THE COMPLETE PLANETARY EPHEMERIS FOR
1950 to 2000 A.D.

Given at midnight ephemeris time
in the true longitude - latitude
and true right ascension - declination
coordinates of date

THE HIERATIC PUBLISHING CO.
P.O. BOX 133 MEDFORD, MASSACHUSETTS 02155
UNITED STATES OF AMERICA, EARTH

Distributed in the United States and Canada by Para
Research, Inc. 964 Washington Street, Gloucester, Massachusetts 01930.

The indestructable stars are under the throne of His face.

(Egyptian Hymn to Osiris, ca. 1500 B.C.)

VIDIMUS ENIM STELLUM EJUS IN ORIENTE, ET VENIMUS ADORARE EUM.

We saw His star as it rose and have come to do Him homage.

(Matthew 2:2-3)

τῶν τε πλείστων καὶ ὁλοσχερῶν συμπτωμάτων ἐναργῶς οἴτω
τὴν ἀπὸ τοῦ περι- έχοντος αἰτίαν ἐμφανιζόντων.

It is clearly evident that most events of a widespread nature draw their causes from the enveloping heavens.

(Claudius Ptolemy's Tetrabiblos I.1, ca 130 A.D.)

An error in the calculation of an ephemeris is as sinful as the murder of a Brahmin.

(Varāha Mihira's Brihat Jātaka, ca. 540 A.D.)

Sir, I have studied it, you have not!

(Sir Isaac Newton's reply to comet-discoverer Halley's questioning the basis of Astrology, ca. 1680)

INTRODUCTION

This ephemeris has been produced not only to satisfy present needs but also to anticipate future desires. Thus, it meets the following criteria: First, the calculations are based on the most accurate, scientific information available. Second, the results are sufficiently precise to satisfy foreseeable future requirements. Third, the data are presented in a convenient and familiar format. For the scientific minded, a somewhat technical discussion of the astronomical basis of these computations follows; those who have no need for such detail may immediately consult the ephemeris.

Time

From ages immemorial, the motions of the celestial bodies have been used to establish numerical time-scales. In the physical sciences natural phenomena are described by formulating laws in mathematical form. Those laws concerning the ordering of events are usually cast with a measure of time as an independent parameter. In particular, by definition, uniform astronomical time is the independent variable in the equations of motion describing the dynamic behavior of the celestial bodies. Therefore, any discrepancies between theory and observation that cannot be attributed to observational error are evidence of inconsistent or incomplete hypotheses.

The rotation of the Earth has been the basis for the astronomical measurement of time. Sidereal Time (i.e. Equinoctial Time) defined by the diurnal motion of the vernal equinox on the celestial sphere is obtained from observations of the diurnal motions of stars. Universal time (i.e. Mean Solar Time) defined by the diurnal motion of a conventional mean sun is consequently obtained from its relation to Sidereal Time. Unfortunately our knowledge of the equations of motion governing the Earth's rotation is not as complete as our knowledge of those governing the orbital motions of the planets. Thus, the fundamental astronomical measurement of time is presently based on the orbital motion of the Earth. Ephemeris Time (i.e. Earth Orbital Time) defined by the apparent annual motion of the Sun is obtained by determining the correction, ΔT, which must be added to Universal Time to obtain Ephemeris Time:

(1) $$\text{E.T.} = \text{U.T.} + \Delta T.$$

The methods of calculation are unaffected by the adoption of the term E.T. to designate the argument in the fundamental ephemerides of the planets, in place of the former U.T. or G.M.T. The actual rotational position of the Earth (consequently ΔT and U.T. to which all civil clocks are adjusted) can only be determined empirically after the fact. Therefore, corrections to former procedures are necessary to calculate quantities that depend upon the Earth's rotation such as Sidereal Time, Hour Angle, and Meridian Transit.

To facilitate such calculations the concept of an auxiliary reference meridian, the Ephemeris Meridian, has been introduced. The position of the Ephemeris Meridian in space is where the Greenwich Meridian would have been if the Earth had rotated uniformly at the rate implicit in the definition of Ephemeris Time. It is 1.002738 ΔT east of the actual Greenwich Meridian on the surface of the Earth.

For example, Ephemeris Sidereal Time, which is the hour angle of the true vernal equinox of date referred to the Ephemeris Meridian, is computed in terms of E.T. in the same manner as the positions of the planets. When ΔT has been determined, the (true) Greenwich Sidereal Time is obtained from the formula:

(2) $$\text{G.S.T.} = \text{E.S.T.} - 1.002738 \ \Delta T.$$

Often the practical consequences of ignoring the above distinction between E.T. and U.T. (i.e. assuming $\Delta T = 0$) are insignificant. As seen in Table 1, the values of ΔT versus year, although irregular, are generally less than 40^s. If greater precision is required the corrections given by (1) and (2) may be used. In the future the current value of ΔT will be obtained from analysis performed in retrospect at the national time services.

Position

Predictions of the motions of celestial bodies can be presented as: (a) complex formulae with time as argument, from which the positions can be computed for any instant; (b) ephemerides, or tables, listing positions at discrete instants from which the positions at any other instant can be obtained by interpolation.

An unperturbed, i.e. gravitationally unaffected by the other planets, orbit of a body about the Sun is completely described by six numerical formulae or Keplerian Elements. These reference orbits may be used as a basis to derive the actual motions of the interacting planets by the general theory of perturbations. Such methods have been used to construct the standard ephemerides. They usually contained complicated approximations to reduce the large amount of hand calculations involved. The advent of large, high-speed, digital computers allows a numerically repetitious approach which is also more fundamental and accurate.

This ephemeris has been generated by an electronic computer. It was programmed to perform a simultaneous numerical integration of the differential equations of motion of all the major planets, including relativistic terms based on the Schwartzschild metric. The results first were corrected using modern astronomical observations, then were referenced to the mean equinox of date using the precessional values of Newcomb, and finally were expressed with respect to the true equinox of date using the nutational values of Woolard. The computations were performed using 16 significant decimal digits. The results were rounded to the nearest $0'.1$ for publication using computer driven, phototypesetting equipment. As $360° = 24^h$ or $0'.1 = 0^s.4$, this precision is equivalent to entering the ephemeris with time known to $0^s.4$ and is also the same expressed in the "Nautical Almanac" as used for marine navigation. Moreover, it is also better than the $0^s.7$ uncertainty in the uncorrected Coordinated Universal Time which is broadcast by most of the world's national time services. Similar precision was maintained by rounding the Ephemeris Sidereal Time to the nearest $0^s.1$.

The "true" positions of the various bodies are their actual geometric locations, relative to the earth's center, as opposed to their "apparent" positions, or observed locations in the sky. The apparent position is derived from the geometric position by the application of corrections for aberration, refraction, and parallax. These corrections depend not only upon the particular body but also upon the position and viewing direction of the observer; they can amount to as much as $1° \ 32'$ for the nearest body, the Moon.

Historically, the ancients used the combination "right ascension/declination" as position coordinates before the combination "longitude/latitude" (which has been standard in star catalogs since Ptolemy's Almagest, ca. 150 A.D.). Moreover, Hipparchus (ca. 150 B.C.) divides not only the ecliptic but also the equator into 30° sections and denotes them by the names of the zodiacal signs. In addition, the main canon of Hindu astronomy, the Sūrya Siddhānta, uses the zodiacal signs in similar fashion to denote arcs on any great circle.

INTRODUCTION

Cet éphéméride a été produit non seulement pour satisfaire aux besoins présents mais aussi pour anticiper les désirs futurs. Donc, il remplit les critères suivants: premièrement, les calculs sont basés sur les informations scientifiques les plus précises que l'on puisse obtenir. Deuxièmement, les résultats sont suffisamment précis pour satisfaire aux exigences futures que l'on peut prévoir. Troisièmement, les indications sont présentées dans un format habituel. Pour ceux doué d'un esprit scientifique, suit une discussion plutôt technique sur la base astronomique de ces calculs; ceux qui n'ont pas besoin de tels détails peuvent consulter immédiatement les éphémérides.

Temps

Depuis les temps immémoriaux, les mouvements des corps célestes ont été employés pour mettre en nombres des échelles périodiques de temps. Dans les sciences physiques les phénomènes naturels sont décrits sous formes de lois mathématiques. Ces lois concernant l'ordre des évènements sont généralement formulées avec une mesure de temps comme paramètre indépendant. En particulier, par définition, le temps uniforme astronomique est la variable indépendante dans les équations de mouvement décrivant le comportement dynamiques des corps célestes. Par conséquent, tout désaccord entre la théorie et l'observation qui ne peut être attribué à une erreur d'observation est la preuve d'hypothèses manquant de suite ou incomplètes.

La rotation de la Terre a été la base des mesures astronomiques de temps. Le Temps Sidéral (i.e. Temps Équinoxial) défini par le mouvement diurne de l'équinoxe vernal sur la sphère céleste est obtenu d'après des observations des mouvements diurnes des étioles. Le Temps Universel (i.e. Temps Solaire Moyen) défini par le mouvement diurne d'un soleil conventionnel moyen est obtenu par conséquent d'après sa relation au Temps Sidéral. Malheureusement nos connaissances des équations des mouvements gouvernant la rotation de la Terre ne sont pas aussi complètes que nos connaissances de celles gouvernant les mouvements orbitaux des planètes. Donc, la mesure fondamentale astronomique de temps est basée à présent sur le mouvement orbital de la Terre. Le Temps Éphéméride (i.e. Temps Orbital Terrestre) défini par le mouvement annuel apparent du mouvement du soleil est obtenu en déterminant la correction, ΔT, qui doit être ajoutée au Temps Universel pour obtenir le Temps Éphéméride:

(1) $$T.E. = T.U. + \Delta T.$$

Les méthodes de calcul ne sont pas affectées par l'adoption du terme T.E. pour désigner l'argument dans les éphémérides fondamentaux des planètes, à la place de l'ancien T.U. ou G.M.T. La position de rotation actuelle de la terre (par conséquent ΔT et T.U. auquel toutes les horloges civiles sont adjustées) peut seulement être déterminée de manière empirique d'après les faits. Donc les corrections de l'ancien procédé sont nécessaires pour calculer les quantités qui dépendent de la rotation de la Terre comme le Temps Sidéral, l'Angle Horaire, et le Passage du Méridien.

Pour faciliter de tels calculs on a introduit le concept d'un méridien de référence auxiliaire, le Méridien Éphéméride. La position du Méridien Éphéméride dans l'espace est là où le Méridien de Greenwich aurait été si la Terre avait tourné uniformément à la vitesse impliquée dans la définition du Temps Éphéméride. Cela se trouve à 1,002738 ΔT à l'est du Meridien de Greenwich réel à la surface de la Terre.

Par exemple, le Temps Éphéméride Sidéral, qui est l'angle horaire du véritable équinoxe vernal de date rattaché au Méridien Éphéméride, est évalué en termes de T.E. de la même manière que les positions des planètes. Quand on a déterminé ΔT, le Temps Sidéral de Greenwich (réel) est obtenu d'après la formule:

(2)   T.S.G. = T.S.E. − 1,002738 ΔT.

Souvent les conséquences pratiques du fait d'ignorer la distinction ci-dessus entre T.E. et T.U. (i.e. sous entendant ΔT = 0) sont insignifiantes. Comme vu à la Table 1, les valeurs de ΔT versus année, quoique irregulières, sont généralement moins de 40^s. Si on requiert une plus grande précision les corrections données par (1) et (2) peuvent être employées. A l'avenir la valeur courante de ΔT sera obtenue d'après l'analyse effectuee en retrospective aux services du temps national.

Position

Les prédictions des mouvements des corps célestes peuvent être présèntées comme: (a) des formules complexes fonction de la variable temps, à partir desquelles on peut calculer les positions à n'importe quel moment; (b) des éphémérides, ou tables donnant des positions à des moments distincts à partir desquels les positions à n'importe quel autre moment peuvent être obtenues par interpolation.

Une orbite non perturbée, i.e. non affectée par la gravitation des autres planètes, d'un corps autour du soleil est complètement décrite par six formules numériques ou Elements de Kepler. Ces orbites de référence peuvent être employées comme bases pour déterminer les mouvements réels des planètes interférant les unes sur les autres selon la théorie générale des perturbations. De telles méthodes ont été employées pour établir des éphémérides standards. Ils contiennent en général des approximations compliquées pour réduire le grand nombre de calculs requis faits à la main. La venue de grands ordinateurs ultra-rapides, à touches et à répétition, permet une approximation numérique plus fonfamentale et plus précise.

Cet éphéméride a été engendré par un ordinateur électronique. Il a été programmé pour accomplir une intégration numérique simultanée des différentes équations de mouvement de toutes les planètes importantes, comprenant les termes de relativité basés sur la métrique de Schwartzschild. Les résultats ont été d'abord corrigés en employant les observations astronomiques modernes, puis compte fut tenu de l'équinoxe moyen de date en se servant des valeurs précessionnelles de Newcomb, et finalement furent exprimées par rapport à l'équinoxe de date réel qui emploie les valeurs nutationnelles de Woolard. On a fait les calculs en se servant de 16 chiffres décimaux significatifs. On a arrondi les résultats au plus proche 0′,1 (zero minute virgule un), pour la publication en se servant d'un matériel de composition-photo par ordinateur.

Les positions "réelles" des différents corps sont leurs positions géometriques vraies, relatives au centre de la Terre, par opposition à leurs positions "apparentes", ou situations observées dans le ciel. La position apparente découle de la position géometrique par l'application de corrections pour l'aberration, la réfraction et la parallaxe. Ces corrections dépendent non seulement du corps particulier mais aussi de la position de l'observateur et de son rayon visuel; elles peuvent aller jusqu'à 1° 32′ (un degre trente deux minutes) pour le corps le plus proche, la Lune.

Historiquement, les anciens se servaient de la combinaison "ascension droite/ déclinaison" comme coordonnées de position avant la combinaison "longitude/ latitude" (qui est standard dans les catalogues d'étoiles depuis l'Almageste de Ptolémée, ca. 150 apr. J.C.). En outre, Hipparque (ca. 150 av. J.C.) divise non seulement l'écliptique mais aussi l'équateur en sections de 30° et les indique par les noms des signes du Zodiaque. De plus, le principal canon de l'astronomie Hindou, le Sūrya Siddhānta, se sert des signes du Zodiaque de manière semblable pour indiquer les arcs sur n'importe quel grand cercle.

INTRODUCCIÓN

Esta efemérides se ha producido no solamente para satisfacer necesidades presentes, sino también para anticipar futuros usos. Por lo tanto, se conforma a los siguientes criterios: Primero, los cálculos se basan en la más exacta información científica que tenemos hoy en día. Segundo, los resultados son suficientemente precisos para satisfacer los futuros requisitos. Tercero, los datos se han presentado en una forma conocida y conveniente. Para las personas que tienen inclinaciones científicas, sigue una discusión técnica de los fundamentos astronómicos de los cálculos; las personas que no necesitan estos detalles pueden consultar directamente el efemérides.

Tiempo

Desde épocas prehistóricas se han usado los movimientos de los cuerpos celestes para establecer tablas numéricas del tiempo. En las ciencias físicas los fenómenos naturales se describen por medio de la formulación de leyes matemáticas. Las leyes que tienen que ver con ordenar una serie de hechos generalmente tienen una medida de tiempo como parámetro independiente. En particular, el Tiempo Uniforme Astronómico, por definición, es la variable independiente en las fórmulas de movimiento que describen el comportamiento de los cuerpos celestes. Por lo tanto, cualquier discrepancia entre teoría y observación que no se pueda atribuir a errores de observacion es evidencia de una hipótesis inconsistente o inexacta.

La rotación de la tierra ha sido la base para la medida astronómica del tiempo. El Tiempo Sideral (i.e. Tiempo Equinoccial), definido por el movimiento diurno del equinoccio vernal en la esfera celestial, se obtiene por medio de observaciones de los movimientos duirnos de las estrellas. Por consiguiente, el Tiempo Universal (i.e. Tiempo Medio Solar), definido por el movimiento diurno de un sol medio convencional se obtiene por su relación al Tiempo Sideral. Desafortunadamente, nuestro conocimiento de las fórmulas de movimiento que rigen la rotación de la tierra no son tan exactas como nuestro conocimiento de las que rigen los movimientos orbitales de los planetas. Así es que la medida fundamental del Tiempo Astronómico se basa en el movimiento orbital de la tierra. El Tiempo Efemérito* (i.e. Tiempo Orbital Terrestre), definido por el movimiento aparente anual del sol, se obtiene determinando la corrección ΔT que hay que añadir al Tiempo Universal para obtener el Tiempo Efemérito:

(1) $$\text{T.E.} = \text{T.U.} + \Delta T$$

Los métodos de cálculos permanecen inalterados si se usa el término T.E. para designar el argumento en las efemérides fundamentales de los planetas, en lugar de los tiempos usados previamente, el Tiempo Universal y el Tiempo Medio de Greenwich. La posición rotacional de la tierra (y por consiguiente ΔT y T.U., al que se ajusta todo reloj civil) solamente se determina empíricamente después del hecho. Por lo tanto, correcciones en las operaciones previamente usadas son necesarias para calcular las cantidades que dependen de la rotación de la tierra, tales como Tiempo Sideral, Ángulo Horario y Tránsito Meridiano.

Para facilitar tales cálculos se ha introducido el concepto de un meridiano auxiliar de referencia, el Meridiano de Efemérides. La posición del Meridiano de Efemérides en el espacio es la posición en que habría estado el Meridiano de Greenwich si la tierra hubiese rotado sobre su eje uniformemente a la velocidad implícita en la definición del Tiempo Efemérito que está a 1.002738 ΔT al este del actual Meridiano de Greenwich sobre la superficie de la tierra.

Por ejemplo, el Tiempo Sideral Efemérito, que es el ángulo horario del verdadero equinoccio vernal de la fecha en referencia al Meridiano Efemérito, se calcula en función del Tiempo Efemérito de igual manera que las posiciones de los planetas. Cuando se ha determinado ΔT, el verdadero Tiempo Sideral de Greenwich se obtiene por medio de la fórmula:

(2) $$\text{T.S. de G.} = \text{T.S.E.} - 1.002738\ \Delta T$$

Muchas veces las consecuencias prácticas de no tomar en cuenta esta distincción son insignificantes. Como se ve en la tabla I, los valores ΔT para cada ano, aunque irregulares, son generalmente menores que 40^s. Si es necesaria una major precisión se puede usar las correcciones dadas en (1) y (2). En el futuro, el valor apropiado de ΔT se obtendrá del análisis en retrospectiva efectuado por los servicios nacionales del tiempo.

Posición

Los prognósticos de los movimientos de los cuerpos celestes se pueden expresar en forma de: (a) fórmulas complicadas con el tiempo como argumento, por medio de las cuales se puede calcular las posiciones para cualquier instante; (b) efemérides, o tablas que enumeran estas posiciones en intervalos discretos por las cuales se calcula por interpolación para las posiciones dentro de los intervalos.

*Se traduce del término del inglés "Ephemeris Time" que refiere no a la tabla especifica de efemérides sino al tiempo téorico desde lo cual se calcula la tabla de efemérides.

Seis fórmulas númericas, o Elementos Keplerianos, describen una órbita no perturbada, i.e. libre de influencia gravitacional de otros planetas. Se puede usar estas órbitas como base para derivar los movimientos actuales de los planetas en interacción, por medio de la teoría general de perturbaciones. Se usan tales métodos para construir el efemérides. Por lo general contiene complicadas aproximaciones para reducir el gran número de cálculos a mano. La llegada de los computadoras digitales ha permitido el uso de más precisas y fundamentale técnicas numéricas.

Esta efemérides se obtuvo con una computadora electrónica que fue programada para hacer una integración numérica simultánea de las fórmulas diferenciales de movimiento de todos los planetas importantes e incluyento términos relativísticos basados en la métrica de Schwartz-child. Primeramente, se corrijieron los resultados usando observaciones modernas astronómicas, luego fueron referidos al equinoccio medio de la fecha usando los valores precesionales de Newcomb y finalmente fueron expresados respecto al equinoccio de la fecha usando los valores nutacionales de Woolard. Los resultados para publicación fueron redondeadas al más cercano 0.1 usando equipo fototipográfico dirigido por una computadora electronic.

Las posiciones "verdaderas" de los varios cuerpos celestes son sus posiciones geométricas con relación al centro de la tierra en oposición a sus posiciones "aparentes", o posiciones observadas en el cielo. La posición aparente se deriva de la geométrica por medio de la aplicación de correcciones por aberración, refracción y paralaje. Estas correcciones dependen no solamente del cuerpo celeste particular, sino que también de la posición y la dirección en que mira el observador, pudiendo llegar a ser 1° 32′ para el cuerpo más cercano, la luna.

Históricamente, el hombre usaba la combinación "ascención recta/declinación" como coordinadas de posición antes que la combinación "longitud/latitud" (que ha sido norma en los catálogos de estrellas desde el Almagest de Ptolomer, c. 150 D.C.). Además, Hiparco (c. 150 A.C.) divide no solamente la eclíptica sino que también el ecuador en secciones de 30° y los denota por los nombres de los signos del zodiaco. Además, el canon principal de la astronomía hindu, el Sūrya Siddhānta, usa los signos zodiacales de manera semejante para designar área en cualquier Círculo Mayor.

INTRODUZIONE

Questa effemeride é stata prodotta con l'intenzione insieme di rispondere alle esigenze attuali e di offrire un valido riferimento in futuro. A questo scopo, ci se é attenuti ai seguenti criteri: a) il calcolo si basa sulla piú accurata informazione scientifica; b) la precisione dei risultati é tale da soddisfare, per quanto é prevedibile, le esigenze future; c) i dati sono presentati in una forma che ne permette una facile consultazione. Per il lettore che abbia esigenze scientifiche segue una discussione delle basi astronomiche di questi calcoli, gli altri possono consultare direttamente l'effemeride.

Tempo

Fin da età immemorabili i moti dei corpi celesti sono stati usati nella determinazione di scale temporali numeriche. Nelle scienze fisiche i fenomeni naturali sono descritti dalla formulazione di leggi in forma matematica; e le leggi che descrivono l'ordinarsi degli eventi richiedono una misura del tempo come parametro indipendente. In particolare il tempo astronomico uniforme é per definizione la variabile indipendente nelle equazioni del moto che descrivono la dinamica dei corpi celesti. Ne deriva quindi che la ragione di qualsiasi discrepanza tra teoria ed osservazione che non possa essere attribuita ad errore di osservazione, si deve ricercare in una formulazione incompleta o errata delle ipotesi di partenza.

La rotazione della Terra é stata la base della misura astronomica del tempo. Il Tempo Sidereo (Tempo Equinoziale) definito dal moto diurno dell'equinozio di primavera sulla sfera celeste, si ottiene da osservazioni del moto diurno delle stelle. Il Tempo Universale (Tempo Solare Medio), definito dal moto diurno di un sole medio convenzionale, si deriva in relazione al tempo sidereo. Sfortunatamente la nostra conoscenza delle equazioni del moto che governano la rotazione della Terra non é cosí completa quanto la nostra conoscenza di quelle che governano i moti orbitali dei pianeti; ne deriva che la misura astronomica fondamentale di tempo si basa presentemente sul moto orbitale della Terra. Il Tempo Effemeride (Tempo Orbitale Terrestre) definito dal moto annuo apparente del Sole, si ottiene determinando la correzione Δt, che aggiunta al Tempo Universale dà il Tempo Effemeride;

(1) $$\text{T.E.} = \text{T.U.} + \Delta T$$

L'adozione, al posto di T.U. o T.M.G. usati in precedenza, del termine T.E. per designare l'argomento nelle effemeridi fondamentali dei pianeti non porta ad alcuna modificazione nei metodi di calcolo. L'effettiva posizione rotazionale della Terra (e di conseguenza ΔT e T.U. secondo cui tutti gli orologi civili sono regolati) si può determinare solo in modo empirico, e quindi bisogna introdurre correzioni nel calcolo di quantità che dipendono dalla rotazione terrestre, come Tempo Sidereo, Angolo Orario e Passaggio del Meridiano. Per facilitare questi calcoli é stato introdotto il concetto di un meridiano ausiliare di riferimento, il Meridiano Effemeride, che si trova sulla superficie terrestre a $1,002738 \Delta T$ ad est del meridiano di Greenwich.

Per esempio, il Tempo Sidereo Effemeride, che é l'angolo orario del vero equinozio de data di primavera relativamente al Meridiano Effemeride, si calcola in termini di T.E. nello stesso modo delle posizioni dei pianeti. Una volta determinato ΔT, il Tempo Sidereo di Greenwich (vero) é dato dalla formula:

(2) $$\text{T.S.G.} = \text{T.S.E.} - 1,002738 \ \Delta T$$

Spesso ignorare la differenza tra T.E. e T.U. (cioe assumere $\Delta T = 0$) porta a conseguenze pratiche irrilevanti. Come si vede dalla tabella 1, i valori di ΔT in funzione dell'anno, sebbene irregolari, sono generalmente inferiori a 40s. Nel caso in cui si richieda maggiore precisione, si possono usare le correzioni date da (1) e (2). In futuro, il valore di ΔT si otterà da analisi eseguite in retrospettiva regli uffici nazionali di tempo.

Posizione

Si possono presentare predizioni dei moti dei corpi celesti sia mediante formule complesse con il tempo come argomento, da cui possono venire calcolate le posizioni per ogni dato istante, sia con effemeridi, o tabelle, che riportano le posizioni dei corpi celesti ad istanti discreti e da cui le posizioni in ogni altro istante si possono ricavare per interpolazione.

Un'orbita non perturbata (cioe escludendo l'interazione gravitazionale con gli altri pianeti) di un pianeta attorno al Sole é descritta completamente da sei formule numeriche o Elementi Kepleriani. Partendo da queste orbite di riferimento ed usando la teoria delle perturbazioni, si possono ricavare i moti dei pianeti interagenti. Questo é il metodo generale con cui si costruiscono le effemeridi. Nel passato data la notevole mole di calcoli, venivano introdotte complicate approssimazioni semplificatrici; con l'introduzione di grandi e veloci calcolatori digitali é possible un approccio numerico ripetitivo che elimina gran parte della inaccuratezza dei calcoli precedenti.

Questa effemeride é stata generata da un calcolatore elettronico, programmato in modo da effettuare una integrazione numerica simultanea delle equazioni differenziali del moto di tutti i pianeti maggiori, includendo i termini relativistici di Schwartzschild. I risultati sono stati prima corretti usando i dati di moderne osservazioni astronomiche, quindi riferiti all'equinozio di data medio per mezzo dei valori precessionali di Newcomb, e finalmente espressi rispetto al vero equinozio di data con l'uso dei valori nutazionali di Woolard. I calcoli sono stati eseguiti usando 16 cifre significative decimali. I resultati sono stati arrotondati al piú vicino $0',1$ per la pubblicazione per mezzo di un'apparecchiatura di phototype, guidata dal calcolatore.

Per i vari corpi celesti si distingue una posizione "vera", che é la loro effettiva posizione geometrica relativa al centro della Terra, ed una posizione "apparente" che é quella che si osserva nel firmamento. La posizione apparente si può ricavare dalla posizione geometrica correggendo per aberrazione, rifrazione e parallasse. Queste correzioni dipendono dal particolare corpo celeste, ed anche dalla posizione dell'osservatore e dalla direzione di osservazione. Possono raggiungere al massimo $1° 32'$, che é quanto si verifica per la Luna, che é il corpo celeste piu vicino.

Una nota storica: gli antichi usarono la combinazione "ascensione retta-declinazione" come coordinate posizionali prima che venisse introdotta la combinazione "longitudine-latitudine" (che é diventata standard nei cataloghi di stelle fin da Tolemeo Almagesto, vissuto attorno al 150 d.C.). Inoltre Ipparco (150 a.C.) divide non solo l'eclittica, ma anche l'equatore in sezioni di $30°$ ciascuna e le denomina dai segni dello Zodiaco. Un simile uso dei segni dello Zodiaco si trova nel Sūrya Siddhānta, il testo principale dell'astronomia indú, dove denotano archi su ogni cerchio massimo.

EINLEITUNG

Dieser astronomische Almanach ist nicht nur zusammengestellt worden, um gegenwärtigem Bedarf entegegenzukommen, sondern auch um zukünftigem Wunsch vorzugreifen. Somit erfüllt er folgende Voraussetzungen: Erstens, die Berechnungen beruhen auf genauesten wissenschaftlichen Kenntnissen. Zweitens, die Ergebnisse sind zulänglich genug, um zukünftigen Bedürfnissen entgegenzukommen. Drittens, die Daten sind in zweckdienlichem und brauchbarem Format angeführt. Fur die wissenschaftlich Gesonnenen folgt eine vorwiegend technische Diskussion, die die astronomischen Grundlagen der Berechnungen erörtert. Die Leser, die diese Darlegung übergehen möchten, wenden sich bitte gleich dem astronomischen Almanach zu.

Die Zeit

Seit urdenklichen Zeiten sind die Bewegungen der Gestirne benutzt worden, um numerische Zeitskalen aufzustellen. In der Physik werden Naturereignisse mit mathematischen Formeln erklärt. Diese Naturgesetze, die die Zeitfolge bestimmter Ereignisse berechnen, benutzen meist das Zeitmaß als unbestimmten Parameter. Im Besonderen ist in der Begriffsbestimmung die einheitliche astronomische Zeit die unabhängige Variabel in den Bewegungsgleichungen, die das dynamische Verhalten der Himmelskörper beschreibt. Demzufolge sind etwaige Widersprüche zwischen Theorie und Beobachtung, die nicht Beobachtungsfehlern zugeschrieben werden können, Beweise von Widersprechenden oder unvollständigen Hypothesen.

Bis vor einigen Jahrzehnten hatte die Erdumdrehung als Basis für astronomische Zeitrechnung gedient. Die Sternzeit (d.h., Äquinoktialzeit), durch die tägliche Bewegung des Frühlingspunktes im Himmelsgewölbe definiert, wird von Beobachtungen der täglichen Bewegungen der Sterne erzielt. Die Weltzeit oder Universal Time (d.h. mittlere Sonnenzeit), definiert von der täglichen Drehung der willkurlich festgesetzten mittleren Sonne, ist infolgedessen von seiner Beziehung zur Sternzeit bestimmt. Unglücklicherweise ist unser Wissen über die Bewegungsgleichungen, die die Erdumdrehung bestimmen, nicht so vollständig wie unser Wissen über diejenigen, die die Planetenbahnen bestimmen. Deshalb beruht die grundlegende astronomische Zeitmessung auf der jährlichen Bahn der Erde. Die Ephemeridenzeit (d.h., Erdbahnzeit), die durch die scheinbare jährliche Bewegung der Sonne berechnet wird, wird erhalten durch die Bestimmung der Korrektur, ΔT, welche zur Universal Time addiert, wird, um die Ephemeridenzeit

$$(1) \qquad \qquad E.T. = U.T. + \Delta T$$

zu erhalten.

* Die Berechnungsmethoden bleiben durch die Verwendung der E.T. Bezeichnung unverändert, um die unabhängige Variabel der grundlegenden Planeten-Ephemeriden zu bestimmen, anstelle der früher gebräuchlichen U.T. oder der mittleren Sonnenzeit des Greenwicher Meridians (G.M.T.). Die tatsächliche (wirkliche) Umdrehungsposition der Erdkugel (folglich ΔT und U.T. nach der alle bürgerlichen Uhren gestellt sind) kann erfahrungsgemäß nur nach dem Tatbestand bestimmt werden. Deshalb ist es wichtig, frühere Verfahren zu korrigieren, um die Grössen zu berechnen, die von der Erdumdrehung abhangen, z.B., Sternzeit, Stundenwinkel and Meridian-Durchgang.

Um solche Berechnungen zu erleichtern, ist das Konzept des zusätzlichen Referenz-Meridians, des Ephemeriden Meridians, eingeführt werden. Die Position des Ephemeriden Meridians im Raum ist dort, wo sich der Greenwicher Meridian befunden hätte, wenn sich die Erdkugel gleichmäßig in der Geschwindigkeit gedreht hatte, die in der Definition der Ephemeridenzeit benutzt wird. Sie befindet sich 1.002738 ΔT östlich des wirklichen Greenwicher Meridians auf der Erdoberfläche.

Sowird zum Beispiel die Ephemeriden Sternzeit, welche der Stundenwinkel des wahren Frühlingsäquinox zur Zeit, bezogen auf den Ephemeriden Meridian ist, bis jetzt in der Form des E.T. auf die gleiche Weise wie die Planeten-positionen berechnet. Wenn ΔT bestimmt ist, wird die wahre Greenwicher Sternzeit von der Formel

$$(2) \qquad \qquad G.S.T. = E.S.T. - 1.002738 \, \Delta T$$

gewonnen.

Oft sind die praktischen Konsequenzen der Mißachtung der obenerwähnten unterscheidenden Merkmale zwischen E.T. und U.T. (vorausgesetzt $\Delta T = 0$) unbedeutend. Wie in Tabelle I ersichtlich ist, sind die Werte ΔT vs. Jahr, wenngleich unregelmäßig, im Allgemeinen weniger als 40ˢ. Falls größere Präzision erforderlich ist, können die in (1) und (2) angeführten Korrektionen verwendet werden. In Zukunft wird der gegenwärtige Wert von ΔT errechnet, indem die Analyse nachträglich zur Normalzeit aus den verschiedenen nationalen Zeit Bureaus geführt wird.

Position

Voraussagen über die Bewegungen der Himmelskörper können wie folgt angeführt werden: (a) komplizierte Formeln mit Zeit als Argument, von denen die Stellungen für jede Sekunde berechnet werden können; (b) Ephemeriden, oder Tabellen, welche Positionen an diskontinuierlichen Zeitpunkten verzeichnen, von den Positionen zu irgenden anderen Zeitpunkten mittels Interpolierung erhalten werden können.

Die ungestörte Bahn eines Himmelskörpers um die Sonne, die schwerkraftsgemäß nicht durch andere Planeten beeinflußt wird, ist ausführlich mittels 6 numerischer Formeln (oder Keplerischer Bahnelemente) beschrieben. Diese Reference-Bahnen können also Basis gebraucht werden, um die wirklichen Bewegungen der sich gegenseitig beeinflussenden Planeten mit Hilfe der gebräuchlichen Störungstheorie zu errechnen. Solche Methoden sind benutzt worden, um die gebrauchlichen Ephemeriden auszuarbeiten. Sie enthielten zumeist komplizierte Naherungswerte, um die große Anzahl der Hand-Kalkulationen zu verringern. Das Aufkommen der großen, schnellen digitalen Komputer ermöglicht wiederholentliche Berechnungen, die viel genauer und grundlegender sind.

Dieser astronomische Almanach ist mit Hilfe eines elektronischen Komputers zusammengestellt worden. Dieser Komputer wurde so programmiert, um eine gleichzeitige numerische Integration der Differential-Bewegungsgleichungen der wichtigeren Planeten ausführen zu können, einschließlich der relativistischen Glieder die auf der Schwartzschildschen Metrik basiert ist. Zuerst wurden die Ergebnisse mit Hilfe neuester astronomischer Beobachtungen korrigiert; dann wurden sie auf dem mittleren Äquinox zur Zeit mit Hilfe der Newcombschen Präzessionsglieder bezogen und wurden schließlich bezüglich des wahren Äquinox mittels der Woolardschen Nutationsglieder präsentiert. Die Berechnungen wurden mit 16 bedeutsamen Dezimal-Digits durchgeführt. Zur Veröffentlichung mittels komputer-gesteuerter photoschriftgesetzter Anlage wurden die Ergebnisse auf die nahesten 0ˑ1 aufgerundet.

Die "wahren" Positionen der verschiedenen Himmelskörper sind ihre tatsächlichen geometrischen Positionen relativ zum Erdzentrum, im Gegensatz zu ihren scheinbaren Stellungen, oder zu den am Himmelsgewölbe beobachteten Stellungen. Die "scheinbare" Position wird von der geometrischen Position durch Anwendung von Korrektionen für Aberration, Refraktion und Parallaxe berechnet. Diese Korrektionen hängen nicht nur vom einzelnen Gestirn ab, sondern auch von der Position und Sehrichtung des Beobachters. Sie können bis zu $1°32'$ für den nahesten Körper, den Mond, betragen.

Geschichtlich betrachtet, gebrauchten die Forscher (Gelehrten) des Altertums die Kombination "Rektaszension/Deklination" als Positions-Koordinaten vor der seit Ptolemäus (150 A.D.) in Sternkundebüchern gebräuchlichen Kombination "Länge/Breite". Ferner teilte Hipparchus (ca. 150 B.C.) nicht nur die Sonnenbahn (Ekliptik) sondern auch den Äquator in $30°$ Abschnitte und kennzeichnete sie mit den Namen der Tierkreiszeichen. Ferner werden schon im hindustanischen astronomischen Hauptkanon, dem Sūrya Siddhānta, die Tierkreiszeichen in ähnlicher Weise benutzt, um Bogen in irgendwelchen größten Kreisen zu kennzeichnen.

REDUCTION FROM UNIVERSAL TO EPHEMERIS TIME
ΔT = E.T. − U.T. VERSUS YEAR — TABLE 1

Year	ΔT^s	Year	ΔT^s	Year	ΔT^s	Year	ΔT^s	Year	ΔT^s
1621	+98	1820.5	+5.3	1860.5	+3.3	1900.5	− 3.8	1940.5	+24.3
1635	+38	1821.5	+4.8	1861.5	+3.1	1901.5	− 2.5	1941.5	+24.7
1639	− 13	1822.5	+4.3	1862.5	+2.9	1902.5	− 1.1	1942.5	+25.2
1645	+13	1823.5	+3.9	1863.5	+2.6	1903.5	+ 0.4	1943.5	+25.2
1653	− 10	1824.5	+3.5	1864.5	+2.3	1904.5	+ 1.8	1944.5	+26.1
1662	− 5	1825.5	+3.2	1865.5	+1.8	1905.5	+ 3.3	1945.5	+26.6
		1826.5	+2.8	1866.5	+1.4	1906.5	+ 4.7	1946.5	+27.1
		1827.5	+2.6	1867.5	+0.9	1907.5	+ 6.1	1947.5	+27.6
		1828.5	+2.4	1868.5	+0.2	1908.5	+ 7.5	1948.5	+28.2
		1829.5	+2.2	1869.5	−0.7	1909.5	+ 8.9	1949.5	+28.9
1681	− 13.5	1830.5	+2.0	1870.5	−1.8	1910.5	+10.3	1950.5	+29.4
1710	− 12.0	1831.5	+1.8	1871.5	−3.1	1911.5	+11.6	1951.5	+29.7
1727	− 7.6	1832.5	+1.5	1872.5	−4.5	1912.5	+13.0	1952.5	+30.3
1738	− 2.9	1833.5	+1.2	1873.5	−5.6	1913.5	+14.2	1953.5	+31.0
1747	− 0.4	1834.5	+0.8	1874.5	−6.6	1914.5	+15.3	1954.5	+31.1
		1835.5	+0.4	1875.5	−7.2	1915.5	+16.4	1955.5	+31.2
		1836.5	0.0	1876.5	−7.7	1916.5	+17.4	1956.5	+31.5
		1837.5	− 0.3	1877.5	−7.9	1917.5	+18.3	1957.5	+31.9
		1838.5	− 0.4	1878.5	−8.0	1918.5	+19.1	1958.5	+32.4
		1839.5	− 0.3	1879.5	−8.1	1919.5	+19.8	1959.5	+32.9
1760.9	+ 2.1	1840.5	− 0.1	1880.5	−8.1	1920.5	+20.5	1960.5	+33.4
1774.1	+ 6.6	1841.5	+0.2	1881.5	−8.2	1921.5	+21.1	1961.5	+33.8
1785.1	+ 8.3	1842.5	+0.6	1882.5	−8.2	1922.5	+21.6	1962.5	+34.2
1792.6	+ 7.4	1843.5	+0.8	1883.5	−8.1	1923.5	+22.0	1963.5	+34.7
1801.8	+ 5.7	1844.5	+1.1	1884.5	−8.1	1924.5	+22.3	1964.5	+35.4
1811.9	+ 4.7	1845.5	+1.4	1885.5	−8.0	1925.5	+22.6	1965.5	+36.1
		1846.5	+1.6	1886.5	−7.8	1926.5	+22.7	1966.5	+37.0
		1847.5	+1.9	1887.5	−7.7	1927.5	+22.8	1967.5	+37.9
		1848.5	+2.1	1888.5	−7.6	1928.5	+22.9	1968.5	+38.8
		1849.5	+2.3	1889.5	−7.6	1929.5	+23.0	1969.5	+39.7
		1850.5	+2.5	1890.5	−7.7	1930.5	+23.2	1970.5	+40.7
		1851.5	+2.7	1891.5	−7.8	1931.5	+23.3	1971.5	+41.7
		1852.5	+2.9	1892.5	−8.0	1932.5	+23.5	1972.5	+42.8
		1853.5	+3.1	1893.5	−8.1	1933.5	+23.6	1973.5	+44.0
		1854.5	+3.2	1894.5	−7.9	1934.5	+23.6	1974.5	+45.2
		1855.5	+3.4	1895.5	−7.6	1935.5	+23.6		
		1856.5	+3.5	1896.5	−7.2	1936.5	+23.6		
		1857.5	+3.5	1897.5	−6.6	1937.5	+23.6		
		1858.5	+3.5	1898.5	−5.8	1938.5	+23.8		
		1859.5	+3.4	1899.5	−4.9	1939.5	+24.0		

JANUARY 1950

DAY	EPHEM. SID. TIME	☉	☊	☽	☿	♀	♂	♃	♄	♅	♆	♇
	h m s	° ′	° ′	° ′	° ′	° ′	° ′	° ′	° ′	° ′	° ′	° ′
		LONGITUDE										
1	6 40 17.9	10♑ .6	12♈ 6.7	1♊ 24.7	29♑ 27.2	16♒ 58.8	2♎ 12.8	6♒ 30.8	19♍ 26.2	2♋ 40.7	17♎ 16.1	17♌ 47.7
2	6 44 14.5	11 1.8	12 3.5	13 43.9	0♒ 28.7	17 19.1	2 34.7	6 44.3	19 R 26.0	2 R 38.1	17 16.6	17 R 46.6
3	6 48 11.1	12 2.9	12 .4	26 18.6	1 24.4	17 37.3	2 56.3	6 57.9	19 25.6	2 35.6	17 17.2	17 45.5
4	6 52 7.6	13 4.0	11 57.2	9♋ 9.5	2 13.4	17 53.5	3 17.5	7 11.5	19 25.1	2 33.1	17 17.7	17 44.4
5	6 56 4.2	14 5.2	11 54.0	22 15.8	2 54.7	18 7.6	3 38.4	7 25.2	19 24.5	2 30.5	17 18.2	17 43.2
6	7 0 .7	15 6.3	11 50.8	5♌ 35.9	3 27.6	18 19.5	3 58.9	7 38.9	19 23.8	2 28.0	17 18.6	17 42.1
7	7 3 57.3	16 7.4	11 47.7	19 7.4	3 51.1	18 29.1	4 19.1	7 52.6	19 23.0	2 25.5	17 19.1	17 40.9
8	7 7 53.8	17 8.6	11 44.5	2♍ 48.0	4 4.3	18 36.4	4 38.9	8 6.4	19 22.1	2 23.1	17 19.4	17 39.7
9	7 11 50.4	18 9.7	11 41.3	16 35.9	4 6.5	18 41.4	4 58.3	8 20.2	19 21.1	2 20.6	17 19.8	17 38.5
10	7 15 47.0	19 10.8	11 38.1	0♎ 29.8	3 R 57.3	18 44.0	5 17.4	8 34.1	19 19.9	2 18.1	17 20.1	17 37.3
11	7 19 43.5	20 12.0	11 35.0	14 28.9	3 36.2	18 44.2	5 36.0	8 48.0	19 18.7	2 15.7	17 20.4	17 36.0
12	7 23 40.1	21 13.1	11 31.8	28 32.9	3 3.3	18 R 41.9	5 54.2	9 1.9	19 17.3	2 13.3	17 20.6	17 34.8
13	7 27 36.6	22 14.3	11 28.6	12♏ 41.2	2 19.2	18 37.1	6 12.0	9 15.9	19 15.9	2 10.9	17 20.8	17 33.5
14	7 31 33.2	23 15.4	11 25.4	26 52.6	1 24.7	18 29.8	6 29.4	9 29.9	19 14.3	2 8.5	17 21.0	17 32.2
15	7 35 29.8	24 16.5	11 22.2	11♐ 4.8	0 21.3	18 20.0	6 46.4	9 43.9	19 12.6	2 6.2	17 21.1	17 30.9
16	7 39 26.3	25 17.7	11 19.1	25 14.2	29♑ 10.8	18 7.7	7 2.9	9 58.0	19 10.9	2 3.9	17 21.3	17 29.6
17	7 43 22.9	26 18.8	11 15.9	9♑ 16.4	27 55.4	17 52.9	7 18.9	10 12.0	19 9.0	2 1.6	17 21.3	17 28.3
18	7 47 19.4	27 19.9	11 12.7	23 6.6	26 37.4	17 35.7	7 34.5	10 26.2	19 7.0	1 59.3	17 21.4	17 27.0
19	7 51 16.0	28 21.0	11 9.5	6♒ 40.6	25 19.4	17 16.1	7 49.6	10 40.3	19 5.0	1 57.0	17 21.4	17 25.6
20	7 55 12.5	29 22.1	11 6.4	19 55.3	24 3.5	16 54.2	8 4.2	10 54.4	19 2.8	1 54.8	17 R 21.3	17 24.3
21	7 59 9.1	0♒ 23.2	11 3.2	2♓ 49.4	22 52.0	16 30.1	8 18.3	11 8.6	19 .5	1 52.6	17 21.3	17 22.9
22	8 3 5.7	1 24.3	11 .0	15 23.4	21 46.7	16 3.9	8 31.9	11 22.8	18 58.2	1 50.5	17 21.2	17 21.6
23	8 7 2.2	2 25.4	10 56.8	27 39.7	20 48.6	15 35.6	8 45.0	11 37.1	18 55.7	1 48.4	17 21.1	17 20.2
24	8 10 58.8	3 26.4	10 53.7	9♈ 41.7	19 58.9	15 5.5	8 57.6	11 51.3	18 53.1	1 46.3	17 20.9	17 18.9
25	8 14 55.3	4 27.4	10 50.5	21 34.2	19 17.9	14 33.8	9 9.6	12 5.5	18 50.5	1 44.2	17 20.7	17 17.5
26	8 18 51.9	5 28.4	10 47.3	3♉ 22.3	18 46.1	14 .6	9 21.1	12 19.8	18 47.7	1 42.2	17 20.5	17 16.1
27	8 22 48.4	6 29.4	10 44.1	15 11.7	18 23.3	13 26.1	9 32.0	12 34.0	18 44.9	1 40.2	17 20.2	17 14.7
28	8 26 45.0	7 30.4	10 40.9	27 7.7	18 9.2	12 50.5	9 42.3	12 48.3	18 42.0	1 38.2	17 19.9	17 13.2
29	8 30 41.6	8 31.3	10 37.8	9♊ 15.4	18 3.6	12 14.2	9 52.1	13 2.6	18 38.9	1 36.3	17 19.5	17 11.8
30	8 34 38.1	9 32.3	10 34.6	21 39.0	18 D 5.8	11 37.3	10 1.3	13 16.9	18 35.8	1 34.4	17 19.2	17 10.4
31	8 38 34.7	10 33.2	10 31.4	4♋ 21.6	18 15.5	11 .1	10 9.9	13 31.2	18 32.6	1 32.6	17 18.8	17 9.0
		LATITUDE										
1	6 40 17.9	0 .0	0 .0	3N 46.9	1S 13.4	0N 37.9	2N 30.8	0S 35.1	2N .4	0N 16.2	1N 35.5	8N 12.1
4	6 52 7.6	0 .0	0 .0	4 59.4	0 37.5	1 14.1	2 34.0	0 35.2	2 1.2	0 16.2	1 35.7	8 12.8
7	7 3 57.3	0 .0	0 .0	3 57.9	0N 8.1	1 53.3	2 37.3	0 35.3	2 2.0	0 16.2	1 35.9	8 13.4
10	7 15 47.0	0 .0	0 .0	0 55.9	1 1.9	2 35.1	2 40.7	0 35.5	2 2.8	0 16.2	1 36.0	8 14.0
13	7 27 36.6	0 .0	0 .0	2S 38.7	1 58.3	3 18.9	2 44.2	0 35.7	2 3.6	0 16.2	1 36.2	8 14.5
16	7 39 26.3	0 .0	0 .0	4 50.3	2 47.9	4 4.0	2 47.7	0 35.8	2 4.4	0 16.2	1 36.4	8 15.1
19	7 51 16.0	0 .0	0 .0	4 30.0	3 20.4	4 49.3	2 51.2	0 36.0	2 5.1	0 16.2	1 36.6	8 15.5
22	8 3 5.7	0 .0	0 .0	2 5.6	3 30.6	5 33.3	2 54.8	0 36.2	2 5.9	0 16.3	1 36.8	8 16.0
25	8 14 55.3	0 .0	0 .0	1N 3.0	3 21.1	6 14.4	2 58.4	0 36.4	2 6.6	0 16.3	1 36.9	8 16.4
28	8 26 45.0	0 .0	0 .0	3 45.3	2 58.1	6 50.8	3 2.0	0 36.6	2 7.3	0 16.3	1 37.1	8 16.8
31	8 38 34.7	0 .0	0 .0	5 3.5	2 27.8	7 20.7	3 5.6	0 36.9	2 7.9	0 16.3	1 37.3	8 17.1
		RIGHT ASCENSION										
1	6 40 17.9	10♑ 53.4	11♈ 8.3	28♉ 26.9	1♒ 53.2	19♒ 14.1	3♎ 1.8	9♒ 3.4	21♍ 5.0	2♋ 55.5	16♎ 31.7	22♌ 57.7
2	6 44 14.5	11 59.7	11 5.3	11♊ 45.7	2 55.3	19 30.4	3 22.3	9 17.3	21 R 4.9	2 R 52.7	16 32.3	22 R 56.7
3	6 48 11.1	13 5.8	11 2.4	25 49.7	3 50.6	19 44.6	3 42.5	9 31.2	21 4.6	2 49.9	16 32.8	22 55.7
4	6 52 7.6	14 11.9	10 59.5	10♋ 21.4	4 38.4	19 56.7	4 2.4	9 45.1	21 4.3	2 47.2	16 33.3	22 54.6
5	6 56 4.2	15 17.8	10 56.5	24 56.2	5 17.9	20 6.5	4 22.0	9 59.1	21 3.8	2 44.4	16 33.8	22 53.5
6	7 0 .7	16 23.7	10 53.6	9♌ 10.9	5 48.1	20 14.0	4 41.3	10 13.1	21 3.3	2 41.7	16 34.2	22 52.4
7	7 3 57.3	17 29.4	10 50.7	22 51.2	6 8.2	20 19.2	5 .2	10 27.2	21 2.7	2 38.9	16 34.6	22 51.2
8	7 7 53.8	18 35.0	10 47.7	5♍ 54.8	6 17.5	20 22.1	5 18.8	10 41.3	21 1.9	2 36.2	16 35.0	22 50.1
9	7 11 50.4	19 40.5	10 44.8	18 29.5	6 R 15.4	20 22.6	5 37.1	10 55.4	21 1.1	2 33.5	16 35.4	22 48.9
10	7 15 47.0	20 45.9	10 41.9	0♎ 49.5	6 1.3	20 R 20.6	5 55.0	11 9.5	21 .1	2 30.9	16 35.7	22 47.8
11	7 19 43.5	21 51.2	10 38.9	13 12.9	5 35.1	20 16.3	6 12.5	11 23.7	20 59.1	2 28.2	16 36.0	22 46.6
12	7 23 40.1	22 56.3	10 36.0	25 58.3	4 56.9	20 9.4	6 29.7	11 37.9	20 57.9	2 25.6	16 36.2	22 45.3
13	7 27 36.6	24 1.2	10 33.1	9♏ 23.5	4 7.4	20 .1	6 46.5	11 52.1	20 56.7	2 23.0	16 36.4	22 44.1
14	7 31 33.2	25 6.1	10 30.1	23 40.5	3 7.5	19 48.4	7 2.9	12 6.4	20 55.4	2 20.4	16 36.6	22 42.9
15	7 35 29.8	26 10.7	10 27.2	8♐ 50.1	1 58.9	19 34.2	7 18.9	12 20.6	20 53.9	2 17.8	16 36.8	22 41.6
16	7 39 26.3	27 15.2	10 24.3	24 36.8	0 43.3	19 17.6	7 34.5	12 34.9	20 52.4	2 15.3	16 36.9	22 40.3
17	7 43 22.9	28 19.6	10 21.3	10♑ 29.3	29♑ 23.1	18 58.6	7 49.7	12 49.2	20 50.8	2 12.8	16 37.0	22 39.0
18	7 47 19.4	29 23.7	10 18.4	25 51.7	28 .7	18 37.3	8 4.5	13 3.5	20 49.0	2 10.3	16 37.0	22 37.7
19	7 51 16.0	0♒ 27.7	10 15.5	10♒ 17.6	26 38.6	18 13.7	8 18.8	13 17.8	20 47.2	2 7.8	16 37.0	22 36.4
20	7 55 12.5	1 31.5	10 12.5	23 37.0	25 19.3	17 48.0	8 32.7	13 32.2	20 45.3	2 5.4	16 37.0	22 35.1
21	7 59 9.1	2 35.1	10 9.6	5♓ 54.3	24 4.7	17 20.2	8 46.1	13 46.5	20 43.3	2 3.0	16 37.0	22 33.7
22	8 3 5.7	3 38.6	10 6.7	17 22.1	22 56.7	16 50.5	8 59.1	14 .9	20 41.2	2 .7	16 37.0	22 32.4
23	8 7 2.2	4 41.8	10 3.7	28 16.6	21 56.6	16 19.0	9 11.6	14 15.3	20 39.0	1 58.4	16 R 36.9	22 31.1
24	8 10 58.8	5 44.8	10 .8	8♈ 54.5	21 5.3	15 45.8	9 23.6	14 29.7	20 36.8	1 56.1	16 36.7	22 29.7
25	8 14 55.3	6 47.7	9 57.9	19 32.2	20 23.4	15 11.2	9 35.1	14 44.0	20 34.4	1 53.8	16 36.6	22 28.3
26	8 18 51.9	7 50.3	9 55.0	0♉ 25.4	19 51.1	14 35.3	9 46.1	14 58.4	20 32.0	1 51.6	16 36.4	22 26.9
27	8 22 48.4	8 52.7	9 52.0	11 48.7	19 28.3	13 58.4	9 56.6	15 12.8	20 29.4	1 49.4	16 36.1	22 25.6
28	8 26 45.0	9 54.9	9 49.1	23 54.2	19 14.8	13 20.7	10 6.6	15 27.2	20 26.8	1 47.3	16 35.9	22 24.1
29	8 30 41.6	10 56.9	9 46.2	6♊ 49.5	19 10.2	12 42.4	10 16.0	15 41.6	20 24.1	1 45.2	16 35.6	22 22.7
30	8 34 38.1	11 58.7	9 43.2	20 33.9	19 D 13.9	12 3.8	10 25.0	15 56.0	20 21.3	1 43.1	16 35.3	22 21.3
31	8 38 34.7	13 .3	9 40.3	4♋ 56.4	19 25.6	11 25.2	10 33.3	16 10.3	20 18.4	1 41.1	16 34.9	22 19.9
		DECLINATION										
1	6 40 17.9	23S 4.2	0N 5.0	24N 9.1	21S 28.2	15S 9.1	1N 25.5	19S 13.0	6N 1.7	23N 41.4	5S 18.7	23N 17.7
4	6 52 7.6	22 48.4	0 5.0	28 6.6	20 16.9	14 17.9	1 2.8	19 2.9	6 2.9	23 41.6	5 19.2	23 19.4
7	7 3 57.3	22 28.5	0 4.9	18 51.5	19 9.9	13 29.7	0 41.4	18 52.5	6 4.5	23 41.7	5 19.6	23 21.1
10	7 15 47.0	22 4.6	0 4.8	0 39.4	18 16.2	12 45.4	0 21.4	18 41.9	6 6.4	23 41.9	5 19.8	23 22.8
13	7 27 36.6	21 36.8	0 4.8	18S 10.2	17 43.7	12 5.8	0 3.0	18 31.0	6 8.7	23 42.0	5 19.9	23 24.5
16	7 39 26.3	21 5.2	0 4.7	28 11.8	17 35.4	11 31.8	0S 13.9	18 19.9	6 11.4	23 42.2	5 19.9	23 26.2
19	7 51 16.0	20 30.0	0 4.6	22 57.8	17 47.8	11 4.0	0 29.0	18 8.6	6 14.4	23 42.3	5 19.8	23 27.9
22	8 3 5.7	19 51.3	0 4.6	7 41.4	18 13.2	10 43.1	0 42.4	17 57.1	6 17.8	23 42.4	5 19.6	23 29.6
25	8 14 55.3	19 9.2	0 4.5	9N 23.1	18 44.5	10 29.5	0 53.9	17 45.4	6 21.4	23 42.5	5 19.2	23 31.3
28	8 26 45.0	18 24.1	0 4.4	23 10.6	19 16.5	10 23.3	1 3.4	17 33.6	6 25.4	23 42.5	5 18.7	23 33.0
31	8 38 34.7	17 35.9	0 4.4	28 25.9	19 45.7	10 24.1	1 10.8	17 21.6	6 29.7	23 42.6	5 18.1	23 34.7

FEBRUARY 1950

LONGITUDE

DAY	EPHEM. SID. TIME h m s	☉ ° ′	☊ ° ′	☽ ° ′	☿ ° ′	♀ ° ′	♂ ° ′	♃ ° ′	♄ ° ′	♅ ° ′	♆ ° ′	♇ ° ′
1	8 42 31.2	11♒34.0	10♈28.2	17♋24.8	18♑32.0	10♒22.8	10♎17.9	13♒45.5	18♍29.4	1♋30.8	17♎18.3	17♌ 7.5
2	8 46 27.8	12 34.9	10 25.1	0♌48.5	18 54.8	9 R 45.8	10 25.2	13 59.8	18 R 26.0	1 R 29.0	17 R 17.9	17 R 6.1
3	8 50 24.3	13 35.8	10 21.9	14 30.7	19 23.4	9 9.3	10 32.0	14 14.1	18 22.6	1 27.3	17 17.4	17 4.7
4	8 54 20.9	14 36.6	10 18.7	28 27.9	19 57.3	8 33.5	10 38.1	14 28.4	18 19.1	1 25.6	17 16.8	17 3.2
5	8 58 17.5	15 37.4	10 15.5	12♍35.9	20 36.0	7 58.7	10 43.5	14 42.7	18 15.5	1 23.9	17 16.3	17 1.8
6	9 2 14.0	16 38.2	10 12.4	26 50.1	21 19.2	7 25.1	10 48.3	14 57.0	18 11.9	1 22.3	17 15.7	17 .3
7	9 6 10.6	17 39.0	10 9.2	11♎ 6.3	22 6.4	6 53.0	10 52.4	15 11.3	18 8.1	1 20.7	17 15.0	16 58.9
8	9 10 7.1	18 39.7	10 6.0	25 21.3	22 57.3	6 22.5	10 55.8	15 25.7	18 4.3	1 19.2	17 14.4	16 57.5
9	9 14 3.7	19 40.5	10 2.8	9♏32.7	23 51.6	5 53.8	10 58.5	15 40.0	18 .5	1 17.7	17 13.7	16 56.0
10	9 18 .2	20 41.2	9 59.6	23 39.0	24 49.0	5 27.0	11 .5	15 54.3	17 56.5	1 16.3	17 13.0	16 54.6
11	9 21 56.8	21 41.9	9 56.5	7♐39.1	25 49.3	5 2.4	11 1.8	16 8.6	17 52.5	1 14.9	17 12.2	16 53.2
12	9 25 53.3	22 42.7	9 53.3	21 32.1	26 52.1	4 40.0	11 2.4	16 22.9	17 48.5	1 13.6	17 11.5	16 51.8
13	9 29 49.9	23 43.4	9 50.1	5♑16.7	27 57.4	4 19.9	11 R 2.2	16 37.2	17 44.4	1 12.3	17 10.7	16 50.3
14	9 33 46.5	24 44.0	9 46.9	18 51.2	29 4.9	4 2.1	11 1.2	16 51.4	17 40.2	1 11.0	17 9.9	16 48.9
15	9 37 43.0	25 44.6	9 43.8	2♒14.1	0♒14.5	3 46.7	10 59.5	17 5.7	17 36.0	1 9.8	17 9.0	16 47.5
16	9 41 39.6	26 45.3	9 40.6	15 23.5	1 25.9	3 33.8	10 57.0	17 19.9	17 31.7	1 8.7	17 8.1	16 46.1
17	9 45 36.1	27 45.8	9 37.4	28 18.2	2 39.2	3 23.4	10 53.8	17 34.1	17 27.4	1 7.6	17 7.2	16 44.6
18	9 49 32.7	28 46.4	9 34.2	10♓57.6	3 54.3	3 15.4	10 49.8	17 48.4	17 23.0	1 6.5	17 6.2	16 43.2
19	9 53 29.2	29 47.0	9 31.1	23 22.0	5 10.9	3 9.9	10 45.0	18 2.5	17 18.6	1 5.5	17 5.2	16 41.8
20	9 57 25.8	0♓47.5	9 27.9	5♈32.8	6 29.0	3 6.9	10 39.4	18 16.7	17 14.1	1 4.6	17 4.2	16 40.4
21	10 1 22.3	1 47.9	9 24.7	17 32.5	7 48.5	3 6.3	10 33.0	18 30.9	17 9.6	1 3.6	17 3.2	16 39.1
22	10 5 18.9	2 48.4	9 21.5	29 24.5	9 9.5	3 D 8.1	10 25.9	18 45.0	17 5.0	1 2.8	17 2.2	16 37.7
23	10 9 15.5	3 48.8	9 18.3	11♉12.8	10 31.8	3 12.2	10 17.9	18 59.1	17 .5	1 2.0	17 1.1	16 36.3
24	10 13 12.0	4 49.2	9 15.2	23 2.1	11 55.3	3 18.7	10 9.2	19 13.2	16 55.8	1 1.2	16 60.0	16 34.9
25	10 17 8.6	5 49.6	9 12.0	4♊57.6	13 20.1	3 27.4	9 59.7	19 27.2	16 51.2	1 .5	16 58.8	16 33.6
26	10 21 5.1	6 49.9	9 8.8	17 4.2	14 46.1	3 38.3	9 49.5	19 41.2	16 46.5	0 59.9	16 57.7	16 32.2
27	10 25 1.7	7 50.2	9 5.6	29 26.8	16 13.3	3 51.3	9 38.5	19 55.2	16 41.8	0 59.3	16 56.5	16 30.9
28	10 28 58.2	8 50.4	9 2.5	12♋ 9.5	17 41.6	4 6.4	9 26.7	20 9.2	16 37.1	0 58.7	16 55.3	16 29.6

LATITUDE

DAY	EPHEM. SID. TIME	☉	☊	☽	☿	♀	♂	♃	♄	♅	♆	♇
1	8 42 31.2	0 .0	0 .0	5N 1.5	2N16.9	7N29.1	3N 6.8	0S36.9	2N 8.2	0N16.3	1N37.3	8N17.2
4	8 54 20.9	0 .0	0 .0	3 17.9	1 43.3	7 48.7	3 10.4	0 37.2	2 8.8	0 16.3	1 37.5	8 17.5
7	9 6 10.6	0 .0	0 .0	0S13.8	1 9.9	8 .1	3 13.9	0 37.4	2 9.4	0 16.3	1 37.7	8 17.7
10	9 18 .2	0 .0	0 .0	3 38.8	0 37.9	8 3.5	3 17.3	0 37.7	2 9.9	0 16.3	1 37.8	8 17.9
13	9 29 49.9	0 .0	0 .0	5 8.0	0 7.9	7 59.6	3 20.6	0 38.0	2 10.5	0 16.2	1 38.0	8 18.1
16	9 41 39.6	0 .0	0 .0	4 6.0	0S19.7	7 49.5	3 23.7	0 38.2	2 11.0	0 16.2	1 38.1	8 18.2
19	9 53 29.2	0 .0	0 .0	1 17.8	0 44.6	7 34.5	3 26.5	0 38.5	2 11.4	0 16.2	1 38.3	8 18.3
22	10 5 18.9	0 .0	0 .0	1N55.4	1 6.7	7 15.5	3 29.1	0 38.8	2 11.8	0 16.2	1 38.4	8 18.3
25	10 17 8.6	0 .0	0 .0	4 23.3	1 25.9	6 53.5	3 31.4	0 39.2	2 12.2	0 16.2	1 38.6	8 18.3
28	10 28 58.2	0 .0	0 .0	5 12.5	1 42.0	6 29.5	3 33.2	0 39.5	2 12.5	0 16.2	1 38.7	8 18.3

RIGHT ASCENSION

DAY	EPHEM. SID. TIME	☉	☊	☽	☿	♀	♂	♃	♄	♅	♆	♇
1	8 42 31.2	14♒ 1.7	9♈37.4	19♋36.1	19♑44.5	10♒46.7	10♎41.1	16♒24.7	20♍15.5	1♋39.1	16♎34.5	22♌18.5
2	8 46 27.8	15 2.9	9 34.4	4♌ 8.9	20 10.1	10 R 8.7	10 48.4	16 39.1	20 R 12.5	1 R 37.2	16 R 34.1	22 R 17.0
3	8 50 24.3	16 3.9	9 31.5	18 15.7	20 41.9	9 31.4	10 55.0	16 53.4	20 9.4	1 35.3	16 33.7	22 15.6
4	8 54 20.9	17 4.6	9 28.6	1♍48.4	21 19.4	8 55.1	11 1.1	17 7.8	20 6.2	1 33.4	16 33.2	22 14.1
5	8 58 17.5	18 5.2	9 25.7	14 49.7	22 2.0	8 19.9	11 6.6	17 22.1	20 3.0	1 31.6	16 32.7	22 12.7
6	9 2 14.0	19 5.6	9 22.7	27 30.7	22 49.3	7 46.2	11 11.4	17 36.5	19 59.7	1 29.9	16 32.2	22 11.3
7	9 6 10.6	20 5.7	9 19.8	10♎ 7.1	23 40.9	7 14.1	11 15.6	17 50.8	19 56.3	1 28.2	16 31.6	22 9.8
8	9 10 7.1	21 5.7	9 16.9	22 56.6	24 36.4	6 43.7	11 19.2	18 5.1	19 52.9	1 26.5	16 31.0	22 8.4
9	9 14 3.7	22 5.5	9 13.9	6♏15.7	25 35.5	6 15.3	11 22.1	18 19.4	19 49.4	1 24.9	16 30.4	22 6.9
10	9 18 .2	23 5.1	9 11.0	20 17.1	26 37.8	5 49.1	11 24.4	18 33.7	19 45.8	1 23.3	16 29.8	22 5.5
11	9 21 56.8	24 4.5	9 8.1	5♐ 3.8	27 43.0	5 25.0	11 26.0	18 47.9	19 42.2	1 21.8	16 29.1	22 4.0
12	9 25 53.3	25 3.7	9 5.2	20 25.9	28 51.0	5 3.3	11 27.0	19 2.2	19 38.5	1 20.4	16 28.4	22 2.6
13	9 29 49.9	26 2.7	9 2.2	5♑58.9	0♒ 1.3	4 44.0	11 27.2	19 16.4	19 34.8	1 19.0	16 27.7	22 1.1
14	9 33 46.5	27 1.6	8 59.3	21 12.2	1 13.9	4 27.1	11 R 26.8	19 30.6	19 31.0	1 17.6	16 26.9	21 59.7
15	9 37 43.0	28 .2	8 56.4	5♒39.8	2 28.5	4 12.8	11 25.6	19 44.8	19 27.1	1 16.3	16 26.1	21 58.3
16	9 41 39.6	28 58.7	8 53.4	19 8.7	3 44.9	4 1.0	11 23.7	19 59.0	19 23.2	1 15.0	16 25.3	21 56.8
17	9 45 36.1	29 57.0	8 50.5	1♓39.0	5 3.0	3 51.7	11 21.1	20 13.1	19 19.3	1 13.8	16 24.5	21 55.4
18	9 49 32.7	0♓55.1	8 47.6	13 20.1	6 22.7	3 45.0	11 17.8	20 27.2	19 15.3	1 12.7	16 23.6	21 53.9
19	9 53 29.2	1 53.0	8 44.7	24 25.5	7 43.7	3 40.8	11 13.7	20 41.3	19 11.2	1 11.6	16 22.7	21 52.5
20	9 57 25.8	2 50.8	8 41.7	5♈10.4	9 6.1	3 39.2	11 9.0	20 55.4	19 7.1	1 10.5	16 21.8	21 51.1
21	10 1 22.3	3 48.4	8 38.8	15 49.9	10 29.7	3 D 40.0	11 3.5	21 9.4	19 3.0	1 9.5	16 20.9	21 49.7
22	10 5 18.9	4 45.8	8 35.9	26 38.8	11 54.3	3 43.3	10 57.2	21 23.4	18 58.9	1 8.6	16 19.9	21 48.3
23	10 9 15.5	5 43.0	8 32.9	7♉50.7	13 20.0	3 49.0	10 50.2	21 37.3	18 54.7	1 7.7	16 18.9	21 46.9
24	10 13 12.0	6 40.1	8 30.0	19 37.6	14 46.5	3 57.1	10 42.5	21 51.3	18 50.4	1 6.9	16 17.9	21 45.5
25	10 17 8.6	7 37.1	8 27.1	2♊ 8.2	16 14.0	4 7.5	10 34.1	22 5.2	18 46.2	1 6.1	16 16.9	21 44.1
26	10 21 5.1	8 33.9	8 24.2	15 25.1	17 42.2	4 20.1	10 24.9	22 19.0	18 41.9	1 5.4	16 15.8	21 42.7
27	10 25 1.7	9 30.5	8 21.2	29 22.3	19 11.2	4 34.9	10 15.0	22 32.8	18 37.6	1 4.7	16 14.8	21 41.3
28	10 28 58.2	10 27.0	8 18.3	13♋45.2	20 41.0	4 51.8	10 4.4	22 46.6	18 33.3	1 4.2	16 13.7	21 40.0

DECLINATION

DAY	EPHEM. SID. TIME	☉	☊	☽	☿	♀	♂	♃	♄	♅	♆	♇
1	8 42 31.2	17S19.2	0N 4.3	27N17.8	19S54.3	10S25.8	1S12.9	17S17.5	6N31.2	23N42.6	5S17.9	23N35.2
4	8 54 20.9	16 27.4	0 4.3	15 6.2	20 15.7	10 34.7	1 17.5	17 5.3	6 35.8	23 42.7	5 17.2	23 36.8
7	9 6 10.6	15 33.0	0 4.2	4S36.4	20 29.0	10 48.3	1 19.9	16 53.0	6 40.6	23 42.7	5 16.4	23 38.4
10	9 18 .2	14 36.1	0 4.1	22 13.3	20 33.1	11 5.4	1 19.9	16 40.5	6 45.7	23 42.8	5 15.4	23 40.0
13	9 29 49.9	13 37.1	0 4.1	28 28.3	20 27.0	11 24.6	1 17.5	16 27.9	6 50.9	23 42.8	5 14.4	23 41.5
16	9 41 39.6	12 36.1	0 4.0	20 8.4	20 10.1	11 44.8	1 12.7	16 15.2	6 56.3	23 42.8	5 13.3	23 42.9
19	9 53 29.2	11 33.2	0 4.0	3 49.5	19 42.0	12 4.8	1 5.3	16 2.4	7 1.9	23 42.9	5 12.1	23 44.3
22	10 5 18.9	10 28.7	0 3.9	13N 3.9	19 2.6	12 23.7	0 55.5	15 49.6	7 7.5	23 42.9	5 10.7	23 45.7
25	10 17 8.6	9 22.7	0 3.8	25 26.7	18 11.7	12 40.8	0 43.2	15 36.7	7 13.3	23 42.9	5 9.4	23 46.9
28	10 28 58.2	8 15.5	0 3.8	28 4.6	17 9.2	12 55.4	0 28.6	15 23.8	7 19.1	23 42.9	5 7.9	23 48.2

MARCH 1950

LONGITUDE

DAY	EPHEM. SID. TIME h m s	☉ ° ′	☊ ° ′	☽ ° ′	☿ ° ′	♀ ° ′	♂ ° ′	♃ ° ′	♄ ° ′	♅ ° ′	♆ ° ′	♇ ° ′
1	10 32 54.8	9 ♓ 50.6	8 ♈ 59.3	25 ♋ 15.4	19 ♒ 11.1	4 ♒ 23.6	9 ♎ 14.2	20 ♒ 23.1	16 ♍ 32.4	0 ♋ 58.2	16 ♎ 54.1	16 ♌ 28.3
2	10 36 51.3	10 50.8	8 56.1	8 ♌ 45.8	20 41.7	4 42.7	9 R .9	20 37.0	16 R 27.7	0 R 57.8	16 R 52.8	16 R 27.0
3	10 40 47.9	11 51.0	8 52.9	22 39.9	22 13.4	5 3.7	8 46.9	20 50.9	16 22.9	0 57.4	16 51.6	16 25.7
4	10 44 44.4	12 51.1	8 49.7	6 ♍ 55.1	23 46.2	5 26.5	8 32.2	21 4.7	16 18.1	0 57.1	16 50.3	16 24.4
5	10 48 41.0	13 51.3	8 46.6	21 26.5	25 20.2	5 51.2	8 16.9	21 18.5	16 13.4	0 56.8	16 49.0	16 23.2
6	10 52 37.6	14 51.3	8 43.4	6 ♎ 7.5	26 55.2	6 17.5	8 .8	21 32.3	16 8.6	0 56.6	16 47.7	16 22.0
7	10 56 34.1	15 51.4	8 40.2	20 51.6	28 31.3	6 45.5	7 44.0	21 46.0	16 3.8	0 56.4	16 46.3	16 20.8
8	11 0 30.7	16 51.4	8 37.0	5 ♏ 32.0	0 ♓ 8.5	7 15.0	7 26.6	21 59.7	15 59.0	0 56.3	16 45.0	16 19.6
9	11 4 27.2	17 51.4	8 33.9	20 3.5	1 46.9	7 46.2	7 8.6	22 13.3	15 54.2	0 56.3	16 43.6	16 18.4
10	11 8 23.8	18 51.3	8 30.7	4 ♐ 22.1	3 26.4	8 18.7	6 50.0	22 26.9	15 49.4	0 56.2	16 42.2	16 17.2
11	11 12 20.3	19 51.2	8 27.5	18 25.5	5 7.0	8 52.7	6 30.7	22 40.5	15 44.7	0 D 56.3	16 40.8	16 16.0
12	11 16 16.9	20 51.1	8 24.3	2 ♑ 12.6	6 48.8	9 28.1	6 11.0	22 54.0	15 39.9	0 56.4	16 39.3	16 14.9
13	11 20 13.4	21 51.0	8 21.1	15 43.4	8 31.7	10 4.7	5 50.7	23 7.5	15 35.1	0 56.5	16 37.9	16 13.7
14	11 24 10.0	22 50.8	8 18.0	28 58.4	10 15.8	10 42.6	5 29.9	23 20.9	15 30.4	0 56.7	16 36.4	16 12.6
15	11 28 6.5	23 50.7	8 14.8	11 ♒ 58.6	12 1.1	11 21.7	5 8.7	23 34.2	15 25.7	0 57.0	16 34.9	16 11.5
16	11 32 3.1	24 50.4	8 11.6	24 44.7	13 47.6	12 1.9	4 47.1	23 47.5	15 21.0	0 57.3	16 33.4	16 10.4
17	11 35 59.6	25 50.2	8 8.4	7 ♓ 18.0	15 35.3	12 43.3	4 25.1	24 .8	15 16.3	0 57.6	16 31.9	16 9.4
18	11 39 56.2	26 49.9	8 5.3	19 39.4	17 24.2	13 25.7	4 2.7	24 14.0	15 11.6	0 58.1	16 30.4	16 8.3
19	11 43 52.8	27 49.6	8 2.1	1 ♈ 50.3	19 14.3	14 9.1	3 40.1	24 27.2	15 7.0	0 58.5	16 28.8	16 7.3
20	11 47 49.3	28 49.3	7 58.9	13 52.2	21 5.7	14 53.4	3 17.2	24 40.3	15 2.4	0 59.1	16 27.3	16 6.3
21	11 51 45.9	29 48.9	7 55.7	25 46.9	22 58.3	15 38.7	2 54.1	24 53.3	14 57.8	0 59.6	16 25.7	16 5.3
22	11 55 42.4	0 ♈ 48.5	7 52.6	7 ♉ 36.9	24 52.1	16 24.9	2 30.8	25 6.3	14 53.3	1 .3	16 24.2	16 4.4
23	11 59 39.0	1 48.0	7 49.4	19 25.1	26 47.1	17 11.9	2 7.5	25 19.2	14 48.8	1 1.0	16 22.6	16 3.4
24	12 3 35.5	2 47.5	7 46.2	1 ♊ 14.9	28 43.4	17 59.8	1 44.0	25 32.0	14 44.4	1 1.7	16 21.0	16 2.5
25	12 7 32.1	3 47.0	7 43.0	13 10.3	0 ♈ 40.8	18 48.5	1 20.6	25 44.8	14 40.0	1 2.5	16 19.4	16 1.6
26	12 11 28.6	4 46.5	7 39.8	25 15.7	2 39.3	19 37.9	0 57.2	25 57.6	14 35.7	1 3.4	16 17.8	16 .8
27	12 15 25.2	5 45.9	7 36.7	7 ♋ 35.4	4 38.9	20 28.1	0 33.8	26 10.2	14 31.4	1 4.3	16 16.2	15 60.0
28	12 19 21.7	6 45.3	7 33.5	20 13.8	6 39.5	21 18.9	0 10.6	26 22.8	14 27.1	1 5.2	16 14.6	15 59.1
29	12 23 18.3	7 44.6	7 30.3	3 ♌ 14.8	8 41.0	22 10.4	29 ♍ 47.5	26 35.3	14 22.9	1 6.2	16 13.0	15 58.3
30	12 27 14.8	8 43.9	7 27.1	16 41.3	10 43.2	23 2.6	29 24.6	26 47.8	14 18.7	1 7.3	16 11.3	15 57.6
31	12 31 11.4	9 43.1	7 24.0	0 ♍ 34.5	12 46.1	23 55.4	29 2.0	27 .1	14 14.7	1 8.4	16 9.7	15 56.8

LATITUDE

DAY	EPHEM. SID. TIME	☉	☊	☽	☿	♀	♂	♃	♄	♅	♆	♇
1	10 32 54.8	0 .0	0 .0	4 N 59.0	1 S 46.7	6 N 21.1	3 N 33.7	0 S 39.6	2 N 12.6	0 N 16.2	1 N 38.7	8 N 18.3
4	10 44 44.4	0 .0	0 .0	2 40.4	1 58.5	5 55.4	3 34.8	0 40.0	2 12.9	0 16.2	1 38.8	8 18.2
7	10 56 34.1	0 .0	0 .0	1 S 13.1	2 6.9	5 28.9	3 35.3	0 40.3	2 13.1	0 16.2	1 38.9	8 18.1
10	11 8 23.8	0 .0	0 .0	4 24.7	2 11.6	5 2.2	3 35.2	0 40.7	2 13.3	0 16.1	1 39.1	8 18.0
13	11 20 13.4	0 .0	0 .0	5 12.8	2 12.5	4 35.5	3 34.4	0 41.1	2 13.4	0 16.1	1 39.1	8 17.8
16	11 32 3.1	0 .0	0 .0	3 34.9	2 9.4	4 9.1	3 32.9	0 41.5	2 13.5	0 16.1	1 39.2	8 17.6
19	11 43 52.8	0 .0	0 .0	0 30.8	2 1.9	3 43.1	3 30.5	0 41.9	2 13.5	0 16.1	1 39.3	8 17.3
22	11 55 42.4	0 .0	0 .0	2 N 40.0	1 49.9	3 17.7	3 27.4	0 42.3	2 13.5	0 16.1	1 39.4	8 17.1
25	12 7 32.1	0 .0	0 .0	4 49.7	1 33.2	2 53.0	3 23.5	0 42.8	2 13.5	0 16.1	1 39.4	8 16.8
28	12 19 21.7	0 .0	0 .0	5 9.8	1 11.8	2 28.9	3 18.8	0 43.3	2 13.4	0 16.0	1 39.5	8 16.5
31	12 31 11.4	0 .0	0 .0	3 11.0	0 45.8	2 5.7	3 13.4	0 43.7	2 13.2	0 16.0	1 39.5	8 16.1

RIGHT ASCENSION

DAY	EPHEM. SID. TIME	☉	☊	☽	☿	♀	♂	♃	♄	♅	♆	♇
1	10 32 54.8	11 ♓ 23.4	8 ♈ 15.4	28 ♋ 13.3	22 ♒ 11.3	5 ♒ 10.8	9 ♎ 53.1	23 ♒ .3	18 ♍ 28.9	1 ♋ 3.6	16 ♎ 12.6	21 ♌ 38.6
2	10 36 51.3	12 19.6	8 12.5	12 ♌ 27.7	23 42.3	5 31.8	9 R 41.1	23 14.0	18 R 24.5	1 R 3.1	16 R 11.4	21 R 37.3
3	10 40 47.9	13 15.7	8 9.5	26 16.9	25 13.9	5 54.7	9 28.5	23 27.7	18 20.1	1 2.7	16 10.3	21 36.0
4	10 44 44.4	14 11.7	8 6.6	9 ♍ 39.4	26 46.1	6 19.4	9 15.1	23 41.3	18 15.8	1 2.3	16 9.1	21 34.6
5	10 48 41.0	15 7.6	8 3.7	22 42.8	28 18.9	6 46.1	9 1.1	23 54.9	18 11.4	1 2.1	16 7.9	21 33.4
6	10 52 37.6	16 3.3	8 .8	5 ♎ 40.4	29 52.1	7 14.4	8 46.4	24 8.4	18 7.0	1 1.8	16 6.7	21 32.1
7	10 56 34.1	16 59.0	7 57.8	18 48.3	1 ♓ 25.9	7 44.3	8 31.1	24 21.9	18 2.6	1 1.6	16 5.5	21 30.8
8	11 0 30.7	17 54.5	7 54.9	2 ♏ 22.6	3 .3	8 15.9	8 15.1	24 35.3	17 58.1	1 1.5	16 4.2	21 29.6
9	11 4 27.2	18 50.0	7 52.0	16 35.3	4 35.1	8 49.0	7 58.6	24 48.7	17 53.7	1 1.4	16 2.9	21 28.3
10	11 8 23.8	19 45.3	7 49.1	1 ♐ 29.5	6 10.5	9 23.6	7 41.5	25 2.1	17 49.3	1 1.4	16 1.6	21 27.1
11	11 12 20.3	20 40.6	7 46.1	16 55.7	7 46.4	9 59.6	7 23.8	25 15.3	17 44.9	1 D 1.5	16 .3	21 25.9
12	11 16 16.9	21 35.8	7 43.2	2 ♑ 30.5	9 22.9	10 36.9	7 5.6	25 28.6	17 40.5	1 1.6	15 59.0	21 24.7
13	11 20 13.4	22 30.9	7 40.3	17 44.8	10 59.9	11 15.5	6 46.8	25 41.7	17 36.0	1 1.7	15 57.7	21 23.5
14	11 24 10.0	23 26.0	7 37.4	2 ♒ 13.6	12 37.5	11 55.4	6 27.6	25 54.9	17 31.7	1 1.9	15 56.3	21 22.3
15	11 28 6.5	24 21.0	7 34.4	15 44.3	14 15.6	12 36.4	6 8.0	26 7.9	17 27.3	1 2.2	15 55.0	21 21.2
16	11 32 3.1	25 15.9	7 31.5	28 17.1	15 54.4	13 18.5	5 47.9	26 20.9	17 22.9	1 2.6	15 53.6	21 20.0
17	11 35 59.6	26 10.8	7 28.6	10 ♓ .6	17 33.8	14 1.6	5 27.4	26 33.9	17 18.6	1 3.0	15 52.2	21 18.9
18	11 39 56.2	27 5.6	7 25.7	21 7.9	19 13.8	14 45.8	5 6.7	26 46.8	17 14.2	1 3.4	15 50.8	21 17.8
19	11 43 52.8	28 .4	7 22.7	1 ♈ 53.4	20 54.6	15 31.0	4 45.6	26 59.6	17 9.9	1 3.9	15 49.4	21 16.8
20	11 47 49.3	28 55.1	7 19.8	12 31.8	22 36.0	16 17.0	4 24.2	27 12.4	17 5.7	1 4.5	15 48.0	21 15.7
21	11 51 45.9	29 49.8	7 16.9	23 16.7	24 18.2	17 3.9	4 2.6	27 25.1	17 1.4	1 5.1	15 46.5	21 14.7
22	11 55 42.4	0 ♈ 44.5	7 14.0	4 ♉ 21.1	26 1.1	17 51.6	3 40.9	27 37.7	16 57.2	1 5.8	15 45.1	21 13.6
23	11 59 39.0	1 39.1	7 11.0	15 56.0	27 44.7	18 40.2	3 19.0	27 50.3	16 53.0	1 6.6	15 43.6	21 12.7
24	12 3 35.5	2 33.7	7 8.1	28 9.6	29 29.2	19 29.4	2 57.0	28 2.8	16 48.9	1 7.4	15 42.1	21 11.7
25	12 7 32.1	3 28.3	7 5.2	11 ♊ 4.7	1 ♈ 14.5	20 19.4	2 34.9	28 15.2	16 44.8	1 8.2	15 40.7	21 10.7
26	12 11 28.6	4 22.9	7 2.3	24 37.6	3 .6	21 10.0	2 12.9	28 27.6	16 40.8	1 9.2	15 39.2	21 9.8
27	12 15 25.2	5 17.5	6 59.3	8 ♋ 36.5	4 47.5	22 1.3	1 50.9	28 39.9	16 36.8	1 10.2	15 37.7	21 8.9
28	12 19 21.7	6 12.1	6 56.4	22 44.6	6 35.2	22 53.1	1 28.9	28 52.1	16 32.8	1 11.2	15 36.3	21 8.0
29	12 23 18.3	7 6.6	6 53.5	6 ♌ 45.3	8 23.6	23 45.5	1 7.0	29 4.3	16 28.9	1 12.3	15 34.7	21 7.2
30	12 27 14.8	8 1.2	6 50.6	20 27.4	10 12.8	24 38.5	0 45.3	29 16.4	16 25.0	1 13.5	15 33.2	21 6.3
31	12 31 11.4	8 55.8	6 47.6	3 ♍ 48.0	12 2.5	25 32.0	0 23.8	29 28.4	16 21.1	1 14.7	15 31.7	21 5.5

DECLINATION

DAY	EPHEM. SID. TIME	☉	☊	☽	☿	♀	♂	♃	♄	♅	♆	♇
1	10 32 54.8	7 S 52.9	0 N 3.7	25 N 59.4	16 S 45.8	12 S 59.6	0 S 23.3	15 S 19.4	7 N 21.0	23 N 42.9	5 S 7.4	23 N 48.6
4	10 44 44.4	6 44.3	0 3.7	11 27.4	15 27.9	13 10.0	0 5.8	15 6.5	7 26.8	23 42.9	5 5.8	23 49.7
7	10 56 34.1	5 34.8	0 3.6	9 S 16.5	13 58.5	13 16.8	0 N 13.7	14 53.5	7 32.6	23 42.9	5 4.2	23 50.7
10	11 8 23.8	4 24.7	0 3.5	25 21.5	12 17.6	13 19.5	0 34.9	14 40.6	7 38.3	23 42.8	5 2.5	23 51.7
13	11 20 13.4	3 14.0	0 3.5	27 41.9	10 25.4	13 18.0	0 57.5	14 27.7	7 44.0	23 42.8	5 .8	23 52.6
16	11 32 3.1	2 3.0	0 3.4	16 39.1	8 22.0	13 12.1	1 21.3	14 14.9	7 49.6	23 42.8	4 59.0	23 53.4
19	11 43 52.8	0 51.9	0 3.3	0 N 15.6	6 7.8	13 1.6	1 45.7	14 2.1	7 55.1	23 42.8	4 57.2	23 54.2
22	11 55 42.4	0 N 19.3	0 3.3	16 34.6	3 43.3	12 46.6	2 10.3	13 49.4	8 .4	23 42.8	4 55.3	23 54.8
25	12 7 32.1	1 30.3	0 3.2	27 10.7	1 9.3	12 27.0	2 34.6	13 36.8	8 5.5	23 42.7	4 53.5	23 55.4
28	12 19 21.7	2 41.0	0 3.1	27 1.7	1 N 32.7	12 2.9	2 58.2	13 24.4	8 10.4	23 42.7	4 51.6	23 55.9
31	12 31 11.4	3 51.1	0 3.1	14 14.9	4 20.5	11 34.4	3 20.5	13 12.0	8 15.1	23 42.6	4 49.7	23 56.3

APRIL 1950

LONGITUDE

DAY	EPHEM. SID. TIME h m s	☉ ° ′	☊ ° ′	☽ ° ′	☿ ° ′	♀ ° ′	♂ ° ′	♃ ° ′	♄ ° ′	♅ ° ′	♆ ° ′	♇ ° ′
1	12 35 8.0	10♈42.3	7♈20.8	14♍53.5	14♈49.4	24♒48.8	28♍39.6	27♒12.4	14♍10.6	1♋ 9.5	16♎ 8.1	15♌56.1
2	12 39 4.5	11 41.5	7 17.6	29 34.6	16 53.0	25 42.8	28 R 17.6	27 24.7	14 R 6.6	1 10.7	16 R 6.4	15 R 55.4
3	12 43 1.1	12 40.6	7 14.4	14♎32.0	18 56.7	26 37.4	27 56.0	27 36.8	14 2.7	1 12.0	16 4.8	15 54.7
4	12 46 57.6	13 39.7	7 11.2	29 37.4	21 .1	27 32.5	27 34.7	27 48.9	13 58.9	1 13.3	16 3.1	15 54.0
5	12 50 54.2	14 38.8	7 8.1	14♏42.0	23 3.1	28 28.1	27 13.9	28 .9	13 55.1	1 14.6	16 1.5	15 53.4
6	12 54 50.7	15 37.8	7 4.9	29 37.0	25 5.2	29 24.3	26 53.5	28 12.8	13 51.4	1 16.0	15 59.8	15 52.8
7	12 58 47.3	16 36.8	7 1.7	14♐15.3	27 6.1	0♓20.9	26 33.6	28 24.6	13 47.8	1 17.5	15 58.2	15 52.2
8	13 2 43.8	17 35.8	6 58.5	28 32.2	29 5.6	1 18.0	26 14.3	28 36.4	13 44.2	1 19.0	15 56.5	15 51.6
9	13 6 40.4	18 34.8	6 55.4	12♑25.3	1♉ 3.2	2 15.6	25 55.5	28 48.0	13 40.7	1 20.5	15 54.9	15 51.1
10	13 10 36.9	19 33.7	6 52.2	25 54.6	2 58.5	3 13.6	25 37.3	28 59.6	13 37.3	1 22.1	15 53.2	15 50.6
11	13 14 33.5	20 32.6	6 49.0	9♒ 1.7	4 51.3	4 12.0	25 19.8	29 11.1	13 33.9	1 23.8	15 51.6	15 50.1
12	13 18 30.0	21 31.4	6 45.8	21 49.0	6 41.1	5 10.9	25 2.8	29 22.5	13 30.6	1 25.4	15 49.9	15 49.6
13	13 22 26.6	22 30.3	6 42.6	4♓19.8	8 27.7	6 10.1	24 46.5	29 33.8	13 27.5	1 27.2	15 48.3	15 49.2
14	13 26 23.2	23 29.1	6 39.5	16 37.0	10 10.7	7 9.7	24 31.0	29 45.0	13 24.3	1 29.0	15 46.6	15 48.8
15	13 30 19.7	24 27.8	6 36.3	28 43.7	11 49.8	8 9.6	24 16.1	29 56.2	13 21.3	1 30.8	15 45.0	15 48.4
16	13 34 16.3	25 26.6	6 33.1	10♈42.6	13 24.9	9 10.0	24 2.0	0♓ 7.2	13 18.4	1 32.7	15 43.4	15 48.1
17	13 38 12.8	26 25.3	6 29.9	22 36.0	14 55.6	10 10.6	23 48.5	0 18.2	13 15.6	1 34.6	15 41.8	15 47.8
18	13 42 9.4	27 24.0	6 26.8	4♉26.0	16 21.7	11 11.6	23 35.9	0 29.0	13 12.8	1 36.6	15 40.2	15 47.5
19	13 46 5.9	28 22.7	6 23.6	16 14.7	17 43.2	12 12.8	23 24.0	0 39.7	13 10.1	1 38.6	15 38.6	15 47.3
20	13 50 2.5	29 21.3	6 20.4	28 4.2	18 59.8	13 14.4	23 12.9	0 50.3	13 7.6	1 40.6	15 37.0	15 47.0
21	13 53 59.0	0♉19.9	6 17.2	9♊56.8	20 11.3	14 16.2	23 2.5	1 .9	13 5.1	1 42.7	15 35.4	15 46.8
22	13 57 55.6	1 18.4	6 14.0	21 55.2	21 17.8	15 18.3	22 53.0	1 11.3	13 2.7	1 44.9	15 33.8	15 46.6
23	14 1 52.1	2 16.9	6 10.9	4♋ 2.4	22 19.0	16 20.7	22 44.3	1 21.6	13 .4	1 47.0	15 32.3	15 46.5
24	14 5 48.7	3 15.4	6 7.7	16 21.9	23 14.9	17 23.4	22 36.3	1 31.8	12 58.2	1 49.3	15 30.7	15 46.3
25	14 9 45.3	4 13.8	6 4.5	28 57.4	24 5.4	18 26.3	22 29.2	1 41.9	12 56.0	1 51.5	15 29.1	15 46.2
26	14 13 41.8	5 12.2	6 1.3	11♌52.5	24 50.5	19 29.4	22 22.8	1 51.9	12 54.0	1 53.8	15 27.6	15 46.2
27	14 17 38.4	6 10.6	5 58.2	25 10.9	25 30.0	20 32.8	22 17.3	2 1.7	12 52.1	1 56.2	15 26.1	15 46.1
28	14 21 34.9	7 8.9	5 55.0	8♍55.0	26 3.9	21 36.4	22 12.5	2 11.5	12 50.3	1 58.5	15 24.6	15 46.1
29	14 25 31.5	8 7.2	5 51.8	23 5.8	26 32.3	22 40.3	22 8.6	2 21.1	12 48.5	2 1.0	15 23.1	15 46.1
30	14 29 28.0	9 5.5	5 48.6	7♎42.0	26 55.1	23 44.3	22 5.4	2 30.6	12 46.9	2 3.4	15 21.6	15 46.1

LATITUDE

DAY	EPHEM. SID. TIME	☉	☊	☽	☿	♀	♂	♃	♄	♅	♆	♇
1	12 35 8.0	0 .0	0 .0	2N 2.2	0S36.2	1N58.2	3N11.5	0S43.9	2N13.2	0N16.0	1N39.5	8N16.0
4	12 46 57.6	0 .0	0 .0	2S .0	0 5.2	1 36.2	3 5.3	0 44.4	2 13.0	0 16.0	1 39.6	8 15.6
7	12 58 47.3	0 .0	0 .0	4 51.7	0N28.3	1 15.1	2 58.6	0 44.9	2 12.8	0 16.0	1 39.6	8 15.3
10	13 10 36.9	0 .0	0 .0	5 .8	1 2.4	0 54.9	2 51.4	0 45.4	2 12.5	0 16.0	1 39.6	8 14.9
13	13 22 26.6	0 .0	0 .0	2 53.4	1 34.9	0 35.8	2 43.9	0 46.0	2 12.3	0 16.0	1 39.6	8 14.4
16	13 34 16.3	0 .0	0 .0	0N17.9	2 3,6	0 17.7	2 36.2	0 46.5	2 11.9	0 16.0	1 39.6	8 14.0
19	13 46 5.9	0 .0	0 .0	3 17.8	2 26.5	0 .7	2 28.3	0 47.1	2 11.6	0 15.9	1 39.6	8 13.6
22	13 57 55.6	0 .0	0 .0	5 3.0	2 41.9	0S15.4	2 20.3	0 47.7	2 11.2	0 15.9	1 39.6	8 13.1
25	14 9 45.3	0 .0	0 .0	4 51.6	2 48.5	0 30.3	2 12.3	0 48.3	2 10.8	0 15.9	1 39.5	8 12.7
28	14 21 34.9	0 .0	0 .0	2 28.7	2 45.3	0 44.2	2 4.3	0 48.9	2 10.4	0 15.9	1 39.5	8 12.2

RIGHT ASCENSION

DAY	EPHEM. SID. TIME	☉	☊	☽	☿	♀	♂	♃	♄	♅	♆	♇
1	12 35 8.0	9♈50.3	6♈44.7	16♍52.9	13♈52.9	26♒25.9	0♎ 2.6	29♒40.3	16♍17.4	1♋15.9	15♎30.2	21♌ 4.7
2	12 39 4.5	10 45.0	6 41.8	29 54.1	15 43.7	27 20.4	29♍41.6	29 52.1	16 R 13.6	1 17.2	15 R 28.7	21 R 4.0
3	12 43 1.1	11 39.6	6 38.9	13♎ 7.4	17 34.8	28 15.2	29 R 20.9	0♓ 3.9	16 10.0	1 18.6	15 27.2	21 3.2
4	12 46 57.6	12 34.3	6 36.0	26 49.5	19 26.1	29 10.5	29 .5	0 15.6	16 6.4	1 20.0	15 25.7	21 2.5
5	12 50 54.2	13 29.0	6 33.0	11♏14.0	21 17.3	0♓ 6.1	28 40.5	0 27.2	16 2.8	1 21.5	15 24.1	21 1.8
6	12 54 50.7	14 23.7	6 30.1	26 26.2	23 8.2	1 2.2	28 20.9	0 38.7	15 59.3	1 23.0	15 22.6	21 1.1
7	12 58 47.3	15 18.5	6 27.2	12♐16.7	24 58.6	1 58.5	28 1.7	0 50.1	15 55.9	1 24.6	15 21.1	21 .5
8	13 2 43.8	16 13.4	6 24.3	28 20.3	26 48.2	2 55.3	27 43.0	1 1.5	15 52.6	1 26.3	15 19.5	20 59.9
9	13 6 40.4	17 8.3	6 21.3	14♑ 3.3	28 36.7	3 52.3	27 24.8	1 12.8	15 49.3	1 27.9	15 18.0	20 59.3
10	13 10 36.9	18 3.3	6 18.4	28 56.3	0♉23.8	4 49.6	27 7.2	1 23.9	15 46.0	1 29.7	15 16.5	20 58.7
11	13 14 33.5	18 58.4	6 15.5	12♒44.6	2 9.1	5 47.2	26 50.0	1 35.0	15 42.9	1 31.5	15 15.0	20 58.2
12	13 18 30.0	19 53.5	6 12.6	25 28.2	3 52.3	6 45.0	26 33.5	1 46.0	15 39.8	1 33.3	15 13.4	20 57.6
13	13 22 26.6	20 48.7	6 9.7	7♓17.0	5 33.2	7 43.1	26 17.5	1 56.9	15 36.8	1 35.2	15 11.9	20 57.1
14	13 26 23.2	21 44.0	6 6.7	18 25.4	7 11.4	8 41.3	26 2.1	2 7.7	15 33.9	1 37.2	15 10.4	20 56.7
15	13 30 19.7	22 39.3	6 3.8	29 9.2	8 46.6	9 39.8	25 47.4	2 18.5	15 31.0	1 39.2	15 8.9	20 56.2
16	13 34 16.3	23 34.8	6 .9	9♈43.6	10 18.5	10 38.6	25 33.4	2 29.1	15 28.3	1 41.2	15 7.4	20 55.9
17	13 38 12.8	24 30.4	5 58.0	20 22.9	11 46.8	11 37.5	25 20.0	2 39.7	15 25.6	1 43.3	15 5.9	20 55.5
18	13 42 9.4	25 26.0	5 55.1	1♉20.0	13 11.3	12 36.5	25 7.3	2 50.1	15 22.9	1 45.5	15 4.4	20 55.2
19	13 46 5.9	26 21.7	5 52.1	12 46.2	14 31.8	13 35.8	24 55.3	3 .4	15 20.4	1 47.7	15 2.9	20 54.8
20	13 50 2.5	27 17.6	5 49.2	24 49.3	15 48.0	14 35.1	24 44.0	3 10.6	15 17.9	1 49.9	15 1.5	20 54.5
21	13 53 59.0	28 13.5	5 46.3	7♊32.3	16 59.7	15 34.7	24 33.4	3 20.8	15 15.6	1 52.2	14 60.0	20 54.3
22	13 57 55.6	29 9.5	5 43.4	20 51.3	18 6.7	16 34.3	24 23.6	3 30.8	15 13.3	1 54.5	14 58.5	20 54.0
23	14 1 52.1	0♉ 5.7	5 40.5	4♋35.1	19 8.9	17 34.1	24 14.5	3 40.7	15 11.1	1 56.9	14 57.1	20 53.8
24	14 5 48.7	1 1.9	5 37.5	18 27.3	20 6.2	18 34.1	24 6.1	3 50.5	15 9.0	1 59.3	14 55.6	20 53.6
25	14 9 45.3	1 58.3	5 34.6	2♌11.8	20 58.3	19 34.1	23 58.5	4 .2	15 6.9	2 1.8	14 54.2	20 53.5
26	14 13 41.8	2 54.8	5 31.7	15 37.4	21 45.1	20 34.3	23 51.6	4 9.8	15 5.0	2 4.3	14 52.7	20 53.3
27	14 17 38.4	3 51.4	5 28.8	28 41.0	22 26.6	21 34.6	23 45.4	4 19.2	15 3.1	2 6.9	14 51.3	20 53.2
28	14 21 34.9	4 48.1	5 25.9	11♍28.0	23 2.7	22 35.0	23 40.0	4 28.6	15 1.4	2 9.5	14 49.9	20 53.2
29	14 25 31.5	5 44.9	5 22.9	24 10.0	23 33.2	23 35.5	23 35.3	4 37.8	14 59.7	2 12.1	14 48.5	20 53.1
30	14 29 28.0	6 41.9	5 20.0	7♎ 3.1	23 58.2	24 36.1	23 31.3	4 47.0	14 58.1	2 14.8	14 47.2	20 53.1

DECLINATION

DAY	EPHEM. SID. TIME	☉	☊	☽	☿	♀	♂	♃	♄	♅	♆	♇
1	12 35 8.0	4N14.3	0N 3.1	7N49.9	5N17.2	11S23.9	3N27.6	13S 8.0	8N16.6	23N42.6	4S49.0	23N56.4
4	12 46 57.6	5 23.6	0 3.0	13S12.9	8 7.2	10 49.5	3 47.8	12 55.9	8 21.0	23 42.6	4 47.1	23 56.7
7	12 58 47.3	6 32.0	0 2.9	27 20.8	10 53.1	10 10.9	4 5.9	12 44.0	8 25.1	23 42.5	4 45.2	23 56.9
10	13 10 36.9	7 39.4	0 2.9	25 53.7	13 29.1	9 28.3	4 21.7	12 32.3	8 28.9	23 42.5	4 43.3	23 57.0
13	13 22 26.6	8 45.6	0 2.8	12 37.0	15 49.6	8 41.8	4 35.0	12 20.8	8 32.4	23 42.4	4 41.4	23 57.0
16	13 34 16.3	9 50.6	0 2.7	4N30.9	17 50.1	7 51.7	4 45.6	12 9.6	8 35.6	23 42.3	4 39.5	23 57.0
19	13 46 5.9	10 54.1	0 2.7	19 51.5	19 27.8	6 58.3	4 53.4	11 58.6	8 38.5	23 42.2	4 37.7	23 56.8
22	13 57 55.6	11 56.0	0 2.6	28 14.5	20 41.6	6 1.8	4 58.4	11 48.0	8 41.0	23 42.1	4 35.9	23 56.6
25	14 9 45.3	12 56.1	0 2.5	25 7.7	21 31.3	5 2.4	5 .5	11 37.6	8 43.2	23 42.0	4 34.1	23 56.3
28	14 21 34.9	13 54.3	0 2.5	10 31.5	21 57.2	4 .4	4 59.8	11 27.6	8 45.0	23 41.9	4 32.4	23 55.9

MAY 1950

LONGITUDE

DAY	EPHEM. SID. TIME h m s	☉ ° ′	☊ ° ′	☽ ° ′	☿ ° ′	♀ ° ′	♂ ° ′	♃ ° ′	♄ ° ′	♅ ° ′	♆ ° ′	♇ ° ′
1	14 33 24.6	10♉ 3.7	5♈45.5	22♎39.4	27♉12.2	24♓48.6	22♍ 3.0	2♓40.0	12♍45.4	2♋ 5.9	15♎20.1	15♌46.2
2	14 37 21.1	11 1.9	5 42.3	7♏51.0	27 23.9	25 53.1	22R 1.3	2 49.3	12R44.0	2 8.4	15R18.7	15D46.3
3	14 41 17.7	12 .1	5 39.1	23 7.1	27 30.1	26 57.8	22 .5	2 58.4	12 42.6	2 11.0	15 17.2	15 46.4
4	14 45 14.3	12 58.2	5 35.9	8♐17.5	27 31.0	28 2.7	22 .3	3 7.5	12 41.4	2 13.6	15 15.8	15 46.6
5	14 49 10.8	13 56.3	5 32.7	23 12.2	27R26.7	29 7.7	22D 1.0	3 16.4	12 40.3	2 16.2	15 14.4	15 46.7
6	14 53 7.4	14 54.4	5 29.6	7♑43.9	27 17.5	0♈13.0	22 2.3	3 25.2	12 39.3	2 18.9	15 13.0	15 46.9
7	14 57 3.9	15 52.5	5 26.4	21 48.2	27 3.6	1 18.5	22 4.5	3 33.8	12 38.4	2 21.7	15 11.7	15 47.2
8	15 1 .5	16 50.6	5 23.2	5♒23.8	26 45.3	2 24.1	22 7.3	3 42.4	12 37.6	2 24.4	15 10.3	15 47.5
9	15 4 57.0	17 48.6	5 20.0	18 32.1	26 23.1	3 29.9	22 10.8	3 50.8	12 36.9	2 27.2	15 9.0	15 47.8
10	15 8 53.6	18 46.6	5 16.9	1♓16.5	25 57.3	4 35.9	22 15.0	3 59.0	12 36.2	2 30.0	15 7.7	15 48.1
11	15 12 50.2	19 44.6	5 13.7	13 41.0	25 28.5	5 42.0	22 19.9	4 7.1	12 35.7	2 32.8	15 6.4	15 48.4
12	15 16 46.7	20 42.5	5 10.5	25 50.3	24 57.1	6 48.2	22 25.5	4 15.1	12 35.3	2 35.7	15 5.1	15 48.8
13	15 20 43.3	21 40.5	5 7.3	7♈48.7	24 23.7	7 54.7	22 31.8	4 23.0	12 35.0	2 38.6	15 3.8	15 49.2
14	15 24 39.8	22 38.4	5 4.1	19 40.4	23 49.0	9 1.2	22 38.8	4 30.7	12 34.8	2 41.5	15 2.6	15 49.6
15	15 28 36.4	23 36.3	5 1.0	1♉28.9	23 13.6	10 7.9	22 46.4	4 38.2	12 34.8	2 44.5	15 1.4	15 50.0
16	15 32 32.9	24 34.1	4 57.8	13 16.9	22 38.1	11 14.7	22 54.6	4 45.6	12 34.8	2 47.5	15 .2	15 50.5
17	15 36 29.5	25 32.0	4 54.6	25 6.8	22 3.1	12 21.7	23 3.5	4 52.9	12D34.9	2 50.5	14 59.0	15 51.0
18	15 40 26.1	26 29.8	4 51.4	7♊ .4	21 29.2	13 28.8	23 13.1	5 .0	12 35.1	2 53.5	14 57.9	15 51.6
19	15 44 22.6	27 27.6	4 48.3	18 59.4	20 56.9	14 36.0	23 23.2	5 7.0	12 35.4	2 56.6	14 56.8	15 52.1
20	15 48 19.2	28 25.4	4 45.1	1♋ 5.3	20 26.9	15 43.3	23 34.0	5 13.8	12 35.9	2 59.7	14 55.7	15 52.7
21	15 52 15.7	29 23.1	4 41.9	13 20.0	19 59.6	16 50.8	23 45.3	5 20.5	12 36.4	3 2.8	14 54.6	15 53.3
22	15 56 12.3	0♊20.8	4 38.7	25 45.3	19 35.3	17 58.3	23 57.2	5 27.0	12 37.1	3 6.0	14 53.5	15 53.9
23	16 0 8.8	1 18.5	4 35.6	8♌23.8	19 14.5	19 6.0	24 9.7	5 33.3	12 37.8	3 9.1	14 52.5	15 54.6
24	16 4 5.4	2 16.2	4 32.4	21 18.3	18 57.5	20 13.7	24 22.8	5 39.5	12 38.7	3 12.3	14 51.5	15 55.3
25	16 8 2.0	3 13.8	4 29.2	4♍31.7	18 44.4	21 21.6	24 36.4	5 45.5	12 39.6	3 15.5	14 50.5	15 56.0
26	16 11 58.5	4 11.4	4 26.0	18 7.0	18 35.6	22 29.6	24 50.5	5 51.4	12 40.7	3 18.8	14 49.6	15 56.8
27	16 15 55.1	5 9.0	4 22.9	2♎ 5.9	18 31.1	23 37.6	25 5.2	5 57.1	12 41.8	3 22.0	14 48.7	15 57.5
28	16 19 51.6	6 6.7	4 19.7	16 28.8	18 31.1	24 45.8	25 20.5	6 2.7	12 43.2	3 25.4	14 47.8	15 58.4
29	16 23 48.2	7 4.2	4 16.5	1♏13.6	18D35.5	25 54.1	25 36.1	6 8.1	12 44.5	3 28.7	14 46.9	15 59.2
30	16 27 44.7	8 1.7	4 13.3	16 15.4	18 44.4	27 2.5	25 52.3	6 13.4	12 46.0	3 32.0	14 46.1	16 .0
31	16 31 41.3	8 59.2	4 10.1	1♐26.2	18 57.8	28 10.9	26 9.0	6 18.4	12 47.6	3 35.3	14 45.3	16 .9

LATITUDE

DAY	EPHEM. SID. TIME	☉	☊	☽	☿	♀	♂	♃	♄	♅	♆	♇
1	14 33 24.6	0 .0	0 .0	1S23.7	2N31.4	0S57.0	1N56.5	0S49.6	2N10.0	0N15.9	1N39.4	8N11.7
4	14 45 14.3	0 .0	0 .0	4 33.2	2 6.6	1 8.8	1 48.8	0 50.2	2 9.5	0 15.9	1 39.4	8 11.2
7	14 57 3.9	0 .0	0 .0	5 .4	1 31.3	1 19.4	1 41.3	0 50.9	2 9.1	0 15.9	1 39.3	8 10.8
10	15 8 53.6	0 .0	0 .0	3 .6	0 47.0	1 29.0	1 34.0	0 51.6	2 8.6	0 15.9	1 39.2	8 10.3
13	15 20 43.3	0 .0	0 .0	0N 5.7	0S 3.4	1 37.5	1 26.9	0 52.3	2 8.1	0 15.9	1 39.1	8 9.8
16	15 32 32.9	0 .0	0 .0	3 4.1	0 55.9	1 45.0	1 20.0	0 53.0	2 7.6	0 15.9	1 39.1	8 9.4
19	15 44 22.6	0 .0	0 .0	4 52.4	1 46.1	1 51.4	1 13.3	0 53.8	2 7.1	0 15.9	1 39.0	8 8.9
22	15 56 12.3	0 .0	0 .0	4 47.6	2 30.3	1 56.8	1 6.9	0 54.5	2 6.6	0 15.9	1 38.9	8 8.5
25	16 8 2.0	0 .0	0 .0	2 38.6	3 5.8	2 1.2	1 .6	0 55.3	2 6.1	0 15.9	1 38.7	8 8.0
28	16 19 51.6	0 .0	0 .0	0S57.6	3 31.4	2 4.7	0 54.7	0 56.1	2 5.6	0 15.9	1 38.6	8 7.6
31	16 31 41.3	0 .0	0 .0	4 12.1	3 46.8	2 7.1	0 48.9	0 56.9	2 5.1	0 15.9	1 38.5	8 7.2

RIGHT ASCENSION

DAY	EPHEM. SID. TIME	☉	☊	☽	☿	♀	♂	♃	♄	♅	♆	♇
1	14 33 24.6	7♉39.0	5♈17.1	20♎25.7	24♉17.7	25♓36.8	23♍28.1	4♓56.0	14♍56.7	2♋17.5	14♎45.8	20♌53.1
2	14 37 21.1	8 36.2	5 14.2	4♏35.1	24 31.7	26 37.7	23R25.5	5 4.9	14R55.3	2 20.3	14R44.4	20 53.1
3	14 41 17.7	9 33.6	5 11.3	19 42.3	24 40.2	27 38.6	23 23.7	5 13.7	14 54.0	2 23.1	14 43.1	20D53.2
4	14 45 14.3	10 31.1	5 8.3	5♐44.3	24 43.5	28 39.7	23 22.6	5 22.3	14 52.8	2 25.9	14 41.8	20 53.3
5	14 49 10.8	11 28.7	5 5.4	22 18.3	24R41.7	29 40.9	23 22.2	5 30.9	14 51.7	2 28.8	14 40.5	20 53.4
6	14 53 7.4	12 26.5	5 2.5	8♑45.6	24 34.9	0♈42.2	23D22.4	5 39.3	14 50.7	2 31.7	14 39.2	20 53.6
7	14 57 3.9	13 24.4	4 59.6	24 26.9	24 23.7	1 43.6	23 23.4	5 47.6	14 49.8	2 34.7	14 37.9	20 53.8
8	15 1 .5	14 22.5	4 56.7	8♒57.9	24 8.1	2 45.1	23 25.0	5 55.8	14 49.0	2 37.7	14 36.7	20 54.0
9	15 4 57.0	15 20.7	4 53.7	22 14.0	23 48.8	3 46.7	23 27.3	6 3.8	14 48.2	2 40.7	14 35.4	20 54.3
10	15 8 53.6	16 19.1	4 50.8	4♓24.5	23 26.0	4 48.5	23 30.2	6 11.8	14 47.6	2 43.8	14 34.2	20 54.5
11	15 12 50.2	17 17.6	4 47.9	15 45.4	23 .3	5 50.3	23 33.8	6 19.5	14 47.1	2 46.9	14 33.0	20 54.8
12	15 16 46.7	18 16.3	4 45.0	26 34.2	22 32.3	6 52.3	23 38.0	6 27.2	14 46.6	2 50.0	14 31.8	20 55.2
13	15 20 43.3	19 15.1	4 42.1	7♈ 8.2	22 2.6	7 54.4	23 42.9	6 34.7	14 46.3	2 53.2	14 30.6	20 55.5
14	15 24 39.8	20 14.0	4 39.1	17 43.1	21 31.6	8 56.6	23 48.4	6 42.1	14 46.0	2 56.4	14 29.5	20 55.9
15	15 28 36.4	21 13.1	4 36.2	28 33.3	21 .1	9 59.0	23 54.4	6 49.3	14 45.9	2 59.6	14 28.3	20 56.3
16	15 32 32.9	22 12.3	4 33.3	9♉51.0	20 28.6	11 1.4	24 1.1	6 56.5	14 45.8	3 2.9	14 27.2	20 56.8
17	15 36 29.5	23 11.7	4 30.4	21 45.6	19 57.8	12 4.0	24 8.4	7 3.4	14D45.9	3 6.2	14 26.1	20 57.2
18	15 40 26.1	24 11.2	4 27.5	4♊21.1	19 28.0	13 6.7	24 16.3	7 10.2	14 46.0	3 9.5	14 25.0	20 57.7
19	15 44 22.6	25 10.9	4 24.6	17 34.3	18 60.0	14 9.6	24 24.8	7 16.9	14 46.3	3 12.8	14 24.0	20 58.2
20	15 48 19.2	26 10.7	4 21.6	1♋14.1	18 34.1	15 12.6	24 33.8	7 23.5	14 46.6	3 16.2	14 23.0	20 58.8
21	15 52 15.7	27 10.6	4 18.7	15 3.1	18 10.8	16 15.8	24 43.4	7 29.9	14 47.0	3 19.6	14 22.0	20 59.4
22	15 56 12.3	28 10.7	4 15.8	28 43.4	17 50.4	17 19.1	24 53.5	7 36.1	14 47.6	3 23.1	14 21.0	20 60.0
23	16 0 8.8	29 10.9	4 12.9	12♌ 1.7	17 33.2	18 22.5	25 4.2	7 42.2	14 48.2	3 26.5	14 20.0	21 .6
24	16 4 5.4	0♊11.2	4 10.0	24 53.5	17 19.6	19 26.2	25 15.4	7 48.2	14 48.9	3 30.0	14 19.1	21 1.3
25	16 8 2.0	1 11.7	4 7.1	7♍22.8	17 9.6	20 29.9	25 27.0	7 54.0	14 49.8	3 33.5	14 18.1	21 1.9
26	16 11 58.5	2 12.2	4 4.1	19 40.7	17 3.6	21 33.9	25 39.2	7 59.6	14 50.7	3 37.1	14 17.3	21 2.7
27	16 15 55.1	3 12.9	4 1.2	2♎ 3.0	17 1.5	22 38.0	25 51.9	8 5.1	14 51.7	3 40.6	14 16.4	21 3.4
28	16 19 51.6	4 13.8	3 58.3	14 48.8	17D 3.5	23 42.4	26 5.2	8 10.5	14 52.9	3 44.3	14 15.6	21 4.2
29	16 23 48.2	5 14.7	3 55.4	28 17.6	17 9.7	24 46.9	26 18.8	8 15.7	14 54.1	3 47.9	14 14.8	21 5.0
30	16 27 44.7	6 15.7	3 52.5	12♏46.6	17 19.9	25 51.6	26 32.9	8 20.7	14 55.4	3 51.5	14 14.0	21 5.8
31	16 31 41.3	7 16.9	3 49.6	28 22.7	17 34.3	26 56.5	26 47.5	8 25.6	14 56.8	3 55.1	14 13.2	21 6.7

DECLINATION

DAY	EPHEM. SID. TIME	☉	☊	☽	☿	♀	♂	♃	♄	♅	♆	♇
1	14 33 24.6	14N50.4	0N 2.4	10S 6.8	21N59.8	2S56.1	4N56.3	11S17.9	8N46.5	23N41.8	4S30.7	23N55.4
4	14 45 14.3	15 44.3	0 2.3	26 11.5	21 40.0	1 49.8	4 50.3	11 8.6	8 47.6	23 41.7	4 29.1	23 54.8
7	14 57 3.9	16 35.8	0 2.3	26 37.4	20 59.3	0 41.7	4 41.8	10 59.7	8 48.3	23 41.5	4 27.6	23 54.2
10	15 8 53.6	17 24.9	0 2.2	13 50.3	20 .7	0N28.0	4 30.9	10 51.2	8 48.7	23 41.4	4 26.1	23 53.5
13	15 20 43.3	18 11.4	0 2.1	3N11.3	18 49.3	1 38.7	4 17.7	10 43.1	8 48.7	23 41.2	4 24.7	23 52.7
16	15 32 32.9	18 55.2	0 2.1	18 45.3	17 32.2	2 50.4	4 2.3	10 35.5	8 48.4	23 41.0	4 23.4	23 51.8
19	15 44 22.6	19 36.0	0 2.0	27 50.9	16 17.6	4 2.6	3 44.9	10 28.4	8 47.7	23 40.8	4 22.1	23 50.9
22	15 56 12.3	20 13.9	0 1.9	25 42.6	15 13.4	5 15.1	3 25.5	10 21.7	8 46.6	23 40.6	4 21.0	23 49.9
25	16 8 2.0	20 48.6	0 1.9	12 18.8	14 25.5	6 27.5	3 4.3	10 15.6	8 45.1	23 40.4	4 19.9	23 48.8
28	16 19 51.6	21 20.1	0 1.8	7S22.1	13 57.3	7 39.6	2 41.3	10 10.0	8 43.3	23 40.1	4 19.0	23 47.7
31	16 31 41.3	21 48.3	0 1.7	24 34.0	13 49.7	8 51.1	2 16.7	10 4.9	8 41.1	23 39.9	4 18.1	23 46.5

JUNE 1950

LONGITUDE

DAY	EPHEM. SID. TIME	☉	☊	☽	☿	♀	♂	♃	♄	♅	♆	♇
	h m s	° ′	° ′	° ′	° ′	° ′	° ′	° ′	° ′	° ′	° ′	° ′
1	16 35 37.9	9♊56.7	4♈ 7.0	16♐36.0	19♉15.6	29♈19.5	26♍26.1	6♓23.3	12♍49.2	3♋38.7	14♎44.5	16♌ 1.8
2	16 39 34.4	10 54.2	4 3.8	1♑34.5	19 37.9	0♉28.1	26 43.7	6 28.0	12 51.0	3 42.1	14R43.7	16 2.7
3	16 43 31.0	11 51.6	4 .6	16 12.6	20 4.4	1 36.8	27 1.8	6 32.6	12 52.9	3 45.5	14 43.0	16 3.6
4	16 47 27.5	12 49.1	3 57.4	0♒24.2	20 35.2	2 45.6	27 20.3	6 36.9	12 54.8	3 48.9	14 42.3	16 4.6
5	16 51 24.1	13 46.5	3 54.3	14 6.4	21 10.2	3 54.5	27 39.2	6 41.1	12 56.9	3 52.3	14 41.6	16 5.6
6	16 55 20.7	14 43.9	3 51.1	27 19.5	21 49.2	5 3.5	27 58.6	6 45.2	12 59.0	3 55.7	14 41.0	16 6.6
7	16 59 17.2	15 41.3	3 47.9	10♓ 6.4	22 32.2	6 12.6	28 18.4	6 49.0	13 1.3	3 59.2	14 40.4	16 7.6
8	17 3 13.8	16 38.7	3 44.7	22 31.2	23 19.1	7 21.8	28 38.6	6 52.7	13 3.6	4 2.7	14 39.8	16 8.7
9	17 7 10.3	17 36.1	3 41.6	4♈39.2	24 9.8	8 31.0	28 59.2	6 56.2	13 6.1	4 6.2	14 39.2	16 9.7
10	17 11 6.9	18 33.5	3 38.4	16 35.5	25 4.2	9 40.3	29 20.2	6 59.5	13 8.6	4 9.7	14 38.7	16 10.8
11	17 15 3.4	19 30.8	3 35.2	28 25.3	26 2.2	10 49.7	29 41.6	7 2.6	13 11.3	4 13.2	14 38.2	16 12.0
12	17 19 .0	20 28.2	3 32.0	10♉12.9	27 3.7	11 59.2	0♎ 3.3	7 5.6	13 14.0	4 16.7	14 37.7	16 13.1
13	17 22 56.6	21 25.5	3 28.9	22 2.1	28 8.7	13 8.7	0 25.5	7 8.3	13 16.8	4 20.2	14 37.3	16 14.3
14	17 26 53.1	22 22.9	3 25.7	3♊55.9	29 17.2	14 18.3	0 48.0	7 10.9	13 19.8	4 23.7	14 36.9	16 15.5
15	17 30 49.7	23 20.2	3 22.5	15 56.4	0♊29.0	15 28.0	1 10.9	7 13.3	13 22.8	4 27.3	14 36.5	16 16.7
16	17 34 46.2	24 17.5	3 19.3	28 5.1	1 44.1	16 37.7	1 34.2	7 15.5	13 25.9	4 30.9	14 36.2	16 17.9
17	17 38 42.8	25 14.8	3 16.1	10♋23.0	3 2.5	17 47.5	1 57.8	7 17.5	13 29.1	4 34.4	14 35.9	16 19.1
18	17 42 39.4	26 12.2	3 13.0	22 50.8	4 24.2	18 57.5	2 21.8	7 19.4	13 32.4	4 38.0	14 35.6	16 20.5
19	17 46 35.9	27 9.5	3 9.8	5♌29.0	5 49.0	20 7.4	2 46.1	7 21.0	13 35.8	4 41.6	14 35.4	16 21.7
20	17 50 32.5	28 6.7	3 6.6	18 18.7	7 17.0	21 17.4	3 10.7	7 22.4	13 39.3	4 45.2	14 35.2	16 23.1
21	17 54 29.0	29 4.0	3 3.4	1♍21.2	8 48.2	22 27.4	3 35.7	7 23.7	13 42.8	4 48.8	14 35.0	16 24.4
22	17 58 25.6	0♋ 1.3	3 .3	14 38.1	10 22.4	23 37.5	4 1.0	7 24.7	13 46.5	4 52.4	14 34.8	16 25.7
23	18 2 22.2	0 58.5	2 57.1	28 11.5	11 59.8	24 47.7	4 26.6	7 25.6	13 50.2	4 56.0	14 34.7	16 27.1
24	18 6 18.7	1 55.7	2 53.9	12♎ 2.8	13 40.2	25 57.9	4 52.4	7 26.2	13 54.0	4 59.6	14 34.6	16 28.5
25	18 10 15.3	2 52.9	2 50.7	26 13.0	15 23.5	27 8.2	5 18.6	7 26.7	13 57.9	5 3.2	14 34.6	16 29.9
26	18 14 11.8	3 50.2	2 47.6	10♏41.1	17 9.9	28 18.5	5 45.1	7 27.0	14 1.9	5 6.8	14 34.5	16 31.3
27	18 18 8.4	4 47.4	2 44.4	25 24.2	18 59.0	29 28.9	6 11.9	7 27.1	14 5.9	5 10.4	14 34.5	16 32.7
28	18 22 5.0	5 44.5	2 41.2	10♐16.5	20 51.0	0♊39.4	6 38.9	7R27.0	14 10.1	5 14.0	14D34.6	16 34.2
29	18 26 1.5	6 41.7	2 38.0	25 10.3	22 45.6	1 49.9	7 6.3	7 26.7	14 14.3	5 17.6	14 34.7	16 35.7
30	18 29 58.1	7 38.9	2 34.9	9♑56.7	24 42.8	3 .5	7 33.9	7 26.2	14 18.6	5 21.2	14 34.8	16 37.2

LATITUDE

DAY	EPHEM. SID. TIME	☉	☊	☽	☿	♀	♂	♃	♄	♅	♆	♇
1	16 35 37.9	0 .0	0 .0	4S47.5	3S49.8	2S 7.7	0N47.0	0S57.2	2N 4.9	0N15.9	1N38.5	8N 7.0
4	16 47 27.5	0 .0	0 .0	4 33.8	3 52.7	2 9.0	0 41.5	0 58.0	2 4.4	0 15.9	1 38.3	8 6.6
7	16 59 17.2	0 .0	0 .0	2 6.6	3 47.3	2 9.3	0 36.3	0 58.8	2 3.9	0 15.9	1 38.2	8 6.3
10	17 11 6.9	0 .0	0 .0	1N 3.0	3 34.6	2 8.7	0 31.2	0 59.6	2 3.4	0 16.0	1 38.1	8 5.9
13	17 22 56.6	0 .0	0 .0	3 43.0	3 15.6	2 7.4	0 26.3	1 .5	2 2.9	0 16.0	1 38.0	8 5.6
16	17 34 46.2	0 .0	0 .0	4 58.6	2 51.2	2 5.2	0 21.6	1 1.3	2 2.5	0 16.0	1 37.8	8 5.2
19	17 46 35.9	0 .0	0 .0	4 14.5	2 22.5	2 2.3	0 17.0	1 2.2	2 2.0	0 16.0	1 37.7	8 4.9
22	17 58 25.6	0 .0	0 .0	1 35.4	1 50.3	1 58.7	0 12.7	1 3.1	2 1.5	0 16.0	1 37.5	8 4.6
25	18 10 15.3	0 .0	0 .0	1S59.5	1 15.7	1 54.5	0 8.4	1 3.9	2 1.1	0 16.1	1 37.4	8 4.4
28	18 22 5.0	0 .0	0 .0	4 38.0	0 40.1	1 49.6	0 4.4	1 4.8	2 .7	0 16.1	1 37.2	8 4.2

RIGHT ASCENSION

DAY	EPHEM. SID. TIME	☉	☊	☽	☿	♀	♂	♃	♄	♅	♆	♇
1	16 35 37.9	8♊18.1	3♈46.6	14♐54.2	17♉52.8	28♈ 1.6	27♍ 2.4	8♓30.3	14♍58.3	3♋58.8	14♎12.5	21♌ 7.5
2	16 39 34.4	9 19.4	3 43.7	1♑47.1	18 15.3	29 6.9	27 17.9	8 34.8	14 59.8	4 2.5	14R11.7	21 8.4
3	16 43 31.0	10 20.9	3 40.8	18 15.2	18 41.9	0♉12.5	27 33.7	8 39.2	15 1.5	4 6.2	14 11.0	21 9.3
4	16 47 27.5	11 22.4	3 37.9	3♒40.6	19 12.5	1 18.2	27 50.0	8 43.5	15 3.3	4 9.9	14 10.4	21 10.3
5	16 51 24.1	12 24.1	3 35.0	17 46.9	19 47.0	2 24.2	28 6.6	8 47.5	15 5.1	4 13.7	14 9.7	21 11.2
6	16 55 20.7	13 25.8	3 32.1	0♓37.3	20 25.4	3 30.5	28 23.7	8 51.4	15 7.1	4 17.4	14 9.1	21 12.2
7	16 59 17.2	14 27.6	3 29.1	12 26.6	21 7.7	4 36.9	28 41.2	8 55.2	15 9.1	4 21.2	14 8.5	21 13.2
8	17 3 13.8	15 29.5	3 26.2	23 33.3	21 53.7	5 43.7	28 59.0	8 58.7	15 11.3	4 25.0	14 8.0	21 14.3
9	17 7 10.3	16 31.5	3 23.3	4♈16.2	22 43.4	6 50.6	29 17.3	9 2.1	15 13.5	4 28.8	14 7.4	21 15.4
10	17 11 6.9	17 33.5	3 20.4	14 52.9	23 36.8	7 57.8	29 35.9	9 5.4	15 15.8	4 32.6	14 6.9	21 16.4
11	17 15 3.4	18 35.6	3 17.5	25 39.4	24 33.9	9 5.3	29 54.8	9 8.4	15 18.2	4 36.4	14 6.5	21 17.6
12	17 19 .0	19 37.8	3 14.6	6♉49.7	25 34.6	10 13.0	0♎14.2	9 11.3	15 20.7	4 40.2	14 6.0	21 18.7
13	17 22 56.6	20 40.0	3 11.6	18 35.1	26 39.0	11 21.0	0 33.9	9 14.0	15 23.3	4 44.1	14 5.6	21 19.8
14	17 26 53.1	21 42.3	3 8.7	1♊ 2.1	27 47.0	12 29.3	0 53.9	9 16.5	15 25.9	4 48.0	14 5.2	21 21.0
15	17 30 49.7	22 44.6	3 5.8	14 10.2	28 58.6	13 37.8	1 14.3	9 18.9	15 28.7	4 51.8	14 4.8	21 22.2
16	17 34 46.2	23 46.9	3 2.9	27 49.9	0♊13.8	14 46.6	1 35.0	9 21.1	15 31.5	4 55.7	14 4.5	21 23.5
17	17 38 42.8	24 49.3	2 60.0	11♋44.0	1 32.7	15 55.7	1 56.1	9 23.1	15 34.4	4 59.6	14 4.2	21 24.7
18	17 42 39.4	25 51.7	2 57.1	25 32.3	2 55.3	17 5.1	2 17.5	9 24.9	15 37.5	5 3.6	14 4.0	21 26.0
19	17 46 35.9	26 54.1	2 54.2	8♌58.3	4 21.5	18 14.7	2 39.2	9 26.6	15 40.6	5 7.5	14 3.7	21 27.3
20	17 50 32.5	27 56.5	2 51.2	21 54.1	5 51.4	19 24.6	3 1.2	9 28.0	15 43.7	5 11.4	14 3.5	21 28.6
21	17 54 29.0	28 59.0	2 48.3	4♍20.9	7 25.1	20 34.8	3 23.5	9 29.3	15 47.0	5 15.3	14 3.3	21 29.9
22	17 58 25.6	0♋ 1.4	2 45.4	16 28.2	9 2.5	21 45.3	3 46.2	9 30.4	15 50.3	5 19.2	14 3.2	21 31.3
23	18 2 22.2	1 3.8	2 42.5	28 30.5	10 43.7	22 56.0	4 9.1	9 31.3	15 53.7	5 23.1	14 3.0	21 32.7
24	18 6 18.7	2 6.1	2 39.6	10♎45.9	12 28.6	24 7.1	4 32.3	9 32.1	15 57.2	5 27.1	14 2.9	21 34.1
25	18 10 15.3	3 8.5	2 36.7	23 34.4	14 17.3	25 18.4	4 55.8	9 32.6	16 .8	5 31.0	14 2.9	21 35.5
26	18 14 11.8	4 10.8	2 33.7	7♏15.1	16 9.7	26 30.0	5 19.6	9 33.0	16 4.4	5 34.9	14 2.8	21 36.9
27	18 18 8.4	5 13.1	2 30.8	22 1.6	18 5.8	27 41.9	5 43.7	9 33.2	16 8.2	5 38.8	14 2.8	21 38.3
28	18 22 5.0	6 15.3	2 27.9	7♐54.2	20 5.5	28 54.1	6 8.0	9 33.2	16 12.0	5 42.8	14 2.8	21 39.8
29	18 26 1.5	7 17.5	2 25.0	24 32.0	22 8.6	0♊ 6.5	6 32.6	9R33.0	16 15.8	5 46.7	14D 2.9	21 41.3
30	18 29 58.1	8 19.7	2 22.1	11♑14.4	24 15.1	1 19.3	6 57.5	9 32.7	16 19.8	5 50.6	14 2.9	21 42.8

DECLINATION

DAY	EPHEM. SID. TIME	☉	☊	☽	☿	♀	♂	♃	♄	♅	♆	♇
1	16 35 37.9	21N57.0	0N 1.7	27S32.4	13N51.6	9N14.7	2N 8.2	10S 3.4	8N40.3	23N39.8	4S17.9	23N46.1
4	16 47 27.5	22 20.6	0 1.6	24 31.6	14 9.8	10 24.9	1 41.6	9 59.1	8 37.7	23 39.5	4 17.1	23 44.9
7	16 59 17.2	22 40.8	0 1.6	9 44.1	14 44.8	11 33.7	1 13.7	9 55.3	8 34.8	23 39.2	4 16.5	23 43.6
10	17 11 6.9	22 57.3	0 1.5	7N29.7	15 34.0	12 40.8	0 44.5	9 52.2	8 31.5	23 38.9	4 16.0	23 42.2
13	17 22 56.6	23 10.3	0 1.4	21 52.3	16 34.5	13 45.9	0 14.0	9 49.7	8 27.9	23 38.6	4 15.6	23 40.8
16	17 34 46.2	23 19.5	0 1.4	28 24.6	17 43.2	14 48.7	0S17.7	9 47.9	8 24.0	23 38.2	4 15.3	23 39.4
19	17 46 35.9	23 25.1	0 1.3	23 1.0	18 56.7	15 48.9	0 50.4	9 46.6	8 19.7	23 37.9	4 15.1	23 37.9
22	17 58 25.6	23 26.9	0 1.3	7 31.1	20 11.6	16 46.1	1 24.2	9 46.0	8 15.2	23 37.5	4 15.0	23 36.4
25	18 10 15.3	23 25.0	0 1.2	11S58.7	21 23.6	17 40.1	1 58.9	9 46.1	8 10.4	23 37.1	4 15.0	23 34.9
28	18 22 5.0	23 19.4	0 1.1	26 34.8	22 27.9	18 30.5	2 34.4	9 46.8	8 5.3	23 36.7	4 15.2	23 33.3

JULY 1950

LONGITUDE

DAY	EPHEM. SID. TIME	☉	☊	☽	☿	♀	♂	♃	♄	♅	♆	♇
	h m s	° ′	° ′	° ′	° ′	° ′	° ′	° ′	° ′	° ′	° ′	° ′
1	18 33 54.6	8♋36.1	2♈31.7	24♑27.4	26♊42.3	4♊11.1	8♎ 1.7	7♓25.5	14♍23.0	5♋24.8	14♎34.9	16♌38.7
2	18 37 51.2	9 33.3	2 28.5	8♒35.6	28 44.0	5 21.8	8 29.8	7 R 24.7	14 27.4	5 28.4	14 35.1	16 40.2
3	18 41 47.7	10 30.5	2 25.3	22 17.6	0♋47.6	6 32.5	8 58.2	7 23.6	14 32.0	5 32.0	14 35.3	16 41.7
4	18 45 44.3	11 27.6	2 22.2	5♓32.4	2 53.0	7 43.3	9 26.8	7 22.3	14 36.6	5 35.6	14 35.5	16 43.3
5	18 49 40.9	12 24.8	2 19.0	18 21.7	4 59.9	8 54.2	9 55.7	7 20.9	14 41.3	5 39.2	14 35.8	16 44.8
6	18 53 37.4	13 22.0	2 15.8	0♈48.8	7 8.0	10 5.1	10 24.8	7 19.2	14 46.0	5 42.8	14 36.1	16 46.4
7	18 57 34.0	14 19.2	2 12.6	12 58.6	9 16.9	11 16.1	10 54.2	7 17.4	14 50.9	5 46.3	14 36.4	16 48.0
8	19 1 30.5	15 16.4	2 9.4	24 56.3	11 26.5	12 27.1	11 23.8	7 15.4	14 55.8	5 49.9	14 36.8	16 49.6
9	19 5 27.1	16 13.7	2 6.3	6♉47.3	13 36.4	13 38.3	11 53.7	7 13.2	15 .8	5 53.5	14 37.2	16 51.3
10	19 9 23.7	17 10.9	2 3.1	18 36.6	15 46.3	14 49.4	12 23.8	7 10.8	15 5.8	5 57.1	14 37.6	16 52.9
11	19 13 20.2	18 8.1	1 59.9	0♊28.8	17 55.9	16 .6	12 54.1	7 8.2	15 11.0	6 .6	14 38.1	16 54.5
12	19 17 16.8	19 5.3	1 56.7	12 27.5	20 5.0	17 11.9	13 24.6	7 5.4	15 16.1	6 4.2	14 38.6	16 56.2
13	19 21 13.3	20 2.6	1 53.6	24 35.8	22 13.4	18 23.2	13 55.4	7 2.4	15 21.4	6 7.7	14 39.1	16 57.9
14	19 25 9.9	20 59.8	1 50.4	6♋55.5	24 20.9	19 34.6	14 26.4	6 59.3	15 26.7	6 11.2	14 39.6	16 59.5
15	19 29 6.4	21 57.1	1 47.2	19 27.5	26 27.3	20 46.0	14 57.6	6 55.9	15 32.1	6 14.7	14 40.2	17 1.2
16	19 33 3.0	22 54.3	1 44.0	2♌12.1	28 32.4	21 57.4	15 29.0	6 52.4	15 37.6	6 18.2	14 40.8	17 2.9
17	19 36 59.6	23 51.6	1 40.9	15 8.9	0♌36.1	23 8.9	16 .6	6 48.7	15 43.1	6 21.7	14 41.5	17 4.7
18	19 40 56.1	24 48.8	1 37.7	28 17.4	2 38.4	24 20.5	16 32.4	6 44.8	15 48.7	6 25.2	14 42.2	17 6.4
19	19 44 52.7	25 46.1	1 34.5	11♍37.1	4 39.1	25 32.1	17 4.5	6 40.8	15 54.3	6 28.7	14 42.9	17 8.1
20	19 48 49.2	26 43.4	1 31.3	25 7.8	6 38.1	26 43.8	17 36.7	6 36.6	16 .0	6 32.1	14 43.6	17 9.9
21	19 52 45.8	27 40.7	1 28.2	8♎49.7	8 35.5	27 55.5	18 9.2	6 32.2	16 5.8	6 35.5	14 44.4	17 11.6
22	19 56 42.4	28 37.9	1 25.0	22 43.1	10 31.2	29 7.2	18 41.8	6 27.6	16 11.6	6 38.9	14 45.2	17 13.4
23	20 0 38.9	29 35.2	1 21.8	6♏47.9	12 25.2	0♋19.0	19 14.6	6 22.9	16 17.5	6 42.3	14 46.0	17 15.1
24	20 4 35.5	0♌32.5	1 18.6	21 3.3	14 17.4	1 30.8	19 47.6	6 18.0	16 23.4	6 45.7	14 46.9	17 16.9
25	20 8 32.0	1 29.8	1 15.4	5♐27.4	16 7.9	2 42.7	20 20.8	6 13.0	16 29.4	6 49.1	14 47.8	17 18.7
26	20 12 28.6	2 27.1	1 12.3	19 56.4	17 56.7	3 54.7	20 54.2	6 7.8	16 35.5	6 52.4	14 48.7	17 20.5
27	20 16 25.1	3 24.4	1 9.1	4♑25.3	19 43.7	5 6.7	21 27.8	6 2.4	16 41.6	6 55.7	14 49.7	17 22.3
28	20 20 21.7	4 21.7	1 5.9	18 48.0	21 29.0	6 18.7	22 1.5	5 56.9	16 47.7	6 59.0	14 50.7	17 24.1
29	20 24 18.3	5 19.1	1 2.7	2♒58.3	23 12.5	7 30.8	22 35.4	5 51.3	16 53.9	7 2.3	14 51.7	17 25.9
30	20 28 14.8	6 16.4	0 59.6	16 51.2	24 54.4	8 43.0	23 9.5	5 45.5	17 .2	7 5.6	14 52.8	17 27.7
31	20 32 11.4	7 13.8	0 56.4	0♓22.8	26 34.5	9 55.2	23 43.7	5 39.6	17 6.5	7 8.9	14 53.8	17 29.6

LATITUDE

DAY	EPHEM. SID. TIME	☉	☊	☽	☿	♀	♂	♃	♄	♅	♆	♇
1	18 33 54.6	0 .0	0 .0	4 S 38.3	0 S 5.0	1 S 44.1	0 N .5	1 S 5.7	2 N .3	0 N 16.1	1 N 37.1	8 N 3.9
4	18 45 44.3	0 .0	0 .0	2 14.1	0 N 27.7	1 38.1	0 S 3.3	1 6.5	1 59.9	0 16.1	1 36.9	8 3.8
7	18 57 34.0	0 .0	0 .0	0 N 59.1	0 56.4	1 31.7	0 7.0	1 7.4	1 59.5	0 16.2	1 36.8	8 3.6
10	19 9 23.7	0 .0	0 .0	3 41.4	1 19.5	1 24.8	0 10.5	1 8.2	1 59.1	0 16.2	1 36.6	8 3.5
13	19 21 13.3	0 .0	0 .0	4 59.6	1 36.0	1 17.5	0 13.9	1 9.1	1 58.8	0 16.2	1 36.5	8 3.4
16	19 33 3.0	0 .0	0 .0	4 17.7	1 45.7	1 9.9	0 17.2	1 9.9	1 58.4	0 16.3	1 36.4	8 3.3
19	19 44 52.7	0 .0	0 .0	1 37.8	1 48.9	1 2.0	0 20.4	1 10.7	1 58.1	0 16.3	1 36.2	8 3.3
22	19 56 42.4	0 .0	0 .0	1 S 56.7	1 45.9	0 53.9	0 23.5	1 11.5	1 57.8	0 16.4	1 36.1	8 3.2
25	20 8 32.0	0 .0	0 .0	4 37.2	1 37.6	0 45.6	0 26.4	1 12.3	1 57.5	0 16.4	1 35.9	8 3.3
28	20 20 21.7	0 .0	0 .0	4 48.6	1 24.6	0 37.2	0 29.3	1 13.0	1 57.3	0 16.4	1 35.8	8 3.3
31	20 32 11.4	0 .0	0 .0	2 29.4	1 7.5	0 28.8	0 32.1	1 13.7	1 57.0	0 16.5	1 35.7	8 3.4

RIGHT ASCENSION

DAY	EPHEM. SID. TIME	☉	☊	☽	☿	♀	♂	♃	♄	♅	♆	♇
1	18 33 54.6	9♋21.8	2♈19.2	27♑16.7	26♊24.7	2♊32.3	7♎22.6	9♓32.1	16♍23.8	5♋54.6	14♎ 3.1	21♌44.3
2	18 37 51.2	10 23.8	2 16.3	12♒ 9.4	28 37.1	3 45.7	7 48.0	9 R 31.4	16 27.9	5 58.5	14 3.2	21 45.8
3	18 41 47.7	11 25.8	2 13.3	25 44.7	0♋52.0	4 59.3	8 13.6	9 30.5	16 32.1	6 2.4	14 3.4	21 47.4
4	18 45 44.3	12 27.7	2 10.4	8♓11.2	3 9.3	6 13.1	8 39.5	9 29.5	16 36.3	6 6.3	14 3.6	21 48.9
5	18 49 40.9	13 29.5	2 7.5	19 45.6	5 28.3	7 27.3	9 5.6	9 28.2	16 40.6	6 10.2	14 3.8	21 50.5
6	18 53 37.4	14 31.3	2 4.6	0♈46.8	7 48.8	8 41.7	9 32.0	9 26.8	16 45.0	6 14.1	14 4.0	21 52.1
7	18 57 34.0	15 33.0	2 1.7	11 33.1	10 10.4	9 56.4	9 58.6	9 25.1	16 49.4	6 18.1	14 4.3	21 53.7
8	19 1 30.5	16 34.6	1 58.8	22 21.5	12 32.5	11 11.3	10 25.5	9 23.3	16 54.0	6 21.9	14 4.6	21 55.4
9	19 5 27.1	17 36.1	1 55.9	3♉27.4	14 54.8	12 26.6	10 52.6	9 21.4	16 58.6	6 25.9	14 5.0	21 57.1
10	19 9 23.7	18 37.5	1 52.9	15 3.7	17 16.8	13 42.0	11 19.9	9 19.2	17 3.2	6 29.8	14 5.4	21 58.7
11	19 13 20.2	19 38.8	1 50.0	27 19.6	19 38.1	14 57.7	11 47.5	9 16.9	17 7.9	6 33.6	14 5.8	22 .4
12	19 17 16.8	20 40.0	1 47.1	10♊17.9	21 58.4	16 13.5	12 15.3	9 14.4	17 12.7	6 37.5	14 6.2	22 2.1
13	19 21 13.3	21 41.1	1 44.2	23 53.0	24 17.3	17 29.7	12 43.4	9 11.7	17 17.5	6 41.3	14 6.7	22 3.8
14	19 25 9.9	22 42.1	1 41.3	7♋50.2	26 34.5	18 46.0	13 11.6	9 8.8	17 22.4	6 45.2	14 7.2	22 5.5
15	19 29 6.4	23 43.0	1 38.4	21 49.5	28 49.7	20 2.5	13 40.1	9 5.8	17 27.4	6 49.0	14 7.7	22 7.2
16	19 33 3.0	24 43.7	1 35.4	5♌31.5	1♌ 2.8	21 19.2	14 8.9	9 2.6	17 32.4	6 52.8	14 8.3	22 8.9
17	19 36 59.6	25 44.4	1 32.5	18 44.2	3 13.5	22 36.1	14 37.8	8 59.2	17 37.5	6 56.6	14 8.8	22 10.7
18	19 40 56.1	26 44.8	1 29.6	1♍25.0	5 21.8	23 53.1	15 7.0	8 55.6	17 42.7	7 .4	14 9.5	22 12.5
19	19 44 52.7	27 45.2	1 26.7	13 40.4	7 27.5	25 10.4	15 36.4	8 51.9	17 47.9	7 4.2	14 10.1	22 14.2
20	19 48 49.2	28 45.4	1 23.8	25 42.7	9 30.6	26 27.7	16 6.0	8 48.0	17 53.1	7 7.9	14 10.8	22 16.0
21	19 52 45.8	29 45.5	1 20.9	7♎48.6	11 31.0	27 45.2	16 35.8	8 44.0	17 58.4	7 11.7	14 11.5	22 17.8
22	19 56 42.4	0♌45.4	1 18.0	20 16.6	13 28.8	29 2.8	17 5.9	8 39.8	18 3.8	7 15.4	14 12.2	22 19.6
23	20 0 38.9	1 45.2	1 15.0	3♏25.3	15 23.9	0♋20.6	17 36.2	8 35.4	18 9.2	7 19.1	14 12.9	22 21.4
24	20 4 35.5	2 44.8	1 12.1	17 30.3	17 16.3	1 38.4	18 6.6	8 30.9	18 14.7	7 22.8	14 13.7	22 23.2
25	20 8 32.0	3 44.3	1 9.2	2♐37.8	19 6.1	2 56.3	18 37.3	8 26.2	18 20.2	7 26.4	14 14.5	22 25.0
26	20 12 28.6	4 43.6	1 6.3	18 37.7	20 53.2	4 14.4	19 8.2	8 21.4	18 25.8	7 30.1	14 15.4	22 26.9
27	20 16 25.1	5 42.8	1 3.4	5♑ .6	22 37.9	5 32.4	19 39.3	8 16.4	18 31.4	7 33.7	14 16.2	22 28.7
28	20 20 21.7	6 41.8	1 .5	21 6.2	24 20.0	6 50.6	20 10.6	8 11.3	18 37.1	7 37.3	14 17.1	22 30.6
29	20 24 18.3	7 40.7	0 57.6	6♒19.9	25 59.7	8 8.7	20 42.1	8 6.1	18 42.8	7 40.8	14 18.0	22 32.4
30	20 28 14.8	8 39.5	0 54.6	20 24.7	27 37.0	9 27.0	21 13.9	8 .8	18 48.6	7 44.5	14 19.0	22 34.3
31	20 32 11.4	9 38.0	0 51.7	3♓21.4	29 12.0	10 45.2	21 45.8	7 55.2	18 54.4	7 48.0	14 20.0	22 36.2

DECLINATION

DAY	EPHEM. SID. TIME	☉	☊	☽	☿	♀	♂	♃	♄	♅	♆	♇
1	18 33 54.6	23 N 10.1	0 N 1.1	25 S 47.9	23 N 19.4	19 N 17.1	3 S 10.7	9 S 48.2	7 N 59.9	23 N 36.3	4 S 15.4	23 N 31.7
4	18 45 44.3	22 57.2	0 1.0	11 33.6	23 52.7	19 59.5	3 47.8	9 50.1	7 54.3	23 35.9	4 15.8	23 30.1
7	18 57 34.0	22 40.7	0 .9	6 N 2.1	24 3.7	20 37.5	4 25.4	9 52.8	7 48.4	23 35.5	4 16.3	23 28.5
10	19 9 23.7	22 20.6	0 .9	20 54.8	23 49.9	21 10.8	5 3.7	9 56.0	7 42.2	23 35.0	4 16.9	23 26.8
13	19 21 13.3	21 57.1	0 .8	28 19.6	23 11.6	21 39.2	5 42.5	9 59.9	7 35.9	23 34.6	4 17.6	23 25.1
16	19 33 3.0	21 30.2	0 .7	23 51.5	22 11.2	22 2.5	6 21.7	10 4.4	7 29.3	23 34.1	4 18.4	23 23.5
19	19 44 52.7	20 59.9	0 .7	8 42.9	20 52.1	22 20.4	7 1.4	10 9.5	7 22.5	23 33.7	4 19.3	23 21.8
22	19 56 42.4	20 26.5	0 .6	10 S 38.7	19 18.3	22 32.8	7 41.4	10 15.1	7 15.5	23 33.2	4 20.3	23 20.1
25	20 8 32.0	19 50.0	0 .5	25 45.9	17 33.5	22 39.6	8 21.7	10 21.2	7 8.3	23 32.7	4 21.5	23 18.5
28	20 20 21.7	19 10.6	0 .5	26 53.4	15 40.9	22 40.7	9 2.1	10 27.8	7 .9	23 32.3	4 22.7	23 16.8
31	20 32 11.4	18 28.3	0 .4	13 40.3	13 43.2	22 35.9	9 42.7	10 34.9	6 53.4	23 31.8	4 24.0	23 15.2

AUGUST 1950

LONGITUDE

DAY	EPHEM. SID. TIME (h m s)	☉ ° ′	☊ ° ′	☽ ° ′	☿ ° ′	♀ ° ′	♂ ° ′	♃ ° ′	♄ ° ′	♅ ° ′	♆ ° ′	♇ ° ′
1	20 36 7.9	8♌11.2	0♈53.2	13♓31.7	28♌13.0	11♋ 7.4	24♎18.1	5♓33.5	17♍12.9	7♋12.1	14♎54.9	17♌31.4
2	20 40 4.5	9 8.6	0 50.0	26 18.6	29 49.7	12 19.7	24 52.7	5R27.4	17 19.3	7 15.3	14 56.0	17 33.2
3	20 44 1.0	10 6.0	0 46.9	8♈45.7	1♍24.8	13 32.1	25 27.5	5 21.0	17 25.7	7 18.5	14 57.2	17 35.0
4	20 47 57.6	11 3.4	0 43.7	20 56.6	2 58.1	14 44.4	26 2.3	5 14.6	17 32.2	7 21.6	14 58.4	17 36.9
5	20 51 54.2	12 .8	0 40.5	2♉56.0	4 29.8	15 56.9	26 37.4	5 8.0	17 38.7	7 24.7	14 59.6	17 38.7
6	20 55 50.7	12 58.3	0 37.3	14 48.7	5 59.7	17 9.4	27 12.6	5 1.3	17 45.3	7 27.8	15 .8	17 40.6
7	20 59 47.3	13 55.8	0 34.1	26 39.8	7 27.9	18 22.0	27 48.0	4 54.5	17 52.0	7 30.9	15 2.1	17 42.4
8	21 3 43.8	14 53.3	0 31.0	8♊34.4	8 54.4	19 34.6	28 23.5	4 47.6	17 58.6	7 33.9	15 3.4	17 44.2
9	21 7 40.4	15 50.8	0 27.8	20 36.7	10 19.2	20 47.2	28 59.2	4 40.6	18 5.3	7 37.0	15 4.7	17 46.1
10	21 11 36.9	16 48.4	0 24.6	2♋50.7	11 42.1	21 59.9	29 35.1	4 33.5	18 12.1	7 40.0	15 6.0	17 47.9
11	21 15 33.5	17 45.9	0 21.4	15 19.0	13 3.3	23 12.7	0♏11.1	4 26.3	18 18.9	7 42.9	15 7.4	17 49.8
12	21 19 30.0	18 43.5	0 18.3	28 3.5	14 22.6	24 25.4	0 47.2	4 19.1	18 25.7	7 45.9	15 8.8	17 51.6
13	21 23 26.6	19 41.2	0 15.1	11♌ 4.5	15 40.0	25 38.3	1 23.5	4 11.7	18 32.6	7 48.8	15 10.2	17 53.5
14	21 27 23.2	20 38.8	0 11.9	24 21.5	16 55.4	26 51.2	1 60.0	4 4.3	18 39.5	7 51.6	15 11.7	17 55.3
15	21 31 19.7	21 36.5	0 8.7	7♍52.9	18 8.8	28 4.1	2 36.6	3 56.8	18 46.4	7 54.5	15 13.2	17 57.2
16	21 35 16.3	22 34.1	0 5.6	21 36.6	19 20.2	29 17.1	3 13.3	3 49.2	18 53.4	7 57.3	15 14.7	17 59.0
17	21 39 12.8	23 31.8	0 2.4	5♎30.3	20 29.4	0♌30.1	3 50.2	3 41.6	19 .4	8 .1	15 16.2	18 .8
18	21 43 9.4	24 29.5	29♓59.2	19 31.5	21 36.3	1 43.2	4 27.3	3 33.9	19 7.4	8 2.8	15 17.7	18 2.7
19	21 47 5.9	25 27.3	29 56.0	3♏38.3	22 41.0	2 56.3	5 4.4	3 26.1	19 14.5	8 5.5	15 19.3	18 4.5
20	21 51 2.5	26 25.1	29 52.8	17 48.6	23 43.2	4 9.5	5 41.8	3 18.4	19 21.6	8 8.3	15 20.9	18 6.4
21	21 54 59.0	27 22.8	29 49.7	2♐ .7	24 42.7	5 22.7	6 19.3	3 10.6	19 28.7	8 10.9	15 22.5	18 8.2
22	21 58 55.6	28 20.6	29 46.5	16 12.4	25 39.6	6 35.9	6 56.8	3 2.8	19 35.9	8 13.5	15 24.2	18 10.0
23	22 2 52.2	29 18.4	29 43.3	0♑21.5	26 33.6	7 49.2	7 34.5	2 54.9	19 43.0	8 16.1	15 25.8	18 11.9
24	22 6 48.7	0♍16.2	29 40.1	14 25.2	27 24.6	9 2.5	8 12.4	2 47.0	19 50.2	8 18.6	15 27.5	18 13.7
25	22 10 45.3	1 14.1	29 37.0	28 20.2	28 12.4	10 15.9	8 50.3	2 39.1	19 57.5	8 21.1	15 29.2	18 15.5
26	22 14 41.8	2 11.9	29 33.8	12♒ 3.7	28 56.8	11 29.3	9 28.4	2 31.2	20 4.7	8 23.6	15 31.0	18 17.3
27	22 18 38.4	3 9.8	29 30.6	25 32.7	29 37.6	12 42.7	10 6.7	2 23.3	20 12.0	8 26.0	15 32.7	18 19.1
28	22 22 34.9	4 7.7	29 27.4	8♓45.3	0♎14.7	13 56.2	10 45.0	2 15.4	20 19.2	8 28.4	15 34.5	18 20.9
29	22 26 31.5	5 5.7	29 24.3	21 40.6	0 47.6	15 9.8	11 23.5	2 7.5	20 26.6	8 30.7	15 36.2	18 22.7
30	22 30 28.0	6 3.7	29 21.1	4♈18.7	1 16.2	16 23.4	12 2.0	1 59.7	20 33.9	8 33.0	15 38.0	18 24.4
31	22 34 24.6	7 1.7	29 17.9	16 41.1	1 40.3	17 37.0	12 40.8	1 51.8	20 41.2	8 35.3	15 39.9	18 26.2

LATITUDE

DAY	EPHEM. SID. TIME	☉	☊	☽	☿	♀	♂	♃	♄	♅	♆	♇
1	20 36 7.9	0 .0	0 .0	1S24.4	1N 1.1	0S25.9	0S33.0	1S13.9	1N57.0	0N16.5	1N35.6	8N 3.4
4	20 47 57.6	0 .0	0 .0	1N53.5	0 39.6	0 17.5	0 35.6	1 14.5	1 56.8	0 16.5	1 35.5	8 3.5
7	20 59 47.3	0 .0	0 .0	4 20.1	0 15.4	0 9.0	0 38.2	1 15.2	1 56.6	0 16.6	1 35.4	8 3.7
10	21 11 36.9	0 .0	0 .0	5 8.3	0S11.0	0 .7	0 40.6	1 15.7	1 56.4	0 16.7	1 35.2	8 3.9
13	21 23 26.6	0 .0	0 .0	3 49.7	0 39.2	0N 7.5	0 43.0	1 16.2	1 56.3	0 16.7	1 35.1	8 4.1
16	21 35 16.3	0 .0	0 .0	0 38.6	1 8.7	0 15.5	0 45.3	1 16.7	1 56.1	0 16.8	1 35.0	8 4.4
19	21 47 5.9	0 .0	0 .0	2S59.1	1 39.0	0 23.2	0 47.5	1 17.1	1 56.0	0 16.8	1 34.9	8 4.6
22	21 58 55.6	0 .0	0 .0	5 5.2	2 9.6	0 30.7	0 49.7	1 17.5	1 56.0	0 16.9	1 34.8	8 5.0
25	22 10 45.3	0 .0	0 .0	4 31.8	2 39.8	0 37.8	0 51.7	1 17.8	1 55.9	0 16.9	1 34.7	8 5.3
28	22 22 34.9	0 .0	0 .0	1 45.9	3 8.6	0 44.6	0 53.7	1 18.1	1 55.9	0 17.0	1 34.6	8 5.7
31	22 34 24.6	0 .0	0 .0	1N39.1	3 34.9	0 51.0	0 55.6	1 18.3	1 55.9	0 17.1	1 34.5	8 6.1

RIGHT ASCENSION

DAY	EPHEM. SID. TIME	☉	☊	☽	☿	♀	♂	♃	♄	♅	♆	♇
1	20 36 7.9	10♌36.5	0♈48.8	15♓22.1	0♍44.7	12♋ 3.4	22♎17.9	7♓49.6	19♍ .3	7♋51.5	14♎21.0	22♌38.1
2	20 40 4.5	11 34.7	0 45.9	26 43.5	2 15.1	13 21.7	22 50.2	7R43.8	19 6.2	7 55.0	14 22.0	22 39.9
3	20 44 1.0	12 32.9	0 43.0	7♈43.0	3 43.4	14 39.9	23 22.7	7 37.9	19 12.1	7 58.4	14 23.1	22 41.8
4	20 47 57.6	13 30.8	0 40.1	18 37.6	5 9.5	15 58.1	23 55.5	7 31.9	19 18.1	8 1.9	14 24.1	22 43.7
5	20 51 54.2	14 28.7	0 37.2	29 42.7	6 33.6	17 16.2	24 28.4	7 25.8	19 24.1	8 5.3	14 25.3	22 45.6
6	20 55 50.7	15 26.4	0 34.2	11♉11.9	7 55.5	18 34.3	25 1.5	7 19.5	19 30.2	8 8.6	14 26.4	22 47.5
7	20 59 47.3	16 23.9	0 31.3	23 15.8	9 15.4	19 52.3	25 34.9	7 13.2	19 36.3	8 12.0	14 27.5	22 49.4
8	21 3 43.8	17 21.3	0 28.4	5♊60.0	10 33.3	21 10.3	26 8.4	7 6.7	19 42.5	8 15.3	14 28.7	22 51.3
9	21 7 40.4	18 18.5	0 25.5	19 22.7	11 49.3	22 28.1	26 42.1	7 .1	19 48.6	8 18.6	14 29.9	22 53.2
10	21 11 36.9	19 15.7	0 22.6	3♋13.6	13 3.2	23 45.9	27 16.1	6 53.5	19 54.9	8 21.8	14 31.1	22 55.1
11	21 15 33.5	20 12.6	0 19.7	17 15.4	14 15.2	25 3.5	27 50.2	6 46.7	20 1.1	8 25.1	14 32.4	22 57.0
12	21 19 30.0	21 9.5	0 16.8	1♌ 8.9	15 25.2	26 21.0	28 24.6	6 39.9	20 7.4	8 28.3	14 33.7	22 58.9
13	21 23 26.6	22 6.1	0 13.8	14 39.4	16 33.2	27 38.4	28 59.2	6 33.0	20 13.8	8 31.4	14 35.0	23 .8
14	21 27 23.2	23 2.7	0 10.9	27 40.5	17 39.1	28 55.7	29 33.9	6 26.0	20 20.1	8 34.6	14 36.3	23 2.7
15	21 31 19.7	23 59.1	0 8.0	10♍15.1	18 43.1	0♌12.8	0♏ 8.9	6 18.9	20 26.5	8 37.7	14 37.7	23 4.6
16	21 35 16.3	24 55.4	0 5.1	22 32.9	19 45.0	1 29.7	0 44.1	6 11.8	20 32.9	8 40.7	14 39.0	23 6.6
17	21 39 12.8	25 51.5	0 2.2	4♎48.5	20 44.8	2 46.5	1 19.5	6 4.6	20 39.4	8 43.7	14 40.4	23 8.5
18	21 43 9.4	26 47.5	29♓59.3	17 18.7	21 42.4	4 3.0	1 55.1	5 57.3	20 45.9	8 46.7	14 41.8	23 10.4
19	21 47 5.9	27 43.4	29 56.4	0♏20.9	22 37.7	5 19.4	2 30.9	5 50.0	20 52.4	8 49.7	14 43.3	23 12.3
20	21 51 2.5	28 39.2	29 53.4	14 10.0	23 30.8	6 35.7	3 6.9	5 42.7	20 59.0	8 52.7	14 44.8	23 14.2
21	21 54 59.0	29 34.8	29 50.5	28 53.5	24 21.5	7 51.7	3 43.1	5 35.3	21 5.6	8 55.5	14 46.3	23 16.1
22	21 58 55.6	0♍30.3	29 47.6	14♐25.7	25 9.6	9 7.5	4 19.5	5 27.9	21 12.2	8 58.4	14 47.8	23 18.0
23	22 2 52.2	1 25.7	29 44.7	0♑24.4	25 55.1	10 23.1	4 56.1	5 20.5	21 18.8	9 1.2	14 49.3	23 19.9
24	22 6 48.7	2 21.0	29 41.8	16 15.8	26 37.9	11 38.5	5 32.9	5 13.0	21 25.4	9 3.9	14 50.8	23 21.8
25	22 10 45.3	3 16.1	29 38.9	1♒27.3	27 17.7	12 53.6	6 9.9	5 5.6	21 32.1	9 6.7	14 52.4	23 23.7
26	22 14 41.8	4 11.2	29 35.9	15 39.3	27 54.5	14 8.6	6 47.1	4 58.1	21 38.8	9 9.3	14 54.0	23 25.6
27	22 18 38.4	5 6.1	29 33.0	28 48.3	28 28.1	15 23.3	7 24.5	4 50.6	21 45.5	9 12.0	14 55.6	23 27.5
28	22 22 34.9	6 1.0	29 30.1	11♓ 2.5	28 58.3	16 37.8	8 2.1	4 43.1	21 52.2	9 14.6	14 57.2	23 29.3
29	22 26 31.5	6 55.7	29 27.2	22 35.9	29 24.9	17 52.1	8 40.0	4 35.6	21 58.9	9 17.1	14 58.8	23 31.2
30	22 30 28.0	7 50.4	29 24.3	3♈44.5	29 47.7	19 6.1	9 18.0	4 28.1	22 5.7	9 19.6	15 .5	23 33.0
31	22 34 24.6	8 44.9	29 21.4	14 44.1	0♎ 6.4	20 20.0	9 56.2	4 20.6	22 12.5	9 22.1	15 2.2	23 34.9

DECLINATION

DAY	EPHEM. SID. TIME	☉	☊	☽	☿	♀	♂	♃	♄	♅	♆	♇
1	20 36 7.9	18N13.6	0N .4	7S46.6	13N 3.2	22N33.1	9S56.2	10S37.3	6N50.8	23N31.6	4S24.5	23N14.6
4	20 47 57.6	17 27.7	0 .3	9N55.8	11 2.1	22 20.6	10 36.8	10 44.9	6 43.1	23 31.1	4 26.0	23 13.0
7	20 59 47.3	16 39.2	0 .3	23 37.9	9 .6	22 2.4	11 17.3	10 52.8	6 35.2	23 30.7	4 27.5	23 11.4
10	21 11 36.9	15 48.3	0 .2	28 33.2	7 .4	21 38.4	11 57.8	11 1.0	6 27.1	23 30.2	4 29.1	23 9.8
13	21 23 26.6	14 55.1	0 .1	21 8.0	5 3.1	21 8.7	12 38.1	11 9.5	6 19.0	23 29.7	4 30.9	23 8.3
16	21 35 16.3	13 59.8	0 .0	3 55.1	3 10.1	20 33.6	13 18.1	11 18.2	6 10.7	23 29.3	4 32.7	23 6.8
19	21 47 5.9	13 2.5	0 .0	15S32.4	1 23.3	19 53.1	13 57.9	11 26.9	6 2.3	23 28.9	4 34.6	23 5.3
22	21 58 55.6	12 3.3	0S .1	27 47.6	0S15.4	19 7.5	14 37.2	11 35.8	5 53.9	23 28.4	4 36.5	23 3.8
25	22 10 45.3	11 2.4	0 .2	24 56.1	1 43.8	18 17.0	15 16.0	11 44.6	5 45.3	23 28.0	4 38.6	23 2.4
28	22 22 34.9	9 59.9	0 .2	9 55.6	2 58.9	17 21.8	15 54.3	11 53.4	5 36.7	23 27.6	4 40.7	23 1.0
31	22 34 24.6	8 56.1	0 .3	8N 5.1	3 57.0	16 22.1	16 31.9	12 2.1	5 28.0	23 27.2	4 42.8	22 59.7

SEPTEMBER 1950

LONGITUDE

DAY	EPHEM. SID. TIME h m s	☉ ° ′	☊ ° ′	☽ ° ′	☿ ° ′	♀ ° ′	♂ ° ′	♃ ° ′	♄ ° ′	♅ ° ′	♆ ° ′	♇ ° ′
1	22 38 21.1	7♍59.7	29♓14.7	28♈50.1	1♎59.5	18♌50.7	13♏19.6	1♓44.0	20♍48.6	8♋37.5	15♎41.7	18♌28.0
2	22 42 17.7	8 57.7	29 11.5	10♉49.2	2 13.6	20 4.4	13 58.5	1R36.2	20 56.0	8 39.7	15 43.6	18 29.7
3	22 46 14.3	9 55.8	29 8.4	22 42.4	2 22.3	21 18.1	14 37.6	1 28.4	21 3.4	8 41.9	15 45.4	18 31.5
4	22 50 10.8	10 53.9	29 5.2	4♊34.0	2 25.2	22 31.9	15 16.8	1 20.7	21 10.8	8 44.0	15 47.3	18 33.2
5	22 54 7.4	11 52.1	29 2.0	16 28.9	2R22.2	23 45.8	15 56.1	1 13.1	21 18.2	8 46.0	15 49.3	18 34.9
6	22 58 3.9	12 50.3	28 58.8	28 31.8	2 13.1	24 59.7	16 35.5	1 5.5	21 25.6	8 48.1	15 51.2	18 36.7
7	23 2 .5	13 48.5	28 55.7	10♋47.1	1 57.6	26 13.6	17 15.1	0 57.9	21 33.1	8 50.0	15 53.1	18 38.4
8	23 5 57.0	14 46.8	28 52.5	23 18.7	1 35.6	27 27.6	17 54.7	0 50.4	21 40.5	8 52.0	15 55.1	18 40.1
9	23 9 53.6	15 45.1	28 49.3	6♌ 9.4	1 7.1	28 41.6	18 34.5	0 43.0	21 48.0	8 53.9	15 57.1	18 41.7
10	23 13 50.1	16 43.4	28 46.1	19 21.0	0 32.3	29 55.7	19 14.5	0 35.8	21 55.5	8 55.8	15 59.1	18 43.5
11	23 17 46.7	17 41.8	28 42.9	2♍53.7	29♍51.3	1♍ 9.7	19 54.5	0 28.5	22 3.0	8 57.6	16 1.1	18 45.1
12	23 21 43.2	18 40.2	28 39.8	16 45.9	29 4.5	2 23.9	20 34.6	0 21.4	22 10.5	8 59.3	16 3.2	18 46.8
13	23 25 39.8	19 38.6	28 36.6	0♎54.6	28 12.5	3 38.0	21 14.9	0 14.3	22 18.0	9 1.0	16 5.2	18 48.4
14	23 29 36.4	20 37.0	28 33.4	15 15.5	27 16.2	4 52.2	21 55.2	0 7.4	22 25.4	9 2.7	16 7.2	18 50.0
15	23 33 32.9	21 35.5	28 30.2	29 43.6	26 16.4	6 6.4	22 35.7	0 .5	22 32.9	9 4.3	16 9.3	18 51.6
16	23 37 29.5	22 34.0	28 27.1	14♏13.5	25 14.3	7 20.7	23 16.2	29♒53.8	22 40.4	9 5.9	16 11.4	18 53.2
17	23 41 26.0	23 32.5	28 23.9	28 40.5	24 11.4	8 35.0	23 56.9	29 47.1	22 47.9	9 7.4	16 13.5	18 54.8
18	23 45 22.6	24 31.1	28 20.7	13♐ .5	23 9.0	9 49.3	24 37.7	29 40.6	22 55.4	9 8.8	16 15.6	18 56.4
19	23 49 19.1	25 29.7	28 17.5	27 10.7	22 8.6	11 3.7	25 18.6	29 34.3	23 2.9	9 10.3	16 17.7	18 57.9
20	23 53 15.7	26 28.3	28 14.3	11♑ 8.9	21 11.8	12 18.0	25 59.6	29 28.0	23 10.4	9 11.6	16 19.8	18 59.5
21	23 57 12.2	27 26.9	28 11.2	24 54.1	20 20.1	13 32.5	26 40.7	29 21.9	23 17.9	9 13.0	16 21.9	19 1.0
22	0 1 8.8	28 25.6	28 8.0	8♒25.6	19 34.8	14 46.9	27 21.9	29 15.9	23 25.3	9 14.2	16 24.1	19 2.5
23	0 5 5.3	29 24.3	28 4.8	21 43.2	18 57.0	16 1.4	28 3.2	29 10.1	23 32.8	9 15.4	16 26.2	19 4.0
24	0 9 1.9	0♎23.0	28 1.6	4♓47.1	18 27.9	17 15.9	28 44.6	29 4.4	23 40.3	9 16.6	16 28.4	19 5.4
25	0 12 58.4	1 21.7	27 58.5	17 37.3	18 8.0	18 30.4	29 26.0	28 58.9	23 47.7	9 17.7	16 30.5	19 6.9
26	0 16 55.0	2 20.5	27 55.3	0♈14.5	17 58.0	19 44.9	0♐ 7.6	28 53.5	23 55.2	9 18.8	16 32.7	19 8.3
27	0 20 51.5	3 19.3	27 52.1	12 39.3	17 58.0	20 59.5	0 49.3	28 48.2	24 2.6	9 19.8	16 34.9	19 9.7
28	0 24 48.1	4 18.2	27 48.9	24 52.9	18D 8.2	22 14.1	1 31.1	28 43.2	24 10.0	9 20.8	16 37.1	19 11.1
29	0 28 44.7	5 17.1	27 45.7	6♉57.0	18 28.4	23 28.8	2 12.9	28 38.2	24 17.4	9 21.7	16 39.3	19 12.5
30	0 32 41.2	6 16.0	27 42.6	18 53.7	18 58.3	24 43.5	2 54.9	28 33.5	24 24.8	9 22.6	16 41.5	19 13.9

LATITUDE

DAY	SID. TIME	☉	☊	☽	☿	♀	♂	♃	♄	♅	♆	♇
1	22 38 21.1	0 .0	0 .0	2N40.0	3S42.7	0N53.0	0S56.2	1S18.4	1N55.9	0N17.1	1N34.5	8N 6.2
4	22 50 10.8	0 .0	0 .0	4 48.8	4 2.6	0 58.8	0 58.0	1 18.5	1 55.9	0 17.2	1 34.4	8 6.7
7	23 2 .5	0 .0	0 .0	5 8.6	4 14.6	1 4.1	0 59.7	1 18.6	1 56.0	0 17.2	1 34.4	8 7.2
10	23 13 50.1	0 .0	0 .0	3 19.4	4 15.2	1 9.0	1 1.4	1 18.6	1 56.0	0 17.3	1 34.3	8 7.7
13	23 25 39.8	0 .0	0 .0	0S14.2	4 .8	1 13.2	1 2.9	1 18.6	1 56.1	0 17.4	1 34.2	8 8.2
16	23 37 29.5	0 .0	0 .0	3 47.8	3 29.3	1 17.0	1 4.4	1 18.5	1 56.2	0 17.4	1 34.2	8 8.8
19	23 49 19.1	0 .0	0 .0	5 16.9	2 42.0	1 20.2	1 5.9	1 18.4	1 56.4	0 17.5	1 34.1	8 9.4
22	0 1 8.8	0 .0	0 .0	4 3.0	1 44.4	1 22.8	1 7.2	1 18.3	1 56.6	0 17.6	1 34.1	8 10.1
25	0 12 58.4	0 .0	0 .0	0 59.4	0 44.6	1 24.8	1 8.5	1 18.1	1 56.7	0 17.6	1 34.1	8 10.7
28	0 24 48.1	0 .0	0 .0	2N21.6	0N10.0	1 26.2	1 9.7	1 17.8	1 57.0	0 17.7	1 34.1	8 11.4

RIGHT ASCENSION

DAY	SID. TIME	☉	☊	☽	☿	♀	♂	♃	♄	♅	♆	♇
1	22 38 21.1	9♍39.4	29♓18.5	25♈49.5	0♎20.9	21♌33.6	10♏34.6	4♓13.2	22♍19.2	9♋24.5	15♎ 3.9	23♌36.7
2	22 42 17.7	10 33.9	29 15.5	7♉13.8	0 30.9	22 47.0	11 13.2	4R 5.8	22 26.1	9 26.9	15 5.6	23 38.6
3	22 46 14.3	11 28.2	29 12.6	19 7.5	0 36.2	24 .1	11 52.0	3 58.4	22 32.9	9 29.3	15 7.3	23 40.4
4	22 50 10.8	12 22.5	29 9.7	1♊37.3	0 36.5	25 13.1	12 31.0	3 51.0	22 39.7	9 31.6	15 9.1	23 42.2
5	22 54 7.4	13 16.7	29 6.8	14 43.8	0R31.8	26 25.8	13 10.3	3 43.7	22 46.6	9 33.8	15 10.8	23 44.0
6	22 58 3.9	14 10.9	29 3.9	28 19.9	0 21.7	27 38.3	13 49.7	3 36.5	22 53.4	9 36.0	15 12.6	23 45.8
7	23 2 .5	15 5.0	29 1.0	12♋12.1	0 6.3	28 50.5	14 29.3	3 29.3	23 .3	9 38.1	15 14.4	23 47.6
8	23 5 57.0	15 59.1	28 58.0	26 3.5	29♍45.5	0♍ 2.6	15 9.2	3 22.1	23 7.2	9 40.3	15 16.2	23 49.4
9	23 9 53.6	16 53.1	28 55.1	9♌39.4	29 19.3	1 14.5	15 49.2	3 15.0	23 14.1	9 42.3	15 18.0	23 51.2
10	23 13 50.1	17 47.1	28 52.2	22 51.9	28 47.9	2 26.1	16 29.6	3 8.1	23 21.0	9 44.4	15 19.9	23 53.0
11	23 17 46.7	18 41.1	28 49.3	5♍41.1	28 11.5	3 37.6	17 10.0	3 1.1	23 27.9	9 46.3	15 21.8	23 54.7
12	23 21 43.2	19 35.0	28 46.4	18 14.3	27 30.5	4 48.8	17 50.7	2 54.3	23 34.8	9 48.2	15 23.6	23 56.5
13	23 25 39.8	20 28.9	28 43.5	0♎44.4	26 45.5	5 59.9	18 31.6	2 47.5	23 41.7	9 50.1	15 25.5	23 58.2
14	23 29 36.4	21 22.8	28 40.6	13 27.1	25 57.3	7 10.7	19 12.7	2 40.8	23 48.6	9 51.9	15 27.4	23 59.9
15	23 33 32.9	22 16.6	28 37.6	26 38.8	25 6.7	8 21.4	19 54.0	2 34.3	23 55.5	9 53.7	15 29.3	24 1.6
16	23 37 29.5	23 10.5	28 34.7	10♏34.0	24 14.8	9 31.9	20 35.5	2 27.8	24 2.5	9 55.4	15 31.2	24 3.3
17	23 41 26.0	24 4.3	28 31.8	25 19.9	23 22.7	10 42.2	21 17.2	2 21.4	24 9.4	9 57.0	15 33.2	24 5.0
18	23 45 22.6	24 58.1	28 28.9	10♐51.5	22 31.7	11 52.3	21 59.1	2 15.2	24 16.3	9 58.6	15 35.1	24 6.7
19	23 49 19.1	25 51.9	28 26.0	26 47.8	21 43.1	13 2.3	22 41.2	2 9.0	24 23.2	10 .1	15 37.0	24 8.3
20	23 53 15.7	26 45.7	28 23.1	12♑36.7	20 58.3	14 12.2	23 23.5	2 3.0	24 30.1	10 1.6	15 39.0	24 9.9
21	23 57 12.2	27 39.5	28 20.1	27 46.9	20 18.3	15 21.9	24 6.0	1 57.1	24 37.0	10 3.1	15 41.0	24 11.5
22	0 1 8.8	28 33.4	28 17.2	11♒59.3	19 44.4	16 31.4	24 48.6	1 51.4	24 43.9	10 4.5	15 43.0	24 13.1
23	0 5 5.3	29 27.2	28 14.3	25 9.7	19 17.5	17 40.8	25 31.5	1 45.7	24 50.8	10 5.8	15 44.9	24 14.7
24	0 9 1.9	0♎21.1	28 11.4	7♓25.6	18 58.5	18 50.1	26 14.6	1 40.3	24 57.7	10 7.1	15 46.9	24 16.3
25	0 12 58.4	1 15.0	28 8.5	19 .3	18 47.9	19 59.3	26 57.9	1 34.9	25 4.6	10 8.3	15 48.9	24 17.9
26	0 16 55.0	2 8.9	28 5.6	0♈ 9.2	18 46.1	21 8.4	27 41.3	1 29.7	25 11.5	10 9.5	15 51.0	24 19.4
27	0 20 51.5	3 2.9	28 2.7	11 7.7	18D53.3	22 17.4	28 25.0	1 24.6	25 18.3	10 10.6	15 53.0	24 20.9
28	0 24 48.1	3 56.9	27 59.7	22 10.0	19 9.5	23 26.3	29 8.8	1 19.7	25 25.2	10 11.6	15 55.0	24 22.4
29	0 28 44.7	4 51.0	27 56.8	3♉28.8	19 34.4	24 35.2	29 52.9	1 15.0	25 32.0	10 12.6	15 57.0	24 23.9
30	0 32 41.2	5 45.2	27 53.9	15 14.3	20 7.8	25 43.9	0♐37.1	1 10.3	25 38.9	10 13.6	15 59.1	24 25.3

DECLINATION

DAY	SID. TIME	☉	☊	☽	☿	♀	♂	♃	♄	♅	♆	♇
1	22 38 21.1	8N34.5	0S .3	13N33.3	4S11.9	16N 1.3	16S44.3	12S 4.9	5N25.1	23N27.1	4S43.5	22N59.3
4	22 50 10.8	7 28.9	0 .4	25 47.4	4 40.3	14 56.1	17 20.9	12 13.4	5 16.4	23 26.8	4 45.8	22 58.0
7	23 2 .5	6 22.3	0 .4	28 8.1	4 40.3	13 47.1	17 56.7	12 21.6	5 7.6	23 26.4	4 48.1	22 56.9
10	23 13 50.1	5 14.6	0 .5	18 10.7	4 6.9	12 34.6	18 31.6	12 29.5	4 58.8	23 26.1	4 50.4	22 55.7
13	23 25 39.8	4 6.2	0 .6	0S34.7	2 58.2	11 19.0	19 5.5	12 37.1	4 50.1	23 25.8	4 52.8	22 54.6
16	23 37 29.5	2 57.1	0 .6	19 44.1	1 18.6	10 .5	19 38.2	12 44.3	4 41.3	23 25.6	4 55.2	22 53.6
19	23 49 19.1	1 47.5	0 .7	28 42.0	0N38.2	8 39.4	20 9.8	12 51.0	4 32.5	23 25.3	4 57.7	22 52.7
22	0 1 8.8	0 37.6	0 .8	22 4.2	2 31.6	7 16.1	20 40.1	12 57.3	4 23.8	23 25.1	5 .2	22 51.8
25	0 12 58.4	0S32.5	0 .8	5 48.2	4 .6	5 50.9	21 9.1	13 3.1	4 15.1	23 24.9	5 2.7	22 51.0
28	0 24 48.1	1 42.7	0 .9	11N50.0	4 50.7	4 24.1	21 36.6	13 8.4	4 6.4	23 24.8	5 5.2	22 50.3

OCTOBER 1950

LONGITUDE

DAY	EPHEM. SID. TIME h m s	☉ ° ′	☊ ° ′	☾ ° ′	☿ ° ′	♀ ° ′	♂ ° ′	♃ ° ′	♄ ° ′	♅ ° ′	♆ ° ′	♇ ° ′
1	0 36 37.8	7♎15.0	27♓39.4	0♊46.0	19♍37.5	25♍58.2	3♐37.0	28♒29.0	24♍32.3	9♋23.5	16♎43.7	19♌15.2
2	0 40 34.3	8 14.0	27 36.2	12 37.1	20 25.2	27 12.9	4 19.2	28 R 24.6	24 39.6	9 24.2	16 45.9	19 16.6
3	0 44 30.9	9 13.0	27 33.0	24 30.9	21 21.0	28 27.7	5 1.4	28 20.3	24 47.0	9 24.9	16 48.2	19 17.9
4	0 48 27.4	10 12.1	27 29.9	6♋31.9	22 24.2	29 42.5	5 43.7	28 16.3	24 54.3	9 25.6	16 50.4	19 19.1
5	0 52 24.0	11 11.2	27 26.7	18 44.6	23 33.9	0♎57.3	6 26.2	28 12.4	25 1.6	9 26.2	16 52.6	19 20.4
6	0 56 20.5	12 10.4	27 23.5	1♌13.4	24 49.5	2 12.1	7 8.7	28 8.7	25 8.9	9 26.7	16 54.8	19 21.6
7	1 0 17.1	13 9.6	27 20.3	14 2.5	26 10.2	3 27.0	7 51.3	28 5.2	25 16.2	9 27.2	16 57.1	19 22.9
8	1 4 13.6	14 8.8	27 17.1	27 15.0	27 35.5	4 41.9	8 34.0	28 1.8	25 23.4	9 27.7	16 59.3	19 24.1
9	1 8 10.2	15 8.1	27 14.0	10♍52.9	29 4.5	5 56.8	9 16.8	27 58.7	25 30.6	9 28.1	17 1.5	19 25.2
10	1 12 6.7	16 7.4	27 10.8	24 56.1	0♎36.8	7 11.7	9 59.7	27 55.7	25 37.8	9 28.4	17 3.8	19 26.4
11	1 16 3.3	17 6.7	27 7.6	9♎22.1	2 11.7	8 26.7	10 42.7	27 53.0	25 45.0	9 28.7	17 6.0	19 27.5
12	1 19 59.9	18 6.1	27 4.4	24 5.9	3 48.8	9 41.6	11 25.8	27 50.4	25 52.1	9 28.9	17 8.2	19 28.6
13	1 23 56.4	19 5.5	27 1.3	9♏ .4	5 27.7	10 56.6	12 8.9	27 48.1	25 59.2	9 29.1	17 10.5	19 29.7
14	1 27 53.0	20 4.9	26 58.1	23 57.3	7 7.9	12 11.6	12 52.2	27 45.9	26 6.3	9 29.3	17 12.7	19 30.8
15	1 31 49.5	21 4.4	26 54.9	8♐48.2	8 49.2	13 26.7	13 35.5	27 43.9	26 13.4	9 29.3	17 14.9	19 31.8
16	1 35 46.1	22 3.9	26 51.7	23 26.1	10 31.2	14 41.7	14 18.9	27 42.1	26 20.4	9 29.3	17 17.2	19 32.8
17	1 39 42.6	23 3.4	26 48.5	7♑46.0	12 13.8	15 56.8	15 2.4	27 40.6	26 27.4	9 29.3	17 19.4	19 33.8
18	1 43 39.2	24 3.0	26 45.4	21 45.1	13 56.7	17 11.8	15 46.0	27 39.2	26 34.3	9 R 29.2	17 21.6	19 34.8
19	1 47 35.7	25 2.5	26 42.2	5♒22.9	15 39.7	18 26.9	16 29.6	27 38.0	26 41.2	9 29.1	17 23.8	19 35.7
20	1 51 32.3	26 2.2	26 39.0	18 40.5	17 22.7	19 42.0	17 13.3	27 37.1	26 48.1	9 28.9	17 26.1	19 36.6
21	1 55 28.8	27 1.8	26 35.8	1♓40.0	19 5.5	20 57.1	17 57.1	27 36.3	26 55.0	9 28.6	17 28.3	19 37.5
22	1 59 25.4	28 1.5	26 32.7	14 23.9	20 48.3	22 12.3	18 41.1	27 35.8	27 1.8	9 28.4	17 30.5	19 38.4
23	2 3 22.0	29 1.2	26 29.5	26 54.6	22 30.7	23 27.4	19 25.0	27 35.5	27 8.6	9 28.0	17 32.7	19 39.2
24	2 7 18.5	0♏ .9	26 26.3	9♈14.4	24 12.7	24 42.6	20 9.1	27 35.3	27 15.3	9 27.6	17 34.9	19 40.1
25	2 11 15.1	1 .7	26 23.1	21 25.2	25 54.4	25 57.8	20 53.2	27 D 35.4	27 22.0	9 27.1	17 37.1	19 40.8
26	2 15 11.6	2 .5	26 20.0	3♉28.8	27 35.6	27 12.9	21 37.3	27 35.6	27 28.6	9 26.6	17 39.3	19 41.6
27	2 19 8.2	3 .3	26 16.8	15 26.7	29 16.4	28 28.1	22 21.6	27 36.1	27 35.2	9 26.1	17 41.5	19 42.3
28	2 23 4.7	4 .2	26 13.6	27 20.5	0♏56.7	29 43.3	23 5.9	27 36.7	27 41.7	9 25.4	17 43.6	19 43.0
29	2 27 1.3	5 .1	26 10.4	9♊11.9	2 36.5	0♏58.5	23 50.3	27 37.6	27 48.2	9 24.8	17 45.8	19 43.7
30	2 30 57.8	6 .0	26 7.2	21 3.2	4 15.9	2 13.8	24 34.7	27 38.6	27 54.7	9 24.1	17 47.9	19 44.4
31	2 34 54.4	6 60.0	26 4.1	2♋57.1	5 54.8	3 29.0	25 19.3	27 39.9	28 1.1	9 23.3	17 50.1	19 45.0

LATITUDE

DAY	EPHEM. SID. TIME	☉	☊	☾	☿	♀	♂	♃	♄	♅	♆	♇
1	0 36 37.8	0 .0	0 .0	4N40.7	0N54.4	1N27.0	1S10.8	1S17.5	1N57.2	0N17.8	1N34.0	8N12.1
4	0 48 27.4	0 .0	0 .0	5 13.1	1 26.6	1 27.2	1 11.9	1 17.2	1 57.5	0 17.9	1 34.0	8 12.9
7	1 0 17.1	0 .0	0 .0	3 41.1	1 46.8	1 26.8	1 12.8	1 16.8	1 57.8	0 17.9	1 34.0	8 13.6
10	1 12 6.7	0 .0	0 .0	0 18.9	1 56.5	1 25.8	1 13.7	1 16.5	1 58.1	0 18.0	1 34.1	8 14.4
13	1 23 56.4	0 .0	0 .0	3S25.5	1 57.5	1 24.2	1 14.6	1 16.0	1 58.4	0 18.1	1 34.1	8 15.2
16	1 35 46.1	0 .0	0 .0	5 13.1	1 51.8	1 22.1	1 15.3	1 15.6	1 58.8	0 18.2	1 34.1	8 16.0
19	1 47 35.7	0 .0	0 .0	4 10.3	1 41.1	1 19.4	1 16.0	1 15.2	1 59.2	0 18.2	1 34.1	8 16.9
22	1 59 25.4	0 .0	0 .0	1 14.9	1 26.8	1 16.2	1 16.6	1 14.7	1 59.6	0 18.3	1 34.2	8 17.7
25	2 11 15.1	0 .0	0 .0	2N 3.4	1 10.0	1 12.4	1 17.2	1 14.2	2 .0	0 18.4	1 34.2	8 18.6
28	2 23 4.7	0 .0	0 .0	4 27.2	0 51.4	1 8.2	1 17.6	1 13.7	2 .5	0 18.5	1 34.3	8 19.5
31	2 34 54.4	0 .0	0 .0	5 8.2	0 31.9	1 3.5	1 18.0	1 13.2	2 1.0	0 18.5	1 34.3	8 20.4

RIGHT ASCENSION

DAY	EPHEM. SID. TIME	☉	☊	☾	☿	♀	♂	♃	♄	♅	♆	♇
1	0 36 37.8	6♎39.4	27♓51.0	27♉32.9	20♍49.3	26♍52.7	1♐21.6	1♓ 6.0	25♍45.7	10♋14.5	16♎ 1.2	24♌26.8
2	0 40 34.3	7 33.7	27 48.1	10♊25.5	21 38.2	28 1.4	2 6.2	1 R 1.7	25 52.5	10 15.3	16 3.2	24 28.3
3	0 44 30.9	8 28.1	27 45.2	23 46.6	22 33.9	29 10.0	2 51.0	0 57.6	25 59.3	10 16.1	16 5.3	24 29.7
4	0 48 27.4	9 22.5	27 42.2	7♋24.4	23 35.7	0♎18.6	3 35.9	0 53.6	26 6.1	10 16.8	16 7.3	24 31.1
5	0 52 24.0	10 17.0	27 39.3	21 3.7	24 43.1	1 27.2	4 21.1	0 49.8	26 12.9	10 17.5	16 9.4	24 32.4
6	0 56 20.5	11 11.6	27 36.4	4♌31.1	25 55.3	2 35.8	5 6.4	0 46.2	26 19.6	10 18.1	16 11.5	24 33.8
7	1 0 17.1	12 6.4	27 33.5	17 38.5	27 11.7	3 44.4	5 51.9	0 42.8	26 26.3	10 18.7	16 13.5	24 35.1
8	1 4 13.6	13 1.2	27 30.6	0♍25.3	28 31.6	4 53.0	6 37.6	0 39.5	26 33.0	10 19.1	16 15.6	24 36.4
9	1 8 10.2	13 56.1	27 27.7	12 58.0	29 54.6	6 1.7	7 23.5	0 36.5	26 39.7	10 19.6	16 17.7	24 37.7
10	1 12 6.7	14 51.1	27 24.7	25 28.6	1♎20.1	7 10.3	8 9.5	0 33.6	26 46.3	10 19.9	16 19.7	24 39.0
11	1 16 3.3	15 46.3	27 21.8	8♎12.6	2 47.6	8 19.0	8 55.7	0 30.9	26 53.0	10 20.3	16 21.8	24 40.2
12	1 19 59.9	16 41.6	27 18.9	21 27.1	4 16.8	9 27.8	9 42.1	0 28.3	26 59.6	10 20.5	16 23.9	24 41.4
13	1 23 56.4	17 37.0	27 16.0	5♏28.0	5 47.3	10 36.6	10 28.7	0 26.0	27 6.2	10 20.7	16 26.0	24 42.6
14	1 27 53.0	18 32.5	27 13.1	20 24.8	7 18.9	11 45.5	11 15.4	0 23.9	27 12.7	10 20.8	16 28.1	24 43.8
15	1 31 49.5	19 28.1	27 10.2	6♐13.8	8 51.2	12 54.5	12 2.3	0 21.9	27 19.2	10 20.9	16 30.1	24 44.9
16	1 35 46.1	20 23.9	27 7.2	22 33.4	10 24.0	14 3.5	12 49.3	0 20.2	27 25.7	10 20.9	16 32.2	24 46.1
17	1 39 42.6	21 19.8	27 4.3	8♑47.9	11 57.3	15 12.7	13 36.5	0 18.6	27 32.2	10 20.9	16 34.3	24 47.2
18	1 43 39.2	22 15.9	27 1.4	24 21.2	13 30.8	16 22.0	14 23.8	0 17.2	27 38.6	10 R 20.8	16 36.3	24 48.2
19	1 47 35.7	23 12.1	26 58.5	8♒50.8	15 4.5	17 31.4	15 11.3	0 16.0	27 45.0	10 20.7	16 38.4	24 49.3
20	1 51 32.3	24 8.4	26 55.6	22 11.7	16 38.3	18 40.9	15 58.9	0 15.1	27 51.4	10 20.4	16 40.5	24 50.3
21	1 55 28.8	25 4.9	26 52.7	4♓32.2	18 12.1	19 50.6	16 46.7	0 14.3	27 57.7	10 20.2	16 42.5	24 51.3
22	1 59 25.4	26 1.6	26 49.7	16 7.0	19 45.9	21 .4	17 34.6	0 13.7	28 4.1	10 19.9	16 44.6	24 52.3
23	2 3 22.0	26 58.5	26 46.8	27 12.7	21 19.6	22 10.4	18 22.6	0 13.3	28 10.3	10 19.5	16 46.7	24 53.3
24	2 7 18.5	27 55.4	26 43.9	8♈ 5.6	22 53.2	23 20.6	19 10.8	0 13.1	28 16.6	10 19.1	16 48.7	24 54.2
25	2 11 15.1	28 52.6	26 41.0	19 .7	24 26.8	24 30.9	19 59.1	0 13.1	28 22.8	10 18.6	16 50.8	24 55.1
26	2 15 11.6	29 49.9	26 38.1	0♉11.2	26 .3	25 41.4	20 47.5	0 D 13.3	28 28.9	10 18.0	16 52.8	24 56.0
27	2 19 8.2	0♏47.5	26 35.2	11 47.7	27 33.7	26 52.1	21 36.0	0 13.7	28 35.0	10 17.4	16 54.8	24 56.8
28	2 23 4.7	1 45.2	26 32.2	23 57.0	29 7.0	28 3.0	22 24.6	0 14.3	28 41.1	10 16.7	16 56.8	24 57.7
29	2 27 1.3	2 43.1	26 29.3	6♊40.3	0♏40.3	29 14.2	23 13.3	0 15.0	28 47.1	10 16.0	16 58.8	24 58.5
30	2 30 57.8	3 41.1	26 26.4	19 52.3	2 13.6	0♏25.5	24 2.2	0 16.0	28 53.1	10 15.2	17 .9	24 59.2
31	2 34 54.4	4 39.4	26 23.5	3♋20.8	3 46.9	1 37.1	24 51.1	0 17.1	28 59.0	10 14.4	17 2.8	24 60.0

DECLINATION

DAY	EPHEM. SID. TIME	☉	☊	☾	☿	♀	♂	♃	♄	♅	♆	♇
1	0 36 37.8	2S52.7	0S 1.0	24N53.5	4N56.6	2N56.0	22S 2.5	13S13.0	3N57.8	23N24.7	5S 7.7	22N49.6
4	0 48 27.4	4 2.5	0 1.0	28 29.9	4 20.5	1 27.0	22 26.9	13 17.2	3 49.3	23 24.6	5 10.3	22 49.1
7	1 0 17.1	5 11.9	0 1.1	20 8.7	3 9.4	0S 2.7	22 49.5	13 20.7	3 40.9	23 24.6	5 12.8	22 48.6
10	1 12 6.7	6 20.7	0 1.2	2 18.2	1 32.2	1 32.6	23 10.4	13 23.6	3 32.6	23 24.6	5 15.4	22 48.2
13	1 23 56.4	7 28.7	0 1.2	17S44.8	0S22.3	3 2.4	23 29.4	13 25.9	3 24.4	23 24.6	5 17.9	22 47.9
16	1 35 46.1	8 35.8	0 1.3	28 29.8	2 27.1	4 31.9	23 46.4	13 27.5	3 16.3	23 24.6	5 20.5	22 47.6
19	1 47 35.7	9 41.8	0 1.4	22 58.4	4 36.6	6 .6	24 1.4	13 28.5	3 8.4	23 24.7	5 23.0	22 47.5
22	1 59 25.4	10 46.6	0 1.4	7 17.8	6 47.0	7 28.3	24 14.3	13 28.8	3 .6	23 24.9	5 25.5	22 47.4
25	2 11 15.1	11 49.8	0 1.5	10N15.7	8 55.5	8 54.4	24 25.1	13 28.5	2 53.0	23 25.0	5 28.0	22 47.5
28	2 23 4.7	12 51.5	0 1.6	23 54.3	11 .2	10 18.9	24 33.6	13 27.6	2 45.6	23 25.2	5 30.4	22 47.6
31	2 34 54.4	13 51.3	0 1.6	28 33.1	12 59.8	11 41.1	24 39.9	13 26.0	2 38.3	23 25.4	5 32.8	22 47.8

NOVEMBER 1950

LONGITUDE

DAY	EPHEM. SID. TIME	☉	☊	☽	☿	♀	♂	♃	♄	♅	♆	♇
	h m s	° ′	° ′	° ′	° ′	° ′	° ′	° ′	° ′	° ′	° ′	° ′
1	2 38 51.0	7♏60.0	26♓ .9	14♋56.9	7♏33.2	4♏44.2	26♐ 3.9	27♒41.4	28♍ 7.4	9♋22.5	17♎52.2	19♌45.6
2	2 42 47.5	9 .0	25 57.7	27 6.6	9 11.2	5 59.5	26 48.6	27 43.0	28 13.7	9 R 21.6	17 54.3	19 46.2
3	2 46 44.1	10 .1	25 54.5	9♌30.5	10 48.7	7 14.8	27 33.3	27 44.9	28 19.9	9 20.7	17 56.4	19 46.7
4	2 50 40.6	11 .2	25 51.4	22 13.1	12 25.7	8 30.1	28 18.1	27 47.0	28 26.1	9 19.7	17 58.5	19 47.2
5	2 54 37.2	12 .3	25 48.2	5♍18.6	14 2.4	9 45.4	29 3.0	27 49.2	28 32.3	9 18.7	18 .6	19 47.7
6	2 58 33.7	13 .5	25 45.0	18 50.7	15 38.6	11 .7	29 47.9	27 51.7	28 38.3	9 17.6	18 2.7	19 48.2
7	3 2 30.3	14 .7	25 41.8	2♎51.2	17 14.4	12 16.0	0♑32.9	27 54.3	28 44.4	9 16.5	18 4.8	19 48.6
8	3 6 26.9	15 1.0	25 38.6	17 19.5	18 49.8	13 31.3	1 18.0	27 57.2	28 50.3	9 15.3	18 6.8	19 49.0
9	3 10 23.4	16 1.2	25 35.5	2♏12.0	20 24.9	14 46.7	2 3.2	28 .2	28 56.2	9 14.1	18 8.8	19 49.4
10	3 14 20.0	17 1.5	25 32.3	17 21.5	21 59.6	16 2.0	2 48.4	28 3.5	29 2.1	9 12.8	18 10.8	19 49.7
11	3 18 16.5	18 1.9	25 29.1	2♐38.2	23 34.0	17 17.4	3 33.7	28 6.9	29 7.9	9 11.5	18 12.9	19 50.0
12	3 22 13.1	19 2.3	25 25.9	17 51.1	25 8.1	18 32.8	4 19.1	28 10.6	29 13.6	9 10.2	18 14.9	19 50.4
13	3 26 9.6	20 2.7	25 22.8	2♑49.7	26 41.8	19 48.1	5 4.5	28 14.4	29 19.3	9 8.8	18 16.9	19 50.6
14	3 30 6.2	21 3.1	25 19.6	17 26.2	28 15.3	21 3.5	5 49.9	28 18.5	29 24.9	9 7.3	18 18.8	19 50.9
15	3 34 2.7	22 3.5	25 16.4	1♒36.1	29 48.4	22 18.9	6 35.4	28 22.7	29 30.4	9 5.9	18 20.8	19 51.1
16	3 37 59.3	23 4.0	25 13.2	15 18.1	1♐21.3	23 34.2	7 21.0	28 27.0	29 35.8	9 4.3	18 22.7	19 51.2
17	3 41 55.9	24 4.5	25 10.1	28 33.7	2 54.0	24 49.6	8 6.6	28 31.6	29 41.2	9 2.7	18 24.6	19 51.4
18	3 45 52.4	25 5.0	25 6.9	11♓26.1	4 26.4	26 5.0	8 52.3	28 36.4	29 46.5	9 1.1	18 26.5	19 51.5
19	3 49 49.0	26 5.5	25 3.7	23 59.5	5 58.5	27 20.4	9 38.0	28 41.3	29 51.7	8 59.4	18 28.3	19 51.6
20	3 53 45.5	27 6.0	25 .5	6♈18.0	7 30.5	28 35.7	10 23.8	28 46.5	29 56.9	8 57.7	18 30.2	19 51.6
21	3 57 42.1	28 6.6	24 57.4	18 25.7	9 2.2	29 51.1	11 9.6	28 51.8	0♎ 2.0	8 56.0	18 32.0	19 51.6
22	4 1 38.7	29 7.2	24 54.2	0♉25.9	10 33.6	1♐ 6.5	11 55.5	28 57.2	0 7.0	8 54.2	18 33.8	19 51.6
23	4 5 35.2	0♐ 7.8	24 51.0	12 21.4	12 4.9	2 21.9	12 41.4	29 2.9	0 12.0	8 52.4	18 35.6	19 51.6
24	4 9 31.8	1 8.4	24 47.8	24 14.3	13 35.9	3 37.3	13 27.4	29 8.7	0 16.8	8 50.5	18 37.4	19 51.6
25	4 13 28.3	2 9.1	24 44.6	6♊ 6.4	15 6.6	4 52.7	14 13.4	29 14.7	0 21.6	8 48.6	18 39.1	19 R 51.5
26	4 17 24.9	3 9.7	24 41.5	17 58.9	16 37.1	6 8.0	14 59.5	29 20.9	0 26.3	8 46.7	18 40.8	19 51.3
27	4 21 21.4	4 10.4	24 38.3	29 53.2	18 7.3	7 23.4	15 45.6	29 27.2	0 30.9	8 44.7	18 42.5	19 51.2
28	4 25 18.0	5 11.1	24 35.1	11♋51.0	19 37.2	8 38.8	16 31.8	29 33.7	0 35.5	8 42.7	18 44.2	19 51.0
29	4 29 14.6	6 11.9	24 31.9	23 54.2	21 6.7	9 54.2	17 18.0	29 40.4	0 40.0	8 40.7	18 45.9	19 50.8
30	4 33 11.1	7 12.7	24 28.8	6♌ 5.7	22 35.9	11 9.6	18 4.3	29 47.2	0 44.3	8 38.6	18 47.5	19 50.6

LATITUDE

DAY	EPHEM. SID. TIME	☉	☊	☽	☿	♀	♂	♃	♄	♅	♆	♇
1	2 38 51.0	0 .0	0 .0	4N55.5	0N25.2	1N 1.9	1S18.1	1S13.1	2N 1.2	0N18.6	1N34.4	8N20.7
4	2 50 40.6	0 .0	0 .0	2 59.0	0 5.0	0 56.6	1 18.4	1 12.6	2 1.7	0 18.6	1 34.4	8 21.6
7	3 2 30.3	0 .0	0 .0	0S29.0	0S15.2	0 51.0	1 18.6	1 12.0	2 2.2	0 18.7	1 34.5	8 22.6
10	3 14 20.0	0 .0	0 .0	3 55.4	0 34.9	0 45.0	1 18.8	1 11.5	2 2.8	0 18.8	1 34.6	8 23.5
13	3 26 9.6	0 .0	0 .0	5 4.4	0 54.0	0 38.8	1 18.9	1 11.0	2 3.4	0 18.9	1 34.7	8 24.4
16	3 37 59.3	0 .0	0 .0	3 23.0	1 12.1	0 32.2	1 18.9	1 10.5	2 4.0	0 18.9	1 34.8	8 25.4
19	3 49 49.0	0 .0	0 .0	0 14.6	1 29.0	0 25.5	1 18.8	1 10.0	2 4.7	0 19.0	1 34.9	8 26.3
22	4 1 38.7	0 .0	0 .0	2N49.5	1 44.2	0 18.6	1 18.6	1 9.5	2 5.3	0 19.0	1 35.0	8 27.2
25	4 13 28.3	0 .0	0 .0	4 43.6	1 57.5	0 11.5	1 18.4	1 9.0	2 6.0	0 19.1	1 35.1	8 28.2
28	4 25 18.0	0 .0	0 .0	4 49.2	2 8.4	0 4.4	1 18.1	1 8.6	2 6.7	0 19.2	1 35.3	8 29.1

RIGHT ASCENSION

DAY	EPHEM. SID. TIME	☉	☊	☽	☿	♀	♂	♃	♄	♅	♆	♇
1	2 38 51.0	5♏37.9	26♓20.6	16♋50.6	5♏20.2	2♏49.0	25♐40.1	0♓18.5	29♍ 4.9	10♋13.5	17♎ 4.8	25♌ .7
2	2 42 47.5	6 36.6	26 17.7	0♌ 7.4	6 53.6	4 1.0	26 29.3	0 20.0	29 10.8	10 R 12.6	17 6.8	25 1.4
3	2 46 44.1	7 35.4	26 14.7	13 2.8	8 27.0	5 13.4	27 18.5	0 21.8	29 16.6	10 11.6	17 8.8	25 2.0
4	2 50 40.6	8 34.5	26 11.8	25 35.5	10 .5	6 26.0	28 7.8	0 23.7	29 22.3	10 10.5	17 10.7	25 2.7
5	2 54 37.2	9 33.8	26 8.9	7♍51.7	11 34.1	7 38.9	28 57.2	0 25.8	29 28.0	10 9.4	17 12.7	25 3.3
6	2 58 33.7	10 33.3	26 6.0	20 3.1	13 7.9	8 52.0	29 46.7	0 28.1	29 33.7	10 8.2	17 14.6	25 3.8
7	3 2 30.3	11 33.1	26 3.1	2♎25.6	14 41.9	10 5.4	0♑36.3	0 30.6	29 39.3	10 7.0	17 16.5	25 4.4
8	3 6 26.9	12 33.0	26 .2	15 17.7	16 16.0	11 19.1	1 25.9	0 33.3	29 44.8	10 5.7	17 18.5	25 4.9
9	3 10 23.4	13 33.1	25 57.2	28 58.3	17 50.4	12 33.1	2 15.6	0 36.2	29 50.3	10 4.4	17 20.4	25 5.4
10	3 14 20.0	14 33.5	25 54.3	13♏42.5	19 25.0	13 47.4	3 5.4	0 39.3	29 55.7	10 3.0	17 22.2	25 5.8
11	3 18 16.5	15 34.1	25 51.4	29 34.1	20 59.8	15 2.0	3 55.2	0 42.5	0♎ 1.1	10 1.6	17 24.1	25 6.3
12	3 22 13.1	16 34.9	25 48.5	16♐16.6	22 34.9	16 16.9	4 45.1	0 46.0	0 6.5	10 .2	17 26.0	25 6.7
13	3 26 9.6	17 35.9	25 45.6	3♑12.3	24 10.3	17 32.1	5 35.0	0 49.6	0 11.8	9 58.7	17 27.9	25 7.1
14	3 30 6.2	18 37.1	25 42.7	19 35.4	25 45.9	18 47.6	6 25.0	0 53.4	0 17.0	9 57.1	17 29.7	25 7.4
15	3 34 2.7	19 38.5	25 39.7	4♒51.7	27 21.8	20 3.4	7 15.0	0 57.4	0 22.1	9 55.5	17 31.5	25 7.8
16	3 37 59.3	20 40.1	25 36.8	18 49.3	28 58.1	21 19.5	8 5.0	1 1.6	0 27.2	9 53.8	17 33.3	25 8.0
17	3 41 55.9	21 41.9	25 33.9	1♓34.7	0♐34.6	22 35.9	8 55.0	1 5.9	0 32.2	9 52.1	17 35.1	25 8.3
18	3 45 52.4	22 44.0	25 31.0	13 23.6	2 11.4	23 52.6	9 45.1	1 10.5	0 37.2	9 50.3	17 36.9	25 8.5
19	3 49 49.0	23 46.2	25 28.1	24 34.8	3 48.4	25 9.6	10 35.2	1 15.2	0 42.0	9 48.5	17 38.6	25 8.7
20	3 53 45.5	24 48.6	25 25.1	5♈26.8	5 25.8	26 26.9	11 25.3	1 20.0	0 46.9	9 46.6	17 40.3	25 8.9
21	3 57 42.1	25 51.3	25 22.2	16 16.2	7 3.4	27 44.5	12 15.4	1 25.1	0 51.6	9 44.8	17 42.0	25 9.0
22	4 1 38.7	26 54.1	25 19.3	27 18.0	8 41.2	29 2.4	13 5.5	1 30.3	0 56.3	9 42.8	17 43.7	25 9.1
23	4 5 35.2	27 57.1	25 16.4	8♉44.4	10 19.3	0♐20.6	13 55.6	1 35.6	1 .9	9 40.8	17 45.4	25 9.2
24	4 9 31.8	29 .3	25 13.5	20 43.7	11 57.5	1 39.1	14 45.7	1 41.2	1 5.5	9 38.8	17 47.1	25 9.3
25	4 13 28.3	0♐ 3.8	25 10.6	3♊19.0	13 35.9	2 57.9	15 35.8	1 46.9	1 10.0	9 36.7	17 48.7	25 9.3
26	4 17 24.9	1 7.4	25 7.6	16 25.8	15 14.4	4 16.9	16 25.9	1 52.8	1 14.4	9 34.6	17 50.3	25 9.3
27	4 21 21.4	2 11.2	25 4.7	29 52.3	16 52.9	5 36.3	17 16.0	1 58.8	1 18.7	9 32.5	17 51.9	25 R 9.2
28	4 25 18.0	3 15.2	25 1.8	13♋21.9	18 31.4	6 55.9	18 6.0	2 5.0	1 23.0	9 30.3	17 53.5	25 9.2
29	4 29 14.6	4 19.3	24 58.9	26 38.0	20 9.9	8 15.8	18 56.0	2 11.3	1 27.2	9 28.1	17 55.1	25 9.1
30	4 33 11.1	5 23.7	24 56.0	9♌29.6	21 48.1	9 35.9	19 46.0	2 17.8	1 31.3	9 25.8	17 56.6	25 9.0

DECLINATION

DAY	EPHEM. SID. TIME	☉	☊	☽	☿	♀	♂	♃	♄	♅	♆	♇
1	2 38 51.0	14S10.8	0S 1.7	27N30.2	13S38.4	12S 8.0	24S41.5	13S25.4	2N36.0	23N25.5	5S33.6	22N47.9
4	2 50 40.6	15 8.0	0 1.7	16 55.8	15 29.6	13 26.9	24 44.7	13 23.0	2 29.0	23 25.8	5 35.9	22 48.2
7	3 2 30.3	16 3.0	0 1.8	1S34.7	17 13.7	14 42.8	24 45.5	13 19.9	2 22.2	23 26.1	5 38.2	22 48.6
10	3 14 20.0	16 55.6	0 1.9	20 46.9	18 50.1	15 55.4	24 43.9	13 16.3	2 15.7	23 26.4	5 40.4	22 49.2
13	3 26 9.6	17 45.6	0 1.9	28 29.4	20 18.0	17 4.3	24 39.9	13 12.0	2 9.4	23 26.8	5 42.6	22 49.7
16	3 37 59.3	18 32.8	0 2.0	19 29.0	21 37.0	18 9.1	24 33.4	13 7.2	2 3.4	23 27.1	5 44.8	22 50.4
19	3 49 49.0	19 17.0	0 2.1	2 36.6	22 46.3	19 9.5	24 24.5	13 1.7	1 57.6	23 27.5	5 46.8	22 51.2
22	4 1 38.7	19 58.1	0 2.1	14N16.3	23 45.5	20 5.2	24 13.1	12 55.7	1 52.2	23 27.9	5 48.8	22 52.1
25	4 13 28.3	20 36.0	0 2.2	25 59.2	24 33.8	20 55.7	23 59.3	12 49.1	1 47.0	23 28.4	5 50.7	22 53.0
28	4 25 18.0	21 10.4	0 2.3	27 43.2	25 10.6	21 40.9	23 43.0	12 42.0	1 42.1	23 28.8	5 52.5	22 54.0

DECEMBER 1950

LONGITUDE

DAY	EPHEM. SID. TIME h m s	☉ ° ′	☊ ° ′	☽ ° ′	☿ ° ′	♀ ° ′	♂ ° ′	♃ ° ′	♄ ° ′	♅ ° ′	♆ ° ′	♇ ° ′
1	4 37 7.7	8♐13.5	24♓25.6	18♌28.6	24♐ 4.6	12♐25.0	18♑50.6	29♒54.2	0♎48.6	8♋36.5	18♎49.1	19♌50.3
2	4 41 4.2	9 14.3	24 22.4	1♍ 7.1	25 32.8	13 40.5	19 36.9	0♓ 1.4	0 52.8	8 R34.3	18 50.7	19 R50.0
3	4 45 .8	10 15.2	24 19.2	14 5.2	27 .5	14 55.9	20 23.3	0 8.7	0 57.0	8 32.2	18 52.3	19 49.8
4	4 48 57.3	11 16.0	24 16.1	27 27.1	28 27.4	16 11.3	21 9.8	0 16.2	1 1.1	8 30.0	18 53.8	19 49.4
5	4 52 53.9	12 16.9	24 12.9	11♎15.8	29 53.6	17 26.8	21 56.2	0 23.8	1 5.0	8 27.8	18 55.3	19 49.1
6	4 56 50.5	13 17.8	24 9.7	25 32.8	1♑18.9	18 42.2	22 42.7	0 31.6	1 8.9	8 25.5	18 56.8	19 48.7
7	5 0 47.0	14 18.8	24 6.5	10♏16.5	2 43.1	19 57.6	23 29.3	0 39.6	1 12.7	8 23.3	18 58.3	19 48.2
8	5 4 43.6	15 19.7	24 3.4	25 21.9	4 6.0	21 13.0	24 15.9	0 47.6	1 16.3	8 21.0	18 59.7	19 47.8
9	5 8 40.1	16 20.7	24 .2	10♐40.4	5 27.6	22 28.5	25 2.5	0 55.9	1 19.9	8 18.6	19 1.1	19 47.3
10	5 12 36.7	17 21.7	23 57.0	26 .6	6 47.4	23 43.9	25 49.2	1 4.3	1 23.4	8 16.3	19 2.5	19 46.8
11	5 16 33.3	18 22.7	23 53.8	11♑10.8	8 5.3	24 59.3	26 35.9	1 12.8	1 26.8	8 13.9	19 3.8	19 46.2
12	5 20 29.8	19 23.7	23 50.6	26 .7	9 20.9	26 14.7	27 22.6	1 21.4	1 30.1	8 11.5	19 5.1	19 45.7
13	5 24 26.4	20 24.7	23 47.5	10♒23.5	10 33.8	27 30.2	28 9.4	1 30.3	1 33.3	8 9.1	19 6.4	19 45.1
14	5 28 22.9	21 25.7	23 44.3	24 15.9	11 43.6	28 45.6	28 56.2	1 39.2	1 36.4	8 6.6	19 7.7	19 44.5
15	5 32 19.5	22 26.8	23 41.1	7♓38.5	12 49.8	0♑ 1.0	29 43.0	1 48.3	1 39.5	8 4.2	19 8.9	19 43.8
16	5 36 16.1	23 27.8	23 37.9	20 34.1	13 51.8	1 16.4	0♒29.8	1 57.5	1 42.4	8 1.7	19 10.1	19 43.2
17	5 40 12.6	24 28.9	23 34.8	3♈ 7.0	14 49.1	2 31.8	1 16.7	2 6.9	1 45.2	7 59.2	19 11.3	19 42.5
18	5 44 9.2	25 30.0	23 31.6	15 22.5	15 40.8	3 47.2	2 3.6	2 16.4	1 47.9	7 56.7	19 12.4	19 41.7
19	5 48 5.7	26 31.0	23 28.4	27 25.5	16 26.3	5 2.6	2 50.5	2 26.0	1 50.5	7 54.2	19 13.5	19 41.0
20	5 52 2.3	27 32.1	23 25.2	9♉20.7	17 4.7	6 18.0	3 37.5	2 35.7	1 53.0	7 51.7	19 14.6	19 40.2
21	5 55 58.8	28 33.2	23 22.1	21 12.0	17 35.2	7 33.4	4 24.5	2 45.6	1 55.5	7 49.1	19 15.7	19 39.4
22	5 59 55.4	29 34.3	23 18.9	3♊ 2.8	17 56.7	8 48.8	5 11.5	2 55.6	1 57.8	7 46.6	19 16.7	19 38.6
23	6 3 52.0	0♑35.4	23 15.7	14 55.2	18 8.5	10 4.1	5 58.5	3 5.7	1 60.0	7 44.0	19 17.7	19 37.8
24	6 7 48.5	1 36.5	23 12.5	26 51.3	18 9.7	11 19.5	6 45.5	3 15.9	2 2.1	7 41.5	19 18.7	19 37.0
25	6 11 45.1	2 37.6	23 9.4	8♋51.9	17 R59.7	12 34.9	7 32.6	3 26.3	2 4.1	7 38.9	19 19.6	19 36.1
26	6 15 41.6	3 38.7	23 6.2	20 58.3	17 38.0	13 50.3	8 19.7	3 36.7	2 6.0	7 36.3	19 20.5	19 35.2
27	6 19 38.2	4 39.8	23 3.0	3♌11.3	17 4.4	15 5.6	9 6.8	3 47.3	2 7.8	7 33.7	19 21.4	19 34.2
28	6 23 34.8	5 40.9	22 59.8	15 32.4	16 19.3	16 21.0	9 53.9	3 58.0	2 9.5	7 31.1	19 22.2	19 33.3
29	6 27 31.3	6 42.1	22 56.6	28 3.4	15 23.4	17 36.3	10 41.0	4 8.8	2 11.1	7 28.6	19 23.0	19 32.3
30	6 31 27.9	7 43.2	22 53.5	10♍46.8	14 18.1	18 51.7	11 28.1	4 19.7	2 12.6	7 26.0	19 23.8	19 31.3
31	6 35 24.4	8 44.4	22 50.3	23 45.7	13 5.1	20 7.0	12 15.3	4 30.7	2 13.9	7 23.4	19 24.5	19 30.3

LATITUDE

DAY	EPHEM. SID. TIME	☉	☊	☽	☿	♀	♂	♃	♄	♅	♆	♇
1	4 37 7.7	0 .0	0 .0	3N .7	2S16.5	0S 2.8	1S17.8	1S 8.1	2N 7.4	0N19.2	1N35.4	8N30.0
4	4 48 57.3	0 .0	0 .0	0S12.7	2 21.2	0 10.1	1 17.3	1 7.6	2 8.2	0 19.3	1 35.5	8 30.9
7	5 0 47.0	0 .0	0 .0	3 34.6	2 21.6	0 17.2	1 16.8	1 7.2	2 8.9	0 19.3	1 35.7	8 31.8
10	5 12 36.7	0 .0	0 .0	4 59.9	2 16.8	0 24.3	1 16.3	1 6.8	2 9.7	0 19.4	1 35.8	8 32.7
13	5 24 26.4	0 .0	0 .0	3 27.6	2 5.7	0 31.2	1 15.6	1 6.4	2 10.5	0 19.4	1 36.0	8 33.6
16	5 36 16.1	0 .0	0 .0	0 17.0	1 46.7	0 38.0	1 14.9	1 6.0	2 11.3	0 19.5	1 36.1	8 34.4
19	5 48 5.7	0 .0	0 .0	2N47.5	1 18.3	0 44.5	1 14.2	1 5.6	2 12.1	0 19.5	1 36.3	8 35.3
22	5 59 55.4	0 .0	0 .0	4 41.2	0 39.0	0 50.8	1 13.3	1 5.2	2 12.9	0 19.5	1 36.5	8 36.1
25	6 11 45.1	0 .0	0 .0	4 47.5	0N11.1	0 56.7	1 12.4	1 4.8	2 13.8	0 19.6	1 36.6	8 36.9
28	6 23 34.8	0 .0	0 .0	2 59.5	1 8.8	1 2.3	1 11.5	1 4.5	2 14.6	0 19.6	1 36.8	8 37.6
31	6 35 24.4	0 .0	0 .0	0S 9.9	2 5.8	1 7.6	1 10.5	1 4.2	2 15.5	0 19.6	1 37.0	8 38.4

RIGHT ASCENSION

DAY	EPHEM. SID. TIME	☉	☊	☽	☿	♀	♂	♃	♄	♅	♆	♇
1	4 37 7.7	6♐28.2	24♓53.0	21♌53.5	23♐26.1	10♐56.3	20♑36.0	2♓24.5	1♎35.3	9♋23.5	17♎58.1	25♌ 8.8
2	4 41 4.2	7 32.9	24 50.1	3♍54.3	25 3.7	12 16.9	21 25.9	2 31.3	1 39.3	9 R21.2	17 59.6	25 R 8.6
3	4 45 .8	8 37.8	24 47.2	15 42.9	26 40.8	13 37.8	22 15.9	2 38.3	1 43.2	9 18.9	18 1.1	25 8.5
4	4 48 57.3	9 42.8	24 44.3	27 34.6	28 17.3	14 58.8	23 5.7	2 45.4	1 47.0	9 16.5	18 2.5	25 8.2
5	4 52 53.9	10 48.0	24 41.4	9♎48.0	29 52.9	16 20.1	23 55.5	2 52.6	1 50.7	9 14.1	18 4.0	25 8.0
6	4 56 50.5	11 53.3	24 38.5	22 43.4	1♑27.5	17 41.6	24 45.2	2 60.0	1 54.4	9 11.6	18 5.4	25 7.7
7	5 0 47.0	12 58.8	24 35.5	6♏40.6	3 .9	19 3.2	25 34.9	3 7.5	1 58.0	9 9.2	18 6.7	25 7.3
8	5 4 43.6	14 4.3	24 32.6	21 53.2	4 32.9	20 25.0	26 24.6	3 15.2	2 1.4	9 6.7	18 8.1	25 7.0
9	5 8 40.1	15 10.1	24 29.7	8♐18.3	6 3.2	21 47.0	27 14.2	3 23.0	2 4.8	9 4.1	18 9.4	25 6.6
10	5 12 36.7	16 15.9	24 26.8	25 28.9	7 31.4	23 9.1	28 3.7	3 31.0	2 8.1	9 1.6	18 10.7	25 6.2
11	5 16 33.3	17 21.8	24 23.9	12♑36.6	8 57.3	24 31.3	28 53.1	3 39.1	2 11.4	8 59.0	18 12.0	25 5.7
12	5 20 29.8	18 27.9	24 20.9	28 53.2	10 20.4	25 53.6	29 42.5	3 47.3	2 14.5	8 56.4	18 13.2	25 5.3
13	5 24 26.4	19 34.0	24 18.0	13♒50.7	11 40.3	27 16.0	0♒31.8	3 55.7	2 17.5	8 53.7	18 14.4	25 4.8
14	5 28 22.9	20 40.2	24 15.1	27 25.8	12 56.6	28 38.5	1 21.1	4 4.2	2 20.5	8 51.1	18 15.6	25 4.2
15	5 32 19.5	21 46.5	24 12.2	9♓51.4	14 8.5	0♑ 1.1	2 10.2	4 12.8	2 23.4	8 48.4	18 16.8	25 3.7
16	5 36 16.1	22 52.9	24 9.3	21 26.8	15 15.5	1 23.7	2 59.3	4 21.5	2 26.2	8 45.7	18 17.9	25 3.1
17	5 40 12.6	23 59.3	24 6.3	2♈32.1	16 17.0	2 46.3	3 48.3	4 30.4	2 28.8	8 43.0	18 19.1	25 2.5
18	5 44 9.2	25 5.8	24 3.4	13 26.1	17 12.1	4 8.9	4 37.2	4 39.4	2 31.4	8 40.3	18 20.1	25 1.9
19	5 48 5.7	26 12.3	24 .5	24 25.6	18 .1	5 31.5	5 26.0	4 48.5	2 34.0	8 37.5	18 21.2	25 1.2
20	5 52 2.3	27 18.8	23 57.6	5♉44.8	18 40.1	6 54.1	6 14.7	4 57.7	2 36.4	8 34.8	18 22.2	25 .5
21	5 55 58.8	28 25.4	23 54.7	17 34.3	19 11.1	8 16.7	7 3.3	5 7.1	2 38.7	8 32.0	18 23.2	24 59.8
22	5 59 55.4	29 31.9	23 51.7	0♊ .1	19 32.2	9 39.2	7 51.8	5 16.5	2 40.9	8 29.2	18 24.2	24 59.1
23	6 3 52.0	0♑38.5	23 48.8	13 .6	19 42.6	11 1.6	8 40.2	5 26.1	2 43.1	8 26.4	18 25.1	24 58.3
24	6 7 48.5	1 45.2	23 45.9	26 26.3	19 R41.5	12 24.0	9 28.6	5 35.8	2 45.1	8 23.7	18 26.1	24 57.6
25	6 11 45.1	2 51.8	23 43.0	10♋ .6	19 28.2	13 46.2	10 16.8	5 45.6	2 47.1	8 20.9	18 27.0	24 56.8
26	6 15 41.6	3 58.3	23 40.1	23 25.4	19 2.3	15 8.4	11 4.9	5 55.5	2 48.9	8 18.1	18 27.8	24 56.0
27	6 19 38.2	5 4.9	23 37.1	6♌26.2	18 23.9	16 30.3	11 53.0	6 5.5	2 50.7	8 15.3	18 28.7	24 55.1
28	6 23 34.8	6 11.4	23 34.2	18 56.3	17 33.2	17 52.2	12 40.9	6 15.6	2 52.4	8 12.4	18 29.5	24 54.2
29	6 27 31.3	7 17.9	23 31.3	0♍57.4	16 31.2	19 13.9	13 28.7	6 25.8	2 53.9	8 9.6	18 30.2	24 53.3
30	6 31 27.9	8 24.3	23 28.4	12 38.3	15 19.5	20 35.4	14 16.4	6 36.1	2 55.4	8 6.8	18 31.0	24 52.4
31	6 35 24.4	9 30.7	23 25.5	24 12.4	13 59.9	21 56.7	15 3.9	6 46.5	2 56.8	8 4.0	18 31.7	24 51.5

DECLINATION

DAY	EPHEM. SID. TIME	☉	☊	☽	☿	♀	♂	♃	♄	♅	♆	♇
1	4 37 7.7	21S41.2	0S 2.3	18N 9.4	25S35.3	22S20.3	23S24.4	12S34.3	1N37.5	23N29.3	5S54.2	22N55.1
4	4 48 57.3	22 8.3	0 2.4	0 49.1	25 47.5	22 53.9	23 3.3	12 26.1	1 33.3	23 29.8	5 55.9	22 56.3
7	5 0 47.0	22 31.6	0 2.5	18S17.9	25 46.8	23 21.2	22 40.0	12 17.5	1 29.4	23 30.2	5 57.4	22 57.5
10	5 12 36.7	22 50.9	0 2.5	28 23.0	25 33.1	23 42.2	22 14.3	12 8.3	1 25.8	23 30.7	5 58.9	22 58.8
13	5 24 26.4	23 6.1	0 2.6	20 58.2	25 6.9	23 56.7	21 46.4	11 58.6	1 22.6	23 31.2	6 .2	23 .2
16	5 36 16.1	23 17.2	0 2.6	3 60.0	24 29.7	24 4.5	21 16.3	11 48.5	1 19.7	23 31.7	6 1.5	23 1.6
19	5 48 5.7	23 24.1	0 2.7	13N 9.8	23 43.8	24 5.6	20 44.0	11 37.9	1 17.2	23 32.2	6 2.6	23 3.1
22	5 59 55.4	23 26.8	0 2.8	25 22.2	22 53.3	23 59.9	20 9.8	11 26.9	1 15.1	23 32.7	6 3.6	23 4.7
25	6 11 45.1	23 25.3	0 2.8	27 55.9	22 3.3	23 47.6	19 33.5	11 15.4	1 13.4	23 33.2	6 4.6	23 6.2
28	6 23 34.8	23 19.6	0 2.9	19 2.3	21 18.7	23 28.7	18 55.3	11 3.6	1 12.0	23 33.7	6 5.4	23 7.9
31	6 35 24.4	23 9.6	0 3.0	2 19.6	20 43.0	23 3.3	18 15.4	10 51.3	1 11.0	23 34.1	6 6.1	23 9.5

JANUARY 1951

LONGITUDE

DAY	EPHEM. SID. TIME h m s	☉ ° ′	☊ ° ′	☽ ° ′	☿ ° ′	♀ ° ′	♂ ° ′	♃ ° ′	♄ ° ′	♅ ° ′	♆ ° ′	♇ ° ′
1	6 39 21.0	9♑45.5	22♓47.1	7♎ 3.1	11♑46.7	21♑22.3	13♒ 2.5	4♓41.8	2♎15.2	7♋20.8	19♎25.2	19♌29.3
2	6 43 17.6	10 46.7	22 43.9	20 42.1	10 R 25.6	22 37.7	13 49.6	4 53.0	2 16.3	7 R 18.2	19 25.9	19 R 28.2
3	6 47 14.1	11 47.8	22 40.8	4♏44.4	9 4.3	23 53.0	14 36.8	5 4.4	2 17.4	7 15.6	19 26.5	19 27.1
4	6 51 10.7	12 49.0	22 37.6	19 10.1	7 45.6	25 8.3	15 24.1	5 15.8	2 18.3	7 13.0	19 27.1	19 26.0
5	6 55 7.2	13 50.2	22 34.4	3♐56.4	6 31.6	26 23.6	16 11.3	5 27.3	2 19.1	7 10.5	19 27.7	19 24.9
6	6 59 3.8	14 51.4	22 31.2	18 57.3	5 24.5	27 38.9	16 58.5	5 38.9	2 19.9	7 7.9	19 28.2	19 23.8
7	7 3 .3	15 52.5	22 28.1	4♑ 4.2	4 25.7	28 54.2	17 45.8	5 50.7	2 20.5	7 5.3	19 28.7	19 22.6
8	7 6 56.9	16 53.7	22 24.9	19 6.8	3 36.2	0♒ 9.5	18 33.0	6 2.5	2 21.0	7 2.8	19 29.2	19 21.5
9	7 10 53.5	17 54.9	22 21.7	3♒55.1	2 56.5	1 24.8	19 20.3	6 14.4	2 21.3	7 .2	19 29.6	19 20.3
10	7 14 50.0	18 56.0	22 18.5	18 21.1	2 26.9	2 40.1	20 7.5	6 26.4	2 21.6	6 57.7	19 30.0	19 19.1
11	7 18 46.6	19 57.2	22 15.4	2♓20.0	2 7.1	3 55.4	20 54.8	6 38.5	2 21.8	6 55.2	19 30.3	19 17.9
12	7 22 43.1	20 58.4	22 12.2	15 50.2	1 56.8	5 10.6	21 42.1	6 50.6	2 21.8	6 52.7	19 30.7	19 16.6
13	7 26 39.7	21 59.5	22 9.0	28 52.9	1 55.6	6 25.9	22 29.4	7 2.9	2 21.8	6 50.2	19 31.0	19 15.4
14	7 30 36.3	23 .7	22 5.8	11♈31.6	2 D 2.7	7 41.1	23 16.7	7 15.3	2 R 21.7	6 47.8	19 31.3	19 14.2
15	7 34 32.8	24 1.8	22 2.7	23 50.7	2 17.6	8 56.3	24 4.0	7 27.7	2 21.4	6 45.4	19 31.5	19 12.9
16	7 38 29.4	25 2.9	21 59.5	5♉55.4	2 39.5	10 11.5	24 51.2	7 40.2	2 21.0	6 42.9	19 31.7	19 11.6
17	7 42 25.9	26 4.0	21 56.3	17 50.9	3 8.0	11 26.7	25 38.5	7 52.7	2 20.5	6 40.5	19 31.8	19 10.3
18	7 46 22.5	27 5.1	21 53.1	29 42.1	3 42.2	12 41.9	26 25.8	8 5.4	2 19.9	6 38.1	19 31.9	19 9.0
19	7 50 19.0	28 6.2	21 49.9	11♊33.1	4 21.8	13 57.0	27 13.0	8 18.1	2 19.2	6 35.8	19 32.0	19 7.7
20	7 54 15.6	29 7.2	21 46.8	23 27.4	5 6.1	15 12.2	28 .3	8 30.9	2 18.4	6 33.4	19 32.1	19 6.3
21	7 58 12.2	0♒ 8.3	21 43.6	5♋27.8	5 54.8	16 27.3	28 47.6	8 43.8	2 17.5	6 31.1	19 32.1	19 5.0
22	8 2 8.7	1 9.3	21 40.4	17 36.2	6 47.3	17 42.4	29 34.8	8 56.7	2 16.5	6 28.8	19 32.1	19 3.6
23	8 6 5.3	2 10.3	21 37.2	29 53.8	7 43.3	18 57.5	0♓22.0	9 9.7	2 15.3	6 26.5	19 R 32.0	19 2.2
24	8 10 1.8	3 11.3	21 34.1	12♌21.2	8 42.5	20 12.5	1 9.2	9 22.7	2 14.1	6 24.3	19 31.9	19 .9
25	8 13 58.4	4 12.3	21 30.9	24 59.0	9 44.5	21 27.6	1 56.5	9 35.9	2 12.7	6 22.1	19 31.8	18 59.5
26	8 17 55.0	5 13.3	21 27.7	7♍47.6	10 49.2	22 42.6	2 43.7	9 49.1	2 11.3	6 19.9	19 31.7	18 58.1
27	8 21 51.5	6 14.3	21 24.5	20 47.6	11 56.2	23 57.6	3 30.9	10 2.3	2 9.8	6 17.7	19 31.5	18 56.7
28	8 25 48.1	7 15.2	21 21.4	3♎60.0	13 5.4	25 12.6	4 18.1	10 15.6	2 8.1	6 15.6	19 31.2	18 55.3
29	8 29 44.6	8 16.2	21 18.2	17 25.9	14 16.6	26 27.5	5 5.2	10 29.0	2 6.3	6 13.5	19 31.0	18 53.8
30	8 33 41.2	9 17.1	21 15.0	1♏ 6.5	15 29.6	27 42.5	5 52.4	10 42.4	2 4.5	6 11.5	19 30.7	18 52.4
31	8 37 37.7	10 18.1	21 11.8	15 2.7	16 44.2	28 57.4	6 39.5	10 55.9	2 2.5	6 9.4	19 30.4	18 51.0

LATITUDE

DAY	EPHEM. SID. TIME	☉	☊	☽	☿	♀	♂	♃	♄	♅	♆	♇
1	6 39 21.0	0 .0	0 .0	1S19.5	2N22.6	1S 9.2	1S10.1	1S 4.1	2N15.8	0N19.7	1N37.0	8N38.6
4	6 51 10.7	0 .0	0 .0	4 15.2	3 .6	1 13.9	1 9.0	1 3.8	2 16.6	0 19.7	1 37.2	8 39.3
7	7 3 .3	0 .0	0 .0	4 55.0	3 16.7	1 18.1	1 7.9	1 3.5	2 17.5	0 19.7	1 37.4	8 40.0
10	7 14 50.0	0 .0	0 .0	2 43.8	3 13.0	1 21.8	1 6.6	1 3.2	2 18.3	0 19.7	1 37.6	8 40.6
13	7 26 39.7	0 .0	0 .0	0N43.1	2 55.7	1 25.0	1 5.4	1 3.0	2 19.2	0 19.7	1 37.8	8 41.2
16	7 38 29.4	0 .0	0 .0	3 37.2	2 30.7	1 27.7	1 4.1	1 2.7	2 20.0	0 19.7	1 37.9	8 41.7
19	7 50 19.0	0 .0	0 .0	5 1.9	2 1.9	1 29.8	1 2.7	1 2.5	2 20.9	0 19.8	1 38.1	8 42.3
22	8 2 8.7	0 .0	0 .0	4 31.6	1 31.8	1 31.3	1 1.3	1 2.3	2 21.7	0 19.8	1 38.3	8 42.7
25	8 13 58.4	0 .0	0 .0	2 9.2	1 2.0	1 32.2	0 59.8	1 2.1	2 22.5	0 19.8	1 38.5	8 43.2
28	8 25 48.1	0 .0	0 .0	1S17.0	0 33.3	1 32.5	0 58.3	1 2.0	2 23.3	0 19.8	1 38.7	8 43.6
31	8 37 37.7	0 .0	0 .0	4 15.7	0 6.1	1 32.2	0 56.8	1 1.8	2 24.1	0 19.8	1 38.8	8 43.9

RIGHT ASCENSION

DAY	EPHEM. SID. TIME	☉	☊	☽	☿	♀	♂	♃	♄	♅	♆	♇
1	6 39 21.0	10♑37.1	23♓22.5	5♎57.0	12♑34.9	23♑17.8	15♒51.4	6♓57.0	2♎58.0	8♋ 1.2	18♎32.3	24♌50.5
2	6 43 17.6	11 43.3	23 19.6	18 11.3	11 R 7.4	24 38.7	16 38.8	7 7.6	2 59.2	7 R 58.3	18 33.0	24 R 49.5
3	6 47 14.1	12 49.5	23 16.7	1♏15.7	9 40.0	25 59.4	17 26.1	7 18.2	3 .3	7 55.5	18 33.6	24 48.5
4	6 51 10.7	13 55.6	23 13.8	15 28.0	8 15.6	27 19.8	18 13.2	7 29.0	3 1.2	7 52.7	18 34.2	24 47.5
5	6 55 7.2	15 1.7	23 10.8	0♐56.6	6 56.7	28 40.0	19 .3	7 39.9	3 2.1	7 49.9	18 34.7	24 46.4
6	6 59 3.8	16 7.6	23 7.9	17 31.1	5 45.1	29 60.0	19 47.2	7 50.8	3 2.9	7 47.1	18 35.2	24 45.4
7	7 3 .3	17 13.4	23 5.0	4♑36.4	4 42.5	1♒19.7	20 34.1	8 1.9	3 3.5	7 44.3	18 35.7	24 44.3
8	7 6 56.9	18 19.1	23 2.1	21 23.6	3 49.9	2 39.1	21 20.8	8 13.0	3 4.1	7 41.5	18 36.2	24 43.2
9	7 10 53.5	19 24.7	22 59.2	7♒11.2	3 7.7	3 58.2	22 7.4	8 24.2	3 4.6	7 38.8	18 36.6	24 42.0
10	7 14 50.0	20 30.1	22 56.2	21 40.4	2 36.3	5 17.0	22 53.9	8 35.5	3 4.9	7 36.0	18 37.0	24 40.9
11	7 18 46.6	21 35.4	22 53.3	4♓54.4	2 15.3	6 35.5	23 40.3	8 46.8	3 5.2	7 33.3	18 37.3	24 39.7
12	7 22 43.1	22 40.6	22 50.4	17 8.2	2 4.5	7 53.7	24 26.6	8 58.3	3 5.4	7 30.6	18 37.7	24 38.5
13	7 26 39.7	23 45.6	22 47.5	28 41.3	2 3.2	9 11.6	25 12.8	9 9.8	3 5.4	7 27.9	18 38.0	24 37.3
14	7 30 36.3	24 50.5	22 44.5	9♈53.1	2 D 11.0	10 29.3	25 58.9	9 21.4	3 5.4	7 25.2	18 38.3	24 36.2
15	7 34 32.8	25 55.2	22 41.6	21 1.3	2 27.0	11 46.6	26 44.8	9 33.1	3 R 5.3	7 22.6	18 38.5	24 34.9
16	7 38 29.4	26 59.7	22 38.7	2♉21.5	2 50.6	13 3.5	27 30.7	9 44.8	3 5.1	7 19.9	18 38.7	24 33.7
17	7 42 25.9	28 4.0	22 35.8	14 6.0	3 21.2	14 20.1	28 16.4	9 56.6	3 4.7	7 17.3	18 38.9	24 32.4
18	7 46 22.5	29 8.2	22 32.9	26 23.2	3 58.2	15 36.4	29 2.0	10 8.5	3 4.3	7 14.7	18 39.0	24 31.1
19	7 50 19.0	0♒12.2	22 29.9	9♊14.9	4 40.9	16 52.4	29 47.5	10 20.4	3 3.8	7 12.1	18 39.1	24 29.9
20	7 54 15.6	1 16.0	22 27.0	22 35.3	5 28.9	18 8.0	0♓32.9	10 32.4	3 3.1	7 9.5	18 39.2	24 28.5
21	7 58 12.2	2 19.6	22 24.1	6♋10.9	6 21.5	19 23.3	1 18.2	10 44.4	3 2.4	7 7.0	18 39.2	24 27.2
22	8 2 8.7	3 23.0	22 21.2	19 44.2	7 18.5	20 38.2	2 3.4	10 56.6	3 1.6	7 4.5	18 39.2	24 25.9
23	8 6 5.3	4 26.2	22 18.2	2♌58.9	8 19.3	21 52.9	2 48.4	11 8.7	3 .6	7 2.0	18 39.2	24 24.6
24	8 10 1.8	5 29.3	22 15.3	15 45.0	9 23.6	23 7.2	3 33.4	11 21.0	2 59.6	6 59.6	18 R 39.1	24 23.2
25	8 13 58.4	6 32.1	22 12.4	28 .9	10 31.1	24 21.2	4 18.3	11 33.2	2 58.5	6 57.2	18 39.0	24 21.9
26	8 17 55.0	7 34.8	22 9.5	9♍52.2	11 41.5	25 34.9	5 3.1	11 45.6	2 57.3	6 54.8	18 38.9	24 20.5
27	8 21 51.5	8 37.2	22 6.5	21 30.1	12 54.5	26 48.2	5 47.7	11 58.0	2 55.9	6 52.5	18 38.8	24 19.1
28	8 25 48.1	9 39.5	22 3.6	3♎ 9.6	14 9.8	28 1.3	6 32.3	12 10.4	2 54.5	6 50.1	18 38.6	24 17.7
29	8 29 44.6	10 41.6	22 .7	15 8.1	15 27.4	29 14.0	7 16.8	12 22.9	2 53.0	6 47.9	18 38.4	24 16.3
30	8 33 41.2	11 43.4	21 57.8	27 44.1	16 46.8	0♓26.5	8 1.2	12 35.4	2 51.4	6 45.6	18 38.1	24 14.9
31	8 37 37.7	12 45.1	21 54.8	11♏14.8	18 8.1	1 38.6	8 45.5	12 48.0	2 49.7	6 43.4	18 37.8	24 13.5

DECLINATION

DAY	EPHEM. SID. TIME	☉	☊	☽	☿	♀	♂	♃	♄	♅	♆	♇
1	6 39 21.0	23S 5.4	0S 3.0	4S 1.0	20S33.5	22S53.4	18S 1.6	10S47.2	1N10.8	23N34.3	6S 6.3	23N10.1
4	6 51 10.7	22 49.8	0 3.1	21 36.6	20 13.0	22 19.5	17 19.4	10 34.4	1 10.3	23 34.7	6 6.9	23 11.8
7	7 3 .3	22 30.2	0 3.1	28 17.9	20 5.9	21 39.6	16 35.5	10 21.3	1 10.3	23 35.2	6 7.3	23 13.5
10	7 14 50.0	22 6.6	0 3.2	17 55.7	20 12.5	20 53.9	15 50.0	10 7.9	1 10.6	23 35.6	6 7.6	23 15.3
13	7 26 39.7	21 39.1	0 3.3	0N12.9	20 30.3	20 2.7	15 3.1	9 54.1	1 11.3	23 36.0	6 7.8	23 17.0
16	7 38 29.4	21 7.8	0 3.3	16 54.8	20 54.6	19 6.2	14 14.9	9 40.0	1 12.4	23 36.4	6 7.9	23 18.8
19	7 50 19.0	20 32.9	0 3.4	27 9.6	21 20.8	18 4.8	13 25.4	9 25.6	1 13.9	23 36.8	6 7.9	23 20.5
22	8 2 8.7	19 54.5	0 3.5	26 46.6	21 44.7	16 58.8	12 34.8	9 10.9	1 15.8	23 37.1	6 7.7	23 22.3
25	8 13 58.4	19 12.8	0 3.5	15 13.6	22 3.6	15 48.6	11 43.1	8 56.0	1 18.0	23 37.4	6 7.5	23 24.1
28	8 25 48.1	18 27.9	0 3.6	2S46.0	22 15.1	14 34.5	10 50.5	8 40.8	1 20.6	23 37.7	6 7.1	23 25.8
31	8 37 37.7	17 40.0	0 3.7	20 25.5	22 17.9	13 16.8	9 57.0	8 25.4	1 23.5	23 38.0	6 6.6	23 27.5

FEBRUARY 1951

LONGITUDE

DAY	EPHEM. SID. TIME	☉	☊	☽	☿	♀	♂	♃	♄	♅	♆	♇
	h m s	° ′	° ′	° ′	° ′	° ′	° ′	° ′	° ′	° ′	° ′	° ′
1	8 41 34.3	11♒19.0	21♓ 8.6	29♏14.2	18♑ .5	0♓12.4	7♓26.7	11♓ 9.5	2♎ .5	6♋ 7.5	19♎30.0	18♌49.6
2	8 45 30.8	12 19.9	21 5.5	13♐39.3	19 18.1	1 27.2	8 13.8	11 23.1	1R58.3	6R 5.5	19R29.6	18R48.1
3	8 49 27.4	13 20.8	21 2.3	28 14.4	20 37.2	2 42.1	9 .9	11 36.7	1 56.1	6 3.6	19 29.2	18 46.7
4	8 53 24.0	14 21.7	20 59.1	12♑54.2	21 57.5	3 57.0	9 48.1	11 50.4	1 53.8	6 1.7	19 28.8	18 45.3
5	8 57 20.5	15 22.6	20 55.9	27 31.9	23 19.1	5 11.9	10 35.2	12 4.2	1 51.3	5 59.9	19 28.3	18 43.8
6	9 1 17.1	16 23.4	20 52.8	12♒ .3	24 41.7	6 26.7	11 22.2	12 18.0	1 48.8	5 58.1	19 27.8	18 42.4
7	9 5 13.6	17 24.2	20 49.6	26 13.0	26 5.5	7 41.5	12 9.3	12 31.8	1 46.2	5 56.3	19 27.2	18 40.9
8	9 9 10.2	18 25.0	20 46.4	10♓ 5.0	27 30.3	8 56.2	12 56.3	12 45.7	1 43.4	5 54.6	19 26.7	18 39.5
9	9 13 6.7	19 25.8	20 43.2	23 33.8	28 56.1	10 11.0	13 43.3	12 59.6	1 40.6	5 52.9	19 26.1	18 38.0
10	9 17 3.3	20 26.6	20 40.1	6♈38.9	0♒22.9	11 25.7	14 30.3	13 13.6	1 37.7	5 51.3	19 25.4	18 36.6
11	9 20 59.9	21 27.3	20 36.9	19 21.8	1 50.7	12 40.4	15 17.3	13 27.6	1 34.7	5 49.7	19 24.7	18 35.1
12	9 24 56.4	22 28.0	20 33.7	1♉45.6	3 19.4	13 55.0	16 4.2	13 41.6	1 31.7	5 48.1	19 24.0	18 33.7
13	9 28 53.0	23 28.7	20 30.5	13 54.3	4 49.1	15 9.6	16 51.1	13 55.7	1 28.5	5 46.6	19 23.3	18 32.2
14	9 32 49.5	24 29.3	20 27.3	25 52.8	6 19.6	16 24.2	17 38.0	14 9.8	1 25.3	5 45.2	19 22.5	18 30.8
15	9 36 46.1	25 30.0	20 24.2	7♊45.7	7 51.0	17 38.8	18 24.9	14 23.9	1 22.0	5 43.7	19 21.7	18 29.4
16	9 40 42.6	26 30.5	20 21.0	19 38.0	9 23.4	18 53.3	19 11.7	14 38.1	1 18.6	5 42.4	19 20.9	18 27.9
17	9 44 39.2	27 31.1	20 17.8	1♋33.9	10 56.7	20 7.8	19 58.5	14 52.3	1 15.1	5 41.0	19 20.0	18 26.5
18	9 48 35.7	28 31.6	20 14.6	13 37.5	12 30.8	21 22.2	20 45.3	15 6.6	1 11.6	5 39.7	19 19.2	18 25.1
19	9 52 32.3	29 32.1	20 11.5	25 51.7	14 5.9	22 36.6	21 32.1	15 20.8	1 8.0	5 38.5	19 18.2	18 23.6
20	9 56 28.9	0♓32.6	20 8.3	8♌19.0	15 41.8	23 51.0	22 18.8	15 35.1	1 4.3	5 37.3	19 17.3	18 22.2
21	10 0 25.4	1 33.1	20 5.1	21 .6	17 18.7	25 5.3	23 5.5	15 49.4	1 .5	5 36.2	19 16.3	18 20.8
22	10 4 22.0	2 33.5	20 1.9	3♍57.1	18 56.6	26 19.6	23 52.2	16 3.7	0 56.7	5 35.1	19 15.4	18 19.4
23	10 8 18.5	3 33.9	19 58.8	17 8.2	20 35.3	27 33.9	24 38.8	16 18.1	0 52.8	5 34.0	19 14.3	18 18.0
24	10 12 15.1	4 34.3	19 55.6	0♎32.9	22 15.1	28 48.1	25 25.4	16 32.5	0 48.9	5 33.1	19 13.3	18 16.6
25	10 16 11.6	5 34.7	19 52.4	14 9.9	23 55.8	0♈ 2.3	26 12.0	16 46.9	0 44.9	5 32.2	19 12.3	18 15.3
26	10 20 8.2	6 35.0	19 49.2	27 57.7	25 37.5	1 16.5	26 58.5	17 1.3	0 40.9	5 31.3	19 11.2	18 13.9
27	10 24 4.7	7 35.3	19 46.0	11♏54.5	27 20.2	2 30.6	27 45.0	17 15.8	0 36.8	5 30.4	19 10.1	18 12.6
28	10 28 1.3	8 35.5	19 42.9	25 58.7	29 3.9	3 44.7	28 31.5	17 30.2	0 32.6	5 29.6	19 8.9	18 11.2

LATITUDE

DAY	EPHEM. SID. TIME	☉	☊	☽	☿	♀	♂	♃	♄	♅	♆	♇
1	8 41 34.3	0 .0	0 .0	4S51.0	0S 2.5	1S31.9	0S56.3	1S 1.8	2N24.4	0N19.8	1N38.9	8N44.1
4	8 53 24.0	0 .0	0 .0	4 45.1	0 27.0	1 30.8	0 54.7	1 1.7	2 25.2	0 19.8	1 39.1	8 44.4
7	9 5 13.6	0 .0	0 .0	2 2.3	0 49.3	1 29.0	0 53.0	1 1.6	2 25.9	0 19.7	1 39.2	8 44.6
10	9 17 3.3	0 .0	0 .0	1N34.1	1 9.3	1 26.6	0 51.3	1 1.5	2 26.6	0 19.7	1 39.4	8 44.9
13	9 28 53.0	0 .0	0 .0	4 16.3	1 26.6	1 23.6	0 49.6	1 1.4	2 27.3	0 19.7	1 39.6	8 45.0
16	9 40 42.6	0 .0	0 .0	5 14.1	1 41.3	1 19.9	0 47.9	1 1.3	2 27.9	0 19.7	1 39.7	8 45.2
19	9 52 32.3	0 .0	0 .0	4 12.2	1 53.0	1 15.7	0 46.1	1 1.3	2 28.5	0 19.7	1 39.9	8 45.3
22	10 4 22.0	0 .0	0 .0	1 22.0	2 1.6	1 10.9	0 44.3	1 1.3	2 29.1	0 19.7	1 40.0	8 45.3
25	10 16 11.6	0 .0	0 .0	2S14.8	2 6.8	1 5.5	0 42.5	1 1.3	2 29.6	0 19.7	1 40.2	8 45.4
28	10 28 1.3	0 .0	0 .0	4 51.3	2 8.4	0 59.6	0 40.7	1 1.3	2 30.1	0 19.6	1 40.3	8 45.3

RIGHT ASCENSION

DAY	EPHEM. SID. TIME	☉	☊	☽	☿	♀	♂	♃	♄	♅	♆	♇
1	8 41 34.3	13♒46.5	21♓51.9	25♏52.0	19♑31.0	2♓50.5	9♓29.7	13♓ .7	2♎48.0	6♋41.2	18♎37.5	24♌12.1
2	8 45 30.8	14 47.8	21 49.0	11♐34.2	20 55.4	4 2.1	10 13.8	13 13.4	2R46.1	6R39.1	18R37.2	24R10.7
3	8 49 27.4	15 48.9	21 46.1	28 .3	22 21.1	5 13.4	10 57.8	13 26.1	2 44.1	6 37.0	18 36.8	24 9.2
4	8 53 24.0	16 49.8	21 43.1	14♑32.3	23 48.2	6 24.4	11 41.8	13 38.9	2 42.1	6 35.0	18 36.5	24 7.8
5	8 57 20.5	17 50.4	21 40.2	0♒29.2	25 16.3	7 35.2	12 25.7	13 51.7	2 40.0	6 33.0	18 36.0	24 6.4
6	9 1 17.1	18 50.9	21 37.3	15 24.2	26 45.4	8 45.7	13 9.5	14 4.6	2 37.7	6 31.0	18 35.6	24 5.0
7	9 5 13.6	19 51.2	21 34.4	29 10.4	28 15.5	9 56.0	13 53.1	14 17.5	2 35.4	6 29.1	18 35.1	24 3.5
8	9 9 10.2	20 51.2	21 31.4	11♓55.8	29 46.5	11 6.0	14 36.8	14 30.4	2 33.0	6 27.2	18 34.5	24 2.1
9	9 13 6.7	21 51.1	21 28.5	23 56.0	1♒18.3	12 15.8	15 20.3	14 43.3	2 30.5	6 25.4	18 34.0	24 .6
10	9 17 3.3	22 50.7	21 25.6	5♈28.9	2 50.8	13 25.4	16 3.8	14 56.3	2 28.0	6 23.6	18 33.4	23 59.1
11	9 20 59.9	23 50.2	21 22.7	16 51.5	4 23.9	14 34.7	16 47.2	15 9.4	2 25.3	6 21.9	18 32.8	23 57.7
12	9 24 56.4	24 49.4	21 19.7	28 19.4	5 57.7	15 43.9	17 30.5	15 22.4	2 22.6	6 20.2	18 32.2	23 56.2
13	9 28 53.0	25 48.5	21 16.8	10♉ 5.4	7 32.1	16 52.8	18 13.7	15 35.5	2 19.8	6 18.5	18 31.5	23 54.8
14	9 32 49.5	26 47.3	21 13.9	22 18.6	9 7.0	18 1.6	18 56.9	15 48.6	2 16.9	6 16.9	18 30.8	23 53.3
15	9 36 46.1	27 46.0	21 10.9	5♊ 3.0	10 42.4	19 10.2	19 40.0	16 1.7	2 14.0	6 15.4	18 30.1	23 51.9
16	9 40 42.6	28 44.5	21 8.0	18 15.6	12 18.3	20 18.6	20 23.0	16 14.9	2 11.0	6 13.9	18 29.3	23 50.4
17	9 44 39.2	29 42.8	21 5.1	1♋46.5	13 54.6	21 26.8	21 6.0	16 28.1	2 7.9	6 12.4	18 28.6	23 49.0
18	9 48 35.7	0♓40.9	21 2.2	15 20.7	15 31.3	22 34.9	21 48.9	16 41.3	2 4.7	6 11.0	18 27.8	23 47.5
19	9 52 32.3	1 38.8	20 59.2	28 42.8	17 8.4	23 42.9	22 31.7	16 54.5	2 1.5	6 9.7	18 26.9	23 46.1
20	9 56 28.9	2 36.6	20 56.3	11♌41.8	18 45.8	24 50.7	23 14.5	17 7.8	1 58.2	6 8.4	18 26.1	23 44.7
21	10 0 25.4	3 34.2	20 53.4	24 13.5	20 23.6	25 58.4	23 57.2	17 21.1	1 54.8	6 7.1	18 25.2	23 43.2
22	10 4 22.0	4 31.6	20 50.4	6♍21.3	22 1.8	27 6.0	24 39.9	17 34.3	1 51.4	6 5.9	18 24.3	23 41.8
23	10 8 18.5	5 28.9	20 47.5	18 14.1	23 40.3	28 13.5	25 22.5	17 47.6	1 47.9	6 4.8	18 23.4	23 40.4
24	10 12 15.1	6 26.0	20 44.6	0♎ 4.9	25 19.1	29 20.9	26 5.1	18 1.0	1 44.3	6 3.7	18 22.4	23 39.0
25	10 16 11.6	7 23.0	20 41.7	12 9.6	26 58.4	0♈28.2	26 47.7	18 14.3	1 40.8	6 2.7	18 21.5	23 37.6
26	10 20 8.2	8 19.8	20 38.7	24 44.6	28 37.9	1 35.5	27 30.2	18 27.7	1 37.1	6 1.8	18 20.5	23 36.2
27	10 24 4.7	9 16.5	20 35.8	8♏ 5.8	0♓17.7	2 42.7	28 12.6	18 41.1	1 33.4	6 .9	18 19.4	23 34.8
28	10 28 1.3	10 13.1	20 32.9	22 24.1	1 57.9	3 49.8	28 55.0	18 54.4	1 29.6	5 60.0	18 18.4	23 33.4

DECLINATION

DAY	EPHEM. SID. TIME	☉	☊	☽	☿	♀	♂	♃	♄	♅	♆	♇
1	8 41 34.3	17S23.4	0S 3.7	24S43.5	22S16.6	12S50.2	9S39.0	8S20.2	1N24.5	23N38.1	6S 6.4	23N28.1
4	8 53 24.0	16 31.7	0 3.7	27 33.0	22 6.1	11 28.4	8 44.4	8 4.4	1 27.9	23 38.4	6 5.8	23 29.8
7	9 5 13.6	15 37.4	0 3.8	14 42.0	21 44.8	10 3.8	7 49.3	7 48.5	1 31.6	23 38.6	6 5.1	23 31.4
10	9 17 3.3	14 40.8	0 3.9	4N 4.8	21 12.2	8 36.9	6 53.5	7 32.4	1 35.6	23 38.8	6 4.2	23 33.0
13	9 28 53.0	13 41.9	0 3.9	20 5.5	20 28.1	7 8.0	5 57.3	7 16.1	1 39.9	23 39.0	6 3.3	23 34.6
16	9 40 42.6	12 41.0	0 4.0	28 15.7	19 32.2	5 37.4	5 .7	6 59.7	1 44.4	23 39.2	6 2.2	23 36.1
19	9 52 32.3	11 38.3	0 4.1	25 6.5	18 24.4	4 5.5	4 3.9	6 43.2	1 49.2	23 39.4	6 1.1	23 37.6
22	10 4 22.0	10 34.0	0 4.1	11 20.2	17 4.5	2 32.7	3 6.9	6 26.5	1 54.2	23 39.5	5 59.9	23 39.0
25	10 16 11.6	9 28.2	0 4.2	7S39.5	15 32.6	0 59.2	2 9.7	6 9.7	1 59.4	23 39.6	5 58.6	23 40.4
28	10 28 1.3	8 21.1	0 4.3	23 58.2	13 48.5	0N34.6	1 12.5	5 52.8	2 4.7	23 39.7	5 57.2	23 41.6

MARCH 1951

LONGITUDE

DAY	EPHEM. SID. TIME h m s	☉ ° ′	☊ ° ′	☽ ° ′	☿ ° ′	♀ ° ′	♂ ° ′	♃ ° ′	♄ ° ′	♅ ° ′	♆ ° ′	♇ ° ′
1	10 31 57.8	9♓35.8	19♓39.7	10♐ 8.5	0♓48.6	4♈58.7	29♓17.9	17♓44.7	0♎28.4	5♋28.9	19♎ 7.7	18♌ 9.9
2	10 35 54.4	10 36.0	19 36.5	24 21.8	2 34.4	6 12.7	0♈ 4.4	17 59.1	0R24.1	5R28.2	19R 6.6	18R 8.6
3	10 39 51.0	11 36.2	19 33.3	8♑36.2	4 21.2	7 26.6	0 50.7	18 13.6	0 19.8	5 27.6	19 5.3	18 7.2
4	10 43 47.5	12 36.4	19 30.2	22 48.9	6 9.0	8 40.6	1 37.1	18 28.1	0 15.4	5 27.0	19 4.1	18 5.9
5	10 47 44.1	13 36.5	19 27.0	6♒56.4	7 58.0	9 54.4	2 23.4	18 42.6	0 11.0	5 26.5	19 2.8	18 4.7
6	10 51 40.6	14 36.6	19 23.8	20 55.3	9 48.0	11 8.3	3 9.7	18 57.2	0 6.5	5 26.0	19 1.6	18 3.4
7	10 55 37.2	15 36.7	19 20.6	4♓42.2	11 39.0	12 22.1	3 55.9	19 11.7	0 2.0	5 25.5	19 .3	18 2.1
8	10 59 33.7	16 36.8	19 17.4	18 14.2	13 31.2	13 35.8	4 42.1	19 26.2	29♍57.5	5 25.2	18 58.9	18 .9
9	11 3 30.3	17 36.8	19 14.3	1♈29.4	15 24.3	14 49.5	5 28.3	19 40.8	29 53.0	5 24.9	18 57.6	17 59.6
10	11 7 26.8	18 36.8	19 11.1	14 26.8	17 18.5	16 3.1	6 14.4	19 55.3	29 48.4	5 24.6	18 56.2	17 58.4
11	11 11 23.4	19 36.8	19 7.9	27 6.6	19 13.6	17 16.7	7 .5	20 9.9	29 43.8	5 24.4	18 54.9	17 57.2
12	11 15 19.9	20 36.7	19 4.7	9♉30.4	21 9.7	18 30.3	7 46.5	20 24.4	29 39.1	5 24.2	18 53.5	17 56.0
13	11 19 16.5	21 36.6	19 1.6	21 40.7	23 6.7	19 43.8	8 32.5	20 38.9	29 34.5	5 24.1	18 52.1	17 54.8
14	11 23 13.1	22 36.4	18 58.4	3♊41.0	25 4.4	20 57.2	9 18.5	20 53.5	29 29.8	5 24.1	18 50.6	17 53.7
15	11 27 9.6	23 36.3	18 55.2	15 35.2	27 2.8	22 10.6	10 4.4	21 8.0	29 25.1	5 24.1	18 49.2	17 52.6
16	11 31 6.2	24 36.0	18 52.0	27 28.0	29 1.8	23 24.0	10 50.3	21 22.5	29 20.4	5 24.1	18 47.7	17 51.4
17	11 35 2.7	25 35.8	18 48.8	9♋24.0	1♈ 1.1	24 37.3	11 36.1	21 37.1	29 15.7	5D24.3	18 46.2	17 50.3
18	11 38 59.3	26 35.5	18 45.7	21 27.9	3 .7	25 50.5	12 21.9	21 51.6	29 11.0	5 24.5	18 44.8	17 49.3
19	11 42 55.8	27 35.2	18 42.5	3♌43.9	5 .3	27 3.7	13 7.7	22 6.1	29 6.3	5 24.7	18 43.3	17 48.2
20	11 46 52.4	28 34.8	18 39.3	16 15.7	6 59.7	28 16.8	13 53.4	22 20.6	29 1.6	5 25.0	18 41.8	17 47.2
21	11 50 48.9	29 34.4	18 36.1	29 6.1	8 58.5	29 29.9	14 39.0	22 35.1	28 56.8	5 25.3	18 40.2	17 46.2
22	11 54 45.5	0♈34.0	18 33.0	12♍16.7	10 56.5	0♉42.8	15 24.7	22 49.6	28 52.1	5 25.7	18 38.7	17 45.2
23	11 58 42.0	1 33.5	18 29.8	25 47.6	12 53.3	1 55.8	16 10.2	23 4.0	28 47.4	5 26.1	18 37.2	17 44.2
24	12 2 38.6	2 33.0	18 26.6	9♎37.2	14 48.6	3 8.6	16 55.7	23 18.5	28 42.6	5 26.6	18 35.6	17 43.2
25	12 6 35.1	3 32.4	18 23.4	23 42.6	16 41.9	4 21.4	17 41.2	23 32.9	28 37.9	5 27.1	18 34.0	17 42.3
26	12 10 31.7	4 31.9	18 20.2	7♏59.5	18 32.9	5 34.2	18 26.6	23 47.3	28 33.2	5 27.7	18 32.4	17 41.4
27	12 14 28.2	5 31.3	18 17.1	22 22.9	20 21.0	6 46.8	19 12.0	24 1.7	28 28.5	5 28.4	18 30.8	17 40.5
28	12 18 24.8	6 30.6	18 13.9	6♐47.8	22 6.0	7 59.5	19 57.4	24 16.1	28 23.9	5 29.1	18 29.2	17 39.6
29	12 22 21.4	7 30.0	18 10.7	21 9.7	23 47.4	9 12.0	20 42.7	24 30.4	28 19.2	5 29.8	18 27.6	17 38.8
30	12 26 17.9	8 29.3	18 7.5	5♑24.9	25 24.7	10 24.5	21 27.9	24 44.7	28 14.6	5 30.6	18 26.0	17 37.9
31	12 30 14.5	9 28.5	18 4.4	19 30.9	26 57.7	11 36.9	22 13.1	24 59.1	28 10.0	5 31.5	18 24.4	17 37.1

LATITUDE

DAY	SID. TIME	☉	☊	☽	☿	♀	♂	♃	♄	♅	♆	♇
1	10 31 57.8	0 .0	0 .0	5S12.7	2S 8.0	0S57.5	0S40.1	1S 1.3	2N30.2	0N19.6	1N40.3	8N45.3
4	10 43 47.5	0 .0	0 .0	4 23.3	2 4.3	0 50.9	0 38.2	1 1.4	2 30.7	0 19.6	1 40.5	8 45.3
7	10 55 37.2	0 .0	0 .0	1 18.4	1 56.3	0 43.9	0 36.3	1 1.4	2 31.0	0 19.6	1 40.6	8 45.1
10	11 7 26.8	0 .0	0 .0	2N16.5	1 43.5	0 36.4	0 34.4	1 1.5	2 31.4	0 19.6	1 40.7	8 45.0
13	11 19 16.5	0 .0	0 .0	4 41.7	1 25.9	0 28.5	0 32.5	1 1.6	2 31.7	0 19.5	1 40.8	8 44.8
16	11 31 6.2	0 .0	0 .0	5 13.4	1 3.3	0 20.2	0 30.5	1 1.7	2 31.9	0 19.5	1 40.9	8 44.6
19	11 42 55.8	0 .0	0 .0	3 45.4	0 35.8	0 11.7	0 28.6	1 1.8	2 32.1	0 19.5	1 41.0	8 44.4
22	11 54 45.5	0 .0	0 .0	0 37.4	0 4.0	0 2.9	0 26.6	1 2.0	2 32.2	0 19.5	1 41.0	8 44.1
25	12 6 35.1	0 .0	0 .0	2S59.9	0N31.0	0N 6.2	0 24.7	1 2.1	2 32.3	0 19.4	1 41.1	8 43.8
28	12 18 24.8	0 .0	0 .0	5 8.1	1 7.3	0 15.4	0 22.7	1 2.3	2 32.3	0 19.4	1 41.2	8 43.5
31	12 30 14.5	0 .0	0 .0	4 31.3	1 42.7	0 24.8	0 20.7	1 2.5	2 32.3	0 19.4	1 41.2	8 43.1

RIGHT ASCENSION

DAY	SID. TIME	☉	☊	☽	☿	♀	♂	♃	♄	♅	♆	♇
1	10 31 57.8	11♓ 9.5	20♓29.9	7♐39.5	3♓38.4	4♈57.0	29♓37.4	19♓ 7.8	1♎25.8	5♋59.2	18♎17.3	23♌32.1
2	10 35 54.4	12 5.8	20 27.0	23 36.3	5 19.3	6 4.1	0♈19.7	19 21.2	1R22.0	5R58.4	18R16.2	23R30.7
3	10 39 51.0	13 1.9	20 24.1	9♑43.8	7 .5	7 11.2	1 2.0	19 34.6	1 18.1	5 57.7	18 15.1	23 29.4
4	10 43 47.5	13 58.0	20 21.1	25 26.4	8 42.2	8 18.2	1 44.3	19 48.0	1 14.1	5 57.1	18 14.0	23 28.0
5	10 47 44.1	14 53.9	20 18.2	10♒18.0	10 24.2	9 25.3	2 26.5	20 1.4	1 10.1	5 56.5	18 12.8	23 26.7
6	10 51 40.6	15 49.7	20 15.3	24 8.6	12 6.6	10 32.5	3 8.7	20 14.9	1 6.1	5 56.0	18 11.7	23 25.4
7	10 55 37.2	16 45.4	20 12.4	7♓ 2.7	13 49.4	11 39.6	3 50.9	20 28.3	1 2.0	5 55.5	18 10.5	23 24.1
8	10 59 33.7	17 41.0	20 9.4	19 12.7	15 32.6	12 46.8	4 33.0	20 41.7	0 57.9	5 55.1	18 9.2	23 22.8
9	11 3 30.3	18 36.5	20 6.5	0♈54.7	17 16.2	13 54.0	5 15.2	20 55.2	0 53.8	5 54.8	18 8.0	23 21.5
10	11 7 26.8	19 31.9	20 3.6	12 24.5	19 .2	15 1.3	5 57.3	21 8.6	0 49.6	5 54.5	18 6.8	23 20.2
11	11 11 23.4	20 27.2	20 .6	23 57.0	20 44.6	16 8.7	6 39.4	21 22.0	0 45.4	5 54.3	18 5.5	23 19.0
12	11 15 19.9	21 22.5	19 57.7	5♉44.5	22 29.4	17 16.1	7 21.5	21 35.4	0 41.2	5 54.1	18 4.2	23 17.7
13	11 19 16.5	22 17.6	19 54.8	17 56.1	24 14.6	18 23.6	8 3.6	21 48.9	0 37.0	5 54.0	18 2.9	23 16.5
14	11 23 13.1	23 12.7	19 51.8	0♊36.1	26 .1	19 31.2	8 45.6	22 2.3	0 32.7	5 53.9	18 1.6	23 15.3
15	11 27 9.6	24 7.7	19 48.9	13 42.7	27 45.8	20 38.9	9 27.7	22 15.7	0 28.5	5 53.9	18 .3	23 14.1
16	11 31 6.2	25 2.6	19 46.0	27 7.5	29 31.7	21 46.7	10 9.7	22 29.1	0 24.2	5D54.0	17 58.9	23 13.0
17	11 35 2.7	25 57.5	19 43.0	10♋37.5	1♈17.8	22 54.7	10 51.7	22 42.5	0 19.9	5 54.1	17 57.5	23 11.8
18	11 38 59.3	26 52.4	19 40.1	23 58.7	3 3.9	24 2.8	11 33.8	22 55.9	0 15.6	5 54.3	17 56.2	23 10.7
19	11 42 55.8	27 47.1	19 37.2	7♌ .1	4 49.8	25 11.0	12 15.8	23 9.3	0 11.3	5 54.6	17 54.8	23 9.6
20	11 46 52.4	28 41.9	19 34.2	19 37.4	6 35.4	26 19.4	12 57.8	23 22.6	0 7.0	5 54.9	17 53.4	23 8.5
21	11 50 48.9	29 36.5	19 31.3	1♍52.7	8 20.6	27 27.9	13 39.8	23 36.0	0 2.6	5 55.2	17 52.0	23 7.4
22	11 54 45.5	0♈31.2	19 28.4	13 54.0	10 5.0	28 36.5	14 21.8	23 49.3	29♍58.3	5 55.7	17 50.6	23 6.4
23	11 58 42.0	1 25.8	19 25.4	25 53.6	11 48.4	29 45.3	15 3.9	24 2.7	29 54.0	5 56.1	17 49.2	23 5.3
24	12 2 38.6	2 20.4	19 22.5	8♎ 6.4	13 30.6	0♉54.3	15 45.9	24 16.0	29 49.7	5 56.7	17 47.7	23 4.3
25	12 6 35.1	3 14.9	19 19.6	20 48.9	15 11.3	2 3.5	16 27.9	24 29.3	29 45.4	5 57.3	17 46.2	23 3.3
26	12 10 31.7	4 9.5	19 16.6	4♏16.5	16 50.0	3 12.9	17 10.0	24 42.5	29 41.0	5 57.9	17 44.8	23 2.3
27	12 14 28.2	5 4.1	19 13.7	18 40.0	18 26.5	4 22.5	17 52.0	24 55.8	29 36.8	5 58.6	17 43.3	23 1.4
28	12 18 24.8	5 58.6	19 10.8	3♐59.4	20 .5	5 32.2	18 34.1	25 9.0	29 32.5	5 59.4	17 41.8	23 .5
29	12 22 21.4	6 53.2	19 7.8	19 59.0	21 31.5	6 42.2	19 16.2	25 22.3	29 28.2	6 .2	17 40.3	22 59.5
30	12 26 17.9	7 47.7	19 4.9	6♑ 7.9	22 59.1	7 52.4	19 58.3	25 35.4	29 24.0	6 1.1	17 38.8	22 58.7
31	12 30 14.5	8 42.3	19 2.0	21 50.8	24 23.1	9 2.8	20 40.4	25 48.6	29 19.7	6 2.0	17 37.3	22 57.8

DECLINATION

DAY	SID. TIME	☉	☊	☽	☿	♀	♂	♃	♄	♅	♆	♇
1	10 31 57.8	7S58.5	0S 4.3	27S 7.9	13S11.1	1N 5.9	0S53.5	5S47.2	2N 6.5	23N39.7	5S56.7	23N42.1
4	10 43 47.5	6 49.9	0 4.4	25 50.6	11 11.0	2 39.7	0N 3.6	5 30.2	2 12.1	23 39.7	5 55.2	23 43.3
7	10 55 37.2	5 40.5	0 4.4	11 .4	8 59.2	4 12.9	1 .5	5 13.2	2 17.8	23 39.8	5 53.6	23 44.4
10	11 7 26.8	4 30.3	0 4.5	7N47.6	6 36.3	5 45.4	1 57.1	4 56.1	2 23.5	23 39.8	5 52.0	23 45.4
13	11 19 16.5	3 19.7	0 4.5	22 43.2	4 3.0	7 16.8	2 53.5	4 39.0	2 29.3	23 39.8	5 50.3	23 46.4
16	11 31 6.2	2 8.7	0 4.6	28 38.7	1 21.2	8 46.7	3 49.4	4 22.0	2 35.1	23 39.8	5 48.6	23 47.3
19	11 42 55.8	0 57.6	0 4.7	22 58.5	1N26.5	10 14.9	4 44.8	4 4.9	2 40.9	23 39.7	5 46.9	23 48.1
22	11 54 45.5	0N13.5	0 4.7	7 32.0	4 16.2	11 40.9	5 39.6	3 47.8	2 46.7	23 39.7	5 45.1	23 48.8
25	12 6 35.1	1 24.5	0 4.8	11S59.6	7 2.5	13 4.5	6 33.8	3 30.8	2 52.4	23 39.6	5 43.2	23 49.4
28	12 18 24.8	2 35.1	0 4.9	26 30.7	9 39.1	14 25.3	7 27.3	3 13.9	2 58.0	23 39.5	5 41.4	23 49.9
31	12 30 14.5	3 45.4	0 4.9	26 30.1	11 59.4	15 43.0	8 20.0	2 57.0	3 3.5	23 39.3	5 39.5	23 50.4

APRIL 1951

LONGITUDE

DAY	EPHEM. SID. TIME h m s	☉ ° ′	☊ ° ′	☽ ° ′	☿ ° ′	♀ ° ′	♂ ° ′	♃ ° ′	♄ ° ′	♅ ° ′	♆ ° ′	♇ ° ′
1	12 34 11.0	10♈27.8	18♓ 1.2	3♒26.3	28♈25.8	12♉49.3	22♈58.3	25♓13.3	28♍ 5.4	5♋32.4	18♎22.8	17♌36.3
2	12 38 7.6	11 27.0	17 58.0	17 10.1	29 48.9	14 1.6	23 43.4	25 27.6	28R .9	5 33.4	18R21.1	17R35.6
3	12 42 4.1	12 26.2	17 54.8	0♓42.0	1♉ 6.5	15 13.8	24 28.5	25 41.8	27 56.3	5 34.4	18 19.5	17 34.8
4	12 46 .7	13 25.3	17 51.6	14 1.6	2 18.5	16 26.0	25 13.5	25 56.0	27 51.9	5 35.5	18 17.8	17 34.1
5	12 49 57.2	14 24.5	17 48.5	27 8.8	3 24.6	17 38.1	25 58.5	26 10.2	27 47.4	5 36.6	18 16.2	17 33.4
6	12 53 53.8	15 23.5	17 45.3	10♈ 3.4	4 24.7	18 50.1	26 43.4	26 24.4	27 43.0	5 37.7	18 14.5	17 32.8
7	12 57 50.3	16 22.6	17 42.1	22 45.2	5 18.4	20 2.1	27 28.3	26 38.5	27 38.6	5 39.0	18 12.9	17 32.2
8	13 1 46.9	17 21.7	17 38.9	5♉14.6	6 5.8	21 14.0	28 13.2	26 52.6	27 34.4	5 40.3	18 11.3	17 31.6
9	13 5 43.4	18 20.7	17 35.8	17 32.2	6 46.6	22 25.8	28 58.0	27 6.7	27 30.1	5 41.6	18 9.6	17 31.0
10	13 9 40.0	19 19.6	17 32.6	29 39.4	7 20.8	23 37.6	29 42.7	27 20.7	27 25.9	5 43.0	18 8.0	17 30.4
11	13 13 36.6	20 18.5	17 29.4	11♊38.4	7 48.4	24 49.2	0♉27.4	27 34.6	27 21.7	5 44.4	18 6.3	17 29.9
12	13 17 33.1	21 17.4	17 26.2	23 32.1	8 9.4	26 .8	1 12.0	27 48.6	27 17.5	5 45.9	18 4.7	17 29.4
13	13 21 29.7	22 16.3	17 23.0	5♋24.1	8 23.8	27 12.3	1 56.6	28 2.5	27 13.5	5 47.4	18 3.0	17 28.9
14	13 25 26.2	23 15.1	17 19.9	17 18.6	8 31.7	28 23.7	2 41.1	28 16.3	27 9.5	5 49.0	18 1.4	17 28.5
15	13 29 22.8	24 13.8	17 16.7	29 20.4	8 33.2	29 35.1	3 25.6	28 30.1	27 5.5	5 50.6	17 59.8	17 28.0
16	13 33 19.3	25 12.6	17 13.5	11♌34.3	8R28.5	0♊46.3	4 10.0	28 43.9	27 1.6	5 52.2	17 58.1	17 27.6
17	13 37 15.9	26 11.2	17 10.3	24 5.1	8 17.9	1 57.5	4 54.4	28 57.6	26 57.8	5 53.9	17 56.5	17 27.3
18	13 41 12.4	27 9.9	17 7.2	6♍56.8	8 1.8	3 8.5	5 38.7	29 11.3	26 54.0	5 55.7	17 54.9	17 26.9
19	13 45 9.0	28 8.5	17 4.0	20 12.7	7 40.5	4 19.5	6 23.0	29 24.9	26 50.3	5 57.5	17 53.2	17 26.6
20	13 49 5.5	29 7.1	17 .8	3♎54.3	7 14.6	5 30.4	7 7.2	29 38.5	26 46.7	5 59.3	17 51.6	17 26.3
21	13 53 2.1	0♉ 5.7	16 57.6	18 .8	6 44.5	6 41.2	7 51.4	29 52.0	26 43.1	6 1.2	17 50.0	17 26.0
22	13 56 58.7	1 4.2	16 54.5	2♏28.8	6 10.8	7 51.9	8 35.5	0♈ 5.5	26 39.7	6 3.2	17 48.4	17 25.8
23	14 0 55.2	2 2.7	16 51.3	17 12.4	5 34.4	9 2.5	9 19.6	0 18.9	26 36.2	6 5.1	17 46.8	17 25.6
24	14 4 51.8	3 1.1	16 48.1	2♐ 3.9	4 55.7	10 13.0	10 3.6	0 32.3	26 32.9	6 7.2	17 45.2	17 25.4
25	14 8 48.3	3 59.5	16 44.9	16 54.9	4 15.7	11 23.4	10 47.6	0 45.6	26 29.6	6 9.2	17 43.7	17 25.3
26	14 12 44.9	4 57.9	16 41.7	1♑37.4	3 35.1	12 33.7	11 31.5	0 58.9	26 26.4	6 11.3	17 42.1	17 25.1
27	14 16 41.4	5 56.3	16 38.6	16 5.7	2 54.5	13 43.9	12 15.4	1 12.1	26 23.3	6 13.5	17 40.6	17 25.0
28	14 20 38.0	6 54.6	16 35.4	0♒15.9	2 14.7	14 54.0	12 59.2	1 25.2	26 20.3	6 15.7	17 39.0	17 25.0
29	14 24 34.5	7 53.0	16 32.2	14 6.9	1 36.5	16 4.0	13 43.0	1 38.4	26 17.4	6 18.0	17 37.5	17 25.0
30	14 28 31.1	8 51.3	16 29.0	27 38.9	1 .4	17 13.9	14 26.7	1 51.4	26 14.5	6 20.2	17 36.0	17 25.0

LATITUDE

DAY	EPHEM. SID. TIME	☉	☊	☽	☿	♀	♂	♃	♄	♅	♆	♇
1	12 34 11.0	0 .0	0 .0	3S44.9	1N53.8	0N27.9	0S20.1	1S 2.6	2N32.3	0N19.4	1N41.2	8N43.0
4	12 46 .7	0 .0	0 .0	0 27.1	2 24.0	0 37.3	0 18.1	1 2.8	2 32.2	0 19.3	1 41.3	8 42.6
7	12 57 50.3	0 .0	0 .0	2N54.6	2 47.5	0 46.8	0 16.1	1 3.1	2 32.1	0 19.3	1 41.3	8 42.2
10	13 9 40.0	0 .0	0 .0	4 54.8	3 2.1	0 56.1	0 14.1	1 3.3	2 31.9	0 19.3	1 41.3	8 41.7
13	13 21 29.7	0 .0	0 .0	4 58.2	3 6.0	1 5.4	0 12.1	1 3.6	2 31.7	0 19.3	1 41.3	8 41.3
16	13 33 19.3	0 .0	0 .0	3 7.2	2 57.6	1 14.4	0 10.2	1 3.9	2 31.4	0 19.3	1 41.3	8 40.8
19	13 45 9.0	0 .0	0 .0	0S 9.4	2 36.2	1 23.3	0 8.2	1 4.2	2 31.1	0 19.2	1 41.3	8 40.4
22	13 56 58.7	0 .0	0 .0	3 35.2	2 2.5	1 31.8	0 6.2	1 4.6	2 30.8	0 19.2	1 41.3	8 39.9
25	14 8 48.3	0 .0	0 .0	5 7.8	1 18.7	1 40.0	0 4.3	1 4.9	2 30.4	0 19.2	1 41.2	8 39.4
28	14 20 38.0	0 .0	0 .0	3 47.7	0 28.9	1 47.8	0 2.3	1 5.3	2 30.0	0 19.2	1 41.2	8 38.9

RIGHT ASCENSION

DAY	EPHEM. SID. TIME	☉	☊	☽	☿	♀	♂	♃	♄	♅	♆	♇
1	12 34 11.0	9♈36.9	18♓59.0	6♒41.5	25♈43.2	10♉13.4	21♈22.5	26♓ 1.8	29♍15.5	6♋ 3.0	17♎35.8	22♌56.9
2	12 38 7.6	10 31.6	18 56.1	20 30.2	26 58.9	11 24.3	22 4.7	26 14.9	29R11.3	6 4.1	17R34.3	22R56.1
3	12 42 4.1	11 26.3	18 53.2	3♓21.3	28 9.9	12 35.4	22 46.9	26 28.0	29 7.2	6 5.2	17 32.8	22 55.3
4	12 46 .7	12 21.0	18 50.2	15 27.7	29 16.1	13 46.7	23 29.1	26 41.1	29 3.0	6 6.3	17 31.3	22 54.6
5	12 49 57.2	13 15.7	18 47.3	27 5.1	0♉17.1	14 58.2	24 11.4	26 54.1	28 58.9	6 7.5	17 29.8	22 53.8
6	12 53 53.8	14 10.5	18 44.3	8♈29.8	1 12.7	16 10.0	24 53.6	27 7.2	28 54.9	6 8.8	17 28.2	22 53.1
7	12 57 50.3	15 5.3	18 41.4	19 56.6	2 2.7	17 22.1	25 35.9	27 20.2	28 50.9	6 10.2	17 26.7	22 52.4
8	13 1 46.9	16 .2	18 38.5	1♉38.1	2 47.0	18 34.4	26 18.3	27 33.2	28 46.9	6 11.6	17 25.2	22 51.8
9	13 5 43.4	16 55.2	18 35.5	13 43.8	3 25.3	19 46.9	27 .7	27 46.1	28 43.0	6 13.0	17 23.7	22 51.1
10	13 9 40.0	17 50.2	18 32.6	26 18.1	3 57.7	20 59.6	27 43.1	27 59.0	28 39.0	6 14.5	17 22.1	22 50.5
11	13 13 36.6	18 45.2	18 29.7	9♊19.7	4 24.0	22 12.5	28 25.5	28 11.9	28 35.2	6 16.1	17 20.6	22 49.9
12	13 17 33.1	19 40.3	18 26.7	22 40.3	4 44.3	23 25.7	29 8.0	28 24.7	28 31.4	6 17.7	17 19.1	22 49.3
13	13 21 29.7	20 35.5	18 23.8	6♋ 6.8	4 58.5	24 39.1	29 50.5	28 37.5	28 27.6	6 19.3	17 17.5	22 48.8
14	13 25 26.2	21 30.8	18 20.9	19 25.0	5 6.7	25 52.8	0♉33.0	28 50.2	28 23.9	6 21.0	17 16.0	22 48.3
15	13 29 22.8	22 26.1	18 17.9	2♌23.4	5 9.2	27 6.6	1 15.6	29 2.9	28 20.2	6 22.8	17 14.5	22 47.8
16	13 33 19.3	23 21.5	18 15.0	14 57.2	5R 6.0	28 20.7	1 58.2	29 15.6	28 16.6	6 24.6	17 13.0	22 47.3
17	13 37 15.9	24 17.0	18 12.0	27 8.1	4 57.5	29 35.0	2 40.8	29 28.2	28 13.1	6 26.5	17 11.5	22 46.9
18	13 41 12.4	25 12.6	18 9.1	9♍ 3.8	4 44.1	0♊49.4	3 23.5	29 40.8	28 9.6	6 28.4	17 9.9	22 46.4
19	13 45 9.0	26 8.3	18 6.2	20 56.7	4 26.0	2 4.1	4 6.3	29 53.4	28 6.1	6 30.3	17 8.4	22 46.1
20	13 49 5.5	27 4.1	18 3.2	3♎ 2.2	4 3.9	3 18.9	4 49.0	0♈ 5.9	28 2.7	6 32.4	17 6.9	22 45.7
21	13 53 2.1	27 59.9	18 .3	15 37.5	3 38.2	4 34.0	5 31.8	0 18.3	27 59.4	6 34.4	17 5.4	22 45.4
22	13 56 58.7	28 55.9	17 57.3	29 .3	3 9.6	5 49.2	6 14.7	0 30.7	27 56.2	6 36.5	17 4.0	22 45.1
23	14 0 55.2	29 52.0	17 54.4	13♏24.4	2 38.7	7 4.5	6 57.6	0 43.1	27 53.0	6 38.7	17 2.5	22 44.8
24	14 4 51.8	0♉48.2	17 51.5	28 53.2	2 6.2	8 20.0	7 40.5	0 55.4	27 49.9	6 40.9	17 1.0	22 44.6
25	14 8 48.3	1 44.5	17 48.5	15♐13.0	1 32.8	9 35.7	8 23.5	1 7.7	27 46.8	6 43.1	16 59.5	22 44.3
26	14 12 44.9	2 41.0	17 45.6	1♑50.4	0 59.0	10 51.4	9 6.5	1 19.9	27 43.8	6 45.4	16 58.1	22 44.2
27	14 16 41.4	3 37.5	17 42.7	18 3.8	0 25.7	12 7.3	9 49.6	1 32.1	27 40.9	6 47.8	16 56.6	22 44.0
28	14 20 38.0	4 34.2	17 39.7	3♒20.6	29♈53.4	13 23.3	10 32.8	1 44.2	27 38.1	6 50.2	16 55.2	22 43.9
29	14 24 34.5	5 31.1	17 36.8	17 27.4	29 22.8	14 39.5	11 16.0	1 56.3	27 35.4	6 52.7	16 53.8	22 43.8
30	14 28 31.1	6 28.0	17 33.8	0♓28.1	28 54.3	15 55.7	11 59.2	2 8.3	27 32.7	6 55.1	16 52.4	22 43.7

DECLINATION

DAY	EPHEM. SID. TIME	☉	☊	☽	☿	♀	♂	♃	♄	♅	♆	♇
1	12 34 11.0	4N 8.6	0S 5.0	23S 2.2	12N41.5	16N 8.1	8N37.4	2S51.4	3N 5.3	23N39.3	5S38.8	23N50.5
4	12 46 .7	5 18.0	0 5.0	6 42.2	14 31.9	17 21.2	9 29.0	2 34.7	3 10.6	23 39.1	5 36.9	23 50.9
7	12 57 50.3	6 26.5	0 5.1	11N33.2	15 55.6	18 30.4	10 19.6	2 18.0	3 15.8	23 39.0	5 35.0	23 51.1
10	13 9 40.0	7 34.1	0 5.2	24 52.9	16 50.2	19 35.5	11 9.3	2 1.5	3 20.7	23 38.8	5 33.2	23 51.2
13	13 21 29.7	8 40.4	0 5.2	28 18.2	17 14.5	20 36.2	11 57.8	1 45.1	3 25.4	23 38.5	5 31.3	23 51.3
16	13 33 19.3	9 45.5	0 5.3	20 18.9	17 8.0	21 32.0	12 45.2	1 28.9	3 29.9	23 38.3	5 29.4	23 51.3
19	13 45 9.0	10 49.1	0 5.4	3 44.1	16 32.2	22 22.8	13 31.4	1 12.9	3 34.1	23 38.1	5 27.6	23 51.1
22	13 56 58.7	11 51.0	0 5.4	15S42.2	15 30.7	23 8.3	14 16.4	0 57.0	3 38.0	23 37.8	5 25.7	23 50.9
25	14 8 48.3	12 51.2	0 5.5	27 54.5	14 10.8	23 48.4	15 .0	0 41.4	3 41.7	23 37.5	5 24.0	23 50.6
28	14 20 38.0	13 49.6	0 5.5	23 48.4	12 42.6	24 22.7	15 42.3	0 26.0	3 45.0	23 37.2	5 22.2	23 50.3

MAY 1951

LONGITUDE

DAY	EPHEM. SID. TIME h m s	☉ ° ′	☊ ° ′	☽ ° ′	☿ ° ′	♀ ° ′	♂ ° ′	♃ ° ′	♄ ° ′	♅ ° ′	♆ ° ′	♇ ° ′
1	14 32 27.7	9♉49.6	16♓25.9	10♓53.6	0♉27.0	18♊23.7	15♉10.4	2♈ 4.4	26♍11.8	6♋22.5	17♎34.5	17♌25.0
2	14 36 24.2	10 47.8	16 22.7	23 53.1	29♈56.8	19 33.4	15 54.0	2 17.3	26 R 9.1	6 24.9	17 R 33.0	17 25.0
3	14 40 20.8	11 46.1	16 19.5	6♈39.4	29 R 30.2	20 43.0	16 37.6	2 30.1	26 6.5	6 27.3	17 31.5	17 D 25.1
4	14 44 17.3	12 44.2	16 16.3	19 14.4	29 7.6	21 52.5	17 21.1	2 42.9	26 3.9	6 29.7	17 30.1	17 25.2
5	14 48 13.9	13 42.4	16 13.1	1♉39.3	28 49.3	23 1.9	18 4.6	2 55.6	26 1.5	6 32.2	17 28.6	17 25.3
6	14 52 10.4	14 40.6	16 10.0	13 55.3	28 35.3	24 11.1	18 48.0	3 8.2	25 59.2	6 34.7	17 27.2	17 25.5
7	14 56 7.0	15 38.7	16 6.8	26 3.3	28 26.0	25 20.2	19 31.3	3 20.8	25 56.9	6 37.3	17 25.8	17 25.6
8	15 0 3.5	16 36.7	16 3.6	8♊ 4.4	28 21.3	26 29.2	20 14.7	3 33.3	25 54.8	6 39.8	17 24.4	17 25.8
9	15 4 .1	17 34.8	16 .4	19 59.9	28 D 21.4	27 38.1	20 57.9	3 45.7	25 52.7	6 42.5	17 23.0	17 26.1
10	15 7 56.7	18 32.8	15 57.3	1♋51.9	28 26.1	28 46.9	21 41.1	3 58.1	25 50.8	6 45.1	17 21.6	17 26.3
11	15 11 53.2	19 30.8	15 54.1	13 42.8	28 35.5	29 55.5	22 24.3	4 10.3	25 48.9	6 47.8	17 20.3	17 26.6
12	15 15 49.8	20 28.8	15 50.9	25 36.1	28 49.5	1♋ 4.0	23 7.4	4 22.5	25 47.1	6 50.5	17 19.0	17 27.0
13	15 19 46.3	21 26.7	15 47.7	7♌35.9	29 8.0	2 12.4	23 50.5	4 34.6	25 45.5	6 53.3	17 17.7	17 27.3
14	15 23 42.9	22 24.6	15 44.6	19 46.9	29 30.9	3 20.6	24 33.5	4 46.6	25 43.9	6 56.1	17 16.4	17 27.7
15	15 27 39.4	23 22.5	15 41.4	2♍14.0	29 58.0	4 28.7	25 16.4	4 58.6	25 42.4	6 58.9	17 15.1	17 28.1
16	15 31 36.0	24 20.3	15 38.2	15 2.1	0♉29.3	5 36.6	25 59.3	5 10.4	25 41.1	7 1.7	17 13.9	17 28.5
17	15 35 32.6	25 18.2	15 35.0	28 15.7	1 4.6	6 44.4	26 42.1	5 22.2	25 39.8	7 4.6	17 12.6	17 29.0
18	15 39 29.1	26 16.0	15 31.8	11♎57.6	1 43.8	7 52.0	27 24.9	5 33.9	25 38.6	7 7.5	17 11.4	17 29.5
19	15 43 25.7	27 13.7	15 28.7	26 8.6	2 26.8	8 59.5	28 7.7	5 45.5	25 37.5	7 10.5	17 10.3	17 30.0
20	15 47 22.2	28 11.5	15 25.5	10♏46.4	3 13.5	10 6.8	28 50.4	5 57.1	25 36.6	7 13.5	17 9.2	17 30.6
21	15 51 18.8	29 9.2	15 22.3	25 45.1	4 3.6	11 14.0	29 33.0	6 8.5	25 35.7	7 16.5	17 8.0	17 31.1
22	15 55 15.3	0♊ 6.9	15 19.1	10♐56.0	4 57.2	12 20.9	0♊15.6	6 19.8	25 34.9	7 19.5	17 6.9	17 31.7
23	15 59 11.9	1 4.6	15 16.0	26 8.3	5 54.1	13 27.7	0 58.1	6 31.0	25 34.3	7 22.6	17 5.8	17 32.3
24	16 3 8.5	2 2.2	15 12.8	11♑11.5	6 54.2	14 34.3	1 40.6	6 42.2	25 33.7	7 25.7	17 4.8	17 33.0
25	16 7 5.0	2 59.9	15 9.6	25 56.9	7 57.4	15 40.8	2 23.1	6 53.2	25 33.2	7 28.8	17 3.7	17 33.7
26	16 11 1.6	3 57.5	15 6.4	10♒19.1	9 3.6	16 47.0	3 5.4	7 4.2	25 32.9	7 31.9	17 2.7	17 34.4
27	16 14 58.1	4 55.1	15 3.3	24 15.8	10 12.9	17 53.1	3 47.8	7 15.0	25 32.6	7 35.1	17 1.7	17 35.1
28	16 18 54.7	5 52.6	15 .1	7♓47.4	11 25.0	18 59.0	4 30.1	7 25.8	25 32.4	7 38.3	17 .8	17 35.8
29	16 22 51.2	6 50.2	14 56.9	20 56.4	12 40.0	20 4.7	5 12.3	7 36.4	25 32.4	7 41.5	16 59.8	17 36.6
30	16 26 47.8	7 47.8	14 53.7	3♈46.0	13 57.7	21 10.2	5 54.5	7 47.0	25 32.4	7 44.7	16 58.9	17 37.4
31	16 30 44.4	8 45.3	14 50.6	16 19.9	15 18.3	22 15.5	6 36.7	7 57.4	25 D 32.6	7 48.0	16 58.0	17 38.2

LATITUDE

DAY	EPHEM. SID. TIME	☉	☊	☽	☿	♀	♂	♃	♄	♅	♆	♇
1	14 32 27.7	0 .0	0 .0	0S37.5	0S22.5	1N55.1	0S .4	1S 5.7	2N29.5	0N19.2	1N41.2	8N38.4
4	14 44 17.3	0 .0	0 .0	2N39.8	1 11.1	2 1.9	0N 1.5	1 6.1	2 29.0	0 19.1	1 41.1	8 37.9
7	14 56 7.0	0 .0	0 .0	4 43.1	1 53.8	2 8.1	0 3.5	1 6.5	2 28.5	0 19.1	1 41.0	8 37.3
10	15 7 56.7	0 .0	0 .0	4 53.1	2 28.9	2 13.6	0 5.4	1 7.0	2 28.0	0 19.1	1 41.0	8 36.8
13	15 19 46.3	0 .0	0 .0	3 11.5	2 55.5	2 18.4	0 7.3	1 7.4	2 27.5	0 19.1	1 40.9	8 36.3
16	15 31 36.0	0 .0	0 .0	0 7.9	3 13.7	2 22.5	0 9.1	1 7.9	2 26.9	0 19.1	1 40.8	8 35.8
19	15 43 25.7	0 .0	0 .0	3S13.6	3 24.0	2 25.7	0 11.0	1 8.5	2 26.3	0 19.1	1 40.7	8 35.3
22	15 55 15.3	0 .0	0 .0	5 .0	3 26.8	2 28.1	0 12.8	1 9.0	2 25.7	0 19.1	1 40.6	8 34.8
25	16 7 5.0	0 .0	0 .0	3 50.1	3 22.8	2 29.5	0 14.7	1 9.5	2 25.1	0 19.1	1 40.5	8 34.3
28	16 18 54.7	0 .0	0 .0	0 40.4	3 12.6	2 30.0	0 16.5	1 10.1	2 24.5	0 19.1	1 40.4	8 33.8
31	16 30 44.4	0 .0	0 .0	2N35.4	2 56.9	2 29.4	0 18.3	1 10.7	2 23.8	0 19.1	1 40.3	8 33.4

RIGHT ASCENSION

DAY	EPHEM. SID. TIME	☉	☊	☽	☿	♀	♂	♃	♄	♅	♆	♇
1	14 32 27.7	7♉25.1	17♓30.9	12♓36.5	28♈28.4	17♊12.0	12♉42.5	2♈20.2	27♍30.1	6♋57.7	16♎51.0	22♌43.7
2	14 36 24.2	8 22.4	17 27.9	24 10.4	28 R 5.5	18 28.3	13 25.8	2 32.1	27 R 27.5	7 .2	16 R 49.6	22 43.7
3	14 40 20.8	9 19.7	17 25.0	5♈27.4	27 46.0	19 44.6	14 9.2	2 44.0	27 25.1	7 2.8	16 48.2	22 43.7
4	14 44 17.3	10 17.2	17 22.1	16 43.8	27 30.1	21 1.0	14 52.6	2 55.7	27 22.7	7 5.5	16 46.9	22 43.7
5	14 48 13.9	11 14.9	17 19.1	28 13.5	27 18.1	22 17.4	15 36.1	3 7.4	27 20.4	7 8.2	16 45.5	22 D 43.8
6	14 52 10.4	12 12.7	17 16.2	10♉ 7.3	27 10.0	23 33.8	16 19.7	3 19.1	27 18.2	7 10.9	16 44.2	22 43.9
7	14 56 7.0	13 10.6	17 13.2	22 31.2	27 6.0	24 50.2	17 3.2	3 30.7	27 16.1	7 13.7	16 42.9	22 44.0
8	15 0 3.5	14 8.7	17 10.3	5♊25.1	27 D 6.1	26 6.5	17 46.9	3 42.2	27 14.0	7 16.5	16 41.6	22 44.2
9	15 4 .1	15 6.9	17 7.4	18 41.4	27 10.3	27 22.8	18 30.5	3 53.7	27 12.1	7 19.4	16 40.3	22 44.3
10	15 7 56.7	16 5.2	17 4.4	2♋ 6.6	27 18.7	28 39.0	19 14.3	4 5.0	27 10.2	7 22.3	16 39.0	22 44.6
11	15 11 53.2	17 3.7	17 1.5	15 24.8	27 31.1	29 55.0	19 58.0	4 16.4	27 8.4	7 25.2	16 37.7	22 44.8
12	15 15 49.8	18 2.3	16 58.5	28 22.7	27 47.5	1♋11.0	20 41.8	4 27.6	27 6.7	7 28.2	16 36.5	22 45.1
13	15 19 46.3	19 1.1	16 55.6	10♌53.2	28 7.7	2 26.9	21 25.7	4 38.8	27 5.1	7 31.2	16 35.3	22 45.4
14	15 23 42.9	19 60.0	16 52.6	22 56.9	28 31.9	3 42.5	22 9.6	4 49.9	27 3.6	7 34.2	16 34.1	22 45.7
15	15 27 39.4	20 59.0	16 49.7	4♍40.7	28 59.7	4 58.1	22 53.6	5 .9	27 2.1	7 37.3	16 32.9	22 46.0
16	15 31 36.0	21 58.2	16 46.8	16 16.4	29 31.1	6 13.4	23 37.5	5 11.9	27 .8	7 40.4	16 31.7	22 46.4
17	15 35 32.6	22 57.5	16 43.8	27 59.7	0♉ 6.1	7 28.5	24 21.6	5 22.7	26 59.5	7 43.5	16 30.6	22 46.8
18	15 39 29.1	23 57.0	16 40.9	10♎ 8.5	0 44.5	8 43.4	25 5.6	5 33.5	26 58.4	7 46.7	16 29.4	22 47.3
19	15 43 25.7	24 56.6	16 37.9	23 2.4	1 26.2	9 58.1	25 49.8	5 44.3	26 57.3	7 49.9	16 28.3	22 47.7
20	15 47 22.2	25 56.4	16 35.0	6♏59.9	2 11.2	11 12.5	26 34.0	5 54.9	26 56.4	7 53.2	16 27.3	22 48.3
21	15 51 18.8	26 56.2	16 32.0	22 12.1	2 59.3	12 26.6	27 18.2	6 5.5	26 55.5	7 56.5	16 26.2	22 48.8
22	15 55 15.3	27 56.2	16 29.1	8♐34.2	3 50.5	13 40.4	28 2.4	6 16.0	26 54.7	7 59.8	16 25.2	22 49.4
23	15 59 11.9	28 56.3	16 26.2	25 37.7	4 44.8	14 53.9	28 46.7	6 26.4	26 54.0	8 3.1	16 24.2	22 49.9
24	16 3 8.5	29 56.6	16 23.2	12♑35.9	5 42.0	16 7.1	29 31.0	6 36.7	26 53.4	8 6.5	16 23.2	22 50.5
25	16 7 5.0	0♊57.0	16 20.3	28 43.7	6 42.2	17 19.9	0♊15.3	6 46.9	26 52.9	8 9.8	16 22.2	22 51.2
26	16 11 1.6	1 57.5	16 17.3	13♒36.4	7 45.2	18 32.4	0 59.7	6 57.0	26 52.5	8 13.3	16 21.2	22 51.8
27	16 14 58.1	2 58.2	16 14.4	27 11.8	8 51.1	19 44.6	1 44.1	7 7.1	26 52.1	8 16.7	16 20.3	22 52.5
28	16 18 54.7	3 59.0	16 11.4	9♓43.1	9 59.9	20 56.3	2 28.6	7 17.0	26 51.9	8 20.2	16 19.4	22 53.2
29	16 22 51.2	4 59.9	16 8.5	21 29.1	11 11.5	22 7.6	3 13.1	7 26.9	26 51.8	8 23.7	16 18.5	22 54.0
30	16 26 47.8	6 .9	16 5.5	2♈49.5	12 26.0	23 18.6	3 57.6	7 36.7	26 51.7	8 27.2	16 17.7	22 54.7
31	16 30 44.4	7 2.1	16 2.6	14 2.4	13 43.3	24 29.1	4 42.2	7 46.3	26 D 51.8	8 30.7	16 16.8	22 55.5

DECLINATION

DAY	EPHEM. SID. TIME	☉	☊	☽	☿	♀	♂	♃	♄	♅	♆	♇
1	14 32 27.7	14N45.9	0S 5.6	8S 3.7	11N17.0	24N51.1	16N23.2	0S10.8	3N48.0	23N36.8	5S20.5	23N49.8
4	14 44 17.3	15 40.0	0 5.7	9N59.9	10 3.6	25 13.6	17 2.6	0N 4.1	3 50.6	23 36.4	5 18.9	23 49.2
7	14 56 7.0	16 31.8	0 5.7	23 51.4	9 8.9	25 30.0	17 40.4	0 18.8	3 53.0	23 36.1	5 17.3	23 48.6
10	15 7 56.7	17 21.1	0 5.8	28 19.2	8 36.2	25 40.2	18 16.7	0 33.2	3 54.9	23 35.6	5 15.8	23 47.9
13	15 19 46.3	18 7.8	0 5.9	21 27.7	8 26.0	25 44.2	18 51.4	0 47.3	3 56.5	23 35.2	5 14.4	23 47.1
16	15 31 36.0	18 51.8	0 5.9	6 1.2	8 37.3	25 42.1	19 24.4	1 1.0	3 57.8	23 34.8	5 13.0	23 46.2
19	15 43 25.7	19 32.8	0 6.0	13S 6.2	9 7.9	25 34.0	19 55.7	1 14.4	3 58.6	23 34.3	5 11.7	23 45.3
22	15 55 15.3	20 10.9	0 6.1	27 2.4	9 55.7	25 19.9	20 25.3	1 27.5	3 59.1	23 33.8	5 10.5	23 44.3
25	16 7 5.0	20 45.9	0 6.1	24 43.8	10 58.0	25 .1	20 53.1	1 40.2	3 59.2	23 33.2	5 9.4	23 43.2
28	16 18 54.7	21 17.7	0 6.2	9 16.5	12 12.4	24 34.7	21 19.1	1 52.6	3 58.9	23 32.7	5 8.4	23 42.0
31	16 30 44.4	21 46.2	0 6.3	8N48.9	13 36.6	24 3.9	21 43.3	2 4.5	3 58.3	23 32.1	5 7.5	23 40.8

JUNE 1951

DAY	EPHEM. SID. TIME	☉	☊	☽	☿	♀	♂	♃	♄	♅	♆	♇
	h m s	° ′	° ′	° ′	° ′	° ′	° ′	° ′	° ′	° ′	° ′	° ′
		LONGITUDE										
1	16 34 40.9	9♊42.8	14♓47.4	28♈41.5	16♉41.5	23♋20.6	7♊18.7	8♈ 7.7	25♍32.8	7♋51.2	16♎57.2	17♌39.1
2	16 38 37.5	10 40.4	14 44.2	10♉53.5	18 7.4	24 25.5	8 .8	8 18.0	25 33.2	7 54.5	16R56.3	17 40.0
3	16 42 34.0	11 37.9	14 41.0	22 58.3	19 36.0	25 30.2	8 42.8	8 28.1	25 33.6	7 57.9	16 55.5	17 40.9
4	16 46 30.6	12 35.3	14 37.8	4♊57.5	21 7.2	26 34.6	9 24.7	8 38.1	25 34.2	8 1.2	16 54.8	17 41.8
5	16 50 27.2	13 32.8	14 34.7	16 52.7	22 41.0	27 38.8	10 6.7	8 47.9	25 34.8	8 4.6	16 54.0	17 42.7
6	16 54 23.7	14 30.3	14 31.5	28 45.1	24 17.4	28 42.8	10 48.5	8 57.7	25 35.6	8 7.9	16 53.3	17 43.7
7	16 58 20.3	15 27.7	14 28.3	10♋36.2	25 56.4	29 46.6	11 30.3	9 7.3	25 36.4	8 11.3	16 52.6	17 44.7
8	17 2 16.8	16 25.1	14 25.1	22 27.8	27 38.0	0♌50.1	12 12.1	9 16.9	25 37.4	8 14.7	16 52.0	17 45.7
9	17 6 13.4	17 22.5	14 22.0	4♌22.5	29 22.1	1 53.3	12 53.8	9 26.3	25 38.5	8 18.2	16 51.3	17 46.8
10	17 10 9.9	18 19.9	14 18.8	16 23.4	1♊ 8.9	2 56.3	13 35.5	9 35.6	25 39.7	8 21.7	16 50.8	17 47.9
11	17 14 6.5	19 17.3	14 15.6	28 34.4	2 58.1	3 59.0	14 17.1	9 44.8	25 41.0	8 25.1	16 50.2	17 49.0
12	17 18 3.1	20 14.7	14 12.4	10♍59.9	4 49.7	5 1.4	14 58.6	9 53.8	25 42.3	8 28.6	16 49.7	17 50.1
13	17 21 59.6	21 12.0	14 9.3	23 44.7	6 43.8	6 3.5	15 40.1	10 2.7	25 43.8	8 32.1	16 49.2	17 51.2
14	17 25 56.2	22 9.3	14 6.1	6♎53.3	8 40.3	7 5.4	16 21.6	10 11.5	25 45.4	8 35.6	16 48.7	17 52.4
15	17 29 52.7	23 6.6	14 2.9	20 29.4	10 39.0	8 6.9	17 3.0	10 20.1	25 47.0	8 39.1	16 48.2	17 53.6
16	17 33 49.3	24 3.9	13 59.7	4♏34.9	12 39.8	9 8.0	17 44.4	10 28.6	25 48.8	8 42.6	16 47.8	17 54.8
17	17 37 45.9	25 1.2	13 56.6	19 9.1	14 42.7	10 8.9	18 25.7	10 37.0	25 50.7	8 46.1	16 47.4	17 56.0
18	17 41 42.4	25 58.4	13 53.4	4♐ 7.4	16 47.5	11 9.4	19 6.9	10 45.3	25 52.6	8 49.7	16 47.1	17 57.2
19	17 45 39.0	26 55.7	13 50.2	19 22.0	18 53.9	12 9.6	19 48.2	10 53.4	25 54.7	8 53.2	16 46.7	17 58.5
20	17 49 35.5	27 52.9	13 47.0	4♑42.2	21 1.9	13 9.3	20 29.3	11 1.3	25 56.8	8 56.8	16 46.4	17 59.8
21	17 53 32.1	28 50.1	13 43.9	19 56.5	23 11.0	14 8.8	21 10.4	11 9.2	25 59.1	9 .4	16 46.2	18 1.1
22	17 57 28.7	29 47.4	13 40.7	4♒54.4	25 21.1	15 7.8	21 51.5	11 16.9	26 1.4	9 3.9	16 45.9	18 2.4
23	18 1 25.2	0♋44.6	13 37.5	19 28.6	27 32.0	16 6.5	22 32.6	11 24.4	26 3.9	9 7.5	16 45.7	18 3.7
24	18 5 21.8	1 41.8	13 34.3	3♓35.1	29 43.3	17 4.7	23 13.5	11 31.8	26 6.4	9 11.1	16 45.6	18 5.1
25	18 9 18.3	2 39.0	13 31.1	17 13.3	1♋54.7	18 2.5	23 54.5	11 39.1	26 9.0	9 14.7	16 45.4	18 6.5
26	18 13 14.9	3 36.2	13 28.0	0♈25.1	4 6.0	18 59.9	24 35.4	11 46.2	26 11.7	9 18.3	16 45.3	18 7.9
27	18 17 11.4	4 33.5	13 24.8	13 14.1	6 17.0	19 56.9	25 16.2	11 53.1	26 14.6	9 21.9	16 45.3	18 9.3
28	18 21 8.0	5 30.7	13 21.6	25 44.3	8 27.3	20 53.4	25 57.1	11 60.0	26 17.5	9 25.5	16 45.2	18 10.7
29	18 25 4.6	6 27.9	13 18.4	8♉ .0	10 36.7	21 49.4	26 37.8	12 6.6	26 20.4	9 29.1	16 45.2	18 12.2
30	18 29 1.1	7 25.1	13 15.3	20 5.3	12 45.0	22 45.0	27 18.6	12 13.1	26 23.5	9 32.8	16 45.2	18 13.6
		LATITUDE										
1	16 34 40.9	0 .0	0 .0	3N27.0	2S50.4	2N29.0	0N18.9	1S10.9	2N23.6	0N19.1	1N40.2	8N33.2
4	16 46 30.6	0 .0	0 .0	4 55.0	2 28.1	2 26.9	0 20.7	1 11.5	2 23.0	0 19.1	1 40.1	8 32.8
7	16 58 20.3	0 .0	0 .0	4 28.4	2 1.6	2 23.7	0 22.5	1 12.1	2 22.3	0 19.1	1 40.0	8 32.4
10	17 10 9.9	0 .0	0 .0	2 18.6	1 31.7	2 19.2	0 24.2	1 12.8	2 21.7	0 19.1	1 39.9	8 31.9
13	17 21 59.6	0 .0	0 .0	0S53.2	0 59.3	2 13.5	0 25.9	1 13.5	2 21.1	0 19.1	1 39.7	8 31.6
16	17 33 49.3	0 .0	0 .0	3 54.9	0 25.8	2 6.5	0 27.7	1 14.2	2 20.4	0 19.1	1 39.6	8 31.2
19	17 45 39.0	0 .0	0 .0	4 59.2	0N 7.4	1 58.2	0 29.3	1 14.9	2 19.8	0 19.1	1 39.4	8 30.8
22	17 57 28.7	0 .0	0 .0	3 5.3	0 38.4	1 48.4	0 31.0	1 15.6	2 19.2	0 19.1	1 39.3	8 30.5
25	18 9 18.3	0 .0	0 .0	0N24.8	1 5.3	1 37.2	0 32.7	1 16.3	2 18.5	0 19.2	1 39.1	8 30.2
28	18 21 8.0	0 .0	0 .0	3 28.2	1 26.8	1 24.5	0 34.3	1 17.1	2 17.9	0 19.2	1 39.0	8 29.9
		RIGHT ASCENSION										
1	16 34 40.9	8♊ 3.3	15♓59.6	25♈23.7	15♉ 3.5	25♋39.2	5♊26.8	7♈55.9	26♍51.9	8♋34.3	16♎16.0	22♌56.3
2	16 38 37.5	9 4.7	15 56.7	7♉ 6.2	16 26.6	26 48.8	6 11.4	8 5.4	26 52.1	8 37.9	16R15.2	22 57.2
3	16 42 34.0	10 6.1	15 53.8	19 18.0	17 52.6	27 57.9	6 56.0	8 14.8	26 52.5	8 41.5	16 14.5	22 58.0
4	16 46 30.6	11 7.7	15 50.8	2♊ 1.6	19 21.6	29 6.6	7 40.7	8 24.0	26 52.9	8 45.1	16 13.7	22 58.9
5	16 50 27.2	12 9.4	15 47.9	15 11.6	20 53.6	0♌14.8	8 25.3	8 33.2	26 53.4	8 48.8	16 13.0	22 59.9
6	16 54 23.7	13 11.1	15 44.9	28 35.2	22 28.7	1 22.5	9 10.0	8 42.3	26 54.0	8 52.5	16 12.3	23 .8
7	16 58 20.3	14 12.9	15 42.0	11♋56.0	24 6.9	2 29.7	9 54.8	8 51.2	26 54.7	8 56.1	16 11.7	23 1.8
8	17 2 16.8	15 14.8	15 39.0	24 58.1	25 48.3	3 36.4	10 39.5	9 .1	26 55.5	8 59.9	16 11.1	23 2.8
9	17 6 13.4	16 16.8	15 36.1	7♌31.7	27 32.8	4 42.5	11 24.2	9 8.8	26 56.4	9 3.6	16 10.5	23 3.8
10	17 10 9.9	17 18.9	15 33.1	19 34.6	29 20.7	5 48.2	12 9.0	9 17.5	26 57.5	9 7.4	16 9.9	23 4.9
11	17 14 6.5	18 21.0	15 30.2	1♍11.6	1♊11.8	6 53.2	12 53.8	9 26.0	26 58.6	9 11.2	16 9.4	23 5.9
12	17 18 3.1	19 23.1	15 27.2	12 33.4	3 6.1	7 57.7	13 38.6	9 34.4	26 59.7	9 14.9	16 8.9	23 7.0
13	17 21 59.6	20 25.3	15 24.3	23 54.4	5 3.8	9 1.6	14 23.3	9 42.7	27 1.0	9 18.7	16 8.4	23 8.1
14	17 25 56.2	21 27.5	15 21.3	5♎32.0	7 4.7	10 4.9	15 8.1	9 50.9	27 2.4	9 22.5	16 7.9	23 9.3
15	17 29 52.7	22 29.8	15 18.4	17 45.8	9 8.9	11 7.6	15 52.9	9 58.9	27 3.8	9 26.3	16 7.5	23 10.4
16	17 33 49.3	23 32.1	15 15.4	0♏56.3	11 16.1	12 9.7	16 37.7	10 6.9	27 5.3	9 30.2	16 7.1	23 11.6
17	17 37 45.9	24 34.4	15 12.5	15 21.0	13 26.3	13 11.2	17 22.4	10 14.7	27 7.0	9 34.0	16 6.7	23 12.8
18	17 41 42.4	25 36.8	15 9.5	1♐ 6.6	15 39.4	14 12.1	18 7.2	10 22.4	27 8.7	9 37.9	16 6.3	23 14.1
19	17 45 39.0	26 39.1	15 6.6	17 59.1	17 55.0	15 12.4	18 51.9	10 29.9	27 10.5	9 41.7	16 6.0	23 15.3
20	17 49 35.5	27 41.5	15 3.6	5♑18.8	20 13.0	16 12.0	19 36.7	10 37.4	27 12.4	9 45.6	16 5.7	23 16.6
21	17 53 32.1	28 43.9	15 .7	22 13.7	22 33.0	17 10.9	20 21.4	10 44.7	27 14.4	9 49.5	16 5.5	23 17.9
22	17 57 28.7	29 46.2	14 57.7	8♒ 3.5	24 54.7	18 9.2	21 6.1	10 51.9	27 16.4	9 53.4	16 5.2	23 19.2
23	18 1 25.2	0♋48.6	14 54.8	22 32.7	27 17.7	19 6.9	21 50.9	10 58.9	27 18.6	9 57.3	16 5.0	23 20.5
24	18 5 21.8	1 51.0	14 51.8	5♓47.5	29 41.7	20 3.9	22 35.5	11 5.9	27 20.8	10 1.2	16 4.9	23 21.9
25	18 9 18.3	2 53.3	14 48.9	18 5.1	2♋ 6.1	21 .2	23 20.2	11 12.6	27 23.2	10 5.1	16 4.7	23 23.2
26	18 13 14.9	3 55.7	14 45.9	29 45.9	4 30.6	21 55.8	24 4.9	11 19.3	27 25.6	10 9.0	16 4.6	23 24.6
27	18 17 11.4	4 58.0	14 43.0	11♈ 9.6	6 54.8	22 50.7	24 49.5	11 25.8	27 28.1	10 12.9	16 4.5	23 26.0
28	18 21 8.0	6 .2	14 40.0	22 33.7	9 18.2	23 45.0	25 34.1	11 32.2	27 30.7	10 16.9	16 4.4	23 27.5
29	18 25 4.6	7 2.5	14 37.1	4♉12.8	11 40.6	24 38.5	26 18.7	11 38.4	27 33.3	10 20.8	16 4.4	23 28.9
30	18 29 1.1	8 4.7	14 34.1	16 17.3	14 1.5	25 31.3	27 3.3	11 44.5	27 36.1	10 24.7	16 4.4	23 30.4
		DECLINATION										
1	16 34 40.9	21N54.9	0S 6.3	14N14.1	14N 6.4	23N52.5	21N51.0	2N 8.4	3N58.0	23N31.9	5S 7.2	23N40.4
4	16 46 30.6	22 18.9	0 6.3	25 57.9	15 39.7	23 15.0	22 12.7	2 19.8	3 56.9	23 31.4	5 6.4	23 39.1
7	16 58 20.3	22 39.3	0 6.4	27 29.0	17 16.7	22 32.7	22 32.5	2 30.7	3 55.4	23 30.7	5 5.7	23 37.8
10	17 10 9.9	22 56.1	0 6.5	18 8.0	18 54.1	21 46.0	22 50.4	2 41.2	3 53.5	23 30.1	5 5.1	23 36.4
13	17 21 59.6	23 9.3	0 6.5	1 40.2	20 28.0	20 55.2	23 6.4	2 51.2	3 51.3	23 29.4	5 4.6	23 35.0
16	17 33 49.3	23 18.9	0 6.6	16S44.1	21 53.9	20 .7	23 20.5	3 .7	3 48.7	23 28.8	5 4.2	23 33.5
19	17 45 39.0	23 24.7	0 6.7	27 59.5	23 6.4	19 2.7	23 32.6	3 9.8	3 45.8	23 28.1	5 3.9	23 32.0
22	17 57 28.7	23 26.9	0 6.7	22 2.5	24 .3	18 1.8	23 42.8	3 18.3	3 42.6	23 27.4	5 3.8	23 30.4
25	18 9 18.3	23 25.3	0 6.8	4 40.1	24 31.4	16 58.2	23 51.1	3 26.3	3 39.0	23 26.6	5 3.7	23 28.8
28	18 21 8.0	23 20.0	0 6.9	13N10.8	24 37.4	15 52.3	23 57.5	3 33.7	3 35.1	23 25.9	5 3.7	23 27.2

JULY 1951

LONGITUDE

DAY	EPHEM. SID. TIME	☉	☊	☽	☿	♀	♂	♃	♄	♅	♆	♇
	h m s	° ′	° ′	° ′	° ′	° ′	° ′	° ′	° ′	° ′	° ′	° ′
1	18 32 57.7	8♋22.4	13♓12.1	2♊ 3.5	14♋52.1	23♌40.1	27♊59.3	12♈19.5	26♍26.8	9♋36.4	16♎45.3	18♌15.2
2	18 36 54.2	9 19.6	13 8.9	13 57.3	16 57.8	24 34.6	28 39.9	12 25.7	26 30.0	9 40.0	16D45.4	18 16.7
3	18 40 50.8	10 16.8	13 5.7	25 49.1	19 1.9	25 28.6	29 20.5	12 31.7	26 33.4	9 43.7	16 45.5	18 18.2
4	18 44 47.4	11 14.0	13 2.6	7♋40.7	21 4.3	26 22.0	0♋ 1.1	12 37.5	26 36.8	9 47.3	16 45.7	18 19.7
5	18 48 43.9	12 11.3	12 59.4	19 33.5	23 5.0	27 14.9	0 41.6	12 43.2	26 40.3	9 50.9	16 45.9	18 21.3
6	18 52 40.5	13 8.5	12 56.2	1♌29.2	25 4.0	28 7.2	1 22.1	12 48.7	26 43.9	9 54.5	16 46.1	18 22.8
7	18 56 37.0	14 5.7	12 53.0	13 29.6	27 1.0	28 58.8	2 2.5	12 54.1	26 47.6	9 58.1	16 46.4	18 24.4
8	19 0 33.6	15 2.9	12 49.9	25 37.0	28 56.1	29 49.8	2 42.8	12 59.3	26 51.4	10 1.8	16 46.6	18 26.0
9	19 4 30.2	16 .1	12 46.7	7♍54.1	0♌49.4	0♍40.1	3 23.2	13 4.3	26 55.3	10 5.4	16 46.9	18 27.6
10	19 8 26.7	16 57.4	12 43.5	20 24.1	2 40.6	1 29.8	4 3.5	13 9.1	26 59.2	10 9.0	16 47.3	18 29.2
11	19 12 23.3	17 54.6	12 40.3	3♎10.9	4 30.0	2 18.7	4 43.7	13 13.8	27 3.3	10 12.6	16 47.7	18 30.9
12	19 16 19.8	18 51.8	12 37.1	16 18.1	6 17.4	3 6.9	5 23.9	13 18.3	27 7.4	10 16.2	16 48.1	18 32.5
13	19 20 16.4	19 49.0	12 34.0	29 49.0	8 2.8	3 54.3	6 4.1	13 22.6	27 11.6	10 19.7	16 48.5	18 34.2
14	19 24 12.9	20 46.2	12 30.8	13♏45.8	9 46.3	4 40.8	6 44.2	13 26.8	27 15.8	10 23.3	16 49.0	18 35.9
15	19 28 9.5	21 43.4	12 27.6	28 8.4	11 27.8	5 26.6	7 24.2	13 30.7	27 20.2	10 26.9	16 49.5	18 37.5
16	19 32 6.1	22 40.6	12 24.4	12♐54.1	13 7.4	6 11.4	8 4.2	13 34.5	27 24.6	10 30.4	16 50.0	18 39.2
17	19 36 2.6	23 37.8	12 21.3	27 57.0	14 45.0	6 55.4	8 44.2	13 38.1	27 29.1	10 34.0	16 50.6	18 41.0
18	19 39 59.2	24 35.0	12 18.1	13♑ 8.5	16 20.7	7 38.4	9 24.2	13 41.5	27 33.7	10 37.5	16 51.2	18 42.7
19	19 43 55.7	25 32.3	12 14.9	28 18.4	17 54.4	8 20.4	10 4.1	13 44.8	27 38.3	10 41.1	16 51.8	18 44.4
20	19 47 52.3	26 29.5	12 11.7	13♒16.4	19 26.1	9 1.4	10 43.9	13 47.8	27 43.0	10 44.6	16 52.5	18 46.1
21	19 51 48.9	27 26.7	12 8.6	27 54.5	20 55.9	9 41.3	11 23.7	13 50.7	27 47.8	10 48.1	16 53.2	18 47.9
22	19 55 45.4	28 24.0	12 5.4	12♓ 7.3	22 23.7	10 20.2	12 3.6	13 53.4	27 52.7	10 51.6	16 54.0	18 49.7
23	19 59 42.0	29 21.3	12 2.2	25 52.4	23 49.5	10 57.9	12 43.3	13 55.9	27 57.7	10 55.1	16 54.7	18 51.5
24	20 3 38.5	0♌18.6	11 59.0	9♈10.4	25 13.2	11 34.5	13 23.0	13 58.2	28 2.7	10 58.6	16 55.5	18 53.2
25	20 7 35.1	1 15.9	11 55.9	22 3.8	26 34.9	12 9.8	14 2.6	14 .3	28 7.7	11 2.1	16 56.3	18 55.0
26	20 11 31.6	2 13.2	11 52.7	4♉36.3	27 54.5	12 43.9	14 42.3	14 2.2	28 12.9	11 5.5	16 57.2	18 56.8
27	20 15 28.2	3 10.5	11 49.5	16 52.2	29 11.9	13 16.7	15 21.9	14 4.0	28 18.1	11 8.9	16 58.1	18 58.6
28	20 19 24.8	4 7.8	11 46.3	28 56.1	0♍27.1	13 48.1	16 1.4	14 5.5	28 23.3	11 12.3	16 59.0	19 .4
29	20 23 21.3	5 5.2	11 43.1	10♊52.1	1 40.1	14 18.1	16 40.9	14 6.8	28 28.7	11 15.7	16 59.9	19 2.2
30	20 27 17.9	6 2.6	11 40.0	22 44.1	2 50.7	14 46.6	17 20.4	14 8.0	28 34.1	11 19.1	17 .9	19 4.1
31	20 31 14.4	6 60.0	11 36.8	4♋35.4	3 58.9	15 13.6	17 59.8	14 8.9	28 39.6	11 22.5	17 1.9	19 5.9

LATITUDE

DAY	EPHEM. SID. TIME	☉	☊	☽	☿	♀	♂	♃	♄	♅	♆	♇
1	18 32 57.7	0 .0	0 .0	4N58.1	1N42.0	1N10.2	0N35.9	1S17.9	2N17.3	0N19.2	1N38.8	8N29.7
4	18 44 47.4	0 .0	0 .0	4 32.6	1 50.4	0 54.3	0 37.5	1 18.7	2 16.8	0 19.2	1 38.7	8 29.4
7	18 56 37.0	0 .0	0 .0	2 22.4	1 52.2	0 36.8	0 39.1	1 19.5	2 16.2	0 19.3	1 38.5	8 29.2
10	19 8 26.7	0 .0	0 .0	0S49.5	1 48.0	0 17.5	0 40.7	1 20.3	2 15.6	0 19.3	1 38.4	8 29.1
13	19 20 16.4	0 .0	0 .0	3 51.2	1 38.3	0S 3.5	0 42.2	1 21.1	2 15.1	0 19.3	1 38.2	8 28.9
16	19 32 6.1	0 .0	0 .0	5 7.2	1 23.6	0 26.3	0 43.8	1 22.0	2 14.6	0 19.4	1 38.1	8 28.8
19	19 43 55.7	0 .0	0 .0	3 27.9	1 4.6	0 51.0	0 45.3	1 22.8	2 14.1	0 19.4	1 37.9	8 28.8
22	19 55 45.4	0 .0	0 .0	0N 8.7	0 41.8	1 17.5	0 46.8	1 23.7	2 13.6	0 19.4	1 37.8	8 28.7
25	20 7 35.1	0 .0	0 .0	3 26.2	0 15.6	1 45.9	0 48.2	1 24.6	2 13.1	0 19.5	1 37.6	8 28.7
28	20 19 24.8	0 .0	0 .0	5 4.4	0S13.4	2 16.1	0 49.7	1 25.4	2 12.7	0 19.5	1 37.5	8 28.7
31	20 31 14.4	0 .0	0 .0	4 43.5	0 44.7	2 48.2	0 51.1	1 26.3	2 12.3	0 19.6	1 37.4	8 28.8

RIGHT ASCENSION

DAY	EPHEM. SID. TIME	☉	☊	☽	☿	♀	♂	♃	♄	♅	♆	♇
1	18 32 57.7	9♋ 6.9	14♓31.2	28♉52.2	16♋20.8	26♌23.5	27♊47.8	11♈50.5	27♍39.0	10♋28.7	16♎ 4.5	23♌31.9
2	18 36 54.2	10 9.0	14 28.2	11♊55.2	18 38.0	27 14.8	28 32.3	11 56.3	27 41.9	10 32.7	16D 4.6	23 33.4
3	18 40 50.8	11 11.0	14 25.3	25 16.1	20 52.9	28 5.4	29 16.8	12 2.0	27 44.9	10 36.6	16 4.7	23 34.9
4	18 44 47.4	12 13.0	14 22.3	8♋39.4	23 5.5	28 55.3	0♋ 1.2	12 7.5	27 48.0	10 40.5	16 4.8	23 36.5
5	18 48 43.9	13 14.9	14 19.3	21 48.3	25 15.5	29 44.3	0 45.6	12 12.8	27 51.1	10 44.5	16 4.9	23 38.0
6	18 52 40.5	14 16.7	14 16.4	4♌30.5	27 22.8	0♍32.6	1 29.9	12 18.0	27 54.4	10 48.4	16 5.1	23 39.6
7	18 56 37.0	15 18.4	14 13.4	16 40.8	29 27.4	1 20.0	2 14.1	12 23.1	27 57.7	10 52.3	16 5.3	23 41.2
8	19 0 33.6	16 20.0	14 10.5	28 21.4	1♌29.1	2 6.7	2 58.4	12 28.0	28 1.1	10 56.2	16 5.6	23 42.8
9	19 4 30.2	17 21.6	14 7.5	9♍40.7	3 28.0	2 52.5	3 42.5	12 32.7	28 4.6	11 .2	16 5.8	23 44.4
10	19 8 26.7	18 23.0	14 4.6	20 51.4	5 24.0	3 37.4	4 26.7	12 37.3	28 8.1	11 4.1	16 6.1	23 46.1
11	19 12 23.3	19 24.3	14 1.6	2♎ 9.2	7 17.2	4 21.5	5 10.7	12 41.7	28 11.7	11 8.0	16 6.5	23 47.7
12	19 16 19.8	20 25.5	13 58.7	13 52.1	9 7.5	5 4.6	5 54.7	12 46.0	28 15.4	11 11.9	16 6.8	23 49.4
13	19 20 16.4	21 26.6	13 55.7	26 19.8	10 54.9	5 46.9	6 38.7	12 50.1	28 19.2	11 15.8	16 7.2	23 51.1
14	19 24 12.9	22 27.6	13 52.8	9♏51.2	12 39.5	6 28.2	7 22.5	12 54.0	28 23.1	11 19.7	16 7.6	23 52.7
15	19 28 9.5	23 28.5	13 49.8	24 39.6	14 21.4	7 8.5	8 6.3	12 57.8	28 27.0	11 23.6	16 8.1	23 54.4
16	19 32 6.1	24 29.2	13 46.8	10♐44.1	16 .5	7 47.8	8 50.1	13 1.4	28 31.0	11 27.4	16 8.6	23 56.2
17	19 36 2.6	25 29.8	13 43.9	27 40.8	17 36.8	8 26.1	9 33.8	13 4.8	28 35.0	11 31.3	16 9.1	23 57.9
18	19 39 59.2	26 30.3	13 40.9	14♑45.4	19 10.5	9 3.4	10 17.4	13 8.1	28 39.2	11 35.1	16 9.6	23 59.6
19	19 43 55.7	27 30.6	13 38.0	1♒10.7	20 41.6	9 39.6	11 .9	13 11.2	28 43.4	11 39.0	16 10.2	24 1.4
20	19 47 52.3	28 30.8	13 35.0	16 27.8	22 10.0	10 14.7	11 44.4	13 14.1	28 47.6	11 42.8	16 10.8	24 3.1
21	19 51 48.9	29 30.9	13 32.0	0♓29.3	23 35.9	10 48.7	12 27.8	13 16.9	28 52.0	11 46.6	16 11.4	24 4.9
22	19 55 45.4	0♌30.9	13 29.1	13 27.6	24 59.3	11 21.5	13 11.1	13 19.5	28 56.4	11 50.4	16 12.1	24 6.8
23	19 59 42.0	1 30.7	13 26.1	25 40.1	26 20.1	11 53.1	13 54.4	13 21.9	29 .9	11 54.2	16 12.8	24 8.6
24	20 3 38.5	2 30.3	13 23.2	7♈26.7	27 38.4	12 23.5	14 37.5	13 24.2	29 5.4	11 58.0	16 13.5	24 10.4
25	20 7 35.1	3 29.8	13 20.2	19 5.3	28 54.1	12 52.7	15 20.6	13 26.2	29 10.0	12 1.7	16 14.2	24 12.2
26	20 11 31.6	4 29.2	13 17.3	0♉51.5	0♍ 7.4	13 20.5	16 3.6	13 28.1	29 14.7	12 5.5	16 15.0	24 14.0
27	20 15 28.2	5 28.4	13 14.3	12 57.3	1 18.2	13 47.0	16 46.5	13 29.8	29 19.4	12 9.2	16 15.8	24 15.8
28	20 19 24.8	6 27.5	13 11.3	25 29.4	2 26.5	14 12.1	17 29.4	13 31.4	29 24.1	12 12.9	16 16.6	24 17.7
29	20 23 21.3	7 26.5	13 8.4	8♊28.2	3 32.3	14 35.8	18 12.1	13 32.7	29 29.0	12 16.6	16 17.5	24 19.5
30	20 27 17.9	8 25.3	13 5.4	21 46.5	4 35.5	14 58.1	18 54.8	13 33.9	29 33.9	12 20.2	16 18.4	24 21.4
31	20 31 14.4	9 23.9	13 2.5	5♋11.2	5 36.1	15 18.8	19 37.3	13 34.9	29 38.9	12 23.9	16 19.3	24 23.2

DECLINATION

DAY	EPHEM. SID. TIME	☉	☊	☽	☿	♀	♂	♃	♄	♅	♆	♇
1	18 32 57.7	23N11.0	0S 6.9	25N26.8	24N18.4	14N44.4	24N 1.9	3N40.6	3N30.8	23N25.1	5S 3.9	23N25.5
4	18 44 47.4	22 58.4	0 7.0	27 45.6	23 36.8	13 35.0	24 4.4	3 46.9	3 26.3	23 24.4	5 4.2	23 23.9
7	18 56 37.0	22 42.1	0 7.0	19 3.0	22 35.8	12 24.4	24 5.1	3 52.6	3 21.5	23 23.6	5 4.6	23 22.2
10	19 8 26.7	22 22.3	0 7.1	3 2.7	21 19.3	11 13.1	24 3.8	3 57.7	3 16.4	23 22.8	5 5.1	23 20.5
13	19 20 16.4	21 59.1	0 7.2	15S .9	19 50.6	10 1.6	24 .7	4 2.2	3 11.0	23 22.0	5 5.7	23 18.8
16	19 32 6.1	21 32.4	0 7.2	27 25.9	18 13.2	8 50.2	23 55.8	4 6.0	3 5.3	23 21.2	5 6.4	23 17.0
19	19 43 55.7	21 2.5	0 7.3	23 54.0	16 29.7	7 39.5	23 49.1	4 9.2	2 59.4	23 20.4	5 7.3	23 15.3
22	19 55 45.4	20 29.3	0 7.4	6 53.0	14 42.7	6 29.9	23 40.6	4 11.7	2 53.2	23 19.6	5 8.2	23 13.5
25	20 7 35.1	19 53.1	0 7.4	11N47.0	12 54.2	5 22.1	23 30.4	4 13.6	2 46.8	23 18.8	5 9.2	23 11.8
28	20 19 24.8	19 13.9	0 7.5	24 52.5	11 6.5	4 16.7	23 18.5	4 14.8	2 40.2	23 18.0	5 10.4	23 10.1
31	20 31 14.4	18 31.8	0 7.6	28 5.4	9 21.5	3 14.2	23 4.9	4 15.4	2 33.3	23 17.1	5 11.6	23 8.4

LONGITUDE

DAY	SID. TIME (h m s)	☉	☊	☽	☿	♀	♂	♃	♄	♅	♆	♇
1	20 35 11.0	7♌57.4	11♓33.6	16♋28.6	5♍ 4.7	15♍39.1	18♋39.2	14♈ 9.7	28♍45.1	11♋25.8	17♎ 2.9	19♌ 7.7
2	20 39 7.5	8 54.8	11 30.4	28 25.9	6 7.8	16 2.9	19 18.6	14 10.2	28 50.7	11 29.1	17 4.0	19 9.5
3	20 43 4.1	9 52.2	11 27.3	10♌29.2	7 8.3	16 25.0	19 57.9	14 10.6	28 56.3	11 32.4	17 5.0	19 11.4
4	20 47 .7	10 49.7	11 24.1	22 40.0	8 6.0	16 45.4	20 37.1	14 10.7	29 2.0	11 35.7	17 6.1	19 13.2
5	20 50 57.2	11 47.1	11 20.9	4♍59.9	9 .7	17 4.0	21 16.4	14 10.7	29 7.8	11 38.9	17 7.3	19 15.1
6	20 54 53.8	12 44.6	11 17.7	17 30.5	9 52.4	17 20.6	21 55.6	14R10.4	29 13.6	11 42.2	17 8.5	19 16.9
7	20 58 50.3	13 42.1	11 14.6	0♎13.5	10 40.9	17 35.4	22 34.7	14 10.0	29 19.5	11 45.4	17 9.7	19 18.8
8	21 2 46.9	14 39.6	11 11.4	13 11.0	11 26.0	17 48.2	23 13.9	14 9.3	29 25.5	11 48.6	17 10.9	19 20.6
9	21 6 43.4	15 37.1	11 8.2	26 25.1	12 7.5	17 58.8	23 52.9	14 8.5	29 31.5	11 51.7	17 12.1	19 22.5
10	21 10 40.0	16 34.7	11 5.0	9♏57.4	12 45.3	18 7.4	24 32.0	14 7.4	29 37.5	11 54.9	17 13.4	19 24.4
11	21 14 36.5	17 32.2	11 1.8	23 49.1	13 19.2	18 13.8	25 11.0	14 6.2	29 43.6	11 58.0	17 14.7	19 26.2
12	21 18 33.1	18 29.8	10 58.7	8♐ .2	13 49.0	18 18.1	25 50.0	14 4.8	29 49.8	12 1.1	17 16.1	19 28.1
13	21 22 29.7	19 27.4	10 55.5	22 28.8	14 14.4	18 20.0	26 28.9	14 3.2	29 56.0	12 4.1	17 17.5	19 30.0
14	21 26 26.2	20 25.0	10 52.3	7♑11.1	14 35.2	18R19.5	27 7.8	14 1.4	0♎ 2.3	12 7.2	17 18.8	19 31.9
15	21 30 22.8	21 22.6	10 49.1	22 1.2	14 51.3	18 16.8	27 46.6	13 59.3	0 8.6	12 10.2	17 20.3	19 33.7
16	21 34 19.3	22 20.2	10 46.0	6♒51.8	15 2.3	18 11.6	28 25.4	13 57.1	0 14.9	12 13.1	17 21.7	19 35.6
17	21 38 15.9	23 17.9	10 42.8	21 35.2	15 8.1	18 4.1	29 4.2	13 54.7	0 21.3	12 16.1	17 23.2	19 37.4
18	21 42 12.4	24 15.5	10 39.6	6♓ 4.3	15 8.6	17 54.2	29 42.9	13 52.1	0 27.7	12 19.0	17 24.6	19 39.3
19	21 46 9.0	25 13.2	10 36.4	20 13.3	15R 3.5	17 41.9	0♌21.6	13 49.3	0 34.2	12 21.9	17 26.1	19 41.2
20	21 50 5.5	26 10.9	10 33.3	3♈59.0	14 52.7	17 27.2	1 .3	13 46.3	0 40.7	12 24.7	17 27.7	19 43.0
21	21 54 2.1	27 8.7	10 30.1	17 20.1	14 36.2	17 10.2	1 38.9	13 43.2	0 47.3	12 27.6	17 29.2	19 44.9
22	21 57 58.7	28 6.4	10 26.9	0♉17.6	14 13.9	16 50.9	2 17.5	13 39.8	0 53.9	12 30.3	17 30.8	19 46.7
23	22 1 55.2	29 4.2	10 23.7	12 53.9	13 45.9	16 29.4	2 56.0	13 36.3	1 .6	12 33.1	17 32.4	19 48.6
24	22 5 51.8	0♍ 2.1	10 20.5	25 12.6	13 12.5	16 5.7	3 34.6	13 32.5	1 7.2	12 35.8	17 34.0	19 50.4
25	22 9 48.3	0 59.9	10 17.4	7♊18.0	12 33.8	15 40.0	4 13.1	13 28.6	1 14.0	12 38.5	17 35.7	19 52.2
26	22 13 44.9	1 57.8	10 14.2	19 14.6	11 50.3	15 12.4	4 51.5	13 24.5	1 20.7	12 41.2	17 37.4	19 54.1
27	22 17 41.4	2 55.7	10 11.0	1♋ 6.8	11 2.7	14 43.0	5 29.9	13 20.3	1 27.5	12 43.8	17 39.1	19 55.9
28	22 21 38.0	3 53.6	10 7.8	12 58.9	10 11.5	14 11.9	6 8.3	13 15.8	1 34.4	12 46.4	17 40.8	19 57.7
29	22 25 34.5	4 51.6	10 4.7	24 54.7	9 17.6	13 39.4	6 46.7	13 11.2	1 41.2	12 48.9	17 42.5	19 59.5
30	22 29 31.1	5 49.6	10 1.5	6♌57.4	8 22.0	13 5.6	7 25.0	13 6.4	1 48.1	12 51.4	17 44.3	20 1.4
31	22 33 27.7	6 47.6	9 58.3	19 9.7	7 25.8	12 30.7	8 3.2	13 1.4	1 55.1	12 53.9	17 46.0	20 3.2

LATITUDE

DAY	SID. TIME (h m s)	☉	☊	☽	☿	♀	♂	♃	♄	♅	♆	♇
1	20 35 11.0	0 .0	0 .0	4N11.1	0S55.6	2S59.3	0N51.6	1S26.6	2N12.1	0N19.6	1N37.3	8N28.8
4	20 47 .7	0 .0	0 .0	1 33.1	1 29.3	3 33.7	0 53.0	1 27.4	2 11.7	0 19.6	1 37.2	8 28.9
7	20 58 50.3	0 .0	0 .0	1S49.0	2 4.0	4 9.5	0 54.4	1 28.3	2 11.3	0 19.7	1 37.0	8 29.0
10	21 10 40.0	0 .0	0 .0	4 32.5	2 38.9	4 46.4	0 55.8	1 29.1	2 11.0	0 19.7	1 36.9	8 29.2
13	21 22 29.7	0 .0	0 .0	5 7.3	3 12.9	5 23.9	0 57.1	1 30.0	2 10.7	0 19.8	1 36.8	8 29.4
16	21 34 19.3	0 .0	0 .0	2 52.0	3 44.3	6 1.2	0 58.5	1 30.8	2 10.4	0 19.8	1 36.7	8 29.6
19	21 46 9.0	0 .0	0 .0	0N57.1	4 11.0	6 37.5	0 59.8	1 31.6	2 10.1	0 19.9	1 36.6	8 29.9
22	21 57 58.7	0 .0	0 .0	4 4.1	4 29.9	7 11.4	1 1.1	1 32.3	2 9.8	0 20.0	1 36.5	8 30.2
25	22 9 48.3	0 .0	0 .0	5 16.2	4 37.4	7 41.7	1 2.4	1 33.1	2 9.6	0 20.0	1 36.3	8 30.5
28	22 21 38.0	0 .0	0 .0	4 25.4	4 29.9	8 6.8	1 3.7	1 33.8	2 9.4	0 20.1	1 36.3	8 30.9
31	22 33 27.7	0 .0	0 .0	1 52.2	4 5.5	8 25.5	1 4.9	1 34.4	2 9.2	0 20.2	1 36.2	8 31.3

RIGHT ASCENSION

DAY	SID. TIME (h m s)	☉	☊	☽	☿	♀	♂	♃	♄	♅	♆	♇
1	20 35 11.0	10♌22.4	12♓59.5	18♋26.4	6♍34.1	15♍38.0	20♋19.8	13♈35.7	29♍43.9	12♋27.5	16♎20.2	24♌25.1
2	20 39 7.5	11 20.7	12 56.5	1♌18.7	7 29.4	15 55.6	21 2.2	13 36.3	29 49.0	12 31.1	16 21.2	24 27.0
3	20 43 4.1	12 18.9	12 53.6	13 40.8	8 22.0	16 11.6	21 44.5	13 36.7	29 54.1	12 34.7	16 22.1	24 28.9
4	20 47 .7	13 17.0	12 50.6	25 32.7	9 11.7	16 25.8	22 26.7	13 37.0	29 59.3	12 38.2	16 23.2	24 30.7
5	20 50 57.2	14 14.9	12 47.6	7♍ .3	9 58.6	16 38.4	23 8.8	13R36.9	0♎ 4.5	12 41.8	16 24.2	24 32.6
6	20 54 53.8	15 12.6	12 44.7	18 14.5	10 42.4	16 49.1	23 50.7	13 36.6	0 9.8	12 45.3	16 25.3	24 34.5
7	20 58 50.3	16 10.2	12 41.7	29 29.0	11 23.1	16 57.9	24 32.6	13 36.6	0 15.2	12 48.7	16 26.4	24 36.4
8	21 2 46.9	17 7.6	12 38.8	11♎ .0	12 .6	17 4.9	25 14.4	13 36.1	0 20.6	12 52.2	16 27.5	24 38.3
9	21 6 43.4	18 4.9	12 35.8	23 5.1	12 34.7	17 10.0	25 56.1	13 35.4	0 26.0	12 55.6	16 28.6	24 40.2
10	21 10 40.0	19 2.1	12 32.8	6♏ 1.9	13 5.3	17 13.0	26 37.7	13 34.6	0 31.5	12 59.0	16 29.8	24 42.2
11	21 14 36.5	19 59.0	12 29.9	20 4.5	13 32.3	17 14.0	27 19.2	13 33.6	0 37.1	13 2.4	16 31.0	24 44.1
12	21 18 33.1	20 55.9	12 26.9	5♐17.7	13 55.5	17R13.0	28 .6	13 32.4	0 42.7	13 5.8	16 32.3	24 46.0
13	21 22 29.7	21 52.6	12 23.9	21 29.0	14 14.7	17 9.9	28 41.8	13 31.0	0 48.4	13 9.1	16 33.5	24 48.0
14	21 26 26.2	22 49.1	12 21.0	7♑ 6.6	14 29.7	17 4.6	29 23.0	13 29.4	0 54.0	13 12.4	16 34.8	24 49.9
15	21 30 22.8	23 45.6	12 18.0	24 28.9	14 40.5	16 57.3	0♌ 4.1	13 27.6	0 59.8	13 15.6	16 36.1	24 51.8
16	21 34 19.3	24 41.8	12 15.0	10♒ 2.1	14 46.8	16 47.7	0 45.0	13 25.7	1 5.6	13 18.9	16 37.4	24 53.7
17	21 38 15.9	25 37.9	12 12.1	24 31.1	14 48.5	16 36.1	1 25.8	13 23.6	1 11.4	13 22.1	16 38.7	24 55.6
18	21 42 12.4	26 33.9	12 9.1	7♓58.7	14R45.4	16 22.3	2 6.6	13 21.3	1 17.2	13 25.2	16 40.1	24 57.5
19	21 46 9.0	27 29.8	12 6.1	20 38.5	14 37.6	16 6.4	2 47.2	13 18.8	1 23.2	13 28.3	16 41.5	24 59.5
20	21 50 5.5	28 25.6	12 3.2	2♈47.8	14 24.8	15 48.4	3 27.7	13 16.1	1 29.1	13 31.4	16 42.9	25 1.4
21	21 54 2.1	29 21.2	12 .2	14 44.0	14 7.2	15 28.4	4 8.1	13 13.3	1 35.1	13 34.5	16 44.3	25 3.3
22	21 57 58.7	0♍16.7	11 57.2	26 42.6	13 44.6	15 6.5	4 48.4	13 10.3	1 41.1	13 37.5	16 45.7	25 5.2
23	22 1 55.2	1 12.1	11 54.3	8♉55.8	13 17.3	14 42.7	5 28.6	13 7.1	1 47.2	13 40.5	16 47.2	25 7.1
24	22 5 51.8	2 7.4	11 51.3	21 4.2	12 45.5	14 17.2	6 8.7	13 3.8	1 53.3	13 43.4	16 48.7	25 9.0
25	22 9 48.3	3 2.6	11 48.3	4♊31.0	12 9.5	13 50.0	6 48.6	13 .3	1 59.4	13 46.4	16 50.3	25 10.9
26	22 13 44.9	3 57.7	11 45.4	17 49.5	11 29.6	13 21.2	7 28.5	12 56.6	2 5.6	13 49.2	16 51.8	25 12.8
27	22 17 41.4	4 52.7	11 42.4	1♋15.7	10 46.5	12 51.1	8 8.3	12 52.7	2 11.8	13 52.1	16 53.4	25 14.7
28	22 21 38.0	5 47.6	11 39.4	14 35.3	10 .7	12 19.7	8 47.9	12 48.7	2 18.0	13 54.9	16 55.0	25 16.6
29	22 25 34.5	6 42.4	11 36.5	27 35.4	9 13.1	11 47.3	9 27.4	12 44.5	2 24.3	13 57.6	16 56.5	25 18.5
30	22 29 31.1	7 37.1	11 33.5	10♌ 8.0	8 24.6	11 14.0	10 6.8	12 40.2	2 30.6	14 .3	16 58.2	25 20.4
31	22 33 27.7	8 31.7	11 30.5	22 11.8	7 36.1	10 40.0	10 40.0	12 35.7	2 37.0	14 3.0	16 59.8	25 22.2

DECLINATION

DAY	SID. TIME (h m s)	☉	☊	☽	☿	♀	♂	♃	♄	♅	♆	♇
1	20 35 11.0	18N17.1	0S 7.6	26N35.0	8N47.4	2N54.2	23N .0	4N15.4	2N31.0	23N16.9	5S12.0	23N 7.8
4	20 47 .7	17 31.4	0 7.6	15 26.0	9 7.9	1 56.9	22 44.3	4 15.0	2 23.9	23 16.1	5 13.4	23 6.1
7	20 58 50.3	16 43.1	0 7.7	1S45.4	5 39.1	1 4.5	22 27.0	4 13.9	2 16.6	23 15.3	5 14.9	23 4.4
10	21 10 40.0	15 52.4	0 7.8	19 6.6	9 19.6	0 18.1	22 8.2	4 12.2	2 9.1	23 14.5	5 16.4	23 2.8
13	21 22 29.7	14 59.4	0 7.8	28 20.9	14 2.0	0S21.3	21 48.0	4 9.7	2 1.5	23 13.7	5 18.1	23 1.1
16	21 34 19.3	14 4.3	0 7.9	21 20.2	16 2.6	0 52.4	21 26.3	4 6.6	1 53.7	23 12.9	5 19.8	22 59.5
19	21 46 9.0	13 7.2	0 8.0	2 60.0	17 2.1	1 14.3	21 3.3	4 2.9	1 45.7	23 12.2	5 21.6	22 58.0
22	21 57 58.7	12 8.2	0 8.0	15N23.1	2 3.3	1 25.9	20 38.9	3 58.5	1 37.6	23 11.5	5 23.5	22 56.4
25	22 9 48.3	11 7.4	0 8.1	23 43.9	2 34.4	1 26.7	20 13.3	3 53.5	1 29.4	23 10.8	5 25.4	22 54.9
28	22 21 38.0	10 5.1	0 8.1	27 13.0	3 34.9	1 16.4	19 46.4	3 47.9	1 21.1	23 10.1	5 27.5	22 53.5
31	22 33 27.7	9 1.3	0 8.2	16 51.5	4 59.1	0 55.4	19 18.3	3 41.7	1 12.7	23 9.4	5 29.6	22 52.1

SEPTEMBER 1951

LONGITUDE

DAY	EPHEM. SID. TIME h m s	☉ ° ′	☊ ° ′	☽ ° ′	☿ ° ′	♀ ° ′	♂ ° ′	♃ ° ′	♄ ° ′	♅ ° ′	♆ ° ′	♇ ° ′
1	22 37 24.2	7♍45.7	9♓55.1	1♍33.5	6♍30.2	11♍54.9	8♌41.5	12♈56.3	2♎ 2.1	12♋56.3	17♎47.8	20♌ 5.0
2	22 41 20.8	8 43.8	9 51.9	14 10.1	5R36.4	11R18.5	9 19.7	12R51.1	2 9.1	12 58.8	17 49.7	20 6.8
3	22 45 17.3	9 41.9	9 48.8	27 .3	4 45.5	10 41.6	9 57.9	12 45.6	2 16.1	13 1.1	17 51.5	20 8.6
4	22 49 13.9	10 40.1	9 45.6	10♎ 4.3	3 58.7	10 4.5	10 36.0	12 40.0	2 23.2	13 3.4	17 53.4	20 10.3
5	22 53 10.4	11 38.2	9 42.4	23 22.1	3 17.2	9 27.5	11 14.1	12 34.2	2 30.3	13 5.7	17 55.3	20 12.1
6	22 57 7.0	12 36.4	9 39.2	6♏53.3	2 42.0	8 50.7	11 52.2	12 28.3	2 37.4	13 7.9	17 57.1	20 13.9
7	23 1 3.5	13 34.6	9 36.1	20 37.3	2 13.9	8 14.4	12 30.2	12 22.3	2 44.5	13 10.1	17 59.1	20 15.6
8	23 5 .1	14 32.9	9 32.9	4♐33.2	1 53.6	7 38.8	13 8.2	12 16.1	2 51.7	13 12.3	18 1.0	20 17.3
9	23 8 56.6	15 31.1	9 29.7	18 39.6	1 41.7	7 4.3	13 46.1	12 9.8	2 58.8	13 14.4	18 2.9	20 19.0
10	23 12 53.2	16 29.4	9 26.5	2♑54.9	1 38.7	6 30.8	14 24.0	12 3.3	3 6.0	13 16.5	18 4.9	20 20.8
11	23 16 49.7	17 27.7	9 23.3	17 16.4	1D44.6	5 58.8	15 1.9	11 56.7	3 13.3	13 18.5	18 6.8	20 22.5
12	23 20 46.3	18 26.1	9 20.2	1♒41.0	1 59.7	5 28.3	15 39.7	11 50.0	3 20.5	13 20.5	18 8.8	20 24.1
13	23 24 42.9	19 24.4	9 17.0	16 4.5	2 23.8	4 59.5	16 17.5	11 43.2	3 27.8	13 22.4	18 10.8	20 25.8
14	23 28 39.4	20 22.8	9 13.8	0♓22.5	2 56.8	4 32.6	16 55.2	11 36.3	3 35.0	13 24.3	18 12.8	20 27.5
15	23 32 36.0	21 21.2	9 10.6	14 30.4	3 38.4	4 7.7	17 33.0	11 29.2	3 42.3	13 26.1	18 14.9	20 29.1
16	23 36 32.5	22 19.7	9 7.5	28 24.0	4 28.3	3 45.0	18 10.7	11 22.1	3 49.6	13 27.9	18 16.9	20 30.8
17	23 40 29.1	23 18.2	9 4.3	12♈ .0	5 25.9	3 24.4	18 48.3	11 14.8	3 57.0	13 29.7	18 19.0	20 32.4
18	23 44 25.6	24 16.7	9 1.1	25 16.5	6 30.8	3 6.2	19 25.9	11 7.5	4 4.3	13 31.4	18 21.0	20 34.0
19	23 48 22.2	25 15.3	8 57.9	8♉12.8	7 42.4	2 50.4	20 3.5	11 .1	4 11.6	13 33.1	18 23.1	20 35.6
20	23 52 18.7	26 13.8	8 54.7	20 49.9	9 .0	2 36.9	20 41.0	10 52.5	4 19.0	13 34.7	18 25.2	20 37.2
21	23 56 15.3	27 12.5	8 51.6	3♊10.2	10 23.1	2 25.9	21 18.6	10 45.0	4 26.4	13 36.2	18 27.3	20 38.7
22	0 0 11.8	28 11.1	8 48.4	15 16.9	11 51.0	2 17.3	21 56.0	10 37.3	4 33.8	13 37.8	18 29.4	20 40.3
23	0 4 8.4	29 9.9	8 45.2	27 14.2	13 23.1	2 11.2	22 33.5	10 29.6	4 41.2	13 39.3	18 31.6	20 41.9
24	0 8 4.9	0♎ 8.6	8 42.0	9♋ 6.6	14 58.8	2 7.5	23 10.9	10 21.8	4 48.6	13 40.7	18 33.8	20 43.4
25	0 12 1.5	1 7.4	8 38.9	20 58.9	16 37.6	2 6.2	23 48.3	10 14.0	4 56.0	13 42.1	18 35.9	20 44.9
26	0 15 58.0	2 6.2	8 35.7	2♌55.9	18 18.8	2D 7.3	24 25.6	10 6.1	5 3.4	13 43.4	18 38.1	20 46.4
27	0 19 54.6	3 5.0	8 32.5	15 2.0	20 2.2	2 10.7	25 2.9	9 58.1	5 10.8	13 44.7	18 40.2	20 47.8
28	0 23 51.2	4 3.9	8 29.3	27 21.0	21 47.1	2 16.5	25 40.2	9 50.1	5 18.2	13 45.9	18 42.4	20 49.3
29	0 27 47.7	5 2.8	8 26.1	9♍56.0	23 33.2	2 24.4	26 17.4	9 42.1	5 25.6	13 47.1	18 44.6	20 50.7
30	0 31 44.3	6 1.8	8 23.0	22 48.8	25 20.2	2 34.6	26 54.6	9 34.1	5 33.0	13 48.2	18 46.8	20 52.1

LATITUDE

DAY	SID. TIME	☉	☊	☽	☿	♀	♂	♃	♄	♅	♆	♇
1	22 37 24.2	0 .0	0 .0	0N45.8	3S53.6	8S30.0	1N 5.4	1S34.7	2N 9.1	0N20.2	1N36.1	8N31.4
4	22 49 13.9	0 .0	0 .0	2S39.9	3 8.5	8 38.3	1 6.6	1 35.3	2 9.0	0 20.3	1 36.0	8 31.9
7	23 1 3.5	0 .0	0 .0	4 59.3	2 13.7	8 38.3	1 7.8	1 35.8	2 8.8	0 20.3	1 36.0	8 32.3
10	23 12 53.2	0 .0	0 .0	4 51.6	1 16.0	8 30.1	1 9.1	1 36.4	2 8.7	0 20.4	1 35.9	8 32.8
13	23 24 42.9	0 .0	0 .0	2 8.0	0 21.4	8 14.4	1 10.3	1 36.8	2 8.7	0 20.5	1 35.8	8 33.4
16	23 36 32.5	0 .0	0 .0	1N40.7	0N25.8	7 52.3	1 11.4	1 37.2	2 8.6	0 20.5	1 35.8	8 34.0
19	23 48 22.2	0 .0	0 .0	4 29.0	1 2.9	7 25.3	1 12.6	1 37.6	2 8.6	0 20.6	1 35.7	8 34.6
22	0 0 11.8	0 .0	0 .0	5 13.8	1 29.3	6 54.6	1 13.8	1 37.8	2 8.6	0 20.7	1 35.7	8 35.2
25	0 12 1.5	0 .0	0 .0	3 57.2	1 45.3	6 21.6	1 14.9	1 38.0	2 8.6	0 20.8	1 35.6	8 35.9
28	0 23 51.2	0 .0	0 .0	1 7.9	1 52.3	5 47.3	1 16.1	1 38.2	2 8.7	0 20.9	1 35.6	8 36.6

RIGHT ASCENSION

DAY	SID. TIME	☉	☊	☽	☿	♀	♂	♃	♄	♅	♆	♇
1	22 37 24.2	9♍26.3	11♓27.5	3♍51.2	6♍48.7	10♍ 5.5	11♌25.4	12♈31.0	2♎43.3	14♋ 5.7	17♎ 1.4	25♌24.1
2	22 41 20.8	10 20.8	11 24.6	15 15.8	6R 3.4	9R30.8	12 4.5	12R26.3	2 49.8	14 8.3	17 3.2	25 26.0
3	22 45 17.3	11 15.2	11 21.6	26 37.9	5 21.3	8 55.9	12 43.5	12 21.3	2 56.2	14 10.9	17 4.9	25 27.9
4	22 49 13.9	12 9.5	11 18.6	8♎12.2	4 43.5	8 21.2	13 22.3	12 16.2	3 2.6	14 13.4	17 6.6	25 29.7
5	22 53 10.4	13 3.8	11 15.7	20 14.7	4 10.8	7 46.9	14 1.1	12 11.0	3 9.1	14 15.8	17 8.3	25 31.6
6	22 57 7.0	13 58.0	11 12.7	3♏ 1.3	3 44.3	7 13.1	14 39.7	12 5.6	3 15.6	14 18.3	17 10.0	25 33.4
7	23 1 3.5	14 52.1	11 9.7	16 45.0	3 24.6	6 40.2	15 18.2	12 .1	3 22.2	14 20.6	17 11.8	25 35.2
8	23 5 .1	15 46.2	11 6.7	1♐30.8	3 12.3	6 8.2	15 56.6	11 54.5	3 28.7	14 23.0	17 13.6	25 37.0
9	23 8 56.6	16 40.2	11 3.8	17 10.1	3 8.0	5 37.4	16 34.9	11 48.7	3 35.3	14 25.2	17 15.4	25 38.8
10	23 12 53.2	17 34.2	11 .8	3♑17.9	3D12.0	5 8.0	17 13.1	11 42.8	3 41.9	14 27.5	17 17.2	25 40.6
11	23 16 49.7	18 28.1	10 57.8	19 19.4	3 24.4	4 40.0	17 51.2	11 36.8	3 48.5	14 29.7	17 19.0	25 42.4
12	23 20 46.3	19 22.0	10 54.9	4♒43.2	3 45.3	4 13.8	18 29.2	11 30.7	3 55.1	14 31.8	17 20.8	25 44.2
13	23 24 42.9	20 15.9	10 51.9	19 12.3	4 14.6	3 49.4	19 7.0	11 24.4	4 1.8	14 33.9	17 22.7	25 46.0
14	23 28 39.4	21 9.7	10 48.9	2♓45.9	4 52.0	3 27.0	19 44.8	11 18.1	4 8.4	14 36.0	17 24.6	25 47.7
15	23 32 36.0	22 3.5	10 45.9	15 34.0	5 37.3	3 6.6	20 22.4	11 11.7	4 15.1	14 38.0	17 26.4	25 49.4
16	23 36 32.5	22 57.3	10 43.0	27 51.9	6 29.9	2 48.4	20 59.9	11 5.1	4 21.8	14 39.9	17 28.3	25 51.2
17	23 40 29.1	23 51.1	10 40.0	9♈55.8	7 29.5	2 32.5	21 37.4	10 58.5	4 28.5	14 41.8	17 30.2	25 52.9
18	23 44 25.6	24 44.9	10 37.0	22 .8	8 35.3	2 18.8	22 14.7	10 51.8	4 35.2	14 43.7	17 32.2	25 54.6
19	23 48 22.2	25 38.7	10 34.0	4♉19.0	9 47.0	2 7.4	22 51.9	10 45.0	4 42.0	14 45.5	17 34.1	25 56.3
20	23 52 18.7	26 32.5	10 31.1	16 58.4	11 3.7	1 58.4	23 29.0	10 38.1	4 48.7	14 47.2	17 36.0	25 57.9
21	23 56 15.3	27 26.3	10 28.1	0♊ 1.0	12 25.0	1 51.8	24 6.0	10 31.2	4 55.5	14 48.9	17 38.0	25 59.6
22	0 0 11.8	28 20.1	10 25.1	13 22.5	13 50.1	1 47.5	24 42.9	10 24.1	5 2.3	14 50.5	17 39.9	26 1.2
23	0 4 8.4	29 14.0	10 22.1	26 52.2	15 18.5	1 45.7	25 19.8	10 17.1	5 9.1	14 52.2	17 42.0	26 2.9
24	0 8 4.9	0♎ 7.9	10 19.1	10♋16.1	16 49.7	1D46.1	25 56.5	10 9.9	5 15.9	14 53.7	17 43.9	26 4.5
25	0 12 1.5	1 1.8	10 16.2	23 21.5	18 23.0	1 48.9	26 33.1	10 2.7	5 22.7	14 55.2	17 45.9	26 6.1
26	0 15 58.0	1 55.8	10 13.2	6♌ .3	19 58.0	1 53.9	27 9.6	9 55.5	5 29.5	14 56.7	17 47.9	26 7.7
27	0 19 54.6	2 49.8	10 10.2	18 10.7	21 34.4	2 1.2	27 46.0	9 48.2	5 36.3	14 58.0	17 49.9	26 9.3
28	0 23 51.2	3 43.8	10 7.2	29 57.0	23 11.7	2 10.6	28 22.4	9 40.9	5 43.1	14 59.4	17 52.0	26 10.8
29	0 27 47.7	4 37.9	10 4.3	11♍28.0	24 49.7	2 22.2	28 58.6	9 33.5	5 49.9	15 .6	17 54.0	26 12.3
30	0 31 44.3	5 32.1	10 1.3	22 56.0	26 28.0	2 35.8	29 34.7	9 26.1	5 56.7	15 1.9	17 56.0	26 13.9

DECLINATION

DAY	SID. TIME	☉	☊	☽	☿	♀	♂	♃	♄	♅	♆	♇
1	22 37 24.2	8N39.7	0S 8.2	11N38.3	5N30.5	0S46.2	19N 8.7	3N39.5	1N 9.9	23N 9.2	5S30.3	22N51.6
4	22 49 13.9	7 34.2	0 8.3	6S26.4	7 7.5	0 12.9	18 39.2	3 32.6	1 1.4	23 8.6	5 32.5	22 50.3
7	23 1 3.5	6 27.6	0 8.3	22 43.0	8 36.1	0N27.7	18 8.6	3 25.2	0 52.8	23 8.0	5 34.7	22 49.0
10	23 12 53.2	5 20.0	0 8.4	28 16.5	9 42.6	1 12.9	17 37.1	3 17.3	0 44.1	23 7.4	5 37.0	22 47.8
13	23 24 42.9	4 11.7	0 8.5	18 3.6	10 17.6	2 .4	17 4.6	3 9.0	0 35.4	23 6.9	5 39.3	22 46.7
16	23 36 32.5	3 2.7	0 8.5	0N54.2	10 16.5	2 47.5	16 31.2	3 .4	0 26.7	23 6.4	5 41.7	22 45.6
19	23 48 22.2	1 53.2	0 8.6	18 29.2	9 39.3	3 32.0	15 57.0	2 51.5	0 18.0	23 6.0	5 44.1	22 44.6
22	0 0 11.8	0 43.3	0 8.7	27 49.9	8 29.8	4 12.3	15 21.9	2 42.4	0 9.2	23 5.6	5 46.5	22 43.6
25	0 12 1.5	0S26.8	0 8.7	25 42.9	6 53.9	4 47.0	14 46.2	2 33.0	0 .4	23 5.2	5 49.0	22 42.7
28	0 23 51.2	1 37.0	0 8.8	13 27.5	4 58.7	5 15.5	14 9.7	2 23.6	0S 8.3	23 4.9	5 51.5	22 41.9

OCTOBER 1951

LONGITUDE

DAY	EPHEM. SID. TIME	☉	☊	☾	☿	♀	♂	♃	♄	♅	♆	♇
	h m s	° ′	° ′	° ′	° ′	° ′	° ′	° ′	° ′	° ′	° ′	° ′
1	0 35 40.8	7♎ .8	8♓19.8	6♎ .1	27♍ 7.9	2♍46.9	27♌31.7	9♈26.0	5♎40.5	13♋49.3	18♎49.0	20♌53.5
2	0 39 37.4	7 59.8	8 16.6	19 29.1	28 55.8	3 1.3	28 8.9	9R18.0	5 47.9	13 50.3	18 51.2	20 54.9
3	0 43 33.9	8 58.9	8 13.4	3♏13.9	0♎43.9	3 17.7	28 45.9	9 9.9	5 55.3	13 51.2	18 53.4	20 56.2
4	0 47 30.5	9 57.9	8 10.3	17 11.2	2 31.9	3 36.0	29 22.9	9 1.8	6 2.7	13 52.2	18 55.6	20 57.6
5	0 51 27.0	10 57.1	8 7.1	1♐17.5	4 19.8	3 56.3	29 59.9	8 53.7	6 10.1	13 53.0	18 57.8	20 58.9
6	0 55 23.6	11 56.2	8 3.9	15 28.9	6 7.3	4 18.4	0♍36.9	8 45.7	6 17.5	13 53.8	19 .0	21 .2
7	0 59 20.1	12 55.4	8 .7	29 42.0	7 54.4	4 42.2	1 13.8	8 37.7	6 24.9	13 54.6	19 2.2	21 1.4
8	1 3 16.7	13 54.6	7 57.5	13♑54.0	9 40.9	5 7.8	1 50.6	8 29.6	6 32.3	13 55.3	19 4.5	21 2.7
9	1 7 13.2	14 53.8	7 54.4	28 2.8	11 27.0	5 35.1	2 27.5	8 21.7	6 39.6	13 55.9	19 6.7	21 3.9
10	1 11 9.8	15 53.1	7 51.2	12♒ 6.8	13 12.4	6 3.9	3 4.2	8 13.7	6 47.0	13 56.5	19 8.9	21 5.1
11	1 15 6.4	16 52.4	7 48.0	26 4.6	14 57.1	6 34.3	3 41.0	8 5.8	6 54.3	13 57.1	19 11.1	21 6.3
12	1 19 2.9	17 51.7	7 44.8	9♓54.9	16 41.2	7 6.2	4 17.7	7 58.0	7 1.7	13 57.6	19 13.4	21 7.5
13	1 22 59.5	18 51.1	7 41.7	23 36.0	18 24.6	7 39.6	4 54.3	7 50.2	7 9.0	13 58.0	19 15.6	21 8.6
14	1 26 56.0	19 50.5	7 38.5	7♈ 6.2	20 7.4	8 14.4	5 31.0	7 42.5	7 16.3	13 58.5	19 17.9	21 9.8
15	1 30 52.6	20 49.9	7 35.3	20 23.5	21 49.5	8 50.5	6 7.6	7 34.9	7 23.6	13 58.8	19 20.1	21 10.9
16	1 34 49.1	21 49.4	7 32.1	3♉26.5	23 30.8	9 27.9	6 44.1	7 27.3	7 30.9	13 59.1	19 22.4	21 11.9
17	1 38 45.7	22 48.9	7 29.0	16 14.2	25 11.5	10 6.6	7 20.6	7 19.8	7 38.1	13 59.3	19 24.6	21 13.0
18	1 42 42.2	23 48.4	7 25.8	28 46.4	26 51.5	10 46.4	7 57.0	7 12.4	7 45.4	13 59.5	19 26.8	21 14.0
19	1 46 38.8	24 48.0	7 22.6	11♊ 4.2	28 30.8	11 27.5	8 33.4	7 5.0	7 52.6	13 59.6	19 29.1	21 15.0
20	1 50 35.3	25 47.6	7 19.4	23 9.7	0♏ 9.5	12 9.6	9 9.8	6 57.8	7 59.8	13 59.6	19 31.3	21 16.0
21	1 54 31.9	26 47.2	7 16.2	5♋ 6.1	1 47.5	12 52.9	9 46.1	6 50.7	8 6.9	13 59.7	19 33.5	21 16.9
22	1 58 28.5	27 46.9	7 13.1	16 57.3	3 25.0	13 37.2	10 22.4	6 43.6	8 14.1	13R59.6	19 35.7	21 17.8
23	2 2 25.0	28 46.6	7 9.9	28 48.1	5 1.8	14 22.5	10 58.7	6 36.7	8 21.2	13 59.5	19 37.9	21 18.7
24	2 6 21.6	29 46.3	7 6.7	10♌43.7	6 38.1	15 8.8	11 34.9	6 29.9	8 28.3	13 59.4	19 40.2	21 19.6
25	2 10 18.1	0♏46.1	7 3.5	22 49.2	8 13.8	15 56.0	12 11.0	6 23.2	8 35.4	13 59.2	19 42.4	21 20.5
26	2 14 14.7	1 46.0	7 .4	5♍ 9.7	9 49.0	16 44.1	12 47.1	6 16.7	8 42.4	13 58.9	19 44.6	21 21.3
27	2 18 11.2	2 45.8	6 57.2	17 49.5	11 23.6	17 33.0	13 23.2	6 10.3	8 49.4	13 58.6	19 46.8	21 22.1
28	2 22 7.8	3 45.7	6 54.0	0♎52.0	12 57.7	18 22.8	13 59.2	6 4.0	8 56.4	13 58.2	19 48.9	21 22.8
29	2 26 4.3	4 45.6	6 50.8	14 18.7	14 31.4	19 13.4	14 35.2	5 57.8	9 3.3	13 57.8	19 51.1	21 23.6
30	2 30 .9	5 45.6	6 47.6	28 8.9	16 4.5	20 4.7	15 11.1	5 51.8	9 10.2	13 57.3	19 53.3	21 24.3
31	2 33 57.5	6 45.6	6 44.5	12♏19.7	17 37.2	20 56.8	15 47.0	5 45.9	9 17.1	13 56.8	19 55.5	21 25.0

LATITUDE

DAY	EPHEM. SID. TIME	☉	☊	☾	☿	♀	♂	♃	♄	♅	♆	♇
1	0 35 40.8	0 .0	0 .0	2S18.8	1N51.6	5S12.6	1N17.2	1S38.3	2N 8.8	0N20.9	1N35.6	8N37.3
4	0 47 30.5	0 .0	0 .0	4 48.6	1 45.0	4 38.0	1 18.3	1 38.3	2 8.9	0 21.0	1 35.6	8 38.1
7	0 59 20.1	0 .0	0 .0	4 52.5	1 33.9	4 4.0	1 19.4	1 38.2	2 9.0	0 21.1	1 35.6	8 38.8
10	1 11 9.8	0 .0	0 .0	2 23.1	1 19.5	3 31.0	1 20.5	1 38.0	2 9.2	0 21.2	1 35.6	8 39.6
13	1 22 59.5	0 .0	0 .0	1N16.2	1 2.6	2 59.2	1 21.6	1 37.8	2 9.4	0 21.3	1 35.6	8 40.5
16	1 34 49.1	0 .0	0 .0	4 10.6	0 44.0	2 28.7	1 22.7	1 37.6	2 9.6	0 21.4	1 35.6	8 41.3
19	1 46 38.8	0 .0	0 .0	5 7.5	0 24.4	1 59.6	1 23.8	1 37.2	2 9.8	0 21.5	1 35.6	8 42.2
22	1 58 28.5	0 .0	0 .0	4 1.7	0 4.2	1 32.1	1 24.8	1 36.8	2 10.1	0 21.5	1 35.7	8 43.1
25	2 10 18.1	0 .0	0 .0	1 23.7	0S16.2	1 6.2	1 25.9	1 36.4	2 10.4	0 21.6	1 35.7	8 44.0
28	2 22 7.8	0 .0	0 .0	1S56.6	0 36.4	0 41.8	1 26.9	1 35.8	2 10.7	0 21.7	1 35.7	8 44.9
31	2 33 57.5	0 .0	0 .0	4 33.7	0 56.1	0 18.9	1 27.9	1 35.3	2 11.1	0 21.8	1 35.8	8 45.8

RIGHT ASCENSION

DAY	EPHEM. SID. TIME	☉	☊	☾	☿	♀	♂	♃	♄	♅	♆	♇
1	0 35 40.8	6♎26.3	9♓58.3	4♎35.4	28♍ 6.5	2♍51.5	0♍10.7	9♈18.7	6♎ 3.5	15♋ 3.0	17♎58.0	26♌15.4
2	0 39 37.4	7 20.6	9 55.3	16 41.9	29 44.9	3 9.1	0 46.6	9R11.3	6 10.3	15 4.1	18 .1	26 16.8
3	0 43 33.9	8 15.0	9 52.3	29 31.1	1♎23.2	3 28.5	1 22.4	9 3.9	6 17.2	15 5.2	18 2.1	26 18.3
4	0 47 30.5	9 9.4	9 49.4	13♏15.5	3 1.2	3 49.8	1 58.1	8 56.4	6 24.0	15 6.2	18 4.2	26 19.7
5	0 51 27.0	10 4.0	9 46.4	28 .2	4 38.8	4 12.9	2 33.8	8 49.0	6 30.8	15 7.1	18 6.3	26 21.1
6	0 55 23.6	10 58.6	9 43.4	13♐36.4	6 16.0	4 37.7	3 9.3	8 41.6	6 37.6	15 8.0	18 8.3	26 22.5
7	0 59 20.1	11 53.3	9 40.4	29 39.6	7 52.7	5 4.0	3 44.7	8 34.2	6 44.4	15 8.8	18 10.4	26 23.9
8	1 3 16.7	12 48.1	9 37.4	15♑35.6	9 29.0	5 32.0	4 20.1	8 26.8	6 51.2	15 9.6	18 12.5	26 25.3
9	1 7 13.2	13 42.9	9 34.4	0♒53.7	11 4.7	6 1.5	4 55.3	8 19.5	6 58.0	15 10.3	18 14.5	26 26.6
10	1 11 9.8	14 37.9	9 31.5	15 17.0	12 40.0	6 32.5	5 30.4	8 12.1	7 4.7	15 10.9	18 16.6	26 27.9
11	1 15 6.4	15 33.0	9 28.5	28 44.6	14 14.7	7 4.8	6 5.5	8 4.9	7 11.5	15 11.5	18 18.7	26 29.2
12	1 19 2.9	16 28.2	9 25.5	11♓26.3	15 49.0	7 38.5	6 40.5	7 57.6	7 18.3	15 12.0	18 20.8	26 30.5
13	1 22 59.5	17 23.5	9 22.5	23 37.3	17 22.9	8 13.5	7 15.4	7 50.4	7 25.0	15 12.5	18 22.9	26 31.7
14	1 26 56.0	18 19.0	9 19.5	5♈34.0	18 56.3	8 49.8	7 50.2	7 43.4	7 31.8	15 13.0	18 25.0	26 33.0
15	1 30 52.6	19 14.6	9 16.6	17 31.9	20 29.4	9 27.3	8 24.9	7 36.3	7 38.5	15 13.4	18 27.1	26 34.2
16	1 34 49.1	20 10.3	9 13.6	29 43.8	22 2.1	10 5.9	8 59.5	7 29.3	7 45.2	15 13.7	18 29.1	26 35.4
17	1 38 45.7	21 6.2	9 10.6	12♉18.6	23 34.4	10 45.6	9 34.1	7 22.3	7 51.9	15 13.9	18 31.2	26 36.6
18	1 42 42.2	22 2.2	9 7.6	25 19.4	25 6.5	11 26.3	10 8.5	7 15.5	7 58.6	15 14.1	18 33.3	26 37.7
19	1 46 38.8	22 58.3	9 4.6	8♊42.1	26 38.3	12 8.1	10 42.9	7 8.7	8 5.2	15 14.2	18 35.4	26 38.8
20	1 50 35.3	23 54.6	9 1.6	22 15.8	28 9.9	12 50.8	11 17.2	7 2.0	8 11.9	15 14.3	18 37.5	26 39.9
21	1 54 31.9	24 51.1	8 58.6	5♋45.5	29 41.4	13 34.4	11 51.4	6 55.4	8 18.5	15 14.3	18 39.5	26 41.0
22	1 58 28.5	25 47.7	8 55.7	18 56.8	1♏12.7	14 19.0	12 25.5	6 48.9	8 25.1	15 14.3	18 41.6	26 42.0
23	2 2 25.0	26 44.5	8 52.7	1♌40.1	2 43.9	15 4.4	12 59.6	6 42.5	8 31.7	15R14.2	18 43.7	26 43.0
24	2 6 21.6	27 41.5	8 49.7	13 52.6	4 15.0	15 50.5	13 33.6	6 36.2	8 38.2	15 14.0	18 45.7	26 44.0
25	2 10 18.1	28 38.7	8 46.7	25 38.4	5 46.0	16 37.5	14 7.5	6 30.0	8 44.8	15 13.8	18 47.8	26 45.0
26	2 14 14.7	29 36.0	8 43.7	7♍ 6.3	7 17.0	17 25.2	14 41.3	6 23.9	8 51.3	15 13.5	18 49.9	26 45.9
27	2 18 11.2	0♏33.5	8 40.7	18 28.9	8 48.1	18 13.5	15 15.0	6 17.9	8 57.8	15 13.2	18 51.9	26 46.8
28	2 22 7.8	1 31.2	8 37.7	0♎ 1.3	10 19.1	19 2.6	15 48.7	6 12.1	9 4.2	15 12.8	18 54.0	26 47.7
29	2 26 4.3	2 29.1	8 34.7	12 .2	11 50.2	19 52.3	16 22.3	6 6.3	9 10.7	15 12.3	18 56.0	26 48.6
30	2 30 .9	3 27.2	8 31.8	24 42.8	13 21.4	20 42.6	16 55.8	6 .7	9 17.1	15 11.8	18 58.0	26 49.4
31	2 33 57.5	4 25.4	8 28.8	8♏24.2	14 52.7	21 33.5	17 29.2	5 55.3	9 23.4	15 11.3	19 .0	26 50.2

DECLINATION

DAY	EPHEM. SID. TIME	☉	☊	☾	☿	♀	♂	♃	♄	♅	♆	♇
1	0 35 40.8	2S47.1	0S 8.8	4S30.5	2N50.9	5N37.2	13N32.6	2N14.0	0S17.1	23N 4.7	5S54.0	22N41.2
4	0 47 30.5	3 56.9	0 8.9	21 34.8	0 35.9	5 52.1	12 54.9	2 4.5	0 25.7	23 4.4	5 56.5	22 40.6
7	0 59 20.1	5 6.3	0 9.0	28 19.4	1S41.9	6 .0	12 16.7	1 55.1	0 34.4	23 4.3	5 59.0	22 40.0
10	1 11 9.8	6 15.2	0 9.0	19 27.5	3 59.7	6 1.1	11 38.0	1 45.8	0 43.0	23 4.2	6 1.5	22 39.6
13	1 22 59.5	7 23.2	0 9.1	1 22.5	6 15.3	5 55.6	10 58.9	1 36.7	0 51.5	23 4.1	6 4.1	22 39.2
16	1 34 49.1	8 30.4	0 9.2	16N35.4	8 27.1	5 43.6	10 19.4	1 27.9	0 59.9	23 4.1	6 6.6	22 38.9
19	1 46 38.8	9 36.5	0 9.2	27 11.0	10 34.2	5 25.5	9 39.5	1 19.5	1 8.2	23 4.1	6 9.1	22 38.7
22	1 58 28.5	10 41.3	0 9.3	26 22.0	12 35.6	5 1.5	8 59.3	1 11.4	1 16.4	23 4.2	6 11.6	22 38.6
25	2 10 18.1	11 44.7	0 9.3	15 14.0	14 30.6	4 32.0	8 18.9	1 3.7	1 24.5	23 4.3	6 14.0	22 38.6
28	2 22 7.8	12 46.6	0 9.4	2S 7.6	16 18.8	3 57.4	7 38.3	0 56.6	1 32.5	23 4.5	6 16.5	22 38.6
31	2 33 57.5	13 46.6	0 9.5	19 52.9	17 59.4	3 18.0	6 57.5	0 50.0	1 40.3	23 4.7	6 18.9	22 38.8

NOVEMBER 1951

LONGITUDE

DAY	EPHEM. SID. TIME	☉	☊	☽	☿	♀	♂	♃	♄	♅	♆	♇
	h m s	° ′	° ′	° ′	° ′	° ′	° ′	° ′	° ′	° ′	° ′	° ′
1	2 37 54.0	7♏45.6	6♓41.3	26♏45.9	19♏ 9.4	21♍49.6	16♍22.8	5♈40.2	9♎24.0	13♋56.2	19♎57.6	21♌25.6
2	2 41 50.6	8 45.7	6 38.1	11♐20.8	20 41.1	22 43.1	16 58.6	5R34.7	9 30.8	13R55.6	19 59.8	21 26.3
3	2 45 47.1	9 45.8	6 34.9	25 57.1	22 12.4	23 37.2	17 34.3	5 29.3	9 37.5	13 54.9	20 1.9	21 26.9
4	2 49 43.7	10 45.9	6 31.8	10♑28.4	23 43.3	24 32.0	18 10.0	5 24.2	9 44.3	13 54.2	20 4.1	21 27.5
5	2 53 40.2	11 46.1	6 28.6	24 50.0	25 13.7	25 27.4	18 45.6	5 19.1	9 51.0	13 53.4	20 6.2	21 28.0
6	2 57 36.8	12 46.2	6 25.4	8♒58.9	26 43.7	26 23.4	19 21.2	5 14.2	9 57.6	13 52.6	20 8.3	21 28.6
7	3 1 33.3	13 46.4	6 22.2	22 54.1	28 13.2	27 19.9	19 56.7	5 9.5	10 4.2	13 51.7	20 10.4	21 29.1
8	3 5 29.9	14 46.6	6 19.1	6♓35.8	29 42.2	28 17.0	20 32.1	5 5.0	10 10.8	13 50.8	20 12.5	21 29.5
9	3 9 26.5	15 46.9	6 15.9	20 4.8	1♐10.8	29 14.7	21 7.5	5 .7	10 17.3	13 49.8	20 14.5	21 29.9
10	3 13 23.0	16 47.1	6 12.7	3♈22.1	2 38.9	0♎12.8	21 42.8	4 56.5	10 23.8	13 48.8	20 16.6	21 30.4
11	3 17 19.6	17 47.4	6 9.5	16 28.3	4 6.5	1 11.5	22 18.1	4 52.6	10 30.2	13 47.7	20 18.6	21 30.7
12	3 21 16.1	18 47.8	6 6.3	29 23.7	5 33.6	2 10.7	22 53.3	4 48.8	10 36.6	13 46.5	20 20.6	21 31.1
13	3 25 12.7	19 48.1	6 3.2	12♉ 8.2	7 .0	3 10.3	23 28.5	4 45.2	10 42.9	13 45.3	20 22.6	21 31.4
14	3 29 9.2	20 48.5	5 60.0	24 41.4	8 25.9	4 10.5	24 3.6	4 41.8	10 49.2	13 44.1	20 24.6	21 31.7
15	3 33 5.8	21 48.9	5 56.8	7♊ 3.3	9 51.1	5 11.0	24 38.6	4 38.6	10 55.4	13 42.8	20 26.6	21 31.9
16	3 37 2.4	22 49.3	5 53.6	19 14.4	11 15.6	6 12.0	25 13.6	4 35.6	11 1.6	13 41.5	20 28.6	21 32.2
17	3 40 58.9	23 49.7	5 50.5	1♋15.7	12 39.3	7 13.4	25 48.6	4 32.8	11 7.7	13 40.1	20 30.5	21 32.4
18	3 44 55.5	24 50.2	5 47.3	13 9.5	14 2.2	8 15.3	26 23.5	4 30.1	11 13.7	13 38.7	20 32.4	21 32.6
19	3 48 52.0	25 50.7	5 44.1	24 58.8	15 24.0	9 17.5	26 58.3	4 27.7	11 19.7	13 37.3	20 34.4	21 32.7
20	3 52 48.6	26 51.3	5 40.9	6♌47.4	16 44.7	10 20.1	27 33.0	4 25.5	11 25.7	13 35.8	20 36.3	21 32.8
21	3 56 45.1	27 51.8	5 37.8	18 40.2	18 4.2	11 23.0	28 7.7	4 23.5	11 31.6	13 34.2	20 38.1	21 32.9
22	4 0 41.7	28 52.4	5 34.6	0♍42.5	19 22.3	12 26.4	28 42.4	4 21.7	11 37.4	13 32.6	20 40.0	21 33.0
23	4 4 38.3	29 53.1	5 31.4	12 59.6	20 38.8	13 30.0	29 16.9	4 20.1	11 43.1	13 31.0	20 41.8	21 33.0
24	4 8 34.8	0♐53.7	5 28.2	25 37.1	21 53.5	14 34.0	29 51.4	4 18.7	11 48.9	13 29.3	20 43.6	21 33.0
25	4 12 31.4	1 54.5	5 25.0	8♎39.6	23 6.2	15 38.4	0♎25.9	4 17.6	11 54.5	13 27.6	20 45.5	21 33.0
26	4 16 27.9	2 55.2	5 21.9	22 10.0	24 16.5	16 43.1	1 .3	4 16.6	12 .1	13 25.9	20 47.3	21R32.9
27	4 20 24.5	3 55.9	5 18.7	6♏ 9.2	25 24.1	17 48.0	1 34.6	4 15.8	12 5.6	13 24.1	20 49.0	21 32.9
28	4 24 21.0	4 56.7	5 15.5	20 35.1	26 28.7	18 53.2	2 8.8	4 15.2	12 11.1	13 22.2	20 50.7	21 32.7
29	4 28 17.6	5 57.5	5 12.3	5♐21.9	27 29.7	19 58.7	2 42.9	4 14.9	12 16.4	13 20.3	20 52.5	21 32.6
30	4 32 14.2	6 58.3	5 9.2	20 21.5	28 26.7	21 4.5	3 17.0	4 14.8	12 21.8	13 18.4	20 54.1	21 32.4

LATITUDE

DAY	EPHEM. SID. TIME	☉	☊	☽	☿	♀	♂	♃	♄	♅	♆	♇
1	2 37 54.0	0 .0	0 .0	4S57.9	1S 2.4	0S11.7	1N28.3	1S35.1	2N11.2	0N21.8	1N35.8	8N46.1
4	2 49 43.7	0 .0	0 .0	4 15.6	1 21.0	0N 9.1	1 29.3	1 34.4	2 11.6	0 21.9	1 35.9	8 47.1
7	3 1 33.3	0 .0	0 .0	1 17.2	1 38.2	0 28.3	1 30.3	1 33.7	2 12.0	0 22.0	1 36.0	8 48.1
10	3 13 23.0	0 .0	0 .0	2N12.5	1 53.9	0 46.1	1 31.3	1 33.0	2 12.5	0 22.1	1 36.0	8 49.0
13	3 25 12.7	0 .0	0 .0	4 32.9	2 7.5	1 2.3	1 32.3	1 32.3	2 13.0	0 22.1	1 36.1	8 50.0
16	3 37 2.4	0 .0	0 .0	4 53.1	2 18.7	1 17.0	1 33.3	1 31.5	2 13.5	0 22.2	1 36.2	8 51.0
19	3 48 52.0	0 .0	0 .0	3 18.3	2 26.8	1 30.3	1 34.3	1 30.7	2 14.0	0 22.3	1 36.3	8 52.0
22	4 0 41.7	0 .0	0 .0	0 27.3	2 31.0	1 42.1	1 35.3	1 29.8	2 14.5	0 22.4	1 36.4	8 52.9
25	4 12 31.4	0 .0	0 .0	2S44.0	2 30.5	1 52.6	1 36.2	1 29.0	2 15.1	0 22.4	1 36.6	8 53.9
28	4 24 21.0	0 .0	0 .0	4 50.2	2 24.0	2 1.7	1 37.2	1 28.1	2 15.7	0 22.5	1 36.7	8 54.9

RIGHT ASCENSION

DAY	EPHEM. SID. TIME	☉	☊	☽	☿	♀	♂	♃	♄	♅	♆	♇
1	2 37 54.0	5♏23.9	8♓25.8	23♏12.4	16♏24.1	22♍25.0	18♍ 2.6	5♈50.0	9♎29.8	15♋10.6	19♎ 2.1	26♌51.0
2	2 41 50.6	6 22.6	8 22.8	9♐ 1.1	17 55.5	23 17.0	18 35.9	5R44.8	9 36.1	15R10.0	19 4.1	26 51.7
3	2 45 47.1	7 21.4	8 19.8	25 25.3	19 27.1	24 9.5	19 9.1	5 39.8	9 42.3	15 9.2	19 6.1	26 52.5
4	2 49 43.7	8 20.5	8 16.8	11♑46.2	20 58.9	25 2.6	19 42.3	5 35.0	9 48.6	15 8.5	19 8.1	26 53.2
5	2 53 40.2	9 19.8	8 13.8	27 26.8	22 30.7	25 56.0	20 15.3	5 30.2	9 54.8	15 7.6	19 10.1	26 53.9
6	2 57 36.8	10 19.2	8 10.8	12♒ 5.9	24 2.6	26 50.0	20 48.3	5 25.7	10 1.0	15 6.7	19 12.0	26 54.5
7	3 1 33.3	11 18.9	8 7.8	25 41.0	25 34.6	27 44.4	21 21.2	5 21.3	10 7.1	15 5.8	19 14.0	26 55.1
8	3 5 29.9	12 18.7	8 4.9	8♓22.5	27 6.7	28 39.2	21 54.0	5 17.0	10 13.2	15 4.8	19 16.0	26 55.7
9	3 9 26.5	13 18.8	8 1.9	20 27.1	28 38.8	29 34.5	22 26.8	5 13.0	10 19.3	15 3.7	19 17.9	26 56.3
10	3 13 23.0	14 19.1	7 58.9	2♈12.8	0♐10.9	0♎30.1	22 59.5	5 9.0	10 25.3	15 2.6	19 19.8	26 56.8
11	3 17 19.6	15 19.6	7 55.9	13 56.4	1 43.1	1 26.2	23 32.1	5 5.3	10 31.2	15 1.4	19 21.7	26 57.3
12	3 21 16.1	16 20.3	7 52.9	25 52.8	3 15.1	2 22.6	24 4.7	5 1.7	10 37.2	15 .2	19 23.6	26 57.8
13	3 25 12.7	17 21.2	7 49.9	8♉12.8	4 47.1	3 19.4	24 37.2	4 58.3	10 43.0	14 58.9	19 25.5	26 58.2
14	3 29 9.2	18 22.3	7 46.9	21 1.9	6 18.8	4 16.6	25 9.6	4 55.1	10 48.9	14 57.6	19 27.4	26 58.6
15	3 33 5.8	19 23.6	7 43.9	4♊17.9	7 50.3	5 14.1	25 42.0	4 52.1	10 54.7	14 56.2	19 29.2	26 59.0
16	3 37 2.4	20 25.1	7 40.9	17 51.1	9 21.4	6 12.0	26 14.3	4 49.2	11 .4	14 54.8	19 31.1	26 59.3
17	3 40 58.9	21 26.9	7 37.9	1♋25.5	10 52.0	7 10.2	26 46.5	4 46.5	11 6.1	14 53.3	19 32.9	26 59.7
18	3 44 55.5	22 28.8	7 34.9	14 44.2	12 22.1	8 8.8	27 18.7	4 44.0	11 11.8	14 51.8	19 34.7	26 60.0
19	3 48 52.0	23 31.0	7 31.9	27 34.5	13 51.4	9 7.7	27 50.8	4 41.7	11 17.3	14 50.2	19 36.5	27 .2
20	3 52 48.6	24 33.4	7 28.9	9♌50.8	15 19.8	10 6.9	28 22.8	4 39.5	11 22.9	14 48.6	19 38.3	27 .5
21	3 56 45.1	25 36.0	7 25.9	21 35.2	16 47.1	11 6.5	28 54.8	4 37.6	11 28.4	14 46.9	19 40.0	27 .7
22	4 0 41.7	26 38.8	7 22.9	2♍55.8	18 13.1	12 6.3	29 26.7	4 35.8	11 33.8	14 45.2	19 41.8	27 .9
23	4 4 38.3	27 41.8	7 20.0	14 5.1	19 37.5	13 6.5	29 58.5	4 34.2	11 39.2	14 43.4	19 43.5	27 1.0
24	4 8 34.8	28 45.0	7 17.0	25 18.1	21 .2	14 7.0	0♎30.3	4 32.8	11 44.5	14 41.6	19 45.2	27 1.1
25	4 12 31.4	29 48.5	7 14.0	6♎52.3	22 20.7	15 7.8	1 2.1	4 31.7	11 49.9	14 39.8	19 47.0	27 1.3
26	4 16 27.9	0♐52.1	7 11.0	19 6.4	23 38.7	16 8.9	1 33.7	4 30.7	11 55.1	14 37.9	19 48.6	27 1.3
27	4 20 24.5	1 55.9	7 8.0	2♏19.3	24 53.7	17 10.3	2 5.3	4 29.9	12 .2	14 35.9	19 50.3	27 1.3
28	4 24 21.0	2 59.9	7 5.0	16 45.3	26 5.4	18 11.9	2 36.8	4 29.2	12 5.3	14 33.9	19 51.9	27 1.3
29	4 28 17.6	4 4.1	7 2.0	2♐27.2	27 13.2	19 13.9	3 8.3	4 28.8	12 10.3	14 31.9	19 53.5	27 1.3
30	4 32 14.2	5 8.4	6 59.0	19 6.8	28 16.5	20 16.2	3 39.7	4 28.5	12 15.3	14 29.8	19 55.1	27 1.3

DECLINATION

DAY	EPHEM. SID. TIME	☉	☊	☽	☿	♀	♂	♃	♄	♅	♆	♇
1	2 37 54.0	14S 6.2	0S 9.5	24S16.0	18S31.2	3N 3.9	6N43.9	0N47.9	1S42.9	23N 4.8	6S19.7	22N38.9
4	2 49 43.7	15 3.6	0 9.5	27 16.9	20 1.0	2 18.7	6 3.0	0 42.1	1 50.5	23 5.1	6 22.0	22 39.2
7	3 1 33.3	15 58.7	0 9.6	15 6.1	21 22.0	1 29.7	5 22.1	0 37.0	1 57.9	23 5.4	6 24.3	22 39.5
10	3 13 23.0	16 51.5	0 9.7	3N21.9	22 33.5	0 37.2	4 41.2	0 32.5	2 5.2	23 5.8	6 26.6	22 40.0
13	3 25 12.7	17 41.6	0 9.7	19 48.5	23 34.9	0S18.5	4 .3	0 28.7	2 12.2	23 6.2	6 28.8	22 40.6
16	3 37 2.4	18 29.0	0 9.8	27 52.8	24 25.5	1 17.0	3 19.5	0 25.6	2 19.1	23 6.7	6 30.9	22 41.2
19	3 48 52.0	19 13.5	0 9.9	24 23.5	25 4.8	2 18.0	2 38.8	0 23.2	2 25.7	23 7.2	6 33.0	22 42.0
22	4 0 41.7	19 54.9	0 9.9	11 39.1	25 31.9	3 20.9	1 58.3	0 21.6	2 32.0	23 7.8	6 35.0	22 42.8
25	4 12 31.4	20 33.0	0 10.0	5S56.8	25 46.4	4 25.6	1 18.0	0 20.7	2 38.2	23 8.3	6 36.9	22 43.7
28	4 24 21.0	21 7.7	0 10.0	22 33.7	25 48.0	5 31.4	0 37.9	0 20.6	2 44.1	23 8.9	6 38.8	22 44.7

DECEMBER 1951

LONGITUDE

DAY	EPHEM. SID. TIME h m s	☉ ° ′	☊ ° ′	☽ ° ′	☿ ° ′	♀ ° ′	♂ ° ′	♃ ° ′	♄ ° ′	♅ ° ′	♆ ° ′	♇ ° ′
1	4 36 10.7	7♐59.1	5♓ 6.0	5♑23.9	29♐19.2	22♎10.5	3♎51.0	4♈14.8	12♎27.0	13♋16.5	20♎55.8	21♌32.2
2	4 40 7.3	8 59.9	5 2.8	20 19.6	0♑ 6.4	23 16.8	4 24.9	4D15.1	12 32.1	13R14.5	20 57.4	21R32.0
3	4 44 3.8	10 .8	4 59.6	5♒ .8	0 47.8	24 23.4	4 58.8	4 15.6	12 37.2	13 12.5	20 59.1	21 31.7
4	4 48 .4	11 1.7	4 56.5	19 22.7	1 22.5	25 30.1	5 32.5	4 16.3	12 42.3	13 10.4	21 .7	21 31.4
5	4 51 57.0	12 2.5	4 53.3	3♓23.3	1 49.8	26 37.1	6 6.2	4 17.2	12 47.2	13 8.3	21 2.2	21 31.1
6	4 55 53.5	13 3.4	4 50.1	17 2.7	2 8.8	27 44.3	6 39.8	4 18.3	12 52.1	13 6.2	21 3.8	21 30.8
7	4 59 50.1	14 4.4	4 46.9	0♈22.9	2 18.7	28 51.8	7 13.3	4 19.6	12 56.8	13 4.0	21 5.3	21 30.4
8	5 3 46.6	15 5.3	4 43.8	13 26.3	2R18.6	29 59.4	7 46.7	4 21.2	13 1.6	13 1.9	21 6.8	21 30.0
9	5 7 43.2	16 6.2	4 40.6	26 15.4	2 7.8	1♏ 7.3	8 20.0	4 22.9	13 6.2	12 59.6	21 8.2	21 29.5
10	5 11 39.7	17 7.2	4 37.4	8♉52.6	1 45.9	2 15.3	8 53.3	4 24.9	13 10.7	12 57.4	21 9.7	21 29.1
11	5 15 36.3	18 8.1	4 34.2	21 19.4	1 12.5	3 23.6	9 26.4	4 27.0	13 15.2	12 55.1	21 11.1	21 28.6
12	5 19 32.9	19 9.1	4 31.0	3♊37.2	0 27.7	4 32.0	9 59.5	4 29.3	13 19.6	12 52.8	21 12.5	21 28.1
13	5 23 29.4	20 10.1	4 27.9	15 46.7	29♐32.2	5 40.6	10 32.5	4 31.9	13 23.9	12 50.5	21 13.8	21 27.5
14	5 27 26.0	21 11.1	4 24.7	27 48.9	28 27.0	6 49.4	11 5.4	4 34.6	13 28.1	12 48.2	21 15.2	21 27.0
15	5 31 22.5	22 12.1	4 21.5	9♋44.8	27 13.8	7 58.4	11 38.2	4 37.6	13 32.2	12 45.8	21 16.5	21 26.4
16	5 35 19.1	23 13.1	4 18.3	21 35.7	25 54.8	9 7.6	12 11.0	4 40.8	13 36.3	12 43.5	21 17.8	21 25.8
17	5 39 15.7	24 14.2	4 15.2	3♌23.9	24 32.4	10 16.9	12 43.6	4 44.1	13 40.3	12 41.1	21 19.0	21 25.2
18	5 43 12.2	25 15.2	4 12.0	15 12.3	23 9.5	11 26.4	13 16.1	4 47.7	13 44.2	12 38.6	21 20.2	21 24.5
19	5 47 8.8	26 16.3	4 8.8	27 4.6	21 48.9	12 36.0	13 48.5	4 51.4	13 48.0	12 36.2	21 21.4	21 23.8
20	5 51 5.3	27 17.4	4 5.6	9♍ 5.2	20 33.2	13 45.8	14 20.8	4 55.3	13 51.7	12 33.7	21 22.6	21 23.1
21	5 55 1.9	28 18.5	4 2.5	21 19.1	19 24.6	14 55.7	14 53.0	4 59.4	13 55.3	12 31.2	21 23.7	21 22.3
22	5 58 58.5	29 19.6	3 59.3	3♎51.7	18 24.7	16 5.8	15 25.1	5 3.7	13 58.8	12 28.7	21 24.8	21 21.5
23	6 2 55.0	0♑20.7	3 56.1	16 47.9	17 34.8	17 16.0	15 57.1	5 8.2	14 2.2	12 26.2	21 25.9	21 20.7
24	6 6 51.6	1 21.8	3 52.9	0♏11.9	16 55.5	18 26.4	16 29.0	5 12.9	14 5.6	12 23.7	21 26.9	21 19.9
25	6 10 48.1	2 23.0	3 49.8	14 6.1	16 27.1	19 36.8	17 .8	5 17.8	14 8.8	12 21.1	21 27.9	21 19.1
26	6 14 44.7	3 24.1	3 46.6	28 30.0	16 9.3	20 47.4	17 32.4	5 22.8	14 11.9	12 18.6	21 28.9	21 18.2
27	6 18 41.2	4 25.3	3 43.4	13♐19.8	16 1.7	21 58.2	18 4.0	5 28.1	14 15.0	12 16.0	21 29.8	21 17.3
28	6 22 37.8	5 26.4	3 40.2	28 28.2	16D 3.8	23 9.0	18 35.4	5 33.5	14 17.9	12 13.5	21 30.7	21 16.4
29	6 26 34.4	6 27.6	3 37.1	13♑45.1	16 14.9	24 19.9	19 6.7	5 39.1	14 20.8	12 10.9	21 31.6	21 15.5
30	6 30 30.9	7 28.8	3 33.9	28 59.3	16 34.1	25 30.9	19 37.8	5 44.9	14 23.5	12 8.3	21 32.5	21 14.5
31	6 34 27.5	8 29.9	3 30.7	14♒ .6	17 .8	26 42.1	20 8.8	5 50.8	14 26.2	12 5.7	21 33.3	21 13.5

LATITUDE

DAY	EPHEM. SID. TIME	☉	☊	☽	☿	♀	♂	♃	♄	♅	♆	♇
1	4 36 10.7	0 .0	0 .0	4S18.8	2S 9.8	2N 9.4	1N38.1	1S27.3	2N16.3	0N22.6	1N36.8	8N55.9
4	4 48 .4	0 .0	0 .0	1 19.2	1 46.0	2 15.9	1 39.1	1 26.4	2 17.0	0 22.6	1 36.9	8 56.8
7	4 59 50.1	0 .0	0 .0	2N12.1	1 10.8	2 21.1	1 40.0	1 25.5	2 17.6	0 22.7	1 37.1	8 57.8
10	5 11 39.7	0 .0	0 .0	4 32.0	0 23.2	2 25.0	1 41.0	1 24.6	2 18.3	0 22.7	1 37.2	8 58.7
13	5 23 29.4	0 .0	0 .0	4 53.8	0N34.3	2 27.8	1 41.9	1 23.7	2 19.0	0 22.8	1 37.4	8 59.6
16	5 35 19.1	0 .0	0 .0	3 20.2	1 33.9	2 29.4	1 42.8	1 22.8	2 19.8	0 22.8	1 37.5	9 .5
19	5 47 8.8	0 .0	0 .0	0 30.4	2 23.2	2 29.9	1 43.7	1 22.0	2 20.5	0 22.9	1 37.7	9 1.4
22	5 58 58.5	0 .0	0 .0	2S37.9	2 53.1	2 29.4	1 44.6	1 21.1	2 21.3	0 22.9	1 37.9	9 2.3
25	6 10 48.1	0 .0	0 .0	4 49.1	3 2.2	2 27.9	1 45.4	1 20.3	2 22.1	0 23.0	1 38.0	9 3.1
28	6 22 37.8	0 .0	0 .0	4 33.6	2 55.4	2 25.4	1 46.3	1 19.4	2 22.9	0 23.0	1 38.2	9 3.9
31	6 34 27.5	0 .0	0 .0	1 34.3	2 38.3	2 22.1	1 47.2	1 18.6	2 23.7	0 23.0	1 38.4	9 4.7

RIGHT ASCENSION

DAY	EPHEM. SID. TIME	☉	☊	☽	☿	♀	♂	♃	♄	♅	♆	♇
1	4 36 10.7	6♐12.9	6♓56.0	6♑ 4.7	29♐14.7	21♎18.7	4♎11.0	4♈28.5	12♎20.2	14♋27.7	19♎56.7	27♌ 1.2
2	4 40 7.3	7 17.6	6 53.0	22 34.0	0♑ 7.1	22 21.6	4 42.2	4D28.6	12 25.1	14R25.6	19 58.2	27R 1.0
3	4 44 3.8	8 22.5	6 50.0	8♒ .6	0 52.9	23 24.7	5 13.4	4 29.0	12 29.8	14 23.4	19 59.8	27 .9
4	4 48 .4	9 27.4	6 47.0	22 13.8	1 31.2	24 28.1	5 44.5	4 29.5	12 34.5	14 21.2	20 1.3	27 .7
5	4 51 57.0	10 32.6	6 44.0	5♓21.1	2 1.2	25 31.8	6 15.5	4 30.2	12 39.2	14 18.9	20 2.8	27 .5
6	4 55 53.5	11 37.9	6 41.0	17 39.4	2 21.9	26 35.8	6 46.5	4 31.1	12 43.8	14 16.6	20 4.2	27 .3
7	4 59 50.1	12 43.3	6 38.0	29 28.4	2 32.5	27 40.1	7 17.4	4 32.2	12 48.3	14 14.3	20 5.7	27 .0
8	5 3 46.6	13 48.8	6 35.0	11♈ 7.2	2R32.1	28 44.7	7 48.2	4 33.5	12 52.7	14 11.9	20 7.1	26 59.7
9	5 7 43.2	14 54.5	6 32.0	22 52.5	2 20.0	29 49.7	8 19.0	4 35.0	12 57.0	14 9.5	20 8.4	26 59.4
10	5 11 39.7	16 .2	6 29.0	4♉57.5	1 55.7	0♏54.9	8 49.7	4 36.6	13 1.3	14 7.1	20 9.8	26 59.1
11	5 15 36.3	17 6.1	6 26.0	17 30.5	1 19.0	2 .4	9 20.3	4 38.5	13 5.5	14 4.6	20 11.1	26 58.7
12	5 19 32.9	18 12.1	6 23.0	0♊33.1	0 30.2	3 6.2	9 50.8	4 40.5	13 9.7	14 2.2	20 12.5	26 58.3
13	5 23 29.4	19 18.1	6 20.0	13 58.4	29♐29.9	4 12.3	10 21.3	4 42.7	13 13.7	13 59.6	20 13.7	26 57.8
14	5 27 26.0	20 24.3	6 17.0	27 32.0	28 19.4	5 18.8	10 51.7	4 45.1	13 17.7	13 57.1	20 15.0	26 57.4
15	5 31 22.5	21 30.5	6 14.0	10♋56.2	27 .6	6 25.6	11 22.1	4 47.7	13 21.6	13 54.5	20 16.2	26 56.9
16	5 35 19.1	22 36.9	6 11.0	23 55.1	25 35.9	7 32.7	11 52.4	4 50.6	13 25.5	13 52.0	20 17.5	26 56.4
17	5 39 15.7	23 43.3	6 8.0	6♌19.7	24 8.1	8 40.1	12 22.6	4 53.5	13 29.3	13 49.4	20 18.7	26 55.9
18	5 43 12.2	24 49.7	6 5.0	18 8.7	22 40.1	9 47.9	12 52.7	4 56.6	13 33.0	13 46.8	20 19.8	26 55.3
19	5 47 8.8	25 56.2	6 2.0	29 27.9	21 14.9	10 55.9	13 22.7	4 59.9	13 36.5	13 44.1	20 21.0	26 54.7
20	5 51 5.3	27 2.8	5 58.9	10♍28.1	19 55.0	12 4.3	13 52.7	5 3.4	13 40.1	13 41.5	20 22.1	26 54.1
21	5 55 1.9	28 9.3	5 55.9	21 23.2	18 42.9	13 13.1	14 22.6	5 7.1	13 43.5	13 38.8	20 23.1	26 53.4
22	5 58 58.5	29 15.9	5 52.9	2♎29.8	17 40.0	14 22.1	14 52.4	5 10.9	13 46.8	13 36.1	20 24.2	26 52.7
23	6 2 55.0	0♑22.5	5 49.9	14 6.2	16 47.7	15 31.5	15 22.1	5 14.9	13 50.1	13 33.3	20 25.2	26 52.0
24	6 6 51.6	1 29.2	5 46.9	26 32.2	16 6.5	16 41.2	15 51.8	5 19.1	13 53.3	13 30.6	20 26.2	26 51.3
25	6 10 48.1	2 35.8	5 43.9	10♏ 6.6	15 36.5	17 51.2	16 21.4	5 23.5	13 56.4	13 27.8	20 27.1	26 50.6
26	6 14 44.7	3 42.4	5 40.9	25 1.6	15 17.6	19 1.6	16 50.8	5 28.0	13 59.4	13 25.1	20 28.1	26 49.8
27	6 18 41.2	4 49.0	5 37.9	11♐13.9	15 9.4	20 12.3	17 20.2	5 32.7	14 2.3	13 22.3	20 29.0	26 49.0
28	6 22 37.8	5 55.6	5 34.9	28 16.4	15D11.3	21 23.3	17 49.5	5 37.6	14 5.1	13 19.5	20 29.8	26 48.2
29	6 26 34.4	7 2.2	5 31.9	15♑22.3	15 22.4	22 34.7	18 18.7	5 42.6	14 7.8	13 16.7	20 30.7	26 47.3
30	6 30 30.9	8 8.6	5 28.9	1♒44.9	15 42.2	23 46.3	18 47.8	5 47.8	14 10.5	13 13.9	20 31.5	26 46.4
31	6 34 27.5	9 15.1	5 25.9	16 57.3	16 9.7	24 58.3	19 16.8	5 53.2	14 13.0	13 11.1	20 32.3	26 45.5

DECLINATION

DAY	EPHEM. SID. TIME	☉	☊	☽	☿	♀	♂	♃	♄	♅	♆	♇
1	4 36 10.7	21S38.9	0S10.1	27S38.8	25S36.5	6S38.1	0S 1.8	0N21.2	2S49.7	23N 9.6	6S40.6	22N45.8
4	4 48 .4	22 6.3	0 10.2	16 16.1	25 12.4	7 45.3	0 41.2	0 22.6	2 55.0	23 10.2	6 42.3	22 47.0
7	4 59 50.1	22 29.8	0 10.2	2N10.3	24 36.4	8 52.5	1 20.1	0 24.8	3 .1	23 10.9	6 43.9	22 48.2
10	5 11 39.7	22 49.4	0 10.3	18 45.1	23 49.4	9 59.4	1 58.7	0 27.6	3 4.8	23 11.6	6 45.4	22 49.5
13	5 23 29.4	23 5.0	0 10.3	27 33.4	22 52.5	11 5.7	2 36.8	0 31.2	3 9.3	23 12.3	6 46.8	22 50.9
16	5 35 19.1	23 16.4	0 10.4	25 .5	21 49.2	12 10.9	3 14.4	0 35.6	3 13.4	23 13.1	6 48.1	22 52.3
19	5 47 8.8	23 23.7	0 10.5	12 58.0	20 48.7	13 14.6	3 51.4	0 40.6	3 17.2	23 13.8	6 49.3	22 53.8
22	5 58 58.5	23 26.8	0 10.5	3S57.1	20 4.1	14 16.5	4 27.9	0 46.3	3 20.7	23 14.5	6 50.4	22 55.4
25	6 10 48.1	23 25.6	0 10.6	20 40.3	19 44.2	15 16.2	5 3.7	0 52.6	3 23.8	23 15.3	6 51.4	22 57.0
28	6 22 37.8	23 20.1	0 10.6	27 59.9	19 48.6	16 13.2	5 38.9	0 59.6	3 26.6	23 16.0	6 52.3	22 58.7
31	6 34 27.5	23 10.5	0 10.7	18 8.1	20 11.3	17 7.3	6 13.4	1 7.2	3 29.1	23 16.8	6 53.1	23 .4

JANUARY 1952

DAY	EPHEM. SID. TIME	☉	☊	☾	☿	♀	♂	♃	♄	♅	♆	♇
	h m s	° ′	° ′	° ′	° ′	° ′	° ′	° ′	° ′	° ′	° ′	° ′
		LONGITUDE										
1	6 38 24.0	9♑31.1	3♓27.5	28♒41.3	17♐34.2	27♏53.3	20♎39.7	5♈56.9	14♎28.7	12♋ 3.1	21♎34.0	21♌12.5
2	6 42 20.6	10 32.3	3 24.3	12♓57.1	18 13.6	29 4.6	21 10.5	6 3.2	14 31.2	12 R .5	21 34.8	21 R 11.5
3	6 46 17.2	11 33.5	3 21.2	26 46.7	18 58.3	0♐16.0	21 41.1	6 9.7	14 33.5	11 57.9	21 35.5	21 10.4
4	6 50 13.7	12 34.6	3 18.0	10♈11.1	19 47.8	1 27.5	22 11.6	6 16.4	14 35.7	11 55.3	21 36.2	21 9.4
5	6 54 10.3	13 35.8	3 14.8	23 13.2	20 41.6	2 39.1	22 41.9	6 23.2	14 37.9	11 52.7	21 36.8	21 8.3
6	6 58 6.8	14 37.0	3 11.6	5♉56.3	21 39.3	3 50.8	23 12.2	6 30.2	14 40.0	11 50.2	21 37.5	21 7.2
7	7 2 3.4	15 38.1	3 8.5	18 23.8	22 40.2	5 2.6	23 42.2	6 37.3	14 41.9	11 47.6	21 38.1	21 6.1
8	7 5 60.0	16 39.3	3 5.3	0♊39.2	23 44.2	6 14.4	24 12.1	6 44.6	14 43.7	11 45.0	21 38.6	21 5.0
9	7 9 56.5	17 40.4	3 2.1	12 45.4	24 50.8	7 26.3	24 41.9	6 52.1	14 45.5	11 42.4	21 39.1	21 3.8
10	7 13 53.1	18 41.5	2 58.9	24 44.7	25 59.9	8 38.3	25 11.5	6 59.7	14 47.1	11 39.8	21 39.6	21 2.6
11	7 17 49.6	19 42.6	2 55.8	6♋39.1	27 11.1	9 50.4	25 40.9	7 7.4	14 48.6	11 37.3	21 40.0	21 1.4
12	7 21 46.2	20 43.8	2 52.6	18 30.3	28 24.2	11 2.5	26 10.2	7 15.3	14 50.0	11 34.7	21 40.4	21 .2
13	7 25 42.7	21 44.9	2 49.4	0♌19.9	29 39.1	12 14.7	26 39.3	7 23.4	14 51.3	11 32.1	21 40.8	20 59.0
14	7 29 39.3	22 46.0	2 46.2	12 9.7	0♑55.6	13 27.0	27 8.3	7 31.6	14 52.5	11 29.6	21 41.2	20 57.8
15	7 33 35.9	23 47.1	2 43.1	24 1.9	2 13.5	14 39.3	27 37.1	7 40.0	14 53.6	11 27.1	21 41.5	20 56.5
16	7 37 32.4	24 48.2	2 39.9	5♍58.9	3 32.8	15 51.7	28 5.7	7 48.5	14 54.6	11 24.6	21 41.7	20 55.2
17	7 41 29.0	25 49.3	2 36.7	18 4.0	4 53.2	17 4.2	28 34.2	7 57.1	14 55.5	11 22.1	21 42.0	20 53.9
18	7 45 25.5	26 50.3	2 33.5	0♎20.8	6 14.8	18 16.7	29 2.4	8 5.9	14 56.3	11 19.6	21 42.2	20 52.6
19	7 49 22.1	27 51.4	2 30.3	12 53.4	7 37.4	19 29.3	29 30.5	8 14.8	14 56.9	11 17.1	21 42.3	20 51.3
20	7 53 18.6	28 52.5	2 27.2	25 45.9	9 1.0	20 41.9	29 58.4	8 23.9	14 57.5	11 14.7	21 42.5	20 50.0
21	7 57 15.2	29 53.6	2 24.0	9♏ 2.1	10 25.5	21 54.6	0♏26.1	8 33.1	14 57.9	11 12.2	21 42.6	20 48.7
22	8 1 11.8	0♒54.6	2 20.8	22 44.9	11 50.9	23 7.4	0 53.6	8 42.4	14 58.3	11 9.8	21 42.6	20 47.3
23	8 5 8.3	1 55.7	2 17.6	6♐55.3	13 17.1	24 20.2	1 20.9	8 51.9	14 58.5	11 7.4	21 42.7	20 46.0
24	8 9 4.9	2 56.7	2 14.5	21 31.5	14 44.1	25 33.0	1 48.0	9 1.5	14 58.6	11 5.1	21 42.7	20 44.6
25	8 13 1.4	3 57.8	2 11.3	6♑28.9	16 11.9	26 45.9	2 14.8	9 11.2	14 58.7	11 2.7	21 R 42.6	20 43.2
26	8 16 58.0	4 58.8	2 8.1	21 39.9	17 40.4	27 58.9	2 41.5	9 21.0	14 R 58.6	11 .4	21 42.6	20 41.8
27	8 20 54.6	5 59.9	2 4.9	6♒54.7	19 9.7	29 11.9	3 8.0	9 31.0	14 58.4	10 58.2	21 42.5	20 40.5
28	8 24 51.1	7 .9	2 1.8	22 3.0	20 39.7	0♑24.9	3 34.1	9 41.1	14 58.1	10 55.9	21 42.4	20 39.1
29	8 28 47.7	8 1.9	1 58.6	6♓55.5	22 10.4	1 38.0	4 .1	9 51.3	14 57.7	10 53.7	21 42.2	20 37.7
30	8 32 44.2	9 2.8	1 55.4	21 25.4	23 41.8	2 51.1	4 25.8	10 1.7	14 57.2	10 51.5	21 42.0	20 36.2
31	8 36 40.8	10 3.8	1 52.2	5♈28.8	25 13.8	4 4.2	4 51.3	10 12.1	14 56.5	10 49.3	21 41.7	20 34.8
		LATITUDE										
1	6 38 24.0	0 .0	0 .0	0S16.9	2N31.1	2N20.8	1N47.4	1S18.3	2N24.0	0N23.1	1N38.4	9N 4.9
4	6 50 13.7	0 .0	0 .0	3N11.5	2 7.0	2 16.3	1 48.3	1 17.5	2 24.8	0 23.1	1 38.6	9 5.7
7	7 2 3.4	0 .0	0 .0	4 59.8	1 40.7	2 11.1	1 49.1	1 16.8	2 25.6	0 23.1	1 38.8	9 6.4
10	7 13 53.1	0 .0	0 .0	4 43.2	1 13.7	2 5.2	1 49.9	1 16.0	2 26.5	0 23.1	1 39.0	9 7.1
13	7 25 42.7	0 .0	0 .0	2 38.5	0 47.0	1 58.6	1 50.6	1 15.2	2 27.3	0 23.2	1 39.2	9 7.7
16	7 37 32.4	0 .0	0 .0	0S27.7	0 21.2	1 51.5	1 51.4	1 14.5	2 28.2	0 23.2	1 39.3	9 8.3
19	7 49 22.1	0 .0	0 .0	3 29.7	0S 3.3	1 43.8	1 52.1	1 13.8	2 29.0	0 23.2	1 39.5	9 8.9
22	8 1 11.8	0 .0	0 .0	5 10.2	0 26.2	1 35.7	1 52.8	1 13.1	2 29.9	0 23.2	1 39.7	9 9.4
25	8 13 1.4	0 .0	0 .0	4 15.0	0 47.2	1 27.3	1 53.4	1 12.5	2 30.8	0 23.2	1 39.9	9 9.9
28	8 24 51.1	0 .0	0 .0	0 47.2	1 6.2	1 18.5	1 54.1	1 11.8	2 31.6	0 23.2	1 40.1	9 10.3
31	8 36 40.8	0 .0	0 .0	3N .6	1 23.0	1 9.4	1 54.6	1 11.2	2 32.4	0 23.2	1 40.3	9 10.7
		RIGHT ASCENSION										
1	6 38 24.0	10♑21.5	5♓22.9	0♓56.2	16♐44.4	26♏10.6	19♎45.7	5♈58.7	14♎15.5	13♋ 8.3	20♎33.0	26♌44.6
2	6 42 20.6	11 27.8	5 19.9	13 54.3	17 25.5	27 23.3	20 14.5	6 4.4	14 17.8	13 R 5.5	20 33.7	26 R 43.7
3	6 46 17.2	12 34.0	5 16.8	26 10.9	18 12.4	28 36.2	20 43.2	6 10.2	14 20.1	13 2.7	20 34.4	26 42.7
4	6 50 13.7	13 40.1	5 13.8	8♈ 5.9	19 4.5	29 49.5	21 11.8	6 16.2	14 22.3	12 59.8	20 35.1	26 41.7
5	6 54 10.3	14 46.1	5 10.8	19 57.6	20 1.3	1♐ 3.0	21 40.3	6 22.3	14 24.4	12 57.0	20 35.7	26 40.7
6	6 58 6.8	15 52.1	5 7.8	2♉ 1.0	21 2.3	2 16.9	22 8.7	6 28.7	14 26.4	12 54.3	20 36.3	26 39.7
7	7 2 3.4	16 57.9	5 4.8	14 26.7	22 7.1	3 31.1	22 37.0	6 35.1	14 28.3	12 51.5	20 36.9	26 38.7
8	7 5 60.0	18 3.6	5 1.8	27 19.2	23 15.3	4 45.6	23 5.1	6 41.7	14 30.1	12 48.6	20 37.4	26 37.6
9	7 9 56.5	19 9.1	4 58.8	10♊35.2	24 26.7	6 .3	23 33.1	6 48.5	14 31.8	12 45.8	20 37.9	26 36.5
10	7 13 53.1	20 14.6	4 55.8	24 3.8	25 40.8	7 15.4	24 1.1	6 55.4	14 33.4	12 43.1	20 38.4	26 35.4
11	7 17 49.6	21 19.9	4 52.8	7♋28.9	26 57.4	8 30.7	24 28.9	7 2.4	14 34.9	12 40.3	20 38.8	26 34.3
12	7 21 46.2	22 25.0	4 49.7	20 34.3	28 16.4	9 46.3	24 56.5	7 9.6	14 36.4	12 37.5	20 39.2	26 33.1
13	7 25 42.7	23 30.0	4 46.7	3♌ 8.4	29 37.4	11 2.2	25 24.1	7 16.9	14 37.7	12 34.7	20 39.6	26 32.0
14	7 29 39.3	24 34.9	4 43.7	15 7.2	1♑ .3	12 18.3	25 51.5	7 24.3	14 38.9	12 32.0	20 40.0	26 30.8
15	7 33 35.9	25 39.6	4 40.7	26 33.5	2 25.0	13 34.7	26 18.8	7 31.9	14 40.0	12 29.2	20 40.3	26 29.6
16	7 37 32.4	26 44.1	4 37.7	7♍35.6	3 51.2	14 51.4	26 45.9	7 39.6	14 41.0	12 26.5	20 40.5	26 28.4
17	7 41 29.0	27 48.5	4 34.7	18 25.5	5 18.9	16 8.3	27 12.9	7 47.5	14 42.0	12 23.8	20 40.8	26 27.1
18	7 45 25.5	28 52.7	4 31.7	29 17.7	6 48.0	17 25.4	27 39.8	7 55.5	14 42.8	12 21.1	20 41.0	26 25.9
19	7 49 22.1	29 56.7	4 28.6	10♎28.9	8 18.2	18 42.8	28 6.5	8 3.6	14 43.5	12 18.4	20 41.2	26 24.6
20	7 53 18.6	1♒ .6	4 25.6	22 17.0	9 49.6	20 .3	28 33.1	8 11.8	14 44.1	12 15.8	20 41.3	26 23.4
21	7 57 15.2	2 4.3	4 22.6	5♏ .5	11 22.0	21 18.1	28 59.5	8 20.2	14 44.7	12 13.1	20 41.4	26 22.1
22	8 1 11.8	3 7.8	4 19.6	18 54.9	12 55.4	22 36.0	29 25.7	8 28.7	14 45.1	12 10.5	20 41.5	26 20.8
23	8 5 8.3	4 11.1	4 16.6	4♐ 6.9	14 29.6	23 54.1	29 51.8	8 37.3	14 45.4	12 7.9	20 41.6	26 19.5
24	8 9 4.9	5 14.2	4 13.6	20 25.3	16 4.6	25 12.4	0♏17.7	8 46.0	14 45.6	12 5.4	20 41.6	26 18.1
25	8 13 1.4	6 17.2	4 10.5	7♑17.6	17 40.4	26 30.8	0 43.4	8 54.9	14 45.8	12 2.8	20 41.6	26 16.8
26	8 16 58.0	7 19.9	4 7.5	23 59.3	19 16.8	27 49.4	1 9.0	9 3.9	14 45.8	12 .3	20 R 41.5	26 15.4
27	8 20 54.6	8 22.5	4 4.5	9♒52.7	20 53.9	29 8.1	1 34.4	9 13.0	14 45.8	11 57.9	20 41.5	26 14.1
28	8 24 51.1	9 24.8	4 1.5	24 40.8	22 31.6	0♑26.9	1 59.5	9 22.2	14 R 45.6	11 55.4	20 41.4	26 12.8
29	8 28 47.7	10 27.0	3 58.5	8♓26.2	24 9.8	1 45.8	2 24.5	9 31.5	14 45.3	11 53.0	20 41.2	26 11.4
30	8 32 44.2	11 28.9	3 55.4	21 23.1	25 48.4	3 4.8	2 49.2	9 41.0	14 44.9	11 50.6	20 41.1	26 10.0
31	8 36 40.8	12 30.6	3 52.4	3♈50.0	27 27.5	4 23.8	3 13.8	9 50.5	14 44.4	11 48.2	20 40.9	26 8.6
		DECLINATION										
1	6 38 24.0	23S 6.4	0S10.7	12S12.0	20S21.5	17S24.6	6S24.7	1N 9.9	3S29.8	23N17.0	6S53.3	23N .9
4	6 50 13.7	22 51.2	0 10.8	6N58.2	20 56.7	18 14.1	6 58.2	1 18.3	3 31.7	23 17.8	6 54.0	23 2.7
7	7 2 3.4	22 31.9	0 10.8	22 6.4	21 34.2	18 59.8	7 30.9	1 27.3	3 33.3	23 18.5	6 54.5	23 4.4
10	7 13 53.1	22 8.6	0 10.9	28 3.5	22 9.6	19 41.4	8 2.8	1 36.8	3 34.6	23 19.2	6 54.9	23 6.2
13	7 25 42.7	21 41.4	0 11.0	22 40.0	22 39.8	20 18.5	8 33.8	1 46.9	3 35.4	23 19.9	6 55.2	23 8.0
16	7 37 32.4	21 10.5	0 11.0	8 53.5	23 2.8	20 50.9	9 4.0	1 57.5	3 35.9	23 20.5	6 55.4	23 9.8
19	7 49 22.1	20 35.8	0 11.1	8S18.5	23 17.0	21 18.4	9 33.3	2 8.5	3 36.0	23 21.2	6 55.4	23 11.7
22	8 1 11.8	19 57.7	0 11.1	23 27.6	23 21.2	21 40.5	10 1.6	2 20.0	3 35.7	23 21.8	6 55.4	23 13.5
25	8 13 1.4	19 16.2	0 11.2	27 32.0	23 14.8	21 57.2	10 28.9	2 31.9	3 35.1	23 22.4	6 55.2	23 15.3
28	8 24 51.1	18 31.5	0 11.3	14 54.5	22 57.0	22 8.4	10 55.3	2 44.3	3 34.1	23 23.0	6 54.9	23 17.1
31	8 36 40.8	17 43.8	0 11.3	4N56.4	22 27.5	22 13.7	11 20.6	2 57.0	3 32.7	23 23.5	6 54.5	23 18.9

FEBRUARY 1952

LONGITUDE

DAY	EPHEM. SID. TIME h m s	☉ ° ′	☊ ° ′	☾ ° ′	☿ ° ′	♀ ° ′	♂ ° ′	♃ ° ′	♄ ° ′	♅ ° ′	♆ ° ′	♇ ° ′
1	8 40 37.3	11♒ 4.7	1♓49.1	19♈ 4.9	26♑46.6	5♑17.4	5♏16.5	10♈22.7	14♎55.8	10♋47.1	21♎41.4	20♌33.4
2	8 44 33.9	12 5.6	1 45.9	2♉14.8	28 20.1	6 30.5	5 41.5	10 33.4	14 R 55.0	10 R 45.0	21 R 41.1	20 R 31.9
3	8 48 30.4	13 6.5	1 42.7	15 1.4	29 54.3	7 43.7	6 6.2	10 44.1	14 54.0	10 42.9	21 40.8	20 30.5
4	8 52 27.0	14 7.4	1 39.5	27 28.7	1♒29.2	8 57.0	6 30.7	10 55.0	14 52.9	10 40.9	21 40.4	20 29.1
5	8 56 23.6	15 8.2	1 36.3	9♊40.7	3 4.8	10 10.3	6 54.9	11 6.0	14 51.8	10 38.9	21 40.0	20 27.6
6	9 0 20.1	16 9.0	1 33.2	21 41.6	4 41.2	11 23.6	7 18.8	11 17.1	14 50.5	10 36.9	21 39.6	20 26.1
7	9 4 16.7	17 9.8	1 30.0	3♋35.3	6 18.3	12 36.9	7 42.4	11 28.3	14 49.2	10 34.9	21 39.1	20 24.7
8	9 8 13.2	18 10.6	1 26.8	15 25.2	7 56.1	13 50.2	8 5.8	11 39.6	14 47.7	10 33.0	21 38.6	20 23.2
9	9 12 9.8	19 11.3	1 23.6	27 14.2	9 34.8	15 3.6	8 28.8	11 51.0	14 46.1	10 31.2	21 38.0	20 21.8
10	9 16 6.3	20 12.0	1 20.5	9♌ 4.8	11 14.2	16 17.0	8 51.6	12 2.5	14 44.5	10 29.3	21 37.5	20 20.3
11	9 20 2.9	21 12.7	1 17.3	20 59.3	12 54.5	17 30.4	9 14.1	12 14.1	14 42.7	10 27.5	21 36.9	20 18.9
12	9 23 59.5	22 13.4	1 14.1	2♍59.6	14 35.5	18 43.9	9 36.2	12 25.8	14 40.8	10 25.8	21 36.2	20 17.4
13	9 27 56.0	23 14.1	1 10.9	15 7.4	16 17.4	19 57.4	9 58.1	12 37.6	14 38.9	10 24.1	21 35.6	20 15.9
14	9 31 52.6	24 14.7	1 7.7	27 24.7	18 .2	21 10.9	10 19.6	12 49.4	14 36.8	10 22.4	21 34.9	20 14.5
15	9 35 49.1	25 15.3	1 4.6	9♎53.5	19 43.8	22 24.4	10 40.8	13 1.4	14 34.7	10 20.8	21 34.2	20 13.0
16	9 39 45.7	26 15.9	1 1.4	22 35.9	21 28.2	23 38.0	11 1.6	13 13.4	14 32.4	10 19.2	21 33.4	20 11.6
17	9 43 42.2	27 16.5	0 58.2	5♏34.4	23 13.6	24 51.6	11 22.2	13 25.6	14 30.1	10 17.7	21 32.7	20 10.2
18	9 47 38.8	28 17.1	0 55.0	18 50.9	24 59.9	26 5.2	11 42.3	13 37.8	14 27.7	10 16.2	21 31.9	20 8.7
19	9 51 35.3	29 17.6	0 51.9	2♐27.3	26 47.0	27 18.8	12 2.1	13 50.1	14 25.1	10 14.7	21 31.0	20 7.3
20	9 55 31.9	0♓18.1	0 48.7	16 24.6	28 35.1	28 32.4	12 21.5	14 2.4	14 22.5	10 13.3	21 30.2	20 5.8
21	9 59 28.5	1 18.6	0 45.5	0♑42.2	0♓24.0	29 46.1	12 40.5	14 14.9	14 19.8	10 11.9	21 29.3	20 4.4
22	10 3 25.0	2 19.1	0 42.3	15 17.8	2 13.8	0♒59.8	12 59.1	14 27.4	14 17.0	10 10.6	21 28.3	20 3.0
23	10 7 21.6	3 19.5	0 39.2	0♒ 7.0	4 4.4	2 13.4	13 17.3	14 40.0	14 14.1	10 9.3	21 27.4	20 1.6
24	10 11 18.1	4 19.9	0 36.0	15 3.3	5 55.9	3 27.1	13 35.1	14 52.7	14 11.2	10 8.1	21 26.4	20 .2
25	10 15 14.7	5 20.3	0 32.8	29 59.1	7 48.1	4 40.9	13 52.5	15 5.4	14 8.1	10 6.9	21 25.4	19 58.8
26	10 19 11.2	6 20.7	0 29.6	14♓46.1	9 41.1	5 54.6	14 9.5	15 18.2	14 5.0	10 5.8	21 24.4	19 57.4
27	10 23 7.8	7 21.0	0 26.4	29 17.0	11 34.7	7 8.3	14 26.0	15 31.1	14 1.8	10 4.7	21 23.3	19 56.0
28	10 27 4.3	8 21.3	0 23.3	13♈26.2	13 28.8	8 22.0	14 42.0	15 44.1	13 58.5	10 3.7	21 22.2	19 54.6
29	10 31 .9	9 21.6	0 20.1	27 10.4	15 23.3	9 35.8	14 57.6	15 57.1	13 55.1	10 2.7	21 21.1	19 53.2

LATITUDE

DAY	EPHEM. SID. TIME	☉	☊	☾	☿	♀	♂	♃	♄	♅	♆	♇
1	8 40 37.3	0 .0	0 .0	3N56.5	1S28.1	1N 6.3	1N54.8	1S11.0	2N32.7	0N23.2	1N40.3	9N10.8
4	8 52 27.0	0 .0	0 .0	5 15.5	1 41.6	0 57.0	1 55.3	1 10.4	2 33.5	0 23.2	1 40.5	9 11.2
7	9 4 16.7	0 .0	0 .0	4 25.5	1 52.4	0 47.6	1 55.8	1 9.8	2 34.3	0 23.2	1 40.7	9 11.5
10	9 16 6.3	0 .0	0 .0	1 56.2	2 .2	0 38.1	1 56.2	1 9.3	2 35.1	0 23.1	1 40.8	9 11.7
13	9 27 56.0	0 .0	0 .0	1S20.2	2 4.8	0 28.6	1 56.5	1 8.7	2 35.9	0 23.1	1 41.0	9 11.9
16	9 39 45.7	0 .0	0 .0	4 10.7	2 5.7	0 19.1	1 56.7	1 8.2	2 36.6	0 23.1	1 41.2	9 12.1
19	9 51 35.3	0 .0	0 .0	5 17.5	2 2.7	0 9.8	1 56.9	1 7.8	2 37.4	0 23.1	1 41.3	9 12.2
22	10 3 25.0	0 .0	0 .0	3 46.0	1 55.4	0 .6	1 57.0	1 7.3	2 38.1	0 23.1	1 41.5	9 12.3
25	10 15 14.7	0 .0	0 .0	0 3.3	1 43.4	0S 8.3	1 56.9	1 6.8	2 38.7	0 23.0	1 41.6	9 12.3
28	10 27 4.3	0 .0	0 .0	3N36.2	1 26.2	0 17.0	1 56.7	1 6.4	2 39.3	0 23.0	1 41.7	9 12.3

RIGHT ASCENSION

DAY	EPHEM. SID. TIME	☉	☊	☾	☿	♀	♂	♃	♄	♅	♆	♇
1	8 40 37.3	13♒32.2	3♓49.4	16♈ 5.1	29♑ 7.0	5♑42.9	3♏38.1	10♈ .1	14♎43.9	11♋45.9	20♎40.6	26♌ 7.2
2	8 44 33.9	14 33.5	3 46.4	28 23.8	0♒46.9	7 2.0	4 2.2	10 9.9	14 R 43.2	11 R 43.6	20 R 40.4	26 R 5.8
3	8 48 30.4	15 34.6	3 43.4	10♉57.9	2 27.2	8 21.1	4 26.1	10 19.8	14 42.4	11 41.3	20 40.1	26 4.3
4	8 52 27.0	16 35.4	3 40.3	23 53.3	4 7.8	9 40.3	4 49.7	10 29.7	14 41.6	11 39.1	20 39.7	26 2.9
5	8 56 23.6	17 36.1	3 37.3	7♊ 8.9	5 48.6	10 59.4	5 13.1	10 39.8	14 40.6	11 36.9	20 39.4	26 1.5
6	9 0 20.1	18 36.6	3 34.3	20 36.6	7 29.8	12 18.6	5 36.3	10 49.9	14 39.5	11 34.7	20 39.0	26 .0
7	9 4 16.7	19 36.9	3 31.3	4♋ 2.8	9 11.2	13 37.7	5 59.2	11 .2	14 38.4	11 32.6	20 38.6	25 58.6
8	9 8 13.2	20 36.9	3 28.2	17 12.6	10 52.8	14 56.8	6 21.9	11 10.5	14 37.1	11 30.6	20 38.1	25 57.2
9	9 12 9.8	21 36.8	3 25.2	29 54.7	12 34.7	16 15.8	6 44.3	11 21.0	14 35.8	11 28.5	20 37.6	25 55.7
10	9 16 6.3	22 36.4	3 22.2	12♌ 3.5	14 16.8	17 34.7	7 6.4	11 31.5	14 34.3	11 26.5	20 37.1	25 54.3
11	9 20 2.9	23 35.9	3 19.2	23 40.3	15 59.0	18 53.6	7 28.3	11 42.1	14 32.8	11 24.6	20 36.6	25 52.8
12	9 23 59.5	24 35.2	3 16.1	4♍51.4	17 41.5	20 12.4	7 49.9	11 52.8	14 31.2	11 22.7	20 36.0	25 51.3
13	9 27 56.0	25 34.3	3 13.1	15 47.1	19 24.2	21 31.1	8 11.2	12 3.6	14 29.5	11 20.8	20 35.4	25 49.9
14	9 31 52.6	26 33.1	3 10.1	26 40.3	21 7.0	22 49.7	8 32.2	12 14.5	14 27.7	11 19.0	20 34.8	25 48.4
15	9 35 49.1	27 31.8	3 7.1	7♎45.5	22 50.0	24 8.1	8 52.9	12 25.5	14 25.8	11 17.2	20 34.1	25 47.0
16	9 39 45.7	28 30.4	3 4.0	19 18.6	24 33.2	25 26.4	9 13.3	12 36.5	14 23.8	11 15.5	20 33.4	25 45.5
17	9 43 42.2	29 28.8	3 1.0	1♏35.6	26 16.5	26 44.7	9 33.4	12 47.7	14 21.8	11 13.9	20 32.8	25 44.1
18	9 47 38.8	0♓26.9	2 58.0	14 51.2	28 .0	28 2.7	9 53.1	12 58.9	14 19.6	11 12.2	20 32.0	25 42.7
19	9 51 35.3	1 24.9	2 54.9	29 13.6	29 43.6	29 20.5	10 12.5	13 10.2	14 17.4	11 10.7	20 31.3	25 41.2
20	9 55 31.9	2 22.7	2 51.9	14♐39.3	1♓27.4	0♒38.2	10 31.5	13 21.6	14 15.0	11 9.1	20 30.5	25 39.8
21	9 59 28.5	3 20.4	2 48.9	0♑47.6	3 11.3	1 55.7	10 50.1	13 33.0	14 12.6	11 7.6	20 29.7	25 38.3
22	10 3 25.0	4 17.9	2 45.9	17 4.7	4 55.3	3 13.0	11 8.4	13 44.6	14 10.1	11 6.2	20 28.8	25 36.9
23	10 7 21.6	5 15.3	2 42.8	2♒55.4	6 39.4	4 30.0	11 26.3	13 56.2	14 7.6	11 4.8	20 27.9	25 35.5
24	10 11 18.1	6 12.4	2 39.8	17 57.5	8 23.5	5 46.9	11 43.8	14 7.8	14 4.9	11 3.5	20 27.0	25 34.0
25	10 15 14.7	7 9.5	2 36.8	2♓ 5.8	10 7.7	7 3.6	12 .9	14 19.6	14 2.2	11 2.2	20 26.1	25 32.6
26	10 19 11.2	8 6.4	2 33.7	15 28.2	11 51.9	8 20.0	12 17.6	14 31.4	13 59.4	11 1.0	20 25.2	25 31.2
27	10 23 7.8	9 3.1	2 30.7	28 19.7	13 36.1	9 36.2	12 33.8	14 43.3	13 56.5	10 59.8	20 24.2	25 29.8
28	10 27 4.3	9 59.7	2 27.7	10♈56.8	15 20.1	10 52.2	12 49.6	14 55.2	13 53.5	10 58.7	20 23.2	25 28.4
29	10 31 .9	10 56.2	2 24.6	23 34.6	17 3.9	12 7.9	13 5.0	15 7.2	13 50.5	10 57.6	20 22.2	25 27.0

DECLINATION

DAY	EPHEM. SID. TIME	☉	☊	☾	☿	♀	♂	♃	♄	♅	♆	♇
1	8 40 37.3	17S27.3	0S11.3	11N 7.1	22S15.0	22S14.2	11S28.8	3N 1.3	3S32.2	23N23.7	6S54.4	23N19.5
4	8 52 27.0	16 35.8	0 11.4	24 43.2	21 29.2	22 11.8	11 52.7	3 14.5	3 30.3	23 24.2	6 53.8	23 21.2
7	9 4 16.7	15 41.8	0 11.5	27 49.4	20 31.1	22 3.6	12 15.6	3 28.1	3 28.1	23 24.6	6 53.2	23 22.9
10	9 16 6.3	14 45.4	0 11.5	19 51.6	19 20.2	21 49.5	12 37.3	3 41.9	3 25.6	23 25.1	6 52.4	23 24.6
13	9 27 56.0	13 46.7	0 11.6	4 37.9	17 56.6	21 29.5	12 58.0	3 56.1	3 22.7	23 25.5	6 51.5	23 26.2
16	9 39 45.7	12 46.0	0 11.6	12S40.2	16 20.1	21 3.9	13 17.5	4 10.5	3 19.5	23 25.8	6 50.6	23 27.8
19	9 51 35.3	11 43.4	0 11.7	25 50.6	14 30.7	20 32.7	13 35.8	4 25.1	3 16.1	23 26.2	6 49.5	23 29.4
22	10 3 25.0	10 39.2	0 11.8	26 18.8	12 28.8	19 56.0	13 53.0	4 40.0	3 12.3	23 26.4	6 48.4	23 30.9
25	10 15 14.7	9 33.4	0 11.8	11 32.0	10 14.7	19 14.1	14 8.9	4 55.1	3 8.2	23 26.7	6 47.2	23 32.3
28	10 27 4.3	8 26.4	0 11.9	8N37.4	7 49.4	18 27.1	14 23.6	5 10.4	3 3.9	23 26.9	6 45.9	23 33.6

MARCH 1952

LONGITUDE

DAY	EPHEM. SID. TIME h m s	☉ ° ′	☊ ° ′	☽ ° ′	☿ ° ′	♀ ° ′	♂ ° ′	♃ ° ′	♄ ° ′	♅ ° ′	♆ ° ′	♇ ° ′
1	10 34 57.4	10♓21.8	0♓16.9	10♉28.7	17♓18.2	10♒49.6	15♏12.7	16♈10.2	13♎51.7	10♋ 1.8	21♎20.0	19♌51.9
2	10 38 54.0	11 22.0	0 13.7	23 22.4	19 13.2	12 3.3	15 27.3	16 23.3	13 R 48.1	10 R .9	21 R 18.8	19 R 50.5
3	10 42 50.6	12 22.2	0 10.6	5♊54.4	21 8.1	13 17.1	15 41.5	16 36.5	13 44.6	10 .1	21 17.6	19 49.2
4	10 46 47.1	13 22.3	0 7.4	18 8.5	23 2.7	14 30.8	15 55.1	16 49.7	13 40.9	9 59.3	21 16.4	19 47.9
5	10 50 43.7	14 22.4	0 4.2	0♋ 9.5	24 56.7	15 44.6	16 8.3	17 3.1	13 37.2	9 58.6	21 15.2	19 46.6
6	10 54 40.2	15 22.5	0 1.0	12 2.0	26 49.8	16 58.4	16 20.9	17 16.4	13 33.4	9 57.9	21 14.0	19 45.3
7	10 58 36.8	16 22.5	29♒57.8	23 50.6	28 41.6	18 12.2	16 33.0	17 29.8	13 29.6	9 57.3	21 12.7	19 44.0
8	11 2 33.3	17 22.5	29 54.7	5♌39.8	0♈31.9	19 26.0	16 44.6	17 43.3	13 25.6	9 56.7	21 11.4	19 42.7
9	11 6 29.9	18 22.5	29 51.5	17 33.1	2 20.1	20 39.8	16 55.7	17 56.9	13 21.7	9 56.3	21 10.1	19 41.5
10	11 10 26.4	19 22.5	29 48.3	29 33.9	4 5.8	21 53.6	17 6.2	18 10.5	13 17.7	9 55.8	21 8.8	19 40.3
11	11 14 23.0	20 22.3	29 45.1	11♍44.5	5 48.5	23 7.5	17 16.1	18 24.1	13 13.6	9 55.4	21 7.5	19 39.0
12	11 18 19.5	21 22.2	29 42.0	24 6.8	7 27.8	24 21.3	17 25.4	18 37.7	13 9.5	9 55.0	21 6.1	19 37.8
13	11 22 16.1	22 22.0	29 38.8	6♎41.9	9 3.0	25 35.1	17 34.1	18 51.5	13 5.3	9 54.7	21 4.7	19 36.6
14	11 26 12.6	23 21.8	29 35.6	19 30.5	10 33.8	26 48.9	17 42.2	19 5.2	13 1.1	9 54.5	21 3.3	19 35.5
15	11 30 9.2	24 21.6	29 32.4	2♏32.6	11 59.5	28 2.8	17 49.8	19 19.0	12 56.8	9 54.3	21 1.9	19 34.3
16	11 34 5.8	25 21.3	29 29.2	15 48.3	13 19.8	29 16.6	17 56.6	19 32.8	12 52.5	9 54.2	21 .4	19 33.2
17	11 38 2.3	26 21.0	29 26.1	29 17.2	14 34.2	0♓30.4	18 2.9	19 46.7	12 48.2	9 54.1	20 59.0	19 32.0
18	11 41 58.9	27 20.7	29 22.9	12♐58.9	15 42.2	1 44.3	18 8.5	20 .6	12 43.8	9 54.0	20 57.5	19 30.9
19	11 45 55.4	28 20.4	29 19.7	26 53.2	16 43.5	2 58.1	18 13.4	20 14.6	12 39.3	9 D 54.1	20 56.0	19 29.9
20	11 49 52.0	29 20.0	29 16.5	10♑59.1	17 37.7	4 12.0	18 17.7	20 28.6	12 34.9	9 54.1	20 54.5	19 28.8
21	11 53 48.5	0♈19.6	29 13.4	25 15.4	18 24.6	5 25.9	18 21.2	20 42.6	12 30.4	9 54.3	20 53.0	19 27.7
22	11 57 45.1	1 19.1	29 10.2	9♒40.0	19 4.0	6 39.7	18 24.1	20 56.6	12 25.8	9 54.4	20 51.5	19 26.7
23	12 1 41.6	2 18.7	29 7.0	24 9.7	19 35.6	7 53.6	18 26.2	21 10.7	12 21.3	9 54.7	20 50.0	19 25.7
24	12 5 38.2	3 18.2	29 3.8	8♓40.0	19 59.5	9 7.5	18 27.7	21 24.9	12 16.7	9 55.0	20 48.4	19 24.7
25	12 9 34.7	4 17.7	29 .6	23 5.8	20 15.5	10 21.3	18 28.4	21 39.0	12 12.1	9 55.3	20 46.9	19 23.8
26	12 13 31.3	5 17.1	28 57.5	7♈21.3	20 23.7	11 35.2	18 28.4	21 53.2	12 7.5	9 55.7	20 45.3	19 22.8
27	12 17 27.8	6 16.5	28 54.3	21 21.4	20 24.3	12 49.1	18 R 27.6	22 7.4	12 2.8	9 56.1	20 43.7	19 21.9
28	12 21 24.4	7 15.9	28 51.1	5♉ 1.9	20 R 17.5	14 2.9	18 26.1	22 21.6	11 58.2	9 56.7	20 42.1	19 21.0
29	12 25 20.9	8 15.2	28 47.9	18 20.5	20 3.5	15 16.8	18 23.8	22 35.9	11 53.5	9 57.2	20 40.5	19 20.1
30	12 29 17.5	9 14.5	28 44.8	1♊16.6	19 43.0	16 30.7	18 20.8	22 50.2	11 48.9	9 57.9	20 39.0	19 19.3
31	12 33 14.1	10 13.8	28 41.6	13 51.5	19 16.2	17 44.6	18 17.0	23 4.5	11 44.2	9 58.5	20 37.3	19 18.5

LATITUDE

DAY	SID. TIME	☉	☊	☽	☿	♀	♂	♃	♄	♅	♆	♇
1	10 34 57.4	0 .0	0 .0	4N58.0	1S11.7	0S22.6	1N56.6	1S 6.1	2N39.7	0N23.0	1N41.8	9N12.3
4	10 46 47.1	0 .0	0 .0	5 2.2	0 45.6	0 30.8	1 56.1	1 5.8	2 40.3	0 23.0	1 42.0	9 12.2
7	10 58 36.8	0 .0	0 .0	3 9.7	0 14.2	0 38.5	1 55.6	1 5.4	2 40.8	0 22.9	1 42.1	9 12.1
10	11 10 26.4	0 .0	0 .0	0 5.7	0N21.6	0 45.9	1 54.8	1 5.0	2 41.3	0 22.9	1 42.2	9 12.0
13	11 22 16.1	0 .0	0 .0	3S 6.0	1 .2	0 52.8	1 53.8	1 4.7	2 41.7	0 22.9	1 42.3	9 11.8
16	11 34 5.8	0 .0	0 .0	5 3.9	1 39.5	0 59.2	1 52.6	1 4.4	2 42.1	0 22.8	1 42.4	9 11.5
19	11 45 55.4	0 .0	0 .0	4 40.8	2 16.5	1 5.1	1 51.1	1 4.1	2 42.4	0 22.8	1 42.5	9 11.3
22	11 57 45.1	0 .0	0 .0	1 50.8	2 48.0	1 10.5	1 49.3	1 3.8	2 42.7	0 22.8	1 42.6	9 11.0
25	12 9 34.7	0 .0	0 .0	2N 1.2	3 11.0	1 15.3	1 47.2	1 3.6	2 42.9	0 22.7	1 42.6	9 10.7
28	12 21 24.4	0 .0	0 .0	4 41.7	3 22.3	1 19.5	1 44.8	1 3.4	2 43.1	0 22.7	1 42.7	9 10.3
31	12 33 14.1	0 .0	0 .0	5 1.2	3 19.4	1 23.1	1 42.0	1 3.1	2 43.2	0 22.7	1 42.7	9 9.9

RIGHT ASCENSION

DAY	SID. TIME	☉	☊	☽	☿	♀	♂	♃	♄	♅	♆	♇
1	10 34 57.4	11♓52.5	2♓21.6	6♉24.5	18♓47.4	13♒23.3	13♏19.9	15♈19.3	13♎47.4	10♋56.6	20♎21.1	25♌25.6
2	10 38 54.0	12 48.7	2 18.6	19 33.0	20 30.5	14 38.6	13 34.3	15 31.4	13 R 44.2	10 R 55.7	20 R 20.1	25 R 24.2
3	10 42 50.6	13 44.7	2 15.5	2♊59.4	22 13.1	15 53.5	13 48.3	15 43.6	13 41.0	10 54.8	20 19.0	25 22.9
4	10 46 47.1	14 40.7	2 12.5	16 36.2	23 54.9	17 8.3	14 1.7	15 55.9	13 37.7	10 53.9	20 17.9	25 21.5
5	10 50 43.7	15 36.5	2 9.5	0♋10.7	25 35.7	18 22.7	14 14.7	16 8.2	13 34.3	10 53.1	20 16.8	25 20.2
6	10 54 40.2	16 32.2	2 6.4	13 28.8	27 15.5	19 36.9	14 27.2	16 20.6	13 30.9	10 52.4	20 15.6	25 18.8
7	10 58 36.8	17 27.8	2 3.4	26 19.3	28 53.8	20 50.9	14 39.1	16 33.0	13 27.4	10 51.7	20 14.4	25 17.5
8	11 2 33.3	18 23.3	2 .4	8♌37.0	0♈30.3	22 4.6	14 50.5	16 45.4	13 23.9	10 51.1	20 13.2	25 16.2
9	11 6 29.9	19 18.7	1 57.3	20 22.7	2 4.9	23 18.0	15 1.5	16 58.0	13 20.3	10 50.6	20 12.1	25 15.0
10	11 10 26.4	20 14.0	1 54.3	1♍42.5	3 37.0	24 31.2	15 11.8	17 10.6	13 16.7	10 50.1	20 10.9	25 13.7
11	11 14 23.0	21 9.3	1 51.3	12 46.2	5 6.3	25 44.2	15 21.5	17 23.2	13 13.0	10 49.6	20 9.6	25 12.4
12	11 18 19.5	22 4.4	1 48.2	23 45.8	6 32.5	26 56.8	15 30.7	17 35.9	13 9.2	10 49.3	20 8.3	25 11.2
13	11 22 16.1	22 59.5	1 45.2	4♎55.1	7 55.0	28 9.3	15 39.3	17 48.6	13 5.4	10 48.9	20 7.1	25 9.9
14	11 26 12.6	23 54.5	1 42.1	16 28.7	9 13.6	29 21.5	15 47.3	18 1.4	13 1.6	10 48.7	20 5.8	25 8.7
15	11 30 9.2	24 49.4	1 39.1	28 41.3	10 27.7	0♓33.4	15 54.6	18 14.2	12 57.7	10 48.4	20 4.5	25 7.5
16	11 34 5.8	25 44.3	1 36.1	11♏45.8	11 36.9	1 45.2	16 1.4	18 27.0	12 53.8	10 48.3	20 3.1	25 6.3
17	11 38 2.3	26 39.1	1 33.0	25 49.6	12 40.9	2 56.6	16 7.5	18 39.9	12 49.8	10 48.2	20 1.8	25 5.1
18	11 41 58.9	27 33.9	1 30.0	10♐49.6	13 39.3	4 7.9	16 12.9	18 52.9	12 45.8	10 48.1	20 .4	25 4.0
19	11 45 55.4	28 28.6	1 26.9	26 28.9	14 31.8	5 19.0	16 17.7	19 5.9	12 41.8	10 D 48.2	19 59.0	25 2.8
20	11 49 52.0	29 23.3	1 23.9	12♑18.8	15 18.0	6 29.8	16 21.7	19 18.9	12 37.7	10 48.2	19 57.7	25 1.7
21	11 53 48.5	0♈18.0	1 20.9	27 48.8	15 57.8	7 40.4	16 25.1	19 31.9	12 33.6	10 48.4	19 56.3	25 .6
22	11 57 45.1	1 12.6	1 17.8	12♒38.0	16 30.9	8 50.8	16 27.8	19 45.0	12 29.4	10 48.6	19 54.8	24 59.5
23	12 1 41.6	2 7.2	1 14.8	26 39.8	16 57.2	10 1.0	16 29.8	19 58.2	12 25.3	10 48.8	19 53.4	24 58.5
24	12 5 38.2	3 1.9	1 11.7	10♓ .1	17 16.6	11 11.0	16 31.0	20 11.3	12 21.1	10 49.1	19 52.0	24 57.4
25	12 9 34.7	3 56.4	1 8.7	22 51.8	17 29.1	12 20.8	16 31.5	20 24.6	12 16.9	10 49.5	19 50.5	24 56.4
26	12 13 31.3	4 51.0	1 5.6	5♈30.5	17 34.8	13 30.5	16 R 31.3	20 37.8	12 12.6	10 50.0	19 49.1	24 55.4
27	12 17 27.8	5 45.6	1 2.6	18 11.2	17 R 33.9	14 40.0	16 30.3	20 51.1	12 8.4	10 50.4	19 47.6	24 54.4
28	12 21 24.4	6 40.2	0 59.6	1♉ 6.0	17 26.6	15 49.3	16 28.5	21 4.4	12 4.1	10 51.0	19 46.1	24 53.5
29	12 25 20.9	7 34.8	0 56.5	14 21.9	17 13.2	16 58.4	16 26.0	21 17.7	11 59.9	10 51.6	19 44.7	24 52.5
30	12 29 17.5	8 29.4	0 53.5	27 58.8	16 54.3	18 7.4	16 22.7	21 31.1	11 55.6	10 52.3	19 43.2	24 51.7
31	12 33 14.1	9 24.1	0 50.4	11♊48.9	16 30.2	19 16.3	16 18.7	21 44.5	11 51.3	10 53.0	19 41.7	24 50.8

DECLINATION

DAY	SID. TIME	☉	☊	☽	☿	♀	♂	♃	♄	♅	♆	♇
1	10 34 57.4	7S41.1	0S11.9	19N40.8	6S 7.1	17S53.2	14S32.7	5N20.7	3S .9	23N27.0	6S44.9	23N34.5
4	10 46 47.1	6 32.3	0 12.0	26 56.1	3 27.6	16 58.5	14 45.3	5 36.2	2 56.3	23 27.2	6 43.5	23 35.7
7	10 58 36.8	5 22.7	0 12.0	24 27.4	0 44.2	15 59.4	14 56.7	5 51.8	2 51.4	23 27.3	6 42.0	23 36.9
10	11 10 26.4	4 12.5	0 12.1	11 43.1	1N57.6	14 56.3	15 6.7	6 7.6	2 46.4	23 27.4	6 40.4	23 38.0
13	11 22 16.1	3 1.8	0 12.1	5S30.4	4 30.7	13 49.5	15 15.5	6 23.5	2 41.2	23 27.5	6 38.8	23 39.0
16	11 34 5.8	1 50.8	0 12.2	21 25.1	6 47.5	12 39.2	15 22.9	6 39.4	2 35.9	23 27.5	6 37.1	23 39.9
19	11 45 55.4	0 39.7	0 12.3	28 5.4	8 40.5	11 25.8	15 29.0	6 55.4	2 30.5	23 27.4	6 35.4	23 40.7
22	11 57 45.1	0N31.5	0 12.3	19 36.9	10 3.5	10 9.6	15 33.6	7 11.5	2 25.0	23 27.4	6 33.6	23 41.5
25	12 9 34.7	1 42.4	0 12.4	0 53.1	10 51.9	8 50.9	15 36.8	7 27.5	2 19.4	23 27.3	6 31.8	23 42.1
28	12 21 24.4	2 53.1	0 12.4	17N37.3	11 3.1	7 30.0	15 38.5	7 43.6	2 13.8	23 27.1	6 30.0	23 42.7
31	12 33 14.1	4 3.2	0 12.5	27 27.3	10 37.2	6 7.2	15 38.7	7 59.7	2 8.3	23 27.0	6 28.2	23 43.2

APRIL 1952

LONGITUDE

DAY	EPHEM. SID. TIME	☉	☊	☾	☿	♀	♂	♃	♄	♅	♆	♇
	h m s	° ′	° ′	° ′	° ′	° ′	° ′	° ′	° ′	° ′	° ′	° ′
1	12 37 10.6	11♈13.0	28♒38.4	26♊ 8.2	18♈44.0	18♓58.4	18♏12.5	23♈18.8	11♎39.6	9♋59.3	20♎35.7	19♌17.7
2	12 41 7.2	12 12.2	28 35.2	8♋10.8	18R 7.0	20 12.2	18R 7.1	23 33.1	11R34.9	10 .0	20R34.1	19R16.9
3	12 45 3.7	13 11.4	28 32.0	20 4.0	17 26.0	21 26.1	18 1.1	23 47.5	11 30.2	10 .9	20 32.5	19 16.1
4	12 49 .3	14 10.5	28 28.9	1♌53.1	16 42.0	22 39.9	17 54.2	24 1.8	11 25.5	10 1.7	20 30.8	19 15.4
5	12 52 56.8	15 9.5	28 25.7	13 43.0	15 55.7	23 53.7	17 46.6	24 16.2	11 20.9	10 2.7	20 29.2	19 14.7
6	12 56 53.4	16 8.6	28 22.5	25 38.9	15 8.3	25 7.6	17 38.2	24 30.6	11 16.2	10 3.6	20 27.6	19 14.0
7	13 0 49.9	17 7.5	28 19.3	7♍44.9	14 20.6	26 21.4	17 29.1	24 45.0	11 11.6	10 4.7	20 25.9	19 13.3
8	13 4 46.5	18 6.5	28 16.2	20 4.8	13 33.5	27 35.2	17 19.2	24 59.4	11 7.0	10 5.8	20 24.3	19 12.7
9	13 8 43.0	19 5.4	28 13.0	2♎40.9	12 47.9	28 49.0	17 8.6	25 13.8	11 2.3	10 6.9	20 22.6	19 12.1
10	13 12 39.6	20 4.3	28 9.8	15 34.6	12 4.6	0♈ 2.8	16 57.2	25 28.2	10 57.8	10 8.1	20 21.0	19 11.5
11	13 16 36.1	21 3.2	28 6.6	28 45.7	11 24.3	1 16.6	16 45.1	25 42.6	10 53.2	10 9.3	20 19.3	19 10.9
12	13 20 32.7	22 2.0	28 3.4	12♏12.9	10 47.5	2 30.4	16 32.3	25 57.1	10 48.6	10 10.6	20 17.7	19 10.4
13	13 24 29.3	23 .8	28 .3	25 53.7	10 14.9	3 44.2	16 18.8	26 11.5	10 44.1	10 11.9	20 16.0	19 9.9
14	13 28 25.8	23 59.5	27 57.1	9♐45.1	9 46.7	4 58.0	16 4.6	26 26.0	10 39.6	10 13.3	20 14.4	19 9.4
15	13 32 22.4	24 58.2	27 53.9	23 44.2	9 23.3	6 11.8	15 49.6	26 40.4	10 35.2	10 14.8	20 12.7	19 9.0
16	13 36 18.9	25 56.9	27 50.7	7♑48.2	9 5.0	7 25.6	15 34.1	26 54.9	10 30.7	10 16.2	20 11.1	19 8.5
17	13 40 15.5	26 55.6	27 47.6	21 55.0	8 51.7	8 39.4	15 17.8	27 9.3	10 26.3	10 17.8	20 9.4	19 8.1
18	13 44 12.0	27 54.2	27 44.4	6♒ 3.0	8 43.7	9 53.2	15 1.0	27 23.8	10 22.0	10 19.3	20 7.8	19 7.8
19	13 48 8.6	28 52.9	27 41.2	20 11.2	8 40.8	11 7.0	14 43.5	27 38.2	10 17.7	10 21.0	20 6.2	19 7.4
20	13 52 5.1	29 51.5	27 38.0	4♓18.2	8D43.1	12 20.8	14 25.5	27 52.7	10 13.4	10 22.7	20 4.6	19 7.1
21	13 56 1.7	0♉50.1	27 34.9	18 22.3	8 50.3	13 34.6	14 6.9	28 7.1	10 9.2	10 24.4	20 3.0	19 6.9
22	13 59 58.2	1 48.6	27 31.7	2♈21.3	9 2.5	14 48.4	13 47.8	28 21.6	10 5.0	10 26.2	20 1.4	19 6.6
23	14 3 54.8	2 47.1	27 28.5	16 12.1	9 19.4	16 2.1	13 28.2	28 36.0	10 .9	10 28.0	19 59.8	19 6.4
24	14 7 51.4	3 45.6	27 25.3	29 51.5	9 41.0	17 15.9	13 8.1	28 50.4	9 56.8	10 29.9	19 58.2	19 6.1
25	14 11 47.9	4 44.0	27 22.1	13♉16.2	10 7.0	18 29.7	12 47.7	29 4.8	9 52.8	10 31.8	19 56.6	19 6.0
26	14 15 44.5	5 42.4	27 19.0	26 24.0	10 37.2	19 43.4	12 26.9	29 19.2	9 48.8	10 33.7	19 55.0	19 5.8
27	14 19 41.0	6 40.8	27 15.8	9♊13.5	11 11.6	20 57.2	12 5.7	29 33.6	9 44.9	10 35.7	19 53.5	19 5.7
28	14 23 37.6	7 39.1	27 12.6	21 45.0	11 49.9	22 10.9	11 44.3	29 48.0	9 41.0	10 37.8	19 51.9	19 5.6
29	14 27 34.1	8 37.5	27 9.4	4♋ .3	12 31.9	23 24.7	11 22.6	0♉ 2.4	9 37.2	10 39.8	19 50.3	19 5.5
30	14 31 30.7	9 35.7	27 6.3	16 2.4	13 17.5	24 38.4	11 .7	0 16.7	9 33.5	10 42.0	19 48.8	19 5.5

LATITUDE

DAY	EPHEM. SID. TIME	☉	☊	☾	☿	♀	♂	♃	♄	♅	♆	♇
1	12 37 10.6	0 .0	0 .0	4N38.3	3N15.1	1S24.2	1N41.0	1S 3.1	2N43.3	0N22.6	1N42.8	9N 9.8
4	12 49 .3	0 .0	0 .0	2 25.3	2 52.1	1 27.0	1 37.6	1 2.9	2 43.3	0 22.6	1 42.8	9 9.4
7	13 0 49.9	0 .0	0 .0	0S43.1	2 16.1	1 29.1	1 33.8	1 2.7	2 43.3	0 22.6	1 42.8	9 8.9
10	13 12 39.6	0 .0	0 .0	3 41.1	1 30.9	1 30.7	1 29.5	1 2.6	2 43.3	0 22.5	1 42.9	9 8.5
13	13 24 29.3	0 .0	0 .0	5 5.3	0 41.7	1 31.6	1 24.7	1 2.4	2 43.2	0 22.5	1 42.9	9 8.0
16	13 36 18.9	0 .0	0 .0	3 58.2	0S 7.1	1 32.0	1 19.5	1 2.3	2 43.0	0 22.5	1 42.9	9 7.5
19	13 48 8.6	0 .0	0 .0	0 46.0	0 51.9	1 31.7	1 13.7	1 2.2	2 42.8	0 22.4	1 42.9	9 7.0
22	13 59 58.2	0 .0	0 .0	2N48.9	1 30.9	1 30.7	1 7.5	1 2.1	2 42.5	0 22.4	1 42.8	9 6.5
25	14 11 47.9	0 .0	0 .0	4 52.4	2 3.2	1 29.2	1 .8	1 2.1	2 42.2	0 22.4	1 42.8	9 5.9
28	14 23 37.6	0 .0	0 .0	4 36.8	2 28.5	1 27.2	0 53.7	1 2.0	2 41.9	0 22.4	1 42.8	9 5.4

RIGHT ASCENSION

DAY	EPHEM. SID. TIME	☉	☊	☾	☿	♀	♂	♃	♄	♅	♆	♇
1	12 37 10.6	10♈18.7	0♓47.4	25♊38.3	16♈ 1.6	20♓25.0	16♏13.8	21♈57.9	11♎47.1	10♋53.8	19♎40.2	24♌49.9
2	12 41 7.2	11 13.3	0 44.3	9♋11.2	15R29.3	21 33.6	16R 8.2	22 11.3	11R42.8	10 54.7	19R38.7	24R49.1
3	12 45 3.7	12 8.0	0 41.3	22 15.0	14 54.0	22 42.0	16 1.8	22 24.7	11 38.5	10 55.6	19 37.2	24 48.2
4	12 49 .3	13 2.7	0 38.2	4♌43.4	14 16.4	23 50.4	15 54.7	22 38.2	11 34.2	10 56.5	19 35.7	24 47.4
5	12 52 56.8	13 57.5	0 35.2	16 37.0	13 37.5	24 58.6	15 46.7	22 51.7	11 29.9	10 57.5	19 34.1	24 46.7
6	12 56 53.4	14 52.3	0 32.1	28 2.3	12 58.1	26 6.8	15 38.0	23 5.2	11 25.6	10 58.6	19 32.6	24 45.9
7	13 0 49.9	15 47.1	0 29.1	9♍ 9.4	12 18.9	27 14.8	15 28.5	23 18.7	11 21.3	10 59.7	19 31.1	24 45.2
8	13 4 46.5	16 42.0	0 26.0	20 10.8	11 40.8	28 22.8	15 18.3	23 32.3	11 17.1	11 .9	19 29.5	24 44.5
9	13 8 43.0	17 36.9	0 23.0	1♎20.8	11 4.5	29 30.8	15 7.3	23 45.8	11 12.8	11 2.1	19 28.0	24 43.8
10	13 12 39.6	18 31.9	0 20.0	12 54.4	10 30.6	0♈38.7	14 55.5	23 59.4	11 8.6	11 3.4	19 26.5	24 43.1
11	13 16 36.1	19 27.0	0 16.9	25 6.7	9 59.7	1 46.5	14 43.1	24 13.0	11 4.4	11 4.7	19 24.9	24 42.5
12	13 20 32.7	20 22.1	0 13.9	8♏11.0	9 32.2	2 54.3	14 29.8	24 26.6	11 .2	11 6.1	19 23.4	24 41.9
13	13 24 29.3	21 17.3	0 10.8	22 15.1	9 8.6	4 2.1	14 15.9	24 40.2	10 56.0	11 7.6	19 21.9	24 41.3
14	13 28 25.8	22 12.6	0 7.7	7♐15.8	8 49.2	5 9.9	14 1.3	24 53.8	10 51.8	11 9.1	19 20.3	24 40.8
15	13 32 22.4	23 8.0	0 4.7	22 55.9	8 34.0	6 17.7	13 45.9	25 7.5	10 47.7	11 10.6	19 18.8	24 40.3
16	13 36 18.9	24 3.5	0 1.6	8♑45.5	8 23.4	7 25.5	13 29.9	25 21.1	10 43.6	11 12.3	19 17.3	24 39.8
17	13 40 15.5	24 59.1	29♒58.6	24 13.1	8 17.3	8 33.3	13 13.3	25 34.8	10 39.6	11 13.9	19 15.7	24 39.3
18	13 44 12.0	25 54.7	29 55.5	8♒57.1	8 15.8	9 41.2	12 56.0	25 48.5	10 35.5	11 15.6	19 14.2	24 38.9
19	13 48 8.6	26 50.5	29 52.5	22 50.7	8D18.8	10 49.0	12 38.1	26 2.1	10 31.5	11 17.4	19 12.7	24 38.5
20	13 52 5.1	27 46.4	29 49.4	5♓60.0	8 26.3	11 57.0	12 19.6	26 15.8	10 27.6	11 19.3	19 11.2	24 38.1
21	13 56 1.7	28 42.4	29 46.4	18 38.4	8 38.1	13 5.0	12 .6	26 29.5	10 23.7	11 21.1	19 9.7	24 37.8
22	13 59 58.2	29 38.5	29 43.3	1♈ 2.4	8 54.2	14 13.1	11 41.1	26 43.2	10 19.8	11 23.1	19 8.2	24 37.4
23	14 3 54.8	0♉34.7	29 40.3	13 28.0	9 14.3	15 21.2	11 21.1	26 56.9	10 16.0	11 25.0	19 6.7	24 37.1
24	14 7 51.4	1 31.1	29 37.2	26 9.2	9 38.3	16 29.4	11 .6	27 10.6	10 12.2	11 27.0	19 5.2	24 36.8
25	14 11 47.9	2 27.5	29 34.2	9♉15.0	10 6.2	17 37.7	10 39.7	27 24.3	10 8.4	11 29.1	19 3.8	24 36.6
26	14 15 44.5	3 24.1	29 31.1	22 48.0	10 37.6	18 46.1	10 18.5	27 37.9	10 4.7	11 31.2	19 2.3	24 36.4
27	14 19 41.0	4 20.8	29 28.0	6♊41.6	11 12.5	19 54.6	9 56.9	27 51.6	10 1.1	11 33.4	19 .8	24 36.2
28	14 23 37.6	5 17.6	29 25.0	20 41.8	11 50.8	21 3.3	9 35.1	28 5.3	9 57.5	11 35.6	18 59.4	24 36.0
29	14 27 34.1	6 14.5	29 21.9	4♋30.2	12 32.2	22 12.1	9 13.0	28 19.0	9 53.9	11 37.9	18 57.9	24 35.9
30	14 31 30.7	7 11.6	29 18.9	17 50.6	13 16.6	23 21.0	8 50.7	28 32.6	9 50.5	11 40.2	18 56.5	24 35.8

DECLINATION

DAY	EPHEM. SID. TIME	☉	☊	☾	☿	♀	♂	♃	♄	♅	♆	♇
1	12 37 10.6	4N26.4	0S12.5	28N 1.7	10N20.9	5S39.3	15S38.4	8N 5.0	2S 6.4	23N26.9	6S27.5	23N43.3
4	12 49 .3	5 35.5	0 12.6	22 6.4	9 12.8	4 14.6	15 36.6	8 21.0	2 .9	23 26.7	6 25.7	23 43.6
7	13 0 49.9	6 43.7	0 12.6	7 59.9	7 44.8	2 48.7	15 33.3	8 37.0	1 55.5	23 26.4	6 23.8	23 43.9
10	13 12 39.6	7 50.9	0 12.7	9S31.9	6 10.2	1 22.1	15 28.5	8 52.9	1 50.1	23 26.1	6 21.9	23 44.1
13	13 24 29.3	8 56.9	0 12.7	24 10.5	4 41.9	0N 5.1	15 22.2	9 8.7	1 44.9	23 25.8	6 20.0	23 44.1
16	13 36 18.9	10 1.6	0 12.8	27 10.9	3 29.6	1 32.4	15 14.4	9 24.5	1 39.8	23 25.4	6 18.2	23 44.1
19	13 48 8.6	11 4.8	0 12.9	15 29.2	2 38.8	2 59.6	15 5.2	9 40.1	1 34.9	23 25.0	6 16.4	23 44.0
22	13 59 58.2	12 6.4	0 12.9	3N31.1	2 11.5	4 26.5	14 54.7	9 55.6	1 30.2	23 24.6	6 14.6	23 43.7
25	14 11 47.9	13 6.2	0 13.0	20 28.1	2 7.1	5 52.5	14 43.1	10 11.0	1 25.7	23 24.1	6 12.8	23 43.4
28	14 23 37.6	14 4.1	0 13.0	27 47.6	2 24.0	7 17.5	14 30.5	10 26.3	1 21.4	23 23.6	6 11.1	23 43.0

MAY 1952

LONGITUDE

DAY	EPHEM. SID. TIME h m s	☉ ° ′	☊ ° ′	☽ ° ′	☿ ° ′	♀ ° ′	♂ ° ′	♃ ° ′	♄ ° ′	♅ ° ′	♆ ° ′	♇ ° ′
1	14 35 27.2	10♉34.0	27♒ 3.1	27♋55.4	14♈ 6.6	25♈52.1	10♏38.7	0♉31.0	9♎29.8	10♋44.1	19♎47.3	19♌ 5.5
2	14 39 23.8	11 32.2	26 59.9	9♌44.3	14 59.0	27 5.9	10R16.6	0 45.3	9R26.2	10 46.3	19R45.8	19 5.5
3	14 43 20.4	12 30.4	26 56.7	21 34.4	15 54.6	28 19.6	9 54.4	0 59.6	9 22.7	10 48.6	19 44.3	19 5.5
4	14 47 16.9	13 28.5	26 53.5	3♍31.1	16 53.3	29 33.3	9 32.2	1 13.9	9 19.2	10 50.9	19 42.8	19D 5.6
5	14 51 13.5	14 26.6	26 50.4	15 39.7	17 54.9	0♉47.0	9 10.0	1 28.1	9 15.8	10 53.2	19 41.3	19 5.7
6	14 55 10.0	15 24.7	26 47.2	28 4.8	18 59.3	2 .7	8 47.9	1 42.3	9 12.5	10 55.6	19 39.9	19 5.9
7	14 59 6.6	16 22.8	26 44.0	10♎50.0	20 6.5	3 14.4	8 25.9	1 56.5	9 9.3	10 58.0	19 38.5	19 6.0
8	15 3 3.1	17 20.8	26 40.8	23 57.5	21 16.3	4 28.0	8 4.1	2 10.7	9 6.1	11 .4	19 37.0	19 6.2
9	15 6 59.7	18 18.8	26 37.7	7♏27.3	22 28.7	5 41.7	7 42.5	2 24.9	9 3.0	11 2.9	19 35.6	19 6.4
10	15 10 56.2	19 16.7	26 34.5	21 17.6	23 43.7	6 55.4	7 21.1	2 39.0	8 60.0	11 5.4	19 34.2	19 6.7
11	15 14 52.8	20 14.7	26 31.3	5♐24.6	25 1.1	8 9.1	7 .1	2 53.1	8 57.1	11 8.1	19 32.9	19 7.0
12	15 18 49.4	21 12.6	26 28.1	19 42.8	26 20.9	9 22.8	6 39.4	3 7.2	8 54.3	11 10.6	19 31.6	19 7.3
13	15 22 45.9	22 10.5	26 25.0	4♑ 6.5	27 43.0	10 36.4	6 19.0	3 21.2	8 51.5	11 13.3	19 30.2	19 7.6
14	15 26 42.5	23 8.4	26 21.8	18 30.3	29 7.5	11 50.1	5 59.0	3 35.2	8 48.8	11 15.9	19 28.9	19 8.0
15	15 30 39.0	24 6.2	26 18.6	2♒49.9	0♉34.3	13 3.8	5 39.4	3 49.2	8 46.2	11 18.6	19 27.6	19 8.3
16	15 34 35.6	25 4.1	26 15.4	17 2.4	2 3.3	14 17.4	5 20.4	4 3.1	8 43.7	11 21.4	19 26.4	19 8.7
17	15 38 32.1	26 1.9	26 12.2	1♓ 6.5	3 34.5	15 31.1	5 1.8	4 17.0	8 41.3	11 24.2	19 25.1	19 9.2
18	15 42 28.7	26 59.7	26 9.1	15 1.5	5 8.0	16 44.8	4 43.8	4 30.9	8 38.9	11 27.0	19 23.9	19 9.6
19	15 46 25.3	27 57.4	26 5.9	28 47.4	6 43.7	17 58.4	4 26.3	4 44.7	8 36.7	11 29.8	19 22.7	19 10.1
20	15 50 21.8	28 55.2	26 2.7	12♈23.8	8 21.6	19 12.1	4 9.5	4 58.5	8 34.5	11 32.7	19 21.5	19 10.7
21	15 54 18.4	29 52.9	25 59.5	25 50.3	10 1.7	20 25.8	3 53.3	5 12.2	8 32.5	11 35.6	19 20.3	19 11.2
22	15 58 14.9	0♊50.6	25 56.4	9♉ 5.8	11 44.0	21 39.4	3 37.8	5 26.0	8 30.5	11 38.5	19 19.1	19 11.8
23	16 2 11.5	1 48.3	25 53.2	22 9.1	13 28.5	22 53.1	3 22.9	5 39.6	8 28.6	11 41.4	19 18.0	19 12.4
24	16 6 8.0	2 46.0	25 50.0	4♊59.0	15 15.2	24 6.8	3 8.8	5 53.2	8 26.8	11 44.4	19 16.9	19 13.0
25	16 10 4.6	3 43.7	25 46.8	17 34.8	17 4.0	25 20.4	2 55.4	6 6.8	8 25.1	11 47.4	19 15.9	19 13.7
26	16 14 1.2	4 41.3	25 43.7	29 56.7	18 55.0	26 34.1	2 42.8	6 20.3	8 23.5	11 50.5	19 14.8	19 14.3
27	16 17 57.7	5 38.9	25 40.5	12♋ 5.7	20 48.2	27 47.7	2 30.9	6 33.8	8 22.0	11 53.6	19 13.8	19 15.1
28	16 21 54.3	6 36.5	25 37.3	24 4.0	22 43.5	29 1.4	2 19.8	6 47.3	8 20.7	11 56.7	19 12.8	19 15.8
29	16 25 50.8	7 34.1	25 34.1	5♌54.8	24 40.9	0♊15.0	2 9.5	7 .6	8 19.3	11 59.8	19 11.8	19 16.5
30	16 29 47.4	8 31.6	25 31.0	17 42.4	26 40.4	1 28.7	2 .1	7 14.0	8 18.1	12 2.9	19 10.9	19 17.3
31	16 33 43.9	9 29.1	25 27.8	29 31.6	28 41.8	2 42.3	1 51.4	7 27.2	8 17.0	12 6.1	19 9.9	19 18.1

LATITUDE

DAY	EPHEM. SID. TIME	☉	☊	☽	☿	♀	♂	♃	♄	♅	♆	♇
1	14 35 27.2	0 .0	0 .0	2N30.2	2S46.9	1S24.5	0N46.3	1S 2.0	2N41.5	0N22.3	1N42.7	9N 4.8
4	14 47 16.9	0 .0	0 .0	0S32.1	2 58.7	1 21.4	0 38.5	1 2.0	2 41.1	0 22.3	1 42.7	9 4.3
7	14 59 6.6	0 .0	0 .0	3 28.2	3 4.3	1 17.7	0 30.6	1 2.0	2 40.6	0 22.3	1 42.6	9 3.7
10	15 10 56.2	0 .0	0 .0	4 59.2	3 3.9	1 13.5	0 22.5	1 2.0	2 40.1	0 22.3	1 42.5	9 3.2
13	15 22 45.9	0 .0	0 .0	3 58.2	2 57.9	1 8.9	0 14.3	1 2.0	2 39.6	0 22.2	1 42.5	9 2.6
16	15 34 35.6	0 .0	0 .0	0 47.9	2 46.6	1 3.9	0 6.2	1 2.1	2 39.0	0 22.2	1 42.4	9 2.1
19	15 46 25.3	0 .0	0 .0	2N43.4	2 30.3	0 58.5	0S 1.9	1 2.2	2 38.4	0 22.2	1 42.3	9 1.5
22	15 58 14.9	0 .0	0 .0	4 48.0	2 9.4	0 52.7	0 9.7	1 2.2	2 37.8	0 22.2	1 42.2	9 1.0
25	16 10 4.6	0 .0	0 .0	4 37.9	1 44.5	0 46.6	0 17.4	1 2.3	2 37.1	0 22.2	1 42.1	9 .4
28	16 21 54.3	0 .0	0 .0	2 34.2	1 16.1	0 40.2	0 24.8	1 2.5	2 36.5	0 22.2	1 42.0	8 59.9
31	16 33 43.9	0 .0	0 .0	0S26.4	0 45.1	0 33.6	0 31.9	1 2.6	2 35.8	0 22.2	1 41.9	8 59.4

RIGHT ASCENSION

DAY	EPHEM. SID. TIME	☉	☊	☽	☿	♀	♂	♃	♄	♅	♆	♇
1	14 35 27.2	8♉ 8.8	29♒15.8	0♌33.4	14♈ 4.0	24♈30.0	8♏28.3	28♈46.3	9♎47.0	11♋42.5	18♎55.1	24♌35.7
2	14 39 23.8	9 6.1	29 12.8	12 37.2	14 54.1	25 39.3	8R 5.8	28 59.9	9R43.7	11 44.9	18R53.6	24 35.7
3	14 43 20.4	10 3.5	29 9.7	24 7.5	15 47.0	26 48.7	7 43.2	29 13.6	9 40.4	11 47.4	18 52.2	24 35.6
4	14 47 16.9	11 1.1	29 6.6	5♍14.5	16 42.5	27 58.2	7 20.7	29 27.2	9 37.1	11 49.9	18 50.9	24 35.6
5	14 51 13.5	11 58.8	29 3.6	16 11.2	17 40.5	29 7.9	6 58.1	29 40.8	9 34.0	11 52.4	18 49.5	24D35.7
6	14 55 10.0	12 56.7	29 .5	27 12.8	18 40.9	0♉17.9	6 35.7	29 54.4	9 30.8	11 55.0	18 48.1	24 35.8
7	14 59 6.6	13 54.7	28 57.5	8♎35.2	19 43.7	1 28.0	6 13.4	0♉ 8.0	9 27.8	11 57.6	18 46.8	24 35.8
8	15 3 3.1	14 52.8	28 54.4	20 35.3	20 48.9	2 38.3	5 51.2	0 21.5	9 24.8	12 .2	18 45.5	24 36.0
9	15 6 59.7	15 51.1	28 51.3	3♏28.8	21 56.3	3 48.9	5 29.2	0 35.1	9 21.9	12 2.9	18 44.1	24 36.1
10	15 10 56.2	16 49.5	28 48.3	17 26.9	23 6.0	4 59.6	5 7.5	0 48.6	9 19.1	12 5.7	18 42.8	24 36.3
11	15 14 52.8	17 48.1	28 45.2	2♐30.7	24 17.9	6 10.7	4 46.2	1 2.2	9 16.4	12 8.5	18 41.6	24 36.6
12	15 18 49.4	18 46.8	28 42.2	18 24.5	25 32.1	7 21.9	4 25.1	1 15.7	9 13.7	12 11.3	18 40.3	24 36.8
13	15 22 45.9	19 45.6	28 39.1	4♑37.0	26 48.4	8 33.4	4 4.4	1 29.1	9 11.1	12 14.2	18 39.1	24 37.1
14	15 26 42.5	20 44.6	28 36.0	20 30.4	28 7.0	9 45.1	3 44.1	1 42.6	9 8.5	12 17.1	18 37.8	24 37.4
15	15 30 39.0	21 43.8	28 33.0	5♒36.6	29 27.8	10 57.1	3 24.2	1 56.0	9 6.1	12 20.0	18 36.6	24 37.7
16	15 34 35.6	22 43.1	28 29.9	19 44.7	0♉50.9	12 9.3	3 4.8	2 9.4	9 3.7	12 23.0	18 35.4	24 38.0
17	15 38 32.1	23 42.5	28 26.8	2♓59.4	2 16.2	13 21.8	2 45.9	2 22.8	9 1.4	12 26.0	18 34.3	24 38.4
18	15 42 28.7	24 42.1	28 23.8	15 34.7	3 43.9	14 34.6	2 27.6	2 36.2	8 59.2	12 29.0	18 33.1	24 38.8
19	15 46 25.3	25 41.8	28 20.7	27 48.3	5 13.9	15 47.6	2 9.8	2 49.5	8 57.0	12 32.1	18 32.0	24 39.3
20	15 50 21.8	26 41.7	28 17.6	9♈58.0	6 46.3	17 .9	1 52.6	3 2.8	8 55.0	12 35.2	18 30.8	24 39.7
21	15 54 18.4	27 41.7	28 14.6	22 19.6	8 21.2	18 14.5	1 36.0	3 16.1	8 53.0	12 38.3	18 29.7	24 40.2
22	15 58 14.9	28 41.8	28 11.5	5♉ 5.1	9 58.7	19 28.3	1 20.1	3 29.3	8 51.1	12 41.5	18 28.7	24 40.7
23	16 2 11.5	29 42.1	28 8.4	18 20.5	11 38.7	20 42.5	1 4.9	3 42.5	8 49.3	12 44.7	18 27.6	24 41.3
24	16 6 8.0	0♊42.5	28 5.4	2♊ 3.0	13 21.3	21 56.9	0 50.4	3 55.7	8 47.5	12 48.0	18 26.6	24 41.9
25	16 10 4.6	1 43.0	28 2.3	16 1.1	15 6.7	23 11.6	0 36.6	4 8.9	8 45.9	12 51.2	18 25.5	24 42.5
26	16 14 1.2	2 43.7	27 59.2	29 56.3	16 54.8	24 26.6	0 23.6	4 22.0	8 44.4	12 54.5	18 24.6	24 43.1
27	16 17 57.7	3 44.5	27 56.2	13♋29.5	18 45.7	25 41.8	0 11.3	4 35.0	8 42.9	12 57.9	18 23.6	24 43.7
28	16 21 54.3	4 45.4	27 53.1	26 26.8	20 39.5	26 57.4	29♎59.7	4 48.1	8 41.5	13 1.2	18 22.6	24 44.4
29	16 25 50.8	5 46.4	27 50.0	8♌42.9	22 36.2	28 13.2	29 49.0	5 1.0	8 40.2	13 4.6	18 21.7	24 45.1
30	16 29 47.4	6 47.5	27 47.0	20 20.7	24 35.8	29 29.3	29 39.0	5 14.0	8 39.0	13 8.0	18 20.8	24 45.9
31	16 33 43.9	7 48.7	27 43.9	1♍28.9	26 38.2	0♊45.6	29 29.9	5 26.9	8 37.9	13 11.5	18 20.0	24 46.6

DECLINATION

DAY	EPHEM. SID. TIME	☉	☊	☽	☿	♀	♂	♃	♄	♅	♆	♇
1	14 35 27.2	14N59.8	0S13.1	23N 2.2	3N .1	8N41.1	14S17.3	10N41.4	1S17.3	23N23.1	6S 9.4	23N42.6
4	14 47 16.9	15 53.3	0 13.1	9 43.3	3 53.1	10 3.0	14 3.8	10 56.3	1 13.6	23 22.5	6 7.7	23 42.0
7	14 59 6.6	16 44.5	0 13.2	7S28.8	5 1.0	11 22.8	13 50.3	11 11.0	1 10.1	23 21.9	6 6.1	23 41.3
10	15 10 56.2	17 33.1	0 13.3	22 53.8	6 21.8	12 40.3	13 37.0	11 25.5	1 6.9	23 21.2	6 4.6	23 40.6
13	15 22 45.9	18 19.1	0 13.3	27 21.1	7 53.8	13 55.1	13 24.3	11 39.9	1 4.1	23 20.6	6 3.2	23 39.8
16	15 34 35.6	19 2.4	0 13.4	16 29.7	9 35.1	15 6.9	13 12.6	11 54.0	1 1.5	23 19.9	6 1.8	23 38.9
19	15 46 25.3	19 42.7	0 13.4	2N 1.0	11 23.9	16 15.4	13 2.0	12 7.9	0 59.3	23 19.1	6 .5	23 37.9
22	15 58 14.9	20 20.0	0 13.5	19 4.5	13 18.4	17 20.2	12 53.0	12 21.5	0 57.5	23 18.3	5 59.3	23 36.9
25	16 10 4.6	20 54.2	0 13.5	27 28.6	15 16.0	18 21.1	12 45.8	12 35.0	0 55.9	23 17.5	5 58.1	23 35.8
28	16 21 54.3	21 25.2	0 13.6	23 50.1	17 14.0	19 17.6	12 40.5	12 48.1	0 54.8	23 16.7	5 57.1	23 34.6
31	16 33 43.9	21 52.8	0 13.7	11 13.8	19 8.5	20 9.5	12 37.4	13 1.0	0 54.0	23 15.8	5 56.1	23 33.3

JUNE 1952

LONGITUDE

DAY	EPHEM. SID. TIME h m s	☉ ° ′	☊ ° ′	☽ ° ′	☿ ° ′	♀ ° ′	♂ ° ′	♃ ° ′	♄ ° ′	♅ ° ′	♆ ° ′	♇ ° ′
1	16 37 40.5	10♊26.7	25♒24.6	11♍27.6	0♊45.1	3♊56.0	1♏43.6	7♉40.5	8♎16.1	12♋ 9.4	19♎ 9.1	19♌19.0
2	16 41 37.1	11 24.1	25 21.4	23 36.0	2 50.1	5 9.7	1R36.6	7 53.7	8R15.2	12 12.6	19R 8.2	19 19.9
3	16 45 33.6	12 21.6	25 18.2	6♎ 1.9	4 56.7	6 23.3	1 30.3	8 6.8	8 14.4	12 15.8	19 7.4	19 20.8
4	16 49 30.2	13 19.0	25 15.1	18 49.8	7 4.8	7 37.0	1 25.0	8 19.8	8 13.7	12 19.1	19 6.6	19 21.7
5	16 53 26.7	14 16.4	25 11.9	2♏ 3.0	9 14.2	8 50.6	1 20.4	8 32.8	8 13.1	12 22.4	19 5.8	19 22.6
6	16 57 23.3	15 13.8	25 8.7	15 42.6	11 24.6	10 4.2	1 16.7	8 45.8	8 12.6	12 25.7	19 5.0	19 23.6
7	17 1 19.9	16 11.2	25 5.5	29 47.4	13 35.8	11 17.9	1 13.8	8 58.6	8 12.1	12 29.0	19 4.3	19 24.6
8	17 5 16.4	17 8.6	25 2.4	14♐13.5	15 47.6	12 31.5	1 11.7	9 11.4	8 11.8	12 32.4	19 3.6	19 25.6
9	17 9 13.0	18 5.9	24 59.2	28 54.4	17 59.6	13 45.1	1 10,4	9 24.2	8 11.6	12 35.8	19 2.9	19 26.6
10	17 13 9.5	19 3.3	24 56.0	13♑42.5	20 11.7	14 58.8	1 9.9	9 36.9	8 11.5	12 39.1	19 2.3	19 27.7
11	17 17 6.1	20 .6	24 52.8	28 29.7	22 23.5	16 12.4	1D10.2	9 49.5	8 11.5	12 42.6	19 1.7	19 28.7
12	17 21 2.7	20 57.9	24 49.7	13♒ 9.4	24 34.7	17 26.1	1 11.3	10 2.0	8D11.6	12 46.0	19 1.1	19 29.8
13	17 24 59.2	21 55.2	24 46.5	27 36.4	26 45.2	18 39.8	1 13.2	10 14.5	8 11.8	12 49.4	19 .5	19 31.0
14	17 28 55.8	22 52.5	24 43.3	11♓47.9	28 54.7	19 53.4	1 15.8	10 26.9	8 12.1	12 52.9	18 60.0	19 32.1
15	17 32 52.3	23 49.8	24 40.1	25 42.9	1♋ 2.9	21 7.1	1 19.2	10 39.2	8 12.5	12 56.3	18 59.5	19 33.3
16	17 36 48.9	24 47.1	24 37.0	9♈21.6	3 9.7	22 20.8	1 23.4	10 51.5	8 13.0	12 59.8	18 59.0	19 34.5
17	17 40 45.4	25 44.4	24 33.8	22 44.8	5 14.9	23 34.4	1 28.3	11 3.7	8 13.6	13 3.3	18 58.6	19 35.7
18	17 44 42.0	26 41.7	24 30.6	5♉53.8	7 18.3	24 48.1	1 34.0	11 15.8	8 14.3	13 6.8	18 58.2	19 36.9
19	17 48 38.6	27 39.0	24 27.4	18 49.5	9 19.9	26 1.8	1 40.4	11 27.9	8 15.1	13 10.4	18 57.8	19 38.2
20	17 52 35.1	28 36.3	24 24.2	1♊32.7	11 19.6	27 15.5	1 47.6	11 39.8	8 16.0	13 13.9	18 57.5	19 39.4
21	17 56 31.7	29 33.5	24 21.1	14 4.0	13 17.2	28 29.2	1 55.5	11 51.7	8 17.0	13 17.4	18 57.2	19 40.7
22	18 0 28.2	0♋30.8	24 17.9	26 24.0	15 12.8	29 43.0	2 4.1	12 3.5	8 18.2	13 21.1	18 56.9	19 42.1
23	18 4 24.8	1 28.1	24 14.7	8♋33.5	17 6.2	0♋56.7	2 13.4	12 15.2	8 19.4	13 24.6	18 56.7	19 43.4
24	18 8 21.4	2 25.3	24 11.5	20 33.8	18 57.4	2 10.4	2 23.4	12 26.9	8 20.7	13 28.2	18 56.5	19 44.8
25	18 12 17.9	3 22.6	24 8.4	2♌26.6	20 46.5	3 24.2	2 34.0	12 38.4	8 22.1	13 31.8	18 56.3	19 46.2
26	18 16 14.5	4 19.8	24 5.2	14 14.6	22 33.4	4 37.9	2 45.4	12 49.8	8 23.6	13 35.4	18 56.1	19 47.6
27	18 20 11.0	5 17.0	24 2.0	26 1.0	24 18.0	5 51.6	2 57.3	13 1.2	8 25.2	13 39.0	18 56.0	19 49.0
28	18 24 7.6	6 14.3	23 58.8	7♍49.7	26 .4	7 5.4	3 10.0	13 12.5	8 26.9	13 42.6	18 55.9	19 50.4
29	18 28 4.2	7 11.5	23 55.7	19 45.4	27 40.6	8 19.1	3 23.3	13 23.6	8 28.7	13 46.2	18 55.9	19 51.9
30	18 32 .7	8 8.7	23 52.5	1♎52.9	29 18.6	9 32.8	3 37.2	13 34.7	8 30.6	13 49.8	18 55.9	19 53.3

LATITUDE

DAY	SID. TIME	☉	☊	☽	☿	♀	♂	♃	♄	♅	♆	♇
1	16 37 40.5	0 .0	0 .0	1S28.6	0S34.5	0S31.3	0S34.2	1S 2.7	2N35.6	0N22.2	1N41.8	8N59.2
4	16 49 30.2	0 .0	0 .0	4 6.9	0 2.1	0 24.5	0 40.9	1 2.8	2 34.9	0 22.2	1 41.7	8 58.8
7	17 1 19.9	0 .0	0 .0	5 1.3	0N29.3	0 17.5	0 47.3	1 3.0	2 34.2	0 22.2	1 41.6	8 58.3
10	17 13 9.5	0 .0	0 .0	3 15.1	0 57.9	0 10.4	0 53.3	1 3.2	2 33.4	0 22.2	1 41.4	8 57.8
13	17 24 59.2	0 .0	0 .0	0N22.2	1 22.1	0 3.2	0 58.9	1 3.4	2 32.7	0 22.2	1 41.3	8 57.4
16	17 36 48.9	0 .0	0 .0	3 40.1	1 40.4	0N 3.9	1 4.2	1 3.6	2 32.0	0 22.2	1 41.1	8 57.0
19	17 48 38.6	0 .0	0 .0	5 4.6	1 52.1	0 11.0	1 9.2	1 3.8	2 31.2	0 22.2	1 41.0	8 56.6
22	18 0 28.2	0 .0	0 .0	4 14.9	1 57.2	0 18.1	1 13.8	1 4.1	2 30.5	0 22.2	1 40.9	8 56.2
25	18 12 17.9	0 .0	0 .0	1 45.4	1 55.7	0 25.0	1 18.2	1 4.4	2 29.8	0 22.2	1 40.7	8 55.9
28	18 24 7.6	0 .0	0 .0	1S22.9	1 48.2	0 31.7	1 22.3	1 4.7	2 29.0	0 22.2	1 40.6	8 55.6

RIGHT ASCENSION

DAY	SID. TIME	☉	☊	☽	☿	♀	♂	♃	♄	♅	♆	♇
1	16 37 40.5	8♊50.1	27♒40.8	12♍20.0	28♉43.6	2♊ 2.3	29♎21.6	5♉39.8	8♎37.0	13♋15.0	18♎19.1	24♌47.5
2	16 41 37.1	9 51.5	27 37.8	23 8.9	0♊51.7	3 19.2	29R14.0	5 52.6	8R36.0	13 18.5	18R18.3	24 48.3
3	16 45 33.6	10 53.0	27 34.7	4♎12.0	3 2.5	4 36.3	29 7.2	6 5.4	8 35.2	13 22.0	18 17.5	24 49.2
4	16 49 30.2	11 54.6	27 31.6	15 46.9	5 15.8	5 53.7	29 1.3	6 18.1	8 34.5	13 25.6	18 16.8	24 50.0
5	16 53 26.7	12 56.3	27 28.5	28 11.4	7 31.4	7 11.4	28 56.2	6 30.7	8 33.8	13 29.1	18 16.0	24 50.9
6	16 57 23.3	13 58.0	27 25.5	11♏41.4	9 49.1	8 29.2	28 51.8	6 43.4	8 33.3	13 32.7	18 15.3	24 51.8
7	17 1 19.9	14 59.9	27 22.4	26 25.1	12 8.7	9 47.4	28 48.3	6 55.9	8 32.8	13 36.3	18 14.6	24 52.8
8	17 5 16.4	16 1.8	27 19.3	12♐15.7	14 29.8	11 5.7	28 45.5	7 8.4	8 32.4	13 39.9	18 13.9	24 53.8
9	17 9 13.0	17 3.7	27 16.2	28 46.2	16 52.1	12 24.3	28 43.6	7 20.9	8 32.1	13 43.6	18 13.3	24 54.7
10	17 13 9.5	18 5.8	27 13.2	15♑15.5	19 15.2	13 43.1	28 42.4	7 33.3	8 31.9	13 47.3	18 12.7	24 55.8
11	17 17 6.1	19 7.9	27 10.1	1♒ 5.1	21 38.7	15 2.1	28 42.0	7 45.6	8 31.8	13 50.9	18 12.1	24 56.8
12	17 21 2.7	20 10.0	27 7.0	15 53.8	24 2.3	16 21.3	28D42.4	7 57.9	8 31.8	13 54.7	18 11.5	24 57.9
13	17 24 59.2	21 12.3	27 3.9	29 40.0	26 25.5	17 40.6	28 43.5	8 10.1	8D31.9	13 58.4	18 11.0	24 59.0
14	17 28 55.8	22 14.5	27 .9	12♓35.8	28 48.0	19 .2	28 45.4	8 22.3	8 32.1	14 2.1	18 10.5	25 .1
15	17 32 52.3	23 16.8	26 57.8	24 59.1	1♋ 9.4	20 19.9	28 48.1	8 34.4	8 32.4	14 5.9	18 10.0	25 1.2
16	17 36 48.9	24 19.1	26 54.7	7♈ 8.7	3 29.4	21 39.7	28 51.5	8 46.4	8 32.7	14 9.7	18 9.5	25 2.4
17	17 40 45.4	25 21.5	26 51.6	19 22.2	5 47.6	22 59.7	28 55.6	8 58.4	8 33.2	14 13.4	18 9.1	25 3.6
18	17 44 42.0	26 23.9	26 48.6	1♉53.5	8 3.9	24 19.9	29 .5	9 10.3	8 33.7	14 17.2	18 8.7	25 4.8
19	17 48 38.6	27 26.3	26 45.5	14 51.8	10 18.0	25 40.1	29 6.1	9 22.2	8 34.4	14 21.1	18 8.4	25 6.0
20	17 52 35.1	28 28.7	26 42.4	28 18.1	12 29.7	27 .5	29 12.4	9 33.9	8 35.1	14 24.9	18 8.0	25 7.2
21	17 56 31.7	29 31.1	26 39.3	12♊ 5.0	14 38.8	28 20.9	29 19.4	9 45.6	8 35.9	14 28.7	18 7.7	25 8.5
22	18 0 28.2	0♋33.6	26 36.2	25 56.8	16 45.2	29 41.4	29 27.2	9 57.3	8 36.9	14 32.6	18 7.5	25 9.9
23	18 4 24.8	1 36.0	26 33.2	9♋34.3	18 48.8	1♋ 2.0	29 35.6	10 8.8	8 37.9	14 36.5	18 7.2	25 11.2
24	18 8 21.4	2 38.4	26 30.1	22 41.3	20 49.4	2 22.6	29 44.8	10 20.3	8 39.0	14 40.4	18 7.0	25 12.5
25	18 12 17.9	3 40.8	26 27.0	5♌ 8.7	22 47.2	3 43.2	29 54.5	10 31.7	8 40.2	14 44.2	18 6.8	25 13.9
26	18 16 14.5	4 43.1	26 23.9	16 55.9	24 41.9	5 3.8	0♏ 5.0	10 43.0	8 41.5	14 48.1	18 6.7	25 15.2
27	18 20 11.0	5 45.4	26 20.8	28 9.1	26 33.5	6 24.4	0 16.1	10 54.2	8 42.8	14 52.0	18 6.5	25 16.6
28	18 24 7.6	6 47.6	26 17.7	8♍58.9	28 22.2	7 45.0	0 27.9	11 5.4	8 44.3	14 55.9	18 6.4	25 18.1
29	18 28 4.2	7 49.8	26 14.7	19 39.0	0♌ 7.7	9 5.6	0 40.2	11 16.4	8 45.9	14 59.8	18 6.4	25 19.5
30	18 32 .7	8 52.0	26 11.6	0♎24.7	1 50.2	10 26.1	0 53.2	11 27.4	8 47.5	15 3.8	18 6.3	25 20.9

DECLINATION

DAY	SID. TIME	☉	☊	☽	☿	♀	♂	♃	♄	♅	♆	♇
1	16 37 40.5	22N 1.3	0S13.7	5N54.1	19N45.2	20N25.8	12S36.8	13N 5.2	0S53.8	23N15.6	5S55.8	23N32.9
4	16 49 30.2	22 24.3	0 13.7	11S10.9	21 27.9	21 11.1	12 36.6	13 17.8	0 53.5	23 14.7	5 55.0	23 31.6
7	17 1 19.9	22 43.8	0 13.8	25 .9	22 55.5	21 51.2	12 38.7	13 30.0	0 53.6	23 13.7	5 54.2	23 30.2
10	17 13 9.5	22 59.8	0 13.8	25 58.6	24 2.9	22 25.7	12 42.9	13 41.9	0 54.0	23 12.8	5 53.6	23 28.7
13	17 24 59.2	23 12.1	0 13.9	11 57.6	24 46.5	22 54.6	12 49.3	13 53.5	0 54.8	23 11.8	5 53.1	23 27.3
16	17 36 48.9	23 20.7	0 13.9	7N 4.8	25 4.9	23 17.5	12 57.9	14 4.9	0 55.9	23 10.8	5 52.6	23 25.7
19	17 48 38.6	23 25.6	0 14.0	22 18.2	24 59.0	23 34.3	13 8.5	14 15.9	0 57.4	23 9.8	5 52.3	23 24.2
22	18 0 28.2	23 26.8	0 14.1	27 38.7	24 31.2	23 44.9	13 21.1	14 26.5	0 59.3	23 8.7	5 52.1	23 22.5
25	18 12 17.9	23 24.2	0 14.1	21 20.0	23 44.9	23 49.2	13 35.5	14 36.9	1 1.5	23 7.6	5 52.0	23 20.9
28	18 24 7.6	23 18.0	0 14.2	7 21.3	22 43.5	23 47.1	13 51.7	14 46.9	1 4.1	23 6.6	5 52.0	23 19.2

JULY 1952

LONGITUDE

DAY	EPHEM. SID. TIME h m s	☉ ° ′	☊ ° ′	☾ ° ′	☿ ° ′	♀ ° ′	♂ ° ′	♃ ° ′	♄ ° ′	♅ ° ′	♆ ° ′	♇ ° ′
1	18 35 57.3	9♋ 5.9	23♒49.3	14♎17.3	0♌54.3	10♋46.6	3♏51.7	13♉45.7	8♎32.5	13♋53.4	18♎55.9	19♌54.8
2	18 39 53.8	10 3.1	23 46.1	27 3.3	2 27.8	12 .3	4 6.8	13 56.6	8 34.6	13 57.1	18 55.9	19 56.3
3	18 43 50.4	11 .3	23 43.0	10♏14.9	3 59.0	13 14.1	4 22.5	14 7.4	8 36.8	14 .7	18D56.0	19 57.8
4	18 47 46.9	11 57.4	23 39.8	23 54.3	5 27.9	14 27.8	4 38.7	14 18.1	8 39.1	14 4.3	18 56.1	19 59.4
5	18 51 43.5	12 54.6	23 36.6	8♐ 1.6	6 54.5	15 41.6	4 55.6	14 28.6	8 41.4	14 8.0	18 56.2	20 .9
6	18 55 40.1	13 51.8	23 33.4	22 34.2	8 18.8	16 55.4	5 12.9	14 39.1	8 43.9	14 11.6	18 56.4	20 2.5
7	18 59 36.6	14 49.0	23 30.3	7♑26.3	9 40.7	18 9.1	5 30.8	14 49.5	8 46.4	14 15.2	18 56.6	20 4.1
8	19 3 33.2	15 46.1	23 27.1	22 30.0	11 .3	19 22.9	5 49.3	14 59.8	8 49.1	14 18.9	18 56.8	20 5.6
9	19 7 29.7	16 43.3	23 23.9	7♒36.1	12 17.4	20 36.7	6 8.2	15 9.9	8 51.8	14 22.5	18 57.1	20 7.3
10	19 11 26.3	17 40.5	23 20.7	22 35.5	13 31.9	21 50.5	6 27.7	15 20.0	8 54.6	14 26.1	18 57.4	20 8.9
11	19 15 22.9	18 37.7	23 17.5	7♓20.8	14 44.0	23 4.2	6 47.7	15 29.9	8 57.5	14 29.7	18 57.7	20 10.5
12	19 19 19.4	19 34.9	23 14.4	21 46.9	15 53.4	24 18.0	7 8.1	15 39.8	9 .5	14 33.4	18 58.1	20 12.2
13	19 23 16.0	20 32.1	23 11.2	5♈51.1	17 .2	25 31.9	7 29.1	15 49.6	9 3.7	14 37.0	18 58.5	20 13.9
14	19 27 12.5	21 29.4	23 8.0	19 32.8	18 4.1	26 45.7	7 50.5	15 59.2	9 6.9	14 40.6	18 58.9	20 15.6
15	19 31 9.1	22 26.6	23 4.8	2♉53.0	19 5.2	27 59.5	8 12.4	16 8.6	9 10.1	14 44.3	18 59.4	20 17.2
16	19 35 5.6	23 23.8	23 1.7	15 53.7	20 3.4	29 13.4	8 34.7	16 18.0	9 13.5	14 47.9	18 59.9	20 18.9
17	19 39 2.2	24 21.1	22 58.5	28 37.2	20 58.4	0♌27.2	8 57.5	16 27.3	9 16.9	14 51.5	19 .4	20 20.7
18	19 42 58.8	25 18.3	22 55.3	11♊ 6.1	21 50.3	1 41.1	9 20.7	16 36.4	9 20.4	14 55.1	19 1.0	20 22.4
19	19 46 55.3	26 15.6	22 52.1	23 22.7	22 38.8	2 54.9	9 44.3	16 45.4	9 24.1	14 58.6	19 1.5	20 24.1
20	19 50 51.9	27 12.9	22 49.0	5♋29.3	23 23.9	4 8.8	10 8.4	16 54.3	9 27.7	15 2.2	19 2.2	20 25.9
21	19 54 48.4	28 10.2	22 45.8	17 27.8	24 5.4	5 22.7	10 32.9	17 3.0	9 31.5	15 5.8	19 2.8	20 27.6
22	19 58 45.0	29 7.5	22 42.6	29 20.3	24 43.1	6 36.5	10 57.8	17 11.6	9 35.4	15 9.3	19 3.5	20 29.4
23	20 2 41.5	0♌ 4.8	22 39.4	11♌ 8.7	25 16.9	7 50.4	11 23.1	17 20.1	9 39.3	15 12.9	19 4.2	20 31.2
24	20 6 38.1	1 2.1	22 36.2	22 55.3	25 46.6	9 4.3	11 48.8	17 28.4	9 43.3	15 16.4	19 4.9	20 33.0
25	20 10 34.7	1 59.4	22 33.1	4♍42.7	26 12.1	10 18.2	12 14.9	17 36.6	9 47.4	15 20.0	19 5.7	20 34.8
26	20 14 31.2	2 56.7	22 29.9	16 33.9	26 33.1	11 32.1	12 41.4	17 44.7	9 51.6	15 23.5	19 6.5	20 36.6
27	20 18 27.8	3 54.1	22 26.7	28 32.3	26 49.5	12 46.0	13 8.3	17 52.7	9 55.9	15 27.0	19 7.4	20 38.4
28	20 22 24.3	4 51.4	22 23.5	10♎41.8	27 1.2	13 59.9	13 35.5	18 .4	10 .2	15 30.4	19 8.2	20 40.2
29	20 26 20.9	5 48.8	22 20.4	23 6.4	27 8.0	15 13.8	14 3.1	18 8.1	10 4.6	15 33.9	19 9.1	20 42.0
30	20 30 17.4	6 46.2	22 17.2	5♏50.3	27 9.8	16 27.7	14 31.0	18 15.6	10 9.1	15 37.4	19 10.0	20 43.8
31	20 34 14.0	7 43.5	22 14.0	18 57.2	27R 6.5	17 41.6	14 59.3	18 23.0	10 13.7	15 40.8	19 11.0	20 45.7

LATITUDE

DAY	SID. TIME	☉	☊	☾	☿	♀	♂	♃	♄	♅	♆	♇
1	18 35 57.3	0 .0	0 .0	4S 4.6	1N34.9	0N38.2	1S26.0	1S 5.0	2N28.3	0N22.2	1N40.4	8N55.3
4	18 47 46.9	0 .0	0 .0	5 10.3	1 16.5	0 44.5	1 29.6	1 5.3	2 27.6	0 22.2	1 40.2	8 55.0
7	18 59 36.6	0 .0	0 .0	3 38.6	0 53.4	0 50.5	1 32.8	1 5.6	2 26.9	0 22.3	1 40.1	8 54.8
10	19 11 26.3	0 .0	0 .0	0N 3.9	0 26.0	0 56.1	1 35.9	1 6.0	2 26.2	0 22.3	1 39.9	8 54.6
13	19 23 16.0	0 .0	0 .0	3 37.8	0S 5.2	1 1.4	1 38.7	1 6.3	2 25.5	0 22.3	1 39.8	8 54.4
16	19 35 5.6	0 .0	0 .0	5 11.8	0 39.6	1 6.3	1 41.3	1 6.7	2 24.8	0 22.4	1 39.6	8 54.3
19	19 46 55.3	0 .0	0 .0	4 27.3	1 16.7	1 10.7	1 43.7	1 7.1	2 24.2	0 22.4	1 39.5	8 54.2
22	19 58 45.0	0 .0	0 .0	1 59.3	1 55.7	1 14.7	1 45.9	1 7.5	2 23.6	0 22.4	1 39.3	8 54.1
25	20 10 34.7	0 .0	0 .0	1S12.3	2 35.5	1 18.2	1 47.9	1 7.9	2 22.9	0 22.5	1 39.2	8 54.1
28	20 22 24.3	0 .0	0 .0	3 59.8	3 14.7	1 21.1	1 49.8	1 8.3	2 22.3	0 22.5	1 39.0	8 54.1
31	20 34 14.0	0 .0	0 .0	5 16.6	3 51.1	1 23.6	1 51.5	1 8.8	2 21.7	0 22.6	1 38.9	8 54.1

RIGHT ASCENSION

DAY	SID. TIME	☉	☊	☾	☿	♀	♂	♃	♄	♅	♆	♇
1	18 35 57.3	9♋54.1	26♒ 8.5	11♎33.0	3♌29.6	11♋46.6	1♏ 6.9	11♉38.3	8♎49.2	15♋ 7.7	18♎ 6.3	25♌22.4
2	18 39 53.8	10 56.1	26 5.4	23 21.8	5 6.0	13 7.0	1 21.1	11 49.0	8 51.0	15 11.6	18 6.3	25 23.9
3	18 43 50.4	11 58.0	26 2.3	6♏ 8.7	6 39.4	14 27.3	1 35.9	11 59.7	8 53.0	15 15.5	18D 6.4	25 25.4
4	18 47 46.9	12 59.9	25 59.2	20 7.7	8 9.6	15 47.5	1 51.3	12 10.4	8 54.9	15 19.4	18 6.4	25 26.9
5	18 51 43.5	14 1.7	25 56.2	5♐22.2	9 36.9	17 7.5	2 7.3	12 20.9	8 57.0	15 23.4	18 6.6	25 28.5
6	18 55 40.1	15 3.4	25 53.1	21 37.6	11 1.1	18 27.5	2 23.8	12 31.3	8 59.2	15 27.3	18 6.7	25 30.0
7	18 59 36.6	16 5.0	25 50.0	8♑19.7	12 22.4	19 47.2	2 40.9	12 41.6	9 1.4	15 31.2	18 6.9	25 31.6
8	19 3 33.2	17 6.5	25 46.9	24 45.4	13 40.6	21 6.9	2 58.5	12 51.8	9 3.8	15 35.1	18 7.1	25 33.2
9	19 7 29.7	18 7.9	25 43.8	10♒21.7	14 55.7	22 26.3	3 16.7	13 1.9	9 6.2	15 39.1	18 7.3	25 34.8
10	19 11 26.3	19 9.3	25 40.7	24 55.3	16 7.8	23 45.6	3 35.3	13 11.9	9 8.7	15 43.0	18 7.5	25 36.4
11	19 15 22.9	20 10.5	25 37.6	8♓31.5	17 16.9	25 4.7	3 54.5	13 21.8	9 11.3	15 46.9	18 7.8	25 38.1
12	19 19 19.4	21 11.6	25 34.5	21 25.4	18 22.8	26 23.6	4 14.2	13 31.6	9 13.9	15 50.8	18 8.2	25 39.7
13	19 23 16.0	22 12.7	25 31.5	3♈55.6	19 25.7	27 42.4	4 34.4	13 41.4	9 16.7	15 54.8	18 8.5	25 41.4
14	19 27 12.5	23 13.5	25 28.4	16 20.2	20 25.4	29 .9	4 55.1	13 51.0	9 19.6	15 58.7	18 8.9	25 43.1
15	19 31 9.1	24 14.3	25 25.3	28 54.4	21 21.8	0♌19.1	5 16.3	14 .4	9 22.5	16 2.6	18 9.3	25 44.8
16	19 35 5.6	25 15.0	25 22.2	11♉48.8	22 15.0	1 37.1	5 38.0	14 9.8	9 25.5	16 6.5	18 9.8	25 46.5
17	19 39 2.2	26 15.5	25 19.1	25 7.5	23 4.9	2 54.9	6 .1	14 19.0	9 28.6	16 10.4	18 10.2	25 48.3
18	19 42 58.8	27 15.9	25 16.0	8♊46.0	23 51.3	4 12.4	6 22.7	14 28.2	9 31.7	16 14.3	18 10.7	25 50.0
19	19 46 55.3	28 16.2	25 12.9	22 32.2	24 34.3	5 29.7	6 45.8	14 37.2	9 34.9	16 18.1	18 11.2	25 51.7
20	19 50 51.9	29 16.3	25 9.8	6♋ 9.3	25 13.7	6 46.7	7 9.3	14 46.1	9 38.3	16 22.0	18 11.8	25 53.5
21	19 54 48.4	0♌16.3	25 6.7	19 20.9	25 49.4	8 3.4	7 33.3	14 54.8	9 41.6	16 25.8	18 12.4	25 55.3
22	19 58 45.0	1 16.2	25 3.6	1♌56.4	26 21.3	9 19.9	7 57.8	15 3.4	9 45.1	16 29.7	18 13.0	25 57.0
23	20 2 41.5	2 15.9	25 .5	13 52.6	26 49.3	10 36.0	8 22.6	15 11.9	9 48.6	16 33.5	18 13.6	25 58.8
24	20 6 38.1	3 15.5	24 57.4	25 13.4	27 13.2	11 51.9	8 48.0	15 20.3	9 52.3	16 37.3	18 14.3	26 .6
25	20 10 34.7	4 14.9	24 54.3	6♍ 7.3	27 33.1	13 7.5	9 13.7	15 28.6	9 56.0	16 41.1	18 15.0	26 2.5
26	20 14 31.2	5 14.2	24 51.2	16 46.1	27 48.6	14 22.8	9 39.9	15 36.7	9 59.7	16 44.9	18 15.7	26 4.3
27	20 18 27.8	6 13.3	24 48.1	27 23.6	27 59.9	15 37.9	10 6.5	15 44.6	10 3.6	16 48.7	18 16.5	26 6.1
28	20 22 24.3	7 12.3	24 45.1	8♎15.0	28 6.6	16 52.6	10 33.5	15 52.5	10 7.5	16 52.5	18 17.3	26 7.9
29	20 26 20.9	8 11.1	24 42.0	19 36.6	28 8.8	18 7.0	11 .9	16 .2	10 11.4	16 56.2	18 18.1	26 9.8
30	20 30 17.4	9 9.8	24 38.9	1♏45.3	28R 6.3	19 21.2	11 28.7	16 7.7	10 15.5	16 59.9	18 18.9	26 11.6
31	20 34 14.0	10 8.3	24 35.8	14 56.1	27 59.1	20 35.0	11 56.9	16 15.1	10 19.6	17 3.6	18 19.8	26 13.5

DECLINATION

DAY	SID. TIME	☉	☊	☾	☿	♀	♂	♃	♄	♅	♆	♇
1	18 35 57.3	23N 8.1	0S14.2	9S23.5	21N30.4	23N38.7	14S 9.5	14N56.5	1S 7.0	23N 5.5	5S52.1	23N17.5
4	18 47 46.9	22 54.5	0 14.3	23 45.6	20 8.8	23 23.9	14 28.8	15 5.8	1 10.2	23 4.3	5 52.3	23 15.7
7	18 59 36.6	22 37.4	0 14.3	26 52.5	18 41.4	23 3.0	14 49.4	15 14.7	1 13.7	23 3.2	5 52.7	23 14.0
10	19 11 26.3	22 16.8	0 14.4	13 55.6	17 10.9	22 35.9	15 11.2	15 23.2	1 17.6	23 2.1	5 53.1	23 12.2
13	19 23 16.0	21 52.6	0 14.4	5N39.4	15 39.8	22 2.9	15 34.1	15 31.4	1 21.8	23 .9	5 53.7	23 10.4
16	19 35 5.6	21 25.2	0 14.5	21 34.2	14 10.5	21 24.0	15 57.9	15 39.2	1 26.2	22 59.8	5 54.4	23 8.6
19	19 46 55.3	20 54.4	0 14.6	27 43.8	12 45.7	20 39.6	16 22.5	15 46.6	1 31.0	22 58.6	5 55.1	23 6.8
22	19 58 45.0	20 20.4	0 14.6	22 14.5	11 28.1	19 49.9	16 47.8	15 53.6	1 36.0	22 57.4	5 56.0	23 5.0
25	20 10 34.7	19 43.4	0 14.7	8 39.9	10 20.9	18 55.2	17 13.8	16 .3	1 41.3	22 56.3	5 57.0	23 3.2
28	20 22 24.3	19 3.4	0 14.7	7S54.6	9 27.5	17 55.6	17 40.1	16 6.5	1 46.9	22 55.1	5 58.1	23 1.4
31	20 34 14.0	18 20.6	0 14.8	22 31.9	8 51.4	16 51.6	18 6.8	16 12.2	1 52.7	22 53.9	5 59.2	22 59.6

AUGUST 1952

LONGITUDE

DAY	EPHEM. SID. TIME h m s	☉ ° ′	☊ ° ′	☽ ° ′	☿ ° ′	♀ ° ′	♂ ° ′	♃ ° ′	♄ ° ′	♅ ° ′	♆ ° ′	♇ ° ′
1	20 38 10.6	8♌40.9	22♒10.8	2♐30.1	26♌58.0	18♌55.5	15♏27.9	18♉30.2	10♎18.3	15♋44.2	19♎12.0	20♌47.5
2	20 42 7.1	9 38.3	22 7.7	16 30.0	26 R 44.3	20 9.4	15 56.8	18 37.2	10 23.0	15 47.6	19 13.0	20 49.4
3	20 46 3.7	10 35.8	22 4.5	0♑56.2	26 25.4	21 23.4	16 26.1	18 44.2	10 27.9	15 51.1	19 14.1	20 51.3
4	20 50 .2	11 33.2	22 1.3	15 44.8	26 1.6	22 37.3	16 55.7	18 51.0	10 32.7	15 54.4	19 15.1	20 53.1
5	20 53 56.8	12 30.6	21 58.1	0♒49.6	25 32.8	23 51.2	17 25.6	18 57.6	10 37.6	15 57.8	19 16.2	20 55.0
6	20 57 53.3	13 28.1	21 55.0	16 2.0	24 59.5	25 5.1	17 55.8	19 4.0	10 42.6	16 1.1	19 17.4	20 56.8
7	21 1 49.9	14 25.5	21 51.8	1♓12.3	24 22.0	26 19.0	18 26.3	19 10.3	10 47.7	16 4.4	19 18.5	20 58.7
8	21 5 46.5	15 23.0	21 48.6	16 11.5	23 40.8	27 33.0	18 57.1	19 16.5	10 52.8	16 7.7	19 19.7	21 .6
9	21 9 43.0	16 20.5	21 45.4	0♈52.1	22 56.5	28 46.9	19 28.1	19 22.4	10 58.0	16 11.0	19 20.9	21 2.5
10	21 13 39.6	17 18.0	21 42.2	15 9.0	22 9.7	0♍ .8	19 59.5	19 28.2	11 3.2	16 14.2	19 22.2	21 4.3
11	21 17 36.1	18 15.6	21 39.1	28 59.9	21 21.3	1 14.7	20 31.1	19 33.9	11 8.5	16 17.4	19 23.4	21 6.2
12	21 21 32.7	19 13.2	21 35.9	12♉24.6	20 32.1	2 28.6	21 3.0	19 39.4	11 13.9	16 20.6	19 24.7	21 8.1
13	21 25 29.2	20 10.8	21 32.7	25 25.2	19 43.0	3 42.6	21 35.2	19 44.7	11 19.3	16 23.8	19 26.0	21 10.0
14	21 29 25.8	21 8.4	21 29.5	8♊ 4.6	18 55.0	4 56.5	22 7.6	19 49.9	11 24.9	16 26.9	19 27.4	21 11.9
15	21 33 22.3	22 6.0	21 26.4	20 26.4	18 8.9	6 10.5	22 40.3	19 54.8	11 30.4	16 30.1	19 28.8	21 13.7
16	21 37 18.9	23 3.7	21 23.2	2♋34.5	17 25.9	7 24.4	23 13.3	19 59.6	11 36.0	16 33.2	19 30.2	21 15.6
17	21 41 15.5	24 1.4	21 20.0	14 32.5	16 46.7	8 38.3	23 46.5	20 4.3	11 41.7	16 36.2	19 31.6	21 17.5
18	21 45 12.0	24 59.1	21 16.8	26 23.8	16 12.2	9 52.3	24 20.0	20 8.7	11 47.5	16 39.3	19 33.0	21 19.4
19	21 49 8.6	25 56.9	21 13.6	8♌11.6	15 43.2	11 6.2	24 53.7	20 13.0	11 53.3	16 42.3	19 34.5	21 21.3
20	21 53 5.1	26 54.7	21 10.5	19 58.6	15 20.3	12 20.2	25 27.7	20 17.1	11 59.1	16 45.3	19 36.0	21 23.1
21	21 57 1.7	27 52.4	21 7.3	1♍47.0	15 4.1	13 34.1	26 1.9	20 21.0	12 5.0	16 48.2	19 37.5	21 25.0
22	22 0 58.2	28 50.3	21 4.1	13 39.3	14 55.1	14 48.1	26 36.3	20 24.7	12 11.0	16 51.2	19 39.1	21 26.9
23	22 4 54.8	29 48.1	21 .9	25 37.6	14 53.5	16 2.0	27 11.0	20 28.3	12 17.0	16 54.1	19 40.6	21 28.8
24	22 8 51.3	0♍46.0	20 57.8	7♎44.3	14 D 59.8	17 16.0	27 46.0	20 31.7	12 23.1	16 57.0	19 42.3	21 30.7
25	22 12 47.9	1 43.9	20 54.6	20 1.5	15 13.9	18 29.9	28 21.1	20 34.8	12 29.2	16 59.8	19 43.9	21 32.5
26	22 16 44.4	2 41.8	20 51.4	2♏32.1	15 36.1	19 43.9	28 56.5	20 37.8	12 35.4	17 2.6	19 45.5	21 34.4
27	22 20 41.0	3 39.7	20 48.2	15 18.6	16 6.1	20 57.8	29 32.1	20 40.6	12 41.6	17 5.4	19 47.2	21 36.2
28	22 24 37.6	4 37.7	20 45.1	28 24.0	16 44.0	22 11.7	0♐ 7.9	20 43.2	12 47.9	17 8.1	19 48.9	21 38.1
29	22 28 34.1	5 35.7	20 41.9	11♐50.4	17 29.6	23 25.6	0 43.9	20 45.6	12 54.2	17 10.8	19 50.6	21 39.9
30	22 32 30.7	6 33.7	20 38.7	25 39.6	18 22.7	24 39.6	1 20.1	20 47.9	13 .6	17 13.4	19 52.3	21 41.7
31	22 36 27.2	7 31.7	20 35.5	9♑51.8	19 22.9	25 53.5	1 56.5	20 49.9	13 7.0	17 16.1	19 54.1	21 43.6

LATITUDE

DAY	EPHEM. SID. TIME	☉	☊	☽	☿	♀	♂	♃	♄	♅	♆	♇
1	20 38 10.6	0 .0	0 .0	5 S 11.2	4 S 2.2	1 N 24.2	1 S 52.0	1 S 8.9	2 N 21.5	0 N 22.6	1 N 38.8	8 N 54.1
4	20 50 .2	0 .0	0 .0	3 5.8	4 30.4	1 25.9	1 53.5	1 9.4	2 21.0	0 22.6	1 38.7	8 54.2
7	21 1 49.9	0 .0	0 .0	0 N 53.6	4 48.1	1 27.0	1 54.8	1 9.9	2 20.4	0 22.7	1 38.6	8 54.3
10	21 13 39.6	0 .0	0 .0	4 16.0	4 51.9	1 27.5	1 56.0	1 10.3	2 19.9	0 22.7	1 38.4	8 54.4
13	21 25 29.2	0 .0	0 .0	5 17.1	4 39.3	1 27.4	1 57.1	1 10.8	2 19.4	0 22.8	1 38.3	8 54.6
16	21 37 18.9	0 .0	0 .0	4 .0	4 10.6	1 26.7	1 58.0	1 11.3	2 19.0	0 22.8	1 38.2	8 54.8
19	21 49 8.6	0 .0	0 .0	1 13.6	3 28.4	1 25.4	1 58.8	1 11.8	2 18.5	0 22.9	1 38.0	8 55.1
22	22 0 58.2	0 .0	0 .0	1 S 59.6	2 37.6	1 23.5	1 59.5	1 12.3	2 18.1	0 23.0	1 37.9	8 55.4
25	22 12 47.9	0 .0	0 .0	4 30.5	1 43.4	1 21.0	2 .0	1 12.9	2 17.7	0 23.0	1 37.8	8 55.7
28	22 24 37.6	0 .0	0 .0	5 14.5	0 50.5	1 17.9	2 .5	1 13.4	2 17.3	0 23.1	1 37.7	8 56.1
31	22 36 27.2	0 .0	0 .0	3 30.6	0 2.5	1 14.3	2 .8	1 13.9	2 16.9	0 23.2	1 37.6	8 56.5

RIGHT ASCENSION

DAY	EPHEM. SID. TIME	☉	☊	☽	☿	♀	♂	♃	♄	♅	♆	♇
1	20 38 10.6	11♌ 6.7	24♒32.7	29♏18.0	27♌47.2	21♌48.5	12♏25.5	16♉22.4	10♎23.8	17♋ 7.3	18♎20.7	26♌15.4
2	20 42 7.1	12 4.9	24 29.6	14♐47.5	27 R 30.7	23 1.8	12 54.5	16 29.5	10 28.1	17 11.0	18 21.6	26 17.3
3	20 46 3.7	13 3.0	24 26.5	1♑ 3.2	27 9.6	24 14.8	13 23.9	16 36.5	10 32.4	17 14.7	18 22.6	26 19.2
4	20 50 .2	14 .8	24 23.4	17 29.2	26 44.1	25 27.5	13 53.6	16 43.3	10 36.8	17 18.3	18 23.6	26 21.1
5	20 53 56.8	14 58.6	24 20.3	3♒28.8	26 14.3	26 39.9	14 23.7	16 50.0	10 41.3	17 21.9	18 24.6	26 23.0
6	20 57 53.3	15 56.2	24 17.2	18 39.0	25 40.6	27 52.0	14 54.2	16 56.5	10 45.8	17 25.5	18 25.6	26 24.9
7	21 1 49.9	16 53.6	24 14.1	2♓55.1	25 3.4	29 3.8	15 25.0	17 2.9	10 50.4	17 29.1	18 26.7	26 26.8
8	21 5 46.5	17 50.9	24 11.0	16 26.0	24 23.1	0♍15.4	15 56.2	17 9.1	10 55.0	17 32.6	18 27.8	26 28.7
9	21 9 43.0	18 48.0	24 7.9	29 27.5	23 40.3	1 26.7	16 27.7	17 15.1	10 59.7	17 36.2	18 28.9	26 30.6
10	21 13 39.6	19 45.0	24 4.7	12♈16.7	22 55.8	2 37.8	16 59.6	17 21.0	11 4.5	17 39.7	18 30.0	26 32.5
11	21 17 36.1	20 41.9	24 1.6	25 9.1	22 10.1	3 48.6	17 31.8	17 26.7	11 9.3	17 43.1	18 31.2	26 34.4
12	21 21 32.7	21 38.6	23 58.5	8♉15.8	21 24.2	4 59.1	18 4.4	17 32.3	11 14.2	17 46.6	18 32.4	26 36.3
13	21 25 29.2	22 35.2	23 55.4	21 41.8	20 38.8	6 9.5	18 37.2	17 37.7	11 19.1	17 50.0	18 33.6	26 38.3
14	21 29 25.8	23 31.7	23 52.3	5♊24.3	19 54.9	7 19.5	19 10.5	17 42.9	11 24.1	17 53.4	18 34.8	26 40.2
15	21 33 22.3	24 28.0	23 49.2	19 13.3	19 13.3	8 29.4	19 44.1	17 47.9	11 29.2	17 56.7	18 36.1	26 42.1
16	21 37 18.9	25 24.2	23 46.1	2♋53.6	18 35.0	9 39.1	20 18.0	17 52.8	11 34.3	18 .1	18 37.4	26 44.0
17	21 41 15.5	26 20.2	23 43.0	16 10.3	18 .7	10 48.5	20 52.2	17 57.5	11 39.5	18 3.4	18 38.7	26 46.0
18	21 45 12.0	27 16.2	23 39.9	28 52.7	17 31.4	11 57.7	21 26.8	18 2.0	11 44.7	18 6.7	18 40.0	26 47.9
19	21 49 8.6	28 12.0	23 36.8	10♌57.1	17 7.6	13 6.8	22 1.6	18 6.4	11 50.0	18 9.9	18 41.4	26 49.8
20	21 53 5.1	29 7.7	23 33.7	22 26.1	16 50.0	14 15.6	22 36.8	18 10.6	11 55.3	18 13.1	18 42.7	26 51.8
21	21 57 1.7	0♍ 3.3	23 30.6	3♍27.0	16 39.2	15 24.3	23 12.4	18 14.5	12 .7	18 16.3	18 44.2	26 53.7
22	22 0 58.2	0 58.7	23 27.5	14 10.4	16 35.5	16 32.8	23 48.2	18 18.3	12 6.2	18 19.5	18 45.6	26 55.6
23	22 4 54.8	1 54.1	23 24.4	24 48.6	16 D 39.4	17 41.1	24 24.4	18 21.9	12 11.7	18 22.6	18 47.0	26 57.5
24	22 8 51.3	2 49.4	23 21.3	5♎35.3	16 51.0	18 49.4	25 .9	18 25.4	12 17.2	18 25.7	18 48.5	26 59.5
25	22 12 47.9	3 44.5	23 18.1	16 45.1	17 10.4	19 57.4	25 37.6	18 28.7	12 22.8	18 28.8	18 50.0	27 1.4
26	22 16 44.4	4 39.5	23 15.0	28 32.7	17 37.7	21 5.3	26 14.7	18 31.7	12 28.5	18 31.8	18 51.5	27 3.3
27	22 20 41.0	5 34.4	23 11.9	11♏12.0	18 12.8	22 13.1	26 52.1	18 34.6	12 34.1	18 34.7	18 53.1	27 5.2
28	22 24 37.6	6 29.2	23 8.8	24 52.5	18 55.6	23 20.8	27 29.7	18 37.2	12 39.9	18 37.7	18 54.6	27 7.2
29	22 28 34.1	7 24.0	23 5.7	9♐34.9	19 45.8	24 28.4	28 7.7	18 39.7	12 45.6	18 40.6	18 56.2	27 9.1
30	22 32 30.7	8 18.6	23 2.6	25 6.5	20 43.2	25 35.9	28 45.9	18 42.0	12 51.5	18 43.4	18 57.8	27 10.9
31	22 36 27.2	9 13.1	22 59.5	11♑ 1.3	21 47.4	26 43.3	29 24.5	18 44.1	12 57.3	18 46.3	18 59.4	27 12.8

DECLINATION

DAY	EPHEM. SID. TIME	☉	☊	☽	☿	♀	♂	♃	♄	♅	♆	♇
1	20 38 10.6	18 N 5.8	0 S 14.8	25 S 45.0	8 N 43.9	16 N 29.4	18 S 15.8	16 N 14.1	1 S 54.7	22 N 53.6	5 S 59.7	22 N 59.0
4	20 50 .2	17 19.4	0 14.8	25 35.6	8 36.2	15 19.9	18 42.7	16 19.3	2 .8	22 52.4	6 1.0	22 57.2
7	21 1 49.9	16 30.6	0 14.9	10 12.9	8 52.2	14 6.8	19 9.6	16 24.1	2 7.2	22 51.3	6 2.4	22 55.5
10	21 13 39.6	15 39.3	0 14.9	9 N 54.2	9 31.2	12 50.2	19 36.4	16 28.5	2 13.7	22 50.2	6 3.9	22 53.7
13	21 25 29.2	14 45.8	0 15.0	24 15.0	10 29.0	11 30.5	20 3.0	16 32.5	2 20.5	22 49.0	6 5.5	22 52.0
16	21 37 18.9	13 50.1	0 15.1	27 25.3	11 38.0	10 8.1	20 29.3	16 36.0	2 27.5	22 48.0	6 7.1	22 50.4
19	21 49 8.6	12 52.4	0 15.1	19 24.5	12 48.6	8 43.3	20 55.1	16 39.1	2 34.6	22 46.9	6 8.9	22 48.7
22	22 0 58.2	11 52.9	0 15.2	4 35.3	13 51.2	7 16.3	21 20.4	16 41.7	2 41.9	22 45.9	6 10.7	22 47.1
25	22 12 47.9	10 51.7	0 15.2	12 S .1	14 37.5	5 47.6	21 45.0	16 43.9	2 49.3	22 44.8	6 12.6	22 45.6
28	22 24 37.6	9 49.0	0 15.3	24 55.0	15 1.4	4 17.4	22 8.8	16 45.6	2 56.9	22 43.8	6 14.6	22 44.1
31	22 36 27.2	8 44.9	0 15.3	26 34.9	14 58.5	2 46.2	22 31.7	16 46.8	3 4.7	22 42.9	6 16.6	22 42.6

SEPTEMBER 1952

LONGITUDE

DAY	EPHEM. SID. TIME (h m s)	☉	☊	☽	☿	♀	♂	♃	♄	♅	♆	♇
1	22 40 23.8	8♍29.7	20♒32.3	24♑25.5	20♌29.9	27♍7.4	2♐33.1	20♉51.7	13♎13.4	17♋18.7	19♎55.8	21♌45.4
2	22 44 20.3	9 27.8	20 29.2	9♒17.0	21 43.3	28 21.2	3 9.9	20 53.4	13 19.9	17 21.2	19 57.6	21 47.2
3	22 48 16.9	10 25.9	20 26.0	24 19.9	23 2.7	29 35.1	3 46.8	20 54.8	13 26.4	17 23.7	19 59.4	21 49.0
4	22 52 13.4	11 24.0	20 22.8	9♓26.2	24 27.6	0♎49.0	4 24.0	20 56.1	13 33.0	17 26.2	20 1.2	21 50.8
5	22 56 10.0	12 22.1	20 19.6	24 27.0	25 57.4	2 2.9	5 1.3	20 57.1	13 39.6	17 28.6	20 3.1	21 52.6
6	23 0 6.5	13 20.3	20 16.5	9♈13.5	27 31.8	3 16.7	5 38.9	20 58.0	13 46.2	17 31.0	20 4.9	21 54.4
7	23 4 3.1	14 18.5	20 13.3	23 38.8	29 10.0	4 30.6	6 16.6	20 58.6	13 52.9	17 33.4	20 6.8	21 56.1
8	23 7 59.7	15 16.7	20 10.1	7♉38.3	0♍51.7	5 44.4	6 54.4	20 59.1	13 59.6	17 35.7	20 8.7	21 57.9
9	23 11 56.2	16 15.0	20 6.9	21 10.2	2 36.3	6 58.3	7 32.5	20 59.3	14 6.4	17 38.0	20 10.6	21 59.6
10	23 15 52.8	17 13.3	20 3.7	4♊15.4	4 23.2	8 12.1	8 10.7	20 59.4	14 13.2	17 40.3	20 12.6	22 1.4
11	23 19 49.3	18 11.6	20 .6	16 56.3	6 12.2	9 26.0	8 49.1	20R59.2	14 20.0	17 42.5	20 14.5	22 3.1
12	23 23 45.9	19 10.0	19 57.4	29 17.1	8 2.6	10 39.8	9 27.7	20 58.9	14 26.9	17 44.6	20 16.5	22 4.8
13	23 27 42.4	20 8.4	19 54.2	11♋22.3	9 54.2	11 53.6	10 6.4	20 58.3	14 33.8	17 46.7	20 18.5	22 6.5
14	23 31 39.0	21 6.9	19 51.0	23 16.8	11 46.7	13 7.5	10 45.3	20 57.6	14 40.7	17 48.9	20 20.5	22 8.3
15	23 35 35.5	22 5.4	19 47.9	5♌5.1	13 39.5	14 21.3	11 24.4	20 56.7	14 47.7	17 50.9	20 22.5	22 10.0
16	23 39 32.1	23 3.9	19 44.7	16 51.6	15 32.6	15 35.1	12 3.6	20 55.5	14 54.6	17 52.9	20 24.5	22 11.6
17	23 43 28.6	24 2.5	19 41.5	28 40.0	17 25.7	16 48.9	12 43.0	20 54.2	15 1.7	17 54.8	20 26.6	22 13.3
18	23 47 25.2	25 1.0	19 38.3	10♍33.4	19 18.6	18 2.7	13 22.5	20 52.6	15 8.7	17 56.7	20 28.6	22 14.9
19	23 51 21.7	25 59.7	19 35.1	22 34.2	21 11.2	19 16.5	14 2.2	20 50.8	15 15.7	17 58.6	20 30.7	22 16.5
20	23 55 18.3	26 58.3	19 32.0	4♎44.2	23 3.2	20 30.3	14 42.1	20 48.9	15 22.8	18 .4	20 32.8	22 18.2
21	23 59 14.8	27 57.0	19 28.8	17 4.9	24 54.7	21 44.1	15 22.0	20 46.7	15 29.9	18 2.1	20 34.9	22 19.7
22	0 3 11.4	28 55.7	19 25.6	29 37.1	26 45.4	22 57.8	16 2.2	20 44.4	15 37.1	18 3.8	20 37.0	22 21.3
23	0 7 8.0	29 54.4	19 22.4	12♏21.7	28 35.4	24 11.6	16 42.5	20 41.8	15 44.2	18 5.5	20 39.1	22 22.9
24	0 11 4.5	0♎53.2	19 19.3	25 19.3	0♎24.6	25 25.4	17 22.9	20 39.0	15 51.4	18 7.1	20 41.2	22 24.4
25	0 15 1.1	1 52.0	19 16.1	8♐31.3	2 13.0	26 39.1	18 3.5	20 36.1	15 58.6	18 8.7	20 43.3	22 26.0
26	0 18 57.6	2 50.8	19 12.9	21 58.2	4 .5	27 52.8	18 44.2	20 32.9	16 5.8	18 10.2	20 45.5	22 27.5
27	0 22 54.2	3 49.7	19 9.7	5♑41.2	5 47.1	29 6.5	19 25.0	20 29.6	16 13.0	18 11.7	20 47.6	22 29.0
28	0 26 50.7	4 48.6	19 6.5	19 40.7	7 32.8	0♏20.2	20 5.9	20 26.1	16 20.2	18 13.1	20 49.8	22 30.5
29	0 30 47.3	5 47.5	19 3.4	3♒56.5	9 17.6	1 33.9	20 47.0	20 22.4	16 27.5	18 14.5	20 52.0	22 32.0
30	0 34 43.8	6 46.5	19 .2	18 26.9	11 1.5	2 47.6	21 28.3	20 18.5	16 34.7	18 15.8	20 54.1	22 33.4

LATITUDE

DAY	SID. TIME (h m s)	☉	☊	☽	☿	♀	♂	♃	♄	♅	♆	♇
1	22 40 23.8	0 .0	0 .0	2S24.4	0N12.0	1N12.9	2S .9	1S14.1	2N16.8	0N23.2	1N37.6	8N56.6
4	22 52 13.4	0 .0	0 .0	1N37.4	0 49.6	1 8.5	2 1.0	1 14.6	2 16.5	0 23.3	1 37.5	8 57.1
7	23 4 3.1	0 .0	0 .0	4 38.6	1 17.9	1 3.5	2 1.1	1 15.1	2 16.2	0 23.3	1 37.4	8 57.6
10	23 15 52.8	0 .0	0 .0	4 5.7	1 36.7	0 58.1	2 1.0	1 15.6	2 15.9	0 23.4	1 37.3	8 58.1
13	23 27 42.4	0 .0	0 .0	3 22.1	1 46.7	0 52.6	2 .9	1 16.0	2 15.7	0 23.5	1 37.3	8 58.6
16	23 39 32.1	0 .0	0 .0	0 24.6	1 49.1	0 45.7	2 .6	1 16.5	2 15.5	0 23.6	1 37.2	8 59.2
19	23 51 21.7	0 .0	0 .0	2S42.3	1 45.1	0 38.9	2 .3	1 17.0	2 15.3	0 23.7	1 37.2	8 59.8
22	0 3 11.4	0 .0	0 .0	4 49.0	1 36.2	0 31.7	1 59.8	1 17.4	2 15.1	0 23.7	1 37.1	9 .5
25	0 15 1.1	0 .0	0 .0	4 55.3	1 23.4	0 24.1	1 59.3	1 17.8	2 15.0	0 23.8	1 37.1	9 1.2
28	0 26 50.7	0 .0	0 .0	2 39.9	1 7.7	0 16.2	1 58.6	1 18.2	2 14.9	0 23.9	1 37.0	9 1.9

RIGHT ASCENSION

DAY	SID. TIME (h m s)	☉	☊	☽	☿	♀	♂	♃	♄	♅	♆	♇
1	22 40 23.8	10♍7.6	22♒56.4	26♑48.0	22♌57.9	27♍50.6	0♐3.2	18♉46.0	13♎3.2	18♋49.1	19♎1.1	27♌14.7
2	22 44 20.3	11 2.0	22 53.2	12♒2.0	24 14.3	28 57.8	0 42.3	18 47.7	13 9.0	18 51.8	19 2.7	27 16.6
3	22 48 16.9	11 56.3	22 50.1	26 32.8	25 36.1	0♎5.0	1 21.6	18 49.2	13 15.1	18 54.5	19 4.4	27 18.5
4	22 52 13.4	12 50.5	22 47.0	10♓23.6	27 2.6	1 12.2	2 1.2	18 50.5	13 21.2	18 57.2	19 6.1	27 20.3
5	22 56 10.0	13 44.7	22 43.9	23 46.2	28 33.5	2 19.3	2 41.1	18 51.6	13 27.2	18 59.9	19 7.8	27 22.2
6	23 0 6.5	14 38.8	22 40.8	6♈55.9	0♍7.3	3 26.4	3 21.2	18 52.5	13 33.3	19 2.4	19 9.5	27 24.0
7	23 4 3.1	15 32.8	22 37.7	20 7.3	1 45.6	4 33.5	4 1.6	18 53.2	13 39.4	19 4.9	19 11.2	27 25.9
8	23 7 59.7	16 26.9	22 34.5	3♉31.9	3 25.7	5 40.6	4 42.2	18 53.7	13 45.6	19 7.4	19 13.0	27 27.7
9	23 11 56.2	17 20.8	22 31.4	17 14.7	5 7.8	6 47.8	5 23.1	18 54.0	13 51.8	19 9.9	19 14.8	27 29.5
10	23 15 52.8	18 14.8	22 28.3	1♊13.3	6 51.5	7 54.9	6 4.3	18 54.1	13 58.0	19 12.3	19 16.6	27 31.4
11	23 19 49.3	19 8.7	22 25.2	15 17.4	8 36.3	9 2.1	6 45.6	18R54.0	14 4.3	19 14.7	19 18.4	27 33.2
12	23 23 45.9	20 2.6	22 22.1	29 11.7	10 21.7	10 9.3	7 27.3	18 53.7	14 10.6	19 17.0	19 20.2	27 35.0
13	23 27 42.4	20 56.4	22 18.9	12♋41.1	12 7.5	11 16.6	8 9.1	18 53.2	14 16.9	19 19.3	19 22.0	27 36.7
14	23 31 39.0	21 50.3	22 15.8	25 34.9	13 53.4	12 24.0	8 51.3	18 52.5	14 23.3	19 21.6	19 23.9	27 38.6
15	23 35 35.5	22 44.1	22 12.7	7♌49.1	15 39.0	13 31.4	9 33.6	18 51.6	14 29.7	19 23.7	19 25.8	27 40.3
16	23 39 32.1	23 38.0	22 9.6	19 26.6	17 24.2	14 38.9	10 16.2	18 50.5	14 36.2	19 25.9	19 27.7	27 42.1
17	23 43 28.6	24 31.8	22 6.5	0♍34.8	19 8.8	15 46.5	10 59.0	18 49.2	14 42.6	19 28.0	19 29.6	27 43.8
18	23 47 25.2	25 25.6	22 3.3	11 24.1	20 52.7	16 54.3	11 42.1	18 47.6	14 49.1	19 30.0	19 31.5	27 45.5
19	23 51 21.7	26 19.4	22 .2	22 6.6	22 36.2	18 2.1	12 25.3	18 45.9	14 55.6	19 32.0	19 33.4	27 47.3
20	23 55 18.3	27 13.3	21 57.1	2♎54.4	24 19.1	19 10.1	13 8.8	18 44.0	15 2.1	19 33.9	19 35.3	27 49.0
21	23 59 14.8	28 7.1	21 54.0	14 4.3	26 0.9	20 18.2	13 52.5	18 41.8	15 8.7	19 35.8	19 37.3	27 50.6
22	0 3 11.4	29 1.0	21 50.8	25 46.8	27 39.7	21 26.5	14 36.4	18 39.5	15 15.2	19 37.7	19 39.2	27 52.3
23	0 7 8.0	29 54.9	21 47.7	9♏15.2	29 21.7	22 34.9	15 20.5	18 36.9	15 21.8	19 39.5	19 41.2	27 54.0
24	0 11 4.5	0♎48.8	21 44.6	21 37.8	1♎3.7	23 43.5	16 4.8	18 34.2	15 28.4	19 41.2	19 43.2	27 55.6
25	0 15 1.1	1 42.8	21 41.5	5♐55.4	2 57.6	24 52.2	16 49.3	18 31.3	15 35.1	19 42.9	19 45.2	27 57.2
26	0 18 57.6	2 36.8	21 38.3	20 57.4	4 22.0	26 1.2	17 34.0	18 28.2	15 41.7	19 44.5	19 47.2	27 58.8
27	0 22 54.2	3 30.8	21 35.2	6♑22.2	5 47.6	27 10.3	18 18.9	18 24.8	15 48.4	19 46.1	19 49.2	28 .4
28	0 26 50.7	4 24.9	21 32.1	21 43.2	7 22.5	28 19.7	19 3.9	18 21.3	15 55.1	19 47.6	19 51.2	28 2.0
29	0 30 47.3	5 19.0	21 29.0	6♒38.3	8 56.6	29 29.2	19 49.2	18 17.6	16 1.8	19 49.1	19 53.2	28 3.6
30	0 34 43.8	6 13.2	21 25.8	20 57.0	10 30.0	0♏39.0	20 34.6	18 13.7	16 8.5	19 50.5	19 55.2	28 5.1

DECLINATION

DAY	SID. TIME (h m s)	☉	☊	☽	☿	♀	♂	♃	♄	♅	♆	♇
1	22 40 23.8	8N23.2	0S15.3	23S36.5	14N51.0	2N15.6	22S39.2	16N47.2	3S7.3	22N42.6	6S17.3	22N42.1
4	22 52 13.4	7 17.5	0 15.4	6S31.7	14 9.1	0 43.3	23 .7	16 47.8	3 15.1	22 41.7	6 19.5	22 40.7
7	23 4 3.1	6 10.7	0 15.4	13N29.9	12 46.7	0S49.3	23 21.1	16 48.0	3 23.1	22 40.8	6 21.6	22 39.4
10	23 15 52.8	5 3.0	0 15.5	26 1.4	11 24.3	2 21.9	23 40.2	16 47.7	3 31.2	22 40.0	6 23.9	22 38.1
13	23 27 42.4	3 54.4	0 15.6	19 10.7	9 30.3	3 54.3	23 57.9	16 47.0	3 39.4	22 39.2	6 26.1	22 36.9
16	23 39 32.1	2 45.2	0 15.6	16 10.7	7 22.6	5 26.0	24 14.2	16 45.8	3 47.6	22 38.5	6 28.5	22 35.8
19	23 51 21.7	1 35.6	0 15.7	0S27.9	5 6.3	6 56.9	24 29.0	16 44.1	3 55.9	22 37.8	6 30.8	22 34.7
22	0 3 11.4	0 25.6	0 15.7	15S50.6	2 45.7	8 26.5	24 42.1	16 42.0	4 4.2	22 37.2	6 33.2	22 33.7
25	0 15 1.1	0S44.6	0 15.8	26 35.4	0 23.6	9 54.4	24 53.4	16 39.4	4 12.6	22 36.7	6 35.7	22 32.8
28	0 26 50.7	1 54.7	0 15.8	24 38.5	1S57.5	11 20.4	25 3.0	16 36.4	4 21.0	22 36.2	6 38.1	22 31.9

OCTOBER 1952

LONGITUDE

DAY	EPHEM. SID. TIME	☉	☊	☽	☿	♀	♂	♃	♄	♅	♆	♇
	h m s	° ′	° ′	° ′	° ′	° ′	° ′	° ′	° ′	° ′	° ′	° ′
1	0 38 40.4	7♎45.4	18♒57.0	3♓ 8.7	12♎44.5	4♏ 1.2	22♐ 9.6	20♉14.4	16♎42.0	18♋17.1	20♎56.3	22♌34.8
2	0 42 36.9	8 44.4	18 53.8	17 56.4	14 26.6	5 14.9	22 51.0	20 R 10.1	16 49.3	18 18.3	20 58.5	22 36.2
3	0 46 33.5	9 43.5	18 50.7	2♈43.2	16 7.9	6 28.5	23 32.6	20 5.7	16 56.6	18 19.5	21 .7	22 37.6
4	0 50 30.0	10 42.5	18 47.5	17 21.2	17 48.4	7 42.1	24 14.3	20 1.1	17 3.9	18 20.6	21 2.9	22 38.9
5	0 54 26.6	11 41.7	18 44.3	1♉43.2	19 28.0	8 55.8	24 56.2	19 56.3	17 11.2	18 21.7	21 5.2	22 40.3
6	0 58 23.2	12 40.8	18 41.1	15 43.3	21 6.8	10 9.4	25 38.1	19 51.4	17 18.5	18 22.7	21 7.4	22 41.7
7	1 2 19.7	13 40.0	18 37.9	29 18.1	22 44.8	11 22.9	26 20.1	19 46.3	17 25.9	18 23.7	21 9.6	22 43.0
8	1 6 16.3	14 39.2	18 34.8	12♊26.8	24 22.0	12 36.5	27 2.2	19 41.0	17 33.2	18 24.6	21 11.8	22 44.3
9	1 10 12.8	15 38.5	18 31.6	25 10.8	25 58.5	13 50.0	27 44.5	19 35.5	17 40.5	18 25.5	21 14.1	22 45.5
10	1 14 9.4	16 37.8	18 28.4	7♋33.4	27 34.2	15 3.6	28 26.8	19 29.9	17 47.9	18 26.3	21 16.3	22 46.8
11	1 18 5.9	17 37.1	18 25.2	19 39.3	29 9.2	16 17.1	29 9.3	19 24.1	17 55.2	18 27.0	21 18.5	22 48.0
12	1 22 2.5	18 36.5	18 22.1	1♌33.5	0♏43.5	17 30.6	29 51.9	19 18.2	18 2.5	18 27.7	21 20.7	22 49.2
13	1 25 59.0	19 35.9	18 18.9	13 21.6	2 17.1	18 44.1	0♑34.5	19 12.1	18 9.9	18 28.4	21 23.0	22 50.4
14	1 29 55.6	20 35.3	18 15.7	25 8.8	3 50.0	19 57.6	1 17.3	19 5.9	18 17.2	18 29.0	21 25.2	22 51.5
15	1 33 52.1	21 34.8	18 12.5	6♍59.8	5 22.2	21 11.1	2 .2	18 59.5	18 24.5	18 29.5	21 27.5	22 52.6
16	1 37 48.7	22 34.3	18 9.3	18 58.9	6 53.8	22 24.6	2 43.2	18 53.0	18 31.9	18 30.0	21 29.7	22 53.7
17	1 41 45.2	23 33.9	18 6.2	1♎ 9.1	8 24.7	23 38.0	3 26.3	18 46.3	18 39.2	18 30.4	21 31.9	22 54.8
18	1 45 41.8	24 33.5	18 3.0	13 32.7	9 54.9	24 51.5	4 9.4	18 39.6	18 46.5	18 30.8	21 34.2	22 55.9
19	1 49 38.4	25 33.1	17 59.8	26 10.6	11 24.5	26 4.9	4 52.7	18 32.7	18 53.8	18 31.1	21 36.4	22 56.9
20	1 53 34.9	26 32.8	17 56.6	9♏ 3.0	12 53.4	27 18.3	5 36.1	18 25.7	19 1.1	18 31.4	21 38.6	22 57.9
21	1 57 31.5	27 32.5	17 53.5	22 8.9	14 21.7	28 31.7	6 19.6	18 18.6	19 8.4	18 31.6	21 40.9	22 58.9
22	2 1 28.0	28 32.2	17 50.3	5♐27.1	15 49.3	29 45.1	7 3.1	18 11.3	19 15.7	18 31.8	21 43.1	22 59.9
23	2 5 24.6	29 32.0	17 47.1	18 56.1	17 16.2	0♐58.5	7 46.8	18 4.0	19 23.0	18 31.9	21 45.3	23 .8
24	2 9 21.1	0♏31.7	17 43.9	2♑34.8	18 42.4	2 11.9	8 30.5	17 56.6	19 30.2	18 32.0	21 47.5	23 1.7
25	2 13 17.7	1 31.6	17 40.7	16 22.4	20 7.9	3 25.2	9 14.3	17 49.1	19 37.5	18 32.0	21 49.7	23 2.6
26	2 17 14.2	2 31.4	17 37.6	0♒18.5	21 32.6	4 38.5	9 58.3	17 41.5	19 44.8	18 32.0	21 52.0	23 3.5
27	2 21 10.8	3 31.3	17 34.4	14 22.8	22 56.5	5 51.8	10 42.2	17 33.8	19 52.0	18 R 31.9	21 54.2	23 4.3
28	2 25 7.3	4 31.2	17 31.2	28 34.9	24 19.6	7 5.1	11 26.3	17 26.1	19 59.2	18 31.7	21 56.4	23 5.1
29	2 29 3.9	5 31.1	17 28.0	12♓53.3	25 41.8	8 18.3	12 10.4	17 18.2	20 6.3	18 31.5	21 58.6	23 5.9
30	2 33 .5	6 31.1	17 24.9	27 15.4	27 3.0	9 31.6	12 54.6	17 10.4	20 13.5	18 31.2	22 .8	23 6.6
31	2 36 57.0	7 31.1	17 21.7	11♈37.0	28 23.2	10 44.8	13 38.9	17 2.4	20 20.6	18 30.9	22 2.9	23 7.3

LATITUDE

DAY	EPHEM. SID. TIME	☉	☊	☽	☿	♀	♂	♃	♄	♅	♆	♇
1	0 38 40.4	0 .0	0 .0	1N 6.9	0N49.9	0N 8.1	1S57.9	1S18.6	2N14.8	0N24.0	1N37.0	9N 2.6
4	0 50 30.0	0 .0	0 .0	4 17.5	0 30.6	0S .2	1 57.0	1 18.9	2 14.8	0 24.1	1 37.0	9 3.4
7	1 2 19.7	0 .0	0 .0	5 2.6	0 10.3	0 8.7	1 56.1	1 19.2	2 14.8	0 24.2	1 37.0	9 4.2
10	1 14 9.4	0 .0	0 .0	3 26.8	0S10.5	0 17.4	1 55.1	1 19.4	2 14.8	0 24.3	1 37.0	9 5.0
13	1 25 59.0	0 .0	0 .0	0 34.6	0 31.4	0 26.1	1 54.0	1 19.6	2 14.8	0 24.4	1 37.0	9 5.9
16	1 37 48.7	0 .0	0 .0	2S29.1	0 52.1	0 34.8	1 52.8	1 19.8	2 14.9	0 24.5	1 37.0	9 6.8
19	1 49 38.4	0 .0	0 .0	4 38.4	1 12.2	0 43.5	1 51.6	1 19.9	2 14.9	0 24.6	1 37.0	9 7.7
22	2 1 28.0	0 .0	0 .0	4 49.5	1 31.5	0 52.1	1 50.2	1 20.0	2 15.1	0 24.6	1 37.0	9 8.6
25	2 13 17.7	0 .0	0 .0	2 41.3	1 49.5	1 .6	1 48.8	1 20.0	2 15.2	0 24.7	1 37.1	9 9.5
28	2 25 7.3	0 .0	0 .0	0N53.6	2 5.9	1 8.8	1 47.3	1 19.9	2 15.4	0 24.8	1 37.1	9 10.5
31	2 36 57.0	0 .0	0 .0	4 2.2	2 20.1	1 16.8	1 45.7	1 19.8	2 15.6	0 24.9	1 37.2	9 11.4

RIGHT ASCENSION

DAY	EPHEM. SID. TIME	☉	☊	☽	☿	♀	♂	♃	♄	♅	♆	♇
1	0 38 40.4	7♎ 7.4	21♒22.7	4♓40.6	12♎ 2.7	1♏49.0	21♐20.2	18♉ 9.7	16♎15.2	19♋51.9	19♎57.3	28♌ 6.6
2	0 42 36.9	8 1.7	21 19.6	17 59.3	13 34.7	2 59.2	22 5.9	18 R 5.4	16 21.9	19 53.2	19 59.3	28 8.1
3	0 46 33.5	8 56.1	21 16.4	1♈ 7.3	15 6.0	4 9.7	22 51.8	18 1.0	16 28.7	19 54.5	20 1.3	28 9.6
4	0 50 30.0	9 50.6	21 13.3	14 19.6	16 36.8	5 20.4	23 37.8	17 56.4	16 35.5	19 55.7	20 3.4	28 11.1
5	0 54 26.6	10 45.2	21 10.2	27 48.4	18 7.1	6 31.4	24 24.0	17 51.6	16 42.3	19 56.9	20 5.5	28 12.6
6	0 58 23.2	11 39.8	21 7.1	11♉40.2	19 36.9	7 42.6	25 10.3	17 46.7	16 49.1	19 58.0	20 7.6	28 14.0
7	1 2 19.7	12 34.6	21 3.9	25 53.4	21 6.2	8 54.1	25 56.8	17 41.6	16 55.8	19 59.0	20 9.6	28 15.4
8	1 6 16.3	13 29.4	21 .8	10♊17.4	22 35.1	10 5.9	26 43.4	17 36.3	17 2.6	20 .0	20 11.7	28 16.8
9	1 10 12.8	14 24.4	20 57.7	24 34.6	24 3.7	11 18.0	27 30.1	17 30.8	17 9.4	20 1.0	20 13.8	28 18.2
10	1 14 9.4	15 19.4	20 54.5	8♋26.9	25 31.9	12 30.3	28 17.0	17 25.2	17 16.2	20 1.8	20 15.9	28 19.5
11	1 18 5.9	16 14.6	20 51.4	21 40.8	26 59.8	13 42.9	29 3.9	17 19.4	17 23.0	20 2.6	20 18.0	28 20.9
12	1 22 2.5	17 9.9	20 48.3	4♌11.0	28 27.4	14 55.8	29 51.0	17 13.5	17 29.9	20 3.4	20 20.0	28 22.2
13	1 25 59.0	18 5.4	20 45.1	16 .0	29 54.8	16 9.1	0♑38.2	17 7.4	17 36.7	20 4.1	20 22.1	28 23.5
14	1 29 55.6	19 .9	20 42.0	27 15.7	1♏22.0	17 22.6	1 25.5	17 1.2	17 43.5	20 4.7	20 24.2	28 24.7
15	1 33 52.1	19 56.7	20 38.8	8♍ 9.3	2 48.9	18 36.4	2 12.9	16 54.8	17 50.3	20 5.3	20 26.3	28 26.0
16	1 37 48.7	20 52.5	20 35.7	18 53.8	4 15.7	19 50.5	3 .4	16 48.3	17 57.1	20 5.9	20 28.4	28 27.2
17	1 41 45.2	21 48.5	20 32.6	29 43.0	5 42.4	21 5.0	3 48.0	16 41.7	18 3.9	20 6.3	20 30.5	28 28.4
18	1 45 41.8	22 44.7	20 29.4	10♎51.2	7 8.9	22 19.7	4 35.7	16 34.9	18 10.8	20 6.8	20 32.6	28 29.6
19	1 49 38.4	23 41.0	20 26.3	22 32.3	8 35.2	23 34.7	5 23.5	16 28.0	18 17.6	20 7.1	20 34.7	28 30.7
20	1 53 34.9	24 37.4	20 23.2	4♏59.0	10 1.4	24 50.1	6 11.3	16 21.0	18 24.4	20 7.4	20 36.8	28 31.8
21	1 57 31.5	25 34.1	20 20.0	18 19.7	11 27.5	26 5.7	6 59.2	16 13.9	18 31.1	20 7.6	20 38.9	28 32.9
22	2 1 28.0	26 30.8	20 16.9	2♐35.0	12 53.4	27 21.6	7 47.2	16 6.7	18 37.9	20 7.8	20 40.9	28 34.0
23	2 5 24.6	27 27.8	20 13.7	17 33.7	14 19.1	28 37.9	8 35.3	15 59.4	18 44.7	20 7.9	20 43.0	28 35.1
24	2 9 21.1	28 24.9	20 10.6	2♑53.5	15 44.7	29 54.4	9 23.4	15 51.9	18 51.5	20 8.0	20 45.1	28 36.1
25	2 13 17.7	29 22.2	20 7.5	18 7.0	17 10.0	1♐11.2	10 11.6	15 44.4	18 58.2	20 8.0	20 47.2	28 37.1
26	2 17 14.2	0♏19.7	20 4.3	2♒51.9	18 35.2	2 28.3	10 59.8	15 36.9	19 5.0	20 8.0	20 49.3	28 38.1
27	2 21 10.8	1 17.3	20 1.2	16 57.4	19 60.0	3 45.6	11 48.1	15 29.2	19 11.8	20 R 7.9	20 51.4	28 39.1
28	2 25 7.3	2 15.1	19 58.0	0♓25.0	21 24.4	5 3.2	12 36.3	15 21.5	19 18.5	20 7.7	20 53.4	28 40.0
29	2 29 3.9	3 13.1	19 54.9	13 25.4	22 48.5	6 21.1	13 24.6	15 13.7	19 25.2	20 7.5	20 55.5	28 40.9
30	2 33 .5	4 11.3	19 51.8	26 13.4	24 12.0	7 39.2	14 13.0	15 5.8	19 31.9	20 7.2	20 57.5	28 41.7
31	2 36 57.0	5 9.7	19 48.6	9♈ 5.2	25 35.0	8 57.5	15 1.3	14 57.9	19 38.5	20 6.9	20 59.6	28 42.6

DECLINATION

DAY	EPHEM. SID. TIME	☉	☊	☽	☿	♀	♂	♃	♄	♅	♆	♇
1	0 38 40.4	3S 4.7	0S15.9	9S18.9	4S16.1	12S44.2	25S10.6	16N33.0	4S29.4	22N35.7	6S40.6	22N31.2
4	0 50 30.0	4 14.4	0 15.9	10N46.7	6 31.1	14 5.3	25 16.3	16 29.1	4 37.8	22 35.3	6 43.1	22 30.5
7	1 2 19.7	5 23.7	0 16.0	24 55.7	8 41.4	15 23.4	25 19.9	16 24.9	4 46.2	22 35.0	6 45.6	22 29.9
10	1 14 9.4	6 32.3	0 16.0	26 40.4	10 46.5	16 38.2	25 21.4	16 20.2	4 54.5	22 34.7	6 48.1	22 29.4
13	1 25 59.0	7 40.2	0 16.1	17 22.1	12 45.7	17 49.3	25 20.8	16 15.2	5 2.9	22 34.5	6 50.6	22 28.9
16	1 37 48.7	8 47.1	0 16.1	2 4.4	14 38.5	18 56.4	25 18.0	16 9.9	5 11.2	22 34.4	6 53.1	22 28.6
19	1 49 38.4	9 53.0	0 16.2	14S25.7	16 24.2	19 59.1	25 12.9	16 4.2	5 19.4	22 34.3	6 55.5	22 28.4
22	2 1 28.0	10 57.5	0 16.2	25 58.0	18 2.4	20 57.2	25 5.7	15 58.3	5 27.5	22 34.3	6 58.0	22 28.3
25	2 13 17.7	12 .5	0 16.3	25 6.6	19 32.4	21 50.2	24 56.1	15 52.1	5 35.6	22 34.4	7 .4	22 28.2
28	2 25 7.3	13 1.9	0 16.3	11 8.0	20 53.5	22 37.9	24 44.2	15 45.8	5 43.6	22 34.5	7 2.9	22 28.2
31	2 36 57.0	14 1.4	0 16.4	8N18.5	22 5.1	23 19.9	24 30.0	15 39.2	5 51.4	22 34.7	7 5.3	22 28.4

NOVEMBER 1952

LONGITUDE

DAY	EPHEM. SID. TIME h m s	☉ ° ′	☊ ° ′	☾ ° ′	☿ ° ′	♀ ° ′	♂ ° ′	♃ ° ′	♄ ° ′	♅ ° ′	♆ ° ′	♇ ° ′
1	2 40 53.6	8 ♏ 31.1	17 ♒ 18.5	25 ♈ 53.0	29 ♏ 42.3	11 ♐ 57.9	14 ♑ 23.2	16 ♉ 54.4	20 ♎ 27.7	18 ♋ 30.5	22 ♎ 5.1	23 ♌ 8.0
2	2 44 50.1	9 31.1	17 15.3	9 ♉ 57.7	1 ♐ .2	13 11.1	15 7.6	16 R 46.4	20 34.8	18 R 30.1	22 7.3	23 8.7
3	2 48 46.7	10 31.2	17 12.2	23 45.8	2 16.8	14 24.2	15 52.1	16 38.3	20 41.9	18 29.6	22 9.4	23 9.3
4	2 52 43.2	11 31.3	17 9.0	7 ♊ 13.5	3 31.9	15 37.3	16 36.6	16 30.2	20 48.9	18 29.1	22 11.6	23 10.0
5	2 56 39.8	12 31.4	17 5.8	20 18.9	4 45.4	16 50.4	17 21.3	16 22.1	20 55.9	18 28.5	22 13.7	23 10.5
6	3 0 36.3	13 31.6	17 2.6	3 ♋ 2.1	5 57.1	18 3.4	18 5.9	16 13.9	21 2.9	18 27.8	22 15.8	23 11.1
7	3 4 32.9	14 31.8	16 59.4	15 25.2	7 6.9	19 16.4	18 50.7	16 5.8	21 9.9	18 27.2	22 17.9	23 11.6
8	3 8 29.5	15 32.0	16 56.3	27 31.9	8 14.4	20 29.4	19 35.5	15 57.6	21 16.8	18 26.4	22 20.0	23 12.1
9	3 12 26.0	16 32.3	16 53.1	9 ♌ 26.8	9 19.5	21 42.4	20 20.3	15 49.4	21 23.7	18 25.6	22 22.1	23 12.6
10	3 16 22.6	17 32.6	16 49.9	21 15.5	10 21.8	22 55.3	21 5.2	15 41.3	21 30.5	18 24.8	22 24.2	23 13.0
11	3 20 19.1	18 32.9	16 46.7	3 ♍ 3.3	11 21.0	24 8.3	21 50.2	15 33.1	21 37.4	18 23.9	22 26.2	23 13.4
12	3 24 15.7	19 33.3	16 43.6	14 56.0	12 16.6	25 21.1	22 35.2	15 24.9	21 44.2	18 22.9	22 28.3	23 13.8
13	3 28 12.2	20 33.7	16 40.4	26 58.5	13 8.3	26 34.0	23 20.3	15 16.8	21 50.9	18 21.9	22 30.3	23 14.2
14	3 32 8.8	21 34.1	16 37.2	9 ♎ 15.1	13 55.6	27 46.9	24 5.5	15 8.7	21 57.6	18 20.9	22 32.3	23 14.5
15	3 36 5.4	22 34.6	16 34.0	21 49.0	14 37.8	28 59.7	24 50.7	15 .7	22 4.3	18 19.8	22 34.3	23 14.8
16	3 40 1.9	23 35.1	16 30.9	4 ♏ 41.9	15 14.5	0 ♑ 12.5	25 36.0	14 52.7	22 11.0	18 18.7	22 36.4	23 15.1
17	3 43 58.5	24 35.6	16 27.7	17 53.7	15 44.8	1 25.2	26 21.3	14 44.8	22 17.6	18 17.5	22 38.3	23 15.3
18	3 47 55.0	25 36.2	16 24.5	1 ♐ 23.0	16 8.1	2 38.0	27 6.7	14 36.9	22 24.2	18 16.2	22 40.3	23 15.5
19	3 51 51.6	26 36.7	16 21.3	15 6.8	16 23.7	3 50.6	27 52.1	14 29.0	22 30.7	18 14.9	22 42.2	23 15.7
20	3 55 48.1	27 37.3	16 18.1	29 1.4	16 30.8	5 3.3	28 37.6	14 21.3	22 37.2	18 13.6	22 44.1	23 15.9
21	3 59 44.7	28 38.0	16 15.0	13 ♑ 3.0	16 R 28.6	6 15.9	29 23.1	14 13.6	22 43.6	18 12.2	22 46.0	23 16.0
22	4 3 41.3	29 38.6	16 11.8	27 8.3	16 16.5	7 28.4	0 ♒ 8.6	14 6.0	22 50.0	18 10.8	22 47.9	23 16.1
23	4 7 37.8	0 ♐ 39.2	16 8.6	11 ♒ 14.8	15 54.0	8 41.0	0 54.2	13 58.4	22 56.3	18 9.3	22 49.8	23 16.1
24	4 11 34.4	1 39.9	16 5.4	25 21.0	15 20.8	9 53.4	1 39.9	13 51.0	23 2.6	18 7.8	22 51.6	23 16.2
25	4 15 30.9	2 40.6	16 2.3	9 ♓ 25.9	14 36.8	11 5.9	2 25.5	13 43.7	23 8.8	18 6.2	22 53.5	23 16.2
26	4 19 27.5	3 41.3	15 59.1	23 28.9	13 42.4	12 18.2	3 11.2	13 36.4	23 15.0	18 4.6	22 55.3	23 R 16.1
27	4 23 24.0	4 42.0	15 55.9	7 ♈ 28.9	12 38.6	13 30.6	3 57.0	13 29.3	23 21.1	18 3.0	22 57.0	23 16.1
28	4 27 20.6	5 42.8	15 52.7	21 24.4	11 26.8	14 42.8	4 42.8	13 22.3	23 27.2	18 1.3	22 58.8	23 16.0
29	4 31 17.2	6 43.5	15 49.6	5 ♉ 12.8	10 8.8	15 55.0	5 28.6	13 15.4	23 33.2	17 59.5	23 .5	23 15.9
30	4 35 13.7	7 44.3	15 46.4	18 51.3	8 47.2	17 7.2	6 14.4	13 8.7	23 39.2	17 57.8	23 2.3	23 15.7

LATITUDE

DAY	SID. TIME	☉	☊	☾	☿	♀	♂	♃	♄	♅	♆	♇
1	2 40 53.6	0 .0	0 .0	4 N 38.7	2 S 24.3	1 S 19.4	1 S 45.2	1 S 19.8	2 N 15.7	0 N 25.0	1 N 37.2	9 N 11.8
4	2 52 43.2	0 .0	0 .0	4 43.0	2 34.9	1 27.0	1 43.5	1 19.6	2 15.9	0 25.0	1 37.2	9 12.8
7	3 4 32.9	0 .0	0 .0	2 38.7	2 41.7	1 34.2	1 41.8	1 19.4	2 16.2	0 25.1	1 37.3	9 13.8
10	3 16 22.6	0 .0	0 .0	0 S 22.8	2 43.8	1 40.9	1 40.0	1 19.1	2 16.5	0 25.2	1 37.4	9 14.8
13	3 28 12.2	0 .0	0 .0	3 14.9	2 39.6	1 47.2	1 38.2	1 18.7	2 16.8	0 25.3	1 37.5	9 15.8
16	3 40 1.9	0 .0	0 .0	4 54.3	2 27.4	1 52.9	1 36.3	1 18.3	2 17.2	0 25.4	1 37.6	9 16.8
19	3 51 51.6	0 .0	0 .0	4 22.4	2 4.9	1 58.0	1 34.3	1 17.9	2 17.6	0 25.5	1 37.7	9 17.8
22	4 3 41.3	0 .0	0 .0	1 35.2	1 29.8	2 2.5	1 32.2	1 17.4	2 18.0	0 25.6	1 37.8	9 18.8
25	4 15 30.9	0 .0	0 .0	2 N 3.9	0 41.3	2 6.2	1 30.2	1 16.8	2 18.4	0 25.6	1 37.9	9 19.9
28	4 27 20.6	0 .0	0 .0	4 37.1	0 N 17.6	2 9.3	1 28.0	1 16.2	2 18.9	0 25.7	1 38.0	9 20.9

RIGHT ASCENSION

DAY	SID. TIME	☉	☊	☾	☿	♀	♂	♃	♄	♅	♆	♇
1	2 40 53.6	6 ♏ 8.3	19 ♒ 45.5	22 ♈ 15.3	26 ♏ 57.3	10 ♐ 16.1	15 ♑ 49.7	14 ♉ 49.9	19 ♎ 45.2	20 ♋ 6.5	21 ♎ 1.6	28 ♌ 43.4
2	2 44 50.1	7 7.0	19 42.3	5 ♉ 53.6	28 18.7	11 34.9	16 38.0	14 R 41.9	19 51.8	20 R 6.0	21 3.6	28 44.2
3	2 48 46.7	8 6.0	19 39.2	20 2.0	29 39.2	12 53.9	17 26.4	14 33.9	19 58.4	20 5.5	21 5.6	28 45.0
4	2 52 43.2	9 5.2	19 36.0	4 ♊ 32.4	0 ♐ 58.6	14 13.1	18 14.7	14 25.8	20 5.0	20 4.9	21 7.6	28 45.7
5	2 56 39.8	10 4.6	19 32.9	19 7.0	2 16.7	15 32.4	19 3.1	14 17.7	20 11.6	20 4.3	21 9.6	28 46.4
6	3 0 36.3	11 4.2	19 29.7	3 ♋ 23.8	3 33.3	16 52.0	19 51.4	14 9.5	20 18.1	20 3.6	21 11.6	28 47.1
7	3 4 32.9	12 4.0	19 26.6	17 4.1	4 48.1	18 11.7	20 39.8	14 1.4	20 24.6	20 2.9	21 13.6	28 47.7
8	3 8 29.5	13 4.0	19 23.5	29 57.7	6 .9	19 31.5	21 28.1	13 53.2	20 31.1	20 2.1	21 15.6	28 48.4
9	3 12 26.0	14 4.2	19 20.3	12 ♌ 4.4	7 11.2	20 51.5	22 16.4	13 45.1	20 37.6	20 1.3	21 17.5	28 48.9
10	3 16 22.6	15 4.7	19 17.2	23 31.0	8 18.9	22 11.6	23 4.7	13 37.0	20 44.0	20 .4	21 19.5	28 49.5
11	3 20 19.1	16 5.3	19 14.0	4 ♍ 29.2	9 23.4	23 31.8	23 52.9	13 28.8	20 50.4	19 59.4	21 21.4	28 50.1
12	3 24 15.7	17 6.2	19 10.9	15 12.6	10 24.3	24 52.1	24 41.2	13 20.7	20 56.8	19 58.4	21 23.4	28 50.6
13	3 28 12.2	18 7.3	19 7.7	25 56.0	11 21.1	26 12.5	25 29.3	13 12.6	21 3.2	19 57.3	21 25.3	28 51.0
14	3 32 8.8	19 8.6	19 4.6	6 ♎ 55.1	12 13.2	27 32.9	26 17.5	13 4.6	21 9.5	19 56.2	21 27.2	28 51.5
15	3 36 5.4	20 10.1	19 1.4	18 25.4	13 .0	28 53.3	27 5.6	12 56.6	21 15.8	19 55.0	21 29.1	28 51.9
16	3 40 1.9	21 11.9	18 58.3	0 ♏ 41.8	13 40.8	0 ♑ 13.8	27 53.7	12 48.6	21 22.1	19 53.8	21 31.0	28 52.4
17	3 43 58.5	22 13.9	18 55.1	13 55.6	14 14.8	1 34.3	28 41.8	12 40.7	21 28.3	19 52.6	21 32.8	28 52.7
18	3 47 55.0	23 16.0	18 52.0	28 10.5	14 41.3	2 54.7	29 29.7	12 32.8	21 34.4	19 51.2	21 34.7	28 53.1
19	3 51 51.6	24 18.4	18 48.8	13 ♐ 17.8	14 59.4	4 15.1	0 ♒ 17.7	12 25.0	21 40.6	19 49.8	21 36.5	28 53.4
20	3 55 48.1	25 21.0	18 45.7	28 54.3	15 8.3	5 35.5	1 5.5	12 17.3	21 46.7	19 48.4	21 38.3	28 53.6
21	3 59 44.7	26 23.8	18 42.5	14 ♑ 28.3	15 R 7.2	6 55.7	1 53.3	12 9.7	21 52.7	19 46.9	21 40.1	28 53.9
22	4 3 41.3	27 26.8	18 39.4	29 31.5	14 55.5	8 15.9	2 41.1	12 2.1	21 58.8	19 45.4	21 41.9	28 54.1
23	4 7 37.8	28 29.9	18 36.2	13 ♒ 48.7	14 32.7	9 36.0	3 28.7	11 54.6	22 4.7	19 43.8	21 43.6	28 54.3
24	4 11 34.4	29 33.3	18 33.0	27 19.2	13 58.5	10 55.9	4 16.3	11 47.2	22 10.7	19 42.2	21 45.4	28 54.4
25	4 15 30.9	0 ♐ 36.8	18 29.9	10 ♓ 13.4	13 13.0	12 15.7	5 3.9	11 39.9	22 16.5	19 40.5	21 47.1	28 54.6
26	4 19 27.5	1 40.6	18 26.7	22 46.8	12 16.8	13 35.3	5 51.3	11 32.7	22 22.4	19 38.8	21 48.8	28 54.7
27	4 23 24.0	2 44.5	18 23.6	5 ♈ 17.0	11 10.9	14 54.7	6 38.7	11 25.6	22 28.2	19 37.0	21 50.5	28 54.7
28	4 27 20.6	3 48.6	18 20.4	18 .6	9 56.9	16 14.0	7 25.9	11 18.6	22 33.9	19 35.2	21 52.2	28 54.8
29	4 31 17.2	4 52.8	18 17.3	1 ♉ 10.8	8 37.0	17 33.0	8 13.1	11 11.8	22 39.6	19 33.3	21 53.8	28 54.8
30	4 35 13.7	5 57.3	18 14.1	14 54.5	7 13.7	18 51.7	9 .2	11 5.1	22 45.3	19 31.4	21 55.4	28 54.8

DECLINATION

DAY	SID. TIME	☉	☊	☾	☿	♀	♂	♃	♄	♅	♆	♇
1	2 40 53.6	14 S 20.8	0 S 16.4	14 N 19.5	22 S 26.6	23 S 32.6	24 S 24.8	15 N 37.0	5 S 54.0	22 N 34.8	7 S 6.0	22 N 28.5
4	2 52 43.2	15 17.6	0 16.4	26 10.4	23 24.0	24 6.7	24 7.6	15 30.3	6 1.7	22 35.1	7 8.4	22 28.7
7	3 4 32.9	16 12.2	0 16.5	25 11.0	24 9.7	24 34.7	23 48.1	15 23.6	6 9.3	22 35.4	7 10.7	22 29.1
10	3 16 22.6	17 4.3	0 16.5	14 3.6	24 42.6	24 56.3	23 26.4	15 16.8	6 16.7	22 35.8	7 12.9	22 29.6
13	3 28 12.2	17 53.8	0 16.6	1 S 46.6	25 1.3	25 11.3	23 2.5	15 10.1	6 24.0	22 36.3	7 15.1	22 30.1
16	3 40 1.9	18 40.5	0 16.6	17 42.3	25 4.3	25 19.7	22 36.3	15 3.4	6 31.1	22 36.8	7 17.3	22 30.8
19	3 51 51.6	19 24.3	0 16.7	26 57.7	24 49.4	25 21.4	29 8.1	14 56.9	6 38.0	22 37.4	7 19.3	22 31.5
22	4 3 41.3	20 4.9	0 16.7	22 17.6	24 13.7	25 16.4	21 37.7	14 50.6	6 44.8	22 38.1	7 21.4	22 32.4
25	4 15 30.9	20 42.1	0 16.8	6 7.3	23 14.6	25 4.8	21 5.3	14 44.6	6 51.3	22 38.8	7 23.3	22 33.3
28	4 27 20.6	21 15.9	0 16.8	12 N 37.6	21 52.2	24 46.5	20 31.0	14 38.8	6 57.6	22 39.5	7 25.2	22 34.3

DECEMBER 1952

DAY	EPHEM. SID. TIME	☉	☊	☽	☿	♀	♂	♃	♄	♅	♆	♇
	h m s	° ′	° ′	° ′	° ′	° ′	° ′	° ′	° ′	° ′	° ′	° ′
		LONGITUDE										
1	4 39 10.3	8♐45.1	15♒43.2	2♊16.9	7♐24.5	18♑19.3	7♒ .3	13♉ 2.1	23♎45.1	17♋55.9	23♎ 4.0	23♌15.5
2	4 43 6.8	9 45.9	15 40.0	15 27.0	6 R 3.6	19 31.3	7 46.2	12 R 55.6	23 50.9	17 R 54.1	23 5.6	23 R 15.3
3	4 47 3.4	10 46.8	15 36.8	28 19.8	4 47.2	20 43.3	8 32.1	12 49.2	23 56.7	17 52.2	23 7.3	23 15.1
4	4 50 60.0	11 47.6	15 33.7	10♋55.2	3 37.6	21 55.2	9 18.0	12 43.0	24 2.5	17 50.3	23 8.9	23 14.8
5	4 54 56.5	12 48.5	15 30.5	23 14.1	2 36.9	23 7.0	10 4.0	12 36.9	24 8.1	17 48.3	23 10.5	23 14.6
6	4 58 53.1	13 49.4	15 27.3	5♌19.0	1 46.3	24 18.8	10 50.0	12 31.0	24 13.7	17 46.3	23 12.1	23 14.2
7	5 2 49.6	14 50.4	15 24.1	17 13.6	1 6.9	25 30.6	11 36.0	12 25.3	24 19.3	17 44.3	23 13.7	23 13.9
8	5 6 46.2	15 51.3	15 21.0	29 2.1	0 38.8	26 42.2	12 22.1	12 19.7	24 24.8	17 42.3	23 15.2	23 13.6
9	5 10 42.7	16 52.2	15 17.8	10♍49.9	0 22.0	27 53.8	13 8.1	12 14.2	24 30.2	17 40.1	23 16.7	23 13.1
10	5 14 39.3	17 53.2	15 14.6	22 42.3	0 16.2	29 5.3	13 54.2	12 8.9	24 35.6	17 38.0	23 18.2	23 12.7
11	5 18 35.9	18 54.2	15 11.4	4♎44.7	0 D 20.6	0♒16.7	14 40.3	12 3.8	24 40.8	17 35.8	23 19.7	23 12.3
12	5 22 32.4	19 55.2	15 8.3	17 2.2	0 34.6	1 28.1	15 26.5	11 58.9	24 46.0	17 33.7	23 21.1	23 11.8
13	5 26 29.0	20 56.3	15 5.1	29 39.1	0 57.3	2 39.4	16 12.6	11 54.1	24 51.2	17 31.4	23 22.5	23 11.2
14	5 30 25.5	21 57.3	15 1.9	12♏38.4	1 28.0	3 50.6	16 58.8	11 49.5	24 56.2	17 29.2	23 23.9	23 10.7
15	5 34 22.1	22 58.4	14 58.7	26 1.3	2 5.6	5 1.7	17 45.0	11 45.1	25 1.2	17 26.9	23 25.2	23 10.1
16	5 38 18.7	23 59.4	14 55.6	9♐47.0	2 49.6	6 12.7	18 31.2	11 40.9	25 6.2	17 24.6	23 26.5	23 9.5
17	5 42 15.2	25 .5	14 52.4	23 52.5	3 39.1	7 23.6	19 17.4	11 36.9	25 11.0	17 22.3	23 27.8	23 8.9
18	5 46 11.8	26 1.6	14 49.2	8♑12.9	4 33.6	8 34.5	20 3.6	11 33.1	25 15.8	17 19.9	23 29.1	23 8.3
19	5 50 8.3	27 2.7	14 46.0	22 42.3	5 32.3	9 45.2	20 49.8	11 29.4	25 20.5	17 17.5	23 30.3	23 7.6
20	5 54 4.9	28 3.9	14 42.9	7♒14.6	6 34.8	10 55.9	21 36.1	11 26.0	25 25.1	17 15.1	23 31.5	23 6.9
21	5 58 1.4	29 5.0	14 39.7	21 44.1	7 40.7	12 6.4	22 22.3	11 22.7	25 29.6	17 12.7	23 32.6	23 6.1
22	6 1 58.0	0♑ 6.1	14 36.5	6♓ 6.8	8 49.5	13 16.8	23 8.6	11 19.7	25 34.1	17 10.2	23 33.8	23 5.4
23	6 5 54.6	1 7.2	14 33.3	20 19.8	10 .8	14 27.1	23 54.9	11 16.8	25 38.4	17 7.8	23 34.9	23 4.6
24	6 9 51.1	2 8.3	14 30.1	4♈21.6	11 14.4	15 37.3	24 41.2	11 14.2	25 42.7	17 5.3	23 36.0	23 3.8
25	6 13 47.7	3 9.5	14 27.0	18 11.5	12 29.9	16 47.4	25 27.4	11 11.7	25 46.9	17 2.8	23 37.0	23 3.0
26	6 17 44.2	4 10.6	14 23.8	1♉49.3	13 47.2	17 57.3	26 13.7	11 9.5	25 51.0	17 .3	23 38.0	23 2.1
27	6 21 40.8	5 11.7	14 20.6	15 14.9	15 6.0	19 7.1	26 60.0	11 7.5	25 55.1	16 57.8	23 39.0	23 1.2
28	6 25 37.4	6 12.9	14 17.4	28 28.1	16 26.3	20 16.8	27 46.3	11 5.7	25 59.1	16 55.3	23 40.0	23 .4
29	6 29 33.9	7 14.0	14 14.3	11♊28.5	17 47.7	21 26.3	28 32.6	11 4.1	26 2.9	16 52.7	23 40.9	22 59.5
30	6 33 30.5	8 15.2	14 11.1	24 15.9	19 10.3	22 35.7	29 18.8	11 2.7	26 6.7	16 50.2	23 41.8	22 58.5
31	6 37 27.0	9 16.3	14 7.9	6♋50.3	20 33.8	23 44.9	0♓ 5.1	11 1.5	26 10.4	16 47.6	23 42.7	22 57.6
		LATITUDE										
1	4 39 10.3	0 .0	0 .0	4 N 48.4	1 N 17.6	2 S 11.5	1 S 25.9	1 S 15.6	2 N 19.4	0 N 25.8	1 N 38.1	9 N 21.9
4	4 50 60.0	0 .0	0 .0	2 47.3	2 6.2	2 12.9	1 23.7	1 14.9	2 19.9	0 25.9	1 38.3	9 22.9
7	5 2 49.6	0 .0	0 .0	0 S 17.0	2 35.9	2 13.5	1 21.4	1 14.1	2 20.4	0 25.9	1 38.4	9 23.9
10	5 14 39.3	0 .0	0 .0	3 12.2	2 46.6	2 13.2	1 19.1	1 13.4	2 21.0	0 26.0	1 38.6	9 24.9
13	5 26 29.0	0 .0	0 .0	4 57.5	2 42.7	2 11.9	1 16.8	1 12.6	2 21.6	0 26.0	1 38.7	9 25.8
16	5 38 18.7	0 .0	0 .0	4 35.4	2 29.3	2 9.7	1 14.4	1 11.8	2 22.2	0 26.1	1 38.9	9 26.8
19	5 50 8.3	0 .0	0 .0	1 48.2	2 10.1	2 6.5	1 12.0	1 10.9	2 22.8	0 26.2	1 39.0	9 27.7
22	6 1 58.0	0 .0	0 .0	2 N 1.4	1 47.6	2 2.2	1 9.6	1 10.1	2 23.5	0 26.2	1 39.2	9 28.6
25	6 13 47.7	0 .0	0 .0	4 41.8	1 23.6	1 57.0	1 7.2	1 9.2	2 24.2	0 26.3	1 39.3	9 29.5
28	6 25 37.4	0 .0	0 .0	4 59.4	0 59.1	1 50.6	1 4.7	1 8.3	2 24.8	0 26.3	1 39.5	9 30.3
31	6 37 27.0	0 .0	0 .0	3 2.7	0 34.8	1 43.3	1 2.3	1 7.4	2 25.6	0 26.3	1 39.7	9 31.2
		RIGHT ASCENSION										
1	4 39 10.3	7♐ 1.9	18♒10.9	29♉ 8.9	5♐49.8	20♑10.3	9♒47.3	10♉58.5	22♎50.9	19♋29.5	21♎57.0	28♌54.7
2	4 43 6.8	8 6.6	18 7.8	13♊40.6	4 R 28.2	21 28.5	10 34.2	10 R 52.0	22 56.4	19 R 27.5	21 58.6	28 R 54.6
3	4 47 3.4	9 11.5	18 4.6	28 7.7	3 11.4	22 46.5	11 21.0	10 45.7	23 1.9	19 25.5	22 .2	28 54.5
4	4 50 60.0	10 16.6	18 1.5	12♋ 7.8	2 1.9	24 4.2	12 7.8	10 39.5	23 7.3	19 23.4	22 1.7	28 54.4
5	4 54 56.5	11 21.8	17 58.3	25 24.7	1 1.5	25 21.6	12 54.4	10 33.4	23 12.7	19 21.3	22 3.2	28 54.2
6	4 58 53.1	12 27.2	17 55.2	7♌52.7	0 11.3	26 38.7	13 41.0	10 27.5	23 18.0	19 19.2	22 4.7	28 54.0
7	5 2 49.6	13 32.7	17 52.0	19 35.2	29♏32.4	27 55.5	14 27.5	10 21.8	23 23.3	19 17.0	22 6.3	28 53.8
8	5 6 46.2	14 38.4	17 48.8	0♍41.9	29 4.7	29 11.9	15 13.8	10 16.2	23 28.5	19 14.8	22 7.7	28 53.6
9	5 10 42.7	15 44.1	17 45.7	11 25.9	28 48.2	0♒28.0	16 .1	10 10.8	23 33.7	19 12.5	22 9.1	28 53.3
10	5 14 39.3	16 50.0	17 42.5	22 2.1	28 42.6	1 43.7	16 46.3	10 5.5	23 38.8	19 10.3	22 10.5	28 53.0
11	5 18 35.9	17 56.0	17 39.3	2♎46.5	28 D 47.1	2 59.1	17 32.3	10 .4	23 43.8	19 7.9	22 11.9	28 52.6
12	5 22 32.4	19 2.1	17 36.2	13 55.4	29 1.2	4 14.0	18 18.3	9 55.5	23 48.7	19 5.6	22 13.3	28 52.3
13	5 26 29.0	20 8.2	17 33.0	25 45.6	29 24.0	5 28.6	19 4.2	9 50.7	23 53.6	19 3.2	22 14.6	28 51.9
14	5 30 25.5	21 14.5	17 29.9	8♏32.0	29 54.7	6 42.8	19 50.0	9 46.1	23 58.5	19 .8	22 15.9	28 51.4
15	5 34 22.1	22 20.8	17 26.7	22 24.6	0♐32.5	7 56.6	20 35.6	9 41.7	24 3.2	18 58.3	22 17.2	28 51.0
16	5 38 18.7	23 27.3	17 23.5	7♐22.2	1 16.8	9 10.0	21 21.2	9 37.5	24 7.9	18 55.8	22 18.4	28 50.5
17	5 42 15.2	24 33.7	17 20.4	23 7.5	2 6.9	10 23.0	22 6.7	9 33.5	24 12.5	18 53.3	22 19.7	28 50.0
18	5 46 11.8	25 40.3	17 17.2	9♑ 8.8	3 2.0	11 35.6	22 52.1	9 29.6	24 17.1	18 50.8	22 20.9	28 49.4
19	5 50 8.3	26 46.8	17 14.0	24 50.5	4 1.8	12 47.8	23 37.3	9 25.9	24 21.6	18 48.2	22 22.0	28 48.9
20	5 54 4.9	27 53.4	17 10.9	9♒47.3	5 5.7	13 59.5	24 22.5	9 22.5	24 26.0	18 45.7	22 23.2	28 48.3
21	5 58 1.4	29 .0	17 7.7	23 51.2	6 13.3	15 10.8	25 7.6	9 19.2	24 30.3	18 43.1	22 24.3	28 47.7
22	6 1 58.0	0♑ 6.6	17 4.5	7♓ 8.2	7 24.2	16 21.7	25 52.6	9 16.1	24 34.6	18 40.4	22 25.4	28 47.0
23	6 5 54.6	1 13.3	17 1.4	19 53.0	8 38.1	17 32.1	26 37.4	9 13.2	24 38.8	18 37.8	22 26.4	28 46.4
24	6 9 51.1	2 19.9	16 58.2	2♈23.5	9 54.6	18 42.1	27 22.2	9 10.5	24 42.9	18 35.1	22 27.5	28 45.7
25	6 13 47.7	3 26.5	16 55.0	14 57.2	11 13.5	19 51.6	28 6.9	9 8.1	24 46.9	18 32.4	22 28.5	28 44.9
26	6 17 44.2	4 33.1	16 51.8	27 49.3	12 34.6	21 .7	28 51.4	9 5.8	24 50.9	18 29.7	22 29.4	28 44.2
27	6 21 40.8	5 39.6	16 48.7	11♉ 9.7	13 57.6	22 9.4	29 35.9	9 3.7	24 54.8	18 27.0	22 30.4	28 43.4
28	6 25 37.4	6 46.2	16 45.5	25 .8	15 22.6	23 17.6	0♓20.3	9 1.8	24 58.6	18 24.3	22 31.3	28 42.7
29	6 29 33.9	7 52.6	16 42.3	9♊14.5	16 49.1	24 25.4	1 4.5	9 .2	25 2.3	18 21.6	22 32.2	28 41.8
30	6 33 30.5	8 59.0	16 39.2	23 33.9	18 17.1	25 32.7	1 48.7	8 58.7	25 6.0	18 18.9	22 33.1	28 41.0
31	6 37 27.0	10 5.4	16 36.0	7♋37.3	19 46.5	26 39.5	2 32.8	8 57.4	25 9.5	18 16.1	22 33.9	28 40.1
		DECLINATION										
1	4 39 10.3	21 S 46.1	0 S 16.9	25 N 20.0	20 S 16.7	24 S 21.9	19 S 54.7	14 N 33.3	7 S 3.8	22 N 40.3	7 S 26.9	22 N 35.4
4	4 50 60.0	22 12.5	0 16.9	25 46.6	18 49.1	23 50.9	19 16.6	14 28.2	7 9.6	22 41.1	7 28.6	22 36.6
7	5 2 49.6	22 35.1	0 17.0	15 24.4	17 50.7	23 13.9	18 36.8	14 23.6	7 15.3	22 41.9	7 30.3	22 37.8
10	5 14 39.3	22 53.7	0 17.0	0 S 2.8	17 29.9	22 31.1	17 55.3	14 19.3	7 20.7	22 42.8	7 31.8	22 39.2
13	5 26 29.0	23 8.2	0 17.1	15 59.2	17 42.1	21 42.8	17 12.2	14 15.6	7 25.8	22 43.8	7 33.2	22 40.6
16	5 38 18.7	23 18.6	0 17.1	26 27.8	18 17.4	20 49.1	16 27.6	14 12.3	7 30.7	22 44.7	7 34.6	22 42.0
19	5 50 8.3	23 24.8	0 17.2	23 18.8	19 6.0	19 50.6	15 41.6	14 9.6	7 35.3	22 45.7	7 35.8	22 43.6
22	6 1 58.0	23 26.8	0 17.2	7 23.4	20 .4	18 47.4	14 54.2	14 7.4	7 39.6	22 46.6	7 37.0	22 45.2
25	6 13 47.7	23 24.5	0 17.3	11 N 28.5	20 55.2	17 40.0	14 5.6	14 5.8	7 43.6	22 47.6	7 38.0	22 46.8
28	6 25 37.4	23 18.0	0 17.3	24 41.2	21 46.6	16 28.7	13 15.8	14 4.8	7 47.4	22 48.6	7 38.9	22 48.5
31	6 37 27.0	23 7.3	0 17.4	26 18.7	22 32.0	15 14.0	12 25.0	14 4.3	7 50.8	22 49.6	7 39.8	22 50.2

JANUARY 1953

DAY	EPHEM. SID. TIME	☉	☊	☽	☿	♀	♂	♃	♄	♅	♆	♇
		LONGITUDE										
	h m s	° ′	° ′	° ′	° ′	° ′	° ′	° ′	° ′	° ′	° ′	° ′
1	6 41 23.6	10♑17.4	14♒ 4.7	19♋11.9	21♐58.2	24♒53.9	0♓51.4	11♉ .5	26♎14.0	16♋45.0	23♎43.5	22♌56.6
2	6 45 20.2	11 18.6	14 1.6	1♌21.8	23 23.4	26 2.8	1 37.6	10 R 59.7	26 17.5	16 R 42.4	23 44.3	22 R 55.6
3	6 49 16.7	12 19.7	13 58.4	13 21.6	24 49.4	27 11.6	2 23.9	10 59.1	26 20.9	16 39.9	23 45.1	22 54.5
4	6 53 13.3	13 20.9	13 55.2	25 13.9	26 16.0	28 20.1	3 10.1	10 58.7	26 24.2	16 37.3	23 45.8	22 53.5
5	6 57 9.8	14 22.0	13 52.0	7♍ 1.8	27 43.4	29 28.5	3 56.3	10 58.5	26 27.5	16 34.7	23 46.5	22 52.4
6	7 1 6.4	15 23.1	13 48.9	18 49.5	29 11.3	0♓36.7	4 42.5	10 D 58.6	26 30.6	16 32.1	23 47.1	22 51.3
7	7 5 2.9	16 24.3	13 45.7	0♎41.2	0♑39.8	1 44.8	5 28.8	10 58.8	26 33.6	16 29.5	23 47.8	22 50.2
8	7 8 59.5	17 25.4	13 42.5	12 42.0	2 8.8	2 52.6	6 15.0	10 59.3	26 36.6	16 26.8	23 48.4	22 49.1
9	7 12 56.1	18 26.6	13 39.3	24 56.8	3 38.4	4 .3	7 1.2	10 60.0	26 39.4	16 24.2	23 48.9	22 47.9
10	7 16 52.6	19 27.7	13 36.1	7♏30.3	5 8.5	5 7.7	7 47.3	11 .8	26 42.2	16 21.6	23 49.4	22 46.8
11	7 20 49.2	20 28.9	13 33.0	20 26.5	6 39.1	6 14.9	8 33.5	11 1.9	26 44.8	16 19.0	23 49.9	22 45.6
12	7 24 45.7	21 30.0	13 29.8	3♐48.4	8 10.3	7 22.0	9 19.7	11 3.2	26 47.4	16 16.5	23 50.4	22 44.4
13	7 28 42.3	22 31.2	13 26.6	17 36.9	9 41.9	8 28.8	10 5.8	11 4.7	26 49.9	16 13.9	23 50.8	22 43.2
14	7 32 38.9	23 32.3	13 23.4	1♑50.7	11 14.0	9 35.4	10 52.0	11 6.4	26 52.2	16 11.3	23 51.2	22 41.9
15	7 36 35.4	24 33.5	13 20.3	16 25.8	12 46.6	10 41.7	11 38.1	11 8.3	26 54.5	16 8.7	23 51.6	22 40.7
16	7 40 32.0	25 34.6	13 17.1	1♒16.0	14 19.7	11 47.9	12 24.2	11 10.4	26 56.6	16 6.1	23 51.9	22 39.4
17	7 44 28.5	26 35.7	13 13.9	16 13.4	15 53.3	12 53.7	13 10.3	11 12.7	26 58.7	16 3.6	23 52.2	22 38.1
18	7 48 25.1	27 36.9	13 10.7	1♓ 9.9	17 27.5	13 59.4	13 56.4	11 15.2	27 .7	16 1.1	23 52.5	22 36.9
19	7 52 21.6	28 38.0	13 7.6	15 57.6	19 2.2	15 4.8	14 42.5	11 17.9	27 2.5	15 58.6	23 52.7	22 35.6
20	7 56 18.2	29 39.1	13 4.4	0♈30.8	20 37.4	16 9.8	15 28.6	11 20.9	27 4.3	15 56.1	23 52.9	22 34.2
21	8 0 14.8	0♒40.1	13 1.2	14 45.4	22 13.2	17 14.6	16 14.6	11 24.0	27 5.9	15 53.6	23 53.0	22 32.9
22	8 4 11.3	1 41.2	12 58.0	28 39.6	23 49.5	18 19.1	17 .6	11 27.3	27 7.4	15 51.1	23 53.1	22 31.6
23	8 8 7.9	2 42.2	12 54.9	12♉13.3	25 26.4	19 23.3	17 46.5	11 30.8	27 8.9	15 48.6	23 53.2	22 30.2
24	8 12 4.4	3 43.2	12 51.7	25 27.6	27 3.8	20 27.1	18 32.5	11 34.4	27 10.2	15 46.2	23 53.2	22 28.8
25	8 16 1.0	4 44.2	12 48.5	8♊24.3	28 41.9	21 30.6	19 18.4	11 38.3	27 11.4	15 43.7	23 53.2	22 27.5
26	8 19 57.5	5 45.2	12 45.3	21 5.4	0♒20.7	22 33.8	20 4.3	11 42.4	27 12.5	15 41.3	23 53.2	22 26.1
27	8 23 54.1	6 46.2	12 42.1	3♋33.2	2 .0	23 36.6	20 50.2	11 46.6	27 13.5	15 38.9	23 53.2	22 24.7
28	8 27 50.7	7 47.1	12 39.0	15 49.5	3 40.0	24 39.1	21 36.0	11 51.1	27 14.4	15 36.6	23 R 53.1	22 23.3
29	8 31 47.2	8 48.0	12 35.8	27 56.4	5 20.7	25 41.1	22 21.8	11 55.7	27 15.2	15 34.2	23 52.9	22 21.9
30	8 35 43.8	9 49.0	12 32.6	9♌55.6	7 2.0	26 42.8	23 7.6	12 .5	27 15.9	15 31.9	23 52.8	22 20.4
31	8 39 40.3	10 49.9	12 29.4	21 49.0	8 44.1	27 44.1	23 53.4	12 5.5	27 16.5	15 29.6	23 52.6	22 19.0
		LATITUDE										
1	6 41 23.6	0 .0	0 .0	2N 4.2	0N26.8	1S40.6	1S 1.4	1S 7.1	2N25.8	0N26.4	1N39.8	9N31.4
4	6 53 13.3	0 .0	0 .0	1S 9.3	0 3.5	1 31.8	0 58.9	1 6.2	2 26.5	0 26.4	1 39.9	9 32.2
7	7 5 2.9	0 .0	0 .0	3 54.8	0S18.6	1 21.9	0 56.4	1 5.3	2 27.3	0 26.4	1 40.1	9 32.9
10	7 16 52.6	0 .0	0 .0	5 14.0	0 39.3	1 11.0	0 53.9	1 4.4	2 28.1	0 26.4	1 40.3	9 33.7
13	7 28 42.3	0 .0	0 .0	4 18.2	0 58.3	0 58.9	0 51.4	1 3.5	2 28.8	0 26.5	1 40.5	9 34.3
16	7 40 32.0	0 .0	0 .0	1 1.1	1 15.4	0 45.8	0 48.9	1 2.6	2 29.6	0 26.5	1 40.7	9 35.0
19	7 52 21.6	0 .0	0 .0	2N55.7	1 30.4	0 31.7	0 46.4	1 1.7	2 30.4	0 26.5	1 40.8	9 35.6
22	8 4 11.3	0 .0	0 .0	5 8.2	1 43.1	0 16.5	0 43.9	1 .9	2 31.2	0 26.5	1 41.0	9 36.1
25	8 16 1.0	0 .0	0 .0	4 45.4	1 53.2	0 .3	0 41.4	1 .0	2 32.1	0 26.5	1 41.2	9 36.6
28	8 27 50.7	0 .0	0 .0	2 22.2	2 .3	0N16.9	0 38.9	0 59.2	2 32.9	0 26.5	1 41.4	9 37.1
31	8 39 40.3	0 .0	0 .0	0S52.4	2 4.3	0 35.1	0 36.4	0 58.3	2 33.7	0 26.5	1 41.6	9 37.5
		RIGHT ASCENSION										
1	6 41 23.6	11♑11.7	16♒32.8	21♋ 6.2	21♐17.2	27♒45.9	3♓16.7	8♉56.3	25♎13.0	18♋13.3	22♎34.7	28♌39.2
2	6 45 20.2	12 17.9	16 29.6	3♌50.3	22 49.1	28 51.9	4 .6	8 R 55.5	25 16.4	18 R 10.5	22 35.5	28 R 38.3
3	6 49 16.7	13 24.0	16 26.5	15 48.3	24 22.1	29 57.4	4 44.4	8 54.8	25 19.7	18 7.7	22 36.2	28 37.4
4	6 53 13.3	14 30.0	16 23.3	27 6.7	25 56.1	1♓ 2.5	5 28.0	8 54.3	25 22.9	18 5.0	22 36.9	28 36.4
5	6 57 9.8	15 35.9	16 20.1	7♍56.3	27 31.0	2 7.2	6 11.6	8 54.1	25 26.0	18 2.2	22 37.6	28 35.4
6	7 1 6.4	16 41.8	16 16.9	18 30.6	29 6.8	3 11.4	6 55.1	8 54.0	25 29.1	17 59.4	22 38.2	28 34.4
7	7 5 2.9	17 47.5	16 13.8	29 4.3	0♑43.5	4 15.2	7 38.5	8 D 54.2	25 32.0	17 56.6	22 38.8	28 33.4
8	7 8 59.5	18 53.1	16 10.6	9♎53.1	2 20.9	5 18.6	8 21.8	8 54.5	25 34.9	17 53.7	22 39.4	28 32.3
9	7 12 56.1	19 58.6	16 7.4	21 13.3	3 59.0	6 21.5	9 5.1	8 55.1	25 37.7	17 50.9	22 40.0	28 31.3
10	7 16 52.6	21 3.9	16 4.2	3♏21.0	5 37.8	7 24.0	9 48.2	8 55.8	25 40.3	17 48.1	22 40.5	28 30.2
11	7 20 49.2	22 9.2	16 1.1	16 29.9	7 17.2	8 26.1	10 31.3	8 56.8	25 42.9	17 45.3	22 41.0	28 29.1
12	7 24 45.7	23 14.3	15 57.9	0♐46.8	8 57.2	9 27.8	11 14.3	8 58.0	25 45.4	17 42.5	22 41.4	28 28.0
13	7 28 42.3	24 19.2	15 54.7	16 5.5	10 37.8	10 29.1	11 57.2	8 59.3	25 47.9	17 39.8	22 41.8	28 26.8
14	7 32 38.9	25 24.0	15 51.5	2♑ 3.9	12 18.8	11 29.9	12 40.0	9 .9	25 50.2	17 37.0	22 42.2	28 25.7
15	7 36 35.4	26 28.6	15 48.3	18 7.7	14 .3	12 30.4	13 22.8	9 2.7	25 52.4	17 34.2	22 42.6	28 24.5
16	7 40 32.0	27 33.0	15 45.2	3♒44.3	15 42.3	13 30.4	14 5.5	9 4.6	25 54.5	17 31.4	22 42.9	28 23.3
17	7 44 28.5	28 37.3	15 42.0	18 34.4	17 24.6	14 30.0	14 48.1	9 6.8	25 56.5	17 28.7	22 43.2	28 22.1
18	7 48 25.1	29 41.5	15 38.8	2♓35.3	19 7.4	15 29.3	15 30.7	9 9.2	25 58.5	17 26.0	22 43.5	28 20.9
19	7 52 21.6	0♒45.4	15 35.6	15 56.6	20 50.5	16 28.1	16 13.2	9 11.8	26 .4	17 23.3	22 43.7	28 19.6
20	7 56 18.2	1 49.1	15 32.4	28 54.0	22 33.9	17 26.5	16 55.6	9 14.5	26 2.1	17 20.6	22 43.9	28 18.4
21	8 0 14.8	2 52.7	15 29.2	11♈44.7	24 17.5	18 24.5	17 37.9	9 17.5	26 3.7	17 17.9	22 44.1	28 17.1
22	8 4 11.3	3 56.0	15 26.1	24 44.1	26 1.4	19 22.0	18 20.2	9 20.6	26 5.3	17 15.2	22 44.2	28 15.8
23	8 8 7.9	4 59.2	15 22.9	8♉ 3.2	27 45.6	20 19.2	19 2.4	9 24.0	26 6.7	17 12.5	22 44.3	28 14.5
24	8 12 4.4	6 2.2	15 19.7	21 46.5	29 29.9	21 15.9	19 44.5	9 27.5	26 8.1	17 9.9	22 44.3	28 13.2
25	8 16 1.0	7 4.9	15 16.5	5♊49.6	1♒14.5	22 12.3	20 26.6	9 31.2	26 9.3	17 7.3	22 44.4	28 11.9
26	8 19 57.5	8 7.5	15 13.3	19 59.5	2 59.2	23 8.2	21 8.6	9 35.1	26 10.5	17 4.7	22 44.4	28 10.5
27	8 23 54.1	9 9.8	15 10.1	3♋58.3	4 44.1	24 3.7	21 50.6	9 39.2	26 11.5	17 2.1	22 R 44.3	28 9.2
28	8 27 50.7	10 12.0	15 6.9	17 28.5	6 29.0	24 58.7	22 32.5	9 43.5	26 12.5	16 59.6	22 44.3	28 7.8
29	8 31 47.2	11 13.9	15 3.8	0♌18.9	8 14.1	25 53.4	23 14.3	9 48.0	26 13.3	16 57.0	22 44.2	28 6.5
30	8 35 43.8	12 15.6	15 .6	12 26.2	9 59.3	26 47.6	23 56.1	9 52.6	26 14.1	16 54.5	22 44.0	28 5.1
31	8 39 40.3	13 17.2	14 57.4	23 54.0	11 44.5	27 41.4	24 37.9	9 57.4	26 14.7	16 52.1	22 43.9	28 3.7
		DECLINATION										
1	6 41 23.6	23S 2.9	0S17.4	24N 7.3	22S45.5	14S48.3	12S 7.8	14N 4.3	7S51.8	22N50.0	7S40.0	22N50.8
4	6 53 13.3	22 46.6	0 17.4	12 1.6	23 20.2	13 29.5	11 15.8	14 4.6	7 54.8	22 50.9	7 40.7	22 52.6
7	7 5 2.9	22 26.3	0 17.5	3S51.8	23 45.3	12 7.9	10 22.8	14 5.5	7 57.5	22 51.9	7 41.2	22 54.4
10	7 16 52.6	22 2.1	0 17.5	18 57.7	24 .1	10 44.1	9 29.1	14 6.9	7 59.9	22 52.9	7 41.7	22 56.2
13	7 28 42.3	21 33.9	0 17.6	27 9.3	24 3.7	9 18.2	8 34.7	14 9.0	8 1.9	22 53.9	7 42.0	22 58.1
16	7 40 32.0	21 2.0	0 17.6	20 52.6	23 55.6	7 50.8	7 39.7	14 11.6	8 3.6	22 54.8	7 42.2	22 60.0
19	7 52 21.6	20 26.4	0 17.7	2 50.4	23 35.2	6 22.0	6 44.2	14 14.8	8 4.9	22 55.7	7 42.4	23 1.8
22	8 4 11.3	19 47.4	0 17.7	15N47.8	23 2.3	4 52.4	5 48.3	14 18.5	8 5.9	22 56.6	7 42.3	23 3.7
25	8 16 1.0	19 5.1	0 17.8	26 24.5	22 16.4	3 22.3	4 52.1	14 22.7	8 6.6	22 57.5	7 42.2	23 5.6
28	8 27 50.7	18 19.7	0 17.8	24 51.7	21 17.3	1 52.0	3 55.6	14 27.4	8 6.9	22 58.3	7 42.0	23 7.4
31	8 39 40.3	17 31.3	0 17.9	13 24.8	20 4.8	0 21.8	2 59.0	14 32.6	8 6.9	22 59.1	7 41.6	23 9.3

FEBRUARY 1953

LONGITUDE

DAY	EPHEM. SID. TIME h m s	☉ ° ′	☊ ° ′	☽ ° ′	☿ ° ′	♀ ° ′	♂ ° ′	♃ ° ′	♄ ° ′	♅ ° ′	♆ ° ′	♇ ° ′
1	8 43 36.9	11♒50.7	12♒26.3	3♍38.6	10♒26.8	28♓45.0	24♓39.1	12♉10.7	27♎17.0	15♋27.4	23♎52.3	22♌17.6
2	8 47 33.4	12 51.6	12 23.1	15 26.7	12 10.3	29 45.4	25 24.8	12 16.0	27 17.4	15 R 25.1	23 R 52.1	22 R 16.1
3	8 51 30.0	13 52.4	12 19.9	27 16.0	13 54.4	0♈45.4	26 10.5	12 21.5	27 17.6	15 22.9	23 51.8	22 14.7
4	8 55 26.5	14 53.3	12 16.7	9♎ 9.6	15 39.3	1 44.9	26 56.1	12 27.2	27 17.8	15 20.8	23 51.5	22 13.2
5	8 59 23.1	15 54.1	12 13.6	21 11.2	17 24.8	2 43.9	27 41.7	12 33.1	27 17.9	15 18.6	23 51.1	22 11.8
6	9 3 19.7	16 54.9	12 10.4	3♏24.5	19 11.1	3 42.5	28 27.3	12 39.1	27 R 17.8	15 16.5	23 50.7	22 10.3
7	9 7 16.2	17 55.7	12 7.2	15 54.0	20 58.0	4 40.6	29 12.8	12 45.3	27 17.7	15 14.4	23 50.3	22 8.8
8	9 11 12.8	18 56.5	12 4.0	28 43.7	22 45.6	5 38.2	29 58.4	12 51.7	27 17.5	15 12.4	23 49.9	22 7.4
9	9 15 9.3	19 57.2	12 .8	11♐57.1	24 33.7	6 35.1	0♈43.9	12 58.2	27 17.1	15 10.4	23 49.4	22 6.0
10	9 19 5.9	20 58.0	11 57.7	25 36.8	26 22.4	7 31.6	1 29.3	13 4.9	27 16.6	15 8.4	23 48.9	22 4.5
11	9 23 2.4	21 58.7	11 54.5	9♑43.7	28 11.5	8 27.5	2 14.8	13 11.8	27 16.0	15 6.5	23 48.3	22 3.0
12	9 26 59.0	22 59.4	11 51.3	24 16.3	0♓ 1.0	9 22.7	3 .2	13 18.8	27 15.4	15 4.6	23 47.7	22 1.6
13	9 30 55.5	24 .1	11 48.1	9♒10.3	1 50.8	10 17.4	3 45.5	13 26.0	27 14.6	15 2.7	23 47.1	22 .1
14	9 34 52.1	25 .7	11 45.0	24 18.5	3 40.8	11 11.4	4 30.8	13 33.3	27 13.7	15 .9	23 46.4	21 58.6
15	9 38 48.7	26 1.4	11 41.8	9♓31.9	5 30.7	12 4.7	5 16.1	13 40.8	27 12.7	14 59.1	23 45.8	21 57.1
16	9 42 45.2	27 2.0	11 38.6	24 40.5	7 20.4	12 57.4	6 1.4	13 48.4	27 11.6	14 57.4	23 45.1	21 55.7
17	9 46 41.8	28 2.5	11 35.4	9♈35.2	9 9.6	13 49.3	6 46.6	13 56.2	27 10.4	14 55.7	23 44.3	21 54.2
18	9 50 38.3	29 3.1	11 32.2	24 8.7	10 58.2	14 40.4	7 31.8	14 4.1	27 9.1	14 54.0	23 43.5	21 52.8
19	9 54 34.9	0♓ 3.6	11 29.1	8♉16.8	12 45.8	15 30.8	8 16.9	14 12.2	27 7.7	14 52.4	23 42.7	21 51.3
20	9 58 31.4	1 4.1	11 25.9	21 58.0	14 32.0	16 20.4	9 2.0	14 20.4	27 6.1	14 50.8	23 41.9	21 49.9
21	10 2 28.0	2 4.6	11 22.7	5♊13.2	16 16.5	17 9.1	9 47.1	14 28.8	27 4.5	14 49.3	23 41.1	21 48.4
22	10 6 24.5	3 5.0	11 19.5	18 5.1	17 58.8	17 57.0	10 32.1	14 37.3	27 2.8	14 47.8	23 40.2	21 47.0
23	10 10 21.1	4 5.4	11 16.4	0♋37.2	19 38.4	18 43.9	11 17.1	14 45.9	27 1.0	14 46.3	23 39.3	21 45.5
24	10 14 17.7	5 5.7	11 13.2	12 53.5	21 14.8	19 29.8	12 2.0	14 54.7	26 59.1	14 44.9	23 38.3	21 44.1
25	10 18 14.2	6 6.1	11 10.0	24 57.9	22 47.4	20 14.8	12 46.9	15 3.6	26 57.1	14 43.6	23 37.3	21 42.7
26	10 22 10.8	7 6.4	11 6.8	6♌54.0	24 15.7	20 58.8	13 31.8	15 12.6	26 55.1	14 42.3	23 36.4	21 41.3
27	10 26 7.3	8 6.6	11 3.7	18 45.1	25 39.1	21 41.6	14 16.6	15 21.8	26 52.9	14 41.0	23 35.3	21 39.9
28	10 30 3.9	9 6.9	11 .5	0♍33.7	26 56.9	22 23.4	15 1.4	15 31.0	26 50.6	14 39.8	23 34.3	21 38.5

LATITUDE

DAY	EPHEM. SID. TIME	☉	☊	☽	☿	♀	♂	♃	♄	♅	♆	♇
1	8 43 36.9	0 .0	0 .0	1S55.6	2S 4.8	0N41.4	0S35.5	0S58.0	2N34.0	0N26.5	1N41.6	9N37.6
4	8 55 26.5	0 .0	0 .0	4 26.1	2 3.8	1 .8	0 33.1	0 57.2	2 34.8	0 26.5	1 41.8	9 38.0
7	9 7 16.2	0 .0	0 .0	5 17.1	1 58.6	1 21.2	0 30.6	0 56.4	2 35.6	0 26.5	1 42.0	9 38.3
10	9 19 5.9	0 .0	0 .0	3 51.7	1 48.8	1 42.4	0 28.1	0 55.6	2 36.4	0 26.5	1 42.2	9 38.6
13	9 30 55.5	0 .0	0 .0	0 17.9	1 33.7	2 4.4	0 25.7	0 54.9	2 37.2	0 26.4	1 42.3	9 38.8
16	9 42 45.2	0 .0	0 .0	3N33.5	1 12.9	2 27.2	0 23.3	0 54.1	2 37.9	0 26.4	1 42.5	9 39.0
19	9 54 34.9	0 .0	0 .0	5 15.5	0 46.1	2 50.6	0 20.9	0 53.4	2 38.7	0 26.4	1 42.7	9 39.1
22	10 6 24.5	0 .0	0 .0	4 16.6	0 13.4	3 14.7	0 18.5	0 52.7	2 39.4	0 26.4	1 42.8	9 39.2
25	10 18 14.2	0 .0	0 .0	1 34.4	0N24.6	3 39.3	0 16.2	0 52.0	2 40.1	0 26.3	1 43.0	9 39.2
28	10 30 3.9	0 .0	0 .0	1S38.6	1 6.4	4 4.4	0 13.8	0 51.3	2 40.8	0 26.3	1 43.1	9 39.2

RIGHT ASCENSION

DAY	EPHEM. SID. TIME	☉	☊	☽	☿	♀	♂	♃	♄	♅	♆	♇
1	8 43 36.9	14♒18.5	14♒54.2	4♍51.0	13♒29.8	28♓34.7	25♓19.6	10♉ 2.4	26♎15.3	16♋49.6	22♎43.7	28♌ 2.3
2	8 47 33.4	15 19.6	14 51.0	15 28.8	15 15.1	29 27.6	26 1.2	10 7.6	26 15.7	16 R 47.2	22 R 43.5	28 R .9
3	8 51 30.0	16 20.5	14 47.8	26 .2	17 .4	0♈20.0	26 42.8	10 12.9	26 16.1	16 44.9	22 43.2	27 59.5
4	8 55 26.5	17 21.3	14 44.6	6♎39.3	18 45.6	1 12.0	27 24.4	10 18.4	26 16.3	16 42.5	22 42.9	27 58.1
5	8 59 23.1	18 21.8	14 41.4	17 40.6	20 30.8	2 3.6	28 5.9	10 24.1	26 16.5	16 40.2	22 42.6	27 56.6
6	9 3 19.7	19 22.1	14 38.2	29 18.8	22 16.0	2 54.6	28 47.4	10 30.0	26 16.5	16 37.9	22 42.3	27 55.2
7	9 7 16.2	20 22.2	14 35.0	11♏47.5	24 .9	3 45.2	29 28.9	10 36.0	26 16.5	16 35.7	22 41.9	27 53.8
8	9 11 12.8	21 22.2	14 31.8	25 16.0	25 45.8	4 35.4	0♈10.4	10 42.2	26 R 16.4	16 33.5	22 41.5	27 52.4
9	9 15 9.3	22 21.9	14 28.7	9♐45.5	27 30.4	5 25.0	0 51.8	10 48.6	26 16.1	16 31.3	22 41.1	27 50.9
10	9 19 5.9	23 21.5	14 25.5	25 4.6	29 14.7	6 14.1	1 33.2	10 55.1	26 15.8	16 29.2	22 40.6	27 49.5
11	9 23 2.4	24 20.8	14 22.3	10♑49.1	0♓58.7	7 2.7	2 14.5	11 1.8	26 15.3	16 27.1	22 40.1	27 48.0
12	9 26 59.0	25 20.0	14 19.1	26 29.4	2 42.3	7 50.8	2 55.8	11 8.6	26 14.8	16 25.0	22 39.6	27 46.6
13	9 30 55.5	26 18.9	14 15.9	11♒41.4	4 25.3	8 38.3	3 37.1	11 15.7	26 14.1	16 23.0	22 39.0	27 45.1
14	9 34 52.1	27 17.7	14 12.7	26 14.5	6 7.7	9 25.2	4 18.4	11 22.8	26 13.4	16 21.1	22 38.4	27 43.6
15	9 38 48.7	28 16.3	14 9.5	10♓11.0	7 49.3	10 11.6	4 59.7	11 30.1	26 12.5	16 19.1	22 37.8	27 42.2
16	9 42 45.2	29 14.7	14 6.3	23 42.2	9 30.0	10 57.3	5 41.0	11 37.6	26 11.6	16 17.2	22 37.2	27 40.7
17	9 46 41.8	0♓13.0	14 3.1	7♈ 2.8	11 9.6	11 42.4	6 22.2	11 45.2	26 10.6	16 15.4	22 36.5	27 39.3
18	9 50 38.3	1 11.0	13 59.9	20 27.4	12 47.8	12 26.9	7 3.4	11 53.0	26 9.4	16 13.6	22 35.8	27 37.8
19	9 54 34.9	2 8.9	13 56.7	4♉ 6.8	14 24.5	13 10.7	7 44.6	12 .9	26 8.2	16 11.8	22 35.1	27 36.4
20	9 58 31.4	3 6.6	13 53.5	18 5.4	15 59.3	13 53.8	8 25.9	12 9.0	26 6.8	16 10.1	22 34.3	27 34.9
21	10 2 28.0	4 4.1	13 50.3	2♊19.5	17 31.9	14 36.1	9 7.0	12 17.2	26 5.4	16 8.5	22 33.5	27 33.5
22	10 6 24.5	5 1.5	13 47.1	16 37.1	19 2.0	15 17.7	9 48.2	12 25.5	26 3.9	16 6.9	22 32.7	27 32.0
23	10 10 21.1	5 58.7	13 43.9	0♋41.6	20 29.2	15 58.5	10 29.4	12 34.0	26 2.3	16 5.3	22 31.9	27 30.6
24	10 14 17.7	6 55.7	13 40.7	14 17.0	21 53.1	16 38.4	11 10.6	12 42.6	26 .6	16 3.8	22 31.0	27 29.1
25	10 18 14.2	7 52.6	13 37.5	27 12.8	23 13.1	17 17.5	11 51.8	12 51.4	25 58.8	16 2.3	22 30.1	27 27.7
26	10 22 10.8	8 49.3	13 34.3	9♌25.8	24 28.9	17 55.7	12 32.9	13 .3	25 56.9	16 .9	22 29.2	27 26.3
27	10 26 7.3	9 45.9	13 31.1	20 59.6	25 39.8	18 32.9	13 14.1	13 9.3	25 55.0	15 59.5	22 28.3	27 24.9
28	10 30 3.9	10 42.4	13 27.9	2♍ 2.3	26 45.6	19 9.1	13 55.3	13 18.5	25 52.9	15 58.2	22 27.3	27 23.5

DECLINATION

DAY	EPHEM. SID. TIME	☉	☊	☽	☿	♀	♂	♃	♄	♅	♆	♇
1	8 43 36.9	17S14.5	0S17.9	8N22.6	19S37.6	0N 8.1	2S40.2	14N34.5	8S 6.8	22N59.4	7S41.5	23N 9.9
4	8 55 26.5	16 22.5	0 17.9	7S42.4	18 7.1	1 37.5	1 43.5	14 40.3	8 6.4	23 .1	7 41.0	23 11.7
7	9 7 16.2	15 27.8	0 18.0	21 39.4	16 23.1	3 6.0	0 46.8	14 46.5	8 5.6	23 .9	7 40.4	23 13.4
10	9 19 5.9	14 30.7	0 18.0	27 14.0	14 26.0	4 33.3	0N 9.7	14 53.2	8 4.4	23 1.5	7 39.7	23 15.2
13	9 30 55.5	13 31.5	0 18.1	18 15.3	12 16.7	5 58.9	1 6.1	15 .2	8 3.0	23 2.1	7 38.9	23 16.9
16	9 42 45.2	12 30.3	0 18.1	1N 9.1	9 56.7	7 22.6	2 2.2	15 7.6	8 1.2	23 2.7	7 38.0	23 18.5
19	9 54 34.9	11 27.3	0 18.2	19 14.5	7 28.9	8 43.9	2 57.9	15 15.4	7 59.1	23 3.3	7 37.0	23 20.1
22	10 6 24.5	10 22.6	0 18.2	27 10.3	4 57.6	10 2.5	3 53.3	15 23.5	7 56.7	23 3.7	7 35.9	23 21.6
25	10 18 14.2	9 16.6	0 18.3	22 41.5	2 29.2	11 17.9	4 48.1	15 31.8	7 54.0	23 4.2	7 34.8	23 23.1
28	10 30 3.9	8 9.3	0 18.3	9 44.4	0 11.9	12 29.6	5 42.4	15 40.5	7 51.0	23 4.6	7 33.5	23 24.5

MARCH 1953

LONGITUDE

DAY	EPHEM. SID. TIME h m s	☉ ° ′	☊ ° ′	☽ ° ′	☿ ° ′	♀ ° ′	♂ ° ′	♃ ° ′	♄ ° ′	♅ ° ′	♆ ° ′	♇ ° ′
1	10 34 .4	10♓ 7.1	10♒57.3	12♍22.3	28♓ 8.5	23♈ 4.0	15♈46.2	15♉40.5	26♎48.3	14♋38.7	23♎33.3	21♌37.1
2	10 37 57.0	11 7.3	10 54.1	24 12.8	29 13.3	23 43.4	16 30.8	15 50.0	26 R 45.8	14 R 37.6	23 R 32.2	21 R 35.8
3	10 41 53.5	12 7.4	10 50.9	6♎ 7.0	0♈10.8	24 21.6	17 15.5	15 59.7	26 43.3	14 36.5	23 31.0	21 34.4
4	10 45 50.1	13 7.6	10 47.8	18 6.9	1 .5	24 58.5	18 .1	16 9.4	26 40.7	14 35.5	23 29.9	21 33.1
5	10 49 46.6	14 7.7	10 44.6	0♏14.6	1 42.0	25 34.0	18 44.6	16 19.3	26 37.9	14 34.5	23 28.7	21 31.7
6	10 53 43.2	15 7.7	10 41.4	12 32.5	2 14.8	26 8.2	19 29.1	16 29.3	26 35.1	14 33.6	23 27.5	21 30.4
7	10 57 39.7	16 7.8	10 38.2	25 3.6	2 38.7	26 40.9	20 13.6	16 39.4	26 32.3	14 32.7	23 26.3	21 29.1
8	11 1 36.3	17 7.8	10 35.1	7♐50.8	2 53.7	27 12.1	20 58.1	16 49.7	26 29.3	14 31.9	23 25.1	21 27.8
9	11 5 32.9	18 7.7	10 31.9	20 57.4	2 59.5	27 41.7	21 42.4	17 .0	26 26.2	14 31.1	23 23.8	21 26.5
10	11 9 29.4	19 7.7	10 28.7	4♑26.4	2 R 56.4	28 9.8	22 26.8	17 10.4	26 23.1	14 30.4	23 22.5	21 25.2
11	11 13 26.0	20 7.6	10 25.5	18 19.8	2 44.6	28 36.1	23 11.1	17 21.0	26 19.9	14 29.8	23 21.2	21 23.9
12	11 17 22.5	21 7.5	10 22.3	2♒38.2	2 24.5	29 .8	23 55.4	17 31.7	26 16.6	14 29.2	23 19.9	21 22.7
13	11 21 19.1	22 7.4	10 19.2	17 19.9	1 56.6	29 23.7	24 39.6	17 42.4	26 13.3	14 28.6	23 18.6	21 21.5
14	11 25 15.6	23 7.2	10 16.0	2♓20.3	1 21.7	29 44.7	25 23.8	17 53.3	26 9.8	14 28.1	23 17.2	21 20.2
15	11 29 12.2	24 7.1	10 12.8	17 31.9	0 40.6	0♉ 3.9	26 7.9	18 4.2	26 6.3	14 27.6	23 15.8	21 19.0
16	11 33 8.7	25 6.8	10 9.6	2♈45.1	29♓54.3	0 21.0	26 52.0	18 15.3	26 2.8	14 27.3	23 14.5	21 17.9
17	11 37 5.3	26 6.6	10 6.5	17 49.4	29 3.9	0 36.1	27 36.0	18 26.4	25 59.1	14 26.9	23 13.0	21 16.7
18	11 41 1.8	27 6.3	10 3.3	2♉35.4	28 10.7	0 49.1	28 20.0	18 37.7	25 55.4	14 26.6	23 11.6	21 15.5
19	11 44 58.4	28 6.0	10 .1	16 56.1	27 15.7	0 60.0	29 4.0	18 49.0	25 51.6	14 26.4	23 10.2	21 14.4
20	11 48 54.9	29 5.6	9 56.9	0♊48.0	26 20.2	1 8.6	29 47.9	19 .5	25 47.8	14 26.2	23 8.7	21 13.3
21	11 52 51.5	0♈ 5.2	9 53.7	14 10.6	25 25.4	1 14.9	0♉31.8	19 12.0	25 43.9	14 26.1	23 7.2	21 12.2
22	11 56 48.0	1 4.8	9 50.6	27 6.0	24 32.4	1 19.0	1 15.6	19 23.6	25 40.0	14 26.0	23 5.8	21 11.2
23	12 0 44.6	2 4.3	9 47.4	9♋38.0	23 42.1	1 20.6	1 59.4	19 35.3	25 36.0	14 26.0	23 4.3	21 10.1
24	12 4 41.2	3 3.8	9 44.2	21 51.5	22 55.3	1 R 19.7	2 43.1	19 47.1	25 32.0	14 D 26.1	23 2.8	21 9.1
25	12 8 37.7	4 3.3	9 41.0	3♌51.6	22 12.9	1 16.4	3 26.8	19 58.9	25 27.9	14 26.2	23 1.2	21 8.1
26	12 12 34.3	5 2.7	9 37.9	15 43.1	21 35.3	1 10.6	4 10.4	20 10.9	25 23.8	14 26.3	22 59.7	21 7.1
27	12 16 30.8	6 2.1	9 34.7	27 30.6	21 2.9	1 2.3	4 54.0	20 22.9	25 19.6	14 26.5	22 58.1	21 6.1
28	12 20 27.4	7 1.4	9 31.5	9♍17.9	20 36.2	0 51.5	5 37.5	20 34.9	25 15.3	14 26.7	22 56.6	21 5.2
29	12 24 23.9	8 .7	9 28.3	21 8.1	20 15.1	0 38.2	6 21.0	20 47.1	25 11.1	14 27.0	22 55.0	21 4.3
30	12 28 20.5	8 60.0	9 25.1	3♎ 3.5	19 59.9	0 22.5	7 4.4	20 59.3	25 6.7	14 27.4	22 53.4	21 3.4
31	12 32 17.0	9 59.2	9 22.0	15 5.9	19 50.6	0 4.3	7 47.8	21 11.6	25 2.4	14 27.8	22 51.8	21 2.5

LATITUDE

DAY	SID. TIME	☉	☊	☽	☿	♀	♂	♃	♄	♅	♆	♇
1	10 34 .4	0 .0	0 .0	2 S 37.6	1 N 20.8	4 N 12.8	0 S 13.1	0 S 51.1	2 N 41.1	0 N 26.3	1 N 43.1	9 N 39.2
4	10 45 50.1	0 .0	0 .0	4 45.6	2 3.5	4 38.1	0 10.8	0 50.4	2 41.7	0 26.2	1 43.3	9 39.1
7	10 57 39.7	0 .0	0 .0	5 3.7	2 42.7	5 3.5	0 8.5	0 49.8	2 42.3	0 26.2	1 43.4	9 39.0
10	11 9 29.4	0 .0	0 .0	3 9.5	3 13.9	5 28.7	0 6.3	0 49.2	2 42.9	0 26.2	1 43.5	9 38.9
13	11 21 19.1	0 .0	0 .0	0 N 30.1	3 32.5	5 53.3	0 4.1	0 48.6	2 43.5	0 26.1	1 43.6	9 38.7
16	11 33 8.7	0 .0	0 .0	4 1.0	3 34.8	6 17.0	0 1.9	0 48.0	2 44.0	0 26.1	1 43.7	9 38.5
19	11 44 58.4	0 .0	0 .0	5 7.1	3 19.8	6 39.3	0 N .3	0 47.4	2 44.5	0 26.0	1 43.8	9 38.2
22	11 56 48.0	0 .0	0 .0	3 35.0	2 49.5	6 59.4	0 2.4	0 46.9	2 44.9	0 26.0	1 43.9	9 37.9
25	12 8 37.7	0 .0	0 .0	0 39.3	2 8.5	7 16.7	0 4.5	0 46.3	2 45.3	0 26.0	1 44.0	9 37.6
28	12 20 27.4	0 .0	0 .0	2 S 25.1	1 22.4	7 30.1	0 6.5	0 45.8	2 45.6	0 25.9	1 44.1	9 37.2
31	12 32 17.0	0 .0	0 .0	4 34.4	0 35.8	7 38.6	0 8.6	0 45.3	2 45.9	0 25.9	1 44.1	9 36.8

RIGHT ASCENSION

DAY	SID. TIME	☉	☊	☽	☿	♀	♂	♃	♄	♅	♆	♇
1	10 34 .4	11♓38.8	13♒24.7	12♍44.5	27♓45.6	19♈44.4	14♈36.5	13♉27.8	25♎50.8	15♋57.0	22♎26.4	27♌22.1
2	10 37 57.0	12 34.9	13 21.5	23 18.2	28 39.3	20 18.6	15 17.7	13 37.2	25 R 48.6	15 R 55.8	22 R 25.3	27 R 20.7
3	10 41 53.5	13 31.0	13 18.3	3♎56.1	29 26.4	20 51.6	15 58.9	13 46.8	25 46.3	15 54.7	22 24.3	27 19.3
4	10 45 50.1	14 27.0	13 15.1	14 51.4	0♈ 6.3	21 23.5	16 40.1	13 56.4	25 43.9	15 53.6	22 23.2	27 17.9
5	10 49 46.6	15 22.8	13 11.8	26 16.9	0 38.9	21 54.1	17 21.4	14 6.2	25 41.4	15 52.5	22 22.2	27 16.6
6	10 53 43.2	16 18.5	13 8.6	8♏24.4	1 3.8	22 23.6	18 2.6	14 16.1	25 38.8	15 51.5	22 21.1	27 15.2
7	10 57 39.7	17 14.1	13 5.4	21 22.5	1 20.8	22 51.7	18 43.9	14 26.1	25 36.2	15 50.6	22 19.9	27 13.9
8	11 1 36.3	18 9.7	13 2.2	5♐13.7	1 30.0	23 18.4	19 25.2	14 36.3	25 33.5	15 49.7	22 18.8	27 12.5
9	11 5 32.9	19 5.1	12 59.0	19 51.0	1 31.2	23 43.7	20 6.5	14 46.5	25 30.7	15 48.9	22 17.6	27 11.2
10	11 9 29.4	20 .4	12 55.8	4♑57.3	1 R 24.7	24 7.6	20 47.8	14 56.9	25 27.8	15 48.1	22 16.5	27 9.9
11	11 13 26.0	20 55.7	12 52.6	20 9.7	1 10.7	24 29.9	21 29.1	15 7.4	25 24.8	15 47.4	22 15.2	27 8.6
12	11 17 22.5	21 50.9	12 49.4	5♒ 7.1	0 49.7	24 50.6	22 10.5	15 18.0	25 21.8	15 46.7	22 14.0	27 7.3
13	11 21 19.1	22 46.0	12 46.2	19 37.4	0 22.3	25 9.6	22 51.9	15 28.7	25 18.7	15 46.1	22 12.8	27 6.1
14	11 25 15.6	23 41.0	12 43.0	3♓39.4	29♓49.2	25 27.0	23 33.4	15 39.5	25 15.6	15 45.6	22 11.5	27 4.8
15	11 29 12.2	24 36.0	12 39.8	17 21.2	29 11.2	25 42.6	24 14.8	15 50.4	25 12.3	15 45.1	22 10.2	27 3.6
16	11 33 8.7	25 30.9	12 36.5	0♈55.4	28 29.2	25 56.3	24 56.3	16 1.5	25 9.0	15 44.7	22 8.9	27 2.3
17	11 37 5.3	26 25.8	12 33.3	14 36.0	27 44.3	26 8.1	25 37.8	16 12.6	25 5.7	15 44.3	22 7.6	27 1.1
18	11 41 1.8	27 20.6	12 30.1	28 34.0	26 57.4	26 18.0	26 19.4	16 23.8	25 2.3	15 44.0	22 6.3	26 59.9
19	11 44 58.4	28 15.4	12 26.9	12♉54.3	26 9.8	26 25.9	27 1.0	16 35.1	24 58.8	15 43.7	22 5.0	26 58.7
20	11 48 54.9	29 10.1	12 23.7	27 32.6	25 22.3	26 31.6	27 42.6	16 46.6	24 55.2	15 43.5	22 3.6	26 57.6
21	11 52 51.5	0♈ 4.8	12 20.5	12♊15.9	24 36.1	26 35.3	28 24.3	16 58.1	24 51.6	15 43.4	22 2.2	26 56.4
22	11 56 48.0	0 59.5	12 17.3	26 45.0	23 52.1	26 36.8	29 6.1	17 9.7	24 48.0	15 43.4	22 .9	26 55.4
23	12 0 44.6	1 54.1	12 14.0	10♋41.9	23 11.0	26 R 36.0	29 47.8	17 21.4	24 44.3	15 43.3	21 59.5	26 54.3
24	12 4 41.2	2 48.7	12 10.8	23 54.8	22 33.5	26 33.0	0♉29.6	17 33.2	24 40.6	15 D 43.4	21 58.1	26 53.2
25	12 8 37.7	3 43.3	12 7.6	6♌20.6	22 .3	26 27.8	1 11.4	17 45.1	24 36.8	15 43.5	21 56.7	26 52.1
26	12 12 34.3	4 37.8	12 4.4	18 3.3	21 31.7	26 20.2	1 53.2	17 57.1	24 32.9	15 43.6	21 55.2	26 51.1
27	12 16 30.8	5 32.4	12 1.2	29 11.9	21 8.0	26 10.4	2 35.1	18 9.2	24 29.0	15 43.8	21 53.8	26 50.0
28	12 20 27.4	6 26.9	11 58.0	9♍57.9	20 49.5	25 58.3	3 17.1	18 21.3	24 25.1	15 44.1	21 52.3	26 49.0
29	12 24 23.9	7 21.5	11 54.7	20 33.7	20 36.4	25 44.1	3 59.1	18 33.5	24 21.1	15 44.4	21 50.9	26 48.1
30	12 28 20.5	8 16.0	11 51.5	1♎12.3	20 28.5	25 27.6	4 41.1	18 45.8	24 17.1	15 44.8	21 49.4	26 47.1
31	12 32 17.0	9 10.6	11 48.3	12 6.6	20 25.9	25 9.0	5 23.1	18 58.2	24 13.1	15 45.2	21 47.9	26 46.2

DECLINATION

DAY	SID. TIME	☉	☊	☽	☿	♀	♂	♃	♄	♅	♆	♇
1	10 34 .4	7 S 46.6	0 S 18.3	4 N 29.6	0 N 29.7	12 N 52.7	6 N .4	15 N 43.4	7 S 49.9	23 N 4.7	7 S 33.1	23 N 24.9
4	10 45 50.1	6 37.9	0 18.4	11 S 30.1	2 17.4	13 58.8	6 53.8	15 52.4	7 46.6	23 5.0	7 31.7	23 26.2
7	10 57 39.7	5 28.4	0 18.4	23 56.7	3 32.4	15 .2	7 46.5	16 1.5	7 43.0	23 5.2	7 30.3	23 27.5
10	11 9 29.4	4 18.2	0 18.4	26 31.7	4 8.1	15 56.0	8 38.5	16 10.9	7 39.2	23 5.4	7 28.8	23 28.6
13	11 21 19.1	3 7.5	0 18.5	15 10.1	4 1.3	16 45.7	9 29.6	16 20.4	7 35.1	23 5.6	7 27.2	23 29.7
16	11 33 8.7	1 56.5	0 18.5	4 N 46.7	3 14.8	17 28.4	10 19.8	16 30.1	7 30.9	23 5.7	7 25.6	23 30.7
19	11 44 58.4	0 45.4	0 18.6	21 48.1	1 58.0	18 3.1	11 9.0	16 39.9	7 26.4	23 5.8	7 23.9	23 31.6
22	11 56 48.0	0 N 25.8	0 18.6	26 59.9	0 25.4	18 28.6	11 57.2	16 49.9	7 21.8	23 5.8	7 22.2	23 32.4
25	12 8 37.7	1 36.7	0 18.7	19 55.8	1 S 7.3	18 43.8	12 44.3	16 59.9	7 17.1	23 5.7	7 20.5	23 33.1
28	12 20 27.4	2 47.3	0 18.7	5 50.6	2 27.7	18 47.5	13 30.2	17 10.0	7 12.2	23 5.6	7 18.7	23 33.7
31	12 32 17.0	3 57.4	0 18.8	10 S 9.8	3 28.5	18 38.5	14 15.0	17 20.1	7 7.3	23 5.4	7 16.9	23 34.3

APRIL 1953

LONGITUDE

DAY	EPHEM. SID. TIME h m s	☉ ° ′	☊ ° ′	☽ ° ′	☿ ° ′	♀ ° ′	♂ ° ′	♃ ° ′	♄ ° ′	♅ ° ′	♆ ° ′	♇ ° ′
1	12 36 13.6	10♈58.4	9♒18.8	27♎16.5	19♓46.9	29♈43.7	8♉31.1	21♉24.0	24♎58.0	14♋28.3	22♎50.2	21♌ 1.6
2	12 40 10.1	11 57.5	9 15.6	9♏36.3	19 D 48.9	29 R 20.9	9 14.4	21 36.4	24 R 53.6	14 28.8	22 R 48.6	21 R .8
3	12 44 6.7	12 56.7	9 12.4	22 6.2	19 56.3	28 55.8	9 57.7	21 48.9	24 49.1	14 29.4	22 47.0	20 60.0
4	12 48 3.2	13 55.8	9 9.3	4♐47.4	20 8.9	28 28.7	10 40.9	22 1.5	24 44.7	14 30.0	22 45.4	20 59.2
5	12 51 59.8	14 54.8	9 6.1	17 41.4	20 26.6	27 59.6	11 24.0	22 14.1	24 40.2	14 30.7	22 43.8	20 58.4
6	12 55 56.4	15 53.9	9 2.9	0♑50.0	20 49.1	27 28.8	12 7.1	22 26.8	24 35.6	14 31.4	22 42.1	20 57.7
7	12 59 52.9	16 52.9	8 59.7	14 15.4	21 16.3	26 56.3	12 50.2	22 39.6	24 31.1	14 32.2	22 40.5	20 57.0
8	13 3 49.5	17 51.9	8 56.5	27 59.4	21 47.8	26 22.4	13 33.2	22 52.4	24 26.5	14 33.0	22 38.9	20 56.3
9	13 7 46.0	18 50.8	8 53.4	12♒ 3.5	22 23.4	25 47.3	14 16.1	23 5.2	24 22.0	14 33.9	22 37.2	20 55.6
10	13 11 42.6	19 49.8	8 50.2	26 27.4	23 3.0	25 11.2	14 59.1	23 18.2	24 17.4	14 34.9	22 35.6	20 55.0
11	13 15 39.1	20 48.7	8 47.0	11♓ 8.9	23 46.3	24 34.3	15 42.0	23 31.2	24 12.8	14 35.8	22 33.9	20 54.4
12	13 19 35.7	21 47.6	8 43.8	26 3.1	24 33.3	23 56.9	16 24.8	23 44.2	24 8.2	14 36.9	22 32.3	20 53.8
13	13 23 32.2	22 46.4	8 40.7	11♈ 2.6	25 23.5	23 19.2	17 7.6	23 57.3	24 3.6	14 38.0	22 30.7	20 53.3
14	13 27 28.8	23 45.2	8 37.5	25 58.3	26 17.0	22 41.5	17 50.4	24 10.5	23 58.9	14 39.2	22 29.0	20 52.7
15	13 31 25.3	24 44.0	8 34.3	10♉40.9	27 13.5	22 3.9	18 33.1	24 23.7	23 54.3	14 40.4	22 27.4	20 52.2
16	13 35 21.9	25 42.7	8 31.1	25 2.6	28 13.0	21 26.8	19 15.7	24 36.9	23 49.7	14 41.6	22 25.7	20 51.8
17	13 39 18.4	26 41.4	8 27.9	8♊58.2	29 15.2	20 50.3	19 58.3	24 50.2	23 45.1	14 42.9	22 24.1	20 51.3
18	13 43 15.0	27 40.1	8 24.8	22 25.5	0♈20.0	20 14.8	20 40.9	25 3.5	23 40.5	14 44.3	22 22.4	20 50.9
19	13 47 11.6	28 38.7	8 21.6	5♋25.4	1 27.5	19 40.3	21 23.4	25 16.9	23 35.9	14 45.7	22 20.8	20 50.5
20	13 51 8.1	29 37.3	8 18.4	18 .9	2 37.3	19 7.2	22 5.9	25 30.3	23 31.3	14 47.1	22 19.2	20 50.1
21	13 55 4.7	0♉35.9	8 15.2	0♌16.5	3 49.6	18 35.7	22 48.3	25 43.8	23 26.7	14 48.6	22 17.5	20 49.8
22	13 59 1.2	1 34.4	8 12.1	12 17.4	5 4.1	18 5.8	23 30.6	25 57.3	23 22.2	14 50.2	22 15.9	20 49.4
23	14 2 57.8	2 32.9	8 8.9	24 9.2	6 20.9	17 37.8	24 13.0	26 10.8	23 17.6	14 51.8	22 14.3	20 49.2
24	14 6 54.3	3 31.3	8 5.7	5♍57.1	7 39.8	17 11.7	24 55.2	26 24.4	23 13.1	14 53.4	22 12.7	20 48.9
25	14 10 50.9	4 29.7	8 2.5	17 45.9	9 .8	16 47.8	25 37.5	26 38.0	23 8.6	14 55.1	22 11.1	20 48.7
26	14 14 47.4	5 28.1	7 59.3	29 39.7	10 23.8	16 26.1	26 19.6	26 51.6	23 4.2	14 56.8	22 9.5	20 48.5
27	14 18 44.0	6 26.4	7 56.2	11♎41.5	11 48.9	16 6.7	27 1.8	27 5.3	22 59.7	14 58.6	22 7.9	20 48.3
28	14 22 40.5	7 24.8	7 53.0	23 53.6	13 16.0	15 49.6	27 43.9	27 19.0	22 55.3	15 .4	22 6.3	20 48.1
29	14 26 37.1	8 23.0	7 49.8	6♏17.2	14 45.0	15 35.0	28 25.9	27 32.7	22 51.0	15 2.3	22 4.7	20 48.0
30	14 30 33.7	9 21.3	7 46.6	18 52.9	16 16.0	15 22.7	29 7.9	27 46.4	22 46.6	15 4.2	22 3.2	20 47.9

LATITUDE

DAY	EPHEM. SID. TIME	☉	☊	☽	☿	♀	♂	♃	♄	♅	♆	♇
1	12 36 13.6	0 .0	0 .0	4S55.7	0N20.8	7N40.2	0N 9.2	0S45.2	2N46.0	0N25.8	1N44.1	9N36.7
4	12 48 3.2	0 .0	0 .0	4 35.8	0S21.7	7 40.7	0 11.2	0 44.7	2 46.2	0 25.8	1 44.2	9 36.2
7	12 59 52.9	0 .0	0 .0	2 11.5	0 59.2	7 34.1	0 13.2	0 44.2	2 46.3	0 25.8	1 44.2	9 35.8
10	13 11 42.6	0 .0	0 .0	1N27.4	1 31.2	7 19.9	0 15.1	0 43.8	2 46.5	0 25.7	1 44.2	9 35.3
13	13 23 32.2	0 .0	0 .0	4 25.6	1 57.5	6 58.1	0 17.0	0 43.3	2 46.5	0 25.7	1 44.3	9 34.8
16	13 35 21.9	0 .0	0 .0	4 49.8	2 18.1	6 29.4	0 18.8	0 42.9	2 46.5	0 25.6	1 44.3	9 34.3
19	13 47 11.6	0 .0	0 .0	2 46.1	2 33.1	5 54.7	0 20.6	0 42.5	2 46.5	0 25.6	1 44.3	9 33.7
22	13 59 1.2	0 .0	0 .0	0S19.7	2 42.7	5 15.8	0 22.4	0 42.1	2 46.4	0 25.5	1 44.3	9 33.2
25	14 10 50.9	0 .0	0 .0	3 11.4	2 47.1	4 34.1	0 24.1	0 41.8	2 46.2	0 25.5	1 44.2	9 32.6
28	14 22 40.5	0 .0	0 .0	4 51.0	2 46.2	3 51.3	0 25.9	0 41.4	2 46.0	0 25.5	1 44.2	9 32.0

RIGHT ASCENSION

DAY	EPHEM. SID. TIME	☉	☊	☽	☿	♀	♂	♃	♄	♅	♆	♇
1	12 36 13.6	10♈ 5.2	11♒45.1	23♎28.9	20♓28.4	24♈48.3	6♉ 5.3	19♉10.7	24♎ 9.0	15♋45.7	21♎46.4	26♌45.2
2	12 40 10.1	10 59.8	11 41.9	5♏30.2	20 D 36.0	24 R 25.8	6 47.4	19 23.2	24 R 4.9	15 46.3	21 R 44.9	26 R 44.3
3	12 44 6.7	11 54.5	11 38.6	18 18.3	20 48.4	24 1.4	7 29.6	19 35.8	24 .7	15 46.9	21 43.4	26 43.5
4	12 48 3.2	12 49.1	11 35.4	1♐54.7	21 5.4	23 35.3	8 11.9	19 48.5	23 56.5	15 47.6	21 41.9	26 42.6
5	12 51 59.8	13 43.9	11 32.2	16 12.4	21 26.9	23 7.7	8 54.2	20 1.3	23 52.4	15 48.3	21 40.4	26 41.8
6	12 55 56.4	14 38.7	11 29.0	0♑55.9	21 52.6	22 38.7	9 36.6	20 14.1	23 48.1	15 49.1	21 38.9	26 41.0
7	12 59 52.9	15 33.5	11 25.7	15 44.2	22 22.3	22 8.5	10 19.0	20 27.0	23 43.9	15 50.0	21 37.3	26 40.2
8	13 3 49.5	16 28.4	11 22.5	0♒18.5	22 55.8	21 37.4	11 1.4	20 40.0	23 39.6	15 50.9	21 35.8	26 39.4
9	13 7 46.0	17 23.3	11 19.3	14 27.8	23 32.9	21 5.5	11 43.9	20 53.1	23 35.4	15 51.8	21 34.3	26 38.7
10	13 11 42.6	18 18.3	11 16.1	28 11.2	24 13.3	20 33.0	12 26.5	21 6.2	23 31.1	15 52.8	21 32.7	26 38.0
11	13 15 39.1	19 13.4	11 12.8	11♓36.1	24 56.9	20 .2	13 9.1	21 19.3	23 26.8	15 53.9	21 31.2	26 37.3
12	13 19 35.7	20 8.6	11 9.6	24 55.5	25 43.6	19 27.3	13 51.9	21 32.6	23 22.5	15 55.1	21 29.7	26 36.7
13	13 23 32.2	21 3.8	11 6.4	8♈24.0	26 33.0	18 54.5	14 34.6	21 45.9	23 18.2	15 56.3	21 28.1	26 36.1
14	13 27 28.8	21 59.2	11 3.2	22 14.7	27 25.1	18 22.0	15 17.4	21 59.3	23 13.9	15 57.5	21 26.6	26 35.5
15	13 31 25.3	22 54.6	10 59.9	6♉35.6	28 19.7	17 50.1	16 .2	22 12.7	23 9.5	15 58.8	21 25.1	26 34.9
16	13 35 21.9	23 50.0	10 56.7	21 25.3	29 16.8	17 18.9	16 43.1	22 26.2	23 5.2	16 .1	21 23.5	26 34.3
17	13 39 18.4	24 45.6	10 53.5	6♊31.1	0♈16.1	16 48.7	17 26.0	22 39.7	23 .9	16 1.5	21 22.0	26 33.8
18	13 43 15.0	25 41.3	10 50.3	21 31.2	1 17.6	16 19.7	18 9.0	22 53.3	22 56.6	16 3.0	21 20.5	26 33.3
19	13 47 11.6	26 37.0	10 47.0	6♋ 2.1	2 21.2	15 52.0	18 52.0	23 7.0	22 52.3	16 4.5	21 18.9	26 32.8
20	13 51 8.1	27 32.9	10 43.8	19 46.6	3 26.8	15 25.8	19 35.1	23 20.7	22 48.0	16 6.1	21 17.4	26 32.4
21	13 55 4.7	28 28.8	10 40.6	2♌38.2	4 34.3	15 1.2	20 18.3	23 34.4	22 43.7	16 7.7	21 15.9	26 32.0
22	13 59 1.2	29 24.9	10 37.3	14 39.6	5 43.6	14 38.4	21 1.4	23 48.2	22 39.4	16 9.4	21 14.3	26 31.6
23	14 2 57.8	0♉21.0	10 34.1	26 .2	6 54.8	14 17.6	21 44.7	24 2.1	22 35.1	16 11.1	21 12.8	26 31.2
24	14 6 54.3	1 17.3	10 30.9	6♍52.5	8 7.8	13 58.7	22 28.0	24 16.0	22 30.9	16 12.9	21 11.3	26 30.9
25	14 10 50.9	2 13.7	10 27.6	17 30.3	9 22.5	13 41.8	23 11.3	24 29.9	22 26.7	16 14.7	21 9.8	26 30.6
26	14 14 47.4	3 10.2	10 24.4	28 7.7	10 39.0	13 27.1	23 54.7	24 43.9	22 22.5	16 16.6	21 8.3	26 30.3
27	14 18 44.0	4 6.8	10 21.2	8♎58.7	11 57.1	13 14.6	24 38.1	24 57.9	22 18.3	16 18.5	21 6.8	26 30.1
28	14 22 40.5	5 3.6	10 17.9	20 16.7	13 17.0	13 4.4	25 21.5	25 12.0	22 14.2	16 20.4	21 5.4	26 29.8
29	14 26 37.1	6 .4	10 14.7	2♏13.8	14 38.6	12 56.3	26 5.0	25 26.1	22 10.1	16 22.5	21 3.9	26 29.6
30	14 30 33.7	6 57.4	10 11.5	14 58.5	16 1.9	12 50.5	26 48.6	25 40.2	22 6.0	16 24.5	21 2.4	26 29.5

DECLINATION

DAY	EPHEM. SID. TIME	☉	☊	☽	☿	♀	♂	♃	♄	♅	♆	♇
1	12 36 13.6	4N20.6	0S18.8	15S 5.9	3S43.7	18N32.5	14N29.6	17N23.4	7S 5.6	23N 5.4	7S16.3	23N34.4
4	12 48 3.2	5 29.8	0 18.8	25 37.1	4 14.1	18 5.8	15 12.6	17 33.6	7 .5	23 5.1	7 14.5	23 34.8
7	12 59 52.9	6 38.1	0 18.9	24 51.8	4 22.2	17 25.7	15 54.3	17 43.8	6 55.5	23 4.8	7 12.6	23 35.1
10	13 11 42.6	7 45.4	0 18.9	11 19.9	4 9.4	16 33.6	16 34.6	17 53.9	6 50.3	23 4.5	7 10.8	23 35.3
13	13 23 32.2	8 51.6	0 19.0	8N26.5	3 37.8	15 31.5	17 13.5	18 4.0	6 45.2	23 4.1	7 8.9	23 35.4
16	13 35 21.9	9 56.4	0 19.0	23 43.0	2 49.3	14 22.4	17 50.9	18 14.1	6 40.2	23 3.7	7 7.1	23 35.4
19	13 47 11.6	10 59.8	0 19.0	26 6.1	1 45.7	13 9.8	18 26.8	18 24.1	6 35.2	23 3.2	7 5.3	23 35.3
22	13 59 1.2	12 1.5	0 19.1	16 48.2	0 28.5	11 57.6	19 1.1	18 34.1	6 30.2	23 2.7	7 3.5	23 35.1
25	14 10 50.9	13 1.4	0 19.1	1 53.9	1N .8	10 49.1	19 33.8	18 43.9	6 25.4	23 2.1	7 1.7	23 34.9
28	14 22 40.5	13 59.4	0 19.2	13S46.7	2 41.2	9 47.1	20 4.8	18 53.7	6 20.7	23 1.4	6 60.0	23 34.5

MAY 1953

LONGITUDE

DAY	EPHEM. SID. TIME h m s	☉ ° ′	☊ ° ′	☽ ° ′	☿ ° ′	♀ ° ′	♂ ° ′	♃ ° ′	♄ ° ′	♅ ° ′	♆ ° ′	♇ ° ′
1	14 34 30.2	10♉19.5	7♒43.5	1♐40.5	17♈48.8	15♈13.0	29♉49.8	28♉ .2	22♎42.3	15♋ 6.2	22♎ 1.6	20♌47.8
2	14 38 26.8	11 17.7	7 40.3	14 39.6	19 23.6	15R 5.6	0♊31.7	28 14.0	22R38.1	15 8.2	22R .1	20 47.8
3	14 42 23.3	12 15.9	7 37.1	27 49.9	21 .3	15 .8	1 13.6	28 27.9	22 33.9	15 10.3	21 58.6	20 47.8
4	14 46 19.9	13 14.1	7 33.9	11♑11.4	22 38.9	14 58.4	1 55.4	28 41.8	22 29.7	15 12.4	21 57.1	20D47.9
5	14 50 16.4	14 12.2	7 30.8	24 44.6	24 19.3	14 58.3	2 37.2	28 55.7	22 25.6	15 14.5	21 55.6	20 47.9
6	14 54 13.0	15 10.3	7 27.6	8♒30.0	26 1.7	15D .6	3 18.9	29 9.6	22 21.5	15 16.7	21 54.1	20 48.0
7	14 58 9.5	16 8.4	7 24.4	22 28.3	27 45.9	15 5.2	4 .6	29 23.5	22 17.5	15 18.9	21 52.6	20 48.1
8	15 2 6.1	17 6.4	7 21.2	6♓39.5	29 32.1	15 12.1	4 42.3	29 37.4	22 13.5	15 21.2	21 51.2	20 48.2
9	15 6 2.7	18 4.5	7 18.0	21 2.4	1♉20.1	15 21.1	5 23.9	29 51.4	22 9.6	15 23.5	21 49.7	20 48.4
10	15 9 59.2	19 2.5	7 14.9	5♈34.0	3 10.1	15 32.4	6 5.4	0♊ 5.4	22 5.7	15 25.8	21 48.3	20 48.6
11	15 13 55.8	20 .4	7 11.7	20 9.6	5 2.0	15 45.6	6 47.0	0 19.4	22 1.9	15 28.2	21 46.9	20 48.8
12	15 17 52.3	20 58.4	7 8.5	4♉42.8	6 55.7	16 .9	7 28.4	0 33.4	21 58.2	15 30.6	21 45.5	20 49.1
13	15 21 48.9	21 56.4	7 5.3	19 6.6	8 51.4	16 18.2	8 9.9	0 47.4	21 54.5	15 33.1	21 44.1	20 49.3
14	15 25 45.4	22 54.3	7 2.2	3♊14.3	10 48.9	16 37.3	8 51.3	1 1.5	21 50.8	15 35.6	21 42.8	20 49.6
15	15 29 42.0	23 52.2	6 59.0	17 1.0	12 48.2	16 58.2	9 32.6	1 15.5	21 47.3	15 38.1	21 41.4	20 50.0
16	15 33 38.6	24 50.0	6 55.8	0♋23.8	14 49.3	17 20.9	10 13.9	1 29.6	21 43.8	15 40.7	21 40.1	20 50.3
17	15 37 35.1	25 47.8	6 52.6	13 22.5	16 52.2	17 45.3	10 55.2	1 43.6	21 40.4	15 43.3	21 38.8	20 50.7
18	15 41 31.7	26 45.7	6 49.5	25 58.8	18 56.7	18 11.3	11 36.4	1 57.7	21 37.0	15 46.0	21 37.5	20 51.1
19	15 45 28.2	27 43.4	6 46.3	8♌16.1	21 2.7	18 38.9	12 17.6	2 11.8	21 33.7	15 48.7	21 36.3	20 51.6
20	15 49 24.8	28 41.2	6 43.1	20 19.0	23 10.1	19 7.9	12 58.7	2 25.9	21 30.5	15 51.4	21 35.0	20 52.0
21	15 53 21.3	29 38.9	6 39.9	2♍12.7	25 18.8	19 38.5	13 39.8	2 40.0	21 27.4	15 54.1	21 33.8	20 52.5
22	15 57 17.9	0♊36.6	6 36.7	14 2.5	27 28.6	20 10.4	14 20.9	2 54.0	21 24.3	15 56.9	21 32.6	20 53.1
23	16 1 14.5	1 34.3	6 33.6	25 53.6	29 39.2	20 43.7	15 1.9	3 8.1	21 21.4	15 59.7	21 31.4	20 53.6
24	16 5 11.0	2 32.0	6 30.4	7♎50.9	1♊50.6	21 18.4	15 42.9	3 22.3	21 18.5	16 2.6	21 30.3	20 54.3
25	16 9 7.6	3 29.6	6 27.2	19 58.1	4 2.3	21 54.2	16 23.8	3 36.4	21 15.7	16 5.5	21 29.2	20 54.9
26	16 13 4.1	4 27.2	6 24.0	2♏18.5	6 14.1	22 31.3	17 4.7	3 50.4	21 12.9	16 8.4	21 28.1	20 55.5
27	16 17 .7	5 24.8	6 20.9	14 54.0	8 25.8	23 9.5	17 45.5	4 4.5	21 10.3	16 11.3	21 27.0	20 56.2
28	16 20 57.2	6 22.3	6 17.7	27 45.3	10 37.1	23 48.9	18 26.3	4 18.6	21 7.7	16 14.3	21 25.9	20 56.9
29	16 24 53.8	7 19.9	6 14.5	10♐52.0	12 47.7	24 29.3	19 7.1	4 32.7	21 5.2	16 17.3	21 24.9	20 57.6
30	16 28 50.4	8 17.4	6 11.3	24 12.9	14 57.4	25 10.8	19 47.8	4 46.7	21 2.8	16 20.3	21 23.9	20 58.3
31	16 32 46.9	9 14.9	6 8.2	7♑46.0	17 5.8	25 53.2	20 28.5	5 .8	21 .5	16 23.4	21 22.9	20 59.1

LATITUDE

DAY	SID. TIME	☉	☊	☽	☿	♀	♂	♃	♄	♅	♆	♇
1	14 34 30.2	0 .0	0 .0	4S33.6	2S40.4	3N 8.7	0N27.5	0S41.1	2N45.8	0N25.4	1N44.2	9N31.4
4	14 46 19.9	0 .0	0 .0	2 11.4	2 29.6	2 27.4	0 29.2	0 40.7	2 45.5	0 25.4	1 44.1	9 30.8
7	14 58 9.5	0 .0	0 .0	1N21.4	2 14.1	1 48.1	0 30.8	0 40.4	2 45.1	0 25.4	1 44.1	9 30.2
10	15 9 59.2	0 .0	0 .0	4 18.3	1 54.2	1 11.3	0 32.4	0 40.1	2 44.7	0 25.3	1 44.0	9 29.6
13	15 21 48.9	0 .0	0 .0	4 53.8	1 30.2	0 37.2	0 33.9	0 39.8	2 44.3	0 25.3	1 43.9	9 29.0
16	15 33 38.6	0 .0	0 .0	2 55.7	1 2.6	0 6.0	0 35.4	0 39.5	2 43.8	0 25.3	1 43.9	9 28.4
19	15 45 28.2	0 .0	0 .0	0S13.8	0 32.4	0S22.4	0 36.9	0 39.2	2 43.3	0 25.2	1 43.8	9 27.8
22	15 57 17.9	0 .0	0 .0	3 9.6	0 .8	0 48.0	0 38.3	0 39.0	2 42.7	0 25.2	1 43.7	9 27.3
25	16 9 7.6	0 .0	0 .0	4 53.1	0N30.5	1 10.9	0 39.7	0 38.7	2 42.1	0 25.2	1 43.6	9 26.7
28	16 20 57.2	0 .0	0 .0	4 40.5	0 59.6	1 31.2	0 41.1	0 38.5	2 41.5	0 25.2	1 43.5	9 26.1
31	16 32 46.9	0 .0	0 .0	2 18.2	1 24.7	1 49.1	0 42.5	0 38.2	2 40.9	0 25.2	1 43.3	9 25.6

RIGHT ASCENSION

DAY	SID. TIME	☉	☊	☽	☿	♀	♂	♃	♄	♅	♆	♇
1	14 34 30.2	7♉54.5	10♒ 8.2	28♏33.1	17♈26.9	12♈47.0	27♉32.2	25♉54.4	22♎ 2.0	16♋26.7	21♎ 1.0	26♌29.3
2	14 38 26.8	8 51.8	10 5.0	12♐50.8	18 53.7	12R45.6	28 15.8	26 8.6	21R58.0	16 28.8	20R59.5	26R29.2
3	14 42 23.3	9 49.3	10 1.8	27 34.7	20 22.3	12D46.6	28 59.6	26 22.9	21 54.0	16 31.1	20 58.1	26 29.2
4	14 46 19.9	10 46.8	9 58.5	12♑22.3	21 52.7	12 49.6	29 43.3	26 37.2	21 50.1	16 33.3	20 56.7	26 29.1
5	14 50 16.4	11 44.5	9 55.3	26 52.6	23 25.0	12 54.8	0♊27.0	26 51.6	21 46.2	16 35.6	20 55.3	26 29.1
6	14 54 13.0	12 42.3	9 52.1	10♒53.2	24 59.2	13 2.1	1 10.8	27 5.9	21 42.3	16 38.0	20 53.9	26 29.1
7	14 58 9.5	13 40.3	9 48.8	24 22.5	26 35.4	13 11.4	1 54.7	27 20.3	21 38.5	16 40.4	20 52.5	26D29.2
8	15 2 6.1	14 38.4	9 45.6	7♓28.0	28 13.7	13 22.7	2 38.6	27 34.7	21 34.8	16 42.8	20 51.1	26 29.2
9	15 6 2.7	15 36.7	9 42.3	20 23.1	29 54.0	13 35.9	3 22.5	27 49.2	21 31.1	16 45.3	20 49.8	26 29.3
10	15 9 59.2	16 35.1	9 39.1	3♈23.7	1♉36.5	13 51.0	4 6.5	28 3.6	21 27.4	16 47.8	20 48.4	26 29.4
11	15 13 55.8	17 33.7	9 35.9	16 45.4	3 21.3	14 7.8	4 50.5	28 18.1	21 23.8	16 50.4	20 47.1	26 29.6
12	15 17 52.3	18 32.4	9 32.6	0♉40.3	5 8.3	14 26.5	5 34.5	28 32.7	21 20.2	16 53.0	20 45.8	26 29.8
13	15 21 48.9	19 31.2	9 29.4	15 12.7	6 57.7	14 46.8	6 18.6	28 47.2	21 16.7	16 55.7	20 44.5	26 30.0
14	15 25 45.4	20 30.2	9 26.1	0♊15.4	8 49.5	15 8.7	7 2.6	29 1.8	21 13.3	16 58.4	20 43.2	26 30.2
15	15 29 42.0	21 29.4	9 22.9	15 28.8	10 43.8	15 32.2	7 46.8	29 16.4	21 9.9	17 1.1	20 42.0	26 30.5
16	15 33 38.6	22 28.6	9 19.6	0♋26.6	12 40.5	15 57.2	8 30.9	29 31.0	21 6.6	17 3.9	20 40.7	26 30.8
17	15 37 35.1	23 28.1	9 16.4	14 44.5	14 39.7	16 23.7	9 15.1	29 45.6	21 3.3	17 6.7	20 39.5	26 31.1
18	15 41 31.7	24 27.6	9 13.2	28 8.8	16 41.5	16 51.5	9 59.3	0♊ .3	21 .2	17 9.5	20 38.3	26 31.4
19	15 45 28.2	25 27.3	9 9.9	10♌37.7	18 45.6	17 20.7	10 43.5	0 14.9	20 57.0	17 12.4	20 37.1	26 31.8
20	15 49 24.8	26 27.1	9 6.7	22 18.1	20 52.2	17 51.2	11 27.7	0 29.6	20 54.0	17 15.4	20 35.9	26 32.2
21	15 53 21.3	27 27.1	9 3.4	3♍22.4	23 1.1	18 22.9	12 11.9	0 44.3	20 51.0	17 18.3	20 34.8	26 32.6
22	15 57 17.9	28 27.2	9 .2	14 4.9	25 12.1	18 55.9	12 56.2	0 59.0	20 48.1	17 21.3	20 33.6	26 33.1
23	16 1 14.5	29 27.4	8 56.9	24 40.8	27 25.2	19 30.0	13 40.4	1 13.7	20 45.2	17 24.4	20 32.5	26 33.6
24	16 5 11.0	0♊27.8	8 53.7	5♎25.2	29 40.1	20 5.3	14 24.8	1 28.4	20 42.5	17 27.5	20 31.5	26 34.2
25	16 9 7.6	1 28.3	8 50.4	16 33.0	1♊56.5	20 41.6	15 9.0	1 43.2	20 39.8	17 30.6	20 30.4	26 34.7
26	16 13 4.1	2 28.9	8 47.2	28 18.2	4 14.1	21 18.9	15 53.3	1 57.9	20 37.2	17 33.7	20 29.4	26 35.3
27	16 17 .7	3 29.6	8 43.9	10♏51.9	6 32.7	21 57.3	16 37.6	2 12.6	20 34.6	17 36.9	20 28.3	26 35.9
28	16 20 57.2	4 30.4	8 40.7	24 20.0	8 52.0	22 36.6	17 21.9	2 27.4	20 32.1	17 40.1	20 27.3	26 36.5
29	16 24 53.8	5 31.3	8 37.5	8♐38.6	11 11.5	23 16.8	18 6.2	2 42.1	20 29.7	17 43.3	20 26.3	26 37.2
30	16 28 50.4	6 32.4	8 34.2	23 32.2	13 30.9	23 58.0	18 50.5	2 56.9	20 27.4	17 46.6	20 25.4	26 37.9
31	16 32 46.9	7 33.6	8 31.0	8♑36.3	15 49.9	24 40.1	19 34.8	3 11.6	20 25.2	17 49.9	20 24.5	26 38.6

DECLINATION

DAY	SID. TIME	☉	☊	☽	☿	♀	♂	♃	♄	♅	♆	♇
1	14 34 30.2	14N55.3	0S19.2	24S58.0	4N31.2	8N53.6	20N34.2	19N 3.3	6S16.1	23N .7	6S58.3	23N34.0
4	14 46 19.9	15 49.0	0 19.3	25 9.5	6 29.8	8 9.9	21 1.8	19 12.8	6 11.8	23 .0	6 56.6	23 33.5
7	14 58 9.5	16 40.3	0 19.3	12 44.6	8 35.6	7 36.4	21 27.6	19 22.1	6 7.6	22 59.2	6 55.0	23 32.8
10	15 9 59.2	17 29.2	0 19.3	6N 9.8	10 47.0	7 12.9	21 51.7	19 31.4	6 3.6	22 58.4	6 53.5	23 32.1
13	15 21 48.9	18 15.4	0 19.4	22 12.6	13 1.9	6 59.1	22 14.0	19 40.4	5 59.8	22 57.5	6 52.0	23 31.3
16	15 33 38.6	18 58.9	0 19.4	26 22.5	15 17.5	6 54.4	22 34.5	19 49.3	5 56.3	22 56.6	6 50.6	23 30.4
19	15 45 28.2	19 39.5	0 19.5	17 58.9	17 30.2	6 57.8	22 53.1	19 58.0	5 53.0	22 55.7	6 49.2	23 29.4
22	15 57 17.9	20 17.1	0 19.5	3 21.8	19 35.4	7 8.8	23 9.8	20 6.5	5 50.0	22 54.7	6 47.9	23 28.4
25	16 9 7.6	20 51.5	0 19.5	12S19.7	21 27.7	7 26.4	23 24.6	20 14.8	5 47.4	22 53.6	6 46.7	23 27.2
28	16 20 57.2	21 22.7	0 19.6	24 13.0	23 1.7	7 49.9	23 37.6	20 22.9	5 45.0	22 52.5	6 45.6	23 26.0
31	16 32 46.9	21 50.6	0 19.6	25 31.1	24 13.5	8 18.6	23 48.6	20 30.8	5 42.9	22 51.4	6 44.6	23 24.8

JUNE 1953

LONGITUDE

DAY	EPHEM. SID. TIME h m s	☉ ° ′	☊ ° ′	☽ ° ′	☿ ° ′	♀ ° ′	♂ ° ′	♃ ° ′	♄ ° ′	♅ ° ′	♆ ° ′	♇ ° ′
1	16 36 43.5	10♊12.4	6♒ 5.0	21♑29.4	19♊12.9	26♈36.6	21♊ 9.1	5♊14.8	20♎58.3	16♋26.5	21♎21.9	20♌59.9
2	16 40 40.0	11 9.9	6 1.8	5♒21.2	21 18.3	27 21.0	21 49.7	5 28.9	20 R 56.1	16 29.6	21 R 21.0	21 .7
3	16 44 36.6	12 7.3	5 58.6	19 19.9	23 21.9	28 6.2	22 30.3	5 42.9	20 54.1	16 32.7	21 20.1	21 1.5
4	16 48 33.1	13 4.8	5 55.4	3♓24.3	25 23.5	28 52.3	23 10.8	5 56.9	20 52.1	16 35.9	21 19.2	21 2.4
5	16 52 29.7	14 2.2	5 52.3	17 33.4	27 23.0	29 39.2	23 51.3	6 10.9	20 50.3	16 39.1	21 18.4	21 3.3
6	16 56 26.3	14 59.6	5 49.1	1♈45.6	29 20.3	0♉26.9	24 31.8	6 24.9	20 48.5	16 42.3	21 17.5	21 4.2
7	17 0 22.8	15 57.1	5 45.9	15 59.1	1♋15.3	1 15.4	25 12.2	6 38.9	20 46.8	16 45.5	21 16.7	21 5.2
8	17 4 19.4	16 54.5	5 42.7	0♉10.9	3 7.9	2 4.5	25 52.6	6 52.9	20 45.2	16 48.8	21 16.0	21 6.1
9	17 8 15.9	17 51.9	5 39.6	14 17.3	4 58.1	2 54.4	26 32.9	7 6.8	20 43.7	16 52.1	21 15.2	21 7.1
10	17 12 12.5	18 49.3	5 36.4	28 14.4	6 45.8	3 45.0	27 13.2	7 20.7	20 42.3	16 55.4	21 14.5	21 8.2
11	17 16 9.1	19 46.6	5 33.2	11♊58.1	8 31.0	4 36.1	27 53.5	7 34.6	20 41.0	16 58.7	21 13.8	21 9.2
12	17 20 5.6	20 44.0	5 30.0	25 25.2	10 13.7	5 27.9	28 33.8	7 48.5	20 39.8	17 2.1	21 13.2	21 10.3
13	17 24 2.2	21 41.4	5 26.9	8♋33.7	11 53.8	6 20.3	29 14.0	8 2.4	20 38.7	17 5.4	21 12.5	21 11.4
14	17 27 58.7	22 38.7	5 23.7	21 23.1	13 31.4	7 13.4	29 54.2	8 16.3	20 37.7	17 8.8	21 12.0	21 12.5
15	17 31 55.3	23 36.1	5 20.5	3♌54.1	15 6.3	8 6.9	0♋34.3	8 30.1	20 36.8	17 12.3	21 11.4	21 13.7
16	17 35 51.8	24 33.4	5 17.3	16 9.3	16 38.7	9 .9	1 14.4	8 43.9	20 36.0	17 15.7	21 10.9	21 14.8
17	17 39 48.4	25 30.7	5 14.2	28 11.9	18 8.4	9 55.5	1 54.5	8 57.6	20 35.3	17 19.1	21 10.4	21 16.0
18	17 43 45.0	26 28.0	5 11.0	10♍ 6.3	19 35.4	10 50.6	2 34.5	9 11.4	20 34.7	17 22.6	21 9.9	21 17.2
19	17 47 41.5	27 25.2	5 7.8	21 57.2	20 59.8	11 46.1	3 14.5	9 25.0	20 34.2	17 26.0	21 9.4	21 18.4
20	17 51 38.1	28 22.5	5 4.6	3♎49.6	22 21.5	12 42.1	3 54.5	9 38.7	20 33.8	17 29.5	21 9.0	21 19.7
21	17 55 34.6	29 19.8	5 1.4	15 48.4	23 40.4	13 38.5	4 34.4	9 52.4	20 33.4	17 33.0	21 8.6	21 20.9
22	17 59 31.2	0♋17.0	4 58.3	27 58.1	24 56.5	14 35.4	5 14.3	10 6.0	20 33.2	17 36.5	21 8.3	21 22.2
23	18 3 27.8	1 14.2	4 55.1	10♏22.8	26 9.7	15 32.7	5 54.1	10 19.5	20 33.1	17 40.1	21 8.0	21 23.5
24	18 7 24.3	2 11.4	4 51.9	23 5.3	27 20.1	16 30.5	6 34.0	10 33.1	20 33.1	17 43.6	21 7.7	21 24.9
25	18 11 20.9	3 8.7	4 48.7	6♐ 7.4	28 27.5	17 28.6	7 13.7	10 46.6	20 D 33.2	17 47.1	21 7.4	21 26.2
26	18 15 17.4	4 5.9	4 45.6	19 29.4	29 31.8	18 27.1	7 53.5	11 .0	20 33.3	17 50.7	21 7.2	21 27.6
27	18 19 14.0	5 3.0	4 42.4	3♑10.1	0♌33.0	19 25.9	8 33.2	11 13.4	20 33.6	17 54.3	21 7.0	21 29.0
28	18 23 10.5	6 .2	4 39.2	17 6.8	1 31.0	20 25.2	9 12.9	11 26.8	20 34.0	17 57.9	21 6.8	21 30.4
29	18 27 7.1	6 57.4	4 36.0	1♒15.9	2 25.6	21 24.8	9 52.6	11 40.2	20 34.5	18 1.4	21 6.7	21 31.8
30	18 31 3.7	7 54.6	4 32.9	15 33.3	3 16.9	22 24.7	10 32.2	11 53.5	20 35.0	18 5.0	21 6.6	21 33.2

LATITUDE

DAY	EPHEM. SID. TIME	☉	☊	☽	☿	♀	♂	♃	♄	♅	♆	♇
1	16 36 43.5	0 .0	0 .0	1S 9.2	1N31.9	1S54.5	0N42.9	0S38.2	2N40.7	0N25.1	1N43.3	9N25.4
4	16 48 33.1	0 .0	0 .0	2N29.1	1 49.4	2 9.4	0 44.2	0 38.0	2 40.0	0 25.1	1 43.2	9 24.8
7	17 0 22.8	0 .0	0 .0	4 52.0	2 .2	2 22.2	0 45.5	0 37.7	2 39.3	0 25.1	1 43.0	9 24.3
10	17 12 12.5	0 .0	0 .0	4 41.1	2 4.3	2 33.0	0 46.7	0 37.5	2 38.5	0 25.1	1 42.9	9 23.8
13	17 24 2.2	0 .0	0 .0	2 12.4	2 1.5	2 41.9	0 47.9	0 37.4	2 37.8	0 25.1	1 42.8	9 23.3
16	17 35 51.8	0 .0	0 .0	1S 6.9	1 52.2	2 49.1	0 49.1	0 37.2	2 37.1	0 25.1	1 42.6	9 22.9
19	17 47 41.5	0 .0	0 .0	3 52.5	1 36.7	2 54.6	0 50.3	0 37.0	2 36.3	0 25.1	1 42.5	9 22.4
22	17 59 31.2	0 .0	0 .0	5 10.3	1 15.3	2 58.6	0 51.4	0 36.9	2 35.5	0 25.1	1 42.3	9 22.0
25	18 11 20.9	0 .0	0 .0	4 23.4	0 48.4	3 1.1	0 52.5	0 36.7	2 34.7	0 25.1	1 42.2	9 21.6
28	18 23 10.5	0 .0	0 .0	1 28.1	0 16.5	3 2.3	0 53.5	0 36.6	2 33.9	0 25.1	1 42.0	9 21.3

RIGHT ASCENSION

DAY	EPHEM. SID. TIME	☉	☊	☽	☿	♀	♂	♃	♄	♅	♆	♇
1	16 36 43.5	8♊34.8	8♒27.7	23♑25.3	18♊ 8.0	25♈23.0	20♊19.1	3♊26.3	20♎23.0	17♋53.2	20♎23.5	26♌39.3
2	16 40 40.0	9 36.2	8 24.5	7♒41.6	20 25.1	26 6.7	21 3.3	3 41.1	20 R 20.9	17 56.5	20 R 22.7	26 40.1
3	16 44 36.6	10 37.7	8 21.2	21 19.8	22 40.6	26 51.2	21 47.6	3 55.8	20 19.0	17 59.9	20 21.8	26 40.9
4	16 48 33.1	11 39.3	8 18.0	4♓25.4	24 54.5	27 36.5	22 31.9	4 10.6	20 17.0	18 3.3	20 21.0	26 41.7
5	16 52 29.7	12 41.0	8 14.7	17 11.3	27 6.4	28 22.5	23 16.1	4 25.3	20 15.2	18 6.7	20 20.1	26 42.5
6	16 56 26.3	13 42.7	8 11.4	29 53.6	29 16.1	29 9.3	24 .4	4 40.0	20 13.5	18 10.2	20 19.4	26 43.4
7	17 0 22.8	14 44.6	8 8.2	12♈49.2	1♋23.3	29 56.8	24 44.6	4 54.7	20 11.8	18 13.7	20 18.6	26 44.3
8	17 4 19.4	15 46.5	8 4.9	26 12.8	3 28.0	0♉44.9	25 28.8	5 9.5	20 10.2	18 17.2	20 17.8	26 45.2
9	17 8 15.9	16 48.5	8 1.7	10♉13.5	5 29.9	1 33.8	26 13.0	5 24.2	20 8.8	18 20.7	20 17.1	26 46.1
10	17 12 12.5	17 50.6	7 58.4	24 50.7	7 28.9	2 23.2	26 57.2	5 38.9	20 7.4	18 24.3	20 16.5	26 47.1
11	17 16 9.1	18 52.7	7 55.2	9♊51.8	9 25.0	3 13.3	27 41.3	5 53.5	20 6.1	18 27.9	20 15.8	26 48.1
12	17 20 5.6	19 54.9	7 51.9	24 53.2	11 18.0	4 4.0	28 25.4	6 8.2	20 4.8	18 31.5	20 15.2	26 49.1
13	17 24 2.2	20 57.2	7 48.7	9♋28.6	13 7.9	4 55.3	29 9.5	6 22.8	20 3.7	18 35.1	20 14.6	26 50.2
14	17 27 58.7	21 59.5	7 45.4	23 18.1	14 54.6	5 47.2	29 53.6	6 37.5	20 2.7	18 38.8	20 14.0	26 51.3
15	17 31 55.3	23 1.8	7 42.1	6♌13.2	16 38.0	6 39.6	0♋37.7	6 52.1	20 1.8	18 42.4	20 13.5	26 52.4
16	17 35 51.8	24 4.2	7 38.9	18 16.2	18 18.1	7 32.6	1 21.6	7 6.7	20 .9	18 46.1	20 13.0	26 53.5
17	17 39 48.4	25 6.6	7 35.6	29 36.7	19 54.9	8 26.2	2 5.6	7 21.3	20 .2	18 49.8	20 12.5	26 54.6
18	17 43 45.0	26 8.9	7 32.4	10♍28.0	21 28.3	9 20.2	2 49.5	7 35.8	19 59.5	18 53.5	20 12.0	26 55.8
19	17 47 41.5	27 11.3	7 29.1	21 .9	22 58.3	10 14.8	3 33.3	7 50.4	19 58.9	18 57.3	20 11.6	26 57.0
20	17 51 38.1	28 13.7	7 25.9	1♎42.9	24 24.8	11 10.0	4 17.2	8 4.9	19 58.4	19 1.0	20 11.2	26 58.2
21	17 55 34.6	29 16.1	7 22.6	12 37.3	25 47.9	12 5.6	5 .9	8 19.3	19 58.0	19 4.8	20 10.8	26 59.4
22	17 59 31.2	0♋18.5	7 19.3	24 3.3	27 7.5	13 1.8	5 44.6	8 33.8	19 57.7	19 8.5	20 10.4	27 .7
23	18 3 27.8	1 20.9	7 16.1	6♏14.5	28 23.6	13 58.4	6 28.3	8 48.2	19 57.5	19 12.3	20 10.1	27 1.9
24	18 7 24.3	2 23.3	7 12.8	19 20.8	29 36.1	14 55.5	7 11.9	9 2.5	19 57.4	19 16.1	20 9.8	27 3.2
25	18 11 20.9	3 25.6	7 9.6	3♐24.1	0♌44.9	15 53.2	7 55.5	9 16.9	19 57.4	19 19.9	20 9.5	27 4.5
26	18 15 17.4	4 27.9	7 6.3	18 14.9	1 50.1	16 51.3	8 38.9	9 31.2	19 D 57.5	19 23.8	20 9.3	27 5.9
27	18 19 14.0	5 30.2	7 3.0	3♑31.4	2 51.6	17 49.8	9 22.4	9 45.5	19 57.6	19 27.6	20 9.1	27 7.2
28	18 23 10.5	6 32.4	6 59.8	18 45.3	3 49.3	18 48.9	10 5.8	9 59.7	19 57.9	19 31.4	20 8.9	27 8.6
29	18 27 7.1	7 34.6	6 56.5	3♒32.6	4 43.2	19 48.4	10 49.1	10 13.9	19 58.2	19 35.3	20 8.8	27 10.0
30	18 31 3.7	8 36.7	6 53.2	17 40.7	5 33.2	20 48.4	11 32.3	10 28.1	19 58.7	19 39.2	20 8.7	27 11.4

DECLINATION

DAY	EPHEM. SID. TIME	☉	☊	☽	☿	♀	♂	♃	♄	♅	♆	♇
1	16 36 43.5	21N59.2	0S19.6	22S52.1	24N32.1	8N29.1	23N51.9	20N33.4	5S42.3	22N51.0	6S44.3	23N24.3
4	16 48 33.1	22 22.5	0 19.7	7 56.6	25 11.3	9 3.6	24 .4	20 41.0	5 40.6	22 49.9	6 43.4	23 23.0
7	17 0 22.8	22 42.3	0 19.7	10N46.7	25 26.7	9 41.5	24 7.0	20 48.4	5 39.3	22 48.7	6 42.6	23 21.6
10	17 12 12.5	22 58.5	0 19.8	24 20.3	25 20.6	10 22.3	24 11.8	20 55.5	5 38.3	22 47.4	6 41.9	23 20.1
13	17 24 2.2	23 11.1	0 19.8	25 22.3	24 55.9	11 5.3	24 14.6	21 2.4	5 37.6	22 46.1	6 41.3	23 18.6
16	17 35 51.8	23 20.1	0 19.8	14 56.1	24 15.9	11 50.0	24 15.6	21 9.1	5 37.3	22 44.8	6 40.8	23 17.0
19	17 47 41.5	23 25.3	0 19.9	0S22.2	23 23.9	12 35.9	24 14.7	21 15.6	5 37.3	22 43.5	6 40.4	23 15.4
22	17 59 31.2	23 26.7	0 19.9	15 34.7	22 23.0	13 22.5	24 11.9	21 21.8	5 37.7	22 42.1	6 40.1	23 13.7
25	18 11 20.9	23 24.5	0 20.0	25 39.5	21 16.0	14 9.2	24 7.4	21 27.7	5 38.4	22 40.7	6 39.9	23 12.0
28	18 23 10.5	23 18.6	0 20.0	23 48.4	20 5.8	14 55.7	24 1.0	21 33.5	5 39.4	22 39.3	6 39.8	23 10.3

JULY 1953

DAY	EPHEM. SID. TIME h m s	☉	☊	☽	☿	♀	♂	♃	♄	♅	♆	♇
		LONGITUDE ° ′	° ′	° ′	° ′	° ′	° ′	° ′	° ′	° ′	° ′	° ′
1	18 35 .2	8♋51.8	4♒29.7	29♒54.6	4♌ 4.6	23♉25.0	11♋11.8	12♊ 6.7	20♎35.7	18♋ 8.6	21♎ 6.5	21♌34.7
2	18 38 56.8	9 49.0	4 26.5	14♓16.1	4 48.7	24 25.6	11 51.3	12 19.9	20 36.5	18 12.3	21R 6.4	21 36.2
3	18 42 53.3	10 46.2	4 23.3	28 34.4	5 29.0	25 26.5	12 30.9	12 33.1	20 37.4	18 15.9	21 6.4	21 37.7
4	18 46 49.9	11 43.4	4 20.2	12♈46.9	6 5.5	26 27.7	13 10.4	12 46.2	20 38.3	18 19.5	21D 6.5	21 39.2
5	18 50 46.5	12 40.7	4 17.0	26 51.5	6 37.9	27 29.2	13 49.9	12 59.3	20 39.4	18 23.2	21 6.6	21 40.8
6	18 54 43.0	13 37.9	4 13.8	10♉46.4	7 6.2	28 31.0	14 29.4	13 12.4	20 40.6	18 26.8	21 6.7	21 42.3
7	18 58 39.6	14 35.1	4 10.6	24 30.1	7 30.2	29 33.1	15 8.8	13 25.3	20 41.9	18 30.5	21 6.8	21 43.9
8	19 2 36.1	15 32.3	4 7.5	8♊ 1.4	7 49.8	0♊35.4	15 48.2	13 38.3	20 43.2	18 34.1	21 6.9	21 45.5
9	19 6 32.7	16 29.5	4 4.3	21 19.1	8 4.9	1 38.0	16 27.6	13 51.1	20 44.7	18 37.8	21 7.1	21 47.1
10	19 10 29.2	17 26.8	4 1.1	4♋22.4	8 15.4	2 40.8	17 6.9	14 4.0	20 46.3	18 41.4	21 7.3	21 48.7
11	19 14 25.8	18 24.0	3 57.9	17 11.1	8 21.3	3 43.9	17 46.2	14 16.7	20 47.9	18 45.0	21 7.6	21 50.3
12	19 18 22.4	19 21.2	3 54.7	29 45.3	8 22.3	4 47.2	18 25.5	14 29.4	20 49.7	18 48.7	21 7.9	21 51.9
13	19 22 18.9	20 18.5	3 51.6	12♌ 6.0	8R18.6	5 50.7	19 4.8	14 42.1	20 51.5	18 52.3	21 8.2	21 53.6
14	19 26 15.5	21 15.7	3 48.4	24 14.8	8 10.1	6 54.5	19 44.0	14 54.6	20 53.5	18 56.0	21 8.5	21 55.3
15	19 30 12.0	22 13.0	3 45.2	6♍14.3	7 56.9	7 58.4	20 23.2	15 7.2	20 55.5	18 59.6	21 8.9	21 57.0
16	19 34 8.6	23 10.2	3 42.0	18 7.4	7 39.1	9 2.6	21 2.4	15 19.6	20 57.6	19 3.3	21 9.3	21 58.6
17	19 38 5.2	24 7.5	3 38.9	29 58.0	7 16.9	10 7.0	21 41.5	15 32.0	20 59.9	19 6.9	21 9.8	22 .4
18	19 42 1.7	25 4.7	3 35.7	11♎50.1	6 50.5	11 11.6	22 20.6	15 44.3	21 2.2	19 10.6	21 10.2	22 2.1
19	19 45 58.3	26 2.0	3 32.5	23 48.4	6 20.2	12 16.4	22 59.7	15 56.6	21 4.6	19 14.2	21 10.7	22 3.8
20	19 49 54.8	26 59.2	3 29.3	5♏57.4	5 46.5	13 21.4	23 38.8	16 8.8	21 7.1	19 17.8	21 11.3	22 5.5
21	19 53 51.4	27 56.5	3 26.2	18 21.5	5 9.7	14 26.6	24 17.8	16 20.9	21 9.7	19 21.4	21 11.9	22 7.3
22	19 57 47.9	28 53.8	3 23.0	1♐ 4.7	4 30.5	15 31.9	24 56.8	16 32.9	21 12.4	19 25.0	21 12.5	22 9.1
23	20 1 44.5	29 51.0	3 19.8	14 9.9	3 49.5	16 37.4	25 35.8	16 44.9	21 15.2	19 28.7	21 13.1	22 10.8
24	20 5 41.1	0♌48.3	3 16.6	27 38.8	3 7.2	17 43.2	26 14.7	16 56.8	21 18.0	19 32.2	21 13.8	22 12.6
25	20 9 37.6	1 45.6	3 13.4	11♑31.3	2 24.5	18 49.1	26 53.7	17 8.6	21 21.0	19 35.8	21 14.5	22 14.4
26	20 13 34.2	2 43.0	3 10.3	25 45.5	1 42.1	19 55.2	27 32.6	17 20.4	21 24.1	19 39.5	21 15.2	22 16.3
27	20 17 30.7	3 40.3	3 7.1	10♒16.9	1 .8	21 1.4	28 11.5	17 32.1	21 27.2	19 43.0	21 16.0	22 18.1
28	20 21 27.3	4 37.6	3 3.9	24 59.9	0 21.3	22 7.8	28 50.3	17 43.7	21 30.4	19 46.6	21 16.8	22 19.9
29	20 25 23.8	5 34.9	3 .7	9♓47.4	29♋44.3	23 14.4	29 29.2	17 55.2	21 33.7	19 50.1	21 17.6	22 21.7
30	20 29 20.4	6 32.3	2 57.6	24 32.5	29 10.7	24 21.1	0♌ 8.0	18 6.7	21 37.1	19 53.7	21 18.4	22 23.5
31	20 33 17.0	7 29.6	2 54.4	9♈ 8.9	28 41.0	25 28.0	0 46.8	18 18.0	21 40.6	19 57.2	21 19.3	22 25.4
		LATITUDE										
1	18 35 .2	0 .0	0 .0	2N20.8	0S20.0	3S 2.2	0N54.6	0S36.4	2N33.1	0N25.1	1N41.9	9N20.9
4	18 46 49.9	0 .0	0 .0	4 54.8	1 .3	3 .8	0 55.6	0 36.3	2 32.4	0 25.1	1 41.7	9 20.6
7	18 58 39.6	0 .0	0 .0	4 53.9	1 43.5	2 58.4	0 56.6	0 36.2	2 31.6	0 25.2	1 41.6	9 20.3
10	19 10 29.2	0 .0	0 .0	2 32.8	2 28.2	2 54.9	0 57.5	0 36.1	2 30.8	0 25.2	1 41.4	9 20.1
13	19 22 18.9	0 .0	0 .0	0S48.9	3 12.2	2 50.5	0 58.4	0 36.0	2 30.0	0 25.2	1 41.2	9 19.9
16	19 34 8.6	0 .0	0 .0	3 43.8	3 52.8	2 45.2	0 59.3	0 35.9	2 29.2	0 25.2	1 41.1	9 19.7
19	19 45 58.3	0 .0	0 .0	5 12.7	4 26.4	2 39.1	1 .2	0 35.8	2 28.5	0 25.3	1 40.9	9 19.5
22	19 57 47.9	0 .0	0 .0	4 40.7	4 49.2	2 32.3	1 1.0	0 35.7	2 27.7	0 25.3	1 40.8	9 19.4
25	20 9 37.6	0 .0	0 .0	1 57.8	4 58.1	2 24.7	1 1.8	0 35.6	2 27.0	0 25.3	1 40.6	9 19.4
28	20 21 27.3	0 .0	0 .0	1N57.7	4 51.2	2 16.6	1 2.6	0 35.6	2 26.2	0 25.4	1 40.5	9 19.3
31	20 33 17.0	0 .0	0 .0	4 49.5	4 29.3	2 7.9	1 3.4	0 35.5	2 25.5	0 25.4	1 40.3	9 19.3
		RIGHT ASCENSION										
1	18 35 .2	9♋38.8	6♒50.0	1♓10.2	6♌19.2	21♉48.9	12♋15.5	10♊42.2	19♎59.2	19♋43.0	20♎ 8.6	27♌12.9
2	18 38 56.8	10 40.8	6 46.7	14 11.1	7 1.1	22 49.8	12 58.6	10 56.3	19 59.8	19 46.9	20R 8.5	27 14.3
3	18 42 53.3	11 42.8	6 43.4	26 58.5	7 38.9	23 51.2	13 41.7	11 10.4	20 .5	19 50.8	20 8.5	27 15.8
4	18 46 49.9	12 44.7	6 40.2	9♈49.1	8 12.5	24 53.0	14 24.7	11 24.4	20 1.3	19 54.7	20 8.5	27 17.3
5	18 50 46.5	13 46.6	6 36.9	22 58.4	8 41.8	25 55.3	15 7.7	11 38.4	20 2.3	19 58.6	20D 8.6	27 18.8
6	18 54 43.0	14 48.4	6 33.6	6♉37.4	9 6.7	26 58.0	15 50.5	11 52.3	20 3.2	20 2.5	20 8.6	27 20.4
7	18 58 39.6	15 50.0	6 30.4	20 50.0	9 27.2	28 1.1	16 33.3	12 6.2	20 4.3	20 6.5	20 8.7	27 21.9
8	19 2 36.1	16 51.6	6 27.1	5♊29.2	9 43.0	29 4.6	17 16.0	12 20.0	20 5.5	20 10.4	20 8.9	27 23.5
9	19 6 32.7	17 53.1	6 23.8	20 17.6	9 54.3	0♊ 8.5	17 58.6	12 33.7	20 6.8	20 14.3	20 9.0	27 25.1
10	19 10 29.2	18 54.5	6 20.6	4♋51.5	10 .8	1 12.9	18 41.2	12 47.4	20 8.1	20 18.2	20 9.2	27 26.7
11	19 14 25.8	19 55.8	6 17.3	18 49.9	10 2.7	2 17.7	19 23.6	13 1.1	20 9.6	20 22.1	20 9.4	27 28.3
12	19 18 22.4	20 57.0	6 14.0	1♌60.0	9R59.9	3 22.8	20 6.0	13 14.7	20 11.1	20 26.0	20 9.6	27 29.9
13	19 22 18.9	21 58.1	6 10.7	14 19.6	9 52.3	4 28.4	20 48.3	13 28.2	20 12.7	20 29.9	20 9.9	27 31.5
14	19 26 15.5	22 59.0	6 7.5	25 54.7	9 40.1	5 34.3	21 30.5	13 41.7	20 14.4	20 33.8	20 10.2	27 33.2
15	19 30 12.0	23 59.8	6 4.2	6♍56.2	9 23.4	6 40.6	22 12.7	13 55.1	20 16.2	20 37.7	20 10.6	27 34.9
16	19 34 8.6	25 .5	6 .9	17 37.4	9 2.3	7 47.3	22 54.7	14 8.5	20 18.1	20 41.7	20 10.9	27 36.6
17	19 38 5.2	26 1.1	5 57.7	28 12.5	8 36.9	8 54.4	23 36.7	14 21.8	20 20.1	20 45.6	20 11.3	27 38.3
18	19 42 1.7	27 1.6	5 54.4	8♎56.3	8 7.7	10 1.8	24 18.5	14 35.0	20 22.2	20 49.5	20 11.7	27 40.0
19	19 45 58.3	28 1.9	5 51.1	20 3.4	7 34.9	11 9.5	25 .3	14 48.1	20 24.3	20 53.3	20 12.2	27 41.7
20	19 49 54.8	29 2.0	5 47.8	1♏48.1	6 59.0	12 17.7	25 42.0	15 1.2	20 26.6	20 57.2	20 12.7	27 43.4
21	19 53 51.4	0♌ 2.0	5 44.6	14 22.4	6 20.4	13 26.1	26 23.6	15 14.2	20 28.9	21 1.1	20 13.2	27 45.2
22	19 57 47.9	1 1.9	5 41.3	27 53.0	5 39.6	14 35.0	27 5.1	15 27.2	20 31.3	21 5.0	20 13.7	27 47.0
23	20 1 44.5	2 1.6	5 38.0	12♐17.7	4 57.4	15 44.1	27 46.5	15 40.0	20 33.8	21 8.8	20 14.3	27 48.7
24	20 5 41.1	3 1.2	5 34.7	27 22.4	4 14.4	16 53.6	28 27.8	15 52.8	20 36.4	21 12.7	20 14.9	27 50.5
25	20 9 37.6	4 .6	5 31.5	12♑42.9	3 31.2	18 3.3	29 9.0	16 5.5	20 39.0	21 16.5	20 15.5	27 52.3
26	20 13 34.2	4 60.0	5 28.2	27 52.8	2 48.7	19 13.5	29 50.2	16 18.2	20 41.8	21 20.4	20 16.2	27 54.2
27	20 17 30.7	5 59.1	5 24.9	12♒32.9	2 7.5	20 23.9	0♌31.2	16 30.8	20 44.7	21 24.2	20 16.9	27 56.0
28	20 21 27.3	6 58.1	5 21.6	26 36.7	1 28.5	21 34.6	1 12.1	16 43.2	20 47.6	21 28.1	20 17.6	27 57.8
29	20 25 23.8	7 56.9	5 18.3	10♓ 8.8	0 52.4	22 45.6	1 52.9	16 55.6	20 50.6	21 31.9	20 18.4	27 59.6
30	20 29 20.4	8 55.6	5 15.1	23 21.2	0 19.8	23 56.8	2 33.7	17 7.9	20 53.6	21 35.6	20 19.2	28 1.5
31	20 33 17.0	9 54.1	5 11.8	6♈29.2	29♋51.5	25 8.4	3 14.3	17 20.2	20 56.8	21 39.4	20 20.0	28 3.3
		DECLINATION										
1	18 35 .2	23N 9.0	0S20.0	9S18.6	18N55.1	15N41.5	23N52.9	21N38.9	5S40.8	22N37.9	6S39.8	23N 8.5
4	18 46 49.9	22 55.7	0 20.1	9N34.3	17 46.9	16 26.2	23 43.0	21 44.2	5 42.5	22 36.5	6 40.0	23 6.7
7	18 58 39.6	22 38.9	0 20.1	23 38.8	16 43.9	17 9.3	23 31.4	21 49.2	5 44.6	22 35.0	6 40.2	23 4.9
10	19 10 29.2	22 18.5	0 20.2	25 55.1	15 49.2	17 50.5	23 18.1	21 53.9	5 46.9	22 33.5	6 40.6	23 3.1
13	19 22 18.9	21 54.6	0 20.2	16 23.3	15 5.9	18 29.3	23 3.2	21 58.4	5 49.6	22 32.0	6 41.1	23 1.2
16	19 34 8.6	21 27.4	0 20.2	1 15.7	14 36.6	19 5.4	22 46.6	22 2.7	5 52.6	22 30.5	6 41.6	22 59.3
19	19 45 58.3	20 56.9	0 20.3	14S 4.8	14 23.5	19 38.5	22 28.5	22 6.7	5 55.9	22 29.0	6 42.3	22 57.5
22	19 57 47.9	20 23.2	0 20.3	24 57.4	14 27.3	20 8.3	22 8.9	22 10.5	5 59.5	22 27.5	6 43.1	22 55.6
25	20 9 37.6	19 46.4	0 20.4	24 54.2	14 47.2	20 34.3	21 47.8	22 14.0	6 3.4	22 26.0	6 44.0	22 53.7
28	20 21 27.3	19 6.7	0 20.4	11 20.7	15 20.2	20 56.4	21 25.2	22 17.4	6 7.6	22 24.4	6 45.0	22 51.8
31	20 33 17.0	18 24.2	0 20.4	8N 3.6	16 2.1	21 14.3	21 1.3	22 20.5	6 12.0	22 22.9	6 46.1	22 50.0

AUGUST 1953

LONGITUDE

DAY	EPHEM. SID. TIME h m s	☉ ° ′	☊ ° ′	☽ ° ′	☿ ° ′	♀ ° ′	♂ ° ′	♃ ° ′	♄ ° ′	♅ ° ′	♆ ° ′	♇ ° ′
1	20 37 13.5	8♌27.0	2♒51.2	23♈31.7	28♋15.8	26♊35.1	1♌25.5	18♊29.3	21♎44.1	20♋ .7	21♎20.2	22♌27.2
2	20 41 10.1	9 24.4	2 48.0	7♉37.8	27 R 55.7	27 42.3	2 4.3	18 40.5	21 47.8	20 4.2	21 21.2	22 29.1
3	20 45 6.6	10 21.9	2 44.9	21 25.8	27 41.2	28 49.6	2 43.0	18 51.5	21 51.5	20 7.7	21 22.1	22 31.0
4	20 49 3.2	11 19.3	2 41.7	4♊55.5	27 32.5	29 57.1	3 21.7	19 2.5	21 55.3	20 11.2	21 23.1	22 32.8
5	20 52 59.7	12 16.8	2 38.5	18 7.8	27 30.0	1♋ 4.8	4 .4	19 13.5	21 59.2	20 14.6	21 24.2	22 34.7
6	20 56 56.3	13 14.3	2 35.3	1♋ 4.1	27 D 34.0	2 12.6	4 39.1	19 24.3	22 3.1	20 18.1	21 25.2	22 36.6
7	21 0 52.8	14 11.8	2 32.1	13 46.0	27 44.6	3 20.5	5 17.7	19 35.0	22 7.2	20 21.5	21 26.3	22 38.4
8	21 4 49.4	15 9.3	2 29.0	26 15.2	28 2.0	4 28.6	5 56.3	19 45.6	22 11.3	20 24.9	21 27.4	22 40.3
9	21 8 46.0	16 6.8	2 25.8	8♌33.3	28 26.2	5 36.8	6 34.9	19 56.2	22 15.5	20 28.3	21 28.6	22 42.2
10	21 12 42.5	17 4.4	2 22.6	20 41.9	28 57.1	6 45.1	7 13.5	20 6.6	22 19.8	20 31.6	21 29.7	22 44.1
11	21 16 39.1	18 2.0	2 19.4	2♍42.7	29 34.9	7 53.5	7 52.1	20 16.9	22 24.1	20 35.0	21 30.9	22 46.0
12	21 20 35.6	18 59.6	2 16.3	14 37.6	0♌19.4	9 2.1	8 30.6	20 27.1	22 28.6	20 38.3	21 32.1	22 47.9
13	21 24 32.2	19 57.2	2 13.1	26 28.7	1 10.5	10 10.8	9 9.1	20 37.2	22 33.1	20 41.6	21 33.4	22 49.8
14	21 28 28.7	20 54.8	2 9.9	8♎18.7	2 8.1	11 19.6	9 47.6	20 47.3	22 37.7	20 44.9	21 34.7	22 51.7
15	21 32 25.3	21 52.5	2 6.7	20 10.6	3 11.9	12 28.5	10 26.1	20 57.2	22 42.3	20 48.1	21 36.0	22 53.6
16	21 36 21.8	22 50.2	2 3.6	2♏ 8.2	4 21.9	13 37.6	11 4.6	21 7.0	22 47.1	20 51.4	21 37.4	22 55.5
17	21 40 18.4	23 47.9	2 .4	14 15.3	5 37.7	14 46.8	11 43.0	21 16.7	22 51.9	20 54.6	21 38.7	22 57.4
18	21 44 15.0	24 45.6	1 57.2	26 36.2	6 59.0	15 56.0	12 21.4	21 26.2	22 56.7	20 57.8	21 40.1	22 59.3
19	21 48 11.5	25 43.3	1 54.0	9♐15.3	8 25.6	17 5.4	12 59.8	21 35.7	23 1.7	21 1.0	21 41.5	23 1.2
20	21 52 8.1	26 41.1	1 50.8	22 16.5	9 57.0	18 14.9	13 38.2	21 45.0	23 6.7	21 4.1	21 43.0	23 3.1
21	21 56 4.6	27 38.8	1 47.7	5♑42.9	11 33.0	19 24.5	14 16.6	21 54.2	23 11.7	21 7.2	21 44.4	23 5.0
22	22 0 1.2	28 36.6	1 44.5	19 36.1	13 13.0	20 34.2	14 54.9	22 3.3	23 16.9	21 10.3	21 45.9	23 6.9
23	22 3 57.7	29 34.4	1 41.3	3♒55.8	14 56.6	21 44.1	15 33.2	22 12.3	23 22.1	21 13.3	21 47.4	23 8.8
24	22 7 54.3	0♍32.2	1 38.1	18 38.5	16 43.5	22 54.0	16 11.5	22 21.2	23 27.3	21 16.4	21 49.0	23 10.7
25	22 11 50.8	1 30.1	1 35.0	3♓38.5	18 33.2	24 4.0	16 49.8	22 29.9	23 32.6	21 19.3	21 50.5	23 12.6
26	22 15 47.4	2 27.9	1 31.8	18 47.1	20 25.1	25 14.2	17 28.0	22 38.5	23 38.0	21 22.3	21 52.1	23 14.5
27	22 19 43.9	3 25.8	1 28.6	3♈54.9	22 19.0	26 24.4	18 6.3	22 47.0	23 43.5	21 25.2	21 53.7	23 16.4
28	22 23 40.5	4 23.7	1 25.4	18 52.2	24 14.4	27 34.8	18 44.5	22 55.3	23 49.0	21 28.2	21 55.3	23 18.2
29	22 27 37.1	5 21.7	1 22.2	3♉31.4	26 10.9	28 45.2	19 22.7	23 3.5	23 54.5	21 31.0	21 57.0	23 20.1
30	22 31 33.6	6 19.7	1 19.1	17 47.6	28 8.1	29 55.8	20 .9	23 11.6	24 .2	21 33.9	21 58.7	23 22.0
31	22 35 30.2	7 17.7	1 15.9	1♊38.4	0♍ 5.8	1♌ 6.5	20 39.1	23 19.6	24 5.8	21 36.7	22 .4	23 23.8

LATITUDE

DAY	EPHEM. SID. TIME h m s	☉	☊	☽	☿	♀	♂	♃	♄	♅	♆	♇
1	20 37 13.5	0 .0	0 .0	5N12.5	4S19.0	2S 4.9	1N 3.6	0S35.5	2N25.3	0N25.4	1N40.3	9N19.3
4	20 49 3.2	0 .0	0 .0	4 30.1	3 41.0	1 55.6	1 4.4	0 35.4	2 24.6	0 25.5	1 40.1	9 19.4
7	21 0 52.8	0 .0	0 .0	1 46.2	2 55.4	1 46.0	1 5.1	0 35.4	2 23.9	0 25.5	1 40.0	9 19.4
10	21 12 42.5	0 .0	0 .0	1S34.7	2 6.0	1 36.0	1 5.8	0 35.4	2 23.3	0 25.6	1 39.8	9 19.5
13	21 24 32.2	0 .0	0 .0	4 12.9	1 16.4	1 25.8	1 6.4	0 35.3	2 22.6	0 25.6	1 39.7	9 19.7
16	21 36 21.8	0 .0	0 .0	5 14.9	0 29.3	1 15.4	1 7.0	0 35.3	2 22.0	0 25.7	1 39.6	9 19.9
19	21 48 11.5	0 .0	0 .0	4 14.4	0N12.7	1 4.9	1 7.7	0 35.3	2 21.4	0 25.7	1 39.4	9 20.1
22	22 0 1.2	0 .0	0 .0	1 13.7	0 47.9	0 54.3	1 8.2	0 35.2	2 20.8	0 25.8	1 39.3	9 20.4
25	22 11 50.8	0 .0	0 .0	2N39.4	1 15.0	0 43.7	1 8.8	0 35.2	2 20.3	0 25.9	1 39.2	9 20.7
28	22 23 40.5	0 .0	0 .0	5 3.0	1 33.5	0 33.2	1 9.4	0 35.2	2 19.8	0 25.9	1 39.1	9 21.1
31	22 35 30.2	0 .0	0 .0	4 33.7	1 43.8	0 22.7	1 9.9	0 35.2	2 19.3	0 26.0	1 39.0	9 21.4

RIGHT ASCENSION

DAY	EPHEM. SID. TIME h m s	☉	☊	☽	☿	♀	♂	♃	♄	♅	♆	♇
1	20 37 13.5	10♌52.5	5♒ 8.5	19♈47.6	29♋28.0	26♊20.1	3♌54.9	17♊32.3	21♎ .0	21♋43.2	20♎20.8	28♌ 5.2
2	20 41 10.1	11 50.8	5 5.2	3♉27.8	29 R 9.9	27 32.2	4 35.3	17 44.3	21 3.3	21 46.9	20 21.7	28 7.1
3	20 45 6.6	12 48.9	5 1.9	17 34.8	28 57.6	28 44.4	5 15.7	17 56.3	21 6.7	21 50.6	20 22.5	28 9.0
4	20 49 3.2	13 46.8	4 58.7	2♊ 4.6	28 51.5	29 56.9	5 55.9	18 8.1	21 10.2	21 54.4	20 23.5	28 10.8
5	20 52 59.7	14 44.6	4 55.4	16 43.4	28 D 51.9	1♋ 9.6	6 36.1	18 19.9	21 13.7	21 58.1	20 24.4	28 12.7
6	20 56 56.3	15 42.3	4 52.1	1♋11.4	28 59.1	2 22.5	7 16.1	18 31.6	21 17.3	22 1.7	20 25.4	28 14.6
7	21 0 52.8	16 39.8	4 48.8	15 9.2	29 13.2	3 35.6	7 56.1	18 43.1	21 21.0	22 5.4	20 26.4	28 16.5
8	21 4 49.4	17 37.2	4 45.5	28 23.7	29 34.4	4 48.9	8 36.0	18 54.6	21 24.8	22 9.0	20 27.4	28 18.4
9	21 8 46.0	18 34.4	4 42.2	10♌51.0	0♌ 2.7	6 2.3	9 15.7	19 6.0	21 28.6	22 12.6	20 28.4	28 20.3
10	21 12 42.5	19 31.5	4 38.9	22 34.8	0 38.1	7 15.9	9 55.4	19 17.2	21 32.5	22 16.2	20 29.5	28 22.3
11	21 16 39.1	20 28.4	4 35.7	3♍43.9	1 20.7	8 29.6	10 35.0	19 28.4	21 36.5	22 19.8	20 30.6	28 24.2
12	21 20 35.6	21 25.2	4 32.4	14 29.9	2 10.2	9 43.5	11 14.5	19 39.4	21 40.6	22 23.4	20 31.7	28 26.1
13	21 24 32.2	22 21.9	4 29.1	25 5.6	3 6.6	10 57.4	11 53.8	19 50.3	21 44.7	22 26.9	20 32.9	28 28.0
14	21 28 28.7	23 18.4	4 25.8	5♎44.3	4 9.6	12 11.5	12 33.1	20 1.1	21 48.9	22 30.4	20 34.1	28 30.0
15	21 32 25.3	24 14.7	4 22.5	16 39.4	5 19.0	13 25.6	13 12.3	20 11.8	21 53.2	22 33.9	20 35.3	28 31.9
16	21 36 21.8	25 11.0	4 19.2	28 3.9	6 34.6	14 39.9	13 51.4	20 22.4	21 57.6	22 37.4	20 36.6	28 33.9
17	21 40 18.4	26 7.1	4 15.9	10♏ 9.5	7 56.0	15 54.1	14 30.4	20 32.9	22 2.0	22 40.8	20 37.8	28 35.8
18	21 44 15.0	27 3.1	4 12.6	23 4.5	9 22.8	17 8.5	15 9.3	20 43.2	22 6.4	22 44.2	20 39.1	28 37.8
19	21 48 11.5	27 58.9	4 9.4	6♐51.0	10 54.6	18 22.8	15 48.0	20 53.5	22 11.0	22 47.6	20 40.4	28 39.7
20	21 52 8.1	28 54.6	4 6.1	21 21.9	12 30.9	19 37.3	16 26.7	21 3.5	22 15.6	22 50.9	20 41.7	28 41.6
21	21 56 4.6	29 50.2	4 2.8	6♑20.5	14 11.4	20 51.7	17 5.3	21 13.5	22 20.3	22 54.3	20 43.1	28 43.6
22	22 0 1.2	0♍45.6	3 59.5	21 24.5	15 55.3	22 6.1	17 43.8	21 23.3	22 25.0	22 57.6	20 44.4	28 45.5
23	22 3 57.7	1 41.0	3 56.2	6♒14.0	17 42.3	23 20.5	18 22.2	21 33.1	22 29.8	23 .8	20 45.8	28 47.4
24	22 7 54.3	2 36.2	3 52.9	20 37.7	19 31.9	24 35.0	19 .5	21 42.6	22 34.6	23 4.0	20 47.3	28 49.4
25	22 11 50.8	3 31.3	3 49.6	4♓35.0	21 23.4	25 49.4	19 38.7	21 52.1	22 39.5	23 7.2	20 48.7	28 51.3
26	22 15 47.4	4 26.3	3 46.3	18 13.7	23 16.3	27 3.7	20 16.8	22 1.4	22 44.5	23 10.4	20 50.2	28 53.2
27	22 19 43.9	5 21.2	3 43.0	1♈46.6	25 10.3	28 18.1	20 54.8	22 10.6	22 49.6	23 13.5	20 51.7	28 55.2
28	22 23 40.5	6 16.1	3 39.7	15 27.1	27 4.9	29 32.3	21 32.8	22 19.6	22 54.6	23 16.6	20 53.2	28 57.1
29	22 27 37.1	7 10.8	3 36.4	29 26.2	28 59.7	0♌46.5	22 10.6	22 28.5	22 59.8	23 19.7	20 54.7	28 59.0
30	22 31 33.6	8 5.4	3 33.1	13♉48.8	0♍54.3	2 .7	22 48.4	22 37.2	23 5.0	23 22.7	20 56.2	29 .9
31	22 35 30.2	8 60.0	3 29.8	28 30.9	2 48.5	3 14.8	23 26.0	22 45.8	23 10.3	23 25.7	20 57.8	29 2.8

DECLINATION

DAY	EPHEM. SID. TIME h m s	☉	☊	☽	☿	♀	♂	♃	♄	♅	♆	♇
1	20 37 13.5	18N 9.4	0S20.4	13N58.4	16N17.1	21N19.3	20N53.0	22N21.5	6S13.6	22N22.4	6S46.5	22N49.4
4	20 49 3.2	17 23.2	0 20.5	25 32.9	17 2.8	21 31.2	20 27.2	22 24.4	6 18.4	22 20.9	6 47.7	22 47.5
7	21 0 52.8	16 34.5	0 20.5	24 29.7	17 45.2	21 38.3	20 .2	22 27.0	6 23.4	22 19.4	6 49.0	22 45.7
10	21 12 42.5	15 43.4	0 20.6	13 6.0	18 19.1	21 40.6	19 31.9	22 29.4	6 28.7	22 18.0	6 50.4	22 43.9
13	21 24 32.2	14 50.0	0 20.6	2S28.0	18 39.7	21 37.8	19 2.4	22 31.7	6 34.2	22 16.5	6 51.9	22 42.1
16	21 36 21.8	13 54.5	0 20.6	17 8.3	18 42.0	21 29.9	18 31.7	22 33.7	6 39.9	22 15.1	6 53.5	22 40.3
19	21 48 11.5	12 57.0	0 20.7	26 2.1	18 22.0	21 16.9	17 60.0	22 35.6	6 45.9	22 13.7	6 55.2	22 38.6
22	22 0 1.2	11 57.7	0 20.7	23 13.8	17 37.3	20 58.6	17 27.2	22 37.3	6 52.0	22 12.3	6 56.9	22 36.9
25	22 11 50.8	10 56.6	0 20.7	7 41.9	16 27.5	20 35.2	16 53.4	22 38.9	6 58.3	22 10.9	6 58.7	22 35.3
28	22 23 40.5	9 54.1	0 20.8	12N 3.6	14 54.9	20 6.6	16 18.7	22 40.3	7 4.8	22 9.6	7 .6	22 33.7
31	22 35 30.2	8 50.1	0 20.8	24 57.6	13 3.6	19 32.9	15 43.0	22 41.5	7 11.4	22 8.4	7 2.6	22 32.2

SEPTEMBER 1953

LONGITUDE

DAY	EPHEM. SID. TIME h m s	☉ ° ′	☊ ° ′	☽ ° ′	☿ ° ′	♀ ° ′	♂ ° ′	♃ ° ′	♄ ° ′	♅ ° ′	♆ ° ′	♇ ° ′
1	22 39 26.7	8♍15.7	1♒12.7	15♊ 4.3	2♍ 3.7	2♌17.2	21♌17.2	23♊27.4	24♎11.6	21♋39.5	22♎ 2.1	23♌25.7
2	22 43 23.3	9 13.8	1 9.5	28 7.4	4 1.5	3 28.1	21 55.4	23 35.1	24 17.4	21 42.2	22 3.8	23 27.5
3	22 47 19.8	10 11.9	1 6.4	10♋50.8	5 59.0	4 39.1	22 33.5	23 42.6	24 23.2	21 44.9	22 5.6	23 29.4
4	22 51 16.4	11 10.1	1 3.2	23 18.1	7 56.0	5 50.1	23 11.7	23 50.0	24 29.1	21 47.6	22 7.3	23 31.2
5	22 55 12.9	12 8.3	1 .0	5♌32.7	9 52.4	7 1.3	23 49.8	23 57.2	24 35.1	21 50.2	22 9.1	23 33.0
6	22 59 9.5	13 6.5	0 56.8	17 38.0	11 48.1	8 12.6	24 27.9	24 4.4	24 41.1	21 52.9	22 11.0	23 34.9
7	23 3 6.0	14 4.8	0 53.6	29 36.4	13 43.0	9 23.9	25 6.0	24 11.3	24 47.2	21 55.4	22 12.8	23 36.7
8	23 7 2.6	15 3.0	0 50.5	11♍30.3	15 36.9	10 35.3	25 44.1	24 18.1	24 53.3	21 58.0	22 14.7	23 38.5
9	23 10 59.1	16 1.3	0 47.3	23 21.5	17 29.8	11 46.8	26 22.1	24 24.7	24 59.5	22 .4	22 16.6	23 40.3
10	23 14 55.7	16 59.7	0 44.1	5♎11.9	19 21.7	12 58.4	27 .1	24 31.2	25 5.7	22 2.9	22 18.5	23 42.0
11	23 18 52.2	17 58.0	0 40.9	17 3.2	21 12.6	14 10.1	27 38.1	24 37.6	25 11.9	22 5.3	22 20.4	23 43.8
12	23 22 48.8	18 56.4	0 37.8	28 57.4	23 2.4	15 21.9	28 16.1	24 43.7	25 18.2	22 7.7	22 22.3	23 45.6
13	23 26 45.4	19 54.8	0 34.6	10♏56.9	24 51.1	16 33.7	28 54.1	24 49.7	25 24.6	22 10.0	22 24.2	23 47.3
14	23 30 41.9	20 53.3	0 31.4	23 4.6	26 38.7	17 45.6	29 32.1	24 55.6	25 31.0	22 12.3	22 26.2	23 49.0
15	23 34 38.5	21 51.7	0 28.2	5♐24.1	28 25.2	18 57.6	0♍10.0	25 1.3	25 37.4	22 14.5	22 28.2	23 50.8
16	23 38 35.0	22 50.2	0 25.0	17 59.1	0♎10.7	20 9.7	0 48.0	25 6.8	25 43.9	22 16.8	22 30.2	23 52.5
17	23 42 31.6	23 48.7	0 21.9	0♑53.9	1 55.0	21 21.8	1 25.9	25 12.2	25 50.4	22 18.9	22 32.2	23 54.2
18	23 46 28.1	24 47.3	0 18.7	14 12.2	3 38.3	22 34.1	2 3.8	25 17.3	25 56.9	22 21.0	22 34.2	23 55.9
19	23 50 24.7	25 45.9	0 15.5	27 57.1	5 20.6	23 46.4	2 41.7	25 22.4	26 3.5	22 23.1	22 36.2	23 57.5
20	23 54 21.2	26 44.5	0 12.3	12♒10.0	7 1.8	24 58.7	3 19.5	25 27.2	26 10.1	22 25.1	22 38.3	23 59.2
21	23 58 17.8	27 43.1	0 9.2	26 49.4	8 42.0	26 11.2	3 57.4	25 31.9	26 16.8	22 27.1	22 40.3	24 .8
22	0 2 14.3	28 41.8	0 6.0	11♓51.1	10 21.3	27 23.7	4 35.2	25 36.4	26 23.5	22 29.1	22 42.4	24 2.4
23	0 6 10.9	29 40.5	0 2.8	27 7.0	11 59.5	28 36.3	5 13.1	25 40.7	26 30.2	22 31.0	22 44.5	24 4.1
24	0 10 7.4	0♎39.2	29♑59.6	12♈26.6	13 36.8	29 49.0	5 50.9	25 44.9	26 37.0	22 32.8	22 46.6	24 5.7
25	0 14 4.0	1 38.0	29 56.4	27 38.7	15 13.1	1♍ 1.8	6 28.7	25 48.8	26 43.8	22 34.6	22 48.7	24 7.2
26	0 18 .5	2 36.7	29 53.3	12♉32.9	16 48.6	2 14.6	7 6.5	25 52.6	26 50.6	22 36.4	22 50.8	24 8.8
27	0 21 57.1	3 35.6	29 50.1	27 2.0	18 23.1	3 27.5	7 44.3	25 56.3	26 57.5	22 38.2	22 53.0	24 10.4
28	0 25 53.7	4 34.5	29 46.9	11♊ 1.9	19 56.7	4 40.5	8 22.1	25 59.7	27 4.4	22 39.8	22 55.1	24 11.9
29	0 29 50.2	5 33.4	29 43.7	24 32.3	21 29.4	5 53.5	8 59.8	26 3.0	27 11.3	22 41.5	22 57.3	24 13.4
30	0 33 46.8	6 32.4	29 40.6	7♋35.5	23 1.2	7 6.7	9 37.6	26 6.0	27 18.2	22 43.0	22 59.4	24 14.9

LATITUDE

DAY	EPHEM. SID. TIME	☉	☊	☽	☿	♀	♂	♃	♄	♅	♆	♇
1	22 39 26.7	0 .0	0 .0	3N51.3	1N45.6	0S19.3	1N10.0	0S35.2	2N19.1	0N26.0	1N39.0	9N21.6
4	22 51 16.4	0 .0	0 .0	0 51.8	1 46.4	0 9.1	1 10.5	0 35.2	2 18.6	0 26.1	1 38.9	9 22.0
7	23 3 6.0	0 .0	0 .0	2S20.0	1 41.4	0N .8	1 11.0	0 35.2	2 18.2	0 26.2	1 38.8	9 22.5
10	23 14 55.7	0 .0	0 .0	4 33.7	1 31.7	0 10.4	1 11.4	0 35.2	2 17.7	0 26.3	1 38.7	9 23.0
13	23 26 45.4	0 .0	0 .0	5 3.5	1 18.3	0 19.7	1 11.8	0 35.2	2 17.3	0 26.4	1 38.6	9 23.5
16	23 38 35.0	0 .0	0 .0	3 33.5	1 2.0	0 28.6	1 12.2	0 35.2	2 17.0	0 26.4	1 38.5	9 24.1
19	23 50 24.7	0 .0	0 .0	0 21.1	0 43.6	0 37.1	1 12.6	0 35.2	2 16.6	0 26.5	1 38.5	9 24.7
22	0 2 14.3	0 .0	0 .0	3N16.9	0 23.7	0 45.2	1 13.0	0 35.2	2 16.3	0 26.6	1 38.4	9 25.4
25	0 14 4.0	0 .0	0 .0	5 3.5	0 2.7	0 52.7	1 13.3	0 35.2	2 16.0	0 26.7	1 38.4	9 26.1
28	0 25 53.7	0 .0	0 .0	3 53.6	0S19.0	0 59.7	1 13.6	0 35.2	2 15.7	0 26.8	1 38.3	9 26.8

RIGHT ASCENSION

DAY	EPHEM. SID. TIME	☉	☊	☽	☿	♀	♂	♃	♄	♅	♆	♇
1	22 39 26.7	9♍54.5	3♒26.5	13♊19.1	4♍42.0	4♌28.8	24♌ 3.6	22♊54.3	23♎15.6	23♋28.7	20♎59.4	29♌ 4.7
2	22 43 23.3	10 48.9	3 23.2	27 54.5	6 34.5	5 42.7	24 41.1	23 2.6	23 21.0	23 31.6	21 1.0	29 6.6
3	22 47 19.8	11 43.3	3 19.9	11♋58.3	8 26.0	6 56.4	25 18.5	23 10.7	23 26.4	23 34.5	21 2.7	29 8.5
4	22 51 16.4	12 37.5	3 16.6	25 18.4	10 16.3	8 10.1	25 55.8	23 18.7	23 31.9	23 37.4	21 4.3	29 10.4
5	22 55 12.9	13 31.8	3 13.3	7♌50.9	12 5.3	9 23.7	26 33.1	23 26.6	23 37.4	23 40.2	21 6.0	29 12.3
6	22 59 9.5	14 26.0	3 10.0	19 39.7	13 52.9	10 37.2	27 10.3	23 34.3	23 43.0	23 43.0	21 7.7	29 14.2
7	23 3 6.0	15 20.1	3 6.7	0♍53.2	15 39.2	11 50.5	27 47.4	23 41.8	23 48.6	23 45.8	21 9.4	29 16.1
8	23 7 2.6	16 14.2	3 3.4	11 42.5	17 24.0	13 3.6	28 24.4	23 49.2	23 54.3	23 48.5	21 11.1	29 18.0
9	23 10 59.1	17 8.2	3 .1	22 19.7	19 7.5	14 16.7	29 1.3	23 56.4	24 .1	23 51.1	21 12.9	29 19.8
10	23 14 55.7	18 2.1	2 56.8	2♎57.2	20 49.5	15 29.5	29 38.1	24 3.4	24 5.8	23 53.7	21 14.6	29 21.7
11	23 18 52.2	18 56.1	2 53.5	13 47.4	22 30.2	16 42.3	0♍14.8	24 10.3	24 11.7	23 56.3	21 16.4	29 23.5
12	23 22 48.8	19 50.0	2 50.2	25 1.8	24 9.5	17 54.8	0 51.5	24 17.0	24 17.5	23 58.8	21 18.2	29 25.3
13	23 26 45.4	20 43.9	2 46.9	6♏50.9	25 47.6	19 7.2	1 28.1	24 23.5	24 23.4	24 1.3	21 20.0	29 27.1
14	23 30 41.9	21 37.7	2 43.6	19 22.2	27 24.4	20 19.5	2 4.6	24 29.8	24 29.4	24 3.7	21 21.8	29 28.9
15	23 34 38.5	22 31.6	2 40.3	2♐38.4	28 60.0	21 31.6	2 41.0	24 36.0	24 35.4	24 6.1	21 23.7	29 30.7
16	23 38 35.0	23 25.4	2 37.0	16 34.9	0♎34.5	22 43.5	3 17.4	24 42.0	24 41.4	24 8.5	21 25.5	29 32.5
17	23 42 31.6	24 19.2	2 33.7	0♑59.9	2 7.8	23 55.3	3 53.7	24 47.8	24 47.5	24 10.8	21 27.4	29 34.3
18	23 46 28.1	25 13.0	2 30.4	15 36.2	3 40.2	25 6.9	4 29.9	24 53.4	24 53.6	24 13.1	21 29.3	29 36.1
19	23 50 24.7	26 6.8	2 27.1	0♒ 7.2	5 11.6	26 18.3	5 6.0	24 58.8	24 59.8	24 15.3	21 31.2	29 37.8
20	23 54 21.2	27 .6	2 23.8	14 21.8	6 42.0	27 29.5	5 42.1	25 4.1	25 6.0	24 17.5	21 33.1	29 39.5
21	23 58 17.8	27 54.4	2 20.5	28 17.7	8 11.5	28 40.6	6 18.1	25 9.2	25 12.2	24 19.6	21 35.0	29 41.3
22	0 2 14.3	28 48.2	2 17.2	12♓ .6	9 40.3	29 51.6	6 54.0	25 14.0	25 18.5	24 21.7	21 36.9	29 43.0
23	0 6 10.9	29 42.1	2 13.9	25 41.3	11 8.2	1♍ 2.4	7 29.9	25 18.7	25 24.8	24 23.7	21 38.9	29 44.7
24	0 10 7.4	0♎36.0	2 10.6	9♈33.1	12 35.4	2 13.0	8 5.7	25 23.2	25 31.1	24 25.7	21 40.8	29 46.4
25	0 14 4.0	1 29.9	2 7.3	23 47.2	14 1.9	3 23.5	8 41.4	25 27.5	25 37.5	24 27.6	21 42.8	29 48.0
26	0 18 .5	2 23.8	2 4.0	8♉29.4	15 27.7	4 33.8	9 17.1	25 31.7	25 43.9	24 29.5	21 44.8	29 49.7
27	0 21 57.1	3 17.9	2 .6	23 35.7	16 53.0	5 44.0	9 52.8	25 35.6	25 50.3	24 31.4	21 46.8	29 51.4
28	0 25 53.7	4 11.9	1 57.3	8♊51.4	18 17.6	6 54.1	10 28.3	25 39.3	25 56.8	24 33.1	21 48.8	29 53.0
29	0 29 50.2	5 6.0	1 54.0	23 54.7	19 41.6	8 4.0	11 3.8	25 42.9	26 3.3	24 34.9	21 50.8	29 54.6
30	0 33 46.8	6 .2	1 50.7	8♋23.6	21 5.2	9 13.7	11 39.3	25 46.2	26 9.8	24 36.5	21 52.8	29 56.2

DECLINATION

DAY	EPHEM. SID. TIME	☉	☊	☽	☿	♀	♂	♃	♄	♅	♆	♇
1	22 39 26.7	8N28.4	0S20.8	26N26.4	12N23.2	19N20.6	15N30.9	22N41.9	7S13.7	22N 7.9	7S 3.3	22N31.7
4	22 51 16.4	7 22.8	0 20.9	22 17.1	10 14.5	18 40.3	14 54.1	22 43.0	7 20.5	22 6.7	7 5.3	22 30.2
7	23 3 6.0	6 16.0	0 20.9	9 25.7	7 57.9	17 55.2	14 16.4	22 44.0	7 27.5	22 5.5	7 7.4	22 28.7
10	23 14 55.7	5 8.2	0 20.9	6S15.1	5 37.1	17 5.5	13 38.0	22 44.8	7 34.7	22 4.4	7 9.6	22 27.4
13	23 26 45.4	3 59.7	0 21.0	19 55.0	3 14.6	16 11.5	12 58.9	22 45.6	7 41.9	22 3.3	7 11.8	22 26.1
16	23 38 35.0	2 50.6	0 21.0	26 26.8	0 52.7	15 13.2	12 19.1	22 46.2	7 49.2	22 2.3	7 14.1	22 24.9
19	23 50 24.7	1 41.0	0 21.1	20 55.3	1S27.4	14 11.1	11 38.8	22 46.8	7 56.6	22 1.4	7 16.4	22 23.7
22	0 2 14.3	0 31.1	0 21.1	4 5.0	3 44.3	13 5.2	10 57.8	22 47.2	8 4.1	22 .5	7 18.7	22 22.6
25	0 14 4.0	0S39.0	0 21.1	15N21.3	5 57.3	11 56.0	10 16.3	22 47.6	8 11.7	21 59.7	7 21.1	22 21.6
28	0 25 53.7	1 49.1	0 21.2	25 57.5	8 5.6	10 43.5	9 34.3	22 48.0	8 19.3	21 58.9	7 23.5	22 20.7

OCTOBER 1953

LONGITUDE

DAY	EPHEM. SID. TIME h m s	☉ ° ′	☊ ° ′	☾ ° ′	☿ ° ′	♀ ° ′	♂ ° ′	♃ ° ′	♄ ° ′	♅ ° ′	♆ ° ′	♇ ° ′
1	0 37 43.3	7♎31.3	29♑37.4	20♋15.2	24♎32.2	8♍19.8	10♍15.3	26♊ 8.9	27♎25.2	22♋44.6	23♎ 1.6	24♌16.4
2	0 41 39.9	8 30.4	29 34.2	2♌36.3	26 2.2	9 33.1	10 53.0	26 11.6	27 32.2	22 46.0	23 3.8	24 17.9
3	0 45 36.4	9 29.4	29 31.0	14 43.5	27 31.4	10 46.4	11 30.7	26 14.1	27 39.2	22 47.5	23 6.0	24 19.3
4	0 49 33.0	10 28.5	29 27.8	26 41.3	28 59.8	11 59.8	12 8.4	26 16.4	27 46.3	22 48.8	23 8.1	24 20.7
5	0 53 29.5	11 27.7	29 24.7	8♍33.7	0♏27.2	13 13.2	12 46.1	26 18.5	27 53.3	22 50.2	23 10.3	24 22.1
6	0 57 26.1	12 26.8	29 21.5	20 23.8	1 53.7	14 26.7	13 23.8	26 20.4	28 .4	22 51.4	23 12.5	24 23.5
7	1 1 22.6	13 26.0	29 18.3	2♎14.0	3 19.4	15 40.2	14 1.4	26 22.1	28 7.5	22 52.7	23 14.8	24 24.9
8	1 5 19.2	14 25.3	29 15.1	14 6.3	4 44.1	16 53.9	14 39.1	26 23.6	28 14.6	22 53.8	23 17.0	24 26.2
9	1 9 15.7	15 24.6	29 12.0	26 2.1	6 7.8	18 7.5	15 16.7	26 24.9	28 21.8	22 55.0	23 19.2	24 27.5
10	1 13 12.3	16 23.9	29 8.8	8♏ 2.7	7 30.6	19 21.2	15 54.3	26 26.0	28 28.9	22 56.0	23 21.4	24 28.8
11	1 17 8.8	17 23.2	29 5.6	20 9.3	8 52.3	20 35.0	16 31.9	26 27.0	28 36.1	22 57.0	23 23.6	24 30.1
12	1 21 5.4	18 22.6	29 2.4	2♐23.6	10 13.0	21 48.9	17 9.5	26 27.7	28 43.3	22 58.0	23 25.9	24 31.4
13	1 25 2.0	19 22.0	28 59.2	14 47.8	11 32.5	23 2.7	17 47.0	26 28.2	28 50.5	22 58.9	23 28.1	24 32.6
14	1 28 58.5	20 21.4	28 56.1	27 24.7	12 50.8	24 16.7	18 24.6	26 28.5	28 57.7	22 59.8	23 30.3	24 33.8
15	1 32 55.1	21 20.9	28 52.9	10♑17.5	14 7.9	25 30.6	19 2.1	26 28.6	29 4.9	23 .6	23 32.6	24 35.0
16	1 36 51.6	22 20.4	28 49.7	23 29.8	15 23.6	26 44.6	19 39.7	26R28.5	29 12.2	23 1.3	23 34.8	24 36.2
17	1 40 48.2	23 19.9	28 46.5	7♒ 4.7	16 37.9	27 58.7	20 17.2	26 28.2	29 19.4	23 2.0	23 37.0	24 37.3
18	1 44 44.7	24 19.5	28 43.4	21 4.7	17 50.7	29 12.9	20 54.7	26 27.8	29 26.7	23 2.7	23 39.3	24 38.5
19	1 48 41.3	25 19.1	28 40.2	5♓30.0	19 1.8	0♎27.0	21 32.2	26 27.1	29 33.9	23 3.3	23 41.6	24 39.6
20	1 52 37.8	26 18.7	28 37.0	20 18.3	20 11.0	1 41.2	22 9.6	26 26.2	29 41.2	23 3.9	23 43.8	24 40.6
21	1 56 34.4	27 18.4	28 33.8	5♈23.8	21 18.2	2 55.5	22 47.1	26 25.1	29 48.5	23 4.4	23 46.0	24 41.7
22	2 0 30.9	28 18.0	28 30.6	20 37.6	22 23.2	4 9.8	23 24.5	26 23.9	29 55.7	23 4.8	23 48.3	24 42.7
23	2 4 27.5	29 17.7	28 27.5	5♉49.0	23 25.8	5 24.1	24 2.0	26 22.4	0♏ 3.0	23 5.2	23 50.5	24 43.7
24	2 8 24.1	0♏17.5	28 24.3	20 46.9	24 25.7	6 38.5	24 39.4	26 20.7	0 10.3	23 5.5	23 52.7	24 44.6
25	2 12 20.6	1 17.3	28 21.1	5♊22.6	25 22.8	7 52.9	25 16.8	26 18.8	0 17.5	23 5.8	23 54.9	24 45.6
26	2 16 17.2	2 17.1	28 17.9	19 30.3	26 16.5	9 7.4	25 54.1	26 16.7	0 24.8	23 6.0	23 57.2	24 46.5
27	2 20 13.7	3 16.9	28 14.8	3♋ 8.0	27 6.7	10 21.9	26 31.5	26 14.4	0 32.0	23 6.1	23 59.4	24 47.4
28	2 24 10.3	4 16.8	28 11.6	16 16.7	27 52.8	11 36.4	27 8.9	26 11.9	0 39.3	23 6.2	24 1.6	24 48.3
29	2 28 6.8	5 16.7	28 8.4	28 59.9	28 34.6	12 51.0	27 46.2	26 9.3	0 46.6	23 6.3	24 3.8	24 49.1
30	2 32 3.4	6 16.7	28 5.2	11♌22.1	29 11.4	14 5.6	28 23.6	26 6.4	0 53.8	23 6.3	24 6.0	24 49.9
31	2 35 59.9	7 16.7	28 2.1	23 28.7	29 42.7	15 20.3	29 .9	26 3.3	1 1.1	23R 6.2	24 8.2	24 50.7

LATITUDE

DAY	EPHEM. SID. TIME	☉	☊	☾	☿	♀	♂	♃	♄	♅	♆	♇
1	0 37 43.3	0 .0	0 .0	0N56.9	0S40.9	1N 6.1	1N13.9	0S35.2	2N15.5	0N26.9	1N38.3	9N27.6
4	0 49 33.0	0 .0	0 .0	2S12.1	1 2.6	1 11.9	1 14.2	0 35.2	2 15.3	0 27.0	1 38.3	9 28.3
7	1 1 22.6	0 .0	0 .0	4 25.2	1 23.9	1 17.1	1 14.4	0 35.2	2 15.1	0 27.1	1 38.2	9 29.2
10	1 13 12.3	0 .0	0 .0	4 57.2	1 44.3	1 21.7	1 14.6	0 35.2	2 14.9	0 27.2	1 38.2	9 30.0
13	1 25 2.0	0 .0	0 .0	3 31.7	2 3.5	1 25.7	1 14.8	0 35.1	2 14.8	0 27.3	1 38.2	9 30.9
16	1 36 51.6	0 .0	0 .0	0 30.2	2 20.9	1 28.9	1 15.0	0 35.1	2 14.7	0 27.4	1 38.2	9 31.8
19	1 48 41.3	0 .0	0 .0	2N58.9	2 36.1	1 31.5	1 15.1	0 35.0	2 14.6	0 27.5	1 38.2	9 32.7
22	2 0 30.9	0 .0	0 .0	4 57.0	2 48.3	1 33.5	1 15.3	0 35.0	2 14.6	0 27.6	1 38.3	9 33.6
25	2 12 20.6	0 .0	0 .0	3 59.8	2 56.5	1 34.7	1 15.4	0 34.9	2 14.5	0 27.7	1 38.3	9 34.6
28	2 24 10.3	0 .0	0 .0	1 1.5	2 59.3	1 35.3	1 15.4	0 34.8	2 14.6	0 27.8	1 38.3	9 35.6
31	2 35 59.9	0 .0	0 .0	2S10.5	2 55.0	1 35.2	1 15.5	0 34.7	2 14.6	0 27.9	1 38.4	9 36.6

RIGHT ASCENSION

DAY	EPHEM. SID. TIME	☉	☊	☾	☿	♀	♂	♃	♄	♅	♆	♇
1	0 37 43.3	6♎54.5	1♒47.4	22♋ 3.8	22♎28.2	10♍23.4	12♍14.6	25♊49.3	26♎16.4	24♋38.2	21♎54.9	29♌57.8
2	0 41 39.9	7 48.8	1 44.1	4♌51.0	23 50.7	11 32.9	12 50.0	25 52.2	26 22.9	24 39.7	21 56.9	29 59.3
3	0 45 36.4	8 43.2	1 40.8	16 49.6	25 12.8	12 42.3	13 25.3	25 54.9	26 29.5	24 41.3	21 58.9	0♍ .8
4	0 49 33.0	9 37.6	1 37.5	28 9.1	26 34.4	13 51.5	14 .5	25 57.4	26 36.2	24 42.7	22 1.0	0 2.4
5	0 53 29.5	10 32.2	1 34.2	9♍ 1.6	27 55.5	15 .7	14 35.7	25 59.7	26 42.8	24 44.2	22 3.1	0 3.9
6	0 57 26.1	11 26.9	1 30.8	19 40.1	29 16.2	16 9.8	15 10.8	26 1.7	26 49.5	24 45.5	22 5.1	0 5.3
7	1 1 22.6	12 21.6	1 27.5	0♎17.2	0♏36.4	17 18.7	15 45.9	26 3.6	26 56.2	24 46.8	22 7.2	0 6.8
8	1 5 19.2	13 16.5	1 24.2	11 5.4	1 56.1	18 27.6	16 20.9	26 5.2	27 2.9	24 48.1	22 9.3	0 8.3
9	1 9 15.7	14 11.4	1 20.9	22 16.1	3 15.3	19 36.4	16 55.9	26 6.6	27 9.6	24 49.3	22 11.3	0 9.7
10	1 13 12.3	15 6.5	1 17.6	3♏59.1	4 34.0	20 45.1	17 30.8	26 7.9	27 16.4	24 50.4	22 13.4	0 11.1
11	1 17 8.8	16 1.7	1 14.3	16 21.2	5 52.1	21 53.8	18 5.7	26 8.9	27 23.1	24 51.5	22 15.5	0 12.5
12	1 21 5.4	16 57.0	1 10.9	29 24.2	7 9.6	23 2.3	18 40.5	26 9.6	27 29.9	24 52.5	22 17.6	0 13.8
13	1 25 2.0	17 52.4	1 7.6	13♐ 3.4	8 26.5	24 10.8	19 15.3	26 10.2	27 36.7	24 53.5	22 19.7	0 15.2
14	1 28 58.5	18 48.0	1 4.3	27 7.3	9 42.6	25 19.3	19 50.1	26 10.5	27 43.5	24 54.4	22 21.8	0 16.5
15	1 32 55.1	19 43.6	1 1.0	11♑20.1	10 57.9	26 27.7	20 24.8	26 10.7	27 50.3	24 55.3	22 23.9	0 17.8
16	1 36 51.6	20 39.4	0 57.7	25 26.8	12 12.3	27 36.1	20 59.5	26R10.6	27 57.2	24 56.1	22 26.0	0 19.1
17	1 40 48.2	21 35.4	0 54.4	9♒17.8	13 25.7	28 44.5	21 34.1	26 10.3	28 4.0	24 56.8	22 28.1	0 20.3
18	1 44 44.7	22 31.5	0 51.0	22 51.1	14 38.0	29 52.9	22 8.7	26 9.8	28 10.9	24 57.6	22 30.2	0 21.6
19	1 48 41.3	23 27.7	0 47.7	6♓12.6	15 49.0	1♎ 1.2	22 43.3	26 9.0	28 17.8	24 58.2	22 32.3	0 22.8
20	1 52 37.8	24 24.1	0 44.4	19 33.3	16 58.5	2 9.6	23 17.8	26 8.1	28 24.7	24 58.8	22 34.4	0 24.0
21	1 56 34.4	25 20.7	0 41.1	3♈ 7.4	18 6.4	3 17.9	23 52.3	26 6.9	28 31.6	24 59.3	22 36.5	0 25.1
22	2 0 30.9	26 17.4	0 37.8	17 8.7	19 12.4	4 26.3	24 26.8	26 5.5	28 38.4	24 59.8	22 38.6	0 26.3
23	2 4 27.5	27 14.2	0 34.4	1♉46.6	20 16.3	5 34.7	25 1.2	26 3.9	28 45.3	25 .2	22 40.7	0 27.4
24	2 8 24.1	28 11.3	0 31.1	17 1.4	21 17.9	6 43.2	25 35.6	26 2.1	28 52.2	25 .5	22 42.8	0 28.5
25	2 12 20.6	29 8.5	0 27.8	2♊40.2	22 16.8	7 51.7	26 10.0	26 .0	28 59.1	25 .8	22 44.9	0 29.5
26	2 16 17.2	0♏ 5.9	0 24.5	18 18.6	23 12.6	9 .3	26 44.4	25 57.7	29 6.0	25 1.1	22 47.0	0 30.6
27	2 20 13.7	1 3.4	0 21.1	3♋28.2	24 4.9	10 8.9	27 18.7	25 55.3	29 12.9	25 1.2	22 49.1	0 31.6
28	2 24 10.3	2 1.2	0 17.8	17 47.5	24 53.4	11 17.6	27 53.0	25 52.6	29 19.8	25 1.4	22 51.1	0 32.6
29	2 28 6.8	2 59.2	0 14.5	1♌ 7.1	25 37.5	12 26.4	28 27.3	25 49.7	29 26.7	25 1.4	22 53.2	0 33.5
30	2 32 3.4	3 57.3	0 11.2	13 29.5	26 16.7	13 35.3	29 1.6	25 46.5	29 33.6	25 1.4	22 55.3	0 34.5
31	2 35 59.9	4 55.7	0 7.8	25 4.6	26 50.4	14 44.3	29 35.8	25 43.2	29 40.5	25 1.4	22 57.4	0 35.4

DECLINATION

DAY	EPHEM. SID. TIME	☉	☊	☾	☿	♀	♂	♃	♄	♅	♆	♇
1	0 37 43.3	2S59.2	0S21.2	22N51.3	10S 8.7	9N28.2	8N51.9	22N48.2	8S27.0	21N58.2	7S25.9	22N19.9
4	0 49 33.0	4 8.9	0 21.2	10 33.1	12 5.8	8 10.3	8 9.1	22 48.5	8 34.7	21 57.6	7 28.4	22 19.1
7	1 1 22.6	5 18.3	0 21.3	4S56.6	13 56.4	6 50.2	7 25.9	22 48.6	8 42.4	21 57.0	7 30.8	22 18.4
10	1 13 12.3	6 27.0	0 21.3	18 52.5	15 39.8	5 28.1	6 42.4	22 48.8	8 50.2	21 56.6	7 33.3	22 17.9
13	1 25 2.0	7 34.9	0 21.3	26 5.1	17 15.4	4 4.4	5 58.6	22 48.9	8 57.9	21 56.2	7 35.8	22 17.4
16	1 36 51.6	8 41.9	0 21.4	21 53.9	18 42.1	2 39.3	5 14.7	22 48.9	9 5.6	21 55.9	7 38.2	22 17.0
19	1 48 41.3	9 47.8	0 21.4	6 43.4	19 59.1	1 13.2	4 30.5	22 48.9	9 13.3	21 55.6	7 40.7	22 16.7
22	2 0 30.9	10 52.4	0 21.4	12N38.4	21 4.9	0S13.5	3 46.2	22 48.9	9 21.0	21 55.5	7 43.1	22 16.5
25	2 12 20.6	11 55.5	0 21.5	26 8.2	21 58.0	1 40.6	3 1.8	22 48.8	9 28.6	21 55.4	7 45.6	22 16.4
28	2 24 10.3	12 57.0	0 21.5	23 28.3	22 36.3	3 7.8	2 17.3	22 48.7	9 36.2	21 55.5	7 48.0	22 16.3
31	2 35 59.9	13 56.7	0 21.5	11 38.5	22 56.6	4 34.6	1 32.8	22 48.5	9 43.7	21 55.5	7 50.3	22 16.4

NOVEMBER 1953

DAY	EPHEM. SID. TIME h m s	☉ ° ′	☊ ° ′	☽ ° ′	☿ ° ′	♀ ° ′	♂ ° ′	♃ ° ′	♄ ° ′	♅ ° ′	♆ ° ′	♇ ° ′
LONGITUDE												
1	2 39 56.5	8♏16.7	27♑58.9	5♍24.9	0♐ 8.0	16♎35.0	29♍38.2	26♊ .0	1♏ 8.3	23♋ 6.1	24♎10.4	24♌51.5
2	2 43 53.0	9 16.7	27 55.7	17 15.6	0 26.6	17 49.7	0♎15.5	25 R 56.6	1 15.5	23 R 5.9	24 12.6	24 52.2
3	2 47 49.6	10 16.8	27 52.5	29 5.0	0 37.9	19 4.5	0 52.8	25 52.9	1 22.7	23 5.7	24 14.7	24 52.9
4	2 51 46.2	11 17.0	27 49.3	10♎56.6	0 41.3	20 19.3	1 30.1	25 49.1	1 30.0	23 5.4	24 16.9	24 53.6
5	2 55 42.7	12 17.1	27 46.2	22 53.0	0 R 36.1	21 34.1	2 7.3	25 45.1	1 37.2	23 5.1	24 19.1	24 54.2
6	2 59 39.3	13 17.3	27 43.0	4♏55.9	0 21.8	22 49.0	2 44.5	25 40.9	1 44.3	23 4.7	24 21.2	24 54.8
7	3 3 35.8	14 17.6	27 39.8	17 6.4	29♏57.8	24 3.9	3 21.8	25 36.5	1 51.5	23 4.3	24 23.3	24 55.4
8	3 7 32.4	15 17.9	27 36.6	29 25.4	29 24.1	25 18.9	3 59.0	25 32.0	1 58.7	23 3.9	24 25.5	24 56.0
9	3 11 28.9	16 18.1	27 33.5	11♐53.4	28 40.4	26 33.8	4 36.2	25 27.2	2 5.8	23 3.3	24 27.6	24 56.6
10	3 15 25.5	17 18.5	27 30.3	24 31.1	27 47.2	27 48.8	5 13.4	25 22.3	2 12.9	23 2.7	24 29.7	24 57.1
11	3 19 22.1	18 18.8	27 27.1	7♑19.7	26 45.2	29 3.8	5 50.5	25 17.2	2 20.0	23 2.1	24 31.8	24 57.5
12	3 23 18.6	19 19.2	27 23.9	20 20.8	25 35.6	0♏18.8	6 27.6	25 12.0	2 27.1	23 1.4	24 33.9	24 58.0
13	3 27 15.2	20 19.5	27 20.8	3♒36.4	24 20.1	1 33.8	7 4.7	25 6.5	2 34.2	23 .6	24 36.0	24 58.4
14	3 31 11.7	21 19.9	27 17.6	17 8.8	23 .8	2 48.9	7 41.8	25 1.0	2 41.2	22 59.8	24 38.0	24 58.8
15	3 35 8.3	22 20.4	27 14.4	0♓59.7	21 40.1	4 3.9	8 18.9	24 55.2	2 48.2	22 58.9	24 40.1	24 59.1
16	3 39 4.8	23 20.8	27 11.2	15 9.9	20 20.7	5 19.0	8 55.9	24 49.3	2 55.2	22 58.0	24 42.1	24 59.5
17	3 43 1.4	24 21.3	27 8.0	29 38.3	19 5.2	6 34.1	9 33.0	24 43.3	3 2.1	22 57.1	24 44.1	24 59.8
18	3 46 57.9	25 21.8	27 4.9	14♈21.4	17 56.1	7 49.3	10 10.0	24 37.1	3 9.1	22 56.1	24 46.1	25 .0
19	3 50 54.5	26 22.3	27 1.7	29 13.2	16 55.3	9 4.4	10 47.0	24 30.8	3 15.9	22 55.0	24 48.1	25 .3
20	3 54 51.1	27 22.9	26 58.5	14♉ 5.7	16 4.6	10 19.6	11 24.0	24 24.3	3 22.8	22 53.9	24 50.0	25 .5
21	3 58 47.6	28 23.4	26 55.3	28 50.0	15 24.9	11 34.8	12 .9	24 17.7	3 29.6	22 52.7	24 52.0	25 .7
22	4 2 44.2	29 24.0	26 52.2	13♊17.9	14 56.8	12 50.0	12 37.9	24 11.0	3 36.4	22 51.5	24 53.9	25 .8
23	4 6 40.7	0♐24.6	26 49.0	27 23.2	14 40.3	14 5.2	13 14.8	24 4.2	3 43.2	22 50.3	24 55.8	25 .9
24	4 10 37.3	1 25.3	26 45.8	11♋ 2.5	14 35.3	15 20.4	13 51.7	23 57.2	3 50.0	22 49.0	24 57.7	25 1.0
25	4 14 33.8	2 25.9	26 42.6	24 15.3	14 D 41.2	16 35.7	14 28.6	23 50.1	3 56.7	22 47.6	24 59.6	25 1.1
26	4 18 30.4	3 26.6	26 39.5	7♌ 3.2	14 57.2	17 51.0	15 5.4	23 43.0	4 3.3	22 46.2	25 1.4	25 1.1
27	4 22 27.0	4 27.3	26 36.3	19 29.9	15 22.5	19 6.3	15 42.3	23 35.7	4 9.9	22 44.8	25 3.2	25 1.1
28	4 26 23.5	5 28.1	26 33.1	1♍39.9	15 56.2	20 21.6	16 19.1	23 28.3	4 16.5	22 43.3	25 5.1	25 1.1
29	4 30 20.1	6 28.9	26 29.9	13 38.4	16 37.5	21 36.9	16 56.0	23 20.8	4 23.1	22 41.8	25 6.9	25 1.1
30	4 34 16.6	7 29.7	26 26.7	25 30.5	17 25.4	22 52.3	17 32.8	23 13.3	4 29.6	22 40.2	25 8.7	25 R 1.0
LATITUDE												
1	2 39 56.5	0 .0	0 .0	3 S 4.1	2 S 51.6	1 N 35.1	1 N 15.5	0 S 34.7	2 N 14.6	0 N 27.9	1 N 38.4	9 N 36.9
4	2 51 46.2	0 .0	0 .0	4 48.2	2 34.1	1 34.1	1 15.5	0 34.6	2 14.7	0 28.0	1 38.4	9 37.9
7	3 3 35.8	0 .0	0 .0	4 42.1	2 3.6	1 32.6	1 15.5	0 34.5	2 14.8	0 28.1	1 38.5	9 39.0
10	3 15 25.5	0 .0	0 .0	2 39.9	1 18.3	1 30.4	1 15.5	0 34.3	2 14.9	0 28.2	1 38.6	9 40.0
13	3 27 15.2	0 .0	0 .0	0 N 39.2	0 20.8	1 27.6	1 15.4	0 34.1	2 15.1	0 28.3	1 38.7	9 41.0
16	3 39 4.8	0 .0	0 .0	3 49.9	0 N 40.5	1 24.3	1 15.3	0 33.9	2 15.3	0 28.4	1 38.7	9 42.1
19	3 50 54.5	0 .0	0 .0	5 3.5	1 33.6	1 20.4	1 15.2	0 33.7	2 15.5	0 28.5	1 38.8	9 43.2
22	4 2 44.2	0 .0	0 .0	3 25.0	2 10.1	1 16.1	1 15.1	0 33.5	2 15.7	0 28.6	1 38.9	9 44.2
25	4 14 33.8	0 .0	0 .0	0 5.4	2 28.6	1 11.2	1 14.9	0 33.2	2 16.0	0 28.7	1 39.0	9 45.3
28	4 26 23.5	0 .0	0 .0	3 S 3.1	2 32.2	1 5.9	1 14.7	0 32.9	2 16.3	0 28.7	1 39.2	9 46.4
RIGHT ASCENSION												
1	2 39 56.5	5♏54.2	0♒ 4.5	6♍ 5.8	27♏18.0	15♎53.5	0♎10.1	25♊39.7	29♎47.4	25♋ 1.3	22♎59.4	0♍36.3
2	2 43 53.0	6 53.0	0 1.2	16 47.6	27 38.8	17 2.7	0 44.3	25 R 35.9	29 54.3	25 R 1.1	23 1.5	0 37.1
3	2 47 49.6	7 51.9	29♑57.9	27 24.2	27 52.1	18 12.1	1 18.5	25 32.0	0♏ 1.2	25 .9	23 3.5	0 38.0
4	2 51 46.2	8 51.1	29 54.5	8♎ 9.5	27 57.4	19 21.6	1 52.7	25 27.8	0 8.1	25 .6	23 5.6	0 38.8
5	2 55 42.7	9 50.5	29 51.2	19 15.9	27 R 53.8	20 31.3	2 26.8	25 23.4	0 14.9	25 .2	23 7.6	0 39.5
6	2 59 39.3	10 50.0	29 47.9	0♏54.4	27 41.0	21 41.2	3 1.0	25 18.9	0 21.8	24 59.8	23 9.6	0 40.3
7	3 3 35.8	11 49.8	29 44.6	13 12.7	27 18.5	22 51.2	3 35.1	25 14.1	0 28.6	24 59.4	23 11.6	0 41.0
8	3 7 32.4	12 49.9	29 41.2	26 13.3	26 46.1	24 1.4	4 9.3	25 9.2	0 35.5	24 58.9	23 13.7	0 41.7
9	3 11 28.9	13 50.1	29 37.9	9♐51.3	26 3.9	25 11.8	4 43.4	25 4.1	0 42.3	24 58.3	23 15.7	0 42.4
10	3 15 25.5	14 50.5	29 34.6	23 54.3	25 12.4	26 22.3	5 17.5	24 58.7	0 49.1	24 57.7	23 17.7	0 43.0
11	3 19 22.1	15 51.1	29 31.2	8♑ 4.8	24 12.3	27 33.1	5 51.6	24 53.2	0 55.9	24 57.0	23 19.6	0 43.7
12	3 23 18.6	16 51.9	29 27.9	22 5.6	23 5.1	28 44.1	6 25.7	24 47.5	1 2.7	24 56.3	23 21.6	0 44.2
13	3 27 15.2	17 53.0	29 24.6	5♒45.5	21 52.6	29 55.2	6 59.8	24 41.6	1 9.4	24 55.5	23 23.5	0 44.8
14	3 31 11.7	18 54.2	29 21.3	19 1.8	20 36.8	1♏ 6.7	7 33.9	24 35.6	1 16.1	24 54.6	23 25.5	0 45.3
15	3 35 8.3	19 55.7	29 17.9	2♓ .1	19 20.2	2 18.3	8 8.0	24 29.4	1 22.9	24 53.7	23 27.4	0 45.8
16	3 39 4.8	20 57.4	29 14.6	14 51.6	18 5.4	3 30.2	8 42.0	24 23.0	1 29.5	24 52.7	23 29.3	0 46.3
17	3 43 1.4	21 59.2	29 11.3	27 51.5	16 54.9	4 42.3	9 16.1	24 16.4	1 36.2	24 51.7	23 31.2	0 46.7
18	3 46 57.9	23 1.3	29 7.9	11♈15.8	15 50.7	5 54.6	9 50.1	24 9.7	1 42.9	24 50.7	23 33.1	0 47.1
19	3 50 54.5	24 3.6	29 4.6	25 18.3	14 54.9	7 7.3	10 24.2	24 2.9	1 49.5	24 49.5	23 35.0	0 47.5
20	3 54 51.1	25 6.0	29 1.3	10♉ 6.4	14 8.7	8 20.2	10 58.3	23 55.9	1 56.1	24 48.4	23 36.8	0 47.8
21	3 58 47.6	26 8.7	28 57.9	25 35.2	13 33.0	9 33.3	11 32.3	23 48.7	2 2.6	24 47.1	23 38.7	0 48.1
22	4 2 44.2	27 11.6	28 54.6	11♊25.2	13 8.2	10 46.7	12 6.4	23 41.5	2 9.2	24 45.9	23 40.5	0 48.4
23	4 6 40.7	28 14.7	28 51.3	27 6.0	12 54.4	12 .5	12 40.5	23 34.0	2 15.7	24 44.5	23 42.3	0 48.7
24	4 10 37.3	29 18.0	28 47.9	12♋ 7.4	12 51.3	13 14.5	13 14.5	23 26.5	2 22.2	24 43.2	23 44.1	0 48.9
25	4 14 33.8	0♐21.5	28 44.6	26 10.4	12 D 58.4	14 28.7	13 48.6	23 18.8	2 28.6	24 41.7	23 45.9	0 49.1
26	4 18 30.4	1 25.1	28 41.2	9♌10.5	13 15.0	15 43.3	14 22.7	23 11.0	2 35.0	24 40.2	23 47.6	0 49.3
27	4 22 27.0	2 29.0	28 37.9	21 14.4	13 40.2	16 58.2	14 56.8	23 3.1	2 41.4	24 38.7	23 49.4	0 49.4
28	4 26 23.5	3 33.0	28 34.6	2♍34.8	14 13.5	18 13.4	15 30.9	22 55.1	2 47.8	24 37.1	23 51.1	0 49.5
29	4 30 20.1	4 37.3	28 31.2	13 27.0	14 53.9	19 28.9	16 5.1	22 47.1	2 54.1	24 35.6	23 52.8	0 49.6
30	4 34 16.6	5 41.7	28 27.9	24 6.5	15 40.7	20 44.7	16 39.2	22 38.9	3 .4	24 33.9	23 54.5	0 49.7
DECLINATION												
1	2 39 56.5	14 S 16.2	0 S 21.5	6 N 40.3	22 S 58.8	5 S 3.4	1 N 17.9	22 N 48.5	9 S 46.2	21 N 55.6	7 S 51.1	22 N 16.5
4	2 51 46.2	15 13.2	0 21.6	8 S 44.9	22 48.8	6 29.3	0 33.5	22 48.3	9 53.6	21 55.8	7 53.5	22 16.7
7	3 3 35.8	16 7.9	0 21.6	21 27.2	22 9.6	7 54.2	0 S 10.9	22 48.0	10 .9	21 56.1	7 55.8	22 17.0
10	3 15 25.5	17 .3	0 21.6	25 59.7	20 56.7	9 17.5	0 55.2	22 47.7	10 8.1	21 56.5	7 58.0	22 17.4
13	3 27 15.2	17 50.0	0 21.7	18 43.1	19 11.8	10 39.1	1 39.3	22 47.3	10 15.2	21 56.9	8 .2	22 18.0
16	3 39 4.8	18 36.9	0 21.7	2 18.7	17 11.3	11 58.4	2 23.3	22 46.8	10 22.1	21 57.4	8 2.4	22 18.6
19	3 50 54.5	19 20.9	0 21.7	15 N 55.4	15 24.0	13 15.2	3 6.9	22 46.3	10 29.0	21 58.0	8 4.5	22 19.3
22	4 2 44.2	20 1.7	0 21.8	25 47.5	14 15.1	14 29.2	3 50.3	22 45.7	10 35.6	21 58.7	8 6.5	22 20.1
25	4 14 33.8	20 39.2	0 21.8	21 21.6	13 52.8	15 39.9	4 33.4	22 45.0	10 42.2	21 59.4	8 8.5	22 21.0
28	4 26 23.5	21 13.3	0 21.8	8 2.0	14 11.0	16 47.0	5 16.2	22 44.2	10 48.6	22 .2	8 10.4	22 22.0

DECEMBER 1953

LONGITUDE

DAY	EPHEM. SID. TIME h m s	☉ ° ′	☊ ° ′	☽ ° ′	☿ ° ′	♀ ° ′	♂ ° ′	♃ ° ′	♄ ° ′	♅ ° ′	♆ ° ′	♇ ° ′
1	4 38 13.2	8♐30.5	26♑23.6	7♎21.2	18♏19.2	24♏ 7.6	18♎ 9.5	23♊ 5.6	4♏36.1	22♋38.6	25♎10.4	25♌ .9
2	4 42 9.8	9 31.4	26 20.4	19 14.8	19 18.2	25 23.0	18 46.3	22 R 57.9	4 42.5	22 R 36.9	25 12.2	25 R .8
3	4 46 6.3	10 32.2	26 17.2	1♏15.0	20 21.6	26 38.4	19 23.0	22 50.1	4 48.9	22 35.2	25 13.9	25 .6
4	4 50 2.9	11 33.1	26 14.0	13 24.7	21 28.9	27 53.8	19 59.7	22 42.2	4 55.2	22 33.5	25 15.5	25 .4
5	4 53 59.4	12 34.0	26 10.9	25 45.6	22 39.6	29 9.2	20 36.4	22 34.3	5 1.5	22 31.7	25 17.2	25 .1
6	4 57 56.0	13 34.9	26 7.7	8♐18.8	23 53.2	0♐24.6	21 13.1	22 26.3	5 7.7	22 29.9	25 18.8	24 59.9
7	5 1 52.5	14 35.9	26 4.5	21 4.5	25 9.3	1 40.0	21 49.7	22 18.2	5 13.9	22 28.0	25 20.5	24 59.6
8	5 5 49.1	15 36.8	26 1.3	4♑ 2.6	26 27.6	2 55.4	22 26.3	22 10.2	5 20.0	22 26.1	25 22.0	24 59.3
9	5 9 45.7	16 37.8	25 58.2	17 12.6	27 47.7	4 10.8	23 2.8	22 2.1	5 26.1	22 24.2	25 23.6	24 58.9
10	5 13 42.2	17 38.8	25 55.0	0♒33.8	29 9.4	5 26.3	23 39.4	21 53.9	5 32.2	22 22.2	25 25.2	24 58.5
11	5 17 38.8	18 39.8	25 51.8	14 6.2	0♐32.5	6 41.7	24 15.9	21 45.8	5 38.1	22 20.2	25 26.7	24 58.1
12	5 21 35.3	19 40.8	25 48.6	27 49.5	1 56.8	7 57.1	24 52.4	21 37.6	5 44.0	22 18.1	25 28.2	24 57.7
13	5 25 31.9	20 41.8	25 45.5	11♓43.5	3 22.1	9 12.6	25 28.8	21 29.4	5 49.9	22 16.0	25 29.6	24 57.2
14	5 29 28.4	21 42.8	25 42.3	25 48.0	4 48.3	10 28.0	26 5.3	21 21.2	5 55.7	22 13.9	25 31.0	24 56.7
15	5 33 25.0	22 43.9	25 39.1	10♈ 1.7	6 15.3	11 43.5	26 41.7	21 13.1	6 1.4	22 11.8	25 32.5	24 56.2
16	5 37 21.6	23 44.9	25 35.9	24 22.4	7 43.0	12 58.9	27 18.0	21 4.9	6 7.1	22 9.6	25 33.8	24 55.7
17	5 41 18.1	24 46.0	25 32.7	8♉46.6	9 11.2	14 14.4	27 54.3	20 56.8	6 12.7	22 7.4	25 35.2	24 55.1
18	5 45 14.7	25 47.0	25 29.6	23 9.7	10 40.0	15 29.9	28 30.7	20 48.7	6 18.3	22 5.1	25 36.5	24 54.5
19	5 49 11.2	26 48.1	25 26.4	7♊26.4	12 9.3	16 45.3	29 6.9	20 40.6	6 23.8	22 2.9	25 37.8	24 53.9
20	5 53 7.8	27 49.2	25 23.2	21 31.3	13 39.0	18 .8	29 43.2	20 32.6	6 29.3	22 .6	25 39.1	24 53.3
21	5 57 4.4	28 50.3	25 20.0	5♋20.0	15 9.0	19 16.3	0♏19.4	20 24.5	6 34.6	21 58.3	25 40.4	24 52.6
22	6 1 .9	29 51.3	25 16.9	18 49.1	16 39.4	20 31.8	0 55.6	20 16.6	6 39.9	21 56.0	25 41.6	24 51.9
23	6 4 57.5	0♑52.4	25 13.7	1♌57.3	18 10.2	21 47.2	1 31.8	20 8.7	6 45.2	21 53.6	25 42.8	24 51.1
24	6 8 54.0	1 53.5	25 10.5	14 44.9	19 41.3	23 2.7	2 7.9	20 .8	6 50.3	21 51.2	25 43.9	24 50.4
25	6 12 50.6	2 54.6	25 7.3	27 13.6	21 12.6	24 18.2	2 44.0	19 53.0	6 55.4	21 48.8	25 45.0	24 49.6
26	6 16 47.2	3 55.8	25 4.2	9♍26.7	22 44.3	25 33.7	3 20.1	19 45.3	7 .4	21 46.4	25 46.1	24 48.8
27	6 20 43.7	4 56.9	25 1.0	21 28.0	24 16.3	26 49.2	3 56.1	19 37.7	7 5.4	21 43.9	25 47.2	24 48.0
28	6 24 40.3	5 58.0	24 57.8	3♎22.2	25 48.5	28 4.6	4 32.1	19 30.1	7 10.3	21 41.5	25 48.2	24 47.1
29	6 28 36.8	6 59.2	24 54.6	15 14.2	27 21.0	29 20.1	5 8.0	19 22.6	7 15.1	21 39.0	25 49.2	24 46.2
30	6 32 33.4	8 .3	24 51.5	27 8.7	28 53.9	0♑35.6	5 44.0	19 15.3	7 19.8	21 36.5	25 50.2	24 45.3
31	6 36 29.9	9 1.5	24 48.3	9♏10.3	0♑27.0	1 51.1	6 19.8	19 8.0	7 24.4	21 34.0	25 51.1	24 44.4

LATITUDE

DAY	SID. TIME	☉	☊	☽	☿	♀	♂	♃	♄	♅	♆	♇
1	4 38 13.2	0 .0	0 .0	4 S 53.2	2 N 25.2	1 N .2	1 N 14.5	0 S 32.6	2 N 16.6	0 N 28.8	1 N 39.3	9 N 47.4
4	4 50 2.9	0 .0	0 .0	4 52.1	2 11.3	0 54.2	1 14.2	0 32.3	2 17.0	0 28.9	1 39.4	9 48.5
7	5 1 52.5	0 .0	0 .0	2 50.7	1 52.9	0 47.9	1 13.9	0 31.9	2 17.3	0 29.0	1 39.5	9 49.5
10	5 13 42.2	0 .0	0 .0	0 N 33.7	1 32.0	0 41.2	1 13.5	0 31.5	2 17.8	0 29.1	1 39.7	9 50.6
13	5 25 31.9	0 .0	0 .0	3 49.8	1 9.8	0 34.4	1 13.2	0 31.1	2 18.2	0 29.1	1 39.8	9 51.6
16	5 37 21.6	0 .0	0 .0	5 12.4	0 47.1	0 27.4	1 12.7	0 30.7	2 18.6	0 29.2	1 40.0	9 52.6
19	5 49 11.2	0 .0	0 .0	3 48.1	0 24.5	0 20.2	1 12.3	0 30.2	2 19.1	0 29.3	1 40.1	9 53.5
22	6 1 .9	0 .0	0 .0	0 28.7	0 2.5	0 12.9	1 11.8	0 29.8	2 19.6	0 29.3	1 40.3	9 54.5
25	6 12 50.6	0 .0	0 .0	2 S 52.7	0 S 18.7	0 5.6	1 11.2	0 29.3	2 20.1	0 29.4	1 40.5	9 55.4
28	6 24 40.3	0 .0	0 .0	4 55.2	0 38.7	0 S 1.7	1 10.6	0 28.8	2 20.7	0 29.4	1 40.6	9 56.3
31	6 36 29.9	0 .0	0 .0	5 4.9	0 57.2	0 8.9	1 10.0	0 28.3	2 21.3	0 29.5	1 40.8	9 57.2

RIGHT ASCENSION

DAY	SID. TIME	☉	☊	☽	☿	♀	♂	♃	♄	♅	♆	♇
1	4 38 13.2	6♐46.3	28♑24.6	4♎48.4	16♏33.2	22♏ .8	17♎13.4	22♊30.6	3♏ 6.6	24♋32.2	23♎56.2	0♍49.7
2	4 42 9.8	7 51.1	28 21.2	15 47.1	17 30.8	23 17.2	17 47.5	22 R 22.2	3 12.8	24 R 30.4	23 57.8	0 49.7
3	4 46 6.3	8 56.0	28 17.9	27 15.4	18 32.9	24 33.9	18 21.7	22 13.7	3 19.0	24 28.6	23 59.4	0 R 49.6
4	4 50 2.9	10 1.1	28 14.5	9♏23.7	19 38.9	25 50.9	18 55.8	22 5.2	3 25.1	24 26.7	24 1.0	0 49.6
5	4 53 59.4	11 6.3	28 11.2	22 17.5	20 48.6	27 8.1	19 30.0	21 56.6	3 31.2	24 24.8	24 2.6	0 49.5
6	4 57 56.0	12 11.7	28 7.9	5♐54.7	22 1.3	28 25.7	20 4.2	21 48.0	3 37.2	24 22.9	24 4.2	0 49.3
7	5 1 52.5	13 17.2	28 4.5	20 4.5	23 16.9	29 43.6	20 38.4	21 39.3	3 43.2	24 20.9	24 5.7	0 49.2
8	5 5 49.1	14 22.8	28 1.2	4♑28.0	24 34.9	1♐ 1.8	21 12.6	21 30.5	3 49.1	24 18.9	24 7.2	0 49.0
9	5 9 45.7	15 28.6	27 57.8	18 44.7	25 55.2	2 20.2	21 46.9	21 21.7	3 55.0	24 16.8	24 8.7	0 48.8
10	5 13 42.2	16 34.4	27 54.5	2♒38.5	27 17.5	3 38.9	22 21.1	21 12.9	4 .9	24 14.7	24 10.2	0 48.5
11	5 17 38.8	17 40.4	27 51.2	16 2.7	28 41.6	4 57.9	22 55.4	21 4.1	4 6.6	24 12.6	24 11.6	0 48.2
12	5 21 35.3	18 46.4	27 47.8	29 .2	0♐ 7.3	6 17.2	23 29.6	20 55.3	4 12.4	24 10.4	24 13.0	0 47.9
13	5 25 31.9	19 52.6	27 44.5	11♓41.1	1 34.6	7 36.7	24 3.9	20 46.4	4 18.1	24 8.2	24 14.4	0 47.6
14	5 29 28.4	20 58.8	27 41.1	24 19.8	3 3.2	8 56.5	24 38.2	20 37.5	4 23.7	24 6.0	24 15.8	0 47.2
15	5 33 25.0	22 5.1	27 37.8	7♈12.8	4 33.0	10 16.5	25 12.5	20 28.7	4 29.3	24 3.7	24 17.2	0 46.9
16	5 37 21.6	23 11.5	27 34.4	20 35.9	6 4.0	11 36.8	25 46.8	20 19.9	4 34.8	24 1.4	24 18.5	0 46.4
17	5 41 18.1	24 17.9	27 31.1	4♉41.0	7 36.1	12 57.2	26 21.2	20 11.1	4 40.3	23 59.0	24 19.8	0 46.0
18	5 45 14.7	25 24.3	27 27.7	19 31.2	9 9.2	14 17.9	26 55.5	20 2.3	4 45.7	23 56.6	24 21.0	0 45.5
19	5 49 11.2	26 30.8	27 24.4	4♊56.8	10 43.3	15 38.8	27 29.9	19 53.5	4 51.0	23 54.2	24 22.3	0 45.0
20	5 53 7.8	27 37.4	27 21.1	20 34.3	12 18.2	16 60.0	28 4.4	19 44.9	4 56.3	23 51.8	24 23.5	0 44.5
21	5 57 4.4	28 44.0	27 17.7	5♋53.1	13 54.0	18 21.2	28 38.8	19 36.2	5 1.6	23 49.4	24 24.7	0 44.0
22	6 1 .9	29 50.6	27 14.4	20 27.0	15 30.6	19 42.7	29 13.2	19 27.6	5 6.7	23 46.9	24 25.9	0 43.4
23	6 4 57.5	0♑57.2	27 11.0	4♌ 2.5	17 7.9	21 4.3	29 47.7	19 19.0	5 11.8	23 44.4	24 27.0	0 42.8
24	6 8 54.0	2 3.7	27 7.7	16 39.2	18 45.9	22 26.0	0♏22.2	19 10.5	5 16.9	23 41.8	24 28.1	0 42.1
25	6 12 50.6	3 10.3	27 4.3	28 25.9	20 24.7	23 47.9	0 56.7	19 2.1	5 21.8	23 39.3	24 29.2	0 41.5
26	6 16 47.2	4 16.9	27 1.0	9♍36.2	22 4.0	25 9.9	1 31.2	18 53.7	5 26.7	23 36.7	24 30.2	0 40.8
27	6 20 43.7	5 23.5	26 57.6	20 25.0	23 44.0	26 32.0	2 5.7	18 45.5	5 31.6	23 34.1	24 31.3	0 40.1
28	6 24 40.3	6 30.0	26 54.3	1♎ 7.8	25 24.6	27 54.2	2 40.3	18 37.3	5 36.4	23 31.4	24 32.2	0 39.3
29	6 28 36.8	7 36.5	26 50.9	11 59.4	27 5.8	29 16.5	3 14.8	18 29.2	5 41.1	23 28.8	24 33.2	0 38.5
30	6 32 33.4	8 42.9	26 47.6	23 14.0	28 47.5	0♑38.9	3 49.4	18 21.3	5 45.7	23 26.1	24 34.1	0 37.8
31	6 36 29.9	9 49.3	26 44.2	5♏ 3.8	0♑29.7	2 1.3	4 24.1	18 13.4	5 50.2	23 23.4	24 35.0	0 36.9

DECLINATION

DAY	SID. TIME	☉	☊	☽	☿	♀	♂	♃	♄	♅	♆	♇
1	4 38 13.2	21 S 43.8	0 S 21.9	7 S 24.3	14 S 57.6	17 S 50.2	5 S 58.5	22 N 43.4	10 S 54.8	22 N 1.1	8 S 12.2	22 N 23.1
4	4 50 2.9	22 10.5	0 21.9	20 30.4	16 1.5	18 49.0	6 40.5	22 42.5	11 .8	22 2.0	8 13.9	22 24.2
7	5 1 52.5	22 33.4	0 21.9	25 59.0	17 13.9	19 43.2	7 21.9	22 41.5	11 6.7	22 3.0	8 15.6	22 25.5
10	5 13 42.2	22 52.3	0 22.0	19 29.2	18 28.7	20 32.4	8 2.8	22 40.4	11 12.3	22 4.0	8 17.2	22 26.8
13	5 25 31.9	23 7.2	0 22.0	3 37.4	19 41.5	21 16.3	8 43.2	22 39.3	11 17.7	22 5.1	8 18.7	22 28.2
16	5 37 21.6	23 17.9	0 22.0	14 N 17.2	20 49.7	21 54.6	9 23.0	22 38.1	11 23.0	22 6.2	8 20.0	22 29.7
19	5 49 11.2	23 24.4	0 22.1	25 18.4	21 51.1	22 27.1	10 2.2	22 36.9	11 28.0	22 7.3	8 21.3	22 31.2
22	6 1 .9	23 26.7	0 22.1	22 35.9	22 44.2	22 53.6	10 40.7	22 35.7	11 32.7	22 8.5	8 22.6	22 32.8
25	6 12 50.6	23 24.8	0 22.1	9 43.9	23 27.9	23 13.8	11 18.5	22 34.4	11 37.3	22 9.7	8 23.7	22 34.5
28	6 24 40.3	23 18.7	0 22.1	5 S 51.3	24 1.4	23 27.6	11 55.6	22 33.2	11 41.6	22 10.9	8 24.6	22 36.2
31	6 36 29.9	23 8.3	0 22.2	19 21.9	24 24.0	23 34.9	12 32.0	22 31.9	11 45.6	22 12.2	8 25.5	22 37.9

JANUARY 1954

LONGITUDE

DAY	EPHEM. SID. TIME h m s	☉ ° ′	☊ ° ′	☽ ° ′	☿ ° ′	♀ ° ′	♂ ° ′	♃ ° ′	♄ ° ′	♅ ° ′	♆ ° ′	♇ ° ′
1	6 40 26.5	10♑ 2.7	24♑45.1	21♏23.0	2♑ .5	3♑ 6.6	6♏55.7	19♊ .8	7♏29.0	21♋31.4	25♎52.0	24♌43.4
2	6 44 23.1	11 3.8	24 41.9	3♐49.9	3 34.2	4 22.1	7 31.5	18 R 53.8	7 33.5	21 R 28.9	25 52.9	24 R 42.5
3	6 48 19.6	12 5.0	24 38.7	16 33.5	5 8.3	5 37.6	8 7.3	18 46.8	7 37.9	21 26.3	25 53.7	24 41.5
4	6 52 16.2	13 6.2	24 35.6	29 34.7	6 42.8	6 53.1	8 43.0	18 40.0	7 42.3	21 23.7	25 54.5	24 40.5
5	6 56 12.7	14 7.4	24 32.4	12♑53.5	8 17.5	8 8.6	9 18.7	18 33.3	7 46.5	21 21.2	25 55.3	24 39.4
6	7 0 9.3	15 8.6	24 29.2	26 28.5	9 52.7	9 24.1	9 54.3	18 26.7	7 50.7	21 18.6	25 56.0	24 38.4
7	7 4 5.8	16 9.7	24 26.0	10♒17.4	11 28.2	10 39.6	10 29.9	18 20.3	7 54.8	21 16.0	25 56.7	24 37.3
8	7 8 2.4	17 10.9	24 22.9	24 17.3	13 4.2	11 55.1	11 5.4	18 14.0	7 58.8	21 13.4	25 57.4	24 36.2
9	7 11 59.0	18 12.1	24 19.7	8♓24.9	14 40.5	13 10.6	11 40.9	18 7.8	8 2.7	21 10.8	25 58.1	24 35.1
10	7 15 55.5	19 13.3	24 16.5	22 37.1	16 17.3	14 26.1	12 16.4	18 1.9	8 6.6	21 8.2	25 58.7	24 34.0
11	7 19 52.1	20 14.4	24 13.3	6♈50.6	17 54.5	15 41.6	12 51.8	17 56.0	8 10.3	21 5.6	25 59.3	24 32.8
12	7 23 48.6	21 15.5	24 10.2	21 2.9	19 32.2	16 57.0	13 27.1	17 50.3	8 14.0	21 3.0	25 59.8	24 31.6
13	7 27 45.2	22 16.7	24 7.0	5♉11.8	21 10.3	18 12.5	14 2.4	17 44.8	8 17.5	21 .4	26 .3	24 30.4
14	7 31 41.8	23 17.8	24 3.8	19 15.1	22 48.9	19 28.0	14 37.7	17 39.4	8 21.0	20 57.8	26 .8	24 29.2
15	7 35 38.3	24 18.9	24 .6	3♊11.0	24 28.0	20 43.4	15 12.9	17 34.2	8 24.4	20 55.2	26 1.2	24 28.0
16	7 39 34.9	25 20.0	23 57.5	16 57.6	26 7.6	21 58.8	15 48.0	17 29.2	8 27.7	20 52.6	26 1.6	24 26.8
17	7 43 31.4	26 21.0	23 54.3	0♋33.0	27 47.7	23 14.3	16 23.1	17 24.4	8 30.9	20 50.0	26 2.0	24 25.5
18	7 47 28.0	27 22.1	23 51.1	13 55.7	29 28.3	24 29.7	16 58.1	17 19.7	8 34.0	20 47.4	26 2.3	24 24.2
19	7 51 24.5	28 23.2	23 47.9	27 4.3	1♒ 9.4	25 45.1	17 33.1	17 15.2	8 37.0	20 44.8	26 2.6	24 22.9
20	7 55 21.1	29 24.2	23 44.7	9♌58.0	2 51.0	27 .5	18 8.0	17 10.8	8 39.9	20 42.2	26 2.9	24 21.6
21	7 59 17.7	0♒25.3	23 41.6	22 36.7	4 33.2	28 15.9	18 42.9	17 6.7	8 42.8	20 39.7	26 3.1	24 20.3
22	8 3 14.2	1 26.3	23 38.4	5♍ 1.2	6 15.8	29 31.3	19 17.7	17 2.7	8 45.5	20 37.1	26 3.3	24 19.0
23	8 7 10.8	2 27.3	23 35.2	17 13.1	7 58.8	0♒46.7	19 52.5	16 59.0	8 48.1	20 34.6	26 3.5	24 17.6
24	8 11 7.3	3 28.3	23 32.0	29 14.9	9 42.3	2 2.1	20 27.2	16 55.4	8 50.7	20 32.0	26 3.6	24 16.3
25	8 15 3.9	4 29.3	23 28.9	11♎10.0	11 26.2	3 17.5	21 1.9	16 52.0	8 53.1	20 29.5	26 3.7	24 14.9
26	8 19 .4	5 30.3	23 25.7	23 2.2	13 10.4	4 32.9	21 36.5	16 48.8	8 55.4	20 27.0	26 3.8	24 13.6
27	8 22 57.0	6 31.3	23 22.5	4♏56.0	14 54.9	5 48.3	22 11.0	16 45.8	8 57.7	20 24.5	26 3.8	24 12.2
28	8 26 53.6	7 32.2	23 19.3	16 56.1	16 39.6	7 3.6	22 45.5	16 43.0	8 59.8	20 22.1	26 3.8	24 10.8
29	8 30 50.1	8 33.2	23 16.2	29 7.2	18 24.3	8 19.0	23 19.8	16 40.4	9 1.9	20 19.6	26 R 3.7	24 9.4
30	8 34 46.7	9 34.1	23 13.0	11♐33.8	20 9.0	9 34.4	23 54.2	16 37.9	9 3.8	20 17.2	26 3.7	24 7.9
31	8 38 43.2	10 35.1	23 9.8	24 19.7	21 53.6	10 49.8	24 28.5	16 35.8	9 5.7	20 14.8	26 3.6	24 6.6

LATITUDE

DAY	EPHEM. SID. TIME	☉	☊	☽	☿	♀	♂	♃	♄	♅	♆	♇
1	6 40 26.5	0 .0	0 .0	4S40.7	1S 3.1	0S11.3	1N 9.8	0S28.1	2N21.5	0N29.5	1N40.9	9N57.5
4	6 52 16.2	0 .0	0 .0	2 11.0	1 19.4	0 18.4	1 9.1	0 27.6	2 22.1	0 29.5	1 41.0	9 58.3
7	7 4 5.8	0 .0	0 .0	1N29.3	1 33.7	0 25.4	1 8.3	0 27.0	2 22.7	0 29.6	1 41.2	9 59.1
10	7 15 55.5	0 .0	0 .0	4 30.9	1 45.7	0 32.2	1 7.5	0 26.4	2 23.3	0 29.6	1 41.4	9 59.9
13	7 27 45.2	0 .0	0 .0	5 11.1	1 55.2	0 38.7	1 6.6	0 25.9	2 24.0	0 29.6	1 41.6	10 .6
16	7 39 34.9	0 .0	0 .0	3 11.4	2 1.9	0 45.0	1 5.6	0 25.3	2 24.6	0 29.6	1 41.8	10 1.3
19	7 51 24.5	0 .0	0 .0	0S17.0	2 5.2	0 50.9	1 4.6	0 24.7	2 25.3	0 29.7	1 42.0	10 1.9
22	8 3 14.2	0 .0	0 .0	3 28.2	2 4.9	0 56.5	1 3.5	0 24.1	2 26.0	0 29.7	1 42.1	10 2.5
25	8 15 3.9	0 .0	0 .0	5 8.6	2 .3	1 1.7	1 2.4	0 23.6	2 26.7	0 29.7	1 42.3	10 3.1
28	8 26 53.6	0 .0	0 .0	4 51.3	1 50.8	1 6.5	1 1.2	0 23.0	2 27.5	0 29.7	1 42.5	10 3.6
31	8 38 43.2	0 .0	0 .0	2 36.6	1 35.9	1 10.8	0 59.8	0 22.4	2 28.2	0 29.7	1 42.7	10 4.0

RIGHT ASCENSION

DAY	EPHEM. SID. TIME	☉	☊	☽	☿	♀	♂	♃	♄	♅	♆	♇
1	6 40 26.5	10♑55.7	26♑40.9	17♏37.9	2♑12.3	3♑23.7	4♏58.7	18♊ 5.6	5♏54.7	23♋20.7	24♎35.9	0♍36.1
2	6 44 23.1	12 1.9	26 37.5	0♐59.4	3 55.5	4 46.1	5 33.3	17 R 58.0	5 59.1	23 R 18.0	24 36.8	0 R 35.2
3	6 48 19.6	13 8.1	26 34.2	15 2.4	5 39.1	6 8.5	6 8.0	17 50.5	6 3.5	23 15.3	24 37.6	0 34.3
4	6 52 16.2	14 14.2	26 30.8	29 32.0	7 23.0	7 30.9	6 42.7	17 43.1	6 7.7	23 12.5	24 38.3	0 33.4
5	6 56 12.7	15 20.2	26 27.5	14♑ 6.9	9 7.4	8 53.3	7 17.4	17 35.9	6 11.9	23 9.8	24 39.1	0 32.5
6	7 0 9.3	16 26.1	26 24.1	28 26.9	10 52.1	10 15.6	7 52.1	17 28.8	6 16.0	23 7.0	24 39.8	0 31.5
7	7 4 5.8	17 31.8	26 20.7	12♒19.3	12 37.2	11 37.9	8 26.8	17 21.8	6 20.0	23 4.3	24 40.5	0 30.6
8	7 8 2.4	18 37.5	26 17.4	25 41.5	14 22.5	13 .1	9 1.5	17 15.0	6 24.0	23 1.5	24 41.2	0 29.6
9	7 11 59.0	19 43.0	26 14.0	8♓39.7	16 8.1	14 22.1	9 36.2	17 8.4	6 27.8	22 58.7	24 41.8	0 28.5
10	7 15 55.5	20 48.5	26 10.7	21 26.3	17 54.0	15 44.1	10 11.0	17 1.9	6 31.6	22 56.0	24 42.4	0 27.5
11	7 19 52.1	21 53.7	26 7.3	4♈16.3	19 40.1	17 6.0	10 45.8	16 55.6	6 35.3	22 53.2	24 43.0	0 26.5
12	7 23 48.6	22 58.8	26 4.0	17 25.0	21 26.3	18 27.6	11 20.5	16 49.5	6 38.9	22 50.4	24 43.5	0 25.4
13	7 27 45.2	24 3.8	26 .6	1♉ 5.2	23 12.7	19 49.2	11 55.3	16 43.5	6 42.5	22 47.6	24 44.0	0 24.3
14	7 31 41.8	25 8.6	25 57.3	15 23.6	24 59.3	21 10.5	12 30.1	16 37.7	6 45.9	22 44.9	24 44.5	0 23.2
15	7 35 38.3	26 13.2	25 53.9	0♊16.7	26 45.9	22 31.7	13 4.9	16 32.1	6 49.2	22 42.1	24 44.9	0 22.0
16	7 39 34.9	27 17.6	25 50.5	15 29.2	28 32.6	23 52.6	13 39.7	16 26.6	6 52.5	22 39.3	24 45.3	0 20.9
17	7 43 31.4	28 21.9	25 47.2	0♋36.6	0♒19.3	25 13.4	14 14.5	16 21.4	6 55.7	22 36.5	24 45.7	0 19.7
18	7 47 28.0	29 26.0	25 43.8	15 13.9	2 6.0	26 34.0	14 49.3	16 16.3	6 58.8	22 33.8	24 46.0	0 18.5
19	7 51 24.5	0♒29.9	25 40.5	29 3.8	3 52.7	27 54.3	15 24.1	16 11.4	7 1.8	22 31.0	24 46.3	0 17.3
20	7 55 21.1	1 33.7	25 37.1	12♌ .3	5 39.2	29 14.4	15 58.9	16 6.7	7 4.7	22 28.2	24 46.6	0 16.1
21	7 59 17.7	2 37.2	25 33.7	24 7.3	7 25.6	0♒34.2	16 33.7	16 2.3	7 7.5	22 25.5	24 46.8	0 14.8
22	8 3 14.2	3 40.6	25 30.4	5♍34.8	9 11.9	1 53.8	17 8.6	15 58.0	7 10.2	22 22.8	24 47.0	0 13.6
23	8 7 10.8	4 43.8	25 27.0	16 35.7	10 57.9	3 13.1	17 43.4	15 53.9	7 12.8	22 20.1	24 47.2	0 12.3
24	8 11 7.3	5 46.8	25 23.7	27 24.0	12 43.6	4 32.1	18 18.2	15 50.0	7 15.4	22 17.4	24 47.4	0 11.0
25	8 15 3.9	6 49.6	25 20.3	8♎13.6	14 28.9	5 50.9	18 53.0	15 46.4	7 17.8	22 14.7	24 47.5	0 9.7
26	8 19 .4	7 52.2	25 16.9	19 18.1	16 13.8	7 9.4	19 27.9	15 42.9	7 20.2	22 12.0	24 47.5	0 8.4
27	8 22 57.0	8 54.6	25 13.6	0♏49.8	17 58.2	8 27.6	20 2.7	15 39.6	7 22.4	22 9.3	24 47.6	0 7.1
28	8 26 53.6	9 56.8	25 10.2	12 59.2	19 41.9	9 45.5	20 37.5	15 36.6	7 24.6	22 6.7	24 47.6	0 5.7
29	8 30 50.1	10 58.8	25 6.8	25 52.6	21 24.9	11 3.1	21 12.3	15 33.7	7 26.6	22 4.1	24 47.6	0 4.4
30	8 34 46.7	12 .6	25 3.5	9♐29.6	23 6.9	12 20.4	21 47.1	15 31.1	7 28.6	22 1.5	24 R 47.5	0 3.0
31	8 38 43.2	13 2.3	25 .1	23 41.8	24 48.0	13 37.5	22 21.9	15 28.8	7 30.5	21 59.0	24 47.5	0 1.7

DECLINATION

DAY	EPHEM. SID. TIME	☉	☊	☽	☿	♀	♂	♃	♄	♅	♆	♇
1	6 40 26.5	23S 3.9	0S22.2	22S37.4	24S28.9	23S35.9	12S43.9	22N31.5	11S46.9	22N12.6	8S25.8	22N38.5
4	6 52 16.2	22 48.0	0 22.2	25 37.7	24 35.8	23 34.4	13 19.2	22 30.3	11 50.6	22 13.8	8 26.6	22 40.3
7	7 4 5.8	22 28.0	0 22.2	16 14.1	24 30.3	23 26.4	13 53.6	22 29.2	11 54.0	22 15.1	8 27.2	22 42.2
10	7 15 55.5	22 4.1	0 22.3	1N13.1	24 12.1	23 11.8	14 27.2	22 28.1	11 57.2	22 16.3	8 27.7	22 44.0
13	7 27 45.2	21 36.2	0 22.3	18 8.3	23 40.6	22 50.8	14 59.8	22 27.1	12 .1	22 17.6	8 28.1	22 45.9
16	7 39 34.9	21 4.6	0 22.3	25 58.9	22 55.5	22 23.5	15 31.6	22 26.2	12 2.7	22 18.8	8 28.4	22 47.8
19	7 51 24.5	20 29.4	0 22.4	20 28.4	21 56.6	21 50.0	16 2.4	22 25.5	12 5.0	22 20.0	8 28.6	22 49.8
22	8 3 14.2	19 50.7	0 22.4	6 26.5	20 43.7	21 10.6	16 32.2	22 24.9	12 7.0	22 21.2	8 28.7	22 51.7
25	8 15 3.9	19 8.7	0 22.4	9S 8.9	19 16.9	20 25.6	17 1.0	22 24.4	12 8.8	22 22.3	8 28.7	22 53.6
28	8 26 53.6	18 23.5	0 22.4	21 32.9	17 36.5	19 35.1	17 28.8	22 24.1	12 10.2	22 23.4	8 28.5	22 55.5
31	8 38 43.2	17 35.3	0 22.5	25 55.9	15 43.6	18 39.4	17 55.6	22 24.0	12 11.4	22 24.5	8 28.3	22 57.4

FEBRUARY 1954

LONGITUDE

DAY	EPHEM. SID. TIME	☉	☊	☽	☿	♀	♂	♃	♄	♅	♆	♇
	h m s	° ′	° ′	° ′	° ′	° ′	° ′	° ′	° ′	° ′	° ′	° ′
1	8 42 39.8	11♒36.1	23♑ 6.6	7♑27.7	23♒37.7	12♒ 5.1	25♏ 2.7	16♊33.7	9♏ 7.4	20♋12.5	26♎ 3.4	24♌ 5.1
2	8 46 36.3	12 37.0	23 3.4	20 59.0	25 21.2	13 20.4	25 36.8	16R31.9	9 9.1	20R10.1	26R 3.3	24R 3.7
3	8 50 32.9	13 37.8	23 .3	4♒53.0	27 3.8	14 35.8	26 10.8	16 30.3	9 10.6	20 7.8	26 3.1	24 2.2
4	8 54 29.4	14 38.7	22 57.1	19 7.0	28 45.3	15 51.1	26 44.8	16 28.9	9 12.0	20 5.4	26 2.8	24 .8
5	8 58 26.0	15 39.6	22 53.9	3♓36.1	0♓25.2	17 6.4	27 18.7	16 27.7	9 13.4	20 3.2	26 2.5	23 59.3
6	9 2 22.6	16 40.4	22 50.7	18 14.2	2 3.3	18 21.7	27 52.5	16 26.7	9 14.6	20 .9	26 2.2	23 57.9
7	9 6 19.1	17 41.2	22 47.6	2♈54.2	3 39.0	19 37.0	28 26.2	16 25.9	9 15.7	19 58.7	26 1.9	23 56.4
8	9 10 15.7	18 42.0	22 44.4	17 29.6	5 11.7	20 52.2	28 59.8	16 25.3	9 16.7	19 56.5	26 1.5	23 54.9
9	9 14 12.2	19 42.8	22 41.2	1♉55.0	6 41.1	22 7.5	29 33.3	16 24.9	9 17.6	19 54.3	26 1.1	23 53.5
10	9 18 8.8	20 43.5	22 38.0	16 6.8	8 6.4	23 22.7	0♐ 6.8	16 24.8	9 18.4	19 52.2	26 .6	23 52.0
11	9 22 5.3	21 44.2	22 34.9	0♊ 3.1	9 27.0	24 38.0	0 40.2	16 24.8	9 19.1	19 50.0	26 .1	23 50.5
12	9 26 1.9	22 44.9	22 31.7	13 43.4	10 42.2	25 53.2	1 13.4	16D25.0	9 19.7	19 48.0	25 59.6	23 49.0
13	9 29 58.4	23 45.5	22 28.5	27 8.4	11 51.3	27 8.4	1 46.6	16 25.4	9 20.2	19 45.9	25 59.1	23 47.6
14	9 33 55.0	24 46.1	22 25.3	10♋19.1	12 53.6	28 23.5	2 19.7	16 26.1	9 20.6	19 43.9	25 58.5	23 46.1
15	9 37 51.6	25 46.7	22 22.1	23 16.7	13 48.3	29 38.7	2 52.7	16 26.9	9 20.9	19 42.0	25 57.9	23 44.6
16	9 41 48.1	26 47.3	22 19.0	6♌ 2.3	14 34.7	0♓53.8	3 25.7	16 27.9	9 21.1	19 40.0	25 57.3	23 43.1
17	9 45 44.7	27 47.8	22 15.8	18 36.9	15 12.3	2 9.0	3 58.5	16 29.2	9 21.1	19 38.1	25 56.6	23 41.6
18	9 49 41.2	28 48.3	22 12.6	1♍ 1.2	15 40.5	3 24.1	4 31.2	16 30.6	9 21.1	19 36.3	25 55.9	23 40.2
19	9 53 37.8	29 48.8	22 9.4	13 16.0	15 58.8	4 39.2	5 3.8	16 32.2	9R21.0	19 34.5	25 55.2	23 38.7
20	9 57 34.3	0♓49.3	22 6.3	25 22.3	16 7.1	5 54.3	5 36.4	16 34.0	9 20.7	19 32.7	25 54.4	23 37.2
21	10 1 30.9	1 49.8	22 3.1	7♎21.5	16R 5.2	7 9.4	6 8.8	16 36.1	9 20.4	19 31.0	25 53.7	23 35.8
22	10 5 27.4	2 50.2	21 59.9	19 15.6	15 53.2	8 24.4	6 41.2	16 38.3	9 20.0	19 29.3	25 52.9	23 34.4
23	10 9 24.0	3 50.6	21 56.7	1♏ 7.3	15 31.4	9 39.5	7 13.4	16 40.7	9 19.4	19 27.6	25 52.0	23 32.9
24	10 13 20.5	4 51.0	21 53.5	13 .1	15 .4	10 54.5	7 45.5	16 43.3	9 18.8	19 26.0	25 51.2	23 31.5
25	10 17 17.1	5 51.3	21 50.4	24 58.0	14 21.0	12 9.5	8 17.5	16 46.1	9 18.0	19 24.4	25 50.3	23 30.0
26	10 21 13.7	6 51.6	21 47.2	7♐ 5.6	13 34.1	13 24.5	8 49.3	16 49.1	9 17.2	19 22.9	25 49.3	23 28.6
27	10 25 10.2	7 51.9	21 44.0	19 27.8	12 41.1	14 39.5	9 21.1	16 52.3	9 16.2	19 21.4	25 48.4	23 27.2
28	10 29 6.8	8 52.2	21 40.8	2♑ 9.4	11 43.3	15 54.4	9 52.7	16 55.6	9 15.1	19 20.0	25 47.4	23 25.7

LATITUDE

DAY	EPHEM. SID. TIME	☉	☊	☽	☿	♀	♂	♃	♄	♅	♆	♇
1	8 42 39.8	0 .0	0 .0	1S30.0	1S29.6	1S12.2	0N59.4	0S22.2	2N28.4	0N29.7	1N42.8	10N 4.2
4	8 54 29.4	0 .0	0 .0	2N14.0	1 6.4	1 15.9	0 58.0	0 21.6	2 29.2	0 29.7	1 42.9	10 4.6
7	9 6 19.1	0 .0	0 .0	4 53.3	0 36.5	1 19.0	0 56.4	0 21.0	2 29.9	0 29.7	1 43.1	10 4.9
10	9 18 8.8	0 .0	0 .0	4 50.3	0N .3	1 21.7	0 54.8	0 20.4	2 30.6	0 29.6	1 43.3	10 5.2
13	9 29 58.4	0 .0	0 .0	2 20.8	0 42.9	1 23.8	0 53.1	0 19.9	2 31.4	0 29.6	1 43.5	10 5.5
16	9 41 48.1	0 .0	0 .0	1S 6.4	1 29.5	1 25.4	0 51.3	0 19.3	2 32.1	0 29.6	1 43.6	10 5.7
19	9 53 37.8	0 .0	0 .0	3 56.8	2 16.4	1 26.4	0 49.3	0 18.8	2 32.8	0 29.6	1 43.8	10 5.8
22	10 5 27.4	0 .0	0 .0	5 8.6	2 58.2	1 26.8	0 47.2	0 18.2	2 33.6	0 29.5	1 43.9	10 6.0
25	10 17 17.1	0 .0	0 .0	4 22.9	3 28.8	1 26.7	0 45.1	0 17.7	2 34.3	0 29.5	1 44.1	10 6.0
28	10 29 6.8	0 .0	0 .0	1 50.5	3 42.5	1 25.9	0 42.7	0 17.2	2 35.0	0 29.5	1 44.2	10 6.0

RIGHT ASCENSION

DAY	EPHEM. SID. TIME	☉	☊	☽	☿	♀	♂	♃	♄	♅	♆	♇
1	8 42 39.8	14♒ 3.7	24♑56.7	8♑13.0	26♒27.8	14♒54.1	22♏56.7	15♊26.6	7♏32.3	21♋56.4	24♎47.4	0♍ .3
2	8 46 36.3	15 4.9	24 53.4	22 44.0	28 6.2	16 10.5	23 31.4	15R24.6	7 33.9	21R53.9	24R47.2	29♌58.9
3	8 50 32.9	16 5.9	24 50.0	6♒58.8	29 42.9	17 26.6	24 6.2	15 22.8	7 35.5	21 51.4	24 47.0	29R57.5
4	8 54 29.4	17 6.7	24 46.6	20 49.7	1♓17.7	18 42.4	24 40.9	15 21.3	7 37.0	21 48.9	24 46.8	29 56.1
5	8 58 26.0	18 7.3	24 43.3	4♓17.7	2 50.2	19 57.8	25 15.5	15 20.0	7 38.3	21 46.5	24 46.6	29 54.7
6	9 2 22.6	19 7.7	24 39.9	17 31.3	4 20.1	21 13.0	25 50.2	15 18.9	7 39.6	21 44.0	24 46.3	29 53.3
7	9 6 19.1	20 7.9	24 36.5	0♈42.8	5 47.1	22 27.8	26 24.8	15 18.0	7 40.8	21 41.7	24 46.0	29 51.9
8	9 10 15.7	21 7.9	24 33.2	14 6.0	7 10.7	23 42.3	26 59.4	15 17.4	7 41.8	21 39.3	24 45.7	29 50.4
9	9 14 12.2	22 7.7	24 29.8	27 52.6	8 30.4	24 56.6	27 33.9	15 16.9	7 42.8	21 37.0	24 45.3	29 49.0
10	9 18 8.8	23 7.2	24 26.4	12♉ 9.1	9 45.6	26 10.5	28 8.4	15 16.7	7 43.6	21 34.7	24 44.9	29 47.6
11	9 22 5.3	24 6.6	24 23.1	26 53.6	10 56.0	27 24.1	28 42.9	15 16.7	7 44.4	21 32.4	24 44.5	29 46.1
12	9 26 1.9	25 5.8	24 19.7	11♊53.7	12 .8	28 37.4	29 17.3	15D16.9	7 45.0	21 30.2	24 44.0	29 44.7
13	9 29 58.4	26 4.8	24 16.3	26 49.6	12 59.5	29 50.4	29 51.7	15 17.4	7 45.6	21 28.0	24 43.5	29 43.2
14	9 33 55.0	27 3.6	24 13.0	11♋19.6	13 51.5	1♓ 3.2	0♐26.0	15 18.0	7 46.1	21 25.9	24 43.0	29 41.8
15	9 37 51.6	28 2.2	24 9.6	25 7.9	14 36.3	2 15.6	1 .3	15 18.9	7 46.4	21 23.8	24 42.5	29 40.3
16	9 41 48.1	29 .6	24 6.2	8♌ 7.8	15 13.2	3 27.8	1 34.5	15 20.0	7 46.7	21 21.7	24 41.9	29 38.8
17	9 45 44.7	29 58.8	24 2.8	20 21.2	15 41.9	4 39.7	2 8.7	15 21.3	7 46.8	21 19.7	24 41.3	29 37.4
18	9 49 41.2	0♓56.9	23 59.5	1♍56.2	16 1.9	5 51.4	2 42.8	15 22.8	7 46.9	21 17.7	24 40.6	29 35.9
19	9 53 37.8	1 54.8	23 56.1	13 3.9	16 12.9	7 2.8	3 16.9	15 24.6	7R46.8	21 15.7	24 40.0	29 34.5
20	9 57 34.3	2 52.5	23 52.7	23 56.6	16 14.8	8 13.9	3 50.9	15 26.5	7 46.6	21 13.8	24 39.3	29 33.0
21	10 1 30.9	3 50.1	23 49.4	4♎46.9	16R 7.6	9 24.9	4 25.0	15 28.7	7 46.4	21 12.0	24 38.6	29 31.6
22	10 5 27.4	4 47.5	23 46.0	15 46.9	15 51.5	10 35.6	4 58.9	15 31.1	7 46.1	21 10.2	24 37.9	29 30.2
23	10 9 24.0	5 44.7	23 42.6	27 7.8	15 26.8	11 46.0	5 32.7	15 33.6	7 45.6	21 8.4	24 37.1	29 28.7
24	10 13 20.5	6 41.8	23 39.2	8♏59.2	14 54.3	12 56.3	6 6.4	15 36.4	7 45.1	21 6.7	24 36.3	29 27.3
25	10 17 17.1	7 38.7	23 35.9	21 27.8	14 14.6	14 6.3	6 40.1	15 39.4	7 44.4	21 5.0	24 35.4	29 25.8
26	10 21 13.7	8 35.5	23 32.5	4♐35.3	13 28.8	15 16.2	7 13.7	15 42.6	7 43.6	21 3.3	24 34.6	29 24.4
27	10 25 10.2	9 32.1	23 29.1	18 17.3	12 38.1	16 25.8	7 47.2	15 46.0	7 42.8	21 1.7	24 33.7	29 22.9
28	10 29 6.8	10 28.6	23 25.7	2♑23.0	11 43.7	17 35.3	8 20.6	15 49.6	7 41.8	21 .2	24 32.8	29 21.5

DECLINATION

DAY	EPHEM. SID. TIME	☉	☊	☽	☿	♀	♂	♃	♄	♅	♆	♇
1	8 42 39.8	17S18.6	0S22.5	24S44.1	15S 3.5	18S19.8	18S 4.3	22N24.0	12S11.7	22N24.9	8S28.2	22N58.0
4	8 54 29.4	16 26.6	0 22.5	12 58.3	12 56.9	17 17.8	18 29.7	22 24.1	12 12.4	22 25.9	8 27.8	22 59.9
7	9 6 19.1	15 32.2	0 22.5	5N38.3	10 44.3	16 11.4	18 54.0	22 24.4	12 12.9	22 26.9	8 27.3	23 1.7
10	9 18 8.8	14 35.3	0 22.6	21 17.5	8 31.7	15 1.0	19 17.2	22 24.8	12 13.1	22 27.8	8 26.7	23 3.5
13	9 29 58.4	13 36.3	0 22.6	25 45.7	6 27.3	13 46.8	19 39.4	22 25.4	12 12.9	22 28.7	8 25.9	23 5.3
16	9 41 48.1	12 35.3	0 22.6	17 41.8	4 41.8	12 29.4	20 .4	22 26.3	12 12.5	22 29.5	8 25.1	23 7.0
19	9 53 37.8	11 32.4	0 22.6	2 55.9	3 26.1	11 8.9	20 20.4	22 27.2	12 11.8	22 30.3	8 24.2	23 8.7
22	10 5 27.4	10 27.9	0 22.7	12S17.8	2 49.7	9 45.7	20 39.4	22 28.4	12 10.8	22 31.0	8 23.2	23 10.3
25	10 17 17.1	9 22.0	0 22.7	23 15.7	2 56.9	8 20.2	20 57.2	22 29.7	12 9.5	22 31.7	8 22.2	23 11.8
28	10 29 6.8	8 14.8	0 22.7	25 16.2	3 44.3	6 52.8	21 14.0	22 31.2	12 7.9	22 32.3	8 21.0	23 13.3

MARCH 1954

LONGITUDE

DAY	EPHEM. SID. TIME h m s	☉ ° ′	☊ ° ′	☽ ° ′	☿ ° ′	♀ ° ′	♂ ° ′	♃ ° ′	♄ ° ′	♅ ° ′	♆ ° ′	♇ ° ′
1	10 33 3.3	9♓52.4	21♑37.7	15♑14.7	10♓42.2	17♓ 9.4	10♐24.2	16♊59.1	9♏14.0	19♋18.6	25♎46.4	23♌24.3
2	10 36 59.9	10 52.6	21 34.5	28 46.8	9 R 39.4	18 24.3	10 55.6	17 2.9	9 R 12.7	19 R 17.2	25 R 45.4	23 R 22.9
3	10 40 56.4	11 52.8	21 31.3	12♒46.8	8 36.4	19 39.2	11 26.8	17 6.8	9 11.3	19 15.9	25 44.3	23 21.5
4	10 44 53.0	12 53.0	21 28.1	27 13.2	7 34.6	20 54.1	11 57.9	17 10.9	9 9.9	19 14.7	25 43.2	23 20.1
5	10 48 49.5	13 53.1	21 24.9	12♓ 1.3	6 35.3	22 9.0	12 28.9	17 15.1	9 8.3	19 13.5	25 42.1	23 18.8
6	10 52 46.1	14 53.3	21 21.8	27 3.4	5 39.7	23 23.8	12 59.7	17 19.6	9 6.7	19 12.3	25 41.0	23 17.4
7	10 56 42.6	15 53.3	21 18.6	12♈ 9.9	4 48.8	24 38.6	13 30.3	17 24.2	9 4.9	19 11.2	25 39.8	23 16.1
8	11 0 39.2	16 53.4	21 15.4	27 10.8	4 3.4	25 53.5	14 .8	17 29.0	9 3.0	19 10.2	25 38.6	23 14.7
9	11 4 35.7	17 53.4	21 12.2	11♉57.2	3 23.8	27 8.2	14 31.2	17 34.0	9 1.1	19 9.2	25 37.4	23 13.4
10	11 8 32.3	18 53.3	21 9.1	26 23.2	2 50.6	28 23.0	15 1.4	17 39.1	8 59.1	19 8.2	25 36.2	23 12.1
11	11 12 28.9	19 53.3	21 5.9	10♊25.8	2 24.0	29 37.7	15 31.4	17 44.4	8 56.9	19 7.3	25 34.9	23 10.8
12	11 16 25.4	20 53.2	21 2.7	24 4.5	2 3.9	0♈52.4	16 1.3	17 49.9	8 54.7	19 6.4	25 33.7	23 9.5
13	11 20 22.0	21 53.0	20 59.5	7♋21.1	1 50.5	2 7.1	16 31.0	17 55.6	8 52.4	19 5.6	25 32.4	23 8.2
14	11 24 18.5	22 52.9	20 56.3	20 18.6	1 43.5	3 21.8	17 .6	18 1.4	8 50.0	19 4.9	25 31.1	23 7.0
15	11 28 15.1	23 52.7	20 53.2	2♌59.9	1 42.7	4 36.5	17 30.0	18 7.4	8 47.5	19 4.2	25 29.8	23 5.8
16	11 32 11.6	24 52.4	20 50.0	15 28.4	1 D 47.9	5 51.1	17 59.2	18 13.5	8 45.0	19 3.6	25 28.4	23 4.6
17	11 36 8.2	25 52.1	20 46.8	27 46.8	1 58.9	7 5.7	18 28.3	18 19.8	8 42.3	19 3.0	25 27.1	23 3.4
18	11 40 4.7	26 51.8	20 43.6	9♍57.2	2 15.3	8 20.2	18 57.1	18 26.3	8 39.6	19 2.4	25 25.7	23 2.2
19	11 44 1.3	27 51.5	20 40.5	22 1.2	2 36.9	9 34.8	19 25.8	18 32.9	8 36.7	19 1.9	25 24.3	23 1.0
20	11 47 57.8	28 51.1	20 37.3	4♎ .3	3 3.4	10 49.3	19 54.3	18 39.6	8 33.8	19 1.5	25 22.9	22 59.8
21	11 51 54.4	29 50.6	20 34.1	15 55.5	3 34.5	12 3.7	20 22.6	18 46.5	8 30.8	19 1.1	25 21.4	22 58.7
22	11 55 50.9	0♈50.2	20 30.9	27 48.2	4 9.9	13 18.2	20 50.7	18 53.6	8 27.8	19 .8	25 20.0	22 57.6
23	11 59 47.5	1 49.7	20 27.7	9♏40.2	4 49.4	14 32.6	21 18.6	19 .8	8 24.6	19 .5	25 18.5	22 56.5
24	12 3 44.0	2 49.2	20 24.6	21 33.8	5 32.7	15 47.0	21 46.3	19 8.1	8 21.4	19 .3	25 17.0	22 55.4
25	12 7 40.6	3 48.6	20 21.4	3♐31.9	6 19.6	17 1.4	22 13.7	19 15.6	8 18.1	19 .1	25 15.5	22 54.4
26	12 11 37.1	4 48.1	20 18.2	15 38.3	7 9.9	18 15.8	22 41.0	19 23.2	8 14.8	18 60.0	25 14.0	22 53.3
27	12 15 33.7	5 47.4	20 15.0	27 57.5	8 3.4	19 30.1	23 8.0	19 31.0	8 11.3	18 59.9	25 12.5	22 52.3
28	12 19 30.3	6 46.8	20 11.9	10♑34.2	8 59.9	20 44.4	23 34.8	19 38.9	8 7.8	18 59.9	25 11.0	22 51.3
29	12 23 26.8	7 46.1	20 8.7	23 33.2	9 59.2	21 58.7	24 1.4	19 46.9	8 4.3	18 D 60.0	25 9.4	22 50.3
30	12 27 23.4	8 45.4	20 5.5	6♒58.6	11 1.3	23 12.9	24 27.7	19 55.1	8 .6	19 .1	25 7.9	22 49.4
31	12 31 19.9	9 44.7	20 2.3	20 53.1	12 5.9	24 27.2	24 53.8	20 3.4	7 56.9	19 .2	25 6.3	22 48.5

LATITUDE

DAY	EPHEM. SID. TIME	☉	☊	☽	☿	♀	♂	♃	♄	♅	♆	♇
1	10 33 3.3	0 .0	0 .0	0 S 42.0	3 N 42.7	1 S 25.6	0 N 41.9	0 S 17.0	2 N 35.2	0 N 29.5	1 N 44.3	10 N 6.0
4	10 44 53.0	0 .0	0 .0	2 N 53.2	3 30.6	1 24.0	0 39.4	0 16.5	2 35.9	0 29.4	1 44.4	10 6.0
7	10 56 42.6	0 .0	0 .0	5 .7	3 2.5	1 22.0	0 36.7	0 16.0	2 36.5	0 29.4	1 44.6	10 5.9
10	11 8 32.3	0 .0	0 .0	4 13.5	2 24.1	1 19.3	0 33.9	0 15.5	2 37.1	0 29.3	1 44.7	10 5.7
13	11 20 22.0	0 .0	0 .0	1 18.8	1 41.1	1 16.1	0 30.8	0 15.0	2 37.8	0 29.3	1 44.8	10 5.5
16	11 32 11.6	0 .0	0 .0	2 S .6	0 57.8	1 12.4	0 27.6	0 14.5	2 38.3	0 29.2	1 44.9	10 5.3
19	11 44 1.3	0 .0	0 .0	4 22.3	0 16.8	1 8.2	0 24.2	0 14.0	2 38.9	0 29.2	1 45.0	10 5.1
22	11 55 50.9	0 .0	0 .0	4 59.3	0 S 20.5	1 3.4	0 20.6	0 13.6	2 39.4	0 29.1	1 45.1	10 4.8
25	12 7 40.6	0 .0	0 .0	3 42.0	0 53.4	0 58.2	0 16.7	0 13.1	2 39.9	0 29.1	1 45.2	10 4.4
28	12 19 30.3	0 .0	0 .0	0 52.9	1 21.7	0 52.6	0 12.7	0 12.7	2 40.3	0 29.0	1 45.3	10 4.0
31	12 31 19.9	0 .0	0 .0	2 N 32.8	1 45.3	0 46.5	0 8.3	0 12.2	2 40.7	0 29.0	1 45.3	10 3.6

RIGHT ASCENSION

DAY	EPHEM. SID. TIME	☉	☊	☽	☿	♀	♂	♃	♄	♅	♆	♇
1	10 33 3.3	11♓25.0	23♑22.3	16♑37.9	10♓47.0	18♓44.6	8♐53.9	15♊53.4	7♏40.8	20♋58.7	24♎31.9	29♌20.1
2	10 36 59.9	12 21.3	23 19.0	0♒47.9	9 R 49.5	19 53.8	9 27.1	15 57.4	7 R 39.6	20 R 57.3	24 R 30.9	29 R 18.7
3	10 40 56.4	13 17.4	23 15.6	14 44.3	8 52.4	21 2.8	10 .3	16 1.6	7 38.4	20 55.9	24 29.9	29 17.3
4	10 44 53.0	14 13.4	23 12.2	28 25.4	7 57.1	22 11.7	10 33.3	16 5.9	7 37.0	20 54.5	24 28.9	29 15.9
5	10 48 49.5	15 9.3	23 8.8	11♓56.7	7 4.8	23 20.4	11 6.1	16 10.5	7 35.6	20 53.2	24 27.9	29 14.5
6	10 52 46.1	16 5.1	23 5.5	25 28.3	6 16.3	24 29.1	11 38.9	16 15.3	7 34.0	20 52.0	24 26.8	29 13.1
7	10 56 42.6	17 .8	23 2.1	9♈12.4	5 32.6	25 37.6	12 11.5	16 20.3	7 32.4	20 50.8	24 25.8	29 11.7
8	11 0 39.2	17 56.3	22 58.7	23 20.0	4 54.3	26 46.0	12 44.1	16 25.4	7 30.7	20 49.7	24 24.7	29 10.4
9	11 4 35.7	18 51.8	22 55.3	7♉56.8	4 21.8	27 54.3	13 16.4	16 30.8	7 28.9	20 48.6	24 23.5	29 9.0
10	11 8 32.3	19 47.2	22 51.9	23 .1	3 55.5	29 2.6	13 48.7	16 36.3	7 27.0	20 47.5	24 22.4	29 7.7
11	11 12 28.9	20 42.5	22 48.6	8♊16.6	3 35.4	0♈10.7	14 20.8	16 42.0	7 25.0	20 46.6	24 21.2	29 6.4
12	11 16 25.4	21 37.6	22 45.2	23 25.6	3 21.7	1 18.9	14 52.8	16 47.9	7 22.9	20 45.7	24 20.1	29 5.0
13	11 20 22.0	22 32.8	22 41.8	8♋ 5.2	3 14.1	2 26.9	15 24.6	16 54.0	7 20.7	20 44.8	24 18.9	29 3.7
14	11 24 18.5	23 27.8	22 38.4	21 59.8	3 12.8	3 35.0	15 56.3	17 .3	7 18.5	20 44.0	24 17.7	29 2.5
15	11 28 15.1	24 22.8	22 35.0	5♌ 3.6	3 D 17.3	4 43.0	16 27.8	17 6.8	7 16.1	20 43.3	24 16.5	29 1.2
16	11 32 11.6	25 17.7	22 31.6	17 19.5	3 27.4	5 51.0	16 59.2	17 13.4	7 13.7	20 42.6	24 15.2	28 60.0
17	11 36 8.2	26 12.5	22 28.3	28 55.9	3 42.8	6 58.9	17 30.4	17 20.1	7 11.2	20 41.9	24 13.9	28 58.7
18	11 40 4.7	27 7.3	22 24.9	10♍ 4.3	4 3.4	8 6.9	18 1.4	17 27.1	7 8.6	20 41.4	24 12.6	28 57.5
19	11 44 1.3	28 2.1	22 21.5	20 56.8	4 28.8	9 14.9	18 32.3	17 34.2	7 5.9	20 40.8	24 11.3	28 56.3
20	11 47 57.8	28 56.8	22 18.1	1♎45.8	4 58.6	10 22.9	19 2.9	17 41.5	7 3.1	20 40.3	24 10.0	28 55.1
21	11 51 54.4	29 51.4	22 14.7	12 42.7	5 32.6	11 31.0	19 33.4	17 48.9	7 .3	20 39.9	24 8.7	28 53.9
22	11 55 50.9	0♈46.0	22 11.3	23 58.0	6 10.6	12 39.1	20 3.7	17 56.5	6 57.4	20 39.6	24 7.3	28 52.7
23	11 59 47.5	1 40.7	22 7.9	5♏40.3	6 52.2	13 47.3	20 33.8	18 4.3	6 54.4	20 39.3	24 5.9	28 51.6
24	12 3 44.0	2 35.2	22 4.6	17 55.3	7 37.2	14 55.5	21 3.7	18 12.2	6 51.4	20 39.0	24 4.6	28 50.5
25	12 7 40.6	3 29.8	22 1.2	0♐44.4	8 25.4	16 3.8	21 33.4	18 20.3	6 48.2	20 38.8	24 3.2	28 49.4
26	12 11 37.1	4 24.4	21 57.8	14 3.8	9 16.5	17 12.2	22 2.9	18 28.5	6 45.0	20 38.7	24 1.7	28 48.3
27	12 15 33.7	5 18.9	21 54.4	27 44.5	10 10.5	18 20.7	22 32.1	18 36.9	6 41.8	20 38.6	24 .3	28 47.2
28	12 19 30.3	6 13.5	21 51.0	11♑34.4	11 6.9	19 29.4	23 1.2	18 45.4	6 38.4	20 38.6	23 58.9	28 46.1
29	12 23 26.8	7 8.1	21 47.6	25 22.0	12 5.8	20 38.1	23 29.9	18 54.1	6 35.0	20 D 38.7	23 57.4	28 45.1
30	12 27 23.4	8 2.6	21 44.2	8♒59.9	13 6.9	21 47.0	23 58.5	19 2.9	6 31.6	20 38.8	23 56.0	28 44.1
31	12 31 19.9	8 57.2	21 40.8	22 26.9	14 10.2	22 56.0	24 26.8	19 11.9	6 28.0	20 38.9	23 54.5	28 43.1

DECLINATION

DAY	EPHEM. SID. TIME	☉	☊	☽	☿	♀	♂	♃	♄	♅	♆	♇
1	10 33 3.3	7 S 52.1	0 S 22.7	23 S 16.2	4 S 7.1	6 S 23.3	21 S 19.4	22 N 31.7	12 S 7.3	22 N 32.5	8 S 20.6	23 N 13.8
4	10 44 53.0	6 43.5	0 22.8	9 43.6	5 28.2	4 53.7	21 34.8	22 33.3	12 5.4	22 33.0	8 19.3	23 15.2
7	10 56 42.6	5 34.0	0 22.8	9 N 25.2	6 54.9	3 22.9	21 49.2	22 35.1	12 3.2	22 33.5	8 17.9	23 16.5
10	11 8 32.3	4 23.8	0 22.8	23 27.4	8 13.3	1 51.4	22 2.6	22 37.0	12 .8	22 33.8	8 16.5	23 17.7
13	11 20 22.0	3 13.2	0 22.8	24 33.2	9 14.9	0 19.3	22 15.1	22 39.0	11 58.1	22 34.2	8 15.0	23 18.8
16	11 32 11.6	2 2.2	0 22.9	14 16.9	9 56.3	1 N 13.0	22 26.7	22 41.0	11 55.2	22 34.4	8 13.5	23 19.9
19	11 44 1.3	0 51.1	0 22.9	0 S 51.1	10 17.1	2 45.1	22 37.4	22 43.2	11 52.1	22 34.6	8 11.9	23 20.8
22	11 55 50.9	0 N 20.0	0 22.9	15 20.8	10 18.2	4 16.7	22 47.3	22 45.4	11 48.7	22 34.7	8 10.2	23 21.7
25	12 7 40.6	1 30.9	0 22.9	24 29.8	10 1.2	5 47.6	22 56.4	22 47.6	11 45.2	22 34.7	8 8.5	23 22.5
28	12 19 30.3	2 41.5	0 23.0	23 54.3	9 27.7	7 17.3	23 4.8	22 49.9	11 41.5	22 34.7	8 6.8	23 23.2
31	12 31 19.9	3 51.7	0 23.0	12 7.4	8 38.9	8 45.5	23 12.5	22 52.2	11 37.6	22 34.6	8 5.0	23 23.8

LONGITUDE

DAY	EPHEM. SID. TIME (h m s)	☉	☊	☽	☿	♀	♂	♃	♄	♅	♆	♇
1	12 35 16.5	10♈44.0	19♑59.1	5♓17.1	13♓12.9	25♈41.4	25♐19.6	20♊11.8	7♏53.2	19♋.4	25♎4.7	22♌47.5
2	12 39 13.0	11 43.2	19 56.0	20 7.4	14 22.3	26 55.5	25 45.2	20 20.4	7R49.4	19 .7	25R3.1	22R46.7
3	12 43 9.6	12 42.3	19 52.8	5♈17.2	15 33.8	28 9.7	26 10.4	20 29.0	7 45.5	19 1.0	25 1.5	22 45.8
4	12 47 6.1	13 41.5	19 49.6	20 36.6	16 47.6	29 23.9	26 35.5	20 37.9	7 41.6	19 1.4	24 60.0	22 45.0
5	12 51 2.7	14 40.7	19 46.4	5♉53.8	18 3.4	0♉38.0	27 .2	20 46.8	7 37.6	19 1.8	24 58.4	22 44.2
6	12 54 59.2	15 39.7	19 43.3	20 57.8	19 21.1	1 52.0	27 24.6	20 55.9	7 33.6	19 2.3	24 56.7	22 43.4
7	12 58 55.8	16 38.8	19 40.1	5♊39.9	20 40.8	3 6.1	27 48.8	21 5.1	7 29.5	19 2.8	24 55.1	22 42.6
8	13 2 52.3	17 37.8	19 36.9	19 55.0	22 2.3	4 20.1	28 12.6	21 14.3	7 25.4	19 3.4	24 53.5	22 41.9
9	13 6 48.9	18 36.7	19 33.7	3♋41.7	23 25.7	5 34.0	28 36.1	21 23.8	7 21.2	19 4.1	24 51.9	22 41.2
10	13 10 45.4	19 35.7	19 30.5	17 1.2	24 50.8	6 48.0	28 59.3	21 33.3	7 17.0	19 4.8	24 50.2	22 40.5
11	13 14 42.0	20 34.5	19 27.4	29 56.9	26 17.6	8 1.9	29 22.2	21 42.9	7 12.8	19 5.5	24 48.6	22 39.8
12	13 18 38.6	21 33.4	19 24.2	12♌32.8	27 46.2	9 15.8	29 44.8	21 52.6	7 8.5	19 6.3	24 46.9	22 39.2
13	13 22 35.1	22 32.2	19 21.0	24 53.3	29 16.4	10 29.6	0♑7.0	22 2.5	7 4.2	19 7.1	24 45.3	22 38.6
14	13 26 31.7	23 31.0	19 17.8	7♍2.6	0♈48.3	11 43.4	0 28.9	22 12.4	6 59.8	19 8.0	24 43.7	22 38.0
15	13 30 28.2	24 29.7	19 14.7	19 4.0	2 21.9	12 57.2	0 50.5	22 22.5	6 55.4	19 9.0	24 42.0	22 37.4
16	13 34 24.8	25 28.4	19 11.5	1♎.5	3 57.1	14 10.9	1 11.6	22 32.6	6 51.0	19 10.0	24 40.4	22 36.9
17	13 38 21.3	26 27.1	19 8.3	12 54.3	5 34.0	15 24.6	1 32.5	22 42.9	6 46.6	19 11.1	24 38.7	22 36.4
18	13 42 17.9	27 25.7	19 5.1	24 46.9	7 12.5	16 38.3	1 52.9	22 53.2	6 42.1	19 12.2	24 37.1	22 35.9
19	13 46 14.4	28 24.3	19 1.9	6♏39.8	8 52.6	17 51.9	2 13.0	23 3.7	6 37.7	19 13.3	24 35.4	22 35.4
20	13 50 11.0	29 22.9	18 58.8	18 34.4	10 34.4	19 5.5	2 32.7	23 14.2	6 33.2	19 14.5	24 33.8	22 35.0
21	13 54 7.5	0♉21.4	18 55.6	0♐32.2	12 17.8	20 19.1	2 52.0	23 24.8	6 28.6	19 15.8	24 32.2	22 34.6
22	13 58 4.1	1 19.9	18 52.4	12 35.3	14 2.9	21 32.6	3 10.8	23 35.6	6 24.1	19 17.1	24 30.5	22 34.2
23	14 2 .6	2 18.4	18 49.2	24 46.3	15 49.6	22 46.1	3 29.3	23 46.4	6 19.6	19 18.5	24 28.9	22 33.9
24	14 5 57.2	3 16.9	18 46.1	7♑8.5	17 38.0	23 59.6	3 47.3	23 57.3	6 15.0	19 19.9	24 27.3	22 33.6
25	14 9 53.8	4 15.4	18 42.9	19 45.8	19 28.2	25 13.1	4 4.9	24 8.3	6 10.5	19 21.4	24 25.7	22 33.3
26	14 13 50.3	5 13.8	18 39.7	2♒42.2	21 20.0	26 26.5	4 22.0	24 19.4	6 5.9	19 22.9	24 24.1	22 33.1
27	14 17 46.9	6 12.1	18 36.5	16 1.7	23 13.4	27 39.9	4 38.7	24 30.5	6 1.4	19 24.4	24 22.5	22 32.8
28	14 21 43.4	7 10.5	18 33.3	29 47.4	25 8.6	28 53.2	4 54.9	24 41.8	5 56.8	19 26.0	24 20.9	22 32.6
29	14 25 40.0	8 8.8	18 30.2	14♓.7	27 5.4	0♊6.6	5 10.5	24 53.1	5 52.3	19 27.7	24 19.3	22 32.5
30	14 29 36.5	9 7.1	18 27.0	28 40.1	29 3.8	1 19.9	5 25.7	25 4.5	5 47.7	19 29.4	24 17.7	22 32.3

LATITUDE

DAY	SID. TIME (h m s)	☉	☊	☽	☿	♀	♂	♃	♄	♅	♆	♇
1	12 35 16.5	0 .0	0 .0	3N32.7	1S52.1	0S44.4	0N 6.8	0S12.1	2N40.8	0N28.9	1N45.4	10N 3.5
4	12 47 6.1	0 .0	0 .0	5 .2	2 9.5	0 37.9	0 2.1	0 11.7	2 41.2	0 28.9	1 45.4	10 3.0
7	12 58 55.8	0 .0	0 .0	3 28.9	2 22.2	0 31.1	0S 2.8	0 11.2	2 41.5	0 28.8	1 45.5	10 2.5
10	13 10 45.4	0 .0	0 .0	0 12.6	2 30.3	0 23.9	0 8.1	0 10.8	2 41.8	0 28.8	1 45.5	10 2.0
13	13 22 35.1	0 .0	0 .0	2S55.5	2 33.7	0 16.5	0 13.7	0 10.4	2 42.0	0 28.7	1 45.5	10 1.5
16	13 34 24.8	0 .0	0 .0	4 45.4	2 32.5	0 9.0	0 19.7	0 10.0	2 42.1	0 28.7	1 45.5	10 1.0
19	13 46 14.4	0 .0	0 .0	4 44.5	2 26.7	0 1.2	0 26.0	0 9.7	2 42.2	0 28.6	1 45.5	10 .4
22	13 58 4.1	0 .0	0 .0	1 49.3	2 16.2	0N 6.7	0 32.6	0 9.3	2 42.3	0 28.6	1 45.5	9 59.8
25	14 9 53.8	0 .0	0 .0	0N11.5	2 1.1	0 14.6	0 39.7	0 8.9	2 42.3	0 28.5	1 45.5	9 59.2
28	14 21 43.4	0 .0	0 .0	3 24.1	1 41.1	0 22.5	0 47.2	0 8.6	2 42.3	0 28.5	1 45.5	9 58.6

RIGHT ASCENSION

DAY	SID. TIME (h m s)	☉	☊	☽	☿	♀	♂	♃	♄	♅	♆	♇
1	12 35 16.5	9♈51.9	21♑37.5	5♓48.1	15♓15.4	24♈5.2	24♐54.8	19♊21.0	6♏24.4	20♋39.1	23♎53.0	28♌42.1
2	12 39 13.0	10 46.5	21 34.1	19 13.3	16 22.4	25 14.5	25 22.5	19 30.2	6R20.8	20 39.4	23R51.6	28R41.2
3	12 43 9.6	11 41.2	21 30.7	2♈55.4	17 31.2	26 25.0	25 50.0	19 39.6	6 17.1	20 39.8	23 50.1	28 40.3
4	12 47 6.1	12 36.0	21 27.3	17 6.5	18 41.8	27 33.7	26 17.2	19 49.2	6 13.4	20 40.2	23 48.6	28 39.4
5	12 51 2.7	13 30.7	21 23.9	1♉54.6	19 53.8	28 43.6	26 44.1	19 58.9	6 9.6	20 40.7	23 47.1	28 38.5
6	12 54 59.2	14 25.5	21 20.5	17 18.7	21 7.4	29 53.6	27 10.7	20 8.7	6 5.7	20 41.2	23 45.6	28 37.7
7	12 58 55.8	15 20.3	21 17.1	3♊5.1	22 22.5	1♉3.8	27 36.9	20 18.6	6 1.8	20 41.7	23 44.1	28 36.9
8	13 2 52.3	16 15.2	21 13.7	18 49.3	23 38.9	2 14.3	28 2.9	20 28.7	5 57.9	20 42.4	23 42.5	28 36.0
9	13 6 48.9	17 10.2	21 10.3	4♋4.1	24 56.8	3 25.0	28 28.5	20 38.9	5 53.9	20 43.0	23 41.0	28 35.3
10	13 10 45.4	18 5.2	21 6.9	18 28.8	26 15.9	4 35.8	28 53.8	20 49.2	5 49.8	20 43.8	23 39.5	28 34.5
11	13 14 42.0	19 .2	21 3.5	1♌53.3	27 36.4	5 46.9	29 18.8	20 59.6	5 45.8	20 44.6	23 37.9	28 33.8
12	13 18 38.6	19 55.3	21 .2	14 26.0	28 58.2	6 58.3	29 43.4	21 10.1	5 41.7	20 45.4	23 36.4	28 33.1
13	13 22 35.1	20 50.5	20 56.8	26 10.9	0♈21.2	8 9.8	0♑7.7	21 20.8	5 37.5	20 46.3	23 34.9	28 32.4
14	13 26 31.7	21 45.8	20 53.5	7♍22.7	1 45.6	9 21.6	0 31.6	21 31.6	5 33.3	20 47.3	23 33.3	28 31.7
15	13 30 28.2	22 41.1	20 50.0	18 15.2	3 11.2	10 33.7	0 55.1	21 42.5	5 29.1	20 48.3	23 31.8	28 31.1
16	13 34 24.8	23 36.5	20 46.6	29 1.7	4 38.1	11 46.0	1 18.3	21 53.5	5 24.9	20 49.4	23 30.2	28 30.5
17	13 38 21.3	24 32.1	20 43.2	9♎54.6	6 6.4	12 58.5	1 41.1	22 4.6	5 20.6	20 50.5	23 28.7	28 29.3
18	13 42 17.9	25 27.7	20 39.8	21 4.9	7 36.0	14 11.4	2 3.5	22 15.8	5 16.4	20 51.7	23 27.1	28 28.8
19	13 46 14.4	26 23.3	20 36.4	2♏41.5	9 7.0	15 24.4	2 25.4	22 27.2	5 12.1	20 52.9	23 25.6	28 28.3
20	13 50 11.0	27 19.1	20 33.0	14 50.2	10 39.4	16 37.8	2 47.0	22 38.6	5 7.7	20 54.2	23 24.1	28 28.3
21	13 54 7.5	28 15.0	20 29.6	27 32.2	12 13.3	17 51.4	3 8.1	22 50.1	5 3.4	20 55.6	23 22.5	28 27.8
22	13 58 4.1	29 11.1	20 26.2	10♐43.0	13 48.6	19 5.3	3 28.8	23 1.8	4 59.0	20 57.0	23 21.0	28 27.4
23	14 2 .6	0♉7.2	20 22.8	24 11.1	15 25.5	20 19.5	3 49.1	23 13.5	4 54.7	20 58.4	23 19.4	28 26.9
24	14 5 57.2	1 3.4	20 19.4	7♑49.8	17 4.0	21 33.9	4 8.9	23 25.3	4 50.3	20 59.9	23 17.9	28 26.5
25	14 9 53.8	1 59.8	20 16.0	21 21.4	18 44.2	22 48.6	4 28.2	23 37.3	4 46.0	21 1.6	23 16.4	28 26.2
26	14 13 50.3	2 56.3	20 12.6	4♒40.1	20 26.1	24 3.6	4 47.0	23 49.4	4 41.6	21 3.2	23 14.9	28 25.9
27	14 17 46.9	3 52.9	20 9.2	17 44.9	22 9.8	25 18.9	5 5.4	24 1.5	4 37.2	21 4.8	23 13.4	28 25.6
28	14 21 43.4	4 49.7	20 5.8	0♓41.1	23 55.3	26 34.3	5 23.4	24 13.7	4 32.8	21 6.5	23 11.9	28 25.3
29	14 25 40.0	5 46.5	20 2.4	13 39.0	25 42.7	27 50.2	5 40.4	24 26.0	4 28.4	21 8.3	23 10.4	28 25.0
30	14 29 36.5	6 43.5	19 59.0	26 52.5	27 32.0	29 6.3	5 57.2	24 38.4	4 24.0	21 10.1	23 8.9	28 24.8

DECLINATION

DAY	SID. TIME (h m s)	☉	☊	☽	☿	♀	♂	♃	♄	♅	♆	♇
1	12 35 16.5	4N15.0	0S23.0	6S16.6	8S19.4	9N14.5	23S15.0	22N53.0	11S36.3	22N34.6	8S 4.5	23N23.9
4	12 47 6.1	5 24.3	0 23.0	12N40.9	7 12.2	10 40.3	23 22.0	22 55.3	11 32.3	22 34.4	8 2.7	23 24.4
7	12 58 55.8	6 32.7	0 23.0	24 40.9	5 52.4	12 3.8	23 28.5	22 57.6	11 28.1	22 34.1	8 .9	23 24.7
10	13 10 45.4	7 40.1	0 23.1	22 34.2	4 20.8	13 24.7	23 34.7	22 59.8	11 23.8	22 33.8	7 59.1	23 25.0
13	13 22 35.1	8 46.3	0 23.1	10 28.3	2 38.3	14 42.7	23 40.5	23 2.0	11 19.5	22 33.4	7 57.2	23 25.1
16	13 34 24.8	9 51.2	0 23.1	4S45.8	0 45.7	15 57.4	23 46.1	23 4.1	11 15.1	22 32.9	7 55.4	23 25.2
19	13 46 14.4	10 54.6	0 23.2	18 13.0	1N16.4	17 8.5	23 51.6	23 6.2	11 10.6	22 32.4	7 53.6	23 25.2
22	13 58 4.1	11 56.4	0 23.2	25 11.1	3 27.0	18 15.7	23 57.1	23 8.2	11 6.2	22 31.8	7 51.8	23 25.0
25	14 9 53.8	12 56.5	0 23.2	21 48.1	5 45.1	19 18.6	24 2.7	23 10.1	11 1.7	22 31.2	7 50.1	23 24.7
28	14 21 43.4	13 54.7	0 23.2	8 21.7	8 9.4	20 17.0	24 8.4	23 11.8	10 57.3	22 30.4	7 48.3	23 24.4

MAY 1954

LONGITUDE

DAY	EPHEM. SID. TIME h m s	☉ ° ′	☊ ° ′	☽ ° ′	☿ ° ′	♀ ° ′	♂ ° ′	♃ ° ′	♄ ° ′	♅ ° ′	♆ ° ′	♇ ° ′
1	14 33 33.1	10♉ 5.4	18♑23.8	13♈40.7	1♉ 3.9	2♊33.1	5♑40.4	25♊16.0	5♏43.1	19♋31.1	24♎16.1	22♌32.2
2	14 37 29.6	11 3.6	18 20.6	28 54.5	3 5.6	3 46.3	5 54.5	25 27.5	5 R38.6	19 32.9	24 R14.6	22 R32.1
3	14 41 26.2	12 1.8	18 17.5	14♉10.7	5 8.8	4 59.5	6 8.1	25 39.2	5 34.1	19 34.8	24 13.0	22 32.0
4	14 45 22.8	13 .0	18 14.3	29 18.2	7 13.4	6 12.7	6 21.1	25 50.9	5 29.5	19 36.7	24 11.5	22 32.0
5	14 49 19.3	13 58.2	18 11.1	14♊ 7.4	9 19.4	7 25.8	6 33.6	26 2.6	5 25.1	19 38.6	24 9.9	22 32.0
6	14 53 15.9	14 56.3	18 7.9	28 31.3	11 26.6	8 38.9	6 45.5	26 14.5	5 20.6	19 40.6	24 8.4	22 32.0
7	14 57 12.4	15 54.4	18 4.8	12♋26.9	13 34.9	9 51.9	6 56.8	26 26.4	5 16.1	19 42.6	24 6.9	22 D32.1
8	15 1 9.0	16 52.5	18 1.6	25 53.8	15 44.1	11 4.9	7 7.6	26 38.4	5 11.7	19 44.7	24 5.4	22 32.1
9	15 5 5.5	17 50.5	17 58.4	8♌54.5	17 54.0	12 17.9	7 17.8	26 50.4	5 7.3	19 46.8	24 3.9	22 32.3
10	15 9 2.1	18 48.5	17 55.2	21 32.8	20 4.4	13 30.8	7 27.3	27 2.5	5 2.9	19 48.9	24 2.5	22 32.4
11	15 12 58.6	19 46.5	17 52.0	3♍53.3	22 15.1	14 43.7	7 36.2	27 14.7	4 58.6	19 51.1	24 1.0	22 32.6
12	15 16 55.2	20 44.4	17 48.9	16 .5	24 25.7	15 56.5	7 44.5	27 26.9	4 54.3	19 53.3	23 59.6	22 32.8
13	15 20 51.8	21 42.3	17 45.7	27 58.9	26 36.1	17 9.3	7 52.2	27 39.2	4 50.0	19 55.6	23 58.2	22 33.0
14	15 24 48.3	22 40.2	17 42.5	9♎52.4	28 45.8	18 22.1	7 59.2	27 51.6	4 45.7	19 57.9	23 56.8	22 33.2
15	15 28 44.9	23 38.1	17 39.3	21 44.2	0♊54.7	19 34.8	8 5.6	28 4.0	4 41.5	20 .3	23 55.4	22 33.5
16	15 32 41.4	24 36.0	17 36.2	3♏36.8	3 2.5	20 47.6	8 11.4	28 16.5	4 37.4	20 2.7	23 54.1	22 33.9
17	15 36 38.0	25 33.8	17 33.0	15 32.4	5 8.8	22 .2	8 16.4	28 29.0	4 33.3	20 5.1	23 52.7	22 34.2
18	15 40 34.5	26 31.5	17 29.8	27 32.4	7 13.5	23 12.8	8 20.7	28 41.5	4 29.3	20 7.6	23 51.4	22 34.6
19	15 44 31.1	27 29.3	17 26.6	9♐38.4	9 16.3	24 25.3	8 24.4	28 54.1	4 25.2	20 10.1	23 50.1	22 35.0
20	15 48 27.6	28 27.0	17 23.5	21 51.7	11 17.0	25 37.9	8 27.3	29 6.8	4 21.3	20 12.7	23 48.8	22 35.4
21	15 52 24.2	29 24.7	17 20.3	4♑14.0	13 15.3	26 50.3	8 29.5	29 19.5	4 17.4	20 15.3	23 47.5	22 35.8
22	15 56 20.8	0♊22.4	17 17.1	16 47.3	15 11.3	28 2.8	8 31.0	29 32.2	4 13.5	20 17.9	23 46.3	22 36.3
23	16 0 17.3	1 20.1	17 13.9	29 33.8	17 4.7	29 15.1	8 31.8	29 45.0	4 9.7	20 20.5	23 45.0	22 36.8
24	16 4 13.9	2 17.8	17 10.7	12♒36.3	18 55.3	0♋27.5	8 31.8	29 57.9	4 5.9	20 23.2	23 43.8	22 37.3
25	16 8 10.4	3 15.4	17 7.6	25 57.4	20 43.3	1 39.8	8 R31.1	0♋10.8	4 2.2	20 25.9	23 42.7	22 37.9
26	16 12 7.0	4 13.0	17 4.4	9♓39.3	22 28.3	2 52.1	8 29.6	0 23.7	3 58.6	20 28.7	23 41.5	22 38.5
27	16 16 3.5	5 10.6	17 1.2	23 42.9	24 10.5	4 4.3	8 27.3	0 36.7	3 55.0	20 31.5	23 40.3	22 39.1
28	16 20 .1	6 8.2	16 58.0	8♈ 7.5	25 49.8	5 16.5	8 24.3	0 49.7	3 51.5	20 34.3	23 39.2	22 39.8
29	16 23 56.7	7 5.8	16 54.9	22 50.0	27 26.0	6 28.6	8 20.5	1 2.7	3 48.1	20 37.2	23 38.1	22 40.4
30	16 27 53.2	8 3.4	16 51.7	7♉44.6	28 59.2	7 40.7	8 16.0	1 15.8	3 44.7	20 40.1	23 37.1	22 41.1
31	16 31 49.8	9 .9	16 48.5	22 43.5	0♋29.4	8 52.8	8 10.7	1 28.9	3 41.4	20 43.0	23 36.0	22 41.8

LATITUDE

DAY	EPHEM. SID. TIME	☉	☊	☽	☿	♀	♂	♃	♄	♅	♆	♇
1	14 33 33.1	0 .0	0 .0	5N 2.0	1S17.9	0N30.5	0S55.1	0S 8.2	2N42.2	0N28.4	1N45.5	9N58.0
4	14 45 22.8	0 .0	0 .0	3 43.9	0 50.5	0 38.3	1 3.4	0 7.8	2 42.0	0 28.4	1 45.4	9 57.3
7	14 57 12.4	0 .0	0 .0	0 22.2	0 20.4	0 46.0	1 12.3	0 7.5	2 41.8	0 28.3	1 45.4	9 56.7
10	15 9 2.1	0 .0	0 .0	2S55.5	0N11.1	0 53.5	1 21.5	0 7.2	2 41.6	0 28.3	1 45.3	9 56.0
13	15 20 51.8	0 .0	0 .0	4 49.8	0 42.3	1 .8	1 31.3	0 6.8	2 41.3	0 28.2	1 45.2	9 55.4
16	15 32 41.4	0 .0	0 .0	4 51.3	1 11.2	1 7.8	1 41.5	0 6.5	2 40.9	0 28.2	1 45.2	9 54.8
19	15 44 31.1	0 .0	0 .0	3 .7	1 36.0	1 14.5	1 52.2	0 6.2	2 40.6	0 28.2	1 45.1	9 54.1
22	15 56 20.8	0 .0	0 .0	0N 7.2	1 55.1	1 20.9	2 3.2	0 5.8	2 40.1	0 28.1	1 45.0	9 53.5
25	16 8 10.4	0 .0	0 .0	3 21.5	2 7.7	1 26.8	2 14.7	0 5.5	2 39.7	0 28.1	1 44.9	9 52.9
28	16 20 .1	0 .0	0 .0	5 7.6	2 13.1	1 32.2	2 26.6	0 5.2	2 39.2	0 28.1	1 44.8	9 52.2
31	16 31 49.8	0 .0	0 .0	4 6.5	2 11.3	1 37.1	2 38.8	0 4.9	2 38.6	0 28.0	1 44.7	9 51.6

RIGHT ASCENSION

DAY	EPHEM. SID. TIME	☉	☊	☽	☿	♀	♂	♃	♄	♅	♆	♇
1	14 33 33.1	7♉40.7	19♑55.6	10♈36.3	29♈23.3	0♊22.6	6♑13.4	24♊50.9	4♏19.6	21♋12.0	23♎ 7.4	28♌24.6
2	14 37 29.6	8 37.9	19 52.2	25 2.9	1♉16.6	1 39.2	6 29.0	25 3.4	4 R15.2	21 13.9	23 R 6.0	28 R24.4
3	14 41 26.2	9 35.4	19 48.8	10♉17.7	3 12.0	2 56.0	6 44.0	25 16.1	4 10.9	21 15.9	23 4.5	28 24.3
4	14 45 22.8	10 32.9	19 45.4	26 12.8	5 9.5	4 13.0	6 58.4	25 28.8	4 6.5	21 17.9	23 3.0	28 24.2
5	14 49 19.3	11 30.6	19 42.0	12♊25.2	7 8.9	5 30.4	7 12.3	25 41.6	4 2.2	21 20.0	23 1.6	28 24.1
6	14 53 15.9	12 28.4	19 38.6	28 22.2	9 10.4	6 47.9	7 25.5	25 54.5	3 57.9	21 22.1	23 .2	28 24.0
7	14 57 12.4	13 26.4	19 35.2	13♋33.9	11 13.8	8 5.6	7 38.1	26 7.5	3 53.6	21 24.2	22 58.8	28 24.0
8	15 1 9.0	14 24.5	19 31.8	27 43.4	13 19.1	9 23.6	7 50.1	26 20.5	3 49.3	21 26.4	22 57.3	28 24.0
9	15 5 5.5	15 22.7	19 28.4	10♌48.6	15 26.1	10 41.8	8 1.4	26 33.6	3 45.0	21 28.7	22 55.9	28 24.0
10	15 9 2.1	16 21.1	19 25.0	22 57.9	17 34.6	12 .1	8 12.1	26 46.8	3 40.8	21 31.0	22 54.6	28 D24.1
11	15 12 58.6	17 19.6	19 21.6	4♍25.1	19 44.4	13 18.7	8 22.1	27 .0	3 36.6	21 33.3	22 53.2	28 24.2
12	15 16 55.2	18 18.2	19 18.2	15 25.3	21 55.4	14 37.4	8 31.4	27 13.3	3 32.4	21 35.7	22 51.8	28 24.3
13	15 20 51.8	19 17.0	19 14.8	26 13.5	24 7.3	15 56.2	8 40.1	27 26.7	3 28.3	21 38.1	22 50.5	28 24.4
14	15 24 48.3	20 15.9	19 11.4	7♎ 3.9	26 19.7	17 15.2	8 48.0	27 40.1	3 24.2	21 40.6	22 49.2	28 24.6
15	15 28 44.9	21 15.0	19 8.0	18 8.9	28 32.4	18 34.4	8 55.2	27 53.6	3 20.1	21 43.1	22 47.9	28 24.8
16	15 32 41.4	22 14.2	19 4.6	29 39.1	0♊45.0	19 53.7	9 1.8	28 7.2	3 16.2	21 45.7	22 46.6	28 25.1
17	15 36 38.0	23 13.6	19 1.2	11♏41.8	2 57.2	21 13.0	9 7.6	28 20.9	3 12.2	21 48.3	22 45.4	28 25.3
18	15 40 34.5	24 13.1	18 57.8	24 19.5	5 8.7	22 32.5	9 12.6	28 34.5	3 8.3	21 51.0	22 44.1	28 25.6
19	15 44 31.1	25 12.7	18 54.4	7♐28.9	7 19.2	23 52.0	9 16.9	28 48.3	3 4.4	21 53.7	22 42.9	28 26.0
20	15 48 27.6	26 12.5	18 51.0	21 .1	9 28.3	25 11.6	9 20.3	29 2.0	3 .5	21 56.4	22 41.6	28 26.3
21	15 52 24.2	27 12.4	18 47.6	4♑38.9	11 35.8	26 31.2	9 23.1	29 15.9	2 56.7	21 59.2	22 40.4	28 26.7
22	15 56 20.8	28 12.4	18 44.2	18 11.2	13 41.3	27 50.9	9 25.0	29 29.8	2 53.0	22 2.0	22 39.3	28 27.1
23	16 0 17.3	29 12.6	18 40.8	1♒27.0	15 44.8	29 10.6	9 26.1	29 43.7	2 49.3	22 4.8	22 38.1	28 27.5
24	16 4 13.9	0♊12.9	18 37.3	14 23.1	17 45.8	0♋30.3	9 26.4	29 57.7	2 45.6	22 7.7	22 36.9	28 28.0
25	16 8 10.4	1 13.4	18 33.9	27 3.4	19 44.3	1 50.0	9 R25.9	0♋11.7	2 42.0	22 10.6	22 35.8	28 28.4
26	16 12 7.0	2 13.9	18 30.5	9♓37.8	21 40.1	3 9.6	9 24.5	0 25.8	2 38.5	22 13.5	22 34.7	28 29.0
27	16 16 3.5	3 14.6	18 27.1	22 19.8	23 32.9	4 29.2	9 22.3	0 39.9	2 35.0	22 16.5	22 33.6	28 29.5
28	16 20 .1	4 15.5	18 23.7	5♈25.4	25 22.7	5 48.8	9 19.3	0 54.1	2 31.6	22 19.5	22 32.6	28 30.1
29	16 23 56.7	5 16.4	18 20.3	19 9.9	27 9.3	7 8.3	9 15.4	1 8.3	2 28.3	22 22.6	22 31.5	28 30.7
30	16 27 53.2	6 17.5	18 16.9	3♉44.8	28 52.6	8 27.7	9 10.6	1 22.6	2 25.0	22 25.7	22 30.5	28 31.3
31	16 31 49.8	7 18.7	18 13.5	19 11.6	0♋32.6	9 47.0	9 5.0	1 36.9	2 21.7	22 28.8	22 29.5	28 31.9

DECLINATION

DAY	EPHEM. SID. TIME	☉	☊	☽	☿	♀	♂	♃	♄	♅	♆	♇
1	14 33 33.1	14N50.8	0S23.2	10N 2.0	10N37.9	21N10.5	24S14.5	23N13.5	10S52.9	22N29.7	7S46.6	23N24.0
4	14 45 22.8	15 44.7	0 23.3	23 38.9	13 7.9	21 58.8	24 21.0	23 15.0	10 48.5	22 28.8	7 45.0	23 23.4
7	14 57 12.4	16 36.3	0 23.3	23 13.9	15 35.7	22 41.6	24 28.0	23 16.4	10 44.3	22 27.9	7 43.3	23 22.8
10	15 9 2.1	17 25.3	0 23.3	11 33.2	17 56.6	23 18.8	24 35.6	23 17.6	10 40.1	22 26.9	7 41.8	23 22.1
13	15 20 51.8	18 11.8	0 23.3	3S37.7	20 5.2	23 50.1	24 43.9	23 18.7	10 36.1	22 25.9	7 40.3	23 21.3
16	15 32 41.4	18 55.5	0 23.3	17 17.1	21 56.2	24 15.2	24 52.9	23 19.6	10 32.3	22 24.8	7 38.8	23 20.4
19	15 44 31.1	19 36.3	0 23.4	24 52.7	23 25.7	24 34.2	25 2.7	23 20.3	10 28.6	22 23.7	7 37.4	23 19.4
22	15 56 20.8	20 14.1	0 23.4	22 16.4	24 31.8	24 46.7	25 13.3	23 20.9	10 25.1	22 22.5	7 36.1	23 18.4
25	16 8 10.4	20 48.8	0 23.4	9 42.4	25 14.6	24 52.9	25 24.8	23 21.2	10 21.7	22 21.3	7 34.9	23 17.2
28	16 20 .1	21 20.3	0 23.4	7N55.9	25 35.9	24 52.6	25 37.0	23 21.4	10 18.6	22 20.0	7 33.7	23 16.0
31	16 31 49.8	21 48.5	0 23.4	22 25.7	25 38.0	24 45.8	25 50.0	23 21.3	10 15.7	22 18.6	7 32.7	23 14.7

JUNE 1954

LONGITUDE

DAY	EPHEM. SID. TIME	☉	☊	☾	☿	♀	♂	♃	♄	♅	♆	♇
	h m s	° ′	° ′	° ′	° ′	° ′	° ′	° ′	° ′	° ′	° ′	° ′
1	16 35 46.3	9 ♊ 58.5	16 ♑ 45.3	7 ♊ 37.8	1 ♋ 56.4	10 ♋ 4.8	8 ♑ 4.6	1 ♋ 42.1	3 ♏ 38.2	20 ♋ 46.0	23 ♎ 35.0	22 ♌ 42.6
2	16 39 42.9	10 56.0	16 42.2	22 19.0	3 20.4	11 16.7	7 R 57.8	1 55.3	3 R 35.0	20 48.9	23 R 34.0	22 43.4
3	16 43 39.4	11 53.5	16 39.0	6 ♋ 40.2	4 41.1	12 28.6	7 50.2	2 8.5	3 31.9	20 52.0	23 33.0	22 44.2
4	16 47 36.0	12 51.0	16 35.8	20 37.1	5 58.7	13 40.5	7 41.9	2 21.8	3 28.9	20 55.0	23 32.1	22 45.0
5	16 51 32.6	13 48.4	16 32.6	4 ♌ 8.0	7 13.0	14 52.3	7 32.8	2 35.0	3 26.0	20 58.1	23 31.2	22 45.9
6	16 55 29.1	14 45.9	16 29.4	17 13.7	8 24.0	16 4.2	7 23.2	2 48.4	3 23.2	21 1.2	23 30.3	22 46.8
7	16 59 25.7	15 43.3	16 26.3	29 56.5	9 31.7	17 15.9	7 12.7	3 1.7	3 20.4	21 4.3	23 29.4	22 47.7
8	17 3 22.2	16 40.7	16 23.1	12 ♍ 20.4	10 35.9	18 27.5	7 1.6	3 15.1	3 17.7	21 7.5	23 28.6	22 48.6
9	17 7 18.8	17 38.1	16 19.9	24 29.7	11 36.5	19 39.1	6 49.9	3 28.5	3 15.1	21 10.7	23 27.8	22 49.6
10	17 11 15.4	18 35.5	16 16.7	6 ♎ 28.9	12 33.7	20 50.7	6 37.5	3 41.9	3 12.5	21 13.9	23 27.0	22 50.6
11	17 15 11.9	19 32.8	16 13.6	18 22.6	13 27.1	22 2.2	6 24.4	3 55.3	3 10.1	21 17.1	23 26.3	22 51.6
12	17 19 8.5	20 30.2	16 10.4	0 ♏ 14.8	14 16.8	23 13.6	6 10.8	4 8.7	3 7.7	21 20.3	23 25.5	22 52.6
13	17 23 5.0	21 27.5	16 7.2	12 9.2	15 2.7	24 25.0	5 56.7	4 22.2	3 5.5	21 23.6	23 24.8	22 53.6
14	17 27 1.6	22 24.8	16 4.0	24 8.8	15 44.6	25 36.3	5 41.9	4 35.7	3 3.3	21 26.9	23 24.2	22 54.7
15	17 30 58.1	23 22.1	16 .9	6 ♐ 15.9	16 22.5	26 47.6	5 26.7	4 49.2	3 1.2	21 30.2	23 23.5	22 55.8
16	17 34 54.7	24 19.4	15 57.7	18 32.5	16 56.3	27 58.8	5 11.0	5 2.7	2 59.2	21 33.5	23 22.9	22 56.9
17	17 38 51.3	25 16.6	15 54.5	0 ♑ 59.8	17 25.8	29 9.9	4 54.8	5 16.2	2 57.2	21 36.9	23 22.3	22 58.1
18	17 42 47.8	26 13.9	15 51.3	13 39.0	17 51.1	0 ♌ 21.0	4 38.2	5 29.8	2 55.4	21 40.3	23 21.8	22 59.3
19	17 46 44.4	27 11.2	15 48.2	26 30.7	18 11.9	1 32.0	4 21.2	5 43.3	2 53.7	21 43.7	23 21.2	23 .5
20	17 50 40.9	28 8.4	15 45.0	9 ♒ 35.6	18 28.2	2 42.9	4 3.9	5 56.9	2 52.0	21 47.1	23 20.7	23 1.7
21	17 54 37.5	29 5.7	15 41.8	22 54.3	18 40.0	3 53.8	3 46.2	6 10.5	2 50.4	21 50.5	23 20.3	23 2.9
22	17 58 34.1	0 ♋ 2.9	15 38.6	6 ♓ 27.3	18 47.3	5 4.6	3 28.3	6 24.1	2 49.0	21 54.0	23 19.9	23 4.2
23	18 2 30.6	1 .1	15 35.4	20 14.7	18 49.9	6 15.4	3 10.1	6 37.7	2 47.6	21 57.4	23 19.4	23 5.4
24	18 6 27.2	1 57.4	15 32.3	4 ♈ 16.2	18 R 48.1	7 26.1	2 51.7	6 51.3	2 46.3	22 .9	23 19.1	23 6.7
25	18 10 23.7	2 54.6	15 29.1	18 30.5	18 41.7	8 36.7	2 33.2	7 4.9	2 45.1	22 4.4	23 18.7	23 8.1
26	18 14 20.3	3 51.8	15 25.9	2 ♉ 55.2	18 30.9	9 47.3	2 14.6	7 18.5	2 44.1	22 7.9	23 18.4	23 9.4
27	18 18 16.8	4 49.1	15 22.7	17 26.7	18 16.0	10 57.8	1 56.0	7 32.2	2 43.1	22 11.5	23 18.2	23 10.8
28	18 22 13.4	5 46.4	15 19.6	2 ♊ .1	17 57.0	12 8.3	1 37.3	7 45.8	2 42.2	22 15.0	23 18.0	23 12.2
29	18 26 10.0	6 43.6	15 16.4	16 29.7	17 34.1	13 18.6	1 18.6	7 59.4	2 41.4	22 18.6	23 17.7	23 13.6
30	18 30 6.5	7 40.8	15 13.2	0 ♋ 49.9	17 7.9	14 28.9	1 .1	8 13.0	2 40.7	22 22.1	23 17.6	23 15.0

LATITUDE

DAY	EPHEM. SID. TIME	☉	☊	☾	☿	♀	♂	♃	♄	♅	♆	♇
1	16 35 46.3	0 .0	0 .0	3 N 9.5	2 N 9.1	1 N 38.7	2 S 42.9	0 S 4.8	2 N 38.4	0 N 28.0	1 N 44.6	9 N 51.4
4	16 47 36.0	0 .0	0 .0	0 S 30.5	1 57.6	1 42.8	2 55.3	0 4.5	2 37.8	0 28.0	1 44.5	9 50.8
7	16 59 25.7	0 .0	0 .0	3 41.3	1 39.0	1 46.4	3 7.8	0 4.2	2 37.2	0 28.0	1 44.4	9 50.3
10	17 11 15.4	0 .0	0 .0	5 9.9	1 13.6	1 49.3	3 20.2	0 3.9	2 36.6	0 28.0	1 44.2	9 49.7
13	17 23 5.0	0 .0	0 .0	4 39.0	0 41.7	1 51.6	3 32.5	0 3.6	2 35.9	0 27.9	1 44.1	9 49.2
16	17 34 54.7	0 .0	0 .0	2 19.3	0 3.8	1 53.1	3 44.4	0 3.3	2 35.2	0 27.9	1 44.0	9 48.7
19	17 46 44.4	0 .0	0 .0	1 N 4.5	0 S 39.3	1 53.9	3 55.8	0 3.0	2 34.5	0 27.9	1 43.8	9 48.2
22	17 58 34.1	0 .0	0 .0	4 8.2	1 26.3	1 54.0	4 6.6	0 2.7	2 33.7	0 27.9	1 43.7	9 47.7
25	18 10 23.7	0 .0	0 .0	5 15.5	2 15.0	1 53.2	4 16.7	0 2.4	2 33.0	0 27.9	1 43.5	9 47.3
28	18 22 13.4	0 .0	0 .0	3 35.0	3 2.8	1 51.6	4 25.8	0 2.1	2 32.2	0 27.9	1 43.4	9 46.9

RIGHT ASCENSION

DAY	EPHEM. SID. TIME	☉	☊	☾	☿	♀	♂	♃	♄	♅	♆	♇
1	16 35 46.3	8 ♊ 20.0	18 ♑ 10.1	5 ♊ 16.4	2 ♋ 9.0	11 ♋ 6.1	8 ♑ 58.6	1 ♋ 51.2	2 ♏ 18.6	22 ♋ 31.9	22 ♎ 28.5	28 ♌ 32.6
2	16 39 42.9	9 21.4	18 6.7	21 30.4	3 41.9	12 25.2	8 R 51.3	2 5.6	2 R 15.5	22 35.1	22 R 27.6	28 33.3
3	16 43 39.4	10 22.9	18 3.3	7 ♋ 18.4	5 11.1	13 44.0	8 43.1	2 20.0	2 12.5	22 38.3	22 26.7	28 34.1
4	16 47 36.0	11 24.5	17 59.9	22 13.0	6 36.6	15 2.7	8 34.2	2 34.4	2 9.5	22 41.6	22 25.8	28 34.8
5	16 51 32.6	12 26.2	17 56.4	6 ♌ 2.2	7 58.2	16 21.3	8 24.4	2 48.9	2 6.7	22 44.9	22 24.9	28 35.6
6	16 55 29.1	13 28.0	17 53.0	18 48.7	9 16.0	17 39.6	8 13.9	3 3.4	2 3.9	22 48.2	22 24.1	28 36.5
7	16 59 25.7	14 29.8	17 49.6	0 ♍ 43.6	10 29.8	18 57.7	8 2.6	3 17.9	2 1.2	22 51.6	22 23.2	28 37.3
8	17 3 22.2	15 31.7	17 46.2	12 2.3	11 39.6	20 15.6	7 50.5	3 32.5	1 58.5	22 54.9	22 22.4	28 38.2
9	17 7 18.8	16 33.7	17 42.8	23 .5	12 45.2	21 33.2	7 37.6	3 47.1	1 56.0	22 58.3	22 21.7	28 39.1
10	17 11 15.4	17 35.7	17 39.4	3 ♎ 53.5	13 46.6	22 50.6	7 24.0	4 1.7	1 53.5	23 1.7	22 20.9	28 40.0
11	17 15 11.9	18 37.8	17 36.0	14 55.4	14 43.8	24 7.7	7 9.8	4 16.3	1 51.1	23 5.2	22 20.2	28 40.9
12	17 19 8.5	19 40.0	17 32.6	26 18.3	15 36.5	25 24.5	6 54.8	4 30.9	1 48.7	23 8.6	22 19.5	28 41.9
13	17 23 5.0	20 42.2	17 29.1	8 ♏ 11.9	16 24.9	26 41.0	6 39.2	4 45.6	1 46.5	23 12.1	22 18.8	28 42.9
14	17 27 1.6	21 44.4	17 25.7	20 41.5	17 8.7	27 57.3	6 22.9	5 .2	1 44.3	23 15.6	22 18.2	28 43.9
15	17 30 58.1	22 46.7	17 22.3	3 ♐ 46.5	17 47.8	29 13.2	6 6.1	5 14.9	1 42.2	23 19.2	22 17.5	28 45.0
16	17 34 54.7	23 49.0	17 18.9	17 19.2	18 22.4	0 ♌ 28.8	5 48.6	5 29.6	1 40.2	23 22.7	22 17.0	28 46.0
17	17 38 51.3	24 51.3	17 15.5	1 ♑ 5.8	18 52.1	1 44.1	5 30.7	5 44.4	1 38.3	23 26.3	22 16.4	28 47.1
18	17 42 47.8	25 53.6	17 12.1	14 50.2	19 17.1	2 59.0	5 12.3	5 59.1	1 36.5	23 29.9	22 15.9	28 48.2
19	17 46 44.4	26 56.0	17 8.7	28 19.0	19 37.2	4 13.6	4 53.3	6 13.9	1 34.7	23 33.5	22 15.3	28 49.4
20	17 50 40.9	27 58.4	17 5.3	11 ♒ 25.3	19 52.3	5 27.9	4 34.0	6 28.6	1 33.1	23 37.2	22 14.9	28 50.5
21	17 54 37.5	29 .8	17 1.8	24 10.0	20 2.6	6 41.8	4 14.3	6 .43.4	1 31.5	23 40.8	22 14.4	28 51.7
22	17 58 34.1	0 ♋ 3.2	16 58.4	6 ♓ 40.6	20 7.9	7 55.3	3 54.3	6 58.2	1 30.0	23 44.5	22 14.0	28 52.9
23	18 2 30.6	1 5.5	16 55.0	19 9.2	20 8.4	9 8.5	3 33.9	7 12.9	1 28.6	23 48.2	22 13.6	28 54.2
24	18 6 27.2	2 7.9	16 51.6	1 ♈ 51.1	20 R 4.0	10 21.4	3 13.4	7 27.7	1 27.3	23 51.9	22 13.2	28 55.4
25	18 10 23.7	3 10.3	16 48.2	15 1.8	19 55.0	11 33.8	2 52.6	7 42.5	1 26.1	23 55.6	22 12.9	28 56.7
26	18 14 20.3	4 12.6	16 44.8	28 55.0	19 41.3	12 45.9	2 31.7	7 57.3	1 25.0	23 59.3	22 12.6	28 58.0
27	18 18 16.8	5 15.0	16 41.3	13 ♉ 38.4	19 23.4	13 57.7	2 10.7	8 12.2	1 24.0	24 3.2	22 12.3	28 59.3
28	18 22 13.4	6 17.3	16 37.9	29 7.4	19 1.2	15 9.1	1 49.7	8 27.0	1 23.0	24 6.9	22 12.1	29 .7
29	18 26 10.0	7 19.5	16 34.5	15 ♊ 3.1	18 35.3	16 ·20.0	1 28.7	8 41.8	1 22.2	24 10.7	22 11.9	29 2.0
30	18 30 6.5	8 21.7	16 31.1	0 ♋ 54.9	18 5.8	17 30.6	1 7.8	8 56.6	1 21.4	24 14.5	22 11.7	29 3.4

DECLINATION

DAY	EPHEM. SID. TIME	☉	☊	☾	☿	♀	♂	♃	♄	♅	♆	♇
1	16 35 46.3	21 N 57.1	0 S 23.5	24 N 42.3	25 N 34.9	24 N 42.1	25 S 54.5	23 N 21.3	10 S 14.8	22 N 18.2	7 S 32.3	23 N 14.3
4	16 47 36.0	22 20.7	0 23.5	21 21.7	25 16.1	24 26.9	26 8.3	23 21.0	10 12.3	22 16.8	7 31.4	23 12.9
7	16 59 25.7	22 40.8	0 23.5	8 2.4	24 45.0	24 5.4	26 22.5	23 20.5	10 10.0	22 15.3	7 30.5	23 11.5
10	17 11 15.4	22 57.3	0 23.5	7 S 18.9	24 4.4	23 37.8	26 36.8	23 19.7	10 7.9	22 13.8	7 29.7	23 10.0
13	17 23 5.0	23 10.2	0 23.5	19 54.5	23 17.2	23 4.3	26 51.0	23 18.8	10 6.2	22 12.3	7 29.1	23 8.4
16	17 34 54.7	23 19.4	0 23.6	25 15.9	22 26.1	22 25.1	27 4.9	23 17.7	10 4.7	22 10.7	7 28.5	23 6.8
19	17 46 44.4	23 24.9	0 23.6	19 48.1	21 33.5	21 40.5	27 18.1	23 16.3	10 3.5	22 9.1	7 28.0	23 5.2
22	17 58 34.1	23 26.7	0 23.6	5 18.0	20 42.2	20 50.7	27 30.6	23 14.7	10 2.6	22 7.4	7 27.6	23 3.5
25	18 10 23.7	23 24.8	0 23.6	12 N 6.8	19 54.7	19 56.0	27 41.9	23 13.0	10 2.0	22 5.7	7 27.4	23 1.7
28	18 22 13.4	23 19.2	0 23.6	24 4.7	19 13.3	18 56.7	27 51.9	23 11.0	10 1.8	22 4.0	7 27.2	22 59.9

JULY 1954

LONGITUDE

DAY	EPHEM. SID. TIME h m s	☉ ° ′	☊ ° ′	☽ ° ′	☿ ° ′	♀ ° ′	♂ ° ′	♃ ° ′	♄ ° ′	♅ ° ′	♆ ° ′	♇ ° ′
1	18 34 3.1	8♋38.1	15♑10.0	14♋55.5	16♋38.5	15♌39.1	0♑41.6	8♋26.7	2♏40.1	22♋25.7	23♎17.4	23♌16.5
2	18 37 59.6	9 35.3	15 6.9	28 42.5	16R 6.5	16 49.3	0R23.4	8 40.3	2R39.6	22 29.3	23R17.3	23 17.9
3	18 41 56.2	10 32.5	15 3.7	12♌ 8.6	15 32.3	17 59.3	0 5.4	8 53.9	2 39.2	22 32.9	23 17.2	23 19.4
4	18 45 52.8	11 29.7	15 .5	25 13.1	14 56.6	19 9.3	29♐47.7	9 7.5	2 38.9	22 36.5	23 17.1	23 20.9
5	18 49 49.3	12 27.0	14 57.3	7♍57.3	14 19.8	20 19.2	29 30.3	9 21.2	2 38.7	22 40.1	23 17.1	23 22.4
6	18 53 45.9	13 24.2	14 54.2	20 23.3	13 42.6	21 29.1	29 13.3	9 34.8	2 38.6	22 43.7	23 17.1	23 23.9
7	18 57 42.4	14 21.4	14 51.0	2♎34.6	13 5.6	22 38.8	28 56.8	9 48.4	2 38.6	22 47.4	23D17.2	23 25.5
8	19 1 39.0	15 18.6	14 47.8	14 35.4	12 29.6	23 48.5	28 40.6	10 1.9	2D38.7	22 51.0	23 17.2	23 27.0
9	19 5 35.5	16 15.8	14 44.6	26 30.0	11 55.0	24 58.0	28 25.0	10 15.5	2 38.8	22 54.6	23 17.4	23 28.6
10	19 9 32.1	17 13.0	14 41.4	8♏23.0	11 22.5	26 7.5	28 9.9	10 29.1	2 39.1	22 58.3	23 17.5	23 30.2
11	19 13 28.7	18 10.2	14 38.3	20 18.9	10 52.7	27 16.8	27 55.4	10 42.6	2 39.5	23 1.9	23 17.7	23 31.8
12	19 17 25.2	19 7.4	14 35.1	2♐21.7	10 26.2	28 26.1	27 41.4	10 56.2	2 40.0	23 5.6	23 17.9	23 33.5
13	19 21 21.8	20 4.6	14 31.9	14 34.9	10 3.4	29 35.3	27 28.1	11 9.7	2 40.6	23 9.2	23 18.1	23 35.1
14	19 25 18.3	21 1.8	14 28.7	27 1.4	9 44.8	0♍44.4	27 15.4	11 23.2	2 41.2	23 12.9	23 18.4	23 36.8
15	19 29 14.9	21 59.0	14 25.6	9♑43.1	9 30.6	1 53.3	27 3.4	11 36.7	2 42.0	23 16.6	23 18.7	23 38.4
16	19 33 11.4	22 56.2	14 22.4	22 41.0	9 21.4	3 2.2	26 52.1	11 50.2	2 42.9	23 20.2	23 19.0	23 40.1
17	19 37 8.0	23 53.5	14 19.2	5♒55.1	9 17.2	4 11.0	26 41.5	12 3.6	2 43.9	23 23.9	23 19.4	23 41.8
18	19 41 4.6	24 50.7	14 16.0	19 24.7	9D18.5	5 19.7	26 31.7	12 17.1	2 45.0	23 27.6	23 19.8	23 43.6
19	19 45 1.1	25 48.0	14 12.9	3♓ 7.9	9 25.1	6 28.2	26 22.6	12 30.5	2 46.1	23 31.3	23 20.2	23 45.3
20	19 48 57.7	26 45.2	14 9.7	17 2.5	9 37.4	7 36.7	26 14.3	12 43.9	2 47.4	23 34.9	23 20.7	23 47.0
21	19 52 54.2	27 42.5	14 6.5	1♈ 6.0	9 55.4	8 45.0	26 6.7	12 57.3	2 48.8	23 38.6	23 21.2	23 48.8
22	19 56 50.8	28 39.7	14 3.3	15 15.6	10 19.1	9 53.2	25 59.9	13 10.6	2 50.2	23 42.2	23 21.7	23 50.5
23	20 0 47.3	29 37.0	14 .2	29 28.7	10 48.6	11 1.3	25 54.0	13 23.9	2 51.8	23 45.9	23 22.3	23 52.3
24	20 4 43.9	0♌34.3	13 57.0	13♉42.9	11 23.8	12 9.3	25 48.8	13 37.2	2 53.4	23 49.5	23 22.8	23 54.1
25	20 8 40.5	1 31.6	13 53.8	27 55.5	12 4.8	13 17.1	25 44.5	13 50.5	2 55.2	23 53.2	23 23.5	23 55.9
26	20 12 37.0	2 29.0	13 50.6	12♊ 4.3	12 51.4	14 24.9	25 41.0	14 3.7	2 57.0	23 56.8	23 24.1	23 57.7
27	20 16 33.6	3 26.3	13 47.4	26 6.6	13 43.6	15 32.5	25 38.3	14 16.9	2 58.9	24 .4	23 24.8	23 59.5
28	20 20 30.1	4 23.7	13 44.3	9♋60.0	14 41.4	16 40.0	25 36.5	14 30.1	3 .9	24 4.0	23 25.5	24 1.3
29	20 24 26.7	5 21.1	13 41.1	23 41.7	15 44.6	17 47.4	25 35.5	14 43.2	3 3.1	24 7.7	23 26.2	24 3.1
30	20 28 23.2	6 18.4	13 37.9	7♌ 9.6	16 53.2	18 54.6	25 35.4	14 56.3	3 5.3	24 11.3	23 27.0	24 5.0
31	20 32 19.8	7 15.9	13 34.7	20 22.0	18 7.0	20 1.7	25D36.1	15 9.4	3 7.6	24 14.9	23 27.8	24 6.8

LATITUDE

DAY	SID. TIME	☉	☊	☽	☿	♀	♂	♃	♄	♅	♆	♇
1	18 34 3.1	0 .0	0 .0	0S 1.1	3S45.9	1N49.2	4S33.9	0S 1.9	2N31.4	0N27.9	1N43.2	9N46.5
4	18 45 52.8	0 .0	0 .0	3 26.0	4 20.6	1 45.9	4 40.9	0 1.6	2 30.6	0 27.9	1 43.0	9 46.1
7	18 57 42.4	0 .0	0 .0	5 9.8	4 43.3	1 41.8	4 46.8	0 1.3	2 29.8	0 27.9	1 42.9	9 45.8
10	19 9 32.1	0 .0	0 .0	4 50.5	4 51.8	1 36.8	4 51.4	0 1.0	2 29.0	0 27.9	1 42.7	9 45.5
13	19 21 21.8	0 .0	0 .0	2 39.7	4 46.0	1 30.9	4 54.9	0 .7	2 28.2	0 28.0	1 42.6	9 45.2
16	19 33 11.4	0 .0	0 .0	0N43.6	4 27.2	1 24.2	4 57.3	0 .4	2 27.4	0 28.0	1 42.4	9 45.0
19	19 45 1.1	0 .0	0 .0	3 56.5	3 57.7	1 16.6	4 58.6	0 .1	2 26.6	0 28.0	1 42.2	9 44.8
22	19 56 50.8	0 .0	0 .0	5 15.8	3 20.5	1 8.1	4 58.9	0N .2	2 25.8	0 28.0	1 42.1	9 44.7
25	20 8 40.5	0 .0	0 .0	3 50.4	2 38.2	0 58.8	4 58.4	0 .5	2 25.0	0 28.1	1 41.9	9 44.5
28	20 20 30.1	0 .0	0 .0	0 26.2	1 53.5	0 48.7	4 57.0	0 .7	2 24.2	0 28.1	1 41.8	9 44.5
31	20 32 19.8	0 .0	0 .0	3S 3.4	1 8.6	0 37.7	4 54.9	0 1.0	2 23.4	0 28.1	1 41.6	9 44.4

RIGHT ASCENSION

DAY	SID. TIME	☉	☊	☽	☿	♀	♂	♃	♄	♅	♆	♇
1	18 34 3.1	9♋23.9	16♑27.7	16♋11.9	17♋33.4	18♌40.9	0♑47.0	9♋11.4	1♏20.7	24♋18.3	22♎11.5	29♌ 4.8
2	18 37 59.6	10 26.0	16 24.3	0♌33.5	16R58.3	19 50.7	0R26.4	9 26.2	1R20.2	24 22.1	22R11.4	29 6.2
3	18 41 56.2	11 28.0	16 20.8	13 54.2	16 21.3	21 .2	0 6.1	9 41.0	1 19.7	24 25.9	22 11.3	29 7.7
4	18 45 52.8	12 29.9	16 17.4	26 19.6	15 42.7	22 9.3	29♐46.1	9 55.8	1 19.3	24 29.8	22 11.2	29 9.1
5	18 49 49.3	13 31.8	16 14.0	8♍ 2.2	15 3.3	23 18.0	29 26.5	10 10.5	1 19.0	24 33.6	22 11.2	29 10.6
6	18 53 45.9	14 33.6	16 10.6	19 16.7	14 23.7	24 26.4	29 7.2	10 25.3	1 18.8	24 37.5	22 11.2	29 12.1
7	18 57 42.4	15 35.3	16 7.2	0♎18.2	13 44.5	25 34.3	28 48.5	10 40.0	1 18.7	24 41.3	22 11.2	29 13.6
8	19 1 39.0	16 36.9	16 3.7	11 21.2	13 6.4	26 41.9	28 30.2	10 54.8	1 18.7	24 45.2	22 11.2	29 15.1
9	19 5 35.5	17 38.4	16 .3	22 38.7	12 30.0	27 49.2	28 12.5	11 9.5	1D18.8	24 49.1	22D11.3	29 16.7
10	19 9 32.1	18 39.8	15 56.9	4♏21.7	11 56.0	28 56.1	27 55.4	11 24.2	1 19.0	24 52.9	22 11.4	29 18.3
11	19 13 28.7	19 41.0	15 53.5	16 38.1	11 24.9	0♍ 2.6	27 38.9	11 38.9	1 19.2	24 56.8	22 11.6	29 19.8
12	19 17 25.2	20 42.2	15 50.0	29 30.8	10 57.3	1 8.7	27 23.1	11 53.5	1 19.6	25 .7	22 11.7	29 21.4
13	19 21 21.8	21 43.3	15 46.6	12♐55.9	10 33.7	2 14.5	27 8.0	12 8.2	1 20.1	25 4.6	22 11.9	29 23.0
14	19 25 18.3	22 44.2	15 43.2	26 42.9	10 14.6	3 20.0	26 53.7	12 22.8	1 20.6	25 8.5	22 12.2	29 24.7
15	19 29 14.9	23 45.0	15 39.8	10♑36.6	10 .2	4 25.1	26 40.1	12 37.4	1 21.3	25 12.4	22 12.4	29 26.3
16	19 33 11.4	24 45.7	15 36.4	24 21.9	9 51.1	5 29.9	26 27.3	12 52.0	1 22.0	25 16.3	22 12.7	29 28.0
17	19 37 8.0	25 46.3	15 32.9	7♒48.1	9 47.3	6 34.3	26 15.3	13 6.5	1 22.8	25 20.1	22 13.0	29 29.7
18	19 41 4.6	26 46.8	15 29.5	20 52.3	9D49.3	7 38.4	26 4.1	13 21.1	1 23.8	25 24.1	22 13.4	29 31.4
19	19 45 1.1	27 47.1	15 26.1	3♓38.4	9 57.2	8 42.2	25 53.8	13 35.6	1 24.8	25 28.0	22 13.8	29 33.1
20	19 48 57.7	28 47.3	15 22.7	16 15.9	10 11.0	9 45.7	25 44.4	13 50.1	1 25.9	25 31.9	22 14.2	29 34.8
21	19 52 54.2	29 47.3	15 19.2	28 58.1	10 30.9	10 48.9	25 35.8	14 4.5	1 27.2	25 35.7	22 14.7	29 36.5
22	19 56 50.8	0♌47.2	15 15.8	11♈59.2	10 57.0	11 51.7	25 28.1	14 19.0	1 28.4	25 39.6	22 15.1	29 38.3
23	20 0 47.3	1 47.0	15 12.4	25 32.6	11 29.3	12 54.3	25 21.4	14 33.3	1 29.8	25 43.5	22 15.6	29 40.0
24	20 4 43.9	2 46.7	15 9.0	9♉47.3	12 7.8	13 56.6	25 15.6	14 47.7	1 31.3	25 47.4	22 16.2	29 41.8
25	20 8 40.5	3 46.2	15 5.5	24 43.5	12 52.6	14 58.6	25 10.7	15 2.0	1 32.9	25 51.2	22 16.7	29 43.6
26	20 12 37.0	4 45.5	15 2.1	10♊ 9.5	13 43.5	16 .3	25 6.7	15 16.3	1 34.5	25 55.1	22 17.3	29 45.4
27	20 16 33.6	5 44.7	14 58.7	25 42.4	14 40.5	17 1.8	25 3.7	15 30.5	1 36.3	25 58.9	22 17.9	29 47.2
28	20 20 30.1	6 43.8	14 55.3	10♋54.9	15 43.6	18 3.0	25 1.7	15 44.8	1 38.1	26 2.8	22 18.6	29 49.0
29	20 24 26.7	7 42.7	14 51.8	25 24.9	16 52.6	19 3.9	25 .6	15 58.9	1 40.1	26 6.6	22 19.2	29 50.8
30	20 28 23.2	8 41.5	14 48.4	9♌ 2.0	18 7.3	20 4.6	25 .5	16 13.0	1 42.1	26 10.4	22 20.0	29 52.7
31	20 32 19.8	9 40.1	14 45.0	21 46.8	19 27.8	21 5.1	25D 1.4	16 27.1	1 44.2	26 14.2	22 20.7	29 54.5

DECLINATION

DAY	SID. TIME	☉	☊	☽	☿	♀	♂	♃	♄	♅	♆	♇
1	18 34 3.1	23N 9.8	0S23.6	22N35.5	18N40.3	17N53.1	28S .6	23N 8.7	10S 1.8	22N 2.3	7S27.2	22N58.1
4	18 45 52.8	22 56.9	0 23.7	9 52.9	18 17.5	16 45.6	28 7.7	23 6.3	10 2.1	22 .5	7 27.2	22 56.3
7	18 57 42.4	22 40.3	0 23.7	5S45.7	18 6.1	15 34.4	28 13.3	23 3.7	10 2.8	21 58.7	7 27.4	22 54.4
10	19 9 32.1	22 20.2	0 23.7	18 52.8	18 6.7	14 19.8	28 17.4	23 .9	10 3.7	21 56.9	7 27.6	22 52.5
13	19 21 21.8	21 56.6	0 23.7	25 11.9	18 18.6	13 2.3	28 20.1	22 57.9	10 5.0	21 55.1	7 28.0	22 50.6
16	19 33 11.4	21 29.7	0 23.7	26 49.3	18 40.4	11 42.1	28 21.7	22 54.7	10 6.5	21 53.3	7 28.5	22 48.7
19	19 45 1.1	20 59.4	0 23.8	6 40.8	19 9.5	10 19.6	28 22.2	22 51.3	10 8.4	21 51.4	7 29.1	22 46.7
22	19 56 50.8	20 26.0	0 23.8	10N51.7	19 42.8	8 54.9	28 21.9	22 47.8	10 10.5	21 49.5	7 29.8	22 44.8
25	20 8 40.5	19 49.5	0 23.8	23 26.5	20 16.2	7 28.6	28 20.8	22 44.0	10 13.0	21 47.7	7 30.6	22 42.8
28	20 20 30.1	19 10.0	0 23.8	23 30.2	20 45.4	6 .7	28 19.2	22 40.1	10 15.7	21 45.8	7 31.5	22 40.9
31	20 32 19.8	18 27.6	0 23.8	11 48.0	21 5.2	4 31.7	28 17.0	22 36.1	10 18.7	21 44.0	7 32.5	22 38.9

AUGUST 1954

LONGITUDE

DAY	EPHEM. SID. TIME h m s	☉ ° ′	☊ ° ′	☽ ° ′	☿ ° ′	♀ ° ′	♂ ° ′	♃ ° ′	♄ ° ′	♅ ° ′	♆ ° ′	♇ ° ′
1	20 36 16.4	8♌13.3	13♑31.6	3♍17.7	19♋25.8	21♍ 8.6	25♐37.7	15♋22.5	3♏10.0	24♋18.4	23♎28.7	24♌ 8.7
2	20 40 12.9	9 10.7	13 28.4	15 56.9	20 49.6	22 15.5	25 40.1	15 35.4	3 12.5	24 22.0	23 29.5	24 10.5
3	20 44 9.5	10 8.1	13 25.2	28 20.7	22 18.1	23 22.1	25 43.4	15 48.4	3 15.1	24 25.6	23 30.4	24 12.4
4	20 48 6.0	11 5.6	13 22.0	10♎31.2	23 51.1	24 28.6	25 47.5	16 1.3	3 17.7	24 29.1	23 31.3	24 14.3
5	20 52 2.6	12 3.0	13 18.9	22 31.6	25 28.4	25 35.0	25 52.5	16 14.2	3 20.5	24 32.7	23 32.3	24 16.1
6	20 55 59.1	13 .5	13 15.7	4♏25.8	27 9.6	26 41.2	25 58.2	16 27.0	3 23.3	24 36.2	23 33.3	24 18.0
7	20 59 55.7	13 58.0	13 12.5	16 18.3	28 54.6	27 47.2	26 4.8	16 39.8	3 26.3	24 39.7	23 34.3	24 19.9
8	21 3 52.2	14 55.6	13 9.3	28 13.7	0♌42.9	28 53.1	26 12.2	16 52.6	3 29.4	24 43.3	23 35.4	24 21.8
9	21 7 48.8	15 53.1	13 6.1	10♐17.0	2 34.2	29 58.8	26 20.4	17 5.3	3 32.5	24 46.7	23 36.5	24 23.7
10	21 11 45.4	16 50.6	13 3.0	22 32.7	4 28.1	1♎ 4.3	26 29.4	17 17.9	3 35.7	24 50.2	23 37.6	24 25.6
11	21 15 41.9	17 48.1	12 59.8	5♑ 4.9	6 24.3	2 9.6	26 39.1	17 30.5	3 39.0	24 53.6	23 38.7	24 27.6
12	21 19 38.5	18 45.7	12 56.6	17 56.7	8 22.4	3 14.7	26 49.5	17 43.1	3 42.3	24 57.1	23 39.8	24 29.5
13	21 23 35.0	19 43.3	12 53.4	1♒ 9.9	10 22.0	4 19.6	27 .7	17 55.6	3 45.8	25 .5	23 41.0	24 31.4
14	21 27 31.6	20 40.9	12 50.3	14 44.8	12 22.7	5 24.3	27 12.7	18 8.0	3 49.3	25 3.9	23 42.2	24 33.3
15	21 31 28.1	21 38.5	12 47.1	28 39.5	14 24.2	6 28.8	27 25.3	18 20.4	3 52.9	25 7.3	23 43.5	24 35.2
16	21 35 24.7	22 36.1	12 43.9	12♓50.5	16 26.1	7 33.1	27 38.7	18 32.7	3 56.6	25 10.6	23 44.7	24 37.1
17	21 39 21.2	23 33.8	12 40.7	27 12.7	18 28.2	8 37.2	27 52.7	18 45.0	4 .4	25 14.0	23 46.0	24 39.0
18	21 43 17.8	24 31.5	12 37.5	11♈40.4	20 30.2	9 41.1	28 7.5	18 57.2	4 4.3	25 17.3	23 47.4	24 41.0
19	21 47 14.3	25 29.2	12 34.4	26 8.0	22 31.9	10 44.7	28 22.9	19 9.3	4 8.2	25 20.6	23 48.7	24 42.9
20	21 51 10.9	26 26.9	12 31.2	10♉30.4	24 33.1	11 48.1	28 38.9	19 21.4	4 12.2	25 23.8	23 50.1	24 44.8
21	21 55 7.5	27 24.7	12 28.0	24 44.4	26 33.6	12 51.3	28 55.6	19 33.5	4 16.3	25 27.1	23 51.5	24 46.7
22	21 59 4.0	28 22.5	12 24.8	8♊47.9	28 33.2	13 54.2	29 12.9	19 45.4	4 20.5	25 30.3	23 52.9	24 48.6
23	22 3 .6	29 20.3	12 21.7	22 39.8	0♍31.9	14 56.9	29 30.9	19 57.3	4 24.8	25 33.5	23 54.4	24 50.5
24	22 6 57.1	0♍18.1	12 18.5	6♋20.0	2 29.6	15 59.3	29 49.4	20 9.2	4 29.1	25 36.7	23 55.8	24 52.5
25	22 10 53.7	1 16.0	12 15.3	19 48.6	4 26.1	17 1.5	0♑ 8.6	20 21.0	4 33.5	25 39.8	23 57.3	24 54.4
26	22 14 50.2	2 13.9	12 12.1	3♌ 5.7	6 21.5	18 3.4	0 28.3	20 32.6	4 38.0	25 42.9	23 58.9	24 56.3
27	22 18 46.8	3 11.8	12 8.9	16 11.1	8 15.6	19 5.0	0 48.7	20 44.3	4 42.5	25 46.0	24 .4	24 58.2
28	22 22 43.3	4 9.8	12 5.8	29 4.5	10 8.5	20 6.3	1 9.6	20 55.8	4 47.1	25 49.1	24 2.0	25 .1
29	22 26 39.9	5 7.8	12 2.6	11♍45.7	12 .2	21 7.4	1 31.1	21 7.4	4 51.9	25 52.2	24 3.6	25 2.0
30	22 30 36.4	6 5.8	11 59.4	24 14.5	13 50.5	22 8.1	1 53.2	21 18.8	4 56.6	25 55.2	24 5.2	25 3.9
31	22 34 33.0	7 3.9	11 56.2	6♎31.4	15 39.6	23 8.5	2 15.7	21 30.1	5 1.5	25 58.2	24 6.9	25 5.8

LATITUDE

DAY	EPHEM. SID. TIME	☉	☊	☽	☿	♀	♂	♃	♄	♅	♆	♇
1	20 36 16.4	0 .0	0 .0	3S55.8	0S53.9	0N33.8	4S54.0	0N 1.1	2N23.1	0N28.1	1N41.6	9N44.4
4	20 48 6.0	0 .0	0 .0	5 12.5	0 12.0	0 21.8	4 51.0	0 1.4	2 22.4	0 28.2	1 41.4	9 44.4
7	20 59 55.7	0 .0	0 .0	4 26.1	0N25.2	0 9.0	4 47.5	0 1.7	2 21.6	0 28.2	1 41.3	9 44.5
10	21 11 45.4	0 .0	0 .0	1 56.9	0 56.3	0S 4.6	4 43.6	0 2.0	2 20.9	0 28.3	1 41.1	9 44.5
13	21 23 35.0	0 .0	0 .0	1N29.8	1 19.9	0 18.8	4 39.3	0 2.3	2 20.1	0 28.3	1 41.0	9 44.7
16	21 35 24.7	0 .0	0 .0	4 24.6	1 35.8	0 33.7	4 34.6	0 2.6	2 19.4	0 28.4	1 40.8	9 44.8
19	21 47 14.3	0 .0	0 .0	5 2.5	1 44.1	0 49.2	4 29.7	0 3.0	2 18.7	0 28.4	1 40.7	9 45.0
22	21 59 4.0	0 .0	0 .0	2 58.4	1 45.6	1 5.3	4 24.6	0 3.3	2 18.0	0 28.5	1 40.6	9 45.3
25	22 10 53.7	0 .0	0 .0	0S31.6	1 41.3	1 22.0	4 19.3	0 3.6	2 17.4	0 28.6	1 40.4	9 45.6
28	22 22 43.3	0 .0	0 .0	3 38.1	1 32.1	1 39.1	4 13.9	0 3.9	2 16.7	0 28.6	1 40.3	9 45.9
31	22 34 33.0	0 .0	0 .0	5 3.1	1 19.0	1 56.6	4 8.3	0 4.2	2 16.1	0 28.7	1 40.2	9 46.3

RIGHT ASCENSION

DAY	EPHEM. SID. TIME	☉	☊	☽	☿	♀	♂	♃	♄	♅	♆	♇
1	20 36 16.4	10♌38.5	14♑41.6	3♍47.8	20♋53.6	22♍ 5.3	25♐ 3.2	16♋41.2	1♏46.4	26♋18.0	22♎21.5	29♌56.3
2	20 40 12.9	11 36.8	14 38.1	15 17.4	22 24.8	23 5.2	25 6.0	16 55.2	1 48.7	26 21.8	22 22.2	29 58.2
3	20 44 9.5	12 35.0	14 34.7	26 29.0	24 .8	24 5.0	25 9.7	17 9.1	1 51.1	26 25.6	22 23.1	0♍ .1
4	20 48 6.0	13 33.0	14 31.3	7♎36.2	25 41.6	25 4.5	25 14.4	17 23.0	1 53.6	26 29.4	22 23.9	0 2.0
5	20 52 2.6	14 30.8	14 27.8	18 51.5	27 26.7	26 3.8	25 20.0	17 36.9	1 56.1	26 33.1	22 24.8	0 3.8
6	20 55 59.1	15 28.5	14 24.4	0♏26.0	29 15.7	27 2.9	25 26.6	17 50.6	1 58.7	26 36.9	22 25.7	0 5.7
7	20 59 55.7	16 26.1	14 21.0	12 28.5	1♌ 8.3	28 1.7	25 34.1	18 4.4	2 1.5	26 40.6	22 26.6	0 7.6
8	21 3 52.2	17 23.5	14 17.6	25 3.9	3 4.0	29 .4	25 42.5	18 18.1	2 4.3	26 44.3	22 27.6	0 9.6
9	21 7 48.8	18 20.7	14 14.1	8♐11.7	5 2.2	29 58.9	25 51.8	18 31.8	2 7.2	26 48.0	22 28.6	0 11.5
10	21 11 45.4	19 17.8	14 10.7	21 45.7	7 2.7	0♎57.2	26 1.9	18 45.3	2 10.2	26 51.7	22 29.6	0 13.4
11	21 15 41.9	20 14.7	14 7.3	5♑34.3	9 4.7	1 55.2	26 12.9	18 58.8	2 13.3	26 55.3	22 30.7	0 15.3
12	21 19 38.5	21 11.5	14 3.8	19 23.8	11 7.9	2 53.1	26 24.8	19 12.3	2 16.4	26 59.0	22 31.7	0 17.2
13	21 23 35.0	22 8.2	14 .4	3♒ 2.9	13 11.8	3 50.8	26 37.5	19 25.7	2 19.6	27 2.6	22 32.8	0 19.2
14	21 27 31.6	23 4.7	13 57.0	16 25.5	15 16.0	4 48.3	26 51.0	19 39.0	2 22.9	27 6.2	22 34.0	0 21.1
15	21 31 28.1	24 1.1	13 53.5	29 32.2	17 20.1	5 45.6	27 5.4	19 52.3	2 26.3	27 9.8	22 35.1	0 23.0
16	21 35 24.7	24 57.3	13 50.1	12♓29.7	19 23.6	6 42.8	27 20.5	20 5.5	2 29.8	27 13.3	22 36.3	0 25.0
17	21 39 21.2	25 53.4	13 46.7	25 28.7	21 26.4	7 39.7	27 36.4	20 18.7	2 33.3	27 16.8	22 37.5	0 26.9
18	21 43 17.8	26 49.4	13 43.2	8♈41.7	23 28.0	8 36.6	27 53.0	20 31.7	2 36.9	27 20.3	22 38.7	0 28.8
19	21 47 14.3	27 45.2	13 39.8	22 20.5	25 28.4	9 33.2	28 10.4	20 44.7	2 40.6	27 23.8	22 39.9	0 30.8
20	21 51 10.9	28 40.9	13 36.4	6♉33.5	27 27.3	10 29.7	28 28.5	20 57.7	2 44.4	27 27.3	22 41.2	0 32.7
21	21 55 7.5	29 36.6	13 32.9	21 21.2	29 24.6	11 26.0	28 47.3	21 10.6	2 48.2	27 30.7	22 42.5	0 34.7
22	21 59 4.0	0♍32.1	13 29.5	6♊34.4	1♍20.1	12 22.2	29 6.9	21 23.3	2 52.2	27 34.1	22 43.8	0 36.6
23	22 3 .6	1 27.4	13 26.1	21 53.8	3 13.9	13 18.2	29 27.1	21 36.1	2 56.2	27 37.5	22 45.2	0 38.6
24	22 6 57.1	2 22.7	13 22.6	6♋56.0	5 5.8	14 14.1	29 48.1	21 48.7	3 .2	27 40.9	22 46.5	0 40.5
25	22 10 53.7	3 17.9	13 19.2	21 21.3	6 55.9	15 9.8	0♑ 9.7	22 1.3	3 4.4	27 44.2	22 47.9	0 42.5
26	22 14 50.2	4 13.0	13 15.8	4♌58.9	8 44.2	16 5.3	0 31.9	22 13.8	3 8.6	27 47.5	22 49.4	0 44.4
27	22 18 46.8	5 8.0	13 12.3	17 48.2	10 30.6	17 .7	0 54.8	22 26.2	3 12.9	27 50.8	22 50.8	0 46.3
28	22 22 43.3	6 2.8	13 8.9	29 55.6	12 15.3	17 55.9	1 18.4	22 38.5	3 17.3	27 54.0	22 52.3	0 48.3
29	22 26 39.9	6 57.7	13 5.5	11♍31.7	13 58.2	18 51.1	1 42.6	22 50.8	3 21.7	27 57.3	22 53.8	0 50.3
30	22 30 36.4	7 52.4	13 2.0	22 48.6	15 39.4	19 46.0	2 7.4	23 2.9	3 26.3	28 .5	22 55.3	0 52.2
31	22 34 33.0	8 47.0	12 58.6	3♎58.5	17 18.9	20 40.7	2 32.7	23 15.0	3 30.8	28 3.6	22 56.8	0 54.1

DECLINATION

DAY	EPHEM. SID. TIME	☉	☊	☽	☿	♀	♂	♃	♄	♅	♆	♇
1	20 36 16.4	18N12.9	0S23.8	6N38.0	21N 8.9	4N 1.8	28S16.2	22N34.7	10S19.7	21N43.3	7S32.8	22N38.3
4	20 48 6.0	17 26.9	0 23.8	8S57.1	21 8.5	2 31.7	28 13.6	22 30.5	10 23.1	21 41.5	7 34.0	22 36.4
7	20 59 55.7	16 38.4	0 23.9	20 57.7	20 47.7	1 1.1	28 10.7	22 26.1	10 26.7	21 39.7	7 35.2	22 34.5
10	21 11 45.4	15 47.5	0 23.9	25 10.9	20 3.6	0S29.8	28 7.4	22 21.6	10 30.5	21 37.8	7 36.5	22 32.6
13	21 23 35.0	14 54.3	0 23.9	18 26.7	18 55.8	2 .5	28 3.9	22 17.0	10 34.6	21 36.0	7 37.9	22 30.7
16	21 35 24.7	13 59.0	0 23.9	2 39.9	17 26.3	3 30.8	28 .1	22 12.3	10 38.9	21 34.2	7 39.4	22 28.9
19	21 47 14.3	13 1.7	0 23.9	14N47.1	15 38.8	5 .5	27 55.9	22 7.5	10 43.5	21 32.5	7 41.0	22 27.1
22	21 59 4.0	12 2.5	0 23.9	24 42.6	13 37.8	6 29.4	27 51.2	22 2.7	10 48.2	21 30.7	7 42.7	22 25.3
25	22 10 53.7	11 1.6	0 24.0	21 27.7	11 27.5	7 57.1	27 46.1	21 57.8	10 53.2	21 29.1	7 44.4	22 23.6
28	22 22 43.3	9 59.1	0 24.0	8 23.3	9 11.3	9 23.4	27 40.3	21 52.8	10 58.3	21 27.4	7 46.2	22 21.9
31	22 34 33.0	8 55.2	0 24.0	7S13.6	6 52.2	10 48.0	27 33.8	21 47.8	11 3.7	21 25.8	7 48.1	22 20.2

SEPTEMBER 1954

LONGITUDE

DAY	EPHEM. SID. TIME	☉	☊	☽	☿	♀	♂	♃	♄	♅	♆	♇
	h m s	° ′	° ′	° ′	° ′	° ′	° ′	° ′	° ′	° ′	° ′	° ′
1	22 38 29.6	8♍ 1.9	11♑53.1	18♎37.6	17♍27.4	24♎ 8.6	2♑38.8	21♋41.3	5♏ 6.4	26♋ 1.1	24♎ 8.5	25♌ 7.7
2	22 42 26.1	9 .0	11 49.9	0♏35.2	19 14.0	25 8.3	3 2.5	21 52.5	5 11.4	26 4.0	24 10.2	25 9.6
3	22 46 22.7	9 58.1	11 46.7	12 27.3	20 59.3	26 7.7	3 26.6	22 3.6	5 16.4	26 6.9	24 11.9	25 11.4
4	22 50 19.2	10 56.3	11 43.5	24 17.6	22 43.4	27 6.7	3 51.2	22 14.6	5 21.5	26 9.8	24 13.7	25 13.3
5	22 54 15.8	11 54.4	11 40.3	6♐10.7	24 26.2	28 5.4	4 16.3	22 25.5	5 26.7	26 12.6	24 15.4	25 15.2
6	22 58 12.3	12 52.6	11 37.2	18 11.6	26 7.8	29 3.6	4 41.9	22 36.3	5 31.9	26 15.4	24 17.2	25 17.0
7	23 2 8.9	13 50.8	11 34.0	0♑25.5	27 48.3	0♏ 1.4	5 8.0	22 47.0	5 37.2	26 18.1	24 19.0	25 18.9
8	23 6 5.4	14 49.0	11 30.8	12 57.5	29 27.5	0 58.8	5 34.4	22 57.7	5 42.6	26 20.8	24 20.8	25 20.7
9	23 10 2.0	15 47.3	11 27.6	25 52.0	1♎ 5.6	1 55.8	6 1.4	23 8.2	5 48.0	26 23.5	24 22.6	25 22.5
10	23 13 58.5	16 45.6	11 24.5	9♒12.2	2 42.6	2 52.3	6 28.7	23 18.7	5 53.4	26 26.2	24 24.5	25 24.3
11	23 17 55.1	17 43.9	11 21.3	22 59.3	4 18.4	3 48.4	6 56.5	23 29.1	5 59.0	26 28.8	24 26.3	25 26.1
12	23 21 51.6	18 42.2	11 18.1	7♓12.0	5 53.1	4 43.9	7 24.7	23 39.3	6 4.6	26 31.4	24 28.2	25 27.9
13	23 25 48.2	19 40.6	11 14.9	21 46.1	7 26.6	5 39.0	7 53.2	23 49.5	6 10.2	26 33.9	24 30.1	25 29.7
14	23 29 44.7	20 39.0	11 11.7	6♈34.5	8 59.1	6 33.5	8 22.2	23 59.6	6 15.9	26 36.4	24 32.0	25 31.5
15	23 33 41.3	21 37.4	11 8.6	21 28.8	10 30.5	7 27.5	8 51.5	24 9.5	6 21.7	26 38.8	24 34.0	25 33.2
16	23 37 37.8	22 35.9	11 5.4	6♉20.0	12 .8	8 21.0	9 21.2	24 19.4	6 27.5	26 41.3	24 35.9	25 35.0
17	23 41 34.4	23 34.4	11 2.2	21 .5	13 29.9	9 13.8	9 51.2	24 29.2	6 33.4	26 43.6	24 37.9	25 36.7
18	23 45 31.0	24 32.9	10 59.0	5♊25.0	14 58.0	10 6.1	10 21.6	24 38.8	6 39.3	26 46.0	24 39.9	25 38.5
19	23 49 27.5	25 31.6	10 55.9	19 30.8	16 25.0	10 57.8	10 52.4	24 48.4	6 45.3	26 48.3	24 41.9	25 40.2
20	23 53 24.1	26 30.2	10 52.7	3♋17.3	17 50.8	11 48.8	11 23.5	24 57.9	6 51.3	26 50.6	24 43.9	25 41.9
21	23 57 20.6	27 28.8	10 49.5	16 45.6	19 15.5	12 39.1	11 54.9	25 7.2	6 57.4	26 52.8	24 46.0	25 43.6
22	0 1 17.2	28 27.5	10 46.3	29 57.7	20 39.0	13 28.8	12 26.6	25 16.4	7 3.5	26 55.0	24 48.0	25 45.3
23	0 5 13.7	29 26.2	10 43.1	12♌55.7	22 1.3	14 17.7	12 58.7	25 25.5	7 9.7	26 57.1	24 50.0	25 46.9
24	0 9 10.3	0♎25.0	10 40.0	25 41.4	23 22.5	15 5.9	13 31.1	25 34.5	7 15.9	26 59.2	24 52.1	25 48.6
25	0 13 6.8	1 23.8	10 36.8	8♍16.3	24 42.3	15 53.3	14 3.8	25 43.4	7 22.2	27 1.2	24 54.2	25 50.2
26	0 17 3.4	2 22.6	10 33.6	20 41.4	26 .8	16 40.0	14 36.7	25 52.1	7 28.5	27 3.2	24 56.3	25 51.8
27	0 20 59.9	3 21.5	10 30.4	2♎57.4	27 18.0	17 25.8	15 10.0	26 .8	7 34.8	27 5.2	24 58.4	25 53.4
28	0 24 56.5	4 20.4	10 27.3	15 4.9	28 33.7	18 10.7	15 43.6	26 9.3	7 41.2	27 7.1	25 .5	25 55.0
29	0 28 53.0	5 19.3	10 24.1	27 4.8	29 47.9	18 54.7	16 17.5	26 17.6	7 47.7	27 9.0	25 2.6	25 56.6
30	0 32 49.6	6 18.2	10 20.9	8♏58.5	1♏ .5	19 37.8	16 51.6	26 25.9	7 54.1	27 10.8	25 4.8	25 58.1

LATITUDE

DAY	EPHEM. SID. TIME	☉	☊	☽	☿	♀	♂	♃	♄	♅	♆	♇
1	22 38 29.6	0 .0	0 .0	5S 3.8	1N13.9	2S 2.5	4S 6.4	0N 4.3	2N15.9	0N28.7	1N40.2	9N46.4
4	22 50 19.2	0 .0	0 .0	3 49.4	0 56.8	2 20.4	4 .7	0 4.7	2 15.3	0 28.8	1 40.1	9 46.8
7	23 2 8.9	0 .0	0 .0	1 5.8	0 37.5	2 38.7	3 54.9	0 5.0	2 14.7	0 28.9	1 40.0	9 47.3
10	23 13 58.5	0 .0	0 .0	2N15.6	0 16.5	2 57.1	3 49.1	0 5.4	2 14.2	0 29.0	1 39.9	9 47.8
13	23 25 48.2	0 .0	0 .0	4 43.0	0S 5.7	3 15.5	3 43.3	0 5.7	2 13.6	0 29.1	1 39.8	9 48.3
16	23 37 37.8	0 .0	0 .0	4 35.5	0 28.6	3 34.0	3 37.4	0 6.1	2 13.1	0 29.1	1 39.7	9 48.9
19	23 49 27.5	0 .0	0 .0	1 55.0	0 51.9	3 52.5	3 31.6	0 6.4	2 12.7	0 29.2	1 39.6	9 49.5
22	0 1 17.2	0 .0	0 .0	1S34.8	1 15.2	4 10.6	3 25.7	0 6.8	2 12.2	0 29.3	1 39.6	9 50.1
25	0 13 6.8	0 .0	0 .0	4 11.8	1 38.1	4 28.5	3 19.8	0 7.2	2 11.8	0 29.4	1 39.5	9 50.8
28	0 24 56.5	0 .0	0 .0	4 58.8	2 .2	4 45.8	3 14.0	0 7.5	2 11.4	0 29.5	1 39.5	9 51.6

RIGHT ASCENSION

DAY	EPHEM. SID. TIME	☉	☊	☽	☿	♀	♂	♃	♄	♅	♆	♇
1	22 38 29.6	9♍41.5	12♑55.2	15♎13.0	18♍56.8	21♎35.3	2♑58.7	23♋27.0	3♏35.5	28♋ 6.7	22♎58.4	0♍56.1
2	22 42 26.1	10 36.0	12 51.7	26 42.3	20 33.2	22 29.6	3 25.2	23 38.9	3 40.2	28 9.8	22 59.9	0 58.0
3	22 46 22.7	11 30.3	12 48.3	8♏34.4	22 8.1	23 23.8	3 52.3	23 50.7	3 44.9	28 12.9	23 1.5	0 59.9
4	22 50 19.2	12 24.6	12 44.9	20 54.5	23 41.6	24 17.8	4 19.9	24 2.4	3 49.8	28 15.9	23 3.1	1 1.8
5	22 54 15.8	13 18.9	12 41.4	3♐43.5	25 13.7	25 11.6	4 48.0	24 14.0	3 54.7	28 18.8	23 4.8	1 3.7
6	22 58 12.3	14 13.0	12 38.0	16 57.4	26 44.5	26 5.1	5 16.6	24 25.5	3 59.7	28 21.8	23 6.4	1 5.6
7	23 2 8.9	15 7.1	12 34.5	0♑28.0	28 14.0	26 58.5	5 45.7	24 36.9	4 4.7	28 24.7	23 8.1	1 7.5
8	23 6 5.4	16 1.2	12 31.1	14 4.7	29 42.4	27 51.6	6 15.3	24 48.2	4 9.8	28 27.6	23 9.8	1 9.4
9	23 10 2.0	16 55.2	12 27.7	27 37.7	1♎ 9.6	28 44.4	6 45.4	24 59.4	4 14.9	28 30.4	23 11.5	1 11.3
10	23 13 58.5	17 49.1	12 24.2	11♒ 1.1	2 35.7	29 37.0	7 15.9	25 10.5	4 20.1	28 33.2	23 13.2	1 13.2
11	23 17 55.1	18 43.0	12 20.8	24 14.4	4 .8	0♏29.3	7 46.9	25 21.5	4 25.4	28 35.9	23 14.9	1 15.0
12	23 21 51.6	19 36.9	12 17.3	7♓22.6	5 24.8	1 21.3	8 18.3	25 32.4	4 30.7	28 38.7	23 16.7	1 16.9
13	23 25 48.2	20 30.8	12 13.9	20 34.8	6 47.9	2 13.0	8 50.1	25 43.2	4 36.1	28 41.3	23 18.5	1 18.7
14	23 29 44.7	21 24.6	12 10.5	4♈ 2.4	8 10.0	3 4.4	9 22.2	25 53.9	4 41.6	28 44.0	23 20.3	1 20.6
15	23 33 41.3	22 18.4	12 7.0	17 56.6	9 31.2	3 55.4	9 54.8	26 4.4	4 47.1	28 46.6	23 22.1	1 22.4
16	23 37 37.8	23 12.2	12 3.6	2♉25.1	10 51.6	4 46.1	10 27.8	26 14.9	4 52.6	28 49.1	23 23.9	1 24.2
17	23 41 34.4	24 6.0	12 .1	17 27.9	12 11.0	5 36.4	11 1.1	26 25.2	4 58.2	28 51.6	23 25.7	1 26.0
18	23 45 31.0	24 59.8	11 56.7	2♊54.8	13 29.6	6 26.3	11 34.7	26 35.5	5 3.9	28 54.1	23 27.6	1 27.8
19	23 49 27.5	25 53.6	11 53.3	18 25.6	14 47.4	7 15.8	12 8.8	26 45.6	5 9.6	28 56.6	23 29.5	1 29.6
20	23 53 24.1	26 47.5	11 49.8	3♋36.2	16 4.4	8 4.8	12 43.1	26 55.6	5 15.4	28 59.0	23 31.4	1 31.4
21	23 57 20.6	27 41.3	11 46.4	18 6.8	17 20.5	8 53.4	13 17.8	27 5.5	5 21.2	29 1.3	23 33.3	1 33.2
22	0 1 17.2	28 35.1	11 42.9	1♌47.4	18 35.8	9 41.4	13 52.8	27 15.2	5 27.1	29 3.6	23 35.2	1 34.9
23	0 5 13.7	29 29.0	11 39.5	14 37.8	19 50.2	10 29.0	14 28.1	27 24.9	5 33.0	29 5.9	23 37.1	1 36.7
24	0 9 10.3	0♎22.9	11 36.1	26 45.2	21 3.7	11 15.9	15 3.7	27 34.4	5 38.9	29 8.1	23 39.1	1 38.4
25	0 13 6.8	1 16.9	11 32.6	8♍20.7	22 16.3	12 2.3	15 39.6	27 43.7	5 44.9	29 10.2	23 41.0	1 40.1
26	0 17 3.4	2 10.8	11 29.2	19 36.3	23 28.0	12 48.1	16 15.7	27 53.0	5 51.0	29 12.3	23 43.0	1 41.8
27	0 20 59.9	3 4.9	11 25.7	0♎44.4	24 38.7	13 33.1	16 52.2	28 2.1	5 57.1	29 14.4	23 44.9	1 43.5
28	0 24 56.5	3 58.9	11 22.3	11 55.9	25 48.4	14 17.5	17 28.9	28 11.0	6 3.2	29 16.4	23 46.9	1 45.1
29	0 28 53.0	4 53.1	11 18.9	23 20.7	26 56.9	15 1.1	18 5.9	28 19.9	6 9.4	29 18.4	23 48.9	1 46.8
30	0 32 49.6	5 47.2	11 15.4	5♏ 6.3	28 4.2	15 44.0	18 43.1	28 28.6	6 15.6	29 20.3	23 50.9	1 48.4

DECLINATION

DAY	EPHEM. SID. TIME	☉	☊	☽	☿	♀	♂	♃	♄	♅	♆	♇
1	22 38 29.6	8N33.6	0S24.0	11S58.7	6N 5.5	11S15.8	27S31.5	21N46.2	11S 5.5	21N25.2	7S48.8	22N19.7
4	22 50 19.2	7 28.0	0 24.0	22 33.2	3 45.5	12 37.8	27 24.0	21 41.2	11 11.1	21 23.7	7 50.7	22 18.2
7	23 2 8.9	6 21.3	0 24.0	24 32.5	1 26.8	13 57.4	27 15.5	21 36.2	11 16.8	21 22.2	7 52.8	22 16.7
10	23 13 58.5	5 13.7	0 24.0	15 46.6	0S49.5	15 14.5	27 6.1	21 31.2	11 22.7	21 20.7	7 54.9	22 15.2
13	23 25 48.2	4 5.3	0 24.1	1N 4.2	3 2.5	16 28.8	26 55.5	21 26.3	11 28.7	21 19.4	7 57.0	22 13.8
16	23 37 37.8	2 56.3	0 24.1	17 57.8	5 11.3	17 40.0	26 43.8	21 21.4	11 34.8	21 18.0	7 59.2	22 12.5
19	23 49 27.5	1 46.7	0 24.1	24 56.5	7 15.3	18 47.9	26 30.9	21 16.6	11 41.1	21 16.8	8 1.5	22 11.3
22	0 1 17.2	0 36.8	0 24.1	18 37.1	9 13.7	19 52.2	26 16.6	21 11.9	11 47.4	21 15.6	8 3.7	22 10.1
25	0 13 6.8	0S33.3	0 24.1	4 34.5	11 5.6	20 52.7	26 .9	21 7.3	11 53.9	21 14.4	8 6.1	22 9.0
28	0 24 56.5	1 43.5	0 24.1	10S31.9	12 50.3	21 49.2	25 43.7	21 2.9	12 .4	21 13.4	8 8.4	22 8.0

OCTOBER 1954

LONGITUDE

DAY	EPHEM. SID. TIME h m s	☉ ° ′	☊ ° ′	☽ ° ′	☿ ° ′	♀ ° ′	♂ ° ′	♃ ° ′	♄ ° ′	♅ ° ′	♆ ° ′	♇ ° ′
1	0 36 46.1	7♎17.2	10♑17.7	20♏48.2	2♏11.4	20♏19.9	17♑26.0	26♋34.0	8♏ .7	27♋12.5	25♎ 6.9	25♌59.7
2	0 40 42.7	8 16.3	10 14.5	2♐36.7	3 20.5	21 .9	18 .7	26 42.0	8 7.2	27 14.3	25 9.1	26 1.2
3	0 44 39.2	9 15.3	10 11.4	14 27.8	4 27.6	21 40.9	18 35.6	26 49.8	8 13.8	27 15.9	25 11.2	26 2.7
4	0 48 35.8	10 14.4	10 8.2	26 26.0	5 32.7	22 19.8	19 10.8	26 57.5	8 20.4	27 17.6	25 13.4	26 4.1
5	0 52 32.4	11 13.5	10 5.0	8♑36.4	6 35.5	22 57.5	19 46.2	27 5.1	8 27.1	27 19.1	25 15.6	26 5.6
6	0 56 28.9	12 12.7	10 1.8	21 4.4	7 35.9	23 34.0	20 21.8	27 12.5	8 33.8	27 20.7	25 17.8	26 7.0
7	1 0 25.5	13 11.8	9 58.7	3♒55.0	8 33.7	24 9.2	20 57.7	27 19.8	8 40.5	27 22.1	25 20.0	26 8.4
8	1 4 22.0	14 11.0	9 55.5	17 12.6	9 28.5	24 43.1	21 33.8	27 27.0	8 47.3	27 23.6	25 22.2	26 9.8
9	1 8 18.6	15 10.3	9 52.3	0♓60.0	10 20.3	25 15.7	22 10.1	27 34.0	8 54.0	27 24.9	25 24.4	26 11.2
10	1 12 15.1	16 9.6	9 49.1	15 17.2	11 8.6	25 46.8	22 46.7	27 40.9	9 .9	27 26.3	25 26.6	26 12.6
11	1 16 11.7	17 8.9	9 45.9	0♈ .9	11 53.1	26 16.5	23 23.4	27 47.6	9 7.7	27 27.6	25 28.9	26 14.0
12	1 20 8.2	18 8.2	9 42.8	15 4.3	12 33.6	26 44.6	24 .3	27 54.1	9 14.6	27 28.8	25 31.1	26 15.3
13	1 24 4.8	19 7.5	9 39.6	0♉17.7	13 9.5	27 11.1	24 37.4	28 .5	9 21.5	27 30.0	25 33.3	26 16.6
14	1 28 1.3	20 6.9	9 36.4	15 30.0	13 40.4	27 35.9	25 14.7	28 6.8	9 28.4	27 31.1	25 35.5	26 17.8
15	1 31 57.9	21 6.4	9 33.2	0♊30.9	14 6.0	27 59.0	25 52.2	28 12.9	9 35.4	27 32.2	25 37.8	26 19.1
16	1 35 54.4	22 5.8	9 30.1	15 12.6	14 25.6	28 20.4	26 29.9	28 18.9	9 42.4	27 33.2	25 40.0	26 20.3
17	1 39 51.0	23 5.3	9 26.9	29 30.5	14 38.9	28 39.9	27 7.7	28 24.6	9 49.3	27 34.2	25 42.2	26 21.5
18	1 43 47.6	24 4.9	9 23.7	13♋23.2	14 45.1	28 57.5	27 45.7	28 30.3	9 56.4	27 35.1	25 44.5	26 22.7
19	1 47 44.1	25 4.5	9 20.5	26 51.6	14 R 43.9	29 13.2	28 23.9	28 35.7	10 3.4	27 36.0	25 46.7	26 23.8
20	1 51 40.7	26 4.1	9 17.3	9♌58.4	14 34.8	29 26.9	29 2.3	28 41.1	10 10.4	27 36.8	25 48.9	26 25.0
21	1 55 37.2	27 3.7	9 14.2	22 46.8	14 17.2	29 38.5	29 40.8	28 46.2	10 17.5	27 37.5	25 51.2	26 26.1
22	1 59 33.8	28 3.4	9 11.0	5♍20.2	13 50.8	29 47.9	0♒19.4	28 51.2	10 24.6	27 38.2	25 53.4	26 27.1
23	2 3 30.3	29 3.2	9 7.8	17 41.6	13 15.6	29 55.2	0 58.3	28 56.0	10 31.7	27 38.9	25 55.7	26 28.2
24	2 7 26.9	0♏ 2.9	9 4.6	29 53.7	12 31.5	0♐ .3	1 37.3	29 .6	10 38.8	27 39.5	25 57.9	26 29.2
25	2 11 23.4	1 2.7	9 1.5	11♎58.3	11 39.0	0 3.1	2 16.4	29 5.0	10 46.0	27 40.0	26 .1	26 30.2
26	2 15 20.0	2 2.6	8 58.3	23 56.9	10 38.5	0 3.5	2 55.7	29 9.3	10 53.1	27 40.5	26 2.4	26 31.2
27	2 19 16.5	3 2.4	8 55.1	5♏51.0	9 31.4	0 R 1.6	3 35.1	29 13.4	11 .3	27 40.9	26 4.6	26 32.2
28	2 23 13.1	4 2.3	8 51.9	17 41.8	8 18.9	29♏57.3	4 14.7	29 17.3	11 7.4	27 41.3	26 6.8	26 33.1
29	2 27 9.6	5 2.3	8 48.7	29 30.9	7 3.1	29 50.5	4 54.4	29 21.1	11 14.6	27 41.6	26 9.0	26 34.0
30	2 31 6.2	6 2.2	8 45.6	11♐20.4	5 45.9	29 41.4	5 34.2	29 24.6	11 21.8	27 41.9	26 11.2	26 34.9
31	2 35 2.8	7 2.3	8 42.4	23 13.1	4 29.9	29 29.8	6 14.2	29 28.1	11 29.1	27 42.1	26 13.5	26 35.8

LATITUDE

DAY	SID. TIME	☉	☊	☽	☿	♀	♂	♃	♄	♅	♆	♇
1	0 36 46.1	0 .0	0 .0	3S48.6	2S21.0	5S 2.5	3S 8.1	0N 7.9	2N11.0	0N29.6	1N39.4	9N52.3
4	0 48 35.8	0 .0	0 .0	1 11.0	2 40.0	5 18.4	3 2.3	0 8.3	2 10.6	0 29.7	1 39.4	9 53.1
7	1 0 25.5	0 .0	0 .0	2N 3.0	2 56.3	5 33.1	2 56.5	0 8.7	2 10.3	0 29.8	1 39.4	9 53.9
10	1 12 15.1	0 .0	0 .0	4 34.2	3 9.0	5 46.5	2 50.8	0 9.1	2 10.0	0 29.9	1 39.3	9 54.8
13	1 24 4.8	0 .0	0 .0	4 40.6	3 16.7	5 58.2	2 45.0	0 9.5	2 9.7	0 30.0	1 39.3	9 55.7
16	1 35 54.4	0 .0	0 .0	2 1.2	3 17.5	6 7.8	2 39.4	0 10.0	2 9.4	0 30.1	1 39.3	9 56.6
19	1 47 44.1	0 .0	0 .0	1S34.5	3 8.7	6 14.8	2 33.8	0 10.4	2 9.2	0 30.2	1 39.3	9 57.5
22	1 59 33.8	0 .0	0 .0	4 13.1	2 47.3	6 18.6	2 28.2	0 10.8	2 9.0	0 30.3	1 39.3	9 58.5
25	2 11 23.4	0 .0	0 .0	5 1.2	2 10.8	6 18.8	2 22.7	0 11.3	2 8.8	0 30.4	1 39.4	9 59.4
28	2 23 13.1	0 .0	0 .0	3 51.7	1 19.2	6 14.4	2 17.2	0 11.7	2 8.7	0 30.5	1 39.4	10 .5
31	2 35 2.8	0 .0	0 .0	1 13.9	0 18.3	6 5.0	2 11.8	0 12.2	2 8.6	0 30.6	1 39.4	10 1.5

RIGHT ASCENSION

DAY	SID. TIME	☉	☊	☽	☿	♀	♂	♃	♄	♅	♆	♇
1	0 36 46.1	6♎41.5	11♑12.0	17♏17.1	29♎10.3	16♏25.9	19♑20.5	28♋37.1	6♏21.9	29♋22.2	23♎52.9	1♍50.0
2	0 40 42.7	7 35.8	11 8.5	29 53.5	0♏14.9	17 7.0	19 58.2	28 45.5	6 28.2	29 24.0	23 55.0	1 51.6
3	0 44 39.2	8 30.2	11 5.1	12♐51.9	1 18.0	17 47.2	20 36.1	28 53.8	6 34.5	29 25.7	23 57.0	1 53.2
4	0 48 35.8	9 24.6	11 1.6	26 4.7	2 19.4	18 26.3	21 14.2	29 1.9	6 40.9	29 27.5	23 59.0	1 54.8
5	0 52 32.4	10 19.2	10 58.2	9♑22.6	3 18.9	19 4.4	21 52.5	29 9.9	6 47.3	29 29.1	24 1.1	1 56.4
6	0 56 28.9	11 13.8	10 54.7	22 37.3	4 16.4	19 41.3	22 31.0	29 17.7	6 53.8	29 30.7	24 3.1	1 57.9
7	1 0 25.5	12 8.5	10 51.3	5♒43.9	5 11.6	20 17.1	23 9.6	29 25.4	7 .3	29 32.3	24 5.2	1 59.4
8	1 4 22.0	13 3.3	10 47.9	18 42.7	6 4.3	20 51.6	23 48.4	29 32.9	7 6.8	29 33.8	24 7.3	2 .9
9	1 8 18.6	13 58.2	10 44.4	1♓38.7	6 54.2	21 24.8	24 27.4	29 40.3	7 13.3	29 35.2	24 9.3	2 2.4
10	1 12 15.1	14 53.2	10 41.0	14 41.3	7 41.1	21 56.7	25 6.6	29 47.6	7 20.0	29 36.7	24 11.5	2 3.9
11	1 16 11.7	15 48.3	10 37.5	28 2.6	8 24.5	22 27.1	25 45.9	29 54.6	7 26.6	29 38.1	24 13.6	2 5.3
12	1 20 8.2	16 43.6	10 34.1	11♈55.3	9 4.1	22 56.0	26 25.3	0♌ 1.6	7 33.2	29 39.3	24 15.6	2 6.7
13	1 24 4.8	17 38.9	10 30.6	26 29.2	9 39.5	23 23.3	27 4.9	0 8.3	7 39.9	29 40.6	24 17.7	2 8.1
14	1 28 1.3	18 34.4	10 27.2	11♉46.8	10 10.3	23 49.0	27 44.5	0 14.9	7 46.6	29 41.8	24 19.8	2 9.5
15	1 31 57.9	19 30.0	10 23.7	27 38.6	10 36.0	24 12.9	28 24.3	0 21.3	7 53.3	29 42.9	24 21.9	2 10.8
16	1 35 54.4	20 25.8	10 20.3	13♊42.1	10 56.0	24 35.1	29 4.2	0 27.6	8 .1	29 44.0	24 24.0	2 12.2
17	1 39 51.0	21 21.7	10 16.8	29 27.7	11 9.9	24 55.4	29 44.2	0 33.7	8 6.8	29 45.0	24 26.1	2 13.5
18	1 43 47.6	22 17.7	10 13.4	14♋29.9	11 17.1	25 13.8	0♒24.3	0 39.6	8 13.6	29 46.0	24 28.2	2 14.8
19	1 47 44.1	23 13.9	10 10.0	28 34.7	11 17.2	25 30.1	1 4.4	0 45.3	8 20.5	29 46.9	24 30.4	2 16.1
20	1 51 40.7	24 10.3	10 6.5	11♌41.3	11 R 9.7	25 44.5	1 44.7	0 50.9	8 27.3	29 47.7	24 32.5	2 17.3
21	1 55 37.2	25 6.8	10 3.1	23 57.6	10 54.3	25 56.7	2 25.1	0 56.3	8 34.2	29 48.5	24 34.6	2 18.5
22	1 59 33.8	26 3.5	9 59.6	5♍36.1	10 30.6	26 6.7	3 5.5	1 1.5	8 41.1	29 49.3	24 36.7	2 19.7
23	2 3 30.3	27 .3	9 56.2	16 50.8	9 58.6	26 14.4	3 46.0	1 6.6	8 48.0	29 50.0	24 38.8	2 20.9
24	2 7 26.9	27 57.4	9 52.7	27 55.1	9 18.4	26 19.9	4 26.6	1 11.5	8 54.9	29 50.6	24 40.9	2 22.0
25	2 11 23.4	28 54.6	9 49.3	9♎ 1.4	8 30.5	26 23.0	5 7.2	1 16.1	9 1.8	29 51.2	24 43.0	2 23.2
26	2 15 20.0	29 52.0	9 45.8	20 29.2	7 35.7	26 23.7	5 47.9	1 20.6	9 8.8	29 51.7	24 45.1	2 24.3
27	2 19 16.5	0♏49.5	9 42.4	1♏59.6	6 35.0	26 R 22.0	6 28.6	1 25.0	9 15.8	29 52.2	24 47.2	2 25.3
28	2 23 13.1	1 47.3	9 38.9	14 4.5	5 30.0	26 17.8	7 9.5	1 29.1	9 22.7	29 52.6	24 49.3	2 26.4
29	2 27 9.6	2 45.2	9 35.5	26 35.2	4 22.3	26 11.1	7 50.3	1 33.0	9 29.7	29 52.9	24 51.4	2 27.4
30	2 31 6.2	3 43.3	9 32.0	9♐27.4	3 14.1	26 2.0	8 31.2	1 36.8	9 36.7	29 53.2	24 53.5	2 28.4
31	2 35 2.8	4 41.7	9 28.6	22 32.8	2 7.5	25 50.5	9 12.2	1 40.4	9 43.8	29 53.5	24 55.7	2 29.5

DECLINATION

DAY	SID. TIME	☉	☊	☽	☿	♀	♂	♃	♄	♅	♆	♇
1	0 36 46.1	2S53.6	0S24.1	21S37.9	14S26.6	22S41.3	25S25.1	20N58.6	12S 7.0	21N12.4	8S10.8	22N 7.1
4	0 48 35.8	4 3.4	0 24.1	24 34.8	15 53.2	23 28.8	25 4.8	20 54.5	12 13.6	21 11.5	8 13.2	22 6.3
7	1 0 25.5	5 12.7	0 24.2	17 17.2	17 8.5	24 11.4	24 43.0	20 50.5	12 20.3	21 10.7	8 15.6	22 5.5
10	1 12 15.1	6 21.4	0 24.2	1 35.1	18 10.1	24 48.7	24 19.6	20 46.8	12 27.1	21 10.0	8 18.0	22 4.8
13	1 24 4.8	7 29.4	0 24.2	15N57.1	18 55.0	25 20.4	23 54.6	20 43.3	12 33.9	21 9.4	8 20.4	22 4.3
16	1 35 54.4	8 36.5	0 24.2	24 38.0	19 18.8	25 45.9	23 28.0	20 40.0	12 40.7	21 8.9	8 22.9	22 3.8
19	1 47 44.1	9 42.4	0 24.2	19 14.7	19 15.9	26 4.8	22 59.8	20 37.0	12 47.5	21 8.4	8 25.3	22 3.4
22	1 59 33.8	10 47.2	0 24.2	5 37.8	18 39.6	26 16.3	22 29.9	20 34.3	12 54.3	21 8.1	8 27.7	22 3.2
25	2 11 23.4	11 50.5	0 24.2	9S21.1	17 24.3	26 19.8	21 58.5	20 31.9	13 1.0	21 7.8	8 30.1	22 3.0
28	2 23 13.1	12 52.1	0 24.2	20 49.0	15 31.8	26 14.3	21 25.4	20 29.8	13 7.8	21 7.7	8 32.5	22 2.9
31	2 35 2.8	13 52.0	0 24.3	24 30.1	13 18.6	25 59.0	20 50.7	20 28.0	13 14.5	21 7.6	8 34.9	22 2.9

NOVEMBER 1954

DAY	EPHEM. SID. TIME	☉	☊	☽	☿	♀	♂	♃	♄	♅	♆	♇
		LONGITUDE										
	h m s	° ′	° ′	° ′	° ′	° ′	° ′	° ′	° ′	° ′	° ′	° ′
1	2 38 59.3	8♏ 2.3	8♑39.2	5♑12.5	3♏17.3	29♏15.8	6♒54.3	29♋31.3	11♏36.3	27♋42.3	26♎15.7	26♌36.6
2	2 42 55.9	9 2.4	8 36.0	17 22.6	2 R 10.4	28 R 59.4	7 34.5	29 34.3	11 43.5	27 42.4	26 17.9	26 37.4
3	2 46 52.4	10 2.4	8 32.9	29 48.2	1 11.4	28 40.7	8 14.8	29 37.1	11 50.7	27 42.4	26 20.1	26 38.2
4	2 50 49.0	11 2.5	8 29.7	12♒34.0	0 21.7	28 19.6	8 55.3	29 39.7	11 57.9	27 42.4	26 22.3	26 38.9
5	2 54 45.5	12 2.7	8 26.5	25 44.6	29♎42.7	27 56.4	9 35.8	29 42.2	12 5.1	27 R 42.3	26 24.5	26 39.6
6	2 58 42.1	13 2.8	8 23.3	9♓23.3	29 15.0	27 31.1	10 16.5	29 44.4	12 12.3	27 42.2	26 26.6	26 40.3
7	3 2 38.6	14 3.0	8 20.2	23 31.8	28 59.0	27 3.7	10 57.2	29 46.5	12 19.5	27 42.0	26 28.8	26 41.0
8	3 6 35.2	15 3.2	8 17.0	8♈ 8.6	28 54.5	26 34.6	11 38.1	29 48.4	12 26.7	27 41.8	26 30.9	26 41.6
9	3 10 31.8	16 3.4	8 13.8	23 8.8	29 D 1.2	26 3.8	12 19.0	29 50.1	12 33.9	27 41.5	26 33.1	26 42.2
10	3 14 28.3	17 3.7	8 10.6	8♉24.1	29 18.5	25 31.4	13 .1	29 51.6	12 41.1	27 41.2	26 35.2	26 42.8
11	3 18 24.9	18 4.0	8 7.4	23 43.9	29 45.6	24 57.8	13 41.2	29 52.9	12 48.3	27 40.8	26 37.3	26 43.3
12	3 22 21.4	19 4.3	8 4.3	8♊56.9	0♏21.6	24 23.1	14 22.4	29 54.0	12 55.5	27 40.4	26 39.4	26 43.8
13	3 26 18.0	20 4.6	8 1.1	23 53.3	1 5.6	23 47.6	15 3.7	29 54.9	13 2.6	27 39.9	26 41.5	26 44.3
14	3 30 14.5	21 5.0	7 57.9	8♋26.1	1 56.8	23 11.5	15 45.0	29 55.6	13 9.8	27 39.3	26 43.6	26 44.7
15	3 34 11.1	22 5.4	7 54.7	22 31.7	2 54.3	22 35.1	16 26.5	29 56.1	13 17.0	27 38.7	26 45.7	26 45.2
16	3 38 7.6	23 5.9	7 51.6	6♌ 9.6	3 57.3	21 58.5	17 8.0	29 56.4	13 24.1	27 38.1	26 47.7	26 45.6
17	3 42 4.2	24 6.3	7 48.4	19 21.4	5 5.0	21 22.2	17 49.6	29 56.5	13 31.2	27 37.3	26 49.8	26 45.9
18	3 46 .8	25 6.8	7 45.2	2♍10.6	6 16.9	20 46.2	18 31.2	29 56.5	13 38.4	27 36.6	26 51.8	26 46.3
19	3 49 57.3	26 7.4	7 42.0	14 40.9	7 32.3	20 10.9	19 13.0	29 R 56.2	13 45.5	27 35.8	26 53.8	26 46.6
20	3 53 53.9	27 7.9	7 38.9	26 56.6	8 50.7	19 36.6	19 54.8	29 55.7	13 52.6	27 34.9	26 55.8	26 46.8
21	3 57 50.4	28 8.6	7 35.7	9♎ 1.4	10 11.7	19 3.3	20 36.7	29 55.1	13 59.7	27 34.0	26 57.9	26 47.1
22	4 1 47.0	29 9.2	7 32.5	20 58.6	11 34.7	18 31.4	21 18.7	29 54.2	14 6.7	27 33.1	26 59.8	26 47.4
23	4 5 43.5	0♐ 9.8	7 29.3	2♏51.3	12 59.7	18 1.0	22 .7	29 53.1	14 13.8	27 32.0	27 1.8	26 47.5
24	4 9 40.1	1 10.5	7 26.1	14 41.6	14 26.1	17 32.3	22 42.8	29 51.8	14 20.8	27 31.0	27 3.7	26 47.7
25	4 13 36.7	2 11.2	7 23.0	26 31.8	15 53.8	17 5.5	23 24.9	29 50.3	14 27.8	27 29.9	27 5.6	26 47.8
26	4 17 33.2	3 11.9	7 19.8	8♐23.4	17 22.5	16 40.6	24 7.1	29 48.6	14 34.8	27 28.7	27 7.5	26 47.9
27	4 21 29.8	4 12.7	7 16.6	20 18.2	18 52.1	16 17.9	24 49.4	29 46.8	14 41.7	27 27.5	27 9.4	26 48.0
28	4 25 26.3	5 13.4	7 13.4	2♑18.3	20 22.4	15 57.4	25 31.7	29 44.7	14 48.6	27 26.2	27 11.3	26 48.0
29	4 29 22.9	6 14.2	7 10.3	14 25.8	21 53.3	15 39.3	26 14.1	29 42.4	14 55.5	27 24.9	27 13.1	26 48.0
30	4 33 19.4	7 15.0	7 7.1	26 43.5	23 24.7	15 23.4	26 56.5	29 39.9	15 2.4	27 23.5	27 15.0	26 48.0
		LATITUDE										
1	2 38 59.3	0 .0	0 .0	0 S 10.4	0 N 2.3	6 S .6	2 S 10.0	0 N 12.3	2 N 8.5	0 N 30.7	1 N 39.5	10 N 1.8
4	2 50 49.0	0 .0	0 .0	2 N 58.2	0 58.8	5 43.3	2 4.7	0 12.8	2 8.5	0 30.8	1 39.5	10 2.9
7	3 2 38.6	0 .0	0 .0	4 58.3	1 41.5	5 19.8	1 59.4	0 13.3	2 8.4	0 30.9	1 39.6	10 3.9
10	3 14 28.3	0 .0	0 .0	4 21.3	2 7.7	4 49.8	1 54.3	0 13.8	2 8.4	0 31.0	1 39.6	10 5.0
13	3 26 18.0	0 .0	0 .0	1 7.1	2 19.0	4 14.0	1 49.1	0 14.3	2 8.4	0 31.1	1 39.7	10 6.1
16	3 38 7.6	0 .0	0 .0	2 S 34.2	2 18.8	3 33.2	1 44.1	0 14.8	2 8.4	0 31.2	1 39.8	10 7.2
19	3 49 57.3	0 .0	0 .0	4 48.4	2 10.4	2 48.7	1 39.1	0 15.3	2 8.4	0 31.3	1 39.9	10 8.3
22	4 1 47.0	0 .0	0 .0	5 .0	1 56.5	2 2.4	1 34.2	0 15.8	2 8.5	0 31.4	1 40.0	10 9.4
25	4 13 36.7	0 .0	0 .0	3 17.5	1 39.0	1 15.9	1 29.4	0 16.3	2 8.6	0 31.5	1 40.1	10 10.5
28	4 25 26.3	0 .0	0 .0	0 18.5	1 19.3	0 30.8	1 24.6	0 16.8	2 8.7	0 31.6	1 40.2	10 11.6
		RIGHT ASCENSION										
1	2 38 59.3	5♏40.2	9♑25.1	5♑40.9	1♏ 4.6	25♏36.5	9♒53.1	1♌43.8	9♏50.8	29♋53.6	24♎57.7	2♍30.4
2	2 42 55.9	6 38.9	9 21.7	18 42.6	0 R 7.3	25 R 20.2	10 34.1	1 46.9	9 57.9	29 53.7	24 59.8	2 31.3
3	2 46 52.4	7 37.8	9 18.2	1♒32.4	29♎17.5	25 1.5	11 15.1	1 49.9	10 4.9	29 53.8	25 1.9	2 32.2
4	2 50 49.0	8 36.9	9 14.8	14 10.2	28 36.3	24 40.6	11 56.1	1 52.7	10 11.9	29 53.8	25 4.0	2 33.1
5	2 54 45.5	9 36.2	9 11.3	26 41.3	28 4.8	24 17.5	12 37.1	1 55.3	10 19.0	29 R 53.7	25 6.0	2 33.9
6	2 58 42.1	10 35.7	9 7.9	9♓15.4	27 43.6	23 52.5	13 18.2	1 57.7	10 26.0	29 53.6	25 8.1	2 34.7
7	3 2 38.6	11 35.4	9 4.4	22 5.6	27 32.9	23 25.6	13 59.2	1 59.9	10 33.1	29 53.4	25 10.1	2 35.5
8	3 6 35.2	12 35.3	9 1.0	5♈26.7	27 32.4	22 57.1	14 40.2	2 1.9	10 40.1	29 53.2	25 12.1	2 36.3
9	3 10 31.8	13 35.4	8 57.5	19 32.8	27 D 41.9	22 27.1	15 21.3	2 3.7	10 47.2	29 52.9	25 14.2	2 37.0
10	3 14 28.3	14 35.7	8 54.1	4♉32.9	28 .7	21 55.7	16 2.3	2 5.3	10 54.3	29 52.6	25 16.2	2 37.7
11	3 18 24.9	15 36.2	8 50.6	20 24.9	28 28.2	21 23.4	16 43.3	2 6.7	11 1.3	29 52.2	25 18.2	2 38.4
12	3 22 21.4	16 37.0	8 47.2	6♊50.4	29 3.7	20 50.2	17 24.3	2 7.8	11 8.3	29 51.7	25 20.2	2 39.0
13	3 26 18.0	17 37.9	8 43.7	23 17.2	29 46.4	20 16.4	18 5.3	2 8.8	11 15.4	29 51.2	25 22.2	2 39.7
14	3 30 14.5	18 39.1	8 40.3	9♋10.1	0♏35.5	19 42.4	18 46.2	2 9.6	11 22.4	29 50.6	25 24.2	2 40.3
15	3 34 11.1	19 40.5	8 36.8	24 4.7	1 30.3	19 8.2	19 27.2	2 10.2	11 29.5	29 50.0	25 26.1	2 40.8
16	3 38 7.6	20 42.1	8 33.4	7♌52.6	2 30.1	18 34.3	20 8.1	2 10.6	11 36.5	29 49.3	25 28.1	2 41.4
17	3 42 4.2	21 43.9	8 29.9	20 39.2	3 34.4	18 .8	20 49.0	2 10.7	11 43.5	29 48.6	25 30.0	2 41.9
18	3 46 .8	22 45.9	8 26.5	2♍37.3	4 42.6	17 28.0	21 29.8	2 10.7	11 50.5	29 47.8	25 31.9	2 42.3
19	3 49 57.3	23 48.2	8 23.0	14 2.4	5 54.2	16 56.1	22 10.7	2 R 10.4	11 57.5	29 46.9	25 33.9	2 42.8
20	3 53 53.9	24 50.6	8 19.6	25 10.0	7 8.8	16 25.3	22 51.5	2 9.9	12 4.5	29 46.0	25 35.8	2 43.2
21	3 57 50.4	25 53.3	8 16.1	6♎14.2	8 26.1	15 55.9	23 32.3	2 9.3	12 11.5	29 45.1	25 37.7	2 43.6
22	4 1 47.0	26 56.2	8 12.7	17 27.4	9 45.6	15♏28.0	24 13.1	2 8.4	12 18.4	29 44.1	25 39.6	2 44.0
23	4 5 43.5	27 59.3	8 9.2	28 59.7	11 7.1	15 1.8	24 53.8	2 7.4	12 25.4	29 43.0	25 41.4	2 44.3
24	4 9 40.1	29 2.6	8 5.8	10♏57.7	12 30.4	14 37.3	25 34.5	2 6.1	12 32.3	29 41.9	25 43.3	2 44.6
25	4 13 36.7	0♐ 6.0	8 2.3	23 23.6	13 55.3	14 14.8	26 15.2	2 4.5	12 39.2	29 40.7	25 45.1	2 44.9
26	4 17 33.2	1 9.7	7 58.9	6♐13.9	15 21.6	13 54.4	26 55.9	2 2.8	12 46.1	29 39.5	25 46.9	2 45.1
27	4 21 29.8	2 13.6	7 55.4	19 20.4	16 49.2	13 36.1	27 36.5	2 .9	12 52.9	29 38.2	25 48.7	2 45.3
28	4 25 26.3	3 17.6	7 52.0	2♑31.1	18 18.0	13 20.1	28 17.1	1 58.8	12 59.8	29 36.9	25 50.4	2 45.5
29	4 29 22.9	4 21.8	7 48.5	15 34.5	19 47.8	13 6.3	28 57.6	1 56.4	13 6.6	29 35.5	25 52.2	2 45.7
30	4 33 19.4	5 26.2	7 45.1	28 22.6	21 18.5	12 54.8	29 38.1	1 53.9	13 13.4	29 34.1	25 53.9	2 45.8
		DECLINATION										
1	2 38 59.3	14 S 11.5	0 S 24.3	23 S 31.0	12 S 34.7	25 S 51.6	20 S 38.9	20 N 27.5	13 S 16.8	21 N 7.6	8 S 35.7	22 N 3.0
4	2 50 49.0	15 8.6	0 24.3	14 11.2	10 41.0	25 22.0	20 2.2	20 26.1	13 23.4	21 7.7	8 38.0	22 3.2
7	3 2 38.6	16 3.6	0 24.3	1 N 59.8	9 32.0	24 41.4	19 24.1	20 25.2	13 30.0	21 7.9	8 40.3	22 3.4
10	3 14 28.3	16 56.1	0 24.3	18 25.7	9 14.4	23 50.0	18 44.5	20 24.6	13 36.6	21 8.1	8 42.5	22 3.8
13	3 26 18.0	17 46.0	0 24.3	24 25.3	9 41.1	22 49.4	18 3.6	20 24.4	13 43.1	21 8.5	8 44.7	22 4.3
16	3 38 7.6	18 33.1	0 24.3	16 14.8	10 39.7	21 41.7	17 21.4	20 24.5	13 49.4	21 9.0	8 46.9	22 4.8
19	3 49 57.3	19 17.3	0 24.3	1 35.8	11 58.4	20 30.2	16 38.0	20 25.1	13 55.7	21 9.5	8 49.0	22 5.5
22	4 1 47.0	19 58.4	0 24.3	12 S 49.1	13 27.8	19 18.2	15 53.3	20 26.0	14 1.9	21 10.1	8 51.1	22 6.3
25	4 13 36.7	20 36.2	0 24.3	22 35.0	15 1.2	18 9.4	15 7.4	20 27.3	14 8.0	21 10.9	8 53.1	22 7.1
28	4 25 26.3	21 10.6	0 24.3	23 44.0	16 34.3	17 6.6	14 20.5	20 29.0	14 14.0	21 11.7	8 55.0	22 8.1

DECEMBER 1954

LONGITUDE

DAY	EPHEM. SID. TIME h m s	☉ ° ′	☊ ° ′	☾ ° ′	☿ ° ′	♀ ° ′	♂ ° ′	♃ ° ′	♄ ° ′	♅ ° ′	♆ ° ′	♇ ° ′
1	4 37 16.0	8♐15.8	7♑ 3.9	9♒14.4	24♏56.5	15♏10.0	27♒38.9	29♋37.3	15♏ 9.2	27♋22.1	27≏16.8	26♌47.9
2	4 41 12.6	9 16.6	7 .7	22 2.0	26 28.6	14 R 59.1	28 21.5	29 R 34.4	15 16.0	27 R 20.7	27 18.5	26 47.9
3	4 45 9.1	10 17.5	6 57.6	5♓ 9.6	28 .9	14 50.6	29 4.0	29 31.4	15 22.8	27 19.2	27 20.3	26 R 47.7
4	4 49 5.7	11 18.4	6 54.4	18 40.1	29 33.5	14 44.6	29 46.6	29 28.1	15 29.6	27 17.6	27 22.0	26 47.6
5	4 53 2.2	12 19.2	6 51.2	2♈35.3	1♐ 6.2	14 41.1	0♓29.2	29 24.7	15 36.3	27 16.0	27 23.8	26 47.4
6	4 56 58.8	13 20.1	6 48.0	16 55.1	2 39.0	14 40.0	1 11.9	29 21.1	15 42.9	27 14.4	27 25.4	26 47.2
7	5 0 55.3	14 21.0	6 44.8	1♉36.9	4 12.0	14 D 41.3	1 54.6	29 17.3	15 49.6	27 12.7	27 27.1	26 47.0
8	5 4 51.9	15 21.9	6 41.7	16 35.5	5 45.0	14 45.1	2 37.3	29 13.3	15 56.2	27 11.0	27 28.8	26 46.7
9	5 8 48.5	16 22.8	6 38.5	1♊43.0	7 18.2	14 51.2	3 20.1	29 9.2	16 2.8	27 9.2	27 30.4	26 46.4
10	5 12 45.0	17 23.8	6 35.3	16 50.1	8 51.4	14 59.6	4 2.9	29 4.8	16 9.3	27 7.4	27 32.0	26 46.1
11	5 16 41.6	18 24.7	6 32.1	1♋47.2	10 24.7	15 10.3	4 45.7	29 .3	16 15.8	27 5.6	27 33.6	26 45.8
12	5 20 38.1	19 25.8	6 29.0	16 26.3	11 58.1	15 23.3	5 28.6	28 55.7	16 22.3	27 3.8	27 35.2	26 45.4
13	5 24 34.7	20 26.7	6 25.8	0♌41.7	13 31.6	15 38.4	6 11.4	28 50.8	16 28.7	27 1.9	27 36.7	26 45.0
14	5 28 31.3	21 27.8	6 22.6	14 30.4	15 5.1	15 55.5	6 54.3	28 45.8	16 35.0	26 59.9	27 38.2	26 44.6
15	5 32 27.8	22 28.8	6 19.4	27 52.1	16 38.7	16 14.7	7 37.2	28 40.6	16 41.3	26 57.9	27 39.7	26 44.1
16	5 36 24.4	23 29.8	6 16.3	10♍48.6	18 12.5	16 35.9	8 20.1	28 35.3	16 47.6	26 55.9	27 41.1	26 43.6
17	5 40 20.9	24 30.9	6 13.1	23 23.2	19 46.3	16 59.0	9 3.0	28 29.8	16 53.8	26 53.8	27 42.5	26 43.1
18	5 44 17.5	25 31.9	6 9.9	5≏40.1	21 20.3	17 23.9	9 46.0	28 24.1	17 .0	26 51.8	27 43.9	26 42.6
19	5 48 14.0	26 33.0	6 6.7	17 43.6	22 54.4	17 50.5	10 29.0	28 18.3	17 6.1	26 49.6	27 45.3	26 42.0
20	5 52 10.6	27 34.1	6 3.6	29 38.4	24 28.7	18 18.9	11 12.0	28 12.3	17 12.2	26 47.5	27 46.6	26 41.4
21	5 56 7.2	28 35.2	6 .4	11♏28.5	26 3.2	18 48.9	11 55.0	28 6.2	17 18.2	26 45.3	27 47.9	26 40.8
22	6 0 3.7	29 36.3	5 57.2	23 17.6	27 37.8	19 20.4	12 38.0	27 60.0	17 24.2	26 43.1	27 49.2	26 40.1
23	6 4 .3	0♑37.5	5 54.0	5♐ 9.1	29 12.6	19 53.5	13 21.1	27 53.6	17 30.1	26 40.8	27 50.5	26 39.4
24	6 7 56.8	1 38.6	5 50.8	17 5.5	0♑47.6	20 28.1	14 4.1	27 47.1	17 36.0	26 38.5	27 51.7	26 38.7
25	6 11 53.4	2 39.8	5 47.7	29 9.0	2 22.9	21 4.0	14 47.2	27 40.4	17 41.8	26 36.2	27 52.9	26 38.0
26	6 15 50.0	3 40.9	5 44.5	11♑21.4	3 58.4	21 41.3	15 30.3	27 33.7	17 47.5	26 33.9	27 54.0	26 37.2
27	6 19 46.5	4 42.1	5 41.3	23 44.0	5 34.2	22 19.9	16 13.4	27 26.8	17 53.2	26 31.6	27 55.2	26 36.4
28	6 23 43.1	5 43.2	5 38.1	6♒18.2	7 10.2	22 59.7	16 56.5	27 19.8	17 58.8	26 29.2	27 56.3	26 35.6
29	6 27 39.6	6 44.4	5 35.0	19 5.0	8 46.5	23 40.6	17 39.6	27 12.7	18 4.4	26 26.8	27 57.4	26 34.8
30	6 31 36.2	7 45.6	5 31.8	2♓ 5.8	10 23.1	24 22.8	18 22.7	27 5.5	18 9.9	26 24.3	27 58.4	26 33.9
31	6 35 32.7	8 46.7	5 28.6	15 21.6	11 59.9	25 6.0	19 5.8	26 58.2	18 15.3	26 21.9	27 59.4	26 33.0

LATITUDE

DAY	EPHEM. SID. TIME	☉	☊	☾	☿	♀	♂	♃	♄	♅	♆	♇
1	4 37 16.0	0 .0	0 .0	2N54.1	0N58.4	0N11.7	1S20.0	0N17.4	2N 8.9	0N31.7	1N40.3	10N12.7
4	4 49 5.7	0 .0	0 .0	5 1.1	0 37.0	0 50.9	1 15.4	0 17.9	2 9.1	0 31.8	1 40.4	10 13.8
7	5 0 55.3	0 .0	0 .0	4 43.5	0 15.6	1 26.2	1 10.9	0 18.4	2 9.3	0 31.9	1 40.5	10 14.9
10	5 12 45.0	0 .0	0 .0	1 41.6	0S 5.4	1 57.3	1 6.5	0 18.9	2 9.5	0 32.0	1 40.7	10 16.0
13	5 24 34.7	0 .0	0 .0	2S14.9	0 25.6	2 24.4	1 2.1	0 19.4	2 9.8	0 32.0	1 40.8	10 17.1
16	5 36 24.4	0 .0	0 .0	4 48.0	0 44.8	2 47.6	0 57.9	0 20.0	2 10.1	0 32.1	1 41.0	10 18.1
19	5 48 14.0	0 .0	0 .0	5 10.0	1 2.7	3 7.1	0 53.7	0 20.5	2 10.4	0 32.2	1 41.1	10 19.2
22	6 0 3.7	0 .0	0 .0	3 33.6	1 19.0	3 23.2	0 49.6	0 21.0	2 10.7	0 32.3	1 41.3	10 20.2
25	6 11 53.4	0 .0	0 .0	0 35.3	1 33.5	3 36.1	0 45.6	0 21.5	2 11.1	0 32.3	1 41.4	10 21.1
28	6 23 43.1	0 .0	0 .0	2N42.9	1 45.9	3 46.2	0 41.7	0 22.0	2 11.4	0 32.4	1 41.6	10 22.1
31	6 35 32.7	0 .0	0 .0	4 58.2	1 55.9	3 53.6	0 37.9	0 22.5	2 11.9	0 32.4	1 41.8	10 23.0

RIGHT ASCENSION

DAY	EPHEM. SID. TIME	☉	☊	☾	☿	♀	♂	♃	♄	♅	♆	♇
1	4 37 16.0	6♐30.7	7♑41.6	10♒52.9	22♏50.2	12♏45.7	0♓18.6	1♌51.2	13♏20.2	29♋32.6	25≏55.7	2♍45.9
2	4 41 12.6	7 35.4	7 38.2	23 9.0	24 22.6	12 R 38.9	0 59.0	1 R 48.2	13 26.9	29 R 31.1	25 57.4	2 45.9
3	4 45 9.1	8 40.3	7 34.7	5♓19.6	25 55.9	12 34.4	1 39.4	1 45.1	13 33.6	29 29.5	25 59.0	2 46.0
4	4 49 5.7	9 45.3	7 31.3	17 37.2	27 29.9	12 32.3	2 19.7	1 41.7	13 40.3	29 27.9	26 .7	2 46.0
5	4 53 2.2	10 50.5	7 27.8	0♈16.9	29 4.6	12 D 32.5	3 .1	1 38.2	13 47.0	29 26.3	26 2.3	2 R 45.9
6	4 56 58.8	11 55.8	7 24.4	13 34.8	0♐39.9	12 35.0	3 40.3	1 34.5	13 53.6	29 24.6	26 3.9	2 45.9
7	5 0 55.3	13 1.2	7 20.9	27 45.1	2 15.9	12 39.8	4 20.5	1 30.5	14 .2	29 22.8	26 5.5	2 45.8
8	5 4 51.9	14 6.7	7 17.4	12♉54.8	3 52.6	12 46.7	5 .7	1 26.4	14 6.7	29 21.0	26 7.1	2 45.6
9	5 8 48.5	15 12.4	7 14.0	28 58.0	5 29.8	12 55.9	5 40.8	1 22.1	14 13.2	29 19.2	26 8.7	2 45.5
10	5 12 45.0	16 18.2	7 10.5	15♊30.8	7 7.7	13 7.2	6 20.9	1 17.6	14 19.7	29 17.3	26 10.2	2 45.3
11	5 16 4196	17 24.1	7 7.1	1♋57.1	8 46.1	13 20.6	7 .9	1 12.9	14 26.2	29 15.3	26 11.7	2 45.1
12	5 20 38.1	18 30.1	7 3.6	17 41.8	10 25.1	13 36.1	7 41.0	1 8.1	14 32.6	29 13.4	26 13.2	2 44.9
13	5 24 34.7	19 36.2	7 .2	2♌23.7	12 4.7	13 53.6	8 20.9	1 3.1	14 39.0	29 11.4	26 14.7	2 44.7
14	5 28 31.3	20 42.4	6 56.7	15 58.8	13 44.8	14 12.9	9 .8	0 57.9	14 45.3	29 9.4	26 16.1	2 44.4
15	5 32 27.8	21 48.7	6 53.3	28 35.5	15 25.4	14 34.1	9 40.7	0 52.5	14 51.6	29 7.3	26 17.5	2 44.0
16	5 36 24.4	22 55.0	6 49.8	10♍28.3	17 6.5	14 57.2	10 20.5	0 46.9	14 57.8	29 5.1	26 18.9	2 43.7
17	5 40 20.9	24 1.4	6 46.4	21 53.2	18 48.2	15 22.0	11 .3	0 41.2	15 4.0	29 3.0	26 20.3	2 43.3
18	5 44 17.5	25 7.9	6 42.9	3≏ 5.7	20 30.3	15 48.5	11 40.0	0 35.3	15 10.2	29 .8	26 21.6	2 42.9
19	5 48 14.0	26 14.4	6 39.4	14 20.0	22 12.9	16 16.6	12 19.7	0 29.2	15 16.3	28 58.6	26 22.9	2 42.5
20	5 52 10.6	27 21.0	6 36.0	25 47.8	23 56.0	16 46.3	12 59.4	0 23.0	15 22.4	28 56.3	26 24.2	2 42.0
21	5 56 7.2	28 27.6	6 32.5	7♏38.3	25 39.5	17 17.5	13 39.0	0 16.7	15 28.4	28 54.0	26 25.5	2 41.5
22	6 0 3.7	29 34.2	6 29.1	19 56.3	27 23.4	17 50.2	14 18.6	0 10.2	15 34.4	28 51.7	26 26.7	2 41.0
23	6 4 .3	0♑40.8	6 25.6	2♐41.5	29 7.8	18 24.4	14 58.2	0 3.5	15 40.3	28 49.3	26 27.9	2 40.4
24	6 7 56.8	1 47.5	6 22.2	15 47.8	0♑52.5	18 59.9	15 37.7	29♋56.7	15 46.1	28 46.9	26 29.1	2 39.8
25	6 11 53.4	2 54.1	6 18.7	29 4.2	2 37.6	19 36.7	16 17.2	29 49.8	15 51.9	28 44.5	26 30.2	2 39.2
26	6 15 50.0	4 .7	6 15.3	12♑17.9	4 23.0	20 14.9	16 56.7	29 42.7	15 57.7	28 42.0	26 31.3	2 38.6
27	6 19 46.5	5 7.3	6 11.8	25 18.1	6 8.7	20 54.2	17 36.1	29 35.5	16 3.4	28 39.5	26 32.4	2 37.9
28	6 23 43.1	6 13.9	6 8.3	7♒59.1	7 54.7	21 34.8	18 15.5	29 28.2	16 9.0	28 37.0	26 33.5	2 37.3
29	6 27 39.6	7 20.4	6 4.9	20 20.9	9 41.0	22 16.5	18 54.9	29 20.7	16 14.6	28 34.5	26 34.5	2 36.5
30	6 31 36.2	8 26.9	6 1.4	2♓29.8	11 27.4	22 59.4	19 34.3	29 13.2	16 20.1	28 32.0	26 35.5	2 35.8
31	6 35 32.7	9 33.3	5 58.0	14 36.1	13 14.1	23 43.3	20 13.6	29 5.6	16 25.5	28 29.4	26 36.5	2 35.0

DECLINATION

DAY	EPHEM. SID. TIME	☉	☊	☾	☿	♀	♂	♃	♄	♅	♆	♇
1	4 37 16.0	21S41.4	0S24.4	15S 8.9	18S 3.7	16S12.1	13S32.6	20N31.1	14S19.8	21N12.6	8S56.8	22N 9.2
4	4 49 5.7	22 8.4	0 24.4	0N 8.2	19 27.5	15 27.2	12 43.8	20 33.5	14 25.5	21 13.6	8 58.6	22 10.3
7	5 0 55.3	22 31.6	0 24.4	16 27.9	20 44.1	14 52.6	11 54.0	20 36.3	14 31.0	21 14.6	9 .3	22 11.5
10	5 12 45.0	22 50.8	0 24.4	24 28.7	21 52.3	14 28.1	11 3.5	20 39.4	14 36.4	21 15.7	9 1.9	22 12.9
13	5 24 34.7	23 6.0	0 24.4	17 48.7	22 51.2	14 13.3	10 12.3	20 42.8	14 41.7	21 16.9	9 3.4	22 14.2
16	5 36 24.4	23 17.1	0 24.4	3 4.2	23 40.0	14 7.5	9 20.5	20 46.5	14 46.8	21 18.1	9 4.9	22 15.7
19	5 48 14.0	23 24.0	0 24.4	11S43.7	24 17.9	14 9.5	8 28.0	20 50.4	14 51.7	21 19.4	9 6.2	22 17.2
22	6 0 3.7	23 26.7	0 24.4	22 2.7	24 44.4	14 18.4	7 35.1	20 54.6	14 56.4	21 20.7	9 7.5	22 18.9
25	6 11 53.4	23 25.1	0 24.4	24 1.9	24 58.9	14 33.1	6 41.7	20 59.0	15 .9	21 22.1	9 8.6	22 20.5
28	6 23 43.1	23 19.3	0 24.4	16 4.3	25 .8	14 52.6	5 47.9	21 3.5	15 5.3	21 23.5	9 9.7	22 22.2
31	6 35 32.7	23 9.2	0 24.4	1 11.1	24 49.7	15 15.9	4 53.8	21 8.2	15 9.4	21 24.9	9 10.6	22 24.0

JANUARY 1955

LONGITUDE

DAY	EPHEM. SID. TIME h m s	☉ ° ′	☊ ° ′	☽ ° ′	☿ ° ′	♀ ° ′	♂ ° ′	♃ ° ′	♄ ° ′	♅ ° ′	♆ ° ′	♇ ° ′
1	6 39 29.3	9♑47.9	5♑25.4	28♓53.5	13♑37.1	25♏50.3	19♓49.0	26♋50.8	18♏20.7	26♋19.4	28♎ .4	26♌32.1
2	6 43 25.9	10 49.1	5 22.3	12♈42.2	15 14.7	26 35.6	20 32.1	26 R 43.4	18 26.1	26 R 17.0	28 1.4	26 R 31.2
3	6 47 22.4	11 50.3	5 19.1	26 47.3	16 52.5	27 21.8	21 15.3	26 35.8	18 31.3	26 14.5	28 2.3	26 30.3
4	6 51 19.0	12 51.4	5 15.9	11♉ 7.7	18 30.6	28 9.0	21 58.4	26 28.2	18 36.5	26 12.0	28 3.2	26 29.3
5	6 55 15.5	13 52.6	5 12.7	25 40.7	20 9.0	28 57.1	22 41.5	26 20.5	18 41.6	26 9.5	28 4.0	26 28.3
6	6 59 12.1	14 53.7	5 9.6	10♊21.9	21 47.7	29 46.1	23 24.6	26 12.7	18 46.6	26 6.9	28 4.8	26 27.3
7	7 3 8.6	15 54.8	5 6.4	25 5.6	23 26.6	0♐35.9	24 7.7	26 4.9	18 51.6	26 4.4	28 5.6	26 26.2
8	7 7 5.2	16 56.0	5 3.2	9♋45.1	25 5.8	1 26.5	24 50.8	25 57.0	18 56.5	26 1.8	28 6.4	26 25.2
9	7 11 1.8	17 57.1	5 .0	24 13.7	26 45.3	2 17.9	25 33.9	25 49.1	19 1.3	25 59.2	28 7.1	26 24.1
10	7 14 58.3	18 58.2	4 56.8	8♌25.4	28 24.8	3 10.0	26 16.9	25 41.1	19 6.1	25 56.7	28 7.8	26 23.0
11	7 18 54.9	19 59.3	4 53.7	22 15.8	0♒ 4.5	4 2.9	27 .0	25 33.2	19 10.7	25 54.1	28 8.4	26 21.8
12	7 22 51.4	21 .4	4 50.5	5♍42.6	1 44.2	4 56.4	27 43.1	25 25.1	19 15.3	25 51.5	28 9.1	26 20.7
13	7 26 48.0	22 1.6	4 47.3	18 45.4	3 23.9	5 50.6	28 26.1	25 17.1	19 19.9	25 48.9	28 9.7	26 19.5
14	7 30 44.5	23 2.7	4 44.1	1♎25.9	5 3.5	6 45.5	29 9.1	25 9.0	19 24.3	25 46.3	28 10.2	26 18.4
15	7 34 41.1	24 3.8	4 41.0	13 47.1	6 42.7	7 40.9	29 52.2	25 .9	19 28.7	25 43.6	28 10.7	26 17.2
16	7 38 37.7	25 4.9	4 37.8	25 53.1	8 21.5	8 37.0	0♈35.2	24 52.9	19 32.9	25 41.0	28 11.2	26 15.9
17	7 42 34.2	26 6.0	4 34.6	7♏48.6	9 59.7	9 33.6	1 18.2	24 44.8	19 37.2	25 38.4	28 11.7	26 14.7
18	7 46 30.8	27 7.1	4 31.4	19 38.6	11 37.1	10 30.8	2 1.2	24 36.7	19 41.3	25 35.8	28 12.1	26 13.5
19	7 50 27.3	28 8.2	4 28.3	1♐27.9	13 13.4	11 28.5	2 44.1	24 28.7	19 45.3	25 33.2	28 12.5	26 12.2
20	7 54 23.9	29 9.3	4 25.1	13 21.0	14 48.3	12 26.7	3 27.1	24 20.6	19 49.3	25 30.6	28 12.8	26 10.9
21	7 58 20.4	0♒10.4	4 21.9	25 22.0	16 21.5	13 25.4	4 10.1	24 12.6	19 53.1	25 28.0	28 13.1	26 9.6
22	8 2 17.0	1 11.5	4 18.7	7♑34.1	17 52.5	14 24.6	4 53.1	24 4.7	19 57.0	25 25.4	28 13.5	26 8.3
23	8 6 13.6	2 12.6	4 15.5	19 59.7	19 21.0	15 24.1	5 36.0	23 56.7	20 .7	25 22.8	28 13.7	26 7.0
24	8 10 10.1	3 13.6	4 12.4	2♒40.3	20 46.3	16 24.2	6 18.9	23 48.8	20 4.3	25 20.2	28 13.9	26 5.7
25	8 14 6.7	4 14.7	4 9.2	15 36.2	22 7.9	17 24.6	7 1.8	23 41.0	20 7.8	25 17.6	28 14.1	26 4.3
26	8 18 3.2	5 15.7	4 6.0	28 47.1	23 25.2	18 25.4	7 44.7	23 33.2	20 11.3	25 15.1	28 14.2	26 3.0
27	8 21 59.8	6 16.7	4 2.8	12♓11.7	24 37.4	19 26.6	8 27.6	23 25.5	20 14.6	25 12.5	28 14.3	26 1.6
28	8 25 56.3	7 17.7	3 59.7	25 48.4	25 43.8	20 28.2	9 10.4	23 17.8	20 17.9	25 10.0	28 14.4	26 .2
29	8 29 52.9	8 18.7	3 56.5	9♈35.3	26 43.6	21 30.1	9 53.2	23 10.2	20 21.0	25 7.4	28 14.4	25 58.8
30	8 33 49.5	9 19.6	3 53.3	23 30.8	27 35.9	22 32.4	10 36.1	23 2.7	20 24.1	25 4.9	28 14.4	25 57.4
31	8 37 46.0	10 20.5	3 50.1	7♉33.3	28 20.0	23 34.9	11 18.8	22 55.3	20 27.1	25 2.4	28 14.4	25 56.0

LATITUDE

DAY	EPHEM. SID. TIME	☉	☊	☽	☿	♀	♂	♃	♄	♅	♆	♇
1	6 39 29.3	0 .0	0 .0	5N15.4	1S58.7	3N55.5	0S36.6	0N22.6	2N12.0	0N32.4	1N41.8	10N23.3
4	6 51 19.0	0 .0	0 .0	4 18.4	2 4.9	3 59.7	0 32.9	0 23.1	2 12.4	0 32.5	1 42.0	10 24.2
7	7 3 8.6	0 .0	0 .0	0 57.8	2 7.7	4 1.8	0 29.3	0 23.6	2 12.8	0 32.6	1 42.2	10 25.1
10	7 14 58.3	0 .0	0 .0	2S52.2	2 6.6	4 1.9	0 25.8	0 24.0	2 13.3	0 32.6	1 42.3	10 25.9
13	7 26 48.0	0 .0	0 .0	5 2.9	2 1.0	4 .3	0 22.3	0 24.4	2 13.8	0 32.6	1 42.5	10 26.7
16	7 38 37.7	0 .0	0 .0	4 56.1	1 50.1	3 57.1	0 19.0	0 24.8	2 14.3	0 32.7	1 42.7	10 27.4
19	7 50 27.3	0 .0	0 .0	2 56.7	1 33.0	3 52.5	0 15.7	0 25.2	2 14.9	0 32.7	1 42.9	10 28.1
22	8 2 17.0	0 .0	0 .0	0N11.4	1 9.1	3 46.5	0 12.5	0 25.6	2 15.4	0 32.7	1 43.1	10 28.7
25	8 14 6.7	0 .0	0 .0	3 22.4	0 37.4	3 39.4	0 9.4	0 26.0	2 16.0	0 32.7	1 43.3	10 29.3
28	8 25 56.3	0 .0	0 .0	5 8.0	0N 2.0	3 31.3	0 6.3	0 26.3	2 16.5	0 32.7	1 43.5	10 29.9
31	8 37 46.0	0 .0	0 .0	4 23.3	0 48.6	3 22.2	0 3.4	0 26.6	2 17.1	0 32.7	1 43.6	10 30.4

RIGHT ASCENSION

DAY	EPHEM. SID. TIME	☉	☊	☽	☿	♀	♂	♃	♄	♅	♆	♇
1	6 39 29.3	10♑39.6	5♑54.5	26♓53.3	15♑ .8	24♏28.3	20♓52.9	28♋57.8	16♏30.9	28♋26.8	26♎37.5	2♍34.3
2	6 43 25.9	11 46.0	5 51.1	9♈36.6	16 47.7	25 14.4	21 32.2	28 R 50.0	16 36.3	28 R 24.2	26 38.4	2 R 33.5
3	6 47 22.4	12 52.1	5 47.6	23 .7	18 34.6	26 1.4	22 11.5	28 42.1	16 41.6	28 21.6	26 39.3	2 32.7
4	6 51 19.0	13 58.2	5 44.2	7♉17.1	20 21.5	26 49.4	22 50.7	28 34.1	16 46.8	28 19.0	26 40.2	2 31.8
5	6 55 15.5	15 4.2	5 40.7	22 28.4	22 8.4	27 38.3	23 29.9	28 26.0	16 51.9	28 16.3	26 41.0	2 30.9
6	6 59 12.1	16 10.1	5 37.2	8♊23.6	23 55.1	28 28.1	24 9.1	28 17.9	16 56.9	28 13.6	26 41.8	2 30.0
7	7 3 8.6	17 15.8	5 33.8	24 36.9	25 41.6	29 18.9	24 48.2	28 9.7	17 1.9	28 10.9	26 42.6	2 29.1
8	7 7 5.2	18 21.5	5 30.3	10♋34.8	27 27.9	0♐10.5	25 27.4	28 1.4	17 6.9	28 8.2	26 43.3	2 28.1
9	7 11 1.8	19 27.0	5 26.9	25 48.8	29 13.8	1 2.9	26 6.5	27 53.1	17 11.7	28 5.5	26 44.0	2 27.2
10	7 14 58.3	20 32.4	5 23.4	10♌ 4.4	0♒59.4	1 56.2	26 45.6	27 44.7	17 16.5	28 2.8	26 44.7	2 26.2
11	7 18 54.9	21 37.6	5 20.0	23 21.4	2 44.4	2 50.3	27 24.6	27 36.3	17 21.2	28 .1	26 45.3	2 25.2
12	7 22 51.4	22 42.8	5 16.5	5♍49.2	4 28.8	3 45.2	28 3.7	27 27.8	17 25.8	27 57.3	26 45.9	2 24.1
13	7 26 48.0	23 47.7	5 13.0	17 41.5	6 12.4	4 40.8	28 42.7	27 19.4	17 30.4	27 54.6	26 46.5	2 23.1
14	7 30 44.5	24 52.6	5 9.6	29 13.0	7 55.2	5 37.2	29 21.8	27 10.9	17 34.9	27 51.8	26 47.0	2 22.0
15	7 34 41.1	25 57.2	5 6.1	10♎37.9	9 36.9	6 34.3	0♈ .8	27 2.4	17 39.3	27 49.1	26 47.5	2 20.9
16	7 38 37.7	27 1.7	5 2.7	22 8.8	11 17.4	7 32.1	0 39.8	26 53.8	17 43.6	27 46.3	26 48.0	2 19.8
17	7 42 34.2	28 6.1	4 59.2	3♏55.7	12 56.4	8 30.6	1 18.8	26 45.3	17 47.9	27 43.5	26 48.5	2 18.6
18	7 46 30.8	29 10.3	4 55.7	16 5.8	14 33.9	9 29.7	1 57.8	26 36.8	17 52.0	27 40.8	26 48.9	2 17.5
19	7 50 27.3	0♒14.3	4 52.3	28 41.7	16 9.3	10 29.5	2 36.8	26 28.3	17 56.1	27 38.0	26 49.3	2 16.3
20	7 54 23.9	1 18.1	4 48.8	11♐40.6	17 42.6	11 30.0	3 15.9	26 19.8	18 .1	27 35.2	26 49.6	2 15.1
21	7 58 20.4	2 21.7	4 45.4	24 55.0	19 13.3	12 31.0	3 54.9	26 11.3	18 4.1	27 32.5	26 50.0	2 13.9
22	8 2 17.0	3 25.3	4 41.9	8♑13.8	20 41.2	13 32.7	4 33.9	26 3.0	18 7.9	27 29.8	26 50.3	2 12.7
23	8 6 13.6	4 28.5	4 38.4	21 25.7	22 5.6	14 34.9	5 12.9	25 54.6	18 11.7	27 27.1	26 50.5	2 11.5
24	8 10 10.1	5 31.6	4 35.0	4♒22.9	23 26.1	15 37.6	5 52.0	25 46.2	18 15.4	27 24.3	26 50.8	2 10.3
25	8 14 6.7	6 34.5	4 31.5	17 2.6	24 42.3	16 40.9	6 31.0	25 37.9	18 18.9	27 21.6	26 50.9	2 9.0
26	8 18 3.2	7 37.2	4 28.1	29 27.5	25 53.5	17 44.7	7 10.0	25 29.7	18 22.4	27 18.9	26 51.1	2 7.7
27	8 21 59.8	8 39.7	4 24.6	11♓45.2	26 59.2	18 49.0	7 49.1	25 21.5	18 25.8	27 16.2	26 51.2	2 6.4
28	8 25 56.3	9 42.0	4 21.2	24 6.8	27 58.6	19 53.8	8 28.1	25 13.4	18 29.1	27 13.5	26 51.3	2 5.1
29	8 29 52.9	10 44.0	4 17.7	6♈45.1	28 51.1	20 59.1	9 7.2	25 5.3	18 32.3	27 10.8	26 51.4	2 3.8
30	8 33 49.5	11 45.9	4 14.2	19 53.2	29 36.0	22 4.9	9 46.3	24 57.4	18 35.5	27 8.1	26 51.4	2 2.4
31	8 37 46.0	12 47.5	4 10.8	3♉41.9	0♓12.5	23 11.0	10 25.4	24 49.5	18 38.5	27 5.5	26 51.4	2 1.1

DECLINATION

DAY	EPHEM. SID. TIME	☉	☊	☽	☿	♀	♂	♃	♄	♅	♆	♇
1	6 39 29.3	23S 5.0	0S24.4	4N22.9	24S42.9	15S24.3	4S35.7	21N 9.8	15S10.8	21N25.4	9S10.9	22N24.6
4	6 51 19.0	22 49.4	0 24.4	19 15.6	24 13.7	15 51.4	3 41.4	21 14.6	15 14.7	21 26.9	9 11.8	22 26.5
7	7 3 8.6	22 29.8	0 24.4	24 19.0	23 30.4	16 20.3	2 46.9	21 19.4	15 18.3	21 28.4	9 12.5	22 28.3
10	7 14 58.3	22 6.2	0 24.5	15 23.4	22 33.0	16 50.2	1 52.4	21 24.3	15 21.8	21 29.9	9 13.1	22 30.3
13	7 26 48.0	21 38.6	0 24.5	0S11.8	21 21.7	17 20.5	0 57.8	21 29.1	15 25.0	21 31.3	9 13.6	22 32.2
16	7 38 37.7	21 7.3	0 24.5	14 35.7	19 57.0	17 50.5	0 3.4	21 33.9	15 28.1	21 32.8	9 14.0	22 34.1
19	7 50 27.3	20 32.4	0 24.5	23 20.5	18 20.4	18 19.5	0N50.9	21 38.6	15 30.9	21 34.3	9 14.2	22 36.1
22	8 2 17.0	19 53.9	0 24.5	23 2.3	16 34.4	18 47.0	1 45.0	21 43.2	15 33.4	21 35.7	9 14.4	22 38.1
25	8 14 6.7	19 12.1	0 24.5	12 56.2	14 43.6	19 12.5	2 38.9	21 47.7	15 35.8	21 37.2	9 14.5	22 40.0
28	8 25 56.3	18 27.1	0 24.5	3N 2.6	12 54.9	19 35.4	3 32.4	21 52.0	15 37.9	21 38.6	9 14.4	22 42.0
31	8 37 46.0	17 39.2	0 24.5	18 10.8	11 17.8	19 55.4	4 25.5	21 56.1	15 39.7	21 40.0	9 14.2	22 44.0

FEBRUARY 1955

LONGITUDE

DAY	EPHEM. SID. TIME h m s	☉ ° ′	☊ ° ′	☽ ° ′	☿ ° ′	♀ ° ′	♂ ° ′	♃ ° ′	♄ ° ′	♅ ° ′	♆ ° ′	♇ ° ′
1	8 41 42.6	11 ♒ 21.5	3 ♑ 47.0	21 ♉ 41.5	28 ♒ 55.0	24 ♐ 37.9	12 ♈ 1.6	22 ♋ 48.0	20 ♏ 29.9	24 ♋ 59.9	28 ♎ 14.3	25 ♌ 54.6
2	8 45 39.1	12 22.3	3 43.8	5 ♊ 53.8	29 20.3	25 41.1	12 44.3	22 R 40.8	20 32.7	24 R 57.5	28 R 14.2	25 R 53.1
3	8 49 35.7	13 23.2	3 40.6	20 8.4	29 35.1	26 44.6	13 27.1	22 33.6	20 35.4	24 55.0	28 14.1	25 51.7
4	8 53 32.2	14 24.1	3 37.4	4 ♋ 22.9	29 39.2	27 48.4	14 9.8	22 26.6	20 38.0	24 52.6	28 13.9	25 50.2
5	8 57 28.8	15 24.9	3 34.2	18 34.1	29 R 32.1	28 52.5	14 52.4	22 19.7	20 40.5	24 50.2	28 13.7	25 48.8
6	9 1 25.3	16 25.7	3 31.1	2 ♌ 38.3	29 14.0	29 56.8	15 35.1	22 12.9	20 42.9	24 47.8	28 13.5	25 47.3
7	9 5 21.9	17 26.5	3 27.9	16 31.3	28 45.2	1 ♑ 1.5	16 17.7	22 6.2	20 45.2	24 45.4	28 13.2	25 45.9
8	9 9 18.5	18 27.2	3 24.7	0 ♍ 9.3	28 6.3	2 6.3	17 .2	21 59.7	20 47.4	24 43.1	28 12.9	25 44.4
9	9 13 15.0	19 27.9	3 21.5	13 29.4	27 18.2	3 11.5	17 42.8	21 53.2	20 49.6	24 40.8	28 12.6	25 42.9
10	9 17 11.6	20 28.7	3 18.4	26 30.0	26 22.3	4 16.8	18 25.3	21 46.9	20 51.6	24 38.5	28 12.3	25 41.4
11	9 21 8.1	21 29.4	3 15.2	9 ♎ 10.9	25 20.1	5 22.5	19 7.8	21 40.8	20 53.5	24 36.3	28 11.9	25 39.9
12	9 25 4.7	22 30.1	3 12.0	21 33.8	24 13.4	6 28.3	19 50.4	21 34.8	20 55.4	24 34.1	28 11.5	25 38.5
13	9 29 1.2	23 30.7	3 8.8	3 ♏ 41.6	23 4.1	7 34.4	20 32.8	21 28.9	20 57.1	24 31.9	28 11.0	25 37.0
14	9 32 57.8	24 31.4	3 5.7	15 38.3	21 54.0	8 40.6	21 15.2	21 23.2	20 58.7	24 29.7	28 10.5	25 35.5
15	9 36 54.3	25 32.0	3 2.5	27 28.6	20 45.0	9 47.1	21 57.6	21 17.6	21 .2	24 27.6	28 10.0	25 34.0
16	9 40 50.9	26 32.6	2 59.3	9 ♐ 17.9	19 38.9	10 53.8	22 40.0	21 12.2	21 1.6	24 25.5	28 9.4	25 32.6
17	9 44 47.5	27 33.2	2 56.1	21 11.5	18 36.9	12 .6	23 22.3	21 6.9	21 2.9	24 23.4	28 8.8	25 31.1
18	9 48 44.0	28 33.8	2 52.9	3 ♑ 14.6	17 40.4	13 7.6	24 4.7	21 1.8	21 4.1	24 21.4	28 8.2	25 29.6
19	9 52 40.6	29 34.3	2 49.8	15 31.6	16 50.2	14 14.8	24 46.9	20 56.9	21 5.2	24 19.4	28 7.6	25 28.1
20	9 56 37.1	0 ♓ 34.8	2 46.6	28 6.4	16 7.0	15 22.2	25 29.2	20 52.1	21 6.2	24 17.4	28 6.9	25 26.6
21	10 0 33.7	1 35.3	2 43.4	11 ♒ 1.3	15 31.1	16 29.7	26 11.4	20 47.5	21 7.1	24 15.5	28 6.2	25 25.1
22	10 4 30.2	2 35.8	2 40.2	24 16.9	15 2.7	17 37.4	26 53.7	20 43.1	21 7.9	24 13.6	28 5.4	25 23.7
23	10 8 26.8	3 36.2	2 37.1	7 ♓ 52.3	14 41.8	18 45.3	27 35.8	20 38.8	21 8.6	24 11.7	28 4.6	25 22.2
24	10 12 23.3	4 36.6	2 33.9	21 44.6	14 28.3	19 53.3	28 18.0	20 34.8	21 9.2	24 9.9	28 3.8	25 20.7
25	10 16 19.9	5 37.0	2 30.7	5 ♈ 49.4	14 22.0	21 1.4	29 .1	20 30.9	21 9.7	24 8.1	28 3.0	25 19.2
26	10 20 16.4	6 37.4	2 27.5	20 2.0	14 D 22.5	22 9.6	29 42.2	20 27.1	21 10.1	24 6.4	28 2.2	25 17.8
27	10 24 13.0	7 37.7	2 24.3	4 ♉ 17.4	14 29.5	23 18.0	0 ♉ 24.3	20 23.6	21 10.3	24 4.7	28 1.3	25 16.3
28	10 28 9.5	8 38.0	2 21.2	18 31.8	14 42.6	24 26.5	1 6.3	20 20.3	21 10.5	24 3.0	28 .3	25 14.9

LATITUDE

DAY	EPHEM. SID. TIME	☉	☊	☽	☿	♀	♂	♃	♄	♅	♆	♇
1	8 41 42.6	0 .0	0 .0	3 N 34.4	1 N 5.2	3 N 18.9	0 S 2.4	0 N 26.7	2 N 17.3	0 N 32.7	1 N 43.7	10 N 30.6
4	8 53 32.2	0 .0	0 .0	0 3.7	1 56.6	3 8.8	0 N .4	0 27.0	2 17.9	0 32.7	1 43.9	10 31.0
7	9 5 21.9	0 .0	0 .0	3 S 25.6	2 45.0	2 57.9	0 3.2	0 27.3	2 18.6	0 32.7	1 44.1	10 31.4
10	9 17 11.6	0 .0	0 .0	5 5.1	3 22.3	2 46.4	0 5.9	0 27.5	2 19.2	0 32.7	1 44.2	10 31.7
13	9 29 1.2	0 .0	0 .0	4 28.7	3 41.3	2 34.5	0 8.5	0 27.7	2 19.8	0 32.7	1 44.4	10 32.0
16	9 40 50.9	0 .0	0 .0	2 10.1	3 39.1	2 22.2	0 11.1	0 28.0	2 20.4	0 32.7	1 44.6	10 32.3
19	9 52 40.6	0 .0	0 .0	1 N .4	3 18.8	2 9.5	0 13.5	0 28.2	2 21.1	0 32.6	1 44.8	10 32.4
22	10 4 30.2	0 .0	0 .0	3 54.8	2 46.5	1 56.6	0 15.9	0 28.3	2 21.7	0 32.6	1 44.9	10 32.6
25	10 16 19.9	0 .0	0 .0	5 3.4	2 8.2	1 43.6	0 18.2	0 28.5	2 22.3	0 32.6	1 45.1	10 32.7
28	10 28 9.5	0 .0	0 .0	3 33.9	1 28.3	1 30.5	0 20.5	0 28.7	2 23.0	0 32.5	1 45.2	10 32.7

RIGHT ASCENSION

DAY	EPHEM. SID. TIME	☉	☊	☽	☿	♀	♂	♃	♄	♅	♆	♇
1	8 41 42.6	13 ♒ 49.0	4 ♑ 7.3	18 ♉ 16.3	0 ♓ 40.1	24 ♐ 17.6	11 ♈ 4.5	24 ♋ 41.8	18 ♏ 41.4	27 ♋ 2.9	26 ♎ 51.4	1 ♍ 59.7
2	8 45 39.1	14 50.2	4 3.9	3 ♊ 31.2	0 58.2	25 24.7	11 43.6	24 R 34.1	18 44.3	27 R .2	26 R 51.3	1 R 58.4
3	8 49 35.7	15 51.3	4 .4	19 9.8	1 6.3	26 32.1	12 22.8	24 26.5	18 47.0	26 57.7	26 51.2	1 57.0
4	8 53 32.2	16 52.1	3 56.9	4 ♋ 46.6	1 R 4.0	27 39.9	13 1.9	24 19.1	18 49.7	26 55.1	26 51.0	1 55.6
5	8 57 28.8	17 52.7	3 53.5	19 56.0	0 51.4	28 48.1	13 41.1	24 11.7	18 52.3	26 52.5	26 50.9	1 54.2
6	9 1 25.3	18 53.1	3 50.0	4 ♌ 20.8	0 28.5	29 56.6	14 20.3	24 4.5	18 54.7	26 50.0	26 50.7	1 52.8
7	9 5 21.9	19 53.3	3 46.5	17 55.4	29 ♒ 55.8	1 ♑ 5.5	14 59.5	23 57.4	18 57.1	26 47.5	26 50.4	1 51.4
8	9 9 18.5	20 53.3	3 43.1	0 ♍ 44.2	29 13.9	2 14.7	15 38.7	23 50.5	18 59.4	26 45.0	26 50.2	1 50.0
9	9 13 15.0	21 53.1	3 39.6	12 56.9	28 23.8	3 24.3	16 18.0	23 43.6	19 1.5	26 42.6	26 49.9	1 48.5
10	9 17 11.6	22 52.7	3 36.2	24 46.0	27 26.9	4 34.1	16 57.3	23 36.9	19 3.6	26 40.2	26 49.6	1 47.1
11	9 21 8.1	23 52.1	3 32.7	6 ♎ 24.1	26 24.6	5 44.2	17 36.6	23 30.4	19 5.6	26 37.8	26 49.2	1 45.7
12	9 25 4.7	24 51.4	3 29.2	18 2.9	25 18.7	6 54.7	18 16.0	23 24.0	19 7.5	26 35.5	26 48.9	1 44.3
13	9 29 1.2	25 50.4	3 25.8	29 52.0	24 10.9	8 5.3	18 55.4	23 17.8	19 9.3	26 33.1	26 48.4	1 42.8
14	9 32 57.8	26 49.3	3 22.3	11 ♏ 58.7	23 3.0	9 16.2	19 34.8	23 11.7	19 11.0	26 30.8	26 48.0	1 41.4
15	9 36 54.3	27 48.0	3 18.9	24 26.6	21 56.8	10 27.3	20 14.2	23 5.7	19 12.5	26 28.6	26 47.5	1 39.9
16	9 40 50.9	28 46.4	3 15.4	7 ♐ 15.2	20 53.7	11 38.6	20 53.7	22 60.0	19 14.0	26 26.3	26 47.0	1 38.5
17	9 44 47.5	29 44.8	3 11.9	20 19.8	19 55.2	12 50.1	21 33.2	22 54.3	19 15.4	26 24.1	26 46.5	1 37.0
18	9 48 44.0	0 ♓ 42.9	3 8.5	3 ♑ 32.2	19 2.4	14 1.7	22 12.8	22 48.9	19 16.7	26 22.0	26 45.9	1 35.5
19	9 52 40.6	1 40.9	3 5.0	16 43.4	18 16.0	15 13.6	22 52.3	22 43.6	19 17.8	26 19.9	26 45.3	1 34.1
20	9 56 37.1	2 38.7	3 1.6	29 46.1	17 36.7	16 25.5	23 32.0	22 38.6	19 18.9	26 17.8	26 44.7	1 32.6
21	10 0 33.7	3 36.3	2 58.1	12 ♒ 36.7	17 4.8	17 37.6	24 11.7	22 33.6	19 19.8	26 15.7	26 44.0	1 31.2
22	10 4 30.2	4 33.8	2 54.6	25 16.2	16 40.4	18 49.8	24 51.4	22 28.9	19 20.7	26 13.7	26 43.3	1 29.7
23	10 8 26.8	5 31.1	2 51.2	7 ♓ 50.3	16 23.5	20 2.0	25 31.2	22 24.4	19 21.4	26 11.7	26 42.6	1 28.2
24	10 12 23.3	6 28.2	2 47.7	20 27.8	16 14.0	21 14.4	26 11.0	22 20.0	19 22.1	26 9.8	26 41.9	1 26.8
25	10 16 19.9	7 25.2	2 44.2	3 ♈ 19.8	16 11.6	22 26.8	26 50.8	22 15.9	19 22.6	26 7.9	26 41.1	1 25.3
26	10 20 16.4	8 22.0	2 40.8	16 37.5	16 D 16.0	23 39.2	27 30.8	22 11.9	19 23.1	26 6.1	26 40.3	1 23.9
27	10 24 13.0	9 18.7	2 37.3	0 ♉ 30.0	16 26.9	24 51.7	28 10.7	22 8.2	19 23.4	26 4.3	26 39.5	1 22.4
28	10 28 9.5	10 15.3	2 33.9	15 1.1	16 43.9	26 4.2	28 50.7	22 4.6	19 23.6	26 2.5	26 38.7	1 21.0

DECLINATION

DAY	EPHEM. SID. TIME	☉	☊	☽	☿	♀	♂	♃	♄	♅	♆	♇
1	8 41 42.6	17 S 22.6	0 S 24.5	21 N 38.4	10 S 50.1	20 S 1.4	4 N 43.1	21 N 57.4	15 S 40.3	21 N 40.4	9 S 14.2	22 N 44.6
4	8 53 32.2	16 30.9	0 24.5	23 26.0	9 46.5	20 16.9	5 35.6	22 1.2	15 41.8	21 41.7	9 13.8	22 46.5
7	9 5 21.9	15 36.7	0 24.5	12 37.0	9 19.9	20 28.6	6 27.5	22 4.8	15 43.1	21 43.0	9 13.4	22 48.4
10	9 17 11.6	14 40.0	0 24.5	3 S 16.5	9 33.4	20 36.2	7 18.8	22 8.1	15 44.2	21 44.2	9 12.9	22 50.3
13	9 29 1.2	13 41.1	0 24.5	16 57.5	10 20.7	20 39.5	8 9.5	22 11.2	15 45.0	21 45.4	9 12.3	22 52.1
16	9 40 50.9	12 40.3	0 24.5	23 59.6	11 27.5	20 38.2	8 59.5	22 14.0	15 45.6	21 46.5	9 11.6	22 53.9
19	9 52 40.6	11 37.5	0 24.5	21 32.5	12 37.9	20 32.2	9 48.6	22 16.6	15 45.9	21 47.6	9 10.8	22 55.6
22	10 4 30.2	10 33.1	0 24.5	9 44.2	13 40.4	20 21.4	10 37.0	22 18.9	15 46.0	21 48.6	9 9.8	22 57.3
25	10 16 19.9	9 27.2	0 24.5	6 N 57.3	14 28.8	20 5.7	11 24.4	22 20.9	15 45.8	21 49.5	9 8.8	22 58.9
28	10 28 9.5	8 20.1	0 24.5	20 46.1	15 1.0	19 45.1	12 10.9	22 22.6	15 45.4	21 50.3	9 7.7	23 .5

MARCH 1955

LONGITUDE

DAY	EPHEM. SID. TIME h m s	☉ ° ′	☊ ° ′	☽ ° ′	☿ ° ′	♀ ° ′	♂ ° ′	♃ ° ′	♄ ° ′	♅ ° ′	♆ ° ′	♇ ° ′
1	10 32 6.1	9♓38.2	2♑18.0	2♊42.4	15♒ 1.4	25♑35.1	1♉48.3	20♋17.1	21♏10.6	24♋ 1.4	27♎59.4	25♌13.5
2	10 36 2.7	10 38.4	2 14.8	16 47.5	15 25.6	26 43.9	2 30.3	20 R 14.1	21 10.6	23 R 59.9	27 R 58.4	25 R 12.0
3	10 39 59.2	11 38.6	2 11.6	0♋46.3	15 54.9	27 52.7	3 12.2	20 11.4	21 R 10.4	23 58.3	27 57.4	25 10.6
4	10 43 55.8	12 38.8	2 8.5	14 38.5	16 28.8	29 1.7	3 54.1	20 8.8	21 10.2	23 56.9	27 56.4	25 9.2
5	10 47 52.3	13 38.9	2 5.3	28 23.7	17 7.1	0♒10.8	4 36.1	20 6.4	21 9.9	23 55.5	27 55.4	25 7.8
6	10 51 48.9	14 39.0	2 2.1	12♌ .7	17 49.4	1 20.0	5 17.9	20 4.2	21 9.4	23 54.1	27 54.3	25 6.4
7	10 55 45.4	15 39.0	1 58.9	25 28.2	18 35.4	2 29.3	5 59.7	20 2.2	21 8.9	23 52.8	27 53.2	25 5.1
8	10 59 42.0	16 39.1	1 55.7	8♍44.3	19 24.9	3 38.7	6 41.5	20 .4	21 8.3	23 51.5	27 52.1	25 3.7
9	11 3 38.5	17 39.0	1 52.6	21 47.3	20 17.7	4 48.2	7 23.2	19 58.8	21 7.5	23 50.2	27 51.0	25 2.3
10	11 7 35.1	18 39.0	1 49.4	4♎35.6	21 13.6	5 57.8	8 4.9	19 57.4	21 6.7	23 49.0	27 49.8	25 1.0
11	11 11 31.6	19 38.9	1 46.2	17 8.7	22 12.3	7 7.5	8 46.5	19 56.1	21 5.7	23 47.9	27 48.6	24 59.7
12	11 15 28.2	20 38.8	1 43.0	29 27.2	23 13.7	8 17.3	9 28.2	19 55.1	21 4.7	23 46.8	27 47.4	24 58.3
13	11 19 24.7	21 38.6	1 39.9	11♏32.8	24 17.6	9 27.2	10 9.8	19 54.2	21 3.5	23 45.7	27 46.2	24 57.0
14	11 23 21.3	22 38.5	1 36.7	23 28.4	25 23.9	10 37.1	10 51.3	19 53.6	21 2.3	23 44.7	27 44.9	24 55.7
15	11 27 17.8	23 38.3	1 33.5	5♐18.1	26 32.4	11 47.2	11 32.9	19 53.1	21 .9	23 43.8	27 43.6	24 54.5
16	11 31 14.4	24 38.0	1 30.3	17 6.7	27 43.1	12 57.3	12 14.4	19 52.9	20 59.5	23 42.9	27 42.3	24 53.2
17	11 35 10.9	25 37.8	1 27.1	28 59.3	28 55.8	14 7.5	12 55.8	19 52.8	20 58.0	23 42.0	27 41.0	24 52.0
18	11 39 7.5	26 37.5	1 24.0	11♑ 1.7	0♓10.4	15 17.8	13 37.3	19 D 52.9	20 56.3	23 41.2	27 39.7	24 50.7
19	11 43 4.1	27 37.2	1 20.8	23 19.2	1 26.9	16 28.2	14 18.7	19 53.2	20 54.6	23 40.5	27 38.3	24 49.5
20	11 47 .6	28 36.8	1 17.6	5♒56.7	2 45.1	17 38.6	15 .0	19 53.8	20 52.8	23 39.8	27 36.9	24 48.3
21	11 50 57.2	29 36.5	1 14.4	18 57.8	4 5.1	18 49.1	15 41.4	19 54.5	20 50.9	23 39.1	27 35.5	24 47.1
22	11 54 53.7	0♈36.1	1 11.3	2♓24.4	5 26.7	19 59.7	16 22.7	19 55.4	20 48.9	23 38.6	27 34.1	24 46.0
23	11 58 50.3	1 35.6	1 8.1	16 16.3	6 49.9	21 10.3	17 4.0	19 56.5	20 46.8	23 38.0	27 32.7	24 44.8
24	12 2 46.8	2 35.2	1 4.9	0♈30.2	8 14.7	22 21.0	17 45.2	19 57.7	20 44.6	23 37.5	27 31.2	24 43.7
25	12 6 43.4	3 34.7	1 1.7	15 .7	9 41.0	23 31.8	18 26.4	19 59.2	20 42.3	23 37.1	27 29.8	24 42.6
26	12 10 39.9	4 34.2	0 58.5	29 40.6	11 8.9	24 42.6	19 7.7	20 .9	20 40.0	23 36.8	27 28.4	24 41.6
27	12 14 36.5	5 33.6	0 55.4	14♉22.0	12 38.2	25 53.5	19 48.8	20 2.8	20 37.5	23 36.5	27 26.9	24 40.5
28	12 18 33.0	6 33.0	0 52.2	28 58.2	14 8.9	27 4.4	20 29.9	20 4.8	20 35.0	23 36.2	27 25.4	24 39.5
29	12 22 29.6	7 32.3	0 49.0	13♊23.9	15 41.1	28 15.4	21 11.0	20 7.1	20 32.4	23 36.0	27 23.9	24 38.4
30	12 26 26.1	8 31.7	0 45.8	27 36.1	17 14.7	29 26.4	21 52.1	20 9.5	20 29.7	23 35.8	27 22.3	24 37.4
31	12 30 22.7	9 30.9	0 42.7	11♋33.7	18 49.7	0♓37.4	22 33.1	20 12.1	20 26.9	23 35.7	27 20.8	24 36.4

LATITUDE

DAY	SID. TIME	☉	☊	☽	☿	♀	♂	♃	♄	♅	♆	♇
1	10 32 6.1	0 .0	0 .0	2N34.3	1N15.2	1N26.1	0N21.2	0N28.7	2N23.2	0N32.5	1N45.3	10N32.7
4	10 43 55.8	0 .0	0 .0	1S 1.1	0 37.2	1 13.1	0 23.4	0 28.8	2 23.8	0 32.5	1 45.4	10 32.7
7	10 55 45.4	0 .0	0 .0	4 .2	0 2.0	1 .1	0 25.5	0 29.0	2 24.4	0 32.4	1 45.6	10 32.6
10	11 7 35.1	0 .0	0 .0	5 .6	0S29.6	0 47.3	0 27.5	0 29.1	2 25.0	0 32.4	1 45.7	10 32.5
13	11 19 24.7	0 .0	0 .0	3 51.9	0 57.6	0 34.7	0 29.5	0 29.2	2 25.6	0 32.3	1 45.8	10 32.3
16	11 31 14.4	0 .0	0 .0	1 15.5	1 21.8	0 22.4	0 31.4	0 29.2	2 26.2	0 32.3	1 45.9	10 32.1
19	11 43 4.1	0 .0	0 .0	1N52.8	1 42.1	0 10.5	0 33.2	0 29.3	2 26.7	0 32.2	1 46.0	10 31.8
22	11 54 53.7	0 .0	0 .0	4 23.9	1 58.4	0S 1.1	0 35.0	0 29.4	2 27.3	0 32.1	1 46.1	10 31.5
25	12 6 43.4	0 .0	0 .0	4 51.0	2 10.8	0 12.2	0 36.7	0 29.5	2 27.8	0 32.1	1 46.2	10 31.1
28	12 18 33.0	0 .0	0 .0	2 36.8	2 19.0	0 22.8	0 38.4	0 29.5	2 28.3	0 32.0	1 46.3	10 30.8
31	12 30 22.7	0 .0	0 .0	1S .2	2 23.1	0 32.9	0 40.0	0 29.6	2 28.7	0 32.0	1 46.4	10 30.3

RIGHT ASCENSION

DAY	SID. TIME	☉	☊	☽	☿	♀	♂	♃	♄	♅	♆	♇
1	10 32 6.1	11♓11.7	2♑30.4	0♊ 6.0	17♒ 6.5	27♑16.8	29♈30.8	22♋ 1.2	19♏23.8	26♋ .8	26♎37.8	1♍19.6
2	10 36 2.7	12 8.0	2 26.9	15 29.7	17 34.4	28 29.3	0♉10.9	21 R 58.1	19 23.8	25 R 59.2	26 R 36.9	1 R 18.1
3	10 39 59.2	13 4.1	2 23.5	0♋50.6	18 7.2	29 41.8	0 51.0	21 55.1	19 R 23.7	25 57.5	26 36.0	1 16.7
4	10 43 55.8	14 .1	2 20.0	15 46.6	18 44.6	0♒54.3	1 31.2	21 52.3	19 23.5	25 56.0	26 35.0	1 15.3
5	10 47 52.3	14 56.1	2 16.5	0♌ 2.8	19 26.2	2 6.7	2 11.5	21 49.8	19 23.3	25 54.5	26 34.1	1 13.9
6	10 51 48.9	15 51.9	2 13.1	13 33.6	20 11.7	3 19.1	2 51.8	21 47.5	19 22.9	25 53.0	26 33.1	1 12.5
7	10 55 45.4	16 47.5	2 9.6	26 22.5	21 .7	4 31.5	3 32.2	21 45.3	19 22.4	25 51.6	26 32.1	1 11.1
8	10 59 42.0	17 43.1	2 6.1	8♍37.9	21 53.0	5 43.8	4 12.6	21 43.4	19 21.8	25 50.2	26 31.0	1 9.8
9	11 3 38.5	18 38.5	2 2.7	20 30.9	22 48.4	6 56.0	4 53.0	21 41.7	19 21.1	25 48.9	26 29.9	1 8.4
10	11 7 35.1	19 33.9	1 59.2	2♎13.0	23 46.6	8 8.1	5 33.5	21 40.2	19 20.3	25 47.6	26 28.8	1 7.0
11	11 11 31.6	20 29.2	1 55.8	13 54.9	24 47.3	9 20.1	6 14.1	21 38.8	19 19.4	25 46.4	26 27.7	1 5.7
12	11 15 28.2	21 24.4	1 52.3	25 45.4	25 50.4	10 32.1	6 54.7	21 37.7	19 18.4	25 45.2	26 26.6	1 4.3
13	11 19 24.7	22 19.5	1 48.8	7♏51.0	26 55.7	11 43.9	7 35.4	21 36.8	19 17.3	25 44.1	26 25.4	1 3.0
14	11 23 21.3	23 14.6	1 45.4	20 14.9	28 3.0	12 55.6	8 16.1	21 36.1	19 16.1	25 43.1	26 24.3	1 1.7
15	11 27 17.8	24 9.6	1 41.9	2♐56.5	29 12.3	14 7.2	8 56.9	21 35.6	19 14.8	25 42.0	26 23.1	1 .4
16	11 31 14.4	25 4.5	1 38.4	15 51.7	0♓23.2	15 18.7	9 37.7	21 35.4	19 13.5	25 41.1	26 21.9	0 59.1
17	11 35 10.9	25 59.4	1 35.0	28 53.8	1 35.8	16 30.1	10 18.7	21 35.3	19 12.0	25 40.2	26 20.6	0 57.8
18	11 39 7.5	26 54.2	1 31.5	11♑55.1	2 49.9	17 41.3	10 59.6	21 D 35.4	19 10.4	25 39.3	26 19.4	0 56.5
19	11 43 4.1	27 49.0	1 28.1	24 49.8	4 5.5	18 52.3	11 40.7	21 35.8	19 8.7	25 38.5	26 18.1	0 55.3
20	11 47 .6	28 43.7	1 24.6	7♒35.2	5 22.3	20 3.3	12 21.8	21 36.3	19 6.9	25 37.8	26 16.8	0 54.1
21	11 50 57.2	29 38.4	1 21.1	20 12.7	6 40.5	21 14.0	13 2.9	21 37.1	19 5.1	25 37.1	26 15.5	0 52.8
22	11 54 53.7	0♈33.1	1 17.7	2♓47.8	7 59.8	22 24.7	13 44.1	21 38.1	19 3.1	25 36.5	26 14.2	0 51.6
23	11 58 50.3	1 27.7	1 14.2	15 29.2	9 20.2	23 35.1	14 25.4	21 39.2	19 1.1	25 35.9	26 12.8	0 50.4
24	12 2 46.8	2 22.4	1 10.7	28 27.9	10 41.8	24 45.4	15 6.7	21 40.6	18 58.9	25 35.4	26 11.5	0 49.3
25	12 6 43.4	3 17.0	1 7.3	11♈55.1	12 4.3	25 55.6	15 48.1	21 42.2	18 56.7	25 34.9	26 10.1	0 48.1
26	12 10 39.9	4 11.6	1 3.8	26 .0	13 28.0	27 5.6	16 29.7	21 44.0	18 54.4	25 34.6	26 8.8	0 47.0
27	12 14 36.5	5 6.2	1 .3	10♉46.2	14 52.5	28 15.4	17 11.2	21 46.0	18 52.0	25 34.2	26 7.4	0 45.9
28	12 18 33.0	6 .8	0 56.9	26 7.8	16 18.0	29 25.1	17 52.8	21 48.2	18 49.5	25 33.9	26 6.0	0 44.8
29	12 22 29.6	6 55.4	0 53.4	11♊48.1	17 44.5	0♓34.6	18 34.4	21 50.6	18 46.9	25 33.7	26 4.6	0 43.8
30	12 26 26.1	7 50.0	0 50.0	27 22.9	19 11.9	1 43.9	19 16.1	21 53.2	18 44.2	25 33.5	26 3.1	0 42.7
31	12 30 22.7	8 44.5	0 46.5	12♋28.6	20 40.3	2 53.0	19 57.9	21 56.0	18 41.5	25 33.4	26 1.7	0 41.7

DECLINATION

DAY	SID. TIME	☉	☊	☽	☿	♀	♂	♃	♄	♅	♆	♇
1	10 32 6.1	7S57.5	0S24.5	23N13.6	15S 8.1	19S37.1	12N26.2	22N23.2	15S45.2	21N50.6	9S 7.4	23N 1.0
4	10 43 55.8	6 48.9	0 24.5	21 37.7	15 18.6	19 10.0	13 11.3	22 24.5	15 44.5	21 51.3	9 6.2	23 2.5
7	10 55 45.4	5 39.5	0 24.5	9 15.7	15 13.6	18 38.0	13 55.4	22 25.6	15 43.6	21 52.0	9 4.9	23 3.8
10	11 7 35.1	4 29.5	0 24.5	6S25.3	14 53.8	18 1.3	14 38.4	22 26.4	15 42.4	21 52.6	9 3.6	23 5.1
13	11 19 24.7	3 18.9	0 24.5	18 58.4	14 20.0	17 20.0	15 20.1	22 27.0	15 41.1	21 53.1	9 2.2	23 6.3
16	11 31 14.4	2 7.9	0 24.5	24 4.4	13 32.9	16 34.3	16 .7	22 27.3	15 39.5	21 53.6	9 .7	23 7.5
19	11 43 4.1	0 56.8	0 24.5	19 34.6	12 33.1	15 44.3	16 39.9	22 27.3	15 37.7	21 53.9	8 59.1	23 8.5
22	11 54 53.7	0N14.4	0 24.5	6 30.6	11 21.1	14 50.2	17 17.9	22 27.1	15 35.6	21 54.2	8 57.6	23 9.4
25	12 6 43.4	1 25.4	0 24.5	10N23.1	9 57.5	13 52.3	17 54.5	22 26.6	15 33.4	21 54.4	8 55.9	23 10.3
28	12 18 33.0	2 36.1	0 24.5	22 29.0	8 22.6	12 50.8	18 29.7	22 25.8	15 31.1	21 54.5	8 54.3	23 11.0
31	12 30 22.7	3 46.3	0 24.5	21 56.6	6 36.9	11 46.1	19 3.4	22 24.8	15 28.5	21 54.5	8 52.6	23 11.7

APRIL 1955

LONGITUDE

DAY	EPHEM. SID. TIME h m s	☉ ° ′	☊ ° ′	☽ ° ′	☿ ° ′	♀ ° ′	♂ ° ′	♃ ° ′	♄ ° ′	♅ ° ′	♆ ° ′	♇ ° ′
1	12 34 19.2	10♈30.2	0♑39.5	25♋16.8	20♓26.2	1♓48.5	23♉14.1	20♋14.9	20♏24.0	23♋35.6	27♎19.2	24♌35.5
2	12 38 15.8	11 29.4	0 36.3	8♌46.4	22 4.1	2 59.7	23 55.0	20 17.8	20 R 21.1	23 35.6	27 R 17.7	24 R 34.6
3	12 42 12.3	12 28.5	0 33.1	22 3.4	23 43.3	4 10.9	24 35.9	20 21.0	20 18.1	23 D 35.7	27 16.1	24 33.6
4	12 46 8.9	13 27.6	0 29.9	5♍ 8.7	25 24.1	5 22.1	25 16.8	20 24.3	20 15.0	23 35.8	27 14.5	24 32.8
5	12 50 5.4	14 26.7	0 26.8	18 2.6	27 6.2	6 33.4	25 57.6	20 27.8	20 11.8	23 36.0	27 12.9	24 31.9
6	12 54 2.0	15 25.8	0 23.6	0♎45.2	28 49.8	7 44.7	26 38.4	20 31.5	20 8.6	23 36.2	27 11.3	24 31.0
7	12 57 58.6	16 24.8	0 20.4	13 16.4	0♈34.8	8 56.0	27 19.2	20 35.3	20 5.2	23 36.5	27 9.7	24 30.2
8	13 1 55.1	17 23.7	0 17.2	25 36.3	2 21.3	10 7.5	27 59.9	20 39.3	20 1.9	23 36.8	27 8.1	24 29.4
9	13 5 51.7	18 22.7	0 14.0	7♏45.5	4 9.3	11 18.9	28 40.6	20 43.5	19 58.4	23 37.2	27 6.5	24 28.7
10	13 9 48.2	19 21.6	0 10.9	19 45.2	5 58.7	12 30.4	29 21.3	20 47.9	19 54.9	23 37.6	27 4.9	24 27.9
11	13 13 44.8	20 20.5	0 7.7	1♐37.7	7 49.7	13 41.9	0♊ 1.9	20 52.4	19 51.3	23 38.1	27 3.3	24 27.2
12	13 17 41.3	21 19.3	0 4.5	13 25.8	9 42.1	14 53.5	0 42.5	20 57.1	19 47.7	23 38.6	27 1.6	24 26.5
13	13 21 37.9	22 18.1	0 1.3	25 13.6	11 36.0	16 5.1	1 23.1	21 1.9	19 44.0	23 39.2	26 60.0	24 25.8
14	13 25 34.4	23 16.9	29♐58.2	7♑ 5.5	13 31.5	17 16.7	2 3.6	21 6.9	19 40.2	23 39.9	26 58.3	24 25.2
15	13 29 31.0	24 15.7	29 55.0	19 6.6	15 28.4	18 28.4	2 44.1	21 12.1	19 36.4	23 40.6	26 56.7	24 24.6
16	13 33 27.5	25 14.5	29 51.8	1♒22.5	17 26.8	19 40.1	3 24.6	21 17.5	19 32.6	23 41.3	26 55.1	24 24.0
17	13 37 24.1	26 13.2	29 48.6	13 58.1	19 26.7	20 51.9	4 5.1	21 23.0	19 28.7	23 42.2	26 53.5	24 23.5
18	13 41 20.6	27 11.9	29 45.4	26 58.2	21 27.9	22 3.7	4 45.5	21 28.6	19 24.7	23 43.0	26 51.8	24 22.9
19	13 45 17.2	28 10.5	29 42.3	10♓25.7	23 30.4	23 15.5	5 25.9	21 34.4	19 20.7	23 43.9	26 50.2	24 22.4
20	13 49 13.7	29 9.1	29 39.1	24 21.6	25 34.3	24 27.3	6 6.2	21 40.4	19 16.6	23 44.9	26 48.5	24 21.9
21	13 53 10.3	0♉ 7.7	29 35.9	8♈44.2	27 39.3	25 39.1	6 46.5	21 46.5	19 12.5	23 45.9	26 46.9	24 21.5
22	13 57 6.9	1 6.3	29 32.7	23 28.4	29 45.3	26 51.0	7 26.8	21 52.8	19 8.4	23 47.0	26 45.2	24 21.0
23	14 1 3.4	2 4.8	29 29.6	8♉26.6	1♉52.3	28 2.9	8 7.1	21 59.2	19 4.2	23 48.1	26 43.6	24 20.6
24	14 4 60.0	3 3.3	29 26.4	23 29.5	3 60.0	29 14.9	8 47.3	22 5.7	18 59.9	23 49.2	26 42.0	24 20.3
25	14 8 56.5	4 1.8	29 23.2	8♊27.9	6 8.2	0♈26.8	9 27.5	22 12.4	18 55.7	23 50.5	26 40.3	24 19.9
26	14 12 53.1	5 .2	29 20.0	23 14.0	8 16.8	1 38.8	10 7.7	22 19.3	18 51.4	23 51.7	26 38.7	24 19.6
27	14 16 49.6	5 58.6	29 16.9	7♋42.3	10 25.4	2 50.8	10 47.9	22 26.2	18 47.0	23 53.1	26 37.1	24 19.3
28	14 20 46.2	6 56.9	29 13.7	21 50.1	12 33.8	4 2.8	11 28.0	22 33.4	18 42.7	23 54.4	26 35.5	24 19.0
29	14 24 42.7	7 55.3	29 10.5	5♌36.7	14 41.7	5 14.8	12 8.0	22 40.6	18 38.3	23 55.8	26 33.9	24 18.8
30	14 28 39.3	8 53.6	29 7.3	19 3.1	16 48.9	6 26.9	12 48.1	22 48.0	18 33.9	23 57.3	26 32.3	24 18.6

LATITUDE

DAY	EPHEM. SID. TIME	☉	☊	☽	☿	♀	♂	♃	♄	♅	♆	♇
1	12 34 19.2	0 .0	0 .0	2S 8.9	2S23.6	0S36.1	0N40.5	0N29.6	2N28.9	0N31.9	1N46.4	10N30.2
4	12 46 8.9	0 .0	0 .0	4 34.0	2 22.0	0 45.4	0 42.0	0 29.6	2 29.3	0 31.9	1 46.5	10 29.7
7	12 57 58.6	0 .0	0 .0	4 52.3	2 16.0	0 54.1	0 43.5	0 29.7	2 29.6	0 31.8	1 46.5	10 29.2
10	13 9 48.2	0 .0	0 .0	3 10.9	2 5.4	1 2.2	0 44.9	0 29.7	2 30.0	0 31.7	1 46.6	10 28.7
13	13 21 37.9	0 .0	0 .0	0 17.8	1 50.3	1 9.6	0 46.3	0 29.8	2 30.3	0 31.7	1 46.6	10 28.2
16	13 33 27.5	0 .0	0 .0	2N46.0	1 30.8	1 16.3	0 47.6	0 29.8	2 30.6	0 31.6	1 46.6	10 27.6
19	13 45 17.2	0 .0	0 .0	4 50.4	1 6.9	1 22.3	0 48.9	0 29.9	2 30.8	0 31.6	1 46.6	10 27.0
22	13 57 6.9	0 .0	0 .0	4 35.7	0 39.3	1 27.5	0 50.1	0 29.9	2 31.0	0 31.5	1 46.6	10 26.4
25	14 8 56.5	0 .0	0 .0	1 41.2	0 8.7	1 32.1	0 51.2	0 29.9	2 31.1	0 31.4	1 46.6	10 25.7
28	14 20 46.2	0 .0	0 .0	2S 6.7	0N23.3	1 35.9	0 52.4	0 30.0	2 31.2	0 31.4	1 46.6	10 25.1

RIGHT ASCENSION

DAY	EPHEM. SID. TIME	☉	☊	☽	☿	♀	♂	♃	♄	♅	♆	♇
1	12 34 19.2	9♈39.2	0♑43.0	26♋49.5	22♓ 9.5	4♓ 2.0	20♉39.7	21♋59.0	18♏38.7	25♋33.4	26♎ .2	0♍40.6
2	12 38 15.8	10 33.8	0 39.6	10♌20.9	23 39.8	5 10.9	21 21.5	22 2.1	18 R 35.8	25 R 33.3	25 R 58.7	0 R 39.7
3	12 42 12.3	11 28.4	0 36.1	23 7.1	25 11.0	6 19.6	22 3.5	22 5.5	18 32.8	25 D 33.4	25 57.3	0 38.7
4	12 46 8.9	12 23.1	0 32.6	5♍17.8	26 43.2	7 28.1	22 45.4	22 9.1	18 29.7	25 33.5	25 55.8	0 37.7
5	12 50 5.4	13 17.8	0 29.2	17 5.2	28 16.4	8 36.5	23 27.5	22 12.8	18 26.6	25 33.7	25 54.3	0 36.8
6	12 54 2.0	14 12.6	0 25.7	28 41.4	29 50.7	9 44.7	24 9.6	22 16.7	18 23.4	25 33.9	25 52.8	0 35.9
7	12 57 58.6	15 7.3	0 22.2	10♎17.5	1♈26.0	10 52.8	24 51.7	22 20.8	18 20.1	25 34.2	25 51.3	0 35.0
8	13 1 55.1	16 2.2	0 18.8	22 2.7	3 2.5	12 .8	25 33.9	22 25.1	18 16.8	25 34.5	25 49.8	0 34.1
9	13 5 51.7	16 57.1	0 15.3	4♏ 3.6	4 40.1	13 8.6	26 16.1	22 29.6	18 13.4	25 34.9	25 48.2	0 33.3
10	13 9 48.2	17 52.0	0 11.8	16 23.3	6 19.0	14 16.3	26 58.4	22 34.3	18 9.9	25 35.4	25 46.7	0 32.5
11	13 13 44.8	18 47.1	0 8.4	29 .7	7 59.0	15 23.9	27 40.8	22 39.1	18 6.3	25 35.9	25 45.2	0 31.7
12	13 17 41.3	19 42.2	0 4.9	11♐51.2	9 40.4	16 31.4	28 23.2	22 44.1	18 2.7	25 36.5	25 43.6	0 30.9
13	13 21 37.9	20 37.3	0 1.5	24 47.2	11 23.1	17 38.8	29 5.6	22 49.3	17 59.1	25 37.1	25 42.1	0 30.2
14	13 25 34.4	21 32.6	29♐58.0	7♑40.7	13 7.3	18 46.1	29 48.1	22 54.6	17 55.3	25 37.8	25 40.6	0 29.5
15	13 29 31.0	22 27.9	29 54.5	20 25.3	14 52.8	19 53.3	0♊30.6	23 .2	17 51.6	25 38.5	25 39.0	0 28.8
16	13 33 27.5	23 23.4	29 51.1	2♒58.4	16 39.9	21 .4	1 13.3	23 5.9	17 47.8	25 39.3	25 37.5	0 28.2
17	13 37 24.1	24 18.9	29 47.6	15 21.7	18 28.5	22 7.4	1 55.9	23 11.8	17 43.9	25 40.2	25 36.0	0 27.5
18	13 41 20.6	25 14.5	29 44.1	27 41.1	20 18.6	23 14.3	2 38.6	23 17.8	17 40.0	25 41.1	25 34.4	0 26.9
19	13 45 17.2	26 10.2	29 40.7	10♓ 6.2	22 10.3	24 21.2	3 21.4	23 24.0	17 36.0	25 42.1	25 32.9	0 26.3
20	13 49 13.7	27 6.0	29 37.2	22 48.8	24 3.5	25 28.0	4 4.1	23 30.4	17 31.9	25 43.1	25 31.3	0 25.7
21	13 53 10.3	28 1.9	29 33.7	6♈ 2.3	25 58.3	26 34.7	4 47.0	23 36.9	17 27.8	25 44.2	25 29.8	0 25.2
22	13 57 6.9	28 58.0	29 30.3	19 58.7	27 54.6	27 41.4	5 29.8	23 43.5	17 23.7	25 45.3	25 28.2	0 24.7
23	14 1 3.4	29 54.1	29 26.8	4♉45.4	29 52.4	28 48.1	6 12.7	23 50.4	17 19.6	25 46.5	25 26.7	0 24.2
24	14 4 60.0	0♉50.3	29 23.4	20 19.9	1♉51.6	29 54.7	6 55.7	23 57.4	17 15.4	25 47.7	25 25.1	0 23.8
25	14 8 56.5	1 46.7	29 19.9	6♊26.3	3 52.1	1♈ 1.3	7 38.7	24 4.5	17 11.1	25 49.0	25 23.6	0 23.3
26	14 12 53.1	2 43.2	29 16.4	22 36.5	5 53.7	2 7.8	8 21.7	24 11.8	17 6.8	25 50.3	25 22.0	0 22.9
27	14 16 49.6	3 39.8	29 13.0	8♋20.0	7 56.3	3 14.4	9 4.7	24 19.2	17 2.5	25 51.7	25 20.5	0 22.6
28	14 20 46.2	4 36.5	29 9.5	23 14.2	9 59.6	4 20.9	9 47.8	24 26.8	16 58.2	25 53.2	25 19.0	0 22.2
29	14 24 42.7	5 33.3	29 6.0	7♌10.4	12 3.4	5 27.4	10 30.9	24 34.5	16 53.9	25 54.7	25 17.5	0 21.9
30	14 28 39.3	6 30.3	29 2.6	20 12.1	14 7.5	6 34.0	11 14.1	24 42.4	16 49.5	25 56.2	25 16.0	0 21.6

DECLINATION

DAY	EPHEM. SID. TIME	☉	☊	☽	☿	♀	♂	♃	♄	♅	♆	♇
1	12 34 19.2	4N 9.5	0S24.6	18N58.3	5S59.4	11S23.8	19N14.3	22N24.4	15S27.6	21N54.5	8S52.0	23N11.9
4	12 46 8.9	5 18.8	0 24.6	5 22.5	3 60.0	10 15.0	19 46.1	22 23.0	15 24.8	21 54.4	8 50.2	23 12.4
7	12 57 58.6	6 27.3	0 24.6	9S43.6	1 50.9	9 3.5	20 16.3	22 21.4	15 21.9	21 54.2	8 48.5	23 12.8
10	13 9 48.2	7 34.8	0 24.6	20 44.4	0N27.3	7 49.6	20 44.9	22 19.5	15 18.8	21 54.0	8 46.7	23 13.1
13	13 21 37.9	8 41.1	0 24.6	23 39.3	2 53.8	6 33.6	21 11.9	22 17.4	15 15.6	21 53.6	8 44.9	23 13.3
16	13 33 27.5	9 46.1	0 24.6	17 9.5	5 27.2	5 15.7	21 37.2	22 15.0	15 12.3	21 53.2	8 43.2	23 13.4
19	13 45 17.2	10 49.7	0 24.6	3 10.6	8 5.7	3 56.2	22 .9	22 12.4	15 8.9	21 52.7	8 41.4	23 13.4
22	13 57 6.9	11 51.7	0 24.6	13N23.0	10 46.6	2 35.5	22 22.9	22 9.5	15 5.4	21 52.1	8 39.6	23 13.3
25	14 8 56.5	12 51.9	0 24.6	23 23.2	13 25.9	1 13.8	22 43.1	22 6.4	15 1.9	21 51.4	8 37.8	23 13.1
28	14 20 46.2	13 50.2	0 24.5	19 35.4	15 58.9	0N 8.5	23 1.6	22 3.0	14 58.2	21 50.7	8 36.1	23 12.8

MAY 1955

DAY	EPHEM. SID. TIME h m s	☉ ° ′	☊ ° ′	☽ ° ′	☿ ° ′	♀ ° ′	♂ ° ′	♃ ° ′	♄ ° ′	♅ ° ′	♆ ° ′	♇ ° ′
		LONGITUDE										
1	14 32 35.8	9♉51.8	29♐ 4.1	2♍11.2	18♉54.9	7♈39.0	13♊28.1	22♋55.5	18♏29.4	23♋58.8	26♎30.7	24♌18.4
2	14 36 32.4	10 50.0	29 1.0	15 3.1	20 59.6	8 51.0	14 8.1	23 3.2	18R25.0	24 .4	26R29.1	24R18.3
3	14 40 29.0	11 48.2	28 57.8	27 41.2	23 2.5	10 3.1	14 48.0	23 11.0	18 20.5	24 2.0	26 27.5	24 18.2
4	14 44 25.5	12 46.4	28 54.6	10♎ 7.1	25 3.5	11 15.3	15 27.9	23 18.9	18 16.1	24 3.7	26 26.0	24 18.1
5	14 48 22.1	13 44.5	28 51.4	22 22.7	27 2.2	12 27.4	16 7.8	23 26.9	18 11.6	24 5.4	26 24.4	24 18.0
6	14 52 18.6	14 42.6	28 48.3	4♏29.4	28 58.4	13 39.6	16 47.7	23 35.1	18 7.1	24 7.1	26 22.9	24 18.0
7	14 56 15.2	15 40.7	28 45.1	16 28.6	0♊52.0	14 51.8	17 27.6	23 43.4	18 2.6	24 9.0	26 21.4	24 18.0
8	15 0 11.7	16 38.8	28 41.9	28 21.8	2 42.7	16 4.0	18 7.4	23 51.8	17 58.1	24 10.8	26 19.8	24 18.0
9	15 4 8.3	17 36.8	28 38.7	10♐10.9	4 30.3	17 16.2	18 47.1	24 .3	17 53.6	24 12.7	26 18.3	24D18.1
10	15 8 4.8	18 34.8	28 35.5	21 58.4	6 14.7	18 28.5	19 26.9	24 8.9	17 49.1	24 14.7	26 16.8	24 18.2
11	15 12 1.4	19 32.7	28 32.4	3♑47.2	7 55.8	19 40.7	20 6.6	24 17.7	17 44.6	24 16.7	26 15.4	24 18.3
12	15 15 58.0	20 30.7	28 29.2	15 40.8	9 33.4	20 53.0	20 46.2	24 26.5	17 40.0	24 18.7	26 13.9	24 18.4
13	15 19 54.5	21 28.6	28 26.0	27 43.4	11 7.6	22 5.3	21 25.9	24 35.5	17 35.5	24 20.7	26 12.4	24 18.6
14	15 23 51.1	22 26.5	28 22.8	9♒59.4	12 38.2	23 17.7	22 5.5	24 44.6	17 31.0	24 22.9	26 11.0	24 18.8
15	15 27 47.6	23 24.3	28 19.7	22 33.5	14 5.2	24 30.0	22 45.1	24 53.8	17 26.5	24 25.0	26 9.6	24 19.0
16	15 31 44.2	24 22.2	28 16.5	5♓30.0	15 28.5	25 42.4	23 24.7	25 3.1	17 22.1	24 27.2	26 8.2	24 19.3
17	15 35 40.7	25 20.0	28 13.3	18 52.5	16 48.1	26 54.7	24 4.3	25 12.5	17 17.6	24 29.5	26 6.8	24 19.6
18	15 39 37.3	26 17.9	28 10.1	2♈43.0	18 3.8	28 7.1	24 43.8	25 22.0	17 13.2	24 31.7	26 5.4	24 19.9
19	15 43 33.8	27 15.7	28 7.0	17 1.2	19 15.7	29 19.5	25 23.3	25 31.6	17 8.8	24 34.1	26 4.0	24 20.2
20	15 47 30.4	28 13.4	28 3.8	1♉44.0	20 23.7	0♉32.0	26 2.8	25 41.3	17 4.4	24 36.4	26 2.7	24 20.6
21	15 51 27.0	29 11.2	28 .6	16 45.1	21 27.7	1 44.4	26 42.2	25 51.1	16 60.0	24 38.8	26 1.4	24 21.0
22	15 55 23.5	0♊ 8.9	27 57.4	1♊56.0	22 27.6	2 56.9	27 21.7	26 1.0	16 55.6	24 41.3	26 .1	24 21.4
23	15 59 20.1	1 6.6	27 54.2	17 7.0	23 23.5	4 9.4	28 1.1	26 11.0	16 51.3	24 43.8	25 58.8	24 21.9
24	16 3 16.6	2 4.3	27 51.1	2♋ 8.6	24 15.2	5 21.8	28 40.4	26 21.1	16 47.0	24 46.3	25 57.5	24 22.3
25	16 7 13.2	3 2.0	27 47.9	16 53.0	25 2.7	6 34.3	29 19.8	26 31.3	16 42.8	24 48.8	25 56.3	24 22.9
26	16 11 9.7	3 59.6	27 44.7	1♌15.0	25 45.9	7 46.8	29 59.1	26 41.6	16 38.6	24 51.4	25 55.1	24 23.4
27	16 15 6.3	4 57.3	27 41.5	15 12.2	26 24.7	8 59.4	0♋38.4	26 52.0	16 34.4	24 54.1	25 53.9	24 24.0
28	16 19 2.9	5 54.9	27 38.4	28 44.4	26 59.0	10 11.9	1 17.8	27 2.5	16 30.3	24 56.8	25 52.8	24 24.6
29	16 22 59.4	6 52.5	27 35.2	11♍53.2	27 28.8	11 24.5	1 57.0	27 13.0	16 26.2	24 59.5	25 51.6	24 25.2
30	16 26 56.0	7 50.0	27 32.0	24 41.1	27 54.1	12 37.0	2 36.2	27 23.6	16 22.1	25 2.2	25 50.5	24 25.9
31	16 30 52.5	8 47.5	27 28.8	7♎11.6	28 14.7	13 49.6	3 15.4	27 34.3	16 18.1	25 5.0	25 49.4	24 26.6
		LATITUDE										
1	14 32 35.8	0 .0	0 .0	4S38.7	0N54.9	1S39.0	0N53.4	0N30.0	2N31.3	0N31.3	1N46.6	10N24.4
4	14 44 25.5	0 .0	0 .0	5 .7	1 24.2	1 41.4	0 54.5	0 30.1	2 31.3	0 31.3	1 46.5	10 23.7
7	14 56 15.2	0 .0	0 .0	3 21.2	1 49.2	1 43.0	0 55.5	0 30.1	2 31.2	0 31.2	1 46.5	10 23.1
10	15 8 4.8	0 .0	0 .0	0 26.1	2 8.2	1 43.9	0 56.4	0 30.2	2 31.1	0 31.1	1 46.4	10 22.4
13	15 19 54.5	0 .0	0 .0	2N41.1	2 20.4	1 44.1	0 57.3	0 30.2	2 31.0	0 31.1	1 46.4	10 21.7
16	15 31 44.2	0 .0	0 .0	4 51.9	2 24.9	1 43.6	0 58.2	0 30.3	2 30.8	0 31.0	1 46.3	10 21.0
19	15 43 33.8	0 .0	0 .0	4 53.9	2 21.4	1 42.4	0 59.0	0 30.4	2 30.6	0 31.0	1 46.2	10 20.3
22	15 55 23.5	0 .0	0 .0	2 11.0	2 9.7	1 40.6	0 59.8	0 30.4	2 30.3	0 30.9	1 46.1	10 19.6
25	16 7 13.2	0 .0	0 .0	1S50.1	1 49.7	1 38.1	1 .6	0 30.5	2 30.0	0 30.9	1 46.0	10 19.0
28	16 19 2.9	0 .0	0 .0	4 39.4	1 21.5	1 35.1	1 1.3	0 30.6	2 29.6	0 30.9	1 45.9	10 18.3
31	16 30 52.5	0 .0	0 .0	5 10.3	0 45.4	1 31.5	1 2.0	0 30.6	2 29.2	0 30.8	1 45.8	10 17.6
		RIGHT ASCENSION										
1	14 32 35.8	7♉27.4	28♐59.1	2♍30.1	16♉11.6	7♈40.6	11♊57.2	24♋50.4	16♏45.1	25♋57.8	25♎14.4	0♍21.3
2	14 36 32.4	8 24.6	28 55.7	14 18.0	18 15.4	8 47.2	12 40.4	24 58.5	16R40.7	25 59.5	25R13.0	0R21.1
3	14 40 29.0	9 21.9	28 52.2	25 49.9	20 18.6	9 53.8	13 23.6	25 6.8	16 36.2	26 1.2	25 11.5	0 20.9
4	14 44 25.5	10 19.4	28 48.7	7♎18.7	22 20.8	11 .5	14 6.8	25 15.2	16 31.8	26 3.0	25 10.0	0 20.7
5	14 48 22.1	11 17.0	28 45.3	18 55.0	24 21.8	12 7.2	14 50.0	25 23.7	16 27.3	26 4.8	25 8.5	0 20.6
6	14 52 18.6	12 14.7	28 41.8	0♏47.1	26 21.3	13 14.1	15 33.3	25 32.4	16 22.8	26 6.6	25 7.0	0 20.5
7	14 56 15.2	13 12.7	28 38.3	12 59.3	28 18.9	14 21.0	16 16.6	25 41.2	16 18.4	26 8.6	25 5.6	0 20.4
8	15 0 11.7	14 10.7	28 34.9	25 31.5	0♊14.5	15 28.0	16 59.9	25 50.1	16 13.9	26 10.5	25 4.2	0 20.4
9	15 4 8.3	15 8.9	28 31.4	8♐19.2	2 7.7	16 35.0	17 43.1	25 59.2	16 9.4	26 12.5	25 2.8	0 20.3
10	15 8 4.8	16 7.2	28 27.9	21 14.0	3 58.2	17 42.2	18 26.4	26 8.3	16 4.9	26 14.6	25 1.4	0 20.3
11	15 12 1.4	17 5.6	28 24.5	4♑ 6.4	5 46.0	18 49.5	19 9.7	26 17.6	16 .4	26 16.7	24 59.9	0 20.3
12	15 15 58.0	18 4.3	28 21.0	16 48.1	7 30.8	19 56.9	19 53.1	26 27.0	15 55.9	26 18.8	24 58.6	0D20.4
13	15 19 54.5	19 3.0	28 17.6	29 14.8	9 12.4	21 4.4	20 36.4	26 36.5	15 51.4	26 21.0	24 57.2	0 20.5
14	15 23 51.1	20 1.9	28 14.1	11♒26.8	10 50.7	22 12.0	21 19.7	26 46.1	15 47.0	26 23.3	24 55.8	0 20.6
15	15 27 47.6	21 .9	28 10.6	23 29.2	12 25.5	23 19.9	22 3.0	26 55.8	15 42.5	26 25.5	24 54.5	0 20.7
16	15 31 44.2	22 .1	28 7.2	5♓31.2	13 56.6	24 27.8	22 46.3	27 5.7	15 38.0	26 27.9	24 53.1	0 20.9
17	15 35 40.7	22 59.5	28 3.7	17 45.1	15 23.9	25 35.9	23 29.6	27 15.6	15 33.6	26 30.2	24 51.8	0 21.1
18	15 39 37.3	23 59.0	28 .2	0♈25.2	16 47.3	26 44.2	24 12.9	27 25.7	15 29.2	26 32.7	24 50.5	0 21.3
19	15 43 33.8	24 58.6	27 56.8	13 46.6	18 6.6	27 52.7	24 56.3	27 35.8	15 24.8	26 35.1	24 49.2	0 21.6
20	15 47 30.4	25 58.4	27 53.3	28 1.7	19 21.8	29 1.3	25 39.6	27 46.1	15 20.4	26 37.6	24 47.9	0 21.8
21	15 51 27.0	26 58.3	27 49.9	13♉16.1	20 32.8	0♉10.2	26 22.8	27 56.5	15 16.0	26 40.2	24 46.7	0 22.2
22	15 55 23.5	27 58.3	27 46.4	29 21.8	21 39.3	1 19.2	27 6.1	28 6.9	15 11.7	26 42.7	24 45.5	0 22.5
23	15 59 20.1	28 58.5	27 42.9	15♊54.7	22 41.4	2 28.4	27 49.4	28 17.5	15 7.4	26 45.4	24 44.2	0 22.9
24	16 3 16.6	29 58.8	27 39.5	2♋19.6	23 38.8	3 37.9	28 32.6	28 28.1	15 3.1	26 48.0	24 43.0	0 23.3
25	16 7 13.2	0♊59.3	27 36.0	18 3.6	24 31.6	4 47.5	29 15.8	28 38.9	14 58.9	26 50.7	24 41.9	0 23.7
26	16 11 9.7	1 59.9	27 32.6	2♌47.6	25 19.5	5 57.4	29 59.0	28 49.7	14 54.7	26 53.5	24 40.7	0 24.1
27	16 15 6.3	3 .5	27 29.1	16 28.6	26 2.6	7 7.5	0♋42.2	29 .7	14 50.5	26 56.3	24 39.6	0 24.6
28	16 19 2.9	4 1.4	27 25.6	29 15.2	26 40.7	8 17.9	1 25.4	29 11.7	14 46.4	26 59.1	24 38.5	0 25.2
29	16 22 59.4	5 2.3	27 22.2	11♍21.3	27 13.8	9 28.4	2 8.5	29 22.8	14 42.3	27 2.0	24 37.4	0 25.7
30	16 26 56.0	6 3.3	27 18.7	23 2.2	27 41.7	10 39.2	2 51.6	29 34.0	14 38.3	27 4.9	24 36.3	0 26.3
31	16 30 52.5	7 4.4	27 15.2	4♎32.7	28 4.5	11 50.3	3 34.7	29 45.3	14 34.3	27 7.8	24 35.3	0 26.9
		DECLINATION										
1	14 32 35.8	14N46.5	0S24.5	6N21.5	18N19.9	1N31.2	23N18.4	21N59.4	14S54.6	21N49.9	8S34.4	23N12.4
4	14 44 25.5	15 40.5	0 24.5	8S36.8	20 23.8	2 53.9	23 33.3	21 55.5	14 50.9	21 48.9	8 32.7	23 11.9
7	14 56 15.2	16 32.3	0 24.5	19 58.7	22 7.0	4 16.5	23 46.4	21 51.4	14 47.3	21 48.0	8 31.1	23 11.2
10	15 8 4.8	17 21.5	0 24.5	23 38.2	23 27.7	5 38.5	23 57.8	21 47.0	14 43.6	21 46.9	8 29.5	23 10.5
13	15 19 54.5	18 8.2	0 24.5	17 59.3	24 26.0	6 59.7	24 7.3	21 42.3	14 40.0	21 45.8	8 28.0	23 9.8
16	15 31 44.2	18 52.1	0 24.5	4 58.1	25 3.2	8 19.8	24 15.0	21 37.4	14 36.5	21 44.6	8 26.5	23 8.9
19	15 43 33.8	19 33.1	0 24.5	11N12.5	25 21.6	9 38.4	24 20.9	21 32.3	14 33.0	21 43.3	8 25.1	23 7.9
22	15 55 23.5	20 11.2	0 24.5	22 41.5	25 23.3	10 55.3	24 24.9	21 26.9	14 29.6	21 42.0	8 23.8	23 6.9
25	16 7 13.2	20 46.2	0 24.5	20 33.5	25 10.7	12 10.1	24 27.2	21 21.2	14 26.3	21 40.6	8 22.5	23 5.7
28	16 19 2.9	21 17.9	0 24.5	7 32.6	24 46.1	13 22.5	24 27.6	21 15.3	14 23.1	21 39.1	8 21.3	23 4.5
31	16 30 52.5	21 46.3	0 24.5	7S36.2	24 11.4	14 32.2	24 26.2	21 9.1	14 20.0	21 37.6	8 20.2	23 3.2

JUNE 1955

LONGITUDE

DAY	EPHEM. SID. TIME h m s	☉ ° ′	☊ ° ′	☾ ° ′	☿ ° ′	♀ ° ′	♂ ° ′	♃ ° ′	♄ ° ′	♅ ° ′	♆ ° ′	♇ ° ′
1	16 34 49.1	9♊45.0	27♐25.7	19♎27.8	28♊30.6	15♉ 2.2	3♋54.6	27♋45.1	16♏14.2	25♋ 7.8	25♎48.3	24♌27.3
2	16 38 45.6	10 42.5	27 22.5	1♏33.1	28 41.9	16 14.8	4 33.8	27 56.0	16 R 10.3	25 10.6	25 R 47.2	24 28.0
3	16 42 42.2	11 40.0	27 19.3	13 30.3	28 48.5	17 27.4	5 12.9	28 6.9	16 6.4	25 13.5	25 46.2	24 28.7
4	16 46 38.8	12 37.4	27 16.1	25 22.1	28 50.6	18 40.0	5 52.0	28 17.9	16 2.6	25 16.4	25 45.2	24 29.5
5	16 50 35.3	13 34.8	27 12.9	7♐11.0	28 R 48.1	19 52.7	6 31.1	28 29.0	15 58.9	25 19.3	25 44.2	24 30.3
6	16 54 31.9	14 32.2	27 9.8	18 59.1	28 41.2	21 5.3	7 10.1	28 40.2	15 55.2	25 22.3	25 43.3	24 31.2
7	16 58 28.4	15 29.6	27 6.6	0♑48.7	28 30.0	22 18.0	7 49.2	28 51.4	15 51.6	25 25.3	25 42.3	24 32.0
8	17 2 25.0	16 27.0	27 3.4	12 42.2	28 14.8	23 30.7	8 28.2	29 2.8	15 48.0	25 28.3	25 41.4	24 32.9
9	17 6 21.5	17 24.4	27 .2	24 42.1	27 55.8	24 43.4	9 7.2	29 14.1	15 44.5	25 31.3	25 40.6	24 33.8
10	17 10 18.1	18 21.7	26 57.1	6♒51.3	27 33.3	25 56.1	9 46.1	29 25.6	15 41.0	25 34.4	25 39.7	24 34.8
11	17 14 14.7	19 19.1	26 53.9	19 12.9	27 7.8	27 8.9	10 25.1	29 37.1	15 37.7	25 37.5	25 38.9	24 35.7
12	17 18 11.2	20 16.4	26 50.7	1♓50.2	26 39.6	28 21.6	11 4.0	29 48.7	15 34.3	25 40.7	25 38.1	24 36.7
13	17 22 7.8	21 13.8	26 47.5	14 46.5	26 9.1	29 34.4	11 42.9	0♌ .3	15 31.1	25 43.8	25 37.3	24 37.7
14	17 26 4.3	22 11.1	26 44.4	28 4.8	25 37.0	0♊47.2	12 21.8	0 12.0	15 27.9	25 47.0	25 36.6	24 38.8
15	17 30 .9	23 8.4	26 41.2	11♈47.2	25 3.7	2 .0	13 .7	0 23.8	15 24.8	25 50.2	25 35.9	24 39.8
16	17 33 57.4	24 5.7	26 38.0	25 54.2	24 29.8	3 12.9	13 39.5	0 35.6	15 21.8	25 53.5	25 35.2	24 40.9
17	17 37 54.0	25 3.0	26 34.8	10♉24.5	23 55.9	4 25.7	14 18.4	0 47.5	15 18.8	25 56.7	25 34.5	24 42.0
18	17 41 50.6	26 .4	26 31.7	25 14.5	23 22.6	5 38.7	14 57.3	0 59.5	15 16.0	26 .0	25 33.9	24 43.2
19	17 45 47.1	26 57.7	26 28.5	10♊17.6	22 50.4	6 51.6	15 36.1	1 11.5	15 13.2	26 3.3	25 33.3	24 44.4
20	17 49 43.7	27 55.0	26 25.3	25 25.7	22 19.8	8 4.5	16 14.9	1 23.5	15 10.5	26 6.7	25 32.8	24 45.6
21	17 53 40.2	28 52.2	26 22.1	10♋29.8	21 51.5	9 17.4	16 53.6	1 35.6	15 7.8	26 10.0	25 32.2	24 46.8
22	17 57 36.8	29 49.5	26 18.9	25 21.2	21 25.9	10 30.4	17 32.4	1 47.8	15 5.3	26 13.4	25 31.7	24 48.0
23	18 1 33.4	0♋46.8	26 15.8	9♌52.8	21 3.3	11 43.3	18 11.1	2 .0	15 2.8	26 16.8	25 31.2	24 49.2
24	18 5 29.9	1 44.0	26 12.6	23 59.8	20 44.3	12 56.3	18 49.8	2 12.3	15 .4	26 20.2	25 30.8	24 50.5
25	18 9 26.5	2 41.3	26 9.4	7♍40.2	20 29.1	14 9.3	19 28.5	2 24.6	14 58.1	26 23.6	25 30.4	24 51.8
26	18 13 23.0	3 38.5	26 6.2	20 54.4	20 18.0	15 22.3	20 7.2	2 36.9	14 55.9	26 27.1	25 30.0	24 53.1
27	18 17 19.6	4 35.7	26 3.1	3♎44.5	20 11.3	16 35.3	20 45.9	2 49.3	14 53.7	26 30.5	25 29.6	24 54.4
28	18 21 16.1	5 32.9	25 59.9	16 14.0	20 9.2	17 48.4	21 24.5	3 1.8	14 51.7	26 34.0	25 29.3	24 55.8
29	18 25 12.7	6 30.1	25 56.7	28 26.8	20 D 11.7	19 1.4	22 3.2	3 14.3	14 49.7	26 37.5	25 29.0	24 57.2
30	18 29 9.3	7 27.3	25 53.5	10♏27.4	20 19.1	20 14.5	22 41.8	3 26.8	14 47.9	26 41.0	25 28.8	24 58.6

LATITUDE

DAY	SID. TIME	☉	☊	☾	☿	♀	♂	♃	♄	♅	♆	♇
1	16 34 49.1	0 .0	0 .0	4 S 50.9	0 N 31.8	1 S 30.2	1 N 2.2	0 N 30.7	2 N 29.1	0 N 30.8	1 N 45.8	10 N 17.4
4	16 46 38.8	0 .0	0 .0	2 43.3	0 S 13.3	1 25.8	1 2.8	0 30.8	2 28.6	0 30.8	1 45.7	10 16.8
7	16 58 28.4	0 .0	0 .0	0 N 24.8	1 3.0	1 21.0	1 3.4	0 30.9	2 28.1	0 30.7	1 45.5	10 16.2
10	17 10 18.1	0 .0	0 .0	3 26.5	1 54.5	1 15.7	1 4.0	0 31.0	2 27.6	0 30.7	1 45.4	10 15.6
13	17 22 7.8	0 .0	0 .0	5 11.3	2 44.2	1 10.0	1 4.5	0 31.1	2 27.1	0 30.7	1 45.3	10 15.0
16	17 33 57.4	0 .0	0 .0	4 36.7	3 28.0	1 4.0	1 5.0	0 31.2	2 26.5	0 30.7	1 45.1	10 14.4
19	17 45 47.1	0 .0	0 .0	1 28.4	4 2.2	0 57.6	1 5.5	0 31.3	2 25.8	0 30.6	1 45.0	10 13.9
22	17 57 36.8	0 .0	0 .0	2 S 34.2	4 24.4	0 50.9	1 5.9	0 31.4	2 25.2	0 30.6	1 44.8	10 13.3
25	18 9 26.5	0 .0	0 .0	5 .9	4 33.7	0 43.9	1 6.3	0 31.5	2 24.5	0 30.6	1 44.7	10 12.8
28	18 21 16.1	0 .0	0 .0	4 58.7	4 30.6	0 36.8	1 6.7	0 31.7	2 23.8	0 30.6	1 44.5	10 12.4

RIGHT ASCENSION

DAY	SID. TIME	☉	☊	☾	☿	♀	♂	♃	♄	♅	♆	♇
1	16 34 49.1	8♊ 5.7	27♐11.8	16♎ 5.4	28♊22.2	13♉ 1.6	4♋17.7	29♋56.6	14♏30.3	27♋10.8	24♎34.2	0♍27.5
2	16 38 45.6	9 7.0	27 8.3	27 50.4	28 34.7	14 13.2	5 .6	0♌ 8.0	14 R 26.4	27 13.8	24 R 33.2	0 28.2
3	16 42 42.2	10 8.4	27 4.9	9♏54.4	28 42.1	15 25.0	5 43.6	0 19.5	14 22.6	27 16.8	24 32.2	0 28.8
4	16 46 38.8	11 10.0	27 1.4	22 19.6	28 44.4	16 37.1	6 26.5	0 31.1	14 18.8	27 19.9	24 31.3	0 29.5
5	16 50 35.3	12 11.6	26 57.9	5♐ 3.1	28 R 41.9	17 49.4	7 9.3	0 42.7	14 15.0	27 23.0	24 30.3	0 30.3
6	16 54 31.9	13 13.3	26 54.5	17 57.6	28 34.6	19 2.1	7 52.1	0 54.4	14 11.3	27 26.1	24 29.4	0 31.0
7	16 58 28.4	14 15.1	26 51.0	0♑52.9	28 22.7	20 15.0	8 34.9	1 6.2	14 7.7	27 29.3	24 28.5	0 31.8
8	17 2 25.0	15 16.9	26 47.6	13 39.2	28 6.5	21 28.2	9 17.6	1 18.1	14 4.1	27 32.5	24 27.7	0 32.6
9	17 6 21.5	16 18.8	26 44.1	26 9.3	27 46.3	22 41.6	10 .2	1 30.0	14 .6	27 35.7	24 26.8	0 33.5
10	17 10 18.1	17 20.9	26 40.6	8♒21.2	27 22.4	23 55.4	10 42.9	1 42.0	13 57.1	27 38.9	24 26.0	0 34.3
11	17 14 14.7	18 22.9	26 37.2	20 17.8	26 55.4	25 9.4	11 25.4	1 54.0	13 53.8	27 42.2	24 25.2	0 35.2
12	17 18 11.2	19 25.1	26 33.7	2♓ 6.7	26 25.6	26 23.7	12 7.9	2 6.1	13 50.4	27 45.5	24 24.4	0 36.1
13	17 22 7.8	20 27.2	26 30.3	13 58.8	25 53.5	27 38.3	12 50.4	2 18.3	13 47.2	27 48.8	24 23.7	0 37.1
14	17 26 4.3	21 29.5	26 26.8	26 7.9	25 19.8	28 53.2	13 32.8	2 30.5	13 44.0	27 52.2	24 23.0	0 38.0
15	17 30 .9	22 31.8	26 23.3	8♈49.0	24 44.9	0♊ 8.3	14 15.1	2 42.8	13 40.9	27 55.6	24 22.3	0 39.0
16	17 33 57.4	23 34.1	26 19.9	22 17.2	24 9.5	1 23.8	14 57.4	2 55.1	13 37.8	27 59.0	24 21.6	0 40.0
17	17 37 54.0	24 36.4	26 16.4	6♉43.9	23 34.1	2 39.4	15 39.6	3 7.5	13 34.8	28 2.4	24 21.0	0 41.1
18	17 41 50.6	25 38.9	26 13.0	22 11.2	22 59.5	3 55.5	16 21.8	3 20.0	13 32.0	28 6.0	24 20.4	0 42.2
19	17 45 47.1	26 41.3	26 9.5	8♊26.5	22 26.0	5 11.7	17 3.9	3 32.5	13 29.2	28 9.4	24 19.8	0 43.3
20	17 49 43.7	27 43.7	26 6.0	25 1.0	21 54.3	6 28.2	17 46.0	3 45.1	13 26.4	28 13.0	24 19.3	0 44.4
21	17 53 40.2	28 46.1	26 2.6	11♋18.5	21 24.9	7 44.9	18 27.9	3 57.7	13 23.7	28 16.5	24 18.8	0 45.5
22	17 57 36.8	29 48.6	25 59.1	26 49.3	20 58.4	9 1.9	19 9.8	4 10.4	13 21.2	28 20.0	24 18.3	0 46.7
23	18 1 33.4	0♋51.0	25 55.7	11♌19.0	20 35.0	10 19.1	19 51.7	4 23.0	13 18.6	28 23.6	24 17.8	0 47.9
24	18 5 29.9	1 53.4	25 52.2	24 48.7	20 15.2	11 36.5	20 33.4	4 35.8	13 16.2	28 27.2	24 17.4	0 49.1
25	18 9 26.5	2 55.7	25 48.7	7♍29.0	19 59.4	12 54.2	21 15.1	4 48.6	13 13.9	28 30.8	24 17.0	0 50.3
26	18 13 23.0	3 58.1	25 45.3	19 34.5	19 47.8	14 12.0	21 56.7	5 1.4	13 11.6	28 34.4	24 16.6	0 51.5
27	18 17 19.6	5 .4	25 41.8	1♎20.4	19 40.7	15 30.1	22 38.2	5 14.2	13 9.4	28 38.1	24 16.2	0 52.8
28	18 21 16.1	6 2.7	25 38.4	13 .5	19 38.3	16 48.4	23 19.7	5 27.1	13 7.4	28 41.8	24 15.9	0 54.1
29	18 25 12.7	7 4.9	25 34.9	24 46.5	19 D 40.7	18 6.9	24 1.1	5 40.1	13 5.3	28 45.4	24 15.6	0 55.4
30	18 29 9.3	8 7.1	25 31.4	6♏46.9	19 48.1	19 25.5	24 42.4	5 53.0	13 3.4	28 49.1	24 15.3	0 56.8

DECLINATION

DAY	SID. TIME	☉	☊	☾	☿	♀	♂	♃	♄	♅	♆	♇
1	16 34 49.1	21 N 55.1	0 S 24.5	12 S 6.1	23 N 58.0	14 N 54.8	24 N 25.4	21 N 7.0	14 S 19.0	21 N 37.1	8 S 19.8	23 N 2.8
4	16 46 38.8	22 18.9	0 24.5	21 45.1	23 13.1	16 .4	24 21.7	21 .5	14 16.2	21 35.5	8 18.8	23 1.4
7	16 58 28.4	22 39.3	0 24.5	23 1.8	22 23.2	17 2.6	24 16.2	20 53.8	14 13.5	21 33.8	8 17.9	22 59.9
10	17 10 18.1	22 56.1	0 24.5	15 13.8	21 30.9	18 1.1	24 8.9	20 46.8	14 11.0	21 32.1	8 17.1	22 58.4
13	17 22 7.8	23 9.3	0 24.5	1 12.5	20 39.2	18 55.4	23 60.0	20 39.6	14 8.7	21 30.3	8 16.3	22 56.8
16	17 33 57.4	23 18.8	0 24.5	14 N 18.1	19 52.0	19 45.5	23 49.3	20 32.1	14 6.6	21 28.5	8 15.7	22 55.2
19	17 45 47.1	23 24.6	0 24.5	23 27.3	19 13.2	20 30.9	23 37.0	20 24.4	14 4.7	21 26.6	8 15.2	22 53.5
22	17 57 36.8	23 26.7	0 24.5	18 32.7	18 46.1	21 11.3	23 23.0	20 16.5	14 3.0	21 24.7	8 14.7	22 51.7
25	18 9 26.5	23 25.0	0 24.5	4 2.2	18 33.1	21 46.6	23 7.5	20 8.3	14 1.6	21 22.8	8 14.4	22 50.0
28	18 21 16.1	23 19.7	0 24.5	10 S 58.7	18 34.8	22 16.5	22 50.3	19 59.9	14 .4	21 20.8	8 14.1	22 48.1

JULY 1955

DAY	EPHEM. SID. TIME	☉	☊	☽	☿	♀	♂	♃	♄	♅	♆	♇
	h m s	° ′	° ′	° ′	° ′	° ′	° ′	° ′	° ′	° ′	° ′	° ′
		LONGITUDE										
1	18 33 5.8	8♋24.5	25♐50.4	22♏20.0	20♊31.3	21♊27.6	23♋20.4	3♌39.4	14♏46.1	26♋44.5	25♎28.5	24♌60.0
2	18 37 2.4	9 21.7	25 47.2	4♐ 8.4	20 48.4	22 40.7	23 58.9	3 52.0	14 R 44.4	26 48.1	25 R 28.3	25 1.4
3	18 40 58.9	10 18.9	25 44.0	15 56.2	21 10.5	23 53.9	24 37.5	4 4.6	14 42.8	26 51.6	25 28.2	25 2.9
4	18 44 55.5	11 16.1	25 40.8	27 46.4	21 37.4	25 7.0	25 16.1	4 17.3	14 41.3	26 55.2	25 28.0	25 4.3
5	18 48 52.0	12 13.3	25 37.6	9♑41.6	22 9.3	26 20.2	25 54.6	4 30.0	14 39.9	26 58.7	25 27.9	25 5.8
6	18 52 48.6	13 10.4	25 34.5	21 44.0	22 46.0	27 33.4	26 33.1	4 42.7	14 38.5	27 2.3	25 27.9	25 7.3
7	18 56 45.2	14 7.6	25 31.3	3♒55.3	23 27.6	28 46.6	27 11.6	4 55.5	14 37.3	27 5.9	25 27.8	25 8.9
8	19 0 41.7	15 4.8	25 28.1	16 17.4	24 13.9	29 59.9	27 50.1	5 8.3	14 36.2	27 9.5	25 27.8	25 10.4
9	19 4 38.3	16 2.0	25 24.9	28 51.8	25 5.1	1♋13.2	28 28.6	5 21.2	14 35.2	27 13.2	25 D 27.9	25 12.0
10	19 8 34.8	16 59.2	25 21.8	11♓39.9	26 .8	2 26.5	29 7.1	5 34.1	14 34.2	27 16.8	25 28.0	25 13.6
11	19 12 31.4	17 56.4	25 18.6	24 43.4	27 1.2	3 39.8	29 45.5	5 47.0	14 33.4	27 20.5	25 28.0	25 15.2
12	19 16 28.0	18 53.6	25 15.4	8♈ 3.7	28 6.1	4 53.1	0♌24.0	5 59.9	14 32.6	27 24.1	25 28.2	25 16.8
13	19 20 24.5	19 50.8	25 12.2	21 42.0	29 15.5	6 6.5	1 2.4	6 12.8	14 32.0	27 27.7	25 28.3	25 18.4
14	19 24 21.1	20 48.1	25 9.1	5♉39.0	0♋29.4	7 19.8	1 40.8	6 25.8	14 31.4	27 31.4	25 28.5	25 20.1
15	19 28 17.6	21 45.3	25 5.9	19 54.2	1 47.6	8 33.3	2 19.3	6 38.8	14 30.9	27 35.1	25 28.7	25 21.7
16	19 32 14.2	22 42.5	25 2.7	4♊25.8	3 10.1	9 46.7	2 57.7	6 51.8	14 30.5	27 38.7	25 29.0	25 23.4
17	19 36 10.7	23 39.8	24 59.5	19 10.1	4 36.8	11 .2	3 36.1	7 4.9	14 30.3	27 42.4	25 29.3	25 25.1
18	19 40 7.3	24 37.0	24 56.4	4♋ 1.6	6 7.5	12 13.6	4 14.5	7 17.9	14 30.1	27 46.1	25 29.6	25 26.8
19	19 44 3.9	25 34.3	24 53.2	18 53.4	7 42.3	13 27.1	4 52.8	7 31.0	14 30.0	27 49.7	25 29.9	25 28.5
20	19 48 .4	26 31.6	24 50.0	3♌37.7	9 20.9	14 40.7	5 31.2	7 44.1	14 30.0	27 53.4	25 30.3	25 30.2
21	19 51 57.0	27 28.9	24 46.8	18 7.2	11 3.2	15 54.2	6 9.6	7 57.3	14 D 30.2	27 57.1	25 30.7	25 32.0
22	19 55 53.5	28 26.2	24 43.6	2♍15.9	12 48.9	17 7.8	6 47.9	8 10.4	14 30.4	28 .7	25 31.2	25 33.7
23	19 59 50.1	29 23.5	24 40.5	16 .0	14 38.0	18 21.4	7 26.3	8 23.5	14 30.7	28 4.4	25 31.6	25 35.5
24	20 3 46.6	0♌20.8	24 37.3	29 18.3	16 30.1	19 35.0	8 4.6	8 36.7	14 31.1	28 8.1	25 32.1	25 37.2
25	20 7 43.2	1 18.1	24 34.1	12♎11.6	18 25.0	20 48.6	8 42.9	8 49.9	14 31.6	28 11.8	25 32.7	25 39.0
26	20 11 39.7	2 15.4	24 30.9	24 42.8	20 22.4	22 2.3	9 21.2	9 3.1	14 32.2	28 15.4	25 33.3	25 40.8
27	20 15 36.3	3 12.7	24 27.8	6♏55.9	22 22.0	23 16.0	9 59.5	9 16.2	14 32.9	28 19.1	25 33.9	25 42.6
28	20 19 32.9	4 10.1	24 24.6	18 55.6	24 23.4	24 29.7	10 37.8	9 29.4	14 33.7	28 22.8	25 34.5	25 44.5
29	20 23 29.4	5 7.4	24 21.4	0♐47.0	26 26.3	25 43.4	11 16.1	9 42.7	14 34.6	28 26.4	25 35.2	25 46.3
30	20 27 26.0	6 4.8	24 18.2	12 35.0	28 30.5	26 57.1	11 54.4	9 55.9	14 35.7	28 30.1	25 35.9	25 48.2
31	20 31 22.5	7 2.2	24 15.1	24 24.1	0♌35.5	28 10.9	12 32.7	10 9.1	14 36.8	28 33.8	25 36.6	25 50.0
		LATITUDE										
1	18 33 5.8	0 .0	0 .0	2S58.1	4S16.6	0S29.5	1N 7.0	0N31.8	2N23.1	0N30.6	1N44.4	10N11.9
4	18 44 55.5	0 .0	0 .0	0N 7.4	3 53.6	0 22.1	1 7.3	0 32.0	2 22.4	0 30.6	1 44.2	10 11.5
7	18 56 45.2	0 .0	0 .0	3 12.7	3 23.5	0 14.6	1 7.6	0 32.1	2 21.6	0 30.6	1 44.0	10 11.2
10	19 8 34.8	0 .0	0 .0	5 5.0	2 48.2	0 7.1	1 7.9	0 32.3	2 20.9	0 30.6	1 43.9	10 10.8
13	19 20 24.5	0 .0	0 .0	4 44.5	2 9.5	0N .4	1 8.1	0 32.5	2 20.1	0 30.6	1 43.7	10 10.5
16	19 32 14.2	0 .0	0 .0	1 57.1	1 29.1	0 7.8	1 8.3	0 32.6	2 19.3	0 30.6	1 43.6	10 10.2
19	19 44 3.9	0 .0	0 .0	2S 1.1	0 48.6	0 15.1	1 8.5	0 32.8	2 18.5	0 30.6	1 43.4	10 10.0
22	19 55 53.5	0 .0	0 .0	4 46.1	0 9.8	0 22.2	1 8.6	0 33.0	2 17.7	0 30.7	1 43.2	10 9.8
25	20 7 43.2	0 .0	0 .0	4 59.7	0N25.4	0 29.1	1 8.7	0 33.2	2 16.9	0 30.7	1 43.1	10 9.6
28	20 19 32.9	0 .0	0 .0	3 7.8	0 55.4	0 35.7	1 8.8	0 33.4	2 16.1	0 30.7	1 42.9	10 9.5
31	20 31 22.5	0 .0	0 .0	0 8.0	1 18.7	0 42.1	1 8.9	0 33.6	2 15.4	0 30.7	1 42.7	10 9.4
		RIGHT ASCENSION										
1	18 33 5.8	9♋ 9.2	25♐28.0	19♏ 6.4	20♊ .5	20♊44.3	25♋23.6	6♌ 6.0	13♏ 1.6	28♋52.9	24♎15.1	0♍58.1
2	18 37 2.4	10 11.2	25 24.5	1♐44.8	20 18.0	22 3.3	26 4.7	6 19.1	12 R 59.9	28 56.6	24 R 14.9	0 59.5
3	18 40 58.9	11 13.2	25 21.1	14 37.1	20 40.7	23 22.4	26 45.8	6 32.1	12 58.2	29 .3	24 14.7	1 .9
4	18 44 55.5	12 15.1	25 17.6	27 34.6	21 8.5	24 41.7	27 26.7	6 45.2	12 56.7	29 4.1	24 14.6	1 2.3
5	18 48 52.0	13 17.0	25 14.1	10♑27.1	21 41.6	26 1.1	28 7.6	6 58.4	12 55.2	29 7.8	24 14.5	1 3.8
6	18 52 48.6	14 18.7	25 10.7	23 6.3	22 19.8	27 20.6	28 48.4	7 11.5	12 53.8	29 11.6	24 14.4	1 5.2
7	18 56 45.2	15 20.4	25 7.2	5♒27.4	23 3.3	28 40.2	29 29.1	7 24.7	12 52.5	29 15.4	24 14.3	1 6.7
8	19 0 41.7	16 22.0	25 3.8	17 31.0	23 52.0	29 59.8	0♌ 9.8	7 37.9	12 51.3	29 19.2	24 14.3	1 8.2
9	19 4 38.3	17 23.6	25 .3	29 22.0	24 45.8	1♋19.6	0 50.4	7 51.1	12 50.3	29 23.0	24 14.3	1 9.7
10	19 8 34.8	18 25.0	24 56.9	11♓ 9.2	25 44.8	2 39.5	1 30.9	8 4.4	12 49.3	29 26.8	24 D 14.4	1 11.3
11	19 12 31.4	19 26.3	24 53.4	23 4.5	26 48.9	3 59.3	2 11.2	8 17.6	12 48.3	29 30.7	24 14.4	1 12.8
12	19 16 28.0	20 27.5	24 49.9	5♈21.5	27 58.1	5 19.2	2 51.5	8 30.9	12 47.5	29 34.5	24 14.5	1 14.4
13	19 20 24.5	21 28.6	24 46.5	18 14.5	29 12.3	6 39.2	3 31.8	8 44.2	12 46.8	29 38.3	24 14.7	1 16.0
14	19 24 21.1	22 29.6	24 43.0	1♉56.1	0♋31.6	7 59.1	4 11.9	8 57.6	12 46.1	29 42.2	24 14.8	1 17.6
15	19 28 17.6	23 30.4	24 39.6	16 33.7	1 55.8	9 19.0	4 51.9	9 10.9	12 45.6	29 46.0	24 15.0	1 19.2
16	19 32 14.2	24 31.2	24 36.1	2♊ 4.0	3 24.9	10 39.0	5 31.9	9 24.3	12 45.2	29 49.9	24 15.2	1 20.8
17	19 36 10.7	25 31.8	24 32.6	18 9.7	4 58.7	11 58.8	6 11.8	9 37.6	12 44.8	29 53.7	24 15.5	1 22.5
18	19 40 7.3	26 32.4	24 29.2	4♋21.9	6 37.2	13 18.7	6 51.6	9 51.0	12 44.6	29 57.6	24 15.7	1 24.1
19	19 44 3.9	27 32.7	24 25.7	20 9.3	8 20.3	14 38.4	7 31.3	10 4.4	12 44.4	0♌ 1.4	24 16.0	1 25.8
20	19 48 .4	28 33.0	24 22.3	5♌10.1	10 7.7	15 58.1	8 10.9	10 17.8	12 44.3	0 5.3	24 16.4	1 27.5
21	19 51 57.0	29 33.1	24 18.8	19 16.3	11 59.2	17 17.7	8 50.4	10 31.2	12 D 44.4	0 9.2	24 16.8	1 29.2
22	19 55 53.5	0♌33.1	24 15.4	2♍31.9	13 54.5	18 37.2	9 29.9	10 44.6	12 44.5	0 13.0	24 17.2	1 30.9
23	19 59 50.1	1 32.9	24 11.9	15 7.8	15 53.5	19 56.6	10 9.2	10 58.1	12 44.7	0 16.9	24 17.6	1 32.7
24	20 3 46.6	2 32.6	24 8.4	27 17.5	17 55.6	21 15.9	10 48.5	11 11.5	12 45.1	0 20.7	24 18.0	1 34.4
25	20 7 43.2	3 32.1	24 5.0	9♎14.1	20 .6	22 35.0	11 27.7	11 24.9	12 45.5	0 24.6	24 18.5	1 36.2
26	20 11 39.7	4 31.5	24 1.5	21 10.3	22 8.1	23 53.9	12 6.8	11 38.3	12 46.0	0 28.4	24 19.0	1 37.9
27	20 15 36.3	5 30.7	23 58.1	3♏14.6	24 17.5	25 12.7	12 45.8	11 51.8	12 46.6	0 32.3	24 19.6	1 39.7
28	20 19 32.9	6 29.8	23 54.6	15 33.3	26 28.5	26 31.4	13 24.7	12 5.2	12 47.4	0 36.1	24 20.2	1 41.5
29	20 23 29.4	7 28.7	23 51.2	28 8.4	28 40.5	27 49.8	14 3.5	12 18.6	12 48.2	0 40.0	24 20.8	1 43.3
30	20 27 26.0	8 27.5	23 47.7	10♐57.3	0♌53.2	29 8.1	14 42.3	12 32.1	12 49.1	0 43.9	24 21.5	1 45.2
31	20 31 22.5	9 26.1	23 44.2	23 53.7	3 6.0	0♌26.2	15 21.0	12 45.5	12 50.1	0 47.7	24 22.1	1 47.0
		DECLINATION										
1	18 33 5.8	23N10.7	0S24.5	21S13.5	18N50.4	22N40.8	22N31.6	19N51.3	13S59.5	21N18.8	8S14.0	22N46.3
4	18 44 55.5	22 58.0	0 24.5	23 18.2	19 17.7	22 59.2	22 11.5	19 42.5	13 58.8	21 16.7	8 14.0	22 44.4
7	18 56 45.2	22 41.7	0 24.5	16 9.3	19 53.8	23 11.8	21 49.8	19 33.5	13 58.3	21 14.6	8 14.0	22 42.5
10	19 8 34.8	22 21.9	0 24.5	2 29.1	20 35.0	23 18.3	21 26.8	19 24.3	13 58.1	21 12.5	8 14.2	22 40.5
13	19 20 24.5	21 58.6	0 24.5	12N51.2	21 17.0	23 18.6	21 2.3	19 14.9	13 58.2	21 10.4	8 14.5	22 38.5
16	19 32 14.2	21 31.9	0 24.5	22 57.1	21 55.4	23 12.8	20 36.5	19 5.2	13 58.6	21 8.2	8 14.9	22 36.5
19	19 44 3.9	21 1.9	0 24.4	20 6.8	22 24.7	23 .9	20 9.4	18 55.5	13 59.2	21 6.1	8 15.4	22 34.5
22	19 55 53.5	20 28.7	0 24.4	6 12.9	22 39.9	22 42.8	19 41.1	18 45.5	14 .0	21 3.9	8 16.0	22 32.5
25	20 7 43.2	19 52.4	0 24.4	9S25.0	22 35.9	22 18.7	19 11.5	18 35.4	14 1.1	21 1.7	8 16.7	22 30.5
28	20 19 32.9	19 13.2	0 24.4	20 27.7	22 9.2	21 48.8	18 40.7	18 25.1	14 2.5	20 59.5	8 17.5	22 28.5
31	20 31 22.5	18 31.1	0 24.4	23 27.6	21 18.6	21 13.1	18 8.8	18 14.6	14 4.2	20 57.3	8 18.5	22 26.4

AUGUST 1955

LONGITUDE

DAY	EPHEM. SID. TIME h m s	☉ ° ′	☊ ° ′	☽ ° ′	☿ ° ′	♀ ° ′	♂ ° ′	♃ ° ′	♄ ° ′	♅ ° ′	♆ ° ′	♇ ° ′
1	20 35 19.1	7♌59.5	24♐11.9	6♑18.3	2♌41.0	29♋24.7	13♌10.9	10♌22.4	14♏38.0	28♋37.4	25♎37.4	25♌51.9
2	20 39 15.6	8 56.9	24 8.7	18 21.1	4 46.7	0♌38.5	13 49.2	10 35.6	14 39.3	28 41.1	25 38.2	25 53.7
3	20 43 12.2	9 54.3	24 5.5	0♒34.9	6 52.4	1 52.3	14 27.4	10 48.8	14 40.6	28 44.7	25 39.0	25 55.6
4	20 47 8.8	10 51.7	24 2.3	13 1.3	8 57.7	3 6.2	15 5.6	11 2.0	14 42.1	28 48.3	25 39.9	25 57.5
5	20 51 5.3	11 49.1	23 59.2	25 41.2	11 2.6	4 20.0	15 43.9	11 15.2	14 43.7	28 51.9	25 40.7	25 59.4
6	20 55 1.9	12 46.6	23 56.0	8♓34.8	13 6.7	5 33.9	16 22.1	11 28.5	14 45.4	28 55.5	25 41.6	26 1.2
7	20 58 58.4	13 44.0	23 52.8	21 41.7	15 9.9	6 47.8	17 .3	11 41.7	14 47.1	28 59.1	25 42.6	26 3.1
8	21 2 55.0	14 41.5	23 49.6	5♈ 1.2	17 12.1	8 1.8	17 38.5	11 54.9	14 49.0	29 2.7	25 43.6	26 5.0
9	21 6 51.5	15 39.0	23 46.5	18 32.9	19 13.2	9 15.7	18 16.7	12 8.1	14 50.9	29 6.2	25 44.6	26 6.9
10	21 10 48.1	16 36.5	23 43.3	2♉16.0	21 13.0	10 29.7	18 55.0	12 21.3	14 53.0	29 9.8	25 45.6	26 8.9
11	21 14 44.6	17 34.1	23 40.1	16 10.4	23 11.5	11 43.7	19 33.2	12 34.5	14 55.1	29 13.3	25 46.6	26 10.8
12	21 18 41.2	18 31.7	23 36.9	0♊15.4	25 8.7	12 57.8	20 11.4	12 47.7	14 57.3	29 16.8	25 47.7	26 12.7
13	21 22 37.7	19 29.3	23 33.7	14 30.3	27 4.5	14 11.8	20 49.6	13 .9	14 59.7	29 20.4	25 48.8	26 14.6
14	21 26 34.3	20 26.9	23 30.6	28 53.3	28 58.8	15 25.9	21 27.8	13 14.1	15 2.1	29 23.9	25 50.0	26 16.5
15	21 30 30.9	21 24.5	23 27.4	13♋21.5	0♍51.7	16 40.0	22 6.0	13 27.2	15 4.6	29 27.3	25 51.2	26 18.5
16	21 34 27.4	22 22.2	23 24.2	27 50.7	2 43.2	17 54.2	22 44.2	13 40.4	15 7.2	29 30.8	25 52.4	26 20.4
17	21 38 24.0	23 19.9	23 21.0	12♌15.5	4 33.2	19 8.3	23 22.4	13 53.5	15 9.9	29 34.2	25 53.6	26 22.3
18	21 42 20.5	24 17.6	23 17.9	26 29.9	6 21.8	20 22.5	24 .6	14 6.6	15 12.6	29 37.7	25 54.8	26 24.3
19	21 46 17.1	25 15.3	23 14.7	10♍28.4	8 8.9	21 36.7	24 38.8	14 19.8	15 15.5	29 41.1	25 56.1	26 26.2
20	21 50 13.6	26 13.1	23 11.5	24 6.8	9 54.7	22 50.9	25 17.0	14 32.9	15 18.5	29 44.5	25 57.5	26 28.2
21	21 54 10.2	27 10.9	23 8.3	7♎22.4	11 39.0	24 5.2	25 55.2	14 46.0	15 21.5	29 47.9	25 58.8	26 30.1
22	21 58 6.7	28 8.7	23 5.2	20 15.1	13 21.9	25 19.4	26 33.4	14 59.0	15 24.7	29 51.2	26 .2	26 32.1
23	22 2 3.3	29 6.5	23 2.0	2♏46.5	15 3.4	26 33.7	27 11.6	15 12.0	15 27.9	29 54.6	26 1.6	26 34.0
24	22 5 59.8	0♍ 4.4	22 58.8	14 59.9	16 43.5	27 48.0	27 49.8	15 25.0	15 31.2	29 57.9	26 3.0	26 36.0
25	22 9 56.4	1 2.2	22 55.6	26 59.7	18 22.2	29 2.3	28 27.9	15 38.0	15 34.6	0♌ 1.2	26 4.4	26 37.9
26	22 13 53.0	2 .1	22 52.4	8♐51.0	19 59.6	0♍16.6	29 6.1	15 50.9	15 38.0	0 4.4	26 5.9	26 39.8
27	22 17 49.5	2 58.0	22 49.3	20 39.3	21 35.7	1 30.9	29 44.3	16 3.9	15 41.6	0 7.7	26 7.4	26 41.8
28	22 21 46.1	3 55.9	22 46.1	2♑29.9	23 10.4	2 45.3	0♍22.5	16 16.8	15 45.2	0 10.9	26 8.9	26 43.7
29	22 25 42.6	4 53.9	22 42.9	14 27.7	24 43.8	3 59.6	1 .6	16 29.6	15 48.9	0 14.1	26 10.4	26 45.6
30	22 29 39.2	5 51.8	22 39.7	26 37.1	26 15.9	5 14.0	1 38.8	16 42.4	15 52.7	0 17.2	26 12.0	26 47.5
31	22 33 35.7	6 49.8	22 36.6	9♒ 1.4	27 46.6	6 28.4	2 17.0	16 55.2	15 56.6	0 20.3	26 13.6	26 49.4

LATITUDE

DAY	EPHEM. SID. TIME h m s	☉	☊	☽	☿	♀	♂	♃	♄	♅	♆	♇
1	20 35 19.1	0 .0	0 .0	0N56.4	1N24.9	0N44.2	1N 8.9	0N33.7	2N15.1	0N30.8	1N42.7	10N 9.4
4	20 47 8.8	0 .0	0 .0	3 47.2	1 38.6	0 50.1	1 9.0	0 34.0	2 14.3	0 30.8	1 42.5	10 9.4
7	20 58 58.4	0 .0	0 .0	5 6.9	1 45.2	0 55.7	1 9.0	0 34.2	2 13.5	0 30.8	1 42.4	10 9.4
10	21 10 48.1	0 .0	0 .0	4 5.2	1 45.4	1 .8	1 8.9	0 34.5	2 12.7	0 30.9	1 42.2	10 9.4
13	21 22 37.7	0 .0	0 .0	0 56.2	1 39.9	1 5.6	1 8.9	0 34.7	2 12.0	0 30.9	1 42.1	10 9.5
16	21 34 27.4	0 .0	0 .0	2S46.5	1 29.7	1 9.8	1 8.8	0 35.0	2 11.2	0 31.0	1 41.9	10 9.6
19	21 46 17.1	0 .0	0 .0	4 55.3	1 15.6	1 13.6	1 8.7	0 35.3	2 10.5	0 31.0	1 41.8	10 9.8
22	21 58 6.7	0 .0	0 .0	4 33.5	0 58.3	1 16.8	1 8.6	0 35.6	2 9.7	0 31.1	1 41.7	10 10.0
25	22 9 56.4	0 .0	0 .0	2 18.6	0 38.4	1 19.6	1 8.5	0 35.9	2 9.0	0 31.1	1 41.5	10 10.3
28	22 21 46.1	0 .0	0 .0	0N45.5	0 16.5	1 21.7	1 8.3	0 36.2	2 8.3	0 31.2	1 41.4	10 10.6
31	22 33 35.7	0 .0	0 .0	3 35.3	0S 7.0	1 23.3	1 8.1	0 36.5	2 7.6	0 31.3	1 41.3	10 10.9

RIGHT ASCENSION

DAY	EPHEM. SID. TIME h m s	☉	☊	☽	☿	♀	♂	♃	♄	♅	♆	♇
1	20 35 19.1	10♌24.6	23♐40.8	6♑49.2	5♌18.6	1♌44.0	15♌59.6	12♌59.0	12♏51.2	0♌51.5	24♎22.8	1♍48.9
2	20 39 15.6	11 22.9	23 37.3	19 35.5	7 30.6	3 1.6	16 38.0	13 12.4	12 52.4	0 55.3	24 23.5	1 50.7
3	20 43 12.2	12 21.0	23 33.9	2♒ 7.3	9 41.5	4 19.0	17 16.4	13 25.8	12 53.7	0 59.1	24 24.3	1 52.6
4	20 47 8.8	13 19.0	23 30.4	14 23.1	11 51.2	5 36.2	17 54.8	13 39.2	12 55.1	1 2.9	24 25.1	1 54.4
5	20 51 5.3	14 16.9	23 27.0	26 25.7	13 59.4	6 53.2	18 33.0	13 52.6	12 56.5	1 6.7	24 25.9	1 56.3
6	20 55 1.9	15 14.6	23 23.5	8♓22.0	16 5.8	8 9.9	19 11.1	14 6.0	12 58.1	1 10.5	24 26.7	1 58.2
7	20 58 58.4	16 12.1	23 20.1	20 21.4	18 10.3	9 26.3	19 49.2	14 19.3	12 59.8	1 14.2	24 27.6	2 .1
8	21 2 55.0	17 9.5	23 16.6	2♈35.7	20 12.8	10 42.5	20 27.2	14 32.7	13 1.5	1 18.0	24 28.5	2 2.0
9	21 6 51.5	18 6.8	23 13.1	15 17.1	22 13.1	11 58.5	21 5.1	14 46.0	13 3.4	1 21.7	24 29.4	2 3.9
10	21 10 48.1	19 3.9	23 9.7	28 37.1	24 11.2	13 14.2	21 43.0	14 59.3	13 5.3	1 25.4	24 30.4	2 5.8
11	21 14 44.6	20 .9	23 6.2	12♉43.3	26 7.2	14 29.7	22 20.7	15 12.7	13 7.3	1 29.1	24 31.3	2 7.7
12	21 18 41.2	20 57.7	23 2.8	27 35.8	28 .9	15 44.9	22 58.4	15 26.0	13 9.4	1 32.8	24 32.3	2 9.6
13	21 22 37.7	21 54.4	22 59.3	13♊ 4.1	29 52.4	16 59.8	23 36.0	15 39.2	13 11.7	1 36.5	24 33.4	2 11.5
14	21 26 34.3	22 51.0	22 55.9	28 47.5	1♍41.6	18 14.4	24 13.5	15 52.5	13 14.0	1 40.2	24 34.4	2 13.5
15	21 30 30.9	23 47.4	22 52.4	14♋20.4	3 28.8	19 28.9	24 51.0	16 5.7	13 16.4	1 43.8	24 35.5	2 15.4
16	21 34 27.4	24 43.7	22 49.0	29 21.3	5 13.8	20 43.0	25 28.4	16 19.0	13 18.8	1 47.4	24 36.6	2 17.3
17	21 38 24.0	25 39.9	22 45.5	13♌38.6	6 56.7	21 56.9	26 5.7	16 32.2	13 21.4	1 51.1	24 37.8	2 19.3
18	21 42 20.5	26 35.9	22 42.0	27 11.5	8 37.7	23 10.5	26 42.9	16 45.3	13 24.1	1 54.6	24 38.9	2 21.2
19	21 46 17.1	27 31.8	22 38.6	10♍ 6.9	10 16.7	24 23.9	27 20.1	16 58.5	13 26.8	1 58.2	24 40.1	2 23.2
20	21 50 13.6	28 27.7	22 35.1	22 35.3	11 53.9	25 37.0	27 57.2	17 11.7	13 29.7	2 1.8	24 41.4	2 25.2
21	21 54 10.2	29 23.3	22 31.7	4♎48.3	13 29.2	26 49.8	28 34.3	17 24.7	13 32.7	2 5.3	24 42.6	2 27.1
22	21 58 6.7	0♍18.9	22 28.2	16 56.7	15 2.8	28 2.4	29 11.2	17 37.8	13 35.7	2 8.8	24 43.9	2 29.1
23	22 2 3.3	1 14.3	22 24.8	29 9.4	16 34.7	29 14.8	29 48.1	17 50.8	13 38.8	2 12.3	24 45.2	2 31.0
24	22 5 59.8	2 9.6	22 21.3	11♏32.3	18 4.9	0♍26.8	0♍24.9	18 3.9	13 42.0	2 15.8	24 46.5	2 33.0
25	22 9 56.4	3 4.8	22 17.9	24 7.8	19 33.5	1 38.7	1 1.7	18 16.8	13 45.2	2 19.2	24 47.9	2 34.9
26	22 13 53.0	3 59.9	22 14.4	6♐54.8	21 .6	2 50.3	1 38.4	18 29.8	13 48.6	2 22.6	24 49.2	2 36.9
27	22 17 49.5	4 54.8	22 11.0	19 48.5	22 26.3	4 1.7	2 15.0	18 42.7	13 52.0	2 26.0	24 50.6	2 38.8
28	22 21 46.1	5 49.7	22 7.5	2♑42.4	23 50.5	5 12.8	2 51.6	18 55.5	13 55.5	2 29.4	24 52.0	2 40.8
29	22 25 42.6	6 44.5	22 4.1	15 29.8	25 13.3	6 23.7	3 28.0	19 8.4	13 59.1	2 32.7	24 53.5	2 42.7
30	22 29 39.2	7 39.2	22 .6	28 5.8	26 34.7	7 34.4	4 4.5	19 21.1	14 2.8	2 36.0	24 54.9	2 44.7
31	22 33 35.7	8 33.8	21 57.1	10♒28.8	27 54.8	8 44.9	4 40.9	19 33.9	14 6.6	2 39.3	24 56.4	2 46.6

DECLINATION

DAY	EPHEM. SID. TIME h m s	☉	☊	☽	☿	♀	♂	♃	♄	♅	♆	♇
1	20 35 19.1	18N16.4	0S24.4	22S21.3	20N56.5	20N59.9	17N58.0	18N11.1	14S 4.8	20N56.6	8S18.8	22N25.8
4	20 47 8.8	17 30.7	0 24.4	13 16.6	19 36.3	20 16.9	17 24.6	18 .5	14 6.7	20 54.4	8 19.8	22 23.8
7	20 58 58.4	16 42.4	0 24.4	1N24.4	17 58.0	19 28.6	16 50.3	17 49.8	14 8.9	20 52.2	8 20.9	22 21.8
10	21 10 48.1	15 51.7	0 24.4	16 5.8	16 5.6	18 35.2	16 14.9	17 39.0	14 11.4	20 50.0	8 22.2	22 19.8
13	21 22 37.7	14 58.7	0 24.4	23 28.5	14 3.2	17 37.2	15 38.6	17 28.0	14 14.1	20 47.9	8 23.5	22 17.9
16	21 34 27.4	14 3.5	0 24.4	17 52.6	11 54.1	16 34.6	15 1.4	17 17.0	14 17.0	20 45.7	8 24.9	22 16.0
19	21 46 17.1	13 6.3	0 24.4	3 5.0	9 41.0	15 27.9	14 23.4	17 5.9	14 20.1	20 43.6	8 26.4	22 14.1
22	21 58 6.7	12 7.3	0 24.4	12S 8.0	7 26.2	14 17.3	13 44.5	16 54.7	14 23.4	20 41.5	8 28.0	22 12.2
25	22 9 56.4	11 6.5	0 24.4	21 44.3	5 11.3	13 3.2	13 4.8	16 43.4	14 27.0	20 39.5	8 29.6	22 10.4
28	22 21 46.1	10 4.2	0 24.3	22 39.8	2 57.7	11 45.9	12 24.5	16 32.2	14 30.7	20 37.5	8 31.4	22 8.6
31	22 33 35.7	9 .4	0 24.3	14 32.5	0 46.7	10 25.7	11 43.4	16 20.9	14 34.6	20 35.5	8 33.2	22 6.9

SEPTEMBER 1955

LONGITUDE

DAY	EPHEM. SID. TIME (h m s)	☉	☊	☽	☿	♀	♂	♃	♄	♅	♆	♇
1	22 37 32.3	7♍47.8	22♐33.4	21♒42.6	29♍16.0	7♍42.8	2♍55.2	17♌8.0	16♏.5	0♌23.4	26♎15.2	26♌51.4
2	22 41 28.8	8 45.9	22 30.2	4♓41.5	0♎44.0	8 57.2	3 33.3	17 20.7	16 4.5	0 26.5	26 16.8	26 53.3
3	22 45 25.4	9 43.9	22 27.0	17 57.4	2 10.7	10 11.7	4 11.5	17 33.4	16 8.7	0 29.6	26 18.5	26 55.2
4	22 49 21.9	10 42.0	22 23.8	1♈28.3	3 36.1	11 26.1	4 49.7	17 46.1	16 12.8	0 32.6	26 20.1	26 57.1
5	22 53 18.5	11 40.1	22 20.7	15 11.4	5 .0	12 40.6	5 27.9	17 58.7	16 17.1	0 35.6	26 21.8	26 58.9
6	22 57 15.0	12 38.3	22 17.5	29 3.7	6 22.6	13 55.1	6 6.1	18 11.3	16 21.4	0 38.5	26 23.6	27 .8
7	23 1 11.6	13 36.5	22 14.3	13♉2.3	7 43.7	15 9.6	6 44.2	18 23.9	16 25.8	0 41.5	26 25.3	27 2.7
8	23 5 8.1	14 34.7	22 11.1	27 4.9	9 3.3	16 24.1	7 22.4	18 36.4	16 30.3	0 44.4	26 27.1	27 4.6
9	23 9 4.7	15 33.0	22 8.0	11♊10.1	10 21.4	17 38.6	8 .6	18 48.8	16 34.9	0 47.2	26 28.8	27 6.4
10	23 13 1.3	16 31.3	22 4.8	25 16.8	11 38.0	18 53.2	8 38.9	19 1.3	16 39.5	0 50.1	26 30.7	27 8.3
11	23 16 57.8	17 29.6	22 1.6	9♋24.2	12 52.8	20 7.8	9 17.1	19 13.7	16 44.2	0 52.9	26 32.5	27 10.2
12	23 20 54.4	18 28.0	21 58.4	23 31.1	14 6.0	21 22.4	9 55.3	19 26.0	16 49.0	0 55.7	26 34.3	27 12.0
13	23 24 50.9	19 26.4	21 55.2	7♌35.6	15 17.5	22 37.0	10 33.5	19 38.3	16 53.8	0 58.4	26 36.2	27 13.8
14	23 28 47.5	20 24.8	21 52.1	21 34.9	16 27.0	23 51.6	11 11.7	19 50.5	16 58.7	1 1.1	26 38.1	27 15.6
15	23 32 44.0	21 23.3	21 48.9	5♍25.5	17 34.6	25 6.2	11 50.0	20 2.7	17 3.7	1 3.8	26 40.0	27 17.5
16	23 36 40.6	22 21.8	21 45.7	19 3.6	18 40.1	26 20.8	12 28.2	20 14.9	17 8.7	1 6.4	26 41.9	27 19.2
17	23 40 37.1	23 20.3	21 42.5	2♎26.1	19 43.3	27 35.5	13 6.4	20 26.9	17 13.8	1 9.0	26 43.8	27 21.0
18	23 44 33.7	24 18.9	21 39.3	15 30.4	20 44.2	28 50.1	13 44.7	20 39.0	17 19.0	1 11.5	26 45.8	27 22.8
19	23 48 30.2	25 17.5	21 36.2	28 15.7	21 42.6	0♎4.8	14 22.9	20 50.9	17 24.2	1 14.0	26 47.7	27 24.6
20	23 52 26.8	26 16.1	21 33.0	10♏42.8	22 38.3	1 19.5	15 1.2	21 2.8	17 29.5	1 16.5	26 49.7	27 26.3
21	23 56 23.3	27 14.7	21 29.8	22 53.8	23 31.1	2 34.2	15 39.4	21 14.7	17 34.9	1 18.9	26 51.7	27 28.0
22	0 0 19.9	28 13.4	21 26.6	4♐52.3	24 20.7	3 48.8	16 17.7	21 26.4	17 40.3	1 21.3	26 53.7	27 29.8
23	0 4 16.4	29 12.1	21 23.5	16 42.9	25 7.5	5 3.5	16 55.9	21 38.2	17 45.8	1 23.7	26 55.7	27 31.5
24	0 8 13.0	0♎10.9	21 20.3	28 30.8	25 49.6	6 18.2	17 34.2	21 49.8	17 51.3	1 26.0	26 57.8	27 33.2
25	0 12 9.5	1 9.6	21 17.1	10♑21.4	26 28.2	7 32.9	18 12.4	22 1.4	17 56.9	1 28.2	26 59.8	27 34.9
26	0 16 6.1	2 8.4	21 13.9	22 20.2	27 2.6	8 47.7	18 50.7	22 12.9	18 2.5	1 30.4	27 1.9	27 36.5
27	0 20 2.6	3 7.2	21 10.7	4♒32.4	27 32.3	10 2.4	19 29.0	22 24.4	18 8.2	1 32.6	27 3.9	27 38.1
28	0 23 59.2	4 6.1	21 7.6	17 2.3	27 57.0	11 17.1	20 7.3	22 35.8	18 14.0	1 34.8	27 6.0	27 39.8
29	0 27 55.7	5 5.0	21 4.4	29 52.9	28 16.3	12 31.8	20 45.5	22 47.1	18 19.8	1 36.9	27 8.1	27 41.4
30	0 31 52.3	6 3.9	21 1.2	13♓5.9	28 29.7	13 46.6	21 23.8	22 58.3	18 25.7	1 38.9	27 10.2	27 43.0

LATITUDE

DAY	EPHEM. SID. TIME (h m s)	☉	☊	☽	☿	♀	♂	♃	♄	♅	♆	♇
1	22 37 32.3	0 .0	0 .0	4N16.6	0S15.1	1N23.8	1N 8.1	0N36.6	2N 7.4	0N31.3	1N41.2	10N11.1
4	22 49 21.9	0 .0	0 .0	4 57.9	0 39.9	1 24.6	1 7.8	0 36.9	2 6.7	0 31.4	1 41.1	10 11.5
7	23 1 11.6	0 .0	0 .0	3 12.7	1 5.2	1 24.9	1 7.6	0 37.3	2 6.1	0 31.4	1 41.0	10 11.9
10	23 13 1.3	0 .0	0 .0	0S14.6	1 30.7	1 24.5	1 7.3	0 37.7	2 5.4	0 31.5	1 40.9	10 12.4
13	23 24 50.9	0 .0	0 .0	3 34.2	1 55.9	1 23.6	1 7.0	0 38.0	2 4.8	0 31.6	1 40.8	10 12.9
16	23 36 40.6	0 .0	0 .0	4 60.0	2 20.3	1 22.1	1 6.7	0 38.4	2 4.2	0 31.7	1 40.7	10 13.5
19	23 48 30.2	0 .0	0 .0	4 .9	2 43.3	1 20.1	1 6.3	0 38.8	2 3.7	0 31.8	1 40.7	10 14.1
22	0 0 19.9	0 .0	0 .0	1 24.6	3 4.0	1 17.5	1 6.0	0 39.2	2 3.1	0 31.9	1 40.6	10 14.7
25	0 12 9.5	0 .0	0 .0	1N40.8	3 21.5	1 14.3	1 5.6	0 39.7	2 2.6	0 32.0	1 40.5	10 15.4
28	0 23 59.2	0 .0	0 .0	4 11.6	3 34.2	1 11.1	1 5.2	0 40.1	2 2.1	0 32.1	1 40.5	10 16.1

RIGHT ASCENSION

DAY	EPHEM. SID. TIME (h m s)	☉	☊	☽	☿	♀	♂	♃	♄	♅	♆	♇
1	22 37 32.3	9♍28.3	21♐53.7	21♒41.1	29♍13.6	9♍55.2	5♍17.2	19♌46.6	14♏10.4	2♌42.5	24♎57.9	2♍48.6
2	22 41 28.8	10 22.7	21 50.2	4♓48.3	0♎31.2	11 5.3	5 53.4	19 59.3	14 14.3	2 45.7	24 59.4	2 50.5
3	22 45 25.4	11 17.1	21 46.8	16 58.5	1 47.4	12 15.2	6 29.6	20 11.9	14 18.3	2 48.9	25 1.0	2 52.5
4	22 49 21.9	12 11.3	21 43.3	29 22.2	3 2.4	13 25.0	7 5.8	20 24.5	14 22.4	2 52.1	25 2.5	2 54.4
5	22 53 18.5	13 5.6	21 39.9	12♈10.0	4 16.2	14 34.6	7 41.9	20 37.0	14 26.6	2 55.2	25 4.1	2 56.3
6	22 57 15.0	13 59.7	21 36.4	25 31.7	5 28.7	15 44.0	8 17.9	20 49.5	14 30.8	2 58.3	25 5.7	2 58.2
7	23 1 11.6	14 53.8	21 33.0	9♉33.6	6 40.0	16 53.2	8 53.9	21 2.0	14 35.1	3 1.3	25 7.4	3 .2
8	23 5 8.1	15 47.9	21 29.5	24 15.4	7 50.0	18 2.4	9 29.9	21 14.4	14 39.5	3 4.4	25 9.0	3 2.1
9	23 9 4.7	16 41.9	21 26.1	9♊27.4	8 58.7	19 11.4	10 5.8	21 26.7	14 43.9	3 7.3	25 10.7	3 4.0
10	23 13 1.3	17 35.9	21 22.6	24 52.0	10 6.1	20 20.3	10 41.7	21 39.1	14 48.5	3 10.4	25 12.4	3 5.9
11	23 16 57.8	18 29.9	21 19.2	10♋5.7	11 12.1	21 29.1	11 17.5	21 51.3	14 53.1	3 13.3	25 14.1	3 7.8
12	23 20 54.4	19 23.8	21 15.7	24 54.5	12 16.6	22 37.7	11 53.3	22 3.5	14 57.8	3 16.2	25 15.8	3 9.7
13	23 24 50.9	20 17.7	21 12.3	9♌3.5	13 19.7	23 46.3	12 29.0	22 15.7	15 2.5	3 19.0	25 17.6	3 11.6
14	23 28 47.5	21 11.5	21 8.8	22 32.9	14 21.2	24 54.8	13 4.7	22 27.8	15 7.3	3 21.8	25 19.3	3 13.4
15	23 32 44.0	22 5.4	21 5.4	5♍28.4	15 21.1	26 3.2	13 40.4	22 39.8	15 12.2	3 24.6	25 21.1	3 15.3
16	23 36 40.6	22 59.2	21 1.9	17 59.3	16 19.2	27 11.5	14 16.0	22 51.8	15 17.1	3 27.3	25 22.9	3 17.1
17	23 40 37.1	23 53.0	20 58.5	0♎16.3	17 15.5	28 19.8	14 51.6	23 3.7	15 22.1	3 30.0	25 24.7	3 19.0
18	23 44 33.7	24 46.9	20 55.0	12 29.3	18 9.8	29 28.1	15 27.3	23 15.5	15 27.3	3 32.7	25 26.5	3 20.8
19	23 48 30.2	25 40.7	20 51.6	24 46.4	19 1.9	0♎36.3	16 2.7	23 27.3	15 32.4	3 35.3	25 28.4	3 22.6
20	23 52 26.8	26 34.5	20 48.1	7♏14.9	19 51.7	1 44.4	16 38.2	23 39.1	15 37.6	3 37.9	25 30.2	3 24.4
21	23 56 23.3	27 28.4	20 44.7	19 51.0	20 38.9	2 52.6	17 13.6	23 50.7	15 42.8	3 40.4	25 32.1	3 26.2
22	0 0 19.9	28 22.2	20 41.2	2♐38.8	21 23.5	4 .8	17 49.1	24 2.3	15 48.2	3 42.9	25 34.0	3 28.0
23	0 4 16.4	29 16.1	20 37.8	15 31.6	22 5.9	5 8.9	18 24.5	24 13.8	15 53.6	3 45.4	25 35.9	3 29.8
24	0 8 13.0	0♎10.0	20 34.3	28 23.2	22 43.4	6 17.1	18 59.8	24 25.3	15 59.0	3 47.8	25 37.8	3 31.5
25	0 12 9.5	1 3.9	20 30.9	11♑7.5	23 18.2	7 25.3	19 35.2	24 36.7	16 4.5	3 50.1	25 39.7	3 33.3
26	0 16 6.1	1 57.8	20 27.4	23 40.3	23 49.2	8 33.5	20 10.5	24 48.0	16 10.1	3 52.5	25 41.7	3 35.0
27	0 20 2.6	2 51.8	20 24.0	6♒.8	24 16.1	9 41.7	20 45.8	24 59.3	16 15.7	3 54.7	25 43.6	3 36.8
28	0 23 59.2	3 45.8	20 20.5	18 11.7	24 38.4	10 50.2	21 21.0	25 10.4	16 21.4	3 57.0	25 45.6	3 38.5
29	0 27 55.7	4 39.9	20 17.1	0♓18.8	24 55.9	11 58.6	21 56.3	25 21.5	16 27.2	3 59.1	25 47.6	3 40.2
30	0 31 52.3	5 34.0	20 13.6	12 30.7	25 8.1	13 7.1	22 31.5	25 32.5	16 33.0	4 1.3	25 49.6	3 41.8

DECLINATION

DAY	EPHEM. SID. TIME (h m s)	☉	☊	☽	☿	♀	♂	♃	♄	♅	♆	♇
1	22 37 32.3	8N38.8	0S24.3	10S13.2	0N 3.7	9N58.4	11N29.6	16N17.1	14S36.0	20N34.9	8S33.8	22N 6.4
4	22 49 21.9	7 33.4	0 24.3	5N 8.4	2S 2.5	8 34.9	10 47.7	16 5.8	14 40.1	20 33.0	8 35.7	22 4.7
7	23 1 11.6	6 26.8	0 24.3	18 48.9	4 3.9	7 9.2	10 5.2	15 54.5	14 44.4	20 31.1	8 37.6	22 3.1
10	23 13 1.3	5 19.2	0 24.3	23 7.0	5 59.6	5 41.7	9 22.1	15 43.2	14 48.9	20 29.3	8 39.7	22 1.5
13	23 24 50.9	4 10.9	0 24.3	14 55.4	7 48.3	4 12.7	8 38.6	15 32.0	14 53.5	20 27.6	8 41.7	22 .1
16	23 36 40.6	3 1.8	0 24.3	0S16.3	9 28.7	2 42.5	7 54.6	15 20.8	14 58.3	20 25.9	8 43.9	21 58.7
19	23 48 30.2	1 52.3	0 24.3	14 36.4	10 59.1	1 11.6	7 10.1	15 9.7	15 3.2	20 24.3	8 46.0	21 57.4
22	0 0 19.9	0 42.4	0 24.3	22 29.9	12 17.4	0S19.9	6 25.3	14 58.7	15 8.1	20 22.8	8 48.3	21 56.1
25	0 12 9.5	0S27.7	0 24.3	21 21.9	13 20.6	1 51.5	5 40.2	14 47.8	15 13.3	20 21.4	8 50.5	21 55.0
28	0 23 59.2	1 37.8	0 24.2	11 44.0	14 4.7	2 32.9	4 54.8	14 37.0	15 18.5	20 20.0	8 52.8	21 53.9

LONGITUDE

DAY	EPHEM. SID. TIME (h m s)	☉	☊	☽	☿	♀	♂	♃	♄	♅	♆	♇
1	0 35 48.9	7♎2.9	20♐58.0	26♓40.7	28♎37.0	15♎1.3	22♍2.2	23♌9.5	18♏31.6	1♌41.0	27♎12.4	27♌44.6
2	0 39 45.4	8 1.8	20 54.9	10♈34.7	28 37.5	16 16.1	22 40.5	23 20.6	18 37.6	1 42.9	27 14.5	27 46.2
3	0 43 42.0	9 .8	20 51.7	24 43.6	28R31.0	17 30.8	23 18.8	23 31.6	18 43.6	1 44.8	27 16.7	27 47.7
4	0 47 38.5	9 59.9	20 48.5	9♉2.1	28 17.0	18 45.6	23 57.1	23 42.5	18 49.7	1 46.7	27 18.8	27 49.3
5	0 51 35.1	10 59.0	20 45.3	23 24.8	27 55.3	20 .3	24 35.4	23 53.4	18 55.8	1 48.5	27 21.0	27 50.8
6	0 55 31.6	11 58.1	20 42.1	7♊46.8	27 25.7	21 15.1	25 13.8	24 4.1	19 2.0	1 50.3	27 23.2	27 52.3
7	0 59 28.2	12 57.2	20 39.0	22 4.5	26 48.2	22 29.9	25 52.1	24 14.8	19 8.2	1 52.0	27 25.3	27 53.7
8	1 3 24.7	13 56.4	20 35.8	6♋15.5	26 3.0	23 44.7	26 30.5	24 25.4	19 14.4	1 53.7	27 27.5	27 55.2
9	1 7 21.3	14 55.7	20 32.6	20 18.6	25 10.5	24 59.4	27 8.8	24 35.9	19 20.7	1 55.3	27 29.7	27 56.6
10	1 11 17.8	15 55.0	20 29.4	4♌13.1	24 11.3	26 14.2	27 47.2	24 46.4	19 27.0	1 56.9	27 31.9	27 58.0
11	1 15 14.4	16 54.3	20 26.3	17 58.8	23 6.6	27 29.0	28 25.6	24 56.7	19 33.4	1 58.4	27 34.1	27 59.4
12	1 19 10.9	17 53.6	20 23.1	1♍34.8	21 57.6	28 43.8	29 4.0	25 7.0	19 39.8	1 59.9	27 36.3	28 .8
13	1 23 7.5	18 53.0	20 19.9	15 .4	20 46.0	29 58.6	29 42.4	25 17.1	19 46.3	2 1.4	27 38.6	28 2.1
14	1 27 4.0	19 52.4	20 16.7	28 14.1	19 33.7	1♏13.5	0♎20.8	25 27.2	19 52.8	2 2.7	27 40.8	28 3.5
15	1 31 .6	20 51.9	20 13.5	11♎14.7	18 22.5	2 28.3	0 59.2	25 37.1	19 59.3	2 4.1	27 43.0	28 4.8
16	1 34 57.1	21 51.4	20 10.4	24 1.1	17 14.8	3 43.1	1 37.7	25 47.0	20 5.9	2 5.4	27 45.2	28 6.1
17	1 38 53.7	22 50.9	20 7.2	6♏33.0	16 12.3	4 57.9	2 16.1	25 56.7	20 12.5	2 6.6	27 47.5	28 7.3
18	1 42 50.3	23 50.5	20 4.0	18 50.8	15 17.0	6 12.7	2 54.5	26 6.4	20 19.1	2 7.8	27 49.7	28 8.6
19	1 46 46.8	24 50.1	20 .8	0♐56.0	14 30.5	7 27.6	3 33.0	26 15.9	20 25.8	2 8.9	27 51.9	28 9.8
20	1 50 43.4	25 49.7	19 57.7	12 51.2	13 53.9	8 42.4	4 11.5	26 25.3	20 32.5	2 10.0	27 54.2	28 11.0
21	1 54 39.9	26 49.4	19 54.5	24 40.0	13 28.0	9 57.2	4 49.9	26 34.7	20 39.3	2 11.0	27 56.4	28 12.1
22	1 58 36.5	27 49.1	19 51.3	6♑26.7	13 13.3	11 12.1	5 28.5	26 43.9	20 46.1	2 12.0	27 58.7	28 13.3
23	2 2 33.0	28 48.8	19 48.1	18 16.1	13 9.9	12 26.9	6 6.9	26 53.0	20 52.9	2 12.9	28 .9	28 14.5
24	2 6 29.6	29 48.6	19 44.9	0♒13.5	13D17.6	13 41.8	6 45.4	27 2.0	20 59.7	2 13.8	28 3.2	28 15.6
25	2 10 26.1	0♏48.3	19 41.8	12 24.3	13 35.9	14 56.6	7 23.9	27 10.9	21 6.5	2 14.6	28 5.4	28 16.6
26	2 14 22.7	1 48.1	19 38.6	24 53.4	14 3.4	16 11.4	8 2.4	27 19.7	21 13.4	2 15.3	28 7.7	28 17.7
27	2 18 19.2	2 48.0	19 35.4	7♓45.0	14 42.0	17 26.2	8 40.9	27 28.3	21 20.3	2 16.0	28 9.9	28 18.7
28	2 22 15.8	3 47.8	19 32.2	21 1.9	15 28.1	18 41.0	9 19.5	27 36.8	21 27.2	2 16.7	28 12.1	28 19.7
29	2 26 12.4	4 47.7	19 29.1	4♈44.9	16 21.8	19 55.8	9 58.0	27 45.2	21 34.2	2 17.3	28 14.3	28 20.6
30	2 30 8.9	5 47.6	19 25.9	18 52.4	17 22.3	21 10.6	10 36.5	27 53.5	21 41.1	2 17.8	28 16.6	28 21.6
31	2 34 5.5	6 47.6	19 22.7	3♉20.3	18 28.7	22 25.5	11 15.1	28 1.6	21 48.1	2 18.3	28 18.8	28 22.5

LATITUDE

DAY	SID. TIME (h m s)	☉	☊	☽	☿	♀	♂	♃	♄	♅	♆	♇
1	0 35 48.9	0 .0	0 .0	4N56.0	3S39.9	1N6.4	1N4.7	0N40.6	2N1.6	0N32.2	1N40.4	10N16.9
4	0 47 38.5	0 .0	0 .0	3 18.3	3 35.8	1 1.8	1 4.2	0 41.0	2 1.1	0 32.3	1 40.4	10 17.7
7	0 59 28.2	0 .0	0 .0	0S12.8	3 18.5	0 56.7	1 3.7	0 41.5	2 .7	0 32.4	1 40.3	10 18.5
10	1 11 17.8	0 .0	0 .0	3 34.3	2 45.2	0 51.1	1 3.2	0 42.0	2 .2	0 32.5	1 40.3	10 19.4
13	1 23 7.5	0 .0	0 .0	5 3.4	1 56.0	0 45.2	1 2.7	0 42.5	1 59.8	0 32.6	1 40.3	10 20.2
16	1 34 57.1	0 .0	0 .0	4 9.6	0 56.2	0 38.9	1 2.1	0 43.0	1 59.5	0 32.7	1 40.3	10 21.2
19	1 46 46.8	0 .0	0 .0	1 33.0	0N4.5	0 32.3	1 1.5	0 43.6	1 59.1	0 32.8	1 40.3	10 22.1
22	1 58 36.5	0 .0	0 .0	1N35.6	0 56.6	0 25.4	1 .9	0 44.1	1 58.8	0 32.9	1 40.3	10 23.1
25	2 10 26.1	0 .0	0 .0	4 10.4	1 34.7	0 18.3	1 .2	0 44.7	1 58.5	0 33.0	1 40.3	10 24.1
28	2 22 15.8	0 .0	0 .0	5 8.9	1 58.1	0 11.0	0 59.5	0 45.3	1 58.2	0 33.1	1 40.3	10 25.1
31	2 34 5.5	0 .0	0 .0	3 38.1	2 8.6	0 3.5	0 58.8	0 45.9	1 57.9	0 33.2	1 40.4	10 26.2

RIGHT ASCENSION

DAY	SID. TIME (h m s)	☉	☊	☽	☿	♀	♂	♃	♄	♅	♆	♇
1	0 35 48.9	6♎28.3	20♐10.2	24♓57.9	25♎14.7	14♎15.7	23♍6.8	25♌43.5	16♏38.9	4♌3.4	25♎51.6	3♍43.6
2	0 39 45.4	7 22.5	20 6.7	7♈51.2	25 15.2	15 24.3	23 42.0	25 54.4	16 44.8	4 5.5	25 53.6	3 45.2
3	0 43 42.0	8 16.8	20 3.3	21 20.6	25R9.4	16 33.1	24 17.2	26 5.2	16 50.7	4 7.5	25 55.6	3 46.8
4	0 47 38.5	9 11.2	19 59.8	5♉32.3	24 57.0	17 42.0	24 52.4	26 15.9	16 56.7	4 9.4	25 57.7	3 48.5
5	0 51 35.1	10 5.7	19 56.4	20 25.3	24 37.7	18 51.1	25 27.5	26 26.5	17 2.8	4 11.3	25 59.7	3 50.0
6	0 55 31.6	11 .3	19 52.9	5♊48.9	24 11.5	20 .3	26 2.7	26 37.0	17 8.9	4 13.2	26 1.7	3 51.6
7	0 59 28.2	11 55.0	19 49.5	21 18.1	23 38.4	21 9.6	26 37.8	26 47.4	17 15.0	4 15.0	26 3.8	3 53.2
8	1 3 24.7	12 49.8	19 46.0	6♋44.5	22 58.8	22 19.1	27 13.0	26 57.8	17 21.2	4 16.7	26 5.9	3 54.7
9	1 7 21.3	13 44.7	19 42.6	21 33.6	22 12.9	23 28.8	27 48.2	27 8.1	17 27.5	4 18.4	26 7.9	3 56.3
10	1 11 17.8	14 39.6	19 39.2	5♌40.2	21 21.7	24 38.7	28 23.3	27 18.3	17 33.8	4 20.1	26 10.0	3 57.8
11	1 15 14.4	15 34.8	19 35.7	19 4.1	20 26.1	25 48.7	28 58.5	27 28.3	17 40.1	4 21.7	26 12.1	3 59.3
12	1 19 10.9	16 30.0	19 32.3	1♍52.0	19 27.2	26 59.0	29 33.6	27 38.3	17 46.5	4 23.2	26 14.2	4 .7
13	1 23 7.5	17 25.4	19 28.8	14 14.5	18 26.7	28 9.5	0♎8.8	27 48.2	17 52.9	4 24.7	26 16.3	4 2.2
14	1 27 4.0	18 20.8	19 25.4	26 23.1	17 26.2	29 20.1	0 43.9	27 58.0	17 59.4	4 26.2	26 18.4	4 3.6
15	1 31 .6	19 16.5	19 21.9	8♎28.6	16 27.4	0♏31.1	1 19.1	28 7.7	18 5.9	4 27.5	26 20.5	4 5.0
16	1 34 57.1	20 12.2	19 18.5	20 39.8	15 32.1	1 42.2	1 54.3	28 17.3	18 12.5	4 28.9	26 22.6	4 6.4
17	1 38 53.7	21 8.1	19 15.0	3♏2.6	14 42.0	2 53.6	2 29.5	28 26.8	18 19.0	4 30.2	26 24.7	4 7.8
18	1 42 50.3	22 4.2	19 11.6	15 38.9	13 58.6	4 5.2	3 4.7	28 36.2	18 25.7	4 31.4	26 26.8	4 9.1
19	1 46 46.8	23 .3	19 8.2	28 26.8	13 23.1	5 17.1	3 39.9	28 45.5	18 32.3	4 32.6	26 28.9	4 10.5
20	1 50 43.4	23 56.7	19 4.7	11♐20.6	12 56.4	6 29.3	4 15.1	28 54.7	18 39.0	4 33.7	26 31.0	4 11.8
21	1 54 39.9	24 53.2	19 1.3	24 12.9	12 39.2	7 41.7	4 50.3	29 3.8	18 45.7	4 34.8	26 33.2	4 13.0
22	1 58 36.5	25 49.9	18 57.8	6♑56.1	12 31.9	8 54.5	5 25.6	29 12.8	18 52.6	4 35.8	26 35.3	4 14.4
23	2 2 33.0	26 46.7	18 54.4	19 18.1	12D34.4	10 7.4	6 .6	29 21.7	18 59.4	4 36.8	26 37.4	4 15.6
24	2 6 29.6	27 43.7	18 50.9	1♒39.1	12 46.4	11 20.7	6 36.1	29 30.4	19 6.2	4 37.7	26 39.6	4 16.8
25	2 10 26.1	28 40.8	18 47.5	13 40.1	13 7.7	12 34.1	7 11.4	29 39.0	19 13.0	4 38.5	26 41.7	4 17.9
26	2 14 22.7	29 38.1	18 44.0	25 34.7	13 37.5	13 48.1	7 46.7	29 47.6	19 19.9	4 39.3	26 43.8	4 19.2
27	2 18 19.2	0♏35.6	18 40.6	7♓32.2	14 15.3	15 2.2	8 22.2	29 56.1	19 26.8	4 40.1	26 45.9	4 20.3
28	2 22 15.8	1 33.3	18 37.2	19 44.1	15 .4	16 16.7	8 57.4	0♍4.4	19 33.8	4 40.7	26 48.0	4 21.4
29	2 26 12.4	2 31.1	18 33.7	2♈23.2	15 52.0	17 31.4	9 32.8	0 12.6	19 40.7	4 41.3	26 50.1	4 22.5
30	2 30 8.9	3 29.2	18 30.3	15 41.8	16 49.3	18 46.5	10 8.2	0 20.7	19 47.7	4 41.9	26 52.3	4 23.6
31	2 34 5.5	4 27.4	18 26.8	29 49.5	17 51.8	20 1.8	10 43.7	0 28.7	19 54.7	4 42.4	26 54.4	4 24.6

DECLINATION

DAY	SID. TIME (h m s)	☉	☊	☽	☿	♀	♂	♃	♄	♅	♆	♇
1	0 35 48.9	2S47.9	0S24.2	3N16.0	14S24.4	4S53.9	4N9.1	14N26.4	15S23.8	20N18.7	8S55.1	21N52.9
4	0 47 38.5	3 57.7	0 24.2	17 38.4	14 13.4	6 23.9	3 23.1	14 16.0	15 29.1	20 17.6	8 57.5	21 51.9
7	0 59 28.2	5 7.0	0 24.2	22 59.7	12 59.7	7 52.8	2 37.1	14 5.7	15 34.5	20 16.5	8 59.8	21 51.1
10	1 11 17.8	6 15.8	0 24.2	15 44.2	11 56.5	9 20.2	1 50.8	13 55.6	15 40.0	20 15.5	9 2.2	21 50.4
13	1 23 7.5	7 23.9	0 24.2	1 14.5	9 54.0	10 45.7	1 4.5	13 45.8	15 45.6	20 14.5	9 4.6	21 49.7
16	1 34 57.1	8 31.1	0 24.2	13S11.0	7 38.4	12 9.0	0 18.1	13 36.2	15 51.1	20 13.8	9 7.0	21 49.2
19	1 46 46.8	9 37.2	0 24.2	21 52.0	5 39.1	13 30.5	0S28.3	13 26.9	15 56.8	20 12.5	9 9.4	21 48.8
22	1 58 36.5	10 42.0	0 24.1	21 41.8	4 21.1	14 49.7	1 14.6	13 17.9	16 2.4	20 12.5	9 11.8	21 48.4
25	2 10 26.1	11 45.4	0 24.1	13 54.8	3 54.8	16 6.7	2 1.1	13 9.2	16 8.0	20 12.0	9 14.1	21 48.2
28	2 22 15.8	12 47.2	0 24.1	1N10.7	4 36.5	17 12.7	2 47.1	13 .8	16 13.6	20 11.7	9 16.5	21 48.0
31	2 34 5.5	13 47.1	0 24.1	16 2.6	5 15.7	18 18.3	3 33.0	12 52.8	16 19.3	20 11.4	9 18.8	21 48.0

NOVEMBER 1955

LONGITUDE

DAY	EPHEM. SID. TIME	☉	☊	☽	☿	♀	♂	♃	♄	♅	♆	♇
	h m s	° ′	° ′	° ′	° ′	° ′	° ′	° ′	° ′	° ′	° ′	° ′
1	2 38 2.0	7♏47.6	19♐19.5	18♉ 2.3	19♎40.3	23♏40.3	11♎53.7	28♌ 9.7	21♏55.1	2♌18.7	28♎21.0	28♌23.4
2	2 41 58.6	8 47.6	19 16.3	2♊51.0	20 56.3	24 55.1	12 32.2	28 17.6	22 2.1	2 19.1	28 23.2	28 24.2
3	2 45 55.1	9 47.6	19 13.2	17 38.7	22 16.1	26 9.9	13 10.8	28 25.3	22 9.2	2 19.4	28 25.4	28 25.1
4	2 49 51.7	10 47.7	19 10.0	2♋18.8	23 39.1	27 24.7	13 49.4	28 33.0	22 16.2	2 19.6	28 27.6	28 25.9
5	2 53 48.2	11 47.8	19 6.8	16 46.4	25 4.8	28 39.5	14 28.0	28 40.5	22 23.3	2 19.9	28 29.8	28 26.7
6	2 57 44.8	12 47.9	19 3.6	0♌58.5	26 32.8	29 54.3	15 6.7	28 47.8	22 30.4	2 20.0	28 32.0	28 27.4
7	3 1 41.3	13 48.1	19 .5	14 53.6	28 2.6	1♐ 9.1	15 45.3	28 55.0	22 37.5	2 20.1	28 34.2	28 28.1
8	3 5 37.9	14 48.3	18 57.3	28 31.8	29 33.9	2 23.9	16 23.9	29 2.1	22 44.6	2 20.1	28 36.4	28 28.8
9	3 9 34.5	15 48.6	18 54.1	11♍53.7	1♏ 6.4	3 38.7	17 2.6	29 9.0	22 51.7	2 20.1	28 38.5	28 29.5
10	3 13 31.0	16 48.9	18 50.9	25 .3	2 39.9	4 53.5	17 41.3	29 15.8	22 58.8	2 20.1	28 40.7	28 30.1
11	3 17 27.6	17 49.2	18 47.8	7♎52.7	4 14.2	6 8.3	18 20.0	29 22.5	23 6.0	2R19.9	28 42.8	28 30.7
12	3 21 24.1	18 49.6	18 44.6	20 32.1	5 49.1	7 23.2	18 58.7	29 29.0	23 13.2	2 19.8	28 45.0	28 31.4
13	3 25 20.7	19 50.0	18 41.4	2♏59.2	7 24.4	8 38.0	19 37.4	29 35.4	23 20.3	2 19.6	28 47.2	28 31.9
14	3 29 17.2	20 50.4	18 38.2	15 15.2	8 59.9	9 52.8	20 16.1	29 41.6	23 27.5	2 19.3	28 49.3	28 32.4
15	3 33 13.8	21 50.8	18 35.0	27 21.2	10 35.7	11 7.6	20 54.8	29 47.6	23 34.6	2 18.9	28 51.4	28 32.9
16	3 37 10.3	22 51.3	18 31.9	9♐18.7	12 11.7	12 22.4	21 33.6	29 53.5	23 41.8	2 18.6	28 53.5	28 33.4
17	3 41 6.9	23 51.8	18 28.7	21 9.7	13 47.6	13 37.2	22 12.3	29 59.2	23 48.9	2 18.1	28 55.5	28 33.8
18	3 45 3.5	24 52.3	18 25.5	2♑56.8	15 23.6	14 52.0	22 51.1	0♍ 4.8	23 56.1	2 17.6	28 57.6	28 34.2
19	3 49 .0	25 52.8	18 22.3	14 43.2	16 59.5	16 6.8	23 29.8	0 10.2	24 3.3	2 17.0	28 59.7	28 34.6
20	3 52 56.6	26 53.4	18 19.2	26 32.4	18 35.3	17 21.6	24 8.6	0 15.4	24 10.4	2 16.4	29 1.7	28 34.9
21	3 56 53.1	27 54.0	18 16.0	8♒29.0	20 11.1	18 36.4	24 47.4	0 20.5	24 17.6	2 15.8	29 3.7	28 35.3
22	4 0 49.7	28 54.6	18 12.8	20 37.4	21 46.7	19 51.2	25 26.2	0 25.4	24 24.7	2 15.0	29 5.7	28 35.5
23	4 4 46.2	29 55.2	18 9.6	3♓ 2.4	23 22.1	21 5.9	26 5.0	0 30.2	24 31.8	2 14.3	29 7.7	28 35.8
24	4 8 42.8	0♐55.8	18 6.5	15 48.6	24 57.5	22 20.7	26 43.8	0 34.7	24 39.0	2 13.4	29 9.7	28 36.0
25	4 12 39.4	1 56.5	18 3.3	28 59.6	26 32.7	23 35.4	27 22.6	0 39.1	24 46.1	2 12.6	29 11.7	28 36.2
26	4 16 35.9	2 57.2	18 .1	12♈38.0	28 7.7	24 50.2	28 1.4	0 43.4	24 53.2	2 11.6	29 13.6	28 36.4
27	4 20 32.5	3 57.9	17 56.9	26 44.0	29 42.6	26 4.9	28 40.3	0 47.4	25 .3	2 10.7	29 15.5	28 36.5
28	4 24 29.0	4 58.6	17 53.7	11♉15.5	1♐17.4	27 19.6	29 19.1	0 51.3	25 7.4	2 9.6	29 17.4	28 36.6
29	4 28 25.6	5 59.3	17 50.6	26 7.5	2 52.1	28 34.4	29 58.0	0 55.0	25 14.5	2 8.5	29 19.3	28 36.7
30	4 32 22.1	7 .1	17 47.4	11♊12.5	4 26.6	29 49.1	0♏36.8	0 58.6	25 21.6	2 7.4	29 21.2	28 36.7

LATITUDE

DAY	EPHEM. SID. TIME	☉	☊	☽	☿	♀	♂	♃	♄	♅	♆	♇
1	2 38 2.0	0 .0	0 .0	2N34.8	2N 9.7	0N 1.0	0N58.5	0N46.1	1N57.9	0N33.3	1N40.4	10N26.5
4	2 49 51.7	0 .0	0 .0	1S18.4	2 7.3	0S 6.6	0 57.8	0 46.7	1 57.6	0 33.4	1 40.4	10 27.6
7	3 1 41.3	0 .0	0 .0	4 22.7	1 58.2	0 14.2	0 57.0	0 47.4	1 57.4	0 33.5	1 40.5	10 28.7
10	3 13 31.0	0 .0	0 .0	5 10.3	1 44.5	0 21.8	0 56.2	0 48.0	1 57.3	0 33.6	1 40.5	10 29.8
13	3 25 20.7	0 .0	0 .0	3 40.1	1 27.6	0 29.4	0 55.3	0 48.7	1 57.1	0 33.7	1 40.6	10 31.0
16	3 37 10.3	0 .0	0 .0	0 44.2	1 8.7	0 36.8	0 54.4	0 49.4	1 57.0	0 33.8	1 40.6	10 32.1
19	3 49 .0	0 .0	0 .0	2N25.5	0 48.7	0 44.2	0 53.5	0 50.1	1 56.9	0 34.0	1 40.7	10 33.2
22	4 0 49.7	0 .0	0 .0	4 42.9	0 28.1	0 51.3	0 52.5	0 50.8	1 56.8	0 34.1	1 40.8	10 34.4
25	4 12 39.4	0 .0	0 .0	5 10.5	0 7.5	0 58.1	0 51.6	0 51.5	1 56.8	0 34.2	1 40.9	10 35.5
28	4 24 29.0	0 .0	0 .0	3 7.2	0S12.9	1 4.7	0 50.5	0 52.2	1 56.7	0 34.3	1 41.0	10 36.7

RIGHT ASCENSION

DAY	EPHEM. SID. TIME	☉	☊	☽	☿	♀	♂	♃	♄	♅	♆	♇
1	2 38 2.0	5♏25.8	18♐23.4	14♉48.8	18♎58.8	21♏17.5	11♎19.1	0♍36.1	20♏ 1.7	4♌42.9	26♎56.5	4♍25.6
2	2 41 58.6	6 24.4	18 20.0	0♊30.9	20 9.6	22 33.5	11 54.6	0 43.8	20 8.8	4 43.3	26 58.6	4 26.6
3	2 45 55.1	7 23.2	18 16.5	16 34.3	21 23.7	23 49.8	12 30.2	0 51.3	20 15.9	4 43.6	27 .7	4 27.6
4	2 49 51.7	8 22.3	18 13.1	2♋29.8	22 40.8	25 6.4	13 5.8	0 58.7	20 22.9	4 43.9	27 2.8	4 28.5
5	2 53 48.2	9 21.5	18 9.6	17 51.2	24 .3	26 23.3	13 41.4	1 6.0	20 30.0	4 44.1	27 4.8	4 29.4
6	2 57 44.8	10 20.9	18 6.2	2♌23.1	25 22.0	27 40.5	14 17.0	1 13.2	20 37.2	4 44.3	27 6.9	4 30.3
7	3 1 41.3	11 20.6	18 2.8	16 3.0	26 45.4	28 58.0	14 52.7	1 20.2	20 44.3	4 44.4	27 9.0	4 31.2
8	3 5 37.9	12 20.5	17 59.3	28 57.8	28 10.5	0♐15.8	15 28.5	1 27.0	20 51.5	4 44.4	27 11.1	4 32.0
9	3 9 34.5	13 20.6	17 55.9	11♍19.6	29 36.8	1 33.9	16 4.3	1 33.8	20 58.6	4 44.4	27 13.1	4 32.8
10	3 13 31.0	14 20.9	17 52.4	23 21.8	1♏ 4.3	2 52.4	16 40.1	1 40.4	21 5.8	4 44.4	27 15.2	4 33.6
11	3 17 27.6	15 21.4	17 49.0	5♎17.3	2 32.8	4 11.1	17 15.9	1 46.8	21 13.0	4R44.3	27 17.2	4 34.3
12	3 21 24.1	16 22.1	17 45.6	17 16.8	4 2.3	5 30.1	17 51.9	1 53.2	21 20.3	4 44.1	27 19.3	4 35.1
13	3 25 20.7	17 23.1	17 42.1	29 28.2	5 32.4	6 49.4	18 27.9	1 59.4	21 27.5	4 43.9	27 21.3	4 35.8
14	3 29 17.2	18 24.3	17 38.7	11♏55.5	7 3.3	8 8.9	19 3.9	2 5.4	21 34.7	4 43.6	27 23.3	4 36.4
15	3 33 13.8	19 25.6	17 35.2	24 37.9	8 34.7	9 28.7	19 39.9	2 11.2	21 41.9	4 43.3	27 25.3	4 37.1
16	3 37 10.3	20 27.2	17 31.8	7♐30.4	10 6.8	10 48.7	20 16.1	2 17.0	21 49.2	4 42.9	27 27.3	4 37.7
17	3 41 6.9	21 29.0	17 28.4	20 24.4	11 39.3	12 9.0	20 52.2	2 22.5	21 56.4	4 42.4	27 29.3	4 38.2
18	3 45 3.5	22 31.0	17 24.9	3♑10.7	13 12.4	13 29.4	21 28.4	2 27.9	22 3.6	4 41.9	27 31.3	4 38.8
19	3 49 .0	23 33.2	17 21.5	15 41.7	14 45.9	14 50.1	22 4.7	2 33.2	22 10.9	4 41.3	27 33.2	4 39.3
20	3 52 56.6	24 35.6	17 18.1	27 54.0	16 19.8	16 11.0	22 41.0	2 38.3	22 18.1	4 40.7	27 35.2	4 39.8
21	3 56 53.1	25 38.2	17 14.6	9♒48.3	17 54.2	17 32.1	23 17.4	2 43.2	22 25.4	4 40.0	27 37.1	4 40.3
22	4 0 49.7	26 41.1	17 11.2	21 30.0	19 29.1	18 53.4	23 53.8	2 48.0	22 32.6	4 39.3	27 39.0	4 40.7
23	4 4 46.2	27 44.1	17 7.8	3♓ 8.0	21 4.3	20 14.8	24 30.3	2 52.6	22 39.8	4 38.5	27 40.9	4 41.1
24	4 8 42.8	28 47.3	17 4.3	14 53.8	22 40.0	21 36.4	25 6.9	2 57.1	22 47.1	4 37.6	27 42.8	4 41.4
25	4 12 39.4	29 50.7	17 .9	27 .9	24 16.1	22 58.1	25 43.5	3 1.4	22 54.3	4 36.7	27 44.7	4 41.8
26	4 16 35.9	0♐54.2	16 57.4	9♈44.0	25 52.6	24 19.9	26 20.2	3 5.5	23 1.5	4 35.8	27 46.5	4 42.1
27	4 20 32.5	1 58.0	16 54.0	23 16.8	27 29.6	25 41.8	26 56.9	3 9.5	23 8.7	4 34.8	27 48.4	4 42.4
28	4 24 29.0	3 2.0	16 50.6	7♉48.6	29 7.0	27 3.8	27 33.7	3 13.3	23 15.9	4 33.7	27 50.2	4 42.6
29	4 28 25.6	4 6.1	16 47.1	23 19.3	0♐44.8	28 25.9	28 10.6	3 16.9	23 23.1	4 32.6	27 52.0	4 42.9
30	4 32 22.1	5 10.4	16 43.7	9♊34.0	2 23.1	29 48.0	28 47.5	3 20.4	23 30.3	4 31.4	27 53.8	4 43.0

DECLINATION

DAY	EPHEM. SID. TIME	☉	☊	☽	☿	♀	♂	♃	♄	♅	♆	♇
1	2 38 2.0	14S 6.7	0S24.1	19N41.1	5S41.7	18S40.7	3S48.3	12N50.2	16S21.1	20N11.3	9S19.6	21N48.0
4	2 49 51.7	15 4.0	0 24.1	22 7.1	7 12.7	19 41.5	4 34.0	12 42.7	16 26.7	20 11.2	9 21.9	21 48.1
7	3 1 41.3	15 59.1	0 24.1	12 10.8	8 56.4	20 37.6	5 19.5	12 35.6	16 32.3	20 11.2	9 24.2	21 48.3
10	3 13 31.0	16 51.8	0 24.1	2S45.7	10 45.8	21 28.4	6 4.7	12 28.9	16 37.8	20 11.4	9 26.4	21 48.6
13	3 25 20.7	17 42.0	0 24.0	15 57.3	12 36.3	22 13.9	6 49.5	12 22.7	16 43.3	20 11.6	9 28.7	21 49.0
16	3 37 10.3	18 29.4	0 24.0	22 34.8	14 24.5	22 53.5	7 33.9	12 17.0	16 48.7	20 11.9	9 30.8	21 49.6
19	3 49 .0	19 13.9	0 24.0	20 13.2	16 8.1	23 27.1	8 17.9	12 11.7	16 54.1	20 12.4	9 32.9	21 50.2
22	4 0 49.7	19 55.2	0 24.0	10 8.7	17 45.7	23 54.5	9 1.4	12 7.0	16 59.3	20 12.9	9 35.0	21 50.9
25	4 12 39.4	20 33.3	0 24.0	4N20.8	19 15.9	24 15.4	9 44.4	12 2.8	17 4.5	20 13.6	9 37.0	21 51.7
28	4 24 29.0	21 7.9	0 24.0	18 10.5	20 38.0	24 29.8	10 26.8	11 59.2	17 9.7	20 14.4	9 38.9	21 52.7

DECEMBER 1955

DAY	EPHEM. SID. TIME	☉	☊	☽	☿	♀	♂	♃	♄	♅	♆	♇
	h m s	° ′	° ′	° ′	° ′	° ′	° ′	° ′	° ′	° ′	° ′	° ′
		LONGITUDE										
1	4 36 18.7	8♐ .9	17♐44.2	26♊21.5	6♐ 1.1	1♑ 3.8	1♏15.7	1♍ 1.9	25♏28.6	2♌ 6.2	29♎23.0	28♌36.7
2	4 40 15.3	9 1.7	17 41.0	11♋25.3	7 35.5	2 18.5	1 54.6	1 5.1	25 35.7	2R 5.0	29 24.9	28 36.7
3	4 44 11.8	10 2.5	17 37.9	26 15.6	9 9.8	3 33.2	2 33.5	1 8.1	25 42.7	2 3.8	29 26.7	28 36.7
4	4 48 8.4	11 3.4	17 34.7	10♌46.4	10 44.1	4 47.9	3 12.5	1 10.9	25 49.7	2 2.5	29 28.5	28R36.6
5	4 52 4.9	12 4.2	17 31.5	24 54.0	12 18.3	6 2.5	3 51.4	1 13.6	25 56.7	2 1.1	29 30.3	28 36.5
6	4 56 1.5	13 5.1	17 28.3	8♍37.4	13 52.5	7 17.2	4 30.3	1 16.0	26 3.7	1 59.7	29 32.0	28 36.4
7	4 59 58.0	14 6.0	17 25.2	21 57.3	15 26.7	8 31.9	5 9.3	1 18.3	26 10.6	1 58.2	29 33.8	28 36.2
8	5 3 54.6	15 7.0	17 22.0	4♎55.7	17 .9	9 46.5	5 48.3	1 20.3	26 17.5	1 56.7	29 35.5	28 36.0
9	5 7 51.2	16 7.9	17 18.8	17 35.6	18 35.2	11 1.1	6 27.2	1 22.2	26 24.4	1 55.2	29 37.1	28 35.8
10	5 11 47.7	17 8.9	17 15.6	0♏ .0	20 9.5	12 15.8	7 6.2	1 23.9	26 31.3	1 53.6	29 38.8	28 35.5
11	5 15 44.3	18 9.9	17 12.4	12 12.0	21 43.8	13 30.4	7 45.2	1 25.4	26 38.1	1 51.9	29 40.4	28 35.2
12	5 19 40.8	19 10.9	17 9.3	24 14.5	23 18.2	14 45.0	8 24.2	1 26.7	26 44.9	1 50.2	29 42.1	28 34.9
13	5 23 37.4	20 11.9	17 6.1	6♐ 9.8	24 52.6	15 59.6	9 3.2	1 27.8	26 51.7	1 48.5	29 43.6	28 34.5
14	5 27 33.9	21 12.9	17 2.9	18 .4	26 27.2	17 14.2	9 42.3	1 28.7	26 58.5	1 46.7	29 45.2	28 34.2
15	5 31 30.5	22 14.0	16 59.7	29 48.3	28 1.8	18 28.8	10 21.3	1 29.4	27 5.2	1 44.9	29 46.7	28 33.8
16	5 35 27.1	23 15.1	16 56.6	11♑35.6	29 36.6	19 43.3	11 .4	1 29.9	27 11.9	1 43.1	29 48.2	28 33.3
17	5 39 23.6	24 16.1	16 53.4	23 24.6	1♑11.4	20 57.9	11 39.4	1 30.2	27 18.6	1 41.2	29 49.7	28 32.9
18	5 43 20.2	25 17.2	16 50.2	5♒17.7	2 46.4	22 12.4	12 18.5	1 30.4	27 25.2	1 39.3	29 51.2	28 32.4
19	5 47 16.7	26 18.3	16 47.0	17 17.8	4 21.4	23 26.9	12 57.5	1R30.3	27 31.8	1 37.3	29 52.6	28 31.8
20	5 51 13.3	27 19.4	16 43.9	29 28.0	5 56.6	24 41.4	13 36.6	1 30.0	27 38.3	1 35.3	29 54.0	28 31.3
21	5 55 9.8	28 20.5	16 40.7	11♓52.0	7 31.8	25 55.9	14 15.7	1 29.6	27 44.8	1 33.3	29 55.4	28 30.7
22	5 59 6.4	29 21.6	16 37.5	24 33.5	9 7.1	27 10.4	14 54.8	1 28.9	27 51.3	1 31.2	29 56.8	28 30.1
23	6 3 3.0	0♑22.7	16 34.3	7♈36.1	10 42.4	28 24.8	15 33.9	1 28.1	27 57.7	1 29.1	29 58.1	28 29.5
24	6 6 59.5	1 23.9	16 31.2	21 3.0	12 17.8	29 39.3	16 13.0	1 27.1	28 4.2	1 27.0	29 59.4	28 28.9
25	6 10 56.1	2 25.0	16 28.0	4♉56.1	13 53.1	0♒53.7	16 52.1	1 25.8	28 10.5	1 24.8	0♏ .7	28 28.2
26	6 14 52.6	3 26.1	16 24.8	19 15.6	15 28.4	2 8.0	17 31.3	1 24.4	28 16.8	1 22.6	0 1.9	28 27.5
27	6 18 49.2	4 27.2	16 21.6	3♊59.3	17 3.5	3 22.4	18 10.4	1 22.7	28 23.1	1 20.4	0 3.1	28 26.7
28	6 22 45.7	5 28.4	16 18.4	19 2.0	18 38.4	4 36.7	18 49.5	1 20.9	28 29.3	1 18.2	0 4.3	28 26.0
29	6 26 42.3	6 29.5	16 15.3	4♋15.8	20 13.0	5 50.9	19 28.7	1 18.9	28 35.4	1 15.9	0 5.4	28 25.2
30	6 30 38.9	7 30.6	16 12.1	19 31.2	21 47.2	7 5.2	20 7.8	1 16.7	28 41.5	1 13.6	0 6.6	28 24.4
31	6 34 35.4	8 31.7	16 8.9	4♌37.7	23 20.8	8 19.4	20 47.0	1 14.3	28 47.6	1 11.2	0 7.6	28 23.5
		LATITUDE										
1	4 36 18.7	0 .0	0 .0	0S50.0	0S32.6	1S11.0	0N49.5	0N53.0	1N56.7	0N34.4	1N41.1	10N37.8
4	4 48 8.4	0 .0	0 .0	4 15.7	0 51.3	1 16.9	0 48.3	0 53.7	1 56.8	0 34.5	1 41.2	10 39.0
7	4 59 58.0	0 .0	0 .0	5 17.1	1 8.8	1 22.3	0 47.2	0 54.5	1 56.8	0 34.6	1 41.4	10 40.1
10	5 11 47.7	0 .0	0 .0	3 54.3	1 24.8	1 27.3	0 46.0	0 55.2	1 56.9	0 34.7	1 41.5	10 41.3
13	5 23 37.4	0 .0	0 .0	1 1.9	1 39.1	1 31.7	0 44.8	0 56.0	1 57.0	0 34.8	1 41.6	10 42.4
16	5 35 27.1	0 .0	0 .0	2N10.7	1 51.3	1 35.7	0 43.5	0 56.8	1 57.1	0 34.8	1 41.8	10 43.5
19	5 47 16.7	0 .0	0 .0	4 35.0	2 1.0	1 39.0	0 42.2	0 57.6	1 57.2	0 34.9	1 41.9	10 44.5
22	5 59 6.4	0 .0	0 .0	5 14.8	2 7.9	1 41.8	0 40.8	0 58.4	1 57.4	0 35.0	1 42.1	10 45.6
25	6 10 56.1	0 .0	0 .0	3 34.0	2 11.4	1 43.9	0 39.4	0 59.1	1 57.6	0 35.1	1 42.2	10 46.6
28	6 22 45.7	0 .0	0 .0	0S 9.4	2 11.0	1 45.4	0 38.0	0 59.9	1 57.8	0 35.1	1 42.4	10 47.7
31	6 34 35.4	0 .0	0 .0	3 52.5	2 5.8	1 46.1	0 36.4	1 .7	1 58.0	0 35.2	1 42.6	10 48.6
		RIGHT ASCENSION										
1	4 36 18.7	6♐14.8	16♐40.3	26♊ 3.4	4♐ 1.9	1♑10.1	29♎24.5	3♍23.7	23♏37.5	4♌30.2	27♎55.6	4♍43.2
2	4 40 15.3	7 19.5	16 36.8	12♋13.2	5 41.1	2 32.3	0♏ 1.6	3 26.8	23 44.6	4R28.9	27 57.3	4 43.3
3	4 44 11.8	8 24.3	16 33.4	27 36.7	7 20.7	3 54.5	0 38.8	3 29.8	23 51.8	4 27.7	27 59.1	4 43.5
4	4 48 8.4	9 29.3	16 30.0	12♌ 2.1	9 .8	5 16.7	1 16.0	3 32.6	23 59.0	4 26.3	28 .8	4 43.6
5	4 52 4.9	10 34.4	16 26.5	25 31.9	10 41.4	6 38.8	1 53.3	3 35.2	24 6.1	4 24.9	28 2.5	4 43.6
6	4 56 1.5	11 39.7	16 23.1	8♍17.0	12 22.4	8 .9	2 30.7	3 37.6	24 13.2	4 23.4	28 4.2	4 43.6
7	4 59 58.0	12 45.1	16 19.7	20 31.7	14 3.8	9 22.9	3 8.2	3 39.8	24 20.2	4 21.9	28 5.8	4 43.6
8	5 3 54.6	13 50.6	16 16.2	2♎30.5	15 45.6	10 44.9	3 45.7	3 41.9	24 27.3	4 20.4	28 7.5	4R43.5
9	5 7 51.2	14 56.3	16 12.8	14 26.3	17 27.9	12 6.7	4 23.3	3 43.8	24 34.3	4 18.8	28 9.1	4 43.5
10	5 11 47.7	16 2.1	16 9.4	26 29.3	19 10.6	13 28.5	5 1.0	3 45.5	24 41.3	4 17.1	28 10.7	4 43.4
11	5 15 44.3	17 8.0	16 6.0	8♏46.3	20 53.7	14 50.1	5 38.7	3 47.0	24 48.3	4 15.4	28 12.2	4 43.2
12	5 19 40.8	18 14.0	16 2.5	21 19.3	22 37.1	16 11.6	6 16.6	3 48.3	24 55.3	4 13.7	28 13.8	4 43.0
13	5 23 37.4	19 20.2	15 59.1	4♐ 5.6	24 20.9	17 32.9	6 54.5	3 49.5	25 2.2	4 11.9	28 15.3	4 42.8
14	5 27 33.9	20 26.4	15 55.7	16 58.1	26 5.0	18 54.0	7 32.5	3 50.4	25 9.1	4 10.0	28 16.8	4 42.6
15	5 31 30.5	21 32.7	15 52.2	29 47.3	27 49.4	20 15.0	8 10.6	3 51.2	25 16.0	4 8.2	28 18.3	4 42.4
16	5 35 27.1	22 39.0	15 48.8	12♑24.1	29 34.1	21 35.7	8 48.7	3 51.8	25 22.8	4 6.2	28 19.7	4 42.1
17	5 39 23.6	23 45.4	15 45.4	24 42.3	1♑19.0	22 56.2	9 27.0	3 52.2	25 29.6	4 4.3	28 21.2	4 41.8
18	5 43 20.2	24 51.9	15 41.9	6♒39.9	3 4.1	24 16.5	10 5.3	3 52.4	25 36.4	4 2.3	28 22.6	4 41.4
19	5 47 16.7	25 58.4	15 38.5	18 19.7	4 49.3	25 36.5	10 43.7	3 52.5	25 43.2	4 .3	28 23.9	4 41.0
20	5 51 13.3	27 5.0	15 35.1	29 48.5	6 34.5	26 56.3	11 22.1	3R52.3	25 49.9	3 58.2	28 25.3	4 40.6
21	5 55 9.8	28 11.6	15 31.7	11♓16.3	8 19.8	28 15.8	12 .7	3 52.0	25 56.6	3 56.1	28 26.6	4 40.2
22	5 59 6.4	29 18.2	15 28.2	22 55.5	10 5.1	29 35.1	12 39.3	3 51.4	26 3.2	3 53.9	28 27.9	4 39.8
23	6 3 3.0	0♑24.8	15 24.8	5♈ .4	11 50.2	0♒54.0	13 18.1	3 50.7	26 9.8	3 51.7	28 29.2	4 39.3
24	6 6 59.5	1 31.4	15 21.4	17 45.6	13 35.2	2 12.7	13 56.9	3 49.8	26 16.4	3 49.6	28 30.5	4 38.8
25	6 10 56.1	2 38.0	15 18.0	1♉24.5	15 19.8	3 31.0	14 35.8	3 48.8	26 22.9	3 47.3	28 31.7	4 38.3
26	6 14 52.6	3 44.6	15 14.5	16 5.1	17 4.1	4 49.0	15 14.8	3 47.5	26 29.4	3 45.0	28 32.9	4 37.7
27	6 18 49.2	4 51.2	15 11.1	1♊44.7	18 47.8	6 6.7	15 53.8	3 46.0	26 35.8	3 42.7	28 34.1	4 37.1
28	6 22 45.7	5 57.7	15 7.7	18 5.2	20 30.9	7 24.1	16 33.0	3 44.4	26 42.2	3 40.4	28 35.2	4 36.5
29	6 26 42.3	7 4.2	15 4.2	4♋35.6	22 13.3	8 41.1	17 12.2	3 42.5	26 48.5	3 38.0	28 36.3	4 35.8
30	6 30 38.9	8 10.6	15 .8	20 42.0	23 54.7	9 57.8	17 51.5	3 40.5	26 54.8	3 35.6	28 37.4	4 35.1
31	6 34 35.4	9 17.0	14 57.4	6♌ .5	25 35.0	11 14.1	18 30.9	3 38.3	27 1.0	3 33.2	28 38.4	4 34.4
		DECLINATION										
1	4 36 18.7	21S39.0	0S24.0	22N33.6	21S51.0	24S37.4	11S 8.5	11N56.1	17S14.7	20N15.2	9S40.8	21N53.7
4	4 48 8.4	22 6.3	0 23.9	13 25.9	22 54.4	24 38.2	11 49.7	11 53.6	17 19.6	20 16.2	9 42.6	21 54.8
7	4 59 58.0	22 29.8	0 23.9	1S39.9	23 47.4	24 32.3	12 30.1	11 51.7	17 24.4	20 17.2	9 44.3	21 56.0
10	5 11 47.7	22 49.4	0 23.9	15 7.6	24 29.4	24 19.6	13 9.7	11 50.4	17 29.2	20 18.4	9 46.0	21 57.3
13	5 23 37.4	23 4.9	0 23.9	22 21.5	24 59.7	24 .2	13 48.6	11 49.7	17 33.7	20 19.6	9 47.5	21 58.7
16	5 35 27.1	23 16.3	0 23.9	20 46.0	25 17.9	23 34.3	14 26.6	11 49.7	17 38.2	20 20.9	9 49.0	22 .2
19	5 47 16.7	23 23.6	0 23.9	11 16.9	25 23.3	23 2.0	15 3.7	11 50.3	17 42.5	20 22.2	9 50.4	22 1.7
22	5 59 6.4	23 26.6	0 23.8	2N39.3	25 15.4	22 23.5	15 39.8	11 51.5	17 46.7	20 23.7	9 51.7	22 3.3
25	6 10 56.1	23 25.3	0 23.8	16 31.6	24 53.9	21 39.1	16 14.9	11 53.4	17 50.8	20 25.1	9 52.9	22 5.0
28	6 22 45.7	23 19.9	0 23.8	22 50.1	24 18.6	20 49.1	16 49.0	11 55.8	17 54.7	20 26.7	9 54.1	22 6.7
31	6 34 35.4	23 10.2	0 23.8	15 20.7	23 29.5	19 53.7	17 22.1	11 58.9	17 58.5	20 28.3	9 55.1	22 8.5

JANUARY 1956

LONGITUDE

DAY	EPHEM. SID. TIME	☉	☊	☽	☿	♀	♂	♃	♄	♅	♆	♇
	h m s	° ′	° ′	° ′	° ′	° ′	° ′	° ′	° ′	° ′	° ′	° ′
1	6 38 32.0	9♑32.9	16♐ 5.7	19♌26.4	24♑53.7	9♒33.6	21♏26.2	1♍11.7	28♏53.6	1♌ 8.9	0♏ 8.7	28♌22.7
2	6 42 28.5	10 34.0	16 2.6	3♍50.7	26 25.8	10 47.8	22 5.4	1R 9.0	28 59.6	1R 6.5	0 9.7	28R21.8
3	6 46 25.1	11 35.1	15 59.4	17 47.1	27 56.8	12 1.9	22 44.6	1 6.0	29 5.5	1 4.1	0 10.7	28 20.9
4	6 50 21.7	12 36.3	15 56.2	1♎14.8	29 26.3	13 16.0	23 23.8	1 2.8	29 11.3	1 1.6	0 11.7	28 19.9
5	6 54 18.2	13 37.5	15 53.0	14 15.8	0♒54.3	14 30.1	24 3.0	0 59.5	29 17.1	0 59.2	0 12.6	28 19.0
6	6 58 14.8	14 38.6	15 49.9	26 53.6	2 20.2	15 44.2	24 42.2	0 56.0	29 22.9	0 56.7	0 13.5	28 18.0
7	7 2 11.3	15 39.8	15 46.7	9♏12.3	3 43.7	16 58.2	25 21.5	0 52.3	29 28.6	0 54.2	0 14.4	28 17.0
8	7 6 7.9	16 40.9	15 43.5	21 16.7	5 4.4	18 12.2	26 .7	0 48.4	29 34.2	0 51.7	0 15.2	28 15.9
9	7 10 4.4	17 42.1	15 40.3	3♐11.3	6 21.6	19 26.1	26 40.0	0 44.4	29 39.8	0 49.2	0 16.0	28 14.9
10	7 14 1.0	18 43.3	15 37.1	15 .1	7 34.8	20 40.1	27 19.2	0 40.1	29 45.3	0 46.7	0 16.8	28 13.8
11	7 17 57.6	19 44.4	15 34.0	26 46.6	8 43.3	21 53.9	27 58.5	0 35.7	29 50.7	0 44.1	0 17.5	28 12.7
12	7 21 54.1	20 45.6	15 30.8	8♑33.9	9 46.5	23 7.8	28 37.8	0 31.1	29 56.1	0 41.6	0 18.2	28 11.6
13	7 25 50.7	21 46.7	15 27.6	20 24.2	10 43.4	24 21.6	29 17.1	0 26.4	0♐ 1.4	0 39.0	0 18.9	28 10.5
14	7 29 47.2	22 47.9	15 24.4	2♒19.6	11 33.3	25 35.4	29 56.4	0 21.5	0 6.7	0 36.4	0 19.6	28 9.4
15	7 33 43.8	23 49.1	15 21.3	14 21.6	12 15.1	26 49.1	0♐35.7	0 16.5	0 11.9	0 33.9	0 20.2	28 8.2
16	7 37 40.3	24 50.2	15 18.1	26 31.6	12 48.2	28 2.8	1 15.0	0 11.2	0 17.0	0 31.3	0 20.7	28 7.0
17	7 41 36.9	25 51.3	15 14.9	8♓51.3	13 11.5	29 16.5	1 54.3	0 5.9	0 22.1	0 28.6	0 21.3	28 5.8
18	7 45 33.5	26 52.5	15 11.7	21 22.5	13 24.4	0♓30.0	2 33.6	0 .3	0 27.1	0 26.0	0 21.8	28 4.6
19	7 49 30.0	27 53.6	15 8.6	4♈ 7.2	13 26.2	1 43.6	3 12.9	29♌54.6	0 32.0	0 23.4	0 22.2	28 3.3
20	7 53 26.6	28 54.6	15 5.4	17 7.9	13R16.4	2 57.1	3 52.2	29 48.8	0 36.8	0 20.8	0 22.6	28 2.1
21	7 57 23.1	29 55.7	15 2.2	0♉27.2	12 55.0	4 10.5	4 31.5	29 42.8	0 41.6	0 18.2	0 23.0	28 .8
22	8 1 19.7	0♒56.8	14 59.0	14 7.2	12 22.1	5 23.9	5 10.8	29 36.7	0 46.2	0 15.6	0 23.4	27 59.5
23	8 5 16.2	1 57.8	14 55.8	28 9.5	11 38.2	6 37.2	5 50.1	29 30.5	0 50.9	0 12.9	0 23.7	27 58.2
24	8 9 12.8	2 58.8	14 52.7	12♊34.0	10 44.6	7 50.4	6 29.4	29 24.1	0 55.4	0 10.3	0 24.0	27 56.9
25	8 13 9.3	3 59.8	14 49.5	27 18.4	9 42.5	9 3.6	7 8.8	29 17.7	0 59.9	0 7.7	0 24.3	27 55.6
26	8 17 5.9	5 .8	14 46.3	12♋17.7	8 33.8	10 16.7	7 48.1	29 11.1	1 4.2	0 5.1	0 24.5	27 54.2
27	8 21 2.5	6 1.8	14 43.1	27 24.5	7 20.6	11 29.8	8 27.4	29 4.3	1 8.5	0 2.5	0 24.7	27 52.9
28	8 24 59.0	7 2.7	14 40.0	12♌29.2	6 5.1	12 42.8	9 6.8	28 57.5	1 12.8	29♋59.9	0 24.9	27 51.5
29	8 28 55.6	8 3.7	14 36.8	27 22.1	4 49.5	13 55.7	9 46.1	28 50.6	1 16.9	29 57.3	0 25.0	27 50.1
30	8 32 52.1	9 4.6	14 33.6	11♍54.6	3 36.1	15 8.6	10 25.5	28 43.6	1 21.0	29 54.7	0 25.1	27 48.7
31	8 36 48.7	10 5.5	14 30.4	26 .8	2 26.7	16 21.4	11 4.9	28 36.4	1 25.0	29 52.2	0 25.1	27 47.3

LATITUDE

DAY	EPHEM. SID. TIME	☉	☊	☽	☿	♀	♂	♃	♄	♅	♆	♇
1	6 38 32.0	0 .0	0 .0	4S39.2	2S 2.9	1S46.2	0N35.9	1N .9	1N58.1	0N35.2	1N42.6	10N49.0
4	6 50 21.7	0 .0	0 .0	5 5.7	1 50.1	1 46.1	0 34.3	1 1.7	1 58.4	0 35.3	1 42.8	10 49.9
7	7 2 11.3	0 .0	0 .0	3 13.8	1 30.2	1 45.2	0 32.7	1 2.4	1 58.7	0 35.3	1 43.0	10 50.8
10	7 14 1.0	0 .0	0 .0	0 11.9	1 2.3	1 43.5	0 31.0	1 3.2	1 59.0	0 35.4	1 43.2	10 51.7
13	7 25 50.7	0 .0	0 .0	2N51.7	0 25.5	1 41.1	0 29.3	1 3.9	1 59.3	0 35.4	1 43.3	10 52.5
16	7 37 40.3	0 .0	0 .0	4 51.3	0N20.3	1 38.0	0 27.4	1 4.6	1 59.6	0 35.5	1 43.5	10 53.3
19	7 49 30.0	0 .0	0 .0	4 55.6	1 13.1	1 34.1	0 25.6	1 5.2	1 60.0	0 35.5	1 43.7	10 54.0
22	8 1 19.7	0 .0	0 .0	2 45.9	2 7.8	1 29.5	0 23.6	1 5.9	2 .4	0 35.5	1 43.9	10 54.7
25	8 13 9.3	0 .0	0 .0	0S58.5	2 55.7	1 24.1	0 21.6	1 6.5	2 .7	0 35.5	1 44.1	10 55.4
28	8 24 59.0	0 .0	0 .0	4 15.7	3 27.0	1 18.1	0 19.5	1 7.0	2 1.2	0 35.6	1 44.3	10 56.0
31	8 36 48.7	0 .0	0 .0	5 1.8	3 36.5	1 11.3	0 17.4	1 7.5	2 1.6	0 35.6	1 44.4	10 56.5

RIGHT ASCENSION

DAY	EPHEM. SID. TIME	☉	☊	☽	☿	♀	♂	♃	♄	♅	♆	♇
1	6 38 32.0	10♑23.3	14♐54.0	20♌22.8	27♑14.0	12♒30.1	19♏10.4	3♍36.0	27♏ 7.2	3♌30.7	28♎39.5	4♍33.7
2	6 42 28.5	11 29.6	14 50.5	3♍53.2	28 51.4	13 45.7	19 50.0	3R33.4	27 13.3	3R28.3	28 40.5	4R33.0
3	6 46 25.1	12 35.8	14 47.1	16 43.1	0♒27.1	15 1.0	20 29.7	3 30.7	27 19.4	3 25.8	28 41.4	4 32.2
4	6 50 21.7	13 41.9	14 43.7	29 6.7	2 .6	16 15.9	21 9.4	3 27.8	27 25.5	3 23.2	28 42.4	4 31.4
5	6 54 18.2	14 47.9	14 40.3	11♎17.5	3 31.8	17 30.5	21 49.3	3 24.7	27 31.4	3 20.7	28 43.3	4 30.6
6	6 58 14.8	15 53.8	14 36.8	23 27.1	5 .1	18 44.7	22 29.2	3 21.4	27 37.4	3 18.1	28 44.1	4 29.7
7	7 2 11.3	16 59.6	14 33.4	5♏43.9	6 25.2	19 58.6	23 9.2	3 17.9	27 43.2	3 15.5	28 45.0	4 28.8
8	7 6 7.9	18 5.4	14 30.0	18 12.6	7 46.7	21 12.2	23 49.3	3 14.3	27 49.0	3 12.9	28 45.8	4 27.9
9	7 10 4.4	19 10.9	14 26.6	0♐53.3	9 3.9	22 25.3	24 29.5	3 10.5	27 54.8	3 10.3	28 46.6	4 27.0
10	7 14 1.0	20 16.4	14 23.2	13 41.8	10 16.3	23 38.2	25 9.8	3 6.6	28 .5	3 7.7	28 47.3	4 26.1
11	7 17 57.6	21 21.7	14 19.7	26 30.7	11 23.2	24 50.6	25 50.2	3 2.4	28 6.1	3 5.0	28 48.0	4 25.1
12	7 21 54.1	22 26.9	14 16.3	9♑11.4	12 24.0	26 2.8	26 30.6	2 58.2	28 11.6	3 2.3	28 48.7	4 24.1
13	7 25 50.7	23 32.0	14 12.9	21 37.1	13 17.9	27 14.6	27 11.1	2 53.7	28 17.1	2 59.6	28 49.4	4 23.1
14	7 29 47.2	24 36.9	14 9.5	3♒43.8	14 4.1	28 26.1	27 51.8	2 49.1	28 22.6	2 57.0	28 50.1	4 22.1
15	7 33 43.8	25 41.7	14 6.0	15 31.8	14 41.8	29 37.2	28 32.5	2 44.4	28 28.0	2 54.3	28 50.7	4 21.1
16	7 37 40.3	26 46.2	14 2.6	27 5.5	15 10.2	0♓48.0	29 13.2	2 39.4	28 33.3	2 51.6	28 51.2	4 20.0
17	7 41 36.9	27 50.6	13 59.2	8♓32.5	15 28.5	1 58.5	29 54.0	2 34.4	28 38.5	2 48.9	28 51.7	4 18.9
18	7 45 33.5	28 54.9	13 55.8	20 3.0	15 36.1	3 8.7	0♐35.0	2 29.1	28 43.6	2 46.2	28 52.2	4 17.8
19	7 49 30.0	29 58.9	13 52.4	1♈49.0	15R32.5	4 18.5	1 15.9	2 23.8	28 48.7	2 43.4	28 52.7	4 16.6
20	7 53 26.6	1♒ 2.8	13 48.9	14 3.6	15 17.4	5 28.1	1 57.0	2 18.3	28 53.7	2 40.7	28 53.1	4 15.5
21	7 57 23.1	2 6.5	13 45.5	26 59.7	14 50.7	6 37.3	2 38.1	2 12.6	28 58.7	2 38.0	28 53.5	4 14.3
22	8 1 19.7	3 10.0	13 42.1	10♉47.5	14 12.8	7 46.2	3 19.4	2 6.8	29 3.5	2 35.2	28 53.9	4 13.1
23	8 5 16.2	4 13.2	13 38.7	25 31.0	13 24.3	8 54.9	4 .6	2 .9	29 8.3	2 32.5	28 54.2	4 11.9
24	8 9 12.8	5 16.3	13 35.3	11♊ 3.4	12 26.4	10 3.3	4 42.0	1 54.9	29 13.0	2 29.8	28 54.5	4 10.7
25	8 13 9.3	6 19.2	13 31.8	27 5.1	11 20.5	11 11.3	5 23.4	1 48.7	29 17.6	2 27.0	28 54.8	4 9.5
26	8 17 5.9	7 21.9	13 28.4	13♋ 8.5	10 8.5	12 19.2	6 4.9	1 42.5	29 22.2	2 24.3	28 55.0	4 8.2
27	8 21 2.5	8 24.4	13 25.0	28 46.9	8 52.5	13 26.7	6 46.5	1 36.1	29 26.7	2 21.6	28 55.2	4 7.0
28	8 24 59.0	9 26.7	13 21.6	13♌43.4	7 34.6	14 34.0	7 28.1	1 29.6	29 31.1	2 18.9	28 55.4	4 5.7
29	8 28 55.6	10 28.8	13 18.2	27 53.5	6 17.3	15 41.1	8 9.9	1 23.0	29 35.4	2 16.2	28 55.5	4 4.4
30	8 32 52.1	11 30.7	13 14.7	11♍22.5	5 2.5	16 47.9	8 51.6	1 16.3	29 39.6	2 13.5	28 55.7	4 3.1
31	8 36 48.7	12 32.4	13 11.3	24 20.7	3 52.1	17 54.6	9 33.5	1 9.5	29 43.7	2 10.8	28 55.7	4 1.8

DECLINATION

DAY	EPHEM. SID. TIME	☉	☊	☽	☿	♀	♂	♃	♄	♅	♆	♇
1	6 38 32.0	23S 6.0	0S23.8	10N34.1	23S10.2	19S34.1	17S32.8	12N .1	17S59.7	20N28.8	9S55.4	22N 9.1
4	6 50 21.7	22 50.8	0 23.8	5S10.1	22 4.0	18 32.0	18 4.3	12 3.9	18 3.3	20 30.5	9 56.3	22 11.0
7	7 2 11.3	22 31.5	0 23.8	17 37.5	20 47.1	17 25.4	18 34.6	12 8.4	18 6.7	20 32.1	9 57.0	22 12.9
10	7 14 1.0	22 8.2	0 23.7	22 47.9	19 23.0	16 14.5	19 3.7	12 13.4	18 9.9	20 33.8	9 57.7	22 14.8
13	7 25 50.7	21 40.9	0 23.7	19 3.9	17 57.5	14 59.6	19 31.5	12 18.9	18 13.0	20 35.5	9 58.3	22 16.8
16	7 37 40.3	21 9.9	0 23.7	8 6.4	16 38.8	13 41.2	19 58.0	12 24.9	18 15.9	20 37.2	9 58.7	22 18.7
19	7 49 30.0	20 35.2	0 23.7	6N 9.5	15 37.4	12 19.7	20 23.1	12 31.4	18 18.6	20 39.0	9 59.1	22 20.8
22	8 1 19.7	19 57.1	0 23.7	18 43.1	15 2.9	10 55.3	20 46.8	12 38.3	18 21.2	20 40.7	9 59.3	22 22.8
25	8 13 9.3	19 15.6	0 23.6	22 26.5	14 60.0	9 28.4	21 9.1	12 45.5	18 23.6	20 42.4	9 59.5	22 24.8
28	8 24 59.0	18 30.9	0 23.6	12 58.0	15 24.6	7 59.5	21 30.0	12 53.1	18 25.8	20 44.0	9 59.5	22 26.8
31	8 36 48.7	17 43.2	0 23.6	3S 1.9	16 6.1	6 28.8	21 49.3	13 1.0	18 27.8	20 45.7	9 59.4	22 28.8

FEBRUARY 1956

LONGITUDE

DAY	EPHEM. SID. TIME h m s	☉ ° ′	☊ ° ′	☾ ° ′	☿ ° ′	♀ ° ′	♂ ° ′	♃ ° ′	♄ ° ′	♅ ° ′	♆ ° ′	♇ ° ′
1	8 40 45.2	11♒ 6.4	14♐27.3	9♎38.0	1♒22.9	17♓34.1	11♐44.2	28♌29.2	1♐28.9	29♋49.6	0♏25.1	27♌45.9
2	8 44 41.8	12 7.3	14 24.1	22 46.3	0 R 26.0	18 46.7	12 23.6	28 R 21.9	1 32.7	29 R 47.1	0 25.1	27 R 44.5
3	8 48 38.4	13 8.2	14 20.9	5♏28.7	29♑36.8	19 59.3	13 3.0	28 14.5	1 36.4	29 44.5	0 25.1	27 43.0
4	8 52 34.9	14 9.1	14 17.7	17 49.3	28 55.8	21 11.8	13 42.4	28 7.1	1 40.1	29 42.0	0 R 25.0	27 41.6
5	8 56 31.5	15 9.9	14 14.5	29 53.4	28 23.4	22 24.3	14 21.8	27 59.6	1 43.7	29 39.5	0 24.9	27 40.2
6	9 0 28.0	16 10.8	14 11.4	11♐46.3	27 59.4	23 36.6	15 1.2	27 52.0	1 47.2	29 37.1	0 24.8	27 38.7
7	9 4 24.6	17 11.6	14 8.2	23 33.4	27 43.7	24 48.9	15 40.6	27 44.3	1 50.5	29 34.6	0 24.6	27 37.3
8	9 8 21.1	18 12.4	14 5.0	5♑19.4	27 36.1	26 1.1	16 20.0	27 36.6	1 53.8	29 32.1	0 24.4	27 35.8
9	9 12 17.7	19 13.2	14 1.8	17 8.5	27 36.0	27 13.2	16 59.4	27 28.8	1 57.1	29 29.7	0 24.1	27 34.3
10	9 16 14.2	20 13.9	13 58.7	29 3.8	27 D 43.2	28 25.2	17 38.8	27 21.0	2 .2	29 27.3	0 23.8	27 32.8
11	9 20 10.8	21 14.7	13 55.5	11♒ 7.8	27 57.0	29 37.1	18 18.1	27 13.2	2 3.2	29 24.9	0 23.5	27 31.3
12	9 24 7.3	22 15.4	13 52.3	23 21.8	28 16.9	0♈49.0	18 57.5	27 5.3	2 6.1	29 22.6	0 23.2	27 29.9
13	9 28 3.9	23 16.1	13 49.1	5♓46.8	28 42.7	2 .7	19 36.9	26 57.4	2 9.0	29 20.2	0 22.8	27 28.4
14	9 32 .5	24 16.8	13 46.0	18 23.0	29 13.7	3 12.4	20 16.3	26 49.5	2 11.7	29 17.9	0 22.4	27 26.9
15	9 35 57.0	25 17.4	13 42.8	1♈10.5	29 49.5	4 24.0	20 55.7	26 41.5	2 14.4	29 15.6	0 21.9	27 25.4
16	9 39 53.6	26 18.1	13 39.6	14 9.3	0♒29.9	5 35.4	21 35.1	26 33.6	2 16.9	29 13.4	0 21.4	27 23.9
17	9 43 50.1	27 18.6	13 36.4	27 19.9	1 14.3	6 46.8	22 14.4	26 25.7	2 19.4	29 11.1	0 20.9	27 22.4
18	9 47 46.7	28 19.2	13 33.2	10♉43.2	2 2.5	7 58.0	22 53.8	26 17.7	2 21.7	29 8.9	0 20.4	27 20.9
19	9 51 43.2	29 19.7	13 30.1	24 20.3	2 54.2	9 9.2	23 33.2	26 9.8	2 24.0	29 6.8	0 19.8	27 19.4
20	9 55 39.8	0♓20.2	13 26.9	8♊12.5	3 49.1	10 20.2	24 12.6	26 1.9	2 26.2	29 4.6	0 19.2	27 17.9
21	9 59 36.3	1 20.7	13 23.7	22 20.3	4 46.9	11 31.1	24 51.9	25 54.0	2 28.2	29 2.5	0 18.5	27 16.4
22	10 3 32.9	2 21.2	13 20.5	6♋43.1	5 47.5	12 41.9	25 31.3	25 46.2	2 30.2	29 .5	0 17.9	27 14.9
23	10 7 29.4	3 21.6	13 17.4	21 18.5	6 50.7	13 52.5	26 10.6	25 38.4	2 32.1	28 58.4	0 17.2	27 13.4
24	10 11 26.0	4 21.9	13 14.2	6♌ 1.9	7 56.2	15 3.1	26 50.0	25 30.6	2 33.9	28 56.4	0 16.4	27 11.9
25	10 15 22.5	5 22.3	13 11.0	20 46.7	9 3.9	16 13.5	27 29.4	25 22.9	2 35.6	28 54.5	0 15.7	27 10.5
26	10 19 19.1	6 22.7	13 7.8	5♍24.8	10 13.7	17 23.8	28 8.7	25 15.2	2 37.2	28 52.6	0 14.9	27 9.0
27	10 23 15.7	7 22.9	13 4.6	19 48.5	11 25.5	18 33.9	28 48.1	25 7.6	2 38.7	28 50.7	0 14.1	27 7.5
28	10 27 12.2	8 23.2	13 1.5	3♎51.2	12 39.1	19 43.9	29 27.4	25 .1	2 40.1	28 48.9	0 13.3	27 6.1
29	10 31 8.8	9 23.4	12 58.3	17 29.0	13 54.5	20 53.8	0♑ 6.8	24 52.6	2 41.3	28 47.0	0 12.4	27 4.6

LATITUDE

DAY	EPHEM. SID. TIME	☉	☊	☾	☿	♀	♂	♃	♄	♅	♆	♇
1	8 40 45.2	0 .0	0 .0	4 S 40.4	3 N 35.0	1 S 8.8	0 N 16.7	1 N 7.7	2 N 1.7	0 N 35.6	1 N 44.5	10 N 56.7
4	8 52 34.9	0 .0	0 .0	2 23.2	3 18.8	1 1.1	0 14.4	1 8.2	2 2.2	0 35.6	1 44.7	10 57.2
7	9 4 24.6	0 .0	0 .0	0 N 42.7	2 50.7	0 52.7	0 12.1	1 8.6	2 2.6	0 35.6	1 44.9	10 57.6
10	9 16 14.2	0 .0	0 .0	3 30.2	2 16.8	0 43.7	0 9.7	1 9.0	2 3.1	0 35.5	1 45.1	10 58.0
13	9 28 3.9	0 .0	0 .0	4 58.3	1 40.9	0 34.1	0 7.3	1 9.4	2 3.6	0 35.5	1 45.2	10 58.3
16	9 39 53.6	0 .0	0 .0	4 22.1	1 5.5	0 23.9	0 4.7	1 9.7	2 4.1	0 35.5	1 45.4	10 58.6
19	9 51 43.2	0 .0	0 .0	1 42.3	0 31.8	0 13.3	0 2.1	1 9.9	2 4.6	0 35.5	1 45.6	10 58.8
22	10 3 32.9	0 .0	0 .0	1 S 57.3	0 .6	0 2.1	0 S .7	1 10.1	2 5.1	0 35.4	1 45.7	10 59.0
25	10 15 22.5	0 .0	0 .0	4 37.4	0 S 27.8	0 N 9.5	0 3.5	1 10.3	2 5.6	0 35.4	1 45.9	10 59.1
28	10 27 12.2	0 .0	0 .0	4 41.3	0 53.2	0 21.5	0 6.4	1 10.4	2 6.1	0 35.4	1 46.1	10 59.2

RIGHT ASCENSION

DAY	EPHEM. SID. TIME	☉	☊	☾	☿	♀	♂	♃	♄	♅	♆	♇
1	8 40 45.2	13♒33.8	13♐ 7.9	6♎59.8	2♒47.8	19♓ .9	10♐15.4	1♍ 2.6	29♏47.8	2♌ 8.1	28♎55.8	4♍ .4
2	8 44 41.8	14 35.1	13 4.5	19 30.7	1 R 50.7	20 7.1	10 57.4	0 R 55.7	29 51.8	2 R 5.5	28 55.8	3 R 59.1
3	8 48 38.4	15 36.2	13 1.1	2♏ 2.1	1 1.7	21 13.1	11 39.4	0 48.6	29 55.6	2 2.8	28 55.8	3 57.7
4	8 52 34.9	16 37.1	12 57.7	14 39.1	0 21.4	22 19.0	12 21.6	0 41.5	29 59.5	2 .2	28 R 55.7	3 56.4
5	8 56 31.5	17 37.8	12 54.2	27 23.2	29♑49.8	23 24.6	13 3.8	0 34.3	0♐ 3.2	1 57.6	28 55.7	3 55.0
6	9 0 28.0	18 38.3	12 50.8	10♐12.3	29 27.2	24 30.1	13 46.0	0 27.0	0 6.8	1 55.0	28 55.5	3 53.7
7	9 4 24.6	19 38.6	12 47.4	23 1.2	29 13.2	25 35.4	14 28.2	0 19.7	0 10.4	1 52.4	28 55.4	3 52.3
8	9 8 21.1	20 38.7	12 44.0	5♑43.5	29 7.5	26 40.5	15 10.6	0 12.3	0 13.8	1 49.9	28 55.2	3 50.9
9	9 12 17.7	21 38.6	12 40.6	18 13.4	29 D 9.8	27 45.5	15 52.9	0 4.9	0 17.1	1 47.3	28 55.0	3 49.4
10	9 16 14.2	22 38.3	12 37.2	0♒27.1	29 19.5	28 50.4	16 35.4	29♌57.4	0 20.4	1 44.8	28 54.7	3 48.0
11	9 20 10.8	23 37.8	12 33.8	12 24.4	29 36.3	29 55.2	17 17.8	29 49.8	0 23.6	1 42.3	28 54.4	3 46.6
12	9 24 7.3	24 37.1	12 30.3	24 8.2	29 59.4	0♈59.8	18 .3	29 42.3	0 26.6	1 39.8	28 54.1	3 45.2
13	9 28 3.9	25 36.2	12 26.9	5♓44.5	0♒28.6	2 4.3	18 42.9	29 34.7	0 29.6	1 37.4	28 53.8	3 43.7
14	9 32 .5	26 35.1	12 23.5	17 21.6	1 3.2	3 8.8	19 25.4	29 27.1	0 32.5	1 35.0	28 53.4	3 42.3
15	9 35 57.0	27 33.9	12 20.1	29 9.3	1 42.9	4 13.1	20 8.1	29 19.4	0 35.2	1 32.6	28 53.0	3 40.8
16	9 39 53.6	28 32.4	12 16.7	11♈18.7	2 27.1	5 17.4	20 50.7	29 11.8	0 37.9	1 30.2	28 52.6	3 39.4
17	9 43 50.1	29 30.8	12 13.3	24 .4	3 15.6	6 21.6	21 33.4	29 4.1	0 40.5	1 27.9	28 52.1	3 37.9
18	9 47 46.7	0♓28.9	12 9.9	7♉23.2	4 8.0	7 25.7	22 16.1	28 56.5	0 43.0	1 25.6	28 51.6	3 36.5
19	9 51 43.2	1 26.9	12 6.5	21 31.5	5 3.8	8 29.7	22 58.8	28 48.9	0 45.3	1 23.3	28 51.1	3 35.0
20	9 55 39.8	2 24.8	12 3.0	6♊21.9	6 2.9	9 33.7	23 41.6	28 41.2	0 47.6	1 21.1	28 50.5	3 33.5
21	9 59 36.3	3 22.4	11 59.6	21 42.2	7 4.9	10 37.7	24 24.4	28 33.6	0 49.8	1 18.9	28 49.9	3 32.1
22	10 3 32.9	4 19.9	11 56.2	7♋12.6	8 9.7	11 41.6	25 7.2	28 26.0	0 51.9	1 16.7	28 49.3	3 30.6
23	10 7 29.4	5 17.2	11 52.8	22 31.8	9 16.8	12 45.5	25 50.0	28 18.5	0 53.9	1 14.6	28 48.6	3 29.2
24	10 11 26.0	6 14.3	11 49.4	7♌23.6	10 26.2	13 49.3	26 32.8	28 11.0	0 55.7	1 12.5	28 48.0	3 27.7
25	10 15 22.5	7 11.4	11 46.0	21 40.7	11 37.7	14 53.2	27 15.8	28 3.5	0 57.6	1 10.4	28 47.3	3 26.3
26	10 19 19.1	8 8.2	11 42.6	5♍24.2	12 51.1	15 57.0	27 58.6	27 56.1	0 59.2	1 8.4	28 46.6	3 24.8
27	10 23 15.7	9 4.9	11 39.2	18 40.9	14 6.1	17 .9	28 41.5	27 48.7	1 .8	1 6.4	28 45.8	3 23.4
28	10 27 12.2	10 1.5	11 35.8	1♎40.0	15 22.8	18 4.7	29 24.4	27 41.4	1 2.3	1 4.5	28 45.0	3 21.9
29	10 31 8.8	10 57.9	11 32.4	14 30.6	16 40.9	19 8.5	0♑ 7.4	27 34.1	1 3.6	1 2.6	28 44.2	3 20.5

DECLINATION

DAY	EPHEM. SID. TIME	☉	☊	☾	☿	♀	♂	♃	♄	♅	♆	♇
1	8 40 45.2	17 S 26.7	0 S 23.6	8 S 6.7	16 S 21.6	5 S 58.2	21 S 55.4	13 N 3.7	18 S 28.5	20 N 46.2	9 S 59.4	22 N 29.5
4	8 52 34.9	16 35.2	0 23.6	19 26.3	17 8.0	4 25.6	22 12.7	13 11.8	18 30.3	20 47.8	9 59.1	22 31.5
7	9 4 24.6	15 41.1	0 23.6	22 34.6	17 49.8	2 52.0	22 28.4	13 20.1	18 31.9	20 49.4	9 58.8	22 33.4
10	9 16 14.2	14 44.6	0 23.5	16 55.3	18 23.2	1 17.8	22 42.5	13 28.5	18 33.3	20 50.9	9 58.4	22 35.4
13	9 28 3.9	13 45.9	0 23.5	4 46.0	18 46.6	0 N 16.7	22 55.0	13 37.0	18 34.6	20 52.4	9 57.8	22 37.3
16	9 39 53.6	12 45.2	0 23.5	9 N 36.4	18 59.0	1 51.3	23 5.9	13 45.4	18 35.7	20 53.8	9 57.2	22 39.1
19	9 51 43.2	11 42.6	0 23.5	20 30.7	18 59.9	3 25.5	23 15.2	13 53.7	18 36.6	20 55.1	9 56.5	22 40.9
22	10 3 32.9	10 38.3	0 23.5	21 19.3	18 49.1	4 59.1	23 22.8	14 2.0	18 37.3	20 56.4	9 55.7	22 42.7
25	10 15 22.5	9 32.6	0 23.4	10 11.1	18 26.4	6 31.7	23 28.7	14 10.0	18 37.8	20 57.6	9 54.8	22 44.4
28	10 27 12.2	8 25.6	0 23.4	5 S 50.0	17 51.9	8 3.1	23 33.0	14 17.8	18 38.2	20 58.7	9 53.8	22 46.0

MARCH 1956

LONGITUDE

DAY	EPHEM. SID. TIME h m s	☉ ° ′	☊ ° ′	☾ ° ′	☿ ° ′	♀ ° ′	♂ ° ′	♃ ° ′	♄ ° ′	♅ ° ′	♆ ° ′	♇ ° ′
1	10 35 5.3	10♓23.6	12♐55.1	0♏40.4	15♒11.5	22♈ 3.5	0♑46.1	24♌45.1	2♐42.5	28♋45.3	0♏11.5	27♌ 3.1
2	10 39 1.9	11 23.8	12 51.9	13 26.7	16 30.1	23 13.1	1 25.4	24 R 37.8	2 43.6	28 R 43.5	0 R 10.6	27 R 1.7
3	10 42 58.4	12 24.0	12 48.8	25 51.0	17 50.2	24 22.5	2 4.8	24 30.5	2 44.6	28 41.9	0 9.6	27 .3
4	10 46 55.0	13 24.1	12 45.6	7♐58.0	19 11.8	25 31.8	2 44.1	24 23.4	2 45.4	28 40.2	0 8.6	26 58.8
5	10 50 51.5	14 24.2	12 42.4	19 53.1	20 34.8	26 40.9	3 23.4	24 16.3	2 46.2	28 38.6	0 7.6	26 57.4
6	10 54 48.1	15 24.3	12 39.2	1♑41.7	21 59.2	27 49.9	4 2.7	24 9.3	2 46.9	28 37.0	0 6.6	26 56.0
7	10 58 44.6	16 24.3	12 36.0	13 29.4	23 24.9	28 58.7	4 42.0	24 2.4	2 47.5	28 35.5	0 5.5	26 54.6
8	11 2 41.2	17 24.4	12 32.9	25 21.3	24 51.9	0♉ 7.4	5 21.3	23 55.6	2 47.9	28 34.0	0 4.4	26 53.2
9	11 6 37.7	18 24.4	12 29.7	7♒21.4	26 20.2	1 15.9	6 .6	23 48.9	2 48.3	28 32.6	0 3.3	26 51.8
10	11 10 34.3	19 24.3	12 26.5	19 33.3	27 49.8	2 24.2	6 39.9	23 42.4	2 48.6	28 31.2	0 2.2	26 50.4
11	11 14 30.8	20 24.3	12 23.3	1♓59.1	29 20.6	3 32.4	7 19.1	23 35.9	2 48.7	28 29.9	0 1.0	26 49.1
12	11 18 27.4	21 24.2	12 20.2	14 39.6	0♓52.7	4 40.4	7 58.4	23 29.6	2 48.8	28 28.6	29♎59.9	26 47.7
13	11 22 23.9	22 24.0	12 17.0	27 34.9	2 25.9	5 48.1	8 37.6	23 23.4	2 R 48.7	28 27.4	29 58.6	26 46.4
14	11 26 20.5	23 23.9	12 13.8	10♈43.9	4 .4	6 55.8	9 16.8	23 17.4	2 48.6	28 26.2	29 57.4	26 45.1
15	11 30 17.1	24 23.7	12 10.6	24 4.8	5 36.1	8 3.2	9 56.0	23 11.5	2 48.4	28 25.0	29 56.2	26 43.8
16	11 34 13.6	25 23.5	12 7.4	7♉36.1	7 13.0	9 10.4	10 35.2	23 5.7	2 48.0	28 23.9	29 54.9	26 42.5
17	11 38 10.2	26 23.2	12 4.3	21 16.4	8 51.2	10 17.5	11 14.4	23 .1	2 47.6	28 22.9	29 53.7	26 41.3
18	11 42 6.7	27 22.9	12 1.1	5♊ 4.6	10 30.5	11 24.3	11 53.6	22 54.6	2 47.1	28 22.0	29 52.3	26 40.0
19	11 46 3.3	28 22.6	11 57.9	19 .4	12 11.1	12 30.8	12 32.7	22 49.3	2 46.4	28 21.0	29 51.0	26 38.8
20	11 49 59.8	29 22.2	11 54.7	3♋ 3.4	13 52.9	13 37.2	13 11.8	22 44.1	2 45.7	28 20.1	29 49.7	26 37.6
21	11 53 56.4	0♈21.8	11 51.5	17 13.2	15 36.0	14 43.3	13 50.9	22 39.1	2 44.8	28 19.3	29 48.3	26 36.4
22	11 57 52.9	1 21.3	11 48.4	1♌28.5	17 20.3	15 49.2	14 30.0	22 34.2	2 43.9	28 18.5	29 46.9	26 35.2
23	12 1 49.5	2 20.8	11 45.2	15 46.7	19 5.9	16 54.9	15 9.0	22 29.5	2 42.8	28 17.7	29 45.5	26 34.0
24	12 5 46.0	3 20.3	11 42.0	0♍ 3.9	20 52.8	18 .3	15 48.1	22 24.9	2 41.7	28 17.1	29 44.1	26 32.9
25	12 9 42.6	4 19.7	11 38.8	14 15.4	22 41.0	19 5.4	16 27.1	22 20.6	2 40.4	28 16.4	29 42.7	26 31.7
26	12 13 39.1	5 19.1	11 35.7	28 15.9	24 30.6	20 10.3	17 6.1	22 16.4	2 39.1	28 15.8	29 41.2	26 30.6
27	12 17 35.7	6 18.5	11 32.5	12♎ .5	26 21.4	21 14.9	17 45.1	22 12.3	2 37.7	28 15.3	29 39.7	26 29.5
28	12 21 32.2	7 17.8	11 29.3	25 25.8	28 13.6	22 19.2	18 24.1	22 8.5	2 36.2	28 14.8	29 38.3	26 28.5
29	12 25 28.8	8 17.1	11 26.1	8♏30.0	0♈ 7.1	23 23.2	19 3.0	22 4.8	2 34.5	28 14.4	29 36.8	26 27.4
30	12 29 25.3	9 16.4	11 22.9	21 13.2	2 1.9	24 27.0	19 41.9	22 1.2	2 32.8	28 14.0	29 35.3	26 26.4
31	12 33 21.9	10 15.6	11 19.8	3♐37.2	3 58.0	25 30.5	20 20.9	21 57.9	2 31.0	28 13.7	29 33.7	26 25.4

LATITUDE

DAY	EPHEM. SID. TIME h m s	☉ ° ′	☊ ° ′	☾ ° ′	☿ ° ′	♀ ° ′	♂ ° ′	♃ ° ′	♄ ° ′	♅ ° ′	♆ ° ′	♇ ° ′
1	10 35 5.3	0 .0	0 .0	3S22.5	1S 8.3	0N29.7	0S 8.4	1N10.5	2N 6.4	0N35.3	1N46.2	10N59.2
4	10 46 55.0	0 .0	0 .0	0 24.7	1 28.4	0 42.2	0 11.5	1 10.5	2 6.9	0 35.3	1 46.3	10 59.1
7	10 58 44.6	0 .0	0 .0	2N35.6	1 45.1	0 54.9	0 14.6	1 10.5	2 7.4	0 35.2	1 46.5	10 59.1
10	11 10 34.3	0 .0	0 .0	4 37.7	1 58.3	1 7.9	0 17.9	1 10.5	2 7.9	0 35.2	1 46.6	10 58.9
13	11 22 23.9	0 .0	0 .0	4 48.9	2 8.0	1 20.9	0 21.3	1 10.4	2 8.4	0 35.1	1 46.7	10 58.8
16	11 34 13.6	0 .0	0 .0	2 47.0	2 14.0	1 33.9	0 24.8	1 10.3	2 8.9	0 35.1	1 46.8	10 58.5
19	11 46 3.3	0 .0	0 .0	0S42.5	2 16.0	1 47.0	0 28.4	1 10.1	2 9.4	0 35.0	1 47.0	10 58.3
22	11 57 52.9	0 .0	0 .0	3 54.5	2 14.0	1 59.9	0 32.1	1 9.9	2 9.9	0 34.9	1 47.1	10 57.9
25	12 9 42.6	0 .0	0 .0	5 2.1	2 7.6	2 12.7	0 35.9	1 9.7	2 10.4	0 34.9	1 47.1	10 57.6
28	12 21 32.2	0 .0	0 .0	3 33.6	1 56.8	2 25.2	0 39.8	1 9.5	2 10.8	0 34.8	1 47.2	10 57.2
31	12 33 21.9	0 .0	0 .0	0 33.0	1 41.4	2 37.4	0 43.9	1 9.2	2 11.2	0 34.7	1 47.3	10 56.7

RIGHT ASCENSION

DAY	EPHEM. SID. TIME h m s	☉ ° ′	☊ ° ′	☾ ° ′	☿ ° ′	♀ ° ′	♂ ° ′	♃ ° ′	♄ ° ′	♅ ° ′	♆ ° ′	♇ ° ′
1	10 35 5.3	11♓54.2	11♐28.9	27♎20.0	18♒ .4	20♈12.4	0♑50.3	27♌26.9	1♐ 4.9	1♌ .7	28♎43.4	3♍19.0
2	10 39 1.9	12 50.3	11 25.5	10♏12.6	19 21.1	21 16.3	1 33.2	27 R 19.8	1 6.0	0 R 58.9	28 R 42.5	3 R 17.6
3	10 42 58.4	13 46.4	11 22.1	23 9.2	20 43.0	22 20.2	2 16.2	27 12.7	1 7.1	0 57.1	28 41.6	3 16.2
4	10 46 55.0	14 42.3	11 18.7	6♐ 7.6	22 6.0	23 24.1	2 59.1	27 5.7	1 8.0	0 55.4	28 40.7	3 14.7
5	10 50 51.5	15 38.1	11 15.3	19 2.9	23 29.9	24 28.1	3 42.0	26 58.8	1 8.9	0 53.7	28 39.8	3 13.3
6	10 54 48.1	16 33.9	11 11.9	1♑49.5	24 54.8	25 32.1	4 24.9	26 52.0	1 9.6	0 52.1	28 38.8	3 11.9
7	10 58 44.6	17 29.5	11 8.5	14 22.6	26 20.6	26 36.2	5 7.8	26 45.3	1 10.2	0 50.5	28 37.8	3 10.5
8	11 2 41.2	18 25.0	11 5.1	26 39.6	27 47.2	27 40.3	5 50.7	26 38.7	1 10.7	0 48.9	28 36.8	3 9.1
9	11 6 37.7	19 20.4	11 1.7	8♒40.9	29 14.6	28 44.5	6 33.6	26 32.2	1 11.1	0 47.4	28 35.8	3 7.7
10	11 10 34.3	20 15.8	10 58.3	20 29.9	0♓42.8	29 48.8	7 16.5	26 25.8	1 11.5	0 46.0	28 34.7	3 6.3
11	11 14 30.8	21 11.0	10 54.9	2♓12.6	2 11.6	0♉53.1	7 59.3	26 19.5	1 11.7	0 44.6	28 33.6	3 5.0
12	11 18 27.4	22 6.2	10 51.5	13 56.8	3 41.2	1 57.5	8 42.1	26 13.3	1 11.8	0 43.2	28 32.5	3 3.6
13	11 22 23.9	23 1.3	10 48.1	25 52.0	5 11.5	3 1.9	9 24.9	26 7.3	1 R 11.7	0 41.9	28 31.4	3 2.3
14	11 26 20.5	23 56.3	10 44.7	8♈ 7.9	6 42.4	4 6.4	10 7.7	26 1.3	1 11.6	0 40.7	28 30.2	3 .9
15	11 30 17.1	24 51.3	10 41.3	20 54.2	8 14.0	5 11.0	10 50.4	25 55.5	1 11.4	0 39.5	28 29.0	2 59.6
16	11 34 13.6	25 46.2	10 37.9	4♉18.0	9 46.2	6 15.6	11 33.1	25 49.9	1 11.1	0 38.3	28 27.8	2 58.3
17	11 38 10.2	26 41.1	10 34.4	18 22.1	11 19.1	7 20.4	12 15.7	25 44.4	1 10.7	0 37.3	28 26.7	2 57.1
18	11 42 6.7	27 35.9	10 31.0	3♊ 2.2	12 52.7	8 25.1	12 58.3	25 39.0	1 10.2	0 36.2	28 25.4	2 55.8
19	11 46 3.3	28 30.6	10 27.6	18 6.4	14 26.9	9 29.9	13 40.9	25 33.8	1 9.5	0 35.2	28 24.2	2 54.5
20	11 49 59.8	29 25.3	10 24.2	3♋17.0	16 1.9	10 34.8	14 23.4	25 28.7	1 8.8	0 34.3	28 22.9	2 53.2
21	11 53 56.4	0♈20.0	10 20.8	18 15.7	17 37.5	11 39.7	15 5.9	25 23.8	1 7.9	0 33.4	28 21.6	2 52.0
22	11 57 52.9	1 14.6	10 17.4	2♌49.0	19 13.8	12 44.6	15 48.3	25 19.0	1 7.0	0 32.6	28 20.3	2 50.8
23	12 1 49.5	2 9.2	10 14.0	16 51.2	20 50.9	13 49.6	16 30.7	25 14.4	1 5.9	0 31.8	28 19.0	2 49.6
24	12 5 46.0	3 3.8	10 10.6	0♍23.8	22 28.8	14 54.6	17 13.0	25 9.9	1 4.8	0 31.1	28 17.7	2 48.4
25	12 9 42.6	3 58.4	10 7.2	13 33.7	24 7.5	15 59.6	17 55.3	25 5.6	1 3.5	0 30.4	28 16.3	2 47.2
26	12 13 39.1	4 52.9	10 3.8	26 29.7	25 47.1	17 4.7	18 37.5	25 1.4	1 2.2	0 29.8	28 15.0	2 46.1
27	12 17 35.7	5 47.5	10 .4	9♎20.8	27 27.5	18 9.7	19 19.6	24 57.4	1 .7	0 29.2	28 13.6	2 44.9
28	12 21 32.2	6 42.0	9 57.0	22 14.2	29 8.8	19 14.8	20 1.7	24 53.6	0 59.2	0 28.7	28 12.2	2 43.8
29	12 25 28.8	7 36.6	9 53.6	5♏13.9	0♈51.1	20 19.8	20 43.8	24 50.0	0 57.6	0 28.3	28 10.8	2 42.7
30	12 29 25.3	8 31.1	9 50.2	18 20.2	2 34.4	21 24.8	21 25.8	24 46.5	0 55.8	0 27.9	28 9.4	2 41.6
31	12 33 21.9	9 25.7	9 46.8	1♐29.6	4 18.7	22 29.8	22 7.7	24 43.2	0 54.0	0 27.5	28 7.9	2 40.6

DECLINATION

DAY	EPHEM. SID. TIME h m s	☉ ° ′	☊ ° ′	☾ ° ′	☿ ° ′	♀ ° ′	♂ ° ′	♃ ° ′	♄ ° ′	♅ ° ′	♆ ° ′	♇ ° ′
1	10 35 5.3	7S40.3	0S23.4	14S52.2	17S22.3	9N 3.1	23S34.9	14N22.9	18S38.3	20N59.4	9S53.0	22N47.0
4	10 46 55.0	6 31.5	0 23.4	22 2.9	16 28.1	10 31.7	23 36.4	14 30.2	18 38.4	21 .4	9 51.9	22 48.5
7	10 58 44.6	5 21.9	0 23.4	20 10.8	15 22.2	11 58.2	23 36.3	14 37.2	18 38.3	21 1.3	9 50.7	22 50.0
10	11 10 34.3	4 11.7	0 23.3	10 33.5	14 4.8	13 22.3	23 34.5	14 43.8	18 38.0	21 2.1	9 49.4	22 51.3
13	11 22 23.9	3 .9	0 23.3	3N27.4	12 36.1	14 43.8	23 31.0	14 50.0	18 37.5	21 2.9	9 48.0	22 52.6
16	11 34 13.6	1 49.9	0 23.3	16 40.8	10 56.1	16 2.3	23 26.0	14 55.7	18 36.9	21 3.5	9 46.6	22 53.8
19	11 46 3.3	0 38.7	0 23.3	22 17.0	9 5.2	17 17.6	23 19.4	15 1.0	18 36.1	21 4.0	9 45.2	22 54.8
22	11 57 52.9	0N32.4	0 23.3	16 1.3	7 3.5	18 29.4	23 11.2	15 5.7	18 35.2	21 4.5	9 43.6	22 55.8
25	12 9 42.6	1 43.3	0 23.2	1 32.9	4 51.5	19 37.4	23 1.5	15 10.0	18 34.1	21 4.8	9 42.0	22 56.7
28	12 21 32.2	2 53.8	0 23.2	13S 8.9	2 29.5	20 41.5	22 50.3	15 13.7	18 32.8	21 5.1	9 40.4	22 57.5
31	12 33 21.9	4 3.8	0 23.2	21 25.3	0N 1.6	21 41.3	22 37.6	15 16.9	18 31.4	21 5.2	9 38.8	22 58.2

APRIL 1956

LONGITUDE

DAY	EPHEM. SID. TIME	☉	☊	☽	☿	♀	♂	♃	♄	♅	♆	♇
	h m s	° ′	° ′	° ′	° ′	° ′	° ′	° ′	° ′	° ′	° ′	° ′
1	12 37 18.4	11♈14.8	11♐16.6	15♐45.5	5♈55.4	26♉33.6	20♑59.7	21♌54.7	2♐29.1	28♋13.5	29♎32.2	26♌24.4
2	12 41 15.0	12 14.0	11 13.4	27 42.5	7 54.1	27 36.4	21 38.6	21 R 51.7	2 R 27.2	28 R 13.3	29 R 30.7	26 R 23.4
3	12 45 11.5	13 13.1	11 10.2	9♑33.1	9 54.0	28 39.0	22 17.4	21 48.9	2 25.1	28 13.1	29 29.1	26 22.5
4	12 49 8.1	14 12.2	11 7.1	21 22.7	11 55.1	29 41.1	22 56.2	21 46.3	2 22.9	28 13.0	29 27.5	26 21.6
5	12 53 4.7	15 11.3	11 3.9	3♒16.6	13 57.3	0♊43.0	23 35.0	21 43.8	2 20.7	28 12.9	29 26.0	26 20.7
6	12 57 1.2	16 10.3	11 .7	15 19.6	16 .4	1 44.5	24 13.7	21 41.6	2 18.3	28 12.9	29 24.4	26 19.8
7	13 0 57.8	17 9.4	10 57.5	27 36.2	18 4.4	2 45.7	24 52.5	21 39.6	2 16.0	28 D 13.1	29 22.8	26 19.0
8	13 4 54.3	18 8.4	10 54.3	10♓ 9.3	20 9.2	3 46.5	25 31.2	21 37.7	2 13.4	28 13.2	29 21.2	26 18.2
9	13 8 50.9	19 7.4	10 51.2	23 1.1	22 14.4	4 46.9	26 9.8	21 36.0	2 10.9	28 13.3	29 19.6	26 17.4
10	13 12 47.4	20 6.3	10 48.0	6♈12.0	24 20.0	5 46.9	26 48.4	21 34.5	2 8.2	28 13.6	29 18.0	26 16.6
11	13 16 44.0	21 5.2	10 44.8	19 40.9	26 25.7	6 46.5	27 27.0	21 33.1	2 5.4	28 13.8	29 16.4	26 15.8
12	13 20 40.5	22 4.0	10 41.6	3♉25.4	28 31.3	7 45.7	28 5.5	21 32.0	2 2.6	28 14.2	29 14.8	26 15.1
13	13 24 37.1	23 2.9	10 38.5	17 22.3	0♉36.5	8 44.4	28 44.0	21 31.0	1 59.7	28 14.6	29 13.1	26 14.4
14	13 28 33.6	24 1.7	10 35.3	1♊27.8	2 40.9	9 42.7	29 22.4	21 30.3	1 56.7	28 15.0	29 11.5	26 13.7
15	13 32 30.2	25 .4	10 32.1	15 38.4	4 44.2	10 40.6	0♒ .8	21 29.7	1 53.6	28 15.5	29 9.9	26 13.1
16	13 36 26.7	25 59.1	10 28.9	29 51.0	6 46.2	11 38.0	0 39.1	21 29.3	1 50.5	28 16.0	29 8.2	26 12.5
17	13 40 23.3	26 57.8	10 25.7	14♋ 3.3	8 46.4	12 34.8	1 17.4	21 29.1	1 47.3	28 16.6	29 6.6	26 11.9
18	13 44 19.8	27 56.5	10 22.6	28 13.5	10 44.6	13 31.2	1 55.6	21 29.1	1 44.0	28 17.3	29 5.0	26 11.3
19	13 48 16.4	28 55.1	10 19.4	12♌19.8	12 40.4	14 27.0	2 33.8	21 D 29.3	1 40.7	28 18.0	29 3.3	26 10.8
20	13 52 12.9	29 53.6	10 16.2	26 20.8	14 33.4	15 22.2	3 11.9	21 29.7	1 37.2	28 18.8	29 1.7	26 10.2
21	13 56 9.5	0♉52.2	10 13.0	10♍14.5	16 23.5	16 16.9	3 50.0	21 30.2	1 33.8	28 19.6	29 .0	26 9.8
22	14 0 6.1	1 50.7	10 9.9	23 59.0	18 10.3	17 11.0	4 28.1	21 31.0	1 30.2	28 20.4	28 58.4	26 9.3
23	14 4 2.6	2 49.1	10 6.7	7♎31.9	19 53.7	18 4.5	5 6.1	21 31.9	1 26.6	28 21.3	28 56.7	26 8.9
24	14 7 59.2	3 47.5	10 3.5	20 51.2	21 33.3	18 57.3	5 44.0	21 33.0	1 23.0	28 22.3	28 55.1	26 8.5
25	14 11 55.7	4 45.9	10 .3	3♏55.3	23 9.0	19 49.5	6 21.9	21 34.3	1 19.3	28 23.3	28 53.5	26 8.1
26	14 15 52.3	5 44.3	9 57.1	16 43.4	24 40.7	20 41.0	6 59.7	21 35.8	1 15.5	28 24.4	28 51.8	26 7.7
27	14 19 48.8	6 42.6	9 54.0	29 15.6	26 8.1	21 31.8	7 37.5	21 37.4	1 11.7	28 25.5	28 50.2	26 7.4
28	14 23 45.4	7 41.0	9 50.8	11♐33.4	27 31.3	22 21.9	8 15.2	21 39.3	1 7.8	28 26.8	28 48.6	26 7.2
29	14 27 41.9	8 39.3	9 47.6	23 38.7	28 50.1	23 11.2	8 52.9	21 41.3	1 3.9	28 28.0	28 47.0	26 6.9
30	14 31 38.5	9 37.5	9 44.4	5♑35.0	0♊ 4.3	23 59.7	9 30.5	21 43.5	0 59.9	28 29.3	28 45.4	26 6.7

LATITUDE

DAY	EPHEM. SID. TIME	☉	☊	☽	☿	♀	♂	♃	♄	♅	♆	♇
1	12 37 18.4	0 .0	0 .0	0N31.9	1S35.2	2N41.3	0S45.3	1N 9.1	2N11.4	0N34.7	1N47.3	10N56.6
4	12 49 8.1	0 .0	0 .0	3 24.1	1 13.6	2 52.9	0 49.5	1 8.8	2 11.8	0 34.6	1 47.4	10 56.1
7	13 0 57.8	0 .0	0 .0	5 .0	0 47.7	3 4.0	0 53.8	1 8.5	2 12.2	0 34.6	1 47.5	10 55.6
10	13 12 47.4	0 .0	0 .0	4 33.7	0 18.1	3 14.5	0 58.3	1 8.1	2 12.5	0 34.5	1 47.5	10 55.0
13	13 24 37.1	0 .0	0 .0	1 53.5	0N14.2	3 24.2	1 3.0	1 7.8	2 12.8	0 34.4	1 47.5	10 54.4
16	13 36 26.7	0 .0	0 .0	1S51.4	0 47.4	3 33.1	1 7.7	1 7.4	2 13.1	0 34.4	1 47.6	10 53.8
19	13 48 16.4	0 .0	0 .0	4 38.0	1 19.5	3 41.0	1 12.6	1 7.1	2 13.4	0 34.3	1 47.6	10 53.2
22	14 0 6.1	0 .0	0 .0	4 59.6	1 48.3	3 48.0	1 17.7	1 6.7	2 13.6	0 34.2	1 47.6	10 52.6
25	14 11 55.7	0 .0	0 .0	2 56.8	2 12.0	3 53.7	1 22.8	1 6.3	2 13.8	0 34.1	1 47.6	10 51.9
28	14 23 45.4	0 .0	0 .0	0N17.7	2 29.0	3 58.2	1 28.1	1 5.9	2 14.0	0 34.1	1 47.6	10 51.2

RIGHT ASCENSION

DAY	EPHEM. SID. TIME	☉	☊	☽	☿	♀	♂	♃	♄	♅	♆	♇
1	12 37 18.4	10♈20.3	9♐43.4	14♐35.8	6♈ 4.0	23♉34.8	22♑49.5	24♌40.0	0♐52.1	0♌27.2	28♎ 6.5	2♍39.5
2	12 41 15.0	11 15.0	9 40.0	27 31.9	7 50.4	24 39.7	23 31.3	24 R 37.1	0 R 50.0	0 R 27.0	28 R 5.0	2 R 38.5
3	12 45 11.5	12 9.7	9 36.6	10♑11.9	9 37.8	25 44.5	24 13.0	24 34.3	0 47.9	0 26.8	28 3.5	2 37.5
4	12 49 8.1	13 4.4	9 33.2	22 32.9	11 26.4	26 49.3	24 54.6	24 31.7	0 45.7	0 26.7	28 2.1	2 36.5
5	12 53 4.7	13 59.1	9 29.8	4♒35.4	13 16.0	27 54.0	25 36.2	24 29.2	0 43.4	0 26.7	28 .6	2 35.6
6	12 57 1.2	14 53.9	9 26.4	16 23.4	15 6.7	28 58.6	26 17.6	24 27.0	0 41.0	0 26.7	27 59.1	2 34.6
7	13 0 57.8	15 48.8	9 23.1	28 3.6	16 58.4	0♊ 3.1	26 59.1	24 25.0	0 38.6	0 D 26.8	27 57.6	2 33.7
8	13 4 54.3	16 43.8	9 19.7	9♓44.9	18 51.0	1 7.4	27 40.4	24 23.1	0 36.0	0 26.9	27 56.1	2 32.9
9	13 8 50.9	17 38.7	9 16.3	21 37.6	20 44.5	2 11.6	28 21.6	24 21.4	0 33.4	0 27.1	27 54.6	2 32.0
10	13 12 47.4	18 33.8	9 12.9	3♈52.5	22 38.7	3 15.5	29 2.7	24 19.8	0 30.6	0 27.3	27 53.1	2 31.1
11	13 16 44.0	19 28.9	9 9.5	16 40.0	24 33.6	4 19.3	29 43.7	24 18.5	0 27.8	0 27.6	27 51.5	2 30.3
12	13 20 40.5	20 24.1	9 6.1	0♉ 8.3	26 28.9	5 22.9	0♒24.6	24 17.3	0 24.9	0 27.9	27 50.0	2 29.5
13	13 24 37.1	21 19.3	9 2.7	14 20.5	28 24.4	6 26.2	1 5.4	24 16.4	0 21.9	0 28.3	27 48.5	2 28.7
14	13 28 33.6	22 14.7	8 59.3	29 11.9	0♉19.9	7 29.2	1 46.1	24 15.6	0 18.8	0 28.8	27 46.9	2 28.0
15	13 32 30.2	23 10.1	8 55.9	14♊28.7	2 15.2	8 31.9	2 26.8	24 15.0	0 15.7	0 29.3	27 45.4	2 27.3
16	13 36 26.7	24 5.6	8 52.5	29 50.3	4 10.0	9 34.3	3 7.3	24 14.6	0 12.5	0 29.9	27 43.8	2 26.6
17	13 40 23.3	25 1.2	8 49.1	14♋55.9	6 4.0	10 36.3	3 47.7	24 14.3	0 9.2	0 30.5	27 42.3	2 25.9
18	13 44 19.8	25 56.9	8 45.7	29 30.3	7 56.8	11 38.0	4 28.0	24 14.3	0 5.8	0 31.2	27 40.7	2 25.2
19	13 48 16.4	26 52.6	8 42.3	13♌27.9	9 48.2	12 39.2	5 8.1	24 D 14.4	0 2.4	0 31.9	27 39.1	2 24.6
20	13 52 12.9	27 48.5	8 38.9	26 51.2	11 37.9	13 40.0	5 48.2	24 14.7	29♏58.9	0 32.7	27 37.6	2 24.0
21	13 56 9.5	28 44.5	8 35.5	9♍48.4	13 25.5	14 40.2	6 28.2	24 15.2	29 55.3	0 33.5	27 36.0	2 23.5
22	14 0 6.1	29 40.5	8 32.2	22 30.0	15 10.8	15 40.0	7 8.0	24 15.9	29 51.7	0 34.4	27 34.5	2 22.9
23	14 4 2.6	0♉36.7	8 28.8	5♎ 6.7	16 53.4	16 39.2	7 47.8	24 16.8	29 48.0	0 35.4	27 32.9	2 22.4
24	14 7 59.2	1 33.0	8 25.4	17 47.6	18 33.2	17 37.9	8 27.4	24 17.8	29 44.2	0 36.4	27 31.4	2 21.9
25	14 11 55.7	2 29.4	8 22.0	0♏38.3	20 9.8	18 35.9	9 6.9	24 19.0	29 40.4	0 37.5	27 29.8	2 21.4
26	14 15 52.3	3 25.9	8 18.6	13 40.6	21 43.0	19 33.2	9 46.3	24 20.4	29 36.6	0 38.6	27 28.3	2 21.0
27	14 19 48.8	4 22.6	8 15.2	26 51.5	23 12.6	20 29.9	10 25.6	24 22.0	29 32.6	0 39.8	27 26.7	2 20.6
28	14 23 45.4	5 19.4	8 11.8	10♐ 4.0	24 38.4	21 25.8	11 4.8	24 23.8	29 28.7	0 41.0	27 25.2	2 20.3
29	14 27 41.9	6 16.3	8 8.4	23 9.0	26 .2	22 21.0	11 43.8	24 25.7	29 24.7	0 42.3	27 23.7	2 19.9
30	14 31 38.5	7 13.4	8 5.0	5♑58.5	27 17.8	23 15.3	12 22.8	24 27.8	29 20.6	0 43.7	27 22.2	2 19.6

DECLINATION

DAY	EPHEM. SID. TIME	☉	☊	☽	☿	♀	♂	♃	♄	♅	♆	♇
1	12 37 18.4	4N27.0	0S23.2	22S 9.2	0N53.8	22N .2	22S33.0	15N17.8	18S30.9	21N 5.3	9S38.2	22N58.4
4	12 49 8.1	5 36.1	0 23.2	18 23.0	3 35.0	22 54.1	22 18.4	15 20.3	18 29.3	21 5.3	9 36.5	22 58.9
7	13 0 57.8	6 44.4	0 23.1	7 36.5	6 21.3	23 43.4	22 2.5	15 22.1	18 27.6	21 5.2	9 34.8	22 59.3
10	13 12 47.4	7 51.6	0 23.1	6N39.0	9 9.3	24 27.9	21 45.2	15 23.5	18 25.7	21 5.0	9 33.1	22 59.7
13	13 24 37.1	8 57.7	0 23.1	18 50.1	11 54.5	25 7.5	21 26.7	15 24.2	18 23.7	21 4.8	9 31.3	22 59.9
16	13 36 26.7	10 2.3	0 23.1	21 35.3	14 31.4	25 42.1	21 7.0	15 24.4	18 21.6	21 4.4	9 29.6	23 .0
19	13 48 16.4	11 5.5	0 23.0	12 39.2	16 54.4	26 11.8	20 46.2	15 24.1	18 19.4	21 3.9	9 27.8	23 .0
22	14 0 6.1	12 7.0	0 23.0	2S11.7	18 58.7	26 36.5	20 24.3	15 23.2	18 17.1	21 3.4	9 26.1	22 59.9
25	14 11 55.7	13 6.8	0 23.0	15 35.9	20 41.6	26 56.3	20 1.3	15 21.8	18 14.7	21 2.7	9 24.3	22 59.7
28	14 23 45.4	14 4.6	0 23.0	21 52.9	22 1.7	27 11.2	19 37.4	15 19.8	18 12.2	21 1.9	9 22.7	22 59.4

MAY 1956

LONGITUDE

DAY	EPHEM. SID. TIME h m s	☉ ° ′	☊ ° ′	☽ ° ′	☿ ° ′	♀ ° ′	♂ ° ′	♃ ° ′	♄ ° ′	♅ ° ′	♆ ° ′	♇ ° ′
1	14 35 35.0	10♉35.8	9♐41.3	17♑26.1	1♊13.9	24♊47.4	10♒ 8.0	21♌45.8	0♐55.9	28♋30.6	28♎43.8	26♌ 6.5
2	14 39 31.6	11 34.0	9 38.1	29 16.5	2 18.8	25 34.3	10 45.4	21 48.4	0 R 51.9	28 32.0	28 R 42.2	26 R 6.3
3	14 43 28.2	12 32.1	9 34.9	11♒11.1	3 19.0	26 20.3	11 22.8	21 51.1	0 47.7	28 33.4	28 40.6	26 6.1
4	14 47 24.7	13 30.3	9 31.7	23 14.5	4 14.3	27 5.4	12 .1	21 54.0	0 43.6	28 34.9	28 39.1	26 6.0
5	14 51 21.3	14 28.4	9 28.5	5♓31.7	5 4.8	27 49.6	12 37.3	21 57.0	0 39.4	28 36.4	28 37.5	26 5.9
6	14 55 17.8	15 26.5	9 25.4	18 6.5	5 50.3	28 32.8	13 14.5	22 .3	0 35.2	28 37.9	28 35.9	26 5.9
7	14 59 14.4	16 24.6	9 22.2	1♈ 2.2	6 30.8	29 15.0	13 51.5	22 3.7	0 30.9	28 39.6	28 34.4	26 5.8
8	15 3 10.9	17 22.7	9 19.0	14 20.6	7 6.2	29 56.2	14 28.5	22 7.2	0 26.7	28 41.2	28 32.8	26 5.8
9	15 7 7.5	18 20.7	9 15.8	28 1.6	7 36.6	0♋36.3	15 5.4	22 11.0	0 22.3	28 42.9	28 31.3	26 5.8
10	15 11 4.0	19 18.7	9 12.7	12♉ 3.5	8 1.8	1 15.3	15 42.2	22 14.9	0 18.0	28 44.7	28 29.8	26 D 5.9
11	15 15 .6	20 16.7	9 9.5	26 22.6	8 22.0	1 53.1	16 18.8	22 19.0	0 13.6	28 46.5	28 28.3	26 6.0
12	15 18 57.1	21 14.6	9 6.3	10♊53.7	8 37.0	2 29.6	16 55.4	22 23.2	0 9.3	28 48.4	28 26.8	26 6.1
13	15 22 53.7	22 12.6	9 3.1	25 30.9	8 46.9	3 5.0	17 31.9	22 27.6	0 4.8	28 50.3	28 25.3	26 6.2
14	15 26 50.3	23 10.5	8 60.0	10♋ 8.1	8 51.9	3 39.0	18 8.2	22 32.2	0 .4	28 52.2	28 23.9	26 6.4
15	15 30 46.8	24 8.3	8 56.8	24 40.0	8 51.9	4 11.6	18 44.5	22 36.9	29♏56.0	28 54.2	28 22.4	26 6.6
16	15 34 43.4	25 6.2	8 53.6	9♌ 2.2	8 R 47.2	4 42.8	19 20.6	22 41.8	29 51.5	28 56.3	28 21.0	26 6.8
17	15 38 39.9	26 4.0	8 50.4	23 11.9	8 37.8	5 12.5	19 56.7	22 46.8	29 47.1	28 58.3	28 19.6	26 7.1
18	15 42 36.5	27 1.8	8 47.2	7♍ 7.2	8 24.2	5 40.7	20 32.6	22 52.0	29 42.6	29 .5	28 18.2	26 7.4
19	15 46 33.0	27 59.6	8 44.1	20 47.3	8 6.5	6 7.3	21 8.4	22 57.4	29 38.2	29 2.7	28 16.9	26 7.7
20	15 50 29.6	28 57.3	8 40.9	4♎12.2	7 45.0	6 32.3	21 44.1	23 2.9	29 33.7	29 4.9	28 15.5	26 8.1
21	15 54 26.2	29 55.0	8 37.7	17 22.1	7 20.2	6 55.5	22 19.7	23 8.5	29 29.2	29 7.1	28 14.1	26 8.5
22	15 58 22.7	0♊52.7	8 34.5	0♏17.6	6 52.5	7 16.9	22 55.1	23 14.3	29 24.7	29 9.4	28 12.8	26 8.9
23	16 2 19.3	1 50.3	8 31.4	12 59.6	6 22.5	7 36.5	23 30.4	23 20.2	29 20.3	29 11.7	28 11.5	26 9.3
24	16 6 15.8	2 47.9	8 28.2	25 28.9	5 50.6	7 54.2	24 5.6	23 26.3	29 15.8	29 14.1	28 10.2	26 9.7
25	16 10 12.4	3 45.6	8 25.0	7♐46.6	5 17.4	8 10.0	24 40.6	23 32.5	29 11.3	29 16.5	28 9.0	26 10.2
26	16 14 8.9	4 43.1	8 21.8	19 54.2	4 43.4	8 23.7	25 15.5	23 38.9	29 6.9	29 19.0	28 7.7	26 10.7
27	16 18 5.5	5 40.7	8 18.7	1♑53.7	4 9.4	8 35.4	25 50.3	23 45.4	29 2.5	29 21.5	28 6.5	26 11.3
28	16 22 2.0	6 38.3	8 15.5	13 47.2	3 35.8	8 45.0	26 24.9	23 52.0	28 58.0	29 24.0	28 5.3	26 11.9
29	16 25 58.6	7 35.8	8 12.3	25 37.6	3 3.3	8 52.3	26 59.3	23 58.8	28 53.6	29 26.5	28 4.1	26 12.5
30	16 29 55.2	8 33.3	8 9.1	7♒28.3	2 32.4	8 57.5	27 33.6	24 5.7	28 49.2	29 29.1	28 2.9	26 13.1
31	16 33 51.7	9 30.8	8 5.9	19 23.0	2 3.6	9 .4	28 7.8	24 12.7	28 44.9	29 31.8	28 1.8	26 13.7

LATITUDE

DAY	EPHEM. SID. TIME	☉	☊	☽	☿	♀	♂	♃	♄	♅	♆	♇
1	14 35 35.0	0 .0	0 .0	3N18.4	2N38.0	4N 1.2	1S33.6	1N 5.5	2N14.1	0N34.0	1N47.5	10N50.5
4	14 47 24.7	0 .0	0 .0	5 3.7	2 38.2	4 2.6	1 39.2	1 5.1	2 14.2	0 33.9	1 47.5	10 49.8
7	14 59 14.4	0 .0	0 .0	4 50.4	2 29.1	4 2.2	1 45.0	1 4.8	2 14.3	0 33.9	1 47.5	10 49.1
10	15 11 4.0	0 .0	0 .0	2 19.2	2 10.1	3 59.7	1 51.0	1 4.4	2 14.3	0 33.8	1 47.4	10 48.3
13	15 22 53.7	0 .0	0 .0	1S34.6	1 41.2	3 55.1	1 57.1	1 4.0	2 14.3	0 33.7	1 47.3	10 47.6
16	15 34 43.4	0 .0	0 .0	4 36.7	1 3.1	3 48.1	2 3.3	1 3.6	2 14.2	0 33.7	1 47.3	10 46.9
19	15 46 33.0	0 .0	0 .0	5 9.2	0 17.1	3 38.4	2 9.7	1 3.3	2 14.1	0 33.6	1 47.2	10 46.1
22	15 58 22.7	0 .0	0 .0	3 14.8	0S34.0	3 25.7	2 16.3	1 2.9	2 14.0	0 33.5	1 47.1	10 45.4
25	16 10 12.4	0 .0	0 .0	0 1.9	1 26.5	3 9.7	2 23.0	1 2.6	2 13.8	0 33.5	1 47.0	10 44.7
28	16 22 2.0	0 .0	0 .0	3N 5.4	2 16.2	2 50.2	2 29.9	1 2.2	2 13.5	0 33.4	1 46.9	10 44.0
31	16 33 51.7	0 .0	0 .0	5 .7	2 59.3	2 26.9	2 37.0	1 1.9	2 13.3	0 33.4	1 46.8	10 43.3

RIGHT ASCENSION

DAY	EPHEM. SID. TIME	☉	☊	☽	☿	♀	♂	♃	♄	♅	♆	♇
1	14 35 35.0	8♉10.5	8♐ 1.7	18♑26.8	28♉31.1	24♊ 8.8	13♒ 1.5	24♌30.1	29♏16.5	0♌45.0	27♎20.7	2♍19.3
2	14 39 31.6	9 7.8	7 58.3	0♒32.9	29 39.8	25 1.4	13 40.2	24 32.6	29 R 12.3	0 46.5	27 R 19.1	2 R 19.0
3	14 43 28.2	10 5.3	7 54.9	12 19.7	0♊44.0	25 53.1	14 18.7	24 35.2	29 8.1	0 48.0	27 17.6	2 18.8
4	14 47 24.7	11 2.9	7 51.5	23 53.9	1 43.3	26 43.8	14 57.1	24 38.0	29 3.8	0 49.5	27 16.1	2 18.6
5	14 51 21.3	12 .6	7 48.1	5♓24.6	2 37.8	27 33.4	15 35.4	24 40.9	28 59.5	0 51.1	27 14.6	2 18.4
6	14 55 17.8	12 58.5	7 44.7	17 2.9	3 27.2	28 22.0	16 13.5	24 44.1	28 55.2	0 52.7	27 13.2	2 18.2
7	14 59 14.4	13 56.5	7 41.4	29 1.2	4 11.6	29 9.5	16 51.4	24 47.3	28 50.8	0 54.4	27 11.7	2 18.1
8	15 3 10.9	14 54.7	7 38.0	11♈32.1	4 50.7	29 55.7	17 29.2	24 50.8	28 46.4	0 56.2	27 10.2	2 18.0
9	15 7 7.5	15 53.0	7 34.6	24 46.8	5 24.6	0♋40.8	18 6.9	24 54.4	28 41.9	0 58.0	27 8.8	2 17.9
10	15 11 4.0	16 51.5	7 31.2	8♉52.3	5 53.1	1 24.6	18 44.4	24 58.2	28 37.5	0 59.8	27 7.3	2 17.9
11	15 15 .6	17 50.1	7 27.8	23 47.8	6 16.3	2 7.0	19 21.8	25 2.2	28 33.0	1 1.7	27 5.9	2 17.9
12	15 18 57.1	18 48.9	7 24.4	9♊21.3	6 34.2	2 48.1	19 59.0	25 6.3	28 28.5	1 3.6	27 4.5	2 17.9
13	15 22 53.7	19 47.7	7 21.1	25 10.3	6 46.7	3 27.7	20 36.0	25 10.5	28 23.9	1 5.6	27 3.1	2 17.9
14	15 26 50.3	20 46.8	7 17.7	10♋47.9	6 54.0	4 5.8	21 12.9	25 14.9	28 19.4	1 7.7	27 1.7	2 D 18.0
15	15 30 46.8	21 45.9	7 14.3	25 52.5	6 56.2	4 42.3	21 49.6	25 19.5	28 14.8	1 9.7	27 .3	2 18.1
16	15 34 43.4	22 45.3	7 10.9	10♌13.3	6 R 53.5	5 17.2	22 26.2	25 24.2	28 10.3	1 11.9	26 58.9	2 18.2
17	15 38 39.9	23 44.7	7 7.5	23 50.6	6 46.0	5 50.4	23 2.6	25 29.1	28 5.7	1 14.0	26 57.6	2 18.4
18	15 42 36.5	24 44.3	7 4.2	6♍52.5	6 34.0	6 21.8	23 38.8	25 34.2	28 1.1	1 16.3	26 56.3	2 18.6
19	15 46 33.0	25 44.0	7 .8	19 30.7	6 17.9	6 51.4	24 14.9	25 39.4	27 56.5	1 18.6	26 55.0	2 18.9
20	15 50 29.6	26 43.9	6 57.4	1♎57.9	5 57.9	7 19.1	24 50.8	25 44.7	27 51.9	1 20.9	26 53.7	2 19.1
21	15 54 26.2	27 43.9	6 54.0	14 25.1	5 34.6	7 44.7	25 26.5	25 50.2	27 47.3	1 23.2	26 52.4	2 19.4
22	15 58 22.7	28 44.0	6 50.6	27 .9	5 8.5	8 8.4	26 2.1	25 55.8	27 42.7	1 25.6	26 51.2	2 19.7
23	16 2 19.3	29 44.2	6 47.3	9♏49.6	4 40.0	8 29.9	26 37.5	26 1.5	27 38.1	1 28.1	26 49.9	2 20.0
24	16 6 15.8	0♊44.6	6 43.9	22 50.9	4 9.7	8 49.3	27 12.7	26 7.4	27 33.5	1 30.5	26 48.7	2 20.4
25	16 10 12.4	1 45.1	6 40.5	5♐59.4	3 38.1	9 6.4	27 47.7	26 13.4	27 28.9	1 33.1	26 47.5	2 20.8
26	16 14 8.9	2 45.7	6 37.1	19 6.3	3 6.0	9 21.3	28 22.6	26 19.6	27 24.3	1 35.6	26 46.3	2 21.2
27	16 18 5.5	3 46.4	6 33.7	2♑ 1.9	2 33.8	9 33.7	28 57.2	26 25.9	27 19.8	1 38.2	26 45.1	2 21.7
28	16 22 2.0	4 47.3	6 30.4	14 38.2	2 2.1	9 43.8	29 31.7	26 32.3	27 15.2	1 40.9	26 43.9	2 22.1
29	16 25 58.6	5 48.2	6 27.0	26 51.0	1 31.5	9 51.5	0♓ 6.0	26 38.9	27 10.7	1 43.5	26 42.8	2 22.6
30	16 29 55.2	6 49.3	6 23.6	8♒40.9	1 2.5	9 56.6	0 40.1	26 45.6	27 6.2	1 46.3	26 41.7	2 23.2
31	16 33 51.7	7 50.5	6 20.2	20 12.8	0 35.6	9 59.1	1 14.0	26 52.4	27 1.7	1 49.0	26 40.6	2 23.7

DECLINATION

DAY	EPHEM. SID. TIME	☉	☊	☽	☿	♀	♂	♃	♄	♅	♆	♇
1	14 35 35.0	15N .3	0S22.9	19S 1.6	22N59.2	27N21.5	19S12.7	15N17.3	18S 9.7	21N 1.1	9S21.0	22N59.0
4	14 47 24.7	15 53.8	0 22.9	8 59.2	23 35.3	27 27.2	18 47.1	15 14.3	18 7.1	21 .2	9 19.3	22 58.5
7	14 59 14.4	16 44.9	0 22.9	4N51.1	23 50.9	27 28.7	18 20.8	15 10.8	18 4.4	20 59.1	9 17.7	22 57.9
10	15 11 4.0	17 33.5	0 22.9	17 39.8	23 47.5	27 26.0	17 53.9	15 6.8	18 1.7	20 58.0	9 16.1	22 57.2
13	15 22 53.7	18 19.5	0 22.8	21 47.5	23 26.2	27 19.5	17 26.4	15 2.3	17 59.0	20 56.8	9 14.6	22 56.4
16	15 34 43.4	19 2.7	0 22.8	13 32.9	22 48.5	27 9.5	16 58.5	14 57.3	17 56.3	20 55.5	9 13.1	22 55.5
19	15 46 33.0	19 43.0	0 22.8	1S 5.2	21 56.7	26 56.3	16 30.1	14 51.8	17 53.6	20 54.1	9 11.7	22 54.5
22	15 58 22.7	20 20.3	0 22.8	14 36.9	20 54.3	26 40.0	16 1.5	14 45.9	17 50.9	20 52.7	9 10.4	22 53.4
25	16 10 12.4	20 54.4	0 22.7	21 38.6	19 46.1	26 20.9	15 32.7	14 39.6	17 48.2	20 51.1	9 9.1	22 52.2
28	16 22 2.0	21 25.3	0 22.7	19 39.4	18 38.8	25 59.1	15 3.8	14 32.8	17 45.6	20 49.5	9 7.9	22 51.0
31	16 33 51.7	21 52.9	0 22.7	10 14.7	17 38.9	25 34.8	14 34.8	14 25.6	17 43.0	20 47.8	9 6.7	22 49.7

JUNE 1956

LONGITUDE

DAY	EPHEM. SID. TIME	☉	☊	☽	☿	♀	♂	♃	♄	♅	♆	♇
	h m s	° ′	° ′	° ′	° ′	° ′	° ′	° ′	° ′	° ′	° ′	° ′
1	16 37 48.3	10♊28.3	8♐ 2.8	1♓25.9	1♊37.4	9♋ 1.0	28♒41.7	24♌19.9	28♏40.5	29♋34.5	28♎ .7	26♌14.4
2	16 41 44.8	11 25.8	7 59.6	13 41.5	1 R 14.2	8 R 59.2	29 15.5	24 27.2	28 R 36.2	29 37.2	27 R 59.6	26 15.1
3	16 45 41.4	12 23.3	7 56.4	26 14.0	0 54.4	8 55.1	29 49.1	24 34.6	28 31.9	29 39.9	27 58.5	26 15.9
4	16 49 37.9	13 20.7	7 53.2	9♈ 7.4	0 38.3	8 48.6	0♓22.6	24 42.1	28 27.7	29 42.7	27 57.5	26 16.6
5	16 53 34.5	14 18.2	7 50.1	22 24.7	0 26.1	8 39.7	0 55.8	24 49.8	28 23.4	29 45.5	27 56.5	26 17.4
6	16 57 31.1	15 15.6	7 46.9	6♉ 7.5	0 18.0	8 28.4	1 28.8	24 57.6	28 19.2	29 48.3	27 55.5	26 18.2
7	17 1 27.6	16 13.0	7 43.7	20 15.7	0 14.2	8 14.7	2 1.6	25 5.5	28 15.1	29 51.2	27 54.5	26 19.1
8	17 5 24.2	17 10.4	7 40.5	4♊46.5	0 D 14.9	7 58.6	2 34.2	25 13.6	28 10.9	29 54.1	27 53.5	26 19.9
9	17 9 20.7	18 7.9	7 37.4	19 34.9	0 20.1	7 40.3	3 6.7	25 21.8	28 6.9	29 57.1	27 52.7	26 20.9
10	17 13 17.3	19 5.2	7 34.2	4♋33.8	0 29.7	7 19.6	3 38.8	25 30.1	28 2.9	0♌ .1	27 51.8	26 21.8
11	17 17 13.8	20 2.6	7 31.0	19 34.6	0 43.9	6 56.8	4 10.7	25 38.5	27 58.9	0 3.1	27 50.9	26 22.8
12	17 21 10.4	20 60.0	7 27.8	4♌28.9	1 2.6	6 31.8	4 42.4	25 47.0	27 54.9	0 6.1	27 50.1	26 23.7
13	17 25 7.0	21 57.3	7 24.6	19 9.5	1 25.7	6 4.7	5 13.9	25 55.6	27 51.0	0 9.2	27 49.3	26 24.7
14	17 29 3.5	22 54.6	7 21.5	3♍31.1	1 53.3	5 35.8	5 45.1	26 4.3	27 47.2	0 12.3	27 48.5	26 25.8
15	17 33 .1	23 51.9	7 18.3	17 30.8	2 25.2	5 5.1	6 16.0	26 13.1	27 43.4	0 15.4	27 47.7	26 26.8
16	17 36 56.6	24 49.2	7 15.1	1♎ 7.8	3 1.4	4 32.9	6 46.7	26 22.1	27 39.7	0 18.5	27 47.0	26 27.9
17	17 40 53.2	25 46.5	7 11.9	14 23.1	3 41.9	3 59.2	7 17.1	26 31.1	27 36.0	0 21.7	27 46.3	26 29.0
18	17 44 49.7	26 43.8	7 8.8	27 18.9	4 26.5	3 24.2	7 47.3	26 40.3	27 32.4	0 24.9	27 45.6	26 30.1
19	17 48 46.3	27 41.0	7 5.6	9♏57.8	5 15.2	2 48.3	8 17.1	26 49.5	27 28.8	0 28.1	27 45.0	26 31.2
20	17 52 42.9	28 38.3	7 2.4	22 22.6	6 7.9	2 11.5	8 46.7	26 58.9	27 25.3	0 31.4	27 44.4	26 32.4
21	17 56 39.4	29 35.5	6 59.2	4♐36.1	7 4.6	1 34.2	9 16.1	27 8.3	27 21.9	0 34.6	27 43.8	26 33.6
22	18 0 36.0	0♋32.7	6 56.1	16 40.7	8 5.1	0 56.6	9 45.1	27 17.9	27 18.5	0 37.9	27 43.3	26 34.8
23	18 4 32.5	1 29.9	6 52.9	28 38.8	9 9.5	0 19.0	10 13.8	27 27.5	27 15.2	0 41.2	27 42.7	26 36.0
24	18 8 29.1	2 27.1	6 49.7	10♑32.3	10 17.6	29♊41.5	10 42.2	27 37.2	27 11.9	0 44.6	27 42.3	26 37.3
25	18 12 25.7	3 24.3	6 46.5	22 23.2	11 29.4	29 4.4	11 10.2	27 47.1	27 8.8	0 47.9	27 41.8	26 38.6
26	18 16 22.2	4 21.5	6 43.3	4♒13.6	12 44.9	28 27.9	11 38.0	27 57.0	27 5.6	0 51.3	27 41.4	26 39.9
27	18 20 18.8	5 18.7	6 40.2	16 5.8	14 4.1	27 52.4	12 5.4	28 7.0	27 2.6	0 54.7	27 41.0	26 41.2
28	18 24 15.3	6 15.9	6 37.0	28 2.5	15 26.8	27 18.0	12 32.4	28 17.1	26 59.7	0 58.1	27 40.6	26 42.5
29	18 28 11.9	7 13.1	6 33.8	10♓ 6.7	16 53.1	26 44.9	12 59.1	28 27.3	26 56.8	1 1.6	27 40.3	26 43.9
30	18 32 8.4	8 10.4	6 30.6	22 21.9	18 22.9	26 13.3	13 25.5	28 37.6	26 54.0	1 5.1	27 40.0	26 45.3

LATITUDE

DAY	EPHEM. SID. TIME	☉	☊	☽	☿	♀	♂	♃	♄	♅	♆	♇
1	16 37 48.3	0 .0	0 .0	5N15.3	3S11.6	2N18.3	2S39.4	1N 1.8	2N13.2	0N33.4	1N46.8	10N43.0
4	16 49 37.9	0 .0	0 .0	4 32.3	3 41.6	1 49.6	2 46.7	1 1.5	2 12.8	0 33.3	1 46.7	10 42.4
7	17 1 27.6	0 .0	0 .0	1 37.8	4 .4	1 17.1	2 54.2	1 1.2	2 12.5	0 33.3	1 46.5	10 41.7
10	17 13 17.3	0 .0	0 .0	2S21.1	4 8.3	0 40.8	3 1.8	1 .9	2 12.1	0 33.3	1 46.4	10 41.0
13	17 25 7.0	0 .0	0 .0	4 59.3	4 6.1	0 1.4	3 9.6	1 .6	2 11.7	0 33.2	1 46.3	10 40.4
16	17 36 56.6	0 .0	0 .0	4 51.2	3 55.3	0S40.1	3 17.6	1 .3	2 11.2	0 33.2	1 46.1	10 39.8
19	17 48 46.3	0 .0	0 .0	2 29.4	3 36.9	1 22.6	3 25.7	1 .1	2 10.7	0 33.2	1 46.0	10 39.2
22	18 0 36.0	0 .0	0 .0	0N46.8	3 12.4	2 4.7	3 34.0	0 59.8	2 10.2	0 33.1	1 45.8	10 38.6
25	18 12 25.7	0 .0	0 .0	3 39.6	2 42.9	2 44.7	3 42.4	0 59.6	2 9.6	0 33.1	1 45.7	10 38.1
28	18 24 15.3	0 .0	0 .0	5 8.4	2 9.6	3 21.3	3 50.9	0 59.4	2 9.0	0 33.1	1 45.5	10 37.6

RIGHT ASCENSION

DAY	EPHEM. SID. TIME	☉	☊	☽	☿	♀	♂	♃	♄	♅	♆	♇
1	16 37 48.3	8♊51.9	6♐16.9	1♓34.7	0♊11.2	9♋59.1	1♓47.7	26♌59.3	26♏57.2	1♌51.8	26♎39.5	2♍24.3
2	16 41 44.8	9 53.3	6 13.5	12 57.2	29♉49.8	9 R 56.5	2 21.2	27 6.4	26 R 52.8	1 54.6	26 R 38.5	2 24.9
3	16 45 41.4	10 54.8	6 10.1	24 32.7	29 R 31.6	9 51.2	2 54.5	27 13.5	26 48.4	1 57.5	26 37.5	2 25.6
4	16 49 37.9	11 56.4	6 6.8	6♈34.8	29 17.0	9 43.3	3 27.5	27 20.8	26 44.0	2 .4	26 36.5	2 26.2
5	16 53 34.5	12 58.1	6 3.4	19 16.8	29 6.2	9 32.7	4 .4	27 28.3	26 39.6	2 3.3	26 35.5	2 26.9
6	16 57 31.1	13 59.9	6 .0	2♉50.4	28 59.3	9 19.5	4 33.0	27 35.8	26 35.3	2 6.3	26 34.5	2 27.7
7	17 1 27.6	15 1.8	5 56.6	17 21.4	28 56.6	9 3.7	5 5.3	27 43.5	26 31.0	2 9.3	26 33.6	2 28.4
8	17 5 24.2	16 3.8	5 53.3	2♊45.5	28 D 58.0	8 45.4	5 37.5	27 51.2	26 26.8	2 12.3	26 32.7	2 29.2
9	17 9 20.7	17 5.8	5 49.9	18 45.4	29 3.9	8 24.5	6 9.4	27 59.2	26 22.6	2 15.5	26 31.8	2 30.0
10	17 13 17.3	18 7.9	5 46.5	4♋53.1	29 14.0	8 1.2	6 41.1	28 7.2	26 18.5	2 18.6	26 31.0	2 30.9
11	17 17 13.8	19 10.1	5 43.2	20 39.4	29 28.5	7 35.4	7 12.5	28 15.3	26 14.3	2 21.7	26 30.2	2 31.7
12	17 21 10.4	20 12.3	5 39.8	5♌44.2	29 47.3	7 7.5	7 43.6	28 23.5	26 10.3	2 24.9	26 29.3	2 32.6
13	17 25 7.0	21 14.5	5 36.4	20 .3	0♊10.5	6 37.4	8 14.5	28 31.8	26 6.3	2 28.0	26 28.6	2 33.5
14	17 29 3.5	22 16.8	5 33.0	3♍31.8	0 38.1	6 5.3	8 45.1	28 40.2	26 2.3	2 31.3	26 27.8	2 34.5
15	17 33 .1	23 19.1	5 29.7	16 29.4	1 10.0	5 31.4	9 15.5	28 48.7	25 58.4	2 34.5	26 27.1	2 35.4
16	17 36 56.6	24 21.4	5 26.3	29 6.1	1 46.1	4 55.8	9 45.6	28 57.4	25 54.5	2 37.8	26 26.4	2 36.4
17	17 40 53.2	25 23.8	5 22.9	11♎34.4	2 26.6	4 18.8	10 15.4	29 6.1	25 50.7	2 41.1	26 25.7	2 37.4
18	17 44 49.7	26 26.2	5 19.6	24 4.7	3 11.2	3 40.7	10 45.0	29 14.9	25 47.0	2 44.4	26 25.1	2 38.5
19	17 48 46.3	27 28.5	5 16.2	6♏43.9	4 .1	3 1.5	11 14.2	29 23.8	25 43.3	2 47.8	26 24.4	2 39.5
20	17 52 42.9	28 30.9	5 12.8	19 34.6	4 53.2	2 21.6	11 43.2	29 32.8	25 39.7	2 51.2	26 23.8	2 40.6
21	17 56 39.4	29 33.3	5 9.5	2♐34.4	5 50.4	1 41.3	12 11.9	29 41.9	25 36.1	2 54.6	26 23.3	2 41.7
22	18 0 36.0	0♋35.7	5 6.1	15 36.7	6 51.7	1 .8	12 40.3	29 51.1	25 32.7	2 58.0	26 22.7	2 42.9
23	18 4 32.5	1 38.0	5 2.7	28 37.7	7 57.3	0 20.3	13 8.4	0♍ .4	25 29.2	3 1.5	26 22.2	2 44.0
24	18 8 29.1	2 40.4	4 59.4	11♑13.5	9 6.9	29♊40.2	13 36.1	0 9.7	25 25.9	3 4.9	26 21.7	2 45.2
25	18 12 25.7	3 42.7	4 56.0	23 33.1	10 20.7	29 .6	14 3.6	0 19.2	25 22.6	3 8.4	26 21.3	2 46.4
26	18 16 22.2	4 45.0	4 52.7	5♒29.5	11 38.7	28 21.9	14 30.7	0 28.7	25 19.4	3 12.0	26 20.9	2 47.6
27	18 20 18.8	5 47.2	4 49.3	17 5.0	13 .8	27 44.2	14 57.5	0 38.3	25 16.2	3 15.5	26 20.5	2 48.9
28	18 24 15.3	6 49.4	4 45.9	28 25.6	14 27.0	27 7.8	15 23.9	0 48.0	25 13.2	3 19.0	26 20.1	2 50.1
29	18 28 11.9	7 51.6	4 42.6	9♓40.2	15 57.4	26 32.9	15 50.0	0 57.8	25 10.2	3 22.6	26 19.7	2 51.4
30	18 32 8.4	8 53.8	4 39.2	20 59.9	17 32.0	25 59.7	16 15.8	1 7.6	25 7.3	3 26.3	26 19.5	2 52.8

DECLINATION

DAY	EPHEM. SID. TIME	☉	☊	☽	☿	♀	♂	♃	♄	♅	♆	♇
1	16 37 48.3	22N 1.3	0S22.7	6S 3.1	17N21.7	25N26.2	14S25.2	14N23.1	17S42.1	20N47.3	9S 6.4	22N49.2
4	16 49 37.9	22 24.3	0 22.6	7N47.2	16 40.5	24 58.5	13 56.4	14 15.4	17 39.7	20 45.5	9 5.4	22 47.8
7	17 1 27.6	22 43.8	0 22.6	19 23.1	16 17.1	24 28.2	13 27.9	14 7.2	17 37.3	20 43.6	9 4.4	22 46.3
10	17 13 17.3	22 59.7	0 22.6	21 .8	16 12.6	23 55.2	12 59.7	13 58.7	17 35.0	20 41.7	9 3.6	22 44.7
13	17 25 7.0	23 12.0	0 22.6	10 20.1	16 25.9	23 19.7	12 32.0	13 49.8	17 32.8	20 39.8	9 2.8	22 43.1
16	17 36 56.6	23 20.5	0 22.5	4S54.1	16 55.1	22 41.8	12 4.9	13 40.5	17 30.7	20 37.7	9 2.1	22 41.4
19	17 48 46.3	23 25.4	0 22.5	17 10.0	17 37.4	22 2.2	11 38.5	13 30.9	17 28.7	20 35.6	9 1.6	22 39.7
22	18 0 36.0	23 26.6	0 22.5	21 60.0	18 29.7	21 21.8	11 12.9	13 20.9	17 26.9	20 33.5	9 1.1	22 37.9
25	18 12 25.7	23 24.0	0 22.5	17 58.3	19 28.5	20 41.8	10 48.2	13 10.6	17 25.3	20 31.3	9 .7	22 36.1
28	18 24 15.3	23 17.7	0 22.4	7 19.6	20 30.1	20 3.7	10 24.6	13 .0	17 23.8	20 29.1	9 .4	22 34.2

JULY 1956

LONGITUDE

DAY	EPHEM. SID. TIME (h m s)	☉	☊	☽	☿	♀	♂	♃	♄	♅	♆	♇
1	18 36 5.0	9♋7.6	6♐27.5	4♈52.0	19♊56.2	25♊43.4	13♓51.4	28♌47.9	26♏51.3	1♌8.5	27♎39.7	26♌46.8
2	18 40 1.6	10 4.8	6 24.3	17 41.0	21 32.8	25R15.2	14 16.9	28 58.4	26R48.6	1 12.0	27R39.5	26 48.2
3	18 43 58.1	11 2.0	6 21.1	0♉52.4	23 12.8	24 49.1	14 42.0	29 8.9	26 46.0	1 15.5	27 39.3	26 49.6
4	18 47 54.7	11 59.2	6 17.9	14 29.2	24 56.0	24 25.0	15 6.7	29 19.5	26 43.5	1 19.0	27 39.1	26 51.1
5	18 51 51.2	12 56.4	6 14.8	28 32.8	26 42.4	24 3.0	15 31.0	29 30.1	26 41.1	1 22.6	27 38.9	26 52.6
6	18 55 47.8	13 53.6	6 11.6	13♊2.4	28 31.8	23 43.3	15 54.8	29 40.9	26 38.8	1 26.1	27 38.8	26 54.1
7	18 59 44.3	14 50.8	6 8.4	27 54.5	0♋24.2	23 26.0	16 18.1	29 51.7	26 36.5	1 29.7	27 38.7	26 55.6
8	19 3 40.9	15 48.1	6 5.2	13♋2.4	2 19.3	23 10.9	16 41.0	0♍2.6	26 34.4	1 33.3	27 38.7	26 57.1
9	19 7 37.5	16 45.3	6 2.1	28 16.9	4 16.9	22 58.2	17 3.4	0 13.6	26 32.3	1 36.8	27 38.6	26 58.7
10	19 11 34.0	17 42.5	5 58.9	13♌27.6	6 16.9	22 47.9	17 25.4	0 24.6	26 30.3	1 40.4	27D38.7	27 .3
11	19 15 30.6	18 39.7	5 55.7	28 24.7	8 19.0	22 39.9	17 46.8	0 35.8	26 28.4	1 44.1	27 38.7	27 1.9
12	19 19 27.1	19 37.0	5 52.5	13♍.3	10 22.9	22 34.4	18 7.7	0 46.9	26 26.6	1 47.7	27 38.8	27 3.5
13	19 23 23.7	20 34.2	5 49.3	27 9.6	12 28.3	22 31.1	18 28.1	0 58.2	26 24.9	1 51.3	27 38.9	27 5.1
14	19 27 20.2	21 31.4	5 46.2	11♎51.0	14 35.0	22 30.2	18 47.9	1 9.5	26 23.3	1 54.9	27 39.0	27 6.7
15	19 31 16.8	22 28.7	5 43.0	24 5.6	16 42.6	22D30.2	19 7.2	1 20.9	26 21.7	1 58.6	27 39.2	27 8.4
16	19 35 13.4	23 25.9	5 39.8	6♏56.3	18 50.8	22 35.3	19 26.0	1 32.3	26 20.3	2 2.2	27 39.4	27 10.1
17	19 39 9.9	24 23.1	5 36.6	19 27.1	20 59.4	22 41.2	19 44.2	1 43.8	26 18.9	2 5.9	27 39.6	27 11.7
18	19 43 6.5	25 20.4	5 33.5	1♐42.2	23 8.0	22 49.2	20 1.8	1 55.4	26 17.7	2 9.6	27 39.9	27 13.4
19	19 47 3.0	26 17.6	5 30.3	13 45.9	25 16.3	22 59.4	20 18.8	2 7.0	26 16.5	2 13.2	27 40.2	27 15.2
20	19 50 59.6	27 14.8	5 27.1	25 42.1	27 24.2	23 11.6	20 35.3	2 18.7	26 15.4	2 16.9	27 40.5	27 16.9
21	19 54 56.1	28 12.1	5 23.9	7♑33.9	29 31.5	23 25.9	20 51.2	2 30.5	26 14.5	2 20.6	27 40.9	27 18.7
22	19 58 52.7	29 9.4	5 20.8	19 24.1	1♌37.8	23 42.2	21 6.4	2 42.3	26 13.6	2 24.3	27 41.3	27 20.4
23	20 2 49.3	0♌6.7	5 17.6	1♒14.7	3 43.0	24 .3	21 21.0	2 54.1	26 12.8	2 28.0	27 41.8	27 22.2
24	20 6 45.8	1 3.9	5 14.4	13 7.6	5 47.0	24 20.2	21 34.9	3 6.0	26 12.1	2 31.7	27 42.2	27 24.0
25	20 10 42.4	2 1.2	5 11.2	25 4.5	7 49.8	24 41.9	21 48.1	3 17.9	26 11.5	2 35.4	27 42.7	27 25.8
26	20 14 38.9	2 58.5	5 8.0	7♓8.0	9 51.1	25 5.4	22 .7	3 29.9	26 11.0	2 39.1	27 43.2	27 27.6
27	20 18 35.5	3 55.8	5 4.9	19 16.6	11 50.9	25 30.5	22 12.6	3 42.0	26 10.6	2 42.7	27 43.8	27 29.4
28	20 22 32.0	4 53.2	5 1.7	1♈36.1	13 49.2	25 57.3	22 23.8	3 54.1	26 10.3	2 46.4	27 44.4	27 31.2
29	20 26 28.6	5 50.5	4 58.5	14 8.1	15 46.0	26 25.5	22 34.2	4 6.2	26 10.1	2 50.1	27 45.0	27 33.0
30	20 30 25.1	6 47.9	4 55.3	26 55.7	17 41.1	26 55.3	22 44.0	4 18.4	26 9.9	2 53.8	27 45.7	27 34.9
31	20 34 21.7	7 45.3	4 52.2	10♉2.5	19 34.6	27 26.6	22 52.9	4 30.6	26 9.9	2 57.5	27 46.3	27 36.7

LATITUDE

DAY	EPHEM. SID. TIME	☉	☊	☽	☿	♀	♂	♃	♄	♅	♆	♇
1	18 36 5.0	0 .0	0 .0	4N38.6	1S33.7	3S53.6	3S59.6	0N59.2	2N 8.4	0N33.1	1N45.4	10N37.1
4	18 47 54.7	0 .0	0 .0	2 3.7	0 56.6	4 20.9	4 8.4	0 59.0	2 7.8	0 33.1	1 45.2	10 36.6
7	18 59 44.3	0 .0	0 .0	1S47.6	0 19.8	4 42.9	4 17.4	0 58.8	2 7.1	0 33.1	1 45.0	10 36.2
10	19 11 34.0	0 .0	0 .0	4 43.2	0N15.0	4 59.7	4 26.4	0 58.6	2 6.5	0 33.1	1 44.9	10 35.8
13	19 23 23.7	0 .0	0 .0	4 51.5	0 45.8	5 11.8	4 35.4	0 58.5	2 5.8	0 33.1	1 44.7	10 35.5
16	19 35 13.4	0 .0	0 .0	2 36.6	1 11.2	5 19.4	4 44.4	0 58.4	2 5.1	0 33.1	1 44.5	10 35.2
19	19 47 3.0	0 .0	0 .0	0N35.0	1 30.1	5 23.3	4 53.5	0 58.3	2 4.4	0 33.1	1 44.4	10 34.9
22	19 58 52.7	0 .0	0 .0	3 26.6	1 42.0	5 23.7	5 2.4	0 58.2	2 3.7	0 33.1	1 44.2	10 34.7
25	20 10 42.4	0 .0	0 .0	4 58.8	1 47.2	5 21.3	5 11.3	0 58.1	2 2.9	0 33.1	1 44.0	10 34.5
28	20 22 32.0	0 .0	0 .0	4 35.7	1 46.1	5 16.6	5 19.9	0 58.0	2 2.2	0 33.1	1 43.9	10 34.2
31	20 34 21.7	0 .0	0 .0	2 14.3	1 39.4	5 9.5	5 28.4	0 57.9	2 1.4	0 33.1	1 43.7	10 34.2

RIGHT ASCENSION

DAY	EPHEM. SID. TIME	☉	☊	☽	☿	♀	♂	♃	♄	♅	♆	♇
1	18 36 5.0	9♋55.9	4♐35.8	2♈37.0	19♊10.7	25♊28.4	16♓41.2	1♍17.6	25♏4.5	3♌29.9	26♎19.2	2♍54.1
2	18 40 1.6	10 57.9	4 32.5	14 45.0	20 53.5	24R59.0	17 6.1	1 27.6	25R 1.7	3 33.5	26R19.0	2 55.5
3	18 43 58.1	11 59.9	4 29.1	27 36.9	22 40.3	24 31.7	17 30.7	1 37.6	24 59.1	3 37.2	26 18.7	2 56.9
4	18 47 54.7	13 1.8	4 25.8	11♉22.9	24 31.2	24 6.7	17 54.9	1 47.8	24 56.5	3 40.8	26 18.5	2 58.2
5	18 51 51.2	14 3.6	4 22.4	26 6.6	26 25.8	23 43.9	18 18.7	1 58.0	24 53.9	3 44.5	26 18.4	2 59.7
6	18 55 47.8	15 5.3	4 19.0	11♊40.7	28 24.3	23 23.6	18 42.0	2 8.3	24 51.5	3 48.2	26 18.2	3 1.1
7	18 59 44.3	16 7.0	4 15.7	27 45.0	0♋25.0	23 5.6	19 4.9	2 18.6	24 49.2	3 51.9	26 18.1	3 2.6
8	19 3 40.9	17 8.5	4 12.3	13♋51.4	2 31.6	22 50.1	19 27.4	2 29.1	24 46.9	3 55.6	26 18.1	3 4.0
9	19 7 37.5	18 10.0	4 9.0	29 32.9	4 40.1	22 37.1	19 49.4	2 39.6	24 44.8	3 59.3	26 18.0	3 5.5
10	19 11 34.0	19 11.4	4 5.6	14♌32.9	6 51.3	22 26.6	20 10.9	2 50.1	24 42.7	4 3.1	26 18.0	3 7.0
11	19 15 30.6	20 12.6	4 2.2	28 47.4	9 4.9	22 18.5	20 32.0	3 .7	24 40.7	4 6.8	26 18.0	3 8.6
12	19 19 27.1	21 13.8	3 58.9	12♍22.1	11 20.6	22 12.9	20 52.6	3 11.4	24 38.8	4 10.6	26D18.1	3 10.1
13	19 23 23.7	22 14.8	3 55.5	25 27.7	13 37.9	22 9.7	21 12.7	3 22.1	24 37.0	4 14.4	26 18.2	3 11.7
14	19 27 20.2	23 15.7	3 52.2	8♎ 6.2	15 56.4	22 8.7	21 32.3	3 32.9	24 35.3	4 18.1	26 18.3	3 13.3
15	19 31 16.8	24 16.5	3 48.8	20 58.4	18 15.7	22D10.6	21 51.4	3 43.8	24 33.6	4 21.9	26 18.4	3 14.9
16	19 35 13.4	25 17.1	3 45.5	3♏42.5	20 35.2	22 14.5	22 10.0	3 54.7	24 32.1	4 25.7	26 18.6	3 16.5
17	19 39 9.9	26 17.6	3 42.1	16 32.7	22 54.7	22 20.8	22 28.0	4 5.6	24 30.7	4 29.5	26 18.8	3 18.1
18	19 43 6.5	27 18.0	3 38.8	29 29.2	25 13.6	22 29.2	22 45.5	4 16.7	24 29.3	4 33.3	26 19.0	3 19.8
19	19 47 3.0	28 18.3	3 35.4	12♐28.0	27 31.5	22 39.9	23 2.5	4 27.7	24 28.1	4 37.1	26 19.3	3 21.4
20	19 50 59.6	29 18.4	3 32.0	25 22.4	29 48.3	22 52.7	23 18.9	4 38.8	24 26.9	4 41.0	26 19.6	3 23.1
21	19 54 56.1	0♌18.4	3 28.7	8♑4.7	2♌3.5	23 7.7	23 34.7	4 50.0	24 25.9	4 44.8	26 20.0	3 24.9
22	19 58 52.7	1 18.2	3 25.3	20 28.9	4 16.8	23 24.6	23 50.0	5 1.2	24 25.0	4 48.6	26 20.3	3 26.6
23	20 2 49.3	2 17.9	3 22.0	2♒31.9	6 28.1	23 43.5	24 4.6	5 12.5	24 24.1	4 52.5	26 20.7	3 28.3
24	20 6 45.8	3 17.4	3 18.6	14 14.3	8 37.2	24 4.3	24 18.7	5 23.8	24 23.3	4 56.3	26 21.1	3 30.0
25	20 10 42.4	4 16.8	3 15.3	25 40.2	10 43.9	24 27.0	24 32.1	5 35.1	24 22.7	5 .1	26 21.6	3 31.8
26	20 14 38.9	5 16.0	3 11.9	6♓56.5	12 48.3	24 51.5	24 44.9	5 46.5	24 22.1	5 3.9	26 22.0	3 33.5
27	20 18 35.5	6 15.1	3 8.6	18 12.3	14 50.1	25 17.7	24 57.0	5 57.9	24 21.6	5 7.8	26 22.5	3 35.3
28	20 22 32.0	7 14.1	3 5.2	29 38.2	16 49.4	25 45.7	25 8.4	6 9.4	24 21.2	5 11.6	26 23.1	3 37.1
29	20 26 28.6	8 12.9	3 1.9	11♈26.1	18 46.2	26 15.2	25 19.2	6 20.9	24 20.9	5 15.4	26 23.6	3 38.9
30	20 30 25.1	9 11.5	2 58.5	23 52.4	20 40.4	26 46.4	25 29.3	6 32.4	24 20.7	5 19.2	26 24.2	3 40.7
31	20 34 21.7	10 10.0	2 55.2	6♉53.6	22 32.2	27 19.1	25 38.7	6 44.0	24 20.7	5 23.0	26 24.9	3 42.5

DECLINATION

DAY	EPHEM. SID. TIME	☉	☊	☽	☿	♀	♂	♃	♄	♅	♆	♇
1	18 36 5.0	23N 7.8	0S22.4	6N11.7	21N30.3	19N29.0	10S 2.1	12N49.1	17S22.5	20N26.8	9S .2	22N32.3
4	18 47 54.7	22 54.2	0 22.3	18 9.4	22 24.3	18 58.9	9 41.0	12 37.9	17 21.3	20 24.4	9 .2	22 30.3
7	18 59 44.3	22 37.0	0 22.3	23 6.8	23 58.8	18 34.3	9 21.3	12 26.4	17 20.3	20 22.1	9 .2	22 28.3
10	19 11 34.0	22 16.3	0 22.3	12 15.5	23 32.6	18 15.6	9 3.3	12 14.6	17 19.6	20 19.7	9 .3	22 26.3
13	19 23 23.7	21 52.1	0 22.3	3S19.7	23 37.2	18 2.7	8 47.0	12 2.6	17 19.0	20 17.3	9 .6	22 24.3
16	19 35 13.4	21 24.6	0 22.3	16 17.9	23 17.6	17 55.2	8 32.5	11 50.3	17 18.6	20 14.8	9 .9	22 22.2
19	19 47 3.0	20 53.8	0 22.2	21 52.6	22 33.7	17 52.7	8 19.9	11 37.8	17 18.4	20 12.3	9 1.3	22 20.1
22	19 58 52.7	20 19.9	0 22.2	18 37.9	21 27.5	17 54.3	8 9.4	11 25.0	17 18.5	20 9.8	9 1.9	22 18.0
25	20 10 42.4	19 42.8	0 22.2	8 28.1	20 2.2	18 1.0	8 1.0	11 12.0	17 18.7	20 7.3	9 2.6	22 16.0
28	20 22 32.0	19 2.9	0 22.1	4N51.1	18 22.4	18 6.6	7 54.8	10 58.8	17 19.1	20 4.8	9 3.3	22 13.9
31	20 34 21.7	18 20.0	0 22.1	16 57.2	16 31.4	18 15.7	7 51.0	10 45.4	17 19.8	20 2.3	9 4.2	22 11.8

AUGUST 1956

LONGITUDE

DAY	EPHEM. SID. TIME	☉	☊	☽	☿	♀	♂	♃	♄	♅	♆	♇
	h m s	° ′	° ′	° ′	° ′	° ′	° ′	° ′	° ′	° ′	° ′	° ′
1	20 38 18.3	8 ♌ 42.7	4 ♐ 49.0	23 ♉ 31.5	21 ♌ 26.5	27 ♊ 59.2	23 ♓ 1.1	4 ♍ 42.9	26 ♏ 10.0	3 ♌ 1.2	27 ♎ 47.1	27 ♌ 38.6
2	20 42 14.8	9 40.1	4 45.8	7 ♊ 25.2	23 16.8	28 33.1	23 8.6	4 55.2	26 D 10.2	3 4.8	27 47.8	27 40.5
3	20 46 11.4	10 37.5	4 42.6	21 44.4	25 5.4	29 8.3	23 15.2	5 7.5	26 10.4	3 8.5	27 48.6	27 42.4
4	20 50 7.9	11 35.0	4 39.5	6 ♋ 27.2	26 52.5	29 44.8	23 21.1	5 19.9	26 10.8	3 12.2	27 49.4	27 44.2
5	20 54 4.5	12 32.5	4 36.3	21 29.0	28 37.9	0 ♋ 22.4	23 26.1	5 32.3	26 11.3	3 15.8	27 50.2	27 46.1
6	20 58 1.0	13 30.0	4 33.1	6 ♌ 41.7	0 ♍ 21.7	1 1.2	23 30.4	5 44.8	26 11.8	3 19.5	27 51.1	27 48.0
7	21 1 57.6	14 27.5	4 29.9	21 55.1	2 3.9	1 41.1	23 33.8	5 57.3	26 12.5	3 23.1	27 52.0	27 49.9
8	21 5 54.1	15 25.0	4 26.7	6 ♍ 58.3	3 44.6	2 22.0	23 36.4	6 9.9	26 13.2	3 26.7	27 52.9	27 51.9
9	21 9 50.7	16 22.6	4 23.6	21 41.8	5 23.7	3 4.0	23 38.2	6 22.4	26 14.1	3 30.4	27 53.9	27 53.8
10	21 13 47.2	17 20.1	4 20.4	5 ♎ 59.1	7 1.2	3 46.9	23 39.1	6 35.0	26 15.1	3 34.0	27 54.8	27 55.7
11	21 17 43.8	18 17.8	4 17.2	19 47.0	8 37.2	4 30.8	23 39.3	6 47.7	26 16.2	3 37.6	27 55.9	27 57.7
12	21 21 40.4	19 15.4	4 14.0	3 ♏ 5.7	10 11.5	5 15.5	23 R 38.7	7 .4	26 17.3	3 41.2	27 56.9	27 59.6
13	21 25 36.9	20 13.0	4 10.9	15 57.8	11 44.4	6 1.2	23 37.2	7 13.0	26 18.5	3 44.8	27 58.0	28 1.6
14	21 29 33.5	21 10.6	4 7.7	28 27.5	13 15.6	6 47.7	23 34.9	7 25.8	26 19.9	3 48.4	27 59.1	28 3.5
15	21 33 30.0	22 8.2	4 4.5	10 ♐ 39.8	14 45.3	7 34.9	23 31.8	7 38.5	26 21.3	3 51.9	28 .3	28 5.5
16	21 37 26.6	23 5.9	4 1.3	22 39.9	16 13.4	8 23.0	23 27.9	7 51.3	26 22.8	3 55.5	28 1.4	28 7.4
17	21 41 23.1	24 3.6	3 58.1	4 ♑ 32.6	17 39.9	9 11.9	23 23.2	8 4.0	26 24.5	3 59.0	28 2.6	28 9.4
18	21 45 19.7	25 1.3	3 55.0	16 22.2	19 4.8	10 1.4	23 17.7	8 16.8	26 26.2	4 2.5	28 3.8	28 11.3
19	21 49 16.2	25 59.0	3 51.8	28 12.2	20 28.0	10 51.7	23 11.5	8 29.7	26 28.0	4 6.0	28 5.1	28 13.3
20	21 53 12.8	26 56.7	3 48.6	10 ♒ 5.4	21 49.6	11 42.7	23 4.5	8 42.5	26 29.9	4 9.5	28 6.3	28 15.2
21	21 57 9.3	27 54.5	3 45.4	22 3.7	23 9.5	12 34.3	22 56.7	8 55.4	26 31.9	4 12.9	28 7.6	28 17.2
22	22 1 5.9	28 52.2	3 42.3	4 ♓ 8.7	24 27.6	13 26.6	22 48.3	9 8.3	26 34.0	4 16.4	28 9.0	28 19.1
23	22 5 2.5	29 50.0	3 39.1	16 21.2	25 44.0	14 19.5	22 39.1	9 21.2	26 36.2	4 19.8	28 10.3	28 21.1
24	22 8 59.0	0 ♍ 47.9	3 35.9	28 42.2	26 58.4	15 13.0	22 29.2	9 34.1	26 38.4	4 23.2	28 11.7	28 23.0
25	22 12 55.6	1 45.7	3 32.7	11 ♈ 12.7	28 11.0	16 7.1	22 18.6	9 47.0	26 40.8	4 26.6	28 13.1	28 25.0
26	22 16 52.1	2 43.6	3 29.5	23 54.1	29 21.6	17 1.8	22 7.4	9 59.9	26 43.3	4 29.9	28 14.5	28 26.9
27	22 20 48.7	3 41.5	3 26.4	6 ♉ 48.1	0 ♎ 30.1	17 57.0	21 55.6	10 12.9	26 45.8	4 33.3	28 16.0	28 28.9
28	22 24 45.2	4 39.5	3 23.2	19 57.1	1 36.4	18 52.7	21 43.1	10 25.9	26 48.5	4 36.6	28 17.4	28 30.8
29	22 28 41.8	5 37.4	3 20.0	3 ♊ 23.5	2 40.4	19 49.0	21 30.1	10 38.8	26 51.2	4 39.9	28 18.9	28 32.8
30	22 32 38.3	6 35.5	3 16.8	17 9.4	3 42.1	20 45.8	21 16.5	10 51.8	26 54.0	4 43.2	28 20.5	28 34.7
31	22 36 34.9	7 33.5	3 13.7	1 ♋ 16.3	4 41.2	21 43.0	21 2.5	11 4.8	26 56.9	4 46.4	28 22.0	28 36.7

LATITUDE

DAY	EPHEM. SID. TIME	☉	☊	☽	☿	♀	♂	♃	♄	♅	♆	♇
1	20 38 18.3	0 .0	0 .0	1 N 6.4	1 N 36.1	5 S 6.8	5 S 31.1	0 N 57.9	2 N 1.2	0 N 33.2	1 N 43.6	10 N 34.2
4	20 50 7.9	0 .0	0 .0	2 S 34.4	1 23.3	4 57.6	5 39.1	0 57.9	2 .4	0 33.2	1 43.5	10 34.1
7	21 1 57.6	0 .0	0 .0	4 54.0	1 6.7	4 47.0	5 46.6	0 57.8	1 59.7	0 33.2	1 43.3	10 34.1
10	21 13 47.2	0 .0	0 .0	4 20.2	0 46.9	4 35.2	5 53.4	0 57.8	1 58.9	0 33.3	1 43.2	10 34.1
13	21 25 36.9	0 .0	0 .0	1 39.3	0 24.5	4 22.4	5 59.5	0 57.8	1 58.2	0 33.3	1 43.0	10 34.2
16	21 37 26.6	0 .0	0 .0	1 N 32.2	0 .0	4 8.8	6 4.8	0 57.9	1 57.5	0 33.3	1 42.9	10 34.3
19	21 49 16.2	0 .0	0 .0	4 2.1	0 S 26.2	3 54.5	6 9.0	0 57.9	1 56.7	0 33.4	1 42.7	10 34.4
22	22 1 5.9	0 .0	0 .0	4 59.8	0 53.6	3 39.6	6 12.1	0 58.0	1 56.0	0 33.4	1 42.6	10 34.6
25	22 12 55.6	0 .0	0 .0	3 58.1	1 21.7	3 24.3	6 13.9	0 58.0	1 55.3	0 33.5	1 42.5	10 34.9
28	22 24 45.2	0 .0	0 .0	1 9.9	1 50.2	3 8.7	6 14.3	0 58.1	1 54.6	0 33.6	1 42.3	10 35.2
31	22 36 34.9	0 .0	0 .0	2 S 22.2	2 18.4	2 52.8	6 13.2	0 58.2	1 53.9	0 33.6	1 42.2	10 35.5

RIGHT ASCENSION

DAY	EPHEM. SID. TIME	☉	☊	☽	☿	♀	♂	♃	♄	♅	♆	♇
1	20 38 18.3	11 ♌ 8.4	2 ♐ 51.8	20 ♉ 50.7	24 ♌ 21.4	27 ♊ 53.2	25 ♓ 47.4	6 ♍ 55.6	24 ♏ 20.7	5 ♌ 26.8	26 ♎ 25.5	3 ♍ 44.4
2	20 42 14.8	12 6.6	2 48.5	5 ♊ 38.3	26 8.3	28 28.8	25 55.3	7 7.3	24 D 20.8	5 30.6	26 26.2	3 46.2
3	20 46 11.4	13 4.7	2 45.1	21 6.0	27 52.7	29 5.8	26 2.5	7 18.9	24 21.0	5 34.4	26 26.9	3 48.0
4	20 50 7.9	14 2.6	2 41.8	6 ♋ 53.7	29 34.9	29 44.0	26 9.0	7 30.7	24 21.3	5 38.2	26 27.7	3 49.9
5	20 54 4.5	15 .4	2 38.4	22 37.3	1 ♍ 14.7	0 ♋ 23.6	26 14.7	7 42.4	24 21.7	5 42.0	26 28.4	3 51.8
6	20 58 1.0	15 58.0	2 35.1	7 ♌ 56.7	2 52.4	1 4.4	26 19.6	7 54.2	24 22.3	5 45.8	26 29.2	3 53.7
7	21 1 57.6	16 55.5	2 31.7	22 41.0	4 27.9	1 46.3	26 23.7	8 6.0	24 22.9	5 49.6	26 30.1	3 55.5
8	21 5 54.1	17 52.8	2 28.4	6 ♍ 49.5	6 1.3	2 29.5	26 27.0	8 17.8	24 23.6	5 53.3	26 30.9	3 57.4
9	21 9 50.7	18 50.0	2 25.0	20 28.1	7 32.7	3 13.7	26 29.6	8 29.7	24 24.4	5 57.1	26 31.8	3 59.3
10	21 13 47.2	19 47.0	2 21.7	3 ♎ 46.0	9 2.1	3 58.9	26 31.4	8 41.6	24 25.3	6 .8	26 32.7	4 1.2
11	21 17 43.8	20 44.0	2 18.4	16 52.8	10 29.6	4 45.3	26 32.4	8 53.5	24 26.4	6 4.6	26 33.7	4 3.2
12	21 21 40.4	21 40.7	2 15.0	29 55.8	11 55.2	5 32.6	26 32.6	9 5.4	24 27.5	6 8.3	26 34.7	4 5.1
13	21 25 36.9	22 37.3	2 11.7	12 ♏ 59.5	13 18.9	6 20.8	26 R 32.0	9 17.4	24 28.7	6 12.0	26 35.7	4 7.1
14	21 29 33.5	23 33.8	2 8.3	26 4.7	14 40.8	7 10.0	26 30.7	9 29.4	24 30.0	6 15.7	26 36.7	4 9.0
15	21 33 30.0	24 30.1	2 5.0	9 ♐ 8.7	16 .9	8 .0	26 28.5	9 41.4	24 31.4	6 19.4	26 37.7	4 10.9
16	21 37 26.6	25 26.3	2 1.6	22 6.3	17 19.3	8 51.0	26 25.6	9 53.4	24 32.9	6 23.1	26 38.8	4 12.9
17	21 41 23.1	26 22.3	1 58.3	4 ♑ 51.5	18 36.0	9 42.7	26 21.9	10 5.4	24 34.5	6 26.7	26 39.9	4 14.8
18	21 45 19.7	27 18.2	1 55.0	17 19.6	19 50.9	10 35.2	26 17.4	10 17.4	24 36.2	6 30.3	26 41.1	4 16.8
19	21 49 16.2	28 14.0	1 51.6	29 27.8	21 4.2	11 28.6	26 12.2	10 29.5	24 37.9	6 33.9	26 42.2	4 18.7
20	21 53 12.8	29 9.6	1 48.3	11 ♒ 16.7	22 15.7	12 22.6	26 6.2	10 41.5	24 39.8	6 37.5	26 43.4	4 20.7
21	21 57 9.3	0 ♍ 5.2	1 44.9	22 49.6	23 25.6	13 17.4	25 59.5	10 53.6	24 41.8	6 41.1	26 44.6	4 22.6
22	22 1 5.9	1 .6	1 41.6	4 ♓ 12.4	24 33.7	14 12.9	25 52.0	11 5.7	24 43.9	6 44.7	26 45.9	4 24.6
23	22 5 2.5	1 55.9	1 38.2	15 32.9	25 40.1	15 9.0	25 43.9	11 17.8	24 46.1	6 48.2	26 47.1	4 26.5
24	22 8 59.0	2 51.1	1 34.9	27 .3	26 44.7	16 5.8	25 35.0	11 29.9	24 48.3	6 51.7	26 48.4	4 28.5
25	22 12 55.6	3 46.2	1 31.6	8 ♈ 44.4	27 47.5	17 3.2	25 25.4	11 42.0	24 50.7	6 55.2	26 49.7	4 30.5
26	22 16 52.1	4 41.2	1 28.2	20 55.2	28 48.5	18 1.2	25 15.2	11 54.2	24 53.1	6 58.7	26 51.0	4 32.4
27	22 20 48.7	5 36.1	1 24.9	3 ♉ 41.9	29 47.5	18 59.7	25 4.3	12 6.3	24 55.7	7 2.1	26 52.4	4 34.4
28	22 24 45.2	6 30.9	1 21.6	17 10.5	0 ♎ 44.6	19 58.8	24 52.8	12 18.5	24 58.3	7 5.5	26 53.8	4 36.4
29	22 28 41.8	7 25.6	1 18.2	1 ♊ 22.0	1 39.6	20 58.4	24 40.7	12 30.6	25 1.0	7 9.0	26 55.2	4 38.3
30	22 32 38.3	8 20.3	1 14.9	16 10.2	2 32.5	21 58.5	24 28.1	12 42.8	25 3.8	7 12.3	26 56.6	4 40.3
31	22 36 34.9	9 14.8	1 11.5	1 ♋ 21.7	3 23.1	22 59.1	24 14.8	12 54.9	25 6.7	7 15.7	26 58.1	4 42.2

DECLINATION

DAY	EPHEM. SID. TIME	☉	☊	☽	☿	♀	♂	♃	♄	♅	♆	♇
1	20 38 18.3	18 N 5.2	0 S 22.1	19 N 43.8	15 N 52.5	18 N 18.9	7 S 50.2	10 N 40.9	17 S 20.0	20 N 1.5	9 S 4.5	22 N 11.1
4	20 50 7.9	17 18.8	0 22.1	20 43.0	13 51.7	18 29.0	7 49.6	10 27.3	17 20.9	19 59.0	9 5.4	22 9.0
7	21 1 57.6	16 29.8	0 22.0	9 33.8	11 46.8	18 39.0	7 51.5	10 13.5	17 22.1	19 56.5	9 6.5	22 7.0
10	21 13 47.2	15 38.5	0 22.0	6 S 21.5	9 39.7	18 48.3	7 55.6	9 59.6	17 23.4	19 54.0	9 7.7	22 4.9
13	21 25 36.9	14 44.9	0 22.0	18 12.2	7 32.3	18 56.2	8 2.0	9 45.4	17 24.9	19 51.5	9 8.9	22 2.9
16	21 37 26.6	13 49.3	0 21.9	21 42.4	5 26.2	19 2.4	8 10.5	9 31.2	17 26.6	19 49.0	9 10.3	22 .9
19	21 49 16.2	12 51.6	0 21.9	16 34.2	3 22.6	19 6.3	8 20.9	9 16.9	17 28.5	19 46.6	9 11.7	21 59.0
22	22 1 5.9	11 52.2	0 21.9	5 20.0	1 22.9	19 7.4	8 32.9	9 2.4	17 30.6	19 44.1	9 13.2	21 57.0
25	22 12 55.6	10 51.0	0 21.9	8 N 5.2	0 S 31.6	19 5.4	8 46.3	8 47.9	17 32.9	19 41.8	9 14.8	21 55.2
28	22 24 45.2	9 48.3	0 21.8	18 51.2	2 19.4	18 60.0	9 .8	8 33.3	17 35.3	19 39.4	9 16.5	21 53.3
31	22 36 34.9	8 44.1	0 21.8	21 4.1	3 58.8	18 50.9	9 15.8	8 18.6	17 37.9	19 37.1	9 18.2	21 51.5

SEPTEMBER 1956

LONGITUDE

DAY	EPHEM. SID. TIME h m s	☉ ° ′	☊ ° ′	☽ ° ′	☿ ° ′	♀ ° ′	♂ ° ′	♃ ° ′	♄ ° ′	♅ ° ′	♆ ° ′	♇ ° ′
1	22 40 31.4	8♍31.6	3♐10.5	15♋43.5	5♎37.8	22♋40.7	20♓48.0	11♍17.8	26♏59.9	4♌49.7	28♎23.6	28♌38.7
2	22 44 28.0	9 29.7	3 7.3	0♌28.2	6 31.4	23 38.9	20 R 33.1	11 30.8	27 3.0	4 52.9	28 25.2	28 40.6
3	22 48 24.5	10 27.8	3 4.1	15 24.6	7 22.0	24 37.5	20 17.7	11 43.8	27 6.2	4 56.1	28 26.9	28 42.5
4	22 52 21.1	11 26.0	3 .9	0♍24.4	8 9.4	25 36.5	20 2.1	11 56.9	27 9.4	4 59.2	28 28.5	28 44.4
5	22 56 17.6	12 24.2	2 57.8	15 18.4	8 53.4	26 35.9	19 46.1	12 9.9	27 12.7	5 2.3	28 30.2	28 46.4
6	23 0 14.2	13 22.4	2 54.6	29 57.1	9 33.8	27 35.7	19 29.9	12 22.9	27 16.2	5 5.4	28 31.9	28 48.3
7	23 4 10.7	14 20.7	2 51.4	14♎13.5	10 10.2	28 35.9	19 13.5	12 35.9	27 19.7	5 8.5	28 33.6	28 50.2
8	23 8 7.3	15 19.0	2 48.2	28 3.0	10 42.4	29 36.4	18 57.0	12 48.9	27 23.3	5 11.5	28 35.3	28 52.1
9	23 12 3.9	16 17.3	2 45.1	11♏24.7	11 10.2	0♌37.3	18 40.5	13 1.9	27 26.9	5 14.5	28 37.0	28 54.0
10	23 16 .4	17 15.6	2 41.9	24 19.8	11 33.1	1 38.6	18 23.8	13 14.9	27 30.7	5 17.5	28 38.8	28 55.8
11	23 19 57.0	18 13.9	2 38.7	6♐52.0	11 51.0	2 40.2	18 7.2	13 27.9	27 34.5	5 20.4	28 40.6	28 57.7
12	23 23 53.5	19 12.3	2 35.5	19 5.8	12 3.4	3 42.2	17 50.7	13 40.8	27 38.4	5 23.3	28 42.4	28 59.6
13	23 27 50.1	20 10.7	2 32.3	1♑ 6.6	12 10.0	4 44.4	17 34.3	13 53.8	27 42.4	5 26.2	28 44.3	29 1.4
14	23 31 46.6	21 9.2	2 29.2	12 59.6	12 10.5	5 47.0	17 18.0	14 6.8	27 46.5	5 29.1	28 46.1	29 3.3
15	23 35 43.2	22 7.6	2 26.0	24 49.8	12 R 4.6	6 49.9	17 2.0	14 19.7	27 50.6	5 31.9	28 48.0	29 5.1
16	23 39 39.7	23 6.1	2 22.8	6♒41.5	11 52.1	7 53.1	16 46.2	14 32.7	27 54.8	5 34.6	28 49.9	29 6.9
17	23 43 36.3	24 4.6	2 19.6	18 38.5	11 32.7	8 56.6	16 30.7	14 45.6	27 59.1	5 37.4	28 51.8	29 8.7
18	23 47 32.8	25 3.2	2 16.5	0♓43.5	11 6.3	10 .3	16 15.6	14 58.5	28 3.5	5 40.1	28 53.7	29 10.5
19	23 51 29.4	26 1.8	2 13.3	12 58.2	10 32.9	11 4.4	16 .8	15 11.4	28 7.9	5 42.7	28 55.6	29 12.3
20	23 55 25.9	27 .4	2 10.1	25 23.8	9 52.7	12 8.8	15 46.4	15 24.3	28 12.4	5 45.4	28 57.6	29 14.1
21	23 59 22.5	27 59.0	2 6.9	8♈ .6	9 6.0	13 13.4	15 32.5	15 37.1	28 17.0	5 48.0	28 59.5	29 15.9
22	0 3 19.0	28 57.7	2 3.7	20 48.6	8 13.4	14 18.3	15 19.1	15 50.0	28 21.7	5 50.6	29 1.6	29 17.7
23	0 7 15.6	29 56.4	2 .6	3♉47.6	7 15.5	15 23.4	15 6.2	16 2.8	28 26.4	5 53.1	29 3.6	29 19.4
24	0 11 12.1	0♎55.2	1 57.4	16 57.8	6 13.5	16 28.8	14 53.8	16 15.6	28 31.2	5 55.6	29 5.6	29 21.1
25	0 15 8.7	1 54.0	1 54.2	0♊19.5	5 8.5	17 34.5	14 42.0	16 28.4	28 36.1	5 58.0	29 7.6	29 22.8
26	0 19 5.2	2 52.8	1 51.0	13 53.5	4 2.0	18 40.3	14 30.8	16 41.1	28 41.0	6 .4	29 9.7	29 24.5
27	0 23 1.8	3 51.6	1 47.8	27 40.7	2 55.5	19 46.5	14 20.2	16 53.8	28 46.0	6 2.8	29 11.7	29 26.2
28	0 26 58.3	4 50.5	1 44.7	11♋41.4	1 51.0	20 52.8	14 10.3	17 6.5	28 51.1	6 5.1	29 13.8	29 27.9
29	0 30 54.9	5 49.5	1 41.5	25 55.2	0 49.9	21 59.4	14 1.1	17 19.2	28 56.2	6 7.4	29 15.9	29 29.5
30	0 34 51.4	6 48.4	1 38.3	10♌20.4	29♍54.1	23 6.2	13 52.5	17 31.8	29 1.4	6 9.6	29 18.0	29 31.2

LATITUDE

DAY	EPHEM. SID. TIME	☉	☊	☽	☿	♀	♂	♃	♄	♅	♆	♇
1	22 40 31.4	0 .0	0 .0	3S24.2	2S27.6	2S47.5	6S12.4	0N58.2	1N53.6	0N33.7	1N42.2	10N35.6
4	22 52 21.1	0 .0	0 .0	5 .4	2 54.5	2 31.4	6 9.2	0 58.4	1 53.0	0 33.7	1 42.0	10 36.0
7	23 4 10.7	0 .0	0 .0	3 44.6	3 19.1	2 15.4	6 4.2	0 58.5	1 52.3	0 33.8	1 41.9	10 36.4
10	23 16 .4	0 .0	0 .0	0 41.0	3 40.2	1 59.4	5 57.7	0 58.7	1 51.6	0 33.9	1 41.8	10 36.9
13	23 27 50.1	0 .0	0 .0	2N27.8	3 55.8	1 43.5	5 49.5	0 58.8	1 51.0	0 34.0	1 41.7	10 37.4
16	23 39 39.7	0 .0	0 .0	4 34.2	4 3.1	1 27.8	5 40.0	0 59.0	1 50.3	0 34.0	1 41.6	10 38.0
19	23 51 29.4	0 .0	0 .0	4 56.2	3 58.8	1 12.3	5 29.1	0 59.2	1 49.7	0 34.1	1 41.5	10 38.6
22	0 3 19.0	0 .0	0 .0	3 15.6	3 39.4	0 57.2	5 17.2	0 59.4	1 49.1	0 34.2	1 41.5	10 39.3
25	0 15 8.7	0 .0	0 .0	0 1.6	3 2.9	0 42.5	5 4.4	0 59.7	1 48.6	0 34.3	1 41.4	10 39.9
28	0 26 58.3	0 .0	0 .0	3S21.7	2 11.4	0 28.2	4 50.8	0 59.9	1 48.0	0 34.4	1 41.3	10 40.7

RIGHT ASCENSION

DAY	EPHEM. SID. TIME	☉	☊	☽	☿	♀	♂	♃	♄	♅	♆	♇
1	22 40 31.4	10♍ 9.3	1♐ 8.2	16♋38.5	4♎11.4	24♋ .1	24♓ 1.2	13♍ 7.1	25♏ 9.8	7♌19.1	26♎59.6	4♍44.2
2	22 44 28.0	11 3.7	1 4.9	1♌43.6	4 57.1	25 1.6	23 R 47.0	13 19.3	25 12.9	7 22.4	27 1.1	4 46.2
3	22 48 24.5	11 58.1	1 1.5	16 26.0	5 40.1	26 3.4	23 32.4	13 31.4	25 16.1	7 25.6	27 2.6	4 48.1
4	22 52 21.1	12 52.4	0 58.2	0♍42.2	6 20.4	27 5.6	23 17.4	13 43.6	25 19.3	7 28.9	27 4.2	4 50.1
5	22 56 17.6	13 46.6	0 54.9	14 34.9	6 57.6	28 8.1	23 2.0	13 55.7	25 22.7	7 32.1	27 5.7	4 52.0
6	23 0 14.2	14 40.7	0 51.5	28 10.9	7 31.5	29 11.0	22 46.4	14 7.9	25 26.1	7 35.3	27 7.3	4 54.0
7	23 4 10.7	15 34.8	0 48.2	11♎37.5	8 2.0	0♌14.2	22 30.5	14 20.0	25 29.6	7 38.5	27 8.9	4 55.9
8	23 8 7.3	16 28.9	0 44.9	25 .8	8 28.8	1 17.7	22 14.4	14 32.2	25 33.3	7 41.6	27 10.6	4 57.8
9	23 12 3.9	17 22.9	0 41.5	8♏24.0	8 51.7	2 21.5	21 58.1	14 44.3	25 37.0	7 44.7	27 12.2	4 59.8
10	23 16 .4	18 16.9	0 38.2	21 47.1	9 10.4	3 25.5	21 41.7	14 56.4	25 40.7	7 47.7	27 13.9	5 1.7
11	23 19 57.0	19 10.8	0 34.9	5♐ 6.3	9 24.6	4 29.8	21 25.3	15 8.5	25 44.6	7 50.8	27 15.6	5 3.6
12	23 23 53.5	20 4.7	0 31.5	18 16.4	9 34.0	5 34.3	21 8.9	15 20.6	25 48.6	7 53.8	27 17.3	5 5.5
13	23 27 50.1	20 58.5	0 28.2	1♑11.2	9 38.4	6 39.1	20 52.5	15 32.7	25 52.6	7 56.7	27 19.0	5 7.4
14	23 31 46.6	21 52.4	0 24.9	13 46.5	9 R 37.4	7 44.0	20 36.2	15 44.8	25 56.7	7 59.7	27 20.7	5 9.3
15	23 35 43.2	22 46.2	0 21.5	26 .4	9 31.0	8 49.1	20 20.0	15 56.9	26 .9	8 2.6	27 22.5	5 11.1
16	23 39 39.7	23 40.0	0 18.2	7♒54.2	9 18.8	9 54.4	20 4.0	16 8.9	26 5.2	8 5.4	27 24.3	5 13.0
17	23 43 36.3	24 33.8	0 14.9	19 31.8	9 .8	10 59.8	19 48.2	16 20.9	26 9.5	8 8.2	27 26.1	5 14.9
18	23 47 32.8	25 27.6	0 11.6	0♓59.4	8 36.9	12 5.4	19 32.6	16 32.9	26 13.9	8 11.0	27 27.9	5 16.7
19	23 51 29.4	26 21.4	0 8.2	12 24.8	8 7.2	13 11.2	19 17.3	16 44.9	26 18.4	8 13.8	27 29.7	5 18.6
20	23 55 25.9	27 15.2	0 4.9	23 57.0	7 31.9	14 17.0	19 2.4	16 56.9	26 23.0	8 16.5	27 31.5	5 20.4
21	23 59 22.5	28 9.0	0 1.6	5♈45.2	6 51.3	15 23.0	18 47.9	17 8.9	26 27.7	8 19.2	27 33.4	5 22.2
22	0 3 19.0	29 2.9	29♏58.2	17 58.5	6 6.1	16 29.1	18 33.8	17 20.8	26 32.4	8 21.9	27 35.3	5 24.1
23	0 7 15.6	29 56.7	29 54.9	0♉44.6	5 16.8	17 35.2	18 20.0	17 32.8	26 37.2	8 24.4	27 37.2	5 25.9
24	0 11 12.1	0♎50.6	29 51.6	14 8.2	4 24.6	18 41.5	18 6.8	17 44.6	26 42.1	8 27.0	27 39.1	5 27.7
25	0 15 8.7	1 44.6	29 48.3	28 9.0	3 30.4	19 47.8	17 54.0	17 56.5	26 47.1	8 29.5	27 41.0	5 29.4
26	0 19 5.2	2 38.5	29 44.9	12♊40.7	2 35.5	20 54.2	17 41.8	18 8.4	26 52.1	8 32.0	27 43.0	5 31.2
27	0 23 1.8	3 32.6	29 41.6	27 30.8	1 41.4	22 .6	17 30.2	18 20.2	26 57.2	8 34.4	27 44.9	5 32.9
28	0 26 58.3	4 26.6	29 38.3	12♋23.8	0 49.5	23 7.1	17 19.1	18 32.0	27 2.3	8 36.8	27 46.9	5 34.7
29	0 30 54.9	5 20.8	29 35.0	27 5.7	0 1.3	24 13.6	17 8.6	18 43.7	27 7.5	8 39.1	27 48.8	5 36.4
30	0 34 51.4	6 15.0	29 31.6	11♌27.6	29♍18.0	25 20.2	16 58.8	18 55.4	27 12.8	8 41.4	27 50.8	5 38.1

DECLINATION

DAY	EPHEM. SID. TIME	☉	☊	☽	☿	♀	♂	♃	♄	♅	♆	♇
1	22 40 31.4	8N22.5	0S21.8	19N 8.2	4S29.7	18N47.0	9S20.9	8N13.6	17S38.8	19N36.4	9S18.9	21N50.9
4	22 52 21.1	7 16.6	0 21.7	6 38.5	5 54.4	18 32.6	9 36.1	7 58.9	17 41.7	19 34.1	9 20.7	21 49.2
7	23 4 10.7	6 9.8	0 21.7	9S 3.5	7 4.7	18 14.1	9 50.7	7 44.1	17 44.6	19 31.9	9 22.6	21 47.5
10	23 16 .4	5 2.0	0 21.7	19 31.1	7 56.8	17 51.4	10 4.2	7 29.2	17 47.7	19 29.8	9 24.5	21 45.9
13	23 27 50.1	3 53.5	0 21.6	20 58.6	8 25.5	17 24.5	10 16.3	7 14.4	17 51.0	19 27.8	9 26.6	21 44.4
16	23 39 39.7	2 44.3	0 21.6	14 10.6	8 25.3	16 53.2	10 26.3	6 59.6	17 54.4	19 25.8	9 28.6	21 43.0
19	23 51 29.4	1 34.7	0 21.6	2 7.7	7 50.2	16 17.6	10 34.2	6 44.8	17 57.9	19 23.9	9 30.7	21 41.6
22	0 3 19.0	0 24.8	0 21.5	11N 8.6	6 37.3	15 37.7	10 39.5	6 30.0	18 1.5	19 22.0	9 32.9	21 40.2
25	0 15 8.7	0S45.3	0 21.5	20 14.9	4 50.5	14 53.7	10 42.1	6 15.3	18 5.2	19 20.3	9 35.1	21 39.0
28	0 26 58.3	1 55.5	0 21.5	19 34.8	2 44.7	14 5.6	10 41.9	6 .7	18 9.0	19 18.6	9 37.3	21 37.9

OCTOBER 1956

DAY	EPHEM. SID. TIME	☉	☊	☽	☿	♀	♂	♃	♄	♅	♆	♇
		LONGITUDE										
	h m s	° ′	° ′	° ′	° ′	° ′	° ′	° ′	° ′	° ′	° ′	° ′
1	0 38 48.0	7♎47.4	1♐35.1	24♌53.2	29♍ 5.0	24♌13.2	13♓44.7	17♍44.4	29♏ 6.7	6♌11.8	29♎20.1	29♌32.8
2	0 42 44.6	8 46.5	1 32.0	9♍28.3	28 R 23.9	25 20.4	13 R 37.6	17 57.0	29 12.0	6 13.9	29 22.2	29 34.4
3	0 46 41.1	9 45.6	1 28.8	23 59.1	27 52.0	26 27.8	13 31.3	18 9.6	29 17.3	6 16.0	29 24.3	29 36.0
4	0 50 37.7	10 44.7	1 25.6	8♎18.7	27 30.0	27 35.4	13 25.7	18 22.1	29 22.8	6 18.1	29 26.5	29 37.5
5	0 54 34.2	11 43.9	1 22.4	22 21.3	27 18.4	28 43.2	13 20.9	18 34.5	29 28.3	6 20.1	29 28.6	29 39.1
6	0 58 30.8	12 43.0	1 19.2	6♏ 2.5	27 17.4	29 51.2	13 17.0	18 47.0	29 33.8	6 22.1	29 30.8	29 40.6
7	1 2 27.3	13 42.3	1 16.1	19 20.3	27 D 26.9	0♍59.4	13 13.8	18 59.4	29 39.5	6 24.0	29 33.0	29 42.1
8	1 6 23.9	14 41.5	1 12.9	2♐14.8	27 46.9	2 7.7	13 11.4	19 11.7	29 45.1	6 25.9	29 35.1	29 43.6
9	1 10 20.4	15 40.8	1 9.7	14 48.3	28 16.7	3 16.3	13 9.9	19 24.0	29 50.8	6 27.7	29 37.3	29 45.1
10	1 14 17.0	16 40.1	1 6.5	27 4.1	28 55.8	4 24.9	13 9.1	19 36.3	29 56.6	6 29.5	29 39.5	29 46.5
11	1 18 13.5	17 39.4	1 3.4	9♑ 6.9	29 43.6	5 33.8	13 D 9.2	19 48.5	0♐ 2.5	6 31.2	29 41.7	29 48.0
12	1 22 10.1	18 38.8	1 .2	21 1.5	0♎39.3	6 42.8	13 10.0	20 .7	0 8.3	6 32.9	29 43.9	29 49.4
13	1 26 6.6	19 38.3	0 57.0	2♒53.0	1 42.2	7 52.0	13 11.8	20 12.8	0 14.3	6 34.6	29 46.2	29 50.8
14	1 30 3.2	20 37.7	0 53.8	14 46.4	2 51.3	9 1.4	13 14.2	20 24.9	0 20.3	6 36.2	29 48.4	29 52.2
15	1 33 59.7	21 37.2	0 50.6	26 46.0	4 6.0	10 10.9	13 17.5	20 36.9	0 26.3	6 37.7	29 50.6	29 53.5
16	1 37 56.3	22 36.6	0 47.5	8♓55.6	5 25.6	11 20.5	13 21.5	20 48.9	0 32.4	6 39.2	29 52.8	29 54.8
17	1 41 52.8	23 36.2	0 44.3	21 18.1	6 49.3	12 30.3	13 26.3	21 .8	0 38.5	6 40.6	29 55.0	29 56.1
18	1 45 49.4	24 35.7	0 41.1	3♈55.2	8 16.6	13 40.2	13 31.9	21 12.7	0 44.7	6 42.0	29 57.3	29 57.4
19	1 49 46.0	25 35.3	0 37.9	16 47.9	9 46.8	14 50.3	13 38.2	21 24.5	0 50.9	6 43.3	29 59.5	29 58.7
20	1 53 42.5	26 34.9	0 34.8	29 55.7	11 19.4	16 .5	13 45.3	21 36.2	0 57.2	6 44.6	0♏ 1.7	29 59.9
21	1 57 39.1	27 34.6	0 31.6	13♉17.8	12 54.1	17 10.9	13 53.1	21 47.9	1 3.5	6 45.8	0 4.0	0♍ 1.1
22	2 1 35.6	28 34.3	0 28.4	26 52.3	14 30.3	18 21.4	14 1.6	21 59.5	1 9.8	6 47.0	0 6.2	0 2.3
23	2 5 32.2	29 34.0	0 25.2	10♊37.5	16 7.9	19 32.0	14 10.8	22 11.1	1 16.2	6 48.2	0 8.5	0 3.5
24	2 9 28.7	0♏33.7	0 22.0	24 31.5	17 46.3	20 42.8	14 20.7	22 22.6	1 22.6	6 49.2	0 10.7	0 4.6
25	2 13 25.3	1 33.5	0 18.9	8♋32.5	19 25.5	21 53.7	14 31.3	22 34.0	1 29.1	6 50.3	0 12.9	0 5.7
26	2 17 21.8	2 33.4	0 15.7	22 39.0	21 5.2	23 4.7	14 42.6	22 45.4	1 35.6	6 51.2	0 15.2	0 6.8
27	2 21 18.4	3 33.2	0 12.5	6♌49.3	22 45.3	24 15.9	14 54.5	22 56.7	1 42.1	6 52.1	0 17.4	0 7.9
28	2 25 14.9	4 33.1	0 9.3	21 1.5	24 25.5	25 27.2	15 7.1	23 8.0	1 48.7	6 53.0	0 19.7	0 8.9
29	2 29 11.5	5 33.1	0 6.2	5♍13.3	26 5.7	26 38.5	15 20.3	23 19.1	1 55.3	6 53.8	0 21.9	0 9.9
30	2 33 8.0	6 33.1	0 3.0	19 21.8	27 46.0	27 50.0	15 34.2	23 30.2	2 2.0	6 54.6	0 24.1	0 10.9
31	2 37 4.6	7 33.1	29♏59.8	3♎23.6	29 26.0	29 1.7	15 48.6	23 41.2	2 8.6	6 55.3	0 26.4	0 11.8
		LATITUDE										
1	0 38 48.0	0 .0	0 .0	5S 4.8	1S11.4	0S14.4	4S36.7	1N .2	1N47.4	0N34.5	1N41.3	10N41.4
4	0 50 37.7	0 .0	0 .0	4 1.2	0 11.9	0 1.1	4 22.3	1 .5	1 46.9	0 34.6	1 41.2	10 42.2
7	1 2 27.3	0 .0	0 .0	0 56.3	0N39.4	0N11.6	4 7.6	1 .8	1 46.4	0 34.7	1 41.2	10 43.1
10	1 14 17.0	0 .0	0 .0	2N22.3	1 18.4	0 23.7	3 53.0	1 1.1	1 45.9	0 34.8	1 41.2	10 44.0
13	1 26 6.6	0 .0	0 .0	4 37.0	1 44.2	0 35.1	3 38.5	1 1.5	1 45.5	0 34.9	1 41.1	10 44.9
16	1 37 56.3	0 .0	0 .0	5 6.4	1 58.0	0 45.8	3 24.2	1 1.8	1 45.0	0 35.0	1 41.1	10 45.8
19	1 49 46.0	0 .0	0 .0	3 30.8	2 1.8	0 55.8	3 10.2	1 2.2	1 44.6	0 35.2	1 41.1	10 46.8
22	2 1 35.6	0 .0	0 .0	0 12.8	1 57.9	1 5.0	2 56.6	1 2.6	1 44.2	0 35.3	1 41.1	10 47.8
25	2 13 25.3	0 .0	0 .0	3S19.2	1 48.3	1 13.4	2 43.5	1 3.0	1 43.8	0 35.4	1 41.1	10 48.8
28	2 25 14.9	0 .0	0 .0	5 11.0	1 34.7	1 21.1	2 30.8	1 3.5	1 43.4	0 35.5	1 41.1	10 49.9
31	2 37 4.6	0 .0	0 .0	4 20.1	1 18.2	1 27.9	2 18.6	1 3.9	1 43.1	0 35.6	1 41.2	10 51.0
		RIGHT ASCENSION										
1	0 38 48.0	7♎ 9.3	29♏28.3	25♌27.5	28♍41.1	26♌26.7	16♓49.6	19♍ 7.1	27♏18.2	8♌43.7	27♎52.8	5♍39.8
2	0 42 44.6	8 3.6	29 25.0	9♍ 8.5	28 R 11.5	27 33.3	16 R 41.0	19 18.8	27 23.6	8 45.9	27 54.8	5 41.5
3	0 46 41.1	8 58.1	29 21.7	22 37.6	27 50.2	28 39.9	16 33.2	19 30.5	27 29.1	8 48.1	27 56.8	5 43.1
4	0 50 37.7	9 52.6	29 18.4	6♎ 2.3	27 37.6	29 46.5	16 26.1	19 42.1	27 34.6	8 50.2	27 58.9	5 44.8
5	0 54 34.2	10 47.2	29 15.0	19 28.9	27 34.2	0♍53.1	16 19.7	19 53.6	27 40.3	8 52.3	28 .9	5 46.4
6	0 58 30.8	11 41.9	29 11.7	3♏ .7	27 D 40.1	1 59.7	16 14.1	20 5.1	27 45.9	8 54.3	28 2.9	5 48.0
7	1 2 27.3	12 36.6	29 8.4	16 36.9	27 55.2	3 6.3	16 9.2	20 16.6	27 51.7	8 56.3	28 5.0	5 49.6
8	1 6 23.9	13 31.5	29 5.1	0♐12.6	28 19.3	4 12.9	16 5.0	20 28.1	27 57.5	8 58.2	28 7.1	5 51.2
9	1 10 20.4	14 26.5	29 1.8	13 40.3	28 51.8	5 19.4	16 1.7	20 39.5	28 3.3	9 .1	28 9.1	5 52.8
10	1 14 17.0	15 21.6	28 58.4	26 51.7	29 32.3	6 25.9	15 59.0	20 50.9	28 9.3	9 1.9	28 11.2	5 54.3
11	1 18 13.5	16 16.8	28 55.1	9♑40.8	0♎20.2	7 32.5	15 57.2	21 2.2	28 15.2	9 3.7	28 13.3	5 55.8
12	1 22 10.1	17 12.1	28 51.8	22 4.8	1 14.7	8 39.0	15 56.1	21 13.4	28 21.3	9 5.4	28 15.4	5 57.3
13	1 26 6.6	18 7.6	28 48.5	4♒ 4.7	2 15.2	9 45.5	15 55.8	21 24.7	28 27.4	9 7.2	28 17.5	5 58.9
14	1 30 3.2	19 3.2	28 45.2	15 45.0	3 20.9	10 51.9	15 D 56.2	21 35.9	28 33.5	9 8.8	28 19.6	6 .3
15	1 33 59.7	19 58.9	28 41.9	27 12.8	4 31.3	11 58.4	15 57.4	21 47.0	28 39.7	9 10.4	28 21.7	6 1.8
16	1 37 56.3	20 54.7	28 38.5	8♓36.8	5 45.6	13 4.8	15 59.3	21 58.1	28 45.9	9 11.9	28 23.8	6 3.2
17	1 41 52.8	21 50.7	28 35.2	20 7.0	7 3.4	14 11.2	16 2.0	22 9.1	28 52.2	9 13.4	28 26.0	6 4.6
18	1 45 49.4	22 46.8	28 31.9	1♈53.6	8 24.0	15 17.6	16 5.4	22 20.1	28 58.6	9 14.8	28 28.1	6 6.0
19	1 49 46.0	23 43.1	28 28.6	14 6.8	9 47.1	16 24.0	16 9.5	22 31.1	29 5.0	9 16.2	28 30.2	6 7.3
20	1 53 42.5	24 39.5	28 25.3	26 55.1	11 12.1	17 30.4	16 14.3	22 41.9	29 11.4	9 17.5	28 32.3	6 8.7
21	1 57 39.1	25 36.1	28 22.0	10♉23.4	12 38.8	18 36.8	16 19.8	22 52.7	29 17.9	9 18.8	28 34.5	6 10.0
22	2 1 35.6	26 32.8	28 18.7	24 31.4	14 6.9	19 43.2	16 25.9	23 3.5	29 24.4	9 20.0	28 36.6	6 11.3
23	2 5 32.2	27 29.7	28 15.3	9♊11.2	15 36.1	20 49.6	16 32.8	23 14.2	29 31.0	9 21.2	28 38.7	6 12.6
24	2 9 28.7	28 26.8	28 12.0	24 8.1	17 6.2	21 56.0	16 40.3	23 24.9	29 37.6	9 22.3	28 40.8	6 13.8
25	2 13 25.3	29 24.1	28 8.7	9♋ 4.2	18 37.0	23 2.4	16 48.5	23 35.4	29 44.2	9 23.4	28 43.0	6 15.0
26	2 17 21.8	0♏21.5	28 5.4	23 43.9	20 8.3	24 8.9	16 57.3	23 46.0	29 50.9	9 24.4	28 45.1	6 16.2
27	2 21 18.4	1 19.2	28 2.1	7♌57.8	21 40.1	25 15.3	17 6.7	23 56.4	29 57.7	9 25.3	28 47.2	6 17.4
28	2 25 14.9	2 17.0	27 58.8	21 44.3	23 12.2	26 21.8	17 16.8	24 6.8	0♐ 4.4	9 26.2	28 49.4	6 18.6
29	2 29 11.5	3 15.0	27 55.5	5♍ 8.1	24 44.7	27 28.3	17 27.5	24 17.2	0 11.3	9 27.1	28 51.5	6 19.7
30	2 33 8.0	4 13.3	27 52.2	18 17.9	26 17.4	28 34.9	17 38.7	24 27.4	0 18.1	9 27.8	28 53.6	6 20.8
31	2 37 4.6	5 11.7	27 48.9	1♎23.2	27 50.2	29 41.4	17 50.6	24 37.6	0 25.0	9 28.6	28 55.8	6 21.9
		DECLINATION										
1	0 38 48.0	3S 5.5	0S21.4	8N26.1	0S43.6	13N13.5	10S38.9	5N46.2	18S12.9	19N17.1	9S39.6	21N36.8
4	0 50 37.7	4 15.2	0 21.4	6S59.4	0N48.8	12 17.7	10 32.9	5 31.7	18 16.9	19 15.6	9 41.9	21 35.8
7	1 2 27.3	5 24.5	0 21.4	18 28.1	1 37.0	11 18.3	10 24.0	5 17.4	18 20.9	19 14.2	9 44.2	21 34.9
10	1 14 17.0	6 33.2	0 21.3	21 2.4	1 37.4	10 15.6	10 12.3	5 3.2	18 25.0	19 12.9	9 46.5	21 34.1
13	1 26 6.6	7 41.0	0 21.3	15 1.3	0 54.9	9 9.8	9 57.9	4 49.1	18 29.2	19 11.8	9 48.9	21 33.4
16	1 37 56.3	8 47.9	0 21.3	3 29.2	0S21.1	8 1.1	9 41.0	4 35.3	18 33.3	19 10.7	9 51.2	21 32.9
19	1 49 46.0	9 53.7	0 21.2	9N50.7	2 .5	6 49.8	9 21.6	4 21.6	18 37.6	19 9.8	9 53.6	21 32.4
22	2 1 35.6	10 58.1	0 21.2	19 40.1	3 54.4	5 36.1	9 .1	4 8.1	18 41.8	19 9.0	9 55.9	21 32.0
25	2 13 25.3	12 1.1	0 21.2	19 51.3	5 55.9	4 20.4	8 36.5	3 54.9	18 46.1	19 8.3	9 58.3	21 31.7
28	2 25 14.9	13 2.4	0 21.1	9 34.5	8 .0	3 2.9	8 10.9	3 41.9	18 50.3	19 7.7	10 .6	21 31.5
31	2 37 4.6	14 2.0	0 21.1	5S19.6	10 3.3	1 43.8	7 43.5	3 29.1	18 54.6	19 7.2	10 2.9	21 31.5

NOVEMBER 1956

LONGITUDE

DAY	EPHEM. SID. TIME	☉	☊	☾	☿	♀	♂	♃	♄	♅	♆	♇
	h m s	° ′	° ′	° ′	° ′	° ′	° ′	° ′	° ′	° ′	° ′	° ′
1	2 41 1.2	8♏33.1	29♏56.6	17♎15.3	1♏ 5.9	0♎13.4	16♓ 3.7	23♍52.2	2♐15.3	6♌55.9	0♏28.6	0♍12.8
2	2 44 57.7	9 33.2	29 53.4	0♏53.6	2 45.6	1 25.2	16 19.4	24 3.0	2 22.1	6 56.5	0 30.8	0 13.7
3	2 48 54.3	10 33.4	29 50.3	14 15.9	4 25.0	2 37.2	16 35.7	24 13.8	2 28.9	6 57.1	0 33.1	0 14.6
4	2 52 50.8	11 33.5	29 47.1	27 20.5	6 4.1	3 49.2	16 52.6	24 24.5	2 35.7	6 57.6	0 35.3	0 15.4
5	2 56 47.4	12 33.7	29 43.9	10♐ 7.3	7 42.8	5 1.3	17 10.0	24 35.2	2 42.5	6 58.0	0 37.5	0 16.2
6	3 0 43.9	13 33.9	29 40.7	22 37.2	9 21.2	6 13.5	17 28.0	24 45.7	2 49.3	6 58.4	0 39.7	0 17.0
7	3 4 40.5	14 34.1	29 37.6	4♑52.2	10 59.2	7 25.8	17 46.5	24 56.1	2 56.2	6 58.7	0 41.9	0 17.8
8	3 8 37.0	15 34.4	29 34.4	16 55.4	12 36.9	8 38.2	18 5.5	25 6.5	3 3.1	6 58.9	0 44.1	0 18.5
9	3 12 33.6	16 34.7	29 31.2	28 50.8	14 14.2	9 50.7	18 25.1	25 16.7	3 10.0	6 59.1	0 46.2	0 19.2
10	3 16 30.1	17 35.0	29 28.0	10♒42.7	15 51.2	11 3.2	18 45.2	25 26.9	3 16.9	6 59.3	0 48.4	0 19.9
11	3 20 26.7	18 35.3	29 24.9	22 35.9	17 27.8	12 15.8	19 5.7	25 37.0	3 23.9	6 59.4	0 50.6	0 20.6
12	3 24 23.3	19 35.6	29 21.7	4♓35.1	19 4.0	13 28.6	19 26.7	25 47.0	3 30.9	6 59.4	0 52.7	0 21.2
13	3 28 19.8	20 36.0	29 18.5	16 44.9	20 40.0	14 41.4	19 48.2	25 56.8	3 37.9	6 59.4	0 54.9	0 21.8
14	3 32 16.4	21 36.4	29 15.3	29 9.4	22 15.6	15 54.2	20 10.2	26 6.6	3 44.9	6R59.3	0 57.0	0 22.3
15	3 36 12.9	22 36.8	29 12.1	11♈51.7	23 51.0	17 7.2	20 32.6	26 16.3	3 51.9	6 59.2	0 59.1	0 22.9
16	3 40 9.5	23 37.3	29 9.0	24 54.1	25 26.1	18 20.2	20 55.4	26 25.9	3 58.9	6 59.0	1 1.2	0 23.4
17	3 44 6.0	24 37.8	29 5.8	8♉17.2	27 .9	19 33.3	21 18.6	26 35.4	4 6.0	6 58.8	1 3.3	0 23.8
18	3 48 2.6	25 38.2	29 2.6	22 .1	28 35.4	20 46.4	21 42.2	26 44.7	4 13.0	6 58.5	1 5.4	0 24.3
19	3 51 59.1	26 38.8	28 59.4	6♊ .5	0♐ 9.7	21 59.7	22 6.2	26 54.0	4 20.1	6 58.1	1 7.5	0 24.7
20	3 55 55.7	27 39.3	28 56.3	20 14.6	1 43.8	23 13.0	22 30.6	27 3.1	4 27.2	6 57.7	1 9.5	0 25.1
21	3 59 52.3	28 39.9	28 53.1	4♋37.5	3 17.7	24 26.4	22 55.4	27 12.2	4 34.3	6 57.3	1 11.6	0 25.4
22	4 3 48.8	29 40.5	28 49.9	19 4.1	4 51.5	25 39.8	23 20.5	27 21.1	4 41.4	6 56.8	1 13.6	0 25.7
23	4 7 45.4	0♐41.1	28 46.7	3♌29.8	6 25.0	26 53.3	23 46.0	27 30.0	4 48.5	6 56.2	1 15.6	0 26.0
24	4 11 41.9	1 41.8	28 43.5	17 50.2	7 58.5	28 6.9	24 11.8	27 38.7	4 55.6	6 55.6	1 17.7	0 26.3
25	4 15 38.5	2 42.5	28 40.4	2♍ 2.3	9 31.8	29 20.5	24 38.0	27 47.3	5 2.7	6 55.0	1 19.7	0 26.6
26	4 19 35.0	3 43.2	28 37.2	16 3.8	11 4.9	0♏34.2	25 4.5	27 55.8	5 9.9	6 54.2	1 21.6	0 26.8
27	4 23 31.6	4 44.0	28 34.0	29 53.5	12 37.9	1 48.0	25 31.3	28 4.1	5 17.0	6 53.5	1 23.6	0 26.9
28	4 27 28.2	5 44.7	28 30.8	13♎30.6	14 10.8	3 1.8	25 58.4	28 12.3	5 24.1	6 52.6	1 25.5	0 27.1
29	4 31 24.7	6 45.5	28 27.7	26 54.8	15 43.6	4 15.6	26 25.9	28 20.4	5 31.2	6 51.7	1 27.4	0 27.2
30	4 35 21.3	7 46.3	28 24.5	10♏ 6.1	17 16.3	5 29.6	26 53.6	28 28.4	5 38.3	6 50.8	1 29.3	0 27.2

LATITUDE

DAY	EPHEM. SID. TIME	☉	☊	☾	☿	♀	♂	♃	♄	♅	♆	♇
1	2 41 1.2	0 .0	0 .0	3S30.1	1N12.2	1N30.0	2S14.6	1N 4.1	1N43.0	0N35.7	1N41.2	10N51.3
4	2 52 50.8	0 .0	0 .0	0 9.2	0 53.3	1 35.7	2 3.1	1 4.5	1 42.6	0 35.8	1 41.2	10 52.4
7	3 4 40.5	0 .0	0 .0	3N 5.6	0 33.5	1 40.6	1 52.1	1 5.1	1 42.3	0 35.9	1 41.2	10 53.6
10	3 16 30.1	0 .0	0 .0	5 .7	0 13.3	1 44.6	1 41.5	1 5.6	1 42.1	0 36.0	1 41.3	10 54.7
13	3 28 19.8	0 .0	0 .0	5 2.0	0S 6.9	1 47.8	1 31.5	1 6.1	1 41.8	0 36.1	1 41.4	10 55.9
16	3 40 9.5	0 .0	0 .0	2 58.2	0 26.8	1 50.2	1 22.0	1 6.7	1 41.6	0 36.3	1 41.4	10 57.1
19	3 51 59.1	0 .0	0 .0	0S38.7	0 46.0	1 51.7	1 12.9	1 7.3	1 41.4	0 36.4	1 41.5	10 58.2
22	4 3 48.8	0 .0	0 .0	4 3.5	1 4.3	1 52.5	1 4.3	1 7.9	1 41.2	0 36.5	1 41.6	10 59.4
25	4 15 38.5	0 .0	0 .0	5 16.8	1 21.3	1 52.4	0 56.1	1 8.5	1 41.0	0 36.6	1 41.7	11 .6
28	4 27 28.2	0 .0	0 .0	3 46.7	1 36.7	1 51.6	0 48.4	1 9.1	1 40.9	0 36.7	1 41.8	11 1.8

RIGHT ASCENSION

DAY	EPHEM. SID. TIME	☉	☊	☾	☿	♀	♂	♃	♄	♅	♆	♇
1	2 41 1.2	6♏10.3	27♏45.6	14♎32.7	29♎23.2	0♎48.1	18♓ 3.1	24♍47.7	0♐31.9	9♌29.2	28♎57.9	6♍23.0
2	2 44 57.7	7 9.1	27 42.3	27 52.3	0♏56.4	1 54.8	18 16.1	24 57.8	0 38.9	9 29.8	28 60.0	6 24.0
3	2 48 54.3	8 8.2	27 38.9	11♏23.1	2 29.8	3 1.5	18 29.7	25 7.8	0 45.9	9 30.5	29 2.2	6 25.0
4	2 52 50.8	9 7.4	27 35.6	25 1.5	4 3.2	4 8.3	18 43.9	25 17.7	0 52.9	9 31.0	29 4.3	6 26.0
5	2 56 47.4	10 6.8	27 32.3	8♐39.0	5 36.8	5 15.2	18 58.5	25 27.5	0 60.0	9 31.4	29 6.4	6 27.0
6	3 0 43.9	11 6.5	27 29.0	22 5.4	7 10.5	6 22.1	19 13.7	25 37.3	1 7.1	9 31.8	29 8.5	6 27.9
7	3 4 40.5	12 6.3	27 25.7	5♑11.0	8 44.4	7 29.1	19 29.5	25 46.9	1 14.2	9 32.1	29 10.6	6 28.8
8	3 8 37.0	13 6.4	27 22.4	17 49.8	10 18.5	8 36.2	19 45.7	25 56.5	1 21.3	9 32.4	29 12.6	6 29.7
9	3 12 33.6	14 6.6	27 19.1	0♒ .5	11 52.7	9 43.4	20 2.4	26 6.0	1 28.5	9 32.6	29 14.7	6 30.5
10	3 16 30.1	15 7.1	27 15.8	11 46.1	13 27.1	10 50.7	20 19.6	26 15.4	1 35.7	9 32.8	29 16.8	6 31.3
11	3 20 26.7	16 7.7	27 12.5	23 13.3	15 1.8	11 58.1	20 37.2	26 24.7	1 42.9	9 32.9	29 18.9	6 32.1
12	3 24 23.3	17 8.6	27 9.2	4♓31.5	16 36.7	13 5.6	20 55.3	26 34.0	1 50.1	9 32.9	29 20.9	6 32.9
13	3 28 19.8	18 9.7	27 5.9	15 51.2	18 11.8	14 13.2	21 13.9	26 43.1	1 57.4	9 32.9	29 23.0	6 33.6
14	3 32 16.4	19 11.0	27 2.6	27 24.3	19 47.2	15 21.0	21 32.9	26 52.2	2 4.6	9 32.9	29 25.0	6 34.3
15	3 36 12.9	20 12.5	26 59.3	9♈22.6	21 22.9	16 28.9	21 52.3	27 1.1	2 11.9	9R32.7	29 27.0	6 35.0
16	3 40 9.5	21 14.2	26 56.0	21 57.4	22 58.9	17 36.9	22 12.0	27 10.0	2 19.2	9 32.6	29 29.0	6 35.6
17	3 44 6.0	22 16.1	26 52.7	5♉17.0	24 35.2	18 45.1	22 32.2	27 18.8	2 26.5	9 32.3	29 31.1	6 36.2
18	3 48 2.6	23 18.2	26 49.4	19 24.5	26 11.8	19 53.5	22 52.8	27 27.5	2 33.9	9 32.0	29 33.0	6 36.8
19	3 51 59.1	24 20.6	26 46.1	4♊14.5	27 48.8	21 2.0	23 13.7	27 36.1	2 41.2	9 31.7	29 35.0	6 37.4
20	3 55 55.7	25 23.1	26 42.8	19 32.1	29 26.1	22 10.7	23 35.1	27 44.6	2 48.6	9 31.3	29 37.0	6 37.9
21	3 59 52.3	26 25.8	26 39.5	4♋55.4	1♐ 3.8	23 19.6	23 56.7	27 52.9	2 56.0	9 30.8	29 39.0	6 38.4
22	4 3 48.8	27 28.8	26 36.2	20 2.8	2 41.9	24 28.7	24 18.7	28 1.2	3 3.3	9 30.3	29 40.9	6 38.9
23	4 7 45.4	28 31.9	26 32.9	4♌39.4	4 20.3	25 38.0	24 41.0	28 9.4	3 10.7	9 29.8	29 42.8	6 39.3
24	4 11 41.9	29 35.3	26 29.6	18 40.0	5 59.1	26 47.5	25 3.7	28 17.5	3 18.2	9 29.2	29 44.8	6 39.8
25	4 15 38.5	0♐38.9	26 26.3	2♍ 8.2	7 38.3	27 57.2	25 26.7	28 25.5	3 25.6	9 28.5	29 46.7	6 40.2
26	4 19 35.0	1 42.6	26 23.0	15 12.9	9 17.8	29 7.2	25 50.0	28 33.3	3 33.0	9 27.8	29 48.6	6 40.5
27	4 23 31.6	2 46.5	26 19.7	28 5.4	10 57.6	0♏17.3	26 13.6	28 41.1	3 40.5	9 27.0	29 50.5	6 40.9
28	4 27 28.2	3 50.7	26 16.4	10♎56.8	12 37.8	1 27.7	26 37.5	28 48.7	3 47.9	9 26.1	29 52.3	6 41.2
29	4 31 24.7	4 55.0	26 13.2	23 55.8	14 18.3	2 38.4	27 1.7	28 56.2	3 55.3	9 25.3	29 54.2	6 41.4
30	4 35 21.3	5 59.4	26 9.9	7♏ 7.5	15 59.0	3 49.2	27 26.2	29 3.6	4 2.7	9 24.3	29 56.0	6 41.7

DECLINATION

DAY	EPHEM. SID. TIME	☉	☊	☾	☿	♀	♂	♃	♄	♅	♆	♇
1	2 41 1.2	14S21.4	0S21.1	10S .7	10S43.8	1N17.2	7S34.0	3N24.9	18S56.0	19N 7.1	10S 3.7	21N31.5
4	2 52 50.8	15 18.2	0 21.1	19 43.1	12 42.4	0S 3.3	7 4.3	3 12.5	19 .3	19 6.8	10 6.0	21 31.5
7	3 4 40.5	16 12.7	0 21.0	20 15.7	14 35.7	1 24.5	6 33.1	3 .5	19 4.5	19 6.6	10 8.2	21 31.7
10	3 16 30.1	17 4.8	0 21.0	12 43.5	16 22.5	2 46.2	6 .4	2 48.7	19 8.8	19 6.6	10 10.4	21 32.0
13	3 28 19.8	17 54.3	0 21.0	0 35.6	18 2.0	4 7.9	5 26.5	2 37.4	19 12.9	19 6.7	10 12.6	21 32.4
16	3 40 9.5	18 40.9	0 20.9	12N24.3	19 33.5	5 29.5	4 51.3	2 26.3	19 17.1	19 6.9	10 14.8	21 32.9
19	3 51 59.1	19 24.6	0 20.9	20 40.7	20 56.3	6 50.4	4 15.0	2 15.7	19 21.2	19 7.2	10 16.8	21 33.5
22	4 3 48.8	20 5.1	0 20.8	18 4.1	22 9.8	8 10.5	3 37.7	2 5.5	19 25.2	19 7.7	10 18.9	21 34.2
25	4 15 38.5	20 42.3	0 20.8	5 48.9	23 13.4	9 29.3	2 59.5	1 55.6	19 29.2	19 8.2	10 20.9	21 35.0
28	4 27 28.2	21 16.1	0 20.8	8S48.7	24 6.4	10 46.5	2 20.4	1 46.2	19 33.1	19 8.9	10 22.8	21 36.0

DECEMBER 1956

DAY	EPHEM. SID. TIME	☉	☊	☾	☿	♀	♂	♃	♄	♅	♆	♇
		LONGITUDE										
	h m s	° ′	° ′	° ′	° ′	° ′	° ′	° ′	° ′	° ′	° ′	° ′
1	4 39 17.8	8♐47.2	28♏21.3	23♏ 4.3	18♐48.9	6♏43.5	27♓21.6	28♍36.3	5♐45.5	6♌49.8	1♏31.2	0♍27.3
2	4 43 14.4	9 48.0	28 18.1	5♐49.5	20 21.4	7 57.5	27 50.0	28 44.0	5 52.6	6R48.8	1 33.1	0 27.3
3	4 47 10.9	10 48.9	28 15.0	18 22.0	21 53.7	9 11.6	28 18.6	28 51.5	5 59.7	6 47.7	1 34.9	0 27.3
4	4 51 7.5	11 49.8	28 11.8	0♑42.6	23 26.0	10 25.6	28 47.5	28 59.0	6 6.8	6 46.6	1 36.7	0R27.2
5	4 55 4.1	12 50.7	28 8.6	12 52.5	24 58.1	11 39.8	29 16.6	29 6.3	6 13.9	6 45.4	1 38.5	0 27.2
6	4 59 .6	13 51.6	28 5.4	24 53.4	26 30.0	12 53.9	29 46.0	29 13.4	6 21.0	6 44.1	1 40.3	0 27.1
7	5 2 57.2	14 52.6	28 2.3	6♒47.9	28 1.8	14 8.1	0♈15.7	29 20.5	6 28.0	6 42.8	1 42.1	0 26.9
8	5 6 53.7	15 53.5	27 59.1	18 39.2	29 33.3	15 22.4	0 45.6	29 27.4	6 35.1	6 41.5	1 43.8	0 26.8
9	5 10 50.3	16 54.5	27 55.9	0♓31.1	1♑ 4.5	16 36.7	1 15.8	29 34.1	6 42.2	6 40.1	1 45.5	0 26.6
10	5 14 46.8	17 55.5	27 52.7	12 27.9	2 35.4	17 51.0	1 46.2	29 40.7	6 49.2	6 38.7	1 47.2	0 26.3
11	5 18 43.4	18 56.5	27 49.5	24 34.2	4 5.9	19 5.3	2 16.8	29 47.1	6 56.2	6 37.2	1 48.9	0 26.1
12	5 22 40.0	19 57.4	27 46.4	6♈54.8	5 35.9	20 19.7	2 47.6	29 53.4	7 3.2	6 35.7	1 50.5	0 25.8
13	5 26 36.5	20 58.5	27 43.2	19 34.2	7 5.4	21 34.1	3 18.6	29 59.6	7 10.2	6 34.1	1 52.1	0 25.5
14	5 30 33.1	21 59.5	27 40.0	2♉36.1	8 34.1	22 48.5	3 49.9	0♎ 5.6	7 17.2	6 32.5	1 53.7	0 25.1
15	5 34 29.6	23 .5	27 36.8	16 3.2	10 2.1	24 3.0	4 21.4	0 11.4	7 24.2	6 30.9	1 55.4	0 24.8
16	5 38 26.2	24 1.6	27 33.7	29 56.2	11 29.0	25 17.5	4 53.0	0 17.1	7 31.1	6 29.2	1 56.9	0 24.4
17	5 42 22.7	25 2.6	27 30.5	14♊13.4	12 54.7	26 32.0	5 24.8	0 22.7	7 38.0	6 27.5	1 58.4	0 23.9
18	5 46 19.3	26 3.7	27 27.3	28 50.9	14 19.0	27 46.6	5 56.8	0 28.0	7 44.9	6 25.7	1 59.9	0 23.5
19	5 50 15.9	27 4.7	27 24.1	13♋41.9	15 41.6	29 1.2	6 28.9	0 33.2	7 51.8	6 23.9	2 1.4	0 23.0
20	5 54 12.4	28 5.8	27 21.0	28 38.2	17 2.2	0♐15.8	7 1.3	0 38.3	7 58.6	6 22.1	2 2.8	0 22.5
21	5 58 9.0	29 6.9	27 17.8	13♌31.2	18 20.5	1 30.4	7 33.8	0 43.2	8 5.5	6 20.2	2 4.2	0 21.9
22	6 2 5.5	0♑ 8.0	27 14.6	28 13.2	19 36.1	2 45.0	8 6.4	0 47.9	8 12.3	6 18.2	2 5.6	0 21.3
23	6 6 2.1	1 9.1	27 11.4	12♍38.5	20 48.4	3 59.7	8 39.2	0 52.4	8 19.0	6 16.3	2 7.0	0 20.7
24	6 9 58.6	2 10.2	27 8.2	26 43.9	21 57.0	5 14.4	9 12.2	0 56.8	8 25.8	6 14.3	2 8.3	0 20.1
25	6 13 55.2	3 11.3	27 5.1	10♎28.3	23 1.2	6 29.2	9 45.3	1 1.0	8 32.5	6 12.2	2 9.6	0 19.4
26	6 17 51.8	4 12.4	27 1.9	23 52.6	24 .4	7 43.9	10 18.6	1 5.1	8 39.1	6 10.1	2 10.9	0 18.8
27	6 21 48.3	5 13.6	26 58.7	6♏58.7	24 53.8	8 58.7	10 52.0	1 8.9	8 45.8	6 8.0	2 12.2	0 18.0
28	6 25 44.9	6 14.7	26 55.5	19 49.0	25 40.6	10 13.5	11 25.6	1 12.6	8 52.4	6 5.9	2 13.4	0 17.3
29	6 29 41.4	7 15.9	26 52.4	2♐26.1	26 19.9	11 28.3	11 59.3	1 16.1	8 58.9	6 3.7	2 14.6	0 16.5
30	6 33 38.0	8 17.1	26 49.2	14 52.0	26 50.9	12 43.1	12 33.1	1 19.5	9 5.5	6 1.5	2 15.7	0 15.7
31	6 37 34.5	9 18.3	26 46.0	27 8.6	27 12.5	13 58.0	13 7.1	1 22.6	9 12.0	5 59.2	2 16.9	0 14.9
		LATITUDE										
1	4 39 17.8	0 .0	0 .0	0S33.2	1S50.3	1N50.1	0S41.0	1N 9.8	1N40.7	0N36.8	1N41.9	11N 3.0
4	4 51 7.5	0 .0	0 .0	2N46.3	2 1.7	1 47.8	0 34.0	1 10.5	1 40.6	0 36.9	1 42.0	11 4.2
7	5 2 57.2	0 .0	0 .0	4 52.4	2 10.4	1 44.8	0 27.4	1 11.2	1 40.5	0 37.0	1 42.1	11 5.4
10	5 14 46.8	0 .0	0 .0	5 6.6	2 15.9	1 41.2	0 21.1	1 11.9	1 40.5	0 37.1	1 42.3	11 6.6
13	5 26 36.5	0 .0	0 .0	3 20.1	2 17.6	1 37.0	0 15.2	1 12.6	1 40.4	0 37.2	1 42.4	11 7.7
16	5 38 26.2	0 .0	0 .0	0S 5.5	2 14.7	1 32.3	0 9.5	1 13.4	1 40.4	0 37.3	1 42.5	11 8.9
19	5 50 15.9	0 .0	0 .0	3 41.1	2 6.1	1 26.9	0 4.2	1 14.1	1 40.4	0 37.4	1 42.7	11 10.0
22	6 2 5.5	0 .0	0 .0	5 12.4	1 50.6	1 21.2	0N .8	1 14.9	1 40.4	0 37.5	1 42.8	11 11.1
25	6 13 55.2	0 .0	0 .0	3 52.8	1 27.0	1 14.9	0 5.6	1 15.7	1 40.5	0 37.6	1 43.0	11 12.2
28	6 25 44.9	0 .0	0 .0	0 47.8	0 53.8	1 8.3	0 10.2	1 16.5	1 40.5	0 37.7	1 43.1	11 13.2
31	6 37 34.5	0 .0	0 .0	2N28.5	0 10.1	1 1.4	0 14.4	1 17.3	1 40.6	0 37.8	1 43.3	11 14.3
		RIGHT ASCENSION										
1	4 39 17.8	7♐ 4.1	26♏ 6.6	20♏31.6	17♐40.1	5♏ .4	27♓51.0	29♍10.9	4♐10.2	9♌23.3	29♎57.8	6♍41.9
2	4 43 14.4	8 8.9	26 3.3	4♐ 2.7	19 21.3	6 11.8	28 16.1	29 18.1	4 17.6	9R22.3	29 59.6	6 42.0
3	4 47 10.9	9 13.9	25 60.0	17 31.0	21 2.7	7 23.4	28 41.4	29 25.1	4 25.0	9 21.1	0♏ 1.3	6 42.2
4	4 51 7.5	10 19.0	25 56.7	0♑45.5	22 44.2	8 35.3	29 7.0	29 32.1	4 32.4	9 20.0	0 3.1	6 42.3
5	4 55 4.1	11 24.2	25 53.4	13 37.1	24 25.8	9 47.5	29 32.8	29 38.8	4 39.9	9 18.8	0 4.8	6 42.4
6	4 59 .6	12 29.6	25 50.1	26 .6	26 7.4	10 59.9	29 58.9	29 45.5	4 47.3	9 17.5	0 6.5	6 42.4
7	5 2 57.2	13 35.2	25 46.8	7♒55.9	27 49.0	12 12.7	0♈25.3	29 52.1	4 54.7	9 16.2	0 8.2	6 42.4
8	5 6 53.7	14 40.8	25 43.5	19 27.6	29 30.4	13 25.7	0 51.9	29 58.5	5 2.1	9 14.9	0 9.9	6 42.4
9	5 10 50.3	15 46.6	25 40.2	0♓43.2	1♑11.5	14 39.0	1 18.7	0♎ 4.7	5 9.4	9 13.5	0 11.6	6 42.4
10	5 14 46.8	16 52.4	25 37.0	11 52.9	2 52.3	15 52.5	1 45.8	0 10.9	5 16.8	9 12.0	0 13.2	6R42.3
11	5 18 43.4	17 58.4	25 33.7	23 8.3	4 32.7	17 6.4	2 13.1	0 16.9	5 24.2	9 10.5	0 14.8	6 42.2
12	5 22 40.0	19 4.5	25 30.4	4♈42.0	6 12.4	18 20.5	2 40.6	0 22.8	5 31.5	9 8.9	0 16.4	6 42.1
13	5 26 36.5	20 10.6	25 27.1	16 46.8	7 51.4	19 35.0	3 8.3	0 28.5	5 38.8	9 7.4	0 17.9	6 42.0
14	5 30 33.1	21 16.9	25 23.8	29 34.6	9 29.4	20 49.7	3 36.2	0 34.1	5 46.2	9 5.7	0 19.5	6 41.8
15	5 34 29.6	22 23.2	25 20.5	13♉13.9	11 6.3	22 4.8	4 4.4	0 39.6	5 53.5	9 4.1	0 21.0	6 41.6
16	5 38 26.2	23 29.6	25 17.2	27 46.3	12 41.9	23 20.1	4 32.7	0 44.9	6 .8	9 2.3	0 22.5	6 41.4
17	5 42 22.7	24 36.0	25 14.0	13♊ 3.5	14 15.8	24 35.7	5 1.2	0 50.1	6 8.0	9 .6	0 24.0	6 41.1
18	5 46 19.3	25 42.5	25 10.7	28 46.1	15 47.9	25 51.7	5 29.9	0 55.1	6 15.3	8 58.8	0 25.5	6 40.8
19	5 50 15.9	26 49.0	25 7.4	14♋28.8	17 17.8	27 7.9	5 58.7	0 60.0	6 22.5	8 56.9	0 26.9	6 40.4
20	5 54 12.4	27 55.5	25 4.1	29 48.4	18 45.1	28 24.4	6 27.8	1 4.7	6 29.7	8 55.0	0 28.3	6 40.1
21	5 58 9.0	29 2.1	25 .8	14♌31.1	20 9.4	29 41.2	6 57.0	1 9.3	6 36.8	8 53.1	0 29.6	6 39.7
22	6 2 5.5	0♑ 8.7	24 57.5	28 34.4	21 30.3	0♐58.3	7 26.4	1 13.7	6 43.9	8 51.1	0 31.0	6 39.3
23	6 6 2.1	1 15.3	24 54.3	12♍ 4.0	22 47.2	2 15.7	7 56.0	1 18.0	6 51.1	8 49.1	0 32.3	6 38.8
24	6 9 58.6	2 21.9	24 51.0	25 10.5	23 59.6	3 33.3	8 25.7	1 22.1	6 58.1	8 47.0	0 33.6	6 38.3
25	6 13 55.2	3 28.5	24 47.7	8♎ 5.3	25 6.8	4 51.3	8 55.6	1 26.1	7 5.2	8 44.9	0 34.9	6 37.8
26	6 17 51.8	4 35.1	24 44.4	20 59.0	26 8.1	6 9.5	9 25.7	1 29.9	7 12.2	8 42.8	0 36.1	6 37.3
27	6 21 48.3	5 41.6	24 41.1	3♏59.0	27 2.8	7 27.9	9 55.9	1 33.6	7 19.2	8 40.7	0 37.3	6 36.8
28	6 25 44.9	6 48.2	24 37.9	17 8.6	27 50.0	8 46.7	10 26.3	1 37.1	7 26.1	8 38.5	0 38.5	6 36.2
29	6 29 41.4	7 54.7	24 34.6	0♐26.0	28 28.9	10 5.6	10 56.9	1 40.4	7 33.1	8 36.2	0 39.6	6 35.6
30	6 33 38.0	9 1.1	24 31.3	13 45.0	28 58.5	11 24.8	11 27.6	1 43.6	7 40.0	8 34.0	0 40.8	6 34.9
31	6 37 34.5	10 7.5	24 28.0	26 56.6	29 18.0	12 44.3	11 58.5	1 46.6	7 46.8	8 31.7	0 41.9	6 34.2
		DECLINATION										
1	4 39 17.8	21S46.2	0S20.7	19S 4.7	24S48.3	12S 1.8	1S40.6	1N37.3	19S37.0	19N 9.8	10S24.7	21N37.0
4	4 51 7.5	22 12.6	0 20.7	20 40.2	25 18.4	13 14.7	1 .0	1 28.9	19 40.8	19 10.7	10 26.5	21 38.1
7	5 2 57.2	22 35.1	0 20.7	13 51.3	25 36.1	14 24.9	0 18.9	1 21.0	19 44.5	19 11.7	10 28.2	21 39.3
10	5 14 46.8	22 53.7	0 20.6	2 9.5	25 41.0	15 32.0	0N22.9	1 13.6	19 48.1	19 12.9	10 29.8	21 40.6
13	5 26 36.5	23 8.2	0 20.6	10N44.6	25 32.6	16 35.8	1 5.1	1 6.8	19 51.6	19 14.1	10 31.4	21 42.0
16	5 38 26.2	23 18.5	0 20.5	20 3.0	25 11.0	17 35.8	1 47.7	1 .5	19 55.0	19 15.4	10 32.9	21 43.5
19	5 50 15.9	23 24.7	0 20.5	19 4.4	24 36.4	18 31.7	2 30.6	0 54.8	19 58.3	19 16.8	10 34.3	21 45.0
22	6 2 5.5	23 26.6	0 20.5	7 12.2	23 50.1	19 23.2	3 13.7	0 49.7	20 1.5	19 18.3	10 35.6	21 46.7
25	6 13 55.2	23 24.3	0 20.4	7S42.8	22 54.5	20 9.9	3 57.1	0 45.2	20 4.7	19 19.9	10 36.9	21 48.4
28	6 25 44.9	23 17.8	0 20.4	18 27.7	21 53.5	20 51.6	4 40.6	0 41.3	20 7.7	19 21.6	10 38.0	21 50.1
31	6 37 34.5	23 7.0	0 20.4	20 56.3	20 53.2	21 27.9	5 24.1	0 38.1	20 10.6	19 23.3	10 39.0	21 51.9

JANUARY 1957

DAY	EPHEM. SID. TIME	☉	☊	☽	☿	♀	♂	♃	♄	♅	♆	♇
		LONGITUDE										
	h m s	° ′	° ′	° ′	° ′	° ′	° ′	° ′	° ′	° ′	° ′	° ′
1	6 41 31.1	10♑19.4	26♏42.8	9♑17.3	27♑24.0	15♐12.8	13♈41.2	1♎25.6	9♐18.4	5♌57.0	2♏18.0	0♍14.1
2	6 45 27.7	11 20.6	26 39.7	21 19.4	27 24.6	16 27.7	14 15.4	1 28.4	9 24.9	5R54.7	2 19.0	0R13.2
3	6 49 24.2	12 21.8	26 36.5	3♒16.1	27R13.6	17 42.6	14 49.8	1 31.0	9 31.2	5 52.4	2 20.1	0 12.3
4	6 53 20.8	13 23.0	26 33.3	15 8.9	26 50.8	18 57.5	15 24.2	1 33.4	9 37.6	5 50.0	2 21.1	0 11.4
5	6 57 17.3	14 24.2	26 30.1	26 59.9	26 16.3	20 12.4	15 58.8	1 35.7	9 43.9	5 47.7	2 22.1	0 10.5
6	7 1 13.9	15 25.4	26 27.0	8♓51.5	25 30.3	21 27.3	16 33.5	1 37.8	9 50.2	5 45.3	2 23.0	0 9.5
7	7 5 10.4	16 26.5	26 23.8	20 46.9	24 33.9	22 42.3	17 8.3	1 39.6	9 56.4	5 42.9	2 23.9	0 8.6
8	7 9 7.0	17 27.7	26 20.6	2♈50.2	23 28.5	23 57.2	17 43.2	1 41.3	10 2.5	5 40.4	2 24.8	0 7.5
9	7 13 3.6	18 28.8	26 17.4	15 5.6	22 15.9	25 12.1	18 18.2	1 42.8	10 8.6	5 38.0	2 25.7	0 6.5
10	7 17 .1	19 30.0	26 14.2	27 38.2	20 58.5	26 27.1	18 53.3	1 44.1	10 14.7	5 35.5	2 26.5	0 5.5
11	7 20 56.7	20 31.1	26 11.1	10♉32.5	19 38.8	27 42.0	19 28.5	1 45.2	10 20.7	5 33.0	2 27.3	0 4.4
12	7 24 53.2	21 32.2	26 7.9	23 52.8	18 19.3	28 57.0	20 3.8	1 46.1	10 26.6	5 30.5	2 28.0	0 3.3
13	7 28 49.8	22 33.3	26 4.7	7♊41.7	17 2.4	0♑11.9	20 39.2	1 46.9	10 32.5	5 28.0	2 28.7	0 2.2
14	7 32 46.3	23 34.4	26 1.5	21 59.9	15 50.4	1 26.9	21 14.6	1 47.4	10 38.4	5 25.4	2 29.4	0 1.0
15	7 36 42.9	24 35.5	25 58.4	6♋44.8	14 45.0	2 41.8	21 50.2	1 47.8	10 44.2	5 22.9	2 30.0	29♌59.9
16	7 40 39.5	25 36.6	25 55.2	21 50.0	13 47.6	3 56.8	22 25.8	1 47.9	10 49.9	5 20.3	2 30.7	29 58.7
17	7 44 36.0	26 37.7	25 52.0	7♌ 6.5	12 59.0	5 11.8	23 1.5	1 47.9	10 55.6	5 17.7	2 31.2	29 57.5
18	7 48 32.6	27 38.7	25 48.8	22 22.9	12 19.7	6 26.8	23 37.2	1R47.7	11 1.2	5 15.1	2 31.8	29 56.3
19	7 52 29.1	28 39.8	25 45.7	7♍28.3	11 50.0	7 41.8	24 13.1	1 47.3	11 6.8	5 12.5	2 32.3	29 55.1
20	7 56 25.7	29 40.8	25 42.5	22 13.6	11 29.6	8 56.8	24 48.9	1 46.7	11 12.3	5 9.9	2 32.8	29 53.8
21	8 0 22.2	0♒41.9	25 39.3	6♎33.4	11 18.3	10 11.8	25 24.9	1 45.9	11 17.8	5 7.3	2 33.2	29 52.5
22	8 4 18.8	1 42.9	25 36.1	20 25.4	11 15.6	11 26.8	26 .9	1 44.9	11 23.1	5 4.7	2 33.6	29 51.3
23	8 8 15.4	2 43.9	25 32.9	3♏50.6	11D20.9	12 41.8	26 37.0	1 43.7	11 28.5	5 2.1	2 34.0	29 50.0
24	8 12 11.9	3 45.0	25 29.8	16 51.6	11 33.7	13 56.8	27 13.2	1 42.3	11 33.7	4 59.5	2 34.4	29 48.7
25	8 16 8.5	4 46.0	25 26.6	29 32.6	11 53.4	15 11.9	27 49.4	1 40.8	11 38.9	4 56.8	2 34.7	29 47.3
26	8 20 5.0	5 47.0	25 23.4	11♐57.6	12 19.5	16 27.0	28 25.8	1 39.0	11 44.1	4 54.3	2 35.0	29 46.0
27	8 24 1.6	6 48.0	25 20.2	24 10.6	12 51.2	17 42.0	29 2.1	1 37.1	11 49.2	4 51.6	2 35.2	29 44.7
28	8 27 58.1	7 49.0	25 17.1	6♑15.1	13 28.2	18 57.0	29 38.5	1 35.0	11 54.2	4 49.0	2 35.4	29 43.3
29	8 31 54.7	8 50.0	25 13.9	18 13.8	14 10.0	20 12.1	0♉15.0	1 32.6	11 59.1	4 46.4	2 35.6	29 41.9
30	8 35 51.2	9 50.9	25 10.7	0♒ 8.8	14 56.0	21 27.1	0 51.5	1 30.1	12 3.9	4 43.8	2 35.7	29 40.5
31	8 39 47.8	10 51.9	25 7.5	12 1.6	15 46.0	22 42.1	1 28.1	1 27.4	12 8.7	4 41.2	2 35.8	29 39.1

DAY	EPHEM. SID. TIME	☉	☊	☽	☿	♀	♂	♃	♄	♅	♆	♇
		LATITUDE										
1	6 41 31.1	0 .0	0 .0	3N22.3	0N 6.6	0N59.0	0N15.8	1N17.6	1N40.6	0N37.8	1N43.4	11N14.6
4	6 53 20.8	0 .0	0 .0	4 59.7	0 1.9	0 51.7	0 19.8	1 18.4	1 40.7	0 37.8	1 43.5	11 15.6
7	7 5 10.4	0 .0	0 .0	4 42.9	1 59.1	0 44.1	0 23.6	1 19.2	1 40.9	0 37.9	1 43.7	11 16.5
10	7 17 .1	0 .0	0 .0	2 33.9	2 47.7	0 36.4	0 27.1	1 20.1	1 41.0	0 38.0	1 43.9	11 17.4
13	7 28 49.8	0 .0	0 .0	0S53.9	3 17.6	0 28.5	0 30.5	1 20.9	1 41.2	0 38.0	1 44.1	11 18.3
16	7 40 39.5	0 .0	0 .0	4 8.1	3 25.2	0 20.6	0 33.7	1 21.8	1 41.3	0 38.0	1 44.2	11 19.1
19	7 52 29.1	0 .0	0 .0	4 58.8	3 14.3	0 12.6	0 36.7	1 22.6	1 41.5	0 38.1	1 44.4	11 19.9
22	8 4 18.8	0 .0	0 .0	3 .4	2 51.4	0 4.7	0 39.6	1 23.4	1 41.7	0 38.1	1 44.6	11 20.7
25	8 16 8.5	0 .0	0 .0	0N15.4	2 22.2	0S 3.1	0 42.2	1 24.2	1 42.0	0 38.1	1 44.8	11 21.3
28	8 27 58.1	0 .0	0 .0	3 13.5	1 50.5	0 10.8	0 44.8	1 25.0	1 42.2	0 38.2	1 45.0	11 22.0
31	8 39 47.8	0 .0	0 .0	4 51.5	1 18.5	0 18.4	0 47.2	1 25.8	1 42.5	0 38.2	1 45.2	11 22.6

DAY	EPHEM. SID. TIME	☉	☊	☽	☿	♀	♂	♃	♄	♅	♆	♇
		RIGHT ASCENSION										
1	6 41 31.1	11♑13.8	24♏24.7	9♑51.5	29♑26.6	14♐ 3.9	12♈29.5	1♎49.4	7♐53.6	8♌29.4	0♏42.9	6♍33.5
2	6 45 27.7	12 20.0	24 21.5	22 22.6	29R23.5	15 23.8	13 .7	1 52.1	8 .4	8R27.0	0 44.0	6R32.8
3	6 49 24.2	13 26.2	24 18.2	4♒27.3	29 8.2	16 43.9	13 32.0	1 54.6	8 7.1	8 24.6	0 45.0	6 32.1
4	6 53 20.8	14 32.3	24 14.9	16 7.0	28 40.5	18 4.1	14 3.4	1 56.9	8 13.8	8 22.2	0 46.0	6 31.3
5	6 57 17.3	15 38.3	24 11.6	27 26.9	28 .6	19 24.6	14 35.1	1 59.1	8 20.5	8 19.8	0 47.0	6 30.6
6	7 1 13.9	16 44.1	24 8.4	8♓34.7	27 9.0	20 45.2	15 6.9	2 1.1	8 27.1	8 17.4	0 47.9	6 29.7
7	7 5 10.4	17 49.9	24 5.1	19 40.6	26 6.6	22 6.0	15 38.8	2 2.9	8 33.6	8 14.9	0 48.8	6 28.9
8	7 9 7.0	18 55.5	24 1.8	0♈55.9	24 55.2	23 26.9	16 10.8	2 4.6	8 40.1	8 12.4	0 49.6	6 28.0
9	7 13 3.6	20 1.0	23 58.5	12 32.5	23 36.7	24 47.9	16 43.0	2 6.1	8 46.5	8 9.9	0 50.5	6 27.1
10	7 17 .1	21 6.3	23 55.3	24 42.9	22 13.5	26 9.0	17 15.3	2 7.4	8 52.9	8 7.3	0 51.3	6 26.2
11	7 20 56.7	22 11.5	23 52.0	7♉37.9	20 48.2	27 30.2	17 47.7	2 8.5	8 59.3	8 4.8	0 52.0	6 25.3
12	7 24 53.2	23 16.5	23 48.7	21 24.8	19 23.6	28 51.6	18 20.3	2 9.5	9 5.6	8 2.2	0 52.8	6 24.3
13	7 28 49.8	24 21.4	23 45.5	6♊ 3.9	18 2.1	0♑12.9	18 53.0	2 10.2	9 11.8	7 59.6	0 53.5	6 23.3
14	7 32 46.3	25 26.1	23 42.2	21 25.6	16 45.9	1 34.4	19 25.8	2 10.8	9 18.0	7 57.0	0 54.1	6 22.3
15	7 36 42.9	26 30.7	23 38.9	7♋10.3	15 36.9	2 55.9	19 58.8	2 11.3	9 24.1	7 54.4	0 54.8	6 21.3
16	7 40 39.5	27 35.1	23 35.6	22 54.1	14 36.5	4 17.4	20 31.8	2 11.5	9 30.2	7 51.7	0 55.4	6 20.3
17	7 44 36.0	28 39.3	23 32.4	8♌16.1	13 45.5	5 38.9	21 5.0	2 11.6	9 36.2	7 49.1	0 56.0	6 19.2
18	7 48 32.6	29 43.4	23 29.1	23 4.8	13 4.4	7 .4	21 38.3	2R11.5	9 42.2	7 46.4	0 56.5	6 18.1
19	7 52 29.1	0♒47.3	23 25.8	7♍18.6	12 33.5	8 22.0	22 11.7	2 11.3	9 48.0	7 43.7	0 57.0	6 17.0
20	7 56 25.7	1 51.0	23 22.6	21 3.3	12 12.6	9 43.5	22 45.3	2 10.8	9 53.9	7 41.1	0 57.5	6 15.9
21	8 0 22.2	2 54.5	23 19.3	4♎28.1	12 1.3	11 4.9	23 18.9	2 10.2	9 59.6	7 38.4	0 58.0	6 14.7
22	8 4 18.8	3 57.8	23 16.0	17 42.6	11 59.2	12 26.3	23 52.7	2 9.4	10 5.3	7 35.7	0 58.4	6 13.6
23	8 8 15.4	5 1.0	23 12.8	0♏54.5	12D 5.7	13 47.6	24 26.6	2 8.4	10 11.0	7 33.0	0 58.8	6 12.4
24	8 12 11.9	6 3.9	23 9.5	14 8.1	12 20.2	15 8.9	25 .6	2 7.3	10 16.6	7 30.3	0 59.1	6 11.2
25	8 16 8.5	7 6.7	23 6.2	27 24.1	12 42.0	16 30.0	25 34.8	2 5.9	10 22.1	7 27.6	0 59.4	6 10.0
26	8 20 5.0	8 9.3	23 3.0	10♐38.8	13 10.7	17 51.1	26 9.1	2 4.5	10 27.5	7 24.9	0 59.8	6 8.8
27	8 24 1.6	9 11.7	22 59.7	23 46.1	13 45.6	19 12.0	26 43.4	2 2.8	10 32.9	7 22.2	1 .0	6 7.5
28	8 27 58.1	10 13.8	22 56.4	6♑38.9	14 26.1	20 32.7	27 17.9	2 1.0	10 38.2	7 19.5	1 .2	6 6.3
29	8 31 54.7	11 15.8	22 53.2	19 11.3	15 11.7	21 53.3	27 52.5	1 58.9	10 43.4	7 16.8	1 .4	6 5.0
30	8 35 51.2	12 17.6	22 49.9	1♒20.3	16 2.0	23 13.8	28 27.2	1 56.7	10 48.6	7 14.1	1 .6	6 3.7
31	8 39 47.8	13 19.1	22 46.7	13 6.2	16 56.5	24 34.0	29 2.1	1 54.4	10 53.6	7 11.5	1 .7	6 2.4

DAY	EPHEM. SID. TIME	☉	☊	☽	☿	♀	♂	♃	♄	♅	♆	♇
		DECLINATION										
1	6 41 31.1	23S 2.5	0S20.3	19S45.3	20S34.5	21S38.8	5N38.7	0N37.1	20S11.5	19N23.9	10S39.3	21N52.6
4	6 53 20.8	22 46.2	0 20.3	11 30.9	19 46.7	22 7.6	6 22.2	0 34.8	20 14.2	19 25.7	10 40.2	21 54.5
7	7 5 10.4	22 25.9	0 20.3	0N40.9	19 15.5	22 30.5	7 5.7	0 33.1	20 16.9	19 27.5	10 41.1	21 56.4
10	7 17 .1	22 1.5	0 20.2	13 1.7	19 2.6	22 47.4	7 49.1	0 32.1	20 19.4	19 29.3	10 41.8	21 58.3
13	7 28 49.8	21 33.4	0 20.2	20 42.7	19 5.4	22 58.1	8 32.3	0 31.7	20 21.8	19 31.2	10 42.4	22 .4
16	7 40 39.5	21 1.4	0 20.1	17 35.4	19 19.6	23 2.5	9 15.1	0 32.1	20 24.0	19 33.2	10 42.8	22 2.4
19	7 52 29.1	20 25.9	0 20.1	4 8.5	19 41.4	23 .6	9 57.7	0 33.1	20 26.2	19 35.1	10 43.2	22 4.4
22	8 4 18.8	19 46.9	0 20.1	10S45.8	20 7.1	22 52.3	10 39.8	0 34.8	20 28.2	19 37.0	10 43.5	22 6.5
25	8 16 8.5	19 4.6	0 20.0	19 48.4	20 33.0	22 37.7	11 21.5	0 37.2	20 30.1	19 38.9	10 43.7	22 8.6
28	8 27 58.1	18 19.1	0 20.0	20 4.4	20 55.7	22 16.9	12 2.8	0 40.2	20 31.9	19 40.9	10 43.8	22 10.6
31	8 39 47.8	17 30.6	0 19.9	12 31.2	21 12.8	21 50.0	12 43.4	0 44.0	20 33.5	19 42.8	10 43.7	22 12.7

LONGITUDE

DAY	EPHEM. SID. TIME (h m s)	☉	☊	☾	☿	♀	♂	♃	♄	♅	♆	♇
1	8 43 44.4	11♒52.8	25♏4.3	23♒53.6	16♑39.6	23♑57.2	2♉4.7	1♎24.6	12♐13.4	4♌38.6	2♏35.9	29♌37.7
2	8 47 40.9	12 53.7	25 1.2	5♓46.0	17 36.3	25 12.2	2 41.4	1R21.5	12 18.0	4R36.0	2 35.9	29R36.3
3	8 51 37.5	13 54.6	24 58.0	17 40.4	18 36.1	26 27.2	3 18.1	1 18.3	12 22.6	4 33.4	2 35.9	29 34.9
4	8 55 34.0	14 55.4	24 54.8	29 38.7	19 38.5	27 42.3	3 54.9	1 14.8	12 27.1	4 30.8	2 35.9	29 33.4
5	8 59 30.6	15 56.3	24 51.6	11♈43.8	20 43.4	28 57.3	4 31.7	1 11.2	12 31.5	4 28.3	2R35.8	29 32.0
6	9 3 27.1	16 57.1	24 48.5	23 59.0	21 50.6	0♒12.3	5 8.6	1 7.4	12 35.8	4 25.7	2 35.7	29 30.5
7	9 7 23.7	17 57.9	24 45.3	6♉28.4	22 59.8	1 27.3	5 45.5	1 3.5	12 40.1	4 23.2	2 35.6	29 29.0
8	9 11 20.2	18 58.7	24 42.1	19 16.4	24 11.0	2 42.3	6 22.4	0 59.4	12 44.2	4 20.7	2 35.4	29 27.6
9	9 15 16.8	19 59.4	24 38.9	2♊27.5	25 24.1	3 57.3	6 59.4	0 55.1	12 48.3	4 18.1	2 35.2	29 26.1
10	9 19 13.3	21 .1	24 35.8	16 5.5	26 38.8	5 12.3	7 36.4	0 50.6	12 52.3	4 15.7	2 35.0	29 24.6
11	9 23 9.9	22 .8	24 32.6	0♋12.4	27 55.0	6 27.3	8 13.4	0 46.0	12 56.3	4 13.2	2 34.7	29 23.1
12	9 27 6.5	23 1.5	24 29.4	14 47.9	29 12.8	7 42.3	8 50.5	0 41.3	13 .1	4 10.7	2 34.4	29 21.6
13	9 31 3.0	24 2.1	24 26.2	29 47.9	0♒32.0	8 57.2	9 27.6	0 36.3	13 3.9	4 8.3	2 34.1	29 20.1
14	9 34 59.6	25 2.7	24 23.0	15♌4.6	1 52.5	10 12.2	10 4.8	0 31.2	13 7.5	4 5.9	2 33.7	29 18.6
15	9 38 56.1	26 3.3	24 19.9	0♍27.3	3 14.2	11 27.2	10 41.9	0 26.0	13 11.1	4 3.5	2 33.3	29 17.1
16	9 42 52.7	27 3.9	24 16.7	15 43.8	4 37.3	12 42.2	11 19.2	0 20.7	13 14.7	4 1.2	2 32.9	29 15.6
17	9 46 49.2	28 4.4	24 13.5	0♎43.2	6 1.5	13 57.1	11 56.4	0 15.2	13 18.1	3 58.9	2 32.4	29 14.1
18	9 50 45.8	29 4.9	24 10.3	15 17.3	7 26.8	15 12.1	12 33.6	0 9.5	13 21.4	3 56.6	2 31.9	29 12.6
19	9 54 42.3	0♓5.4	24 7.2	29 21.9	8 53.3	16 27.0	13 10.9	0 3.7	13 24.7	3 54.3	2 31.4	29 11.1
20	9 58 38.9	1 5.9	24 4.0	12♏56.4	10 20.8	17 42.0	13 48.2	29♍57.7	13 27.8	3 52.0	2 30.8	29 9.6
21	10 2 35.4	2 6.3	24 .8	26 2.9	11 49.4	18 56.9	14 25.5	29 51.7	13 30.9	3 49.8	2 30.3	29 8.1
22	10 6 32.0	3 6.8	23 57.6	8♐45.4	13 19.1	20 11.8	15 2.8	29 45.5	13 33.9	3 47.6	2 29.6	29 6.6
23	10 10 28.5	4 7.2	23 54.4	21 8.7	14 49.8	21 26.8	15 40.2	29 39.1	13 36.8	3 45.4	2 29.0	29 5.1
24	10 14 25.1	5 7.6	23 51.3	3♑17.7	16 21.5	22 41.7	16 17.5	29 32.7	13 39.6	3 43.3	2 28.3	29 3.6
25	10 18 21.7	6 7.9	23 48.2	15 16.9	17 54.2	23 56.6	16 54.9	29 26.1	13 42.3	3 41.2	2 27.6	29 2.1
26	10 22 18.2	7 8.2	23 44.9	27 10.5	19 28.1	25 11.5	17 32.4	29 19.5	13 44.9	3 39.1	2 26.8	29 .6
27	10 26 14.8	8 8.5	23 41.7	9♒1.6	21 2.8	26 26.4	18 9.8	29 12.7	13 47.4	3 37.1	2 26.1	28 59.1
28	10 30 11.3	9 8.8	23 38.6	20 52.8	22 38.6	27 41.3	18 47.3	29 5.8	13 49.8	3 35.1	2 25.3	28 57.6

LATITUDE

DAY	SID. TIME	☉	☊	☾	☿	♀	♂	♃	♄	♅	♆	♇
1	8 43 44.4	0 .0	0 .0	4N59.8	1N8.0	0S20.8	0N48.0	1N26.1	1N42.6	0N38.2	1N45.2	11N22.8
4	8 55 34.0	0 .0	0 .0	4 7.8	0 37.4	0 28.1	0 50.2	1 26.9	1 42.8	0 38.2	1 45.4	11 23.3
7	9 7 23.7	0 .0	0 .0	1 35.2	0N8.6	0 35.1	0 52.3	1 27.6	1 43.1	0 38.2	1 45.6	11 23.7
10	9 19 13.3	0 .0	0 .1	1S50.0	0S18.1	0 41.7	0 54.2	1 28.3	1 43.4	0 38.2	1 45.8	11 24.1
13	9 31 3.0	0 .0	0 .0	4 33.0	0 42.3	0 48.1	0 56.1	1 29.0	1 43.7	0 38.1	1 46.0	11 24.5
16	9 42 52.7	0 .0	0 .0	4 38.8	1 3.9	0 54.0	0 57.9	1 29.6	1 44.1	0 38.1	1 46.1	11 24.8
19	9 54 42.3	0 .0	0 .0	2 4.1	1 22.8	0 59.5	0 59.5	1 30.2	1 44.4	0 38.1	1 46.3	11 25.0
22	10 6 32.0	0 .0	0 .0	1N19.6	1 38.8	1 4.6	1 1.1	1 30.8	1 44.8	0 38.1	1 46.5	11 25.2
25	10 18 21.7	0 .0	0 .0	3 57.5	1 51.8	1 9.2	1 2.5	1 31.3	1 45.1	0 38.0	1 46.6	11 25.3
28	10 30 11.3	0 .0	0 .0	5 .3	2 1.5	1 13.3	1 3.9	1 31.8	1 45.5	0 38.0	1 46.8	11 25.4

RIGHT ASCENSION

DAY	SID. TIME	☉	☊	☾	☿	♀	♂	♃	♄	♅	♆	♇
1	8 43 44.4	14♒20.5	22♏43.4	24♒32.4	17♑54.9	25♑54.1	29♈37.0	1♎51.8	10♐58.6	7♌8.8	1♏.8	6♍1.1
2	8 47 40.9	15 21.7	22 40.1	5♓44.8	18 56.7	27 14.0	0♉12.1	1R49.1	11 3.5	7R6.1	1 .8	5R59.8
3	8 51 37.5	16 22.6	22 36.9	16 51.5	20 1.7	28 33.6	0 47.3	1 46.2	11 8.4	7 3.4	1 .8	5 58.4
4	8 55 34.0	17 23.4	22 33.6	28 1.8	21 9.6	29 53.0	1 22.6	1 43.2	11 13.1	7 .8	1 .8	5 57.1
5	8 59 30.6	18 23.9	22 30.4	9♈25.7	22 20.1	1♒12.2	1 58.0	1 40.0	11 17.8	6 58.1	1 .8	5 55.7
6	9 3 27.1	19 24.2	22 27.1	21 16.0	23 33.0	2 31.2	2 33.5	1 36.6	11 22.4	6 55.5	1R.7	5 54.3
7	9 7 23.7	20 24.4	22 23.8	3♉6.2	24 48.0	3 49.9	3 9.2	1 33.1	11 26.9	6 52.9	1 .6	5 52.9
8	9 11 20.2	21 24.3	22 20.6	16 40.8	26 5.0	5 8.3	3 44.9	1 29.4	11 31.4	6 50.3	1 .4	5 51.5
9	9 15 16.8	22 24.0	22 17.3	0♊31.6	27 23.8	6 26.5	4 20.7	1 25.6	11 35.7	6 47.7	1 .3	5 50.1
10	9 19 13.3	23 23.5	22 14.1	15 5.9	28 44.2	7 44.4	4 56.7	1 21.6	11 40.0	6 45.1	1 .1	5 48.7
11	9 23 9.9	24 22.8	22 10.8	0♋13.3	0♒6.1	9 2.1	5 32.8	1 17.5	11 44.1	6 42.6	0 59.8	5 47.3
12	9 27 6.5	25 21.9	22 7.5	15 30.0	1 29.4	10 19.4	6 8.9	1 13.2	11 48.2	6 40.1	0 59.6	5 45.5
13	9 31 3.0	26 20.9	22 4.2	0♌58.6	2 53.9	11 36.5	6 45.2	1 8.7	11 52.2	6 37.5	0 59.3	5 44.5
14	9 34 59.6	27 19.6	22 1.0	16 3.9	4 19.6	12 53.3	7 21.5	1 4.2	11 56.1	6 35.1	0 58.9	5 43.0
15	9 38 56.1	28 18.1	21 57.8	0♍45.6	5 46.3	14 9.8	7 58.0	0 59.4	11 60.0	6 32.6	0 58.6	5 41.6
16	9 42 52.7	29 16.6	21 54.5	15 4.0	7 14.0	15 26.1	8 34.6	0 54.6	12 3.7	6 30.2	0 58.2	5 40.2
17	9 46 49.2	0♓14.7	21 51.3	29 3.8	8 42.6	16 42.1	9 11.3	0 49.6	12 7.4	6 27.8	0 57.8	5 38.7
18	9 50 45.8	1 12.8	21 48.0	12♎51.6	10 12.0	17 57.7	9 48.1	0 44.5	12 10.9	6 25.4	0 57.3	5 37.3
19	9 54 42.3	2 10.6	21 44.8	26 33.2	11 42.2	19 13.1	10 24.9	0 39.3	12 14.4	6 23.0	0 56.8	5 35.8
20	9 58 38.9	3 8.3	21 41.5	10♏11.7	13 13.1	20 28.1	11 1.9	0 33.9	12 17.8	6 20.7	0 56.3	5 34.4
21	10 2 35.4	4 5.8	21 38.2	23 46.9	14 44.6	21 42.9	11 39.0	0 28.4	12 21.0	6 18.4	0 55.8	5 32.9
22	10 6 32.0	5 3.2	21 35.0	7♐15.4	16 16.8	22 57.4	12 16.2	0 22.8	12 24.2	6 16.1	0 55.2	5 31.4
23	10 10 28.5	6 .4	21 31.7	20 31.8	17 49.5	24 11.6	12 53.4	0 17.1	12 27.3	6 13.9	0 54.6	5 30.0
24	10 14 25.1	6 57.4	21 28.5	3♑30.3	19 22.5	25 25.5	13 30.8	0 11.2	12 30.2	6 11.7	0 53.9	5 28.5
25	10 18 21.7	7 54.3	21 25.2	16 6.6	20 56.6	26 39.2	14 8.3	0 5.3	12 33.1	6 9.5	0 53.3	5 27.0
26	10 22 18.2	8 51.1	21 22.0	28 19.1	22 30.9	27 52.6	14 45.9	29♍59.2	12 35.9	6 7.4	0 52.6	5 25.6
27	10 26 14.8	9 47.7	21 18.7	10♒8.7	24 5.6	29 5.7	15 23.6	29 53.1	12 38.6	6 5.2	0 51.9	5 24.1
28	10 30 11.3	10 44.2	21 15.5	21 39.3	25 40.8	0♓18.5	16 1.3	29 46.8	12 41.2	6 3.2	0 51.1	5 22.7

DECLINATION

DAY	SID. TIME	☉	☊	☾	☿	♀	♂	♃	♄	♅	♆	♇
1	8 43 44.4	17S13.8	0S19.9	8S50.3	21S16.8	21S39.7	12N56.9	0N45.4	20S34.0	19N43.4	10S43.7	22N13.4
4	8 55 34.0	16 21.7	0 19.9	3N38.8	21 24.0	21 .5	13 36.7	0 49.9	20 35.5	19 45.3	10 43.5	22 15.4
7	9 7 23.7	15 27.0	0 19.9	10 17.7	21 20.5	20 24.6	13 56.5	0 55.1	20 36.9	19 47.1	10 43.3	22 17.4
10	9 19 13.3	14 29.9	0 19.8	20 53.6	21 7.5	19 38.1	14 15.9	1 .9	20 38.1	19 48.9	10 42.9	22 19.4
13	9 31 3.0	13 30.7	0 19.8	15 44.7	20 43.7	18 47.7	14 34.7	1 7.2	20 39.3	19 50.6	10 42.4	22 21.4
16	9 42 52.7	12 29.5	0 19.7	1 20.5	20 8.7	17 51.8	14 52.7	1 14.0	20 40.3	19 52.3	10 41.8	22 23.3
19	9 54 42.3	11 26.5	0 19.7	13S11.0	19 22.2	16 51.3	15 9.9	1 21.3	20 41.2	19 53.9	10 41.2	22 25.1
22	10 6 32.0	10 20.1	0 19.7	21 9.9	18 24.2	15 46.5	15 26.4	1 29.0	20 42.0	19 55.4	10 40.4	22 26.9
25	10 18 21.7	9 15.8	0 19.6	18 38.1	17 14.4	14 37.8	15 42.3	1 37.2	20 42.6	19 56.9	10 39.5	22 28.7
28	10 30 11.3	8 8.5	0 19.6	9 47.4	15 53.0	13 25.5	15 57.5	1 45.7	20 43.1	19 58.3	10 38.6	22 30.4

MARCH 1957

LONGITUDE

DAY	EPHEM. SID. TIME	☉	☊	☽	☿	♀	♂	♃	♄	♅	♆	♇
	h m s	° ′	° ′	° ′	° ′	° ′	° ′	° ′	° ′	° ′	° ′	° ′
1	10 34 7.9	10♓ 9.1	23♏35.4	2♓45.9	24♒15.4	28♒56.2	19♉24.8	28♍58.9	13♐52.1	3♌33.1	2♏24.4	28♌56.1
2	10 38 4.4	11 9.3	23 32.2	14 42.3	25 53.3	0♓11.1	20 2.3	28R51.8	13 54.3	3R31.2	2R23.6	28R54.7
3	10 42 1.0	12 9.5	23 29.0	26 43.2	27 32.2	1 26.0	20 39.8	28 44.7	13 56.5	3 29.3	2 22.7	28 53.2
4	10 45 57.5	13 9.6	23 25.8	8♈49.9	29 12.1	2 40.8	21 17.4	28 37.4	13 58.5	3 27.5	2 21.7	28 51.7
5	10 49 54.1	14 9.8	23 22.7	21 3.8	0♓53.2	3 55.7	21 54.9	28 30.1	14 .4	3 25.7	2 20.8	28 50.3
6	10 53 50.6	15 9.9	23 19.5	3♉27.1	2 35.3	5 10.5	22 32.5	28 22.8	14 2.3	3 23.9	2 19.8	28 48.9
7	10 57 47.2	16 9.9	23 16.3	16 2.4	4 18.5	6 25.3	23 10.1	28 15.3	14 4.0	3 22.2	2 18.8	28 47.4
8	11 1 43.7	17 9.9	23 13.1	28 52.9	6 2.7	7 40.1	23 47.7	28 7.8	14 5.7	3 20.5	2 17.8	28 46.0
9	11 5 40.3	18 10.0	23 10.0	12♊ 2.0	7 48.2	8 55.0	24 25.3	28 .3	14 7.3	3 18.9	2 16.8	28 44.6
10	11 9 36.8	19 9.9	23 6.8	25 32.9	9 34.7	10 9.7	25 3.0	27 52.7	14 8.7	3 17.3	2 15.7	28 43.2
11	11 13 33.4	20 9.8	23 3.6	9♋27.9	11 22.4	11 24.5	25 40.6	27 45.1	14 10.0	3 15.7	2 14.6	28 41.8
12	11 17 29.9	21 9.7	23 .4	23 47.5	13 11.2	12 39.3	26 18.2	27 37.4	14 11.3	3 14.2	2 13.5	28 40.5
13	11 21 26.5	22 9.6	22 57.2	8♌29.6	15 1.2	13 54.0	26 55.9	27 29.7	14 12.4	3 12.8	2 12.4	28 39.1
14	11 25 23.0	23 9.4	22 54.1	23 29.1	16 52.3	15 8.7	27 33.5	27 22.0	14 13.5	3 11.3	2 11.2	28 37.7
15	11 29 19.6	24 9.1	22 50.9	8♍37.6	18 44.6	16 23.4	28 11.2	27 14.2	14 14.4	3 10.0	2 10.0	28 36.4
16	11 33 16.1	25 8.9	22 47.7	23 45.2	20 38.1	17 38.1	28 48.8	27 6.4	14 15.3	3 8.6	2 8.8	28 35.1
17	11 37 12.7	26 8.6	22 44.5	8♎41.5	22 32.6	18 52.8	29 26.5	26 58.7	14 16.0	3 7.3	2 7.5	28 33.8
18	11 41 9.3	27 8.2	22 41.3	23 17.8	24 28.3	20 7.5	0♊ 4.2	26 50.9	14 16.7	3 6.1	2 6.3	28 32.5
19	11 45 5.8	28 7.9	22 38.2	7♏28.4	26 25.1	21 22.2	0 41.8	26 43.1	14 17.2	3 4.9	2 5.0	28 31.2
20	11 49 2.4	29 7.5	22 35.0	21 10.7	28 22.9	22 36.8	1 19.5	26 35.3	14 17.7	3 3.8	2 3.7	28 29.9
21	11 52 58.9	0♈ 7.0	22 31.8	4♐25.1	0♈21.7	23 51.5	1 57.2	26 27.5	14 18.0	3 2.7	2 2.4	28 28.7
22	11 56 55.5	1 6.6	22 28.6	17 14.3	2 21.4	25 6.1	2 34.9	26 19.8	14 18.3	3 1.7	2 1.1	28 27.5
23	12 0 52.0	2 6.1	22 25.5	29 42.2	4 21.8	26 20.7	3 12.6	26 12.1	14 18.4	3 .7	1 59.7	28 26.2
24	12 4 48.6	3 5.6	22 22.3	11♑53.8	6 22.9	27 35.3	3 50.3	26 4.4	14 18.4	2 59.7	1 58.3	28 25.0
25	12 8 45.1	4 5.1	22 19.1	23 54.0	8 24.5	28 49.9	4 28.0	25 56.7	14 18.4	2 58.8	1 56.9	28 23.9
26	12 12 41.7	5 4.5	22 15.9	5♒47.3	10 26.4	0♈ 4.5	5 5.7	25 49.1	14R18.2	2 58.0	1 55.5	28 22.7
27	12 16 38.2	6 3.9	22 12.7	17 38.2	12 28.5	1 19.1	5 43.4	25 41.5	14 18.0	2 57.2	1 54.1	28 21.6
28	12 20 34.8	7 3.3	22 9.6	29 30.1	14 30.4	2 33.6	6 21.1	25 33.9	14 17.6	2 56.5	1 52.6	28 20.4
29	12 24 31.3	8 2.6	22 6.4	11♓26.0	16 31.9	3 48.2	6 58.8	25 26.5	14 17.2	2 55.8	1 51.2	28 19.3
30	12 28 27.9	9 2.0	22 3.2	23 28.2	18 32.7	5 2.8	7 36.6	25 19.1	14 16.7	2 55.2	1 49.8	28 18.3
31	12 32 24.4	10 1.2	22 .0	5♈38.0	20 32.4	6 17.3	8 14.3	25 11.7	14 16.0	2 54.6	1 48.3	28 17.3

LATITUDE

DAY	EPHEM. SID. TIME	☉	☊	☽	☿	♀	♂	♃	♄	♅	♆	♇
1	10 34 7.9	0 .0	0 .0	4N55.8	2S 4.0	1S14.5	1N 4.3	1N31.9	1N45.6	0N38.0	1N46.9	11N25.4
4	10 45 57.5	0 .0	0 .0	3 27.0	2 9.2	1 17.9	1 5.5	1 32.3	1 45.9	0 37.9	1 47.0	11 25.4
7	10 57 47.2	0 .0	0 .0	0 30.5	2 10.6	1 20.8	1 6.7	1 32.7	1 46.3	0 37.9	1 47.2	11 25.3
10	11 9 36.8	0 .0	0 .0	2S49.9	2 8.0	1 23.1	1 7.8	1 32.9	1 46.7	0 37.8	1 47.3	11 25.2
13	11 21 26.5	0 .0	0 .0	4 56.6	2 1.2	1 24.8	1 8.8	1 33.2	1 47.1	0 37.8	1 47.4	11 25.1
16	11 33 16.1	0 .0	0 .0	4 17.1	1 49.8	1 26.0	1 9.8	1 33.3	1 47.4	0 37.7	1 47.6	11 24.9
19	11 45 5.8	0 .0	0 .0	1 11.4	1 33.7	1 26.6	1 10.6	1 33.4	1 47.8	0 37.6	1 47.7	11 24.6
22	11 56 55.5	0 .0	0 .0	2N17.0	1 12.8	1 26.6	1 11.5	1 33.5	1 48.2	0 37.6	1 47.8	11 24.3
25	12 8 45.1	0 .0	0 .0	4 34.8	0 47.1	1 26.0	1 12.2	1 33.5	1 48.5	0 37.5	1 47.9	11 23.9
28	12 20 34.8	0 .0	0 .0	5 4.3	0 17.2	1 24.8	1 12.9	1 33.4	1 48.9	0 37.4	1 48.0	11 23.5
31	12 32 24.4	0 .0	0 .0	3 37.2	0N16.0	1 23.1	1 13.5	1 33.3	1 49.2	0 37.4	1 48.1	11 23.1

RIGHT ASCENSION

DAY	EPHEM. SID. TIME	☉	☊	☽	☿	♀	♂	♃	♄	♅	♆	♇
1	10 34 7.9	11♓40.5	21♏12.2	2♓56.5	27♒16.5	1♓31.0	16♉39.2	29♍40.5	12♐43.7	6♌ 1.1	0♏50.3	5♍21.2
2	10 38 4.4	12 36.8	21 9.0	14 7.5	28 52.6	2 43.3	17 17.2	29R34.1	12 46.0	5R59.1	0R49.5	5R19.8
3	10 42 1.0	13 32.9	21 5.7	25 20.7	0♓29.1	3 55.4	17 55.3	29 27.6	12 48.3	5 57.2	0 48.7	5 18.3
4	10 45 57.5	14 28.9	21 2.5	6♈44.7	2 6.1	5 7.1	18 33.5	29 21.0	12 50.5	5 55.3	0 47.8	5 16.9
5	10 49 54.1	15 24.7	20 59.3	18 28.3	3 43.5	6 18.7	19 11.8	29 14.3	12 52.5	5 53.4	0 47.0	5 15.4
6	10 53 50.6	16 20.5	20 56.0	0♉39.7	5 21.3	7 30.0	19 50.1	29 7.6	12 54.5	5 51.6	0 46.0	5 14.0
7	10 57 47.2	17 16.1	20 52.8	13 25.2	6 59.6	8 41.0	20 28.6	29 .8	12 56.4	5 49.8	0 45.1	5 12.6
8	11 1 43.7	18 11.6	20 49.5	26 48.1	8 38.4	9 51.9	21 7.1	28 54.0	12 58.1	5 48.0	0 44.1	5 11.2
9	11 5 40.3	19 7.1	20 46.3	10♊47.0	10 17.6	11 2.6	21 45.8	28 47.1	12 59.8	5 46.4	0 43.2	5 9.8
10	11 9 36.8	20 2.5	20 43.0	25 15.1	11 57.4	12 13.0	22 24.6	28 40.2	13 1.4	5 44.7	0 42.2	5 8.4
11	11 13 33.4	20 57.7	20 39.8	10♋ .9	13 37.6	13 23.2	23 3.4	28 33.2	13 2.8	5 43.1	0 41.2	5 7.0
12	11 17 29.9	21 52.9	20 36.5	24 51.5	15 18.4	14 33.2	23 42.3	28 26.2	13 4.2	5 41.5	0 40.1	5 5.6
13	11 21 26.5	22 48.0	20 33.3	9♌35.8	16 59.7	15 43.0	24 21.3	28 19.2	13 5.4	5 40.0	0 39.0	5 4.3
14	11 25 23.0	23 43.0	20 30.1	24 7.6	18 41.6	16 52.6	25 .3	28 12.1	13 6.5	5 38.5	0 37.9	5 2.9
15	11 29 19.6	24 37.9	20 26.8	8♍25.9	20 24.0	18 2.1	25 39.5	28 5.0	13 7.5	5 37.1	0 36.8	5 1.6
16	11 33 16.1	25 32.8	20 23.6	22 34.2	22 7.1	19 11.4	26 18.7	27 57.9	13 8.5	5 35.7	0 35.6	5 .2
17	11 37 12.7	26 27.6	20 20.3	6♎37.3	23 50.8	20 20.6	26 58.0	27 50.7	13 9.3	5 34.4	0 34.5	4 58.9
18	11 41 9.3	27 22.4	20 17.1	20 39.7	25 35.1	21 29.7	27 37.4	27 43.6	13 10.0	5 33.1	0 33.3	4 57.6
19	11 45 5.8	28 17.1	20 13.8	4♏43.1	27 20.1	22 38.6	28 16.9	27 36.5	13 10.6	5 31.8	0 32.1	4 56.3
20	11 49 2.4	29 11.8	20 10.6	18 45.3	29 5.7	23 47.4	28 56.5	27 29.3	13 11.1	5 30.7	0 30.9	4 55.0
21	11 52 58.9	0♈ 6.5	20 7.4	2♐40.8	0♈51.9	24 56.0	29 36.1	27 22.2	13 11.4	5 29.5	0 29.6	4 53.7
22	11 56 55.5	1 1.1	20 4.1	16 21.9	2 38.6	26 4.6	0♊15.8	27 15.1	13 11.7	5 28.4	0 28.3	4 52.4
23	12 0 52.0	1 55.7	20 .9	29 41.1	4 26.0	27 13.1	0 55.6	27 8.0	13 11.9	5 27.4	0 27.1	4 51.2
24	12 4 48.6	2 50.3	19 57.7	12♑33.4	6 13.8	28 21.6	1 35.4	27 .9	13 11.9	5 26.4	0 25.8	4 50.0
25	12 8 45.1	3 44.9	19 54.4	24 57.2	8 2.0	29 29.9	2 15.3	26 53.9	13 11.9	5 25.5	0 24.4	4 48.8
26	12 12 41.7	4 39.5	19 51.2	6♒54.3	9 50.5	0♈38.2	2 55.3	26 46.9	13R11.8	5 24.6	0 23.1	4 47.6
27	12 16 38.2	5 34.0	19 47.9	18 29.5	11 39.2	1 46.5	3 35.4	26 39.9	13 11.5	5 23.8	0 21.8	4 46.4
28	12 20 34.8	6 28.6	19 44.7	29 49.7	13 27.9	2 54.7	4 15.6	26 32.9	13 11.1	5 23.0	0 20.4	4 45.2
29	12 24 31.3	7 23.2	19 41.5	11♓ 2.9	15 16.4	4 2.9	4 55.8	26 26.1	13 10.7	5 22.3	0 19.0	4 44.1
30	12 28 27.9	8 17.9	19 38.2	22 18.0	17 4.6	5 11.1	5 36.1	26 19.3	13 10.1	5 21.7	0 17.7	4 43.0
31	12 32 24.4	9 12.5	19 35.0	3♈43.8	18 52.1	6 19.3	6 16.5	26 12.5	13 9.5	5 21.1	0 16.2	4 41.9

DECLINATION

DAY	EPHEM. SID. TIME	☉	☊	☽	☿	♀	♂	♃	♄	♅	♆	♇
1	10 34 7.9	7S45.8	0S19.6	5S53.2	15S23.2	13S .6	18N37.0	1N48.7	20S43.3	19N58.7	10S38.3	22N30.9
4	10 45 57.5	6 37.1	0 19.5	6N40.3	13 46.2	11 44.0	19 8.4	1 57.5	20 43.7	20 .0	10 37.2	22 32.5
7	10 57 47.2	5 27.5	0 19.5	17 7.7	11 57.5	10 24.5	19 38.6	2 6.7	20 44.0	20 1.2	10 36.1	22 34.0
10	11 9 36.8	4 17.3	0 19.4	20 32.3	9 57.3	9 2.5	20 7.7	2 15.9	20 44.1	20 2.3	10 34.9	22 35.4
13	11 21 26.5	3 6.7	0 19.4	13 21.9	7 45.9	7 38.3	20 35.5	2 25.3	20 44.2	20 3.3	10 33.6	22 36.8
16	11 33 16.1	1 55.7	0 19.3	1S27.3	5 23.7	6 12.4	21 1.9	2 34.7	20 44.2	20 4.2	10 32.3	22 38.0
19	11 45 5.8	0 44.6	0 19.3	15 7.9	2 51.4	4 44.9	21 27.1	2 44.1	20 44.0	20 5.0	10 30.9	22 39.2
22	11 56 55.5	0N26.5	0 19.3	20 33.5	0 10.5	3 16.3	21 50.9	2 53.4	20 43.8	20 5.6	10 29.4	22 40.2
25	12 8 45.1	1 37.4	0 19.2	16 49.0	2N36.8	1 46.8	22 13.2	3 2.5	20 43.4	20 6.2	10 27.9	22 41.2
28	12 20 34.8	2 48.0	0 19.2	6 53.5	5 27.3	0 16.7	22 34.2	3 11.5	20 43.0	20 6.7	10 26.3	22 42.0
31	12 32 24.4	3 58.2	0 19.1	5N33.6	8 16.3	1N13.5	22 53.6	3 20.2	20 42.5	20 7.1	10 24.8	22 42.8

APRIL 1957

LONGITUDE

DAY	EPHEM. SID. TIME h m s	☉ ° ′	☊ ° ′	☽ ° ′	☿ ° ′	♀ ° ′	♂ ° ′	♃ ° ′	♄ ° ′	♅ ° ′	♆ ° ′	♇ ° ′
1	12 36 21.0	11♈ .5	21♏56.9	17♈56.8	22♈30.7	7♈31.8	8♊52.0	25♍ 4.4	14♐15.2	2♌54.1	1♏46.8	28♌16.2
2	12 40 17.5	11 59.7	21 53.7	0♉25.4	24 27.2	8 46.3	9 29.8	24 R 57.2	14 R 14.4	2 R 53.6	1 R 45.3	28 R 15.2
3	12 44 14.1	12 58.8	21 50.5	13 4.8	26 21.6	10 .7	10 7.5	24 50.1	14 13.4	2 53.2	1 43.7	28 14.2
4	12 48 10.6	13 58.0	21 47.3	25 56.0	28 13.4	11 15.2	10 45.2	24 43.0	14 12.4	2 52.8	1 42.2	28 13.2
5	12 52 7.2	14 57.1	21 44.1	9♊ .4	0♉ 2.3	12 29.6	11 23.0	24 36.1	14 11.2	2 52.5	1 40.6	28 12.3
6	12 56 3.7	15 56.1	21 41.0	22 19.2	1 47.9	13 44.0	12 .7	24 29.2	14 10.0	2 52.3	1 39.1	28 11.4
7	13 0 .3	16 55.1	21 37.8	5♋54.1	3 29.8	14 58.5	12 38.4	24 22.5	14 8.7	2 52.1	1 37.5	28 10.5
8	13 3 56.8	17 54.1	21 34.6	19 45.9	5 7.8	16 12.8	13 16.2	24 15.8	14 7.2	2 51.9	1 35.9	28 9.6
9	13 7 53.4	18 53.1	21 31.4	3♌54.6	6 41.4	17 27.2	13 53.9	24 9.3	14 5.7	2 51.8	1 34.4	28 8.7
10	13 11 50.0	19 52.0	21 28.3	18 18.8	8 10.4	18 41.5	14 31.6	24 2.9	14 4.1	2 51.8	1 32.8	28 7.9
11	13 15 46.5	20 50.8	21 25.1	2♍55.1	9 34.7	19 55.9	15 9.4	23 56.5	14 2.4	2 51.8	1 31.2	28 7.1
12	13 19 43.1	21 49.6	21 21.9	17 38.3	10 53.8	21 10.2	15 47.1	23 50.4	14 .6	2 D 51.9	1 29.5	28 6.3
13	13 23 39.6	22 48.4	21 18.7	2♎21.5	12 7.8	22 24.5	16 24.8	23 44.3	13 58.7	2 52.0	1 27.9	28 5.5
14	13 27 36.2	23 47.2	21 15.5	16 57.6	13 16.3	23 38.8	17 2.5	23 38.3	13 56.7	2 52.1	1 26.3	28 4.8
15	13 31 32.7	24 45.9	21 12.4	1♏19.6	14 19.3	24 53.0	17 40.2	23 32.5	13 54.7	2 52.4	1 24.7	28 4.1
16	13 35 29.3	25 44.6	21 9.2	15 22.2	15 16.6	26 7.3	18 17.9	23 26.9	13 52.5	2 52.7	1 23.1	28 3.4
17	13 39 25.8	26 43.3	21 6.0	29 2.1	16 8.1	27 21.5	18 55.6	23 21.3	13 50.3	2 53.0	1 21.4	28 2.8
18	13 43 22.4	27 41.9	21 2.8	12♐18.0	16 53.8	28 35.7	19 33.3	23 15.9	13 48.0	2 53.4	1 19.8	28 2.1
19	13 47 18.9	28 40.5	20 59.7	25 11.1	17 33.5	29 49.9	20 11.0	23 10.7	13 45.6	2 53.8	1 18.2	28 1.5
20	13 51 15.5	29 39.1	20 56.5	7♑43.7	18 7.3	1♉ 4.1	20 48.8	23 5.6	13 43.1	2 54.4	1 16.6	28 1.0
21	13 55 12.0	0♉37.7	20 53.3	19 59.5	18 35.0	2 18.3	21 26.4	23 .6	13 40.5	2 54.9	1 14.9	28 .5
22	13 59 8.6	1 36.2	20 50.1	2♒ 2.9	18 56.8	3 32.5	22 4.1	22 55.8	13 37.9	2 55.5	1 13.3	27 59.9
23	14 3 5.1	2 34.7	20 46.9	13 58.5	19 12.6	4 46.6	22 41.8	22 51.2	13 35.2	2 56.2	1 11.6	27 59.5
24	14 7 1.7	3 33.1	20 43.8	25 50.9	19 22.5	6 .8	23 19.5	22 46.6	13 32.3	2 56.9	1 10.0	27 59.0
25	14 10 58.3	4 31.6	20 40.6	7♓44.5	19 26.6	7 14.9	23 57.2	22 42.3	13 29.5	2 57.6	1 8.4	27 58.6
26	14 14 54.8	5 30.0	20 37.4	19 43.3	19 R 25.1	8 29.0	24 34.9	22 38.1	13 26.5	2 58.5	1 6.7	27 58.1
27	14 18 51.4	6 28.3	20 34.2	1♈50.6	19 18.1	9 43.1	25 12.6	22 34.1	13 23.5	2 59.3	1 5.1	27 57.8
28	14 22 47.9	7 26.7	20 31.1	14 9.0	19 6.0	10 57.2	25 50.2	22 30.3	13 20.3	3 .2	1 3.5	27 57.4
29	14 26 44.5	8 25.0	20 27.9	26 40.4	18 49.1	12 11.2	26 27.9	22 26.6	13 17.2	3 1.2	1 1.8	27 57.1
30	14 30 41.0	9 23.3	20 24.7	9♉25.8	18 27.7	13 25.3	27 5.6	22 23.1	13 13.9	3 2.2	1 .2	27 56.8

LATITUDE

DAY	EPHEM. SID. TIME	☉	☊	☽	☿	♀	♂	♃	♄	♅	♆	♇
1	12 36 21.0	0 .0	0 .0	2N45.2	0N27.6	1S22.4	1N13.7	1N33.2	1N49.3	0N37.3	1N48.1	11N22.9
4	12 48 10.6	0 .0	0 .0	0S32.3	1 2.5	1 20.0	1 14.3	1 33.0	1 49.7	0 37.2	1 48.2	11 22.4
7	13 0 .3	0 .0	0 .0	3 44.5	1 36.3	1 17.0	1 14.8	1 32.8	1 50.0	0 37.2	1 48.2	11 21.9
10	13 11 50.0	0 .0	0 .0	5 12.5	2 6.5	1 13.5	1 15.2	1 32.4	1 50.3	0 37.1	1 48.3	11 21.3
13	13 23 39.6	0 .0	0 .0	3 51.0	2 31.0	1 9.5	1 15.7	1 32.1	1 50.6	0 37.0	1 48.3	11 20.7
16	13 35 29.3	0 .0	0 .0	0 24.0	2 48.0	1 5.1	1 16.0	1 31.7	1 50.9	0 36.9	1 48.3	11 20.1
19	13 47 18.9	0 .0	0 .0	3N 3.0	2 55.7	1 .2	1 16.3	1 31.2	1 51.1	0 36.8	1 48.4	11 19.4
22	13 59 8.6	0 .0	0 .0	5 .5	2 52.8	0 54.9	1 16.6	1 30.8	1 51.4	0 36.8	1 48.4	11 18.8
25	14 10 58.3	0 .0	0 .0	5 .2	2 38.5	0 49.3	1 16.9	1 30.2	1 51.6	0 36.7	1 48.4	11 18.1
28	14 22 47.9	0 .0	0 .0	3 3.9	2 12.4	0 43.3	1 17.0	1 29.7	1 51.7	0 36.6	1 48.4	11 17.4

RIGHT ASCENSION

DAY	EPHEM. SID. TIME	☉	☊	☽	☿	♀	♂	♃	♄	♅	♆	♇
1	12 36 21.0	10♈ 7.1	19♏31.8	15♈29.1	20♈38.8	7♈27.4	6♊56.9	26♍ 5.8	13♐ 8.7	5♌20.6	0♏14.8	4♍40.8
2	12 40 17.5	11 1.8	19 28.5	27 41.3	22 24.2	8 35.6	7 37.4	25 R 59.1	13 R 7.8	5 R 20.1	0 R 13.4	4 R 39.7
3	12 44 14.1	11 56.5	19 25.3	10♉25.8	24 8.1	9 43.8	8 17.9	25 52.5	13 6.8	5 19.6	0 11.9	4 38.7
4	12 48 10.6	12 51.2	19 22.1	23 44.6	25 50.2	10 52.1	8 58.5	25 46.0	13 5.7	5 19.2	0 10.5	4 37.6
5	12 52 7.2	13 45.9	19 18.8	7♊34.7	27 30.2	12 .3	9 39.2	25 39.6	13 4.5	5 18.9	0 9.0	4 36.6
6	12 56 3.7	14 40.7	19 15.6	21 48.7	29 7.6	13 8.7	10 19.9	25 33.3	13 3.2	5 18.6	0 7.5	4 35.7
7	13 0 .3	15 35.6	19 12.4	6♋15.1	0♉42.2	14 17.1	11 .6	25 27.0	13 1.8	5 18.4	0 6.0	4 34.7
8	13 3 56.8	16 30.5	19 9.2	20 42.3	2 13.6	15 25.6	11 41.4	25 20.9	13 .3	5 18.2	0 4.5	4 33.7
9	13 7 53.4	17 25.4	19 5.9	5♌ 1.0	3 41.5	16 34.1	12 22.3	25 14.8	12 58.7	5 18.1	0 3.0	4 32.8
10	13 11 50.0	18 20.4	19 2.7	19 7.3	5 5.6	17 42.8	13 3.2	25 8.8	12 57.0	5 18.1	0 1.5	4 31.9
11	13 15 46.5	19 15.5	18 59.5	3♍ 1.9	6 25.7	18 51.5	13 44.1	25 3.0	12 55.2	5 18.1	29♎60.0	4 31.0
12	13 19 43.1	20 10.6	18 56.2	16 49.9	7 41.5	20 .4	14 25.1	24 57.2	12 53.3	5 D 18.2	29 58.5	4 30.2
13	13 23 39.6	21 5.8	18 53.0	0♎37.8	8 52.7	21 9.4	15 6.1	24 51.6	12 51.3	5 18.3	29 56.9	4 29.4
14	13 27 36.2	22 1.1	18 49.8	14 31.8	9 59.1	22 18.5	15 47.2	24 46.1	12 49.2	5 18.4	29 55.4	4 28.6
15	13 31 32.7	22 56.4	18 46.6	28 35.3	11 .5	23 27.8	16 28.3	24 40.7	12 47.0	5 18.7	29 53.8	4 27.8
16	13 35 29.3	23 51.9	18 43.3	12♏47.0	11 56.8	24 37.2	17 9.4	24 35.4	12 44.7	5 19.0	29 52.3	4 27.0
17	13 39 25.8	24 47.4	18 40.1	27 .6	12 47.7	25 46.8	17 50.6	24 30.3	12 42.4	5 19.3	29 50.7	4 26.3
18	13 43 22.4	25 43.0	18 36.9	11♐ 6.1	13 33.2	26 56.6	18 31.8	24 25.2	12 39.9	5 19.7	29 49.2	4 25.6
19	13 47 18.9	26 38.8	18 33.7	24 52.3	14 13.2	28 6.5	19 13.0	24 20.3	12 37.4	5 20.2	29 47.6	4 24.9
20	13 51 15.5	27 34.6	18 30.4	8♑10.4	14 47.5	29 16.7	19 54.3	24 15.6	12 34.8	5 20.7	29 46.1	4 24.3
21	13 55 12.0	28 30.6	18 27.2	20 55.8	15 16.1	0♉27.0	20 35.6	24 11.0	12 32.1	5 21.3	29 44.5	4 23.7
22	13 59 8.6	29 26.6	18 24.0	3♒ 8.9	15 39.0	1 37.6	21 16.9	24 6.5	12 29.3	5 21.9	29 43.0	4 23.1
23	14 3 5.1	0♉22.8	18 20.8	14 54.2	15 56.1	2 48.3	21 58.2	24 2.1	12 26.4	5 22.6	29 41.4	4 22.5
24	14 7 1.7	1 19.1	18 17.6	26 19.3	16 7.7	3 59.3	22 39.6	23 57.9	12 23.4	5 23.3	29 39.9	4 21.9
25	14 10 58.3	2 15.5	18 14.3	7♓33.2	16 13.7	5 10.5	23 21.0	23 53.8	12 20.4	5 24.1	29 38.3	4 21.4
26	14 14 54.8	3 12.0	18 11.1	18 46.0	16 14.3	6 21.9	24 2.4	23 49.9	12 17.2	5 24.9	29 36.7	4 20.9
27	14 18 51.4	4 8.7	18 7.9	0♈ 8.1	16 R 9.8	7 33.6	24 43.8	23 46.2	12 14.0	5 25.8	29 35.2	4 20.4
28	14 22 47.9	5 5.5	18 4.7	11 49.4	16 .4	8 45.5	25 25.2	23 42.5	12 10.7	5 26.7	29 33.6	4 20.0
29	14 26 44.5	6 2.4	18 1.5	23 59.0	15 46.4	9 57.7	26 6.6	23 39.1	12 7.4	5 27.8	29 32.1	4 19.6
30	14 30 41.0	6 59.4	17 58.2	6♉43.4	15 28.3	11 10.1	26 48.1	23 35.8	12 3.9	5 28.8	29 30.5	4 19.2

DECLINATION

DAY	EPHEM. SID. TIME	☉	☊	☽	☿	♀	♂	♃	♄	♅	♆	♇
1	12 36 21.0	4N21.4	0S19.1	9N35.1	9N11.3	1N43.6	22N59.8	3N23.0	20S42.3	20N 7.1	10S24.2	22N43.0
4	12 48 10.6	5 30.6	0 19.1	18 43.2	11 49.1	3 13.6	23 17.2	3 31.3	20 41.6	20 7.4	10 22.6	22 43.6
7	13 0 .3	6 38.9	0 19.0	19 34.4	14 11.5	4 43.0	23 33.1	3 39.3	20 40.8	20 7.5	10 20.9	22 44.1
10	13 11 50.0	7 46.2	0 19.0	10 23.0	16 13.7	6 11.5	23 47.5	3 46.8	20 40.0	20 7.4	10 19.2	22 44.5
13	13 23 39.6	8 52.3	0 18.9	4S28.2	17 52.4	7 38.8	24 .3	3 53.8	20 39.1	20 7.3	10 17.5	22 44.8
16	13 35 29.3	9 57.0	0 18.9	16 49.7	19 5.7	9 4.6	24 11.4	4 .3	20 38.1	20 7.1	10 15.8	22 45.0
19	13 47 18.9	11 .3	0 18.9	20 18.5	19 52.9	10 28.5	24 20.9	4 6.3	20 37.0	20 6.7	10 14.1	22 45.0
22	13 59 8.6	12 2.0	0 18.8	14 49.4	20 13.6	11 50.2	24 28.8	4 11.8	20 35.9	20 6.3	10 12.4	22 45.0
25	14 10 58.3	13 1.9	0 18.8	4 1.2	20 8.1	13 9.4	24 35.1	4 16.6	20 34.6	20 5.7	10 10.7	22 44.8
28	14 22 47.9	13 59.9	0 18.7	8N24.3	19 37.4	14 25.8	24 39.7	4 20.9	20 33.4	20 5.0	10 9.0	22 44.6

MAY 1957

LONGITUDE

DAY	EPHEM. SID. TIME h m s	☉ ° ′	☊ ° ′	☽ ° ′	☿ ° ′	♀ ° ′	♂ ° ′	♃ ° ′	♄ ° ′	♅ ° ′	♆ ° ′	♇ ° ′
1	14 34 37.6	10♉21.6	20♏21.5	22♉25.6	18♉ 2.3	14♉39.3	27♊43.3	22♍19.7	13♐10.6	3♌ 3.3	0♏58.6	27♌56.5
2	14 38 34.1	11 19.8	20 18.3	5♊39.6	17 R 33.4	15 53.3	28 21.0	22 R 16.6	13 R 7.2	3 4.5	0 R 57.0	27 R 56.3
3	14 42 30.7	12 18.0	20 15.2	19 7.0	17 1.5	17 7.3	28 58.6	22 13.6	13 3.8	3 5.6	0 55.4	27 56.1
4	14 46 27.2	13 16.2	20 12.0	2♋46.9	16 27.3	18 21.3	29 36.3	22 10.8	13 .2	3 6.9	0 53.8	27 55.9
5	14 50 23.8	14 14.3	20 8.8	16 37.9	15 51.3	19 35.3	0♋14.0	22 8.1	12 56.7	3 8.1	0 52.2	27 55.7
6	14 54 20.3	15 12.4	20 5.6	0♌38.7	15 14.2	20 49.2	0 51.6	22 5.7	12 53.0	3 9.5	0 50.6	27 55.6
7	14 58 16.9	16 10.5	20 2.5	14 47.4	14 36.8	22 3.2	1 29.3	22 3.4	12 49.3	3 10.9	0 49.0	27 55.5
8	15 2 13.5	17 8.5	19 59.3	29 2.1	13 59.6	23 17.1	2 6.9	22 1.3	12 45.6	3 12.3	0 47.5	27 55.5
9	15 6 10.0	18 6.6	19 56.1	13♍20.2	13 23.3	24 31.0	2 44.6	21 59.4	12 41.8	3 13.8	0 45.9	27 55.4
10	15 10 6.6	19 4.5	19 52.9	27 38.5	12 48.6	25 44.9	3 22.2	21 57.6	12 38.0	3 15.3	0 44.4	27 55.4
11	15 14 3.1	20 2.5	19 49.7	11♎53.5	12 16.0	26 58.8	3 59.9	21 56.1	12 34.1	3 16.9	0 42.9	27 D 55.5
12	15 17 59.7	21 .4	19 46.6	26 1.3	11 45.9	28 12.6	4 37.5	21 54.7	12 30.2	3 18.6	0 41.4	27 55.6
13	15 21 56.2	21 58.3	19 43.4	9♏58.1	11 19.0	29 26.5	5 15.2	21 53.6	12 26.2	3 20.2	0 39.9	27 55.6
14	15 25 52.8	22 56.2	19 40.2	23 40.7	10 55.5	0♊40.3	5 52.8	21 52.5	12 22.2	3 21.9	0 38.4	27 55.8
15	15 29 49.3	23 54.0	19 37.0	7♐ 6.4	10 35.8	1 54.1	6 30.4	21 51.7	12 18.1	3 23.7	0 36.9	27 55.9
16	15 33 45.9	24 51.9	19 33.9	20 14.0	10 20.1	3 7.9	7 8.0	21 51.1	12 14.0	3 25.5	0 35.4	27 56.1
17	15 37 42.5	25 49.7	19 30.7	3♑ 3.2	10 8.8	4 21.6	7 45.6	21 50.6	12 9.8	3 27.4	0 34.0	27 56.3
18	15 41 39.0	26 47.4	19 27.5	15 35.1	10 1.8	5 35.4	8 23.2	21 50.3	12 5.6	3 29.3	0 32.5	27 56.5
19	15 45 35.6	27 45.2	19 24.3	27 52.0	9 59.3	6 49.1	9 .8	21 50.2	12 1.4	3 31.2	0 31.1	27 56.8
20	15 49 32.1	28 42.9	19 21.1	9♒57.0	10 D 1.4	8 2.9	9 38.4	21 D 50.3	11 57.2	3 33.2	0 29.7	27 57.0
21	15 53 28.7	29 40.6	19 18.0	21 54.0	10 8.1	9 16.6	10 16.0	21 50.5	11 52.9	3 35.3	0 28.3	27 57.4
22	15 57 25.2	0♊38.3	19 14.8	3♓47.4	10 19.3	10 30.3	10 53.6	21 51.0	11 48.6	3 37.4	0 27.0	27 57.7
23	16 1 21.8	1 36.0	19 11.6	15 41.8	10 35.0	11 44.0	11 31.2	21 51.6	11 44.3	3 39.5	0 25.6	27 58.1
24	16 5 18.3	2 33.7	19 8.4	27 41.8	10 55.1	12 57.7	12 8.8	21 52.4	11 39.9	3 41.7	0 24.3	27 58.5
25	16 9 14.9	3 31.3	19 5.3	9♈51.8	11 19.5	14 11.4	12 46.4	21 53.4	11 35.5	3 43.9	0 23.0	27 58.9
26	16 13 11.5	4 28.9	19 2.1	22 15.5	11 48.2	15 25.0	13 24.0	21 54.5	11 31.2	3 46.1	0 21.7	27 59.4
27	16 17 8.0	5 26.6	18 58.9	4♉56.0	12 21.0	16 38.7	14 1.6	21 55.9	11 26.7	3 48.4	0 20.4	27 59.9
28	16 21 4.6	6 24.1	18 55.7	17 55.5	12 57.8	17 52.3	14 39.2	21 57.4	11 22.3	3 50.7	0 19.1	28 .4
29	16 25 1.1	7 21.7	18 52.6	1♊14.4	13 38.6	19 6.0	15 16.8	21 59.1	11 17.9	3 53.1	0 17.9	28 .9
30	16 28 57.7	8 19.3	18 49.4	14 52.1	14 23.1	20 19.6	15 54.4	22 .9	11 13.5	3 55.5	0 16.7	28 1.5
31	16 32 54.2	9 16.8	18 46.2	28 46.3	15 11.4	21 33.2	16 32.0	22 3.0	11 9.0	3 58.0	0 15.5	28 2.1

LATITUDE

DAY	SID. TIME	☉	☊	☽	☿	♀	♂	♃	♄	♅	♆	♇
1	14 34 37.6	0 .0	0 .0	0S15.5	1N35.4	0S37.0	1N17.2	1N29.1	1N51.9	0N36.5	1N48.4	11N16.6
4	14 46 27.2	0 .0	0 .0	3 37.0	0 49.5	0 30.4	1 17.3	1 28.5	1 52.0	0 36.4	1 48.3	11 15.9
7	14 58 16.9	0 .0	0 .0	5 15.8	0S 1.6	0 23.6	1 17.4	1 27.9	1 52.1	0 36.4	1 48.3	11 15.1
10	15 10 6.6	0 .0	0 .0	4 10.2	0 53.6	0 16.6	1 17.5	1 27.2	1 52.2	0 36.3	1 48.2	11 14.3
13	15 21 56.2	0 .0	0 .0	0 53.6	1 42.1	0 9.5	1 17.5	1 26.6	1 52.3	0 36.2	1 48.2	11 13.6
16	15 33 45.9	0 .0	0 .0	2N41.4	2 23.9	0 2.3	1 17.5	1 25.9	1 52.3	0 36.1	1 48.1	11 12.8
19	15 45 35.6	0 .0	0 .0	4 54.1	2 57.1	0N 5.0	1 17.4	1 25.2	1 52.3	0 36.1	1 48.1	11 12.0
22	15 57 25.2	0 .0	0 .0	5 6.9	3 20.8	0 12.3	1 17.3	1 24.5	1 52.2	0 36.0	1 48.0	11 11.2
25	16 9 14.9	0 .0	0 .0	3 22.7	3 35.4	0 19.5	1 17.2	1 23.9	1 52.1	0 35.9	1 47.9	11 10.5
28	16 21 4.6	0 .0	0 .0	0 9.7	3 41.2	0 26.7	1 17.1	1 23.2	1 52.0	0 35.9	1 47.8	11 9.7
31	16 32 54.2	0 .0	0 .0	3S19.0	3 39.2	0 33.7	1 16.9	1 22.5	1 51.9	0 35.8	1 47.7	11 8.9

RIGHT ASCENSION

DAY	SID. TIME	☉	☊	☽	☿	♀	♂	♃	♄	♅	♆	♇
1	14 34 37.6	7♉56.6	17♏55.0	20♉ 5.2	15♉ 6.5	12♉22.8	27♊29.5	23♍32.6	12♐ .4	5♌29.9	29♎29.0	4♍18.8
2	14 38 34.1	8 53.9	17 51.8	4♊ 1.6	14 R 41.6	13 35.8	28 11.0	23 R 29.6	11 R 56.9	5 31.1	29 R 27.4	4 R 18.5
3	14 42 30.7	9 51.4	17 48.6	18 23.4	14 14.0	14 49.0	28 52.5	23 26.8	11 53.2	5 32.3	29 25.9	4 18.2
4	14 46 27.2	10 48.9	17 45.4	2♋57.0	13 44.4	16 2.5	29 33.9	23 24.1	11 49.5	5 33.6	29 24.4	4 17.9
5	14 50 23.8	11 46.6	17 42.2	17 27.7	13 13.3	17 16.3	0♋15.4	23 21.6	11 45.7	5 34.9	29 22.9	4 17.6
6	14 54 20.3	12 44.5	17 38.9	1♌44.2	12 41.5	18 30.3	0 56.8	23 19.2	11 41.9	5 36.3	29 21.4	4 17.4
7	14 58 16.9	13 42.5	17 35.7	15 41.4	12 9.5	19 44.6	1 38.3	23 17.1	11 38.0	5 37.7	29 19.9	4 17.2
8	15 2 13.5	14 40.6	17 32.5	29 20.4	11 37.9	20 59.2	2 19.7	23 15.0	11 34.0	5 39.2	29 18.4	4 17.1
9	15 6 10.0	15 38.8	17 29.3	12♍47.3	11 7.4	22 14.1	3 1.1	23 13.2	11 30.0	5 40.7	29 16.9	4 16.9
10	15 10 6.6	16 37.2	17 26.1	26 10.7	10 38.4	23 29.2	3 42.5	23 11.5	11 25.9	5 42.3	29 15.4	4 16.8
11	15 14 3.1	17 35.8	17 22.9	9♎39.5	10 11.5	24 44.7	4 24.0	23 10.0	11 21.9	5 43.9	29 14.0	4 16.8
12	15 17 59.7	18 34.5	17 19.7	23 20.4	9 47.1	26 .4	5 5.4	23 8.7	11 17.7	5 45.6	29 12.5	4 16.7
13	15 21 56.2	19 33.3	17 16.5	7♏16.1	9 25.6	27 16.4	5 46.7	23 7.5	11 13.5	5 47.3	29 11.1	4 16.7
14	15 25 52.8	20 32.2	17 13.2	21 23.5	9 7.4	28 32.6	6 28.1	23 6.5	11 9.2	5 49.1	29 9.7	4 16.7
15	15 29 49.3	21 31.3	17 10.0	5♐34.0	8 52.6	29 49.1	7 9.4	23 5.6	11 4.9	5 50.9	29 8.3	4 D 16.8
16	15 33 45.9	22 30.6	17 6.8	19 35.1	8 41.5	1♊ 5.9	7 50.7	23 4.9	11 .6	5 52.8	29 6.9	4 16.8
17	15 37 42.5	23 30.0	17 3.6	3♑14.3	8 34.3	2 23.0	8 31.9	23 4.4	10 56.2	5 54.7	29 5.5	4 16.9
18	15 41 39.0	24 29.5	17 .4	16 22.7	8 31.0	3 40.3	9 13.1	23 4.1	10 51.8	5 56.7	29 4.1	4 17.1
19	15 45 35.6	25 29.2	16 57.2	28 56.7	8 D 31.8	4 57.9	9 54.3	23 3.9	10 47.3	5 58.7	29 2.7	4 17.2
20	15 49 32.1	26 29.0	16 54.0	10♒58.0	8 36.7	6 15.7	10 35.5	23 3.9	10 42.8	6 .8	29 1.4	4 17.4
21	15 53 28.7	27 28.9	16 50.8	22 32.9	8 45.7	7 33.8	11 16.7	23 D 4.0	10 38.3	6 2.9	29 .1	4 17.6
22	15 57 25.2	28 29.0	16 47.6	3♓50.1	8 58.7	8 52.1	11 57.8	23 4.3	10 33.7	6 5.0	28 58.7	4 17.8
23	16 1 21.8	29 29.2	16 44.4	15 .0	9 15.8	10 10.6	12 38.8	23 4.8	10 29.2	6 7.2	28 57.4	4 18.1
24	16 5 18.3	0♊29.6	16 41.2	26 14.0	9 36.8	11 29.4	13 19.9	23 5.4	10 24.6	6 9.4	28 56.2	4 18.4
25	16 9 14.9	1 30.1	16 38.0	7♈43.5	10 1.7	12 48.4	14 .9	23 6.2	10 19.9	6 11.7	28 54.9	4 18.7
26	16 13 11.5	2 30.7	16 34.8	19 39.5	10 30.5	14 7.5	14 41.8	23 7.2	10 15.3	6 14.0	28 53.7	4 19.1
27	16 17 8.0	3 31.5	16 31.6	2♉11.3	11 3.0	15 26.9	15 22.8	23 8.4	10 10.6	6 16.4	28 52.4	4 19.5
28	16 21 4.6	4 32.3	16 28.4	15 24.8	11 39.2	16 46.4	16 3.6	23 9.7	10 6.0	6 18.8	28 51.2	4 19.9
29	16 25 1.1	5 33.3	16 25.2	29 20.4	12 19.0	18 6.1	16 44.5	23 11.1	10 1.3	6 21.3	28 50.0	4 20.3
30	16 28 57.7	6 34.4	16 22.0	13♊50.7	13 2.3	19 26.0	17 25.3	23 12.8	9 56.6	6 23.8	28 48.9	4 20.8
31	16 32 54.2	7 35.6	16 18.7	28 41.6	13 49.1	20 46.0	18 6.0	23 14.5	9 51.9	6 26.3	28 47.7	4 21.3

DECLINATION

DAY	SID. TIME	☉	☊	☽	☿	♀	♂	♃	♄	♅	♆	♇
1	14 34 37.6	14N55.8	0S18.7	18N 7.9	18N44.0	15N38.9	24N42.6	4N24.5	20S32.0	20N 4.2	10S 7.3	22N44.2
4	14 46 27.2	15 49.5	0 18.6	19 47.9	17 33.0	16 48.5	24 43.9	4 27.5	20 30.6	20 3.3	10 5.7	22 43.7
7	14 58 16.9	16 40.8	0 18.6	11 21.6	16 11.9	17 54.2	24 43.5	4 29.8	20 29.1	20 2.3	10 4.1	22 43.2
10	15 10 6.6	17 29.6	0 18.5	2S53.2	14 50.0	18 55.7	24 41.4	4 31.5	20 27.6	20 1.2	10 2.5	22 42.5
13	15 21 56.2	18 15.8	0 18.5	15 39.2	13 36.5	19 52.8	24 37.7	4 32.5	20 26.1	19 60.0	10 1.0	22 41.7
16	15 33 45.9	18 59.2	0 18.5	20 24.0	12 38.6	20 44.9	24 32.4	4 32.9	20 24.5	19 58.7	9 59.5	22 40.8
19	15 45 35.6	19 39.7	0 18.4	15 47.1	12 .6	21 32.0	24 25.4	4 32.6	20 22.9	19 57.3	9 58.1	22 39.8
22	15 57 25.2	20 17.3	0 18.4	5 20.9	11 44.2	22 13.7	24 16.8	4 31.7	20 21.2	19 55.8	9 56.7	22 38.8
25	16 9 14.9	20 51.7	0 18.3	7N .8	11 48.9	22 49.8	24 6.6	4 30.1	20 19.6	19 54.2	9 55.4	22 37.6
28	16 21 4.6	21 22.9	0 18.3	17 19.9	12 12.9	23 20.0	23 54.8	4 27.9	20 17.9	19 52.5	9 54.2	22 36.4
31	16 32 54.2	21 50.7	0 18.2	20 7.3	12 53.9	23 44.1	23 41.5	4 25.0	20 16.2	19 50.7	9 53.0	22 35.1

JUNE 1957

DAY	EPHEM. SID. TIME	☉	☊	☽	☿	♀	♂	♃	♄	♅	♆	♇
		LONGITUDE										
	h m s	° ′	° ′	° ′	° ′	° ′	° ′	° ′	° ′	° ′	° ′	° ′
1	16 36 50.8	10♊14.4	18♏43.0	12♋53.6	16♉ 3.3	22♊46.8	17♋ 9.6	22♍ 5.2	11♐ 4.6	4♌ .5	0♏14.4	28♌ 2.8
2	16 40 47.4	11 11.9	18 39.8	27 9.6	16 58.7	24 .4	17 47.2	22 7.6	11R .2	4 3.1	0R13.2	28 3.4
3	16 44 43.9	12 9.4	18 36.7	11♌29.8	17 57.5	25 14.0	18 24.8	22 10.2	10 55.7	4 5.6	0 12.1	28 4.1
4	16 48 40.5	13 6.8	18 33.5	25 49.9	18 59.6	26 27.5	19 2.4	22 12.9	10 51.3	4 8.3	0 11.0	28 4.8
5	16 52 37.0	14 4.3	18 30.3	10♍ 6.4	20 5.0	27 41.1	19 40.0	22 15.8	10 46.8	4 10.9	0 9.9	28 5.6
6	16 56 33.6	15 1.7	18 27.1	24 16.4	21 13.6	28 54.6	20 17.6	22 18.9	10 42.4	4 13.6	0 8.8	28 6.4
7	17 0 30.1	15 59.1	18 24.0	8♎18.1	22 25.4	0♋ 8.1	20 55.2	22 22.2	10 37.9	4 16.3	0 7.8	28 7.2
8	17 4 26.7	16 56.5	18 20.8	22 10.2	23 40.2	1 21.6	21 32.7	22 25.6	10 33.5	4 19.0	0 6.8	28 8.0
9	17 8 23.3	17 53.8	18 17.6	5♏51.7	24 58.1	2 35.0	22 10.3	22 29.2	10 29.1	4 21.8	0 5.8	28 8.8
10	17 12 19.8	18 51.2	18 14.4	19 21.8	26 19.0	3 48.5	22 47.9	22 32.9	10 24.8	4 24.7	0 4.9	28 9.7
11	17 16 16.4	19 48.5	18 11.3	2♐39.8	27 42.9	5 1.9	23 25.5	22 36.8	10 20.4	4 27.5	0 3.9	28 10.6
12	17 20 12.9	20 45.8	18 8.1	15 45.0	29 9.7	6 15.3	24 3.0	22 40.9	10 16.1	4 30.4	0 3.0	28 11.5
13	17 24 9.5	21 43.1	18 4.9	28 36.7	0♊39.5	7 28.7	24 40.6	22 45.1	10 11.7	4 33.3	0 2.2	28 12.5
14	17 28 6.0	22 40.4	18 1.7	11♑14.9	2 12.1	8 42.1	25 18.2	22 49.5	10 7.4	4 36.3	0 1.3	28 13.5
15	17 32 2.6	23 37.7	17 58.6	23 40.0	3 47.7	9 55.5	25 55.7	22 54.0	10 3.2	4 39.2	0 .5	28 14.5
16	17 35 59.2	24 35.0	17 55.4	5♒53.1	5 26.1	11 8.9	26 33.3	22 58.7	9 58.9	4 42.2	29♎59.7	28 15.5
17	17 39 55.7	25 32.3	17 52.2	17 56.3	7 7.4	12 22.2	27 10.9	23 3.5	9 54.7	4 45.3	29 58.9	28 16.6
18	17 43 52.3	26 29.5	17 49.0	29 52.4	8 51.4	13 35.6	27 48.5	23 8.5	9 50.6	4 48.3	29 58.2	28 17.6
19	17 47 48.8	27 26.8	17 45.8	11♓45.1	10 38.3	14 48.9	28 26.0	23 13.6	9 46.4	4 51.4	29 57.5	28 18.7
20	17 51 45.4	28 24.0	17 42.7	23 38.5	12 27.8	16 2.2	29 3.6	23 18.9	9 42.3	4 54.6	29 56.8	28 19.9
21	17 55 41.9	29 21.3	17 39.5	5♈37.4	14 20.0	17 15.5	29 41.2	23 24.4	9 38.2	4 57.7	29 56.1	28 21.0
22	17 59 38.5	0♋18.6	17 36.3	17 46.7	16 14.8	18 28.9	0♌18.8	23 30.0	9 34.3	5 .9	29 55.6	28 22.2
23	18 3 35.1	1 15.8	17 33.1	0♉11.2	18 12.0	19 42.2	0 56.4	23 35.8	9 30.3	5 4.1	29 55.0	28 23.4
24	18 7 31.6	2 13.1	17 30.0	12 55.1	20 11.5	20 55.4	1 34.0	23 41.6	9 26.4	5 7.4	29 54.4	28 24.7
25	18 11 28.2	3 10.3	17 26.8	26 1.9	22 13.2	22 8.7	2 11.6	23 47.7	9 22.5	5 10.6	29 53.9	28 25.9
26	18 15 24.7	4 7.5	17 23.6	9♊33.2	24 16.9	23 21.9	2 49.2	23 53.8	9 18.6	5 13.9	29 53.4	28 27.2
27	18 19 21.3	5 4.8	17 20.4	23 28.9	26 22.4	24 35.2	3 26.8	24 .1	9 14.8	5 17.2	29 52.9	28 28.5
28	18 23 17.8	6 2.0	17 17.3	7♋46.1	28 29.4	25 48.4	4 4.5	24 6.6	9 11.1	5 20.5	29 52.4	28 29.8
29	18 27 14.4	6 59.2	17 14.1	22 19.8	0♋37.7	27 1.6	4 42.1	24 13.1	9 7.4	5 23.9	29 52.0	28 31.1
30	18 31 11.0	7 56.5	17 10.9	7♌ 3.0	2 47.0	28 14.8	5 19.7	24 19.8	9 3.8	5 27.2	29 51.6	28 32.5
		LATITUDE										
1	16 36 50.8	0 .0	0 .0	4S12.4	3S36.9	0N36.0	1N16.8	1N22.2	1N51.8	0N35.8	1N47.6	11N 8.7
4	16 48 40.5	0 .0	0 .0	5 12.3	3 25.6	0 42.8	1 16.6	1 21.6	1 51.6	0 35.7	1 47.5	11 8.0
7	17 0 30.1	0 .0	0 .0	3 27.1	3 8.3	0 49.4	1 16.4	1 20.9	1 51.4	0 35.7	1 47.4	11 7.2
10	17 12 19.8	0 .0	0 .0	0 .9	2 45.8	0 55.7	1 16.1	1 20.2	1 51.1	0 35.6	1 47.3	11 6.5
13	17 24 9.5	0 .0	0 .0	3N17.3	2 18.8	1 1.7	1 15.9	1 19.5	1 50.8	0 35.6	1 47.1	11 5.8
16	17 35 59.2	0 .0	0 .0	5 2.4	1 48.2	1 7.4	1 15.6	1 18.9	1 50.5	0 35.5	1 47.0	11 5.2
19	17 47 48.8	0 .0	0 .0	4 46.5	1 15.1	1 12.6	1 15.2	1 18.2	1 50.1	0 35.5	1 46.9	11 4.5
22	17 59 38.5	0 .0	0 .0	2 41.0	0 40.6	1 17.4	1 14.9	1 17.6	1 49.7	0 35.5	1 46.7	11 3.9
25	18 11 28.2	0 .0	0 .0	0S38.2	0 6.2	1 21.7	1 14.5	1 17.0	1 49.3	0 35.4	1 46.6	11 3.3
28	18 23 17.8	0 .0	0 .0	3 52.3	0N26.3	1 25.6	1 14.1	1 16.4	1 48.9	0 35.4	1 46.4	11 2.7
		RIGHT ASCENSION										
1	16 36 50.8	8♊37.0	16♏15.5	13♋34.9	14♉39.4	22♊ 6.2	18♋46.8	23♍16.5	9♐47.2	6♌28.9	28♎46.6	4♍21.9
2	16 40 47.4	9 38.4	16 12.3	28 14.2	15 33.1	23 26.4	19 27.4	23 18.7	9R42.5	6 31.5	28R45.5	4 22.4
3	16 44 43.9	10 39.9	16 9.1	12♌29.5	16 30.0	24 46.8	20 8.0	23 20.9	9 37.8	6 34.2	28 44.4	4 23.0
4	16 48 40.5	11 41.5	16 5.9	26 18.9	17 30.3	26 7.2	20 48.5	23 23.4	9 33.1	6 36.9	28 43.4	4 23.6
5	16 52 37.0	12 43.2	16 2.8	9♍46.9	18 33.8	27 27.7	21 29.0	23 25.9	9 28.4	6 39.6	28 42.3	4 24.2
6	16 56 33.6	13 45.0	15 59.6	23 2.3	19 40.6	28 48.3	22 9.5	23 28.7	9 23.7	6 42.4	28 41.3	4 24.9
7	17 0 30.1	14 46.8	15 56.4	6♎15.3	20 50.7	0♋ 8.9	22 49.8	23 31.6	9 19.0	6 45.2	28 40.3	4 25.6
8	17 4 26.7	15 48.7	15 53.2	19 35.1	22 4.1	1 29.5	23 30.1	23 34.6	9 14.4	6 48.0	28 39.4	4 26.3
9	17 8 23.3	16 50.7	15 50.0	3♏ 7.6	23 20.7	2 50.1	24 10.4	23 37.8	9 9.7	6 50.9	28 38.4	4 27.1
10	17 12 19.8	17 52.7	15 46.8	16 54.4	24 40.6	4 10.7	24 50.5	23 41.2	9 5.1	6 53.8	28 37.5	4 27.8
11	17 16 16.4	18 54.8	15 43.6	0♐50.8	26 3.9	5 31.3	25 30.7	23 44.7	9 .5	6 56.7	28 36.6	4 28.6
12	17 20 12.9	19 56.9	15 40.4	14 47.3	27 30.5	6 51.9	26 10.7	23 48.4	8 55.9	6 59.7	28 35.7	4 29.5
13	17 24 9.5	20 59.1	15 37.2	28 31.4	29 .5	8 12.4	26 50.7	23 52.1	8 51.3	7 2.7	28 34.9	4 30.3
14	17 28 6.0	22 1.4	15 34.0	11♑52.1	0♊34.0	9 32.9	27 30.6	23 56.1	8 46.8	7 5.7	28 34.0	4 31.2
15	17 32 2.6	23 3.6	15 30.8	24 41.9	2 10.9	10 53.2	28 10.5	24 .2	8 42.3	7 8.8	28 33.3	4 32.1
16	17 35 59.2	24 5.9	15 27.6	6♒58.9	3 51.4	12 13.5	28 50.3	24 4.4	8 37.8	7 11.9	28 32.5	4 33.0
17	17 39 55.7	25 8.3	15 24.4	18 46.1	5 35.3	13 33.7	29 30.0	24 8.8	8 33.3	7 15.0	28 31.7	4 34.0
18	17 43 52.3	26 10.6	15 21.2	0♓10.4	7 22.8	14 53.7	0♌ 9.7	24 13.3	8 28.9	7 18.1	28 31.0	4 35.0
19	17 47 48.8	27 13.0	15 18.0	11 21.0	9 13.9	16 13.7	0 49.3	24 17.9	8 24.6	7 21.3	28 30.3	4 36.0
20	17 51 45.4	28 15.4	15 14.8	22 28.6	11 8.5	17 33.4	1 28.8	24 22.7	8 20.2	7 24.5	28 29.7	4 37.0
21	17 55 41.9	29 17.8	15 11.6	3♈44.8	13 6.6	18 53.0	2 8.3	24 27.6	8 15.9	7 27.8	28 29.0	4 38.1
22	17 59 38.5	0♋20.2	15 8.4	15 21.3	15 8.2	20 12.5	2 47.7	24 32.7	8 11.7	7 31.1	28 28.4	4 39.2
23	18 3 35.1	1 22.6	15 5.3	27 29.2	17 13.1	21 31.7	3 27.0	24 37.9	8 7.5	7 34.4	28 27.9	4 40.3
24	18 7 31.6	2 25.0	15 2.1	10♉17.8	19 21.1	22 50.8	4 6.3	24 43.3	8 3.3	7 37.7	28 27.3	4 41.4
25	18 11 28.2	3 27.4	14 58.9	23 52.0	21 32.2	24 9.6	4 45.5	24 48.7	7 59.2	7 41.1	28 26.8	4 42.6
26	18 15 24.7	4 29.7	14 55.7	8♊10.5	23 46.0	25 28.2	5 24.6	24 54.3	7 55.2	7 44.4	28 26.3	4 43.7
27	18 19 21.3	5 32.0	14 52.5	23 3.2	26 2.4	26 46.6	6 3.6	25 .0	7 51.2	7 47.8	28 25.8	4 44.9
28	18 23 17.8	6 34.3	14 49.3	8♋13.1	28 20.9	28 4.7	6 42.6	25 5.9	7 47.2	7 51.2	28 25.4	4 46.2
29	18 27 14.4	7 36.5	14 46.1	23 20.3	0♋41.3	29 22.6	7 21.5	25 11.8	7 43.3	7 54.7	28 24.9	4 47.4
30	18 31 11.0	8 38.7	14 42.9	8♌ 8.8	3 3.1	0♌40.2	8 .4	25 17.9	7 39.5	7 58.1	28 24.6	4 48.7
		DECLINATION										
1	16 36 50.8	21N59.3	0S18.2	18N37.8	13N10.9	23N50.8	23N36.7	4N23.9	20S15.7	19N50.1	9S52.6	22N34.6
4	16 48 40.5	22 22.6	0 18.2	8 .4	14 10.4	24 6.6	23 21.3	4 20.3	20 14.0	19 48.2	9 51.6	22 33.1
7	17 0 30.1	22 42.3	0 18.1	6S27.8	15 20.6	24 16.0	23 4.4	4 16.0	20 12.4	19 46.3	9 50.6	22 31.6
10	17 12 19.8	22 58.5	0 18.1	17 35.2	16 38.7	24 19.0	22 46.0	4 11.1	20 10.8	19 44.2	9 49.7	22 30.1
13	17 24 9.5	23 11.1	0 18.0	20 8.9	18 1.7	24 15.5	22 26.2	4 5.7	20 9.2	19 42.1	9 48.8	22 28.4
16	17 35 59.2	23 19.9	0 18.0	13 54.8	19 26.2	24 5.6	22 5.0	3 59.7	20 7.7	19 39.9	9 48.1	22 26.7
19	17 47 48.8	23 25.1	0 17.9	2 44.3	20 48.4	23 49.3	21 42.3	3 53.2	20 6.3	19 37.7	9 47.5	22 25.0
22	17 59 38.5	23 26.6	0 17.9	9N27.4	22 3.6	23 26.7	21 18.3	3 46.1	20 4.9	19 35.3	9 46.9	22 23.1
25	18 11 28.2	23 24.3	0 17.8	18 38.8	23 6.7	22 58.0	20 53.0	3 38.6	20 3.5	19 33.0	9 46.5	22 21.3
28	18 23 17.8	23 18.3	0 17.8	19 21.0	23 52.4	22 23.3	20 26.4	3 30.5	20 2.3	19 30.5	9 46.1	22 19.3

JULY 1957

LONGITUDE

DAY	EPHEM. SID. TIME	☉	☊	☽	☿	♀	♂	♃	♄	♅	♆	♇
	h m s	° ′	° ′	° ′	° ′	° ′	° ′	° ′	° ′	° ′	° ′	° ′
1	18 35 7.5	8♋53.7	17♏ 7.7	21♌48.0	4♋57.1	29♋28.0	5♌57.3	24♍26.7	9♐ .3	5♌30.6	29♎51.3	28♌33.8
2	18 39 4.1	9 50.9	17 4.5	6♍27.3	7 7.6	0♌41.1	6 35.0	24 33.7	8 R 56.8	5 34.0	29 R 51.0	28 35.2
3	18 43 .6	10 48.1	17 1.4	20 55.3	9 18.3	1 54.3	7 12.6	24 40.8	8 53.3	5 37.5	29 50.7	28 36.7
4	18 46 57.2	11 45.3	16 58.2	5♎ 8.2	11 28.9	3 7.4	7 50.2	24 48.0	8 49.9	5 40.9	29 50.4	28 38.1
5	18 50 53.7	12 42.5	16 55.0	19 4.2	13 39.0	4 20.5	8 27.9	24 55.4	8 46.6	5 44.4	29 50.2	28 39.6
6	18 54 50.3	13 39.7	16 51.8	2♏43.5	15 48.6	5 33.6	9 5.5	25 2.9	8 43.4	5 47.8	29 50.0	28 41.0
7	18 58 46.9	14 36.9	16 48.7	16 6.9	17 57.2	6 46.6	9 43.1	25 10.5	8 40.2	5 51.3	29 49.8	28 42.5
8	19 2 43.4	15 34.1	16 45.5	29 16.1	20 4.9	7 59.7	10 20.8	25 18.2	8 37.1	5 54.9	29 49.7	28 44.0
9	19 6 40.0	16 31.3	16 42.3	12♐12.5	22 11.3	9 12.7	10 58.4	25 26.1	8 34.1	5 58.4	29 49.6	28 45.6
10	19 10 36.5	17 28.5	16 39.1	24 57.4	24 16.4	10 25.7	11 36.1	25 34.0	8 31.1	6 1.9	29 49.5	28 47.1
11	19 14 33.1	18 25.7	16 36.0	7♑31.5	26 20.0	11 38.7	12 13.8	25 42.1	8 28.2	6 5.5	29 49.5	28 48.7
12	19 18 29.6	19 22.8	16 32.8	19 55.6	28 22.0	12 51.6	12 51.4	25 50.3	8 25.4	6 9.1	29 49.5	28 50.3
13	19 22 26.2	20 20.1	16 29.6	2♒10.3	0♌22.4	14 4.6	13 29.1	25 58.7	8 22.7	6 12.7	29 49.5	28 51.9
14	19 26 22.8	21 17.3	16 26.4	14 16.4	2 21.0	15 17.5	14 6.8	26 7.1	8 20.1	6 16.3	29 D 49.6	28 53.6
15	19 30 19.3	22 14.5	16 23.2	26 15.3	4 17.9	16 30.4	14 44.5	26 15.7	8 17.5	6 19.9	29 49.7	28 55.2
16	19 34 15.9	23 11.7	16 20.1	8♓ 8.8	6 13.0	17 43.3	15 22.2	26 24.3	8 15.0	6 23.5	29 49.8	28 56.9
17	19 38 12.4	24 8.9	16 16.9	19 59.7	8 6.2	18 56.1	15 59.9	26 33.1	8 12.6	6 27.1	29 50.0	28 58.5
18	19 42 9.0	25 6.2	16 13.7	1♈51.6	9 57.7	20 9.0	16 37.6	26 41.9	8 10.2	6 30.8	29 50.2	29 .2
19	19 46 5.5	26 3.4	16 10.5	13 48.6	11 47.4	21 21.8	17 15.3	26 50.9	8 8.0	6 34.4	29 50.4	29 1.9
20	19 50 2.1	27 .7	16 7.4	25 55.5	13 35.2	22 34.6	17 53.1	26 60.0	8 5.8	6 38.1	29 50.6	29 3.6
21	19 53 58.6	27 57.9	16 4.2	8♉17.5	15 21.2	23 47.4	18 30.8	27 9.1	8 3.7	6 41.7	29 50.9	29 5.4
22	19 57 55.2	28 55.2	16 1.0	20 59.6	17 5.4	25 .1	19 8.5	27 18.4	8 1.7	6 45.4	29 51.2	29 7.1
23	20 1 51.8	29 52.5	15 57.8	4♊ 6.3	18 47.8	26 12.9	19 46.3	27 27.8	7 59.8	6 49.1	29 51.6	29 8.9
24	20 5 48.3	0♌49.8	15 54.7	17 40.6	20 28.4	27 25.6	20 24.1	27 37.2	7 58.0	6 52.8	29 52.0	29 10.6
25	20 9 44.9	1 47.2	15 51.5	1♋43.6	22 7.2	28 38.3	21 1.9	27 46.8	7 56.2	6 56.5	29 52.4	29 12.4
26	20 13 41.4	2 44.5	15 48.3	16 13.3	23 44.2	29 51.0	21 39.6	27 56.5	7 54.6	7 .2	29 52.8	29 14.2
27	20 17 38.0	3 41.9	15 45.1	1♌ 4.3	25 19.3	1♍ 3.6	22 17.4	28 6.2	7 53.0	7 3.9	29 53.3	29 16.0
28	20 21 34.5	4 39.2	15 41.9	16 8.5	26 52.7	2 16.2	22 55.3	28 16.1	7 51.5	7 7.5	29 53.8	29 17.8
29	20 25 31.1	5 36.6	15 38.8	1♍15.7	28 24.3	3 28.8	23 33.1	28 26.0	7 50.2	7 11.2	29 54.3	29 19.7
30	20 29 27.6	6 34.0	15 35.6	16 15.8	29 54.1	4 41.4	24 10.9	28 36.1	7 48.9	7 14.9	29 54.9	29 21.5
31	20 33 24.2	7 31.4	15 32.4	1♎ .6	1♍22.0	5 54.0	24 48.8	28 46.2	7 47.7	7 18.7	29 55.5	29 23.4

LATITUDE

DAY	EPHEM. SID. TIME	☉	☊	☽	☿	♀	♂	♃	♄	♅	♆	♇
1	18 35 7.5	0 .0	0 .0	5S 6.3	0N55.1	1N28.9	1N13.6	1N15.8	1N48.4	0N35.4	1N46.2	11N 2.2
4	18 46 57.2	0 .0	0 .0	3 30.2	1 18.7	1 31.6	1 13.2	1 15.2	1 47.9	0 35.3	1 46.1	11 1.7
7	18 58 46.9	0 .0	0 .0	0 11.5	1 35.9	1 33.7	1 12.7	1 14.7	1 47.4	0 35.3	1 45.9	11 1.2
10	19 10 36.5	0 .0	0 .0	3N 2.9	1 46.3	1 35.3	1 12.2	1 14.1	1 46.8	0 35.3	1 45.7	11 .8
13	19 22 26.2	0 .0	0 .0	4 52.0	1 50.1	1 36.2	1 11.7	1 13.6	1 46.3	0 35.3	1 45.6	11 .4
16	19 34 15.9	0 .0	0 .0	4 43.0	1 47.8	1 36.4	1 11.2	1 13.1	1 45.7	0 35.3	1 45.4	11 .0
19	19 46 5.5	0 .0	0 .0	2 46.2	1 39.9	1 36.0	1 10.6	1 12.6	1 45.1	0 35.3	1 45.2	10 59.7
22	19 57 55.2	0 .0	0 .0	0S21.8	1 27.1	1 34.9	1 10.0	1 12.1	1 44.5	0 35.3	1 45.1	10 59.4
25	20 9 44.9	0 .0	0 .0	3 33.9	1 10.0	1 33.1	1 9.4	1 11.6	1 43.8	0 35.3	1 44.9	10 59.1
28	20 21 34.5	0 .0	0 .0	5 .9	0 49.3	1 30.7	1 8.8	1 11.2	1 43.2	0 35.3	1 44.7	10 58.9
31	20 33 24.2	0 .0	0 .0	3 33.0	0 25.4	1 27.5	1 8.2	1 10.8	1 42.6	0 35.3	1 44.6	10 58.8

RIGHT ASCENSION

DAY	EPHEM. SID. TIME	☉	☊	☽	☿	♀	♂	♃	♄	♅	♆	♇
1	18 35 7.5	9♋40.8	14♏39.8	22♌30.3	5♋26.0	1♌57.5	8♌39.2	25♍24.1	7♐35.7	8♌ 1.6	28♎24.2	4♍50.0
2	18 39 4.1	10 42.9	14 36.6	6♍24.6	7 49.4	3 14.6	9 17.8	25 30.5	7 R 32.0	8 5.1	28 R 23.9	4 51.3
3	18 43 .6	11 44.9	14 33.4	19 57.9	10 13.0	4 31.3	9 56.5	25 36.9	7 28.4	8 8.7	28 23.6	4 52.6
4	18 46 57.2	12 46.8	14 30.2	3♎19.2	12 36.4	5 47.8	10 35.0	25 43.5	7 24.8	8 12.2	28 23.3	4 54.0
5	18 50 53.7	13 48.6	14 27.0	16 38.1	14 59.1	7 3.9	11 13.5	25 50.2	7 21.3	8 15.8	28 23.1	4 55.3
6	18 54 50.3	14 50.3	14 23.8	0♏ 2.2	17 20.8	8 19.8	11 51.9	25 57.0	7 17.8	8 19.3	28 22.9	4 56.7
7	18 58 46.9	15 52.0	14 20.7	13 35.4	19 41.0	9 35.3	12 30.2	26 3.9	7 14.5	8 22.9	28 22.7	4 58.2
8	19 2 43.4	16 53.5	14 17.5	27 16.9	21 59.6	10 50.5	13 8.5	26 11.0	7 11.2	8 26.5	28 22.6	4 59.6
9	19 6 40.0	17 55.0	14 14.3	11♐ .7	24 16.3	12 5.4	13 46.7	26 18.1	7 8.0	8 30.2	28 22.4	5 1.0
10	19 10 36.5	18 56.3	14 11.1	24 37.7	26 30.8	13 20.0	14 24.8	26 25.4	7 4.8	8 33.8	28 22.4	5 2.5
11	19 14 33.1	19 57.6	14 7.9	7♑57.7	28 42.9	14 34.3	15 2.8	26 32.7	7 1.8	8 37.4	28 22.3	5 4.0
12	19 18 29.6	20 58.7	14 4.8	20 52.6	0♌52.5	15 48.2	15 40.8	26 40.2	6 58.8	8 41.1	28 22.3	5 5.5
13	19 22 26.2	21 59.8	14 1.6	3♒18.3	2 59.6	17 1.9	16 18.7	26 47.8	6 55.9	8 44.8	28 22.3	5 7.1
14	19 26 22.8	23 .7	13 58.4	15 15.1	5 3.9	18 15.1	16 56.5	26 55.5	6 53.1	8 48.5	28 D 22.4	5 8.6
15	19 30 19.3	24 1.4	13 55.2	26 47.3	7 5.5	19 28.1	17 34.3	27 3.2	6 50.4	8 52.2	28 22.4	5 10.2
16	19 34 15.9	25 2.1	13 52.0	8♓ 2.1	9 4.4	20 40.7	18 12.0	27 11.1	6 47.7	8 55.9	28 22.5	5 11.8
17	19 38 12.4	26 2.6	13 48.9	19 8.4	11 .4	21 53.1	18 49.6	27 19.1	6 45.1	8 59.6	28 22.7	5 13.4
18	19 42 9.0	27 3.1	13 45.7	0♈16.6	12 53.8	23 5.1	19 27.2	27 27.2	6 42.6	9 3.4	28 22.8	5 15.0
19	19 46 5.5	28 3.3	13 42.5	11 37.4	14 44.3	24 16.7	20 4.7	27 35.3	6 40.2	9 7.1	28 23.0	5 16.6
20	19 50 2.1	29 3.5	13 39.3	23 21.7	16 32.2	25 28.1	20 42.1	27 43.6	6 37.9	9 10.9	28 23.2	5 18.3
21	19 53 58.6	0♌ 3.5	13 36.2	5♉39.9	18 17.4	26 39.2	21 19.4	27 52.0	6 35.7	9 14.6	28 23.5	5 20.0
22	19 57 55.2	1 3.4	13 33.0	18 39.7	20 .0	27 49.9	21 56.7	28 .4	6 33.5	9 18.4	28 23.7	5 21.6
23	20 1 51.8	2 3.1	13 29.8	2♊24.6	21 40.0	29 .4	22 34.0	28 8.9	6 31.5	9 22.1	28 24.1	5 23.3
24	20 5 48.3	3 2.7	13 26.6	16 51.7	23 17.5	0♍10.6	23 11.1	28 17.6	6 29.5	9 25.9	28 24.4	5 25.0
25	20 9 44.9	4 2.2	13 23.5	1♋49.9	24 52.5	1 20.5	23 48.2	28 26.3	6 27.7	9 29.7	28 24.8	5 26.8
26	20 13 41.4	5 1.5	13 20.3	17 2.7	26 25.1	2 30.1	24 25.3	28 35.1	6 25.9	9 33.5	28 25.2	5 28.5
27	20 17 38.0	6 .7	13 17.1	2♌12.1	27 55.3	3 39.4	25 2.3	28 44.0	6 24.2	9 37.3	28 25.6	5 30.3
28	20 21 34.5	6 59.7	13 13.9	17 4.5	29 23.1	4 48.4	25 39.2	28 53.0	6 22.7	9 41.0	28 26.1	5 32.0
29	20 25 31.1	7 58.6	13 10.8	1♍33.7	0♍48.6	5 57.2	26 16.0	29 2.1	6 21.2	9 44.8	28 26.6	5 33.8
30	20 29 27.6	8 57.3	13 7.6	15 40.6	2 11.8	7 5.7	26 52.9	29 11.2	6 19.8	9 48.6	28 27.1	5 35.6
31	20 33 24.2	9 55.9	13 4.4	29 30.7	3 32.8	8 14.0	27 29.6	29 20.4	6 18.5	9 52.4	28 27.6	5 37.4

DECLINATION

DAY	EPHEM. SID. TIME	☉	☊	☽	☿	♀	♂	♃	♄	♅	♆	♇
1	18 35 7.5	23N 8.7	0S17.8	9N24.3	24N16.1	21N42.8	19N58.5	3N22.0	20S 1.1	19N28.0	9S45.9	22N17.4
4	18 46 57.2	22 55.4	0 17.7	5S15.4	24 15.2	20 56.8	19 29.4	3 13.0	20 .0	19 25.5	9 45.7	22 15.4
7	18 58 46.9	22 38.5	0 17.7	16 50.8	23 49.3	20 5.6	18 59.2	3 3.6	19 59.0	19 22.9	9 45.7	22 13.3
10	19 10 36.5	22 18.1	0 17.6	20 18.0	23 .5	19 9.4	18 27.8	2 53.7	19 58.2	19 20.3	9 45.7	22 11.3
13	19 22 26.2	21 54.2	0 17.6	14 56.0	21 52.0	18 8.5	17 55.3	2 43.5	19 57.4	19 17.6	9 45.9	22 9.2
16	19 34 15.9	21 27.0	0 17.5	4 8.3	20 27.7	17 3.2	17 21.8	2 32.8	19 56.8	19 14.9	9 46.1	22 7.0
19	19 46 5.5	20 56.4	0 17.5	8N .1	18 51.2	15 53.9	16 47.2	2 21.8	19 56.3	19 12.1	9 46.5	22 4.9
22	19 57 55.2	20 22.7	0 17.4	17 39.4	17 5.9	14 40.8	16 11.6	2 10.4	19 55.9	19 9.4	9 47.0	22 2.8
25	20 9 44.9	19 45.9	0 17.4	19 52.1	15 14.6	13 24.3	15 35.1	1 58.7	19 55.6	19 6.6	9 47.5	22 .6
28	20 21 34.5	19 6.1	0 17.3	11 12.5	13 19.6	12 4.7	14 57.7	1 46.7	19 55.5	19 3.8	9 48.2	21 58.5
31	20 33 24.2	18 23.5	0 17.3	3S39.5	11 23.1	10 42.3	14 19.4	1 34.3	19 55.5	19 1.0	9 48.9	21 56.3

AUGUST 1957

LONGITUDE

DAY	EPHEM. SID. TIME h m s	☉ ° ′	☊ ° ′	☽ ° ′	☿ ° ′	♀ ° ′	♂ ° ′	♃ ° ′	♄ ° ′	♅ ° ′	♆ ° ′	♇ ° ′
1	20 37 20.8	8♌28.8	15♏29.2	15♎24.4	2♍48.1	7♍ 6.5	25♌26.6	28♍56.4	7♐46.6	7♌22.4	29♎56.2	29♌25.2
2	20 41 17.3	9 26.2	15 26.1	29 24.9	4 12.3	8 19.0	26 4.5	29 6.7	7R45.6	7 26.1	29 56.8	29 27.1
3	20 45 13.9	10 23.7	15 22.9	13♏ 2.2	5 34.6	9 31.5	26 42.4	29 17.1	7 44.7	7 29.8	29 57.6	29 29.0
4	20 49 10.4	11 21.1	15 19.7	26 18.1	6 55.0	10 43.9	27 20.3	29 27.5	7 43.9	7 33.5	29 58.3	29 30.9
5	20 53 7.0	12 18.6	15 16.5	9♐15.6	8 13.3	11 56.3	27 58.2	29 38.1	7 43.2	7 37.2	29 59.1	29 32.8
6	20 57 3.5	13 16.0	15 13.4	21 57.8	9 29.6	13 8.7	28 36.1	29 48.7	7 42.6	7 40.9	29 59.8	29 34.7
7	21 1 .1	14 13.5	15 10.2	4♑27.5	10 43.9	14 21.0	29 14.0	29 59.4	7 42.1	7 44.6	0♏ .7	29 36.6
8	21 4 56.6	15 11.0	15 7.0	16 47.1	11 55.9	15 33.3	29 51.9	0♎10.1	7 41.6	7 48.2	0 1.5	29 38.5
9	21 8 53.2	16 8.5	15 3.8	28 58.4	13 5.8	16 45.6	0♍29.9	0 21.0	7 41.3	7 51.9	0 2.4	29 40.5
10	21 12 49.8	17 6.0	15 .6	11♒ 2.8	14 13.3	17 57.8	1 7.8	0 31.9	7 41.1	7 55.6	0 3.3	29 42.4
11	21 16 46.3	18 3.5	14 57.5	23 1.7	15 18.4	19 10.0	1 45.8	0 42.9	7 40.9	7 59.2	0 4.3	29 44.3
12	21 20 42.9	19 1.1	14 54.3	4♓56.0	16 21.1	20 22.2	2 23.7	0 53.9	7 40.9	8 2.9	0 5.2	29 46.3
13	21 24 39.4	19 58.7	14 51.1	16 47.4	17 21.1	21 34.3	3 1.7	1 5.0	7 40.9	8 6.5	0 6.2	29 48.2
14	21 28 36.0	20 56.3	14 47.9	28 37.8	18 18.4	22 46.4	3 39.7	1 16.2	7D41.1	8 10.2	0 7.3	29 50.2
15	21 32 32.5	21 53.9	14 44.8	10♈29.9	19 12.8	23 58.5	4 17.7	1 27.5	7 41.3	8 13.8	0 8.3	29 52.1
16	21 36 29.1	22 51.6	14 41.6	22 27.0	20 4.2	25 10.5	4 55.8	1 38.8	7 41.7	8 17.4	0 9.4	29 54.1
17	21 40 25.6	23 49.2	14 38.4	4♉33.3	20 52.4	26 22.5	5 33.8	1 50.2	7 42.1	8 21.0	0 10.5	29 56.1
18	21 44 22.2	24 46.9	14 35.2	16 53.4	21 37.3	27 34.5	6 11.9	2 1.6	7 42.7	8 24.6	0 11.7	29 58.0
19	21 48 18.7	25 44.7	14 32.0	29 32.3	22 18.6	28 46.4	6 50.0	2 13.1	7 43.3	8 28.2	0 12.8	29 60.0
20	21 52 15.3	26 42.4	14 28.9	12♊34.7	22 56.2	29 58.3	7 28.1	2 24.7	7 44.0	8 31.8	0 14.0	0♍ 2.0
21	21 56 11.8	27 40.2	14 25.7	26 4.6	23 29.8	1♎10.1	8 6.2	2 36.3	7 44.8	8 35.3	0 15.3	0 3.9
22	22 0 8.4	28 38.0	14 22.5	10♋ 4.1	23 59.2	2 22.0	8 44.3	2 48.0	7 45.8	8 38.9	0 16.5	0 5.9
23	22 4 5.0	29 35.8	14 19.3	24 32.7	24 24.2	3 33.8	9 22.5	2 59.8	7 46.8	8 42.4	0 17.8	0 7.9
24	22 8 1.5	0♍33.8	14 16.2	9♌26.4	24 44.5	4 45.6	10 .7	3 11.6	7 48.0	8 45.9	0 19.2	0 9.9
25	22 11 58.1	1 31.6	14 13.0	24 37.5	24 59.9	5 57.3	10 38.9	3 23.5	7 49.2	8 49.4	0 20.5	0 11.9
26	22 15 54.6	2 29.6	14 9.8	9♍55.7	25 10.0	7 8.9	11 17.1	3 35.4	7 50.5	8 52.9	0 21.9	0 13.9
27	22 19 51.2	3 27.5	14 6.6	25 9.6	25 14.7	8 20.6	11 55.3	3 47.3	7 51.9	8 56.4	0 23.3	0 15.8
28	22 23 47.7	4 25.5	14 3.4	10♎ 8.9	25R13.7	9 32.2	12 33.6	3 59.4	7 53.4	8 59.8	0 24.7	0 17.8
29	22 27 44.3	5 23.5	14 .3	24 46.1	25 6.9	10 43.7	13 11.8	4 11.4	7 55.0	9 3.2	0 26.1	0 19.8
30	22 31 40.8	6 21.5	13 57.1	8♏57.0	24 54.0	11 55.2	13 50.1	4 23.5	7 56.7	9 6.6	0 27.6	0 21.8
31	22 35 37.4	7 19.5	13 53.9	22 40.6	24 34.9	13 6.7	14 28.4	4 35.7	7 58.5	9 10.0	0 29.1	0 23.7

LATITUDE

DAY	EPHEM. SID. TIME	☉	☊	☽	☿	♀	♂	♃	♄	♅	♆	♇
1	20 37 20.8	0 .0	0 .0	2S33.0	0N16.8	1N26.3	1N 7.9	1N10.7	1N42.3	0N35.3	1N44.5	10N58.7
4	20 49 10.4	0 .0	0 .0	0N55.6	0S10.5	1 22.3	1 7.3	1 10.3	1 41.7	0 35.4	1 44.3	10 58.6
7	21 1 .1	0 .0	0 .0	3 47.0	0 39.8	1 17.6	1 6.6	1 9.9	1 41.0	0 35.4	1 44.2	10 58.6
10	21 12 49.8	0 .0	0 .0	4 58.9	1 10.7	1 12.2	1 5.9	1 9.5	1 40.3	0 35.4	1 44.0	10 58.5
13	21 24 39.4	0 .0	0 .0	4 13.7	1 42.7	1 6.2	1 5.1	1 9.2	1 39.7	0 35.5	1 43.9	10 58.6
16	21 36 29.1	0 .0	0 .0	1 51.4	2 15.0	0 59.6	1 4.4	1 8.9	1 39.0	0 35.5	1 43.7	10 58.6
19	21 48 18.7	0 .0	0 .0	1S21.6	2 47.0	0 52.4	1 3.6	1 8.6	1 38.3	0 35.5	1 43.6	10 58.8
22	22 0 8.4	0 .0	0 .0	4 11.6	3 17.5	0 44.6	1 2.8	1 8.3	1 37.7	0 35.6	1 43.4	10 58.9
25	22 11 58.1	0 .0	0 .0	4 56.2	3 45.2	0 36.2	1 2.0	1 8.0	1 37.0	0 35.6	1 43.3	10 59.1
28	22 23 47.7	0 .0	0 .0	2 44.7	4 7.7	0 27.4	1 1.2	1 7.8	1 36.3	0 35.7	1 43.1	10 59.4
31	22 35 37.4	0 .0	0 .0	0N51.9	4 22.3	0 18.1	1 .3	1 7.5	1 35.7	0 35.8	1 43.0	10 59.7

RIGHT ASCENSION

DAY	EPHEM. SID. TIME	☉	☊	☽	☿	♀	♂	♃	♄	♅	♆	♇
1	20 37 20.8	10♌54.3	13♏ 1.3	13♎11.7	4♍51.6	9♍22.0	28♌ 6.3	29♍29.7	6♐17.3	9♌56.2	28♎28.2	5♍39.2
2	20 41 17.3	11 52.5	12 58.1	26 50.2	6 8.1	10 29.8	28 42.9	29 39.1	6R16.2	9 60.0	28 28.8	5 41.0
3	20 45 13.9	12 50.7	12 54.9	10♏30.5	7 22.5	11 37.3	29 19.5	29 48.6	6 15.3	10 3.8	28 29.5	5 42.9
4	20 49 10.4	13 48.6	12 51.7	24 13.0	8 34.7	12 44.7	29 56.0	29 58.2	6 14.4	10 7.6	28 30.2	5 44.8
5	20 53 7.0	14 46.4	12 48.6	7♐53.9	9 44.6	13 51.8	0♍32.5	0♎ 7.8	6 13.6	10 11.4	28 30.9	5 46.6
6	20 57 3.5	15 44.0	12 45.4	21 26.6	10 52.3	14 58.6	1 8.9	0 17.5	6 12.9	10 15.1	28 31.6	5 48.5
7	21 1 .1	16 41.5	12 42.2	4♑43.3	11 57.8	16 5.3	1 45.3	0 27.2	6 12.4	10 18.9	28 32.4	5 50.3
8	21 4 56.6	17 38.8	12 39.1	17 37.5	13 1.1	17 11.8	2 21.6	0 37.1	6 11.9	10 22.7	28 33.2	5 52.2
9	21 8 53.2	18 36.0	12 35.9	0♒ 5.3	14 2.0	18 18.1	2 57.8	0 47.0	6 11.5	10 26.4	28 34.0	5 54.1
10	21 12 49.8	19 33.1	12 32.7	12 6.4	15 .7	19 24.3	3 34.0	0 56.9	6 11.2	10 30.2	28 34.9	5 56.0
11	21 16 46.3	20 29.9	12 29.6	23 43.9	15 56.9	20 30.2	4 10.2	1 6.9	6 11.0	10 33.9	28 35.7	5 57.9
12	21 20 42.9	21 26.7	12 26.4	5♓ 3.3	16 50.7	21 36.0	4 46.3	1 17.0	6 10.9	10 37.6	28 36.6	5 59.8
13	21 24 39.4	22 23.3	12 23.2	16 12.2	17 41.9	22 41.7	5 22.3	1 27.2	6 10.9	10 41.4	28 37.6	6 1.7
14	21 28 36.0	23 19.8	12 20.1	27 18.9	18 30.5	23 47.3	5 58.3	1 37.4	6D11.1	10 45.1	28 38.5	6 3.7
15	21 32 32.5	24 16.1	12 16.9	8♈32.9	19 16.4	24 52.7	6 34.3	1 47.7	6 11.3	10 48.8	28 39.5	6 5.6
16	21 36 29.1	25 12.3	12 13.8	20 3.5	19 59.5	25 58.0	7 10.3	1 58.0	6 11.6	10 52.5	28 40.5	6 7.5
17	21 40 25.6	26 8.4	12 10.6	1♉60.0	20 39.6	27 3.2	7 46.2	2 8.4	6 12.0	10 56.1	28 41.6	6 9.5
18	21 44 22.2	27 4.3	12 7.4	14 30.0	21 16.6	28 8.3	8 22.0	2 18.9	6 12.5	10 59.8	28 42.7	6 11.4
19	21 48 18.7	28 .2	12 4.3	27 38.7	21 50.4	29 13.3	8 57.8	2 29.4	6 13.2	11 3.5	28 43.7	6 13.4
20	21 52 15.3	28 55.9	12 1.1	11♊27.0	22 20.8	0♎18.2	9 33.6	2 40.0	6 13.9	11 7.1	28 44.9	6 15.3
21	21 56 11.8	29 51.5	11 57.9	25 49.9	22 47.6	1 23.1	10 9.4	2 50.6	6 14.7	11 10.7	28 46.0	6 17.3
22	22 0 8.4	0♍46.9	11 54.8	10♋37.1	23 10.6	2 28.0	10 45.1	3 1.3	6 15.7	11 14.3	28 47.2	6 19.3
23	22 4 5.0	1 42.3	11 51.6	25 35.0	23 29.7	3 32.8	11 20.8	3 12.0	6 16.7	11 17.9	28 48.4	6 21.2
24	22 8 1.5	2 37.6	11 48.5	10♌30.7	23 44.7	4 37.6	11 56.5	3 22.9	6 17.9	11 21.6	28 49.7	6 23.2
25	22 11 58.1	3 32.8	11 45.3	25 15.4	23 55.3	5 42.3	12 32.2	3 33.7	6 19.1	11 25.1	28 50.9	6 25.2
26	22 15 54.6	4 27.8	11 42.1	9♍46.0	24 1.3	6 47.0	13 7.8	3 44.6	6 20.5	11 28.7	28 52.2	6 27.2
27	22 19 51.2	5 22.8	11 39.0	24 4.3	24 2.6	7 51.8	13 43.4	3 55.6	6 21.9	11 32.2	28 53.5	6 29.1
28	22 23 47.7	6 17.7	11 35.8	8♎14.5	23R59.0	8 56.5	14 18.9	4 6.6	6 23.4	11 35.7	28 54.9	6 31.1
29	22 27 44.3	7 12.4	11 32.7	22 21.2	23 50.4	10 1.3	14 54.4	4 17.6	6 25.1	11 39.2	28 56.2	6 33.1
30	22 31 40.8	8 7.1	11 29.5	6♏26.7	23 36.6	11 6.0	15 30.0	4 28.7	6 26.8	11 42.6	28 57.6	6 35.1
31	22 35 37.4	9 1.7	11 26.4	20 30.2	23 17.7	12 10.8	16 5.4	4 39.8	6 28.7	11 46.1	28 59.0	6 37.0

DECLINATION

DAY	EPHEM. SID. TIME	☉	☊	☽	☿	♀	♂	♃	♄	♅	♆	♇
1	20 37 20.8	18N 8.7	0S17.3	8S25.1	10N44.3	10N14.3	14N 6.5	1N30.1	19S55.6	19N .0	9S49.2	21N55.6
4	20 49 10.4	17 22.6	0 17.2	18 25.7	8 48.7	8 48.8	13 27.1	1 17.4	19 55.8	18 57.2	9 50.1	21 53.4
7	21 1 .1	16 33.9	0 17.2	19 35.2	6 55.8	7 21.2	12 46.9	1 4.4	19 56.2	18 54.4	9 51.1	21 51.3
10	21 12 49.8	15 42.8	0 17.1	12 39.8	5 7.3	5 52.0	12 6.0	0 51.1	19 56.7	18 51.6	9 52.2	21 49.2
13	21 24 39.4	14 49.4	0 17.1	1 19.1	3 25.3	4 21.4	11 24.5	0 37.6	19 57.3	18 48.8	9 53.3	21 47.1
16	21 36 29.1	13 53.9	0 17.0	10N27.6	1 51.9	2 49.8	10 42.2	0 23.9	19 58.1	18 46.0	9 54.6	21 45.0
19	21 48 18.7	12 56.4	0 17.0	18 43.6	0 29.7	1 17.3	9 59.4	0 9.9	19 59.0	18 43.2	9 55.9	21 43.0
22	22 0 8.4	11 57.1	0 16.9	18 52.8	0S38.1	0S15.6	9 15.9	0S 4.2	20 .1	18 40.5	9 57.3	21 41.0
25	22 11 58.1	10 56.0	0 16.9	8 39.4	1 27.4	1 48.6	8 31.9	0 18.5	20 1.3	18 37.7	9 58.9	21 39.0
28	22 23 47.7	9 53.4	0 16.8	6S32.7	1 53.6	3 21.5	7 47.4	0 33.0	20 2.6	18 35.1	10 .4	21 37.1
31	22 35 37.4	8 49.3	0 16.8	17 36.4	1 51.7	4 54.0	7 2.5	0 47.6	20 4.1	18 32.4	10 2.1	21 35.2

SEPTEMBER 1957

LONGITUDE

DAY	EPHEM. SID. TIME h m s	☉ ° ′	☊ ° ′	☾ ° ′	☿ ° ′	♀ ° ′	♂ ° ′	♃ ° ′	♄ ° ′	♅ ° ′	♆ ° ′	♇ ° ′
1	22 39 33.9	8♍17.6	13♏50.7	5♐58.6	24♍ 9.7	14♎18.1	15♍ 6.7	4♎47.9	8♐ .4	9♌13.3	0♏30.6	0♍25.7
2	22 43 30.5	9 15.6	13 47.6	18 54.0	23 R 38.4	15 29.5	15 45.0	5 .1	8 2.3	9 16.7	0 32.1	0 27.7
3	22 47 27.0	10 13.7	13 44.4	1♑30.6	23 1.2	16 40.8	16 23.4	5 12.4	8 4.4	9 20.0	0 33.7	0 29.6
4	22 51 23.6	11 11.9	13 41.2	13 52.5	22 18.4	17 52.1	17 1.7	5 24.7	8 6.6	9 23.3	0 35.3	0 31.6
5	22 55 20.1	12 10.0	13 38.0	26 3.2	21 30.5	19 3.3	17 40.1	5 37.1	8 8.8	9 26.5	0 36.9	0 33.5
6	22 59 16.7	13 8.2	13 34.8	8♒ 5.8	20 38.1	20 14.4	18 18.5	5 49.5	8 11.2	9 29.8	0 38.5	0 35.4
7	23 3 13.2	14 6.4	13 31.7	20 2.9	19 42.2	21 25.5	18 56.9	6 1.9	8 13.6	9 33.0	0 40.2	0 37.4
8	23 7 9.8	15 4.6	13 28.5	1♓56.6	18 43.7	22 36.6	19 35.3	6 14.4	8 16.1	9 36.2	0 41.9	0 39.3
9	23 11 6.3	16 2.9	13 25.3	13 48.5	17 43.7	23 47.6	20 13.8	6 26.9	8 18.8	9 39.3	0 43.6	0 41.2
10	23 15 2.9	17 1.2	13 22.1	25 40.1	16 43.6	24 58.5	20 52.3	6 39.4	8 21.5	9 42.5	0 45.3	0 43.1
11	23 18 59.5	17 59.5	13 19.0	7♈33.2	15 44.7	26 9.4	21 30.7	6 52.0	8 24.3	9 45.6	0 47.0	0 45.1
12	23 22 56.0	18 57.8	13 15.8	19 29.6	14 48.5	27 20.3	22 9.3	7 4.6	8 27.1	9 48.6	0 48.8	0 47.0
13	23 26 52.6	19 56.2	13 12.6	1♉31.9	13 56.2	28 31.0	22 47.8	7 17.2	8 30.1	9 51.7	0 50.6	0 48.8
14	23 30 49.1	20 54.7	13 9.4	13 43.0	13 9.2	29 41.8	23 26.4	7 29.9	8 33.2	9 54.7	0 52.4	0 50.8
15	23 34 45.7	21 53.1	13 6.2	26 6.3	12 28.7	0♏52.5	24 5.0	7 42.6	8 36.3	9 57.7	0 54.2	0 52.7
16	23 38 42.2	22 51.6	13 3.1	8♊46.0	11 55.7	2 3.1	24 43.6	7 55.3	8 39.6	10 .7	0 56.1	0 54.5
17	23 42 38.8	23 50.2	12 59.9	21 46.1	11 31.0	3 13.6	25 22.2	8 8.1	8 42.9	10 3.6	0 57.9	0 56.4
18	23 46 35.3	24 48.7	12 56.7	5♋10.1	11 15.3	4 24.1	26 .8	8 20.8	8 46.3	10 6.5	0 59.8	0 58.2
19	23 50 31.9	25 47.3	12 53.5	19 .6	11 9.1	5 34.5	26 39.5	8 33.6	8 49.8	10 9.3	1 1.7	1 .0
20	23 54 28.4	26 46.0	12 50.3	3♌18.0	11 D 12.5	6 44.9	27 18.2	8 46.4	8 53.3	10 12.2	1 3.6	1 1.9
21	23 58 25.0	27 44.6	12 47.2	18 .2	11 25.7	7 55.2	27 56.9	8 59.3	8 57.0	10 15.0	1 5.6	1 3.7
22	0 2 21.5	28 43.3	12 44.0	3♍ 1.7	11 48.5	9 5.5	28 35.7	9 12.1	9 .7	10 17.7	1 7.5	1 5.5
23	0 6 18.1	29 42.1	12 40.8	18 13.9	12 20.6	10 15.6	29 14.5	9 25.0	9 4.5	10 20.4	1 9.5	1 7.3
24	0 10 14.6	0♎40.9	12 37.6	3♎26.7	13 1.7	11 25.8	29 53.2	9 37.9	9 8.4	10 23.1	1 11.5	1 9.0
25	0 14 11.2	1 39.7	12 34.5	18 29.7	13 51.2	12 35.8	0♎32.1	9 50.8	9 12.4	10 25.8	1 13.5	1 10.8
26	0 18 7.7	2 38.5	12 31.3	3♏14.2	14 48.7	13 45.8	1 10.9	10 3.7	9 16.4	10 28.4	1 15.5	1 12.5
27	0 22 4.3	3 37.4	12 28.1	17 34.2	15 53.4	14 55.7	1 49.8	10 16.6	9 20.5	10 30.9	1 17.5	1 14.3
28	0 26 .8	4 36.3	12 24.9	1♐26.8	17 4.6	16 5.5	2 28.6	10 29.6	9 24.7	10 33.5	1 19.5	1 16.0
29	0 29 57.4	5 35.2	12 21.7	14 52.2	18 21.8	17 15.3	3 7.6	10 42.5	9 29.0	10 35.9	1 21.6	1 17.7
30	0 33 53.9	6 34.2	12 18.6	27 52.3	19 44.2	18 25.0	3 46.5	10 55.5	9 33.4	10 38.4	1 23.7	1 19.4

LATITUDE

DAY	EPHEM. SID. TIME	☉	☊	☾	☿	♀	♂	♃	♄	♅	♆	♇
1	22 39 33.9	0 .0	0 .0	1N59.8	4S24.9	0N14.9	1N .1	1N 7.5	1N35.4	0N35.8	1N43.0	10N59.8
4	22 51 23.6	0 .0	0 .0	4 26.7	4 23.3	0 5.1	0 59.2	1 7.2	1 34.8	0 35.8	1 42.8	11 .2
7	23 3 13.2	0 .0	0 .0	5 1.4	4 5.7	0S 5.1	0 58.3	1 7.1	1 34.1	0 35.9	1 42.7	11 .6
10	23 15 2.9	0 .0	0 .0	3 40.6	3 31.0	0 15.7	0 57.4	1 6.9	1 33.5	0 36.0	1 42.6	11 1.0
13	23 26 52.6	0 .0	0 .0	0 53.9	2 41.6	0 26.5	0 56.4	1 6.7	1 32.9	0 36.1	1 42.5	11 1.5
16	23 38 42.2	0 .0	0 .0	2S21.5	1 43.8	0 37.5	0 55.4	1 6.6	1 32.3	0 36.1	1 42.4	11 2.1
19	23 50 31.9	0 .0	0 .0	4 45.6	0 45.2	0 48.6	0 54.5	1 6.5	1 31.6	0 36.2	1 42.3	11 2.7
22	0 2 21.5	0 .0	0 .0	4 47.4	0N 7.9	0 59.9	0 53.5	1 6.4	1 31.1	0 36.3	1 42.2	11 3.3
25	0 14 11.2	0 .0	0 .0	1 59.4	0 51.2	1 11.1	0 52.4	1 6.3	1 30.5	0 36.4	1 42.1	11 4.0
28	0 26 .8	0 .0	0 .0	1N49.1	1 23.0	1 22.4	0 51.4	1 6.3	1 29.9	0 36.5	1 42.1	11 4.7

RIGHT ASCENSION

DAY	EPHEM. SID. TIME	☉	☊	☾	☿	♀	♂	♃	♄	♅	♆	♇
1	22 39 33.9	9♍56.2	11♏23.2	4♐27.3	22♍53.6	13♎15.7	16♍40.9	4♎51.0	6♐30.6	11♌49.5	29♎ .4	6♍39.0
2	22 43 30.5	10 50.6	11 20.1	18 11.6	22 R 24.5	14 20.6	17 16.4	5 2.2	6 32.7	11 52.9	29 1.9	6 41.0
3	22 47 27.0	11 44.9	11 16.9	1♑36.0	21 50.5	15 25.5	17 51.8	5 13.4	6 34.8	11 56.3	29 3.4	6 42.9
4	22 51 23.6	12 39.2	11 13.7	14 35.1	21 12.2	16 30.5	18 27.2	5 24.7	6 37.0	11 59.6	29 4.9	6 44.9
5	22 55 20.1	13 33.4	11 10.6	27 6.4	20 29.8	17 35.6	19 2.6	5 36.0	6 39.4	12 2.9	29 6.4	6 46.8
6	22 59 16.7	14 27.5	11 7.4	9♒10.5	19 44.1	18 40.8	19 38.0	5 47.4	6 41.8	12 6.2	29 7.9	6 48.8
7	23 3 13.2	15 21.6	11 4.3	20 51.0	18 55.9	19 46.1	20 13.4	5 58.8	6 44.3	12 9.5	29 9.5	6 50.8
8	23 7 9.8	16 15.6	11 1.1	2♓13.6	18 5.9	20 51.4	20 48.7	6 10.2	6 46.9	12 12.7	29 11.1	6 52.7
9	23 11 6.3	17 9.6	10 58.0	13 25.3	17 15.3	21 56.9	21 24.1	6 21.7	6 49.7	12 15.9	29 12.7	6 54.6
10	23 15 2.9	18 3.5	10 54.8	24 34.0	16 25.3	23 2.5	21 59.4	6 33.2	6 52.5	12 19.1	29 14.3	6 56.6
11	23 18 59.5	18 57.4	10 51.7	5♈47.9	15 36.8	24 8.3	22 34.8	6 44.7	6 55.4	12 22.3	29 15.9	6 58.5
12	23 22 56.0	19 51.3	10 48.5	17 15.1	14 51.3	25 14.1	23 10.1	6 56.2	6 58.4	12 25.4	29 17.6	7 .4
13	23 26 52.6	20 45.2	10 45.4	29 3.4	14 9.8	26 20.2	23 45.5	7 7.8	7 1.5	12 28.5	29 19.3	7 2.4
14	23 30 49.1	21 39.0	10 42.2	11♉19.1	13 33.5	27 26.4	24 20.9	7 19.5	7 4.7	12 31.6	29 21.0	7 4.3
15	23 34 45.7	22 32.9	10 39.1	24 6.3	13 3.4	28 32.7	24 56.2	7 31.1	7 8.0	12 34.7	29 22.8	7 6.2
16	23 38 42.2	23 26.7	10 35.9	7♊26.1	12 40.3	29 39.2	25 31.6	7 42.8	7 11.3	12 37.7	29 24.5	7 8.1
17	23 42 38.8	24 20.5	10 32.8	21 15.5	12 24.9	0♏45.9	26 6.9	7 54.5	7 14.8	12 40.6	29 26.3	7 10.0
18	23 46 35.3	25 14.3	10 29.6	5♋27.5	12 17.8	1 52.7	26 42.3	8 6.2	7 18.3	12 43.6	29 28.0	7 11.9
19	23 50 31.9	26 8.1	10 26.5	19 53.1	12 D 19.3	2 59.8	27 17.7	8 18.0	7 21.9	12 46.5	29 29.8	7 13.8
20	23 54 28.4	27 1.9	10 23.3	4♌23.1	12 29.6	4 7.0	27 53.1	8 29.8	7 25.7	12 49.3	29 31.7	7 15.6
21	23 58 25.0	27 55.8	10 20.2	18 51.0	12 48.7	5 14.5	28 28.5	8 41.6	7 29.5	12 52.2	29 33.5	7 17.5
22	0 2 21.5	28 49.7	10 17.1	3♍14.3	13 16.3	6 22.1	29 3.9	8 53.4	7 33.4	12 55.0	29 35.3	7 19.3
23	0 6 18.1	29 43.6	10 13.9	17 34.2	13 52.3	7 30.0	29 39.3	9 5.2	7 37.4	12 57.7	29 37.2	7 21.2
24	0 10 14.6	0♎37.5	10 10.8	1♎54.1	14 36.1	8 38.1	0♎14.8	9 17.1	7 41.4	13 .5	29 39.1	7 23.0
25	0 14 11.2	1 31.4	10 7.6	16 17.7	15 27.4	9 46.4	0 50.3	9 28.9	7 45.6	13 3.2	29 41.0	7 24.8
26	0 18 7.7	2 25.4	10 4.5	0♏46.1	16 25.4	10 54.9	1 25.8	9 40.8	7 49.8	13 5.8	29 42.9	7 26.6
27	0 22 4.3	3 19.5	10 1.3	15 16.7	17 29.6	12 3.6	2 1.3	9 52.7	7 54.1	13 8.4	29 44.8	7 28.4
28	0 26 .8	4 13.6	9 58.2	29 43.0	18 39.3	13 12.6	2 36.8	10 4.6	7 58.5	13 11.0	29 46.7	7 30.2
29	0 29 57.4	5 7.7	9 55.1	13♐55.5	19 53.8	14 21.7	3 12.4	10 16.6	8 3.0	13 13.5	29 48.7	7 31.9
30	0 33 53.9	6 1.9	9 51.9	27 44.8	21 12.7	15 31.1	3 48.0	10 28.5	8 7.6	13 16.0	29 50.7	7 33.7

DECLINATION

DAY	EPHEM. SID. TIME	☉	☊	☾	☿	♀	♂	♃	♄	♅	♆	♇
1	22 39 33.9	8N27.7	0S16.8	19S20.5	1S44.1	5S24.6	6N47.4	0S52.5	20S 4.6	18N31.6	10S 2.7	21N34.6
4	22 51 23.6	7 22.0	0 16.7	18 17.9	0 58.8	6 56.0	6 1.9	1 7.3	20 6.2	18 29.0	10 4.4	21 32.8
7	23 3 13.2	6 15.3	0 16.7	10 1.8	0N18.6	8 26.1	5 16.0	1 22.2	20 8.0	18 26.5	10 6.2	21 31.0
10	23 15 2.9	5 7.6	0 16.6	1N39.2	1 60.0	9 54.8	4 29.9	1 37.2	20 9.8	18 24.0	10 8.1	21 29.3
13	23 26 52.6	3 59.2	0 16.6	12 51.0	3 50.0	11 21.7	3 43.4	1 52.2	20 11.8	18 21.6	10 10.0	21 27.7
16	23 38 42.2	2 50.0	0 16.5	19 26.2	5 29.3	12 46.4	2 56.6	2 7.4	20 13.9	18 19.3	10 12.0	21 26.1
19	23 50 31.9	1 40.4	0 16.5	17 22.8	6 41.3	14 8.8	2 9.7	2 22.6	20 16.0	18 17.0	10 14.1	21 24.7
22	0 2 21.5	0 30.5	0 16.4	5 55.4	7 15.4	15 28.4	1 22.6	2 37.8	20 18.3	18 14.8	10 16.2	21 23.2
25	0 14 11.2	0S39.7	0 16.4	9S 5.4	7 8.4	16 45.0	0 35.3	2 53.1	20 20.6	18 12.7	10 18.3	21 21.9
28	0 26 .8	1 49.8	0 16.3	18 40.4	6 22.7	17 58.2	0S12.0	3 8.3	20 23.0	18 10.7	10 20.5	21 20.7

OCTOBER 1957

LONGITUDE

DAY	EPHEM. SID. TIME	☉	☊	☽	☿	♀	♂	♃	♄	♅	♆	♇
	h m s	° ′	° ′	° ′	° ′	° ′	° ′	° ′	° ′	° ′	° ′	° ′
1	0 37 50.5	7♎33.2	12♏15.4	10♑30.8	21♍11.1	19♏34.6	4♎25.4	11♎ 8.4	9♐37.8	10♌40.8	1♏25.7	1♍21.0
2	0 41 47.0	8 32.2	12 12.2	22 51.8	22 42.0	20 44.1	5 4.4	11 21.4	9 42.3	10 43.2	1 27.8	1 22.7
3	0 45 43.6	9 31.2	12 9.0	4♒59.7	24 16.1	21 53.5	5 43.4	11 34.4	9 46.9	10 45.5	1 29.9	1 24.3
4	0 49 40.1	10 30.3	12 5.9	16 58.4	25 53.1	23 2.8	6 22.4	11 47.4	9 51.5	10 47.8	1 32.0	1 25.9
5	0 53 36.7	11 29.5	12 2.7	28 51.9	27 32.3	24 12.1	7 1.5	12 .4	9 56.3	10 50.1	1 34.2	1 27.6
6	0 57 33.3	12 28.6	11 59.5	10♓43.2	29 13.3	25 21.2	7 40.6	12 13.4	10 1.0	10 52.3	1 36.4	1 29.2
7	1 1 29.8	13 27.8	11 56.3	22 35.1	0♎55.7	26 30.2	8 19.7	12 26.4	10 5.9	10 54.4	1 38.5	1 30.7
8	1 5 26.4	14 27.0	11 53.1	4♈29.7	2 39.2	27 39.2	8 58.8	12 39.4	10 10.8	10 56.5	1 40.7	1 32.3
9	1 9 22.9	15 26.2	11 50.0	16 29.1	4 23.4	28 48.0	9 38.0	12 52.3	10 15.8	10 58.6	1 42.8	1 33.8
10	1 13 19.5	16 25.5	11 46.8	28 34.7	6 8.2	29 56.7	10 17.1	13 5.3	10 20.8	11 .6	1 45.0	1 35.3
11	1 17 16.0	17 24.8	11 43.6	10♉48.4	7 53.2	1♐ 5.4	10 56.3	13 18.3	10 26.0	11 2.6	1 47.2	1 36.8
12	1 21 12.6	18 24.1	11 40.4	23 11.9	9 38.3	2 13.9	11 35.5	13 31.3	10 31.1	11 4.5	1 49.4	1 38.3
13	1 25 9.1	19 23.5	11 37.3	5♊47.1	11 23.4	3 22.3	12 14.8	13 44.2	10 36.4	11 6.4	1 51.6	1 39.7
14	1 29 5.7	20 22.9	11 34.1	18 36.4	13 8.4	4 30.5	12 54.1	13 57.2	10 41.7	11 8.2	1 53.8	1 41.2
15	1 33 2.2	21 22.4	11 30.9	1♋42.1	14 53.0	5 38.7	13 33.4	14 10.2	10 47.0	11 10.0	1 56.0	1 42.6
16	1 36 58.8	22 21.9	11 27.7	15 6.2	16 37.3	6 46.8	14 12.7	14 23.1	10 52.5	11 11.8	1 58.2	1 44.0
17	1 40 55.3	23 21.4	11 24.5	28 50.5	18 21.2	7 54.7	14 52.1	14 36.0	10 57.9	11 13.4	2 .4	1 45.3
18	1 44 51.9	24 21.0	11 21.4	12♌55.3	20 4.7	9 2.5	15 31.5	14 48.9	11 3.5	11 15.1	2 2.6	1 46.7
19	1 48 48.4	25 20.6	11 18.2	27 19.6	21 47.6	10 10.2	16 10.9	15 1.8	11 9.1	11 16.7	2 4.8	1 48.0
20	1 52 45.0	26 20.2	11 15.0	12♍ .1	23 30.0	11 17.7	16 50.4	15 14.7	11 14.7	11 18.2	2 7.1	1 49.3
21	1 56 41.5	27 19.9	11 11.8	26 51.4	25 11.8	12 25.1	17 29.9	15 27.6	11 20.4	11 19.7	2 9.3	1 50.5
22	2 0 38.1	28 19.7	11 8.7	11♎46.2	26 53.1	13 32.4	18 9.4	15 40.5	11 26.2	11 21.2	2 11.5	1 51.8
23	2 4 34.7	29 19.4	11 5.5	26 36.6	28 33.8	14 39.5	18 48.9	15 53.3	11 32.0	11 22.5	2 13.8	1 53.0
24	2 8 31.2	0♏19.2	11 2.3	11♏14.6	0♏13.9	15 46.5	19 28.5	16 6.1	11 37.9	11 23.9	2 16.0	1 54.2
25	2 12 27.8	1 19.0	10 59.1	25 33.9	1 53.4	16 53.4	20 8.1	16 18.9	11 43.8	11 25.2	2 18.3	1 55.4
26	2 16 24.3	2 18.9	10 55.9	9♐30.2	3 32.5	18 .1	20 47.8	16 31.7	11 49.9	11 26.5	2 20.6	1 56.6
27	2 20 20.9	3 18.8	10 52.8	23 1.3	5 11.0	19 6.6	21 27.4	16 44.4	11 55.9	11 27.6	2 22.8	1 57.7
28	2 24 17.4	4 18.7	10 49.6	6♑ 7.6	6 48.9	20 12.9	22 7.1	16 57.1	12 1.9	11 28.8	2 25.0	1 58.8
29	2 28 14.0	5 18.6	10 46.4	18 51.1	8 26.3	21 19.1	22 46.8	17 9.8	12 8.1	11 29.8	2 27.3	1 59.9
30	2 32 10.5	6 18.6	10 43.2	1♒15.4	10 3.1	22 25.0	23 26.5	17 22.5	12 14.2	11 30.9	2 29.5	2 .9
31	2 36 7.1	7 18.6	10 40.1	13 24.5	11 39.5	23 30.8	24 6.3	17 35.1	12 20.4	11 31.8	2 31.8	2 2.0

LATITUDE

DAY	EPHEM. SID. TIME	☉	☊	☽	☿	♀	♂	♃	♄	♅	♆	♇
1	0 37 50.5	0 .0	0 .0	4N29.3	1N43.4	1S33.5	0N50.3	1N 6.2	1N29.3	0N36.6	1N42.0	11N 5.5
4	0 49 40.1	0 .0	0 .0	5 10.7	1 53.6	1 44.5	0 49.2	1 6.2	1 28.8	0 36.7	1 42.0	11 6.3
7	1 1 29.8	0 .0	0 .0	3 53.4	1 55.3	1 55.2	0 48.1	1 6.2	1 28.3	0 36.8	1 41.9	11 7.1
10	1 13 19.5	0 .0	0 .0	1 5.5	1 50.4	2 5.7	0 47.0	1 6.2	1 27.8	0 36.9	1 41.9	11 8.0
13	1 25 9.1	0 .0	0 .0	2S14.8	1 40.3	2 15.7	0 45.8	1 6.3	1 27.3	0 37.0	1 41.8	11 8.9
16	1 36 58.8	0 .0	0 .0	4 45.4	1 26.6	2 25.3	0 44.6	1 6.3	1 26.8	0 37.1	1 41.8	11 9.8
19	1 48 48.4	0 .0	0 .0	5 2.9	1 10.1	2 34.3	0 43.4	1 6.4	1 26.3	0 37.3	1 41.8	11 10.8
22	2 0 38.1	0 .0	0 .0	2 32.6	0 51.9	2 42.8	0 42.2	1 6.5	1 25.9	0 37.4	1 41.8	11 11.8
25	2 12 27.8	0 .0	0 .0	1N22.6	0 32.5	2 50.5	0 40.9	1 6.6	1 25.4	0 37.5	1 41.8	11 12.9
28	2 24 17.4	0 .0	0 .0	4 22.1	0 12.5	2 57.5	0 39.6	1 6.7	1 25.0	0 37.6	1 41.8	11 14.0
31	2 36 7.1	0 .0	0 .0	5 17.1	0S 7.8	3 3.6	0 38.3	1 6.9	1 24.6	0 37.7	1 41.8	11 15.1

RIGHT ASCENSION

DAY	EPHEM. SID. TIME	☉	☊	☽	☿	♀	♂	♃	♄	♅	♆	♇
1	0 37 50.5	6♎56.1	9♏48.8	11♑ 3.8	22♍35.1	16♏40.7	4♎23.6	10♎40.5	8♐12.2	13♌18.5	29♎52.6	7♍35.4
2	0 41 47.0	7 50.5	9 45.6	23 49.6	24 .6	17 50.6	4 59.2	10 52.4	8 16.9	13 20.9	29 54.6	7 37.1
3	0 45 43.6	8 44.8	9 42.5	6♒ 3.5	25 28.5	19 .6	5 34.9	11 4.4	8 21.7	13 23.2	29 56.6	7 38.8
4	0 49 40.1	9 39.3	9 39.3	17 50.0	26 58.6	20 10.9	6 10.6	11 16.3	8 26.6	13 25.5	29 58.6	7 40.5
5	0 53 36.7	10 33.9	9 36.2	29 16.1	28 30.3	21 21.4	6 46.4	11 28.4	8 31.6	13 27.9	0♏ .7	7 42.2
6	0 57 33.3	11 28.5	9 33.1	10♓29.6	0♎ 3.1	22 32.1	7 22.1	11 40.4	8 36.6	13 30.1	0 2.7	7 43.9
7	1 1 29.8	12 23.3	9 29.9	21 39.3	1 37.0	23 43.0	7 57.9	11 52.3	8 41.7	13 32.3	0 4.8	7 45.5
8	1 5 26.4	13 18.1	9 26.8	2♈53.8	3 11.5	24 54.1	8 33.8	12 4.3	8 46.9	13 34.4	0 6.8	7 47.2
9	1 9 22.9	14 13.0	9 23.7	14 21.4	4 46.4	26 5.4	9 9.7	12 16.3	8 52.1	13 36.5	0 8.9	7 48.8
10	1 13 19.5	15 8.0	9 20.5	26 9.5	6 21.7	27 16.9	9 45.6	12 28.3	8 57.4	13 38.6	0 10.9	7 50.4
11	1 17 16.0	16 3.2	9 17.4	8♉23.4	7 57.0	28 28.6	10 21.6	12 40.3	9 2.8	13 40.6	0 13.0	7 51.9
12	1 21 12.6	16 58.5	9 14.3	21 6.5	9 32.4	29 40.4	10 57.6	12 52.3	9 8.2	13 42.5	0 15.1	7 53.5
13	1 25 9.1	17 53.9	9 11.1	4♊18.2	11 7.6	0♐52.5	11 33.7	13 4.3	9 13.8	13 44.5	0 17.2	7 55.0
14	1 29 5.7	18 49.4	9 8.0	17 54.4	12 42.7	2 4.7	12 9.8	13 16.3	9 19.3	13 46.3	0 19.3	7 56.6
15	1 33 2.2	19 45.0	9 4.9	1♋47.9	14 17.7	3 17.0	12 46.0	13 28.3	9 25.0	13 48.1	0 21.4	7 58.1
16	1 36 58.8	20 40.9	9 1.7	15 49.9	15 52.4	4 29.5	13 22.2	13 40.2	9 30.7	13 49.9	0 23.5	7 59.5
17	1 40 55.3	21 36.8	8 58.6	29 52.8	17 26.9	5 42.2	13 58.5	13 52.2	9 36.5	13 51.6	0 25.6	8 1.0
18	1 44 51.9	22 32.9	8 55.5	13♌52.0	19 1.1	6 54.9	14 34.9	14 4.2	9 42.3	13 53.3	0 27.7	8 2.4
19	1 48 48.4	23 29.2	8 52.3	27 47.0	20 35.1	8 7.8	15 11.3	14 16.1	9 48.2	13 54.9	0 29.9	8 3.9
20	1 52 45.0	24 25.6	8 49.2	11♍41.1	22 8.8	9 20.8	15 47.7	14 28.1	9 54.2	13 56.5	0 32.0	8 5.3
21	1 56 41.5	25 22.2	8 46.1	25 39.9	23 42.3	10 33.9	16 24.3	14 40.0	10 .2	13 58.0	0 34.1	8 6.6
22	2 0 38.1	26 18.9	8 42.9	9♎49.3	25 15.7	11 47.1	17 .9	14 51.9	10 6.3	13 59.5	0 36.3	8 8.0
23	2 4 34.7	27 15.9	8 39.8	24 12.9	26 48.8	13 .3	17 37.5	15 3.8	10 12.4	14 .9	0 38.4	8 9.3
24	2 8 31.2	28 12.9	8 36.7	8♏50.1	28 21.8	14 13.6	18 14.3	15 15.7	10 18.6	14 2.3	0 40.6	8 10.6
25	2 12 27.8	29 10.2	8 33.5	23 34.4	29 54.7	15 26.9	18 51.1	15 27.6	10 24.9	14 3.6	0 42.7	8 11.9
26	2 16 24.3	0♏ 7.7	8 30.4	8♐14.3	1♏27.5	16 40.2	19 28.0	15 39.5	10 31.3	14 4.9	0 44.9	8 13.2
27	2 20 20.9	1 5.3	8 27.3	22 36.0	3 .2	17 53.5	20 4.9	15 51.3	10 37.6	14 6.1	0 47.0	8 14.5
28	2 24 17.4	2 3.1	8 24.2	6♑27.5	4 32.9	19 6.7	20 41.9	16 3.1	10 44.0	14 7.2	0 49.2	8 15.7
29	2 28 14.0	3 1.1	8 21.0	19 42.0	6 5.5	20 19.9	21 19.0	16 14.9	10 50.5	14 8.3	0 51.3	8 16.9
30	2 32 10.5	3 59.3	8 17.9	2♒18.2	7 38.2	21 33.1	21 56.1	16 26.7	10 57.0	14 9.4	0 53.5	8 18.1
31	2 36 7.1	4 57.6	8 14.8	14 20.2	9 10.9	22 46.1	22 33.3	16 38.5	11 3.6	14 10.4	0 55.6	8 19.2

DECLINATION

DAY	EPHEM. SID. TIME	☉	☊	☽	☿	♀	♂	♃	♄	♅	♆	♇
1	0 37 50.5	2S59.8	0S16.2	18S33.1	5N 4.8	19S 7.8	0S59.3	3S23.6	20S25.5	18N 8.8	10S22.7	21N19.5
4	0 49 40.1	4 9.6	0 16.2	10 48.5	3 22.5	20 13.3	1 46.7	3 38.8	20 28.1	18 7.0	10 24.9	21 18.5
7	1 1 29.8	5 18.9	0 16.1	0N37.9	1 23.7	21 14.6	2 34.0	3 54.0	20 30.7	18 5.3	10 27.2	21 17.5
10	1 13 19.5	6 27.5	0 16.1	11 59.4	0S44.9	22 11.3	3 21.2	4 9.1	20 33.4	18 3.7	10 29.4	21 16.6
13	1 25 9.1	7 35.4	0 16.0	19 3.7	2 58.0	23 3.1	4 8.3	4 24.2	20 36.1	18 2.2	10 31.7	21 15.8
16	1 36 58.8	8 42.4	0 16.0	17 51.6	5 12.1	23 49.9	4 55.2	4 39.2	20 38.8	18 .8	10 34.0	21 15.2
19	1 48 48.4	9 48.3	0 15.9	7 39.3	7 24.5	24 31.3	5 41.9	4 54.1	20 41.6	17 59.6	10 36.3	21 14.6
22	2 0 38.1	10 52.9	0 15.9	6S59.8	9 33.4	25 7.2	6 28.3	5 8.9	20 44.3	17 58.5	10 38.6	21 14.1
25	2 12 27.8	11 56.0	0 15.8	17 49.1	11 37.5	25 37.5	7 14.4	5 23.5	20 47.1	17 57.5	10 40.9	21 13.8
28	2 24 17.4	12 57.5	0 15.8	18 56.2	13 35.7	26 1.9	8 .1	5 38.0	20 49.9	17 56.6	10 43.2	21 13.5
31	2 36 7.1	13 57.2	0 15.7	11 43.7	15 27.4	26 20.4	8 45.4	5 52.4	20 52.7	17 55.9	10 45.5	21 13.4

NOVEMBER 1957

LONGITUDE

DAY	EPHEM. SID. TIME h m s	☉ ° ′	☊ ° ′	☾ ° ′	☿ ° ′	♀ ° ′	♂ ° ′	♃ ° ′	♄ ° ′	♅ ° ′	♆ ° ′	♇ ° ′
1	2 40 3.6	8♏18.6	10♏36.9	25♒23.0	13♏15.4	24♐36.3	24♎46.1	17♎47.7	12♐26.7	11♌32.8	2♏34.0	2♍3.0
2	2 44 .2	9 18.7	10 33.7	7♓15.5	14 50.9	25 41.7	25 25.9	18 .3	12 33.0	11 33.6	2 36.2	2 3.9
3	2 47 56.7	10 18.7	10 30.5	19 6.3	16 25.9	26 46.8	26 5.8	18 12.8	12 39.3	11 34.4	2 38.5	2 4.9
4	2 51 53.3	11 18.8	10 27.3	0♈59.4	18 .5	27 51.7	26 45.6	18 25.3	12 45.7	11 35.2	2 40.7	2 5.8
5	2 55 49.9	12 19.0	10 24.2	12 58.1	19 34.6	28 56.4	27 25.5	18 37.7	12 52.1	11 35.9	2 42.9	2 6.7
6	2 59 46.4	13 19.1	10 21.0	25 5.2	21 8.4	0♑ .9	28 5.5	18 50.1	12 58.5	11 36.5	2 45.1	2 7.5
7	3 3 43.0	14 19.3	10 17.8	7♉22.8	22 41.8	1 5.1	28 45.4	19 2.5	13 5.0	11 37.1	2 47.3	2 8.4
8	3 7 39.5	15 19.5	10 14.6	19 52.4	24 14.8	2 9.0	29 25.4	19 14.8	13 11.6	11 37.6	2 49.5	2 9.2
9	3 11 36.1	16 19.8	10 11.5	2♊34.9	25 47.5	3 12.7	0♏ 5.4	19 27.1	13 18.1	11 38.1	2 51.7	2 9.9
10	3 15 32.6	17 20.0	10 8.3	15 30.9	27 19.9	4 16.0	0 45.5	19 39.3	13 24.7	11 38.5	2 53.9	2 10.7
11	3 19 29.2	18 20.3	10 5.1	28 40.3	28 51.9	5 19.2	1 25.6	19 51.5	13 31.3	11 38.9	2 56.1	2 11.4
12	3 23 25.7	19 20.7	10 1.9	12♋ 3.0	0♐23.5	6 22.0	2 5.7	20 3.7	13 38.0	11 39.2	2 58.3	2 12.1
13	3 27 22.3	20 21.0	9 58.7	25 38.7	1 54.9	7 24.5	2 45.8	20 15.8	13 44.7	11 39.5	3 .4	2 12.7
14	3 31 18.8	21 21.4	9 55.6	9♌26.9	3 25.9	8 26.7	3 26.0	20 27.8	13 51.4	11 39.7	3 2.6	2 13.4
15	3 35 15.4	22 21.9	9 52.4	23 26.9	4 56.7	9 28.6	4 6.2	20 39.8	13 58.1	11 39.8	3 4.7	2 14.0
16	3 39 12.0	23 22.4	9 49.2	7♍37.5	6 27.1	10 30.2	4 46.5	20 51.8	14 5.0	11 40.0	3 6.9	2 14.6
17	3 43 8.5	24 22.9	9 46.0	21 56.6	7 57.2	11 31.4	5 26.8	21 3.7	14 11.8	11 40.0	3 9.0	2 15.1
18	3 47 5.1	25 23.4	9 42.9	6♎21.5	9 27.0	12 32.3	6 7.1	21 15.5	14 18.6	11 40.0	3 11.2	2 15.6
19	3 51 1.6	26 24.0	9 39.7	20 48.5	10 56.3	13 32.8	6 47.5	21 27.3	14 25.4	11 R 39.9	3 13.3	2 16.1
20	3 54 58.2	27 24.6	9 36.5	5♏12.9	12 25.4	14 32.9	7 27.9	21 39.0	14 32.3	11 39.8	3 15.4	2 16.6
21	3 58 54.7	28 25.2	9 33.3	19 29.9	13 54.0	15 32.6	8 8.3	21 50.7	14 39.2	11 39.6	3 17.4	2 17.0
22	4 2 51.3	29 25.8	9 30.2	3♐34.3	15 22.1	16 31.9	8 48.7	22 2.3	14 46.1	11 39.4	3 19.5	2 17.4
23	4 6 47.8	0♐26.5	9 27.0	17 22.1	16 49.8	17 30.8	9 29.2	22 13.8	14 53.1	11 39.1	3 21.5	2 17.8
24	4 10 44.4	1 27.1	9 23.8	0♑50.1	18 16.9	18 29.2	10 9.7	22 25.2	15 .0	11 38.7	3 23.6	2 18.1
25	4 14 41.0	2 27.8	9 20.6	13 56.9	19 43.5	19 27.1	10 50.2	22 36.6	15 7.0	11 38.3	3 25.6	2 18.4
26	4 18 37.5	3 28.6	9 17.4	26 42.9	21 9.3	20 24.6	11 30.8	22 48.0	15 14.0	11 37.8	3 27.6	2 18.6
27	4 22 34.1	4 29.3	9 14.3	9♒10.0	22 34.4	21 21.6	12 11.4	22 59.2	15 21.0	11 37.3	3 29.6	2 18.9
28	4 26 30.6	5 30.1	9 11.1	21 21.2	23 58.6	22 18.0	12 52.0	23 10.4	15 28.0	11 36.7	3 31.6	2 19.1
29	4 30 27.2	6 30.8	9 7.9	3♓20.7	25 21.8	23 13.9	13 32.6	23 21.5	15 35.0	11 36.1	3 33.5	2 19.3
30	4 34 23.7	7 31.6	9 4.7	15 13.2	26 43.8	24 9.2	14 13.3	23 32.5	15 42.1	11 35.4	3 35.5	2 19.4

LATITUDE

DAY	SID. TIME	☉	☊	☾	☿	♀	♂	♃	♄	♅	♆	♇
1	2 40 3.6	0 .0	0 .0	5N 7.0	0S14.5	3S 5.4	0N37.9	1N 6.9	1N24.5	0N37.8	1N41.8	11N15.4
4	2 51 53.3	0 .0	0 .0	3 22.6	0 34.5	3 10.3	0 36.5	1 7.1	1 24.1	0 37.9	1 41.8	11 16.6
7	3 3 43.0	0 .0	0 .0	0 17.7	0 53.8	3 14.0	0 35.2	1 7.3	1 23.7	0 38.0	1 41.9	11 17.7
10	3 15 32.6	0 .0	0 .0	3S 2.1	1 12.3	3 16.7	0 33.7	1 7.5	1 23.4	0 38.1	1 41.9	11 18.9
13	3 27 22.3	0 .0	0 .0	5 6.3	1 29.5	3 18.1	0 32.3	1 7.7	1 23.1	0 38.3	1 42.0	11 20.1
16	3 39 12.0	0 .0	0 .0	4 42.1	1 45.2	3 18.2	0 30.9	1 8.0	1 22.7	0 38.4	1 42.0	11 21.3
19	3 51 1.6	0 .0	0 .0	1 47.1	1 59.1	3 16.8	0 29.4	1 8.3	1 22.4	0 38.5	1 42.1	11 22.5
22	4 2 51.3	0 .0	0 .0	2N 3.8	2 10.6	3 13.9	0 27.9	1 8.6	1 22.2	0 38.6	1 42.2	11 23.8
25	4 14 41.0	0 .0	0 .0	4 41.9	2 19.3	3 9.4	0 26.3	1 8.9	1 21.9	0 38.8	1 42.3	11 25.0
28	4 26 30.6	0 .0	0 .0	5 8.6	2 24.5	3 3.1	0 24.8	1 9.2	1 21.7	0 38.9	1 42.4	11 26.2

RIGHT ASCENSION

DAY	SID. TIME	☉	☊	☾	☿	♀	♂	♃	♄	♅	♆	♇
1	2 40 3.6	5♏56.2	8♏11.7	25♒55.1	10♏43.7	23♐59.0	23♎10.6	16♎50.2	11♐10.2	14♌11.3	0♏57.8	8♍20.3
2	2 44 .2	6 54.9	8 8.5	7♓12.3	12 16.5	25 11.8	23 48.0	17 1.9	11 16.9	14 12.2	0 59.9	8 21.4
3	2 47 56.7	7 53.8	8 5.4	18 21.8	13 49.5	26 24.4	24 25.5	17 13.5	11 23.6	14 13.0	1 2.0	8 22.5
4	2 51 53.3	8 53.0	8 2.3	29 33.8	15 22.6	27 36.8	25 3.0	17 25.2	11 30.3	14 13.8	1 4.2	8 23.5
5	2 55 49.9	9 52.3	7 59.2	10♈57.9	16 55.9	28 49.0	25 40.7	17 36.8	11 37.1	14 14.5	1 6.3	8 24.6
6	2 59 46.4	10 51.9	7 56.0	22 43.0	18 29.4	0♑ 1.0	26 18.4	17 48.4	11 43.9	14 15.2	1 8.4	8 25.5
7	3 3 43.0	11 51.6	7 52.9	4♉55.7	20 3.1	1 12.7	26 56.2	17 59.9	11 50.8	14 15.8	1 10.5	8 26.5
8	3 7 39.5	12 51.6	7 49.8	17 40.0	21 37.0	2 24.1	27 34.1	18 11.4	11 57.7	14 16.3	1 12.6	8 27.5
9	3 11 36.1	13 51.7	7 46.7	0♊55.6	23 11.0	3 35.3	28 12.0	18 22.9	12 4.7	14 16.8	1 14.7	8 28.4
10	3 15 32.6	14 52.1	7 43.6	14 37.2	24 45.4	4 46.1	28 50.1	18 34.3	12 11.7	14 17.3	1 16.8	8 29.2
11	3 19 29.2	15 52.7	7 40.4	28 35.6	26 19.9	5 56.5	29 28.3	18 45.7	12 18.7	14 17.7	1 18.9	8 30.1
12	3 23 25.7	16 53.5	7 37.3	12♋39.4	27 54.7	7 6.6	0♏ 6.5	18 57.1	12 25.8	14 18.0	1 21.0	8 30.9
13	3 27 22.3	17 54.5	7 34.2	26 38.6	29 29.7	8 16.3	0 44.9	19 8.4	12 32.9	14 18.3	1 23.1	8 31.7
14	3 31 18.8	18 55.8	7 31.1	10♌27.1	1♐ 4.9	9 25.6	1 23.4	19 19.7	12 40.0	14 18.5	1 25.2	8 32.5
15	3 35 15.4	19 57.3	7 28.0	24 4.0	2 40.3	10 34.4	2 1.9	19 30.9	12 47.2	14 18.6	1 27.2	8 33.3
16	3 39 12.0	20 59.0	7 24.8	7♍33.4	4 16.0	11 42.9	2 40.6	19 42.1	12 54.4	14 18.8	1 29.3	8 34.0
17	3 43 8.5	22 .9	7 21.7	21 2.3	5 51.7	12 50.7	3 19.4	19 53.3	13 1.7	14 18.8	1 31.4	8 34.7
18	3 47 5.1	23 3.0	7 18.6	4♎39.5	7 27.6	13 58.1	3 58.2	20 4.4	13 8.9	14 18.8	1 33.4	8 35.4
19	3 51 1.6	24 5.3	7 15.5	18 32.5	9 3.5	15 4.9	4 37.2	20 15.4	13 16.2	14 18.8	1 35.4	8 36.0
20	3 54 58.2	25 7.8	7 12.4	2♏45.4	10 39.5	16 11.2	5 16.3	20 26.4	13 23.5	14 R 18.6	1 37.4	8 36.6
21	3 58 54.7	26 10.6	7 9.3	17 16.8	12 15.5	17 16.9	5 55.5	20 37.3	13 30.8	14 18.5	1 39.4	8 37.2
22	4 2 51.3	27 13.5	7 6.1	1♐58.1	13 51.3	18 21.9	6 34.8	20 48.2	13 38.2	14 18.2	1 41.4	8 37.8
23	4 6 47.8	28 16.7	7 3.0	16 35.3	15 27.0	19 26.4	7 14.2	20 59.1	13 45.6	14 17.9	1 43.4	8 38.3
24	4 10 44.4	29 20.0	6 59.9	0♑52.9	17 2.4	20 30.1	7 53.7	21 9.8	13 53.0	14 17.6	1 45.4	8 38.8
25	4 14 41.0	0♐23.5	6 56.8	14 38.1	18 37.5	21 33.2	8 33.3	21 20.5	14 .4	14 17.2	1 47.3	8 39.2
26	4 18 37.5	1 27.2	6 53.7	27 44.2	20 12.0	22 35.5	9 13.0	21 31.2	14 7.9	14 16.7	1 49.3	8 39.6
27	4 22 34.1	2 31.1	6 50.6	10♒11.0	21 45.9	23 37.0	9 52.8	21 41.8	14 15.3	14 16.2	1 51.2	8 40.0
28	4 26 30.6	3 35.2	6 47.5	22 3.9	23 19.1	24 37.8	10 32.7	21 52.3	14 22.8	14 15.7	1 53.1	8 40.4
29	4 30 27.2	4 39.4	6 44.4	3♓31.4	24 51.2	25 37.8	11 12.8	22 2.8	14 30.3	14 15.0	1 55.0	8 40.7
30	4 34 23.7	5 43.8	6 41.3	14 43.9	26 22.2	26 37.0	11 52.9	22 13.2	14 37.8	14 14.4	1 56.8	8 41.1

DECLINATION

DAY	SID. TIME	☉	☊	☾	☿	♀	♂	♃	♄	♅	♆	♇
1	2 40 3.6	14S16.7	0S15.7	8S14.3	16S 3.1	26S25.2	9S .4	5S57.1	20S53.7	17N55.6	10S46.3	21N13.3
4	2 51 53.3	15 13.6	0 15.7	3N29.5	17 45.0	26 35.8	9 45.1	6 11.3	20 56.5	17 55.1	10 48.5	21 13.3
7	3 3 43.0	16 8.3	0 15.6	14 15.3	19 19.0	26 40.3	10 29.2	6 25.2	20 59.3	17 54.7	10 50.7	21 13.5
10	3 15 32.6	17 .6	0 15.6	19 38.3	20 44.3	26 39.0	11 12.7	6 38.9	21 2.0	17 54.4	10 52.9	21 13.7
13	3 27 22.3	17 50.3	0 15.5	15 59.8	22 .6	26 31.9	11 55.6	6 52.4	21 4.7	17 54.2	10 55.1	21 14.0
16	3 39 12.0	18 37.2	0 15.5	4 20.6	23 7.0	26 19.2	12 37.8	7 5.7	21 7.4	17 54.2	10 57.2	21 14.5
19	3 51 1.6	19 21.1	0 15.4	9S46.7	24 3.1	26 1.0	13 19.3	7 18.7	21 10.1	17 54.4	10 59.3	21 15.0
22	4 2 51.3	20 1.9	0 15.4	18 50.7	24 48.1	25 37.6	13 59.9	7 31.5	21 12.7	17 54.6	11 1.4	21 15.7
25	4 14 41.0	20 39.4	0 15.3	18 2.3	25 21.5	25 9.3	14 39.7	7 43.9	21 15.3	17 55.0	11 3.4	21 16.5
28	4 26 30.6	21 13.4	0 15.2	9 30.5	25 42.7	24 36.4	15 18.5	7 56.1	21 17.8	17 55.6	11 5.3	21 17.3

DECEMBER 1957

LONGITUDE

DAY	EPHEM. SID. TIME h m s	☉ ° ′	☊ ° ′	☽ ° ′	☿ ° ′	♀ ° ′	♂ ° ′	♃ ° ′	♄ ° ′	♅ ° ′	♆ ° ′	♇ ° ′
1	4 38 20.3	8♐32.4	9♏ 1.6	27♓ 3.6	28♐ 4.5	25♑ 3.9	14♏54.0	23♎43.5	15♐49.1	11♌34.7	3♏37.4	2♍19.5
2	4 42 16.9	9 33.3	8 58.4	8♈57.0	29 23.7	25 58.0	15 34.8	23 54.3	15 56.2	11 R33.9	3 39.3	2 19.6
3	4 46 13.4	10 34.1	8 55.2	20 57.8	0♑41.1	26 51.4	16 15.5	24 5.1	16 3.3	11 33.1	3 41.2	2 19.7
4	4 50 10.0	11 34.9	8 52.0	3♉10.4	1 56.5	27 44.1	16 56.3	24 15.8	16 10.3	11 32.2	3 43.1	2 19.7
5	4 54 6.5	12 35.8	8 48.9	15 37.9	3 9.5	28 36.2	17 37.2	24 26.4	16 17.4	11 31.3	3 44.9	2 19.7
6	4 58 3.1	13 36.7	8 45.7	28 22.7	4 19.8	29 27.5	18 18.0	24 37.0	16 24.5	11 30.3	3 46.7	2 R19.6
7	5 1 59.6	14 37.6	8 42.5	11♊25.6	5 27.0	0♒18.1	18 59.0	24 47.5	16 31.7	11 29.3	3 48.6	2 19.6
8	5 5 56.2	15 38.6	8 39.3	24 46.2	6 30.6	1 7.8	19 39.9	24 57.8	16 38.7	11 28.2	3 50.4	2 19.5
9	5 9 52.8	16 39.5	8 36.1	8♋22.8	7 30.0	1 56.8	20 20.9	25 8.1	16 45.8	11 27.0	3 52.2	2 19.4
10	5 13 49.3	17 40.4	8 33.0	22 12.5	8 24.6	2 44.8	21 1.9	25 18.3	16 52.9	11 25.8	3 53.9	2 19.2
11	5 17 45.9	18 41.4	8 29.8	6♌11.9	9 13.9	3 32.0	21 42.9	25 28.4	17 .0	11 24.6	3 55.6	2 19.0
12	5 21 42.4	19 42.4	8 26.6	20 17.5	9 56.9	4 18.3	22 24.0	25 38.4	17 7.1	11 23.3	3 57.3	2 18.8
13	5 25 39.0	20 43.4	8 23.4	4♍26.1	10 33.0	5 3.6	23 5.1	25 48.3	17 14.2	11 22.0	3 59.0	2 18.5
14	5 29 35.5	21 44.4	8 20.3	18 35.1	11 1.2	5 47.9	23 46.2	25 58.1	17 21.3	11 20.6	4 .7	2 18.3
15	5 33 32.1	22 45.4	8 17.1	2♎42.8	11 20.7	6 31.1	24 27.4	26 7.8	17 28.4	11 19.2	4 2.3	2 17.9
16	5 37 28.7	23 46.5	8 13.9	16 47.8	11 30.6	7 13.3	25 8.6	26 17.4	17 35.4	11 17.7	4 3.9	2 17.6
17	5 41 25.2	24 47.6	8 10.7	0♏48.9	11 R30.1	7 54.3	25 49.8	26 26.8	17 42.5	11 16.1	4 5.5	2 17.2
18	5 45 21.8	25 48.7	8 7.6	14 44.8	11 18.6	8 34.2	26 31.1	26 36.2	17 49.6	11 14.6	4 7.0	2 16.8
19	5 49 18.3	26 49.8	8 4.4	28 33.6	10 55.5	9 12.8	27 12.4	26 45.5	17 56.6	11 13.0	4 8.6	2 16.4
20	5 53 14.9	27 50.9	8 1.2	12♐13.1	10 20.7	9 50.2	27 53.7	26 54.7	18 3.6	11 11.3	4 10.1	2 15.9
21	5 57 11.4	28 52.0	7 58.0	25 40.8	9 34.4	10 26.3	28 35.1	27 3.7	18 10.7	11 9.6	4 11.6	2 15.4
22	6 1 8.0	29 53.1	7 54.8	8♑54.4	8 37.4	11 .9	29 16.5	27 12.7	18 17.7	11 7.9	4 13.0	2 14.9
23	6 5 4.6	0♑54.3	7 51.7	21 52.2	7 31.0	11 34.2	29 57.9	27 21.5	18 24.7	11 6.1	4 14.4	2 14.4
24	6 9 1.1	1 55.4	7 48.5	4♒33.4	6 17.0	12 5.9	0♐39.4	27 30.2	18 31.6	11 4.2	4 15.8	2 13.8
25	6 12 57.7	2 56.5	7 45.3	16 58.4	4 57.7	12 36.1	1 20.9	27 38.8	18 38.6	11 2.4	4 17.2	2 13.2
26	6 16 54.2	3 57.7	7 42.1	29 9.0	3 35.6	13 4.6	2 2.4	27 47.2	18 45.6	11 .5	4 18.6	2 12.5
27	6 20 50.8	4 58.8	7 39.0	11♓ 8.1	2 13.6	13 31.5	2 44.0	27 55.6	18 52.5	10 58.5	4 19.9	2 11.9
28	6 24 47.3	6 .0	7 35.8	22 59.9	0 54.4	13 56.6	3 25.6	28 3.8	18 59.4	10 56.6	4 21.2	2 11.2
29	6 28 43.9	7 1.2	7 32.6	4♈49.0	29♐40.3	14 19.9	4 7.2	28 11.9	19 6.3	10 54.6	4 22.5	2 10.5
30	6 32 40.5	8 2.3	7 29.4	16 40.7	28 33.4	14 41.3	4 48.8	28 19.9	19 13.2	10 52.5	4 23.7	2 9.8
31	6 36 37.0	9 3.5	7 26.3	28 40.5	27 35.1	15 .7	5 30.5	28 27.7	19 20.0	10 50.4	4 24.9	2 9.0

LATITUDE

DAY	SID. TIME	☉	☊	☽	☿	♀	♂	♃	♄	♅	♆	♇
1	4 38 20.3	0 .0	0 .0	3N35.5	2S25.5	2S55.0	0N23.2	1N 9.6	1N21.4	0N39.0	1N42.5	11N27.5
4	4 50 10.0	0 .0	0 .0	0 39.1	2 21.2	2 44.9	0 21.5	1 9.9	1 21.2	0 39.1	1 42.6	11 28.7
7	5 1 59.6	0 .0	0 .0	2S41.6	2 10.4	2 32.7	0 19.9	1 10.3	1 21.0	0 39.2	1 42.7	11 29.9
10	5 13 49.3	0 .0	0 .0	4 55.6	1 51.4	2 18.2	0 18.2	1 10.7	1 20.9	0 39.3	1 42.8	11 31.1
13	5 25 39.0	0 .0	0 .0	4 42.0	1 22.4	2 1.4	0 16.5	1 11.2	1 20.7	0 39.4	1 42.9	11 32.4
16	5 37 28.7	0 .0	0 .0	2 1.2	0 42.1	1 42.0	0 14.7	1 11.6	1 20.6	0 39.5	1 43.1	11 33.6
19	5 49 18.3	0 .0	0 .0	1N39.7	0N 9.5	1 19.9	0 12.9	1 12.1	1 20.5	0 39.7	1 43.2	11 34.7
22	6 1 8.0	0 .0	0 .0	4 24.2	1 8.4	0 55.0	0 11.1	1 12.6	1 20.3	0 39.7	1 43.4	11 35.9
25	6 12 57.7	0 .0	0 .0	5 2.9	2 5.0	0 27.1	0 9.3	1 13.1	1 20.3	0 39.8	1 43.5	11 37.0
28	6 24 47.3	0 .0	0 .0	3 39.6	2 47.4	0N 3.8	0 7.4	1 13.6	1 20.2	0 39.9	1 43.7	11 38.1
31	6 36 37.0	0 .0	0 .0	0 53.3	3 8.5	0 37.9	0 5.4	1 14.1	1 20.1	0 40.0	1 43.8	11 39.2

RIGHT ASCENSION

DAY	SID. TIME	☉	☊	☽	☿	♀	♂	♃	♄	♅	♆	♇
1	4 38 20.3	6♐48.4	6♏38.1	25♓52.5	27♐51.8	27♑35.2	12♏33.2	22♎23.5	14♐45.3	14♌13.6	1♏58.7	8♍41.3
2	4 42 16.9	7 53.2	6 35.0	7♈ 8.5	29 19.7	28 32.6	13 13.6	22 33.7	14 52.9	14 R12.9	2 .5	8 41.6
3	4 46 13.4	8 58.0	6 31.9	18 42.4	0♑45.6	29 29.1	13 54.1	22 43.9	15 .4	14 12.0	2 2.4	8 41.8
4	4 50 10.0	10 3.1	6 28.8	0♉43.5	2 9.3	0♒24.6	14 34.7	22 54.0	15 7.9	14 11.1	2 4.2	8 42.0
5	4 54 6.5	11 8.3	6 25.7	13 18.7	3 30.2	1 19.1	15 15.5	23 4.1	15 15.5	14 10.2	2 5.9	8 42.1
6	4 58 3.1	12 13.6	6 22.6	26 30.6	4 47.9	2 12.6	15 56.3	23 14.0	15 23.1	14 9.2	2 7.7	8 42.3
7	5 1 59.6	13 19.1	6 19.5	10♊16.5	6 2.2	3 5.1	16 37.3	23 23.9	15 30.7	14 8.2	2 9.5	8 42.4
8	5 5 56.2	14 24.7	6 16.4	24 27.3	7 12.1	3 56.5	17 18.4	23 33.7	15 38.2	14 7.1	2 11.2	8 42.5
9	5 9 52.8	15 30.4	6 13.3	8♋49.7	8 17.3	4 46.7	17 59.6	23 43.5	15 45.8	14 6.0	2 12.9	8 42.5
10	5 13 49.3	16 36.2	6 10.2	23 9.4	9 17.1	5 35.9	18 40.9	23 53.1	15 53.4	14 4.8	2 14.6	8 42.5
11	5 17 45.9	17 42.1	6 7.1	7♌15.8	10 10.6	6 23.8	19 22.4	24 2.7	16 1.0	14 3.5	2 16.3	8 42.5
12	5 21 42.4	18 48.2	6 4.0	21 3.9	10 57.1	7 10.6	20 4.0	24 12.1	16 8.6	14 2.3	2 18.0	8 R42.4
13	5 25 39.0	19 54.3	6 .9	4♍35.1	11 35.6	7 56.1	20 45.7	24 21.5	16 16.1	14 .9	2 19.6	8 42.4
14	5 29 35.5	21 .5	5 57.8	17 55.8	12 5.4	8 40.4	21 27.5	24 30.8	16 23.7	13 59.5	2 21.2	8 42.2
15	5 33 32.1	22 6.8	5 54.7	1♎14.9	12 25.4	9 23.3	22 9.4	24 40.0	16 31.3	13 58.1	2 22.8	8 42.1
16	5 37 28.7	23 13.2	5 51.5	14 41.8	12 34.8	10 5.0	22 51.5	24 49.1	16 38.8	13 56.6	2 24.3	8 41.9
17	5 41 25.2	24 19.6	5 48.4	28 24.1	12 R32.8	10 45.2	23 33.7	24 58.2	16 46.4	13 55.1	2 25.9	8 41.7
18	5 45 21.8	25 26.1	5 45.3	12♏25.2	12 18.7	11 24.0	24 16.0	25 7.1	16 53.9	13 53.5	2 27.4	8 41.5
19	5 49 18.3	26 32.7	5 42.2	26 42.4	11 52.0	12 1.3	24 58.4	25 15.9	17 1.5	13 51.9	2 28.9	8 41.2
20	5 53 14.9	27 39.3	5 39.1	11♐ 7.0	11 12.7	12 37.2	25 40.9	25 24.6	17 9.0	13 50.2	2 30.3	8 40.9
21	5 57 11.4	28 45.9	5 36.0	25 25.3	10 21.2	13 11.5	26 23.6	25 33.2	17 16.5	13 48.5	2 31.8	8 40.6
22	6 1 8.0	29 52.5	5 32.9	9♑23.0	9 18.4	13 44.1	27 6.4	25 41.7	17 24.0	13 46.7	2 33.2	8 40.3
23	6 5 4.6	0♑59.1	5 29.8	22 49.2	8 5.7	14 15.1	27 49.3	25 50.2	17 31.5	13 44.9	2 34.6	8 39.9
24	6 9 1.1	2 5.8	5 26.7	5♒38.7	6 45.2	14 44.5	28 32.3	25 58.5	17 39.0	13 43.1	2 35.9	8 39.5
25	6 12 57.7	3 12.4	5 23.6	17 52.3	5 19.3	15 12.0	29 15.4	26 6.6	17 46.5	13 41.2	2 37.3	8 39.0
26	6 16 54.2	4 19.0	5 20.5	29 35.7	3 50.9	15 37.7	29 58.7	26 14.7	17 53.9	13 39.3	2 38.6	8 38.6
27	6 20 50.8	5 25.6	5 17.4	10♓57.3	2 22.8	16 1.6	0♐42.1	26 22.7	18 1.3	13 37.3	2 39.9	8 38.1
28	6 24 47.3	6 32.2	5 14.4	22 7.5	0 58.1	16 23.5	1 25.6	26 30.6	18 8.8	13 35.4	2 41.2	8 37.6
29	6 28 43.9	7 38.6	5 11.3	3♈17.2	29♐39.0	16 43.4	2 9.2	26 38.3	18 16.1	13 33.3	2 42.4	8 37.0
30	6 32 40.5	8 45.1	5 8.2	14 37.6	28 27.7	17 1.3	2 52.9	26 45.9	18 23.5	13 31.3	2 43.6	8 36.5
31	6 36 37.0	9 51.5	5 5.1	26 19.4	27 25.8	17 17.1	3 36.7	26 53.4	18 30.8	13 29.2	2 44.8	8 35.9

DECLINATION

DAY	SID. TIME	☉	☊	☽	☿	♀	♂	♃	♄	♅	♆	♇
1	4 38 20.3	21S43.9	0S15.2	2N 7.6	25S51.2	23S59.4	15S56.4	8S 8.0	21S20.3	17N56.3	11S 7.2	21N18.3
4	4 50 10.0	22 10.6	0 15.1	13 11.2	25 46.9	23 18.6	16 33.2	8 19.5	21 22.7	17 57.1	11 9.0	21 19.4
7	5 1 59.6	22 33.4	0 15.1	19 29.2	25 30.1	22 34.4	17 8.9	8 30.7	21 25.0	17 58.0	11 10.7	21 20.6
10	5 13 49.3	22 52.3	0 15.0	16 44.9	25 1.7	21 47.4	17 43.5	8 41.6	21 27.3	17 59.0	11 12.4	21 21.9
13	5 25 39.0	23 7.1	0 15.0	5 30.3	24 23.6	20 58.0	18 16.9	8 52.0	21 29.5	18 .2	11 14.0	21 23.2
16	5 37 28.7	23 17.8	0 14.9	8S28.0	23 38.6	20 6.8	18 48.9	9 2.1	21 31.6	18 1.5	11 15.5	21 24.7
19	5 49 18.3	23 24.3	0 14.9	18 13.2	22 50.1	19 14.2	19 19.7	9 11.9	21 33.6	18 2.9	11 16.9	21 26.2
22	6 1 8.0	23 26.5	0 14.8	18 45.0	22 1.5	18 20.9	19 49.0	9 21.2	21 35.6	18 4.4	11 18.3	21 27.8
25	6 12 57.7	23 24.6	0 14.8	10 56.0	21 16.1	17 27.7	20 16.9	9 30.0	21 37.5	18 6.0	11 19.6	21 29.5
28	6 24 47.3	23 18.4	0 14.7	0N34.9	20 39.0	16 35.0	20 43.3	9 38.5	21 39.3	18 7.7	11 20.7	21 31.3
31	6 36 37.0	23 8.0	0 14.7	11 50.1	20 16.8	15 43.9	21 8.2	9 46.5	21 41.0	18 9.4	11 21.8	21 33.1

JANUARY 1958

DAY	EPHEM. SID. TIME	LONGITUDE ☉	☊	☽	☿	♀	♂	♃	♄	♅	♆	♇
	h m s	° ′	° ′	° ′	° ′	° ′	° ′	° ′	° ′	° ′	° ′	° ′
1	6 40 33.6	10♑ 4.6	7♏23.1	10♉53.6	26♐46.6	15♒18.1	6♐12.2	28≏35.4	19♐26.8	10♌48.3	4♏26.1	2♍ 8.2
2	6 44 30.1	11 5.8	7 19.9	23 24.7	26R 8.3	15 33.5	6 54.0	28 43.0	19 33.6	10R46.2	4 27.2	2R 7.4
3	6 48 26.7	12 6.9	7 16.7	6♊17.6	25 40.4	15 46.6	7 35.7	28 50.4	19 40.3	10 44.0	4 28.3	2 6.5
4	6 52 23.2	13 8.0	7 13.5	19 34.1	25 22.7	15 57.5	8 17.5	28 57.7	19 47.0	10 41.8	4 29.4	2 5.7
5	6 56 19.8	14 9.2	7 10.4	3♋14.5	25 14.7	16 6.2	8 59.4	29 4.9	19 53.7	10 39.5	4 30.5	2 4.8
6	7 0 16.4	15 10.3	7 7.2	17 16.3	25D16.0	16 12.5	9 41.2	29 11.9	20 .4	10 37.2	4 31.5	2 3.9
7	7 4 12.9	16 11.4	7 4.0	1♌34.9	25 25.8	16 16.4	10 23.1	29 18.8	20 7.0	10 34.9	4 32.5	2 2.9
8	7 8 9.5	17 12.5	7 .8	16 4.0	25 43.4	16 17.9	11 5.1	29 25.5	20 13.6	10 32.6	4 33.4	2 1.9
9	7 12 6.0	18 13.7	6 57.7	0♍36.7	26 8.3	16R17.0	11 47.0	29 32.1	20 20.2	10 30.3	4 34.3	2 1.0
10	7 16 2.6	19 14.8	6 54.5	15 6.7	26 39.6	16 13.5	12 29.0	29 38.5	20 26.7	10 27.9	4 35.2	1 59.9
11	7 19 59.1	20 15.9	6 51.3	29 29.0	27 16.7	16 7.6	13 11.1	29 44.8	20 33.2	10 25.5	4 36.1	1 58.9
12	7 23 55.7	21 17.1	6 48.1	13≏40.5	27 59.1	15 59.1	13 53.2	29 51.0	20 39.6	10 23.1	4 36.9	1 57.8
13	7 27 52.3	22 18.2	6 45.0	27 39.8	28 46.2	15 48.2	14 35.3	29 57.0	20 46.1	10 20.6	4 37.7	1 56.8
14	7 31 48.8	23 19.3	6 41.8	11♏27.0	29 37.6	15 34.7	15 17.4	0♏ 2.8	20 52.4	10 18.2	4 38.5	1 55.7
15	7 35 45.4	24 20.4	6 38.6	25 2.6	0♑32.7	15 18.8	15 59.6	0 8.5	20 58.8	10 15.7	4 39.2	1 54.5
16	7 39 41.9	25 21.5	6 35.4	8♐27.3	1 31.3	15 .5	16 41.8	0 14.0	21 5.1	10 13.2	4 39.9	1 53.4
17	7 43 38.5	26 22.7	6 32.2	21 41.7	2 32.9	14 39.8	17 24.0	0 19.4	21 11.3	10 10.7	4 40.6	1 52.2
18	7 47 35.0	27 23.8	6 29.1	4♑45.5	3 37.3	14 17.0	18 6.3	0 24.7	21 17.5	10 8.2	4 41.2	1 51.1
19	7 51 31.6	28 24.9	6 25.9	17 38.4	4 44.1	13 51.9	18 48.6	0 29.7	21 23.7	10 5.6	4 41.8	1 49.9
20	7 55 28.1	29 26.0	6 22.7	0♒19.5	5 53.2	13 24.8	19 31.0	0 34.6	21 29.8	10 3.1	4 42.4	1 48.7
21	7 59 24.7	0♒27.1	6 19.5	12 48.5	7 4.3	12 55.7	20 13.3	0 39.3	21 35.9	10 .5	4 42.9	1 47.4
22	8 3 21.3	1 28.2	6 16.4	25 5.4	8 17.2	12 25.0	20 55.7	0 43.9	21 41.9	9 57.9	4 43.4	1 46.2
23	8 7 17.8	2 29.2	6 13.2	7♓11.1	9 31.9	11 52.6	21 38.1	0 48.2	21 47.8	9 55.3	4 43.9	1 44.9
24	8 11 14.4	3 30.3	6 10.0	19 7.4	10 48.1	11 18.9	22 20.6	0 52.4	21 53.7	9 52.7	4 44.3	1 43.6
25	8 15 10.9	4 31.3	6 6.8	0♈57.3	12 5.7	10 44.0	23 3.1	0 56.5	21 59.6	9 50.1	4 44.7	1 42.3
26	8 19 7.5	5 32.3	6 3.7	12 44.6	13 24.7	10 8.2	23 45.6	1 .3	22 5.4	9 47.5	4 45.0	1 41.0
27	8 23 4.0	6 33.3	6 .5	24 34.1	14 44.9	9 31.7	24 28.1	1 4.0	22 11.1	9 44.8	4 45.4	1 39.7
28	8 27 .6	7 34.2	5 57.3	6♉31.1	16 6.3	8 54.7	25 10.7	1 7.5	22 16.8	9 42.2	4 45.7	1 38.3
29	8 30 57.1	8 35.2	5 54.1	18 41.1	17 28.7	8 17.6	25 53.3	1 10.9	22 22.5	9 39.6	4 45.9	1 37.0
30	8 34 53.7	9 36.1	5 50.9	1♊ 9.7	18 52.2	7 40.5	26 35.9	1 14.0	22 28.0	9 37.0	4 46.1	1 35.6
31	8 38 50.3	10 37.0	5 47.8	14 1.7	20 16.7	7 3.8	27 18.5	1 17.0	22 33.6	9 34.3	4 46.3	1 34.2

DAY	EPHEM. SID. TIME	LATITUDE ☉	☊	☽	☿	♀	♂	♃	♄	♅	♆	♇
1	6 40 33.6	0 .0	0 .0	0S11.9	3N10.8	0N49.9	0N 4.8	1N14.3	1N20.1	0N40.0	1N43.9	11N39.6
4	6 52 23.2	0 .0	0 .0	3 19.8	3 6.2	1 28.0	0 2.8	1 14.9	1 20.1	0 40.1	1 44.1	11 40.6
7	7 4 12.9	0 .0	0 .0	5 .3	2 49.2	2 9.0	0 .8	1 15.5	1 20.1	0 40.2	1 44.2	11 41.6
10	7 16 2.6	0 .0	0 .0	4 .2	2 25.2	2 52.3	0S 1.2	1 16.1	1 20.1	0 40.2	1 44.4	11 42.6
13	7 27 52.3	0 .0	0 .0	0 51.7	1 57.8	3 37.4	0 3.3	1 16.7	1 20.1	0 40.3	1 44.6	11 43.5
16	7 39 41.9	0 .0	0 .0	2N36.2	1 29.2	4 23.1	0 5.4	1 17.3	1 20.1	0 40.4	1 44.8	11 44.4
19	7 51 31.6	0 .0	0 .0	4 43.4	1 .7	5 8.1	0 7.5	1 18.0	1 20.1	0 40.4	1 44.9	11 45.2
22	8 3 21.3	0 .0	0 .0	4 44.1	0 33.1	5 50.7	0 9.7	1 18.6	1 20.2	0 40.4	1 45.1	11 46.0
25	8 15 10.9	0 .0	0 .0	2 52.6	0 6.8	6 29.2	0 11.9	1 19.3	1 20.2	0 40.5	1 45.3	11 46.8
28	8 27 .6	0 .0	0 .0	0S 4.6	0S17.7	7 1.9	0 14.2	1 19.9	1 20.3	0 40.5	1 45.5	11 47.5
31	8 38 50.3	0 .0	0 .0	3 8.2	0 40.2	7 27.5	0 16.5	1 20.6	1 20.4	0 40.5	1 45.7	11 48.1

DAY	EPHEM. SID. TIME	RIGHT ASCENSION ☉	☊	☽	☿	♀	♂	♃	♄	♅	♆	♇
1	6 40 33.6	10♑57.8	5♏ 2.0	8♉31.9	26♐34.2	17♒30.7	4♐20.6	27≏ .8	18♐38.1	13♌27.0	2♏45.9	8♍35.2
2	6 44 30.1	12 4.0	4 58.9	21 21.8	25R53.5	17 42.1	5 4.7	27 8.0	18 45.4	13R24.9	2 47.0	8R34.6
3	6 48 26.7	13 10.1	4 55.8	4♊51.1	25 23.7	17 51.2	5 48.8	27 15.1	18 52.6	13 22.7	2 48.1	8 33.9
4	6 52 23.2	14 16.1	4 52.7	18 55.8	25 4.8	17 58.1	6 33.1	27 22.1	18 59.8	13 20.4	2 49.2	8 33.2
5	6 56 19.8	15 22.1	4 49.6	3♋25.5	24 56.1	18 2.5	7 17.4	27 29.0	19 7.0	13 18.2	2 50.2	8 32.4
6	7 0 16.4	16 27.9	4 46.5	18 5.4	24D57.2	18 4.6	8 1.9	27 35.7	19 14.1	13 15.9	2 51.2	8 31.7
7	7 4 12.9	17 33.6	4 43.4	2♌40.7	25 7.5	18R 4.2	8 46.5	27 42.4	19 21.3	13 13.5	2 52.2	8 30.9
8	7 8 9.5	18 39.3	4 40.3	17 .7	25 26.0	18 1.3	9 31.2	27 48.8	19 28.3	13 11.2	2 53.1	8 30.1
9	7 12 6.0	19 44.7	4 37.2	1♍ 1.4	25 52.3	17 56.0	10 15.9	27 55.2	19 35.4	13 8.8	2 54.0	8 29.3
10	7 16 2.6	20 50.1	4 34.1	14 44.7	26 25.5	17 48.1	11 .8	28 1.4	19 42.4	13 6.4	2 54.9	8 28.4
11	7 19 59.1	21 55.3	4 31.0	28 17.2	27 5.1	17 37.8	11 45.8	28 7.4	19 49.4	13 4.0	2 55.7	8 27.5
12	7 23 55.7	23 .4	4 27.9	11≏47.0	27 50.3	17 25.0	12 30.9	28 13.3	19 56.3	13 1.5	2 56.5	8 26.6
13	7 27 52.3	24 5.3	4 24.9	25 22.2	28 40.8	17 9.7	13 16.1	28 19.1	20 3.2	12 59.1	2 57.3	8 25.7
14	7 31 48.8	25 10.1	4 21.8	9♏ 7.8	29 35.9	16 52.0	14 1.4	28 24.8	20 10.0	12 56.6	2 58.1	8 24.7
15	7 35 45.4	26 14.8	4 18.7	23 4.8	0♑35.2	16 32.0	14 46.8	28 30.2	20 16.8	12 54.1	2 58.8	8 23.7
16	7 39 41.9	27 19.2	4 15.6	7♐ 9.0	1 38.4	16 9.6	15 32.3	28 35.6	20 23.6	12 51.5	2 59.5	8 22.7
17	7 43 38.5	28 23.6	4 12.5	21 11.5	2 45.0	15 45.0	16 17.8	28 40.8	20 30.3	12 49.0	3 .1	8 21.7
18	7 47 35.0	29 27.7	4 9.4	5♑ 1.4	3 54.7	15 18.3	17 3.5	28 45.9	20 37.0	12 46.5	3 .8	8 20.7
19	7 51 31.6	0♒31.7	4 6.3	18 28.2	5 7.2	14 49.5	17 49.3	28 50.7	20 43.6	12 43.9	3 1.4	8 19.7
20	7 55 28.1	1 35.5	4 3.2	1♒25.3	6 22.2	14 18.8	18 35.1	28 55.5	20 50.2	12 41.3	3 2.0	8 18.6
21	7 59 24.7	2 39.1	4 .2	13 50.4	7 39.6	13 46.5	19 21.0	29 .0	20 56.7	12 38.7	3 2.5	8 17.5
22	8 3 21.3	3 42.5	3 57.1	25 46.0	8 59.0	13 12.5	20 7.0	29 4.4	21 3.2	12 36.0	3 3.0	8 16.4
23	8 7 17.8	4 45.7	3 54.0	7♓17.9	10 20.4	12 37.2	20 53.0	29 8.7	21 9.6	12 33.4	3 3.5	8 15.2
24	8 11 14.4	5 48.7	3 50.9	18 34.1	11 43.5	12 .8	21 39.1	29 12.8	21 15.9	12 30.8	3 3.9	8 14.1
25	8 15 10.9	6 51.6	3 47.8	29 43.8	13 8.1	11 23.3	22 25.3	29 16.7	21 22.2	12 28.1	3 4.3	8 12.9
26	8 19 7.5	7 54.2	3 44.7	10♈57.0	14 34.3	10 45.2	23 11.5	29 20.5	21 28.5	12 25.5	3 4.6	8 11.7
27	8 23 4.0	8 56.6	3 41.6	22 23.5	16 1.7	10 6.6	23 57.9	29 24.1	21 34.7	12 22.8	3 5.0	8 10.5
28	8 27 .6	9 58.8	3 38.6	4♉12.9	17 30.4	9 27.8	24 44.2	29 27.5	21 40.8	12 20.2	3 5.3	8 9.3
29	8 30 57.1	11 .8	3 35.5	16 33.2	19 .2	8 49.0	25 30.7	29 30.8	21 46.8	12 17.5	3 5.5	8 8.0
30	8 34 53.7	12 2.6	3 32.4	29 29.9	20 30.9	8 10.6	26 17.1	29 33.9	21 52.8	12 14.8	3 5.8	8 6.8
31	8 38 50.3	13 4.2	3 29.3	13♊ 4.0	22 2.7	7 32.6	27 3.7	29 36.8	21 58.8	12 12.1	3 6.0	8 5.5

DAY	EPHEM. SID. TIME	DECLINATION ☉	☊	☽	☿	♀	♂	♃	♄	♅	♆	♇
1	6 40 33.6	23S 3.6	0S14.6	14N54.5	20S13.5	15S27.3	21S16.1	9S49.0	21S41.5	18N10.0	11S22.2	21N33.7
4	6 52 23.2	22 47.7	0 14.6	19 42.8	20 15.7	14 39.2	21 38.7	9 56.4	21 43.1	18 11.9	11 23.1	21 35.6
7	7 4 12.9	22 27.7	0 14.5	14 55.6	20 32.7	13 54.5	21 59.7	10 3.3	21 44.6	18 13.8	11 24.0	21 37.6
10	7 16 2.6	22 3.7	0 14.5	2 10.3	20 58.9	13 14.0	22 18.9	10 9.7	21 46.1	18 15.8	11 24.7	21 39.6
13	7 27 52.3	21 35.8	0 14.4	11S26.9	21 28.4	12 38.4	22 36.4	10 15.5	21 47.4	18 17.8	11 25.4	21 41.6
16	7 39 41.9	21 4.1	0 14.4	19 8.8	21 56.9	12 8.4	22 52.0	10 20.9	21 48.7	18 19.9	11 26.0	21 43.7
19	7 51 31.6	20 28.9	0 14.3	17 35.7	22 20.8	11 44.7	23 5.8	10 25.8	21 49.8	18 22.0	11 26.4	21 45.8
22	8 3 21.3	19 50.1	0 14.3	8 41.7	22 38.0	11 27.8	23 17.6	10 30.1	21 50.9	18 24.1	11 26.8	21 47.9
25	8 15 10.9	19 8.0	0 14.2	3N 1.1	22 46.7	11 17.8	23 27.5	10 33.9	21 51.9	18 26.3	11 27.0	21 50.0
28	8 27 .6	18 22.8	0 14.1	13 37.3	22 45.8	11 14.4	23 35.5	10 37.1	21 52.9	18 28.4	11 27.2	21 52.1
31	8 38 50.3	17 34.6	0 14.1	19 22.4	22 34.5	11 17.1	23 41.4	10 39.7	21 53.7	18 30.5	11 27.2	21 54.2

FEBRUARY 1958

LONGITUDE

DAY	EPHEM. SID. TIME h m s	☉ ° ′	☊ ° ′	☽ ° ′	☿ ° ′	♀ ° ′	♂ ° ′	♃ ° ′	♄ ° ′	♅ ° ′	♆ ° ′	♇ ° ′
1	8 42 46.8	11♒37.9	5♏44.6	27♊20.7	21♑42.2	6♒27.6	28♐ 1.2	1♏19.8	22♐39.0	9♌31.7	4♏46.5	1♍32.8
2	8 46 43.4	12 38.8	5 41.4	11♋ 8.2	23 8.6	5R52.3	28 43.9	1 22.4	22 44.4	9R29.1	4 46.6	1R31.4
3	8 50 39.9	13 39.6	5 38.2	25 23.0	24 35.8	5 18.0	29 26.7	1 24.9	22 49.7	9 26.5	4 46.7	1 30.0
4	8 54 36.5	14 40.5	5 35.1	10♌ .6	26 3.9	4 45.1	0♑ 9.5	1 27.1	22 55.0	9 23.8	4 46.7	1 28.5
5	8 58 33.0	15 41.3	5 31.9	24 53.5	27 32.9	4 13.6	0 52.3	1 29.2	23 .2	9 21.2	4 46.7	1 27.1
6	9 2 29.6	16 42.0	5 28.7	9♍52.8	29 2.7	3 43.9	1 35.1	1 31.1	23 5.3	9 18.6	4 46.7	1 25.6
7	9 6 26.1	17 42.8	5 25.5	24 48.8	0♒33.4	3 16.0	2 18.0	1 32.8	23 10.4	9 16.0	4 46.7	1 24.2
8	9 10 22.7	18 43.6	5 22.3	9♎33.8	2 4.9	2 50.2	3 .9	1 34.4	23 15.5	9 13.5	4R46.6	1 22.7
9	9 14 19.2	19 44.3	5 19.2	24 1.9	3 37.2	2 26.5	3 43.8	1 35.7	23 20.4	9 10.9	4 46.5	1 21.3
10	9 18 15.8	20 45.1	5 16.0	8♏10.5	5 10.3	2 5.1	4 26.8	1 36.9	23 25.3	9 8.4	4 46.3	1 19.8
11	9 22 12.4	21 45.8	5 12.8	21 59.0	6 44.2	1 46.0	5 9.8	1 37.9	23 30.1	9 5.8	4 46.1	1 18.3
12	9 26 8.9	22 46.5	5 9.6	5♐28.5	8 19.0	1 29.3	5 52.8	1 38.6	23 34.8	9 3.3	4 45.9	1 16.8
13	9 30 5.5	23 47.1	5 6.5	18 41.0	9 54.6	1 15.0	6 35.9	1 39.2	23 39.4	9 .7	4 45.7	1 15.3
14	9 34 2.0	24 47.8	5 3.3	1♑38.8	11 31.0	1 3.3	7 19.0	1 39.6	23 44.0	8 58.2	4 45.4	1 13.8
15	9 37 58.6	25 48.4	5 .1	14 23.7	13 8.3	0 54.0	8 2.1	1 39.8	23 48.5	8 55.7	4 45.1	1 12.3
16	9 41 55.1	26 49.0	4 56.9	26 57.5	14 46.5	0 47.2	8 45.2	1 39.8	23 53.0	8 53.3	4 44.7	1 10.8
17	9 45 51.7	27 49.6	4 53.8	9♒21.0	16 25.5	0 42.9	9 28.4	1R39.7	23 57.3	8 50.8	4 44.3	1 9.3
18	9 49 48.2	28 50.1	4 50.6	21 35.3	18 5.4	0 41.1	10 11.6	1 39.3	24 1.6	8 48.4	4 43.9	1 7.7
19	9 53 44.8	29 50.7	4 47.4	3♓41.0	19 46.3	0D41.7	10 54.8	1 38.7	24 5.8	8 46.0	4 43.4	1 6.2
20	9 57 41.3	0♓51.2	4 44.2	15 39.1	21 28.0	0 44.6	11 38.1	1 38.0	24 9.9	8 43.6	4 43.0	1 4.7
21	10 1 37.9	1 51.7	4 41.0	27 31.1	23 10.7	0 49.9	12 21.3	1 37.1	24 14.0	8 41.2	4 42.4	1 3.2
22	10 5 34.4	2 52.1	4 37.9	9♈19.1	24 54.3	0 57.5	13 4.6	1 35.9	24 17.9	8 38.9	4 41.9	1 1.7
23	10 9 31.0	3 52.5	4 34.7	21 5.9	26 38.8	1 7.3	13 48.0	1 34.6	24 21.8	8 36.6	4 41.3	1 .1
24	10 13 27.6	4 52.9	4 31.5	2♉55.2	28 24.4	1 19.3	14 31.3	1 33.1	24 25.6	8 34.3	4 40.7	0 58.6
25	10 17 24.1	5 53.3	4 28.3	14 51.3	0♓10.9	1 33.3	15 14.7	1 31.4	24 29.3	8 32.1	4 40.1	0 57.1
26	10 21 20.7	6 53.6	4 25.2	26 59.2	1 58.4	1 49.5	15 58.1	1 29.6	24 32.9	8 29.8	4 39.4	0 55.6
27	10 25 17.2	7 53.9	4 22.0	9♊24.1	3 46.9	2 7.6	16 41.5	1 27.5	24 36.5	8 27.6	4 38.7	0 54.1
28	10 29 13.8	8 54.2	4 18.8	22 11.0	5 36.3	2 27.6	17 24.9	1 25.2	24 39.9	8 25.5	4 37.9	0 52.6

LATITUDE

DAY	EPHEM. SID. TIME	☉	☊	☽	☿	♀	♂	♃	♄	♅	♆	♇
1	8 42 46.8	0 .0	0 .0	3S57.4	0S47.3	7N34.2	0S17.2	1N20.8	1N20.5	0N40.5	1N45.7	11N48.3
4	8 54 36.5	0 .0	0 .0	4 59.6	1 6.9	7 49.1	0 19.6	1 21.5	1 20.6	0 40.5	1 45.9	11 48.9
7	9 6 26.1	0 .0	0 .0	3 13.0	1 24.1	7 55.9	0 21.9	1 22.2	1 20.7	0 40.5	1 46.1	11 49.4
10	9 18 15.8	0 .0	0 .0	0N20.3	1 38.8	7 55.3	0 24.3	1 22.9	1 20.8	0 40.5	1 46.3	11 49.8
13	9 30 5.5	0 .0	0 .0	3 32.4	1 50.6	7 48.2	0 26.7	1 23.6	1 21.0	0 40.5	1 46.5	11 50.2
16	9 41 55.1	0 .0	0 .0	5 .2	1 59.5	7 35.8	0 29.2	1 24.3	1 21.1	0 40.5	1 46.7	11 50.6
19	9 53 44.8	0 .0	0 .0	4 21.5	2 5.1	7 19.1	0 31.7	1 24.9	1 21.3	0 40.5	1 46.8	11 50.8
22	10 5 34.4	0 .0	0 .0	2 2.3	2 7.1	6 59.1	0 34.2	1 25.6	1 21.5	0 40.5	1 47.0	11 51.1
25	10 17 24.1	0 .0	0 .0	1S 4.4	2 5.3	6 36.7	0 36.8	1 26.2	1 21.7	0 40.4	1 47.2	11 51.2
28	10 29 13.8	0 .0	0 .0	3 53.8	1 59.3	6 12.7	0 39.3	1 26.9	1 21.8	0 40.4	1 47.3	11 51.3

RIGHT ASCENSION

DAY	EPHEM. SID. TIME	☉	☊	☽	☿	♀	♂	♃	♄	♅	♆	♇
1	8 42 46.8	14♒ 5.5	3♏26.2	27♊11.4	23♑35.2	6♒55.5	27♐50.3	29♎39.5	22♐ 4.6	12♌ 9.5	3♏ 6.1	8♍ 4.2
2	8 46 43.4	15 6.7	3 23.2	11♋42.5	25 8.6	6R19.4	28 36.9	29 42.1	22 10.4	12R 6.8	3 6.3	8R 2.9
3	8 50 39.9	16 7.7	3 20.1	26 24.4	26 42.6	5 44.6	29 23.6	29 44.5	22 16.2	12 4.2	3 6.4	8 1.6
4	8 54 36.5	17 8.4	3 17.0	11♌ 4.9	28 17.4	5 11.2	0♑10.3	29 46.8	22 21.8	12 1.5	3 6.4	8 .3
5	8 58 33.0	18 9.0	3 13.9	25 35.2	29 52.7	4 39.5	0 57.1	29 48.8	22 27.4	11 58.8	3 6.5	7 58.9
6	9 2 29.6	19 9.3	3 10.8	9♍52.3	1♒28.6	4 9.7	1 43.9	29 50.7	22 33.0	11 56.2	3 6.5	7 57.6
7	9 6 26.1	20 9.5	3 7.7	23 57.9	3 5.1	3 41.9	2 30.8	29 52.5	22 38.4	11 53.6	3R 6.4	7 56.2
8	9 10 22.7	21 9.4	3 4.7	7♎56.9	4 42.0	3 16.3	3 17.7	29 54.0	22 43.9	11 51.0	3 6.4	7 54.9
9	9 14 19.2	22 9.2	3 1.6	21 54.6	6 19.4	2 53.0	4 4.6	29 55.4	22 49.2	11 48.4	3 6.3	7 53.5
10	9 18 15.8	23 8.8	2 58.5	5♏55.0	7 57.2	2 32.0	4 51.6	29 56.6	22 54.4	11 45.7	3 6.2	7 52.1
11	9 22 12.4	24 8.1	2 55.4	19 58.8	9 35.3	2 13.5	5 38.6	29 57.6	22 59.6	11 43.1	3 6.0	7 50.7
12	9 26 8.9	25 7.3	2 52.4	4♐ 2.9	11 13.9	1 57.5	6 25.6	29 58.4	23 4.7	11 40.6	3 5.8	7 49.3
13	9 30 5.5	26 6.3	2 49.3	18 .8	12 52.7	1 44.0	7 12.6	29 59.0	23 9.7	11 38.0	3 5.6	7 47.9
14	9 34 2.0	27 5.1	2 46.2	1♑44.3	14 31.9	1 33.2	7 59.6	29 59.5	23 14.6	11 35.4	3 5.4	7 46.5
15	9 37 58.6	28 3.8	2 43.1	15 5.7	16 11.4	1 24.9	8 46.7	29 59.8	23 19.5	11 32.9	3 5.1	7 45.0
16	9 41 55.1	29 2.2	2 40.1	27 60.0	17 51.2	1 19.1	9 33.7	29 59.9	23 24.3	11 30.4	3 4.7	7 43.6
17	9 45 51.7	0♓ .5	2 37.0	10♒25.5	19 31.2	1 16.0	10 20.8	29R59.8	23 29.0	11 27.9	3 4.4	7 42.1
18	9 49 48.2	0 58.6	2 33.9	22 24.1	21 11.5	1 15.3	11 7.9	29 59.5	23 33.6	11 25.4	3 4.0	7 40.7
19	9 53 44.8	1 56.5	2 30.8	4♓ .4	22 52.1	1D17.2	11 55.0	29 59.1	23 38.1	11 23.0	3 3.6	7 39.2
20	9 57 41.3	2 54.2	2 27.8	15 20.8	24 33.0	1 21.5	12 42.0	29 58.4	23 42.5	11 20.5	3 3.1	7 37.8
21	10 1 37.9	3 51.8	2 24.7	26 33.1	26 14.1	1 28.2	13 29.1	29 57.6	23 46.9	11 18.1	3 2.7	7 36.3
22	10 5 34.4	4 49.2	2 21.6	7♈45.3	27 55.5	1 37.2	14 16.1	29 56.6	23 51.2	11 15.7	3 2.2	7 34.9
23	10 9 31.0	5 46.5	2 18.5	19 5.9	29 37.1	1 48.5	15 3.1	29 55.4	23 55.3	11 13.4	3 1.6	7 33.4
24	10 13 27.6	6 43.6	2 15.5	0♉42.8	1♓19.0	2 2.1	15 50.2	29 54.1	23 59.4	11 11.0	3 1.1	7 31.9
25	10 17 24.1	7 40.5	2 12.4	12 43.0	3 1.1	2 17.8	16 37.2	29 52.5	24 3.4	11 8.7	3 .5	7 30.5
26	10 21 20.7	8 37.3	2 9.3	25 12.1	4 43.6	2 35.6	17 24.1	29 50.8	24 7.3	11 6.5	2 59.8	7 29.0
27	10 25 17.2	9 34.0	2 6.3	8♊12.6	6 26.3	2 55.5	18 11.1	29 48.9	24 11.1	11 4.2	2 59.2	7 27.6
28	10 29 13.8	10 30.5	2 3.2	21 44.0	8 9.2	3 17.3	18 58.0	29 46.8	24 14.9	11 2.0	2 58.5	7 26.1

DECLINATION

DAY	EPHEM. SID. TIME	☉	☊	☽	☿	♀	♂	♃	♄	♅	♆	♇
1	8 42 46.8	17S17.9	0S14.1	19N27.6	22S28.2	11S19.2	23S42.9	10S40.5	21S54.0	18N31.2	11S27.2	21N54.9
4	8 54 36.5	16 26.0	0 14.0	12 55.6	22 2.0	11 28.8	23 46.1	10 42.4	21 54.7	18 33.3	11 27.1	21 57.0
7	9 6 26.1	15 31.6	0 14.0	0S53.6	21 24.2	11 42.2	23 47.3	10 43.7	21 55.4	18 35.4	11 26.9	21 59.1
10	9 18 15.8	14 34.7	0 13.9	13 54.8	20 34.5	11 58.2	23 46.4	10 44.4	21 56.0	18 37.5	11 26.7	22 1.1
13	9 30 5.5	13 35.6	0 13.9	19 25.9	19 32.6	12 15.7	23 43.4	10 44.6	21 56.6	18 39.5	11 26.3	22 3.1
16	9 41 55.1	12 34.6	0 13.8	15 51.5	18 18.5	12 33.7	23 38.3	10 44.2	21 57.0	18 41.4	11 25.8	22 5.1
19	9 53 44.8	11 31.7	0 13.7	6 5.5	16 52.0	12 51.2	23 31.2	10 43.2	21 57.4	18 43.3	11 25.2	22 7.1
22	10 5 34.4	10 27.2	0 13.7	5N34.0	15 13.1	13 7.4	23 22.0	10 41.6	21 57.8	18 45.2	11 24.5	22 8.9
25	10 17 24.1	9 21.2	0 13.6	15 16.2	13 21.8	13 21.7	23 10.8	10 39.4	21 58.1	18 46.9	11 23.7	22 10.8
28	10 29 13.8	8 14.0	0 13.6	19 19.3	11 18.3	13 33.5	22 57.5	10 36.7	21 58.3	18 48.6	11 22.9	22 12.5

MARCH 1958

LONGITUDE

DAY	EPHEM. SID. TIME	☉	☊	☾	☿	♀	♂	♃	♄	♅	♆	♇
	h m s	° ′	° ′	° ′	° ′	° ′	° ′	° ′	° ′	° ′	° ′	° ′
1	10 33 10.3	9♓54.5	4♏15.6	5♋24.5	7♓26.9	2♒49.6	18♑ 8.4	1♏22.9	24♐43.3	8♌23.4	4♏37.2	0♍51.1
2	10 37 6.9	10 54.6	4 12.4	19 7.1	9 18.3	3 13.3	18 51.9	1 R 20.3	24 46.6	8 R 21.3	4 R 36.4	0 R 49.6
3	10 41 3.4	11 54.8	4 9.3	3♌19.5	11 10.7	3 38.7	19 35.4	1 17.5	24 49.8	8 19.2	4 35.6	0 48.1
4	10 44 60.0	12 54.9	4 6.1	17 58.8	13 4.0	4 5.8	20 19.0	1 14.5	24 52.9	8 17.2	4 34.8	0 46.7
5	10 48 56.5	13 55.0	4 2.9	2♍59.2	14 58.1	4 34.5	21 2.5	1 11.4	24 55.9	8 15.2	4 33.9	0 45.2
6	10 52 53.1	14 55.1	3 59.7	18 11.5	16 53.1	5 4.8	21 46.1	1 8.1	24 58.9	8 13.2	4 33.0	0 43.7
7	10 56 49.6	15 55.1	3 56.5	3♎25.4	18 48.9	5 36.6	22 29.7	1 4.6	25 1.7	8 11.3	4 32.1	0 42.3
8	11 0 46.2	16 55.1	3 53.4	18 30.6	20 45.3	6 9.8	23 13.4	1 .9	25 4.5	8 9.4	4 31.1	0 40.8
9	11 4 42.7	17 55.1	3 50.2	3♏18.8	22 42.3	6 44.4	23 57.1	0 57.1	25 7.1	8 7.6	4 30.1	0 39.4
10	11 8 39.3	18 55.0	3 47.0	17 44.6	24 39.7	7 20.4	24 40.7	0 53.1	25 9.7	8 5.8	4 29.1	0 37.9
11	11 12 35.8	19 55.0	3 43.8	1♐45.6	26 37.3	7 57.7	25 24.5	0 48.9	25 12.1	8 4.0	4 28.1	0 36.5
12	11 16 32.4	20 54.8	3 40.7	15 21.7	28 35.0	8 36.1	26 8.2	0 44.6	25 14.5	8 2.3	4 27.0	0 35.1
13	11 20 28.9	21 54.7	3 37.5	28 34.9	0♈32.5	9 15.8	26 52.0	0 40.1	25 16.8	8 .6	4 25.9	0 33.7
14	11 24 25.5	22 54.5	3 34.3	11♑27.8	2 29.5	9 56.6	27 35.8	0 35.4	25 19.0	7 58.9	4 24.8	0 32.3
15	11 28 22.0	23 54.4	3 31.1	24 3.7	4 25.8	10 38.5	28 19.6	0 30.6	25 21.1	7 57.3	4 23.7	0 30.9
16	11 32 18.6	24 54.1	3 27.9	6♒25.7	6 21.0	11 21.4	29 3.4	0 25.7	25 23.1	7 55.8	4 22.5	0 29.6
17	11 36 15.2	25 53.9	3 24.8	18 36.6	8 14.8	12 5.3	29 47.3	0 20.5	25 25.0	7 54.3	4 21.3	0 28.2
18	11 40 11.7	26 53.6	3 21.6	0♓39.0	10 6.8	12 50.2	0♒31.1	0 15.3	25 26.8	7 52.8	4 20.1	0 26.9
19	11 44 8.3	27 53.3	3 18.4	12 35.0	11 56.4	13 36.0	1 15.0	0 9.9	25 28.5	7 51.4	4 18.9	0 25.6
20	11 48 4.8	28 52.9	3 15.2	24 26.4	13 43.3	14 22.6	1 58.9	0 4.3	25 30.1	7 50.0	4 17.7	0 24.3
21	11 52 1.4	29 52.6	3 12.1	6♈15.0	15 27.1	15 10.1	2 42.8	29♎58.7	25 31.6	7 48.7	4 16.4	0 23.0
22	11 55 57.9	0♈52.2	3 8.9	18 2.8	17 7.3	15 58.5	3 26.8	29 52.9	25 33.1	7 47.4	4 15.1	0 21.7
23	11 59 54.5	1 51.8	3 5.7	29 52.0	18 43.3	16 47.6	4 10.8	29 46.9	25 34.4	7 46.2	4 13.8	0 20.5
24	12 3 51.0	2 51.3	3 2.5	11♉45.3	20 14.8	17 37.4	4 54.7	29 40.9	25 35.6	7 45.0	4 12.5	0 19.2
25	12 7 47.6	3 50.8	2 59.3	23 45.7	21 41.4	18 28.0	5 38.7	29 34.7	25 36.7	7 43.9	4 11.2	0 18.0
26	12 11 44.1	4 50.2	2 56.2	5♊57.0	23 2.6	19 19.2	6 22.7	29 28.4	25 37.7	7 42.8	4 9.8	0 16.8
27	12 15 40.7	5 49.6	2 53.0	18 23.1	24 18.1	20 11.1	7 6.7	29 21.9	25 38.7	7 41.8	4 8.4	0 15.6
28	12 19 37.2	6 49.0	2 49.8	1♋ 8.2	25 27.6	21 3.7	7 50.7	29 15.4	25 39.5	7 40.8	4 7.0	0 14.5
29	12 23 33.8	7 48.3	2 46.6	14 16.0	26 30.9	21 56.8	8 34.8	29 8.8	25 40.2	7 39.8	4 5.6	0 13.3
30	12 27 30.3	8 47.6	2 43.5	27 49.8	27 27.5	22 50.6	9 18.8	29 2.1	25 40.8	7 39.0	4 4.1	0 12.2
31	12 31 26.9	9 46.9	2 40.3	11♌50.8	28 17.4	23 44.9	10 2.9	28 55.2	25 41.3	7 38.1	4 2.7	0 11.1

LATITUDE

DAY	EPHEM. SID. TIME	☉	☊	☾	☿	♀	♂	♃	♄	♅	♆	♇
1	10 33 10.3	0 .0	0 .0	4 S 33.3	1 S 56.3	6 N 4.5	0 S 40.2	1 N 27.1	1 N 21.9	0 N 40.4	1 N 47.4	11 N 51.3
4	10 44 60.0	0 .0	0 .0	4 56.3	1 44.1	5 39.2	0 42.8	1 27.7	1 22.1	0 40.3	1 47.5	11 51.4
7	10 56 49.6	0 .0	0 .0	2 28.5	1 27.0	5 13.4	0 45.5	1 28.3	1 22.3	0 40.3	1 47.7	11 51.3
10	11 8 39.3	0 .0	0 .0	1 N 24.1	1 4.7	4 47.4	0 48.1	1 28.8	1 22.5	0 40.2	1 47.8	11 51.2
13	11 20 28.9	0 .0	0 .0	4 19.4	0 37.3	4 21.6	0 50.8	1 29.3	1 22.7	0 40.2	1 48.0	11 51.1
16	11 32 18.6	0 .0	0 .0	5 9.8	0 5.2	3 56.0	0 53.5	1 29.8	1 23.0	0 40.1	1 48.1	11 50.9
19	11 44 8.3	0 .0	0 .0	3 55.5	0 N 30.4	3 30.8	0 56.2	1 30.3	1 23.2	0 40.1	1 48.2	11 50.7
22	11 55 57.9	0 .0	0 .0	1 12.6	1 7.8	3 6.2	0 59.0	1 30.7	1 23.4	0 40.0	1 48.3	11 50.4
25	12 7 47.6	0 .0	0 .0	2 S .0	1 44.6	2 42.3	1 1.7	1 31.0	1 23.6	0 39.9	1 48.5	11 50.0
28	12 19 37.2	0 .0	0 .0	4 32.4	2 18.3	2 19.1	1 4.5	1 31.3	1 23.8	0 39.8	1 48.6	11 49.6
31	12 31 26.9	0 .0	0 .0	5 10.3	2 46.0	1 56.7	1 7.3	1 31.6	1 24.1	0 39.7	1 48.6	11 49.2

RIGHT ASCENSION

DAY	EPHEM. SID. TIME	☉	☊	☾	☿	♀	♂	♃	♄	♅	♆	♇
1	10 33 10.3	11♓26.9	2♏ .1	5♋41.7	9♓52.5	3♒41.1	19♑45.0	29♎44.6	24♐18.6	10♌59.9	2♏57.8	7♍24.7
2	10 37 6.9	12 23.1	1 57.0	19 58.0	11 36.0	4 6.7	20 31.8	29 R 42.2	24 22.1	10 R 57.7	2 R 57.1	7 R 23.2
3	10 41 3.4	13 19.2	1 54.0	4♌24.2	13 19.8	4 34.0	21 18.7	29 39.6	24 25.5	10 55.6	2 56.3	7 21.8
4	10 44 60.0	14 15.2	1 50.9	18 52.9	15 3.9	5 3.0	22 5.5	29 36.9	24 28.9	10 53.6	2 55.5	7 20.3
5	10 48 56.5	15 11.0	1 47.8	3♍20.0	16 48.1	5 33.7	22 52.2	29 34.0	24 32.1	10 51.5	2 54.7	7 18.9
6	10 52 53.1	16 6.8	1 44.8	17 44.8	18 32.6	6 5.9	23 39.0	29 30.9	24 35.3	10 49.5	2 53.8	7 17.4
7	10 56 49.6	17 2.4	1 41.7	2♎ 9.4	20 17.3	6 39.7	24 25.7	29 27.6	24 38.4	10 47.5	2 52.9	7 16.0
8	11 0 46.2	17 57.9	1 38.6	16 36.5	22 2.0	7 14.9	25 12.3	29 24.2	24 41.3	10 45.6	2 52.0	7 14.5
9	11 4 42.7	18 53.4	1 35.6	1♏ 7.7	23 46.8	7 51.5	25 58.9	29 20.6	24 44.2	10 43.7	2 51.1	7 13.1
10	11 8 39.3	19 48.7	1 32.5	15 41.3	25 31.6	8 29.5	26 45.5	29 16.8	24 46.9	10 41.9	2 50.2	7 11.7
11	11 12 35.8	20 44.0	1 29.4	0♐11.8	27 16.3	9 8.7	27 32.0	29 12.9	24 49.6	10 40.1	2 49.2	7 10.3
12	11 16 32.4	21 39.2	1 26.4	14 31.1	29 .7	9 49.2	28 18.5	29 8.9	24 52.2	10 38.3	2 48.2	7 8.9
13	11 20 28.9	22 34.3	1 23.3	28 30.1	0♈44.6	10 30.8	29 4.9	29 4.6	24 54.6	10 36.6	2 47.1	7 7.5
14	11 24 25.5	23 29.3	1 20.2	12♑ 1.5	2 27.9	11 13.5	29 51.2	29 .3	24 57.0	10 34.9	2 46.1	7 6.1
15	11 28 22.0	24 24.3	1 17.2	25 1.3	4 10.5	11 57.3	0♒37.5	28 55.7	24 59.3	10 33.3	2 45.0	7 4.7
16	11 32 18.6	25 19.3	1 14.1	7♒29.4	5 51.9	12 42.1	1 23.8	28 51.1	25 1.4	10 31.7	2 43.9	7 3.4
17	11 36 15.2	26 14.1	1 11.1	19 29.0	7 32.0	13 27.8	2 9.9	28 46.3	25 3.5	10 30.1	2 42.8	7 2.0
18	11 40 11.7	27 9.0	1 8.0	1♓ 5.7	9 10.4	14 14.4	2 56.0	28 41.3	25 5.4	10 28.6	2 41.7	7 .7
19	11 44 8.3	28 3.7	1 4.9	12 26.5	10 46.9	15 1.9	3 42.1	28 36.2	25 7.2	10 27.1	2 40.5	6 59.3
20	11 48 4.8	28 58.5	1 1.9	23 39.1	12 21.0	15 50.3	4 28.0	28 31.0	25 9.0	10 25.7	2 39.3	6 58.0
21	11 52 1.4	29 53.2	0 58.8	4♈51.3	13 52.4	16 39.3	5 13.9	28 25.6	25 10.6	10 24.4	2 38.1	6 56.7
22	11 55 57.9	0♈47.9	0 55.7	16 10.7	15 20.7	17 29.2	5 59.8	28 20.2	25 12.2	10 23.1	2 36.9	6 55.4
23	11 59 54.5	1 42.5	0 52.7	27 44.0	16 45.5	18 19.7	6 45.6	28 14.6	25 13.6	10 21.8	2 35.7	6 54.2
24	12 3 51.0	2 37.2	0 49.6	9♉37.1	18 6.4	19 10.9	7 31.3	28 8.9	25 14.9	10 20.6	2 34.4	6 52.9
25	12 7 47.6	3 31.8	0 46.6	21 54.0	19 23.1	20 2.7	8 16.8	28 3.0	25 16.1	10 19.4	2 33.1	6 51.6
26	12 11 44.1	4 26.4	0 43.5	4♊36.4	20 35.2	20 55.1	9 2.4	27 57.1	25 17.2	10 18.3	2 31.8	6 50.4
27	12 15 40.7	5 20.9	0 40.4	17 43.5	21 42.4	21 48.0	9 47.8	27 51.0	25 18.2	10 17.3	2 30.5	6 49.2
28	12 19 37.2	6 15.5	0 37.4	1♋11.8	22 44.3	22 41.5	10 33.2	27 44.8	25 19.1	10 16.2	2 29.2	6 48.0
29	12 23 33.8	7 10.1	0 34.3	14 55.9	23 40.7	23 35.5	11 18.4	27 38.6	25 19.9	10 15.3	2 27.8	6 46.8
30	12 27 30.3	8 4.7	0 31.3	28 50.2	24 31.3	24 29.9	12 3.6	27 32.2	25 20.5	10 14.4	2 26.5	6 45.6
31	12 31 26.9	8 59.2	0 28.2	12♌50.4	25 16.0	25 24.8	12 48.8	27 25.8	25 21.1	10 13.5	2 25.1	6 44.5

DECLINATION

DAY	EPHEM. SID. TIME	☉	☊	☾	☿	♀	♂	♃	♄	♅	♆	♇
1	10 33 10.3	7 S 51.3	0 S 13.6	18 N 46.8	10 S 34.5	13 S 36.7	22 S 52.7	10 S 35.7	21 S 58.4	18 N 49.1	11 S 22.6	22 N 13.1
4	10 44 60.0	6 42.7	0 13.5	10 44.4	8 15.4	13 44.2	22 36.7	10 32.2	21 58.6	18 50.7	11 21.6	22 14.7
7	10 56 49.6	5 33.3	0 13.4	3 S 38.0	5 45.6	13 48.2	22 18.8	10 28.2	21 58.7	18 52.2	11 20.6	22 16.3
10	11 8 39.3	4 23.2	0 13.4	15 46.7	3 6.7	13 48.1	21 58.9	10 23.7	21 58.8	18 53.6	11 19.5	22 17.8
13	11 20 28.9	3 12.5	0 13.3	19 6.7	0 21.3	13 44.0	21 37.1	10 18.7	21 58.8	18 54.9	11 18.3	22 19.2
16	11 32 18.6	2 1.5	0 13.3	13 39.8	2 N 26.5	13 35.5	21 13.4	10 13.3	21 58.8	18 56.0	11 17.0	22 20.6
19	11 44 8.3	0 50.4	0 13.2	3 12.6	5 11.2	13 22.5	20 47.9	10 7.3	21 58.8	18 57.1	11 15.7	22 21.8
22	11 55 57.9	0 N 20.8	0 13.2	8 N 11.9	7 46.1	13 5.1	20 20.6	10 1.0	21 58.7	18 58.1	11 14.3	22 22.9
25	12 7 47.6	1 31.7	0 13.1	16 46.7	10 4.3	12 43.2	19 51.6	9 54.3	21 58.6	18 58.9	11 12.9	22 24.0
28	12 19 37.2	2 42.4	0 13.0	18 53.9	11 59.5	12 16.9	19 20.9	9 47.2	21 58.5	18 59.6	11 11.4	22 24.9
31	12 31 26.9	3 52.5	0 13.0	12 16.0	13 27.0	11 46.2	18 48.6	9 39.9	21 58.3	19 .2	11 9.9	22 25.7

APRIL 1958

LONGITUDE

DAY	EPHEM. SID. TIME h m s	☉ ° ′	☊ ° ′	☽ ° ′	☿ ° ′	♀ ° ′	♂ ° ′	♃ ° ′	♄ ° ′	♅ ° ′	♆ ° ′	♇ ° ′
1	12 35 23.4	10♈46.1	2♏37.1	26♌18.4	29♈ .4	24♒39.7	10♒46.9	28♎48.3	25♐41.7	7♌37.3	4♏ 1.2	0♍10.0
2	12 39 20.0	11 45.2	2 33.9	11♍ 8.8	29 36.3	25 35.1	11 31.0	28 R 41.3	25 42.1	7 R 36.6	3 R 59.8	0 R 8.9
3	12 43 16.5	12 44.4	2 30.7	26 15.4	0♉ 5.2	26 31.0	12 15.1	28 34.2	25 42.3	7 35.9	3 58.3	0 7.9
4	12 47 13.1	13 43.5	2 27.6	11♎29.4	0 26.8	27 27.4	12 59.2	28 27.1	25 42.4	7 35.3	3 56.8	0 6.8
5	12 51 9.6	14 42.5	2 24.4	26 40.7	0 41.4	28 24.3	13 43.4	28 19.8	25 42.4	7 34.7	3 55.2	0 5.8
6	12 55 6.2	15 41.6	2 21.2	11♏40.0	0 48.9	29 21.7	14 27.5	28 12.6	25 42.4	7 34.2	3 53.7	0 4.9
7	12 59 2.7	16 40.6	2 18.0	26 19.5	0 49.6	0♓19.5	15 11.6	28 5.2	25 R 42.2	7 33.7	3 52.2	0 3.9
8	13 2 59.3	17 39.6	2 14.8	10♐34.4	0 R 43.6	1 17.7	15 55.8	27 57.8	25 41.9	7 33.3	3 50.6	0 3.0
9	13 6 55.8	18 38.5	2 11.7	24 22.3	0 31.3	2 16.4	16 40.0	27 50.3	25 41.5	7 33.0	3 49.0	0 2.1
10	13 10 52.4	19 37.4	2 8.5	7♑43.8	0 13.0	3 15.4	17 24.2	27 42.8	25 41.1	7 32.7	3 47.5	0 1.2
11	13 14 49.0	20 36.3	2 5.3	20 40.7	29♈49.2	4 14.9	18 8.4	27 35.3	25 40.5	7 32.4	3 45.9	0 .3
12	13 18 45.5	21 35.2	2 2.1	3♒16.6	29 20.5	5 14.7	18 52.6	27 27.7	25 39.9	7 32.2	3 44.4	29♌59.5
13	13 22 42.1	22 34.0	1 59.0	15 35.3	28 47.4	6 14.9	19 36.8	27 20.1	25 39.1	7 32.1	3 42.8	29 58.7
14	13 26 38.6	23 32.8	1 55.8	27 40.7	28 10.6	7 15.4	20 21.0	27 12.5	25 38.3	7 32.0	3 41.2	29 57.9
15	13 30 35.2	24 31.6	1 52.6	9♓36.8	27 31.0	8 16.2	21 5.2	27 4.8	25 37.3	7 32.0	3 39.5	29 57.1
16	13 34 31.7	25 30.4	1 49.4	21 27.1	26 49.3	9 17.4	21 49.5	26 57.1	25 36.3	7 32.0	3 37.9	29 56.4
17	13 38 28.3	26 29.1	1 46.2	3♈14.9	26 6.3	10 18.9	22 33.7	26 49.4	25 35.1	7 32.0	3 36.3	29 55.7
18	13 42 24.8	27 27.7	1 43.1	15 2.8	25 22.8	11 20.6	23 17.9	26 41.7	25 33.9	7 D 32.2	3 34.7	29 55.0
19	13 46 21.4	28 26.4	1 39.9	26 53.4	24 39.7	12 22.7	24 2.1	26 34.0	25 32.5	7 32.3	3 33.0	29 54.3
20	13 50 17.9	29 25.0	1 36.7	8♉48.7	23 57.7	13 25.0	24 46.3	26 26.3	25 31.1	7 32.6	3 31.4	29 53.7
21	13 54 14.5	0♉23.6	1 33.5	20 50.9	23 17.5	14 27.6	25 30.5	26 18.7	25 29.6	7 32.8	3 29.8	29 53.1
22	13 58 11.0	1 22.1	1 30.4	3♊ 1.9	22 39.8	15 30.5	26 14.8	26 11.0	25 28.0	7 33.2	3 28.1	29 52.5
23	14 2 7.6	2 20.7	1 27.2	15 24.1	22 5.2	16 33.5	26 59.0	26 3.4	25 26.3	7 33.6	3 26.5	29 52.0
24	14 6 4.1	3 19.1	1 24.0	27 59.6	21 34.1	17 36.9	27 43.1	25 55.8	25 24.5	7 34.0	3 24.9	29 51.4
25	14 10 .7	4 17.6	1 20.8	10♋50.9	21 7.0	18 40.4	28 27.3	25 48.2	25 22.6	7 34.5	3 23.2	29 50.9
26	14 13 57.2	5 16.0	1 17.6	24 .4	20 44.2	19 44.2	29 11.5	25 40.7	25 20.6	7 35.1	3 21.6	29 50.5
27	14 17 53.8	6 14.4	1 14.5	7♌30.0	20 25.9	20 48.2	29 55.7	25 33.3	25 18.5	7 35.7	3 19.9	29 50.0
28	14 21 50.4	7 12.7	1 11.3	21 20.9	20 12.4	21 52.5	0♓39.9	25 25.8	25 16.4	7 36.3	3 18.3	29 49.6
29	14 25 46.9	8 11.0	1 8.1	5♍33.3	20 3.7	22 56.9	1 24.0	25 18.5	25 14.1	7 37.1	3 16.7	29 49.2
30	14 29 43.5	9 9.3	1 4.9	20 5.3	19 59.9	24 1.5	2 8.2	25 11.2	25 11.8	7 37.8	3 15.0	29 48.9

LATITUDE

DAY	SID. TIME	☉	☊	☽	☿	♀	♂	♃	♄	♅	♆	♇
1	12 35 23.4	0 .0	0 .0	4 S 46.3	2 N 53.4	1 N 49.4	1 S 8.2	1 N 31.7	1 N 24.1	0 N 39.7	1 N 48.7	11 N 49.0
4	12 47 13.1	0 .0	0 .0	1 47.4	3 9.2	1 28.1	1 11.0	1 31.9	1 24.3	0 39.6	1 48.7	11 48.5
7	12 59 2.7	0 .0	0 .0	2 N 14.5	3 13.3	1 7.7	1 13.7	1 32.0	1 24.6	0 39.6	1 48.8	11 48.0
10	13 10 52.4	0 .0	0 .0	4 50.9	3 4.1	0 48.2	1 16.5	1 32.1	1 24.8	0 39.5	1 48.9	11 47.4
13	13 22 42.1	0 .0	0 .0	5 7.6	2 41.0	0 29.8	1 19.3	1 32.1	1 25.0	0 39.4	1 48.9	11 46.8
16	13 34 31.7	0 .0	0 .0	3 23.7	2 5.3	0 12.2	1 22.1	1 32.1	1 25.1	0 39.3	1 49.0	11 46.1
19	13 46 21.4	0 .0	0 .0	0 24.3	1 20.2	0 S 4.3	1 24.8	1 32.0	1 25.3	0 39.2	1 49.0	11 45.5
22	13 58 11.0	0 .0	0 .0	2 S 47.7	0 30.1	0 19.8	1 27.6	1 31.8	1 25.5	0 39.1	1 49.0	11 44.7
25	14 10 .7	0 .0	0 .0	4 58.0	0 S 20.2	0 34.2	1 30.3	1 31.6	1 25.6	0 39.0	1 49.0	11 44.0
28	14 21 50.4	0 .0	0 .0	4 58.5	1 6.8	0 47.6	1 33.0	1 31.3	1 25.8	0 38.9	1 49.0	11 43.3

RIGHT ASCENSION

DAY	SID. TIME	☉	☊	☽	☿	♀	♂	♃	♄	♅	♆	♇
1	12 35 23.4	9♈53.8	0♏25.2	26♌54.6	25♈54.4	26♒20.1	13♒33.8	27♎19.2	25♐21.6	10♌12.7	2♏23.7	6♍43.4
2	12 39 20.0	10 48.5	0 22.1	11♍ 4.0	26 26.6	27 15.8	14 18.7	27 R 12.6	25 21.9	10 R 12.0	2 R 22.3	6 R 42.2
3	12 43 16.5	11 43.1	0 19.0	25 21.7	26 52.4	28 11.9	15 3.6	27 5.9	25 22.1	10 11.2	2 20.8	6 41.1
4	12 47 13.1	12 37.8	0 16.0	9♎51.6	27 11.8	29 8.4	15 48.4	26 59.2	25 22.3	10 10.6	2 19.4	6 40.1
5	12 51 9.6	13 32.5	0 12.9	24 35.7	27 24.9	0♓ 5.2	16 33.1	26 52.3	25 22.3	10 10.0	2 18.0	6 39.0
6	12 55 6.2	14 27.3	0 9.9	9♏32.1	27 31.6	1 2.3	17 17.7	26 45.5	25 R 22.2	10 9.5	2 16.5	6 38.0
7	12 59 2.7	15 22.1	0 6.8	24 33.6	27 32.3	1 59.8	18 2.2	26 38.5	25 22.1	10 9.0	2 15.0	6 37.0
8	13 2 59.3	16 16.9	0 3.8	9♐28.6	27 R 27.1	2 57.5	18 46.7	26 31.5	25 21.8	10 8.5	2 13.6	6 36.0
9	13 6 55.8	17 11.8	0 .7	24 3.6	27 16.3	3 55.4	19 31.0	26 24.4	25 21.4	10 8.2	2 12.1	6 35.0
10	13 10 52.4	18 6.8	29♎57.7	8♑ 7.1	27 .3	4 53.7	20 15.3	26 17.3	25 20.9	10 7.8	2 10.6	6 34.0
11	13 14 49.0	19 1.9	29 54.6	21 32.5	26 39.7	5 52.1	20 59.5	26 10.2	25 20.3	10 7.6	2 9.1	6 33.1
12	13 18 45.5	19 57.1	29 51.6	4♒19.1	26 14.9	6 50.9	21 43.7	26 3.1	25 19.6	10 7.4	2 7.6	6 32.2
13	13 22 42.1	20 52.3	29 48.5	16 30.3	25 46.5	7 49.8	22 27.7	25 55.9	25 18.8	10 7.2	2 6.1	6 31.4
14	13 26 38.6	21 47.6	29 45.5	28 13.2	25 15.2	8 48.9	23 11.6	25 48.6	25 17.9	10 7.1	2 4.5	6 30.5
15	13 30 35.2	22 42.9	29 42.4	9♓36.3	24 41.8	9 48.1	23 55.5	25 41.4	25 16.8	10 7.1	2 3.0	6 29.7
16	13 34 31.7	23 38.4	29 39.4	20 48.7	24 6.8	10 47.6	24 39.2	25 34.1	25 15.7	10 7.1	2 1.4	6 28.8
17	13 38 28.3	24 34.0	29 36.3	1♈59.3	23 31.2	11 47.2	25 22.9	25 26.9	25 14.5	10 7.1	1 59.9	6 28.1
18	13 42 24.8	25 29.6	29 33.3	13 16.7	22 55.6	12 46.9	26 6.5	25 19.6	25 13.1	10 D 7.3	1 58.3	6 27.3
19	13 46 21.4	26 25.4	29 30.2	24 48.1	22 20.6	13 46.8	26 49.9	25 12.3	25 11.7	10 7.4	1 56.8	6 26.5
20	13 50 17.9	27 21.2	29 27.2	6♉39.4	21 47.1	14 46.8	27 33.3	25 5.0	25 10.1	10 7.7	1 55.2	6 25.8
21	13 54 14.5	28 17.2	29 24.1	18 54.1	21 15.5	15 47.0	28 16.6	24 57.8	25 8.5	10 7.9	1 53.6	6 25.1
22	13 58 11.0	29 13.2	29 21.1	1♊33.3	20 46.4	16 47.2	28 59.8	24 50.5	25 6.8	10 8.3	1 52.1	6 24.5
23	14 2 7.6	0♉ 9.4	29 18.0	14 34.5	20 20.2	17 47.6	29 42.9	24 43.3	25 4.9	10 8.7	1 50.5	6 23.8
24	14 6 4.1	1 5.6	29 15.0	27 53.1	19 57.4	18 48.1	0♓26.0	24 36.2	25 3.0	10 9.1	1 48.9	6 23.2
25	14 10 .7	2 2.0	29 11.9	11♋22.5	19 38.3	19 48.7	1 8.9	24 29.0	25 1.0	10 9.6	1 47.4	6 22.6
26	14 13 57.2	2 58.5	29 8.9	24 56.7	19 23.0	20 49.4	1 51.7	24 21.9	24 58.8	10 10.2	1 45.8	6 22.1
27	14 17 53.8	3 55.2	29 5.8	8♌31.7	19 11.9	21 50.2	2 34.5	24 14.8	24 56.6	10 10.8	1 44.2	6 21.5
28	14 21 50.4	4 51.9	29 2.8	22 6.8	19 4.9	22 51.0	3 17.2	24 7.8	24 54.3	10 11.5	1 42.6	6 21.0
29	14 25 46.9	5 48.7	28 59.8	5♍44.9	19 2.2	23 52.0	3 59.7	24 .8	24 51.9	10 12.2	1 41.1	6 20.5
30	14 29 43.5	6 45.7	28 56.7	19 31.2	19 D 3.7	24 53.1	4 42.2	23 53.9	24 49.4	10 13.0	1 39.5	6 20.1

DECLINATION

DAY	SID. TIME	☉	☊	☽	☿	♀	♂	♃	♄	♅	♆	♇
1	12 35 23.4	4 N 15.7	0 S 13.0	8 N 15.4	13 N 49.4	11 S 35.0	18 S 37.5	9 S 37.4	21 S 58.3	19 N .4	11 S 9.3	22 N 26.0
4	12 47 13.1	5 25.0	0 12.9	6 S 11.5	14 34.9	10 58.7	18 3.2	9 29.7	21 58.1	19 .9	11 7.8	22 26.6
7	12 59 2.7	6 33.3	0 12.9	17 9.2	14 46.8	10 18.2	17 27.3	9 21.8	21 57.9	19 1.2	11 6.2	22 27.2
10	13 10 52.4	7 40.7	0 12.8	18 22.6	14 25.2	9 33.8	16 50.1	9 13.7	21 57.6	19 1.4	11 4.5	22 27.7
13	13 22 42.1	8 46.9	0 12.7	11 15.8	13 33.2	8 45.6	16 11.5	9 5.6	21 57.4	19 1.4	11 2.9	22 28.0
16	13 34 31.7	9 51.8	0 12.7	0 16.2	12 17.3	7 53.9	15 31.7	8 57.4	21 57.1	19 1.4	11 1.2	22 28.3
19	13 46 21.4	10 55.3	0 12.6	10 N 44.6	10 47.9	6 59.0	14 50.7	8 49.2	21 56.8	19 1.2	10 59.5	22 28.4
22	13 58 11.0	11 57.1	0 12.6	18 1.4	9 17.0	6 1.0	14 8.6	8 41.0	21 56.5	19 .9	10 57.9	22 28.4
25	14 10 .7	12 57.2	0 12.5	18 2.9	7 55.7	5 .3	13 25.4	8 33.0	21 56.1	19 .5	10 56.2	22 28.3
28	14 21 50.4	13 55.3	0 12.5	9 40.2	6 52.0	3 57.2	12 41.3	8 25.1	21 55.8	18 59.9	10 54.5	22 28.1

MAY 1958

DAY	EPHEM. SID. TIME	☉	☊	☽	☿	♀	♂	♃	♄	♅	♆	♇
		LONGITUDE										
	h m s	° ′	° ′	° ′	° ′	° ′	° ′	° ′	° ′	° ′	° ′	° ′
1	14 33 40.0	10♉ 7.5	1♏ 1.8	4♎53.0	20♈ .9	25♓ 6.3	2♓52.3	25♎ 3.9	25♐ 9.4	7♌38.7	3♏13.4	29♌48.6
2	14 37 36.6	11 5.7	0 58.6	19 50.6	20D 6.8	26 11.3	3 36.4	24R56.8	25R 6.9	7 39.5	3R11.8	29R48.3
3	14 41 33.1	12 4.0	0 55.4	4♏50.6	20 17.5	27 16.6	4 20.6	24 49.7	25 4.4	7 40.5	3 10.2	29 48.0
4	14 45 29.7	13 2.1	0 52.2	19 44.6	20 32.8	28 21.9	5 4.7	24 42.7	25 1.8	7 41.5	3 8.6	29 47.8
5	14 49 26.2	14 .2	0 49.0	4♐24.7	20 52.6	29 27.5	5 48.8	24 35.8	24 59.1	7 42.5	3 7.0	29 47.6
6	14 53 22.8	14 58.3	0 45.9	18 44.5	21 16.9	0♈33.2	6 32.9	24 28.9	24 56.3	7 43.6	3 5.4	29 47.4
7	14 57 19.3	15 56.4	0 42.7	2♑39.7	21 45.4	1 39.1	7 17.0	24 22.2	24 53.4	7 44.7	3 3.8	29 47.2
8	15 1 15.9	16 54.4	0 39.5	16 8.7	22 18.1	2 45.2	8 1.1	24 15.5	24 50.4	7 45.9	3 2.2	29 47.1
9	15 5 12.4	17 52.4	0 36.3	29 11.9	22 54.8	3 51.4	8 45.1	24 9.0	24 47.4	7 47.1	3 .6	29 47.0
10	15 9 9.0	18 50.4	0 33.2	11♒51.9	23 35.3	4 57.8	9 29.1	24 2.5	24 44.3	7 48.4	2 59.1	29 47.0
11	15 13 5.6	19 48.4	0 30.0	24 12.2	24 19.5	6 4.3	10 13.2	23 56.2	24 41.2	7 49.7	2 57.5	29 46.9
12	15 17 2.1	20 46.4	0 26.8	6♓17.4	25 7.2	7 11.0	10 57.2	23 50.0	24 37.9	7 51.1	2 56.0	29 46.9
13	15 20 58.7	21 44.3	0 23.6	18 12.0	25 58.4	8 17.8	11 41.1	23 43.9	24 34.6	7 52.6	2 54.4	29 46.9
14	15 24 55.2	22 42.2	0 20.4	0♈ .8	26 52.9	9 24.7	12 25.1	23 37.9	24 31.3	7 54.0	2 52.9	29D47.0
15	15 28 51.8	23 40.1	0 17.3	11 48.2	27 50.6	10 31.8	13 9.0	23 32.0	24 27.8	7 55.6	2 51.4	29 47.1
16	15 32 48.3	24 38.0	0 14.1	23 38.1	28 51.4	11 39.0	13 52.9	23 26.3	24 24.3	7 57.1	2 49.9	29 47.2
17	15 36 44.9	25 35.8	0 10.9	5♉33.8	29 55.1	12 46.3	14 36.8	23 20.7	24 20.8	7 58.8	2 48.4	29 47.3
18	15 40 41.4	26 33.6	0 7.7	17 37.9	1♉ 1.8	13 53.8	15 20.6	23 15.2	24 17.2	8 .5	2 46.9	29 47.5
19	15 44 38.0	27 31.4	0 4.6	29 52.7	2 11.3	15 1.3	16 4.4	23 9.9	24 13.5	8 2.2	2 45.5	29 47.7
20	15 48 34.6	28 29.2	0 1.4	12♊19.4	3 23.5	16 9.0	16 48.2	23 4.7	24 9.8	8 3.9	2 44.0	29 47.9
21	15 52 31.1	29 26.9	29♎58.2	24 59.1	4 38.4	17 16.7	17 31.9	22 59.7	24 6.0	8 5.8	2 42.6	29 48.2
22	15 56 27.7	0♊24.7	29 55.0	7♋52.2	5 56.0	18 24.6	18 15.6	22 54.8	24 2.2	8 7.6	2 41.2	29 48.5
23	16 0 24.2	1 22.4	29 51.9	20 59.2	7 16.1	19 32.6	18 59.3	22 50.0	23 58.3	8 9.5	2 39.8	29 48.8
24	16 4 20.8	2 20.1	29 48.7	4♌20.1	8 38.8	20 40.7	19 42.9	22 45.5	23 54.4	8 11.5	2 38.5	29 49.2
25	16 8 17.3	3 17.7	29 45.5	17 55.2	10 3.9	21 48.9	20 26.5	22 41.0	23 50.5	8 13.5	2 37.1	29 49.5
26	16 12 13.9	4 15.4	29 42.3	1♍44.2	11 31.6	22 57.1	21 10.0	22 36.8	23 46.4	8 15.6	2 35.8	29 50.0
27	16 16 10.4	5 13.0	29 39.1	15 47.0	13 1.7	24 5.5	21 53.5	22 32.7	23 42.4	8 17.7	2 34.5	29 50.4
28	16 20 7.0	6 10.6	29 36.0	0♎ 2.5	14 34.2	25 13.9	22 37.0	22 28.7	23 38.3	8 19.8	2 33.2	29 50.9
29	16 24 3.6	7 8.1	29 32.8	14 28.9	16 9.2	26 22.4	23 20.4	22 24.9	23 34.2	8 22.0	2 31.9	29 51.3
30	16 28 .1	8 5.6	29 29.6	29 3.0	17 46.6	27 31.1	24 3.7	22 21.3	23 30.0	8 24.2	2 30.6	29 51.9
31	16 31 56.7	9 3.1	29 26.4	13♏40.1	19 26.4	28 39.8	24 47.0	22 17.8	23 25.8	8 26.5	2 29.4	29 52.4
		LATITUDE										
1	14 33 40.0	0 .0	0 .0	2S21.5	1S47.3	0S60.0	1S35.7	1N31.0	1N25.9	0N38.8	1N49.0	11N42.5
4	14 45 29.7	0 .0	0 .0	1N40.7	2 20.4	1 11.2	1 38.4	1 30.6	1 26.0	0 38.7	1 49.0	11 41.7
7	14 57 19.3	0 .0	0 .0	4 38.3	2 45.6	1 21.5	1 41.0	1 30.2	1 26.1	0 38.7	1 49.0	11 40.9
10	15 9 9.0	0 .0	0 .0	5 11.0	3 3.2	1 30.7	1 43.6	1 29.7	1 26.2	0 38.6	1 48.9	11 40.1
13	15 20 58.7	0 .0	0 .0	3 36.0	3 13.5	1 38.8	1 46.1	1 29.2	1 26.2	0 38.5	1 48.9	11 39.3
16	15 32 48.3	0 .0	0 .0	0 41.9	3 16.9	1 45.9	1 48.7	1 28.6	1 26.2	0 38.4	1 48.8	11 38.5
19	15 44 38.0	0 .0	0 .0	2S31.1	3 14.0	1 52.0	1 51.1	1 28.0	1 26.2	0 38.3	1 48.7	11 37.7
22	15 56 27.7	0 .0	0 .0	4 48.0	3 5.2	1 57.1	1 53.5	1 27.4	1 26.2	0 38.2	1 48.7	11 36.8
25	16 8 17.3	0 .0	0 .0	4 59.1	2 50.9	2 1.2	1 55.9	1 26.7	1 26.2	0 38.2	1 48.6	11 36.0
28	16 20 7.0	0 .0	0 .0	2 40.3	2 31.7	2 4.3	1 58.2	1 26.0	1 26.1	0 38.1	1 48.5	11 35.2
31	16 31 56.7	0 .0	0 .0	1N 9.3	2 8.0	2 6.5	2 .4	1 25.3	1 26.0	0 38.0	1 48.4	11 34.4
		RIGHT ASCENSION										
1	14 33 40.0	7♉42.8	28♎53.7	3♎32.7	19♈ 9.5	25♓54.3	5♓24.6	23♎47.1	24♐46.8	10♌13.8	1♏38.0	6♍19.7
2	14 37 36.6	8 40.1	28 50.6	17 55.1	19 19.5	26 55.5	6 7.0	23R40.3	24R44.1	10 14.7	1R36.4	6R19.3
3	14 41 33.1	9 37.5	28 47.6	2♏40.8	19 33.6	27 56.9	6 49.3	23 33.6	24 41.4	10 15.7	1 34.9	6 18.9
4	14 45 29.7	10 35.0	28 44.5	17 46.0	19 51.7	28 58.4	7 31.4	23 27.0	24 38.6	10 16.7	1 33.4	6 18.6
5	14 49 26.2	11 32.6	28 41.5	2♐59.9	20 13.6	29 59.9	8 13.5	23 20.4	24 35.7	10 17.7	1 31.8	6 18.3
6	14 53 22.8	12 30.4	28 38.5	18 6.3	20 39.4	1♈ 1.6	8 55.5	23 13.9	24 32.6	10 18.8	1 30.3	6 18.0
7	14 57 19.3	13 28.4	28 35.4	2♑48.2	21 8.8	2 3.4	9 37.4	23 7.5	24 29.6	10 19.9	1 28.8	6 17.7
8	15 1 15.9	14 26.4	28 32.4	16 52.4	21 41.8	3 5.2	10 19.3	23 1.2	24 26.4	10 21.1	1 27.2	6 17.5
9	15 5 12.4	15 24.7	28 29.3	0♒13.1	22 18.2	4 7.2	11 1.0	22 55.0	24 23.1	10 22.4	1 25.7	6 17.3
10	15 9 9.0	16 23.0	28 26.3	12 51.2	22 57.9	5 9.3	11 42.7	22 48.9	24 19.8	10 23.7	1 24.2	6 17.1
11	15 13 5.6	17 21.5	28 23.3	24 53.0	23 40.8	6 11.5	12 24.3	22 42.9	24 16.4	10 25.0	1 22.7	6 17.0
12	15 17 2.1	18 20.2	28 20.2	6♓27.3	24 26.7	7 13.8	13 5.9	22 37.0	24 12.9	10 26.4	1 21.2	6 16.9
13	15 20 58.7	19 19.0	28 17.2	17 44.6	25 15.7	8 16.2	13 47.3	22 31.2	24 9.4	10 27.9	1 19.8	6 16.8
14	15 24 55.2	20 18.0	28 14.1	28 55.5	26 7.6	9 18.7	14 28.7	22 25.5	24 5.7	10 29.4	1 18.3	6 16.7
15	15 28 51.8	21 17.1	28 11.1	10♈ 9.8	27 2.3	10 21.4	15 10.0	22 19.9	24 2.0	10 31.0	1 16.8	6 16.7
16	15 32 48.3	22 16.3	28 8.1	21 36.8	27 59.7	11 24.2	15 51.2	22 14.5	23 58.3	10 32.6	1 15.4	6 16.7
17	15 36 44.9	23 15.7	28 5.0	3♉23.8	28 59.8	12 27.1	16 32.4	22 9.1	23 54.5	10 34.2	1 14.0	6 16.7
18	15 40 41.4	24 15.3	28 2.0	15 36.0	0♉ 2.6	13 30.1	17 13.5	22 3.9	23 50.6	10 35.9	1 12.6	6D16.8
19	15 44 38.0	25 14.9	27 59.0	28 15.1	1 8.0	14 33.3	17 54.4	21 58.9	23 46.6	10 37.7	1 11.2	6 16.9
20	15 48 34.6	26 14.8	27 55.9	11♊19.2	2 16.0	15 36.6	18 35.4	21 53.9	23 42.6	10 39.5	1 9.8	6 17.0
21	15 52 31.1	27 14.7	27 52.9	24 42.3	3 26.6	16 40.0	19 16.2	21 49.1	23 38.6	10 41.3	1 8.4	6 17.1
22	15 56 27.7	28 14.8	27 49.9	8♋16.1	4 39.7	17 43.6	19 57.0	21 44.4	23 34.4	10 43.2	1 7.0	6 17.3
23	16 0 24.2	29 15.0	27 46.8	21 52.1	5 55.3	18 47.4	20 37.6	21 39.9	23 30.3	10 45.2	1 5.7	6 17.5
24	16 4 20.8	0♊15.4	27 43.8	5♌23.7	7 13.6	19 51.4	21 18.3	21 35.6	23 26.1	10 47.2	1 4.4	6 17.8
25	16 8 17.3	1 15.9	27 40.8	18 48.5	8 34.4	20 55.4	21 58.8	21 31.3	23 21.8	10 49.2	1 3.1	6 18.0
26	16 12 13.9	2 16.4	27 37.7	2♍ 8.4	9 57.8	21 59.7	22 39.3	21 27.3	23 17.5	10 51.3	1 1.8	6 18.3
27	16 16 10.4	3 17.2	27 34.7	15 29.0	11 23.8	23 4.1	23 19.7	21 23.3	23 13.1	10 53.4	1 .5	6 18.6
28	16 20 7.0	4 18.0	27 31.7	28 58.5	12 52.5	24 8.7	24 .0	21 19.5	23 8.7	10 55.6	0 59.3	6 19.0
29	16 24 3.6	5 18.9	27 28.6	12♎45.4	14 24.0	25 13.5	24 40.3	21 15.9	23 4.3	10 57.8	0 58.0	6 19.4
30	16 28 .1	6 19.9	27 25.6	26 56.6	15 58.2	26 18.5	25 20.5	21 12.4	22 59.8	11 .1	0 56.8	6 19.8
31	16 31 56.7	7 21.1	27 22.6	11♏34.2	17 35.3	27 23.6	26 .6	21 9.1	22 55.3	11 2.4	0 55.6	6 20.2
		DECLINATION										
1	14 33 40.0	14N51.3	0S12.4	4S 6.3	6N10.1	2S51.8	11S56.4	8S17.5	21S55.4	18N59.2	10S52.9	22N27.8
4	14 45 29.7	15 45.2	0 12.3	16 3.5	5 51.4	1 44.4	11 10.5	8 10.1	21 55.0	18 58.4	10 51.3	22 27.3
7	14 57 19.3	16 36.7	0 12.3	18 46.7	5 55.1	0 35.3	10 24.0	8 3.0	21 54.6	18 57.5	10 49.7	22 26.8
10	15 9 9.0	17 25.7	0 12.2	12 14.9	6 19.2	0N35.1	9 36.8	7 56.2	21 54.2	18 56.5	10 48.1	22 26.1
13	15 20 58.7	18 12.1	0 12.2	1 21.1	7 1.6	1 46.6	8 49.0	7 49.8	21 53.8	18 55.3	10 46.6	22 25.4
16	15 32 48.3	18 55.8	0 12.1	9N49.6	7 59.9	2 58.9	8 .7	7 43.9	21 53.3	18 54.0	10 45.1	22 24.5
19	15 44 38.0	19 36.6	0 12.0	17 40.0	9 11.9	4 11.7	7 12.1	7 38.4	21 52.8	18 52.6	10 43.6	22 23.6
22	15 56 27.7	20 14.4	0 12.0	18 25.0	10 35.2	5 24.7	6 23.1	7 33.4	21 52.4	18 51.2	10 42.3	22 22.5
25	16 8 17.3	20 49.0	0 11.9	10 42.8	12 7.9	6 37.6	5 33.8	7 29.0	21 51.9	18 49.5	10 40.9	22 21.4
28	16 20 7.0	21 20.5	0 11.9	2S28.1	13 47.7	7 50.0	4 44.4	7 25.0	21 51.4	18 47.8	10 39.7	22 20.1
31	16 31 56.7	21 48.6	0 11.8	14 50.5	15 32.2	9 1.7	3 54.9	7 21.7	21 50.8	18 46.0	10 38.5	22 18.8

JUNE 1958

DAY	EPHEM. SID. TIME	☉	☊	☽	☿	♀	♂	♃	♄	♅	♆	♇
	h m s	° ′	° ′	° ′	° ′	° ′	° ′	° ′	° ′	° ′	° ′	° ′
		LONGITUDE										
1	16 35 53.2	10♊ .6	29♎23.3	28♏14.8	21♉ 8.5	29♈48.6	25♓30.3	22♎14.5	23♐21.6	8♌28.8	2♏28.1	29♌53.0
2	16 39 49.8	10 58.1	29 20.1	12♐40.6	22 53.1	0♉57.4	26 13.5	22 R 11.4	23 R 17.3	8 31.1	2 R 26.9	29 53.6
3	16 43 46.3	11 55.6	29 16.9	26 51.6	24 40.1	2 6.4	26 56.7	22 8.5	23 13.1	8 33.5	2 25.7	29 54.2
4	16 47 42.9	12 53.0	29 13.7	10♑42.9	26 29.5	3 15.4	27 39.8	22 5.7	23 8.7	8 35.9	2 24.6	29 54.9
5	16 51 39.5	13 50.4	29 10.6	24 11.5	28 21.2	4 24.6	28 22.9	22 3.1	23 4.4	8 38.4	2 23.5	29 55.6
6	16 55 36.0	14 47.8	29 7.4	7♒16.3	0♊15.2	5 33.8	29 5.9	22 .7	23 .1	8 40.9	2 22.3	29 56.3
7	16 59 32.6	15 45.2	29 4.2	19 58.5	2 11.4	6 43.1	29 48.9	21 58.4	22 55.7	8 43.4	2 21.2	29 57.0
8	17 3 29.1	16 42.6	29 1.0	2♓20.8	4 9.9	7 52.4	0♈31.8	21 56.3	22 51.3	8 46.0	2 20.2	29 57.8
9	17 7 25.7	17 40.0	28 57.8	14 27.1	6 10.5	9 1.9	1 14.6	21 54.4	22 46.9	8 48.6	2 19.1	29 58.6
10	17 11 22.2	18 37.4	28 54.7	26 22.4	8 13.0	10 11.4	1 57.4	21 52.7	22 42.5	8 51.2	2 18.1	29 59.4
11	17 15 18.8	19 34.7	28 51.5	8♈11.7	10 17.5	11 21.0	2 40.1	21 51.1	22 38.1	8 53.9	2 17.1	0♍ .3
12	17 19 15.4	20 32.1	28 48.3	20 .2	12 23.6	12 30.6	3 22.8	21 49.8	22 33.7	8 56.6	2 16.2	0 1.2
13	17 23 11.9	21 29.4	28 45.1	1♉52.8	14 31.3	13 40.4	4 5.4	21 48.6	22 29.2	8 59.4	2 15.2	0 2.1
14	17 27 8.5	22 26.8	28 42.0	13 54.0	16 40.4	14 50.2	4 47.9	21 47.6	22 24.9	9 2.2	2 14.3	0 3.1
15	17 31 5.0	23 24.1	28 38.8	26 7.2	18 50.5	16 .1	5 30.4	21 46.8	22 20.4	9 5.0	2 13.5	0 4.0
16	17 35 1.6	24 21.5	28 35.6	8♊35.1	21 1.4	17 10.0	6 12.7	21 46.2	22 16.0	9 7.9	2 12.6	0 5.0
17	17 38 58.1	25 18.8	28 32.4	21 19.2	23 13.0	18 20.0	6 55.0	21 45.7	22 11.6	9 10.8	2 11.8	0 6.0
18	17 42 54.7	26 16.1	28 29.3	4♋19.7	25 24.8	19 30.0	7 37.2	21 45.4	22 7.2	9 13.7	2 10.9	0 7.1
19	17 46 51.3	27 13.4	28 26.1	17 35.6	27 36.6	20 40.1	8 19.3	21 45.3	22 2.7	9 16.7	2 10.2	0 8.1
20	17 50 47.8	28 10.6	28 22.9	1♌ 5.4	29 48.2	21 50.3	9 1.3	21 D 45.4	21 58.3	9 19.7	2 9.4	0 9.2
21	17 54 44.4	29 7.9	28 19.7	14 46.8	1♋59.2	23 .5	9 43.2	21 45.6	21 54.0	9 22.7	2 8.7	0 10.3
22	17 58 40.9	0♋ 5.2	28 16.5	28 37.4	4 9.5	24 10.8	10 25.0	21 46.1	21 49.6	9 25.7	2 8.0	0 11.5
23	18 2 37.5	1 2.4	28 13.4	12♍35.2	6 18.8	25 21.1	11 6.8	21 46.7	21 45.2	9 28.8	2 7.3	0 12.6
24	18 6 34.0	1 59.7	28 10.2	26 38.6	8 26.9	26 31.5	11 48.4	21 47.5	21 40.9	9 31.9	2 6.7	0 13.8
25	18 10 30.6	2 56.9	28 7.0	10♎46.4	10 33.6	27 42.0	12 29.9	21 48.5	21 36.6	9 35.0	2 6.1	0 15.0
26	18 14 27.2	3 54.1	28 3.8	24 57.5	12 38.7	28 52.4	13 11.4	21 49.6	21 32.3	9 38.2	2 5.5	0 16.3
27	18 18 23.7	4 51.3	28 .7	9♏10.4	14 42.2	0♊ 3.0	13 52.7	21 51.0	21 28.1	9 41.4	2 4.9	0 17.5
28	18 22 20.3	5 48.5	27 57.5	23 23.0	16 44.0	1 13.6	14 34.0	21 52.5	21 23.8	9 44.6	2 4.4	0 18.8
29	18 26 16.8	6 45.7	27 54.3	7♐32.3	18 43.9	2 24.2	15 15.1	21 54.2	21 19.6	9 47.8	2 3.9	0 20.1
30	18 30 13.4	7 42.9	27 51.1	21 34.6	20 41.8	3 35.0	15 56.2	21 56.0	21 15.5	9 51.1	2 3.5	0 21.4
		LATITUDE										
1	16 35 53.2	0 .0	0 .0	2N23.6	1S59.3	2S 7.0	2S 1.1	1N25.1	1N26.0	0N38.0	1N48.4	11N34.1
4	16 47 42.9	0 .0	0 .0	4 51.4	1 30.7	2 8.0	2 3.3	1 24.3	1 25.9	0 37.9	1 48.2	11 33.3
7	16 59 32.6	0 .0	0 .0	4 51.5	0 59.4	2 8.1	2 5.3	1 23.5	1 25.7	0 37.9	1 48.1	11 32.6
10	17 11 22.2	0 .0	0 .0	2 52.6	0 26.6	2 7.4	2 7.3	1 22.8	1 25.5	0 37.8	1 48.0	11 31.8
13	17 23 11.9	0 .0	0 .0	0S 9.0	0N 6.2	2 5.8	2 9.2	1 22.0	1 25.3	0 37.7	1 47.9	11 31.0
16	17 35 1.6	0 .0	0 .0	3 11.2	0 37.1	2 3.5	2 11.1	1 21.1	1 25.1	0 37.7	1 47.7	11 30.3
19	17 46 51.3	0 .0	0 .0	4 58.3	1 4.4	2 .4	2 12.8	1 20.3	1 24.9	0 37.6	1 47.6	11 29.6
22	17 58 40.9	0 .0	0 .0	4 26.1	1 26.6	1 56.7	2 14.4	1 19.5	1 24.6	0 37.6	1 47.4	11 28.9
25	18 10 30.6	0 .0	0 .0	1 36.6	1 42.4	1 52.3	2 16.0	1 18.7	1 24.3	0 37.5	1 47.3	11 28.3
28	18 22 20.3	0 .0	0 .0	2N 5.3	1 51.7	1 47.3	2 17.4	1 17.9	1 23.9	0 37.5	1 47.1	11 27.7
		RIGHT ASCENSION										
1	16 35 53.2	8♊22.3	27♎19.5	26♏33.3	19♉15.3	28♈29.0	26♓40.6	21♎ 5.9	22♐50.7	11♌ 4.7	0♏54.4	6♍20.7
2	16 39 49.8	9 23.7	27 16.5	11♐41.5	20 58.2	29 34.6	27 20.6	21 R 2.9	22 R 46.2	11 7.1	0 R 53.3	6 21.1
3	16 43 46.3	10 25.1	27 13.5	26 41.1	22 44.2	0♉40.4	28 .6	21 .0	22 41.6	11 9.5	0 52.1	6 21.7
4	16 47 42.9	11 26.7	27 10.4	11♑14.6	24 33.2	1 46.5	28 40.4	20 57.4	22 36.9	11 12.0	0 51.0	6 22.2
5	16 51 39.5	12 28.3	27 7.4	25 9.3	26 25.3	2 52.7	29 20.3	20 54.8	22 32.3	11 14.5	0 49.9	6 22.8
6	16 55 36.0	13 30.1	27 4.4	8♒20.4	28 20.5	3 59.2	29 60.0	20 52.4	22 27.6	11 17.0	0 48.8	6 23.4
7	16 59 32.6	14 31.9	27 1.4	20 49.9	0♊18.8	5 6.0	0♈39.7	20 50.2	22 22.9	11 19.6	0 47.8	6 24.0
8	17 3 29.1	15 33.8	26 58.3	2♓44.9	2 20.3	6 13.0	1 19.3	20 48.2	22 18.2	11 22.2	0 46.7	6 24.7
9	17 7 25.7	16 35.7	26 55.3	14 15.2	4 24.8	7 20.2	1 58.9	20 46.3	22 13.4	11 24.8	0 45.7	6 25.4
10	17 11 22.2	17 37.8	26 52.3	25 31.8	6 32.3	8 27.7	2 38.4	20 44.6	22 8.7	11 27.5	0 44.7	6 26.1
11	17 15 18.8	18 39.9	26 49.3	6♈45.6	8 42.7	9 35.4	3 17.8	20 43.1	22 4.0	11 30.3	0 43.8	6 26.8
12	17 19 15.4	19 42.0	26 46.2	18 7.2	10 55.9	10 43.5	3 57.2	20 41.7	21 59.2	11 33.0	0 42.8	6 27.6
13	17 23 11.9	20 44.3	26 43.2	29 45.8	13 11.5	11 51.7	4 36.5	20 40.5	21 54.4	11 35.8	0 41.9	6 28.4
14	17 27 8.5	21 46.6	26 40.2	11♉49.0	15 29.5	13 .3	5 15.7	20 39.5	21 49.7	11 38.7	0 41.1	6 29.2
15	17 31 5.0	22 48.9	26 37.1	24 21.2	17 49.5	14 9.1	5 54.9	20 38.6	21 44.9	11 41.6	0 40.2	6 30.1
16	17 35 1.6	23 51.2	26 34.1	7♊22.8	20 11.1	15 18.2	6 34.0	20 37.9	21 40.2	11 44.5	0 39.4	6 30.9
17	17 38 58.1	24 53.6	26 31.1	20 49.7	22 34.1	16 27.6	7 13.1	20 37.3	21 35.4	11 47.4	0 38.5	6 31.8
18	17 42 54.7	25 56.0	26 28.1	4♋33.4	24 58.0	17 37.2	7 52.0	20 37.0	21 30.7	11 50.4	0 37.8	6 32.8
19	17 46 51.3	26 58.4	26 25.1	18 23.4	27 22.4	18 47.1	8 30.9	20 36.8	21 25.9	11 53.4	0 37.0	6 33.7
20	17 50 47.8	28 .8	26 22.0	2♌10.1	29 47.0	19 57.3	9 9.7	20 36.8	21 21.2	11 56.4	0 36.3	6 34.7
21	17 54 44.4	29 3.2	26 19.0	15 47.1	2♋11.2	21 7.7	9 48.5	20 D 36.9	21 16.5	11 59.5	0 35.5	6 35.7
22	17 58 40.9	0♋ 5.6	26 16.0	29 13.2	4 34.8	22 18.5	10 27.2	20 37.2	21 11.8	12 2.6	0 34.9	6 36.7
23	18 2 37.5	1 8.0	26 13.0	12♍31.8	6 57.4	23 29.5	11 5.8	20 37.7	21 7.1	12 5.7	0 34.2	6 37.8
24	18 6 34.0	2 10.4	26 9.9	25 49.8	9 18.6	24 40.8	11 44.3	20 38.3	21 2.4	12 8.8	0 33.6	6 38.8
25	18 10 30.6	3 12.8	26 6.9	9♎16.1	11 38.0	25 52.4	12 22.8	20 39.1	20 57.8	12 12.0	0 33.0	6 39.9
26	18 14 27.2	4 15.1	26 3.9	22 59.0	13 55.5	27 4.3	13 1.2	20 40.1	20 53.2	12 15.2	0 32.4	6 41.1
27	18 18 23.7	5 17.4	26 .9	7♏ 4.2	16 10.8	28 16.5	13 39.6	20 41.3	20 48.6	12 18.4	0 31.9	6 42.2
28	18 22 20.3	6 19.6	25 57.9	21 32.3	18 23.8	29 29.0	14 17.8	20 42.6	20 44.0	12 21.7	0 31.4	6 43.4
29	18 26 16.8	7 21.8	25 54.8	6♐17.2	20 34.1	0♊41.7	14 56.0	20 44.1	20 39.5	12 25.0	0 30.9	6 44.6
30	18 30 13.4	8 24.0	25 51.8	21 6.1	22 41.8	1 54.7	15 34.2	20 45.7	20 35.1	12 28.3	0 30.4	6 45.8
		DECLINATION										
1	16 35 53.2	21N57.2	0S11.8	17S26.3	16N 7.7	9N25.4	3S38.4	7S20.7	21S50.7	18N45.4	10S38.1	22N18.3
4	16 47 42.9	22 20.8	0 11.7	18 10.1	17 54.2	10 35.7	2 48.8	7 18.1	21 50.2	18 43.5	10 37.0	22 16.9
7	16 59 32.6	22 40.8	0 11.7	10 12.5	19 37.9	11 44.5	1 59.4	7 16.1	21 49.6	18 41.4	10 36.0	22 15.4
10	17 11 22.2	22 57.3	0 11.6	1N11.9	21 14.5	12 51.6	1 10.1	7 14.7	21 49.1	18 39.3	10 35.0	22 13.8
13	17 23 11.9	23 10.1	0 11.6	11 59.3	22 38.8	13 56.6	0 21.1	7 13.9	21 48.6	18 37.1	10 34.1	22 12.2
16	17 35 1.6	23 19.3	0 11.5	18 35.4	23 45.3	14 59.2	0N27.7	7 13.8	21 48.0	18 34.8	10 33.4	22 10.4
19	17 46 51.3	23 24.8	0 11.4	17 21.2	24 29.7	15 59.1	1 16.0	7 14.2	21 47.5	18 32.4	10 32.7	22 8.6
22	17 58 40.9	23 26.5	0 11.4	7 47.5	24 49.1	16 56.0	2 3.8	7 15.3	21 47.0	18 30.0	10 32.1	22 6.8
25	18 10 30.6	23 24.5	0 11.3	5S44.7	24 43.4	17 49.6	2 51.1	7 16.9	21 46.5	18 27.4	10 31.5	22 4.9
28	18 22 20.3	23 18.9	0 11.3	16 35.9	24 14.4	18 39.5	3 37.8	7 19.2	21 46.0	18 24.9	10 31.1	22 2.9

JULY 1958

LONGITUDE

DAY	EPHEM. SID. TIME h m s	☉ ° ′	☊ ° ′	☽ ° ′	☿ ° ′	♀ ° ′	♂ ° ′	♃ ° ′	♄ ° ′	♅ ° ′	♆ ° ′	♇ ° ′
1	18 34 9.9	8♋40.1	27♎48.0	5♑25.8	22♋37.8	4♊45.7	16♈37.1	21♎58.1	21♐11.4	9♌54.4	2♏ 3.0	0♍22.8
2	18 38 6.5	9 37.3	27 44.8	19 1.9	24 31.8	5 56.5	17 18.0	22 .3	21 R 7.3	9 57.7	2 R 2.6	0 24.1
3	18 42 3.1	10 34.4	27 41.6	2♒19.9	26 23.8	7 7.4	17 58.7	22 2.7	21 3.2	10 1.0	2 2.3	0 25.5
4	18 45 59.6	11 31.6	27 38.4	15 18.1	28 13.8	8 18.3	18 39.3	22 5.2	20 59.2	10 4.3	2 1.9	0 26.9
5	18 49 56.2	12 28.8	27 35.3	27 56.7	0♌ 1.7	9 29.4	19 19.8	22 8.0	20 55.3	10 7.8	2 1.7	0 28.4
6	18 53 52.7	13 26.0	27 32.1	10♓17.3	1 47.6	10 40.4	20 .2	22 10.9	20 51.4	10 11.2	2 1.4	0 29.8
7	18 57 49.3	14 23.2	27 28.9	22 23.1	3 31.4	11 51.5	20 40.5	22 13.9	20 47.5	10 14.6	2 1.2	0 31.3
8	19 1 45.8	15 20.4	27 25.7	4♈18.2	5 13.1	13 2.7	21 20.6	22 17.2	20 43.7	10 18.0	2 1.0	0 32.8
9	19 5 42.4	16 17.6	27 22.5	16 7.6	6 52.8	14 13.9	22 .6	22 20.5	20 39.9	10 21.5	2 .8	0 34.3
10	19 9 38.9	17 14.8	27 19.4	27 56.7	8 30.4	15 25.2	22 40.4	22 24.1	20 36.2	10 24.9	2 .6	0 35.8
11	19 13 35.5	18 12.0	27 16.2	9♉51.0	10 5.9	16 36.5	23 20.2	22 27.8	20 32.5	10 28.4	2 .5	0 37.4
12	19 17 32.1	19 9.3	27 13.0	21 55.6	11 39.4	17 47.8	23 59.7	22 31.7	20 28.9	10 31.9	2 .4	0 38.9
13	19 21 28.6	20 6.5	27 9.8	4♊15.0	13 10.8	18 59.3	24 39.2	22 35.7	20 25.3	10 35.5	2 .4	0 40.5
14	19 25 25.2	21 3.7	27 6.7	16 52.9	14 40.1	20 10.7	25 18.5	22 39.9	20 21.8	10 39.0	2 .3	0 42.1
15	19 29 21.7	22 1.0	27 3.5	29 51.2	16 7.3	21 22.3	25 57.6	22 44.3	20 18.4	10 42.5	2 .3	0 43.7
16	19 33 18.3	22 58.2	27 .3	13♋10.5	17 32.4	22 33.8	26 36.6	22 48.8	20 15.0	10 46.1	2 D .4	0 45.4
17	19 37 14.8	23 55.5	26 57.1	26 49.2	18 55.2	23 45.4	27 15.4	22 53.5	20 11.7	10 49.7	2 .5	0 47.0
18	19 41 11.4	24 52.8	26 54.0	10♌44.1	20 15.9	24 57.1	27 54.1	22 58.4	20 8.4	10 53.3	2 .6	0 48.7
19	19 45 8.0	25 50.0	26 50.8	24 50.8	21 34.4	26 8.8	28 32.5	23 3.3	20 5.3	10 56.9	2 .7	0 50.4
20	19 49 4.5	26 47.3	26 47.6	9♍ 4.5	22 50.5	27 20.6	29 10.8	23 8.5	20 2.1	11 .5	2 .9	0 52.1
21	19 53 1.1	27 44.6	26 44.4	23 20.7	24 4.3	28 32.4	29 49.0	23 13.8	19 59.1	11 4.2	2 1.1	0 53.8
22	19 56 57.6	28 41.9	26 41.2	7♎35.6	25 15.6	29 44.2	0♉26.9	23 19.2	19 56.1	11 7.8	2 1.3	0 55.5
23	20 0 54.2	29 39.2	26 38.1	21 47.0	26 24.5	0♋56.1	1 4.7	23 24.8	19 53.3	11 11.4	2 1.6	0 57.3
24	20 4 50.7	0♌36.5	26 34.9	5♏53.2	27 30.8	2 8.1	1 42.3	23 30.6	19 50.4	11 15.1	2 1.9	0 59.0
25	20 8 47.3	1 33.8	26 31.7	19 53.6	28 34.5	3 20.1	2 19.7	23 36.5	19 47.7	11 18.8	2 2.2	1 .8
26	20 12 43.8	2 31.1	26 28.5	3♐47.5	29 35.4	4 32.2	2 57.0	23 42.5	19 45.1	11 22.5	2 2.6	1 2.6
27	20 16 40.4	3 28.4	26 25.4	17 33.9	0♍33.4	5 44.2	3 34.0	23 48.7	19 42.5	11 26.2	2 3.0	1 4.4
28	20 20 37.0	4 25.7	26 22.2	1♑11.5	1 28.5	6 56.4	4 10.8	23 55.0	19 40.0	11 29.9	2 3.5	1 6.2
29	20 24 33.5	5 23.1	26 19.0	14 38.5	2 20.4	8 8.5	4 47.5	24 1.5	19 37.6	11 33.6	2 3.9	1 8.1
30	20 28 30.1	6 20.4	26 15.8	27 52.9	3 9.1	9 20.8	5 23.9	24 8.1	19 35.2	11 37.3	2 4.4	1 9.9
31	20 32 26.6	7 17.8	26 12.6	10♒52.9	3 54.3	10 33.0	6 .1	24 14.8	19 33.0	11 41.0	2 5.0	1 11.7

LATITUDE

DAY	EPHEM. SID. TIME	☉	☊	☽	☿	♀	♂	♃	♄	♅	♆	♇
1	18 34 9.9	0 .0	0 .0	4N37.9	1N54.3	1S41.7	2S18.7	1N17.1	1N23.6	0N37.5	1N47.0	11N27.1
4	18 45 59.6	0 .0	0 .0	4 49.1	1 50.7	1 35.6	2 19.9	1 16.3	1 23.2	0 37.4	1 46.8	11 26.5
7	18 57 49.3	0 .0	0 .0	2 56.6	1 41.3	1 29.1	2 21.1	1 15.5	1 22.8	0 37.4	1 46.7	11 26.0
10	19 9 38.9	0 .0	0 .0	0S .5	1 26.8	1 22.1	2 22.1	1 14.7	1 22.4	0 37.4	1 46.5	11 25.5
13	19 21 28.6	0 .0	0 .0	3 .2	1 7.6	1 14.8	2 22.9	1 13.9	1 22.0	0 37.4	1 46.3	11 25.0
16	19 33 18.3	0 .0	0 .0	4 51.8	0 44.2	1 7.2	2 23.7	1 13.1	1 21.5	0 37.3	1 46.1	11 24.6
19	19 45 8.0	0 .0	0 .0	4 25.7	0 17.2	0 59.3	2 24.3	1 12.4	1 21.1	0 37.3	1 46.0	11 24.2
22	19 56 57.6	0 .0	0 .0	1 38.1	0S12.9	0 51.1	2 24.8	1 11.6	1 20.6	0 37.3	1 45.8	11 23.9
25	20 8 47.3	0 .0	0 .0	2N .7	0 45.7	0 42.9	2 25.1	1 10.9	1 20.1	0 37.3	1 45.6	11 23.6
28	20 20 37.0	0 .0	0 .0	4 33.3	1 20.7	0 34.5	2 25.4	1 10.2	1 19.6	0 37.3	1 45.5	11 23.3
31	20 32 26.6	0 .0	0 .0	4 50.6	1 57.1	0 26.1	2 25.4	1 9.5	1 19.0	0 37.3	1 45.3	11 23.1

RIGHT ASCENSION

DAY	EPHEM. SID. TIME	☉	☊	☽	☿	♀	♂	♃	♄	♅	♆	♇
1	18 34 9.9	9♋26.1	25♎48.8	5♑42.9	24♋46.7	3♊ 8.0	16♈12.2	20♎47.5	20♐30.6	12♌31.6	0♏30.0	6♍47.0
2	18 38 6.5	10 28.1	25 45.8	19 52.7	26 48.7	4 21.6	16 50.2	20 49.5	20 R 26.2	12 35.0	0 R 29.6	6 48.3
3	18 42 3.1	11 30.1	25 42.8	3♒25.7	28 47.9	5 35.4	17 28.1	20 51.6	20 21.9	12 38.3	0 29.2	6 49.6
4	18 45 59.6	12 31.9	25 39.8	16 19.1	0♌44.1	6 49.6	18 6.0	20 53.9	20 17.5	12 41.7	0 28.9	6 50.9
5	18 49 56.2	13 33.8	25 36.7	28 35.9	2 37.4	8 4.0	18 43.8	20 56.4	20 13.3	12 45.2	0 28.6	6 52.3
6	18 53 52.7	14 35.6	25 33.7	10♓23.3	4 27.8	9 18.7	19 21.5	20 59.0	20 9.1	12 48.6	0 28.3	6 53.6
7	18 57 49.3	15 37.2	25 30.7	21 50.7	6 15.1	10 33.6	19 59.1	21 1.7	20 4.9	12 52.1	0 28.1	6 55.0
8	19 1 45.8	16 38.8	25 27.7	3♈ 8.6	7 59.6	11 48.7	20 36.6	21 4.7	20 .8	12 55.6	0 27.8	6 56.4
9	19 5 42.4	17 40.3	25 24.7	14 27.4	9 41.2	13 4.2	21 14.0	21 7.7	19 56.7	12 59.1	0 27.6	6 57.8
10	19 9 38.9	18 41.7	25 21.7	25 57.3	11 19.9	14 19.8	21 51.4	21 11.0	19 52.7	13 2.6	0 27.5	6 59.2
11	19 13 35.5	19 43.0	25 18.6	7♉47.2	12 55.7	15 35.7	22 28.7	21 14.4	19 48.8	13 6.1	0 27.4	7 .7
12	19 17 32.1	20 44.2	25 15.6	20 3.9	14 28.8	16 51.8	23 5.8	21 17.9	19 44.9	13 9.7	0 27.3	7 2.1
13	19 21 28.6	21 45.3	25 12.6	2♊51.2	15 59.0	18 8.1	23 42.9	21 21.6	19 41.0	13 13.2	0 27.2	7 3.6
14	19 25 25.2	22 46.2	25 9.6	16 8.5	17 26.5	19 24.6	24 19.9	21 25.4	19 37.3	13 16.8	0 27.1	7 5.1
15	19 29 21.7	23 47.1	25 6.6	29 50.8	18 51.2	20 41.4	24 56.8	21 29.4	19 33.6	13 20.4	0 27.1	7 6.7
16	19 33 18.3	24 47.8	25 3.6	13♋48.7	20 13.1	21 58.3	25 33.5	21 33.6	19 29.9	13 24.0	0 27.1	7 8.2
17	19 37 14.8	25 48.4	25 .6	27 51.4	21 32.4	23 15.3	26 10.2	21 37.9	19 26.4	13 27.7	0 D 27.2	7 9.8
18	19 41 11.4	26 48.9	24 57.5	11♌49.8	22 48.9	24 32.6	26 46.7	21 42.3	19 22.9	13 31.3	0 27.3	7 11.4
19	19 45 8.0	27 49.2	24 54.5	25 38.2	24 2.7	25 50.0	27 23.2	21 46.9	19 19.5	13 34.9	0 27.4	7 13.0
20	19 49 4.5	28 49.4	24 51.5	9♍16.3	25 13.8	27 7.5	27 59.5	21 51.6	19 16.1	13 38.6	0 27.5	7 14.6
21	19 53 1.1	29 49.5	24 48.5	22 47.9	26 22.1	28 25.2	28 35.7	21 56.5	19 12.8	13 42.3	0 27.7	7 16.2
22	19 56 57.6	0♌49.4	24 45.5	6♎19.6	27 27.7	29 42.9	29 11.7	22 1.5	19 9.6	13 46.0	0 27.9	7 17.9
23	20 0 54.2	1 49.2	24 42.5	19 58.7	28 30.4	1♋ .8	29 47.7	22 6.7	19 6.5	13 49.7	0 28.2	7 19.5
24	20 4 50.7	2 48.8	24 39.5	3♏51.5	29 30.3	2 18.8	0♉23.5	22 12.0	19 3.5	13 53.3	0 28.4	7 21.2
25	20 8 47.3	3 48.3	24 36.5	18 .5	0♍27.4	3 36.9	0 59.2	22 17.4	19 .5	13 57.1	0 28.7	7 22.9
26	20 12 43.8	4 47.7	24 33.5	2♐23.4	1 21.5	4 55.0	1 34.7	22 23.0	18 57.7	14 .8	0 29.1	7 24.7
27	20 16 40.4	5 46.8	24 30.4	16 52.3	2 12.6	6 13.2	2 10.2	22 28.7	18 54.9	14 4.5	0 29.5	7 26.4
28	20 20 37.0	6 45.9	24 27.4	1♑15.4	3 .6	7 31.4	2 45.4	22 34.6	18 52.2	14 8.3	0 29.9	7 28.1
29	20 24 33.5	7 44.7	24 24.4	15 20.0	3 45.5	8 49.7	3 20.6	22 40.5	18 49.6	14 12.0	0 30.3	7 29.9
30	20 28 30.1	8 43.4	24 21.4	28 56.2	4 27.0	10 8.0	3 55.5	22 46.6	18 47.1	14 15.7	0 30.7	7 31.6
31	20 32 26.6	9 42.0	24 18.4	11♒58.9	5 5.3	11 26.3	4 30.4	22 52.9	18 44.7	14 19.5	0 31.2	7 33.4

DECLINATION

DAY	EPHEM. SID. TIME	☉	☊	☽	☿	♀	♂	♃	♄	♅	♆	♇
1	18 34 9.9	23N 9.5	0S11.2	18S42.1	23N25.3	19N25.4	4N23.8	7S22.0	21S45.5	18N22.2	10S30.8	22N .9
4	18 45 59.6	22 56.5	0 11.1	11 38.4	22 19.5	20 7.2	5 9.2	7 25.4	21 45.1	18 19.5	10 30.6	21 58.9
7	18 57 49.3	22 39.9	0 11.1	0 19.0	21 .6	20 44.5	5 53.7	7 29.4	21 44.7	18 16.7	10 30.5	21 56.8
10	19 9 38.9	22 19.8	0 11.0	10N44.2	19 32.0	21 17.0	6 37.3	7 33.9	21 44.3	18 13.8	10 30.4	21 54.7
13	19 21 28.6	21 56.2	0 11.0	18 2.7	17 56.6	21 44.6	7 20.1	7 38.9	21 44.0	18 11.0	10 30.5	21 52.5
16	19 33 18.3	21 29.2	0 10.9	17 57.0	16 16.8	22 7.0	8 1.8	7 44.5	21 43.7	18 8.0	10 30.7	21 50.4
19	19 45 8.0	20 58.9	0 10.8	9 3.8	14 35.2	22 23.9	8 42.5	7 50.6	21 43.5	18 5.1	10 31.0	21 48.2
22	19 56 57.6	20 25.4	0 10.8	4S30.9	12 54.0	22 35.4	9 22.1	7 57.1	21 43.3	18 2.1	10 31.3	21 46.0
25	20 8 47.3	19 48.9	0 10.7	15 46.6	11 15.4	22 41.2	10 .6	8 4.2	21 43.1	17 59.1	10 31.8	21 43.8
28	20 20 37.0	19 9.3	0 10.7	18 53.0	9 41.7	22 41.2	10 38.0	8 11.6	21 43.1	17 56.0	10 32.4	21 41.5
31	20 32 26.6	18 27.0	0 10.6	12 50.5	8 15.5	22 35.4	11 14.1	8 19.5	21 43.0	17 52.9	10 33.1	21 39.3

AUGUST 1958

LONGITUDE

DAY	EPHEM. SID. TIME	☉	☊	☽	☿	♀	♂	♃	♄	♅	♆	♇
	h m s	° ′	° ′	° ′	° ′	° ′	° ′	° ′	° ′	° ′	° ′	° ′
1	20 36 23.2	8♌15.1	26♎ 9.5	23♒37.4	4♍36.0	11♋45.4	6♉36.2	24♎21.6	19♐30.8	11♌44.7	2♏ 5.5	1♍13.6
2	20 40 19.7	9 12.5	26 6.3	6♓ 6.3	5 14.0	12 57.7	7 12.0	24 28.6	19R28.7	11 48.4	2 6.1	1 15.5
3	20 44 16.3	10 9.9	26 3.1	18 20.6	5 48.1	14 10.1	7 47.5	24 35.7	19 26.7	11 52.1	2 6.7	1 17.3
4	20 48 12.8	11 7.3	25 59.9	0♈22.5	6 18.1	15 22.6	8 22.9	24 43.0	19 24.8	11 55.8	2 7.4	1 19.2
5	20 52 9.4	12 4.8	25 56.8	12 15.5	6 43.8	16 35.1	8 58.0	24 50.4	19 23.0	11 59.5	2 8.0	1 21.1
6	20 56 6.0	13 2.2	25 53.6	24 3.8	7 5.0	17 47.7	9 32.9	24 57.9	19 21.2	12 3.2	2 8.8	1 23.0
7	21 0 2.5	13 59.7	25 50.4	5♉52.3	7 21.6	19 .3	10 7.5	25 5.5	19 19.6	12 6.9	2 9.5	1 24.9
8	21 3 59.1	14 57.2	25 47.2	17 46.4	7 33.3	20 13.0	10 41.9	25 13.3	19 18.0	12 10.6	2 10.3	1 26.9
9	21 7 55.6	15 54.7	25 44.1	29 51.4	7 39.9	21 25.7	11 16.0	25 21.1	19 16.5	12 14.3	2 11.1	1 28.8
10	21 11 52.2	16 52.3	25 40.9	12♊12.6	7 41.4	22 38.5	11 49.9	25 29.1	19 15.1	12 18.0	2 11.9	1 30.7
11	21 15 48.7	17 49.8	25 37.7	24 54.4	7R37.5	23 51.3	12 23.5	25 37.2	19 13.8	12 21.7	2 12.8	1 32.7
12	21 19 45.3	18 47.4	25 34.5	7♋59.8	7 28.2	25 4.2	12 56.8	25 45.5	19 12.6	12 25.4	2 13.7	1 34.6
13	21 23 41.8	19 45.0	25 31.3	21 30.3	7 13.5	26 17.1	13 29.9	25 53.8	19 11.5	12 29.1	2 14.6	1 36.6
14	21 27 38.4	20 42.7	25 28.2	5♌24.9	6 53.2	27 30.0	14 2.6	26 2.3	19 10.5	12 32.8	2 15.6	1 38.6
15	21 31 34.9	21 40.3	25 25.0	19 40.1	6 27.5	28 43.0	14 35.1	26 10.9	19 9.6	12 36.5	2 16.6	1 40.5
16	21 35 31.5	22 38.0	25 21.8	4♍10.6	5 56.7	29 56.1	15 7.2	26 19.6	19 8.8	12 40.2	2 17.6	1 42.5
17	21 39 28.0	23 35.7	25 18.6	18 49.2	5 20.9	1♌ 9.2	15 39.1	26 28.5	19 8.1	12 43.9	2 18.7	1 44.5
18	21 43 24.6	24 33.5	25 15.5	3♎29.1	4 40.5	2 22.4	16 10.6	26 37.4	19 7.5	12 47.6	2 19.7	1 46.5
19	21 47 21.2	25 31.2	25 12.3	18 4.0	3 56.0	3 35.5	16 41.8	26 46.4	19 6.9	12 51.2	2 20.8	1 48.5
20	21 51 17.7	26 28.9	25 9.1	2♏29.4	3 8.1	4 48.7	17 12.6	26 55.5	19 6.5	12 54.9	2 22.0	1 50.5
21	21 55 14.3	27 26.7	25 5.9	16 42.3	2 17.6	6 2.0	17 43.1	27 4.8	19 6.2	12 58.5	2 23.1	1 52.5
22	21 59 10.8	28 24.5	25 2.7	0♐41.4	1 25.2	7 15.3	18 13.3	27 14.1	19 5.9	13 2.1	2 24.3	1 54.5
23	22 3 7.4	29 22.3	24 59.6	14 26.5	0 32.0	8 28.6	18 43.1	27 23.6	19 5.8	13 5.7	2 25.5	1 56.4
24	22 7 3.9	0♍20.1	24 56.4	27 57.9	29♌38.9	9 42.0	19 12.6	27 33.1	19 5.7	13 9.3	2 26.8	1 58.4
25	22 11 .5	1 18.0	24 53.2	11♑16.1	28 47.2	10 55.4	19 41.7	27 42.7	19D 5.8	13 12.9	2 28.1	2 .4
26	22 14 57.0	2 15.8	24 50.0	24 21.4	27 57.9	12 8.9	20 10.5	27 52.5	19 5.9	13 16.4	2 29.4	2 2.4
27	22 18 53.6	3 13.7	24 46.9	7♒14.0	27 12.1	13 22.4	20 38.9	28 2.3	19 6.2	13 20.0	2 30.7	2 4.4
28	22 22 50.1	4 11.7	24 43.7	19 54.0	26 30.7	14 35.9	21 6.9	28 12.2	19 6.5	13 23.5	2 32.0	2 6.4
29	22 26 46.7	5 9.6	24 40.5	2♓21.6	25 54.9	15 49.5	21 34.5	28 22.2	19 6.9	13 27.0	2 33.4	2 8.4
30	22 30 43.2	6 7.6	24 37.3	14 37.4	25 25.3	17 3.2	22 1.7	28 32.3	19 7.5	13 30.6	2 34.8	2 10.4
31	22 34 39.8	7 5.5	24 34.1	26 42.5	25 2.8	18 16.8	22 28.4	28 42.5	19 8.1	13 34.0	2 36.3	2 12.4

LATITUDE

DAY	EPHEM. SID. TIME	☉	☊	☽	☿	♀	♂	♃	♄	♅	♆	♇
1	20 36 23.2	0 .0	0 .0	4N25.9	2S 9.4	0S23.3	2S25.4	1N 9.2	1N18.9	0N37.3	1N45.2	11N23.0
4	20 48 12.8	0 .0	0 .0	2 7.0	2 46.3	0 14.8	2 25.3	1 8.6	1 18.3	0 37.3	1 45.1	11 22.9
7	21 0 2.5	0 .0	0 .0	0S57.7	3 22.1	0 6.5	2 25.0	1 7.9	1 17.8	0 37.4	1 44.9	11 22.8
10	21 11 52.2	0 .0	0 .0	3 44.1	3 54.8	0N 1.8	2 24.5	1 7.2	1 17.2	0 37.4	1 44.7	11 22.7
13	21 23 41.8	0 .0	0 .0	5 3.5	4 21.8	0 9.9	2 23.9	1 6.6	1 16.7	0 37.4	1 44.6	11 22.7
16	21 35 31.5	0 .0	0 .0	3 53.4	4 39.6	0 17.8	2 23.1	1 6.0	1 16.1	0 37.4	1 44.4	11 22.7
19	21 47 21.2	0 .0	0 .0	0 31.2	4 44.6	0 25.4	2 22.1	1 5.4	1 15.5	0 37.5	1 44.3	11 22.8
22	21 59 10.8	0 .0	0 .0	3N 4.3	4 33.5	0 32.8	2 20.9	1 4.8	1 15.0	0 37.5	1 44.1	11 22.9
25	22 11 .5	0 .0	0 .0	4 59.7	4 5.6	0 39.8	2 19.6	1 4.3	1 14.4	0 37.6	1 44.0	11 23.1
28	22 22 50.1	0 .0	0 .0	4 35.0	3 22.9	0 46.4	2 18.0	1 3.7	1 13.8	0 37.6	1 43.8	11 23.3
31	22 34 39.8	0 .0	0 .0	2 17.2	2 30.4	0 52.7	2 16.2	1 3.2	1 13.2	0 37.7	1 43.7	11 23.6

RIGHT ASCENSION

DAY	EPHEM. SID. TIME	☉	☊	☽	☿	♀	♂	♃	♄	♅	♆	♇
1	20 36 23.2	10♌40.4	24♎15.4	24♒28.1	5♍40.0	12♋44.6	5♉ 5.1	22♎59.2	18♐42.3	14♌23.2	0♏31.7	7♍35.2
2	20 40 19.7	11 38.7	24 12.4	6♓28.1	6 11.1	14 2.9	5 39.6	23 5.7	18R40.0	14 26.9	0 32.3	7 37.0
3	20 44 16.3	12 36.8	24 9.4	18 5.9	6 38.6	15 21.1	6 13.9	23 12.3	18 37.9	14 30.7	0 32.8	7 38.8
4	20 48 12.8	13 34.7	24 6.4	29 30.1	7 2.1	16 39.3	6 48.1	23 19.1	18 35.8	14 34.4	0 33.4	7 40.7
5	20 52 9.4	14 32.5	24 3.4	10♈50.0	7 21.6	17 57.5	7 22.1	23 25.9	18 33.8	14 38.2	0 34.1	7 42.5
6	20 56 6.0	15 30.2	24 .4	22 14.9	7 37.0	19 15.6	7 55.9	23 32.9	18 31.9	14 41.9	0 34.7	7 44.3
7	21 0 2.5	16 27.7	23 57.4	3♉53.3	7 48.2	20 33.7	8 29.6	23 40.0	18 30.1	14 45.7	0 35.4	7 46.2
8	21 3 59.1	17 25.1	23 54.4	15 52.9	7 54.9	21 51.6	9 3.0	23 47.2	18 28.5	14 49.4	0 36.1	7 48.1
9	21 7 55.6	18 22.3	23 51.4	28 19.1	7 57.0	23 9.5	9 36.2	23 54.6	18 26.9	14 53.1	0 36.9	7 49.9
10	21 11 52.2	19 19.4	23 48.3	11♊14.4	7R54.5	24 27.2	10 9.2	24 2.0	18 25.4	14 56.9	0 37.7	7 51.8
11	21 15 48.7	20 16.4	23 45.3	24 37.8	7 47.3	25 44.8	10 42.0	24 9.6	18 23.9	15 .6	0 38.5	7 53.7
12	21 19 45.3	21 13.2	23 42.3	8♋23.9	7 35.3	27 2.3	11 14.6	24 17.3	18 22.6	15 4.3	0 39.3	7 55.6
13	21 23 41.8	22 9.9	23 39.3	22 24.9	7 18.5	28 19.7	11 46.9	24 25.1	18 21.4	15 8.1	0 40.2	7 57.5
14	21 27 38.4	23 6.4	23 36.3	6♌31.7	6 57.0	29 36.9	12 19.0	24 33.0	18 20.3	15 11.8	0 41.1	7 59.4
15	21 31 34.9	24 2.8	23 33.3	20 37.4	6 31.0	0♌54.0	12 50.9	24 41.1	18 19.3	15 15.5	0 42.0	8 1.4
16	21 35 31.5	24 59.1	23 30.3	4♍38.2	6 .5	2 10.9	13 22.5	24 49.2	18 18.5	15 19.2	0 43.0	8 3.3
17	21 39 28.0	25 55.2	23 27.3	18 34.4	5 26.0	3 27.6	13 53.8	24 57.5	18 17.7	15 22.9	0 44.0	8 5.3
18	21 43 24.6	26 51.3	23 24.3	2♎29.3	4 47.7	4 44.1	14 24.8	25 5.9	18 17.0	15 26.6	0 45.0	8 7.2
19	21 47 21.2	27 47.1	23 21.3	16 27.7	4 6.1	6 .5	14 55.6	25 14.3	18 16.4	15 30.3	0 46.0	8 9.2
20	21 51 17.7	28 42.9	23 18.3	0♏33.9	3 22.0	7 16.6	15 26.1	25 22.9	18 15.9	15 33.9	0 47.1	8 11.1
21	21 55 14.3	29 38.5	23 15.3	14 49.4	2 35.9	8 32.5	15 56.3	25 31.5	18 15.6	15 37.6	0 48.2	8 13.1
22	21 59 10.8	0♍34.0	23 12.3	29 12.3	1 48.7	9 48.3	16 26.1	25 40.3	18 15.3	15 41.2	0 49.3	8 15.1
23	22 3 7.4	1 29.4	23 9.3	13♐36.0	1 1.3	11 3.8	16 55.7	25 49.2	18 15.1	15 44.9	0 50.5	8 17.0
24	22 7 3.9	2 24.6	23 6.3	27 51.4	0 14.6	12 19.1	17 25.0	25 58.1	18 15.0	15 48.5	0 51.6	8 19.0
25	22 11 .5	3 19.8	23 3.3	11♑48.6	29♌29.6	13 34.2	17 53.9	26 7.2	18D15.1	15 52.1	0 52.8	8 21.0
26	22 14 57.0	4 14.8	23 .3	25 19.6	28 47.3	14 49.0	18 22.5	26 16.4	18 15.2	15 55.7	0 54.1	8 22.9
27	22 18 53.6	5 9.7	22 57.3	8♒20.4	28 8.7	16 3.7	18 50.7	26 25.6	18 15.4	15 59.2	0 55.3	8 24.9
28	22 22 50.1	6 4.6	22 54.3	20 50.7	27 34.7	17 18.1	19 18.6	26 35.0	18 15.8	16 2.8	0 56.6	8 26.9
29	22 26 46.7	6 59.3	22 51.3	2♓54.0	27 6.1	18 32.2	19 46.2	26 44.4	18 16.2	16 6.3	0 57.9	8 28.9
30	22 30 43.2	7 54.0	22 48.3	14 36.2	26 43.9	19 46.2	20 13.4	26 53.9	18 16.8	16 9.9	0 59.2	8 30.8
31	22 34 39.8	8 48.5	22 45.3	26 4.2	26 28.4	20 59.9	20 40.2	27 3.5	18 17.5	16 13.4	1 .6	8 32.8

DECLINATION

DAY	EPHEM. SID. TIME	☉	☊	☽	☿	♀	♂	♃	♄	♅	♆	♇
1	20 36 23.2	18N12.3	0S10.6	9S27.6	7N48.9	22N32.2	11N25.9	8S22.3	21S43.1	17N51.9	10S33.3	21N38.6
4	20 48 12.8	17 26.3	0 10.5	2N 5.4	6 37.4	22 18.6	12 .4	8 30.7	21 43.1	17 48.8	10 34.1	21 36.3
7	21 0 2.5	16 37.8	0 10.5	12 34.4	5 40.8	21 59.3	12 33.6	8 39.5	21 43.3	17 45.7	10 35.0	21 34.1
10	21 11 52.2	15 46.9	0 10.4	18 33.4	5 3.1	21 34.2	13 5.6	8 48.7	21 43.5	17 42.6	10 36.0	21 31.9
13	21 23 41.8	14 53.7	0 10.3	16 43.6	4 48.3	21 3.5	13 36.2	8 58.3	21 43.7	17 39.5	10 37.0	21 29.8
16	21 35 31.5	13 58.3	0 10.3	6 21.2	4 59.7	20 27.4	14 5.5	9 8.2	21 44.1	17 36.4	10 38.2	21 27.6
19	21 47 21.2	13 .9	0 10.2	7S34.1	5 38.7	19 45.9	14 33.4	9 18.4	21 44.5	17 33.3	10 39.5	21 25.5
22	21 59 10.8	12 1.7	0 10.2	17 17.5	6 42.4	18 59.3	14 60.0	9 28.9	21 45.0	17 30.3	10 40.8	21 23.4
25	22 11 .5	11 .8	0 10.1	17 59.2	8 3.4	18 7.8	15 25.2	9 39.7	21 45.6	17 27.2	10 42.2	21 21.3
28	22 22 50.1	9 58.4	0 10.0	10 29.6	9 29.8	17 11.7	15 49.2	9 50.7	21 46.2	17 24.2	10 43.7	21 19.3
31	22 34 39.8	8 54.5	0 10.0	0N47.4	10 48.7	16 11.2	16 11.8	10 1.9	21 46.9	17 21.3	10 45.3	21 17.4

SEPTEMBER 1958

LONGITUDE

DAY	EPHEM. SID. TIME	☉	☊	☽	☿	♀	♂	♃	♄	♅	♆	♇
	h m s	° ′	° ′	° ′	° ′	° ′	° ′	° ′	° ′	° ′	° ′	° ′
1	22 38 36.3	8♍ 3.6	24♎31.0	8♈38.6	24♌47.9	19♌30.5	22♉54.8	28♎52.8	19♐ 8.8	13♌37.5	2♏37.7	2♍14.4
2	22 42 32.9	9 1.6	24 27.8	20 28.4	24R41.1	20 44.3	23 20.8	29 3.2	19 9.6	13 41.0	2 39.2	2 16.4
3	22 46 29.4	9 59.7	24 24.6	2♉15.2	24D42.6	21 58.1	23 46.3	29 13.7	19 10.6	13 44.4	2 40.7	2 18.4
4	22 50 26.0	10 57.8	24 21.4	14 3.1	24 52.8	23 11.9	24 11.3	29 24.2	19 11.6	13 47.8	2 42.2	2 20.3
5	22 54 22.6	11 56.0	24 18.3	25 56.5	25 11.6	24 25.8	24 35.9	29 34.8	19 12.7	13 51.2	2 43.8	2 22.3
6	22 58 19.1	12 54.2	24 15.1	8♊ .5	25 39.0	25 39.8	25 .1	29 45.6	19 14.0	13 54.6	2 45.4	2 24.3
7	23 2 15.7	13 52.4	24 11.9	20 20.1	26 14.9	26 53.8	25 23.7	29 56.4	19 15.3	13 57.9	2 47.0	2 26.3
8	23 6 12.2	14 50.6	24 8.7	3♋ .1	26 59.0	28 7.8	25 46.8	0♏ 7.2	19 16.7	14 1.3	2 48.6	2 28.3
9	23 10 8.8	15 48.9	24 5.5	16 4.5	27 50.9	29 21.8	26 9.4	0 18.2	19 18.2	14 4.6	2 50.3	2 30.2
10	23 14 5.3	16 47.2	24 2.4	29 35.9	28 50.4	0♍35.9	26 31.5	0 29.2	19 19.7	14 7.8	2 51.9	2 32.2
11	23 18 1.9	17 45.6	23 59.2	13♌34.5	29 57.0	1 50.0	26 53.1	0 40.3	19 21.4	14 11.1	2 53.6	2 34.1
12	23 21 58.4	18 44.0	23 56.0	27 58.3	1♍10.0	3 4.2	27 14.1	0 51.5	19 23.2	14 14.3	2 55.3	2 36.1
13	23 25 55.0	19 42.4	23 52.8	12♍42.3	2 29.1	4 18.4	27 34.6	1 2.7	19 25.1	14 17.5	2 57.1	2 38.0
14	23 29 51.5	20 40.8	23 49.6	27 39.3	3 53.6	5 32.6	27 54.4	1 14.0	19 27.1	14 20.7	2 58.8	2 39.9
15	23 33 48.1	21 39.3	23 46.5	12♎40.6	5 23.0	6 46.8	28 13.7	1 25.4	19 29.1	14 23.8	3 .6	2 41.8
16	23 37 44.6	22 37.8	23 43.3	27 37.7	6 56.6	8 1.1	28 32.4	1 36.9	19 31.3	14 27.0	3 2.4	2 43.7
17	23 41 41.2	23 36.3	23 40.1	12♏23.2	8 33.9	9 15.5	28 50.5	1 48.4	19 33.5	14 30.0	3 4.2	2 45.6
18	23 45 37.7	24 34.9	23 36.9	26 51.7	10 14.3	10 29.8	29 8.0	1 60.0	19 35.9	14 33.1	3 6.0	2 47.5
19	23 49 34.3	25 33.5	23 33.8	11♐ .2	11 57.4	11 44.2	29 24.8	2 11.6	19 38.3	14 36.1	3 7.9	2 49.4
20	23 53 30.8	26 32.1	23 30.6	24 47.7	13 42.6	12 58.6	29 41.0	2 23.3	19 40.9	14 39.1	3 9.8	2 51.2
21	23 57 27.4	27 30.7	23 27.4	8♑14.6	15 29.4	14 13.0	29 56.6	2 35.1	19 43.5	14 42.1	3 11.7	2 53.1
22	0 1 23.9	28 29.4	23 24.2	21 22.4	17 17.6	15 27.5	0♊11.5	2 46.9	19 46.2	14 45.0	3 13.6	2 54.9
23	0 5 20.5	29 28.1	23 21.0	4♒13.1	19 6.7	16 42.0	0 25.7	2 58.8	19 49.0	14 47.9	3 15.5	2 56.8
24	0 9 17.0	0♎26.8	23 17.9	16 49.0	20 56.5	17 56.5	0 39.2	3 10.7	19 51.9	14 50.8	3 17.4	2 58.6
25	0 13 13.6	1 25.6	23 14.7	29 12.0	22 46.5	19 11.1	0 52.1	3 22.7	19 54.8	14 53.6	3 19.4	3 .4
26	0 17 10.1	2 24.4	23 11.5	11♓24.2	24 36.8	20 25.7	1 4.2	3 34.8	19 57.9	14 56.4	3 21.4	3 2.2
27	0 21 6.7	3 23.2	23 8.3	23 27.5	26 27.0	21 40.3	1 15.6	3 46.9	20 1.1	14 59.2	3 23.4	3 4.0
28	0 25 3.2	4 22.1	23 5.2	5♈23.4	28 16.9	22 55.0	1 26.3	3 59.1	20 4.3	15 2.0	3 25.4	3 5.8
29	0 28 59.8	5 21.0	23 2.0	17 14.2	0♎ 6.5	24 9.6	1 36.2	4 11.3	20 7.6	15 4.6	3 27.4	3 7.5
30	0 32 56.4	6 19.9	22 58.8	29 1.8	1 55.6	25 24.3	1 45.4	4 23.5	20 11.0	15 7.3	3 29.5	3 9.3

LATITUDE

DAY	EPHEM. SID. TIME	☉	☊	☽	☿	♀	♂	♃	♄	♅	♆	♇
1	22 38 36.3	0 .0	0 .0	1N16.7	2S11.7	0N54.6	2S15.5	1N 3.0	1N13.0	0N37.7	1N43.6	11N23.7
4	22 50 26.0	0 .0	0 .0	1S52.4	1 15.4	1 .3	2 13.4	1 2.5	1 12.5	0 37.7	1 43.5	11 24.0
7	23 2 15.7	0 .0	0 .0	4 22.9	0 22.4	1 5.4	2 11.1	1 2.1	1 11.9	0 37.8	1 43.4	11 24.4
10	23 14 5.3	0 .0	0 .0	5 9.8	0N23.4	1 10.1	2 8.5	1 1.6	1 11.3	0 37.9	1 43.3	11 24.8
13	23 25 55.0	0 .0	0 .0	3 20.8	0 60.0	1 14.2	2 5.6	1 1.2	1 10.8	0 37.9	1 43.1	11 25.3
16	23 37 44.6	0 .0	0 .0	0N28.1	1 26.3	1 17.8	2 2.4	1 .7	1 10.2	0 38.0	1 43.0	11 25.8
19	23 49 34.3	0 .0	0 .0	3 55.9	1 42.7	1 20.8	1 58.8	1 .3	1 9.7	0 38.1	1 42.9	11 26.4
22	0 1 23.9	0 .0	0 .0	5 14.8	1 50.2	1 23.3	1 55.0	0 59.9	1 9.1	0 38.2	1 42.8	11 27.0
25	0 13 13.6	0 .0	0 .0	4 12.6	1 50.3	1 25.1	1 50.8	0 59.6	1 8.6	0 38.3	1 42.8	11 27.7
28	0 25 3.2	0 .0	0 .0	1 32.0	1 44.3	1 26.3	1 46.2	0 59.2	1 8.0	0 38.4	1 42.7	11 28.4

RIGHT ASCENSION

DAY	EPHEM. SID. TIME	☉	☊	☽	☿	♀	♂	♃	♄	♅	♆	♇
1	22 38 36.3	9♍43.0	22♎42.3	7♈26.0	26♌20.4	22♌13.4	21♉ 6.6	27♎13.3	18♐18.2	16♌16.8	1♏ 1.9	8♍34.8
2	22 42 32.9	10 37.4	22 39.3	18 49.5	26R20.2	23 26.7	21 32.6	27 23.0	18 19.1	16 20.3	1 3.3	8 36.8
3	22 46 29.4	11 31.8	22 36.3	0♉21.9	26D28.1	24 39.7	21 58.1	27 32.9	18 20.1	16 23.8	1 4.8	8 38.7
4	22 50 26.0	12 26.1	22 33.3	12 10.0	26 44.2	25 52.6	22 23.3	27 42.9	18 21.1	16 27.2	1 6.2	8 40.7
5	22 54 22.6	13 20.3	22 30.3	24 18.8	27 8.6	27 5.2	22 48.0	27 52.9	18 22.3	16 30.6	1 7.7	8 42.7
6	22 58 19.1	14 14.5	22 27.3	6♊51.7	27 41.1	28 17.6	23 12.3	28 3.1	18 23.6	16 34.0	1 9.2	8 44.7
7	23 2 15.7	15 8.6	22 24.3	19 49.2	28 21.5	29 29.8	23 36.0	28 13.3	18 25.0	16 37.4	1 10.7	8 46.7
8	23 6 12.2	16 2.6	22 21.4	3♋ 9.3	29 9.6	0♍41.7	23 59.3	28 23.6	18 26.5	16 40.7	1 12.3	8 48.6
9	23 10 8.8	16 56.7	22 18.4	16 47.6	0♍ 5.0	1 53.5	24 22.1	28 34.0	18 28.1	16 44.0	1 13.8	8 50.6
10	23 14 5.3	17 50.6	22 15.4	0♌38.6	1 7.2	3 5.0	24 44.4	28 44.4	18 29.8	16 47.3	1 15.4	8 52.6
11	23 18 1.9	18 44.6	22 12.4	14 37.2	2 15.7	4 16.4	25 6.1	28 55.0	18 31.6	16 50.6	1 17.0	8 54.5
12	23 21 58.4	19 38.5	22 9.4	28 40.0	3 30.0	5 27.5	25 27.4	29 5.6	18 33.5	16 53.8	1 18.6	8 56.5
13	23 25 55.0	20 32.4	22 6.4	12♍46.5	4 49.4	6 38.4	25 48.0	29 16.3	18 35.5	16 57.0	1 20.3	8 58.4
14	23 29 51.5	21 26.3	22 3.4	26 58.4	6 13.4	7 49.2	26 8.1	29 27.0	18 37.6	17 .2	1 22.0	9 .3
15	23 33 48.1	22 20.1	22 .4	11♎18.6	7 41.3	8 59.8	26 27.6	29 37.8	18 39.8	17 3.4	1 23.6	9 2.3
16	23 37 44.6	23 13.9	21 57.4	25 49.3	9 12.6	10 10.2	26 46.5	29 48.7	18 42.1	17 6.5	1 25.4	9 4.2
17	23 41 41.2	24 7.8	21 54.4	10♏30.1	10 46.7	11 20.4	27 4.7	29 59.7	18 44.5	17 9.6	1 27.1	9 6.1
18	23 45 37.7	25 1.6	21 51.4	25 16.7	12 23.1	12 30.5	27 22.4	0♏10.7	18 47.0	17 12.7	1 28.8	9 8.0
19	23 49 34.3	25 55.4	21 48.4	10♐ .6	14 1.2	13 40.4	27 39.4	0 21.8	18 49.6	17 15.7	1 30.6	9 9.9
20	23 53 30.8	26 49.2	21 45.4	24 31.3	15 40.6	14 50.2	27 55.8	0 33.0	18 52.3	17 18.7	1 32.4	9 11.8
21	23 57 27.4	27 43.0	21 42.4	8♑38.5	17 21.0	15 59.8	28 11.5	0 44.2	18 55.1	17 21.7	1 34.2	9 13.7
22	0 1 23.9	28 36.9	21 39.5	22 14.9	19 2.0	17 9.3	28 26.6	0 55.5	18 58.0	17 24.6	1 36.0	9 15.6
23	0 5 20.5	29 30.7	21 36.5	5♒17.6	20 43.2	18 18.6	28 40.9	1 6.9	19 1.0	17 27.5	1 37.8	9 17.5
24	0 9 17.0	0♎24.6	21 33.5	17 48.1	22 24.5	19 27.9	28 54.6	1 18.3	19 4.1	17 30.4	1 39.7	9 19.3
25	0 13 13.6	1 18.5	21 30.5	29 50.6	24 5.7	20 37.0	29 7.5	1 29.8	19 7.3	17 33.2	1 41.5	9 21.2
26	0 17 10.1	2 12.5	21 27.5	11♓31.8	25 46.6	21 46.1	29 19.7	1 41.3	19 10.5	17 36.1	1 43.4	9 23.0
27	0 21 6.7	3 6.5	21 24.5	22 59.2	27 27.0	22 55.1	29 31.2	1 53.0	19 14.0	17 38.9	1 45.4	9 24.9
28	0 25 3.2	4 .5	21 21.5	4♈20.4	29 6.9	24 3.9	29 41.9	2 4.6	19 17.4	17 41.6	1 47.3	9 26.7
29	0 28 59.8	4 54.6	21 18.5	15 42.6	0♎46.2	25 12.7	29 51.8	2 16.3	19 21.0	17 44.3	1 49.2	9 28.5
30	0 32 56.4	5 48.8	21 15.5	27 12.6	2 24.9	26 21.5	0♊ .9	2 28.1	19 24.6	17 47.0	1 51.1	9 30.3

DECLINATION

DAY	EPHEM. SID. TIME	☉	☊	☽	☿	♀	♂	♃	♄	♅	♆	♇
1	22 38 36.3	8N32.9	0S10.0	4N36.2	11N11.3	15N50.1	16N19.0	10S 5.7	21S47.1	17N20.3	10S45.8	21N16.7
4	22 50 26.0	7 27.3	0 9.9	14 16.1	12 2.8	14 44.2	16 39.9	10 17.3	21 47.9	17 17.4	10 47.5	21 14.8
7	23 2 15.7	6 20.6	0 9.8	18 43.2	12 25.1	13 34.5	16 59.5	10 29.0	21 48.8	17 14.5	10 49.2	21 13.0
10	23 14 5.3	5 13.0	0 9.8	15 11.2	12 14.7	12 21.3	17 17.8	10 40.9	21 49.7	17 11.7	10 51.0	21 11.2
13	23 25 55.0	4 4.6	0 9.7	3 41.9	11 31.4	11 5.1	17 35.0	10 53.0	21 50.7	17 9.0	10 52.9	21 9.5
16	23 37 44.6	2 55.5	0 9.6	10S11.6	10 18.0	9 46.0	17 50.9	11 5.2	21 51.7	17 6.3	10 54.8	21 7.8
19	23 49 34.3	1 45.9	0 9.6	18 12.1	8 39.6	8 24.4	18 5.6	11 17.6	21 52.8	17 3.7	10 56.7	21 6.2
22	0 1 23.9	0 36.0	0 9.5	16 33.6	6 42.7	7 .7	18 19.2	11 30.0	21 54.0	17 1.2	10 58.7	21 4.7
25	0 13 13.6	0S34.0	0 9.5	7 48.3	4 33.3	5 35.1	18 31.6	11 42.6	21 55.2	16 58.8	11 .8	21 3.3
28	0 25 3.2	1 44.2	0 9.4	3N33.0	2 16.7	4 8.0	18 43.0	11 55.2	21 56.4	16 56.4	11 2.9	21 2.0

OCTOBER 1958

LONGITUDE

DAY	EPHEM. SID. TIME h m s	☉ ° ′	☊ ° ′	☽ ° ′	☿ ° ′	♀ ° ′	♂ ° ′	♃ ° ′	♄ ° ′	♅ ° ′	♆ ° ′	♇ ° ′
1	0 36 52.9	7♎18.8	22♎55.6	10♉48.9	3♎44.1	26♍39.0	1♊53.8	4♏35.8	20♐14.5	15♌ 9.9	3♏31.5	3♍11.0
2	0 40 49.5	8 17.8	22 52.4	22 38.4	5 32.0	27 53.8	2 1.4	4 48.2	20 18.1	15 12.5	3 33.6	3 12.7
3	0 44 46.0	9 16.9	22 49.3	4♊33.7	7 19.2	29 8.5	2 8.1	5 .6	20 21.7	15 15.0	3 35.6	3 14.4
4	0 48 42.6	10 15.9	22 46.1	16 38.6	9 5.7	0♎23.3	2 14.1	5 13.0	20 25.5	15 17.5	3 37.7	3 16.0
5	0 52 39.1	11 15.0	22 42.9	28 57.4	10 51.5	1 38.2	2 19.2	5 25.5	20 29.3	15 20.0	3 39.8	3 17.7
6	0 56 35.7	12 14.2	22 39.7	11♋34.2	12 36.5	2 53.0	2 23.5	5 38.0	20 33.2	15 22.4	3 41.9	3 19.3
7	1 0 32.2	13 13.4	22 36.5	24 33.1	14 20.8	4 7.9	2 27.0	5 50.6	20 37.1	15 24.8	3 44.1	3 21.0
8	1 4 28.8	14 12.6	22 33.4	7♌57.2	16 4.2	5 22.8	2 29.5	6 3.2	20 41.2	15 27.1	3 46.2	3 22.6
9	1 8 25.3	15 11.8	22 30.2	21 48.5	17 46.9	6 37.7	2 31.2	6 15.8	20 45.3	15 29.4	3 48.3	3 24.1
10	1 12 21.9	16 11.1	22 27.0	6♍ 6.6	19 28.8	7 52.6	2 32.0	6 28.5	20 49.5	15 31.7	3 50.5	3 25.7
11	1 16 18.4	17 10.5	22 23.8	20 48.8	21 10.0	9 7.6	2R31.9	6 41.2	20 53.8	15 33.9	3 52.6	3 27.3
12	1 20 15.0	18 9.8	22 20.7	5♎49.3	22 50.4	10 22.6	2 30.9	6 54.0	20 58.2	15 36.0	3 54.8	3 28.8
13	1 24 11.5	19 9.3	22 17.5	21 .1	24 30.1	11 37.6	2 29.1	7 6.7	21 2.6	15 38.2	3 57.0	3 30.3
14	1 28 8.1	20 8.7	22 14.3	6♏11.7	26 9.0	12 52.6	2 26.3	7 19.5	21 7.1	15 40.2	3 59.2	3 31.8
15	1 32 4.6	21 8.2	22 11.1	21 14.8	27 47.3	14 7.6	2 22.6	7 32.4	21 11.7	15 42.3	4 1.4	3 33.2
16	1 36 1.2	22 7.7	22 7.9	6♐ 1.1	29 24.9	15 22.7	2 18.0	7 45.3	21 16.3	15 44.2	4 3.6	3 34.7
17	1 39 57.7	23 7.2	22 4.8	20 24.8	1♏ 1.7	16 37.8	2 12.5	7 58.2	21 21.1	15 46.2	4 5.8	3 36.1
18	1 43 54.3	24 6.8	22 1.6	4♑23.0	2 38.0	17 52.9	2 6.1	8 11.1	21 25.9	15 48.1	4 8.0	3 37.6
19	1 47 50.8	25 6.4	21 58.4	17 55.0	4 13.6	19 8.0	1 58.9	8 24.1	21 30.8	15 50.0	4 10.3	3 39.0
20	1 51 47.4	26 6.0	21 55.2	1♒ 2.3	5 48.6	20 23.1	1 50.7	8 37.0	21 35.7	15 51.7	4 12.5	3 40.3
21	1 55 44.0	27 5.7	21 52.1	13 47.8	7 22.9	21 38.2	1 41.7	8 50.0	21 40.7	15 53.5	4 14.7	3 41.6
22	1 59 40.5	28 5.4	21 48.9	26 14.8	8 56.7	22 53.4	1 31.8	9 3.1	21 45.7	15 55.2	4 16.9	3 43.0
23	2 3 37.1	29 5.1	21 45.7	8♓27.3	10 29.9	24 8.5	1 21.1	9 16.1	21 50.9	15 56.8	4 19.2	3 44.2
24	2 7 33.6	0♏ 4.8	21 42.5	20 28.8	12 2.5	25 23.7	1 9.6	9 29.1	21 56.0	15 58.4	4 21.4	3 45.5
25	2 11 30.2	1 4.6	21 39.3	2♈22.9	13 34.6	26 38.8	0 57.2	9 42.2	22 1.3	15 60.0	4 23.6	3 46.7
26	2 15 26.7	2 4.4	21 36.2	14 12.4	15 6.1	27 54.0	0 44.0	9 55.3	22 6.6	16 1.5	4 25.9	3 48.0
27	2 19 23.3	3 4.2	21 33.0	26 .2	16 37.1	29 9.2	0 30.1	10 8.4	22 12.0	16 2.9	4 28.1	3 49.2
28	2 23 19.8	4 4.1	21 29.8	7♉48.4	18 7.5	0♏24.4	0 15.4	10 21.5	22 17.4	16 4.3	4 30.4	3 50.3
29	2 27 16.4	5 4.0	21 26.6	19 39.2	19 37.4	1 39.6	29♉59.9	10 34.6	22 22.9	16 5.7	4 32.6	3 51.5
30	2 31 12.9	6 3.9	21 23.5	1♊34.7	21 6.8	2 54.8	29 43.8	10 47.7	22 28.5	16 6.9	4 34.8	3 52.6
31	2 35 9.5	7 3.8	21 20.3	13 37.2	22 35.7	4 10.1	29 27.0	11 .9	22 34.1	16 8.2	4 37.1	3 53.7

LATITUDE

DAY	SID. TIME	☉	☊	☽	☿	♀	♂	♃	♄	♅	♆	♇
1	0 36 52.9	0 .0	0 .0	1S41.2	1N33.8	1N27.0	1S41.3	0N58.9	1N 7.5	0N38.5	1N42.6	11N29.1
4	0 48 42.6	0 .0	0 .0	4 18.4	1 19.7	1 27.0	1 35.9	0 58.5	1 7.0	0 38.6	1 42.5	11 29.9
7	1 0 32.2	0 .0	0 .0	5 17.6	1 3.2	1 26.4	1 30.1	0 58.2	1 6.5	0 38.7	1 42.5	11 30.8
10	1 12 21.9	0 .0	0 .0	3 49.7	0 44.8	1 25.3	1 23.8	0 58.0	1 6.0	0 38.8	1 42.4	11 31.6
13	1 24 11.5	0 .0	0 .0	0 7.1	0 25.2	1 23.5	1 17.1	0 57.7	1 5.5	0 38.9	1 42.4	11 32.6
16	1 36 1.2	0 .0	0 .0	3N40.3	0 4.9	1 21.2	1 9.9	0 57.4	1 5.1	0 39.0	1 42.4	11 33.5
19	1 47 50.8	0 .0	0 .0	5 17.3	0S15.6	1 18.4	1 2.2	0 57.2	1 4.6	0 39.1	1 42.3	11 34.5
22	1 59 40.5	0 .0	0 .0	4 24.1	0 36.1	1 15.0	0 54.1	0 57.0	1 4.2	0 39.2	1 42.3	11 35.5
25	2 11 30.2	0 .0	0 .0	1 48.7	0 56.1	1 11.1	0 45.6	0 56.8	1 3.7	0 39.3	1 42.3	11 36.6
28	2 23 19.8	0 .0	0 .0	1S24.8	1 15.4	1 6.8	0 36.7	0 56.6	1 3.3	0 39.5	1 42.3	11 37.7
31	2 35 9.5	0 .0	0 .0	4 7.5	1 33.7	1 2.0	0 27.4	0 56.4	1 2.9	0 39.6	1 42.3	11 38.8

RIGHT ASCENSION

DAY	SID. TIME	☉	☊	☽	☿	♀	♂	♃	♄	♅	♆	♇
1	0 36 52.9	6♎43.0	21♎12.6	8♉56.0	4♎ 2.9	27♍30.2	0♊ 9.2	2♏39.9	19♐28.3	17♌49.6	1♏53.1	9♍32.0
2	0 40 49.5	7 37.3	21 9.6	20 56.6	5 40.2	28 38.8	0 16.7	2 51.8	19 32.2	17 52.2	1 55.1	9 33.8
3	0 44 46.0	8 31.6	21 6.6	3♊16.8	7 16.8	29 47.4	0 23.4	3 3.7	19 36.1	17 54.7	1 57.0	9 35.5
4	0 48 42.6	9 26.0	21 3.6	15 56.6	8 52.8	0♎56.0	0 29.2	3 15.6	19 40.1	17 57.2	1 59.0	9 37.3
5	0 52 39.1	10 20.6	21 .6	28 54.2	10 28.1	2 4.6	0 34.1	3 27.6	19 44.2	17 59.7	2 1.0	9 39.0
6	0 56 35.7	11 15.2	20 57.6	12♋ 6.4	12 2.8	3 13.2	0 38.2	3 39.7	19 48.3	18 2.1	2 3.1	9 40.7
7	1 0 32.2	12 9.9	20 54.6	25 29.6	13 36.9	4 21.8	0 41.3	3 51.8	19 52.6	18 4.5	2 5.1	9 42.4
8	1 4 28.8	13 4.7	20 51.6	9♌ 1.2	15 10.4	5 30.4	0 43.6	4 4.0	19 56.9	18 6.8	2 7.1	9 44.1
9	1 8 25.3	13 59.7	20 48.7	22 40.3	16 43.4	6 39.0	0 44.9	4 16.2	20 1.4	18 9.1	2 9.2	9 45.7
10	1 12 21.9	14 54.7	20 45.7	6♍28.1	18 15.9	7 47.7	0 45.3	4 28.4	20 5.9	18 11.4	2 11.2	9 47.4
11	1 16 18.4	15 49.9	20 42.7	20 28.1	19 48.0	8 56.4	0R44.8	4 40.7	20 10.5	18 13.6	2 13.3	9 49.0
12	1 20 15.0	16 45.1	20 39.7	4♎44.7	21 19.6	10 5.2	0 43.3	4 53.0	20 15.1	18 15.8	2 15.4	9 50.6
13	1 24 11.5	17 40.5	20 36.7	19 21.4	22 50.9	11 14.1	0 40.8	5 5.4	20 19.9	18 17.9	2 17.5	9 52.2
14	1 28 8.1	18 36.1	20 33.7	4♏18.5	24 21.8	12 23.0	0 37.4	5 17.8	20 24.7	18 20.0	2 19.6	9 53.7
15	1 32 4.6	19 31.7	20 30.8	19 31.0	25 52.4	13 32.1	0 33.1	5 30.2	20 29.7	18 22.0	2 21.7	9 55.3
16	1 36 1.2	20 27.5	20 27.8	4♐48.1	27 22.8	14 41.2	0 27.8	5 42.7	20 34.7	18 24.0	2 23.8	9 56.8
17	1 39 57.7	21 23.5	20 24.8	19 54.7	28 53.0	15 50.4	0 21.6	5 55.2	20 39.7	18 25.9	2 25.9	9 58.3
18	1 43 54.3	22 19.6	20 21.8	4♑36.0	0♏23.0	16 59.8	0 14.5	6 7.8	20 44.9	18 27.9	2 28.1	9 59.9
19	1 47 50.8	23 15.8	20 18.8	18 41.0	1 52.8	18 9.3	0 6.3	6 20.4	20 50.2	18 29.7	2 30.2	10 1.4
20	1 51 47.4	24 12.2	20 15.8	2♒ 4.8	3 22.4	19 18.9	29♉57.3	6 33.0	20 55.4	18 31.5	2 32.3	10 2.8
21	1 55 44.0	25 8.7	20 12.9	14 48.9	4 52.0	20 28.6	29 47.4	6 45.7	21 .8	18 33.3	2 34.4	10 4.3
22	1 59 40.5	26 5.4	20 9.9	26 58.7	6 21.5	21 38.5	29 36.5	6 58.3	21 6.3	18 35.0	2 36.6	10 5.7
23	2 3 37.1	27 2.2	20 6.9	8♓42.4	7 50.9	22 48.6	29 24.8	7 11.0	21 11.8	18 36.6	2 38.7	10 7.1
24	2 7 33.6	27 59.2	20 3.9	20 9.1	9 20.3	23 58.8	29 12.1	7 23.7	21 17.3	18 38.2	2 40.9	10 8.4
25	2 11 30.2	28 56.4	20 .9	1♈27.8	10 49.6	25 9.2	28 58.7	7 36.5	21 23.0	18 39.8	2 43.0	10 9.8
26	2 15 26.7	29 53.7	19 58.0	12 47.0	12 19.0	26 19.9	28 44.3	7 49.2	21 28.7	18 41.3	2 45.2	10 11.1
27	2 19 23.3	0♏51.3	19 55.0	24 14.1	13 48.3	27 30.7	28 29.2	8 2.0	21 34.5	18 42.7	2 47.3	10 12.4
28	2 23 19.8	1 49.0	19 52.0	5♉54.8	15 17.7	28 41.7	28 13.3	8 14.8	21 40.3	18 44.1	2 49.5	10 13.7
29	2 27 16.4	2 46.9	19 49.0	17 53.1	16 47.1	29 53.0	27 56.6	8 27.7	21 46.3	18 45.5	2 51.6	10 14.9
30	2 31 12.9	3 45.0	19 46.1	0♊10.4	18 16.5	1♏ 4.4	27 39.1	8 40.5	21 52.2	18 46.8	2 53.8	10 16.2
31	2 35 9.5	4 43.2	19 43.1	12 45.7	19 45.9	2 16.2	27 21.0	8 53.4	21 58.3	18 48.0	2 56.0	10 17.4

DECLINATION

DAY	SID. TIME	☉	☊	☽	☿	♀	♂	♃	♄	♅	♆	♇
1	0 36 52.9	2S54.2	0S 9.3	13N28.1	0S 3.0	2N39.7	18N53.4	12S 7.9	21S57.7	16N54.1	11S 5.0	21N .7
4	0 48 42.6	4 3.9	0 9.3	18 29.2	2 23.0	1 10.5	19 2.6	12 20.6	21 59.0	16 52.0	11 7.2	20 59.6
7	1 0 32.2	5 13.3	0 9.2	16 .2	4 41.2	0S19.2	19 10.9	12 33.3	22 .3	16 49.9	11 9.4	20 58.5
10	1 12 21.9	6 22.0	0 9.2	5 42.6	6 56.0	1 49.2	19 18.0	12 46.1	22 1.6	16 48.0	11 11.6	20 57.6
13	1 24 11.5	7 30.0	0 9.1	8S18.4	9 6.3	3 19.0	19 24.0	12 58.8	22 3.0	16 46.2	11 13.8	20 56.7
16	1 36 1.2	8 37.1	0 9.0	17 41.8	11 11.4	4 48.4	19 28.9	13 11.5	22 4.4	16 44.5	11 16.1	20 55.9
19	1 47 50.8	9 43.1	0 9.0	16 60.0	13 10.5	6 17.0	19 32.7	13 24.2	22 5.7	16 42.9	11 18.3	20 55.3
22	1 59 40.5	10 47.8	0 8.9	8 37.5	15 3.1	7 44.4	19 35.2	13 36.9	22 7.1	16 41.4	11 20.6	20 54.7
25	2 11 30.2	11 51.0	0 8.8	2N36.6	16 48.5	9 10.3	19 36.5	13 49.5	22 8.5	16 40.1	11 22.8	20 54.3
28	2 23 19.8	12 52.6	0 8.8	12 46.6	18 26.3	10 34.4	19 36.6	14 2.0	22 9.9	16 38.9	11 25.1	20 53.9
31	2 35 9.5	13 52.4	0 8.7	18 20.6	19 55.9	11 56.3	19 35.4	14 14.4	22 11.2	16 37.9	11 27.3	20 53.7

LONGITUDE

DAY	EPHEM. SID. TIME (h m s)	☉	☊	☽	☿	♀	♂	♃	♄	♅	♆	♇
1	2 39 6.0	8♏3.8	21≏17.1	25♉48.9	24♏3.9	5♏25.3	29♉9.5	11♏14.0	22♐39.7	16♌9.4	4♏39.3	3♍54.7
2	2 43 2.6	9 3.9	21 13.9	8♊12.4	25 31.7	6 40.6	28R51.4	11 27.2	22 45.4	16 10.5	4 41.6	3 55.8
3	2 46 59.1	10 3.9	21 10.7	20 50.7	26 58.8	7 55.8	28 32.8	11 40.4	22 51.2	16 11.6	4 43.8	3 56.8
4	2 50 55.7	11 4.0	21 7.6	3♋46.7	28 25.4	9 11.1	28 13.5	11 53.5	22 57.0	16 12.6	4 46.0	3 57.8
5	2 54 52.3	12 4.2	21 4.4	17 3.2	29 51.3	10 26.4	27 53.8	12 6.7	23 2.9	16 13.6	4 48.3	3 58.7
6	2 58 48.8	13 4.3	21 1.2	0♌42.7	1♐16.6	11 41.7	27 33.7	12 19.9	23 8.6	16 14.5	4 50.5	3 59.7
7	3 2 45.4	14 4.5	20 58.0	14 46.1	2 41.1	12 57.0	27 13.1	12 33.1	23 14.8	16 15.4	4 52.7	4 .6
8	3 6 41.9	15 4.8	20 54.9	29 13.1	4 5.0	14 12.4	26 52.1	12 46.3	23 20.9	16 16.2	4 55.0	4 1.5
9	3 10 38.5	16 5.1	20 51.7	14♍.6	5 28.0	15 27.7	26 30.9	12 59.5	23 27.0	16 17.0	4 57.2	4 2.3
10	3 14 35.0	17 5.4	20 48.5	29 3.2	6 50.0	16 43.1	26 9.3	13 12.6	23 33.1	16 17.7	4 59.4	4 3.1
11	3 18 31.6	18 5.8	20 45.3	14♎12.9	8 11.2	17 58.4	25 47.5	13 25.8	23 39.3	16 18.3	5 1.6	4 3.9
12	3 22 28.1	19 6.1	20 42.1	29 20.2	9 31.2	19 13.8	25 25.6	13 39.0	23 45.5	16 18.9	5 3.8	4 4.7
13	3 26 24.7	20 6.5	20 39.0	14♏15.8	10 50.0	20 29.2	25 3.6	13 52.1	23 51.8	16 19.5	5 6.0	4 5.4
14	3 30 21.2	21 6.9	20 35.8	28 51.3	12 7.5	21 44.5	24 41.5	14 5.3	23 58.1	16 19.9	5 8.2	4 6.1
15	3 34 17.8	22 7.4	20 32.6	13♐1.1	13 23.4	22 59.9	24 19.4	14 18.4	24 4.4	16 20.4	5 10.3	4 6.8
16	3 38 14.4	23 7.8	20 29.4	26 42.7	14 37.7	24 15.3	23 57.4	14 31.5	24 10.8	16 20.7	5 12.5	4 7.4
17	3 42 10.9	24 8.3	20 26.3	9♑56.2	15 50.1	25 30.6	23 35.5	14 44.6	24 17.2	16 21.0	5 14.7	4 8.1
18	3 46 7.5	25 8.8	20 23.1	22 44.0	17 .3	26 46.0	23 13.7	14 57.7	24 23.7	16 21.3	5 16.8	4 8.6
19	3 50 4.0	26 9.4	20 19.9	5♒10.1	18 8.0	28 1.4	22 52.2	15 10.8	24 30.2	16 21.5	5 18.9	4 9.2
20	3 54 .6	27 9.9	20 16.7	17 19.1	19 13.1	29 16.8	22 30.9	15 23.9	24 36.7	16 21.6	5 21.0	4 9.7
21	3 57 57.1	28 10.5	20 13.6	29 16.1	20 14.9	0♐32.1	22 10.0	15 36.9	24 43.3	16 21.7	5 23.2	4 10.2
22	4 1 53.7	29 11.1	20 10.4	11♓5.7	21 13.3	1 47.5	21 49.4	15 50.0	24 49.9	16 21.8	5 25.2	4 10.7
23	4 5 50.2	0♐11.7	20 7.2	22 52.4	22 7.5	3 2.9	21 29.2	16 3.0	24 56.5	16R21.7	5 27.3	4 11.1
24	4 9 46.8	1 12.3	20 4.0	4♈39.9	22 57.2	4 18.3	21 9.4	16 15.9	25 3.2	16 21.7	5 29.4	4 11.5
25	4 13 43.4	2 13.0	20 .8	16 31.4	23 41.8	5 33.7	20 50.1	16 28.9	25 9.8	16 21.5	5 31.5	4 11.9
26	4 17 39.9	3 13.7	19 57.7	28 29.2	24 20.4	6 49.0	20 31.3	16 41.8	25 16.6	16 21.3	5 33.5	4 12.2
27	4 21 36.5	4 14.3	19 54.5	10♉35.2	24 52.6	8 4.4	20 13.1	16 54.7	25 23.3	16 21.1	5 35.5	4 12.5
28	4 25 33.0	5 15.1	19 51.3	22 50.6	25 17.3	9 19.8	19 54.9	17 7.6	25 29.9	16 20.5	5 39.6	4 13.1
29	4 29 29.6	6 15.9	19 48.1	5♊16.4	25 34.0	10 35.2	19 38.4	17 20.1	25 36.9	16 20.1	5 41.6	4 13.3
30	4 33 26.1	7 16.6	19 45.0	17 53.4	25 41.7	11 50.6	19 22.0	17 33.3	25 43.8	16 19.9	5 42.8	4 13.9

LATITUDE

DAY	SID. TIME	☉	☊	☽	☿	♀	♂	♃	♄	♅	♆	♇
1	2 39 6.0	0 .0	0 .0	4S43.5	1S39.4	1N .3	0S24.3	0N56.4	1N 2.8	0N39.6	1N42.3	11N39.2
4	2 50 55.7	0 .0	0 .0	5 9.7	1 55.7	0 54.9	0 14.7	0 56.2	1 2.4	0 39.7	1 42.4	11 40.3
7	3 2 45.4	0 .0	0 .0	3 12.2	2 10.0	0 49.2	0 4.9	0 56.1	1 2.0	0 39.9	1 42.4	11 41.5
10	3 14 35.0	0 .0	0 .0	0N37.7	2 21.9	0 43.2	0N 4.9	0 56.0	1 1.6	0 40.0	1 42.4	11 42.7
13	3 26 24.7	0 .0	0 .0	4 8.2	2 30.7	0 36.8	0 14.7	0 55.9	1 1.3	0 40.1	1 42.5	11 43.9
16	3 38 14.4	0 .0	0 .0	5 12.4	2 35.6	0 30.2	0 24.3	0 55.8	1 .9	0 40.3	1 42.5	11 45.2
19	3 50 4.0	0 .0	0 .0	4 48.3	2 35.7	0 23.4	0 33.6	0 55.7	1 .6	0 40.4	1 42.6	11 46.4
22	4 1 53.7	0 .0	0 .0	0 58.7	2 29.5	0 16.5	0 42.5	0 55.7	1 .3	0 40.5	1 42.7	11 47.7
25	4 13 43.4	0 .0	0 .0	2S10.0	2 15.4	0 9.4	0 51.0	0 55.6	0 60.0	0 40.6	1 42.7	11 49.0
28	4 25 33.0	0 .0	0 .0	4 31.0	1 58.3	0 .1	0 59.1	0 55.6	0 59.7	0 40.8	1 42.8	11 50.2

RIGHT ASCENSION

DAY	SID. TIME	☉	☊	☽	☿	♀	♂	♃	♄	♅	♆	♇
1	2 39 6.0	5♏41.7	19≏40.1	25♊35.8	21♏15.3	3♏28.1	27♉2.2	9♏6.3	22♐4.4	18♌49.2	2♏58.1	10♍18.6
2	2 43 2.6	6 40.4	19 37.1	8♋36.1	22 44.7	4 40.3	26R42.7	9 19.2	22 10.5	18 50.4	3 .3	10 19.7
3	2 46 59.1	7 39.3	19 34.1	21 42.1	24 14.0	5 52.8	26 22.6	9 32.1	22 16.7	18 51.5	3 2.4	10 20.9
4	2 50 55.7	8 38.4	19 31.2	4♌50.8	25 43.2	7 5.5	26 2.0	9 45.0	22 23.0	18 52.5	3 4.6	10 22.0
5	2 54 52.3	9 37.7	19 28.2	18 1.9	27 12.3	8 18.5	25 40.8	9 58.0	22 29.3	18 53.5	3 6.7	10 23.1
6	2 58 48.8	10 37.2	19 25.2	1♍17.9	28 41.2	9 31.8	25 19.2	10 10.9	22 35.7	18 54.4	3 8.9	10 24.1
7	3 2 45.4	11 36.9	19 22.2	14 44.2	0♐9.9	10 45.1	24 57.2	10 23.9	22 42.2	18 55.3	3 11.0	10 25.2
8	3 6 41.9	12 36.9	19 19.3	28 27.9	1 38.3	11 59.3	24 34.8	10 36.9	22 48.7	18 56.1	3 13.2	10 26.2
9	3 10 38.5	13 37.1	19 16.3	12♎36.1	3 6.3	13 13.4	24 12.0	10 49.9	22 55.3	18 56.9	3 15.3	10 27.2
10	3 14 35.0	14 37.5	19 13.3	27 14.0	4 33.7	14 27.9	23 49.0	11 2.9	23 1.9	18 57.6	3 17.5	10 28.2
11	3 18 31.6	15 38.0	19 10.3	12♏21.4	6 .5	15 42.6	23 25.7	11 15.9	23 8.5	18 58.3	3 19.6	10 29.1
12	3 22 28.1	16 38.8	19 7.4	27 26.6	7 26.6	16 57.7	23 2.4	11 28.9	23 15.2	18 58.9	3 21.7	10 30.0
13	3 26 24.7	17 39.9	19 4.4	13♐26.1	8 51.7	18 13.0	22 38.9	11 41.9	23 22.0	18 59.4	3 23.8	10 30.9
14	3 30 21.2	18 41.1	19 1.4	28 17.7	10 15.7	19 28.7	22 15.3	11 54.9	23 28.8	18 59.9	3 25.9	10 31.7
15	3 34 17.8	19 42.5	18 58.4	13♑37.1	11 38.4	20 44.6	21 51.8	12 7.9	23 35.6	19 .3	3 28.0	10 32.5
16	3 38 14.4	20 44.1	18 55.5	27 42.6	12 59.5	22 .2	21 28.4	12 20.9	23 42.5	19 .7	3 30.1	10 33.3
17	3 42 10.9	21 46.0	18 52.5	11♒1.0	14 18.9	23 17.5	21 5.1	12 33.8	23 49.4	19 1.0	3 32.2	10 34.1
18	3 46 7.5	22 48.0	18 49.5	23 35.9	15 36.0	24 35.3	20 42.0	12 46.8	23 56.4	19 1.3	3 34.2	10 34.8
19	3 50 4.0	23 50.3	18 46.6	5♓35.8	16 50.7	25 51.5	20 19.2	12 59.8	24 3.4	19 1.5	3 36.3	10 35.5
20	3 54 .6	24 52.7	18 43.6	17 10.8	18 2.6	27 9.0	19 56.6	13 12.8	24 10.5	19 1.7	3 38.3	10 36.2
21	3 57 57.1	25 55.4	18 40.6	28 31.7	19 11.1	28 26.7	19 34.4	13 25.7	24 17.6	19 1.8	3 40.4	10 36.9
22	4 1 53.7	26 58.2	18 37.6	9♈48.8	20 15.8	29 44.8	19 12.5	13 38.7	24 24.7	19 1.8	3 42.4	10 37.5
23	4 5 50.2	28 1.3	18 34.7	21 11.5	21 16.0	1♐2.3	18 51.1	13 51.6	24 31.8	19 1.8	3 44.4	10 38.1
24	4 9 46.8	29 4.5	18 31.7	2♉47.3	22 11.3	2 21.8	18 30.2	14 4.5	24 39.0	19R1.8	3 46.4	10 38.6
25	4 13 43.4	0♐7.9	18 28.7	14 41.8	23 .9	3 40.7	18 9.7	14 17.4	24 46.1	19 1.6	3 48.4	10 39.2
26	4 17 39.9	1 11.6	18 25.8	26 57.6	23 44.0	4 60.0	17 49.9	14 30.3	24 53.5	19 1.5	3 50.4	10 39.7
27	4 21 36.5	2 15.4	18 22.8	9♊14.3	24 19.9	6 19.4	17 30.6	14 43.2	25 .8	19 1.2	3 52.4	10 40.1
28	4 25 33.0	3 19.4	18 19.8	22 27.9	24 47.7	7 39.2	17 11.9	14 56.0	25 8.1	19 .9	3 54.3	10 40.6
29	4 29 29.6	4 23.6	18 16.9	5♋32.3	25 6.5	8 59.2	16 53.9	15 8.9	25 15.5	19 .6	3 56.3	10 41.0
30	4 33 26.1	5 27.9	18 13.9	18 40.5	25 15.4	10 19.5	16 36.5	15 21.7	25 22.9	19 .3	3 58.2	10 41.4

DECLINATION

DAY	SID. TIME	☉	☊	☽	☿	♀	♂	♃	♄	♅	♆	♇
1	2 39 6.0	14S11.9	0S 8.7	18N39.2	20S23.8	12S23.0	19N34.7	14S18.5	22S11.7	16N37.6	11S28.1	20N53.7
4	2 50 55.7	15 9.0	0 8.6	14 17.2	21 41.5	13 41.4	19 31.7	14 30.8	22 13.0	16 36.7	11 30.3	20 53.6
7	3 2 45.4	16 3.9	0 8.6	3 2.5	22 49.5	14 56.7	19 27.6	14 43.0	22 14.3	16 36.0	11 32.5	20 53.8
10	3 14 35.0	16 56.4	0 8.5	10S33.1	23 47.0	16 8.7	19 22.4	14 55.0	22 15.6	16 35.4	11 34.7	20 53.8
13	3 26 24.7	17 46.3	0 8.4	18 24.3	24 33.5	17 16.9	19 16.2	15 6.9	22 16.8	16 35.0	11 36.8	20 54.4
16	3 38 14.4	18 33.4	0 8.4	15 42.1	25 7.6	18 20.9	19 9.3	15 18.6	22 18.0	16 34.8	11 38.9	20 54.4
19	3 50 4.0	19 17.6	0 8.3	6 4.1	25 29.8	19 20.5	19 2.0	15 30.2	22 19.1	16 34.7	11 41.0	20 54.9
22	4 1 53.7	19 58.7	0 8.3	5N17.5	25 38.3	20 15.2	18 54.5	15 41.5	22 20.2	16 34.7	11 43.0	20 55.6
25	4 13 43.4	20 36.4	0 8.2	14 42.1	25 32.8	21 4.8	18 47.2	15 52.7	22 21.3	16 34.9	11 45.0	20 56.3
28	4 25 33.0	21 10.7	0 8.1	18 44.3	25 12.6	21 49.0	18 40.2	16 3.7	22 22.3	16 35.2	11 46.9	20 57.1

DECEMBER 1958

LONGITUDE

DAY	EPHEM. SID. TIME	☉	☊	☾	☿	♀	♂	♃	♄	♅	♆	♇
	h m s	° ′	° ′	° ′	° ′	° ′	° ′	° ′	° ′	° ′	° ′	° ′
1	4 37 22.7	8♐17.4	19♎41.8	0♌42.4	25♐39.6	13♐ 6.0	19♉ 6.3	17♏46.1	25♐50.6	16♌19.6	5♏43.5	4♍13.5
2	4 41 19.3	9 18.2	19 38.6	13 44.7	25R27.2	14 21.4	18R51.2	17 58.9	25 57.5	16R19.1	5 45.5	4 13.6
3	4 45 15.8	10 19.1	19 35.4	27 1.7	25 3.8	15 36.8	18 36.9	18 11.6	26 4.4	16 18.5	5 47.4	4 13.8
4	4 49 12.4	11 19.9	19 32.3	10♍34.9	24 29.2	16 52.2	18 23.3	18 24.3	26 11.3	16 17.9	5 49.3	4 13.8
5	4 53 8.9	12 20.8	19 29.1	24 25.5	23 43.6	18 7.6	18 10.4	18 36.9	26 18.2	16 17.2	5 51.2	4 13.9
6	4 57 5.5	13 21.7	19 25.9	8♎34.3	22 47.4	19 23.1	17 58.3	18 49.5	26 25.2	16 16.5	5 53.1	4 13.9
7	5 1 2.0	14 22.6	19 22.7	23 .4	21 41.7	20 38.5	17 47.0	19 2.1	26 32.2	16 15.7	5 55.0	4 13.9
8	5 4 58.6	15 23.6	19 19.5	7♏41.2	20 28.2	21 53.9	17 36.5	19 14.6	26 39.2	16 14.8	5 56.8	4 13.9
9	5 8 55.2	16 24.6	19 16.4	22 31.8	19 9.0	23 9.3	17 26.8	19 27.1	26 46.2	16 13.9	5 58.6	4R13.8
10	5 12 51.7	17 25.6	19 13.2	7♐25.1	17 46.5	24 24.7	17 17.9	19 39.5	26 53.2	16 13.0	6 .4	4 13.7
11	5 16 48.3	18 26.6	19 10.0	22 12.7	16 23.7	25 40.1	17 9.8	19 51.9	27 .2	16 12.0	6 2.2	4 13.6
12	5 20 44.8	19 27.6	19 6.8	6♑46.1	15 3.2	26 55.5	17 2.6	20 4.3	27 7.2	16 10.9	6 4.0	4 13.5
13	5 24 41.4	20 28.6	19 3.7	20 58.4	13 47.8	28 11.0	16 56.2	20 16.6	27 14.3	16 9.8	6 5.7	4 13.3
14	5 28 37.9	21 29.6	19 .5	4♒45.0	12 39.6	29 26.4	16 50.6	20 28.8	27 21.3	16 8.7	6 7.4	4 13.0
15	5 32 34.5	22 30.7	18 57.3	18 4.1	11 40.4	0♑41.8	16 45.9	20 41.0	27 28.4	16 7.5	6 9.1	4 12.8
16	5 36 31.0	23 31.7	18 54.1	0♓56.8	10 51.4	1 57.2	16 42.0	20 53.1	27 35.5	16 6.2	6 10.8	4 12.5
17	5 40 27.6	24 32.8	18 51.0	13 26.2	10 13.3	3 12.6	16 38.9	21 5.2	27 42.6	16 4.9	6 12.4	4 12.2
18	5 44 24.2	25 33.9	18 47.8	25 36.8	9 46.3	4 28.0	16 36.7	21 17.2	27 49.6	16 3.6	6 14.0	4 11.9
19	5 48 20.7	26 35.0	18 44.6	7♈33.9	9 30.3	5 43.4	16 35.3	21 29.2	27 56.7	16 2.2	6 15.6	4 11.5
20	5 52 17.3	27 36.1	18 41.4	19 23.1	9 24.7	6 58.8	16 34.7	21 41.1	28 3.9	16 .8	6 17.2	4 11.1
21	5 56 13.8	28 37.2	18 38.2	1♉ 9.7	9D29.0	8 14.2	16D34.9	21 53.0	28 10.9	15 59.3	6 18.8	4 10.7
22	6 0 10.4	29 38.3	18 35.1	12 58.7	9 42.4	9 29.5	16 35.8	22 4.8	28 18.0	15 57.8	6 20.3	4 10.2
23	6 4 6.9	0♑39.4	18 31.9	24 54.3	10 4.0	10 44.9	16 37.6	22 16.5	28 25.1	15 56.2	6 21.8	4 9.8
24	6 8 3.5	1 40.5	18 28.7	6♊59.8	10 33.3	12 .3	16 40.1	22 28.1	28 32.2	15 54.6	6 23.2	4 9.2
25	6 12 .1	2 41.6	18 25.5	19 17.6	11 9.2	13 15.6	16 43.3	22 39.7	28 39.2	15 52.9	6 24.7	4 8.7
26	6 15 56.6	3 42.7	18 22.4	1♋48.6	11 51.2	14 30.9	16 47.3	22 51.2	28 46.3	15 51.2	6 26.1	4 8.1
27	6 19 53.2	4 43.8	18 19.2	14 33.3	12 38.6	15 46.3	16 52.0	23 2.6	28 53.4	15 49.5	6 27.5	4 7.5
28	6 23 49.7	5 44.9	18 16.0	27 30.8	13 30.8	17 1.6	16 57.5	23 14.0	29 .4	15 47.7	6 28.8	4 6.9
29	6 27 46.3	6 46.0	18 12.8	10♌40.3	14 27.1	18 16.9	17 3.6	23 25.3	29 7.5	15 45.8	6 30.2	4 6.2
30	6 31 42.8	7 47.2	18 9.7	24 .5	15 27.2	19 32.3	17 10.4	23 36.5	29 14.5	15 44.0	6 31.5	4 5.5
31	6 35 39.4	8 48.3	18 6.5	7♍30.6	16 30.6	20 47.6	17 17.9	23 47.6	29 21.5	15 42.0	6 32.7	4 4.8

LATITUDE

DAY	EPHEM. SID. TIME	☉	☊	☾	☿	♀	♂	♃	♄	♅	♆	♇
1	4 37 22.7	0 .0	0 .0	5S 3.9	1S15.0	0S 5.0	1N 6.6	0N55.6	0N59.4	0N40.9	1N42.9	11N51.5
4	4 49 12.4	0 .0	0 .0	3 20.2	0 25.9	0 12.2	1 13.5	0 55.6	0 59.1	0 41.0	1 43.0	11 52.8
7	5 1 2.0	0 .0	0 .0	0N10.9	0N32.8	0 19.4	1 19.8	0 55.6	0 58.9	0 41.1	1 43.1	11 54.1
10	5 12 51.7	0 .0	0 .0	3 42.5	1 32.2	0 26.4	1 25.6	0 55.7	0 58.6	0 41.3	1 43.2	11 55.3
13	5 24 41.4	0 .0	0 .0	5 4.7	2 19.8	0 33.3	1 30.7	0 55.7	0 58.4	0 41.4	1 43.4	11 56.6
16	5 36 31.0	0 .0	0 .0	3 50.9	2 47.5	0 40.0	1 35.4	0 55.8	0 58.2	0 41.5	1 43.5	11 57.8
19	5 48 20.7	0 .0	0 .0	1 5.6	2 55.6	0 46.5	1 39.4	0 55.9	0 58.0	0 41.6	1 43.6	11 59.1
22	6 0 10.4	0 .0	0 .0	1S59.5	2 48.9	0 52.7	1 43.0	0 56.0	0 57.8	0 41.7	1 43.8	12 .3
25	6 12 .1	0 .0	0 .0	4 20.9	2 32.7	0 58.6	1 46.2	0 56.1	0 57.6	0 41.8	1 43.9	12 1.5
28	6 23 49.7	0 .0	0 .0	4 57.5	2 11.0	1 4.1	1 48.9	0 56.2	0 57.4	0 41.9	1 44.1	12 2.6
31	6 35 39.4	0 .0	0 .0	3 18.0	1 46.4	1 9.2	1 51.3	0 56.4	0 57.3	0 42.0	1 44.2	12 3.8

RIGHT ASCENSION

DAY	EPHEM. SID. TIME	☉	☊	☾	☿	♀	♂	♃	♄	♅	♆	♇
1	4 37 22.7	6♐32.5	18♎10.9	1♌47.1	25♐13.6	11♐40.0	16♉19.8	15♏34.5	25♐30.3	18♌59.8	4♏ .1	10♍41.8
2	4 41 19.3	7 37.1	18 7.9	14 49.3	25R .5	13 .7	16R 3.9	15 47.3	25 37.7	18R59.3	4 2.0	10 42.1
3	4 45 15.8	8 42.0	18 5.0	27 48.2	24 35.5	14 21.7	15 48.7	15 60.0	25 45.2	18 58.7	4 3.9	10 42.4
4	4 49 12.4	9 47.0	18 2.0	10♍48.7	23 58.5	15 42.8	15 34.3	16 12.7	25 52.6	18 58.1	4 5.7	10 42.7
5	4 53 8.9	10 52.2	17 59.0	23 58.2	23 9.7	17 4.2	15 20.6	16 25.4	26 .1	18 57.5	4 7.6	10 42.9
6	4 57 5.5	11 57.5	17 56.1	7♎26.1	22 9.7	18 25.8	15 7.7	16 38.0	26 7.7	18 56.7	4 9.4	10 43.1
7	5 1 2.0	13 3.0	17 53.1	21 21.1	20 59.8	19 47.5	14 55.7	16 50.7	26 15.2	18 56.0	4 11.2	10 43.3
8	5 4 58.6	14 8.6	17 50.1	5♏49.1	19 42.0	21 9.4	14 44.5	17 3.2	26 22.7	18 55.1	4 13.0	10 43.4
9	5 8 55.2	15 14.3	17 47.2	20 50.0	18 18.4	22 31.4	14 34.1	17 15.8	26 30.3	18 54.3	4 14.8	10 43.5
10	5 12 51.7	16 20.1	17 44.2	6♐15.3	16 51.8	23 53.5	14 24.5	17 28.3	26 37.9	18 53.3	4 16.5	10 43.6
11	5 16 48.3	17 26.1	17 41.3	21 47.8	15 25.3	25 15.8	14 15.9	17 40.8	26 45.5	18 52.4	4 18.2	10 43.6
12	5 20 44.8	18 32.1	17 38.3	7♑ 6.4	14 1.5	26 38.2	14 8.0	17 53.2	26 53.1	18 51.3	4 19.9	10 43.7
13	5 24 41.4	19 38.3	17 35.3	21 51.8	12 43.4	28 .7	14 1.1	18 5.6	27 .7	18 50.2	4 21.6	10 43.7
14	5 28 37.9	20 44.5	17 32.4	5♒52.6	11 32.9	29 23.2	13 55.0	18 17.9	27 8.4	18 49.1	4 23.3	10R43.6
15	5 32 34.5	21 50.8	17 29.4	19 6.2	10 31.9	0♑45.8	13 49.7	18 30.2	27 16.0	18 47.9	4 24.9	10 43.5
16	5 36 31.0	22 57.2	17 26.4	1♓37.1	9 41.5	2 8.4	13 45.4	18 42.5	27 23.6	18 46.7	4 26.6	10 43.4
17	5 40 27.6	24 3.6	17 23.5	13 34.2	9 2.4	3 31.0	13 41.8	18 54.7	27 31.3	18 45.4	4 28.2	10 43.3
18	5 44 24.2	25 10.1	17 20.5	25 8.4	8 34.5	4 53.6	13 39.2	19 6.8	27 39.0	18 44.1	4 29.7	10 43.1
19	5 48 20.7	26 16.6	17 17.5	6♈30.8	8 17.8	6 16.2	13 37.3	19 18.9	27 46.6	18 42.7	4 31.3	10 43.0
20	5 52 17.3	27 23.2	17 14.6	17 52.3	8 11.9	7 38.8	13 36.4	19 31.0	27 54.3	18 41.3	4 32.9	10 42.8
21	5 56 13.8	28 29.7	17 11.6	29 22.3	8D16.0	9 1.4	13 36.2	19 43.0	28 2.0	18 39.8	4 34.4	10 42.5
22	6 0 10.4	29 36.3	17 8.7	11♉ 8.8	8 29.4	10 23.8	13D36.8	19 54.9	28 9.7	18 38.3	4 35.9	10 42.2
23	6 4 6.9	0♑42.9	17 5.7	23 17.1	8 51.4	11 46.2	13 38.2	20 6.8	28 17.3	18 36.8	4 37.3	10 41.9
24	6 8 3.5	1 49.5	17 2.7	5♊49.2	9 21.2	13 8.5	13 40.4	20 18.6	28 25.0	18 35.2	4 38.7	10 41.6
25	6 12 .1	2 56.1	16 59.8	18 43.4	9 58.1	14 30.6	13 43.4	20 30.4	28 32.6	18 33.5	4 40.1	10 41.2
26	6 15 56.6	4 2.6	16 56.8	1♋54.3	10 41.3	15 52.7	13 47.1	20 42.1	28 40.3	18 31.8	4 41.5	10 40.8
27	6 19 53.2	5 9.2	16 53.8	15 14.0	11 30.2	17 14.6	13 51.6	20 53.7	28 47.9	18 30.1	4 42.9	10 40.4
28	6 23 49.7	6 15.7	16 50.9	28 34.5	12 24.3	18 36.3	13 56.9	21 5.2	28 55.5	18 28.3	4 44.2	10 40.0
29	6 27 46.3	7 22.2	16 47.9	11♌49.5	13 22.9	19 57.9	14 2.8	21 16.7	29 3.2	18 26.5	4 45.5	10 39.5
30	6 31 42.8	8 28.6	16 45.0	24 56.9	14 25.8	21 19.3	14 9.5	21 28.1	29 10.8	18 24.6	4 46.8	10 39.0
31	6 35 39.4	9 35.0	16 42.0	7♍58.2	15 32.3	22 40.5	14 16.8	21 39.5	29 18.4	18 22.7	4 48.0	10 38.4

DECLINATION

DAY	EPHEM. SID. TIME	☉	☊	☾	☿	♀	♂	♃	♄	♅	♆	♇
1	4 37 22.7	21S41.5	0S 8.1	15N 3.2	24S37.2	22S27.4	18N34.1	16S14.5	22S23.2	16N35.7	11S48.8	20N58.0
4	4 49 12.4	22 8.5	0 8.0	4 30.6	23 45.5	22 59.8	18 28.8	16 25.0	22 24.1	16 36.3	11 50.6	20 59.1
7	5 1 2.0	22 31.6	0 7.9	8S46.6	22 38.2	23 26.0	18 24.7	16 35.4	22 24.9	16 37.1	11 52.4	21 .2
10	5 12 51.7	22 50.8	0 7.9	17 53.5	21 21.0	23 45.8	18 22.0	16 45.5	22 25.7	16 38.0	11 54.1	21 1.5
13	5 24 41.4	23 6.0	0 7.8	16 47.1	20 8.8	23 59.1	18 20.8	16 55.3	22 26.4	16 39.1	11 55.7	21 2.8
16	5 36 31.0	23 17.0	0 7.8	7 32.3	19 18.6	24 5.7	18 21.1	17 4.9	22 27.0	16 40.3	11 57.2	21 4.2
19	5 48 20.7	23 23.9	0 7.7	4N .4	18 59.0	24 5.5	18 23.1	17 14.2	22 27.6	16 41.6	11 58.7	21 5.8
22	6 0 10.4	23 26.5	0 7.6	13 50.2	19 7.5	23 58.7	18 26.7	17 23.3	22 28.1	16 43.0	12 .1	21 7.4
25	6 12 .1	23 24.9	0 7.6	18 40.5	19 35.8	23 45.1	18 31.9	17 32.1	22 28.5	16 44.6	12 1.4	21 9.0
28	6 23 49.7	23 19.0	0 7.5	15 47.7	20 15.5	23 25.0	18 38.6	17 40.6	22 28.9	16 46.2	12 2.6	21 10.8
31	6 35 39.4	23 9.0	0 7.4	5 41.3	20 59.6	22 58.4	18 46.7	17 48.8	22 29.1	16 48.0	12 3.7	21 12.6

JANUARY 1959

LONGITUDE

DAY	EPHEM. SID. TIME h m s	☉ ° ′	☊ ° ′	☽ ° ′	☿ ° ′	♀ ° ′	♂ ° ′	♃ ° ′	♄ ° ′	♅ ° ′	♆ ° ′	♇ ° ′
1	6 39 36.0	9♑49.4	18♎ 3.3	21♍10.4	17♐36.9	22♑ 2.9	17♉26.1	23♏58.7	29♐28.6	15♌40.1	6♏34.0	4♍ 4.1
2	6 43 32.5	10 50.6	18 .1	4♎59.7	18 45.9	23 18.2	17 34.9	24 9.7	29 35.6	15 R 38.1	6 35.2	4 R 3.3
3	6 47 29.1	11 51.7	17 56.9	18 59.0	19 57.1	24 33.5	17 44.4	24 20.6	29 42.5	15 36.1	6 36.4	4 2.5
4	6 51 25.6	12 52.9	17 53.8	3♏ 8.1	21 10.4	25 48.8	17 54.5	24 31.4	29 49.5	15 34.0	6 37.5	4 1.7
5	6 55 22.2	13 54.1	17 50.6	17 26.1	22 25.5	27 4.1	18 5.2	24 42.1	29 56.5	15 31.9	6 38.6	4 .8
6	6 59 18.7	14 55.2	17 47.4	1♐50.6	23 42.2	28 19.4	18 16.5	24 52.7	0♑ 3.4	15 29.8	6 39.7	3 60.0
7	7 3 15.3	15 56.4	17 44.2	16 17.6	25 .4	29 34.7	18 28.4	25 3.3	0 10.3	15 27.7	6 40.8	3 59.1
8	7 7 11.9	16 57.6	17 41.1	0♑41.6	26 20.0	0♒50.0	18 40.9	25 13.7	0 17.2	15 25.5	6 41.8	3 58.1
9	7 11 8.4	17 58.8	17 37.9	14 56.2	27 40.8	2 5.2	18 53.9	25 24.1	0 24.1	15 23.2	6 42.8	3 57.2
10	7 15 5.0	18 60.0	17 34.7	28 55.5	29 2.7	3 20.5	19 7.6	25 34.4	0 31.0	15 21.0	6 43.9	3 56.3
11	7 19 1.5	20 1.1	17 31.5	12♒34.6	0♑25.5	4 35.8	19 21.8	25 44.6	0 37.8	15 18.8	6 44.8	3 55.3
12	7 22 58.1	21 2.3	17 28.4	25 50.7	1 49.3	5 51.0	19 36.5	25 54.7	0 44.7	15 16.4	6 45.7	3 54.3
13	7 26 54.6	22 3.4	17 25.2	8♓43.4	3 14.0	7 6.2	19 51.7	26 4.6	0 51.4	15 14.1	6 46.6	3 53.2
14	7 30 51.2	23 4.6	17 22.0	21 14.4	4 39.5	8 21.4	20 7.5	26 14.5	0 58.2	15 11.7	6 47.4	3 52.2
15	7 34 47.8	24 5.7	17 18.8	3♈27.0	6 5.7	9 36.6	20 23.7	26 24.3	1 4.9	15 9.4	6 48.2	3 51.1
16	7 38 44.3	25 6.8	17 15.6	15 25.8	7 32.7	10 51.8	20 40.5	26 33.9	1 11.6	15 7.0	6 49.0	3 50.0
17	7 42 40.9	26 7.9	17 12.5	27 16.2	9 .3	12 7.0	20 57.7	26 43.5	1 18.3	15 4.5	6 49.7	3 48.8
18	7 46 37.4	27 9.0	17 9.3	9♉ 3.9	10 28.7	13 22.1	21 15.3	26 52.9	1 24.9	15 2.1	6 50.4	3 47.7
19	7 50 34.0	28 10.1	17 6.1	20 54.2	11 57.7	14 37.2	21 33.4	27 2.3	1 31.5	14 59.6	6 51.1	3 46.5
20	7 54 30.5	29 11.2	17 2.9	2♊52.5	13 27.3	15 52.3	21 52.0	27 11.5	1 38.1	14 57.1	6 51.8	3 45.3
21	7 58 27.1	0♒12.2	16 59.8	15 3.0	14 57.5	17 7.4	22 11.0	27 20.6	1 44.6	14 54.6	6 52.4	3 44.1
22	8 2 23.6	1 13.2	16 56.6	27 29.1	16 28.4	18 22.5	22 30.4	27 29.6	1 51.1	14 52.1	6 52.9	3 42.9
23	8 6 20.2	2 14.3	16 53.4	10♋12.9	17 59.9	19 37.6	22 50.2	27 38.5	1 57.5	14 49.5	6 53.5	3 41.6
24	8 10 16.8	3 15.3	16 50.2	23 14.8	19 31.9	20 52.6	23 10.4	27 47.3	2 4.0	14 47.0	6 54.0	3 40.4
25	8 14 13.3	4 16.3	16 47.1	6♌34.0	21 4.6	22 7.6	23 30.9	27 55.9	2 10.3	14 44.4	6 54.5	3 39.1
26	8 18 9.9	5 17.2	16 43.9	20 8.0	22 38.0	23 22.6	23 51.9	28 4.4	2 16.7	14 41.8	6 54.9	3 37.8
27	8 22 6.4	6 18.2	16 40.7	3♍53.9	24 11.9	24 37.6	24 13.2	28 12.8	2 23.0	14 39.3	6 55.3	3 36.5
28	8 26 3.0	7 19.2	16 37.5	17 48.4	25 46.5	25 52.5	24 34.8	28 21.1	2 29.2	14 36.7	6 55.7	3 35.2
29	8 29 59.5	8 20.1	16 34.3	1♎48.4	27 21.7	27 7.5	24 56.8	28 29.2	2 35.4	14 34.1	6 56.0	3 33.8
30	8 33 56.1	9 21.0	16 31.2	15 51.6	28 57.6	28 22.4	25 19.2	28 37.3	2 41.6	14 31.4	6 56.3	3 32.5
31	8 37 52.6	10 22.0	16 28.0	29 56.6	0♒34.3	29 37.3	25 41.9	28 45.2	2 47.7	14 28.9	6 56.6	3 31.2

LATITUDE

DAY	SID. TIME	☉	☊	☽	☿	♀	♂	♃	♄	♅	♆	♇
1	6 39 36.0	0 .0	0 .0	2 S 18.3	1 N 37.9	1 S 10.8	1 N 52.0	0 N 56.4	0 N 57.2	0 N 42.0	1 N 44.3	12 N 4.2
4	6 51 25.6	0 .0	0 .0	1 N 17.6	1 12.1	1 15.4	1 53.9	0 56.6	0 57.1	0 42.1	1 44.4	12 5.3
7	7 3 15.3	0 .0	0 .0	4 16.0	0 46.4	1 19.5	1 55.6	0 56.8	0 57.0	0 42.2	1 44.6	12 6.3
10	7 15 5.0	0 .0	0 .0	4 54.4	0 21.4	1 23.0	1 56.9	0 57.0	0 56.8	0 42.3	1 44.8	12 7.3
13	7 26 54.6	0 .0	0 .0	3 7.1	0 S 2.4	1 26.1	1 58.0	0 57.2	0 56.7	0 42.3	1 45.0	12 8.3
16	7 38 44.3	0 .0	0 .0	0 7.4	0 24.8	1 28.6	1 58.8	0 57.4	0 56.6	0 42.4	1 45.1	12 9.3
19	7 50 34.0	0 .0	0 .0	2 S 50.4	0 45.5	1 30.5	1 59.5	0 57.6	0 56.6	0 42.4	1 45.3	12 10.2
22	8 2 23.6	0 .0	0 .0	4 45.5	1 4.4	1 31.9	1 60.0	0 57.9	0 56.5	0 42.5	1 45.5	12 11.0
25	8 14 13.3	0 .0	0 .0	4 42.2	1 21.1	1 32.6	2 .3	0 58.1	0 56.4	0 42.5	1 45.7	12 11.8
28	8 26 3.0	0 .0	0 .0	2 20.8	1 35.5	1 32.8	2 .5	0 58.4	0 56.4	0 42.6	1 45.9	12 12.6
31	8 37 52.6	0 .0	0 .0	1 N 17.3	1 47.4	1 32.3	2 .6	0 58.7	0 56.3	0 42.6	1 46.0	12 13.3

RIGHT ASCENSION

DAY	SID. TIME	☉	☊	☽	☿	♀	♂	♃	♄	♅	♆	♇
1	6 39 36.0	10♑41.3	16♎39.0	20♍59.0	16♐42.2	24♑ 1.5	14♉24.9	21♏50.7	29♐26.0	18♌20.8	4♏49.2	10♍37.9
2	6 43 32.5	11 47.5	16 36.1	4♎ 7.3	17 55.1	25 22.2	14 33.6	22 1.9	29 33.6	18 R 18.8	4 50.4	10 R 37.3
3	6 47 29.1	12 53.7	16 33.1	17 32.3	19 10.7	26 42.8	14 43.0	22 13.1	29 41.1	18 16.8	4 51.6	10 36.7
4	6 51 25.6	13 59.8	16 30.2	1♏22.0	20 28.7	28 3.1	14 53.1	22 24.1	29 48.7	18 14.8	4 52.7	10 36.0
5	6 55 22.2	15 5.8	16 27.2	15 41.1	21 49.0	29 23.1	15 3.7	22 35.1	29 56.2	18 12.7	4 53.8	10 35.3
6	6 59 18.7	16 11.7	16 24.2	0♐28.2	23 11.4	0♒42.9	15 15.1	22 45.9	0♑ 3.7	18 10.6	4 54.9	10 34.6
7	7 3 15.3	17 17.5	16 21.3	15 34.4	24 35.5	2 2.4	15 27.0	22 56.7	0 11.2	18 8.4	4 56.0	10 33.9
8	7 7 11.9	18 23.2	16 18.3	0♑43.8	26 1.4	3 21.6	15 39.6	23 7.4	0 18.7	18 6.3	4 57.0	10 33.2
9	7 11 8.4	19 28.8	16 15.4	15 37.9	27 28.8	4 40.6	15 52.7	23 18.0	0 26.1	18 4.0	4 58.0	10 32.4
10	7 15 5.0	20 34.3	16 12.4	0♒ 1.0	28 57.7	5 59.3	16 6.5	23 28.6	0 33.6	18 1.9	4 59.0	10 31.6
11	7 19 1.5	21 39.6	16 9.5	13 44.1	0♑27.8	7 17.6	16 20.8	23 39.0	0 41.0	17 59.6	4 59.9	10 30.8
12	7 22 58.1	22 44.7	16 6.5	26 45.6	1 59.1	8 35.7	16 35.7	23 49.3	0 48.3	17 57.3	5 .8	10 29.9
13	7 26 54.6	23 49.7	16 3.5	9♓10.0	3 31.5	9 53.4	16 51.2	23 59.6	0 55.7	17 55.0	5 1.6	10 29.1
14	7 30 51.2	24 54.5	16 .6	21 5.5	5 4.9	11 10.8	17 7.2	24 9.7	1 3.0	17 52.6	5 2.5	10 28.2
15	7 34 47.8	25 59.2	15 57.6	2♈42.0	6 39.2	12 27.9	17 23.7	24 19.7	1 10.2	17 50.2	5 3.3	10 27.2
16	7 38 44.3	27 3.7	15 54.7	14 9.8	8 14.4	13 44.6	17 40.8	24 29.7	1 17.5	17 47.8	5 4.0	10 26.3
17	7 42 40.9	28 8.1	15 51.7	25 38.8	9 50.4	15 1.1	17 58.3	24 39.5	1 24.7	17 45.4	5 4.8	10 25.3
18	7 46 37.4	29 12.2	15 48.8	7♉18.1	11 27.1	16 17.1	18 16.4	24 49.2	1 31.9	17 43.0	5 5.5	10 24.3
19	7 50 34.0	0♒16.2	15 45.8	19 14.7	13 4.6	17 32.9	18 34.9	24 58.8	1 39.0	17 40.5	5 6.2	10 23.3
20	7 54 30.5	1 20.0	15 42.9	1♊33.7	14 42.6	18 48.3	18 53.9	25 8.3	1 46.1	17 38.0	5 6.8	10 22.3
21	7 58 27.1	2 23.6	15 39.9	14 16.5	16 21.2	20 3.5	19 13.4	25 17.7	1 53.2	17 35.5	5 7.4	10 21.2
22	8 2 23.6	3 27.0	15 36.9	27 21.3	18 .4	21 18.2	19 33.3	25 26.9	2 .2	17 33.0	5 8.0	10 20.2
23	8 6 20.2	4 30.2	15 34.0	10♋42.5	19 40.1	22 32.7	19 53.6	25 36.1	2 7.2	17 30.5	5 8.5	10 19.1
24	8 10 16.8	5 33.3	15 31.0	24 12.8	21 20.2	23 46.8	20 14.4	25 45.1	2 14.1	17 27.9	5 9.0	10 18.0
25	8 14 13.3	6 36.1	15 28.1	7♌44.6	23 .8	25 .6	20 35.6	25 54.0	2 21.0	17 25.4	5 9.5	10 16.8
26	8 18 9.9	7 38.7	15 25.1	21 12.4	24 41.7	26 14.1	20 57.2	26 2.8	2 27.9	17 22.8	5 10.0	10 15.7
27	8 22 6.4	8 41.2	15 22.2	4♍34.3	26 23.1	27 27.2	21 19.3	26 11.5	2 34.7	17 20.2	5 10.4	10 14.5
28	8 26 3.0	9 43.4	15 19.2	17 52.2	28 4.7	28 40.1	21 41.7	26 20.0	2 41.5	17 17.6	5 10.8	10 13.3
29	8 29 59.5	10 45.4	15 16.3	1♎11.1	29 46.7	29 52.7	22 4.5	26 28.5	2 48.2	17 15.0	5 11.1	10 12.1
30	8 33 56.1	11 47.3	15 13.3	14 37.7	1♒28.9	1♓ 4.9	22 27.7	26 36.8	2 54.8	17 12.4	5 11.4	10 10.9
31	8 37 52.6	12 49.0	15 10.4	28 19.0	3 11.4	2 16.9	22 51.3	26 45.0	3 1.5	17 9.8	5 11.7	10 9.7

DECLINATION

DAY	SID. TIME	☉	☊	☽	☿	♀	♂	♃	♄	♅	♆	♇
1	6 39 36.0	23 S 4.7	0 S 7.4	1 N 22.8	21 S 14.4	22 S 48.1	18 N 49.7	17 S 51.5	22 S 29.2	16 N 48.6	12 S 4.1	21 N 13.2
4	6 51 25.6	22 49.1	0 7.4	11 S 20.6	21 56.9	22 13.2	18 59.6	17 59.3	22 29.4	16 50.5	12 5.1	21 15.2
7	7 3 15.3	22 29.4	0 7.3	18 29.5	22 34.5	21 32.2	19 10.6	18 6.8	22 29.5	16 52.4	12 6.0	21 17.1
10	7 15 5.0	22 5.7	0 7.2	15 34.3	23 4.9	20 45.4	19 22.8	18 14.0	22 29.6	16 54.5	12 6.8	21 19.1
13	7 26 54.6	21 38.1	0 7.2	5 24.4	23 26.5	19 53.2	19 35.9	18 21.0	22 29.6	16 56.6	12 7.5	21 21.2
16	7 38 44.3	21 6.8	0 7.1	6 N 11.4	23 38.4	18 55.8	19 49.9	18 27.6	22 29.6	16 58.8	12 8.2	21 23.3
19	7 50 34.0	20 31.8	0 7.0	15 14.6	23 39.6	17 53.5	20 4.6	18 33.8	22 29.6	17 1.0	12 8.7	21 25.4
22	8 2 23.6	19 53.4	0 7.0	18 39.7	23 29.4	16 46.7	20 19.9	18 39.8	22 29.4	17 3.2	12 9.1	21 27.5
25	8 14 13.3	19 11.6	0 6.9	14 4.5	23 7.5	15 35.8	20 35.7	18 45.5	22 29.3	17 5.5	12 9.4	21 29.7
28	8 26 3.0	18 26.6	0 6.8	2 39.6	22 33.4	14 21.0	20 51.9	18 50.8	22 29.0	17 7.8	12 9.6	21 31.8
31	8 37 52.6	17 38.6	0 6.8	10 S 14.8	21 46.7	13 2.7	21 8.3	18 55.8	22 28.8	17 10.1	12 9.8	21 34.0

FEBRUARY 1959

LONGITUDE

DAY	EPHEM. SID. TIME h m s	☉ ° ′	☊ ° ′	☽ ° ′	☿ ° ′	♀ ° ′	♂ ° ′	♃ ° ′	♄ ° ′	♅ ° ′	♆ ° ′	♇ ° ′
1	8 41 49.2	11 ♒ 22.9	16 ♎ 24.8	14 ♏ 2.3	2 ♒ 11.5	0 ♓ 52.2	26 ♉ 4.9	28 ♏ 53.0	2 ♑ 53.8	14 ♌ 26.2	6 ♏ 56.9	3 ♍ 29.8
2	8 45 45.8	12 23.8	16 21.6	28 7.9	3 49.5	2 7.1	26 28.2	29 .6	2 59.8	14 R 23.6	6 57.1	3 R 28.4
3	8 49 42.3	13 24.7	16 18.5	12 ♐ 12.2	5 28.1	3 21.9	26 51.8	29 8.1	3 5.8	14 21.0	6 57.2	3 27.0
4	8 53 38.9	14 25.6	16 15.3	26 13.5	7 7.5	4 36.7	27 15.7	29 15.4	3 11.7	14 18.3	6 57.4	3 25.6
5	8 57 35.4	15 26.4	16 12.1	10 ♑ 9.1	8 47.6	5 51.5	27 39.9	29 22.6	3 17.6	14 15.7	6 57.5	3 24.1
6	9 1 32.0	16 27.2	16 8.9	23 55.8	10 28.5	7 6.3	28 4.4	29 29.7	3 23.4	14 13.1	6 57.5	3 22.7
7	9 5 28.5	17 28.1	16 5.8	7 ♒ 30.3	12 10.2	8 21.0	28 29.2	29 36.6	3 29.2	14 10.5	6 57.6	3 21.2
8	9 9 25.1	18 28.9	16 2.6	20 49.5	13 52.6	9 35.8	28 54.2	29 43.4	3 34.9	14 7.8	6 57.6	3 19.8
9	9 13 21.6	19 29.6	15 59.4	3 ♓ 51.2	15 35.8	10 50.5	29 19.5	29 50.0	3 40.5	14 5.2	6 R 57.5	3 18.3
10	9 17 18.2	20 30.4	15 56.2	16 34.9	17 19.9	12 5.1	29 45.1	29 56.5	3 46.1	14 2.6	6 57.4	3 16.8
11	9 21 14.7	21 31.1	15 53.0	29 1.0	19 4.7	13 19.8	0 ♊ 11.0	0 ♐ 2.8	3 51.7	13 60.0	6 57.3	3 15.3
12	9 25 11.3	22 31.8	15 49.9	11 ♈ 11.9	20 50.3	14 34.4	0 37.1	0 9.0	3 57.1	13 57.4	6 57.2	3 13.8
13	9 29 7.9	23 32.5	15 46.7	23 10.7	22 36.8	15 49.0	1 3.4	0 15.1	4 2.5	13 54.8	6 57.0	3 12.3
14	9 33 4.4	24 33.2	15 43.5	5 ♉ 1.7	24 24.0	17 3.5	1 30.0	0 20.9	4 7.9	13 52.2	6 56.8	3 10.8
15	9 37 1.0	25 33.8	15 40.3	16 50.0	26 12.1	18 18.0	1 56.8	0 26.6	4 13.2	13 49.6	6 56.6	3 9.3
16	9 40 57.5	26 34.4	15 37.2	28 40.7	28 .9	19 32.5	2 23.8	0 32.2	4 18.4	13 47.1	6 56.3	3 7.8
17	9 44 54.1	27 35.0	15 34.0	10 ♊ 39.1	29 50.5	20 46.9	2 51.0	0 37.6	4 23.6	13 44.6	6 56.0	3 6.3
18	9 48 50.6	28 35.5	15 30.8	22 50.4	1 ♓ 40.8	22 1.3	3 18.5	0 42.8	4 28.7	13 42.0	6 55.6	3 4.8
19	9 52 47.2	29 36.0	15 27.6	5 ♋ 18.8	3 31.7	23 15.7	3 46.1	0 47.9	4 33.7	13 39.5	6 55.3	3 3.2
20	9 56 43.7	0 ♓ 36.5	15 24.4	18 7.7	5 23.2	24 30.0	4 13.9	0 52.8	4 38.7	13 37.0	6 54.8	3 1.7
21	10 0 40.3	1 37.0	15 21.3	1 ♌ 18.9	7 15.3	25 44.4	4 42.0	0 57.6	4 43.6	13 34.6	6 54.5	3 .2
22	10 4 36.8	2 37.4	15 18.1	14 52.3	9 7.8	26 58.6	5 10.3	1 2.2	4 48.4	13 32.2	6 54.0	2 58.7
23	10 8 33.4	3 37.8	15 14.9	28 46.0	11 .5	28 12.8	5 38.7	1 6.6	4 53.2	13 29.7	6 53.5	2 57.2
24	10 12 29.9	4 38.2	15 11.7	12 ♍ 56.3	12 53.3	29 27.0	6 7.3	1 10.9	4 57.9	13 27.3	6 52.9	2 55.6
25	10 16 26.5	5 38.5	15 8.6	27 18.1	14 46.1	0 ♈ 41.1	6 36.0	1 15.0	5 2.5	13 24.9	6 52.4	2 54.1
26	10 20 23.0	6 38.8	15 5.4	11 ♎ 45.9	16 38.6	1 55.2	7 4.9	1 18.9	5 7.0	13 22.6	6 51.8	2 52.6
27	10 24 19.6	7 39.1	15 2.2	26 14.3	18 30.5	3 9.2	7 34.0	1 22.6	5 11.5	13 20.2	6 51.2	2 51.1
28	10 28 16.1	8 39.3	14 59.0	10 ♏ 38.9	20 21.7	4 23.3	8 3.3	1 26.2	5 15.8	13 17.9	6 50.5	2 49.5

LATITUDE

DAY	EPHEM. SID. TIME	☉	☊	☽	☿	♀	♂	♃	♄	♅	♆	♇
1	8 41 49.2	0 .0	0 .0	2 N 27.0	1 S 50.8	1 S 32.0	2 N .6	0 N 58.8	0 N 56.3	0 N 42.6	1 N 46.1	12 N 13.5
4	8 53 38.9	0 .0	0 .0	4 48.2	1 58.9	1 30.6	2 .5	0 59.1	0 56.3	0 42.6	1 46.3	12 14.1
7	9 5 28.5	0 .0	0 .0	4 41.0	2 3.8	1 28.6	2 .3	0 59.4	0 56.3	0 42.6	1 46.5	12 14.7
10	9 17 18.2	0 .0	0 .0	2 22.8	2 5.2	1 26.1	2 .1	0 59.7	0 56.2	0 42.7	1 46.7	12 15.2
13	9 29 7.9	0 .0	0 .0	0 S 48.5	2 2.7	1 22.8	1 59.7	1 .0	0 56.2	0 42.7	1 46.8	12 15.6
16	9 40 57.5	0 .0	0 .0	3 37.1	1 55.9	1 19.0	1 59.3	1 .3	0 56.2	0 42.6	1 47.0	12 16.0
19	9 52 47.2	0 .0	0 .0	5 5.7	1 44.4	1 14.6	1 58.8	1 .7	0 56.2	0 42.6	1 47.2	12 16.3
22	10 4 36.8	0 .0	0 .0	4 25.3	1 27.6	1 9.6	1 58.2	1 1.0	0 56.3	0 42.6	1 47.4	12 16.6
25	10 16 26.5	0 .0	0 .0	1 27.0	1 5.3	1 4.1	1 57.6	1 1.4	0 56.3	0 42.6	1 47.5	12 16.8
28	10 28 16.1	0 .0	0 .0	2 N 23.0	0 37.3	0 58.0	1 57.0	1 1.7	0 56.3	0 42.6	1 47.7	12 16.9

RIGHT ASCENSION

DAY	EPHEM. SID. TIME	☉	☊	☽	☿	♀	♂	♃	♄	♅	♆	♇
1	8 41 49.2	13 ♒ 50.4	15 ♎ 7.4	12 ♏ 19.7	4 ♒ 54.2	3 ♓ 28.6	23 ♉ 15.2	26 ♏ 53.0	3 ♑ 8.1	17 ♌ 7.2	5 ♏ 12.0	10 ♍ 8.4
2	8 45 45.8	14 51.6	15 4.5	26 40.9	6 37.1	4 40.0	23 39.5	27 .9	3 14.6	17 R 4.6	5 12.2	10 R 7.2
3	8 49 42.3	15 52.7	15 1.5	11 ♐ 18.3	8 20.3	5 51.1	24 4.1	27 8.6	3 21.1	17 1.9	5 12.4	10 5.9
4	8 53 38.9	16 53.5	14 58.6	26 1.8	10 3.6	7 2.0	24 29.1	27 16.2	3 27.5	16 59.3	5 12.5	10 4.6
5	8 57 35.4	17 54.2	14 55.6	10 ♑ 38.3	11 47.1	8 12.6	24 54.4	27 23.7	3 33.8	16 56.6	5 12.6	10 3.3
6	9 1 32.0	18 54.6	14 52.6	24 54.6	13 30.8	9 22.9	25 20.1	27 31.0	3 40.1	16 54.0	5 12.7	10 2.0
7	9 5 28.5	19 54.9	14 49.7	8 ♒ 41.0	15 14.6	10 33.0	25 46.1	27 38.2	3 46.3	16 51.4	5 12.8	10 .6
8	9 9 25.1	20 54.9	14 46.7	21 53.3	16 58.5	11 42.9	26 12.4	27 45.3	3 52.5	16 48.7	5 12.8	9 59.3
9	9 13 21.6	21 54.7	14 43.8	4 ♓ 32.6	18 42.5	12 52.6	26 39.0	27 52.1	3 58.6	16 46.1	5 12.8	9 57.9
10	9 17 18.2	22 54.4	14 40.8	16 43.6	20 26.6	14 2.0	27 6.0	27 58.9	4 4.7	16 43.5	5 R 12.7	9 56.5
11	9 21 14.7	23 53.8	14 37.9	28 33.8	22 10.8	15 11.2	27 33.2	28 5.4	4 10.7	16 40.9	5 12.6	9 55.2
12	9 25 11.3	24 53.1	14 34.9	10 ♈ 11.3	23 55.1	16 20.2	28 .8	28 11.9	4 16.6	16 38.3	5 12.5	9 53.8
13	9 29 7.9	25 52.1	14 32.0	21 44.8	25 39.5	17 29.0	28 28.6	28 18.1	4 22.4	16 35.7	5 12.4	9 52.4
14	9 33 4.4	26 51.0	14 29.0	3 ♉ 22.4	27 23.8	18 37.7	28 56.7	28 24.2	4 28.2	16 33.1	5 12.2	9 51.0
15	9 37 1.0	27 49.6	14 26.1	15 11.0	29 8.2	19 46.1	29 25.1	28 30.2	4 33.9	16 30.5	5 12.0	9 49.5
16	9 40 57.5	28 48.1	14 23.1	27 16.4	0 ♓ 52.6	20 54.4	29 53.8	28 36.0	4 39.6	16 28.0	5 11.7	9 48.1
17	9 44 54.1	29 46.4	14 20.2	9 ♊ 41.9	2 36.9	22 2.5	0 ♊ 22.7	28 41.6	4 45.2	16 25.4	5 11.4	9 46.7
18	9 48 50.6	0 ♓ 44.5	14 17.2	22 28.6	4 21.2	23 10.5	0 51.9	28 47.0	4 50.7	16 22.9	5 11.1	9 45.3
19	9 52 47.2	1 42.5	14 14.3	5 ♋ 34.4	6 5.4	24 18.4	1 21.4	28 52.3	4 56.1	16 20.4	5 10.8	9 43.8
20	9 56 43.7	2 40.2	14 11.3	18 55.2	7 49.3	25 26.1	1 51.1	28 57.4	5 1.5	16 17.9	5 10.4	9 42.4
21	10 0 40.3	3 37.9	14 8.4	2 ♌ 25.7	9 33.1	26 33.7	2 21.1	29 2.5	5 6.8	16 15.4	5 10.1	9 41.0
22	10 4 36.8	4 35.3	14 5.5	16 .9	11 16.5	27 41.2	2 51.3	29 7.2	5 12.0	16 13.0	5 9.6	9 39.5
23	10 8 33.4	5 32.5	14 2.5	29 37.7	12 59.5	28 48.6	3 21.7	29 11.8	5 17.2	16 10.5	5 9.2	9 38.0
24	10 12 29.9	6 29.6	13 59.6	13 ♍ 15.6	14 42.0	29 56.0	3 52.3	29 16.3	5 22.2	16 8.1	5 8.7	9 36.6
25	10 16 26.5	7 26.6	13 56.6	26 56.9	16 23.8	1 ♈ 3.2	4 23.2	29 20.5	5 27.2	16 5.7	5 8.1	9 35.1
26	10 20 23.0	8 23.4	13 53.7	10 ♎ 45.4	18 4.8	2 10.4	4 54.2	29 24.6	5 32.1	16 3.3	5 7.6	9 33.7
27	10 24 19.6	9 20.0	13 50.7	24 45.4	19 44.7	3 17.5	5 25.5	29 28.5	5 36.9	16 1.0	5 7.0	9 32.2
28	10 28 16.1	10 16.6	13 47.8	8 ♏ 59.5	21 23.3	4 24.6	5 57.0	29 32.2	5 41.7	15 58.7	5 6.4	9 30.7

DECLINATION

DAY	EPHEM. SID. TIME	☉	☊	☽	☿	♀	♂	♃	♄	♅	♆	♇
1	8 41 49.2	17 S 22.0	0 S 6.8	13 S 42.8	21 S 28.3	12 S 35.9	21 N 13.8	18 S 57.4	22 S 28.3	17 N 10.9	12 S 9.8	21 N 34.7
4	8 53 38.9	16 30.3	0 6.7	18 35.2	20 24.6	11 13.6	21 30.3	19 1.9	22 28.0	17 13.2	12 9.8	21 36.9
7	9 5 28.5	15 36.0	0 6.6	13 51.9	19 7.7	9 48.6	21 46.8	19 6.2	22 27.5	17 15.5	12 9.7	21 39.0
10	9 17 18.2	14 39.3	0 6.6	3 6.3	17 37.8	8 21.3	22 3.3	19 10.1	22 27.1	17 17.8	12 9.5	21 41.1
13	9 29 7.9	13 40.4	0 6.5	8 N 15.5	15 54.7	6 52.0	22 19.5	19 13.7	22 26.6	17 20.1	12 9.1	21 43.2
16	9 40 57.5	12 39.5	0 6.4	16 20.1	13 58.7	5 21.2	22 35.5	19 16.9	22 26.1	17 22.3	12 8.7	21 45.2
19	9 52 47.2	11 36.8	0 6.4	18 14.6	11 50.1	3 49.1	22 51.0	19 19.8	22 25.6	17 24.5	12 8.2	21 47.2
22	10 4 36.8	10 32.4	0 6.3	12 8.7	9 30.1	2 16.0	23 6.2	19 22.4	22 25.1	17 26.6	12 7.7	21 49.2
25	10 16 26.5	9 26.6	0 6.2	0 S 15.4	7 .2	0 42.4	23 20.8	19 24.7	22 24.5	17 28.6	12 7.0	21 51.1
28	10 28 16.1	8 19.5	0 6.2	12 45.2	4 23.5	0 N 51.4	23 34.7	19 26.6	22 24.0	17 30.6	12 6.2	21 52.9

MARCH 1959

DAY	EPHEM. SID. TIME	☉	☊	☽	☿	♀	♂	♃	♄	♅	♆	♇
	h m s	° ′	° ′	° ′	° ′	° ′	° ′	° ′	° ′	° ′	° ′	° ′
		LONGITUDE										
1	10 32 12.7	9♓39.6	14♎55.8	24♏56.5	22♓11.6	5♈37.2	8♊32.7	1♐29.5	5♑20.2	13♌15.7	6♏49.8	2♍48.0
2	10 36 9.3	10 39.8	14 52.7	9♐ 4.6	24 .1	6 51.1	9 2.3	1 32.8	5 24.4	13 R 13.4	6 R 49.1	2 R 46.5
3	10 40 5.8	11 40.0	14 49.5	23 2.1	25 46.5	8 5.0	9 32.0	1 35.8	5 28.6	13 11.2	6 48.3	2 45.0
4	10 44 2.4	12 40.1	14 46.3	6♑48.0	27 30.6	9 18.9	10 1.9	1 38.6	5 32.6	13 9.0	6 47.6	2 43.5
5	10 47 58.9	13 40.3	14 43.1	20 21.9	29 11.8	10 32.7	10 31.9	1 41.3	5 36.6	13 6.8	6 46.8	2 42.0
6	10 51 55.5	14 40.4	14 39.9	3♒43.1	0♈49.5	11 46.4	11 2.0	1 43.8	5 40.6	13 4.7	6 45.9	2 40.5
7	10 55 52.0	15 40.5	14 36.8	16 51.4	2 23.2	13 .1	11 32.3	1 46.1	5 44.4	13 2.6	6 45.1	2 39.0
8	10 59 48.6	16 40.5	14 33.6	29 46.2	3 52.5	14 13.8	12 2.8	1 48.2	5 48.2	13 .5	6 44.2	2 37.5
9	11 3 45.1	17 40.5	14 30.4	12♓27.3	5 16.7	15 27.4	12 33.4	1 50.2	5 51.8	12 58.5	6 43.3	2 36.0
10	11 7 41.7	18 40.5	14 27.2	24 55.2	6 35.2	16 41.0	13 4.1	1 51.9	5 55.4	12 56.5	6 42.3	2 34.6
11	11 11 38.2	19 40.5	14 24.1	7♈10.5	7 47.7	17 54.5	13 34.9	1 53.5	5 58.9	12 54.5	6 41.3	2 33.1
12	11 15 34.8	20 40.4	14 20.9	19 14.9	8 53.5	19 8.0	14 5.9	1 54.9	6 2.3	12 52.6	6 40.3	2 31.7
13	11 19 31.3	21 40.3	14 17.7	1♉10.7	9 52.3	20 21.4	14 37.0	1 56.1	6 5.7	12 50.7	6 39.3	2 30.2
14	11 23 27.9	22 40.2	14 14.5	13 .9	10 43.6	21 34.9	15 8.2	1 57.2	6 9.0	12 48.9	6 38.3	2 28.9
15	11 27 24.4	23 40.0	14 11.3	24 49.1	11 27.1	22 48.2	15 39.6	1 58.0	6 12.1	12 47.1	6 37.2	2 27.5
16	11 31 21.0	24 39.8	14 8.2	6♊39.8	12 2.6	24 1.4	16 11.0	1 58.6	6 15.2	12 45.3	6 36.1	2 26.1
17	11 35 17.5	25 39.6	14 5.0	18 37.4	12 29.8	25 14.6	16 42.6	1 59.1	6 18.2	12 43.6	6 35.0	2 24.7
18	11 39 14.1	26 39.3	14 1.8	0♋46.9	12 48.7	26 27.8	17 14.2	1 59.3	6 21.0	12 41.9	6 33.9	2 23.3
19	11 43 10.6	27 38.9	13 58.6	13 12.8	12 59.2	27 40.9	17 46.0	1 59.4	6 23.8	12 40.3	6 32.7	2 21.9
20	11 47 7.2	28 38.6	13 55.5	25 59.5	13 1.4	28 53.9	18 17.8	1 R 59.3	6 26.6	12 38.7	6 31.5	2 20.6
21	11 51 3.7	29 38.2	13 52.3	9♌10.0	12 R 55.5	0♉ 6.8	18 49.8	1 59.0	6 29.2	12 37.1	6 30.3	2 19.3
22	11 55 .3	0♈37.7	13 49.1	22 45.9	12 41.9	1 19.7	19 21.9	1 58.5	6 31.7	12 35.6	6 29.0	2 17.9
23	11 58 56.8	1 37.3	13 45.9	6♍47.1	12 20.9	2 32.6	19 54.0	1 57.8	6 34.1	12 34.2	6 27.8	2 16.6
24	12 2 53.4	2 36.7	13 42.7	21 10.8	11 53.1	3 45.3	20 26.2	1 56.9	6 36.5	12 32.7	6 26.5	2 15.4
25	12 6 49.9	3 36.2	13 39.6	5♎52.1	11 19.3	4 58.0	20 58.6	1 55.9	6 38.7	12 31.4	6 25.2	2 14.1
26	12 10 46.5	4 35.6	13 36.4	20 44.1	10 40.1	6 10.7	21 31.0	1 54.6	6 40.9	12 30.0	6 23.9	2 12.8
27	12 14 43.1	5 35.0	13 33.2	5♏39.2	9 56.6	7 23.2	22 3.5	1 53.2	6 42.9	12 28.8	6 22.5	2 11.6
28	12 18 39.6	6 34.3	13 30.0	20 29.5	9 9.6	8 35.8	22 36.0	1 51.6	6 44.9	12 27.5	6 21.2	2 10.4
29	12 22 36.2	7 33.7	13 26.9	5♐ 8.6	8 20.3	9 48.2	23 8.7	1 49.8	6 46.8	12 26.4	6 19.8	2 9.2
30	12 26 32.7	8 33.0	13 23.7	19 31.5	7 29.6	11 .6	23 41.4	1 47.9	6 48.6	12 25.2	6 18.4	2 8.0
31	12 30 29.3	9 32.2	13 20.5	3♑35.3	6 38.6	12 12.9	24 14.2	1 45.7	6 50.2	12 24.1	6 17.0	2 6.9
		LATITUDE										
1	10 32 12.7	0 .0	0 .0	3N27.4	0S26.8	0S55.8	1N56.8	1N 1.8	0N56.3	0N42.5	1N47.8	12N16.9
4	10 44 2.4	0 .0	0 .0	5 10.8	0N 8.2	0 49.1	1 56.1	1 2.2	0 56.4	0 42.5	1 47.9	12 17.0
7	10 55 52.0	0 .0	0 .0	4 21.3	0 47.1	0 41.8	1 55.3	1 2.5	0 56.4	0 42.5	1 48.1	12 17.0
10	11 7 41.7	0 .0	0 .0	1 38.4	1 27.8	0 34.2	1 54.5	1 2.9	0 56.5	0 42.4	1 48.2	12 16.9
13	11 19 31.3	0 .0	0 .0	1S38.3	2 7.7	0 26.2	1 53.7	1 3.3	0 56.5	0 42.3	1 48.4	12 16.8
16	11 31 21.0	0 .0	0 .0	4 14.7	2 43.2	0 17.8	1 52.9	1 3.6	0 56.6	0 42.3	1 48.5	12 16.6
19	11 43 10.6	0 .0	0 .0	5 16.7	3 10.8	0 9.1	1 52.0	1 3.9	0 56.6	0 42.2	1 48.6	12 16.4
22	11 55 .3	0 .0	0 .0	4 4.2	3 26.6	0 .1	1 51.1	1 4.3	0 56.7	0 42.1	1 48.8	12 16.1
25	12 6 49.9	0 .0	0 .0	0 39.8	3 27.6	0N 9.0	1 50.2	1 4.6	0 56.8	0 42.1	1 48.9	12 15.8
28	12 18 39.6	0 .0	0 .0	3N13.4	3 12.5	0 18.4	1 49.3	1 4.9	0 56.8	0 42.0	1 49.0	12 15.4
31	12 30 29.3	0 .0	0 .0	5 13.5	2 42.6	0 27.8	1 48.4	1 5.2	0 56.9	0 41.9	1 49.1	12 14.9
		RIGHT ASCENSION										
1	10 32 12.7	11♓13.0	13♎44.8	23♏27.3	23♓ .5	5♈31.7	6♊28.7	29♏35.8	5♑46.3	15♌56.4	5♏ 5.7	9♍29.3
2	10 36 9.3	12 9.2	13 41.9	8♐ 4.1	24 35.8	6 38.7	7 .6	29 39.2	5 50.9	15 R 54.1	5 R 5.0	9 R 27.8
3	10 40 5.8	13 5.4	13 38.9	22 41.1	26 9.0	7 45.7	7 32.7	29 42.3	5 55.4	15 51.9	5 4.3	9 26.3
4	10 44 2.4	14 1.4	13 36.0	7♑ 7.6	27 39.7	8 52.8	8 5.1	29 45.3	5 59.8	15 49.6	5 3.6	9 24.9
5	10 47 58.9	14 57.3	13 33.0	21 13.3	29 7.5	9 59.8	8 37.6	29 48.1	6 4.1	15 47.5	5 2.8	9 23.4
6	10 51 55.5	15 53.1	13 30.1	4♒51.1	0♈32.0	11 6.9	9 10.2	29 50.7	6 8.4	15 45.3	5 2.1	9 22.0
7	10 55 52.0	16 48.8	13 27.1	17 58.2	1 52.7	12 14.0	9 43.1	29 53.2	6 12.5	15 43.2	5 1.2	9 20.5
8	10 59 48.6	17 44.4	13 24.2	0♓35.7	3 9.3	13 21.2	10 16.2	29 55.4	6 16.6	15 41.1	5 .4	9 19.1
9	11 3 45.1	18 39.9	13 21.3	12 48.0	4 21.2	14 28.4	10 49.4	29 57.4	6 20.5	15 39.1	4 59.5	9 17.6
10	11 7 41.7	19 35.3	13 18.3	24 41.2	5 28.0	15 35.7	11 22.8	29 59.3	6 24.4	15 37.0	4 58.6	9 16.2
11	11 11 38.2	20 30.7	13 15.4	6♈22.4	6 29.3	16 43.0	11 56.4	0♐ .9	6 28.2	15 35.1	4 57.7	9 14.7
12	11 15 34.8	21 25.9	13 12.4	17 58.8	7 24.7	17 50.4	12 30.2	0 2.4	6 31.9	15 33.1	4 56.7	9 13.3
13	11 19 31.3	22 21.0	13 9.5	29 37.0	8 13.8	18 57.9	13 4.1	0 3.7	6 35.5	15 31.2	4 55.8	9 11.9
14	11 23 27.9	23 16.2	13 6.5	11♉22.8	8 56.3	20 5.6	13 38.3	0 4.8	6 39.0	15 29.4	4 54.8	9 10.5
15	11 27 24.4	24 11.2	13 3.6	23 20.8	9 31.8	21 13.3	14 12.5	0 5.7	6 42.4	15 27.6	4 53.8	9 9.1
16	11 31 21.0	25 6.1	13 .6	5♊34.0	10 .3	22 21.1	14 46.9	0 6.4	6 45.7	15 25.8	4 52.7	9 7.8
17	11 35 17.5	26 1.0	12 57.7	18 3.6	10 21.4	23 29.1	15 21.4	0 6.8	6 49.0	15 24.1	4 51.7	9 6.4
18	11 39 14.1	26 55.8	12 54.8	0♋49.2	10 35.3	24 37.2	15 56.1	0 7.1	6 52.1	15 22.4	4 50.6	9 5.0
19	11 43 10.6	27 50.6	12 51.8	13 48.6	10 41.9	25 45.4	16 30.9	0 7.2	6 55.1	15 20.7	4 49.5	9 3.6
20	11 47 7.2	28 45.3	12 48.9	26 59.3	10 R 41.2	26 53.7	17 5.9	0 R 7.1	6 58.0	15 19.1	4 48.3	9 2.3
21	11 51 3.7	29 40.0	12 45.9	10♌18.8	10 33.7	28 2.3	17 41.0	0 6.8	7 .8	15 17.5	4 47.2	9 1.0
22	11 55 .3	0♈34.6	12 43.0	23 45.9	10 19.5	29 10.9	18 16.2	0 6.4	7 3.6	15 16.0	4 46.0	8 59.6
23	11 58 56.8	1 29.2	12 40.0	7♍21.2	9 59.2	0♉19.8	18 51.5	0 5.7	7 6.2	15 14.5	4 44.8	8 58.3
24	12 2 53.4	2 23.8	12 37.1	21 7.2	9 33.4	1 28.8	19 26.9	0 4.8	7 8.7	15 13.1	4 43.6	8 57.0
25	12 6 49.9	3 18.4	12 34.2	5♎ 7.4	9 2.6	2 38.0	20 2.5	0 3.7	7 11.2	15 11.7	4 42.3	8 55.7
26	12 10 46.5	4 12.9	12 31.2	19 25.3	8 27.6	3 47.4	20 38.2	0 2.5	7 13.5	15 10.3	4 41.0	8 54.5
27	12 14 43.1	5 7.5	12 28.3	4♏ 2.5	7 49.4	4 57.0	21 14.0	0 1.0	7 15.7	15 9.0	4 39.8	8 53.2
28	12 18 39.6	6 2.0	12 25.3	18 56.3	7 8.7	6 6.8	21 49.9	29♏59.4	7 17.8	15 7.8	4 38.5	8 52.0
29	12 22 36.2	6 56.6	12 22.4	3♐59.5	6 26.5	7 16.8	22 25.9	29 57.5	7 19.8	15 6.6	4 37.2	8 50.7
30	12 26 32.7	7 51.2	12 19.5	19 .4	5 43.8	8 27.0	23 2.0	29 55.5	7 21.8	15 5.4	4 35.8	8 49.5
31	12 30 29.3	8 45.8	12 16.5	3♑45.7	5 1.4	9 37.5	23 38.2	29 53.3	7 23.6	15 4.3	4 34.5	8 48.3
		DECLINATION										
1	10 32 12.7	7S56.9	0S 6.2	15S38.9	3S30.5	1N22.7	23N39.2	19S27.2	22S23.8	17N31.2	12S 5.9	21N53.5
4	10 44 2.4	6 48.3	0 6.1	18 5.6	0 51.9	2 56.4	23 52.2	19 28.6	22 23.2	17 33.1	12 5.1	21 55.2
7	10 55 52.0	5 38.9	0 6.0	11 37.8	1N40.1	4 29.6	24 4.4	19 29.8	22 22.7	17 34.9	12 4.1	21 56.9
10	11 7 41.7	4 28.8	0 6.0	0 30.8	3 57.6	6 1.9	24 15.8	19 30.6	22 22.2	17 36.5	12 3.1	21 58.5
13	11 19 31.3	3 18.2	0 5.9	10N20.9	5 52.0	7 33.0	24 26.3	19 31.1	22 21.7	17 38.1	12 1.9	21 60.0
16	11 31 21.0	2 7.2	0 5.8	17 14.3	7 15.9	9 2.7	24 35.8	19 31.3	22 21.2	17 39.6	12 .8	22 1.4
19	11 43 10.6	0 56.1	0 5.8	17 32.0	8 3.4	10 30.5	24 44.3	19 31.1	22 20.7	17 41.0	11 59.5	22 2.7
22	11 55 .3	0N15.0	0 5.7	10 4.7	8 11.1	11 56.1	24 51.7	19 30.6	22 20.3	17 42.2	11 58.2	22 3.9
25	12 6 49.9	1 26.0	0 5.6	2S56.4	7 39.7	13 19.3	24 58.1	19 29.8	22 19.8	17 43.3	11 56.9	22 5.0
28	12 18 39.6	2 36.6	0 5.6	14 45.9	6 34.8	14 39.6	25 3.3	19 28.6	22 19.5	17 44.3	11 55.5	22 6.0
31	12 30 29.3	3 46.8	0 5.5	18 10.2	5 7.5	15 56.7	25 7.3	19 27.1	22 19.1	17 45.2	11 54.0	22 6.9

APRIL 1959

DAY	EPHEM. SID. TIME	☉	☊	☽	☿	♀	♂	♃	♄	♅	♆	♇
	h m s	° ′	° ′	° ′	° ′	° ′	° ′	° ′	° ′	° ′	° ′	° ′
		LONGITUDE										
1	12 34 25.8	10♈31.5	13♎17.3	17♑19.0	5♈48.3	13♉25.1	24♊47.1	1♐43.4	6♑51.8	12♌23.1	6♏15.6	2♍ 5.7
2	12 38 22.4	11 30.7	13 14.1	0♒43.0	4R59.7	14 37.3	25 20.1	1R40.8	6 53.3	12R22.1	6R14.1	2R 4.6
3	12 42 18.9	12 29.9	13 11.0	13 48.6	4 13.6	15 49.4	25 53.2	1 38.1	6 54.7	12 21.2	6 12.7	2 3.5
4	12 46 15.5	13 29.0	13 7.8	26 37.7	3 30.8	17 1.5	26 26.3	1 35.3	6 56.0	12 20.3	6 11.3	2 2.5
5	12 50 12.0	14 28.2	13 4.6	9♓12.3	2 51.9	18 13.5	26 59.5	1 32.2	6 57.2	12 19.5	6 9.8	2 1.4
6	12 54 8.6	15 27.3	13 1.4	21 34.4	2 17.4	19 25.4	27 32.8	1 29.0	6 58.3	12 18.7	6 8.3	2 .4
7	12 58 5.1	16 26.3	12 58.2	3♈46.0	1 47.7	20 37.2	28 6.2	1 25.6	6 59.3	12 18.0	6 6.8	1 59.4
8	13 2 1.7	17 25.3	12 55.1	15 49.0	1 23.1	21 48.9	28 39.6	1 22.0	7 .2	12 17.3	6 5.2	1 58.4
9	13 5 58.2	18 24.3	12 51.9	27 45.2	1 3.9	23 .6	29 13.1	1 18.3	7 1.0	12 16.7	6 3.7	1 57.4
10	13 9 54.8	19 23.3	12 48.7	9♉36.7	0 50.0	24 12.2	29 46.6	1 14.3	7 1.7	12 16.1	6 2.2	1 56.5
11	13 13 51.3	20 22.2	12 45.5	21 25.5	0 41.5	25 23.7	0♋20.2	1 10.2	7 2.3	12 15.6	6 .6	1 55.5
12	13 17 47.9	21 21.1	12 42.4	3♊14.5	0 38.4	26 35.2	0 53.9	1 6.0	7 2.8	12 15.1	5 59.0	1 54.6
13	13 21 44.4	22 19.9	12 39.2	15 6.4	0D40.7	27 46.5	1 27.6	1 1.6	7 3.2	12 14.7	5 57.5	1 53.8
14	13 25 41.0	23 18.7	12 36.0	27 4.9	0 48.1	28 57.8	2 1.4	0 57.0	7 3.5	12 14.3	5 55.9	1 52.9
15	13 29 37.5	24 17.5	12 32.8	9♋13.6	1 .5	0♊ 9.0	2 35.3	0 52.3	7 3.7	12 14.0	5 54.3	1 52.1
16	13 33 34.1	25 16.2	12 29.6	21 36.9	1 17.9	1 20.0	3 9.2	0 47.4	7 3.8	12 13.8	5 52.7	1 51.3
17	13 37 30.6	26 14.9	12 26.5	4♌18.7	1 39.9	2 31.0	3 43.2	0 42.4	7 3.8	12 13.6	5 51.1	1 50.5
18	13 41 27.2	27 13.6	12 23.3	17 22.9	2 6.4	3 42.0	4 17.2	0 37.2	7R 3.7	12 13.4	5 49.5	1 49.8
19	13 45 23.8	28 12.2	12 20.1	0♍52.5	2 37.1	4 52.8	4 51.3	0 31.9	7 3.5	12 13.3	5 47.8	1 49.1
20	13 49 20.3	29 10.8	12 16.9	14 48.9	3 12.1	6 3.5	5 25.4	0 26.5	7 3.2	12 13.3	5 46.2	1 48.4
21	13 53 16.9	0♉ 9.4	12 13.8	29 11.7	3 50.9	7 14.1	5 59.6	0 20.9	7 2.9	12 13.3	5 44.6	1 47.7
22	13 57 13.4	1 7.9	12 10.6	13♎57.6	4 33.5	8 24.6	6 33.8	0 15.2	7 2.4	12D13.4	5 43.0	1 47.1
23	14 1 10.0	2 6.4	12 7.4	29 .5	5 19.7	9 35.0	7 8.1	0 9.3	7 1.8	12 13.5	5 41.3	1 46.4
24	14 5 6.5	3 4.8	12 4.2	14♏12.1	6 9.3	10 45.3	7 42.4	0 3.4	7 1.1	12 13.7	5 39.7	1 45.9
25	14 9 3.1	4 3.3	12 1.0	29 22.6	7 2.2	11 55.6	8 16.8	29♏57.3	7 .4	12 14.0	5 38.1	1 45.3
26	14 12 59.6	5 1.7	11 57.9	14♐22.6	7 58.2	13 5.7	8 51.2	29 51.1	6 59.5	12 14.3	5 36.5	1 44.8
27	14 16 56.2	6 .0	11 54.7	28 3.9	8 57.2	14 15.7	9 25.7	29 44.8	6 58.6	12 14.6	5 34.8	1 44.3
28	14 20 52.7	6 58.4	11 51.5	13♑21.4	9 59.0	15 25.6	10 .2	29 38.4	6 57.5	12 15.0	5 33.2	1 43.8
29	14 24 49.3	7 56.7	11 48.3	27 12.5	11 3.7	16 35.4	10 34.7	29 31.8	6 56.4	12 15.4	5 31.5	1 43.4
30	14 28 45.8	8 55.0	11 45.2	10♒37.4	12 11.0	17 45.1	11 9.3	29 25.2	6 55.1	12 15.9	5 29.9	1 43.0
		LATITUDE										
1	12 34 25.8	0 .0	0 .0	5N17.0	2N29.8	0N31.0	1N48.0	1N 5.3	0N56.9	0N41.9	1N49.1	12N14.8
4	12 46 15.5	0 .0	0 .0	3 50.7	1 46.1	0 40.5	1 47.1	1 5.5	0 57.0	0 41.8	1 49.2	12 14.3
7	12 58 5.1	0 .0	0 .0	0 51.7	0 58.0	0 50.0	1 46.1	1 5.8	0 57.0	0 41.7	1 49.3	12 13.7
10	13 9 54.8	0 .0	0 .0	2S22.1	0 10.1	0 59.4	1 45.1	1 6.0	0 57.1	0 41.6	1 49.3	12 13.1
13	13 21 44.4	0 .0	0 .0	4 40.4	0S34.3	1 8.6	1 44.1	1 6.2	0 57.2	0 41.5	1 49.4	12 12.5
16	13 33 34.1	0 .0	0 .0	5 13.5	1 13.3	1 17.7	1 43.0	1 6.3	0 57.2	0 41.4	1 49.4	12 11.8
19	13 45 23.8	0 .0	0 .0	3 33.0	1 46.2	1 26.6	1 42.0	1 6.5	0 57.3	0 41.3	1 49.5	12 11.2
22	13 57 13.4	0 .0	0 .0	0N 5.0	2 12.6	1 35.1	1 41.0	1 6.6	0 57.3	0 41.2	1 49.5	12 10.4
25	14 9 3.1	0 .0	0 .0	3 48.6	2 32.7	1 43.3	1 39.9	1 6.6	0 57.4	0 41.1	1 49.5	12 9.7
28	14 20 52.7	0 .0	0 .0	5 15.0	2 46.6	1 51.1	1 38.8	1 6.7	0 57.4	0 41.0	1 49.5	12 8.9
		RIGHT ASCENSION										
1	12 34 25.8	9♈40.4	12♎13.6	18♑ 3.8	4♈20.2	10♉48.1	24♊14.5	29♏50.9	7♑25.3	15♌ 3.3	4♏33.1	8♍47.1
2	12 38 22.4	10 35.0	12 10.6	1♒47.9	3R41.0	11 59.0	24 50.9	29R48.3	7 26.9	15R 2.3	4R31.7	8R46.0
3	12 42 18.9	11 29.7	12 7.7	14 56.3	3 4.5	13 10.1	25 27.4	29 45.5	7 28.4	15 1.3	4 30.3	8 44.8
4	12 46 15.5	12 24.4	12 4.8	27 31.8	2 31.3	14 21.5	26 4.0	29 42.5	7 29.8	15 .5	4 29.0	8 43.8
5	12 50 12.0	13 19.2	12 1.8	9♓40.5	2 1.9	15 33.1	26 40.7	29 39.4	7 31.1	14 59.6	4 27.5	8 42.7
6	12 54 8.6	14 14.0	11 58.9	21 29.5	1 36.6	16 44.9	27 17.4	29 36.0	7 32.3	14 58.8	4 26.1	8 41.6
7	12 58 5.1	15 8.8	11 55.9	3♈ 6.9	1 15.8	17 56.9	27 54.2	29 32.5	7 33.4	14 58.1	4 24.7	8 40.5
8	13 2 1.7	16 3.7	11 53.0	14 40.0	0 59.7	19 9.2	28 31.2	29 28.8	7 34.3	14 57.4	4 23.2	8 39.5
9	13 5 58.2	16 58.6	11 50.1	26 15.5	0 48.3	20 21.7	29 8.1	29 24.9	7 35.2	14 56.7	4 21.7	8 38.4
10	13 9 54.8	17 53.6	11 47.1	7♉58.6	0 41.8	21 34.4	29 45.2	29 20.9	7 35.9	14 56.2	4 20.2	8 37.4
11	13 13 51.3	18 48.7	11 44.2	19 53.2	0 40.1	22 47.4	0♋22.3	29 16.7	7 36.6	14 55.6	4 18.7	8 36.5
12	13 17 47.9	19 43.8	11 41.2	2♊ 1.2	0D43.2	24 .6	0 59.5	29 12.3	7 37.1	14 55.1	4 17.2	8 35.5
13	13 21 44.4	20 39.0	11 38.3	14 22.7	0 50.9	25 14.0	1 36.8	29 7.7	7 37.6	14 54.7	4 15.7	8 34.6
14	13 25 41.0	21 34.3	11 35.4	26 56.2	1 3.2	26 27.6	2 14.1	29 3.0	7 37.9	14 54.3	4 14.2	8 33.6
15	13 29 37.5	22 29.6	11 32.4	9♋39.5	1 19.8	27 41.5	2 51.5	28 58.1	7 38.1	14 54.0	4 12.7	8 32.7
16	13 33 34.1	23 25.1	11 29.5	22 30.0	1 40.6	28 55.5	3 28.9	28 53.1	7 38.2	14 53.8	4 11.1	8 31.9
17	13 37 30.6	24 20.6	11 26.5	5♌26.3	2 5.4	0♊ 9.8	4 6.4	28 47.9	7 38.2	14 53.5	4 9.6	8 31.0
18	13 41 27.2	25 16.2	11 23.6	18 28.6	2 34.1	1 24.2	4 43.9	28 42.5	7R38.1	14 53.4	4 8.0	8 30.2
19	13 45 23.8	26 11.9	11 20.7	1♍39.3	3 6.4	2 38.9	5 21.5	28 37.0	7 37.9	14 53.3	4 6.5	8 29.4
20	13 49 20.3	27 7.7	11 17.7	15 3.0	3 42.2	3 53.7	5 59.1	28 31.4	7 37.6	14 53.2	4 4.9	8 28.6
21	13 53 16.9	28 3.5	11 14.8	28 45.5	4 21.3	5 8.6	6 36.7	28 25.6	7 37.2	14 53.2	4 3.3	8 27.9
22	13 57 13.4	28 59.5	11 11.9	12♎52.8	5 3.6	6 23.8	7 14.4	28 19.7	7 36.7	14D53.3	4 1.8	8 27.2
23	14 1 10.0	29 55.6	11 8.9	27 29.2	5 48.9	7 39.1	7 52.1	28 13.7	7 36.0	14 53.4	4 .2	8 26.5
24	14 5 6.5	0♉51.8	11 6.0	12♏34.4	6 37.0	8 54.5	8 29.9	28 7.5	7 35.3	14 53.6	3 58.6	8 25.8
25	14 9 3.1	1 48.2	11 3.1	28 1.6	7 28.0	10 10.1	9 7.7	28 1.3	7 34.5	14 53.9	3 57.1	8 25.2
26	14 12 59.6	2 44.7	11 .1	13♐36.6	8 21.5	11 25.8	9 45.5	27 54.9	7 33.6	14 54.1	3 55.5	8 24.6
27	14 16 56.2	3 41.2	10 57.2	29 1.1	9 17.5	12 41.6	10 23.3	27 48.3	7 32.6	14 54.5	3 54.0	8 24.0
28	14 20 52.7	4 37.9	10 54.3	13♑57.7	10 15.9	13 57.5	11 1.1	27 41.7	7 31.4	14 54.9	3 52.4	8 23.4
29	14 24 49.3	5 34.7	10 51.3	28 14.3	11 16.6	15 13.5	11 39.0	27 34.9	7 30.2	14 55.3	3 50.8	8 22.8
30	14 28 45.8	6 31.7	10 48.4	11♒46.8	12 19.6	16 29.5	12 16.9	27 28.1	7 28.8	14 55.8	3 49.2	8 22.3
		DECLINATION										
1	12 34 25.8	4N10.0	0S 5.5	17S 4.8	4N35.9	16N21.7	25N 8.3	19S26.6	22S19.0	17N45.5	11S53.5	22N 7.2
4	12 46 15.5	5 19.4	0 5.4	9 1.3	3 1.2	17 34.1	25 10.7	19 24.7	22 18.7	17 46.2	11 52.0	22 8.0
7	12 58 5.1	6 27.8	0 5.4	2N17.3	1 36.0	18 42.7	25 11.8	19 22.5	22 18.5	17 46.8	11 50.5	22 8.6
10	13 9 54.8	7 35.3	0 5.3	12 26.8	0 29.2	19 47.0	25 11.6	19 20.0	22 18.3	17 47.2	11 48.9	22 9.1
13	13 21 44.4	8 41.6	0 5.2	17 57.9	0S15.3	20 46.9	25 10.1	19 17.3	22 18.2	17 47.5	11 47.3	22 9.6
16	13 33 34.1	9 46.7	0 5.2	16 32.7	0 36.3	21 41.9	25 7.3	19 14.2	22 18.1	17 47.7	11 45.7	22 9.9
19	13 45 23.8	10 50.2	0 5.1	7 50.6	0 34.9	22 31.9	25 3.1	19 10.9	22 18.1	17 47.7	11 44.0	22 10.0
22	13 57 13.4	11 52.1	0 5.0	5S25.9	0 13.0	23 16.6	24 57.6	19 7.3	22 18.1	17 47.6	11 42.4	22 10.1
25	14 9 3.1	12 52.3	0 5.0	16 17.8	0N27.3	23 55.7	24 50.7	19 3.5	22 18.1	17 47.3	11 40.8	22 10.0
28	14 20 52.7	13 50.6	0 4.9	17 32.8	1 24.1	24 29.1	24 42.5	18 59.4	22 18.2	17 47.0	11 39.2	22 9.9

MAY 1959

LONGITUDE

DAY	EPHEM. SID. TIME	☉	☊	☽	☿	♀	♂	♃	♄	♅	♆	♇
	h m s	° ′	° ′	° ′	° ′	° ′	° ′	° ′	° ′	° ′	° ′	° ′
1	14 32 42.4	9♉53.2	11♎42.0	23♒38.2	13♈20.9	18♊54.6	11♋44.0	29♏18.4	6♑53.8	12♌16.5	5♏28.3	1♍42.6
2	14 36 38.9	10 51.5	11 38.8	6♓18.1	14 33.2	20 4.1	12 18.7	29R11.6	6R52.4	12 17.1	5R26.6	1R42.2
3	14 40 35.5	11 49.7	11 35.6	18 41.0	15 48.0	21 13.4	12 53.4	29 4.7	6 50.8	12 17.7	5 25.0	1 41.9
4	14 44 32.1	12 47.9	11 32.4	0♈50.7	17 5.1	22 22.7	13 28.2	28 57.7	6 49.2	12 18.5	5 23.4	1 41.6
5	14 48 28.6	13 46.0	11 29.3	12 50.7	18 24.6	23 31.8	14 3.0	28 50.6	6 47.5	12 19.2	5 21.8	1 41.3
6	14 52 25.2	14 44.2	11 26.1	24 44.4	19 46.2	24 40.8	14 37.8	28 43.4	6 45.7	12 20.0	5 20.2	1 41.1
7	14 56 21.7	15 42.3	11 22.9	6♉34.4	21 10.1	25 49.6	15 12.7	28 36.2	6 43.8	12 20.9	5 18.5	1 40.8
8	15 0 18.3	16 40.4	11 19.7	18 23.1	22 36.1	26 58.4	15 47.7	28 28.9	6 41.9	12 21.8	5 16.9	1 40.6
9	15 4 14.8	17 38.4	11 16.6	0♊12.4	24 4.2	28 7.0	16 22.7	28 21.6	6 39.8	12 22.8	5 15.3	1 40.5
10	15 8 11.4	18 36.5	11 13.4	12 4.3	25 34.4	29 15.5	16 57.7	28 14.2	6 37.7	12 23.9	5 13.8	1 40.4
11	15 12 7.9	19 34.5	11 10.2	24 .8	27 6.7	0♋23.8	17 32.7	28 6.7	6 35.4	12 24.9	5 12.2	1 40.3
12	15 16 4.5	20 32.4	11 7.0	6♋ 4.0	28 41.1	1 32.0	18 7.8	27 59.2	6 33.1	12 26.1	5 10.6	1 40.2
13	15 20 1.0	21 30.4	11 3.8	18 16.5	0♉17.6	2 40.1	18 43.0	27 51.7	6 30.7	12 27.3	5 9.1	1 40.2
14	15 23 57.6	22 28.3	11 .7	0♌41.2	1 56.1	3 48.0	19 18.1	27 44.1	6 28.2	12 28.5	5 7.5	1 40.1
15	15 27 54.2	23 26.2	10 57.5	13 21.5	3 36.6	4 55.8	19 53.3	27 36.5	6 25.7	12 29.8	5 6.0	1D40.2
16	15 31 50.7	24 24.1	10 54.3	26 20.7	5 19.3	6 3.5	20 28.6	27 29.0	6 23.1	12 31.2	5 4.5	1 40.3
17	15 35 47.3	25 21.9	10 51.1	9♍42.2	7 4.0	7 10.9	21 3.9	27 21.3	6 20.4	12 32.5	5 3.0	1 40.3
18	15 39 43.8	26 19.7	10 48.0	23 28.5	8 50.7	8 18.2	21 39.2	27 13.7	6 17.6	12 34.0	5 1.5	1 40.5
19	15 43 40.4	27 17.5	10 44.8	7♎40.7	10 39.5	9 25.3	22 14.6	27 6.1	6 14.7	12 35.5	4 60.0	1 40.6
20	15 47 36.9	28 15.2	10 41.6	22 17.8	12 30.3	10 32.3	22 49.9	26 58.4	6 11.7	12 37.0	4 58.5	1 40.8
21	15 51 33.5	29 12.9	10 38.4	7♏15.7	14 23.2	11 39.1	23 25.3	26 50.8	6 8.7	12 38.6	4 57.0	1 41.0
22	15 55 30.0	0♊10.6	10 35.3	22 27.4	16 18.1	12 45.7	24 .8	26 43.1	6 5.6	12 40.2	4 55.6	1 41.2
23	15 59 26.6	1 8.3	10 32.1	7♐43.4	18 15.0	13 52.1	24 36.2	26 35.5	6 2.5	12 41.9	4 54.1	1 41.4
24	16 3 23.2	2 5.9	10 28.9	22 53.0	20 13.8	14 58.3	25 11.7	26 28.0	5 59.3	12 43.6	4 52.7	1 41.7
25	16 7 19.7	3 3.6	10 25.7	7♑46.1	22 14.6	16 4.3	25 47.2	26 20.4	5 56.0	12 45.4	4 51.3	1 42.1
26	16 11 16.3	4 1.2	10 22.5	22 15.2	24 17.2	17 10.2	26 22.8	26 12.9	5 52.6	12 47.2	4 49.9	1 42.4
27	16 15 12.8	4 58.8	10 19.4	6♒15.9	26 21.6	18 15.8	26 58.4	26 5.4	5 49.2	12 49.1	4 48.6	1 42.8
28	16 19 9.4	5 56.3	10 16.2	19 47.0	28 27.6	19 21.3	27 34.0	25 57.9	5 45.7	12 51.0	4 47.2	1 43.2
29	16 23 5.9	6 53.9	10 13.0	2♓50.3	0♊35.1	20 26.5	28 9.6	25 50.5	5 42.2	12 52.9	4 45.9	1 43.6
30	16 27 2.5	7 51.5	10 9.8	15 29.4	2 43.9	21 31.5	28 45.3	25 43.1	5 38.6	12 54.9	4 44.6	1 44.1
31	16 30 59.0	8 49.0	10 6.7	27 48.8	4 53.8	22 36.4	29 21.0	25 35.8	5 34.9	12 57.0	4 43.3	1 44.6

LATITUDE

DAY	EPHEM. SID. TIME	☉	☊	☽	☿	♀	♂	♃	♄	♅	♆	♇
1	14 32 42.4	0 .0	0 .0	3N58.7	2S54.6	1N58.3	1N37.8	1N 6.7	0N57.4	0N40.9	1N49.5	12N 8.1
4	14 44 32.1	0 .0	0 .0	1 5.9	2 56.8	2 5.0	1 36.7	1 6.6	0 57.4	0 40.8	1 49.5	12 7.3
7	14 56 21.7	0 .0	0 .0	2S 5.9	2 53.7	2 11.1	1 35.6	1 6.5	0 57.4	0 40.7	1 49.5	12 6.5
10	15 8 11.4	0 .0	0 .0	4 27.9	2 45.3	2 16.5	1 34.5	1 6.4	0 57.4	0 40.6	1 49.4	12 5.6
13	15 20 1.0	0 .0	0 .0	5 8.7	2 32.0	2 21.2	1 33.4	1 6.2	0 57.4	0 40.5	1 49.4	12 4.8
16	15 31 50.7	0 .0	0 .0	3 43.1	2 13.9	2 25.1	1 32.2	1 6.0	0 57.4	0 40.5	1 49.3	12 3.9
19	15 43 40.4	0 .0	0 .0	0 24.7	1 51.5	2 28.1	1 31.1	1 5.8	0 57.4	0 40.4	1 49.3	12 3.0
22	15 55 30.0	0 .0	0 .0	3N19.7	1 25.3	2 30.3	1 30.0	1 5.5	0 57.3	0 40.3	1 49.2	12 2.2
25	16 7 19.7	0 .0	0 .0	5 6.5	0 56.0	2 31.5	1 28.8	1 5.1	0 57.2	0 40.2	1 49.1	12 1.3
28	16 19 9.4	0 .0	0 .0	4 1.7	0 24.6	2 31.7	1 27.7	1 4.7	0 57.2	0 40.1	1 49.0	12 .4
31	16 30 59.0	0 .0	0 .0	1 13.0	0N 7.4	2 30.8	1 26.5	1 4.3	0 57.1	0 40.0	1 49.0	11 59.6

RIGHT ASCENSION

DAY	EPHEM. SID. TIME	☉	☊	☽	☿	♀	♂	♃	♄	♅	♆	♇
1	14 32 42.4	7♉28.8	10♎45.4	24♒37.8	13♈24.8	17♊45.6	12♋54.8	27♏21.1	7♑27.4	14♌56.3	3♏47.6	8♍21.8
2	14 36 38.9	8 26.0	10 42.5	6♓54.2	14 32.0	19 1.8	13 32.7	27R14.0	7R25.8	14 56.9	3R46.1	8R21.4
3	14 40 35.5	9 23.4	10 39.6	18 45.2	15 41.4	20 17.9	14 10.6	27 6.9	7 24.2	14 57.6	3 44.5	8 20.9
4	14 44 32.1	10 20.9	10 36.6	0♈20.3	16 52.8	21 34.1	14 48.5	26 59.7	7 22.5	14 58.3	3 42.9	8 20.5
5	14 48 28.6	11 18.6	10 33.7	11 48.8	18 6.1	22 50.3	15 26.5	26 52.4	7 20.6	14 59.1	3 41.4	8 20.1
6	14 52 25.2	12 16.4	10 30.8	23 18.9	19 21.5	24 6.5	16 4.4	26 45.0	7 18.7	14 59.9	3 39.8	8 19.8
7	14 56 21.7	13 14.3	10 27.8	4♉56.9	20 38.9	25 22.6	16 42.4	26 37.5	7 16.6	15 .8	3 38.3	8 19.4
8	15 0 18.3	14 12.4	10 24.9	16 47.4	21 58.2	26 38.7	17 20.3	26 30.0	7 14.5	15 1.7	3 36.7	8 19.1
9	15 4 14.8	15 10.6	10 22.0	28 52.4	23 19.6	27 54.7	17 58.3	26 22.4	7 12.3	15 2.7	3 35.2	8 18.9
10	15 8 11.4	16 9.0	10 19.0	11♊11.7	24 42.9	29 10.6	18 36.3	26 14.8	7 10.0	15 3.7	3 33.6	8 18.6
11	15 12 7.9	17 7.5	10 16.1	23 42.8	26 8.3	0♋26.4	19 14.2	26 7.1	7 7.6	15 4.8	3 32.1	8 18.4
12	15 16 4.5	18 6.1	10 13.2	6♋21.7	27 35.8	1 42.1	19 52.2	25 59.4	7 5.0	15 5.9	3 30.6	8 18.2
13	15 20 1.0	19 4.9	10 10.2	19 4.3	29 5.4	2 57.7	20 30.1	25 51.6	7 2.5	15 7.1	3 29.1	8 18.1
14	15 23 57.6	20 3.8	10 7.3	1♌47.9	0♉37.1	4 13.0	21 8.1	25 43.8	6 59.8	15 8.3	3 27.6	8 18.0
15	15 27 54.2	21 2.9	10 4.4	14 31.8	2 11.0	5 28.2	21 46.0	25 36.0	6 57.0	15 9.6	3 26.1	8 17.9
16	15 31 50.7	22 2.1	10 1.5	27 18.2	3 47.2	6 43.2	22 23.9	25 28.2	6 54.2	15 11.0	3 24.7	8 17.8
17	15 35 47.3	23 1.5	9 58.5	10♍12.2	5 25.8	7 58.0	23 1.8	25 20.3	6 51.3	15 12.4	3 23.2	8 17.8
18	15 39 43.8	24 .9	9 55.6	23 21.0	7 6.7	9 12.5	23 39.7	25 12.5	6 48.3	15 13.8	3 21.8	8 17.8
19	15 43 40.4	25 .5	9 52.7	6♎53.3	8 50.0	10 26.8	24 17.5	25 4.6	6 45.2	15 15.3	3 20.3	8 17.8
20	15 47 36.9	26 .3	9 49.7	20 57.4	10 35.9	11 40.8	24 55.4	24 56.8	6 42.0	15 16.8	3 18.9	8D17.9
21	15 51 33.5	27 .1	9 46.8	5♏38.5	12 24.4	12 54.4	25 33.2	24 48.9	6 38.7	15 18.4	3 17.5	8 17.9
22	15 55 30.0	28 .2	9 43.9	20 55.7	14 15.4	14 7.8	26 10.9	24 41.1	6 35.4	15 20.0	3 16.1	8 18.0
23	15 59 26.6	29 .3	9 40.9	6♐39.5	16 9.2	15 20.9	26 48.7	24 33.2	6 32.0	15 21.7	3 14.7	8 18.2
24	16 3 23.2	0♊ .6	9 38.0	22 31.4	18 5.7	16 33.6	27 26.4	24 25.4	6 28.5	15 23.4	3 13.3	8 18.3
25	16 7 19.7	1 1.0	9 35.1	8♑ 8.6	20 4.9	17 45.9	28 4.1	24 17.6	6 25.0	15 25.2	3 12.0	8 18.5
26	16 11 16.3	2 1.5	9 32.1	23 11.2	22 6.9	18 57.9	28 41.8	24 9.9	6 21.4	15 27.0	3 10.6	8 18.7
27	16 15 12.8	3 2.2	9 29.2	7♒27.3	24 11.6	20 9.5	29 19.4	24 2.2	6 17.7	15 28.9	3 9.3	8 19.0
28	16 19 9.4	4 3.0	9 26.3	20 54.5	26 18.9	21 20.7	29 57.0	23 54.5	6 13.9	15 30.8	3 8.0	8 19.3
29	16 23 5.9	5 3.9	9 23.4	3♓37.7	28 28.7	22 31.5	0♌34.6	23 46.9	6 10.1	15 32.8	3 6.7	8 19.6
30	16 27 2.5	6 4.9	9 20.4	15 46.1	0♊41.0	23 41.8	1 12.1	23 39.4	6 6.2	15 34.8	3 5.4	8 19.9
31	16 30 59.0	7 6.0	9 17.5	27 30.6	2 55.5	24 51.8	1 49.6	23 31.8	6 2.3	15 36.8	3 4.2	8 20.3

DECLINATION

DAY	EPHEM. SID. TIME	☉	☊	☽	☿	♀	♂	♃	♄	♅	♆	♇
1	14 32 42.4	14N46.8	0S 4.8	9S53.0	2N35.3	24N56.6	24N32.8	18S55.2	22S18.4	17N46.4	11S37.5	22N 9.6
4	14 44 32.1	15 40.9	0 4.8	1N20.6	3 59.3	25 18.1	24 21.8	18 50.7	22 18.6	17 45.8	11 35.9	22 9.2
7	14 56 21.7	16 32.6	0 4.7	11 43.8	5 34.4	25 33.6	24 9.4	18 46.2	22 18.9	17 45.0	11 34.3	22 8.7
10	15 8 11.4	17 21.8	0 4.7	17 48.8	7 19.2	25 42.9	23 55.7	18 41.4	22 19.2	17 44.1	11 32.8	22 8.1
13	15 20 1.0	18 8.5	0 4.6	17 5.7	9 12.1	25 46.0	23 40.5	18 36.6	22 19.6	17 43.0	11 31.3	22 7.4
16	15 31 50.7	18 52.4	0 4.5	9 14.1	11 11.5	25 43.1	23 24.1	18 31.7	22 19.9	17 41.8	11 29.8	22 6.6
19	15 43 40.4	19 33.4	0 4.5	3S25.5	13 15.3	25 34.2	23 6.2	18 26.8	22 20.4	17 40.5	11 28.4	22 5.6
22	15 55 30.0	20 11.4	0 4.4	15 10.0	15 21.2	25 19.4	22 47.1	18 21.8	22 20.8	17 39.1	11 27.0	22 4.6
25	16 7 19.7	20 46.3	0 4.3	18 6.9	17 25.8	24 58.9	22 26.7	18 16.9	22 21.3	17 37.6	11 25.6	22 3.5
28	16 19 9.4	21 18.0	0 4.3	11 3.3	19 25.2	24 32.8	22 5.0	18 12.0	22 21.9	17 35.9	11 24.3	22 2.3
31	16 30 59.0	21 46.4	0 4.2	0N14.8	21 14.2	24 1.5	21 42.0	18 7.2	22 22.4	17 34.1	11 23.1	22 1.0

JUNE 1959

LONGITUDE

DAY	EPHEM. SID. TIME h m s	☉ ° ′	☊ ° ′	☽ ° ′	☿ ° ′	♀ ° ′	♂ ° ′	♃ ° ′	♄ ° ′	♅ ° ′	♆ ° ′	♇ ° ′
1	16 34 55.6	9♊46.5	10♎ 3.5	9♈53.5	7♊ 4.7	23♋41.0	29♋56.8	25♏28.6	5♑31.2	12♌59.1	4♏42.0	1♍45.1
2	16 38 52.2	10 44.0	10 .3	21 48.3	9 16.2	24 45.3	0♌32.5	25R21.4	5R27.5	13 1.2	4R40.8	1 45.6
3	16 42 48.7	11 41.5	9 57.1	3♉37.7	11 28.2	25 49.5	1 8.3	25 14.3	5 23.7	13 3.4	4 39.5	1 46.2
4	16 46 45.3	12 39.0	9 54.0	15 25.3	13 40.3	26 53.4	1 44.2	25 7.2	5 19.8	13 5.6	4 38.3	1 46.8
5	16 50 41.8	13 36.5	9 50.8	27 14.2	15 52.3	27 57.0	2 20.0	25 .3	5 15.9	13 7.9	4 37.1	1 47.5
6	16 54 38.4	14 34.0	9 47.6	9♊ 6.9	18 4.0	29 .5	2 56.0	24 53.5	5 12.0	13 10.2	4 36.0	1 48.2
7	16 58 34.9	15 31.4	9 44.4	21 5.0	20 14.9	0♌ 3.7	3 31.9	24 46.7	5 8.0	13 12.5	4 34.8	1 48.9
8	17 2 31.5	16 28.8	9 41.2	3♋ 9.9	22 24.9	1 6.6	4 7.9	24 40.0	5 3.9	13 14.9	4 33.7	1 49.6
9	17 6 28.1	17 26.2	9 38.1	15 22.9	24 33.8	2 9.2	4 43.9	24 33.4	4 59.8	13 17.4	4 32.6	1 50.3
10	17 10 24.6	18 23.6	9 34.9	27 45.2	26 41.3	3 11.5	5 19.9	24 27.0	4 55.7	13 19.8	4 31.5	1 51.1
11	17 14 21.2	19 21.0	9 31.7	10♌18.3	28 47.3	4 13.5	5 56.0	24 20.6	4 51.6	13 22.3	4 30.5	1 51.9
12	17 18 17.7	20 18.4	9 28.5	23 4.1	0♋51.5	5 15.3	6 32.0	24 14.3	4 47.4	13 24.9	4 29.4	1 52.8
13	17 22 14.3	21 15.7	9 25.4	6♍ 5.1	2 53.8	6 16.7	7 8.1	24 8.2	4 43.2	13 27.4	4 28.4	1 53.6
14	17 26 10.8	22 13.0	9 22.2	19 23.7	4 54.1	7 17.8	7 44.3	24 2.2	4 38.9	13 30.1	4 27.5	1 54.5
15	17 30 7.4	23 10.3	9 19.0	3♎ 2.4	6 52.4	8 18.6	8 20.4	23 56.3	4 34.7	13 32.7	4 26.5	1 55.4
16	17 34 4.0	24 7.6	9 15.8	17 3.0	8 48.5	9 19.0	8 56.6	23 50.5	4 30.4	13 35.4	4 25.6	1 56.4
17	17 38 .5	25 4.9	9 12.7	1♏25.6	10 42.4	10 19.1	9 32.8	23 44.8	4 26.0	13 38.1	4 24.7	1 57.3
18	17 41 57.1	26 2.2	9 9.5	16 8.1	12 34.0	11 18.8	10 9.1	23 39.3	4 21.7	13 40.9	4 23.8	1 58.3
19	17 45 53.6	26 59.4	9 6.3	1♐ 5.8	14 23.3	12 18.1	10 45.3	23 34.0	4 17.3	13 43.7	4 23.0	1 59.3
20	17 49 50.2	27 56.7	9 3.1	16 10.8	16 10.3	13 17.0	11 21.6	23 28.7	4 13.0	13 46.5	4 22.1	2 .4
21	17 53 46.7	28 53.9	8 59.9	1♑13.8	17 55.0	14 15.6	11 57.9	23 23.6	4 8.6	13 49.4	4 21.3	2 1.4
22	17 57 43.3	29 51.1	8 56.8	16 4.7	19 37.3	15 13.7	12 34.3	23 18.7	4 4.2	13 52.3	4 20.6	2 2.5
23	18 1 39.9	0♋48.4	8 53.6	0♒35.2	21 17.3	16 11.4	13 10.6	23 13.9	3 59.8	13 55.2	4 19.8	2 3.7
24	18 5 36.4	1 45.6	8 50.4	14 39.4	22 54.9	17 8.6	13 47.0	23 9.3	3 55.4	13 58.1	4 19.1	2 4.8
25	18 9 33.0	2 42.8	8 47.2	28 14.8	24 30.1	18 5.4	14 23.4	23 4.8	3 51.0	14 1.1	4 18.4	2 6.0
26	18 13 29.5	3 40.0	8 44.1	11♓21.9	26 2.9	19 1.7	14 59.9	23 .4	3 46.5	14 4.2	4 17.8	2 7.2
27	18 17 26.1	4 37.3	8 40.9	24 3.7	27 33.3	19 57.6	15 36.4	22 56.3	3 42.2	14 7.2	4 17.2	2 8.4
28	18 21 22.6	5 34.5	8 37.7	6♈24.5	29 1.3	20 53.0	16 12.9	22 52.3	3 37.7	14 10.3	4 16.6	2 9.7
29	18 25 19.2	6 31.7	8 34.5	18 29.5	0♌26.8	21 47.8	16 49.5	22 48.4	3 33.3	14 13.4	4 16.1	2 10.9
30	18 29 15.8	7 28.9	8 31.4	0♉24.0	1 49.9	22 42.2	17 26.0	22 44.7	3 28.9	14 16.6	4 15.5	2 12.2

LATITUDE

DAY	EPHEM. SID. TIME	☉	☊	☽	☿	♀	♂	♃	♄	♅	♆	♇
1	16 34 55.6	0 .0	0 .0	0N 8.8	0N17.9	2N30.3	1N26.1	1N 4.2	0N57.0	0N40.0	1N48.9	11N59.3
4	16 46 45.3	0 .0	0 .0	2S50.9	0 47.9	2 27.9	1 25.0	1 3.7	0 56.9	0 39.9	1 48.8	11 58.4
7	16 58 34.9	0 .0	0 .0	4 45.0	1 14.2	2 24.3	1 23.8	1 3.2	0 56.8	0 39.8	1 48.7	11 57.6
10	17 10 24.6	0 .0	0 .0	4 49.0	1 35.3	2 19.5	1 22.6	1 2.7	0 56.6	0 39.8	1 48.6	11 56.8
13	17 22 14.3	0 .0	0 .0	2 50.1	1 50.2	2 13.4	1 21.4	1 2.1	0 56.5	0 39.7	1 48.4	11 56.0
16	17 34 4.0	0 .0	0 .0	0N37.0	1 58.4	2 5.9	1 20.2	1 1.5	0 56.3	0 39.6	1 48.3	11 55.2
19	17 45 53.6	0 .0	0 .0	3 55.6	1 59.8	1 57.1	1 19.0	1 .9	0 56.1	0 39.6	1 48.2	11 54.4
22	17 57 43.3	0 .0	0 .0	4 59.1	1 54.9	1 46.8	1 17.8	1 .2	0 55.9	0 39.5	1 48.0	11 53.7
25	18 9 33.0	0 .0	0 .0	3 17.6	1 43.8	1 35.0	1 16.6	0 59.6	0 55.7	0 39.4	1 47.9	11 53.0
28	18 21 22.6	0 .0	0 .0	0 13.2	1 27.0	1 21.6	1 15.3	0 58.9	0 55.4	0 39.4	1 47.7	11 52.3

RIGHT ASCENSION

DAY	EPHEM. SID. TIME	☉	☊	☽	☿	♀	♂	♃	♄	♅	♆	♇
1	16 34 55.6	8♊ 7.3	9♎14.6	9♈ 1.9	5♊12.1	26♋ 1.2	2♌27.1	23♏24.4	5♑58.3	15♌38.9	3♏ 2.9	8♍20.7
2	16 38 52.2	9 8.7	9 11.6	20 30.0	7 30.4	27 10.2	3 4.6	23R17.0	5R54.2	15 41.1	3R 1.7	8 21.1
3	16 42 48.7	10 10.1	9 8.7	2♉ 3.4	9 50.2	28 18.7	3 42.0	23 9.7	5 50.1	15 43.2	3 .5	8 21.5
4	16 46 45.3	11 11.7	9 5.8	13 48.5	12 11.2	29 26.8	4 19.4	23 2.5	5 45.9	15 45.5	2 59.3	8 22.0
5	16 50 41.8	12 13.4	9 2.9	25 49.1	14 32.9	0♌34.3	4 56.7	22 55.4	5 41.7	15 47.7	2 58.2	8 22.5
6	16 54 38.4	13 15.2	8 59.9	8♊ 6.3	16 55.2	1 41.4	5 34.1	22 48.4	5 37.5	15 50.1	2 57.1	8 23.1
7	16 58 34.9	14 17.0	8 57.0	20 37.9	19 17.5	2 47.9	6 11.3	22 41.4	5 33.1	15 52.4	2 56.0	8 23.7
8	17 2 31.5	15 18.9	8 54.1	3♋19.4	21 39.4	3 53.8	6 48.6	22 34.6	5 28.8	15 54.8	2 54.9	8 24.3
9	17 6 28.1	16 20.9	8 51.1	16 5.4	24 .7	4 59.2	7 25.7	22 27.8	5 24.4	15 57.2	2 53.8	8 24.9
10	17 10 24.6	17 22.9	8 48.2	28 50.7	26 20.9	6 4.0	8 2.9	22 21.1	5 19.9	15 59.7	2 52.8	8 25.5
11	17 14 21.2	18 25.0	8 45.3	11♌32.4	28 39.7	7 8.3	8 40.0	22 14.6	5 15.4	16 2.2	2 51.7	8 26.2
12	17 18 17.7	19 27.2	8 42.4	24 10.5	0♋56.9	8 12.0	9 17.1	22 8.2	5 10.9	16 4.8	2 50.7	8 26.9
13	17 22 14.3	20 29.4	8 39.4	6♍48.6	3 12.1	9 15.1	9 54.1	22 1.9	5 6.3	16 7.3	2 49.7	8 27.7
14	17 26 10.8	21 31.6	8 36.5	19 33.0	5 25.1	10 17.6	10 31.1	21 55.7	5 1.7	16 10.0	2 48.8	8 28.4
15	17 30 7.4	22 33.9	8 33.6	2♎32.6	7 35.8	11 19.5	11 8.0	21 49.6	4 57.1	16 12.6	2 47.9	8 29.2
16	17 34 4.0	23 36.2	8 30.7	15 57.1	9 43.9	12 20.7	11 44.9	21 43.7	4 52.5	16 15.3	2 46.9	8 30.0
17	17 38 .5	24 38.5	8 27.7	29 55.5	11 49.3	13 21.3	12 21.7	21 37.9	4 47.8	16 18.0	2 46.1	8 30.8
18	17 41 57.1	25 40.9	8 24.8	14♏33.1	13 51.8	14 21.3	12 58.5	21 32.3	4 43.1	16 20.8	2 45.2	8 31.7
19	17 45 53.6	26 43.2	8 21.9	29 48.0	15 51.5	15 20.6	13 35.3	21 26.8	4 38.4	16 23.6	2 44.4	8 32.6
20	17 49 50.2	27 45.6	8 18.9	15♐29.4	17 48.1	16 19.3	14 12.0	21 21.4	4 33.7	16 26.4	2 43.6	8 33.5
21	17 53 46.7	28 48.0	8 16.0	1♑17.5	19 41.7	17 17.2	14 48.6	21 16.2	4 29.0	16 29.3	2 42.8	8 34.5
22	17 57 43.3	29 50.3	8 13.1	16 49.1	21 32.2	18 14.5	15 25.2	21 11.1	4 24.2	16 32.2	2 42.0	8 35.4
23	18 1 39.9	0♋52.7	8 10.2	1♒44.8	23 19.6	19 11.1	16 1.8	21 6.1	4 19.5	16 35.1	2 41.3	8 36.4
24	18 5 36.4	1 55.1	8 7.2	15 54.0	25 3.8	20 7.0	16 38.3	21 1.4	4 14.7	16 38.1	2 40.6	8 37.4
25	18 9 33.0	2 57.4	8 4.3	29 15.5	26 44.9	21 2.2	17 14.8	20 56.7	4 9.9	16 41.1	2 39.9	8 38.5
26	18 13 29.5	3 59.7	8 1.4	11♓55.0	28 22.8	21 56.7	17 51.2	20 52.3	4 5.1	16 44.1	2 39.3	8 39.5
27	18 17 26.1	5 2.1	7 58.5	24 2.1	29 57.5	22 50.5	18 27.6	20 48.0	4 .4	16 47.2	2 38.7	8 40.7
28	18 21 22.6	6 4.3	7 55.5	5♈47.7	1♌29.0	23 43.6	19 4.0	20 43.9	3 55.6	16 50.3	2 38.1	8 41.8
29	18 25 19.2	7 6.6	7 52.6	17 22.8	2 57.3	24 35.8	19 40.3	20 39.9	3 50.9	16 53.4	2 37.6	8 42.9
30	18 29 15.8	8 8.8	7 49.7	28 57.1	4 22.4	25 27.4	20 16.5	20 36.1	3 46.1	16 56.5	2 37.0	8 44.1

DECLINATION

DAY	EPHEM. SID. TIME	☉	☊	☽	☿	♀	♂	♃	♄	♅	♆	♇
1	16 34 55.6	21N55.1	0S 4.2	4N 3.2	21N47.3	23N49.9	21N34.0	18S 5.6	22S22.6	17N33.5	11S22.7	22N .5
4	16 46 45.3	22 19.0	0 4.1	13 44.1	23 14.1	23 12.0	21 9.4	18 1.0	22 23.2	17 31.6	11 21.6	21 59.1
7	16 58 34.9	22 39.3	0 4.0	18 24.2	24 19.0	22 29.3	20 43.5	17 56.6	22 23.8	17 29.5	11 20.5	21 57.6
10	17 10 24.6	22 56.1	0 4.0	15 53.4	24 59.3	21 42.4	20 16.4	17 52.3	22 24.4	17 27.3	11 19.6	21 56.0
13	17 22 14.3	23 9.2	0 3.9	6 38.6	25 14.8	20 51.5	19 48.2	17 48.3	22 25.0	17 25.1	11 18.6	21 54.3
16	17 34 4.0	23 18.7	0 3.8	6S 7.8	25 7.1	19 56.9	19 18.8	17 44.5	22 25.6	17 22.7	11 17.8	21 52.6
19	17 45 53.6	23 24.4	0 3.8	16 32.2	24 39.0	18 59.0	18 48.3	17 41.0	22 26.3	17 20.3	11 17.1	21 50.7
22	17 57 43.3	23 26.5	0 3.7	17 31.3	23 54.0	17 58.3	18 16.8	17 37.9	22 26.9	17 17.8	11 16.4	21 48.9
25	18 9 33.0	23 24.8	0 3.6	8 59.6	22 55.5	16 55.0	17 44.2	17 35.0	22 27.5	17 15.1	11 15.8	21 47.0
28	18 21 22.6	23 19.4	0 3.6	2N44.9	21 46.5	15 49.5	17 10.6	17 32.6	22 28.1	17 12.4	11 15.4	21 44.9

JULY 1959

DAY	EPHEM. SID. TIME	☉	☊	☽	☿	♀	♂	♃	♄	♅	♆	♇
	h m s	° ′	° ′	° ′	° ′	° ′	° ′	° ′	° ′	° ′	° ′	° ′
LONGITUDE												
1	18 33 12.3	8♋26.1	8♎28.2	12♉13.2	3♌10.4	23♌35.9	18♌ 2.6	22♏41.2	3♑24.5	14♌19.7	4♏15.0	2♍13.5
2	18 37 8.9	9 23.3	8 25.0	24 1.8	4 28.4	24 29.2	18 39.2	22R37.8	3R20.1	14 22.9	4R14.5	2 14.8
3	18 41 5.4	10 20.5	8 21.8	5♊53.6	5 43.8	25 21.8	19 15.9	22 34.6	3 15.7	14 26.1	4 14.1	2 16.2
4	18 45 2.0	11 17.8	8 18.6	17 51.6	6 56.5	26 13.8	19 52.6	22 31.6	3 11.4	14 29.4	4 13.7	2 17.6
5	18 48 58.5	12 15.0	8 15.5	29 58.1	8 6.5	27 5.2	20 29.3	22 28.7	3 7.0	14 32.6	4 13.3	2 19.0
6	18 52 55.1	13 12.2	8 12.3	12♋14.4	9 13.7	27 56.0	21 6.0	22 26.0	3 2.7	14 35.9	4 12.9	2 20.4
7	18 56 51.6	14 9.4	8 9.1	24 41.2	10 18.0	28 46.0	21 42.8	22 23.5	2 58.4	14 39.3	4 12.6	2 21.8
8	19 0 48.2	15 6.6	8 5.9	7♌18.9	11 19.4	29 35.4	22 19.6	22 21.2	2 54.1	14 42.6	4 12.3	2 23.3
9	19 4 44.8	16 3.9	8 2.8	20 7.5	12 17.7	0♍24.1	22 56.4	22 19.1	2 49.9	14 45.9	4 12.1	2 24.8
10	19 8 41.3	17 1.1	7 59.6	3♍ 7.5	13 12.8	1 12.0	23 33.3	22 17.1	2 45.6	14 49.3	4 11.8	2 26.3
11	19 12 37.9	17 58.3	7 56.4	16 19.6	14 4.7	1 59.1	24 10.2	22 15.3	2 41.5	14 52.7	4 11.6	2 27.8
12	19 16 34.4	18 55.5	7 53.2	29 44.8	14 53.2	2 45.4	24 47.1	22 13.7	2 37.3	14 56.2	4 11.5	2 29.3
13	19 20 31.0	19 52.7	7 50.1	13♎24.4	15 38.1	3 30.8	25 24.0	22 12.3	2 33.2	14 59.6	4 11.3	2 30.9
14	19 24 27.5	20 50.0	7 46.9	27 19.5	16 19.4	4 15.4	26 1.0	22 11.1	2 29.1	15 3.1	4 11.2	2 32.5
15	19 28 24.1	21 47.2	7 43.7	11♏30.4	16 56.9	4 59.0	26 38.0	22 10.0	2 25.0	15 6.5	4 11.2	2 34.1
16	19 32 20.7	22 44.4	7 40.5	25 55.9	17 30.4	5 41.7	27 15.0	22 9.1	2 21.0	15 10.0	4 11.1	2 35.7
17	19 36 17.2	23 41.6	7 37.3	10♐33.0	17 59.8	6 23.4	27 52.0	22 8.4	2 17.1	15 13.6	4 11.1	2 37.3
18	19 40 13.8	24 38.9	7 34.2	25 16.4	18 25.0	7 4.0	28 29.2	22 8.0	2 13.2	15 17.1	4D11.2	2 39.0
19	19 44 10.3	25 36.1	7 31.0	9♑58.9	18 45.8	7 43.6	29 6.3	22 7.6	2 9.3	15 20.7	4 11.3	2 40.7
20	19 48 6.9	26 33.3	7 27.8	24 32.9	19 2.0	8 22.1	29 43.4	22 7.5	2 5.5	15 24.2	4 11.4	2 42.3
21	19 52 3.4	27 30.6	7 24.6	8♒51.0	19 13.5	8 59.4	0♍20.5	22 7.5	2 1.7	15 27.8	4 11.5	2 44.0
22	19 55 60.0	28 27.8	7 21.5	22 47.6	19 20.2	9 35.5	0 57.7	22D 7.7	1 58.0	15 31.4	4 11.6	2 45.8
23	19 59 56.5	29 25.1	7 18.3	6♓19.4	19 22.1	10 10.3	1 34.9	22 8.1	1 54.3	15 35.0	4 11.8	2 47.5
24	20 3 53.1	0♌22.3	7 15.1	19 26.0	19R19.0	10 43.9	2 12.2	22 8.7	1 50.7	15 38.6	4 12.0	2 49.2
25	20 7 49.7	1 19.6	7 11.9	2♈ 8.8	19 10.9	11 16.1	2 49.4	22 9.4	1 47.1	15 42.3	4 12.3	2 51.0
26	20 11 46.2	2 16.9	7 8.8	14 31.5	18 57.8	11 47.0	3 26.7	22 10.4	1 43.6	15 45.9	4 12.6	2 52.8
27	20 15 42.8	3 14.2	7 5.6	26 38.4	18 39.8	12 16.4	4 4.1	22 11.5	1 40.2	15 49.5	4 12.9	2 54.5
28	20 19 39.3	4 11.6	7 2.4	8♉34.7	18 17.1	12 44.3	4 41.4	22 12.8	1 36.8	15 53.2	4 13.2	2 56.3
29	20 23 35.9	5 8.9	6 59.2	20 25.7	17 49.8	13 10.7	5 18.8	22 14.3	1 33.5	15 56.9	4 13.6	2 58.2
30	20 27 32.4	6 6.3	6 56.0	2♊16.4	17 18.2	13 35.5	5 56.2	22 15.9	1 30.3	16 .5	4 14.0	2 60.0
31	20 31 29.0	7 3.7	6 52.9	14 11.5	16 42.7	13 58.7	6 33.7	22 17.8	1 27.1	16 4.2	4 14.5	3 1.8
LATITUDE												
1	18 33 12.3	0 .0	0 .0	2S46.5	1N 5.0	1N 6.6	1N14.1	0N58.2	0N55.2	0N39.3	1N47.6	11N51.6
4	18 45 2.0	0 .0	0 .0	4 41.4	0 38.2	0 50.0	1 12.9	0 57.5	0 54.9	0 39.3	1 47.4	11 51.0
7	18 56 51.6	0 .0	0 .0	4 47.4	0 7.0	0 31.6	1 11.6	0 56.7	0 54.6	0 39.3	1 47.2	11 50.4
10	19 8 41.3	0 .0	0 .0	2 50.0	0S28.0	0 11.5	1 10.3	0 56.0	0 54.3	0 39.2	1 47.1	11 49.9
13	19 20 31.0	0 .0	0 .0	0N32.7	1 6.2	0S10.5	1 9.1	0 55.3	0 53.9	0 39.2	1 46.9	11 49.4
16	19 32 20.7	0 .0	0 .0	3 47.9	1 46.8	0 34.3	1 7.8	0 54.5	0 53.6	0 39.2	1 46.7	11 48.9
19	19 44 10.3	0 .0	0 .0	5 1.6	2 28.7	1 .1	1 6.5	0 53.8	0 53.2	0 39.1	1 46.6	11 48.4
22	19 55 60.0	0 .0	0 .0	3 29.0	3 10.2	1 27.8	1 5.2	0 53.0	0 52.9	0 39.1	1 46.4	11 48.0
25	20 7 49.7	0 .0	0 .0	0 21.2	3 48.9	1 57.5	1 3.9	0 52.3	0 52.5	0 39.1	1 46.2	11 47.7
28	20 19 39.3	0 .0	0 .0	2S44.4	4 21.9	2 29.0	1 2.6	0 51.6	0 52.1	0 39.1	1 46.0	11 47.4
31	20 31 29.0	0 .0	0 .0	4 43.5	4 45.5	3 2.5	1 1.2	0 50.8	0 51.7	0 39.1	1 45.9	11 47.1
RIGHT ASCENSION												
1	18 33 12.3	9♋10.9	7♎46.8	10♉38.9	5♌44.3	26♌18.1	20♌52.7	20♏32.4	3♑41.3	16♌59.7	2♏36.5	8♍45.3
2	18 37 8.9	10 13.0	7 43.8	22 34.1	7 2.9	27 8.1	21 28.9	20R28.9	3R36.6	17 2.8	2R36.1	8 46.5
3	18 41 5.4	11 15.0	7 40.9	4♊46.2	8 18.3	27 57.3	22 5.0	20 25.6	3 31.8	17 6.1	2 35.6	8 47.7
4	18 45 2.0	12 16.9	7 38.0	17 15.1	9 30.5	28 45.7	22 41.1	20 22.5	3 27.1	17 9.3	2 35.2	8 49.0
5	18 48 58.5	13 18.8	7 35.1	29 58.0	10 39.3	29 33.3	23 17.2	20 19.5	3 22.4	17 12.6	2 34.8	8 50.3
6	18 52 55.1	14 20.6	7 32.1	12♋49.4	11 44.8	0♍20.0	23 53.2	20 16.8	3 17.8	17 15.9	2 34.5	8 51.6
7	18 56 51.6	15 22.4	7 29.2	25 43.4	12 46.9	1 5.9	24 29.2	20 14.2	3 13.1	17 19.2	2 34.1	8 52.9
8	19 0 48.2	16 24.0	7 26.3	8♌34.6	13 45.6	1 50.9	25 5.1	20 11.8	3 8.5	17 22.5	2 33.8	8 54.3
9	19 4 44.8	17 25.5	7 23.4	21 20.6	14 40.8	2 35.0	25 41.0	20 9.5	3 3.9	17 25.9	2 33.6	8 55.6
10	19 8 41.3	18 26.9	7 20.5	4♍ 2.0	15 32.5	3 18.2	26 16.8	20 7.5	2 59.3	17 29.2	2 33.3	8 57.0
11	19 12 37.9	19 28.3	7 17.5	16 43.0	16 20.6	4 .5	26 52.6	20 5.6	2 54.8	17 32.6	2 33.1	8 58.4
12	19 16 34.4	20 29.5	7 14.6	29 30.3	17 4.9	4 41.8	27 28.4	20 3.9	2 50.3	17 36.1	2 32.9	8 59.8
13	19 20 31.0	21 30.6	7 11.7	12♎32.9	17 45.5	5 22.1	28 4.1	20 2.4	2 45.8	17 39.5	2 32.8	9 1.3
14	19 24 27.5	22 31.6	7 8.8	25 59.8	18 22.2	6 1.4	28 39.8	20 1.1	2 41.4	17 43.0	2 32.7	9 2.8
15	19 28 24.1	23 32.4	7 5.8	9♏58.5	18 55.0	6 39.6	29 15.5	19 59.9	2 37.0	17 46.4	2 32.6	9 4.3
16	19 32 20.7	24 33.1	7 2.9	24 32.2	19 23.7	7 16.8	29 51.1	19 59.0	2 32.7	17 49.9	2 32.5	9 5.8
17	19 36 17.2	25 33.7	6 60.0	9♐37.4	19 48.2	7 52.9	0♍26.7	19 58.2	2 28.4	17 53.4	2 32.5	9 7.3
18	19 40 13.8	26 34.2	6 57.1	25 2.1	20 8.4	8 27.9	1 2.3	19 57.7	2 24.2	17 57.0	2D32.6	9 8.9
19	19 44 10.3	27 34.6	6 54.1	10♑27.8	20 24.3	9 1.7	1 37.8	19 57.3	2 20.0	18 .5	2 32.6	9 10.4
20	19 48 6.9	28 34.8	6 51.2	25 34.9	20 35.7	9 34.3	2 13.3	19 57.0	2 15.8	18 4.1	2 32.7	9 12.0
21	19 52 3.4	29 34.8	6 48.3	10♒ 7.8	20 42.5	10 5.7	2 48.7	19 57.0	2 11.8	18 7.7	2 32.8	9 13.6
22	19 55 60.0	0♌34.7	6 45.4	23 59.1	20 44.8	10 35.9	3 24.1	19D57.2	2 7.7	18 11.2	2 32.9	9 15.2
23	19 59 56.5	1 34.5	6 42.5	7♓ 8.8	20R42.3	11 4.7	3 59.5	19 57.5	2 3.8	18 14.8	2 33.1	9 16.9
24	20 3 53.1	2 34.2	6 39.5	19 42.8	20 35.2	11 32.2	4 34.8	19 58.0	1 59.9	18 18.4	2 33.2	9 18.5
25	20 7 49.7	3 33.7	6 36.6	1♈49.8	20 23.5	11 58.3	5 10.1	19 58.7	1 56.0	18 22.0	2 33.5	9 20.2
26	20 11 46.2	4 33.0	6 33.7	13 39.6	20 7.1	12 23.1	5 45.4	19 59.6	1 52.2	18 25.7	2 33.7	9 21.8
27	20 15 42.8	5 32.2	6 30.8	25 22.0	19 46.3	12 46.3	6 20.7	20 .6	1 48.5	18 29.3	2 34.0	9 23.5
28	20 19 39.3	6 31.3	6 27.8	7♉ 5.8	19 21.1	13 8.1	6 56.0	20 1.9	1 44.8	18 32.9	2 34.3	9 25.3
29	20 23 35.9	7 30.2	6 24.9	18 58.0	18 51.9	13 28.4	7 31.2	20 3.3	1 41.3	18 36.6	2 34.7	9 27.0
30	20 27 32.4	8 29.0	6 22.0	1♊ 3.9	18 18.9	13 47.1	8 6.4	20 4.9	1 37.7	18 40.3	2 35.0	9 28.7
31	20 31 29.0	9 27.6	6 19.1	13 25.9	17 42.5	14 4.1	8 41.6	20 6.7	1 34.3	18 43.9	2 35.4	9 30.5
DECLINATION												
1	18 33 12.3	23N10.4	0S 3.5	12N51.7	20N30.2	14N42.2	16N36.0	17S30.4	22S28.7	17N 9.7	11S15.0	21N42.9
4	18 45 2.0	22 57.7	0 3.5	18 13.0	19 9.3	13 33.5	16 .4	17 28.7	22 29.3	17 6.8	11 14.7	21 40.8
7	18 56 51.6	22 41.3	0 3.4	16 28.5	17 46.5	12 23.9	15 23.9	17 27.4	22 29.9	17 3.9	11 14.5	21 38.7
10	19 8 41.3	22 21.5	0 3.3	7 43.0	16 24.4	11 13.7	14 46.6	17 26.4	22 30.5	17 .9	11 14.4	21 36.5
13	19 20 31.0	21 58.2	0 3.3	4S47.4	15 5.8	10 3.4	14 8.4	17 25.9	22 31.1	16 57.8	11 14.4	21 34.4
16	19 32 20.7	21 31.4	0 3.2	15 32.8	13 53.5	8 55.4	13 29.3	17 25.8	22 31.7	16 54.7	11 14.5	21 32.1
19	19 44 10.3	21 1.4	0 3.1	18 3.2	12 50.7	7 44.6	12 49.5	17 26.1	22 32.2	16 51.6	11 14.7	21 29.9
22	19 55 60.0	20 28.2	0 3.1	10 37.5	12 .7	6 37.1	12 9.0	17 26.9	22 32.8	16 48.4	11 15.0	21 27.6
25	20 7 49.7	19 51.9	0 3.0	1N10.7	11 26.7	5 31.7	11 27.7	17 28.1	22 33.3	16 45.2	11 15.3	21 25.3
28	20 19 39.3	19 12.7	0 2.9	11 46.0	11 11.6	4 29.0	10 45.8	17 29.6	22 33.8	16 41.9	11 15.8	21 23.0
31	20 31 29.0	18 30.5	0 2.9	17 48.7	11 17.2	3 29.7	10 3.2	17 31.6	22 34.3	16 38.6	11 16.4	21 20.8

LONGITUDE

DAY	EPHEM. SID. TIME (h m s)	☉	☊	☽	☿	♀	♂	♃	♄	♅	♆	♇
1	20 35 25.5	8♌ 1.1	6♎49.7	26♊14.8	16♌ 3.8	14♍20.1	7♍11.2	22♏19.8	1♑24.0	16♌ 7.9	4♏15.0	3♍ 3.7
2	20 39 22.1	8 58.5	6 46.5	8♋29.2	15 R22.1	14 39.7	7 48.7	22 22.0	1 R20.9	16 11.6	4 15.5	3 5.5
3	20 43 18.7	9 55.9	6 43.3	20 56.8	14 38.1	14 57.6	8 26.3	22 24.3	1 18.0	16 15.3	4 16.0	3 7.4
4	20 47 15.2	10 53.4	6 40.2	3♌38.5	13 52.5	15 13.5	9 3.9	22 26.9	1 15.1	16 19.0	4 16.6	3 9.3
5	20 51 11.8	11 50.8	6 37.0	16 34.3	13 6.2	15 27.5	9 41.5	22 29.6	1 12.2	16 22.7	4 17.2	3 11.2
6	20 55 8.3	12 48.3	6 33.8	29 43.4	12 20.1	15 39.5	10 19.1	22 32.5	1 9.5	16 26.5	4 17.8	3 13.1
7	20 59 4.9	13 45.8	6 30.6	13♍ 4.7	11 34.8	15 49.4	10 56.8	22 35.5	1 6.8	16 30.2	4 18.5	3 15.0
8	21 3 1.4	14 43.4	6 27.4	26 37.1	10 51.5	15 57.2	11 34.6	22 38.8	1 4.3	16 34.0	4 19.2	3 17.0
9	21 6 58.0	15 40.9	6 24.3	10♎19.4	10 10.7	16 2.8	12 12.3	22 42.2	1 1.8	16 37.7	4 20.0	3 18.9
10	21 10 54.5	16 38.4	6 21.1	24 10.9	9 33.5	16 6.2	12 50.1	22 45.8	0 59.3	16 41.4	4 20.7	3 20.9
11	21 14 51.1	17 36.0	6 17.9	8♏11.0	9 .5	16 7.2	13 27.9	22 49.6	0 57.0	16 45.1	4 21.5	3 22.8
12	21 18 47.6	18 33.5	6 14.7	22 18.8	8 32.4	16 R 6.0	14 5.7	22 53.5	0 54.7	16 48.8	4 22.3	3 24.8
13	21 22 44.2	19 31.1	6 11.6	6♐33.0	8 10.0	16 2.4	14 43.6	22 57.6	0 52.6	16 52.6	4 23.2	3 26.7
14	21 26 40.8	20 28.7	6 8.4	20 51.4	7 53.6	15 56.4	15 21.5	23 1.8	0 50.5	16 56.3	4 24.1	3 28.7
15	21 30 37.3	21 26.3	6 5.2	5♑10.7	7 43.7	15 48.0	15 59.4	23 6.2	0 48.5	17 .0	4 25.0	3 30.7
16	21 34 33.9	22 24.0	6 2.0	19 26.7	7 40.8	15 37.2	16 37.4	23 10.8	0 46.5	17 3.7	4 25.9	3 32.6
17	21 38 30.4	23 21.6	5 58.8	3♒45.0	7 D45.0	15 24.0	17 15.4	23 15.5	0 44.7	17 7.4	4 26.9	3 34.6
18	21 42 27.0	24 19.3	5 55.7	17 29.5	7 56.6	15 8.5	17 53.4	23 20.4	0 43.0	17 11.1	4 27.9	3 36.6
19	21 46 23.5	25 17.0	5 52.5	1♓ 7.6	8 15.6	14 50.6	18 31.5	23 25.4	0 41.3	17 14.8	4 28.9	3 38.6
20	21 50 20.1	26 14.7	5 49.3	14 26.3	8 42.1	14 30.4	19 9.5	23 30.6	0 39.7	17 18.5	4 30.0	3 40.6
21	21 54 16.6	27 12.4	5 46.1	27 24.6	9 16.0	14 8.1	19 47.7	23 36.0	0 38.3	17 22.2	4 31.1	3 42.6
22	21 58 13.2	28 10.2	5 43.0	10♈ 3.4	9 57.4	13 43.6	20 25.8	23 41.5	0 36.9	17 25.9	4 32.2	3 44.6
23	22 2 9.7	29 7.9	5 39.8	22 24.7	10 45.9	13 17.1	21 4.0	23 47.1	0 35.6	17 29.6	4 33.4	3 46.6
24	22 6 6.3	0♍ 5.8	5 36.6	4♉35.0	11 41.5	12 48.7	21 42.3	23 52.9	0 34.4	17 33.2	4 34.5	3 48.6
25	22 10 2.8	1 3.6	5 33.4	16 29.4	12 43.9	12 18.6	22 20.5	23 58.9	0 33.3	17 36.9	4 35.7	3 50.6
26	22 13 59.4	2 1.5	5 30.2	28 21.7	13 52.8	11 46.9	22 58.8	24 5.0	0 32.3	17 40.5	4 37.0	3 52.7
27	22 17 55.9	2 59.4	5 27.1	10♊13.8	15 7.8	11 13.8	23 37.1	24 11.3	0 31.4	17 44.1	4 38.2	3 54.7
28	22 21 52.5	3 57.3	5 23.9	22 10.5	16 28.7	10 39.4	24 15.5	24 17.7	0 30.5	17 47.8	4 39.5	3 56.7
29	22 25 49.1	4 55.3	5 20.7	4♋16.4	17 54.9	10 4.1	24 53.9	24 24.2	0 29.9	17 51.4	4 40.9	3 58.8
30	22 29 45.6	5 53.3	5 17.5	17 35.3	19 26.0	9 28.0	25 32.4	24 30.9	0 29.2	17 55.0	4 42.2	4 .8
31	22 33 42.2	6 51.3	5 14.4	29 10.2	21 1.6	8 51.1	26 10.9	24 37.8	0 28.7	17 58.6	4 43.6	4 2.8

LATITUDE

DAY	EPHEM. SID. TIME	☉	☊	☽	☿	♀	♂	♃	♄	♅	♆	♇
1	20 35 25.5	0 .0	0 .0	5S .8	4S50.6	3S14.0	1N .8	0N50.6	0N51.6	0N39.1	1N45.8	11N47.0
4	20 47 15.2	0 .0	0 .0	4 29.1	4 56.0	3 49.6	0 59.5	0 49.9	0 51.2	0 39.1	1 45.6	11 46.8
7	20 59 4.9	0 .0	0 .0	1 55.1	4 45.3	4 26.5	0 58.1	0 49.1	0 50.7	0 39.1	1 45.5	11 46.7
10	21 10 54.5	0 .0	0 .0	1N41.8	4 18.8	5 4.3	0 56.8	0 48.4	0 50.3	0 39.1	1 45.3	11 46.5
13	21 22 44.2	0 .0	0 .0	4 31.9	3 39.4	5 42.2	0 55.4	0 47.7	0 49.9	0 39.1	1 45.1	11 46.5
16	21 34 33.9	0 .0	0 .0	5 2.0	2 51.2	6 19.5	0 54.0	0 47.0	0 49.4	0 39.2	1 45.0	11 46.5
19	21 46 23.5	0 .0	0 .0	2 50.8	1 59.1	6 55.0	0 52.6	0 46.4	0 49.0	0 39.2	1 44.8	11 46.5
22	21 58 13.2	0 .0	0 .0	0S30.9	1 7.1	7 27.4	0 51.2	0 45.7	0 48.5	0 39.2	1 44.7	11 46.6
25	22 10 2.8	0 .0	0 .0	3 29.9	0 18.8	7 55.1	0 49.8	0 45.0	0 48.1	0 39.2	1 44.5	11 46.7
28	22 21 52.5	0 .0	0 .0	5 5.9	0N23.3	8 16.7	0 48.4	0 44.4	0 47.6	0 39.3	1 44.4	11 46.8
31	22 33 42.2	0 .0	0 .0	4 44.2	0 57.5	8 30.9	0 47.0	0 43.8	0 47.2	0 39.3	1 44.2	11 47.1

RIGHT ASCENSION

DAY	EPHEM. SID. TIME	☉	☊	☽	☿	♀	♂	♃	♄	♅	♆	♇
1	20 35 25.5	10♌26.1	6♎16.2	26♊ 3.5	17♌ 3.1	14♍19.5	9♍16.7	20♏ 8.7	1♑30.9	18♌47.6	2♏35.9	9♍32.2
2	20 39 22.1	11 24.4	6 13.2	8♋53.8	16 R21.5	14 33.1	9 51.9	20 10.9	1 R27.6	18 51.3	2 36.4	9 34.0
3	20 43 18.7	12 22.6	6 10.3	21 51.8	15 38.0	14 45.0	10 27.0	20 13.2	1 24.4	18 55.0	2 36.9	9 35.8
4	20 47 15.2	13 20.6	6 7.4	4♌52.2	14 53.6	14 55.1	11 2.1	20 15.7	1 21.3	18 58.7	2 37.4	9 37.6
5	20 51 11.8	14 18.5	6 4.5	17 51.0	14 8.8	15 3.3	11 37.2	20 18.4	1 18.2	19 2.4	2 37.9	9 39.4
6	20 55 8.3	15 16.2	6 1.5	0♍46.5	13 24.5	15 9.5	12 12.3	20 21.3	1 15.3	19 6.1	2 38.5	9 41.3
7	20 59 4.9	16 13.8	5 58.6	13 40.0	12 41.6	15 13.9	12 47.4	20 24.3	1 12.4	19 9.8	2 39.2	9 43.1
8	21 3 1.4	17 11.3	5 55.7	26 36.0	12 .9	15 16.2	13 22.5	20 27.6	1 9.6	19 13.5	2 39.9	9 45.0
9	21 6 58.0	18 8.6	5 52.8	9♎34.2	11 23.1	15 16.5	13 57.5	20 31.0	1 6.9	19 17.2	2 40.5	9 46.8
10	21 10 54.5	19 5.7	5 49.9	23 1.2	10 49.1	15 R14.7	14 32.6	20 34.6	1 4.3	19 20.9	2 41.2	9 48.7
11	21 14 51.1	20 2.7	5 46.9	6♏41.0	10 19.5	15 10.8	15 7.6	20 38.3	1 1.7	19 24.6	2 42.0	9 50.6
12	21 18 47.6	20 59.5	5 44.0	20 54.3	9 55.1	15 4.8	15 42.6	20 42.2	0 59.3	19 28.3	2 42.8	9 52.5
13	21 22 44.2	21 56.2	5 41.1	5♐30.7	9 36.5	14 56.6	16 17.6	20 46.3	0 56.9	19 32.0	2 43.6	9 54.4
14	21 26 40.8	22 52.7	5 38.2	20 24.7	9 24.1	14 46.2	16 52.6	20 50.5	0 54.7	19 35.7	2 44.4	9 56.3
15	21 30 37.3	23 49.1	5 35.3	5♑25.8	9 18.5	14 33.7	17 27.6	20 55.0	0 52.5	19 39.4	2 45.3	9 58.2
16	21 34 33.9	24 45.4	5 32.3	20 18.2	9 D19.9	14 19.1	18 2.6	20 59.5	0 50.4	19 43.1	2 46.1	10 .1
17	21 38 30.4	25 41.5	5 29.4	4♒47.8	9 27.9	14 2.3	18 37.6	21 4.3	0 48.4	19 46.8	2 47.1	10 2.1
18	21 42 27.0	26 37.5	5 26.5	18 45.9	9 44.9	13 43.5	19 12.6	21 9.2	0 46.5	19 50.5	2 48.0	10 4.0
19	21 46 23.5	27 33.4	5 23.6	2♓ 8.6	10 8.7	13 22.7	19 47.6	21 14.3	0 44.8	19 54.2	2 49.0	10 5.9
20	21 50 20.1	28 29.1	5 20.7	14 58.3	10 40.1	12 59.9	20 22.6	21 19.5	0 43.1	19 57.8	2 50.0	10 7.9
21	21 54 16.6	29 24.7	5 17.7	27 22.4	11 19.0	12 35.3	20 57.6	21 24.9	0 41.5	20 1.5	2 51.0	10 9.8
22	21 58 13.2	0♍20.2	5 14.8	9♈26.6	12 5.3	12 8.9	21 32.6	21 30.4	0 40.0	20 5.1	2 52.1	10 11.8
23	22 2 9.7	1 15.6	5 11.9	21 19.8	12 40.8	11 40.8	22 7.7	21 36.2	0 38.6	20 8.8	2 53.1	10 13.7
24	22 6 6.3	2 10.9	5 9.0	3♉ 9.7	13 29.2	11 11.3	22 42.7	21 42.0	0 37.3	20 12.4	2 54.3	10 15.7
25	22 10 2.8	3 6.1	5 6.1	15 3.1	14 15.3	10 40.4	23 17.7	21 48.0	0 36.1	20 16.0	2 55.4	10 17.7
26	22 13 59.4	4 1.1	5 3.1	27 5.3	15 19.6	10 8.4	23 52.8	21 54.2	0 35.0	20 19.6	2 56.6	10 19.7
27	22 17 55.9	4 56.1	5 .2	9♊17.9	16 32.7	9 38.8	24 27.9	22 .5	0 34.0	20 23.2	2 57.7	10 21.6
28	22 21 52.5	5 51.0	4 57.3	21 47.8	19 3.3	9 1.4	25 3.0	22 7.0	0 33.1	20 26.8	2 59.0	10 23.6
29	22 25 49.1	6 45.8	4 54.4	4♋28.7	20 32.7	8 26.9	25 38.1	22 13.7	0 32.4	20 30.5	3 .3	10 25.6
30	22 29 45.6	7 40.5	4 51.5	17 19.9	22 6.5	7 52.0	26 13.2	22 20.4	0 31.7	20 34.0	3 1.5	10 27.6
31	22 33 42.2	8 35.2	4 48.5	0♌18.1	23 44.0	7 16.9	26 48.4	22 27.3	0 31.1	20 37.6	3 2.8	10 29.6

DECLINATION

DAY	EPHEM. SID. TIME	☉	☊	☽	☿	♀	♂	♃	♄	♅	♆	♇
1	20 35 25.5	18N15.9	0S 2.8	18N22.7	11N23.7	3N10.9	9N48.8	17S32.4	22S34.5	16N37.5	11S16.6	21N20.0
4	20 47 15.2	17 30.1	0 2.8	14 58.6	11 56.1	2 17.5	9 5.4	17 34.9	22 35.0	16 34.2	11 17.3	21 17.7
7	20 59 4.9	16 41.8	0 2.7	4 54.5	12 44.3	1 29.7	8 21.5	17 37.8	22 35.5	16 30.8	11 18.1	21 15.4
10	21 10 54.5	15 51.0	0 2.6	7S48.1	13 42.0	0 48.4	7 37.0	17 41.0	22 36.0	16 27.4	11 19.0	21 13.1
13	21 22 44.2	14 58.0	0 2.6	16 56.2	14 41.6	0 14.8	6 52.0	17 44.7	22 36.5	16 24.1	11 20.0	21 10.9
16	21 34 33.9	14 2.9	0 2.5	17 5.9	15 35.5	0S 9.9	6 6.6	17 48.7	22 37.0	16 20.7	11 21.1	21 8.7
19	21 46 23.5	13 5.7	0 2.4	8 25.9	16 17.1	0 24.9	5 20.8	17 53.0	22 37.4	16 17.4	11 22.2	21 6.5
22	21 58 13.2	12 6.7	0 2.4	3N30.5	16 40.6	0 29.3	4 34.6	17 57.6	22 37.9	16 14.0	11 23.5	21 4.3
25	22 10 2.8	11 5.9	0 2.3	13 24.9	16 41.4	0 22.9	3 48.1	18 2.6	22 38.4	16 10.7	11 24.8	21 2.1
28	22 21 52.5	10 3.6	0 2.2	18 7.2	16 16.3	0 5.8	3 1.3	18 7.8	22 38.8	16 7.4	11 26.2	21 .0
31	22 33 42.2	8 59.7	0 2.2	15 41.4	15 23.8	0N20.9	2 14.2	18 13.3	22 39.3	16 4.1	11 27.7	20 58.0

SEPTEMBER 1959

DAY	EPHEM. SID. TIME	☉	☊	☽	☿	♀	♂	♃	♄	♅	♆	♇
	h m s	° ′	° ′	° ′	° ′	° ′	° ′	° ′	° ′	° ′	° ′	° ′
		LONGITUDE										
1	22 37 38.7	7♍49.4	5♎11.2	12♌ 3.1	22♌41.1	8♍14.3	26♍49.4	24♏44.7	0♑28.3	18♌ 2.2	4♏45.0	4♍ 4.8
2	22 41 35.3	8 47.4	5 8.0	25 14.6	24 24.1	7R37.2	27 27.9	24 51.8	0R27.9	18 5.7	4 46.4	4 6.8
3	22 45 31.8	9 45.6	5 4.8	8♍43.9	26 10.2	7 .2	28 6.5	24 59.1	0 27.7	18 9.2	4 47.8	4 8.8
4	22 49 28.4	10 43.7	5 1.6	22 29.1	27 58.7	6 23.6	28 45.2	25 6.5	0 27.5	18 12.8	4 49.3	4 10.8
5	22 53 24.9	11 41.9	4 58.5	6♎27.3	29 49.3	5 47.6	29 23.8	25 14.0	0 27.5	18 16.3	4 50.8	4 12.8
6	22 57 21.5	12 40.0	4 55.3	20 35.1	1♍41.5	5 12.4	0♎ 2.5	25 21.6	0 27.5	18 19.7	4 52.3	4 14.8
7	23 1 18.0	13 38.3	4 52.1	4♏48.9	3 34.9	4 38.3	0 41.3	25 29.4	0D27.7	18 23.2	4 53.8	4 16.8
8	23 5 14.6	14 36.5	4 48.9	19 5.4	5 29.2	4 5.4	1 20.0	25 37.3	0 27.9	18 26.7	4 55.4	4 18.8
9	23 9 11.1	15 34.8	4 45.8	3♐21.5	7 24.1	3 33.9	1 58.8	25 45.3	0 28.3	18 30.1	4 57.0	4 20.8
10	23 13 7.7	16 33.1	4 42.6	17 34.7	9 19.3	3 4.1	2 37.7	25 53.5	0 28.7	18 33.5	4 58.6	4 22.8
11	23 17 4.2	17 31.4	4 39.4	1♑42.7	11 14.4	2 36.0	3 16.6	26 1.8	0 29.2	18 36.9	5 .3	4 24.8
12	23 21 .8	18 29.7	4 36.2	15 43.4	13 9.4	2 9.8	3 55.5	26 10.2	0 29.9	18 40.2	5 1.9	4 26.7
13	23 24 57.3	19 28.1	4 33.0	29 34.9	15 4.0	1 45.7	4 34.4	26 18.7	0 30.6	18 43.5	5 3.6	4 28.7
14	23 28 53.9	20 26.5	4 29.9	13♒15.4	16 58.1	1 23.7	5 13.4	26 27.3	0 31.4	18 46.9	5 5.3	4 30.7
15	23 32 50.4	21 24.9	4 26.7	26 43.2	18 51.5	1 3.9	5 52.4	26 36.1	0 32.4	18 50.1	5 7.0	4 32.6
16	23 36 47.0	22 23.3	4 23.5	9♓57.0	20 44.2	0 46.5	6 31.5	26 45.0	0 33.4	18 53.4	5 8.8	4 34.6
17	23 40 43.5	23 21.8	4 20.3	22 55.7	22 36.2	0 31.4	7 10.6	26 53.9	0 34.5	18 56.6	5 10.5	4 36.5
18	23 44 40.1	24 20.3	4 17.2	5♈39.3	24 27.2	0 18.8	7 49.7	27 3.0	0 35.8	18 59.9	5 12.3	4 38.4
19	23 48 36.6	25 18.9	4 14.0	18 8.3	26 17.4	0 8.6	8 28.9	27 12.3	0 37.1	19 3.1	5 14.2	4 40.4
20	23 52 33.2	26 17.5	4 10.8	0♉24.0	28 6.6	0 .8	9 8.2	27 21.6	0 38.5	19 6.2	5 16.0	4 42.3
21	23 56 29.7	27 16.1	4 7.6	12 28.6	29 54.9	29♌55.4	9 47.4	27 31.1	0 40.0	19 9.4	5 17.8	4 44.2
22	0 0 26.3	28 14.8	4 4.4	24 25.2	1♎42.1	29 52.5	10 26.7	27 40.6	0 41.6	19 12.5	5 19.7	4 46.1
23	0 4 22.9	29 13.5	4 1.3	6♊17.3	3 28.4	29 52.0	11 6.0	27 50.2	0 43.3	19 15.5	5 21.6	4 47.9
24	0 8 19.4	0♎12.2	3 58.1	18 9.1	5 13.7	29D53.8	11 45.4	27 60.0	0 45.1	19 18.6	5 23.5	4 49.8
25	0 12 16.0	1 11.0	3 54.9	0♋ 5.2	6 58.1	29 58.0	12 24.8	28 9.8	0 47.0	19 21.6	5 25.4	4 51.6
26	0 16 12.5	2 9.8	3 51.7	12 10.0	8 41.5	0♍ 4.5	13 4.3	28 19.8	0 49.0	19 24.6	5 27.3	4 53.5
27	0 20 9.1	3 8.6	3 48.5	24 28.2	10 23.9	0 13.2	13 43.8	28 29.8	0 51.1	19 27.5	5 29.3	4 55.3
28	0 24 5.6	4 7.5	3 45.4	7♌ 3.9	12 5.5	0 24.1	14 23.3	28 40.0	0 53.3	19 30.4	5 31.3	4 57.1
29	0 28 2.2	5 6.4	3 42.2	20 .3	13 46.1	0 37.1	15 2.9	28 50.2	0 55.5	19 33.3	5 33.2	4 58.9
30	0 31 58.7	6 5.3	3 39.0	3♍19.4	15 25.8	0 52.2	15 42.5	29 .6	0 57.9	19 36.2	5 35.2	5 .7
		LATITUDE										
1	22 37 38.7	0 .0	0 .0	4S 7.7	1N 6.9	8S33.9	0N46.5	0N43.5	0N47.0	0N39.3	1N44.2	11N47.2
4	22 49 28.4	0 .0	0 .0	1 3.2	1 29.0	8 37.2	0 45.0	0 42.9	0 46.6	0 39.4	1 44.0	11 47.5
7	23 1 18.0	0 .0	0 .0	2N41.7	1 42.4	8 32.3	0 43.6	0 42.3	0 46.1	0 39.5	1 43.9	11 47.8
10	23 13 7.7	0 .0	0 .0	5 2.8	1 47.8	8 19.8	0 42.1	0 41.8	0 45.6	0 39.5	1 43.8	11 48.2
13	23 24 57.3	0 .0	0 .0	4 45.2	1 46.4	8 .6	0 40.6	0 41.2	0 45.2	0 39.6	1 43.6	11 48.7
16	23 36 47.0	0 .0	0 .0	2 9.1	1 39.6	7 36.0	0 39.1	0 40.6	0 44.7	0 39.6	1 43.5	11 49.2
19	23 48 36.6	0 .0	0 .0	1S17.8	1 28.4	7 7.3	0 37.6	0 40.1	0 44.3	0 39.7	1 43.4	11 49.7
22	0 0 26.3	0 .0	0 .0	4 4.8	1 13.9	6 35.9	0 36.1	0 39.5	0 43.8	0 39.8	1 43.3	11 50.3
25	0 12 16.0	0 .0	0 .0	5 16.6	0 56.9	6 2.7	0 34.6	0 39.0	0 43.4	0 39.9	1 43.2	11 51.0
28	0 24 5.6	0 .0	0 .0	4 26.2	0 38.1	5 28.8	0 33.1	0 38.5	0 42.9	0 40.0	1 43.1	11 51.7
		RIGHT ASCENSION										
1	22 37 38.7	9♍29.7	4♎45.6	13♌20.0	25♌24.7	6♍41.7	27♍23.6	22♏34.4	0♑30.6	20♌41.1	3♏ 4.1	10♍31.6
2	22 41 35.3	10 24.2	4 42.7	26 23.9	27 8.1	6R 6.9	27 58.8	22 41.6	0R30.2	20 44.6	3 5.5	10 33.6
3	22 45 31.8	11 18.5	4 39.8	9♍30.1	28 53.6	5 32.4	28 34.0	22 49.0	0 30.0	20 48.1	3 6.9	10 35.6
4	22 49 28.4	12 12.9	4 36.9	22 41.0	0♍40.8	4 58.7	29 9.2	22 56.5	0 29.8	20 51.6	3 8.3	10 37.6
5	22 53 24.9	13 7.1	4 33.9	6♎ .9	2 29.1	4 25.8	29 44.5	23 4.1	0 29.8	20 55.1	3 9.7	10 39.5
6	22 57 21.5	14 1.3	4 31.0	19 34.9	4 18.2	3 53.9	0♎19.8	23 11.9	0 29.8	20 58.5	3 11.1	10 41.5
7	23 1 18.0	14 55.4	4 28.1	3♏27.5	6 7.7	3 23.3	0 55.2	23 19.8	0D30.0	21 2.0	3 12.6	10 43.5
8	23 5 14.6	15 49.5	4 25.2	17 41.0	7 57.1	2 54.2	1 30.6	23 27.8	0 30.2	21 5.4	3 14.1	10 45.5
9	23 9 11.1	16 43.5	4 22.3	2♐13.8	9 46.3	2 26.6	2 6.0	23 36.0	0 30.6	21 8.8	3 15.6	10 47.5
10	23 13 7.7	17 37.5	4 19.3	16 59.5	11 35.0	2 .7	2 41.4	23 44.3	0 31.1	21 12.1	3 17.2	10 49.4
11	23 17 4.2	18 31.5	4 16.4	1♑47.6	13 23.1	1 36.7	3 16.9	23 52.8	0 31.7	21 15.5	3 18.7	10 51.4
12	23 21 .8	19 25.3	4 13.5	16 25.7	15 10.3	1 14.7	3 52.4	24 1.3	0 32.4	21 18.8	3 20.3	10 53.4
13	23 24 57.3	20 19.2	4 10.6	0♒42.9	16 56.5	0 54.8	4 28.0	24 10.0	0 33.2	21 22.1	3 21.9	10 55.3
14	23 28 53.9	21 13.0	4 7.7	14 31.9	18 41.7	0 37.1	5 3.6	24 18.9	0 34.1	21 25.4	3 23.5	10 57.3
15	23 32 50.4	22 6.9	4 4.8	27 50.4	20 25.8	0 21.6	5 39.2	24 27.8	0 35.1	21 28.7	3 25.2	10 59.3
16	23 36 47.0	23 .6	4 1.8	10♓40.2	22 8.8	0 8.4	6 14.9	24 36.9	0 36.2	21 31.9	3 26.8	11 1.2
17	23 40 43.5	23 54.4	3 58.9	23 6.4	23 50.6	29♌57.6	6 50.7	24 46.1	0 37.4	21 35.1	3 28.5	11 3.1
18	23 44 40.1	24 48.2	3 56.0	5♈15.2	25 31.3	29 49.1	7 26.4	24 55.4	0 38.7	21 38.3	3 30.2	11 5.1
19	23 48 36.6	25 42.0	3 53.1	17 13.5	27 10.9	29 43.0	8 2.3	25 4.9	0 40.2	21 41.5	3 32.0	11 7.1
20	23 52 33.2	26 35.8	3 50.2	29 7.7	28 49.3	29 39.3	8 38.2	25 14.4	0 41.8	21 44.6	3 33.7	11 9.0
21	23 56 29.7	27 29.6	3 47.2	11♉ 3.5	0♎26.7	29 37.9	9 14.2	25 24.1	0 43.4	21 47.7	3 35.5	11 10.9
22	0 0 26.3	28 23.5	3 44.3	23 5.1	2 3.1	29D38.9	9 50.2	25 33.9	0 45.1	21 50.7	3 37.3	11 12.8
23	0 4 22.9	29 17.3	3 41.4	5♊15.5	3 38.5	29 42.2	10 26.2	25 43.8	0 47.0	21 53.8	3 39.1	11 14.7
24	0 8 19.4	0♎11.2	3 38.5	17 35.6	5 12.9	29 47.8	11 2.4	25 53.8	0 48.9	21 56.8	3 40.9	11 16.6
25	0 12 16.0	1 5.1	3 35.6	0♋ 5.4	6 46.4	29 55.6	11 38.6	26 3.9	0 51.0	21 59.8	3 42.7	11 18.5
26	0 16 12.5	1 59.0	3 32.7	12 43.5	8 19.1	0♍ 5.6	12 14.8	26 14.1	0 53.1	22 2.7	3 44.6	11 20.3
27	0 20 9.1	2 53.0	3 29.7	25 28.3	9 50.9	0 17.7	12 51.1	26 24.5	0 55.4	22 5.6	3 46.5	11 22.2
28	0 24 5.6	3 47.1	3 26.8	8♌18.5	11 22.0	0 31.9	13 27.5	26 34.9	0 57.7	22 8.5	3 48.4	11 24.0
29	0 28 2.2	4 41.2	3 23.9	21 13.9	12 52.4	0 48.1	14 4.0	26 45.5	1 .2	22 11.4	3 50.3	11 25.9
30	0 31 58.7	5 35.4	3 21.0	4♍16.0	14 22.2	1 6.2	14 40.5	26 56.1	1 2.7	22 14.2	3 52.2	11 27.7
		DECLINATION										
1	22 37 38.7	8N38.2	0S 2.2	13N12.8	15N .5	0N31.7	1N58.5	18S15.2	22S39.5	16N 3.1	11S28.2	20N57.3
4	22 49 28.4	7 32.7	0 2.1	2 .8	13 34.2	1 8.7	1 11.1	18 21.0	22 39.9	15 59.8	11 29.8	20 55.3
7	23 1 18.0	6 26.1	0 2.0	10S35.3	11 47.1	1 51.0	0 23.6	18 27.1	22 40.4	15 56.7	11 31.4	20 53.4
10	23 13 7.7	5 18.5	0 2.0	17 50.1	9 44.4	2 36.0	0S24.1	18 33.3	22 40.8	15 53.5	11 33.1	20 51.5
13	23 24 57.3	4 10.2	0 1.9	15 35.4	7 31.2	3 21.4	1 11.8	18 39.8	22 41.3	15 50.5	11 34.9	20 49.7
16	23 36 47.0	3 1.2	0 1.8	5 50.7	5 11.8	4 5.0	1 59.5	18 46.4	22 41.7	15 47.5	11 36.7	20 48.0
19	23 48 36.6	1 51.7	0 1.8	5N54.9	2 49.6	4 44.9	2 47.2	18 53.2	22 42.2	15 44.5	11 38.6	20 46.3
22	0 0 26.3	0 41.8	0 1.7	14 55.1	0 27.2	5 19.9	3 34.9	19 .1	22 42.6	15 41.7	11 40.5	20 44.7
25	0 12 16.0	0S28.2	0 1.6	18 9.9	1S53.7	5 49.1	4 22.5	19 7.2	22 43.0	15 38.9	11 42.5	20 43.2
28	0 24 5.6	1 38.4	0 1.6	14 12.7	4 11.7	6 12.0	5 9.9	19 14.3	22 43.4	15 36.2	11 44.5	20 41.8

OCTOBER 1959

DAY	EPHEM. SID. TIME	☉	☊	☽	☿	♀	♂	♃	♄	♅	♆	♇
	h m s	° ′	° ′	° ′	° ′	° ′	° ′	° ′	° ′	° ′	° ′	° ′
						LONGITUDE						
1	0 35 55.3	7≏ 4.3	3≏35.8	17♍ 1.8	17≏ 4.6	1♍ 9.3	16≏22.2	29♏11.0	1♑ .3	19♌39.0	5♏37.2	5♍ 2.5
2	0 39 51.8	8 3.3	3 32.7	1≏ 5.9	18 42.5	1 28.3	17 1.9	29 21.5	1 2.9	19 41.7	5 39.3	5 4.2
3	0 43 48.4	9 2.4	3 29.5	15 28.1	20 19.6	1 49.2	17 41.7	29 32.2	1 5.5	19 44.5	5 41.3	5 6.0
4	0 47 44.9	10 1.5	3 26.3	0♏ 3.4	21 55.9	2 11.9	18 21.5	29 42.9	1 8.2	19 47.2	5 43.4	5 7.7
5	0 51 41.5	11 .6	3 23.1	14 45.1	23 31.3	2 36.4	19 1.3	29 53.7	1 11.0	19 49.8	5 45.4	5 9.4
6	0 55 38.0	11 59.8	3 19.9	29 26.7	25 6.0	3 2.5	19 41.2	0♐ 4.6	1 13.9	19 52.5	5 47.5	5 11.1
7	0 59 34.6	12 58.9	3 16.8	14♐ 1.8	26 39.8	3 30.3	20 21.1	0 15.5	1 16.9	19 55.1	5 49.6	5 12.8
8	1 3 31.1	13 58.1	3 13.6	28 25.5	28 12.9	3 59.7	21 1.0	0 26.6	1 20.0	19 57.6	5 51.7	5 14.5
9	1 7 27.7	14 57.4	3 10.4	12♑34.6	29 45.2	4 30.6	21 41.0	0 37.7	1 23.2	20 .1	5 53.8	5 16.1
10	1 11 24.2	15 56.7	3 7.2	26 27.3	1♏16.8	5 3.0	22 21.1	0 49.0	1 26.5	20 2.6	5 56.0	5 17.8
11	1 15 20.8	16 56.0	3 4.1	10♒ 3.0	2 47.6	5 36.8	23 1.2	1 .3	1 29.8	20 5.1	5 58.2	5 19.4
12	1 19 17.3	17 55.3	3 .9	23 22.6	4 17.6	6 12.0	23 41.3	1 11.7	1 33.3	20 7.4	6 .3	5 21.0
13	1 23 13.9	18 54.7	2 57.7	6♓26.8	5 46.9	6 48.5	24 21.5	1 23.1	1 36.8	20 9.8	6 2.5	5 22.5
14	1 27 10.4	19 54.1	2 54.5	19 17.1	7 15.4	7 26.2	25 1.7	1 34.6	1 40.4	20 12.1	6 4.6	5 24.1
15	1 31 7.0	20 53.5	2 51.3	1♈54.8	8 43.1	8 5.2	25 41.9	1 46.2	1 44.0	20 14.3	6 6.8	5 25.6
16	1 35 3.5	21 53.0	2 48.2	14 21.0	10 10.1	8 45.4	26 22.2	1 57.9	1 47.8	20 16.6	6 9.0	5 27.1
17	1 39 .1	22 52.5	2 45.0	26 37.0	11 36.3	9 26.8	27 2.5	2 9.6	1 51.6	20 18.7	6 11.2	5 28.6
18	1 42 56.7	23 52.0	2 41.8	8♉44.1	13 1.7	10 9.2	27 42.9	2 21.4	1 55.5	20 20.9	6 13.4	5 30.0
19	1 46 53.2	24 51.5	2 38.6	20 43.8	14 26.3	10 52.8	28 23.3	2 33.3	1 59.5	20 22.9	6 15.6	5 31.5
20	1 50 49.8	25 51.1	2 35.5	2♊38.1	15 50.0	11 37.3	29 3.7	2 45.3	2 3.6	20 25.0	6 17.8	5 32.9
21	1 54 46.3	26 50.8	2 32.3	14 29.4	17 12.8	12 22.9	29 44.2	2 57.3	2 7.8	20 27.0	6 20.0	5 34.3
22	1 58 42.9	27 50.4	2 29.1	26 20.7	18 34.6	13 9.3	0♏24.8	3 9.3	2 12.0	20 28.9	6 22.2	5 35.7
23	2 2 39.4	28 50.1	2 25.9	8♋15.5	19 55.5	13 56.8	1 5.4	3 21.5	2 16.3	20 30.8	6 24.5	5 37.0
24	2 6 36.0	29 49.9	2 22.7	20 17.9	21 15.3	14 45.1	1 46.0	3 33.6	2 20.7	20 32.6	6 26.7	5 38.4
25	2 10 32.5	0♏49.6	2 19.6	2♌32.2	22 34.0	15 34.2	2 26.7	3 45.9	2 25.1	20 34.5	6 28.9	5 39.7
26	2 14 29.1	1 49.5	2 16.4	15 3.2	23 51.5	16 24.2	3 7.4	3 58.2	2 29.7	20 36.2	6 31.2	5 41.0
27	2 18 25.6	2 49.3	2 13.2	27 55.0	25 7.7	17 15.0	3 48.2	4 10.6	2 34.3	20 37.9	6 33.4	5 42.2
28	2 22 22.2	3 49.2	2 10.0	11♍11.5	26 22.5	18 6.5	4 29.0	4 23.0	2 38.9	20 39.6	6 35.6	5 43.5
29	2 26 18.7	4 49.1	2 6.9	24 54.7	27 35.6	18 58.8	5 9.9	4 35.5	2 43.7	20 41.2	6 37.9	5 44.7
30	2 30 15.3	5 49.1	2 3.7	9≏ 5.1	28 47.1	19 51.8	5 50.8	4 48.0	2 48.5	20 42.7	6 40.1	5 45.9
31	2 34 11.8	6 49.1	2 .5	23 40.3	29 56.8	20 45.5	6 31.8	5 .6	2 53.4	20 44.3	6 42.4	5 47.1
						LATITUDE						
1	0 35 55.3	0 .0	0 .0	1S33.0	0N18.0	4S54.7	0N31.5	0N38.0	0N42.5	0N40.1	1N43.1	11N52.4
4	0 47 44.9	0 .0	0 .0	2N19.5	0S 2.8	4 21.1	0 29.9	0 37.5	0 42.1	0 40.2	1 43.0	11 53.2
7	0 59 34.6	0 .0	0 .0	4 57.9	0 24.0	3 48.2	0 28.4	0 37.1	0 41.7	0 40.3	1 42.9	11 54.0
10	1 11 24.2	0 .0	0 .0	4 52.8	0 45.3	3 16.4	0 26.8	0 36.6	0 41.2	0 40.4	1 42.9	11 54.9
13	1 23 13.9	0 .0	0 .0	2 26.8	1 6.2	2 45.8	0 25.2	0 36.2	0 40.8	0 40.5	1 42.8	11 55.8
16	1 35 3.5	0 .0	0 .0	0S56.7	1 26.4	2 16.5	0 23.5	0 35.8	0 40.4	0 40.6	1 42.8	11 56.8
19	1 46 53.2	0 .0	0 .0	3 49.6	1 45.5	1 48.7	0 21.9	0 35.3	0 40.0	0 40.7	1 42.8	11 57.8
22	1 58 42.9	0 .0	0 .0	5 11.4	2 3.3	1 22.3	0 20.3	0 34.9	0 39.6	0 40.8	1 42.7	11 58.8
25	2 10 32.5	0 .0	0 .0	4 35.2	2 19.1	0 57.4	0 18.6	0 34.5	0 39.3	0 40.9	1 42.7	11 59.9
28	2 22 22.2	0 .0	0 .0	2 .4	2 32.5	0 34.0	0 16.9	0 34.2	0 38.9	0 41.0	1 42.7	12 1.0
31	2 34 11.8	0 .0	0 .0	1N46.7	2 42.7	0 12.0	0 15.2	0 33.8	0 38.5	0 41.2	1 42.7	12 2.1
						RIGHT ASCENSION						
1	0 35 55.3	6≏29.6	3≏18.1	17♍27.8	15≏51.3	1♍26.3	15≏17.1	27♏ 6.9	1♑ 5.4	22♌17.0	3♏54.1	11♍29.5
2	0 39 51.8	7 23.9	3 15.1	0≏54.0	17 19.9	1 48.1	15 53.8	27 17.8	1 8.2	22 19.7	3 56.1	11 31.3
3	0 43 48.4	8 18.3	3 12.2	14 39.2	18 47.9	2 11.7	16 30.6	27 28.7	1 11.0	22 22.4	3 58.0	11 33.1
4	0 47 44.9	9 12.7	3 9.3	28 47.5	20 15.4	2 37.0	17 7.4	27 39.8	1 14.0	22 25.1	3 60.0	11 34.9
5	0 51 41.5	10 7.3	3 6.4	13♏19.8	21 42.5	3 3.9	17 44.3	27 51.0	1 17.0	22 27.7	4 2.0	11 36.6
6	0 55 38.0	11 1.9	3 3.5	28 12.8	23 9.1	3 32.4	18 21.3	28 2.2	1 20.2	22 30.3	4 4.0	11 38.4
7	0 59 34.6	11 56.6	3 .6	13♐17.5	24 35.3	4 2.4	18 58.4	28 13.6	1 23.4	22 32.9	4 6.0	11 40.1
8	1 3 31.1	12 51.4	2 57.6	28 21.0	26 1.2	4 33.8	19 35.6	28 25.0	1 26.8	22 35.4	4 8.0	11 41.8
9	1 7 27.7	13 46.3	2 54.7	13♑ 9.2	27 26.7	5 6.6	20 12.8	28 36.5	1 30.2	22 37.9	4 10.1	11 43.5
10	1 11 24.2	14 41.3	2 51.8	27 30.7	28 52.0	5 40.8	20 50.2	28 48.2	1 33.8	22 40.4	4 12.1	11 45.3
11	1 15 20.8	15 36.4	2 48.9	11♒19.0	0♏16.9	6 16.2	21 27.6	28 59.9	1 37.4	22 42.8	4 14.2	11 46.9
12	1 19 17.3	16 31.6	2 46.0	24 33.5	1 41.5	6 52.9	22 5.1	29 11.7	1 41.1	22 45.1	4 16.3	11 48.6
13	1 23 13.9	17 27.0	2 43.1	7♓17.5	3 5.8	7 30.7	22 42.7	29 23.6	1 44.9	22 47.4	4 18.3	11 50.2
14	1 27 10.4	18 22.4	2 40.1	19 37.4	4 29.8	8 9.7	23 20.4	29 35.6	1 48.8	22 49.7	4 20.4	11 51.9
15	1 31 7.0	19 18.0	2 37.2	1♈40.6	5 53.6	8 49.7	23 58.2	29 47.6	1 52.8	22 51.9	4 22.5	11 53.5
16	1 35 3.5	20 13.7	2 34.3	13 34.5	7 17.1	9 30.8	24 36.1	29 59.8	1 56.9	22 54.1	4 24.6	11 55.0
17	1 39 .1	21 9.6	2 31.4	25 25.8	8 40.3	10 12.9	25 14.1	0♐12.0	2 1.0	22 56.3	4 26.7	11 56.6
18	1 42 56.7	22 5.6	2 28.5	7♉19.8	10 3.2	10 56.0	25 52.1	0 24.3	2 5.3	22 58.4	4 28.9	11 58.2
19	1 46 53.2	23 1.7	2 25.6	19 20.3	11 25.8	11 39.9	26 30.3	0 36.6	2 9.6	23 .4	4 31.0	11 59.7
20	1 50 49.8	23 58.0	2 22.6	1♊29.0	12 48.0	12 24.8	27 8.6	0 49.1	2 14.0	23 2.4	4 33.1	12 1.2
21	1 54 46.3	24 54.5	2 19.7	13 46.1	14 9.8	13 10.4	27 47.0	1 1.6	2 18.5	23 4.4	4 35.2	12 2.7
22	1 58 42.9	25 51.1	2 16.8	26 10.1	15 31.1	13 56.9	28 25.5	1 14.2	2 23.1	23 6.3	4 37.4	12 4.2
23	2 2 39.4	26 48.0	2 13.9	8♋38.9	16 51.9	14 44.1	29 4.1	1 26.8	2 27.8	23 8.2	4 39.5	12 5.6
24	2 6 36.0	27 44.9	2 11.0	21 10.6	18 12.2	15 32.1	29 42.8	1 39.6	2 32.6	23 10.0	4 41.7	12 7.0
25	2 10 32.5	28 42.1	2 8.1	3♌44.2	19 31.8	16 20.8	0♏21.7	1 52.4	2 37.4	23 11.8	4 43.8	12 8.4
26	2 14 29.1	29 39.4	2 5.1	16 20.2	20 50.6	17 10.1	1 .6	2 5.2	2 42.3	23 13.6	4 46.0	12 9.8
27	2 18 25.6	0♏36.9	2 2.2	29 1.5	22 8.5	18 .1	1 39.7	2 18.2	2 47.3	23 15.2	4 48.2	12 11.2
28	2 22 22.2	1 34.6	1 59.3	11♍52.8	23 25.4	18 50.7	2 18.9	2 31.2	2 52.4	23 16.9	4 50.3	12 12.5
29	2 26 18.7	2 32.5	1 56.4	25 .7	24 41.1	19 41.8	2 58.2	2 44.3	2 57.5	23 18.5	4 52.5	12 13.9
30	2 30 15.3	3 30.6	1 53.5	8≏32.3	25 55.5	20 33.5	3 37.6	2 57.4	3 2.7	23 20.0	4 54.7	12 15.2
31	2 34 11.8	4 28.9	1 50.6	22 34.3	27 8.3	21 25.8	4 17.2	3 10.6	3 8.1	23 21.5	4 56.9	12 16.5
						DECLINATION						
1	0 35 55.3	2S48.4	0S 1.5	3N41.7	6S25.9	6N28.1	5S57.2	19S21.5	22S43.8	15N33.6	11S46.6	20N40.4
4	0 47 44.9	3 58.2	0 1.4	9S18.9	8 35.3	6 37.6	6 44.2	19 28.8	22 44.1	15 31.1	11 48.7	20 39.2
7	0 59 34.6	5 7.6	0 1.4	17 33.3	10 39.4	6 40.4	7 30.9	19 36.2	22 44.5	15 28.7	11 50.8	20 38.0
10	1 11 24.2	6 16.4	0 1.3	16 4.2	12 37.7	6 36.7	8 17.3	19 43.6	22 44.8	15 26.4	11 53.0	20 36.9
13	1 23 13.9	7 24.5	0 1.2	6 52.3	14 29.4	6 26.7	9 3.2	19 51.0	22 45.1	15 24.3	11 55.1	20 36.0
16	1 35 3.5	8 31.6	0 1.2	4N47.3	16 14.1	6 10.6	9 48.7	19 58.4	22 45.4	15 22.2	11 57.3	20 35.1
19	1 46 53.2	9 37.6	0 1.1	14 14.7	17 51.1	5 48.6	10 33.7	20 5.8	22 45.6	15 20.3	11 59.5	20 34.4
22	1 58 42.9	10 42.4	0 1.0	18 12.2	19 19.8	5 21.1	11 18.1	20 13.1	22 45.8	15 18.5	12 1.7	20 33.8
25	2 10 32.5	11 45.8	0 1.0	15 7.6	20 39.3	4 48.4	12 1.9	20 20.4	22 45.9	15 16.8	12 3.9	20 33.2
28	2 22 22.2	12 47.5	0 .9	5 30.7	21 48.9	4 10.8	12 45.0	20 27.7	22 46.1	15 15.3	12 6.1	20 32.8
31	2 34 11.8	13 47.5	0 .8	7S32.2	22 47.4	3 28.7	13 27.5	20 34.9	22 46.1	15 13.9	12 8.3	20 32.5

NOVEMBER 1959

LONGITUDE

DAY	EPHEM. SID. TIME	☉	☊	☽	☿	♀	♂	♃	♄	♅	♆	♇
	h m s	° ′	° ′	° ′	° ′	° ′	° ′	° ′	° ′	° ′	° ′	° ′
1	2 38 8.4	7♏49.2	1♎57.3	8♏34.7	1♐ 4.3	21♍39.8	7♏12.8	5♐13.3	2♑58.4	20♌45.7	6♏44.7	5♍48.2
2	2 42 5.0	8 49.2	1 54.1	23 40.3	2 9.5	22 34.8	7 53.8	5 25.9	3 3.4	20 47.1	6 46.9	5 49.3
3	2 46 1.5	9 49.3	1 51.0	8♐47.5	3 12.1	23 30.3	8 34.9	5 38.7	3 8.5	20 48.5	6 49.1	5 50.4
4	2 49 58.1	10 49.4	1 47.8	23 46.5	4 11.8	24 26.5	9 16.0	5 51.5	3 13.7	20 49.8	6 51.4	5 51.4
5	2 53 54.6	11 49.6	1 44.6	8♑29.3	5 8.4	25 23.2	9 57.2	6 4.3	3 18.9	20 51.0	6 53.6	5 52.5
6	2 57 51.2	12 49.7	1 41.4	22 50.3	6 1.3	26 20.4	10 38.4	6 17.1	3 24.2	20 52.2	6 55.9	5 53.5
7	3 1 47.7	13 49.9	1 38.3	6♒46.8	6 50.2	27 18.2	11 19.7	6 30.0	3 29.5	20 53.3	6 58.1	5 54.4
8	3 5 44.3	14 50.2	1 35.1	20 18.9	7 34.7	28 16.5	12 1.0	6 43.0	3 34.9	20 54.4	7 .3	5 55.4
9	3 9 40.8	15 50.4	1 31.9	3♓28.5	8 14.0	29 15.3	12 42.3	6 56.0	3 40.4	20 55.4	7 2.6	5 56.3
10	3 13 37.4	16 50.7	1 28.7	16 18.5	8 47.8	0♎14.6	13 23.7	7 9.0	3 45.9	20 56.4	7 4.8	5 57.2
11	3 17 33.9	17 51.0	1 25.5	28 52.4	9 15.3	1 14.3	14 5.2	7 22.0	3 51.5	20 57.3	7 7.0	5 58.1
12	3 21 30.5	18 51.3	1 22.4	11♈13.5	9 35.9	2 14.5	14 46.6	7 35.1	3 57.1	20 58.2	7 9.2	5 58.9
13	3 25 27.1	19 51.6	1 19.2	23 24.7	9 48.8	3 15.2	15 28.2	7 48.2	4 2.8	20 59.0	7 11.4	5 59.7
14	3 29 23.6	20 52.0	1 16.0	5♉28.6	9 53.4	4 16.3	16 9.7	8 1.4	4 8.5	20 59.8	7 13.6	6 .5
15	3 33 20.2	21 52.4	1 12.8	17 27.1	9R49.0	5 17.7	16 51.4	8 14.6	4 14.3	21 .5	7 15.8	6 1.2
16	3 37 16.7	22 52.8	1 9.7	29 21.9	9 34.9	6 19.6	17 33.0	8 27.8	4 20.2	21 1.1	7 18.0	6 1.9
17	3 41 13.3	23 53.3	1 6.5	11♊14.3	9 10.7	7 21.9	18 14.7	8 41.0	4 26.1	21 1.7	7 20.1	6 2.6
18	3 45 9.8	24 53.8	1 3.3	23 6.0	8 36.1	8 24.6	18 56.5	8 54.3	4 32.1	21 2.2	7 22.3	6 3.3
19	3 49 6.4	25 54.3	1 .1	4♋58.7	7 51.1	9 27.6	19 38.3	9 7.6	4 38.1	21 2.7	7 24.5	6 3.9
20	3 53 2.9	26 54.8	0 56.9	16 54.8	6 56.1	10 31.0	20 20.1	9 20.9	4 44.1	21 3.1	7 26.6	6 4.5
21	3 56 59.5	27 55.4	0 53.8	28 57.2	5 52.1	11 34.7	21 2.0	9 34.3	4 50.3	21 3.6	7 28.8	6 5.1
22	4 0 56.1	28 56.0	0 50.6	11♌ 9.5	4 40.4	12 38.8	21 44.0	9 47.6	4 56.4	21 3.9	7 30.9	6 5.6
23	4 4 52.6	29 56.6	0 47.4	23 35.8	3 22.8	13 43.2	22 26.0	10 1.0	5 2.6	21 4.1	7 33.0	6 6.1
24	4 8 49.2	0♐57.3	0 44.2	6♍20.5	2 1.7	14 47.9	23 8.0	10 14.4	5 8.8	21 4.3	7 35.1	6 6.6
25	4 12 45.7	1 58.0	0 41.1	19 28.2	0 39.7	15 52.9	23 50.1	10 27.9	5 15.1	21 4.5	7 37.2	6 7.1
26	4 16 42.3	2 58.7	0 37.9	3♎ 2.4	29♏19.6	16 58.1	24 32.2	10 41.3	5 21.5	21 4.6	7 39.3	6 7.5
27	4 20 38.8	3 59.4	0 34.7	17 5.4	28 4.1	18 3.7	25 14.4	10 54.8	5 27.8	21 4.6	7 41.4	6 7.9
28	4 24 35.4	5 .2	0 31.5	1♏36.9	26 55.5	19 9.6	25 56.6	11 8.2	5 34.2	21 4.6	7 43.4	6 8.2
29	4 28 31.9	6 1.0	0 28.4	16 33.2	25 55.8	20 15.7	26 38.9	11 21.7	5 40.7	21R 4.5	7 45.5	6 8.5
30	4 32 28.5	7 1.8	0 25.2	1♐47.1	25 6.3	21 22.0	27 21.2	11 35.2	5 47.2	21 4.4	7 47.5	6 8.8

LATITUDE

DAY	EPHEM. SID. TIME	☉	☊	☽	☿	♀	♂	♃	♄	♅	♆	♇
1	2 38 8.4	0 .0	0 .0	2N58.6	2S45.2	0S 5.1	0N14.7	0N33.7	0N38.4	0N41.2	1N42.7	12N 2.5
4	2 49 58.1	0 .0	0 .0	5 6.3	2 49.7	0N14.9	0 13.0	0 33.3	0 38.0	0 41.3	1 42.7	12 3.6
7	3 1 47.7	0 .0	0 .0	4 19.3	2 48.3	0 33.3	0 11.3	0 33.0	0 37.7	0 41.5	1 42.7	12 4.8
10	3 13 37.4	0 .0	0 .0	2 30.9	2 39.2	0 50.3	0 9.5	0 32.7	0 37.3	0 41.6	1 42.8	12 6.1
13	3 25 27.1	0 .0	0 .0	1S46.5	2 20.0	1 5.8	0 7.8	0 32.3	0 37.0	0 41.7	1 42.8	12 7.3
16	3 37 16.7	0 .0	0 .0	4 15.3	1 48.2	1 19.9	0 6.0	0 32.0	0 36.7	0 41.8	1 42.9	12 8.6
19	3 49 6.4	0 .0	0 .0	5 5.1	1 2.5	1 32.5	0 4.3	0 31.7	0 36.3	0 42.0	1 42.9	12 9.9
22	4 0 56.1	0 .0	0 .0	3 57.8	0 4.9	1 43.8	0 2.5	0 31.4	0 36.0	0 42.1	1 43.0	12 11.2
25	4 12 45.7	0 .0	0 .0	1 7.0	0N56.0	1 53.8	0 .7	0 31.2	0 35.7	0 42.2	1 43.0	12 12.5
28	4 24 35.4	0 .0	0 .0	2N30.6	1 48.2	2 2.4	0S 1.1	0 30.9	0 35.4	0 42.4	1 43.1	12 13.8

RIGHT ASCENSION

DAY	EPHEM. SID. TIME	☉	☊	☽	☿	♀	♂	♃	♄	♅	♆	♇
1	2 38 8.4	5♏27.4	1♎47.6	7♏10.3	28♏19.3	22♍18.6	4♏56.9	3♐23.9	3♑13.5	23♌23.0	4♏59.1	12♍17.7
2	2 42 5.0	6 26.1	1 44.7	22 18.7	29 28.1	23 11.9	5 36.6	3 37.2	3 18.9	23 24.4	5 1.2	12 19.0
3	2 46 1.5	7 25.0	1 41.8	7♐50.2	0♐34.6	24 5.6	6 16.6	3 50.6	3 24.4	23 25.7	5 3.4	12 20.2
4	2 49 58.1	8 24.0	1 38.9	23 28.4	1 38.4	24 59.8	6 56.6	4 4.0	3 30.0	23 27.0	5 5.6	12 21.3
5	2 53 54.6	9 23.3	1 36.0	8♑53.6	2 39.0	25 54.4	7 36.7	4 17.5	3 35.7	23 28.2	5 7.7	12 22.5
6	2 57 51.2	10 22.8	1 33.1	23 48.7	3 36.0	26 49.4	8 17.0	4 31.0	3 41.4	23 29.4	5 9.9	12 23.6
7	3 1 47.7	11 22.4	1 30.1	8♒ 3.2	4 29.0	27 44.8	8 57.4	4 44.6	3 47.2	23 30.5	5 12.1	12 24.7
8	3 5 44.3	12 22.3	1 27.2	21 34.7	5 17.3	28 40.6	9 38.0	4 58.2	3 53.1	23 31.6	5 14.2	12 25.8
9	3 9 40.8	13 22.4	1 24.3	4♓27.3	6 .4	29 36.8	10 18.6	5 11.9	3 59.0	23 32.6	5 16.4	12 26.8
10	3 13 37.4	14 22.7	1 21.4	16 48.7	6 37.7	0♎33.4	10 59.4	5 25.6	4 5.0	23 33.6	5 18.5	12 27.9
11	3 17 33.9	15 23.2	1 18.5	28 48.4	7 8.4	1 30.3	11 40.3	5 39.4	4 11.0	23 34.5	5 20.7	12 28.9
12	3 21 30.5	16 23.9	1 15.6	10♈35.9	7 31.7	2 27.6	12 21.4	5 53.2	4 17.2	23 35.4	5 22.8	12 29.8
13	3 25 27.1	17 24.8	1 12.7	22 19.6	7 47.0	3 25.2	13 2.6	6 7.1	4 23.3	23 36.2	5 25.0	12 30.8
14	3 29 23.6	18 25.9	1 9.7	4♉ 6.5	7 53.5	4 23.2	13 43.9	6 21.0	4 29.6	23 37.0	5 27.1	12 31.7
15	3 33 20.2	19 27.3	1 6.8	16 1.4	7R50.5	5 21.5	14 25.3	6 34.9	4 35.9	23 37.7	5 29.2	12 32.6
16	3 37 16.7	20 28.8	1 3.9	28 6.6	7 37.2	6 20.1	15 6.9	6 48.9	4 42.2	23 38.3	5 31.3	12 33.5
17	3 41 13.3	21 30.6	1 1.0	10♊22.1	7 13.4	7 19.1	15 48.6	7 2.9	4 48.6	23 38.9	5 33.4	12 34.3
18	3 45 9.8	22 32.6	0 58.1	22 45.6	6 38.8	8 18.3	16 30.5	7 16.9	4 55.1	23 39.4	5 35.5	12 35.1
19	3 49 6.4	23 34.7	0 55.2	5♋13.3	5 53.6	9 17.9	17 12.5	7 31.0	5 1.6	23 39.9	5 37.6	12 35.9
20	3 53 2.9	24 37.1	0 52.2	17 41.4	4 58.2	10 17.8	17 54.6	7 45.1	5 8.1	23 40.4	5 39.7	12 36.6
21	3 56 59.5	25 39.8	0 49.3	0♌ 7.2	3 53.8	11 18.0	18 37.0	7 59.3	5 14.8	23 40.8	5 41.8	12 37.4
22	4 0 56.1	26 42.6	0 46.4	12 29.8	2 41.8	12 18.5	19 19.4	8 13.5	5 21.5	23 41.1	5 43.9	12 38.1
23	4 4 52.6	27 45.6	0 43.5	24 51.4	1 24.3	13 19.2	20 2.0	8 27.7	5 28.2	23 41.4	5 46.0	12 38.8
24	4 8 49.2	28 48.8	0 40.6	7♍16.7	0 3.8	14 20.3	20 44.7	8 41.9	5 34.9	23 41.6	5 48.0	12 39.4
25	4 12 45.7	29 52.2	0 37.7	19 53.0	28♏42.8	15 21.7	21 27.5	8 56.2	5 41.8	23 41.7	5 50.0	12 40.0
26	4 16 42.3	0♐55.9	0 34.8	2♎49.4	27 24.2	16 23.3	22 10.5	9 10.5	5 48.6	23 41.8	5 52.1	12 40.6
27	4 20 38.8	1 59.7	0 31.8	16 15.6	26 10.5	17 25.2	22 53.6	9 24.8	5 55.5	23 41.9	5 54.1	12 41.1
28	4 24 35.4	3 3.7	0 28.9	0♏20.2	25 4.0	18 27.4	23 36.9	9 39.1	6 2.5	23 41.9	5 56.1	12 41.7
29	4 28 31.9	4 7.8	0 26.0	15 7.9	24 6.4	19 29.9	24 20.3	9 53.5	6 9.4	23R41.8	5 58.0	12 42.1
30	4 32 28.5	5 12.2	0 23.1	0♐35.7	23 19.0	20 32.7	25 3.8	10 7.8	6 16.5	23 41.7	6 .0	12 42.6

DECLINATION

DAY	EPHEM. SID. TIME	☉	☊	☽	☿	♀	♂	♃	♄	♅	♆	♇
1	2 38 8.4	14S 7.1	0S .8	11S32.5	23S 4.2	3N13.7	13S41.4	20S37.3	22S46.1	15N13.5	12S 9.0	20N32.4
4	2 49 58.1	15 4.4	0 .7	18 11.8	23 45.9	2 26.1	14 22.7	20 44.3	22 46.1	15 12.4	12 11.2	20 32.3
7	3 1 47.7	15 59.5	0 .7	14 23.6	24 13.1	1 34.9	15 3.1	20 51.3	22 46.1	15 11.3	12 13.4	20 32.2
10	3 13 37.4	16 52.2	0 .6	4 .4	24 23.4	0 40.3	15 42.6	20 58.2	22 46.0	15 10.5	12 15.5	20 32.3
13	3 25 27.1	17 42.3	0 .5	7N26.8	24 13.9	0S17.2	16 21.0	21 4.9	22 45.8	15 9.8	12 17.6	20 32.5
16	3 37 16.7	18 29.7	0 .5	15 51.6	23 40.4	1 17.4	16 58.4	21 11.5	22 45.6	15 9.2	12 19.7	20 32.8
19	3 49 6.4	19 14.1	0 .4	18 16.0	22 38.9	2 19.8	17 34.6	21 17.9	22 45.3	15 8.8	12 21.8	20 33.3
22	4 0 56.1	19 55.4	0 .4	13 36.8	21 9.3	3 24.1	18 9.6	21 24.2	22 45.0	15 8.6	12 23.8	20 33.8
25	4 12 45.7	20 33.4	0 .3	3 8.5	19 22.7	4 29.9	18 43.3	21 30.3	22 44.6	15 8.5	12 25.8	20 34.5
28	4 24 35.4	21 8.0	0 .2	9S40.9	17 43.0	5 36.8	19 15.7	21 36.3	22 44.1	15 8.6	12 27.7	20 35.2

DECEMBER 1959

LONGITUDE

DAY	EPHEM. SID. TIME	☉	☊	☽	☿	♀	♂	♃	♄	♅	♆	♇
	h m s	° ′	° ′	° ′	° ′	° ′	° ′	° ′	° ′	° ′	° ′	° ′
1	4 36 25.1	8♐ 2.6	0♎22.0	17♐ 8.2	24♏28.0	22♎28.6	28♏ 3.6	11♐48.7	5♑53.7	21♌ 4.2	7♏49.5	6♍ 9.1
2	4 40 21.6	9 3.5	0 18.8	2♑24.8	24R 1.2	23 35.5	28 46.0	12 2.2	6 .2	21R 3.9	7 51.5	6 9.3
3	4 44 18.2	10 4.3	0 15.6	17 25.9	23 46.0	24 42.5	29 28.4	12 15.7	6 6.8	21 3.6	7 53.4	6 9.5
4	4 48 14.7	11 5.2	0 12.5	2♒ 3.0	23 41.8	25 49.8	0♐10.9	12 29.3	6 13.4	21 3.2	7 55.4	6 9.6
5	4 52 11.3	12 6.1	0 9.3	16 11.6	23D48.1	26 57.3	0 53.5	12 42.8	6 20.1	21 2.8	7 57.3	6 9.8
6	4 56 7.8	13 7.0	0 6.1	29 50.6	24 4.1	28 5.0	1 36.0	12 56.3	6 26.8	21 2.4	7 59.3	6 9.9
7	5 0 4.4	14 7.9	0 2.9	13♓ 1.8	24 28.9	29 12.9	2 18.7	13 9.8	6 33.5	21 1.8	8 1.2	6 9.9
8	5 4 1.0	15 8.9	29♍59.8	25 48.9	25 1.8	0♏21.0	3 1.3	13 23.4	6 40.3	21 1.3	8 3.1	6 10.0
9	5 7 57.5	16 9.8	29 56.6	8♈16.4	25 41.8	1 29.3	3 44.1	13 36.9	6 47.0	21 .6	8 4.9	6 10.0
10	5 11 54.1	17 10.8	29 53.4	20 29.2	26 28.2	2 37.8	4 26.8	13 50.4	6 53.8	20 59.9	8 6.8	6 10.0
11	5 15 50.6	18 11.7	29 50.2	2♉31.6	27 20.2	3 46.5	5 9.6	14 4.0	7 .6	20 59.2	8 8.6	6R 9.9
12	5 19 47.2	19 12.7	29 47.1	14 27.7	28 17.1	4 55.4	5 52.5	14 17.5	7 7.5	20 58.4	8 10.4	6 9.9
13	5 23 43.7	20 13.7	29 43.9	26 20.3	29 18.3	6 4.4	6 35.4	14 31.0	7 14.4	20 57.6	8 12.2	6 9.7
14	5 27 40.3	21 14.7	29 40.7	8♊11.9	0♐23.2	7 13.6	7 18.3	14 44.5	7 21.3	20 56.7	8 14.0	6 9.6
15	5 31 36.8	22 15.7	29 37.5	20 4.3	1 31.5	8 22.9	8 1.3	14 58.0	7 28.2	20 55.8	8 15.7	6 9.4
16	5 35 33.4	23 16.8	29 34.3	1♋58.8	2 42.6	9 32.4	8 44.3	15 11.5	7 35.1	20 54.7	8 17.5	6 9.2
17	5 39 30.0	24 17.8	29 31.2	13 56.6	3 56.2	10 42.1	9 27.4	15 25.0	7 42.1	20 53.7	8 19.2	6 8.9
18	5 43 26.5	25 18.9	29 28.0	25 58.9	5 11.9	11 51.9	10 10.5	15 38.4	7 49.0	20 52.6	8 20.8	6 8.7
19	5 47 23.1	26 19.9	29 24.8	8♌ 7.4	6 29.6	13 1.9	10 53.7	15 51.9	7 56.0	20 51.4	8 22.5	6 8.4
20	5 51 19.6	27 21.0	29 21.6	20 24.3	7 48.9	14 12.0	11 36.9	16 5.3	8 3.0	20 50.2	8 24.1	6 8.0
21	5 55 16.2	28 22.1	29 18.5	2♍52.7	9 9.7	15 22.2	12 20.1	16 18.7	8 10.0	20 49.0	8 25.7	6 7.7
22	5 59 12.7	29 23.2	29 15.3	15 35.8	10 31.7	16 32.6	13 3.4	16 32.1	8 17.1	20 47.7	8 27.3	6 7.3
23	6 3 9.3	0♑24.3	29 12.1	28 37.8	11 54.9	17 43.1	13 46.8	16 45.5	8 24.1	20 46.3	8 28.9	6 6.8
24	6 7 5.9	1 25.4	29 8.9	12♎ 2.2	13 19.1	18 53.7	14 30.2	16 58.8	8 31.1	20 44.9	8 30.4	6 6.4
25	6 11 2.4	2 26.6	29 5.8	25 52.2	14 44.1	20 4.5	15 13.6	17 12.2	8 38.2	20 43.5	8 31.9	6 5.9
26	6 14 59.0	3 27.7	29 2.6	10♏ 8.9	16 10.0	21 15.4	15 57.1	17 25.5	8 45.3	20 42.0	8 33.4	6 5.4
27	6 18 55.5	4 28.9	28 59.4	24 51.0	17 36.6	22 26.3	16 40.6	17 38.7	8 52.3	20 40.4	8 34.8	6 4.8
28	6 22 52.1	5 30.0	28 56.2	9♐53.5	19 3.8	23 37.4	17 24.2	17 52.0	8 59.4	20 38.9	8 36.2	6 4.3
29	6 26 48.6	6 31.2	28 53.0	25 8.1	20 31.6	24 48.6	18 7.8	18 5.2	9 6.5	20 37.2	8 37.6	6 3.7
30	6 30 45.2	7 32.4	28 49.9	10♑24.0	21 59.9	25 59.9	18 51.5	18 18.4	9 13.6	20 35.6	8 39.0	6 3.0
31	6 34 41.8	8 33.6	28 46.7	25 29.8	23 28.8	27 11.3	19 35.2	18 31.6	9 20.7	20 33.8	8 40.3	6 2.4

LATITUDE

DAY	EPHEM. SID. TIME	☉	☊	☽	☿	♀	♂	♃	♄	♅	♆	♇
1	4 36 25.1	0 .0	0 .0	4N53.1	2N22.9	2N 9.7	0S 2.9	0N30.6	0N35.1	0N42.5	1N43.2	12N15.1
4	4 48 14.7	0 .0	0 .0	4 20.1	2 38.6	2 15.7	0 4.7	0 30.4	0 34.9	0 42.6	1 43.3	12 16.4
7	5 0 4.4	0 .0	0 .0	1 34.0	2 39.2	2 20.5	0 6.6	0 30.1	0 34.6	0 42.8	1 43.4	12 17.7
10	5 11 54.1	0 .0	0 .0	1S41.3	2 29.3	2 24.1	0 8.4	0 29.9	0 34.3	0 42.9	1 43.5	12 19.0
13	5 23 43.7	0 .0	0 .0	4 8.4	2 12.8	2 26.6	0 10.3	0 29.7	0 34.1	0 43.0	1 43.6	12 20.4
16	5 35 33.4	0 .0	0 .0	4 59.2	1 52.4	2 27.9	0 12.1	0 29.4	0 33.8	0 43.1	1 43.8	12 21.7
19	5 47 23.1	0 .0	0 .0	3 54.4	1 29.8	2 28.1	0 14.0	0 29.2	0 33.6	0 43.2	1 43.9	12 22.9
22	5 59 12.7	0 .0	0 .0	1 10.7	1 6.2	2 27.4	0 15.9	0 29.0	0 33.3	0 43.4	1 44.0	12 24.2
25	6 11 2.4	0 .0	0 .0	2N16.4	0 42.6	2 25.6	0 17.8	0 28.8	0 33.1	0 43.5	1 44.2	12 25.5
28	6 22 52.1	0 .0	0 .0	4 44.5	0 19.3	2 23.0	0 19.7	0 28.6	0 32.9	0 43.6	1 44.3	12 26.7
31	6 34 41.8	0 .0	0 .0	4 27.3	0S 3.2	2 19.5	0 21.6	0 28.5	0 32.7	0 43.7	1 44.5	12 27.9

RIGHT ASCENSION

DAY	EPHEM. SID. TIME	☉	☊	☽	☿	♀	♂	♃	♄	♅	♆	♇
1	4 36 25.1	6♐16.7	0♎20.2	16♐31.0	22♏42.5	21♎35.8	25♏47.5	10♐22.2	6♑23.5	23♌41.5	6♏ 2.0	12♍43.0
2	4 40 21.6	7 21.4	0 17.3	2♑32.0	22R17.3	22 39.1	26 31.3	10 36.6	6 30.6	23R41.3	6 3.9	12 43.4
3	4 44 18.2	8 26.3	0 14.4	18 14.3	22 3.2	23 42.7	27 15.3	10 51.1	6 37.8	23 41.0	6 5.8	12 43.8
4	4 48 14.7	9 31.3	0 11.4	3♒18.1	21 59.9	24 46.6	27 59.4	11 5.5	6 45.0	23 40.7	6 7.7	12 44.1
5	4 52 11.3	10 36.4	0 8.5	17 33.6	22D 6.6	25 50.8	28 43.6	11 19.9	6 52.2	23 40.3	6 9.6	12 44.4
6	4 56 7.8	11 41.7	0 5.6	1♓ .5	22 22.8	26 55.3	29 28.0	11 34.4	6 59.4	23 39.8	6 11.5	12 44.7
7	5 0 4.4	12 47.1	0 2.7	13 45.4	22 47.6	28 .0	0♐12.5	11 48.8	7 6.7	23 39.3	6 13.4	12 45.0
8	5 4 1.0	13 52.7	29♍59.8	25 58.6	23 20.3	29 5.1	0 57.2	12 3.3	7 14.0	23 38.8	6 15.2	12 45.2
9	5 7 57.5	14 58.4	29 56.9	7♈51.1	23 60.0	0♏10.4	1 41.9	12 17.7	7 21.3	23 38.2	6 17.0	12 45.4
10	5 11 54.1	16 4.1	29 54.0	19 33.6	24 46.0	1 16.1	2 26.8	12 32.2	7 28.7	23 37.5	6 18.8	12 45.5
11	5 15 50.6	17 10.0	29 51.0	1♉15.2	25 37.8	2 22.0	3 11.9	12 46.7	7 36.1	23 36.8	6 20.6	12 45.7
12	5 19 47.2	18 16.1	29 48.1	13 3.0	26 34.6	3 28.3	3 57.1	13 1.2	7 43.6	23 36.1	6 22.4	12 45.8
13	5 23 43.7	19 22.2	29 45.2	25 1.6	27 35.9	4 34.9	4 42.4	13 15.7	7 51.0	23 35.2	6 24.2	12 45.9
14	5 27 40.3	20 28.3	29 42.3	7♊12.7	28 41.1	5 41.7	5 27.8	13 30.1	7 58.5	23 34.4	6 25.9	12 45.9
15	5 31 36.8	21 34.6	29 39.4	19 35.0	29 50.0	6 48.9	6 13.4	13 44.6	8 5.9	23 33.5	6 27.6	12 45.9
16	5 35 33.4	22 40.9	29 36.5	2♋ 4.8	1♐ 2.1	7 56.4	6 59.0	13 59.0	8 13.4	23 32.5	6 29.3	12 45.9
17	5 39 30.0	23 47.3	29 33.5	14 36.8	2 17.0	9 4.2	7 44.8	14 13.5	8 21.0	23 31.5	6 30.9	12R45.8
18	5 43 26.5	24 53.7	29 30.6	27 6.3	3 34.5	10 12.3	8 30.8	14 27.9	8 28.5	23 30.4	6 32.6	12 45.7
19	5 47 23.1	26 .2	29 27.7	9♌30.0	4 54.4	11 20.8	9 16.8	14 42.4	8 36.1	23 29.3	6 34.2	12 45.6
20	5 51 19.6	27 6.7	29 24.8	21 47.3	6 16.3	12 29.5	10 3.0	14 56.8	8 43.6	23 28.1	6 35.8	12 45.5
21	5 55 16.2	28 13.3	29 21.9	4♍ 1.1	7 40.1	13 38.6	10 49.3	15 11.2	8 51.2	23 26.9	6 37.4	12 45.3
22	5 59 12.7	29 19.9	29 19.0	16 17.1	9 5.7	14 48.1	11 35.7	15 25.6	8 58.8	23 25.6	6 38.9	12 45.1
23	6 3 9.3	0♑26.5	29 16.1	28 43.6	10 32.8	15 57.8	12 22.3	15 39.9	9 6.4	23 24.3	6 40.4	12 44.8
24	6 7 5.9	1 33.1	29 13.1	11♎30.7	12 1.4	17 7.9	13 8.9	15 54.3	9 14.1	23 22.9	6 41.9	12 44.6
25	6 11 2.4	2 39.7	29 10.2	24 49.1	13 31.3	18 18.3	13 55.7	16 8.6	9 21.7	23 21.5	6 43.4	12 44.3
26	6 14 59.0	3 46.3	29 7.3	8♏48.0	15 2.4	19 29.0	14 42.6	16 22.9	9 29.3	23 20.1	6 44.9	12 44.0
27	6 18 55.5	4 52.9	29 4.4	23 32.2	16 34.7	20 40.1	15 29.6	16 37.2	9 37.0	23 18.6	6 46.3	12 43.6
28	6 22 52.1	5 59.5	29 1.5	8♐58.6	18 8.1	21 51.5	16 16.7	16 51.5	9 44.6	23 17.0	6 47.7	12 43.2
29	6 26 48.6	7 6.1	28 58.6	24 53.6	19 42.4	23 3.2	17 3.9	17 5.8	9 52.3	23 15.4	6 49.1	12 42.8
30	6 30 45.2	8 12.6	28 55.7	10♑54.7	21 17.7	24 15.2	17 51.1	17 20.0	9 60.0	23 13.8	6 50.4	12 42.4
31	6 34 41.8	9 19.0	28 52.7	26 36.8	22 53.8	25 27.6	18 38.5	17 34.2	10 7.6	23 12.1	6 51.7	12 41.9

DECLINATION

DAY	EPHEM. SID. TIME	☉	☊	☽	☿	♀	♂	♃	♄	♅	♆	♇
1	4 36 25.1	21S39.1	0S .2	17S57.4	16S34.7	6S44.4	19S46.6	21S42.0	22S43.5	15N 8.8	12S29.5	20N36.1
4	4 48 14.7	22 6.4	0 .1	15 28.7	16 8.2	7 52.4	20 16.1	21 47.6	22 42.9	15 9.3	12 31.4	20 37.1
7	5 0 4.4	22 29.9	0 .0	5 13.2	16 19.1	9 .3	20 44.0	21 53.0	22 42.2	15 9.8	12 33.1	20 38.2
10	5 11 54.1	22 49.4	0 .0	6N26.3	16 56.7	10 7.7	21 10.3	21 58.2	22 41.4	15 10.6	12 34.8	20 39.4
13	5 23 43.7	23 4.9	0N .1	15 18.5	17 50.5	11 14.4	21 34.8	22 3.1	22 40.6	15 11.4	12 36.4	20 40.7
16	5 35 33.4	23 16.3	0 .2	18 26.5	18 52.0	12 19.9	21 57.7	22 7.9	22 39.7	15 12.5	12 38.0	20 42.1
19	5 47 23.1	23 23.4	0 .2	14 27.7	19 55.3	13 23.8	22 18.7	22 12.4	22 38.7	15 13.6	12 39.5	20 43.6
22	5 59 12.7	23 26.4	0 .3	4 35.6	20 56.2	14 25.8	22 37.8	22 16.8	22 37.7	15 14.9	12 40.9	20 45.2
25	6 11 2.4	23 25.1	0 .4	7S52.6	21 51.8	15 25.4	22 55.1	22 20.9	22 36.6	15 16.4	12 42.2	20 46.9
28	6 22 52.1	23 19.6	0 .4	17 14.7	22 40.2	16 22.3	23 10.3	22 24.7	22 35.4	15 18.0	12 43.5	20 48.6
31	6 34 41.8	23 9.9	0 .5	16 39.7	23 20.0	17 16.2	23 23.5	22 28.4	22 34.1	15 19.6	12 44.6	20 50.4

JANUARY 1960

DAY	EPHEM. SID. TIME	☉	☊	☾	☿	♀	♂	♃	♄	♅	♆	♇
	h m s	° ′	° ′	° ′	° ′	° ′	° ′	° ′	° ′	° ′	° ′	° ′
		LONGITUDE										
1	6 38 38.3	9♑34.8	28♍43.5	10♒15.5	24♐58.1	28♏22.8	20♐18.9	18♐44.7	9♑27.8	20♌32.1	8♏41.7	6♍ 1.7
2	6 42 34.9	10 36.0	28 40.3	24 34.4	26 28.0	29 34.4	21 2.8	18 57.9	9 34.9	20 R 30.3	8 43.0	6 R 1.0
3	6 46 31.4	11 37.2	28 37.2	8♓23.4	27 58.2	0♐46.0	21 46.6	19 10.9	9 42.0	20 28.5	8 44.2	6 .3
4	6 50 28.0	12 38.3	28 34.0	21 42.7	29 28.8	1 57.8	22 30.5	19 23.9	9 49.1	20 26.6	8 45.5	5 59.5
5	6 54 24.5	13 39.5	28 30.8	4♈35.2	0♑59.9	3 9.6	23 14.4	19 36.9	9 56.2	20 24.7	8 46.7	5 58.7
6	6 58 21.1	14 40.7	28 27.6	17 5.3	2 31.3	4 21.5	23 58.3	19 49.9	10 3.2	20 22.7	8 47.8	5 57.9
7	7 2 17.7	15 41.8	28 24.5	29 18.2	4 3.2	5 33.4	24 42.3	20 2.8	10 10.3	20 20.7	8 49.0	5 57.0
8	7 6 14.2	16 43.0	28 21.3	11♉18.9	5 35.5	6 45.5	25 26.3	20 15.6	10 17.4	20 18.7	8 50.1	5 56.2
9	7 10 10.8	17 44.1	28 18.1	23 12.5	7 8.2	7 57.6	26 10.4	20 28.4	10 24.4	20 16.6	8 51.1	5 55.3
10	7 14 7.3	18 45.2	28 14.9	5♊ 3.0	8 41.3	9 9.7	26 54.5	20 41.2	10 31.5	20 14.5	8 52.2	5 54.3
11	7 18 3.9	19 46.4	28 11.7	16 54.1	10 14.8	10 22.0	27 38.6	20 53.9	10 38.5	20 12.4	8 53.2	5 53.4
12	7 22 .4	20 47.5	28 8.6	28 48.4	11 48.7	11 34.3	28 22.8	21 6.6	10 45.5	20 10.2	8 54.2	5 52.4
13	7 25 57.0	21 48.6	28 5.4	10♋47.7	13 23.1	12 46.7	29 7.1	21 19.2	10 52.5	20 8.1	8 55.1	5 51.4
14	7 29 53.6	22 49.7	28 2.2	22 53.5	14 58.0	13 59.1	29 51.3	21 31.8	10 59.5	20 5.8	8 56.0	5 50.4
15	7 33 50.1	23 50.8	27 59.0	5♌ 6.6	16 33.3	15 11.6	0♑35.6	21 44.3	11 6.5	20 3.6	8 56.9	5 49.3
16	7 37 46.7	24 51.9	27 55.9	17 27.7	18 9.1	16 24.2	1 20.0	21 56.7	11 13.5	20 1.3	8 57.8	5 48.3
17	7 41 43.2	25 53.0	27 52.7	29 58.0	19 45.4	17 36.8	2 4.4	22 9.2	11 20.4	19 59.0	8 58.6	5 47.2
18	7 45 39.8	26 54.1	27 49.5	12♍38.5	21 22.2	18 49.5	2 48.8	22 21.5	11 27.3	19 56.6	8 59.4	5 46.1
19	7 49 36.3	27 55.2	27 46.3	25 31.3	22 59.6	20 2.2	3 33.3	22 33.8	11 34.2	19 54.3	9 .1	5 45.0
20	7 53 32.9	28 56.2	27 43.2	8♎38.5	24 37.5	21 15.0	4 17.8	22 46.0	11 41.1	19 51.9	9 .9	5 43.8
21	7 57 29.4	29 57.3	27 40.0	22 2.5	26 16.0	22 27.9	5 2.4	22 58.2	11 48.0	19 49.5	9 1.6	5 42.6
22	8 1 26.0	0♒58.4	27 36.8	5♏45.5	27 55.0	23 40.8	5 47.0	23 10.3	11 54.9	19 47.1	9 2.3	5 41.5
23	8 5 22.6	1 59.5	27 33.6	19 48.8	29 34.7	24 53.7	6 31.7	23 22.4	12 1.7	19 44.6	9 2.9	5 40.3
24	8 9 19.1	3 .5	27 30.4	4♐11.8	1♒14.9	26 6.7	7 16.3	23 34.4	12 8.5	19 42.2	9 3.5	5 39.0
25	8 13 15.7	4 1.5	27 27.3	18 51.9	2 55.7	27 19.8	8 1.1	23 46.3	12 15.3	19 39.7	9 4.0	5 37.8
26	8 17 12.2	5 2.6	27 24.1	3♑43.6	4 37.2	28 32.8	8 45.8	23 58.1	12 22.0	19 37.1	9 4.6	5 36.5
27	8 21 8.8	6 3.6	27 20.9	18 39.2	6 19.2	29 46.0	9 30.6	24 9.9	12 28.7	19 34.6	9 5.0	5 35.2
28	8 25 5.3	7 4.6	27 17.7	3♒29.8	8 1.9	0♑59.1	10 15.4	24 21.6	12 35.4	19 32.1	9 5.5	5 33.9
29	8 29 1.9	8 5.6	27 14.6	18 6.7	9 45.3	2 12.3	11 .3	24 33.2	12 42.1	19 29.5	9 5.9	5 32.6
30	8 32 58.4	9 6.6	27 11.4	2♓22.8	11 29.2	3 25.5	11 45.2	24 44.7	12 48.7	19 26.9	9 6.3	5 31.3
31	8 36 55.0	10 7.5	27 8.2	16 13.9	13 13.8	4 38.8	12 30.1	24 56.2	12 55.3	19 24.4	9 6.7	5 29.9
		LATITUDE										
1	6 38 38.3	0 .0	0 .0	3 N 43.3	0 S 10.4	2 N 18.1	0 S 22.2	0 N 28.4	0 N 32.6	0 N 43.7	1 N 44.5	12 N 28.3
4	6 50 28.0	0 .0	0 .0	0 32.4	0 31.3	2 13.5	0 24.2	0 28.2	0 32.4	0 43.8	1 44.6	12 29.4
7	7 2 17.7	0 .0	0 .0	2 S 38.7	0 50.8	2 8.1	0 26.1	0 28.0	0 32.2	0 43.9	1 44.8	12 30.6
10	7 14 7.3	0 .0	0 .0	4 39.3	1 8.5	2 2.1	0 28.0	0 27.9	0 32.0	0 44.0	1 45.0	12 31.6
13	7 25 57.0	0 .0	0 .0	4 53.2	1 24.3	1 55.4	0 29.9	0 27.7	0 31.8	0 44.1	1 45.2	12 32.7
16	7 37 46.7	0 .0	0 .0	3 11.1	1 37.9	1 48.3	0 31.8	0 27.6	0 31.6	0 44.2	1 45.3	12 33.7
19	7 49 36.3	0 .0	0 .0	0 3.7	1 49.1	1 40.6	0 33.7	0 27.4	0 31.5	0 44.2	1 45.5	12 34.6
22	8 1 26.0	0 .0	0 .0	3 N 15.5	1 57.6	1 32.4	0 35.6	0 27.3	0 31.3	0 44.3	1 45.7	12 35.5
25	8 13 15.7	0 .0	0 .0	5 4.0	2 3.0	1 24.0	0 37.5	0 27.2	0 31.1	0 44.3	1 45.9	12 36.4
28	8 25 5.3	0 .0	0 .0	4 2.7	2 5.0	1 15.2	0 39.4	0 27.1	0 31.0	0 44.4	1 46.1	12 37.2
31	8 36 55.0	0 .0	0 .0	0 49.5	2 3.2	1 6.1	0 41.3	0 26.9	0 30.8	0 44.4	1 46.2	12 38.0
		RIGHT ASCENSION										
1	6 38 38.3	10♑25.4	28♍49.8	11♒40.3	24♐30.7	26♏40.2	19♐26.0	17♐48.3	10♑15.3	23♌10.4	6♏53.0	12♍41.4
2	6 42 34.9	11 31.7	28 46.9	25 55.8	26 8.4	27 53.2	20 13.6	18 2.5	10 23.0	23 R 8.7	6 54.3	12 R 40.9
3	6 46 31.4	12 37.9	28 44.0	9♓23.5	27 46.8	29 6.5	21 1.3	18 16.6	10 30.7	23 6.9	6 55.6	12 40.4
4	6 50 28.0	13 44.1	28 41.1	22 10.4	29 25.9	0♐20.1	21 49.0	18 30.6	10 38.3	23 5.1	6 56.8	12 39.8
5	6 54 24.5	14 50.1	28 38.2	4♈26.8	1♑ 5.6	1 34.0	22 36.9	18 44.6	10 46.0	23 3.2	6 57.9	12 39.2
6	6 58 21.1	15 56.0	28 35.3	16 23.6	2 45.9	2 48.2	23 24.8	18 58.6	10 53.6	23 1.3	6 59.1	12 38.5
7	7 2 17.7	17 1.8	28 32.3	28 11.5	4 26.7	4 2.7	24 12.8	19 12.5	11 1.3	22 59.3	7 .2	12 37.9
8	7 6 14.2	18 7.5	28 29.4	9♉59.2	6 8.1	5 17.5	25 .8	19 26.4	11 8.9	22 57.3	7 1.3	12 37.2
9	7 10 10.8	19 13.1	28 26.5	21 53.7	7 49.9	6 32.5	25 48.9	19 40.3	11 16.5	22 55.3	7 2.4	12 36.5
10	7 14 7.3	20 18.5	28 23.6	3♊59.0	9 32.2	7 47.9	26 37.1	19 54.0	11 24.1	22 53.3	7 3.4	12 35.7
11	7 18 3.9	21 23.8	28 20.7	16 16.6	11 15.0	9 3.5	27 25.4	20 7.8	11 31.7	22 51.2	7 4.4	12 35.0
12	7 22 .4	22 28.9	28 17.8	28 44.8	12 58.1	10 19.4	28 13.7	20 21.5	11 39.3	22 49.1	7 5.4	12 34.2
13	7 25 57.0	23 33.9	28 14.8	11♋19.5	14 41.7	11 35.6	29 2.1	20 35.1	11 46.8	22 46.9	7 6.3	12 33.4
14	7 29 53.6	24 38.8	28 11.9	23 55.6	16 25.5	12 52.0	29 50.5	20 48.7	11 54.4	22 44.7	7 7.2	12 32.5
15	7 33 50.1	25 43.5	28 9.0	6♌28.4	18 9.7	14 8.7	0♑39.0	21 2.3	12 1.9	22 42.5	7 8.1	12 31.6
16	7 37 46.7	26 48.0	28 6.1	18 55.0	19 54.2	15 25.6	1 27.5	21 15.7	12 9.4	22 40.3	7 9.0	12 30.8
17	7 41 43.2	27 52.4	28 3.2	1♍15.3	21 38.9	16 42.8	2 16.1	21 29.2	12 16.9	22 38.0	7 9.8	12 29.8
18	7 45 39.8	28 56.6	28 .3	13 32.3	23 23.9	18 .2	3 4.8	21 42.5	12 24.4	22 35.7	7 10.6	12 28.9
19	7 49 36.3	0♒ .6	27 57.4	25 51.9	25 9.1	19 17.8	3 53.4	21 55.8	12 31.8	22 33.4	7 11.3	12 28.0
20	7 53 32.9	1 4.4	27 54.4	8♎22.9	26 54.5	20 35.5	4 42.1	22 9.1	12 39.3	22 31.0	7 12.0	12 27.0
21	7 57 29.4	2 8.1	27 51.5	21 12.9	28 40.0	21 53.5	5 30.9	22 22.2	12 46.7	22 28.7	7 12.7	12 26.0
22	8 1 26.0	3 11.6	27 48.6	4♏33.1	0♒25.8	23 11.8	6 19.7	22 35.4	12 54.1	22 26.3	7 13.4	12 25.0
23	8 5 22.6	4 14.9	27 45.7	18 30.4	2 11.6	24 30.1	7 8.5	22 48.5	13 1.5	22 23.9	7 14.1	12 23.9
24	8 9 19.1	5 18.0	27 42.8	3♐ 7.6	3 57.5	25 48.6	7 57.3	23 1.4	13 8.8	22 21.5	7 14.7	12 22.9
25	8 13 15.7	6 21.0	27 39.9	18 20.1	5 43.4	27 7.2	8 46.2	23 14.3	13 16.1	22 19.0	7 15.2	12 21.8
26	8 17 12.2	7 23.7	27 36.9	3♑54.6	7 29.4	28 26.0	9 35.0	23 27.2	13 23.3	22 16.6	7 15.7	12 20.7
27	8 21 8.8	8 26.2	27 34.0	19 31.4	9 15.4	29 44.8	10 23.9	23 39.9	13 30.6	22 14.1	7 16.2	12 19.6
28	8 25 5.3	9 28.6	27 31.1	4♒49.7	11 1.4	1♑ 3.8	11 12.8	23 52.6	13 37.8	22 11.6	7 16.7	12 18.4
29	8 29 1.9	10 30.7	27 28.2	19 34.1	12 47.3	2 22.9	12 1.7	24 5.2	13 44.9	22 9.0	7 17.1	12 17.2
30	8 32 58.4	11 32.6	27 25.3	3♓37.5	14 33.1	3 42.0	12 50.6	24 17.7	13 52.1	22 6.5	7 17.5	12 16.1
31	8 36 55.0	12 34.3	27 22.4	17 .5	16 18.8	5 1.2	13 39.4	24 30.1	13 59.1	22 4.0	7 17.9	12 14.9
		DECLINATION										
1	6 38 38.3	23 S 5.7	0 N .5	14 S 5.2	23 S 31.2	17 S 33.4	23 S 27.4	22 S 29.6	22 S 33.7	15 N 20.2	12 S 45.0	20 N 51.1
4	6 50 28.0	22 50.5	0 .6	2 47.5	23 57.8	18 22.6	23 37.9	22 33.0	22 32.4	15 22.1	12 46.1	20 53.0
7	7 2 17.7	22 31.1	0 .7	8 N 45.1	24 13.5	19 7.9	23 46.2	22 36.1	22 31.0	15 24.0	12 47.0	20 54.9
10	7 14 7.3	22 7.8	0 .7	16 33.7	24 17.8	19 48.9	23 52.3	22 39.1	22 29.6	15 26.1	12 47.9	20 57.0
13	7 25 57.0	21 40.5	0 .8	18 7.9	24 10.0	20 25.4	23 56.2	22 41.8	22 28.1	15 28.2	12 48.7	20 59.0
16	7 37 46.7	21 9.5	0 .9	12 33.9	23 49.7	20 57.1	23 57.9	22 44.3	22 26.5	15 30.4	12 49.4	21 1.1
19	7 49 36.3	20 34.8	0 .9	1 43.4	23 16.5	21 23.8	23 57.3	22 46.6	22 24.9	15 32.7	12 49.9	21 3.3
22	8 1 26.0	19 56.6	0 1.0	10 S 22.0	22 30.0	21 45.1	23 54.5	22 48.7	22 23.3	15 35.0	12 50.4	21 5.4
25	8 13 15.7	19 15.1	0 1.1	17 55.6	21 30.0	22 1.0	23 49.4	22 50.6	22 21.6	15 37.4	12 50.8	21 7.6
28	8 25 5.3	18 30.3	0 1.1	15 26.4	20 16.4	22 11.1	23 42.0	22 52.3	22 19.9	15 39.9	12 51.1	21 9.8
31	8 36 55.0	17 42.6	0 1.2	4 40.3	18 49.0	22 15.6	23 32.4	22 53.8	22 18.2	15 42.3	12 51.3	21 12.0

FEBRUARY 1960

DAY	EPHEM. SID. TIME	LONGITUDE										
		☉	☊	☾	☿	♀	♂	♃	♄	♅	♆	♇
	h m s	° ′	° ′	° ′	° ′	° ′	° ′	° ′	° ′	° ′	° ′	° ′
1	8 40 51.6	11♒ 8.5	27♍ 5.0	29♓38.3	14♒58.9	5♑52.0	13♑15.1	25♐ 7.6	13♑ 1.8	19♌21.8	9♏ 7.0	5♍28.6
2	8 44 48.1	12 9.4	27 1.9	12♈37.0	16 44.6	7 5.3	14 .1	25 18.8	13 8.3	19R19.2	9 7.3	5R27.2
3	8 48 44.7	13 10.3	26 58.7	25 13.0	18 30.8	8 18.7	14 45.1	25 30.1	13 14.8	19 16.5	9 7.5	5 25.8
4	8 52 41.2	14 11.1	26 55.5	7♉30.5	20 17.4	9 32.0	15 30.2	25 41.2	13 21.2	19 13.9	9 7.7	5 24.4
5	8 56 37.8	15 12.0	26 52.3	19 34.3	22 4.5	10 45.4	16 15.3	25 52.2	13 27.6	19 11.3	9 7.9	5 23.0
6	9 0 34.3	16 12.8	26 49.1	1♊29.6	23 51.9	11 58.8	17 .4	26 3.2	13 34.0	19 8.7	9 8.0	5 21.6
7	9 4 30.9	17 13.6	26 46.0	13 21.1	25 39.5	13 12.3	17 45.6	26 14.1	13 40.3	19 6.0	9 8.1	5 20.1
8	9 8 27.4	18 14.4	26 42.8	25 13.2	27 27.2	14 25.7	18 30.8	26 24.8	13 46.6	19 3.4	9 8.2	5 18.7
9	9 12 24.0	19 15.1	26 39.6	7♋ 9.8	29 14.9	15 39.2	19 16.0	26 35.5	13 52.8	19 .8	9 8.3	5 17.2
10	9 16 20.5	20 15.8	26 36.4	19 14.0	1♓ 2.4	16 52.7	20 1.3	26 46.1	13 59.0	18 58.1	9 8.3	5 15.7
11	9 20 17.1	21 16.5	26 33.3	1♌27.9	2 49.4	18 6.2	20 46.6	26 56.6	14 5.1	18 55.5	9R 8.2	5 14.3
12	9 24 13.7	22 17.3	26 30.1	13 53.0	4 35.8	19 19.8	21 31.9	27 7.0	14 11.3	18 52.9	9 8.2	5 12.8
13	9 28 10.2	23 17.9	26 26.9	26 30.1	6 21.2	20 33.4	22 17.3	27 17.3	14 17.3	18 50.3	9 8.1	5 11.3
14	9 32 6.8	24 18.6	26 23.7	9♍19.4	8 5.3	21 47.0	23 2.7	27 27.5	14 23.3	18 47.7	9 8.0	5 9.8
15	9 36 3.3	25 19.2	26 20.5	22 20.9	9 47.6	23 .6	23 48.1	27 37.6	14 29.2	18 45.1	9 7.9	5 8.3
16	9 39 59.9	26 19.7	26 17.4	5♎34.4	11 27.9	24 14.2	24 33.5	27 47.6	14 35.1	18 42.5	9 7.7	5 6.8
17	9 43 56.4	27 20.3	26 14.2	18 60.0	13 5.6	25 27.9	25 19.0	27 57.5	14 41.0	18 39.9	9 7.4	5 5.3
18	9 47 53.0	28 20.9	26 11.0	2♏37.5	14 40.2	26 41.6	26 4.5	28 7.3	14 46.8	18 37.3	9 7.2	5 3.8
19	9 51 49.5	29 21.4	26 7.8	16 27.0	16 11.1	27 55.2	26 50.1	28 17.0	14 52.5	18 34.7	9 6.9	5 2.2
20	9 55 46.1	0♓21.9	26 4.7	0♐28.1	17 37.7	29 9.0	27 35.6	28 26.5	14 58.2	18 32.1	9 6.6	5 .7
21	9 59 42.6	1 22.4	26 1.5	14 39.8	18 59.4	0♒22.7	28 21.3	28 36.0	15 3.8	18 29.6	9 6.2	4 59.2
22	10 3 39.2	2 22.8	25 58.3	29 .0	20 15.4	1 36.4	29 6.9	28 45.3	15 9.4	18 27.0	9 5.8	4 57.6
23	10 7 35.7	3 23.3	25 55.1	13♑25.6	21 25.2	2 50.2	29 52.5	28 54.5	15 14.9	18 24.5	9 5.4	4 56.1
24	10 11 32.3	4 23.7	25 51.9	27 52.1	22 28.1	4 4.0	0♒38.2	29 3.6	15 20.3	18 22.0	9 4.9	4 54.5
25	10 15 28.8	5 24.1	25 48.8	12♒14.2	23 23.5	5 17.8	1 23.9	29 12.6	15 25.7	18 19.5	9 4.4	4 53.0
26	10 19 25.4	6 24.4	25 45.6	26 26.6	24 10.8	6 31.6	2 9.7	29 21.5	15 31.1	18 17.0	9 3.9	4 51.5
27	10 23 22.0	7 24.8	25 42.4	10♓24.3	24 49.5	7 45.4	2 55.4	29 30.2	15 36.3	18 14.6	9 3.4	4 49.9
28	10 27 18.5	8 25.1	25 39.2	24 3.5	25 19.1	8 59.2	3 41.2	29 38.8	15 41.5	18 12.1	9 2.8	4 48.4
29	10 31 15.1	9 25.3	25 36.1	7♈22.2	25 39.4	10 13.0	4 27.0	29 47.3	15 46.6	18 9.7	9 2.2	4 46.8

DAY	EPHEM. SID. TIME	LATITUDE										
		☉	☊	☾	☿	♀	♂	♃	♄	♅	♆	♇
1	8 40 51.6	0 .0	0 .0	0S22.8	2S 1.6	1N 3.0	0S41.9	0N26.9	0N30.8	0N44.4	1N46.3	12N38.2
4	8 52 41.2	0 .0	0 .0	3 28.2	1 53.8	0 53.8	0 43.8	0 26.8	0 30.6	0 44.5	1 46.5	12 38.9
7	9 4 30.9	0 .0	0 .0	5 3.6	1 41.0	0 44.4	0 45.7	0 26.7	0 30.5	0 44.5	1 46.7	12 39.5
10	9 16 20.5	0 .0	0 .0	4 43.6	1 22.4	0 34.9	0 47.5	0 26.6	0 30.4	0 44.5	1 46.9	12 40.0
13	9 28 10.2	0 .0	0 .0	2 28.4	0 57.8	0 25.5	0 49.4	0 26.5	0 30.2	0 44.5	1 47.0	12 40.5
16	9 39 59.9	0 .0	0 .0	0N58.8	0 26.8	0 16.2	0 51.2	0 26.4	0 30.1	0 44.5	1 47.2	12 41.0
19	9 51 49.5	0 .0	0 .0	4 6.6	0N10.3	0 7.0	0 53.0	0 26.3	0 30.0	0 44.5	1 47.4	12 41.3
22	10 3 39.2	0 .0	0 .0	5 13.6	0 52.3	0S 2.1	0 54.7	0 26.2	0 29.9	0 44.5	1 47.6	12 41.6
25	10 15 28.8	0 .0	0 .0	3 32.9	1 36.9	0 10.9	0 56.5	0 26.1	0 29.8	0 44.5	1 47.7	12 41.9
28	10 27 18.5	0 .0	0 .0	0 3.1	2 20.8	0 19.5	0 58.2	0 26.0	0 29.7	0 44.4	1 47.9	12 42.1

DAY	EPHEM. SID. TIME	RIGHT ASCENSION										
		☉	☊	☾	☿	♀	♂	♃	♄	♅	♆	♇
1	8 40 51.6	13♒35.9	27♍19.4	29♓49.1	18♒ 4.3	6♑20.4	14♑28.3	24♐42.5	14♑ 6.2	22♌ 1.4	7♏18.2	12♍13.6
2	8 44 48.1	14 37.2	27 16.5	12♈12.1	19 49.6	7 39.7	15 17.2	24 54.7	14 13.2	21R58.9	7 18.5	12R12.4
3	8 48 44.7	15 38.3	27 13.6	24 18.8	21 34.6	8 59.0	16 6.0	25 6.9	14 20.2	21 56.3	7 18.8	12 11.2
4	8 52 41.2	16 39.1	27 10.7	6♉18.1	23 19.2	10 18.3	16 54.8	25 19.0	14 27.1	21 53.7	7 19.0	12 9.9
5	8 56 37.8	17 39.8	27 7.8	18 17.4	25 3.5	11 37.5	17 43.6	25 30.9	14 34.0	21 51.1	7 19.2	12 8.6
6	9 0 34.3	18 40.3	27 4.9	0♊22.3	26 47.2	12 56.8	18 32.4	25 42.8	14 40.8	21 48.5	7 19.3	12 7.3
7	9 4 30.9	19 40.6	27 2.0	12 36.0	28 30.3	14 16.0	19 21.2	25 54.6	14 47.6	21 45.9	7 19.5	12 6.0
8	9 8 27.4	20 40.6	26 59.0	24 59.3	0♓12.7	15 35.1	20 9.9	26 6.3	14 54.3	21 43.3	7 19.6	12 4.7
9	9 12 24.0	21 40.5	26 56.1	7♋30.8	1 54.3	16 54.2	20 58.6	26 17.9	15 1.0	21 40.7	7 19.6	12 3.4
10	9 16 20.5	22 40.1	26 53.2	20 7.2	3 34.8	18 13.3	21 47.3	26 29.4	15 7.7	21 38.1	7 19.7	12 2.0
11	9 20 17.1	23 39.6	26 50.3	2♌44.8	5 14.2	19 32.2	22 35.9	26 40.8	15 14.3	21 35.5	7 19.7	12 .7
12	9 24 13.7	24 38.9	26 47.4	15 20.5	6 52.2	20 51.1	22 24.5	26 52.1	15 20.9	21 33.0	7 19.7	11 59.3
13	9 28 10.2	25 37.9	26 44.4	27 52.7	8 28.5	22 9.8	24 13.1	27 3.3	15 27.4	21 30.4	7R19.6	11 58.0
14	9 32 6.8	26 36.8	26 41.5	10♍22.4	10 2.8	23 28.4	25 1.6	27 14.4	15 33.8	21 27.8	7 19.5	11 56.6
15	9 36 3.3	27 35.5	26 38.6	22 53.1	11 34.9	24 46.9	25 50.0	27 25.3	15 40.2	21 25.2	7 19.3	11 55.2
16	9 39 59.9	28 34.0	26 35.7	5♎30.3	13 4.4	26 5.2	26 38.4	27 36.2	15 46.5	21 22.6	7 19.2	11 53.8
17	9 43 56.4	29 32.3	26 32.8	18 21.0	14 30.9	27 23.4	27 26.8	27 46.9	15 52.8	21 20.1	7 19.0	11 52.4
18	9 47 53.0	0♓30.5	26 29.9	1♏32.6	15 54.0	28 41.4	28 15.1	27 57.6	15 59.0	21 17.5	7 18.7	11 50.9
19	9 51 49.5	1 28.5	26 26.9	15 11.3	17 13.2	29 59.2	29 3.3	28 8.1	16 5.2	21 15.0	7 18.5	11 49.5
20	9 55 46.1	2 26.3	26 24.0	29 20.5	18 28.0	1♒16.8	29 51.5	28 18.4	16 11.3	21 12.4	7 18.2	11 48.1
21	9 59 42.6	3 23.9	26 21.1	13♐58.3	19 37.9	2 34.3	0♒39.6	28 28.7	16 17.3	21 9.9	7 17.8	11 46.6
22	10 3 39.2	4 21.4	26 18.2	28 57.2	20 42.3	3 51.6	1 27.7	28 38.9	16 23.3	21 7.4	7 17.5	11 45.2
23	10 7 35.7	5 18.8	26 15.3	14♑ 3.8	21 40.7	5 8.6	2 15.7	28 48.9	16 29.2	21 4.9	7 17.1	11 43.7
24	10 11 32.3	6 15.9	26 12.4	29 2.8	22 32.7	6 25.5	3 3.6	28 58.8	16 35.1	21 2.4	7 16.7	11 42.3
25	10 15 28.8	7 13.0	26 9.4	13♒40.8	23 17.6	7 42.1	3 51.4	29 8.5	16 40.8	20 59.9	7 16.2	11 40.8
26	10 19 25.4	8 9.8	26 6.5	27 49.0	23 55.1	8 58.5	4 39.2	29 18.1	16 46.6	20 57.5	7 15.7	11 39.4
27	10 23 22.0	9 6.6	26 3.6	11♓25.1	24 24.8	10 14.6	5 26.9	29 27.6	16 52.2	20 55.0	7 15.2	11 37.9
28	10 27 18.5	10 3.2	26 .7	24 31.5	24 46.4	11 30.5	6 14.6	29 37.0	16 57.8	20 52.6	7 14.7	11 36.4
29	10 31 15.1	10 59.6	25 57.8	7♈13.6	24 59.6	12 46.2	7 2.1	29 46.2	17 3.3	20 50.2	7 14.1	11 35.0

DAY	EPHEM. SID. TIME	DECLINATION										
		☉	☊	☾	☿	♀	♂	♃	♄	♅	♆	♇
1	8 40 51.6	17S26.0	0N 1.2	0S29.6	18S16.8	22S15.7	23S28.6	22S54.2	22S17.6	15N43.2	12S51.3	21N12.8
4	8 52 41.2	16 34.5	0 1.3	10N44.0	16 31.4	22 12.3	23 16.0	22 55.5	22 15.8	15 45.6	12 51.4	21 15.0
7	9 4 30.9	15 40.4	0 1.3	17 22.9	14 33.1	22 3.0	23 1.1	22 56.6	22 14.1	15 48.1	12 51.4	21 17.2
10	9 16 20.5	14 44.0	0 1.4	17 22.9	12 23.4	21 47.9	22 43.9	22 57.6	22 12.3	15 50.6	12 51.2	21 19.3
13	9 28 10.2	13 45.3	0 1.5	10 21.3	10 4.6	21 26.9	22 24.6	22 58.4	22 10.5	15 53.1	12 51.0	21 21.5
16	9 39 59.9	12 44.5	0 1.5	1S18.8	7 40.7	21 .2	22 3.1	22 59.0	22 8.7	15 55.5	12 50.7	21 23.6
19	9 51 49.5	11 41.9	0 1.6	12 49.0	5 17.6	20 28.0	21 39.5	22 59.6	22 6.9	15 57.9	12 50.3	21 25.6
22	10 3 39.2	10 37.7	0 1.7	18 12.7	3 3.6	19 50.3	21 13.8	22 60.0	22 5.2	16 .3	12 49.8	21 27.7
25	10 15 28.8	9 31.9	0 1.7	13 43.3	1 8.4	19 7.4	20 46.1	23 .3	22 3.4	16 2.6	12 49.2	21 29.6
28	10 27 18.5	8 24.9	0 1.8	2 18.7	0N17.6	18 19.6	20 16.4	23 .5	22 1.7	16 4.8	12 48.5	21 31.5

MARCH 1960

LONGITUDE

DAY	EPHEM. SID. TIME h m s	☉ ° ′	☊ ° ′	☽ ° ′	☿ ° ′	♀ ° ′	♂ ° ′	♃ ° ′	♄ ° ′	♅ ° ′	♆ ° ′	♇ ° ′
1	10 35 11.6	10♓25.6	25♍32.9	20♈19.9	25♓50.2	11♒26.8	5♒12.9	29♐55.7	15♑51.7	18♌ 7.3	9♏ 1.5	4♍45.3
2	10 39 8.2	11 25.8	25 29.7	2♉57.8	25 5.4	12 40.7	5 58.7	0♑ 3.9	15 56.7	18R 5.0	9R .8	4R43.8
3	10 43 4.7	12 26.0	25 26.5	15 18.5	25R43.2	13 54.5	6 44.6	0 12.0	16 1.7	18 2.6	9 .1	4 42.2
4	10 47 1.3	13 26.2	25 23.3	27 25.7	25 25.9	15 8.4	7 30.5	0 20.0	16 6.6	18 .4	8 59.4	4 40.8
5	10 50 57.8	14 26.3	25 20.2	9♊23.6	24 59.9	16 22.2	8 16.4	0 27.8	16 11.4	17 58.1	8 58.7	4 39.3
6	10 54 54.4	15 26.3	25 17.0	21 16.7	24 25.9	17 36.1	9 2.3	0 35.5	16 16.1	17 55.8	8 57.9	4 37.7
7	10 58 50.9	16 26.4	25 13.8	3♋ 9.9	23 44.9	18 49.9	9 48.3	0 43.1	16 20.7	17 53.6	8 57.1	4 36.2
8	11 2 47.5	17 26.4	25 10.6	15 7.6	22 57.7	20 3.8	10 34.2	0 50.5	16 25.3	17 51.4	8 56.2	4 34.7
9	11 6 44.0	18 26.3	25 7.5	27 14.2	22 5.7	21 17.6	11 20.2	0 57.8	16 29.8	17 49.3	8 55.3	4 33.2
10	11 10 40.6	19 26.3	25 4.3	9♌33.0	21 10.0	22 31.5	12 6.2	1 4.9	16 34.3	17 47.1	8 54.4	4 31.8
11	11 14 37.1	20 26.2	25 1.1	22 6.9	20 12.1	23 45.4	12 52.2	1 11.9	16 38.6	17 45.0	8 53.5	4 30.3
12	11 18 33.7	21 26.0	24 57.9	4♍57.5	19 13.3	24 59.2	13 38.3	1 18.7	16 42.9	17 43.0	8 52.5	4 28.8
13	11 22 30.2	22 25.8	24 54.7	18 5.4	18 14.8	26 13.1	14 24.3	1 25.4	16 47.1	17 40.9	8 51.5	4 27.4
14	11 26 26.8	23 25.6	24 51.6	1♎30.2	17 18.0	27 27.0	15 10.4	1 32.0	16 51.2	17 38.9	8 50.5	4 25.9
15	11 30 23.3	24 25.4	24 48.4	15 10.3	16 23.9	28 40.9	15 56.5	1 38.4	16 55.3	17 37.0	8 49.5	4 24.5
16	11 34 19.9	25 25.1	24 45.2	29 3.2	15 33.5	29 54.8	16 42.6	1 44.6	16 59.3	17 35.1	8 48.4	4 23.1
17	11 38 16.4	26 24.8	24 42.0	13♏ 6.0	14 47.6	1♓ 8.6	17 28.7	1 50.7	17 3.1	17 33.2	8 47.3	4 21.7
18	11 42 13.0	27 24.5	24 38.8	27 15.5	14 6.8	2 22.5	18 14.8	1 56.7	17 7.0	17 31.3	8 46.2	4 20.3
19	11 46 9.5	28 24.1	24 35.7	11♐28.7	13 31.6	3 36.4	19 1.0	2 2.5	17 10.7	17 29.5	8 45.1	4 18.9
20	11 50 6.1	29 23.7	24 32.5	25 42.5	13 2.3	4 50.3	19 47.1	2 8.1	17 14.3	17 27.8	8 43.9	4 17.5
21	11 54 2.6	0♈23.3	24 29.3	9♑54.5	12 39.1	6 4.3	20 33.3	2 13.6	17 17.9	17 26.0	8 42.7	4 16.1
22	11 57 59.2	1 22.9	24 26.1	24 2.3	12 22.1	7 18.2	21 19.5	2 18.9	17 21.4	17 24.3	8 41.5	4 14.8
23	12 1 55.8	2 22.4	24 23.0	8♒ 3.8	12 11.1	8 32.1	22 5.7	2 24.0	17 24.8	17 22.7	8 40.3	4 13.5
24	12 5 52.3	3 21.9	24 19.8	21 57.1	12 6.2	9 46.0	22 51.9	2 29.0	17 28.1	17 21.1	8 39.1	4 12.2
25	12 9 48.9	4 21.4	24 16.6	5♓40.2	12D 7.2	10 60.0	23 38.2	2 33.8	17 31.4	17 19.6	8 37.8	4 10.9
26	12 13 45.4	5 20.9	24 13.4	19 11.1	12 13.9	12 13.9	24 24.4	2 38.5	17 34.5	17 18.1	8 36.6	4 9.6
27	12 17 42.0	6 20.3	24 10.2	2♈28.4	12 25.9	13 27.8	25 10.7	2 43.0	17 37.5	17 16.6	8 35.2	4 8.4
28	12 21 38.5	7 19.6	24 7.1	15 30.8	12 43.2	14 41.7	25 56.9	2 47.3	17 40.5	17 15.2	8 33.9	4 7.1
29	12 25 35.1	8 19.0	24 3.9	28 18.0	13 5.4	15 55.6	26 43.1	2 51.4	17 43.4	17 13.8	8 32.6	4 5.9
30	12 29 31.6	9 18.3	24 .7	10♉50.2	13 32.3	17 9.5	27 29.4	2 55.4	17 46.1	17 12.5	8 31.2	4 4.7
31	12 33 28.2	10 17.5	23 57.5	23 8.7	14 3.6	18 23.4	28 15.6	2 59.1	17 48.8	17 11.2	8 29.8	4 3.5

LATITUDE

DAY	SID. TIME	☉	☊	☽	☿	♀	♂	♃	♄	♅	♆	♇
1	10 35 11.6	0 .0	0 .0	2S17.4	2N47.4	0S25.0	0S59.4	0N26.0	0N29.6	0N44.4	1N48.0	12N42.1
4	10 47 1.3	0 .0	0 .0	4 41.7	3 19.3	0 33.0	1 1.0	0 25.9	0 29.5	0 44.4	1 48.2	12 42.2
7	10 58 50.9	0 .0	0 .0	5 13.3	3 37.3	0 40.6	1 2.7	0 25.8	0 29.4	0 44.3	1 48.3	12 42.2
10	11 10 40.6	0 .0	0 .0	3 44.8	3 37.5	0 47.8	1 4.3	0 25.7	0 29.3	0 44.3	1 48.5	12 42.2
13	11 22 30.2	0 .0	0 .0	0 36.3	3 19.8	0 54.6	1 5.9	0 25.6	0 29.2	0 44.2	1 48.6	12 42.1
16	11 34 19.9	0 .0	0 .0	2N59.5	2 47.4	1 .8	1 7.4	0 25.5	0 29.1	0 44.2	1 48.8	12 41.9
19	11 46 9.5	0 .0	0 .0	5 8.8	2 5.7	1 6.5	1 8.9	0 25.5	0 29.0	0 44.1	1 48.9	12 41.6
22	11 57 59.2	0 .0	0 .0	4 36.4	1 20.4	1 11.7	1 10.3	0 25.4	0 28.9	0 44.0	1 49.0	12 41.4
25	12 9 48.9	0 .0	0 .0	1 43.4	0 35.6	1 16.3	1 11.7	0 25.3	0 28.8	0 44.0	1 49.1	12 41.0
28	12 21 38.5	0 .0	0 .0	1S52.7	0S 6.2	1 20.3	1 13.1	0 25.2	0 28.7	0 43.9	1 49.3	12 40.6
31	12 33 28.2	0 .0	0 .0	4 29.4	0 43.6	1 23.8	1 14.4	0 25.1	0 28.6	0 43.8	1 49.4	12 40.2

RIGHT ASCENSION

DAY	SID. TIME	☉	☊	☽	☿	♀	♂	♃	♄	♅	♆	♇
1	10 35 11.6	11♓56.0	25♍54.8	19♈38.5	25♓ 4.3	14♒ 1.6	7♒49.6	29♐55.3	17♑ 8.7	20♌47.9	7♏13.5	11♍33.5
2	10 39 8.2	12 52.2	25 51.9	1♉53.2	25R .7	15 16.8	8 36.9	0♑ 4.2	17 14.1	20R45.5	7R12.8	11R32.0
3	10 43 4.7	13 48.2	25 49.0	14 3.8	24 48.9	16 31.7	9 24.2	0 13.0	17 19.4	20 43.2	7 12.2	11 30.6
4	10 47 1.3	14 44.2	25 46.1	26 15.3	24 29.4	17 46.4	10 11.5	0 21.7	17 24.6	20 41.0	7 11.5	11 29.1
5	10 50 57.8	15 40.0	25 43.2	8♊30.9	24 2.5	19 .8	10 58.6	0 30.2	17 29.8	20 38.7	7 10.8	11 27.7
6	10 54 54.4	16 35.7	25 40.3	20 52.2	23 28.9	20 14.9	11 45.7	0 38.6	17 34.8	20 36.5	7 10.0	11 26.2
7	10 58 50.9	17 31.3	25 37.3	3♋19.0	22 49.7	21 28.8	12 32.6	0 46.8	17 39.8	20 34.3	7 9.2	11 24.8
8	11 2 47.5	18 26.8	25 34.4	15 50.1	22 5.6	22 42.4	13 19.5	0 54.9	17 44.7	20 32.1	7 8.4	11 23.3
9	11 6 44.0	19 22.2	25 31.5	28 23.5	21 17.8	23 55.7	14 6.2	1 2.8	17 49.5	20 29.9	7 7.6	11 21.9
10	11 10 40.6	20 17.5	25 28.6	10♌57.7	20 27.6	25 8.8	14 52.9	1 10.5	17 54.3	20 27.8	7 6.7	11 20.4
11	11 14 37.1	21 12.7	25 25.7	23 32.3	19 36.0	26 21.7	15 39.5	1 18.1	17 59.0	20 25.7	7 5.8	11 19.0
12	11 18 33.7	22 7.9	25 22.7	6♍ 8.3	18 44.3	27 34.3	16 26.0	1 25.6	18 3.5	20 23.7	7 4.9	11 17.5
13	11 22 30.2	23 2.9	25 19.8	18 48.7	17 53.6	28 46.6	17 12.4	1 32.8	18 8.0	20 21.6	7 4.0	11 16.1
14	11 26 26.8	23 57.9	25 16.9	1♎37.8	17 4.9	29 58.8	17 58.7	1 39.9	18 12.5	20 19.7	7 3.0	11 14.7
15	11 30 23.3	24 52.9	25 14.0	14 41.3	16 19.3	1♓10.6	18 44.9	1 46.9	18 16.8	20 17.7	7 2.0	11 13.3
16	11 34 19.9	25 47.7	25 11.1	28 4.7	15 37.5	2 22.3	19 31.0	1 53.7	18 21.0	20 15.8	7 1.0	11 11.9
17	11 38 16.4	26 42.5	25 8.1	11♏52.1	15 .2	3 33.7	20 17.0	2 .3	18 25.2	20 13.9	6 59.9	11 10.5
18	11 42 13.0	27 37.3	25 5.2	26 5.0	14 27.9	4 44.8	21 3.0	2 6.8	18 29.3	20 12.1	6 58.9	11 9.1
19	11 46 9.5	28 32.0	25 2.3	10♐40.4	14 .9	5 55.8	21 48.8	2 13.0	18 33.3	20 10.3	6 57.8	11 7.7
20	11 50 6.1	29 26.7	24 59.4	25 30.2	13 39.4	7 6.6	22 34.6	2 19.2	18 37.2	20 8.5	6 56.7	11 6.3
21	11 54 2.6	0♈21.4	24 56.5	10♑22.9	13 23.7	8 17.1	23 20.3	2 25.1	18 41.0	20 6.8	6 55.5	11 5.0
22	11 57 59.2	1 16.0	24 53.5	25 5.5	13 13.7	9 27.4	24 5.9	2 30.9	18 44.7	20 5.1	6 54.4	11 3.6
23	12 1 55.8	2 10.7	24 50.6	9♒27.4	13 9.4	10 37.6	24 51.3	2 36.4	18 48.4	20 3.5	6 53.2	11 2.3
24	12 5 52.3	3 5.3	24 47.7	23 22.6	13D10.5	11 47.5	25 36.7	2 41.9	18 51.9	20 1.9	6 52.0	11 1.0
25	12 9 48.9	3 59.9	24 44.8	6♓49.8	13 17.1	12 57.3	26 22.1	2 47.1	18 55.4	20 .4	6 50.8	10 59.7
26	12 13 45.4	4 54.5	24 41.9	19 51.6	13 28.8	14 6.9	27 7.3	2 52.2	18 58.7	19 58.9	6 49.6	10 58.4
27	12 17 42.0	5 49.1	24 38.9	2♈33.2	13 45.4	15 16.3	27 52.4	2 57.0	19 2.0	19 57.4	6 48.3	10 57.2
28	12 21 38.5	6 43.7	24 36.0	15 .9	14 6.6	16 25.6	28 37.4	3 1.7	19 5.2	19 56.0	6 47.0	10 55.9
29	12 25 35.1	7 38.3	24 33.1	27 20.5	14 32.3	17 34.7	29 22.3	3 6.2	19 8.2	19 54.6	6 45.7	10 54.6
30	12 29 31.6	8 32.9	24 30.2	9♉37.3	15 2.2	18 43.6	0♓ 7.2	3 10.5	19 11.2	19 53.3	6 44.4	10 53.4
31	12 33 28.2	9 27.5	24 27.3	21 54.9	15 35.9	19 52.4	0 51.9	3 14.6	19 14.1	19 52.0	6 43.1	10 52.2

DECLINATION

DAY	SID. TIME	☉	☊	☽	☿	♀	♂	♃	♄	♅	♆	♇
1	10 35 11.6	7S39.5	0N 1.9	5N49.4	0N54.3	17S45.0	19S55.6	23S .6	22S .6	16N 6.3	12S48.0	21N32.8
4	10 47 1.3	6 30.7	0 1.9	15 .8	1 14.1	16 49.4	19 22.7	23 .6	21 58.9	16 8.4	12 47.2	21 34.5
7	10 58 50.9	5 21.1	0 2.0	18 11.0	0 50.6	15 49.5	18 48.1	23 .6	21 57.3	16 10.4	12 46.3	21 36.3
10	11 10 40.6	4 10.9	0 2.1	14 14.9	0S10.1	14 45.6	18 11.7	23 .6	21 55.8	16 12.4	12 45.3	21 37.9
13	11 22 30.2	3 .2	0 2.1	4 9.1	1 34.9	13 38.1	17 33.7	23 .4	21 54.3	16 14.2	12 44.2	21 39.5
16	11 34 19.9	1 49.2	0 2.2	8S20.4	3 7.3	12 27.1	16 54.0	23 .3	21 52.9	16 16.0	12 43.1	21 40.9
19	11 46 9.5	0 38.1	0 2.2	17 3.7	4 32.5	11 13.1	16 12.9	23 .1	21 51.5	16 17.6	12 41.9	21 42.3
22	11 57 59.2	0N33.0	0 2.3	16 46.0	5 40.9	9 56.3	15 30.3	22 59.9	21 50.3	16 19.1	12 40.7	21 43.5
25	12 9 48.9	1 43.9	0 2.4	7 49.8	6 28.0	8 37.1	14 46.3	22 59.7	21 49.1	16 20.5	12 39.7	21 44.7
28	12 21 38.5	2 54.5	0 2.4	4N22.4	6 52.9	7 15.8	14 1.0	22 59.6	21 48.0	16 21.8	12 38.1	21 45.7
31	12 33 28.2	4 4.5	0 2.5	14 12.8	6 56.6	5 52.6	13 14.5	22 59.4	21 47.0	16 22.9	12 36.7	21 46.7

APRIL 1960

LONGITUDE

DAY	EPHEM. SID. TIME h m s	☉ ° ′	☊ ° ′	☾ ° ′	☿ ° ′	♀ ° ′	♂ ° ′	♃ ° ′	♄ ° ′	♅ ° ′	♆ ° ′	♇ ° ′
1	12 37 24.7	11♈16.7	23♍54.4	5♊15.6	14♓39.2	19♓37.3	29♒ 1.9	3♑ 2.7	17♑51.4	17♌10.0	8♏28.4	4♍ 2.3
2	12 41 21.3	12 15.9	23 51.2	17 13.9	15 18.7	20 51.2	29 48.1	3 6.2	17 53.9	17R 8.8	8R27.0	4R 1.2
3	12 45 17.8	13 15.1	23 48.0	29 7.4	16 2.0	22 5.0	0♓34.4	3 9.4	17 56.3	17 7.7	8 25.6	4 .0
4	12 49 14.4	14 14.2	23 44.8	11♋ .3	16 48.9	23 18.9	1 20.7	3 12.5	17 58.7	17 6.6	8 24.1	3 58.9
5	12 53 10.9	15 13.3	23 41.6	22 57.3	17 39.1	24 32.8	2 6.9	3 15.4	18 .9	17 5.6	8 22.6	3 57.8
6	12 57 7.5	16 12.3	23 38.5	5♌ 3.0	18 32.5	25 46.6	2 53.2	3 18.1	18 3.0	17 4.6	8 21.2	3 56.8
7	13 1 4.0	17 11.3	23 35.3	17 22.1	19 29.0	27 .5	3 39.4	3 20.6	18 5.1	17 3.6	8 19.7	3 55.7
8	13 5 .6	18 10.2	23 32.1	29 58.7	20 28.3	28 14.3	4 25.7	3 23.0	18 7.0	17 2.8	8 18.2	3 54.7
9	13 8 57.1	19 9.2	23 28.9	12♍56.0	21 30.4	29 28.2	5 11.9	3 25.2	18 8.9	17 1.9	8 16.6	3 53.7
10	13 12 53.7	20 8.0	23 25.7	26 15.9	22 35.1	0♈42.0	5 58.1	3 27.2	18 10.6	17 1.1	8 15.1	3 52.7
11	13 16 50.2	21 6.9	23 22.6	9♎58.6	23 42.3	1 55.9	6 44.4	3 29.0	18 12.3	17 .4	8 13.6	3 51.8
12	13 20 46.8	22 5.7	23 19.4	24 2.2	24 51.9	3 9.7	7 30.6	3 30.6	18 13.8	16 59.7	8 12.0	3 50.9
13	13 24 43.3	23 4.5	23 16.2	8♏22.9	26 3.8	4 23.5	8 16.9	3 32.0	18 15.3	16 59.1	8 10.5	3 49.9
14	13 28 39.9	24 3.2	23 13.0	22 55.0	27 17.9	5 37.3	9 3.1	3 33.3	18 16.7	16 58.5	8 8.9	3 49.1
15	13 32 36.4	25 2.0	23 9.9	7♐32.2	28 34.2	6 51.2	9 49.4	3 34.4	18 18.0	16 58.1	8 7.4	3 48.3
16	13 36 33.0	26 .7	23 6.7	22 7.7	29 52.6	8 5.0	10 35.6	3 35.3	18 19.2	16 57.6	8 5.8	3 47.4
17	13 40 29.6	26 59.4	23 3.5	6♑35.9	1♈13.0	9 18.8	11 21.8	3 36.0	18 20.3	16 57.2	8 4.2	3 46.6
18	13 44 26.1	27 58.0	23 .3	20 52.6	2 35.3	10 32.7	12 8.0	3 36.5	18 21.3	16 56.8	8 2.6	3 45.8
19	13 48 22.7	28 56.6	22 57.1	4♒55.5	3 59.6	11 46.5	12 54.2	3 36.8	18 22.1	16 56.5	8 1.0	3 45.1
20	13 52 19.2	29 55.2	22 54.0	18 43.5	5 25.8	13 .3	13 40.4	3 36.9	18 22.9	16 56.2	7 59.4	3 44.3
21	13 56 15.8	0♉53.7	22 50.8	2♓16.8	6 53.9	14 14.1	14 26.6	3R36.8	18 23.6	16 56.0	7 57.7	3 43.6
22	14 0 12.3	1 52.2	22 47.6	15 36.1	8 23.8	15 27.9	15 12.8	3 36.6	18 24.2	16 55.9	7 56.1	3 43.0
23	14 4 8.9	2 50.7	22 44.4	28 42.4	9 55.5	16 41.7	15 59.0	3 36.2	18 24.7	16 55.8	7 54.5	3 42.3
24	14 8 5.4	3 49.2	22 41.3	11♈36.5	11 29.0	17 55.5	16 45.1	3 35.5	18 25.1	16 55.8	7 52.9	3 41.7
25	14 12 2.0	4 47.7	22 38.1	24 18.9	13 4.3	19 9.3	17 31.2	3 34.7	18 25.4	16 55.8	7 51.2	3 41.1
26	14 15 58.5	5 46.1	22 34.9	6♉50.3	14 41.3	20 23.1	18 17.4	3 33.7	18 25.6	16 55.8	7 49.6	3 40.5
27	14 19 55.1	6 44.4	22 31.7	19 11.2	16 20.2	21 36.9	19 3.5	3 32.5	18 25.7	16D56.0	7 47.9	3 40.0
28	14 23 51.6	7 42.8	22 28.5	1♊22.4	18 .8	22 50.6	19 49.5	3 31.1	18 25.7	16 56.1	7 46.3	3 39.5
29	14 27 48.2	8 41.1	22 25.4	13 25.1	19 43.2	24 4.4	20 35.6	3 29.5	18R25.6	16 56.4	7 44.7	3 39.0
30	14 31 44.7	9 39.4	22 22.2	25 21.2	21 27.3	25 18.2	21 21.6	3 27.8	18 25.4	16 56.7	7 43.0	3 38.5

LATITUDE

DAY	EPHEM. SID. TIME	☉	☊	☾	☿	♀	♂	♃	♄	♅	♆	♇
1	12 37 24.7	0 .0	0 .0	4S57.8	0S55.0	1S24.8	1S14.8	0N25.1	0N28.6	0N43.8	1N49.4	12N40.0
4	12 49 14.4	0 .0	0 .0	5 2.3	1 25.6	1 27.4	1 16.0	0 25.0	0 28.5	0 43.7	1 49.5	12 39.5
7	13 1 4.0	0 .0	0 .0	3 10.6	1 50.9	1 29.4	1 17.2	0 24.9	0 28.4	0 43.6	1 49.5	12 38.9
10	13 12 53.7	0 .0	0 .0	0N 9.4	2 11.0	1 30.8	1 18.2	0 24.8	0 28.3	0 43.5	1 49.6	12 38.3
13	13 24 43.3	0 .0	0 .0	3 37.2	2 25.9	1 31.5	1 19.3	0 24.7	0 28.3	0 43.4	1 49.7	12 37.7
16	13 36 33.0	0 .0	0 .0	5 12.0	2 35.7	1 31.6	1 20.3	0 24.5	0 28.2	0 43.3	1 49.7	12 37.0
19	13 48 22.7	0 .0	0 .0	3 56.8	2 40.6	1 31.2	1 21.2	0 24.4	0 28.1	0 43.2	1 49.8	12 36.3
22	14 0 12.3	0 .0	0 .0	0 46.9	2 40.5	1 30.1	1 22.0	0 24.3	0 28.0	0 43.1	1 49.8	12 35.5
25	14 12 2.0	0 .0	0 .0	2S35.8	2 35.6	1 28.5	1 22.8	0 24.1	0 27.9	0 43.0	1 49.8	12 34.7
28	14 23 51.6	0 .0	0 .0	4 44.8	2 26.0	1 26.2	1 23.5	0 24.0	0 27.8	0 42.9	1 49.8	12 33.9

RIGHT ASCENSION

DAY	EPHEM. SID. TIME	☉	☊	☾	☿	♀	♂	♃	♄	♅	♆	♇
1	12 37 24.7	10♈22.2	24♍24.3	4♊15.2	16♓13.4	21♓ 1.1	1♓36.6	3♑18.5	19♑16.9	19♌50.8	6♏41.7	10♍51.0
2	12 41 21.3	11 16.8	24 21.4	16 38.8	16 54.3	22 9.6	2 21.1	3 22.2	19 19.5	19R49.6	6R40.4	10R49.8
3	12 45 17.8	12 11.5	24 18.5	29 4.9	17 38.5	23 18.1	3 5.6	3 25.8	19 22.1	19 48.5	6 39.0	10 48.6
4	12 49 14.4	13 6.2	24 15.6	11♋31.9	18 25.7	24 26.4	3 50.0	3 29.1	19 24.6	19 47.4	6 37.6	10 47.5
5	12 53 10.9	14 1.0	24 12.6	23 58.5	19 15.7	25 34.6	4 34.2	3 32.3	19 27.0	19 46.4	6 36.2	10 46.3
6	12 57 7.5	14 55.8	24 9.7	6♌24.2	20 8.5	26 42.8	5 18.4	3 35.2	19 29.3	19 45.4	6 34.8	10 45.2
7	13 1 4.0	15 50.6	24 6.8	18 49.7	21 3.8	27 50.8	6 2.6	3 38.0	19 31.4	19 44.4	6 33.3	10 44.1
8	13 5 .6	16 45.5	24 3.9	1♍17.5	22 1.4	28 58.8	6 46.6	3 40.5	19 33.5	19 43.5	6 31.9	10 43.1
9	13 8 57.1	17 40.5	24 1.0	13 51.7	23 1.3	0♈ 6.8	7 30.5	3 42.9	19 35.5	19 42.7	6 30.4	10 42.0
10	13 12 53.7	18 35.5	23 58.0	26 38.1	24 3.4	1 14.7	8 14.4	3 45.0	19 37.4	19 41.9	6 28.9	10 41.0
11	13 16 50.2	19 30.5	23 55.1	9♎42.9	25 7.4	2 22.5	8 58.2	3 47.0	19 39.1	19 41.2	6 27.4	10 40.0
12	13 20 46.8	20 25.7	23 52.2	23 12.6	26 13.4	3 30.3	9 41.9	3 48.8	19 40.8	19 40.5	6 25.9	10 39.0
13	13 24 43.3	21 20.9	23 49.3	7♏11.5	27 21.2	4 38.2	10 25.5	3 50.3	19 42.4	19 39.9	6 24.4	10 38.0
14	13 28 39.9	22 16.2	23 46.4	21 40.6	28 30.8	5 46.0	11 9.1	3 51.7	19 43.9	19 39.3	6 22.9	10 37.1
15	13 32 36.4	23 11.6	23 43.4	6♐35.4	29 42.2	6 53.8	11 52.6	3 52.9	19 45.3	19 38.8	6 21.4	10 36.2
16	13 36 33.0	24 7.1	23 40.5	21 45.2	0♈55.2	8 1.6	12 36.1	3 53.9	19 46.5	19 38.3	6 19.9	10 35.3
17	13 40 29.6	25 2.7	23 37.6	6♑55.2	2 9.8	9 9.5	13 19.4	3 54.6	19 47.7	19 37.9	6 18.4	10 34.4
18	13 44 26.1	25 58.3	23 34.7	21 49.8	3 25.9	10 17.4	14 2.7	3 55.2	19 48.8	19 37.5	6 16.8	10 33.5
19	13 48 22.7	26 54.1	23 31.7	6♒17.3	4 43.7	11 25.3	14 45.9	3 55.5	19 49.7	19 37.2	6 15.3	10 32.7
20	13 52 19.2	27 50.0	23 28.8	20 11.8	6 2.9	12 33.3	15 29.0	3 55.6	19 50.6	19 37.0	6 13.7	10 31.9
21	13 56 15.8	28 46.0	23 25.9	3♓33.4	7 23.7	13 41.3	16 12.1	3 55.6	19 51.3	19 36.7	6 12.1	10 31.1
22	14 0 12.3	29 42.1	23 23.0	16 26.6	8 46.0	14 49.4	16 55.1	3R55.3	19 51.9	19 36.6	6 10.6	10 30.3
23	14 4 8.9	0♉38.3	23 20.0	28 58.5	10 9.8	15 57.6	17 38.1	3 54.8	19 52.5	19 36.5	6 9.0	10 29.6
24	14 8 5.4	1 34.6	23 17.1	11♈16.7	11 35.2	17 5.9	18 21.0	3 54.1	19 52.9	19 36.4	6 7.4	10 28.9
25	14 12 2.0	2 31.1	23 14.2	23 28.7	13 2.1	18 14.3	19 3.8	3 53.2	19 53.2	19 36.4	6 5.8	10 28.2
26	14 15 58.5	3 27.7	23 11.3	5♉40.1	14 30.6	19 22.8	19 46.5	3 52.2	19 53.4	19D36.5	6 4.2	10 27.5
27	14 19 55.1	4 24.4	23 8.4	17 55.0	16 .7	20 31.4	20 29.2	3 50.9	19 53.5	19 36.6	6 2.7	10 26.9
28	14 23 51.6	5 21.2	23 5.4	0♊15.2	17 32.5	21 40.2	21 11.9	3 49.4	19 53.5	19 36.8	6 1.1	10 26.3
29	14 27 48.2	6 18.1	23 2.5	12 40.1	19 6.0	22 49.0	21 54.5	3 47.6	19R53.4	19 37.0	5 59.5	10 25.7
30	14 31 44.7	7 15.2	22 59.6	25 7.6	20 41.2	23 58.0	22 37.0	3 45.7	19 53.2	19 37.3	5 57.9	10 25.2

DECLINATION

DAY	EPHEM. SID. TIME	☉	☊	☾	☿	♀	♂	♃	♄	♅	♆	♇
1	12 37 24.7	4N27.8	0N 2.5	16N17.7	6S53.3	5S24.6	12S58.8	22S59.3	21S46.7	16N23.2	12S36.2	21N47.0
4	12 49 14.4	5 36.9	0 2.6	17 57.8	6 31.2	3 59.5	12 10.9	22 59.2	21 45.8	16 24.2	12 34.7	21 47.8
7	13 1 4.0	6 45.1	0 2.7	12 36.2	5 51.8	2 33.4	11 22.0	22 59.1	21 45.0	16 25.0	12 33.2	21 48.5
10	13 12 53.7	7 52.2	0 2.7	1 37.7	4 56.9	1 6.6	10 32.1	22 59.1	21 44.4	16 25.7	12 31.7	21 49.0
13	13 24 43.3	8 58.2	0 2.8	10S52.2	3 47.8	0N20.7	9 41.5	22 59.0	21 43.8	16 26.2	12 30.2	21 49.5
16	13 36 33.0	10 2.9	0 2.9	18 1.1	2 25.8	1 48.2	8 50.0	22 59.1	21 43.4	16 26.5	12 28.6	21 49.8
19	13 48 22.7	11 6.0	0 2.9	15 12.2	0 52.1	3 15.4	7 57.9	22 59.2	21 43.1	16 26.8	12 27.0	21 50.0
22	14 0 12.3	12 7.5	0 3.0	4 57.4	0N52.3	4 42.2	7 5.2	22 59.3	21 42.9	16 26.9	12 25.4	21 50.1
25	14 12 2.0	13 7.3	0 3.1	7N .7	2 46.3	6 8.2	6 12.1	22 59.5	21 42.9	16 26.8	12 23.9	21 50.1
28	14 23 51.6	14 5.1	0 3.1	15 47.3	4 49.0	7 33.0	5 18.5	22 59.7	21 42.9	16 26.6	12 22.3	21 49.9

MAY 1960

DAY	EPHEM. SID. TIME	☉	☊	☽	☿	♀	♂	♃	♄	♅	♆	♇
		LONGITUDE										
	h m s	° ′	° ′	° ′	° ′	° ′	° ′	° ′	° ′	° ′	° ′	° ′
1	14 35 41.3	10♉37.6	22♍19.0	7♋13.4	23♈13.3	26♈31.9	22♓ 7.6	3♑25.8	18♑25.1	16♌57.0	7♏41.4	3♍38.1
2	14 39 37.9	11 35.8	22 15.8	19 5.1	25 1.0	27 45.7	22 53.6	3 R 23.7	18 R 24.7	16 57.4	7 R 39.8	3 R 37.7
3	14 43 34.4	12 34.0	22 12.7	1♌ .2	26 50.6	28 59.4	23 39.6	3 21.4	18 24.2	16 57.8	7 38.1	3 37.4
4	14 47 31.0	13 32.2	22 9.5	13 3.5	28 41.9	0♉13.1	24 25.6	3 18.9	18 23.6	16 58.3	7 36.5	3 37.0
5	14 51 27.5	14 30.3	22 6.3	25 19.8	0♉35.1	1 26.9	25 11.5	3 16.3	18 23.0	16 58.9	7 34.9	3 36.7
6	14 55 24.1	15 28.4	22 3.1	7♍54.1	2 30.1	2 40.6	25 57.4	3 13.5	18 22.2	16 59.6	7 33.3	3 36.5
7	14 59 20.6	16 26.5	21 59.9	20 50.8	4 26.8	3 54.3	26 43.3	3 10.4	18 21.4	17 .2	7 31.7	3 36.2
8	15 3 17.2	17 24.5	21 56.8	4♎13.4	6 25.3	5 8.0	27 29.1	3 7.2	18 20.4	17 .9	7 30.1	3 36.0
9	15 7 13.7	18 22.5	21 53.6	18 3.5	8 25.5	6 21.7	28 14.9	3 3.9	18 19.3	17 1.7	7 28.5	3 35.8
10	15 11 10.3	19 20.5	21 50.4	2♏20.2	10 27.3	7 35.4	29 .7	3 .3	18 18.2	17 2.5	7 26.9	3 35.6
11	15 15 6.8	20 18.4	21 47.2	16 59.8	12 30.8	8 49.1	29 46.5	2 56.6	18 16.9	17 3.4	7 25.3	3 35.5
12	15 19 3.4	21 16.3	21 44.1	1♐55.3	14 35.9	10 2.8	0♈32.2	2 52.7	18 15.6	17 4.3	7 23.7	3 35.4
13	15 22 60.0	22 14.2	21 40.9	16 57.9	16 42.3	11 16.5	1 17.9	2 48.7	18 14.2	17 5.3	7 22.1	3 35.3
14	15 26 56.5	23 12.0	21 37.7	1♑57.8	18 50.1	12 30.2	2 3.6	2 44.5	18 12.7	17 6.3	7 20.6	3 35.3
15	15 30 53.1	24 9.9	21 34.5	16 46.2	20 59.0	13 43.9	2 49.3	2 40.1	18 11.0	17 7.4	7 19.0	3 35.3
16	15 34 49.6	25 7.7	21 31.4	1♒16.8	23 8.8	14 57.5	3 34.9	2 35.6	18 9.3	17 8.5	7 17.5	3 35.3
17	15 38 46.2	26 5.5	21 28.2	15 25.9	25 19.5	16 11.2	4 20.5	2 30.9	18 7.6	17 9.7	7 15.9	3 35.3
18	15 42 42.7	27 3.3	21 25.0	29 12.5	27 30.6	17 24.9	5 6.0	2 26.1	18 5.7	17 11.0	7 14.4	3 D 35.4
19	15 46 39.3	28 1.1	21 21.8	12♓37.7	29 42.0	18 38.6	5 51.6	2 21.1	18 3.7	17 12.2	7 12.9	3 35.5
20	15 50 35.8	28 58.8	21 18.6	25 44.0	1♊53.5	19 52.3	6 37.1	2 15.9	18 1.7	17 13.6	7 11.4	3 35.7
21	15 54 32.4	29 56.5	21 15.5	8♈34.0	4 4.6	21 5.9	7 22.5	2 10.7	17 59.5	17 15.0	7 9.9	3 35.8
22	15 58 28.9	0♊54.2	21 12.3	21 10.6	6 15.2	22 19.6	8 7.9	2 5.2	17 57.3	17 16.4	7 8.4	3 36.0
23	16 2 25.5	1 51.9	21 9.1	3♉36.2	8 25.0	23 33.3	8 53.3	1 59.7	17 55.0	17 17.9	7 7.0	3 36.2
24	16 6 22.1	2 49.6	21 5.9	15 52.7	10 33.7	24 47.0	9 38.6	1 54.0	17 52.6	17 19.4	7 5.6	3 36.5
25	16 10 18.6	3 47.2	21 2.8	28 1.5	12 41.1	26 .6	10 23.9	1 48.1	17 50.1	17 21.0	7 4.1	3 36.8
26	16 14 15.2	4 44.9	20 59.6	10♊ 3.9	14 46.9	27 14.3	11 9.2	1 42.2	17 47.5	17 22.6	7 2.7	3 37.1
27	16 18 11.7	5 42.5	20 56.4	22 .9	16 50.9	28 28.0	11 54.4	1 36.1	17 45.0	17 24.3	7 1.4	3 37.5
28	16 22 8.3	6 40.1	20 53.2	3♋54.0	18 52.9	29 41.7	12 39.6	1 29.9	17 42.2	17 26.1	6 60.0	3 37.9
29	16 26 4.8	7 37.7	20 50.0	15 44.9	20 52.8	0♊55.4	13 24.7	1 23.6	17 39.5	17 27.8	6 58.6	3 38.3
30	16 30 1.4	8 35.2	20 46.9	27 36.0	22 50.4	2 9.0	14 9.7	1 17.2	17 36.6	17 29.7	6 57.3	3 38.7
31	16 33 58.0	9 32.8	20 43.7	9♌30.7	24 45.6	3 22.7	14 54.7	1 10.6	17 33.7	17 31.5	6 56.0	3 39.2
		LATITUDE										
1	14 35 41.3	0 .0	0 .0	4 S 59.0	2 S 11.6	1 S 23.5	1 S 24.1	0 N 23.8	0 N 27.7	0 N 42.8	1 N 49.8	12 N 33.1
4	14 47 31.0	0 .0	0 .0	3 19.4	1 52.7	1 20.1	1 24.6	0 23.6	0 27.5	0 42.7	1 49.8	12 32.2
7	14 59 20.6	0 .0	0 .0	0 13.5	1 29.7	1 16.3	1 25.1	0 23.4	0 27.4	0 42.6	1 49.8	12 31.4
10	15 11 10.3	0 .0	0 .0	3 N 13.0	1 2.9	1 12.0	1 25.4	0 23.3	0 27.3	0 42.5	1 49.8	12 30.5
13	15 22 60.0	0 .0	0 .0	3 2.7	0 33.2	1 7.3	1 25.7	0 23.0	0 27.2	0 42.4	1 49.7	12 29.6
16	15 34 49.6	0 .0	0 .0	3 57.8	0 1.9	1 2.2	1 25.9	0 22.8	0 27.1	0 42.3	1 49.7	12 28.7
19	15 46 39.3	0 .0	0 .0	0 52.2	0 N 29.5	0 56.6	1 26.1	0 22.6	0 26.9	0 42.2	1 49.6	12 27.8
22	15 58 28.9	0 .0	0 .0	2 S 26.3	0 59.1	0 50.8	1 26.1	0 22.3	0 26.8	0 42.1	1 49.6	12 26.8
25	16 10 18.6	0 .0	0 .0	4 35.4	1 24.9	0 44.6	1 26.0	0 22.0	0 26.6	0 42.0	1 49.5	12 25.9
28	16 22 8.3	0 .0	0 .0	4 53.7	1 45.4	0 38.2	1 25.9	0 21.8	0 26.5	0 41.9	1 49.4	12 25.0
31	16 33 58.0	0 .0	0 .0	3 20.0	1 59.5	0 31.5	1 25.7	0 21.5	0 26.3	0 41.8	1 49.3	12 24.1
		RIGHT ASCENSION										
1	14 35 41.3	8♉12.4	22♍56.7	7♋34.8	22♈18.3	25♈ 7.2	23♓19.5	3♑43.6	19♑52.9	19♌37.6	5♏56.3	10♍24.6
2	14 39 37.9	9 9.7	22 53.7	19 58.9	23 57.1	26 16.6	24 1.9	3 R 41.3	19 R 52.5	19 38.0	5 R 54.7	10 R 24.1
3	14 43 34.4	10 7.2	22 50.8	2♌18.2	25 38.0	27 26.1	24 44.3	3 38.8	19 52.0	19 38.4	5 53.1	10 23.7
4	14 47 31.0	11 4.8	22 47.9	14 33.2	27 20.8	28 35.7	25 26.6	3 36.1	19 51.4	19 38.9	5 51.6	10 23.2
5	14 51 27.5	12 2.5	22 45.0	26 46.6	29 5.6	29 45.6	26 8.9	3 33.2	19 50.7	19 39.4	5 50.0	10 22.8
6	14 55 24.1	13 .5	22 42.0	9♍ 3.3	0♉52.6	0♉55.7	26 51.1	3 30.2	19 49.9	19 40.1	5 48.5	10 22.4
7	14 59 20.6	13 58.5	22 39.1	21 30.1	2 41.7	2 6.0	27 33.3	3 26.9	19 49.0	19 40.7	5 46.9	10 22.1
8	15 3 17.2	14 56.6	22 36.2	4♎15.6	4 33.1	3 16.4	28 15.5	3 23.4	19 48.0	19 41.4	5 45.3	10 21.7
9	15 7 13.7	15 54.9	22 33.3	17 28.4	6 26.7	4 27.1	28 57.6	3 19.8	19 46.8	19 42.2	5 43.8	10 21.4
10	15 11 10.3	16 53.3	22 30.3	1♏16.2	8 22.6	5 38.0	29 39.6	3 15.9	19 45.6	19 43.0	5 42.2	10 21.2
11	15 15 6.8	17 51.9	22 27.4	15 43.5	10 20.8	6 49.2	0♈21.6	3 11.9	19 44.3	19 43.8	5 40.7	10 20.9
12	15 19 3.4	18 50.6	22 24.5	0♐48.5	12 21.4	8 .5	1 3.6	3 7.7	19 42.9	19 44.7	5 39.2	10 20.7
13	15 22 60.0	19 49.4	22 21.6	16 21.2	14 24.2	9 12.2	1 45.6	3 3.3	19 41.3	19 45.7	5 37.6	10 20.5
14	15 26 56.5	20 48.4	22 18.6	2♑ 3.7	16 29.3	10 24.0	2 27.5	2 58.7	19 39.7	19 46.7	5 36.1	10 20.3
15	15 30 53.1	21 47.6	22 15.7	17 34.8	18 36.4	11 36.2	3 9.4	2 54.0	19 38.0	19 47.8	5 34.6	10 20.2
16	15 34 49.6	22 46.9	22 12.8	2♒36.4	20 45.7	12 48.6	3 51.3	2 49.1	19 36.2	19 48.9	5 33.1	10 20.1
17	15 38 46.2	23 46.3	22 9.9	16 57.9	22 56.7	14 1.2	4 33.2	2 44.0	19 34.3	19 50.0	5 31.6	10 20.0
18	15 42 42.7	24 45.9	22 6.9	0♓37.2	25 9.5	15 14.1	5 15.0	2 38.7	19 32.3	19 51.3	5 30.1	10 19.9
19	15 46 39.3	25 45.6	22 4.0	13 39.1	27 23.7	16 27.3	5 56.8	2 33.3	19 30.2	19 52.5	5 28.7	10 19.9
20	15 50 35.8	26 45.5	22 1.1	26 11.9	29 39.0	17 40.8	6 38.6	2 27.7	19 28.0	19 53.8	5 27.2	10 19.9
21	15 54 32.4	27 45.5	21 58.2	8♈25.5	1♊55.2	18 54.6	7 20.4	2 22.0	19 25.7	19 55.2	5 25.8	10 19.9
22	15 58 28.9	28 45.6	21 55.2	20 29.1	4 12.0	20 8.6	8 2.1	2 16.1	19 23.4	19 56.6	5 24.3	10 D 20.0
23	16 2 25.5	29 45.9	21 52.3	2♉30.9	6 28.9	21 22.9	8 43.8	2 10.1	19 20.9	19 58.1	5 22.9	10 20.1
24	16 6 22.1	0♊46.3	21 49.4	14 36.8	8 45.7	22 37.5	9 25.5	2 3.9	19 18.4	19 59.6	5 21.5	10 20.2
25	16 10 18.6	1 46.9	21 46.5	26 49.9	11 2.1	23 52.4	10 7.2	1 57.5	19 15.7	20 1.1	5 20.1	10 20.4
26	16 14 15.2	2 47.5	21 43.5	9♊10.8	13 17.6	25 7.5	10 48.9	1 51.0	19 13.0	20 2.7	5 18.8	10 20.6
27	16 18 11.7	3 48.4	21 40.6	21 37.5	15 32.0	26 23.0	11 30.6	1 44.5	19 10.2	20 4.4	5 17.4	10 20.8
28	16 22 8.3	4 49.3	21 37.7	4♋ 5.9	17 44.9	27 38.7	12 12.2	1 37.7	19 7.4	20 6.1	5 16.1	10 21.1
29	16 26 4.8	5 50.3	21 34.8	16 31.5	19 56.1	28 54.7	12 53.8	1 30.9	19 4.4	20 7.9	5 14.8	10 21.3
30	16 30 1.4	6 51.4	21 31.8	28 50.8	22 5.3	0♊11.0	13 35.4	1 23.9	19 1.3	20 9.7	5 13.5	10 21.6
31	16 33 58.0	7 52.6	21 28.9	11♌ 2.1	24 12.3	1 27.5	14 17.0	1 16.8	18 58.2	20 11.5	5 12.2	10 21.9
		DECLINATION										
1	14 35 41.3	15 N .8	0 N 3.2	18 N 16.1	6 N 59.2	8 N 56.3	4 S 24.6	23 S .0	21 S 43.1	16 N 26.2	12 S 20.7	21 N 49.7
4	14 47 31.0	15 54.2	0 3.3	13 42.5	9 15.4	10 17.9	3 30.5	23 .4	21 43.4	16 25.7	12 19.1	21 49.3
7	14 59 20.6	16 45.3	0 3.3	3 25.3	11 35.8	11 37.4	2 36.3	23 .8	21 43.8	16 25.0	12 17.6	21 48.8
10	15 11 10.3	17 33.9	0 3.4	9 S 15.8	13 57.8	12 54.5	1 42.0	23 1.2	21 44.4	16 24.2	12 16.0	21 48.2
13	15 22 60.0	18 19.8	0 3.5	17 46.9	16 18.0	14 8.8	0 47.6	23 1.7	21 45.1	16 23.3	12 14.6	21 47.5
16	15 34 49.6	19 3.0	0 3.5	16 .5	18 31.9	15 20.1	0 N 6.6	23 2.2	21 45.8	16 22.2	12 13.1	21 46.7
19	15 46 39.3	19 43.2	0 3.6	6 1.0	20 34.1	16 28.0	1 .6	23 2.7	21 46.7	16 21.0	12 11.7	21 45.7
22	15 58 28.9	20 20.5	0 3.7	6 N .1	22 19.4	17 32.1	1 54.4	23 3.2	21 47.7	16 19.6	12 10.3	21 44.7
25	16 10 18.6	20 54.6	0 3.7	15 14.7	23 43.4	18 32.2	2 47.9	23 3.7	21 48.8	16 18.1	12 9.0	21 43.6
28	16 22 8.3	21 25.5	0 3.8	18 29.5	24 43.6	19 28.0	3 41.0	23 4.2	21 50.0	16 16.5	12 7.7	21 42.3
31	16 33 58.0	21 53.1	0 3.8	14 39.5	25 19.7	20 19.1	4 33.5	23 4.7	21 51.3	16 14.7	12 6.5	21 41.0

JUNE 1960

DAY	EPHEM. SID. TIME	☉	☊	☾	☿	♀	♂	♃	♄	♅	♆	♇
		LONGITUDE										
	h m s	° ′	° ′	° ′	° ′	° ′	° ′	° ′	° ′	° ′	° ′	° ′
1	16 37 54.5	10♊30.3	20♍40.5	21♌32.7	26♊38.3	4♊36.4	15♈39.7	1♑ 4.0	17♑30.6	17♌33.4	6♏54.7	3♍39.7
2	16 41 51.1	11 27.8	20 37.3	3♍46.6	28 28.5	5 50.0	16 24.6	0R57.2	17R27.6	17 35.4	6R53.4	3 40.2
3	16 45 47.6	12 25.2	20 34.2	16 17.4	0♋16.1	7 3.7	17 9.5	0 50.4	17 24.4	17 37.4	6 52.1	3 40.7
4	16 49 44.2	13 22.7	20 31.0	29 10.0	2 1.0	8 17.3	17 54.3	0 43.5	17 21.2	17 39.4	6 50.9	3 41.3
5	16 53 40.7	14 20.1	20 27.8	12♎28.6	3 43.2	9 31.0	18 39.0	0 36.5	17 17.9	17 41.5	6 49.7	3 41.9
6	16 57 37.3	15 17.5	20 24.6	26 16.3	5 22.7	10 44.7	19 23.7	0 29.4	17 14.6	17 43.7	6 48.5	3 42.6
7	17 1 33.8	16 14.9	20 21.5	10♏33.7	6 59.5	11 58.3	20 8.4	0 22.2	17 11.1	17 45.8	6 47.3	3 43.2
8	17 5 30.4	17 12.2	20 18.3	25 18.0	8 33.5	13 12.0	20 53.0	0 15.0	17 7.7	17 48.1	6 46.1	3 43.9
9	17 9 27.0	18 9.6	20 15.1	10♐23.2	10 4.7	14 25.6	21 37.5	0 7.7	17 4.1	17 50.3	6 45.0	3 44.7
10	17 13 23.5	19 6.9	20 11.9	25 39.7	11 33.0	15 39.3	22 22.0	0 .4	17 .5	17 52.6	6 43.9	3 45.4
11	17 17 20.1	20 4.2	20 8.7	10♑56.3	12 58.5	16 52.9	23 6.4	29♐52.9	16 56.9	17 55.0	6 42.8	3 46.2
12	17 21 16.6	21 1.6	20 5.6	26 1.9	14 21.2	18 6.6	23 50.8	29 45.5	16 53.2	17 57.4	6 41.7	3 47.0
13	17 25 13.2	21 58.9	20 2.4	10♒47.9	15 40.9	19 20.3	24 35.1	29 38.0	16 49.4	17 59.8	6 40.7	3 47.8
14	17 29 9.7	22 56.2	19 59.2	25 8.6	16 57.7	20 33.9	25 19.4	29 30.4	16 45.6	18 2.2	6 39.7	3 48.7
15	17 33 6.3	23 53.4	19 56.0	9♓ 2.2	18 11.4	21 47.6	26 3.6	29 22.9	16 41.8	18 4.7	6 38.7	3 49.6
16	17 37 2.9	24 50.7	19 52.9	22 29.5	19 22.2	23 1.3	26 47.8	29 15.3	16 37.9	18 7.3	6 37.7	3 50.5
17	17 40 59.4	25 48.1	19 49.7	5♈33.1	20 29.8	24 15.0	27 31.9	29 7.7	16 34.0	18 9.9	6 36.8	3 51.5
18	17 44 56.0	26 45.3	19 46.5	18 16.8	21 34.2	25 28.7	28 15.9	29 .0	16 30.0	18 12.5	6 35.9	3 52.5
19	17 48 52.5	27 42.6	19 43.3	0♉44.4	22 35.4	26 42.4	28 59.9	28 52.3	16 25.9	18 15.2	6 35.0	3 53.5
20	17 52 49.1	28 39.9	19 40.2	12 59.8	23 33.2	27 56.1	29 43.8	28 44.7	16 21.9	18 17.9	6 34.1	3 54.5
21	17 56 45.6	29 37.1	19 37.0	25 6.2	24 27.6	29 9.8	0♉27.6	28 37.0	16 17.7	18 20.6	6 33.3	3 55.5
22	18 0 42.2	0♋34.4	19 33.8	7♊ 6.1	25 18.5	0♋23.5	1 11.4	28 29.3	16 13.6	18 23.4	6 32.5	3 56.6
23	18 4 38.8	1 31.7	19 30.6	19 1.6	26 5.8	1 37.3	1 55.1	28 21.6	16 9.4	18 26.2	6 31.7	3 57.7
24	18 8 35.3	2 28.9	19 27.5	0♋54.3	26 49.3	2 51.0	2 38.7	28 14.0	16 5.2	18 29.0	6 31.0	3 58.8
25	18 12 31.9	3 26.1	19 24.3	12 45.7	27 28.9	4 4.7	3 22.2	28 6.4	16 .9	18 31.9	6 30.2	3 60.0
26	18 16 28.4	4 23.4	19 21.1	24 37.3	28 4.6	5 18.5	4 5.7	27 58.7	15 56.7	18 34.8	6 29.5	4 1.2
27	18 20 25.0	5 20.6	19 17.9	6♌30.9	28 36.2	6 32.2	4 49.1	27 51.2	15 52.4	18 37.7	6 28.9	4 2.4
28	18 24 21.5	6 17.8	19 14.7	18 28.7	29 3.5	7 45.9	5 32.4	27 43.6	15 48.1	18 40.7	6 28.2	4 3.6
29	18 28 18.1	7 15.1	19 11.6	0♍33.8	29 26.6	8 59.7	6 15.6	27 36.1	15 43.7	18 43.6	6 27.6	4 4.8
30	18 32 14.7	8♋12.3	19♍ 8.4	12♍49.8	29♋45.3	10♋13.4	6♉58.8	27♐28.7	15♑39.4	18♌46.7	6♏27.0	4♍ 6.1
		LATITUDE										
1	16 37 54.5	0 .0	0 .0	2S28.3	2N 2.7	0S29.2	1S25.6	0N21.4	0N26.3	0N41.7	1N49.3	12N23.8
4	16 49 44.2	0 .0	0 .0	0N44.1	2 7.7	0 22.3	1 25.2	0 21.0	0 26.1	0 41.7	1 49.2	12 22.9
7	17 1 33.8	0 .0	0 .0	3 50.7	2 5.7	0 15.3	1 24.8	0 20.7	0 25.9	0 41.6	1 49.1	12 22.0
10	17 13 23.5	0 .0	0 .0	4 59.0	1 56.9	0 8.2	1 24.2	0 20.4	0 25.7	0 41.5	1 48.9	12 21.2
13	17 25 13.2	0 .0	0 .0	3 9.8	1 41.4	0 1.0	1 23.6	0 20.0	0 25.5	0 41.4	1 48.8	12 20.3
16	17 37 2.9	0 .0	0 .0	0S15.0	1 19.6	0N 6.1	1 22.9	0 19.6	0 25.3	0 41.3	1 48.7	12 19.5
19	17 48 52.5	0 .0	0 .0	3 18.9	0 51.9	0 13.2	1 22.1	0 19.2	0 25.1	0 41.2	1 48.5	12 18.7
22	18 0 42.2	0 .0	0 .0	4 53.9	0 18.6	0 20.2	1 21.2	0 18.8	0 24.9	0 41.2	1 48.4	12 17.9
25	18 12 31.9	0 .0	0 .0	4 34.3	0S19.7	0 27.0	1 20.2	0 18.4	0 24.7	0 41.1	1 48.2	12 17.1
28	18 24 21.5	0 .0	0 .0	2 29.7	1 2.1	0 33.7	1 19.1	0 18.0	0 24.4	0 41.0	1 48.1	12 16.4
		RIGHT ASCENSION										
1	16 37 54.5	8♊54.0	21♍26.0	23♌ 6.6	26♊16.8	2♊44.3	14♈58.6	1♑ 9.5	18♑55.0	20♌13.4	5♏10.9	10♍22.3
2	16 41 51.1	9 55.4	21 23.1	5♍ 8.3	28 18.7	4 1.3	15 40.2	1R 2.2	18R51.7	20 15.4	5R 9.7	10 22.7
3	16 45 47.6	10 56.9	21 20.1	17 13.7	0♋17.8	5 18.6	16 21.8	0 54.8	18 48.3	20 17.3	5 8.4	10 23.1
4	16 49 44.2	11 58.5	21 17.2	29 31.6	2 14.0	6 36.2	17 3.3	0 47.3	18 44.9	20 19.3	5 7.2	10 23.5
5	16 53 40.7	13 .2	21 14.3	12♎12.2	4 7.2	7 54.0	17 44.9	0 39.6	18 41.4	20 21.4	5 6.0	10 24.0
6	16 57 37.3	14 2.0	21 11.3	25 26.1	5 57.3	9 12.0	18 26.4	0 31.9	18 37.8	20 23.5	5 4.8	10 24.5
7	17 1 33.8	15 3.8	21 8.4	9♏22.1	7 44.1	10 30.3	19 8.0	0 24.2	18 34.2	20 25.7	5 3.7	10 25.0
8	17 5 30.4	16 5.7	21 5.5	24 4.8	9 27.7	11 48.8	19 49.5	0 16.3	18 30.5	20 27.9	5 2.6	10 25.6
9	17 9 27.0	17 7.7	21 2.6	9♐31.0	11 7.8	13 7.5	20 31.1	0 8.4	18 26.7	20 30.1	5 1.5	10 26.2
10	17 13 23.5	18 9.8	20 59.6	25 26.7	12 44.6	14 26.4	21 12.6	0 .4	18 22.9	20 32.4	5 .4	10 26.8
11	17 17 20.1	19 11.9	20 56.7	11♑29.5	14 17.9	15 45.5	21 54.2	29♐52.3	18 19.0	20 34.7	4 59.3	10 27.4
12	17 21 16.6	20 14.0	20 53.8	27 14.3	15 47.6	17 4.8	22 35.7	29 44.2	18 15.0	20 37.0	4 58.3	10 28.1
13	17 25 13.2	21 16.2	20 50.8	12♒21.7	17 13.8	18 24.3	23 17.3	29 36.1	18 11.0	20 39.4	4 57.2	10 28.8
14	17 29 9.7	22 18.5	20 47.9	26 42.4	18 36.3	19 43.9	23 58.8	29 27.9	18 7.0	20 41.8	4 56.2	10 29.5
15	17 33 6.3	23 20.8	20 45.0	10♓16.9	19 55.2	21 3.7	24 40.4	29 19.6	18 2.9	20 44.3	4 55.3	10 30.2
16	17 37 2.9	24 23.1	20 42.1	23 12.2	21 10.3	22 23.7	25 22.0	29 11.4	17 58.7	20 46.8	4 54.3	10 31.0
17	17 40 59.4	25 25.5	20 39.1	5♈38.7	22 21.7	23 43.8	26 3.6	29 3.1	17 54.5	20 49.4	4 53.4	10 31.9
18	17 44 56.0	26 27.9	20 36.2	17 47.0	23 29.2	25 4.0	26 45.2	28 54.8	17 50.2	20 52.0	4 52.5	10 32.7
19	17 48 52.5	27 30.3	20 33.3	29 47.3	24 32.9	26 24.3	27 26.8	28 46.4	17 45.9	20 54.6	4 51.7	10 33.5
20	17 52 49.1	28 32.7	20 30.3	11♉47.6	25 32.5	27 44.7	28 8.4	28 38.1	17 41.6	20 57.3	4 50.8	10 34.4
21	17 56 45.6	29 35.1	20 27.4	23 53.5	26 28.2	29 5.2	28 50.0	28 29.7	17 37.2	20 60.0	4 50.0	10 35.3
22	18 0 42.2	0♋37.5	20 24.5	6♊ 7.7	27 19.7	0♋25.7	29 31.6	28 21.4	17 32.7	21 2.7	4 49.2	10 36.3
23	18 4 38.8	1 39.9	20 21.6	18 29.9	28 7.1	1 46.3	0♉13.2	28 13.1	17 28.3	21 5.4	4 48.4	10 37.2
24	18 8 35.3	2 42.3	20 18.6	0♋57.1	28 50.2	3 6.9	0 54.8	28 4.7	17 23.8	21 8.2	4 47.7	10 38.2
25	18 12 31.9	3 44.6	20 15.7	13 24.5	29 29.0	4 27.6	1 36.5	27 56.4	17 19.2	21 11.1	4 47.0	10 39.2
26	18 16 28.4	4 47.0	20 12.8	25 47.4	0♌ 3.3	5 48.2	2 18.1	27 48.2	17 14.7	21 13.9	4 46.3	10 40.3
27	18 20 25.0	5 49.3	20 9.8	8♌ 2.1	0 33.2	7 8.8	2 59.7	27 39.9	17 10.1	21 16.8	4 45.6	10 41.3
28	18 24 21.5	6 51.5	20 6.9	20 7.3	0 58.5	8 29.4	3 41.3	27 31.7	17 5.4	21 19.7	4 45.0	10 42.4
29	18 28 18.1	7 53.7	20 4.0	2♍ 5.0	1 19.1	9 50.0	4 23.0	27 23.6	17 .8	21 22.7	4 44.4	10 43.5
30	18 32 14.7	8♋55.9	20♍ 1.0	13♍59.9	1♌35.1	11♋10.5	5♉ 4.6	27♐15.5	16♑56.1	21♌25.7	4♏43.8	10♍44.7
		DECLINATION										
1	16 37 54.5	22N 1.5	0N 3.9	11N58.9	25N26.6	20N35.0	4N50.9	23S 4.9	21S51.7	16N14.1	12S 6.1	21N40.5
4	16 49 44.2	22 24.5	0 3.9	1 .4	25 33.3	21 19.4	5 42.7	23 5.3	21 53.1	16 12.2	12 4.9	21 39.1
7	17 1 33.8	22 43.9	0 4.0	11S20.3	25 21.0	21 58.5	6 33.8	23 5.8	21 54.5	16 10.2	12 3.9	21 37.5
10	17 13 23.5	22 59.8	0 4.1	18 23.4	24 52.8	22 32.0	7 24.2	23 6.2	21 56.1	16 8.0	12 2.9	21 35.9
13	17 25 13.2	23 12.0	0 4.1	14 28.9	24 11.9	22 59.8	8 13.8	23 6.5	21 57.6	16 5.7	12 2.0	21 34.2
16	17 37 2.9	23 20.5	0 4.2	3 12.6	23 21.4	23 21.6	9 2.5	23 6.8	21 59.3	16 3.3	12 1.1	21 32.5
19	17 48 52.5	23 25.3	0 4.3	8N37.5	22 24.1	23 37.2	9 50.4	23 7.0	22 .9	16 .8	12 .4	21 30.6
22	18 0 42.2	23 26.4	0 4.3	16 40.0	21 23.0	23 46.7	10 37.2	23 7.2	22 2.6	15 58.2	11 59.7	21 28.7
25	18 12 31.9	23 23.8	0 4.4	18 16.7	20 20.7	23 49.8	11 23.0	23 7.3	22 4.4	15 55.5	11 59.1	21 26.7
28	18 24 21.5	23 17.5	0 4.5	12 55.0	19 20.1	23 46.5	12 7.6	23 7.4	22 6.1	15 52.8	11 58.6	21 24.7

JULY 1960

DAY	EPHEM. SID. TIME	☉	☊	☾	☿	♀	♂	♃	♄	♅	♆	♇
	h m s	° ′	° ′	° ′	° ′	° ′	° ′	° ′	° ′	° ′	° ′	° ′
		LONGITUDE										
1	18 36 11.2	9♋ 9.5	19♍ 5.2	25♍20.7	29♋59.4	11♋27.2	7♉41.9	27♐21.3	15♑35.0	18♌49.7	6♏26.5	4♍ 7.4
2	18 40 7.8	10 6.7	19 2.0	8♎11.1	0♌ 8.9	12 40.9	8 24.9	27 R 13.9	15 R 30.6	18 52.8	6 R 26.0	4 8.7
3	18 44 4.3	11 3.9	18 58.9	21 25.1	0 13.8	13 54.7	9 7.8	27 6.7	15 26.2	18 55.9	6 25.5	4 10.0
4	18 48 .9	12 1.1	18 55.7	5♏ 6.0	0 14.1	15 8.5	9 50.6	26 59.5	15 21.8	18 59.1	6 25.0	4 11.4
5	18 51 57.4	12 58.3	18 52.5	19 15.3	0 R 9.6	16 22.2	10 33.3	26 52.3	15 17.4	19 2.2	6 24.6	4 12.8
6	18 55 54.0	13 55.4	18 49.3	3♐52.0	0 .6	17 36.0	11 16.0	26 45.3	15 13.0	19 5.4	6 24.2	4 14.2
7	18 59 50.6	14 52.6	18 46.2	18 51.3	29♋47.0	18 49.7	11 58.6	26 38.3	15 8.5	19 8.6	6 23.8	4 15.6
8	19 3 47.1	15 49.8	18 43.0	4♑ 5.4	29 29.1	20 3.6	12 41.2	26 31.4	15 4.2	19 11.9	6 23.5	4 17.1
9	19 7 43.7	16 47.0	18 39.8	19 23.7	29 6.9	21 17.3	13 23.6	26 24.6	14 59.7	19 15.2	6 23.2	4 18.6
10	19 11 40.2	17 44.2	18 36.6	4♒34.9	28 40.9	22 31.1	14 5.9	26 17.9	14 55.3	19 18.5	6 22.9	4 20.1
11	19 15 36.8	18 41.4	18 33.4	19 29.2	28 11.3	23 44.9	14 48.1	26 11.3	14 50.9	19 21.8	6 22.7	4 21.6
12	19 19 33.3	19 38.6	18 30.3	3♓59.4	27 38.6	24 58.7	15 30.3	26 4.8	14 46.5	19 25.2	6 22.5	4 23.1
13	19 23 29.9	20 35.8	18 27.1	18 1.9	27 3.2	26 12.5	16 12.4	25 58.4	14 42.1	19 28.5	6 22.3	4 24.7
14	19 27 26.5	21 33.0	18 23.9	1♈36.1	26 25.6	27 26.3	16 54.4	25 52.1	14 37.7	19 31.9	6 22.2	4 26.2
15	19 31 23.0	22 30.2	18 20.7	14 44.0	25 46.6	28 40.1	17 36.3	25 46.0	14 33.4	19 35.3	6 22.0	4 27.8
16	19 35 19.6	23 27.4	18 17.6	27 29.0	25 6.6	29 54.0	18 18.1	25 39.9	14 29.0	19 38.7	6 22.0	4 29.4
17	19 39 16.1	24 24.7	18 14.4	9♉55.3	24 26.5	1♌ 7.8	18 59.8	25 34.0	14 24.7	19 42.2	6 21.9	4 31.1
18	19 43 12.7	25 21.9	18 11.2	22 7.4	23 46.9	2 21.6	19 41.4	25 28.2	14 20.4	19 45.7	6 21.9	4 32.7
19	19 47 9.2	26 19.2	18 8.0	4♊ 9.3	23 8.4	3 35.5	20 22.9	25 22.5	14 16.1	19 49.1	6 21.9	4 34.4
20	19 51 5.8	27 16.4	18 4.9	16 4.7	22 31.9	4 49.3	21 4.3	25 17.0	14 11.8	19 52.7	6 21.9	4 36.0
21	19 55 2.3	28 13.7	18 1.7	27 56.8	21 57.9	6 3.2	21 45.6	25 11.6	14 7.6	19 56.2	6 D 22.0	4 37.7
22	19 58 58.9	29 11.0	17 58.5	9♋48.1	21 27.1	7 17.1	22 26.8	25 6.3	14 3.4	19 59.7	6 22.1	4 39.4
23	20 2 55.5	0♌ 8.3	17 55.3	21 40.5	21 .1	8 30.9	23 7.9	25 1.2	13 59.2	20 3.3	6 22.3	4 41.2
24	20 6 52.0	1 5.6	17 52.1	3♌35.9	20 37.4	9 44.8	23 48.9	24 56.3	13 55.1	20 6.8	6 22.4	4 42.9
25	20 10 48.6	2 3.0	17 49.0	15 35.8	20 19.4	10 58.7	24 29.8	24 51.5	13 51.0	20 10.4	6 22.6	4 44.7
26	20 14 45.1	3 .3	17 45.8	27 42.0	20 6.6	12 12.6	25 10.6	24 46.8	13 46.9	20 14.0	6 22.9	4 46.4
27	20 18 41.7	3 57.7	17 42.6	9♍56.5	19 59.3	13 26.5	25 51.2	24 42.3	13 42.9	20 17.6	6 23.1	4 48.2
28	20 22 38.2	4 55.0	17 39.4	22 21.6	19 57.8	14 40.3	26 31.8	24 38.0	13 38.9	20 21.3	6 23.4	4 50.0
29	20 26 34.8	5 52.4	17 36.3	5♎ .1	20 D 2.2	15 54.3	27 12.2	24 33.9	13 35.1	20 24.9	6 23.8	4 51.9
30	20 30 31.3	6 49.8	17 33.1	17 55.1	20 12.8	17 8.2	27 52.5	24 29.9	13 31.2	20 28.6	6 24.2	4 53.7
31	20 34 27.9	7 47.2	17 29.9	1♏ 9.6	20 29.6	18 22.1	28 32.7	24 26.0	13 27.3	20 32.3	6 24.6	4 55.6
		LATITUDE										
1	18 36 11.2	0 .0	0 .0	0N39.3	1S47.6	0N40.2	1S17.9	0N17.5	0N24.2	0N41.0	1N47.9	12N15.7
4	18 48 .9	0 .0	0 .0	3 43.5	2 34.1	0 46.4	1 16.6	0 17.1	0 24.0	0 40.9	1 47.8	12 15.0
7	18 59 50.6	0 .0	0 .0	5 3.7	3 19.3	0 52.3	1 15.2	0 16.6	0 23.7	0 40.9	1 47.6	12 14.3
10	19 11 40.2	0 .0	0 .0	3 26.6	3 59.8	0 57.8	1 13.8	0 16.2	0 23.4	0 40.8	1 47.4	12 13.7
13	19 23 29.9	0 .0	0 .0	0S 5.3	4 31.8	1 3.0	1 12.2	0 15.7	0 23.2	0 40.8	1 47.3	12 13.2
16	19 35 19.6	0 .0	0 .0	3 19.4	4 51.6	1 7.7	1 10.5	0 15.2	0 22.9	0 40.8	1 47.1	12 12.7
19	19 47 9.2	0 .0	0 .0	4 59.2	4 56.8	1 12.1	1 8.8	0 14.7	0 22.6	0 40.7	1 46.9	12 12.2
22	19 58 58.9	0 .0	0 .0	4 42.1	4 46.7	1 15.9	1 6.9	0 14.2	0 22.3	0 40.7	1 46.7	12 11.7
25	20 10 48.6	0 .0	0 .0	2 37.1	4 22.9	1 19.2	1 5.0	0 13.8	0 22.0	0 40.7	1 46.6	12 11.3
28	20 22 38.2	0 .0	0 .0	0N34.3	3 48.1	1 22.1	1 2.9	0 13.3	0 21.7	0 40.7	1 46.4	12 11.0
31	20 34 27.9	0 .0	0 .0	3 40.9	3 5.6	1 24.3	1 .8	0 12.8	0 21.4	0 40.6	1 46.2	12 10.7
		RIGHT ASCENSION										
1	18 36 11.2	9♋58.0	19♍58.1	25♍59.3	1♌46.3	12♋30.9	5♉46.2	27♐ 7.4	16♑51.5	21♌28.7	4♏43.2	10♍45.8
2	18 40 7.8	10 60.0	19 55.2	8♎12.7	1 52.7	13 51.3	6 27.8	26 R 59.4	16 R 46.8	21 31.7	4 R 42.7	10 47.0
3	18 44 4.3	12 1.9	19 52.2	20 50.8	1 54.3	15 11.5	7 9.5	26 51.5	16 42.1	21 34.8	4 42.2	10 48.2
4	18 48 .9	13 3.8	19 49.3	4♏ 4.6	1 R 51.1	16 31.6	7 51.1	26 43.7	16 37.3	21 37.9	4 41.8	10 49.4
5	18 51 57.4	14 5.6	19 46.4	18 2.8	1 43.1	17 51.6	8 32.7	26 35.9	16 32.6	21 41.0	4 41.3	10 50.7
6	18 55 54.0	15 7.3	19 43.5	2♐49.4	1 30.6	19 11.5	9 14.4	26 28.2	16 27.9	21 44.1	4 40.9	10 52.0
7	18 59 50.6	16 8.9	19 40.5	18 19.5	1 13.5	20 31.2	9 56.0	26 20.6	16 23.1	21 47.3	4 40.6	10 53.3
8	19 3 47.1	17 10.4	19 37.6	4♑17.9	0 52.2	21 50.8	10 37.7	26 13.2	16 18.5	21 50.6	4 40.3	10 54.6
9	19 7 43.7	18 11.9	19 34.7	20 21.0	0 26.7	23 10.1	11 19.3	26 5.8	16 13.7	21 53.8	4 39.9	10 56.0
10	19 11 40.2	19 13.2	19 31.7	6♒ 4.0	29♋57.5	24 29.3	12 1.0	25 58.5	16 9.0	21 57.0	4 39.7	10 57.3
11	19 15 36.8	20 14.4	19 28.8	21 48.8	29 24.9	25 48.3	12 42.6	25 51.3	16 4.3	22 .3	4 39.4	10 58.7
12	19 19 33.3	21 15.5	19 25.9	5♓27.5	28 49.3	27 7.1	13 24.3	25 44.2	15 59.6	22 3.6	4 39.2	11 .1
13	19 23 29.9	22 16.5	19 22.9	19 1.7	28 11.3	28 25.7	14 5.9	25 37.3	15 54.9	22 6.9	4 39.0	11 1.5
14	19 27 26.5	23 17.3	19 20.0	1♈58.9	27 31.5	29 44.0	14 47.5	25 30.5	15 50.2	22 10.2	4 38.8	11 3.0
15	19 31 23.0	24 18.1	19 17.1	14 29.2	26 50.4	1♌ 2.1	15 29.2	25 23.7	15 45.5	22 13.6	4 38.7	11 4.4
16	19 35 19.6	25 18.7	19 14.1	26 43.0	26 8.6	2 20.0	16 10.8	25 17.2	15 40.8	22 17.0	4 38.6	11 5.9
17	19 39 16.1	26 19.2	19 11.2	8♉49.5	25 27.0	3 37.6	16 52.4	25 10.7	15 36.2	22 20.4	4 38.5	11 7.4
18	19 43 12.7	27 19.6	19 8.3	20 56.2	24 46.1	4 55.0	17 34.0	25 4.4	15 31.6	22 23.8	4 38.5	11 8.9
19	19 47 9.2	28 19.9	19 5.3	3♊ 7.8	24 6.7	6 12.1	18 15.6	24 58.2	15 27.0	22 27.2	4 38.5	11 10.5
20	19 51 5.8	29 20.0	19 2.4	15 26.2	23 29.5	7 28.9	18 57.1	24 52.2	15 22.4	22 30.6	4 38.5	11 12.0
21	19 55 2.3	0♌20.0	18 59.5	27 50.7	22 55.1	8 45.5	19 38.7	24 46.4	15 17.9	22 34.1	4 38.5	11 13.6
22	19 58 58.9	1 19.9	18 56.5	10♋17.9	22 24.2	10 1.7	20 20.2	24 40.6	15 13.3	22 37.6	4 D 38.6	11 15.2
23	20 2 55.5	2 19.6	18 53.6	22 43.7	21 57.4	11 17.7	21 1.7	24 35.1	15 8.9	22 41.1	4 38.7	11 16.8
24	20 6 52.0	3 19.1	18 50.6	5♌ 3.9	21 35.2	12 33.5	21 43.2	24 29.7	15 4.4	22 44.6	4 38.9	11 18.5
25	20 10 48.6	4 18.6	18 47.7	17 15.7	21 18.0	13 48.9	22 24.6	24 24.5	15 .0	22 48.1	4 39.1	11 20.1
26	20 14 45.1	5 17.8	18 44.8	29 19.0	21 6.3	15 4.0	23 6.0	24 19.4	14 55.7	22 51.7	4 39.3	11 21.8
27	20 18 41.7	6 17.0	18 41.8	11♍16.2	21 .5	16 18.9	23 47.4	24 14.5	14 51.4	22 55.2	4 39.5	11 23.4
28	20 22 38.2	7 15.9	18 38.9	23 12.6	21 D .8	17 33.4	24 28.8	24 9.8	14 47.1	22 58.8	4 39.8	11 25.1
29	20 26 34.8	8 14.8	18 36.0	5♎15.6	21 7.5	18 47.7	25 10.1	24 5.3	14 42.9	23 2.4	4 40.1	11 26.9
30	20 30 31.3	9 13.5	18 33.0	17 34.4	21 20.7	20 1.7	25 51.4	24 .9	14 38.8	23 6.0	4 40.5	11 28.6
31	20 34 27.9	10 12.0	18 30.1	0♏18.8	21 40.5	21 15.3	26 32.6	23 56.8	14 34.6	23 9.6	4 40.8	11 30.4
		DECLINATION										
1	18 36 11.2	23N 7.5	0N 4.5	2N27.0	18N24.1	23N36.9	12N51.0	23S 7.4	22S 7.9	15N49.9	11S58.2	21N22.6
4	18 48 .9	22 53.9	0 4.6	9S42.6	17 35.5	23 21.0	13 33.3	23 7.4	22 9.6	15 46.9	11 57.8	21 20.5
7	18 59 50.6	22 36.7	0 4.7	17 55.8	16 57.0	22 58.9	14 14.2	23 7.3	22 11.4	15 43.9	11 57.6	21 18.3
10	19 11 40.2	22 16.0	0 4.7	15 46.4	16 30.7	22 30.7	14 53.8	23 7.3	22 13.1	15 40.8	11 57.5	21 16.1
13	19 23 29.9	21 51.8	0 4.8	4 48.8	16 18.2	21 56.5	15 32.1	23 7.2	22 14.8	15 37.6	11 57.4	21 13.8
16	19 35 19.6	21 24.2	0 4.8	7N28.5	16 19.9	21 16.6	16 9.0	23 7.0	22 16.5	15 34.3	11 57.5	21 11.5
19	19 47 9.2	20 53.4	0 4.9	16 4.6	16 34.8	20 31.2	16 44.4	23 6.9	22 18.2	15 31.0	11 57.6	21 9.2
22	19 58 58.9	20 19.4	0 5.0	18 23.5	17 .6	19 40.5	17 18.3	23 6.8	22 19.8	15 27.7	11 57.9	21 6.9
25	20 10 48.6	19 42.3	0 5.0	13 39.5	17 34.2	18 44.9	17 50.8	23 6.8	22 21.4	15 24.2	11 58.2	21 4.6
28	20 22 38.2	19 2.3	0 5.1	3 33.4	18 11.8	17 44.5	18 21.7	23 6.7	22 22.9	15 20.8	11 58.6	21 2.2
31	20 34 27.9	18 19.5	0 5.2	8S25.5	18 49.1	16 39.7	18 51.0	23 6.7	22 24.4	15 17.3	11 59.2	20 59.9

AUGUST 1960

LONGITUDE

DAY	EPHEM. SID. TIME h m s	☉ ° ′	☊ ° ′	☽ ° ′	☿ ° ′	♀ ° ′	♂ ° ′	♃ ° ′	♄ ° ′	♅ ° ′	♆ ° ′	♇ ° ′
1	20 38 24.5	8♌44.6	17♍26.7	14♏46.2	20♋52.7	19♌36.0	29♉12.8	24♐22.3	13♑23.5	20♌35.9	6♏25.0	4♍57.4
2	20 42 21.0	9 42.0	17 23.5	28 46.2	21 22.2	20 49.9	29 52.8	24 R 18.8	13 R 19.8	20 39.6	6 25.5	4 59.3
3	20 46 17.6	10 39.4	17 20.4	13♐ 9.2	21 58.0	22 3.8	0♊32.6	24 15.5	13 16.1	20 43.3	6 26.0	5 1.2
4	20 50 14.1	11 36.8	17 17.2	27 52.3	22 40.1	23 17.6	1 12.3	24 12.4	13 12.5	20 47.0	6 26.5	5 3.1
5	20 54 10.7	12 34.2	17 14.0	12♑49.8	23 28.4	24 31.5	1 51.9	24 9.4	13 8.9	20 50.7	6 27.0	5 5.0
6	20 58 7.2	13 31.7	17 10.8	27 53.7	24 22.8	25 45.4	2 31.4	24 6.6	13 5.4	20 54.4	6 27.6	5 6.9
7	21 2 3.8	14 29.2	17 7.7	12♒54.8	25 23.3	26 59.3	3 10.7	24 4.0	13 2.0	20 58.1	6 28.3	5 8.8
8	21 6 .3	15 26.6	17 4.5	27 44.1	26 29.7	28 13.2	3 49.9	24 1.5	12 58.6	21 1.8	6 28.9	5 10.7
9	21 9 56.9	16 24.1	17 1.3	12♓14.2	27 41.8	29 27.1	4 29.0	23 59.3	12 55.3	21 5.5	6 29.6	5 12.7
10	21 13 53.4	17 21.7	16 58.1	26 20.1	28 59.4	0♍41.0	5 8.0	23 57.2	12 52.0	21 9.3	6 30.3	5 14.6
11	21 17 50.0	18 19.2	16 55.0	9♈59.6	0♌22.3	1 54.9	5 46.8	23 55.3	12 48.9	21 13.0	6 31.0	5 16.6
12	21 21 46.6	19 16.8	16 51.8	23 13.1	1 50.1	3 8.8	6 25.5	23 53.6	12 45.7	21 16.7	6 31.8	5 18.5
13	21 25 43.1	20 14.4	16 48.6	6♉ 2.8	3 22.7	4 22.7	7 4.1	23 52.1	12 42.7	21 20.5	6 32.6	5 20.5
14	21 29 39.7	21 12.0	16 45.4	18 32.2	4 59.7	5 36.6	7 42.5	23 50.7	12 39.7	21 24.2	6 33.5	5 22.5
15	21 33 36.2	22 9.6	16 42.2	0♊45.5	6 40.8	6 50.5	8 20.8	23 49.5	12 36.8	21 27.9	6 34.3	5 24.5
16	21 37 32.8	23 7.3	16 39.1	12 47.3	8 25.5	8 4.4	8 59.0	23 48.6	12 34.0	21 31.7	6 35.2	5 26.5
17	21 41 29.3	24 5.0	16 35.9	24 42.0	10 13.4	9 18.3	9 37.0	23 47.8	12 31.2	21 35.4	6 36.2	5 28.5
18	21 45 25.9	25 2.7	16 32.7	6♋33.4	12 4.2	10 32.2	10 14.8	23 47.2	12 28.6	21 39.1	6 37.1	5 30.5
19	21 49 22.4	26 .5	16 29.5	18 25.4	13 57.5	11 46.2	10 52.6	23 46.8	12 26.0	21 42.9	6 38.2	5 32.5
20	21 53 19.0	26 58.2	16 26.4	0♌20.9	15 52.7	13 .1	11 30.2	23 46.6	12 23.5	21 46.6	6 39.2	5 34.5
21	21 57 15.5	27 56.0	16 23.2	12 22.4	17 49.6	14 14.0	12 7.5	23 46.6	12 21.0	21 50.3	6 40.2	5 36.6
22	22 1 12.1	28 53.8	16 20.0	24 31.8	19 47.7	15 27.9	12 44.8	23 D 46.7	12 18.7	21 54.1	6 41.3	5 38.6
23	22 5 8.6	29 51.7	16 16.8	6♍50.8	21 46.6	16 41.8	13 21.8	23 47.1	12 16.4	21 57.8	6 42.4	5 40.6
24	22 9 5.2	0♍49.5	16 13.6	19 20.7	23 46.1	17 55.7	13 58.8	23 47.6	12 14.2	22 1.5	6 43.5	5 42.6
25	22 13 1.7	1 47.4	16 10.5	2♎ 2.7	25 45.8	19 9.6	14 35.5	23 48.3	12 12.1	22 5.2	6 44.7	5 44.7
26	22 16 58.3	2 45.3	16 7.3	14 57.7	27 45.6	20 23.5	15 12.1	23 49.2	12 10.1	22 8.9	6 45.9	5 46.7
27	22 20 54.9	3 43.3	16 4.1	28 6.9	29 45.0	21 37.4	15 48.5	23 50.3	12 8.2	22 12.6	6 47.1	5 48.7
28	22 24 51.4	4 41.2	16 .9	11♏31.4	1♍44.0	22 51.3	16 24.7	23 51.6	12 6.4	22 16.2	6 48.4	5 50.8
29	22 28 48.0	5 39.2	15 57.8	25 11.6	3 42.4	24 5.2	17 .7	23 53.1	12 4.6	22 19.9	6 49.6	5 52.8
30	22 32 44.5	6 37.2	15 54.6	9♐ 8.0	5 40.1	25 19.1	17 36.6	23 54.7	12 3.0	22 23.5	6 50.9	5 54.8
31	22 36 41.1	7 35.2	15 51.4	23 19.6	7 36.9	26 32.9	18 12.3	23 56.6	12 1.4	22 27.2	6 52.3	5 56.9

LATITUDE

DAY	EPHEM. SID. TIME	☉	☊	☽	☿	♀	♂	♃	♄	♅	♆	♇
1	20 38 24.5	0 .0	0 .0	4N26.4	2S50.4	1N25.0	1S .0	0N12.6	0N21.3	0N40.6	1N46.2	12N10.6
4	20 50 14.1	0 .0	0 .0	5 4.9	2 3.0	1 26.5	0 57.7	0 12.2	0 21.0	0 40.6	1 46.0	12 10.3
7	21 2 3.8	0 .0	0 .0	2 49.7	1 15.4	1 27.4	0 55.4	0 11.7	0 20.7	0 40.6	1 45.8	12 10.1
10	21 13 53.4	0 .0	0 .0	0S58.1	0 29.9	1 27.8	0 52.9	0 11.2	0 20.4	0 40.6	1 45.6	12 10.0
13	21 25 43.1	0 .0	0 .0	4 2.2	0N11.0	1 27.5	0 50.3	0 10.7	0 20.1	0 40.6	1 45.5	12 9.9
16	21 37 32.8	0 .0	0 .0	5 14.1	0 45.7	1 26.6	0 47.6	0 10.3	0 19.7	0 40.6	1 45.3	12 9.8
19	21 49 22.4	0 .0	0 .0	4 24.7	1 12.8	1 25.1	0 44.8	0 9.8	0 19.4	0 40.7	1 45.1	12 9.8
22	22 1 12.1	0 .0	0 .0	1 53.1	1 31.7	1 23.1	0 41.9	0 9.3	0 19.1	0 40.7	1 45.0	12 9.9
25	22 13 1.7	0 .0	0 .0	1N30.5	1 42.6	1 20.4	0 38.9	0 8.9	0 18.8	0 40.7	1 44.8	12 10.0
28	22 24 51.4	0 .0	0 .0	4 22.9	1 46.3	1 17.1	0 35.8	0 8.4	0 18.4	0 40.8	1 44.7	12 10.1
31	22 36 41.1	0 .0	0 .0	5 14.0	1 43.7	1 13.3	0 32.6	0 8.0	0 18.1	0 40.8	1 44.5	12 10.3

RIGHT ASCENSION

DAY	EPHEM. SID. TIME	☉	☊	☽	☿	♀	♂	♃	♄	♅	♆	♇
1	20 38 24.5	11♌10.3	18♍27.2	13♏38.4	22♋ 7.0	22♌28.7	27♉13.8	23♐52.8	14♑30.6	23♌13.2	4♏41.2	11♍32.1
2	20 42 21.0	12 8.5	18 24.2	27 39.9	22 40.3	23 41.8	27 54.9	23 R 49.0	14 R 26.6	23 16.8	4 41.7	11 33.9
3	20 46 17.6	13 6.5	18 21.3	12♐24.7	23 20.3	24 54.6	28 36.0	23 45.3	14 22.6	23 20.4	4 42.1	11 35.7
4	20 50 14.1	14 4.4	18 18.3	27 46.0	24 7.0	26 7.1	29 17.0	23 41.9	14 18.7	23 24.0	4 42.6	11 37.4
5	20 54 10.7	15 2.1	18 15.4	13♑28.4	25 .4	27 19.3	29 58.0	23 38.7	14 14.9	23 27.7	4 43.1	11 39.3
6	20 58 7.2	15 59.7	18 12.5	29 10.9	26 .3	28 31.2	0♊38.9	23 35.6	14 11.1	23 31.3	4 43.7	11 41.1
7	21 2 3.8	16 57.1	18 9.5	14♒33.2	27 6.5	29 42.9	1 19.8	23 32.8	14 7.4	23 34.9	4 44.2	11 42.9
8	21 6 .3	17 54.4	18 6.6	29 21.3	28 18.9	0♍54.3	2 .6	23 30.1	14 3.8	23 38.6	4 44.9	11 44.7
9	21 9 56.9	18 51.5	18 3.7	13♓30.0	29 37.2	2 5.4	2 41.3	23 27.7	14 .3	23 42.2	4 45.5	11 46.6
10	21 13 53.4	19 48.5	18 .7	27 1.3	1♌ 1.2	3 16.3	3 22.0	23 25.4	13 56.8	23 45.9	4 46.2	11 48.4
11	21 17 50.0	20 45.4	17 57.8	10♈ 1.9	2 30.5	4 27.0	4 2.6	23 23.3	13 53.3	23 49.6	4 46.9	11 50.3
12	21 21 46.6	21 42.1	17 54.8	22 40.3	4 4.8	5 37.4	4 43.2	23 21.5	13 50.0	23 53.2	4 47.6	11 52.2
13	21 25 43.1	22 38.6	17 51.9	5♉ 5.1	5 43.7	6 47.5	5 23.6	23 19.8	13 46.7	23 56.9	4 48.4	11 54.1
14	21 29 39.7	23 35.1	17 49.0	17 23.7	7 26.8	7 57.4	6 4.0	23 18.3	13 43.5	24 .5	4 49.1	11 56.0
15	21 33 36.2	24 31.4	17 46.0	29 41.7	9 13.5	9 7.1	6 44.3	23 17.0	13 40.4	24 4.2	4 50.0	11 57.9
16	21 37 32.8	25 27.6	17 43.1	12♊ 2.4	11 3.5	10 16.6	7 24.5	23 16.0	13 37.4	24 7.9	4 50.8	11 59.8
17	21 41 29.3	26 23.6	17 40.1	24 26.6	12 56.1	11 25.9	8 4.6	23 15.1	13 34.4	24 11.5	4 51.7	12 1.7
18	21 45 25.9	27 19.6	17 37.2	6♋53.2	14 51.0	12 35.0	8 44.6	23 14.5	13 31.5	24 15.2	4 52.6	12 3.7
19	21 49 22.4	28 15.4	17 34.3	19 19.6	16 47.5	13 43.9	9 24.6	23 14.1	13 28.8	24 18.9	4 53.6	12 5.7
20	21 53 19.0	29 11.1	17 31.3	1♌42.8	18 45.2	14 52.7	10 4.4	23 13.8	13 26.1	24 22.5	4 54.5	12 7.6
21	21 57 15.5	0♍ 6.7	17 28.4	14 .2	20 43.7	16 1.2	10 44.1	23 13.8	13 23.5	24 26.2	4 55.5	12 9.6
22	22 1 12.1	1 2.1	17 25.4	26 11.2	22 42.5	17 9.6	11 23.6	23 D 13.9	13 20.9	24 29.8	4 56.6	12 11.5
23	22 5 8.6	1 57.5	17 22.5	8♍16.9	24 41.2	18 17.8	12 3.1	23 14.3	13 18.5	24 33.5	4 57.6	12 13.5
24	22 9 5.2	2 52.7	17 19.5	20 20.9	26 39.5	19 25.9	12 42.4	23 14.9	13 16.2	24 37.1	4 58.7	12 15.4
25	22 13 1.7	3 47.8	17 16.6	2♎28.5	28 37.0	20 33.8	13 21.6	23 15.6	13 13.9	24 40.7	4 59.8	12 17.4
26	22 16 58.3	4 42.8	17 13.7	14 47.0	0♍33.7	21 41.6	14 .6	23 16.6	13 11.7	24 44.3	5 .9	12 19.4
27	22 20 54.9	5 37.7	17 10.7	27 24.2	2 29.2	22 49.3	14 39.6	23 17.8	13 9.7	24 47.9	5 2.1	12 21.4
28	22 24 51.4	6 32.5	17 7.8	10♏28.0	4 23.4	23 56.9	15 18.3	23 19.2	13 7.7	24 51.5	5 3.3	12 23.4
29	22 28 48.0	7 27.3	17 4.8	24 4.5	6 16.2	25 4.4	15 56.9	23 20.8	13 5.8	24 55.1	5 4.5	12 25.3
30	22 32 44.5	8 21.9	17 1.9	8♐16.3	8 7.5	26 11.8	16 35.4	23 22.6	13 4.1	24 58.7	5 5.7	12 27.3
31	22 36 41.1	9 16.4	16 58.9	23 .5	9 57.2	27 19.1	17 13.7	23 24.6	13 2.4	25 2.2	5 7.0	12 29.3

DECLINATION

DAY	EPHEM. SID. TIME	☉	☊	☽	☿	♀	♂	♃	♄	♅	♆	♇
1	20 38 24.5	18N 4.6	0N 5.2	12S 1.4	19N .8	16N17.2	19N .4	23S 6.7	22S24.9	15N16.1	11S59.4	20N59.1
4	20 50 14.1	17 18.2	0 5.3	18 20.7	19 30.8	15 7.0	19 27.7	23 6.8	22 26.3	15 12.6	12 .0	20 56.7
7	21 2 3.8	16 29.3	0 5.3	14 13.5	19 49.7	13 53.2	19 53.4	23 6.9	22 27.6	15 9.0	12 .7	20 54.4
10	21 13 53.4	15 38.0	0 5.4	2 20.8	19 52.5	12 36.0	20 17.4	23 7.0	22 28.9	15 5.4	12 1.6	20 52.0
13	21 25 43.1	14 44.4	0 5.5	9N43.5	19 34.9	11 15.8	20 40.0	23 7.3	22 30.1	15 1.9	12 2.5	20 49.7
16	21 37 32.8	13 48.7	0 5.5	17 8.4	18 53.7	9 52.9	21 .9	23 7.6	22 31.2	14 58.3	12 3.5	20 47.4
19	21 49 22.4	12 51.0	0 5.6	17 48.2	17 48.1	8 27.6	21 20.3	23 8.0	22 32.3	14 54.6	12 4.6	20 45.1
22	22 1 12.1	11 51.5	0 5.6	11 34.1	16 19.9	7 .4	21 38.1	23 8.4	22 33.3	14 51.1	12 5.8	20 42.9
25	22 13 1.7	10 50.3	0 5.7	0 34.3	14 32.5	5 31.4	21 54.5	23 8.9	22 34.2	14 47.5	12 7.0	20 40.7
28	22 24 51.4	9 47.6	0 5.8	11S 7.1	12 30.8	4 1.0	22 9.3	23 9.5	22 35.1	14 43.9	12 8.4	20 38.5
31	22 36 41.1	8 43.5	0 5.8	18 2.8	10 19.0	2 29.6	22 22.7	23 10.2	22 35.9	14 40.4	12 9.8	20 36.4

SEPTEMBER 1960

LONGITUDE

DAY	EPHEM. SID. TIME h m s	☉ ° ′	☊ ° ′	☽ ° ′	☿ ° ′	♀ ° ′	♂ ° ′	♃ ° ′	♄ ° ′	♅ ° ′	♆ ° ′	♇ ° ′
1	22 40 37.6	8♍33.3	15♍48.2	7♑44.4	9♍32.7	27♍46.8	18♊47.8	23♐58.6	11♑59.9	22♌30.8	6♏53.6	5♍58.9
2	22 44 34.2	9 31.3	15 45.0	22 18.9	11 27.5	29 .6	19 23.1	24 .8	11 R 58.5	22 34.4	6 55.0	6 .9
3	22 48 30.7	10 29.4	15 41.9	6♒58.1	13 21.2	0♎14.5	19 58.2	24 3.2	11 57.3	22 38.0	6 56.4	6 3.0
4	22 52 27.3	11 27.5	15 38.7	21 36.1	15 13.8	1 28.3	20 33.2	24 5.8	11 56.1	22 41.6	6 57.8	6 5.0
5	22 56 23.8	12 25.7	15 35.5	6♓6.6	17 5.2	2 42.1	21 7.9	24 8.5	11 55.0	22 45.2	6 59.3	6 7.0
6	23 0 20.4	13 23.8	15 32.3	20 23.4	18 55.5	3 56.0	21 42.5	24 11.5	11 53.9	22 48.8	7 .8	6 9.1
7	23 4 16.9	14 22.0	15 29.1	4♈22.0	20 44.7	5 9.8	22 16.8	24 14.6	11 53.0	22 52.3	7 2.3	6 11.1
8	23 8 13.5	15 20.3	15 26.0	17 59.1	22 32.6	6 23.6	22 51.0	24 17.9	11 52.2	22 55.8	7 3.8	6 13.1
9	23 12 10.0	16 18.6	15 22.8	1♉13.6	24 19.5	7 37.4	23 25.0	24 21.4	11 51.5	22 59.4	7 5.4	6 15.1
10	23 16 6.6	17 16.9	15 19.6	14 6.0	26 5.1	8 51.2	23 58.7	24 25.0	11 50.9	23 2.9	7 7.0	6 17.2
11	23 20 3.1	18 15.2	15 16.4	26 38.5	27 49.6	10 5.0	24 32.3	24 28.8	11 50.4	23 6.4	7 8.6	6 19.2
12	23 23 59.7	19 13.6	15 13.3	8♊54.3	29 33.0	11 18.8	25 5.6	24 32.8	11 50.0	23 9.8	7 10.2	6 21.2
13	23 27 56.2	20 12.0	15 10.1	20 57.6	1♎15.3	12 32.5	25 38.7	24 37.0	11 49.6	23 13.3	7 11.9	6 23.2
14	23 31 52.8	21 10.4	15 6.9	2♋52.9	2 56.4	13 46.3	26 11.5	24 41.3	11 49.4	23 16.7	7 13.5	6 25.1
15	23 35 49.3	22 8.9	15 3.7	14 44.7	4 36.5	15 .0	26 44.2	24 45.8	11 49.2	23 20.1	7 15.2	6 27.1
16	23 39 45.9	23 7.4	15 .5	26 37.7	6 15.6	16 13.8	27 16.6	24 50.5	11 49.2	23 23.4	7 16.9	6 29.1
17	23 43 42.4	24 5.9	14 57.4	8♌35.9	7 53.5	17 27.5	27 48.7	24 55.3	11 D 49.3	23 26.8	7 18.7	6 31.1
18	23 47 39.0	25 4.5	14 54.2	20 43.1	9 30.5	18 41.3	28 20.7	25 .3	11 49.4	23 30.1	7 20.4	6 33.0
19	23 51 35.6	26 3.1	14 51.0	3♍2.1	11 6.4	19 55.0	28 52.3	25 5.5	11 49.7	23 33.4	7 22.2	6 35.0
20	23 55 32.1	27 1.7	14 47.8	15 35.2	12 41.3	21 8.7	29 23.7	25 10.8	11 50.0	23 36.7	7 24.0	6 36.9
21	23 59 28.7	28 .4	14 44.7	28 23.5	14 15.3	22 22.5	29 54.9	25 16.3	11 50.5	23 39.9	7 25.8	6 38.8
22	0 3 25.2	28 59.1	14 41.5	11♎27.4	15 48.2	23 36.2	0♋25.7	25 22.0	11 51.0	23 43.2	7 27.7	6 40.7
23	0 7 21.8	29 57.9	14 38.3	24 46.4	17 20.2	24 49.9	0 56.3	25 27.8	11 51.7	23 46.4	7 29.5	6 42.6
24	0 11 18.3	0♎56.7	14 35.1	8♏19.3	18 51.2	26 3.6	1 26.7	25 33.8	11 52.4	23 49.5	7 31.4	6 44.5
25	0 15 14.9	1 55.5	14 31.9	22 4.2	20 21.2	27 17.2	1 56.7	25 39.9	11 53.3	23 52.7	7 33.3	6 46.4
26	0 19 11.4	2 54.3	14 28.8	5♐59.3	21 50.3	28 30.9	2 26.4	25 46.2	11 54.2	23 55.8	7 35.2	6 48.3
27	0 23 8.0	3 53.2	14 25.6	20 2.4	23 18.4	29 44.6	2 55.9	25 52.7	11 55.3	23 58.9	7 37.1	6 50.2
28	0 27 4.5	4 52.0	14 22.4	4♑11.4	24 45.5	0♏58.2	3 25.1	25 59.2	11 56.4	24 1.9	7 39.1	6 52.0
29	0 31 1.1	5 51.0	14 19.2	18 24.1	26 11.6	2 11.8	3 53.9	26 6.0	11 57.7	24 4.9	7 41.0	6 53.8
30	0 34 57.6	6 50.0	14 16.0	2♒38.6	27 36.7	3 25.5	4 22.5	26 12.9	11 59.0	24 8.0	7 43.0	6 55.7

LATITUDE

DAY	EPHEM. SID. TIME	☉	☊	☽	☿	♀	♂	♃	♄	♅	♆	♇
1	22 40 37.6	0 .0	0 .0	4N53.5	1N41.6	1N11.8	0S31.5	0N 7.9	0N18.0	0N40.8	1N44.5	12N10.4
4	22 52 27.3	0 .0	0 .0	2 8.7	1 32.4	1 7.3	0 28.1	0 7.4	0 17.7	0 40.8	1 44.3	12 10.7
7	23 4 16.9	0 .0	0 .0	1S42.9	1 19.3	1 2.1	0 24.6	0 7.0	0 17.3	0 40.9	1 44.2	12 11.0
10	23 16 6.6	0 .0	0 .0	4 31.0	1 3.2	0 56.5	0 20.9	0 6.6	0 17.0	0 40.9	1 44.1	12 11.4
13	23 27 56.2	0 .0	0 .0	5 15.8	0 44.8	0 50.4	0 17.2	0 6.2	0 16.7	0 41.0	1 43.9	12 11.8
16	23 39 45.9	0 .0	0 .0	3 59.2	0 24.7	0 43.8	0 13.3	0 5.8	0 16.4	0 41.1	1 43.8	12 12.3
19	23 51 35.6	0 .0	0 .0	1 8.8	0 3.4	0 36.9	0 9.2	0 5.4	0 16.0	0 41.1	1 43.7	12 12.9
22	0 3 25.2	0 .0	0 .0	2N18.5	0S18.6	0 29.5	0 5.0	0 5.0	0 15.7	0 41.2	1 43.6	12 13.4
25	0 15 14.9	0 .0	0 .0	4 49.7	0 41.0	0 21.8	0 .7	0 4.6	0 15.4	0 41.3	1 43.5	12 14.1
28	0 27 4.5	0 .0	0 .0	4 58.6	1 3.4	0 13.8	0N 3.8	0 4.2	0 15.1	0 41.4	1 43.4	12 14.8

RIGHT ASCENSION

DAY	EPHEM. SID. TIME	☉	☊	☽	☿	♀	♂	♃	♄	♅	♆	♇
1	22 40 37.6	10♍10.9	16♍56.0	8♑7.6	11♍45.3	28♍26.4	17♊51.9	23♐26.8	13♑.8	25♌5.8	5♏8.3	12♍31.3
2	22 44 34.2	11 5.3	16 53.1	23 22.9	13 31.8	29 33.5	18 29.9	23 29.2	12 R 59.3	25 9.3	5 9.6	12 33.3
3	22 48 30.7	11 59.6	16 50.1	8♒30.2	15 16.7	0♎40.7	19 7.7	23 31.8	12 58.0	25 12.9	5 11.0	12 35.3
4	22 52 27.3	12 53.8	16 47.2	23 16.4	17 .1	1 47.8	19 45.4	23 34.5	12 56.7	25 16.4	5 12.3	12 37.3
5	22 56 23.8	13 47.9	16 44.2	7♓33.7	18 41.9	2 54.8	20 22.8	23 37.5	12 55.5	25 19.9	5 13.7	12 39.3
6	23 0 20.4	14 42.0	16 41.3	21 21.0	20 22.2	4 1.9	21 .2	23 40.7	12 54.4	25 23.4	5 15.1	12 41.3
7	23 4 16.9	15 36.1	16 38.3	4♈41.3	22 1.1	5 9.0	21 37.3	23 44.1	12 53.4	25 26.8	5 16.6	12 43.3
8	23 8 13.5	16 30.1	16 35.4	17 40.4	23 38.6	6 16.0	22 14.2	23 47.7	12 52.6	25 30.3	5 18.0	12 45.3
9	23 12 10.0	17 24.1	16 32.4	0♉24.9	25 14.7	7 23.1	22 51.0	23 51.5	12 51.9	25 33.8	5 19.6	12 47.3
10	23 16 6.6	18 18.0	16 29.5	13 .6	26 49.6	8 30.2	23 27.5	23 55.4	12 51.2	25 37.2	5 21.1	12 49.3
11	23 20 3.1	19 11.9	16 26.6	25 32.1	28 23.2	9 37.4	24 3.9	23 59.6	12 50.6	25 40.6	5 22.6	12 51.3
12	23 23 59.7	20 5.8	16 23.6	8♊2.3	29 55.6	10 44.6	24 40.0	24 3.9	12 50.2	25 43.9	5 24.2	12 53.3
13	23 27 56.2	20 59.7	16 20.7	20 32.3	1♎26.9	11 51.8	25 15.9	24 8.4	12 49.8	25 47.3	5 25.8	12 55.2
14	23 31 52.8	21 53.5	16 17.7	3♋1.5	2 57.1	12 59.2	25 51.6	24 13.1	12 49.6	25 50.6	5 27.4	12 57.2
15	23 35 49.3	22 47.3	16 14.8	15 28.5	4 26.3	14 6.6	26 27.0	24 18.0	12 49.4	25 53.9	5 29.0	12 59.2
16	23 39 45.9	23 41.1	16 11.8	27 51.7	5 54.6	15 14.1	27 2.2	24 23.1	12 49.4	25 57.2	5 30.6	13 1.1
17	23 43 42.4	24 35.0	16 8.9	10♌10.0	7 21.9	16 21.7	27 37.2	24 28.3	12 D 49.5	26 .5	5 32.3	13 3.1
18	23 47 39.0	25 28.8	16 5.9	22 23.4	8 48.3	17 29.5	28 11.9	24 33.8	12 49.7	26 3.8	5 34.0	13 5.0
19	23 51 35.6	26 22.6	16 3.0	4♍33.6	10 14.0	18 37.3	28 46.3	24 39.4	12 49.9	26 7.0	5 35.7	13 7.0
20	23 55 32.1	27 16.4	16 .0	16 44.0	11 38.8	19 45.3	29 20.5	24 45.2	12 50.3	26 10.2	5 37.4	13 8.9
21	23 59 28.7	28 10.3	15 57.1	28 59.5	13 2.9	20 53.4	29 54.4	24 51.1	12 50.8	26 13.4	5 39.2	13 10.9
22	0 3 25.2	29 4.2	15 54.1	11♎26.2	14 26.2	22 1.7	0♋28.0	24 57.3	12 51.4	26 16.5	5 40.9	13 12.8
23	0 7 21.8	29 58.1	15 51.2	24 10.7	15 48.9	23 10.2	1 1.4	25 3.6	12 52.1	26 19.6	5 42.7	13 14.7
24	0 11 18.3	0♎52.0	15 48.2	7♏19.2	17 10.9	24 18.8	1 34.4	25 10.1	12 53.0	26 22.7	5 44.5	13 16.6
25	0 15 14.9	1 45.9	15 45.3	20 56.0	18 32.2	25 27.6	2 7.2	25 16.8	12 53.9	26 25.8	5 46.4	13 18.5
26	0 19 11.4	2 39.9	15 42.3	5♐2.3	19 52.9	26 36.6	2 39.6	25 23.6	12 54.9	26 28.8	5 48.2	13 20.4
27	0 23 8.0	3 34.0	15 39.4	19 34.5	21 12.9	27 45.8	3 11.8	25 30.6	12 56.1	26 31.8	5 50.1	13 22.3
28	0 27 4.5	4 28.0	15 36.4	4♑23.9	22 32.4	28 55.2	3 43.6	25 37.8	12 57.3	26 34.8	5 51.9	13 24.2
29	0 31 1.1	5 22.2	15 33.5	19 18.3	23 51.2	0♏4.8	4 15.1	25 45.1	12 58.7	26 37.8	5 53.8	13 26.0
30	0 34 57.6	6 16.4	15 30.5	4♒4.6	25 9.5	1 14.7	4 46.3	25 52.7	13 .2	26 40.7	5 55.8	13 27.9

DECLINATION

DAY	EPHEM. SID. TIME	☉	☊	☽	☿	♀	♂	♃	♄	♅	♆	♇
1	22 40 37.6	8N21.8	0N 5.9	18S19.9	9N33.6	1N58.9	22N26.8	23S10.4	22S36.1	14N39.2	12S10.3	20N35.7
4	22 52 27.3	7 16.1	0 5.9	12 16.4	7 14.4	0 26.6	22 38.3	23 11.2	22 36.8	14 35.7	12 11.8	20 33.6
7	23 4 16.9	6 9.2	0 6.0	0N 9.7	4 53.0	1S 6.1	22 48.5	23 12.0	22 37.4	14 32.3	12 13.4	20 31.6
10	23 16 6.6	5 1.5	0 6.1	11 45.3	2 31.4	2 38.7	22 57.4	23 12.9	22 37.9	14 28.9	12 15.0	20 29.6
13	23 27 56.2	3 53.0	0 6.1	17 53.0	0 11.2	4 11.0	23 5.1	23 13.8	22 38.3	14 25.5	12 16.7	20 27.8
16	23 39 45.9	2 43.8	0 6.2	16 55.0	2S 6.5	5 42.6	23 11.6	23 14.7	22 38.7	14 22.2	12 18.5	20 26.0
19	23 51 35.6	1 34.2	0 6.2	9 19.4	4 20.6	7 13.2	23 17.0	23 15.7	22 39.0	14 19.0	12 20.3	20 24.2
22	0 3 25.2	0 24.2	0 6.3	2S24.4	6 30.4	8 42.5	23 21.5	23 16.7	22 39.2	14 15.8	12 22.1	20 22.6
25	0 15 14.9	0S45.9	0 6.4	13 37.0	8 35.2	10 10.1	23 25.0	23 17.7	22 39.3	14 12.8	12 24.0	20 21.0
28	0 27 4.5	1 56.1	0 6.4	18 24.1	10 34.4	11 35.8	23 27.7	23 18.6	22 39.3	14 9.8	12 26.0	20 19.5

OCTOBER 1960

LONGITUDE

DAY	EPHEM. SID. TIME	☉	☊	☽	☿	♀	♂	♃	♄	♅	♆	♇
	h m s	° ′	° ′	° ′	° ′	° ′	° ′	° ′	° ′	° ′	° ′	° ′
1	0 38 54.2	7♎48.9	14♍12.9	16♒52.1	29♎ .7	4♏39.1	4♋50.8	26♐20.0	12♑ .5	24♌10.9	7♏45.0	6♍57.5
2	0 42 50.7	8 47.9	14 9.7	1♓ 2.1	0♏23.7	5 52.6	5 18.7	26 27.2	12 2.0	24 13.9	7 47.0	6 59.3
3	0 46 47.3	9 47.0	14 6.5	15 5.3	1 45.5	7 6.2	5 46.3	26 34.5	12 3.6	24 16.7	7 49.1	7 1.1
4	0 50 43.8	10 46.0	14 3.3	28 58.7	3 6.3	8 19.7	6 13.6	26 42.0	12 5.4	24 19.6	7 51.1	7 2.8
5	0 54 40.4	11 45.1	14 .2	12♈39.0	4 25.8	9 33.3	6 40.6	26 49.6	12 7.2	24 22.4	7 53.2	7 4.6
6	0 58 36.9	12 44.3	13 57.0	26 3.5	5 44.1	10 46.8	7 7.2	26 57.3	12 9.1	24 25.2	7 55.2	7 6.3
7	1 2 33.5	13 43.5	13 53.8	9♉10.6	7 1.2	12 .3	7 33.5	27 5.2	12 11.1	24 27.9	7 57.3	7 8.0
8	1 6 30.0	14 42.7	13 50.6	21 59.5	8 16.8	13 13.8	7 59.4	27 13.2	12 13.2	24 30.7	7 59.4	7 9.7
9	1 10 26.6	15 41.9	13 47.4	4♊31.1	9 31.0	14 27.3	8 24.9	27 21.4	12 15.4	24 33.3	8 1.5	7 11.4
10	1 14 23.1	16 41.2	13 44.3	16 47.1	10 43.6	15 40.7	8 50.1	27 29.6	12 17.7	24 36.0	8 3.6	7 13.1
11	1 18 19.7	17 40.5	13 41.1	28 50.8	11 54.5	16 54.2	9 14.9	27 38.1	12 20.1	24 38.6	8 5.7	7 14.7
12	1 22 16.2	18 39.9	13 37.9	10♋46.1	13 3.7	18 7.6	9 39.3	27 46.6	12 22.6	24 41.1	8 7.9	7 16.4
13	1 26 12.8	19 39.3	13 34.7	22 37.4	14 10.9	19 21.0	10 3.3	27 55.3	12 25.2	24 43.6	8 10.0	7 18.0
14	1 30 9.4	20 38.7	13 31.6	4♌29.8	15 15.9	20 34.4	10 26.9	28 4.1	12 27.8	24 46.1	8 12.2	7 19.5
15	1 34 5.9	21 38.2	13 28.4	16 28.4	16 18.7	21 47.8	10 50.1	28 13.0	12 30.6	24 48.6	8 14.3	7 21.1
16	1 38 2.5	22 37.7	13 25.2	28 37.8	17 19.0	23 1.2	11 12.8	28 22.0	12 33.4	24 51.0	8 16.5	7 22.7
17	1 41 59.0	23 37.2	13 22.0	11♍ 2.4	18 16.5	24 14.6	11 35.1	28 31.2	12 36.3	24 53.3	8 18.7	7 24.2
18	1 45 55.6	24 36.8	13 18.8	23 45.5	19 10.9	25 28.0	11 57.0	28 40.5	12 39.4	24 55.6	8 20.9	7 25.7
19	1 49 52.1	25 36.4	13 15.7	6♎49.3	20 2.0	26 41.3	12 18.4	28 49.9	12 42.5	24 57.9	8 23.1	7 27.2
20	1 53 48.7	26 36.1	13 12.5	20 14.1	20 49.4	27 54.6	12 39.3	28 59.4	12 45.7	25 .1	8 25.3	7 28.7
21	1 57 45.2	27 35.8	13 9.3	3♏58.8	21 32.7	29 8.0	12 59.8	29 9.1	12 49.0	25 2.4	8 27.5	7 30.1
22	2 1 41.8	28 35.6	13 6.1	17 60.0	22 11.5	0♐21.3	13 19.8	29 18.9	12 52.4	25 4.5	8 29.7	7 31.6
23	2 5 38.3	29 35.3	13 3.0	2♐13.2	22 45.4	1 34.6	13 39.3	29 28.8	12 55.8	25 6.6	8 32.0	7 33.0
24	2 9 34.9	0♏35.1	12 59.8	16 33.1	23 13.7	2 47.9	13 58.3	29 38.7	12 59.4	25 8.6	8 34.2	7 34.3
25	2 13 31.4	1 34.9	12 56.6	0♑54.7	23 36.0	4 1.1	14 16.7	29 48.8	13 3.0	25 10.6	8 36.4	7 35.7
26	2 17 28.0	2 34.8	12 53.4	15 13.3	23 51.7	5 14.3	14 34.6	29 59.0	13 6.7	25 12.6	8 38.6	7 37.0
27	2 21 24.5	3 34.6	12 50.2	29 25.9	24 .1	6 27.5	14 52.0	0♑ 9.3	13 10.5	25 14.5	8 40.9	7 38.3
28	2 25 21.1	4 34.5	12 47.1	13♒30.5	24 .7	7 40.7	15 8.9	0 19.7	13 14.4	25 16.3	8 43.1	7 39.6
29	2 29 17.6	5 34.5	12 43.9	27 26.2	23 R 53.0	8 53.9	15 25.2	0 30.2	13 18.4	25 18.1	8 45.4	7 40.8
30	2 33 14.2	6 34.4	12 40.7	11♓12.7	23 36.3	10 7.0	15 40.9	0 40.8	13 22.4	25 19.9	8 47.6	7 42.1
31	2 37 10.8	7 34.4	12 37.5	24 49.6	23 10.4	11 20.1	15 56.0	0 51.5	13 26.5	25 21.6	8 49.8	7 43.3

LATITUDE

DAY	EPHEM. SID. TIME	☉	☊	☽	☿	♀	♂	♃	♄	♅	♆	♇
1	0 38 54.2	0 .0	0 .0	2N30.9	1S25.4	0N 5.6	0N 8.5	0N 3.9	0N14.8	0N41.5	1N43.3	12N15.5
4	0 50 43.8	0 .0	0 .0	1S13.7	1 46.7	0S 2.8	0 13.3	0 3.5	0 14.5	0 41.5	1 43.3	12 16.3
7	1 2 33.5	0 .0	0 .0	4 12.9	2 6.8	0 11.5	0 18.4	0 3.1	0 14.2	0 41.6	1 43.2	12 17.1
10	1 14 23.1	0 .0	0 .0	5 12.2	2 25.2	0 20.2	0 23.6	0 2.8	0 13.8	0 41.7	1 43.1	12 18.0
13	1 26 12.8	0 .0	0 .0	4 7.6	2 41.4	0 28.9	0 29.0	0 2.5	0 13.5	0 41.8	1 43.1	12 18.9
16	1 38 2.5	0 .0	0 .0	1 28.2	2 54.5	0 37.7	0 34.6	0 2.1	0 13.3	0 42.0	1 43.0	12 19.9
19	1 49 52.1	0 .0	0 .0	1N55.5	3 3.5	0 46.4	0 40.5	0 1.8	0 13.0	0 42.1	1 43.0	12 20.9
22	2 1 41.8	0 .0	0 .0	4 35.5	3 7.0	0 55.0	0 46.6	0 1.5	0 12.7	0 42.2	1 43.0	12 21.9
25	2 13 31.4	0 .0	0 .0	4 55.4	3 2.9	1 3.5	0 52.9	0 1.1	0 12.4	0 42.3	1 42.9	12 23.0
28	2 25 21.1	0 .0	0 .0	2 38.2	2 48.7	1 11.8	0 59.4	0 .8	0 12.1	0 42.4	1 42.9	12 24.1
31	2 37 10.8	0 .0	0 .0	0S56.0	2 21.5	1 19.7	1 6.2	0 .5	0 11.8	0 42.5	1 42.9	12 25.3

RIGHT ASCENSION

DAY	EPHEM. SID. TIME	☉	☊	☽	☿	♀	♂	♃	♄	♅	♆	♇
1	0 38 54.2	7♎10.7	15♍27.6	18♒32.5	26♎27.0	2♏24.7	5♋17.2	26♐ .4	13♑ 1.7	26♌43.6	5♏57.7	13♍29.8
2	0 42 50.7	8 5.0	15 24.6	2♓36.3	27 43.9	3 35.0	5 47.7	26 8.2	13 3.4	26 46.5	5 59.6	13 31.6
3	0 46 47.3	8 59.4	15 21.7	16 15.5	29 .2	4 45.5	6 17.8	26 16.1	13 5.2	26 49.3	6 1.6	13 33.4
4	0 50 43.8	9 53.8	15 18.7	29 33.1	0♏15.7	5 56.3	6 47.6	26 24.3	13 7.0	26 52.1	6 3.6	13 35.2
5	0 54 40.4	10 48.4	15 15.8	12♈34.2	1 30.5	7 7.4	7 17.1	26 32.6	13 9.0	26 54.8	6 5.5	13 37.0
6	0 58 36.9	11 43.0	15 12.8	25 24.5	2 44.4	8 18.7	7 46.1	26 41.0	13 11.1	26 57.5	6 7.5	13 38.8
7	1 2 33.5	12 37.8	15 9.9	8♉ 8.9	3 57.5	9 30.2	8 14.9	26 49.6	13 13.3	27 .2	6 9.5	13 40.5
8	1 6 30.0	13 32.6	15 6.9	20 50.7	5 9.7	10 42.1	8 43.2	26 58.3	13 15.6	27 2.8	6 11.6	13 42.3
9	1 10 26.6	14 27.6	15 4.0	3♊31.5	6 20.8	11 54.2	9 11.1	27 7.2	13 17.9	27 5.5	6 13.6	13 44.0
10	1 14 23.1	15 22.6	15 1.0	16 10.9	7 30.8	13 6.6	9 38.6	27 16.2	13 20.4	27 8.0	6 15.6	13 45.7
11	1 18 19.7	16 17.8	14 58.1	28 47.4	8 39.5	14 19.3	10 5.7	27 25.4	13 23.0	27 10.6	6 17.7	13 47.4
12	1 22 16.2	17 13.1	14 55.1	11♋18.7	9 46.9	15 32.3	10 32.4	27 34.7	13 25.7	27 13.1	6 19.7	13 49.1
13	1 26 12.8	18 8.6	14 52.2	23 43.1	10 52.7	16 45.6	10 58.7	27 44.1	13 28.5	27 15.5	6 21.8	13 50.8
14	1 30 9.4	19 4.1	14 49.2	5♌59.8	11 56.7	17 59.2	11 24.5	27 53.7	13 31.3	27 17.9	6 23.9	13 52.4
15	1 34 5.9	19 59.8	14 46.3	18 9.7	12 58.8	19 13.1	11 49.9	28 3.4	13 34.3	27 20.3	6 26.0	13 54.1
16	1 38 2.5	20 55.7	14 43.3	0♍15.6	13 58.8	20 27.3	12 14.8	28 13.3	13 37.4	27 22.7	6 28.1	13 55.7
17	1 41 59.0	21 51.7	14 40.4	12 22.0	14 56.3	21 41.8	12 39.2	28 23.3	13 40.6	27 25.0	6 30.2	13 57.3
18	1 45 55.6	22 47.9	14 37.4	24 34.9	15 51.0	22 56.6	13 3.1	28 33.4	13 43.8	27 27.2	6 32.3	13 58.9
19	1 49 52.1	23 44.2	14 34.4	7♎ 1.4	16 42.7	24 11.7	13 26.6	28 43.6	13 47.2	27 29.4	6 34.5	14 .4
20	1 53 48.7	24 40.6	14 31.5	19 48.9	17 30.9	25 27.2	13 49.5	28 54.0	13 50.7	27 31.6	6 36.6	14 2.0
21	1 57 45.2	25 37.3	14 28.5	3♏ 3.9	18 15.2	26 42.9	14 12.0	29 4.6	13 54.3	27 33.8	6 38.8	14 3.6
22	2 1 41.8	26 34.1	14 25.6	16 50.9	18 55.2	27 58.9	14 33.9	29 15.2	13 57.9	27 35.9	6 40.9	14 5.1
23	2 5 38.3	27 31.0	14 22.6	1♐10.0	19 30.3	29 15.2	14 55.3	29 26.0	14 1.7	27 37.9	6 43.1	14 6.5
24	2 9 34.9	28 28.2	14 19.7	15 55.9	20 .1	0♐31.8	15 16.1	29 36.8	14 5.5	27 39.9	6 45.2	14 8.0
25	2 13 31.4	29 25.5	14 16.7	0♑57.4	20 23.9	1 48.6	15 36.4	29 47.8	14 9.4	27 41.8	6 47.4	14 9.5
26	2 17 28.0	0♏22.9	14 13.8	15 59.7	20 41.1	3 5.8	15 56.0	29 58.9	14 13.4	27 43.7	6 49.6	14 10.9
27	2 21 24.5	1 20.6	14 10.8	0♒48.0	20 51.2	4 23.2	16 15.2	0♑10.2	14 17.5	27 45.6	6 51.8	14 12.3
28	2 25 21.1	2 18.4	14 7.9	15 11.9	20 53.5	5 40.8	16 33.7	0 21.5	14 21.7	27 47.4	6 53.9	14 13.7
29	2 29 17.6	3 16.4	14 4.9	29 6.7	20 R 47.4	6 58.7	16 51.6	0 33.0	14 26.0	27 49.2	6 56.1	14 15.0
30	2 33 14.2	4 14.6	14 1.9	12♓33.5	20 32.6	8 16.9	17 8.9	0 44.5	14 30.4	27 50.9	6 58.3	14 16.4
31	2 37 10.8	5 13.0	13 59.0	25 37.4	20 8.7	9 35.3	17 25.7	0 56.2	14 34.8	27 52.6	7 .5	14 17.7

DECLINATION

DAY	EPHEM. SID. TIME	☉	☊	☽	☿	♀	♂	♃	♄	♅	♆	♇
1	0 38 54.2	3S 6.1	0N 6.5	13S23.0	12S27.3	12S59.1	23N29.7	23S19.6	22S39.3	14N 6.9	12S28.0	20N18.1
4	0 50 43.8	4 15.7	0 6.6	1 32.0	14 13.2	14 19.7	23 31.1	23 20.5	22 39.1	14 4.1	12 30.0	20 16.8
7	1 2 33.5	5 25.0	0 6.6	10N33.3	15 51.2	15 37.3	23 31.9	23 21.4	22 38.9	14 1.4	12 32.1	20 15.5
10	1 14 23.1	6 33.6	0 6.7	17 36.4	17 20.5	16 51.4	23 32.4	23 22.3	22 38.6	13 58.8	12 34.2	20 14.4
13	1 26 12.8	7 41.4	0 6.8	17 28.3	18 39.8	18 1.9	23 32.6	23 23.1	22 38.2	13 56.3	12 36.3	20 13.4
16	1 38 2.5	8 48.3	0 6.8	10 34.4	19 47.5	19 8.3	23 32.6	23 23.8	22 37.8	13 54.0	12 38.4	20 12.5
19	1 49 52.1	9 54.0	0 6.9	0S56.4	20 41.8	20 10.2	23 32.7	23 24.4	22 37.2	13 51.7	12 40.5	20 11.7
22	2 1 41.8	10 58.5	0 7.0	12 46.9	21 19.7	21 7.5	23 32.8	23 25.0	22 36.5	13 49.6	12 42.7	20 11.0
25	2 13 31.4	12 1.5	0 7.0	18 30.9	21 37.5	21 59.6	23 33.2	23 25.4	22 35.8	13 47.7	12 44.8	20 10.4
28	2 25 21.1	13 2.9	0 7.1	14 14.5	21 30.0	22 46.4	23 33.9	23 25.7	22 35.0	13 45.9	12 47.0	20 9.9
31	2 37 10.8	14 2.3	0 7.1	2 54.8	20 51.0	23 27.5	23 35.2	23 25.8	22 34.0	13 44.2	12 49.1	20 9.6

NOVEMBER 1960

DAY	EPHEM. SID. TIME	☉	☊	☽	☿	♀	♂	♃	♄	♅	♆	♇
	h m s	° ′	° ′	° ′	° ′	° ′	° ′	° ′	° ′	° ′	° ′	° ′
		LONGITUDE										
1	2 41 7.3	8♏34.4	12♍34.4	8♈16.6	22♏35.0	12♐33.2	16♋10.6	1♑ 2.3	13♑30.7	25♌23.2	8♏52.1	7♍44.4
2	2 45 3.9	9 34.5	12 31.2	21 33.0	21 R 50.2	13 46.2	16 24.6	1 13.2	13 35.0	25 24.9	8 54.3	7 45.6
3	2 49 .4	10 34.5	12 28.0	4♉37.6	20 56.2	14 59.2	16 37.9	1 24.2	13 39.3	25 26.4	8 56.6	7 46.7
4	2 52 57.0	11 34.6	12 24.8	17 29.5	19 54.0	16 12.2	16 50.7	1 35.3	13 43.8	25 27.9	8 58.8	7 47.8
5	2 56 53.5	12 34.7	12 21.6	0♊ 7.9	18 44.6	17 25.2	17 2.8	1 46.5	13 48.3	25 29.4	9 1.1	7 48.9
6	3 0 50.1	13 34.9	12 18.5	12 32.7	17 29.7	18 38.1	17 14.2	1 57.7	13 52.8	25 30.8	9 3.3	7 49.9
7	3 4 46.6	14 35.1	12 15.3	24 44.9	16 11.4	19 51.0	17 25.0	2 9.1	13 57.5	25 32.1	9 5.5	7 51.0
8	3 8 43.2	15 35.3	12 12.1	6♋46.4	14 52.1	21 3.9	17 35.1	2 20.5	14 2.2	25 33.4	9 7.8	7 52.0
9	3 12 39.7	16 35.6	12 8.9	18 40.0	13 34.1	22 16.8	17 44.5	2 32.0	14 7.0	25 34.7	9 10.0	7 52.9
10	3 16 36.3	17 35.9	12 5.8	0♌29.6	12 20.2	23 29.6	17 53.2	2 43.7	14 11.8	25 35.9	9 12.2	7 53.8
11	3 20 32.9	18 36.2	12 2.6	12 19.9	11 12.7	24 42.5	18 1.3	2 55.4	14 16.8	25 37.1	9 14.5	7 54.8
12	3 24 29.4	19 36.6	11 59.4	24 16.0	10 13.5	25 55.2	18 8.6	3 7.2	14 21.8	25 38.1	9 16.7	7 55.7
13	3 28 26.0	20 37.0	11 56.2	6♍23.4	9 24.2	27 8.0	18 15.1	3 19.0	14 26.9	25 39.2	9 18.9	7 56.5
14	3 32 22.5	21 37.4	11 53.0	18 47.4	8 46.0	28 20.7	18 20.9	3 30.9	14 32.0	25 40.2	9 21.2	7 57.3
15	3 36 19.1	22 37.9	11 49.9	1♎32.7	8 19.3	29 33.4	18 25.9	3 42.9	14 37.2	25 41.1	9 23.4	7 58.1
16	3 40 15.6	23 38.4	11 46.7	14 42.9	8 4.4	0♑46.0	18 30.1	3 55.0	14 42.5	25 42.0	9 25.5	7 58.9
17	3 44 12.2	24 38.9	11 43.5	28 19.7	8 .9	1 58.6	18 33.6	4 7.1	14 47.8	25 42.8	9 27.7	7 59.6
18	3 48 8.7	25 39.4	11 40.3	12♏22.3	8 D 8.5	3 11.2	18 36.2	4 19.4	14 53.2	25 43.5	9 29.9	8 .3
19	3 52 5.3	26 40.0	11 37.2	26 47.1	8 26.2	4 23.7	18 38.0	4 31.7	14 58.6	25 44.2	9 32.1	8 1.0
20	3 56 1.9	27 40.6	11 34.0	11♐27.8	8 53.4	5 36.2	18 39.0	4 44.0	15 4.1	25 44.9	9 34.2	8 1.6
21	3 59 58.4	28 41.2	11 30.8	26 16.2	9 29.2	6 48.7	18 39.2	4 56.5	15 9.7	25 45.5	9 36.4	8 2.3
22	4 3 55.0	29 41.8	11 27.6	11♑ 3.7	10 12.5	8 1.1	18 R 38.5	5 9.0	15 15.3	25 46.0	9 38.5	8 2.8
23	4 7 51.5	0♐42.5	11 24.5	25 43.0	11 2.6	9 13.5	18 37.0	5 21.5	15 21.0	25 46.5	9 40.7	8 3.4
24	4 11 48.1	1 43.2	11 21.3	10♒ 8.5	11 58.7	10 25.8	18 34.6	5 34.1	15 26.7	25 46.9	9 42.8	8 3.9
25	4 15 44.6	2 43.9	11 18.1	24 17.3	12 60.0	11 38.1	18 31.4	5 46.8	15 32.5	25 47.3	9 44.9	8 4.4
26	4 19 41.2	3 44.6	11 14.9	8♓ 8.7	14 5.8	12 50.3	18 27.4	5 59.6	15 38.4	25 47.6	9 47.0	8 4.8
27	4 23 37.7	4 45.3	11 11.7	21 43.4	15 15.5	14 2.5	18 22.5	6 12.4	15 44.3	25 47.8	9 49.1	8 5.3
28	4 27 34.3	5 46.1	11 8.6	5♈ 3.1	16 28.5	15 14.6	18 16.7	6 25.2	15 50.2	25 48.0	9 51.1	8 5.7
29	4 31 30.9	6 46.8	11 5.4	18 9.5	17 44.4	16 26.7	18 10.1	6 38.1	15 56.2	25 48.2	9 53.2	8 6.0
30	4 35 27.4	7 47.6	11 2.2	1♉ 4.0	19 2.8	17 38.7	18 2.6	6 51.1	16 2.3	25 48.3	9 55.2	8 6.3
		LATITUDE										
1	2 41 7.3	0 .0	0 .0	2S 4.8	2S 9.1	1S 22.3	1N 8.5	0N .4	0N 11.7	0N 42.6	1N 42.9	12N 25.7
4	2 52 57.0	0 .0	0 .0	4 32.6	1 22.0	1 29.9	1 15.6	0 .1	0 11.4	0 42.7	1 42.9	12 26.9
7	3 4 46.6	0 .0	0 .0	4 57.9	0 23.2	1 37.0	1 23.0	0S .2	0 11.2	0 42.8	1 42.9	12 28.1
10	3 16 36.3	0 .0	0 .0	3 26.4	0N 37.8	1 43.7	1 30.7	0 .5	0 10.9	0 43.0	1 43.0	12 29.3
13	3 28 26.0	0 .0	0 .0	0 35.4	1 29.5	1 49.8	1 38.6	0 .8	0 10.6	0 43.1	1 43.0	12 30.6
16	3 40 15.6	0 .0	0 .0	2N 39.8	2 4.7	1 55.4	1 46.7	0 1.1	0 10.4	0 43.2	1 43.0	12 31.9
19	3 52 5.3	0 .0	0 .0	4 50.0	2 22.8	2 .4	1 55.1	0 1.4	0 10.1	0 43.3	1 43.1	12 33.2
22	4 3 55.0	0 .0	0 .0	4 23.6	2 26.8	2 4.7	2 3.6	0 1.7	0 9.9	0 43.5	1 43.2	12 34.6
25	4 15 44.6	0 .0	0 .0	1 31.1	2 20.7	2 8.4	2 12.3	0 2.0	0 9.6	0 43.6	1 43.2	12 35.9
28	4 27 34.3	0 .0	0 .0	1S 59.7	2 7.7	2 11.2	2 21.1	0 2.3	0 9.4	0 43.7	1 43.3	12 37.3
		RIGHT ASCENSION										
1	2 41 7.3	6♏11.6	13♍56.0	8♈25.4	19♏35.5	10♐53.8	17♋41.7	1♑ 8.0	14♑39.3	27♌54.2	7♏ 2.6	14♍19.0
2	2 45 3.9	7 10.4	13 53.1	21 4.7	18 R 53.3	12 12.7	17 57.2	1 19.8	14 44.0	27 55.7	7 4.8	14 20.2
3	2 49 .4	8 9.4	13 50.1	3♉41.6	18 2.4	13 31.7	18 11.9	1 31.8	14 48.7	27 57.3	7 7.0	14 21.5
4	2 52 57.0	9 8.5	13 47.1	16 20.1	17 3.8	14 50.8	18 26.1	1 43.9	14 53.4	27 58.7	7 9.2	14 22.7
5	2 56 53.5	10 7.9	13 44.2	29 1.9	15 58.8	16 10.2	18 39.5	1 56.1	14 58.3	28 .2	7 11.4	14 23.9
6	3 0 50.1	11 7.5	13 41.2	11♊45.9	14 49.0	17 29.7	18 52.2	2 8.3	15 3.2	28 1.5	7 13.6	14 25.1
7	3 4 46.6	12 7.3	13 38.3	24 29.2	13 36.4	18 49.4	19 4.3	2 20.7	15 8.2	28 2.9	7 15.7	14 26.2
8	3 8 43.2	13 7.3	13 35.3	7♋ 7.5	12 23.4	20 9.2	19 15.6	2 33.2	15 13.3	28 4.1	7 17.9	14 27.3
9	3 12 39.7	14 7.6	13 32.4	19 37.1	11 12.4	21 29.2	19 26.1	2 45.7	15 18.5	28 5.4	7 20.1	14 28.4
10	3 16 36.3	15 8.0	13 29.4	1♌55.4	10 5.5	22 49.2	19 35.9	2 58.4	15 23.7	28 6.5	7 22.3	14 29.5
11	3 20 32.9	16 8.7	13 26.4	14 2.6	9 5.0	24 9.4	19 45.0	3 11.1	15 29.1	28 7.7	7 24.5	14 30.6
12	3 24 29.4	17 9.6	13 23.5	26 1.0	8 12.6	25 29.6	19 53.3	3 24.0	15 34.5	28 8.8	7 26.6	14 31.6
13	3 28 26.0	18 10.7	13 20.5	7♍55.7	7 29.6	26 49.9	20 .8	3 36.9	15 39.9	28 9.8	7 28.8	14 32.6
14	3 32 22.5	19 12.0	13 17.6	19 53.7	6 56.8	28 10.2	20 7.4	3 49.9	15 45.5	28 10.8	7 30.9	14 33.5
15	3 36 19.1	20 13.6	13 14.6	2♎ 3.5	6 34.8	29 30.5	20 13.3	4 2.9	15 51.0	28 11.7	7 33.1	14 34.5
16	3 40 15.6	21 15.3	13 11.6	14 34.7	6 23.5	0♑50.9	20 18.2	4 16.1	15 56.7	28 12.5	7 35.2	14 35.4
17	3 44 12.2	22 17.3	13 8.7	27 36.6	6 22.7	2 11.2	20 22.4	4 29.3	16 2.5	28 13.3	7 37.4	14 36.3
18	3 48 8.7	23 19.4	13 5.7	11♏16.7	6 D 31.9	3 31.5	20 25.7	4 42.7	16 8.3	28 14.1	7 39.5	14 37.1
19	3 52 5.3	24 21.8	13 2.8	25 38.4	6 50.5	4 51.8	20 28.1	4 56.0	16 14.1	28 14.8	7 41.6	14 37.9
20	3 56 1.9	25 24.4	12 59.8	10♐38.4	7 17.8	6 12.0	20 29.6	5 9.5	16 20.1	28 15.4	7 43.7	14 38.7
21	3 59 58.4	26 27.2	12 56.8	26 4.8	7 52.9	7 32.1	20 30.2	5 23.0	16 26.0	28 16.0	7 45.8	14 39.5
22	4 3 55.0	27 30.2	12 53.9	11♑38.7	8 35.0	8 52.1	20 R 29.9	5 36.6	16 32.1	28 16.5	7 47.9	14 40.3
23	4 7 51.5	28 33.4	12 50.9	26 59.6	9 23.5	10 12.0	20 28.7	5 50.3	16 38.2	28 17.0	7 50.0	14 41.0
24	4 11 48.1	29 36.7	12 47.9	11♒51.0	10 17.6	11 31.7	20 26.6	6 4.1	16 44.4	28 17.4	7 52.1	14 41.6
25	4 15 44.6	0♐40.3	12 45.0	26 4.7	11 16.6	12 51.3	20 23.6	6 17.9	16 50.6	28 17.8	7 54.1	14 42.3
26	4 19 41.2	1 44.0	12 42.0	9♓40.6	12 20.1	14 10.7	20 19.6	6 31.7	16 56.9	28 18.1	7 56.2	14 42.9
27	4 23 37.7	2 48.0	12 39.1	22 44.6	13 27.5	15 30.0	20 14.7	6 45.7	17 3.3	28 18.4	7 58.2	14 43.5
28	4 27 34.3	3 52.1	12 36.1	5♈25.7	14 38.3	16 49.0	20 8.9	6 59.6	17 9.7	28 18.6	8 .2	14 44.1
29	4 31 30.9	4 56.3	12 33.1	17 53.3	15 52.1	18 7.7	20 2.1	7 13.7	17 16.1	28 18.7	8 2.3	14 44.6
30	4 35 27.4	6 .8	12 30.2	0♉16.3	17 8.6	19 26.3	19 54.4	7 27.8	17 22.6	28 18.8	8 4.3	14 45.1
		DECLINATION										
1	2 41 7.3	14S 21.7	0N 7.2	1N 22.3	20S 29.9	23S 39.9	23N 35.7	23S 25.9	22S 33.7	13N 43.7	12S 49.8	20N 9.5
4	2 52 57.0	15 18.5	0 7.2	12 41.4	19 1.9	24 13.0	23 37.9	23 25.9	22 32.7	13 42.2	12 52.0	20 9.3
7	3 4 46.6	16 13.0	0 7.3	18 22.6	17 3.2	24 39.9	23 40.8	23 25.7	22 31.5	13 40.9	12 54.1	20 9.2
10	3 16 36.3	17 5.0	0 7.4	16 41.2	14 56.4	25 .5	23 44.7	23 25.3	22 30.3	13 39.8	12 56.2	20 9.3
13	3 28 26.0	17 54.5	0 7.4	8 37.2	13 12.7	25 14.4	23 49.5	23 24.8	22 28.9	13 38.8	12 58.3	20 9.4
16	3 40 15.6	18 41.1	0 7.5	3S 20.6	12 13.9	25 21.8	23 55.6	23 24.1	22 27.5	13 38.0	13 .3	20 9.7
19	3 52 5.3	19 24.8	0 7.5	14 44.0	12 3.8	25 22.5	24 2.7	23 23.3	22 26.0	13 37.3	13 2.3	20 10.1
22	4 3 55.0	20 5.3	0 7.6	18 36.1	12 33.5	25 16.5	24 11.1	23 22.2	22 24.4	13 36.9	13 4.3	20 10.6
25	4 15 44.6	20 42.5	0 7.7	11 59.6	13 30.4	25 3.8	24 20.7	23 20.9	22 22.6	13 36.6	13 6.2	20 11.2
28	4 27 34.3	21 16.2	0 7.7	0N 10.5	14 43.5	24 44.6	24 31.5	23 19.4	22 20.8	13 36.4	13 8.1	20 12.0

DECEMBER 1960

LONGITUDE

DAY	EPHEM. SID. TIME	☉	☊	☽	☿	♀	♂	♃	♄	♅	♆	♇
	h m s	° ′	° ′	° ′	° ′	° ′	° ′	° ′	° ′	° ′	° ′	° ′
1	4 39 24.0	8 ♐ 48.4	10 ♍ 59.0	13 ♉ 47.8	20 ♏ 23.3	18 ♑ 50.6	17 ♋ 54.3	7 ♑ 4.1	16 ♑ 8.4	25 ♌ 48.3	9 ♏ 57.3	8 ♍ 6.6
2	4 43 20.5	9 49.3	10 55.9	26 21.5	21 45.7	20 2.5	17 R 45.2	7 17.2	16 14.6	25 48.3	9 59.3	8 7.0
3	4 47 17.1	10 50.1	10 52.7	8 ♊ 45.2	23 9.5	21 14.3	17 35.2	7 30.3	16 20.7	25 R 48.2	10 1.3	8 7.2
4	4 51 13.6	11 51.0	10 49.5	20 59.2	24 34.6	22 26.1	17 24.3	7 43.5	16 27.0	25 48.1	10 3.3	8 7.4
5	4 55 10.2	12 51.8	10 46.3	3 ♋ 4.2	26 .8	23 37.7	17 12.6	7 56.7	16 33.3	25 47.9	10 5.3	8 7.6
6	4 59 6.8	13 52.7	10 43.2	15 1.2	27 28.0	24 49.3	17 .1	8 9.9	16 39.6	25 47.7	10 7.2	8 7.7
7	5 3 3.3	14 53.6	10 40.0	26 52.3	28 56.0	26 .8	16 46.8	8 23.2	16 45.9	25 47.3	10 9.1	8 7.8
8	5 6 59.9	15 54.6	10 36.8	8 ♌ 40.2	0 ♐ 24.7	27 12.3	16 32.6	8 36.6	16 52.3	25 47.0	10 11.1	8 7.9
9	5 10 56.4	16 55.5	10 33.6	20 28.8	1 53.9	28 23.6	16 17.7	8 49.9	16 58.8	25 46.6	10 13.0	8 7.9
10	5 14 53.0	17 56.5	10 30.4	2 ♍ 22.5	3 23.7	29 34.9	16 2.0	9 3.3	17 5.3	25 46.1	10 14.8	8 8.0
11	5 18 49.5	18 57.5	10 27.3	14 26.5	4 53.9	0 ♒ 46.1	15 45.6	9 16.8	17 11.8	25 45.6	10 16.7	8 R 7.9
12	5 22 46.1	19 58.5	10 24.1	26 46.3	6 24.4	1 57.3	15 28.4	9 30.3	17 18.3	25 45.0	10 18.5	8 7.9
13	5 26 42.7	20 59.5	10 20.9	9 ♎ 27.2	7 55.3	3 8.3	15 10.5	9 43.8	17 24.9	25 44.4	10 20.3	8 7.8
14	5 30 39.2	22 .5	10 17.7	22 34.0	9 26.5	4 19.3	14 52.0	9 57.4	17 31.6	25 43.7	10 22.1	8 7.7
15	5 34 35.8	23 1.6	10 14.6	6 ♏ 9.9	10 58.0	5 30.1	14 32.8	10 11.0	17 38.2	25 42.9	10 23.9	8 7.6
16	5 38 32.3	24 2.7	10 11.4	20 15.8	12 29.7	6 40.9	14 13.0	10 24.6	17 44.9	25 42.1	10 25.7	8 7.4
17	5 42 28.9	25 3.8	10 8.2	4 ♐ 49.4	14 1.6	7 51.6	13 52.6	10 38.3	17 51.6	25 41.3	10 27.4	8 7.2
18	5 46 25.4	26 4.9	10 5.0	19 44.8	15 33.7	9 2.2	13 31.7	10 52.0	17 58.4	25 40.4	10 29.1	8 6.9
19	5 50 22.0	27 6.0	10 1.9	4 ♑ 53.0	17 6.0	10 12.7	13 10.3	11 5.7	18 5.2	25 39.4	10 30.8	8 6.7
20	5 54 18.6	28 7.1	9 58.7	20 3.6	18 38.5	11 23.0	12 48.4	11 19.4	18 12.0	25 38.4	10 32.4	8 6.4
21	5 58 15.1	29 8.2	9 55.5	5 ♒ 6.2	20 11.2	12 33.3	12 26.1	11 33.2	18 18.8	25 37.4	10 34.1	8 6.0
22	6 2 11.7	0 ♑ 9.4	9 52.3	19 52.4	21 44.1	13 43.4	12 3.4	11 47.0	18 25.7	25 36.2	10 35.7	8 5.7
23	6 6 8.2	1 10.5	9 49.1	4 ♓ 17.1	23 17.3	14 53.5	11 40.5	12 .9	18 32.6	25 35.1	10 37.3	8 5.3
24	6 10 4.8	2 11.7	9 46.0	18 17.8	24 50.6	16 3.4	11 17.2	12 14.7	18 39.5	25 33.9	10 38.9	8 4.9
25	6 14 1.3	3 12.8	9 42.8	1 ♈ 55.0	26 24.1	17 13.1	10 53.7	12 28.5	18 46.4	25 32.7	10 40.4	8 4.5
26	6 17 57.9	4 14.0	9 39.6	15 10.6	27 57.9	18 22.8	10 30.1	12 42.4	18 53.4	25 31.4	10 42.0	8 4.0
27	6 21 54.5	5 15.1	9 36.4	28 7.7	29 31.9	19 32.2	10 6.3	12 56.3	19 .3	25 30.0	10 43.4	8 3.5
28	6 25 51.0	6 16.2	9 33.3	10 ♉ 49.2	1 ♑ 6.2	20 41.6	9 42.5	13 10.2	19 7.3	25 28.6	10 44.9	8 2.9
29	6 29 47.6	7 17.4	9 30.1	23 17.9	2 40.7	21 50.8	9 18.6	13 24.1	19 14.3	25 27.1	10 46.3	8 2.3
30	6 33 44.1	8 18.5	9 26.9	5 ♊ 36.3	4 15.5	22 59.8	8 54.7	13 38.0	19 21.3	25 25.6	10 47.7	8 1.7
31	6 37 40.7	9 19.7	9 23.7	17 46.2	5 50.6	24 8.6	8 31.0	13 52.0	19 28.3	25 24.1	10 49.1	8 1.1

LATITUDE

DAY	EPHEM. SID. TIME	☉	☊	☽	☿	♀	♂	♃	♄	♅	♆	♇
1	4 39 24.0	0 .0	0 .0	4 S 26.1	1 N 50.4	2 S 13.3	2 N 30.0	0 S 2.6	0 N 9.1	0 N 43.9	1 N 43.4	12 N 38.6
4	4 51 13.6	0 .0	0 .0	4 54.8	1 30.4	2 14.5	2 38.8	0 2.8	0 8.9	0 44.0	1 43.5	12 40.0
7	5 3 3.3	0 .0	0 .0	3 26.6	1 8.9	2 14.8	2 47.5	0 3.1	0 8.6	0 44.1	1 43.6	12 41.3
10	5 14 53.0	0 .0	0 .0	0 39.9	0 46.9	2 14.3	2 56.1	0 3.4	0 8.4	0 44.3	1 43.7	12 42.7
13	5 26 42.7	0 .0	0 .0	2 N 29.8	0 24.8	2 12.7	3 4.3	0 3.7	0 8.2	0 44.4	1 43.8	12 44.0
16	5 38 32.3	0 .0	0 .0	4 44.8	0 3.1	2 10.2	3 12.1	0 4.0	0 7.9	0 44.5	1 43.9	12 45.4
19	5 50 22.0	0 .0	0 .0	4 31.9	0 S 17.8	2 6.7	3 19.4	0 4.2	0 7.7	0 44.7	1 44.0	12 46.7
22	6 2 11.7	0 .0	0 .0	1 38.4	0 37.6	2 2.1	3 26.0	0 4.5	0 7.5	0 44.8	1 44.2	12 48.0
25	6 14 1.3	0 .0	0 .0	2 S .4	0 56.1	1 56.5	3 31.9	0 4.8	0 7.2	0 44.9	1 44.3	12 49.3
28	6 25 51.0	0 .0	0 .0	4 29.4	1 13.1	1 49.9	3 37.0	0 5.1	0 7.0	0 45.0	1 44.4	12 50.6
31	6 37 40.7	0 .0	0 .0	4 59.6	1 28.2	1 42.1	3 41.2	0 5.4	0 6.8	0 45.1	1 44.6	12 51.8

RIGHT ASCENSION

DAY	EPHEM. SID. TIME	☉	☊	☽	☿	♀	♂	♃	♄	♅	♆	♇
1	4 39 24.0	7 ♐ 5.4	12 ♍ 27.2	12 ♉ 41.5	18 ♏ 27.5	20 ♑ 44.5	19 ♋ 45.8	7 ♑ 41.9	17 ♑ 29.2	28 ♌ 18.9	8 ♏ 6.2	14 ♍ 45.6
2	4 43 20.5	8 10.2	12 24.2	25 12.7	19 48.5	22 2.6	19 R 36.3	7 56.2	17 35.8	28 18.9	8 8.3	14 46.1
3	4 47 17.1	9 15.1	12 21.3	7 ♊ 50.5	21 11.4	23 20.3	19 25.8	8 10.5	17 42.5	28 18.9	8 10.2	14 46.5
4	4 51 13.6	10 20.2	12 18.3	20 32.5	22 36.0	24 37.7	19 14.4	8 24.8	17 49.2	28 R 18.7	8 12.2	14 46.9
5	4 55 10.2	11 25.4	12 15.3	3 ♋ 13.9	24 2.1	25 54.8	19 2.0	8 39.1	17 55.9	28 18.6	8 14.1	14 47.2
6	4 59 6.8	12 30.8	12 12.4	15 49.1	25 29.7	27 11.6	18 48.7	8 53.5	18 2.7	28 18.3	8 16.0	14 47.6
7	5 3 3.3	13 36.3	12 9.4	28 13.0	26 58.5	28 28.0	18 34.6	9 8.0	18 9.5	28 18.1	8 17.9	14 47.9
8	5 6 59.9	14 41.9	12 6.4	10 ♌ 23.2	28 28.5	29 44.1	18 19.5	9 22.5	18 16.4	28 17.7	8 19.8	14 48.1
9	5 10 56.4	15 47.7	12 3.5	22 19.9	29 59.5	0 ♒ 59.8	18 3.5	9 37.0	18 23.3	28 17.3	8 21.6	14 48.4
10	5 14 53.0	16 53.5	12 .5	4 ♍ 6.6	1 ♐ 31.6	2 15.2	17 46.7	9 51.6	18 30.3	28 16.9	8 23.5	14 48.6
11	5 18 49.5	17 59.5	11 57.5	15 49.5	3 4.6	3 30.2	17 29.0	10 6.2	18 37.3	28 16.4	8 25.3	14 48.7
12	5 22 46.1	19 5.6	11 54.6	27 37.3	4 38.5	4 44.8	17 10.5	10 20.8	18 44.3	28 15.9	8 27.1	14 48.9
13	5 26 42.7	20 11.8	11 51.6	9 ♎ 40.0	6 13.3	5 59.0	16 51.2	10 35.5	18 51.4	28 15.3	8 28.9	14 49.0
14	5 30 39.2	21 18.0	11 48.6	22 9.0	7 48.8	7 12.8	16 31.2	10 50.2	18 58.5	28 14.6	8 30.6	14 49.1
15	5 34 35.8	22 24.4	11 45.7	5 ♏ 15.2	9 25.1	8 26.3	16 10.3	11 5.0	19 5.6	28 13.9	8 32.4	14 49.1
16	5 38 32.3	23 30.8	11 42.7	19 7.4	11 2.1	9 39.3	15 48.8	11 19.8	19 12.8	28 13.2	8 34.1	14 49.1
17	5 42 28.9	24 37.3	11 39.7	3 ♐ 49.0	12 39.8	10 51.9	15 26.6	11 34.6	19 20.0	28 12.3	8 35.8	14 49.1
18	5 46 25.4	25 43.8	11 36.8	19 14.7	14 18.2	12 4.0	15 3.8	11 49.4	19 27.3	28 11.5	8 37.5	14 49.1
19	5 50 22.0	26 50.3	11 33.8	5 ♑ 8.7	15 57.1	13 15.8	14 40.4	12 4.3	19 34.5	28 10.6	8 39.1	14 R 49.0
20	5 54 18.6	27 56.9	11 30.8	21 6.9	17 36.7	14 27.1	14 16.4	12 19.2	19 41.8	28 9.6	8 40.8	14 48.9
21	5 58 15.1	29 3.6	11 27.9	6 ♒ 45.0	19 16.9	15 38.0	13 51.9	12 34.1	19 49.1	28 8.6	8 42.4	14 48.8
22	6 2 11.7	0 ♑ 10.2	11 24.9	21 45.3	20 57.7	16 48.4	13 27.0	12 49.0	19 56.5	28 7.5	8 44.0	14 48.6
23	6 6 8.2	1 16.9	11 21.9	6 ♓ 1.0	22 39.0	17 58.5	13 1.8	13 4.0	20 3.9	28 6.5	8 45.6	14 48.5
24	6 10 4.8	2 23.5	11 18.9	19 34.3	24 20.8	19 8.0	12 36.2	13 19.0	20 11.3	28 5.3	8 47.1	14 48.2
25	6 14 1.3	3 30.1	11 16.0	2 ♈ 33.4	26 3.1	20 17.2	12 10.3	13 34.0	20 18.7	28 4.1	8 48.7	14 48.0
26	6 17 57.9	4 36.7	11 13.0	15 8.7	27 45.9	21 25.8	11 44.2	13 49.0	20 26.1	28 2.9	8 50.2	14 47.7
27	6 21 54.5	5 43.3	11 10.0	27 30.9	29 29.1	22 34.0	11 17.9	14 4.0	20 33.6	28 1.5	8 51.6	14 47.4
28	6 25 51.0	6 49.8	11 7.1	9 ♉ 49.2	1 ♑ 12.8	23 41.7	10 51.4	14 19.0	20 41.0	28 .2	8 53.1	14 47.1
29	6 29 47.6	7 56.2	11 4.1	22 10.2	2 56.9	24 49.0	10 25.0	14 34.0	20 48.5	27 58.8	8 54.5	14 46.7
30	6 33 44.1	9 2.6	11 1.1	4 ♊ 37.4	4 41.3	25 55.9	9 58.5	14 49.1	20 56.0	27 57.4	8 55.9	14 46.3
31	6 37 40.7	10 9.0	10 58.1	17 11.2	6 26.2	27 2.3	9 32.0	15 4.1	21 3.5	27 55.9	8 57.2	14 45.9

DECLINATION

DAY	EPHEM. SID. TIME	☉	☊	☽	☿	♀	♂	♃	♄	♅	♆	♇
1	4 39 24.0	21 S 46.3	0 N 7.8	11 N 44.7	16 S 4.4	24 S 19.0	24 N 43.3	23 S 17.7	22 S 18.9	13 N 36.5	13 S 10.0	20 N 12.9
4	4 51 13.6	22 12.7	0 7.9	18 14.0	17 27.3	23 47.1	24 56.0	23 15.8	22 16.9	13 36.6	13 11.8	20 13.8
7	5 3 3.3	22 35.2	0 7.9	17 24.3	18 48.1	23 9.3	25 9.5	23 13.7	22 14.8	13 37.0	13 13.5	20 14.9
10	5 14 53.0	22 53.7	0 8.0	10 .5	20 4.1	22 25.7	25 23.5	23 11.3	22 12.6	13 37.6	13 15.2	20 16.1
13	5 26 42.7	23 8.1	0 8.1	1 S 27.1	21 13.5	21 36.6	25 37.8	23 8.8	22 10.4	13 38.3	13 16.8	20 17.4
16	5 38 32.3	23 18.5	0 8.1	13 14.1	22 14.7	20 42.3	25 52.0	23 6.0	22 8.0	13 39.1	13 18.3	20 18.8
19	5 50 22.0	23 24.6	0 8.2	18 49.4	23 6.7	19 43.1	26 5.8	23 2.9	22 5.6	13 40.2	13 19.8	20 20.3
22	6 2 11.7	23 26.5	0 8.2	13 17.9	23 48.6	18 39.4	26 18.9	22 59.7	22 3.0	13 41.4	13 21.2	20 21.9
25	6 14 1.3	23 24.2	0 8.3	1 4.8	24 19.7	17 31.6	26 30.9	22 56.2	22 .4	13 42.7	13 22.5	20 23.5
28	6 25 51.0	23 17.6	0 8.4	10 N 48.1	24 39.3	16 19.9	26 41.6	22 52.5	21 57.7	13 44.2	13 23.8	20 25.3
31	6 37 40.7	23 6.8	0 8.4	17 54.4	24 46.9	15 4.8	26 50.9	22 48.5	21 55.0	13 45.8	13 24.9	20 27.1

JANUARY 1961

LONGITUDE

DAY	EPHEM. SID. TIME h m s	☉ ° ′	☊ ° ′	☽ ° ′	☿ ° ′	♀ ° ′	♂ ° ′	♃ ° ′	♄ ° ′	♅ ° ′	♆ ° ′	♇ ° ′
1	6 41 37.2	10♑20.8	9♍20.6	29♊48.9	7♑26.0	25♒17.3	8♋ 7.3	14♑ 5.9	19♑35.4	25♌22.5	10♏50.5	8♍ .5
2	6 45 33.8	11 21.9	9 17.4	11♋45.9	9 1.7	26 25.9	7 R43.8	14 19.8	19 42.4	25 R20.9	10 51.8	7 R59.8
3	6 49 30.3	12 23.1	9 14.2	23 38.3	10 37.8	27 34.2	7 20.5	14 33.8	19 49.5	25 19.2	10 53.1	7 59.1
4	6 53 26.9	13 24.2	9 11.0	5♌27.7	12 14.3	28 42.4	6 57.5	14 47.8	19 56.6	25 17.5	10 54.4	7 58.3
5	6 57 23.5	14 25.4	9 7.8	17 16.1	13 51.1	29 50.3	6 34.7	15 1.7	20 3.6	25 15.7	10 55.6	7 57.6
6	7 1 20.0	15 26.5	9 4.7	29 6.3	15 28.3	0♓58.1	6 12.3	15 15.7	20 10.7	25 13.9	10 56.8	7 56.8
7	7 5 16.6	16 27.6	9 1.5	11♍ 1.5	17 5.9	2 5.7	5 50.3	15 29.6	20 17.8	25 12.1	10 58.0	7 55.9
8	7 9 13.1	17 28.8	8 58.3	23 6.0	18 43.9	3 13.1	5 28.7	15 43.6	20 24.9	25 10.2	10 59.1	7 55.1
9	7 13 9.7	18 29.9	8 55.1	5♎24.1	20 22.4	4 20.3	5 7.6	15 57.6	20 32.0	25 8.3	11 .2	7 54.2
10	7 17 6.2	19 31.1	8 52.0	18 .9	22 1.2	5 27.2	4 47.0	16 11.6	20 39.1	25 6.3	11 1.3	7 53.3
11	7 21 2.8	20 32.2	8 48.8	1♏ .9	23 40.5	6 34.0	4 26.9	16 25.5	20 46.2	25 4.3	11 2.4	7 52.4
12	7 24 59.4	21 33.4	8 45.6	14 28.1	25 20.2	7 40.5	4 7.3	16 39.5	20 53.3	25 2.3	11 3.4	7 51.4
13	7 28 55.9	22 34.6	8 42.4	28 24.7	27 .4	8 46.8	3 48.4	16 53.5	21 .5	25 .3	11 4.5	7 50.5
14	7 32 52.5	23 35.7	8 39.3	12♐50.2	28 41.0	9 52.8	3 30.1	17 7.4	21 7.6	24 58.2	11 5.4	7 49.5
15	7 36 49.0	24 36.8	8 36.1	27 41.0	0♒21.9	10 58.6	3 12.5	17 21.4	21 14.7	24 56.0	11 6.4	7 48.5
16	7 40 45.6	25 38.0	8 32.9	12♑50.1	2 3.3	12 4.2	2 55.5	17 35.3	21 21.8	24 53.9	11 7.3	7 47.5
17	7 44 42.1	26 39.1	8 29.7	28 7.8	3 45.0	13 9.4	2 39.3	17 49.2	21 28.9	24 51.7	11 8.1	7 46.4
18	7 48 38.7	27 40.2	8 26.5	13♒23.0	5 27.0	14 14.4	2 23.7	18 3.1	21 36.0	24 49.4	11 9.0	7 45.3
19	7 52 35.3	28 41.3	8 23.4	28 25.6	7 9.2	15 19.2	2 9.0	18 17.0	21 43.1	24 47.2	11 9.8	7 44.2
20	7 56 31.8	29 42.4	8 20.2	13♓ 7.6	8 51.7	16 23.6	1 55.0	18 30.8	21 50.1	24 44.9	11 10.5	7 43.0
21	8 0 28.4	0♒43.5	8 17.0	27 24.2	10 34.3	17 27.7	1 41.7	18 44.7	21 57.2	24 42.5	11 11.3	7 41.9
22	8 4 24.9	1 44.6	8 13.8	11♈13.7	12 16.9	18 31.5	1 29.3	18 58.5	22 4.2	24 40.2	11 12.0	7 40.7
23	8 8 21.5	2 45.6	8 10.7	24 36.9	13 59.3	19 34.9	1 17.7	19 12.3	22 11.3	24 37.8	11 12.6	7 39.5
24	8 12 18.0	3 46.7	8 7.5	7♉36.4	15 41.6	20 38.0	1 6.9	19 26.1	22 18.3	24 35.4	11 13.3	7 38.3
25	8 16 14.6	4 47.7	8 4.3	20 15.7	17 23.4	21 40.8	0 56.8	19 39.9	22 25.3	24 33.0	11 13.9	7 37.1
26	8 20 11.1	5 48.7	8 1.1	2♊38.5	19 4.6	22 43.2	0 47.6	19 53.6	22 32.3	24 30.6	11 14.4	7 35.8
27	8 24 7.7	6 49.6	7 58.0	14 48.7	20 44.9	23 45.2	0 39.3	20 7.3	22 39.2	24 28.1	11 15.0	7 34.5
28	8 28 4.3	7 50.6	7 54.8	26 49.7	22 24.0	24 46.8	0 31.7	20 21.0	22 46.2	24 25.7	11 15.5	7 33.2
29	8 32 .8	8 51.5	7 51.6	8♋44.4	24 1.6	25 48.0	0 24.9	20 34.7	22 53.1	24 23.2	11 15.9	7 31.9
30	8 35 57.4	9 52.4	7 48.4	20 35.5	25 37.4	26 48.8	0 19.0	20 48.3	23 .0	24 20.6	11 16.4	7 30.6
31	8 39 53.9	10 53.3	7 45.2	2♌25.0	27 10.9	27 49.1	0 13.8	21 1.9	23 6.9	24 18.1	11 16.8	7 29.3

LATITUDE

DAY	SID. TIME	☉	☊	☽	☿	♀	♂	♃	♄	♅	♆	♇
1	6 41 37.2	0 .0	0 .0	4 S 42.3	1 S 32.8	1 S 39.3	3 N 42.4	0 S 5.5	0 N 6.7	0 N 45.1	1 N 44.6	12 N 52.2
4	6 53 26.9	0 .0	0 .0	2 42.4	1 45.1	1 30.1	3 45.5	0 5.7	0 6.5	0 45.2	1 44.8	12 53.4
7	7 5 16.6	0 .0	0 .0	0 N 20.2	1 55.0	1 19.8	3 47.6	0 6.0	0 6.3	0 45.3	1 45.0	12 54.6
10	7 17 6.2	0 .0	0 .0	3 22.1	2 2.0	1 8.4	3 48.9	0 6.3	0 6.1	0 45.4	1 45.1	12 55.7
13	7 28 55.9	0 .0	0 .0	5 5.7	2 5.8	0 55.9	3 49.3	0 6.6	0 5.9	0 45.5	1 45.3	12 56.8
16	7 40 45.6	0 .0	0 .0	4 11.0	2 5.9	0 42.3	3 48.9	0 6.9	0 5.6	0 45.6	1 45.5	12 57.9
19	7 52 35.3	0 .0	0 .0	0 44.9	2 1.8	0 27.6	3 47.8	0 7.2	0 5.4	0 45.7	1 45.6	12 58.9
22	8 4 24.9	0 .0	0 .0	2 S 57.4	1 52.8	0 11.9	3 46.1	0 7.5	0 5.2	0 45.7	1 45.8	12 59.8
25	8 16 14.6	0 .0	0 .0	5 .0	1 38.2	0 N 4.9	3 43.9	0 7.8	0 5.0	0 45.8	1 46.0	13 .7
28	8 28 4.3	0 .0	0 .0	4 53.6	1 17.4	0 22.7	3 41.2	0 8.1	0 4.8	0 45.9	1 46.2	13 1.6
31	8 39 53.9	0 .0	0 .0	2 55.4	0 49.6	0 41.5	3 38.2	0 8.4	0 4.6	0 45.9	1 46.4	13 2.4

RIGHT ASCENSION

DAY	SID. TIME	☉	☊	☽	☿	♀	♂	♃	♄	♅	♆	♇
1	6 41 37.2	11♑15.3	10♍55.2	29♊48.4	8♑11.3	28♒ 8.2	9♋ 5.7	15♑19.2	21♑11.0	27♌54.4	8♏58.6	14♍45.4
2	6 45 33.8	12 21.5	10 52.2	12♋23.9	9 56.8	29 13.7	8 R39.5	15 34.2	21 18.5	27 R52.8	8 59.9	14 R44.9
3	6 49 30.3	13 27.6	10 49.2	24 52.1	11 42.6	0♓18.7	8 13.6	15 49.3	21 26.1	27 51.2	9 1.2	14 44.4
4	6 53 26.9	14 33.6	10 46.2	7♌ 8.2	13 28.7	1 23.3	7 47.9	16 4.3	21 33.6	27 49.5	9 2.4	14 43.9
5	6 57 23.5	15 39.5	10 43.3	19 10.0	15 14.9	2 27.4	7 22.5	16 19.4	21 41.2	27 47.8	9 3.6	14 43.3
6	7 1 20.0	16 45.4	10 40.3	0♍58.4	17 1.4	3 31.1	6 57.5	16 34.4	21 48.7	27 46.1	9 4.8	14 42.7
7	7 5 16.6	17 51.1	10 37.3	12 37.3	18 48.1	4 34.3	6 32.8	16 49.5	21 56.3	27 44.3	9 6.0	14 42.1
8	7 9 13.1	18 56.7	10 34.3	24 13.3	20 34.9	5 37.2	6 8.7	17 4.5	22 3.9	27 42.5	9 7.1	14 41.4
9	7 13 9.7	20 2.1	10 31.4	5♎55.4	22 21.7	6 39.5	5 45.0	17 19.6	22 11.5	27 40.6	9 8.3	14 40.7
10	7 17 6.2	21 7.5	10 28.4	17 54.0	24 8.7	7 41.5	5 21.9	17 34.6	22 19.0	27 38.8	9 9.3	14 40.0
11	7 21 2.8	22 12.7	10 25.4	0♏20.6	25 55.7	8 43.0	4 59.4	17 49.6	22 26.6	27 36.8	9 10.4	14 39.3
12	7 24 59.4	23 17.7	10 22.4	13 26.4	27 42.6	9 44.1	4 37.5	18 4.6	22 34.2	27 34.9	9 11.4	14 38.6
13	7 28 55.9	24 22.7	10 19.5	27 20.0	29 29.6	10 44.8	4 16.3	18 19.7	22 41.8	27 32.9	9 12.5	14 37.8
14	7 32 52.5	25 27.5	10 16.5	12♐ 4.5	1♒16.3	11 45.0	3 55.8	18 34.7	22 49.4	27 30.9	9 13.4	14 37.0
15	7 36 49.0	26 32.1	10 13.5	27 33.9	3 2.9	12 44.8	3 36.0	18 49.6	22 56.9	27 28.8	9 14.3	14 36.2
16	7 40 45.6	27 36.6	10 10.5	13♑31.4	4 49.3	13 44.2	3 17.0	19 4.6	23 4.5	27 26.7	9 15.2	14 35.3
17	7 44 42.1	28 40.8	10 7.6	29 33.1	6 35.3	14 43.2	2 58.7	19 19.5	23 12.0	27 24.6	9 16.1	14 34.4
18	7 48 38.7	29 44.9	10 4.6	15♒14.6	8 21.0	15 41.7	2 41.3	19 34.4	23 19.6	27 22.4	9 16.9	14 33.5
19	7 52 35.3	0♒48.9	10 1.6	0♓19.1	10 6.2	16 39.8	2 24.7	19 49.3	23 27.1	27 20.2	9 17.7	14 32.6
20	7 56 31.8	1 52.6	9 58.6	14 40.5	11 50.9	17 37.5	2 9.0	20 4.2	23 34.6	27 18.0	9 18.5	14 31.7
21	8 0 28.4	2 56.2	9 55.6	28 21.0	13 34.9	18 34.8	1 54.2	20 19.0	23 42.1	27 15.8	9 19.2	14 30.7
22	8 4 24.9	3 59.5	9 52.7	11♈28.8	15 18.1	19 31.6	1 40.2	20 33.8	23 49.6	27 13.5	9 20.0	14 29.7
23	8 8 21.5	5 2.7	9 49.7	24 13.5	17 .4	20 28.0	1 27.1	20 48.6	23 57.1	27 11.2	9 20.6	14 28.7
24	8 12 18.0	6 5.6	9 46.7	6♉45.0	18 41.6	21 24.0	1 15.0	21 3.4	24 4.6	27 8.9	9 21.3	14 27.6
25	8 16 14.6	7 8.4	9 43.7	19 11.3	20 21.5	22 19.5	1 3.8	21 18.1	24 12.0	27 6.6	9 21.9	14 26.6
26	8 20 11.1	8 10.9	9 40.7	1♊37.9	21 59.9	23 14.6	0 53.4	21 32.8	24 19.4	27 4.2	9 22.5	14 25.5
27	8 24 7.7	9 13.3	9 37.8	14 7.6	23 36.7	24 9.3	0 44.0	21 47.4	24 26.8	27 1.8	9 23.0	14 24.4
28	8 28 4.3	10 15.4	9 34.8	26 40.0	25 11.5	25 3.5	0 35.5	22 2.0	24 34.2	26 59.4	9 23.5	14 23.3
29	8 32 .8	11 17.4	9 31.8	9♋12.4	26 44.0	25 57.3	0 28.0	22 16.6	24 41.6	26 57.0	9 24.0	14 22.1
30	8 35 57.4	12 19.1	9 28.8	21 40.5	28 13.8	26 50.5	0 21.3	22 31.1	24 48.9	26 54.6	9 24.4	14 21.0
31	8 39 53.9	13 20.6	9 25.8	3♌59.9	29 40.7	27 43.4	0 15.5	22 45.6	24 56.2	26 52.1	9 24.8	14 19.8

DECLINATION

DAY	SID. TIME	☉	☊	☽	☿	♀	♂	♃	♄	♅	♆	♇
1	6 41 37.2	23 S 2.3	0 N 8.4	18 N 44.2	24 S 46.7	14 S 39.1	26 N 53.6	22 S 47.2	21 S 54.0	13 N 46.4	13 S 25.3	20 N 27.8
4	6 53 26.9	22 46.0	0 8.5	16 16.8	24 37.4	13 20.0	27 .7	22 42.9	21 51.2	13 48.1	13 26.4	20 29.7
7	7 5 16.6	22 25.7	0 8.6	7 44.6	24 14.9	11 58.3	27 6.2	22 38.5	21 48.3	13 50.1	13 27.3	20 31.7
10	7 17 6.2	22 1.3	0 8.6	3 S 57.1	23 38.9	10 34.3	27 10.0	22 33.9	21 45.3	13 52.1	13 28.2	20 33.7
13	7 28 55.9	21 33.1	0 8.7	14 50.2	22 48.9	9 8.5	27 12.4	22 29.0	21 42.2	13 54.2	13 29.0	20 35.8
16	7 40 45.6	21 1.1	0 8.8	18 39.4	21 44.9	7 41.2	27 13.4	22 24.0	21 39.2	13 56.4	13 29.7	20 37.9
19	7 52 35.3	20 25.5	0 8.8	11 19.2	20 26.9	6 12.6	27 13.3	22 18.7	21 36.0	13 58.7	13 30.3	20 40.1
22	8 4 24.9	19 46.5	0 8.9	1 N 43.3	18 55.3	4 43.3	27 12.1	22 13.3	21 32.9	14 1.1	13 30.8	20 42.3
25	8 16 14.6	19 4.1	0 8.9	12 59.4	17 11.0	3 13.5	27 10.2	22 7.8	21 29.7	14 3.6	13 31.2	20 44.5
28	8 28 4.3	18 18.6	0 9.0	18 30.7	15 16.0	1 43.6	27 7.7	22 2.0	21 26.4	14 6.1	13 31.6	20 46.8
31	8 39 53.9	17 30.1	0 9.1	16 46.4	13 13.6	0 13.9	27 4.7	21 56.1	21 23.2	14 8.7	13 31.8	20 49.0

FEBRUARY 1961

LONGITUDE

DAY	EPHEM. SID. TIME h m s	☉ ° ′	☊ ° ′	☾ ° ′	☿ ° ′	♀ ° ′	♂ ° ′	♃ ° ′	♄ ° ′	♅ ° ′	♆ ° ′	♇ ° ′
1	8 43 50.5	11♒54.2	7♍42.1	14♌15.0	28♒41.5	28♓49.0	0♋ 9.5	21♑15.4	23♑13.8	24♌15.6	11♏17.1	7♍27.9
2	8 47 47.0	12 55.1	7 38.9	26 7.3	0♓ 8.8	29 48.4	0 R 5.9	21 29.0	23 20.7	24 R 13.0	11 17.5	7 R 26.6
3	8 51 43.6	13 56.0	7 35.7	8♍ 3.9	1 32.2	0♈47.4	0 3.2	21 42.5	23 27.5	24 10.5	11 17.8	7 25.2
4	8 55 40.1	14 56.8	7 32.5	20 7.1	2 50.9	1 45.8	0 1.2	21 55.9	23 34.3	24 7.9	11 18.1	7 23.8
5	8 59 36.7	15 57.6	7 29.4	2♎19.4	4 4.2	2 43.8	29♊60.0	22 9.4	23 41.1	24 5.3	11 18.3	7 22.4
6	9 3 33.2	16 58.4	7 26.2	14 44.0	5 11.5	3 41.1	29 59.5	22 22.7	23 47.8	24 2.7	11 18.5	7 21.0
7	9 7 29.8	17 59.2	7 23.0	27 24.1	6 11.8	4 38.0	29 D 59.8	22 36.1	23 54.5	24 .1	11 18.7	7 19.6
8	9 11 26.4	18 60.0	7 19.8	10♏23.1	7 4.6	5 34.3	0♋ .8	22 49.4	24 1.2	23 57.5	11 18.8	7 18.1
9	9 15 22.9	20 .7	7 16.6	23 44.0	7 49.0	6 30.0	0 2.6	23 2.6	24 7.9	23 54.8	11 18.9	7 16.6
10	9 19 19.5	21 1.5	7 13.5	7♐29.0	8 24.3	7 25.0	0 5.1	23 15.8	24 14.5	23 52.2	11 18.9	7 15.2
11	9 23 16.0	22 2.2	7 10.3	21 38.8	8 50.0	8 19.5	0 8.3	23 29.0	24 21.1	23 49.6	11 19.0	7 13.7
12	9 27 12.6	23 2.9	7 7.1	6♑11.8	9 5.5	9 13.3	0 12.2	23 42.1	24 27.6	23 46.9	11 19.0	7 12.2
13	9 31 9.1	24 3.6	7 3.9	21 3.9	9 10.5	10 6.4	0 16.8	23 55.2	24 34.1	23 44.3	11 R 18.9	7 10.7
14	9 35 5.7	25 4.2	7 .8	6♒ 8.3	9 R 5.0	10 58.8	0 22.1	24 8.2	24 40.6	23 41.7	11 18.8	7 9.2
15	9 39 2.2	26 4.9	6 57.6	21 16.5	8 48.9	11 50.5	0 28.0	24 21.1	24 47.0	23 39.0	11 18.7	7 7.7
16	9 42 58.8	27 5.5	6 54.4	6♓18.9	8 22.7	12 41.5	0 34.7	24 34.0	24 53.4	23 36.4	11 18.6	7 6.2
17	9 46 55.3	28 6.1	6 51.2	21 6.8	7 47.0	13 31.6	0 41.9	24 46.9	24 59.8	23 33.8	11 18.4	7 4.7
18	9 50 51.9	29 6.6	6 48.0	5♈33.5	7 2.7	14 21.0	0 49.8	24 59.7	25 6.1	23 31.1	11 18.2	7 3.1
19	9 54 48.4	0♓ 7.1	6 44.9	19 34.6	6 11.0	15 9.5	0 58.4	25 12.4	25 12.4	23 28.5	11 17.9	7 1.6
20	9 58 45.0	1 7.6	6 41.7	3♉ 8.9	5 13.2	15 57.1	1 7.5	25 25.1	25 18.6	23 25.9	11 17.6	7 .0
21	10 2 41.6	2 8.1	6 38.5	16 16.9	4 10.9	16 43.7	1 17.3	25 37.7	25 24.8	23 23.3	11 17.3	6 58.5
22	10 6 38.1	3 8.6	6 35.3	29 1.4	3 5.8	17 29.5	1 27.6	25 50.2	25 30.9	23 20.7	11 17.0	6 57.0
23	10 10 34.7	4 9.0	6 32.2	11♊26.1	1 59.6	18 14.2	1 38.5	26 2.7	25 37.0	23 18.1	11 16.6	6 55.4
24	10 14 31.2	5 9.4	6 29.0	23 35.3	0 53.9	18 57.9	1 50.0	26 15.2	25 43.1	23 15.6	11 16.2	6 53.9
25	10 18 27.8	6 9.7	6 25.8	5♋33.4	29♒50.3	19 40.5	2 2.0	26 27.5	25 49.1	23 13.1	11 15.8	6 52.4
26	10 22 24.3	7 10.0	6 22.6	17 24.8	28 50.2	20 21.9	2 14.6	26 39.8	25 55.0	23 10.5	11 15.3	6 50.8
27	10 26 20.9	8 10.3	6 19.4	29 13.3	27 54.6	21 2.2	2 27.7	26 52.0	26 .9	23 8.0	11 14.8	6 49.3
28	10 30 17.4	9 10.5	6 16.3	11♌ 2.5	27 4.5	21 41.3	2 41.2	27 4.2	26 6.7	23 5.5	11 14.3	6 47.7

LATITUDE

DAY	EPHEM. SID. TIME	☉	☊	☾	☿	♀	♂	♃	♄	♅	♆	♇
1	8 43 50.5	0 .0	0 .0	1 S 58.1	0 S 38.7	0 N 48.0	3 N 37.1	0 S 8.5	0 N 4.5	0 N 45.9	1 N 46.4	13 N 2.6
4	8 55 40.1	0 .0	0 .0	1 N 16.0	0 1.2	1 8.2	3 33.7	0 8.8	0 4.3	0 46.0	1 46.6	13 3.3
7	9 7 29.8	0 .0	0 .0	4 6.7	0 N 42.7	1 29.2	3 30.1	0 9.2	0 4.1	0 46.0	1 46.8	13 4.0
10	9 19 19.5	0 .0	0 .0	5 16.7	1 31.0	1 51.1	3 26.3	0 9.5	0 3.9	0 46.0	1 47.0	13 4.6
13	9 31 9.1	0 .0	0 .0	3 45.1	2 19.6	2 13.9	3 22.4	0 9.8	0 3.7	0 46.0	1 47.2	13 5.1
16	9 42 58.8	0 .0	0 .0	0 S .6	3 2.4	2 37.4	3 18.4	0 10.1	0 3.5	0 46.0	1 47.3	13 5.6
19	9 54 48.4	0 .0	0 .0	3 38.5	3 32.3	3 1.7	3 14.3	0 10.5	0 3.3	0 46.0	1 47.5	13 6.0
22	10 6 38.1	0 .0	0 .0	5 15.4	3 43.6	3 26.6	3 10.3	0 10.8	0 3.0	0 46.0	1 47.7	13 6.3
25	10 18 27.8	0 .0	0 .0	4 37.4	3 34.9	3 52.1	3 6.3	0 11.2	0 2.8	0 46.0	1 47.9	13 6.6
28	10 30 17.4	0 .0	0 .0	2 15.7	3 9.3	4 17.9	3 2.3	0 11.5	0 2.6	0 46.0	1 48.0	13 6.8

RIGHT ASCENSION

DAY	EPHEM. SID. TIME	☉	☊	☾	☿	♀	♂	♃	♄	♅	♆	♇
1	8 43 50.5	14♒21.9	9♍22.8	16♌ 7.6	1♓ 4.1	28♓35.7	0♋10.6	23♑ .1	25♑ 3.5	26♌49.6	9♏25.2	14♍18.6
2	8 47 47.0	15 23.1	9 19.9	28 2.8	2 23.5	29 27.6	0 R 6.7	23 14.5	25 10.8	26 R 47.2	9 25.6	14 R 17.4
3	8 51 43.6	16 24.0	9 16.9	9♍47.2	3 38.5	0♈19.1	0 3.6	23 28.9	25 18.0	26 44.7	9 25.9	14 16.2
4	8 55 40.1	17 24.7	9 13.9	21 25.1	4 48.5	1 10.0	0 1.4	23 43.3	25 25.2	26 42.2	9 26.2	14 15.0
5	8 59 36.7	18 25.2	9 10.9	3♎ 3.3	5 52.8	2 .4	29♊60.0	23 57.5	25 32.4	26 39.7	9 26.4	14 13.7
6	9 3 33.2	19 25.5	9 7.9	14 50.2	6 50.9	2 50.3	29 59.5	24 11.8	25 39.5	26 37.1	9 26.6	14 12.5
7	9 7 29.8	20 25.7	9 4.9	26 55.3	7 42.1	3 39.7	29 D 59.8	24 25.9	25 46.7	26 34.6	9 26.8	14 11.2
8	9 11 26.4	21 25.6	9 2.0	9♏28.9	8 25.7	4 28.5	0♋ .9	24 40.1	25 53.7	26 32.1	9 27.0	14 9.9
9	9 15 22.9	22 25.3	8 59.0	22 40.0	9 1.3	5 16.9	0 2.9	24 54.1	26 .8	26 29.5	9 27.1	14 8.5
10	9 19 19.5	23 24.8	8 56.0	6♐35.0	9 28.2	6 4.6	0 5.7	25 8.2	26 7.8	26 26.9	9 27.1	14 7.2
11	9 23 16.0	24 24.2	8 53.0	21 14.6	9 46.0	6 51.8	0 9.3	25 22.1	26 14.7	26 24.4	9 27.2	14 5.9
12	9 27 12.6	25 23.3	8 50.0	6♑31.4	9 54.4	7 38.4	0 13.6	25 36.0	26 21.7	26 21.8	9 27.2	14 4.5
13	9 31 9.1	26 22.3	8 47.0	22 10.0	9 R 53.1	8 24.4	0 18.8	25 49.9	26 28.5	26 19.2	9 27.2	14 3.2
14	9 35 5.7	27 21.1	8 44.0	7♒50.0	9 42.2	9 9.8	0 24.7	26 3.7	26 35.4	26 16.7	9 R 27.1	14 1.8
15	9 39 2.2	28 19.6	8 41.1	23 12.5	9 21.9	9 54.5	0 31.3	26 17.4	26 42.2	26 14.1	9 27.0	14 .4
16	9 42 58.8	29 18.1	8 38.1	8♓ 4.9	8 52.5	10 38.6	0 38.7	26 31.1	26 48.9	26 11.5	9 26.9	13 59.0
17	9 46 55.3	0♓16.3	8 35.1	22 22.6	8 14.9	11 22.0	0 46.9	26 44.7	26 55.7	26 9.0	9 26.7	13 57.6
18	9 50 51.9	1 14.4	8 32.1	6♈ 7.9	7 29.8	12 4.6	0 55.7	26 58.2	27 2.3	26 6.4	9 26.5	13 56.2
19	9 54 48.4	2 12.2	8 29.1	19 27.1	6 38.5	12 46.5	1 5.2	27 11.7	27 9.0	26 3.9	9 26.3	13 54.8
20	9 58 45.0	3 9.9	8 26.1	2♉27.6	5 42.3	13 27.6	1 15.4	27 25.1	27 15.5	26 1.3	9 26.1	13 53.3
21	10 2 41.6	4 7.5	8 23.1	15 16.5	4 42.6	14 7.9	1 26.3	27 38.4	27 22.0	25 58.8	9 25.8	13 51.9
22	10 6 38.1	5 4.8	8 20.1	27 59.1	3 41.0	14 47.4	1 37.8	27 51.6	27 28.5	25 56.3	9 25.5	13 50.5
23	10 10 34.7	6 2.0	8 17.1	10♊38.8	2 39.0	15 25.9	1 50.0	28 4.8	27 34.9	25 53.7	9 25.1	13 49.0
24	10 14 31.2	6 59.1	8 14.1	23 16.5	1 38.3	16 3.6	2 2.8	28 17.9	27 41.4	25 51.3	9 24.8	13 47.6
25	10 18 27.8	7 56.0	8 11.2	5♋50.9	0 40.0	16 40.3	2 16.2	28 31.0	27 47.7	25 48.8	9 24.3	13 46.2
26	10 22 24.3	8 52.8	8 8.2	18 19.9	29♒45.5	17 16.0	2 30.2	28 43.9	27 53.9	25 46.3	9 23.9	13 44.7
27	10 26 20.9	9 49.3	8 5.2	0♌40.7	28 55.7	17 50.6	2 44.7	28 56.8	28 .1	25 43.9	9 23.4	13 43.2
28	10 30 17.4	10 45.8	8 2.2	12 51.3	28 11.5	18 24.1	2 59.9	29 9.5	28 6.3	25 41.4	9 22.9	13 41.8

DECLINATION

DAY	EPHEM. SID. TIME	☉	☊	☾	☿	♀	♂	♃	♄	♅	♆	♇
1	8 43 50.5	17 S 13.4	0 N 9.1	14 N 40.3	12 S 32.1	0 N 15.8	27 N 3.6	21 S 54.1	21 S 22.1	14 N 9.5	13 S 31.8	20 N 49.8
4	8 55 40.1	16 21.2	0 9.2	5 4.8	10 28.7	1 44.6	27 .2	21 48.1	21 18.8	14 12.1	13 31.9	20 52.0
7	9 7 29.8	15 26.5	0 9.2	6 S 42.6	8 34.6	3 12.4	26 56.6	21 41.9	21 15.6	14 14.7	13 32.0	20 54.2
10	9 19 19.5	14 29.4	0 9.3	16 21.1	7 .7	4 38.7	26 52.8	21 35.6	21 12.3	14 17.4	13 31.9	20 56.5
13	9 31 9.1	13 30.2	0 9.3	18 5.0	5 58.4	6 3.3	26 48.9	21 29.2	21 9.0	14 20.0	13 31.7	20 58.7
16	9 42 58.8	12 28.9	0 9.4	9 12.4	5 36.5	7 25.8	26 44.8	21 22.7	21 5.8	14 22.6	13 31.4	21 .8
19	9 54 48.4	11 25.9	0 9.5	4 N 17.2	5 57.2	8 45.8	26 40.6	21 16.1	21 2.6	14 25.2	13 31.0	21 2.9
22	10 6 38.1	10 21.2	0 9.5	14 48.6	6 53.5	10 2.8	26 36.3	21 9.5	20 59.4	14 27.8	13 30.6	21 5.0
25	10 18 27.8	9 15.1	0 9.6	18 42.4	8 10.4	11 16.5	26 31.8	21 2.8	20 56.3	14 30.3	13 30.1	21 7.0
28	10 30 17.4	8 7.8	0 9.6	15 17.1	9 31.3	12 26.2	26 27.1	20 56.2	20 53.2	14 32.8	13 29.4	21 9.0

MARCH 1961

LONGITUDE

DAY	EPHEM. SID. TIME	☉	☊	☽	☿	♀	♂	♃	♄	♅	♆	♇
	h m s	° ′	° ′	° ′	° ′	° ′	° ′	° ′	° ′	° ′	° ′	° ′
1	10 34 14.0	10♓10.8	6♍13.1	22♌55.3	26♒20.5	22♈19.1	2♋55.3	27♑16.2	26♑12.5	23♌ 3.0	11♏13.7	6♍46.2
2	10 38 10.5	11 10.9	6 9.9	4♍54.2	25 R 43.2	22 55.6	3 9.9	27 28.2	26 18.2	23 R .5	11 R 13.1	6 R 44.6
3	10 42 7.1	12 11.1	6 6.7	17 1.2	25 12.8	23 30.7	3 24.9	27 40.1	26 23.9	22 58.1	11 12.5	6 43.1
4	10 46 3.6	13 11.2	6 3.6	29 18.0	24 49.4	24 4.4	3 40.4	27 52.0	26 29.5	22 55.6	11 11.8	6 41.5
5	10 50 .2	14 11.3	6 .4	11♎45.9	24 32.9	24 36.7	3 56.3	28 3.7	26 35.1	22 53.2	11 11.1	6 40.0
6	10 53 56.7	15 11.4	5 57.2	24 26.2	24 23.3	25 7.4	4 12.7	28 15.4	26 40.6	22 50.8	11 10.4	6 38.5
7	10 57 53.3	16 11.4	5 54.0	7♏20.3	24 20.3	25 36.5	4 29.6	28 27.0	26 46.0	22 48.5	11 9.6	6 36.9
8	11 1 49.8	17 11.4	5 50.8	20 29.2	24 D 23.6	26 4.0	4 46.8	28 38.5	26 51.4	22 46.2	11 8.9	6 35.4
9	11 5 46.4	18 11.4	5 47.7	3♐54.1	24 33.0	26 29.8	5 4.4	28 50.0	26 56.7	22 43.8	11 8.1	6 33.9
10	11 9 42.9	19 11.3	5 44.5	17 35.7	24 48.2	26 53.9	5 22.5	29 1.3	27 2.0	22 41.6	11 7.2	6 32.4
11	11 13 39.5	20 11.3	5 41.3	1♑34.4	25 8.7	27 16.1	5 40.9	29 12.6	27 7.2	22 39.3	11 6.3	6 30.9
12	11 17 36.0	21 11.2	5 38.1	15 49.4	25 34.3	27 36.5	5 59.8	29 23.7	27 12.3	22 37.1	11 5.5	6 29.4
13	11 21 32.6	22 11.0	5 35.0	0♒18.6	26 4.6	27 55.0	6 19.0	29 34.8	27 17.4	22 34.9	11 4.5	6 27.9
14	11 25 29.2	23 10.9	5 31.8	14 58.4	26 39.5	28 11.4	6 38.6	29 45.8	27 22.4	22 32.7	11 3.6	6 26.4
15	11 29 25.7	24 10.7	5 28.6	29 43.6	27 18.5	28 25.8	6 58.5	29 56.7	27 27.3	22 30.6	11 2.6	6 24.9
16	11 33 22.3	25 10.5	5 25.4	14♓27.8	28 1.3	28 38.1	7 18.9	0♒ 7.5	27 32.1	22 28.5	11 1.6	6 23.5
17	11 37 18.8	26 10.3	5 22.2	29 4.0	28 47.9	28 48.2	7 39.6	0 18.2	27 37.0	22 26.5	11 .6	6 22.1
18	11 41 15.4	27 10.0	5 19.1	13♈25.5	29 37.9	28 56.1	8 .6	0 28.8	27 41.7	22 24.4	10 59.6	6 20.7
19	11 45 11.9	28 9.7	5 15.9	27 27.1	0♓31.1	29 1.7	8 21.9	0 39.3	27 46.3	22 22.4	10 58.5	6 19.2
20	11 49 8.5	29 9.3	5 12.7	11♉ 5.3	1 27.2	29 4.9	8 43.6	0 49.7	27 50.9	22 20.5	10 57.4	6 17.8
21	11 53 5.0	0♈ 8.9	5 9.5	24 19.0	2 26.3	29 5.7	9 5.5	0 60.0	27 55.4	22 18.5	10 56.3	6 16.4
22	11 57 1.6	1 8.5	5 6.4	7♊ 8.9	3 28.0	29 R 4.1	9 27.8	1 10.1	27 59.8	22 16.7	10 55.1	6 15.0
23	12 0 58.1	2 8.0	5 3.2	19 37.8	4 32.2	29 .0	9 50.4	1 20.2	28 4.2	22 14.8	10 53.9	6 13.7
24	12 4 54.7	3 7.5	4 60.0	1♋49.4	5 38.8	28 53.4	10 13.3	1 30.2	28 8.5	22 13.0	10 52.7	6 12.3
25	12 8 51.2	4 7.0	4 56.8	13 48.4	6 47.7	28 44.3	10 36.5	1 40.0	28 12.7	22 11.2	10 51.5	6 11.0
26	12 12 47.8	5 6.4	4 53.6	25 39.6	7 58.8	28 32.7	10 59.9	1 49.8	28 16.8	22 9.5	10 50.3	6 9.6
27	12 16 44.3	6 5.8	4 50.5	7♌28.1	9 12.0	28 18.7	11 23.6	1 59.4	28 20.8	22 7.8	10 49.0	6 8.3
28	12 20 40.9	7 5.1	4 47.3	19 18.5	10 27.1	28 2.1	11 47.6	2 8.9	28 24.8	22 6.2	10 47.8	6 7.1
29	12 24 37.4	8 4.4	4 44.1	1♍14.9	11 44.2	27 43.1	12 11.8	2 18.3	28 28.7	22 4.6	10 46.5	6 5.8
30	12 28 34.0	9 3.7	4 40.9	13 21.0	13 3.2	27 21.8	12 36.3	2 27.5	28 32.5	22 3.1	10 45.1	6 4.5
31	12 32 30.5	10 2.9	4 37.7	25 39.5	14 23.9	26 58.2	13 1.1	2 36.7	28 36.2	22 1.5	10 43.8	6 3.3

LATITUDE

DAY	EPHEM. SID. TIME	☉	☊	☽	☿	♀	♂	♃	♄	♅	♆	♇
1	10 34 14.0	0 .0	0 .0	1S13.5	2N58.1	4N26.6	3N .9	0S11.7	0N 2.6	0N46.0	1N48.1	13N 6.8
4	10 46 3.6	0 .0	0 .0	2N 4.6	2 19.6	4 52.8	2 57.0	0 12.0	0 2.3	0 46.0	1 48.3	13 6.9
7	10 57 53.3	0 .0	0 .0	4 37.9	1 37.7	5 18.9	2 53.1	0 12.4	0 2.1	0 45.9	1 48.4	13 7.0
10	11 9 42.9	0 .0	0 .0	5 10.7	0 56.2	5 44.6	2 49.3	0 12.8	0 1.9	0 45.9	1 48.6	13 6.9
13	11 21 32.6	0 .0	0 .0	3 6.0	0 17.2	6 9.7	2 45.6	0 13.2	0 1.7	0 45.8	1 48.7	13 6.9
16	11 33 22.3	0 .0	0 .0	0S45.5	0S18.3	6 33.5	2 41.9	0 13.6	0 1.5	0 45.8	1 48.9	13 6.7
19	11 45 11.9	0 .0	0 .0	4 6.3	0 49.8	6 55.5	2 38.2	0 14.0	0 1.3	0 45.7	1 49.0	13 6.5
22	11 57 1.6	0 .0	0 .0	5 14.6	1 17.0	7 14.9	2 34.7	0 14.4	0 1.0	0 45.6	1 49.1	13 6.2
25	12 8 51.2	0 .0	0 .0	4 8.6	1 39.9	7 30.8	2 31.2	0 14.8	0 .8	0 45.6	1 49.2	13 5.9
28	12 20 40.9	0 .0	0 .0	1 30.4	1 58.5	7 42.2	2 27.8	0 15.3	0 .6	0 45.5	1 49.4	13 5.5
31	12 32 30.5	0 .0	0 .0	1N45.4	2 12.7	7 48.0	2 24.5	0 15.7	0 .4	0 45.4	1 49.5	13 5.1

RIGHT ASCENSION

DAY	EPHEM. SID. TIME	☉	☊	☽	☿	♀	♂	♃	♄	♅	♆	♇
1	10 34 14.0	11♓42.1	7♍59.2	24♌51.3	27♒33.4	18♈56.5	3♋15.5	29♑22.2	28♑12.4	25♌39.0	9♏22.4	13♍40.3
2	10 38 10.5	12 38.3	7 56.2	6♍42.0	27 R 1.9	19 27.8	3 31.7	29 34.8	28 18.4	25 R 36.6	9 R 21.8	13 R 38.8
3	10 42 7.1	13 34.4	7 53.2	18 26.8	26 37.1	19 57.7	3 48.4	29 47.4	28 24.4	25 34.2	9 21.2	13 37.4
4	10 46 3.6	14 30.3	7 50.2	0♎11.0	26 19.2	20 26.4	4 5.6	29 59.8	28 30.3	25 31.8	9 20.6	13 35.9
5	10 50 .2	15 26.1	7 47.2	12 1.2	26 8.0	20 53.8	4 23.4	0♒12.1	28 36.2	25 29.4	9 19.9	13 34.4
6	10 53 56.7	16 21.8	7 44.2	24 5.2	26 3.5	21 19.7	4 41.6	0 24.4	28 41.9	25 27.1	9 19.2	13 33.0
7	10 57 53.3	17 17.5	7 41.2	6♏31.0	26 D 5.3	21 44.2	5 .2	0 36.6	28 47.7	25 24.8	9 18.5	13 31.5
8	11 1 49.8	18 13.0	7 38.2	19 26.0	26 13.3	22 7.3	5 19.4	0 48.7	28 53.3	25 22.5	9 17.8	13 30.0
9	11 5 46.4	19 8.4	7 35.2	2♐55.6	26 27.0	22 28.7	5 38.9	1 .6	28 58.9	25 20.2	9 17.0	13 28.6
10	11 9 42.9	20 3.8	7 32.2	17 1.3	26 46.3	22 48.5	5 59.0	1 12.5	29 4.5	25 18.0	9 16.2	13 27.1
11	11 13 39.5	20 59.0	7 29.2	1♑39.3	27 10.6	23 6.7	6 19.4	1 24.3	29 9.9	25 15.8	9 15.4	13 25.7
12	11 17 36.0	21 54.2	7 26.2	16 39.7	27 39.8	23 23.1	6 40.3	1 36.0	29 15.3	25 13.6	9 14.5	13 24.2
13	11 21 32.6	22 49.3	7 23.3	1♒48.7	28 13.5	23 37.8	7 1.6	1 47.6	29 20.6	25 11.5	9 13.6	13 22.8
14	11 25 29.2	23 44.4	7 20.3	16 51.5	28 51.3	23 50.5	7 23.2	1 59.1	29 25.9	25 9.3	9 12.7	13 21.3
15	11 29 25.7	24 39.3	7 17.3	1♓36.9	29 33.0	24 1.4	7 45.3	2 10.5	29 31.1	25 7.2	9 11.8	13 19.9
16	11 33 22.3	25 34.3	7 14.3	15 59.1	0♓18.2	24 10.3	8 7.8	2 21.8	29 36.2	25 5.2	9 10.8	13 18.5
17	11 37 18.8	26 29.2	7 11.3	29 57.6	1 6.9	24 17.3	8 30.7	2 33.0	29 41.3	25 3.2	9 9.9	13 17.1
18	11 41 15.4	27 24.0	7 8.3	13♈35.5	1 58.5	24 22.1	8 53.8	2 44.0	29 46.2	25 1.2	9 8.8	13 15.7
19	11 45 11.9	28 18.8	7 5.3	26 58.0	2 53.0	24 24.8	9 17.4	2 55.0	29 51.1	24 59.3	9 7.8	13 14.3
20	11 49 8.5	29 13.5	7 2.3	10♉ 9.8	3 50.2	24 25.3	9 41.3	3 5.8	29 55.9	24 57.3	9 6.7	13 12.9
21	11 53 5.0	0♈ 8.2	6 59.3	23 14.6	4 49.8	24 R 23.6	10 5.5	3 16.6	0♒ .6	24 55.4	9 5.6	13 11.5
22	11 57 1.6	1 2.8	6 56.3	6♊14.1	5 51.6	24 19.7	10 30.1	3 27.2	0 5.3	24 53.6	9 4.5	13 10.1
23	12 0 58.1	1 57.5	6 53.3	19 8.2	6 55.6	24 13.5	10 54.9	3 37.7	0 9.8	24 51.8	9 3.4	13 8.8
24	12 4 54.7	2 52.1	6 50.3	1♋55.1	8 1.6	24 5.1	11 20.1	3 48.0	0 14.3	24 50.0	9 2.2	13 7.4
25	12 8 51.2	3 46.6	6 47.3	14 32.7	9 9.4	23 54.4	11 45.6	3 58.3	0 18.7	24 48.3	9 1.1	13 6.1
26	12 12 47.8	4 41.2	6 44.3	26 58.9	10 19.0	23 41.4	12 11.3	4 8.4	0 23.1	24 46.6	8 59.9	13 4.8
27	12 16 44.3	5 35.8	6 41.3	9♌12.7	11 30.1	23 26.3	12 37.4	4 18.4	0 27.3	24 44.9	8 58.7	13 3.4
28	12 20 40.9	6 30.3	6 38.3	21 14.7	12 42.9	23 9.0	13 3.7	4 28.3	0 31.5	24 43.3	8 57.4	13 2.1
29	12 24 37.4	7 24.9	6 35.3	3♍ 7.4	13 57.0	22 49.7	13 30.2	4 38.1	0 35.5	24 41.7	8 56.2	13 .9
30	12 28 34.0	8 19.4	6 32.3	14 54.9	15 12.6	22 28.3	13 57.1	4 47.7	0 39.5	24 40.2	8 54.9	12 59.6
31	12 32 30.5	9 14.0	6 29.3	26 42.8	16 29.5	22 5.0	14 24.1	4 57.2	0 43.4	24 38.7	8 53.6	12 58.3

DECLINATION

DAY	EPHEM. SID. TIME	☉	☊	☽	☿	♀	♂	♃	♄	♅	♆	♇
1	10 34 14.0	7S45.2	0N 9.7	12N43.2	9S56.6	12N48.5	26N25.5	20S53.9	20S52.2	14N33.6	13S29.2	21N 9.6
4	10 46 3.6	6 36.5	0 9.7	2 11.0	11 3.3	13 52.2	26 20.4	20 47.2	20 49.2	14 36.0	13 28.5	21 11.5
7	10 57 53.3	5 26.9	0 9.8	9S34.8	11 52.4	14 50.7	26 15.0	20 40.6	20 46.2	14 38.3	13 27.6	21 13.3
10	11 9 42.9	4 16.8	0 9.9	17 42.4	12 22.3	15 43.1	26 9.1	20 33.9	20 43.4	14 40.5	13 26.7	21 15.0
13	11 21 32.6	3 6.1	0 9.9	17 3.4	12 33.5	16 28.7	26 2.8	20 27.4	20 40.6	14 42.6	13 25.8	21 16.6
16	11 33 22.3	1 55.1	0 10.0	6 49.0	12 26.9	17 6.5	25 56.0	20 20.9	20 37.9	14 44.7	13 24.7	21 18.2
19	11 45 11.9	0 43.9	0 10.0	6N44.0	12 4.0	17 35.5	25 48.6	20 14.4	20 35.3	14 46.6	13 23.7	21 19.6
22	11 57 1.6	0N27.2	0 10.1	16 20.0	11 26.0	17 54.5	25 40.6	20 8.1	20 32.9	14 48.4	13 22.5	21 20.9
25	12 8 51.2	1 38.2	0 10.2	18 36.2	10 33.9	18 2.1	25 31.8	20 1.9	20 30.5	14 50.1	13 21.3	21 22.2
28	12 20 40.9	2 48.8	0 10.2	13 36.1	9 28.6	17 57.3	25 22.4	19 55.9	20 28.3	14 51.7	13 20.0	21 23.3
31	12 32 30.5	3 58.8	0 10.3	3 20.3	8 10.9	17 39.3	25 12.1	19 50.0	20 26.2	14 53.1	13 18.7	21 24.4

APRIL 1961

LONGITUDE

DAY	EPHEM. SID. TIME h m s	☉ ° ′	☊ ° ′	☽ ° ′	☿ ° ′	♀ ° ′	♂ ° ′	♃ ° ′	♄ ° ′	♅ ° ′	♆ ° ′	♇ ° ′
1	12 36 27.1	11♈ 2.1	4♍34.6	8♎12.1	15♓46.4	26♈32.4	13♋26.0	2♒45.7	28♑39.8	22♌ .1	10♏42.4	6♍ 2.1
2	12 40 23.6	12 1.3	4 31.4	20 59.7	17 10.6	26 R 4.6	13 51.2	2 54.6	28 43.4	21 R 58.7	10 R 41.1	6 R .9
3	12 44 20.2	13 .4	4 28.2	4♏ 2.2	18 36.5	25 34.9	14 16.7	3 3.4	28 46.9	21 57.3	10 39.7	5 59.7
4	12 48 16.7	13 59.5	4 25.0	17 18.9	20 4.0	25 3.4	14 42.3	3 12.1	28 50.3	21 56.0	10 38.3	5 58.5
5	12 52 13.3	14 58.5	4 21.9	0♐48.4	21 33.1	24 30.4	15 8.2	3 20.6	28 53.6	21 54.7	10 36.8	5 57.4
6	12 56 9.8	15 57.6	4 18.7	14 29.2	23 3.9	23 56.0	15 34.3	3 29.0	28 56.8	21 53.5	10 35.4	5 56.3
7	13 0 6.4	16 56.6	4 15.5	28 19.9	24 36.2	23 20.4	16 .6	3 37.3	28 60.0	21 52.3	10 34.0	5 55.2
8	13 4 3.0	17 55.6	4 12.3	12♑19.1	26 10.0	22 44.0	16 27.1	3 45.5	29 3.0	21 51.2	10 32.5	5 54.1
9	13 7 59.5	18 54.5	4 9.1	26 25.5	27 45.4	22 6.8	16 53.8	3 53.5	29 6.0	21 50.1	10 31.0	5 53.1
10	13 11 56.1	19 53.5	4 6.0	10♒38.0	29 22.4	21 29.2	17 20.7	4 1.3	29 8.8	21 49.1	10 29.5	5 52.0
11	13 15 52.6	20 52.4	4 2.8	24 54.8	1♈ .8	20 51.4	17 47.9	4 9.0	29 11.6	21 48.1	10 28.0	5 51.0
12	13 19 49.2	21 51.2	3 59.6	9♓13.6	2 40.9	20 13.6	18 15.1	4 16.6	29 14.3	21 47.1	10 26.5	5 50.0
13	13 23 45.7	22 50.0	3 56.4	23 31.1	4 22.4	19 36.1	18 42.6	4 24.1	29 16.9	21 46.2	10 25.0	5 49.1
14	13 27 42.3	23 48.8	3 53.3	7♈43.2	6 5.6	18 59.2	19 10.3	4 31.4	29 19.4	21 45.4	10 23.4	5 48.1
15	13 31 38.8	24 47.6	3 50.1	21 45.3	7 50.3	18 23.1	19 38.2	4 38.5	29 21.8	21 44.6	10 21.9	5 47.2
16	13 35 35.4	25 46.4	3 46.9	5♉33.2	9 36.5	17 48.0	20 6.2	4 45.5	29 24.1	21 43.9	10 20.3	5 46.3
17	13 39 31.9	26 45.1	3 43.7	19 3.0	11 24.4	17 14.1	20 34.4	4 52.4	29 26.4	21 43.2	10 18.7	5 45.4
18	13 43 28.5	27 43.7	3 40.5	2♊12.7	13 13.8	16 41.5	21 2.8	4 59.1	29 28.5	21 42.6	10 17.1	5 44.6
19	13 47 25.0	28 42.4	3 37.4	15 1.6	15 4.8	16 10.6	21 31.3	5 5.6	29 30.6	21 42.0	10 15.5	5 43.8
20	13 51 21.6	29 41.0	3 34.2	27 31.0	16 57.4	15 41.5	22 .0	5 12.0	29 32.5	21 41.5	10 13.9	5 43.0
21	13 55 18.1	0♉39.5	3 31.0	9♋43.7	18 51.6	15 14.2	22 28.9	5 18.3	29 34.3	21 41.0	10 12.3	5 42.2
22	13 59 14.7	1 38.0	3 27.8	21 43.5	20 47.4	14 49.0	22 57.9	5 24.4	29 36.1	21 40.6	10 10.7	5 41.5
23	14 3 11.2	2 36.5	3 24.7	3♌35.2	22 44.8	14 25.9	23 27.1	5 30.3	29 37.8	21 40.2	10 9.1	5 40.8
24	14 7 7.8	3 35.0	3 21.5	15 24.0	24 43.7	14 5.1	23 56.4	5 36.1	29 39.3	21 39.9	10 7.5	5 40.1
25	14 11 4.3	4 33.4	3 18.3	27 15.3	26 44.2	13 46.5	24 25.9	5 41.7	29 40.8	21 39.7	10 5.9	5 39.4
26	14 15 .9	5 31.8	3 15.1	9♍14.3	28 46.1	13 30.3	24 55.5	5 47.1	29 42.2	21 39.5	10 4.2	5 38.8
27	14 18 57.5	6 30.1	3 11.9	21 25.5	0♉49.5	13 16.6	25 25.2	5 52.4	29 43.4	21 39.3	10 2.6	5 38.2
28	14 22 54.0	7 28.5	3 8.8	3♎52.9	2 54.3	13 5.3	25 55.1	5 57.6	29 44.7	21 39.3	10 1.0	5 37.7
29	14 26 50.6	8 26.8	3 5.6	16 38.9	5 .2	12 56.4	26 25.1	6 2.5	29 45.8	21 39.2	9 59.4	5 37.1
30	14 30 47.1	9 25.0	3 2.4	29 44.8	7 7.3	12 49.9	26 55.3	6 7.3	29 46.7	21 D 39.3	9 57.7	5 36.6

LATITUDE

DAY	SID. TIME	☉	☊	☽	☿	♀	♂	♃	♄	♅	♆	♇
1	12 36 27.1	0 .0	0 .0	2N46.7	2S16.5	7N48.5	2N23.4	0S15.8	0N .3	0N45.4	1N49.5	13N 4.9
4	12 48 16.7	0 .0	0 .0	4 54.7	2 24.8	7 45.2	2 20.2	0 16.3	0 .1	0 45.3	1 49.6	13 4.4
7	13 0 6.4	0 .0	0 .0	4 45.9	2 28.8	7 34.3	2 17.1	0 16.8	0S .2	0 45.2	1 49.7	13 3.8
10	13 11 56.1	0 .0	0 .0	2 10.2	2 28.3	7 15.6	2 14.0	0 17.2	0 .4	0 45.1	1 49.8	13 3.2
13	13 23 45.7	0 .0	0 .0	1S36.3	2 23.3	6 49.6	2 10.9	0 17.7	0 .7	0 45.0	1 49.8	13 2.6
16	13 35 35.4	0 .0	0 .0	4 27.2	2 13.7	6 17.2	2 8.0	0 18.2	0 .9	0 44.9	1 49.9	13 1.9
19	13 47 25.0	0 .0	0 .0	5 1.6	1 59.6	5 39.9	2 5.1	0 18.7	0 1.1	0 44.8	1 49.9	13 1.2
22	13 59 14.7	0 .0	0 .0	3 28.6	1 40.9	4 59.2	2 2.2	0 19.2	0 1.4	0 44.7	1 50.0	13 .4
25	14 11 4.3	0 .0	0 .0	0 38.5	1 18.0	4 16.9	1 59.4	0 19.7	0 1.6	0 44.6	1 50.0	12 59.6
28	14 22 54.0	0 .0	0 .0	2N30.4	0 51.3	3 34.2	1 56.7	0 20.3	0 1.9	0 44.5	1 50.0	12 58.8

RIGHT ASCENSION

DAY	SID. TIME	☉	☊	☽	☿	♀	♂	♃	♄	♅	♆	♇
1	12 36 27.1	10♈ 8.6	6♍26.2	8♎37.7	17♓47.7	21♈40.0	14♋51.4	5♒ 6.6	0♒47.3	24♌37.3	8♏52.3	12♍57.1
2	12 40 23.6	11 3.3	6 23.2	20 46.9	19 7.1	21 R 13.3	15 19.0	5 15.9	0 51.0	24 R 35.9	8 R 50.9	12 R 55.9
3	12 44 20.2	11 57.9	6 20.2	3♏17.6	20 27.8	20 45.1	15 46.7	5 25.0	0 54.6	24 34.5	8 49.6	12 54.7
4	12 48 16.7	12 52.6	6 17.2	16 16.0	21 49.6	20 15.6	16 14.7	5 34.0	0 58.2	24 33.2	8 48.2	12 53.5
5	12 52 13.3	13 47.3	6 14.2	29 45.8	23 12.5	19 45.1	16 42.9	5 42.8	1 1.7	24 32.0	8 46.8	12 52.3
6	12 56 9.8	14 42.1	6 11.2	13♐47.0	24 36.6	19 13.6	17 11.3	5 51.5	1 5.0	24 30.7	8 45.4	12 51.1
7	13 0 6.4	15 37.0	6 8.2	28 14.7	26 1.9	18 41.4	17 40.0	6 .2	1 8.4	24 29.6	8 44.1	12 50.0
8	13 4 3.0	16 31.9	6 5.2	12♑59.1	27 28.3	18 8.8	18 8.8	6 8.6	1 11.6	24 28.5	8 42.6	12 48.9
9	13 7 59.5	17 26.8	6 2.2	27 47.7	28 55.8	17 35.9	18 37.7	6 16.9	1 14.7	24 27.4	8 41.2	12 47.8
10	13 11 56.1	18 21.8	5 59.2	12♒28.4	0♈24.5	17 3.0	19 6.9	6 25.0	1 17.7	24 26.4	8 39.8	12 46.7
11	13 15 52.6	19 16.9	5 56.2	26 52.6	1 54.4	16 30.3	19 36.3	6 33.0	1 20.6	24 25.4	8 38.3	12 45.7
12	13 19 49.2	20 12.1	5 53.2	10♓56.5	3 25.4	15 58.0	20 5.8	6 40.9	1 23.4	24 24.5	8 36.8	12 44.6
13	13 23 45.7	21 7.3	5 50.2	24 41.1	4 57.7	15 26.4	20 35.5	6 48.6	1 26.1	24 23.6	8 35.3	12 43.6
14	13 27 42.3	22 2.6	5 47.2	8♈10.6	6 31.3	14 55.6	21 5.4	6 56.2	1 28.8	24 22.8	8 33.8	12 42.6
15	13 31 38.8	22 58.0	5 44.2	21 30.3	8 6.1	14 25.9	21 35.4	7 3.6	1 31.3	24 22.0	8 32.3	12 41.6
16	13 35 35.4	23 53.5	5 41.2	4♉45.1	9 42.3	13 57.4	22 5.6	7 10.8	1 33.8	24 21.3	8 30.8	12 40.7
17	13 39 31.9	24 49.1	5 38.1	17 58.3	11 19.9	13 30.3	22 35.9	7 17.9	1 36.1	24 20.6	8 29.2	12 39.7
18	13 43 28.5	25 44.8	5 35.1	1♊10.5	12 58.9	13 4.8	23 6.4	7 24.9	1 38.3	24 20.0	8 27.7	12 38.8
19	13 47 25.0	26 40.6	5 32.1	14 20.1	14 39.4	12 41.0	23 37.0	7 31.6	1 40.5	24 19.4	8 26.2	12 37.9
20	13 51 21.6	27 36.4	5 29.1	27 23.2	16 21.5	12 19.1	24 7.8	7 38.3	1 42.5	24 18.9	8 24.6	12 37.0
21	13 55 18.1	28 32.4	5 26.1	10♋15.7	18 5.1	11 59.0	24 38.7	7 44.7	1 44.5	24 18.4	8 23.0	12 36.2
22	13 59 14.7	29 28.5	5 23.1	22 53.7	19 50.5	11 41.0	25 9.7	7 51.0	1 46.3	24 18.0	8 21.5	12 35.4
23	14 3 11.2	0♉24.6	5 20.1	5♌15.4	21 37.5	11 25.0	25 40.8	7 57.2	1 48.1	24 17.6	8 19.9	12 34.6
24	14 7 7.8	1 20.9	5 17.1	17 21.2	23 26.3	11 11.2	26 12.1	8 3.1	1 49.7	24 17.3	8 18.3	12 33.8
25	14 11 4.3	2 17.3	5 14.1	29 14.0	25 16.8	10 59.6	26 43.5	8 8.9	1 51.3	24 17.0	8 16.7	12 33.1
26	14 15 .9	3 13.8	5 11.1	10♍59.0	27 9.2	10 50.2	27 14.9	8 14.6	1 52.7	24 16.8	8 15.1	12 32.3
27	14 18 57.5	4 10.5	5 8.0	22 42.8	29 3.5	10 43.1	27 46.5	8 20.0	1 54.1	24 16.7	8 13.6	12 31.6
28	14 22 54.0	5 7.3	5 5.0	4♎33.4	0♉59.6	10 38.2	28 18.2	8 25.4	1 55.4	24 16.6	8 12.0	12 31.0
29	14 26 50.6	6 4.1	5 2.0	16 39.4	2 57.5	10 35.5	28 50.0	8 30.5	1 56.5	24 16.6	8 10.4	12 30.4
30	14 30 47.1	7 1.1	4 59.0	29 9.1	4 57.3	10 35.0	29 21.8	8 35.5	1 57.6	24 16.6	8 8.8	12 29.7

DECLINATION

DAY	SID. TIME	☉	☊	☽	☿	♀	♂	♃	♄	♅	♆	♇
1	12 36 27.1	4N22.0	0N10.3	0S42.0	7S42.4	17N30.2	25N 8.6	19S48.1	20S25.5	14N53.6	13S18.2	21N24.7
4	12 48 16.7	5 31.2	0 10.4	12 17.2	6 9.3	16 54.1	24 57.2	19 42.5	20 23.6	14 54.8	13 16.8	21 25.6
7	13 0 6.4	6 39.5	0 10.4	18 40.0	4 25.3	16 5.4	24 45.0	19 37.0	20 21.9	14 55.9	13 15.4	21 26.3
10	13 11 56.1	7 46.7	0 10.5	15 29.0	2 31.0	15 6.0	24 31.9	19 31.9	20 20.3	14 56.9	13 14.0	21 26.9
13	13 23 45.7	8 52.9	0 10.5	4 2.9	0 27.2	13 58.8	24 17.8	19 26.9	20 18.8	14 57.7	13 12.5	21 27.5
16	13 35 35.4	9 57.6	0 10.6	9N10.3	1N45.5	12 47.3	24 2.8	19 22.3	20 17.6	14 58.3	13 11.0	21 27.9
19	13 47 25.0	11 .9	0 10.7	17 36.3	4 6.1	11 35.2	23 46.7	19 17.9	20 16.5	14 58.8	13 9.4	21 28.2
22	13 59 14.7	12 2.6	0 10.7	18 15.3	6 33.5	10 26.0	23 29.7	19 13.8	20 15.6	14 59.2	13 7.9	21 28.3
25	14 11 4.3	13 2.5	0 10.8	11 49.4	9 5.9	9 22.7	23 11.7	19 10.1	20 14.8	14 59.4	13 6.4	21 28.4
28	14 22 54.0	14 .4	0 10.8	0 45.5	11 40.7	8 27.4	22 52.6	19 6.7	20 14.2	14 59.4	13 4.8	21 28.3

MAY 1961

DAY	EPHEM. SID. TIME	☉	☊	☽	☿	♀	♂	♃	♄	♅	♆	♇
	h m s	° ′	° ′	° ′	° ′	° ′	° ′	° ′	° ′	° ′	° ′	° ′
		LONGITUDE										
1	14 34 43.7	10♉23.3	2♍59.2	13♏10.0	9♉15.3	12♈45.9	27♋25.5	6♒12.0	29♑47.6	21♌39.3	9♏56.1	5♍36.1
2	14 38 40.2	11 21.4	2 56.1	26 52.2	11 24.2	12R44.3	27 55.9	6 16.4	29 48.4	21 39.5	9R54.5	5R35.7
3	14 42 36.8	12 19.6	2 52.9	10♐48.1	13 33.6	12D45.0	28 26.4	6 20.7	29 49.1	21 39.6	9 52.8	5 35.2
4	14 46 33.3	13 17.7	2 49.7	24 53.3	15 43.4	12 48.1	28 57.1	6 24.8	29 49.7	21 39.9	9 51.2	5 34.8
5	14 50 29.9	14 15.9	2 46.5	9♑ 3.6	17 53.3	12 53.5	29 27.8	6 28.7	29 50.2	21 40.1	9 49.6	5 34.4
6	14 54 26.4	15 13.9	2 43.3	23 15.4	20 3.0	13 1.2	29 58.7	6 32.5	29 50.6	21 40.5	9 47.9	5 34.1
7	14 58 23.0	16 12.0	2 40.2	7♒26.0	22 12.3	13 11.0	0♌29.7	6 36.1	29 50.9	21 40.9	9 46.3	5 33.8
8	15 2 19.5	17 10.1	2 37.0	21 33.7	24 20.9	13 23.0	1 .8	6 39.5	29 51.1	21 41.3	9 44.7	5 33.5
9	15 6 16.1	18 8.1	2 33.8	5♓37.5	26 28.4	13 37.0	1 32.0	6 42.7	29 51.3	21 41.8	9 43.1	5 33.2
10	15 10 12.7	19 6.1	2 30.6	19 36.5	28 34.6	13 53.0	2 3.3	6 45.8	29 51.3	21 42.4	9 41.5	5 33.0
11	15 14 9.2	20 4.1	2 27.5	3♈29.9	0♊39.2	14 11.0	2 34.7	6 48.6	29R51.2	21 43.0	9 39.8	5 32.8
12	15 18 5.8	21 2.0	2 24.3	17 16.1	2 42.0	14 30.8	3 6.3	6 51.3	29 51.0	21 43.6	9 38.2	5 32.6
13	15 22 2.3	21 60.0	2 21.1	0♉53.3	4 42.7	14 52.5	3 37.9	6 53.8	29 50.7	21 44.3	9 36.7	5 32.5
14	15 25 58.9	22 57.9	2 17.9	14 18.9	6 41.1	15 15.8	4 9.7	6 56.1	29 50.3	21 45.1	9 35.1	5 32.4
15	15 29 55.4	23 55.7	2 14.7	27 30.6	8 37.0	15 40.9	4 41.5	6 58.2	29 49.9	21 45.9	9 33.5	5 32.3
16	15 33 52.0	24 53.6	2 11.6	10♊26.7	10 30.2	16 7.5	5 13.5	7 .2	29 49.3	21 46.8	9 31.9	5 32.3
17	15 37 48.5	25 51.4	2 8.4	23 6.4	12 20.7	16 35.7	5 45.5	7 1.9	29 48.6	21 47.7	9 30.4	5 32.2
18	15 41 45.1	26 49.3	2 5.2	5♋30.1	14 8.2	17 5.4	6 17.7	7 3.5	29 47.8	21 48.7	9 28.8	5D32.3
19	15 45 41.7	27 47.1	2 2.0	17 39.5	15 52.8	17 36.6	6 50.0	7 4.9	29 47.0	21 49.8	9 27.3	5 32.3
20	15 49 38.2	28 44.8	1 58.9	29 37.5	17 34.2	18 9.1	7 22.4	7 6.1	29 46.1	21 50.8	9 25.8	5 32.4
21	15 53 34.8	29 42.6	1 55.7	11♌28.2	19 12.5	18 43.0	7 54.8	7 7.1	29 45.0	21 52.0	9 24.3	5 32.5
22	15 57 31.3	0♊40.3	1 52.5	23 16.5	20 47.6	19 18.1	8 27.3	7 7.9	29 43.9	21 53.2	9 22.8	5 32.7
23	16 1 27.9	1 38.0	1 49.3	5♍ 7.5	22 19.5	19 54.4	8 60.0	7 8.5	29 42.6	21 54.4	9 21.3	5 32.8
24	16 5 24.4	2 35.6	1 46.2	17 6.8	23 48.0	20 32.0	9 32.7	7 8.9	29 41.3	21 55.7	9 19.8	5 33.0
25	16 9 21.0	3 33.2	1 43.0	29 19.7	25 13.2	21 10.6	10 5.5	7 9.2	29 39.9	21 57.0	9 18.4	5 33.2
26	16 13 17.5	4 30.8	1 39.8	11♎51.0	26 35.0	21 50.4	10 38.4	7 9.2	29 38.4	21 58.4	9 16.9	5 33.5
27	16 17 14.1	5 28.4	1 36.6	24 44.5	27 53.4	22 31.2	11 11.3	7R 9.1	29 36.7	21 59.8	9 15.5	5 33.8
28	16 21 10.7	6 26.0	1 33.4	8♏ 2.0	29 8.3	23 13.1	11 44.4	7 8.7	29 35.1	22 1.3	9 14.1	5 34.1
29	16 25 7.2	7 23.5	1 30.3	21 43.7	0♋19.6	23 55.9	12 17.5	7 8.2	29 33.3	22 2.8	9 12.7	5 34.4
30	16 29 3.8	8 21.0	1 27.1	5♐47.1	1 27.4	24 39.6	12 50.7	7 7.5	29 31.4	22 4.4	9 11.3	5 34.8
31	16 33 .3	9 18.5	1 23.9	20 7.5	2 31.6	25 24.3	13 24.0	7 6.6	29 29.4	22 6.0	9 9.9	5 35.2
		LATITUDE										
1	14 34 43.7	0 .0	0 .0	4N43.3	0S21.5	2N52.4	1N54.0	0S20.8	0S 2.1	0N44.4	1N50.0	12N57.9
4	14 46 33.3	0 .0	0 .0	4 42.0	0N10.0	2 12.3	1 51.4	0 21.4	0 2.4	0 44.3	1 50.0	12 57.0
7	14 58 23.0	0 .0	0 .0	2 12.5	0 41.5	1 34.5	1 48.8	0 21.9	0 2.6	0 44.1	1 50.0	12 56.1
10	15 10 12.7	0 .0	0 .0	1S25.7	1 11.2	0 59.3	1 46.2	0 22.5	0 2.9	0 44.0	1 50.0	12 55.2
13	15 22 2.3	0 .0	0 .0	4 15.6	1 36.9	0 26.8	1 43.7	0 23.1	0 3.2	0 43.9	1 49.9	12 54.3
16	15 33 52.0	0 .0	0 .0	4 57.7	1 57.2	0S 2.9	1 41.2	0 23.6	0 3.4	0 43.8	1 49.9	12 53.3
19	15 45 41.7	0 .0	0 .0	3 30.8	2 10.9	0 29.8	1 38.8	0 24.2	0 3.7	0 43.7	1 49.8	12 52.4
22	15 57 31.3	0 .0	0 .0	0 44.6	2 17.4	0 54.0	1 36.4	0 24.8	0 4.0	0 43.6	1 49.8	12 51.4
25	16 9 21.0	0 .0	0 .0	2N20.8	2 16.4	1 15.7	1 34.0	0 25.4	0 4.2	0 43.5	1 49.7	12 50.4
28	16 21 10.7	0 .0	0 .0	4 36.7	2 7.8	1 34.9	1 31.7	0 26.0	0 4.5	0 43.4	1 49.6	12 49.5
31	16 33 .3	0 .0	0 .0	4 44.2	1 51.6	1 51.8	1 29.4	0 26.6	0 4.8	0 43.3	1 49.5	12 48.5
		RIGHT ASCENSION										
1	14 34 43.7	7♉58.3	4♍56.0	12♏ 9.8	6♉58.7	10♈36.8	29♋53.7	8♒40.2	1♒58.5	24♌16.6	8♏ 7.2	12♍29.2
2	14 38 40.2	8 55.5	4 53.0	25 46.0	9 1.8	10D40.6	0♌25.7	8 44.9	1 59.4	24D16.7	8R 5.6	12R28.6
3	14 42 36.8	9 52.9	4 50.0	9♐57.3	11 6.4	10 46.6	0 57.8	8 49.3	2 .1	24 16.9	8 4.0	12 28.0
4	14 46 33.3	10 50.5	4 46.9	24 37.3	13 12.4	10 54.7	1 30.0	8 53.5	2 .7	24 17.1	8 2.5	12 27.5
5	14 50 29.9	11 48.2	4 43.9	9♑33.8	15 19.5	11 4.7	2 2.2	8 57.6	2 1.3	24 17.4	8 .9	12 27.0
6	14 54 26.4	12 46.0	4 40.9	24 31.3	17 27.5	11 16.8	2 34.6	9 1.5	2 1.7	24 17.7	7 59.3	12 26.6
7	14 58 23.0	13 44.0	4 37.9	9♒15.2	19 36.2	11 30.7	3 6.9	9 5.2	2 2.1	24 18.1	7 57.7	12 26.1
8	15 2 19.5	14 42.1	4 34.9	23 36.0	21 45.3	11 46.6	3 39.4	9 8.8	2 2.3	24 18.5	7 56.1	12 25.7
9	15 6 16.1	15 40.4	4 31.9	7♓30.3	23 54.6	12 4.2	4 11.9	9 12.1	2 2.4	24 18.9	7 54.5	12 25.4
10	15 10 12.7	16 38.8	4 28.9	21 .8	26 3.6	12 23.5	4 44.5	9 15.3	2 2.5	24 19.5	7 53.0	12 25.0
11	15 14 9.2	17 37.4	4 25.8	4♈13.4	28 12.0	12 44.5	5 17.1	9 18.3	2R 2.4	24 20.1	7 51.4	12 24.7
12	15 18 5.8	18 36.1	4 22.8	17 15.9	0♊19.6	13 7.1	5 49.8	9 21.1	2 2.2	24 20.7	7 49.8	12 24.4
13	15 22 2.3	19 34.9	4 19.8	0♉15.4	2 26.1	13 31.3	6 22.6	9 23.7	2 1.9	24 21.4	7 48.3	12 24.1
14	15 25 58.9	20 34.0	4 16.8	13 17.4	4 31.1	13 56.9	6 55.4	9 26.1	2 1.6	24 22.1	7 46.7	12 23.9
15	15 29 55.4	21 33.1	4 13.8	26 24.3	6 34.3	14 24.0	7 28.2	9 28.3	2 1.1	24 22.9	7 45.2	12 23.7
16	15 33 52.0	22 32.4	4 10.7	9♊34.9	8 35.5	14 52.5	8 1.1	9 30.3	2 .5	24 23.7	7 43.7	12 23.5
17	15 37 48.5	23 31.8	4 7.7	22 45.0	10 34.5	15 22.3	8 34.1	9 32.2	1 59.8	24 24.6	7 42.1	12 23.4
18	15 41 45.1	24 31.4	4 4.7	5♋48.5	12 31.0	15 53.3	9 7.1	9 33.8	1 59.0	24 25.6	7 40.6	12 23.2
19	15 45 41.7	25 31.1	4 1.7	18 39.1	14 24.9	16 25.6	9 40.1	9 35.3	1 58.2	24 26.6	7 39.2	12 23.2
20	15 49 38.2	26 31.0	3 58.7	1♌12.0	16 15.8	16 59.1	10 13.2	9 36.6	1 57.2	24 27.7	7 37.7	12 23.1
21	15 53 34.8	27 31.0	3 55.6	13 25.6	18 3.7	17 33.7	10 46.3	9 37.7	1 56.2	24 28.8	7 36.2	12 23.1
22	15 57 31.3	28 31.1	3 52.6	25 21.5	19 48.4	18 9.4	11 19.5	9 38.5	1 55.0	24 29.9	7 34.7	12 23.1
23	16 1 27.9	29 31.3	3 49.6	7♍ 4.0	21 29.8	18 46.1	11 52.6	9 39.2	1 53.7	24 31.1	7 33.3	12 23.1
24	16 5 24.4	0♊31.6	3 46.6	18 40.3	23 7.7	19 23.9	12 25.8	9 39.7	1 52.3	24 32.3	7 31.8	12D23.2
25	16 9 21.0	1 32.1	3 43.6	0♎19.1	24 42.1	20 2.6	12 59.1	9 40.0	1 50.9	24 33.6	7 30.4	12 23.2
26	16 13 17.5	2 32.7	3 40.5	12 10.2	26 12.8	20 42.3	13 32.3	9 40.1	1 49.3	24 35.0	7 29.0	12 23.4
27	16 17 14.1	3 33.4	3 37.5	24 24.1	27 39.7	21 22.9	14 5.6	9R40.0	1 47.7	24 36.4	7 27.6	12 23.5
28	16 21 10.7	4 34.3	3 34.5	7♏10.6	29 2.7	22 4.4	14 38.9	9 39.7	1 45.9	24 37.8	7 26.2	12 23.7
29	16 25 7.2	5 35.2	3 31.5	20 37.5	0♋21.7	22 46.7	15 12.2	9 39.3	1 44.1	24 39.3	7 24.8	12 23.9
30	16 29 3.8	6 36.3	3 28.4	4♐47.8	1 36.7	23 29.9	15 45.5	9 38.6	1 42.2	24 40.8	7 23.5	12 24.1
31	16 33 .3	7 37.5	3 25.4	19 37.6	2 47.6	24 13.9	16 18.8	9 37.7	1 40.1	24 42.4	7 22.1	12 24.3
		DECLINATION										
1	14 34 43.7	14N56.3	0N10.9	11S17.2	14N14.4	7N41.3	22N32.4	19S 3.7	20S13.9	14N59.3	13S 3.3	21N28.1
4	14 46 33.3	15 49.9	0 11.0	18 38.8	16 42.5	7 5.3	22 11.3	19 1.0	20 13.7	14 59.0	13 1.8	21 27.7
7	14 58 23.0	16 41.2	0 11.0	16 16.7	18 59.5	6 39.4	21 49.0	18 58.7	20 13.7	14 58.6	13 .2	21 27.3
10	15 10 12.7	17 30.0	0 11.1	5 25.7	21 .1	6 23.3	21 25.8	18 56.8	20 13.8	14 58.0	12 58.7	21 26.8
13	15 22 2.3	18 16.2	0 11.1	7N47.3	22 40.2	6 16.4	21 1.4	18 55.4	20 14.2	14 57.3	12 57.3	21 26.1
16	15 33 52.0	18 59.6	0 11.2	17 6.3	23 57.4	6 17.9	20 36.0	18 54.3	20 14.8	14 56.4	12 55.8	21 25.3
19	15 45 41.7	19 40.1	0 11.3	18 47.6	24 51.8	6 27.2	20 9.6	18 53.7	20 15.5	14 55.3	12 54.4	21 24.4
22	15 57 31.3	20 17.6	0 11.3	13 3.6	25 24.4	6 43.4	19 42.1	18 53.5	20 16.4	14 54.1	12 53.0	21 23.4
25	16 9 21.0	20 52.0	0 11.4	2 25.2	25 37.7	7 5.6	19 13.6	18 53.8	20 17.5	14 52.7	12 51.7	21 22.3
28	16 21 10.7	21 23.1	0 11.4	9S49.2	25 34.2	7 33.2	18 44.1	18 54.5	20 18.8	14 51.3	12 50.4	21 21.1
31	16 33 .3	21 50.9	0 11.5	18 21.0	25 16.7	8 5.5	18 13.7	18 55.6	20 20.3	14 49.6	12 49.2	21 19.8

JUNE 1961

DAY	EPHEM. SID. TIME	☉	☊	☽	☿	♀	♂	♃	♄	♅	♆	♇
		LONGITUDE										
	h m s	° ′	° ′	° ′	° ′	° ′	° ′	° ′	° ′	° ′	° ′	° ′
1	16 36 56.9	10♊16.0	1♍20.7	4♑38.7	3♋32.0	26♈ 9.9	13♌57.3	7♒ 5.5	29♑27.4	22♌ 7.7	9♏ 8.6	5♍35.6
2	16 40 53.4	11 13.5	1 17.6	19 13.9	4 28.7	26 56.2	14 30.8	7R 4.2	29R25.3	22 9.4	9R 7.2	5 36.1
3	16 44 50.0	12 10.9	1 14.4	3♒46.6	5 21.5	27 43.4	15 4.3	7 2.8	29 23.0	22 11.2	9 5.9	5 36.6
4	16 48 46.6	13 8.4	1 11.2	18 12.1	6 10.4	28 31.4	15 37.9	7 1.1	29 20.7	22 13.0	9 4.6	5 37.1
5	16 52 43.1	14 5.8	1 8.0	2♓27.1	6 55.3	29 20.2	16 11.5	6 59.3	29 18.4	22 14.9	9 3.3	5 37.7
6	16 56 39.7	15 3.2	1 4.9	16 30.1	7 36.1	0♉ 9.6	16 45.3	6 57.2	29 15.9	22 16.8	9 2.1	5 38.2
7	17 0 36.2	16 .6	1 1.7	0♈20.6	8 12.8	0 59.7	17 19.1	6 55.0	29 13.4	22 18.8	9 .9	5 38.9
8	17 4 32.8	16 58.0	0 58.5	13 59.0	8 45.1	1 50.6	17 53.0	6 52.6	29 10.7	22 20.8	8 59.6	5 39.5
9	17 8 29.3	17 55.5	0 55.3	27 25.5	9 13.2	2 42.1	18 27.0	6 50.1	29 8.1	22 22.8	8 58.5	5 40.2
10	17 12 25.9	18 52.8	0 52.1	10♉40.4	9 36.8	3 34.1	19 1.0	6 47.3	29 5.3	22 24.9	8 57.3	5 40.9
11	17 16 22.5	19 50.2	0 49.0	23 43.4	9 56.0	4 26.8	19 35.1	6 44.4	29 2.4	22 27.1	8 56.2	5 41.6
12	17 20 19.0	20 47.6	0 45.8	6♊34.1	10 10.6	5 20.0	20 9.3	6 41.2	28 59.5	22 29.2	8 55.1	5 42.4
13	17 24 15.6	21 44.9	0 42.6	19 12.2	10 20.6	6 13.8	20 43.6	6 37.9	28 56.5	22 31.5	8 54.0	5 43.2
14	17 28 12.1	22 42.3	0 39.4	1♋37.6	10 26.1	7 8.0	21 17.9	6 34.4	28 53.4	22 33.7	8 52.9	5 44.0
15	17 32 8.7	23 39.6	0 36.3	13 50.8	10 27.1	8 2.8	21 52.3	6 30.8	28 50.3	22 36.0	8 51.8	5 44.8
16	17 36 5.2	24 36.9	0 33.1	25 53.2	10R23.5	8 58.1	22 26.8	6 26.9	28 47.1	22 38.4	8 50.8	5 45.7
17	17 40 1.8	25 34.2	0 29.9	7♌47.0	10 15.6	9 53.9	23 1.3	6 22.9	28 43.8	22 40.8	8 49.8	5 46.6
18	17 43 58.3	26 31.5	0 26.7	19 35.4	10 3.4	10 50.1	23 35.9	6 18.7	28 40.4	22 43.2	8 48.8	5 47.5
19	17 47 54.9	27 28.8	0 23.6	1♍22.3	9 47.1	11 46.8	24 10.6	6 14.4	28 37.0	22 45.6	8 47.9	5 48.4
20	17 51 51.5	28 26.0	0 20.4	13 12.5	9 27.0	12 43.8	24 45.3	6 9.9	28 33.5	22 48.2	8 46.9	5 49.4
21	17 55 48.0	29 23.3	0 17.2	25 10.9	9 3.4	13 41.3	25 20.1	6 5.2	28 30.0	22 50.7	8 46.0	5 50.4
22	17 59 44.6	0♋20.5	0 14.0	7♎23.0	8 36.7	14 39.2	25 55.0	6 .4	28 26.4	22 53.3	8 45.2	5 51.4
23	18 3 41.1	1 17.8	0 10.8	19 53.9	8 7.1	15 37.5	26 29.9	5 55.4	28 22.8	22 55.9	8 44.3	5 52.5
24	18 7 37.7	2 15.0	0 7.7	2♏48.1	7 35.3	16 36.1	27 4.9	5 50.3	28 19.1	22 58.6	8 43.5	5 53.6
25	18 11 34.3	3 12.2	0 4.5	16 8.5	7 1.7	17 35.1	27 39.9	5 45.0	28 15.3	23 1.2	8 42.7	5 54.7
26	18 15 30.8	4 9.4	0 1.3	29 56.5	6 26.9	18 34.5	28 15.0	5 39.6	28 11.5	23 4.0	8 41.9	5 55.8
27	18 19 27.4	5 6.6	29♌58.1	14♐10.4	5 51.4	19 34.2	28 50.2	5 34.0	28 7.6	23 6.7	8 41.2	5 57.0
28	18 23 23.9	6 3.8	29 55.0	28 46.1	5 15.9	20 34.3	29 25.4	5 28.3	28 3.7	23 9.5	8 40.5	5 58.2
29	18 27 20.5	7 1.0	29 51.8	13♑36.7	4 41.0	21 34.6	0♍ .7	5 22.5	27 59.8	23 12.4	8 39.8	5 59.4
30	18 31 17.0	7 58.2	29 48.6	28 33.9	4 7.3	22 35.4	0 36.0	5 16.6	27 55.8	23 15.3	8 39.2	6 .6
		LATITUDE										
1	16 36 56.9	0 .0	0 .0	4N10.2	1N44.5	1S57.0	1N28.6	0S26.8	0S 4.9	0N43.2	1N49.5	12N48.2
4	16 48 46.6	0 .0	0 .0	1 4.3	1 18.4	2 11.0	1 26.3	0 27.5	0 5.1	0 43.1	1 49.4	12 47.2
7	17 0 36.2	0 .0	0 .0	2S31.8	0 45.2	2 23.0	1 24.1	0 28.1	0 5.4	0 43.0	1 49.3	12 46.3
10	17 12 25.9	0 .0	0 .0	4 45.2	0 5.4	2 33.1	1 21.9	0 28.7	0 5.7	0 42.9	1 49.2	12 45.4
13	17 24 15.6	0 .0	0 .0	4 45.0	0S39.7	2 41.5	1 19.7	0 29.3	0 6.0	0 42.9	1 49.1	12 44.5
16	17 36 5.2	0 .0	0 .0	2 47.1	1 28.7	2 48.1	1 17.5	0 29.9	0 6.2	0 42.8	1 48.9	12 43.6
19	17 47 54.9	0 .0	0 .0	0N12.7	2 18.8	2 53.2	1 15.3	0 30.5	0 6.5	0 42.7	1 48.8	12 42.7
22	17 59 44.6	0 .0	0 .0	3 10.9	3 6.8	2 56.7	1 13.2	0 31.1	0 6.8	0 42.6	1 48.7	12 41.8
25	18 11 34.3	0 .0	0 .0	4 59.0	3 48.7	2 58.9	1 11.1	0 31.7	0 7.1	0 42.5	1 48.5	12 41.0
28	18 23 23.9	0 .0	0 .0	4 25.0	4 20.7	2 59.7	1 9.0	0 32.3	0 7.4	0 42.4	1 48.4	12 40.2
		RIGHT ASCENSION										
1	16 36 56.9	8♊38.7	3♍22.4	4♑54.4	3♋54.1	24♈58.6	16♌52.2	9♒36.7	1♒38.0	24♌44.0	7♏20.8	12♍24.6
2	16 40 53.4	9 40.1	3 19.4	20 19.3	4 56.4	25 44.1	17 25.6	9R35.4	1R35.8	24 45.7	7R19.5	12 24.9
3	16 44 50.0	10 41.6	3 16.3	5♒32.3	5 54.2	26 30.4	17 59.0	9 34.0	1 33.5	24 47.4	7 18.2	12 25.3
4	16 48 46.6	11 43.2	3 13.3	20 18.0	6 47.5	27 17.3	18 32.4	9 32.3	1 31.1	24 49.2	7 16.9	12 25.7
5	16 52 43.1	12 44.9	3 10.3	4♓29.5	7 36.2	28 5.0	19 5.8	9 30.5	1 28.7	24 51.0	7 15.7	12 26.1
6	16 56 39.7	13 46.6	3 7.3	18 7.7	8 20.2	28 53.3	19 39.2	9 28.5	1 26.1	24 52.9	7 14.5	12 26.5
7	17 0 36.2	14 48.5	3 4.2	1♈19.3	8 59.5	29 42.3	20 12.7	9 26.3	1 23.5	24 54.8	7 13.2	12 26.9
8	17 4 32.8	15 50.4	3 1.2	14 13.4	9 33.9	0♉31.9	20 46.1	9 23.9	1 20.8	24 56.7	7 12.1	12 27.4
9	17 8 29.3	16 52.4	2 58.2	26 59.5	10 3.5	1 22.1	21 19.6	9 21.3	1 18.0	24 58.7	7 10.9	12 28.0
10	17 12 25.9	17 54.5	2 55.2	9♉45.7	10 28.1	2 13.0	21 53.1	9 18.5	1 15.1	25 .8	7 9.8	12 28.5
11	17 16 22.5	18 56.7	2 52.1	22 37.2	10 47.6	3 4.4	22 26.6	9 15.6	1 12.2	25 2.8	7 8.7	12 29.1
12	17 20 19.0	19 58.8	2 49.1	5♊36.0	11 2.2	3 56.3	23 .1	9 12.4	1 9.1	25 5.0	7 7.5	12 29.7
13	17 24 15.6	21 1.1	2 46.1	18 39.7	11 11.8	4 48.8	23 33.6	9 9.1	1 6.0	25 7.1	7 6.5	12 30.3
14	17 28 12.1	22 3.4	2 43.0	1♋43.0	11 16.3	5 41.9	24 7.2	9 5.6	1 2.8	25 9.3	7 5.4	12 31.0
15	17 32 8.7	23 5.7	2 40.0	14 38.7	11R16.0	6 35.5	24 40.7	9 1.9	0 59.6	25 11.6	7 4.4	12 31.7
16	17 36 5.2	24 8.0	2 37.0	27 19.9	11 10.8	7 29.6	25 14.2	8 58.0	0 56.2	25 13.8	7 3.3	12 32.4
17	17 40 1.8	25 10.4	2 33.9	9♌42.1	11 .9	8 24.3	25 47.8	8 53.9	0 52.8	25 16.2	7 2.4	12 33.1
18	17 43 58.3	26 12.8	2 30.9	21 44.2	10 46.5	9 19.4	26 21.3	8 49.7	0 49.3	25 18.5	7 1.4	12 33.9
19	17 47 54.9	27 15.2	2 27.9	3♍28.5	10 27.9	10 15.1	26 54.9	8 45.3	0 45.8	25 20.9	7 .4	12 34.7
20	17 51 51.5	28 17.6	2 24.9	15 .7	10 5.2	11 11.2	27 28.5	8 40.7	0 42.2	25 23.4	6 59.5	12 35.5
21	17 55 48.0	29 20.0	2 21.8	26 28.6	9 39.0	12 7.8	28 2.0	8 36.0	0 38.5	25 25.8	6 58.6	12 36.3
22	17 59 44.6	0♋22.4	2 18.8	8♎ 2.2	9 9.5	13 4.9	28 35.6	8 31.1	0 34.7	25 28.3	6 57.8	12 37.2
23	18 3 41.1	1 24.8	2 15.8	19 52.5	8 37.2	14 2.5	29 9.2	8 26.0	0 30.9	25 30.9	6 56.9	12 38.1
24	18 7 37.7	2 27.1	2 12.7	2♏10.9	8 2.6	15 .5	29 42.7	8 20.8	0 27.1	25 33.5	6 56.1	12 39.0
25	18 11 34.3	3 29.5	2 9.7	15 8.3	7 26.4	15 59.1	0♍16.3	8 15.5	0 23.2	25 36.1	6 55.3	12 40.0
26	18 15 30.8	4 31.8	2 6.7	28 52.7	6 49.0	16 58.0	0 49.9	8 10.0	0 19.2	25 38.7	6 54.6	12 41.0
27	18 19 27.4	5 34.0	2 3.6	13♐26.2	6 11.0	17 57.4	1 23.5	8 4.3	0 15.2	25 41.4	6 53.8	12 42.0
28	18 23 23.9	6 36.3	2 .6	28 42.1	5 33.2	18 57.3	1 57.0	7 58.5	0 11.1	25 44.1	6 53.1	12 43.0
29	18 27 20.5	7 38.4	1 57.5	14♑23.8	4 56.1	19 57.6	2 30.6	7 52.5	0 7.0	25 46.9	6 52.5	12 44.0
30	18 31 17.0	8 40.6	1 54.5	0♒ 8.5	4 20.4	20 58.5	3 4.3	7 46.5	0 2.9	25 49.7	6 51.9	12 45.2
		DECLINATION										
1	16 36 56.9	21N59.5	0N11.5	19S11.6	25N 8.2	8N17.1	18N 3.3	18S56.1	20S20.8	14N49.0	12S48.8	21N19.3
4	16 48 46.6	22 22.7	0 11.6	14 21.4	24 36.2	8 54.6	17 31.5	18 57.8	20 22.4	14 47.2	12 47.6	21 17.9
7	17 0 36.2	22 42.4	0 11.6	2 11.1	23 56.3	9 35.2	16 58.8	18 59.9	20 24.2	14 45.3	12 46.6	21 16.3
10	17 12 25.9	22 58.6	0 11.7	10N30.4	23 11.0	10 18.3	16 25.2	19 2.5	20 26.2	14 43.2	12 45.5	21 14.7
13	17 24 15.6	23 11.1	0 11.8	18 16.0	22 22.7	11 3.4	15 50.6	19 5.4	20 28.2	14 40.9	12 44.6	21 13.0
16	17 36 5.2	23 19.9	0 11.8	18 14.0	21 33.7	11 49.9	15 15.2	19 8.8	20 30.5	14 38.6	12 43.7	21 11.2
19	17 47 54.9	23 25.1	0 11.9	11 11.2	20 46.4	12 37.3	14 38.9	19 12.5	20 32.8	14 36.1	12 42.9	21 9.4
22	17 59 44.6	23 26.5	0 11.9	0S .4	20 3.3	13 25.2	14 1.8	19 16.5	20 35.2	14 33.6	12 42.2	21 7.5
25	18 11 34.3	23 24.2	0 12.0	11 53.5	19 27.0	14 13.0	13 23.9	19 20.9	20 37.7	14 30.9	12 41.5	21 5.5
28	18 23 23.9	23 18.2	0 12.0	19 1.2	18 59.7	15 .4	12 45.1	19 25.6	20 40.3	14 28.1	12 41.0	21 3.4

JULY 1961

LONGITUDE

DAY	EPHEM. SID. TIME h m s	☉ ° ′	☊ ° ′	☽ ° ′	☿ ° ′	♀ ° ′	♂ ° ′	♃ ° ′	♄ ° ′	♅ ° ′	♆ ° ′	♇ ° ′
1	18 35 13.6	8♋55.4	29♌45.4	13♒28.9	3♋35.4	23♉36.4	1♍11.4	5♒10.5	27♑51.8	23♌18.2	8♏38.6	6♍ 1.9
2	18 39 10.2	9 52.6	29 42.3	28 14.5	3R 5.7	24 37.7	1 46.9	5R 4.3	27R47.7	23 21.1	8R38.0	6 3.2
3	18 43 6.7	10 49.8	29 39.1	12♓45.2	2 38.9	25 39.3	2 22.4	4 57.9	27 43.6	23 24.1	8 37.4	6 4.5
4	18 47 3.3	11 47.0	29 35.9	26 57.7	2 15.5	26 41.1	2 58.0	4 51.5	27 39.4	23 27.1	8 36.9	6 5.8
5	18 50 59.8	12 44.2	29 32.7	10♈50.8	1 55.8	27 43.3	3 33.6	4 44.9	27 35.3	23 30.1	8 36.4	6 7.1
6	18 54 56.4	13 41.4	29 29.5	24 25.0	1 40.2	28 45.7	4 9.3	4 38.2	27 31.0	23 33.1	8 35.9	6 8.5
7	18 58 52.9	14 38.6	29 26.4	7♉41.3	1 29.1	29 48.4	4 45.1	4 31.5	27 26.8	23 36.2	8 35.4	6 9.9
8	19 2 49.5	15 35.8	29 23.2	20 41.6	1 22.6	0♊51.3	5 20.9	4 24.6	27 22.5	23 39.3	8 35.0	6 11.3
9	19 6 46.0	16 33.0	29 20.0	3♊27.3	1 21.0	1 54.5	5 56.8	4 17.6	27 18.2	23 42.5	8 34.6	6 12.7
10	19 10 42.6	17 30.2	29 16.8	16 .0	1D24.5	2 57.9	6 32.7	4 10.5	27 13.9	23 45.7	8 34.3	6 14.2
11	19 14 39.2	18 27.5	29 13.7	28 21.2	1 33.2	4 1.5	7 8.7	4 3.4	27 9.5	23 48.9	8 34.0	6 15.7
12	19 18 35.7	19 24.7	29 10.5	10♋32.1	1 47.1	5 5.4	7 44.7	3 56.2	27 5.2	23 52.1	8 33.7	6 17.2
13	19 22 32.3	20 21.9	29 7.3	22 34.1	2 6.4	6 9.4	8 20.9	3 48.9	27 .8	23 55.3	8 33.4	6 18.7
14	19 26 28.8	21 19.2	29 4.1	4♌28.8	2 31.0	7 13.7	8 57.0	3 41.5	26 56.4	23 58.6	8 33.2	6 20.2
15	19 30 25.4	22 16.4	29 1.0	16 18.1	3 1.0	8 18.2	9 33.2	3 34.0	26 52.0	24 1.9	8 33.0	6 21.8
16	19 34 21.9	23 13.7	28 57.8	28 4.7	3 36.3	9 22.8	10 9.5	3 26.6	26 47.5	24 5.2	8 32.8	6 23.4
17	19 38 18.5	24 10.9	28 54.6	9♍51.5	4 16.9	10 27.7	10 45.9	3 19.0	26 43.1	24 8.6	8 32.7	6 25.0
18	19 42 15.1	25 8.2	28 51.4	21 42.3	5 2.8	11 32.8	11 22.3	3 11.4	26 38.7	24 12.0	8 32.6	6 26.6
19	19 46 11.6	26 5.5	28 48.3	3♎41.3	5 53.9	12 38.0	11 58.7	3 3.8	26 34.2	24 15.3	8 32.5	6 28.2
20	19 50 8.2	27 2.7	28 45.1	15 53.0	6 50.1	13 43.4	12 35.2	2 56.1	26 29.8	24 18.8	8 32.5	6 29.9
21	19 54 4.7	28 .0	28 41.9	28 22.2	7 51.5	14 49.1	13 11.8	2 48.4	26 25.4	24 22.2	8 32.5	6 31.6
22	19 58 1.3	28 57.3	28 38.7	11♏13.3	8 57.9	15 54.8	13 48.5	2 40.7	26 21.0	24 25.7	8D32.6	6 33.3
23	20 1 57.8	29 54.6	28 35.5	24 30.0	10 9.1	17 .8	14 25.1	2 33.0	26 16.5	24 29.2	8 32.6	6 35.0
24	20 5 54.4	0♌51.9	28 32.4	8♐14.3	11 25.3	18 6.9	15 1.8	2 25.2	26 12.1	24 32.7	8 32.7	6 36.7
25	20 9 50.9	1 49.2	28 29.2	22 26.5	12 46.1	19 13.2	15 38.6	2 17.4	26 7.7	24 36.2	8 32.8	6 38.5
26	20 13 47.5	2 46.5	28 26.0	7♑ 3.7	14 11.5	20 19.6	16 15.4	2 9.7	26 3.3	24 39.7	8 33.0	6 40.2
27	20 17 44.1	3 43.8	28 22.8	22 .4	15 41.4	21 26.2	16 52.3	2 1.9	25 58.9	24 43.2	8 33.2	6 42.0
28	20 21 40.6	4 41.1	28 19.7	7♒ 8.5	17 15.6	22 32.9	17 29.2	1 54.1	25 54.6	24 46.8	8 33.4	6 43.8
29	20 25 37.2	5 38.4	28 16.5	22 18.8	18 53.8	23 39.8	18 6.2	1 46.4	25 50.2	24 50.4	8 33.6	6 45.6
30	20 29 33.7	6 35.8	28 13.3	7♓21.8	20 35.9	24 46.9	18 43.3	1 38.7	25 45.9	24 54.0	8 33.9	6 47.4
31	20 33 30.3	7 33.1	28 10.1	22 9.7	22 21.6	25 54.1	19 20.3	1 31.0	25 41.6	24 57.6	8 34.2	6 49.2

LATITUDE

DAY	SID. TIME	☉	☊	☽	☿	♀	♂	♃	♄	♅	♆	♇
1	18 35 13.6	0 .0	0 .0	1N18.5	4S40.0	2S59.3	1N 6.9	0S32.9	0S 7.6	0N42.4	1N48.2	12N39.5
4	18 47 3.3	0 .0	0 .0	2S29.3	4 45.5	2 57.8	1 4.8	0 33.4	0 7.9	0 42.3	1 48.1	12 38.7
7	18 58 52.9	0 .0	0 .0	4 50.2	4 37.7	2 55.1	1 2.8	0 34.0	0 8.2	0 42.2	1 47.9	12 38.0
10	19 10 42.6	0 .0	0 .0	4 54.5	4 18.2	2 51.5	1 .7	0 34.5	0 8.5	0 42.2	1 47.7	12 37.3
13	19 22 32.3	0 .0	0 .0	2 58.7	3 49.4	2 46.9	0 58.7	0 35.0	0 8.7	0 42.1	1 47.6	12 36.7
16	19 34 21.9	0 .0	0 .0	0N 3.4	3 13.8	2 41.5	0 56.7	0 35.5	0 9.0	0 42.1	1 47.4	12 36.1
19	19 46 11.6	0 .0	0 .0	3 5.8	2 33.6	2 35.2	0 54.7	0 36.0	0 9.3	0 42.0	1 47.2	12 35.6
22	19 58 1.3	0 .0	0 .0	5 1.8	1 50.9	2 28.3	0 52.7	0 36.4	0 9.5	0 42.0	1 47.0	12 35.1
25	20 9 50.9	0 .0	0 .0	4 45.1	1 7.9	2 20.7	0 50.7	0 36.8	0 9.8	0 42.0	1 46.9	12 34.6
28	20 21 40.6	0 .0	0 .0	1 48.8	0 26.3	2 12.5	0 48.7	0 37.2	0 10.0	0 41.9	1 46.7	12 34.2
31	20 33 30.3	0 .0	0 .0	2S13.4	0N11.9	2 3.9	0 46.8	0 37.6	0 10.3	0 41.9	1 46.5	12 33.8

RIGHT ASCENSION

DAY	SID. TIME	☉	☊	☽	☿	♀	♂	♃	♄	♅	♆	♇
1	18 35 13.6	9♋42.7	1♍51.5	15♒33.7	3♋46.7	21♉59.7	3♍37.8	7♒40.3	29♑58.7	25♌52.6	6♏51.2	12♍46.3
2	18 39 10.2	10 44.7	1 48.4	0♓24.6	3R15.4	23 1.3	4 11.4	7R33.9	29R54.4	25 55.4	6R50.6	12 47.4
3	18 43 6.7	11 46.7	1 45.4	14 36.2	2 47.2	24 3.4	4 45.0	7 27.5	29 50.1	25 58.3	6 50.1	12 48.5
4	18 47 3.3	12 48.6	1 42.4	28 12.1	2 22.5	25 6.0	5 18.6	7 20.9	29 45.8	26 1.2	6 49.5	12 49.7
5	18 50 59.8	13 50.4	1 39.3	11♈20.5	2 1.8	26 8.9	5 52.2	7 14.1	29 41.4	26 4.1	6 49.0	12 50.9
6	18 54 56.4	14 52.1	1 36.3	24 11.7	1 45.5	27 12.3	6 25.9	7 7.3	29 37.0	26 7.1	6 48.5	12 52.1
7	18 58 52.9	15 53.8	1 33.3	6♉55.2	1 33.8	28 16.1	6 59.5	7 .4	29 32.6	26 10.1	6 48.1	12 53.4
8	19 2 49.5	16 55.3	1 30.2	19 38.7	1 27.0	29 20.3	7 33.1	6 53.3	29 28.1	26 13.1	6 47.7	12 54.6
9	19 6 46.0	17 56.8	1 27.2	2♊26.7	1 25.4	0♊24.8	8 6.8	6 46.2	29 23.6	26 16.2	6 47.3	12 55.9
10	19 10 42.6	18 58.2	1 24.1	15 20.1	1D29.2	1 29.8	8 40.4	6 38.9	29 19.1	26 19.3	6 46.9	12 57.2
11	19 14 39.2	19 59.5	1 21.1	28 15.9	1 38.5	2 35.2	9 14.1	6 31.6	29 14.5	26 22.4	6 46.6	12 58.6
12	19 18 35.7	21 .7	1 18.1	11♋ 8.5	1 53.3	3 41.0	9 47.8	6 24.1	29 10.0	26 25.5	6 46.3	12 59.9
13	19 22 32.3	22 1.7	1 15.0	23 51.3	2 13.9	4 47.2	10 21.5	6 16.6	29 5.4	26 28.7	6 46.0	13 1.3
14	19 26 28.8	23 2.7	1 12.0	6♌18.5	2 40.2	5 53.7	10 55.2	6 9.1	29 .8	26 31.8	6 45.8	13 2.7
15	19 30 25.4	24 3.5	1 8.9	18 26.8	3 12.2	7 .6	11 28.9	6 1.4	28 56.2	26 35.0	6 45.6	13 4.1
16	19 34 21.9	25 4.2	1 5.9	0♍16.2	3 50.1	8 7.9	12 2.6	5 53.7	28 51.5	26 38.3	6 45.4	13 5.6
17	19 38 18.5	26 4.7	1 2.8	11 49.9	4 33.7	9 15.5	12 36.4	5 45.9	28 46.9	26 41.5	6 45.2	13 7.0
18	19 42 15.1	27 5.2	0 59.8	23 14.0	5 23.0	10 23.5	13 10.1	5 38.1	28 42.3	26 44.8	6 45.1	13 8.5
19	19 46 11.6	28 5.5	0 56.8	4♎36.8	6 18.1	11 31.8	13 43.9	5 30.2	28 37.6	26 48.1	6 45.0	13 10.0
20	19 50 8.2	29 5.6	0 53.7	16 8.4	7 18.9	12 40.4	14 17.7	5 22.3	28 33.0	26 51.4	6 45.0	13 11.5
21	19 54 4.7	0♌ 5.7	0 50.7	27 59.9	8 25.4	13 49.5	14 51.5	5 14.4	28 28.4	26 54.8	6 45.0	13 13.1
22	19 58 1.3	1 5.6	0 47.6	10♏22.6	9 37.3	14 58.8	15 25.3	5 6.4	28 23.7	26 58.1	6 45.0	13 14.7
23	20 1 57.8	2 5.3	0 44.6	23 27.0	10 54.7	16 8.5	15 59.2	4 58.4	28 19.1	27 1.5	6 45.0	13 16.2
24	20 5 54.4	3 4.9	0 41.5	7♐20.3	12 17.5	17 18.4	16 33.0	4 50.4	28 14.4	27 4.9	6D45.1	13 17.8
25	20 9 50.9	4 4.3	0 38.5	22 3.3	13 45.5	18 28.7	17 6.9	4 42.4	28 9.8	27 8.3	6 45.2	13 19.4
26	20 13 47.5	5 3.5	0 35.4	7♑27.7	15 18.5	19 39.2	17 40.8	4 34.4	28 5.2	27 11.7	6 45.3	13 21.1
27	20 17 44.1	6 2.7	0 32.4	23 15.6	16 56.4	20 50.1	18 14.7	4 26.3	28 .6	27 15.2	6 45.5	13 22.7
28	20 21 40.6	7 1.6	0 29.3	9♒ 3.8	18 38.9	22 1.2	18 48.6	4 18.3	27 56.0	27 18.6	6 45.7	13 24.4
29	20 25 37.2	8 .5	0 26.3	24 31.2	20 25.7	23 12.6	19 22.5	4 10.3	27 51.5	27 22.1	6 45.9	13 26.0
30	20 29 33.7	8 59.1	0 23.2	9♓24.8	22 16.6	24 24.3	19 56.5	4 2.3	27 46.9	27 25.6	6 46.2	13 27.7
31	20 33 30.3	9 57.6	0 20.2	23 41.0	24 11.1	25 36.2	20 30.5	3 54.3	27 42.4	27 29.1	6 46.5	13 29.4

DECLINATION

DAY	SID. TIME	☉	☊	☽	☿	♀	♂	♃	♄	♅	♆	♇
1	18 35 13.6	23N 8.5	0N12.1	15S31.4	18N43.6	15N46.9	12N 5.7	19S30.5	20S43.0	14N25.2	12S40.5	21N 1.3
4	18 47 3.3	22 55.2	0 12.2	3 29.5	18 39.9	16 32.0	11 25.5	19 35.6	20 45.7	14 22.2	12 40.1	20 59.1
7	18 58 52.9	22 38.2	0 12.2	9N29.8	18 48.3	17 15.5	10 44.6	19 41.0	20 48.4	14 19.1	12 39.8	20 56.9
10	19 10 42.6	22 17.8	0 12.3	17 49.4	19 7.9	17 56.9	10 3.1	19 46.5	20 51.2	14 15.9	12 39.6	20 54.7
13	19 22 32.3	21 53.9	0 12.3	18 36.8	19 36.1	18 35.8	9 20.9	19 52.1	20 54.0	14 12.7	12 39.5	20 52.4
16	19 34 21.9	21 26.6	0 12.4	12 11.8	20 9.9	19 11.9	8 38.1	19 57.8	20 56.8	14 9.3	12 39.5	20 50.1
19	19 46 11.6	20 56.0	0 12.5	1 22.6	20 45.2	19 44.9	7 54.7	20 3.5	20 59.7	14 5.9	12 39.5	20 47.7
22	19 58 1.3	20 22.2	0 12.5	10S24.7	21 17.7	20 14.3	7 10.8	20 9.3	21 2.4	14 2.4	12 39.7	20 45.3
25	20 9 50.9	19 45.4	0 12.6	18 29.0	21 42.2	20 40.0	6 26.4	20 15.0	21 5.2	13 58.9	12 40.0	20 42.9
28	20 21 40.6	19 5.7	0 12.6	16 44.1	21 53.6	21 1.6	5 41.6	20 20.6	21 7.9	13 55.3	12 40.3	20 40.5
31	20 33 30.3	18 23.1	0 12.7	5 9.2	21 46.9	21 18.9	4 56.3	20 26.2	21 10.6	13 51.7	12 40.8	20 38.1

AUGUST 1961

LONGITUDE

DAY	EPHEM. SID. TIME	☉	☊	☽	☿	♀	♂	♃	♄	♅	♆	♇
	h m s	° ′	° ′	° ′	° ′	° ′	° ′	° ′	° ′	° ′	° ′	° ′
1	20 37 26.8	8♌30.5	28♌ 6.9	6♈37.0	24♋10.7	27♊ 1.5	19♍57.5	1♒23.3	25♑37.3	25♌ 1.2	8♏34.6	6♍51.1
2	20 41 23.4	9 27.9	28 3.8	20 40.4	26 2.7	28 9.0	20 34.7	1R15.6	25R33.1	25 4.8	8 35.0	6 52.9
3	20 45 19.9	10 25.3	28 .6	4♉19.4	27 57.5	29 16.7	21 11.9	1 8.0	25 28.9	25 8.5	8 35.4	6 54.8
4	20 49 16.5	11 22.8	27 57.4	17 35.0	29 54.6	0♋24.5	21 49.2	1 .5	25 24.7	25 12.1	8 35.8	6 56.7
5	20 53 13.1	12 20.2	27 54.2	0♊29.5	1♌53.6	1 32.4	22 26.6	0 53.0	25 20.5	25 15.8	8 36.3	6 58.6
6	20 57 9.6	13 17.7	27 51.1	13 5.7	3 54.3	2 40.5	23 4.0	0 45.5	25 16.4	25 19.5	8 36.8	7 .5
7	21 1 6.2	14 15.2	27 47.9	25 26.9	5 56.3	3 48.7	23 41.5	0 38.1	25 12.3	25 23.2	8 37.4	7 2.4
8	21 5 2.7	15 12.7	27 44.7	7♋35.9	7 59.2	4 57.0	24 19.0	0 30.8	25 8.3	25 26.8	8 37.9	7 4.3
9	21 8 59.3	16 10.3	27 41.5	19 35.8	10 2.6	6 5.5	24 56.6	0 23.6	25 4.3	25 30.5	8 38.5	7 6.3
10	21 12 55.8	17 7.8	27 38.4	1♌29.0	12 6.4	7 14.1	25 34.3	0 16.4	25 .3	25 34.3	8 39.2	7 8.2
11	21 16 52.4	18 5.4	27 35.2	13 18.0	14 10.2	8 22.8	26 12.0	0 9.4	24 56.5	25 38.0	8 39.9	7 10.2
12	21 20 48.9	19 3.0	27 32.0	25 5.1	16 13.7	9 31.6	26 49.8	0 2.4	24 52.6	25 41.7	8 40.6	7 12.2
13	21 24 45.5	20 .7	27 28.8	6♍52.4	18 16.7	10 40.6	27 27.6	29♑55.5	24 48.8	25 45.5	8 41.3	7 14.2
14	21 28 42.0	20 58.3	27 25.6	18 42.4	20 19.0	11 49.6	28 5.5	29 48.7	24 45.0	25 49.2	8 42.1	7 16.1
15	21 32 38.6	21 56.0	27 22.5	0♎37.9	22 20.5	12 58.8	28 43.4	29 42.0	24 41.3	25 52.9	8 42.9	7 18.1
16	21 36 35.2	22 53.6	27 19.3	12 41.7	24 21.1	14 8.1	29 21.4	29 35.4	24 37.7	25 56.7	8 43.7	7 20.1
17	21 40 31.7	23 51.3	27 16.1	24 57.2	26 20.6	15 17.5	29 59.4	29 28.9	24 34.1	26 .4	8 44.5	7 22.1
18	21 44 28.3	24 49.0	27 12.9	7♏27.9	28 19.0	16 27.0	0♎37.5	29 22.6	24 30.6	26 4.2	8 45.4	7 24.1
19	21 48 24.8	25 46.8	27 9.8	20 17.3	0♍16.1	17 36.6	1 15.6	29 16.4	24 27.1	26 7.9	8 46.3	7 26.2
20	21 52 21.4	26 44.5	27 6.6	3♐28.8	2 12.0	18 46.3	1 53.8	29 10.2	24 23.7	26 11.7	8 47.3	7 28.2
21	21 56 17.9	27 42.3	27 3.4	17 4.9	4 6.5	19 56.1	2 32.0	29 4.3	24 20.4	26 15.4	8 48.3	7 30.2
22	22 0 14.5	28 40.1	27 .2	1♑ 6.6	5 59.7	21 6.0	3 10.3	28 58.4	24 17.1	26 19.1	8 49.3	7 32.2
23	22 4 11.0	29 37.9	26 57.0	15 33.1	7 51.6	22 16.0	3 48.6	28 52.7	24 13.9	26 22.9	8 50.3	7 34.3
24	22 8 7.6	0♍35.7	26 53.9	0♒21.2	9 42.1	23 26.1	4 27.0	28 47.2	24 10.8	26 26.6	8 51.4	7 36.3
25	22 12 4.1	1 33.5	26 50.7	15 24.9	11 31.3	24 36.4	5 5.5	28 41.7	24 7.7	26 30.4	8 52.5	7 38.4
26	22 16 .7	2 31.4	26 47.5	0♓36.1	13 19.1	25 46.7	5 44.0	28 36.5	24 4.7	26 34.1	8 53.6	7 40.4
27	22 19 57.2	3 29.3	26 44.3	15 45.5	15 5.6	26 57.1	6 22.5	28 31.4	24 1.8	26 37.8	8 54.7	7 42.5
28	22 23 53.8	4 27.2	26 41.2	0♈43.8	16 50.8	28 7.7	7 1.1	28 26.4	23 59.0	26 41.5	8 55.9	7 44.5
29	22 27 50.3	5 25.1	26 38.0	15 23.2	18 34.7	29 18.3	7 39.8	28 21.6	23 56.2	26 45.3	8 57.1	7 46.6
30	22 31 46.9	6 23.1	26 34.8	29 38.3	20 17.2	0♌29.0	8 18.5	28 16.9	23 53.5	26 49.0	8 58.3	7 48.6
31	22 35 43.4	7 21.1	26 31.6	13♉26.4	21 58.5	1 39.9	8 57.3	28 12.4	23 50.9	26 52.7	8 59.6	7 50.7

LATITUDE

DAY	EPHEM. SID. TIME	☉	☊	☽	☿	♀	♂	♃	♄	♅	♆	♇
1	20 37 26.8	0 .0	0 .0	3S20.9	0N23.5	2S .9	0N46.1	0S37.7	0S10.4	0N41.9	1N46.4	12N33.7
4	20 49 16.5	0 .0	0 .0	5 12.1	0 54.4	1 51.6	0 44.2	0 38.1	0 10.6	0 41.9	1 46.3	12 33.4
7	21 1 6.2	0 .0	0 .0	4 39.3	1 18.3	1 42.0	0 42.2	0 38.4	0 10.9	0 41.9	1 46.1	12 33.2
10	21 12 55.8	0 .0	0 .0	2 17.8	1 34.6	1 32.0	0 40.3	0 38.7	0 11.1	0 41.9	1 45.9	12 32.9
13	21 24 45.5	0 .0	0 .0	0N53.7	1 43.5	1 21.9	0 38.4	0 38.9	0 11.3	0 41.9	1 45.7	12 32.8
16	21 36 35.2	0 .0	0 .0	3 47.1	1 45.7	1 11.5	0 36.4	0 39.2	0 11.6	0 41.9	1 45.6	12 32.7
19	21 48 24.8	0 .0	0 .0	5 15.7	1 41.9	1 1.1	0 34.5	0 39.4	0 11.8	0 41.9	1 45.4	12 32.6
22	22 0 14.5	0 .0	0 .0	4 24.2	1 33.2	0 50.6	0 32.6	0 39.6	0 12.0	0 41.9	1 45.2	12 32.6
25	22 12 4.1	0 .0	0 .0	1 5.2	1 20.4	0 40.1	0 30.7	0 39.7	0 12.2	0 41.9	1 45.1	12 32.7
28	22 23 53.8	0 .0	0 .0	2S55.8	1 4.3	0 29.7	0 28.8	0 39.9	0 12.5	0 41.9	1 44.9	12 32.8
31	22 35 43.4	0 .0	0 .0	5 8.4	0 45.6	0 19.5	0 26.9	0 40.0	0 12.7	0 41.9	1 44.8	12 33.0

RIGHT ASCENSION

DAY	EPHEM. SID. TIME	☉	☊	☽	☿	♀	♂	♃	♄	♅	♆	♇
1	20 37 26.8	10♌56.0	0♍17.1	7♈23.9	26♋ 8.9	26♊48.4	21♍ 4.5	3♒46.3	27♑37.9	27♌32.6	6♏46.8	13♍31.2
2	20 41 23.4	11 54.2	0 14.1	20 41.5	28 9.5	28 .8	21 38.5	3R38.4	27R33.5	27 36.1	6 47.1	13 32.9
3	20 45 19.9	12 52.3	0 11.0	3♉43.0	0♌12.6	29 13.4	22 12.6	3 30.5	27 29.0	27 39.6	6 47.5	13 34.7
4	20 49 16.5	13 50.3	0 8.0	16 36.6	2 17.6	0♋26.3	22 46.7	3 22.7	27 24.6	27 43.2	6 47.9	13 36.4
5	20 53 13.1	14 48.1	0 4.9	29 28.1	4 24.0	1 39.4	23 20.9	3 14.9	27 20.3	27 46.7	6 48.4	13 38.2
6	20 57 9.6	15 45.7	0 1.9	12♊20.2	6 31.4	2 52.6	23 55.1	3 7.1	27 15.9	27 50.3	6 48.9	13 40.0
7	21 1 6.2	16 43.2	29♌58.8	25 12.5	8 39.3	4 6.0	24 29.3	2 59.4	27 11.6	27 53.8	6 49.4	13 41.8
8	21 5 2.7	17 40.6	29 55.8	8♋ 1.8	10 47.3	5 19.6	25 3.5	2 51.8	27 7.4	27 57.4	6 49.9	13 43.6
9	21 8 59.3	18 37.8	29 52.7	20 43.1	12 55.0	6 33.4	25 37.8	2 44.3	27 3.2	28 1.0	6 50.5	13 45.4
10	21 12 55.8	19 34.8	29 49.7	3♌11.5	15 2.0	7 47.2	26 12.1	2 36.8	26 59.0	28 4.6	6 51.1	13 47.3
11	21 16 52.4	20 31.8	29 46.6	15 23.5	17 8.1	9 1.3	26 46.6	2 29.5	26 55.0	28 8.3	6 51.7	13 49.2
12	21 20 48.9	21 28.6	29 43.6	27 17.9	19 12.9	10 15.4	27 21.0	2 22.2	26 50.9	28 11.9	6 52.4	13 51.0
13	21 24 45.5	22 25.2	29 40.5	8♍56.4	21 16.2	11 29.7	27 55.4	2 15.0	26 46.9	28 15.5	6 53.1	13 52.9
14	21 28 42.0	23 21.7	29 37.5	20 23.1	23 17.9	12 44.0	28 29.9	2 7.9	26 43.0	28 19.1	6 53.8	13 54.8
15	21 32 38.6	24 18.1	29 34.4	1♎44.6	25 17.7	13 58.4	29 4.5	2 .9	26 39.1	28 22.7	6 54.6	13 56.7
16	21 36 35.2	25 14.3	29 31.3	13 9.1	27 15.7	15 12.8	29 39.0	1 54.1	26 35.2	28 26.3	6 55.3	13 58.6
17	21 40 31.7	26 10.4	29 28.3	24 45.9	29 11.7	16 27.3	0♎13.7	1 47.3	26 31.4	28 29.9	6 56.2	14 .5
18	21 44 28.3	27 6.4	29 25.2	6♏45.3	1♍ 5.7	17 41.9	0 48.4	1 40.7	26 27.7	28 33.6	6 57.0	14 2.4
19	21 48 24.8	28 2.2	29 22.2	19 17.1	2 57.6	18 56.5	1 23.1	1 34.2	26 24.1	28 37.2	6 57.9	14 4.4
20	21 52 21.4	28 57.9	29 19.1	2♐29.8	4 47.6	20 11.1	1 57.9	1 27.8	26 20.5	28 40.8	6 58.8	14 6.3
21	21 56 17.9	29 53.5	29 16.1	16 28.1	6 35.5	21 25.7	2 32.7	1 21.5	26 17.0	28 44.4	6 59.7	14 8.2
22	22 0 14.5	0♍48.9	29 13.0	1♑10.2	8 21.5	22 40.3	3 7.6	1 15.4	26 13.5	28 48.0	7 .7	14 10.2
23	22 4 11.0	1 44.2	29 9.9	16 26.7	10 5.6	23 54.9	3 42.5	1 9.5	26 10.2	28 51.7	7 1.6	14 12.1
24	22 8 7.6	2 39.5	29 6.9	2♒ .7	11 47.8	25 9.5	4 17.5	1 3.6	26 6.9	28 55.3	7 2.7	14 14.1
25	22 12 4.1	3 34.6	29 3.8	17 32.8	13 28.2	26 24.0	4 52.6	0 58.0	26 3.7	28 58.9	7 3.7	14 16.1
26	22 16 .7	4 29.6	29 .8	2♓46.7	15 6.8	27 38.5	5 27.7	0 52.5	26 .5	29 2.5	7 4.8	14 18.0
27	22 19 57.2	5 24.5	28 57.7	17 33.0	16 43.8	28 52.9	6 2.8	0 47.1	25 57.4	29 6.1	7 5.9	14 20.0
28	22 23 53.8	6 19.3	28 54.6	1♈50.1	18 19.1	0♌ 7.3	6 38.1	0 41.9	25 54.4	29 9.7	7 7.0	14 22.0
29	22 27 50.3	7 14.0	28 51.6	15 41.6	19 52.8	1 21.6	7 13.4	0 36.8	25 51.5	29 13.3	7 8.1	14 24.0
30	22 31 46.9	8 8.6	28 48.5	29 13.8	21 25.1	2 35.9	7 48.7	0 32.0	25 48.7	29 16.9	7 9.3	14 26.0
31	22 35 43.4	9 3.2	28 45.5	12♉33.3	22 55.8	3 50.0	8 24.1	0 27.3	25 45.9	29 20.4	7 10.5	14 28.0

DECLINATION

DAY	EPHEM. SID. TIME	☉	☊	☽	☿	♀	♂	♃	♄	♅	♆	♇
1	20 37 26.8	18N 8.3	0N12.7	0S26.9	21N39.9	21N23.7	4N41.1	20S28.0	21S11.4	13N50.5	12S40.9	20N37.3
4	20 49 16.5	17 22.1	0 12.8	12N 5.0	21 3.5	21 34.9	3 55.3	20 33.3	21 14.0	13 46.8	12 41.5	20 34.9
7	21 1 6.2	16 33.3	0 12.8	18 42.7	20 3.2	21 41.3	3 9.1	20 38.5	21 16.5	13 43.1	12 42.2	20 32.4
10	21 12 55.8	15 42.2	0 12.9	17 35.4	18 40.8	21 42.8	2 22.6	20 43.5	21 18.9	13 39.3	12 42.9	20 30.0
13	21 24 45.5	14 48.8	0 12.9	9 49.3	16 59.6	21 39.2	1 35.8	20 48.2	21 21.2	13 35.5	12 43.7	20 27.6
16	21 36 35.2	13 53.2	0 13.0	1S31.7	15 4.0	21 30.4	0 48.8	20 52.6	21 23.4	13 31.7	12 44.7	20 25.2
19	21 48 24.8	12 55.7	0 13.0	12 44.7	12 58.1	21 16.4	0 1.6	20 56.8	21 25.5	13 27.9	12 45.7	20 22.9
22	22 0 14.5	11 56.3	0 13.1	19 2.1	10 45.4	20 57.2	0S45.8	21 .7	21 27.5	13 24.1	12 46.7	20 20.6
25	22 12 4.1	10 55.3	0 13.2	15 10.7	8 28.9	20 32.8	1 33.2	21 4.3	21 29.4	13 20.3	12 47.9	20 18.3
28	22 23 53.8	9 52.7	0 13.2	2 23.9	6 10.9	20 3.2	2 20.8	21 7.6	21 31.1	13 16.5	12 49.2	20 16.0
31	22 35 43.4	8 48.7	0 13.3	10N58.0	3 52.9	19 28.5	3 8.3	21 10.5	21 32.7	13 12.7	12 50.5	20 13.8

SEPTEMBER 1961

LONGITUDE

DAY	EPHEM. SID. TIME	☉	☊	☽	☿	♀	♂	♃	♄	♅	♆	♇
	h m s	° ′	° ′	° ′	° ′	° ′	° ′	° ′	° ′	° ′	° ′	° ′
1	22 39 40.0	8♍19.2	26♌28.4	26♉47.6	23♍38.6	2♌50.8	9♎36.1	28♑ 8.2	23♑48.4	26♌56.4	9♏ .9	7♍52.8
2	22 43 36.6	9 17.3	26 25.3	9♊43.5	25 17.4	4 1.9	10 15.0	28 R 4.0	23 R 46.0	27 .1	9 2.2	7 54.8
3	22 47 33.1	10 15.4	26 22.1	22 17.6	26 54.9	5 13.0	10 53.9	28 .0	23 43.6	27 3.8	9 3.6	7 56.9
4	22 51 29.7	11 13.5	26 18.9	4♋34.0	28 31.3	6 24.2	11 32.9	27 56.2	23 41.3	27 7.4	9 4.9	7 59.0
5	22 55 26.2	12 11.7	26 15.7	16 36.9	0♎ 6.4	7 35.5	12 12.0	27 52.6	23 39.1	27 11.1	9 6.3	8 1.0
6	22 59 22.8	13 9.9	26 12.5	28 30.6	1 40.3	8 46.9	12 51.1	27 49.1	23 37.0	27 14.7	9 7.8	8 3.1
7	23 3 19.3	14 8.1	26 9.4	10♌19.0	3 13.0	9 58.4	13 30.2	27 45.8	23 35.0	27 18.4	9 9.2	8 5.1
8	23 7 15.9	15 6.4	26 6.2	22 5.7	4 44.6	11 9.9	14 9.5	27 42.7	23 33.1	27 22.0	9 10.7	8 7.2
9	23 11 12.4	16 4.7	26 3.0	3♍53.6	6 14.9	12 21.6	14 48.7	27 39.8	23 31.2	27 25.6	9 12.2	8 9.2
10	23 15 9.0	17 3.0	25 59.8	15 45.2	7 44.0	13 33.3	15 28.1	27 37.1	23 29.5	27 29.2	9 13.7	8 11.2
11	23 19 5.5	18 1.4	25 56.7	27 42.7	9 12.0	14 45.1	16 7.5	27 34.5	23 27.8	27 32.7	9 15.2	8 13.3
12	23 23 2.1	18 59.8	25 53.5	9♎48.1	10 38.7	15 57.0	16 46.9	27 32.2	23 26.2	27 36.3	9 16.8	8 15.3
13	23 26 58.6	19 58.2	25 50.3	22 3.0	12 4.2	17 9.0	17 26.4	27 30.0	23 24.8	27 39.8	9 18.4	8 17.3
14	23 30 55.2	20 56.6	25 47.1	4♏29.1	13 28.4	18 21.1	18 5.9	27 28.0	23 23.4	27 43.4	9 20.0	8 19.3
15	23 34 51.7	21 55.1	25 43.9	17 8.4	14 51.4	19 33.2	18 45.6	27 26.3	23 22.1	27 46.9	9 21.7	8 21.4
16	23 38 48.3	22 53.6	25 40.8	0♐ 2.8	16 13.1	20 45.4	19 25.2	27 24.7	23 20.9	27 50.4	9 23.3	8 23.4
17	23 42 44.8	23 52.1	25 37.6	13 14.2	17 33.4	21 57.7	20 4.9	27 23.3	23 19.8	27 53.8	9 25.0	8 25.4
18	23 46 41.4	24 50.7	25 34.4	26 44.4	18 52.3	23 10.0	20 44.7	27 22.1	23 18.8	27 57.3	9 26.7	8 27.4
19	23 50 37.9	25 49.3	25 31.2	10♑34.8	20 9.8	24 22.4	21 24.5	27 21.1	23 17.9	28 .7	9 28.4	8 29.3
20	23 54 34.5	26 47.9	25 28.1	24 45.7	21 25.8	25 34.9	22 4.4	27 20.3	23 17.1	28 4.1	9 30.2	8 31.3
21	23 58 31.0	27 46.5	25 24.9	9♒15.8	22 40.3	26 47.5	22 44.3	27 19.7	23 16.4	28 7.5	9 32.0	8 33.3
22	0 2 27.6	28 45.2	25 21.7	24 1.9	23 53.1	28 .2	23 24.4	27 19.3	23 15.8	28 10.9	9 33.8	8 35.3
23	0 6 24.1	29 43.9	25 18.5	8♓58.6	25 4.2	29 12.9	24 4.4	27 19.1	23 15.3	28 14.2	9 35.6	8 37.2
24	0 10 20.7	0♎42.6	25 15.3	23 58.4	26 13.5	0♍25.7	24 44.5	27 19.1	23 14.8	28 17.5	9 37.4	8 39.2
25	0 14 17.3	1 41.4	25 12.2	8♈52.8	27 20.8	1 38.5	25 24.6	27 D 19.2	23 14.5	28 20.8	9 39.3	8 41.1
26	0 18 13.8	2 40.2	25 9.0	23 33.5	28 26.0	2 51.4	26 4.8	27 19.6	23 14.3	28 24.1	9 41.1	8 43.0
27	0 22 10.4	3 39.0	25 5.8	7♉53.5	29 29.0	4 4.4	26 45.1	27 20.2	23 14.2	28 27.3	9 43.0	8 44.9
28	0 26 6.9	4 37.9	25 2.6	21 48.0	0♏29.7	5 17.5	27 25.4	27 20.9	23 14.1	28 30.5	9 44.9	8 46.8
29	0 30 3.5	5 36.8	24 59.5	5♊15.1	1 27.7	6 30.6	28 5.8	27 21.9	23 D 14.2	28 33.7	9 46.8	8 48.7
30	0 34 .0	6 35.7	24 56.3	18 15.6	2 23.0	7 43.8	28 46.2	27 23.0	23 14.4	28 36.9	9 48.8	8 50.6

LATITUDE

DAY	EPHEM. SID. TIME	☉	☊	☽	☿	♀	♂	♃	♄	♅	♆	♇
1	22 39 40.0	0 .0	0 .0	5 S 17.4	0 N 38.9	0 S 16.1	0 N 26.2	0 S 40.0	0 S 12.7	0 N 42.0	1 N 44.7	12 N 33.0
4	22 51 29.7	0 .0	0 .0	4 12.4	0 17.6	0 6.0	0 24.3	0 40.1	0 12.9	0 42.0	1 44.6	12 33.3
7	23 3 19.3	0 .0	0 .0	1 32.4	0 S 5.0	0 N 3.7	0 22.4	0 40.2	0 13.1	0 42.0	1 44.4	12 33.6
10	23 15 9.0	0 .0	0 .0	1 N 40.6	0 28.5	0 13.2	0 20.6	0 40.2	0 13.3	0 42.1	1 44.3	12 33.9
13	23 26 58.6	0 .0	0 .0	4 17.8	0 52.6	0 22.3	0 18.7	0 40.2	0 13.5	0 42.1	1 44.2	12 34.3
16	23 38 48.3	0 .0	0 .0	5 13.8	1 16.7	0 31.1	0 16.8	0 40.3	0 13.7	0 42.2	1 44.0	12 34.7
19	23 50 37.9	0 .0	0 .0	3 47.5	1 40.6	0 39.4	0 14.9	0 40.3	0 13.9	0 42.2	1 43.9	12 35.3
22	0 2 27.6	0 .0	0 .0	0 16.0	2 3.8	0 47.2	0 13.1	0 40.3	0 14.1	0 42.3	1 43.8	12 35.8
25	0 14 17.3	0 .0	0 .0	3 S 29.2	2 25.8	0 54.5	0 11.2	0 40.2	0 14.3	0 42.4	1 43.7	12 36.4
28	0 26 6.9	0 .0	0 .0	5 10.1	2 45.9	1 1.3	0 9.3	0 40.2	0 14.4	0 42.5	1 43.6	12 37.1

RIGHT ASCENSION

DAY	EPHEM. SID. TIME	☉	☊	☽	☿	♀	♂	♃	♄	♅	♆	♇
1	22 39 40.0	9♍57.7	28♌42.4	25♉45.2	24♍25.3	5♌ 4.2	8♎59.7	0♒22.8	25♑43.3	29♌24.1	7♏11.8	14♍30.0
2	22 43 36.6	10 52.1	28 39.3	8♊52.1	25 53.3	6 18.1	9 35.3	0 R 18.4	25 R 40.8	29 27.6	7 13.1	14 32.0
3	22 47 33.1	11 46.4	28 36.3	21 54.2	27 20.1	7 32.0	10 10.9	0 14.2	25 38.3	29 31.2	7 14.4	14 34.0
4	22 51 29.7	12 40.7	28 33.2	4♋49.3	28 45.6	8 45.7	10 46.6	0 10.2	25 35.9	29 34.7	7 15.7	14 36.0
5	22 55 26.2	13 34.9	28 30.1	17 34.1	0♎ 9.9	9 59.3	11 22.4	0 6.4	25 33.5	29 38.2	7 17.0	14 38.0
6	22 59 22.8	14 29.1	28 27.1	0♌ 5.2	1 33.1	11 12.8	11 58.3	0 2.8	25 31.3	29 41.7	7 18.4	14 40.0
7	23 3 19.3	15 23.2	28 24.0	12 20.0	2 55.1	12 26.1	12 34.3	29♑59.3	25 29.2	29 45.3	7 19.8	14 42.0
8	23 7 15.9	16 17.2	28 20.9	24 18.1	4 16.1	13 39.3	13 10.3	29 56.1	25 27.1	29 48.7	7 21.2	14 44.0
9	23 11 12.4	17 11.3	28 17.9	6♍ 1.0	5 36.0	14 52.4	13 46.5	29 53.0	25 25.2	29 52.2	7 22.6	14 46.0
10	23 15 9.0	18 5.2	28 14.8	17 32.5	6 54.9	16 5.3	14 22.7	29 50.1	25 23.4	29 55.7	7 24.1	14 48.0
11	23 19 5.5	18 59.2	28 11.7	28 57.9	8 12.7	17 18.0	14 59.0	29 47.5	25 21.6	29 59.1	7 25.6	14 50.0
12	23 23 2.1	19 53.1	28 8.7	10♎24.3	9 29.5	18 30.6	15 35.4	29 45.0	25 19.9	0♍ 2.6	7 27.1	14 52.0
13	23 26 58.6	20 47.0	28 5.6	21 59.5	10 45.3	19 43.1	16 11.9	29 42.7	25 18.4	0 6.0	7 28.6	14 54.0
14	23 30 55.2	21 40.8	28 2.5	3♏51.9	12 .2	20 55.3	16 48.4	29 40.7	25 16.9	0 9.4	7 30.2	14 56.0
15	23 34 51.7	22 34.7	27 59.5	16 10.0	13 14.0	22 7.4	17 25.1	29 38.8	25 15.6	0 12.8	7 31.8	14 58.0
16	23 38 48.3	23 28.5	27 56.4	29 .7	14 26.7	23 19.3	18 1.9	29 37.1	25 14.3	0 16.1	7 33.4	14 60.0
17	23 42 44.8	24 22.3	27 53.3	12♐28.6	15 38.5	24 31.1	18 38.7	29 35.7	25 13.2	0 19.5	7 35.0	15 1.9
18	23 46 41.4	25 16.1	27 50.2	26 33.9	16 49.1	25 42.7	19 15.6	29 34.4	25 12.1	0 22.8	7 36.7	15 3.9
19	23 50 37.9	26 9.9	27 47.2	11♑11.3	17 58.7	26 54.1	19 52.7	29 33.3	25 11.2	0 26.1	7 38.3	15 5.9
20	23 54 34.5	27 3.7	27 44.1	26 9.9	19 7.1	28 5.3	20 29.8	29 32.5	25 10.3	0 29.4	7 40.0	15 7.9
21	23 58 31.0	27 57.5	27 41.0	11♒15.6	20 14.2	29 16.4	21 7.1	29 31.8	25 9.6	0 32.7	7 41.7	15 9.8
22	0 2 27.6	28 51.4	27 38.0	26 15.2	21 20.2	0♍27.4	21 44.5	29 31.5	25 9.0	0 35.9	7 43.5	15 11.8
23	0 6 24.1	29 45.2	27 34.9	10♓59.5	22 24.7	1 38.1	22 21.9	29 31.2	25 8.4	0 39.2	7 45.2	15 13.7
24	0 10 20.7	0♎39.1	27 31.8	25 24.6	23 27.8	2 48.7	22 59.5	29 31.2	25 8.0	0 42.3	7 47.0	15 15.7
25	0 14 17.3	1 33.0	27 28.7	9♈31.8	24 29.3	3 59.2	23 37.1	29 D 31.4	25 7.7	0 45.5	7 48.8	15 17.6
26	0 18 13.8	2 27.0	27 25.7	23 24.9	25 29.1	5 9.5	24 14.9	29 31.8	25 7.4	0 48.7	7 50.6	15 19.5
27	0 22 10.4	3 21.0	27 22.6	7♉ 8.3	26 27.1	6 19.6	24 52.8	29 32.4	25 7.3	0 51.8	7 52.4	15 21.4
28	0 26 6.9	4 15.0	27 19.5	20 45.2	27 23.0	7 29.7	25 30.8	29 33.1	25 7.3	0 54.9	7 54.3	15 23.3
29	0 30 3.5	5 9.1	27 16.4	4♊16.5	28 16.9	8 39.5	26 8.9	29 34.1	25 D 7.4	0 57.9	7 56.1	15 25.2
30	0 34 .0	6 3.3	27 13.4	17 40.9	29 8.3	9 49.3	26 47.1	29 35.3	25 7.6	1 1.0	7 58.0	15 27.1

DECLINATION

DAY	EPHEM. SID. TIME	☉	☊	☽	☿	♀	♂	♃	♄	♅	♆	♇
1	22 39 40.0	8 N 27.0	0 N 13.3	14 N 17.5	3 N 7.2	19 N 15.9	3 S 24.2	21 S 11.4	21 S 33.2	13 N 11.5	12 S 50.9	20 N 13.1
4	22 51 29.7	7 21.4	0 13.3	19 9.6	0 51.5	18 34.6	4 11.7	21 13.9	21 34.6	13 7.7	12 52.4	20 10.9
7	23 3 19.3	6 14.6	0 13.4	16 10.5	1 S 21.4	17 48.6	4 59.1	21 16.0	21 35.9	13 4.0	12 53.8	20 8.8
10	23 15 9.0	5 6.9	0 13.5	7 9.8	3 30.3	16 58.1	5 46.5	21 17.8	21 37.1	13 .3	12 55.4	20 6.8
13	23 26 58.6	3 58.4	0 13.5	4 S 35.9	5 34.7	16 3.1	6 33.6	21 19.3	21 38.1	12 56.7	12 57.0	20 4.8
16	23 38 48.3	2 49.3	0 13.6	15 2.9	7 33.6	15 4.1	7 20.5	21 20.3	21 38.9	12 53.1	12 58.7	20 2.9
19	23 50 37.9	1 39.7	0 13.6	19 14.4	9 26.1	14 1.1	8 7.1	21 21.0	21 39.6	12 49.6	13 .4	20 1.1
22	0 2 27.6	0 29.8	0 13.7	13 15.7	11 11.2	12 54.5	8 53.4	21 21.4	21 40.1	12 46.1	13 2.2	19 59.3
25	0 14 17.3	0 S 40.3	0 13.7	0 N 18.9	12 47.8	11 44.5	9 39.3	21 21.4	21 40.5	12 42.8	13 4.0	19 57.6
28	0 26 6.9	1 50.4	0 13.8	13 13.3	14 14.1	10 31.4	10 24.8	21 21.0	21 40.8	12 39.5	13 5.9	19 56.0

OCTOBER 1961

LONGITUDE

DAY	EPHEM. SID. TIME (h m s)	☉ (° ′)	☊ (° ′)	☾ (° ′)	☿ (° ′)	♀ (° ′)	♂ (° ′)	♃ (° ′)	♄ (° ′)	♅ (° ′)	♆ (° ′)	♇ (° ′)
1	0 37 56.6	7♎34.7	24♌53.1	0♋52.1	3♏15.3	8♍57.1	29♎26.7	27♑24.3	23♑14.7	28♌40.0	9♏50.7	8♍52.4
2	0 41 53.1	8 33.7	24 49.9	13 8.7	4 4.3	10 10.4	0♏ 7.2	27 25.9	23 15.0	28 43.1	9 52.7	8 54.3
3	0 45 49.7	9 32.7	24 46.7	25 10.4	4 49.8	11 23.8	0 47.8	27 27.6	23 15.5	28 46.1	9 54.7	8 56.1
4	0 49 46.2	10 31.8	24 43.6	7♌ 2.2	5 31.5	12 37.3	1 28.5	27 29.5	23 16.1	28 49.2	9 56.7	8 57.9
5	0 53 42.8	11 30.9	24 40.4	18 49.3	6 8.9	13 50.8	2 9.2	27 31.6	23 16.7	28 52.2	9 58.7	8 59.7
6	0 57 39.3	12 30.1	24 37.2	0♍36.4	6 41.7	15 4.4	2 50.0	27 33.9	23 17.5	28 55.1	10 .7	9 1.5
7	1 1 35.9	13 29.3	24 34.0	12 27.3	7 9.5	16 18.0	3 30.8	27 36.4	23 18.4	28 58.1	10 2.8	9 3.3
8	1 5 32.4	14 28.5	24 30.8	24 25.5	7 31.8	17 31.7	4 11.7	27 39.1	23 19.3	29 1.0	10 4.8	9 5.0
9	1 9 29.0	15 27.8	24 27.7	6♎33.5	7 48.3	18 45.4	4 52.7	27 42.0	23 20.4	29 3.8	10 6.9	9 6.8
10	1 13 25.5	16 27.1	24 24.5	18 52.8	7 58.4	19 59.2	5 33.7	27 45.1	23 21.6	29 6.7	10 9.0	9 8.5
11	1 17 22.1	17 26.5	24 21.3	1♏24.3	8 1.5	21 13.1	6 14.7	27 48.3	23 22.8	29 9.5	10 11.1	9 10.2
12	1 21 18.6	18 25.8	24 18.1	14 8.4	7 R 57.3	22 27.0	6 55.9	27 51.8	23 24.2	29 12.2	10 13.2	9 11.9
13	1 25 15.2	19 25.3	24 15.0	27 5.1	7 45.4	23 41.0	7 37.1	27 55.4	23 25.7	29 15.0	10 15.4	9 13.6
14	1 29 11.7	20 24.7	24 11.8	10♐13.9	7 25.3	24 55.0	8 18.3	27 59.2	23 27.3	29 17.7	10 17.5	9 15.3
15	1 33 8.3	21 24.2	24 8.6	23 35.1	6 56.7	26 9.0	8 59.6	28 3.2	23 28.9	29 20.3	10 19.7	9 16.9
16	1 37 4.8	22 23.7	24 5.4	7♑ 8.6	6 19.7	27 23.1	9 41.0	28 7.4	23 30.7	29 22.9	10 21.8	9 18.5
17	1 41 1.4	23 23.2	24 2.2	20 55.0	5 34.3	28 37.2	10 22.3	28 11.8	23 32.5	29 25.5	10 24.0	9 20.1
18	1 44 58.0	24 22.8	23 59.1	4♒54.4	4 40.9	29 51.4	11 3.8	28 16.3	23 34.5	29 28.0	10 26.1	9 21.6
19	1 48 54.5	25 22.4	23 55.9	19 6.7	3 40.3	1♎ 5.6	11 45.3	28 21.0	23 36.5	29 30.5	10 28.3	9 23.2
20	1 52 51.1	26 22.0	23 52.7	3♓30.7	2 33.5	2 19.9	12 26.9	28 25.9	23 38.7	29 33.0	10 30.5	9 24.7
21	1 56 47.6	27 21.6	23 49.5	18 3.6	1 22.0	3 34.2	13 8.5	28 31.0	23 40.9	29 35.4	10 32.7	9 26.2
22	2 0 44.2	28 21.3	23 46.4	2♈40.8	0 7.5	4 48.5	13 50.2	28 36.2	23 43.3	29 37.7	10 34.9	9 27.7
23	2 4 40.7	29 21.0	23 43.2	17 16.4	28♎52.2	6 2.9	14 31.9	28 41.6	23 45.7	29 40.0	10 37.1	9 29.2
24	2 8 37.3	0♏20.7	23 40.0	1♉43.3	27 38.2	7 17.4	15 13.7	28 47.2	23 48.2	29 42.3	10 39.3	9 30.6
25	2 12 33.8	1 20.5	23 36.8	15 54.9	26 27.9	8 31.8	15 55.5	28 52.9	23 50.8	29 44.6	10 41.5	9 32.0
26	2 16 30.4	2 20.3	23 33.6	29 45.8	25 23.4	9 46.3	16 37.4	28 58.9	23 53.5	29 46.7	10 43.8	9 33.4
27	2 20 26.9	3 20.1	23 30.5	13♊12.7	24 26.5	11 .9	17 19.4	29 4.9	23 56.3	29 48.9	10 46.0	9 34.8
28	2 24 23.5	4 20.0	23 27.3	26 14.7	23 39.0	12 15.5	18 1.4	29 11.2	23 59.2	29 51.0	10 48.2	9 36.1
29	2 28 20.0	5 19.9	23 24.1	8♋53.3	23 2.0	13 30.1	18 43.4	29 17.6	24 2.2	29 53.0	10 50.4	9 37.5
30	2 32 16.6	6 19.9	23 20.9	21 11.7	22 36.1	14 44.8	19 25.6	29 24.1	24 5.2	29 55.0	10 52.7	9 38.8
31	2 36 13.1	7 19.8	23 17.8	3♌14.4	22 21.8	15 59.5	20 7.8	29 30.8	24 8.4	29 57.0	10 54.9	9 40.0

LATITUDE

DAY	SID. TIME	☉	☊	☾	☿	♀	♂	♃	♄	♅	♆	♇
1	0 37 56.6	0 .0	0 .0	4S16.9	3S 3.4	1N 7.6	0N 7.5	0S40.2	0S14.6	0N42.5	1N43.5	12N37.8
4	0 49 46.2	0 .0	0 .0	1 43.6	3 17.1	1 13.2	0 5.6	0 40.1	0 14.8	0 42.6	1 43.4	12 38.6
7	1 1 35.9	0 .0	0 .0	1N25.5	3 25.5	1 18.2	0 3.8	0 40.1	0 15.0	0 42.7	1 43.4	12 39.4
10	1 13 25.5	0 .0	0 .0	4 4.4	3 26.4	1 22.6	0 1.9	0 40.0	0 15.1	0 42.8	1 43.3	12 40.2
13	1 25 15.2	0 .0	0 .0	5 5.9	3 17.0	1 26.3	0 .1	0 40.0	0 15.3	0 42.9	1 43.2	12 41.2
16	1 37 4.8	0 .0	0 .0	3 48.9	2 54.1	1 29.4	0S 1.8	0 39.9	0 15.4	0 43.0	1 43.2	12 42.1
19	1 48 54.5	0 .0	0 .0	0 33.6	2 15.3	1 31.8	0 3.6	0 39.9	0 15.6	0 43.1	1 43.1	12 43.1
22	2 0 44.2	0 .0	0 .0	3S 5.2	1 21.7	1 33.5	0 5.4	0 39.8	0 15.8	0 43.2	1 43.1	12 44.2
25	2 12 33.8	0 .0	0 .0	4 59.4	0 20.3	1 34.6	0 7.3	0 39.7	0 15.9	0 43.3	1 43.1	12 45.2
28	2 24 23.5	0 .0	0 .0	4 17.9	0N38.2	1 35.0	0 9.1	0 39.7	0 16.1	0 43.4	1 43.0	12 46.4
31	2 36 13.1	0 .0	0 .0	1 49.1	1 24.8	1 34.7	0 10.9	0 39.6	0 16.2	0 43.5	1 43.0	12 47.5

RIGHT ASCENSION

DAY	SID. TIME	☉	☊	☾	☿	♀	♂	♃	♄	♅	♆	♇
1	0 37 56.6	6♎57.5	27♌10.3	0♋55.0	29♎57.1	10♍58.9	27♎25.5	29♑36.8	25♑ 7.9	1♍ 4.0	7♏59.9	15♍29.0
2	0 41 53.1	7 51.8	27 7.2	13 54.7	0♏43.0	12 8.4	28 4.0	29 38.4	25 8.3	1 7.0	8 1.8	15 30.9
3	0 45 49.7	8 46.2	27 4.1	26 36.5	1 25.8	13 17.7	28 42.6	29 40.2	25 8.8	1 9.9	8 3.7	15 32.7
4	0 49 46.2	9 40.7	27 1.0	8♌58.8	2 5.1	14 27.0	29 21.3	29 42.2	25 9.4	1 12.8	8 5.7	15 34.6
5	0 53 42.8	10 35.3	26 58.0	21 1.8	2 40.6	15 36.1	0♏ .1	29 44.4	25 10.1	1 15.7	8 7.6	15 36.4
6	0 57 39.3	11 29.9	26 54.9	2♍48.2	3 11.9	16 45.2	0 39.1	29 46.8	25 10.9	1 18.6	8 9.6	15 38.2
7	1 1 35.9	12 24.7	26 51.8	14 22.5	3 38.5	17 54.1	1 18.2	29 49.5	25 11.9	1 21.4	8 11.6	15 40.0
8	1 5 32.4	13 19.5	26 48.7	25 50.7	4 .1	19 3.0	1 57.4	29 52.3	25 12.9	1 24.2	8 13.6	15 41.8
9	1 9 29.0	14 14.5	26 45.7	7♎20.0	4 16.3	20 11.8	2 36.8	29 55.3	25 14.0	1 27.0	8 15.6	15 43.6
10	1 13 25.5	15 9.6	26 42.6	18 58.0	4 26.4	21 20.5	3 16.3	29 58.5	25 15.3	1 29.7	8 17.6	15 45.3
11	1 17 22.1	16 4.7	26 39.5	0♏52.8	4 30.2	22 29.1	3 55.9	0♒ 1.9	25 16.6	1 32.4	8 19.7	15 47.1
12	1 21 18.6	17 .1	26 36.4	13 11.5	4 R 27.1	23 37.7	4 35.7	0 5.5	25 18.1	1 35.0	8 21.7	15 48.8
13	1 25 15.2	17 55.5	26 33.3	26 .1	4 16.9	24 46.3	5 15.6	0 9.4	25 19.7	1 37.7	8 23.8	15 50.6
14	1 29 11.7	18 51.1	26 30.2	9♐21.4	3 59.1	25 54.8	5 55.7	0 13.4	25 21.4	1 40.3	8 25.9	15 52.3
15	1 33 8.3	19 46.8	26 27.2	23 14.6	3 33.6	27 3.2	6 35.9	0 17.6	25 23.2	1 42.8	8 28.0	15 54.0
16	1 37 4.8	20 42.6	26 24.1	7♑33.7	3 .5	28 11.6	7 16.2	0 22.0	25 25.0	1 45.4	8 30.1	15 55.6
17	1 41 1.4	21 38.5	26 21.0	22 8.8	2 19.9	29 20.0	7 56.6	0 26.6	25 27.0	1 47.8	8 32.2	15 57.3
18	1 44 58.0	22 34.6	26 17.9	6♒48.2	1 32.3	0♎28.4	8 37.2	0 31.3	25 29.1	1 50.3	8 34.3	15 58.9
19	1 48 54.5	23 30.9	26 14.8	21 21.4	0 38.5	1 36.7	9 17.9	0 36.3	25 31.3	1 52.7	8 36.4	16 .5
20	1 52 51.1	24 27.3	26 11.7	5♓41.8	29♎39.6	2 45.1	9 58.8	0 41.4	25 33.5	1 55.0	8 38.6	16 2.1
21	1 56 47.6	25 23.8	26 8.7	19 47.6	28 37.0	3 53.5	10 39.8	0 46.7	25 35.9	1 57.3	8 40.7	16 3.7
22	2 0 44.2	26 20.5	26 5.6	3♈41.2	27 32.4	5 1.9	11 21.0	0 52.2	25 38.4	1 59.6	8 42.9	16 5.3
23	2 4 40.7	27 17.4	26 2.5	17 27.2	26 27.6	6 10.4	12 2.3	0 57.9	25 41.0	2 1.8	8 45.0	16 6.8
24	2 8 37.3	28 14.4	25 59.4	1♉10.7	25 24.6	7 18.9	12 43.7	1 3.7	25 43.7	2 4.0	8 47.2	16 8.3
25	2 12 33.8	29 11.6	25 56.3	14 55.1	24 25.4	8 27.4	13 25.3	1 9.7	25 46.4	2 6.2	8 49.3	16 9.8
26	2 16 30.4	0♏ 9.0	25 53.2	28 40.9	23 31.8	9 36.0	14 7.1	1 15.9	25 49.3	2 8.3	8 51.5	16 11.3
27	2 20 26.9	1 6.6	25 50.1	12♊25.2	22 45.5	10 44.7	14 49.0	1 22.3	25 52.3	2 10.4	8 53.7	16 12.8
28	2 24 23.5	2 4.4	25 47.0	26 2.2	22 7.6	11 53.5	15 31.0	1 28.8	25 55.3	2 12.4	8 55.8	16 14.2
29	2 28 20.0	3 2.3	25 44.0	9♋25.0	21 39.2	13 2.4	16 13.2	1 35.5	25 58.5	2 14.4	8 58.0	16 15.6
30	2 32 16.6	4 .5	25 40.9	22 27.5	21 20.8	14 11.3	16 55.5	1 42.4	26 1.8	2 16.3	9 .2	16 17.0
31	2 36 13.1	4 58.8	25 37.8	5♌ 5.9	21 12.6	15 20.4	17 38.0	1 49.4	26 5.1	2 18.2	9 2.4	16 18.4

DECLINATION

DAY	SID. TIME	☉	☊	☾	☿	♀	♂	♃	♄	♅	♆	♇
1	0 37 56.6	3S .4	0N13.9	19N 9.4	15S28.3	9N15.5	11S 9.7	21S20.3	21S40.8	12N36.2	13S 7.8	19N54.5
4	0 49 46.2	4 10.2	0 13.9	16 50.7	16 27.6	7 57.1	11 54.1	21 19.2	21 40.8	12 33.1	13 9.7	19 53.1
7	1 1 35.9	5 19.5	0 14.0	8 12.2	17 8.3	6 36.4	12 37.8	21 17.8	21 40.5	12 30.1	13 11.7	19 51.8
10	1 13 25.5	6 28.2	0 14.0	3S37.5	17 25.3	5 13.9	13 20.8	21 16.1	21 40.2	12 27.2	13 13.7	19 50.6
13	1 25 15.2	7 36.1	0 14.1	14 32.6	17 12.1	3 49.8	14 3.2	21 13.9	21 39.6	12 24.4	13 15.8	19 49.4
16	1 37 4.8	8 43.1	0 14.1	19 26.4	16 22.1	2 24.4	14 44.6	21 11.5	21 38.9	12 21.7	13 17.8	19 48.4
19	1 48 54.5	9 48.9	0 14.2	14 33.7	14 51.7	0 58.1	15 25.2	21 8.7	21 38.1	12 19.1	13 19.9	19 47.5
22	2 0 44.2	10 53.5	0 14.2	1 46.0	12 47.5	0S28.8	16 4.8	21 5.5	21 37.1	12 16.7	13 22.0	19 46.8
25	2 12 33.8	11 56.5	0 14.3	11N49.3	10 31.7	1 56.1	16 43.4	21 2.0	21 35.9	12 14.4	13 24.1	19 46.1
28	2 24 23.5	12 58.0	0 14.3	19 5.6	8 35.5	3 23.3	17 20.9	20 58.2	21 34.6	12 12.2	13 26.1	19 45.5
31	2 36 13.1	13 57.6	0 14.4	17 39.9	7 23.6	4 50.1	17 57.2	20 54.0	21 33.2	12 10.2	13 28.2	19 45.1

NOVEMBER 1961

LONGITUDE

DAY	EPHEM. SID. TIME	☉	☊	☽	☿	♀	♂	♃	♄	♅	♆	♇
	h m s	° ′	° ′	° ′	° ′	° ′	° ′	° ′	° ′	° ′	° ′	° ′
1	2 40 9.7	8♏19.9	23♌14.6	15♌ 6.8	22♎19.0	17♎14.2	20♏50.0	29♑37.7	24♑11.6	29♌58.9	10♏57.2	9♍41.3
2	2 44 6.3	9 19.9	23 11.4	26 54.3	22 D 27.3	18 29.0	21 32.3	29 44.8	24 15.0	0♍ .8	10 59.4	9 42.5
3	2 48 2.8	10 20.0	23 8.2	8♍42.6	22 46.3	19 43.8	22 14.7	29 52.0	24 18.4	0 2.6	11 1.7	9 43.8
4	2 51 59.4	11 20.2	23 5.0	20 36.5	23 15.1	20 58.7	22 57.1	29 59.3	24 21.9	0 4.4	11 4.0	9 44.9
5	2 55 55.9	12 20.3	23 1.9	2♎40.5	23 52.9	22 13.5	23 39.6	0♒ 6.8	24 25.5	0 6.1	11 6.2	9 46.1
6	2 59 52.5	13 20.5	22 58.7	14 58.0	24 38.8	23 28.4	24 22.1	0 14.5	24 29.2	0 7.8	11 8.4	9 47.2
7	3 3 49.0	14 20.7	22 55.5	27 31.2	25 32.0	24 43.4	25 4.7	0 22.3	24 33.0	0 9.4	11 10.7	9 48.3
8	3 7 45.6	15 21.0	22 52.3	10♏20.8	26 31.5	25 58.3	25 47.4	0 30.2	24 36.8	0 10.9	11 12.9	9 49.4
9	3 11 42.1	16 21.3	22 49.2	23 26.5	27 36.7	27 13.3	26 30.1	0 38.3	24 40.7	0 12.5	11 15.2	9 50.4
10	3 15 38.7	17 21.6	22 46.0	6♐46.5	28 46.6	28 28.3	27 12.9	0 46.5	24 44.7	0 13.9	11 17.4	9 51.4
11	3 19 35.2	18 21.9	22 42.8	20 18.8	0♏ .8	29 43.3	27 55.7	0 54.9	24 48.8	0 15.3	11 19.6	9 52.4
12	3 23 31.8	19 22.3	22 39.6	4♑ .6	1 18.5	0♏58.4	28 38.5	1 3.4	24 53.0	0 16.7	11 21.9	9 53.3
13	3 27 28.4	20 22.7	22 36.5	17 49.9	2 39.2	2 13.4	29 21.5	1 12.0	24 57.2	0 18.0	11 24.1	9 54.3
14	3 31 24.9	21 23.1	22 33.3	1♒44.9	4 2.4	3 28.5	0♐ 4.4	1 20.8	25 1.6	0 19.2	11 26.3	9 55.1
15	3 35 21.5	22 23.5	22 30.1	15 44.7	5 27.8	4 43.6	0 47.5	1 29.7	25 6.0	0 20.4	11 28.5	9 56.0
16	3 39 18.0	23 24.0	22 26.9	29 48.9	6 55.0	5 58.7	1 30.6	1 38.8	25 10.5	0 21.6	11 30.8	9 56.8
17	3 43 14.6	24 24.4	22 23.7	13♓56.8	8 23.6	7 13.9	2 13.7	1 48.0	25 15.0	0 22.7	11 33.0	9 57.7
18	3 47 11.1	25 24.9	22 20.6	28 7.3	9 53.4	8 29.0	2 56.9	1 57.3	25 19.6	0 23.7	11 35.2	9 58.4
19	3 51 7.7	26 25.4	22 17.4	12♈18.3	11 24.2	9 44.2	3 40.1	2 6.7	25 24.3	0 24.7	11 37.3	9 59.2
20	3 55 4.2	27 26.0	22 14.2	26 26.8	12 55.8	10 59.4	4 23.4	2 16.3	25 29.1	0 25.6	11 39.5	9 59.9
21	3 59 .8	28 26.5	22 11.0	10♉28.4	14 28.0	12 14.6	5 6.8	2 25.9	25 34.0	0 26.5	11 41.7	10 .6
22	4 2 57.4	29 27.1	22 7.9	24 18.7	16 .7	13 29.8	5 50.2	2 35.7	25 38.9	0 27.3	11 43.9	10 1.2
23	4 6 53.9	0♐27.7	22 4.7	7♊53.5	17 33.9	14 45.1	6 33.7	2 45.7	25 43.8	0 28.0	11 46.0	10 1.9
24	4 10 50.5	1 28.4	22 1.5	21 9.5	19 7.3	16 .4	7 17.2	2 55.7	25 48.9	0 28.8	11 48.2	10 2.5
25	4 14 47.0	2 29.1	21 58.3	4♋ 5.1	20 41.0	17 15.6	8 .8	3 5.9	25 54.1	0 29.4	11 50.4	10 3.1
26	4 18 43.6	3 29.8	21 55.1	16 40.8	22 14.8	18 30.9	8 44.4	3 16.2	25 59.2	0 30.0	11 52.5	10 3.6
27	4 22 40.1	4 30.5	21 52.0	28 58.4	23 48.8	19 46.2	9 28.1	3 26.5	26 4.5	0 30.6	11 54.6	10 4.1
28	4 26 36.7	5 31.2	21 48.8	11♌ 1.3	25 22.8	21 1.5	10 11.8	3 37.0	26 9.8	0 31.1	11 56.7	10 4.6
29	4 30 33.3	6 32.0	21 45.6	22 54.2	26 56.8	22 16.9	10 55.6	3 47.6	26 15.2	0 31.5	11 58.8	10 5.0
30	4 34 29.8	7 32.7	21 42.4	4♍42.2	28 30.9	23 32.2	11 39.4	3 58.3	26 20.6	0 31.9	12 .9	10 5.4

LATITUDE

DAY	EPHEM. SID. TIME	☉	☊	☽	☿	♀	♂	♃	♄	♅	♆	♇
1	2 40 9.7	0 .0	0 .0	0 S 48.1	1 N 36.9	1 N 34.5	0 S 11.5	0 S 39.6	0 S 16.3	0 N 43.6	1 N 43.0	12 N 47.9
4	2 51 59.4	0 .0	0 .0	2 N 15.4	2 2.5	1 33.4	0 13.3	0 39.5	0 16.4	0 43.7	1 43.0	12 49.1
7	3 3 49.0	0 .0	0 .0	4 30.1	2 14.0	1 31.6	0 15.1	0 39.5	0 16.6	0 43.8	1 43.0	12 50.4
10	3 15 38.7	0 .0	0 .0	4 51.9	2 14.5	1 29.3	0 16.8	0 39.4	0 16.7	0 44.0	1 43.0	12 51.6
13	3 27 28.4	0 .0	0 .0	2 52.6	2 7.1	1 26.4	0 18.6	0 39.4	0 16.9	0 44.1	1 43.1	12 52.9
16	3 39 18.0	0 .0	0 .0	0 S 38.2	1 54.1	1 22.9	0 20.4	0 39.4	0 17.1	0 44.2	1 43.1	12 54.2
19	3 51 7.7	0 .0	0 .0	3 50.7	1 37.4	1 18.9	0 22.1	0 39.3	0 17.2	0 44.4	1 43.1	12 55.6
22	4 2 57.4	0 .0	0 .0	5 .2	1 18.4	1 14.4	0 23.8	0 39.3	0 17.4	0 44.5	1 43.2	12 56.9
25	4 14 47.0	0 .0	0 .0	3 41.8	0 58.1	1 9.4	0 25.6	0 39.3	0 17.5	0 44.6	1 43.3	12 58.3
28	4 26 36.7	0 .0	0 .0	0 53.2	0 37.2	1 4.0	0 27.3	0 39.3	0 17.7	0 44.8	1 43.3	12 59.7

RIGHT ASCENSION

DAY	EPHEM. SID. TIME	☉	☊	☽	☿	♀	♂	♃	♄	♅	♆	♇
1	2 40 9.7	5♏57.4	25♌34.7	17♌20.0	21♎14.5	16♎29.6	18♏20.7	1♒56.6	26♑ 8.5	2♍20.0	9♏ 4.6	16♍19.8
2	2 44 6.3	6 56.1	25 31.6	29 12.4	21 D 26.1	17 39.0	19 3.5	2 3.9	26 12.1	2 21.8	9 6.8	16 21.1
3	2 48 2.8	7 55.1	25 28.5	10♍48.6	21 47.1	18 48.5	19 46.5	2 11.5	26 15.8	2 23.6	9 9.0	16 22.5
4	2 51 59.4	8 54.3	25 25.4	22 15.8	22 16.5	19 58.1	20 29.7	2 19.2	26 19.5	2 25.3	9 11.2	16 23.7
5	2 55 55.9	9 53.6	25 22.3	3♎42.4	22 53.9	21 7.9	21 12.9	2 27.0	26 23.3	2 27.0	9 13.4	16 25.0
6	2 59 52.5	10 53.2	25 19.2	15 17.6	23 38.4	22 17.8	21 56.4	2 35.0	26 27.2	2 28.6	9 15.6	16 26.2
7	3 3 49.0	11 53.0	25 16.1	27 10.3	24 29.2	23 27.9	22 40.0	2 43.1	26 31.2	2 30.1	9 17.8	16 27.4
8	3 7 45.6	12 53.0	25 13.0	9♏29.1	25 25.7	24 38.2	23 23.7	2 51.4	26 35.2	2 31.7	9 20.0	16 28.6
9	3 11 42.1	13 53.2	25 9.9	22 20.4	26 27.2	25 48.7	24 7.6	2 59.8	26 39.4	2 33.1	9 22.2	16 29.8
10	3 15 38.7	14 53.7	25 6.9	5♐47.4	27 33.0	26 59.4	24 51.7	3 8.4	26 43.7	2 34.5	9 24.4	16 30.9
11	3 19 35.2	15 54.3	25 3.8	19 48.1	28 42.7	28 10.3	25 35.9	3 17.1	26 48.0	2 35.9	9 26.6	16 32.0
12	3 23 31.8	16 55.1	25 .7	4♑14.9	29 55.6	29 21.4	26 20.2	3 26.0	26 52.4	2 37.2	9 28.8	16 33.1
13	3 27 28.4	17 56.2	24 57.6	18 55.2	1♏11.5	0♏32.7	27 4.7	3 35.0	26 56.9	2 38.5	9 31.0	16 34.2
14	3 31 24.9	18 57.4	24 54.5	3♒34.6	2 29.8	1 44.2	27 49.4	3 44.2	27 1.5	2 39.7	9 33.1	16 35.2
15	3 35 21.5	19 58.9	24 51.4	18 1.3	3 50.4	2 56.0	28 34.2	3 53.4	27 6.1	2 40.8	9 35.3	16 36.2
16	3 39 18.0	21 .6	24 48.3	2♓ 8.5	5 12.8	4 8.0	29 19.2	4 2.8	27 10.9	2 41.9	9 37.5	16 37.2
17	3 43 14.6	22 2.5	24 45.2	15 55.5	6 36.9	5 20.3	0♐ 4.3	4 12.4	27 15.7	2 43.0	9 39.6	16 38.2
18	3 47 11.1	23 4.5	24 42.1	29 26.6	8 2.4	6 32.8	0 49.5	4 22.1	27 20.6	2 44.0	9 41.8	16 39.1
19	3 51 7.7	24 6.8	24 39.0	12♈49.0	9 29.3	7 45.6	1 34.9	4 31.9	27 25.6	2 45.0	9 44.0	16 40.0
20	3 55 4.2	25 9.3	24 35.9	26 10.3	10 57.2	8 58.6	2 20.4	4 41.8	27 30.6	2 45.9	9 46.1	16 40.9
21	3 59 .8	26 12.0	24 32.8	9♉37.0	12 26.2	10 11.9	3 6.1	4 51.8	27 35.7	2 46.7	9 48.2	16 41.7
22	4 2 57.4	27 14.9	24 29.7	23 12.4	13 56.2	11 25.5	3 52.0	5 2.0	27 40.9	2 47.5	9 50.4	16 42.5
23	4 6 53.9	28 18.0	24 26.6	6♊55.6	15 27.0	12 39.4	4 37.9	5 12.3	27 46.2	2 48.2	9 52.5	16 43.3
24	4 10 50.5	29 21.3	24 23.5	20 41.0	16 58.6	13 53.6	5 24.1	5 22.7	27 51.6	2 49.0	9 54.6	16 44.1
25	4 14 47.0	0♐24.8	24 20.4	4♋19.8	18 30.9	15 8.1	6 10.4	5 33.2	27 57.0	2 49.6	9 56.7	16 44.8
26	4 18 43.6	1 28.5	24 17.3	17 42.7	20 3.8	16 22.8	6 56.8	5 43.9	28 2.5	2 50.2	9 58.8	16 45.5
27	4 22 40.1	2 32.3	24 14.2	0♌41.8	21 37.5	17 37.9	7 43.3	5 54.6	28 8.0	2 50.7	10 .9	16 46.2
28	4 26 36.7	3 36.4	24 11.1	13 13.5	23 11.7	18 53.2	8 30.0	6 5.5	28 13.6	2 51.2	10 3.0	16 46.9
29	4 30 33.3	4 40.6	24 8.0	25 18.1	24 46.5	20 8.9	9 16.8	6 16.4	28 19.3	2 51.6	10 5.0	16 47.5
30	4 34 29.8	5 45.0	24 4.9	7♍ .2	26 21.9	21 24.8	10 3.7	6 27.5	28 25.0	2 52.0	10 7.1	16 48.1

DECLINATION

DAY	EPHEM. SID. TIME	☉	☊	☽	☿	♀	♂	♃	♄	♅	♆	♇
1	2 40 9.7	14 S 17.1	0 N 14.4	15 N 32.3	7 S 11.4	5 S 18.9	18 S 9.0	20 S 52.6	21 S 32.7	12 N 9.6	13 S 28.9	19 N 45.0
4	2 51 59.4	15 14.0	0 14.5	5 47.7	7 8.3	6 44.7	18 43.6	20 47.9	21 31.0	12 7.8	13 31.0	19 44.7
7	3 3 49.0	16 8.7	0 14.5	6 S 23.2	7 47.5	8 9.4	19 16.9	20 43.0	21 29.2	12 6.1	13 33.1	19 44.5
10	3 15 38.7	17 1.0	0 14.6	16 38.8	8 56.6	9 32.5	19 48.7	20 37.7	21 27.3	12 4.6	13 35.1	19 44.5
13	3 27 28.4	17 50.6	0 14.6	19 24.1	10 24.3	10 53.7	20 19.1	20 32.1	21 25.2	12 3.3	13 37.2	19 44.5
16	3 39 18.0	18 37.5	0 14.7	12 8.1	12 1.6	12 12.7	20 47.9	20 26.1	21 22.9	12 2.2	13 39.2	19 44.7
19	3 51 7.7	19 21.4	0 14.7	1 N 19.4	13 42.6	13 29.1	21 15.0	20 19.8	21 20.5	12 1.2	13 41.2	19 45.1
22	4 2 57.4	20 2.2	0 14.8	13 59.8	15 22.8	14 42.6	21 40.4	20 13.2	21 18.0	12 .4	13 43.1	19 45.5
25	4 14 47.0	20 39.6	0 14.9	19 41.1	16 59.5	15 52.7	22 4.1	20 6.3	21 15.3	11 59.8	13 45.0	19 46.1
28	4 26 36.7	21 13.6	0 14.9	16 36.8	18 30.5	16 59.1	22 25.8	19 59.0	21 12.5	11 59.3	13 46.9	19 46.7

DECEMBER 1961

LONGITUDE

DAY	EPHEM. SID. TIME	☉	☊	☽	☿	♀	♂	♃	♄	♅	♆	♇
	h m s	° ′	° ′	° ′	° ′	° ′	° ′	° ′	° ′	° ′	° ′	° ′
1	4 38 26.4	8♐33.5	21♌39.3	16♍30.8	0♐ 5.0	24♏47.6	12♐23.3	4♒ 9.1	26♑26.1	0♍32.2	12♏ 2.9	10♍ 5.8
2	4 42 22.9	9 34.4	21 36.1	28 25.7	1 39.1	26 2.9	13 7.3	4 20.1	26 31.7	0 32.4	12 5.0	10 6.1
3	4 46 19.5	10 35.2	21 32.9	10♎31.9	3 13.1	27 18.3	13 51.3	4 31.1	26 37.3	0 32.6	12 7.0	10 6.4
4	4 50 16.0	11 36.1	21 29.7	22 54.1	4 47.2	28 33.7	14 35.4	4 42.2	26 43.0	0 32.8	12 9.0	10 6.7
5	4 54 12.6	12 37.0	21 26.6	5♏35.4	6 21.2	29 49.1	15 19.5	4 53.4	26 48.7	0 32.9	12 11.0	10 7.0
6	4 58 9.2	13 37.9	21 23.4	18 37.8	7 55.3	1♐ 4.6	16 3.6	5 4.7	26 54.5	0 32.9	12 13.0	10 7.2
7	5 2 5.7	14 38.9	21 20.2	2♐ 1.2	9 29.3	2 20.0	16 47.9	5 16.2	27 .4	0 32.9	12 15.0	10 7.4
8	5 6 2.3	15 39.8	21 17.0	15 43.7	11 3.3	3 35.4	17 32.1	5 27.7	27 6.3	0R32.8	12 16.9	10 7.5
9	5 9 58.8	16 40.8	21 13.8	29 41.7	12 37.4	4 50.9	18 16.4	5 39.3	27 12.2	0 32.6	12 18.9	10 7.6
10	5 13 55.4	17 41.8	21 10.7	13♑50.8	14 11.4	6 6.3	19 .8	5 51.0	27 18.2	0 32.4	12 20.8	10 7.7
11	5 17 51.9	18 42.8	21 7.5	28 5.8	15 45.5	7 21.8	19 45.2	6 2.8	27 24.3	0 32.2	12 22.7	10 7.8
12	5 21 48.5	19 43.8	21 4.3	12♒22.6	17 19.7	8 37.2	20 29.7	6 14.6	27 30.4	0 31.9	12 24.6	10 7.8
13	5 25 45.0	20 44.8	21 1.1	26 37.5	18 53.9	9 52.7	21 14.2	6 26.6	27 36.5	0 31.5	12 26.5	10 7.8
14	5 29 41.6	21 45.9	20 58.0	10♓48.3	20 28.2	11 8.1	21 58.8	6 38.6	27 42.7	0 31.1	12 28.3	10 7.8
15	5 33 38.2	22 46.9	20 54.8	24 53.6	22 2.7	12 23.6	22 43.5	6 50.8	27 49.0	0 30.7	12 30.2	10R 7.7
16	5 37 34.7	23 48.0	20 51.6	8♈52.6	23 37.1	13 39.1	23 28.1	7 3.0	27 55.3	0 30.1	12 32.0	10 7.6
17	5 41 31.3	24 49.0	20 48.4	22 44.5	25 11.8	14 54.6	24 12.8	7 15.3	28 1.7	0 29.6	12 33.8	10 7.5
18	5 45 27.8	25 50.1	20 45.3	6♉28.5	26 46.5	16 10.0	24 57.6	7 27.7	28 8.0	0 28.9	12 35.5	10 7.3
19	5 49 24.4	26 51.2	20 42.1	20 3.0	28 21.4	17 25.5	25 42.4	7 40.1	28 14.5	0 28.2	12 37.2	10 7.1
20	5 53 21.0	27 52.2	20 38.9	3♊26.5	29 56.5	18 41.0	26 27.2	7 52.6	28 20.9	0 27.5	12 39.0	10 6.9
21	5 57 17.5	28 53.3	20 35.7	16 37.0	1♑31.8	19 56.5	27 12.1	8 5.2	28 27.4	0 26.7	12 40.7	10 6.6
22	6 1 14.1	29 54.4	20 32.6	29 33.2	3 7.2	21 11.9	27 57.1	8 17.9	28 33.9	0 25.8	12 42.3	10 6.3
23	6 5 10.6	0♑55.5	20 29.4	12♋14.2	4 42.9	22 27.4	28 42.1	8 30.6	28 40.5	0 24.9	12 44.0	10 6.0
24	6 9 7.2	1 56.6	20 26.2	24 40.1	6 18.7	23 42.9	29 27.1	8 43.4	28 47.1	0 24.0	12 45.6	10 5.7
25	6 13 3.7	2 57.7	20 23.0	6♌52.1	7 54.8	24 58.4	0♑12.2	8 56.2	28 53.8	0 23.0	12 47.2	10 5.3
26	6 17 .3	3 58.8	20 19.8	18 52.4	9 31.1	26 13.9	0 57.3	9 9.2	29 .4	0 21.9	12 48.8	10 4.9
27	6 20 56.9	4 59.9	20 16.7	0♍44.4	11 7.7	27 29.3	1 42.5	9 22.1	29 7.1	0 20.8	12 50.3	10 4.4
28	6 24 53.4	6 1.1	20 13.5	12 32.2	12 44.4	28 44.8	2 27.7	9 35.2	29 13.9	0 19.6	12 51.8	10 3.9
29	6 28 50.0	7 2.2	20 10.3	24 20.5	14 21.4	0♑ .3	3 13.0	9 48.3	29 20.6	0 18.4	12 53.3	10 3.4
30	6 32 46.5	8 3.3	20 7.1	6♎14.5	15 58.6	1 15.8	3 58.3	10 1.5	29 27.4	0 17.2	12 54.8	10 2.9
31	6 36 43.1	9 4.5	20 4.0	18 19.5	17 36.0	2 31.3	4 43.7	10 14.7	29 34.3	0 15.9	12 56.3	10 2.3

LATITUDE

DAY	EPHEM. SID. TIME	☉	☊	☽	☿	♀	♂	♃	♄	♅	♆	♇
1	4 38 26.4	0 .0	0 .0	2N11.0	0N16.1	0N58.3	0S29.0	0S39.2	0S17.8	0N44.9	1N43.4	13N 1.1
4	4 50 16.0	0 .0	0 .0	4 28.1	0S 4.7	0 52.2	0 30.6	0 39.2	0 18.0	0 45.0	1 43.5	13 2.5
7	5 2 5.7	0 .0	0 .0	4 56.7	0 24.8	0 45.8	0 32.3	0 39.3	0 18.2	0 45.2	1 43.6	13 3.9
10	5 13 55.4	0 .0	0 .0	2 59.4	0 43.9	0 39.1	0 33.9	0 39.3	0 18.3	0 45.3	1 43.7	13 5.3
13	5 25 45.0	0 .0	0 .0	0S36.8	1 1.9	0 32.2	0 35.6	0 39.3	0 18.5	0 45.4	1 43.8	13 6.7
16	5 37 34.7	0 .0	0 .0	3 52.2	1 18.4	0 25.1	0 37.2	0 39.3	0 18.7	0 45.6	1 43.9	13 8.1
19	5 49 24.4	0 .0	0 .0	5 6.2	1 33.1	0 17.9	0 38.7	0 39.4	0 18.8	0 45.7	1 44.0	13 9.4
22	6 1 14.1	0 .0	0 .0	3 53.7	1 45.9	0 10.7	0 40.3	0 39.4	0 19.0	0 45.8	1 44.1	13 10.8
25	6 13 3.7	0 .0	0 .0	1 3.9	1 56.2	0 3.4	0 41.8	0 39.5	0 19.2	0 45.9	1 44.3	13 12.1
28	6 24 53.4	0 .0	0 .0	2N 5.7	2 3.9	0S 3.9	0 43.3	0 39.5	0 19.4	0 46.1	1 44.4	13 13.5
31	6 36 43.1	0 .0	0 .0	4 28.7	2 8.3	0 11.1	0 44.8	0 39.6	0 19.5	0 46.2	1 44.5	13 14.8

RIGHT ASCENSION

DAY	EPHEM. SID. TIME	☉	☊	☽	☿	♀	♂	♃	♄	♅	♆	♇
1	4 38 26.4	6♐49.6	24♌ 1.8	18♍26.8	27♏57.9	22♏41.1	10♐50.8	6♒38.6	28♑30.8	2♍52.3	10♏ 9.1	16♍48.6
2	4 42 22.9	7 54.4	23 58.7	29 47.1	29 34.4	23 57.6	11 38.0	6 49.9	28 36.7	2 52.6	10 11.1	16 49.1
3	4 46 19.5	8 59.3	23 55.6	11♎11.5	1♐11.5	25 14.5	12 25.4	7 1.3	28 42.6	2 52.8	10 13.1	16 49.6
4	4 50 16.0	10 4.3	23 52.5	22 50.8	2 49.0	26 31.6	13 12.8	7 12.8	28 48.6	2 52.9	10 15.1	16 50.1
5	4 54 12.6	11 9.6	23 49.4	4♏55.7	4 27.2	27 49.1	14 .4	7 24.3	28 54.6	2 53.0	10 17.1	16 50.5
6	4 58 9.2	12 14.9	23 46.2	17 35.6	6 5.8	29 6.8	14 48.1	7 36.0	29 .7	2 53.1	10 19.0	16 50.9
7	5 2 5.7	13 20.4	23 43.1	0♐56.9	7 44.9	0♐24.9	15 36.0	7 47.7	29 6.9	2 53.1	10 21.0	16 51.3
8	5 6 2.3	14 26.1	23 40.0	15 .8	9 24.5	1 43.2	16 23.9	7 59.6	29 13.1	2R53.0	10 22.9	16 51.6
9	5 9 58.8	15 31.8	23 36.9	29 40.7	11 4.7	3 1.8	17 11.9	8 11.5	29 19.4	2 52.9	10 24.8	16 51.9
10	5 13 55.4	16 37.7	23 33.8	14♑42.6	12 45.3	4 20.7	18 .1	8 23.6	29 25.7	2 52.7	10 26.7	16 52.2
11	5 17 51.9	17 43.6	23 30.7	29 47.9	14 26.4	5 39.9	18 48.4	8 35.7	29 32.1	2 52.5	10 28.6	16 52.5
12	5 21 48.5	18 49.7	23 27.6	14♒38.9	16 8.0	6 59.3	19 36.7	8 47.9	29 38.5	2 52.2	10 30.5	16 52.7
13	5 25 45.0	19 55.9	23 24.5	29 4.0	17 50.0	8 19.0	20 25.2	9 .1	29 45.0	2 51.9	10 32.3	16 52.9
14	5 29 41.6	21 2.1	23 21.4	12♓59.5	19 32.5	9 38.9	21 13.8	9 12.5	29 51.5	2 51.5	10 34.1	16 53.0
15	5 33 38.2	22 8.5	23 18.3	26 29.1	21 15.5	10 59.1	22 2.5	9 25.0	29 58.1	2 51.1	10 36.0	16 53.2
16	5 37 34.7	23 14.8	23 15.2	9♈40.6	22 58.9	12 19.5	22 51.2	9 37.5	0♒ 4.7	2 50.6	10 37.7	16 53.3
17	5 41 31.3	24 21.2	23 12.1	22 43.9	24 42.6	13 40.1	23 40.0	9 50.1	0 11.4	2 50.1	10 39.5	16 53.4
18	5 45 27.8	25 27.7	23 8.9	5♉48.2	26 26.8	15 .9	24 28.9	10 2.7	0 18.1	2 49.5	10 41.2	16 53.4
19	5 49 24.4	26 34.2	23 5.8	19 .5	28 11.3	16 21.9	25 17.9	10 15.4	0 24.8	2 48.8	10 43.0	16 53.4
20	5 53 21.0	27 40.7	23 2.7	2♊23.8	29 56.2	17 43.1	26 7.0	10 28.2	0 31.6	2 48.1	10 44.7	16 53.4
21	5 57 17.5	28 47.3	22 59.6	15 56.3	1♑41.3	19 4.5	26 56.1	10 41.1	0 38.4	2 47.4	10 46.3	16R53.3
22	6 1 14.1	29 53.9	22 56.5	29 31.7	3 26.8	20 26.0	27 45.3	10 54.0	0 45.3	2 46.6	10 48.0	16 53.2
23	6 5 10.6	1♑ .5	22 53.4	13♋ .1	5 12.5	21 47.7	28 34.6	11 7.0	0 52.2	2 45.7	10 49.6	16 53.1
24	6 9 7.2	2 7.1	22 50.3	26 11.7	6 58.5	23 9.6	29 23.9	11 20.0	0 59.1	2 44.8	10 51.2	16 53.0
25	6 13 3.7	3 13.6	22 47.2	8♌58.9	8 44.6	24 31.5	0♑13.3	11 33.1	1 6.1	2 43.9	10 52.8	16 52.8
26	6 17 .3	4 20.2	22 44.0	21 18.3	10 30.9	25 53.6	1 2.8	11 46.3	1 13.0	2 42.9	10 54.4	16 52.6
27	6 20 56.9	5 26.7	22 40.9	3♍11.2	12 17.2	27 15.8	1 52.3	11 59.5	1 20.1	2 41.8	10 55.9	16 52.4
28	6 24 53.4	6 33.3	22 37.8	14 42.6	14 3.7	28 38.0	2 41.9	12 12.7	1 27.1	2 40.8	10 57.4	16 52.1
29	6 28 50.0	7 39.7	22 34.7	26 .5	15 50.1	0♑ .4	3 31.5	12 26.1	1 34.2	2 39.6	10 58.9	16 51.8
30	6 32 46.5	8 46.2	22 31.6	7♎14.7	17 36.4	1 22.7	4 21.1	12 39.4	1 41.3	2 38.4	11 .4	16 51.5
31	6 36 43.1	9 52.6	22 28.5	18 36.4	19 22.7	2 45.1	5 10.8	12 52.9	1 48.5	2 37.2	11 1.8	16 51.1

DECLINATION

DAY	EPHEM. SID. TIME	☉	☊	☽	☿	♀	♂	♃	♄	♅	♆	♇
1	4 38 26.4	21S44.0	0N15.0	7N20.1	19S54.5	18S 1.6	22S45.7	19S51.4	21S 9.6	11N59.1	13S48.7	19N47.5
4	4 50 16.0	22 10.7	0 15.0	4S45.2	21 10.3	18 59.6	23 3.5	19 43.5	21 6.6	11 59.0	13 50.5	19 48.5
7	5 2 5.7	22 33.5	0 15.1	15 43.1	22 17.1	19 53.0	23 19.4	19 35.3	21 3.4	11 59.1	13 52.2	19 49.5
10	5 13 55.4	22 52.4	0 15.1	19 44.9	23 14.0	20 41.3	23 33.1	19 26.8	21 .1	11 59.3	13 53.9	19 50.6
13	5 25 45.0	23 7.2	0 15.2	13 13.1	24 .4	21 24.2	23 44.6	19 17.9	20 56.6	11 59.8	13 55.5	19 51.9
16	5 37 34.7	23 17.8	0 15.2	0 2.3	24 35.6	22 1.5	23 54.0	19 8.8	20 53.1	12 .4	13 57.1	19 53.2
19	5 49 24.4	23 24.3	0 15.3	12N50.1	24 59.1	22 33.0	24 1.1	18 59.3	20 49.4	12 1.2	13 58.5	19 54.7
22	6 1 14.1	23 26.5	0 15.3	19 32.8	25 10.1	22 58.3	24 5.9	18 49.6	20 45.6	12 2.2	13 59.9	19 56.3
25	6 13 3.7	23 24.5	0 15.4	17 31.6	25 8.4	23 17.4	24 8.3	18 39.6	20 41.7	12 3.3	14 1.3	19 57.9
28	6 24 53.4	23 18.3	0 15.4	8 47.5	24 53.2	23 30.1	24 8.5	18 29.3	20 37.8	12 4.6	14 2.6	19 59.6
31	6 36 43.1	23 7.9	0 15.5	3S 2.4	24 24.3	23 36.2	24 6.2	18 18.8	20 33.7	12 6.0	14 3.7	20 1.4

JANUARY 1962

LONGITUDE

DAY	EPHEM. SID. TIME h m s	☉ ° ′	☊ ° ′	☽ ° ′	☿ ° ′	♀ ° ′	♂ ° ′	♃ ° ′	♄ ° ′	♅ ° ′	♆ ° ′	♇ ° ′
1	6 40 39.6	10♑ 5.7	20♌ .8	0♏ 40.4	19♑ 13.5	3♑ 46.8	5♑ 29.1	10♒ 28.0	29♑ 41.1	0♍ 14.5	12♏ 57.7	10♍ 1.7
2	6 44 36.2	11 6.8	19 57.6	13 21.7	20 51.1	5 2.3	6 14.5	10 41.3	29 48.0	0 R 13.1	12 59.1	10 R 1.1
3	6 48 32.8	12 8.0	19 54.4	26 26.6	22 28.9	6 17.8	7 .0	10 54.7	29 54.9	0 11.6	13 .4	10 .5
4	6 52 29.3	13 9.2	19 51.3	9♐ 56.6	24 6.7	7 33.3	7 45.5	11 8.2	0♒ 1.8	0 10.1	13 1.8	9 59.8
5	6 56 25.9	14 10.4	19 48.1	23 51.2	25 44.4	8 48.9	8 31.2	11 21.7	0 8.8	0 8.6	13 3.1	9 59.1
6	7 0 22.4	15 11.6	19 44.9	8♑ 7.1	27 22.0	10 4.4	9 16.8	11 35.3	0 15.8	0 7.0	13 4.4	9 58.4
7	7 4 19.0	16 12.8	19 41.7	22 39.5	28 59.4	11 19.9	10 2.5	11 48.9	0 22.8	0 5.4	13 5.7	9 57.6
8	7 8 15.5	17 13.9	19 38.5	7♒ 21.5	0♒ 36.5	12 35.4	10 48.2	12 2.5	0 29.8	0 3.7	13 6.9	9 56.8
9	7 12 12.1	18 15.1	19 35.4	22 6.1	2 13.0	13 50.9	11 33.9	12 16.2	0 36.8	0 2.0	13 8.1	9 56.0
10	7 16 8.6	19 16.3	19 32.2	6♓ 46.5	3 48.9	15 6.3	12 19.7	12 29.9	0 43.9	0 .2	13 9.2	9 55.2
11	7 20 5.2	20 17.4	19 29.0	21 17.5	5 23.9	16 21.8	13 5.5	12 43.7	0 50.9	29♌ 58.4	13 10.4	9 54.3
12	7 24 1.8	21 18.6	19 25.8	5♈ 35.2	6 57.8	17 37.3	13 51.4	12 57.5	0 58.0	29 56.6	13 11.5	9 53.4
13	7 27 58.3	22 19.7	19 22.7	19 37.7	8 30.3	18 52.8	14 37.3	13 11.4	1 5.1	29 54.7	13 12.5	9 52.5
14	7 31 54.9	23 20.8	19 19.5	3♉ 24.0	10 1.1	20 8.2	15 23.2	13 25.2	1 12.1	29 52.8	13 13.6	9 51.5
15	7 35 51.4	24 21.9	19 16.3	16 54.5	11 29.7	21 23.7	16 9.2	13 39.2	1 19.2	29 50.8	13 14.6	9 50.5
16	7 39 48.0	25 23.0	19 13.1	0♊ 9.6	12 55.8	22 39.1	16 55.2	13 53.1	1 26.4	29 48.8	13 15.5	9 49.5
17	7 43 44.5	26 24.1	19 10.0	13 10.4	14 18.8	23 54.5	17 41.2	14 7.1	1 33.5	29 46.8	13 16.5	9 48.5
18	7 47 41.1	27 25.2	19 6.8	25 57.6	15 38.1	25 10.0	18 27.3	14 21.1	1 40.6	29 44.7	13 17.4	9 47.5
19	7 51 37.7	28 26.2	19 3.6	8♋ 32.1	16 53.2	26 25.4	19 13.4	14 35.2	1 47.7	29 42.6	13 18.3	9 46.4
20	7 55 34.2	29 27.3	19 .4	20 54.9	18 3.3	27 40.8	19 59.5	14 49.2	1 54.9	29 40.4	13 19.1	9 45.3
21	7 59 30.8	0♒ 28.3	18 57.2	3♌ 7.0	19 7.7	28 56.2	20 45.7	15 3.3	2 2.0	29 38.3	13 19.9	9 44.2
22	8 3 27.3	1 29.4	18 54.1	15 9.8	20 5.5	0♒ 11.6	21 31.9	15 17.5	2 9.1	29 36.1	13 20.7	9 43.1
23	8 7 23.9	2 30.4	18 50.9	27 5.0	20 55.9	1 27.0	22 18.1	15 31.6	2 16.3	29 33.8	13 21.5	9 41.9
24	8 11 20.4	3 31.4	18 47.7	8♍ 55.1	21 38.0	2 42.4	23 4.4	15 45.8	2 23.4	29 31.6	13 22.2	9 40.7
25	8 15 17.0	4 32.4	18 44.5	20 42.8	22 11.0	3 57.8	23 50.7	15 60.0	2 30.5	29 29.3	13 22.9	9 39.5
26	8 19 13.5	5 33.4	18 41.4	2♎ 31.7	22 34.3	5 13.2	24 37.1	16 14.2	2 37.7	29 27.0	13 23.6	9 38.3
27	8 23 10.1	6 34.4	18 38.2	14 25.7	22 46.9	6 28.6	25 23.5	16 28.5	2 44.9	29 24.7	13 24.2	9 37.1
28	8 27 6.7	7 35.4	18 35.0	26 29.2	22 48.5	7 44.0	26 9.9	16 42.7	2 52.0	29 22.3	13 24.8	9 35.9
29	8 31 3.2	8 36.3	18 31.8	8♏ 47.0	22 R 38.7	8 59.3	26 56.3	16 57.0	2 59.1	29 19.9	13 25.3	9 34.6
30	8 34 59.8	9 37.3	18 28.7	21 23.4	22 17.7	10 14.7	27 42.8	17 11.3	3 6.2	29 17.5	13 25.8	9 33.3
31	8 38 56.3	10 38.2	18 25.5	4♐ 22.6	21 45.5	11 30.0	28 29.3	17 25.6	3 13.3	29 15.1	13 26.3	9 32.0

LATITUDE

DAY	EPHEM. SID. TIME	☉	☊	☽	☿	♀	♂	♃	♄	♅	♆	♇
1	6 40 39.6	0 .0	0 .0	4N 56.2	2S 9.0	0S 13.5	0S 45.3	0S 39.6	0S 19.6	0N 46.2	1N 44.6	13N 15.2
4	6 52 29.3	0 .0	0 .0	4 50.2	2 8.4	0 20.6	0 46.7	0 39.7	0 19.8	0 46.3	1 44.7	13 16.4
7	7 4 19.0	0 .0	0 .0	2 15.6	2 3.2	0 27.5	0 48.1	0 39.8	0 20.0	0 46.4	1 44.9	13 17.7
10	7 16 8.6	0 .0	0 .0	1S 40.1	1 52.7	0 34.2	0 49.5	0 40.0	0 20.2	0 46.5	1 45.1	13 18.9
13	7 27 58.3	0 .0	0 .0	4 36.4	1 35.9	0 40.6	0 50.8	0 40.1	0 20.4	0 46.6	1 45.2	13 20.0
16	7 39 48.0	0 .0	0 .0	5 8.1	1 11.9	0 46.8	0 52.1	0 40.2	0 20.6	0 46.7	1 45.4	13 21.1
19	7 51 37.7	0 .0	0 .0	3 21.1	0 39.9	0 52.6	0 53.4	0 40.4	0 20.8	0 46.8	1 45.6	13 22.2
22	8 3 27.3	0 .0	0 .0	0 15.6	0N .5	0 58.1	0 54.6	0 40.5	0 21.0	0 46.9	1 45.7	13 23.2
25	8 15 17.0	0 .0	0 .0	2N 51.8	0 48.5	1 3.2	0 55.8	0 40.7	0 21.2	0 46.9	1 45.9	13 24.2
28	8 27 6.7	0 .0	0 .0	4 55.5	1 41.1	1 7.9	0 57.0	0 40.8	0 21.4	0 47.0	1 46.1	13 25.1
31	8 38 56.3	0 .0	0 .0	5 5.0	2 32.4	1 12.1	0 58.1	0 41.0	0 21.6	0 47.1	1 46.3	13 25.9

RIGHT ASCENSION

DAY	EPHEM. SID. TIME	☉	☊	☽	☿	♀	♂	♃	♄	♅	♆	♇
1	6 40 39.6	10♑ 58.9	22♌ 25.3	0♏ 17.4	21♑ 8.7	4♑ 7.6	6♑ .5	13♒ 6.3	1♒ 55.6	2♍ 35.9	11♏ 3.2	16♍ 50.7
2	6 44 36.2	12 5.1	22 22.2	12 29.3	22 54.4	5 30.0	6 50.3	13 19.9	2 2.8	2 R 34.6	11 4.6	16 R 50.3
3	6 48 32.8	13 11.3	22 19.1	25 22.2	24 39.8	6 52.4	7 40.0	13 33.4	2 10.0	2 33.2	11 6.0	16 49.9
4	6 52 29.3	14 17.4	22 16.0	9♐ 2.7	26 24.6	8 14.8	8 29.8	13 47.0	2 17.3	2 31.8	11 7.3	16 49.4
5	6 56 25.9	15 23.4	22 12.9	23 30.8	28 8.9	9 37.3	9 19.7	14 .8	2 24.6	2 30.3	11 8.6	16 49.0
6	7 0 22.4	16 29.3	22 9.7	8♑ 37.2	29 52.5	10 59.6	10 9.5	14 14.4	2 31.9	2 28.8	11 9.9	16 48.4
7	7 4 19.0	17 35.1	22 6.6	24 4.3	1♒ 35.2	12 21.8	10 59.4	14 28.2	2 39.2	2 27.3	11 11.2	16 47.9
8	7 8 15.5	18 40.7	22 3.5	9♒ 30.0	3 16.8	13 43.9	11 49.2	14 42.0	2 46.5	2 25.7	11 12.4	16 47.3
9	7 12 12.1	19 46.3	22 .4	24 35.0	4 57.3	15 5.9	12 39.1	14 55.8	2 53.8	2 24.0	11 13.6	16 46.7
10	7 16 8.6	20 51.7	21 57.2	9♓ 8.3	6 36.3	16 27.8	13 28.9	15 9.6	3 1.2	2 22.4	11 14.7	16 46.0
11	7 20 5.2	21 56.9	21 54.1	23 8.1	8 13.7	17 49.6	14 18.8	15 23.5	3 8.5	2 20.6	11 15.8	16 45.4
12	7 24 1.8	23 2.0	21 51.0	6♈ 39.4	9 49.2	19 11.2	15 8.6	15 37.4	3 15.9	2 18.9	11 16.9	16 44.7
13	7 27 58.3	24 7.0	21 47.9	19 51.7	11 22.4	20 32.7	15 58.4	15 51.3	3 23.3	2 17.1	11 18.0	16 44.0
14	7 31 54.9	25 11.7	21 44.8	2♉ 54.8	12 53.1	21 53.9	16 48.2	16 5.3	3 30.7	2 15.3	11 19.1	16 43.2
15	7 35 51.4	26 16.4	21 41.6	15 57.7	14 20.8	23 15.0	17 38.0	16 19.3	3 38.1	2 13.4	11 20.1	16 42.4
16	7 39 48.0	27 20.8	21 38.5	29 6.4	15 45.2	24 35.9	18 27.7	16 33.3	3 45.5	2 11.5	11 21.0	16 41.6
17	7 43 44.5	28 25.1	21 35.4	12♊ 22.6	17 5.7	25 56.5	19 17.4	16 47.3	3 52.9	2 9.5	11 22.0	16 40.8
18	7 47 41.1	29 29.2	21 32.3	25 43.9	18 21.8	27 17.0	20 7.1	17 1.4	4 .3	2 7.6	11 22.9	16 40.0
19	7 51 37.7	0♒ 33.1	21 29.1	9♋ 3.7	19 32.9	28 37.2	20 56.8	17 15.4	4 7.7	2 5.6	11 23.8	16 39.1
20	7 55 34.2	1 36.8	21 26.0	22 13.5	20 38.4	29 57.1	21 46.4	17 29.5	4 15.1	2 3.5	11 24.6	16 38.2
21	7 59 30.8	2 40.4	21 22.9	5♌ 5.0	21 37.6	1♒ 16.8	22 35.9	17 43.6	4 22.5	2 1.4	11 25.4	16 37.3
22	8 3 27.3	3 43.8	21 19.7	17 32.9	22 29.8	2 36.3	23 25.5	17 57.7	4 30.0	1 59.3	11 26.2	16 36.4
23	8 7 23.9	4 46.9	21 16.6	29 35.3	23 14.1	3 55.5	24 15.0	18 11.9	4 37.4	1 57.2	11 27.0	16 35.4
24	8 11 20.4	5 49.9	21 13.5	11♍ 14.5	23 50.0	5 14.4	25 4.4	18 26.0	4 44.8	1 55.1	11 27.7	16 34.4
25	8 15 17.0	6 52.7	21 10.4	22 36.0	24 16.7	6 33.0	25 53.8	18 40.2	4 52.2	1 52.9	11 28.4	16 33.4
26	8 19 13.5	7 55.3	21 7.2	3♎ 47.8	24 33.5	7 51.4	26 43.1	18 54.4	4 59.7	1 50.7	11 29.1	16 32.4
27	8 23 10.1	8 57.7	21 4.1	14 59.3	24 39.9	9 9.4	27 32.4	19 8.6	5 7.1	1 48.5	11 29.7	16 31.4
28	8 27 6.7	9 59.9	21 1.0	26 21.5	24 R 35.5	10 27.2	28 21.6	19 22.8	5 14.5	1 46.2	11 30.3	16 30.3
29	8 31 3.2	11 1.9	20 57.8	8♏ 5.5	24 20.3	11 44.6	29 10.8	19 37.0	5 21.9	1 43.9	11 30.9	16 29.2
30	8 34 59.8	12 3.7	20 54.7	20 22.7	23 54.2	13 1.7	29 59.9	19 51.2	5 29.2	1 41.6	11 31.4	16 28.1
31	8 38 56.3	13 5.3	20 51.6	3♐ 22.5	23 17.7	14 18.6	0♒ 48.9	20 5.4	5 36.6	1 39.3	11 31.9	16 27.0

DECLINATION

DAY	EPHEM. SID. TIME	☉	☊	☽	☿	♀	♂	♃	♄	♅	♆	♇
1	6 40 39.6	23S 3.5	0N 15.5	7S 4.7	24S 11.5	23S 36.8	24S 4.9	18S 15.2	20S 32.3	12N 6.5	14S 4.1	20N 2.1
4	6 52 29.3	22 47.5	0 15.6	17 9.5	23 23.9	23 34.1	23 59.5	18 4.3	20 28.1	12 8.2	14 5.2	20 4.0
7	7 4 19.0	22 27.5	0 15.6	19 18.5	22 22.4	23 24.9	23 51.7	17 53.1	20 23.8	12 9.9	14 6.2	20 6.0
10	7 16 8.6	22 3.4	0 15.7	10 34.5	21 7.6	23 9.2	23 41.5	17 41.7	20 19.5	12 11.9	14 7.1	20 8.0
13	7 27 58.3	21 35.5	0 15.7	3N 24.7	19 40.9	22 47.0	23 28.9	17 30.1	20 15.0	12 13.9	14 8.0	20 10.1
16	7 39 48.0	21 3.9	0 15.8	15 9.9	18 5.1	22 18.5	23 14.0	17 18.2	20 10.6	12 16.1	14 8.7	20 12.2
19	7 51 37.7	20 28.6	0 15.8	19 49.4	16 24.6	21 43.9	22 56.7	17 6.1	20 6.0	12 18.3	14 9.4	20 14.4
22	8 3 27.3	19 49.8	0 15.9	16 2.5	14 46.8	21 3.5	22 37.1	16 53.9	20 1.4	12 20.7	14 9.9	20 16.7
25	8 15 17.0	19 7.7	0 15.9	6 18.7	13 21.2	20 17.4	22 15.3	16 41.4	19 56.8	12 23.1	14 10.4	20 18.9
28	8 27 6.7	18 22.5	0 16.0	5S 37.4	12 19.3	19 25.9	21 51.1	16 28.7	19 52.1	12 25.7	14 10.8	20 21.2
31	8 38 56.3	17 34.3	0 16.0	16 1.3	11 51.0	18 29.3	21 24.8	16 15.9	19 47.4	12 28.2	14 11.1	20 23.4

FEBRUARY 1962

LONGITUDE

DAY	EPHEM. SID. TIME (h m s)	☉ (° ′)	☊ (° ′)	☽ (° ′)	☿ (° ′)	♀ (° ′)	♂ (° ′)	♃ (° ′)	♄ (° ′)	♅ (° ′)	♆ (° ′)	♇ (° ′)
1	8 42 52.9	11♒39.1	18♌22.3	17♐47.5	21♒ 3.1	12♒45.4	29♑15.8	17♒39.9	3♒20.4	29♌12.6	13♏26.8	9♍30.6
2	8 46 49.4	12 40.0	18 19.1	1♑39.6	20R11.3	14 .7	0♒ 2.3	17 54.2	3 27.5	29R10.1	13 27.2	9R29.3
3	8 50 46.0	13 40.9	18 15.9	15 57.8	19 11.7	15 16.0	0 48.9	18 8.6	3 34.6	29 7.6	13 27.6	9 27.9
4	8 54 42.5	14 41.8	18 12.8	0♒38.8	18 5.9	16 31.4	1 35.5	18 22.9	3 41.7	29 5.1	13 27.9	9 26.6
5	8 58 39.1	15 42.7	18 9.6	15 36.2	16 55.8	17 46.7	2 22.2	18 37.3	3 48.7	29 2.6	13 28.2	9 25.2
6	9 2 35.7	16 43.5	18 6.4	0♓42.0	15 43.5	19 2.0	3 8.8	18 51.6	3 55.7	29 .0	13 28.5	9 23.8
7	9 6 32.2	17 44.3	18 3.2	15 47.0	14 31.0	20 17.3	3 55.5	19 6.0	4 2.8	28 57.4	13 28.7	9 22.3
8	9 10 28.8	18 45.1	18 .1	0♈42.6	13 20.4	21 32.5	4 42.2	19 20.3	4 9.8	28 54.9	13 28.9	9 20.9
9	9 14 25.3	19 45.9	17 56.9	15 21.6	12 13.3	22 47.8	5 28.9	19 34.7	4 16.7	28 52.3	13 29.1	9 19.5
10	9 18 21.9	20 46.6	17 53.7	29 39.3	11 11.1	24 3.0	6 15.7	19 49.1	4 23.7	28 49.7	13 29.3	9 18.0
11	9 22 18.4	21 47.3	17 50.5	13♉33.4	10 15.1	25 18.2	7 2.4	20 3.4	4 30.6	28 47.1	13 29.4	9 16.6
12	9 26 15.0	22 48.0	17 47.3	27 3.7	9 26.2	26 33.5	7 49.2	20 17.8	4 37.6	28 44.5	13 29.4	9 15.1
13	9 30 11.5	23 48.7	17 44.2	10♊11.8	8 44.8	27 48.7	8 36.0	20 32.1	4 44.5	28 41.8	13 29.5	9 13.6
14	9 34 8.1	24 49.3	17 41.0	23 .3	8 11.2	29 3.8	9 22.8	20 46.5	4 51.3	28 39.2	13 29.5	9 12.1
15	9 38 4.6	25 49.9	17 37.8	5♋32.1	7 45.6	0♓19.0	10 9.7	21 .8	4 58.2	28 36.6	13R29.4	9 10.6
16	9 42 1.2	26 50.6	17 34.6	17 50.4	7 27.9	1 34.2	10 56.6	21 15.2	5 5.0	28 34.0	13 29.4	9 9.1
17	9 45 57.7	27 51.1	17 31.5	29 57.9	7 17.8	2 49.3	11 43.4	21 29.5	5 11.8	28 31.4	13 29.3	9 7.6
18	9 49 54.3	28 51.6	17 28.3	11♌57.4	7 15.0	4 4.4	12 30.3	21 43.8	5 18.6	28 28.7	13 29.2	9 6.1
19	9 53 50.9	29 52.1	17 25.1	23 51.2	7D19.1	5 19.5	13 17.2	21 58.1	5 25.3	28 26.1	13 29.0	9 4.6
20	9 57 47.4	0♓52.6	17 21.9	5♍41.5	7 29.8	6 34.6	14 4.1	22 12.4	5 32.0	28 23.5	13 28.8	9 3.0
21	10 1 44.0	1 53.0	17 18.7	17 30.2	7 46.6	7 49.7	14 51.1	22 26.7	5 38.7	28 20.8	13 28.6	9 1.5
22	10 5 40.5	2 53.5	17 15.6	29 19.5	8 9.1	9 4.7	15 38.0	22 41.0	5 45.3	28 18.2	13 28.3	8 59.9
23	10 9 37.1	3 53.9	17 12.4	11♎11.7	8 36.9	10 19.7	16 25.0	22 55.2	5 51.9	28 15.6	13 28.0	8 58.4
24	10 13 33.6	4 54.2	17 9.2	23 9.3	9 9.6	11 34.7	17 12.0	23 9.4	5 58.5	28 13.0	13 27.7	8 56.8
25	10 17 30.2	5 54.6	17 6.0	5♏15.5	9 46.8	12 49.7	17 58.9	23 23.6	6 5.0	28 10.4	13 27.3	8 55.3
26	10 21 26.7	6 54.9	17 2.9	17 33.5	10 28.3	14 4.7	18 46.0	23 37.8	6 11.5	28 7.8	13 26.9	8 53.7
27	10 25 23.3	7 55.2	16 59.7	0♐ 7.0	11 13.6	15 19.7	19 33.0	23 52.0	6 17.9	28 5.2	13 26.5	8 52.1
28	10 29 19.8	8 55.4	16 56.5	12 59.8	12 2.6	16 34.6	20 20.0	24 6.1	6 24.4	28 2.6	13 26.0	8 50.6

LATITUDE

DAY	EPHEM. SID. TIME	☉	☊	☽	☿	♀	♂	♃	♄	♅	♆	♇
1	8 42 52.9	0 .0	0 .0	4N36.1	2N47.7	1S13.4	0S58.4	0S41.1	0S21.7	0N47.1	1N46.3	13N26.2
4	8 54 42.5	0 .0	0 .0	1 35.2	3 24.0	1 16.9	0 59.5	0 41.3	0 22.0	0 47.1	1 46.5	13 27.0
7	9 6 32.2	0 .0	0 .0	2S28.4	3 40.2	1 20.0	1 .5	0 41.5	0 22.2	0 47.2	1 46.7	13 27.7
10	9 18 21.9	0 .0	0 .0	5 1.9	3 35.2	1 22.5	1 1.4	0 41.8	0 22.4	0 47.2	1 46.9	13 28.3
13	9 30 11.5	0 .0	0 .0	4 54.6	3 13.1	1 24.5	1 2.3	0 42.0	0 22.7	0 47.2	1 47.1	13 28.9
16	9 42 1.2	0 .0	0 .0	2 40.3	2 40.7	1 25.9	1 3.1	0 42.2	0 22.9	0 47.3	1 47.2	13 29.4
19	9 53 50.9	0 .0	0 .0	0N32.0	2 3.5	1 26.7	1 3.9	0 42.5	0 23.2	0 47.3	1 47.4	13 29.9
22	10 5 40.5	0 .0	0 .0	3 29.1	1 25.3	1 27.0	1 4.6	0 42.8	0 23.4	0 47.3	1 47.6	13 30.2
25	10 17 30.2	0 .0	0 .0	5 8.3	0 48.4	1 26.6	1 5.3	0 43.1	0 23.7	0 47.3	1 47.8	13 30.6
28	10 29 19.8	0 .0	0 .0	4 46.0	0 13.9	1 25.7	1 5.9	0 43.4	0 24.0	0 47.2	1 48.0	13 30.8

RIGHT ASCENSION

DAY	EPHEM. SID. TIME	☉	☊	☽	☿	♀	♂	♃	♄	♅	♆	♇
1	8 42 52.9	14♒ 6.7	20♌48.4	17♐10.4	22♒31.7	15♒35.1	1♒37.8	20♒19.6	5♒44.0	1♍36.9	11♏32.4	16♍25.8
2	8 46 49.4	15 7.9	20 45.3	1♑45.5	21R37.0	16 51.3	2 26.7	20 33.8	5 51.3	1R34.5	11 32.8	16R24.6
3	8 50 46.0	16 8.9	20 42.2	16 57.8	20 35.3	18 7.3	3 15.5	20 48.1	5 58.6	1 32.1	11 33.2	16 23.5
4	8 54 42.5	17 9.7	20 39.0	2♒29.6	19 28.2	19 22.9	4 4.2	21 2.3	6 5.9	1 29.7	11 33.5	16 22.3
5	8 58 39.1	18 10.3	20 35.9	17 59.8	18 17.5	20 38.2	4 52.9	21 16.5	6 13.2	1 27.3	11 33.9	16 21.0
6	9 2 35.7	19 10.7	20 32.8	3♓10.8	17 5.2	21 53.1	5 41.4	21 30.7	6 20.5	1 24.9	11 34.2	16 19.8
7	9 6 32.2	20 10.9	20 29.6	17 53.0	15 53.3	23 7.8	6 29.9	21 44.9	6 27.8	1 22.4	11 34.4	16 18.5
8	9 10 28.8	21 10.9	20 26.5	2♈ 5.1	14 43.7	24 22.2	7 18.3	21 59.1	6 35.0	1 19.9	11 34.6	16 17.3
9	9 14 25.3	22 10.7	20 23.3	15 52.1	13 38.1	25 36.2	8 6.6	22 13.3	6 42.2	1 17.5	11 34.8	16 16.0
10	9 18 21.9	23 10.3	20 20.2	29 21.9	12 37.7	26 50.0	8 54.8	22 27.5	6 49.4	1 15.0	11 35.0	16 14.7
11	9 22 18.4	24 9.7	20 17.1	12♉42.6	11 43.8	28 3.5	9 42.9	22 41.6	6 56.6	1 12.5	11 35.1	16 13.4
12	9 26 15.0	25 8.9	20 13.9	26 .6	10 57.1	29 16.6	10 30.9	22 55.8	7 3.7	1 10.0	11 35.2	16 12.1
13	9 30 11.5	26 7.8	20 10.8	9♊19.0	10 18.2	0♓29.5	11 18.8	23 9.9	7 10.9	1 7.4	11 35.2	16 10.7
14	9 34 8.1	27 6.6	20 7.6	22 37.5	9 47.3	1 42.1	12 6.7	23 24.0	7 17.9	1 4.9	11 35.3	16 9.4
15	9 38 4.6	28 5.2	20 4.5	5♋52.2	9 24.5	2 54.4	12 54.4	23 38.1	7 25.0	1 2.4	11 35.3	16 8.0
16	9 42 1.2	29 3.7	20 1.4	18 57.4	9 9.8	4 6.5	13 42.1	23 52.3	7 32.1	0 59.9	11 35.3	16 6.7
17	9 45 57.7	0♓ 1.9	19 58.2	1♌46.6	9 2.8	5 18.3	14 29.6	24 6.3	7 39.1	0 57.4	11R35.2	16 5.3
18	9 49 54.3	0 60.0	19 55.1	14 15.3	9D 3.2	6 29.8	15 17.0	24 20.4	7 46.1	0 54.8	11 35.1	16 3.9
19	9 53 50.9	1 57.9	19 51.9	26 21.2	9 10.7	7 41.1	16 4.4	24 34.4	7 53.0	0 52.3	11 34.9	16 2.5
20	9 57 47.4	2 55.6	19 48.8	8♍ 5.4	9 24.8	8 52.1	16 51.6	24 48.4	7 59.9	0 49.8	11 34.7	16 1.1
21	10 1 44.0	3 53.1	19 45.6	19 31.7	9 45.1	10 2.9	17 38.7	25 2.4	8 6.8	0 47.3	11 34.5	15 59.7
22	10 5 40.5	4 50.5	19 42.5	0♎46.1	10 11.2	11 13.4	18 25.8	25 16.4	8 13.6	0 44.7	11 34.3	15 58.3
23	10 9 37.1	5 47.7	19 39.4	11 56.6	10 42.6	12 23.8	19 12.7	25 30.3	8 20.4	0 42.2	11 34.0	15 56.8
24	10 13 33.6	6 44.8	19 36.2	23 12.0	11 19.0	13 33.9	19 59.5	25 44.2	8 27.2	0 39.7	11 33.7	15 55.4
25	10 17 30.2	7 41.7	19 33.1	4♏41.9	11 59.9	14 43.8	20 46.3	25 58.1	8 33.9	0 37.2	11 33.4	15 53.9
26	10 21 26.7	8 38.5	19 29.9	16 36.2	12 44.9	15 53.6	21 32.9	26 12.0	8 40.6	0 34.7	11 33.0	15 52.5
27	10 25 23.3	9 35.1	19 26.8	29 3.8	13 33.8	17 3.1	22 19.4	26 25.8	8 47.2	0 32.2	11 32.6	15 51.0
28	10 29 19.8	10 31.7	19 23.6	12♐11.7	14 26.3	18 12.5	23 5.9	26 39.6	8 53.8	0 29.7	11 32.1	15 49.6

DECLINATION

DAY	EPHEM. SID. TIME	☉	☊	☽	☿	♀	♂	♃	♄	♅	♆	♇
1	8 42 52.9	17S17.5	0N16.0	18S17.9	11S49.9	18S 9.4	21S15.6	16S11.6	19S45.8	12N29.1	14S11.1	20N24.2
4	8 54 42.5	16 25.6	0 16.1	18 27.9	12 10.2	17 6.5	20 46.4	15 58.5	19 41.1	12 31.8	14 11.3	20 26.5
7	9 6 32.2	15 31.1	0 16.1	7 53.2	12 57.9	15 59.4	20 15.3	15 45.3	19 36.4	12 34.5	14 11.4	20 28.8
10	9 18 21.9	14 34.2	0 16.2	6N38.3	13 58.2	14 48.2	19 42.1	15 32.0	19 31.6	12 37.2	14 11.4	20 31.0
13	9 30 11.5	13 35.1	0 16.3	17 7.3	14 58.0	13 33.4	19 7.0	15 18.6	19 26.9	12 40.0	14 11.3	20 33.3
16	9 42 1.2	12 34.0	0 16.3	19 36.2	15 49.0	12 15.3	18 30.0	15 5.1	19 22.2	12 42.7	14 11.1	20 35.5
19	9 53 50.9	11 31.2	0 16.4	14 4.5	16 27.2	10 54.2	17 51.2	14 51.5	19 17.5	12 45.5	14 10.8	20 37.7
22	10 5 40.5	10 26.7	0 16.4	3 28.0	16 51.4	9 30.6	17 10.8	14 37.8	19 12.8	12 48.3	14 10.4	20 39.8
25	10 17 30.2	9 20.7	0 16.5	8S25.7	17 1.5	8 4.7	16 28.8	14 24.1	19 8.2	12 51.0	14 9.9	20 41.9
28	10 29 19.8	8 13.5	0 16.5	17 37.8	16 57.7	6 36.9	15 45.2	14 10.3	19 3.7	12 53.7	14 9.4	20 43.9

MARCH 1962

LONGITUDE

DAY	EPHEM. SID. TIME h m s	☉ ° ′	☊ ° ′	☽ ° ′	☿ ° ′	♀ ° ′	♂ ° ′	♃ ° ′	♄ ° ′	♅ ° ′	♆ ° ′	♇ ° ′
1	10 33 16.4	9♓55.7	16♌53.3	26♐15.4	12♒54.9	17♓49.6	21♒ 7.0	24♒20.3	6♒30.7	28♌ .0	13♏25.5	8♍49.0
2	10 37 12.9	10 55.9	16 50.1	9♑56.3	13 50.3	19 4.5	21 54.1	24 34.3	6 37.1	27 R 57.5	13 R 25.0	8 R 47.5
3	10 41 9.5	11 56.1	16 47.0	24 3.8	14 48.6	20 19.4	22 41.1	24 48.4	6 43.3	27 54.9	13 24.5	8 45.9
4	10 45 6.0	12 56.3	16 43.8	8♒36.8	15 49.6	21 34.3	23 28.2	25 2.5	6 49.6	27 52.4	13 23.9	8 44.3
5	10 49 2.6	13 56.4	16 40.6	23 31.6	16 53.1	22 49.1	24 15.3	25 16.5	6 55.8	27 49.9	13 23.3	8 42.8
6	10 52 59.1	14 56.5	16 37.4	8♓41.2	17 59.0	24 4.0	25 2.4	25 30.4	7 1.9	27 47.4	13 22.6	8 41.2
7	10 56 55.7	15 56.6	16 34.3	23 56.8	19 7.2	25 18.8	25 49.5	25 44.4	7 8.1	27 44.9	13 21.9	8 39.7
8	11 0 52.3	16 56.7	16 31.1	9♈ 7.8	20 17.4	26 33.6	26 36.5	25 58.3	7 14.1	27 42.5	13 21.2	8 38.1
9	11 4 48.8	17 56.7	16 27.9	24 4.5	21 29.6	27 48.4	27 23.7	26 12.2	7 20.2	27 40.1	13 20.5	8 36.6
10	11 8 45.4	18 56.7	16 24.7	8♉39.1	22 43.7	29 3.2	28 10.8	26 26.1	7 26.1	27 37.7	13 19.8	8 35.1
11	11 12 41.9	19 56.7	16 21.5	22 46.7	23 59.6	0♈17.9	28 57.9	26 39.9	7 32.0	27 35.3	13 19.0	8 33.6
12	11 16 38.5	20 56.6	16 18.4	6♊25.8	25 17.2	1 32.6	29 44.9	26 53.6	7 37.9	27 32.9	13 18.1	8 32.1
13	11 20 35.0	21 56.4	16 15.2	19 37.3	26 36.5	2 47.3	0♓32.0	27 7.3	7 43.7	27 30.6	13 17.3	8 30.5
14	11 24 31.6	22 56.3	16 12.0	2♋24.2	27 57.3	4 1.9	1 19.1	27 21.0	7 49.4	27 28.3	13 16.4	8 29.0
15	11 28 28.1	23 56.1	16 8.8	14 50.6	29 19.7	5 16.6	2 6.2	27 34.7	7 55.1	27 26.0	13 15.5	8 27.5
16	11 32 24.7	24 55.8	16 5.7	27 1.1	0♓43.6	6 31.2	2 53.3	27 48.3	8 .7	27 23.7	13 14.5	8 26.0
17	11 36 21.2	25 55.6	16 2.5	9♌ .3	2 9.0	7 45.7	3 40.3	28 1.8	8 6.3	27 21.5	13 13.6	8 24.6
18	11 40 17.8	26 55.2	15 59.3	20 52.2	3 35.8	9 .3	4 27.4	28 15.3	8 11.8	27 19.3	13 12.6	8 23.1
19	11 44 14.3	27 54.9	15 56.1	2♍40.5	5 4.0	10 14.8	5 14.5	28 28.7	8 17.3	27 17.2	13 11.6	8 21.6
20	11 48 10.9	28 54.5	15 52.9	14 28.3	6 33.5	11 29.3	6 1.5	28 42.1	8 22.7	27 15.0	13 10.5	8 20.2
21	11 52 7.4	29 54.1	15 49.8	26 18.1	8 4.5	12 43.7	6 48.6	28 55.5	8 28.0	27 12.9	13 9.5	8 18.8
22	11 56 4.0	0♈53.6	15 46.6	8♎11.7	9 36.7	13 58.2	7 35.6	29 8.8	8 33.3	27 10.9	13 8.4	8 17.3
23	12 0 .5	1 53.2	15 43.4	20 11.0	11 10.4	15 12.6	8 22.7	29 22.0	8 38.5	27 8.8	13 7.3	8 15.9
24	12 3 57.1	2 52.6	15 40.2	2♏17.2	12 45.3	16 27.0	9 9.7	29 35.2	8 43.6	27 6.8	13 6.1	8 14.5
25	12 7 53.6	3 52.1	15 37.0	14 32.1	14 21.6	17 41.3	9 56.7	29 48.3	8 48.7	27 4.9	13 5.0	8 13.2
26	12 11 50.2	4 51.5	15 33.9	26 57.5	15 59.3	18 55.6	10 43.8	0♓ 1.4	8 53.7	27 3.0	13 3.8	8 11.8
27	12 15 46.7	5 50.9	15 30.7	9♐35.4	17 38.2	20 10.0	11 30.8	0 14.4	8 58.6	27 1.1	13 2.6	8 10.4
28	12 19 43.3	6 50.3	15 27.5	22 28.5	19 18.6	21 24.2	12 17.8	0 27.4	9 3.5	26 59.2	13 1.4	8 9.1
29	12 23 39.8	7 49.6	15 24.3	5♑39.5	21 .2	22 38.5	13 4.8	0 40.3	9 8.3	26 57.4	13 .1	8 7.8
30	12 27 36.4	8 48.9	15 21.2	19 11.1	22 43.3	23 52.8	13 51.8	0 53.2	9 13.1	26 55.7	12 58.9	8 6.5
31	12 31 33.0	9 48.2	15 18.0	3♒ 5.2	24 27.7	25 7.0	14 38.8	1 5.9	9 17.8	26 54.0	12 57.6	8 5.2

LATITUDE

DAY	EPHEM. SID. TIME	☉	☊	☽	☿	♀	♂	♃	♄	♅	♆	♇
1	10 33 16.4	0 .0	0 .0	4N 7.8	0N 3.1	1S25.3	1S 6.1	0S43.5	0S24.1	0N47.2	1N48.0	13N30.9
4	10 45 6.0	0 .0	0 .0	0 51.1	0S27.3	1 23.6	1 6.6	0 43.8	0 24.4	0 47.2	1 48.2	13 31.0
7	10 56 55.7	0 .0	0 .0	3S 5.2	0 54.3	1 21.4	1 7.1	0 44.1	0 24.6	0 47.2	1 48.3	13 31.1
10	11 8 45.4	0 .0	0 .0	5 9.3	1 17.8	1 18.5	1 7.5	0 44.5	0 24.9	0 47.2	1 48.5	13 31.1
13	11 20 35.0	0 .0	0 .0	4 25.5	1 37.6	1 15.2	1 7.9	0 44.9	0 25.2	0 47.1	1 48.6	13 31.1
16	11 32 24.7	0 .0	0 .0	1 50.1	1 53.8	1 11.3	1 8.1	0 45.2	0 25.5	0 47.1	1 48.8	13 31.0
19	11 44 14.3	0 .0	0 .0	1N21.1	2 6.2	1 6.9	1 8.4	0 45.6	0 25.8	0 47.0	1 48.9	13 30.8
22	11 56 4.0	0 .0	0 .0	3 59.7	2 14.8	1 2.0	1 8.5	0 46.0	0 26.2	0 46.9	1 49.1	13 30.5
25	12 7 53.6	0 .0	0 .0	5 7.5	2 19.3	0 56.7	1 8.6	0 46.5	0 26.5	0 46.9	1 49.2	13 30.2
28	12 19 43.3	0 .0	0 .0	4 10.0	2 19.8	0 50.9	1 8.6	0 46.9	0 26.8	0 46.8	1 49.3	13 29.9
31	12 31 33.0	0 .0	0 .0	1 12.4	2 15.9	0 44.7	1 8.5	0 47.4	0 27.1	0 46.7	1 49.4	13 29.4

RIGHT ASCENSION

DAY	EPHEM. SID. TIME	☉	☊	☽	☿	♀	♂	♃	♄	♅	♆	♇
1	10 33 16.4	11♓28.0	19♌20.5	26♐ 2.6	15♒21.9	19♓21.7	23♒52.2	26♒53.4	9♒ .3	0♍27.2	11♏31.7	15♍48.1
2	10 37 12.9	12 24.3	19 17.3	10♑33.3	16 20.6	20 30.8	24 38.4	27 7.1	9 6.9	0 R 24.8	11 R 31.2	15 R 46.7
3	10 41 9.5	13 20.4	19 14.2	25 33.7	17 21.9	21 39.7	25 24.6	27 20.8	9 13.3	0 22.3	11 30.6	15 45.2
4	10 45 6.0	14 16.4	19 11.0	10♒48.5	18 25.7	22 48.5	26 10.6	27 34.5	9 19.7	0 19.9	11 30.1	15 43.7
5	10 49 2.6	15 12.3	19 7.9	26 1.7	19 31.8	23 57.2	26 56.6	27 48.1	9 26.1	0 17.5	11 29.5	15 42.3
6	10 52 59.1	16 8.1	19 4.7	11♓ .9	20 40.1	25 5.8	27 42.4	28 1.7	9 32.4	0 15.0	11 28.9	15 40.8
7	10 56 55.7	17 3.8	19 1.6	25 40.2	21 50.2	26 14.2	28 28.1	28 15.2	9 38.7	0 12.7	11 28.2	15 39.3
8	11 0 52.3	17 59.4	18 58.4	9♈59.6	23 2.2	27 22.6	29 13.8	28 28.7	9 44.9	0 10.3	11 27.5	15 37.8
9	11 4 48.8	18 54.9	18 55.3	24 3.3	24 15.8	28 30.9	29 59.3	28 42.2	9 51.1	0 8.0	11 26.9	15 36.4
10	11 8 45.4	19 50.3	18 52.1	7♉56.6	25 30.9	29 39.1	0♓44.8	28 55.7	9 57.2	0 5.7	11 26.1	15 34.9
11	11 12 41.9	20 45.6	18 49.0	21 43.8	26 47.5	0♈47.2	1 30.1	29 9.0	10 3.3	0 3.4	11 25.4	15 33.5
12	11 16 38.5	21 40.8	18 45.8	5♊26.8	28 5.3	1 55.3	2 15.4	29 22.4	10 9.3	0 1.1	11 24.6	15 32.0
13	11 20 35.0	22 35.9	18 42.7	19 4.4	29 24.4	3 3.4	3 .5	29 35.6	10 15.2	29♌58.8	11 23.7	15 30.6
14	11 24 31.6	23 30.9	18 39.5	2♋32.9	0♓44.7	4 11.4	3 45.6	29 48.9	10 21.1	29 56.6	11 22.9	15 29.1
15	11 28 28.1	24 25.9	18 36.4	15 46.9	2 6.0	5 19.4	4 30.5	0♓ 2.1	10 26.9	29 54.4	11 22.0	15 27.7
16	11 32 24.7	25 20.8	18 33.2	28 41.5	3 28.4	6 27.3	5 15.4	0 15.2	10 32.7	29 52.2	11 21.1	15 26.2
17	11 36 21.2	26 15.7	18 30.0	11♌13.3	4 51.7	7 35.3	6 .1	0 28.3	10 38.4	29 50.1	11 20.2	15 24.8
18	11 40 17.8	27 10.5	18 26.9	23 21.6	6 16.0	8 43.3	6 44.8	0 41.3	10 44.1	29 47.9	11 19.2	15 23.4
19	11 44 14.3	28 5.2	18 23.7	5♍ 8.0	7 41.2	9 51.3	7 29.4	0 54.3	10 49.6	29 45.8	11 18.2	15 21.9
20	11 48 10.9	28 59.9	18 20.6	16 36.8	9 7.2	10 59.3	8 13.9	1 7.2	10 55.2	29 43.8	11 17.2	15 20.5
21	11 52 7.4	29 54.6	18 17.4	27 53.7	10 34.1	12 7.4	8 58.3	1 20.1	11 .6	29 41.8	11 16.2	15 19.1
22	11 56 4.0	0♈49.2	18 14.2	9♎ 6.1	12 1.8	13 15.5	9 42.7	1 32.9	11 6.0	29 39.8	11 15.1	15 17.7
23	12 0 .5	1 43.8	18 11.1	20 21.9	13 30.4	14 23.7	10 26.9	1 45.6	11 11.3	29 37.8	11 14.0	15 16.3
24	12 3 57.1	2 38.4	18 7.9	1♏49.4	14 59.8	15 32.0	11 11.1	1 58.3	11 16.6	29 35.9	11 12.9	15 15.0
25	12 7 53.6	3 33.0	18 4.8	13 36.9	16 30.0	16 40.3	11 55.2	2 10.9	11 21.8	29 34.0	11 11.8	15 13.6
26	12 11 50.2	4 27.5	18 1.6	25 51.8	18 1.0	17 48.8	12 39.2	2 23.5	11 26.9	29 32.1	11 10.7	15 12.2
27	12 15 46.7	5 22.1	17 58.4	8♐39.8	19 32.8	18 57.3	13 23.2	2 36.0	11 32.0	29 30.3	11 9.5	15 10.9
28	12 19 43.3	6 16.7	17 55.3	22 3.4	21 5.5	20 6.0	14 7.0	2 48.5	11 37.0	29 28.5	11 8.3	15 9.6
29	12 23 39.8	7 11.2	17 52.1	6♑ .7	22 39.1	21 14.8	14 50.8	3 .9	11 41.9	29 26.7	11 7.1	15 8.2
30	12 27 36.4	8 5.9	17 49.0	20 24.9	24 13.6	22 23.8	15 34.6	3 13.2	11 46.8	29 25.1	11 5.9	15 7.0
31	12 31 33.0	9 .5	17 45.8	5♒ 5.4	25 49.0	23 32.9	16 18.3	3 25.5	11 51.6	29 23.4	11 4.6	15 5.7

DECLINATION

DAY	EPHEM. SID. TIME	☉	☊	☽	☿	♀	♂	♃	♄	♅	♆	♇
1	10 33 16.4	7S50.8	0N16.5	19S15.7	16S53.4	6S 7.2	15S30.3	14S 5.7	19S 2.2	12N54.5	14S 9.2	20N44.6
4	10 45 6.0	6 42.2	0 16.6	17 17.3	16 31.7	4 37.4	14 44.8	13 51.9	18 57.7	12 57.2	14 8.5	20 46.5
7	10 56 55.7	5 32.7	0 16.6	5 14.3	15 57.1	3 6.4	13 57.9	13 38.0	18 53.3	12 59.7	14 7.8	20 48.4
10	11 8 45.4	4 22.5	0 16.7	9N30.0	15 9.9	1 34.7	13 9.8	13 24.2	18 49.0	13 2.2	14 7.0	20 50.2
13	11 20 35.0	3 11.8	0 16.7	18 37.5	14 10.6	0 2.5	12 20.6	13 10.5	18 44.8	13 4.6	14 6.1	20 51.9
16	11 32 24.7	2 .9	0 16.8	18 57.4	12 59.4	1N29.8	11 30.3	12 56.7	18 40.7	13 6.9	14 5.2	20 53.5
19	11 44 14.3	0 49.8	0 16.8	11 47.0	11 36.7	3 1.9	10 39.0	12 43.1	18 36.7	13 9.1	14 4.2	20 55.1
22	11 56 4.0	0N21.4	0 16.9	0 25.3	10 2.8	4 33.5	9 46.9	12 29.5	18 32.8	13 11.2	14 3.1	20 56.5
25	12 7 53.6	1 32.3	0 16.9	11S18.0	8 17.9	6 4.2	8 53.9	12 16.0	18 29.1	13 13.2	14 1.9	20 57.8
28	12 19 43.3	2 42.9	0 17.0	19 4.1	6 22.5	7 33.7	8 .3	12 2.6	18 25.5	13 15.1	14 .7	20 59.0
31	12 31 33.0	3 53.0	0 17.0	18 17.8	4 16.8	9 1.6	7 6.0	11 49.4	18 22.0	13 16.8	13 59.5	21 .1

APRIL 1962

LONGITUDE

DAY	EPHEM. SID. TIME (h m s)	☉ (° ′)	☊ (° ′)	☽ (° ′)	☿ (° ′)	♀ (° ′)	♂ (° ′)	♃ (° ′)	♄ (° ′)	♅ (° ′)	♆ (° ′)	♇ (° ′)
1	12 35 29.5	10♈47.5	15♌14.8	17♒22.5	26♓13.5	26♈21.1	15♓25.7	1♓18.6	9♒22.4	26♌52.3	12♏56.3	8♍4.0
2	12 39 26.1	11 46.7	15 11.6	2♓ 1.5	28 .7	27 35.3	16 12.7	1 31.3	9 26.9	26R50.6	12R54.9	8R 2.7
3	12 43 22.6	12 45.8	15 8.4	16 58.1	29 49.2	28 49.4	16 59.6	1 43.8	9 31.3	26 49.0	12 53.6	8 1.5
4	12 47 19.2	13 45.0	15 5.3	2♈ 5.3	1♈39.2	0♉ 3.5	17 46.5	1 56.3	9 35.7	26 47.5	12 52.2	8 .3
5	12 51 15.7	14 44.1	15 2.1	17 13.6	3 30.6	1 17.6	18 33.4	2 8.8	9 40.0	26 46.0	12 50.8	7 59.1
6	12 55 12.3	15 43.2	14 58.9	2♉13.0	5 23.5	2 31.6	19 20.3	2 21.1	9 44.2	26 44.5	12 49.4	7 57.9
7	12 59 8.8	16 42.2	14 55.7	16 54.2	7 17.7	3 45.6	20 7.1	2 33.4	9 48.4	26 43.1	12 48.0	7 56.7
8	13 3 5.4	17 41.3	14 52.6	1♊10.2	9 13.4	4 59.6	20 54.0	2 45.6	9 52.4	26 41.7	12 46.6	7 55.6
9	13 7 1.9	18 40.2	14 49.4	14 57.4	11 10.4	6 13.5	21 40.8	2 57.7	9 56.4	26 40.4	12 45.1	7 54.5
10	13 10 58.5	19 39.2	14 46.2	28 15.4	13 8.9	7 27.4	22 27.6	3 9.7	10 .3	26 39.1	12 43.7	7 53.4
11	13 14 55.0	20 38.1	14 43.0	11♋ 6.5	15 8.7	8 41.3	23 14.4	3 21.7	10 4.1	26 37.9	12 42.2	7 52.3
12	13 18 51.6	21 36.9	14 39.8	23 34.5	17 9.8	9 55.1	24 1.1	3 33.6	10 7.9	26 36.7	12 40.7	7 51.3
13	13 22 48.1	22 35.8	14 36.7	5♌44.5	19 12.1	11 9.0	24 47.8	3 45.4	10 11.5	26 35.6	12 39.2	7 50.3
14	13 26 44.7	23 34.5	14 33.5	17 41.9	21 15.6	12 22.7	25 34.5	3 57.1	10 15.1	26 34.5	12 37.7	7 49.3
15	13 30 41.2	24 33.3	14 30.3	29 31.8	23 20.2	13 36.5	26 21.2	4 8.7	10 18.6	26 33.4	12 36.2	7 48.3
16	13 34 37.8	25 32.0	14 27.1	11♍19.0	25 25.7	14 50.2	27 7.8	4 20.2	10 22.0	26 32.5	12 34.6	7 47.3
17	13 38 34.3	26 30.7	14 24.0	23 7.6	27 31.9	16 3.8	27 54.4	4 31.7	10 25.3	26 31.5	12 33.1	7 46.4
18	13 42 30.9	27 29.3	14 20.8	5♎ .8	29 38.8	17 17.5	28 41.0	4 43.0	10 28.5	26 30.6	12 31.5	7 45.5
19	13 46 27.4	28 27.9	14 17.6	17 1.1	1♉46.1	18 31.1	29 27.6	4 54.3	10 31.7	26 29.8	12 29.9	7 44.6
20	13 50 24.0	29 26.5	14 14.4	29 10.3	3 53.6	19 44.7	0♈14.2	5 5.5	10 34.8	26 29.1	12 28.4	7 43.8
21	13 54 20.6	0♉25.1	14 11.2	11♏29.3	6 1.0	20 58.2	1 .7	5 16.6	10 37.8	26 28.3	12 26.8	7 43.0
22	13 58 17.1	1 23.6	14 8.1	23 58.6	8 8.0	22 11.7	1 47.2	5 27.6	10 40.7	26 27.6	12 25.2	7 42.2
23	14 2 13.7	2 22.1	14 4.9	6♐38.6	10 14.3	23 25.2	2 33.6	5 38.4	10 43.5	26 27.0	12 23.6	7 41.4
24	14 6 10.2	3 20.5	14 1.7	19 29.8	12 19.7	24 38.6	3 20.1	5 49.2	10 46.2	26 26.4	12 22.0	7 40.7
25	14 10 6.8	4 18.9	13 58.5	2♑33.2	14 23.8	25 52.0	4 6.5	5 59.9	10 48.8	26 25.9	12 20.4	7 40.0
26	14 14 3.3	5 17.3	13 55.4	15 49.7	16 26.3	27 5.3	4 52.8	6 10.5	10 51.3	26 25.4	12 18.8	7 39.3
27	14 17 59.9	6 15.7	13 52.2	29 21.1	18 26.8	28 18.7	5 39.2	6 20.9	10 53.8	26 25.0	12 17.2	7 38.6
28	14 21 56.4	7 14.1	13 49.0	13♒ 8.6	20 25.2	29 32.0	6 25.5	6 31.3	10 56.1	26 24.7	12 15.5	7 38.0
29	14 25 53.0	8 12.4	13 45.8	27 13.4	22 21.0	0♊45.2	7 11.7	6 41.6	10 58.4	26 24.3	12 13.9	7 37.3
30	14 29 49.5	9 10.7	13 42.6	11♓35.1	24 14.1	1 58.4	7 58.0	6 51.7	11 .5	26 24.1	12 12.3	7 36.8

LATITUDE

DAY	EPHEM. SID. TIME	☉	☊	☽	☿	♀	♂	♃	♄	♅	♆	♇
1	12 35 29.5	0 .0	0 .0	0S 3.9	2S13.7	0S42.6	1S 8.5	0S47.5	0S27.3	0N46.7	1N49.5	13N29.3
4	12 47 19.2	0 .0	0 .0	3 38.6	2 4.0	0 36.0	1 8.4	0 48.0	0 27.6	0 46.6	1 49.6	13 28.8
7	12 59 8.8	0 .0	0 .0	5 4.6	1 49.7	0 29.0	1 8.1	0 48.5	0 28.0	0 46.5	1 49.6	13 28.2
10	13 10 58.5	0 .0	0 .0	3 45.2	1 30.8	0 21.8	1 7.8	0 49.0	0 28.3	0 46.4	1 49.7	13 27.6
13	13 22 48.1	0 .0	0 .0	0 52.9	1 7.6	0 14.3	1 7.5	0 49.5	0 28.7	0 46.3	1 49.8	13 27.0
16	13 34 37.8	0 .0	0 .0	2N11.9	0 40.3	0 6.6	1 7.1	0 50.1	0 29.0	0 46.2	1 49.9	13 26.3
19	13 46 27.4	0 .0	0 .0	4 25.9	0 9.9	0N 1.2	1 6.6	0 50.6	0 29.4	0 46.1	1 49.9	13 25.5
22	13 58 17.1	0 .0	0 .0	4 56.9	0N22.3	0 9.1	1 6.0	0 51.2	0 29.8	0 46.0	1 50.0	13 24.7
25	14 10 6.8	0 .0	0 .0	3 20.8	0 54.6	0 17.1	1 5.3	0 51.8	0 30.1	0 45.9	1 50.0	13 23.9
28	14 21 56.4	0 .0	0 .0	0 4.9	1 24.8	0 25.1	1 4.6	0 52.4	0 30.5	0 45.8	1 50.0	13 23.1

RIGHT ASCENSION

DAY	EPHEM. SID. TIME	☉	☊	☽	☿	♀	♂	♃	♄	♅	♆	♇
1	12 35 29.5	9♈55.1	17♌42.6	19♒50.6	27♓25.3	24♈42.1	17♓ 1.9	3♓37.7	11♒56.3	29♌21.7	11♏ 3.3	15♍ 4.4
2	12 39 26.1	10 49.8	17 39.5	4♓31.1	29 2.6	25 51.5	17 45.4	3 49.8	12 .9	29R20.1	11R 2.1	15R 3.1
3	12 43 22.6	11 44.5	17 36.3	19 1.6	0♈41.0	27 1.1	18 28.9	4 1.8	12 5.4	29 18.6	11 .7	15 1.9
4	12 47 19.2	12 39.2	17 33.1	3♈21.9	2 20.3	28 10.8	19 12.3	4 13.8	12 9.9	29 17.1	10 59.4	15 .6
5	12 51 15.7	13 34.0	17 30.0	17 34.9	4 .8	29 20.7	19 55.6	4 25.7	12 14.3	29 15.6	10 58.1	14 59.4
6	12 55 12.3	14 28.8	17 26.8	1♉44.7	5 42.4	0♉30.9	20 38.9	4 37.5	12 18.6	29 14.2	10 56.7	14 58.2
7	12 59 8.8	15 23.6	17 23.6	15 54.6	7 25.3	1 41.2	21 22.1	4 49.2	12 22.8	29 12.8	10 55.3	14 57.0
8	13 3 5.4	16 18.5	17 20.5	0♊ 4.7	9 9.3	2 51.8	22 5.3	5 .9	12 27.0	29 11.5	10 53.9	14 55.9
9	13 7 1.9	17 13.5	17 17.3	14 11.7	10 54.6	4 2.5	22 48.4	5 12.5	12 31.1	29 10.2	10 52.5	14 54.7
10	13 10 58.5	18 8.5	17 14.1	28 9.2	12 41.2	5 13.5	23 31.4	5 24.0	12 35.0	29 8.9	10 51.1	14 53.6
11	13 14 55.0	19 3.5	17 11.0	11♋49.3	14 29.1	6 24.7	24 14.4	5 35.4	12 39.0	29 7.7	10 49.6	14 52.5
12	13 18 51.6	19 58.7	17 7.8	25 5.3	16 18.4	7 36.1	24 57.4	5 46.7	12 42.8	29 6.6	10 48.2	14 51.4
13	13 22 48.1	20 53.9	17 4.6	7♌53.1	18 9.0	8 47.8	25 40.3	5 58.0	12 46.5	29 5.5	10 46.7	14 50.3
14	13 26 44.7	21 49.2	17 1.5	20 11.9	20 .9	9 59.7	26 23.1	6 9.2	12 50.2	29 4.4	10 45.2	14 49.3
15	13 30 41.2	22 44.5	16 58.3	2♍ 4.7	21 54.3	11 11.9	27 5.9	6 20.2	12 53.7	29 3.4	10 43.7	14 48.2
16	13 34 37.8	23 40.0	16 55.1	13 36.6	23 48.9	12 24.3	27 48.7	6 31.2	12 57.2	29 2.4	10 42.2	14 47.2
17	13 38 34.3	24 35.5	16 51.9	24 54.8	25 44.7	13 37.0	28 31.4	6 42.1	13 .6	29 1.5	10 40.7	14 46.2
18	13 42 30.9	25 31.1	16 48.8	6♎ 7.4	27 41.7	14 50.0	29 14.1	6 53.0	13 3.9	29 .6	10 39.2	14 45.2
19	13 46 27.4	26 26.8	16 45.6	17 23.0	29 39.7	16 3.2	29 56.8	7 3.7	13 7.2	28 59.8	10 37.6	14 44.3
20	13 50 24.0	27 22.7	16 42.4	28 50.4	1♉38.6	17 16.7	0♈39.4	7 14.4	13 10.3	28 59.1	10 36.1	14 43.4
21	13 54 20.6	28 18.6	16 39.3	10♏37.5	3 38.2	18 30.4	1 22.0	7 24.9	13 13.4	28 58.4	10 34.6	14 42.5
22	13 58 17.1	29 14.6	16 36.1	22 51.5	5 38.3	19 44.4	2 4.6	7 35.4	13 16.4	28 57.7	10 33.0	14 41.6
23	14 2 13.7	0♉10.7	16 32.9	5♐36.9	7 38.7	20 58.7	2 47.1	7 45.7	13 19.2	28 57.1	10 31.4	14 40.8
24	14 6 10.2	1 7.0	16 29.7	18 55.1	9 39.1	22 13.3	3 29.6	7 56.0	13 22.0	28 56.5	10 29.9	14 40.0
25	14 10 6.8	2 3.3	16 26.6	2♑42.8	11 39.2	23 28.1	4 12.1	8 6.1	13 24.7	28 56.0	10 28.3	14 39.1
26	14 14 3.3	2 59.8	16 23.4	16 52.4	13 38.7	24 43.2	4 54.6	8 16.2	13 27.3	28 55.5	10 26.7	14 38.4
27	14 17 59.9	3 56.4	16 20.2	1♒13.4	15 37.3	25 58.5	5 37.0	8 26.1	13 29.8	28 55.1	10 25.1	14 37.6
28	14 21 56.4	4 53.2	16 17.0	15 35.2	17 34.8	27 14.2	6 19.5	8 36.0	13 32.2	28 54.7	10 23.5	14 36.9
29	14 25 53.0	5 50.1	16 13.8	29 50.0	19 30.8	28 30.1	7 1.9	8 45.8	13 34.5	28 54.4	10 21.9	14 36.2
30	14 29 49.5	6 47.1	16 10.7	13♓54.8	21 24.9	29 46.2	7 44.3	8 55.4	13 36.7	28 54.2	10 20.3	14 35.5

DECLINATION

DAY	EPHEM. SID. TIME	☉	☊	☽	☿	♀	♂	♃	♄	♅	♆	♇
1	12 35 29.5	4N16.3	0N17.0	15S41.4	3S32.7	9N30.6	6S47.8	11S45.0	18S20.9	13N17.3	13S59.1	21N .5
4	12 47 19.2	5 25.5	0 17.1	2 30.8	1 14.3	10 56.0	5 52.9	11 32.0	18 17.7	13 18.9	13 57.8	21 1.4
7	12 59 8.8	6 34.0	0 17.1	12N .9	1N13.0	12 19.1	4 57.5	11 19.1	18 14.7	13 20.3	13 56.4	21 2.3
10	13 10 58.5	7 41.3	0 17.2	19 40.6	3 47.8	13 39.5	4 1.9	11 6.5	18 11.8	13 21.6	13 55.0	21 3.0
13	13 22 48.1	8 47.6	0 17.2	17 59.0	6 28.6	14 57.0	3 6.0	10 54.1	18 9.1	13 22.7	13 53.6	21 3.6
16	13 34 37.8	9 52.4	0 17.3	9 21.3	9 12.6	16 11.1	2 10.0	10 41.9	18 6.6	13 23.7	13 52.2	21 4.1
19	13 46 27.4	10 55.8	0 17.3	2S35.5	11 56.1	17 21.5	1 13.9	10 29.9	18 4.3	13 24.5	13 50.7	21 4.4
22	13 58 17.1	11 57.6	0 17.4	13 58.2	14 34.4	18 28.0	0 17.9	10 18.3	18 2.3	13 25.1	13 49.2	21 4.7
25	14 10 6.8	12 57.6	0 17.4	20 4.3	17 1.8	19 30.2	0N38.0	10 6.9	18 .4	13 25.6	13 47.7	21 4.8
28	14 21 56.4	13 55.7	0 17.5	16 47.7	19 13.0	20 27.7	1 33.7	9 55.9	17 58.8	13 25.9	13 46.2	21 4.8

MAY 1962

LONGITUDE

DAY	EPHEM. SID. TIME h m s	☉ ° ′	☊ ° ′	☽ ° ′	☿ ° ′	♀ ° ′	♂ ° ′	♃ ° ′	♄ ° ′	♅ ° ′	♆ ° ′	♇ ° ′
1	14 33 46.1	10♉ 8.9	13♌39.5	26♓11.4	26♉ 4.3	3♊11.6	8♈44.2	7♓ 1.8	11♒ 2.6	26♌23.9	12♏10.6	7♍36.2
2	14 37 42.6	11 7.2	13 36.3	10♈57.8	27 51.2	4 24.8	9 30.4	7 11.7	11 4.6	26 R 23.7	12 R 9.0	7 R 35.7
3	14 41 39.2	12 5.4	13 33.1	25 47.5	29 34.9	5 37.9	10 16.5	7 21.5	11 6.5	26 23.6	12 7.4	7 35.2
4	14 45 35.8	13 3.6	13 29.9	10♉32.3	1♊15.0	6 51.0	11 2.6	7 31.2	11 8.2	26 23.6	12 5.7	7 34.7
5	14 49 32.3	14 1.8	13 26.8	25 3.8	2 51.5	8 4.1	11 48.6	7 40.8	11 9.9	26 23.6	12 4.1	7 34.2
6	14 53 28.9	14 59.9	13 23.6	9♊14.9	4 24.3	9 17.1	12 34.7	7 50.2	11 11.5	26 D 23.7	12 2.4	7 33.8
7	14 57 25.4	15 58.0	13 20.4	23 1.2	5 53.2	10 30.1	13 20.6	7 59.6	11 13.0	26 23.8	12 .8	7 33.5
8	15 1 22.0	16 56.1	13 17.2	6♋20.7	7 18.2	11 43.0	14 6.6	8 8.8	11 14.4	26 24.0	11 59.2	7 33.1
9	15 5 18.5	17 54.1	13 14.0	19 14.3	8 39.2	12 55.9	14 52.5	8 17.9	11 15.7	26 24.2	11 57.6	7 32.8
10	15 9 15.1	18 52.1	13 10.9	1♌45.1	9 56.1	14 8.8	15 38.3	8 26.8	11 16.9	26 24.5	11 55.9	7 32.5
11	15 13 11.6	19 50.1	13 7.7	13 57.5	11 8.9	15 21.7	16 24.2	8 35.7	11 18.1	26 24.8	11 54.4	7 32.3
12	15 17 8.2	20 48.1	13 4.5	25 56.5	12 17.5	16 34.5	17 9.9	8 44.4	11 19.1	26 25.2	11 52.7	7 32.0
13	15 21 4.7	21 46.0	13 1.3	7♍47.8	13 21.8	17 47.2	17 55.6	8 53.0	11 20.0	26 25.7	11 51.1	7 31.8
14	15 25 1.3	22 43.9	12 58.2	19 36.5	14 21.8	18 59.9	18 41.3	9 1.4	11 20.8	26 26.2	11 49.5	7 31.6
15	15 28 57.9	23 41.8	12 55.0	1♎27.6	15 17.4	20 12.5	19 26.9	9 9.8	11 21.5	26 26.7	11 47.9	7 31.5
16	15 32 54.4	24 39.6	12 51.8	13 25.2	16 8.6	21 25.2	20 12.5	9 17.9	11 22.2	26 27.3	11 46.3	7 31.4
17	15 36 51.0	25 37.4	12 48.6	25 32.7	16 55.2	22 37.7	20 58.1	9 26.0	11 22.7	26 28.0	11 44.8	7 31.3
18	15 40 47.5	26 35.2	12 45.5	7♏52.2	17 37.3	23 50.2	21 43.5	9 33.9	11 23.1	26 28.7	11 43.2	7 31.2
19	15 44 44.1	27 32.9	12 42.3	20 24.9	18 14.7	25 2.7	22 29.0	9 41.6	11 23.4	26 29.5	11 41.6	7 31.2
20	15 48 40.6	28 30.7	12 39.1	3♐11.2	18 47.4	26 15.2	23 14.4	9 49.2	11 23.7	26 30.3	11 40.1	7 31.2
21	15 52 37.2	29 28.4	12 35.9	16 10.6	19 15.4	27 27.5	23 59.7	9 56.7	11 23.8	26 31.1	11 38.5	7 D 31.3
22	15 56 33.7	0♊26.1	12 32.7	29 22.0	19 38.6	28 39.9	24 45.0	10 4.1	11 23.8	26 32.1	11 37.0	7 31.3
23	16 0 30.3	1 23.7	12 29.6	12♑44.6	19 57.0	29 52.2	25 30.3	10 11.2	11 23.8	26 33.0	11 35.5	7 31.4
24	16 4 26.9	2 21.4	12 26.4	26 17.4	20 10.5	1♋ 4.4	26 15.5	10 18.3	11 R 23.6	26 34.0	11 34.0	7 31.6
25	16 8 23.4	3 19.0	12 23.2	10♒ .2	20 19.4	2 16.7	27 .7	10 25.2	11 23.4	26 35.1	11 32.5	7 31.7
26	16 12 20.0	4 16.6	12 20.0	23 52.7	20 23.4	3 28.8	27 45.8	10 31.9	11 23.0	26 36.2	11 31.0	7 31.9
27	16 16 16.5	5 14.2	12 16.9	7♓54.9	20 R 22.9	4 40.9	28 30.9	10 38.5	11 22.6	26 37.4	11 29.5	7 32.1
28	16 20 13.1	6 11.8	12 13.7	22 6.3	20 17.8	5 53.0	29 15.9	10 44.9	11 22.0	26 38.7	11 28.1	7 32.4
29	16 24 9.6	7 9.4	12 10.5	6♈25.3	20 8.4	7 5.1	0♉ .9	10 51.2	11 21.4	26 39.9	11 26.6	7 32.7
30	16 28 6.2	8 6.9	12 7.3	20 49.2	19 54.8	8 17.1	0 45.8	10 57.3	11 20.6	26 41.3	11 25.2	7 33.0
31	16 32 2.8	9 4.5	12 4.1	5♉13.6	19 37.3	9 29.0	1 30.7	11 3.3	11 19.8	26 42.6	11 23.8	7 33.3

LATITUDE

DAY	EPHEM. SID. TIME	☉	☊	☽	☿	♀	♂	♃	♄	♅	♆	♇
1	14 33 46.1	0 .0	0 .0	3S22.9	1N51.0	0N33.0	1S 3.9	0S53.0	0S30.9	0N45.7	1N50.0	13N22.2
4	14 45 35.8	0 .0	0 .0	5 .1	2 11.4	0 40.8	1 3.0	0 53.7	0 31.3	0 45.6	1 50.0	13 21.3
7	14 57 25.4	0 .0	0 .0	3 51.0	2 24.8	0 48.5	1 2.1	0 54.3	0 31.7	0 45.4	1 50.0	13 20.4
10	15 9 15.1	0 .0	0 .0	0 58.1	2 30.5	0 56.0	1 1.1	0 55.0	0 32.1	0 45.3	1 50.0	13 19.4
13	15 21 4.7	0 .0	0 .0	2N 8.4	2 27.8	1 3.3	1 .1	0 55.7	0 32.5	0 45.2	1 50.0	13 18.4
16	15 32 54.4	0 .0	0 .0	4 23.8	2 16.4	1 10.3	0 58.9	0 56.4	0 32.9	0 45.1	1 50.0	13 17.4
19	15 44 44.1	0 .0	0 .0	4 57.8	1 56.0	1 16.9	0 57.8	0 57.2	0 33.3	0 45.0	1 49.9	13 16.4
22	15 56 33.7	0 .0	0 .0	3 22.9	1 26.7	1 23.2	0 56.5	0 57.9	0 33.7	0 44.9	1 49.9	13 15.4
25	16 8 23.4	0 .0	0 .0	0 6.7	0 49.0	1 29.0	0 55.2	0 58.7	0 34.1	0 44.7	1 49.8	13 14.4
28	16 20 13.1	0 .0	0 .0	3S19.5	0 4.1	1 34.3	0 53.8	0 59.5	0 34.5	0 44.6	1 49.7	13 13.4
31	16 32 2.8	0 .0	0 .0	5 2.4	0S46.0	1 39.1	0 52.4	1 .3	0 34.9	0 44.5	1 49.6	13 12.4

RIGHT ASCENSION

DAY	EPHEM. SID. TIME	☉	☊	☽	☿	♀	♂	♃	♄	♅	♆	♇
1	14 33 46.1	7♉44.2	16♌ 7.5	27♓51.0	23♉17.0	1♊ 2.6	8♈26.7	9♓ 4.9	13♒38.9	28♌53.9	10♏18.7	14♍34.8
2	14 37 42.6	8 41.5	16 4.3	11♈43.7	25 6.8	2 19.3	9 9.1	9 14.4	13 40.9	28 R 53.8	10 R 17.1	14 R 34.2
3	14 41 39.2	9 38.9	16 1.1	25 39.1	26 53.9	3 36.2	9 51.4	9 23.7	13 42.8	28 53.7	10 15.5	14 33.6
4	14 45 35.8	10 36.5	15 58.0	9♉42.5	28 38.3	4 53.4	10 33.8	9 32.9	13 44.7	28 53.6	10 13.9	14 33.0
5	14 49 32.3	11 34.2	15 54.8	23 55.9	0♊19.5	6 10.8	11 16.2	9 42.0	13 46.4	28 53.6	10 12.3	14 32.4
6	14 53 28.9	12 32.0	15 51.6	8♊16.6	1 57.5	7 28.4	11 58.5	9 51.0	13 48.1	28 D 53.7	10 10.7	14 31.9
7	14 57 25.4	13 30.0	15 48.4	22 36.8	3 32.0	8 46.2	12 40.8	9 59.8	13 49.6	28 53.8	10 9.1	14 31.4
8	15 1 22.0	14 28.1	15 45.2	6♋45.4	5 2.9	10 4.3	13 23.2	10 8.6	13 51.1	28 53.9	10 7.5	14 30.9
9	15 5 18.5	15 26.3	15 42.0	20 31.3	6 30.0	11 22.5	14 5.5	10 17.2	13 52.4	28 54.1	10 5.9	14 30.5
10	15 9 15.1	16 24.7	15 38.9	3♌46.4	7 53.2	12 40.9	14 47.9	10 25.7	13 53.7	28 54.4	10 4.3	14 30.1
11	15 13 11.6	17 23.3	15 35.7	16 27.4	9 12.3	13 59.5	15 30.2	10 34.1	13 54.9	28 54.7	10 2.8	14 29.7
12	15 17 8.2	18 22.0	15 32.5	28 35.7	10 27.1	15 18.3	16 12.6	10 42.4	13 55.9	28 55.1	10 1.2	14 29.4
13	15 21 4.7	19 20.8	15 29.3	10♍16.9	11 37.6	16 37.2	16 54.9	10 50.5	13 56.9	28 55.5	9 59.6	14 29.0
14	15 25 1.3	20 19.7	15 26.1	21 38.8	12 43.5	17 56.2	17 37.3	10 58.5	13 57.8	28 56.0	9 58.0	14 28.7
15	15 28 57.9	21 18.8	15 22.9	2♎51.0	13 44.9	19 15.4	18 19.7	11 6.4	13 58.5	28 56.5	9 56.5	14 28.4
16	15 32 54.4	22 18.0	15 19.8	14 3.3	14 41.5	20 34.6	19 2.0	11 14.2	13 59.2	28 57.1	9 54.9	14 28.2
17	15 36 51.0	23 17.4	15 16.6	25 26.1	15 33.3	21 54.0	19 44.4	11 21.8	13 59.8	28 57.7	9 53.4	14 28.0
18	15 40 47.5	24 16.9	15 13.4	7♏ 8.8	16 20.2	23 13.5	20 26.8	11 29.3	14 .2	28 58.4	9 51.8	14 27.8
19	15 44 44.1	25 16.5	15 10.2	19 19.8	17 2.0	24 33.0	21 9.2	11 36.7	14 .6	28 59.1	9 50.3	14 27.6
20	15 48 40.6	26 16.3	15 7.0	2♐ 5.1	17 38.7	25 52.5	21 51.6	11 43.9	14 .9	28 59.9	9 48.8	14 27.5
21	15 52 37.2	27 16.2	15 3.8	15 26.2	18 10.3	27 12.1	22 34.1	11 51.0	14 1.1	29 .7	9 47.2	14 27.4
22	15 56 33.7	28 16.2	15 .6	29 19.6	18 36.6	28 31.8	23 16.6	11 58.0	14 1.1	29 1.6	9 45.7	14 27.3
23	16 0 30.3	29 16.4	14 57.4	13♑36.0	18 57.7	29 51.4	23 59.1	12 4.8	14 1.1	29 2.5	9 44.2	14 27.2
24	16 4 26.9	0♊16.7	14 54.3	28 2.3	19 13.6	1♋11.0	24 41.6	12 11.5	14 R 1.0	29 3.5	9 42.8	14 27.2
25	16 8 23.4	1 17.2	14 51.1	12♒25.0	19 24.3	2 30.6	25 24.1	12 18.0	14 .8	29 4.5	9 41.3	14 27.2
26	16 12 20.0	2 17.8	14 47.9	26 34.5	19 29.9	3 50.2	26 6.7	12 24.4	14 .5	29 5.6	9 39.8	14 D 27.3
27	16 16 16.5	3 18.5	14 44.7	10♓26.9	19 30.5	5 9.7	26 49.3	12 30.7	14 .0	29 6.7	9 38.4	14 27.3
28	16 20 13.1	4 19.3	14 41.5	24 4.1	19 R 26.2	6 29.2	27 31.9	12 36.8	13 59.5	29 7.9	9 36.9	14 27.4
29	16 24 9.6	5 20.3	14 38.3	7♈32.7	19 17.3	7 48.5	28 14.5	12 42.8	13 58.9	29 9.1	9 35.5	14 27.6
30	16 28 6.2	6 21.3	14 35.1	21 1.2	19 4.0	9 7.8	28 57.2	12 48.6	13 58.2	29 10.3	9 34.1	14 27.7
31	16 32 2.8	7 22.5	14 31.9	4♉38.2	18 46.5	10 26.9	29 39.9	12 54.3	13 57.4	29 11.7	9 32.7	14 27.9

DECLINATION

DAY	EPHEM. SID. TIME	☉	☊	☽	☿	♀	♂	♃	♄	♅	♆	♇
1	14 33 46.1	14N51.8	0N17.5	4S37.1	21N 4.3	21N20.3	2N29.2	9S45.1	17S57.4	13N26.1	13S44.7	21N 4.6
4	14 45 35.8	15 45.6	0 17.6	10N13.8	22 33.4	22 7.6	3 24.2	9 34.8	17 56.2	13 26.1	13 43.3	21 4.4
7	14 57 25.4	16 37.2	0 17.6	19 24.8	23 40.1	22 49.5	4 18.9	9 24.8	17 55.2	13 25.9	13 41.8	21 4.0
10	15 9 15.1	17 26.2	0 17.7	18 49.7	24 25.4	23 25.7	5 13.0	9 15.2	17 54.5	13 25.5	13 40.3	21 3.5
13	15 21 4.7	18 12.6	0 17.7	10 37.9	24 51.0	23 55.9	6 6.5	9 6.1	17 54.1	13 25.0	13 38.9	21 2.8
16	15 32 54.4	18 56.2	0 17.8	1S14.8	24 58.9	24 20.0	6 59.3	8 57.3	17 53.9	13 24.3	13 37.4	21 2.1
19	15 44 44.1	19 36.9	0 17.8	13 3.9	24 50.8	24 37.8	7 51.4	8 49.1	17 53.9	13 23.5	13 36.0	21 1.2
22	15 56 33.7	20 14.7	0 17.8	20 3.5	24 28.7	24 49.3	8 42.7	8 41.3	17 54.2	13 22.5	13 34.7	21 .3
25	16 8 23.4	20 49.3	0 17.9	17 38.1	23 54.3	24 54.3	9 33.1	8 34.0	17 54.7	13 21.4	13 33.3	20 59.2
28	16 20 13.1	21 20.7	0 17.9	6 11.2	23 9.3	24 52.9	10 22.5	8 27.2	17 55.5	13 20.1	13 32.1	20 58.0
31	16 32 2.8	21 48.8	0 18.0	8N30.6	22 16.3	24 45.0	11 10.9	8 21.0	17 56.5	13 18.6	13 30.8	20 56.7

JUNE 1962

LONGITUDE

DAY	EPHEM. SID. TIME h m s	☉ ° ′	☊ ° ′	☽ ° ′	☿ ° ′	♀ ° ′	♂ ° ′	♃ ° ′	♄ ° ′	♅ ° ′	♆ ° ′	♇ ° ′
1	16 35 59.3	10♊ 2.1	12♌ 1.0	19♉33.2	19♊16.3	10♋41.0	2♉15.5	11♓ 9.1	11♒18.9	26♌44.1	11♏22.5	7♍33.7
2	16 39 55.9	10 59.6	11 57.8	3♊42.2	18 R 52.0	11 52.8	3 .3	11 14.8	11 R 17.9	26 45.6	11 R 21.1	7 34.1
3	16 43 52.4	11 57.1	11 54.6	17 35.3	18 24.9	13 4.6	3 45.0	11 20.2	11 16.8	26 47.1	11 19.7	7 34.6
4	16 47 49.0	12 54.6	11 51.4	1♋ 8.7	17 55.4	14 16.4	4 29.6	11 25.5	11 15.6	26 48.7	11 18.4	7 35.0
5	16 51 45.5	13 52.0	11 48.3	14 20.2	17 24.2	15 28.1	5 14.2	11 30.6	11 14.2	26 50.3	11 17.1	7 35.5
6	16 55 42.1	14 49.5	11 45.1	27 9.9	16 51.5	16 39.8	5 58.7	11 35.6	11 12.8	26 52.0	11 15.8	7 36.0
7	16 59 38.7	15 46.9	11 41.9	9♌39.5	16 18.2	17 51.4	6 43.2	11 40.4	11 11.3	26 53.7	11 14.5	7 36.6
8	17 3 35.2	16 44.3	11 38.7	21 52.4	15 44.6	19 2.9	7 27.6	11 45.0	11 9.8	26 55.5	11 13.2	7 37.2
9	17 7 31.8	17 41.7	11 35.6	3♍52.8	15 11.5	20 14.4	8 12.0	11 49.5	11 8.1	26 57.3	11 12.0	7 37.8
10	17 11 28.3	18 39.1	11 32.4	15 45.7	14 39.3	21 25.8	8 56.3	11 53.7	11 6.3	26 59.2	11 10.7	7 38.4
11	17 15 24.9	19 36.4	11 29.2	27 36.2	14 8.6	22 37.2	9 40.5	11 57.8	11 4.5	27 1.1	11 9.5	7 39.1
12	17 19 21.4	20 33.8	11 26.0	9♎29.4	13 40.0	23 48.5	10 24.7	12 1.7	11 2.5	27 3.0	11 8.4	7 39.8
13	17 23 18.0	21 31.1	11 22.9	21 30.2	13 13.8	24 59.8	11 8.8	12 5.5	11 .5	27 5.0	11 7.2	7 40.5
14	17 27 14.6	22 28.4	11 19.7	3♏42.5	12 50.6	26 11.0	11 52.8	12 9.0	10 58.4	27 7.1	11 6.1	7 41.3
15	17 31 11.1	23 25.7	11 16.5	16 9.5	12 30.8	27 22.1	12 36.8	12 12.4	10 56.2	27 9.2	11 5.0	7 42.0
16	17 35 7.7	24 23.0	11 13.3	28 53.4	12 14.6	28 33.2	13 20.8	12 15.6	10 53.9	27 11.3	11 3.9	7 42.8
17	17 39 4.2	25 20.2	11 10.1	11♐54.8	12 2.4	29 44.1	14 4.6	12 18.6	10 51.5	27 13.5	11 2.8	7 43.7
18	17 43 .8	26 17.5	11 7.0	25 13.2	11 54.3	0♌55.1	14 48.4	12 21.5	10 49.1	27 15.7	11 1.8	7 44.6
19	17 46 57.3	27 14.7	11 3.8	8♑47.1	11 50.6	2 5.9	15 32.2	12 24.1	10 46.5	27 17.9	11 .7	7 45.4
20	17 50 53.9	28 12.0	11 .6	22 33.9	11 D 51.4	3 16.7	16 15.9	12 26.6	10 43.9	27 20.2	10 59.8	7 46.4
21	17 54 50.5	29 9.2	10 57.4	6♒30.8	11 56.9	4 27.5	16 59.5	12 28.9	10 41.2	27 22.6	10 58.8	7 47.3
22	17 58 47.0	0♋ 6.5	10 54.3	20 35.0	12 7.0	5 38.2	17 43.1	12 31.0	10 38.5	27 25.0	10 57.9	7 48.3
23	18 2 43.6	1 3.7	10 51.1	4♓43.9	12 21.8	6 48.8	18 26.6	12 32.9	10 35.7	27 27.4	10 57.0	7 49.3
24	18 6 40.1	2 1.0	10 47.9	18 55.3	12 41.3	7 59.3	19 10.0	12 34.6	10 32.8	27 29.9	10 56.1	7 50.4
25	18 10 36.7	2 58.2	10 44.7	3♈ 7.2	13 5.5	9 9.8	19 53.4	12 36.1	10 29.8	27 32.4	10 55.2	7 51.4
26	18 14 33.2	3 55.4	10 41.6	17 17.9	13 34.4	10 20.1	20 36.7	12 37.5	10 26.7	27 34.9	10 54.4	7 52.5
27	18 18 29.8	4 52.6	10 38.4	1♉25.2	14 7.9	11 30.5	21 20.0	12 38.6	10 23.6	27 37.5	10 53.6	7 53.6
28	18 22 26.4	5 49.9	10 35.2	15 26.8	14 46.0	12 40.7	22 3.2	12 39.5	10 20.4	27 40.1	10 52.8	7 54.8
29	18 26 22.9	6 47.1	10 32.0	29 19.9	15 28.5	13 50.9	22 46.3	12 40.3	10 17.1	27 42.8	10 52.1	7 55.9
30	18 30 19.5	7 44.3	10 28.8	13♊ 1.7	16 15.6	15 1.0	23 29.4	12 40.8	10 13.7	27 45.5	10 51.3	7 57.1

LATITUDE

DAY	EPHEM. SID. TIME	☉	☊	☽	☿	♀	♂	♃	♄	♅	♆	♇
1	16 35 59.3	0 .0	0 .0	5S .5	1S 3.3	1N40.6	0S51.9	1S .5	0S35.1	0N44.5	1N49.6	13N12.1
4	16 47 49.0	0 .0	0 .0	3 13.5	1 55.4	1 44.5	0 50.4	1 1.3	0 35.5	0 44.4	1 49.5	13 11.1
7	16 59 38.7	0 .0	0 .0	0 3.2	2 44.2	1 48.1	0 48.8	1 2.2	0 35.9	0 44.3	1 49.4	13 10.1
10	17 11 28.3	0 .0	0 .0	2N59.2	3 25.8	1 50.8	0 47.2	1 3.0	0 36.3	0 44.2	1 49.3	13 9.1
13	17 23 18.0	0 .0	0 .0	4 51.8	3 57.1	1 52.9	0 45.5	1 3.9	0 36.7	0 44.1	1 49.2	13 8.1
16	17 35 7.7	0 .0	0 .0	4 51.2	4 16.5	1 54.3	0 43.8	1 4.7	0 37.1	0 44.0	1 49.1	13 7.2
19	17 46 57.3	0 .0	0 .0	2 38.4	4 23.8	1 54.8	0 42.0	1 5.6	0 37.5	0 43.9	1 48.9	13 6.2
22	17 58 47.0	0 .0	0 .0	1S .2	4 19.9	1 54.7	0 40.1	1 6.5	0 37.9	0 43.8	1 48.8	13 5.3
25	18 10 36.7	0 .0	0 .0	4 11.2	4 6.2	1 53.7	0 38.2	1 7.4	0 38.3	0 43.7	1 48.6	13 4.4
28	18 22 26.4	0 .0	0 .0	5 9.9	3 44.4	1 51.8	0 36.3	1 8.3	0 38.6	0 43.6	1 48.5	13 3.6

RIGHT ASCENSION

DAY	EPHEM. SID. TIME	☉	☊	☽	☿	♀	♂	♃	♄	♅	♆	♇
1	16 35 59.3	8♊23.9	14♌28.7	18♉29.5	18♊25.4	11♋46.0	0♉22.7	12♓59.8	13♒56.6	29♌13.1	9♏31.4	14♍28.2
2	16 39 55.9	9 25.3	14 25.5	2♊36.5	18 R .8	13 4.9	1 5.4	13 5.2	13 R 55.6	29 14.5	9 R 30.1	14 28.4
3	16 43 52.4	10 26.8	14 22.3	16 54.5	17 33.4	14 23.6	1 48.2	13 10.4	13 54.5	29 16.0	9 28.7	14 28.7
4	16 47 49.0	11 28.4	14 19.1	1♋13.1	17 3.6	15 42.1	2 31.0	13 15.5	13 53.3	29 17.5	9 27.4	14 29.0
5	16 51 45.5	12 30.1	14 15.9	15 18.7	16 31.9	17 .4	3 13.8	13 20.4	13 52.0	29 19.0	9 26.1	14 29.3
6	16 55 42.1	13 31.8	14 12.7	28 58.8	15 58.9	18 18.5	3 56.7	13 25.1	13 50.6	29 20.6	9 24.8	14 29.7
7	16 59 38.7	14 33.7	14 9.6	12♌ 5.1	15 25.2	19 36.4	4 39.6	13 29.7	13 49.1	29 22.3	9 23.5	14 30.1
8	17 3 35.2	15 35.6	14 6.4	24 35.4	14 51.4	20 54.1	5 22.5	13 34.1	13 47.6	29 24.0	9 22.3	14 30.5
9	17 7 31.8	16 37.6	14 3.2	6♍32.6	14 18.0	22 11.5	6 5.5	13 38.3	13 45.9	29 25.7	9 21.1	14 30.9
10	17 11 28.3	17 39.6	13 60.0	18 3.8	13 45.7	23 28.7	6 48.5	13 42.4	13 44.2	29 27.5	9 19.9	14 31.4
11	17 15 24.9	18 41.7	13 56.8	29 18.4	13 14.9	24 45.5	7 31.5	13 46.4	13 42.3	29 29.3	9 18.7	14 31.9
12	17 19 21.4	19 43.9	13 53.6	10♎27.3	12 46.2	26 2.1	8 14.6	13 50.1	13 40.4	29 31.2	9 17.5	14 32.4
13	17 23 18.0	20 46.1	13 50.4	21 41.7	12 20.1	27 18.4	8 57.7	13 53.7	13 38.4	29 33.1	9 16.4	14 33.0
14	17 27 14.6	21 48.3	13 47.2	3♏12.8	11 56.9	28 34.4	9 40.8	13 57.2	13 36.3	29 35.1	9 15.2	14 33.6
15	17 31 11.1	22 50.6	13 44.0	15 11.3	11 37.0	29 50.0	10 23.9	14 .4	13 34.1	29 37.1	9 14.1	14 34.2
16	17 35 7.7	23 52.9	13 40.8	27 45.7	11 20.9	1♌ 5.4	11 7.1	14 3.5	13 31.8	29 39.1	9 13.1	14 34.8
17	17 39 4.2	24 55.2	13 37.6	11♐ .9	11 8.6	2 20.4	11 50.3	14 6.5	13 29.5	29 41.2	9 12.0	14 35.5
18	17 43 .8	25 57.5	13 34.4	24 55.9	11 .6	3 35.1	12 33.6	14 9.2	13 27.0	29 43.3	9 11.0	14 36.2
19	17 46 57.3	26 59.9	13 31.2	9♑22.5	10 56.9	4 49.4	13 16.9	14 11.8	13 24.5	29 45.5	9 10.0	14 36.9
20	17 50 53.9	28 2.3	13 28.0	24 6.2	10 D 57.8	6 3.3	14 .2	14 14.2	13 21.9	29 47.7	9 9.0	14 37.7
21	17 54 50.5	29 4.7	13 24.7	8♒49.8	11 3.2	7 16.9	14 43.6	14 16.4	13 19.2	29 50.0	9 8.0	14 38.5
22	17 58 47.0	0♋ 7.1	13 21.5	23 18.7	11 13.4	8 30.2	15 27.0	14 18.5	13 16.5	29 52.3	9 7.1	14 39.3
23	18 2 43.6	1 9.5	13 18.3	7♓24.7	11 28.3	9 43.1	16 10.4	14 20.4	13 13.7	29 54.6	9 6.2	14 40.2
24	18 6 40.1	2 11.8	13 15.1	21 7.2	11 48.0	10 55.6	16 53.9	14 22.1	13 10.7	29 57.0	9 5.4	14 41.0
25	18 10 36.7	3 14.2	13 11.9	4♈31.6	12 12.5	12 7.8	17 37.4	14 23.7	13 7.7	29 59.4	9 4.5	14 41.9
26	18 14 33.2	4 16.5	13 8.7	17 47.2	12 41.8	13 19.5	18 20.9	14 25.0	13 4.7	0♍ 1.8	9 3.7	14 42.8
27	18 18 29.8	5 18.8	13 5.5	1♉ 3.9	13 16.0	14 30.9	19 4.4	14 26.2	13 1.5	0 4.3	9 2.9	14 43.8
28	18 22 26.4	6 21.1	13 2.3	14 30.7	13 54.9	15 41.9	19 48.0	14 27.2	12 58.3	0 6.8	9 2.1	14 44.7
29	18 26 22.9	7 23.3	12 59.1	28 12.8	14 38.5	16 52.6	20 31.6	14 28.0	12 55.0	0 9.3	9 1.3	14 45.7
30	18 30 19.5	8 25.5	12 55.9	12♊10.3	15 27.0	18 2.8	21 15.3	14 28.6	12 51.7	0 11.9	9 .6	14 46.7

DECLINATION

DAY	EPHEM. SID. TIME	☉	☊	☽	☿	♀	♂	♃	♄	♅	♆	♇
1	16 35 59.3	21N57.4	0N18.0	12N47.9	21N57.4	24N41.0	11N26.8	8S19.0	17S56.9	13N18.0	13S30.5	20N56.3
4	16 47 49.0	22 21.0	0 18.0	20 12.8	20 58.7	24 24.7	12 13.7	8 13.5	17 58.2	13 16.4	13 29.3	20 54.9
7	16 59 38.7	22 41.0	0 18.1	17 47.0	20 .9	24 2.2	12 59.5	8 8.6	17 59.7	13 14.6	13 28.2	20 53.3
10	17 11 28.3	22 57.5	0 18.1	8 22.1	19 9.1	23 33.6	13 44.0	8 4.3	18 1.5	13 12.6	13 27.1	20 51.7
13	17 23 18.0	23 10.3	0 18.2	3S52.2	18 28.0	22 59.1	14 27.2	8 .6	18 3.5	13 10.5	13 26.2	20 50.0
16	17 35 7.7	23 19.4	0 18.2	15 10.4	18 1.4	22 19.0	15 9.1	7 57.6	18 5.7	13 8.2	13 25.3	20 48.3
19	17 46 57.3	23 24.8	0 18.3	20 31.0	17 51.1	21 33.6	15 49.5	7 55.1	18 8.1	13 5.9	13 24.4	20 46.4
22	17 58 47.0	23 26.5	0 18.3	15 35.0	17 57.2	20 43.0	16 28.5	7 53.3	18 10.6	13 3.4	13 23.7	20 44.5
25	18 10 36.7	23 24.5	0 18.4	2 36.0	18 18.1	19 47.6	17 6.0	7 52.1	18 13.4	13 .7	13 23.0	20 42.5
28	18 22 26.4	23 18.8	0 18.4	11N31.3	18 51.4	18 47.6	17 42.0	7 51.7	18 16.3	12 58.0	13 22.4	20 40.4

JULY 1962

DAY	EPHEM. SID. TIME	☉	☊	☽	☿	♀	♂	♃	♄	♅	♆	♇
		LONGITUDE										
	h m s	° ′	° ′	° ′	° ′	° ′	° ′	° ′	° ′	° ′	° ′	° ′
1	18 34 16.0	8♋41.5	10♌25.7	26♊29.8	17♊ 7.0	16♌11.0	24♉12.3	12♓41.2	10♒10.3	27♌48.2	10♏50.6	7♍58.3
2	18 38 12.6	9 38.8	10 22.5	9♋42.1	18 2.8	17 21.0	24 55.2	12 41.4	10R 6.9	27 51.0	10R50.0	7 59.6
3	18 42 9.1	10 36.0	10 19.3	22 37.6	19 2.8	18 30.8	25 38.1	12R41.3	10 3.3	27 53.8	10 49.3	8 .8
4	18 46 5.7	11 33.2	10 16.1	5♌16.2	20 7.1	19 40.6	26 20.9	12 41.1	9 59.7	27 56.6	10 48.7	8 2.1
5	18 50 2.3	12 30.4	10 13.0	17 39.1	21 15.5	20 50.3	27 3.6	12 40.7	9 56.1	27 59.5	10 48.1	8 3.4
6	18 53 58.8	13 27.6	10 9.8	29 48.6	22 28.1	21 59.9	27 46.2	12 40.0	9 52.4	28 2.4	10 47.6	8 4.7
7	18 57 55.4	14 24.9	10 6.6	11♍47.9	23 44.7	23 9.4	28 28.8	12 39.2	9 48.6	28 5.3	10 47.1	8 6.1
8	19 1 51.9	15 22.1	10 3.4	23 40.8	25 5.3	24 18.9	29 11.2	12 38.2	9 44.8	28 8.3	10 46.6	8 7.5
9	19 5 48.5	16 19.3	10 .3	5♎31.7	26 29.8	25 28.2	29 53.6	12 37.0	9 40.9	28 11.3	10 46.1	8 8.9
10	19 9 45.0	17 16.5	9 57.1	17 25.5	27 58.3	26 37.5	0♊36.0	12 35.6	9 37.0	28 14.3	10 45.7	8 10.3
11	19 13 41.6	18 13.7	9 53.9	29 26.7	29 30.5	27 46.6	1 18.2	12 34.0	9 33.1	28 17.4	10 45.3	8 11.7
12	19 17 38.2	19 10.9	9 50.7	11♏40.1	1♋ 6.4	28 55.6	2 .4	12 32.3	9 29.1	28 20.5	10 44.9	8 13.2
13	19 21 34.7	20 8.2	9 47.5	24 9.7	2 46.0	0♍ 4.6	2 42.6	12 30.3	9 25.1	28 23.6	10 44.6	8 14.7
14	19 25 31.3	21 5.4	9 44.4	6♐58.6	4 29.1	1 13.5	3 24.6	12 28.2	9 21.0	28 26.8	10 44.3	8 16.3
15	19 29 27.8	22 2.6	9 41.2	20 8.7	6 15.5	2 22.2	4 6.6	12 25.8	9 16.8	28 29.9	10 44.0	8 17.8
16	19 33 24.4	22 59.8	9 38.0	3♑40.6	8 5.0	3 30.8	4 48.5	12 23.3	9 12.7	28 33.1	10 43.8	8 19.3
17	19 37 20.9	23 57.0	9 34.8	17 32.8	9 57.6	4 39.3	5 30.3	12 20.6	9 8.5	28 36.4	10 43.6	8 20.9
18	19 41 17.5	24 54.2	9 31.7	1♒42.5	11 52.9	5 47.7	6 12.0	12 17.7	9 4.3	28 39.6	10 43.4	8 22.5
19	19 45 14.1	25 51.4	9 28.5	16 5.3	13 50.8	6 55.9	6 53.7	12 14.6	8 60.0	28 42.9	10 43.3	8 24.1
20	19 49 10.6	26 48.7	9 25.3	0♓36.0	15 50.9	8 4.1	7 35.3	12 11.3	8 55.7	28 46.2	10 43.1	8 25.7
21	19 53 7.2	27 45.9	9 22.1	15 9.1	17 52.9	9 12.1	8 16.8	12 7.8	8 51.4	28 49.5	10 43.1	8 27.4
22	19 57 3.7	28 43.2	9 19.0	29 39.4	19 56.6	10 20.0	8 58.3	12 4.2	8 47.0	28 52.9	10 43.0	8 29.0
23	20 1 .3	29 40.5	9 15.8	14♈ 2.8	22 1.6	11 27.8	9 39.7	12 .4	8 42.7	28 56.2	10 43.0	8 30.7
24	20 4 56.8	0♌37.8	9 12.6	28 15.8	24 7.5	12 35.5	10 20.9	11 56.4	8 38.3	28 59.6	10 43.0	8 32.4
25	20 8 53.4	1 35.1	9 9.4	12♉16.4	26 14.2	13 43.0	11 2.2	11 52.2	8 33.9	29 3.1	10 43.0	8 34.1
26	20 12 49.9	2 32.4	9 6.2	26 3.1	28 21.2	14 50.4	11 43.3	11 47.9	8 29.5	29 6.5	10D43.1	8 35.9
27	20 16 46.5	3 29.7	9 3.1	9♊35.5	0♌28.3	15 57.7	12 24.4	11 43.4	8 25.0	29 10.0	10 43.2	8 37.6
28	20 20 43.1	4 27.1	8 59.9	22 53.4	2 35.1	17 4.8	13 5.4	11 38.7	8 20.6	29 13.4	10 43.3	8 39.4
29	20 24 39.6	5 24.5	8 56.7	5♋56.9	4 41.6	18 11.8	13 46.3	11 33.9	8 16.1	29 16.9	10 43.5	8 41.2
30	20 28 36.2	6 21.8	8 53.5	18 46.5	6 47.3	19 18.7	14 27.1	11 28.9	8 11.7	29 20.4	10 43.7	8 43.0
31	20 32 32.7	7 19.2	8 50.4	1♌22.7	8 52.3	20 25.4	15 7.8	11 23.7	8 7.2	29 24.0	10 44.0	8 44.8
		LATITUDE										
1	18 34 16.0	0 .0	0 .0	3S32.0	3S16.1	1N49.2	0S34.3	1S 9.2	0S39.0	0N43.5	1N48.3	13N 2.8
4	18 46 5.7	0 .0	0 .0	0 20.7	2 42.9	1 45.6	0 32.2	1 10.0	0 39.4	0 43.4	1 48.2	13 2.0
7	18 57 55.4	0 .0	0 .0	2N50.5	2 6.3	1 41.2	0 30.1	1 10.9	0 39.7	0 43.4	1 48.0	13 1.2
10	19 9 45.0	0 .0	0 .0	4 53.0	1 27.7	1 36.0	0 27.9	1 11.8	0 40.1	0 43.3	1 47.9	13 .5
13	19 21 34.7	0 .0	0 .0	5 4.5	0 48.6	1 29.8	0 25.7	1 12.7	0 40.4	0 43.2	1 47.7	12 59.8
16	19 33 24.4	0 .0	0 .0	3 2.7	0 10.9	1 22.8	0 23.5	1 13.5	0 40.7	0 43.2	1 47.5	12 59.1
19	19 45 14.1	0 .0	0 .0	0S39.6	0N23.8	1 14.8	0 21.2	1 14.4	0 41.0	0 43.1	1 47.3	12 58.5
22	19 57 3.7	0 .0	0 .0	4 5.5	0 53.7	1 6.0	0 18.9	1 15.2	0 41.3	0 43.1	1 47.2	12 57.9
25	20 8 53.4	0 .0	0 .0	5 16.4	1 17.4	0 56.4	0 16.5	1 16.0	0 41.6	0 43.0	1 47.0	12 57.4
28	20 20 43.1	0 .0	0 .0	3 48.6	1 34.0	0 45.9	0 14.1	1 16.8	0 41.9	0 43.0	1 46.8	12 56.9
31	20 32 32.7	0 .0	0 .0	0 41.8	1 43.6	0 34.5	0 11.6	1 17.6	0 42.2	0 42.9	1 46.6	12 56.5
		RIGHT ASCENSION										
1	18 34 16.0	9♋27.6	12♌52.7	26♊16.9	16♊20.1	19♌12.7	21♉58.9	14♓29.1	12♒48.3	0♍14.5	8♏59.9	14♍47.8
2	18 38 12.6	10 29.7	12 49.5	10♋21.4	17 18.0	20 22.2	22 42.6	14 29.4	12R44.8	0 17.2	8R59.2	14 48.9
3	18 42 9.1	11 31.7	12 46.3	24 10.3	18 20.6	21 31.4	23 26.3	14 29.4	12 41.2	0 19.9	8 58.6	14 49.9
4	18 46 5.7	12 33.7	12 43.1	7♌32.4	19 27.9	22 40.1	24 10.1	14R29.3	12 37.6	0 22.6	8 58.0	14 51.1
5	18 50 2.3	13 35.5	12 39.8	20 20.8	20 39.8	23 48.5	24 53.8	14 29.1	12 33.9	0 25.3	8 57.4	14 52.2
6	18 53 58.8	14 37.3	12 36.6	2♍34.8	21 56.4	24 56.5	25 37.6	14 28.6	12 30.2	0 28.1	8 56.8	14 53.4
7	18 57 55.4	15 39.0	12 33.4	14 18.6	23 17.6	26 4.1	26 21.3	14 27.9	12 26.4	0 30.9	8 56.3	14 54.6
8	19 1 51.9	16 40.6	12 30.2	25 39.9	24 43.5	27 11.4	27 5.1	14 27.1	12 22.6	0 33.8	8 55.8	14 55.8
9	19 5 48.5	17 42.1	12 27.0	6♎48.6	26 13.9	28 18.3	27 48.9	14 26.1	12 18.7	0 36.7	8 55.3	14 57.0
10	19 9 45.0	18 43.5	12 23.8	17 55.8	27 48.8	29 24.8	28 32.8	14 24.9	12 14.7	0 39.6	8 54.9	14 58.3
11	19 13 41.6	19 44.8	12 20.6	29 13.2	29 28.1	0♍30.9	29 16.6	14 23.6	12 10.8	0 42.5	8 54.5	14 59.6
12	19 17 38.2	20 45.9	12 17.4	10♏52.5	1♋11.8	1 36.7	0♊ .4	14 22.0	12 6.7	0 45.5	8 54.1	15 .9
13	19 21 34.7	21 47.0	12 14.1	23 4.5	2 59.8	2 42.2	0 44.3	14 20.3	12 2.7	0 48.5	8 53.8	15 2.2
14	19 25 31.3	22 48.0	12 10.9	5♐57.5	4 51.8	3 47.3	1 28.2	14 18.4	11 58.6	0 51.5	8 53.5	15 3.6
15	19 29 27.8	23 48.8	12 7.7	19 35.4	6 47.8	4 52.1	2 12.0	14 16.4	11 54.4	0 54.6	8 53.2	15 5.0
16	19 33 24.4	24 49.5	12 4.5	3♑54.9	8 47.3	5 56.5	2 55.9	14 14.1	11 50.2	0 57.6	8 53.0	15 6.4
17	19 37 20.9	25 50.0	12 1.3	18 45.0	10 50.2	7 .5	3 39.7	14 11.7	11 45.9	1 .7	8 52.7	15 7.8
18	19 41 17.5	26 50.4	11 58.1	3♒48.0	12 56.2	8 4.3	4 23.6	14 9.1	11 41.7	1 3.8	8 52.5	15 9.2
19	19 45 14.1	27 50.7	11 54.8	18 45.1	15 5.0	9 7.7	5 7.5	14 6.3	11 37.4	1 7.0	8 52.4	15 10.7
20	19 49 10.6	28 50.9	11 51.6	3♓22.2	17 16.0	10 10.8	5 51.3	14 3.3	11 33.0	1 10.1	8 52.2	15 12.1
21	19 53 7.2	29 50.9	11 48.4	17 33.0	19 28.9	11 13.5	6 35.2	14 .2	11 28.7	1 13.3	8 52.1	15 13.6
22	19 57 3.7	0♌50.8	11 45.2	1♈18.9	21 43.2	12 16.0	7 19.0	13 56.9	11 24.3	1 16.5	8 52.1	15 15.1
23	20 1 .3	1 50.6	11 42.0	14 47.0	23 58.6	13 18.2	8 2.9	13 53.5	11 19.8	1 19.8	8 52.0	15 16.7
24	20 4 56.8	2 50.2	11 38.7	28 6.9	26 14.4	14 20.1	8 46.7	13 49.9	11 15.4	1 23.0	8 52.0	15 18.2
25	20 8 53.4	3 49.7	11 35.5	11♉27.9	28 30.4	15 21.7	9 30.5	13 46.1	11 10.9	1 26.3	8 52.0	15 19.8
26	20 12 49.9	4 49.0	11 32.3	24 57.4	0♌46.0	16 23.0	10 14.3	13 42.1	11 6.5	1 29.6	8D52.1	15 21.4
27	20 16 46.5	5 48.2	11 29.1	8♊38.3	3 .9	17 24.1	10 58.1	13 38.0	11 2.0	1 32.9	8 52.2	15 23.0
28	20 20 43.1	6 47.2	11 25.9	22 28.5	5 14.8	18 24.8	11 41.8	13 33.8	10 57.5	1 36.2	8 52.3	15 24.6
29	20 24 39.6	7 46.1	11 22.6	6♋20.5	7 27.2	19 25.4	12 25.6	13 29.3	10 52.9	1 39.6	8 52.4	15 26.2
30	20 28 36.2	8 44.9	11 19.4	20 3.7	9 38.0	20 25.6	13 9.3	13 24.8	10 48.4	1 42.9	8 52.6	15 27.9
31	20 32 32.7	9 43.5	11 16.2	3♌27.1	11 47.0	21 25.7	13 52.9	13 20.0	10 43.9	1 46.3	8 52.8	15 29.6
		DECLINATION										
1	18 34 16.0	23N 9.4	0N18.5	19N51.9	19N33.9	17N43.4	18N16.3	7S51.8	18S19.4	12N55.1	13S21.8	20N38.3
4	18 46 5.7	22 56.4	0 18.5	18 37.1	20 22.0	16 35.3	18 49.0	7 52.7	18 22.6	12 52.1	13 21.4	20 36.1
7	18 57 55.4	22 39.8	0 18.5	9 45.9	21 11.5	15 23.6	19 20.1	7 54.2	18 25.9	12 49.1	13 21.0	20 33.8
10	19 9 45.0	22 19.6	0 18.6	2S19.6	21 57.9	14 8.7	19 49.4	7 56.4	18 29.4	12 45.9	13 20.8	20 31.6
13	19 21 34.7	21 55.9	0 18.6	13 53.5	22 36.2	12 50.8	20 17.0	7 59.3	18 32.9	12 42.6	13 20.6	20 29.2
16	19 33 24.4	21 28.9	0 18.7	20 20.8	23 .9	11 30.3	20 42.9	8 2.8	18 36.5	12 39.2	13 20.5	20 26.8
19	19 45 14.1	20 58.6	0 18.7	16 38.7	23 7.0	10 7.6	21 6.9	8 6.9	18 40.1	12 35.8	13 20.5	20 24.4
22	19 57 3.7	20 25.1	0 18.8	3 53.4	22 50.8	8 42.8	21 29.2	8 11.6	18 43.8	12 32.2	13 20.6	20 22.0
25	20 8 53.4	19 48.6	0 18.8	10N29.7	22 10.3	7 16.3	21 49.7	8 16.9	18 47.6	12 28.6	13 20.8	20 19.6
28	20 20 43.1	19 9.0	0 18.9	19 26.8	21 6.6	5 48.4	22 8.4	8 22.8	18 51.3	12 25.0	13 21.1	20 17.1
31	20 32 32.7	18 26.6	0 18.9	19 10.5	19 42.5	4 19.5	22 25.3	8 29.2	18 55.1	12 21.3	13 21.4	20 14.6

AUGUST 1962

LONGITUDE

DAY	EPHEM. SID. TIME h m s	☉ ° ′	☊ ° ′	☽ ° ′	☿ ° ′	♀ ° ′	♂ ° ′	♃ ° ′	♄ ° ′	♅ ° ′	♆ ° ′	♇ ° ′
1	20 36 29.3	8♌16.6	8♌47.2	13♌46.5	10♌56.2	21♍32.0	15♊48.4	11♓18.4	8♒ 2.8	29♌27.5	10♏44.2	8♍46.6
2	20 40 25.8	9 14.1	8 44.0	25 59.0	12 59.0	22 38.4	16 29.0	11 R 12.9	7 R 58.3	29 31.1	10 44.5	8 48.5
3	20 44 22.4	10 11.6	8 40.8	8♍ 2.2	15 .6	23 44.7	17 9.5	11 7.3	7 53.9	29 34.7	10 44.9	8 50.4
4	20 48 18.9	11 9.0	8 37.7	19 58.1	17 .8	24 50.8	17 49.9	11 1.6	7 49.4	29 38.3	10 45.3	8 52.3
5	20 52 15.5	12 6.5	8 34.5	1♎49.5	18 59.7	25 56.7	18 30.2	10 55.7	7 45.0	29 41.9	10 45.7	8 54.1
6	20 56 12.1	13 4.0	8 31.3	13 39.9	20 57.0	27 2.5	19 10.4	10 49.6	7 40.5	29 45.6	10 46.1	8 56.0
7	21 0 8.6	14 1.4	8 28.1	25 33.0	22 52.9	28 8.1	19 50.6	10 43.4	7 36.1	29 49.2	10 46.6	8 57.9
8	21 4 5.2	14 59.0	8 24.9	7♏33.0	24 47.3	29 13.5	20 30.6	10 37.1	7 31.7	29 52.9	10 47.1	8 59.9
9	21 8 1.7	15 56.5	8 21.8	19 44.5	26 40.2	0♎18.7	21 10.5	10 30.7	7 27.3	29 56.5	10 47.6	9 1.8
10	21 11 58.3	16 54.0	8 18.6	2♐11.8	28 31.5	1 23.7	21 50.4	10 24.2	7 22.9	0♍ .2	10 48.1	9 3.7
11	21 15 54.8	17 51.5	8 15.4	14 59.0	0♍21.3	2 28.5	22 30.2	10 17.5	7 18.6	0 3.9	10 48.7	9 5.7
12	21 19 51.4	18 49.1	8 12.2	28 9.3	2 9.6	3 33.1	23 9.8	10 10.7	7 14.2	0 7.6	10 49.4	9 7.7
13	21 23 47.9	19 46.7	8 9.1	11♑44.8	3 56.4	4 37.5	23 49.4	10 3.8	7 9.9	0 11.3	10 50.0	9 9.6
14	21 27 44.5	20 44.3	8 5.9	25 45.5	5 41.6	5 41.7	24 28.9	9 56.8	7 5.6	0 15.0	10 50.7	9 11.6
15	21 31 41.0	21 41.9	8 2.7	10♒ 9.5	7 25.4	6 45.7	25 8.3	9 49.8	7 1.4	0 18.7	10 51.4	9 13.6
16	21 35 37.6	22 39.5	7 59.5	24 52.1	9 7.7	7 49.4	25 47.6	9 42.6	6 57.2	0 22.4	10 52.2	9 15.6
17	21 39 34.2	23 37.2	7 56.3	9♓46.7	10 48.5	8 52.9	26 26.9	9 35.3	6 53.0	0 26.1	10 52.9	9 17.6
18	21 43 30.7	24 34.8	7 53.2	24 45.2	12 27.9	9 56.2	27 6.0	9 28.0	6 48.9	0 29.9	10 53.7	9 19.6
19	21 47 27.3	25 32.5	7 50.0	9♈39.1	14 5.8	10 59.2	27 45.0	9 20.6	6 44.7	0 33.6	10 54.6	9 21.6
20	21 51 23.8	26 30.3	7 46.8	24 21.2	15 42.3	12 2.0	28 24.0	9 13.1	6 40.7	0 37.4	10 55.4	9 23.7
21	21 55 20.4	27 28.0	7 43.6	8♉45.9	17 17.3	13 4.5	29 2.8	9 5.5	6 36.7	0 41.1	10 56.3	9 25.7
22	21 59 16.9	28 25.8	7 40.5	22 50.0	18 51.0	14 6.7	29 41.6	8 57.9	6 32.7	0 44.9	10 57.3	9 27.7
23	22 3 13.5	29 23.6	7 37.3	6♊32.2	20 23.2	15 8.7	0♋20.3	8 50.2	6 28.7	0 48.6	10 58.2	9 29.8
24	22 7 10.0	0♍21.5	7 34.1	19 53.5	21 54.0	16 10.4	0 58.9	8 42.5	6 24.9	0 52.4	10 59.3	9 31.9
25	22 11 6.6	1 19.4	7 30.9	2♋55.4	23 23.4	17 11.9	1 37.3	8 34.7	6 21.0	0 56.2	11 .3	9 33.9
26	22 15 3.1	2 17.3	7 27.7	15 40.5	24 51.3	18 13.0	2 15.7	8 26.9	6 17.3	0 59.9	11 1.3	9 36.0
27	22 18 59.7	3 15.2	7 24.6	28 11.4	26 17.8	19 13.8	2 54.0	8 19.0	6 13.5	1 3.7	11 2.4	9 38.1
28	22 22 56.2	4 13.1	7 21.4	10♌30.4	27 42.8	20 14.3	3 32.1	8 11.1	6 9.8	1 7.4	11 3.5	9 40.1
29	22 26 52.8	5 11.1	7 18.2	22 40.0	29 6.3	21 14.5	4 10.2	8 3.2	6 6.2	1 11.2	11 4.7	9 42.2
30	22 30 49.3	6 9.1	7 15.0	4♍41.9	0♎28.3	22 14.4	4 48.1	7 55.3	6 2.7	1 14.9	11 5.8	9 44.3
31	22 34 45.9	7 7.2	7 11.9	16 38.2	1 48.8	23 13.9	5 25.9	7 47.4	5 59.2	1 18.7	11 7.0	9 46.4

LATITUDE

DAY	h m s	☉	☊	☽	☿	♀	♂	♃	♄	♅	♆	♇
1	20 36 29.3	0 .0	0 .0	0N26.8	1N45.3	0N30.6	0S10.7	1S17.8	0S42.3	0N42.9	1N46.6	12N56.4
4	20 48 18.9	0 .0	0 .0	3 28.5	1 46.1	0 18.2	0 8.2	1 18.5	0 42.5	0 42.9	1 46.4	12 56.0
7	21 0 8.6	0 .0	0 .0	5 8.5	1 41.1	0 5.0	0 5.6	1 19.2	0 42.8	0 42.9	1 46.2	12 55.7
10	21 11 58.3	0 .0	0 .0	4 51.4	1 31.3	0S 8.9	0 3.0	1 19.8	0 43.0	0 42.8	1 46.0	12 55.4
13	21 23 47.9	0 .0	0 .0	2 25.2	1 17.4	0 23.6	0 .3	1 20.4	0 43.2	0 42.8	1 45.9	12 55.2
16	21 35 37.6	0 .0	0 .0	1S26.9	1 .1	0 38.9	0N 2.4	1 21.0	0 43.4	0 42.8	1 45.7	12 55.0
19	21 47 27.3	0 .0	0 .0	4 35.7	0 40.0	0 54.8	0 5.1	1 21.5	0 43.6	0 42.8	1 45.5	12 54.9
22	21 59 16.9	0 .0	0 .0	5 6.2	0 17.7	1 11.4	0 7.9	1 21.9	0 43.7	0 42.8	1 45.4	12 54.9
25	22 11 6.6	0 .0	0 .0	3 5.4	0S 6.4	1 28.4	0 10.8	1 22.3	0 43.9	0 42.8	1 45.2	12 54.9
28	22 22 56.2	0 .0	0 .0	0N 8.8	0 31.6	1 45.9	0 13.7	1 22.6	0 44.0	0 42.8	1 45.0	12 54.9
31	22 34 45.9	0 .0	0 .0	3 12.2	0 57.8	2 3.9	0 16.6	1 22.9	0 44.2	0 42.8	1 44.9	12 55.0

RIGHT ASCENSION

DAY	h m s	☉	☊	☽	☿	♀	♂	♃	♄	♅	♆	♇
1	20 36 29.3	10♌41.9	11♌13.0	16♌22.6	13♌54.0	22♍25.4	14♊36.6	13♓15.1	10♒39.4	1♍49.7	8♏53.1	15♍31.3
2	20 40 25.8	11 40.2	11 9.7	28 46.6	15 58.7	23 25.0	15 20.2	13 R 10.1	10 R 34.8	1 53.1	8 53.4	15 33.0
3	20 44 22.4	12 38.4	11 6.5	10♍40.5	18 1.3	24 24.3	16 3.8	13 5.0	10 30.3	1 56.6	8 53.7	15 34.7
4	20 48 18.9	13 36.4	11 3.3	22 9.4	20 1.5	25 23.4	16 47.3	12 59.7	10 25.8	2 .1	6 54.0	15 36.5
5	20 52 15.5	14 34.3	11 .1	3♎21.2	21 59.3	26 22.3	17 30.7	12 54.3	10 21.3	2 3.5	8 54.4	15 38.2
6	20 56 12.1	15 31.9	10 56.8	14 25.8	23 54.8	27 20.9	18 14.1	12 48.7	10 16.8	2 7.0	8 54.8	15 40.0
7	21 0 8.6	16 29.5	10 53.6	25 33.6	25 47.9	28 19.3	18 57.5	12 43.0	10 12.3	2 10.5	8 55.3	15 41.8
8	21 4 5.2	17 26.9	10 50.4	6♏55.9	27 38.7	29 17.5	19 40.8	12 37.2	10 7.8	2 14.0	8 55.7	15 43.6
9	21 8 1.7	18 24.1	10 47.1	18 43.6	29 27.1	0♎15.5	20 24.0	12 31.2	10 3.3	2 17.5	8 56.2	15 45.4
10	21 11 58.3	19 21.2	10 43.9	1♐ 6.7	1♍13.3	1 13.2	21 7.2	12 25.2	9 58.8	2 21.0	8 56.7	15 47.2
11	21 15 54.8	20 18.1	10 40.7	14 12.2	2 57.2	2 10.8	21 50.4	12 19.0	9 54.4	2 24.5	8 57.3	15 49.0
12	21 19 51.4	21 14.9	10 37.5	28 2.4	4 39.0	3 8.2	22 33.4	12 12.8	9 50.0	2 28.0	8 57.9	15 50.8
13	21 23 47.9	22 11.5	10 34.2	12♑32.5	6 18.8	4 5.4	23 16.4	12 6.4	9 45.6	2 31.6	8 58.5	15 52.7
14	21 27 44.5	23 8.0	10 31.0	27 30.2	7 56.4	5 2.3	23 59.3	11 59.9	9 41.2	2 35.1	8 59.2	15 54.6
15	21 31 41.0	24 4.3	10 27.8	12♒38.2	9 32.2	5 59.1	24 42.2	11 53.3	9 36.9	2 38.7	8 59.8	15 56.4
16	21 35 37.6	25 .6	10 24.5	27 39.3	11 6.0	6 55.7	25 24.9	11 46.7	9 32.6	2 42.2	9 .5	15 58.3
17	21 39 34.2	25 56.6	10 21.3	12♓21.8	12 37.9	7 52.1	26 7.6	11 39.9	9 28.3	2 45.8	9 1.3	16 .2
18	21 43 30.7	26 52.6	10 18.1	26 41.3	14 8.1	8 48.3	26 50.3	11 33.1	9 24.1	2 49.4	9 2.1	16 2.1
19	21 47 27.3	27 48.4	10 14.8	10♈40.4	15 36.5	9 44.4	27 32.8	11 26.2	9 19.9	2 53.0	9 2.9	16 4.0
20	21 51 23.8	28 44.2	10 11.6	24 25.7	17 3.3	10 40.2	28 15.3	11 19.2	9 15.7	2 56.5	9 3.7	16 6.0
21	21 55 20.4	29 39.8	10 8.4	8♉ 5.2	18 28.4	11 35.9	28 57.6	11 12.2	9 11.6	3 .1	9 4.5	16 7.9
22	21 59 16.9	0♍35.2	10 5.1	21 45.6	19 51.9	12 31.4	29 39.9	11 5.1	9 7.6	3 3.7	9 5.4	16 9.8
23	22 3 13.5	1 30.6	10 1.9	5♊30.5	21 13.9	13 26.8	0♋22.1	10 57.9	9 3.5	3 7.3	9 6.4	16 11.8
24	22 7 10.0	2 25.9	9 58.6	19 19.3	22 34.4	14 22.0	1 4.2	10 50.7	8 59.6	3 10.9	9 7.4	16 13.8
25	22 11 6.6	3 21.1	9 55.4	3♋ 6.8	23 53.4	15 17.0	1 46.2	10 43.5	8 55.7	3 14.5	9 8.3	16 15.7
26	22 15 3.1	4 16.2	9 52.2	16 45.0	25 10.9	16 11.8	2 28.1	10 36.2	8 51.8	3 18.1	9 9.3	16 17.7
27	22 18 59.7	5 11.1	9 48.9	0♌ 5.0	26 26.9	17 6.4	3 9.9	10 28.8	8 48.0	3 21.7	9 10.4	16 19.7
28	22 22 56.2	6 6.0	9 45.7	13 .0	27 41.5	18 .8	3 51.5	10 21.4	8 44.2	3 25.2	9 11.4	16 21.6
29	22 26 52.8	7 .8	9 42.5	25 26.3	28 54.7	18 55.1	4 33.1	10 14.0	8 40.5	3 28.8	9 12.5	16 23.6
30	22 30 49.3	7 55.5	9 39.2	7♍24.2	0♎ 6.5	19 49.2	5 14.5	10 6.6	8 36.9	3 32.4	9 13.7	16 25.6
31	22 34 45.9	8 50.1	9 36.0	18 57.7	1 16.8	20 43.0	5 55.8	9 59.2	8 33.3	3 36.0	9 14.8	16 27.6

DECLINATION

DAY	h m s	☉	☊	☽	☿	♀	♂	♃	♄	♅	♆	♇
1	20 36 29.3	18N11.9	0N18.9	17N 7.3	19N10.6	3N49.6	22N30.5	8S31.5	18S56.3	12N20.0	13S21.6	20N13.8
4	20 48 18.9	17 25.9	0 19.0	7 10.1	17 25.4	2 19.6	22 45.0	8 38.6	18 60.0	12 16.2	13 22.0	20 11.3
7	21 0 8.6	16 37.3	0 19.0	5S 5.2	15 29.0	0 49.1	22 57.6	8 46.1	19 3.7	12 12.3	13 22.6	20 8.8
10	21 11 58.3	15 46.4	0 19.0	15 50.5	13 24.9	0S41.5	23 8.5	8 54.0	19 7.3	12 8.4	13 23.3	20 6.3
13	21 23 47.9	14 53.2	0 19.1	20 30.8	11 16.0	2 11.9	23 17.6	9 2.2	19 10.8	12 4.5	13 24.0	20 3.9
16	21 35 37.6	13 57.8	0 19.1	14 35.9	9 4.6	3 42.0	23 24.9	9 10.8	19 14.2	12 .6	13 24.8	20 1.4
19	21 47 27.3	13 .5	0 19.2	0 24.1	6 52.4	5 11.3	23 30.5	9 19.5	19 17.5	11 56.6	13 25.8	19 59.0
22	21 59 16.9	12 1.3	0 19.2	13N32.5	4 41.0	6 39.8	23 34.5	9 28.5	19 20.7	11 52.6	13 26.8	19 56.6
25	22 11 6.6	11 .3	0 19.3	20 19.3	2 31.7	8 7.0	23 36.7	9 37.6	19 23.8	11 48.6	13 27.8	19 54.2
28	22 22 56.2	9 57.8	0 19.3	17 44.9	0 25.5	9 32.7	23 37.4	9 46.7	19 26.7	11 44.6	13 29.0	19 51.9
31	22 34 45.9	8 53.9	0 19.3	8 13.6	1S36.3	10 56.7	23 36.5	9 55.9	19 29.5	11 40.6	13 30.2	19 49.6

SEPTEMBER 1962

DAY	EPHEM. SID. TIME	☉	☊	☽	☿	♀	♂	♃	♄	♅	♆	♇
	h m s	° ′	° ′	° ′	° ′	° ′	° ′	° ′	° ′	° ′	° ′	° ′
		LONGITUDE										
1	22 38 42.5	8♍ 5.2	7♌ 8.7	28♍30.4	3♎ 7.6	24♎13.0	6♋ 3.7	7♓39.4	5♒55.7	1♍22.4	11♏ 8.2	9♍48.4
2	22 42 39.0	9 3.3	7 5.5	10♎20.8	4 24.9	25 11.8	6 41.3	7 R31.5	5 R52.4	1 26.1	11 9.5	9 50.5
3	22 46 35.6	10 1.4	7 2.3	22 11.3	5 40.4	26 10.2	7 18.8	7 23.6	5 49.1	1 29.9	11 10.8	9 52.6
4	22 50 32.1	10 59.6	6 59.1	4♏ 4.9	6 54.1	27 8.2	7 56.2	7 15.7	5 45.8	1 33.6	11 12.1	9 54.7
5	22 54 28.7	11 57.7	6 56.0	16 4.7	8 6.0	28 5.8	8 33.4	7 7.8	5 42.7	1 37.3	11 13.4	9 56.7
6	22 58 25.2	12 55.9	6 52.8	28 14.3	9 16.0	29 3.0	9 10.6	6 59.9	5 39.6	1 41.0	11 14.7	9 58.8
7	23 2 21.8	13 54.1	6 49.6	10♐37.9	10 24.0	29 59.7	9 47.6	6 52.1	5 36.6	1 44.7	11 16.1	10 .9
8	23 6 18.3	14 52.4	6 46.4	23 19.8	11 29.9	0♏56.0	10 24.6	6 44.3	5 33.6	1 48.4	11 17.5	10 3.0
9	23 10 14.9	15 50.6	6 43.3	6♑24.0	12 33.6	1 51.8	11 1.4	6 36.6	5 30.8	1 52.1	11 19.0	10 5.0
10	23 14 11.4	16 48.9	6 40.1	19 53.9	13 34.8	2 47.1	11 38.1	6 28.9	5 28.0	1 55.7	11 20.4	10 7.1
11	23 18 8.0	17 47.2	6 36.9	3♒51.5	14 33.6	3 41.9	12 14.6	6 21.2	5 25.3	1 59.4	11 21.9	10 9.2
12	23 22 4.5	18 45.6	6 33.7	18 16.4	15 29.7	4 36.1	12 51.1	6 13.7	5 22.6	2 3.0	11 23.4	10 11.2
13	23 26 1.1	19 43.9	6 30.5	3♓ 5.5	16 22.9	5 29.8	13 27.4	6 6.2	5 20.1	2 6.6	11 25.0	10 13.3
14	23 29 57.6	20 42.4	6 27.4	18 12.5	17 13.1	6 23.0	14 3.7	5 58.8	5 17.7	2 10.3	11 26.6	10 15.4
15	23 33 54.2	21 40.8	6 24.2	3♈28.1	17 60.0	7 15.5	14 39.8	5 51.4	5 15.3	2 13.9	11 28.1	10 17.4
16	23 37 50.7	22 39.3	6 21.0	18 41.7	18 43.3	8 7.4	15 15.7	5 44.1	5 13.0	2 17.5	11 29.7	10 19.5
17	23 41 47.3	23 37.8	6 17.8	3♉43.0	19 22.9	8 58.7	15 51.6	5 37.0	5 10.8	2 21.0	11 31.4	10 21.5
18	23 45 43.8	24 36.3	6 14.7	18 23.7	19 58.3	9 49.3	16 27.3	5 29.9	5 8.7	2 24.6	11 33.0	10 23.5
19	23 49 40.4	25 34.9	6 11.5	2♊38.6	20 29.4	10 39.2	17 2.9	5 22.9	5 6.6	2 28.1	11 34.7	10 25.6
20	23 53 36.9	26 33.5	6 8.3	16 25.6	20 55.7	11 28.4	17 38.3	5 16.0	5 4.7	2 31.6	11 36.4	10 27.6
21	23 57 33.5	27 32.1	6 5.1	29 45.7	21 17.0	12 16.9	18 13.7	5 9.2	5 2.8	2 35.1	11 38.1	10 29.6
22	0 1 30.0	28 30.8	6 1.9	12♋41.6	21 32.8	13 4.7	18 48.8	5 2.5	5 1.0	2 38.6	11 39.8	10 31.6
23	0 5 26.6	29 29.5	5 58.8	25 17.2	21 42.7	13 51.6	19 23.9	4 56.0	4 59.4	2 42.1	11 41.6	10 33.6
24	0 9 23.2	0♎28.2	5 55.6	7♌36.8	21 46.4	14 37.8	19 58.8	4 49.5	4 57.8	2 45.5	11 43.4	10 35.6
25	0 13 19.7	1 27.0	5 52.4	19 44.5	21 R43.6	15 23.0	20 33.6	4 43.2	4 56.3	2 48.9	11 45.2	10 37.5
26	0 17 16.3	2 25.8	5 49.2	1♍43.8	21 33.8	16 7.4	21 8.2	4 37.1	4 54.9	2 52.3	11 47.0	10 39.5
27	0 21 12.8	3 24.7	5 46.0	13 38.0	21 16.8	16 50.9	21 42.7	4 31.0	4 53.6	2 55.7	11 48.8	10 41.4
28	0 25 9.4	4 23.6	5 42.9	25 29.3	20 52.3	17 33.4	22 17.0	4 25.1	4 52.4	2 59.1	11 50.7	10 43.4
29	0 29 5.9	5 22.5	5 39.7	7♎19.9	20 20.4	18 14.9	22 51.1	4 19.4	4 51.3	3 2.4	11 52.6	10 45.3
30	0 33 2.5	6 21.5	5 36.5	19 11.3	19 41.0	18 55.4	23 25.2	4 13.8	4 50.3	3 5.7	11 54.5	10 47.2
		LATITUDE										
1	22 38 42.5	0 .0	0 .0	3N58.8	1S 6.6	2S10.0	0N17.6	1S23.0	0S44.2	0N42.9	1N44.8	12N55.1
4	22 50 32.1	0 .0	0 .0	5 10.8	1 33.3	2 28.4	0 20.6	1 23.2	0 44.3	0 42.9	1 44.7	12 55.3
7	23 2 21.8	0 .0	0 .0	4 23.7	1 59.7	2 47.1	0 23.7	1 23.3	0 44.4	0 42.9	1 44.5	12 55.5
10	23 14 11.4	0 .0	0 .0	1 38.9	2 25.5	3 5.9	0 26.8	1 23.4	0 44.5	0 42.9	1 44.4	12 55.8
13	23 26 1.1	0 .0	0 .0	2S10.0	2 49.9	3 24.9	0 30.0	1 23.4	0 44.6	0 43.0	1 44.2	12 56.2
16	23 37 50.7	0 .0	0 .0	4 51.1	3 12.0	3 43.9	0 33.2	1 23.4	0 44.7	0 43.0	1 44.1	12 56.6
19	23 49 40.4	0 .0	0 .0	4 40.1	3 30.7	4 2.7	0 36.5	1 23.3	0 44.8	0 43.1	1 44.0	12 57.1
22	0 1 30.0	0 .0	0 .0	2 11.1	3 44.0	4 21.4	0 39.9	1 23.2	0 44.8	0 43.1	1 43.9	12 57.6
25	0 13 19.7	0 .0	0 .0	1N 3.8	3 49.8	4 39.6	0 43.3	1 23.0	0 44.9	0 43.2	1 43.8	12 58.2
28	0 25 9.4	0 .0	0 .0	3 46.6	3 44.7	4 57.3	0 46.8	1 22.7	0 44.9	0 43.3	1 43.7	12 58.8
		RIGHT ASCENSION										
1	22 38 42.5	9♍44.6	9♌32.7	0♎13.0	2♎25.7	21♎36.7	6♋37.0	9♓51.7	8♒29.8	3♍39.5	9♏16.0	16♍29.6
2	22 42 39.0	10 39.0	9 29.5	11 18.3	3 33.1	22 30.1	7 18.0	9 R44.3	8 R26.3	3 43.1	9 17.2	16 31.6
3	22 46 35.6	11 33.4	9 26.2	22 22.6	4 38.9	23 23.3	7 58.9	9 36.9	8 22.9	3 46.7	9 18.4	16 33.6
4	22 50 32.1	12 27.7	9 23.0	3♏35.7	5 43.3	24 16.3	8 39.7	9 29.4	8 19.6	3 50.2	9 19.7	16 35.6
5	22 54 28.7	13 21.9	9 19.8	15 7.4	6 46.0	25 9.1	9 20.4	9 22.0	8 16.4	3 53.8	9 21.0	16 37.6
6	22 58 25.2	14 16.1	9 16.5	27 6.8	7 47.0	26 1.6	10 .9	9 14.6	8 13.2	3 57.3	9 22.3	16 39.6
7	23 2 21.8	15 10.2	9 13.3	9♐41.5	8 46.3	26 53.8	10 41.3	9 7.3	8 10.1	4 .8	9 23.6	16 41.6
8	23 6 18.3	16 4.3	9 10.0	22 55.9	9 43.8	27 45.8	11 21.5	8 59.9	8 7.1	4 4.3	9 25.0	16 43.6
9	23 10 14.9	16 58.3	9 6.8	6♑49.7	10 39.3	28 37.4	12 1.6	8 52.6	8 4.1	4 7.8	9 26.4	16 45.6
10	23 14 11.4	17 52.2	9 3.5	21 16.5	11 32.8	29 28.8	12 41.5	8 45.4	8 1.3	4 11.3	9 27.8	16 47.7
11	23 18 8.0	18 46.1	9 .3	6♒ 4.5	12 24.1	0♏19.8	13 21.3	8 38.2	7 58.5	4 14.8	9 29.2	16 49.7
12	23 22 4.5	19 40.0	8 57.0	20 59.7	13 13.1	1 10.4	14 .9	8 31.0	7 55.8	4 18.3	9 30.7	16 51.7
13	23 26 1.1	20 33.8	8 53.8	5♓49.9	13 59.6	2 .8	14 40.4	8 23.9	7 53.2	4 21.8	9 32.2	16 53.7
14	23 29 57.6	21 27.7	8 50.5	20 27.8	14 43.4	2 50.7	15 19.7	8 17.0	7 50.7	4 25.2	9 33.7	16 55.7
15	23 33 54.2	22 21.5	8 47.3	4♈51.9	15 24.4	3 40.2	15 58.9	8 10.0	7 48.3	4 28.7	9 35.3	16 57.7
16	23 37 50.7	23 15.3	8 44.1	19 5.4	16 2.2	4 29.3	16 37.9	8 3.1	7 45.9	4 32.1	9 36.8	16 59.7
17	23 41 47.3	24 9.1	8 40.8	3♉13.9	16 36.7	5 18.0	17 16.7	7 56.3	7 43.6	4 35.5	9 38.4	17 1.7
18	23 45 43.8	25 2.9	8 37.6	17 21.9	17 7.6	6 6.2	17 55.4	7 49.6	7 41.4	4 38.9	9 40.0	17 3.7
19	23 49 40.4	25 56.7	8 34.3	1♊31.7	17 34.6	6 53.9	18 33.9	7 43.0	7 39.4	4 42.2	9 41.6	17 5.7
20	23 53 36.9	26 50.5	8 31.0	15 41.2	17 57.4	7 41.0	19 12.2	7 36.4	7 37.3	4 45.6	9 43.3	17 7.7
21	23 57 33.5	27 44.3	8 27.8	29 44.8	18 15.7	8 27.6	19 50.4	7 30.0	7 35.4	4 48.9	9 44.9	17 9.7
22	0 1 30.0	28 38.1	8 24.5	13♋34.3	18 29.2	9 13.7	20 28.4	7 23.7	7 33.6	4 52.2	9 46.6	17 11.6
23	0 5 26.6	29 32.0	8 21.3	27 1.8	18 37.5	9 59.1	21 6.2	7 17.4	7 31.9	4 55.5	9 48.3	17 13.6
24	0 9 23.2	0♎25.9	8 18.0	10♌ 1.2	18 40.2	10 43.9	21 43.8	7 11.3	7 30.3	4 58.8	9 50.1	17 15.6
25	0 13 19.7	1 19.8	8 14.8	22 30.2	18 R37.2	11 28.0	22 21.2	7 5.3	7 28.7	5 2.1	9 51.8	17 17.5
26	0 17 16.3	2 13.8	8 11.5	4♍30.0	18 28.1	12 11.3	22 58.4	6 59.4	7 27.3	5 5.3	9 53.6	17 19.5
27	0 21 12.8	3 7.8	8 8.3	16 5.1	18 12.6	12 53.9	23 35.5	6 53.7	7 26.0	5 8.5	9 55.4	17 21.4
28	0 25 9.4	4 1.9	8 5.0	27 21.8	17 50.8	13 35.7	24 12.3	6 48.1	7 24.7	5 11.7	9 57.2	17 23.4
29	0 29 5.9	4 56.0	8 1.8	8♎27.9	17 22.6	14 16.6	24 48.9	6 42.6	7 23.6	5 14.9	9 59.0	17 25.3
30	0 33 2.5	5 50.2	7 58.5	19 31.9	16 48.0	14 56.6	25 25.4	6 37.2	7 22.5	5 18.0	10 .9	17 27.2
		DECLINATION										
1	22 38 42.5	8N32.3	0N19.4	4N14.7	2S15.8	11S24.3	23N35.8	9S58.9	19S30.4	11N39.3	13S30.6	19N48.8
4	22 50 32.1	7 26.7	0 19.4	8S .1	4 10.1	12 45.6	23 32.9	10 8.0	19 33.0	11 35.4	13 32.0	19 46.6
7	23 2 21.8	6 20.0	0 19.4	17 41.5	5 57.2	14 4.6	23 28.5	10 16.9	19 35.3	11 31.4	13 33.4	19 44.4
10	23 14 11.4	5 12.4	0 19.5	20 20.2	7 35.6	15 21.0	23 22.7	10 25.6	19 37.5	11 27.5	13 34.8	19 42.2
13	23 26 1.1	4 4.0	0 19.5	12 23.5	9 3.3	16 34.4	23 15.6	10 34.0	19 39.6	11 23.6	13 36.3	19 40.2
16	23 37 50.7	2 54.9	0 19.6	2N50.2	10 17.7	17 44.7	23 7.2	10 42.1	19 41.4	11 19.8	13 37.9	19 38.2
19	23 49 40.4	1 45.4	0 19.6	16 6.7	11 15.3	18 51.6	22 57.6	10 49.9	19 43.0	11 16.0	13 39.6	19 36.2
22	0 1 30.0	0 35.5	0 19.7	20 39.7	11 51.7	19 54.9	22 46.8	10 57.2	19 44.4	11 12.3	13 41.3	19 34.4
25	0 13 19.7	0S34.6	0 19.7	15 54.4	12 1.1	20 54.2	22 35.0	11 4.1	19 45.6	11 8.6	13 43.0	19 32.6
28	0 25 9.4	1 44.8	0 19.7	5 15.5	11 37.0	21 49.3	22 22.2	11 10.5	19 46.6	11 5.0	13 44.8	19 30.9

OCTOBER 1962

DAY	EPHEM. SID. TIME	☉	☊	☽	☿	♀	♂	♃	♄	♅	♆	♇
	h m s	° ′	° ′	° ′	° ′	° ′	° ′	° ′	° ′	° ′	° ′	° ′
		LONGITUDE										
1	0 36 59.0	7♎20.5	5♌33.3	1♏ 4.9	18♎54.5	19♏34.8	23♋59.0	4♓ 8.3	4♒49.3	3♍ 9.0	11♏56.4	10♍49.1
2	0 40 55.6	8 19.5	5 30.2	13 2.6	18R 1.2	20 13.1	24 32.7	4R 3.1	4R48.5	3 12.2	11 58.3	10 51.0
3	0 44 52.1	9 18.5	5 27.0	25 6.2	17 2.0	20 50.1	25 6.2	3 57.9	4 47.8	3 15.4	12 .3	10 52.9
4	0 48 48.7	10 17.6	5 23.8	7♐18.2	15 57.9	21 26.0	25 39.6	3 53.0	4 47.2	3 18.6	12 2.2	10 54.8
5	0 52 45.2	11 16.8	5 20.6	19 41.9	14 50.3	22 .6	26 12.8	3 48.2	4 46.7	3 21.8	12 4.3	10 56.7
6	0 56 41.8	12 15.9	5 17.4	2♑20.7	13 40.6	22 33.8	26 45.9	3 43.6	4 46.3	3 25.0	12 6.3	10 58.5
7	1 0 38.3	13 15.1	5 14.3	15 18.7	12 30.6	23 5.7	27 18.7	3 39.1	4 46.0	3 28.1	12 8.3	11 .3
8	1 4 34.9	14 14.3	5 11.1	28 39.6	11 22.3	23 36.1	27 51.4	3 34.9	4 45.8	3 31.1	12 10.3	11 2.1
9	1 8 31.4	15 13.6	5 7.9	12♒26.5	10 17.6	24 4.9	28 23.9	3 30.8	4 45.7	3 34.2	12 12.3	11 3.9
10	1 12 28.0	16 12.8	5 4.7	26 40.8	9 18.4	24 32.3	28 56.2	3 26.8	4 45.7	3 37.2	12 14.4	11 5.7
11	1 16 24.5	17 12.1	5 1.6	11♓21.4	8 26.2	24 58.0	29 28.4	3 23.1	4 45.7	3 40.2	12 16.5	11 7.5
12	1 20 21.1	18 11.4	4 58.4	26 23.8	7 42.7	25 22.0	0♌ .4	3 19.6	4D45.9	3 43.1	12 18.5	11 9.2
13	1 24 17.6	19 10.8	4 55.2	11♈40.1	7 8.8	25 44.2	0 32.1	3 16.2	4 46.2	3 46.0	12 20.6	11 10.9
14	1 28 14.2	20 10.2	4 52.0	26 59.5	6 45.5	26 4.6	1 3.7	3 13.0	4 46.6	3 48.9	12 22.7	11 12.6
15	1 32 10.8	21 9.6	4 48.8	12♉10.6	6 33.0	26 23.2	1 35.1	3 10.0	4 47.1	3 51.7	12 24.8	11 14.3
16	1 36 7.3	22 9.1	4 45.7	27 2.8	6 31.6	26 39.8	2 6.4	3 7.2	4 47.7	3 54.5	12 27.0	11 16.0
17	1 40 3.9	23 8.6	4 42.5	11♊28.9	6D41.2	26 54.5	2 37.4	3 4.6	4 48.4	3 57.3	12 29.1	11 17.7
18	1 44 .4	24 8.1	4 39.3	25 25.1	7 1.3	27 7.1	3 8.2	3 2.2	4 49.1	4 .0	12 31.3	11 19.3
19	1 47 57.0	25 7.7	4 36.1	8♋51.2	7 31.3	27 17.6	3 38.8	3 .0	4 50.0	4 2.7	12 33.4	11 20.9
20	1 51 53.5	26 7.3	4 33.0	21 49.6	8 10.6	27 25.9	4 9.2	2 58.0	4 51.0	4 5.4	12 35.6	11 22.5
21	1 55 50.1	27 6.9	4 29.8	4♌24.6	8 58.4	27 32.1	4 39.4	2 56.2	4 52.1	4 8.0	12 37.8	11 24.1
22	1 59 46.6	28 6.6	4 26.6	16 41.2	9 53.9	27 35.9	5 9.4	2 54.6	4 53.3	4 10.6	12 39.9	11 25.6
23	2 3 43.2	29 6.3	4 23.4	28 44.4	10 56.2	27 37.5	5 39.1	2 53.2	4 54.6	4 13.1	12 42.1	11 27.1
24	2 7 39.7	0♏ 6.1	4 20.2	10♍39.2	12 4.6	27R36.7	6 8.6	2 52.0	4 56.0	4 15.6	12 44.3	11 28.7
25	2 11 36.3	1 5.9	4 17.1	22 29.6	13 18.1	27 33.6	6 37.9	2 51.0	4 57.5	4 18.1	12 46.5	11 30.1
26	2 15 32.8	2 5.8	4 13.9	4♎19.3	14 36.3	27 28.1	7 7.0	2 50.2	4 59.1	4 20.5	12 48.8	11 31.7
27	2 19 29.4	3 5.6	4 10.7	16 10.7	15 58.3	27 20.2	7 35.8	2 49.6	5 .8	4 22.9	12 51.0	11 33.1
28	2 23 25.9	4 5.5	4 7.5	28 5.8	17 23.5	27 9.8	8 4.4	2 49.2	5 2.6	4 25.2	12 53.2	11 34.5
29	2 27 22.5	5 5.5	4 4.4	10♏ 6.0	18 51.5	26 57.0	8 32.7	2 49.0	5 4.5	4 27.5	12 55.5	11 35.9
30	2 31 19.1	6 5.4	4 1.2	22 12.3	20 21.8	26 41.9	9 .7	2 49.0	5 6.5	4 29.7	12 57.7	11 37.3
31	2 35 15.6	7 5.4	3 58.0	4♐25.7	21 53.9	26 24.4	9 28.5	2D49.3	5 8.5	4 31.9	12 59.9	11 38.6
		LATITUDE										
1	0 36 59.0	0 .0	0 .0	5N 1.7	3S25.3	5S14.3	0N50.4	1S22.5	0S44.9	0N43.3	1N43.6	12N59.5
4	0 48 48.7	0 .0	0 .0	4 21.1	2 49.3	5 30.4	0 54.0	1 22.1	0 45.0	0 43.4	1 43.5	13 .3
7	1 0 38.3	0 .0	0 .0	1 49.6	1 57.9	5 45.3	0 57.8	1 21.8	0 45.0	0 43.5	1 43.4	13 1.0
10	1 12 28.0	0 .0	0 .0	1S45.6	0 57.4	5 58.6	1 1.6	1 21.4	0 45.0	0 43.6	1 43.3	13 1.9
13	1 24 17.6	0 .0	0 .0	4 34.8	0N 2.4	6 10.1	1 5.5	1 21.0	0 45.0	0 43.7	1 43.2	13 2.8
16	1 36 7.3	0 .0	0 .0	4 40.6	0 53.1	6 19.2	1 9.4	1 20.5	0 45.0	0 43.7	1 43.2	13 3.7
19	1 47 57.0	0 .0	0 .0	2 14.9	1 30.4	6 25.3	1 13.5	1 20.0	0 45.0	0 43.8	1 43.1	13 4.7
22	1 59 46.6	0 .0	0 .0	1N .2	1 53.6	6 27.9	1 17.7	1 19.5	0 45.0	0 43.9	1 43.1	13 5.8
25	2 11 36.3	0 .0	0 .0	3 41.9	2 4.5	6 26.3	1 22.0	1 19.0	0 45.0	0 44.1	1 43.0	13 6.8
28	2 23 25.9	0 .0	0 .0	4 57.5	2 5.6	6 19.7	1 26.4	1 18.4	0 45.0	0 44.2	1 43.0	13 8.0
31	2 35 15.6	0 .0	0 .0	4 18.1	1 59.3	6 7.5	1 31.0	1 17.9	0 45.0	0 44.3	1 43.0	13 9.1
		RIGHT ASCENSION										
1	0 36 59.0	6♎44.5	7♌55.3	0♏42.5	16♎ 7.5	15♏35.7	26♋ 1.6	6♓32.0	7♒21.6	5♍21.1	10♏ 2.7	17♍29.1
2	0 40 55.6	7 38.8	7 52.0	12 8.1	15R21.5	16 13.7	26 37.6	6R27.0	7R20.8	5 24.2	10 4.6	17 31.0
3	0 44 52.1	8 33.2	7 48.7	23 56.7	14 30.9	16 50.7	27 13.4	6 22.1	7 20.0	5 27.3	10 6.5	17 32.9
4	0 48 48.7	9 27.6	7 45.5	6♐14.7	13 36.5	17 26.6	27 49.0	6 17.3	7 19.4	5 30.3	10 8.4	17 34.8
5	0 52 45.2	10 22.2	7 42.2	19 5.8	12 39.7	18 1.3	28 24.4	6 12.7	7 18.9	5 33.4	10 10.4	17 36.7
6	0 56 41.8	11 16.8	7 39.0	2♑30.1	11 41.7	18 34.7	28 59.6	6 8.3	7 18.5	5 36.4	10 12.4	17 38.5
7	1 0 38.3	12 11.5	7 35.7	16 23.6	10 44.1	19 6.7	29 34.5	6 4.0	7 18.2	5 39.3	10 14.3	17 40.4
8	1 4 34.9	13 6.3	7 32.4	0♒38.2	9 48.6	19 37.4	0♌ 9.3	5 59.9	7 17.9	5 42.3	10 16.3	17 42.2
9	1 8 31.4	14 1.2	7 29.2	15 3.8	8 56.9	20 6.6	0 43.7	5 56.0	7 17.8	5 45.2	10 18.3	17 44.0
10	1 12 28.0	14 56.3	7 25.9	29 31.4	8 10.3	20 34.3	1 18.0	5 52.2	7 17.8	5 48.0	10 20.3	17 45.8
11	1 16 24.5	15 51.4	7 22.7	13♓55.3	7 30.4	21 .4	1 52.1	5 48.6	7D17.9	5 50.9	10 22.3	17 47.6
12	1 20 21.1	16 46.6	7 19.4	28 14.2	6 58.2	21 24.9	2 25.9	5 45.2	7 18.1	5 53.7	10 24.4	17 49.4
13	1 24 17.6	17 42.0	7 16.1	12♈31.0	6 34.7	21 47.5	2 59.4	5 41.9	7 18.4	5 56.4	10 26.4	17 51.1
14	1 28 14.2	18 37.4	7 12.9	26 50.6	6 20.4	22 8.4	3 32.8	5 38.8	7 18.8	5 59.2	10 28.5	17 52.9
15	1 32 10.8	19 33.1	7 9.6	11♉17.1	6 15.7	22 27.4	4 5.9	5 36.0	7 19.3	6 1.9	10 30.5	17 54.6
16	1 36 7.3	20 28.8	7 6.3	25 52.0	6D20.6	22 44.4	4 38.8	5 33.2	7 19.9	6 4.5	10 32.6	17 56.3
17	1 40 3.9	21 24.7	7 3.1	10♊31.7	6 34.9	22 59.5	5 11.4	5 30.7	7 20.6	6 7.2	10 34.7	17 58.0
18	1 44 .4	22 20.8	6 59.8	25 7.7	6 58.3	23 12.4	5 43.8	5 28.4	7 21.4	6 9.8	10 36.8	17 59.7
19	1 47 57.0	23 17.0	6 56.5	9♋28.5	7 30.1	23 23.2	6 15.9	5 26.2	7 22.3	6 12.3	10 38.9	18 1.4
20	1 51 53.5	24 13.3	6 53.3	23 23.1	8 9.9	23 31.8	6 47.8	5 24.2	7 23.4	6 14.9	10 41.0	18 3.0
21	1 55 50.1	25 9.8	6 50.0	6♌43.6	8 56.9	23 38.1	7 19.4	5 22.4	7 24.5	6 17.4	10 43.2	18 4.7
22	1 59 46.6	26 6.5	6 46.7	19 27.4	9 50.4	23 42.2	7 50.7	5 20.8	7 25.7	6 19.8	10 45.3	18 6.3
23	2 3 43.2	27 3.4	6 43.5	1♍36.3	10 49.7	23 43.9	8 21.8	5 19.4	7 27.0	6 22.2	10 47.5	18 7.9
24	2 7 39.7	28 .4	6 40.2	13 16.1	11 54.0	23R43.2	8 52.6	5 18.2	7 28.5	6 24.6	10 49.6	18 9.5
25	2 11 36.3	28 57.6	6 36.9	24 34.5	13 2.8	23 40.1	9 23.2	5 17.2	7 30.0	6 27.0	10 51.8	18 11.0
26	2 15 32.8	29 55.0	6 33.7	5♎40.6	14 15.5	23 34.7	9 53.5	5 16.4	7 31.7	6 29.3	10 54.0	18 12.6
27	2 19 29.4	0♏52.6	6 30.4	16 43.5	15 31.5	23 26.7	10 23.5	5 15.8	7 33.4	6 31.6	10 56.2	18 14.1
28	2 23 25.9	1 50.4	6 27.1	27 52.5	16 50.2	23 16.3	10 53.2	5 15.3	7 35.3	6 33.8	10 58.4	18 15.6
29	2 27 22.5	2 48.3	6 23.9	9♏16.4	18 11.4	23 3.6	11 22.6	5 15.1	7 37.2	6 36.0	11 .6	18 17.1
30	2 31 19.1	3 46.4	6 20.6	21 2.7	19 34.5	22 48.5	11 51.7	5 15.0	7 39.3	6 38.1	11 2.7	18 18.6
31	2 35 15.6	4 44.8	6 17.3	3♐16.9	20 59.4	22 31.0	12 20.5	5D15.2	7 41.4	6 40.2	11 4.9	18 20.0
		DECLINATION										
1	0 36 59.0	2S54.8	0N19.8	7S 8.0	10S34.2	22S40.0	22N 8.5	11S16.4	19S47.3	11N 1.5	13S46.6	19N29.3
4	0 48 48.7	4 4.6	0 19.8	17 14.3	8 53.1	23 25.9	21 54.0	11 21.7	19 47.9	10 58.1	13 48.5	19 27.8
7	1 0 38.3	5 13.9	0 19.9	20 44.9	6 45.1	24 6.7	21 38.7	11 26.4	19 48.2	10 54.7	13 50.4	19 26.4
10	1 12 28.0	6 22.7	0 19.9	14 16.6	4 34.1	24 41.8	21 22.7	11 30.5	19 48.3	10 51.5	13 52.3	19 25.1
13	1 24 17.6	7 30.6	0 19.9	0N23.8	2 48.0	25 10.8	21 6.2	11 33.9	19 48.2	10 48.4	13 54.3	19 23.8
16	1 36 7.3	8 37.6	0 20.0	14 56.8	1 46.7	25 33.2	20 49.3	11 36.8	19 47.8	10 45.4	13 56.2	19 22.7
19	1 47 57.0	9 43.6	0 20.0	20 54.3	1 36.1	25 48.2	20 31.9	11 38.9	19 47.3	10 42.5	13 58.2	19 21.7
22	1 59 46.6	10 48.2	0 20.1	16 47.6	2 10.8	25 55.0	20 14.3	11 40.4	19 46.5	10 39.7	14 .3	19 20.9
25	2 11 36.3	11 51.5	0 20.1	6 22.5	3 20.4	25 52.9	19 56.5	11 41.2	19 45.5	10 37.1	14 2.3	19 20.1
28	2 23 25.9	12 53.1	0 20.1	6S 9.8	4 53.7	25 40.9	19 38.5	11 41.4	19 44.2	10 34.6	14 4.3	19 19.4
31	2 35 15.6	13 52.9	0 20.2	16 48.0	6 41.2	25 18.1	19 20.7	11 40.8	19 42.8	10 32.2	14 6.3	19 18.9

NOVEMBER 1962

DAY	EPHEM. SID. TIME	☉	☊	☾	☿	♀	♂	♃	♄	♅	♆	♇
		LONGITUDE										
	h m s	° ′	° ′	° ′	° ′	° ′	° ′	° ′	° ′	° ′	° ′	° ′
1	2 39 12.2	8♏ 5.4	3♌54.8	16♐47.4	23♎27.4	26♏ 4.5	9♌56.0	2♓49.7	5♒10.7	4♍34.1	13♏ 2.2	11♍39.9
2	2 43 8.7	9 5.5	3 51.6	29 19.1	25 2.2	25 R 42.5	10 23.3	2 50.3	5 13.0	4 36.2	13 4.4	11 41.2
3	2 47 5.3	10 5.6	3 48.5	12♑ 3.0	26 37.9	25 18.3	10 50.2	2 51.2	5 15.4	4 38.2	13 6.7	11 42.5
4	2 51 1.8	11 5.7	3 45.3	25 1.9	28 14.3	24 52.1	11 16.9	2 52.2	5 17.8	4 40.3	13 8.9	11 43.7
5	2 54 58.4	12 5.8	3 42.1	8♒18.8	29 51.2	24 23.9	11 43.3	2 53.4	5 20.4	4 42.2	13 11.2	11 45.0
6	2 58 54.9	13 6.0	3 38.9	21 56.7	1♏28.5	23 54.0	12 9.4	2 54.9	5 23.1	4 44.1	13 13.4	11 46.2
7	3 2 51.5	14 6.1	3 35.8	5♓57.3	3 6.0	23 22.5	12 35.2	2 56.5	5 25.8	4 46.0	13 15.6	11 47.3
8	3 6 48.0	15 6.4	3 32.6	20 21.1	4 43.6	22 49.6	13 .7	2 58.4	5 28.6	4 47.8	13 17.9	11 48.5
9	3 10 44.6	16 6.6	3 29.4	5♈ 5.4	6 21.2	22 15.5	13 25.9	3 .4	5 31.6	4 49.6	13 20.1	11 49.6
10	3 14 41.2	17 6.8	3 26.2	20 5.0	7 58.9	21 40.4	13 50.8	3 2.7	5 34.6	4 51.3	13 22.4	11 50.6
11	3 18 37.7	18 7.1	3 23.1	5♉11.5	9 36.4	21 4.6	14 15.4	3 5.2	5 37.7	4 53.0	13 24.6	11 51.7
12	3 22 34.3	19 7.4	3 19.9	20 14.6	11 13.8	20 28.3	14 39.6	3 7.8	5 40.9	4 54.6	13 26.9	11 52.7
13	3 26 30.8	20 7.8	3 16.7	5♊ 4.5	12 51.0	19 51.7	15 3.5	3 10.6	5 44.2	4 56.2	13 29.1	11 53.7
14	3 30 27.4	21 8.1	3 13.5	19 32.6	14 28.0	19 15.1	15 27.1	3 13.7	5 47.6	4 57.7	13 31.3	11 54.7
15	3 34 23.9	22 8.5	3 10.3	3♋33.8	16 4.9	18 38.8	15 50.3	3 16.9	5 51.1	4 59.1	13 33.6	11 55.6
16	3 38 20.5	23 9.0	3 7.2	17 6.2	17 41.5	18 3.1	16 13.2	3 20.4	5 54.7	5 .6	13 35.8	11 56.6
17	3 42 17.0	24 9.5	3 4.0	0♌10.5	19 17.9	17 28.1	16 35.7	3 24.0	5 58.3	5 2.0	13 38.0	11 57.5
18	3 46 13.6	25 10.0	3 .8	12 50.2	20 54.0	16 54.1	16 57.9	3 27.8	6 2.0	5 3.3	13 40.3	11 58.3
19	3 50 10.2	26 10.5	2 57.6	25 9.8	22 29.9	16 21.4	17 19.6	3 31.8	6 5.8	5 4.5	13 42.5	11 59.2
20	3 54 6.7	27 11.0	2 54.5	7♍14.4	24 5.6	15 50.1	17 41.0	3 36.0	6 9.7	5 5.7	13 44.7	11 60.0
21	3 58 3.3	28 11.6	2 51.3	19 9.5	25 41.1	15 20.4	18 2.0	3 40.4	6 13.7	5 6.9	13 46.9	12 .7
22	4 1 59.8	29 12.2	2 48.1	0♎59.9	27 16.4	14 52.5	18 22.5	3 44.9	6 17.8	5 8.0	13 49.1	12 1.5
23	4 5 56.4	0♐12.9	2 44.9	12 50.2	28 51.5	14 26.5	18 42.7	3 49.7	6 21.9	5 9.0	13 51.2	12 2.2
24	4 9 52.9	1 13.5	2 41.7	24 44.0	0♐26.3	14 2.6	19 2.4	3 54.6	6 26.1	5 10.0	13 53.4	12 2.8
25	4 13 49.5	2 14.2	2 38.6	6♏44.0	2 1.1	13 40.9	19 21.7	3 59.7	6 30.5	5 10.9	13 55.6	12 3.5
26	4 17 46.1	3 14.9	2 35.4	18 52.4	3 35.6	13 21.5	19 40.5	4 5.0	6 34.8	5 11.8	13 57.7	12 4.1
27	4 21 42.6	4 15.7	2 32.2	1♐10.2	5 10.1	13 4.4	19 58.9	4 10.5	6 39.3	5 12.6	13 59.9	12 4.7
28	4 25 39.2	5 16.4	2 29.0	13 38.1	6 44.4	12 49.7	20 16.8	4 16.1	6 43.8	5 13.4	14 2.0	12 5.2
29	4 29 35.7	6 17.2	2 25.9	26 16.4	8 18.6	12 37.5	20 34.2	4 21.9	6 48.4	5 14.1	14 4.1	12 5.7
30	4 33 32.3	7 18.0	2 22.7	9♑ 5.3	9 52.7	12 27.7	20 51.2	4 27.9	6 53.1	5 14.7	14 6.2	12 6.2
		LATITUDE										
1	2 39 12.2	0 .0	0 .0	3N39.3	1N56.0	6S 2.1	1N32.5	1S17.7	0S45.0	0N44.3	1N43.0	13N 9.5
4	2 51 1.8	0 .0	0 .0	0 43.9	1 43.0	5 41.5	1 37.2	1 17.1	0 45.0	0 44.4	1 43.0	13 10.7
7	3 2 51.5	0 .0	0 .0	2S43.3	1 26.8	5 14.4	1 42.0	1 16.6	0 45.0	0 44.6	1 43.0	13 12.0
10	3 14 41.2	0 .0	0 .0	4 53.6	1 8.5	4 41.0	1 47.0	1 16.0	0 45.0	0 44.7	1 43.0	13 13.2
13	3 26 30.8	0 .0	0 .0	4 14.3	0 48.9	4 2.1	1 52.1	1 15.4	0 45.1	0 44.8	1 43.0	13 14.5
16	3 38 20.5	0 .0	0 .0	1 19.2	0 28.6	3 19.0	1 57.4	1 14.8	0 45.1	0 44.9	1 43.0	13 15.9
19	3 50 10.2	0 .0	0 .0	1N59.3	0 8.1	2 33.2	2 2.8	1 14.2	0 45.1	0 45.1	1 43.1	13 17.2
22	4 1 59.8	0 .0	0 .0	4 20.7	0S12.1	1 46.7	2 8.5	1 13.7	0 45.1	0 45.2	1 43.1	13 18.6
25	4 13 49.5	0 .0	0 .0	5 2.3	0 31.8	1 .9	2 14.2	1 13.1	0 45.1	0 45.3	1 43.1	13 20.0
28	4 25 39.2	0 .0	0 .0	3 44.6	0 50.6	0 17.2	2 20.2	1 12.6	0 45.1	0 45.5	1 43.2	13 21.4
		RIGHT ASCENSION										
1	2 39 12.2	5♏43.3	6♌14.1	16♐ 1.8	22♎25.7	22♏11.4	12♌49.0	5♓15.5	7♒43.7	6♍42.2	11♏ 7.1	18♍21.4
2	2 43 8.7	6 42.0	6 10.8	29 16.4	23 53.2	21 R 49.6	13 17.2	5 16.0	7 46.0	6 44.2	11 9.3	18 22.8
3	2 47 5.3	7 40.9	6 7.5	12♑55.3	25 21.7	21 25.8	13 45.1	5 16.7	7 48.4	6 46.2	11 11.5	18 24.2
4	2 51 1.8	8 40.0	6 4.2	26 50.1	26 51.1	21 .1	14 12.7	5 17.7	7 51.0	6 48.1	11 13.8	18 25.5
5	2 54 58.4	9 39.3	6 1.0	10♒51.4	28 21.2	20 32.7	14 39.9	5 18.8	7 53.6	6 50.0	11 16.0	18 26.9
6	2 58 54.9	10 38.8	5 57.7	24 51.2	29 51.9	20 3.7	15 6.8	5 20.1	7 56.4	6 51.8	11 18.2	18 28.2
7	3 2 51.5	11 38.5	5 54.4	8♓45.7	1♏23.2	19 33.3	15 33.4	5 21.6	7 59.2	6 53.6	11 20.4	18 29.4
8	3 6 48.0	12 38.4	5 51.1	22 35.7	2 54.9	19 1.7	15 59.7	5 23.3	8 2.1	6 55.3	11 22.6	18 30.7
9	3 10 44.6	13 38.6	5 47.9	6♈25.9	4 27.1	18 29.3	16 25.7	5 25.2	8 5.1	6 57.0	11 24.8	18 31.9
10	3 14 41.2	14 38.9	5 44.6	20 23.4	5 59.6	17 56.1	16 51.3	5 27.2	8 8.2	6 58.7	11 27.0	18 33.1
11	3 18 37.7	15 39.4	5 41.3	4♉35.6	7 32.5	17 22.4	17 16.5	5 29.5	8 11.4	7 .2	11 29.2	18 34.3
12	3 22 34.3	16 40.2	5 38.0	19 6.8	9 5.7	16 48.6	17 41.4	5 31.9	8 14.7	7 1.8	11 31.4	18 35.5
13	3 26 30.8	17 41.1	5 34.8	3♊55.9	10 39.3	16 14.8	18 6.0	5 34.6	8 18.1	7 3.3	11 33.6	18 36.6
14	3 30 27.4	18 42.3	5 31.5	18 54.7	12 13.2	15 41.3	18 30.2	5 37.4	8 21.6	7 4.7	11 35.8	18 37.7
15	3 34 23.9	19 43.7	5 28.2	3♋48.8	13 47.4	15 8.4	18 54.1	5 40.4	8 25.2	7 6.1	11 38.0	18 38.8
16	3 38 20.5	20 45.3	5 24.9	18 21.7	15 22.0	14 36.3	19 17.6	5 43.6	8 28.9	7 7.5	11 40.3	18 39.9
17	3 42 17.0	21 47.1	5 21.6	2♌19.5	16 56.9	14 5.2	19 40.7	5 47.0	8 32.6	7 8.8	11 42.5	18 40.9
18	3 46 13.6	22 49.2	5 18.4	15 35.0	18 32.1	13 35.3	20 3.4	5 50.5	8 36.5	7 10.1	11 44.6	18 41.9
19	3 50 10.2	23 51.4	5 15.1	28 7.8	20 7.6	13 6.9	20 25.7	5 54.3	8 40.4	7 11.3	11 46.8	18 42.9
20	3 54 6.7	24 53.9	5 11.8	10♍ 3.3	21 43.5	12 40.0	20 47.6	5 58.2	8 44.4	7 12.5	11 49.0	18 43.8
21	3 58 3.3	25 56.5	5 8.5	21 30.2	23 19.8	12 14.9	21 9.1	6 2.3	8 48.5	7 13.6	11 51.2	18 44.7
22	4 1 59.8	26 59.4	5 5.2	2♎38.8	24 56.4	11 51.7	21 30.2	6 6.5	8 52.6	7 14.6	11 53.3	18 45.6
23	4 5 56.4	28 2.5	5 2.0	13 40.2	26 33.5	11 30.4	21 50.8	6 11.0	8 56.9	7 15.6	11 55.5	18 46.5
24	4 9 52.9	29 5.8	4 58.7	24 45.3	28 10.9	11 11.3	22 11.0	6 15.6	9 1.2	7 16.6	11 57.6	18 47.3
25	4 13 49.5	0♐ 9.2	4 55.4	6♏ 4.3	29 48.7	10 54.4	22 30.8	6 20.3	9 5.6	7 17.5	11 59.8	18 48.1
26	4 17 46.1	1 12.9	4 52.1	17 46.4	1♐26.9	10 39.7	22 50.1	6 25.3	9 10.1	7 18.3	12 1.9	18 48.9
27	4 21 42.6	2 16.7	4 48.8	29 58.4	3 5.5	10 27.4	23 9.0	6 30.4	9 14.7	7 19.1	12 4.0	18 49.7
28	4 25 39.2	3 20.8	4 45.5	12♐43.9	4 44.5	10 17.3	23 27.4	6 35.7	9 19.4	7 19.8	12 6.1	18 50.4
29	4 29 35.7	4 25.0	4 42.3	26 1.6	6 24.0	10 9.6	23 45.3	6 41.2	9 24.1	7 20.5	12 8.2	18 51.1
30	4 33 32.3	5 29.4	4 39.0	9♑45.0	8 3.8	10 4.2	24 2.8	6 46.8	9 28.9	7 21.1	12 10.3	18 51.7
		DECLINATION										
1	2 39 12.2	14S12.4	0N20.2	19S 9.0	7S18.9	25S 8.0	19N14.8	11S40.5	19S42.2	10N31.5	14S 7.0	19N18.7
4	2 51 1.8	15 9.5	0 20.2	20 24.6	9 14.7	24 30.2	18 57.1	11 39.1	19 40.5	10 29.3	14 9.0	19 18.3
7	3 2 51.5	16 4.4	0 20.3	11 51.4	11 11.2	23 41.2	18 39.8	11 37.0	19 38.6	10 27.3	14 11.1	19 18.1
10	3 14 41.2	16 56.9	0 20.3	3N19.0	13 5.5	22 42.2	18 22.8	11 34.2	19 36.4	10 25.5	14 13.1	19 18.0
13	3 26 30.8	17 46.7	0 20.3	16 58.6	14 55.3	21 35.3	18 6.4	11 30.8	19 34.1	10 23.9	14 15.0	19 18.0
16	3 38 20.5	18 33.8	0 20.4	21 2.4	16 39.2	20 23.6	17 50.6	11 26.7	19 31.5	10 22.3	14 17.0	19 18.1
19	3 50 10.2	19 17.9	0 20.4	15 .5	18 16.0	19 10.6	17 35.6	11 22.0	19 28.7	10 21.0	14 19.0	19 18.3
22	4 1 59.8	19 58.9	0 20.5	3 35.3	19 45.0	17 60.0	17 21.5	11 16.7	19 25.8	10 19.9	14 20.9	19 18.7
25	4 13 49.5	20 36.7	0 20.5	9S .0	21 5.3	16 54.9	17 8.4	11 10.8	19 22.6	10 18.9	14 22.8	19 19.2
28	4 25 39.2	21 11.0	0 20.5	18 43.4	22 16.2	15 57.8	16 56.6	11 4.3	19 19.3	10 18.1	14 24.6	19 19.8

DECEMBER 1962

LONGITUDE

DAY	EPHEM. SID. TIME	☉	☊	☽	☿	♀	♂	♃	♄	♅	♆	♇
	h m s	° ′	° ′	° ′	° ′	° ′	° ′	° ′	° ′	° ′	° ′	° ′
1	4 37 28.8	8♐18.8	2♌19.5	22♑ 5.2	11♐26.7	12♏20.4	21♌ 7.6	4♓34.1	6♒57.9	5♍15.3	14♏ 8.3	12♍ 6.7
2	4 41 25.4	9 19.7	2 16.3	5♒17.0	13 .7	12 R 15.5	21 23.6	4 40.4	7 2.7	5 15.9	14 10.4	12 7.1
3	4 45 22.0	10 20.5	2 13.2	18 41.8	14 34.6	12 13.2	21 39.0	4 47.0	7 7.6	5 16.3	14 12.5	12 7.5
4	4 49 18.5	11 21.4	2 10.0	2♓21.0	16 8.4	12 13.2	21 53.9	4 53.6	7 12.6	5 16.8	14 14.5	12 7.8
5	4 53 15.1	12 22.2	2 6.8	16 15.4	17 42.3	12 D 15.7	22 8.3	5 .5	7 17.7	5 17.1	14 16.6	12 8.2
6	4 57 11.6	13 23.1	2 3.6	0♈25.2	19 16.1	12 20.5	22 22.2	5 7.5	7 22.8	5 17.5	14 18.6	12 8.5
7	5 1 8.2	14 24.1	2 .4	14 49.0	20 50.0	12 27.7	22 35.5	5 14.7	7 28.0	5 17.8	14 20.6	12 8.8
8	5 5 4.7	15 25.0	1 57.3	29 23.6	22 23.8	12 37.1	22 48.2	5 22.0	7 33.3	5 18.0	14 22.6	12 9.0
9	5 9 1.3	16 25.9	1 54.1	14♉ 3.6	23 57.6	12 48.8	23 .4	5 29.5	7 38.6	5 18.1	14 24.6	12 9.2
10	5 12 57.9	17 26.9	1 50.9	28 42.3	25 31.4	13 2.7	23 12.0	5 37.1	7 43.9	5 18.2	14 26.6	12 9.4
11	5 16 54.4	18 27.8	1 47.7	13♊12.3	27 5.3	13 18.6	23 22.9	5 44.9	7 49.4	5 18.2	14 28.5	12 9.5
12	5 20 51.0	19 28.8	1 44.6	27 26.9	28 39.2	13 36.6	23 33.3	5 52.9	7 54.9	5 18.2	14 30.4	12 9.6
13	5 24 47.5	20 29.8	1 41.4	11♋20.8	0♑13.0	13 56.7	23 43.1	6 .9	8 .5	5 R 18.1	14 32.4	12 9.7
14	5 28 44.1	21 30.8	1 38.2	24 51.1	1 46.9	14 18.6	23 52.2	6 9.2	8 6.1	5 18.0	14 34.2	12 9.7
15	5 32 40.6	22 31.8	1 35.0	7♌57.2	3 20.7	14 42.5	24 .7	6 17.6	8 11.8	5 17.8	14 36.1	12 9.7
16	5 36 37.2	23 32.8	1 31.9	20 40.6	4 54.5	15 8.1	24 8.5	6 26.1	8 17.5	5 17.5	14 38.0	12 9.7
17	5 40 33.8	24 33.8	1 28.7	3♍ 4.4	6 28.3	15 35.5	24 15.6	6 34.8	8 23.3	5 17.2	14 39.8	12 R 9.6
18	5 44 30.3	25 34.9	1 25.5	15 12.8	8 1.9	16 4.6	24 22.1	6 43.6	8 29.2	5 16.9	14 41.6	12 9.5
19	5 48 26.9	26 36.0	1 22.3	27 10.7	9 35.3	16 35.2	24 27.9	6 52.5	8 35.1	5 16.4	14 43.4	12 9.4
20	5 52 23.4	27 37.0	1 19.2	9♎ 3.0	11 8.6	17 7.5	24 32.9	7 1.6	8 41.0	5 16.0	14 45.2	12 9.2
21	5 56 20.0	28 38.1	1 16.0	20 54.7	12 41.5	17 41.2	24 37.3	7 10.8	8 47.0	5 15.4	14 46.9	12 9.1
22	6 0 16.5	29 39.3	1 12.8	2♏50.3	14 14.1	18 16.4	24 40.9	7 20.2	8 53.1	5 14.9	14 48.6	12 8.8
23	6 4 13.1	0♑40.4	1 9.6	14 53.8	15 46.1	18 53.0	24 43.8	7 29.6	8 59.2	5 14.2	14 50.4	12 8.6
24	6 8 9.7	1 41.5	1 6.4	27 8.2	17 17.6	19 30.8	24 45.9	7 39.3	9 5.4	5 13.5	14 52.0	12 8.3
25	6 12 6.2	2 42.7	1 3.3	9♐35.9	18 48.3	20 10.0	24 47.3	7 49.0	9 11.6	5 12.8	14 53.7	12 8.0
26	6 16 2.8	3 43.8	1 .1	22 18.1	20 18.0	20 50.4	24 47.8	7 58.9	9 17.9	5 12.0	14 55.3	12 7.6
27	6 19 59.3	4 45.0	0 56.9	5♑15.1	21 46.6	21 31.9	24 R 47.6	8 8.9	9 24.2	5 11.1	14 56.9	12 7.3
28	6 23 55.9	5 46.2	0 53.7	18 26.4	23 13.9	22 14.6	24 46.7	8 19.0	9 30.6	5 10.3	14 58.6	12 6.9
29	6 27 52.4	6 47.4	0 50.6	1♒50.9	24 39.4	22 58.4	24 44.9	8 29.3	9 37.0	5 9.3	15 .1	12 6.5
30	6 31 49.0	7 48.5	0 47.4	15 27.0	26 2.8	23 43.1	24 42.3	8 39.6	9 43.4	5 8.3	15 1.7	12 6.0
31	6 35 45.6	8 49.7	0 44.2	29 13.4	27 23.9	24 28.9	24 39.0	8 50.1	9 49.9	5 7.2	15 3.2	12 5.5

LATITUDE

DAY	EPHEM. SID. TIME	☉	☊	☽	☿	♀	♂	♃	♄	♅	♆	♇
1	4 37 28.8	0 .0	0 .0	0N46.5	1S 8.4	0N23.5	2N26.3	1S12.0	0S45.2	0N45.6	1N43.3	13N22.8
4	4 49 18.5	0 .0	0 .0	2S41.7	1 24.7	1 .5	2 32.6	1 11.5	0 45.2	0 45.7	1 43.3	13 24.3
7	5 1 8.2	0 .0	0 .0	4 56.5	1 39.3	1 33.6	2 39.1	1 11.0	0 45.2	0 45.9	1 43.4	13 25.7
10	5 12 57.9	0 .0	0 .0	4 31.8	1 51.8	2 2.7	2 45.7	1 10.5	0 45.3	0 46.0	1 43.5	13 27.2
13	5 24 47.5	0 .0	0 .0	1 40.2	2 2.0	2 28.0	2 52.5	1 10.0	0 45.3	0 46.1	1 43.6	13 28.6
16	5 36 37.2	0 .0	0 .0	1N49.7	2 9.4	2 49.5	2 59.5	1 9.5	0 45.4	0 46.3	1 43.7	13 30.0
19	5 48 26.9	0 .0	0 .0	4 22.2	2 13.4	3 7.5	3 6.6	1 9.0	0 45.5	0 46.4	1 43.8	13 31.4
22	6 0 16.5	0 .0	0 .0	5 12.0	2 13.5	3 22.4	3 13.9	1 8.6	0 45.5	0 46.5	1 44.0	13 32.9
25	6 12 6.2	0 .0	0 .0	4 .8	2 8.8	3 34.2	3 21.2	1 8.1	0 45.6	0 46.7	1 44.1	13 34.3
28	6 23 55.9	0 .0	0 .0	1 1.5	1 58.4	3 43.3	3 28.5	1 7.7	0 45.7	0 46.8	1 44.2	13 35.6
31	6 35 45.6	0 .0	0 .0	2S35.7	1 41.2	3 49.9	3 35.8	1 7.3	0 45.8	0 46.9	1 44.4	13 37.0

RIGHT ASCENSION

DAY	EPHEM. SID. TIME	☉	☊	☽	☿	♀	♂	♃	♄	♅	♆	♇
1	4 37 28.8	6♐33.9	4♌35.7	23♑43.5	9♐44.1	10♏ 1.1	24♌19.7	6♓52.6	9♒33.8	7♍21.7	12♏12.4	18♍52.4
2	4 41 25.4	7 38.7	4 32.4	7♒44.7	11 24.8	10 R .4	24 36.2	6 58.5	9 38.8	7 22.2	12 14.4	18 53.0
3	4 45 22.0	8 43.5	4 29.1	21 38.4	13 5.8	10 D 1.9	24 52.1	7 4.6	9 43.8	7 22.7	12 16.5	18 53.5
4	4 49 18.5	9 48.6	4 25.8	5♓19.2	14 47.3	10 5.7	25 7.5	7 10.9	9 48.9	7 23.1	12 18.5	18 54.1
5	4 53 15.1	10 53.7	4 22.5	18 47.6	16 29.1	10 11.8	25 22.4	7 17.3	9 54.1	7 23.5	12 20.5	18 54.6
6	4 57 11.6	11 59.0	4 19.2	2♈ 9.2	18 11.3	10 20.0	25 36.8	7 23.8	9 59.3	7 23.8	12 22.5	18 55.1
7	5 1 8.2	13 4.5	4 16.0	15 33.0	19 53.9	10 30.4	25 50.7	7 30.6	10 4.7	7 24.1	12 24.6	18 55.6
8	5 5 4.7	14 10.1	4 12.7	29 9.3	21 36.7	10 42.8	26 3.9	7 37.5	10 10.0	7 24.3	12 26.5	18 56.0
9	5 9 1.3	15 15.7	4 9.4	13♉ 6.8	23 19.8	10 57.3	26 16.6	7 44.5	10 15.5	7 24.5	12 28.5	18 56.4
10	5 12 57.9	16 21.5	4 6.1	27 30.2	25 3.2	11 13.7	26 28.8	7 51.6	10 21.0	7 24.6	12 30.5	18 56.7
11	5 16 54.4	17 27.4	4 2.8	12♊17.1	26 46.8	11 32.1	26 40.3	7 58.9	10 26.5	7 24.6	12 32.4	18 57.1
12	5 20 51.0	18 33.4	3 59.5	27 16.6	28 30.6	11 52.4	26 51.3	8 6.4	10 32.2	7 24.6	12 34.3	18 57.4
13	5 24 47.5	19 39.5	3 56.2	12♋11.1	0♑14.4	12 14.5	27 1.7	8 14.0	10 37.8	7 R 24.5	12 36.2	18 57.6
14	5 28 44.1	20 45.7	3 52.9	26 41.6	1 58.4	12 38.4	27 11.4	8 21.7	10 43.6	7 24.4	12 38.1	18 57.9
15	5 32 40.6	21 52.0	3 49.6	10♌33.7	3 42.3	13 3.9	27 20.6	8 29.5	10 49.4	7 24.3	12 39.9	18 58.1
16	5 36 37.2	22 58.3	3 46.3	23 40.7	5 26.2	13 31.2	27 29.0	8 37.5	10 55.3	7 24.0	12 41.8	18 58.2
17	5 40 33.8	24 4.7	3 43.0	6♍ 3.8	7 10.0	14 .0	27 36.9	8 45.6	11 1.2	7 23.8	12 43.6	18 58.4
18	5 44 30.3	25 11.1	3 39.8	17 49.8	8 53.5	14 30.5	27 44.0	8 53.9	11 7.2	7 23.4	12 45.4	18 58.5
19	5 48 26.9	26 17.7	3 36.5	29 9.2	10 36.6	15 2.4	27 50.5	9 2.2	11 13.2	7 23.1	12 47.2	18 58.6
20	5 52 23.4	27 24.2	3 33.2	10♎13.5	12 19.4	15 35.7	27 56.3	9 10.7	11 19.3	7 22.6	12 48.9	18 58.6
21	5 56 20.0	28 30.8	3 29.9	21 14.9	14 1.5	16 10.5	28 1.4	9 19.4	11 25.4	7 22.2	12 50.7	18 58.7
22	6 0 16.5	29 37.4	3 26.6	2♏25.5	15 43.0	16 46.6	28 5.8	9 28.1	11 31.6	7 21.6	12 52.4	18 58.7
23	6 4 13.1	0♑44.0	3 23.3	13 56.3	17 23.6	17 24.0	28 9.5	9 37.0	11 37.8	7 21.0	12 54.1	18 R 58.6
24	6 8 9.7	1 50.6	3 20.0	25 56.9	19 3.1	18 2.6	28 12.4	9 46.0	11 44.1	7 20.4	12 55.8	18 58.5
25	6 12 6.2	2 57.3	3 16.7	8♐33.8	20 41.3	18 42.5	28 14.6	9 55.1	11 50.5	7 19.7	12 57.4	18 58.4
26	6 16 2.8	4 3.9	3 13.4	21 48.9	22 18.1	19 23.6	28 16.1	10 4.3	11 56.8	7 19.0	12 59.0	18 58.3
27	6 19 59.3	5 10.5	3 10.1	5♑37.8	23 53.1	20 5.7	28 16.7	10 13.7	12 3.3	7 18.2	13 .6	18 58.2
28	6 23 55.9	6 17.1	3 6.8	19 49.4	25 26.1	20 49.1	28 16.7	10 23.2	12 9.8	7 17.4	13 2.3	18 58.0
29	6 27 52.4	7 23.6	3 3.5	4♒ 8.9	26 56.7	21 33.4	28 R 15.8	10 32.8	12 16.3	7 16.5	13 3.8	18 57.8
30	6 31 49.0	8 30.1	3 .2	18 21.3	28 24.6	22 18.8	28 14.1	10 42.4	12 22.9	7 15.5	13 5.4	18 57.5
31	6 35 45.6	9 36.5	2 56.9	2♓16.8	29 49.2	23 5.2	28 11.7	10 52.2	12 29.5	7 14.6	13 6.9	18 57.3

DECLINATION

DAY	EPHEM. SID. TIME	☉	☊	☽	☿	♀	♂	♃	♄	♅	♆	♇
1	4 37 28.8	21S41.7	0N20.6	20S52.0	23S17.1	15S10.2	16N46.0	10S57.2	19S15.7	10N17.6	14S26.4	19N20.5
4	4 49 18.5	22 8.7	0 20.6	13 9.2	24 7.5	14 32.7	16 36.9	10 49.6	19 12.0	10 17.1	14 28.2	19 21.4
7	5 1 8.2	22 31.8	0 20.6	1N16.8	24 46.6	14 5.6	16 29.4	10 41.4	19 8.1	10 16.9	14 29.9	19 22.3
10	5 12 57.9	22 51.0	0 20.7	15 27.1	25 13.8	13 48.3	16 23.7	10 32.6	19 4.1	10 16.9	14 31.5	19 23.4
13	5 24 47.5	23 6.1	0 20.7	21 17.6	25 28.6	13 40.2	16 19.7	10 23.4	18 59.9	10 17.0	14 33.1	19 24.6
16	5 36 37.2	23 17.1	0 20.8	16 20.0	25 30.4	13 40.5	16 17.8	10 13.7	18 55.5	10 17.4	14 34.7	19 25.9
19	5 48 26.9	23 23.9	0 20.8	5 7.8	25 18.8	13 48.0	16 18.0	10 3.4	18 51.0	10 17.9	14 36.1	19 27.3
22	6 0 16.5	23 26.5	0 20.8	7S34.1	24 53.6	14 1.8	16 20.4	9 52.7	18 46.3	10 18.6	14 37.6	19 28.8
25	6 12 6.2	23 24.9	0 20.9	17 55.4	24 14.9	14 20.8	16 25.1	9 41.5	18 41.5	10 19.5	14 38.9	19 30.5
28	6 23 55.9	23 19.0	0 20.9	21 9.4	23 23.3	14 44.0	16 32.2	9 29.9	18 36.5	10 20.5	14 40.2	19 32.1
31	6 35 45.6	23 8.9	0 20.9	14 10.5	22 20.2	15 10.5	16 41.7	9 17.9	18 31.4	10 21.7	14 41.4	19 33.9

JANUARY 1963

LONGITUDE

DAY	EPHEM. SID. TIME (h m s)	☉	Ω	☽	☿	♀	♂	♃	♄	♅	♆	♇
1	6 39 42.1	9♑50.9	0♌41.0	13♓ 8.4	28♑42.0	25♏15.6	24♌34.8	9♓ .7	9♒56.4	5♍ 6.1	15♏ 4.7	12♍ 5.0
2	6 43 38.7	10 52.0	0 37.9	27 10.7	29 56.8	26 3.3	24R29.7	9 11.4	10 3.0	5R 4.9	15 6.1	12R 4.4
3	6 47 35.2	11 53.2	0 34.7	11♈18.8	1♒ 7.7	26 51.8	24 23.9	9 22.2	10 9.6	5 3.7	15 7.5	12 3.8
4	6 51 31.8	12 54.3	0 31.5	25 30.8	2 13.9	27 41.1	24 17.3	9 33.1	10 16.2	5 2.5	15 8.9	12 3.2
5	6 55 28.3	13 55.5	0 28.3	9♉44.6	3 14.8	28 31.3	24 9.8	9 44.2	10 22.9	5 1.2	15 10.3	12 2.5
6	6 59 24.9	14 56.6	0 25.1	23 57.3	4 9.5	29 22.3	24 1.6	9 55.3	10 29.6	4 59.8	15 11.7	12 1.9
7	7 3 21.5	15 57.8	0 22.0	8♊ 5.6	4 57.3	0♐14.0	23 52.5	10 6.5	10 36.3	4 58.4	15 13.0	12 1.2
8	7 7 18.0	16 58.9	0 18.8	22 5.6	5 37.2	1 6.5	23 42.6	10 17.9	10 43.1	4 56.9	15 14.3	12 .4
9	7 11 14.6	18 .0	0 15.6	5♋53.9	6 8.3	1 59.6	23 32.0	10 29.3	10 49.9	4 55.4	15 15.5	11 59.7
10	7 15 11.1	19 1.1	0 12.4	19 27.3	6 29.7	2 53.5	23 20.5	10 40.8	10 56.7	4 53.9	15 16.8	11 58.9
11	7 19 7.7	20 2.3	0 9.3	2♌43.7	6 40.7	3 48.0	23 8.2	10 52.4	11 3.6	4 52.3	15 18.0	11 58.0
12	7 23 4.2	21 3.4	0 6.1	15 41.9	6R40.5	4 43.1	22 55.2	11 4.2	11 10.5	4 50.7	15 19.1	11 57.2
13	7 27 .8	22 4.5	0 2.9	28 22.2	6 28.7	5 38.8	22 41.3	11 16.0	11 17.4	4 49.0	15 20.3	11 56.3
14	7 30 57.4	23 5.6	29♋59.7	10♍46.2	6 5.1	6 35.1	22 26.8	11 27.9	11 24.3	4 47.2	15 21.4	11 55.4
15	7 34 53.9	24 6.7	29 56.6	22 56.4	5 29.9	7 32.0	22 11.4	11 39.9	11 31.2	4 45.5	15 22.5	11 54.5
16	7 38 50.5	25 7.8	29 53.4	4♎56.4	4 43.6	8 29.4	21 55.4	11 52.0	11 38.2	4 43.7	15 23.5	11 53.6
17	7 42 47.0	26 8.9	29 50.2	16 50.3	3 47.3	9 27.4	21 38.6	12 4.1	11 45.2	4 41.8	15 24.5	11 52.6
18	7 46 43.6	27 10.0	29 47.0	28 42.7	2 42.7	10 25.9	21 21.2	12 16.4	11 52.3	4 40.0	15 25.6	11 51.6
19	7 50 40.1	28 11.1	29 43.9	10♏38.3	1 31.4	11 24.8	21 3.0	12 28.8	11 59.3	4 38.1	15 26.5	11 50.6
20	7 54 36.7	29 12.2	29 40.7	22 41.8	0 15.8	12 24.2	20 44.3	12 41.2	12 6.4	4 36.1	15 27.5	11 49.6
21	7 58 33.3	0♒13.3	29 37.5	4♐57.5	28♑58.2	13 24.0	20 24.9	12 53.7	12 13.5	4 34.1	15 28.3	11 48.5
22	8 2 29.8	1 14.4	29 34.3	17 29.2	27 41.0	14 24.2	20 4.9	13 6.3	12 20.6	4 32.1	15 29.2	11 47.4
23	8 6 26.4	2 15.4	29 31.1	0♑19.5	26 26.5	15 24.9	19 44.3	13 18.9	12 27.7	4 30.0	15 30.0	11 46.3
24	8 10 22.9	3 16.5	29 28.0	13 29.9	25 16.6	16 26.0	19 23.2	13 31.6	12 34.8	4 27.9	15 30.8	11 45.2
25	8 14 19.5	4 17.5	29 24.8	27 .5	24 13.0	17 27.4	19 1.7	13 44.4	12 41.9	4 25.7	15 31.6	11 44.0
26	8 18 16.0	5 18.6	29 21.6	10♒54.6	23 16.8	18 29.2	18 39.7	13 57.3	12 49.1	4 23.6	15 32.3	11 42.8
27	8 22 12.6	6 19.6	29 18.4	24 54.6	22 29.0	19 31.3	18 17.3	14 10.2	12 56.2	4 21.4	15 33.0	11 41.6
28	8 26 9.1	7 20.6	29 15.3	9♓10.7	21 49.9	20 33.8	17 54.5	14 23.3	13 3.4	4 19.1	15 33.7	11 40.4
29	8 30 5.7	8 21.5	29 12.1	23 33.3	21 19.7	21 36.6	17 31.4	14 36.3	13 10.6	4 16.9	15 34.3	11 39.2
30	8 34 2.3	9 22.5	29 8.9	7♈57.5	20 58.4	22 39.7	17 8.1	14 49.5	13 17.8	4 14.6	15 34.9	11 37.9
31	8 37 58.8	10 23.5	29 5.7	22 18.8	20 45.6	23 42.4	16 44.5	15 2.7	13 24.9	4 12.2	15 35.5	11 36.6

LATITUDE

DAY	SID. TIME (h m s)	☉	Ω	☽	☿	♀	♂	♃	♄	♅	♆	♇
1	6 39 42.1	0 .0	0 .0	3S37.1	1S33.7	3N51.6	3N38.3	1S 7.2	0S45.8	0N46.9	1N44.4	13N37.4
4	6 51 31.8	0 .0	0 .0	5 14.8	1 5.5	3 55.3	3 45.5	1 6.8	0 45.9	0 47.1	1 44.5	13 38.7
7	7 3 21.5	0 .0	0 .0	4 7.8	0 27.9	3 56.9	3 52.6	1 6.4	0 46.0	0 47.2	1 44.7	13 40.0
10	7 15 11.1	0 .0	0 .0	0 56.0	0N19.2	3 56.7	3 59.4	1 6.1	0 46.2	0 47.3	1 44.9	13 41.3
13	7 27 .8	0 .0	0 .0	2N32.7	1 13.6	3 54.8	4 5.9	1 5.8	0 46.3	0 47.4	1 45.0	13 42.5
16	7 38 50.5	0 .0	0 .0	4 48.3	2 9.3	3 51.4	4 11.9	1 5.5	0 46.4	0 47.5	1 45.2	13 43.7
19	7 50 40.1	0 .0	0 .0	5 11.5	2 56.4	3 46.6	4 17.4	1 5.2	0 46.6	0 47.6	1 45.3	13 44.8
22	8 2 29.8	0 .0	0 .0	3 33.4	3 25.3	3 40.5	4 22.2	1 4.9	0 46.7	0 47.7	1 45.5	13 45.9
25	8 14 19.5	0 .0	0 .0	0 14.8	3 32.0	3 33.3	4 26.3	1 4.7	0 46.9	0 47.7	1 45.7	13 46.9
28	8 26 9.1	0 .0	0 .0	3S21.8	3 19.5	3 25.1	4 29.5	1 4.4	0 47.1	0 47.8	1 45.9	13 47.8
31	8 37 58.8	0 .0	0 .0	5 14.0	2 54.5	3 16.4	4 31.8	1 4.2	0 47.3	0 47.9	1 46.0	13 48.8

RIGHT ASCENSION

DAY	SID. TIME (h m s)	☉	Ω	☽	☿	♀	♂	♃	♄	♅	♆	♇
1	6 39 42.1	10♑42.8	2♌53.6	15♓52.2	1♒10.2	23♏52.6	28♌8.4	11♓2.1	12♒36.1	7♍13.5	13♏8.3	18♍56.9
2	6 43 38.7	11 49.1	2 50.3	29 10.8	2 27.0	24 40.9	28R4.4	11 12.1	12 42.8	7R12.4	13 9.8	18R56.6
3	6 47 35.2	12 55.3	2 47.0	12♈21.1	3 39.1	25 30.1	27 59.5	11 22.2	12 49.5	7 11.3	13 11.2	18 56.2
4	6 51 31.8	14 1.4	2 43.7	25 33.9	4 45.7	26 20.2	27 53.8	11 32.4	12 56.2	7 10.1	13 12.6	18 55.8
5	6 55 28.3	15 7.3	2 40.4	9♉ .0	5 46.1	27 11.1	27 47.4	11 42.7	13 3.0	7 8.9	13 14.0	18 55.4
6	6 59 24.9	16 13.2	2 37.1	22 48.1	6 39.6	28 3.0	27 40.1	11 53.1	13 9.8	7 7.6	13 15.3	18 54.9
7	7 3 21.5	17 19.0	2 33.8	7♊11.3	7 25.4	28 55.6	27 32.0	12 3.5	13 16.6	7 6.3	13 16.7	18 54.5
8	7 7 18.0	18 24.6	2 30.5	21 35.8	8 2.6	29 49.0	27 23.1	12 14.1	13 23.5	7 4.9	13 17.9	18 53.9
9	7 11 14.6	19 30.1	2 27.2	6♋19.4	8 30.3	0♐43.3	27 13.4	12 24.8	13 30.4	7 3.5	13 19.2	18 53.4
10	7 15 11.1	20 35.5	2 23.9	20 54.9	8 47.9	1 38.3	27 2.8	12 35.5	13 37.3	7 2.1	13 20.4	18 52.8
11	7 19 7.7	21 40.8	2 20.6	5♌ 4.8	8 54.5	2 34.0	26 51.5	12 46.3	13 44.3	7 .6	13 21.6	18 52.2
12	7 23 4.2	22 45.9	2 17.3	18 36.9	8R49.5	3 30.5	26 39.4	12 57.3	13 51.2	6 59.0	13 22.8	18 51.6
13	7 27 .8	23 50.8	2 13.9	1♍26.4	8 32.7	4 27.7	26 26.5	13 8.3	13 58.2	6 57.5	13 24.0	18 51.0
14	7 30 57.4	24 55.6	2 10.6	13 26.7	8 3.8	5 25.6	26 12.8	13 19.3	14 5.3	6 55.8	13 25.1	18 50.3
15	7 34 53.9	26 .3	2 7.3	25 12.3	7 23.3	6 24.1	25 58.3	13 30.5	14 12.3	6 54.2	13 26.2	18 49.6
16	7 38 50.5	27 4.8	2 4.0	6♎24.4	6 31.8	7 23.4	25 43.1	13 41.7	14 19.4	6 52.5	13 27.2	18 48.8
17	7 42 47.0	28 9.1	2 .7	17 29.6	5 30.5	8 23.2	25 27.1	13 52.9	14 26.5	6 50.8	13 28.3	18 48.1
18	7 46 43.6	29 13.3	1 57.4	28 34.1	4 20.9	9 23.8	25 10.5	14 4.5	14 33.6	6 49.0	13 29.3	18 47.3
19	7 50 40.1	0♒17.3	1 54.1	9♏51.8	3 5.1	10 24.9	24 53.0	14 16.0	14 40.7	6 47.2	13 30.3	18 46.5
20	7 54 36.7	1 21.1	1 50.8	21 33.9	1 45.3	11 26.6	24 34.9	14 27.5	14 47.9	6 45.4	13 31.2	18 45.7
21	7 58 33.3	2 24.7	1 47.5	3♐49.7	0 23.9	12 28.8	24 16.2	14 39.1	14 55.0	6 43.5	13 32.1	18 44.8
22	8 2 29.8	3 28.2	1 44.2	16 45.2	29♑ 3.3	13 31.7	23 56.8	14 50.8	15 2.2	6 41.6	13 33.0	18 44.0
23	8 6 26.4	4 31.5	1 40.9	0♑20.8	27 45.9	14 35.0	23 36.7	15 2.5	15 9.4	6 39.6	13 33.8	18 43.1
24	8 10 22.9	5 34.5	1 37.5	14 30.2	26 33.6	15 38.9	23 16.1	15 14.4	15 16.6	6 37.6	13 34.6	18 42.1
25	8 14 19.5	6 37.4	1 34.2	29 3.1	25 28.0	16 43.3	22 55.0	15 26.2	15 23.8	6 35.6	13 35.4	18 41.2
26	8 18 16.0	7 40.1	1 30.9	13♒34.7	24 30.3	17 48.2	22 33.3	15 38.2	15 31.0	6 33.6	13 36.1	18 40.2
27	8 22 12.6	8 42.6	1 27.6	27 58.7	23 41.5	18 53.5	22 11.2	15 50.2	15 38.2	6 31.5	13 36.8	18 39.2
28	8 26 9.1	9 44.9	1 24.3	12♓ 3.2	23 1.9	19 59.4	21 48.6	16 2.3	15 45.4	6 29.4	13 37.5	18 38.2
29	8 30 5.7	10 46.9	1 21.0	25 46.9	22 31.7	21 5.6	21 25.7	16 14.4	15 52.6	6 27.2	13 38.1	18 37.1
30	8 34 2.3	11 48.8	1 17.7	9♈14.6	22 10.8	22 12.3	21 2.4	16 26.6	15 59.9	6 25.1	13 38.8	18 36.1
31	8 37 58.8	12 50.5	1 14.3	22 35.0	21 59.0	23 19.4	20 38.8	16 38.8	16 7.1	6 22.9	13 39.3	18 35.0

DECLINATION

DAY	SID. TIME (h m s)	☉	Ω	☽	☿	♀	♂	♃	♄	♅	♆	♇
1	6 39 42.1	23S 4.6	0N21.0	9S58.0	21S57.1	15S19.9	16N45.5	9S13.8	18S29.7	10N22.2	14S41.8	19N34.5
4	6 51 31.8	22 49.0	0 21.0	4N58.5	21 43.7	15 49.5	16 58.1	9 1.2	18 24.5	10 23.6	14 42.9	19 36.4
7	7 3 21.5	22 29.3	0 21.0	17 34.9	19 28.9	16 20.4	17 13.1	8 48.3	18 19.1	10 25.2	14 43.9	19 38.4
10	7 15 11.1	22 5.6	0 21.1	21 6.5	18 20.5	16 52.1	17 30.3	8 35.0	18 13.6	10 27.0	14 44.9	19 40.4
13	7 27 .8	21 38.0	0 21.1	14 25.7	17 28.1	17 23.8	17 49.4	8 21.3	18 8.1	10 28.9	14 45.7	19 42.5
16	7 38 50.5	21 6.6	0 21.1	2 26.8	16 59.6	17 54.8	18 10.3	8 7.3	18 2.4	10 30.9	14 46.5	19 44.7
19	7 50 40.1	20 31.6	0 21.2	10S 4.8	16 57.3	18 24.7	18 32.6	7 52.9	17 56.7	10 33.1	14 47.2	19 46.9
22	8 2 29.8	19 53.1	0 21.2	19 18.8	17 16.3	18 52.8	18 56.0	7 38.3	17 50.9	10 35.3	14 47.8	19 49.1
25	8 14 19.5	19 11.3	0 21.2	20 31.0	17 47.7	19 18.7	19 20.2	7 23.4	17 45.0	10 37.7	14 48.4	19 51.4
28	8 26 9.1	18 26.3	0 21.3	11 14.7	18 23.4	19 41.8	19 44.2	7 8.2	17 39.1	10 40.2	14 48.8	19 53.7
31	8 37 58.8	17 38.3	0 21.3	3N49.6	18 57.9	20 1.8	20 8.1	6 52.8	17 33.1	10 42.8	14 49.1	19 56.0

FEBRUARY 1963

LONGITUDE

DAY	EPHEM. SID. TIME	☉	☊	☾	☿	♀	♂	♃	♄	♅	♆	♇
	h m s	° ′	° ′	° ′	° ′	° ′	° ′	° ′	° ′	° ′	° ′	° ′
1	8 41 55.4	11 ♒ 24.4	29 ♋ 2.5	6 ♉ 33.7	20 ♑ 41.1	24 ♐ 46.9	16 ♌ 20.7	15 ♓ 15.9	13 ♒ 32.1	4 ♍ 9.9	15 ♏ 36.0	11 ♍ 35.3
2	8 45 51.9	12 25.3	28 59.4	20 39.7	20 D 44.3	25 50.9	15 R 56.8	15 29.3	13 39.3	4 R 7.5	15 36.5	11 R 34.0
3	8 49 48.5	13 26.1	28 56.2	4 ♊ 35.3	20 54.7	26 55.1	15 32.9	15 42.6	13 46.5	4 5.1	15 37.0	11 32.7
4	8 53 45.0	14 27.0	28 53.0	18 19.4	21 11.8	27 59.6	15 8.9	15 56.1	13 53.7	4 2.7	15 37.4	11 31.3
5	8 57 41.6	15 27.8	28 49.8	1 ♋ 51.6	21 35.0	29 4.4	14 44.8	16 9.6	14 .9	4 .3	15 37.8	11 30.0
6	9 1 38.1	16 28.6	28 46.7	15 11.5	22 4.0	0 ♑ 9.5	14 20.9	16 23.1	14 8.1	3 57.8	15 38.1	11 28.6
7	9 5 34.7	17 29.4	28 43.5	28 19.0	22 38.2	1 14.7	13 57.0	16 36.7	14 15.2	3 55.3	15 38.5	11 27.2
8	9 9 31.3	18 30.2	28 40.3	11 ♌ 13.9	23 17.1	2 20.3	13 33.3	16 50.4	14 22.5	3 52.9	15 38.8	11 25.8
9	9 13 27.8	19 31.0	28 37.1	23 55.9	24 .4	3 26.0	13 9.8	17 4.1	14 29.6	3 50.4	15 39.1	11 24.4
10	9 17 24.4	20 31.7	28 34.0	6 ♍ 25.5	24 47.7	4 32.0	12 46.5	17 17.8	14 36.8	3 47.8	15 39.3	11 23.0
11	9 21 20.9	21 32.4	28 30.8	18 43.4	25 38.6	5 38.2	12 23.4	17 31.6	14 44.0	3 45.3	15 39.5	11 21.5
12	9 25 17.5	22 33.0	28 27.6	0 ♎ 51.0	26 32.8	6 44.6	12 .7	17 45.5	14 51.1	3 42.7	15 39.6	11 20.1
13	9 29 14.0	23 33.7	28 24.4	12 50.2	27 30.2	7 51.2	11 38.3	17 59.3	14 58.2	3 40.2	15 39.7	11 18.6
14	9 33 10.6	24 34.3	28 21.2	24 44.1	28 30.3	8 57.9	11 16.3	18 13.3	15 5.4	3 37.6	15 39.8	11 17.1
15	9 37 7.1	25 35.0	28 18.1	6 ♏ 36.1	29 33.1	10 4.9	10 54.7	18 27.2	15 12.5	3 35.0	15 39.9	11 15.6
16	9 41 3.7	26 35.6	28 14.9	18 30.4	0 ♒ 38.2	11 12.1	10 33.6	18 41.2	15 19.6	3 32.4	15 39.9	11 14.1
17	9 45 .2	27 36.1	28 11.7	0 ♐ 31.5	1 45.7	12 19.4	10 13.0	18 55.2	15 26.7	3 29.8	15 39.9	11 12.6
18	9 48 56.8	28 36.7	28 8.5	12 44.3	2 55.2	13 26.9	9 52.9	19 9.3	15 33.8	3 27.1	15 R 39.8	11 11.1
19	9 52 53.3	29 37.2	28 5.4	25 13.5	4 6.6	14 34.6	9 33.4	19 23.4	15 40.8	3 24.5	15 39.7	11 9.6
20	9 56 49.9	0 ♓ 37.7	28 2.2	8 ♑ 3.4	5 19.9	15 42.4	9 14.5	19 37.6	15 47.9	3 21.9	15 39.6	11 8.0
21	10 0 46.5	1 38.2	27 59.0	21 17.2	6 34.9	16 50.4	8 56.2	19 51.7	15 54.9	3 19.2	15 39.5	11 6.5
22	10 4 43.0	2 38.7	27 55.8	4 ♒ 56.6	7 51.5	17 58.5	8 38.5	20 6.0	16 1.9	3 16.6	15 39.3	11 4.9
23	10 8 39.6	3 39.1	27 52.6	19 1.1	9 9.6	19 6.7	8 21.5	20 20.2	16 8.9	3 14.0	15 39.1	11 3.4
24	10 12 36.1	4 39.6	27 49.5	3 ♓ 27.7	10 29.2	20 15.1	8 5.2	20 34.5	16 15.8	3 11.3	15 38.8	11 1.8
25	10 16 32.7	5 40.0	27 46.3	18 10.8	11 50.3	21 23.6	7 49.6	20 48.7	16 22.8	3 8.7	15 38.5	11 .3
26	10 20 29.2	6 40.3	27 43.1	3 ♈ 2.7	13 12.6	22 32.3	7 34.8	21 3.1	16 29.7	3 6.1	15 38.2	10 58.7
27	10 24 25.8	7 40.6	27 39.9	17 54.9	14 36.3	23 41.0	7 20.6	21 17.4	16 36.6	3 3.4	15 37.9	10 57.1
28	10 28 22.3	8 40.9	27 36.8	2 ♉ 39.5	16 1.3	24 49.9	7 7.3	21 31.8	16 43.4	3 .8	15 37.5	10 55.6

LATITUDE

DAY	EPHEM. SID. TIME	☉	☊	☾	☿	♀	♂	♃	♄	♅	♆	♇
1	8 41 55.4	0 .0	0 .0	5 S 14.2	2 N 44.4	3 N 12.8	4 N 32.3	1 S 4.2	0 S 47.3	0 N 47.9	1 N 46.1	13 N 49.1
4	8 53 45.0	0 .0	0 .0	3 29.2	2 11.6	3 2.7	4 33.3	1 4.0	0 47.5	0 48.0	1 46.3	13 49.9
7	9 5 34.7	0 .0	0 .0	0 7.5	1 37.4	2 51.9	4 33.3	1 3.8	0 47.8	0 48.0	1 46.5	13 50.7
10	9 17 24.4	0 .0	0 .0	3 N 8.8	1 3.6	2 40.6	4 32.4	1 3.6	0 48.0	0 48.1	1 46.7	13 51.4
13	9 29 14.0	0 .0	0 .0	5 .7	0 31.5	2 28.7	4 30.4	1 3.5	0 48.2	0 48.1	1 46.8	13 52.0
16	9 41 3.7	0 .0	0 .0	4 56.3	0 1.6	2 16.5	4 27.6	1 3.4	0 48.4	0 48.1	1 47.0	13 52.6
19	9 52 53.3	0 .0	0 .0	2 56.1	0 S 25.8	2 4.0	4 24.0	1 3.3	0 48.7	0 48.1	1 47.2	13 53.1
22	10 4 43.0	0 .0	0 .0	0 S 30.4	0 50.4	1 51.3	4 19.6	1 3.2	0 49.0	0 48.2	1 47.4	13 53.5
25	10 16 32.7	0 .0	0 .0	3 54.5	1 12.1	1 38.4	4 14.6	1 3.2	0 49.2	0 48.2	1 47.5	13 53.9
28	10 28 22.3	0 .0	0 .0	5 9.3	1 30.7	1 25.5	4 9.1	1 3.1	0 49.5	0 48.2	1 47.7	13 54.2

RIGHT ASCENSION

DAY	EPHEM. SID. TIME	☉	☊	☾	☿	♀	♂	♃	♄	♅	♆	♇
1	8 41 55.4	13 ♒ 51.9	1 ♌ 11.0	5 ♉ 58.4	21 ♑ 55.8	24 ♐ 27.0	20 ♌ 15.0	16 ♓ 51.1	16 ♒ 14.4	6 ♍ 20.7	13 ♏ 39.9	18 ♍ 33.9
2	8 45 51.9	14 53.1	1 7.7	19 33.8	22 D .8	25 34.9	19 R 51.0	17 3.4	16 21.6	6 R 18.4	13 40.4	18 R 32.8
3	8 49 48.5	15 54.2	1 4.4	3 ♊ 26.9	22 13.4	26 43.1	19 26.8	17 15.8	16 28.8	6 16.1	13 40.8	18 31.6
4	8 53 45.0	16 55.0	1 1.1	17 37.7	22 33.1	27 51.8	19 2.5	17 28.3	16 36.1	6 13.9	13 41.3	18 30.5
5	8 57 41.6	17 55.6	0 57.8	1 ♋ 59.4	22 59.4	29 .8	18 38.1	17 40.7	16 43.3	6 11.6	13 41.7	18 29.3
6	9 1 38.1	18 56.0	0 54.4	16 19.7	23 31.7	0 ♑ 10.1	18 13.7	17 53.3	16 50.5	6 9.2	13 42.1	18 28.1
7	9 5 34.7	19 56.2	0 51.1	0 ♌ 23.9	24 9.5	1 19.7	17 49.3	18 5.9	16 57.7	6 6.9	13 42.4	18 26.9
8	9 9 31.3	20 56.2	0 47.8	13 59.6	24 52.4	2 29.7	17 25.1	18 18.5	17 5.0	6 4.6	13 42.8	18 25.7
9	9 13 27.8	21 56.0	0 44.5	26 59.4	25 39.8	3 40.0	17 .9	18 31.2	17 12.2	6 2.2	13 43.0	18 24.4
10	9 17 24.4	22 55.6	0 41.2	9 ♍ 22.2	26 31.4	4 50.5	16 36.9	18 43.9	17 19.4	5 59.8	13 43.3	18 23.2
11	9 21 20.9	23 55.0	0 37.8	21 12.0	27 26.8	6 1.3	16 13.2	18 56.6	17 26.6	5 57.4	13 43.5	18 21.9
12	9 25 17.5	24 54.3	0 34.5	2 ♎ 36.5	28 25.7	7 12.3	15 49.6	19 9.4	17 33.8	5 55.0	13 43.6	18 20.6
13	9 29 14.0	25 53.3	0 31.2	13 45.5	29 27.8	8 23.6	15 26.4	19 22.2	17 40.9	5 52.5	13 43.8	18 19.3
14	9 33 10.6	26 52.1	0 27.9	24 49.5	0 ♒ 32.8	9 35.0	15 3.5	19 35.1	17 48.1	5 50.1	13 43.9	18 18.0
15	9 37 7.1	27 50.8	0 24.6	5 ♏ 59.6	1 40.4	10 46.7	14 41.0	19 48.0	17 55.2	5 47.6	13 44.0	18 16.7
16	9 41 3.7	28 49.3	0 21.2	17 26.5	2 50.3	11 58.6	14 18.9	20 .9	18 2.3	5 45.1	13 44.0	18 15.3
17	9 45 .2	29 47.6	0 17.9	29 20.1	4 2.5	13 10.6	13 57.3	20 13.8	18 9.5	5 42.7	13 44.0	18 14.0
18	9 48 56.8	0 ♓ 45.7	0 14.6	11 ♐ 48.0	5 16.7	14 22.8	13 36.2	20 26.8	18 16.5	5 40.2	13 44.0	18 12.6
19	9 52 53.3	1 43.6	0 11.3	24 54.6	6 32.6	15 35.1	13 15.6	20 39.8	18 23.6	5 37.7	13 R 43.9	18 11.2
20	9 56 49.9	2 41.4	0 7.9	8 ♑ 38.8	7 50.3	16 47.5	12 55.6	20 52.9	18 30.7	5 35.2	13 43.8	18 9.8
21	10 0 46.5	3 39.1	0 4.6	22 53.2	9 9.5	18 .1	12 36.2	21 6.0	18 37.7	5 32.7	13 43.7	18 8.4
22	10 4 43.0	4 36.5	0 1.3	7 ♒ 25.3	10 30.0	19 12.7	12 17.4	21 19.1	18 44.7	5 30.2	13 43.5	18 7.0
23	10 8 39.6	5 33.8	29 ♋ 58.0	22 .8	11 51.9	20 25.4	11 59.3	21 32.2	18 51.7	5 27.7	13 43.3	18 5.6
24	10 12 36.1	6 31.0	29 54.6	6 ♓ 27.9	13 14.9	21 38.2	11 41.9	21 45.3	18 58.7	5 25.2	13 43.1	18 4.2
25	10 16 32.7	7 28.0	29 51.3	20 40.4	14 39.1	22 51.0	11 25.2	21 58.5	19 5.6	5 22.7	13 42.8	18 2.8
26	10 20 29.2	8 24.8	29 48.0	4 ♈ 38.5	16 4.2	24 3.9	11 9.2	22 11.7	19 12.5	5 20.2	13 42.5	18 1.3
27	10 24 25.8	9 21.5	29 44.6	18 27.3	17 30.3	25 16.8	10 54.0	22 24.9	19 19.4	5 17.7	13 42.2	17 59.9
28	10 28 22.3	10 18.1	29 41.3	2 ♉ 14.4	18 57.2	26 29.6	10 39.5	22 38.1	19 26.3	5 15.2	13 41.8	17 58.4

DECLINATION

DAY	EPHEM. SID. TIME	☉	☊	☾	☿	♀	♂	♃	♄	♅	♆	♇
1	8 41 55.4	17 S 21.7	0 N 21.3	8 N 45.5	19 S 8.5	20 S 7.7	20 N 15.9	6 S 47.6	17 S 31.1	10 N 43.6	14 S 49.2	19 N 56.8
4	8 53 45.0	16 29.9	0 21.3	19 27.4	19 36.3	20 23.0	20 38.7	6 31.8	17 25.1	10 46.3	14 49.5	19 59.1
7	9 5 34.7	15 35.6	0 21.4	20 22.7	19 56.5	20 34.3	21 .1	6 15.9	17 19.0	10 49.1	14 49.6	20 1.4
10	9 17 24.4	14 39.0	0 21.4	12 4.6	20 7.7	20 41.4	21 19.7	5 59.7	17 13.0	10 51.8	14 49.7	20 3.7
13	9 29 14.0	13 40.1	0 21.4	0 S 27.2	20 8.9	20 44.1	21 37.4	5 43.4	17 6.9	10 54.6	14 49.6	20 6.0
16	9 41 3.7	12 39.2	0 21.5	12 35.2	19 59.5	20 42.2	21 52.8	5 26.9	17 .8	10 57.5	14 49.5	20 8.3
19	9 52 53.3	11 36.4	0 21.5	20 25.4	19 39.0	20 35.5	22 5.9	5 10.2	16 54.8	11 .4	14 49.3	20 10.5
22	10 4 43.0	10 32.0	0 21.6	19 31.5	19 7.1	20 23.8	22 16.6	4 53.5	16 48.7	11 3.2	14 49.0	20 12.7
25	10 16 32.7	9 26.1	0 21.6	8 16.2	18 23.7	20 7.3	22 24.7	4 36.6	16 42.7	11 6.1	14 48.6	20 14.8
28	10 28 22.3	8 18.9	0 21.6	7 N 32.9	17 28.8	19 45.8	22 30.5	4 19.6	16 36.8	11 9.0	14 48.1	20 16.9

MARCH 1963

DAY	EPHEM. SID. TIME	☉	☊	☾	☿	♀	♂	♃	♄	♅	♆	♇
	h m s	° ′	° ′	° ′	° ′	° ′	° ′	° ′	° ′	° ′	° ′	° ′
LONGITUDE												
1	10 32 18.9	9♓41.3	27♋33.6	17♉10.1	17♒27.5	25♑59.0	6♌54.8	21♓46.2	16♒50.3	2♍58.2	15♏37.1	10♍54.0
2	10 36 15.4	10 41.5	27 30.4	1♊22.6	18 54.9	27 8.0	6 R 43.0	22 .6	16 57.1	2 R 55.6	15 R 36.7	10 R 52.5
3	10 40 12.0	11 41.7	27 27.2	15 15.3	20 23.4	28 17.3	6 32.0	22 15.0	17 3.9	2 53.0	15 36.2	10 50.9
4	10 44 8.5	12 41.8	27 24.0	28 48.5	21 53.2	29 26.6	6 21.7	22 29.5	17 10.6	2 50.4	15 35.7	10 49.3
5	10 48 5.1	13 42.0	27 20.9	12♋3.7	23 24.0	0♒36.0	6 12.3	22 43.9	17 17.3	2 47.9	15 35.1	10 47.7
6	10 52 1.6	14 42.1	27 17.7	25 3.1	24 56.0	1 45.5	6 3.7	22 58.4	17 24.0	2 45.3	15 34.5	10 46.2
7	10 55 58.2	15 42.1	27 14.5	7♌48.9	26 29.2	2 55.1	5 55.8	23 12.8	17 30.7	2 42.7	15 33.9	10 44.6
8	10 59 54.8	16 42.1	27 11.3	20 23.2	28 3.5	4 4.8	5 48.8	23 27.3	17 37.3	2 40.2	15 33.3	10 43.0
9	11 3 51.3	17 42.1	27 8.2	2♍47.6	29 38.9	5 14.5	5 42.5	23 41.8	17 43.8	2 37.7	15 32.6	10 41.5
10	11 7 47.9	18 42.1	27 5.0	15 3.3	1♓15.4	6 24.4	5 37.0	23 56.3	17 50.4	2 35.2	15 31.9	10 39.9
11	11 11 44.4	19 42.0	27 1.8	27 11.4	2 53.1	7 34.4	5 32.3	24 10.8	17 56.8	2 32.7	15 31.2	10 38.4
12	11 15 41.0	20 41.9	26 58.6	9♎12.9	4 31.9	8 44.4	5 28.4	24 25.4	18 3.3	2 30.2	15 30.5	10 36.8
13	11 19 37.5	21 41.8	26 55.4	21 9.2	6 11.9	9 54.6	5 25.2	24 39.9	18 9.7	2 27.8	15 29.7	10 35.3
14	11 23 34.1	22 41.6	26 52.3	3♏2.0	7 53.1	11 4.8	5 22.8	24 54.4	18 16.1	2 25.3	15 28.9	10 33.8
15	11 27 30.6	23 41.4	26 49.1	14 53.6	9 35.4	12 15.1	5 21.2	25 9.0	18 22.4	2 22.9	15 28.0	10 32.2
16	11 31 27.2	24 41.2	26 45.9	26 47.2	11 18.9	13 25.5	5 20.3	25 23.5	18 28.7	2 20.5	15 27.2	10 30.7
17	11 35 23.7	25 40.9	26 42.7	8♐46.6	13 3.7	14 35.9	5 20.1	25 38.0	18 34.9	2 18.2	15 26.3	10 29.2
18	11 39 20.3	26 40.6	26 39.5	20 56.1	14 49.6	15 46.4	5 D 20.7	25 52.6	18 41.1	2 15.8	15 25.3	10 27.7
19	11 43 16.8	27 40.3	26 36.4	3♑20.8	16 36.8	16 57.0	5 22.0	26 7.1	18 47.3	2 13.5	15 24.4	10 26.2
20	11 47 13.4	28 40.0	26 33.2	16 5.3	18 25.2	18 7.7	5 24.0	26 21.6	18 53.3	2 11.3	15 23.4	10 24.7
21	11 51 9.9	29 39.6	26 30.0	29 14.4	20 14.9	19 18.4	5 26.7	26 36.2	18 59.4	2 9.0	15 22.4	10 23.3
22	11 55 6.5	0♈39.2	26 26.8	12♒51.3	22 5.8	20 29.2	5 30.1	26 50.7	19 5.4	2 6.8	15 21.4	10 21.9
23	11 59 3.0	1 38.8	26 23.7	26 57.3	23 58.0	21 40.1	5 34.2	27 5.3	19 11.4	2 4.6	15 20.4	10 20.4
24	12 2 59.6	2 38.3	26 20.5	11♓30.9	25 51.4	22 51.0	5 39.0	27 19.8	19 17.3	2 2.5	15 19.3	10 19.0
25	12 6 56.1	3 37.8	26 17.3	26 27.1	27 46.1	24 2.0	5 44.4	27 34.3	19 23.1	2 .3	15 18.2	10 17.6
26	12 10 52.7	4 37.3	26 14.1	11♈37.6	29 42.1	25 13.0	5 50.5	27 48.8	19 28.9	1 58.2	15 17.0	10 16.1
27	12 14 49.2	5 36.7	26 10.9	26 51.9	1♈39.2	26 24.0	5 57.2	28 3.2	19 34.6	1 56.2	15 15.9	10 14.7
28	12 18 45.8	6 36.1	26 7.8	11♉58.9	3 37.5	27 35.1	6 4.6	28 17.7	19 40.3	1 54.1	15 14.7	10 13.4
29	12 22 42.3	7 35.5	26 4.6	26 49.2	5 36.9	28 46.3	6 12.5	28 32.2	19 45.9	1 52.1	15 13.5	10 12.0
30	12 26 38.9	8 34.8	26 1.4	11♊16.4	7 37.4	29 57.5	6 21.1	28 46.6	19 51.5	1 50.2	15 12.3	10 10.7
31	12 30 35.5	9 34.1	25 58.2	25 17.5	9 38.8	1♓8.7	6 30.3	29 1.0	19 57.0	1 48.3	15 11.1	10 9.3
LATITUDE												
1	10 32 18.9	0 .0	0 .0	4 S 54.5	1 S 36.3	1 N 21.2	4 N 7.2	1 S 3.1	0 S 49.6	0 N 48.2	1 N 47.8	13 N 54.3
4	10 44 8.5	0 .0	0 .0	2 35.5	1 50.7	1 8.3	4 1.2	1 3.1	0 49.9	0 48.2	1 47.9	13 54.5
7	10 55 58.2	0 .0	0 .0	0 N 48.0	2 1.7	0 55.6	3 54.9	1 3.1	0 50.2	0 48.1	1 48.1	13 54.6
10	11 7 47.9	0 .0	0 .0	3 42.1	2 9.2	0 43.0	3 48.4	1 3.1	0 50.5	0 48.1	1 48.3	13 54.7
13	11 19 37.5	0 .0	0 .0	5 2.8	2 13.0	0 30.6	3 41.8	1 3.1	0 50.9	0 48.1	1 48.4	13 54.7
16	11 31 27.2	0 .0	0 .0	4 27.2	2 12.9	0 18.6	3 35.2	1 3.2	0 51.2	0 48.0	1 48.6	13 54.6
19	11 43 16.8	0 .0	0 .0	2 6.2	2 8.7	0 6.8	3 28.5	1 3.3	0 51.6	0 48.0	1 48.7	13 54.4
22	11 55 6.5	0 .0	0 .0	1 S 20.1	2 .0	0 S 4.5	3 21.8	1 3.3	0 51.9	0 47.9	1 48.9	13 54.2
25	12 6 56.1	0 .0	0 .0	4 19.9	1 46.8	0 15.4	3 15.2	1 3.5	0 52.3	0 47.9	1 49.0	13 53.9
28	12 18 45.8	0 .0	0 .0	4 51.9	1 29.0	0 25.7	3 8.7	1 3.6	0 52.7	0 47.8	1 49.1	13 53.6
31	12 30 35.5	0 .0	0 .0	2 38.0	1 6.4	0 35.6	3 2.4	1 3.7	0 53.1	0 47.7	1 49.2	13 53.2
RIGHT ASCENSION												
1	10 32 18.9	11♓14.5	29♋38.0	16♉7.3	20♒25.0	27♑42.6	10♌25.9	22♓51.4	19♒33.1	5♍12.7	13♏41.4	17♍57.0
2	10 36 15.4	12 10.8	29 34.7	0♊10.6	21 53.5	28 55.4	10 R 13.1	23 4.7	19 39.9	5 R 10.3	13 R 41.0	17 R 55.6
3	10 40 12.0	13 7.0	29 31.3	14 24.4	23 22.7	0♒8.2	10 1.0	23 18.0	19 46.7	5 7.8	13 40.6	17 54.1
4	10 44 8.5	14 3.0	29 28.0	28 43.5	24 52.5	1 21.0	9 49.8	23 31.2	19 53.4	5 5.3	13 40.1	17 52.6
5	10 48 5.1	14 58.9	29 24.7	12♋57.9	26 23.0	2 33.7	9 39.4	23 44.5	20 .1	5 2.9	13 39.5	17 51.2
6	10 52 1.6	15 54.7	29 21.3	26 55.8	27 54.2	3 46.4	9 29.8	23 57.9	20 6.8	5 .4	13 39.0	17 49.7
7	10 55 58.2	16 50.4	29 18.0	10♌26.8	29 25.9	4 59.0	9 21.0	24 11.2	20 13.4	4 58.0	13 38.4	17 48.2
8	10 59 54.8	17 45.9	29 14.7	23 24.8	0♓58.2	6 11.5	9 13.0	24 24.5	20 20.0	4 55.6	13 37.8	17 46.8
9	11 3 51.3	18 41.4	29 11.3	5♍48.5	2 31.1	7 23.9	9 5.9	24 37.8	20 26.5	4 53.2	13 37.2	17 45.3
10	11 7 47.9	19 36.8	29 8.0	17 41.3	4 4.5	8 36.3	8 59.6	24 51.2	20 33.0	4 50.8	13 36.5	17 43.8
11	11 11 44.4	20 32.0	29 4.7	29 9.5	5 38.5	9 48.5	8 54.1	25 4.5	20 39.5	4 48.4	13 35.8	17 42.3
12	11 15 41.0	21 27.2	29 1.3	10♎21.4	7 13.0	11 .6	8 49.3	25 17.9	20 45.9	4 46.1	13 35.0	17 40.9
13	11 19 37.5	22 22.4	28 58.0	21 26.3	8 48.1	12 12.7	8 45.4	25 31.2	20 52.3	4 43.7	13 34.3	17 39.4
14	11 23 34.1	23 17.4	28 54.7	2♏33.8	10 23.8	13 24.6	8 42.3	25 44.6	20 58.6	4 41.4	13 33.5	17 37.9
15	11 27 30.6	24 12.4	28 51.3	13 53.2	12 .1	14 36.3	8 40.0	25 58.0	21 4.9	4 39.1	13 32.7	17 36.5
16	11 31 27.2	25 7.3	28 48.0	25 33.2	13 37.0	15 48.0	8 38.5	26 11.3	21 11.2	4 36.8	13 31.8	17 35.0
17	11 35 23.7	26 2.2	28 44.7	7♐41.0	15 14.4	16 59.5	8 37.7	26 24.7	21 17.4	4 34.6	13 31.0	17 33.6
18	11 39 20.3	26 57.0	28 41.3	20 21.4	16 52.6	18 10.8	8 37.7	26 38.1	21 23.6	4 32.4	13 30.1	17 32.1
19	11 43 16.8	27 51.8	28 38.0	3♑35.3	18 31.4	19 22.0	8 D 38.4	26 51.4	21 29.7	4 30.2	13 29.1	17 30.7
20	11 47 13.4	28 46.6	28 34.6	17 19.2	20 10.9	20 33.1	8 39.9	27 4.8	21 35.7	4 28.0	13 28.2	17 29.3
21	11 51 9.9	29 41.3	28 31.3	1♒25.2	21 51.1	21 43.9	8 42.1	27 18.1	21 41.8	4 25.8	13 27.2	17 27.8
22	11 55 6.5	0♈36.0	28 28.0	15 43.1	23 32.1	22 54.7	8 45.1	27 31.5	21 47.8	4 23.7	13 26.2	17 26.5
23	11 59 3.0	1 30.6	28 24.6	0♓2.9	25 13.8	24 5.3	8 48.8	27 44.9	21 53.7	4 21.6	13 25.2	17 25.0
24	12 2 59.6	2 25.3	28 21.3	14 18.5	26 56.3	25 15.7	8 53.2	27 58.2	21 59.5	4 19.6	13 24.2	17 23.6
25	12 6 56.1	3 19.9	28 17.9	28 28.2	28 39.7	26 26.0	8 58.2	28 11.5	22 5.3	4 17.5	13 23.1	17 22.2
26	12 10 52.7	4 14.5	28 14.6	12♈35.2	0♈23.9	27 36.0	9 4.0	28 24.8	22 11.1	4 15.5	13 22.0	17 20.9
27	12 14 49.2	5 9.1	28 11.3	26 45.0	2 9.0	28 45.9	9 10.4	28 38.1	22 16.8	4 13.5	13 20.9	17 19.5
28	12 18 45.8	6 3.7	28 7.9	11♉3.5	3 54.9	29 55.7	9 17.5	28 51.4	22 22.4	4 11.6	13 19.7	17 18.1
29	12 22 42.3	6 58.3	28 4.6	25 33.9	5 41.7	1♓5.2	9 25.2	29 4.7	22 28.0	4 9.7	13 18.5	17 16.8
30	12 26 38.9	7 52.9	28 1.2	10♊14.6	7 29.4	2 14.6	9 33.6	29 18.0	22 33.5	4 7.8	13 17.3	17 15.4
31	12 30 35.5	8 47.5	27 57.9	24 58.2	9 18.0	3 23.8	9 42.5	29 31.2	22 39.0	4 6.0	13 16.1	17 14.1
DECLINATION												
1	10 32 18.9	7 S 56.3	0 N 21.6	12 N 15.1	17 S 7.9	19 S 37.5	22 N 31.9	4 S 13.9	16 S 34.8	11 N 9.9	14 S 48.0	20 N 17.6
4	10 44 8.5	6 47.7	0 21.7	20 50.7	15 57.6	19 9.4	22 34.5	3 56.8	16 28.9	11 12.7	14 47.4	20 19.6
7	10 55 58.2	5 38.3	0 21.7	19 5.5	14 35.8	18 36.5	22 35.0	3 39.6	16 23.1	11 15.4	14 46.7	20 21.6
10	11 7 47.9	4 28.2	0 21.7	9 18.1	13 2.5	17 58.8	22 33.5	3 22.4	16 17.4	11 18.1	14 46.0	20 23.5
13	11 19 37.5	3 17.6	0 21.8	3 S 34.3	11 17.9	17 16.6	22 30.0	3 5.2	16 11.7	11 20.8	14 45.2	20 25.2
16	11 31 27.2	2 6.7	0 21.8	15 6.3	9 22.2	16 29.9	22 24.8	2 47.9	16 6.2	11 23.3	14 44.3	20 27.0
19	11 43 16.8	0 55.6	0 21.8	21 17.9	7 15.6	15 39.0	22 17.9	2 30.6	16 .8	11 25.8	14 43.4	20 28.6
22	11 55 6.5	0 N 15.6	0 21.9	18 14.2	4 58.4	14 44.0	22 9.4	2 13.4	15 55.4	11 28.2	14 42.4	20 30.1
25	12 6 56.1	1 26.6	0 21.9	5 23.1	2 31.3	13 45.2	21 59.5	1 56.2	15 50.2	11 30.4	14 41.4	20 31.5
28	12 18 45.8	2 37.3	0 21.9	10 N 47.8	0 N 4.8	12 43.0	21 48.1	1 39.0	15 45.2	11 32.6	14 40.2	20 32.8
31	12 30 35.5	3 47.5	0 21.9	20 43.7	2 48.3	11 37.4	21 35.5	1 21.9	15 40.3	11 34.6	14 39.1	20 34.0

APRIL 1963

LONGITUDE

DAY	EPHEM. SID. TIME h m s	☉ ° ′	☊ ° ′	☽ ° ′	☿ ° ′	♀ ° ′	♂ ° ′	♃ ° ′	♄ ° ′	♅ ° ′	♆ ° ′	♇ ° ′
1	12 34 32.0	10♈33.4	25♋55.1	8♋52.5	11♈41.1	2♓20.0	6♌40.1	29♓15.4	20♒ 2.4	1♍46.4	15♏ 9.8	10♍ 8.0
2	12 38 28.6	11 32.6	25 51.9	22 3.6	13 44.2	3 31.3	6 50.4	29 29.8	20 7.8	1R44.5	15R 8.5	10R 6.7
3	12 42 25.1	12 31.7	25 48.7	4♌54.3	15 47.8	4 42.7	7 1.3	29 44.1	20 13.1	1 42.7	15 7.2	10 5.4
4	12 46 21.7	13 30.9	25 45.5	17 28.2	17 51.8	5 54.1	7 12.8	29 58.5	20 18.3	1 41.0	15 5.9	10 4.2
5	12 50 18.2	14 30.0	25 42.3	29 49.3	19 56.1	7 5.5	7 24.8	0♈12.8	20 23.5	1 39.2	15 4.6	10 2.9
6	12 54 14.8	15 29.0	25 39.2	12♍ .6	22 .2	8 17.0	7 37.3	0 27.0	20 28.6	1 37.6	15 3.2	10 1.7
7	12 58 11.3	16 28.0	25 36.0	24 4.8	24 4.1	9 28.5	7 50.3	0 41.3	20 33.7	1 35.9	15 1.8	10 .5
8	13 2 7.9	17 27.0	25 32.8	6♎ 4.0	26 7.3	10 40.0	8 3.8	0 55.5	20 38.7	1 34.3	15 .4	9 59.3
9	13 6 4.4	18 26.0	25 29.6	17 59.6	28 9.5	11 51.6	8 17.8	1 9.7	20 43.6	1 32.8	14 59.0	9 58.1
10	13 10 1.0	19 24.9	25 26.5	29 53.0	0♉10.5	13 3.3	8 32.3	1 23.9	20 48.4	1 31.3	14 57.6	9 57.0
11	13 13 57.5	20 23.8	25 23.3	11♏45.4	2 9.9	14 14.9	8 47.3	1 38.1	20 53.2	1 29.8	14 56.2	9 55.9
12	13 17 54.1	21 22.7	25 20.1	23 38.5	4 7.3	15 26.7	9 2.7	1 52.2	20 58.0	1 28.4	14 54.7	9 54.8
13	13 21 50.6	22 21.5	25 16.9	5♐34.3	6 2.3	16 38.4	9 18.6	2 6.3	21 2.6	1 27.0	14 53.3	9 53.7
14	13 25 47.2	23 20.3	25 13.7	17 35.6	7 54.6	17 50.2	9 34.9	2 20.3	21 7.2	1 25.7	14 51.8	9 52.7
15	13 29 43.7	24 19.1	25 10.6	29 45.9	9 43.8	19 2.0	9 51.6	2 34.4	21 11.7	1 24.4	14 50.3	9 51.6
16	13 33 40.3	25 17.8	25 7.4	12♑ 9.3	11 29.8	20 13.8	10 8.8	2 48.3	21 16.1	1 23.2	14 48.8	9 50.6
17	13 37 36.9	26 16.5	25 4.2	24 50.4	13 12.1	21 25.7	10 26.3	3 2.3	21 20.4	1 22.0	14 47.3	9 49.6
18	13 41 33.4	27 15.2	25 1.0	7♒53.6	14 50.6	22 37.6	10 44.3	3 16.2	21 24.7	1 20.9	14 45.7	9 48.7
19	13 45 30.0	28 13.8	24 57.9	21 23.1	16 25.0	23 49.5	11 2.7	3 30.0	21 28.9	1 19.8	14 44.2	9 47.7
20	13 49 26.5	29 12.4	24 54.7	5♓21.3	17 55.1	25 1.4	11 21.4	3 43.9	21 33.0	1 18.7	14 42.6	9 46.8
21	13 53 23.1	0♉11.0	24 51.5	19 48.4	19 20.7	26 13.4	11 40.6	3 57.6	21 37.0	1 17.8	14 41.1	9 45.9
22	13 57 19.6	1 9.6	24 48.3	4♈41.1	20 41.6	27 25.4	12 .1	4 11.4	21 41.0	1 16.8	14 39.5	9 45.1
23	14 1 16.2	2 8.1	24 45.1	19 52.5	21 57.8	28 37.5	12 19.9	4 25.1	21 44.8	1 15.9	14 37.9	9 44.2
24	14 5 12.7	3 6.6	24 42.0	5♉12.5	23 9.1	29 49.5	12 40.2	4 38.7	21 48.6	1 15.1	14 36.3	9 43.4
25	14 9 9.3	4 5.1	24 38.8	20 29.4	24 15.4	1♈ 1.6	13 .8	4 52.3	21 52.3	1 14.3	14 34.7	9 42.6
26	14 13 5.8	5 3.5	24 35.6	5♊32.1	25 16.6	2 13.7	13 21.7	5 5.8	21 56.0	1 13.6	14 33.1	9 41.9
27	14 17 2.4	6 1.9	24 32.4	20 12.2	26 12.6	3 25.8	13 43.0	5 19.3	21 59.5	1 12.9	14 31.5	9 41.1
28	14 20 58.9	7 .3	24 29.3	4♋24.7	27 3.4	4 37.9	14 4.6	5 32.8	22 3.0	1 12.2	14 29.9	9 40.4
29	14 24 55.5	7 58.6	24 26.1	18 8.2	27 48.8	5 50.0	14 26.5	5 46.2	22 6.3	1 11.7	14 28.3	9 39.7
30	14 28 52.0	8 56.9	24 22.9	1♌24.1	28 28.8	7 2.2	14 48.8	5 59.5	22 9.6	1 11.1	14 26.6	9 39.1

LATITUDE

DAY	SID. TIME	☉	☊	☽	☿	♀	♂	♃	♄	♅	♆	♇
1	12 34 32.0	0 .0	0 .0	1S32.6	0S57.9	0S38.7	3N .3	1S 3.8	0S53.2	0N47.7	1N49.3	13N53.0
4	12 46 21.7	0 .0	0 .0	1N48.1	0 29.6	0 47.8	2 54.1	1 3.9	0 53.6	0 47.6	1 49.4	13 52.5
7	12 58 11.3	0 .0	0 .0	4 14.4	0N 2.1	0 56.2	2 48.1	1 4.1	0 54.1	0 47.5	1 49.5	13 52.0
10	13 10 1.0	0 .0	0 .0	4 58.6	0 35.7	1 4.0	2 42.2	1 4.3	0 54.5	0 47.4	1 49.5	13 51.4
13	13 21 50.6	0 .0	0 .0	3 48.6	1 9.3	1 11.2	2 36.5	1 4.6	0 54.9	0 47.3	1 49.6	13 50.7
16	13 33 40.3	0 .0	0 .0	1 6.2	1 40.7	1 17.6	2 31.0	1 4.8	0 55.4	0 47.2	1 49.7	13 50.0
19	13 45 30.0	0 .0	0 .0	2S15.6	2 7.8	1 23.4	2 25.6	1 5.1	0 55.8	0 47.1	1 49.8	13 49.3
22	13 57 19.6	0 .0	0 .0	4 43.0	2 28.6	1 28.4	2 20.3	1 5.4	0 56.3	0 47.0	1 49.8	13 48.5
25	14 9 9.3	0 .0	0 .0	4 29.2	2 41.8	1 32.8	2 15.2	1 5.7	0 56.8	0 46.9	1 49.8	13 47.7
28	14 20 58.9	0 .0	0 .0	1 39.8	2 46.1	1 36.4	2 10.3	1 6.0	0 57.3	0 46.8	1 49.9	13 46.8

RIGHT ASCENSION

DAY	SID. TIME	☉	☊	☽	☿	♀	♂	♃	♄	♅	♆	♇
1	12 34 32.0	9♈42.1	27♋54.5	9♋32.9	11♈ 7.3	4♓32.9	9♌52.1	29♓44.5	22♒44.4	4♍ 4.2	13♏14.9	17♍12.8
2	12 38 28.6	10 36.8	27 51.2	23 45.8	12 57.5	5 41.8	10 2.3	29 57.7	22 49.7	4R 2.4	13R13.6	17R11.5
3	12 42 25.1	11 31.4	27 47.9	7♌26.4	14 48.3	6 50.5	10 13.0	0♈10.9	22 55.0	4 .7	13 12.3	17 10.2
4	12 46 21.7	12 26.1	27 44.5	20 29.5	16 39.7	7 59.1	10 24.3	0 24.0	23 .2	3 59.0	13 11.1	17 8.9
5	12 50 18.2	13 20.8	27 41.2	2♍55.2	18 31.6	9 7.6	10 36.2	0 37.2	23 5.3	3 57.3	13 9.7	17 7.7
6	12 54 14.8	14 15.6	27 37.8	14 48.0	20 23.8	10 15.9	10 48.5	0 50.3	23 10.4	3 55.7	13 8.4	17 6.4
7	12 58 11.3	15 10.4	27 34.5	26 15.3	22 16.2	11 24.0	11 1.4	1 3.4	23 15.4	3 54.1	13 7.1	17 5.2
8	13 2 7.9	16 5.3	27 31.1	7♎25.7	24 8.5	12 32.0	11 14.8	1 16.5	23 20.4	3 52.6	13 5.7	17 4.0
9	13 6 4.4	17 .2	27 27.8	18 28.7	26 .4	13 39.9	11 28.7	1 29.5	23 25.3	3 51.1	13 4.3	17 2.8
10	13 10 1.0	17 55.1	27 24.4	29 33.6	27 51.8	14 47.7	11 43.1	1 42.6	23 30.1	3 49.7	13 2.9	17 1.6
11	13 13 57.5	18 50.2	27 21.1	10♏49.1	29 42.4	15 55.3	11 58.0	1 55.6	23 34.8	3 48.3	13 1.5	17 .5
12	13 17 54.1	19 45.3	27 17.7	22 23.2	1♉31.8	17 2.9	12 13.3	2 8.6	23 39.5	3 46.9	13 .1	16 59.4
13	13 21 50.6	20 40.5	27 14.4	4♐21.9	3 19.7	18 10.3	12 29.1	2 21.5	23 44.1	3 45.6	12 58.7	16 58.2
14	13 25 47.2	21 35.7	27 11.0	16 49.0	5 5.8	19 17.6	12 45.3	2 34.5	23 48.7	3 44.3	12 57.2	16 57.1
15	13 29 43.7	22 31.1	27 7.7	29 44.9	6 49.7	20 24.9	13 1.9	2 47.4	23 53.1	3 43.1	12 55.7	16 56.1
16	13 33 40.3	23 26.5	27 4.3	13♑ 6.3	8 31.3	21 32.0	13 18.9	3 .2	23 57.5	3 41.9	12 54.2	16 55.0
17	13 37 36.9	24 22.0	27 1.0	26 46.5	10 10.1	22 39.1	13 36.3	3 13.0	24 1.8	3 40.8	12 52.7	16 54.0
18	13 41 33.4	25 17.7	26 57.6	10♒37.3	11 45.8	23 46.0	13 54.2	3 25.8	24 6.1	3 39.7	12 51.2	16 52.9
19	13 45 30.0	26 13.4	26 54.3	24 31.4	13 18.3	24 53.0	14 12.4	3 38.6	24 10.2	3 38.6	12 49.7	16 51.9
20	13 49 26.5	27 9.2	26 50.9	8♓24.3	14 47.2	25 59.8	14 31.0	3 51.3	24 14.3	3 37.6	12 48.2	16 50.9
21	13 53 23.1	28 5.1	26 47.6	22 15.9	16 12.3	27 6.6	14 49.9	4 4.0	24 18.3	3 36.6	12 46.6	16 50.0
22	13 57 19.6	29 1.2	26 44.2	6♈10.3	17 33.4	28 13.4	15 9.3	4 16.6	24 22.2	3 35.7	12 45.1	16 49.0
23	14 1 16.2	29 57.3	26 40.9	20 14.1	18 50.3	29 20.1	15 29.0	4 29.2	24 26.1	3 34.9	12 43.5	16 48.1
24	14 5 12.7	0♉53.6	26 37.5	4♉34.6	20 2.7	0♈26.7	15 49.0	4 41.8	24 29.9	3 34.1	12 42.0	16 47.2
25	14 9 9.3	1 50.0	26 34.2	19 16.6	21 10.5	1 33.4	16 9.3	4 54.3	24 33.5	3 33.3	12 40.4	16 46.4
26	14 13 5.8	2 46.4	26 30.8	4♊19.1	22 13.6	2 40.0	16 30.0	5 6.8	24 37.1	3 32.6	12 38.8	16 45.5
27	14 17 2.4	3 43.1	26 27.5	19 33.6	23 11.7	3 46.6	16 51.0	5 19.2	24 40.7	3 31.9	12 37.2	16 44.7
28	14 20 58.9	4 39.8	26 24.1	4♋44.9	24 4.8	4 53.3	17 12.3	5 31.6	24 44.1	3 31.3	12 35.6	16 43.9
29	14 24 55.5	5 36.6	26 20.8	19 34.7	24 52.7	5 59.9	17 33.9	5 43.9	24 47.5	3 30.7	12 34.0	16 43.1
30	14 28 52.0	6 33.6	26 17.4	3♌48.0	25 35.3	7 6.5	17 55.8	5 56.2	24 50.7	3 30.2	12 32.4	16 42.4

DECLINATION

DAY	SID. TIME	☉	☊	☽	☿	♀	♂	♃	♄	♅	♆	♇
1	12 34 32.0	4N10.8	0N22.0	21N36.4	3N44.0	11S14.8	21N31.0	1S16.3	15S38.7	11N35.3	14S38.7	20N34.4
4	12 46 21.7	5 20.1	0 22.0	17 18.9	6 33.2	10 5.3	21 16.6	0 59.3	15 34.1	11 37.1	14 37.4	20 35.4
7	12 58 11.3	6 28.5	0 22.0	6 14.6	9 22.2	8 53.2	21 1.1	0 42.4	15 29.6	11 38.9	14 36.2	20 36.3
10	13 10 1.0	7 36.0	0 22.0	6S46.2	12 5.5	7 38.7	20 44.4	0 25.7	15 25.3	11 40.4	14 34.8	20 37.1
13	13 21 50.6	8 42.3	0 22.1	17 29.2	14 37.5	6 22.0	20 26.5	0 9.0	15 21.2	11 41.9	14 33.5	20 37.8
16	13 33 40.3	9 47.3	0 22.1	21 47.3	16 52.7	5 3.6	20 7.6	0N 7.5	15 17.2	11 43.1	14 32.1	20 38.4
19	13 45 30.0	10 50.8	0 22.1	16 30.9	18 47.3	3 43.7	19 47.5	0 23.8	15 13.6	11 44.3	14 30.7	20 38.8
22	13 57 19.6	11 52.7	0 22.2	2 28.1	20 19.0	2 22.6	19 26.5	0 39.9	15 10.1	11 45.2	14 29.3	20 39.1
25	14 9 9.3	12 53.0	0 22.2	13N32.8	21 27.1	1 .6	19 4.3	0 55.9	15 6.9	11 46.0	14 27.9	20 39.3
28	14 20 58.9	13 51.2	0 22.2	21 42.4	22 11.8	0N22.0	18 41.1	1 11.6	15 3.9	11 46.6	14 26.4	20 39.3

MAY 1963

LONGITUDE

DAY	EPHEM. SID. TIME (h m s)	☉ (° ′)	☊ (° ′)	☽ (° ′)	☿ (° ′)	♀ (° ′)	♂ (° ′)	♃ (° ′)	♄ (° ′)	♅ (° ′)	♆ (° ′)	♇ (° ′)
1	14 32 48.6	9♉55.2	24♋19.7	14♌15.9	29♉ 3.5	8♈14.4	15♌11.3	6♈12.8	22♒12.8	1♍10.7	14♏25.0	9♍38.5
2	14 36 45.2	10 53.5	24 16.5	26 47.7	29 32.6	9 26.5	15 34.2	6 26.0	22 15.9	1R10.2	14R23.4	9R37.9
3	14 40 41.7	11 51.7	24 13.4	9♍ 4.1	29 56.4	10 38.8	15 57.4	6 39.2	22 19.0	1 9.9	14 21.8	9 37.4
4	14 44 38.3	12 49.9	24 10.2	21 9.5	0♊14.7	11 51.0	16 20.8	6 52.3	22 21.9	1 9.6	14 20.1	9 36.8
5	14 48 34.8	13 48.0	24 7.0	3♎ 7.6	0 27.5	13 3.3	16 44.5	7 5.3	22 24.8	1 9.4	14 18.5	9 36.3
6	14 52 31.4	14 46.1	24 3.8	15 1.6	0 35.0	14 15.5	17 8.5	7 18.3	22 27.5	1 9.1	14 16.9	9 35.8
7	14 56 27.9	15 44.2	24 .7	26 53.9	0 37.2	15 27.8	17 32.7	7 31.2	22 30.2	1 9.0	14 15.2	9 35.4
8	15 0 24.5	16 42.2	23 57.5	8♏46.4	0R34.4	16 40.1	17 57.2	7 44.1	22 32.8	1 8.9	14 13.6	9 35.0
9	15 4 21.0	17 40.2	23 54.3	20 40.8	0 26.6	17 52.4	18 22.0	7 56.9	22 35.3	1 8.8	14 12.0	9 34.6
10	15 8 17.6	18 38.2	23 51.1	2♐38.3	0 14.1	19 4.7	18 47.0	8 9.6	22 37.7	1D 8.9	14 10.3	9 34.2
11	15 12 14.2	19 36.2	23 47.9	14 40.6	29♉57.3	20 17.1	19 12.2	8 22.2	22 40.0	1 8.9	14 8.7	9 33.9
12	15 16 10.7	20 34.1	23 44.8	26 49.4	29 36.5	21 29.4	19 37.7	8 34.8	22 42.2	1 9.0	14 7.1	9 33.6
13	15 20 7.3	21 32.0	23 41.6	9♑ 7.1	29 12.0	22 41.8	20 3.5	8 47.3	22 44.3	1 9.2	14 5.5	9 33.3
14	15 24 3.8	22 29.9	23 38.4	21 36.5	28 44.4	23 54.2	20 29.4	8 59.7	22 46.3	1 9.4	14 3.9	9 33.1
15	15 28 .4	23 27.8	23 35.2	4♒21.1	28 14.2	25 6.6	20 55.6	9 12.1	22 48.3	1 9.7	14 2.2	9 32.8
16	15 31 56.9	24 25.7	23 32.1	17 24.4	27 41.8	26 19.0	21 22.1	9 24.4	22 50.1	1 10.0	14 .6	9 32.7
17	15 35 53.5	25 23.5	23 28.9	0♓49.7	27 7.9	27 31.5	21 48.7	9 36.6	22 51.8	1 10.4	13 59.0	9 32.5
18	15 39 50.0	26 21.3	23 25.7	14 39.6	26 33.2	28 44.0	22 15.6	9 48.7	22 53.5	1 10.8	13 57.4	9 32.4
19	15 43 46.6	27 19.1	23 22.5	28 54.8	25 58.1	29 56.5	22 42.6	10 .8	22 55.0	1 11.3	13 55.9	9 32.3
20	15 47 43.2	28 16.9	23 19.4	13♈33.5	25 23.4	1♉ 9.0	23 9.9	10 12.8	22 56.5	1 11.9	13 54.3	9 32.2
21	15 51 39.7	29 14.6	23 16.2	28 30.8	24 49.5	2 21.5	23 37.4	10 24.7	22 57.8	1 12.5	13 52.7	9 32.2
22	15 55 36.3	0♊12.4	23 13.0	13♉39.1	24 17.2	3 34.0	24 5.1	10 36.5	22 59.1	1 13.1	13 51.2	9 32.2
23	15 59 32.8	1 10.1	23 9.8	28 48.3	23 46.9	4 46.6	24 33.0	10 48.2	23 .3	1 13.8	13 49.6	9 32.2
24	16 3 29.4	2 7.8	23 6.6	13♊48.3	23 19.1	5 59.2	25 1.1	10 59.9	23 1.4	1 14.6	13 48.1	9D32.3
25	16 7 25.9	3 5.5	23 3.5	28 30.0	22 54.2	7 11.7	25 29.4	11 11.4	23 2.3	1 15.4	13 46.6	9 32.4
26	16 11 22.5	4 3.1	23 .3	12♋47.4	22 32.7	8 24.3	25 57.9	11 22.9	23 3.2	1 16.3	13 45.1	9 32.5
27	16 15 19.0	5 .8	22 57.1	26 37.4	22 14.8	9 36.9	26 26.6	11 34.2	23 4.0	1 17.2	13 43.6	9 32.7
28	16 19 15.6	5 58.4	22 53.9	9♌59.8	22 .7	10 49.5	26 55.4	11 45.5	23 4.6	1 18.2	13 42.1	9 32.9
29	16 23 12.2	6 56.0	22 50.8	22 56.9	21 50.8	12 2.1	27 24.4	11 56.7	23 5.2	1 19.2	13 40.6	9 33.1
30	16 27 8.7	7 53.5	22 47.6	5♍32.1	21 45.2	13 14.7	27 53.6	12 7.7	23 5.7	1 20.3	13 39.2	9 33.3
31	16 31 5.3	8 51.0	22 44.4	17 50.1	21 43.9	14 27.4	28 23.0	12 18.7	23 6.1	1 21.4	13 37.7	9 33.6

LATITUDE

DAY	EPHEM. SID. TIME	☉	☊	☽	☿	♀	♂	♃	♄	♅	♆	♇
1	14 32 48.6	0 .0	0 .0	1N47.2	2N40.5	1S39.2	2N 5.5	1S 6.3	0S57.7	0N46.7	1N49.9	13N45.9
4	14 44 38.3	0 .0	0 .0	4 15.8	2 24.6	1 41.3	2 .9	1 6.7	0 58.2	0 46.6	1 49.9	13 45.0
7	14 56 27.9	0 .0	0 .0	5 1.0	1 57.9	1 42.8	1 56.3	1 7.0	0 58.8	0 46.4	1 49.9	13 44.0
10	15 8 17.6	0 .0	0 .0	3 51.3	1 21.1	1 43.5	1 51.9	1 7.4	0 59.3	0 46.3	1 49.9	13 43.0
13	15 20 7.3	0 .0	0 .0	1 8.6	0 35.8	1 43.5	1 47.7	1 7.8	0 59.8	0 46.2	1 49.9	13 42.0
16	15 31 56.9	0 .0	0 .0	2S11.4	0S15.1	1 42.8	1 43.5	1 8.3	1 .3	0 46.1	1 49.9	13 41.0
19	15 43 46.6	0 .0	0 .0	4 41.8	1 7.6	1 41.4	1 39.5	1 8.7	1 .8	0 46.0	1 49.8	13 40.0
22	15 55 36.3	0 .0	0 .0	4 44.0	1 57.5	1 39.5	1 35.5	1 9.2	1 1.4	0 45.8	1 49.8	13 38.9
25	16 7 25.9	0 .0	0 .0	1 59.9	2 40.9	1 36.9	1 31.7	1 9.7	1 1.9	0 45.7	1 49.7	13 37.9
28	16 19 15.6	0 .0	0 .0	1N39.2	3 15.2	1 33.7	1 27.9	1 10.2	1 2.5	0 45.6	1 49.6	13 36.8
31	16 31 5.3	0 .0	0 .0	4 18.3	3 39.3	1 29.9	1 24.3	1 10.7	1 3.0	0 45.5	1 49.6	13 35.8

RIGHT ASCENSION

DAY	EPHEM. SID. TIME	☉	☊	☽	☿	♀	♂	♃	♄	♅	♆	♇
1	14 32 48.6	7♉30.7	26♋14.0	17♌16.6	26♉12.5	8♈13.2	18♌18.0	6♈ 8.5	24♒53.9	3♍29.7	12♏30.8	16♍41.7
2	14 36 45.2	8 28.0	26 10.7	29 59.7	26 44.3	9 19.9	18 40.5	6 20.7	24 57.0	3R29.3	12R29.2	16R41.0
3	14 40 41.7	9 25.4	26 7.3	12♍ 2.6	27 10.6	10 26.7	19 3.2	6 32.8	25 .1	3 29.0	12 27.7	16 40.3
4	14 44 38.3	10 22.9	26 4.0	23 34.2	27 31.4	11 33.4	19 26.2	6 44.9	25 3.0	3 28.7	12 26.0	16 39.7
5	14 48 34.8	11 20.5	26 .6	4♎44.9	27 46.8	12 40.3	19 49.4	6 56.9	25 5.9	3 28.4	12 24.4	16 39.1
6	14 52 31.4	12 18.3	25 57.3	15 45.5	27 56.7	13 47.2	20 12.9	7 8.9	25 8.6	3 28.2	12 22.8	16 38.5
7	14 56 27.9	13 16.2	25 53.9	26 46.5	28 1.4	14 54.2	20 36.6	7 20.8	25 11.3	3 28.1	12 21.2	16 37.9
8	15 0 24.5	14 14.2	25 50.5	7♏57.6	28R .9	16 1.3	21 .5	7 32.7	25 13.9	3 28.0	12 19.6	16 37.4
9	15 4 21.0	15 12.4	25 47.2	19 27.2	27 55.5	17 8.5	21 24.7	7 44.5	25 16.3	3 27.9	12 18.0	16 36.9
10	15 8 17.6	16 10.7	25 43.8	1♐21.7	27 45.5	18 15.7	21 49.1	7 56.3	25 18.7	3 27.9	12 16.4	16 36.4
11	15 12 14.2	17 9.2	25 40.5	13 44.6	27 31.1	19 23.1	22 13.6	8 7.9	25 21.1	3 27.9	12 14.8	16 35.9
12	15 16 10.7	18 7.8	25 37.1	26 35.6	27 12.8	20 30.6	22 38.4	8 19.6	25 23.3	3D28.0	12 13.2	16 35.5
13	15 20 7.3	19 6.6	25 33.7	9♑50.3	26 50.9	21 38.3	23 3.4	8 31.1	25 25.4	3 28.2	12 11.6	16 35.1
14	15 24 3.8	20 5.5	25 30.4	23 20.7	26 26.0	22 46.1	23 28.6	8 42.6	25 27.4	3 28.4	12 10.0	16 34.7
15	15 28 .4	21 4.5	25 27.0	6♒57.6	25 58.6	23 54.0	23 54.0	8 54.1	25 29.4	3 28.6	12 8.4	16 34.4
16	15 31 56.9	22 3.7	25 23.7	20 33.1	25 29.3	25 2.1	24 19.5	9 5.4	25 31.2	3 28.9	12 6.8	16 34.0
17	15 35 53.5	23 3.1	25 20.3	4♓ 3.0	24 58.6	26 10.4	24 45.2	9 16.7	25 33.0	3 29.3	12 5.2	16 33.7
18	15 39 50.0	24 2.6	25 16.9	17 27.7	24 27.1	27 18.8	25 11.2	9 28.0	25 34.7	3 29.7	12 3.6	16 33.5
19	15 43 46.6	25 2.2	25 13.6	0♈52.5	23 55.5	28 27.4	25 37.2	9 39.1	25 36.3	3 30.1	12 2.1	16 33.2
20	15 47 43.2	26 2.0	25 10.2	14 26.0	23 24.2	29 36.2	26 3.5	9 50.2	25 37.7	3 30.6	12 .5	16 33.0
21	15 51 39.7	27 1.9	25 6.8	28 18.3	22 54.0	0♉45.2	26 29.9	10 1.2	25 39.1	3 31.2	11 59.0	16 32.9
22	15 55 36.3	28 2.0	25 3.5	12♉38.3	22 25.2	1 54.4	26 56.5	10 12.2	25 40.4	3 31.8	11 57.4	16 32.7
23	15 59 32.8	29 2.2	25 .1	27 30.1	21 58.4	3 3.8	27 23.3	10 23.0	25 41.6	3 32.4	11 55.9	16 32.6
24	16 3 29.4	0♊ 2.5	24 56.7	12♊49.9	21 34.1	4 13.5	27 50.2	10 33.8	25 42.8	3 33.2	11 54.4	16 32.5
25	16 7 25.9	1 3.0	24 53.4	28 23.4	21 12.6	5 23.3	28 17.3	10 44.6	25 43.8	3 34.0	11 52.9	16 32.5
26	16 11 22.5	2 3.6	24 50.0	13♋49.2	20 54.2	6 33.3	28 44.5	10 55.2	25 44.7	3 34.8	11 51.4	16 32.5
27	16 15 19.0	3 4.3	24 46.6	28 44.9	20 39.2	7 43.6	29 11.8	11 5.7	25 45.5	3 35.6	11 49.9	16 32.4
28	16 19 15.6	4 5.1	24 43.3	12♌54.8	20 27.8	8 54.1	29 39.3	11 16.2	25 46.2	3 36.5	11 48.5	16D32.5
29	16 23 12.2	5 6.0	24 39.9	26 12.8	20 20.4	10 4.9	0♍ 6.9	11 26.5	25 46.8	3 37.5	11 47.0	16 32.5
30	16 27 8.7	6 7.1	24 36.5	8♍41.9	20 16.8	11 15.9	0 34.7	11 36.8	25 47.3	3 38.5	11 45.6	16 32.6
31	16 31 5.3	7 8.2	24 33.2	20 30.7	20D17.4	12 27.1	1 2.6	11 47.0	25 47.8	3 39.6	11 44.1	16 32.7

DECLINATION

DAY	EPHEM. SID. TIME	☉	☊	☽	☿	♀	♂	♃	♄	♅	♆	♇
1	14 32 48.6	14N47.5	0N22.3	18N15.7	22N33.7	1N44.9	18N16.9	1N27.2	15S 1.1	11N47.1	14S25.0	20N39.3
4	14 44 38.3	15 41.5	0 22.3	7 25.3	22 33.6	3 7.9	17 51.6	1 42.5	14 58.6	11 47.3	14 23.6	20 39.1
7	14 56 27.9	16 33.2	0 22.3	5S41.1	22 12.3	4 30.5	17 25.4	1 57.5	14 56.4	11 47.5	14 22.1	20 38.7
10	15 8 17.6	17 22.4	0 22.3	16 54.5	21 31.5	5 52.5	16 58.2	2 12.2	14 54.5	11 47.4	14 20.7	20 38.3
13	15 20 7.3	18 9.0	0 22.4	21 59.3	20 33.9	7 13.7	16 30.0	2 26.7	14 52.8	11 47.2	14 19.3	20 37.7
16	15 31 56.9	18 52.8	0 22.4	17 42.3	19 24.3	8 33.7	16 .9	2 40.9	14 51.4	11 46.7	14 17.9	20 37.0
19	15 43 46.6	19 33.8	0 22.4	4 44.4	18 9.3	9 52.2	15 30.8	2 54.8	14 50.3	11 46.2	14 16.5	20 36.2
22	15 55 36.3	20 11.8	0 22.5	11N25.1	16 56.8	11 8.9	14 59.8	3 8.3	14 49.4	11 45.4	14 15.1	20 35.3
25	16 7 25.9	20 46.7	0 22.5	21 26.2	15 54.3	12 23.4	14 27.8	3 21.5	14 48.9	11 44.5	14 13.8	20 34.3
28	16 19 15.6	21 18.4	0 22.5	19 20.2	15 7.7	13 35.5	13 55.0	3 34.4	14 48.6	11 43.4	14 12.6	20 33.1
31	16 31 5.3	21 46.8	0 22.5	8 46.3	14 40.2	14 44.8	13 21.3	3 46.8	14 48.7	11 42.1	14 11.3	20 31.8

JUNE 1963

LONGITUDE

DAY	EPHEM. SID. TIME h m s	☉ ° ′	☊ ° ′	☽ ° ′	☿ ° ′	♀ ° ′	♂ ° ′	♃ ° ′	♄ ° ′	♅ ° ′	♆ ° ′	♇ ° ′
1	16 35 1.8	9♊48.5	22♋41.2	29♍55.2	21♉47.1	15♉40.0	28♌52.5	12♈29.6	23♒ 6.3	1♍22.6	13♏36.3	9♍33.9
2	16 38 58.4	10 46.0	22 38.1	11♎52.1	21 D 54.8	16 52.7	29 22.2	12 40.4	23 6.5	1 23.8	13 R 34.9	9 34.3
3	16 42 54.9	11 43.5	22 34.9	23 44.8	22 7.0	18 5.3	29 52.1	12 51.0	23 6.6	1 25.1	13 33.5	9 34.6
4	16 46 51.5	12 40.9	22 31.7	5♏36.7	22 23.6	19 18.0	0♍22.1	13 1.6	23 6.6	1 26.4	13 32.1	9 35.0
5	16 50 48.1	13 38.4	22 28.5	17 30.8	22 44.7	20 30.7	0 52.3	13 12.1	23 R 6.5	1 27.8	13 30.7	9 35.5
6	16 54 44.6	14 35.8	22 25.3	29 29.3	23 10.1	21 43.4	1 22.6	13 22.4	23 6.3	1 29.2	13 29.4	9 35.9
7	16 58 41.2	15 33.2	22 22.2	11♐34.1	23 39.8	22 56.2	1 53.1	13 32.7	23 6.0	1 30.7	13 28.0	9 36.4
8	17 2 37.7	16 30.6	22 19.0	23 46.7	24 13.8	24 8.9	2 23.7	13 42.8	23 5.6	1 32.2	13 26.7	9 36.9
9	17 6 34.3	17 27.9	22 15.8	6♑ 8.3	24 51.8	25 21.7	2 54.5	13 52.8	23 5.1	1 33.8	13 25.4	9 37.5
10	17 10 30.8	18 25.3	22 12.6	18 40.3	25 33.9	26 34.4	3 25.4	14 2.7	23 4.5	1 35.4	13 24.2	9 38.0
11	17 14 27.4	19 22.6	22 9.5	1♒24.2	26 19.9	27 47.2	3 56.5	14 12.6	23 3.8	1 37.1	13 22.9	9 38.7
12	17 18 24.0	20 19.9	22 6.3	14 21.6	27 9.8	29 .1	4 27.7	14 22.2	23 3.0	1 38.8	13 21.7	9 39.3
13	17 22 20.5	21 17.3	22 3.1	27 34.4	28 3.5	0♊12.9	4 59.0	14 31.8	23 2.1	1 40.6	13 20.5	9 40.0
14	17 26 17.1	22 14.6	21 59.9	11♓ 4.3	29 1.0	1 25.8	5 30.5	14 41.3	23 1.1	1 42.4	13 19.3	9 40.7
15	17 30 13.6	23 11.9	21 56.8	24 52.4	0♊ 2.0	2 38.7	6 2.1	14 50.6	23 .1	1 44.3	13 18.2	9 41.4
16	17 34 10.2	24 9.2	21 53.6	8♈58.9	1 6.6	3 51.5	6 33.9	14 59.9	22 58.9	1 46.2	13 17.0	9 42.2
17	17 38 6.7	25 6.5	21 50.4	23 22.4	2 14.7	5 4.4	7 5.8	15 8.9	22 57.6	1 48.1	13 15.9	9 43.0
18	17 42 3.3	26 3.8	21 47.2	7♉59.7	3 26.3	6 17.4	7 37.8	15 17.9	22 56.3	1 50.1	13 14.8	9 43.8
19	17 45 59.9	27 1.1	21 44.1	22 45.6	4 41.3	7 30.3	8 9.9	15 26.7	22 54.8	1 52.2	13 13.7	9 44.6
20	17 49 56.4	27 58.4	21 40.9	7♊33.3	5 59.6	8 43.3	8 42.2	15 35.4	22 53.3	1 54.2	13 12.6	9 45.5
21	17 53 53.0	28 55.7	21 37.7	22 15.2	7 21.3	9 56.2	9 14.6	15 44.0	22 51.6	1 56.4	13 11.6	9 46.4
22	17 57 49.5	29 53.0	21 34.5	6♋44.2	8 46.3	11 9.2	9 47.1	15 52.4	22 49.9	1 58.5	13 10.6	9 47.3
23	18 1 46.1	0♋50.2	21 31.3	20 54.4	10 14.5	12 22.3	10 19.8	16 .7	22 48.1	2 .8	13 9.6	9 48.3
24	18 5 42.7	1 47.5	21 28.2	4♌42.1	11 45.9	13 35.3	10 52.5	16 8.9	22 46.2	2 3.0	13 8.7	9 49.2
25	18 9 39.2	2 44.7	21 25.0	18 5.7	13 20.5	14 48.3	11 25.4	16 16.9	22 44.2	2 5.3	13 7.8	9 50.2
26	18 13 35.8	3 42.0	21 21.8	1♍ 5.9	14 58.3	16 1.4	11 58.5	16 24.8	22 42.1	2 7.7	13 6.8	9 51.3
27	18 17 32.3	4 39.2	21 18.6	13 44.8	16 39.2	17 14.5	12 31.6	16 32.5	22 39.9	2 10.0	13 6.0	9 52.3
28	18 21 28.9	5 36.4	21 15.5	26 5.8	18 23.2	18 27.5	13 4.8	16 40.1	22 37.6	2 12.5	13 5.1	9 53.4
29	18 25 25.4	6 33.6	21 12.3	8♎13.1	20 10.1	19 40.6	13 38.2	16 47.5	22 35.3	2 14.9	13 4.3	9 54.5
30	18 29 22.0	7 30.8	21 9.1	20 11.2	21 59.9	20 53.8	14 11.7	16 54.8	22 32.9	2 17.4	13 3.5	9 55.7

LATITUDE

DAY	EPHEM. SID. TIME	☉	☊	☽	☿	♀	♂	♃	♄	♅	♆	♇
1	16 35 1.8	0 .0	0 .0	4N48.3	3S45.0	1S28.5	1N23.1	1S10.9	1S 3.2	0N45.4	1N49.5	13N35.4
4	16 46 51.5	0 .0	0 .0	4 59.7	3 55.4	1 24.1	1 19.5	1 11.5	1 3.7	0 45.3	1 49.5	13 34.4
7	16 58 41.2	0 .0	0 .0	3 16.6	3 56.4	1 19.1	1 16.1	1 12.0	1 4.3	0 45.2	1 49.4	13 33.3
10	17 10 30.8	0 .0	0 .0	0 10.7	3 49.0	1 13.8	1 12.7	1 12.6	1 4.8	0 45.1	1 49.3	13 32.3
13	17 22 20.5	0 .0	0 .0	3S 8.6	3 34.4	1 8.0	1 9.4	1 13.3	1 5.3	0 45.0	1 49.1	13 31.2
16	17 34 10.2	0 .0	0 .0	5 7.2	3 13.6	1 1.9	1 6.1	1 13.9	1 5.9	0 44.9	1 49.0	13 30.2
19	17 45 59.9	0 .0	0 .0	4 25.8	2 47.6	0 55.4	1 3.0	1 14.5	1 6.4	0 44.8	1 48.9	13 29.2
22	17 57 49.5	0 .0	0 .0	1 14.8	2 17.3	0 48.6	0 59.9	1 15.2	1 6.9	0 44.7	1 48.8	13 28.3
25	18 9 39.2	0 .0	0 .0	2N26.7	1 43.9	0 41.7	0 56.8	1 15.9	1 7.4	0 44.6	1 48.6	13 27.3
28	18 21 28.9	0 .0	0 .0	4 47.8	1 8.5	0 34.5	0 53.8	1 16.6	1 8.0	0 44.5	1 48.5	13 26.4

RIGHT ASCENSION

DAY	EPHEM. SID. TIME	☉	☊	☽	☿	♀	♂	♃	♄	♅	♆	♇
1	16 35 1.8	8♊ 9.4	24♋29.8	1♎50.6	20♉22.1	13♉38.6	1♍30.6	11♈57.1	25♒48.1	3♍40.7	11♏42.7	16♍32.9
2	16 38 58.4	9 10.8	24 26.4	12 54.0	20 31.0	14 50.4	1 58.7	12 7.1	25 48.3	3 41.8	11 R 41.3	16 33.0
3	16 42 54.9	10 12.2	24 23.1	23 53.1	20 44.0	16 2.4	2 26.9	12 17.1	25 48.5	3 43.0	11 39.9	16 33.2
4	16 46 51.5	11 13.8	24 19.7	4♏59.3	21 1.2	17 14.7	2 55.3	12 26.9	25 48.5	3 44.3	11 38.5	16 33.5
5	16 50 48.1	12 15.4	24 16.3	16 22.7	21 22.6	18 27.2	3 23.7	12 36.6	25 48.5	3 45.6	11 37.2	16 33.7
6	16 54 44.6	13 17.1	24 13.0	28 11.4	21 48.1	19 40.1	3 52.3	12 46.3	25 R 48.3	3 46.9	11 35.9	16 34.0
7	16 58 41.2	14 18.9	24 9.6	10♐30.4	22 17.6	20 53.2	4 21.0	12 55.8	25 48.1	3 48.3	11 34.5	16 34.3
8	17 2 37.7	15 20.7	24 6.2	23 20.5	22 51.2	22 6.5	4 49.8	13 5.3	25 47.8	3 49.8	11 33.2	16 34.7
9	17 6 34.3	16 22.7	24 2.8	6♑37.2	23 28.8	23 20.2	5 18.7	13 14.6	25 47.3	3 51.2	11 32.0	16 35.1
10	17 10 30.8	17 24.7	23 59.5	20 11.6	24 10.3	24 34.1	5 47.6	13 23.9	25 46.8	3 52.8	11 30.7	16 35.5
11	17 14 27.4	18 26.8	23 56.1	3♒52.2	24 55.7	25 48.4	6 16.7	13 33.0	25 46.2	3 54.4	11 29.4	16 35.9
12	17 18 24.0	19 28.9	23 52.7	17 28.3	25 45.0	27 2.9	6 45.9	13 42.1	25 45.5	3 56.0	11 28.2	16 36.4
13	17 22 20.5	20 31.1	23 49.4	0♓53.1	26 38.0	28 17.6	7 15.2	13 51.0	25 44.7	3 57.6	11 27.0	16 36.8
14	17 26 17.1	21 33.3	23 46.0	14 5.6	27 35.0	29 32.8	7 44.6	13 59.9	25 43.8	3 59.4	11 25.9	16 37.4
15	17 30 13.6	22 35.6	23 42.6	27 10.2	28 35.6	0♊48.1	8 14.0	14 8.6	25 42.8	4 1.2	11 24.7	16 38.0
16	17 34 10.2	23 37.9	23 39.2	10♈15.8	29 40.1	2 3.7	8 43.6	14 17.2	25 41.7	4 3.0	11 23.6	16 38.5
17	17 38 6.7	24 40.3	23 35.9	23 33.8	0♊48.2	3 19.6	9 13.3	14 25.7	25 40.6	4 4.8	11 22.5	16 39.1
18	17 42 3.3	25 42.7	23 32.5	7♉15.8	2 .2	4 35.7	9 43.0	14 34.1	25 39.3	4 6.7	11 21.4	16 39.8
19	17 45 59.9	26 45.1	23 29.1	21 31.0	3 15.9	5 52.1	10 12.8	14 42.3	25 37.9	4 8.6	11 20.3	16 40.4
20	17 49 56.4	27 47.5	23 25.7	6♊22.4	4 35.4	7 8.8	10 42.7	14 50.5	25 36.5	4 10.6	11 19.2	16 41.1
21	17 53 53.0	28 49.9	23 22.4	21 43.3	5 58.6	8 25.7	11 12.8	14 58.5	25 34.9	4 12.6	11 18.2	16 41.8
22	17 57 49.5	29 52.3	23 19.0	7♋16.1	7 25.7	9 42.8	11 42.9	15 6.4	25 33.3	4 14.7	11 17.2	16 42.6
23	18 1 46.1	0♋54.7	23 15.6	22 36.7	8 56.6	11 .2	12 13.0	15 14.2	25 31.6	4 16.8	11 16.2	16 43.3
24	18 5 42.7	1 57.1	23 12.2	7♌22.6	10 31.3	12 17.8	12 43.3	15 21.8	25 29.8	4 18.9	11 15.3	16 44.1
25	18 9 39.2	2 59.5	23 8.9	21 19.4	12 9.9	13 35.7	13 13.7	15 29.3	25 27.9	4 21.1	11 14.4	16 45.0
26	18 13 35.8	4 1.9	23 5.5	4♍23.6	13 52.4	14 53.7	13 44.1	15 36.7	25 25.9	4 23.3	11 13.5	16 45.8
27	18 17 32.3	5 4.2	23 2.1	16 40.4	15 38.7	16 11.9	14 14.6	15 44.0	25 23.8	4 25.6	11 12.6	16 46.7
28	18 21 28.9	6 6.5	22 58.7	28 19.8	17 28.8	17 30.4	14 45.2	15 51.1	25 21.7	4 27.8	11 11.7	16 47.6
29	18 25 25.4	7 8.7	22 55.3	9♎34.5	19 22.7	18 49.0	15 15.9	15 58.1	25 19.4	4 30.2	11 10.9	16 48.5
30	18 29 22.0	8 10.9	22 52.0	20 37.5	21 20.2	20 7.8	15 46.6	16 5.0	25 17.1	4 32.5	11 10.1	16 49.5

DECLINATION

DAY	EPHEM. SID. TIME	☉	☊	☽	☿	♀	♂	♃	♄	♅	♆	♇
1	16 35 1.8	21N55.5	0N22.6	4N26.4	14N35.4	15N 7.2	13N 9.9	3N50.9	14S48.7	11N41.7	14S10.9	20N31.4
4	16 46 51.5	22 19.3	0 22.6	8S40.7	14 34.6	16 12.3	12 35.0	4 2.8	14 49.2	11 40.2	14 9.8	20 30.0
7	16 58 41.2	22 39.6	0 22.6	18 55.6	14 52.4	17 14.0	11 59.4	4 14.4	14 49.9	11 38.6	14 8.7	20 28.5
10	17 10 30.8	22 56.3	0 22.6	21 57.9	15 26.7	18 11.8	11 22.9	4 25.5	14 50.9	11 36.8	14 7.6	20 26.9
13	17 22 20.5	23 9.4	0 22.7	15 16.0	16 14.7	19 5.4	10 45.7	4 36.1	14 52.2	11 34.8	14 6.6	20 25.3
16	17 34 10.2	23 18.8	0 22.7	1 8.8	17 13.5	19 54.7	10 7.7	4 46.4	14 53.7	11 32.7	14 5.7	20 23.5
19	17 45 59.9	23 24.5	0 22.7	14N10.6	18 19.9	20 39.3	9 29.0	4 56.1	14 55.6	11 30.5	14 4.8	20 21.6
22	17 57 49.5	23 26.6	0 22.7	22 1.5	19 30.4	21 18.9	8 49.5	5 5.4	14 57.7	11 28.1	14 4.0	20 19.7
25	18 9 39.2	23 24.9	0 22.8	17 44.0	20 41.1	21 53.2	8 9.4	5 14.1	15 .1	11 25.6	14 3.3	20 17.7
28	18 21 28.9	23 19.4	0 22.8	5 57.2	21 47.9	22 22.1	7 28.6	5 22.4	15 2.7	11 22.9	14 2.7	20 15.6

JULY 1963

LONGITUDE

DAY	EPHEM. SID. TIME h m s	☉ ° ′	☊ ° ′	☽ ° ′	☿ ° ′	♀ ° ′	♂ ° ′	♃ ° ′	♄ ° ′	♅ ° ′	♆ ° ′	♇ ° ′
1	18 33 18.6	8♋28.0	21♋ 5.9	2♏ 4.5	23♊52.5	22♊ 6.9	14♍45.3	17♈ 2.0	22♒30.4	2♍20.0	13♏ 2.7	9♍56.8
2	18 37 15.1	9 25.2	21 2.8	13 57.5	25 47.8	23 20.1	15 19.0	17 9.0	22R27.8	2 22.5	13R 2.0	9 58.0
3	18 41 11.7	10 22.4	20 59.6	25 53.9	27 45.5	24 33.2	15 52.8	17 15.9	22 25.1	2 25.2	13 1.3	9 59.2
4	18 45 8.2	11 19.6	20 56.4	7♐57.1	29 45.6	25 46.4	16 26.7	17 22.5	22 22.3	2 27.8	13 .6	10 .5
5	18 49 4.8	12 16.8	20 53.2	20 10.0	1♋47.9	26 59.7	17 .7	17 29.1	22 19.6	2 30.6	13 .0	10 1.8
6	18 53 1.3	13 14.0	20 50.0	2♑34.3	3 52.0	28 12.9	17 34.8	17 35.5	22 16.7	2 33.3	12 59.4	10 3.1
7	18 56 57.9	14 11.2	20 46.9	15 11.7	5 57.8	29 26.2	18 9.0	17 41.8	22 13.7	2 36.0	12 58.8	10 4.4
8	19 0 54.5	15 8.3	20 43.7	28 2.8	8 4.9	0♋39.4	18 43.3	17 47.8	22 10.6	2 38.8	12 58.2	10 5.7
9	19 4 51.0	16 5.5	20 40.5	11♒ 7.9	10 13.0	1 52.7	19 17.8	17 53.7	22 7.5	2 41.7	12 57.7	10 7.1
10	19 8 47.6	17 2.7	20 37.3	24 26.8	12 22.0	3 6.0	19 52.3	17 59.5	22 4.3	2 44.5	12 57.2	10 8.5
11	19 12 44.1	17 59.9	20 34.2	7♓59.1	14 31.4	4 19.4	20 26.9	18 5.1	22 1.1	2 47.4	12 56.7	10 9.9
12	19 16 40.7	18 57.1	20 31.0	21 43.8	16 40.9	5 32.8	21 1.6	18 10.5	21 57.7	2 50.4	12 56.3	10 11.3
13	19 20 37.2	19 54.3	20 27.8	5♈40.1	18 50.4	6 46.1	21 36.4	18 15.8	21 54.3	2 53.3	12 55.9	10 12.8
14	19 24 33.8	20 51.5	20 24.6	19 46.3	20 59.6	7 59.6	22 11.3	18 20.8	21 50.9	2 56.3	12 55.5	10 14.2
15	19 28 30.4	21 48.7	20 21.5	4♉ .7	23 8.1	9 13.0	22 46.3	18 25.7	21 47.4	2 59.3	12 55.1	10 15.7
16	19 32 26.9	22 46.0	20 18.3	18 20.7	25 15.8	10 26.4	23 21.4	18 30.5	21 43.8	3 2.4	12 54.8	10 17.3
17	19 36 23.5	23 43.2	20 15.1	2♊43.2	27 22.5	11 39.9	23 56.6	18 35.1	21 40.1	3 5.5	12 54.5	10 18.8
18	19 40 20.0	24 40.4	20 11.9	17 4.2	29 28.0	12 53.4	24 31.9	18 39.4	21 36.4	3 8.6	12 54.2	10 20.4
19	19 44 16.6	25 37.7	20 8.8	1♋19.6	1♌32.3	14 7.0	25 7.3	18 43.6	21 32.7	3 11.8	12 54.0	10 21.9
20	19 48 13.1	26 35.0	20 5.6	15 25.1	3 35.1	15 20.5	25 42.8	18 47.7	21 28.8	3 14.9	12 53.8	10 23.5
21	19 52 9.7	27 32.3	20 2.4	29 16.8	5 36.5	16 34.1	26 18.4	18 51.5	21 25.0	3 18.1	12 53.6	10 25.2
22	19 56 6.3	28 29.6	19 59.2	12♌51.6	7 36.2	17 47.7	26 54.1	18 55.2	21 21.1	3 21.4	12 53.5	10 26.8
23	20 0 2.8	29 26.9	19 56.0	26 7.6	9 34.4	19 1.3	27 29.9	18 58.7	21 17.1	3 24.6	12 53.4	10 28.5
24	20 3 59.4	0♌24.2	19 52.9	9♍ 4.3	11 30.9	20 15.0	28 5.8	19 2.0	21 13.1	3 27.9	12 53.3	10 30.1
25	20 7 55.9	1 21.5	19 49.7	21 42.4	13 25.7	21 28.6	28 41.7	19 5.1	21 9.0	3 31.2	12 53.3	10 31.8
26	20 11 52.5	2 18.9	19 46.5	4♎ 4.2	15 18.8	22 42.4	29 17.8	19 8.0	21 5.0	3 34.6	12 53.3	10 33.6
27	20 15 49.0	3 16.2	19 43.3	16 12.5	17 10.2	23 56.1	29 54.0	19 10.8	21 .8	3 37.9	12D53.4	10 35.3
28	20 19 45.6	4 13.5	19 40.2	28 11.3	18 59.9	25 9.8	0♎30.2	19 13.3	20 56.6	3 41.3	12 53.4	10 37.1
29	20 23 42.1	5 10.9	19 37.0	10♏ 5.0	20 47.9	26 23.5	1 6.5	19 15.7	20 52.4	3 44.7	12 53.5	10 38.8
30	20 27 38.7	6 8.2	19 33.8	21 58.2	22 34.2	27 37.3	1 42.9	19 17.9	20 48.2	3 48.1	12 53.7	10 40.6
31	20 31 35.3	7 5.6	19 30.6	3♐55.7	24 18.7	28 51.1	2 19.4	19 19.8	20 43.9	3 51.6	12 53.8	10 42.4

LATITUDE

DAY	EPHEM. SID. TIME	☉	☊	☽	☿	♀	♂	♃	♄	♅	♆	♇
1	18 33 18.6	0 .0	0 .0	5N 9.6	0S32.5	0S27.2	0N50.9	1S17.3	1S 8.5	0N44.4	1N48.3	13N25.5
4	18 45 8.2	0 .0	0 .0	3 33.9	0N 2.5	0 19.8	0 48.0	1 18.1	1 8.9	0 44.3	1 48.2	13 24.6
7	18 56 57.9	0 .0	0 .0	0 28.9	0 34.6	0 12.3	0 45.2	1 18.8	1 9.4	0 44.2	1 48.0	13 23.8
10	19 8 47.6	0 .0	0 .0	2S57.7	1 2.1	0 4.8	0 42.4	1 19.6	1 9.9	0 44.1	1 47.8	13 23.0
13	19 20 37.2	0 .0	0 .0	5 6.5	1 23.7	0N 2.6	0 39.6	1 20.4	1 10.3	0 44.0	1 47.7	13 22.3
16	19 32 26.9	0 .0	0 .0	4 40.2	1 38.6	0 10.0	0 36.9	1 21.2	1 10.8	0 44.0	1 47.5	13 21.5
19	19 44 16.6	0 .0	0 .0	1 44.0	1 46.7	0 17.2	0 34.3	1 22.0	1 11.2	0 43.9	1 47.3	13 20.9
22	19 56 6.3	0 .0	0 .0	2N 1.0	1 48.2	0 24.2	0 31.7	1 22.8	1 11.6	0 43.8	1 47.2	13 20.2
25	20 7 55.9	0 .0	0 .0	4 37.5	1 43.9	0 31.1	0 29.1	1 23.6	1 12.0	0 43.8	1 47.0	13 19.6
28	20 19 45.6	0 .0	0 .0	5 13.1	1 34.4	0 37.6	0 26.5	1 24.5	1 12.4	0 43.7	1 46.8	13 19.1
31	20 31 35.3	0 .0	0 .0	3 49.2	1 20.4	0 43.9	0 24.0	1 25.3	1 12.7	0 43.7	1 46.6	13 18.6

RIGHT ASCENSION

DAY	EPHEM. SID. TIME	☉	☊	☽	☿	♀	♂	♃	♄	♅	♆	♇
1	18 33 18.6	9♋13.0	22♋48.6	1♏41.4	23♊21.3	21♊26.7	16♍17.4	16♈11.7	25♒14.7	4♍35.0	11♏ 9.3	16♍50.5
2	18 37 15.1	10 15.0	22 45.2	12 58.0	25 25.9	22 45.8	16 48.3	16 18.3	25R12.2	4 37.4	11R 8.6	16 51.5
3	18 41 11.7	11 17.0	22 41.8	24 37.4	27 33.6	24 5.0	17 19.3	16 24.8	25 9.7	4 39.9	11 7.9	16 52.5
4	18 45 8.2	12 18.9	22 38.4	6♐47.1	29 44.3	25 24.4	17 50.4	16 31.1	25 7.0	4 42.4	11 7.2	16 53.6
5	18 49 4.8	13 20.8	22 35.1	19 30.6	1♋57.8	26 43.9	18 21.5	16 37.3	25 4.4	4 45.0	11 6.6	16 54.7
6	18 53 1.3	14 22.6	22 31.7	2♑46.2	4 13.6	28 3.5	18 52.7	16 43.3	25 1.6	4 47.6	11 6.0	16 55.8
7	18 56 57.9	15 24.2	22 28.3	16 25.9	6 31.4	29 23.2	19 24.0	16 49.2	24 58.7	4 50.2	11 5.4	16 56.9
8	19 0 54.5	16 25.8	22 24.9	0♒17.6	8 50.8	0♋42.9	19 55.3	16 55.0	24 55.8	4 52.8	11 4.8	16 58.1
9	19 4 51.0	17 27.3	22 21.5	14 7.9	11 11.3	2 2.8	20 26.7	17 .6	24 52.8	4 55.5	11 4.3	16 59.3
10	19 8 47.6	18 28.7	22 18.1	27 46.4	13 32.7	3 22.6	20 58.2	17 6.0	24 49.7	4 58.2	11 3.7	17 .5
11	19 12 44.1	19 30.0	22 14.8	11♓ 8.1	15 54.3	4 42.5	21 29.8	17 11.3	24 46.6	5 1.0	11 3.3	17 1.7
12	19 16 40.7	20 31.2	22 11.4	24 14.8	18 15.8	6 2.5	22 1.4	17 16.4	24 43.3	5 3.8	11 2.8	17 3.0
13	19 20 37.2	21 32.2	22 8.0	7♈13.6	20 36.7	7 22.4	22 33.1	17 21.4	24 40.1	5 6.6	11 2.4	17 4.2
14	19 24 33.8	22 33.2	22 4.6	20 14.9	22 56.7	8 42.4	23 4.9	17 26.2	24 36.7	5 9.4	11 2.0	17 5.5
15	19 28 30.4	23 34.1	22 1.2	3♉30.9	25 15.5	10 2.3	23 36.8	17 30.9	24 33.3	5 12.3	11 1.6	17 6.8
16	19 32 26.9	24 34.8	21 57.8	17 12.6	27 32.6	11 22.3	24 8.7	17 35.4	24 29.8	5 15.2	11 1.3	17 8.2
17	19 36 23.5	25 35.4	21 54.4	1♊27.3	29 48.0	12 42.1	24 40.7	17 39.8	24 26.3	5 18.1	11 1.0	17 9.5
18	19 40 20.0	26 35.9	21 51.1	16 15.0	2♌ 1.2	14 1.9	25 12.8	17 43.9	24 22.7	5 21.0	11 .7	17 10.9
19	19 44 16.6	27 36.3	21 47.7	1♋25.6	4 12.2	15 21.7	25 45.0	17 48.0	24 19.1	5 24.0	11 .5	17 12.3
20	19 48 13.1	28 36.5	21 44.3	16 40.4	6 20.7	16 41.4	26 17.3	17 51.8	24 15.4	5 27.0	11 .2	17 13.8
21	19 52 9.7	29 36.6	21 40.9	1♌36.7	8 26.8	18 .9	26 49.6	17 55.5	24 11.6	5 30.1	11 .1	17 15.2
22	19 56 6.3	0♌36.6	21 37.5	15 55.7	10 30.3	19 20.4	27 22.0	17 59.0	24 7.8	5 33.1	10 59.9	17 16.7
23	20 0 2.8	1 36.4	21 34.1	29 27.4	12 31.2	20 39.7	27 54.5	18 2.4	24 4.0	5 36.2	10 59.8	17 18.2
24	20 3 59.4	2 36.1	21 30.7	12♍11.1	14 29.4	21 58.9	28 27.1	18 5.5	24 .1	5 39.3	10 59.7	17 19.7
25	20 7 55.9	3 35.6	21 27.3	24 13.3	16 25.0	23 18.0	28 59.8	18 8.5	23 56.1	5 42.4	10 59.7	17 21.2
26	20 11 52.5	4 35.0	21 24.0	5♎44.6	18 18.0	24 36.9	29 32.6	18 11.4	23 52.2	5 45.6	10 59.7	17 22.8
27	20 15 49.0	5 34.2	21 20.6	16 57.0	20 8.4	25 55.7	0♎ 5.4	18 14.1	23 48.1	5 48.8	10 59.7	17 24.4
28	20 19 45.6	6 33.3	21 17.2	28 3.2	21 56.2	27 14.2	0 38.3	18 16.5	23 44.1	5 52.0	10 59.7	17 25.9
29	20 23 42.1	7 32.2	21 13.8	9♏15.4	23 41.4	28 32.6	1 11.3	18 18.8	23 40.0	5 55.2	10D59.8	17 27.6
30	20 27 38.7	8 31.0	21 10.4	20 44.7	25 24.2	29 50.7	1 44.3	18 20.9	23 35.8	5 58.5	10 59.9	17 29.2
31	20 31 35.3	9 29.6	21 7.0	2♐40.6	27 4.6	1♌ 8.7	2 17.5	18 22.9	23 31.6	6 1.7	11 .0	17 30.8

DECLINATION

DAY	EPHEM. SID. TIME	☉	☊	☽	☿	♀	♂	♃	♄	♅	♆	♇
1	18 33 18.6	23N10.3	0N22.8	7S20.9	22N45.6	22N45.4	6N47.2	5N30.1	15S 5.5	11N20.1	14S 2.1	20N13.4
4	18 45 8.2	22 57.6	0 22.8	18 7.1	23 29.0	23 2.8	6 5.3	5 37.2	15 8.6	11 17.2	14 1.6	20 11.2
7	18 56 57.9	22 41.2	0 22.9	22 6.0	23 53.1	23 14.2	5 22.7	5 43.9	15 11.9	11 14.2	14 1.2	20 9.0
10	19 8 47.6	22 21.3	0 22.9	16 9.9	23 53.9	23 19.6	4 39.7	5 49.9	15 15.4	11 11.1	14 .9	20 6.6
13	19 20 37.2	21 58.0	0 22.9	2 26.4	23 30.0	23 18.8	3 56.2	5 55.4	15 19.1	11 7.8	14 .7	20 4.3
16	19 32 26.9	21 31.2	0 22.9	12N48.0	22 42.2	23 11.9	3 12.2	6 .2	15 22.9	11 4.5	14 .5	20 1.9
19	19 44 16.6	21 1.2	0 23.0	21 42.1	21 33.2	22 58.8	2 27.8	6 4.5	15 26.9	11 1.0	14 .4	19 59.5
22	19 56 6.3	20 27.9	0 23.0	18 53.3	20 6.9	22 39.6	1 43.0	6 8.1	15 31.0	10 57.5	14 .5	19 57.0
25	20 7 55.9	19 51.6	0 23.0	7 32.2	18 27.1	22 14.4	0 57.8	6 11.0	15 35.3	10 53.9	14 .6	19 54.5
28	20 19 45.6	19 12.3	0 23.0	5S57.2	16 37.5	21 43.3	0 12.3	6 13.4	15 39.6	10 50.2	14 .8	19 52.0
31	20 31 35.3	18 30.1	0 23.1	17 11.0	14 41.0	21 6.6	0S33.4	6 15.1	15 44.0	10 46.4	14 1.1	19 49.4

AUGUST 1963

LONGITUDE

DAY	EPHEM. SID. TIME	☉	☊	☽	☿	♀	♂	♃	♄	♅	♆	♇
	h m s	° ′	° ′	° ′	° ′	° ′	° ′	° ′	° ′	° ′	° ′	° ′
1	20 35 31.8	8♌ 2.9	19♋27.4	16♐ 1.6	26♌ 1.6	0♌ 4.9	2♎56.0	19♈21.6	20♒39.6	3♍55.0	12♏54.0	10♍44.2
2	20 39 28.4	9 .3	19 24.3	28 20.0	27 42.8	1 18.7	3 32.6	19 23.2	20 R35.2	3 58.5	12 54.2	10 46.1
3	20 43 24.9	9 57.7	19 21.1	10♑54.0	29 22.3	2 32.5	4 9.4	19 24.6	20 30.9	4 2.0	12 54.5	10 47.9
4	20 47 21.5	10 55.1	19 17.9	23 45.8	1♍ .2	3 46.4	4 46.2	19 25.8	20 26.5	4 5.5	12 54.8	10 49.8
5	20 51 18.0	11 52.5	19 14.7	6♒56.2	2 36.4	5 .3	5 23.1	19 26.8	20 22.1	4 9.1	12 55.1	10 51.6
6	20 55 14.6	12 50.0	19 11.6	20 24.9	4 10.9	6 14.2	6 .1	19 27.6	20 17.7	4 12.6	12 55.4	10 53.5
7	20 59 11.1	13 47.4	19 8.4	4♓10.2	5 43.8	7 28.1	6 37.2	19 28.2	20 13.2	4 16.2	12 55.8	10 55.4
8	21 3 7.7	14 44.9	19 5.2	18 9.0	7 15.0	8 42.1	7 14.3	19 28.6	20 8.8	4 19.8	12 56.2	10 57.3
9	21 7 4.3	15 42.4	19 2.0	2♈17.7	8 44.5	9 56.0	7 51.6	19 28.9	20 4.3	4 23.4	12 56.7	10 59.2
10	21 11 .8	16 39.9	18 58.9	16 32.2	10 12.4	11 10.0	8 28.9	19 28.9	19 59.8	4 27.0	12 57.1	11 1.2
11	21 14 57.4	17 37.4	18 55.7	0♉48.7	11 38.5	12 24.1	9 6.3	19 R28.7	19 55.3	4 30.6	12 57.7	11 3.1
12	21 18 53.9	18 35.0	18 52.5	15 3.9	13 3.0	13 38.1	9 43.7	19 28.3	19 50.8	4 34.3	12 58.2	11 5.1
13	21 22 50.5	19 32.6	18 49.3	29 15.1	14 25.6	14 52.2	10 21.3	19 27.8	19 46.3	4 37.9	12 58.8	11 7.0
14	21 26 47.0	20 30.2	18 46.1	13♊20.3	15 46.5	16 6.3	10 59.0	19 27.0	19 41.8	4 41.6	12 59.4	11 9.0
15	21 30 43.6	21 27.8	18 43.0	27 18.1	17 5.6	17 20.4	11 36.7	19 26.0	19 37.3	4 45.3	13 .0	11 11.0
16	21 34 40.1	22 25.5	18 39.8	11♋ 7.2	18 22.9	18 34.6	12 14.6	19 24.9	19 32.9	4 49.0	13 .7	11 13.1
17	21 38 36.7	23 23.2	18 36.6	24 46.1	19 38.2	19 48.7	12 52.5	19 23.5	19 28.4	4 52.7	13 1.4	11 15.1
18	21 42 33.2	24 20.9	18 33.4	8♌13.6	20 51.5	21 2.9	13 30.4	19 21.9	19 23.9	4 56.4	13 2.2	11 17.1
19	21 46 29.8	25 18.6	18 30.3	21 28.3	22 2.7	22 17.1	14 8.5	19 20.2	19 19.4	5 .1	13 2.9	11 19.1
20	21 50 26.4	26 16.4	18 27.1	4♍29.0	23 11.9	23 31.3	14 46.6	19 18.2	19 15.0	5 3.9	13 3.7	11 21.1
21	21 54 22.9	27 14.2	18 23.9	17 15.1	24 18.8	24 45.6	15 24.9	19 16.0	19 10.5	5 7.6	13 4.5	11 23.2
22	21 58 19.5	28 12.0	18 20.7	29 46.6	25 23.4	25 59.8	16 3.2	19 13.7	19 6.1	5 11.3	13 5.4	11 25.2
23	22 2 16.0	29 9.8	18 17.5	12♎ 4.5	26 25.6	27 14.1	16 41.5	19 11.1	19 1.7	5 15.1	13 6.3	11 27.3
24	22 6 12.6	0♍ 7.6	18 14.4	24 10.7	27 25.2	28 28.4	17 20.0	19 8.4	18 57.3	5 18.8	13 7.2	11 29.4
25	22 10 9.1	1 5.5	18 11.2	6♏ 8.1	28 22.2	29 42.7	17 58.5	19 5.4	18 53.0	5 22.6	13 8.1	11 31.4
26	22 14 5.7	2 3.4	18 8.0	18 .5	29 16.3	0♍57.0	18 37.2	19 2.3	18 48.7	5 26.3	13 9.1	11 33.5
27	22 18 2.2	3 1.3	18 4.8	29 52.3	0♎ 7.4	2 11.4	19 15.9	18 59.0	18 44.4	5 30.1	13 10.1	11 35.6
28	22 21 58.8	3 59.2	18 1.7	11♐48.2	0 55.3	3 25.7	19 54.6	18 55.5	18 40.1	5 33.9	13 11.2	11 37.6
29	22 25 55.3	4 57.1	17 58.5	23 53.5	1 39.8	4 40.1	20 33.5	18 51.8	18 35.9	5 37.6	13 12.2	11 39.7
30	22 29 51.9	5 55.1	17 55.3	6♑12.9	2 20.8	5 54.5	21 12.4	18 47.9	18 31.7	5 41.4	13 13.3	11 41.8
31	22 33 48.4	6 53.1	17 52.1	18 50.9	2 57.9	7 8.9	21 51.4	18 43.9	18 27.5	5 45.1	13 14.4	11 43.9

LATITUDE

DAY	EPHEM. SID. TIME	☉	☊	☽	☿	♀	♂	♃	♄	♅	♆	♇
1	20 35 31.8	0 .0	0 .0	2N58.6	1N14.9	0N45.9	0N23.2	1S25.6	1S12.8	0N43.7	1N46.6	13N18.4
4	20 47 21.5	0 .0	0 .0	0S18.4	0 55.9	0 51.8	0 20.8	1 26.4	1 13.1	0 43.6	1 46.4	13 18.0
7	20 59 11.1	0 .0	0 .0	3 37.6	0 34.0	0 57.2	0 18.3	1 27.2	1 13.4	0 43.6	1 46.2	13 17.6
10	21 11 .8	0 .0	0 .0	5 12.7	0 9.5	1 2.2	0 15.9	1 28.1	1 13.7	0 43.6	1 46.0	13 17.3
13	21 22 50.5	0 .0	0 .0	4 3.3	0S17.0	1 6.8	0 13.6	1 28.9	1 14.0	0 43.5	1 45.9	13 17.0
16	21 34 40.1	0 .0	0 .0	0 49.4	0 45.1	1 11.0	0 11.2	1 29.7	1 14.2	0 43.5	1 45.7	13 16.8
19	21 46 29.8	0 .0	0 .0	2N42.1	1 14.3	1 14.6	0 8.9	1 30.5	1 14.4	0 43.5	1 45.5	13 16.6
22	21 58 19.5	0 .0	0 .0	4 51.0	1 44.2	1 17.7	0 6.7	1 31.2	1 14.6	0 43.5	1 45.3	13 16.5
25	22 10 9.1	0 .0	0 .0	4 56.8	2 14.1	1 20.2	0 4.4	1 32.0	1 14.7	0 43.5	1 45.2	13 16.5
28	22 21 58.8	0 .0	0 .0	3 9.7	2 43.5	1 22.3	0 2.2	1 32.7	1 14.9	0 43.5	1 45.0	13 16.5
31	22 33 48.4	0 .0	0 .0	0 3.7	3 11.3	1 23.7	0 .0	1 33.4	1 15.0	0 43.5	1 44.8	13 16.5

RIGHT ASCENSION

DAY	EPHEM. SID. TIME	☉	☊	☽	☿	♀	♂	♃	♄	♅	♆	♇
1	20 35 31.8	10♌28.0	21♋ 3.6	15♐ 9.3	28♌42.6	2♌26.4	2♎50.7	18♈24.7	23♒27.4	6♍ 5.0	11♏ .2	17♍32.5
2	20 39 28.4	11 26.3	21 .2	28 12.6	0♍18.4	3 43.9	3 24.0	18 26.2	23 R23.2	6 8.3	11 .4	17 34.1
3	20 43 24.9	12 24.4	20 56.8	11♑46.6	1 51.8	5 1.2	3 57.4	18 27.6	23 18.9	6 11.6	11 .6	17 35.8
4	20 47 21.5	13 22.4	20 53.4	25 41.5	3 23.1	6 18.3	4 30.9	18 28.9	23 14.7	6 14.9	11 .9	17 37.5
5	20 51 18.0	14 20.2	20 50.0	9♒44.1	4 52.3	7 35.1	5 4.5	18 29.9	23 10.4	6 18.3	11 1.2	17 39.2
6	20 55 14.6	15 17.9	20 46.6	23 41.3	6 19.3	8 51.7	5 38.1	18 30.8	23 6.0	6 21.7	11 1.5	17 41.0
7	20 59 11.1	16 15.4	20 43.2	7♓24.5	7 44.3	10 8.0	6 11.9	18 31.5	23 1.7	6 25.0	11 1.9	17 42.7
8	21 3 7.7	17 12.8	20 39.9	20 51.2	9 7.3	11 24.1	6 45.7	18 31.9	22 57.3	6 28.4	11 2.3	17 44.5
9	21 7 4.3	18 10.1	20 36.5	4♈ 5.0	10 28.2	12 39.9	7 19.7	18 32.3	22 52.9	6 31.8	11 2.7	17 46.3
10	21 11 .8	19 7.2	20 33.1	17 14.2	11 47.3	13 55.5	7 53.7	18 32.4	22 48.6	6 35.2	11 3.1	17 48.0
11	21 14 57.4	20 4.1	20 29.7	0♉29.3	13 4.4	15 10.8	8 27.8	18 R32.3	22 44.2	6 38.7	11 3.6	17 49.8
12	21 18 53.9	21 .9	20 26.3	14 .9	14 19.6	16 25.8	9 2.0	18 32.1	22 39.7	6 42.1	11 4.1	17 51.7
13	21 22 50.5	21 57.6	20 22.9	27 57.1	15 32.9	17 40.6	9 36.3	18 31.6	22 35.3	6 45.6	11 4.7	17 53.5
14	21 26 47.0	22 54.2	20 19.5	12♊20.6	16 44.3	18 55.1	10 10.8	18 31.0	22 30.9	6 49.1	11 5.2	17 55.3
15	21 30 43.6	23 50.6	20 16.1	27 6.2	17 53.7	20 9.4	10 45.3	18 30.2	22 26.5	6 52.5	11 5.9	17 57.2
16	21 34 40.1	24 46.9	20 12.7	12♋ 1.0	19 1.4	21 23.4	11 19.9	18 29.3	22 22.1	6 56.1	11 6.5	17 59.1
17	21 38 36.7	25 43.1	20 9.3	26 46.7	20 7.0	22 37.1	11 54.7	18 28.1	22 17.7	6 59.6	11 7.2	18 1.0
18	21 42 33.2	26 39.1	20 5.9	11♌ 5.5	21 10.7	23 50.6	12 29.5	18 26.7	22 13.3	7 3.1	11 7.9	18 2.9
19	21 46 29.8	27 35.0	20 2.5	24 45.5	22 12.4	25 3.8	13 4.4	18 25.2	22 8.9	7 6.6	11 8.6	18 4.8
20	21 50 26.4	28 30.8	19 59.1	7♍42.4	23 12.0	26 16.8	13 39.5	18 23.4	22 4.5	7 10.1	11 9.4	18 6.7
21	21 54 22.9	29 26.4	19 55.7	19 59.3	24 9.5	27 29.5	14 14.6	18 21.5	22 .2	7 13.6	11 10.2	18 8.6
22	21 58 19.5	0♍22.0	19 52.3	1♎43.7	25 4.8	28 41.9	14 49.9	18 19.4	21 55.8	7 17.2	11 11.0	18 10.5
23	22 2 16.0	1 17.4	19 48.9	13 5.8	25 57.9	29 54.1	15 25.2	18 17.1	21 51.5	7 20.7	11 11.9	18 12.4
24	22 6 12.6	2 12.7	19 45.5	24 16.9	26 48.6	1♍ 6.0	16 .7	18 14.7	21 47.2	7 24.2	11 12.8	18 14.4
25	22 10 9.1	3 7.9	19 42.1	5♏28.2	27 36.9	2 17.7	16 36.3	18 12.0	21 42.9	7 27.8	11 13.7	18 16.3
26	22 14 5.7	4 3.0	19 38.7	16 50.5	28 22.6	3 29.2	17 12.0	18 9.2	21 38.6	7 31.3	11 14.6	18 18.3
27	22 18 2.2	4 57.9	19 35.3	28 33.3	29 5.5	4 40.4	17 47.8	18 6.2	21 34.4	7 34.9	11 15.6	18 20.2
28	22 21 58.8	5 52.8	19 31.9	10♐44.2	29 45.6	5 51.5	18 23.8	18 3.1	21 30.2	7 38.4	11 16.6	18 22.2
29	22 25 55.3	6 47.6	19 28.5	23 27.4	0♎22.7	7 2.3	18 59.8	17 59.7	21 26.0	7 42.0	11 17.6	18 24.2
30	22 29 51.9	7 42.2	19 25.1	6♑42.5	0 56.6	8 12.8	19 36.0	17 56.2	21 21.8	7 45.5	11 18.7	18 26.2
31	22 33 48.4	8 36.8	19 21.7	20 24.0	1 27.0	9 23.2	20 12.2	17 52.5	21 17.7	7 49.1	11 19.8	18 28.2

DECLINATION

DAY	EPHEM. SID. TIME	☉	☊	☽	☿	♀	♂	♃	♄	♅	♆	♇
1	20 35 31.8	18N15.5	0N23.1	19S45.0	14N 1.1	20N53.1	0S48.7	6N15.5	15S45.5	10N45.1	14S 1.2	19N48.6
4	20 47 21.5	17 29.7	0 23.1	21 39.3	11 59.5	20 9.0	1 34.7	6 16.3	15 50.0	10 41.3	14 1.6	19 46.0
7	20 59 11.1	16 41.4	0 23.1	13 21.4	9 56.3	19 19.7	2 20.9	6 16.5	15 54.5	10 37.3	14 2.1	19 43.5
10	21 11 .8	15 50.6	0 23.1	1N41.2	7 53.3	18 25.5	3 7.2	6 15.9	15 59.0	10 33.4	14 2.6	19 40.9
13	21 22 50.5	14 57.6	0 23.2	16 1.9	5 52.2	17 26.5	3 53.6	6 14.8	16 3.5	10 29.3	14 3.3	19 38.4
16	21 34 40.1	14 2.4	0 23.2	22 9.4	3 54.2	16 23.1	4 40.0	6 12.9	16 7.9	10 25.3	14 4.0	19 35.9
19	21 46 29.8	13 5.2	0 23.2	16 54.3	2 1.1	15 15.7	5 26.4	6 10.4	16 12.4	10 21.2	14 4.9	19 33.4
22	21 58 19.5	12 6.1	0 23.2	4 32.2	0 14.3	14 4.4	6 12.8	6 7.3	16 16.7	10 17.1	14 5.8	19 30.9
25	22 10 9.1	11 5.3	0 23.3	8S53.7	1S24.1	12 49.6	6 59.1	6 3.4	16 21.0	10 12.9	14 6.8	19 28.4
28	22 21 58.8	10 2.9	0 23.3	19 4.4	2 52.0	11 31.7	7 45.1	5 59.0	16 25.1	10 8.8	14 7.8	19 26.0
31	22 33 48.4	8 59.1	0 23.3	22 3.4	4 6.3	10 11.0	8 31.0	5 54.0	16 29.2	10 4.6	14 8.9	19 23.6

SEPTEMBER 1963

DAY	EPHEM. SID. TIME	☉	☊	☾	☿	♀	♂	♃	♄	♅	♆	♇
		LONGITUDE										
	h m s	° ′	° ′	° ′	° ′	° ′	° ′	° ′	° ′	° ′	° ′	° ′
1	22 37 45.0	7 ♍ 51.1	17 ♋ 48.9	1 ♒ 51.0	3 ♎ 30.9	8 ♍ 23.3	22 ♎ 30.5	18 ♈ 39.6	18 ♒ 23.4	5 ♍ 48.9	13 ♏ 15.6	11 ♍ 46.0
2	22 41 41.5	8 49.1	17 45.8	15 15.0	3 59.6	9 37.7	23 9.6	18 R 35.2	18 R 19.3	5 52.7	13 16.8	11 48.1
3	22 45 38.1	9 47.2	17 42.6	29 3.0	4 23.7	10 52.1	23 48.8	18 30.7	18 15.3	5 56.4	13 18.0	11 50.2
4	22 49 34.7	10 45.3	17 39.4	13 ♓ 12.5	4 42.9	12 6.6	24 28.1	18 25.9	18 11.3	6 .2	13 19.2	11 52.3
5	22 53 31.2	11 43.4	17 36.2	27 38.9	4 56.9	13 21.0	25 7.5	18 21.0	18 7.4	6 3.9	13 20.5	11 54.4
6	22 57 27.8	12 41.6	17 33.1	12 ♈ 15.7	5 5.5	14 35.6	25 47.0	18 16.0	18 3.6	6 7.7	13 21.8	11 56.5
7	23 1 24.3	13 39.8	17 29.9	26 55.5	5 8.3	15 50.1	26 26.5	18 10.7	17 59.7	6 11.4	13 23.1	11 58.6
8	23 5 20.9	14 38.0	17 26.7	11 ♉ 31.4	5 R 5.0	17 4.6	27 6.1	18 5.3	17 56.0	6 15.2	13 24.5	12 .7
9	23 9 17.4	15 36.2	17 23.5	25 57.9	4 55.4	18 19.1	27 45.7	17 59.7	17 52.2	6 18.9	13 25.8	12 2.8
10	23 13 14.0	16 34.5	17 20.3	10 ♊ 11.4	4 39.3	19 33.6	28 25.5	17 54.0	17 48.6	6 22.6	13 27.2	12 4.9
11	23 17 10.5	17 32.8	17 17.2	24 10.2	4 16.7	20 48.2	29 5.3	17 48.2	17 45.0	6 26.3	13 28.6	12 7.0
12	23 21 7.1	18 31.2	17 14.0	7 ♋ 54.1	3 47.4	22 2.8	29 45.2	17 42.1	17 41.4	6 30.0	13 30.1	12 9.1
13	23 25 3.6	19 29.6	17 10.8	21 23.9	3 11.7	23 17.3	0 ♏ 25.1	17 36.0	17 38.0	6 33.7	13 31.6	12 11.2
14	23 29 .2	20 28.0	17 7.6	4 ♌ 40.6	2 29.7	24 31.9	1 5.2	17 29.7	17 34.5	6 37.4	13 33.1	12 13.3
15	23 32 56.7	21 26.4	17 4.5	17 45.2	1 41.8	25 46.6	1 45.3	17 23.3	17 31.2	6 41.1	13 34.6	12 15.3
16	23 36 53.3	22 24.9	17 1.3	0 ♍ 38.4	0 48.7	27 1.2	2 25.5	17 16.7	17 27.9	6 44.8	13 36.1	12 17.4
17	23 40 49.8	23 23.5	16 58.1	13 20.6	29 ♍ 51.1	28 15.8	3 5.8	17 10.0	17 24.7	6 48.4	13 37.7	12 19.5
18	23 44 46.4	24 22.0	16 54.9	25 51.9	28 50.2	29 30.5	3 46.1	17 3.2	17 21.6	6 52.1	13 39.3	12 21.5
19	23 48 42.9	25 20.6	16 51.7	8 ♎ 12.4	27 47.0	0 ♎ 45.1	4 26.6	16 56.3	17 18.5	6 55.7	13 40.9	12 23.6
20	23 52 39.5	26 19.2	16 48.6	20 22.8	26 43.1	1 59.8	5 7.1	16 49.2	17 15.5	6 59.3	13 42.6	12 25.7
21	23 56 36.0	27 17.9	16 45.4	2 ♏ 24.1	25 39.9	3 14.5	5 47.6	16 42.1	17 12.6	7 2.9	13 44.2	12 27.7
22	0 0 32.6	28 16.6	16 42.2	14 18.4	24 39.0	4 29.1	6 28.3	16 34.8	17 9.8	7 6.5	13 45.9	12 29.7
23	0 4 29.2	29 15.3	16 39.0	26 8.4	23 41.9	5 43.8	7 9.0	16 27.5	17 7.0	7 10.0	13 47.6	12 31.8
24	0 8 25.7	0 ♎ 14.0	16 35.9	7 ♐ 57.7	22 50.3	6 58.5	7 49.8	16 20.1	17 4.4	7 13.6	13 49.4	12 33.8
25	0 12 22.3	1 12.8	16 32.7	19 51.0	22 5.3	8 13.2	8 30.6	16 12.5	17 1.8	7 17.1	13 51.1	12 35.8
26	0 16 18.8	2 11.6	16 29.5	1 ♑ 53.1	21 28.3	9 27.9	9 11.6	16 5.0	16 59.3	7 20.6	13 52.9	12 37.8
27	0 20 15.4	3 10.4	16 26.3	14 9.5	21 .2	10 42.7	9 52.6	15 57.3	16 56.9	7 24.2	13 54.7	12 39.9
28	0 24 11.9	4 9.3	16 23.1	26 45.4	20 41.7	11 57.4	10 33.7	15 49.6	16 54.6	7 27.6	13 56.5	12 41.8
29	0 28 8.5	5 8.2	16 20.0	9 ♒ 45.4	20 33.1	13 12.1	11 14.8	15 41.8	16 52.4	7 31.1	13 58.4	12 43.8
30	0 32 5.0	6 7.1	16 16.8	23 12.9	20 D 34.9	14 26.8	11 56.0	15 34.0	16 50.2	7 34.5	14 .2	12 45.8
		LATITUDE										
1	22 37 45.0	0 .0	0 .0	1 S 5.9	3 S 20.1	1 N 24.1	0 S .7	1 S 33.6	1 S 15.0	0 N 43.5	1 N 44.8	13 N 16.6
4	22 49 34.7	0 .0	0 .0	4 7.6	3 43.8	1 24.7	0 2.8	1 34.3	1 15.1	0 43.5	1 44.6	13 16.7
7	23 1 24.3	0 .0	0 .0	5 2.6	4 2.1	1 24.8	0 5.0	1 34.9	1 15.2	0 43.5	1 44.5	13 16.9
10	23 13 14.0	0 .0	0 .0	3 10.9	4 12.2	1 24.3	0 7.1	1 35.4	1 15.2	0 43.5	1 44.3	13 17.1
13	23 25 3.6	0 .0	0 .0	0 N 14.3	4 10.6	1 23.3	0 9.1	1 36.0	1 15.2	0 43.6	1 44.2	13 17.5
16	23 36 53.3	0 .0	0 .0	3 23.6	3 53.8	1 21.6	0 11.1	1 36.4	1 15.2	0 43.6	1 44.0	13 17.8
19	23 48 42.9	0 .0	0 .0	4 57.4	3 19.9	1 19.4	0 13.2	1 36.8	1 15.2	0 43.6	1 43.9	13 18.3
22	0 0 32.6	0 .0	0 .0	4 29.7	2 30.6	1 16.6	0 15.1	1 37.2	1 15.2	0 43.7	1 43.8	13 18.7
25	0 12 22.3	0 .0	0 .0	2 19.7	1 31.9	1 13.3	0 17.1	1 37.4	1 15.1	0 43.7	1 43.7	13 19.3
28	0 24 11.9	0 .0	0 .0	0 S 50.4	0 32.2	1 9.5	0 19.0	1 37.7	1 15.1	0 43.8	1 43.6	13 19.9
		RIGHT ASCENSION										
1	22 37 45.0	9 ♍ 31.3	19 ♋ 18.3	4 ♒ 21.9	1 ♎ 53.9	10 ♍ 33.4	20 ♎ 48.6	17 ♈ 48.7	21 ♒ 13.7	7 ♍ 52.6	11 ♏ 20.9	18 ♍ 30.2
2	22 41 41.5	10 25.7	19 14.9	18 24.4	2 16.9	11 43.4	21 25.2	17 R 44.7	21 R 9.6	7 56.2	11 22.0	18 32.2
3	22 45 38.1	11 20.1	19 11.5	2 ♓ 21.6	2 35.9	12 53.2	22 1.8	17 40.5	21 5.7	7 59.7	11 23.2	18 34.2
4	22 49 34.7	12 14.4	19 8.1	16 8.0	2 50.6	14 2.8	22 38.6	17 36.1	21 1.7	8 3.3	11 24.4	18 36.2
5	22 53 31.2	13 8.6	19 4.7	29 44.1	3 .7	15 12.3	23 15.5	17 31.7	20 57.8	8 6.8	11 25.6	18 38.2
6	22 57 27.8	14 2.8	19 1.2	13 ♈ 14.8	3 6.1	16 21.7	23 52.5	17 27.1	20 54.0	8 10.4	11 26.9	18 40.2
7	23 1 24.3	14 56.9	18 57.8	26 48.5	3 6.5	17 30.8	24 29.7	17 22.3	20 50.2	8 13.9	11 28.2	18 42.2
8	23 5 20.9	15 50.9	18 54.4	10 ♉ 33.9	3 R 1.7	18 39.9	25 6.9	17 17.3	20 46.5	8 17.5	11 29.5	18 44.2
9	23 9 17.4	16 44.9	18 51.0	24 38.0	2 51.5	19 48.8	25 44.3	17 12.2	20 42.8	8 21.0	11 30.8	18 46.3
10	23 13 14.0	17 38.9	18 47.6	9 ♊ 3.2	2 35.9	20 57.6	26 21.9	17 7.0	20 39.2	8 24.5	11 32.2	18 48.3
11	23 17 10.5	18 32.8	18 44.2	23 45.0	2 14.7	22 6.2	26 59.6	17 1.6	20 35.6	8 28.0	11 33.6	18 50.3
12	23 21 7.1	19 26.7	18 40.8	8 ♋ 32.5	1 48.0	23 14.8	27 37.4	16 56.1	20 32.1	8 31.5	11 35.0	18 52.3
13	23 25 3.6	20 20.6	18 37.4	23 10.1	1 16.0	24 23.3	28 15.4	16 50.4	20 28.6	8 35.0	11 36.4	18 54.3
14	23 29 .2	21 14.4	18 34.0	7 ♌ 22.6	0 38.9	25 31.7	28 53.5	16 44.6	20 25.2	8 38.5	11 37.9	18 56.3
15	23 32 56.7	22 8.3	18 30.6	20 59.4	29 ♍ 57.2	26 40.1	29 31.7	16 38.7	20 21.9	8 41.9	11 39.4	18 58.4
16	23 36 53.3	23 2.1	18 27.2	3 ♍ 56.4	29 11.5	27 48.4	0 ♏ 10.1	16 32.7	20 18.6	8 45.4	11 40.9	19 .4
17	23 40 49.8	23 55.9	18 23.8	16 15.7	28 22.5	28 56.6	0 48.6	16 26.5	20 15.5	8 48.8	11 42.4	19 2.4
18	23 44 46.4	24 49.8	18 20.4	28 3.7	27 31.1	0 ♎ 4.8	1 27.3	16 20.2	20 12.3	8 52.3	11 44.0	19 4.4
19	23 48 42.9	25 43.6	18 16.9	9 ♎ 29.5	26 38.5	1 13.0	2 6.1	16 13.9	20 9.3	8 55.7	11 45.6	19 6.4
20	23 52 39.5	26 37.4	18 13.5	20 42.8	25 45.8	2 21.1	2 45.1	16 7.4	20 6.3	8 59.1	11 47.2	19 8.4
21	23 56 36.0	27 31.2	18 10.1	1 ♏ 53.9	24 54.5	3 29.3	3 24.2	16 .8	20 3.4	9 2.5	11 48.8	19 10.4
22	0 0 32.6	28 25.1	18 6.7	13 12.3	24 5.7	4 37.4	4 3.5	15 54.1	20 .6	9 5.9	11 50.4	19 12.4
23	0 4 29.2	29 19.0	18 3.3	24 46.7	23 20.8	5 45.6	4 42.9	15 47.4	19 57.9	9 9.2	11 52.1	19 14.4
24	0 8 25.7	0 ♎ 12.8	17 59.9	6 ♐ 44.1	22 41.2	6 53.7	5 22.5	15 40.5	19 55.2	9 12.6	11 53.8	19 16.4
25	0 12 22.3	1 6.8	17 56.5	19 8.9	22 7.8	8 1.9	6 2.2	15 33.6	19 52.6	9 15.9	11 55.5	19 18.4
26	0 16 18.8	2 .7	17 53.1	2 ♑ 2.1	21 41.8	9 10.2	6 42.1	15 26.6	19 50.1	9 19.2	11 57.2	19 20.3
27	0 20 15.4	2 54.7	17 49.7	15 20.6	21 23.8	10 18.5	7 22.2	15 19.6	19 47.8	9 22.5	11 59.1	19 22.3
28	0 24 11.9	3 48.8	17 46.2	28 57.8	21 14.4	11 26.9	8 2.3	15 12.4	19 45.4	9 25.8	12 .8	19 24.3
29	0 28 8.5	4 42.9	17 42.8	12 ♒ 45.0	21 13.9	12 35.3	8 42.7	15 5.2	19 43.2	9 29.0	12 2.6	19 26.2
30	0 32 5.0	5 37.0	17 39.4	26 34.0	21 D 22.5	13 43.8	9 23.2	14 58.0	19 41.1	9 32.3	12 4.4	19 28.2
		DECLINATION										
1	22 37 45.0	8 N 37.6	0 N 23.3	20 S 49.3	4 S 27.4	9 N 43.5	8 S 46.2	5 N 52.2	16 S 30.5	10 N 3.3	14 S 9.3	19 N 22.8
4	22 49 34.7	7 32.1	0 23.3	10 24.5	5 17.8	8 19.5	9 31.7	5 46.4	16 34.3	9 59.1	14 10.6	19 20.5
7	23 1 24.3	6 25.5	0 23.4	5 N 40.2	5 44.7	6 53.4	10 16.9	5 40.0	16 37.9	9 55.0	14 11.9	19 18.2
10	23 13 14.0	5 18.0	0 23.4	18 50.0	5 42.5	5 25.6	11 1.6	5 33.2	16 41.4	9 50.9	14 13.3	19 16.0
13	23 25 3.6	4 9.6	0 23.4	21 58.6	5 6.2	3 56.3	11 45.8	5 25.8	16 44.7	9 46.8	14 14.7	19 13.8
16	23 36 53.3	3 .6	0 23.4	14 25.2	3 53.9	2 26.0	12 29.5	5 18.1	16 47.8	9 42.7	14 16.2	19 11.7
19	23 48 42.9	1 51.1	0 23.4	1 18.0	2 10.5	0 54.9	13 12.6	5 9.9	16 50.6	9 38.7	14 17.7	19 9.7
22	0 0 32.6	0 41.2	0 23.5	11 S 50.2	0 10.7	0 S 36.6	13 55.0	5 1.4	16 53.3	9 34.7	14 19.3	19 7.8
25	0 12 22.3	0 S 28.9	0 23.5	20 44.0	1 N 43.9	2 8.3	14 36.8	4 52.6	16 55.7	9 30.8	14 21.0	19 5.9
28	0 24 11.9	1 39.1	0 23.5	21 38.0	3 11.7	3 39.7	15 17.7	4 43.6	16 57.8	9 27.0	14 22.7	19 4.1

OCTOBER 1963

DAY	EPHEM. SID. TIME	☉	☊	☽	☿	♀	♂	♃	♄	♅	♆	♇
	h m s	° ′	° ′	° ′	° ′	° ′	° ′	° ′	° ′	° ′	° ′	° ′
		LONGITUDE										
1	0 36 1.6	7♎ 6.0	16♋13.6	7♓ 9.2	20♍46.9	15♎41.5	12♏37.3	15♈26.1	16♒48.1	7♍37.9	14♏ 2.1	12♍47.7
2	0 39 58.1	8 5.0	16 10.4	21 32.7	21 8.9	16 56.3	13 18.7	15 R 18.1	16 R 46.2	7 41.3	14 4.0	12 49.7
3	0 43 54.7	9 4.0	16 7.2	6♈18.4	21 40.6	18 11.0	14 .1	15 10.1	16 44.3	7 44.6	14 5.9	12 51.6
4	0 47 51.2	10 3.0	16 4.1	21 18.4	22 21.4	19 25.7	14 41.6	15 2.1	16 42.5	7 48.0	14 7.8	12 53.5
5	0 51 47.8	11 2.1	16 .9	6♉23.0	23 10.8	20 40.5	15 23.1	14 54.1	16 40.8	7 51.3	14 9.7	12 55.4
6	0 55 44.3	12 1.2	15 57.7	21 22.2	24 8.1	21 55.2	16 4.8	14 46.0	16 39.2	7 54.6	14 11.7	12 57.3
7	0 59 40.9	13 .4	15 54.5	6♊ 7.7	25 12.5	23 10.0	16 46.5	14 38.0	16 37.7	7 57.8	14 13.7	12 59.2
8	1 3 37.4	13 59.6	15 51.4	20 34.0	26 23.3	24 24.7	17 28.2	14 29.9	16 36.3	8 1.0	14 15.7	13 1.0
9	1 7 34.0	14 58.8	15 48.2	4♋38.2	27 39.8	25 39.5	18 10.1	14 21.8	16 34.9	8 4.2	14 17.7	13 2.9
10	1 11 30.5	15 58.1	15 45.0	18 20.4	29 1.2	26 54.2	18 52.0	14 13.7	16 33.7	8 7.4	14 19.7	13 4.7
11	1 15 27.1	16 57.4	15 41.8	1♌42.2	0♎26.8	28 9.0	19 34.0	14 5.6	16 32.6	8 10.6	14 21.7	13 6.5
12	1 19 23.7	17 56.7	15 38.6	14 46.1	1 56.1	29 23.8	20 16.0	13 57.6	16 31.6	8 13.7	14 23.8	13 8.3
13	1 23 20.2	18 56.1	15 35.5	27 34.8	3 28.4	0♏38.6	20 58.1	13 49.5	16 30.6	8 16.8	14 25.8	13 10.1
14	1 27 16.8	19 55.5	15 32.3	10♍11.0	5 3.3	1 53.4	21 40.3	13 41.5	16 29.8	8 19.8	14 27.9	13 11.9
15	1 31 13.3	20 55.0	15 29.1	22 36.7	6 40.1	3 8.2	22 22.6	13 33.6	16 29.1	8 22.8	14 30.0	13 13.6
16	1 35 9.9	21 54.5	15 25.9	4♎53.3	8 18.6	4 22.9	23 4.9	13 25.6	16 28.5	8 25.8	14 32.1	13 15.4
17	1 39 6.4	22 54.0	15 22.8	17 1.9	9 58.4	5 37.7	23 47.4	13 17.7	16 27.9	8 28.8	14 34.2	13 17.1
18	1 43 3.0	23 53.6	15 19.6	29 3.6	11 39.2	6 52.6	24 29.9	13 10.0	16 27.5	8 31.7	14 36.4	13 18.8
19	1 46 59.5	24 53.2	15 16.4	10♏59.3	13 20.6	8 7.4	25 12.4	13 2.2	16 27.2	8 34.6	14 38.5	13 20.5
20	1 50 56.1	25 52.8	15 13.2	22 50.4	15 2.5	9 22.2	25 55.0	12 54.5	16 27.0	8 37.5	14 40.7	13 22.2
21	1 54 52.6	26 52.5	15 10.0	4♐38.9	16 44.7	10 37.0	26 37.7	12 46.9	16 26.9	8 40.3	14 42.8	13 23.8
22	1 58 49.2	27 52.2	15 6.9	16 27.6	18 27.0	11 51.8	27 20.5	12 39.3	16 26.9	8 43.1	14 45.0	13 25.4
23	2 2 45.7	28 51.9	15 3.7	28 19.9	20 9.3	13 6.6	28 3.3	12 31.9	16 D 27.0	8 45.8	14 47.2	13 27.0
24	2 6 42.3	29 51.6	15 .5	10♑20.3	21 51.4	14 21.4	28 46.2	12 24.5	16 27.1	8 48.5	14 49.3	13 28.6
25	2 10 38.8	0♏51.4	14 57.3	22 33.5	23 33.4	15 36.2	29 29.1	12 17.2	16 27.4	8 51.2	14 51.5	13 30.1
26	2 14 35.4	1 51.2	14 54.2	5♒ 4.8	25 15.0	16 51.0	0♐12.1	12 10.0	16 27.8	8 53.8	14 53.7	13 31.7
27	2 18 32.0	2 51.0	14 51.0	17 59.2	26 56.4	18 5.8	0 55.2	12 3.0	16 28.3	8 56.4	14 55.9	13 33.2
28	2 22 28.5	3 50.9	14 47.8	1♓21.2	28 37.3	19 20.6	1 38.4	11 56.0	16 28.9	8 58.9	14 58.1	13 34.7
29	2 26 25.1	4 50.8	14 44.6	15 13.2	0♏17.9	20 35.4	2 21.6	11 49.2	16 29.6	9 1.4	15 .4	13 36.1
30	2 30 21.6	5 50.7	14 41.5	29 35.3	1 58.0	21 50.2	3 4.8	11 42.4	16 30.4	9 3.9	15 2.6	13 37.6
31	2 34 18.2	6 50.7	14 38.3	14♈24.2	3 37.7	23 4.9	3 48.2	11 35.9	16 31.3	9 6.3	15 4.8	13 39.0
		LATITUDE										
1	0 36 1.6	0 .0	0 .0	3S51.5	0N21.0	1N 5.1	0S20.9	1S37.8	1S15.0	0N43.9	1N43.5	13N20.6
4	0 47 51.2	0 .0	0 .0	4 59.3	1 3.3	1 .3	0 22.8	1 37.9	1 14.9	0 43.9	1 43.4	13 21.3
7	0 59 40.9	0 .0	0 .0	3 13.7	1 33.1	0 55.1	0 24.6	1 37.9	1 14.8	0 44.0	1 43.3	13 22.0
10	1 11 30.5	0 .0	0 .0	0N12.5	1 50.9	0 49.4	0 26.4	1 37.8	1 14.7	0 44.1	1 43.2	13 22.9
13	1 23 20.2	0 .0	0 .0	3 20.7	1 58.4	0 43.4	0 28.2	1 37.7	1 14.6	0 44.1	1 43.1	13 23.7
16	1 35 9.9	0 .0	0 .0	4 54.8	1 57.6	0 37.0	0 30.0	1 37.5	1 14.4	0 44.2	1 43.0	13 24.7
19	1 46 59.5	0 .0	0 .0	4 29.3	1 50.5	0 30.3	0 31.7	1 37.3	1 14.3	0 44.3	1 43.0	13 25.6
22	1 58 49.2	0 .0	0 .0	2 21.1	1 38.7	0 23.3	0 33.4	1 36.9	1 14.1	0 44.4	1 42.9	13 26.7
25	2 10 38.8	0 .0	0 .0	0S44.6	1 23.6	0 16.1	0 35.0	1 36.5	1 14.0	0 44.5	1 42.9	13 27.7
28	2 22 28.5	0 .0	0 .0	3 43.2	1 6.1	0 8.8	0 36.6	1 36.1	1 13.8	0 44.6	1 42.8	13 28.8
31	2 34 18.2	0 .0	0 .0	5 2.8	0 47.2	0 1.3	0 38.2	1 35.5	1 13.7	0 44.7	1 42.8	13 30.0
		RIGHT ASCENSION										
1	0 36 1.6	6♎31.2	17♋36.0	10♓19.9	21♍40.1	14♎52.4	10♏ 3.8	14♈50.7	19♒39.0	9♍35.5	12♏ 6.3	19♍30.1
2	0 39 58.1	7 25.4	17 32.6	24 2.1	22 6.5	16 1.1	10 44.6	14 R 43.4	19 R 37.0	9 38.7	12 8.1	19 32.1
3	0 43 54.7	8 19.8	17 29.2	7♈44.3	22 41.3	17 10.0	11 25.6	14 36.0	19 35.1	9 41.8	12 10.0	19 34.0
4	0 47 51.2	9 14.2	17 25.8	21 33.5	23 23.9	18 18.9	12 6.7	14 28.6	19 33.3	9 45.0	12 11.9	19 35.9
5	0 51 47.8	10 8.6	17 22.3	5♉37.7	24 13.9	19 28.0	12 48.0	14 21.1	19 31.6	9 48.1	12 13.8	19 37.8
6	0 55 44.3	11 3.2	17 18.9	20 2.8	25 10.5	20 37.2	13 29.5	14 13.7	19 30.0	9 51.2	12 15.7	19 39.7
7	0 59 40.9	11 57.9	17 15.5	4♊50.2	26 13.1	21 46.6	14 11.1	14 6.2	19 28.5	9 54.3	12 17.6	19 41.6
8	1 3 37.4	12 52.7	17 12.1	19 53.9	27 21.0	22 56.2	14 52.9	13 58.7	19 27.1	9 57.3	12 19.6	19 43.4
9	1 7 34.0	13 47.6	17 8.7	5♋ .9	28 33.6	24 6.0	15 34.8	13 51.3	19 25.8	10 .3	12 21.6	19 45.3
10	1 11 30.5	14 42.5	17 5.3	19 53.8	29 50.2	25 15.9	16 16.9	13 43.8	19 24.5	10 3.3	12 23.5	19 47.1
11	1 15 27.1	15 37.7	17 1.8	4♌16.6	1♎10.1	26 26.0	16 59.2	13 36.3	19 23.4	10 6.3	12 25.5	19 49.0
12	1 19 23.7	16 32.9	16 58.4	17 59.0	2 33.0	27 36.4	17 41.7	13 28.8	19 22.3	10 9.2	12 27.6	19 50.8
13	1 23 20.2	17 28.2	16 55.0	0♍57.9	3 58.3	28 46.9	18 24.3	13 21.4	19 21.4	10 12.1	12 29.6	19 52.6
14	1 27 16.8	18 23.7	16 51.6	13 16.7	5 25.5	29 57.7	19 7.1	13 14.0	19 20.6	10 15.0	12 31.6	19 54.4
15	1 31 13.3	19 19.4	16 48.2	25 2.9	6 54.3	1♏ 8.7	19 50.0	13 6.6	19 19.8	10 17.8	12 33.7	19 56.1
16	1 35 9.9	20 15.1	16 44.8	6♎26.1	8 24.4	2 20.0	20 33.2	12 59.2	19 19.2	10 20.6	12 35.8	19 57.9
17	1 39 6.4	21 11.0	16 41.3	17 36.5	9 55.4	3 31.5	21 16.5	12 51.9	19 18.6	10 23.4	12 37.8	19 59.7
18	1 43 3.0	22 7.1	16 37.9	28 44.4	11 27.3	4 43.2	21 60.0	12 44.7	19 18.3	10 26.2	12 40.0	20 1.4
19	1 46 59.5	23 3.3	16 34.5	9♏58.9	12 59.6	5 55.3	22 43.6	12 37.5	19 17.9	10 29.0	12 42.1	20 3.2
20	1 50 56.1	23 59.6	16 31.1	21 28.1	14 32.4	7 7.5	23 27.4	12 30.3	19 17.7	10 31.6	12 44.2	20 4.9
21	1 54 52.6	24 56.1	16 27.7	3♐18.2	16 5.5	8 20.1	24 11.4	12 23.3	19 17.5	10 34.3	12 46.3	20 6.5
22	1 58 49.2	25 52.8	16 24.2	15 32.7	17 38.8	9 32.9	24 55.5	12 16.3	19 17.5	10 36.9	12 48.4	20 8.2
23	2 2 45.7	26 49.6	16 20.8	28 12.1	19 12.2	10 46.0	25 39.8	12 9.3	19 D 17.6	10 39.5	12 50.6	20 9.9
24	2 6 42.3	27 46.6	16 17.4	11♑13.0	20 45.7	11 59.4	26 24.3	12 2.5	19 17.8	10 42.0	12 52.7	20 11.5
25	2 10 38.8	28 43.8	16 14.0	24 29.5	22 19.2	13 13.1	27 8.9	11 55.7	19 18.0	10 44.5	12 54.9	20 13.1
26	2 14 35.4	29 41.1	16 10.6	7♒54.1	23 52.7	14 27.1	27 53.7	11 49.0	19 18.4	10 47.0	12 57.1	20 14.7
27	2 18 32.0	0♏38.6	16 7.1	21 20.4	25 26.2	15 41.3	28 38.7	11 42.4	19 18.9	10 49.5	12 59.2	20 16.3
28	2 22 28.5	1 36.3	16 3.7	4♓44.8	26 59.6	16 55.9	29 23.8	11 36.0	19 19.5	10 51.9	13 1.4	20 17.8
29	2 26 25.1	2 34.1	16 .3	18 7.8	28 33.1	18 10.8	0♐ 9.0	11 29.6	19 20.2	10 54.2	13 3.6	20 19.4
30	2 30 21.6	3 32.2	15 56.9	1♈34.4	0♏ 6.5	19 26.0	0 54.5	11 23.3	19 20.9	10 56.5	13 5.8	20 20.9
31	2 34 18.2	4 30.4	15 53.5	15 12.6	1 39.9	20 41.5	1 40.1	11 17.2	19 21.8	10 58.8	13 8.0	20 22.4
		DECLINATION										
1	0 36 1.6	2S49.1	0N23.5	12S28.0	3N58.6	5S10.5	15S57.7	4N34.4	16S59.7	9N23.2	14S24.4	19N 2.4
4	0 47 51.2	3 58.9	0 23.5	3N41.0	4 .2	6 40.4	16 36.7	4 25.1	17 1.3	9 19.5	14 26.2	19 .8
7	0 59 40.9	5 8.2	0 23.6	18 9.2	3 19.7	8 9.1	17 14.7	4 15.8	17 2.7	9 15.9	14 28.0	18 59.3
10	1 11 30.5	6 17.0	0 23.6	22 23.7	2 5.1	9 36.1	17 51.6	4 6.5	17 3.7	9 12.4	14 29.9	18 57.8
13	1 23 20.2	7 25.0	0 23.6	15 27.2	0 25.8	11 1.3	18 27.3	3 57.2	17 4.6	9 8.9	14 31.7	18 56.5
16	1 35 9.9	8 32.2	0 23.6	2 34.1	1S29.7	12 24.2	19 1.8	3 48.2	17 5.1	9 5.6	14 33.6	18 55.3
19	1 46 59.5	9 38.3	0 23.6	10S51.4	3 34.3	13 44.4	19 34.9	3 39.3	17 5.3	9 2.4	14 35.6	18 54.2
22	1 58 49.2	10 43.1	0 23.7	20 24.8	5 42.7	15 1.6	20 6.6	3 30.7	17 5.3	8 59.3	14 37.5	18 53.2
25	2 10 38.8	11 46.4	0 23.7	22 17.3	7 51.3	16 15.4	20 36.8	3 22.5	17 5.0	8 56.4	14 39.5	18 52.3
28	2 22 28.5	12 48.2	0 23.7	14 28.2	9 57.4	17 25.6	21 5.5	3 14.7	17 4.4	8 53.6	14 41.4	18 51.6
31	2 34 18.2	13 48.1	0 23.7	1N 1.4	11 59.3	18 31.6	21 32.4	3 7.3	17 3.5	8 50.9	14 43.4	18 50.9

NOVEMBER 1963

DAY	EPHEM. SID. TIME	☉	☊	☾	☿	♀	♂	♃	♄	♅	♆	♇
		LONGITUDE										
	h m s	° ′	° ′	° ′	° ′	° ′	° ′	° ′	° ′	° ′	° ′	° ′
1	2 38 14.7	7♏50.6	14♋35.1	29♈32.7	5♏17.0	24♏19.7	4♐31.5	11♈29.4	16♒32.3	9♍ 8.7	15♏ 7.0	13♍40.4
2	2 42 11.3	8 50.6	14 31.9	14♉50.9	6 55.8	25 34.5	5 15.0	11 R 23.1	16 33.5	9 11.0	15 9.3	13 41.7
3	2 46 7.8	9 50.7	14 28.7	0♊ 7.2	8 34.2	26 49.3	5 58.5	11 16.9	16 34.7	9 13.3	15 11.5	13 43.1
4	2 50 4.4	10 50.8	14 25.6	15 11.2	10 12.1	28 4.0	6 42.1	11 10.8	16 36.0	9 15.5	15 13.7	13 44.4
5	2 54 .9	11 50.9	14 22.4	29 54.7	11 49.6	29 18.8	7 25.7	11 4.9	16 37.4	9 17.7	15 16.0	13 45.7
6	2 57 57.5	12 51.0	14 19.2	14♋12.8	13 26.6	0♐33.6	8 9.5	10 59.2	16 38.9	9 19.9	15 18.2	13 46.9
7	3 1 54.1	13 51.2	14 16.0	28 4.1	15 3.3	1 48.4	8 53.2	10 53.6	16 40.5	9 22.0	15 20.5	13 48.2
8	3 5 50.6	14 51.4	14 12.9	11♌29.7	16 39.6	3 3.2	9 37.1	10 48.2	16 42.3	9 24.1	15 22.8	13 49.4
9	3 9 47.2	15 51.7	14 9.7	24 32.2	18 15.5	4 17.9	10 21.0	10 43.0	16 44.1	9 26.1	15 25.0	13 50.6
10	3 13 43.7	16 51.9	14 6.5	7♍15.3	19 51.0	5 32.7	11 5.0	10 37.9	16 46.0	9 28.1	15 27.3	13 51.8
11	3 17 40.3	17 52.3	14 3.3	19 42.6	21 26.2	6 47.5	11 49.0	10 32.9	16 48.0	9 30.0	15 29.5	13 52.9
12	3 21 36.8	18 52.6	14 .1	1♎57.7	23 1.0	8 2.3	12 33.1	10 28.2	16 50.1	9 31.9	15 31.8	13 54.0
13	3 25 33.4	19 53.0	13 57.0	14 3.6	24 35.6	9 17.0	13 17.3	10 23.6	16 52.3	9 33.7	15 34.0	13 55.1
14	3 29 29.9	20 53.4	13 53.8	26 2.8	26 9.8	10 31.8	14 1.5	10 19.2	16 54.6	9 35.5	15 36.2	13 56.2
15	3 33 26.5	21 53.8	13 50.6	7♏57.2	27 43.7	11 46.6	14 45.8	10 15.0	16 57.0	9 37.2	15 38.5	13 57.2
16	3 37 23.1	22 54.3	13 47.4	19 48.6	29 17.4	13 1.3	15 30.1	10 10.9	16 59.6	9 38.9	15 40.7	13 58.2
17	3 41 19.6	23 54.8	13 44.3	1♐38.4	0♐50.8	14 16.1	16 14.5	10 7.1	17 2.1	9 40.5	15 43.0	13 59.1
18	3 45 16.2	24 55.3	13 41.1	13 28.3	2 24.0	15 30.9	16 59.0	10 3.4	17 4.8	9 42.1	15 45.2	14 .1
19	3 49 12.7	25 55.8	13 37.9	25 20.4	3 57.0	16 45.6	17 43.5	9 60.0	17 7.6	9 43.6	15 47.4	14 1.0
20	3 53 9.3	26 56.4	13 34.7	7♑17.0	5 29.7	18 .4	18 28.1	9 56.7	17 10.5	9 45.1	15 49.6	14 1.8
21	3 57 5.8	27 57.0	13 31.6	19 21.2	7 2.2	19 15.1	19 12.7	9 53.7	17 13.5	9 46.5	15 51.8	14 2.7
22	4 1 2.4	28 57.6	13 28.4	1♒36.8	8 34.5	20 29.9	19 57.4	9 50.8	17 16.6	9 47.9	15 54.0	14 3.5
23	4 4 59.0	29 58.2	13 25.2	14 7.8	10 6.6	21 44.6	20 42.2	9 48.1	17 19.7	9 49.2	15 56.2	14 4.3
24	4 8 55.5	0♐58.8	13 22.0	26 58.6	11 38.5	22 59.3	21 27.0	9 45.7	17 23.0	9 50.4	15 58.4	14 5.0
25	4 12 52.1	1 59.5	13 18.8	10♓13.1	13 10.2	24 14.0	22 11.9	9 43.4	17 26.3	9 51.7	16 .6	14 5.8
26	4 16 48.6	3 .2	13 15.7	23 54.4	14 41.7	25 28.7	22 56.8	9 41.4	17 29.7	9 52.8	16 2.8	14 6.5
27	4 20 45.2	4 .9	13 12.5	8♈ 3.8	16 13.0	26 43.4	23 41.7	9 39.5	17 33.3	9 53.9	16 5.0	14 7.1
28	4 24 41.7	5 1.6	13 9.3	22 39.8	17 44.1	27 58.1	24 26.8	9 37.9	17 36.9	9 54.9	16 7.1	14 7.7
29	4 28 38.3	6 2.4	13 6.1	7♉37.9	19 14.9	29 12.9	25 11.9	9 36.5	17 40.6	9 56.0	16 9.3	14 8.4
30	4 32 34.9	7 3.1	13 3.0	22 50.2	20 45.5	0♑27.5	25 57.0	9 35.3	17 44.4	9 56.9	16 11.4	14 9.0
		LATITUDE										
1	2 38 14.7	0 .0	0 .0	4S51.3	0N40.7	0S 1.3	0S38.7	1S35.4	1S13.6	0N44.8	1N42.8	13N30.4
4	2 50 4.4	0 .0	0 .0	2 23.1	0 20.7	0 8.9	0 40.3	1 34.8	1 13.5	0 44.9	1 42.8	13 31.6
7	3 1 54.1	0 .0	0 .0	1N19.3	0 .5	0 16.5	0 41.8	1 34.1	1 13.3	0 45.0	1 42.8	13 32.8
10	3 13 43.7	0 .0	0 .0	4 8.4	0S19.6	0 24.2	0 43.2	1 33.4	1 13.1	0 45.1	1 42.8	13 34.1
13	3 25 33.4	0 .0	0 .0	5 5.5	0 39.2	0 31.7	0 44.7	1 32.7	1 13.0	0 45.2	1 42.8	13 35.4
16	3 37 23.1	0 .0	0 .0	4 3.2	0 58.0	0 39.2	0 46.1	1 32.0	1 12.8	0 45.3	1 42.8	13 36.8
19	3 49 12.7	0 .0	0 .0	1 28.3	1 15.8	0 46.5	0 47.4	1 31.2	1 12.7	0 45.5	1 42.8	13 38.2
22	4 1 2.4	0 .0	0 .0	1S45.1	1 32.2	0 53.6	0 48.7	1 30.3	1 12.5	0 45.6	1 42.9	13 39.6
25	4 12 52.1	0 .0	0 .0	4 24.9	1 46.9	1 .4	0 50.0	1 29.5	1 12.4	0 45.7	1 42.9	13 41.0
28	4 24 41.7	0 .0	0 .0	5 5.6	1 59.5	1 6.9	0 51.2	1 28.6	1 12.2	0 45.9	1 43.0	13 42.4
		RIGHT ASCENSION										
1	2 38 14.7	5♏28.8	15♋50.0	29♈12.0	3♏13.4	21♏57.3	2♐25.8	11♈11.2	19♒22.8	11♍ 1.1	13♏10.2	20♍23.9
2	2 42 11.3	6 27.5	15 46.6	13♉40.7	4 46.9	23 13.4	3 11.7	11 R 5.3	19 23.9	11 3.3	13 12.4	20 25.3
3	2 46 7.8	7 26.3	15 43.2	28 42.5	6 20.4	24 29.8	3 57.8	10 59.5	19 25.1	11 5.4	13 14.6	20 26.7
4	2 50 4.4	8 25.3	15 39.8	14♊12.0	7 54.0	25 46.6	4 44.0	10 53.8	19 26.4	11 7.5	13 16.8	20 28.2
5	2 54 .9	9 24.5	15 36.3	29 54.3	9 27.7	27 3.6	5 30.4	10 48.3	19 27.8	11 9.6	13 19.1	20 29.5
6	2 57 57.5	10 24.0	15 32.9	15♋26.7	11 1.5	28 21.0	6 16.9	10 42.9	19 29.3	11 11.7	13 21.3	20 30.9
7	3 1 54.1	11 23.6	15 29.5	0♌27.1	12 35.5	29 38.6	7 3.6	10 37.7	19 30.9	11 13.7	13 23.5	20 32.3
8	3 5 50.6	12 23.6	15 26.1	14 40.1	14 9.7	0♐56.6	7 50.4	10 32.7	19 32.6	11 15.6	13 25.8	20 33.6
9	3 9 47.2	13 23.6	15 22.6	28 .6	15 44.1	2 14.8	8 37.4	10 27.7	19 34.4	11 17.6	13 28.0	20 34.9
10	3 13 43.7	14 23.9	15 19.2	10♍32.2	17 18.6	3 33.4	9 24.5	10 22.9	19 36.3	11 19.4	13 30.2	20 36.2
11	3 17 40.3	15 24.5	15 15.8	22 24.0	18 53.4	4 52.2	10 11.8	10 18.3	19 38.3	11 21.2	13 32.4	20 37.4
12	3 21 36.8	16 25.2	15 12.4	3♎47.5	20 28.4	6 11.3	10 59.2	10 13.8	19 40.3	11 23.0	13 34.7	20 38.7
13	3 25 33.4	17 26.1	15 8.9	14 54.8	22 3.7	7 30.7	11 46.7	10 9.5	19 42.5	11 24.7	13 36.9	20 39.9
14	3 29 29.9	18 27.3	15 5.5	25 57.4	23 39.3	8 50.3	12 34.4	10 5.4	19 44.8	11 26.4	13 39.1	20 41.0
15	3 33 26.5	19 28.7	15 2.1	7♏ 5.9	25 15.2	10 10.2	13 22.2	10 1.4	19 47.2	11 28.0	13 41.3	20 42.2
16	3 37 23.1	20 30.3	14 58.7	18 29.1	26 51.4	11 30.3	14 10.2	9 57.6	19 49.7	11 29.6	13 43.6	20 43.3
17	3 41 19.6	21 32.1	14 55.2	0♐13.9	28 27.8	12 50.6	14 58.3	9 53.9	19 52.2	11 31.2	13 45.8	20 44.4
18	3 45 16.2	22 34.1	14 51.8	12 23.8	0♐ 4.6	14 11.2	15 46.5	9 50.5	19 54.9	11 32.7	13 48.0	20 45.5
19	3 49 12.7	23 36.3	14 48.4	24 58.7	1 41.7	15 32.0	16 34.8	9 47.2	19 57.7	11 34.1	13 50.2	20 46.5
20	3 53 9.3	24 38.7	14 45.0	7♑54.3	3 19.2	16 53.0	17 23.2	9 44.1	20 .5	11 35.5	13 52.4	20 47.6
21	3 57 5.8	25 41.4	14 41.5	21 3.2	4 56.9	18 14.1	18 11.8	9 41.1	20 3.4	11 36.8	13 54.6	20 48.5
22	4 1 2.4	26 44.2	14 38.1	4♒16.5	6 34.9	19 35.4	19 .5	9 38.4	20 6.5	11 38.1	13 56.8	20 49.5
23	4 4 59.0	27 47.2	14 34.7	17 26.7	8 13.2	20 56.9	19 49.2	9 35.8	20 9.6	11 39.4	13 59.0	20 50.4
24	4 8 55.5	28 50.4	14 31.2	0♓29.8	9 51.8	22 18.5	20 38.1	9 33.5	20 12.8	11 40.6	14 1.1	20 51.4
25	4 12 52.1	29 53.8	14 27.8	13 26.5	11 30.6	23 40.3	21 27.1	9 31.3	20 16.1	11 41.7	14 3.3	20 52.2
26	4 16 48.6	0♐57.4	14 24.4	26 22.3	13 9.6	25 2.1	22 16.2	9 29.3	20 19.5	11 42.8	14 5.5	20 53.1
27	4 20 45.2	2 1.2	14 21.0	9♈26.7	14 48.7	26 24.0	23 5.4	9 27.5	20 23.0	11 43.8	14 7.6	20 53.9
28	4 24 41.7	3 5.1	14 17.5	22 51.3	16 28.0	27 46.1	23 54.6	9 25.8	20 26.6	11 44.8	14 9.8	20 54.7
29	4 28 38.3	4 9.3	14 14.1	6♉48.5	18 7.5	29 8.2	24 44.1	9 24.4	20 30.3	11 45.8	14 11.9	20 55.5
30	4 32 34.9	5 13.6	14 10.7	21 27.5	19 46.9	0♑30.3	25 33.5	9 23.2	20 34.0	11 46.7	14 14.1	20 56.3
		DECLINATION										
1	2 38 14.7	14S 7.7	0N23.7	6N46.0	12S38.8	18S52.6	21S41.0	3N 4.9	17S 3.1	8N50.0	14S44.0	18N50.8
4	2 50 4.4	15 4.9	0 23.7	20 15.0	14 33.2	19 52.6	22 5.6	2 58.2	17 1.9	8 47.5	14 46.0	18 50.3
7	3 1 54.1	15 60.0	0 23.7	21 50.7	16 20.8	20 47.8	22 28.4	2 52.1	17 .4	8 45.2	14 48.0	18 49.9
10	3 13 43.7	16 52.6	0 23.8	12 41.3	18 1.1	21 37.7	22 49.3	2 46.6	16 58.5	8 43.0	14 49.9	18 49.7
13	3 25 33.4	17 42.7	0 23.8	0S51.0	19 33.3	22 22.2	23 8.2	2 41.6	16 56.5	8 41.0	14 51.9	18 49.6
16	3 37 23.1	18 30.1	0 23.8	13 47.2	20 56.7	23 .8	23 25.1	2 37.4	16 54.1	8 39.2	14 53.8	18 49.6
19	3 49 12.7	19 14.5	0 23.8	21 53.4	22 10.9	23 33.3	23 39.8	2 33.8	16 51.5	8 37.5	14 55.7	18 49.8
22	4 1 2.4	19 55.8	0 23.8	21 30.7	23 15.2	23 59.6	23 52.4	2 31.0	16 48.7	8 36.0	14 57.5	18 50.1
25	4 12 52.1	20 33.8	0 23.9	11 49.4	24 9.0	24 19.4	24 2.7	2 28.9	16 45.5	8 34.7	14 59.4	18 50.5
28	4 24 41.7	21 8.4	0 23.9	4N 5.1	24 51.6	24 32.6	24 10.7	2 27.5	16 42.2	8 33.6	15 1.2	18 51.0

DECEMBER 1963

LONGITUDE

DAY	EPHEM. SID. TIME h m s	☉ ° ′	☊ ° ′	☾ ° ′	☿ ° ′	♀ ° ′	♂ ° ′	♃ ° ′	♄ ° ′	♅ ° ′	♆ ° ′	♇ ° ′
1	4 36 31.4	8♐ 3.9	12♋59.8	8♊ 6.8	22♐15.8	1♑42.2	26♐42.2	9♈34.2	17♒48.3	9♍57.8	16♏13.6	14♍ 9.5
2	4 40 28.0	9 4.7	12 56.6	23 17.0	23 45.7	2 56.8	27 27.4	9R33.4	17 52.2	9 58.6	16 15.7	14 10.0
3	4 44 24.5	10 5.5	12 53.4	8♋11.2	25 15.3	4 11.5	28 12.7	9 32.8	17 56.3	9 59.4	16 17.8	14 10.5
4	4 48 21.1	11 6.4	12 50.3	22 42.4	26 44.5	5 26.1	28 58.0	9 32.4	18 .4	10 .1	16 19.9	14 10.9
5	4 52 17.6	12 7.2	12 47.1	6♌46.8	28 13.2	6 40.7	29 43.4	9 32.2	18 4.6	10 .7	16 21.9	14 11.3
6	4 56 14.2	13 8.1	12 43.9	20 23.2	29 41.3	7 55.3	0♑28.9	9D32.3	18 8.8	10 1.3	16 24.0	14 11.7
7	5 0 10.8	14 9.0	12 40.7	3♍33.3	1♑ 8.7	9 9.9	1 14.4	9 32.5	18 13.2	10 1.9	16 26.0	14 12.0
8	5 4 7.3	15 9.9	12 37.5	16 20.0	2 35.3	10 24.5	1 59.9	9 32.9	18 17.6	10 2.4	16 28.1	14 12.3
9	5 8 3.9	16 10.9	12 34.4	28 47.2	4 1.1	11 39.1	2 45.5	9 33.6	18 22.2	10 2.8	16 30.1	14 12.6
10	5 12 .4	17 11.8	12 31.2	10♎59.3	5 25.7	12 53.7	3 31.2	9 34.4	18 26.7	10 3.2	16 32.1	14 12.9
11	5 15 57.0	18 12.8	12 28.0	23 .5	6 49.1	14 8.3	4 16.9	9 35.5	18 31.4	10 3.5	16 34.1	14 13.1
12	5 19 53.5	19 13.8	12 24.8	4♏54.5	8 11.1	15 22.8	5 2.6	9 36.7	18 36.2	10 3.7	16 36.1	14 13.2
13	5 23 50.1	20 14.8	12 21.7	16 44.8	9 31.3	16 37.4	5 48.4	9 38.2	18 41.0	10 3.9	16 38.0	14 13.4
14	5 27 46.7	21 15.9	12 18.5	28 34.3	10 49.4	17 51.9	6 34.3	9 39.9	18 45.9	10 4.1	16 39.9	14 13.5
15	5 31 43.2	22 16.9	12 15.3	10♐25.3	12 5.2	19 6.4	7 20.2	9 41.8	18 50.8	10 4.2	16 41.9	14 13.6
16	5 35 39.8	23 18.0	12 12.1	22 19.8	13 18.2	20 20.9	8 6.1	9 43.9	18 55.9	10 4.2	16 43.8	14 13.6
17	5 39 36.3	24 19.0	12 9.0	4♑19.8	14 28.0	21 35.4	8 52.1	9 46.2	19 1.0	10 4.2	16 45.6	14 13.7
18	5 43 32.9	25 20.1	12 5.8	16 26.9	15 34.1	22 49.9	9 38.1	9 48.7	19 6.2	10R 4.1	16 47.5	14R13.6
19	5 47 29.4	26 21.2	12 2.6	28 43.0	16 35.8	24 4.4	10 24.2	9 51.4	19 11.4	10 4.0	16 49.3	14 13.6
20	5 51 26.0	27 22.4	11 59.4	11♒10.2	17 32.6	25 18.9	11 10.4	9 54.3	19 16.8	10 3.8	16 51.2	14 13.6
21	5 55 22.6	28 23.5	11 56.3	23 50.7	18 23.6	26 33.3	11 56.5	9 57.4	19 22.2	10 3.6	16 53.0	14 13.4
22	5 59 19.1	29 24.6	11 53.1	6♓47.0	19 8.1	27 47.7	12 42.7	10 .7	19 27.6	10 3.3	16 54.8	14 13.3
23	6 3 15.7	0♑25.7	11 49.9	20 1.5	19 45.3	29 2.1	13 29.0	10 4.2	19 33.1	10 2.9	16 56.5	14 13.1
24	6 7 12.2	1 26.8	11 46.7	3♈36.2	20 14.2	0♒16.4	14 15.3	10 7.9	19 38.7	10 2.5	16 58.3	14 12.9
25	6 11 8.8	2 27.9	11 43.5	17 32.3	20 33.9	1 30.7	15 1.6	10 11.8	19 44.3	10 2.0	16 60.0	14 12.7
26	6 15 5.3	3 29.0	11 40.4	1♉49.5	20 43.5	2 45.0	15 47.9	10 15.9	19 50.0	10 1.5	17 1.7	14 12.4
27	6 19 1.9	4 30.2	11 37.2	16 25.3	20R42.4	3 59.3	16 34.3	10 20.2	19 55.8	10 .9	17 3.3	14 12.1
28	6 22 58.5	5 31.3	11 34.0	1♊15.3	20 29.8	5 13.6	17 20.8	10 24.6	20 1.6	10 .2	17 5.0	14 11.7
29	6 26 55.0	6 32.4	11 30.8	16 12.9	20 5.4	6 27.8	18 7.2	10 29.3	20 7.4	9 59.5	17 6.6	14 11.4
30	6 30 51.6	7 33.5	11 27.7	1♋10.0	19 29.2	7 42.0	18 53.7	10 34.1	20 13.3	9 58.8	17 8.2	14 11.0
31	6 34 48.1	8 34.7	11 24.5	15 58.2	18 41.5	8 56.1	19 40.3	10 39.1	20 19.3	9 58.0	17 9.8	14 10.5

LATITUDE

DAY	EPHEM. SID. TIME	☉	☊	☾	☿	♀	♂	♃	♄	♅	♆	♇
1	4 36 31.4	0 .0	0 .0	2S52.2	2S 9.7	1S13.1	0S52.4	1S27.7	1S12.1	0N46.0	1N43.0	13N43.9
4	4 48 21.1	0 .0	0 .0	1N 1.3	2 16.9	1 18.9	0 53.5	1 26.8	1 12.0	0 46.1	1 43.1	13 45.3
7	5 0 10.8	0 .0	0 .0	4 8.0	2 20.5	1 24.2	0 54.6	1 25.9	1 11.8	0 46.3	1 43.2	13 46.8
10	5 12 .4	0 .0	0 .0	5 14.3	2 19.7	1 29.1	0 55.6	1 25.0	1 11.7	0 46.4	1 43.2	13 48.3
13	5 23 50.1	0 .0	0 .0	4 16.6	2 13.6	1 33.4	0 56.6	1 24.1	1 11.6	0 46.5	1 43.3	13 49.8
16	5 35 39.8	0 .0	0 .0	1 42.2	2 .8	1 37.2	0 57.5	1 23.2	1 11.5	0 46.7	1 43.4	13 51.2
19	5 47 29.4	0 .0	0 .0	1S35.7	1 40.0	1 40.4	0 58.4	1 22.3	1 11.5	0 46.8	1 43.5	13 52.7
22	5 59 19.1	0 .0	0 .0	4 21.9	1 9.6	1 43.0	0 59.2	1 21.4	1 11.4	0 46.9	1 43.6	13 54.2
25	6 11 8.8	0 .0	0 .0	5 15.4	0 28.4	1 45.0	1 .0	1 20.5	1 11.3	0 47.1	1 43.8	13 55.6
28	6 22 58.5	0 .0	0 .0	3 24.2	0N23.2	1 46.3	1 .8	1 19.6	1 11.3	0 47.2	1 43.9	13 57.0
31	6 34 48.1	0 .0	0 .0	0N26.6	1 21.3	1 46.8	1 1.4	1 18.8	1 11.2	0 47.3	1 44.0	13 58.4

RIGHT ASCENSION

DAY	EPHEM. SID. TIME	☉	☊	☾	☿	♀	♂	♃	♄	♅	♆	♇
1	4 36 31.4	6♐18.1	14♋ 7.2	6♊50.2	21♐26.2	1♑52.4	26♐23.0	9♈22.1	20♒37.9	11♍47.5	14♏16.2	20♍57.0
2	4 40 28.0	7 22.7	14 3.8	22 46.4	23 5.5	3 14.6	27 12.6	9R21.3	20 41.8	11 48.3	14 18.3	20 57.6
3	4 44 24.5	8 27.5	14 .4	8♋53.5	24 44.5	4 36.7	28 2.3	9 20.6	20 45.8	11 49.1	14 20.4	20 58.3
4	4 48 21.1	9 32.5	13 57.0	24 42.1	26 23.2	5 58.8	28 52.0	9 20.1	20 49.8	11 49.7	14 22.4	20 58.9
5	4 52 17.6	10 37.6	13 53.5	9♌46.5	28 1.5	7 20.9	29 41.8	9 19.8	20 54.0	11 50.4	14 24.5	20 59.5
6	4 56 14.2	11 42.9	13 50.1	23 53.1	29 39.2	8 42.9	0♑31.7	9 19.7	20 58.2	11 51.0	14 26.6	21 .1
7	5 0 10.8	12 48.3	13 46.7	7♍ .7	1♑16.2	10 4.8	1 21.6	9D19.8	21 2.5	11 51.5	14 28.6	21 .6
8	5 4 7.3	13 53.8	13 43.2	19 17.4	2 52.4	11 26.7	2 11.6	9 20.1	21 6.9	11 51.9	14 30.6	21 1.1
9	5 8 3.9	14 59.5	13 39.8	0♎55.6	4 27.4	12 48.5	3 1.6	9 20.6	21 11.4	11 52.4	14 32.6	21 1.6
10	5 12 .4	16 5.3	13 36.4	12 9.0	6 1.2	14 10.1	3 51.7	9 21.2	21 15.9	11 52.7	14 34.6	21 2.0
11	5 15 57.0	17 11.2	13 32.9	23 11.4	7 33.4	15 31.6	4 41.9	9 22.1	21 20.5	11 53.0	14 36.6	21 2.4
12	5 19 53.5	18 17.2	13 29.5	4♏15.3	9 3.9	16 52.9	5 32.0	9 23.1	21 25.2	11 53.3	14 38.6	21 2.8
13	5 23 50.1	19 23.3	13 26.1	15 31.7	10 32.1	18 14.1	6 22.2	9 24.4	21 30.0	11 53.5	14 40.5	21 3.2
14	5 27 46.7	20 29.5	13 22.6	27 9.1	11 57.9	19 35.1	7 12.5	9 25.8	21 34.8	11 53.7	14 42.5	21 3.5
15	5 31 43.2	21 35.8	13 19.2	9♐13.2	13 20.8	20 55.9	8 2.7	9 27.4	21 39.7	11 53.8	14 44.4	21 3.8
16	5 35 39.8	22 42.2	13 15.8	21 45.3	14 40.3	22 16.5	8 53.0	9 29.2	21 44.7	11 53.8	14 46.3	21 4.0
17	5 39 36.3	23 48.6	13 12.3	4♑41.7	15 56.0	23 36.8	9 43.3	9 31.2	21 49.7	11 53.8	14 48.2	21 4.2
18	5 43 32.9	24 55.1	13 8.9	17 54.2	17 7.2	24 56.9	10 33.6	9 33.4	21 54.9	11R53.7	14 50.0	21 4.4
19	5 47 29.4	26 1.6	13 5.5	1♒11.7	18 13.3	26 16.8	11 24.0	9 35.8	22 .0	11 53.6	14 51.9	21 4.6
20	5 51 26.0	27 8.2	13 2.0	14 24.0	19 13.6	27 36.5	12 14.3	9 38.4	22 5.3	11 53.5	14 53.7	21 4.8
21	5 55 22.6	28 14.8	12 58.6	27 24.1	20 7.3	28 55.8	13 4.7	9 41.1	22 10.6	11 53.3	14 55.5	21 4.9
22	5 59 19.1	29 21.4	12 55.2	10♓10.5	20 53.6	0♒14.8	13 55.0	9 44.0	22 16.0	11 53.0	14 57.3	21 4.9
23	6 3 15.7	0♑28.0	12 51.7	22 47.4	21 31.6	1 33.6	14 45.3	9 47.1	22 21.4	11 52.7	14 59.1	21 5.0
24	6 7 12.2	1 34.6	12 48.3	5♈23.4	22 .4	2 52.0	15 35.6	9 50.4	22 26.9	11 52.3	15 .8	21 5.0
25	6 11 8.8	2 41.2	12 44.9	18 10.7	22 19.1	4 10.1	16 25.9	9 53.9	22 32.5	11 51.9	15 2.5	21 5.0
26	6 15 5.3	3 47.8	12 41.4	1♉22.9	22 26.8	5 27.9	17 16.1	9 57.5	22 38.1	11 51.4	15 4.2	21R 4.9
27	6 19 1.9	4 54.4	12 38.0	15 13.4	22R22.7	6 45.4	18 6.3	10 1.3	22 43.8	11 50.9	15 5.9	21 4.8
28	6 22 58.5	6 .9	12 34.5	29 51.2	22 6.4	8 2.5	18 56.5	10 5.3	22 49.5	11 50.3	15 7.5	21 4.7
29	6 26 55.0	7 7.4	12 31.1	15♊16.4	21 37.4	9 19.3	19 46.7	10 9.5	22 55.3	11 49.7	15 9.1	21 4.6
30	6 30 51.6	8 13.8	12 27.7	1♋15.7	20 56.0	10 35.8	20 36.8	10 13.8	23 1.1	11 49.0	15 10.7	21 4.4
31	6 34 48.1	9 20.2	12 24.2	17 22.9	20 2.6	11 51.9	21 26.9	10 18.3	23 7.0	11 48.3	15 12.3	21 4.2

DECLINATION

DAY	EPHEM. SID. TIME	☉	☊	☾	☿	♀	♂	♃	♄	♅	♆	♇
1	4 36 31.4	21S39.4	0N23.9	18N49.9	25S22.5	24S39.0	24S16.5	2N26.9	16S38.5	8N32.6	15S 3.0	18N51.7
4	4 48 21.1	22 6.7	0 23.9	22 32.3	25 41.0	24 38.7	24 19.8	2 27.0	16 34.7	8 31.9	15 4.7	18 52.4
7	5 0 10.8	22 30.1	0 23.9	14 3.3	25 46.8	24 31.6	24 20.8	2 27.8	16 30.6	8 31.4	15 6.4	18 53.3
10	5 12 .4	22 49.6	0 23.9	0 28.4	25 39.5	24 17.7	24 19.4	2 29.4	16 26.3	8 31.0	15 8.0	18 54.4
13	5 23 50.1	23 5.1	0 23.9	12S44.4	25 19.3	23 57.2	24 15.5	2 31.8	16 21.8	8 30.8	15 9.6	18 55.5
16	5 35 39.8	23 16.4	0 24.0	21 31.2	24 46.9	23 30.2	24 9.2	2 34.8	16 17.0	8 30.8	15 11.1	18 56.8
19	5 47 29.4	23 23.6	0 24.0	21 58.9	24 4.0	22 56.8	24 .4	2 38.6	16 12.1	8 31.1	15 12.6	18 58.1
22	5 59 19.1	23 26.5	0 24.0	13 4.4	23 13.6	22 17.3	23 49.1	2 43.1	16 7.0	8 31.4	15 14.0	18 59.6
25	6 11 8.8	23 25.2	0 24.0	2N 1.5	22 20.3	21 31.9	23 35.4	2 48.2	16 1.6	8 32.0	15 15.4	19 1.1
28	6 22 58.5	23 19.7	0 24.0	17 4.9	21 29.8	20 40.9	23 19.3	2 54.1	15 56.1	8 32.8	15 16.7	19 2.8
31	6 34 48.1	23 9.9	0 24.0	22 55.6	20 47.8	19 44.7	23 .8	3 .6	15 50.5	8 33.8	15 17.9	19 4.6

JANUARY 1964

LONGITUDE

DAY	EPHEM. SID. TIME	☉	☊	☽	☿	♀	♂	♃	♄	♅	♆	♇
	h m s	° ′	° ′	° ′	° ′	° ′	° ′	° ′	° ′	° ′	° ′	° ′
1	6 38 44.7	9♑35.8	11♋21.3	0♌30.2	17♑43.4	10♒10.2	20♑26.8	10♈44.3	20♒25.4	9♍57.1	17♏11.3	14♍10.1
2	6 42 41.3	10 36.9	11 18.1	14 40.3	16 R 36.3	11 24.3	21 13.4	10 49.7	20 31.4	9 R 56.2	17 12.8	14 R 9.6
3	6 46 37.8	11 38.1	11 15.0	28 25.2	15 22.1	12 38.4	22 .1	10 55.2	20 37.6	9 55.3	17 14.3	14 9.1
4	6 50 34.4	12 39.2	11 11.8	11♍44.2	14 3.2	13 52.4	22 46.8	11 1.0	20 43.7	9 54.3	17 15.8	14 8.5
5	6 54 30.9	13 40.3	11 8.6	24 38.5	12 42.1	15 6.4	23 33.5	11 6.9	20 50.0	9 53.2	17 17.2	14 7.9
6	6 58 27.5	14 41.5	11 5.4	7♎11.1	11 21.5	16 20.4	24 20.2	11 12.9	20 56.3	9 52.1	17 18.7	14 7.3
7	7 2 24.0	15 42.6	11 2.2	19 25.9	10 4.0	17 34.3	25 7.0	11 19.2	21 2.6	9 50.9	17 20.0	14 6.7
8	7 6 20.6	16 43.8	10 59.1	1♏27.5	8 51.8	18 48.2	25 53.8	11 25.6	21 9.0	9 49.7	17 21.4	14 6.0
9	7 10 17.2	17 44.9	10 55.9	13 20.6	7 46.6	20 2.1	26 40.7	11 32.2	21 15.4	9 48.5	17 22.7	14 5.3
10	7 14 13.7	18 46.2	10 52.7	25 9.7	6 50.0	21 16.0	27 27.6	11 39.0	21 21.9	9 47.2	17 24.1	14 4.6
11	7 18 10.3	19 47.3	10 49.5	6♐59.2	6 2.7	22 29.8	28 14.5	11 45.9	21 28.4	9 45.8	17 25.3	14 3.9
12	7 22 6.8	20 48.5	10 46.4	18 52.6	5 25.2	23 43.5	29 1.5	11 53.0	21 34.9	9 44.4	17 26.6	14 3.1
13	7 26 3.4	21 49.6	10 43.2	0♑53.2	4 57.5	24 57.2	29 48.4	12 .3	21 41.5	9 43.0	17 27.8	14 2.3
14	7 29 59.9	22 50.8	10 40.0	13 3.4	4 39.5	26 10.9	0♒35.4	12 7.7	21 48.2	9 41.5	17 29.0	14 1.4
15	7 33 56.5	23 51.9	10 36.8	25 24.9	4 30.9	27 24.5	1 22.4	12 15.2	21 54.8	9 39.9	17 30.1	14 .6
16	7 37 53.1	24 53.0	10 33.7	7♒58.9	4 D 31.0	28 38.1	2 9.5	12 22.9	22 1.5	9 38.3	17 31.3	13 59.7
17	7 41 49.6	25 54.2	10 30.5	20 46.0	4 39.3	29 51.6	2 56.6	12 30.8	22 8.3	9 36.7	17 32.4	13 58.8
18	7 45 46.2	26 55.3	10 27.3	3♓46.6	4 55.1	1♓ 5.1	3 43.6	12 38.8	22 15.0	9 35.0	17 33.4	13 57.8
19	7 49 42.7	27 56.4	10 24.1	17 .6	5 17.8	2 18.5	4 30.8	12 47.0	22 21.8	9 33.3	17 34.5	13 56.8
20	7 53 39.3	28 57.5	10 21.0	0♈27.8	5 46.9	3 31.9	5 17.9	12 55.3	22 28.7	9 31.5	17 35.5	13 55.8
21	7 57 35.8	29 58.5	10 17.8	14 8.1	6 21.6	4 45.2	6 5.1	13 3.8	22 35.5	9 29.7	17 36.4	13 54.8
22	8 1 32.4	0♒59.6	10 14.6	28 1.1	7 1.5	5 58.5	6 52.2	13 12.4	22 42.4	9 27.9	17 37.4	13 53.8
23	8 5 29.0	2 .6	10 11.4	12♉ 6.0	7 46.1	7 11.7	7 39.4	13 21.2	22 49.3	9 26.0	17 38.3	13 52.7
24	8 9 25.5	3 1.7	10 8.2	26 21.6	8 34.9	8 24.8	8 26.6	13 30.1	22 56.3	9 24.0	17 39.1	13 51.6
25	8 13 22.1	4 2.7	10 5.1	10♊45.6	9 27.4	9 37.9	9 13.9	13 39.1	23 3.3	9 22.1	17 40.0	13 50.5
26	8 17 18.6	5 3.7	10 1.9	25 14.8	10 23.5	10 50.9	10 1.1	13 48.2	23 10.3	9 20.1	17 40.8	13 49.4
27	8 21 15.2	6 4.6	9 58.7	9♋44.8	11 22.6	12 3.9	10 48.4	13 57.5	23 17.3	9 18.0	17 41.6	13 48.2
28	8 25 11.7	7 5.6	9 55.5	24 10.5	12 24.6	13 16.7	11 35.6	14 6.9	23 24.3	9 16.0	17 42.3	13 47.0
29	8 29 8.3	8 6.5	9 52.4	8♌26.3	13 29.2	14 29.5	12 22.9	14 16.5	23 31.4	9 13.9	17 43.0	13 45.8
30	8 33 4.8	9 7.5	9 49.2	22 27.0	14 36.1	15 42.3	13 10.2	14 26.2	23 38.5	9 11.7	17 43.7	13 44.6
31	8 37 1.4	10 8.4	9 46.0	6♍ 8.7	15 45.2	16 55.0	13 57.6	14 36.0	23 45.6	9 9.6	17 44.4	13 43.4

LATITUDE

DAY	EPHEM. SID. TIME	☉	☊	☽	☿	♀	♂	♃	♄	♅	♆	♇
1	6 38 44.7	0 .0	0 .0	1N45.3	1N40.6	1S46.9	1S 1.6	1S18.5	1S11.2	0N47.4	1N44.1	13N58.9
4	6 50 34.4	0 .0	0 .0	4 36.8	2 32.6	1 46.5	1 2.2	1 17.6	1 11.2	0 47.5	1 44.2	14 .3
7	7 2 24.0	0 .0	0 .0	5 14.4	3 7.2	1 45.4	1 2.8	1 16.8	1 11.2	0 47.6	1 44.4	14 1.6
10	7 14 13.7	0 .0	0 .0	3 49.0	3 19.5	1 43.5	1 3.2	1 16.0	1 11.2	0 47.7	1 44.5	14 2.9
13	7 26 3.4	0 .0	0 .0	0 57.2	3 12.8	1 40.9	1 3.7	1 15.2	1 11.2	0 47.8	1 44.7	14 4.2
16	7 37 53.1	0 .0	0 .0	2S22.7	2 53.3	1 37.6	1 4.0	1 14.4	1 11.2	0 47.9	1 44.8	14 5.4
19	7 49 42.7	0 .0	0 .0	4 48.3	2 26.7	1 33.5	1 4.3	1 13.7	1 11.3	0 48.0	1 45.0	14 6.6
22	8 1 32.4	0 .0	0 .0	5 2.0	1 57.0	1 28.6	1 4.6	1 12.9	1 11.4	0 48.1	1 45.2	14 7.7
25	8 13 22.1	0 .0	0 .0	2 39.6	1 26.4	1 23.0	1 4.8	1 12.2	1 11.4	0 48.2	1 45.3	14 8.8
28	8 25 11.7	0 .0	0 .0	1N11.2	0 56.3	1 16.6	1 4.9	1 11.5	1 11.5	0 48.3	1 45.5	14 9.9
31	8 37 1.4	0 .0	0 .0	4 17.2	0 27.5	1 9.6	1 4.9	1 10.8	1 11.6	0 48.4	1 45.7	14 10.8

RIGHT ASCENSION

DAY	EPHEM. SID. TIME	☉	☊	☽	☿	♀	♂	♃	♄	♅	♆	♇
1	6 38 44.7	10♑26.5	12♋20.8	3♌ 6.8	18♑58.3	13♒ 7.6	22♑17.0	10♈23.0	23♒12.9	11♍47.5	15♏13.9	21♍ 4.0
2	6 42 41.3	11 32.7	12 17.4	18 2.5	17 R 44.7	14 23.0	23 7.0	10 27.9	23 18.9	11 R 46.6	15 15.4	21 R 3.7
3	6 46 37.8	12 38.9	12 13.9	1♍58.7	16 24.0	15 38.1	23 56.9	10 32.9	23 24.9	11 45.8	15 16.9	21 3.4
4	6 50 34.4	13 45.0	12 10.5	14 56.8	14 58.6	16 52.8	24 46.8	10 38.0	23 31.0	11 44.8	15 18.4	21 3.1
5	6 54 30.9	14 51.0	12 7.1	27 6.4	13 31.3	18 7.1	25 36.7	10 43.4	23 37.1	11 43.8	15 19.8	21 2.7
6	6 58 27.5	15 56.9	12 3.6	8♎41.0	12 4.9	19 21.1	26 26.5	10 48.9	23 43.3	11 42.8	15 21.2	21 2.3
7	7 2 24.0	17 2.7	12 .2	19 55.1	10 42.0	20 34.7	27 16.2	10 54.5	23 49.5	11 41.7	15 22.6	21 1.9
8	7 6 20.6	18 8.4	11 56.7	1♏ 2.5	9 25.0	21 48.0	28 5.9	11 .3	23 55.8	11 40.6	15 24.0	21 1.5
9	7 10 17.2	19 14.0	11 53.3	12 15.8	8 15.7	23 .9	28 55.5	11 6.3	24 2.1	11 39.5	15 25.3	21 1.0
10	7 14 13.7	20 19.5	11 49.9	23 46.0	7 15.6	24 13.5	29 45.1	11 12.5	24 8.5	11 38.3	15 26.7	21 .6
11	7 18 10.3	21 24.8	11 46.4	5♐41.0	6 25.4	25 25.8	0♒34.5	11 18.7	24 14.9	11 37.0	15 28.0	21 .0
12	7 22 6.8	22 30.0	11 43.0	18 5.1	5 45.6	26 37.7	1 23.9	11 25.2	24 21.3	11 35.7	15 29.2	20 59.5
13	7 26 3.4	23 35.0	11 39.5	0♑57.6	5 16.4	27 49.2	2 13.3	11 31.7	24 27.8	11 34.4	15 30.4	20 58.9
14	7 29 59.9	24 39.9	11 36.1	14 12.2	4 57.5	29 .4	3 2.5	11 38.5	24 34.3	11 33.0	15 31.6	20 58.3
15	7 33 56.5	25 44.6	11 32.7	27 38.1	4 48.5	0♓11.3	3 51.6	11 45.4	24 40.8	11 31.5	15 32.8	20 57.7
16	7 37 53.1	26 49.2	11 29.2	11♒ 3.2	4 D 48.9	1 21.9	4 40.7	11 52.4	24 47.4	11 30.1	15 33.9	20 57.0
17	7 41 49.6	27 53.6	11 25.8	24 17.1	4 58.1	2 32.1	5 29.7	11 59.5	24 54.0	11 28.5	15 35.0	20 56.3
18	7 45 46.2	28 57.8	11 22.3	7♓14.7	5 15.3	3 42.0	6 18.6	12 6.9	25 .7	11 27.0	15 36.1	20 55.6
19	7 49 42.7	0♒ 1.9	11 18.9	19 56.7	5 40.0	4 51.6	7 7.4	12 14.3	25 7.3	11 25.4	15 37.2	20 54.8
20	7 53 39.3	1 5.7	11 15.4	2♈29.2	6 11.4	6 .9	7 56.1	12 21.9	25 14.0	11 23.7	15 38.2	20 54.1
21	7 57 35.8	2 9.4	11 12.0	15 2.6	6 49.1	7 10.0	8 44.7	12 29.6	25 20.8	11 22.0	15 39.1	20 53.3
22	8 1 32.4	3 12.9	11 8.6	27 49.7	7 32.4	8 18.7	9 33.2	12 37.5	25 27.5	11 20.3	15 40.1	20 52.4
23	8 5 29.0	4 16.2	11 5.1	11♉ 3.9	8 20.7	9 27.1	10 21.6	12 45.5	25 34.3	11 18.6	15 41.0	20 51.6
24	8 9 25.5	5 19.3	11 1.7	24 56.8	9 13.7	10 35.2	11 9.9	12 53.6	25 41.1	11 16.8	15 41.9	20 50.7
25	8 13 22.1	6 22.1	10 58.2	9♊34.2	10 10.8	11 43.1	11 58.1	13 1.8	25 47.9	11 14.9	15 42.7	20 49.8
26	8 17 18.6	7 24.8	10 54.8	24 52.6	11 11.8	12 50.7	12 46.3	13 10.2	25 54.8	11 13.1	15 43.6	20 48.9
27	8 21 15.2	8 27.3	10 51.4	10♋35.7	12 16.1	13 58.0	13 34.3	13 18.7	26 1.6	11 11.2	15 44.4	20 48.0
28	8 25 11.7	9 29.6	10 47.9	26 17.8	13 23.6	15 5.1	14 22.1	13 27.3	26 8.5	11 9.2	15 45.1	20 47.0
29	8 29 8.3	10 31.7	10 44.5	11♌31.9	14 33.9	16 12.0	15 9.9	13 36.0	26 15.4	11 7.3	15 45.8	20 46.0
30	8 33 4.8	11 33.5	10 41.0	25 59.1	15 46.8	17 18.6	15 57.6	13 44.9	26 22.3	11 5.3	15 46.5	20 45.0
31	8 37 1.4	12 35.3	10 37.6	9♍32.4	17 2.0	18 25.0	16 45.2	13 53.9	26 29.3	11 3.3	15 47.2	20 44.0

DECLINATION

DAY	EPHEM. SID. TIME	☉	☊	☽	☿	♀	♂	♃	♄	♅	♆	♇
1	6 38 44.7	23S 5.7	0N24.0	21N45.6	20S36.4	19S24.8	22S54.1	3N 2.8	15S48.5	8N34.2	15S18.3	19N 5.2
4	6 50 34.4	22 50.4	0 24.1	11 25.5	20 10.3	18 21.9	22 32.5	3 10.1	15 42.6	8 35.4	15 19.4	19 7.0
7	7 2 24.0	22 31.1	0 24.1	2S45.1	19 57.0	17 14.5	22 8.6	3 18.0	15 36.6	8 36.7	15 20.4	19 9.0
10	7 14 13.7	22 7.7	0 24.1	15 21.1	19 56.7	16 2.9	21 42.3	3 26.5	15 30.4	8 38.2	15 21.4	19 11.0
13	7 26 3.4	21 40.4	0 24.1	22 29.2	20 8.4	14 47.4	21 13.9	3 35.5	15 24.0	8 39.9	15 22.3	19 13.1
16	7 37 53.1	21 9.3	0 24.1	20 34.3	20 28.8	13 28.5	20 43.3	3 45.1	15 17.6	8 41.8	15 23.1	19 15.2
19	7 49 42.7	20 34.6	0 24.1	9 33.2	20 53.6	12 6.5	20 10.7	3 55.2	15 11.0	8 43.8	15 23.9	19 17.4
22	8 1 32.4	19 56.4	0 24.1	6N 4.0	21 18.6	10 41.6	19 36.0	4 5.7	15 4.3	8 45.9	15 24.5	19 19.7
25	8 13 22.1	19 14.9	0 24.1	19 25.7	21 40.2	9 14.4	18 59.4	4 16.7	14 57.6	8 48.2	15 25.1	19 21.9
28	8 25 11.7	18 30.1	0 24.2	22 27.0	21 55.8	7 45.1	18 20.9	4 28.2	14 50.7	8 50.6	15 25.6	19 24.2
31	8 37 1.4	17 42.4	0 24.2	13 14.4	22 3.5	6 14.1	17 40.7	4 40.0	14 43.7	8 53.0	15 26.0	19 26.6

FEBRUARY 1964

LONGITUDE

DAY	EPHEM. SID. TIME h m s	☉ ° ′	☊ ° ′	☽ ° ′	☿ ° ′	♀ ° ′	♂ ° ′	♃ ° ′	♄ ° ′	♅ ° ′	♆ ° ′	♇ ° ′
1	8 40 58.0	11 ♒ 9.3	9 ♋ 42.8	19 ♍ 28.7	16 ♑ 56.2	18 ♓ 7.5	14 ♒ 44.9	14 ♈ 45.9	23 ♒ 52.8	9 ♍ 7.4	17 ♏ 45.0	13 ♍ 42.1
2	8 44 54.5	12 10.2	9 39.6	2 ♎ 26.5	18 9.1	19 20.0	15 32.2	14 56.0	23 59.9	9 R 5.2	17 45.6	13 R 40.9
3	8 48 51.1	13 11.1	9 36.5	15 3.2	19 23.6	20 32.5	16 19.6	15 6.1	24 7.0	9 2.9	17 46.1	13 39.6
4	8 52 47.6	14 11.9	9 33.3	27 21.6	20 39.8	21 44.8	17 6.9	15 16.4	24 14.2	9 .6	17 46.6	13 38.3
5	8 56 44.2	15 12.8	9 30.1	9 ♏ 25.5	21 57.4	22 57.1	17 54.3	15 26.8	24 21.4	8 58.3	17 47.1	13 36.9
6	9 0 40.7	16 13.6	9 26.9	21 19.6	23 16.3	24 9.3	18 41.7	15 37.3	24 28.6	8 56.0	17 47.5	13 35.6
7	9 4 37.3	17 14.4	9 23.8	3 ♐ 9.0	24 36.6	25 21.4	19 29.1	15 47.9	24 35.8	8 53.6	17 48.0	13 34.2
8	9 8 33.8	18 15.2	9 20.6	14 58.9	25 58.1	26 33.4	20 16.5	15 58.7	24 43.0	8 51.2	17 48.3	13 32.8
9	9 12 30.4	19 16.0	9 17.4	26 54.2	27 20.8	27 45.3	21 3.9	16 9.5	24 50.2	8 48.8	17 48.7	13 31.4
10	9 16 27.0	20 16.7	9 14.2	8 ♑ 59.2	28 44.5	28 57.1	21 51.3	16 20.4	24 57.5	8 46.3	17 49.0	13 30.0
11	9 20 23.5	21 17.5	9 11.1	21 17.8	0 ♒ 9.4	0 ♈ 8.9	22 38.8	16 31.5	25 4.7	8 43.9	17 49.2	13 28.6
12	9 24 20.1	22 18.2	9 7.9	3 ♒ 52.5	1 35.3	1 20.6	23 26.2	16 42.7	25 11.9	8 41.4	17 49.5	13 27.1
13	9 28 16.6	23 18.9	9 4.7	16 44.8	3 2.2	2 32.1	24 13.6	16 53.9	25 19.2	8 38.9	17 49.7	13 25.7
14	9 32 13.2	24 19.6	9 1.5	29 54.8	4 30.1	3 43.6	25 1.1	17 5.3	25 26.4	8 36.4	17 49.8	13 24.2
15	9 36 9.7	25 20.2	8 58.3	13 ♓ 21.2	5 59.0	4 55.0	25 48.5	17 16.7	25 33.7	8 33.8	17 50.0	13 22.7
16	9 40 6.3	26 20.8	8 55.2	27 1.6	7 28.9	6 6.2	26 35.9	17 28.3	25 40.9	8 31.3	17 50.1	13 21.2
17	9 44 2.8	27 21.4	8 52.0	10 ♈ 53.1	8 59.6	7 17.4	27 23.4	17 39.9	25 48.2	8 28.7	17 50.1	13 19.7
18	9 47 59.4	28 22.0	8 48.8	24 52.4	10 31.3	8 28.4	28 10.8	17 51.6	25 55.4	8 26.2	17 50.2	13 18.2
19	9 51 55.9	29 22.6	8 45.6	8 ♉ 56.5	12 4.0	9 39.3	28 58.2	18 3.5	26 2.7	8 23.6	17 50.2	13 16.7
20	9 55 52.5	0 ♓ 23.1	8 42.5	23 3.1	13 37.5	10 50.1	29 45.7	18 15.4	26 9.9	8 21.0	17 R 50.1	13 15.2
21	9 59 49.1	1 23.6	8 39.3	7 ♊ 10.5	15 12.1	12 .9	0 ♓ 33.1	18 27.4	26 17.2	8 18.4	17 50.1	13 13.7
22	10 3 45.6	2 24.0	8 36.1	21 17.4	16 47.5	13 11.4	1 20.5	18 39.5	26 24.4	8 15.8	17 50.0	13 12.2
23	10 7 42.2	3 24.5	8 32.9	5 ♋ 22.7	18 23.9	14 21.9	2 8.0	18 51.7	26 31.7	8 13.2	17 49.9	13 10.6
24	10 11 38.7	4 24.8	8 29.7	19 24.9	20 1.2	15 32.2	2 55.4	19 3.9	26 38.9	8 10.6	17 49.7	13 9.1
25	10 15 35.3	5 25.2	8 26.6	3 ♌ 22.1	21 39.5	16 42.3	3 42.7	19 16.2	26 46.1	8 7.9	17 49.5	13 7.5
26	10 19 31.8	6 25.5	8 23.4	17 11.6	23 18.8	17 52.3	4 30.1	19 28.6	26 53.3	8 5.3	17 49.2	13 5.9
27	10 23 28.4	7 25.8	8 20.2	0 ♍ 50.5	24 59.0	19 2.2	5 17.5	19 41.1	27 .4	8 2.7	17 49.0	13 4.4
28	10 27 24.9	8 26.1	8 17.0	14 15.8	26 40.3	20 12.0	6 4.9	19 53.6	27 7.6	8 .1	17 48.7	13 2.8
29	10 31 21.5	9 26.3	8 13.9	27 25.0	28 22.5	21 21.5	6 52.2	20 6.3	27 14.7	7 57.4	17 48.3	13 1.2

LATITUDE

DAY	EPHEM. SID. TIME	☉	☊	☽	☿	♀	♂	♃	♄	♅	♆	♇
1	8 40 58.0	0 .0	0 .0	4 N 51.3	0 N 18.2	1 S 7.1	1 S 4.9	1 S 10.6	1 S 11.6	0 N 48.4	1 N 45.7	14 N 11.1
4	8 52 47.6	0 .0	0 .0	4 59.5	0 S 8.2	0 59.1	1 4.9	1 10.0	1 11.8	0 48.5	1 45.9	14 12.0
7	9 4 37.3	0 .0	0 .0	3 10.6	0 32.5	0 50.5	1 4.8	1 9.3	1 11.9	0 48.5	1 46.1	14 12.9
10	9 16 27.0	0 .0	0 .0	0 9.5	0 54.5	0 41.2	1 4.7	1 8.7	1 12.1	0 48.6	1 46.3	14 13.6
13	9 28 16.6	0 .0	0 .0	3 S 2.7	1 14.1	0 31.4	1 4.5	1 8.1	1 12.2	0 48.6	1 46.4	14 14.4
16	9 40 6.3	0 .0	0 .0	4 59.7	1 30.9	0 20.9	1 4.2	1 7.6	1 12.4	0 48.7	1 46.6	14 15.0
19	9 51 55.9	0 .0	0 .0	4 29.5	1 44.9	0 10.0	1 3.8	1 7.0	1 12.6	0 48.7	1 46.8	14 15.6
22	10 3 45.6	0 .0	0 .0	1 38.6	1 56.0	0 N 1.4	1 3.4	1 6.5	1 12.8	0 48.7	1 47.0	14 16.0
25	10 15 35.3	0 .0	0 .0	2 N 2.3	2 3.7	0 13.3	1 3.0	1 6.0	1 13.0	0 48.7	1 47.2	14 16.5
28	10 27 24.9	0 .0	0 .0	4 35.3	2 8.1	0 25.5	1 2.4	1 5.5	1 13.3	0 48.7	1 47.3	14 16.8

RIGHT ASCENSION

DAY	EPHEM. SID. TIME	☉	☊	☽	☿	♀	♂	♃	♄	♅	♆	♇
1	8 40 58.0	13 ♒ 36.7	10 ♋ 34.1	22 ♍ 15.2	18 ♑ 19.3	19 ♓ 31.2	17 ♒ 32.7	14 ♈ 3.0	26 ♒ 36.3	11 ♍ 1.3	15 ♏ 47.9	20 ♍ 43.0
2	8 44 54.5	14 38.0	10 30.7	4 ♎ 17.5	19 38.5	20 37.2	18 20.1	14 12.2	26 43.3	10 R 59.2	15 48.5	20 R 41.9
3	8 48 51.1	15 39.1	10 27.2	15 51.9	20 59.5	21 43.0	19 7.3	14 21.6	26 50.2	10 57.1	15 49.0	20 40.8
4	8 52 47.6	16 39.9	10 23.8	27 11.8	22 22.1	22 48.6	19 54.5	14 31.0	26 57.2	10 54.9	15 49.5	20 39.7
5	8 56 44.2	17 40.6	10 20.4	8 ♏ 30.0	23 46.1	23 54.0	20 41.6	14 40.5	27 4.2	10 52.8	15 50.0	20 38.6
6	9 0 40.7	18 41.1	10 16.9	19 57.9	25 11.5	24 59.2	21 28.5	14 50.2	27 11.3	10 50.6	15 50.5	20 37.4
7	9 4 37.3	19 41.4	10 13.5	1 ♐ 45.1	26 38.1	26 4.3	22 15.3	14 59.9	27 18.3	10 48.3	15 50.9	20 36.2
8	9 8 33.8	20 41.4	10 10.0	13 58.1	28 5.8	27 9.3	23 2.1	15 9.8	27 25.3	10 46.1	15 51.3	20 35.1
9	9 12 30.4	21 41.3	10 6.6	26 39.4	29 34.5	28 14.1	23 48.7	15 19.8	27 32.4	10 43.8	15 51.6	20 33.9
10	9 16 27.0	22 41.0	10 3.1	9 ♑ 46.1	1 ♒ 4.2	29 18.7	24 35.2	15 29.9	27 39.4	10 41.6	15 52.0	20 32.6
11	9 20 23.5	23 40.5	9 59.7	23 10.8	2 34.7	0 ♈ 23.3	25 21.6	15 40.0	27 46.5	10 39.3	15 52.3	20 31.4
12	9 24 20.1	24 39.8	9 56.2	6 ♒ 42.5	4 6.0	1 27.7	26 7.9	15 50.3	27 53.5	10 36.9	15 52.5	20 30.1
13	9 28 16.6	25 38.9	9 52.8	20 10.1	5 38.1	2 32.0	26 54.1	16 .7	28 .6	10 34.6	15 52.7	20 28.9
14	9 32 13.2	26 37.8	9 49.3	3 ♓ 25.7	7 10.8	3 36.3	27 40.2	16 11.1	28 7.6	10 32.2	15 52.9	20 27.6
15	9 36 9.7	27 36.5	9 45.9	16 26.7	8 44.1	4 40.4	28 26.2	16 21.7	28 14.7	10 29.9	15 53.1	20 26.3
16	9 40 6.3	28 35.1	9 42.4	29 15.9	10 18.0	5 44.5	29 12.1	16 32.4	28 21.7	10 27.5	15 53.2	20 25.0
17	9 44 2.8	29 33.4	9 39.0	12 ♈ .7	11 52.4	6 48.5	29 57.9	16 43.1	28 28.8	10 25.1	15 53.3	20 23.6
18	9 47 59.4	0 ♓ 31.6	9 35.5	24 51.7	13 27.3	7 52.4	0 ♓ 43.6	16 53.9	28 35.8	10 22.7	15 53.3	20 22.3
19	9 51 55.9	1 29.6	9 32.1	8 ♉ .6	15 2.7	8 56.2	1 29.1	17 4.9	28 42.9	10 20.2	15 53.3	20 21.0
20	9 55 52.5	2 27.4	9 28.6	21 37.9	16 38.5	10 .0	2 14.6	17 15.9	28 49.9	10 17.8	15 53.3	20 19.6
21	9 59 49.1	3 25.1	9 25.2	5 ♊ 50.6	18 14.8	11 3.8	3 .0	17 27.0	28 57.0	10 15.4	15 53.3	20 18.3
22	10 3 45.6	4 22.6	9 21.7	20 38.1	19 51.4	12 7.6	3 45.3	17 38.2	29 4.0	10 13.0	15 R 53.2	20 16.9
23	10 7 42.2	5 19.9	9 18.3	5 ♋ 50.4	21 28.4	13 11.2	4 30.5	17 49.5	29 11.0	10 10.5	15 53.1	20 15.5
24	10 11 38.7	6 17.1	9 14.8	21 8.8	23 5.8	14 14.9	5 15.5	18 .8	29 18.0	10 8.0	15 52.9	20 14.1
25	10 15 35.3	7 14.1	9 11.4	6 ♌ 10.8	24 43.5	15 18.5	6 .5	18 12.2	29 25.0	10 5.6	15 52.7	20 12.7
26	10 19 31.8	8 10.9	9 8.0	20 38.0	26 21.6	16 22.2	6 45.4	18 23.7	29 32.0	10 3.1	15 52.5	20 11.3
27	10 23 28.4	9 7.6	9 4.5	4 ♍ 20.7	28 .1	17 25.8	7 30.1	18 35.3	29 39.0	10 .6	15 52.3	20 9.8
28	10 27 24.9	10 4.1	9 1.1	17 18.1	29 38.9	18 29.4	8 14.8	18 46.9	29 45.9	9 58.2	15 52.0	20 8.4
29	10 31 21.5	11 .6	8 57.6	29 36.4	1 ♓ 18.0	19 33.0	8 59.4	18 58.6	29 52.9	9 55.7	15 51.7	20 7.0

DECLINATION

DAY	EPHEM. SID. TIME	☉	☊	☽	☿	♀	♂	♃	♄	♅	♆	♇
1	8 40 58.0	17 S 25.8	0 N 24.2	8 N 37.7	22 S 4.1	5 S 43.5	17 S 26.9	4 N 44.1	14 S 41.4	8 N 53.9	15 S 26.1	19 N 27.3
4	8 52 47.6	16 34.3	0 24.2	5 S 52.3	21 59.4	4 10.8	16 44.4	4 56.4	14 34.4	8 56.5	15 26.4	19 29.7
7	9 4 37.3	15 40.2	0 24.2	17 40.3	21 44.3	2 37.1	16 .3	5 9.1	14 27.3	8 59.2	15 26.6	19 32.0
10	9 16 27.0	14 43.7	0 24.2	22 58.9	21 18.3	1 2.8	15 14.7	5 22.1	14 20.2	9 2.0	15 26.7	19 34.4
13	9 28 16.6	13 45.0	0 24.2	18 43.3	20 41.0	0 N 31.7	14 27.7	5 35.5	14 13.0	9 4.8	15 26.7	19 36.7
16	9 40 6.3	12 44.2	0 24.2	5 45.9	19 52.1	2 6.2	13 39.4	5 49.1	14 5.8	9 7.7	15 26.6	19 39.1
19	9 51 55.9	11 41.6	0 24.2	10 N 13.2	18 51.4	3 40.4	12 49.9	6 3.0	13 58.6	9 10.6	15 26.5	19 41.3
22	10 3 45.6	10 37.3	0 24.3	21 31.1	17 38.9	5 13.8	11 59.2	6 17.2	13 51.4	9 13.5	15 26.3	19 43.6
25	10 15 35.3	9 31.5	0 24.3	21 23.3	16 14.4	6 46.3	11 7.6	6 31.6	13 44.3	9 16.5	15 26.0	19 45.8
28	10 27 24.9	8 24.5	0 24.3	10 25.6	14 37.9	8 17.4	10 15.0	6 46.1	13 37.1	9 19.5	15 25.6	19 48.0

MARCH 1964

DAY	EPHEM. SID. TIME	☉	☊	☽	☿	♀	♂	♃	♄	♅	♆	♇
		LONGITUDE										
	h m s	° ′	° ′	° ′	° ′	° ′	° ′	° ′	° ′	° ′	° ′	° ′
1	10 35 18.0	10♓26.5	8♋10.7	10♎16.6	0♓ 5.8	22♈31.0	7♓39.6	20♈18.9	27♒21.9	7♍54.8	17♏48.0	12♍59.6
2	10 39 14.6	11 26.7	8 7.5	22 50.6	1 50.1	23 40.3	8 26.9	20 31.7	27 29.0	7 R 52.2	17 R 47.6	12 R 58.1
3	10 43 11.1	12 26.8	8 4.3	5♏ 8.4	3 35.5	24 49.4	9 14.2	20 44.5	27 36.1	7 49.5	17 47.1	12 56.5
4	10 47 7.7	13 27.0	8 1.1	17 12.6	5 22.0	25 58.4	10 1.5	20 57.4	27 43.2	7 46.9	17 46.7	12 54.9
5	10 51 4.2	14 27.1	7 58.0	29 7.0	7 9.5	27 7.2	10 48.8	21 10.4	27 50.2	7 44.3	17 46.2	12 53.3
6	10 55 .8	15 27.1	7 54.8	10♐56.4	8 58.1	28 15.8	11 36.1	21 23.4	27 57.3	7 41.7	17 45.6	12 51.7
7	10 58 57.4	16 27.2	7 51.6	22 46.0	10 47.8	29 24.3	12 23.4	21 36.5	28 4.3	7 39.1	17 45.1	12 50.2
8	11 2 53.9	17 27.2	7 48.4	4♑41.2	12 38.6	0♉32.6	13 10.7	21 49.6	28 11.3	7 36.5	17 44.5	12 48.6
9	11 6 50.5	18 27.2	7 45.3	16 47.5	14 30.5	1 40.8	13 57.9	22 2.8	28 18.3	7 33.9	17 43.9	12 47.0
10	11 10 47.0	19 27.2	7 42.1	29 9.8	16 23.5	2 48.7	14 45.2	22 16.1	28 25.2	7 31.4	17 43.2	12 45.4
11	11 14 43.6	20 27.1	7 38.9	11♒51.9	18 17.5	3 56.5	15 32.4	22 29.4	28 32.1	7 28.8	17 42.5	12 43.9
12	11 18 40.1	21 27.0	7 35.7	24 56.5	20 12.6	5 4.1	16 19.6	22 42.8	28 39.0	7 26.3	17 41.8	12 42.3
13	11 22 36.7	22 26.9	7 32.5	8♓24.3	22 8.7	6 11.6	17 6.8	22 56.2	28 45.9	7 23.8	17 41.1	12 40.8
14	11 26 33.2	23 26.8	7 29.4	22 13.7	24 5.6	7 18.8	17 54.0	23 9.7	28 52.8	7 21.3	17 40.4	12 39.3
15	11 30 29.8	24 26.6	7 26.2	6♈20.9	26 3.5	8 25.8	18 41.1	23 23.3	28 59.6	7 18.8	17 39.6	12 37.7
16	11 34 26.3	25 26.4	7 23.0	20 40.7	28 2.1	9 32.6	19 28.2	23 36.8	29 6.3	7 16.3	17 38.7	12 36.2
17	11 38 22.9	26 26.1	7 19.8	5♉ 6.7	0♈ 1.3	10 39.1	20 15.3	23 50.4	29 13.1	7 13.9	17 37.9	12 34.6
18	11 42 19.4	27 25.8	7 16.7	19 33.1	2 1.1	11 45.5	21 2.4	24 4.1	29 19.8	7 11.5	17 37.0	12 33.1
19	11 46 16.0	28 25.5	7 13.5	3♊54.9	4 1.2	12 51.6	21 49.4	24 17.8	29 26.4	7 9.1	17 36.1	12 31.6
20	11 50 12.5	29 25.1	7 10.3	18 8.7	6 1.4	13 57.5	22 36.5	24 31.6	29 33.1	7 6.7	17 35.1	12 30.1
21	11 54 9.1	0♈24.7	7 7.1	2♋13.0	8 1.6	15 3.2	23 23.5	24 45.4	29 39.7	7 4.3	17 34.2	12 28.6
22	11 58 5.6	1 24.3	7 3.9	16 7.1	10 1.5	16 8.5	24 10.4	24 59.2	29 46.2	7 2.0	17 33.2	12 27.1
23	12 2 2.2	2 23.8	7 .8	29 51.3	12 .7	17 13.7	24 57.4	25 13.1	29 52.7	6 59.7	17 32.1	12 25.7
24	12 5 58.7	3 23.3	6 57.6	13♌25.6	13 59.0	18 18.6	25 44.3	25 27.0	29 59.2	6 57.4	17 31.1	12 24.2
25	12 9 55.3	4 22.7	6 54.4	26 50.2	15 55.9	19 23.2	26 31.1	25 40.9	0♓ 5.6	6 55.1	17 30.0	12 22.8
26	12 13 51.9	5 22.1	6 51.2	10♍ 4.4	17 51.2	20 27.5	27 18.0	25 54.9	0 12.0	6 52.9	17 28.9	12 21.3
27	12 17 48.4	6 21.5	6 48.1	23 7.3	19 44.4	21 31.5	28 4.8	26 8.9	0 18.4	6 50.7	17 27.8	12 19.9
28	12 21 45.0	7 20.8	6 44.9	5♎57.9	21 35.1	22 35.2	28 51.6	26 22.9	0 24.7	6 48.6	17 26.7	12 18.5
29	12 25 41.5	8 20.1	6 41.7	18 35.3	23 22.8	23 38.7	29 38.4	26 37.0	0 30.9	6 46.4	17 25.5	12 17.1
30	12 29 38.1	9 19.3	6 38.5	0♏59.4	25 7.3	24 41.8	0♈25.1	26 51.1	0 37.1	6 44.3	17 24.3	12 15.7
31	12 33 34.6	10 18.6	6 35.3	13 10.9	26 48.0	25 44.6	1 11.8	27 5.2	0 43.3	6 42.3	17 23.1	12 14.4
		LATITUDE										
1	10 35 18.0	0 .0	0 .0	5N 3.8	2S 8.9	0N33.8	1S 2.1	1S 5.2	1S13.4	0N48.7	1N47.4	14N17.0
4	10 47 7.7	0 .0	0 .0	3 58.8	2 6.9	0 46.6	1 1.4	1 4.8	1 13.7	0 48.7	1 47.6	14 17.2
7	10 58 57.4	0 .0	0 .0	1 23.8	2 .6	0 59.5	1 .7	1 4.4	1 14.0	0 48.7	1 47.8	14 17.4
10	11 10 47.0	0 .0	0 .0	1S46.7	1 49.9	1 12.6	0 60.0	1 4.0	1 14.3	0 48.7	1 47.9	14 17.5
13	11 22 36.7	0 .0	0 .0	4 21.6	1 34.3	1 25.9	0 59.2	1 3.6	1 14.6	0 48.7	1 48.1	14 17.5
16	11 34 26.3	0 .0	0 .0	4 53.5	1 13.9	1 39.1	0 58.3	1 3.2	1 15.0	0 48.6	1 48.2	14 17.4
19	11 46 16.0	0 .0	0 .0	2 46.9	0 48.5	1 52.3	0 57.4	1 2.9	1 15.3	0 48.6	1 48.4	14 17.3
22	11 58 5.6	0 .0	0 .0	0N46.3	0 18.5	2 5.4	0 56.4	1 2.6	1 15.7	0 48.5	1 48.5	14 17.1
25	12 9 55.3	0 .0	0 .0	3 49.7	0N15.0	2 18.4	0 55.4	1 2.2	1 16.0	0 48.5	1 48.7	14 16.8
28	12 21 45.0	0 .0	0 .0	4 59.9	0 50.7	2 31.0	0 54.3	1 2.0	1 16.4	0 48.4	1 48.8	14 16.5
31	12 33 34.6	0 .0	0 .0	3 59.8	1 26.4	2 43.3	0 53.1	1 1.7	1 16.8	0 48.4	1 48.9	14 16.1
		RIGHT ASCENSION										
1	10 35 18.0	11♓56.8	8♋54.1	11♎25.8	2♓57.6	20♈36.6	9♓43.9	19♈10.4	29♒59.8	9♍53.2	15♏51.3	20♍ 5.5
2	10 39 14.6	12 53.0	8 50.7	22 57.6	4 37.5	21 40.3	10 28.4	19 22.2	0♓ 6.7	9 R 50.8	15 R 50.9	20 R 4.1
3	10 43 11.1	13 49.0	8 47.2	4♏23.4	6 17.8	22 44.0	11 12.7	19 34.2	0 13.6	9 48.3	15 50.5	20 2.6
4	10 47 7.7	14 45.0	8 43.8	15 53.8	7 58.5	23 47.7	11 57.0	19 46.2	0 20.4	9 45.8	15 50.1	20 1.1
5	10 51 4.2	15 40.8	8 40.3	27 38.1	9 39.6	24 51.4	12 41.2	19 58.2	0 27.3	9 43.4	15 49.6	19 59.7
6	10 55 .8	16 36.5	8 36.9	9♐43.0	11 21.1	25 55.2	13 25.2	20 10.3	0 34.1	9 40.9	15 49.1	19 58.2
7	10 58 57.4	17 32.1	8 33.4	22 12.3	13 3.1	26 59.0	14 9.3	20 22.5	0 40.9	9 38.5	15 48.5	19 56.7
8	11 2 53.9	18 27.6	8 30.0	5♑ 5.6	14 45.5	28 2.9	14 53.2	20 34.8	0 47.7	9 36.0	15 48.0	19 55.3
9	11 6 50.5	19 23.0	8 26.5	18 18.2	16 28.4	29 6.8	15 37.1	20 47.1	0 54.4	9 33.6	15 47.4	19 53.8
10	11 10 47.0	20 18.4	8 23.1	1♒42.4	18 11.7	0♉10.8	16 20.9	20 59.4	1 1.1	9 31.2	15 46.7	19 52.3
11	11 14 43.6	21 13.6	8 19.6	15 8.9	19 55.5	1 14.8	17 4.6	21 11.9	1 7.8	9 28.8	15 46.1	19 50.8
12	11 18 40.1	22 8.8	8 16.2	28 30.2	21 39.7	2 18.9	17 48.3	21 24.4	1 14.5	9 26.4	15 45.4	19 49.4
13	11 22 36.7	23 3.9	8 12.7	11♓42.6	23 24.5	3 23.0	18 31.9	21 36.9	1 21.2	9 24.1	15 44.7	19 48.0
14	11 26 33.2	23 59.0	8 9.3	24 47.0	25 9.7	4 27.2	19 15.5	21 49.5	1 27.8	9 21.7	15 43.9	19 46.5
15	11 30 29.8	24 54.0	8 5.8	7♈48.7	26 55.2	5 31.5	19 58.9	22 2.2	1 34.4	9 19.3	15 43.1	19 45.0
16	11 34 26.3	25 48.9	8 2.4	20 56.4	28 41.2	6 35.8	20 42.3	22 14.9	1 40.9	9 17.0	15 42.3	19 43.6
17	11 38 22.9	26 43.7	7 58.9	4♉20.0	0♈27.4	7 40.1	21 25.7	22 27.6	1 47.4	9 14.7	15 41.5	19 42.1
18	11 42 19.4	27 38.5	7 55.5	18 8.6	2 13.9	8 44.5	22 8.9	22 40.4	1 53.9	9 12.4	15 40.6	19 40.6
19	11 46 16.0	28 33.3	7 52.0	2♊27.7	4 .6	9 48.9	22 52.1	22 53.3	2 .4	9 10.1	15 39.7	19 39.2
20	11 50 12.5	29 28.0	7 48.6	17 16.3	5 47.2	10 53.4	23 35.3	23 6.2	2 6.8	9 7.9	15 38.8	19 37.7
21	11 54 9.1	0♈22.7	7 45.1	2♋24.4	7 33.8	11 57.9	24 18.4	23 19.1	2 13.1	9 5.7	15 37.9	19 36.3
22	11 58 5.6	1 17.3	7 41.6	17 35.1	9 20.0	13 2.4	25 1.5	23 32.1	2 19.5	9 3.5	15 36.9	19 34.9
23	12 2 2.2	2 11.9	7 38.2	2♌28.2	11 5.7	14 7.0	25 44.5	23 45.1	2 25.7	9 1.3	15 35.9	19 33.4
24	12 5 58.7	3 6.5	7 34.7	16 47.7	12 50.7	15 11.5	26 27.4	23 58.2	2 32.0	8 59.1	15 34.9	19 32.0
25	12 9 55.3	4 1.1	7 31.3	0♍24.9	14 34.7	16 16.1	27 10.4	24 11.3	2 38.2	8 57.0	15 33.8	19 30.6
26	12 13 51.9	4 55.6	7 27.8	13 19.5	16 17.4	17 20.6	27 53.2	24 24.4	2 44.4	8 54.9	15 32.7	19 29.2
27	12 17 48.4	5 50.2	7 24.4	25 37.2	17 58.5	18 25.2	28 36.0	24 37.6	2 50.5	8 52.8	15 31.6	19 27.8
28	12 21 45.0	6 44.7	7 20.9	7♎27.2	19 37.7	19 29.7	29 18.8	24 50.8	2 56.6	8 50.8	15 30.5	19 26.5
29	12 25 41.5	7 39.3	7 17.5	19 .3	21 14.6	20 34.2	0♈ 1.6	25 4.1	3 2.6	8 48.8	15 29.4	19 25.1
30	12 29 38.1	8 33.9	7 14.0	0♏27.2	22 48.8	21 38.6	0 44.3	25 17.4	3 8.6	8 46.8	15 28.2	19 23.7
31	12 33 34.6	9 28.5	7 10.6	11 57.6	24 20.1	22 43.0	1 27.0	25 30.7	3 14.5	8 44.8	15 27.0	19 22.4
		DECLINATION										
1	10 35 18.0	7S39.2	0N24.3	0N35.3	13S27.0	9N17.2	9S39.5	6N55.9	13S32.3	9N21.4	15S25.3	19N49.4
4	10 47 7.7	6 30.4	0 24.3	13S 9.3	11 30.7	10 45.4	8 45.5	7 10.8	13 25.2	9 24.4	15 24.7	19 51.4
7	10 58 57.4	5 20.8	0 24.3	21 51.1	9 22.7	12 11.5	7 50.9	7 25.8	13 18.2	9 27.3	15 24.1	19 53.4
10	11 10 47.0	4 10.6	0 24.3	22 4.1	7 3.5	13 35.2	6 55.7	7 40.9	13 11.2	9 30.1	15 23.5	19 55.4
13	11 22 36.7	2 59.8	0 24.3	12 27.6	4 33.7	14 56.3	5 59.9	7 56.1	13 4.3	9 32.9	15 22.7	19 57.2
16	11 34 26.3	1 48.8	0 24.3	3N32.4	1 54.7	16 14.3	5 3.8	8 11.4	12 57.5	9 35.7	15 21.9	19 58.9
19	11 46 16.0	0 37.6	0 24.3	18 12.1	0N51.4	17 29.1	4 7.3	8 26.8	12 50.7	9 38.3	15 21.1	20 .6
22	11 58 5.6	0N33.5	0 24.4	23 14.2	3 41.2	18 40.3	3 10.7	8 42.2	12 44.1	9 40.9	15 20.1	20 2.2
25	12 9 55.3	1 44.4	0 24.4	16 9.9	6 30.1	19 47.8	2 13.8	8 57.7	12 37.6	9 43.4	15 19.1	20 3.6
28	12 21 45.0	2 55.0	0 24.4	2 13.2	9 12.0	20 51.3	1 17.0	9 13.2	12 31.3	9 45.8	15 18.1	20 5.0
31	12 33 34.6	4 5.0	0 24.4	11S59.1	11 40.6	21 50.5	0 20.2	9 28.6	12 25.0	9 48.1	15 17.0	20 6.2

APRIL 1964

LONGITUDE

DAY	EPHEM. SID. TIME	☉	☊	☽	☿	♀	♂	♃	♄	♅	♆	♇
	h m s	° ′	° ′	° ′	° ′	° ′	° ′	° ′	° ′	° ′	° ′	° ′
1	12 37 31.2	11♈17.8	6♋32.2	25♏11.6	28♈24.7	26♉47.0	1♈58.5	27♈19.3	0♓49.4	6♍40.2	17♏21.9	12♍13.0
2	12 41 27.7	12 16.9	6 29.0	7♐ 4.2	29 56.9	27 49.2	2 45.1	27 33.5	0 55.4	6 R38.3	17 R20.7	12 R11.7
3	12 45 24.3	13 16.1	6 25.8	18 52.5	1♉24.3	28 51.0	3 31.7	27 47.7	1 1.5	6 36.3	17 19.4	12 10.4
4	12 49 20.8	14 15.2	6 22.6	0♑41.2	2 46.6	29 52.5	4 18.3	28 1.9	1 7.5	6 34.4	17 18.1	12 9.1
5	12 53 17.4	15 14.3	6 19.5	12 35.3	4 3.5	0♊53.5	5 4.9	28 16.2	1 13.4	6 32.5	17 16.8	12 7.9
6	12 57 13.9	16 13.4	6 16.3	24 40.5	5 14.9	1 54.2	5 51.4	28 30.4	1 19.2	6 30.7	17 15.5	12 6.6
7	13 1 10.5	17 12.4	6 13.1	7♒ 2.2	6 20.4	2 54.5	6 37.8	28 44.7	1 25.0	6 28.9	17 14.1	12 5.4
8	13 5 7.0	18 11.4	6 9.9	19 45.2	7 20.0	3 54.5	7 24.3	28 59.0	1 30.8	6 27.1	17 12.8	12 4.1
9	13 9 3.6	19 10.3	6 6.7	2♓53.3	8 13.4	4 54.0	8 10.7	29 13.3	1 36.4	6 25.4	17 11.4	12 2.9
10	13 13 .1	20 9.3	6 3.6	16 28.5	9 .5	5 53.1	8 57.1	29 27.6	1 42.1	6 23.7	17 10.0	12 1.8
11	13 16 56.7	21 8.2	6 .4	0♈30.3	9 41.3	6 51.7	9 43.4	29 42.0	1 47.6	6 22.1	17 8.6	12 .6
12	13 20 53.3	22 7.0	5 57.2	14 55.1	10 15.7	7 49.9	10 29.7	29 56.3	1 53.1	6 20.5	17 7.1	11 59.5
13	13 24 49.8	23 5.9	5 54.0	29 37.0	10 43.6	8 47.7	11 15.9	0♉10.7	1 58.6	6 18.9	17 5.7	11 58.3
14	13 28 46.4	24 4.7	5 50.9	14♉27.8	11 5.0	9 44.9	12 2.2	0 25.1	2 4.0	6 17.4	17 4.2	11 57.3
15	13 32 42.9	25 3.4	5 47.7	29 19.0	11 20.1	10 41.7	12 48.3	0 39.5	2 9.3	6 15.9	17 2.7	11 56.2
16	13 36 39.5	26 2.2	5 44.5	14♊ 2.9	11 28.8	11 37.9	13 34.5	0 53.9	2 14.5	6 14.5	17 1.3	11 55.1
17	13 40 36.0	27 .9	5 41.3	28 33.8	11 31.2	12 33.7	14 20.5	1 8.2	2 19.7	6 13.1	16 59.7	11 54.1
18	13 44 32.6	27 59.5	5 38.1	12♋48.1	11 R27.7	13 28.8	15 6.6	1 22.6	2 24.8	6 11.8	16 58.2	11 53.1
19	13 48 29.1	28 58.1	5 35.0	26 44.8	11 18.4	14 23.4	15 52.6	1 37.0	2 29.9	6 10.5	16 56.7	11 52.1
20	13 52 25.7	29 56.7	5 31.8	10♌24.0	11 3.6	15 17.4	16 38.5	1 51.4	2 34.9	6 9.3	16 55.2	11 51.2
21	13 56 22.2	0♉55.3	5 28.6	23 47.1	10 43.7	16 10.7	17 24.5	2 5.9	2 39.8	6 8.1	16 53.6	11 50.3
22	14 0 18.8	1 53.8	5 25.4	6♍55.4	10 19.1	17 3.4	18 10.3	2 20.3	2 44.7	6 7.0	16 52.1	11 49.4
23	14 4 15.3	2 52.2	5 22.3	19 50.5	9 50.5	17 55.5	18 56.2	2 34.7	2 49.4	6 5.9	16 50.5	11 48.5
24	14 8 11.9	3 50.7	5 19.1	2♎33.5	9 18.3	18 46.9	19 42.0	2 49.1	2 54.2	6 4.9	16 49.0	11 47.7
25	14 12 8.4	4 49.1	5 15.9	15 5.2	8 43.2	19 37.5	20 27.7	3 3.5	2 58.8	6 3.9	16 47.4	11 46.9
26	14 16 5.0	5 47.5	5 12.7	27 26.3	8 5.8	20 27.4	21 13.4	3 17.9	3 3.4	6 2.9	16 45.8	11 46.1
27	14 20 1.6	6 45.8	5 9.5	9♏37.5	7 26.9	21 16.6	21 59.0	3 32.3	3 7.9	6 2.1	16 44.2	11 45.3
28	14 23 58.1	7 44.2	5 6.4	21 39.7	6 47.2	22 4.9	22 44.6	3 46.6	3 12.3	6 1.2	16 42.6	11 44.5
29	14 27 54.7	8 42.4	5 3.2	3♐34.6	6 7.4	22 52.4	23 30.2	4 1.0	3 16.6	6 .4	16 41.0	11 43.8
30	14 31 51.2	9 40.7	5 .0	15 24.2	5 28.3	23 39.1	24 15.7	4 15.4	3 20.9	5 59.7	16 39.3	11 43.1

LATITUDE

DAY	EPHEM. SID. TIME	☉	☊	☽	☿	♀	♂	♃	♄	♅	♆	♇
1	12 37 31.2	0 .0	0 .0	3N16.6	1N37.8	2N47.3	0S52.7	1S 1.6	1S17.0	0N48.3	1N48.9	14N15.9
4	12 49 20.8	0 .0	0 .0	0 26.3	2 9.7	2 59.0	0 51.5	1 1.4	1 17.4	0 48.3	1 49.0	14 15.4
7	13 1 10.5	0 .0	0 .0	2S38.3	2 35.9	3 10.2	0 50.2	1 1.1	1 17.9	0 48.2	1 49.1	14 14.9
10	13 13 .1	0 .0	0 .0	4 45.8	2 54.3	3 20.7	0 48.9	1 .9	1 18.3	0 48.1	1 49.2	14 14.3
13	13 24 49.8	0 .0	0 .0	4 34.3	3 3.0	3 30.4	0 47.6	1 .7	1 18.8	0 48.0	1 49.3	14 13.6
16	13 36 39.5	0 .0	0 .0	1 46.2	3 .3	3 39.3	0 46.2	1 .6	1 19.3	0 47.9	1 49.4	14 12.9
19	13 48 29.1	0 .0	0 .0	1N56.0	2 45.2	3 47.2	0 44.7	1 .4	1 19.8	0 47.8	1 49.5	14 12.1
22	14 0 18.8	0 .0	0 .0	4 30.4	2 17.6	3 54.1	0 43.2	1 .3	1 20.3	0 47.7	1 49.5	14 11.3
25	14 12 8.4	0 .0	0 .0	4 58.3	1 38.7	3 59.7	0 41.7	1 .2	1 20.8	0 47.6	1 49.6	14 10.5
28	14 23 58.1	0 .0	0 .0	3 23.7	0 51.5	4 3.9	0 40.1	1 .1	1 21.4	0 47.5	1 49.6	14 9.6

RIGHT ASCENSION

DAY	EPHEM. SID. TIME	☉	☊	☽	☿	♀	♂	♃	♄	♅	♆	♇
1	12 37 31.2	10♈23.1	7♋ 7.1	23♏39.9	25♈48.0	23♉47.3	2♈ 9.6	25♈44.1	3♓20.4	8♍42.9	15♏25.8	19♍21.1
2	12 41 27.7	11 17.7	7 3.6	5♐40.3	27 12.2	24 51.6	2 52.3	25 57.4	3 26.3	8 R41.0	15 R24.6	19 R19.7
3	12 45 24.3	12 12.5	7 .2	18 2.0	28 32.5	25 55.8	3 34.9	26 10.9	3 32.1	8 39.2	15 23.4	19 18.5
4	12 49 20.8	13 7.2	6 56.7	0♑44.7	29 48.4	26 59.9	4 17.5	26 24.3	3 37.9	8 37.4	15 22.1	19 17.2
5	12 53 17.4	14 1.9	6 53.3	13 44.6	0♉59.7	28 3.8	5 .1	26 37.8	3 43.6	8 35.6	15 20.8	19 15.9
6	12 57 13.9	14 56.8	6 49.8	26 55.2	2 6.2	29 7.6	5 42.6	26 51.3	3 49.2	8 33.9	15 19.5	19 14.6
7	13 1 10.5	15 51.6	6 46.4	10♒ 9.0	3 7.5	0♊11.2	6 25.1	27 4.9	3 54.8	8 32.1	15 18.1	19 13.4
8	13 5 7.0	16 46.6	6 42.9	23 19.9	4 3.5	1 14.7	7 7.7	27 18.4	4 .4	8 30.5	15 16.8	19 12.1
9	13 9 3.6	17 41.5	6 39.5	6♓25.1	4 54.0	2 17.9	7 50.2	27 32.0	4 5.8	8 28.8	15 15.4	19 10.9
10	13 13 .1	18 36.6	6 36.0	19 25.9	5 38.8	3 21.0	8 32.6	27 45.6	4 11.3	8 27.2	15 14.0	19 9.7
11	13 16 56.7	19 31.7	6 32.5	2♈27.7	6 17.9	4 23.8	9 15.1	27 59.2	4 16.6	8 25.7	15 12.6	19 8.5
12	13 20 53.3	20 26.9	6 29.1	15 39.0	6 51.0	5 26.3	9 57.6	28 12.8	4 22.0	8 24.1	15 11.2	19 7.4
13	13 24 49.8	21 22.2	6 25.6	29 10.0	7 18.2	6 28.6	10 40.1	28 26.5	4 27.2	8 22.7	15 9.8	19 6.2
14	13 28 46.4	22 17.5	6 22.2	13♉10.4	7 39.4	7 30.5	11 22.5	28 40.2	4 32.4	8 21.2	15 8.3	19 5.1
15	13 32 42.9	23 13.0	6 18.7	27 46.0	7 54.7	8 32.1	12 5.0	28 53.9	4 37.5	8 19.8	15 6.9	19 4.0
16	13 36 39.5	24 8.5	6 15.3	12♊55.2	8 4.1	9 33.3	12 47.4	29 7.6	4 42.6	8 18.5	15 5.4	19 2.9
17	13 40 36.0	25 4.1	6 11.8	28 26.4	8 7.8	10 34.1	13 29.9	29 21.3	4 47.6	8 17.2	15 3.9	19 1.8
18	13 44 32.6	25 59.8	6 8.3	13♋59.3	8 R 5.9	11 34.5	14 12.3	29 35.1	4 52.6	8 15.9	15 2.4	19 .7
19	13 48 29.1	26 55.6	6 4.9	29 10.9	7 58.7	12 34.4	14 54.8	29 48.8	4 57.4	8 14.7	15 .9	18 59.7
20	13 52 25.7	27 51.4	6 1.4	13♌42.8	7 46.6	13 33.8	15 37.2	0♉ 2.6	5 2.2	8 13.5	14 59.4	18 58.7
21	13 56 22.2	28 47.4	5 58.0	27 26.3	7 29.9	14 32.6	16 19.7	0 16.3	5 7.0	8 12.4	14 57.8	18 57.7
22	14 0 18.8	29 43.5	5 54.5	10♍21.8	7 9.0	15 30.9	17 2.1	0 30.1	5 11.7	8 11.3	14 56.3	18 56.7
23	14 4 15.3	0♉39.7	5 51.1	22 36.7	6 44.6	16 28.6	17 44.6	0 43.9	5 16.3	8 10.2	14 54.7	18 55.8
24	14 8 11.9	1 36.1	5 47.6	4♎21.8	6 17.1	17 25.6	18 27.2	0 57.7	5 20.9	8 9.3	14 53.2	18 54.9
25	14 12 8.4	2 32.5	5 44.1	15 48.6	5 47.2	18 22.0	19 9.7	1 11.5	5 25.4	8 8.3	14 51.6	18 54.0
26	14 16 5.0	3 29.0	5 40.7	27 8.8	5 15.6	19 17.6	19 52.2	1 25.3	5 29.8	8 7.4	14 50.1	18 53.1
27	14 20 1.6	4 25.7	5 37.2	8♏32.8	4 42.8	20 12.4	20 34.7	1 39.1	5 34.1	8 6.6	14 48.5	18 52.3
28	14 23 58.1	5 22.5	5 33.8	20 9.1	4 9.6	21 6.4	21 17.3	1 52.9	5 38.4	8 5.8	14 46.9	18 51.4
29	14 27 54.7	6 19.4	5 30.3	2♐ 3.9	3 36.6	21 59.6	21 59.8	2 6.7	5 42.6	8 5.0	14 45.3	18 50.6
30	14 31 51.2	7 16.5	5 26.8	14 20.2	3 4.5	22 51.8	22 42.4	2 20.6	5 46.7	8 4.3	14 43.7	18 49.8

DECLINATION

DAY	EPHEM. SID. TIME	☉	☊	☽	☿	♀	♂	♃	♄	♅	♆	♇
1	12 37 31.2	4N28.2	0N24.4	15S53.0	12N26.1	22N 9.2	0S 1.3	9N33.8	12S23.0	9N48.8	15S16.6	20N 6.6
4	12 49 20.8	5 37.3	0 24.4	23 .2	14 28.1	23 2.5	0N55.4	9 49.3	12 17.0	9 50.9	15 15.4	20 7.7
7	13 1 10.5	6 45.5	0 24.4	21 4.1	16 5.3	23 51.2	1 51.8	10 4.7	12 11.1	9 52.9	15 14.2	20 8.7
10	13 13 .1	7 52.7	0 24.4	9 43.5	17 15.2	24 35.0	2 48.0	10 20.0	12 5.4	9 54.7	15 13.0	20 9.5
13	13 24 49.8	8 58.7	0 24.4	7N 3.4	17 56.4	25 14.1	3 43.7	10 35.3	11 60.0	9 56.4	15 11.7	20 10.2
16	13 36 39.5	10 3.4	0 24.4	20 43.9	18 8.1	25 48.3	4 38.9	10 50.5	11 54.7	9 57.9	15 10.4	20 10.8
19	13 48 29.1	11 6.6	0 24.4	22 42.4	17 50.5	26 17.5	5 33.6	11 5.6	11 49.6	9 59.3	15 9.0	20 11.3
22	14 0 18.8	12 8.1	0 24.4	13 9.2	17 5.6	26 41.8	6 27.7	11 20.6	11 44.8	10 .5	15 7.7	20 11.7
25	14 12 8.4	13 7.8	0 24.4	1S21.3	15 58.1	27 1.2	7 21.1	11 35.5	11 40.2	10 1.5	15 6.3	20 11.9
28	14 23 58.1	14 5.6	0 24.4	14 54.2	14 35.6	27 15.9	8 13.6	11 50.2	11 35.8	10 2.4	15 4.9	20 11.9

MAY 1964

LONGITUDE

DAY	EPHEM. SID. TIME	☉	☊	☽	☿	♀	♂	♃	♄	♅	♆	♇
	h m s	° ′	° ′	° ′	° ′	° ′	° ′	° ′	° ′	° ′	° ′	° ′
1	14 35 47.8	10♉38.9	4♋56.8	27♐11.5	4♉50.5	24♊24.8	25♈ 1.1	4♉29.7	3♓25.1	5♍59.0	16♏37.7	11♍42.5
2	14 39 44.3	11 37.1	4 53.7	9♑ .1	4R14.7	25 9.7	25 46.6	4 44.0	3 29.2	5R58.4	16R36.1	11R41.8
3	14 43 40.9	12 35.3	4 50.5	20 54.3	3 41.3	25 53.6	26 31.9	4 58.4	3 33.2	5 57.8	16 34.5	11 41.2
4	14 47 37.4	13 33.5	4 47.3	2♒58.9	3 11.0	26 36.5	27 17.3	5 12.7	3 37.2	5 57.2	16 32.8	11 40.7
5	14 51 34.0	14 31.6	4 44.1	15 19.1	2 44.2	27 18.4	28 2.5	5 27.0	3 41.0	5 56.8	16 31.2	11 40.1
6	14 55 30.6	15 29.7	4 40.9	27 59.7	2 21.1	27 59.3	28 47.8	5 41.3	3 44.8	5 56.3	16 29.6	11 39.6
7	14 59 27.1	16 27.8	4 37.8	11♓ 5.1	2 2.2	28 39.0	29 32.9	5 55.5	3 48.5	5 56.0	16 27.9	11 39.1
8	15 3 23.7	17 25.8	4 34.6	24 38.2	1 47.7	29 17.6	0♉18.1	6 9.8	3 52.2	5 55.6	16 26.3	11 38.6
9	15 7 20.2	18 23.9	4 31.4	8♈40.0	1 37.7	29 55.0	1 3.2	6 24.0	3 55.7	5 55.4	16 24.7	11 38.2
10	15 11 16.8	19 21.9	4 28.2	23 8.4	1 32.2	0♋31.2	1 48.2	6 38.2	3 59.1	5 55.2	16 23.0	11 37.8
11	15 15 13.3	20 19.9	4 25.1	7♉58.5	1 31.4	1 6.2	2 33.2	6 52.4	4 2.5	5 55.0	16 21.4	11 37.4
12	15 19 9.9	21 17.8	4 21.9	23 2.4	1D35.3	1 39.8	3 18.1	7 6.6	4 5.8	5 54.9	16 19.8	11 37.1
13	15 23 6.4	22 15.8	4 18.7	8♊10.7	1 43.8	2 12.0	4 3.0	7 20.7	4 9.0	5 54.9	16 18.1	11 36.8
14	15 27 3.0	23 13.7	4 15.5	23 13.9	1 56.9	2 42.8	4 47.8	7 34.8	4 12.1	5 54.9	16 16.5	11 36.5
15	15 30 59.6	24 11.6	4 12.3	8♋ 3.7	2 14.5	3 12.1	5 32.7	7 48.9	4 15.2	5D55.0	16 14.9	11 36.3
16	15 34 56.1	25 9.4	4 9.2	22 34.3	2 36.4	3 39.9	6 17.4	8 3.0	4 18.1	5 55.1	16 13.3	11 36.1
17	15 38 52.7	26 7.3	4 6.0	6♌42.5	3 2.7	4 6.0	7 2.0	8 17.0	4 20.9	5 55.2	16 11.7	11 35.9
18	15 42 49.2	27 5.1	4 2.8	20 27.6	3 33.1	4 30.5	7 46.7	8 31.0	4 23.7	5 55.5	16 10.1	11 35.7
19	15 46 45.8	28 2.8	3 59.6	3♍50.4	4 7.6	4 53.2	8 31.2	8 45.0	4 26.3	5 55.7	16 8.5	11 35.6
20	15 50 42.3	29 .6	3 56.5	16 53.0	4 46.0	5 14.2	9 15.7	8 58.9	4 28.9	5 56.1	16 6.9	11 35.5
21	15 54 38.9	29 58.3	3 53.3	29 38.0	5 28.2	5 33.3	10 .2	9 12.8	4 31.4	5 56.4	16 5.4	11 35.4
22	15 58 35.4	0♊56.0	3 50.1	12♎ 8.2	6 14.1	5 50.4	10 44.6	9 26.7	4 33.8	5 56.9	16 3.8	11 35.4
23	16 2 32.0	1 53.6	3 46.9	24 26.1	7 3.5	6 5.6	11 28.9	9 40.5	4 36.1	5 57.4	16 2.2	11 35.4
24	16 6 28.6	2 51.3	3 43.8	6♏33.9	7 56.5	6 18.8	12 13.2	9 54.3	4 38.3	5 57.9	16 .7	11 35.4
25	16 10 25.1	3 48.9	3 40.6	18 33.9	8 52.8	6 29.9	12 57.4	10 8.0	4 40.4	5 58.5	15 59.1	11 35.4
26	16 14 21.7	4 46.5	3 37.4	0♐27.9	9 52.3	6 38.8	13 41.6	10 21.7	4 42.4	5 59.1	15 57.6	11D35.5
27	16 18 18.2	5 44.1	3 34.2	12 17.8	10 55.1	6 45.5	14 25.7	10 35.4	4 44.3	5 59.8	15 56.1	11 35.6
28	16 22 14.8	6 41.6	3 31.1	24 5.7	12 .9	6 50.0	15 9.8	10 49.0	4 46.1	6 .6	15 54.6	11 35.8
29	16 26 11.3	7 39.1	3 27.9	5♑54.1	13 9.8	6 52.2	15 53.8	11 2.6	4 47.8	6 1.4	15 53.1	11 36.0
30	16 30 7.9	8 36.7	3 24.7	17 45.5	14 21.6	6R52.0	16 37.7	11 16.1	4 49.5	6 2.2	15 51.6	11 36.2
31	16 34 4.5	9 34.2	3 21.5	29 43.4	15 36.4	6 49.5	17 21.7	11 29.6	4 51.0	6 3.2	15 50.1	11 36.4

LATITUDE

DAY	EPHEM. SID. TIME	☉	☊	☽	☿	♀	♂	♃	♄	♅	♆	♇
1	14 35 47.8	0 .0	0 .0	0N32.2	0N .1	4N 6.6	0S38.5	0S60.0	1S21.9	0N47.3	1N49.6	14N 8.6
4	14 47 37.4	0 .0	0 .0	2S33.9	0S50.7	4 7.6	0 36.8	0 59.9	1 22.5	0 47.2	1 49.6	14 7.7
7	14 59 27.1	0 .0	0 .0	4 46.6	1 37.2	4 6.8	0 35.1	0 59.8	1 23.1	0 47.1	1 49.6	14 6.7
10	15 11 16.8	0 .0	0 .0	4 50.1	2 16.7	4 3.8	0 33.4	0 59.8	1 23.7	0 47.0	1 49.6	14 5.7
13	15 23 6.4	0 .0	0 .0	2 8.7	2 47.8	3 58.5	0 31.7	0 59.8	1 24.3	0 46.9	1 49.6	14 4.6
16	15 34 56.1	0 .0	0 .0	1N46.9	3 10.2	3 50.6	0 29.9	0 59.8	1 24.9	0 46.7	1 49.6	14 3.6
19	15 46 45.8	0 .0	0 .0	4 33.9	3 24.2	3 39.8	0 28.1	0 59.8	1 25.5	0 46.6	1 49.5	14 2.5
22	15 58 35.4	0 .0	0 .0	5 7.9	3 30.2	3 25.8	0 26.2	0 59.8	1 26.1	0 46.5	1 49.5	14 1.4
25	16 10 25.1	0 .0	0 .0	3 36.5	3 29.0	3 8.4	0 24.4	0 59.9	1 26.8	0 46.4	1 49.5	14 .3
28	16 22 14.8	0 .0	0 .0	0 44.0	3 21.1	2 47.1	0 22.5	0 59.9	1 27.4	0 46.2	1 49.4	13 59.2
31	16 34 4.5	0 .0	0 .0	2S26.5	3 7.3	2 21.9	0 20.5	0 60.0	1 28.1	0 46.1	1 49.3	13 58.1

RIGHT ASCENSION

DAY	EPHEM. SID. TIME	☉	☊	☽	☿	♀	♂	♃	♄	♅	♆	♇
1	14 35 47.8	8♉13.7	5♋23.4	26♐57.1	2♉33.8	23♊43.2	23♈25.1	2♉34.4	5♓50.7	8♍ 3.6	14♏42.1	18♍49.1
2	14 39 44.3	9 11.0	5 19.9	9♑50.1	2R 5.1	24 33.5	24 7.7	2 48.2	5 54.7	8R 3.0	14R40.5	18R48.3
3	14 43 40.9	10 8.5	5 16.5	22 51.9	1 38.8	25 22.9	24 50.4	3 2.0	5 58.6	8 2.5	14 38.8	18 47.6
4	14 47 37.4	11 6.1	5 13.0	5♒54.5	1 15.5	26 11.1	25 33.1	3 15.8	6 2.4	8 1.9	14 37.2	18 46.9
5	14 51 34.0	12 3.8	5 9.6	18 51.8	0 55.3	26 58.2	26 15.8	3 29.6	6 6.2	8 1.5	14 35.6	18 46.3
6	14 55 30.6	13 1.7	5 6.1	1♓41.0	0 38.7	27 44.2	26 58.6	3 43.4	6 9.9	8 1.1	14 34.0	18 45.6
7	14 59 27.1	13 59.7	5 2.6	14 23.9	0 25.8	28 28.9	27 41.4	3 57.1	6 13.5	8 .7	14 32.4	18 45.0
8	15 3 23.7	14 57.9	4 59.2	27 6.5	0 16.8	29 12.3	28 24.2	4 10.9	6 17.0	8 .4	14 30.7	18 44.4
9	15 7 20.2	15 56.2	4 55.7	9♈58.7	0 11.8	29 54.4	29 7.1	4 24.7	6 20.4	8 .1	14 29.1	18 43.9
10	15 11 16.8	16 54.7	4 52.3	23 12.2	0 10.9	0♋35.1	29 50.0	4 38.4	6 23.8	7 59.9	14 27.5	18 43.4
11	15 15 13.3	17 53.3	4 48.8	6♉59.6	0D14.1	1 14.4	0♉32.9	4 52.2	6 27.0	7 59.7	14 25.9	18 42.9
12	15 19 9.9	18 52.1	4 45.3	21 30.3	0 21.4	1 52.1	1 15.9	5 5.9	6 30.2	7 59.6	14 24.3	18 42.4
13	15 23 6.4	19 51.0	4 41.9	6♊47.1	0 32.8	2 28.3	1 58.9	5 19.6	6 33.3	7 59.5	14 22.6	18 41.9
14	15 27 3.0	20 50.1	4 38.4	22 40.5	0 48.2	3 2.8	2 41.9	5 33.3	6 36.3	7 59.5	14 21.0	18 41.5
15	15 30 59.6	21 49.3	4 35.0	8♋48.6	1 7.5	3 35.7	3 25.1	5 47.1	6 39.3	7D59.6	14 19.5	18 41.2
16	15 34 56.1	22 48.6	4 31.5	24 41.6	1 30.7	4 6.8	4 8.2	6 .7	6 42.2	7 59.7	14 17.9	18 40.8
17	15 38 52.7	23 48.1	4 28.0	9♌53.3	1 57.6	4 36.0	4 51.3	6 14.4	6 45.0	7 59.8	14 16.3	18 40.5
18	15 42 49.2	24 47.7	4 24.6	24 9.0	2 28.1	5 3.3	5 34.5	6 28.0	6 47.6	8 .0	14 14.7	18 40.2
19	15 46 45.8	25 47.4	4 21.1	7♍26.9	3 2.3	5 28.6	6 17.7	6 41.6	6 50.2	8 .3	14 13.1	18 39.9
20	15 50 42.3	26 47.3	4 17.7	19 54.6	3 39.9	5 51.8	7 1.0	6 55.2	6 52.8	8 .6	14 11.5	18 39.7
21	15 54 38.9	27 47.3	4 14.2	1♎44.2	4 21.0	6 12.9	7 44.3	7 8.7	6 55.2	8 .9	14 10.0	18 39.4
22	15 58 35.4	28 47.4	4 10.7	13 9.7	5 5.3	6 31.9	8 27.7	7 22.3	6 57.5	8 1.3	14 8.4	18 39.2
23	16 2 32.0	29 47.7	4 7.3	24 24.4	5 52.9	6 48.6	9 11.1	7 35.8	6 59.8	8 1.7	14 6.8	18 39.1
24	16 6 28.6	0♊48.1	4 3.8	5♏40.4	6 43.7	7 2.9	9 54.5	7 49.2	7 1.9	8 2.2	14 5.3	18 38.9
25	16 10 25.1	1 48.6	4 .4	17 7.8	7 37.6	7 14.9	10 38.0	8 2.7	7 4.0	8 2.8	14 3.8	18 38.8
26	16 14 21.7	2 49.2	3 56.9	28 54.3	8 34.6	7 24.5	11 21.5	8 16.1	7 6.0	8 3.4	14 2.2	18 38.8
27	16 18 18.2	3 49.9	3 53.4	11♐ 3.8	9 34.6	7 31.5	12 5.1	8 29.5	7 7.9	8 4.0	14 .7	18 38.7
28	16 22 14.8	4 50.8	3 50.0	23 36.2	10 37.6	7 36.1	12 48.7	8 42.9	7 9.7	8 4.7	13 59.2	18 38.7
29	16 26 11.3	5 51.8	3 46.5	6♑26.7	11 43.5	7 38.0	13 32.3	8 56.2	7 11.4	8 5.5	13 57.7	18 38.7
30	16 30 7.9	6 52.9	3 43.1	19 26.8	12 52.4	7R37.3	14 16.0	9 9.5	7 13.0	8 6.2	13 56.3	18 38.7
31	16 34 4.5	7 54.1	3 39.6	2♒27.0	14 4.3	7 34.0	14 59.8	9 22.7	7 14.6	8 7.1	13 54.8	18D38.8

DECLINATION

DAY	EPHEM. SID. TIME	☉	☊	☽	☿	♀	♂	♃	♄	♅	♆	♇
1	14 35 47.8	15N 1.2	0N24.5	22S52.7	13N 8.4	27N26.0	9N 5.4	12N 4.8	11S31.7	10N 3.1	15S 3.5	20N11.9
4	14 47 37.4	15 54.7	0 24.5	21 59.4	11 46.9	27 31.6	9 56.2	12 19.2	11 27.8	10 3.7	15 2.1	20 11.7
7	14 59 27.1	16 45.7	0 24.5	11 49.5	10 39.7	27 33.0	10 46.0	12 33.5	11 24.2	10 4.0	15 .7	20 11.4
10	15 11 16.8	17 34.3	0 24.5	4N30.0	9 52.3	27 30.3	11 34.8	12 47.5	11 20.9	10 4.2	14 59.3	20 11.0
13	15 23 6.4	18 20.3	0 24.5	19 33.4	9 27.1	27 23.9	12 22.5	13 1.4	11 17.9	10 4.2	14 58.0	20 10.5
16	15 34 56.1	19 3.5	0 24.5	23 18.6	9 24.0	27 14.0	13 9.0	13 15.1	11 15.1	10 4.0	14 56.6	20 9.8
19	15 46 45.8	19 43.7	0 24.5	14 21.1	9 41.5	27 .8	13 54.2	13 28.5	11 12.7	10 3.6	14 55.3	20 9.0
22	15 58 35.4	20 20.9	0 24.5	0S 4.3	10 17.5	26 44.5	14 38.1	13 41.7	11 10.5	10 3.1	14 54.0	20 8.1
25	16 10 25.1	20 55.0	0 24.5	13 53.0	11 9.5	26 25.2	15 20.6	13 54.7	11 8.7	10 2.4	14 52.7	20 7.0
28	16 22 14.8	21 25.9	0 24.5	22 34.8	12 15.1	26 2.9	16 1.7	14 7.4	11 7.2	10 1.5	14 51.5	20 5.9
31	16 34 4.5	21 53.4	0 24.5	22 36.0	13 31.6	25 37.8	16 41.4	14 19.9	11 6.0	10 .4	14 50.3	20 4.6

JUNE 1964

LONGITUDE

DAY	EPHEM. SID. TIME (h m s)	☉ (° ′)	☊ (° ′)	☾ (° ′)	☿ (° ′)	♀ (° ′)	♂ (° ′)	♃ (° ′)	♄ (° ′)	♅ (° ′)	♆ (° ′)	♇ (° ′)
1	16 38 1.0	10♊31.7	3♋18.3	11♒51.3	16♉54.0	6♋44.6	18♉ 5.5	11♉43.1	4♓52.4	6♍ 4.1	15♏48.7	11♍36.7
2	16 41 57.6	11 29.1	3 15.2	24 13.2	18 14.4	6R37.3	18 49.3	11 56.5	4 53.8	6 5.1	15R47.2	11 37.0
3	16 45 54.1	12 26.6	3 12.0	6♓53.2	19 37.6	6 27.5	19 33.0	12 9.8	4 55.0	6 6.2	15 45.8	11 37.3
4	16 49 50.7	13 24.1	3 8.8	19 55.2	21 3.6	6 15.4	20 16.7	12 23.1	4 56.2	6 7.3	15 44.4	11 37.7
5	16 53 47.2	14 21.5	3 5.6	3♈22.4	22 32.3	6 1.0	21 .4	12 36.4	4 57.3	6 8.5	15 43.1	11 38.1
6	16 57 43.8	15 19.0	3 2.5	17 16.3	24 3.7	5 44.1	21 44.0	12 49.6	4 58.2	6 9.7	15 41.7	11 38.5
7	17 1 40.4	16 16.4	2 59.3	1♉36.6	25 37.8	5 25.0	22 27.5	13 2.8	4 59.1	6 11.0	15 40.3	11 39.0
8	17 5 36.9	17 13.8	2 56.1	16 20.3	27 14.5	5 3.6	23 11.0	13 15.8	4 59.8	6 12.3	15 39.0	11 39.5
9	17 9 33.5	18 11.2	2 52.9	1♊21.6	28 53.9	4 40.0	23 54.4	13 28.9	5 .5	6 13.7	15 37.7	11 40.0
10	17 13 30.0	19 8.6	2 49.8	16 32.2	0♊36.0	4 14.3	24 37.8	13 41.8	5 1.0	6 15.1	15 36.4	11 40.5
11	17 17 26.6	20 6.0	2 46.6	1♋42.8	2 20.6	3 46.7	25 21.1	13 54.8	5 1.5	6 16.6	15 35.1	11 41.1
12	17 21 23.1	21 3.3	2 43.4	16 44.0	4 7.9	3 17.3	26 4.3	14 7.6	5 1.8	6 18.1	15 33.8	11 41.7
13	17 25 19.7	22 .7	2 40.2	1♌27.8	5 57.7	2 46.1	26 47.5	14 20.4	5 2.1	6 19.7	15 32.6	11 42.3
14	17 29 16.3	22 58.0	2 37.0	15 48.8	7 50.0	2 13.4	27 30.6	14 33.1	5 2.3	6 21.3	15 31.4	11 43.0
15	17 33 12.8	23 55.3	2 33.9	29 44.2	9 44.8	1 39.3	28 13.6	14 45.8	5 2.3	6 23.0	15 30.2	11 43.7
16	17 37 9.4	24 52.6	2 30.7	13♍13.5	11 41.9	1 4.1	28 56.6	14 58.4	5 2.3	6 24.7	15 29.0	11 44.4
17	17 41 5.9	25 49.9	2 27.5	26 18.3	13 41.3	0 28.0	29 39.6	15 10.9	5R 2.1	6 26.4	15 27.8	11 45.2
18	17 45 2.5	26 47.2	2 24.3	9♎ 1.4	15 42.8	29♊51.1	0♊22.5	15 23.3	5 1.9	6 28.2	15 26.7	11 46.0
19	17 48 59.1	27 44.4	2 21.2	21 26.4	17 46.3	29 13.7	1 5.3	15 35.7	5 1.5	6 30.1	15 25.6	11 46.8
20	17 52 55.6	28 41.7	2 18.0	3♏37.1	19 51.6	28 36.1	1 48.0	15 48.0	5 1.1	6 32.0	15 24.5	11 47.6
21	17 56 52.2	29 38.9	2 14.8	15 37.2	21 58.5	27 58.4	2 30.7	16 .3	5 .6	6 33.9	15 23.4	11 48.5
22	18 0 48.7	0♋36.2	2 11.6	27 30.2	24 6.9	27 21.0	3 13.4	16 12.4	4 60.0	6 35.9	15 22.4	11 49.4
23	18 4 45.3	1 33.4	2 8.5	9♐19.2	26 16.3	26 44.1	3 55.9	16 24.5	4 59.2	6 38.0	15 21.4	11 50.3
24	18 8 41.8	2 30.6	2 5.3	21 7.1	28 26.6	26 7.9	4 38.5	16 36.5	4 58.4	6 40.0	15 20.4	11 51.3
25	18 12 38.4	3 27.8	2 2.1	2♑56.3	0♋37.5	25 32.7	5 20.9	16 48.4	4 57.5	6 42.2	15 19.4	11 52.2
26	18 16 35.0	4 25.0	1 58.9	14 49.3	2 48.8	24 58.7	6 3.4	17 .3	4 56.5	6 44.4	15 18.5	11 53.3
27	18 20 31.5	5 22.2	1 55.8	26 48.0	5 .0	24 26.0	6 45.7	17 12.1	4 55.4	6 46.6	15 17.6	11 54.3
28	18 24 28.1	6 19.4	1 52.6	8♒54.8	7 11.0	23 54.8	7 28.0	17 23.8	4 54.2	6 48.8	15 16.7	11 55.4
29	18 28 24.6	7 16.6	1 49.4	21 12.0	9 21.5	23 25.3	8 10.2	17 35.4	4 52.9	6 51.1	15 15.9	11 56.5
30	18 32 21.2	8 13.8	1 46.2	3♓42.0	11 31.2	22 57.8	8 52.4	17 46.9	4 51.5	6 53.5	15 15.0	11 57.6

LATITUDE

DAY	EPHEM. SID. TIME	☉	☊	☾	☿	♀	♂	♃	♄	♅	♆	♇
1	16 38 1.0	0 .0	0 .0	3S22.1	3S 1.5	2N12.6	0S19.9	1S .0	1S28.3	0N46.1	1N49.3	13N57.7
4	16 49 50.7	0 .0	0 .0	5 9.0	2 40.7	1 42.0	0 17.9	1 .1	1 28.9	0 45.9	1 49.2	13 56.6
7	17 1 40.4	0 .0	0 .0	4 35.5	2 15.4	1 7.5	0 16.0	1 .2	1 29.6	0 45.8	1 49.1	13 55.5
10	17 13 30.0	0 .0	0 .0	1 25.0	1 46.4	0 29.5	0 14.0	1 .3	1 30.3	0 45.7	1 49.0	13 54.5
13	17 25 19.7	0 .0	0 .0	2N36.1	1 14.6	0S11.2	0 12.0	1 .5	1 30.9	0 45.6	1 48.9	13 53.4
16	17 37 9.4	0 .0	0 .0	5 .5	0 41.0	0 53.4	0 9.9	1 .6	1 31.6	0 45.5	1 48.8	13 52.3
19	17 48 59.1	0 .0	0 .0	4 59.7	0 7.3	1 35.8	0 7.9	1 .8	1 32.2	0 45.4	1 48.7	13 51.3
22	18 0 48.7	0 .0	0 .0	3 .6	0N25.0	2 16.9	0 5.8	1 1.0	1 32.9	0 45.2	1 48.5	13 50.2
25	18 12 38.4	0 .0	0 .0	0S 4.8	0 54.0	2 55.3	0 3.8	1 1.2	1 33.5	0 45.1	1 48.4	13 49.2
28	18 24 28.1	0 .0	0 .0	3 10.7	1 17.9	3 29.7	0 1.7	1 1.4	1 34.2	0 45.0	1 48.2	13 48.3

RIGHT ASCENSION

DAY	EPHEM. SID. TIME	☉	☊	☾	☿	♀	♂	♃	♄	♅	♆	♇
1	16 38 1.0	8♊55.4	3♋36.1	15♒18.9	15♉19.1	7♋28.1	15♉43.6	9♉35.9	7♓16.0	8♍ 8.0	13♏53.4	18♍38.9
2	16 41 57.6	9 56.9	3 32.7	27 58.3	16 36.9	7R19.4	16 27.4	9 49.1	7 17.4	8 8.9	13R51.9	18 39.0
3	16 45 54.1	10 58.4	3 29.2	10♓25.7	17 57.7	7 8.1	17 11.3	10 2.3	7 18.6	8 9.9	13 50.5	18 39.2
4	16 49 50.7	12 .0	3 25.8	22 46.8	19 21.5	6 54.2	17 55.2	10 15.4	7 19.8	8 10.9	13 49.1	18 39.4
5	16 53 47.2	13 1.8	3 22.3	5♈11.4	20 48.4	6 37.7	18 39.2	10 28.5	7 20.9	8 12.1	13 47.8	18 39.6
6	16 57 43.8	14 3.6	3 18.8	17 52.0	22 18.3	6 18.6	19 23.2	10 41.5	7 21.9	8 13.2	13 46.4	18 39.9
7	17 1 40.4	15 5.5	3 15.4	1♉ 3.3	23 51.4	5 57.0	20 7.3	10 54.4	7 22.8	8 14.4	13 45.0	18 40.2
8	17 5 36.9	16 7.4	3 11.9	14 59.1	25 27.7	5 33.0	20 51.4	11 7.4	7 23.6	8 15.6	13 43.7	18 40.5
9	17 9 33.5	17 9.5	3 8.5	29 48.8	27 7.1	5 6.7	21 35.5	11 20.2	7 24.3	8 16.9	13 42.4	18 40.8
10	17 13 30.0	18 11.6	3 5.0	15♊31.7	28 49.9	4 38.2	22 19.7	11 33.1	7 24.9	8 18.2	13 41.1	18 41.1
11	17 17 26.6	19 13.7	3 1.5	1♋52.0	0♊36.0	4 7.6	23 3.9	11 45.8	7 25.4	8 19.6	13 39.8	18 41.5
12	17 21 23.1	20 15.9	2 58.1	18 19.5	2 25.4	3 35.0	23 48.2	11 58.6	7 25.8	8 21.0	13 38.5	18 42.0
13	17 25 19.7	21 18.2	2 54.6	4♌19.4	4 18.2	3 .8	24 32.5	12 11.2	7 26.2	8 22.5	13 37.3	18 42.4
14	17 29 16.3	22 20.5	2 51.2	19 25.7	6 14.3	2 24.9	25 16.8	12 23.8	7 26.4	8 24.0	13 36.1	18 42.9
15	17 33 12.8	23 22.8	2 47.7	3♍28.0	8 13.7	1 47.7	26 1.1	12 36.4	7 26.5	8 25.6	13 34.9	18 43.4
16	17 37 9.4	24 25.1	2 44.2	16 29.8	10 16.4	1 9.4	26 45.5	12 48.9	7 26.6	8 27.2	13 33.7	18 43.9
17	17 41 5.9	25 27.5	2 40.8	28 42.6	12 22.4	0 30.2	27 29.9	13 1.3	7R26.5	8 28.8	13 32.6	18 44.5
18	17 45 2.5	26 29.9	2 37.3	10♎21.3	14 31.3	29♊50.4	28 14.4	13 13.7	7 26.4	8 30.5	13 31.4	18 45.1
19	17 48 59.1	27 32.3	2 33.8	21 41.1	16 43.2	29 10.1	28 58.9	13 26.0	7 26.1	8 32.2	13 30.3	18 45.7
20	17 52 55.6	28 34.7	2 30.4	2♏55.8	18 57.8	28 29.8	29 43.4	13 38.3	7 25.8	8 34.0	13 29.2	18 46.3
21	17 56 52.2	29 37.0	2 26.9	14 17.7	21 14.9	27 49.5	0♊27.9	13 50.5	7 25.4	8 35.8	13 28.1	18 47.0
22	18 0 48.7	0♋39.4	2 23.5	25 56.4	23 34.1	27 9.7	1 12.4	14 2.6	7 24.9	8 37.7	13 27.1	18 47.7
23	18 4 45.3	1 41.8	2 20.0	7♐58.0	25 55.2	26 30.5	1 57.0	14 14.6	7 24.2	8 39.6	13 26.1	18 48.5
24	18 8 41.8	2 44.1	2 16.5	20 24.4	28 17.6	25 52.2	2 41.6	14 26.6	7 23.6	8 41.5	13 25.1	18 49.2
25	18 12 38.4	3 46.4	2 13.1	3♑12.3	0♋41.2	25 15.1	3 26.2	14 38.5	7 22.8	8 43.5	13 24.1	18 50.0
26	18 16 35.0	4 48.8	2 9.6	16 13.8	3 5.4	24 39.3	4 10.9	14 50.4	7 21.9	8 45.6	13 23.2	18 50.9
27	18 20 31.5	5 51.0	2 6.2	29 17.9	5 29.8	24 5.0	4 55.6	15 2.2	7 21.0	8 47.7	13 22.3	18 51.7
28	18 24 28.1	6 53.2	2 2.7	12♒14.4	7 54.0	23 32.4	5 40.3	15 13.9	7 19.9	8 49.8	13 21.4	18 52.6
29	18 28 24.6	7 55.4	1 59.2	24 56.1	10 17.5	23 1.8	6 25.0	15 25.5	7 18.7	8 51.9	13 20.6	18 53.4
30	18 32 21.2	8 57.5	1 55.8	7♓21.0	12 40.1	22 33.1	7 9.7	15 37.0	7 17.5	8 54.1	13 19.7	18 54.4

DECLINATION

DAY	EPHEM. SID. TIME	☉	☊	☾	☿	♀	♂	♃	♄	♅	♆	♇
1	16 38 1.0	22N 1.8	0N24.5	20S28.3	13N59.1	25N28.8	16N54.2	14N24.0	11S 5.7	10N .0	14S49.9	20N 4.2
4	16 49 50.7	22 24.7	0 24.5	8 43.5	15 26.4	24 59.6	17 31.8	14 36.2	11 4.9	9 58.8	14 48.7	20 2.8
7	17 1 40.4	22 44.1	0 24.5	7N43.4	16 58.7	24 27.4	18 7.9	14 48.0	11 4.5	9 57.3	14 47.6	20 1.3
10	17 13 30.0	22 60.0	0 24.5	21 21.2	18 32.7	23 52.0	18 42.2	14 59.6	11 4.4	9 55.6	14 46.6	19 59.7
13	17 25 19.7	23 12.1	0 24.5	22 22.4	20 4.9	23 13.7	19 14.9	15 10.9	11 4.6	9 53.9	14 45.6	19 58.0
16	17 37 9.4	23 20.7	0 24.5	11 12.9	21 30.9	22 32.9	19 45.9	15 21.9	11 5.1	9 51.9	14 44.7	19 56.2
19	17 48 59.1	23 25.4	0 24.5	3S43.6	22 45.6	21 50.6	20 15.1	15 32.6	11 6.0	9 49.8	14 43.8	19 54.3
22	18 0 48.7	23 26.5	0 24.5	16 40.4	23 43.7	21 8.1	20 42.6	15 42.9	11 7.2	9 47.5	14 43.0	19 52.4
25	18 12 38.4	23 23.9	0 24.5	23 29.5	24 20.5	20 26.9	21 8.2	15 53.0	11 8.7	9 45.1	14 42.3	19 50.3
28	18 24 28.1	23 17.5	0 24.5	21 5.9	24 32.8	19 48.8	21 31.9	16 2.7	11 10.5	9 42.5	14 41.7	19 48.2

JULY 1964

DAY	EPHEM. SID. TIME	☉	☊	☽	☿	♀	♂	♃	♄	♅	♆	♇
	LONGITUDE											
	h m s	° ′	° ′	° ′	° ′	° ′	° ′	° ′	° ′	° ′	° ′	° ′
1	18 36 17.7	9♋11.0	1♋43.0	16♓27.4	13♋40.0	22♊32.2	9♊34.5	17♉58.3	4♓50.0	6♍55.9	15♏14.2	11♍58.7
2	18 40 14.3	10 8.2	1 39.9	29 30.9	15 47.6	22R 8.7	10 16.6	18 9.7	4R48.4	6 58.3	15R13.4	11 59.9
3	18 44 10.9	11 5.4	1 36.7	12♈54.5	17 53.9	21 47.4	10 58.6	18 20.9	4 46.8	7 .7	15 12.7	12 1.1
4	18 48 7.4	12 2.6	1 33.5	26 40.1	19 58.8	21 28.4	11 40.5	18 32.1	4 45.0	7 3.2	15 12.0	12 2.3
5	18 52 4.0	12 59.8	1 30.3	10♉47.8	22 2.0	21 11.8	12 22.4	18 43.2	4 43.1	7 5.8	15 11.3	12 3.6
6	18 56 .5	13 57.0	1 27.2	25 16.5	24 3.6	20 57.4	13 4.2	18 54.1	4 41.2	7 8.3	15 10.6	12 4.8
7	18 59 57.1	14 54.2	1 24.0	10♊ 2.7	26 3.5	20 45.5	13 46.0	19 5.0	4 39.2	7 10.9	15 10.0	12 6.1
8	19 3 53.7	15 51.5	1 20.8	25 .8	28 1.5	20 36.0	14 27.7	19 15.8	4 37.0	7 13.6	15 9.3	12 7.4
9	19 7 50.2	16 48.7	1 17.6	10♋ 3.4	29 57.7	20 28.9	15 9.4	19 26.5	4 34.8	7 16.3	15 8.8	12 8.8
10	19 11 46.8	17 45.9	1 14.5	25 1.9	1♌52.0	20 24.1	15 50.9	19 37.1	4 32.5	7 19.0	15 8.2	12 10.2
11	19 15 43.3	18 43.1	1 11.3	9♌48.1	3 44.4	20 21.7	16 32.5	19 47.5	4 30.1	7 21.8	15 7.7	12 11.5
12	19 19 39.9	19 40.4	1 8.1	24 14.9	5 34.9	20 21.6	17 13.9	19 57.9	4 27.7	7 24.6	15 7.2	12 13.0
13	19 23 36.4	20 37.6	1 4.9	8♍17.4	7 23.5	20D23.8	17 55.3	20 8.2	4 25.1	7 27.4	15 6.7	12 14.4
14	19 27 33.0	21 34.8	1 1.8	21 53.4	9 10.2	20 28.2	18 36.7	20 18.3	4 22.5	7 30.3	15 6.3	12 15.9
15	19 31 29.6	22 32.1	0 58.6	5♎ 3.1	10 54.9	20 34.8	19 17.9	20 28.4	4 19.7	7 33.2	15 5.9	12 17.3
16	19 35 26.1	23 29.3	0 55.4	17 48.8	12 37.7	20 43.6	19 59.1	20 38.3	4 16.9	7 36.1	15 5.5	12 18.8
17	19 39 22.7	24 26.6	0 52.2	0♏13.8	14 18.7	20 54.5	20 40.3	20 48.2	4 14.1	7 39.1	15 5.3	12 20.4
18	19 43 19.2	25 23.8	0 49.0	12 22.6	15 57.7	21 7.4	21 21.4	20 57.9	4 11.2	7 42.1	15 5.0	12 22.0
19	19 47 15.8	26 21.1	0 45.9	24 19.8	17 34.8	21 22.3	22 2.4	21 7.5	4 8.1	7 45.1	15 4.7	12 23.5
20	19 51 12.3	27 18.3	0 42.7	6♐10.0	19 10.0	21 39.1	22 43.4	21 16.9	4 5.0	7 48.2	15 4.4	12 25.1
21	19 55 8.9	28 15.6	0 39.5	17 57.6	20 43.3	21 57.8	23 24.3	21 26.3	4 1.9	7 51.3	15 4.2	12 26.7
22	19 59 5.5	29 12.9	0 36.3	29 46.5	22 14.6	22 18.3	24 5.1	21 35.5	3 58.6	7 54.4	15 4.0	12 28.4
23	20 3 2.0	0♌10.1	0 33.2	11♑39.9	23 44.0	22 40.6	24 45.9	21 44.6	3 55.3	7 57.5	15 3.9	12 30.0
24	20 6 58.6	1 7.4	0 30.0	23 40.5	25 11.4	23 4.5	25 26.6	21 53.6	3 51.9	8 .7	15 3.8	12 31.7
25	20 10 55.1	2 4.7	0 26.8	5♒50.5	26 36.9	23 30.1	26 7.3	22 2.5	3 48.5	8 3.9	15 3.7	12 33.4
26	20 14 51.7	3 2.0	0 23.6	18 11.3	28 .4	23 57.3	26 47.8	22 11.2	3 45.0	8 7.1	15 3.6	12 35.1
27	20 18 48.2	3 59.3	0 20.5	0♓44.2	29 21.8	24 26.0	27 28.4	22 19.8	3 41.4	8 10.4	15 3.6	12 36.8
28	20 22 44.8	4 56.6	0 17.3	13 29.8	0♍41.2	24 56.2	28 8.8	22 28.3	3 37.8	8 13.7	15 3.6	12 38.5
29	20 26 41.3	5 53.9	0 14.1	26 28.8	1 58.4	25 27.8	28 49.3	22 36.6	3 34.1	8 17.0	15D 3.7	12 40.3
30	20 30 37.9	6 51.3	0 10.9	9♈42.0	3 13.5	26 .8	29 29.6	22 44.8	3 30.3	8 20.3	15 3.8	12 42.1
31	20 34 34.5	7 48.7	0 7.7	23 9.8	4 26.3	26 35.2	0♋ 9.9	22 52.9	3 26.5	8 23.7	15 3.9	12 43.9
	LATITUDE											
1	18 36 17.7	0 .0	0 .0	5S 5.7	1N35.8	3S59.3	0N .4	1S 1.6	1S34.8	0N44.9	1N48.1	13N47.3
4	18 48 7.4	0 .0	0 .0	4 48.5	1 47.0	4 23.8	0 2.5	1 1.9	1 35.4	0 44.8	1 47.9	13 46.4
7	18 59 57.1	0 .0	0 .0	1 59.2	1 51.6	4 43.2	0 4.7	1 2.1	1 36.1	0 44.7	1 47.8	13 45.5
10	19 11 46.8	0 .0	0 .0	2N 3.7	1 49.8	4 57.8	0 6.8	1 2.4	1 36.7	0 44.7	1 47.6	13 44.7
13	19 23 36.4	0 .0	0 .0	4 49.3	1 42.4	5 7.8	0 9.0	1 2.7	1 37.2	0 44.6	1 47.5	13 43.8
16	19 35 26.1	0 .0	0 .0	5 3.6	1 29.8	5 14.0	0 11.1	1 3.0	1 37.8	0 44.5	1 47.3	13 43.1
19	19 47 15.8	0 .0	0 .0	3 12.8	1 12.7	5 16.6	0 13.3	1 3.3	1 38.4	0 44.4	1 47.1	13 42.3
22	19 59 5.5	0 .0	0 .0	0 12.2	0 51.7	5 16.1	0 15.5	1 3.7	1 38.9	0 44.3	1 46.9	13 41.6
25	20 10 55.1	0 .0	0 .0	2S55.0	0 27.2	5 13.1	0 17.6	1 4.0	1 39.4	0 44.3	1 46.8	13 41.0
28	20 22 44.8	0 .0	0 .0	4 56.3	0S .2	5 7.8	0 19.8	1 4.4	1 39.9	0 44.2	1 46.6	13 40.4
31	20 34 34.5	0 .0	0 .0	4 49.7	0 30.1	5 .6	0 22.0	1 4.7	1 40.4	0 44.1	1 46.4	13 39.9
	RIGHT ASCENSION											
1	18 36 17.7	9♋59.6	1♋52.3	19♓32.8	15♋ 1.4	22♊ 6.7	7♊54.4	15♉48.5	7♓16.2	8♍56.3	13♏18.9	18♍55.3
2	18 40 14.3	11 1.6	1 48.8	1♈39.7	17 21.0	21R42.4	8 39.2	15 59.8	7R14.7	8 58.6	13R18.1	18 56.3
3	18 44 10.9	12 3.6	1 45.4	13 53.7	19 38.7	21 20.5	9 23.9	16 11.1	7 13.2	9 .9	13 17.3	18 57.3
4	18 48 7.4	13 5.5	1 41.9	26 29.1	21 54.2	21 1.0	10 8.7	16 22.3	7 11.6	9 3.2	13 16.6	18 58.3
5	18 52 4.0	14 7.3	1 38.5	9♉41.1	24 7.3	20 44.0	10 53.4	16 33.5	7 10.0	9 5.6	13 15.9	18 59.3
6	18 56 .5	15 9.0	1 35.0	23 43.3	26 18.0	20 29.4	11 38.2	16 44.5	7 8.2	9 8.0	13 15.2	19 .4
7	18 59 57.1	16 10.6	1 31.5	8♊43.1	28 26.0	20 17.3	12 23.0	16 55.4	7 6.3	9 10.5	13 14.6	19 1.5
8	19 3 53.7	17 12.2	1 28.1	24 35.6	0♌31.3	20 7.7	13 7.7	17 6.3	7 4.4	9 13.0	13 14.0	19 2.6
9	19 7 50.2	18 13.7	1 24.6	11♋ .1	2 33.9	20 .6	13 52.5	17 17.0	7 2.4	9 15.5	13 13.4	19 3.8
10	19 11 46.8	19 15.0	1 21.2	27 22.9	4 33.6	19 55.9	14 37.2	17 27.7	7 .3	9 18.0	13 12.8	19 5.0
11	19 15 43.3	20 16.3	1 17.7	13♌10.2	6 30.4	19 53.7	15 22.0	17 38.2	6 58.1	9 20.6	13 12.3	19 6.2
12	19 19 39.9	21 17.4	1 14.2	28 .1	8 24.4	19D53.8	16 6.7	17 48.7	6 55.8	9 23.2	13 11.8	19 7.4
13	19 23 36.4	22 18.4	1 10.8	11♍46.8	10 15.6	19 56.3	16 51.4	17 59.0	6 53.4	9 25.9	13 11.3	19 8.6
14	19 27 33.0	23 19.3	1 7.3	24 36.8	12 4.0	20 1.1	17 36.1	18 9.3	6 51.0	9 28.6	13 10.9	19 9.9
15	19 31 29.6	24 20.1	1 3.8	6♎43.2	13 49.5	20 8.2	18 20.8	18 19.4	6 48.5	9 31.3	13 10.5	19 11.2
16	19 35 26.1	25 20.8	1 .4	18 21.3	15 32.4	20 17.5	19 5.4	18 29.5	6 45.9	9 34.0	13 10.1	19 12.5
17	19 39 22.7	26 21.3	0 56.9	29 46.0	17 12.5	20 28.9	19 50.1	18 39.4	6 43.3	9 36.9	13 9.8	19 13.9
18	19 43 19.2	27 21.7	0 53.5	11♏10.7	18 49.9	20 42.5	20 34.7	18 49.3	6 40.6	9 39.7	13 9.5	19 15.2
19	19 47 15.8	28 21.9	0 50.0	22 46.8	20 24.7	20 58.1	21 19.2	18 59.0	6 37.8	9 42.5	13 9.2	19 16.6
20	19 51 12.3	29 22.0	0 46.5	4♐42.5	21 56.9	21 15.6	22 3.7	19 8.6	6 34.9	9 45.4	13 8.9	19 18.0
21	19 55 8.9	0♌22.0	0 43.1	17 2.2	23 26.5	21 35.2	22 48.2	19 18.0	6 31.9	9 48.3	13 8.7	19 19.4
22	19 59 5.5	1 21.8	0 39.6	29 45.3	24 53.6	21 56.6	23 32.7	19 27.4	6 28.9	9 51.2	13 8.5	19 20.9
23	20 3 2.0	2 21.5	0 36.1	12♑46.0	26 18.2	22 19.8	24 17.1	19 36.6	6 25.8	9 54.1	13 8.3	19 22.3
24	20 6 58.6	3 21.0	0 32.7	25 54.3	27 40.4	22 44.8	25 1.5	19 45.8	6 22.7	9 57.1	13 8.2	19 23.8
25	20 10 55.1	4 20.4	0 29.2	8♒59.2	29 .1	23 11.5	25 45.8	19 54.8	6 19.5	10 .1	13 8.1	19 25.3
26	20 14 51.7	5 19.6	0 25.8	21 51.2	0♍17.3	23 39.9	26 30.1	20 3.6	6 16.2	10 3.1	13 8.0	19 26.8
27	20 18 48.2	6 18.7	0 22.3	4♓25.7	1 32.2	24 9.9	27 14.4	20 12.4	6 12.9	10 6.2	13 8.0	19 28.4
28	20 22 44.8	7 17.6	0 18.8	16 43.3	2 44.6	24 41.4	27 58.5	20 21.0	6 9.5	10 9.2	13 8.0	19 29.9
29	20 26 41.3	8 16.4	0 15.4	28 50.1	3 54.6	25 14.5	28 42.7	20 29.5	6 6.0	10 12.3	13 8.0	19 31.5
30	20 30 37.9	9 15.0	0 11.9	10♈55.9	5 2.2	25 49.0	29 26.8	20 37.8	6 2.5	10 15.5	13D 8.1	19 33.1
31	20 34 34.5	10 13.5	0 8.4	23 13.4	6 7.3	26 24.9	0♋10.8	20 46.0	5 58.9	10 18.6	13 8.1	19 34.7
	DECLINATION											
1	18 36 17.7	23N 7.5	0N24.5	10S 2.2	24N19.8	19N15.1	21N53.9	16N12.1	11S12.6	9N39.8	14S41.1	19N46.0
4	18 48 7.4	22 53.8	0 24.5	5N47.9	23 43.2	18 46.9	22 13.9	16 21.2	11 15.1	9 37.0	14 40.6	19 43.8
7	18 59 57.1	22 36.6	0 24.5	19 59.7	22 46.0	18 24.7	22 32.0	16 30.0	11 17.8	9 34.1	14 40.1	19 41.5
10	19 11 46.8	22 15.8	0 24.5	23 9.4	21 31.9	18 8.8	22 48.3	16 38.4	11 20.8	9 31.0	14 39.8	19 39.1
13	19 23 36.4	21 51.6	0 24.5	12 55.8	20 4.6	17 58.7	23 2.6	16 46.4	11 24.0	9 27.8	14 39.5	19 36.7
16	19 35 26.1	21 24.0	0 24.5	2S18.6	18 27.4	17 53.9	23 15.0	16 54.1	11 27.6	9 24.5	14 39.3	19 34.3
19	19 47 15.8	20 53.1	0 24.5	15 44.4	16 43.3	17 53.9	23 25.5	17 1.5	11 31.3	9 21.0	14 39.3	19 31.8
22	19 59 5.5	20 19.1	0 24.5	23 14.5	14 54.8	17 57.6	23 34.1	17 8.4	11 35.3	9 17.5	14 39.2	19 29.3
25	20 10 55.1	19 42.0	0 24.5	21 38.4	13 4.3	18 4.3	23 40.8	17 15.0	11 39.4	9 13.9	14 39.3	19 26.7
28	20 22 44.8	19 2.0	0 24.5	11 2.7	11 13.7	18 13.2	23 45.7	17 21.3	11 43.8	9 10.2	14 39.5	19 24.2
31	20 34 34.5	18 19.1	0 24.6	4N30.9	9 25.0	18 23.5	23 48.7	17 27.2	11 48.3	9 6.4	14 39.7	19 21.6

AUGUST 1964

LONGITUDE

DAY	EPHEM. SID. TIME	☉	☊	☾	☿	♀	♂	♃	♄	♅	♆	♇
	h m s	° ′	° ′	° ′	° ′	° ′	° ′	° ′	° ′	° ′	° ′	° ′
1	20 38 31.0	8♌46.1	0♋ 4.6	6♉52.9	5♍36.9	27♊10.8	0♋50.1	23♉ .8	3♓22.6	8♍27.0	15♏ 4.0	12♍45.7
2	20 42 27.6	9 43.5	0 1.4	20 51.3	6 45.1	27 47.6	1 30.3	23 8.6	3R18.7	8 30.4	15 4.2	12 47.5
3	20 46 24.1	10 40.9	29♊58.2	5♊ 4.7	7 50.8	28 25.6	2 10.4	23 16.3	3 14.8	8 33.9	15 4.4	12 49.3
4	20 50 20.7	11 38.4	29 55.0	19 31.4	8 54.0	29 4.7	2 50.4	23 23.8	3 10.7	8 37.3	15 4.6	12 51.2
5	20 54 17.2	12 35.8	29 51.9	4♋ 8.4	9 54.5	29 44.9	3 30.4	23 31.2	3 6.7	8 40.8	15 4.9	12 53.1
6	20 58 13.8	13 33.3	29 48.7	18 51.0	10 52.3	0♋26.2	4 10.3	23 38.4	3 2.6	8 44.3	15 5.2	12 54.9
7	21 2 10.4	14 30.9	29 45.5	3♌33.1	11 47.2	1 8.5	4 50.2	23 45.5	2 58.4	8 47.8	15 5.6	12 56.9
8	21 6 6.9	15 28.4	29 42.3	18 7.6	12 39.0	1 51.7	5 30.0	23 52.4	2 54.3	8 51.3	15 5.9	12 58.8
9	21 10 3.5	16 26.0	29 39.1	2♍27.7	13 27.6	2 35.9	6 9.8	23 59.2	2 50.0	8 54.9	15 6.3	13 .7
10	21 14 .0	17 23.5	29 36.0	16 27.9	14 12.9	3 20.9	6 49.4	24 5.8	2 45.7	8 58.4	15 6.8	13 2.7
11	21 17 56.6	18 21.1	29 32.8	0♎ 4.5	14 54.7	4 6.8	7 29.0	24 12.3	2 41.4	9 2.0	15 7.2	13 4.6
12	21 21 53.1	19 18.7	29 29.6	13 16.1	15 32.7	4 53.5	8 8.5	24 18.5	2 37.1	9 5.6	15 7.7	13 6.6
13	21 25 49.7	20 16.3	29 26.4	26 3.7	16 6.8	5 41.1	8 48.0	24 24.7	2 32.7	9 9.2	15 8.2	13 8.6
14	21 29 46.2	21 13.9	29 23.3	8♏30.0	16 36.8	6 29.4	9 27.4	24 30.7	2 28.3	9 12.8	15 8.8	13 10.5
15	21 33 42.8	22 11.6	29 20.1	20 39.2	17 2.4	7 18.4	10 6.7	24 36.5	2 23.9	9 16.5	15 9.4	13 12.5
16	21 37 39.3	23 9.2	29 16.9	2♐36.1	17 23.4	8 8.2	10 46.0	24 42.1	2 19.5	9 20.1	15 10.0	13 14.5
17	21 41 35.9	24 6.9	29 13.7	14 26.0	17 39.6	8 58.7	11 25.1	24 47.6	2 15.0	9 23.8	15 10.7	13 16.6
18	21 45 32.5	25 4.6	29 10.6	26 14.1	17 50.8	9 49.8	12 4.3	24 52.9	2 10.5	9 27.4	15 11.4	13 18.6
19	21 49 29.0	26 2.3	29 7.4	8♑ 5.1	17 56.8	10 41.6	12 43.3	24 58.0	2 6.1	9 31.1	15 12.1	13 20.6
20	21 53 25.6	27 .1	29 4.2	20 3.6	17 57.2	11 34.0	13 22.3	25 3.0	2 1.5	9 34.8	15 12.8	13 22.7
21	21 57 22.1	27 57.8	29 1.0	2♒12.8	17R52.1	12 27.1	14 1.2	25 7.8	1 57.0	9 38.5	15 13.6	13 24.7
22	22 1 18.7	28 55.6	28 57.8	14 35.4	17 41.2	13 20.7	14 40.1	25 12.4	1 52.5	9 42.2	15 14.4	13 26.8
23	22 5 15.2	29 53.4	28 54.7	27 12.8	17 24.4	14 14.9	15 18.9	25 16.9	1 48.0	9 46.0	15 15.3	13 28.8
24	22 9 11.8	0♍51.2	28 51.5	10♓ 5.4	17 1.8	15 9.7	15 57.6	25 21.2	1 43.4	9 49.7	15 16.1	13 30.9
25	22 13 8.3	1 49.1	28 48.3	23 12.5	16 33.4	16 5.0	16 36.3	25 25.3	1 38.9	9 53.4	15 17.0	13 33.0
26	22 17 4.9	2 46.9	28 45.1	6♈32.9	15 59.4	17 .8	17 14.9	25 29.2	1 34.3	9 57.2	15 18.0	13 35.1
27	22 21 1.4	3 44.8	28 42.0	20 4.9	15 20.0	17 57.2	17 53.4	25 32.9	1 29.8	10 .9	15 18.9	13 37.1
28	22 24 58.0	4 42.8	28 38.8	3♉46.9	14 35.8	18 54.1	18 31.9	25 36.5	1 25.3	10 4.7	15 20.0	13 39.3
29	22 28 54.5	5 40.8	28 35.6	17 37.4	13 47.2	19 51.4	19 10.3	25 39.9	1 20.8	10 8.5	15 21.0	13 41.4
30	22 32 51.1	6 38.8	28 32.4	1♊35.6	12 55.0	20 49.2	19 48.6	25 43.1	1 16.3	10 12.2	15 22.0	13 43.5
31	22 36 47.7	7 36.8	28 29.2	15 40.6	12 .1	21 47.4	20 26.9	25 46.1	1 11.8	10 16.0	15 23.1	13 45.6

LATITUDE

DAY	EPHEM. SID. TIME	☉	☊	☾	☿	♀	♂	♃	♄	♅	♆	♇
1	20 38 31.0	0 .0	0 .0	4S14.2	0S40.6	4S57.8	0N22.8	1S 4.8	1S40.5	0N44.1	1N46.3	13N39.7
4	20 50 20.7	0 .0	0 .0	1 4.7	1 13.0	4 48.5	0 25.0	1 5.2	1 41.0	0 44.1	1 46.2	13 39.2
7	21 2 10.4	0 .0	0 .0	2N44.9	1 46.6	4 37.8	0 27.2	1 5.6	1 41.4	0 44.0	1 46.0	13 38.8
10	21 14 .0	0 .0	0 .0	4 58.4	2 20.9	4 26.1	0 29.5	1 6.0	1 41.7	0 44.0	1 45.8	13 38.4
13	21 25 49.7	0 .0	0 .0	4 39.1	2 54.7	4 13.4	0 31.7	1 6.4	1 42.1	0 44.0	1 45.6	13 38.1
16	21 37 39.3	0 .0	0 .0	2 25.9	3 27.0	3 60.0	0 33.9	1 6.9	1 42.4	0 43.9	1 45.4	13 37.8
19	21 49 29.0	0 .0	0 .0	0S39.2	3 55.8	3 45.9	0 36.2	1 7.3	1 42.7	0 43.9	1 45.3	13 37.6
22	22 1 18.7	0 .0	0 .0	3 32.3	4 18.7	3 31.3	0 38.5	1 7.7	1 43.0	0 43.9	1 45.1	13 37.5
25	22 13 8.3	0 .0	0 .0	5 1.6	4 32.4	3 16.2	0 40.7	1 8.2	1 43.2	0 43.9	1 44.9	13 37.4
28	22 24 58.0	0 .0	0 .0	4 12.1	4 33.2	3 .9	0 43.0	1 8.6	1 43.4	0 43.8	1 44.8	13 37.3
31	22 36 47.7	0 .0	0 .0	1 13.5	4 17.8	2 45.3	0 45.3	1 9.0	1 43.5	0 43.8	1 44.6	13 37.3

RIGHT ASCENSION

DAY	EPHEM. SID. TIME	☉	☊	☾	☿	♀	♂	♃	♄	♅	♆	♇
1	20 38 31.0	11♌11.8	0♋ 5.0	5♉57.0	7♍10.0	27♊ 2.2	0♋54.8	20♉54.1	5♓55.3	10♍21.8	13♏ 8.3	19♍36.3
2	20 42 27.6	12 10.0	0 1.5	19 20.6	8 10.2	27 40.9	1 38.7	21 2.1	5R51.6	10 25.0	13 8.4	19 38.0
3	20 46 24.1	13 8.1	29♊58.1	3♊34.7	9 7.7	28 20.7	2 22.5	21 9.9	5 47.9	10 28.2	13 8.6	19 39.7
4	20 50 20.7	14 6.0	29 54.6	18 41.7	10 2.7	29 1.8	3 6.3	21 17.5	5 44.1	10 31.4	13 8.8	19 41.3
5	20 54 17.2	15 3.8	29 51.1	4♋31.1	10 55.0	29 44.1	3 50.0	21 25.1	5 40.3	10 34.6	13 9.1	19 43.0
6	20 58 13.8	16 1.4	29 47.7	20 38.7	11 44.6	0♋27.5	4 33.7	21 32.4	5 36.5	10 37.9	13 9.3	19 44.8
7	21 2 10.4	16 58.9	29 44.2	6♌33.1	12 31.3	1 12.1	5 17.3	21 39.7	5 32.6	10 41.2	13 9.7	19 46.5
8	21 6 6.9	17 56.2	29 40.7	21 47.1	13 15.1	1 57.7	6 .8	21 46.8	5 28.7	10 44.5	13 10.0	19 48.3
9	21 10 3.5	18 53.4	29 37.3	6♍ 6.5	13 55.8	2 44.3	6 44.2	21 53.7	5 24.7	10 47.8	13 10.4	19 50.0
10	21 14 .0	19 50.4	29 33.8	19 30.3	14 33.3	3 31.8	7 27.5	22 .4	5 20.6	10 51.2	13 10.8	19 51.8
11	21 17 56.6	20 47.3	29 30.3	2♎ 7.0	15 7.5	4 20.3	8 10.7	22 7.0	5 16.6	10 54.5	13 11.3	19 53.6
12	21 21 53.1	21 44.0	29 26.9	14 9.4	15 38.2	5 9.7	8 53.9	22 13.5	5 12.5	10 57.9	13 11.7	19 55.4
13	21 25 49.7	22 40.6	29 23.4	25 51.6	16 5.4	6 .0	9 36.9	22 19.8	5 8.4	11 1.3	13 12.2	19 57.2
14	21 29 46.2	23 37.0	29 20.0	7♏27.0	16 28.7	6 51.2	10 19.9	22 25.9	5 4.2	11 4.7	13 12.8	19 59.1
15	21 33 42.8	24 33.3	29 16.5	19 7.5	16 48.1	7 43.2	11 2.8	22 31.8	5 .0	11 8.1	13 13.3	20 .9
16	21 37 39.3	25 29.5	29 13.0	1♐ 2.2	17 3.4	8 35.9	11 45.5	22 37.6	4 55.8	11 11.5	13 13.9	20 2.7
17	21 41 35.9	26 25.6	29 9.6	13 17.3	17 14.4	9 29.4	12 28.2	22 43.3	4 51.6	11 14.9	13 14.6	20 4.6
18	21 45 32.5	27 21.5	29 6.1	25 54.5	17 21.0	10 23.7	13 10.8	22 48.7	4 47.4	11 18.3	13 15.2	20 6.5
19	21 49 29.0	28 17.2	29 2.6	8♑50.7	17 22.9	11 18.7	13 53.2	22 54.0	4 43.1	11 21.8	13 15.9	20 8.4
20	21 53 25.6	29 12.9	28 59.2	21 58.5	17R20.0	12 14.3	14 35.6	22 59.1	4 38.9	11 25.2	13 16.6	20 10.3
21	21 57 22.1	0♍ 8.4	28 55.7	5♒ 7.7	17 12.3	13 10.6	15 17.8	23 4.0	4 34.6	11 28.7	13 17.4	20 12.2
22	22 1 18.7	1 3.8	28 52.3	18 9.1	16 59.7	14 7.6	15 60.0	23 8.8	4 30.3	11 32.2	13 18.2	20 14.1
23	22 5 15.2	1 59.1	28 48.8	0♓56.1	16 42.0	15 5.1	16 42.0	23 13.4	4 26.0	11 35.7	13 19.0	20 16.0
24	22 9 11.8	2 54.3	28 45.3	13 27.3	16 19.5	16 3.3	17 24.0	23 17.8	4 21.7	11 39.2	13 19.8	20 18.0
25	22 13 8.3	3 49.4	28 41.9	25 46.0	15 52.1	17 2.0	18 5.8	23 22.0	4 17.4	11 42.7	13 20.7	20 19.9
26	22 17 4.9	4 44.3	28 38.4	8♈ .1	15 20.0	18 1.2	18 47.5	23 26.0	4 13.0	11 46.2	13 21.6	20 21.8
27	22 21 1.4	5 39.2	28 34.9	20 20.2	14 43.7	19 1.0	19 29.1	23 29.9	4 8.7	11 49.7	13 22.6	20 23.8
28	22 24 58.0	6 34.1	28 31.5	2♉58.8	14 3.5	20 1.3	20 10.6	23 33.6	4 4.5	11 53.2	13 23.6	20 25.8
29	22 28 54.5	7 28.8	28 28.0	16 8.4	13 20.0	21 2.1	20 52.0	23 37.1	4 .2	11 56.7	13 24.6	20 27.8
30	22 32 51.1	8 23.4	28 24.5	29 59.2	12 33.8	22 3.3	21 33.2	23 40.4	3 55.9	12 .3	13 25.6	20 29.8
31	22 36 47.7	9 17.9	28 21.1	14♊35.3	11 45.8	23 4.9	22 14.4	23 43.5	3 51.6	12 3.8	13 26.6	20 31.8

DECLINATION

DAY	EPHEM. SID. TIME	☉	☊	☾	☿	♀	♂	♃	♄	♅	♆	♇
1	20 38 31.0	18N 4.2	0N24.6	9N48.4	8N49.5	18N27.1	23N49.2	17N29.0	11S49.9	9N 5.1	14S39.8	19N20.7
4	20 50 20.7	17 17.8	0 24.6	21 57.3	7 6.4	18 38.0	23 49.8	17 34.4	11 54.6	9 1.2	14 40.1	19 18.1
7	21 2 10.4	16 28.8	0 24.6	22 2.1	5 30.0	18 48.5	23 48.5	17 39.4	11 59.4	8 57.2	14 40.6	19 15.5
10	21 14 .0	15 37.5	0 24.5	9 55.3	4 2.7	18 58.1	23 45.5	17 44.0	12 4.4	8 53.2	14 41.1	19 12.9
13	21 25 49.7	14 43.9	0 24.5	5S43.7	2 47.7	19 6.1	23 40.7	17 48.2	12 9.4	8 49.1	14 41.7	19 10.3
16	21 37 39.3	13 48.1	0 24.5	18 18.0	1 48.3	19 12.1	23 34.3	17 52.0	12 14.5	8 45.0	14 42.4	19 7.7
19	21 49 29.0	12 50.5	0 24.5	23 50.9	1 8.8	19 15.6	23 26.2	17 55.4	12 19.6	8 40.8	14 43.2	19 5.1
22	22 1 18.7	11 51.0	0 24.5	19 50.4	0 53.7	19 16.2	23 16.4	17 58.5	12 24.7	8 36.6	14 44.0	19 2.6
25	22 13 8.3	10 49.8	0 24.5	7 18.6	1 7.3	19 13.6	23 5.1	18 1.1	12 29.8	8 32.3	14 44.9	19 .0
28	22 24 58.0	9 47.0	0 24.5	8N49.5	1 51.8	19 7.5	22 52.3	18 3.3	12 34.8	8 28.1	14 45.9	18 57.5
31	22 36 47.7	8 42.9	0 24.5	21 27.4	3 5.2	18 57.6	22 38.1	18 5.2	12 39.8	8 23.8	14 47.0	18 55.1

SEPTEMBER 1964

LONGITUDE

DAY	EPHEM. SID. TIME (h m s)	☉ (° ′)	☊ (° ′)	☾ (° ′)	☿ (° ′)	♀ (° ′)	♂ (° ′)	♃ (° ′)	♄ (° ′)	♅ (° ′)	♆ (° ′)	♇ (° ′)
1	22 40 44.2	8♍34.9	28♊26.1	29♊51.9	11♍ 3.4	22♋46.0	21♋ 5.1	25♉48.9	1♓ 7.3	10♍19.8	15♏24.2	13♍47.7
2	22 44 40.8	9 33.0	28 22.9	14♋ 7.9	10 R 6.2	23 45.1	21 43.2	25 51.5	1 R 2.8	10 23.5	15 25.3	13 49.8
3	22 48 37.3	10 31.1	28 19.7	28 26.4	9 9.6	24 44.6	22 21.3	25 53.9	0 58.3	10 27.3	15 26.5	13 51.9
4	22 52 33.9	11 29.2	28 16.5	12♌43.9	8 14.9	25 44.5	22 59.2	25 56.2	0 53.9	10 31.1	15 27.7	13 54.0
5	22 56 30.4	12 27.4	28 13.4	26 56.0	7 23.2	26 44.7	23 37.1	25 58.2	0 49.5	10 34.8	15 28.9	13 56.2
6	23 0 27.0	13 25.6	28 10.2	10♍57.6	6 36.0	27 45.4	24 15.0	26 .0	0 45.1	10 38.6	15 30.2	13 58.3
7	23 4 23.5	14 23.9	28 7.0	24 43.8	5 54.2	28 46.4	24 52.7	26 1.7	0 40.8	10 42.4	15 31.5	14 .4
8	23 8 20.1	15 22.2	28 3.8	8♎11.1	5 18.9	29 47.7	25 30.4	26 3.1	0 36.4	10 46.1	15 32.8	14 2.5
9	23 12 16.6	16 20.5	28 .6	21 17.2	4 50.9	0♌49.4	26 8.0	26 4.4	0 32.1	10 49.9	15 34.1	14 4.6
10	23 16 13.2	17 18.8	27 57.5	4♏ 2.0	4 31.1	1 51.4	26 45.6	26 5.4	0 27.9	10 53.7	15 35.5	14 6.8
11	23 20 9.7	18 17.1	27 54.3	16 27.2	4 19.9	2 53.7	27 23.0	26 6.3	0 23.7	10 57.4	15 36.8	14 8.9
12	23 24 6.3	19 15.5	27 51.1	28 35.9	4 17.7	3 56.3	28 .4	26 6.9	0 19.5	11 1.1	15 38.3	14 11.0
13	23 28 2.8	20 13.9	27 47.9	10♐32.6	4 D 24.8	4 59.2	28 37.7	26 7.4	0 15.3	11 4.9	15 39.7	14 13.1
14	23 31 59.4	21 12.4	27 44.8	22 22.3	4 41.1	6 2.4	29 14.9	26 7.6	0 11.2	11 8.6	15 41.2	14 15.2
15	23 35 55.9	22 10.8	27 41.6	4♑10.7	5 6.6	7 6.0	29 52.1	26 7.7	0 7.2	11 12.3	15 42.6	14 17.3
16	23 39 52.5	23 9.3	27 38.4	16 3.0	5 41.1	8 9.8	0♌29.1	26 R 7.5	0 3.2	11 16.1	15 44.2	14 19.4
17	23 43 49.1	24 7.8	27 35.2	28 4.6	6 24.2	9 13.8	1 6.1	26 7.2	29♒59.3	11 19.8	15 45.7	14 21.5
18	23 47 45.6	25 6.4	27 32.0	10♒19.9	7 15.6	10 18.2	1 43.1	26 6.7	29 55.4	11 23.5	15 47.3	14 23.7
19	23 51 42.2	26 5.0	27 28.9	22 52.3	8 14.6	11 22.8	2 19.9	26 5.9	29 51.6	11 27.2	15 48.9	14 25.7
20	23 55 38.7	27 3.6	27 25.7	5♓43.9	9 20.8	12 27.7	2 56.6	26 5.0	29 47.8	11 30.9	15 50.5	14 27.8
21	23 59 35.3	28 2.3	27 22.5	18 55.2	10 33.5	13 32.8	3 33.3	26 3.8	29 44.1	11 34.5	15 52.1	14 29.9
22	0 3 31.8	29 .9	27 19.3	2♈25.0	11 52.2	14 38.2	4 9.9	26 2.5	29 40.4	11 38.2	15 53.8	14 32.0
23	0 7 28.4	29 59.6	27 16.2	16 10.5	13 16.1	15 43.8	4 46.4	26 .9	29 36.8	11 41.8	15 55.5	14 34.0
24	0 11 24.9	0♎58.4	27 13.0	0♉ 7.8	14 44.6	16 49.7	5 22.8	25 59.1	29 33.3	11 45.4	15 57.2	14 36.1
25	0 15 21.5	1 57.1	27 9.8	14 12.8	16 17.1	17 55.8	5 59.2	25 57.2	29 29.8	11 49.0	15 58.9	14 38.1
26	0 19 18.0	2 55.9	27 6.6	28 21.7	17 53.1	19 2.1	6 35.4	25 55.0	29 26.4	11 52.6	16 .6	14 40.2
27	0 23 14.6	3 54.8	27 3.4	12♊31.4	19 31.9	20 8.7	7 11.6	25 52.7	29 23.1	11 56.2	16 2.4	14 42.2
28	0 27 11.1	4 53.7	27 .3	26 39.9	21 13.1	21 15.5	7 47.7	25 50.2	29 19.8	11 59.7	16 4.2	14 44.2
29	0 31 7.7	5 52.6	26 57.1	10♋46.0	22 56.2	22 22.5	8 23.7	25 47.4	29 16.6	12 3.3	16 6.0	14 46.2
30	0 35 4.2	6 51.5	26 53.9	24 48.9	24 40.7	23 29.7	8 59.7	25 44.5	29 13.5	12 6.8	16 7.8	14 48.2

LATITUDE

DAY	SID. TIME	☉	☊	☾	☿	♀	♂	♃	♄	♅	♆	♇
1	22 40 44.2	0 .0	0 .0	0N 1.4	4S 8.9	2S40.1	0N46.1	1S 9.2	1S43.6	0N43.8	1N44.5	13N37.4
4	22 52 33.9	0 .0	0 .0	3 27.7	3 31.1	2 24.3	0 48.4	1 9.6	1 43.7	0 43.8	1 44.4	13 37.5
7	23 4 23.5	0 .0	0 .0	5 .6	2 40.3	2 8.6	0 50.8	1 10.1	1 43.8	0 43.9	1 44.2	13 37.6
10	23 16 13.2	0 .0	0 .0	4 5.9	1 42.8	1 52.9	0 53.1	1 10.5	1 43.8	0 43.9	1 44.1	13 37.9
13	23 28 2.8	0 .0	0 .0	1 32.4	0 45.6	1 37.3	0 55.5	1 10.9	1 43.9	0 43.9	1 43.9	13 38.1
16	23 39 52.5	0 .0	0 .0	1S33.0	0N 6.0	1 22.0	0 57.9	1 11.4	1 43.9	0 43.9	1 43.8	13 38.5
19	23 51 42.2	0 .0	0 .0	4 6.6	0 48.2	1 6.8	1 .2	1 11.8	1 43.8	0 43.9	1 43.7	13 38.9
22	0 3 31.8	0 .0	0 .0	4 59.2	1 19.7	0 52.1	1 2.7	1 12.2	1 43.7	0 44.0	1 43.5	13 39.4
25	0 15 21.5	0 .0	0 .0	3 24.6	1 40.3	0 37.6	1 5.1	1 12.5	1 43.7	0 44.0	1 43.4	13 39.9
28	0 27 11.1	0 .0	0 .0	0 .4	1 51.0	0 23.6	1 7.6	1 12.9	1 43.5	0 44.1	1 43.3	13 40.5

RIGHT ASCENSION

DAY	SID. TIME	☉	☊	☾	☿	♀	♂	♃	♄	♅	♆	♇
1	22 40 44.2	10♍12.4	28♊17.6	29♊51.1	10♍56.8	24♋ 6.9	22♋55.4	23♉46.4	3♓47.3	12♍ 7.3	13♏27.7	20♍33.7
2	22 44 40.8	11 6.8	28 14.2	15♋29.5	10 R 7.8	25 9.3	23 36.3	23 49.1	3 R 43.0	12 10.8	13 28.8	20 35.7
3	22 48 37.3	12 1.1	28 10.7	1♌ 5.5	9 20.0	26 12.1	24 17.0	23 51.6	3 38.8	12 14.3	13 30.0	20 37.7
4	22 52 33.9	12 55.4	28 7.2	16 14.4	8 34.5	27 15.2	24 57.6	23 53.9	3 34.5	12 17.9	13 31.1	20 39.8
5	22 56 30.4	13 49.6	28 3.8	0♍39.8	7 52.3	28 18.7	25 38.1	23 56.0	3 30.3	12 21.4	13 32.3	20 41.8
6	23 0 27.0	14 43.7	28 .3	14 16.8	7 14.4	29 22.4	26 18.5	23 58.0	3 26.1	12 24.9	13 33.5	20 43.8
7	23 4 23.5	15 37.8	27 56.8	27 9.7	6 42.0	0♌26.5	26 58.7	23 59.7	3 22.0	12 28.4	13 34.8	20 45.8
8	23 8 20.1	16 31.9	27 53.4	9♎28.2	6 15.8	1 30.8	27 38.8	24 1.2	3 17.8	12 32.0	13 36.1	20 47.8
9	23 12 16.6	17 25.9	27 49.9	21 24.6	5 56.6	2 35.3	28 18.8	24 2.5	3 13.7	12 35.5	13 37.4	20 49.8
10	23 16 13.2	18 19.8	27 46.4	3♏11.1	5 45.1	3 40.1	28 58.6	24 3.6	3 9.6	12 39.0	13 38.7	20 51.9
11	23 20 9.7	19 13.7	27 43.0	14 58.6	5 41.7	4 45.1	29 38.3	24 4.5	3 5.6	12 42.5	13 40.1	20 53.9
12	23 24 6.3	20 7.6	27 39.5	26 56.4	5 D 46.7	5 50.3	0♌17.8	24 5.2	3 1.6	12 46.0	13 41.4	20 55.9
13	23 28 2.8	21 1.5	27 36.1	9♐10.5	6 .2	6 55.7	0 57.2	24 5.7	2 57.6	12 49.5	13 42.9	20 57.9
14	23 31 59.4	21 55.3	27 32.6	21 43.7	6 22.3	8 1.2	1 36.5	24 6.0	2 53.7	12 53.0	13 44.3	20 60.0
15	23 35 55.9	22 49.1	27 29.1	4♑34.2	6 52.7	9 6.9	2 15.6	24 6.1	2 49.8	12 56.5	13 45.8	21 2.0
16	23 39 52.5	23 42.9	27 25.7	17 36.8	7 31.3	10 12.8	2 54.5	24 R 6.0	2 46.0	12 59.9	13 47.2	21 4.0
17	23 43 49.1	24 36.7	27 22.2	0♒43.3	8 17.6	11 18.8	3 33.4	24 5.7	2 42.2	13 3.4	13 48.7	21 6.0
18	23 47 45.6	25 30.6	27 18.7	13 45.6	9 11.3	12 25.0	4 12.1	24 5.2	2 38.5	13 6.9	13 50.3	21 8.1
19	23 51 42.2	26 24.4	27 15.3	26 37.6	10 11.7	13 31.2	4 50.6	24 4.4	2 34.8	13 10.3	13 51.9	21 10.1
20	23 55 38.7	27 18.1	27 11.8	9♓17.1	11 18.2	14 37.5	5 29.0	24 3.5	2 31.2	13 13.8	13 53.5	21 12.1
21	23 59 35.3	28 12.0	27 8.4	21 46.5	12 30.4	15 43.9	6 7.3	24 2.4	2 27.6	13 17.2	13 55.1	21 14.1
22	0 3 31.8	29 5.8	27 4.9	4♈12.1	13 47.4	16 50.5	6 45.4	24 1.0	2 24.1	13 20.6	13 56.7	21 16.1
23	0 7 28.4	29 59.6	27 1.4	16 43.3	15 8.8	17 57.0	7 23.3	23 59.4	2 20.6	13 24.0	13 58.3	21 18.2
24	0 11 24.9	0♎53.5	26 58.0	29 31.3	16 33.9	19 3.7	8 1.2	23 57.7	2 17.2	13 27.4	14 .0	21 20.2
25	0 15 21.5	1 47.5	26 54.5	12♉47.4	18 2.0	20 10.4	8 38.8	23 55.7	2 13.8	13 30.7	14 1.7	21 22.1
26	0 19 18.0	2 41.4	26 51.0	26 40.5	19 32.7	21 17.1	9 16.3	23 53.6	2 10.5	13 34.1	14 3.4	21 24.1
27	0 23 14.6	3 35.4	26 47.6	11♊13.9	21 5.5	22 23.9	9 53.7	23 51.2	2 7.3	13 37.4	14 5.2	21 26.1
28	0 27 11.1	4 29.5	26 44.1	26 22.0	22 39.9	23 30.7	10 30.9	23 48.6	2 4.2	13 40.7	14 6.9	21 28.1
29	0 31 7.7	5 23.7	26 40.7	11♋49.1	24 15.5	24 37.6	11 8.0	23 45.8	2 1.1	13 44.1	14 8.7	21 30.1
30	0 35 4.2	6 17.9	26 37.2	27 12.7	25 52.0	25 44.4	11 44.9	23 42.9	1 58.1	13 47.3	14 10.5	21 32.0

DECLINATION

DAY	SID. TIME	☉	☊	☾	☿	♀	♂	♃	♄	♅	♆	♇
1	22 40 44.2	8N21.2	0N24.5	23N28.0	3N34.8	18N53.4	22N33.0	18N 5.7	12S41.5	8N22.4	14S47.4	18N54.3
4	22 52 33.9	7 15.4	0 24.5	20 18.6	5 12.8	18 38.2	22 16.9	18 6.9	12 46.4	8 18.1	14 48.5	18 51.9
7	23 4 23.5	6 8.6	0 24.5	6 41.5	6 51.8	18 18.7	21 59.4	18 7.8	12 51.1	8 13.8	14 49.8	18 49.5
10	23 16 13.2	5 .8	0 24.5	9S .4	8 15.6	17 55.0	21 40.6	18 8.3	12 55.7	8 9.5	14 51.1	18 47.2
13	23 28 2.8	3 52.2	0 24.5	20 30.5	9 11.2	17 26.9	21 20.7	18 8.3	13 .2	8 5.3	14 52.4	18 45.0
16	23 39 52.5	2 43.1	0 24.5	24 1.1	9 31.3	16 54.6	20 59.5	18 7.9	13 4.5	8 1.1	14 53.9	18 42.8
19	23 51 42.2	1 33.4	0 24.5	17 46.6	9 13.5	16 17.9	20 37.3	18 7.2	13 8.6	7 56.9	14 55.3	18 40.7
22	0 3 31.8	0 23.5	0 24.5	3 36.8	8 20.4	15 36.9	20 14.1	18 6.0	13 12.5	7 52.7	14 56.9	18 38.7
25	0 15 21.5	0S46.6	0 24.5	12N50.9	6 57.1	14 51.8	19 49.8	18 4.4	13 16.1	7 48.6	14 58.4	18 36.8
28	0 27 11.1	1 56.7	0 24.5	23 23.7	5 10.9	14 2.6	19 24.7	18 2.4	13 19.5	7 44.6	15 .1	18 34.9

OCTOBER 1964

LONGITUDE

DAY	EPHEM. SID. TIME	☉	☊	☽	☿	♀	♂	♃	♄	♅	♆	♇
	h m s	° ′	° ′	° ′	° ′	° ′	° ′	° ′	° ′	° ′	° ′	° ′
1	0 39 .8	7♎50.5	26♊50.7	8♌47.7	26♍26.4	24♌37.1	9♌35.5	25♉41.3	29♒10.4	12♍10.3	16♏ 9.6	14♍50.2
2	0 42 57.3	8 49.6	26 47.5	22 41.2	28 12.8	25 44.7	10 11.3	25 R 38.0	29 R 7.5	12 13.8	16 11.5	14 52.2
3	0 46 53.9	9 48.7	26 44.4	6♍27.5	29 59.8	26 52.5	10 46.9	25 34.5	29 4.6	12 17.2	16 13.4	14 54.2
4	0 50 50.5	10 47.8	26 41.2	20 4.0	1♎47.1	28 .4	11 22.5	25 30.8	29 1.8	12 20.7	16 15.3	14 56.1
5	0 54 47.0	11 46.9	26 38.0	3♎28.0	3 34.4	29 8.6	11 58.0	25 26.9	28 59.1	12 24.1	16 17.2	14 58.0
6	0 58 43.6	12 46.1	26 34.8	16 37.1	5 21.7	0♍16.9	12 33.3	25 22.8	28 56.4	12 27.5	16 19.1	14 60.0
7	1 2 40.1	13 45.3	26 31.7	29 29.6	7 8.7	1 25.4	13 8.6	25 18.5	28 53.9	12 30.8	16 21.1	15 1.9
8	1 6 36.7	14 44.6	26 28.5	12♏ 5.2	8 55.4	2 34.1	13 43.8	25 14.1	28 51.4	12 34.2	16 23.1	15 3.8
9	1 10 33.2	15 43.9	26 25.3	24 24.6	10 41.7	3 43.0	14 18.9	25 9.5	28 49.1	12 37.5	16 25.1	15 5.7
10	1 14 29.8	16 43.2	26 22.1	6♐30.0	12 27.5	4 52.0	14 53.9	25 4.7	28 46.8	12 40.8	16 27.1	15 7.6
11	1 18 26.3	17 42.5	26 18.9	18 24.9	14 12.7	6 1.2	15 28.8	24 59.8	28 44.6	12 44.1	16 29.1	15 9.5
12	1 22 22.9	18 41.9	26 15.8	0♑13.6	15 57.3	7 10.5	16 3.5	24 54.6	28 42.5	12 47.3	16 31.1	15 11.3
13	1 26 19.4	19 41.3	26 12.6	12 1.1	17 41.3	8 20.0	16 38.2	24 49.3	28 40.4	12 50.5	16 33.2	15 13.1
14	1 30 16.0	20 40.8	26 9.4	23 52.8	19 24.7	9 29.6	17 12.8	24 43.8	28 38.5	12 53.7	16 35.2	15 14.9
15	1 34 12.5	21 40.2	26 6.2	5♒54.2	21 7.4	10 39.4	17 47.2	24 38.2	28 36.7	12 56.9	16 37.3	15 16.7
16	1 38 9.1	22 39.7	26 3.1	18 10.5	22 49.5	11 49.3	18 21.6	24 32.4	28 34.9	12 60.0	16 39.4	15 18.5
17	1 42 5.6	23 39.2	25 59.9	0♓46.1	24 30.9	12 59.3	18 55.8	24 26.5	28 33.3	13 3.1	16 41.5	15 20.2
18	1 46 2.2	24 38.8	25 56.7	13 44.4	26 11.6	14 9.5	19 29.9	24 20.4	28 31.8	13 6.1	16 43.6	15 22.0
19	1 49 58.8	25 38.4	25 53.5	27 6.8	27 51.7	15 19.9	20 4.0	24 14.2	28 30.3	13 9.2	16 45.7	15 23.7
20	1 53 55.3	26 38.0	25 50.3	10♈52.7	29 31.1	16 30.3	20 37.9	24 7.8	28 29.0	13 12.2	16 47.8	15 25.4
21	1 57 51.9	27 37.6	25 47.2	24 59.2	1♏ 9.9	17 40.9	21 11.7	24 1.3	28 27.7	13 15.1	16 50.0	15 27.1
22	2 1 48.4	28 37.3	25 44.0	9♉21.4	2 48.1	18 51.7	21 45.4	23 54.7	28 26.5	13 18.0	16 52.1	15 28.7
23	2 5 45.0	29 37.0	25 40.8	23 53.2	4 25.7	20 2.5	22 18.9	23 47.9	28 25.5	13 20.9	16 54.3	15 30.4
24	2 9 41.5	0♏36.8	25 37.6	8♊27.9	6 2.8	21 13.5	22 52.4	23 41.1	28 24.5	13 23.8	16 56.5	15 32.0
25	2 13 38.1	1 36.6	25 34.5	22 59.8	7 39.2	22 24.6	23 25.7	23 34.1	28 23.7	13 26.6	16 58.6	15 33.6
26	2 17 34.6	2 36.4	25 31.3	7♋24.4	9 15.1	23 35.8	23 59.0	23 26.9	28 22.9	13 29.4	17 .8	15 35.2
27	2 21 31.2	3 36.2	25 28.1	21 38.6	10 50.5	24 47.2	24 32.1	23 19.7	28 22.3	13 32.2	17 3.0	15 36.7
28	2 25 27.7	4 36.1	25 24.9	5♌41.0	12 25.4	25 58.7	25 5.1	23 12.4	28 21.7	13 34.9	17 5.2	15 38.3
29	2 29 24.3	5 36.1	25 21.8	19 31.0	13 59.8	27 10.2	25 37.9	23 5.0	28 21.3	13 37.5	17 7.4	15 39.8
30	2 33 20.9	6 36.1	25 18.6	3♍ 8.6	15 33.8	28 22.0	26 10.7	22 57.5	28 21.0	13 40.2	17 9.7	15 41.3
31	2 37 17.4	7 36.1	25 15.4	16 33.8	17 7.2	29 33.8	26 43.3	22 49.9	28 20.7	13 42.8	17 11.9	15 42.8

LATITUDE

DAY	EPHEM. SID. TIME	☉	☊	☽	☿	♀	♂	♃	♄	♅	♆	♇
1	0 39 .8	0 .0	0 .0	3N23.0	1N53.4	0S10.1	1N10.0	1S13.2	1S43.4	0N44.1	1N43.2	13N41.1
4	0 50 50.5	0 .0	0 .0	4 59.5	1 49.1	0N 2.8	1 12.5	1 13.5	1 43.2	0 44.2	1 43.1	13 41.8
7	1 2 40.1	0 .0	0 .0	4 11.2	1 39.7	0 15.2	1 15.1	1 13.8	1 43.0	0 44.2	1 43.0	13 42.6
10	1 14 29.8	0 .0	0 .0	1 38.5	1 26.4	0 26.9	1 17.6	1 14.1	1 42.8	0 44.3	1 42.9	13 43.4
13	1 26 19.4	0 .0	0 .0	1S28.1	1 10.4	0 38.0	1 20.2	1 14.3	1 42.6	0 44.4	1 42.8	13 44.2
16	1 38 9.1	0 .0	0 .0	4 3.9	0 52.4	0 48.4	1 22.8	1 14.5	1 42.3	0 44.4	1 42.7	13 45.2
19	1 49 58.8	0 .0	0 .0	5 4.6	0 33.2	0 58.1	1 25.5	1 14.6	1 42.1	0 44.5	1 42.7	13 46.1
22	2 1 48.4	0 .0	0 .0	3 36.8	0 13.2	1 7.0	1 28.2	1 14.7	1 41.8	0 44.6	1 42.6	13 47.1
25	2 13 38.1	0 .0	0 .0	0 6.7	0S 7.1	1 15.2	1 30.9	1 14.7	1 41.5	0 44.7	1 42.6	13 48.2
28	2 25 27.7	0 .0	0 .0	3N24.5	0 27.4	1 22.5	1 33.7	1 14.7	1 41.2	0 44.8	1 42.5	13 49.3
31	2 37 17.4	0 .0	0 .0	5 5.6	0 47.2	1 29.0	1 36.5	1 14.7	1 40.9	0 44.9	1 42.5	13 50.5

RIGHT ASCENSION

DAY	EPHEM. SID. TIME	☉	☊	☽	☿	♀	♂	♃	♄	♅	♆	♇
1	0 39 .8	7♎12.1	26♊33.7	12♌10.7	27♍29.1	26♌51.3	12♌21.7	23♉39.7	1♓55.1	13♍50.6	14♏12.3	21♍34.0
2	0 42 57.3	8 6.5	26 30.3	26 28.1	29 6.5	27 58.2	12 58.3	23 R 36.3	1 R 52.2	13 53.9	14 14.1	21 35.9
3	0 46 53.9	9 .9	26 26.8	10♍ .3	0♎44.1	29 5.0	13 34.8	23 32.7	1 49.4	13 57.1	14 16.0	21 37.9
4	0 50 50.5	9 55.4	26 23.4	22 51.1	2 21.6	0♍11.9	14 11.1	23 29.0	1 46.7	14 .3	14 17.9	21 39.8
5	0 54 47.0	10 50.0	26 19.9	5♎ 9.6	3 59.0	1 18.8	14 47.2	23 25.0	1 44.1	14 3.5	14 19.8	21 41.7
6	0 58 43.6	11 44.7	26 16.4	17 7.0	5 36.2	2 25.6	15 23.2	23 20.9	1 41.5	14 6.7	14 21.7	21 43.7
7	1 2 40.1	12 39.5	26 13.0	28 55.0	7 13.0	3 32.4	15 59.1	23 16.6	1 39.0	14 9.8	14 23.6	21 45.6
8	1 6 36.7	13 34.4	26 9.5	10♏43.9	8 49.5	4 39.2	16 34.7	23 12.0	1 36.6	14 12.9	14 25.6	21 47.5
9	1 10 33.2	14 29.4	26 6.0	22 42.5	10 25.6	5 46.0	17 10.3	23 7.4	1 34.4	14 16.1	14 27.6	21 49.4
10	1 14 29.8	15 24.5	26 2.6	4♐56.4	12 1.2	6 52.8	17 45.7	23 2.5	1 32.1	14 19.1	14 29.5	21 51.3
11	1 18 26.3	16 19.7	25 59.1	17 27.7	13 36.4	7 59.5	18 20.8	22 57.5	1 30.0	14 22.2	14 31.5	21 53.1
12	1 22 22.9	17 15.0	25 55.7	0♑14.9	15 11.2	9 6.2	18 55.9	22 52.2	1 27.9	14 25.2	14 33.5	21 55.0
13	1 26 19.4	18 10.5	25 52.2	13 12.5	16 45.6	10 12.8	19 30.7	22 46.9	1 25.9	14 28.2	14 35.6	21 56.8
14	1 30 16.0	19 6.0	25 48.7	26 13.3	18 19.6	11 19.5	20 5.5	22 41.3	1 24.1	14 31.2	14 37.6	21 58.6
15	1 34 12.5	20 1.8	25 45.3	9♒ 9.6	19 53.2	12 26.1	20 40.0	22 35.6	1 22.3	14 34.1	14 39.7	22 .4
16	1 38 9.1	20 57.6	25 41.8	21 56.2	21 26.4	13 32.7	21 14.4	22 29.7	1 20.6	14 37.1	14 41.7	22 2.2
17	1 42 5.6	21 53.6	25 38.4	4♓31.5	22 59.3	14 39.3	21 48.6	22 23.7	1 18.9	14 39.9	14 43.8	22 4.0
18	1 46 2.2	22 49.7	25 34.9	16 58.1	24 32.0	15 45.8	22 22.7	22 17.5	1 17.4	14 42.8	14 45.9	22 5.8
19	1 49 58.8	23 46.0	25 31.4	29 22.6	26 4.4	16 52.4	22 56.6	22 11.2	1 16.0	14 45.6	14 48.0	22 7.5
20	1 53 55.3	24 42.4	25 28.0	11♈54.6	27 36.5	17 58.9	23 30.3	22 4.7	1 14.7	14 48.4	14 50.1	22 9.2
21	1 57 51.9	25 39.0	25 24.5	24 45.7	29 8.5	19 5.4	24 3.9	21 58.1	1 13.4	14 51.2	14 52.2	22 11.0
22	2 1 48.4	26 35.7	25 21.1	8♉ 7.8	0♏40.4	20 12.0	24 37.3	21 51.4	1 12.3	14 53.9	14 54.3	22 12.7
23	2 5 45.0	27 32.6	25 17.6	22 10.5	2 12.1	21 18.5	25 10.5	21 44.5	1 11.2	14 56.6	14 56.5	22 14.3
24	2 9 41.5	28 29.7	25 14.1	6♊57.6	3 43.7	22 25.0	25 43.6	21 37.5	1 10.3	14 59.3	14 58.6	22 16.0
25	2 13 38.1	29 27.0	25 10.7	22 22.8	5 15.3	23 31.6	26 16.5	21 30.4	1 9.4	15 1.9	15 .8	22 17.7
26	2 17 34.6	0♏24.5	25 7.2	8♋ 8.2	6 46.8	24 38.1	26 49.3	21 23.2	1 8.6	15 4.5	15 3.0	22 19.3
27	2 21 31.2	1 22.1	25 3.8	23 47.9	8 18.4	25 44.7	27 21.9	21 15.9	1 8.0	15 7.1	15 5.1	22 20.9
28	2 25 27.7	2 19.9	25 .3	8♌57.2	9 50.0	26 51.3	27 54.3	21 8.4	1 7.4	15 9.6	15 7.3	22 22.5
29	2 29 24.3	3 18.0	24 56.8	23 20.1	11 21.6	27 58.0	28 26.6	21 .9	1 7.0	15 12.1	15 9.5	22 24.1
30	2 33 20.9	4 16.2	24 53.4	6♍52.2	12 53.4	29 4.7	28 58.7	20 53.3	1 6.6	15 14.7	15 11.8	22 25.7
31	2 37 17.4	5 14.6	24 49.9	19 38.7	14 25.2	0♎11.4	29 30.6	20 45.6	1 6.4	15 17.1	15 14.0	22 27.2

DECLINATION

DAY	EPHEM. SID. TIME	☉	☊	☽	☿	♀	♂	♃	♄	♅	♆	♇
1	0 39 .8	3S 6.7	0N24.5	21N19.6	3N 9.0	13N 9.6	18N58.7	17N60.0	13S22.7	7N40.6	15S 1.7	18N33.1
4	0 50 50.5	4 16.4	0 24.5	8 31.4	0 57.5	12 12.8	18 32.0	17 57.2	13 25.5	7 36.7	15 3.4	18 31.4
7	1 2 40.1	5 25.7	0 24.5	7S22.6	1S18.6	11 12.4	18 4.5	17 54.0	13 28.1	7 32.8	15 5.2	18 29.9
10	1 14 29.8	6 34.3	0 24.5	19 46.9	3 35.8	10 8.8	17 36.4	17 50.4	13 30.4	7 29.1	15 7.0	18 28.4
13	1 26 19.4	7 42.2	0 24.5	24 21.8	5 51.5	9 2.1	17 7.7	17 46.5	13 32.4	7 25.4	15 8.8	18 27.0
16	1 38 9.1	8 49.1	0 24.5	19 15.0	8 4.0	7 52.6	16 38.5	17 42.3	13 34.1	7 21.8	15 10.6	18 25.7
19	1 49 58.8	9 54.8	0 24.5	5 48.3	10 11.9	6 40.5	16 8.9	17 37.7	13 35.5	7 18.4	15 12.5	18 24.5
22	2 1 48.4	10 59.2	0 24.5	11N11.1	12 14.4	5 26.1	15 38.9	17 32.9	13 36.5	7 15.1	15 14.3	18 23.5
25	2 13 38.1	12 2.1	0 24.5	23 8.9	14 10.7	4 9.8	15 8.6	17 27.7	13 37.3	7 11.9	15 16.2	18 22.5
28	2 25 27.7	13 3.4	0 24.5	22 9.3	16 .2	2 51.7	14 38.0	17 22.4	13 37.7	7 8.8	15 18.1	18 21.7
31	2 37 17.4	14 2.9	0 24.5	9 59.7	17 42.3	1 32.1	14 7.3	17 16.8	13 37.7	7 5.8	15 20.0	18 21.0

NOVEMBER 1964

DAY	EPHEM. SID. TIME	☉	☊	☾	☿	♀	♂	♃	♄	♅	♆	♇
		LONGITUDE										
	h m s	° ′	° ′	° ′	° ′	° ′	° ′	° ′	° ′	° ′	° ′	° ′
1	2 41 14.0	8♏36.1	25♊12.2	29♍46.5	18♏40.2	0♎45.7	27♌15.7	22♉42.2	28♒20.6	13♍45.4	17♏14.1	15♍44.2
2	2 45 10.5	9 36.2	25 9.0	12♎46.6	20 12.8	1 57.7	27 48.0	22R34.5	28 20.6	13 47.9	17 16.4	15 45.6
3	2 49 7.1	10 36.3	25 5.9	25 33.9	21 44.9	3 9.8	28 20.2	22 26.6	28 20.6	13 50.3	17 18.6	15 47.0
4	2 53 3.6	11 36.5	25 2.7	8♏ 8.1	23 16.6	4 22.0	28 52.2	22 18.7	28D20.8	13 52.8	17 20.8	15 48.4
5	2 57 .2	12 36.6	24 59.5	20 29.6	24 47.9	5 34.3	29 24.1	22 10.8	28 21.1	13 55.2	17 23.1	15 49.7
6	3 0 56.7	13 36.8	24 56.3	2♐39.3	26 18.8	6 46.6	29 55.9	22 2.8	28 21.5	13 57.5	17 25.3	15 51.0
7	3 4 53.3	14 37.1	24 53.2	14 38.7	27 49.3	7 59.1	0♍27.5	21 54.7	28 22.0	13 59.8	17 27.6	15 52.3
8	3 8 49.8	15 37.3	24 50.0	26 30.4	29 19.4	9 11.6	0 58.9	21 46.6	28 22.6	14 2.1	17 29.8	15 53.6
9	3 12 46.4	16 37.6	24 46.8	8♑17.5	0♐49.0	10 24.3	1 30.2	21 38.5	28 23.3	14 4.3	17 32.1	15 54.8
10	3 16 43.0	17 37.9	24 43.6	20 4.0	2 18.3	11 37.0	2 1.3	21 30.4	28 24.1	14 6.4	17 34.3	15 56.0
11	3 20 39.5	18 38.3	24 40.4	1♒54.6	3 47.1	12 49.8	2 32.2	21 22.2	28 25.0	14 8.5	17 36.6	15 57.2
12	3 24 36.1	19 38.6	24 37.3	13 54.1	5 15.4	14 2.6	3 3.0	21 14.0	28 26.0	14 10.6	17 38.8	15 58.4
13	3 28 32.6	20 39.0	24 34.1	26 7.6	6 43.2	15 15.6	3 33.7	21 5.8	28 27.1	14 12.6	17 41.1	15 59.5
14	3 32 29.2	21 39.4	24 30.9	8♓40.2	8 10.6	16 28.6	4 4.1	20 57.7	28 28.3	14 14.6	17 43.3	16 .6
15	3 36 25.7	22 39.8	24 27.7	21 35.9	9 37.4	17 41.6	4 34.4	20 49.5	28 29.7	14 16.5	17 45.6	16 1.7
16	3 40 22.3	23 40.3	24 24.6	4♈57.8	11 3.6	18 54.8	5 4.6	20 41.3	28 31.1	14 18.4	17 47.8	16 2.7
17	3 44 18.9	24 40.7	24 21.4	18 46.8	12 29.2	20 8.0	5 34.5	20 33.2	28 32.6	14 20.2	17 50.0	16 3.7
18	3 48 15.4	25 41.2	24 18.2	3♉ 1.6	13 54.0	21 21.3	6 4.3	20 25.1	28 34.2	14 22.0	17 52.3	16 4.7
19	3 52 12.0	26 41.8	24 15.0	17 38.2	15 18.1	22 34.6	6 33.9	20 17.0	28 36.0	14 23.7	17 54.5	16 5.7
20	3 56 8.5	27 42.4	24 11.9	2♊30.0	16 41.3	23 48.1	7 3.3	20 9.0	28 37.9	14 25.5	17 56.8	16 6.6
21	4 0 5.1	28 42.9	24 8.7	17 28.9	18 3.6	25 1.6	7 32.5	20 1.0	28 39.8	14 27.1	17 59.0	16 7.5
22	4 4 1.6	29 43.5	24 5.5	2♋26.5	19 24.7	26 15.1	8 1.6	19 53.0	28 41.8	14 28.7	18 1.2	16 8.4
23	4 7 58.2	0♐44.1	24 2.3	17 15.1	20 44.6	27 28.7	8 30.4	19 45.1	28 44.0	14 30.2	18 3.4	16 9.2
24	4 11 54.8	1 44.8	23 59.1	1♌48.8	22 3.0	28 42.4	8 59.1	19 37.3	28 46.2	14 31.7	18 5.6	16 10.0
25	4 15 51.3	2 45.5	23 56.0	16 3.7	23 19.8	29 56.1	9 27.5	19 29.5	28 48.5	14 33.1	18 7.8	16 10.8
26	4 19 47.9	3 46.2	23 52.8	29 58.2	24 34.8	1♏ 9.9	9 55.7	19 21.8	28 50.9	14 34.5	18 10.0	16 11.5
27	4 23 44.4	4 46.9	23 49.6	13♍32.3	25 47.7	2 23.8	10 23.8	19 14.2	28 53.5	14 35.8	18 12.2	16 12.3
28	4 27 41.0	5 47.7	23 46.4	26 47.0	26 58.2	3 37.7	10 51.6	19 6.7	28 56.1	14 37.1	18 14.3	16 12.9
29	4 31 37.5	6 48.4	23 43.3	9♎44.2	28 5.9	4 51.6	11 19.1	18 59.3	28 58.8	14 38.3	18 16.5	16 13.6
30	4 35 34.1	7 49.2	23 40.1	22 25.8	29 10.5	6 5.6	11 46.5	18 51.9	29 1.6	14 39.4	18 18.7	16 14.2
		LATITUDE										
1	2 41 14.0	0 .0	0 .0	5N 6.7	0S53.7	1N31.0	1N37.4	1S14.7	1S40.8	0N44.9	1N42.5	13N50.9
4	2 53 3.6	0 .0	0 .0	3 40.8	1 12.5	1 36.5	1 40.3	1 14.5	1 40.5	0 45.0	1 42.5	13 52.1
7	3 4 53.3	0 .0	0 .0	0 47.5	1 30.2	1 41.1	1 43.2	1 14.4	1 40.2	0 45.1	1 42.4	13 53.4
10	3 16 43.0	0 .0	0 .0	2S20.7	1 46.5	1 44.8	1 46.2	1 14.1	1 39.8	0 45.3	1 42.4	13 54.7
13	3 28 32.6	0 .0	0 .0	4 38.6	2 .9	1 47.8	1 49.3	1 13.8	1 39.5	0 45.4	1 42.4	13 56.0
16	3 40 22.3	0 .0	0 .0	5 7.1	2 13.0	1 49.9	1 52.4	1 13.5	1 39.2	0 45.5	1 42.5	13 57.4
19	3 52 12.0	0 .0	0 .0	3 2.9	2 22.3	1 51.2	1 55.5	1 13.1	1 38.9	0 45.6	1 42.5	13 58.8
22	4 4 1.6	0 .0	0 .0	0N51.4	2 28.2	1 51.8	1 58.8	1 12.7	1 38.5	0 45.7	1 42.5	14 .2
25	4 15 51.3	0 .0	0 .0	4 12.4	2 29.8	1 51.5	2 2.1	1 12.2	1 38.2	0 45.9	1 42.5	14 1.6
28	4 27 41.0	0 .0	0 .0	5 15.5	2 26.0	1 50.5	2 5.4	1 11.7	1 37.9	0 46.0	1 42.6	14 3.1
		RIGHT ASCENSION										
1	2 41 14.0	6♏13.3	24♊46.5	1♎49.9	15♏57.2	1♎18.1	0♍ 2.3	20♉37.8	1♓ 6.2	15♍19.5	15♏16.2	22♍28.7
2	2 45 10.5	7 12.1	24 43.0	13 38.7	17 29.2	2 24.9	0 33.9	20R30.0	1R 6.1	15 21.8	15 18.4	22 30.2
3	2 49 7.1	8 11.1	24 39.5	25 17.8	19 1.4	3 31.8	1 5.3	20 22.0	1D 6.2	15 24.1	15 20.6	22 31.7
4	2 53 3.6	9 10.3	24 36.1	6♏58.4	20 33.8	4 38.7	1 36.5	20 14.0	1 6.3	15 26.4	15 22.9	22 33.1
5	2 57 .2	10 9.8	24 32.6	18 49.8	22 6.2	5 45.7	2 7.5	20 6.0	1 6.5	15 28.6	15 25.1	22 34.6
6	3 0 56.7	11 9.4	24 29.2	0♐58.3	23 38.9	6 52.8	2 38.4	19 57.8	1 6.9	15 30.8	15 27.3	22 36.0
7	3 4 53.3	12 9.3	24 25.7	13 26.1	25 11.7	7 59.9	3 9.0	19 49.7	1 7.3	15 33.0	15 29.6	22 37.4
8	3 8 49.8	13 9.3	24 22.3	26 11.1	26 44.6	9 7.1	3 39.5	19 41.5	1 7.8	15 35.1	15 31.8	22 38.7
9	3 12 46.4	14 9.6	24 18.8	9♑ 7.1	28 17.6	10 14.4	4 9.8	19 33.3	1 8.5	15 37.1	15 34.0	22 40.1
10	3 16 43.0	15 10.0	24 15.3	22 5.3	29 50.7	11 21.9	4 39.9	19 25.0	1 9.2	15 39.2	15 36.3	22 41.4
11	3 20 39.5	16 10.7	24 11.9	4♒57.2	1♐23.9	12 29.4	5 9.8	19 16.8	1 10.0	15 41.2	15 38.5	22 42.7
12	3 24 36.1	17 11.6	24 8.4	17 36.4	2 57.1	13 37.0	5 39.5	19 8.5	1 11.0	15 43.1	15 40.8	22 44.0
13	3 28 32.6	18 12.7	24 5.0	0♓ 1.0	4 30.3	14 44.8	6 9.1	19 .2	1 12.0	15 45.0	15 43.0	22 45.2
14	3 32 29.2	19 14.0	24 1.5	12 13.8	6 3.4	15 52.7	6 38.4	18 51.9	1 13.1	15 46.8	15 45.2	22 46.4
15	3 36 25.7	20 15.5	23 58.1	24 21.6	7 36.4	17 .8	7 7.6	18 43.7	1 14.4	15 48.6	15 47.5	22 47.6
16	3 40 22.3	21 17.2	23 54.6	6♈35.1	9 9.2	18 9.0	7 36.5	18 35.4	1 15.7	15 50.4	15 49.7	22 48.8
17	3 44 18.9	22 19.2	23 51.1	19 7.2	10 41.7	19 17.3	8 5.3	18 27.2	1 17.1	15 52.1	15 51.9	22 49.9
18	3 48 15.4	23 21.3	23 47.7	2♉12.1	12 13.8	20 25.8	8 33.9	18 19.0	1 18.7	15 53.8	15 54.2	22 51.0
19	3 52 12.0	24 23.6	23 44.2	16 3.2	13 45.5	21 34.5	9 2.2	18 10.8	1 20.3	15 55.4	15 56.4	22 52.1
20	3 56 8.5	25 26.2	23 40.8	0♊48.7	15 16.5	22 43.4	9 30.5	18 2.7	1 22.1	15 57.0	15 58.7	22 53.2
21	4 0 5.1	26 29.0	23 37.3	16 26.8	16 46.7	23 52.4	9 58.4	17 54.6	1 23.9	15 58.6	16 .9	22 54.3
22	4 4 1.6	27 31.9	23 33.9	2♋40.7	18 15.9	25 1.7	10 26.2	17 46.6	1 25.8	16 .0	16 3.1	22 55.3
23	4 7 58.2	28 35.1	23 30.4	19 .1	19 44.0	26 11.1	10 53.8	17 38.6	1 27.8	16 1.5	16 5.3	22 56.3
24	4 11 54.8	29 38.4	23 27.0	4♌51.7	21 10.8	27 20.8	11 21.1	17 30.7	1 29.9	16 2.9	16 7.5	22 57.2
25	4 15 51.3	0♐42.0	23 23.5	19 51.3	22 35.8	28 30.7	11 48.3	17 22.9	1 32.1	16 4.2	16 9.7	22 58.2
26	4 19 47.9	1 45.7	23 20.0	3♍49.9	23 59.0	29 40.8	12 15.2	17 15.1	1 34.4	16 5.5	16 11.9	22 59.1
27	4 23 44.4	2 49.6	23 16.6	16 51.8	25 19.9	0♏51.1	12 41.9	17 7.4	1 36.8	16 6.7	16 14.0	22 59.9
28	4 27 41.0	3 53.8	23 13.1	29 8.9	26 38.2	2 1.7	13 8.4	16 59.8	1 39.3	16 7.9	16 16.2	23 .8
29	4 31 37.5	4 58.1	23 9.7	10♎55.8	27 53.4	3 12.5	13 34.7	16 52.3	1 41.9	16 9.1	16 18.4	23 1.6
30	4 35 34.1	6 2.5	23 6.2	22 27.4	29 5.1	4 23.6	14 .7	16 44.9	1 44.6	16 10.1	16 20.5	23 2.4
		DECLINATION										
1	2 41 14.0	14S22.3	0N24.5	4N46.7	18S14.6	1N 5.3	13N57.0	17N14.9	13S37.7	7N 4.9	15S20.6	18N20.8
4	2 53 3.6	15 19.1	0 24.5	10S44.2	19 46.0	0S15.6	13 26.2	17 9.0	13 37.3	7 2.1	15 22.5	18 20.3
7	3 4 53.3	16 13.6	0 24.4	21 46.4	21 8.6	1 37.2	12 55.3	17 3.1	13 36.6	6 59.5	15 24.4	18 19.9
10	3 16 43.0	17 5.7	0 24.4	24 15.7	22 21.9	2 59.2	12 24.6	16 57.0	13 35.6	6 57.0	15 26.3	18 19.6
13	3 28 32.6	17 55.1	0 24.4	17 10.5	23 25.3	4 21.2	11 54.0	16 50.9	13 34.2	6 54.8	15 28.2	18 19.4
16	3 40 22.3	18 41.7	0 24.4	2 43.6	24 18.0	5 42.8	11 23.6	16 44.8	13 32.5	6 52.6	15 30.0	18 19.4
19	3 52 12.0	19 25.3	0 24.4	14N10.1	24 59.5	7 3.9	10 53.6	16 38.7	13 30.5	6 50.7	15 31.9	18 19.5
22	4 4 1.6	20 5.7	0 24.4	24 16.7	25 29.0	8 23.9	10 23.8	16 32.8	13 28.1	6 48.9	15 33.7	18 19.7
25	4 15 51.3	20 42.9	0 24.4	20 2.2	25 46.2	9 42.7	9 54.5	16 26.9	13 25.5	6 47.3	15 35.5	18 20.1
28	4 27 41.0	21 16.6	0 24.4	6 6.2	25 50.5	10 59.7	9 25.8	16 21.3	13 22.5	6 45.9	15 37.2	18 20.6

DECEMBER 1964

LONGITUDE

DAY	EPHEM. SID. TIME	☉	☊	☽	☿	♀	♂	♃	♄	♅	♆	♇
	h m s	° ′	° ′	° ′	° ′	° ′	° ′	° ′	° ′	° ′	° ′	° ′
1	4 39 30.7	8♐50.1	23♊36.9	4♏54.0	0♑11.4	7♏19.7	12♍13.6	18♉44.7	29♒ 4.5	14♍40.5	18♏20.8	16♍14.8
2	4 43 27.2	9 50.9	23 33.7	17 10.7	1 8.2	8 33.8	12 40.5	18R37.5	29 7.5	14 41.6	18 22.9	16 15.3
3	4 47 23.8	10 51.8	23 30.6	29 17.6	2 .3	9 47.9	13 7.2	18 30.5	29 10.6	14 42.6	18 25.1	16 15.9
4	4 51 20.3	11 52.7	23 27.4	11♐16.6	2 46.9	11 2.1	13 33.5	18 23.6	29 13.8	14 43.5	18 27.2	16 16.4
5	4 55 16.9	12 53.6	23 24.2	23 9.3	3 27.5	12 16.3	13 59.7	18 16.8	29 17.1	14 44.4	18 29.3	16 16.8
6	4 59 13.4	13 54.5	23 21.0	4♑57.9	4 1.2	13 30.5	14 25.6	18 10.2	29 20.5	14 45.2	18 31.3	16 17.2
7	5 3 10.0	14 55.5	23 17.9	16 44.6	4 27.2	14 44.8	14 51.2	18 3.7	29 24.0	14 46.0	18 33.4	16 17.6
8	5 7 6.6	15 56.4	23 14.7	28 32.3	4 44.6	15 59.1	15 16.5	17 57.3	29 27.5	14 46.7	18 35.5	16 18.0
9	5 11 3.1	16 57.4	23 11.5	10♒24.2	4 52.6	17 13.5	15 41.6	17 51.1	29 31.2	14 47.3	18 37.5	16 18.3
10	5 14 59.7	17 58.4	23 8.3	22 24.1	4R50.4	18 27.9	16 6.4	17 45.0	29 34.9	14 47.9	18 39.5	16 18.6
11	5 18 56.2	18 59.4	23 5.1	4♓36.0	4 37.3	19 42.3	16 31.0	17 39.1	29 38.8	14 48.5	18 41.6	16 18.9
12	5 22 52.8	20 .4	23 2.0	17 4.3	4 12.8	20 56.8	16 55.2	17 33.3	29 42.7	14 49.0	18 43.6	16 19.1
13	5 26 49.3	21 1.4	22 58.8	29 53.2	3 36.8	22 11.3	17 19.1	17 27.7	29 46.7	14 49.4	18 45.5	16 19.3
14	5 30 45.9	22 2.5	22 55.6	13♈ 6.3	2 49.4	23 25.8	17 42.8	17 22.3	29 50.8	14 49.8	18 47.5	16 19.5
15	5 34 42.5	23 3.5	22 52.4	26 46.3	1 51.5	24 40.3	18 6.1	17 17.0	29 55.0	14 50.1	18 49.5	16 19.6
16	5 38 39.0	24 4.5	22 49.3	10♉53.9	0 44.2	25 54.9	18 29.1	17 11.9	29 59.2	14 50.4	18 51.4	16 19.7
17	5 42 35.6	25 5.6	22 46.1	25 27.4	29♐29.4	27 9.4	18 51.8	17 6.9	0♓ 3.6	14 50.6	18 53.3	16 19.8
18	5 46 32.1	26 6.6	22 42.9	10♊22.4	28 9.3	28 24.0	19 14.2	17 2.2	0 8.0	14 50.7	18 55.2	16 19.8
19	5 50 28.7	27 7.7	22 39.7	25 31.6	26 46.6	29 38.7	19 36.2	16 57.6	0 12.5	14 50.8	18 57.0	16 19.8
20	5 54 25.3	28 8.7	22 36.6	10♋45.7	25 24.1	0♐53.3	19 57.9	16 53.2	0 17.0	14 50.8	18 58.9	16 19.8
21	5 58 21.8	29 9.8	22 33.4	25 55.0	24 4.6	2 8.0	20 19.3	16 49.0	0 21.7	14 50.8	19 .7	16R19.7
22	6 2 18.4	0♑10.9	22 30.2	10♌50.4	22 50.5	3 22.7	20 40.3	16 44.9	0 26.4	14R50.7	19 2.5	16 19.6
23	6 6 14.9	1 12.0	22 27.0	25 24.7	21 43.9	4 37.5	21 1.0	16 41.1	0 31.2	14 50.6	19 4.3	16 19.5
24	6 10 11.5	2 13.1	22 23.9	9♍33.7	20 46.3	5 52.2	21 21.2	16 37.5	0 36.1	14 50.4	19 6.1	16 19.3
25	6 14 8.0	3 14.2	22 20.7	23 16.0	19 58.8	7 7.0	21 41.1	16 34.0	0 41.0	14 50.2	19 7.8	16 19.1
26	6 18 4.6	4 15.4	22 17.5	6♎32.3	19 22.0	8 21.8	22 .6	16 30.7	0 46.0	14 49.9	19 9.5	16 18.9
27	6 22 1.2	5 16.5	22 14.3	19 25.2	18 55.8	9 36.6	22 19.8	16 27.7	0 51.1	14 49.5	19 11.2	16 18.6
28	6 25 57.7	6 17.7	22 11.1	1♏58.2	18 40.1	10 51.5	22 38.5	16 24.8	0 56.3	14 49.1	19 12.9	16 18.3
29	6 29 54.3	7 18.8	22 8.0	14 15.1	18 34.5	12 6.3	22 56.8	16 22.1	1 1.5	14 48.6	19 14.6	16 18.0
30	6 33 50.8	8 20.0	22 4.8	26 19.9	18D38.2	13 21.2	23 14.6	16 19.6	1 6.8	14 48.1	19 16.2	16 17.7
31	6 37 47.4	9 21.1	22 1.6	8♐16.0	18 50.7	14 36.1	23 32.0	16 17.4	1 12.2	14 47.5	19 17.8	16 17.3

LATITUDE

DAY	EPHEM. SID. TIME	☉	☊	☽	☿	♀	♂	♃	♄	♅	♆	♇
1	4 39 30.7	0 .0	0 .0	3N56.0	2S15.4	1N48.8	2N 8.9	1S11.1	1S37.6	0N46.1	1N42.6	14N 4.6
4	4 51 20.3	0 .0	0 .0	1 4.4	1 56.3	1 46.3	2 12.4	1 10.5	1 37.3	0 46.3	1 42.7	14 6.1
7	5 3 10.0	0 .0	0 .0	2S 8.4	1 26.8	1 43.2	2 16.0	1 9.8	1 37.0	0 46.4	1 42.8	14 7.6
10	5 14 59.7	0 .0	0 .0	4 34.0	0 45.3	1 39.5	2 19.7	1 9.1	1 36.7	0 46.5	1 42.9	14 9.1
13	5 26 49.3	0 .0	0 .0	5 15.8	0N 7.7	1 35.1	2 23.5	1 8.4	1 36.4	0 46.6	1 42.9	14 10.6
16	5 38 39.0	0 .0	0 .0	3 33.7	1 7.5	1 30.2	2 27.4	1 7.6	1 36.2	0 46.8	1 43.0	14 12.1
19	5 50 28.7	0 .0	0 .0	0N13.9	2 3.4	1 24.8	2 31.3	1 6.8	1 35.9	0 46.9	1 43.1	14 13.6
22	6 2 18.4	0 .0	0 .0	3 55.8	2 43.6	1 18.9	2 35.4	1 6.0	1 35.7	0 47.0	1 43.2	14 15.1
25	6 14 8.0	0 .0	0 .0	5 17.6	3 2.6	1 12.6	2 39.6	1 5.2	1 35.4	0 47.2	1 43.4	14 16.6
28	6 25 57.7	0 .0	0 .0	4 7.1	3 2.6	1 6.0	2 43.9	1 4.3	1 35.2	0 47.3	1 43.5	14 18.1
31	6 37 47.4	0 .0	0 .0	1 21.0	2 49.3	0 58.9	2 48.2	1 3.5	1 35.0	0 47.4	1 43.6	14 19.5

RIGHT ASCENSION

DAY	EPHEM. SID. TIME	☉	☊	☽	☿	♀	♂	♃	♄	♅	♆	♇
1	4 39 30.7	7♐ 7.2	23♊ 2.8	3♏57.3	0♑12.7	5♏34.9	14♍26.5	16♉37.5	1♓47.3	16♍11.2	16♏22.7	23♍ 3.1
2	4 43 27.2	8 12.0	22 59.3	15 36.8	1 15.6	6 46.5	14 52.1	16R30.3	1 50.2	16 12.2	16 24.8	23 3.9
3	4 47 23.8	9 17.0	22 55.9	27 34.0	2 13.2	7 58.3	15 17.4	16 23.3	1 53.1	16 13.1	16 26.9	23 4.6
4	4 51 20.3	10 22.1	22 52.4	9♐52.9	3 4.6	9 10.4	15 42.5	16 16.3	1 56.2	16 14.0	16 29.0	23 5.2
5	4 55 16.9	11 27.3	22 48.9	22 32.7	3 49.3	10 22.8	16 7.3	16 9.4	1 59.3	16 14.8	16 31.1	23 5.9
6	4 59 13.4	12 32.7	22 45.5	5♑27.3	4 26.1	11 35.4	16 31.9	16 2.7	2 2.5	16 15.6	16 33.2	23 6.5
7	5 3 10.0	13 38.3	22 42.0	18 26.8	4 54.3	12 48.4	16 56.2	15 56.1	2 5.8	16 16.3	16 35.3	23 7.1
8	5 7 6.6	14 43.9	22 38.6	1♒20.4	5 13.0	14 1.6	17 20.2	15 49.7	2 9.2	16 17.0	16 37.4	23 7.6
9	5 11 3.1	15 49.7	22 35.1	13 59.3	5 21.2	15 15.1	17 44.0	15 43.4	2 12.7	16 17.6	16 39.4	23 8.2
10	5 14 59.7	16 55.6	22 31.7	26 19.2	5R18.2	16 28.8	18 7.5	15 37.3	2 16.2	16 18.2	16 41.4	23 8.6
11	5 18 56.2	18 1.6	22 28.2	8♓21.2	5 3.2	17 43.0	18 30.8	15 31.3	2 19.9	16 18.8	16 43.5	23 9.1
12	5 22 52.8	19 7.7	22 24.8	20 11.3	4 35.8	18 57.3	18 53.8	15 25.5	2 23.6	16 19.2	16 45.5	23 9.6
13	5 26 49.3	20 13.9	22 21.3	1♈59.7	3 56.0	20 12.0	19 16.5	15 19.8	2 27.5	16 19.7	16 47.5	23 10.0
14	5 30 45.9	21 20.1	22 17.9	13 59.5	3 4.0	21 26.9	19 38.9	15 14.3	2 31.3	16 20.0	16 49.4	23 10.3
15	5 34 42.5	22 26.4	22 14.4	26 26.3	2 .8	22 42.1	20 1.0	15 9.0	2 35.3	16 20.3	16 51.4	23 10.7
16	5 38 39.0	23 32.8	22 11.0	9♉36.3	0 47.8	23 57.7	20 22.8	15 3.8	2 39.4	16 20.6	16 53.3	23 11.0
17	5 42 35.6	24 39.2	22 7.5	23 43.9	29♐27.0	25 13.5	20 44.3	14 58.8	2 43.5	16 20.8	16 55.2	23 11.3
18	5 46 32.1	25 45.7	22 4.1	8♊56.3	28 .9	26 29.6	21 5.6	14 54.0	2 47.7	16 21.0	16 57.1	23 11.5
19	5 50 28.7	26 52.2	22 .6	25 7.0	26 32.5	27 46.0	21 26.5	14 49.3	2 52.0	16 21.1	16 59.0	23 11.7
20	5 54 25.3	27 58.7	21 57.2	11♋50.9	25 4.6	29 2.8	21 47.1	14 44.8	2 56.3	16 21.1	17 .9	23 11.9
21	5 58 21.8	29 5.3	21 53.7	28 29.7	23 40.2	0♐19.8	22 7.3	14 40.6	3 .7	16 21.1	17 2.7	23 12.0
22	6 2 18.4	0♑11.9	21 50.3	14♌26.6	22 21.7	1 37.0	22 27.3	14 36.5	3 5.2	16R21.0	17 4.5	23 12.2
23	6 6 14.9	1 18.5	21 46.8	29 20.1	21 11.4	2 54.6	22 46.9	14 32.5	3 9.8	16 20.9	17 6.3	23 12.3
24	6 10 11.5	2 25.1	21 43.4	13♍ 6.6	20 10.7	4 12.5	23 6.1	14 28.8	3 14.4	16 20.8	17 8.1	23 12.3
25	6 14 8.0	3 31.7	21 39.9	25 55.6	19 20.6	5 30.6	23 25.0	14 25.3	3 19.2	16 20.6	17 9.9	23 12.3
26	6 18 4.6	4 38.2	21 36.5	8♎ 2.3	18 41.7	6 49.0	23 43.6	14 22.0	3 23.9	16 20.3	17 11.6	23 12.3
27	6 22 1.2	5 44.8	21 33.0	19 43.2	18 14.0	8 7.6	24 1.8	14 18.8	3 28.8	16 20.0	17 13.3	23 12.3
28	6 25 57.7	6 51.3	21 29.6	1♏13.9	17 57.2	9 26.5	24 19.6	14 15.9	3 33.7	16 19.6	17 15.0	23R12.2
29	6 29 54.3	7 57.8	21 26.1	12 48.0	17 50.9	10 45.7	24 37.0	14 13.1	3 38.7	16 19.2	17 16.7	23 12.2
30	6 33 50.8	9 4.2	21 22.7	24 36.0	17D54.5	12 5.0	24 54.0	14 10.6	3 43.7	16 18.7	17 18.3	23 12.0
31	6 37 47.4	10 10.6	21 19.2	6♐44.6	18 7.2	13 24.7	25 10.6	14 8.3	3 48.8	16 18.2	17 19.9	23 11.9

DECLINATION

DAY	EPHEM. SID. TIME	☉	☊	☽	☿	♀	♂	♃	♄	♅	♆	♇
1	4 39 30.7	21S46.7	0N24.4	9S27.0	25S42.0	12S14.8	8N57.6	16N15.8	13S19.3	6N44.7	15S39.0	18N21.2
4	4 51 20.3	22 13.0	0 24.4	21 4.3	25 21.2	13 27.4	8 30.1	16 10.7	13 15.7	6 43.7	15 40.6	18 22.0
7	5 3 10.0	22 35.5	0 24.4	24 31.1	24 48.9	14 37.2	8 3.4	16 5.8	13 11.9	6 42.8	15 42.3	18 22.8
10	5 14 59.7	22 54.0	0 24.4	18 21.7	24 6.6	15 44.0	7 37.6	16 1.3	13 7.8	6 42.2	15 43.9	18 23.8
13	5 26 49.3	23 8.4	0 24.4	4 52.4	23 15.9	16 47.2	7 12.7	15 57.2	13 3.4	6 41.7	15 45.4	18 24.9
16	5 38 39.0	23 18.7	0 24.3	11N42.7	22 19.0	17 46.6	6 48.9	15 53.5	12 58.7	6 41.5	15 46.9	18 26.1
19	5 50 28.7	23 24.7	0 24.3	23 36.0	21 20.9	18 41.9	6 26.2	15 50.2	12 53.8	6 41.4	15 48.4	18 27.5
22	6 2 18.4	23 26.6	0 24.3	21 17.7	20 31.6	19 32.6	6 4.7	15 47.4	12 48.6	6 41.6	15 49.8	18 28.9
25	6 14 8.0	23 24.2	0 24.3	7 32.0	20 1.8	20 18.5	5 44.5	15 45.1	12 43.2	6 41.9	15 51.1	18 30.5
28	6 25 57.7	23 17.6	0 24.3	8S17.6	19 55.7	20 59.3	5 25.7	15 43.3	12 37.6	6 42.5	15 52.3	18 32.1
31	6 37 47.4	23 6.8	0 24.3	20 21.3	20 9.8	21 34.7	5 8.5	15 42.0	12 31.7	6 43.2	15 53.5	18 33.9

JANUARY 1965

DAY	EPHEM. SID. TIME	☉	☊	☽	☿	♀	♂	♃	♄	♅	♆	♇
		LONGITUDE										
	h m s	° ′	° ′	° ′	° ′	° ′	° ′	° ′	° ′	° ′	° ′	° ′
1	6 41 43.9	10♑22.4	21♊58.4	20♐ 6.6	19♐11.1	15♐51.0	23♍49.1	16♉15.4	1♓17.7	14♍46.9	19♏19.4	16♍16.9
2	6 45 40.5	11 23.5	21 55.3	1♑54.5	19 38.7	17 5.9	24 5.6	16R13.5	1 23.2	14R46.2	19 21.0	16R16.4
3	6 49 37.1	12 24.7	21 52.1	13 41.9	20 12.8	18 20.9	24 21.7	16 11.9	1 28.8	14 45.5	19 22.5	16 16.0
4	6 53 33.6	13 25.9	21 48.9	25 30.9	20 52.8	19 35.8	24 37.2	16 10.4	1 34.4	14 44.7	19 24.0	16 15.5
5	6 57 30.2	14 27.1	21 45.7	7♒23.6	21 37.9	20 50.8	24 52.3	16 9.2	1 40.1	14 43.8	19 25.5	16 14.9
6	7 1 26.7	15 28.2	21 42.6	19 21.8	22 27.8	22 5.7	25 6.9	16 8.2	1 45.8	14 42.9	19 27.0	16 14.3
7	7 5 23.3	16 29.4	21 39.4	1♓27.9	23 21.7	23 20.7	25 21.0	16 7.4	1 51.6	14 42.0	19 28.4	16 13.7
8	7 9 19.9	17 30.6	21 36.2	13 44.3	24 19.4	24 35.7	25 34.6	16 6.8	1 57.5	14 40.9	19 29.8	16 13.1
9	7 13 16.4	18 31.7	21 33.0	26 13.9	25 20.4	25 50.6	25 47.7	16 6.4	2 3.5	14 39.9	19 31.1	16 12.4
10	7 17 13.0	19 32.9	21 29.9	8♈59.8	26 24.3	27 5.6	26 .2	16 6.2	2 9.4	14 38.8	19 32.5	16 11.7
11	7 21 9.5	20 34.0	21 26.7	22 5.4	27 30.8	28 20.6	26 12.2	16 6.2	2 15.5	14 37.6	19 33.8	16 11.0
12	7 25 6.1	21 35.1	21 23.5	5♉33.3	28 39.7	29 35.6	26 23.6	16D 6.5	2 21.6	14 36.4	19 35.1	16 10.3
13	7 29 2.6	22 36.3	21 20.3	19 25.8	29 50.8	0♑50.6	26 34.5	16 6.9	2 27.7	14 35.1	19 36.3	16 9.5
14	7 32 59.2	23 37.4	21 17.1	3♊43.4	1♑ 3.7	2 5.6	26 44.8	16 7.6	2 33.9	14 33.8	19 37.6	16 8.7
15	7 36 55.8	24 38.5	21 14.0	18 24.3	2 18.4	3 20.6	26 54.5	16 8.4	2 40.2	14 32.5	19 38.8	16 7.8
16	7 40 52.3	25 39.5	21 10.8	3♋24.1	3 34.7	4 35.6	27 3.6	16 9.5	2 46.5	14 31.0	19 39.9	16 7.0
17	7 44 48.9	26 40.6	21 7.6	18 35.6	4 52.4	5 50.6	27 12.1	16 10.7	2 52.8	14 29.6	19 41.1	16 6.1
18	7 48 45.4	27 41.7	21 4.4	3♌49.3	6 11.5	7 5.6	27 20.0	16 12.2	2 59.2	14 28.1	19 42.2	16 5.2
19	7 52 42.0	28 42.7	21 1.3	18 54.8	7 31.8	8 20.6	27 27.3	16 13.9	3 5.6	14 26.5	19 43.2	16 4.2
20	7 56 38.5	29 43.8	20 58.1	3♍42.8	8 53.2	9 35.7	27 33.9	16 15.8	3 12.1	14 25.0	19 44.3	16 3.3
21	8 0 35.1	0♒44.8	20 54.9	18 6.1	10 15.7	10 50.7	27 39.9	16 17.8	3 18.7	14 23.3	19 45.3	16 2.3
22	8 4 31.7	1 45.9	20 51.7	2♎ .9	11 39.2	12 5.8	27 45.2	16 20.1	3 25.3	14 21.7	19 46.3	16 1.3
23	8 8 28.2	2 46.9	20 48.6	15 26.1	13 3.6	13 20.8	27 49.9	16 22.6	3 31.9	14 20.0	19 47.3	16 .3
24	8 12 24.8	3 47.9	20 45.4	28 23.8	14 28.9	14 35.9	27 53.8	16 25.3	3 38.5	14 18.2	19 48.2	15 59.2
25	8 16 21.3	4 48.9	20 42.2	10♏57.5	15 55.1	15 50.9	27 57.0	16 28.2	3 45.2	14 16.4	19 49.1	15 58.1
26	8 20 17.9	5 49.9	20 39.0	23 12.1	17 22.1	17 6.0	27 59.6	16 31.2	3 52.0	14 14.6	19 49.9	15 57.0
27	8 24 14.4	6 50.9	20 35.8	5♐12.5	18 49.9	18 21.1	28 1.4	16 34.5	3 58.7	14 12.7	19 50.8	15 55.9
28	8 28 11.0	7 51.9	20 32.7	17 3.7	20 18.4	19 36.1	28 2.4	16 37.9	4 5.5	14 10.7	19 51.6	15 54.7
29	8 32 7.6	8 52.9	20 29.5	28 50.5	21 47.8	20 51.2	28 2.7	16 41.6	4 12.4	14 8.8	19 52.3	15 53.5
30	8 36 4.1	9 53.8	20 26.3	10♑36.6	23 17.8	22 6.2	28R 2.3	16 45.4	4 19.2	14 6.8	19 53.0	15 52.3
31	8 40 .7	10 54.7	20 23.1	22 25.5	24 48.6	23 21.3	28 1.1	16 49.4	4 26.1	14 4.7	19 53.7	15 51.1
		LATITUDE										
1	6 41 43.9	0 .0	0 .0	0N16.3	2N42.9	0N56.5	2N49.7	1S 3.2	1S35.0	0N47.5	1N43.6	14N20.0
4	6 53 33.6	0 .0	0 .0	2S49.9	2 20.1	0 49.1	2 54.2	1 2.3	1 34.8	0 47.6	1 43.7	14 21.4
7	7 5 23.3	0 .0	0 .0	4 53.0	1 54.0	0 41.6	2 58.8	1 1.4	1 34.6	0 47.7	1 43.9	14 22.8
10	7 17 13.0	0 .0	0 .0	5 1.7	1 26.7	0 33.8	3 3.4	1 .6	1 34.5	0 47.9	1 44.0	14 24.2
13	7 29 2.6	0 .0	0 .0	2 52.6	0 59.4	0 26.0	3 8.1	0 59.7	1 34.3	0 48.0	1 44.2	14 25.5
16	7 40 52.3	0 .0	0 .0	0N58.2	0 32.8	0 18.1	3 12.9	0 58.8	1 34.2	0 48.1	1 44.3	14 26.7
19	7 52 42.0	0 .0	0 .0	4 19.6	0 7.4	0 10.2	3 17.7	0 58.0	1 34.1	0 48.2	1 44.5	14 28.0
22	8 4 31.7	0 .0	0 .0	5 6.6	0S16.4	0 2.3	3 22.6	0 57.1	1 34.0	0 48.3	1 44.7	14 29.2
25	8 16 21.3	0 .0	0 .0	3 25.4	0 38.5	0S 5.5	3 27.4	0 56.3	1 34.0	0 48.4	1 44.8	14 30.3
28	8 28 11.0	0 .0	0 .0	0 28.1	0 58.6	0 13.1	3 32.1	0 55.4	1 33.9	0 48.5	1 45.0	14 31.4
31	8 40 .7	0 .0	0 .0	2S35.6	1 16.5	0 20.6	3 36.8	0 54.6	1 33.9	0 48.5	1 45.2	14 32.4
		RIGHT ASCENSION										
1	6 41 43.9	11♑17.0	21♊15.8	19♐15.7	18♐28.4	14♐44.5	25♍26.9	14♉ 6.2	3♓54.1	16♍17.7	17♏21.6	23♍11.7
2	6 45 40.5	12 23.2	21 12.3	2♑ 5.5	18 57.1	16 4.6	25 42.7	14R 4.2	3 59.3	16R17.0	17 23.1	23R11.5
3	6 49 37.1	13 29.4	21 8.9	15 5.2	19 32.8	17 24.8	25 58.1	14 2.5	4 4.6	16 16.4	17 24.7	23 11.3
4	6 53 33.6	14 35.4	21 5.4	28 3.2	20 14.8	18 45.2	26 13.0	14 1.0	4 10.0	16 15.6	17 26.2	23 11.0
5	6 57 30.2	15 41.4	21 2.0	10♒48.6	21 2.4	20 5.8	26 27.5	13 59.7	4 15.4	16 14.8	17 27.7	23 10.7
6	7 1 26.7	16 47.3	20 58.5	23 13.9	21 55.1	21 26.5	26 41.5	13 58.6	4 20.9	16 14.0	17 29.1	23 10.4
7	7 5 23.3	17 53.0	20 55.1	5♓17.4	22 52.4	22 47.4	26 55.1	13 57.7	4 26.4	16 13.1	17 30.6	23 10.0
8	7 9 19.9	18 58.6	20 51.6	17 2.5	23 53.8	24 8.4	27 8.2	13 57.0	4 32.0	16 12.2	17 32.0	23 9.6
9	7 13 16.4	20 4.1	20 48.2	28 37.7	24 59.0	25 29.5	27 20.8	13 56.5	4 37.6	16 11.2	17 33.4	23 9.2
10	7 17 13.0	21 9.4	20 44.7	10♈14.6	26 7.5	26 50.8	27 33.0	13 56.3	4 43.3	16 10.2	17 34.7	23 8.7
11	7 21 9.5	22 14.6	20 41.3	22 7.7	27 19.0	28 12.1	27 44.6	13 56.2	4 49.1	16 9.2	17 36.1	23 8.2
12	7 25 6.1	23 19.7	20 37.8	4♉33.1	28 33.3	29 33.5	27 55.7	13D56.4	4 54.9	16 8.1	17 37.4	23 7.7
13	7 29 2.6	24 24.5	20 34.4	17 47.1	29 50.0	0♑55.0	28 6.3	13 56.7	5 .7	16 6.9	17 38.6	23 7.2
14	7 32 59.2	25 29.3	20 30.9	2♊ 3.2	1♑ 9.0	2 16.5	28 16.4	13 57.3	5 6.6	16 5.7	17 39.9	23 6.6
15	7 36 55.8	26 33.8	20 27.5	17 25.8	2 30.1	3 38.0	28 26.0	13 58.0	5 12.6	16 4.4	17 41.1	23 6.0
16	7 40 52.3	27 38.2	20 24.0	3♋44.1	3 53.0	4 59.6	28 35.0	13 59.0	5 18.5	16 3.1	17 42.3	23 5.4
17	7 44 48.9	28 42.4	20 20.6	20 28.8	5 17.6	6 21.2	28 43.4	14 .2	5 24.6	16 1.8	17 43.4	23 4.7
18	7 48 45.4	29 46.5	20 17.1	7♌ .7	6 43.8	7 42.7	28 51.3	14 1.6	5 30.7	16 .4	17 44.5	23 4.1
19	7 52 42.0	0♒50.4	20 13.7	22 45.9	8 11.4	9 4.3	28 58.6	14 3.1	5 36.8	15 59.0	17 45.6	23 3.4
20	7 56 38.5	1 54.0	20 10.2	7♍27.7	9 40.3	10 25.8	29 5.4	14 4.9	5 42.9	15 57.5	17 46.7	23 2.6
21	8 0 35.1	2 57.5	20 6.8	21 6.3	11 10.4	11 47.2	29 11.5	14 6.9	5 49.1	15 56.0	17 47.7	23 1.9
22	8 4 31.7	4 .9	20 3.3	3♎53.0	12 41.7	13 8.7	29 17.0	14 9.1	5 55.4	15 54.5	17 48.8	23 1.1
23	8 8 28.2	5 4.0	19 59.9	16 3.2	14 13.9	14 30.0	29 21.9	14 11.5	6 1.7	15 52.9	17 49.7	23 .3
24	8 12 24.8	6 7.0	19 56.4	27 53.0	15 47.0	15 51.2	29 26.2	14 14.1	6 8.0	15 51.3	17 50.7	22 59.5
25	8 16 21.3	7 9.7	19 53.0	9♏37.2	17 21.0	17 12.3	29 29.8	14 16.8	6 14.4	15 49.7	17 51.6	22 58.6
26	8 20 17.9	8 12.3	19 49.6	21 28.0	18 55.8	18 33.3	29 32.7	14 19.8	6 20.8	15 48.0	17 52.5	22 57.8
27	8 24 14.4	9 14.6	19 46.1	3♐33.9	20 31.3	19 54.2	29 35.0	14 23.0	6 27.2	15 46.2	17 53.3	22 56.9
28	8 28 11.0	10 16.8	19 42.7	15 59.5	22 7.5	21 14.9	29 36.6	14 26.3	6 33.6	15 44.4	17 54.1	22 55.9
29	8 32 7.6	11 18.7	19 39.2	28 43.9	23 44.2	22 35.5	29 37.6	14 29.9	6 40.1	15 42.6	17 54.9	22 55.0
30	8 36 4.1	12 20.5	19 35.8	11♑41.0	25 21.5	23 55.8	29 37.8	14 33.6	6 46.6	15 40.8	17 55.6	22 54.0
31	8 40 .7	13 22.1	19 32.3	24 40.9	26 59.4	25 16.0	29R37.3	14 37.6	6 53.2	15 38.9	17 56.3	22 53.0
		DECLINATION										
1	6 41 43.9	23S 2.3	0N24.3	22S48.3	20S17.8	21S45.3	5N 3.1	15N41.7	12S29.7	6N43.5	15S54.0	18N34.5
4	6 53 33.6	22 46.0	0 24.3	23 49.5	20 48.1	22 13.2	4 48.1	15 41.1	12 23.6	6 44.5	15 55.1	18 36.3
7	7 5 23.3	22 25.6	0 24.3	15 30.8	21 22.8	22 35.1	4 34.9	15 41.1	12 17.2	6 45.6	15 56.1	18 38.3
10	7 17 13.0	22 1.2	0 24.3	1 3.3	21 57.0	22 50.9	4 23.6	15 41.6	12 10.7	6 47.0	15 57.1	18 40.3
13	7 29 2.6	21 32.9	0 24.3	14N49.3	22 27.2	23 .5	4 14.3	15 42.6	12 4.0	6 48.5	15 58.0	18 42.4
16	7 40 52.3	21 .9	0 24.2	24 22.2	22 50.9	23 3.8	4 7.2	15 44.2	11 57.1	6 50.1	15 58.8	18 44.6
19	7 52 42.0	20 25.3	0 24.2	19 15.9	23 6.4	23 .7	4 2.2	15 46.3	11 50.1	6 52.0	15 59.5	18 46.8
22	8 4 31.7	19 46.3	0 24.2	3 53.2	23 12.3	22 51.3	3 59.4	15 48.9	11 42.9	6 53.9	16 .2	18 49.0
25	8 16 21.3	19 3.9	0 24.2	11S51.7	23 7.9	22 35.6	3 59.2	15 52.0	11 35.6	6 56.1	16 .8	18 51.3
28	8 28 11.0	18 18.4	0 24.2	22 21.0	22 52.4	22 13.7	4 1.4	15 55.6	11 28.1	6 58.3	16 1.2	18 53.6
31	8 40 .7	17 29.9	0 24.2	24 8.2	22 25.4	21 45.7	4 6.2	15 59.6	11 20.6	7 .7	16 1.7	18 56.0

FEBRUARY 1965

LONGITUDE

DAY	EPHEM. SID. TIME	☉	☊	☾	☿	♀	♂	♃	♄	♅	♆	♇
	h m s	° ′	° ′	° ′	° ′	° ′	° ′	° ′	° ′	° ′	° ′	° ′
1	8 43 57.2	11♒55.7	20♊20.0	4♒19.5	26♑20.2	24♑36.4	27♍59.2	16♉53.7	4♓33.1	14♍ 2.7	19♏54.4	15♍49.9
2	8 47 53.8	12 56.6	20 16.8	16 20.6	27 52.4	25 51.4	27R56.5	16 58.1	4 40.0	14R .6	19 55.0	15R48.6
3	8 51 50.3	13 57.5	20 13.6	28 30.1	29 25.5	27 6.5	27 52.9	17 2.6	4 47.0	13 58.4	19 55.6	15 47.3
4	8 55 46.9	14 58.3	20 10.4	10♓48.9	0♒59.2	28 21.5	27 48.7	17 7.4	4 54.0	13 56.3	19 56.2	15 46.0
5	8 59 43.4	15 59.2	20 7.3	23 18.1	2 33.7	29 36.6	27 43.6	17 12.4	5 1.1	13 54.1	19 56.7	15 44.7
6	9 3 40.0	16 60.0	20 4.1	5♈58.5	4 8.9	0♒51.6	27 37.7	17 17.5	5 8.1	13 51.8	19 57.2	15 43.4
7	9 7 36.6	18 .8	20 .9	18 51.5	5 44.9	2 6.7	27 31.1	17 22.8	5 15.2	13 49.6	19 57.6	15 42.0
8	9 11 33.1	19 1.6	19 57.7	1♉58.9	7 21.6	3 21.7	27 23.6	17 28.3	5 22.3	13 47.3	19 58.0	15 40.6
9	9 15 29.7	20 2.3	19 54.5	15 22.4	8 59.2	4 36.7	27 15.4	17 33.9	5 29.5	13 45.0	19 58.4	15 39.3
10	9 19 26.2	21 3.0	19 51.4	29 4.1	10 37.5	5 51.7	27 6.4	17 39.8	5 36.6	13 42.6	19 58.8	15 37.9
11	9 23 22.8	22 3.7	19 48.2	13♊ 5.3	12 16.6	7 6.7	26 56.6	17 45.7	5 43.8	13 40.2	19 59.1	15 36.4
12	9 27 19.3	23 4.4	19 45.0	27 26.1	13 56.6	8 21.8	26 46.1	17 52.0	5 51.1	13 37.9	19 59.4	15 35.1
13	9 31 15.9	24 5.1	19 41.8	12♋ 4.5	15 37.3	9 36.8	26 34.8	17 58.3	5 58.3	13 35.5	19 59.7	15 33.6
14	9 35 12.4	25 5.7	19 38.7	26 56.3	17 19.0	10 51.8	26 22.7	18 4.8	6 5.5	13 33.1	19 59.9	15 32.2
15	9 39 9.0	26 6.3	19 35.5	11♌54.6	19 1.5	12 6.7	26 9.8	18 11.4	6 12.7	13 30.6	20 .1	15 30.7
16	9 43 5.5	27 6.8	19 32.3	26 50.8	20 44.8	13 21.7	25 56.3	18 18.2	6 20.0	13 28.1	20 .2	15 29.2
17	9 47 2.1	28 7.4	19 29.1	11♍35.6	22 29.1	14 36.7	25 41.9	18 25.2	6 27.2	13 25.6	20 .3	15 27.7
18	9 50 58.7	29 7.9	19 25.9	26 .8	24 14.2	15 51.7	25 26.9	18 32.3	6 34.5	13 23.1	20 .4	15 26.2
19	9 54 55.2	0♓ 8.4	19 22.8	10♎ .6	26 .3	17 6.6	25 11.2	18 39.6	6 41.8	13 20.6	20 .5	15 24.7
20	9 58 51.8	1 8.8	19 19.6	23 32.4	27 47.3	18 21.6	24 54.7	18 47.0	6 49.1	13 18.1	20 .5	15 23.2
21	10 2 48.3	2 9.3	19 16.4	6♏36.3	29 35.2	19 36.5	24 37.6	18 54.6	6 56.4	13 15.5	20 .5	15 21.6
22	10 6 44.9	3 9.7	19 13.2	19 14.9	1♓24.0	20 51.5	24 19.9	19 2.3	7 3.7	13 12.9	20R .4	15 20.1
23	10 10 41.4	4 10.1	19 10.1	1♐32.5	3 13.8	22 6.4	24 1.5	19 10.2	7 11.0	13 10.4	20 .3	15 18.6
24	10 14 38.0	5 10.4	19 6.9	13 34.3	5 4.4	23 21.3	23 42.5	19 18.2	7 18.3	13 7.8	20 .2	15 17.0
25	10 18 34.5	6 10.8	19 3.7	25 26.0	6 55.9	24 36.3	23 22.9	19 26.4	7 25.6	13 5.2	20 .0	15 15.4
26	10 22 31.1	7 11.1	19 .5	7♑12.9	8 48.2	25 51.2	23 2.8	19 34.7	7 32.9	13 2.6	19 59.8	15 13.9
27	10 26 27.6	8 11.4	18 57.3	19 .2	10 41.3	27 6.1	22 42.2	19 43.1	7 40.3	12 59.9	19 59.6	15 12.3
28	10 30 24.2	9 11.7	18 54.2	0♒52.1	12 35.1	28 21.0	22 21.0	19 51.7	7 47.6	12 57.3	19 59.4	15 10.7

LATITUDE

DAY	EPHEM. SID. TIME	☉	☊	☾	☿	♀	♂	♃	♄	♅	♆	♇
1	8 43 57.2	0 .0	0 .0	3S26.9	1S21.9	0S23.0	3N38.3	0S54.3	1S33.9	0N48.6	1N45.2	14N32.7
4	8 55 46.9	0 .0	0 .0	5 .2	1 36.6	0 30.2	3 42.8	0 53.5	1 33.9	0 48.6	1 45.4	14 33.7
7	9 7 36.6	0 .0	0 .0	4 30.8	1 48.6	0 37.1	3 47.0	0 52.7	1 33.9	0 48.7	1 45.6	14 34.5
10	9 19 26.2	0 .0	0 .0	1 54.7	1 57.7	0 43.6	3 51.0	0 51.9	1 34.0	0 48.8	1 45.8	14 35.4
13	9 31 15.9	0 .0	0 .0	1N49.8	2 3.6	0 49.8	3 54.6	0 51.2	1 34.0	0 48.8	1 45.9	14 36.1
16	9 43 5.5	0 .0	0 .0	4 37.3	2 6.1	0 55.6	3 57.7	0 50.4	1 34.1	0 48.9	1 46.1	14 36.8
19	9 54 55.2	0 .0	0 .0	4 44.9	2 4.8	1 1.0	4 .3	0 49.7	1 34.2	0 48.9	1 46.3	14 37.4
22	10 6 44.9	0 .0	0 .0	2 35.2	1 59.3	1 5.9	4 2.3	0 49.0	1 34.3	0 49.0	1 46.5	14 37.9
25	10 18 34.5	0 .0	0 .0	0S29.5	1 49.2	1 10.4	4 3.6	0 48.3	1 34.5	0 49.0	1 46.6	14 38.4
28	10 30 24.2	0 .0	0 .0	3 18.9	1 34.3	1 14.3	4 4.1	0 47.6	1 34.6	0 49.0	1 46.8	14 38.7

RIGHT ASCENSION

DAY	EPHEM. SID. TIME	☉	☊	☾	☿	♀	♂	♃	♄	♅	♆	♇
1	8 43 57.2	14♒23.4	19♊28.9	7♒32.6	28♑37.7	26♑36.0	29♍36.1	14♉41.7	6♓59.8	15♍37.0	17♏57.0	22♍52.0
2	8 47 53.8	15 24.6	19 25.4	20 7.4	0♒16.4	27 55.8	29R34.2	14 46.0	7 6.4	15R35.0	17 57.6	22R50.9
3	8 51 50.3	16 25.5	19 22.0	2♓20.9	1 55.6	29 15.4	29 31.6	14 50.5	7 13.0	15 33.1	17 58.3	22 49.9
4	8 55 46.9	17 26.3	19 18.6	14 14.1	3 35.1	0♒34.7	29 28.3	14 55.2	7 19.6	15 31.0	17 58.8	22 48.8
5	8 59 43.4	18 26.8	19 15.1	25 52.6	5 14.9	1 53.8	29 24.2	15 .0	7 26.3	15 29.0	17 59.4	22 47.7
6	9 3 40.0	19 27.1	19 11.7	7♈26.1	6 55.1	3 12.7	29 19.4	15 5.1	7 33.0	15 26.9	17 59.9	22 46.6
7	9 7 36.6	20 27.2	19 8.2	19 6.8	8 35.6	4 31.3	29 13.8	15 10.3	7 39.7	15 24.8	18 .3	22 45.4
8	9 11 33.1	21 27.1	19 4.8	1♉ 9.1	10 16.3	5 49.6	29 7.5	15 15.7	7 46.5	15 22.7	18 .8	22 44.3
9	9 15 29.7	22 26.9	19 1.3	13 48.0	11 57.3	7 7.7	29 .5	15 21.3	7 53.2	15 20.6	18 1.2	22 43.1
10	9 19 26.2	23 26.4	18 57.9	27 17.2	13 38.5	8 25.5	28 52.8	15 27.0	8 .0	15 18.4	18 1.6	22 41.9
11	9 23 22.8	24 25.7	18 54.4	11♊45.6	15 20.0	9 43.0	28 44.3	15 33.0	8 6.8	15 16.2	18 1.9	22 40.7
12	9 27 19.3	25 24.8	18 51.0	27 11.5	17 1.7	11 .3	28 35.1	15 39.1	8 13.7	15 14.0	18 2.2	22 39.5
13	9 31 15.9	26 23.8	18 47.6	13♋18.4	18 43.6	12 17.3	28 25.1	15 45.4	8 20.5	15 11.8	18 2.5	22 38.2
14	9 35 12.4	27 22.5	18 44.1	29 36.6	20 25.7	13 33.9	28 14.5	15 51.8	8 27.3	15 9.5	18 2.7	22 37.0
15	9 39 9.0	28 21.0	18 40.7	15♌32.8	22 7.9	14 50.3	28 3.1	15 58.4	8 34.2	15 7.3	18 2.9	22 35.7
16	9 43 5.5	29 19.4	18 37.2	0♍42.8	23 50.4	16 6.4	27 51.0	16 5.1	8 41.0	15 5.0	18 3.1	22 34.4
17	9 47 2.1	0♓17.6	18 33.8	14 57.4	25 33.1	17 22.2	27 38.2	16 12.0	8 47.9	15 2.6	18 3.2	22 33.1
18	9 50 58.7	1 15.6	18 30.4	28 20.6	27 15.9	18 37.7	27 24.8	16 19.1	8 54.8	15 .3	18 3.3	22 31.8
19	9 54 55.2	2 13.4	18 26.9	11♎ 3.7	28 58.9	19 52.9	27 10.6	16 26.3	9 1.7	14 58.0	18 3.4	22 30.5
20	9 58 51.8	3 11.1	18 23.5	23 20.9	0♓42.1	21 7.9	26 55.8	16 33.7	9 8.5	14 55.6	18 3.4	22 29.1
21	10 2 48.3	4 8.6	18 20.0	5♏26.1	2 25.5	22 22.5	26 40.3	16 41.3	9 15.4	14 53.2	18 3.4	22 27.8
22	10 6 44.9	5 5.9	18 16.6	17 31.4	4 9.1	23 36.9	26 24.2	16 49.0	9 22.4	14 50.9	18 3.4	22 26.4
23	10 10 41.4	6 3.1	18 13.1	29 46.0	5 52.8	24 50.9	26 7.5	16 56.8	9 29.3	14 48.5	18R 3.3	22 25.0
24	10 14 38.0	7 .2	18 9.7	12♐15.4	7 36.7	26 4.7	25 50.2	17 4.8	9 36.2	14 46.0	18 3.2	22 23.6
25	10 18 34.5	7 57.0	18 6.3	25 .3	9 20.7	27 18.2	25 32.3	17 12.9	9 43.1	14 43.6	18 3.1	22 22.2
26	10 22 31.1	8 53.8	18 2.8	7♑56.9	11 4.8	28 31.5	25 13.9	17 21.2	9 50.0	14 41.2	18 2.9	22 20.8
27	10 26 27.6	9 50.4	17 59.4	20 57.2	12 48.9	29 44.4	24 55.0	17 29.6	9 56.9	14 38.8	18 2.7	22 19.4
28	10 30 24.2	10 46.9	17 55.9	3♒52.1	14 33.1	0♓57.1	24 35.5	17 38.2	10 3.8	14 36.3	18 2.4	22 18.0

DECLINATION

DAY	EPHEM. SID. TIME	☉	☊	☾	☿	♀	♂	♃	♄	♅	♆	♇
1	8 43 57.2	17S13.1	0N24.2	22S31.8	22S13.8	21S35.0	4N 8.3	16N 1.1	11S18.0	7N 1.6	16S 1.8	18N56.8
4	8 55 46.9	16 20.9	0 24.2	12 8.3	21 30.8	20 59.2	4 16.6	16 5.7	11 10.4	7 4.1	16 2.1	18 59.1
7	9 7 36.6	15 26.1	0 24.2	3N12.7	20 35.5	20 17.7	4 27.5	16 10.8	11 2.6	7 6.7	16 2.3	19 1.5
10	9 19 26.2	14 29.0	0 24.1	18 5.3	19 27.8	19 30.9	4 40.9	16 16.3	10 54.7	7 9.5	16 2.4	19 3.9
13	9 31 15.9	13 29.8	0 24.1	24 43.1	18 7.4	18 38.9	4 56.8	16 22.2	10 46.8	7 12.3	16 2.5	19 6.3
16	9 43 5.5	12 28.5	0 24.1	16 54.3	16 34.3	17 42.1	5 15.0	16 28.5	10 38.8	7 15.1	16 2.5	19 8.6
19	9 54 55.2	11 25.5	0 24.1	0 24.2	14 48.5	16 40.8	5 35.3	16 35.1	10 30.8	7 18.1	16 2.4	19 11.0
22	10 6 44.9	10 20.9	0 24.1	15S 3.1	12 50.2	15 35.2	5 57.5	16 42.0	10 22.8	7 21.0	16 2.2	19 13.3
25	10 18 34.5	9 14.8	0 24.1	23 51.4	10 39.6	14 25.7	6 21.3	16 49.2	10 14.7	7 24.0	16 1.9	19 15.5
28	10 30 24.2	8 7.4	0 24.1	23 12.2	8 17.4	13 12.7	6 46.3	16 56.6	10 6.7	7 27.1	16 1.6	19 17.7

MARCH 1965

DAY	EPHEM. SID. TIME	☉	☊	☽	☿	♀	♂	♃	♄	♅	♆	♇
	h m s	° ′	° ′	° ′	° ′	° ′	° ′	° ′	° ′	° ′	° ′	° ′
		LONGITUDE										
1	10 34 20.8	10♓11.9	18♊51.0	12♒52.2	14♓29.5	29♒35.9	21♍59.5	20♉ .4	7♓54.9	12♍54.7	19♏59.1	15♍ 9.1
2	10 38 17.3	11 12.2	18 47.8	25 2.9	16 24.5	0♓50.8	21R37.5	20 9.2	8 2.2	12R52.1	19R58.7	15R 7.6
3	10 42 13.9	12 12.4	18 44.6	7♓25.7	18 19.8	2 5.7	21 15.2	20 18.2	8 9.5	12 49.4	19 58.4	15 6.0
4	10 46 10.4	13 12.5	18 41.5	20 1.0	20 15.5	3 20.6	20 52.5	20 27.3	8 16.8	12 46.8	19 58.0	15 4.4
5	10 50 7.0	14 12.7	18 38.3	2♈48.9	22 11.2	4 35.5	20 29.6	20 36.6	8 24.2	12 44.2	19 57.6	15 2.8
6	10 54 3.5	15 12.8	18 35.1	15 48.5	24 6.8	5 50.3	20 6.5	20 45.9	8 31.5	12 41.6	19 57.2	15 1.2
7	10 58 .1	16 12.9	18 31.9	28 59.2	26 1.9	7 5.2	19 43.1	20 55.4	8 38.8	12 39.0	19 56.7	14 59.7
8	11 1 56.6	17 12.9	18 28.7	12♉20.6	27 56.4	8 20.0	19 19.6	21 5.0	8 46.0	12 36.3	19 56.2	14 58.1
9	11 5 53.2	18 12.9	18 25.6	25 52.7	29 49.9	9 34.8	18 56.0	21 14.7	8 53.3	12 33.7	19 55.6	14 56.5
10	11 9 49.7	19 12.8	18 22.4	9♊36.1	1♈42.0	10 49.6	18 32.3	21 24.5	9 .5	12 31.1	19 55.1	14 54.9
11	11 13 46.3	20 12.8	18 19.2	23 31.2	3 32.3	12 4.4	18 8.6	21 34.5	9 7.8	12 28.5	19 54.4	14 53.3
12	11 17 42.8	21 12.7	18 16.0	7♋38.4	5 20.4	13 19.1	17 45.0	21 44.5	9 15.0	12 25.9	19 53.8	14 51.7
13	11 21 39.4	22 12.5	18 12.9	21 56.8	7 5.9	14 33.9	17 21.4	21 54.7	9 22.2	12 23.3	19 53.1	14 50.1
14	11 25 35.9	23 12.3	18 9.7	6♌24.4	8 48.3	15 48.6	16 58.0	22 5.0	9 29.4	12 20.8	19 52.4	14 48.6
15	11 29 32.5	24 12.1	18 6.5	20 57.0	10 27.0	17 3.4	16 34.7	22 15.4	9 36.6	12 18.2	19 51.7	14 47.0
16	11 33 29.0	25 11.8	18 3.3	5♍28.9	12 1.6	18 18.1	16 11.6	22 25.9	9 43.7	12 15.7	19 50.9	14 45.4
17	11 37 25.6	26 11.5	18 .1	19 53.3	13 31.6	19 32.8	15 48.8	22 36.4	9 50.9	12 13.1	19 50.2	14 43.9
18	11 41 22.2	27 11.2	17 57.0	4♎ 3.6	14 56.5	20 47.4	15 26.3	22 47.1	9 58.0	12 10.6	19 49.3	14 42.3
19	11 45 18.7	28 10.8	17 53.8	17 54.1	16 15.8	22 2.1	15 4.1	22 57.9	10 5.1	12 8.1	19 48.5	14 40.8
20	11 49 15.3	29 10.4	17 50.6	1♏21.6	17 29.2	23 16.8	14 42.3	23 8.8	10 12.1	12 5.6	19 47.6	14 39.3
21	11 53 11.8	0♈10.0	17 47.4	14 24.8	18 36.3	24 31.4	14 20.9	23 19.8	10 19.2	12 3.2	19 46.7	14 37.8
22	11 57 8.4	1 9.5	17 44.3	27 5.0	19 36.7	25 46.1	13 59.9	23 30.9	10 26.2	12 .7	19 45.8	14 36.2
23	12 1 4.9	2 9.1	17 41.1	9♐25.2	20 30.1	27 .7	13 39.4	23 42.0	10 33.2	11 58.3	19 44.9	14 34.7
24	12 5 1.5	3 8.5	17 37.9	21 29.7	21 16.2	28 15.3	13 19.4	23 53.3	10 40.2	11 55.9	19 43.9	14 33.2
25	12 8 58.0	4 8.0	17 34.7	3♑23.8	21 55.0	29 29.9	12 59.9	24 4.7	10 47.1	11 53.5	19 42.9	14 31.8
26	12 12 54.6	5 7.5	17 31.5	15 12.8	22 26.2	0♈44.5	12 41.1	24 16.2	10 54.1	11 51.2	19 41.9	14 30.3
27	12 16 51.1	6 6.9	17 28.4	27 2.3	22 49.7	1 59.1	12 22.8	24 27.7	11 .9	11 48.9	19 40.8	14 28.9
28	12 20 47.7	7 6.2	17 25.2	8♒57.2	23 5.6	3 13.7	12 5.1	24 39.3	11 7.8	11 46.6	19 39.8	14 27.4
29	12 24 44.2	8 5.6	17 22.0	21 2.0	23 13.9	4 28.2	11 48.1	24 51.0	11 14.6	11 44.3	19 38.6	14 26.0
30	12 28 40.8	9 4.9	17 18.8	3♓20.2	23 14.8	5 42.7	11 31.7	25 2.8	11 21.4	11 42.0	19 37.5	14 24.6
31	12 32 37.3	10 4.1	17 15.7	15 54.0	23R 8.4	6 57.3	11 16.0	25 14.6	11 28.2	11 39.8	19 36.4	14 23.2
		LATITUDE										
1	10 34 20.8	0 .0	0 .0	4S 1.6	1S28.2	1S15.5	4N 4.1	0S47.3	1S34.7	0N49.0	1N46.9	14N38.9
4	10 46 10.4	0 .0	0 .0	4 59.8	1 6.2	1 18.8	4 3.5	0 46.7	1 34.9	0 49.0	1 47.0	14 39.1
7	10 58 .1	0 .0	0 .0	3 48.5	0 38.9	1 21.5	4 2.1	0 46.0	1 35.1	0 49.0	1 47.2	14 39.3
10	11 9 49.7	0 .0	0 .0	0 45.0	0 6.6	1 23.6	3 59.7	0 45.4	1 35.3	0 49.0	1 47.4	14 39.5
13	11 21 39.4	0 .0	0 .0	2N48.4	0N29.7	1 25.2	3 56.5	0 44.8	1 35.5	0 49.0	1 47.5	14 39.5
16	11 33 29.0	0 .0	0 .0	4 53.7	1 8.3	1 26.1	3 52.5	0 44.2	1 35.8	0 48.9	1 47.7	14 39.5
19	11 45 18.7	0 .0	0 .0	4 18.9	1 46.7	1 26.6	3 47.7	0 43.6	1 36.1	0 48.9	1 47.8	14 39.4
22	11 57 8.4	0 .0	0 .0	1 42.5	2 22.2	1 26.4	3 42.1	0 43.1	1 36.4	0 48.9	1 48.0	14 39.2
25	12 8 58.0	0 .0	0 .0	1S27.1	2 51.6	1 25.6	3 36.0	0 42.5	1 36.7	0 48.8	1 48.1	14 39.0
28	12 20 47.7	0 .0	0 .0	4 .2	3 12.0	1 24.3	3 29.3	0 42.0	1 37.0	0 48.8	1 48.2	14 38.7
31	12 32 37.3	0 .0	0 .0	5 2.6	3 20.4	1 22.5	3 22.2	0 41.5	1 37.4	0 48.7	1 48.4	14 38.3
		RIGHT ASCENSION										
1	10 34 20.8	11♓43.2	17♊52.5	16♒33.3	16♓17.3	2♓ 9.5	24♍15.7	17♉46.9	10♓10.8	14♍33.9	18♏ 2.2	22♍16.5
2	10 38 17.3	12 39.5	17 49.1	28 55.9	18 1.4	3 21.7	23R55.4	17 55.7	10 17.7	14R31.4	18R 1.8	22R15.1
3	10 42 13.9	13 35.6	17 45.6	10♓59.6	19 45.4	4 33.6	23 34.7	18 4.7	10 24.6	14 29.0	18 1.5	22 13.7
4	10 46 10.4	14 31.5	17 42.2	22 48.6	21 29.0	5 45.3	23 13.6	18 13.8	10 31.5	14 26.5	18 1.1	22 12.2
5	10 50 7.0	15 27.4	17 38.7	4♈30.7	23 12.3	6 56.8	22 52.3	18 23.1	10 38.4	14 24.1	18 .8	22 10.8
6	10 54 3.5	16 23.2	17 35.3	16 16.4	24 55.0	8 7.9	22 30.7	18 32.5	10 45.3	14 21.7	18 .3	22 9.3
7	10 58 .1	17 18.8	17 31.9	28 18.2	26 36.9	9 18.9	22 8.9	18 42.0	10 52.2	14 19.2	17 59.9	22 7.9
8	11 1 56.6	18 14.4	17 28.4	10♉49.2	28 18.0	10 29.6	21 46.9	18 51.7	10 59.0	14 16.8	17 59.4	22 6.4
9	11 5 53.2	19 9.8	17 25.0	24 1.5	29 57.8	11 40.2	21 24.7	19 1.4	11 5.9	14 14.3	17 58.8	22 4.9
10	11 9 49.7	20 5.2	17 21.6	8♊ 3.3	1♈36.2	12 50.5	21 2.4	19 11.3	11 12.7	14 11.9	17 58.3	22 3.5
11	11 13 46.3	21 .4	17 18.1	22 55.0	3 12.8	14 .6	20 40.1	19 21.3	11 19.5	14 9.5	17 57.7	22 2.0
12	11 17 42.8	21 55.6	17 14.7	8♋25.5	4 47.3	15 10.5	20 17.7	19 31.5	11 26.4	14 7.1	17 57.0	22 .5
13	11 21 39.4	22 50.7	17 11.2	24 12.3	6 19.3	16 20.2	19 55.4	19 41.7	11 33.2	14 4.7	17 56.4	21 59.0
14	11 25 35.9	23 45.7	17 7.8	9♌48.3	7 48.5	17 29.8	19 33.2	19 52.1	11 39.9	14 2.3	17 55.7	21 57.6
15	11 29 32.5	24 40.6	17 4.4	24 50.8	9 14.5	18 39.2	19 11.0	20 2.6	11 46.7	13 59.9	17 55.0	21 56.1
16	11 33 29.0	25 35.5	17 .9	9♍ 8.6	10 36.8	19 48.5	18 49.0	20 13.1	11 53.4	13 57.5	17 54.2	21 54.6
17	11 37 25.6	26 30.3	16 57.5	22 41.6	11 55.0	20 57.6	18 27.2	20 23.8	12 .2	13 55.1	17 53.5	21 53.2
18	11 41 22.2	27 25.1	16 54.1	5♎37.9	13 8.7	22 6.5	18 5.6	20 34.7	12 6.9	13 52.8	17 52.7	21 51.7
19	11 45 18.7	28 19.8	16 50.6	18 9.3	14 17.6	23 15.4	17 44.3	20 45.6	12 13.6	13 50.4	17 51.8	21 50.2
20	11 49 15.3	29 14.5	16 47.2	0♏28.4	15 21.3	24 24.1	17 23.3	20 56.6	12 20.2	13 48.1	17 51.0	21 48.8
21	11 53 11.8	0♈ 9.2	16 43.8	12 46.5	16 19.4	25 32.7	17 2.6	21 7.7	12 26.9	13 45.8	17 50.1	21 47.3
22	11 57 8.4	1 3.8	16 40.3	25 12.3	17 11.6	26 41.3	16 42.2	21 18.9	12 33.5	13 43.5	17 49.2	21 45.9
23	12 1 4.9	1 58.4	16 36.9	7♐50.8	17 57.6	27 49.7	16 22.3	21 30.3	12 40.1	13 41.3	17 48.2	21 44.4
24	12 5 1.5	2 53.0	16 33.5	20 42.8	18 37.2	28 58.1	16 2.8	21 41.7	12 46.6	13 39.0	17 47.3	21 43.0
25	12 8 58.0	3 47.6	16 30.0	3♑44.5	19 10.3	0♈ 6.5	15 43.8	21 53.2	12 53.2	13 36.8	17 46.3	21 41.6
26	12 12 54.6	4 42.2	16 26.6	16 48.8	19 36.7	1 14.8	15 25.3	22 4.9	12 59.7	13 34.6	17 45.3	21 40.2
27	12 16 51.1	5 36.8	16 23.2	29 46.8	19 56.4	2 23.0	15 7.3	22 16.6	13 6.2	13 32.4	17 44.2	21 38.8
28	12 20 47.7	6 31.4	16 19.7	12♒31.2	20 9.3	3 31.2	14 49.9	22 28.4	13 12.7	13 30.3	17 43.2	21 37.4
29	12 24 44.2	7 25.9	16 16.3	24 57.6	20 15.5	4 39.4	14 33.0	22 40.3	13 19.1	13 28.1	17 42.1	21 36.0
30	12 28 40.8	8 20.5	16 12.9	7♓ 6.0	20R15.2	5 47.6	14 16.8	22 52.3	13 25.5	13 26.0	17 41.0	21 34.6
31	12 32 37.3	9 15.2	16 9.4	19 .5	20 8.7	6 55.7	14 1.1	23 4.4	13 31.8	13 24.0	17 39.8	21 33.2
		DECLINATION										
1	10 34 20.8	7S44.7	0N24.1	20S48.7	7S27.7	12S47.6	6N54.8	16N59.2	10S 4.0	7N28.1	16S 1.5	19N18.4
4	10 46 10.4	6 36.0	0 24.0	8 32.8	4 52.5	11 30.4	7 20.8	17 7.0	9 55.9	7 31.1	16 1.0	19 20.6
7	10 58 .1	5 26.4	0 24.0	7N33.2	2 10.3	10 10.3	7 46.8	17 15.0	9 47.9	7 34.1	16 .5	19 22.6
10	11 9 49.7	4 16.2	0 24.0	21 9.2	0N34.5	8 47.8	8 12.6	17 23.2	9 39.9	7 37.1	15 59.9	19 24.6
13	11 21 39.4	3 5.5	0 24.0	24 25.5	3 16.4	7 23.3	8 37.4	17 31.6	9 32.0	7 40.1	15 59.2	19 26.5
16	11 33 29.0	1 54.5	0 24.0	14 3.1	5 48.2	5 56.9	9 1.0	17 40.2	9 24.1	7 43.0	15 58.5	19 28.4
19	11 45 18.7	0 43.4	0 24.0	3S 2.1	8 2.3	4 29.1	9 22.9	17 48.9	9 16.3	7 45.8	15 57.7	19 30.1
22	11 57 8.4	0N27.7	0 24.0	17 50.8	9 52.0	3 .2	9 42.7	17 57.6	9 8.5	7 48.6	15 56.9	19 31.8
25	12 8 58.0	1 38.6	0 23.9	24 51.2	11 11.5	1 30.6	10 .2	18 6.5	9 .9	7 51.3	15 56.0	19 33.3
28	12 20 47.7	2 49.2	0 23.9	21 52.9	11 56.8	0 .4	10 15.2	18 15.5	8 53.3	7 53.9	15 55.0	19 34.7
31	12 32 37.3	3 59.3	0 23.9	10 12.4	12 5.7	1N29.9	10 27.4	18 24.5	8 45.9	7 56.5	15 54.0	19 36.1

APRIL 1965

LONGITUDE

DAY	EPHEM. SID. TIME	☉	☊	☽	☿	♀	♂	♃	♄	♅	♆	♇
	h m s	° ′	° ′	° ′	° ′	° ′	° ′	° ′	° ′	° ′	° ′	° ′
1	12 36 33.9	11♈ 3.4	17♊12.5	28♓44.6	22♈55.2	8♈11.8	11♍ 1.0	25♉26.6	11♓34.9	11♍37.6	19♏35.2	14♍21.8
2	12 40 30.4	12 2.6	17 9.3	11♈51.5	22 R 35.4	9 26.3	10 R 46.8	25 38.6	11 41.5	11 R 35.4	19 R 34.0	14 R 20.4
3	12 44 27.0	13 1.8	17 6.1	25 13.3	22 9.7	10 40.7	10 33.3	25 50.7	11 48.2	11 33.3	19 32.8	14 19.0
4	12 48 23.6	14 .9	17 2.9	8♉47.9	21 38.6	11 55.2	10 20.6	26 2.8	11 54.8	11 31.2	19 31.5	14 17.7
5	12 52 20.1	15 .0	16 59.8	22 32.6	21 2.8	13 9.6	10 8.6	26 15.1	12 1.3	11 29.2	19 30.3	14 16.4
6	12 56 16.7	15 59.1	16 56.6	6♊25.2	20 23.1	14 24.1	9 57.4	26 27.4	12 7.9	11 27.1	19 29.0	14 15.1
7	13 0 13.2	16 58.1	16 53.4	20 23.8	19 40.3	15 38.5	9 47.0	26 39.7	12 14.3	11 25.1	19 27.7	14 13.8
8	13 4 9.8	17 57.1	16 50.2	4♋26.9	18 55.4	16 52.9	9 37.4	26 52.2	12 20.8	11 23.2	19 26.4	14 12.5
9	13 8 6.3	18 56.0	16 47.1	18 33.6	18 9.2	18 7.2	9 28.6	27 4.7	12 27.1	11 21.3	19 25.0	14 11.3
10	13 12 2.9	19 55.0	16 43.9	2♌42.8	17 22.6	19 21.6	9 20.5	27 17.2	12 33.5	11 19.4	19 23.7	14 10.0
11	13 15 59.4	20 53.8	16 40.7	16 52.9	16 36.5	20 35.9	9 13.3	27 29.9	12 39.8	11 17.5	19 22.3	14 8.8
12	13 19 56.0	21 52.7	16 37.5	1♍ 1.8	15 51.7	21 50.3	9 6.8	27 42.5	12 46.0	11 15.7	19 20.9	14 7.6
13	13 23 52.5	22 51.5	16 34.3	15 6.4	15 9.1	23 4.6	9 1.2	27 55.3	12 52.2	11 14.0	19 19.5	14 6.4
14	13 27 49.1	23 50.2	16 31.2	29 2.9	14 29.4	24 18.8	8 56.3	28 8.1	12 58.4	11 12.2	19 18.1	14 5.3
15	13 31 45.6	24 49.0	16 28.0	12♎47.6	13 53.0	25 33.1	8 52.2	28 20.9	13 4.5	11 10.6	19 16.6	14 4.2
16	13 35 42.2	25 47.7	16 24.8	26 16.9	13 20.6	26 47.4	8 48.9	28 33.9	13 10.6	11 9.0	19 15.2	14 3.1
17	13 39 38.8	26 46.4	16 21.6	9♏28.5	12 52.5	28 1.6	8 46.3	28 46.8	13 16.6	11 7.4	19 13.7	14 2.0
18	13 43 35.3	27 45.0	16 18.5	22 21.2	12 29.0	29 15.8	8 44.5	28 59.9	13 22.5	11 5.8	19 12.3	14 1.0
19	13 47 31.9	28 43.6	16 15.3	4♐55.5	12 10.5	0♉30.0	8 43.5	29 12.9	13 28.4	11 4.3	19 10.8	13 59.9
20	13 51 28.4	29 42.2	16 12.1	17 13.4	11 56.9	1 44.2	8 43.2	29 26.0	13 34.2	11 2.8	19 9.3	13 58.9
21	13 55 25.0	0♉40.7	16 8.9	29 17.8	11 48.4	2 58.4	8 D 43.6	29 39.2	13 40.0	11 1.4	19 7.7	13 57.9
22	13 59 21.5	1 39.2	16 5.7	11♑12.9	11 45.0	4 12.5	8 44.8	29 52.4	13 45.7	11 .0	19 6.2	13 57.0
23	14 3 18.1	2 37.7	16 2.6	23 3.4	11 D 46.7	5 26.7	8 46.7	0♊ 5.6	13 51.4	10 58.7	19 4.7	13 56.0
24	14 7 14.6	3 36.2	15 59.4	4♒54.3	11 53.4	6 40.8	8 49.2	0 18.9	13 57.0	10 57.4	19 3.1	13 55.1
25	14 11 11.2	4 34.6	15 56.2	16 50.7	12 5.0	7 54.9	8 52.5	0 32.3	14 2.5	10 56.2	19 1.5	13 54.2
26	14 15 7.7	5 33.0	15 53.0	28 57.5	12 21.3	9 9.0	8 56.5	0 45.7	14 8.0	10 55.0	18 60.0	13 53.4
27	14 19 4.3	6 31.4	15 49.9	11♓18.9	12 42.2	10 23.1	9 1.2	0 59.1	14 13.4	10 53.8	18 58.4	13 52.5
28	14 23 .8	7 29.7	15 46.7	23 58.4	13 7.6	11 37.2	9 6.6	1 12.5	14 18.8	10 52.7	18 56.8	13 51.7
29	14 26 57.4	8 28.0	15 43.5	6♈58.1	13 37.2	12 51.2	9 12.6	1 26.0	14 24.1	10 51.7	18 55.2	13 50.9
30	14 30 54.0	9 26.3	15 40.3	20 18.6	14 10.9	14 5.3	9 19.3	1 39.6	14 29.3	10 50.7	18 53.6	13 50.2

LATITUDE

DAY	EPHEM. SID. TIME	☉	☊	☽	☿	♀	♂	♃	♄	♅	♆	♇
1	12 36 33.9	0 .0	0 .0	4 S 55.3	3 N 20.2	1 S 21.7	3 N 19.8	0 S 41.3	1 S 37.5	0 N 48.7	1 N 48.4	14 N 38.2
4	12 48 23.6	0 .0	0 .0	3 2.3	3 9.7	1 19.1	3 12.3	0 40.8	1 37.9	0 48.6	1 48.5	14 37.7
7	13 0 13.2	0 .0	0 .0	0 N 26.6	2 44.6	1 16.0	3 4.6	0 40.4	1 38.3	0 48.5	1 48.6	14 37.2
10	13 12 2.9	0 .0	0 .0	3 45.5	2 6.9	1 12.4	2 56.8	0 39.9	1 38.8	0 48.5	1 48.7	14 36.6
13	13 23 52.5	0 .0	0 .0	5 6.1	1 20.7	1 8.2	2 49.0	0 39.4	1 39.2	0 48.4	1 48.8	14 35.9
16	13 35 42.2	0 .0	0 .0	3 50.2	0 31.0	1 3.7	2 41.1	0 39.0	1 39.7	0 48.3	1 48.9	14 35.2
19	13 47 31.9	0 .0	0 .0	0 51.8	0 S 17.8	0 58.7	2 33.4	0 38.6	1 40.2	0 48.2	1 48.9	14 34.5
22	13 59 21.5	0 .0	0 .0	2 S 19.5	1 2.3	0 53.3	2 25.7	0 38.2	1 40.7	0 48.1	1 49.0	14 33.7
25	14 11 11.2	0 .0	0 .0	4 35.2	1 40.7	0 47.5	2 18.2	0 37.8	1 41.2	0 48.0	1 49.1	14 32.8
28	14 23 .8	0 .0	0 .0	5 6.4	2 12.0	0 41.4	2 10.8	0 37.4	1 41.8	0 47.9	1 49.1	14 31.9

RIGHT ASCENSION

DAY	EPHEM. SID. TIME	☉	☊	☽	☿	♀	♂	♃	♄	♅	♆	♇
1	12 36 33.9	10♈ 9.8	16♊ 6.0	0♈48.6	19♈56.2	8♈ 3.9	13♍46.2	23♉16.6	13♓38.2	13♍21.9	17♏38.7	21♍31.9
2	12 40 30.4	11 4.5	16 2.6	12 40.6	19 R 38.2	9 12.1	13 R 31.8	23 28.9	13 44.5	13 R 19.9	17 R 37.5	21 R 30.5
3	12 44 27.0	11 59.2	15 59.1	24 48.3	19 15.3	10 20.3	13 18.2	23 41.2	13 50.7	13 17.9	17 36.3	21 29.2
4	12 48 23.6	12 53.9	15 55.7	7♉24.3	18 47.9	11 28.6	13 5.3	23 53.6	13 56.9	13 15.9	17 35.0	21 27.8
5	12 52 20.1	13 48.7	15 52.3	20 39.8	18 16.8	12 36.9	12 53.0	24 6.2	14 3.1	13 14.0	17 33.8	21 26.5
6	12 56 16.7	14 43.5	15 48.8	4♊42.2	17 42.7	13 45.3	12 41.5	24 18.7	14 9.2	13 12.1	17 32.5	21 25.2
7	13 0 13.2	15 38.3	15 45.4	19 30.9	17 6.4	14 53.8	12 30.7	24 31.4	14 15.3	13 10.2	17 31.2	21 23.9
8	13 4 9.8	16 33.2	15 42.0	4♋54.6	16 28.6	16 2.3	12 20.7	24 44.2	14 21.4	13 8.4	17 29.9	21 22.6
9	13 8 6.3	17 28.2	15 38.5	20 31.4	15 50.2	17 10.9	12 11.4	24 57.0	14 27.4	13 6.6	17 28.6	21 21.4
10	13 12 2.9	18 23.2	15 35.1	5♌55.7	15 12.0	18 19.6	12 2.8	25 9.9	14 33.4	13 4.8	17 27.2	21 20.1
11	13 15 59.4	19 18.3	15 31.7	20 46.6	14 34.7	19 28.4	11 55.0	25 22.8	14 39.3	13 3.0	17 25.8	21 18.9
12	13 19 56.0	20 13.4	15 28.3	4♍53.7	13 59.1	20 37.4	11 47.9	25 35.9	14 45.2	13 1.4	17 24.4	21 17.7
13	13 23 52.5	21 8.6	15 24.8	18 17.5	13 25.7	21 46.5	11 41.6	25 49.0	14 51.0	12 59.7	17 23.0	21 16.5
14	13 27 49.1	22 3.9	15 21.4	1♎ 6.2	12 55.2	22 55.7	11 36.0	26 2.1	14 56.8	12 58.1	17 21.6	21 15.3
15	13 31 45.6	22 59.3	15 18.0	13 31.5	12 28.0	24 5.0	11 31.1	26 15.4	15 2.6	12 56.5	17 20.2	21 14.2
16	13 35 42.2	23 54.8	15 14.5	25 46.3	12 4.5	25 14.6	11 27.0	26 28.7	15 8.3	12 55.0	17 18.8	21 13.1
17	13 39 38.8	24 50.3	15 11.1	8♏ 2.1	11 45.0	26 24.3	11 23.6	26 42.1	15 14.0	12 53.5	17 17.3	21 11.9
18	13 43 35.3	25 46.0	15 7.7	20 27.8	11 29.6	27 34.1	11 20.9	26 55.5	15 19.6	12 52.0	17 15.9	21 10.8
19	13 47 31.9	26 41.7	15 4.3	3♐ 8.7	11 18.7	28 44.2	11 18.9	27 9.0	15 25.1	12 50.6	17 14.4	21 9.8
20	13 51 28.4	27 37.5	15 .8	16 5.5	11 12.2	29 54.4	11 17.7	27 22.5	15 30.6	12 49.2	17 12.9	21 8.7
21	13 55 25.0	28 33.5	14 57.4	29 13.6	11 10.2	1♉ 4.9	11 17.1	27 36.1	15 36.1	12 47.9	17 11.3	21 7.6
22	13 59 21.5	29 29.5	14 54.0	12♑24.7	11 D 12.7	2 15.5	11 D 17.2	27 49.8	15 41.5	12 46.6	17 9.8	21 6.6
23	14 3 18.1	0♉25.7	14 50.5	25 29.0	11 19.5	3 26.4	11 18.0	28 3.5	15 46.8	12 45.3	17 8.3	21 5.6
24	14 7 14.6	1 22.0	14 47.1	8♒17.8	11 30.7	4 37.5	11 19.5	28 17.2	15 52.1	12 44.1	17 6.7	21 4.6
25	14 11 11.2	2 18.4	14 43.7	20 46.2	11 46.0	5 48.8	11 21.6	28 31.1	15 57.3	12 42.9	17 5.2	21 3.7
26	14 15 7.7	3 15.0	14 40.3	2♓54.2	12 5.5	7 .4	11 24.4	28 44.9	16 2.5	12 41.8	17 3.6	21 2.7
27	14 19 4.3	4 11.6	14 36.8	14 46.2	12 28.8	8 12.2	11 27.9	28 58.8	16 7.6	12 40.7	17 2.0	21 1.8
28	14 23 .8	5 8.4	14 33.4	26 30.2	12 56.0	9 24.2	11 32.0	29 12.8	16 12.6	12 39.7	17 .4	21 .9
29	14 26 57.4	6 5.3	14 30.0	8♈17.3	13 26.7	10 36.6	11 36.7	29 26.8	16 17.6	12 38.7	16 58.8	21 .0
30	14 30 54.0	7 2.4	14 26.6	20 20.2	14 1.0	11 49.1	11 42.1	29 40.9	16 22.6	12 37.7	16 57.2	20 59.2

DECLINATION

DAY	EPHEM. SID. TIME	☉	☊	☽	☿	♀	♂	♃	♄	♅	♆	♇
1	12 36 33.9	4 N 22.6	0 N 23.9	5 S .9	12 N .6	1 N 60.0	10 N 30.9	18 N 27.5	8 S 43.5	7 N 57.3	15 S 53.6	19 N 36.5
4	12 48 23.6	5 31.8	0 23.9	11 N 33.3	11 22.1	3 30.0	10 39.4	18 36.5	8 36.2	7 59.6	15 52.5	19 37.7
7	13 0 13.2	6 40.1	0 23.9	23 32.4	10 14.1	4 59.3	10 45.0	18 45.6	8 29.1	8 1.9	15 51.4	19 38.7
10	13 12 2.9	7 47.4	0 23.9	23 12.9	8 46.6	6 27.8	10 47.9	18 54.6	8 22.2	8 4.0	15 50.2	19 39.6
13	13 23 52.5	8 53.4	0 23.8	10 34.2	7 12.6	7 54.9	10 47.9	19 3.6	8 15.4	8 6.0	15 49.0	19 40.5
16	13 35 42.2	9 58.2	0 23.8	6 S 34.1	5 44.7	9 20.4	10 45.3	19 12.6	8 8.8	8 7.8	15 47.8	19 41.1
19	13 47 31.9	11 1.5	0 23.8	20 16.4	4 32.4	10 44.0	10 40.1	19 21.5	8 2.4	8 9.5	15 46.5	19 41.7
22	13 59 21.5	12 3.1	0 23.8	25 17.3	3 41.5	12 5.4	10 32.6	19 30.4	7 56.2	8 11.0	15 45.2	19 42.1
25	14 11 11.2	13 3.0	0 23.8	20 9.5	3 13.9	13 24.1	10 22.7	19 39.1	7 50.2	8 12.4	15 43.9	19 42.4
28	14 23 .8	14 .9	0 23.8	7 4.9	3 9.4	14 39.9	10 10.6	19 47.8	7 44.4	8 13.6	15 42.6	19 42.6

MAY 1965

LONGITUDE

DAY	EPHEM. SID. TIME	☉	☊	☾	☿	♀	♂	♃	♄	♅	♆	♇
	h m s	° ′	° ′	° ′	° ′	° ′	° ′	° ′	° ′	° ′	° ′	° ′
1	14 34 50.5	10♉24.6	15♊37.1	3♉58.7	14♈48.6	15♉19.3	9♍26.6	1♊53.1	14♓34.4	10♍49.8	18♏52.0	13♍49.4
2	14 38 47.1	11 22.9	15 34.0	17 56.0	15 30.1	16 33.3	9 34.6	2 6.7	14 39.5	10 R 48.9	18 R 50.4	13 R 48.7
3	14 42 43.6	12 21.1	15 30.8	2♊ 6.4	16 15.3	17 47.3	9 43.2	2 20.3	14 44.6	10 48.0	18 48.7	13 48.1
4	14 46 40.2	13 19.3	15 27.6	16 25.4	17 3.9	19 1.3	9 52.4	2 34.0	14 49.5	10 47.2	18 47.1	13 47.4
5	14 50 36.7	14 17.4	15 24.4	0♋48.3	17 55.8	20 15.3	10 2.2	2 47.7	14 54.4	10 46.5	18 45.5	13 46.8
6	14 54 33.3	15 15.5	15 21.3	15 11.1	18 51.0	21 29.2	10 12.6	3 1.4	14 59.2	10 45.8	18 43.9	13 46.2
7	14 58 29.8	16 13.7	15 18.1	29 30.2	19 49.3	22 43.2	10 23.7	3 15.2	15 4.0	10 45.2	18 42.3	13 45.7
8	15 2 26.4	17 11.7	15 14.9	13♌42.9	20 50.5	23 57.1	10 35.2	3 29.0	15 8.7	10 44.6	18 40.6	13 45.2
9	15 6 23.0	18 9.7	15 11.7	27 47.4	21 54.6	25 11.0	10 47.4	3 42.8	15 13.3	10 44.1	18 39.0	13 44.7
10	15 10 19.5	19 7.7	15 8.6	11♍42.0	23 1.5	26 24.9	11 .0	3 56.6	15 17.8	10 43.6	18 37.4	13 44.2
11	15 14 16.1	20 5.7	15 5.4	25 25.5	24 11.1	27 38.8	11 13.3	4 10.4	15 22.2	10 43.2	18 35.7	13 43.7
12	15 18 12.6	21 3.6	15 2.2	8♎56.9	25 23.3	28 52.6	11 27.0	4 24.2	15 26.6	10 42.8	18 34.1	13 43.3
13	15 22 9.2	22 1.5	14 59.0	22 15.2	26 38.1	0♊ 6.4	11 41.2	4 38.1	15 30.9	10 42.5	18 32.5	13 42.9
14	15 26 5.7	22 59.4	14 55.8	5♏19.6	27 55.4	1 20.2	11 56.0	4 52.0	15 35.1	10 42.2	18 30.9	13 42.6
15	15 30 2.3	23 57.2	14 52.7	18 9.7	29 15.1	2 34.0	12 11.2	5 5.9	15 39.2	10 42.0	18 29.2	13 42.3
16	15 33 58.8	24 55.1	14 49.5	0♐45.7	0♉37.2	3 47.8	12 26.9	5 19.8	15 43.3	10 41.8	18 27.6	13 42.0
17	15 37 55.4	25 52.8	14 46.3	13 8.1	2 1.7	5 1.6	12 43.1	5 33.8	15 47.3	10 41.7	18 26.0	13 41.7
18	15 41 52.0	26 50.6	14 43.1	25 18.6	3 28.5	6 15.3	12 59.8	5 47.7	15 51.2	10 41.7	18 24.4	13 41.5
19	15 45 48.5	27 48.4	14 40.0	7♑19.3	4 57.7	7 29.0	13 16.9	6 1.7	15 55.0	10 41.6	18 22.8	13 41.3
20	15 49 45.1	28 46.1	14 36.8	19 13.1	6 29.1	8 42.8	13 34.4	6 15.6	15 58.7	10 D 41.7	18 21.2	13 41.1
21	15 53 41.6	29 43.8	14 33.6	1♒ 3.6	8 2.8	9 56.5	13 52.4	6 29.6	16 2.4	10 41.8	18 19.6	13 41.0
22	15 57 38.2	0♊41.5	14 30.4	12 54.8	9 38.8	11 10.2	14 10.8	6 43.6	16 5.9	10 42.0	18 18.0	13 40.9
23	16 1 34.7	1 39.2	14 27.3	24 51.3	11 17.0	12 23.8	14 29.6	6 57.6	16 9.4	10 42.2	18 16.4	13 40.8
24	16 5 31.3	2 36.9	14 24.1	6♓57.7	12 57.5	13 37.5	14 48.8	7 11.6	16 12.8	10 42.4	18 14.8	13 40.7
25	16 9 27.9	3 34.5	14 20.9	19 18.5	14 40.2	14 51.2	15 8.5	7 25.6	16 16.1	10 42.7	18 13.3	13 40.7
26	16 13 24.4	4 32.1	14 17.7	1♈57.8	16 25.2	16 4.8	15 28.5	7 39.6	16 19.4	10 43.1	18 11.7	13 40.7
27	16 17 21.0	5 29.7	14 14.5	14 58.9	18 12.4	17 18.5	15 48.9	7 53.6	16 22.5	10 43.5	18 10.2	13 D 40.8
28	16 21 17.5	6 27.4	14 11.4	28 24.0	20 1.9	18 32.1	16 9.7	8 7.7	16 25.6	10 44.1	18 8.7	13 40.9
29	16 25 14.1	7 25.0	14 8.2	12♉13.1	21 53.6	19 45.7	16 30.9	8 21.7	16 28.5	10 44.6	18 7.1	13 41.0
30	16 29 10.6	8 22.5	14 5.0	26 24.7	23 47.4	20 59.3	16 52.5	8 35.8	16 31.4	10 45.2	18 5.6	13 41.1
31	16 33 7.2	9 20.1	14 1.8	10♊54.7	25 43.4	22 12.9	17 14.4	8 49.8	16 34.2	10 45.8	18 4.1	13 41.3

LATITUDE

DAY	EPHEM. SID. TIME	☉	☊	☾	☿	♀	♂	♃	♄	♅	♆	♇
1	14 34 50.5	0 .0	0 .0	3S21.2	2S36.2	0S35.0	2N 3.7	0S37.0	1S42.3	0N47.7	1N49.1	14N31.0
4	14 46 40.2	0 .0	0 .0	0N13.2	2 53.3	0 28.4	1 56.7	0 36.7	1 42.9	0 47.6	1 49.1	14 30.0
7	14 58 29.8	0 .0	0 .0	3 44.0	3 3.7	0 21.5	1 50.0	0 36.3	1 43.5	0 47.5	1 49.2	14 29.0
10	15 10 19.5	0 .0	0 .0	5 13.7	3 7.8	0 14.5	1 43.5	0 36.0	1 44.1	0 47.4	1 49.2	14 27.9
13	15 22 9.2	0 .0	0 .0	4 6.8	3 5.8	0 7.3	1 37.1	0 35.7	1 44.7	0 47.3	1 49.2	14 26.9
16	15 33 58.8	0 .0	0 .0	1 11.3	2 58.3	0 .1	1 31.0	0 35.4	1 45.4	0 47.1	1 49.1	14 25.8
19	15 45 48.5	0 .0	0 .0	2S 6.5	2 45.4	0N 7.2	1 25.1	0 35.1	1 46.0	0 47.0	1 49.1	14 24.7
22	15 57 38.2	0 .0	0 .0	4 31.8	2 27.7	0 14.5	1 19.4	0 34.8	1 46.7	0 46.9	1 49.1	14 23.6
25	16 9 27.9	0 .0	0 .0	5 15.4	2 5.4	0 21.8	1 13.9	0 34.5	1 47.4	0 46.7	1 49.0	14 22.4
28	16 21 17.5	0 .0	0 .0	3 46.1	1 39.2	0 28.9	1 8.6	0 34.2	1 48.1	0 46.6	1 49.0	14 21.3
31	16 33 7.2	0 .0	0 .0	0 16.1	1 9.8	0 35.9	1 3.4	0 34.0	1 48.8	0 46.5	1 48.9	14 20.1

RIGHT ASCENSION

DAY	EPHEM. SID. TIME	☉	☊	☾	☿	♀	♂	♃	♄	♅	♆	♇
1	14 34 50.5	7♉59.6	14♊23.2	2♉52.8	14♈38.6	13♉ 2.0	11♍48.1	29♉55.0	16♓27.4	12♍36.8	16♏55.6	20♍58.4
2	14 38 47.1	8 56.9	14 19.7	16 7.9	15 19.4	14 15.1	11 54.7	0♊ 9.2	16 32.3	12 R 36.0	16 R 54.0	20 R 57.6
3	14 42 43.6	9 54.4	14 16.3	0♊14.6	16 3.3	15 28.4	12 1.8	0 23.4	16 37.0	12 35.2	16 52.4	20 56.8
4	14 46 40.2	10 52.0	14 12.9	15 13.7	16 50.2	16 42.1	12 9.6	0 37.6	16 41.7	12 34.4	16 50.8	20 56.1
5	14 50 36.7	11 49.7	14 9.5	0♋53.3	17 39.9	17 56.0	12 18.0	0 51.9	16 46.3	12 33.7	16 49.2	20 55.3
6	14 54 33.3	12 47.6	14 6.0	16 49.1	18 32.4	19 10.2	12 26.9	1 6.2	16 50.8	12 33.1	16 47.5	20 54.6
7	14 58 29.8	13 45.6	14 2.6	2♌31.0	19 27.5	20 24.7	12 36.4	1 20.6	16 55.4	12 32.5	16 46.0	20 54.0
8	15 2 26.4	14 43.7	13 59.2	17 34.3	20 25.2	21 39.5	12 46.3	1 35.0	16 59.8	12 31.9	16 44.3	20 53.4
9	15 6 23.0	15 42.0	13 55.8	1♍46.8	21 25.4	22 54.5	12 56.9	1 49.4	17 4.1	12 31.4	16 42.7	20 52.7
10	15 10 19.5	16 40.4	13 52.4	15 9.2	22 28.0	24 9.8	13 7.9	2 3.8	17 8.4	12 30.9	16 41.1	20 52.1
11	15 14 16.1	17 39.0	13 48.9	27 50.9	23 33.1	25 25.4	13 19.4	2 18.3	17 12.6	12 30.5	16 39.4	20 51.6
12	15 18 12.6	18 37.7	13 45.5	10♎ 5.3	24 40.5	26 41.3	13 31.5	2 32.8	17 16.8	12 30.2	16 37.8	20 51.0
13	15 22 9.2	19 36.5	13 42.1	22 6.7	25 50.2	27 57.4	13 44.0	2 47.3	17 20.8	12 29.8	16 36.2	20 50.5
14	15 26 5.7	20 35.5	13 38.7	4♏ 8.5	27 2.2	29 13.8	13 57.0	3 1.9	17 24.8	12 29.6	16 34.6	20 50.0
15	15 30 2.3	21 34.6	13 35.3	16 21.3	28 16.6	0♊30.5	14 10.4	3 16.5	17 28.8	12 29.4	16 32.9	20 49.6
16	15 33 58.8	22 33.8	13 31.8	28 52.3	29 33.2	1 47.4	14 24.3	3 31.1	17 32.6	12 29.2	16 31.3	20 49.1
17	15 37 55.4	23 33.2	13 28.4	11♐43.4	0♉52.2	3 4.6	14 38.6	3 45.7	17 36.4	12 29.1	16 29.7	20 48.7
18	15 41 52.0	24 32.8	13 25.0	24 50.9	2 13.5	4 22.1	14 53.4	4 .4	17 40.1	12 29.0	16 28.1	20 48.4
19	15 45 48.5	25 32.4	13 21.6	8♑ 6.0	3 37.1	5 39.8	15 8.5	4 15.0	17 43.7	12 29.0	16 26.5	20 48.0
20	15 49 45.1	26 32.3	13 18.2	21 16.9	5 3.1	6 57.8	15 24.1	4 29.7	17 47.3	12 29.0	16 24.9	20 47.7
21	15 53 41.6	27 32.2	13 14.7	4♒12.4	6 31.6	8 16.0	15 40.1	4 44.5	17 50.7	12 D 29.1	16 23.3	20 47.4
22	15 57 38.2	28 32.3	13 11.3	16 45.3	8 2.5	9 34.4	15 56.5	4 59.2	17 54.1	12 29.2	16 21.7	20 47.1
23	16 1 34.7	29 32.6	13 7.9	28 53.7	9 35.9	10 53.0	16 13.3	5 14.0	17 57.5	12 29.4	16 20.1	20 46.9
24	16 5 31.3	0♊32.9	13 4.5	10♓41.1	11 11.9	12 11.9	16 30.4	5 28.7	18 .7	12 29.6	16 18.5	20 46.7
25	16 9 27.9	1 33.4	13 1.1	22 15.4	12 50.5	13 31.0	16 47.9	5 43.5	18 3.9	12 29.9	16 17.0	20 46.5
26	16 13 24.4	2 34.1	12 57.7	3♈48.0	14 31.8	14 50.2	17 5.8	5 58.3	18 6.9	12 30.2	16 15.4	20 46.3
27	16 17 21.0	3 34.8	12 54.2	15 32.5	16 15.9	16 9.7	17 24.1	6 13.1	18 9.9	12 30.6	16 13.9	20 46.2
28	16 21 17.5	4 35.8	12 50.8	27 44.2	18 2.9	17 29.4	17 42.7	6 28.0	18 12.9	12 31.1	16 12.4	20 46.2
29	16 25 14.1	5 36.8	12 47.4	10♉38.7	19 52.7	18 49.2	18 1.7	6 42.8	18 15.7	12 31.6	16 10.8	20 46.1
30	16 29 10.6	6 37.9	12 44.0	24 29.3	21 45.3	20 9.1	18 21.0	6 57.6	18 18.5	12 32.1	16 9.3	20 46.1
31	16 33 7.2	7 39.1	12 40.6	9♊22.5	23 41.0	21 29.2	18 40.6	7 12.5	18 21.2	12 32.7	16 7.8	20 46.1

DECLINATION

DAY	EPHEM. SID. TIME	☉	☊	☾	☿	♀	♂	♃	♄	♅	♆	♇
1	14 34 50.5	14N56.8	0N23.7	9N41.4	3N26.1	15N52.5	9N56.4	19N56.3	7S38.9	8N14.6	15S41.2	19N42.6
4	14 46 40.2	15 50.5	0 23.7	22 58.2	4 2.1	17 1.5	9 40.2	20 4.7	7 33.6	8 15.5	15 39.9	19 42.5
7	14 58 29.8	16 41.8	0 23.7	23 54.5	4 55.0	18 6.5	9 22.1	20 13.0	7 28.5	8 16.1	15 38.6	19 42.3
10	15 10 19.5	17 30.6	0 23.7	12 .4	6 2.7	19 7.3	9 2.2	20 21.1	7 23.7	8 16.6	15 37.2	19 41.9
13	15 22 9.2	18 16.7	0 23.7	4S50.8	7 23.1	20 3.5	8 40.7	20 29.1	7 19.2	8 16.9	15 35.9	19 41.4
16	15 33 58.8	19 .1	0 23.6	19 9.1	8 54.4	20 54.8	8 17.5	20 36.9	7 15.0	8 17.0	15 34.6	19 40.8
19	15 45 48.5	19 40.5	0 23.6	25 20.8	10 34.7	21 40.9	7 52.9	20 44.5	7 11.0	8 17.0	15 33.3	19 40.1
22	15 57 38.2	20 18.0	0 23.6	21 16.9	12 22.2	22 21.6	7 26.9	20 52.0	7 7.4	8 16.8	15 32.0	19 39.2
25	16 9 27.9	20 52.4	0 23.6	9 3.9	14 14.6	22 56.7	6 59.5	20 59.2	7 4.1	8 16.3	15 30.8	19 38.2
28	16 21 17.5	21 23.5	0 23.6	7N23.1	16 9.6	23 25.8	6 30.8	21 6.3	7 1.0	8 15.7	15 29.6	19 37.1
31	16 33 7.2	21 51.3	0 23.6	21 49.2	18 3.8	23 48.8	6 .9	21 13.1	6 58.3	8 14.9	15 28.4	19 35.9

JUNE 1965

LONGITUDE

DAY	EPHEM. SID. TIME (h m s)	☉ (° ′)	☊ (° ′)	☾ (° ′)	☿ (° ′)	♀ (° ′)	♂ (° ′)	♃ (° ′)	♄ (° ′)	♅ (° ′)	♆ (° ′)	♇ (° ′)
1	16 37 3.8	10♊17.6	13♊58.7	25♊37.5	27♉41.5	23♊26.5	17♍36.6	9♊ 3.8	16♓36.9	10♍46.5	18♏ 2.6	13♍41.5
2	16 41 .3	11 15.1	13 55.5	10♋26.2	29 41.7	24 40.1	17 59.3	9 17.8	16 39.5	10 47.3	18R 1.2	13 41.7
3	16 44 56.9	12 12.6	13 52.3	25 13.6	1♊43.8	25 53.6	18 22.2	9 31.8	16 42.0	10 48.1	17 59.7	13 42.0
4	16 48 53.4	13 10.1	13 49.1	9♌53.0	3 47.8	27 7.1	18 45.5	9 45.8	16 44.4	10 48.9	17 58.3	13 42.3
5	16 52 50.0	14 7.5	13 46.0	24 19.4	5 53.4	28 20.7	19 9.1	9 59.8	16 46.7	10 49.8	17 56.8	13 42.6
6	16 56 46.5	15 5.0	13 42.8	8♍29.1	8 .7	29 34.2	19 33.1	10 13.8	16 48.9	10 50.8	17 55.4	13 43.0
7	17 0 43.1	16 2.4	13 39.6	22 20.5	10 9.3	0♋47.6	19 57.3	10 27.8	16 51.0	10 51.8	17 54.0	13 43.4
8	17 4 39.7	16 59.8	13 36.4	5♎53.3	12 19.1	2 1.1	20 21.9	10 41.7	16 53.0	10 52.8	17 52.6	13 43.8
9	17 8 36.2	17 57.1	13 33.3	19 8.1	14 29.9	3 14.6	20 46.7	10 55.7	16 55.0	10 54.0	17 51.3	13 44.2
10	17 12 32.8	18 54.5	13 30.1	2♏ 6.3	16 41.3	4 28.0	21 11.9	11 9.6	16 56.8	10 55.1	17 49.9	13 44.7
11	17 16 29.3	19 51.8	13 26.9	14 49.6	18 53.2	5 41.4	21 37.3	11 23.5	16 58.6	10 56.3	17 48.6	13 45.2
12	17 20 25.9	20 49.2	13 23.7	27 19.9	21 5.3	6 54.8	22 3.0	11 37.4	17 .2	10 57.6	17 47.3	13 45.8
13	17 24 22.5	21 46.5	13 20.5	9♐38.7	23 17.2	8 8.2	22 29.0	11 51.3	17 1.8	10 58.9	17 46.0	13 46.3
14	17 28 19.0	22 43.8	13 17.4	21 47.9	25 28.8	9 21.5	22 55.2	12 5.2	17 3.2	11 .3	17 44.7	13 47.0
15	17 32 15.6	23 41.1	13 14.2	3♑49.2	27 39.7	10 34.9	23 21.8	12 19.0	17 4.6	11 1.7	17 43.5	13 47.6
16	17 36 12.1	24 38.3	13 11.0	15 44.5	29 49.7	11 48.2	23 48.6	12 32.9	17 5.8	11 3.2	17 42.2	13 48.2
17	17 40 8.7	25 35.6	13 7.8	27 36.0	1♋58.6	13 1.6	24 15.6	12 46.7	17 7.0	11 4.7	17 41.0	13 48.9
18	17 44 5.2	26 32.9	13 4.7	9♒26.3	4 6.2	14 14.9	24 42.9	13 .5	17 8.1	11 6.3	17 39.9	13 49.7
19	17 48 1.8	27 30.2	13 1.5	21 18.2	6 12.3	15 28.2	25 10.5	13 14.3	17 9.0	11 7.9	17 38.7	13 50.5
20	17 51 58.4	28 27.4	12 58.3	3♓15.1	8 16.8	16 41.5	25 38.2	13 28.0	17 9.9	11 9.5	17 37.6	13 51.2
21	17 55 54.9	29 24.7	12 55.1	15 21.0	10 19.4	17 54.8	26 6.3	13 41.7	17 10.7	11 11.2	17 36.5	13 52.0
22	17 59 51.5	0♋21.9	12 52.0	27 39.9	12 20.2	19 8.0	26 34.5	13 55.4	17 11.3	11 13.0	17 35.4	13 52.9
23	18 3 48.0	1 19.2	12 48.8	10♈15.9	14 19.1	20 21.3	27 3.0	14 9.1	17 11.9	11 14.8	17 34.3	13 53.7
24	18 7 44.6	2 16.4	12 45.6	23 13.1	16 15.9	21 34.5	27 31.7	14 22.7	17 12.4	11 16.6	17 33.2	13 54.6
25	18 11 41.2	3 13.7	12 42.4	6♉34.6	18 10.6	22 47.7	28 .7	14 36.3	17 12.7	11 18.5	17 32.2	13 55.6
26	18 15 37.7	4 10.9	12 39.3	20 22.3	20 3.3	24 .9	28 29.8	14 49.9	17 13.0	11 20.5	17 31.2	13 56.5
27	18 19 34.3	5 8.1	12 36.1	4♊36.3	21 53.8	25 14.1	28 59.2	15 3.5	17 13.2	11 22.5	17 30.2	13 57.5
28	18 23 30.8	6 5.4	12 32.9	19 14.0	23 42.1	26 27.3	29 28.9	15 17.0	17 13.2	11 24.5	17 29.3	13 58.5
29	18 27 27.4	7 2.6	12 29.7	4♋10.0	25 28.3	27 40.4	29 58.7	15 30.4	17 13.2	11 26.6	17 28.3	13 59.5
30	18 31 23.9	7 59.8	12 26.5	19 16.8	27 12.4	28 53.6	0♎28.7	15 43.9	17R13.1	11 28.7	17 27.4	14 .6

LATITUDE

DAY	SID. TIME	☉	☊	☾	☿	♀	♂	♃	♄	♅	♆	♇
1	16 37 3.8	0 .0	0 .0	1N 5.1	0S59.5	0N38.2	1N 1.7	0S33.9	1S49.0	0N46.4	1N48.9	14N19.8
4	16 48 53.4	0 .0	0 .0	4 23.5	0 27.4	0 45.0	0 56.8	0 33.6	1 49.7	0 46.3	1 48.8	14 18.6
7	17 0 43.1	0 .0	0 .0	5 13.8	0N 5.0	0 51.5	0 52.1	0 33.4	1 50.5	0 46.2	1 48.7	14 17.5
10	17 12 32.8	0 .0	0 .0	3 31.5	0 36.0	0 57.8	0 47.5	0 33.2	1 51.2	0 46.1	1 48.6	14 16.3
13	17 24 22.5	0 .0	0 .0	0 23.3	1 3.7	1 3.7	0 43.0	0 32.9	1 51.9	0 45.9	1 48.5	14 15.2
16	17 36 12.1	0 .0	0 .0	2S47.6	1 26.4	1 9.2	0 38.7	0 32.7	1 52.7	0 45.8	1 48.4	14 14.1
19	17 48 1.8	0 .0	0 .0	4 52.1	1 43.1	1 14.3	0 34.5	0 32.5	1 53.4	0 45.7	1 48.3	14 13.0
22	17 59 51.5	0 .0	0 .0	5 6.6	1 53.2	1 19.0	0 30.5	0 32.3	1 54.2	0 45.6	1 48.2	14 11.9
25	18 11 41.2	0 .0	0 .0	3 11.0	1 56.6	1 23.2	0 26.5	0 32.1	1 55.0	0 45.5	1 48.0	14 10.8
28	18 23 30.8	0 .0	0 .0	0N30.1	1 53.6	1 26.9	0 22.7	0 31.9	1 55.7	0 45.4	1 47.9	14 9.8

RIGHT ASCENSION

DAY	SID. TIME	☉	☊	☾	☿	♀	♂	♃	♄	♅	♆	♇
1	16 37 3.8	8♊40.4	12♊37.2	25♊11.7	25♉39.6	22♊49.4	19♍ .5	7♊27.3	18♓23.7	12♍33.3	16♏ 6.3	20♍46.1
2	16 41 .3	9 41.9	12 33.8	11♋33.5	27 41.1	24 9.7	19 20.8	7 42.2	18 26.2	12 34.0	16R 4.9	20D46.2
3	16 44 56.9	10 43.4	12 30.3	27 52.9	29 45.6	25 30.1	19 41.4	7 57.0	18 28.6	12 34.7	16 3.4	20 46.2
4	16 48 53.4	11 45.0	12 26.9	13♌35.8	1♊52.9	26 50.5	20 2.3	8 11.9	18 31.0	12 35.5	16 1.9	20 46.3
5	16 52 50.0	12 46.7	12 23.5	28 22.1	4 2.9	28 11.1	20 23.4	8 26.7	18 33.2	12 36.3	16 .5	20 46.5
6	16 56 46.5	13 48.5	12 20.1	12♍ 8.3	6 15.7	29 31.7	20 44.9	8 41.6	18 35.4	12 37.2	15 59.1	20 46.7
7	17 0 43.1	14 50.3	12 16.7	25 3.0	8 30.8	0♋52.3	21 6.7	8 56.4	18 37.4	12 38.1	15 57.7	20 46.9
8	17 4 39.7	15 52.3	12 13.3	7♎20.8	10 48.2	2 12.9	21 28.7	9 11.2	18 39.4	12 39.1	15 56.3	20 47.1
9	17 8 36.2	16 54.3	12 9.9	19 17.8	13 7.5	3 33.5	21 51.0	9 26.1	18 41.3	12 40.1	15 54.9	20 47.3
10	17 12 32.8	17 56.3	12 6.5	1♏ 9.3	15 28.5	4 54.1	22 13.6	9 40.9	18 43.1	12 41.2	15 53.6	20 47.6
11	17 16 29.3	18 58.4	12 3.1	13 8.4	17 50.8	6 14.7	22 36.4	9 55.7	18 44.8	12 42.3	15 52.3	20 48.0
12	17 20 25.9	20 .6	11 59.6	25 24.6	20 14.0	7 35.2	22 59.5	10 10.5	18 46.4	12 43.5	15 50.9	20 48.3
13	17 24 22.5	21 2.8	11 56.2	8♐ 2.7	22 37.8	8 55.7	23 22.9	10 25.3	18 48.0	12 44.7	15 49.6	20 48.7
14	17 28 19.0	22 5.0	11 52.8	21 1.3	25 1.8	10 16.1	23 46.5	10 40.1	18 49.4	12 46.0	15 48.4	20 49.1
15	17 32 15.6	23 7.3	11 49.4	4♑13.2	27 25.5	11 36.4	24 10.3	10 54.9	18 50.8	12 47.3	15 47.1	20 49.5
16	17 36 12.1	24 9.6	11 46.0	17 26.4	29 48.7	12 56.6	24 34.3	11 9.6	18 52.0	12 48.6	15 45.9	20 50.0
17	17 40 8.7	25 11.9	11 42.6	0♒27.9	2♋10.8	14 16.7	24 58.6	11 24.4	18 53.2	12 50.0	15 44.7	20 50.5
18	17 44 5.2	26 14.3	11 39.2	13 7.4	4 31.7	15 36.7	25 23.2	11 39.1	18 54.3	12 51.5	15 43.5	20 51.0
19	17 48 1.8	27 16.7	11 35.8	25 20.1	6 50.9	16 56.5	25 48.0	11 53.8	18 55.3	12 53.0	15 42.3	20 51.6
20	17 51 58.4	28 19.1	11 32.4	7♓ 7.2	9 8.1	18 16.2	26 12.9	12 8.5	18 56.2	12 54.5	15 41.2	20 52.2
21	17 55 54.9	29 21.5	11 29.0	18 35.0	11 23.3	19 35.7	26 38.1	12 23.2	18 57.0	12 56.1	15 40.1	20 52.8
22	17 59 51.5	0♋23.9	11 25.6	29 53.8	13 36.0	20 55.0	27 3.5	12 37.8	18 57.7	12 57.7	15 38.9	20 53.4
23	18 3 48.0	1 26.3	11 22.2	11♈16.9	15 46.3	22 14.1	27 29.2	12 52.5	18 58.4	12 59.4	15 37.9	20 54.0
24	18 7 44.6	2 28.7	11 18.8	22 59.6	17 53.8	23 33.0	27 55.0	13 7.1	18 58.9	13 1.1	15 36.8	20 54.7
25	18 11 41.2	3 31.0	11 15.3	5♉18.7	19 58.6	24 51.7	28 21.1	13 21.6	18 59.3	13 2.9	15 35.8	20 55.5
26	18 15 37.7	4 33.4	11 11.9	18 30.6	22 .5	26 10.1	28 47.3	13 36.2	18 59.7	13 4.6	15 34.8	20 56.2
27	18 19 34.3	5 35.7	11 8.5	2♊48.3	23 59.5	27 28.3	29 13.8	13 50.7	18 59.9	13 6.5	15 33.8	20 57.0
28	18 23 30.8	6 38.0	11 5.1	18 14.7	25 55.5	28 46.3	29 40.5	14 5.2	19 .1	13 8.4	15 32.8	20 57.8
29	18 27 27.4	7 40.2	11 1.7	4♋36.3	27 48.6	0♌ 4.0	0♎ 7.3	14 19.6	19 .1	13 10.3	15 31.9	20 58.6
30	18 31 23.9	8 42.4	10 58.3	21 20.9	29 38.6	1 21.4	0 34.4	14 34.1	19 .1	13 12.2	15 31.0	20 59.4

DECLINATION

DAY	SID. TIME	☉	☊	☾	☿	♀	♂	♃	♄	♅	♆	♇
1	16 37 3.8	21N59.8	0N23.5	24N27.4	18N41.0	23N55.1	5N50.6	21N15.3	6S57.5	8N14.6	15S28.0	19N35.5
4	16 48 53.4	22 23.1	0 23.5	22 .2	20 27.9	24 9.8	5 19.2	21 21.9	6 55.2	8 13.6	15 26.8	19 34.1
7	17 0 43.1	22 42.8	0 23.5	7 50.5	22 3.6	24 18.1	4 46.6	21 28.2	6 53.3	8 12.4	15 25.8	19 32.6
10	17 12 32.8	22 58.9	0 23.5	8S53.8	23 22.5	24 19.9	4 13.0	21 34.3	6 51.7	8 11.0	15 24.7	19 31.1
13	17 24 22.5	23 11.4	0 23.5	21 31.0	24 20.0	24 15.2	3 38.5	21 40.2	6 50.5	8 9.5	15 23.7	19 29.4
16	17 36 12.1	23 20.2	0 23.4	25 17.4	24 53.1	24 4.1	3 3.1	21 45.9	6 49.6	8 7.7	15 22.8	19 27.6
19	17 48 1.8	23 25.2	0 23.4	19 .5	25 .9	23 46.7	2 26.8	21 51.3	6 49.0	8 5.8	15 21.9	19 25.7
22	17 59 51.5	23 26.6	0 23.4	5 36.9	24 45.0	23 23.0	1 49.7	21 56.5	6 48.8	8 3.8	15 21.1	19 23.8
25	18 11 41.2	23 24.3	0 23.4	10N42.4	24 8.1	22 53.1	1 11.8	22 1.4	6 49.0	8 1.6	15 20.4	19 21.8
28	18 23 30.8	23 18.3	0 23.4	23 30.5	23 13.7	22 17.4	0 33.2	22 6.1	6 49.5	7 59.2	15 19.7	19 19.7

JULY 1965

LONGITUDE

DAY	EPHEM. SID. TIME h m s	☉ ° ′	☊ ° ′	☾ ° ′	☿ ° ′	♀ ° ′	♂ ° ′	♃ ° ′	♄ ° ′	♅ ° ′	♆ ° ′	♇ ° ′
1	18 35 20.5	8♋57.1	12♊23.4	4♌24.9	28♋54.2	0♌ 6.7	0♎59.0	15♊57.3	17♓12.8	11♍30.8	17♏26.6	14♍ 1.7
2	18 39 17.1	9 54.3	12 20.2	19 24.9	0♌33.9	1 19.8	1 29.4	16 10.6	17 R 12.5	11 33.0	17 R 25.7	14 2.8
3	18 43 13.6	10 51.5	12 17.0	4♍ 8.6	2 11.4	2 32.9	2 .1	16 24.0	17 12.0	11 35.3	17 24.9	14 4.0
4	18 47 10.2	11 48.7	12 13.8	18 30.4	3 46.7	3 46.0	2 31.0	16 37.3	17 11.5	11 37.6	17 24.1	14 5.1
5	18 51 6.7	12 45.9	12 10.7	2♎27.3	5 19.7	4 59.1	3 2.0	16 50.5	17 10.9	11 39.9	17 23.3	14 6.3
6	18 55 3.3	13 43.1	12 7.5	15 58.9	6 50.6	6 12.1	3 33.2	17 3.7	17 10.1	11 42.3	17 22.6	14 7.5
7	18 58 59.9	14 40.3	12 4.3	29 6.9	8 19.2	7 25.1	4 4.7	17 16.8	17 9.3	11 44.7	17 21.9	14 8.8
8	19 2 56.4	15 37.5	12 1.1	11♏54.1	9 45.6	8 38.1	4 36.3	17 29.9	17 8.4	11 47.2	17 21.2	14 10.1
9	19 6 53.0	16 34.8	11 58.0	24 24.1	11 9.7	9 51.1	5 8.1	17 43.0	17 7.4	11 49.7	17 20.6	14 11.4
10	19 10 49.5	17 32.0	11 54.8	6♐40.4	12 31.4	11 4.1	5 40.1	17 56.0	17 6.3	11 52.2	17 20.0	14 12.7
11	19 14 46.1	18 29.2	11 51.6	18 46.4	13 50.8	12 17.0	6 12.2	18 9.0	17 5.1	11 54.8	17 19.4	14 14.1
12	19 18 42.6	19 26.4	11 48.4	0♑45.1	15 7.8	13 29.9	6 44.5	18 21.9	17 3.7	11 57.4	17 18.8	14 15.5
13	19 22 39.2	20 23.6	11 45.3	12 38.9	16 22.4	14 42.8	7 17.0	18 34.8	17 2.3	12 .1	17 18.3	14 16.8
14	19 26 35.8	21 20.8	11 42.1	24 30.2	17 34.4	15 55.6	7 49.7	18 47.6	17 .8	12 2.7	17 17.8	14 18.3
15	19 30 32.3	22 18.0	11 38.9	6♒20.7	18 43.8	17 8.5	8 22.5	19 .3	16 59.2	12 5.5	17 17.3	14 19.7
16	19 34 28.9	23 15.2	11 35.7	18 12.4	19 50.6	18 21.3	8 55.5	19 13.0	16 57.5	12 8.2	17 16.9	14 21.2
17	19 38 25.4	24 12.4	11 32.5	0♓ 7.3	20 54.7	19 34.1	9 28.6	19 25.6	16 55.8	12 11.0	17 16.4	14 22.7
18	19 42 22.0	25 9.6	11 29.4	12 7.5	21 55.9	20 46.8	10 1.9	19 38.2	16 53.9	12 13.8	17 16.1	14 24.2
19	19 46 18.5	26 6.9	11 26.2	24 15.9	22 54.2	21 59.6	10 35.4	19 50.7	16 51.9	12 16.7	17 15.7	14 25.7
20	19 50 15.1	27 4.1	11 23.0	6♈35.4	23 49.4	23 12.3	11 9.0	20 3.2	16 49.9	12 19.6	17 15.4	14 27.3
21	19 54 11.7	28 1.4	11 19.8	19 9.6	24 41.5	24 25.0	11 42.7	20 15.6	16 47.7	12 22.5	17 15.1	14 28.8
22	19 58 8.2	28 58.7	11 16.7	2♉ 2.4	25 30.3	25 37.7	12 16.7	20 27.9	16 45.5	12 25.5	17 14.8	14 30.4
23	20 2 4.8	29 56.0	11 13.5	15 17.2	26 15.7	26 50.3	12 50.7	20 40.2	16 43.2	12 28.5	17 14.6	14 32.0
24	20 6 1.3	0♌53.3	11 10.3	28 57.1	26 57.5	28 3.0	13 25.0	20 52.4	16 40.8	12 31.5	17 14.4	14 33.7
25	20 9 57.9	1 50.6	11 7.1	13♊ 3.6	27 35.5	29 15.6	13 59.3	21 4.5	16 38.3	12 34.6	17 14.2	14 35.3
26	20 13 54.4	2 47.9	11 4.0	27 36.1	28 9.7	0♍28.2	14 33.9	21 16.6	16 35.7	12 37.6	17 14.1	14 37.0
27	20 17 51.0	3 45.3	11 .8	12♋31.0	28 39.8	1 40.8	15 8.5	21 28.6	16 33.0	12 40.8	17 14.0	14 38.7
28	20 21 47.6	4 42.6	10 57.6	27 41.5	29 5.6	2 53.3	15 43.4	21 40.5	16 30.3	12 43.9	17 13.9	14 40.4
29	20 25 44.1	5 40.0	10 54.4	12♌58.1	29 27.0	4 5.8	16 18.3	21 52.4	16 27.4	12 47.1	17 13.9	14 42.2
30	20 29 40.7	6 37.5	10 51.2	28 9.9	29 43.9	5 18.4	16 53.5	22 4.2	16 24.6	12 50.3	17 D 14.0	14 44.0
31	20 33 37.2	7 34.9	10 48.1	13♍ 6.6	29 56.0	6 30.8	17 28.8	22 15.9	16 21.6	12 53.6	17 14.0	14 45.7

LATITUDE

DAY	SID. TIME	☉	☊	☾	☿	♀	♂	♃	♄	♅	♆	♇
1	18 35 20.5	0 .0	0 .0	4N 3.3	1N44.6	1N30.1	0N19.0	0S31.8	1S56.5	0N45.2	1N47.7	14N 8.7
4	18 47 10.2	0 .0	0 .0	5 12.3	1 30.2	1 32.7	0 15.5	0 31.6	1 57.2	0 45.1	1 47.6	14 7.8
7	18 58 59.9	0 .0	0 .0	3 39.5	1 10.8	1 34.7	0 12.0	0 31.4	1 57.9	0 45.0	1 47.4	14 6.8
10	19 10 49.5	0 .0	0 .0	0 37.5	0 46.9	1 36.0	0 8.6	0 31.3	1 58.7	0 44.9	1 47.3	14 5.9
13	19 22 39.2	0 .0	0 .0	2S31.8	0 19.0	1 36.7	0 5.3	0 31.1	1 59.4	0 44.8	1 47.1	14 5.0
16	19 34 28.9	0 .0	0 .0	4 40.4	0S12.4	1 36.8	0 2.1	0 31.0	2 .1	0 44.8	1 46.9	14 4.2
19	19 46 18.5	0 .0	0 .0	5 2.8	0 46.8	1 36.2	0S 1.0	0 30.9	2 .8	0 44.7	1 46.8	14 3.4
22	19 58 8.2	0 .0	0 .0	3 21.9	1 23.7	1 34.9	0 4.0	0 30.7	2 1.5	0 44.6	1 46.6	14 2.6
25	20 9 57.9	0 .0	0 .0	0N 1.5	2 2.2	1 32.9	0 7.0	0 30.6	2 2.1	0 44.5	1 46.4	14 1.9
28	20 21 47.6	0 .0	0 .0	3 37.3	2 41.3	1 30.3	0 9.9	0 30.5	2 2.8	0 44.4	1 46.2	14 1.2
31	20 33 37.2	0 .0	0 .0	5 5.7	3 19.5	1 26.9	0 12.6	0 30.4	2 3.4	0 44.4	1 46.1	14 .6

RIGHT ASCENSION

DAY	SID. TIME	☉	☊	☾	☿	♀	♂	♃	♄	♅	♆	♇
1	18 35 20.5	9♋44.5	10♊54.9	7♌47.9	1♌25.5	2♌38.5	1♎ 1.7	14♊48.4	18♓60.0	13♍14.3	15♏30.1	21♍ .3
2	18 39 17.1	10 46.6	10 51.5	23 25.0	3 9.4	3 55.4	1 29.2	15 2.8	18 R 59.8	13 16.3	15 R 29.2	21 1.2
3	18 43 13.6	11 48.6	10 48.1	7♍57.9	4 50.4	5 12.0	1 56.8	15 17.1	18 59.5	13 18.4	15 28.4	21 2.2
4	18 47 10.2	12 50.5	10 44.7	21 29.6	6 28.3	6 28.2	2 24.7	15 31.4	18 59.1	13 20.5	15 27.6	21 3.1
5	18 51 6.7	13 52.3	10 41.3	4♎13.2	8 3.2	7 44.2	2 52.7	15 45.6	18 58.6	13 22.7	15 26.8	21 4.1
6	18 55 3.3	14 54.0	10 37.9	16 25.1	9 35.1	8 59.8	3 20.9	15 59.8	18 58.0	13 24.9	15 26.1	21 5.1
7	18 58 59.9	15 55.7	10 34.5	28 22.3	11 4.0	10 15.2	3 49.3	16 13.9	18 57.3	13 27.1	15 25.3	21 6.2
8	19 2 56.4	16 57.2	10 31.1	10♏19.6	12 30.0	11 30.2	4 17.9	16 28.0	18 56.5	13 29.4	15 24.6	21 7.2
9	19 6 53.0	17 58.7	10 27.7	22 28.5	13 53.1	12 44.9	4 46.7	16 42.1	18 55.7	13 31.8	15 24.0	21 8.4
10	19 10 49.5	19 .1	10 24.3	4♐56.4	15 13.2	13 59.3	5 15.6	16 56.1	18 54.8	13 34.1	15 23.4	21 9.5
11	19 14 46.1	20 1.3	10 20.9	17 44.9	16 30.3	15 13.3	5 44.7	17 10.1	18 53.8	13 36.5	15 22.8	21 10.6
12	19 18 42.6	21 2.5	10 17.5	0♑49.7	17 44.5	16 27.0	6 13.9	17 24.0	18 52.6	13 38.9	15 22.2	21 11.8
13	19 22 39.2	22 3.5	10 14.1	14 .6	18 55.7	17 40.4	6 43.4	17 37.8	18 51.4	13 41.4	15 21.7	21 13.0
14	19 26 35.8	23 4.4	10 10.7	27 4.8	20 4.0	18 53.5	7 13.0	17 51.6	18 50.1	13 43.9	15 21.1	21 14.2
15	19 30 32.3	24 5.1	10 7.3	9♒50.5	21 9.2	20 6.2	7 42.8	18 5.4	18 48.7	13 46.4	15 20.6	21 15.4
16	19 34 28.9	25 5.8	10 3.9	22 10.3	22 11.4	21 18.6	8 12.7	18 19.0	18 47.3	13 48.9	15 20.2	21 16.7
17	19 38 25.4	26 6.3	10 .5	4♓ 2.6	23 10.4	22 30.7	8 42.8	18 32.7	18 45.7	13 51.5	15 19.8	21 17.9
18	19 42 22.0	27 6.7	9 57.1	15 31.3	24 6.4	23 42.5	9 13.1	18 46.2	18 44.1	13 54.2	15 19.4	21 19.2
19	19 46 18.5	28 7.0	9 53.7	26 44.8	24 59.1	24 53.9	9 43.5	18 59.8	18 42.3	13 56.8	15 19.0	21 20.6
20	19 50 15.1	29 7.1	9 50.3	7♈54.8	25 48.6	26 5.1	10 14.2	19 13.2	18 40.5	13 59.5	15 18.7	21 21.9
21	19 54 11.7	0♌ 7.1	9 46.9	19 15.4	26 34.8	27 15.9	10 44.9	19 26.6	18 38.6	14 2.2	15 18.4	21 23.3
22	19 58 8.2	1 7.0	9 43.5	1♉ 2.3	27 17.5	28 26.5	11 15.9	19 39.9	18 36.6	14 5.0	15 18.1	21 24.7
23	20 2 4.8	2 6.7	9 40.1	13 32.2	27 56.8	29 36.7	11 47.0	19 53.2	18 34.6	14 7.7	15 17.8	21 26.1
24	20 6 1.3	3 6.3	9 36.7	27 .7	28 32.4	0♍46.6	12 18.3	20 6.3	18 32.4	14 10.5	15 17.6	21 27.5
25	20 9 57.9	4 5.8	9 33.3	11♊37.9	29 4.3	1 56.3	12 49.7	20 19.5	18 30.2	14 13.4	15 17.4	21 29.0
26	20 13 54.4	5 5.1	9 29.9	27 21.6	29 32.3	3 5.7	13 21.3	20 32.5	18 27.9	14 16.3	15 17.3	21 30.4
27	20 17 51.0	6 4.3	9 26.5	13♋52.0	29 56.4	4 14.8	13 53.1	20 45.5	18 25.5	14 19.1	15 17.2	21 31.9
28	20 21 47.6	7 3.3	9 23.1	0♌33.3	0♍16.4	5 23.6	14 25.1	20 58.4	18 23.0	14 22.1	15 17.1	21 33.4
29	20 25 44.1	8 2.1	9 19.7	16 47.0	0 32.2	6 32.2	14 57.2	21 11.2	18 20.5	14 25.0	15 17.0	21 35.0
30	20 29 40.7	9 .9	9 16.3	2♍ 6.9	0 43.8	7 40.5	15 29.5	21 24.0	18 17.9	14 28.0	15 D 17.1	21 36.6
31	20 33 37.2	9 59.5	9 13.0	16 25.4	0 50.8	8 48.6	16 2.0	21 36.6	18 15.2	14 31.0	15 17.1	21 38.2

DECLINATION

DAY	SID. TIME	☉	☊	☾	☿	♀	♂	♃	♄	♅	♆	♇
1	18 35 20.5	23N 8.5	0N23.3	23N 5.8	22N 5.4	21N35.9	0S 6.0	22N10.6	6S50.3	7N56.7	15S19.1	19N17.5
4	18 47 10.2	22 55.2	0 23.3	9 20.0	20 46.3	20 48.9	0 45.9	22 14.9	6 51.5	7 54.0	15 18.5	19 15.2
7	18 58 59.9	22 38.2	0 23.3	7S44.3	19 19.7	19 56.7	1 26.3	22 18.9	6 53.1	7 51.2	15 18.1	19 12.9
10	19 10 49.5	22 17.7	0 23.3	20 48.7	17 48.1	18 59.6	2 7.2	22 22.6	6 54.9	7 48.2	15 17.7	19 10.5
13	19 22 39.2	21 53.8	0 23.2	25 21.6	16 14.1	17 57.9	2 48.6	22 26.2	6 57.1	7 45.2	15 17.4	19 8.1
16	19 34 28.9	21 26.5	0 23.2	19 49.1	14 40.2	16 51.9	3 30.4	22 29.5	6 59.6	7 42.0	15 17.1	19 5.6
19	19 46 18.5	20 55.9	0 23.2	6 54.6	13 8.8	15 41.8	4 12.5	22 32.6	7 2.5	7 38.6	15 17.0	19 3.1
22	19 58 8.2	20 22.1	0 23.2	9N 1.5	11 42.5	14 28.1	4 54.9	22 35.4	7 5.6	7 35.2	15 16.9	19 .6
25	20 9 57.9	19 45.2	0 23.2	22 23.8	10 23.9	13 11.1	5 37.6	22 38.1	7 9.0	7 31.7	15 16.9	18 58.0
28	20 21 47.6	19 5.4	0 23.1	24 10.5	9 16.3	11 51.0	6 20.5	22 40.5	7 12.7	7 28.0	15 17.0	18 55.4
31	20 33 37.2	18 22.8	0 23.1	11 20.3	8 23.0	10 28.1	7 3.5	22 42.8	7 16.7	7 24.2	15 17.2	18 52.7

AUGUST 1965

LONGITUDE

DAY	EPHEM. SID. TIME h m s	☉ ° ′	☊ ° ′	☽ ° ′	☿ ° ′	♀ ° ′	♂ ° ′	♃ ° ′	♄ ° ′	♅ ° ′	♆ ° ′	♇ ° ′
1	20 37 33.8	8♌32.3	10♊44.9	27♍40.2	0♍ 3.1	7♍43.3	18♎ 4.2	22♊27.5	16♓18.5	12♍56.8	17♏14.0	14♍47.5
2	20 41 30.3	9 29.7	10 41.7	11♎46.0	0 5.2	8 55.7	18 39.7	22 39.0	16 R 15.4	13 .1	17 14.1	14 49.3
3	20 45 26.9	10 27.1	10 38.5	25 22.6	0 R 2.2	10 8.1	19 15.4	22 50.5	16 12.2	13 3.4	17 14.3	14 51.1
4	20 49 23.5	11 24.6	10 35.4	8♏31.5	29♌53.9	11 20.4	19 51.2	23 1.9	16 8.9	13 6.7	17 14.4	14 53.0
5	20 53 20.0	12 22.0	10 32.2	21 16.1	29 40.3	12 32.7	20 27.1	23 13.2	16 5.5	13 10.1	17 14.6	14 54.8
6	20 57 16.6	13 19.5	10 29.0	3♐40.8	29 21.5	13 45.0	21 3.2	23 24.4	16 2.1	13 13.5	17 14.8	14 56.7
7	21 1 13.1	14 17.0	10 25.8	15 50.4	28 57.5	14 57.2	21 39.4	23 35.5	15 58.6	13 16.9	17 15.1	14 58.6
8	21 5 9.7	15 14.5	10 22.7	27 49.5	28 28.6	16 9.4	22 15.7	23 46.5	15 55.1	13 20.3	17 15.4	15 .5
9	21 9 6.2	16 12.0	10 19.5	9♑42.3	27 55.0	17 21.6	22 52.1	23 57.4	15 51.4	13 23.7	17 15.7	15 2.4
10	21 13 2.8	17 9.5	10 16.3	21 32.4	27 17.1	18 33.7	23 28.7	24 8.3	15 47.8	13 27.2	17 16.0	15 4.3
11	21 16 59.3	18 7.0	10 13.1	3♒22.5	26 35.3	19 45.8	24 5.4	24 19.0	15 44.0	13 30.7	17 16.4	15 6.3
12	21 20 55.9	19 4.6	10 9.9	15 14.8	25 50.3	20 57.9	24 42.2	24 29.7	15 40.2	13 34.2	17 16.8	15 8.2
13	21 24 52.5	20 2.2	10 6.8	27 11.1	25 2.7	22 9.9	25 19.1	24 40.3	15 36.4	13 37.7	17 17.3	15 10.2
14	21 28 49.0	20 59.8	10 3.6	9♓12.6	24 13.4	23 21.9	25 56.2	24 50.7	15 32.5	13 41.3	17 17.8	15 12.1
15	21 32 45.6	21 57.4	10 .4	21 20.8	23 23.1	24 33.8	26 33.3	25 1.1	15 28.5	13 44.8	17 18.3	15 14.1
16	21 36 42.1	22 55.0	9 57.2	3♈37.0	22 32.9	25 45.8	27 10.6	25 11.3	15 24.5	13 48.4	17 18.8	15 16.1
17	21 40 38.7	23 52.7	9 54.1	16 3.0	21 43.8	26 57.6	27 48.0	25 21.5	15 20.4	13 52.0	17 19.4	15 18.1
18	21 44 35.2	24 50.4	9 50.9	28 41.3	20 56.7	28 9.5	28 25.5	25 31.6	15 16.3	13 55.6	17 20.0	15 20.2
19	21 48 31.8	25 48.1	9 47.7	11♉34.6	20 12.6	29 21.3	29 3.2	25 41.5	15 12.1	13 59.2	17 20.6	15 22.2
20	21 52 28.3	26 45.9	9 44.5	24 46.1	19 32.5	0♎33.1	29 41.0	25 51.4	15 8.0	14 2.9	17 21.4	15 24.3
21	21 56 24.9	27 43.7	9 41.3	8♊18.6	18 57.2	1 44.8	0♏18.9	26 1.2	15 3.7	14 6.5	17 22.1	15 26.3
22	22 0 21.4	28 41.5	9 38.2	22 14.4	18 27.5	2 56.5	0 56.9	26 10.8	14 59.4	14 10.2	17 22.8	15 28.4
23	22 4 18.0	29 39.3	9 35.0	6♋34.1	18 4.1	4 8.1	1 35.0	26 20.3	14 55.1	14 13.9	17 23.6	15 30.5
24	22 8 14.6	0♍37.2	9 31.8	21 16.0	17 47.6	5 19.8	2 13.2	26 29.7	14 50.8	14 17.6	17 24.4	15 32.5
25	22 12 11.1	1 35.0	9 28.6	6♌15.3	17 38.5	6 31.3	2 51.5	26 39.0	14 46.4	14 21.3	17 25.2	15 34.6
26	22 16 7.7	2 32.9	9 25.5	21 24.1	17 37.1	7 42.9	3 30.0	26 48.1	14 42.0	14 25.0	17 26.0	15 36.7
27	22 20 4.2	3 30.9	9 22.3	6♍32.5	17 D 43.7	8 54.4	4 8.5	26 57.2	14 37.5	14 28.7	17 26.9	15 38.8
28	22 24 .8	4 28.9	9 19.1	21 29.9	17 58.3	10 5.8	4 47.2	27 6.1	14 33.0	14 32.4	17 27.8	15 40.9
29	22 27 57.3	5 26.8	9 15.9	6♎ 7.2	18 21.1	11 17.2	5 26.0	27 14.9	14 28.5	14 36.2	17 28.8	15 43.0
30	22 31 53.9	6 24.9	9 12.7	20 18.1	18 52.0	12 28.6	6 4.9	27 23.6	14 24.0	14 39.9	17 29.8	15 45.1
31	22 35 50.4	7 22.9	9 9.6	3♏59.9	19 30.9	13 39.9	6 43.9	27 32.1	14 19.5	14 43.7	17 30.8	15 47.2

LATITUDE

DAY	SID. TIME	☉	☊	☽	☿	♀	♂	♃	♄	♅	♆	♇
1	20 37 33.8	0 .0	0 .0	4N54.7	3S31.6	1N25.7	0S13.6	0S30.4	2S 3.6	0N44.3	1N46.0	14N .4
4	20 49 23.5	0 .0	0 .0	2 49.1	4 5.2	1 21.4	0 16.3	0 30.3	2 4.2	0 44.3	1 45.8	13 59.9
7	21 1 13.1	0 .0	0 .0	0S20.5	4 31.9	1 16.5	0 18.9	0 30.2	2 4.7	0 44.2	1 45.6	13 59.4
10	21 13 2.8	0 .0	0 .0	3 14.1	4 47.9	1 10.9	0 21.4	0 30.1	2 5.3	0 44.2	1 45.5	13 58.9
13	21 24 52.5	0 .0	0 .0	4 52.5	4 49.6	1 4.6	0 23.9	0 30.0	2 5.8	0 44.1	1 45.3	13 58.5
16	21 36 42.1	0 .0	0 .0	4 38.1	4 34.9	0 57.8	0 26.3	0 29.9	2 6.2	0 44.1	1 45.1	13 58.2
19	21 48 31.8	0 .0	0 .0	2 26.5	4 3.9	0 50.4	0 28.7	0 29.8	2 6.7	0 44.0	1 44.9	13 57.9
22	22 0 21.4	0 .0	0 .0	1N 2.0	3 19.8	0 42.4	0 31.0	0 29.7	2 7.0	0 44.0	1 44.7	13 57.7
25	22 12 11.1	0 .0	0 .0	4 9.9	2 27.5	0 33.8	0 33.2	0 29.6	2 7.4	0 44.0	1 44.6	13 57.5
28	22 24 .8	0 .0	0 .0	4 54.2	1 32.6	0 24.8	0 35.4	0 29.6	2 7.7	0 44.0	1 44.4	13 57.4
31	22 35 50.4	0 .0	0 .0	2 54.7	0 39.8	0 15.3	0 37.5	0 29.5	2 8.0	0 43.9	1 44.2	13 57.4

RIGHT ASCENSION

DAY	SID. TIME	☉	☊	☽	☿	♀	♂	♃	♄	♅	♆	♇
1	20 37 33.8	10♌57.9	9♊ 9.6	29♍49.3	0♍53.3	9♍56.4	16♎34.6	21♊49.2	18♓12.5	14♍34.1	15♏17.1	21♍39.7
2	20 41 30.3	11 56.1	9 6.2	12♎33.0	0R51.1	11 4.0	17 7.4	22 1.7	18R 9.6	14 37.1	15 17.2	21 41.4
3	20 45 26.9	12 54.2	9 2.8	24 52.8	0 44.3	12 11.3	17 40.4	22 14.1	18 6.7	14 40.2	15 17.3	21 43.0
4	20 49 23.5	13 52.1	8 59.4	7♏ 4.2	0 32.7	13 18.4	18 13.5	22 26.4	18 3.7	14 43.3	15 17.4	21 44.6
5	20 53 20.0	14 49.9	8 56.0	19 20.0	0 16.5	14 25.3	18 46.7	22 38.6	18 .7	14 46.4	15 17.6	21 46.3
6	20 57 16.6	15 47.5	8 52.6	1♐49.0	29♌55.6	15 32.0	19 20.2	22 50.7	17 57.6	14 49.5	15 17.8	21 48.0
7	21 1 13.1	16 45.0	8 49.2	14 35.1	29 30.2	16 38.5	19 53.8	23 2.8	17 54.4	14 52.7	15 18.0	21 49.7
8	21 5 9.7	17 42.3	8 45.8	27 36.3	29 .6	17 44.8	20 27.6	23 14.7	17 51.2	14 55.9	15 18.3	21 51.4
9	21 9 6.2	18 39.5	8 42.4	10♑45.1	28 27.0	18 51.0	21 1.5	23 26.6	17 47.9	14 59.1	15 18.6	21 53.1
10	21 13 2.8	19 36.5	8 39.0	23 50.4	27 49.8	19 56.9	21 35.6	23 38.3	17 44.6	15 2.3	15 18.9	21 54.8
11	21 16 59.3	20 33.4	8 35.6	6♒40.7	27 9.4	21 2.7	22 9.9	23 50.0	17 41.2	15 5.5	15 19.3	21 56.6
12	21 20 55.9	21 30.1	8 32.2	19 7.8	26 26.5	22 8.4	22 44.3	24 1.5	17 37.7	15 8.8	15 19.7	21 58.4
13	21 24 52.5	22 26.7	8 28.9	1♓ 8.1	25 41.6	23 13.9	23 18.9	24 13.0	17 34.2	15 12.0	15 20.1	22 .2
14	21 28 49.0	23 23.2	8 25.5	12 43.7	24 55.6	24 19.2	23 53.7	24 24.3	17 30.6	15 15.3	15 20.6	22 2.0
15	21 32 45.6	24 19.5	8 22.1	24 .9	24 9.3	25 24.5	24 28.6	24 35.6	17 27.0	15 18.6	15 21.1	22 3.8
16	21 36 42.1	25 15.7	8 18.7	5♈ 9.6	23 23.5	26 29.6	25 3.7	24 46.7	17 23.3	15 21.9	15 21.6	22 5.6
17	21 40 38.7	26 11.7	8 15.3	16 21.9	22 39.2	27 34.7	25 38.9	24 57.7	17 19.6	15 25.3	15 22.2	22 7.4
18	21 44 35.2	27 7.7	8 11.9	27 52.0	21 57.2	28 39.6	26 14.4	25 8.6	17 15.8	15 28.6	15 22.7	22 9.3
19	21 48 31.8	28 3.5	8 8.5	9♉54.9	21 18.5	29 44.5	26 50.0	25 19.4	17 12.0	15 32.0	15 23.4	22 11.2
20	21 52 28.3	28 59.2	8 5.1	22 45.5	20 44.0	0♎49.4	27 25.8	25 30.2	17 8.2	15 35.4	15 24.1	22 13.1
21	21 56 24.9	29 54.8	8 1.8	6♊35.6	20 14.4	1 54.1	28 1.8	25 40.7	17 4.3	15 38.8	15 24.7	22 15.0
22	22 0 21.4	0♍50.3	7 58.4	21 29.1	19 50.5	2 58.8	28 37.9	25 51.2	17 .4	15 42.2	15 25.5	22 16.9
23	22 4 18.0	1 45.6	7 55.0	7♋16.5	19 33.0	4 3.4	29 14.2	26 1.5	16 56.4	15 45.6	15 26.2	22 18.8
24	22 8 14.6	2 40.9	7 51.6	23 33.2	19 22.3	5 8.1	29 50.7	26 11.7	16 52.4	15 49.0	15 27.0	22 20.7
25	22 12 11.1	3 36.0	7 48.2	9♌45.5	19 19.0	6 12.7	0♏27.4	26 21.8	16 48.3	15 52.5	15 27.8	22 22.6
26	22 16 7.7	4 31.1	7 44.8	25 23.5	19D23.3	7 17.3	1 4.2	26 31.7	16 44.3	15 55.9	15 28.6	22 24.6
27	22 20 4.2	5 26.0	7 41.4	10♍11.5	19 35.4	8 21.9	1 41.2	26 41.5	16 40.2	15 59.4	15 29.5	22 26.5
28	22 24 .8	6 20.9	7 38.1	24 8.4	19 55.5	9 26.5	2 18.4	26 51.2	16 36.1	16 2.8	15 30.4	22 28.5
29	22 27 57.3	7 15.6	7 34.7	7♎23.6	20 23.6	10 31.1	2 55.8	27 .7	16 31.9	16 6.3	15 31.3	22 30.4
30	22 31 53.9	8 10.3	7 31.3	20 10.9	20 59.5	11 35.7	3 33.4	27 10.2	16 27.7	16 9.8	15 32.3	22 32.4
31	22 35 50.4	9 4.9	7 27.9	2♏44.9	21 43.2	12 40.4	4 11.1	27 19.4	16 23.6	16 13.3	15 33.3	22 34.4

DECLINATION

DAY	SID. TIME	☉	☊	☽	☿	♀	♂	♃	♄	♅	♆	♇
1	20 37 33.8	18N 7.9	0N23.1	5N25.9	8N 9.1	9N60.0	7S17.9	22N43.5	7S18.1	7N23.0	15S17.2	18N51.8
4	20 49 23.5	17 21.7	0 23.1	11S40.6	7 40.8	8 34.1	8 1.0	22 45.5	7 22.4	7 19.1	15 17.5	18 49.2
7	21 1 13.1	16 32.9	0 23.1	23 1.9	7 35.2	7 6.2	8 44.1	22 47.2	7 26.9	7 15.2	15 17.9	18 46.5
10	21 13 2.8	15 41.8	0 23.0	24 54.9	7 54.3	5 36.7	9 27.1	22 48.9	7 31.6	7 11.1	15 18.3	18 43.9
13	21 24 52.5	14 48.4	0 23.0	17 1.6	8 37.4	4 5.9	10 10.1	22 50.3	7 36.5	7 7.1	15 18.8	18 41.2
16	21 36 42.1	13 52.8	0 23.0	2 48.9	9 39.9	2 34.1	10 52.8	22 51.6	7 41.5	7 2.9	15 19.4	18 38.5
19	21 48 31.8	12 55.3	0 23.0	12N59.1	10 53.5	1 1.6	11 35.2	22 52.7	7 46.7	6 58.7	15 20.1	18 35.9
22	22 0 21.4	11 55.9	0 22.9	24 15.0	12 7.8	0S31.3	12 17.4	22 53.7	7 52.0	6 54.4	15 20.9	18 33.3
25	22 12 11.1	10 54.8	0 22.9	22 44.6	13 12.4	2 4.3	12 59.2	22 54.5	7 57.4	6 50.1	15 21.7	18 30.7
28	22 24 .8	9 52.2	0 22.9	7 52.5	13 58.7	3 37.2	13 40.5	22 55.2	8 2.8	6 45.8	15 22.6	18 28.1
31	22 35 50.4	8 48.1	0 22.9	10S 6.7	14 20.4	5 9.5	14 21.3	22 55.8	8 8.3	6 41.5	15 23.6	18 25.6

SEPTEMBER 1965

LONGITUDE

DAY	EPHEM. SID. TIME h m s	☉ ° ′	☊ ° ′	☾ ° ′	☿ ° ′	♀ ° ′	♂ ° ′	♃ ° ′	♄ ° ′	♅ ° ′	♆ ° ′	♇ ° ′
1	22 39 47.0	8♍21.0	9♊ 6.4	17♏12.9	20♌17.6	14♎51.2	7♏23.0	27♊40.5	14♓14.9	14♍47.4	17♏31.8	15♍49.4
2	22 43 43.5	9 19.0	9 3.2	29 59.9	21 11.8	16 2.4	8 2.2	27 48.8	14 R 10.4	14 51.2	17 32.9	15 51.5
3	22 47 40.1	10 17.1	9 .0	12♐25.2	22 13.2	17 13.5	8 41.5	27 57.0	14 5.8	14 54.9	17 34.0	15 53.6
4	22 51 36.6	11 15.3	8 56.9	24 34.0	23 21.3	18 24.7	9 20.9	28 5.0	14 1.2	14 58.7	17 35.1	15 55.8
5	22 55 33.2	12 13.4	8 53.7	6♑31.7	24 35.9	19 35.7	10 .5	28 12.9	13 56.6	15 2.5	17 36.3	15 57.9
6	22 59 29.8	13 11.6	8 50.5	18 23.1	25 56.3	20 46.7	10 40.1	28 20.6	13 52.0	15 6.2	17 37.4	16 .0
7	23 3 26.3	14 9.8	8 47.3	0♒12.7	27 22.1	21 57.7	11 19.8	28 28.2	13 47.4	15 10.0	17 38.7	16 2.2
8	23 7 22.9	15 8.0	8 44.2	12 4.3	28 52.7	23 8.5	11 59.6	28 35.7	13 42.8	15 13.8	17 39.9	16 4.3
9	23 11 19.4	16 6.3	8 41.0	24 .7	0♍27.7	24 19.4	12 39.5	28 43.0	13 38.2	15 17.6	17 41.2	16 6.4
10	23 15 16.0	17 4.6	8 37.8	6♓ 4.1	2 6.5	25 30.2	13 19.6	28 50.2	13 33.7	15 21.4	17 42.5	16 8.6
11	23 19 12.5	18 2.9	8 34.6	18 15.5	3 48.5	26 40.9	13 59.7	28 57.2	13 29.1	15 25.2	17 43.8	16 10.8
12	23 23 9.1	19 1.3	8 31.4	0♈36.0	5 33.2	27 51.5	14 39.9	29 4.1	13 24.6	15 28.9	17 45.2	16 12.9
13	23 27 5.6	19 59.6	8 28.3	13 6.1	7 20.1	29 2.1	15 20.2	29 10.8	13 20.0	15 32.7	17 46.5	16 15.0
14	23 31 2.2	20 58.1	8 25.1	25 46.1	9 8.9	0♏12.6	16 .6	29 17.4	13 15.5	15 36.5	17 47.9	16 17.2
15	23 34 58.7	21 56.5	8 21.9	8♉37.0	10 59.0	1 23.1	16 41.1	29 23.8	13 11.0	15 40.2	17 49.4	16 19.3
16	23 38 55.3	22 55.0	8 18.7	21 40.0	12 50.1	2 33.5	17 21.7	29 30.1	13 6.5	15 44.0	17 50.8	16 21.4
17	23 42 51.8	23 53.5	8 15.5	4♊56.8	14 42.0	3 43.9	18 2.4	29 36.2	13 2.0	15 47.7	17 52.3	16 23.6
18	23 46 48.4	24 52.0	8 12.4	18 29.1	16 34.2	4 54.1	18 43.2	29 42.2	12 57.5	15 51.5	17 53.8	16 25.7
19	23 50 44.9	25 50.6	8 9.2	2♋18.7	18 26.6	6 4.3	19 24.1	29 48.0	12 53.1	15 55.2	17 55.3	16 27.8
20	23 54 41.5	26 49.2	8 6.0	16 26.3	20 18.9	7 14.5	20 5.1	29 53.6	12 48.7	15 58.9	17 56.9	16 29.9
21	23 58 38.0	27 47.9	8 2.8	0♌51.1	22 10.9	8 24.6	20 46.1	29 59.1	12 44.3	16 2.7	17 58.4	16 32.0
22	0 2 34.6	28 46.6	7 59.7	15 30.3	24 2.6	9 34.6	21 27.3	0♋ 4.4	12 40.0	16 6.4	18 .0	16 34.1
23	0 6 31.2	29 45.3	7 56.5	0♍18.3	25 53.8	10 44.5	22 8.6	0 9.5	12 35.7	16 10.1	18 1.7	16 36.2
24	0 10 27.7	0♎44.1	7 53.3	15 7.8	27 44.4	11 54.4	22 49.9	0 14.5	12 31.4	16 13.8	18 3.3	16 38.3
25	0 14 24.3	1 42.9	7 50.1	29 50.2	29 34.3	13 4.2	23 31.4	0 19.2	12 27.2	16 17.5	18 5.0	16 40.4
26	0 18 20.8	2 41.7	7 46.9	14♎17.5	1♎23.4	14 14.0	24 12.9	0 23.9	12 23.1	16 21.1	18 6.7	16 42.5
27	0 22 17.4	3 40.6	7 43.8	28 23.3	3 11.7	15 23.6	24 54.5	0 28.3	12 18.9	16 24.8	18 8.4	16 44.6
28	0 26 13.9	4 39.5	7 40.6	12♏ 3.8	4 59.3	16 33.2	25 36.3	0 32.6	12 14.8	16 28.4	18 10.1	16 46.6
29	0 30 10.5	5 38.4	7 37.4	25 18.1	6 45.9	17 42.7	26 18.1	0 36.6	12 10.8	16 32.1	18 11.9	16 48.7
30	0 34 7.0	6 37.4	7 34.2	8♐ 7.5	8 31.7	18 52.1	26 60.0	0 40.5	12 6.8	16 35.7	18 13.6	16 50.7

LATITUDE

DAY	EPHEM. SID. TIME	☉	☊	☾	☿	♀	♂	♃	♄	♅	♆	♇
1	22 39 47.0	0 .0	0 .0	1N53.7	0S23.3	0N12.0	0S38.1	0S29.5	2S 8.1	0N43.9	1N44.2	13N57.4
4	22 51 36.6	0 .0	0 .0	1S20.1	0N21.3	0 2.0	0 40.2	0 29.4	2 8.3	0 43.9	1 44.0	13 57.5
7	23 3 26.3	0 .0	0 .0	3 54.7	0 57.2	0S 8.4	0 42.1	0 29.4	2 8.5	0 43.9	1 43.9	13 57.6
10	23 15 16.0	0 .0	0 .0	4 59.6	1 23.5	0 19.1	0 44.0	0 29.3	2 8.6	0 43.9	1 43.7	13 57.7
13	23 27 5.6	0 .0	0 .0	4 5.8	1 40.3	0 30.1	0 45.9	0 29.2	2 8.8	0 43.9	1 43.6	13 58.0
16	23 38 55.3	0 .0	0 .0	1 23.0	1 48.4	0 41.2	0 47.6	0 29.2	2 8.8	0 43.9	1 43.4	13 58.3
19	23 50 44.9	0 .0	0 .0	2N 7.5	1 49.1	0 52.5	0 49.4	0 29.1	2 8.8	0 44.0	1 43.3	13 58.6
22	0 2 34.6	0 .0	0 .0	4 41.1	1 43.8	1 3.9	0 51.0	0 29.0	2 8.8	0 44.0	1 43.1	13 59.0
25	0 14 24.3	0 .0	0 .0	4 38.9	1 33.8	1 15.3	0 52.6	0 29.0	2 8.8	0 44.0	1 43.0	13 59.5
28	0 26 13.9	0 .0	0 .0	2 6.3	1 20.1	1 26.7	0 54.1	0 28.9	2 8.7	0 44.0	1 42.9	14 .0

RIGHT ASCENSION

DAY	EPHEM. SID. TIME	☉	☊	☾	☿	♀	♂	♃	♄	♅	♆	♇
1	22 39 47.0	9♍59.4	7♊24.5	15♏18.2	22♌34.3	13♎45.2	4♏49.0	27♊28.6	16♓19.3	16♍16.7	15♏34.3	22♍36.4
2	22 43 43.5	10 53.8	7 21.1	27 59.9	23 32.4	14 49.9	5 27.1	27 37.5	16 R 15.1	16 20.2	15 35.3	22 38.3
3	22 47 40.1	11 48.1	7 17.8	10♐54.5	24 37.3	15 54.8	6 5.4	27 46.4	16 10.9	16 23.7	15 36.4	22 40.3
4	22 51 36.6	12 42.4	7 14.4	24 1.3	25 48.5	16 59.7	6 43.9	27 55.1	16 6.7	16 27.2	15 37.5	22 42.3
5	22 55 33.2	13 36.5	7 11.0	7♑14.1	27 5.4	18 4.7	7 22.5	28 3.6	16 2.4	16 30.7	15 38.6	22 44.3
6	22 59 29.8	14 30.7	7 7.6	20 23.4	28 27.5	19 9.8	8 1.3	28 12.1	15 58.2	16 34.2	15 39.8	22 46.4
7	23 3 26.3	15 24.8	7 4.2	3♒18.9	29 54.2	20 14.9	8 40.3	28 20.3	15 53.9	16 37.7	15 41.0	22 48.4
8	23 7 22.9	16 18.8	7 .9	15 52.5	1♍25.0	21 20.2	9 19.5	28 28.4	15 49.6	16 41.2	15 42.2	22 50.4
9	23 11 19.4	17 12.7	6 57.5	28 .6	2 59.3	22 25.6	9 58.9	28 36.4	15 45.4	16 44.7	15 43.4	22 52.4
10	23 15 16.0	18 6.7	6 54.1	9♓44.3	4 36.5	23 31.1	10 38.5	28 44.2	15 41.2	16 48.3	15 44.8	22 54.5
11	23 19 12.5	19 .6	6 50.7	21 9.1	6 16.0	24 36.8	11 18.2	28 51.8	15 36.9	16 51.8	15 46.1	22 56.5
12	23 23 9.1	19 54.5	6 47.3	2♈23.6	7 57.4	25 42.6	11 58.1	28 59.3	15 32.7	16 55.3	15 47.4	22 58.5
13	23 27 5.6	20 48.3	6 44.0	13 38.7	9 40.1	26 48.5	12 38.3	29 6.6	15 28.4	16 58.8	15 48.8	23 .6
14	23 31 2.2	21 42.1	6 40.6	25 7.1	11 23.8	27 54.5	13 18.5	29 13.7	15 24.2	17 2.3	15 50.1	23 2.6
15	23 34 58.7	22 35.9	6 37.2	7♉ 2.2	13 8.1	29 .8	13 59.0	29 20.7	15 20.0	17 5.7	15 51.5	23 4.6
16	23 38 55.3	23 29.7	6 33.8	19 37.2	14 52.6	0♏ 7.2	14 39.7	29 27.5	15 15.8	17 9.2	15 53.0	23 6.7
17	23 42 51.8	24 23.5	6 30.4	3♊ 2.7	16 37.2	1 13.7	15 20.5	29 34.2	15 11.7	17 12.7	15 54.4	23 8.7
18	23 46 48.4	25 17.3	6 27.1	17 23.4	18 21.5	2 20.5	16 1.6	29 40.6	15 7.5	17 16.2	15 55.9	23 10.7
19	23 50 44.9	26 11.1	6 23.7	2♋33.6	20 5.4	3 27.4	16 42.8	29 46.9	15 3.4	17 19.7	15 57.4	23 12.8
20	23 54 41.5	27 5.0	6 20.3	18 15.4	21 48.7	4 34.6	17 24.2	29 53.1	14 59.3	17 23.1	15 59.0	23 14.8
21	23 58 38.0	27 58.8	6 16.9	4♌ 1.9	23 31.3	5 41.9	18 5.8	29 59.0	14 55.2	17 26.6	16 .5	23 16.8
22	0 2 34.6	28 52.7	6 13.6	19 26.7	25 13.1	6 49.4	18 47.6	0♋ 4.7	14 51.1	17 30.0	16 2.1	23 18.8
23	0 6 31.2	29 46.5	6 10.2	4♍13.0	26 54.2	7 57.2	19 29.6	0 10.3	14 47.1	17 33.4	16 3.7	23 20.9
24	0 10 27.7	0♎40.5	6 6.8	18 16.2	28 34.4	9 5.1	20 11.8	0 15.7	14 43.1	17 36.9	16 5.3	23 22.9
25	0 14 24.3	1 34.4	6 3.4	1♎42.2	0♎13.7	10 13.3	20 54.2	0 20.9	14 39.2	17 40.3	16 7.0	23 24.9
26	0 18 20.8	2 28.4	6 .1	14 42.5	1 52.1	11 21.7	21 36.8	0 25.9	14 35.3	17 43.7	16 8.7	23 26.9
27	0 22 17.4	3 22.4	5 56.7	27 30.1	3 29.7	12 30.3	22 19.5	0 30.7	14 31.4	17 47.1	16 10.3	23 28.9
28	0 26 13.9	4 16.5	5 53.3	10♏17.1	5 6.4	13 39.1	23 2.5	0 35.4	14 27.6	17 50.5	16 12.1	23 30.9
29	0 30 10.5	5 10.7	5 50.0	23 12.4	6 42.3	14 48.1	23 45.6	0 39.8	14 23.8	17 53.8	16 13.8	23 32.9
30	0 34 7.0	6 4.9	5 46.6	6♐20.4	8 17.5	15 57.3	24 28.9	0 44.0	14 20.1	17 57.2	16 15.6	23 34.9

DECLINATION

DAY	EPHEM. SID. TIME	☉	☊	☾	☿	♀	♂	♃	♄	♅	♆	♇
1	22 39 47.0	8N26.5	0N22.9	15S 9.5	14N21.4	5S40.1	14S34.8	22N56.0	8S10.2	6N40.0	15S24.0	18N24.7
4	22 51 36.6	7 20.8	0 22.8	24 40.1	14 4.3	7 11.3	15 14.8	22 56.4	8 15.7	6 35.6	15 25.0	18 22.2
7	23 3 26.3	6 14.0	0 22.8	23 55.8	13 17.0	8 41.2	15 54.0	22 56.8	8 21.2	6 31.3	15 26.2	18 19.8
10	23 15 16.0	5 6.3	0 22.8	13 55.5	12 1.5	10 9.6	16 32.5	22 57.1	8 26.6	6 26.9	15 27.4	18 17.4
13	23 27 5.6	3 57.8	0 22.7	1N23.9	10 22.2	11 36.2	17 10.2	22 57.3	8 32.0	6 22.5	15 28.7	18 15.1
16	23 38 55.3	2 48.7	0 22.7	16 50.9	8 24.7	13 .5	17 46.8	22 57.5	8 37.3	6 18.1	15 30.0	18 12.8
19	23 50 44.9	1 39.1	0 22.7	25 32.9	6 14.7	14 22.5	18 22.5	22 57.6	8 42.4	6 13.8	15 31.4	18 10.6
22	0 2 34.6	0 29.2	0 22.7	20 39.7	3 57.2	15 41.6	18 57.0	22 57.7	8 47.4	6 9.5	15 32.8	18 8.5
25	0 14 24.3	0S40.9	0 22.6	4 19.7	1 36.3	16 57.7	19 30.4	22 57.7	8 52.3	6 5.2	15 34.3	18 6.5
28	0 26 13.9	1 51.1	0 22.6	13S27.3	0S45.4	18 10.4	20 2.5	22 57.7	8 56.9	6 1.0	15 35.8	18 4.5

OCTOBER 1965

LONGITUDE

DAY	EPHEM. SID. TIME	☉	☊	☾	☿	♀	♂	♃	♄	♅	♆	♇
	h m s	° ′	° ′	° ′	° ′	° ′	° ′	° ′	° ′	° ′	° ′	° ′
1	0 38 3.6	7♎36.4	7♊31.1	20♐35.6	10♎16.7	20♏ 1.5	27♏42.0	0♋44.3	12♓ 3.0	16♍39.3	18♏15.5	16♍52.8
2	0 42 .1	8 35.5	7 27.9	2♑46.6	12 .8	21 10.7	28 24.1	0 47.8	11 R 59.1	16 42.9	18 17.3	16 54.8
3	0 45 56.7	9 34.5	7 24.7	14 45.7	13 44.0	22 19.8	29 6.3	0 51.2	11 55.3	16 46.5	18 19.1	16 56.8
4	0 49 53.2	10 33.6	7 21.5	26 38.3	15 26.4	23 28.9	29 48.5	0 54.3	11 51.6	16 50.0	18 21.0	16 58.8
5	0 53 49.8	11 32.7	7 18.3	8♒29.2	17 7.9	24 37.8	0♐30.8	0 57.3	11 47.9	16 53.5	18 22.9	17 .8
6	0 57 46.3	12 31.8	7 15.2	20 23.0	18 48.6	25 46.6	1 13.2	1 .1	11 44.3	16 57.0	18 24.8	17 2.8
7	1 1 42.9	13 31.0	7 12.0	2♓23.5	20 28.4	26 55.4	1 55.7	1 2.7	11 40.7	17 .5	18 26.7	17 4.8
8	1 5 39.5	14 30.2	7 8.8	14 33.7	22 7.5	28 4.0	2 38.3	1 5.1	11 37.2	17 4.0	18 28.6	17 6.7
9	1 9 36.0	15 29.4	7 5.6	26 55.5	23 45.8	29 12.5	3 20.9	1 7.4	11 33.8	17 7.4	18 30.5	17 8.7
10	1 13 32.6	16 28.7	7 2.5	9♈29.9	25 23.4	0♐20.9	4 3.7	1 9.4	11 30.5	17 10.8	18 32.5	17 10.6
11	1 17 29.1	17 28.0	6 59.3	22 17.3	27 .2	1 29.2	4 46.5	1 11.2	11 27.2	17 14.2	18 34.5	17 12.5
12	1 21 25.7	18 27.3	6 56.1	5♉17.2	28 36.2	2 37.4	5 29.4	1 12.9	11 24.0	17 17.6	18 36.5	17 14.4
13	1 25 22.2	19 26.7	6 52.9	18 29.0	0♏11.6	3 45.4	6 12.3	1 14.3	11 20.9	17 21.0	18 38.5	17 16.3
14	1 29 18.8	20 26.1	6 49.7	1♊52.0	1 46.3	4 53.3	6 55.4	1 15.6	11 17.9	17 24.3	18 40.5	17 18.1
15	1 33 15.3	21 25.6	6 46.6	15 25.6	3 20.2	6 1.1	7 38.5	1 16.6	11 14.9	17 27.6	18 42.6	17 20.0
16	1 37 11.9	22 25.0	6 43.4	29 9.7	4 53.6	7 8.8	8 21.7	1 17.5	11 12.0	17 30.9	18 44.6	17 21.8
17	1 41 8.4	23 24.6	6 40.2	13♋ 3.9	6 26.2	8 16.3	9 5.0	1 18.1	11 9.2	17 34.1	18 46.7	17 23.6
18	1 45 5.0	24 24.1	6 37.0	27 7.9	7 58.3	9 23.7	9 48.4	1 18.6	11 6.5	17 37.3	18 48.7	17 25.4
19	1 49 1.5	25 23.7	6 33.9	11♌20.7	9 29.7	10 31.0	10 31.8	1 18.9	11 3.9	17 40.5	18 50.8	17 27.2
20	1 52 58.1	26 23.4	6 30.7	25 40.2	11 .5	11 38.1	11 15.4	1 18.9	11 1.3	17 43.7	18 52.9	17 29.0
21	1 56 54.7	27 23.0	6 27.5	10♍ 3.2	12 30.6	12 45.0	11 59.0	1 R 18.8	10 58.9	17 46.8	18 55.1	17 30.7
22	2 0 51.2	28 22.8	6 24.3	24 25.3	14 .2	13 51.9	12 42.7	1 18.5	10 56.6	17 50.0	18 57.2	17 32.5
23	2 4 47.8	29 22.5	6 21.2	8♎41.1	15 29.1	14 58.6	13 26.4	1 17.9	10 54.3	17 53.0	18 59.4	17 34.2
24	2 8 44.3	0♏22.3	6 18.0	22 45.3	16 57.4	16 5.1	14 10.3	1 17.2	10 52.1	17 56.1	19 1.5	17 35.9
25	2 12 40.9	1 22.1	6 14.8	6♏33.4	18 25.0	17 11.4	14 54.2	1 16.2	10 50.0	17 59.1	19 3.7	17 37.6
26	2 16 37.4	2 22.0	6 11.6	20 2.1	19 52.0	18 17.6	15 38.2	1 15.0	10 48.0	18 2.0	19 5.9	17 39.2
27	2 20 34.0	3 21.9	6 8.4	3♐ 9.8	21 18.3	19 23.6	16 22.2	1 13.7	10 46.1	18 5.0	19 8.0	17 40.8
28	2 24 30.5	4 21.8	6 5.3	15 56.8	22 43.9	20 29.4	17 6.4	1 12.1	10 44.3	18 7.9	19 10.2	17 42.4
29	2 28 27.1	5 21.7	6 2.1	28 24.9	24 8.8	21 35.0	17 50.6	1 10.4	10 42.6	18 10.7	19 12.4	17 44.0
30	2 32 23.6	6 21.7	5 58.9	10♑37.4	25 32.9	22 40.4	18 34.8	1 8.4	10 41.0	18 13.6	19 14.6	17 45.6
31	2 36 20.2	7 21.7	5 55.7	22 38.2	26 56.1	23 45.6	19 19.2	1 6.2	10 39.5	18 16.4	19 16.8	17 47.1

LATITUDE

DAY	EPHEM. SID. TIME	☉	☊	☾	☿	♀	♂	♃	♄	♅	♆	♇
1	0 38 3.6	0 .0	0 .0	1 S 15.0	1 N 3.8	1 S 37.9	0 S 55.6	0 S 28.8	2 S 8.5	0 N 44.1	1 N 42.8	14 N .7
4	0 49 53.2	0 .0	0 .0	3 55.6	0 45.6	1 49.0	0 57.0	0 28.8	2 8.4	0 44.1	1 42.7	14 1.3
7	1 1 42.9	0 .0	0 .0	5 5.2	0 26.0	1 59.8	0 58.4	0 28.7	2 8.2	0 44.2	1 42.6	14 2.0
10	1 13 32.6	0 .0	0 .0	4 14.9	0 5.7	2 10.3	0 59.7	0 28.6	2 7.9	0 44.2	1 42.5	14 2.8
13	1 25 22.2	0 .0	0 .0	1 30.0	0 S 15.1	2 20.3	1 .9	0 28.5	2 7.7	0 44.3	1 42.4	14 3.6
16	1 37 11.9	0 .0	0 .0	2 N 5.2	0 35.9	2 29.9	1 2.1	0 28.4	2 7.4	0 44.4	1 42.3	14 4.5
19	1 49 1.5	0 .0	0 .0	4 43.4	0 56.3	2 39.0	1 3.2	0 28.3	2 7.1	0 44.4	1 42.2	14 5.5
22	2 0 51.2	0 .0	0 .0	4 53.1	1 16.1	2 47.4	1 4.2	0 28.2	2 6.7	0 44.5	1 42.2	14 6.5
25	2 12 40.9	0 .0	0 .0	2 28.4	1 34.9	2 55.1	1 5.2	0 28.1	2 6.3	0 44.6	1 42.1	14 7.5
28	2 24 30.5	0 .0	0 .0	1 S .2	1 52.4	3 2.0	1 6.1	0 27.9	2 5.9	0 44.7	1 42.0	14 8.6
31	2 36 20.2	0 .0	0 .0	3 52.5	2 8.1	3 8.0	1 7.0	0 27.8	2 5.5	0 44.8	1 42.0	14 9.8

RIGHT ASCENSION

DAY	EPHEM. SID. TIME	☉	☊	☾	☿	♀	♂	♃	♄	♅	♆	♇
1	0 38 3.6	6♎59.1	5♊43.2	19♐40.0	9♎51.8	17♏ 6.9	25♏12.5	0♋48.1	14♓16.5	18♍ .6	16♏17.4	23♍36.9
2	0 42 .1	7 53.5	5 39.8	3♑ 4.7	11 25.5	18 16.5	25 56.1	0 51.9	14 R 12.8	18 3.9	16 19.2	23 38.9
3	0 45 56.7	8 47.9	5 36.5	16 24.7	12 58.5	19 26.4	26 40.0	0 55.6	14 9.2	18 7.2	16 21.0	23 40.9
4	0 49 53.2	9 42.3	5 33.1	29 29.4	14 30.8	20 36.5	27 24.1	0 59.0	14 5.7	18 10.5	16 22.9	23 42.9
5	0 53 49.8	10 36.9	5 29.7	12♒11.0	16 2.5	21 46.8	28 8.3	1 2.3	14 2.3	18 13.7	16 24.7	23 44.8
6	0 57 46.3	11 31.5	5 26.4	24 25.9	17 33.7	22 57.3	28 52.7	1 5.3	13 58.8	18 17.0	16 26.6	23 46.8
7	1 1 42.9	12 26.2	5 23.0	6♓15.5	19 4.4	24 8.0	29 37.3	1 8.1	13 55.5	18 20.2	16 28.5	23 48.7
8	1 5 39.5	13 21.0	5 19.6	17 45.5	20 34.6	25 18.9	0♐22.1	1 10.7	13 52.2	18 23.4	16 30.4	23 50.6
9	1 9 36.0	14 16.0	5 16.3	29 4.6	22 4.4	26 30.0	1 7.0	1 13.2	13 49.0	18 26.6	16 32.4	23 52.5
10	1 13 32.6	15 11.0	5 12.9	10♈23.8	23 33.9	27 41.3	1 52.1	1 15.4	13 45.8	18 29.8	16 34.3	23 54.4
11	1 17 29.1	16 6.2	5 9.5	21 55.3	25 2.9	28 52.8	2 37.4	1 17.4	13 42.7	18 33.0	16 36.3	23 56.3
12	1 21 25.7	17 1.4	5 6.2	3♉52.3	26 31.7	0♐ 4.4	3 22.9	1 19.1	13 39.7	18 36.1	16 38.3	23 58.2
13	1 25 22.2	17 56.8	5 2.8	16 27.3	28 .2	1 16.1	4 8.5	1 20.7	13 36.8	18 39.2	16 40.2	24 .1
14	1 29 18.8	18 52.3	4 59.4	29 50.0	29 28.5	2 28.1	4 54.3	1 22.1	13 33.9	18 42.3	16 42.3	24 2.0
15	1 33 15.3	19 48.0	4 56.1	14♊ 4.3	0♏56.5	3 40.1	5 40.3	1 23.2	13 31.1	18 45.3	16 44.3	24 3.8
16	1 37 11.9	20 43.8	4 52.7	29 4.3	2 24.4	4 52.3	6 26.4	1 24.2	13 28.4	18 48.4	16 46.3	24 5.6
17	1 41 8.4	21 39.7	4 49.3	14♋32.3	3 52.1	6 4.7	7 12.7	1 24.9	13 25.7	18 51.4	16 48.4	24 7.5
18	1 45 5.0	22 35.8	4 46.0	0♌ 3.1	5 19.7	7 17.1	7 59.2	1 25.4	13 23.1	18 54.4	16 50.5	24 9.3
19	1 49 1.5	23 32.1	4 42.6	15 12.3	6 47.1	8 29.6	8 45.8	1 25.6	13 20.6	18 57.3	16 52.5	24 11.1
20	1 52 58.1	24 28.5	4 39.2	29 44.0	8 14.4	9 42.3	9 32.6	1 25.7	13 18.2	19 .3	16 54.6	24 12.8
21	1 56 54.7	25 25.1	4 35.9	13♍34.5	9 41.7	10 55.0	10 19.5	1 R 25.5	13 15.8	19 3.2	16 56.8	24 14.6
22	2 0 51.2	26 21.9	4 32.5	26 49.6	11 8.8	12 7.8	11 6.7	1 25.2	13 13.6	19 6.1	16 58.9	24 16.4
23	2 4 47.8	27 18.8	4 29.2	9♎40.6	12 35.9	13 20.6	11 53.9	1 24.6	13 11.5	19 8.9	17 1.1	24 18.1
24	2 8 44.3	28 15.9	4 25.8	22 21.0	14 2.8	14 33.4	12 41.3	1 23.8	13 9.4	19 11.8	17 3.2	24 19.9
25	2 12 40.9	29 13.2	4 22.4	5♏ 3.4	15 29.6	15 46.2	13 28.9	1 22.8	13 7.4	19 14.5	17 5.4	24 21.6
26	2 16 37.4	0♏10.6	4 19.1	17 57.8	16 56.3	16 59.1	14 16.6	1 21.5	13 5.4	19 17.3	17 7.5	24 23.2
27	2 20 34.0	1 8.2	4 15.7	1♐ 9.4	18 22.9	18 11.9	15 4.4	1 20.0	13 3.6	19 20.0	17 9.7	24 24.9
28	2 24 30.5	2 6.0	4 12.3	14 37.4	19 49.2	19 24.6	15 52.4	1 18.3	13 1.9	19 22.7	17 11.9	24 26.6
29	2 28 27.1	3 4.0	4 9.0	28 14.7	21 15.4	20 37.3	16 40.5	1 16.4	13 .2	19 25.4	17 14.1	24 28.2
30	2 32 23.6	4 2.2	4 5.6	11♑49.5	22 41.2	21 49.8	17 28.8	1 14.3	12 58.7	19 28.0	17 16.3	24 29.8
31	2 36 20.2	5 .6	4 2.3	25 9.0	24 6.8	23 2.3	18 17.1	1 11.9	12 57.2	19 30.6	17 18.5	24 31.4

DECLINATION

DAY	EPHEM. SID. TIME	☉	☊	☾	☿	♀	♂	♃	♄	♅	♆	♇
1	0 38 3.6	3 S 1.2	0 N 22.6	24 S 21.4	3 S 5.6	19 S 19.4	20 S 33.3	22 N 57.7	9 S 1.4	5 N 56.8	15 S 37.4	18 N 2.6
4	0 49 53.2	4 10.9	0 22.6	24 41.1	5 22.8	20 24.4	21 2.6	22 57.8	9 5.6	5 52.6	15 39.0	18 .8
7	1 1 42.9	5 20.2	0 22.5	15 22.0	7 35.9	21 25.0	21 30.3	22 57.8	9 9.6	5 48.6	15 40.7	17 59.2
10	1 13 32.6	6 28.8	0 22.5	0 8.5	9 44.1	22 21.0	21 56.5	22 57.8	9 13.2	5 44.6	15 42.4	17 57.6
13	1 25 22.2	7 36.7	0 22.5	15 N 53.4	11 46.7	23 12.2	22 20.9	22 57.8	9 16.7	5 40.7	15 44.1	17 56.1
16	1 37 11.9	8 43.6	0 22.4	25 31.7	13 43.1	23 58.3	22 43.6	22 57.9	9 19.8	5 36.9	15 45.8	17 54.7
19	1 49 1.5	9 49.5	0 22.4	21 54.9	15 32.9	24 39.1	23 4.4	22 58.0	9 22.6	5 33.2	15 47.6	17 53.4
22	2 0 51.2	10 54.1	0 22.4	6 41.9	17 15.4	25 14.3	23 23.3	22 58.1	9 25.0	5 29.6	15 49.4	17 52.2
25	2 12 40.9	11 57.2	0 22.4	11 S 22.3	18 50.0	25 43.9	23 40.2	22 58.3	9 27.2	5 26.1	15 51.2	17 51.2
28	2 24 30.5	12 58.7	0 22.3	23 42.1	20 16.2	26 7.7	23 55.0	22 58.4	9 29.0	5 22.7	15 53.0	17 50.3
31	2 36 20.2	13 58.3	0 22.3	25 21.8	21 33.3	26 25.6	24 7.7	22 58.6	9 30.4	5 19.5	15 54.8	17 49.5

NOVEMBER 1965

LONGITUDE

DAY	EPHEM. SID. TIME h m s	☉ ° ′	☊ ° ′	☽ ° ′	☿ ° ′	♀ ° ′	♂ ° ′	♃ ° ′	♄ ° ′	♅ ° ′	♆ ° ′	♇ ° ′
1	2 40 16.8	8♏21.7	5♊52.6	4♒32.1	28♏18.6	24♐50.6	20♐ 3.6	1♋ 3.9	10♓38.1	18♍19.1	19♏19.0	17♍48.6
2	2 44 13.3	9 21.7	5 49.4	16 24.0	29 40.0	25 55.3	20 48.0	1R 1.3	10R36.8	18 21.8	19 21.3	17 50.1
3	2 48 9.9	10 21.8	5 46.2	28 18.6	1♐ .5	26 59.8	21 32.6	0 58.6	10 35.6	18 24.5	19 23.5	17 51.6
4	2 52 6.4	11 21.9	5 43.0	10♓20.7	2 19.9	28 4.1	22 17.2	0 55.6	10 34.5	18 27.1	19 25.7	17 53.0
5	2 56 3.0	12 22.0	5 39.8	22 34.1	3 38.1	29 8.1	23 1.9	0 52.5	10 33.5	18 29.7	19 27.9	17 54.4
6	2 59 59.5	13 22.2	5 36.7	5♈ 2.1	4 55.0	0♑11.9	23 46.6	0 49.2	10 32.6	18 32.3	19 30.2	17 55.8
7	3 3 56.1	14 22.4	5 33.5	17 46.9	6 10.4	1 15.4	24 31.4	0 45.6	10 31.8	18 34.8	19 32.4	17 57.2
8	3 7 52.6	15 22.6	5 30.3	0♉49.4	7 24.2	2 18.6	25 16.2	0 41.9	10 31.1	18 37.3	19 34.7	17 58.5
9	3 11 49.2	16 22.8	5 27.1	14 9.4	8 36.2	3 21.5	26 1.2	0 38.0	10 30.5	18 39.7	19 36.9	17 59.8
10	3 15 45.8	17 23.1	5 24.0	27 45.4	9 46.2	4 24.1	26 46.1	0 34.0	10 30.1	18 42.1	19 39.2	18 1.1
11	3 19 42.3	18 23.4	5 20.8	11♊35.2	10 53.9	5 26.4	27 31.2	0 29.7	10 29.7	18 44.5	19 41.4	18 2.4
12	3 23 38.9	19 23.8	5 17.6	25 35.7	11 59.2	6 28.5	28 16.3	0 25.3	10 29.5	18 46.8	19 43.7	18 3.7
13	3 27 35.4	20 24.1	5 14.4	9♋43.7	13 1.6	7 30.1	29 1.5	0 20.7	10 29.3	18 49.1	19 45.9	18 4.9
14	3 31 32.0	21 24.5	5 11.3	23 56.0	14 .8	8 31.4	29 46.7	0 15.9	10 29.2	18 51.3	19 48.2	18 6.0
15	3 35 28.5	22 24.9	5 8.1	8♌ 9.7	14 56.4	9 32.4	0♑32.0	0 11.0	10D29.3	18 53.5	19 50.4	18 7.2
16	3 39 25.1	23 25.4	5 4.9	22 22.3	15 47.9	10 33.0	1 17.3	0 5.8	10 29.4	18 55.6	19 52.7	18 8.3
17	3 43 21.7	24 25.9	5 1.7	6♍31.6	16 34.8	11 33.2	2 2.7	0 .5	10 29.7	18 57.7	19 54.9	18 9.4
18	3 47 18.2	25 26.4	4 58.5	20 35.4	17 16.6	12 33.1	2 48.2	29♊55.1	10 30.0	18 59.7	19 57.2	18 10.5
19	3 51 14.8	26 26.9	4 55.4	4♎31.7	17 52.6	13 32.5	3 33.7	29 49.5	10 30.5	19 1.7	19 59.4	18 11.5
20	3 55 11.3	27 27.5	4 52.2	18 18.5	18 22.0	14 31.5	4 19.3	29 43.7	10 31.0	19 3.6	20 1.7	18 12.5
21	3 59 7.9	28 28.1	4 49.0	1♏54.0	18 44.3	15 30.1	5 4.9	29 37.7	10 31.7	19 5.5	20 3.9	18 13.5
22	4 3 4.4	29 28.7	4 45.8	15 16.3	18 58.5	16 28.2	5 50.6	29 31.7	10 32.5	19 7.3	20 6.1	18 14.4
23	4 7 1.0	0♐29.4	4 42.7	28 24.1	19 4.0	17 25.9	6 36.4	29 25.4	10 33.4	19 9.1	20 8.4	18 15.4
24	4 10 57.6	1 30.1	4 39.5	11♐16.7	19R .0	18 23.1	7 22.2	29 19.1	10 34.4	19 10.8	20 10.6	18 16.3
25	4 14 54.1	2 30.8	4 36.3	23 54.0	18 45.9	19 19.7	8 8.0	29 12.6	10 35.5	19 12.5	20 12.8	18 17.1
26	4 18 50.7	3 31.5	4 33.1	6♑17.0	18 21.0	20 15.9	8 53.9	29 5.9	10 36.7	19 14.2	20 15.0	18 17.9
27	4 22 47.2	4 32.2	4 30.0	18 27.4	17 45.3	21 11.4	9 39.9	28 59.2	10 38.0	19 15.7	20 17.2	18 18.7
28	4 26 43.8	5 33.0	4 26.8	0♒27.9	16 58.9	22 6.4	10 25.9	28 52.3	10 39.4	19 17.3	20 19.4	18 19.5
29	4 30 40.3	6 33.8	4 23.6	12 21.9	16 2.1	23 .8	11 12.0	28 45.3	10 40.9	19 18.7	20 21.6	18 20.2
30	4 34 36.9	7 34.6	4 20.4	24 13.5	14 56.1	23 54.6	11 58.1	28 38.2	10 42.6	19 20.2	20 23.7	18 20.9

LATITUDE

DAY	SID. TIME	☉	☊	☽	☿	♀	♂	♃	♄	♅	♆	♇
1	2 40 16.8	0 .0	0 .0	4S31.0	2S12.9	3S 9.8	1S 7.3	0S27.7	2S 5.4	0N44.8	1N42.0	14N10.2
4	2 52 6.4	0 .0	0 .0	5 12.7	2 25.5	3 14.5	1 8.0	0 27.6	2 5.0	0 44.9	1 42.0	14 11.4
7	3 3 56.1	0 .0	0 .0	3 50.2	2 35.1	3 18.1	1 8.7	0 27.4	2 4.5	0 45.0	1 41.9	14 12.7
10	3 15 45.8	0 .0	0 .0	0 38.0	2 40.7	3 20.5	1 9.4	0 27.2	2 4.0	0 45.1	1 41.9	14 13.9
13	3 27 35.4	0 .0	0 .0	3N 2.0	2 41.4	3 21.6	1 9.9	0 27.0	2 3.6	0 45.2	1 41.9	14 15.3
16	3 39 25.1	0 .0	0 .0	5 9.2	2 35.6	3 21.4	1 10.4	0 26.8	2 3.1	0 45.3	1 41.9	14 16.6
19	3 51 14.8	0 .0	0 .0	4 34.8	2 21.4	3 19.7	1 10.9	0 26.5	2 2.6	0 45.4	1 41.9	14 18.0
22	4 3 4.4	0 .0	0 .0	1 45.4	1 56.7	3 16.3	1 11.2	0 26.3	2 2.1	0 45.5	1 42.0	14 19.5
25	4 14 54.1	0 .0	0 .0	1S44.8	1 19.3	3 11.3	1 11.5	0 26.0	2 1.6	0 45.7	1 42.0	14 20.9
28	4 26 43.8	0 .0	0 .0	4 22.5	0 28.7	3 4.5	1 11.8	0 25.7	2 1.2	0 45.8	1 42.0	14 22.4

RIGHT ASCENSION

DAY	SID. TIME	☉	☊	☽	☿	♀	♂	♃	♄	♅	♆	♇
1	2 40 16.8	5♏59.1	3♊58.9	8♒ 2.9	25♏31.9	24♐14.6	19♐ 5.6	1♋ 9.4	12♓55.8	19♍33.2	17♏20.7	24♍33.0
2	2 44 13.3	6 57.9	3 55.6	20 26.7	26 56.5	25 26.8	19 54.2	1R 6.6	12R54.6	19 35.7	17 22.9	24 34.5
3	2 48 9.9	7 56.8	3 52.2	2♓21.2	28 20.6	26 38.7	20 42.9	1 3.6	12 53.4	19 38.2	17 25.1	24 36.1
4	2 52 6.4	8 56.0	3 48.8	13 52.4	29 44.0	27 50.5	21 31.8	1 .4	12 52.3	19 40.6	17 27.4	24 37.6
5	2 56 3.0	9 55.3	3 45.5	25 9.7	1♐ 6.5	29 2.0	22 20.7	0 57.0	12 51.3	19 43.0	17 29.6	24 39.1
6	2 59 59.5	10 54.9	3 42.1	6♈25.0	2 28.1	0♑13.3	23 9.7	0 53.4	12 50.4	19 45.4	17 31.8	24 40.5
7	3 3 56.1	11 54.6	3 38.8	17 51.7	3 48.5	1 24.3	23 58.9	0 49.6	12 49.6	19 47.7	17 34.1	24 42.0
8	3 7 52.6	12 54.6	3 35.4	29 43.9	5 7.6	2 34.9	24 48.1	0 45.6	12 48.9	19 50.0	17 36.3	24 43.4
9	3 11 49.2	13 54.8	3 32.1	12♉15.7	6 25.1	3 45.3	25 37.4	0 41.3	12 48.3	19 52.3	17 38.6	24 44.8
10	3 15 45.8	14 55.1	3 28.7	25 38.5	7 40.7	4 55.2	26 26.9	0 36.9	12 47.8	19 54.5	17 40.8	24 46.2
11	3 19 42.3	15 55.7	3 25.4	9♊57.7	8 54.2	6 4.8	27 16.4	0 32.3	12 47.3	19 56.7	17 43.1	24 47.6
12	3 23 38.9	16 56.6	3 22.0	25 7.9	10 5.3	7 14.1	28 6.0	0 27.5	12 47.1	19 58.9	17 45.4	24 48.9
13	3 27 35.4	17 57.6	3 18.7	10♋49.9	11 13.5	8 22.8	28 55.6	0 22.5	12 46.8	20 1.0	17 47.6	24 50.3
14	3 31 32.0	18 58.9	3 15.3	26 34.9	12 18.5	9 31.1	29 45.4	0 17.3	12 46.7	20 3.1	17 49.9	24 51.5
15	3 35 28.5	20 .3	3 12.0	11♌54.3	13 19.7	10 39.0	0♑35.2	0 11.9	12 46.7	20 5.1	17 52.1	24 52.8
16	3 39 25.1	21 2.0	3 8.6	26 29.9	14 16.5	11 46.3	1 25.0	0 6.3	12D46.8	20 7.0	17 54.4	24 54.0
17	3 43 21.7	22 3.9	3 5.2	10♍17.0	15 8.5	12 53.1	2 15.0	0 .6	12 46.9	20 9.0	17 56.6	24 55.3
18	3 47 18.2	23 6.0	3 1.9	23 22.2	15 55.0	13 59.3	3 4.9	29♊54.7	12 47.2	20 10.9	17 58.9	24 56.5
19	3 51 14.8	24 8.3	2 58.5	5♎58.4	16 35.1	15 5.0	3 55.0	29 48.6	12 47.6	20 12.7	18 1.1	24 57.6
20	3 55 11.3	25 10.9	2 55.2	18 20.7	17 8.2	16 10.1	4 45.1	29 42.3	12 48.1	20 14.5	18 3.4	24 58.8
21	3 59 7.9	26 13.6	2 51.9	0♏43.9	17 33.5	17 14.5	5 35.2	29 35.8	12 48.6	20 16.3	18 5.6	24 59.9
22	4 3 4.4	27 16.5	2 48.5	13 20.2	17 50.0	18 18.3	6 25.4	29 29.2	12 49.3	20 18.0	18 7.9	25 1.0
23	4 7 1.0	28 19.7	2 45.2	26 17.6	17 57.1	19 21.4	7 15.6	29 22.5	12 50.1	20 19.6	18 10.1	25 2.0
24	4 10 57.6	29 23.0	2 41.8	9♐38.1	17R53.8	20 23.8	8 5.8	29 15.5	12 50.9	20 21.3	18 12.3	25 3.1
25	4 14 54.1	0♐26.5	2 38.5	23 16.0	17 39.6	21 25.4	8 56.1	29 8.5	12 51.9	20 22.8	18 14.6	25 4.1
26	4 18 50.7	1 30.3	2 35.1	6♑59.4	17 14.0	22 26.3	9 46.4	29 1.3	12 53.0	20 24.4	18 16.8	25 5.0
27	4 22 47.2	2 34.2	2 31.8	20 32.6	16 36.8	23 26.3	10 36.7	28 53.9	12 54.2	20 25.8	18 19.0	25 6.0
28	4 26 43.8	3 38.3	2 28.4	3♒41.8	15 48.2	24 25.6	11 27.0	28 46.4	12 55.4	20 27.3	18 21.2	25 6.9
29	4 30 40.3	4 42.5	2 25.1	16 18.4	14 49.0	25 23.9	12 17.3	28 38.8	12 56.8	20 28.6	18 23.4	25 7.8
30	4 34 36.9	5 46.9	2 21.7	28 20.8	13 40.2	26 21.4	13 7.6	28 31.1	12 58.2	20 30.0	18 25.6	25 8.7

DECLINATION

DAY	SID. TIME	☉	☊	☽	☿	♀	♂	♃	♄	♅	♆	♇
1	2 40 16.8	14S17.8	0N22.3	23S30.9	21S56.8	26S30.3	24S11.4	22N58.7	9S30.8	5N18.5	15S55.5	17N49.2
4	2 52 6.4	15 14.7	0 22.3	12 30.6	23 .5	26 40.3	24 21.1	22 58.9	9 31.8	5 15.4	15 57.3	17 48.6
7	3 3 56.1	16 9.3	0 22.2	3N25.8	23 53.3	26 44.4	24 28.6	22 59.2	9 32.4	5 12.5	15 59.1	17 48.1
10	3 15 45.8	17 1.5	0 22.2	19 2.8	24 34.1	26 42.7	24 33.7	22 59.4	9 32.7	5 9.7	16 .9	17 47.7
13	3 27 35.4	17 51.2	0 22.2	26 6.7	25 2.1	26 35.2	24 36.4	22 59.7	9 32.5	5 7.1	16 2.7	17 47.5
16	3 39 25.1	18 38.0	0 22.1	18 55.5	25 15.9	26 22.3	24 36.7	22 59.9	9 32.1	5 4.7	16 4.5	17 47.3
19	3 51 14.8	19 21.9	0 22.1	2 24.2	25 14.3	26 4.0	24 34.6	23 .1	9 31.2	5 2.4	16 6.3	17 47.3
22	4 3 4.4	20 2.6	0 22.1	14S44.3	24 55.5	25 40.6	24 30.1	23 .3	9 30.0	5 .3	16 8.1	17 47.5
25	4 14 54.1	20 40.1	0 22.1	25 2.9	24 17.2	25 12.4	24 23.1	23 .5	9 28.4	4 58.3	16 9.8	17 47.8
28	4 26 43.8	21 14.1	0 22.0	24 19.5	23 17.0	24 39.9	24 13.6	23 .7	9 26.4	4 56.6	16 11.5	17 48.2

DECEMBER 1965

LONGITUDE

DAY	EPHEM. SID. TIME h m s	☉ ° ′	☊ ° ′	☽ ° ′	☿ ° ′	♀ ° ′	♂ ° ′	♃ ° ′	♄ ° ′	♅ ° ′	♆ ° ′	♇ ° ′
1	4 38 33.5	8♐35.4	4♊17.2	6♓ 7.0	13♐42.5	24♑47.7	12♑44.2	28♊30.9	10♓44.3	19♍21.5	20♏25.9	18♍21.6
2	4 42 30.0	9 36.2	4 14.1	18 7.3	12 R 23.2	25 40.1	13 30.4	28 R 23.6	10 46.1	19 22.9	20 28.1	18 22.2
3	4 46 26.6	10 37.1	4 10.9	0♈19.0	11 .9	26 31.8	14 16.7	28 16.3	10 48.1	19 24.2	20 30.3	18 22.9
4	4 50 23.1	11 38.0	4 7.7	12 46.4	9 38.3	27 22.8	15 3.0	28 8.8	10 50.2	19 25.4	20 32.4	18 23.5
5	4 54 19.7	12 38.8	4 4.5	25 33.2	8 18.2	28 13.0	15 49.3	28 1.2	10 52.3	19 26.5	20 34.5	18 24.0
6	4 58 16.2	13 39.7	4 1.4	8♉42.2	7 3.1	29 2.4	16 35.6	27 53.5	10 54.5	19 27.6	20 36.6	18 24.5
7	5 2 12.8	14 40.6	3 58.2	22 14.3	5 55.5	29 50.9	17 22.0	27 45.8	10 56.9	19 28.7	20 38.7	18 25.0
8	5 6 9.4	15 41.5	3 55.0	6♊ 8.9	4 57.0	0♒38.5	18 8.5	27 37.9	10 59.3	19 29.7	20 40.8	18 25.4
9	5 10 5.9	16 42.5	3 51.8	20 23.3	4 9.0	1 25.3	18 55.0	27 30.1	11 1.9	19 30.6	20 42.9	18 25.8
10	5 14 2.5	17 43.4	3 48.7	4♋52.7	3 32.1	2 11.1	19 41.5	27 22.1	11 4.5	19 31.5	20 44.9	18 26.2
11	5 17 59.0	18 44.4	3 45.5	19 31.0	3 6.5	2 55.9	20 28.0	27 14.2	11 7.2	19 32.3	20 47.0	18 26.6
12	5 21 55.6	19 45.3	3 42.3	4♌11.4	2 52.1	3 39.7	21 14.6	27 6.1	11 10.0	19 33.1	20 49.0	18 26.9
13	5 25 52.2	20 46.3	3 39.1	18 47.5	2 48.4	4 22.4	22 1.3	26 58.1	11 13.0	19 33.8	20 51.0	18 27.2
14	5 29 48.7	21 47.3	3 36.0	3♍13.8	2 D 54.7	5 4.0	22 47.9	26 50.0	11 16.0	19 34.5	20 53.0	18 27.4
15	5 33 45.3	22 48.4	3 32.8	17 26.8	3 10.4	5 44.4	23 34.6	26 41.9	11 19.1	19 35.1	20 55.0	18 27.6
16	5 37 41.8	23 49.4	3 29.6	1♎24.2	3 34.5	6 23.7	24 21.4	26 33.7	11 22.3	19 35.6	20 57.0	18 27.8
17	5 41 38.4	24 50.5	3 26.4	15 5.4	4 6.2	7 1.7	25 8.2	26 25.6	11 25.6	19 36.1	20 58.9	18 27.9
18	5 45 34.9	25 51.6	3 23.2	28 31.0	4 44.8	7 38.4	25 55.0	26 17.4	11 29.0	19 36.5	21 .9	18 28.1
19	5 49 31.5	26 52.7	3 20.1	11♏41.8	5 29.4	8 13.8	26 41.8	26 9.2	11 32.5	19 36.9	21 2.8	18 28.1
20	5 53 28.1	27 53.8	3 16.9	24 39.0	6 19.4	8 47.8	27 28.7	26 1.0	11 36.1	19 37.2	21 4.7	18 28.2
21	5 57 24.6	28 54.9	3 13.7	7♐23.8	7 14.1	9 20.3	28 15.6	25 52.9	11 39.8	19 37.5	21 6.6	18 28.2
22	6 1 21.2	29 56.0	3 10.5	19 57.1	8 13.1	9 51.3	29 2.6	25 44.8	11 43.6	19 37.7	21 8.4	18 28.2
23	6 5 17.7	0♑57.1	3 7.4	2♑19.9	9 15.7	10 20.7	29 49.5	25 36.6	11 47.4	19 37.9	21 10.3	18 R 28.1
24	6 9 14.3	1 58.3	3 4.2	14 33.1	10 21.6	10 48.5	0♒36.6	25 28.6	11 51.4	19 38.0	21 12.1	18 28.1
25	6 13 10.9	2 59.5	3 1.0	26 37.7	11 30.2	11 14.6	1 23.6	25 20.6	11 55.4	19 38.0	21 13.9	18 28.0
26	6 17 7.4	4 .6	2 57.8	8♒35.5	12 41.4	11 38.9	2 10.7	25 12.6	11 59.5	19 38.0	21 15.7	18 27.8
27	6 21 4.0	5 1.8	2 54.7	20 28.4	13 54.8	12 1.3	2 57.8	25 4.6	12 3.7	19 R 37.9	21 17.5	18 27.6
28	6 25 .5	6 2.9	2 51.5	2♓19.2	15 10.1	12 21.8	3 44.9	24 56.7	12 8.0	19 37.8	21 19.2	18 27.4
29	6 28 57.1	7 4.1	2 48.3	14 11.4	16 27.2	12 40.4	4 32.0	24 48.9	12 12.4	19 37.6	21 20.9	18 27.2
30	6 32 53.6	8 5.3	2 45.1	26 8.8	17 45.7	12 56.9	5 19.1	24 41.1	12 16.8	19 37.3	21 22.6	18 26.9
31	6 36 50.2	9 6.4	2 42.0	8♈16.2	19 5.7	13 11.3	6 6.3	24 33.5	12 21.4	19 37.0	21 24.2	18 26.6

LATITUDE

DAY	EPHEM. SID. TIME	☉	☊	☽	☿	♀	♂	♃	♄	♅	♆	♇
1	4 38 33.5	0 .0	0 .0	5 S 17.0	0 N 31.0	2 S 55.8	1 S 11.9	0 S 25.4	2 S .7	0 N 45.9	1 N 42.1	14 N 23.9
4	4 50 23.1	0 .0	0 .0	4 9.7	1 29.9	2 44.9	1 12.0	0 25.1	2 .2	0 46.0	1 42.1	14 25.4
7	5 2 12.8	0 .0	0 .0	1 8.5	2 15.6	2 31.9	1 12.1	0 24.7	1 59.7	0 46.2	1 42.2	14 27.0
10	5 14 2.5	0 .0	0 .0	2 N 39.3	2 41.7	2 16.4	1 12.0	0 24.4	1 59.2	0 46.3	1 42.3	14 28.5
13	5 25 52.2	0 .0	0 .0	5 3.7	2 49.1	1 58.5	1 11.9	0 24.0	1 58.8	0 46.4	1 42.3	14 30.0
16	5 37 41.8	0 .0	0 .0	4 41.7	2 42.7	1 37.9	1 11.8	0 23.6	1 58.3	0 46.6	1 42.4	14 31.6
19	5 49 31.5	0 .0	0 .0	2 3.0	2 27.4	1 14.5	1 11.5	0 23.1	1 57.9	0 46.7	1 42.5	14 33.1
22	6 1 21.2	0 .0	0 .0	1 S 23.1	2 6.9	0 48.1	1 11.2	0 22.7	1 57.5	0 46.8	1 42.6	14 34.7
25	6 13 10.9	0 .0	0 .0	4 6.9	1 43.6	0 18.5	1 10.9	0 22.3	1 57.0	0 46.9	1 42.7	14 36.2
28	6 25 .5	0 .0	0 .0	5 11.5	1 19.0	0 N 14.2	1 10.4	0 21.8	1 56.6	0 47.1	1 42.8	14 37.7
31	6 36 50.2	0 .0	0 .0	4 18.1	0 54.1	0 50.1	1 9.9	0 21.3	1 56.2	0 47.2	1 43.0	14 39.2

RIGHT ASCENSION

DAY	EPHEM. SID. TIME	☉	☊	☽	☿	♀	♂	♃	♄	♅	♆	♇
1	4 38 33.5	6♐51.5	2♊18.4	9♓53.9	12♐23.8	27♑18.0	13♑57.9	28♊23.3	12♓59.8	20♍31.2	18♏27.7	25♍ 9.5
2	4 42 30.0	7 56.3	2 15.0	21 6.6	11 R 1.9	28 13.6	14 48.2	28 R 15.3	13 1.5	20 32.5	18 29.9	25 10.3
3	4 46 26.6	9 1.2	2 11.7	2♈11.4	9 37.4	29 8.2	15 38.6	28 7.3	13 3.2	20 33.7	18 32.1	25 11.1
4	4 50 23.1	10 6.3	2 8.4	13 22.2	8 12.8	0♒ 1.8	16 28.9	27 59.1	13 5.1	20 34.8	18 34.3	25 11.9
5	4 54 19.7	11 11.5	2 5.0	24 54.6	6 51.2	0 54.4	17 19.1	27 50.9	13 7.0	20 35.9	18 36.4	25 12.6
6	4 58 16.2	12 16.8	2 1.7	7♉ 4.8	5 35.2	1 45.8	18 9.3	27 42.6	13 9.1	20 37.0	18 38.5	25 13.3
7	5 2 12.8	13 22.3	1 58.3	20 7.9	4 27.0	2 36.2	18 59.5	27 34.1	13 11.2	20 37.9	18 40.7	25 14.0
8	5 6 9.4	14 27.9	1 55.0	4♊14.8	3 28.2	3 25.3	19 49.7	27 25.7	13 13.4	20 38.9	18 42.8	25 14.6
9	5 10 5.9	15 33.6	1 51.7	19 25.7	2 40.1	4 13.3	20 39.8	27 17.1	13 15.7	20 39.8	18 44.8	25 15.2
10	5 14 2.5	16 39.4	1 48.3	5♋25.4	2 3.2	5 .1	21 29.9	27 8.5	13 18.1	20 40.6	18 46.9	25 15.8
11	5 17 59.0	17 45.3	1 45.0	21 42.9	1 37.6	5 45.6	22 20.0	26 59.8	13 20.6	20 41.4	18 49.0	25 16.3
12	5 21 55.6	18 51.4	1 41.6	7♌41.4	1 23.2	6 29.8	23 10.0	26 51.1	13 23.2	20 42.1	18 51.0	25 16.8
13	5 25 52.2	19 57.5	1 38.3	22 53.4	1 19.5	7 12.6	23 59.9	26 42.3	13 25.9	20 42.8	18 53.1	25 17.3
14	5 29 48.7	21 3.7	1 35.0	7♍ 7.8	1 D 25.9	7 54.1	24 49.8	26 33.5	13 28.7	20 43.4	18 55.1	25 17.7
15	5 33 45.3	22 10.0	1 31.6	20 28.7	1 41.6	8 34.2	25 39.7	26 24.7	13 31.5	20 44.0	18 57.1	25 18.2
16	5 37 41.8	23 16.4	1 28.3	3♎ 9.4	2 5.8	9 12.8	26 29.5	26 15.9	13 34.5	20 44.5	18 59.1	25 18.6
17	5 41 38.4	24 22.8	1 24.9	15 26.5	2 37.8	9 49.9	27 19.2	26 7.0	13 37.5	20 45.0	19 1.0	25 18.9
18	5 45 34.9	25 29.3	1 21.6	27 36.6	3 16.8	10 25.5	28 8.9	25 58.1	13 40.6	20 45.4	19 3.0	25 19.2
19	5 49 31.5	26 35.8	1 18.3	9♏54.5	4 2.0	10 59.5	28 58.5	25 49.2	13 43.9	20 45.8	19 4.9	25 19.5
20	5 53 28.1	27 42.4	1 14.9	22 31.4	4 52.9	11 31.9	29 48.0	25 40.4	13 47.2	20 46.1	19 6.9	25 19.8
21	5 57 24.6	28 49.0	1 11.6	5♐32.8	5 48.8	12 2.6	0♒37.5	25 31.5	13 50.5	20 46.3	19 8.7	25 20.0
22	6 1 21.2	29 55.6	1 8.3	18 57.2	6 49.2	12 31.5	1 26.8	25 22.7	13 54.0	20 46.5	19 10.6	25 20.2
23	6 5 17.7	1♑ 2.3	1 4.9	2♑35.3	7 53.7	12 58.7	2 16.1	25 13.9	13 57.5	20 46.7	19 12.5	25 20.4
24	6 9 14.3	2 9.0	1 1.6	16 12.1	9 1.8	13 24.0	3 5.4	25 5.1	14 1.2	20 46.8	19 14.4	25 20.6
25	6 13 10.9	3 15.6	0 58.3	29 31.3	10 13.1	13 47.4	3 54.5	24 56.4	14 4.9	20 46.9	19 16.2	25 20.7
26	6 17 7.4	4 22.2	0 54.9	12♒20.6	11 27.3	14 8.8	4 43.6	24 47.7	14 8.7	20 46.9	19 18.0	25 20.8
27	6 21 4.0	5 28.8	0 51.6	24 34.2	12 44.2	14 28.2	5 32.6	24 39.1	14 12.6	20 R 46.8	19 19.8	25 20.8
28	6 25 .5	6 35.3	0 48.3	6♓13.8	14 3.4	14 45.6	6 21.4	24 30.5	14 16.6	20 46.7	19 21.5	25 20.8
29	6 28 57.1	7 41.8	0 44.9	17 26.5	15 24.7	15 .8	7 10.2	24 22.0	14 20.6	20 46.5	19 23.3	25 20.8
30	6 32 53.6	8 48.3	0 41.6	28 23.2	16 48.1	15 13.8	7 58.9	24 13.6	14 24.7	20 46.3	19 25.0	25 20.8
31	6 36 50.2	9 54.6	0 38.3	9♈17.4	18 13.2	15 24.5	8 47.4	24 5.2	14 28.9	20 46.1	19 26.6	25 R 20.7

DECLINATION

DAY	EPHEM. SID. TIME	☉	☊	☽	☿	♀	♂	♃	♄	♅	♆	♇
1	4 38 33.5	21 S 44.5	0 N 22.0	14 S 10.4	21 S 56.2	24 S 3.3	24 S 1.7	23 N .8	9 S 24.1	4 N 55.0	16 S 13.2	17 N 48.7
4	4 50 23.1	22 11.1	0 22.0	1 N 12.7	20 25.2	23 23.0	23 47.3	23 .8	9 21.5	4 53.6	16 14.9	17 49.3
7	5 2 12.8	22 33.9	0 21.9	17 13.7	19 4.4	22 39.6	23 30.5	23 .8	9 18.5	4 52.5	16 16.5	17 50.1
10	5 14 2.5	22 52.7	0 21.9	26 .4	18 13.1	21 53.5	23 11.2	23 .8	9 15.1	4 51.5	16 18.0	17 51.1
13	5 25 52.2	23 7.4	0 21.9	20 .1	17 57.6	21 5.3	22 49.6	23 .6	9 11.5	4 50.7	16 19.6	17 52.1
16	5 37 41.8	23 18.0	0 21.8	3 45.0	18 12.6	20 15.5	22 25.7	23 .4	9 7.5	4 50.1	16 21.0	17 53.2
19	5 49 31.5	23 24.5	0 21.8	13 S 23.7	18 48.3	19 24.6	21 59.7	23 .2	9 3.2	4 49.7	16 22.5	17 54.5
22	6 1 21.2	23 26.7	0 21.8	24 26.7	19 35.6	18 33.3	21 31.0	22 59.9	8 58.6	4 49.5	16 23.8	17 55.9
25	6 13 10.9	23 24.7	0 21.7	24 52.3	20 27.4	17 42.3	21 .3	22 59.5	8 53.6	4 49.5	16 25.2	17 57.4
28	6 25 .5	23 18.4	0 21.7	15 29.5	21 18.7	16 52.2	20 27.6	22 59.1	8 48.4	4 49.7	16 26.4	17 59.0
31	6 36 50.2	23 7.9	0 21.7	0 40.4	22 5.9	16 3.8	19 52.8	22 58.7	8 43.0	4 50.1	16 27.6	18 .7

JANUARY 1966

DAY	EPHEM. SID. TIME	☉	☊	☽	☿	♀	♂	♃	♄	♅	♆	♇
	h m s	° ′	° ′	° ′	° ′	° ′	° ′	° ′	° ′	° ′	° ′	° ′
		LONGITUDE										
1	6 40 46.8	10♑ 7.6	2♊38.8	20♈38.2	20♐26.8	13♒23.5	6♒53.5	24♊25.8	12♓26.0	19♍36.7	21♏25.9	18♍26.2
2	6 44 43.3	11 8.7	2 35.6	3♉19.5	21 49.1	13 33.5	7 40.7	24 R 18.3	12 30.7	19 R 36.3	21 27.5	18 R 25.8
3	6 48 39.9	12 9.8	2 32.4	16 24.5	23 12.3	13 41.1	8 27.9	24 10.9	12 35.4	19 35.8	21 29.1	18 25.4
4	6 52 36.4	13 11.0	2 29.3	29 56.1	24 36.5	13 46.4	9 15.2	24 3.6	12 40.3	19 35.3	21 30.7	18 25.0
5	6 56 33.0	14 12.1	2 26.1	13♊55.7	26 1.5	13 49.3	10 2.4	23 56.3	12 45.2	19 34.7	21 32.2	18 24.5
6	7 0 29.6	15 13.3	2 22.9	28 21.8	27 27.2	13 49.8	10 49.7	23 49.2	12 50.2	19 34.0	21 33.7	18 24.0
7	7 4 26.1	16 14.4	2 19.7	13♋ 9.9	28 53.7	13 R 47.7	11 36.9	23 42.2	12 55.3	19 33.4	21 35.2	18 23.5
8	7 8 22.7	17 15.5	2 16.5	28 12.7	0♑20.8	13 43.2	12 24.2	23 35.3	13 .4	19 32.6	21 36.7	18 22.9
9	7 12 19.2	18 16.6	2 13.4	13♌20.6	1 48.6	13 36.1	13 11.5	23 28.5	13 5.6	19 31.8	21 38.1	18 22.3
10	7 16 15.8	19 17.7	2 10.2	28 23.6	3 17.0	13 26.5	13 58.9	23 21.9	13 10.9	19 31.0	21 39.5	18 21.7
11	7 20 12.3	20 18.9	2 7.0	13♍12.6	4 45.9	13 14.4	14 46.2	23 15.4	13 16.2	19 30.1	21 40.9	18 21.1
12	7 24 8.9	21 20.0	2 3.8	27 41.3	6 15.5	12 59.7	15 33.5	23 9.0	13 21.7	19 29.1	21 42.2	18 20.4
13	7 28 5.5	22 21.1	2 .7	11♎46.2	7 45.5	12 42.7	16 20.9	23 2.7	13 27.1	19 28.1	21 43.6	18 19.7
14	7 32 2.0	23 22.3	1 57.5	25 26.7	9 16.2	12 23.3	17 8.3	22 56.7	13 32.7	19 27.1	21 44.9	18 19.0
15	7 35 58.6	24 23.4	1 54.3	8♏44.3	10 47.3	12 1.6	17 55.6	22 50.7	13 38.4	19 26.0	21 46.2	18 18.2
16	7 39 55.1	25 24.5	1 51.1	21 41.7	12 19.0	11 37.6	18 43.0	22 44.9	13 44.0	19 24.8	21 47.4	18 17.4
17	7 43 51.7	26 25.6	1 48.0	4♐22.4	13 51.2	11 11.6	19 30.4	22 39.3	13 49.8	19 23.6	21 48.6	18 16.6
18	7 47 48.2	27 26.7	1 44.8	16 49.7	15 23.9	10 43.6	20 17.8	22 33.8	13 55.6	19 22.3	21 49.8	18 15.7
19	7 51 44.8	28 27.8	1 41.6	29 6.4	16 57.2	10 13.7	21 5.2	22 28.4	14 1.4	19 21.0	21 50.9	18 14.8
20	7 55 41.4	29 28.9	1 38.4	11♑15.1	18 31.0	9 42.2	21 52.6	22 23.3	14 7.4	19 19.7	21 52.1	18 13.9
21	7 59 37.9	0♒30.0	1 35.2	23 17.5	20 5.3	9 9.2	22 40.0	22 18.3	14 13.4	19 18.3	21 53.2	18 13.0
22	8 3 34.5	1 31.1	1 32.1	5♒15.2	21 40.3	8 35.0	23 27.4	22 13.5	14 19.4	19 16.8	21 54.2	18 12.0
23	8 7 31.0	2 32.1	1 28.9	17 9.3	23 15.7	7 59.8	24 14.9	22 8.8	14 25.5	19 15.3	21 55.2	18 11.0
24	8 11 27.6	3 33.2	1 25.7	29 1.2	24 51.8	7 23.7	25 2.3	22 4.3	14 31.6	19 13.8	21 56.2	18 10.0
25	8 15 24.1	4 34.2	1 22.5	10♓52.5	26 28.5	6 47.0	25 49.7	22 .1	14 37.9	19 12.2	21 57.2	18 9.0
26	8 19 20.7	5 35.2	1 19.4	22 45.5	28 5.8	6 10.1	26 37.1	21 56.0	14 44.1	19 10.6	21 58.1	18 7.9
27	8 23 17.3	6 36.2	1 16.2	4♈43.0	29 43.7	5 33.0	27 24.5	21 52.0	14 50.4	19 8.9	21 59.0	18 6.8
28	8 27 13.8	7 37.2	1 13.0	16 48.5	1♒22.2	4 56.2	28 11.9	21 48.3	14 56.8	19 7.2	21 59.9	18 5.7
29	8 31 10.4	8 38.1	1 9.8	29 6.4	3 1.4	4 19.8	28 59.3	21 44.8	15 3.2	19 5.4	22 .7	18 4.6
30	8 35 6.9	9 39.1	1 6.7	11♉41.2	4 41.3	3 44.2	29 46.7	21 41.4	15 9.6	19 3.6	22 1.5	18 3.4
31	8 39 3.5	10 40.0	1 3.5	24 37.8	6 21.9	3 9.4	0♓34.1	21 38.3	15 16.1	19 1.7	22 2.3	18 2.3
		LATITUDE										
1	6 40 46.8	0 .0	0 .0	3S34.7	0N45.9	1N 2.8	1S 9.8	0S21.2	1S56.1	0N47.2	1N43.0	14N39.7
4	6 52 36.4	0 .0	0 .0	0 22.8	0 21.7	1 42.8	1 9.2	0 20.7	1 55.7	0 47.4	1 43.1	14 41.2
7	7 4 26.1	0 .0	0 .0	3N15.3	0S 1.6	2 25.5	1 8.5	0 20.2	1 55.4	0 47.5	1 43.3	14 42.6
10	7 16 15.8	0 .0	0 .0	5 6.7	0 23.6	3 10.2	1 7.8	0 19.6	1 55.1	0 47.6	1 43.4	14 44.0
13	7 28 5.5	0 .0	0 .0	4 2.1	0 44.0	3 56.1	1 7.0	0 19.1	1 54.7	0 47.7	1 43.5	14 45.4
16	7 39 55.1	0 .0	0 .0	1 3.1	1 2.7	4 41.7	1 6.2	0 18.6	1 54.5	0 47.8	1 43.7	14 46.7
19	7 51 44.8	0 .0	0 .0	2S12.8	1 19.4	5 25.7	1 5.3	0 18.1	1 54.2	0 48.0	1 43.8	14 48.0
22	8 3 34.5	0 .0	0 .0	4 28.7	1 33.9	6 6.2	1 4.4	0 17.5	1 53.9	0 48.1	1 44.0	14 49.3
25	8 15 24.1	0 .0	0 .0	4 59.6	1 46.0	6 41.4	1 3.4	0 17.0	1 53.7	0 48.2	1 44.2	14 50.5
28	8 27 13.8	0 .0	0 .0	3 35.9	1 55.3	7 10.0	1 2.3	0 16.5	1 53.5	0 48.3	1 44.3	14 51.6
31	8 39 3.5	0 .0	0 .0	0 39.0	2 1.7	7 31.0	1 1.2	0 16.0	1 53.3	0 48.3	1 44.5	14 52.7
		RIGHT ASCENSION										
1	6 40 46.8	11♑ .9	0♊34.9	20♈24.6	19♐39.9	15♒32.9	9♒35.9	23♊57.0	14♓33.1	20♍45.8	19♏28.3	25♍20.6
2	6 44 43.3	12 7.2	0 31.6	2♉ 1.2	21 8.1	15 39.0	10 24.3	23 R 48.8	14 37.5	20 R 45.4	19 29.9	25 R 20.5
3	6 48 39.9	13 13.3	0 28.3	14 24.6	22 37.7	15 42.7	11 12.6	23 40.7	14 41.9	20 45.0	19 31.6	25 20.3
4	6 52 36.4	14 19.3	0 25.0	27 50.2	24 8.5	15 43.9	12 .7	23 32.8	14 46.3	20 44.5	19 33.1	25 20.1
5	6 56 33.0	15 25.3	0 21.6	12♊27.1	25 40.6	15 R 42.7	12 48.8	23 24.9	14 50.9	20 44.0	19 34.7	25 19.9
6	7 0 29.6	16 31.1	0 18.3	28 11.2	27 13.6	15 38.9	13 36.7	23 17.2	14 55.5	20 43.4	19 36.2	25 19.6
7	7 4 26.1	17 36.8	0 15.0	14♋39.5	28 47.7	15 32.6	14 24.6	23 9.6	15 .2	20 42.8	19 37.8	25 19.3
8	7 8 22.7	18 42.4	0 11.6	1♌14.3	0♑22.7	15 23.8	15 12.3	23 2.1	15 4.9	20 42.1	19 39.2	25 19.0
9	7 12 19.2	19 47.9	0 8.3	17 17.1	1 58.6	15 12.5	15 59.9	22 54.7	15 9.7	20 41.4	19 40.7	25 18.6
10	7 16 15.8	20 53.3	0 5.0	2♍24.0	3 35.3	14 58.6	16 47.4	22 47.5	15 14.6	20 40.6	19 42.1	25 18.3
11	7 20 12.3	21 58.5	0 1.7	16 30.3	5 12.7	14 42.2	17 34.8	22 40.4	15 19.6	20 39.8	19 43.5	25 17.9
12	7 24 8.9	23 3.6	29♉58.3	29 44.9	6 50.9	14 23.5	18 22.1	22 33.5	15 24.6	20 38.9	19 44.9	25 17.4
13	7 28 5.5	24 8.5	29 55.0	12♎23.9	8 29.7	14 2.3	19 9.3	22 26.7	15 29.6	20 38.0	19 46.3	25 17.0
14	7 32 2.0	25 13.3	29 51.7	24 44.8	10 9.1	13 38.9	19 56.4	22 20.1	15 34.8	20 37.1	19 47.6	25 16.5
15	7 35 58.6	26 17.9	29 48.4	7♏ 3.6	11 49.0	13 13.2	20 43.4	22 13.6	15 40.0	20 36.1	19 48.9	25 16.0
16	7 39 55.1	27 22.4	29 45.0	19 33.5	13 29.5	12 45.4	21 30.3	22 7.3	15 45.3	20 35.0	19 50.2	25 15.4
17	7 43 51.7	28 26.7	29 41.7	2♐22.9	15 10.4	12 15.6	22 17.0	22 1.2	15 50.6	20 33.9	19 51.4	25 14.9
18	7 47 48.2	29 30.8	29 38.4	15 33.7	16 51.8	11 44.1	23 3.7	21 55.2	15 55.9	20 32.8	19 52.6	25 14.2
19	7 51 44.8	0♒34.8	29 35.1	29 .6	18 33.7	11 10.8	23 50.2	21 49.4	16 1.4	20 31.6	19 53.8	25 13.6
20	7 55 41.4	1 38.6	29 31.7	12♑31.7	20 15.8	10 36.1	24 36.6	21 43.8	16 6.9	20 30.4	19 54.9	25 13.0
21	7 59 37.9	2 42.1	29 28.4	25 51.9	21 58.4	10 .1	25 22.9	21 38.4	16 12.4	20 29.1	19 56.0	25 12.3
22	8 3 34.5	3 45.5	29 25.1	8♒47.6	23 41.3	9 23.0	26 9.1	21 33.2	16 18.0	20 27.7	19 57.1	25 11.5
23	8 7 31.0	4 48.8	29 21.8	21 10.5	25 24.4	8 45.1	26 55.2	21 28.1	16 23.6	20 26.4	19 58.2	25 10.8
24	8 11 27.6	5 51.8	29 18.5	2♓58.9	27 7.8	8 6.6	27 41.2	21 23.3	16 29.3	20 25.0	19 59.2	25 10.0
25	8 15 24.1	6 54.6	29 15.1	14 17.2	28 51.5	7 27.7	28 27.1	21 18.6	16 35.1	20 23.5	20 .2	25 9.2
26	8 19 20.7	7 57.2	29 11.8	25 14.1	0♒35.4	6 48.7	29 12.8	21 14.2	16 40.8	20 22.0	20 1.1	25 8.4
27	8 23 17.3	8 59.6	29 8.5	6♈ 1.2	2 19.5	6 9.9	29 58.5	21 9.9	16 46.7	20 20.5	20 2.0	25 7.6
28	8 27 13.8	10 1.8	29 5.2	16 52.3	4 3.7	5 31.5	0♓44.0	21 5.9	16 52.6	20 18.9	20 2.9	25 6.7
29	8 31 10.4	11 3.8	29 1.9	28 2.6	5 48.1	4 53.7	1 29.5	21 2.0	16 58.5	20 17.3	20 3.8	25 5.8
30	8 35 6.9	12 5.6	28 58.6	9♉48.5	7 32.7	4 16.8	2 14.8	20 58.4	17 4.5	20 15.6	20 4.6	25 4.9
31	8 39 3.5	13 7.2	28 55.2	22 26.1	9 17.3	3 41.1	3 .1	20 55.0	17 10.5	20 13.9	20 5.4	25 4.0
		DECLINATION										
1	6 40 46.8	23S 3.5	0N21.7	4N44.6	22S20.3	15S48.1	19S40.7	22N58.5	8S41.1	4N50.3	16S28.0	18N 1.3
4	6 52 36.4	22 47.5	0 21.6	19 46.2	22 58.4	15 3.3	19 3.3	22 58.0	8 35.3	4 51.0	16 29.1	18 3.1
7	7 4 26.1	22 27.4	0 21.6	26 2.0	23 28.0	14 22.0	18 24.1	22 57.6	8 29.2	4 51.8	16 30.1	18 5.0
10	7 16 15.8	22 3.4	0 21.6	16 49.4	23 47.8	13 45.1	17 43.1	22 57.1	8 22.9	4 52.9	16 31.1	18 7.0
13	7 28 5.5	21 35.4	0 21.5	0S56.4	23 57.0	13 13.3	17 .4	22 56.6	8 16.3	4 54.1	16 32.0	18 9.1
16	7 39 55.1	21 3.7	0 21.5	17 10.6	23 54.9	12 47.1	16 16.0	22 56.2	8 9.5	4 55.5	16 32.9	18 11.2
19	7 51 44.8	20 28.4	0 21.5	25 39.3	23 40.9	12 27.1	15 30.2	22 55.8	8 2.6	4 57.1	16 33.6	18 13.4
22	8 3 34.5	19 49.6	0 21.4	23 18.0	23 14.7	12 13.4	14 43.0	22 55.5	7 55.4	4 58.8	16 34.3	18 15.6
25	8 15 24.1	19 7.5	0 21.4	12 6.3	22 35.8	12 5.9	13 54.4	22 55.2	7 48.0	5 .8	16 34.9	18 17.9
28	8 27 13.8	18 22.2	0 21.4	3N16.9	21 44.0	12 4.4	13 4.6	22 55.0	7 40.5	5 2.8	16 35.4	18 20.3
31	8 39 3.5	17 33.9	0 21.3	18 18.0	20 39.0	12 8.1	12 13.7	22 54.9	7 32.8	5 5.0	16 35.9	18 22.6

FEBRUARY 1966

LONGITUDE

DAY	EPHEM. SID. TIME	☉	☊	☾	☿	♀	♂	♃	♄	♅	♆	♇
	h m s	° ′	° ′	° ′	° ′	° ′	° ′	° ′	° ′	° ′	° ′	° ′
1	8 43 .0	11♒40.9	1♊ .3	8♊ .4	8♒ 3.1	2♒35.8	1♓21.4	21♊35.3	15♓22.7	18♍59.9	22♏ 3.0	18♍ 1.1
2	8 46 56.6	12 41.8	0 57.1	21 52.1	9 45.1	2R 3.6	2 8.8	21R32.6	15 29.3	18R57.9	22 3.7	17R59.8
3	8 50 53.2	13 42.6	0 53.9	6♋13.5	11 27.8	1 33.0	2 56.1	21 30.0	15 35.9	18 56.0	22 4.4	17 58.6
4	8 54 49.7	14 43.5	0 50.8	21 2.2	13 11.2	1 4.1	3 43.5	21 27.7	15 42.6	18 54.0	22 5.1	17 57.4
5	8 58 46.3	15 44.3	0 47.6	6♌11.9	14 55.3	0 37.2	4 30.9	21 25.5	15 49.3	18 52.0	22 5.7	17 56.1
6	9 2 42.8	16 45.1	0 44.4	21 33.0	16 40.2	0 12.3	5 18.2	21 23.6	15 56.1	18 49.9	22 6.3	17 54.8
7	9 6 39.4	17 45.9	0 41.2	6♍53.6	18 25.8	29♑49.6	6 5.5	21 21.8	16 2.9	18 47.8	22 6.8	17 53.5
8	9 10 35.9	18 46.6	0 38.1	22 2.1	20 12.1	29 29.2	6 52.8	21 20.2	16 9.7	18 45.7	22 7.3	17 52.2
9	9 14 32.5	19 47.3	0 34.9	6♎49.2	21 59.2	29 11.2	7 40.0	21 18.9	16 16.6	18 43.5	22 7.8	17 50.8
10	9 18 29.0	20 48.1	0 31.7	21 8.9	23 46.9	28 55.6	8 27.3	21 17.7	16 23.5	18 41.3	22 8.2	17 49.4
11	9 22 25.6	21 48.8	0 28.5	4♏59.2	25 35.2	28 42.5	9 14.5	21 16.7	16 30.4	18 39.1	22 8.6	17 48.0
12	9 26 22.2	22 49.4	0 25.4	18 21.2	27 24.2	28 31.8	10 1.8	21 16.0	16 37.4	18 36.9	22 9.0	17 46.6
13	9 30 18.7	23 50.1	0 22.2	1♐17.9	29 13.7	28 23.7	10 49.0	21 15.4	16 44.4	18 34.6	22 9.3	17 45.2
14	9 34 15.3	24 50.7	0 19.0	13 53.8	1♓ 3.6	28 18.1	11 36.2	21 15.1	16 51.4	18 32.3	22 9.6	17 43.8
15	9 38 11.8	25 51.4	0 15.8	26 13.4	2 54.0	28 15.0	12 23.4	21 14.9	16 58.4	18 29.9	22 9.9	17 42.3
16	9 42 8.4	26 52.0	0 12.6	8♑21.1	4 44.6	28 14.3	13 10.6	21 14.9	17 5.5	18 27.6	22 10.1	17 40.9
17	9 46 4.9	27 52.5	0 9.5	20 20.8	6 35.3	28D16.0	13 57.7	21D15.2	17 12.6	18 25.2	22 10.3	17 39.4
18	9 50 1.5	28 53.1	0 6.3	2♒15.7	8 25.9	28 20.1	14 44.8	21 15.6	17 19.8	18 22.8	22 10.5	17 37.9
19	9 53 58.0	29 53.6	0 3.1	14 8.1	10 16.3	28 26.6	15 32.0	21 16.3	17 26.9	18 20.3	22 10.6	17 36.4
20	9 57 54.6	0♓54.1	29♉59.9	25 59.8	12 6.1	28 35.3	16 19.1	21 17.1	17 34.1	18 17.9	22 10.7	17 34.9
21	10 1 51.2	1 54.6	29 56.8	7♓52.3	13 55.2	28 46.2	17 6.1	21 18.2	17 41.3	18 15.4	22 10.8	17 33.4
22	10 5 47.7	2 55.1	29 53.6	19 46.8	15 43.2	28 59.2	17 53.2	21 19.4	17 48.5	18 12.9	22 10.8	17 31.9
23	10 9 44.3	3 55.5	29 50.4	1♈44.6	17 29.7	29 14.4	18 40.2	21 20.9	17 55.8	18 10.4	22 10.8	17 30.3
24	10 13 40.8	4 55.9	29 47.2	13 47.4	19 14.3	29 31.5	19 27.2	21 22.5	18 3.1	18 7.9	22R10.7	17 28.8
25	10 17 37.4	5 56.3	29 44.0	25 57.7	20 56.7	29 50.7	20 14.2	21 24.4	18 10.4	18 5.4	22 10.7	17 27.3
26	10 21 33.9	6 56.7	29 40.9	8♉18.3	22 36.1	0♒11.7	21 1.2	21 26.5	18 17.7	18 2.8	22 10.6	17 25.7
27	10 25 30.5	7 57.0	29 37.7	20 53.0	24 12.2	0 34.5	21 48.1	21 28.7	18 25.0	18 .3	22 10.5	17 24.1
28	10 29 27.0	8 57.2	29 34.5	3♊45.8	25 44.4	0 59.1	22 35.0	21 31.1	18 32.3	17 57.7	22 10.3	17 22.6

LATITUDE

DAY	EPHEM. SID. TIME	☉	☊	☾	☿	♀	♂	♃	♄	♅	♆	♇
1	8 43 .0	0 .0	0 .0	0N31.9	2S 3.1	7N36.2	1S .8	0S15.8	1S53.2	0N48.4	1N44.6	14N53.1
4	8 54 49.7	0 .0	0 .0	3 48.8	2 5.0	7 46.5	0 59.6	0 15.3	1 53.1	0 48.5	1 44.7	14 54.1
7	9 6 39.4	0 .0	0 .0	4 59.3	2 3.0	7 49.2	0 58.4	0 14.7	1 52.9	0 48.5	1 44.9	14 55.0
10	9 18 29.0	0 .0	0 .0	3 13.2	1 56.7	7 45.1	0 57.1	0 14.2	1 52.8	0 48.6	1 45.1	14 55.9
13	9 30 18.7	0 .0	0 .0	0S 2.6	1 45.6	7 35.3	0 55.8	0 13.7	1 52.7	0 48.7	1 45.3	14 56.7
16	9 42 8.4	0 .0	0 .0	3 4.1	1 29.2	7 21.0	0 54.4	0 13.2	1 52.6	0 48.7	1 45.4	14 57.4
19	9 53 58.0	0 .0	0 .0	4 47.5	1 7.2	7 3.1	0 53.0	0 12.7	1 52.6	0 48.8	1 45.6	14 58.1
22	10 5 47.7	0 .0	0 .0	4 40.7	0 39.2	6 42.6	0 51.5	0 12.2	1 52.5	0 48.8	1 45.8	14 58.7
25	10 17 37.4	0 .0	0 .0	2 44.3	0 5.4	6 20.2	0 50.0	0 11.7	1 52.5	0 48.9	1 46.0	14 59.2
28	10 29 27.0	0 .0	0 .0	0N25.9	0N33.2	5 56.5	0 48.5	0 11.2	1 52.6	0 48.9	1 46.1	14 59.7

RIGHT ASCENSION

DAY	EPHEM. SID. TIME	☉	☊	☾	☿	♀	♂	♃	♄	♅	♆	♇
1	8 43 .0	14♒ 8.6	28♉51.9	6♊ 8.8	11♒ 2.1	3♒ 6.7	3♓45.2	20♊51.8	17♓16.6	20♍12.2	20♏ 6.2	25♍ 3.0
2	8 46 56.6	15 9.7	28 48.6	21 1.9	12 46.9	2R33.8	4 30.2	20R48.8	17 22.6	20R10.4	20 6.9	25R 2.0
3	8 50 53.2	16 10.7	28 45.3	6♋55.7	14 31.8	2 2.8	5 15.1	20 46.0	17 28.8	20 8.6	20 7.6	25 1.0
4	8 54 49.7	17 11.5	28 42.0	23 23.6	16 16.8	1 33.6	6 .0	20 43.4	17 35.0	20 6.9	20 8.3	25 .0
5	8 58 46.3	18 12.0	28 38.7	9♌48.1	18 1.8	1 6.5	6 44.7	20 41.1	17 41.2	20 5.0	20 8.9	24 59.0
6	9 2 42.8	19 12.4	28 35.3	25 36.3	19 46.7	0 41.6	7 29.4	20 38.9	17 47.5	20 3.1	20 9.5	24 57.9
7	9 6 39.4	20 12.5	28 32.0	10♍31.3	21 31.7	0 19.1	8 13.9	20 37.0	17 53.8	20 1.2	20 10.1	24 56.8
8	9 10 35.9	21 12.4	28 28.7	24 32.9	23 16.6	29♑58.9	8 58.3	20 35.3	18 .1	19 59.2	20 10.6	24 55.7
9	9 14 32.5	22 12.2	28 25.4	7♎52.3	25 1.4	29 41.3	9 42.7	20 33.8	18 6.4	19 57.2	20 11.1	24 54.6
10	9 18 29.0	23 11.7	28 22.1	20 45.1	26 46.1	29 26.2	10 26.9	20 32.5	18 12.8	19 55.2	20 11.5	24 53.4
11	9 22 25.6	24 11.1	28 18.8	3♏27.3	28 30.6	29 13.6	11 11.1	20 31.5	18 19.2	19 53.1	20 11.9	24 52.2
12	9 26 22.2	25 10.2	28 15.5	16 12.4	0♓14.9	29 3.7	11 55.2	20 30.6	18 25.7	19 51.1	20 12.3	24 51.1
13	9 30 18.7	26 9.2	28 12.2	29 9.8	1 59.0	28 56.3	12 39.2	20 30.0	18 32.1	19 49.0	20 12.7	24 49.9
14	9 34 15.3	27 8.0	28 8.8	12♐23.0	3 42.8	28 51.6	13 23.1	20 29.6	18 38.6	19 46.8	20 13.0	24 48.6
15	9 38 11.8	28 6.6	28 5.5	25 48.9	5 26.1	28 49.4	14 7.0	20 29.4	18 45.2	19 44.7	20 13.3	24 47.4
16	9 42 8.4	29 5.1	28 2.2	9♑18.4	7 8.9	28D49.8	14 50.8	20D29.5	18 51.7	19 42.5	20 13.5	24 46.1
17	9 46 4.9	0♓ 3.3	27 58.9	22 38.5	8 51.1	28 52.6	15 34.5	20 29.7	18 58.3	19 40.3	20 13.7	24 44.9
18	9 50 1.5	1 1.4	27 55.6	5♒36.9	10 32.5	28 57.9	16 18.1	20 30.2	19 4.9	19 38.1	20 13.9	24 43.6
19	9 53 58.0	1 59.3	27 52.3	18 5.2	12 13.0	29 5.6	17 1.6	20 30.9	19 11.5	19 35.8	20 14.1	24 42.3
20	9 57 54.6	2 57.1	27 49.0	0♓ .5	13 52.3	29 15.7	17 45.1	20 31.8	19 18.2	19 33.6	20 14.2	24 41.0
21	10 1 51.2	3 54.7	27 45.7	11 25.7	15 30.3	29 28.0	18 28.5	20 32.9	19 24.9	19 31.3	20 14.3	24 39.6
22	10 5 47.7	4 52.1	27 42.4	22 27.7	17 6.6	29 42.5	19 11.8	20 34.3	19 31.5	19 29.0	20 14.3	24 38.3
23	10 9 44.3	5 49.3	27 39.1	3♈16.6	18 41.1	29 59.2	19 55.1	20 35.8	19 38.2	19 26.7	20 14.3	24 37.0
24	10 13 40.8	6 46.4	27 35.8	14 4.4	20 13.3	0♒18.0	20 38.3	20 37.6	19 45.0	19 24.4	20 14.3	24 35.6
25	10 17 37.4	7 43.4	27 32.5	25 4.4	21 43.0	0 38.8	21 21.5	20 39.6	19 51.8	19 22.1	20 14.3	24 34.3
26	10 21 33.9	8 40.2	27 29.2	6♉30.9	23 9.6	1 1.5	22 4.6	20 41.8	19 58.5	19 19.7	20R14.2	24 32.9
27	10 25 30.5	9 36.9	27 25.8	18 38.5	24 32.9	1 26.1	22 47.6	20 44.2	20 5.3	19 17.3	20 14.0	24 31.5
28	10 29 27.0	10 33.4	27 22.5	1♊40.0	25 52.2	1 52.4	23 30.5	20 46.9	20 12.0	19 15.0	20 13.9	24 30.1

DECLINATION

DAY	EPHEM. SID. TIME	☉	☊	☾	☿	♀	♂	♃	♄	♅	♆	♇
1	8 43 .0	17S17.2	0N21.3	22N10.4	20S14.4	12S10.4	11S56.5	22N54.9	7S30.2	5N 5.8	16S36.0	18N23.4
4	8 54 49.7	16 25.2	0 21.3	25 33.9	18 51.6	12 19.8	11 4.2	22 55.0	7 22.3	5 8.2	16 36.4	18 25.8
7	9 6 39.4	15 30.7	0 21.3	13 36.7	17 15.4	12 32.4	10 11.0	22 55.1	7 14.3	5 10.7	16 36.7	18 28.2
10	9 18 29.0	14 33.8	0 21.2	5S16.0	15 25.9	12 47.1	9 17.0	22 55.4	7 6.2	5 13.3	16 36.8	18 30.6
13	9 30 18.7	13 34.7	0 21.2	20 28.0	13 23.6	13 2.9	8 22.3	22 55.7	6 58.0	5 16.0	16 37.0	18 33.0
16	9 42 8.4	12 33.7	0 21.2	26 14.7	11 9.5	13 18.8	7 27.0	22 56.2	6 49.7	5 18.8	16 37.0	18 35.4
19	9 53 58.0	11 30.7	0 21.1	21 10.4	8 45.3	13 33.9	6 31.1	22 56.8	6 41.2	5 21.6	16 36.9	18 37.8
22	10 5 47.7	10 26.2	0 21.1	8 20.9	6 14.0	13 47.7	5 34.8	22 57.5	6 32.8	5 24.6	16 36.8	18 40.1
25	10 17 37.4	9 20.1	0 21.0	7N28.7	3 40.4	13 59.3	4 38.1	22 58.3	6 24.2	5 27.6	16 36.6	18 42.4
28	10 29 27.0	8 12.9	0 21.0	21 20.0	1 11.1	14 8.4	3 41.2	22 59.2	6 15.6	5 30.6	16 36.4	18 44.7

MARCH 1966

LONGITUDE

DAY	EPHEM. SID. TIME (h m s)	☉ (° ′)	☊ (° ′)	☽ (° ′)	☿ (° ′)	♀ (° ′)	♂ (° ′)	♃ (° ′)	♄ (° ′)	♅ (° ′)	♆ (° ′)	♇ (° ′)
1	10 33 23.6	9♓57.5	29♉31.3	17♊ .8	27♓12.0	1♒25.4	23♓21.8	21♊33.7	18♓39.6	17♍55.1	22♏10.1	17♍21.0
2	10 37 20.1	10 57.7	29 28.2	0♋41.4	28 34.5	1 53.3	24 8.6	21 36.5	18 47.0	17 R 52.5	22 R 9.8	17 R 19.4
3	10 41 16.7	11 57.8	29 25.0	14 49.6	29 51.3	2 22.8	24 55.4	21 39.5	18 54.3	17 49.9	22 9.6	17 17.8
4	10 45 13.2	12 58.0	29 21.8	29 24.7	1♈ 1.8	2 53.9	25 42.2	21 42.7	19 1.7	17 47.3	22 9.2	17 16.2
5	10 49 9.8	13 58.1	29 18.6	14♌22.8	2 5.5	3 26.4	26 28.9	21 46.1	19 9.1	17 44.7	22 8.9	17 14.6
6	10 53 6.4	14 58.1	29 15.4	29 36.3	3 1.8	4 .3	27 15.6	21 49.7	19 16.5	17 42.1	22 8.5	17 13.0
7	10 57 2.9	15 58.2	29 12.3	14♍54.9	3 50.2	4 35.5	28 2.3	21 53.4	19 23.8	17 39.4	22 8.1	17 11.4
8	11 0 59.5	16 58.2	29 9.1	0♎ 6.8	4 30.5	5 12.1	28 48.9	21 57.3	19 31.2	17 36.8	22 7.7	17 9.8
9	11 4 56.0	17 58.1	29 5.9	15 1.8	5 2.2	5 49.9	29 35.5	22 1.4	19 38.6	17 34.2	22 7.2	17 8.2
10	11 8 52.6	18 58.1	29 2.7	29 31.8	5 25.2	6 29.0	0♈22.1	22 5.7	19 46.0	17 31.6	22 6.7	17 6.7
11	11 12 49.1	19 58.0	28 59.6	13♏32.9	5 39.2	7 9.2	1 8.6	22 10.1	19 53.4	17 28.9	22 6.2	17 5.1
12	11 16 45.7	20 57.9	28 56.4	27 4.3	5 44.5	7 50.5	1 55.1	22 14.7	20 .8	17 26.3	22 5.6	17 3.5
13	11 20 42.2	21 57.7	28 53.2	10♐ 8.0	5 R 40.9	8 32.9	2 41.5	22 19.5	20 8.2	17 23.7	22 5.0	17 1.9
14	11 24 38.8	22 57.6	28 50.0	22 47.9	5 28.9	9 16.4	3 28.0	22 24.5	20 15.6	17 21.1	22 4.4	17 .3
15	11 28 35.3	23 57.4	28 46.8	5♑ 8.7	5 8.8	10 .8	4 14.4	22 29.6	20 23.0	17 18.5	22 3.7	16 58.7
16	11 32 31.9	24 57.1	28 43.7	17 15.4	4 41.2	10 46.2	5 .7	22 34.9	20 30.4	17 15.9	22 3.1	16 57.1
17	11 36 28.4	25 56.9	28 40.5	29 12.7	4 6.7	11 32.4	5 47.1	22 40.4	20 37.8	17 13.3	22 2.3	16 55.5
18	11 40 25.0	26 56.7	28 37.3	11♒ 5.0	3 26.4	12 19.6	6 33.4	22 46.1	20 45.2	17 10.8	22 1.7	16 54.0
19	11 44 21.5	27 56.3	28 34.1	22 55.6	2 40.9	13 7.6	7 19.6	22 51.8	20 52.5	17 8.2	22 .9	16 52.4
20	11 48 18.1	28 56.0	28 31.0	4♓47.4	1 51.6	13 56.3	8 5.8	22 57.8	20 59.9	17 5.6	22 .1	16 50.9
21	11 52 14.7	29 55.6	28 27.8	16 42.6	0 59.4	14 45.9	8 52.0	23 3.9	21 7.3	17 3.1	21 59.2	16 49.3
22	11 56 11.2	0♈55.2	28 24.6	28 42.7	0 5.6	15 36.1	9 38.2	23 10.2	21 14.6	17 .6	21 58.4	16 47.8
23	12 0 7.8	1 54.8	28 21.4	10♈48.9	29♓11.3	16 27.1	10 24.2	23 16.6	21 21.9	16 58.0	21 57.5	16 46.2
24	12 4 4.3	2 54.3	28 18.2	23 2.5	28 17.6	17 18.7	11 10.3	23 23.2	21 29.2	16 55.5	21 56.6	16 44.7
25	12 8 .9	3 53.8	28 15.1	5♉24.7	27 25.7	18 11.0	11 56.3	23 29.9	21 36.5	16 53.1	21 55.6	16 43.2
26	12 11 57.4	4 53.2	28 11.9	17 57.1	26 36.4	19 3.9	12 42.3	23 36.8	21 43.8	16 50.6	21 54.7	16 41.7
27	12 15 54.0	5 52.6	28 8.7	0♊41.8	25 50.5	19 57.5	13 28.2	23 43.9	21 51.1	16 48.2	21 53.7	16 40.2
28	12 19 50.5	6 52.0	28 5.5	13 41.2	25 8.8	20 51.6	14 14.1	23 51.0	21 58.3	16 45.7	21 52.7	16 38.7
29	12 23 47.1	7 51.4	28 2.4	26 58.1	24 31.8	21 46.2	14 59.9	23 58.4	22 5.5	16 43.3	21 51.6	16 37.2
30	12 27 43.6	8 50.7	27 59.2	10♋34.7	23 59.9	22 41.4	15 45.7	24 5.8	22 12.7	16 41.0	21 50.5	16 35.8
31	12 31 40.2	9 49.9	27 56.0	24 32.7	23 33.5	23 37.1	16 31.5	24 13.4	22 19.9	16 38.6	21 49.5	16 34.3

LATITUDE

DAY	EPHEM. SID. TIME (h m s)	☉	☊	☽	☿	♀	♂	♃	♄	♅	♆	♇
1	10 33 23.6	0 .0	0 .0	1N34.5	0N46.9	5N48.4	0S48.0	0S11.1	1S52.6	0N48.9	1N46.2	14N59.8
4	10 45 13.2	0 .0	0 .0	4 23.2	1 29.3	5 23.6	0 46.4	0 10.6	1 52.6	0 48.9	1 46.4	15 .1
7	10 57 2.9	0 .0	0 .0	4 48.6	2 11.0	4 58.5	0 44.8	0 10.1	1 52.7	0 48.9	1 46.5	15 .4
10	11 8 52.6	0 .0	0 .0	2 23.7	2 48.3	4 33.3	0 43.1	0 9.7	1 52.8	0 48.9	1 46.7	15 .6
13	11 20 42.2	0 .0	0 .0	1S 5.5	3 16.8	4 8.2	0 41.4	0 9.2	1 52.9	0 48.9	1 46.8	15 .7
16	11 32 31.9	0 .0	0 .0	3 51.8	3 32.4	3 43.4	0 39.7	0 8.8	1 53.1	0 48.9	1 47.0	15 .7
19	11 44 21.5	0 .0	0 .0	5 2.6	3 31.9	3 19.1	0 38.0	0 8.4	1 53.3	0 48.9	1 47.1	15 .7
22	11 56 11.2	0 .0	0 .0	4 18.3	3 14.3	2 55.3	0 36.2	0 8.0	1 53.4	0 48.8	1 47.3	15 .5
25	12 8 .9	0 .0	0 .0	1 50.0	2 42.1	2 32.2	0 34.4	0 7.6	1 53.7	0 48.8	1 47.4	15 .3
28	12 19 50.5	0 .0	0 .0	1N32.0	1 59.8	2 9.7	0 32.6	0 7.1	1 53.9	0 48.7	1 47.6	15 .1
31	12 31 40.2	0 .0	0 .0	4 22.3	1 13.0	1 48.0	0 30.8	0 6.8	1 54.2	0 48.7	1 47.7	14 59.7

RIGHT ASCENSION

DAY	EPHEM. SID. TIME (h m s)	☉	☊	☽	☿	♀	♂	♃	♄	♅	♆	♇
1	10 33 23.6	11♓29.7	27♉19.2	15♊43.3	27♓ 7.2	2♒20.6	24♓13.4	20♊49.7	20♓18.8	19♍12.6	20♏13.7	24♍28.7
2	10 37 20.1	12 25.9	27 15.9	0♋46.1	28 17.3	2 50.4	24 56.3	20 52.7	20 25.6	19 R 10.2	20 R 13.5	24 R 27.2
3	10 41 16.7	13 22.0	27 12.6	16 32.4	29 22.2	3 21.8	25 39.1	20 56.0	20 32.4	19 7.8	20 13.2	24 25.8
4	10 45 13.2	14 18.0	27 9.3	2♌34.4	0♈21.2	3 54.8	26 21.8	20 59.4	20 39.3	19 5.4	20 12.9	24 24.4
5	10 49 9.8	15 13.9	27 6.0	18 21.7	1 14.0	4 29.2	27 4.5	21 3.0	20 46.1	19 2.9	20 12.6	24 22.9
6	10 53 6.4	16 9.6	27 2.7	3♍32.6	2 .1	5 5.1	27 47.2	21 6.9	20 52.9	19 .5	20 12.2	24 21.5
7	10 57 2.9	17 5.2	26 59.4	17 59.8	2 39.2	5 42.4	28 29.8	21 10.9	20 59.7	18 58.1	20 11.8	24 20.0
8	11 0 59.5	18 .8	26 56.1	1♎48.2	3 10.9	6 21.0	29 12.4	21 15.2	21 6.6	18 55.7	20 11.4	24 18.6
9	11 4 56.0	18 56.2	26 52.8	15 9.9	3 35.1	7 .9	29 54.9	21 19.6	21 13.4	18 53.2	20 10.9	24 17.1
10	11 8 52.6	19 51.5	26 49.5	28 19.0	3 51.6	7 41.9	0♈37.4	21 24.2	21 20.3	18 50.8	20 10.4	24 15.7
11	11 12 49.1	20 46.8	26 46.2	11♏28.6	4 .2	8 24.1	1 19.9	21 29.0	21 27.1	18 48.4	20 9.9	24 14.2
12	11 16 45.7	21 42.0	26 42.9	24 47.7	4 1.2	9 7.5	2 2.3	21 34.0	21 34.0	18 46.0	20 9.4	24 12.7
13	11 20 42.2	22 37.1	26 39.6	8♐19.8	3 R 54.6	9 51.8	2 44.7	21 39.2	21 40.8	18 43.5	20 8.8	24 11.2
14	11 24 38.8	23 32.1	26 36.3	22 1.7	3 40.9	10 37.2	3 27.1	21 44.6	21 47.6	18 41.1	20 8.2	24 9.8
15	11 28 35.3	24 27.1	26 33.0	5♑44.4	3 20.3	11 23.5	4 9.4	21 50.2	21 54.5	18 38.7	20 7.5	24 8.3
16	11 32 31.9	25 22.0	26 29.7	19 15.3	2 53.5	12 10.7	4 51.8	21 55.9	22 1.3	18 36.3	20 6.8	24 6.8
17	11 36 28.4	26 16.9	26 26.4	2♒22.6	2 21.1	12 58.8	5 34.1	22 1.8	22 8.2	18 33.9	20 6.1	24 5.4
18	11 40 25.0	27 11.8	26 23.1	14 58.5	1 44.1	13 47.7	6 16.4	22 8.0	22 15.0	18 31.6	20 5.4	24 3.9
19	11 44 21.5	28 6.5	26 19.8	27 .5	1 3.3	14 37.4	6 58.7	22 14.3	22 21.8	18 29.2	20 4.7	24 2.5
20	11 48 18.1	29 1.3	26 16.5	8♓31.7	0 19.6	15 27.8	7 41.0	22 20.7	22 28.7	18 26.8	20 3.9	24 1.0
21	11 52 14.7	29 56.0	26 13.3	19 39.0	29♓34.0	16 18.8	8 23.2	22 27.4	22 35.5	18 24.4	20 3.0	23 59.5
22	11 56 11.2	0♈50.7	26 10.0	0♈32.0	28 47.7	17 10.6	9 5.5	22 34.2	22 42.2	18 22.1	20 2.2	23 58.1
23	12 0 7.8	1 45.3	26 6.7	11 22.2	28 1.7	18 2.9	9 47.7	22 41.1	22 49.0	18 19.8	20 1.3	23 56.6
24	12 4 4.3	2 39.9	26 3.4	22 21.9	27 16.8	18 55.9	10 29.9	22 48.3	22 55.8	18 17.4	20 .4	23 55.2
25	12 8 .9	3 34.5	26 .1	3♉44.3	26 34.0	19 49.3	11 12.2	22 55.6	23 2.6	18 15.1	19 59.5	23 53.7
26	12 11 57.4	4 29.1	25 56.8	15 42.4	25 54.0	20 43.3	11 54.4	23 3.1	23 9.3	18 12.8	19 58.5	23 52.3
27	12 15 54.0	5 23.7	25 53.5	28 27.4	25 17.6	21 37.8	12 36.6	23 10.7	23 16.0	18 10.6	19 57.5	23 50.8
28	12 19 50.5	6 18.3	25 50.2	12♊ 6.3	24 45.2	22 32.8	13 18.8	23 18.5	23 22.7	18 8.3	19 56.5	23 49.4
29	12 23 47.1	7 12.9	25 46.9	26 37.7	24 17.3	23 28.2	14 1.0	23 26.4	23 29.4	18 6.1	19 55.5	23 48.0
30	12 27 43.6	8 7.5	25 43.6	11♋49.5	23 54.3	24 24.0	14 43.2	23 34.5	23 36.1	18 3.9	19 54.4	23 46.6
31	12 31 40.2	9 2.0	25 40.3	27 19.3	23 36.2	25 20.2	15 25.4	23 42.8	23 42.7	18 1.7	19 53.3	23 45.2

DECLINATION

DAY	EPHEM. SID. TIME (h m s)	☉	☊	☽	☿	♀	♂	♃	♄	♅	♆	♇
1	10 33 23.6	7S50.2	0N21.0	24N22.7	0S23.8	14S10.8	3S22.2	22N59.5	6S12.8	5N31.6	16S36.3	18N45.4
4	10 45 13.2	6 41.6	0 21.0	24 34.0	1N46.5	14 15.7	2 25.1	23 .6	6 4.2	5 34.7	16 35.9	18 47.6
7	10 57 2.9	5 32.1	0 20.9	10 22.6	3 31.7	14 17.1	1 27.9	23 1.7	5 55.5	5 37.8	16 35.4	18 49.8
10	11 8 52.6	4 22.0	0 20.9	9S 4.0	4 43.7	14 14.6	0 30.8	23 2.9	5 46.9	5 40.8	16 34.9	18 51.8
13	11 20 42.2	3 11.3	0 20.9	23 3.3	5 16.1	14 8.0	0N26.2	23 4.1	5 38.3	5 43.9	16 34.3	18 53.8
16	11 32 31.9	2 .4	0 20.8	26 9.7	5 6.7	13 57.1	1 23.1	23 5.4	5 29.7	5 46.9	16 33.7	18 55.7
19	11 44 21.5	0 49.2	0 20.8	18 38.2	4 18.4	13 41.9	2 19.6	23 6.8	5 21.1	5 49.9	16 33.0	18 57.5
22	11 56 11.2	0N22.0	0 20.7	4 27.7	3 .5	13 22.2	3 15.8	23 8.2	5 12.6	5 52.9	16 32.2	18 59.3
25	12 8 .9	1 33.0	0 20.7	11N36.0	1 27.3	12 58.1	4 11.6	23 9.6	5 4.2	5 55.7	16 31.4	19 .9
28	12 19 50.5	2 43.6	0 20.7	23 58.2	0S 5.7	12 29.7	5 6.8	23 11.0	4 55.8	5 58.6	16 30.5	19 2.4
31	12 31 40.2	3 53.8	0 20.6	25 31.1	1 26.5	11 57.0	6 1.4	23 12.4	4 47.5	6 1.3	16 29.5	19 3.8

APRIL 1966

LONGITUDE

DAY	EPHEM. SID. TIME h m s	☉ ° ′	☊ ° ′	☽ ° ′	☿ ° ′	♀ ° ′	♂ ° ′	♃ ° ′	♄ ° ′	♅ ° ′	♆ ° ′	♇ ° ′
1	12 35 36.7	10♈49.1	27♉52.8	8♌51.9	23♓12.6	24♒33.3	17♈17.2	24♊21.2	22♓27.1	16♍36.3	21♏48.3	16♍32.9
2	12 39 33.3	11 48.3	27 49.6	23 30.1	22 R 57.5	25 30.0	18 2.8	24 29.0	22 34.2	16 R 34.0	21 R 47.2	16 R 31.5
3	12 43 29.8	12 47.5	27 46.5	8♍22.1	22 48.0	26 27.1	18 48.4	24 37.1	22 41.3	16 31.7	21 46.0	16 30.1
4	12 47 26.4	13 46.6	27 43.3	23 20.7	22 44.3	27 24.7	19 34.0	24 45.2	22 48.4	16 29.5	21 44.8	16 28.7
5	12 51 23.0	14 45.6	27 40.1	8♎17.0	22 D 46.0	28 22.8	20 19.5	24 53.5	22 55.5	16 27.2	21 43.6	16 27.3
6	12 55 19.5	15 44.7	27 36.9	23 2.0	22 53.1	29 21.2	21 4.9	25 1.9	23 2.5	16 25.0	21 42.4	16 26.0
7	12 59 16.1	16 43.7	27 33.8	7♏28.1	23 5.5	0♓20.1	21 50.4	25 10.4	23 9.5	16 22.9	21 41.2	16 24.6
8	13 3 12.6	17 42.7	27 30.6	21 30.3	23 22.9	1 19.4	22 35.8	25 19.1	23 16.6	16 20.8	21 39.9	16 23.4
9	13 7 9.2	18 41.6	27 27.4	5♐6.1	23 45.0	2 19.0	23 21.1	25 27.9	23 23.5	16 18.7	21 38.6	16 22.1
10	13 11 5.7	19 40.6	27 24.2	18 15.9	24 11.7	3 19.1	24 6.4	25 36.7	23 30.4	16 16.7	21 37.3	16 20.8
11	13 15 2.3	20 39.4	27 21.0	1♑1.8	24 42.8	4 19.4	24 51.6	25 45.8	23 37.3	16 14.6	21 36.0	16 19.5
12	13 18 58.8	21 38.3	27 17.9	13 27.7	25 18.1	5 20.1	25 36.8	25 54.9	23 44.1	16 12.6	21 34.7	16 18.3
13	13 22 55.4	22 37.1	27 14.7	25 37.9	25 57.3	6 21.2	26 22.0	26 4.1	23 51.0	16 10.7	21 33.3	16 17.0
14	13 26 51.9	23 35.9	27 11.5	7♒37.3	26 40.3	7 22.6	27 7.1	26 13.5	23 57.7	16 8.8	21 31.9	16 15.8
15	13 30 48.5	24 34.7	27 8.3	19 30.6	27 26.8	8 24.2	27 52.1	26 22.9	24 4.5	16 6.9	21 30.5	16 14.6
16	13 34 45.0	25 33.4	27 5.2	1♓22.1	28 16.7	9 26.2	28 37.1	26 32.5	24 11.2	16 5.0	21 29.1	16 13.5
17	13 38 41.6	26 32.1	27 2.0	13 15.7	29 9.9	10 28.4	29 22.1	26 42.2	24 17.8	16 3.2	21 27.7	16 12.3
18	13 42 38.2	27 30.8	26 58.8	25 14.5	0♈6.2	11 31.0	0♉7.0	26 52.0	24 24.5	16 1.4	21 26.2	16 11.2
19	13 46 34.7	28 29.4	26 55.6	7♈21.2	1 5.4	12 33.7	0 51.8	27 1.9	24 31.1	15 59.7	21 24.7	16 10.1
20	13 50 31.3	29 28.1	26 52.5	19 37.5	2 7.4	13 36.8	1 36.6	27 11.9	24 37.6	15 58.0	21 23.3	16 9.0
21	13 54 27.8	0♉26.7	26 49.3	2♉4.8	3 12.0	14 40.1	2 21.4	27 22.0	24 44.1	15 56.4	21 21.8	16 8.0
22	13 58 24.4	1 25.2	26 46.1	14 43.9	4 19.3	15 43.6	3 6.1	27 32.2	24 50.5	15 54.8	21 20.3	16 7.0
23	14 2 20.9	2 23.7	26 42.9	27 35.3	5 29.1	16 47.3	3 50.8	27 42.5	24 57.0	15 53.2	21 18.8	16 6.0
24	14 6 17.5	3 22.2	26 39.7	10♊39.4	6 41.3	17 51.3	4 35.4	27 53.0	25 3.3	15 51.7	21 17.2	16 5.0
25	14 10 14.0	4 20.7	26 36.6	23 56.7	7 55.7	18 55.5	5 19.9	28 3.5	25 9.6	15 50.2	21 15.7	16 4.0
26	14 14 10.6	5 19.1	26 33.4	7♋27.4	9 12.5	19 59.9	6 4.4	28 14.0	25 15.9	15 48.8	21 14.1	16 3.1
27	14 18 7.1	6 17.5	26 30.2	21 11.9	10 31.4	21 4.4	6 48.9	28 24.7	25 22.1	15 47.4	21 12.6	16 2.2
28	14 22 3.7	7 15.8	26 27.0	5♌10.0	11 52.4	22 9.2	7 33.3	28 35.5	25 28.3	15 46.1	21 11.0	16 1.3
29	14 26 .3	8 14.2	26 23.9	19 20.7	13 15.6	23 14.2	8 17.7	28 46.4	25 34.4	15 44.9	21 9.5	16 .5
30	14 29 56.8	9 12.5	26 20.7	3♍42.1	14 40.8	24 19.4	9 2.0	28 57.3	25 40.5	15 43.6	21 7.9	15 59.7

LATITUDE

DAY	SID. TIME	☉	☊	☽	☿	♀	♂	♃	♄	♅	♆	♇
1	12 35 36.7	0 .0	0 .0	4N54.2	0N57.2	1N41.0	0S30.2	0S 6.6	1S54.3	0N48.7	1N47.7	14N59.6
4	12 47 26.4	0 .0	0 .0	4 34.3	0 11.2	1 20.4	0 28.3	0 6.2	1 54.6	0 48.6	1 47.8	14 59.1
7	12 59 16.1	0 .0	0 .0	1 37.8	0S31.1	1 .7	0 26.5	0 5.9	1 54.9	0 48.5	1 47.9	14 58.6
10	13 11 5.7	0 .0	0 .0	1S59.3	1 8.2	0 41.8	0 24.6	0 5.5	1 55.2	0 48.5	1 48.0	14 58.1
13	13 22 55.4	0 .0	0 .0	4 29.8	1 39.6	0 23.9	0 22.7	0 5.1	1 55.6	0 48.4	1 48.1	14 57.4
16	13 34 45.0	0 .0	0 .0	5 10.5	2 5.0	0 7.0	0 20.8	0 4.8	1 56.0	0 48.3	1 48.2	14 56.7
19	13 46 34.7	0 .0	0 .0	3 53.1	2 24.5	0S 9.0	0 18.9	0 4.4	1 56.4	0 48.2	1 48.3	14 56.0
22	13 58 24.4	0 .0	0 .0	0 58.0	2 38.4	0 23.9	0 17.0	0 4.1	1 56.9	0 48.1	1 48.4	14 55.2
25	14 10 14.0	0 .0	0 .0	2N31.0	2 46.7	0 37.9	0 15.0	0 3.7	1 57.3	0 48.0	1 48.4	14 54.3
28	14 22 3.7	0 .0	0 .0	4 55.9	2 49.7	0 50.8	0 13.1	0 3.4	1 57.8	0 47.9	1 48.5	14 53.4

RIGHT ASCENSION

DAY	SID. TIME	☉	☊	☽	☿	♀	♂	♃	♄	♅	♆	♇
1	12 35 36.7	9♈56.7	25♉37.0	12♌41.5	23♓23.3	26♒16.8	16♈7.7	23♊51.2	23♓49.4	17♍59.5	19♏52.2	23♍43.8
2	12 39 33.3	10 51.3	25 33.8	27 36.6	23 R 15.6	27 13.7	16 49.9	23 59.8	23 56.0	17 R 57.4	19 R 51.0	23 R 42.4
3	12 43 29.8	11 45.9	25 30.5	11♍56.0	23 13.0	28 10.9	17 32.1	24 8.5	24 2.6	17 55.3	19 49.9	23 41.0
4	12 47 26.4	12 40.6	25 27.2	25 42.6	23 D 15.5	29 8.5	18 14.4	24 17.3	24 9.2	17 53.2	19 48.7	23 39.7
5	12 51 23.0	13 35.3	25 23.9	9♎6.6	23 22.9	0♓6.3	18 56.7	24 26.3	24 15.7	17 51.1	19 47.5	23 38.3
6	12 55 19.5	14 30.1	25 20.6	22 21.1	23 35.0	1 4.5	19 38.9	24 35.4	24 22.2	17 49.1	19 46.3	23 37.0
7	12 59 16.1	15 24.9	25 17.3	5♏39.4	23 51.7	2 2.9	20 21.2	24 44.7	24 28.7	17 47.1	19 45.0	23 35.7
8	13 3 12.6	16 19.8	25 14.0	19 11.1	24 12.9	3 1.5	21 3.6	24 54.2	24 35.2	17 45.2	19 43.8	23 34.4
9	13 7 9.2	17 14.8	25 10.8	3♐.1	24 38.2	4 .4	21 45.9	25 3.7	24 41.6	17 43.2	19 42.5	23 33.1
10	13 11 5.7	18 9.7	25 7.5	17 2.9	25 7.4	4 59.5	22 28.3	25 13.4	24 48.1	17 41.3	19 41.2	23 31.8
11	13 15 2.3	19 4.8	25 4.2	1♑9.0	25 40.4	5 58.8	23 10.7	25 23.2	24 54.4	17 39.4	19 39.9	23 30.5
12	13 18 58.8	19 59.9	25 .9	15 3.3	26 16.9	6 58.3	23 53.1	25 33.1	25 .8	17 37.5	19 38.5	23 29.3
13	13 22 55.4	20 55.1	24 57.6	28 31.6	26 56.9	7 57.9	24 35.5	25 43.1	25 7.1	17 35.7	19 37.1	23 28.0
14	13 26 51.9	21 50.4	24 54.3	11♒24.4	27 40.0	8 57.7	25 18.0	25 53.3	25 13.4	17 33.9	19 35.8	23 26.8
15	13 30 48.5	22 45.8	24 51.1	23 38.9	28 26.1	9 57.7	26 .5	26 3.6	25 19.6	17 32.2	19 34.4	23 25.6
16	13 34 45.0	23 41.3	24 47.8	5♓18.4	29 15.0	10 57.8	26 43.0	26 14.0	25 25.9	17 30.4	19 32.9	23 24.4
17	13 38 41.6	24 36.8	24 44.5	16 30.6	0♈6.6	11 58.1	27 25.6	26 24.6	25 32.1	17 28.8	19 31.5	23 23.3
18	13 42 38.2	25 32.5	24 41.2	27 26.2	1 .8	12 58.4	28 8.2	26 35.3	25 38.2	17 27.1	19 30.1	23 22.1
19	13 46 34.7	26 28.2	24 37.9	8♈17.1	1 57.5	13 58.9	28 50.9	26 46.0	25 44.3	17 25.5	19 28.6	23 21.0
20	13 50 31.3	27 24.1	24 34.6	19 16.5	2 56.4	14 59.5	29 33.5	26 56.9	25 50.4	17 23.9	19 27.1	23 19.8
21	13 54 27.8	28 20.0	24 31.4	0♉37.7	3 57.6	16 .2	0♉16.2	27 7.9	25 56.4	17 22.4	19 25.6	23 18.8
22	13 58 24.4	29 16.1	24 28.1	12 33.7	5 .8	17 1.0	0 59.0	27 19.0	26 2.4	17 20.9	19 24.1	23 17.7
23	14 2 20.9	0♉12.3	24 24.8	25 15.9	6 6.2	18 2.0	1 41.8	27 30.3	26 8.4	17 19.4	19 22.6	23 16.6
24	14 6 17.5	1 8.6	24 21.5	8♊50.8	7 13.5	19 2.9	2 24.6	27 41.6	26 14.3	17 18.0	19 21.1	23 15.6
25	14 10 14.0	2 5.0	24 18.3	23 16.6	8 22.7	20 4.0	3 7.5	27 53.0	26 20.1	17 16.6	19 19.5	23 14.6
26	14 14 10.6	3 1.5	24 15.0	8♋20.5	9 33.8	21 5.2	3 50.4	28 4.6	26 25.9	17 15.3	19 18.0	23 13.6
27	14 18 7.1	3 58.1	24 11.7	23 40.0	10 46.7	22 6.4	4 33.3	28 16.2	26 31.7	17 14.0	19 16.4	23 12.6
28	14 22 3.7	4 54.9	24 8.4	8♌49.6	12 1.4	23 7.8	5 16.3	28 27.9	26 37.5	17 12.7	19 14.8	23 11.6
29	14 26 .3	5 51.8	24 5.2	23 30.1	13 18.0	24 9.2	5 59.3	28 39.8	26 43.2	17 11.6	19 13.3	23 10.8
30	14 29 56.8	6 48.8	24 1.9	7♍33.5	14 36.3	25 10.7	6 42.4	28 51.7	26 48.8	17 10.4	19 11.7	23 9.9

DECLINATION

DAY	SID. TIME	☉	☊	☽	☿	♀	♂	♃	♄	♅	♆	♇
1	12 35 36.7	4N17.0	0N20.6	22N46.4	1S49.2	11S45.2	6N19.5	23N12.9	4S44.7	6N 2.2	16S29.2	19N 4.3
4	12 47 26.4	5 26.2	0 20.6	6 50.4	2 42.7	11 6.9	7 13.2	23 14.2	4 36.6	6 4.8	16 28.2	19 5.5
7	12 59 16.1	6 34.6	0 20.5	12S27.9	3 13.2	10 24.6	8 6.2	23 15.6	4 28.5	6 7.3	16 27.2	19 6.7
10	13 11 5.7	7 41.9	0 20.5	24 54.5	3 21.0	9 38.5	8 58.3	23 16.9	4 20.5	6 9.6	16 26.1	19 7.7
13	13 22 55.4	8 48.1	0 20.5	25 26.3	3 7.9	8 48.7	9 49.5	23 18.1	4 12.7	6 11.9	16 24.9	19 8.6
16	13 34 45.0	9 53.0	0 20.4	15 49.2	2 35.7	7 55.5	10 39.7	23 19.2	4 5.1	6 14.0	16 23.8	19 9.4
19	13 46 34.7	10 56.4	0 20.4	0 39.0	1 46.6	6 59.2	11 28.9	23 20.3	3 57.6	6 15.9	16 22.6	19 10.0
22	13 58 24.4	11 58.3	0 20.4	15N20.2	0 42.3	5 59.8	12 17.1	23 21.3	3 50.2	6 17.8	16 21.4	19 10.5
25	14 10 14.0	12 58.3	0 20.3	25 49.2	0N35.6	4 57.9	13 4.0	23 22.1	3 43.1	6 19.4	16 20.1	19 10.9
28	14 22 3.7	13 56.4	0 20.3	23 45.7	2 5.5	3 53.5	13 49.7	23 22.9	3 36.1	6 21.0	16 18.9	19 11.2

MAY 1966

DAY	EPHEM. SID. TIME	☉	☊	☽	☿	♀	♂	♃	♄	♅	♆	♇
	LONGITUDE											
	h m s	° ′	° ′	° ′	° ′	° ′	° ′	° ′	° ′	° ′	° ′	° ′
1	14 33 53.4	10♉10.7	26♉17.5	18♍10.8	16♈ 8.0	25♓24.7	9♉46.2	29♊ 8.4	25♓46.5	15♍42.4	21♏ 6.3	15♍58.9
2	14 37 49.9	11 8.9	26 14.3	2♎42.5	17 37.2	26 30.2	10 30.4	29 19.5	25 52.4	15 R 41.3	21 R 4.7	15 R 58.1
3	14 41 46.5	12 7.1	26 11.1	17 11.7	19 8.4	27 35.9	11 14.5	29 30.7	25 58.3	15 40.2	21 3.1	15 57.4
4	14 45 43.0	13 5.3	26 8.0	1♏32.8	20 41.5	28 41.7	11 58.6	29 41.9	26 4.2	15 39.2	21 1.5	15 56.7
5	14 49 39.6	14 3.4	26 4.8	15 40.3	22 16.6	29 47.7	12 42.6	29 53.3	26 10.0	15 38.2	20 59.9	15 56.0
6	14 53 36.1	15 1.5	26 1.6	29 30.0	23 53.6	0♈53.9	13 26.6	0♋ 4.7	26 15.7	15 37.2	20 58.3	15 55.3
7	14 57 32.7	15 59.5	25 58.4	12♐59.3	25 32.5	2 .2	14 10.5	0 16.2	26 21.3	15 36.3	20 56.6	15 54.7
8	15 1 29.3	16 57.6	25 55.3	26 7.2	27 13.4	3 6.7	14 54.4	0 27.8	26 26.9	15 35.5	20 55.0	15 54.1
9	15 5 25.8	17 55.6	25 52.1	8♑54.4	28 56.2	4 13.3	15 38.2	0 39.4	26 32.5	15 34.7	20 53.4	15 53.5
10	15 9 22.4	18 53.6	25 48.9	21 23.1	0♉41.0	5 20.1	16 22.0	0 51.1	26 38.0	15 33.9	20 51.8	15 53.0
11	15 13 18.9	19 51.6	25 45.7	3♒36.4	2 27.7	6 27.0	17 5.7	1 2.9	26 43.4	15 33.2	20 50.1	15 52.4
12	15 17 15.5	20 49.5	25 42.6	15 38.5	4 16.3	7 34.0	17 49.4	1 14.8	26 48.7	15 32.6	20 48.5	15 52.0
13	15 21 12.0	21 47.4	25 39.4	27 33.7	6 6.9	8 41.2	18 33.0	1 26.7	26 54.0	15 32.0	20 46.9	15 51.5
14	15 25 8.6	22 45.3	25 36.2	9♓26.6	7 59.4	9 48.5	19 16.6	1 38.7	26 59.3	15 31.4	20 45.2	15 51.1
15	15 29 5.1	23 43.2	25 33.0	21 21.8	9 53.8	10 55.9	20 .1	1 50.7	27 4.4	15 31.0	20 43.6	15 50.7
16	15 33 1.7	24 41.1	25 29.8	3♈23.3	11 50.2	12 3.5	20 43.6	2 2.8	27 9.5	15 30.5	20 42.0	15 50.3
17	15 36 58.3	25 38.9	25 26.7	15 35.0	13 48.4	13 11.1	21 27.0	2 15.0	27 14.5	15 30.1	20 40.3	15 50.0
18	15 40 54.8	26 36.8	25 23.5	27 59.9	15 48.5	14 18.9	22 10.3	2 27.2	27 19.5	15 29.8	20 38.7	15 49.7
19	15 44 51.4	27 34.6	25 20.3	10♉39.9	17 50.4	15 26.8	22 53.7	2 39.5	27 24.4	15 29.5	20 37.1	15 49.4
20	15 48 47.9	28 32.4	25 17.1	23 36.4	19 54.0	16 34.8	23 37.0	2 51.9	27 29.2	15 29.3	20 35.5	15 49.2
21	15 52 44.5	29 30.1	25 14.0	6♊49.4	21 59.3	17 42.9	24 20.2	3 4.3	27 33.9	15 29.2	20 33.9	15 49.0
22	15 56 41.0	0♊27.9	25 10.8	20 18.2	24 6.0	18 51.1	25 3.3	3 16.7	27 38.6	15 29.1	20 32.3	15 48.8
23	16 0 37.6	1 25.6	25 7.6	4♋ 1.0	26 14.1	19 59.3	25 46.4	3 29.2	27 43.2	15 29.0	20 30.7	15 48.7
24	16 4 34.2	2 23.3	25 4.4	17 55.5	28 23.4	21 7.7	26 29.5	3 41.8	27 47.7	15 29.0	20 29.1	15 48.5
25	16 8 30.7	3 20.9	25 1.3	1♌59.1	0♊33.6	22 16.1	27 12.5	3 54.4	27 52.1	15 29.0	20 27.5	15 48.4
26	16 12 27.3	4 18.6	24 58.1	16 8.9	2 44.7	23 24.7	27 55.4	4 7.0	27 56.5	15 D 29.1	20 26.0	15 48.4
27	16 16 23.8	5 16.2	24 54.9	0♍22.2	4 56.3	24 33.3	28 38.3	4 19.7	28 .8	15 29.3	20 24.4	15 48.4
28	16 20 20.4	6 13.8	24 51.7	14 36.3	7 8.2	25 42.0	29 21.1	4 32.5	28 5.0	15 29.5	20 22.8	15 48.4
29	16 24 16.9	7 11.3	24 48.5	28 48.8	9 20.2	26 50.8	0♊ 3.9	4 45.3	28 9.1	15 29.7	20 21.3	15 48.4
30	16 28 13.5	8 8.9	24 45.4	12♎57.2	11 31.8	27 59.6	0 46.6	4 58.1	28 13.1	15 30.1	20 19.7	15 D 48.5
31	16 32 10.1	9 6.4	24 42.2	26 59.0	13 43.0	29 8.6	1 29.3	5 11.0	28 17.1	15 30.4	20 18.2	15 48.6
	LATITUDE											
1	14 33 53.4	0 .0	0 .0	4N50.9	2S47.5	1S 2.7	0S11.2	0S 3.1	1S58.3	0N47.8	1N48.5	14N52.5
4	14 45 43.0	0 .0	0 .0	2 7.5	2 40.2	1 13.6	0 9.2	0 2.7	1 58.8	0 47.7	1 48.5	14 51.5
7	14 57 32.7	0 .0	0 .0	1S36.4	2 28.1	1 23.4	0 7.3	0 2.4	1 59.4	0 47.6	1 48.6	14 50.5
10	15 9 22.4	0 .0	0 .0	4 23.0	2 11.2	1 32.2	0 5.4	0 2.1	1 60.0	0 47.4	1 48.6	14 49.4
13	15 21 12.0	0 .0	0 .0	5 16.5	1 50.0	1 40.0	0 3.4	0 1.8	2 .5	0 47.3	1 48.6	14 48.3
16	15 33 1.7	0 .0	0 .0	4 9.7	1 24.8	1 46.7	0 1.5	0 1.5	2 1.2	0 47.2	1 48.5	14 47.2
19	15 44 51.4	0 .0	0 .0	1 20.4	0 56.3	1 52.5	0N .4	0 1.2	2 1.8	0 47.1	1 48.5	14 46.1
22	15 56 41.0	0 .0	0 .0	2N13.9	0 25.5	1 57.3	0 2.4	0 .9	2 2.4	0 46.9	1 48.5	14 44.9
25	16 8 30.7	0 .0	0 .0	4 50.6	0N 6.2	2 1.1	0 4.3	0 .6	2 3.1	0 46.8	1 48.5	14 43.8
28	16 20 20.4	0 .0	0 .0	4 58.5	0 37.2	2 3.9	0 6.2	0 .3	2 3.8	0 46.7	1 48.4	14 42.6
31	16 32 10.1	0 .0	0 .0	2 30.3	1 5.4	2 5.8	0 8.1	0 .0	2 4.5	0 46.5	1 48.3	14 41.4
	RIGHT ASCENSION											
1	14 33 53.4	7♉45.9	23♉58.6	21♍ 2.9	15♈56.3	26♓12.3	7♉25.5	29♊ 3.8	26♓54.4	17♍ 9.3	19♏10.1	23♍ 9.0
2	14 37 49.9	8 43.2	23 55.3	4♎ 8.9	17 18.2	27 13.9	8 8.7	29 15.9	26 59.9	17 R 8.2	19 R 8.5	23 R 8.1
3	14 41 46.5	9 40.6	23 52.1	17 5.9	18 41.8	28 15.6	8 51.9	29 28.0	27 5.4	17 7.2	19 6.9	23 7.3
4	14 45 43.0	10 38.1	23 48.8	0♏ 8.2	20 7.3	29 17.5	9 35.1	29 40.3	27 10.9	17 6.2	19 5.3	23 6.5
5	14 49 39.6	11 35.7	23 45.5	13 28.2	21 34.6	0♈19.4	10 18.4	29 52.7	27 16.2	17 5.3	19 3.6	23 5.7
6	14 53 36.1	12 33.5	23 42.2	27 12.5	23 3.8	1 21.4	11 1.7	0♋ 5.1	27 21.6	17 4.4	19 2.0	23 4.9
7	14 57 32.7	13 31.5	23 39.0	11♐20.2	24 34.9	2 23.5	11 45.1	0 17.7	27 26.8	17 3.5	19 .4	23 4.2
8	15 1 29.3	14 29.6	23 35.7	25 41.0	26 7.9	3 25.7	12 28.5	0 30.3	27 32.1	17 2.7	18 58.8	23 3.5
9	15 5 25.8	15 27.8	23 32.4	9♑58.0	27 43.1	4 28.0	13 12.0	0 42.9	27 37.2	17 2.0	18 57.1	23 2.8
10	15 9 22.4	16 26.2	23 29.2	23 52.5	29 20.3	5 30.4	13 55.5	0 55.7	27 42.3	17 1.3	18 55.5	23 2.1
11	15 13 18.9	17 24.7	23 25.9	7♒10.3	0♉59.6	6 32.9	14 39.1	1 8.5	27 47.4	17 .6	18 53.8	23 1.5
12	15 17 15.5	18 23.4	23 22.6	19 45.3	2 41.2	7 35.5	15 22.7	1 21.5	27 52.4	16 60.0	18 52.2	23 .9
13	15 21 12.0	19 22.2	23 19.4	1♓39.0	4 25.0	8 38.2	16 6.4	1 34.4	27 57.3	16 59.4	18 50.6	23 .3
14	15 25 8.6	20 21.1	23 16.1	12 59.2	6 11.1	9 41.0	16 50.1	1 47.5	28 2.2	16 58.9	18 48.9	22 59.7
15	15 29 5.1	21 20.2	23 12.8	23 57.1	7 59.7	10 44.0	17 33.9	2 .6	28 7.0	16 58.4	18 47.3	22 59.2
16	15 33 1.7	22 19.5	23 9.6	4♈45.8	9 50.7	11 47.0	18 17.7	2 13.8	28 11.8	16 58.0	18 45.6	22 58.7
17	15 36 58.3	23 18.9	23 6.3	15 39.4	11 44.3	12 50.2	19 1.6	2 27.1	28 16.5	16 57.6	18 44.0	22 58.2
18	15 40 54.8	24 18.5	23 3.0	26 52.8	13 40.3	13 53.5	19 45.5	2 40.4	28 21.1	16 57.3	18 42.4	22 57.8
19	15 44 51.4	25 18.1	22 59.8	8♉40.5	15 39.0	14 57.0	20 29.5	2 53.8	28 25.7	16 57.0	18 40.7	22 57.3
20	15 48 47.9	26 18.0	22 56.5	21 15.8	17 40.2	16 .6	21 13.6	3 7.3	28 30.2	16 56.9	18 39.2	22 57.0
21	15 52 44.5	27 18.0	22 53.2	4♊47.6	19 44.0	17 4.4	21 57.6	3 20.8	28 34.6	16 56.7	18 37.6	22 56.6
22	15 56 41.0	28 18.1	22 50.0	19 16.2	21 50.2	18 8.3	22 41.7	3 34.4	28 39.0	16 56.6	18 35.9	22 56.3
23	16 0 37.6	29 18.3	22 46.7	4♋29.3	23 58.8	19 12.3	23 25.9	3 48.0	28 43.3	16 56.5	18 34.3	22 56.0
24	16 4 34.2	0♊18.7	22 43.5	20 2.4	26 9.7	20 16.5	24 10.1	4 1.7	28 47.5	16 56.5	18 32.7	22 55.7
25	16 8 30.7	1 19.2	22 40.2	5♌26.0	28 22.7	21 20.8	24 54.3	4 15.4	28 51.7	16 56.5	18 31.1	22 55.4
26	16 12 27.3	2 19.8	22 36.9	20 16.2	0♊37.7	22 25.4	25 38.5	4 29.2	28 55.8	16 D 56.6	18 29.5	22 55.2
27	16 16 23.8	3 20.5	22 33.7	4♍22.2	2 54.3	23 30.0	26 22.9	4 43.0	28 59.8	16 56.7	18 28.0	22 55.0
28	16 20 20.4	4 21.3	22 30.4	17 46.5	5 12.3	24 34.9	27 7.2	4 56.9	29 3.7	16 56.9	18 26.4	22 54.9
29	16 24 16.9	5 22.3	22 27.2	0♎39.9	7 31.5	25 40.0	27 51.6	5 10.8	29 7.6	16 57.1	18 24.8	22 54.7
30	16 28 13.5	6 23.4	22 23.9	13 18.0	9 51.4	26 45.2	28 36.0	5 24.8	29 11.4	16 57.4	18 23.3	22 54.6
31	16 32 10.1	7 24.5	22 20.6	25 57.0	12 11.7	27 50.7	29 20.4	5 38.8	29 15.1	16 57.7	18 21.8	22 54.5
	DECLINATION											
1	14 33 53.4	14N52.5	0N20.2	9N 8.0	3N46.2	2S47.0	14N34.1	23N23.5	3S29.4	6N22.3	16S17.6	19N11.3
4	14 45 43.0	15 46.3	0 20.2	10S 1.2	5 36.4	1 38.6	15 17.2	23 24.0	3 22.8	6 23.4	16 16.3	19 11.2
7	14 57 32.7	16 37.7	0 20.2	23 57.4	7 34.7	0 28.7	15 58.8	23 24.3	3 16.5	6 24.4	16 15.0	19 11.1
10	15 9 22.4	17 26.7	0 20.1	26 4.3	9 39.8	0N42.5	16 39.0	23 24.4	3 10.4	6 25.3	16 13.8	19 10.8
13	15 21 12.0	18 13.1	0 20.1	17 16.1	11 49.9	1 54.8	17 17.7	23 24.4	3 4.6	6 25.9	16 12.5	19 10.4
16	15 33 1.7	18 56.7	0 20.0	2 28.3	14 2.6	3 7.8	17 54.9	23 24.3	2 59.0	6 26.3	16 11.2	19 9.8
19	15 44 51.4	19 37.4	0 20.0	13N45.2	16 15.1	4 21.1	18 30.5	23 23.9	2 53.7	6 26.6	16 9.9	19 9.2
22	15 56 41.0	20 15.2	0 20.0	25 19.0	18 23.4	5 34.6	19 4.4	23 23.4	2 48.6	6 26.7	16 8.7	19 8.3
25	16 8 30.7	20 49.8	0 19.9	24 26.3	20 22.5	6 47.9	19 36.6	23 22.7	2 43.8	6 26.6	16 7.5	19 7.4
28	16 20 20.4	21 21.2	0 19.9	10 38.9	22 7.1	8 .7	20 7.1	23 21.8	2 39.3	6 26.3	16 6.3	19 6.4
31	16 32 10.1	21 49.3	0 19.8	8S 3.7	23 32.0	9 12.6	20 35.8	23 20.6	2 35.2	6 25.8	16 5.1	19 5.2

JUNE 1966

LONGITUDE

DAY	EPHEM. SID. TIME h m s	☉ ° ′	☊ ° ′	☽ ° ′	☿ ° ′	♀ ° ′	♂ ° ′	♃ ° ′	♄ ° ′	♅ ° ′	♆ ° ′	♇ ° ′
1	16 36 6.6	10♊ 3.9	24♉39.0	10♏51.8	15♊53.3	0♉17.6	2♊11.9	5♋23.9	28♓21.0	15♍30.8	20♏16.7	15♍48.7
2	16 40 3.2	11 1.4	24 35.8	24 33.3	18 2.6	1 26.7	2 54.5	5 36.8	28 24.7	15 31.3	20 R 15.2	15 48.9
3	16 43 59.7	11 58.8	24 32.7	8♐ 1.4	20 10.5	2 35.9	3 37.0	5 49.8	28 28.5	15 31.8	20 13.7	15 49.1
4	16 47 56.3	12 56.3	24 29.5	21 14.4	22 17.0	3 45.2	4 19.4	6 2.8	28 32.1	15 32.4	20 12.2	15 49.3
5	16 51 52.9	13 53.7	24 26.3	4♑11.5	24 21.8	4 54.5	5 1.8	6 15.9	28 35.6	15 33.1	20 10.8	15 49.5
6	16 55 49.4	14 51.1	24 23.1	16 52.4	26 24.7	6 3.9	5 44.2	6 29.0	28 39.1	15 33.7	20 9.3	15 49.8
7	16 59 46.0	15 48.5	24 20.0	29 18.2	28 25.6	7 13.4	6 26.5	6 42.1	28 42.4	15 34.5	20 7.9	15 50.1
8	17 3 42.5	16 45.9	24 16.8	11♒30.8	0♋24.4	8 23.0	7 8.7	6 55.2	28 45.7	15 35.3	20 6.5	15 50.5
9	17 7 39.1	17 43.3	24 13.6	23 33.1	2 20.9	9 32.6	7 51.0	7 8.4	28 48.9	15 36.1	20 5.0	15 50.9
10	17 11 35.6	18 40.7	24 10.4	5♓28.7	4 15.2	10 42.4	8 33.2	7 21.7	28 52.1	15 37.1	20 3.7	15 51.3
11	17 15 32.2	19 38.0	24 7.3	17 21.7	6 7.1	11 52.2	9 15.3	7 34.9	28 55.1	15 38.0	20 2.3	15 51.8
12	17 19 28.8	20 35.4	24 4.1	29 16.8	7 56.6	13 2.0	9 57.3	7 48.2	28 58.0	15 39.0	20 1.0	15 52.3
13	17 23 25.3	21 32.7	24 .9	11♈18.7	9 43.7	14 11.9	10 39.3	8 1.5	29 .9	15 40.0	19 59.6	15 52.8
14	17 27 21.9	22 30.1	23 57.7	23 32.0	11 28.3	15 21.9	11 21.3	8 14.8	29 3.6	15 41.2	19 58.3	15 53.3
15	17 31 18.4	23 27.4	23 54.5	6♉ 1.0	13 10.4	16 31.9	12 3.2	8 28.1	29 6.3	15 42.3	19 57.0	15 53.9
16	17 35 15.0	24 24.7	23 51.4	18 49.1	14 50.0	17 42.0	12 45.0	8 41.5	29 8.8	15 43.5	19 55.7	15 54.5
17	17 39 11.6	25 22.0	23 48.2	1♊58.4	16 27.1	18 52.2	13 26.8	8 54.9	29 11.3	15 44.8	19 54.5	15 55.1
18	17 43 8.1	26 19.3	23 45.0	15 29.7	18 1.7	20 2.4	14 8.6	9 8.3	29 13.6	15 46.1	19 53.2	15 55.7
19	17 47 4.7	27 16.6	23 41.8	29 21.7	19 33.7	21 12.7	14 50.3	9 21.7	29 15.9	15 47.4	19 52.0	15 56.4
20	17 51 1.2	28 13.9	23 38.7	13♋31.3	21 3.1	22 23.0	15 32.0	9 35.1	29 18.1	15 48.8	19 50.8	15 57.1
21	17 54 57.8	29 11.2	23 35.5	27 53.8	22 29.9	23 33.4	16 13.6	9 48.6	29 20.2	15 50.3	19 49.6	15 57.9
22	17 58 54.3	0♋ 8.5	23 32.3	12♌23.3	23 54.1	24 43.8	16 55.1	10 2.1	29 22.2	15 51.8	19 48.5	15 58.7
23	18 2 50.9	1 5.7	23 29.1	26 53.9	25 15.7	25 54.3	17 36.6	10 15.6	29 24.1	15 53.4	19 47.3	15 59.5
24	18 6 47.5	2 3.0	23 26.0	11♍20.2	26 34.6	27 4.8	18 18.1	10 29.1	29 25.9	15 55.0	19 46.2	16 .3
25	18 10 44.0	3 .2	23 22.8	25 38.1	27 50.7	28 15.4	18 59.5	10 42.6	29 27.6	15 56.6	19 45.2	16 1.2
26	18 14 40.6	3 57.5	23 19.6	9♎44.9	29 4.0	29 26.1	19 40.8	10 56.1	29 29.1	15 58.3	19 44.1	16 2.1
27	18 18 37.1	4 54.7	23 16.4	23 39.3	0♌14.5	0♊36.8	20 22.1	11 9.6	29 30.6	16 .1	19 43.1	16 3.0
28	18 22 33.7	5 51.9	23 13.3	7♏20.9	1 22.0	1 47.5	21 3.3	11 23.1	29 32.0	16 1.8	19 42.0	16 3.9
29	18 26 30.3	6 49.1	23 10.1	20 50.0	2 26.5	2 58.3	21 44.5	11 36.7	29 33.3	16 3.7	19 41.1	16 4.9
30	18 30 26.8	7 46.3	23 6.9	4♐ 6.7	3 28.0	4 9.2	22 25.7	11 50.2	29 34.5	16 5.6	19 40.1	16 5.9

LATITUDE

DAY	SID. TIME	☉	☊	☽	☿	♀	♂	♃	♄	♅	♆	♇
1	16 36 6.6	0 .0	0 .0	1N19.1	1N13.9	2S 6.3	0N 8.7	0N .1	2S 4.7	0N46.5	1N48.3	14N41.0
4	16 47 56.3	0 .0	0 .0	2S18.0	1 35.8	2 7.0	0 10.6	0 .4	2 5.5	0 46.4	1 48.3	14 39.8
7	16 59 46.0	0 .0	0 .0	4 42.9	1 51.6	2 6.9	0 12.5	0 .7	2 6.2	0 46.2	1 48.2	14 38.6
10	17 11 35.6	0 .0	0 .0	5 9.0	2 .7	2 5.9	0 14.4	0 1.0	2 7.0	0 46.1	1 48.1	14 37.4
13	17 23 25.3	0 .0	0 .0	3 37.5	2 3.0	2 4.2	0 16.3	0 1.3	2 7.7	0 46.0	1 48.0	14 36.2
16	17 35 15.0	0 .0	0 .0	0 34.6	1 58.7	2 1.7	0 18.1	0 1.6	2 8.5	0 45.9	1 47.9	14 35.0
19	17 47 4.7	0 .0	0 .0	2N55.9	1 47.9	1 58.4	0 20.0	0 1.9	2 9.3	0 45.7	1 47.8	14 33.9
22	17 58 54.3	0 .0	0 .0	5 3.4	1 31.1	1 54.5	0 21.8	0 2.1	2 10.1	0 45.6	1 47.6	14 32.7
25	18 10 44.0	0 .0	0 .0	4 26.7	1 8.7	1 50.0	0 23.7	0 2.4	2 10.9	0 45.5	1 47.5	14 31.6
28	18 22 33.7	0 .0	0 .0	1 32.9	0 41.0	1 44.9	0 25.5	0 2.7	2 11.7	0 45.4	1 47.4	14 30.5

RIGHT ASCENSION

DAY	SID. TIME	☉	☊	☽	☿	♀	♂	♃	♄	♅	♆	♇
1	16 36 6.6	8♊25.8	22♉17.4	8♏51.7	14♊32.0	28♈56.3	0♊ 4.9	5♋52.8	29♓18.8	16♍58.1	18♏20.2	22♍54.5
2	16 40 3.2	9 27.2	22 14.1	22 12.7	16 52.1	0♉ 2.2	0 49.4	6 6.9	29 22.4	16 58.5	18 R 18.7	22 54.5
3	16 43 59.7	10 28.6	22 10.9	6♐ 3.4	19 11.4	1 8.3	1 34.0	6 21.0	29 25.9	16 58.9	18 17.2	22 54.5
4	16 47 56.3	11 30.2	22 7.6	20 17.9	21 29.8	2 14.6	2 18.6	6 35.2	29 29.3	16 59.5	18 15.7	22 54.5
5	16 51 52.9	12 31.8	22 4.4	4♑41.0	23 46.8	3 21.1	3 3.2	6 49.4	29 32.6	17 .0	18 14.2	22 D 54.6
6	16 55 49.4	13 33.6	22 1.1	18 52.1	26 2.2	4 27.9	3 47.8	7 3.6	29 35.9	17 .7	18 12.8	22 54.7
7	16 59 46.0	14 35.4	21 57.8	2♒32.1	28 15.7	5 34.9	4 32.5	7 17.9	29 39.1	17 1.3	18 11.3	22 54.8
8	17 3 42.5	15 37.3	21 54.6	15 29.5	0♋27.0	6 42.1	5 17.2	7 32.2	29 42.2	17 2.0	18 9.9	22 54.9
9	17 7 39.1	16 39.2	21 51.3	27 41.7	2 35.9	7 49.6	6 1.9	7 46.6	29 45.2	17 2.8	18 8.5	22 55.1
10	17 11 35.6	17 41.3	21 48.1	9♓14.2	4 42.4	8 57.4	6 46.7	8 1.0	29 48.2	17 3.7	18 7.1	22 55.4
11	17 15 32.2	18 43.4	21 44.8	20 17.2	6 46.1	10 5.4	7 31.5	8 15.4	29 51.1	17 4.5	18 5.7	22 55.6
12	17 19 28.8	19 45.6	21 41.6	1♈ 3.9	8 47.0	11 13.7	8 16.3	8 29.8	29 53.9	17 5.4	18 4.4	22 55.9
13	17 23 25.3	20 47.8	21 38.3	11 49.0	10 45.0	12 22.2	9 1.1	8 44.2	29 56.6	17 6.4	18 3.0	22 56.2
14	17 27 21.9	21 50.1	21 35.1	22 48.0	12 40.0	13 31.0	9 45.9	8 58.7	29 59.2	17 7.4	18 1.7	22 56.5
15	17 31 18.4	22 52.4	21 31.8	4♉16.9	14 31.8	14 40.1	10 30.8	9 13.2	0♈ 1.7	17 8.4	18 .4	22 56.9
16	17 35 15.0	23 54.8	21 28.6	16 31.5	16 20.5	15 49.5	11 15.6	9 27.7	0 4.2	17 9.5	17 59.1	22 57.3
17	17 39 11.6	24 57.1	21 25.3	29 44.6	18 6.0	16 59.1	12 .5	9 42.2	0 6.6	17 10.7	17 57.8	22 57.7
18	17 43 8.1	25 59.5	21 22.1	14♊ 2.2	19 48.2	18 9.0	12 45.4	9 56.8	0 8.8	17 11.9	17 56.6	22 58.1
19	17 47 4.7	27 2.0	21 18.8	29 17.3	21 27.2	19 19.2	13 30.3	10 11.4	0 11.0	17 13.1	17 55.3	22 58.6
20	17 51 1.2	28 4.4	21 15.6	15♋ 7.6	23 2.9	20 29.6	14 15.1	10 26.0	0 13.1	17 14.4	17 54.1	22 59.1
21	17 54 57.8	29 6.8	21 12.3	0♌60.0	24 35.2	21 40.4	15 .0	10 40.6	0 15.1	17 15.7	17 52.9	22 59.7
22	17 58 54.3	0♋ 9.2	21 9.1	16 22.9	26 4.1	22 51.4	15 44.9	10 55.2	0 17.1	17 17.1	17 51.8	23 .2
23	18 2 50.9	1 11.7	21 5.8	0♍57.9	27 29.7	24 2.7	16 29.8	11 9.8	0 18.9	17 18.6	17 50.6	23 .8
24	18 6 47.5	2 14.0	21 2.6	14 42.5	28 51.9	25 14.3	17 14.7	11 24.4	0 20.7	17 20.0	17 49.5	23 1.4
25	18 10 44.0	3 16.4	20 59.4	27 46.0	0♌10.6	26 26.2	17 59.5	11 39.1	0 22.3	17 21.5	17 48.4	23 2.1
26	18 14 40.6	4 18.8	20 56.1	10♎23.8	1 25.9	27 38.3	18 44.4	11 53.7	0 23.9	17 23.1	17 47.3	23 2.7
27	18 18 37.1	5 21.0	20 52.9	22 53.3	2 37.6	28 50.8	19 29.2	12 8.4	0 25.4	17 24.7	17 46.3	23 3.5
28	18 22 33.7	6 23.3	20 49.6	5♏30.9	3 45.8	0♊ 3.5	20 14.1	12 23.1	0 26.8	17 26.3	17 45.2	23 4.2
29	18 26 30.3	7 25.5	20 46.4	18 29.7	4 50.4	1 16.5	20 58.9	12 37.7	0 28.1	17 28.0	17 44.2	23 4.9
30	18 30 26.8	8 27.7	20 43.1	1♐57.2	5 51.4	2 29.8	21 43.6	12 52.4	0 29.3	17 29.8	17 43.2	23 5.7

DECLINATION

DAY	SID. TIME	☉	☊	☽	☿	♀	♂	♃	♄	♅	♆	♇
1	16 36 6.6	21N57.9	0N19.8	13S50.1	23N55.3	9N36.3	20N44.9	23N20.2	2S33.8	6N25.6	16S 4.8	19N 4.8
4	16 47 56.3	22 21.3	0 19.8	25 27.0	24 48.9	10 46.7	21 11.2	23 18.8	2 30.1	6 24.8	16 3.6	19 3.5
7	16 59 46.0	22 41.3	0 19.7	24 54.6	25 17.8	11 55.6	21 35.7	23 17.2	2 26.6	6 23.9	16 2.6	19 2.0
10	17 11 35.6	22 57.7	0 19.7	14 17.3	25 23.3	13 2.7	21 58.3	23 15.4	2 23.5	6 22.8	16 1.5	19 .5
13	17 23 25.3	23 10.5	0 19.7	1N 8.3	25 8.0	14 7.6	22 19.1	23 13.4	2 20.7	6 21.5	16 .6	18 58.8
16	17 35 15.0	23 19.6	0 19.6	16 52.2	24 35.1	15 10.0	22 37.9	23 11.2	2 18.2	6 20.1	15 59.6	18 57.1
19	17 47 4.7	23 25.0	0 19.6	26 22.5	23 47.9	16 9.6	22 54.8	23 8.7	2 16.1	6 18.4	15 58.7	18 55.2
22	17 58 54.3	23 26.7	0 19.5	21 56.2	22 49.6	17 6.2	23 9.8	23 6.1	2 14.4	6 16.6	15 57.9	18 53.3
25	18 10 44.0	23 24.7	0 19.5	5 48.8	21 43.2	17 59.3	23 22.9	23 3.2	2 13.0	6 14.6	15 57.1	18 51.3
28	18 22 33.7	23 18.9	0 19.5	12S30.2	20 31.6	18 48.7	23 34.0	23 .1	2 11.9	6 12.5	15 56.4	18 49.2

JULY 1966

LONGITUDE

DAY	EPHEM. SID. TIME	☉	☊	☽	☿	♀	♂	♃	♄	♅	♆	♇
	h m s	° ′	° ′	° ′	° ′	° ′	° ′	° ′	° ′	° ′	° ′	° ′
1	18 34 23.4	8♋43.5	23♉ 3.7	17♐11.5	4♌26.4	5♊20.1	23♊ 6.8	12♋ 3.8	29♓35.7	16♍ 7.6	19♏39.2	16♍ 7.0
2	18 38 19.9	9 40.7	23 .5	0♑ 4.3	5 21.4	6 31.1	23 47.8	12 17.4	29 36.7	16 9.5	19R38.3	16 8.1
3	18 42 16.5	10 37.9	22 57.4	12 45.3	6 13.0	7 42.1	24 28.8	12 30.9	29 37.6	16 11.6	19 37.4	16 9.2
4	18 46 13.1	11 35.1	22 54.2	25 14.4	7 1.2	8 53.1	25 9.8	12 44.5	29 38.4	16 13.6	19 36.5	16 10.3
5	18 50 9.6	12 32.3	22 51.0	7♒32.3	7 45.8	10 4.2	25 50.7	12 58.0	29 39.1	16 15.7	19 35.7	16 11.4
6	18 54 6.2	13 29.4	22 47.8	19 40.1	8 26.6	11 15.4	26 31.5	13 11.6	29 39.7	16 17.9	19 34.9	16 12.6
7	18 58 2.7	14 26.6	22 44.7	1♓39.5	9 3.6	12 26.6	27 12.3	13 25.2	29 40.2	16 20.1	19 34.1	16 13.8
8	19 1 59.3	15 23.8	22 41.5	13 33.3	9 36.6	13 37.9	27 53.1	13 38.7	29 40.6	16 22.3	19 33.4	16 15.0
9	19 5 55.8	16 21.0	22 38.3	25 24.9	10 5.5	14 49.2	28 33.8	13 52.3	29 40.9	16 24.6	19 32.6	16 16.3
10	19 9 52.4	17 18.2	22 35.1	7♈18.3	10 30.1	16 .6	29 14.4	14 5.8	29 41.1	16 26.9	19 31.9	16 17.5
11	19 13 49.0	18 15.4	22 32.0	19 18.4	10 50.3	17 12.0	29 55.0	14 19.3	29 41.2	16 29.3	19 31.3	16 18.8
12	19 17 45.5	19 12.7	22 28.8	1♉30.2	11 6.1	18 23.5	0♋35.6	14 32.9	29 41.2	16 31.7	19 30.6	16 20.2
13	19 21 42.1	20 9.9	22 25.6	13 58.6	11 17.2	19 35.0	1 16.1	14 46.4	29R41.1	16 34.1	19 30.0	16 21.5
14	19 25 38.6	21 7.1	22 22.4	26 48.2	11 23.6	20 46.6	1 56.6	14 59.9	29 40.9	16 36.6	19 29.5	16 22.9
15	19 29 35.2	22 4.4	22 19.3	10♊ 2.6	11 25.2	21 58.2	2 37.0	15 13.4	29 40.6	16 39.2	19 28.9	16 24.3
16	19 33 31.7	23 1.6	22 16.1	23 43.6	11R22.0	23 9.9	3 17.4	15 26.9	29 40.2	16 41.7	19 28.4	16 25.7
17	19 37 28.3	23 58.9	22 12.9	7♋50.9	11 14.0	24 21.6	3 57.8	15 40.4	29 39.7	16 44.3	19 27.9	16 27.2
18	19 41 24.9	24 56.2	22 9.7	22 20.9	11 1.2	25 33.4	4 38.1	15 53.8	29 39.1	16 47.0	19 27.4	16 28.6
19	19 45 21.4	25 53.4	22 6.5	7♌ 7.7	10 43.8	26 45.2	5 18.3	16 7.3	29 38.4	16 49.7	19 27.0	16 30.1
20	19 49 18.0	26 50.7	22 3.4	22 2.8	10 21.8	27 57.1	5 58.5	16 20.7	29 37.6	16 52.4	19 26.6	16 31.6
21	19 53 14.5	27 48.0	22 .2	6♍57.3	9 55.5	29 9.0	6 38.6	16 34.1	29 36.7	16 55.1	19 26.2	16 33.2
22	19 57 11.1	28 45.4	21 57.0	21 43.0	9 25.3	0♋21.0	7 18.8	16 47.6	29 35.7	16 58.0	19 26.0	16 34.8
23	20 1 7.7	29 42.7	21 53.8	6♎13.4	8 51.4	1 33.0	7 58.8	17 .9	29 34.6	17 .8	19 25.7	16 36.4
24	20 5 4.2	0♌40.0	21 50.7	20 25.0	8 14.4	2 45.0	8 38.8	17 14.3	29 33.4	17 3.6	19 25.4	16 38.0
25	20 9 .8	1 37.3	21 47.5	4♏16.4	7 34.7	3 57.1	9 18.8	17 27.6	29 32.1	17 6.5	19 25.1	16 39.6
26	20 12 57.3	2 34.6	21 44.3	17 48.4	6 53.0	5 9.2	9 58.7	17 40.9	29 30.7	17 9.5	19 24.9	16 41.2
27	20 16 53.9	3 31.9	21 41.1	1♐ 2.8	6 10.0	6 21.4	10 38.5	17 54.2	29 29.2	17 12.4	19 24.7	16 42.9
28	20 20 50.4	4 29.2	21 38.0	14 1.9	5 26.4	7 33.6	11 18.4	18 7.4	29 27.6	17 15.4	19 24.6	16 44.6
29	20 24 47.0	5 26.6	21 34.8	26 47.8	4 43.0	8 45.9	11 58.1	18 20.7	29 25.9	17 18.4	19 24.5	16 46.3
30	20 28 43.5	6 23.9	21 31.6	9♑22.4	4 .6	9 58.2	12 37.8	18 33.9	29 24.1	17 21.5	19 24.4	16 48.0
31	20 32 40.1	7 21.3	21 28.4	21 47.2	3 19.9	11 10.5	13 17.5	18 47.0	29 22.3	17 24.6	19 24.4	16 49.8

LATITUDE

DAY	EPHEM. SID. TIME	☉	☊	☽	☿	♀	♂	♃	♄	♅	♆	♇
1	18 34 23.4	0 .0	0 .0	1S58.4	0N 8.6	1S39.2	0N27.3	0N 3.0	2S12.5	0N45.3	1N47.2	14N29.4
4	18 46 13.1	0 .0	0 .0	4 28.2	0S28.2	1 33.1	0 29.1	0 3.3	2 13.3	0 45.1	1 47.1	14 28.4
7	18 58 2.7	0 .0	0 .0	5 3.7	1 8.5	1 26.4	0 30.8	0 3.6	2 14.1	0 45.0	1 46.9	14 27.3
10	19 9 52.4	0 .0	0 .0	3 42.7	1 51.3	1 19.4	0 32.6	0 3.8	2 15.0	0 44.9	1 46.8	14 26.3
13	19 21 42.1	0 .0	0 .0	0 52.3	2 35.3	1 12.1	0 34.3	0 4.1	2 15.8	0 44.8	1 46.6	14 25.4
16	19 33 31.7	0 .0	0 .0	2N32.8	3 18.3	1 4.4	0 36.1	0 4.4	2 16.6	0 44.7	1 46.5	14 24.5
19	19 45 21.4	0 .0	0 .0	4 51.3	3 57.7	0 56.5	0 37.8	0 4.7	2 17.4	0 44.6	1 46.3	14 23.6
22	19 57 11.1	0 .0	0 .0	4 26.1	4 29.9	0 48.4	0 39.5	0 5.0	2 18.2	0 44.5	1 46.1	14 22.8
25	20 9 .8	0 .0	0 .0	1 36.8	4 51.1	0 40.1	0 41.2	0 5.3	2 18.9	0 44.4	1 46.0	14 22.0
28	20 20 50.4	0 .0	0 .0	1S50.0	4 58.0	0 31.8	0 42.9	0 5.6	2 19.7	0 44.4	1 45.8	14 21.3
31	20 32 40.1	0 .0	0 .0	4 19.0	4 49.1	0 23.4	0 44.6	0 5.9	2 20.5	0 44.3	1 45.6	14 20.6

RIGHT ASCENSION

DAY	EPHEM. SID. TIME	☉	☊	☽	☿	♀	♂	♃	♄	♅	♆	♇
1	18 34 23.4	9♋29.8	20♉39.9	15♐52.5	6♌48.7	3♊43.4	22♊28.5	13♋ 7.1	0♈30.5	17♍31.6	17♏42.3	23♍ 6.6
2	18 38 19.9	10 31.8	20 36.7	0♑ 4.8	7 42.2	4 57.2	23 13.2	13 21.8	0 31.5	17 33.4	17R41.4	23 7.4
3	18 42 16.5	11 33.8	20 33.4	14 16.0	8 31.9	6 11.3	23 57.9	13 36.4	0 32.4	17 35.3	17 40.5	23 8.3
4	18 46 13.1	12 35.7	20 30.2	28 5.7	9 17.7	7 25.7	24 42.6	13 51.1	0 33.3	17 37.2	17 39.6	23 9.2
5	18 50 9.6	13 37.5	20 26.9	11♒18.3	9 59.5	8 40.3	25 27.3	14 5.7	0 34.0	17 39.1	17 38.8	23 10.1
6	18 54 6.2	14 39.3	20 23.7	23 46.8	10 37.2	9 55.2	26 11.9	14 20.4	0 34.7	17 41.1	17 38.0	23 11.0
7	18 58 2.7	15 40.9	20 20.5	5♓32.6	11 10.8	11 10.4	26 56.5	14 35.0	0 35.3	17 43.1	17 37.2	23 12.0
8	19 1 59.3	16 42.5	20 17.2	16 43.7	11 40.2	12 25.8	27 41.1	14 49.7	0 35.7	17 45.2	17 36.4	23 13.0
9	19 5 55.8	17 44.0	20 14.0	27 31.7	12 5.2	13 41.4	28 25.6	15 4.3	0 36.1	17 47.3	17 35.7	23 14.0
10	19 9 52.4	18 45.4	20 10.7	8♈10.5	12 25.8	14 57.3	29 10.1	15 18.9	0 36.4	17 49.4	17 35.0	23 15.1
11	19 13 49.0	19 46.7	20 7.5	18 55.2	12 42.0	16 13.4	29 54.6	15 33.5	0 36.6	17 51.6	17 34.3	23 16.2
12	19 17 45.5	20 47.8	20 4.3	0♉ 1.9	12 53.5	17 29.7	0♋39.0	15 48.1	0 36.7	17 53.8	17 33.6	23 17.3
13	19 21 42.1	21 48.9	20 1.0	11 47.1	13 .5	18 46.2	1 23.3	16 2.7	0 36.7	17 56.1	17 33.0	23 18.4
14	19 25 38.6	22 49.9	19 57.8	24 26.3	13 2.8	20 2.9	2 7.7	16 17.3	0R36.6	17 58.3	17 32.4	23 19.5
15	19 29 35.2	23 50.7	19 54.6	8♊10.7	13R .3	21 19.9	2 51.9	16 31.8	0 36.5	18 .7	17 31.8	23 20.7
16	19 33 31.7	24 51.4	19 51.3	23 2.1	12 53.2	22 37.0	3 36.1	16 46.3	0 36.2	18 3.0	17 31.3	23 21.9
17	19 37 28.3	25 52.1	19 48.1	8♋46.7	12 41.5	23 54.2	4 20.3	17 .9	0 35.8	18 5.4	17 30.8	23 23.1
18	19 41 24.9	26 52.5	19 44.9	24 55.3	12 25.2	25 11.6	5 4.4	17 15.4	0 35.4	18 7.9	17 30.3	23 24.4
19	19 45 21.4	27 52.9	19 41.6	10♌51.9	12 4.4	26 29.2	5 48.4	17 29.8	0 34.8	18 10.3	17 29.9	23 25.7
20	19 49 18.0	28 53.1	19 38.4	26 8.4	11 39.5	27 46.9	6 32.4	17 44.3	0 34.2	18 12.8	17 29.5	23 26.9
21	19 53 14.5	29 53.1	19 35.2	10♍32.9	11 10.6	29 4.7	7 16.3	17 58.7	0 33.5	18 15.4	17 29.1	23 28.3
22	19 57 11.1	0♌53.1	19 31.9	24 9.2	10 38.0	0♋22.7	8 .2	18 13.1	0 32.7	18 18.0	17 28.8	23 29.6
23	20 1 7.7	1 52.9	19 28.7	7♎10.3	10 2.2	1 40.7	8 43.9	18 27.5	0 31.8	18 20.6	17 28.4	23 31.0
24	20 5 4.2	2 52.5	19 25.5	19 52.9	9 23.6	2 58.9	9 27.6	18 41.9	0 30.8	18 23.2	17 28.2	23 32.4
25	20 9 .8	3 52.0	19 22.2	2♏34.2	8 42.8	4 17.0	10 11.2	18 56.2	0 29.7	18 25.9	17 27.9	23 33.8
26	20 12 57.3	4 51.3	19 19.0	15 28.3	8 .4	5 35.3	10 54.8	19 10.4	0 28.5	18 28.6	17 27.7	23 35.2
27	20 16 53.9	5 50.5	19 15.8	28 44.9	7 17.0	6 53.6	11 38.2	19 24.7	0 27.2	18 31.3	17 27.5	23 36.7
28	20 20 50.4	6 49.5	19 12.5	12♐26.3	6 33.4	8 11.9	12 21.6	19 38.9	0 25.9	18 34.1	17 27.3	23 38.1
29	20 24 47.0	7 48.4	19 9.3	26 25.9	5 50.3	9 30.3	13 4.9	19 53.1	0 24.4	18 36.9	17 27.2	23 39.6
30	20 28 43.5	8 47.1	19 6.1	10♑29.4	5 8.5	10 48.6	13 48.1	20 7.2	0 22.9	18 39.7	17 27.1	23 41.1
31	20 32 40.1	9 45.6	19 2.9	24 18.2	4 28.8	12 7.0	14 31.2	20 21.3	0 21.3	18 42.5	17 27.0	23 42.7

DECLINATION

DAY	EPHEM. SID. TIME	☉	☊	☽	☿	♀	♂	♃	♄	♅	♆	♇
1	18 34 23.4	23N 9.5	0N19.4	24S47.5	19N17.6	19N34.1	23N43.2	22N56.8	2S11.2	6N10.2	15S55.8	18N47.0
4	18 46 13.1	22 56.4	0 19.4	25 29.2	18 4.1	20 15.3	23 50.4	22 53.3	2 10.9	6 7.7	15 55.2	18 44.7
7	18 58 2.7	22 39.7	0 19.3	15 36.6	16 53.7	20 51.8	23 55.7	22 49.6	2 10.9	6 5.1	15 54.7	18 42.4
10	19 9 52.4	22 19.5	0 19.3	0 30.6	15 49.4	21 23.6	23 59.2	22 45.8	2 11.3	6 2.3	15 54.3	18 40.0
13	19 21 42.1	21 55.8	0 19.2	15N12.3	14 54.4	21 50.3	24 .7	22 41.7	2 12.1	5 59.4	15 54.0	18 37.6
16	19 33 31.7	21 28.8	0 19.2	25 50.5	14 11.6	22 11.8	24 .3	22 37.4	2 13.2	5 56.4	15 53.7	18 35.1
19	19 45 21.4	20 58.4	0 19.2	23 11.2	13 44.0	22 27.9	23 58.1	22 33.0	2 14.6	5 53.2	15 53.5	18 32.6
22	19 57 11.1	20 24.9	0 19.1	7 21.5	13 33.6	22 38.3	23 54.1	22 28.4	2 16.4	5 49.9	15 53.4	18 30.0
25	20 9 .8	19 48.2	0 19.1	11S25.6	13 41.2	22 43.1	23 48.2	22 23.6	2 18.6	5 46.5	15 53.3	18 27.3
28	20 20 50.4	19 8.6	0 19.0	24 18.6	14 5.6	22 42.0	23 40.6	22 18.6	2 21.1	5 42.9	15 53.3	18 24.7
31	20 32 40.1	18 26.2	0 19.0	25 56.5	14 43.5	22 35.2	23 31.2	22 13.5	2 23.9	5 39.3	15 53.4	18 22.0

AUGUST 1966

LONGITUDE

DAY	EPHEM. SID. TIME h m s	☉ ° ′	☊ ° ′	☽ ° ′	☿ ° ′	♀ ° ′	♂ ° ′	♃ ° ′	♄ ° ′	♅ ° ′	♆ ° ′	♇ ° ′
1	20 36 36.7	8♌18.7	21♉25.3	4♒ 3.2	2♌41.7	12♋22.9	13♋57.1	19♋ .1	29♓20.3	17♍27.7	19♏24.3	16♍51.5
2	20 40 33.2	9 16.0	21 22.1	16 11.2	2R 6.8	13 35.4	14 36.7	19 13.2	29R18.2	17 30.8	19 24.3	16 53.3
3	20 44 29.8	10 13.4	21 18.9	28 12.3	1 35.9	14 47.9	15 16.2	19 26.3	29 16.1	17 34.0	19D24.4	16 55.1
4	20 48 26.3	11 10.9	21 15.7	10♓ 7.6	1 9.6	16 .4	15 55.7	19 39.3	29 13.9	17 37.2	19 24.5	16 56.9
5	20 52 22.9	12 8.3	21 12.5	21 59.0	0 48.4	17 13.0	16 35.2	19 52.3	29 11.5	17 40.4	19 24.6	16 58.7
6	20 56 19.4	13 5.7	21 9.4	3♈49.2	0 32.8	18 25.7	17 14.6	20 5.3	29 9.1	17 43.7	19 24.7	17 .6
7	21 0 16.0	14 3.2	21 6.2	15 41.5	0 23.3	19 38.4	17 54.0	20 18.2	29 6.6	17 46.9	19 24.9	17 2.4
8	21 4 12.6	15 .7	21 3.0	27 40.0	0 20.1	20 51.1	18 33.3	20 31.1	29 4.0	17 50.3	19 25.1	17 4.3
9	21 8 9.1	15 58.2	20 59.8	9♉49.5	0D23.6	22 3.9	19 12.6	20 44.0	29 1.4	17 53.6	19 25.3	17 6.2
10	21 12 5.7	16 55.8	20 56.7	22 14.9	0 33.8	23 16.7	19 51.8	20 56.8	28 58.6	17 56.9	19 25.6	17 8.1
11	21 16 2.2	17 53.3	20 53.5	5♊ 1.5	0 51.0	24 29.6	20 31.0	21 9.5	28 55.8	18 .3	19 25.9	17 10.1
12	21 19 58.8	18 50.9	20 50.3	18 13.7	1 15.2	25 42.6	21 10.2	21 22.3	28 52.9	18 3.8	19 26.3	17 12.0
13	21 23 55.3	19 48.6	20 47.1	1♋54.6	1 46.3	26 55.6	21 49.3	21 35.0	28 49.9	18 7.2	19 26.7	17 14.0
14	21 27 51.9	20 46.2	20 43.9	16 5.1	2 24.4	28 8.6	22 28.3	21 47.6	28 46.8	18 10.6	19 27.1	17 16.0
15	21 31 48.4	21 43.8	20 40.8	0♌42.8	3 9.4	29 21.6	23 7.4	22 .2	28 43.6	18 14.1	19 27.5	17 17.9
16	21 35 45.0	22 41.5	20 37.6	15 42.0	4 1.1	0♌34.8	23 46.3	22 12.7	28 40.4	18 17.6	19 28.0	17 19.9
17	21 39 41.6	23 39.2	20 34.4	0♍53.7	4 59.4	1 47.9	24 25.3	22 25.2	28 37.1	18 21.1	19 28.5	17 21.9
18	21 43 38.1	24 36.9	20 31.2	16 7.0	6 4.1	3 1.1	25 4.1	22 37.6	28 33.7	18 24.6	19 29.0	17 23.9
19	21 47 34.7	25 34.7	20 28.1	1♎11.2	7 14.9	4 14.4	25 43.0	22 50.0	28 30.3	18 28.2	19 29.5	17 26.0
20	21 51 31.2	26 32.4	20 24.9	15 57.7	8 31.6	5 27.6	26 21.8	23 2.3	28 26.7	18 31.7	19 30.1	17 28.0
21	21 55 27.8	27 30.2	20 21.7	0♏21.0	9 53.9	6 41.0	27 .5	23 14.6	28 23.1	18 35.3	19 30.8	17 30.1
22	21 59 24.3	28 28.0	20 18.5	14 18.8	11 21.4	7 54.3	27 39.2	23 26.8	28 19.5	18 38.9	19 31.4	17 32.1
23	22 3 20.9	29 25.8	20 15.4	27 51.6	12 53.6	9 7.7	28 17.8	23 38.9	28 15.8	18 42.5	19 32.1	17 34.2
24	22 7 17.4	0♍23.7	20 12.2	11♐ 1.8	14 30.3	10 21.2	28 56.4	23 51.0	28 12.0	18 46.1	19 32.8	17 36.3
25	22 11 14.0	1 21.5	20 9.0	23 52.5	16 11.0	11 34.6	29 35.0	24 3.0	28 8.2	18 49.8	19 33.6	17 38.3
26	22 15 10.5	2 19.4	20 5.8	6♑27.5	17 55.1	12 48.1	0♌13.5	24 15.0	28 4.3	18 53.4	19 34.4	17 40.4
27	22 19 7.1	3 17.3	20 2.6	18 49.9	19 42.4	14 1.7	0 52.0	24 26.9	28 .3	18 57.1	19 35.2	17 42.5
28	22 23 3.7	4 15.2	19 59.5	1♒ 2.5	21 32.2	15 15.3	1 30.4	24 38.7	27 56.3	19 .8	19 36.0	17 44.6
29	22 27 .2	5 13.1	19 56.3	13 7.7	23 24.3	16 28.9	2 8.8	24 50.4	27 52.2	19 4.5	19 36.9	17 46.7
30	22 30 56.8	6 11.1	19 53.1	25 7.1	25 18.1	17 42.6	2 47.1	25 2.1	27 48.1	19 8.2	19 37.8	17 48.9
31	22 34 53.3	7 9.1	19 49.9	7♓ 2.3	27 13.2	18 56.3	3 25.4	25 13.7	27 44.0	19 11.9	19 38.7	17 51.0

LATITUDE

DAY	EPHEM. SID. TIME	☉	☊	☽	☿	♀	♂	♃	♄	♅	♆	♇
1	20 36 36.7	0 .0	0 .0	4S45.5	4S42.7	0S20.6	0N45.1	0N 6.0	2S20.7	0N44.3	1N45.5	14N20.4
4	20 48 26.3	0 .0	0 .0	4 44.9	4 14.0	0 12.2	0 46.8	0 6.3	2 21.4	0 44.2	1 45.4	14 19.7
7	21 0 16.0	0 .0	0 .0	2 55.6	3 34.1	0 3.9	0 48.4	0 6.6	2 22.1	0 44.1	1 45.2	14 19.2
10	21 12 5.7	0 .0	0 .0	0N 5.8	2 46.9	0N 4.3	0 50.1	0 6.9	2 22.8	0 44.0	1 45.0	14 18.7
13	21 23 55.3	0 .0	0 .0	3 17.4	1 56.5	0 12.3	0 51.7	0 7.2	2 23.5	0 44.0	1 44.8	14 18.2
16	21 35 45.0	0 .0	0 .0	4 59.1	1 6.5	0 20.1	0 53.3	0 7.6	2 24.1	0 43.9	1 44.6	14 17.8
19	21 47 34.7	0 .0	0 .0	3 47.2	0 19.7	0 27.6	0 54.9	0 7.9	2 24.7	0 43.9	1 44.5	14 17.4
22	21 59 24.3	0 .0	0 .0	0 29.8	0N21.4	0 34.8	0 56.5	0 8.2	2 25.2	0 43.8	1 44.3	14 17.2
25	22 11 14.0	0 .0	0 .0	2S49.1	0 55.0	0 41.7	0 58.1	0 8.5	2 25.7	0 43.8	1 44.1	14 16.9
28	22 23 3.7	0 .0	0 .0	4 45.4	1 20.3	0 48.2	0 59.6	0 8.9	2 26.2	0 43.8	1 43.9	14 16.8
31	22 34 53.3	0 .0	0 .0	4 46.2	1 36.9	0 54.3	1 1.2	0 9.2	2 26.7	0 43.7	1 43.8	14 16.7

RIGHT ASCENSION

DAY	EPHEM. SID. TIME	☉	☊	☽	☿	♀	♂	♃	♄	♅	♆	♇
1	20 36 36.7	10♌44.0	18♉59.6	7♒36.3	3♌52.0	13♋25.4	15♋14.2	20♋35.4	0♈19.6	18♍45.4	17♏27.0	23♍44.2
2	20 40 33.2	11 42.3	18 56.4	20 14.0	3R18.7	14 43.7	15 57.2	20 49.4	0R17.8	18 48.3	17 27.0	23 45.8
3	20 44 29.8	12 40.4	18 53.2	2♓ 9.9	2 49.7	16 2.0	16 40.1	21 3.4	0 15.9	18 51.2	17 27.0	23 47.4
4	20 48 26.3	13 38.3	18 49.9	13 29.1	2 25.5	17 20.3	17 22.8	21 17.3	0 14.0	18 54.2	17D27.1	23 49.0
5	20 52 22.9	14 36.1	18 46.7	24 21.3	2 6.7	18 38.5	18 5.5	21 31.2	0 11.9	18 57.1	17 27.2	23 50.6
6	20 56 19.4	15 33.8	18 43.5	4♈58.7	1 53.9	19 56.6	18 48.1	21 45.1	0 9.8	19 .1	17 27.3	23 52.2
7	21 0 16.0	16 31.3	18 40.3	15 35.0	1 47.4	21 14.7	19 30.6	21 58.9	0 7.6	19 3.2	17 27.4	23 53.9
8	21 4 12.6	17 28.6	18 37.1	26 25.0	1 47.4	22 32.6	20 13.0	22 12.6	0 5.3	19 6.2	17 27.6	23 55.5
9	21 8 9.1	18 25.8	18 33.8	7♉44.4	1D54.4	23 50.5	20 55.3	22 26.3	0 3.0	19 9.3	17 27.8	23 57.2
10	21 12 5.7	19 22.9	18 30.6	19 48.5	2 8.5	25 8.2	21 37.5	22 40.0	0 .5	19 12.4	17 28.1	23 58.9
11	21 16 2.2	20 19.9	18 27.4	2♊50.8	2 29.8	26 25.8	22 19.6	22 53.6	29♓58.0	19 15.5	17 28.4	24 .7
12	21 19 58.8	21 16.7	18 24.2	16 58.7	2 58.3	27 43.3	23 1.7	23 7.2	29 55.5	19 18.7	17 28.8	24 2.5
13	21 23 55.3	22 13.4	18 20.9	2♋ 8.1	3 34.1	29 .7	23 43.6	23 20.7	29 52.8	19 21.8	17 29.1	24 4.2
14	21 27 51.9	23 9.9	18 17.7	17 59.8	4 17.1	0♌17.9	24 25.4	23 34.2	29 50.0	19 25.0	17 29.5	24 6.0
15	21 31 48.4	24 6.3	18 14.5	4♌ 2.5	5 7.1	1 34.9	25 7.1	23 47.6	29 47.2	19 28.2	17 29.9	24 7.8
16	21 35 45.0	25 2.5	18 11.3	19 44.6	6 4.1	2 51.7	25 48.7	24 .9	29 44.3	19 31.4	17 30.4	24 9.6
17	21 39 41.6	25 58.7	18 8.1	4♍45.3	7 7.7	4 8.4	26 30.2	24 14.2	29 41.4	19 34.6	17 30.8	24 11.4
18	21 43 38.1	26 54.7	18 4.8	18 59.8	8 17.7	5 24.9	27 11.5	24 27.4	29 38.4	19 37.9	17 31.3	24 13.2
19	21 47 34.7	27 50.5	18 1.6	2♎35.8	9 33.9	6 41.1	27 52.8	24 40.5	29 35.3	19 41.2	17 31.9	24 15.0
20	21 51 31.2	28 46.3	17 58.4	15 47.4	10 55.8	7 57.2	28 33.9	24 53.6	29 32.1	19 44.4	17 32.5	24 16.9
21	21 55 27.8	29 41.9	17 55.2	28 50.8	12 23.0	9 13.1	29 15.0	25 6.6	29 28.9	19 47.7	17 33.1	24 18.8
22	21 59 24.3	0♍37.4	17 52.0	12♏ .2	13 55.1	10 28.7	29 55.9	25 19.6	29 25.6	19 51.1	17 33.7	24 20.6
23	22 3 20.9	1 32.8	17 48.8	25 25.8	15 31.6	11 44.2	0♌36.7	25 32.5	29 22.3	19 54.4	17 34.4	24 22.5
24	22 7 17.4	2 28.0	17 45.5	9♐10.9	17 11.9	12 59.4	1 17.4	25 45.3	29 18.9	19 57.7	17 35.1	24 24.4
25	22 11 14.0	3 23.2	17 42.3	23 11.1	18 55.7	14 14.4	1 57.9	25 58.0	29 15.4	20 1.1	17 35.8	24 26.3
26	22 15 10.5	4 18.2	17 39.1	7♑14.0	20 42.2	15 29.2	2 38.4	26 10.7	29 11.9	20 4.5	17 36.6	24 28.2
27	22 19 7.1	5 13.1	17 35.9	21 3.5	22 31.1	16 43.7	3 18.7	26 23.3	29 8.3	20 7.8	17 37.4	24 30.2
28	22 23 3.7	6 8.0	17 32.7	4♒24.3	24 21.8	17 58.0	3 59.0	26 35.8	29 4.7	20 11.2	17 38.2	24 32.1
29	22 27 .2	7 2.7	17 29.5	17 7.0	26 13.7	19 12.1	4 39.1	26 48.2	29 1.0	20 14.6	17 39.1	24 34.1
30	22 30 56.8	7 57.3	17 26.3	29 9.1	28 6.5	20 25.9	5 19.1	27 .6	28 57.3	20 18.1	17 40.0	24 36.0
31	22 34 53.3	8 51.9	17 23.0	10♓34.5	29 59.8	21 39.6	5 58.9	27 12.8	28 53.6	20 21.5	17 40.9	24 38.0

DECLINATION

DAY	EPHEM. SID. TIME	☉	☊	☽	☿	♀	♂	♃	♄	♅	♆	♇
1	20 36 36.7	18N11.5	0N19.0	23S52.0	14N58.3	22N31.6	23N27.7	22N11.8	2S24.9	5N38.1	15S53.5	18N21.1
4	20 48 26.3	17 25.5	0 18.9	12 9.9	15 46.3	22 17.0	23 16.1	22 6.5	2 28.1	5 34.3	15 53.7	18 18.4
7	21 0 16.0	16 36.9	0 18.9	3N28.5	16 35.2	21 56.6	23 2.9	22 1.1	2 31.6	5 30.4	15 54.0	18 15.7
10	21 12 5.7	15 46.0	0 18.8	18 25.8	17 19.1	21 30.4	22 48.0	21 55.6	2 35.4	5 26.4	15 54.4	18 13.0
13	21 23 55.3	14 52.7	0 18.8	26 43.3	17 52.6	20 58.7	22 31.6	21 50.0	2 39.5	5 22.4	15 54.8	18 10.3
16	21 35 45.0	13 57.3	0 18.8	20 53.3	18 10.7	20 21.5	22 13.7	21 44.3	2 43.8	5 18.3	15 55.3	18 7.5
19	21 47 34.7	12 59.9	0 18.7	3 .1	18 8.8	19 39.0	21 54.3	21 38.5	2 48.4	5 14.1	15 55.9	18 4.8
22	21 59 24.3	12 .6	0 18.7	15S39.8	17 43.1	18 51.4	21 33.5	21 32.6	2 53.2	5 9.8	15 56.6	18 2.2
25	22 11 14.0	10 59.7	0 18.6	26 7.1	16 51.9	17 59.0	21 11.4	21 26.7	2 58.2	5 5.5	15 57.4	17 59.5
28	22 23 3.7	9 57.1	0 18.6	24 34.2	15 35.7	17 2.0	20 47.9	21 20.8	3 3.4	5 1.2	15 58.2	17 56.8
31	22 34 53.3	8 53.2	0 18.5	13 21.2	13 57.4	16 .6	20 23.2	21 14.8	3 8.7	4 56.8	15 59.1	17 54.2

SEPTMBER 1966

LONGITUDE

DAY	EPHEM. SID. TIME	☉	☊	☽	☿	♀	♂	♃	♄	♅	♆	♇
	h m s	° ′	° ′	° ′	° ′	° ′	° ′	° ′	° ′	° ′	° ′	° ′
1	22 38 49.9	8 ♍ 7.1	19 ♉ 46.8	18 ♓ 54.5	29 ♌ 9.3	20 ♌ 10.1	4 ♌ 3.6	25 ♋ 25.3	27 ♓ 39.8	19 ♍ 15.6	19 ♏ 39.7	17 ♍ 53.1
2	22 42 46.4	9 5.2	19 43.6	0 ♈ 45.4	1 ♍ 6.1	21 23.9	4 41.9	25 36.8	27 R 35.6	19 19.4	19 40.7	17 55.3
3	22 46 43.0	10 3.3	19 40.4	12 36.7	3 3.2	22 37.8	5 20.1	25 48.2	27 31.3	19 23.1	19 41.8	17 57.4
4	22 50 39.5	11 1.4	19 37.2	24 30.9	5 .4	23 51.7	5 58.2	25 59.5	27 26.9	19 26.8	19 42.8	17 59.6
5	22 54 36.1	11 59.5	19 34.0	6 ♉ 31.3	6 57.4	25 5.6	6 36.2	26 10.8	27 22.6	19 30.6	19 43.9	18 1.7
6	22 58 32.6	12 57.7	19 30.9	18 41.7	8 54.1	26 19.5	7 14.3	26 21.9	27 18.2	19 34.4	19 45.0	18 3.9
7	23 2 29.2	13 55.9	19 27.7	1 ♊ 6.4	10 50.2	27 33.5	7 52.3	26 33.0	27 13.7	19 38.1	19 46.1	18 6.0
8	23 6 25.7	14 54.1	19 24.5	13 50.2	12 45.7	28 47.6	8 30.2	26 44.0	27 9.2	19 41.9	19 47.3	18 8.2
9	23 10 22.3	15 52.4	19 21.3	26 57.5	14 40.5	0 ♍ 1.7	9 8.1	26 54.9	27 4.7	19 45.7	19 48.5	18 10.4
10	23 14 18.9	16 50.7	19 18.2	10 ♋ 31.9	16 34.4	1 15.8	9 46.0	27 5.8	27 .2	19 49.4	19 49.7	18 12.5
11	23 18 15.4	17 49.1	19 15.0	24 35.3	18 27.4	2 29.9	10 23.8	27 16.5	26 55.7	19 53.2	19 51.0	18 14.7
12	23 22 12.0	18 47.4	19 11.8	9 ♌ 7.0	20 19.4	3 44.1	11 1.6	27 27.2	26 51.1	19 57.0	19 52.3	18 16.8
13	23 26 8.5	19 45.8	19 8.6	24 2.8	22 10.4	4 58.3	11 39.3	27 37.8	26 46.5	20 .8	19 53.6	18 19.0
14	23 30 5.1	20 44.3	19 5.4	9 ♍ 14.9	24 .4	6 12.6	12 17.0	27 48.2	26 41.9	20 4.6	19 54.9	18 21.2
15	23 34 1.6	21 42.7	19 2.3	24 33.2	25 49.3	7 26.9	12 54.6	27 58.6	26 37.3	20 8.3	19 56.3	18 23.3
16	23 37 58.2	22 41.3	18 59.1	9 ♎ 46.4	27 37.2	8 41.2	13 32.2	28 8.9	26 32.6	20 12.1	19 57.7	18 25.5
17	23 41 54.7	23 39.8	18 55.9	24 44.4	29 24.0	9 55.6	14 9.7	28 19.1	26 28.0	20 15.9	19 59.1	18 27.6
18	23 45 51.3	24 38.3	18 52.7	9 ♏ 19.6	1 ♎ 9.7	11 10.0	14 47.2	28 29.2	26 23.3	20 19.7	20 .5	18 29.8
19	23 49 47.8	25 36.9	18 49.6	23 28.0	2 54.4	12 24.4	15 24.6	28 39.2	26 18.7	20 23.4	20 2.0	18 31.9
20	23 53 44.4	26 35.6	18 46.4	7 ♐ 8.7	4 38.1	13 38.8	16 2.0	28 49.0	26 14.0	20 27.2	20 3.5	18 34.1
21	23 57 40.9	27 34.2	18 43.2	20 23.1	6 20.7	14 53.3	16 39.4	28 58.8	26 9.4	20 31.0	20 5.0	18 36.2
22	0 1 37.5	28 32.9	18 40.0	3 ♑ 14.5	8 2.3	16 7.8	17 16.7	29 8.5	26 4.7	20 34.7	20 6.5	18 38.4
23	0 5 34.1	29 31.6	18 36.8	15 46.8	9 43.0	17 22.4	17 53.9	29 18.1	26 .1	20 38.5	20 8.2	18 40.5
24	0 9 30.6	0 ♎ 30.4	18 33.7	28 4.1	11 22.7	18 36.9	18 31.1	29 27.6	25 55.5	20 42.3	20 9.8	18 42.7
25	0 13 27.2	1 29.1	18 30.5	10 ♒ 10.4	13 1.4	19 51.5	19 8.3	29 36.9	25 50.9	20 46.0	20 11.4	18 44.8
26	0 17 23.7	2 27.9	18 27.3	22 9.0	14 39.1	21 6.1	19 45.4	29 46.1	25 46.3	20 49.7	20 13.0	18 46.9
27	0 21 20.3	3 26.7	18 24.1	4 ♓ 3.1	16 15.9	22 20.7	20 22.4	29 55.2	25 41.7	20 53.5	20 14.7	18 49.0
28	0 25 16.8	4 25.6	18 21.0	15 54.9	17 51.8	23 35.4	20 59.4	0 ♌ 4.3	25 37.1	20 57.2	20 16.3	18 51.1
29	0 29 13.4	5 24.4	18 17.8	27 46.5	19 26.9	24 50.1	21 36.4	0 13.1	25 32.5	21 .9	20 18.0	18 53.2
30	0 33 9.9	6 23.4	18 14.6	9 ♈ 39.6	21 1.0	26 4.8	22 13.3	0 21.9	25 28.0	21 4.5	20 19.8	18 55.3

LATITUDE

DAY	EPHEM. SID. TIME	☉	☊	☽	☿	♀	♂	♃	♄	♅	♆	♇
1	22 38 49.9	0 .0	0 .0	4 S 20.8	1 N 40.6	0 N 56.2	1 N 1.7	0 N 9.3	2 S 26.8	0 N 43.7	1 N 43.7	14 N 16.7
4	22 50 39.5	0 .0	0 .0	2 3.0	1 46.7	1 1.7	1 3.2	0 9.7	2 27.2	0 43.7	1 43.5	14 16.6
7	23 2 29.2	0 .0	0 .0	1 N 7.8	1 45.9	1 6.7	1 4.8	0 10.0	2 27.5	0 43.7	1 43.4	14 16.7
10	23 14 18.9	0 .0	0 .0	4 1.5	1 39.7	1 11.2	1 6.3	0 10.4	2 27.8	0 43.7	1 43.2	14 16.8
13	23 26 8.5	0 .0	0 .0	5 3.0	1 28.9	1 15.2	1 7.8	0 10.8	2 28.1	0 43.7	1 43.1	14 17.0
16	23 37 58.2	0 .0	0 .0	3 7.7	1 14.8	1 18.6	1 9.3	0 11.2	2 28.3	0 43.7	1 42.9	14 17.2
19	23 49 47.8	0 .0	0 .0	0 S 32.3	0 57.9	1 21.4	1 10.8	0 11.5	2 28.4	0 43.7	1 42.8	14 17.5
22	0 1 37.5	0 .0	0 .0	3 41.1	0 39.1	1 23.7	1 12.3	0 11.9	2 28.5	0 43.7	1 42.6	14 17.9
25	0 13 27.2	0 .0	0 .0	5 5.5	0 18.9	1 25.3	1 13.8	0 12.3	2 28.6	0 43.7	1 42.5	14 18.3
28	0 25 16.8	0 .0	0 .0	4 29.9	0 S 2.2	1 26.4	1 15.3	0 12.7	2 28.6	0 43.7	1 42.4	14 18.8

RIGHT ASCENSION

DAY	EPHEM. SID. TIME	☉	☊	☽	☿	♀	♂	♃	♄	♅	♆	♇
1	22 38 49.9	9 ♍ 46.4	17 ♉ 19.8	21 ♓ 31.4	1 ♍ 53.1	22 ♌ 53.0	6 ♌ 38.7	27 ♋ 25.0	28 ♓ 49.8	20 ♍ 24.9	17 ♏ 41.8	24 ♍ 40.0
2	22 42 46.4	10 40.8	17 16.6	2 ♈ 10.9	3 46.1	24 6.2	7 18.4	27 37.2	28 R 46.0	20 28.4	17 42.9	24 42.0
3	22 46 43.0	11 35.2	17 13.4	12 45.2	5 38.7	25 19.1	7 57.9	27 49.3	28 42.1	20 31.8	17 43.9	24 44.0
4	22 50 39.5	12 29.4	17 10.2	23 27.8	7 30.5	26 31.8	8 37.3	28 1.2	28 38.1	20 35.3	17 44.9	24 46.0
5	22 54 36.1	13 23.6	17 7.0	4 ♉ 32.6	9 21.3	27 44.3	9 16.6	28 13.1	28 34.2	20 38.8	17 46.0	24 48.0
6	22 58 32.6	14 17.8	17 3.8	16 13.6	11 11.1	28 56.6	9 55.8	28 24.8	28 30.2	20 42.2	17 47.1	24 50.0
7	23 2 29.2	15 11.9	17 .6	28 43.4	12 59.7	0 ♍ 8.7	10 34.8	28 36.5	28 26.2	20 45.7	17 48.2	24 52.0
8	23 6 25.7	16 5.9	16 57.4	12 ♊ 10.7	14 47.0	1 20.5	11 13.8	28 48.1	28 22.1	20 49.2	17 49.4	24 54.0
9	23 10 22.3	16 59.9	16 54.1	26 36.2	16 33.1	2 32.2	11 52.6	28 59.6	28 18.0	20 52.6	17 50.6	24 56.0
10	23 14 18.9	17 53.9	16 50.9	11 ♋ 48.7	18 17.8	3 43.6	12 31.3	29 11.0	28 13.9	20 56.1	17 51.8	24 58.0
11	23 18 15.4	18 47.8	16 47.7	27 25.6	20 1.2	4 54.8	13 9.9	29 22.3	28 9.7	20 59.6	17 53.0	25 .1
12	23 22 12.0	19 41.7	16 44.5	12 ♌ 59.2	21 43.2	6 5.9	13 48.4	29 33.6	28 5.6	21 3.1	17 54.3	25 2.1
13	23 26 8.5	20 35.6	16 41.3	28 7.1	23 24.0	7 16.7	14 26.7	29 44.7	28 1.4	21 6.6	17 55.6	25 4.1
14	23 30 5.1	21 29.5	16 38.1	12 ♍ 39.1	25 3.4	8 27.4	15 5.0	29 55.7	27 57.2	21 10.1	17 56.9	25 6.2
15	23 34 1.6	22 23.3	16 34.9	26 37.4	26 41.7	9 37.9	15 43.1	0 ♌ 6.6	27 53.0	21 13.6	17 58.3	25 8.2
16	23 37 58.2	23 17.1	16 31.7	10 ♎ 12.6	28 18.7	10 48.2	16 21.1	0 17.4	27 48.7	21 17.0	17 59.6	25 10.2
17	23 41 54.7	24 11.0	16 28.5	23 38.9	29 54.6	11 58.4	16 59.0	0 28.1	27 44.5	21 20.5	18 1.0	25 12.3
18	23 45 51.3	25 4.8	16 25.3	7 ♏ 10.0	1 ♎ 29.3	13 8.4	17 36.7	0 38.7	27 40.2	21 24.0	18 2.5	25 14.3
19	23 49 47.8	25 58.6	16 22.1	20 56.1	3 3.1	14 18.2	18 14.4	0 49.1	27 36.0	21 27.5	18 3.9	25 16.4
20	23 53 44.4	26 52.4	16 18.9	5 ♐ .7	4 35.8	15 27.9	18 51.9	0 59.5	27 31.7	21 31.0	18 5.4	25 18.4
21	23 57 40.9	27 46.2	16 15.7	19 18.9	6 7.6	16 37.4	19 29.3	1 9.8	27 27.5	21 34.4	18 6.9	25 20.4
22	0 1 37.5	28 40.1	16 12.5	3 ♑ 38.1	7 38.4	17 46.8	20 6.5	1 19.9	27 23.2	21 37.9	18 8.5	25 22.5
23	0 5 34.1	29 34.0	16 9.3	17 41.7	9 8.5	18 56.2	20 43.8	1 30.0	27 19.0	21 41.4	18 10.1	25 24.6
24	0 9 30.6	0 ♎ 27.8	16 6.1	1 ♒ 14.2	10 37.7	20 5.4	21 20.8	1 39.9	27 14.7	21 44.9	18 11.7	25 26.6
25	0 13 27.2	1 21.8	16 2.9	14 6.3	12 6.2	21 14.5	21 57.7	1 49.6	27 10.5	21 48.3	18 13.3	25 28.6
26	0 17 23.7	2 15.7	15 59.7	26 15.8	13 33.9	22 23.4	22 34.5	1 59.3	27 6.3	21 51.7	18 14.9	25 30.7
27	0 21 20.3	3 9.7	15 56.5	7 ♓ 47.0	15 1.0	23 32.3	23 11.2	2 8.8	27 2.0	21 55.2	18 16.5	25 32.7
28	0 25 16.8	4 3.7	15 53.3	18 48.3	16 27.5	24 41.2	23 47.8	2 18.3	26 57.8	21 58.6	18 18.2	25 34.7
29	0 29 13.4	4 57.8	15 50.1	29 30.5	17 53.4	25 49.9	24 24.3	2 27.5	26 53.6	22 2.0	18 19.9	25 36.7
30	0 33 9.9	5 51.9	15 46.9	10 ♈ 5.9	19 18.7	26 58.6	25 .7	2 36.7	26 49.5	22 5.4	18 21.6	25 38.7

DECLINATION

DAY	EPHEM. SID. TIME	☉	☊	☽	☿	♀	♂	♃	♄	♅	♆	♇
1	22 38 49.9	8 N 31.6	0 N 18.5	8 S 23.2	13 N 20.5	15 N 39.2	20 N 14.7	21 N 12.8	3 S 10.5	4 N 55.4	15 S 59.4	17 N 53.4
4	22 50 39.5	7 26.0	0 18.5	7 N 35.7	11 19.9	14 32.5	19 48.4	21 6.8	3 15.9	4 50.9	16 .4	17 50.8
7	23 2 29.2	6 19.4	0 18.4	21 29.5	9 8.3	13 22.1	19 20.9	21 .8	3 21.5	4 46.5	16 1.4	17 48.3
10	23 14 18.9	5 11.7	0 18.4	27 2.4	6 49.9	12 8.3	18 52.4	20 54.9	3 27.1	4 42.0	16 2.5	17 45.8
13	23 26 8.5	4 3.3	0 18.3	18 16.1	4 28.1	10 51.4	18 22.8	20 49.0	3 32.8	4 37.6	16 3.7	17 43.4
16	23 37 58.2	2 54.2	0 18.3	0 S 59.7	2 5.4	9 31.7	17 52.3	20 43.2	3 38.5	4 33.1	16 5.0	17 41.1
19	23 49 47.8	1 44.6	0 18.2	19 10.0	0 S 16.2	8 9.7	17 20.8	20 37.4	3 44.2	4 28.7	16 6.2	17 38.8
22	0 1 37.5	0 34.7	0 18.2	27 5.4	2 35.4	6 45.5	16 48.5	20 31.8	3 49.9	4 24.2	16 7.6	17 36.6
25	0 13 27.2	0 S 35.5	0 18.2	22 35.8	4 51.2	5 19.5	16 15.4	20 26.3	3 55.4	4 19.8	16 9.0	17 34.4
28	0 25 16.8	1 45.6	0 18.1	9 42.0	7 2.6	3 52.1	15 41.6	20 20.9	4 .9	4 15.4	16 10.4	17 32.3

OCTOBER 1966

LONGITUDE

DAY	EPHEM. SID. TIME (h m s)	☉ (° ′)	☊ (° ′)	☽ (° ′)	☿ (° ′)	♀ (° ′)	♂ (° ′)	♃ (° ′)	♄ (° ′)	♅ (° ′)	♆ (° ′)	♇ (° ′)
1	0 37 6.5	7♎22.3	18♉11.4	21♈35.9	22♎34.3	27♍19.5	22♌50.1	0♌30.5	25♓23.5	21♍ 8.2	20♏21.5	18♍57.4
2	0 41 3.0	8 21.3	18 8.2	3♉37.3	24 6.7	28 34.2	23 26.9	0 39.1	25R19.0	21 11.9	20 23.3	18 59.4
3	0 44 59.6	9 20.3	18 5.1	15 45.8	25 38.2	29 49.0	24 3.7	0 47.5	25 14.6	21 15.5	20 25.1	19 1.5
4	0 48 56.1	10 19.4	18 1.9	28 4.1	27 8.9	1♎ 3.8	24 40.4	0 55.7	25 10.2	21 19.2	20 26.9	19 3.5
5	0 52 52.7	11 18.5	17 58.7	10♊35.2	28 38.8	2 18.7	25 17.0	1 3.9	25 5.8	21 22.8	20 28.7	19 5.6
6	0 56 49.2	12 17.6	17 55.5	23 22.2	0♏ 7.8	3 33.5	25 53.7	1 11.9	25 1.4	21 26.4	20 30.6	19 7.6
7	1 0 45.8	13 16.8	17 52.4	6♋28.8	1 36.0	4 48.4	26 30.2	1 19.8	24 57.1	21 30.0	20 32.4	19 9.6
8	1 4 42.4	14 16.0	17 49.2	19 57.6	3 3.3	6 3.3	27 6.7	1 27.5	24 52.9	21 33.5	20 34.3	19 11.6
9	1 8 38.9	15 15.2	17 46.0	3♌50.8	4 29.8	7 18.2	27 43.2	1 35.1	24 48.6	21 37.1	20 36.2	19 13.6
10	1 12 35.5	16 14.5	17 42.8	18 8.3	5 55.4	8 33.2	28 19.6	1 42.6	24 44.5	21 40.6	20 38.1	19 15.6
11	1 16 32.0	17 13.8	17 39.6	2♍47.9	7 20.0	9 48.1	28 55.9	1 49.9	24 40.4	21 44.1	20 40.1	19 17.6
12	1 20 28.6	18 13.2	17 36.5	17 44.4	8 43.8	11 3.1	29 32.2	1 57.1	24 36.3	21 47.6	20 42.0	19 19.5
13	1 24 25.1	19 12.6	17 33.3	2♎50.2	10 6.6	12 18.1	0♍ 8.5	2 4.2	24 32.3	21 51.1	20 44.0	19 21.5
14	1 28 21.7	20 12.1	17 30.1	17 55.9	11 28.4	13 33.2	0 44.7	2 11.1	24 28.4	21 54.6	20 46.0	19 23.4
15	1 32 18.2	21 11.5	17 26.9	2♏52.1	12 49.2	14 48.3	1 20.9	2 17.9	24 24.4	21 58.0	20 48.0	19 25.3
16	1 36 14.8	22 11.0	17 23.8	17 30.6	14 8.8	16 3.3	1 56.9	2 24.5	24 20.6	22 1.4	20 50.1	19 27.2
17	1 40 11.3	23 10.6	17 20.6	1♐45.7	15 27.3	17 18.4	2 32.9	2 30.9	24 16.8	22 4.8	20 52.1	19 29.1
18	1 44 7.9	24 10.1	17 17.4	15 34.4	16 44.6	18 33.5	3 8.9	2 37.2	24 13.1	22 8.2	20 54.1	19 31.0
19	1 48 4.4	25 9.7	17 14.2	28 56.5	18 .5	19 48.6	3 44.8	2 43.4	24 9.5	22 11.5	20 56.2	19 32.8
20	1 52 1.0	26 9.4	17 11.0	11♑53.8	19 15.0	21 3.7	4 20.6	2 49.4	24 5.9	22 14.8	20 58.3	19 34.6
21	1 55 57.6	27 9.0	17 7.9	24 29.4	20 27.9	22 18.8	4 56.4	2 55.2	24 2.4	22 18.1	21 .4	19 36.4
22	1 59 54.1	28 8.7	17 4.7	6♒47.6	21 39.2	23 34.0	5 32.1	3 .9	23 58.9	22 21.3	21 2.5	19 38.2
23	2 3 50.7	29 8.4	17 1.5	18 52.7	22 48.6	24 49.1	6 7.7	3 6.4	23 55.6	22 24.6	21 4.6	19 40.0
24	2 7 47.2	0♏ 8.1	16 58.3	0♓49.1	23 56.0	26 4.3	6 43.3	3 11.7	23 52.3	22 27.8	21 6.7	19 41.7
25	2 11 43.8	1 7.9	16 55.2	12 40.9	25 1.2	27 19.4	7 18.9	3 16.9	23 49.1	22 30.9	21 8.8	19 43.5
26	2 15 40.3	2 7.7	16 52.0	24 31.8	26 4.0	28 34.6	7 54.3	3 21.9	23 45.9	22 34.1	21 11.0	19 45.2
27	2 19 36.9	3 7.5	16 48.8	6♈24.8	27 4.1	29 49.8	8 29.7	3 26.7	23 42.9	22 37.2	21 13.1	19 46.9
28	2 23 33.4	4 7.4	16 45.6	18 22.6	28 1.2	1♏ 5.0	9 5.1	3 31.4	23 39.9	22 40.2	21 15.3	19 48.5
29	2 27 30.0	5 7.3	16 42.5	0♉27.2	28 55.0	2 20.2	9 40.3	3 35.9	23 37.0	22 43.3	21 17.5	19 50.2
30	2 31 26.6	6 7.2	16 39.3	12 40.4	29 45.1	3 35.4	10 15.5	3 40.3	23 34.2	22 46.3	21 19.7	19 51.8
31	2 35 23.1	7 7.1	16 36.1	25 3.6	0♐31.1	4 50.7	10 50.7	3 44.4	23 31.5	22 49.3	21 21.9	19 53.4

LATITUDE

DAY	EPHEM. SID. TIME	☉	☊	☽	☿	♀	♂	♃	♄	♅	♆	♇
1	0 37 6.5	0 .0	0 .0	2S11.4	0S23.7	1N26.9	1N16.8	0N13.2	2S28.6	0N43.8	1N42.2	14N19.4
4	0 48 56.1	0 .0	0 .0	1N 2.5	0 45.4	1 26.7	1 18.3	0 13.6	2 28.5	0 43.8	1 42.1	14 20.0
7	1 0 45.8	0 .0	0 .0	3 59.5	1 6.9	1 26.0	1 19.7	0 14.0	2 28.4	0 43.8	1 42.0	14 20.7
10	1 12 35.5	0 .0	0 .0	5 12.7	1 27.7	1 24.7	1 21.2	0 14.4	2 28.2	0 43.9	1 41.9	14 21.4
13	1 24 25.1	0 .0	0 .0	3 36.1	1 47.7	1 22.8	1 22.7	0 14.9	2 28.0	0 43.9	1 41.8	14 22.2
16	1 36 14.8	0 .0	0 .0	0S 6.8	2 6.2	1 20.3	1 24.2	0 15.3	2 27.7	0 44.0	1 41.7	14 23.1
19	1 48 4.4	0 .0	0 .0	3 33.9	2 22.9	1 17.3	1 25.6	0 15.8	2 27.4	0 44.0	1 41.7	14 24.0
22	1 59 54.1	0 .0	0 .0	5 11.2	2 37.2	1 13.8	1 27.1	0 16.3	2 27.1	0 44.1	1 41.6	14 25.0
25	2 11 43.8	0 .0	0 .0	4 42.9	2 48.3	1 9.8	1 28.6	0 16.8	2 26.7	0 44.2	1 41.5	14 26.0
28	2 23 33.4	0 .0	0 .0	2 27.8	2 55.2	1 5.3	1 30.0	0 17.3	2 26.3	0 44.3	1 41.5	14 27.1
31	2 35 23.1	0 .0	0 .0	0N49.3	2 56.5	1 .4	1 31.5	0 17.8	2 25.8	0 44.3	1 41.4	14 28.2

RIGHT ASCENSION

DAY	EPHEM. SID. TIME	☉	☊	☽	☿	♀	♂	♃	♄	♅	♆	♇
1	0 37 6.5	6♎46.1	15♉43.7	20♈47.1	20♎43.5	28♍ 7.3	25♌36.9	2♌45.7	26♓45.3	22♍ 8.8	18♏23.4	25♍40.7
2	0 41 3.0	7 40.4	15 40.5	1♉47.3	22 7.8	29 15.9	26 13.0	2 54.6	26R41.2	22 12.2	18 25.1	25 42.7
3	0 44 59.6	8 34.8	15 37.3	13 19.1	23 31.7	0♎24.5	26 49.1	3 3.4	26 37.1	22 15.5	18 26.9	25 44.7
4	0 48 56.1	9 29.2	15 34.1	25 33.8	24 55.0	1 33.1	27 25.0	3 12.0	26 33.0	22 18.9	18 28.7	25 46.7
5	0 52 52.7	10 23.7	15 30.9	8♊39.2	26 18.0	2 41.6	28 .8	3 20.5	26 29.0	22 22.2	18 30.6	25 48.7
6	0 56 49.2	11 18.3	15 27.7	22 36.4	27 40.5	3 50.2	28 36.5	3 28.9	26 25.0	22 25.5	18 32.4	25 50.7
7	1 0 45.8	12 13.0	15 24.5	7♋16.6	29 2.7	4 58.8	29 12.1	3 37.1	26 21.0	22 28.9	18 34.3	25 52.7
8	1 4 42.4	13 7.9	15 21.3	22 21.6	0♏24.4	6 7.4	29 47.6	3 45.2	26 17.1	22 32.1	18 36.1	25 54.6
9	1 8 38.9	14 2.8	15 18.1	7♌28.4	1 45.7	7 16.1	0♍22.9	3 53.1	26 13.2	22 35.4	18 38.1	25 56.6
10	1 12 35.5	14 57.8	15 15.0	22 17.1	3 6.6	8 24.8	0 58.2	4 .9	26 9.3	22 38.7	18 40.0	25 58.5
11	1 16 32.0	15 53.0	15 11.8	6♍37.2	4 27.0	9 33.5	1 33.4	4 8.6	26 5.5	22 41.9	18 41.9	26 .4
12	1 20 28.6	16 48.2	15 8.6	20 29.2	5 47.0	10 42.3	2 8.4	4 16.1	26 1.7	22 45.2	18 43.9	26 2.4
13	1 24 25.1	17 43.6	15 5.4	4♎ 2.1	7 6.5	11 51.2	2 43.4	4 23.4	25 58.0	22 48.4	18 45.8	26 4.3
14	1 28 21.7	18 39.2	15 2.2	17 29.3	8 25.5	13 .2	3 18.3	4 30.7	25 54.3	22 51.6	18 47.9	26 6.2
15	1 32 18.2	19 34.9	14 59.0	1♏ 5.1	9 43.9	14 9.3	3 53.0	4 37.7	25 50.7	22 54.8	18 49.9	26 8.1
16	1 36 14.8	20 30.7	14 55.8	15 .7	11 1.7	15 18.4	4 27.6	4 44.6	25 47.2	22 57.9	18 51.9	26 10.0
17	1 40 11.3	21 26.6	14 52.6	29 21.1	12 18.8	16 27.7	5 2.1	4 51.3	25 43.6	23 1.0	18 53.9	26 11.8
18	1 44 7.9	22 22.7	14 49.4	14♐ 1.9	13 35.1	17 37.1	5 36.6	4 57.8	25 40.2	23 4.1	18 56.0	26 13.7
19	1 48 4.4	23 18.9	14 46.2	28 48.9	14 50.5	18 46.7	6 10.9	5 4.2	25 36.8	23 7.2	18 58.1	26 15.5
20	1 52 1.0	24 15.3	14 43.1	13♑22.0	16 4.9	19 56.3	6 45.1	5 10.5	25 33.4	23 10.2	19 .1	26 17.4
21	1 55 57.6	25 11.8	14 39.9	27 21.9	17 18.1	21 6.2	7 19.2	5 16.5	25 30.2	23 13.3	19 2.2	26 19.2
22	1 59 54.1	26 8.5	14 36.7	10♒36.5	18 30.1	22 16.1	7 53.1	5 22.4	25 27.0	23 16.3	19 4.4	26 21.0
23	2 3 50.7	27 5.3	14 33.5	23 2.6	19 40.6	23 26.3	8 27.0	5 28.2	25 23.8	23 19.3	19 6.5	26 22.8
24	2 7 47.2	28 2.3	14 30.3	4♓44.7	20 49.5	24 36.6	9 .8	5 33.7	25 20.7	23 22.2	19 8.6	26 24.5
25	2 11 43.8	28 59.5	14 27.1	15 52.3	21 56.4	25 47.1	9 34.5	5 39.1	25 17.7	23 25.1	19 10.7	26 26.3
26	2 15 40.3	29 56.9	14 24.0	26 37.5	23 1.2	26 57.9	10 8.1	5 44.3	25 14.8	23 28.0	19 12.9	26 28.0
27	2 19 36.9	0♏54.4	14 20.8	7♈13.4	24 3.6	28 8.8	10 41.6	5 49.4	25 11.9	23 30.9	19 15.1	26 29.7
28	2 23 33.4	1 52.1	14 17.6	17 53.4	25 3.2	29 19.9	11 15.0	5 54.2	25 9.1	23 33.7	19 17.2	26 31.4
29	2 27 30.0	2 50.0	14 14.4	28 51.1	25 59.7	0♏31.3	11 48.2	5 58.9	25 6.4	23 36.5	19 19.4	26 33.1
30	2 31 26.6	3 48.1	14 11.2	10♉19.5	26 52.5	1 42.9	12 21.4	6 3.4	25 3.8	23 39.3	19 21.6	26 34.8
31	2 35 23.1	4 46.4	14 8.0	22 29.9	27 41.4	2 54.7	12 54.5	6 7.8	25 1.2	23 42.1	19 23.8	26 36.4

DECLINATION

DAY	EPHEM. SID. TIME	☉	☊	☽	☿	♀	♂	♃	♄	♅	♆	♇
1	0 37 6.5	2S55.6	0N18.1	6N23.4	9S 9.1	2N23.5	15N 7.0	20N15.7	4S 6.3	4N11.1	16S11.9	17N30.4
4	0 48 56.1	4 5.3	0 18.0	20 45.0	11 10.0	0 54.2	14 31.8	20 10.6	4 11.5	4 6.8	16 13.4	17 28.5
7	1 0 45.8	5 14.6	0 18.0	27 16.4	13 4.7	0S35.7	13 56.0	20 5.8	4 16.5	4 2.6	16 15.0	17 26.7
10	1 12 35.5	6 23.3	0 17.9	21 20.0	14 52.7	2 5.7	13 19.7	20 1.1	4 21.4	3 58.4	16 16.6	17 25.0
13	1 24 25.1	7 31.3	0 17.9	2 10.6	16 33.3	3 35.6	12 42.9	19 56.8	4 26.0	3 54.3	16 18.2	17 23.4
16	1 36 14.8	8 38.4	0 17.8	17S10.2	18 5.8	5 4.9	12 5.6	19 52.6	4 30.4	3 50.3	16 19.9	17 21.9
19	1 48 4.4	9 44.4	0 17.8	27 .4	19 29.2	6 33.4	11 28.0	19 48.8	4 34.6	3 46.4	16 21.6	17 20.5
22	1 59 54.1	10 49.1	0 17.7	23 35.6	20 42.7	8 .6	10 50.0	19 45.2	4 38.4	3 42.6	16 23.3	17 19.3
25	2 11 43.8	11 52.3	0 17.7	11 9.2	21 44.8	9 26.3	10 11.8	19 42.0	4 42.0	3 38.8	16 25.0	17 18.1
28	2 23 33.4	12 53.8	0 17.6	4N55.7	22 34.1	10 50.0	9 33.4	19 39.1	4 45.3	3 35.2	16 26.8	17 17.1
31	2 35 23.1	13 53.6	0 17.6	19 49.9	23 8.4	12 11.5	8 54.7	19 36.5	4 48.2	3 31.7	16 28.5	17 16.2

NOVEMBER 1966

LONGITUDE

DAY	EPHEM. SID. TIME (h m s)	☉	☊	☽	☿	♀	♂	♃	♄	♅	♆	♇
1	2 39 19.7	8♏7.1	16♉32.9	7♊38.0	1♐12.6	6♏5.9	11♍25.8	3♌48.4	23♓28.9	22♍52.2	21♏24.1	19♍55.0
2	2 43 16.2	9 7.1	16 29.7	20 24.9	1 49.0	7 21.2	12 .8	3 52.2	23R26.3	22 55.1	21 26.3	19 56.6
3	2 47 12.8	10 7.2	16 26.6	3♋25.7	2 19.8	8 36.4	12 35.7	3 55.8	23 23.9	22 58.0	21 28.5	19 58.1
4	2 51 9.3	11 7.3	16 23.4	16 41.5	2 44.4	9 51.7	13 10.7	3 59.3	23 21.6	23 .9	21 30.7	19 59.7
5	2 55 5.9	12 7.4	16 20.2	0♌13.1	3 2.7	11 7.0	13 45.5	4 2.6	23 19.3	23 3.7	21 33.0	20 1.1
6	2 59 2.4	13 7.6	16 17.0	14 1.9	3 12.4	12 22.3	14 20.2	4 5.7	23 17.1	23 6.4	21 35.2	20 2.6
7	3 2 59.0	14 7.8	16 13.9	28 7.1	3 14.5	13 37.6	14 54.9	4 8.5	23 15.0	23 9.2	21 37.4	20 4.1
8	3 6 55.6	15 8.0	16 10.7	12♍27.5	3R7.7	14 52.9	15 29.5	4 11.3	23 13.0	23 11.8	21 39.7	20 5.5
9	3 10 52.1	16 8.3	16 7.5	27 .3	2 51.6	16 8.3	16 4.0	4 13.8	23 11.2	23 14.5	21 41.9	20 6.9
10	3 14 48.7	17 8.6	16 4.3	11♎40.9	2 25.7	17 23.6	16 38.5	4 16.1	23 9.4	23 17.1	21 44.1	20 8.2
11	3 18 45.2	18 8.9	16 1.1	26 23.6	1 49.7	18 38.9	17 12.8	4 18.2	23 7.7	23 19.7	21 46.4	20 9.6
12	3 22 41.8	19 9.3	15 58.0	11♏1.7	1 8.4	19 54.3	17 47.1	4 20.2	23 6.1	23 22.2	21 48.6	20 10.9
13	3 26 38.3	20 9.7	15 54.8	25 28.5	0 8.4	21 9.6	18 21.3	4 21.9	23 4.6	23 24.7	21 50.9	20 12.2
14	3 30 34.9	21 10.1	15 51.6	9♐38.3	29♏4.3	22 25.0	18 55.5	4 23.5	23 3.2	23 27.1	21 53.1	20 13.4
15	3 34 31.4	22 10.5	15 48.4	23 27.1	27 52.8	23 40.3	19 29.5	4 24.8	23 1.9	23 29.5	21 55.4	20 14.7
16	3 38 28.0	23 11.0	15 45.3	6♑52.5	26 35.8	24 55.7	20 3.5	4 26.0	23 .8	23 31.8	21 57.6	20 15.9
17	3 42 24.6	24 11.5	15 42.1	19 54.5	25 15.6	26 11.1	20 37.4	4 27.0	22 59.7	23 34.2	21 59.9	20 17.0
18	3 46 21.1	25 12.0	15 38.9	2♒34.8	23 54.6	27 26.4	21 11.1	4 27.7	22 58.7	23 36.4	22 2.1	20 18.2
19	3 50 17.7	26 12.5	15 35.7	14 56.4	22 35.6	28 41.8	21 44.8	4 28.3	22 57.8	23 38.6	22 4.4	20 19.3
20	3 54 14.2	27 13.0	15 32.6	27 3.3	21 21.1	29 57.2	22 18.4	4 28.7	22 57.1	23 40.8	22 6.6	20 20.4
21	3 58 10.8	28 13.6	15 29.4	9♓.0	20 13.6	1♐12.6	22 52.0	4 28.9	22 56.4	23 42.9	22 8.9	20 21.4
22	4 2 7.3	29 14.2	15 26.2	20 51.5	19 14.9	2 27.9	23 25.4	4 28.9	22 55.9	23 45.0	22 11.1	20 22.5
23	4 6 3.9	0♐14.8	15 23.0	2♈42.3	18 26.6	3 43.3	23 58.7	4R28.6	22 55.4	23 47.0	22 13.4	20 23.5
24	4 10 .5	1 15.5	15 19.9	14 36.8	17 49.5	4 58.7	24 32.0	4 28.2	22 55.1	23 49.0	22 15.6	20 24.5
25	4 13 57.0	2 16.2	15 16.7	26 38.9	17 24.0	6 14.1	25 5.2	4 27.7	22 54.9	23 51.0	22 17.9	20 25.4
26	4 17 53.6	3 16.8	15 13.5	8♉51.9	17 10.2	7 29.5	25 38.2	4 26.8	22 54.8	23 52.9	22 20.1	20 26.3
27	4 21 50.1	4 17.5	15 10.3	21 18.0	17 7.5	8 44.8	26 11.2	4 25.8	22 54.8	23 54.7	22 22.3	20 27.2
28	4 25 46.7	5 18.2	15 7.1	3♊58.7	17D15.5	10 .2	26 44.0	4 24.6	22D54.9	23 56.5	22 24.5	20 28.1
29	4 29 43.3	6 19.0	15 4.0	16 54.6	17 33.4	11 15.6	27 16.8	4 23.2	22 55.1	23 58.3	22 26.7	20 28.9
30	4 33 39.8	7 19.7	15 .8	0♋5.4	18 .3	12 31.0	27 49.4	4 21.6	22 55.4	23 59.9	22 28.9	20 29.7

LATITUDE

DAY	SID. TIME	☉	☊	☽	☿	♀	♂	♃	♄	♅	♆	♇
1	2 39 19.7	0 .0	0 .0	1N56.4	2S55.4	0N58.7	1N32.0	0N17.9	2S25.7	0N44.4	1N41.4	14N28.6
4	2 51 9.3	0 .0	0 .0	4 36.4	2 46.3	0 53.2	1 33.5	0 18.4	2 25.2	0 44.5	1 41.4	14 29.8
7	3 2 59.0	0 .0	0 .0	5 10.5	2 26.6	0 47.4	1 34.9	0 19.0	2 24.7	0 44.5	1 41.3	14 31.0
10	3 14 48.7	0 .0	0 .0	3 .1	1 53.5	0 41.3	1 36.4	0 19.5	2 24.1	0 44.6	1 41.3	14 32.3
13	3 26 38.3	0 .0	0 .0	0S51.3	1 6.0	0 34.8	1 37.9	0 20.0	2 23.6	0 44.7	1 41.3	14 33.6
16	3 38 28.0	0 .0	0 .0	4 5.6	0 7.2	0 28.2	1 39.4	0 20.6	2 23.0	0 44.8	1 41.3	14 35.0
19	3 50 17.7	0 .0	0 .0	5 16.8	0N53.5	0 21.3	1 40.9	0 21.1	2 22.4	0 44.9	1 41.4	14 36.4
22	4 2 7.3	0 .0	0 .0	4 20.6	1 44.2	0 14.3	1 42.4	0 21.7	2 21.8	0 45.0	1 41.3	14 37.8
25	4 13 57.0	0 .0	0 .0	1 46.1	2 17.3	0 7.2	1 43.9	0 22.2	2 21.2	0 45.2	1 41.3	14 39.3
28	4 25 46.7	0 .0	0 .0	1N36.5	2 32.5	0 .0	1 45.4	0 22.8	2 20.6	0 45.3	1 41.4	14 40.8

RIGHT ASCENSION

DAY	SID. TIME	☉	☊	☽	☿	♀	♂	♃	♄	♅	♆	♇
1	2 39 19.7	5♏44.9	14♉4.9	5♊29.9	28♏25.7	4♏6.8	13♍27.5	6♌11.9	24♓58.7	23♍44.8	19♏26.0	26♍38.1
2	2 43 16.2	6 43.6	14 1.7	19 19.9	29 4.9	5 19.1	14 .4	6 15.9	24R56.3	23 47.5	19 28.2	26 39.7
3	2 47 12.8	7 42.5	13 58.5	3♋50.9	29 38.4	6 31.7	14 33.2	6 19.7	24 54.0	23 50.1	19 30.5	26 41.3
4	2 51 9.3	8 41.6	13 55.3	18 44.2	0♐5.6	7 44.6	15 6.0	6 23.3	24 51.8	23 52.8	19 32.7	26 42.9
5	2 55 5.9	9 40.9	13 52.1	3♌36.6	0 25.6	8 57.8	15 38.6	6 26.7	24 49.7	23 55.4	19 35.0	26 44.4
6	2 59 2.4	10 40.4	13 49.0	18 8.4	0 37.9	10 11.2	16 11.1	6 29.9	24 47.6	23 57.9	19 37.2	26 46.0
7	3 2 59.0	11 40.1	13 45.8	2♍9.4	0 41.8	11 24.9	16 43.6	6 33.0	24 45.6	24 .4	19 39.5	26 47.5
8	3 6 55.6	12 40.1	13 42.6	15 40.5	0R36.6	12 38.9	17 15.9	6 35.8	24 43.7	24 2.9	19 41.7	26 49.0
9	3 10 52.1	13 40.2	13 39.4	28 51.0	0 21.8	13 53.2	17 48.1	6 38.4	24 41.9	24 5.4	19 44.0	26 50.4
10	3 14 48.7	14 40.6	13 36.3	11♎54.9	29♏57.0	15 7.8	18 20.3	6 40.9	24 40.2	24 7.8	19 46.2	26 51.9
11	3 18 45.2	15 41.2	13 33.1	25 8.2	29 22.1	16 22.7	18 52.3	6 43.1	24 38.6	24 10.1	19 48.5	26 53.3
12	3 22 41.8	16 42.0	13 29.9	8♏45.2	28 37.2	17 37.8	19 24.3	6 45.2	24 37.0	24 12.5	19 50.8	26 54.7
13	3 26 38.3	17 43.0	13 26.7	22 55.2	27 42.9	18 53.4	19 56.1	6 47.0	24 35.6	24 14.8	19 53.0	26 56.1
14	3 30 34.9	18 44.2	13 23.6	7♐37.9	26 40.1	20 9.2	20 27.9	6 48.7	24 34.2	24 17.0	19 55.3	26 57.4
15	3 34 31.4	19 45.6	13 20.4	22 41.4	25 30.4	21 25.3	20 59.5	6 50.1	24 33.0	24 19.2	19 57.6	26 58.8
16	3 38 28.0	20 47.3	13 17.2	7♑45.3	24 15.7	22 41.7	21 31.1	6 51.4	24 31.8	24 21.4	19 59.8	27 .1
17	3 42 24.6	21 49.1	13 14.0	22 19.0	23 2.3	23 58.4	22 2.5	6 52.4	24 30.7	24 23.6	20 2.1	27 1.4
18	3 46 21.1	22 51.2	13 10.9	6♒8.5	21 40.7	25 15.4	22 33.9	6 53.2	24 29.8	24 25.7	20 4.4	27 2.6
19	3 50 17.7	23 53.4	13 7.7	19 3.9	20 25.5	26 32.8	23 5.1	6 53.9	24 28.9	24 27.7	20 6.7	27 3.9
20	3 54 14.2	24 55.9	13 4.5	1♓7.3	19 15.1	27 50.4	23 36.3	6 54.3	24 28.1	24 29.7	20 8.9	27 5.1
21	3 58 10.8	25 58.6	13 1.4	12 28.2	18 11.8	29 8.3	24 7.4	6 54.6	24 27.4	24 31.7	20 11.2	27 6.3
22	4 2 7.3	27 1.4	12 58.2	23 19.5	17 17.2	0♐26.6	24 38.3	6 54.6	24 26.9	24 33.6	20 13.4	27 7.4
23	4 6 3.9	28 4.5	12 55.0	3♈55.6	16 32.6	1 45.1	25 9.2	6R54.4	24 26.4	24 35.5	20 15.7	27 8.6
24	4 10 .5	29 7.7	12 51.9	14 31.5	15 58.8	3 3.9	25 40.0	6 54.0	24 26.0	24 37.3	20 18.0	27 9.7
25	4 13 57.0	0♐11.2	12 48.7	25 22.1	15 36.1	4 23.0	26 10.7	6 53.5	24 25.7	24 39.2	20 20.3	27 10.8
26	4 17 53.6	1 14.9	12 45.5	6♉42.0	15 24.3	5 42.4	26 41.3	6 52.7	24 25.5	24 40.9	20 22.5	27 11.8
27	4 21 50.1	2 18.7	12 42.4	18 41.1	15 23.2	7 2.0	27 11.7	6 51.7	24 25.4	24 42.6	20 24.7	27 12.9
28	4 25 46.7	3 22.7	12 39.2	1♊39.4	15D32.0	8 21.9	27 42.1	6 50.5	24 25.4	24 44.3	20 27.0	27 13.9
29	4 29 43.3	4 26.8	12 36.0	15 29.3	15 50.3	9 42.0	28 12.4	6 49.1	24D25.6	24 45.9	20 29.2	27 14.8
30	4 33 39.8	5 31.2	12 32.9	0♋6.1	16 17.0	11 2.4	28 42.6	6 47.5	24 25.8	24 47.5	20 31.4	27 15.8

DECLINATION

DAY	SID. TIME	☉	☊	☽	☿	♀	♂	♃	♄	♅	♆	♇
1	2 39 19.7	14S13.1	0N17.6	23N30.1	23S16.1	12S38.1	8N41.8	19N35.8	4S49.1	3N30.6	16S29.1	17N15.9
4	2 51 9.3	15 10.1	0 17.5	26 58.3	23 25.9	13 56.0	8 3.0	19 33.7	4 51.5	3 27.2	16 30.8	17 15.1
7	3 2 59.0	16 5.0	0 17.5	26 58.8	23 12.4	15 10.8	7 24.2	19 32.0	4 53.7	3 24.0	16 32.6	17 14.5
10	3 14 48.7	16 57.5	0 17.4	1S51.4	22 30.4	16 22.1	6 45.3	19 30.7	4 55.4	3 21.0	16 34.3	17 14.0
13	3 26 38.3	17 47.3	0 17.4	19 57.9	21 15.6	17 29.6	6 6.5	19 29.8	4 56.8	3 18.1	16 36.1	17 13.7
16	3 38 28.0	18 34.4	0 17.3	27 21.2	19 31.0	18 32.9	5 27.7	19 29.4	4 57.8	3 15.3	16 37.8	17 13.5
19	3 50 17.7	19 18.5	0 17.2	17 33.3	17 33.7	19 31.7	4 49.1	19 29.4	4 58.4	3 12.7	16 39.5	17 13.4
22	4 2 7.3	19 59.5	0 17.2	7 36.9	15 52.3	20 25.5	4 10.7	19 29.8	4 58.6	3 10.3	16 41.2	17 13.4
25	4 13 57.0	20 37.2	0 17.2	8N37.8	14 50.0	21 14.2	3 32.6	19 30.6	4 58.4	3 8.0	16 42.9	17 13.6
28	4 25 46.7	21 11.5	0 17.1	22 31.7	14 33.0	21 57.4	2 54.7	19 31.9	4 57.9	3 6.0	16 44.6	17 13.9

DECEMBER 1966

DAY	EPHEM. SID. TIME	☉	☊	☾	☿	♀	♂	♃	♄	♅	♆	♇
	h m s	° ′	° ′	° ′	° ′	° ′	° ′	° ′	° ′	° ′	° ′	° ′
		LONGITUDE										
1	4 37 36.4	8♐20.5	14♉57.6	13♋30.1	18♏35.4	13♐46.3	28♍22.0	4♌19.8	22♓55.8	24♍ 1.6	22♏31.1	20♍30.4
2	4 41 32.9	9 21.3	14 54.4	27 7.1	19 17.7	15 1.7	28 54.5	4 R 17.8	22 56.3	24 3.2	22 33.3	20 31.2
3	4 45 29.5	10 22.1	14 51.3	10♌54.7	20 6.4	16 17.1	29 26.8	4 15.6	22 57.0	24 4.7	22 35.4	20 31.8
4	4 49 26.0	11 23.0	14 48.1	24 51.1	21 .8	17 32.5	29 59.0	4 13.3	22 57.7	24 6.2	22 37.6	20 32.5
5	4 53 22.6	12 23.9	14 44.9	8♍54.6	22 .1	18 47.9	0♎31.2	4 10.7	22 58.6	24 7.6	22 39.8	20 33.1
6	4 57 19.2	13 24.8	14 41.7	23 3.6	23 3.8	20 3.3	1 3.2	4 7.9	22 59.5	24 9.0	22 41.9	20 33.7
7	5 1 15.7	14 25.7	14 38.6	7♎16.3	24 11.2	21 18.7	1 35.1	4 4.9	23 .6	24 10.3	22 44.0	20 34.3
8	5 5 12.3	15 26.6	14 35.4	21 30.9	25 21.9	22 34.1	2 6.9	4 1.8	23 1.7	24 11.6	22 46.1	20 34.8
9	5 9 8.8	16 27.6	14 32.2	5♏44.6	26 35.3	23 49.5	2 38.5	3 58.4	23 3.0	24 12.8	22 48.3	20 35.3
10	5 13 5.4	17 28.6	14 29.0	19 54.4	27 51.2	25 4.9	3 10.1	3 54.9	23 4.4	24 14.0	22 50.3	20 35.8
11	5 17 2.0	18 29.6	14 25.9	3♐56.7	29 9.3	26 20.3	3 41.5	3 51.2	23 5.9	24 15.1	22 52.4	20 36.2
12	5 20 58.5	19 30.6	14 22.7	17 47.6	0♐29.1	27 35.7	4 12.7	3 47.3	23 7.5	24 16.1	22 54.5	20 36.6
13	5 24 55.1	20 31.6	14 19.5	1♑23.7	1 50.5	28 51.1	4 43.9	3 43.2	23 9.2	24 17.1	22 56.5	20 37.0
14	5 28 51.6	21 32.6	14 16.3	14 42.1	3 13.2	0♑ 6.5	5 14.9	3 38.9	23 11.0	24 18.0	22 58.6	20 37.3
15	5 32 48.2	22 33.7	14 13.1	27 41.5	4 37.1	1 21.9	5 45.8	3 34.5	23 12.9	24 18.9	23 .6	20 37.6
16	5 36 44.7	23 34.8	14 10.0	10♒21.9	6 2.1	2 37.3	6 16.5	3 29.9	23 15.0	24 19.8	23 2.7	20 37.9
17	5 40 41.3	24 35.9	14 6.8	22 44.7	7 28.0	3 52.7	6 47.1	3 25.1	23 17.1	24 20.6	23 4.7	20 38.2
18	5 44 37.9	25 36.9	14 3.6	4♓52.8	8 54.6	5 8.1	7 17.6	3 20.2	23 19.3	24 21.3	23 6.6	20 38.3
19	5 48 34.4	26 38.0	14 .4	16 50.1	10 21.9	6 23.5	7 47.9	3 15.0	23 21.6	24 22.0	23 8.6	20 38.5
20	5 52 31.0	27 39.1	13 57.3	28 41.2	11 49.8	7 38.8	8 18.0	3 9.7	23 24.1	24 22.6	23 10.5	20 38.6
21	5 56 27.5	28 40.2	13 54.1	10♈31.2	13 18.3	8 54.2	8 48.0	3 4.3	23 26.6	24 23.1	23 12.5	20 38.7
22	6 0 24.1	29 41.3	13 50.9	22 25.3	14 47.2	10 9.6	9 17.9	2 58.7	23 29.2	24 23.6	23 14.4	20 38.8
23	6 4 20.7	0♑42.4	13 47.7	4♉28.7	16 16.6	11 24.9	9 47.5	2 53.0	23 31.9	24 24.0	23 16.2	20 38.8
24	6 8 17.2	1 43.5	13 44.6	16 45.9	17 46.4	12 40.3	10 17.1	2 47.1	23 34.8	24 24.4	23 18.1	20 38.8
25	6 12 13.8	2 44.6	13 41.4	29 20.6	19 16.6	13 55.6	10 46.4	2 41.0	23 37.7	24 24.7	23 20.0	20 38.8
26	6 16 10.3	3 45.7	13 38.2	12♊15.3	20 47.1	15 10.9	11 15.6	2 34.9	23 40.7	24 25.0	23 21.8	20 R 38.7
27	6 20 6.9	4 46.8	13 35.0	25 30.9	22 18.0	16 26.3	11 44.7	2 28.5	23 43.8	24 25.2	23 23.6	20 38.6
28	6 24 3.5	5 47.9	13 31.9	9♋ 6.6	23 49.2	17 41.6	12 13.5	2 22.1	23 47.0	24 25.3	23 25.4	20 38.5
29	6 28 .0	6 49.0	13 28.7	22 59.5	25 20.8	18 56.9	12 42.2	2 15.5	23 50.3	24 25.4	23 27.1	20 38.3
30	6 31 56.6	7 50.2	13 25.5	7♌ 5.6	26 52.6	20 12.2	13 10.7	2 8.8	23 53.7	24 25.5	23 28.9	20 38.1
31	6 35 53.1	8 51.3	13 22.3	21 19.9	28 24.8	21 27.5	13 39.1	2 2.0	23 57.2	24 25.5	23 30.6	20 37.9
		LATITUDE										
1	4 37 36.4	0 .0	0 .0	4 N 25.0	2 N 33.4	0 S 7.2	1 N 47.0	0 N 23.4	2 S 20.0	0 N 45.4	1 N 41.4	14 N 42.3
4	4 49 26.0	0 .0	0 .0	5 10.2	2 24.4	0 14.4	1 48.5	0 23.9	2 19.3	0 45.5	1 41.4	14 43.8
7	5 1 15.7	0 .0	0 .0	3 16.4	2 9.0	0 21.6	1 50.0	0 24.5	2 18.7	0 45.6	1 41.5	14 45.4
10	5 13 5.4	0 .0	0 .0	0 S 21.5	1 49.6	0 28.6	1 51.6	0 25.1	2 18.1	0 45.8	1 41.6	14 47.0
13	5 24 55.1	0 .0	0 .0	3 42.4	1 28.0	0 35.4	1 53.2	0 25.6	2 17.4	0 45.9	1 41.6	14 48.5
16	5 36 44.7	0 .0	0 .0	5 9.0	1 5.3	0 42.1	1 54.7	0 26.2	2 16.8	0 46.0	1 41.7	14 50.1
19	5 48 34.4	0 .0	0 .0	4 24.8	0 42.3	0 48.5	1 56.3	0 26.7	2 16.2	0 46.1	1 41.8	14 51.7
22	6 0 24.1	0 .0	0 .0	2 1.0	0 19.6	0 54.6	1 57.9	0 27.3	2 15.6	0 46.3	1 41.9	14 53.3
25	6 12 13.8	0 .0	0 .0	1 N 14.8	0 S 2.4	1 .4	1 59.6	0 27.8	2 15.0	0 46.4	1 42.0	14 54.8
28	6 24 3.5	0 .0	0 .0	4 8.1	0 23.4	1 5.8	2 1.2	0 28.4	2 14.4	0 46.5	1 42.1	14 56.4
31	6 35 53.1	0 .0	0 .0	5 3.5	0 43.2	1 10.8	2 2.8	0 28.9	2 13.8	0 46.6	1 42.2	14 57.9
		RIGHT ASCENSION										
1	4 37 36.4	6♐35.7	12♉29.7	15♋10.0	16♏51.6	12♐23.0	29♍12.7	6♌45.7	24♓26.1	24♍49.0	20♏33.6	27♍16.7
2	4 41 32.9	7 40.4	12 26.5	0♌14.1	17 33.1	13 43.8	29 42.6	6 R 43.7	24 26.5	24 50.5	20 35.8	27 17.6
3	4 45 29.5	8 45.3	12 23.4	14 54.4	18 20.9	15 4.9	0♎12.5	6 41.5	24 27.0	24 51.9	20 38.0	27 18.4
4	4 49 26.0	9 50.3	12 20.2	28 57.3	19 14.3	16 26.2	0 42.3	6 39.1	24 27.5	24 53.3	20 40.2	27 19.3
5	4 53 22.6	10 55.4	12 17.0	12♍21.9	20 12.6	17 47.6	1 12.0	6 36.5	24 28.2	24 54.6	20 42.4	27 20.1
6	4 57 19.2	12 .8	12 13.9	25 17.3	21 15.3	19 9.2	1 41.5	6 33.6	24 29.0	24 55.9	20 44.6	27 20.8
7	5 1 15.7	13 6.2	12 10.7	7♎58.2	22 22.0	20 31.0	2 11.0	6 30.6	24 29.9	24 57.1	20 46.7	27 21.6
8	5 5 12.3	14 11.8	12 7.6	20 41.9	23 32.1	21 53.0	2 40.4	6 27.4	24 30.9	24 58.3	20 48.9	27 22.3
9	5 9 8.8	15 17.5	12 4.4	3♏45.2	24 45.3	23 15.1	3 9.6	6 24.0	24 32.0	24 59.4	20 51.0	27 23.0
10	5 13 5.4	16 23.3	12 1.2	17 21.5	26 1.3	24 37.3	3 38.7	6 20.4	24 33.2	25 .5	20 53.1	27 23.6
11	5 17 2.0	17 29.3	11 58.1	1♐37.2	27 19.7	25 59.6	4 7.8	6 16.6	24 34.5	25 1.5	20 55.2	27 24.3
12	5 20 58.5	18 35.3	11 54.9	16 27.3	28 40.4	27 22.0	4 36.7	6 12.6	24 35.9	25 2.5	20 57.3	27 24.9
13	5 24 55.1	19 41.5	11 51.8	1♑33.9	0♐ 3.0	28 44.5	5 5.4	6 8.5	24 37.3	25 3.5	20 59.4	27 25.4
14	5 28 51.6	20 47.7	11 48.6	16 30.3	1 27.4	0♑ 7.1	5 34.1	6 4.1	24 38.9	25 4.3	21 1.5	27 25.9
15	5 32 48.2	21 54.0	11 45.4	0♒50.9	2 53.5	1 29.7	6 2.6	5 59.6	24 40.6	25 5.2	21 3.5	27 26.4
16	5 36 44.7	23 .4	11 42.3	14 19.4	4 21.1	2 52.4	6 31.1	5 54.9	24 42.4	25 6.0	21 5.6	27 27.0
17	5 40 41.3	24 6.9	11 39.1	26 51.6	5 50.0	4 15.0	6 59.4	5 50.0	24 44.3	25 6.7	21 7.6	27 27.4
18	5 44 37.9	25 13.4	11 36.0	8♓33.7	7 20.2	5 37.6	7 27.6	5 44.9	24 46.3	25 7.4	21 9.7	27 27.8
19	5 48 34.4	26 19.9	11 32.8	19 37.6	8 51.6	7 .2	7 55.6	5 39.6	24 48.3	25 8.0	21 11.6	27 28.2
20	5 52 31.0	27 26.4	11 29.7	0♈17.7	10 24.0	8 22.8	8 23.5	5 34.2	24 50.5	25 8.6	21 13.6	27 28.5
21	5 56 27.5	28 33.0	11 26.5	10 49.7	11 57.4	9 45.3	8 51.3	5 28.6	24 52.7	25 9.1	21 15.6	27 28.9
22	6 0 24.1	29 39.6	11 23.4	21 29.4	13 31.8	11 7.7	9 18.9	5 22.9	24 55.0	25 9.6	21 17.5	27 29.1
23	6 4 20.7	0♑46.2	11 20.2	2♉32.9	15 7.0	12 30.0	9 46.4	5 17.0	24 57.5	25 10.0	21 19.4	27 29.4
24	6 8 17.2	1 52.8	11 17.1	14 15.6	16 43.1	13 52.2	10 13.8	5 10.9	24 60.0	25 10.3	21 21.3	27 29.6
25	6 12 13.8	2 59.4	11 13.9	26 50.8	18 20.0	15 14.3	10 41.1	5 4.7	25 2.6	25 10.7	21 23.2	27 29.8
26	6 16 10.3	4 5.9	11 10.7	10♊26.1	19 57.6	16 36.3	11 8.2	4 58.4	25 5.3	25 10.9	21 25.0	27 30.0
27	6 20 6.9	5 12.5	11 7.6	24 59.3	21 36.0	17 58.1	11 35.1	4 51.9	25 8.1	25 11.1	21 26.9	27 30.1
28	6 24 3.5	6 19.0	11 4.4	10♋13.9	23 15.0	19 19.8	12 1.9	4 45.2	25 11.0	25 11.3	21 28.7	27 30.2
29	6 28 .0	7 25.5	11 1.3	25 42.0	24 54.6	20 41.2	12 28.6	4 38.5	25 13.9	25 11.4	21 30.5	27 30.3
30	6 31 56.6	8 31.9	10 58.1	10♌53.0	26 34.9	22 2.5	12 55.1	4 31.5	25 17.0	25 11.4	21 32.3	27 30.3
31	6 35 53.1	9 38.2	10 55.0	25 25.8	28 15.7	23 23.6	13 21.5	4 24.5	25 20.1	25 11.4	21 34.0	27 30.3
		DECLINATION										
1	4 37 36.4	21 S 42.1	0 N 17.1	27 N 9.2	14 S 54.1	22 S 34.7	2 N 17.1	19 N 33.6	4 S 56.9	3 N 4.1	16 S 46.2	17 N 14.3
4	4 49 26.0	22 9.1	0 17.1	18 6.4	15 41.5	23 6.1	1 39.9	19 35.7	4 55.6	3 2.4	16 47.8	17 14.9
7	5 1 15.7	22 32.2	0 17.0	0 7.2	16 44.3	23 31.1	1 3.1	19 38.2	4 53.9	3 .8	16 49.4	17 15.6
10	5 13 5.4	22 51.3	0 17.0	18 S 3.9	17 54.4	23 49.8	0 26.8	19 41.1	4 51.8	2 59.5	16 50.9	17 16.5
13	5 24 55.1	23 6.4	0 16.9	27 8.7	19 5.9	24 1.9	0 S 9.0	19 44.4	4 49.3	2 58.4	16 52.4	17 17.4
16	5 36 44.7	23 17.4	0 16.9	22 35.9	20 14.9	24 7.2	0 44.2	19 48.1	4 46.5	2 57.4	16 53.9	17 18.5
19	5 48 34.4	23 24.2	0 16.8	9 15.7	21 18.6	24 5.9	1 18.8	19 52.1	4 43.3	2 56.7	16 55.3	17 19.7
22	6 0 24.1	23 26.7	0 16.8	6 N 51.4	22 15.1	23 57.8	1 52.7	19 56.4	4 39.7	2 56.1	16 56.6	17 21.0
25	6 12 13.8	23 25.0	0 16.7	21 13.9	23 3.1	23 43.1	2 25.9	20 1.0	4 35.8	2 55.8	16 57.9	17 22.4
28	6 24 3.5	23 19.1	0 16.7	27 15.4	23 41.5	23 21.8	2 58.4	20 5.8	4 31.5	2 55.7	16 59.1	17 24.0
31	6 35 53.1	23 9.0	0 16.6	19 10.8	24 9.3	22 54.0	3 30.1	20 10.8	4 27.0	2 55.7	17 .3	17 25.6

JANUARY 1967

LONGITUDE

DAY	EPHEM. SID. TIME	☉	☊	☾	☿	♀	♂	♃	♄	♅	♆	♇
	h m s	° ′	° ′	° ′	° ′	° ′	° ′	° ′	° ′	° ′	° ′	° ′
1	6 39 49.7	9♑52.4	13♉19.1	5♍37.3	29♐57.3	22♑42.8	14♎ 7.2	1♌55.1	24♓ .8	24♍25.4	23♏32.3	20♍37.6
2	6 43 46.2	10 53.6	13 16.0	19 53.5	1♑30.2	23 58.1	14 35.2	1 R 48.1	24 4.5	24 R 25.2	23 34.0	20 R 37.3
3	6 47 42.8	11 54.7	13 12.8	4♎ 5.4	3 3.3	25 13.4	15 2.9	1 40.9	24 8.3	24 25.1	23 35.6	20 37.0
4	6 51 39.4	12 55.9	13 9.6	18 11.0	4 36.8	26 28.6	15 30.5	1 33.7	24 12.1	24 24.8	23 37.2	20 36.6
5	6 55 35.9	13 57.0	13 6.4	2♏ 9.5	6 10.7	27 43.9	15 57.9	1 26.3	24 16.1	24 24.5	23 38.8	20 36.2
6	6 59 32.5	14 58.3	13 3.3	16 .6	7 45.0	28 59.2	16 25.1	1 19.0	24 20.2	24 24.2	23 40.5	20 35.9
7	7 3 29.0	15 59.4	13 .1	29 43.8	9 19.6	0♒14.5	16 52.0	1 11.5	24 24.3	24 23.8	23 42.0	20 35.4
8	7 7 25.6	17 .6	12 56.9	13♐18.6	10 54.6	1 29.7	17 18.7	1 3.9	24 28.5	24 23.3	23 43.5	20 34.9
9	7 11 22.2	18 1.8	12 53.7	26 43.8	12 30.0	2 45.0	17 45.2	0 56.2	24 32.8	24 22.8	23 45.0	20 34.4
10	7 15 18.7	19 2.9	12 50.6	9♑57.9	14 5.8	4 .2	18 11.5	0 48.5	24 37.2	24 22.2	23 46.5	20 33.8
11	7 19 15.3	20 4.1	12 47.4	22 59.3	15 42.0	5 15.4	18 37.5	0 40.7	24 41.6	24 21.6	23 48.0	20 33.2
12	7 23 11.8	21 5.2	12 44.2	5♒46.7	17 18.7	6 30.7	19 3.3	0 32.8	24 46.2	24 20.9	23 49.4	20 32.6
13	7 27 8.4	22 6.4	12 41.0	18 19.5	18 55.9	7 45.9	19 28.9	0 24.9	24 50.8	24 20.1	23 50.8	20 32.0
14	7 31 4.9	23 7.5	12 37.9	0♓38.0	20 33.5	9 1.0	19 54.2	0 17.0	24 55.5	24 19.3	23 52.1	20 31.3
15	7 35 1.5	24 8.7	12 34.7	12 43.9	22 11.6	10 16.2	20 19.2	0 9.0	25 .3	24 18.5	23 53.5	20 30.6
16	7 38 58.1	25 9.8	12 31.5	24 39.9	23 50.2	11 31.4	20 44.0	0 1.0	25 5.2	24 17.6	23 54.8	20 29.9
17	7 42 54.6	26 10.9	12 28.3	6♈29.7	25 29.3	12 46.5	21 8.5	29♋53.0	25 10.1	24 16.6	23 56.1	20 29.1
18	7 46 51.2	27 12.0	12 25.1	18 17.9	27 8.9	14 1.7	21 32.8	29 45.0	25 15.1	24 15.6	23 57.3	20 28.3
19	7 50 47.7	28 13.1	12 22.0	0♉10.0	28 49.1	15 16.8	21 56.7	29 36.9	25 20.2	24 14.6	23 58.5	20 27.5
20	7 54 44.3	29 14.2	12 18.8	12 11.3	0♒29.8	16 31.9	22 20.4	29 28.9	25 25.4	24 13.5	23 59.7	20 26.7
21	7 58 40.8	0♒15.2	12 15.6	24 27.3	2 11.0	17 46.9	22 43.8	29 20.8	25 30.7	24 12.3	24 .9	20 25.8
22	8 2 37.4	1 16.3	12 12.4	7♊ 3.2	3 52.8	19 2.0	23 7.0	29 12.8	25 36.0	24 11.1	24 2.0	20 24.9
23	8 6 34.0	2 17.3	12 9.3	20 2.9	5 35.1	20 17.0	23 29.8	29 4.7	25 41.3	24 9.8	24 3.1	20 23.9
24	8 10 30.5	3 18.3	12 6.1	3♋28.6	7 18.0	21 32.0	23 52.3	28 56.7	25 46.8	24 8.5	24 4.2	20 23.0
25	8 14 27.1	4 19.3	12 2.9	17 20.4	9 1.3	22 47.0	24 14.5	28 48.7	25 52.3	24 7.2	24 5.2	20 22.0
26	8 18 23.6	5 20.3	11 59.7	1♌35.4	10 45.1	24 2.0	24 36.4	28 40.7	25 57.9	24 5.8	24 6.2	20 21.0
27	8 22 20.2	6 21.3	11 56.6	16 8.2	12 29.4	25 17.0	24 58.0	28 32.9	26 3.6	24 4.4	24 7.3	20 20.0
28	8 26 16.7	7 22.2	11 53.4	0♍51.3	14 14.1	26 31.9	25 19.3	28 25.0	26 9.3	24 2.9	24 8.2	20 19.0
29	8 30 13.3	8 23.2	11 50.2	15 36.5	15 59.1	27 46.8	25 40.2	28 17.1	26 15.1	24 1.3	24 9.1	20 17.9
30	8 34 9.9	9 24.1	11 47.0	0♎16.3	17 44.4	29 1.7	26 .7	28 9.3	26 20.9	23 59.7	24 10.0	20 16.8
31	8 38 6.4	10 25.0	11 43.9	14 44.9	19 29.8	0♓16.6	26 20.9	28 1.6	26 26.8	23 58.1	24 10.8	20 15.7

LATITUDE

DAY	EPHEM. SID. TIME	☉	☊	☾	☿	♀	♂	♃	♄	♅	♆	♇
1	6 39 49.7	0 .0	0 .0	4N45.3	0S49.4	1S12.4	2N 3.4	0N29.0	2S13.6	0N46.7	1N42.2	14N58.5
4	6 51 39.4	0 .0	0 .0	2 15.6	1 7.1	1 16.9	2 5.0	0 29.5	2 13.1	0 46.8	1 42.4	14 60.0
7	7 3 29.0	0 .0	0 .0	1S20.7	1 23.0	1 20.8	2 6.7	0 30.0	2 12.5	0 46.9	1 42.5	15 1.5
10	7 15 18.7	0 .0	0 .0	4 10.7	1 36.8	1 24.3	2 8.3	0 30.5	2 12.0	0 47.0	1 42.6	15 2.9
13	7 27 8.4	0 .0	0 .0	5 .8	1 48.2	1 27.2	2 10.0	0 30.9	2 11.5	0 47.2	1 42.8	15 4.4
16	7 38 58.1	0 .0	0 .0	3 46.6	1 57.0	1 29.5	2 11.7	0 31.4	2 11.0	0 47.3	1 42.9	15 5.8
19	7 50 47.7	0 .0	0 .0	1 7.1	2 2.9	1 31.3	2 13.4	0 31.8	2 10.5	0 47.4	1 43.1	15 7.1
22	8 2 37.4	0 .0	0 .0	2N 4.2	2 5.3	1 32.5	2 15.0	0 32.2	2 10.1	0 47.5	1 43.2	15 8.4
25	8 14 27.1	0 .0	0 .0	4 32.1	2 4.0	1 33.1	2 16.7	0 32.5	2 9.6	0 47.6	1 43.4	15 9.7
28	8 26 16.7	0 .0	0 .0	4 44.1	1 58.2	1 33.0	2 18.4	0 32.9	2 9.2	0 47.7	1 43.5	15 10.9
31	8 38 6.4	0 .0	0 .0	2 16.4	1 47.6	1 32.3	2 20.0	0 33.2	2 8.9	0 47.8	1 43.7	15 12.0

RIGHT ASCENSION

DAY	EPHEM. SID. TIME	☉	☊	☾	☿	♀	♂	♃	♄	♅	♆	♇
1	6 39 49.7	10♑44.6	10♉51.8	9♍13.3	29♐57.1	24♑44.4	13♎47.7	4♌17.4	25♓23.3	25♍11.4	21♏35.7	27♍30.3
2	6 43 46.2	11 50.8	10 48.7	22 21.5	1♑39.0	26 5.1	14 13.7	4 R 10.1	25 26.7	25 R 11.3	21 37.5	27 R 30.2
3	6 47 42.8	12 57.0	10 45.5	5♎ 3.9	3 21.3	27 25.5	14 39.6	4 2.7	25 30.0	25 11.1	21 39.1	27 30.1
4	6 51 39.4	14 3.0	10 42.4	17 38.1	5 4.2	28 45.6	15 5.3	3 55.2	25 33.5	25 10.9	21 40.8	27 30.0
5	6 55 35.9	15 9.0	10 39.3	0♏21.6	6 47.5	0♒ 5.5	15 30.8	3 47.6	25 37.1	25 10.6	21 42.4	27 29.9
6	6 59 32.5	16 15.0	10 36.1	13 30.0	8 31.2	1 25.2	15 56.2	3 40.0	25 40.8	25 10.4	21 44.1	27 29.7
7	7 3 29.0	17 20.8	10 33.0	27 13.7	10 15.3	2 44.5	16 21.4	3 32.2	25 44.5	25 10.0	21 45.7	27 29.5
8	7 7 25.6	18 26.5	10 29.8	11♐34.0	11 59.8	4 3.6	16 46.4	3 24.4	25 48.3	25 9.6	21 47.2	27 29.3
9	7 11 22.2	19 32.0	10 26.7	26 20.5	13 44.5	5 22.4	17 11.1	3 16.4	25 52.2	25 9.1	21 48.8	27 29.0
10	7 15 18.7	20 37.4	10 23.5	11♑11.5	15 29.6	6 40.9	17 35.7	3 8.4	25 56.1	25 8.6	21 50.3	27 28.7
11	7 19 15.3	21 42.7	10 20.4	25 41.4	17 15.0	7 59.0	18 .1	3 .3	26 .2	25 8.0	21 51.7	27 28.4
12	7 23 11.8	22 47.9	10 17.2	9♒29.1	19 .6	9 16.9	18 24.3	2 52.2	26 4.3	25 7.4	21 53.2	27 28.0
13	7 27 8.4	23 52.9	10 14.1	22 24.3	20 46.4	10 34.4	18 48.2	2 44.0	26 8.5	25 6.8	21 54.6	27 27.6
14	7 31 4.9	24 57.7	10 11.0	4♓27.6	22 32.4	11 51.6	19 12.0	2 35.7	26 12.7	25 6.0	21 56.0	27 27.2
15	7 35 1.5	26 2.4	10 7.8	15 47.4	24 18.5	13 8.5	19 35.5	2 27.5	26 17.1	25 5.3	21 57.4	27 26.8
16	7 38 58.1	27 6.9	10 4.7	26 36.3	26 4.8	14 25.1	19 58.8	2 19.1	26 21.5	25 4.5	21 58.7	27 26.3
17	7 42 54.6	28 11.2	10 1.5	7♈ 9.1	27 51.2	15 41.4	20 21.9	2 10.8	26 26.0	25 3.6	22 .0	27 25.8
18	7 46 51.2	29 15.4	9 58.4	17 41.1	29 37.7	16 57.3	20 44.7	2 2.4	26 30.5	25 2.7	22 1.3	27 25.2
19	7 50 47.7	0♒19.4	9 55.2	28 28.1	1♒24.2	18 12.8	21 7.3	1 54.0	26 35.1	25 1.7	22 2.6	27 24.7
20	7 54 44.3	1 23.2	9 52.1	9♉45.9	3 10.7	19 28.1	21 29.6	1 45.6	26 39.8	25 .7	22 3.8	27 24.1
21	7 58 40.8	2 26.8	9 49.0	21 49.6	4 57.2	20 43.0	21 51.7	1 37.2	26 44.6	24 59.7	22 5.0	27 23.5
22	8 2 37.4	3 30.2	9 45.8	4♊51.1	6 43.6	21 57.6	22 13.6	1 28.8	26 49.4	24 58.6	22 6.1	27 22.8
23	8 6 34.0	4 33.4	9 42.7	18 55.2	8 29.9	23 11.9	22 35.1	1 20.4	26 54.3	24 57.4	22 7.3	27 22.1
24	8 10 30.5	5 36.4	9 39.6	3♋54.3	10 16.1	24 25.8	22 56.4	1 12.1	26 59.2	24 56.2	22 8.4	27 21.4
25	8 14 27.1	6 39.3	9 36.4	19 26.7	12 2.1	25 39.4	23 17.5	1 3.7	27 4.3	24 55.0	22 9.4	27 20.7
26	8 18 23.6	7 41.9	9 33.3	5♌ 1.8	13 47.8	26 52.7	23 38.2	0 55.4	27 9.3	24 53.7	22 10.5	27 20.0
27	8 22 20.2	8 44.4	9 30.1	20 11.2	15 33.2	28 5.7	23 58.7	0 47.2	27 14.5	24 52.5	22 11.5	27 19.2
28	8 26 16.7	9 46.6	9 27.0	4♍38.7	17 18.2	29 18.4	24 18.8	0 38.9	27 19.7	24 51.1	22 12.5	27 18.4
29	8 30 13.3	10 48.6	9 23.9	18 23.2	19 2.8	0♓30.8	24 38.7	0 30.7	27 25.0	24 49.7	22 13.4	27 17.6
30	8 34 9.9	11 50.4	9 20.7	1♎34.3	20 46.8	1 42.8	24 58.2	0 22.6	27 30.3	24 48.2	22 14.3	27 16.7
31	8 38 6.4	12 52.1	9 17.6	14 27.5	22 30.1	2 54.6	25 17.4	0 14.5	27 35.7	24 46.8	22 15.2	27 15.9

DECLINATION

DAY	EPHEM. SID. TIME	☉	☊	☾	☿	♀	♂	♃	♄	♅	♆	♇
1	6 39 49.7	23S 4.7	0N16.6	13N52.2	24S16.1	22S43.3	3S40.5	20N12.6	4S25.4	2N55.8	17S .7	17N26.2
4	6 51 39.4	22 49.0	0 16.5	5S 2.5	24 29.0	22 7.3	4 11.0	20 17.8	4 20.4	2 56.2	17 1.8	17 28.0
7	7 3 29.0	22 29.2	0 16.5	21 24.7	24 29.8	21 25.2	4 40.7	20 23.2	4 15.0	2 56.7	17 2.9	17 29.8
10	7 15 18.7	22 5.5	0 16.4	27 14.3	24 18.2	20 37.4	5 9.4	20 28.7	4 9.4	2 57.4	17 3.8	17 31.8
13	7 27 8.4	21 37.9	0 16.4	20 6.1	23 53.6	19 44.2	5 37.1	20 34.2	4 3.6	2 58.3	17 4.8	17 33.8
16	7 38 58.1	21 6.4	0 16.3	5 35.1	23 15.8	18 45.9	6 3.8	20 39.8	3 57.4	2 59.5	17 5.6	17 35.9
19	7 50 47.7	20 31.4	0 16.3	10N29.1	22 24.3	17 42.7	6 29.3	20 45.3	3 51.0	3 .8	17 6.4	17 38.1
22	8 2 37.4	19 52.9	0 16.2	23 32.0	21 19.1	16 35.1	6 53.7	20 50.7	3 44.3	3 2.2	17 7.1	17 40.3
25	8 14 27.1	19 11.0	0 16.2	26 49.0	19 59.9	15 23.4	7 17.0	20 56.0	3 37.5	3 3.9	17 7.7	17 42.6
28	8 26 16.7	18 26.0	0 16.1	15 35.8	18 26.9	14 7.9	7 39.0	21 1.2	3 30.3	3 5.7	17 8.3	17 44.9
31	8 38 6.4	17 38.0	0 16.1	3S42.9	16 40.7	12 49.0	7 59.7	21 6.2	3 23.0	3 7.7	17 8.8	17 47.3

FEBRUARY 1967

LONGITUDE

DAY	EPHEM. SID. TIME h m s	☉ ° ′	☊ ° ′	☾ ° ′	☿ ° ′	♀ ° ′	♂ ° ′	♃ ° ′	♄ ° ′	♅ ° ′	♆ ° ′	♇ ° ′
1	8 42 3.0	11♒25.9	11♉40.7	28♎58.8	21♒15.3	1♓31.4	26♎40.8	27♋53.9	26♓32.8	23♍56.4	24♏11.7	20♍14.5
2	8 45 59.5	12 26.8	11 37.5	12♏56.7	23 .8	2 46.2	27 .3	27 R 46.4	26 38.8	23 R 54.7	24 12.5	20 R 13.3
3	8 49 56.1	13 27.7	11 34.3	26 39.0	24 46.0	4 1.0	27 19.4	27 38.8	26 44.9	23 53.0	24 13.2	20 12.1
4	8 53 52.6	14 28.6	11 31.1	10♐ 6.7	26 30.7	5 15.8	27 38.1	27 31.4	26 51.0	23 51.2	24 13.9	20 10.9
5	8 57 49.2	15 29.4	11 28.0	23 21.3	28 14.8	6 30.6	27 56.4	27 24.0	26 57.2	23 49.3	24 14.6	20 9.7
6	9 1 45.8	16 30.2	11 24.8	6♑24.1	29 58.0	7 45.3	28 14.2	27 16.8	27 3.5	23 47.5	24 15.3	20 8.4
7	9 5 42.3	17 31.1	11 21.6	19 15.9	1♓39.8	9 .0	28 31.7	27 9.6	27 9.8	23 45.5	24 15.9	20 7.1
8	9 9 38.9	18 31.9	11 18.4	1♒56.9	3 20.1	10 14.7	28 48.7	27 2.5	27 16.1	23 43.6	24 16.5	20 5.8
9	9 13 35.4	19 32.6	11 15.3	14 27.2	4 58.3	11 29.3	29 5.3	26 55.6	27 22.5	23 41.6	24 17.0	20 4.5
10	9 17 32.0	20 33.4	11 12.1	26 46.8	6 34.0	12 44.0	29 21.5	26 48.7	27 29.0	23 39.6	24 17.5	20 3.2
11	9 21 28.5	21 34.1	11 8.9	8♓56.2	8 6.6	13 58.6	29 37.2	26 42.0	27 35.5	23 37.5	24 18.0	20 1.8
12	9 25 25.1	22 34.8	11 5.7	20 56.3	9 35.7	15 13.1	29 52.4	26 35.4	27 42.0	23 35.4	24 18.5	20 .5
13	9 29 21.6	23 35.5	11 2.5	2♈49.0	11 .5	16 27.7	0♏ 7.1	26 28.9	27 48.6	23 33.3	24 18.9	19 59.1
14	9 33 18.2	24 36.2	10 59.4	14 37.0	12 20.4	17 42.2	0 21.4	26 22.6	27 55.3	23 31.1	24 19.3	19 57.7
15	9 37 14.8	25 36.8	10 56.2	26 23.9	13 34.7	18 56.7	0 35.1	26 16.4	28 2.0	23 28.9	24 19.6	19 56.2
16	9 41 11.3	26 37.4	10 53.0	8♉14.2	14 42.7	20 11.1	0 48.4	26 10.3	28 8.7	23 26.7	24 19.9	19 54.8
17	9 45 7.9	27 38.1	10 49.8	20 13.1	15 43.7	21 25.5	1 1.2	26 4.4	28 15.5	23 24.5	24 20.2	19 53.4
18	9 49 4.4	28 38.6	10 46.7	2♊25.8	16 37.0	22 39.9	1 13.4	25 58.6	28 22.3	23 22.2	24 20.5	19 51.9
19	9 53 1.0	29 39.1	10 43.5	14 58.0	17 21.9	23 54.2	1 25.1	25 53.0	28 29.1	23 19.9	24 20.7	19 50.5
20	9 56 57.5	0♓39.6	10 40.3	27 54.4	17 57.9	25 8.5	1 36.2	25 47.5	28 36.0	23 17.6	24 20.9	19 49.0
21	10 0 54.1	1 40.1	10 37.1	11♋18.8	18 24.5	26 22.7	1 46.8	25 42.2	28 43.0	23 15.2	24 21.0	19 47.5
22	10 4 50.6	2 40.5	10 34.0	25 12.7	18 41.4	27 36.9	1 56.8	25 37.0	28 49.9	23 12.8	24 21.1	19 46.0
23	10 8 47.2	3 40.9	10 30.8	9♌34.8	18 48.2	28 51.1	2 6.3	25 32.0	28 56.9	23 10.4	24 21.2	19 44.4
24	10 12 43.7	4 41.3	10 27.6	24 20.5	18 R 45.0	0♈ 5.2	2 15.1	25 27.2	29 3.9	23 8.0	24 21.2	19 42.9
25	10 16 40.3	5 41.6	10 24.4	9♍22.0	18 31.9	1 19.3	2 23.4	25 22.5	29 11.0	23 5.5	24 21.3	19 41.4
26	10 20 36.9	6 41.9	10 21.2	24 29.6	18 9.3	2 33.3	2 31.1	25 18.0	29 18.0	23 3.1	24 R 21.2	19 39.8
27	10 24 33.4	7 42.2	10 18.1	9♎33.3	17 37.8	3 47.3	2 38.1	25 13.7	29 25.2	23 .6	24 21.2	19 38.3
28	10 28 30.0	8 42.5	10 14.9	24 24.4	16 58.1	5 1.3	2 44.5	25 9.6	29 32.3	22 58.1	24 21.1	19 36.7

LATITUDE

DAY	EPHEM. SID. TIME	☉	☊	☾	☿	♀	♂	♃	♄	♅	♆	♇
1	8 42 3.0	0 .0	0 .0	1N 5.9	1S42.8	1S32.0	2N20.5	0N33.3	2S 8.7	0N47.8	1N43.7	15N12.4
4	8 53 52.6	0 .0	0 .0	2S24.7	1 24.6	1 30.4	2 22.1	0 33.6	2 8.4	0 47.9	1 43.9	15 13.5
7	9 5 42.3	0 .0	0 .0	4 38.6	0 60.0	1 28.3	2 23.7	0 33.8	2 8.1	0 48.0	1 44.1	15 14.5
10	9 17 32.0	0 .0	0 .0	4 48.0	0 28.7	1 25.5	2 25.3	0 34.1	2 7.8	0 48.1	1 44.2	15 15.4
13	9 29 21.6	0 .0	0 .0	3 2.4	0N 9.1	1 22.1	2 26.8	0 34.3	2 7.5	0 48.2	1 44.4	15 16.3
16	9 41 11.3	0 .0	0 .0	0 8.1	0 52.4	1 18.1	2 28.2	0 34.5	2 7.2	0 48.2	1 44.6	15 17.1
19	9 53 1.0	0 .0	0 .0	2N55.7	1 38.7	1 13.5	2 29.5	0 34.6	2 7.0	0 48.3	1 44.8	15 17.9
22	10 4 50.6	0 .0	0 .0	4 53.9	2 24.4	1 8.3	2 30.7	0 34.8	2 6.8	0 48.3	1 44.9	15 18.5
25	10 16 40.3	0 .0	0 .0	4 22.0	3 4.1	1 2.6	2 31.9	0 34.9	2 6.6	0 48.4	1 45.1	15 19.1
28	10 28 30.0	0 .0	0 .0	1 15.5	3 31.8	0 56.3	2 32.8	0 35.0	2 6.5	0 48.4	1 45.3	15 19.6

RIGHT ASCENSION

DAY	EPHEM. SID. TIME	☉	☊	☾	☿	♀	♂	♃	♄	♅	♆	♇
1	8 42 3.0	13♒53.5	9♉14.5	27♎19.9	24♒12.7	4♓ 6.1	25♎36.3	0♌ 6.4	27♓41.1	24♍45.2	22♏16.0	27♍15.0
2	8 45 59.5	14 54.7	9 11.3	10♏27.3	25 54.3	5 17.3	25 54.9	29♋58.5	27 46.6	24 R 43.7	22 16.9	27 R 14.0
3	8 49 56.1	15 55.7	9 8.2	24 1.2	27 34.9	6 28.3	26 13.1	29 R 50.6	27 52.1	24 42.1	22 17.6	27 13.1
4	8 53 52.6	16 56.6	9 5.1	8♐ 5.6	29 14.3	7 39.0	26 30.9	29 42.8	27 57.7	24 40.4	22 18.4	27 12.1
5	8 57 49.2	17 57.2	9 1.9	22 34.5	0♓52.1	8 49.4	26 48.4	29 35.1	28 3.3	24 38.7	22 19.1	27 11.1
6	9 1 45.8	18 57.6	8 58.8	7♑11.8	2 28.3	9 59.6	27 5.4	29 27.5	28 9.0	24 37.0	22 19.8	27 10.1
7	9 5 42.3	19 57.9	8 55.7	21 35.4	4 2.5	11 9.6	27 22.1	29 19.9	28 14.8	24 35.3	22 20.4	27 9.1
8	9 9 38.9	20 57.9	8 52.5	5♒25.0	5 34.3	12 19.3	27 38.4	29 12.5	28 20.6	24 33.5	22 21.0	27 8.0
9	9 13 35.4	21 57.7	8 49.4	18 28.4	7 3.5	13 28.8	27 54.3	29 5.2	28 26.4	24 31.7	22 21.6	27 6.9
10	9 17 32.0	22 57.4	8 46.3	0♓42.8	8 29.6	14 38.0	28 9.8	28 58.0	28 32.3	24 29.8	22 22.1	27 5.8
11	9 21 28.5	23 56.8	8 43.1	12 13.6	9 52.3	15 47.1	28 24.8	28 50.9	28 38.2	24 27.9	22 22.6	27 4.7
12	9 25 25.1	24 56.1	8 40.0	23 10.9	11 10.9	16 56.0	28 39.4	28 44.0	28 44.2	24 26.0	22 23.1	27 3.6
13	9 29 21.6	25 55.1	8 36.9	3♈47.6	12 25.1	18 4.7	28 53.6	28 37.2	28 50.2	24 24.0	22 23.5	27 2.4
14	9 33 18.2	26 54.0	8 33.8	14 17.4	13 34.2	19 13.2	29 7.3	28 30.5	28 56.3	24 22.1	22 23.9	27 1.2
15	9 37 14.8	27 52.6	8 30.6	24 54.8	14 37.7	20 21.5	29 20.5	28 24.0	29 2.4	24 20.1	22 24.3	27 .0
16	9 41 11.3	28 51.1	8 27.5	5♉54.5	15 35.0	21 29.7	29 33.3	28 17.6	29 8.5	24 18.0	22 24.6	26 58.8
17	9 45 7.9	29 49.4	8 24.4	17 30.8	16 25.6	22 37.7	29 45.6	28 11.4	29 14.7	24 16.0	22 25.0	26 57.6
18	9 49 4.4	0♓47.6	8 21.3	29 56.3	17 8.8	23 45.6	29 57.4	28 5.3	29 20.9	24 13.9	22 25.2	26 56.4
19	9 53 1.0	1 45.5	8 18.1	13♊19.2	17 44.2	24 53.4	0♏ 8.6	27 59.3	29 27.2	24 11.8	22 25.5	26 55.1
20	9 56 57.5	2 43.3	8 15.0	27 39.1	18 11.3	26 1.0	0 19.4	27 53.6	29 33.5	24 9.7	22 25.7	26 53.8
21	10 0 54.1	3 40.8	8 11.9	12♋43.6	18 29.9	27 8.5	0 29.6	27 47.9	29 39.8	24 7.5	22 25.8	26 52.6
22	10 4 50.6	4 38.3	8 8.7	28 9.3	18 39.6	28 15.9	0 39.3	27 42.5	29 46.2	24 5.3	22 26.0	26 51.2
23	10 8 47.2	5 35.5	8 5.6	13♌28.7	18 40.3	29 23.2	0 48.4	27 37.2	29 52.6	24 3.1	22 26.0	26 49.9
24	10 12 43.7	6 32.6	8 2.5	28 20.9	18 R 32.2	0♈30.5	0 57.0	27 32.1	29 59.0	24 .9	22 26.1	26 48.6
25	10 16 40.3	7 29.6	7 59.4	12♍37.2	18 15.4	1 37.6	1 5.0	27 27.2	0♈ 5.4	23 58.6	22 26.1	26 47.2
26	10 20 36.9	8 26.4	7 56.3	26 21.4	17 50.4	2 44.7	1 12.4	27 22.4	0 11.9	23 56.4	22 26.1	26 45.9
27	10 24 33.4	9 23.0	7 53.1	9♎45.3	17 17.7	3 51.8	1 19.2	27 17.9	0 18.4	23 54.1	22 26.1	26 44.5
28	10 28 30.0	10 19.5	7 50.0	23 4.1	16 38.3	4 58.8	1 25.4	27 13.5	0 24.9	23 51.8	22 R 26.0	26 43.1

DECLINATION

DAY	EPHEM. SID. TIME	☉	☊	☾	☿	♀	♂	♃	♄	♅	♆	♇
1	8 42 3.0	17S21.3	0N16.1	10S 5.3	16S 2.5	12S22.0	8S 6.4	21N 7.8	3S20.5	3N 8.3	17S 8.9	17N48.1
4	8 53 52.6	16 29.6	0 16.0	24 21.4	14 .4	10 59.1	8 25.3	21 12.6	3 13.0	3 10.5	17 9.3	17 50.5
7	9 5 42.3	15 35.3	0 16.0	26 39.4	11 49.2	9 33.7	8 42.9	21 17.1	3 5.2	3 12.8	17 9.6	17 52.9
10	9 17 32.0	14 38.5	0 15.9	17 5.7	9 32.9	8 5.9	8 59.0	21 21.4	2 57.3	3 15.3	17 9.9	17 55.4
13	9 29 21.6	13 39.6	0 15.9	1 40.2	7 18.0	6 36.3	9 13.5	21 25.4	2 49.2	3 17.8	17 10.0	17 57.8
16	9 41 11.3	12 38.6	0 15.8	14N 7.7	5 13.0	5 5.1	9 26.5	21 29.1	2 41.0	3 20.5	17 10.1	18 .2
19	9 53 1.0	11 35.8	0 15.8	25 30.4	3 28.6	3 32.8	9 37.9	21 32.5	2 32.7	3 23.2	17 10.1	18 2.6
22	10 4 50.6	10 31.4	0 15.7	25 54.7	2 15.6	1 59.6	9 47.7	21 35.7	2 24.2	3 26.1	17 10.1	18 5.0
25	10 16 40.3	9 25.6	0 15.7	12 6.1	1 42.7	0 25.8	9 55.7	21 38.5	2 15.7	3 29.0	17 9.9	18 7.4
28	10 28 30.0	8 18.4	0 15.6	8S17.5	1 53.7	1N 8.1	10 2.0	21 40.9	2 7.0	3 32.0	17 9.7	18 9.7

MARCH 1967

DAY	EPHEM. SID. TIME	☉	☊	☽	☿	♀	♂	♃	♄	♅	♆	♇
		LONGITUDE										
	h m s	° ′	° ′	° ′	° ′	° ′	° ′	° ′	° ′	° ′	° ′	° ′
1	10 32 26.5	9♓42.7	10♉11.7	8♏56.7	16♓11.3	6♈15.2	2♏50.2	25♋ 5.6	29♓39.5	22♍55.6	24♏20.9	19♍35.1
2	10 36 23.1	10 42.9	10 8.5	23 7.1	15 R 18.7	7 29.0	2 55.3	25 R 1.8	29 46.7	22 R 53.0	24 R 20.8	19 R 33.5
3	10 40 19.6	11 43.1	10 5.4	6♐54.9	14 21.5	8 42.8	2 59.8	24 58.2	29 53.9	22 50.5	24 20.6	19 32.0
4	10 44 16.2	12 43.2	10 2.2	20 21.2	13 21.3	9 56.6	3 3.5	24 54.7	0♈ 1.1	22 47.9	24 20.4	19 30.4
5	10 48 12.7	13 43.4	9 59.0	3♑28.3	12 19.4	11 10.3	3 6.6	24 51.5	0 8.4	22 45.4	24 20.1	19 28.8
6	10 52 9.3	14 43.5	9 55.8	16 18.9	11 17.5	12 24.0	3 8.9	24 48.4	0 15.7	22 42.8	24 19.8	19 27.2
7	10 56 5.8	15 43.6	9 52.6	28 55.4	10 16.9	13 37.7	3 10.5	24 45.5	0 23.0	22 40.2	24 19.5	19 25.6
8	11 0 2.4	16 43.6	9 49.5	11♒20.1	9 18.8	14 51.3	3 11.4	24 42.8	0 30.3	22 37.6	24 19.1	19 24.0
9	11 3 59.0	17 43.6	9 46.3	23 34.8	8 24.4	16 4.8	3 11.6	24 40.3	0 37.7	22 35.0	24 18.7	19 22.4
10	11 7 55.5	18 43.7	9 43.1	5♓41.1	7 34.7	17 18.3	3 R 11.1	24 38.1	0 45.1	22 32.4	24 18.4	19 20.8
11	11 11 52.1	19 43.6	9 39.9	17 40.3	6 50.2	18 31.8	3 9.8	24 36.0	0 52.5	22 29.8	24 17.9	19 19.2
12	11 15 48.6	20 43.6	9 36.8	29 33.6	6 11.5	19 45.2	3 7.7	24 34.0	0 59.9	22 27.2	24 17.4	19 17.6
13	11 19 45.2	21 43.5	9 33.6	11♈22.9	5 39.1	20 58.5	3 4.9	24 32.3	1 7.3	22 24.6	24 16.9	19 16.0
14	11 23 41.7	22 43.3	9 30.4	23 10.1	5 13.1	22 11.8	3 1.3	24 30.8	1 14.7	22 21.9	24 16.4	19 14.4
15	11 27 38.3	23 43.2	9 27.2	4♉57.9	4 53.5	23 25.1	2 56.9	24 29.4	1 22.1	22 19.3	24 15.8	19 12.8
16	11 31 34.8	24 43.0	9 24.0	16 49.8	4 40.4	24 38.2	2 51.8	24 28.3	1 29.6	22 16.7	24 15.2	19 11.2
17	11 35 31.4	25 42.7	9 20.9	28 49.7	4 33.7	25 51.3	2 45.9	24 27.3	1 37.0	22 14.1	24 14.5	19 9.6
18	11 39 27.9	26 42.4	9 17.7	11♊ 2.0	4 33.1	27 4.4	2 39.2	24 26.6	1 44.5	22 11.5	24 13.8	19 8.0
19	11 43 24.5	27 42.1	9 14.5	23 31.6	4 D 38.4	28 17.4	2 31.7	24 26.0	1 51.9	22 8.9	24 13.1	19 6.4
20	11 47 21.0	28 41.8	9 11.3	6♋23.2	4 49.4	29 30.3	2 23.5	24 25.7	1 59.4	22 6.3	24 12.4	19 4.8
21	11 51 17.6	29 41.4	9 8.2	19 40.7	5 5.7	0♉43.2	2 14.5	24 25.5	2 6.9	22 3.7	24 11.7	19 3.2
22	11 55 14.1	0♈40.9	9 5.0	3♌26.8	5 27.3	1 56.0	2 4.8	24 25.5	2 14.4	22 1.1	24 10.9	19 1.7
23	11 59 10.7	1 40.5	9 1.8	17 41.8	5 53.6	3 8.7	1 54.3	24 D 25.7	2 21.8	21 58.5	24 10.0	19 .1
24	12 3 7.3	2 40.0	8 58.6	2♍23.1	6 24.5	4 21.4	1 43.0	24 26.1	2 29.3	21 55.9	24 9.2	18 58.5
25	12 7 3.8	3 39.4	8 55.4	17 24.9	6 59.7	5 34.0	1 31.1	24 26.7	2 36.8	21 53.4	24 8.3	18 57.0
26	12 11 .4	4 38.8	8 52.3	2♎38.7	7 39.0	6 46.6	1 18.3	24 27.5	2 44.3	21 50.9	24 7.4	18 55.5
27	12 14 56.9	5 38.2	8 49.1	17 54.0	8 22.1	7 59.0	1 4.9	24 28.5	2 51.7	21 48.3	24 6.5	18 53.9
28	12 18 53.5	6 37.6	8 45.9	3♏ .8	9 8.8	9 11.4	0 50.7	24 29.7	2 59.2	21 45.8	24 5.5	18 52.4
29	12 22 50.0	7 36.9	8 42.7	17 50.6	9 58.9	10 23.7	0 35.9	24 31.0	3 6.7	21 43.3	24 4.6	18 50.9
30	12 26 46.6	8 36.2	8 39.6	2♐17.5	10 52.2	11 36.0	0 20.4	24 32.6	3 14.1	21 40.9	24 3.6	18 49.4
31	12 30 43.1	9 35.5	8 36.4	16 18.7	11 48.6	12 48.2	0 4.2	24 34.4	3 21.6	21 38.4	24 2.6	18 48.0
		LATITUDE										
1	10 32 26.5	0 .0	0 .0	0S 1.5	3N37.4	0S54.1	2N33.1	0N35.1	2S 6.4	0N48.4	1N45.3	15N19.8
4	10 44 16.2	0 .0	0 .0	3 24.1	3 41.4	0 47.2	2 33.8	0 35.2	2 6.3	0 48.4	1 45.5	15 20.2
7	10 56 5.8	0 .0	0 .0	5 1.8	3 26.6	0 39.8	2 34.3	0 35.2	2 6.2	0 48.5	1 45.7	15 20.5
10	11 7 55.5	0 .0	0 .0	4 31.5	2 56.4	0 32.0	2 34.6	0 35.3	2 6.2	0 48.5	1 45.8	15 20.7
13	11 19 45.2	0 .0	0 .0	2 16.7	2 16.6	0 23.8	2 34.5	0 35.3	2 6.1	0 48.5	1 46.0	15 20.9
16	11 31 34.8	0 .0	0 .0	0N50.2	1 32.9	0 15.3	2 34.2	0 35.4	2 6.1	0 48.5	1 46.2	15 21.0
19	11 43 24.5	0 .0	0 .0	3 44.1	0 49.3	0 6.4	2 33.4	0 35.4	2 6.1	0 48.5	1 46.3	15 21.0
22	11 55 14.1	0 .0	0 .0	5 10.7	0 8.2	0N 2.7	2 32.2	0 35.4	2 6.2	0 48.4	1 46.4	15 20.9
25	12 7 3.8	0 .0	0 .0	3 58.7	0S28.8	0 11.9	2 30.6	0 35.4	2 6.2	0 48.4	1 46.6	15 20.7
28	12 18 53.5	0 .0	0 .0	0 22.6	1 1.3	0 21.4	2 28.4	0 35.4	2 6.3	0 48.4	1 46.7	15 20.5
31	12 30 43.1	0 .0	0 .0	3S18.6	1 29.0	0 30.9	2 25.7	0 35.4	2 6.5	0 48.3	1 46.9	15 20.2
		RIGHT ASCENSION										
1	10 32 26.5	11♓15.9	7♉46.9	6♏32.9	15♓53.1	6♈ 5.8	1♏31.0	27♋ 9.3	0♈31.5	23♍49.5	22♏25.9	26♍41.8
2	10 36 23.1	12 12.2	7 43.8	20 22.9	15 R 3.2	7 12.8	1 35.9	27 R 5.3	0 38.1	23 R 47.2	22 R 25.7	26 R 40.4
3	10 40 19.6	13 8.3	7 40.6	4♐38.3	14 9.9	8 19.8	1 40.3	27 1.4	0 44.7	23 44.8	22 25.5	26 38.9
4	10 44 16.2	14 4.3	7 37.5	19 13.7	13 14.6	9 26.8	1 43.9	26 57.8	0 51.3	23 42.5	22 25.3	26 37.5
5	10 48 12.7	15 .2	7 34.4	3♑54.5	12 18.6	10 33.8	1 46.9	26 54.4	0 58.0	23 40.1	22 25.1	26 36.1
6	10 52 9.3	15 56.0	7 31.3	18 20.1	11 23.2	11 40.8	1 49.2	26 51.1	1 4.6	23 37.7	22 24.8	26 34.7
7	10 56 5.8	16 51.7	7 28.2	2♒12.0	10 29.6	12 47.9	1 50.8	26 48.1	1 11.3	23 35.3	22 24.5	26 33.2
8	11 0 2.4	17 47.3	7 25.1	15 18.4	9 38.9	13 55.0	1 51.7	26 45.2	1 18.0	23 33.0	22 24.1	26 31.8
9	11 3 59.0	18 42.8	7 21.9	27 36.7	8 52.1	15 2.2	1 51.9	26 42.6	1 24.8	23 30.6	22 23.7	26 30.3
10	11 7 55.5	19 38.3	7 18.8	9♓11.7	8 10.0	16 9.5	1 R 51.4	26 40.2	1 31.6	23 28.2	22 23.4	26 28.9
11	11 11 52.1	20 33.6	7 15.7	20 12.7	7 33.1	17 16.8	1 50.2	26 38.0	1 38.3	23 25.8	22 22.9	26 27.5
12	11 15 48.6	21 28.8	7 12.6	0♈51.6	7 1.8	18 24.2	1 48.2	26 35.9	1 45.1	23 23.4	22 22.4	26 26.0
13	11 19 45.2	22 24.0	7 9.5	11 21.3	6 36.6	19 31.7	1 45.4	26 34.1	1 51.9	23 21.0	22 21.9	26 24.5
14	11 23 41.7	23 19.1	7 6.4	21 54.9	6 17.4	20 39.3	1 42.0	26 32.5	1 58.7	23 18.6	22 21.4	26 23.1
15	11 27 38.3	24 14.1	7 3.2	2♉45.8	6 4.5	21 47.0	1 37.8	26 31.1	2 5.5	23 16.1	22 20.8	26 21.6
16	11 31 34.8	25 9.0	7 .1	14 6.8	5 57.6	22 54.8	1 32.8	26 29.8	2 12.3	23 13.7	22 20.2	26 20.1
17	11 35 31.4	26 3.9	6 57.0	26 9.3	5 56.6	24 2.8	1 27.1	26 28.8	2 19.2	23 11.3	22 19.6	26 18.6
18	11 39 27.9	26 58.7	6 53.9	9♊ 1.4	6 D 1.4	25 10.9	1 20.7	26 28.0	2 26.0	23 8.9	22 18.9	26 17.2
19	11 43 24.5	27 53.5	6 50.8	22 44.7	6 11.7	26 19.1	1 13.4	26 27.4	2 32.9	23 6.5	22 18.2	26 15.7
20	11 47 21.0	28 48.2	6 47.7	7♋11.8	6 27.2	27 27.5	1 5.5	26 27.1	2 39.7	23 4.1	22 17.5	26 14.2
21	11 51 17.6	29 42.9	6 44.6	22 5.8	6 47.7	28 36.0	0 56.8	26 26.9	2 46.6	23 1.7	22 16.7	26 12.7
22	11 55 14.1	0♈37.6	6 41.5	7♌ 4.4	7 13.0	29 44.7	0 47.4	26 26.9	2 53.4	22 59.3	22 15.9	26 11.3
23	11 59 10.7	1 32.2	6 38.3	21 48.2	7 42.6	0♉53.6	0 37.2	26 D 27.1	3 .3	22 57.0	22 15.1	26 9.8
24	12 3 7.3	2 26.8	6 35.2	6♍ 6.5	8 16.3	2 2.6	0 26.3	26 27.6	3 7.2	22 54.6	22 14.3	26 8.3
25	12 7 3.8	3 21.3	6 32.1	19 59.6	8 53.9	3 11.9	0 14.7	26 28.2	3 14.0	22 52.2	22 13.4	26 6.9
26	12 11 .4	4 15.9	6 29.0	3♎36.2	9 35.2	4 21.3	0 2.3	26 29.0	3 20.9	22 49.9	22 12.5	26 5.4
27	12 14 56.9	5 10.5	6 25.9	17 10.0	10 19.8	5 30.9	29♎49.3	26 30.1	3 27.8	22 47.6	22 11.6	26 4.0
28	12 18 53.5	6 5.0	6 22.8	0♏55.9	11 7.5	6 40.7	29 35.6	26 31.3	3 34.6	22 45.3	22 10.6	26 2.5
29	12 22 50.0	6 59.6	6 19.7	15 5.6	11 58.2	7 50.7	29 21.2	26 32.8	3 41.5	22 43.0	22 9.6	26 1.1
30	12 26 46.6	7 54.1	6 16.6	29 44.0	12 51.6	9 1.0	29 6.1	26 34.4	3 48.4	22 40.7	22 8.6	25 59.7
31	12 30 43.1	8 48.8	6 13.5	14♐45.4	13 47.7	10 11.5	28 50.4	26 36.3	3 55.3	22 38.4	22 7.6	25 58.3
		DECLINATION										
1	10 32 26.5	7S55.8	0N15.6	14S30.4	2S 6.6	1N39.3	10S 3.7	21N41.7	2S 4.1	3N33.0	17S 9.6	18N10.4
4	10 44 16.2	6 47.2	0 15.5	26 29.2	3 8.1	3 13.0	10 7.5	21 43.8	1 55.4	3 36.0	17 9.3	18 12.7
7	10 56 5.8	5 37.8	0 15.5	25 18.0	4 31.5	4 46.1	10 9.4	21 45.5	1 46.6	3 39.1	17 9.0	18 14.9
10	11 7 55.5	4 27.6	0 15.4	13 38.0	5 59.9	6 18.3	10 9.3	21 46.9	1 37.8	3 42.2	17 8.5	18 17.0
13	11 19 45.2	3 17.0	0 15.4	2N24.3	7 19.4	7 49.3	10 7.3	21 48.0	1 28.9	3 45.3	17 8.0	18 19.1
16	11 31 34.8	2 6.0	0 15.3	17 40.3	8 21.5	9 18.7	10 3.2	21 48.7	1 20.1	3 48.4	17 7.4	18 21.1
19	11 43 24.5	0 54.8	0 15.3	27 1.1	9 2.9	10 46.2	9 57.1	21 49.1	1 11.2	3 51.5	17 6.8	18 23.0
22	11 55 14.1	0N16.3	0 15.2	24 25.2	9 23.2	12 11.4	9 49.0	21 49.2	1 2.3	3 54.5	17 6.1	18 24.8
25	12 7 3.8	1 27.3	0 15.2	8 38.1	9 23.5	13 34.1	9 39.0	21 49.0	0 53.5	3 57.5	17 5.4	18 26.5
28	12 18 53.5	2 37.9	0 15.1	12S 9.9	9 5.4	14 54.0	9 27.1	21 48.5	0 44.7	4 .5	17 4.5	18 28.1
31	12 30 43.1	3 48.1	0 15.1	26 2.1	8 30.4	16 10.6	9 13.5	21 47.7	0 35.9	4 3.4	17 3.7	18 29.6

APRIL 1967

LONGITUDE

DAY	EPHEM. SID. TIME	☉	☊	☽	☿	♀	♂	♃	♄	♅	♆	♇
	h m s	° ′	° ′	° ′	° ′	° ′	° ′	° ′	° ′	° ′	° ′	° ′
1	12 34 39.7	10♈34.7	8♉33.2	29♐53.8	12♓47.7	14♉ .4	29♎47.3	24♋36.3	3♈29.1	21♍36.0	24♏ 1.5	18♍46.5
2	12 38 36.2	11 33.9	8 30.0	13♑ 4.4	13 49.7	15 12.4	29 R 29.9	24 38.4	3 36.5	21 R 33.6	24 R .4	18 R 45.0
3	12 42 32.8	12 33.1	8 26.8	25 53.4	14 54.1	16 24.4	29 11.8	24 40.7	3 43.9	21 31.2	23 59.3	18 43.6
4	12 46 29.3	13 32.2	8 23.7	8♒24.3	16 1.1	17 36.3	28 53.1	24 43.1	3 51.4	21 28.8	23 58.2	18 42.2
5	12 50 25.9	14 31.4	8 20.5	20 40.6	17 10.4	18 48.1	28 33.9	24 45.8	3 58.8	21 26.5	23 57.1	18 40.7
6	12 54 22.5	15 30.4	8 17.3	2♓45.7	18 22.0	19 59.9	28 14.2	24 48.6	4 6.2	21 24.1	23 55.9	18 39.3
7	12 58 19.0	16 29.5	8 14.1	14 42.8	19 35.7	21 11.6	27 53.9	24 51.6	4 13.5	21 21.8	23 54.7	18 38.0
8	13 2 15.6	17 28.5	8 11.0	26 34.4	20 51.5	22 23.2	27 33.3	24 54.8	4 20.9	21 19.6	23 53.5	18 36.6
9	13 6 12.1	18 27.5	8 7.8	8♈23.1	22 9.3	23 34.7	27 12.2	24 58.2	4 28.2	21 17.3	23 52.2	18 35.2
10	13 10 8.7	19 26.5	8 4.6	20 10.9	23 29.0	24 46.1	26 50.8	25 1.8	4 35.6	21 15.1	23 51.0	18 33.9
11	13 14 5.2	20 25.4	8 1.4	2♉ .0	24 50.7	25 57.5	26 29.0	25 5.5	4 42.9	21 12.9	23 49.7	18 32.6
12	13 18 1.8	21 24.3	7 58.2	13 52.6	26 14.2	27 8.8	26 6.9	25 9.4	4 50.2	21 10.7	23 48.4	18 31.3
13	13 21 58.3	22 23.1	7 55.1	25 51.0	27 39.5	28 20.0	25 44.6	25 13.4	4 57.4	21 8.6	23 47.1	18 30.0
14	13 25 54.9	23 22.0	7 51.9	7♊58.1	29 6.5	29 31.1	25 22.1	25 17.7	5 4.7	21 6.5	23 45.7	18 28.7
15	13 29 51.4	24 20.7	7 48.7	20 16.7	0♈35.4	0♊42.1	24 59.4	25 22.1	5 11.9	21 4.5	23 44.4	18 27.5
16	13 33 48.0	25 19.5	7 45.5	2♋50.3	2 5.9	1 53.0	24 36.6	25 26.7	5 19.1	21 2.4	23 43.0	18 26.3
17	13 37 44.5	26 18.2	7 42.4	15 42.3	3 38.1	3 3.9	24 13.8	25 31.4	5 26.3	21 .4	23 41.6	18 25.1
18	13 41 41.1	27 16.9	7 39.2	28 55.8	5 12.0	4 14.6	23 51.0	25 36.3	5 33.4	20 58.5	23 40.2	18 23.9
19	13 45 37.7	28 15.5	7 36.0	12♌33.2	6 47.6	5 25.2	23 28.1	25 41.4	5 40.5	20 56.6	23 38.8	18 22.7
20	13 49 34.2	29 14.1	7 32.8	26 35.6	8 24.8	6 35.8	23 5.4	25 46.6	5 47.6	20 54.7	23 37.3	18 21.6
21	13 53 30.8	0♉12.7	7 29.6	11♍ 2.1	10 3.8	7 46.3	22 42.8	25 52.0	5 54.7	20 52.9	23 35.9	18 20.5
22	13 57 27.3	1 11.2	7 26.5	25 49.4	11 44.4	8 56.6	22 20.3	25 57.5	6 1.8	20 51.1	23 34.5	18 19.5
23	14 1 23.9	2 9.7	7 23.3	10♎51.6	13 26.7	10 6.8	21 58.1	26 3.2	6 8.8	20 49.3	23 33.0	18 18.4
24	14 5 20.4	3 8.2	7 20.1	26 .5	15 10.6	11 16.9	21 36.0	26 9.1	6 15.7	20 47.6	23 31.5	18 17.3
25	14 9 17.0	4 6.6	7 16.9	11♏ 7.1	16 56.3	12 27.0	21 14.3	26 15.0	6 22.6	20 45.9	23 30.0	18 16.3
26	14 13 13.5	5 5.0	7 13.8	26 2.2	18 43.6	13 36.8	20 52.9	26 21.2	6 29.5	20 44.3	23 28.4	18 15.3
27	14 17 10.1	6 3.3	7 10.6	10♐38.4	20 32.7	14 46.6	20 31.8	26 27.5	6 36.4	20 42.7	23 26.9	18 14.4
28	14 21 6.6	7 1.7	7 7.4	24 50.5	22 23.4	15 56.3	20 11.2	26 33.9	6 43.2	20 41.1	23 25.4	18 13.4
29	14 25 3.2	7 60.0	7 4.2	8♑35.9	24 15.9	17 5.9	19 50.9	26 40.5	6 50.0	20 39.6	23 23.8	18 12.5
30	14 28 59.8	8 58.3	7 1.1	21 54.7	26 10.1	18 15.3	19 31.2	26 47.2	6 56.8	20 38.1	23 22.3	18 11.6

LATITUDE

DAY	EPHEM. SID. TIME	☉	☊	☽	☿	♀	♂	♃	♄	♅	♆	♇
1	12 34 39.7	0 .0	0 .0	4S10.3	1S37.2	0N34.1	2N24.7	0N35.4	2S 6.5	0N48.3	1N46.9	15N20.1
4	12 46 29.3	0 .0	0 .0	5 14.4	1 58.4	0 43.7	2 21.2	0 35.4	2 6.7	0 48.3	1 47.0	15 19.7
7	12 58 19.0	0 .0	0 .0	4 9.3	2 14.8	0 53.2	2 17.1	0 35.4	2 6.9	0 48.2	1 47.1	15 19.2
10	13 10 8.7	0 .0	0 .0	1 31.0	2 26.5	1 2.7	2 12.4	0 35.4	2 7.1	0 48.1	1 47.2	15 18.6
13	13 21 58.3	0 .0	0 .0	1N43.2	2 33.4	1 12.0	2 7.1	0 35.4	2 7.3	0 48.1	1 47.3	15 18.0
16	13 33 48.0	0 .0	0 .0	4 22.9	2 35.7	1 21.1	2 1.3	0 35.3	2 7.6	0 48.0	1 47.4	15 17.3
19	13 45 37.7	0 .0	0 .0	5 15.8	2 33.2	1 30.0	1 54.9	0 35.3	2 7.9	0 47.9	1 47.5	15 16.6
22	13 57 27.3	0 .0	0 .0	3 29.0	2 26.1	1 38.5	1 48.0	0 35.3	2 8.2	0 47.8	1 47.6	15 15.8
25	14 9 17.0	0 .0	0 .0	0S23.4	2 14.3	1 46.7	1 40.8	0 35.3	2 8.5	0 47.7	1 47.6	15 15.0
28	14 21 6.6	0 .0	0 .0	3 56.1	1 57.9	1 54.3	1 33.3	0 35.3	2 8.9	0 47.6	1 47.7	15 14.1

RIGHT ASCENSION

DAY	EPHEM. SID. TIME	☉	☊	☽	☿	♀	♂	♃	♄	♅	♆	♇
1	12 34 39.7	9♈43.4	6♉10.4	29♐53.0	14♓46.1	11♉22.1	28♎34.1	26♋38.3	4♈ 2.1	22♍36.2	22♏ 6.6	25♍56.9
2	12 38 36.2	10 38.0	6 7.3	14♑43.8	15 46.7	12 33.0	28 R 17.1	26 40.6	4 8.9	22 R 34.0	22 R 5.5	25 R 55.5
3	12 42 32.8	11 32.7	6 4.2	28 56.6	16 49.5	13 44.2	27 59.6	26 43.0	4 15.8	22 31.7	22 4.4	25 54.1
4	12 46 29.3	12 27.4	6 1.0	12♒18.7	17 54.3	14 55.5	27 41.5	26 45.6	4 22.6	22 29.5	22 3.2	25 52.7
5	12 50 25.9	13 22.1	5 57.9	24 47.5	19 .9	16 7.1	27 22.8	26 48.4	4 29.4	22 27.4	22 2.1	25 51.3
6	12 54 22.5	14 16.9	5 54.8	6♓28.7	20 9.3	17 18.9	27 3.7	26 51.4	4 36.2	22 25.2	22 .9	25 49.9
7	12 58 19.0	15 11.7	5 51.7	17 33.0	21 19.4	18 31.0	26 44.1	26 54.6	4 43.0	22 23.1	21 59.7	25 48.6
8	13 2 15.6	16 6.6	5 48.6	28 12.8	22 31.2	19 43.2	26 24.0	26 58.0	4 49.8	22 21.0	21 58.5	25 47.2
9	13 6 12.1	17 1.6	5 45.5	8♈41.6	23 44.5	20 55.7	26 3.6	27 1.5	4 56.6	22 18.9	21 57.2	25 45.9
10	13 10 8.7	17 56.6	5 42.4	19 12.6	24 59.2	22 8.5	25 42.8	27 5.3	5 3.3	22 16.8	21 56.0	25 44.6
11	13 14 5.2	18 51.7	5 39.3	29 59.0	26 15.5	23 21.5	25 21.6	27 9.2	5 10.1	22 14.8	21 54.7	25 43.3
12	13 18 1.8	19 46.8	5 36.2	11♉13.0	27 33.1	24 34.6	25 .2	27 13.4	5 16.8	22 12.8	21 53.4	25 42.0
13	13 21 58.3	20 42.0	5 33.1	23 5.2	28 52.2	25 48.0	24 38.5	27 17.7	5 23.5	22 10.9	21 52.0	25 40.7
14	13 25 54.9	21 37.3	5 30.0	5♊43.0	0♈12.6	27 1.7	24 16.7	27 22.1	5 30.2	22 8.9	21 50.7	25 39.4
15	13 29 51.4	22 32.6	5 26.9	19 7.5	1 34.3	28 15.5	23 54.7	27 26.8	5 36.8	22 7.0	21 49.3	25 38.2
16	13 33 48.0	23 28.1	5 23.8	3♋12.0	2 57.4	29 29.5	23 32.5	27 31.6	5 43.5	22 5.1	21 47.9	25 36.9
17	13 37 44.5	24 23.6	5 20.7	17 41.2	4 21.8	0♊43.7	23 10.3	27 36.6	5 50.1	22 3.3	21 46.5	25 35.7
18	13 41 41.1	25 19.2	5 17.6	2♌15.4	5 47.6	1 58.2	22 48.1	27 41.8	5 56.7	22 1.5	21 45.1	25 34.5
19	13 45 37.7	26 14.9	5 14.5	16 36.9	7 14.8	3 12.8	22 25.9	27 47.2	6 3.2	21 59.7	21 43.7	25 33.3
20	13 49 34.2	27 10.7	5 11.4	0♍35.8	8 43.4	4 27.5	22 3.8	27 52.7	6 9.8	21 57.9	21 42.2	25 32.2
21	13 53 30.8	28 6.7	5 8.3	14 11.9	10 13.4	5 42.5	21 41.8	27 58.4	6 16.3	21 56.3	21 40.8	25 31.1
22	13 57 27.3	29 2.7	5 5.2	27 33.3	11 44.8	6 57.6	21 19.9	28 4.3	6 22.8	21 54.6	21 39.3	25 29.9
23	14 1 23.9	29 58.8	5 2.1	10♎53.7	13 17.7	8 12.8	20 58.2	28 10.3	6 29.3	21 53.0	21 37.8	25 28.8
24	14 5 20.4	0♉55.0	4 59.0	24 29.0	14 52.2	9 28.1	20 36.7	28 16.4	6 35.7	21 51.4	21 36.3	25 27.7
25	14 9 17.0	1 51.4	4 56.0	8♏33.8	16 28.2	10 43.6	20 15.5	28 22.7	6 42.1	21 49.8	21 34.8	25 26.7
26	14 13 13.5	2 47.8	4 52.9	23 16.6	18 5.9	11 59.2	19 54.6	28 29.2	6 48.5	21 48.3	21 33.3	25 25.6
27	14 17 10.1	3 44.4	4 49.8	8♐34.9	19 45.3	13 14.9	19 34.0	28 35.8	6 54.9	21 46.8	21 31.7	25 24.6
28	14 21 6.6	4 41.1	4 46.7	24 12.5	21 26.5	14 30.6	19 13.7	28 42.6	7 1.2	21 45.3	21 30.2	25 23.6
29	14 25 3.2	5 37.9	4 43.6	9♑42.0	23 9.4	15 46.4	18 53.9	28 49.5	7 7.5	21 43.9	21 28.6	25 22.6
30	14 28 59.8	6 34.9	4 40.5	24 35.2	24 54.3	17 2.3	18 34.5	28 56.6	7 13.7	21 42.5	21 27.0	25 21.6

DECLINATION

DAY	EPHEM. SID. TIME	☉	☊	☽	☿	♀	♂	♃	♄	♅	♆	♇
1	12 34 39.7	4N11.3	0N15.0	27S37.1	8S15.2	16N35.3	9S 8.6	21N47.3	0S33.0	4N 4.3	17S 3.4	18N30.0
4	12 46 29.3	5 20.6	0 15.0	23 13.2	7 20.1	17 47.2	8 52.8	21 46.1	0 24.3	4 7.1	17 2.5	18 31.4
7	12 58 19.0	6 29.1	0 14.9	9 51.1	6 11.2	18 55.1	8 35.7	21 44.5	0 15.6	4 9.8	17 1.5	18 32.6
10	13 10 8.7	7 36.6	0 14.9	6N29.1	4 49.8	19 58.8	8 17.5	21 42.7	0 7.1	4 12.4	17 .5	18 33.7
13	13 21 58.3	8 42.9	0 14.8	20 53.7	3 16.7	20 57.9	7 58.6	21 40.6	0N 1.3	4 14.9	16 59.4	18 34.7
16	13 33 48.0	9 47.9	0 14.8	27 47.8	1 32.8	21 52.1	7 39.4	21 38.1	0 9.7	4 17.3	16 58.3	18 35.6
19	13 45 37.7	10 51.5	0 14.7	22 5.3	0N21.1	22 41.3	7 20.2	21 35.4	0 17.9	4 19.5	16 57.2	18 36.3
22	13 57 27.3	11 53.4	0 14.7	4 51.4	2 24.1	23 25.1	7 1.6	21 32.3	0 26.0	4 21.6	16 56.1	18 36.9
25	14 9 17.0	12 53.5	0 14.6	15S32.3	4 35.3	24 3.4	6 43.7	21 29.0	0 33.9	4 23.5	16 54.9	18 37.4
28	14 21 6.6	13 51.8	0 14.6	27 16.6	6 53.6	24 35.9	6 27.1	21 25.4	0 41.7	4 25.3	16 53.7	18 37.7

MAY 1967

LONGITUDE

DAY	EPHEM. SID. TIME	☉	☊	☾	☿	♀	♂	♃	♄	♅	♆	♇
	h m s	° ′	° ′	° ′	° ′	° ′	° ′	° ′	° ′	° ′	° ′	° ′
1	14 32 56.3	9♉56.5	6♉57.9	4♒48.6	28♈ 6.0	19♊24.6	19♎11.9	26♋54.0	7♈ 3.5	20♍36.7	23♏20.7	18♍10.7
2	14 36 52.9	10 54.8	6 54.7	17 21.0	0♉ 3.6	20 33.9	18 R 53.2	27 1.0	7 10.1	20 R 35.3	23 R 19.1	18 R 9.9
3	14 40 49.4	11 53.0	6 51.5	29 35.9	2 2.8	21 43.0	18 35.1	27 8.2	7 16.8	20 34.0	23 17.5	18 9.1
4	14 44 46.0	12 51.2	6 48.3	11♓37.8	4 3.7	22 51.9	18 17.5	27 15.4	7 23.3	20 32.7	23 15.9	18 8.3
5	14 48 42.5	13 49.3	6 45.2	23 30.9	6 6.2	24 .8	18 .6	27 22.8	7 29.9	20 31.4	23 14.3	18 7.5
6	14 52 39.1	14 47.4	6 42.0	5♈19.2	8 10.2	25 9.5	17 44.3	27 30.3	7 36.4	20 30.2	23 12.7	18 6.8
7	14 56 35.7	15 45.6	6 38.8	17 6.5	10 15.6	26 18.1	17 28.7	27 38.0	7 42.8	20 29.1	23 11.1	18 6.1
8	15 0 32.2	16 43.6	6 35.6	28 55.8	12 22.3	27 26.5	17 13.8	27 45.8	7 49.2	20 28.0	23 9.5	18 5.4
9	15 4 28.8	17 41.7	6 32.5	10♉49.8	14 30.2	28 34.9	16 59.6	27 53.7	7 55.6	20 26.9	23 7.9	18 4.8
10	15 8 25.3	18 39.7	6 29.3	22 50.9	16 39.1	29 43.1	16 46.2	28 1.8	8 1.9	20 25.9	23 6.3	18 4.2
11	15 12 21.9	19 37.7	6 26.1	5♊ .8	18 48.9	0♋51.1	16 33.5	28 9.9	8 8.1	20 25.0	23 4.6	18 3.6
12	15 16 18.4	20 35.8	6 22.9	17 21.4	20 59.3	1 59.1	16 21.6	28 18.3	8 14.4	20 24.1	23 3.0	18 3.1
13	15 20 15.0	21 33.7	6 19.8	29 54.1	23 10.1	3 6.8	16 10.5	28 26.7	8 20.5	20 23.3	23 1.4	18 2.5
14	15 24 11.5	22 31.6	6 16.6	12♋40.4	25 21.0	4 14.4	16 .2	28 35.2	8 26.6	20 22.5	22 59.8	18 2.0
15	15 28 8.1	23 29.5	6 13.4	25 41.7	27 31.8	5 21.9	15 50.6	28 43.8	8 32.7	20 21.7	22 58.1	18 1.6
16	15 32 4.7	24 27.4	6 10.2	8♌59.6	29 42.2	6 29.1	15 41.9	28 52.6	8 38.7	20 21.0	22 56.5	18 1.1
17	15 36 1.2	25 25.2	6 7.0	22 35.0	1♊51.9	7 36.2	15 34.0	29 1.5	8 44.6	20 20.4	22 54.9	18 .7
18	15 39 57.8	26 23.0	6 3.9	6♍28.7	4 .6	8 43.2	15 26.9	29 10.5	8 50.5	20 19.8	22 53.3	18 .4
19	15 43 54.3	27 20.8	6 .7	20 40.3	6 8.0	9 49.9	15 20.6	29 19.5	8 56.3	20 19.2	22 51.6	18 .0
20	15 47 50.9	28 18.6	5 57.5	5♎ 8.2	8 13.9	10 56.5	15 15.1	29 28.7	9 2.0	20 18.7	22 50.0	17 59.7
21	15 51 47.4	29 16.3	5 54.3	19 49.1	10 18.1	12 2.9	15 10.5	29 38.0	9 7.7	20 18.3	22 48.4	17 59.4
22	15 55 44.0	0♊14.0	5 51.2	4♏38.1	12 20.3	13 9.1	15 6.6	29 47.4	9 13.4	20 17.9	22 46.8	17 59.1
23	15 59 40.6	1 11.7	5 48.0	19 28.5	14 20.3	14 15.1	15 3.5	29 56.9	9 18.9	20 17.6	22 45.2	17 58.9
24	16 3 37.1	2 9.3	5 44.8	4♐13.0	16 18.0	15 21.0	15 1.3	0♌ 6.6	9 24.4	20 17.3	22 43.6	17 58.7
25	16 7 33.7	3 6.9	5 41.6	18 44.4	18 13.3	16 26.6	14 59.8	0 16.3	9 29.9	20 17.0	22 42.0	17 58.6
26	16 11 30.2	4 4.5	5 38.5	2♑56.5	20 6.0	17 32.0	14 59.1	0 26.1	9 35.3	20 16.9	22 40.4	17 58.4
27	16 15 26.8	5 2.1	5 35.3	16 45.2	21 56.1	18 37.2	14 D 59.2	0 35.9	9 40.6	20 16.7	22 38.8	17 58.3
28	16 19 23.3	5 59.7	5 32.1	0♒ 8.6	23 43.3	19 42.1	15 .0	0 45.9	9 45.8	20 16.7	22 37.2	17 58.3
29	16 23 19.9	6 57.3	5 28.9	13 7.1	25 27.8	20 46.9	15 1.6	0 56.0	9 51.0	20 16.6	22 35.6	17 58.2
30	16 27 16.5	7 54.8	5 25.7	25 42.9	27 9.5	21 51.4	15 4.0	1 6.2	9 56.1	20 D 16.7	22 34.1	17 58.2
31	16 31 13.0	8 52.3	5 22.6	7♓59.7	28 48.2	22 55.7	15 7.1	1 16.5	10 1.2	20 16.8	22 32.5	17 58.2

LATITUDE

DAY	EPHEM. SID. TIME	☉	☊	☾	☿	♀	♂	♃	♄	♅	♆	♇
1	14 32 56.3	0 .0	0 .0	5 S 17.5	1 S 37.1	2 N 1.5	1 N 25.5	0 N 35.2	2 S 9.3	0 N 47.5	1 N 47.7	15 N 13.1
4	14 44 46.0	0 .0	0 .0	4 21.4	1 12.4	2 8.1	1 17.6	0 35.2	2 9.7	0 47.4	1 47.8	15 12.1
7	14 56 35.7	0 .0	0 .0	1 48.0	0 44.2	2 14.1	1 9.6	0 35.2	2 10.2	0 47.3	1 47.8	15 11.1
10	15 8 25.3	0 .0	0 .0	1 N 26.9	0 13.5	2 19.4	1 1.7	0 35.2	2 10.6	0 47.2	1 47.8	15 10.0
13	15 20 15.0	0 .0	0 .0	4 12.7	0 N 18.1	2 24.0	0 53.8	0 35.2	2 11.1	0 47.1	1 47.8	15 8.9
16	15 32 4.7	0 .0	0 .0	5 15.6	0 48.8	2 27.7	0 46.0	0 35.2	2 11.7	0 46.9	1 47.8	15 7.8
19	15 43 54.3	0 .0	0 .0	3 47.9	1 16.8	2 30.6	0 38.4	0 35.2	2 12.2	0 46.8	1 47.8	15 6.6
22	15 55 44.0	0 .0	0 .0	0 12.2	1 40.1	2 32.5	0 31.0	0 35.2	2 12.8	0 46.7	1 47.8	15 5.4
25	16 7 33.7	0 .0	0 .0	3 S 30.2	1 57.6	2 33.5	0 23.9	0 35.3	2 13.4	0 46.6	1 47.7	15 4.2
28	16 19 23.3	0 .0	0 .0	5 11.4	2 8.2	2 33.4	0 17.0	0 35.3	2 14.0	0 46.4	1 47.7	15 3.0
31	16 31 13.0	0 .0	0 .0	4 27.4	2 11.8	2 32.2	0 10.4	0 35.3	2 14.6	0 46.3	1 47.6	15 1.8

RIGHT ASCENSION

DAY	EPHEM. SID. TIME	☉	☊	☾	☿	♀	♂	♃	♄	♅	♆	♇
1	14 32 56.3	7♉32.0	4♉37.4	8♒32.9	26♈41.1	18♊18.3	18♎15.6	29♋ 3.8	7♈19.9	21♍41.2	21♏25.4	25♍20.7
2	14 36 52.9	8 29.2	4 34.3	21 29.2	28 29.8	19 34.3	17 R 57.2	29 11.2	7 26.1	21 R 39.9	21 R 23.8	25 R 19.8
3	14 40 49.4	9 26.6	4 31.2	3♓29.3	0♉20.7	20 50.2	17 39.3	29 18.7	7 32.2	21 38.7	21 22.2	25 18.9
4	14 44 46.0	10 24.1	4 28.1	14 44.7	2 13.6	22 6.2	17 22.0	29 26.3	7 38.3	21 37.5	21 20.6	25 18.0
5	14 48 42.5	11 21.8	4 25.0	25 29.7	4 8.6	23 22.2	17 5.2	29 34.1	7 44.4	21 36.3	21 19.0	25 17.1
6	14 52 39.1	12 19.6	4 21.9	5♈59.1	6 5.7	24 38.1	16 49.1	29 42.1	7 50.4	21 35.2	21 17.4	25 16.3
7	14 56 35.7	13 17.5	4 18.8	16 27.6	8 5.0	25 54.0	16 33.6	29 50.1	7 56.4	21 34.1	21 15.8	25 15.5
8	15 0 32.2	14 15.6	4 15.8	27 9.3	10 6.3	27 9.8	16 18.7	29 58.3	8 2.4	21 33.1	21 14.1	25 14.7
9	15 4 28.8	15 13.8	4 12.7	8♉17.4	12 9.7	28 25.6	16 4.5	0♌ 6.6	8 8.3	21 32.1	21 12.5	25 14.0
10	15 8 25.3	16 12.2	4 9.6	20 3.4	14 15.1	29 41.2	15 51.0	0 15.1	8 14.1	21 31.1	21 10.8	25 13.2
11	15 12 21.9	17 10.7	4 6.5	2♊35.0	16 22.3	0♋56.7	15 38.2	0 23.7	8 19.9	21 30.3	21 9.2	25 12.5
12	15 16 18.4	18 9.4	4 3.4	15 54.0	18 31.2	2 12.1	15 26.2	0 32.4	8 25.7	21 29.4	21 7.6	25 11.9
13	15 20 15.0	19 8.2	4 .3	29 53.4	20 41.6	3 27.4	15 14.9	0 41.2	8 31.4	21 28.6	21 5.9	25 11.3
14	15 24 11.5	20 7.2	3 57.2	14♋17.1	22 53.3	4 42.4	15 4.3	0 50.2	8 37.1	21 27.9	21 4.3	25 10.6
15	15 28 8.1	21 6.2	3 54.2	28 44.3	25 5.9	5 57.2	14 54.4	0 59.2	8 42.7	21 27.2	21 2.6	25 10.0
16	15 32 4.7	22 5.5	3 51.1	12♌55.8	27 19.4	7 11.8	14 45.4	1 8.4	8 48.3	21 26.5	21 1.0	25 9.5
17	15 36 1.2	23 4.8	3 48.0	26 40.6	29 33.2	8 26.2	14 37.0	1 17.7	8 53.8	21 25.9	20 59.3	25 8.9
18	15 39 57.8	24 4.3	3 44.9	9♍58.1	1♊47.1	9 40.3	14 29.5	1 27.1	8 59.3	21 25.3	20 57.7	25 8.4
19	15 43 54.3	25 3.9	3 41.8	22 56.1	4 .9	10 54.2	14 22.7	1 36.6	9 4.7	21 24.8	20 56.1	25 7.9
20	15 47 50.9	26 3.7	3 38.7	5♎48.7	6 14.0	12 7.7	14 16.6	1 46.3	9 10.1	21 24.3	20 54.4	25 7.4
21	15 51 47.4	27 3.6	3 35.7	18 52.9	8 26.3	13 21.0	14 11.3	1 56.0	9 15.4	21 23.9	20 52.8	25 7.0
22	15 55 44.0	28 3.6	3 32.6	2♏26.0	10 37.3	14 33.9	14 6.8	2 5.8	9 20.6	21 23.6	20 51.1	25 6.6
23	15 59 40.6	29 3.8	3 29.5	16 41.6	12 46.8	15 46.5	14 3.0	2 15.7	9 25.8	21 23.2	20 49.5	25 6.2
24	16 3 37.1	0♊ 4.1	3 26.4	1♐44.6	14 54.6	16 58.7	14 .0	2 25.8	9 31.0	21 22.9	20 47.9	25 5.9
25	16 7 33.7	1 4.5	3 23.3	17 25.5	17 .3	18 10.6	13 57.7	2 35.9	9 36.1	21 22.7	20 46.3	25 5.5
26	16 11 30.2	2 5.0	3 20.2	3♑18.9	19 3.8	19 22.0	13 56.2	2 46.1	9 41.1	21 22.5	20 44.7	25 5.2
27	16 15 26.8	3 5.7	3 17.2	18 51.0	21 4.7	20 33.1	13 55.4	2 56.5	9 46.0	21 22.4	20 43.1	25 5.0
28	16 19 23.3	4 6.5	3 14.1	3♒33.0	23 3.0	21 43.7	13 55.3	3 6.9	9 51.0	21 22.3	20 41.5	25 4.7
29	16 23 19.9	5 7.4	3 11.0	17 10.3	24 58.5	22 53.9	13 D 55.9	3 17.4	9 55.8	21 22.3	20 39.9	25 4.5
30	16 27 16.5	6 8.4	3 7.9	29 43.1	26 51.0	24 3.6	13 57.2	3 28.0	10 .6	21 22.3	20 38.3	25 4.3
31	16 31 13.0	7 9.6	3 4.9	11♓21.5	28 40.4	25 12.9	13 59.3	3 38.7	10 5.3	21 D 22.4	20 36.7	25 4.2

DECLINATION

DAY	EPHEM. SID. TIME	☉	☊	☾	☿	♀	♂	♃	♄	♅	♆	♇
1	14 32 56.3	14 N 48.0	0 N 14.5	24 S 11.9	9 N 17.3	25 N 2.5	6 S 11.9	21 N 21.5	0 N 49.3	4 N 27.0	16 S 52.5	18 N 37.9
4	14 44 46.0	15 42.0	0 14.4	11 13.7	11 44.5	25 23.1	5 58.6	21 17.4	0 56.8	4 28.4	16 51.3	18 38.0
7	14 56 35.7	16 33.7	0 14.4	5 N 3.5	14 12.1	25 37.7	5 47.4	21 12.9	1 4.1	4 29.8	16 50.1	18 37.9
10	15 8 25.3	17 22.9	0 14.3	19 53.4	16 36.1	25 46.1	5 38.6	21 8.2	1 11.1	4 30.9	16 48.9	18 37.7
13	15 20 15.0	18 9.5	0 14.3	27 39.5	18 51.7	25 48.5	5 32.2	21 3.2	1 18.0	4 31.8	16 47.7	18 37.3
16	15 32 4.7	18 53.4	0 14.2	23 4.9	20 53.2	25 44.7	5 28.3	20 57.9	1 24.7	4 32.6	16 46.4	18 36.8
19	15 43 54.3	19 34.3	0 14.2	7 11.3	22 35.8	25 35.0	5 27.1	20 52.3	1 31.1	4 33.2	16 45.2	18 36.2
22	15 55 44.0	20 12.3	0 14.1	12 S 52.7	23 56.0	25 19.5	5 28.5	20 46.4	1 37.3	4 33.6	16 44.0	18 35.5
25	16 7 33.7	20 47.1	0 14.1	26 27.5	24 52.5	24 58.3	5 32.5	20 40.3	1 43.2	4 33.8	16 42.8	18 34.6
28	16 19 23.3	21 18.8	0 14.0	25 11.5	25 25.9	24 31.7	5 39.0	20 33.9	1 48.9	4 33.8	16 41.7	18 33.6
31	16 31 13.0	21 47.1	0 13.9	12 42.2	25 38.2	23 59.8	5 47.8	20 27.3	1 54.4	4 33.7	16 40.6	18 32.5

JUNE 1967

LONGITUDE

DAY	EPHEM. SID. TIME h m s	☉ ° ′	☊ ° ′	☽ ° ′	☿ ° ′	♀ ° ′	♂ ° ′	♃ ° ′	♄ ° ′	♅ ° ′	♆ ° ′	♇ ° ′
1	16 35 9.6	9♊49.9	5♉19.4	20♓ 2.0	0♋24.0	23♋59.8	15♎11.0	1♌26.8	10♈ 6.1	20♍16.9	22♏31.0	17♍58.3
2	16 39 6.1	10 47.4	5 16.2	1♈54.8	1 56.9	25 3.7	15 15.6	1 37.3	10 11.1	20 17.2	22 R 29.5	17 D 58.4
3	16 43 2.7	11 44.9	5 13.0	13 42.9	3 26.8	26 7.3	15 20.9	1 47.8	10 15.9	20 17.4	22 28.0	17 58.5
4	16 46 59.3	12 42.4	5 9.9	25 31.1	4 53.6	27 10.6	15 26.9	1 58.4	10 20.7	20 17.7	22 26.5	17 58.7
5	16 50 55.8	13 39.8	5 6.7	7♉23.8	6 17.4	28 13.7	15 33.7	2 9.1	10 25.4	20 18.1	22 25.0	17 58.9
6	16 54 52.4	14 37.3	5 3.5	19 24.4	7 38.0	29 16.5	15 41.1	2 19.9	10 30.0	20 18.5	22 23.5	17 59.1
7	16 58 48.9	15 34.7	5 .3	1♊35.9	8 55.6	0♌19.0	15 49.2	2 30.7	10 34.5	20 18.9	22 22.0	17 59.3
8	17 2 45.5	16 32.2	4 57.2	14 .2	10 10.0	1 21.2	15 58.0	2 41.7	10 39.0	20 19.5	22 20.5	17 59.6
9	17 6 42.0	17 29.6	4 54.0	26 38.5	11 21.1	2 23.2	16 7.5	2 52.7	10 43.3	20 20.0	22 19.1	17 59.9
10	17 10 38.6	18 27.0	4 50.8	9♋31.0	12 28.9	3 24.8	16 17.6	3 3.8	10 47.6	20 20.6	22 17.7	18 .3
11	17 14 35.2	19 24.4	4 47.6	22 37.6	13 33.4	4 26.2	16 28.3	3 14.9	10 51.8	20 21.3	22 16.3	18 .6
12	17 18 31.7	20 21.7	4 44.5	5♌57.3	14 34.5	5 27.2	16 39.7	3 26.2	10 56.0	20 22.1	22 14.9	18 1.0
13	17 22 28.3	21 19.1	4 41.3	19 29.4	15 32.1	6 27.8	16 51.8	3 37.4	11 .0	20 22.8	22 13.5	18 1.5
14	17 26 24.8	22 16.4	4 38.1	3♍13.0	16 26.1	7 28.2	17 4.4	3 48.8	11 4.0	20 23.7	22 12.1	18 1.9
15	17 30 21.4	23 13.7	4 34.9	17 7.2	17 16.3	8 28.2	17 17.6	4 .2	11 7.9	20 24.6	22 10.8	18 2.4
16	17 34 18.0	24 11.0	4 31.8	1♎11.3	18 2.9	9 27.8	17 31.5	4 11.7	11 11.7	20 25.5	22 9.4	18 3.0
17	17 38 14.5	25 8.3	4 28.6	15 24.3	18 45.5	10 27.0	17 45.9	4 23.3	11 15.4	20 26.5	22 8.1	18 3.5
18	17 42 11.1	26 5.6	4 25.4	29 44.6	19 24.2	11 25.8	18 .8	4 34.9	11 19.0	20 27.5	22 6.9	18 4.1
19	17 46 7.6	27 2.9	4 22.2	14♏ 9.6	19 58.7	12 24.3	18 16.4	4 46.6	11 22.6	20 28.6	22 5.6	18 4.7
20	17 50 4.2	28 .1	4 19.0	28 35.6	20 29.1	13 22.3	18 32.4	4 58.4	11 26.0	20 29.8	22 4.3	18 5.4
21	17 54 .8	28 57.3	4 15.9	12♐58.0	20 55.2	14 19.8	18 49.0	5 10.2	11 29.4	20 31.0	22 3.1	18 6.1
22	17 57 57.3	29 54.6	4 12.7	27 11.4	21 16.9	15 17.0	19 6.1	5 22.0	11 32.7	20 32.2	22 1.9	18 6.8
23	18 1 53.9	0♋51.8	4 9.5	11♑10.7	21 34.2	16 13.7	19 23.8	5 34.0	11 36.0	20 33.6	22 .8	18 7.6
24	18 5 50.4	1 49.1	4 6.3	24 51.3	21 47.0	17 9.8	19 41.9	5 46.0	11 39.1	20 34.9	21 59.6	18 8.4
25	18 9 47.0	2 46.3	4 3.2	8♒10.6	21 55.2	18 5.5	20 .5	5 58.0	11 42.1	20 36.3	21 58.5	18 9.2
26	18 13 43.5	3 43.5	3 60.0	21 7.7	21 58.8	19 .7	20 19.6	6 10.1	11 45.0	20 37.8	21 57.3	18 10.0
27	18 17 40.1	4 40.7	3 56.8	3♓43.6	21 R 57.8	19 55.4	20 39.1	6 22.2	11 47.8	20 39.2	21 56.2	18 10.8
28	18 21 36.7	5 37.9	3 53.6	16 1.1	21 52.2	20 49.5	20 59.1	6 34.4	11 50.6	20 40.8	21 55.2	18 11.7
29	18 25 33.2	6 35.1	3 50.5	28 4.0	21 42.2	21 43.1	21 19.6	6 46.6	11 53.2	20 42.4	21 54.1	18 12.6
30	18 29 29.8	7 32.3	3 47.3	9♈57.2	21 27.9	22 36.1	21 40.5	6 58.9	11 55.8	20 44.0	21 53.1	18 13.6

LATITUDE

DAY	SID. TIME	☉	☊	☽	☿	♀	♂	♃	♄	♅	♆	♇
1	16 35 9.6	0 .0	0 .0	3S47.4	2N11.4	2N31.6	0N 8.2	0N35.3	2S14.8	0N46.2	1N47.6	15N 1.4
4	16 46 59.3	0 .0	0 .0	0 60.0	2 5.4	2 28.9	0 2.0	0 35.4	2 15.5	0 46.1	1 47.6	15 .1
7	16 58 48.9	0 .0	0 .0	2N12.0	1 52.4	2 24.9	0S 4.0	0 35.4	2 16.2	0 46.0	1 47.5	14 58.9
10	17 10 38.6	0 .0	0 .0	4 36.2	1 32.4	2 19.7	0 9.7	0 35.5	2 16.9	0 45.9	1 47.4	14 57.7
13	17 22 28.3	0 .0	0 .0	5 .1	1 5.9	2 13.2	0 15.1	0 35.5	2 17.6	0 45.7	1 47.3	14 56.4
16	17 34 18.0	0 .0	0 .0	2 55.8	0 33.1	2 5.3	0 20.3	0 35.6	2 18.3	0 45.6	1 47.2	14 55.2
19	17 46 7.6	0 .0	0 .0	0S44.7	0S 5.3	1 55.9	0 25.3	0 35.7	2 19.1	0 45.5	1 47.1	14 54.0
22	17 57 57.3	0 .0	0 .0	3 59.9	0 48.6	1 45.0	0 30.0	0 35.7	2 19.8	0 45.3	1 47.0	14 52.8
25	18 9 47.0	0 .0	0 .0	5 4.9	1 35.4	1 32.6	0 34.4	0 35.8	2 20.6	0 45.2	1 46.9	14 51.6
28	18 21 36.7	0 .0	0 .0	3 50.6	2 23.7	1 18.6	0 38.7	0 35.9	2 21.4	0 45.1	1 46.7	14 50.4

RIGHT ASCENSION

DAY	SID. TIME	☉	☊	☽	☿	♀	♂	♃	♄	♅	♆	♇
1	16 35 9.6	8♊10.8	3♉ 1.8	22♓20.5	0♋26.6	26♋21.8	14♎ 2.0	3♌49.5	10♈10.0	21♍22.5	20♏35.1	25♍ 4.0
2	16 39 6.1	9 12.2	2 58.7	2♈56.1	2 9.5	27 30.2	14 5.5	4 .4	10 14.6	21 22.7	20 R 33.6	25 4.0
3	16 43 2.7	10 13.7	2 55.6	13 24.5	3 49.0	28 38.0	14 9.6	4 11.3	10 19.1	21 22.9	20 32.1	25 3.9
4	16 46 59.3	11 15.3	2 52.5	24 1.3	5 25.0	29 45.4	14 14.4	4 22.3	10 23.6	21 23.2	20 30.6	25 3.9
5	16 50 55.8	12 17.0	2 49.5	5♉ 1.1	6 57.4	0♌52.2	14 19.9	4 33.5	10 28.0	21 23.5	20 29.1	25 3.9
6	16 54 52.4	13 18.7	2 46.4	16 37.3	8 26.2	1 58.5	14 26.0	4 44.6	10 32.3	21 23.8	20 27.5	25 3.9
7	16 58 48.9	14 20.5	2 43.3	29 .2	9 51.2	3 4.2	14 32.8	4 55.9	10 36.6	21 24.2	20 26.1	25 3.9
8	17 2 45.5	15 22.5	2 40.2	12♊13.9	11 12.5	4 9.4	14 40.2	5 7.2	10 40.8	21 24.7	20 24.6	25 D 4.0
9	17 6 42.0	16 24.5	2 37.2	26 13.6	12 29.9	5 14.0	14 48.2	5 18.7	10 44.9	21 25.2	20 23.1	25 4.1
10	17 10 38.6	17 26.5	2 34.1	10♋43.6	13 43.4	6 18.1	14 56.9	5 30.1	10 48.9	21 25.8	20 21.7	25 4.3
11	17 14 35.2	18 28.6	2 31.0	25 21.1	14 52.9	7 21.5	15 6.2	5 41.7	10 52.9	21 26.4	20 20.2	25 4.4
12	17 18 31.7	19 30.8	2 28.0	9♌43.0	15 58.4	8 24.4	15 16.1	5 53.3	10 56.8	21 27.0	20 18.8	25 4.6
13	17 22 28.3	20 33.0	2 24.9	23 34.3	16 59.7	9 26.6	15 26.6	6 5.0	11 .6	21 27.7	20 17.4	25 4.9
14	17 26 24.8	21 35.3	2 21.8	6♍51.3	17 56.8	10 28.2	15 37.7	6 16.8	11 4.4	21 28.5	20 16.0	25 5.1
15	17 30 21.4	22 37.6	2 18.7	19 40.6	18 49.6	11 29.2	15 49.3	6 28.6	11 8.0	21 29.3	20 14.7	25 5.4
16	17 34 18.0	23 39.9	2 15.7	2♎15.4	19 38.0	12 29.6	16 1.5	6 40.5	11 11.6	21 30.1	20 13.3	25 5.7
17	17 38 14.5	24 42.2	2 12.6	14 53.0	20 21.9	13 29.2	16 14.3	6 52.4	11 15.2	21 31.0	20 12.0	25 6.1
18	17 42 11.1	25 44.6	2 9.5	27 51.6	21 1.4	14 28.2	16 27.6	7 4.4	11 18.6	21 32.0	20 10.7	25 6.4
19	17 46 7.6	26 46.9	2 6.5	11♏28.0	21 36.2	15 26.5	16 41.5	7 16.4	11 22.0	21 33.0	20 9.4	25 6.8
20	17 50 4.2	27 49.3	2 3.4	25 53.1	22 6.3	16 24.2	16 55.9	7 28.6	11 25.3	21 34.0	20 8.1	25 7.3
21	17 54 .8	28 51.7	2 .3	11♐ 6.1	22 31.6	17 21.1	17 10.7	7 40.7	11 28.5	21 35.1	20 6.9	25 7.7
22	17 57 57.3	29 54.1	1 57.3	26 50.6	22 52.2	18 17.3	17 26.1	7 52.9	11 31.6	21 36.2	20 5.6	25 8.2
23	18 1 53.9	0♋56.5	1 54.2	12♑35.6	23 8.0	19 12.9	17 42.0	8 5.2	11 34.7	21 37.5	20 4.5	25 8.8
24	18 5 50.4	1 58.9	1 51.1	27 47.3	23 18.8	20 7.6	17 58.4	8 17.5	11 37.6	21 38.7	20 3.3	25 9.3
25	18 9 47.0	3 1.2	1 48.1	12♒ 1.6	23 24.7	21 1.6	18 15.2	8 29.9	11 40.5	21 40.0	20 2.1	25 9.9
26	18 13 43.5	4 3.5	1 45.0	25 10.2	23 25.8	21 54.9	18 32.5	8 42.3	11 43.3	21 41.3	20 1.0	25 10.5
27	18 17 40.1	5 5.8	1 41.9	7♓18.3	23 R 22.0	22 47.4	18 50.3	8 54.8	11 46.0	21 42.6	19 59.9	25 11.1
28	18 21 36.7	6 8.1	1 38.9	18 38.5	23 13.5	23 39.2	19 8.5	9 7.3	11 48.7	21 44.0	19 58.8	25 11.8
29	18 25 33.2	7 10.3	1 35.8	29 26.7	23 .5	24 30.1	19 27.2	9 19.8	11 51.2	21 45.5	19 57.7	25 12.5
30	18 29 29.8	8 12.5	1 32.7	9♈59.5	22 43.0	25 20.3	19 46.3	9 32.4	11 53.7	21 47.0	19 56.7	25 13.2

DECLINATION

DAY	SID. TIME	☉	☊	☽	☿	♀	♂	♃	♄	♅	♆	♇
1	16 35 9.6	21N55.8	0N13.9	7S26.0	25N38.1	23N48.1	5S51.3	20N25.0	1N56.1	4N33.6	16S40.2	18N32.1
4	16 46 59.3	22 19.6	0 13.9	8N56.3	25 26.6	23 9.7	6 3.2	20 18.0	2 1.2	4 33.1	16 39.1	18 30.8
7	16 58 48.9	22 39.9	0 13.8	22 38.4	25 .8	22 26.8	6 17.3	20 10.7	2 6.0	4 32.5	16 38.0	18 29.4
10	17 10 38.6	22 56.6	0 13.8	27 41.7	24 23.6	21 39.7	6 33.5	20 3.2	2 10.5	4 31.8	16 37.0	18 27.9
13	17 22 28.3	23 9.7	0 13.7	19 43.3	23 37.9	20 48.6	6 51.6	19 55.4	2 14.6	4 30.8	16 36.1	18 26.3
16	17 34 18.0	23 19.1	0 13.6	2 12.9	22 46.5	19 54.0	7 11.6	19 47.4	2 18.5	4 29.6	16 35.1	18 24.6
19	17 46 7.6	23 24.8	0 13.6	16S48.2	21 52.2	18 56.3	7 33.3	19 39.1	2 22.1	4 28.2	16 34.2	18 22.8
22	17 57 57.3	23 26.7	0 13.5	27 24.8	20 57.6	17 55.8	7 56.6	19 30.6	2 25.3	4 26.7	16 33.4	18 20.9
25	18 9 47.0	23 25.0	0 13.5	23 7.7	20 5.4	16 52.8	8 21.3	19 21.8	2 28.2	4 25.0	16 32.7	18 18.9
28	18 21 36.7	23 19.5	0 13.4	9 3.4	19 18.2	15 47.8	8 47.4	19 12.9	2 30.8	4 23.1	16 31.9	18 16.8

JULY 1967

LONGITUDE

DAY	EPHEM. SID. TIME h m s	☉ ° ′	☊ ° ′	☽ ° ′	☿ ° ′	♀ ° ′	♂ ° ′	♃ ° ′	♄ ° ′	♅ ° ′	♆ ° ′	♇ ° ′
1	18 33 26.3	8♋29.5	3♉44.1	21♈45.9	21♋ 9.5	23♌28.5	22♎ 1.8	7♌11.2	11♈58.2	20♍45.7	21♏52.1	18♍14.6
2	18 37 22.9	9 26.7	3 40.9	3♉35.6	20 R 47.1	24 20.2	22 23.6	7 23.6	12 .6	20 47.5	21 R 51.1	18 15.6
3	18 41 19.5	10 24.0	3 37.8	15 31.3	20 21.2	25 11.4	22 45.8	7 36.0	12 2.9	20 49.2	21 50.2	18 16.6
4	18 45 16.0	11 21.2	3 34.6	27 37.6	19 52.0	26 1.9	23 8.4	7 48.4	12 5.1	20 51.1	21 49.2	18 17.7
5	18 49 12.6	12 18.4	3 31.4	9♊58.3	19 20.0	26 51.7	23 31.5	8 .9	12 7.1	20 52.9	21 48.3	18 18.8
6	18 53 9.1	13 15.6	3 28.2	22 36.0	18 45.7	27 40.8	23 54.9	8 13.5	12 9.1	20 54.9	21 47.5	18 19.9
7	18 57 5.7	14 12.8	3 25.0	5♋32.0	18 9.7	28 29.2	24 18.7	8 26.0	12 11.0	20 56.8	21 46.6	18 21.0
8	19 1 2.2	15 10.1	3 21.9	18 46.1	17 32.4	29 16.8	24 42.9	8 38.7	12 12.8	20 58.9	21 45.8	18 22.2
9	19 4 58.8	16 7.3	3 18.7	2♌16.6	16 54.6	0♍ 3.6	25 7.5	8 51.3	12 14.5	21 .9	21 45.0	18 23.4
10	19 8 55.4	17 4.5	3 15.5	16 .8	16 16.8	0 49.6	25 32.5	9 4.0	12 16.0	21 3.0	21 44.2	18 24.6
11	19 12 51.9	18 1.7	3 12.3	29 55.3	15 39.8	1 34.7	25 57.9	9 16.7	12 17.5	21 5.2	21 43.5	18 25.9
12	19 16 48.5	18 59.0	3 9.2	13♍56.7	15 4.2	2 19.0	26 23.6	9 29.5	12 18.9	21 7.4	21 42.8	18 27.1
13	19 20 45.0	19 56.2	3 6.0	28 2.2	14 30.5	3 2.3	26 49.6	9 42.3	12 20.2	21 9.6	21 42.1	18 28.4
14	19 24 41.6	20 53.5	3 2.8	12♎ 9.6	13 59.5	3 44.7	27 16.1	9 55.1	12 21.4	21 11.9	21 41.5	18 29.8
15	19 28 38.2	21 50.7	2 59.6	26 17.5	13 31.7	4 26.0	27 42.8	10 8.0	12 22.5	21 14.2	21 40.9	18 31.2
16	19 32 34.7	22 47.9	2 56.5	10♏24.7	13 7.5	5 6.3	28 9.9	10 20.8	12 23.5	21 16.6	21 40.3	18 32.5
17	19 36 31.3	23 45.2	2 53.3	24 30.4	12 47.4	5 45.5	28 37.3	10 33.7	12 24.3	21 19.0	21 39.7	18 33.9
18	19 40 27.8	24 42.4	2 50.1	8♐32.8	12 32.0	6 23.6	29 5.0	10 46.6	12 25.1	21 21.4	21 39.2	18 35.4
19	19 44 24.4	25 39.6	2 46.9	22 29.9	12 21.4	7 .5	29 33.1	10 59.6	12 25.8	21 23.9	21 38.7	18 36.8
20	19 48 20.9	26 36.9	2 43.8	6♑18.8	12 16.0	7 36.2	0♏ 1.4	11 12.5	12 26.4	21 26.4	21 38.2	18 38.3
21	19 52 17.5	27 34.1	2 40.6	19 56.3	12 16.0	8 10.6	0 30.0	11 25.5	12 26.8	21 29.0	21 37.8	18 39.8
22	19 56 14.1	28 31.4	2 37.4	3♒19.2	12 D 21.6	8 43.7	0 58.9	11 38.5	12 27.2	21 31.6	21 37.4	18 41.3
23	20 0 10.6	29 28.6	2 34.2	16 25.3	12 33.0	9 15.4	1 28.2	11 51.6	12 27.5	21 34.2	21 37.0	18 42.9
24	20 4 7.2	0♌25.9	2 31.0	29 13.3	12 50.1	9 45.7	1 57.6	12 4.6	12 27.6	21 36.9	21 36.6	18 44.4
25	20 8 3.7	1 23.2	2 27.9	11♓43.5	13 13.2	10 14.6	2 27.4	12 17.7	12 27.7	21 39.6	21 36.3	18 46.0
26	20 12 .3	2 20.5	2 24.7	23 57.7	13 42.1	10 41.9	2 57.5	12 30.7	12 27.7	21 42.4	21 36.0	18 47.6
27	20 15 56.8	3 17.8	2 21.5	5♈59.0	14 17.0	11 7.7	3 27.8	12 43.8	12 R 27.5	21 45.1	21 35.8	18 49.2
28	20 19 53.4	4 15.1	2 18.3	17 51.3	14 57.7	11 31.8	3 58.4	12 56.9	12 27.3	21 48.0	21 35.5	18 50.9
29	20 23 50.0	5 12.5	2 15.2	29 39.8	15 44.2	11 54.3	4 29.2	13 10.1	12 26.9	21 50.8	21 35.3	18 52.6
30	20 27 46.5	6 9.8	2 12.0	11♉29.6	16 36.6	12 15.0	5 .3	13 23.2	12 26.5	21 53.7	21 35.2	18 54.3
31	20 31 43.1	7 7.2	2 8.8	23 26.4	17 34.5	12 34.0	5 31.7	13 36.3	12 25.9	21 56.6	21 35.0	18 56.0

LATITUDE

DAY	SID. TIME	☉	☊	☽	☿	♀	♂	♃	♄	♅	♆	♇
1	18 33 26.3	0 .0	0 .0	1 S 9.4	3 S 10.6	1 N 2.9	0 S 42.7	0 N 36.0	2 S 22.2	0 N 45.0	1 N 46.6	14 N 49.3
4	18 45 16.0	0 .0	0 .0	1 N 58.3	3 52.6	0 45.4	0 46.5	0 36.1	2 23.0	0 44.8	1 46.5	14 48.2
7	18 57 5.7	0 .0	0 .0	4 24.8	4 25.9	0 26.2	0 50.2	0 36.3	2 23.9	0 44.7	1 46.3	14 47.1
10	19 8 55.4	0 .0	0 .0	4 55.2	4 46.9	0 5.1	0 53.6	0 36.4	2 24.7	0 44.6	1 46.2	14 46.0
13	19 20 45.0	0 .0	0 .0	2 56.4	4 53.6	0 S 17.9	0 56.9	0 36.5	2 25.5	0 44.5	1 46.0	14 45.0
16	19 32 34.7	0 .0	0 .0	0 S 36.2	4 45.8	0 42.8	1 .1	0 36.7	2 26.4	0 44.4	1 45.8	14 44.0
19	19 44 24.4	0 .0	0 .0	3 48.1	4 24.8	1 9.8	1 3.0	0 36.8	2 27.2	0 44.3	1 45.7	14 43.1
22	19 56 14.1	0 .0	0 .0	5 .4	3 53.3	1 38.7	1 5.9	0 37.0	2 28.1	0 44.2	1 45.5	14 42.2
25	20 8 3.7	0 .0	0 .0	3 53.1	3 14.2	2 9.7	1 8.5	0 37.2	2 28.9	0 44.1	1 45.3	14 41.3
28	20 19 53.4	0 .0	0 .0	1 14.7	2 30.5	2 42.6	1 11.1	0 37.3	2 29.7	0 44.0	1 45.2	14 40.5
31	20 31 43.1	0 .0	0 .0	1 N 50.6	1 44.8	3 17.3	1 13.4	0 37.5	2 30.6	0 43.9	1 45.0	14 39.7

RIGHT ASCENSION

DAY	SID. TIME	☉	☊	☽	☿	♀	♂	♃	♄	♅	♆	♇
1	18 33 26.3	9♋14.6	1♉29.7	20♈33.3	22♋21.3	26♌ 9.6	20♎ 5.9	9♌45.0	11♈56.0	21♍48.5	19♏55.6	25♍13.9
2	18 37 22.9	10 16.7	1 26.6	1♉23.8	21 R 55.6	26 58.1	20 25.9	9 57.7	11 58.3	21 50.1	19 R 54.7	25 14.7
3	18 41 19.5	11 18.7	1 23.5	12 46.0	21 26.5	27 45.8	20 46.3	10 10.4	12 .5	21 51.7	19 53.7	25 15.5
4	18 45 16.0	12 20.7	1 20.5	24 52.5	20 54.2	28 32.6	21 7.1	10 23.1	12 2.6	21 53.4	19 52.7	25 16.3
5	18 49 12.6	13 22.5	1 17.4	7♊51.4	20 19.1	29 18.6	21 28.3	10 35.9	12 4.7	21 55.1	19 51.8	25 17.2
6	18 53 9.1	14 24.3	1 14.4	21 42.4	19 41.9	0♍ 3.7	21 50.0	10 48.7	12 6.6	21 56.9	19 50.9	25 18.0
7	18 57 5.7	15 26.1	1 11.3	6♋14.2	19 3.1	0 47.8	22 12.0	11 1.5	12 8.4	21 58.7	19 50.1	25 19.0
8	19 1 2.2	16 27.7	1 8.2	21 4.5	18 23.3	1 31.0	22 34.5	11 14.4	12 10.2	22 .5	19 49.2	25 19.9
9	19 4 58.8	17 29.2	1 5.2	5♌47.4	17 43.1	2 13.3	22 57.3	11 27.3	12 11.8	22 2.4	19 48.4	25 20.8
10	19 8 55.4	18 30.7	1 2.1	20 2.3	17 3.2	2 54.6	23 20.5	11 40.2	12 13.4	22 4.3	19 47.6	25 21.8
11	19 12 51.9	19 32.0	0 59.1	3♍39.9	16 24.2	3 34.9	23 44.1	11 53.1	12 14.9	22 6.3	19 46.9	25 22.8
12	19 16 48.5	20 33.2	0 56.0	16 42.7	15 46.9	4 14.2	24 8.1	12 6.1	12 16.3	22 8.3	19 46.1	25 23.9
13	19 20 45.0	21 34.3	0 52.9	29 22.2	15 11.8	4 52.4	24 32.5	12 19.1	12 17.5	22 10.3	19 45.4	25 24.9
14	19 24 41.6	22 35.4	0 49.9	11♎54.3	14 39.7	5 29.5	24 57.2	12 32.2	12 18.8	22 12.5	19 44.8	25 26.1
15	19 28 38.2	23 36.2	0 46.8	24 37.1	14 10.9	6 5.5	25 22.3	12 45.2	12 19.9	22 14.6	19 44.2	25 27.2
16	19 32 34.7	24 36.9	0 43.8	7♏47.9	13 46.1	6 40.4	25 47.7	12 58.3	12 20.9	22 16.8	19 43.6	25 28.3
17	19 36 31.3	25 37.5	0 40.7	21 40.2	13 25.8	7 14.0	26 13.5	13 11.3	12 21.8	22 19.0	19 43.0	25 29.5
18	19 40 27.8	26 38.0	0 37.6	6♐18.9	13 10.3	7 46.5	26 39.6	13 24.4	12 22.6	22 21.2	19 42.4	25 30.7
19	19 44 24.4	27 38.3	0 34.6	21 35.5	13 .0	8 17.7	27 6.1	13 37.5	12 23.4	22 23.5	19 41.9	25 31.9
20	19 48 20.9	28 38.5	0 31.5	7♑ 7.0	12 55.3	8 47.6	27 32.9	13 50.7	12 24.0	22 25.8	19 41.4	25 33.1
21	19 52 17.5	29 38.6	0 28.5	22 22.3	12 D 56.3	9 16.2	27 60.0	14 3.8	12 24.6	22 28.1	19 41.0	25 34.4
22	19 56 14.1	0♌38.5	0 25.4	6♒53.7	13 3.3	9 43.4	28 27.4	14 17.0	12 25.0	22 30.5	19 40.5	25 35.7
23	20 0 10.6	1 38.3	0 22.4	20 26.1	13 16.4	10 9.2	28 55.2	14 30.1	12 25.4	22 32.9	19 40.1	25 37.0
24	20 4 7.2	2 37.9	0 19.3	2♓58.3	13 35.7	10 33.6	29 23.2	14 43.3	12 25.6	22 35.4	19 39.8	25 38.3
25	20 8 3.7	3 37.4	0 16.3	14 39.0	14 1.4	10 56.5	29 51.6	14 56.5	12 25.8	22 37.8	19 39.4	25 39.6
26	20 12 .3	4 36.7	0 13.2	25 41.9	14 33.4	11 17.8	0♏20.3	15 9.7	12 25.9	22 40.4	19 39.1	25 41.0
27	20 15 56.8	5 35.9	0 10.2	6♈22.4	15 11.8	11 37.6	0 49.3	15 22.8	12 R 25.8	22 42.9	19 38.8	25 42.4
28	20 19 53.4	6 35.0	0 7.1	16 56.5	15 56.6	11 55.8	1 18.6	15 36.1	12 25.7	22 45.5	19 38.6	25 43.8
29	20 23 50.0	7 33.9	0 4.0	27 39.9	16 47.6	12 12.3	1 48.3	15 49.3	12 25.5	22 48.1	19 38.4	25 45.3
30	20 27 46.5	8 32.6	0 1.0	8♉47.6	17 44.9	12 27.1	2 18.2	16 2.5	12 25.2	22 50.7	19 38.2	25 46.7
31	20 31 43.1	9 31.3	29♈57.9	20 33.5	18 48.3	12 40.1	2 48.4	16 15.7	12 24.8	22 53.4	19 38.1	25 48.2

DECLINATION

DAY	SID. TIME	☉	☊	☽	☿	♀	♂	♃	♄	♅	♆	♇
1	18 33 26.3	23 N 10.4	0 N 13.4	7 N 24.6	18 N 38.5	14 N 41.2	9 S 14.6	19 N 3.7	2 N 33.1	4 N 21.1	16 S 31.3	18 N 14.6
4	18 45 16.0	22 57.6	0 13.3	21 33.3	18 8.3	13 33.4	9 43.0	18 54.2	2 35.0	4 18.8	16 30.7	18 12.4
7	18 57 5.7	22 41.2	0 13.3	27 44.3	17 49.3	12 24.8	10 12.3	18 44.6	2 36.5	4 16.5	16 30.2	18 10.1
10	19 8 55.4	22 21.3	0 13.2	20 43.8	17 42.3	11 15.8	10 42.6	18 34.7	2 37.7	4 13.9	16 29.7	18 7.7
13	19 20 45.0	21 57.9	0 13.1	3 28.7	17 47.4	10 6.9	11 13.8	18 24.7	2 38.6	4 11.2	16 29.3	18 5.2
16	19 32 34.7	21 31.1	0 13.1	15 S 31.3	18 3.4	8 58.7	11 45.6	18 14.4	2 39.1	4 8.4	16 29.0	18 2.7
19	19 44 24.4	21 1.0	0 13.0	27 1.7	18 28.6	7 51.6	12 18.0	18 4.0	2 39.2	4 5.4	16 28.7	18 .1
22	19 56 14.1	20 27.7	0 13.0	24 17.0	18 59.9	6 46.4	12 50.8	17 53.4	2 39.0	4 2.3	16 28.6	17 57.5
25	20 8 3.7	19 51.4	0 12.9	10 45.4	19 34.0	5 43.6	13 24.1	17 42.6	2 38.4	3 59.0	16 28.5	17 54.9
28	20 19 53.4	19 12.0	0 12.9	5 N 51.4	20 6.7	4 44.0	13 57.6	17 31.7	2 37.4	3 55.6	16 28.4	17 52.2
31	20 31 43.1	18 29.8	0 12.8	20 25.3	20 33.5	3 48.3	14 31.3	17 20.6	2 36.2	3 52.1	16 28.5	17 49.5

AUGUST 1967

LONGITUDE

DAY	EPHEM. SID. TIME	☉	☊	☽	☿	♀	♂	♃	♄	♅	♆	♇
	h m s	° ′	° ′	° ′	° ′	° ′	° ′	° ′	° ′	° ′	° ′	° ′
1	20 35 39.6	8♌ 4.6	2♉ 5.6	5♊35.3	18♋38.1	12♍51.0	6♏ 3.3	13♌49.5	12♈25.3	21♍59.6	21♏35.0	18♍57.7
2	20 39 36.2	9 2.0	2 2.5	18 1.1	19 47.1	13 6.2	6 35.1	14 2.7	12 R 24.5	22 2.6	21 R 34.9	18 59.4
3	20 43 32.7	9 59.4	1 59.3	0♋47.3	21 1.5	13 19.4	7 7.2	14 15.8	12 23.7	22 5.6	21 34.8	19 1.2
4	20 47 29.3	10 56.9	1 56.1	13 56.0	22 21.1	13 30.6	7 39.6	14 29.1	12 22.8	22 8.7	21 D 34.9	19 3.0
5	20 51 25.9	11 54.4	1 52.9	27 27.4	23 45.6	13 39.7	8 12.2	14 42.3	12 21.7	22 11.7	21 34.9	19 4.9
6	20 55 22.4	12 51.9	1 49.7	11♌19.5	25 14.8	13 46.7	8 45.1	14 55.4	12 20.5	22 14.9	21 35.0	19 6.7
7	20 59 19.0	13 49.4	1 46.6	25 28.3	26 48.6	13 51.4	9 18.1	15 8.6	12 19.3	22 18.0	21 35.1	19 8.5
8	21 3 15.5	14 46.9	1 43.4	9♍48.4	28 26.6	13 53.9	9 51.4	15 21.8	12 17.9	22 21.2	21 35.2	19 10.4
9	21 7 12.1	15 44.4	1 40.2	24 14.0	0♌ 8.6	13 54.2	10 24.9	15 35.0	12 16.5	22 24.4	21 35.4	19 12.3
10	21 11 8.6	16 42.0	1 37.0	8♎39.7	1 54.2	13 R 52.1	10 58.7	15 48.2	12 14.9	22 27.6	21 35.6	19 14.1
11	21 15 5.2	17 39.5	1 33.9	23 1.0	3 43.0	13 47.6	11 32.6	16 1.4	12 13.3	22 30.8	21 35.8	19 16.0
12	21 19 1.8	18 37.1	1 30.7	7♏15.2	5 34.8	13 40.8	12 6.8	16 14.6	12 11.5	22 34.1	21 36.0	19 18.0
13	21 22 58.3	19 34.7	1 27.5	21 20.6	7 29.0	13 31.6	12 41.2	16 27.8	12 9.7	22 37.4	21 36.3	19 19.9
14	21 26 54.9	20 32.3	1 24.3	5♐16.5	9 25.4	13 19.9	13 15.8	16 40.9	12 7.7	22 40.7	21 36.6	19 21.9
15	21 30 51.4	21 29.9	1 21.2	19 2.6	11 23.5	13 5.9	13 50.6	16 54.1	12 5.7	22 44.1	21 37.0	19 23.8
16	21 34 48.0	22 27.6	1 18.0	2♑38.7	13 22.9	12 49.5	14 25.6	17 7.3	12 3.6	22 47.5	21 37.4	19 25.8
17	21 38 44.5	23 25.2	1 14.8	16 4.0	15 23.4	12 30.8	15 .7	17 20.4	12 1.3	22 50.9	21 37.8	19 27.8
18	21 42 41.1	24 22.9	1 11.6	29 17.7	17 24.5	12 9.8	15 36.1	17 33.5	11 59.0	22 54.3	21 38.3	19 29.8
19	21 46 37.6	25 20.6	1 8.4	12♒18.8	19 26.0	11 46.7	16 11.7	17 46.7	11 56.6	22 57.7	21 38.7	19 31.8
20	21 50 34.2	26 18.3	1 5.3	25 6.2	21 27.5	11 21.4	16 47.4	17 59.8	11 54.1	23 1.2	21 39.3	19 33.8
21	21 54 30.8	27 16.0	1 2.1	7♓39.5	23 28.8	10 54.2	17 23.3	18 12.9	11 51.6	23 4.7	21 39.8	19 35.9
22	21 58 27.3	28 13.8	0 58.9	19 59.2	25 29.7	10 25.1	17 59.4	18 26.0	11 48.9	23 8.2	21 40.4	19 37.9
23	22 2 23.9	29 11.6	0 55.7	2♈ 6.4	27 30.0	9 54.3	18 35.7	18 39.0	11 46.2	23 11.7	21 41.0	19 40.0
24	22 6 20.4	0♍ 9.4	0 52.6	14 3.4	29 29.6	9 22.0	19 12.2	18 52.1	11 43.3	23 15.3	21 41.6	19 42.1
25	22 10 17.0	1 7.3	0 49.4	25 53.5	1♍28.4	8 48.4	19 48.8	19 5.2	11 40.5	23 18.9	21 42.3	19 44.2
26	22 14 13.5	2 5.1	0 46.2	7♉40.6	3 26.1	8 13.6	20 25.6	19 18.2	11 37.5	23 22.4	21 43.1	19 46.3
27	22 18 10.1	3 3.0	0 43.0	19 29.7	5 22.8	7 37.9	21 2.6	19 31.2	11 34.4	23 26.0	21 43.8	19 48.4
28	22 22 6.6	4 1.0	0 39.8	1♊25.7	7 18.4	7 1.4	21 39.8	19 44.1	11 31.2	23 29.6	21 44.6	19 50.5
29	22 26 3.2	4 58.9	0 36.7	13 34.1	9 12.8	6 24.5	22 17.1	19 57.1	11 28.0	23 33.3	21 45.4	19 52.6
30	22 29 59.7	5 56.9	0 33.5	25 59.9	11 6.0	5 47.3	22 54.6	20 10.0	11 24.7	23 36.9	21 46.2	19 54.7
31	22 33 56.3	6 54.9	0 30.3	8♋47.6	12 58.0	5 10.2	23 32.2	20 22.9	11 21.3	23 40.6	21 47.0	19 56.8

LATITUDE

DAY	EPHEM. SID. TIME	☉	☊	☽	☿	♀	♂	♃	♄	♅	♆	♇
1	20 35 39.6	0 .0	0 .0	2N47.5	1S29.6	3S29.3	1S14.2	0N37.6	2S30.8	0N43.9	1N44.9	14N39.5
4	20 47 29.3	0 .0	0 .0	4 47.0	0 44.8	4 6.1	1 16.4	0 37.8	2 31.6	0 43.8	1 44.7	14 38.8
7	20 59 19.0	0 .0	0 .0	4 34.7	0 3.3	4 44.0	1 18.5	0 38.0	2 32.4	0 43.7	1 44.6	14 38.2
10	21 11 8.6	0 .0	0 .0	1 54.4	0N33.0	5 22.5	1 20.5	0 38.2	2 33.2	0 43.6	1 44.4	14 37.6
13	21 22 58.3	0 .0	0 .0	1S47.1	1 2.6	6 .7	1 22.4	0 38.5	2 34.0	0 43.6	1 44.2	14 37.0
16	21 34 48.0	0 .0	0 .0	4 28.0	1 24.5	6 37.5	1 24.1	0 38.7	2 34.7	0 43.5	1 44.0	14 36.6
19	21 46 37.6	0 .0	0 .0	4 56.2	1 38.5	7 11.6	1 25.7	0 39.0	2 35.5	0 43.5	1 43.8	14 36.2
22	21 58 27.3	0 .0	0 .0	3 14.7	1 45.1	7 41.7	1 27.2	0 39.3	2 36.2	0 43.4	1 43.7	14 35.8
25	22 10 17.0	0 .0	0 .0	0 19.2	1 45.1	8 6.0	1 28.7	0 39.5	2 36.8	0 43.4	1 43.5	14 35.5
28	22 22 6.6	0 .0	0 .0	2N43.1	1 39.5	8 23.4	1 30.0	0 39.8	2 37.5	0 43.3	1 43.3	14 35.3
31	22 33 56.3	0 .0	0 .0	4 47.9	1 29.3	8 32.9	1 31.2	0 40.1	2 38.1	0 43.3	1 43.1	14 35.1

RIGHT ASCENSION

DAY	EPHEM. SID. TIME	☉	☊	☽	☿	♀	♂	♃	♄	♅	♆	♇
1	20 35 39.6	10♌29.7	29♈54.9	3♊ 8.4	19♋57.8	12♍51.3	3♏18.9	16♌28.9	12♈24.3	22♍56.1	19♏37.9	25♍49.7
2	20 39 36.2	11 28.0	29 51.8	16 36.7	21 13.1	13 .7	3 49.8	16 42.1	12 R 23.7	22 58.9	19 37.9	25 51.2
3	20 43 32.7	12 26.2	29 48.8	0♋53.3	22 34.1	13 8.2	4 20.9	16 55.3	12 23.0	23 1.6	19 37.8	25 52.8
4	20 47 29.3	13 24.3	29 45.7	15 41.5	24 .6	13 13.9	4 52.4	17 8.6	12 22.3	23 4.5	19 37.8	25 54.4
5	20 51 25.9	14 22.2	29 42.7	0♌36.8	25 32.3	13 17.4	5 24.1	17 21.8	12 21.4	23 7.3	19 37.8	25 55.9
6	20 55 22.4	15 19.9	29 39.6	15 15.0	27 8.9	13 19.0	5 56.1	17 35.0	12 20.5	23 10.2	19 D 37.9	25 57.5
7	20 59 19.0	16 17.5	29 36.6	29 21.1	28 50.1	13 R 18.5	6 28.4	17 48.2	12 19.4	23 13.0	19 38.0	25 59.2
8	21 3 15.5	17 14.9	29 33.5	12♍51.8	0♌35.5	13 16.0	7 1.0	18 1.4	12 18.3	23 15.9	19 38.1	26 .8
9	21 7 12.1	18 12.2	29 30.5	25 54.3	2 24.8	13 11.3	7 33.8	18 14.6	12 17.0	23 18.9	19 38.2	26 2.4
10	21 11 8.6	19 9.3	29 27.5	8♎42.4	4 17.3	13 4.4	8 7.0	18 27.8	12 15.7	23 21.8	19 38.4	26 4.1
11	21 15 5.2	20 6.3	29 24.4	21 33.0	6 12.8	12 55.4	8 40.4	18 40.9	12 14.3	23 24.8	19 38.6	26 5.8
12	21 19 1.8	21 3.1	29 21.4	4♏42.7	8 10.7	12 44.3	9 14.1	18 54.1	12 12.7	23 27.8	19 38.9	26 7.5
13	21 22 58.3	21 59.8	29 18.3	18 25.1	10 10.4	12 31.0	9 48.1	19 7.2	12 11.1	23 30.9	19 39.1	26 9.2
14	21 26 54.9	22 56.3	29 15.3	2♐47.1	12 11.6	12 15.5	10 22.4	19 20.3	12 9.5	23 33.9	19 39.4	26 11.0
15	21 30 51.4	23 52.7	29 12.2	17 44.2	14 13.8	11 57.9	10 56.9	19 33.5	12 7.7	23 37.0	19 39.8	26 12.7
16	21 34 48.0	24 49.0	29 9.2	2♑59.0	16 16.4	11 38.3	11 31.7	19 46.5	12 5.8	23 40.1	19 40.2	26 14.5
17	21 38 44.5	25 45.1	29 6.1	18 5.0	18 19.1	11 16.6	12 6.7	19 59.6	12 3.9	23 43.2	19 40.6	26 16.3
18	21 42 41.1	26 41.1	29 3.1	2♒36.3	20 21.5	10 53.1	12 42.1	20 12.7	12 1.8	23 46.3	19 41.0	26 18.1
19	21 46 37.6	27 36.9	29 .0	16 16.0	22 23.3	10 27.6	13 17.7	20 25.7	11 59.7	23 49.5	19 41.5	26 19.9
20	21 50 34.2	28 32.7	28 57.0	28 59.4	24 24.2	10 .4	13 53.5	20 38.7	11 57.5	23 52.7	19 42.0	26 21.7
21	21 54 30.8	29 28.3	28 54.0	10♓52.0	26 23.9	9 31.6	14 29.6	20 51.7	11 55.2	23 55.9	19 42.5	26 23.5
22	21 58 27.3	0♍23.8	28 50.9	22 4.9	28 22.3	9 1.4	15 6.0	21 4.7	11 52.9	23 59.1	19 43.1	26 25.4
23	22 2 23.9	1 19.1	28 47.9	2♈52.0	0♍19.2	8 29.8	15 42.6	21 17.6	11 50.4	24 2.3	19 43.7	26 27.2
24	22 6 20.4	2 14.4	28 44.8	13 27.9	2 14.5	7 57.1	16 19.5	21 30.6	11 47.9	24 5.6	19 44.3	26 29.1
25	22 10 17.0	3 9.6	28 41.8	24 7.3	4 8.1	7 23.4	16 56.6	21 43.5	11 45.4	24 8.9	19 45.0	26 31.0
26	22 14 13.5	4 4.7	28 38.7	5♉ 4.3	5 59.9	6 48.9	17 34.0	21 56.4	11 42.7	24 12.2	19 45.7	26 32.9
27	22 18 10.1	4 59.6	28 35.7	16 32.3	7 50.0	6 13.9	18 11.7	22 9.2	11 39.9	24 15.5	19 46.4	26 34.8
28	22 22 6.6	5 54.5	28 32.7	28 42.4	9 38.2	5 38.5	18 49.6	22 22.0	11 37.1	24 18.8	19 47.2	26 36.8
29	22 26 3.2	6 49.3	28 29.6	11♊41.8	11 24.7	5 3.1	19 27.7	22 34.8	11 34.2	24 22.1	19 48.0	26 38.7
30	22 29 59.7	7 44.0	28 26.6	25 29.6	13 9.5	4 27.6	20 6.1	22 47.6	11 31.2	24 25.5	19 48.8	26 40.6
31	22 33 56.3	8 38.6	28 23.5	9♋55.8	14 52.6	3 52.6	20 44.7	23 .3	11 28.2	24 28.8	19 49.6	26 42.6

DECLINATION

DAY	EPHEM. SID. TIME	☉	☊	☽	☿	♀	♂	♃	♄	♅	♆	♇
1	20 35 39.6	18N15.2	0N12.8	23N59.4	20N40.2	3N30.8	14S42.6	17N16.9	2N35.6	3N51.0	16S28.5	17N48.6
4	20 47 29.3	17 29.3	0 12.7	27 28.3	20 51.3	2 41.7	15 16.4	17 5.6	2 33.9	3 47.3	16 28.7	17 45.8
7	20 59 19.0	16 40.9	0 12.7	17 20.4	20 44.7	1 58.8	15 50.2	16 54.2	2 31.8	3 43.5	16 28.9	17 43.1
10	21 11 8.6	15 50.1	0 12.6	1S41.0	20 16.6	1 23.0	16 23.9	16 42.7	2 29.4	3 39.7	16 29.2	17 40.3
13	21 22 58.3	14 57.0	0 12.6	19 49.4	19 24.8	0 55.5	16 57.4	16 31.1	2 26.7	3 35.7	16 29.6	17 37.6
16	21 34 48.0	14 1.8	0 12.5	27 53.1	18 9.5	0 37.3	17 30.6	16 19.4	2 23.6	3 31.7	16 30.0	17 34.8
19	21 46 37.6	13 4.6	0 12.4	21 50.6	16 33.3	0 29.4	18 3.3	16 7.6	2 20.2	3 27.6	16 30.5	17 32.0
22	21 58 27.3	12 5.5	0 12.4	6 57.0	14 40.5	0 32.0	18 35.5	15 55.8	2 16.6	3 23.4	16 31.1	17 29.3
25	22 10 17.0	11 4.7	0 12.3	9N42.5	12 35.4	0 45.2	19 7.1	15 43.8	2 12.7	3 19.1	16 31.8	17 26.5
28	22 22 6.6	10 2.3	0 12.3	23 6.8	10 22.2	1 8.0	19 37.9	15 31.9	2 8.5	3 14.8	16 32.5	17 23.8
31	22 33 56.3	8 58.5	0 12.2	27 56.5	8 4.1	1 39.2	20 8.0	15 19.9	2 4.1	3 10.4	16 33.4	17 21.1

SEPTEMBER 1967

DAY	EPHEM. SID. TIME	☉	☊	☾	☿	♀	♂	♃	♄	♅	♆	♇
		LONGITUDE										
	h m s	° ′	° ′	° ′	° ′	° ′	° ′	° ′	° ′	° ′	° ′	° ′
1	22 37 52.9	7♍53.0	0♉27.1	22♋ .4	14♍48.7	4♍33.2	24♏10.0	20♌35.8	11♈17.8	23♍44.2	21♏47.9	19♍59.0
2	22 41 49.4	8 51.0	0 24.0	5♌39.4	16 38.2	3R56.8	24 48.0	20 48.7	11R14.3	23 47.9	21 48.9	20 1.1
3	22 45 46.0	9 49.2	0 20.8	19 43.8	18 26.4	3 21.1	25 26.1	21 1.5	11 10.7	23 51.6	21 49.8	20 3.3
4	22 49 42.5	10 47.3	0 17.6	4♍ 9.7	20 13.4	2 46.2	26 4.4	21 14.3	11 7.0	23 55.3	21 50.8	20 5.4
5	22 53 39.1	11 45.5	0 14.4	18 51.1	21 59.2	2 12.6	26 42.9	21 27.0	11 3.3	23 59.0	21 51.8	20 7.6
6	22 57 35.6	12 43.7	0 11.3	3♎40.4	23 43.8	1 40.2	27 21.5	21 39.7	10 59.5	24 2.7	21 52.8	20 9.8
7	23 1 32.2	13 41.9	0 8.1	18 29.9	25 27.1	1 9.4	28 .2	21 52.4	10 55.6	24 6.5	21 53.9	20 11.9
8	23 5 28.7	14 40.1	0 4.9	3♏12.4	27 9.3	0 40.2	28 39.1	22 5.1	10 51.7	24 10.2	21 55.0	20 14.1
9	23 9 25.3	15 38.4	0 1.7	17 42.8	28 50.3	0 12.8	29 18.2	22 17.7	10 47.7	24 14.0	21 56.1	20 16.3
10	23 13 21.8	16 36.7	29♈58.5	1♐57.5	0♎30.2	29♌47.4	29 57.4	22 30.3	10 43.6	24 17.7	21 57.3	20 18.4
11	23 17 18.4	17 35.0	29 55.4	15 55.2	2 8.9	29 24.1	0♐36.7	22 42.8	10 39.6	24 21.5	21 58.5	20 20.6
12	23 21 14.9	18 33.4	29 52.2	29 35.6	3 46.4	29 2.9	1 16.2	22 55.3	10 35.4	24 25.3	21 59.7	20 22.8
13	23 25 11.5	19 31.8	29 49.0	12♑59.5	5 22.9	28 44.0	1 55.8	23 7.7	10 31.2	24 29.0	22 .9	20 25.0
14	23 29 8.1	20 30.2	29 45.8	26 8.0	6 58.3	28 27.4	2 35.6	23 20.1	10 27.0	24 32.8	22 2.2	20 27.2
15	23 33 4.6	21 28.6	29 42.7	9♒ 2.1	8 32.6	28 13.2	3 15.5	23 32.6	10 22.7	24 36.6	22 3.6	20 29.4
16	23 37 1.2	22 27.1	29 39.5	21 43.0	10 5.8	28 1.4	3 55.5	23 44.9	10 18.4	24 40.4	22 4.9	20 31.6
17	23 40 57.7	23 25.6	29 36.3	4♓11.6	11 37.9	27 52.0	4 35.7	23 57.1	10 14.0	24 44.2	22 6.2	20 33.8
18	23 44 54.3	24 24.1	29 33.1	16 29.0	13 8.9	27 45.0	5 15.9	24 9.3	10 9.6	24 48.0	22 7.6	20 35.9
19	23 48 50.8	25 22.6	29 29.9	28 36.4	14 38.9	27 40.5	5 56.3	24 21.5	10 5.1	24 51.8	22 9.0	20 38.1
20	23 52 47.4	26 21.2	29 26.8	10♈35.0	16 7.8	27 38.3	6 36.9	24 33.6	10 .7	24 55.5	22 10.4	20 40.3
21	23 56 43.9	27 19.8	29 23.6	22 27.0	17 35.7	27D38.6	7 17.5	24 45.7	9 56.1	24 59.3	22 11.9	20 42.5
22	0 0 40.5	28 18.5	29 20.4	4♉14.7	19 2.4	27 41.2	7 58.3	24 57.7	9 51.6	25 3.1	22 13.4	20 44.6
23	0 4 37.0	29 17.1	29 17.2	16 1.4	20 28.1	27 46.1	8 39.2	25 9.6	9 47.0	25 6.9	22 14.9	20 46.8
24	0 8 33.6	0♎15.9	29 14.1	27 50.5	21 52.6	27 53.3	9 20.2	25 21.5	9 42.4	25 10.7	22 16.4	20 48.9
25	0 12 30.1	1 14.6	29 10.9	9♊46.4	23 16.0	28 2.7	10 1.3	25 33.4	9 37.8	25 14.4	22 18.0	20 51.1
26	0 16 26.7	2 13.4	29 7.7	21 53.8	24 38.3	28 14.2	10 42.5	25 45.1	9 33.2	25 18.2	22 19.5	20 53.3
27	0 20 23.2	3 12.2	29 4.5	4♋17.2	25 59.3	28 27.9	11 23.9	25 56.9	9 28.5	25 22.0	22 21.1	20 55.4
28	0 24 19.8	4 11.1	29 1.3	17 1.4	27 19.1	28 43.7	12 5.4	26 8.5	9 23.8	25 25.7	22 22.8	20 57.5
29	0 28 16.4	5 10.0	28 58.2	0♌10.1	28 37.6	29 1.4	12 47.0	26 20.1	9 19.1	25 29.5	22 24.4	20 59.7
30	0 32 12.9	6 9.0	28 55.0	13 45.9	29 54.8	29 21.0	13 28.7	26 31.6	9 14.4	25 33.2	22 26.1	21 1.8
		LATITUDE										
1	22 37 52.9	0 .0	0 .0	5N 4.9	1N25.0	8S34.3	1S31.5	0N40.2	2S38.3	0N43.3	1N43.1	14N35.1
4	22 49 42.5	0 .0	0 .0	4 11.6	1 10.1	8 32.8	1 32.6	0 40.6	2 38.8	0 43.2	1 42.9	14 35.0
7	23 1 32.2	0 .0	0 .0	0 54.9	0 52.4	8 23.5	1 33.6	0 40.9	2 39.3	0 43.2	1 42.7	14 35.0
10	23 13 21.8	0 .0	0 .0	2S50.7	0 32.8	8 7.2	1 34.5	0 41.2	2 39.8	0 43.2	1 42.6	14 35.0
13	23 25 11.5	0 .0	0 .0	4 59.2	0 11.6	7 45.1	1 35.2	0 41.6	2 40.2	0 43.2	1 42.4	14 35.1
16	23 37 1.2	0 .0	0 .0	4 45.7	0S10.7	7 18.6	1 35.9	0 42.0	2 40.6	0 43.1	1 42.3	14 35.3
19	23 48 50.8	0 .0	0 .0	2 34.3	0 33.5	6 48.8	1 36.5	0 42.3	2 40.9	0 43.1	1 42.1	14 35.6
22	0 0 40.5	0 .0	0 .0	0N33.8	0 56.6	6 17.0	1 37.0	0 42.7	2 41.2	0 43.1	1 42.0	14 35.9
25	0 12 30.1	0 .0	0 .0	3 29.6	1 19.5	5 44.0	1 37.4	0 43.1	2 41.4	0 43.1	1 41.8	14 36.2
28	0 24 19.8	0 .0	0 .0	5 9.3	1 42.0	5 10.7	1 37.7	0 43.6	2 41.6	0 43.2	1 41.7	14 36.7
		RIGHT ASCENSION										
1	22 37 52.9	9♍33.1	28♈20.5	24♋41.1	16♍34.0	3♍18.0	21♏23.6	23♌13.0	11♈25.1	24♍32.2	19♏50.5	26♍44.5
2	22 41 49.4	10 27.6	28 17.5	9♌23.2	18 13.7	2R44.2	22 2.8	23 25.6	11R21.9	24 35.6	19 51.4	26 46.5
3	22 45 46.0	11 22.0	28 14.4	23 44.4	19 52.0	2 11.3	22 42.2	23 38.3	11 18.7	24 39.0	19 52.4	26 48.5
4	22 49 42.5	12 16.3	28 11.4	7♍36.9	21 28.7	1 39.6	23 21.8	23 50.8	11 15.4	24 42.4	19 53.4	26 50.5
5	22 53 39.1	13 10.5	28 8.3	21 3.3	23 4.0	1 9.2	24 1.7	24 3.4	11 12.0	24 45.8	19 54.4	26 52.5
6	22 57 35.6	14 4.7	28 5.3	4♎14.3	24 37.9	0 40.3	24 41.9	24 15.9	11 8.5	24 49.2	19 55.4	26 54.4
7	23 1 32.2	14 58.8	28 2.3	17 24.8	26 10.4	0 13.1	25 22.2	24 28.3	11 5.1	24 52.6	19 56.5	26 56.5
8	23 5 28.7	15 52.9	27 59.2	0♏50.5	27 41.7	29♌47.6	26 2.8	24 40.8	11 1.5	24 56.1	19 57.5	26 58.5
9	23 9 25.3	16 46.9	27 56.2	14 44.9	29 11.8	29 24.1	26 43.7	24 53.1	10 57.9	24 59.5	19 58.7	27 .5
10	23 13 21.8	17 40.9	27 53.2	29 14.6	0♎40.7	29 2.5	27 24.8	25 5.5	10 54.2	25 3.0	19 59.8	27 2.5
11	23 17 18.4	18 34.8	27 50.1	14♐15.8	2 8.5	28 43.1	28 6.1	25 17.7	10 50.5	25 6.4	20 1.0	27 4.5
12	23 21 14.9	19 28.7	27 47.1	29 32.5	3 35.2	28 25.9	28 47.6	25 30.0	10 46.8	25 9.9	20 2.2	27 6.6
13	23 25 11.5	20 22.6	27 44.1	14♑39.8	5 1.0	28 11.0	29 29.4	25 42.2	10 43.0	25 13.3	20 3.5	27 8.6
14	23 29 8.1	21 16.4	27 41.0	29 12.9	6 25.7	27 58.3	0♐11.4	25 54.3	10 39.1	25 16.8	20 4.7	27 10.6
15	23 33 4.6	22 10.3	27 38.0	12♒55.4	7 49.6	27 48.1	0 53.7	26 6.4	10 35.3	25 20.3	20 6.1	27 12.7
16	23 37 1.2	23 4.1	27 35.0	25 42.6	9 12.5	27 40.2	1 36.1	26 18.5	10 31.3	25 23.8	20 7.4	27 14.7
17	23 40 57.7	23 57.9	27 31.9	7♓39.1	10 34.5	27 34.6	2 18.7	26 30.4	10 27.3	25 27.3	20 8.7	27 16.8
18	23 44 54.3	24 51.7	27 28.9	18 55.4	11 55.7	27 31.4	3 1.6	26 42.4	10 23.3	25 30.7	20 10.1	27 18.8
19	23 48 50.8	25 45.4	27 25.9	29 44.7	13 16.1	27 30.6	3 44.7	26 54.2	10 19.3	25 34.2	20 11.5	27 20.9
20	23 52 47.4	26 39.2	27 22.8	10♈20.7	14 35.6	27D32.2	4 28.0	27 6.0	10 15.2	25 37.7	20 12.9	27 22.9
21	23 56 43.9	27 33.0	27 19.8	20 57.2	15 54.4	27 36.0	5 11.4	27 17.8	10 11.1	25 41.2	20 14.4	27 25.0
22	0 0 40.5	28 26.8	27 16.8	1♉47.5	17 12.4	27 42.1	5 55.1	27 29.5	10 6.9	25 44.6	20 15.9	27 27.0
23	0 4 37.0	29 20.7	27 13.7	13 3.8	18 29.7	27 50.5	6 39.0	27 41.1	10 2.8	25 48.1	20 17.4	27 29.1
24	0 8 33.6	0♎14.6	27 10.7	24 56.6	19 46.1	28 1.0	7 23.1	27 52.7	9 58.6	25 51.6	20 18.9	27 31.1
25	0 12 30.1	1 8.5	27 7.7	7♊32.8	21 1.8	28 13.6	8 7.4	28 4.2	9 54.3	25 55.0	20 20.5	27 33.2
26	0 16 26.7	2 2.4	27 4.7	20 53.2	22 16.7	28 28.3	8 51.9	28 15.7	9 50.1	25 58.5	20 22.1	27 35.2
27	0 20 23.2	2 56.4	27 1.6	4♋50.9	23 30.7	28 45.1	9 36.6	28 27.1	9 45.8	26 2.0	20 23.7	27 37.3
28	0 24 19.8	3 50.4	26 58.6	19 11.2	24 43.9	29 3.7	10 21.5	28 38.4	9 41.5	26 5.4	20 25.3	27 39.3
29	0 28 16.4	4 44.5	26 55.6	3♌35.5	25 56.2	29 24.3	11 6.6	28 49.7	9 37.3	26 8.9	20 27.0	27 41.3
30	0 32 12.9	5 38.7	26 52.5	17 47.7	27 7.5	29 46.6	11 51.8	29 .8	9 32.9	26 12.3	20 28.6	27 43.4
		DECLINATION										
1	22 37 52.9	8N36.9	0N12.2	26N39.6	7N17.4	1N51.1	20S17.8	15N15.9	2N 2.6	3N 9.0	16S33.6	17N20.2
4	22 49 42.5	7 31.4	0 12.1	13 53.3	4 56.9	2 30.2	20 46.6	15 3.9	1 57.8	3 4.6	16 34.5	17 17.6
7	23 1 32.2	6 24.8	0 12.1	6S24.4	2 36.6	3 12.7	21 14.4	14 51.9	1 52.9	3 .1	16 35.5	17 15.0
10	23 13 21.8	5 17.2	0 12.0	23 20.7	0 18.1	3 56.0	21 41.1	14 39.9	1 47.8	2 55.6	16 36.5	17 12.5
13	23 25 11.5	4 8.8	0 11.9	27 46.4	1S57.7	4 38.3	22 6.5	14 28.0	1 42.6	2 51.1	16 37.6	17 10.0
16	23 37 1.2	2 59.8	0 11.9	18 46.3	4 9.8	5 17.6	22 30.6	14 16.1	1 37.2	2 46.6	16 38.8	17 7.5
19	23 48 50.8	1 50.3	0 11.8	2 54.8	6 17.4	5 52.7	22 53.2	14 4.3	1 31.7	2 42.1	16 40.0	17 5.1
22	0 0 40.5	0 40.4	0 11.8	13N28.2	8 19.8	6 22.4	23 14.3	13 52.6	1 26.2	2 37.6	16 41.2	17 2.8
25	0 12 30.1	0S29.7	0 11.7	25 22.6	10 16.4	6 46.2	23 33.8	13 40.9	1 20.5	2 33.1	16 42.5	17 .6
28	0 24 19.8	1 39.8	0 11.7	27 28.5	12 6.4	7 3.6	23 51.6	13 29.4	1 14.9	2 28.7	16 43.9	16 58.4

OCTOBER 1967

LONGITUDE

DAY	EPHEM. SID. TIME	☉	☊	☽	☿	♀	♂	♃	♄	♅	♆	♇
	h m s	° ′	° ′	° ′	° ′	° ′	° ′	° ′	° ′	° ′	° ′	° ′
1	0 36 9.5	7♎ 7.9	28♈51.8	27♌49.4	1♏10.6	29♌42.6	14♐10.5	26♌43.1	9♈ 9.7	25♍36.9	22♏27.8	21♍ 3.9
2	0 40 6.0	8 7.0	28 48.6	12♍18.4	2 24.8	0♍ 5.9	14 52.4	26 54.5	9R 5.0	25 40.7	22 29.5	21 6.0
3	0 44 2.6	9 6.0	28 45.5	27 8.3	3 37.5	0 30.9	15 34.5	27 5.8	9 .3	25 44.4	22 31.2	21 8.1
4	0 47 59.1	10 5.1	28 42.3	12♎11.7	4 48.5	0 57.7	16 16.6	27 17.0	8 55.6	25 48.1	22 33.0	21 10.2
5	0 51 55.7	11 4.2	28 39.1	27 19.6	5 57.7	1 26.0	16 58.9	27 28.2	8 50.8	25 51.8	22 34.8	21 12.3
6	0 55 52.2	12 3.4	28 35.9	12♏23.0	7 5.1	1 56.0	17 41.3	27 39.3	8 46.2	25 55.5	22 36.6	21 14.4
7	0 59 48.8	13 2.6	28 32.7	27 13.5	8 10.3	2 27.4	18 23.8	27 50.3	8 41.5	25 59.2	22 38.5	21 16.5
8	1 3 45.3	14 1.8	28 29.6	11♐45.2	9 13.3	3 .2	19 6.4	28 1.3	8 36.8	26 2.8	22 40.3	21 18.5
9	1 7 41.9	15 1.1	28 26.4	25 54.4	10 13.8	3 34.5	19 49.1	28 12.1	8 32.1	26 6.5	22 42.2	21 20.6
10	1 11 38.4	16 .3	28 23.2	9♑39.8	11 11.7	4 10.1	20 31.8	28 22.9	8 27.4	26 10.1	22 44.0	21 22.6
11	1 15 35.0	16 59.7	28 20.0	23 2.2	12 6.6	4 47.0	21 14.7	28 33.6	8 22.8	26 13.7	22 45.9	21 24.6
12	1 19 31.6	17 59.0	28 16.9	6♒ 3.4	12 58.4	5 25.1	21 57.7	28 44.2	8 18.2	26 17.3	22 47.9	21 26.6
13	1 23 28.1	18 58.3	28 13.7	18 45.9	13 46.8	6 4.5	22 40.8	28 54.7	8 13.6	26 20.9	22 49.8	21 28.6
14	1 27 24.7	19 57.7	28 10.5	1♓12.9	14 31.3	6 45.0	23 23.9	29 5.1	8 9.0	26 24.4	22 51.7	21 30.6
15	1 31 21.2	20 57.2	28 7.3	13 27.1	15 11.6	7 26.7	24 7.2	29 15.4	8 4.5	26 27.9	22 53.7	21 32.6
16	1 35 17.8	21 56.6	28 4.1	25 31.4	15 47.3	8 9.4	24 50.5	29 25.7	7 60.0	26 31.5	22 55.7	21 34.5
17	1 39 14.3	22 56.1	28 1.0	7♈28.1	16 18.0	8 53.2	25 33.9	29 35.8	7 55.5	26 35.0	22 57.7	21 36.4
18	1 43 10.9	23 55.6	27 57.8	19 19.5	16 43.2	9 38.0	26 17.4	29 45.9	7 51.0	26 38.4	22 59.7	21 38.3
19	1 47 7.4	24 55.2	27 54.6	1♉ 8.0	17 2.3	10 23.8	27 1.0	29 55.8	7 46.6	26 41.9	23 1.7	21 40.2
20	1 51 4.0	25 54.8	27 51.4	12 55.5	17 14.8	11 10.5	27 44.7	0♍ 5.7	7 42.3	26 45.3	23 3.8	21 42.1
21	1 55 .5	26 54.4	27 48.3	24 44.4	17 20.3	11 58.1	28 28.5	0 15.4	7 38.0	26 48.7	23 5.8	21 44.0
22	1 58 57.1	27 54.0	27 45.1	6♊37.3	17R18.0	12 46.6	29 12.3	0 25.1	7 33.7	26 52.1	23 7.9	21 45.8
23	2 2 53.7	28 53.7	27 41.9	18 37.2	17 7.6	13 36.0	29 56.2	0 34.6	7 29.5	26 55.5	23 10.0	21 47.7
24	2 6 50.2	29 53.5	27 38.7	0♋47.2	16 48.5	14 26.1	0♑40.2	0 44.1	7 25.3	26 58.8	23 12.1	21 49.5
25	2 10 46.8	0♏53.2	27 35.5	13 10.9	16 20.5	15 17.1	1 24.3	0 53.4	7 21.2	27 2.1	23 14.2	21 51.3
26	2 14 43.3	1 53.0	27 32.4	25 52.2	15 43.5	16 8.8	2 8.5	1 2.7	7 17.1	27 5.4	23 16.3	21 53.1
27	2 18 39.9	2 52.9	27 29.2	8♌54.5	14 57.5	17 1.3	2 52.8	1 11.8	7 13.1	27 8.7	23 18.5	21 54.9
28	2 22 36.4	3 52.8	27 26.0	22 20.9	14 3.0	17 54.5	3 37.1	1 20.8	7 9.2	27 12.0	23 20.6	21 56.6
29	2 26 33.0	4 52.7	27 22.8	6♍13.3	13 .7	18 48.3	4 21.5	1 29.7	7 5.3	27 15.2	23 22.8	21 58.3
30	2 30 29.5	5 52.7	27 19.7	20 31.7	11 51.8	19 42.8	5 6.0	1 38.5	7 1.4	27 18.3	23 24.9	22 .0
31	2 34 26.1	6 52.7	27 16.5	5♎13.6	10 37.9	20 37.9	5 50.5	1 47.2	6 57.7	27 21.5	23 27.1	22 1.7

LATITUDE

DAY	EPHEM. SID. TIME	☉	☊	☽	☿	♀	♂	♃	♄	♅	♆	♇
1	0 36 9.5	0 .0	0 .0	4N33.9	2S 3.5	4S37.5	1S37.9	0N44.0	2S41.7	0N43.2	1N41.6	14N37.2
4	0 47 59.1	0 .0	0 .0	1 26.0	2 23.6	4 4.9	1 38.0	0 44.5	2 41.8	0 43.2	1 41.4	14 37.8
7	0 59 48.8	0 .0	0 .0	2S35.3	2 41.7	3 33.2	1 38.1	0 44.9	2 41.8	0 43.2	1 41.3	14 38.4
10	1 11 38.4	0 .0	0 .0	5 1.1	2 56.9	3 2.6	1 38.0	0 45.4	2 41.7	0 43.3	1 41.2	14 39.1
13	1 23 28.1	0 .0	0 .0	4 56.6	3 8.4	2 33.2	1 37.9	0 45.9	2 41.6	0 43.3	1 41.1	14 39.9
16	1 35 17.8	0 .0	0 .0	2 50.4	3 14.6	2 5.1	1 37.7	0 46.4	2 41.5	0 43.3	1 41.0	14 40.7
19	1 47 7.4	0 .0	0 .0	0N17.9	3 13.5	1 38.3	1 37.4	0 47.0	2 41.3	0 43.4	1 40.9	14 41.6
22	1 58 57.1	0 .0	0 .0	3 19.1	3 2.6	1 13.0	1 37.0	0 47.5	2 41.0	0 43.4	1 40.9	14 42.5
25	2 10 46.8	0 .0	0 .0	5 7.4	2 38.7	0 49.0	1 36.5	0 48.1	2 40.8	0 43.5	1 40.8	14 43.5
28	2 22 36.4	0 .0	0 .0	4 49.4	1 59.6	0 26.6	1 35.9	0 48.7	2 40.4	0 43.6	1 40.7	14 44.6
31	2 34 26.1	0 .0	0 .0	2 2.9	1 6.1	0 5.5	1 35.3	0 49.3	2 40.0	0 43.6	1 40.7	14 45.7

RIGHT ASCENSION

DAY	EPHEM. SID. TIME	☉	☊	☽	☿	♀	♂	♃	♄	♅	♆	♇
1	0 36 9.5	6♎32.9	26♈49.5	1♍38.7	28♎17.8	0♍10.8	12♐37.3	29♌12.0	9♈28.6	26♍15.7	20♏30.3	27♍45.4
2	0 40 6.0	7 27.2	26 46.5	15 9.0	29 27.1	0 36.6	13 22.9	29 23.0	9R24.3	26 19.2	20 32.1	27 47.4
3	0 44 2.6	8 21.6	26 43.5	28 27.1	0♏35.1	1 4.0	14 8.7	29 34.0	9 20.0	26 22.6	20 33.8	27 49.4
4	0 47 59.1	9 16.0	26 40.4	11♎46.5	1 42.0	1 33.0	14 54.7	29 44.9	9 15.7	26 26.0	20 35.6	27 51.5
5	0 51 55.7	10 10.6	26 37.4	25 23.1	2 47.4	2 3.4	15 40.8	29 55.7	9 11.3	26 29.4	20 37.4	27 53.5
6	0 55 52.2	11 5.2	26 34.4	9♏31.0	3 51.3	2 35.4	16 27.2	0♍ 6.5	9 7.0	26 32.8	20 39.2	27 55.5
7	0 59 48.8	11 59.9	26 31.4	24 18.1	4 53.5	3 8.7	17 13.7	0 17.1	9 2.7	26 36.2	20 41.0	27 57.5
8	1 3 45.3	12 54.7	26 28.3	9♐41.2	5 53.9	3 43.3	18 .3	0 27.7	8 58.4	26 39.5	20 42.9	27 59.5
9	1 7 41.9	13 49.6	26 25.3	25 22.9	6 52.2	4 19.1	18 47.1	0 38.2	8 54.1	26 42.9	20 44.8	28 1.5
10	1 11 38.4	14 44.7	26 22.3	10♑55.7	7 48.2	4 56.2	19 34.1	0 48.6	8 49.8	26 46.2	20 46.7	28 3.4
11	1 15 35.0	15 39.8	26 19.3	25 51.1	8 41.6	5 34.5	20 21.2	0 58.9	8 45.6	26 49.5	20 48.6	28 5.4
12	1 19 31.6	16 35.0	26 16.2	9♒50.8	9 32.2	6 13.8	21 8.4	1 9.2	8 41.3	26 52.8	20 50.5	28 7.4
13	1 23 28.1	17 30.3	26 13.2	22 49.5	10 19.7	6 54.3	21 55.8	1 19.3	8 37.1	26 56.1	20 52.4	28 9.3
14	1 27 24.7	18 25.8	26 10.2	4♓52.6	11 3.7	7 35.7	22 43.3	1 29.4	8 32.9	26 59.4	20 54.4	28 11.2
15	1 31 21.2	19 21.4	26 7.2	16 11.9	11 43.7	8 18.1	23 30.9	1 39.4	8 28.7	27 2.6	20 56.4	28 13.2
16	1 35 17.8	20 17.1	26 4.2	27 1.3	12 19.5	9 1.5	24 18.6	1 49.3	8 24.5	27 5.9	20 58.4	28 15.1
17	1 39 14.3	21 13.0	26 1.1	7♈35.4	12 50.4	9 45.8	25 6.5	1 59.0	8 20.4	27 9.1	21 .4	28 17.0
18	1 43 10.9	22 9.0	25 58.1	18 8.3	13 16.1	10 30.9	25 54.5	2 8.7	8 16.3	27 12.3	21 2.4	28 18.9
19	1 47 7.4	23 5.1	25 55.1	28 53.2	13 35.9	11 16.9	26 42.5	2 18.3	8 12.2	27 15.5	21 4.5	28 20.8
20	1 51 4.0	24 1.5	25 52.1	10♉ 2.3	13 49.4	12 3.7	27 30.7	2 27.8	8 8.2	27 18.6	21 6.5	28 22.6
21	1 55 .5	24 57.9	25 49.1	21 45.5	13 56.1	12 51.2	28 19.0	2 37.2	8 4.2	27 21.8	21 8.6	28 24.5
22	1 58 57.1	25 54.6	25 46.0	4♊ 9.1	13R55.3	13 39.4	29 7.4	2 46.5	8 .2	27 24.9	21 10.7	28 26.3
23	2 2 53.7	26 51.4	25 43.0	17 14.0	13 46.6	14 28.3	29 55.8	2 55.7	7 56.3	27 28.0	21 12.8	28 28.1
24	2 6 50.2	27 48.3	25 40.0	0♋53.3	13 29.7	15 17.9	0♑44.4	3 4.8	7 52.4	27 31.0	21 14.9	28 30.0
25	2 10 46.8	28 45.5	25 37.0	14 53.5	13 4.2	16 8.2	1 33.0	3 13.8	7 48.6	27 34.1	21 17.0	28 31.8
26	2 14 43.3	29 42.8	25 34.0	28 57.2	12 30.3	16 59.0	2 21.8	3 22.7	7 44.8	27 37.1	21 19.2	28 33.5
27	2 18 39.9	0♏40.4	25 30.9	12♌49.5	11 48.0	17 50.4	3 10.6	3 31.5	7 41.1	27 40.2	21 21.4	28 35.4
28	2 22 36.4	1 38.1	25 27.9	26 21.6	10 57.9	18 42.4	3 59.5	3 40.2	7 37.4	27 43.1	21 23.5	28 37.1
29	2 26 33.0	2 36.0	25 24.9	9♍33.9	10 .9	19 34.9	4 48.4	3 48.8	7 33.8	27 46.1	21 25.7	28 38.8
30	2 30 29.5	3 34.0	25 21.9	22 34.4	8 58.1	20 27.9	5 37.4	3 57.2	7 30.2	27 49.0	21 27.9	28 40.6
31	2 34 26.1	4 32.3	25 18.9	5♎36.6	7 51.1	21 21.4	6 26.5	4 5.5	7 26.7	27 51.9	21 30.1	28 42.3

DECLINATION

DAY	EPHEM. SID. TIME	☉	☊	☽	☿	♀	♂	♃	♄	♅	♆	♇
1	0 36 9.5	2S49.9	0N11.6	16N30.8	13S48.9	7N14.5	24S 7.7	13N18.1	1N 9.3	2N24.2	16S45.2	16N56.4
4	0 47 59.1	3 59.7	0 11.5	3S30.1	15 22.9	7 18.9	24 21.8	13 6.9	1 3.6	2 19.8	16 46.7	16 54.4
7	0 59 48.8	5 9.1	0 11.5	22 3.8	16 47.0	7 17.0	24 34.0	12 55.8	0 58.1	2 15.4	16 48.2	16 52.5
10	1 11 38.4	6 17.9	0 11.4	28 5.9	17 59.6	7 8.8	24 44.2	12 45.0	0 52.6	2 11.1	16 49.7	16 50.7
13	1 23 28.1	7 26.0	0 11.4	19 53.9	18 58.4	6 54.7	24 52.3	12 34.4	0 47.3	2 6.9	16 51.2	16 49.0
16	1 35 17.8	8 33.0	0 11.3	4 23.2	19 40.3	6 34.7	24 58.3	12 24.0	0 42.0	2 2.7	16 52.8	16 47.4
19	1 47 7.4	9 39.1	0 11.2	12N 9.1	20 1.1	6 9.3	25 2.1	12 13.9	0 37.0	1 58.6	16 54.4	16 45.9
22	1 58 57.1	10 43.8	0 11.2	24 41.4	19 55.2	5 38.5	25 3.6	12 4.1	0 32.1	1 54.6	16 56.0	16 44.5
25	2 10 46.8	11 47.1	0 11.1	27 53.4	19 15.7	5 2.8	25 2.8	11 54.6	0 27.4	1 50.7	16 57.6	16 43.3
28	2 22 36.4	12 48.9	0 11.1	18 37.4	17 57.7	4 22.4	24 59.7	11 45.4	0 23.0	1 46.8	16 59.3	16 42.1
31	2 34 26.1	13 48.8	0 11.0	0S11.8	16 3.7	3 37.7	24 54.2	11 36.5	0 18.8	1 43.1	17 1.0	16 41.1

NOVEMBER 1967

DAY	EPHEM. SID. TIME	☉	☊	☾	☿	♀	♂	♃	♄	♅	♆	♇
	h m s	° ′	° ′	° ′	° ′	° ′	° ′	° ′	° ′	° ′	° ′	° ′
		LONGITUDE										
1	2 38 22.7	7♏52.7	27♈13.3	20♎14.2	9♏20.9	21♍33.6	6♑35.2	1♍55.7	6♈54.0	27♍24.6	23♏29.3	22♍ 3.4
2	2 42 19.2	8 52.7	27 10.1	5♏25.5	8R 3.2	22 29.9	7 19.9	2 4.1	6R50.3	27 27.7	23 31.5	22 5.0
3	2 46 15.8	9 52.8	27 7.0	20 38.4	6 47.1	23 26.8	8 4.6	2 12.4	6 46.8	27 30.7	23 33.7	22 6.6
4	2 50 12.3	10 52.9	27 3.8	5♐42.9	5 35.1	24 24.2	8 49.5	2 20.6	6 43.3	27 33.7	23 35.9	22 8.2
5	2 54 8.9	11 53.1	27 .6	20 30.4	4 29.5	25 22.1	9 34.4	2 28.6	6 39.9	27 36.7	23 38.1	22 9.8
6	2 58 5.4	12 53.3	26 57.4	4♑54.4	3 32.1	26 20.5	10 19.4	2 36.5	6 36.5	27 39.7	23 40.3	22 11.3
7	3 2 2.0	13 53.5	26 54.2	18 51.5	2 44.5	27 19.4	11 4.4	2 44.3	6 33.3	27 42.6	23 42.5	22 12.8
8	3 5 58.5	14 53.7	26 51.1	2♒20.8	2 7.8	28 18.8	11 49.5	2 51.9	6 30.1	27 45.4	23 44.8	22 14.3
9	3 9 55.1	15 53.9	26 47.9	15 23.9	1 42.7	29 18.7	12 34.7	2 59.4	6 27.0	27 48.3	23 47.0	22 15.8
10	3 13 51.7	16 54.2	26 44.7	28 4.0	1 29.2	0♎19.0	13 19.9	3 6.8	6 24.0	27 51.1	23 49.2	22 17.2
11	3 17 48.2	17 54.5	26 41.5	10♓25.2	1 27.2	1 19.7	14 5.2	3 14.0	6 21.1	27 53.8	23 51.5	22 18.6
12	3 21 44.8	18 54.8	26 38.4	22 31.8	1D36.3	2 20.8	14 50.6	3 21.1	6 18.3	27 56.6	23 53.7	22 20.0
13	3 25 41.3	19 55.2	26 35.2	4♈28.2	1 55.7	3 22.4	15 36.0	3 28.1	6 15.5	27 59.3	23 56.0	22 21.4
14	3 29 37.9	20 55.5	26 32.0	16 18.3	2 24.6	4 24.3	16 21.4	3 34.9	6 12.9	28 1.9	23 58.2	22 22.7
15	3 33 34.4	21 55.9	26 28.8	28 5.6	3 2.2	5 26.7	17 6.9	3 41.5	6 10.3	28 4.5	24 .5	22 24.0
16	3 37 31.0	22 56.4	26 25.7	9♉53.3	3 47.5	6 29.4	17 52.5	3 48.0	6 7.8	28 7.1	24 2.7	22 25.3
17	3 41 27.6	23 56.9	26 22.5	21 43.7	4 39.8	7 32.5	18 38.1	3 54.4	6 5.5	28 9.7	24 5.0	22 26.6
18	3 45 24.1	24 57.3	26 19.3	3♊38.9	5 38.0	8 35.9	19 23.8	4 .7	6 3.2	28 12.1	24 7.3	22 27.8
19	3 49 20.7	25 57.8	26 16.1	15 40.6	6 41.5	9 39.7	20 9.5	4 6.7	6 1.0	28 14.6	24 9.5	22 29.0
20	3 53 17.2	26 58.4	26 12.9	27 50.6	7 49.6	10 43.8	20 55.2	4 12.6	5 58.9	28 17.0	24 11.8	22 30.2
21	3 57 13.8	27 58.9	26 9.8	10♋10.4	9 1.7	11 48.2	21 41.0	4 18.4	5 56.9	28 19.3	24 14.0	22 31.4
22	4 1 10.3	28 59.5	26 6.6	22 42.0	10 17.1	12 52.9	22 26.9	4 24.0	5 55.0	28 21.7	24 16.3	22 32.5
23	4 5 6.9	0♐ .1	26 3.4	5♌27.4	11 35.3	13 58.0	23 12.8	4 29.4	5 53.2	28 23.9	24 18.5	22 33.6
24	4 9 3.5	1 .7	26 .2	18 28.9	12 56.1	15 3.3	23 58.7	4 34.7	5 51.5	28 26.1	24 20.8	22 34.6
25	4 13 .0	2 1.4	25 57.1	1♍48.8	14 18.9	16 8.9	24 44.7	4 39.8	5 49.9	28 28.3	24 23.0	22 35.6
26	4 16 56.6	3 2.1	25 53.9	15 29.1	15 43.4	17 14.8	25 30.7	4 44.7	5 48.4	28 30.4	24 25.2	22 36.6
27	4 20 53.1	4 2.8	25 50.7	29 31.1	17 9.4	18 20.9	26 16.8	4 49.5	5 47.1	28 32.5	24 27.5	22 37.6
28	4 24 49.7	5 3.6	25 47.5	13♎54.5	18 36.7	19 27.3	27 2.9	4 54.1	5 45.8	28 34.6	24 29.7	22 38.5
29	4 28 46.2	6 4.3	25 44.4	28 37.1	20 4.9	20 34.0	27 49.0	4 58.5	5 44.6	28 36.6	24 31.9	22 39.4
30	4 32 42.8	7 5.1	25 41.2	13♏33.9	21 34.1	21 40.9	28 35.2	5 2.8	5 43.5	28 38.5	24 34.1	22 40.3
		LATITUDE										
1	2 38 22.7	0 .0	0 .0	0N42.7	0S46.0	0N 1.1	1S35.1	0N49.5	2S39.9	0N43.6	1N40.7	14N46.0
4	2 50 12.3	0 .0	0 .0	3S14.5	0N15.7	0 20.2	1 34.3	0 50.1	2 39.4	0 43.7	1 40.6	14 47.2
7	3 2 2.0	0 .0	0 .0	5 12.7	1 10.3	0 37.9	1 33.5	0 50.7	2 39.0	0 43.8	1 40.6	14 48.4
10	3 13 51.7	0 .0	0 .0	4 33.6	1 50.1	0 54.2	1 32.6	0 51.4	2 38.4	0 43.9	1 40.5	14 49.7
13	3 25 41.3	0 .0	0 .0	2 5.9	2 13.0	1 9.1	1 31.6	0 52.0	2 37.9	0 44.0	1 40.5	14 51.0
16	3 37 31.0	0 .0	0 .0	1N 5.5	2 21.5	1 22.5	1 30.6	0 52.7	2 37.3	0 44.1	1 40.5	14 52.4
19	3 49 20.7	0 .0	0 .0	3 52.7	2 19.1	1 34.7	1 29.5	0 53.4	2 36.7	0 44.2	1 40.5	14 53.8
22	4 1 10.3	0 .0	0 .0	5 11.3	2 9.1	1 45.4	1 28.3	0 54.1	2 36.0	0 44.3	1 40.5	14 55.2
25	4 13 .0	0 .0	0 .0	4 17.9	1 53.9	1 54.9	1 27.0	0 54.8	2 35.4	0 44.4	1 40.5	14 56.7
28	4 24 49.7	0 .0	0 .0	1 13.1	1 35.6	2 3.0	1 25.7	0 55.6	2 34.7	0 44.5	1 40.5	14 58.2
		RIGHT ASCENSION										
1	2 38 22.7	5♏30.8	25♈15.9	18♎57.4	6♏41.9	22♍15.3	7♑15.6	4♍13.7	7♈23.3	27♍54.8	21♏32.3	28♍44.0
2	2 42 19.2	6 29.5	25 12.9	2♏53.5	5R32.6	23 9.7	8 4.7	4 21.8	7R19.9	27 57.6	21 34.5	28 45.6
3	2 46 15.8	7 28.4	25 9.8	17 37.5	4 25.4	24 4.5	8 53.9	4 29.8	7 16.6	28 .4	21 36.7	28 47.3
4	2 50 12.3	8 27.4	25 6.8	3♐11.2	3 22.4	24 59.8	9 43.2	4 37.7	7 13.3	28 3.2	21 39.0	28 48.9
5	2 54 8.9	9 26.7	25 3.8	19 20.0	2 25.6	25 55.4	10 32.5	4 45.4	7 10.1	28 5.9	21 41.2	28 50.5
6	2 58 5.4	10 26.2	25 .8	5♑33.0	1 36.6	26 51.4	11 21.8	4 53.0	7 7.0	28 8.6	21 43.4	28 52.1
7	3 2 2.0	11 25.9	24 57.8	21 13.9	0 56.8	27 47.7	12 11.1	5 .4	7 3.9	28 11.3	21 45.7	28 53.7
8	3 5 58.5	12 25.8	24 54.8	5♒55.5	0 27.0	28 44.5	13 .4	5 7.8	7 1.0	28 14.0	21 48.0	28 55.2
9	3 9 55.1	13 25.9	24 51.8	19 27.0	0 7.6	29 41.5	13 49.8	5 15.0	6 58.1	28 16.6	21 50.2	28 56.8
10	3 13 51.7	14 26.2	24 48.8	1♓52.8	29♎58.7	0♎39.0	14 39.1	5 22.1	6 55.2	28 19.2	21 52.5	28 58.3
11	3 17 48.2	15 26.7	24 45.7	13 25.5	0♏ .2	1 36.7	15 28.5	5 29.0	6 52.5	28 21.7	21 54.8	28 59.8
12	3 21 44.8	16 27.4	24 42.7	24 21.2	0D11.4	2 34.8	16 17.8	5 35.8	6 49.8	28 24.2	21 57.0	29 1.2
13	3 25 41.3	17 28.3	24 39.7	4♈56.0	0 32.0	3 33.2	17 7.2	5 42.5	6 47.2	28 26.7	21 59.3	29 2.7
14	3 29 37.9	18 29.5	24 36.7	15 25.9	1 1.1	4 31.8	17 56.5	5 49.1	6 44.7	28 29.2	22 1.6	29 4.1
15	3 33 34.4	19 30.8	24 33.7	26 5.2	1 37.9	5 30.8	18 45.8	5 55.5	6 42.3	28 31.6	22 3.9	29 5.5
16	3 37 31.0	20 32.4	24 30.7	7♉ 7.3	2 21.7	6 30.2	19 35.1	6 1.7	6 39.9	28 33.9	22 6.1	29 6.9
17	3 41 27.6	21 34.2	24 27.7	18 43.2	3 11.9	7 29.8	20 24.4	6 7.9	6 37.7	28 36.3	22 8.5	29 8.3
18	3 45 24.1	22 36.2	24 24.7	1♊ .0	4 7.6	8 29.7	21 13.7	6 13.9	6 35.5	28 38.6	22 10.8	29 9.6
19	3 49 20.7	23 38.4	24 21.7	13 59.1	5 8.1	9 29.9	22 2.9	6 19.7	6 33.4	28 40.9	22 13.0	29 10.9
20	3 53 17.2	24 40.7	24 18.7	27 33.9	6 13.0	10 30.3	22 52.1	6 25.4	6 31.4	28 43.1	22 15.3	29 12.2
21	3 57 13.8	25 43.3	24 15.7	11♋29.8	7 21.7	11 31.1	23 41.2	6 30.9	6 29.5	28 45.2	22 17.6	29 13.4
22	4 1 10.3	26 46.1	24 12.6	25 28.0	8 33.7	12 32.1	24 30.3	6 36.3	6 27.7	28 47.4	22 19.9	29 14.7
23	4 5 6.9	27 49.2	24 9.6	9♌11.6	9 48.7	13 33.4	25 19.3	6 41.5	6 25.9	28 49.5	22 22.2	29 15.9
24	4 9 3.5	28 52.4	24 6.6	22 30.6	11 6.2	14 35.0	26 8.3	6 46.6	6 24.3	28 51.5	22 24.5	29 17.1
25	4 13 .0	29 55.8	24 3.6	5♍24.3	12 26.0	15 36.9	26 57.3	6 51.6	6 22.7	28 53.5	22 26.7	29 18.2
26	4 16 56.6	0♐59.4	24 .6	18 .2	13 47.8	16 39.1	27 46.2	6 56.3	6 21.3	28 55.5	22 29.0	29 19.3
27	4 20 53.1	2 3.2	23 57.6	0♎31.8	15 11.3	17 41.5	28 35.0	7 .9	6 19.9	28 57.4	22 31.3	29 20.4
28	4 24 49.7	3 7.2	23 54.6	13 16.4	16 36.5	18 44.2	29 23.8	7 5.4	6 18.7	28 59.3	22 33.5	29 21.5
29	4 28 46.2	4 11.4	23 51.6	26 33.1	18 3.1	19 47.2	0♒12.5	7 9.7	6 17.5	29 1.1	22 35.8	29 22.6
30	4 32 42.8	5 15.7	23 48.6	10♏39.3	19 30.9	20 50.4	1 1.1	7 13.8	6 16.4	29 2.9	22 38.0	29 23.6
		DECLINATION										
1	2 38 22.7	14S 8.4	0N11.0	7S15.0	15S20.3	3N21.9	24S51.9	11N33.7	0N17.5	1N41.9	17S 1.5	16N40.8
4	2 50 12.3	15 5.7	0 10.9	24 27.3	13 8.5	2 32.0	24 43.2	11 25.3	0 13.7	1 38.3	17 3.2	16 39.9
7	3 2 2.0	16 .8	0 10.9	27 16.6	11 19.5	1 38.7	24 32.2	11 17.4	0 10.2	1 34.9	17 4.9	16 39.2
10	3 13 51.7	16 53.4	0 10.8	16 25.3	10 16.4	0 42.2	24 18.8	11 9.8	0 7.0	1 31.5	17 6.5	16 38.6
13	3 25 41.3	17 43.4	0 10.7	0 8.9	10 3.9	0S17.1	24 3.0	11 2.8	0 4.2	1 28.4	17 8.2	16 38.2
16	3 37 31.0	18 30.7	0 10.7	15N49.1	10 33.9	1 18.8	23 44.9	10 56.1	0 1.7	1 25.3	17 9.9	16 37.9
19	3 49 20.7	19 15.1	0 10.6	26 31.8	11 33.7	2 22.7	23 24.4	10 50.0	0S .5	1 22.5	17 11.5	16 37.6
22	4 1 10.3	19 56.3	0 10.6	26 38.9	12 51.9	3 28.2	23 1.6	10 44.4	0 2.2	1 19.7	17 13.2	16 37.6
25	4 13 .0	20 34.3	0 10.5	14 50.6	14 19.4	4 35.2	22 36.6	10 39.3	0 3.6	1 17.2	17 14.8	16 37.7
28	4 24 49.7	21 8.9	0 10.4	4S21.9	15 50.2	5 43.1	22 9.3	10 34.7	0 4.6	1 14.8	17 16.4	16 37.9

DECEMBER 1967

DAY	EPHEM. SID. TIME	☉	☊	☽	☿	♀	♂	♃	♄	♅	♆	♇
	h m s	° ′	° ′	° ′	° ′	° ′	° ′	° ′	° ′	° ′	° ′	° ′
		LONGITUDE										
1	4 36 39.4	8♐ 6.0	25♈38.0	28♏38.0	23♏ 3.9	22♎48.0	29♑21.5	5♍ 6.9	5♈42.6	28♍40.4	24♏36.3	22♍41.2
2	4 40 35.9	9 6.8	25 34.8	13♐40.1	24 34.3	23 55.4	0♒ 7.7	5 10.8	5R41.7	28 42.2	24 38.5	22 42.0
3	4 44 32.5	10 7.7	25 31.7	28 31.1	26 5.3	25 2.9	0 54.1	5 14.5	5 40.9	28 44.0	24 40.7	22 42.7
4	4 48 29.0	11 8.6	25 28.5	13♑ 2.6	27 36.6	26 10.7	1 40.4	5 18.1	5 40.3	28 45.8	24 42.9	22 43.5
5	4 52 25.6	12 9.4	25 25.3	27 8.7	29 8.2	27 18.7	2 26.8	5 21.5	5 39.8	28 47.4	24 45.1	22 44.2
6	4 56 22.2	13 10.4	25 22.1	10♒46.6	0♐40.1	28 26.8	3 13.2	5 24.7	5 39.3	28 49.1	24 47.3	22 44.9
7	5 0 18.7	14 11.3	25 18.9	23 56.4	2 12.3	29 35.2	3 59.6	5 27.7	5 39.0	28 50.7	24 49.4	22 45.5
8	5 4 15.3	15 12.3	25 15.8	6♓40.3	3 44.7	0♏43.7	4 46.1	5 30.5	5 38.9	28 52.3	24 51.6	22 46.2
9	5 8 11.8	16 13.2	25 12.6	19 2.5	5 17.2	1 52.5	5 32.6	5 33.2	5 38.8	28 53.7	24 53.7	22 46.8
10	5 12 8.4	17 14.2	25 9.4	1♈ 8.0	6 49.8	3 1.3	6 19.1	5 35.7	5 38.8	28 55.2	24 55.9	22 47.3
11	5 16 5.0	18 15.1	25 6.2	13 2.1	8 22.6	4 10.4	7 5.7	5 37.9	5D38.9	28 56.5	24 58.0	22 47.9
12	5 20 1.5	19 16.1	25 3.1	24 49.9	9 55.5	5 19.6	7 52.2	5 40.0	5 39.1	28 57.9	25 .1	22 48.3
13	5 23 58.1	20 17.1	24 59.9	6♉36.3	11 28.4	6 29.0	8 38.8	5 41.9	5 39.5	28 59.1	25 2.2	22 48.8
14	5 27 54.6	21 18.1	24 56.7	18 25.5	13 1.5	7 38.5	9 25.4	5 43.6	5 39.9	29 .3	25 4.2	22 49.2
15	5 31 51.2	22 19.1	24 53.5	0♊20.7	14 34.7	8 48.2	10 12.0	5 45.1	5 40.5	29 1.5	25 6.3	22 49.6
16	5 35 47.7	23 20.1	24 50.4	12 24.6	16 8.0	9 58.1	10 58.7	5 46.5	5 41.1	29 2.6	25 8.3	22 50.0
17	5 39 44.3	24 21.2	24 47.2	24 38.8	17 41.4	11 8.0	11 45.3	5 47.6	5 41.9	29 3.7	25 10.4	22 50.3
18	5 43 40.9	25 22.2	24 44.0	7♋ 4.1	19 15.0	12 18.2	12 32.0	5 48.6	5 42.8	29 4.7	25 12.4	22 50.6
19	5 47 37.4	26 23.3	24 40.8	19 41.0	20 48.7	13 28.4	13 18.7	5 49.3	5 43.8	29 5.6	25 14.4	22 50.8
20	5 51 34.0	27 24.3	24 37.7	2♌29.5	22 22.5	14 38.8	14 5.4	5 49.9	5 44.9	29 6.5	25 16.4	22 51.0
21	5 55 30.5	28 25.4	24 34.5	15 29.6	23 56.5	15 49.4	14 52.1	5 50.2	5 46.1	29 7.3	25 18.3	22 51.2
22	5 59 27.1	29 26.5	24 31.3	28 41.5	25 30.7	17 .0	15 38.8	5 50.4	5 47.4	29 8.1	25 20.3	22 51.4
23	6 3 23.7	0♑27.6	24 28.1	12♍ 5.7	27 5.0	18 10.8	16 25.5	5 50.4	5 48.9	29 8.8	25 22.2	22 51.5
24	6 7 20.2	1 28.7	24 24.9	25 43.2	28 39.6	19 21.7	17 12.3	5R50.2	5 50.4	29 9.5	25 24.1	22 51.6
25	6 11 16.8	2 29.8	24 21.8	9♎34.8	0♑14.3	20 32.7	17 59.1	5 49.8	5 52.0	29 10.1	25 26.0	22 51.6
26	6 15 13.3	3 31.0	24 18.6	23 41.2	1 49.3	21 43.8	18 45.8	5 49.1	5 53.8	29 10.6	25 27.9	22 51.6
27	6 19 9.9	4 32.1	24 15.4	8♏ 1.8	3 24.6	22 55.1	19 32.6	5 48.3	5 55.6	29 11.1	25 29.7	22 51.6
28	6 23 6.5	5 33.3	24 12.2	22 34.4	5 .1	24 6.4	20 19.4	5 47.3	5 57.6	29 11.6	25 31.6	22 51.6
29	6 27 3.0	6 34.5	24 9.1	7♐15.0	6 35.9	25 17.9	21 6.3	5 46.2	5 59.7	29 12.0	25 33.4	22R51.5
30	6 30 59.6	7 35.7	24 5.9	21 57.1	8 12.0	26 29.4	21 53.1	5 44.8	6 1.9	29 12.3	25 35.2	22 51.4
31	6 34 56.1	8 36.8	24 2.7	6♑33.5	9 48.4	27 41.0	22 39.9	5 43.2	6 4.2	29 12.6	25 37.0	22 51.3
		LATITUDE										
1	4 36 39.4	0 .0	0 .0	2S41.3	1N15.3	2N 9.8	1S24.3	0N56.3	2S34.0	0N44.6	1N40.6	14N59.7
4	4 48 29.0	0 .0	0 .0	4 59.8	0 54.0	2 15.5	1 22.9	0 57.1	2 33.2	0 44.7	1 40.6	15 1.3
7	5 0 18.7	0 .0	0 .0	4 35.1	0 32.3	2 19.9	1 21.4	0 57.9	2 32.5	0 44.8	1 40.7	15 2.8
10	5 12 8.4	0 .0	0 .0	2 13.9	0 10.9	2 23.2	1 19.8	0 58.6	2 31.8	0 44.9	1 40.7	15 4.4
13	5 23 58.1	0 .0	0 .0	0N52.7	0S10.1	2 25.3	1 18.2	0 59.4	2 31.0	0 45.0	1 40.8	15 6.0
16	5 35 47.7	0 .0	0 .0	3 39.3	0 30.1	2 26.3	1 16.6	1 .2	2 30.3	0 45.2	1 40.8	15 7.6
19	5 47 37.4	0 .0	0 .0	5 1.8	0 49.1	2 26.3	1 14.8	1 1.0	2 29.5	0 45.3	1 40.9	15 9.2
22	5 59 27.1	0 .0	0 .0	4 14.7	1 6.6	2 25.3	1 13.1	1 1.8	2 28.7	0 45.4	1 41.0	15 10.8
25	6 11 16.8	0 .0	0 .0	1 23.3	1 22.5	2 23.4	1 11.3	1 2.6	2 28.0	0 45.5	1 41.1	15 12.5
28	6 23 6.5	0 .0	0 .0	2S18.9	1 36.5	2 20.5	1 9.4	1 3.4	2 27.2	0 45.6	1 41.2	15 14.0
31	6 34 56.1	0 .0	0 .0	4 46.1	1 48.4	2 16.8	1 7.5	1 4.2	2 26.5	0 45.8	1 41.3	15 15.6
		RIGHT ASCENSION										
1	4 36 39.4	6♐20.3	23♈45.6	25♏45.4	20♏60.0	21♎53.9	1♒49.7	7♍17.8	6♈15.4	29♍ 4.7	22♏40.3	29♍24.6
2	4 40 35.9	7 25.0	23 42.6	11♐47.0	22 30.1	22 57.7	2 38.2	7 21.6	6R14.5	29 6.4	22 42.5	29 25.5
3	4 44 32.5	8 29.8	23 39.6	28 19.7	24 1.1	24 1.8	3 26.6	7 25.2	6 13.7	29 8.1	22 44.8	29 26.5
4	4 48 29.0	9 34.8	23 36.6	14♑43.3	25 33.1	25 6.1	4 15.0	7 28.6	6 13.1	29 9.7	22 47.0	29 27.4
5	4 52 25.6	10 40.0	23 33.6	0♒18.5	27 6.0	26 10.8	5 3.2	7 31.9	6 12.5	29 11.2	22 49.2	29 28.3
6	4 56 22.2	11 45.3	23 30.6	14 42.2	28 39.6	27 15.7	5 51.4	7 35.1	6 12.0	29 12.7	22 51.4	29 29.1
7	5 0 18.7	12 50.7	23 27.6	27 50.9	0♐14.0	28 20.8	6 39.5	7 38.0	6 11.6	29 14.2	22 53.6	29 29.9
8	5 4 15.3	13 56.3	23 24.6	9♓54.8	1 49.2	29 26.4	7 27.6	7 40.8	6 11.4	29 15.7	22 55.8	29 30.8
9	5 8 11.8	15 2.0	23 21.6	21 10.4	3 25.0	0♏32.1	8 15.5	7 43.4	6 11.2	29 17.1	22 58.0	29 31.5
10	5 12 8.4	16 7.8	23 18.6	1♈55.7	5 1.4	1 38.2	9 3.3	7 45.8	6 11.1	29 18.4	23 .2	29 32.3
11	5 16 5.0	17 13.7	23 15.6	12 28.1	6 38.6	2 44.5	9 51.0	7 48.1	6 11.1	29 19.7	23 2.3	29 33.0
12	5 20 1.5	18 19.7	23 12.6	23 4.1	8 16.3	3 51.2	10 38.7	7 50.2	6D11.2	29 20.9	23 4.5	29 33.7
13	5 23 58.1	19 25.8	23 9.6	3♉58.5	9 54.6	4 58.1	11 26.2	7 52.0	6 11.4	29 22.1	23 6.6	29 34.3
14	5 27 54.6	20 31.9	23 6.6	15 24.5	11 33.5	6 5.3	12 13.6	7 53.8	6 11.7	29 23.2	23 8.7	29 34.9
15	5 31 51.2	21 38.2	23 3.6	27 31.9	13 13.0	7 12.9	13 .9	7 55.3	6 12.2	29 24.3	23 10.8	29 35.5
16	5 35 47.7	22 44.5	23 .6	10♊24.5	14 53.0	8 20.7	13 48.1	7 56.7	6 12.7	29 25.3	23 12.9	29 36.1
17	5 39 44.3	23 50.9	22 57.6	23 58.2	16 33.6	9 28.9	14 35.2	7 57.8	6 13.3	29 26.3	23 15.0	29 36.6
18	5 43 40.9	24 57.3	22 54.6	7♋59.2	18 14.7	10 37.4	15 22.3	7 58.8	6 14.0	29 27.2	23 17.0	29 37.1
19	5 47 37.4	26 3.8	22 51.6	22 7.0	19 56.3	11 46.2	16 9.2	7 59.6	6 14.8	29 28.1	23 19.1	29 37.5
20	5 51 34.0	27 10.3	22 48.6	6♌ 1.2	21 38.4	12 55.4	16 56.0	8 .3	6 15.7	29 28.9	23 21.1	29 38.0
21	5 55 30.5	28 16.9	22 45.6	19 27.6	23 21.0	14 4.8	17 42.6	8 .7	6 16.7	29 29.7	23 23.1	29 38.4
22	5 59 27.1	29 23.5	22 42.6	2♍22.2	25 4.0	15 14.6	18 29.2	8 1.0	6 17.8	29 30.4	23 25.1	29 38.7
23	6 3 23.7	0♑30.1	22 39.6	14 50.4	26 47.5	16 24.7	19 15.7	8 1.1	6 19.0	29 31.1	23 27.1	29 39.1
24	6 7 20.2	1 36.7	22 36.6	27 4.4	28 31.5	17 35.1	20 2.1	8R .9	6 20.4	29 31.7	23 29.0	29 39.4
25	6 11 16.8	2 43.3	22 33.6	9♎20.9	0♑15.8	18 45.9	20 48.3	8 .7	6 21.8	29 32.3	23 30.9	29 39.7
26	6 15 13.3	3 49.9	22 30.6	21 58.9	2 .5	19 56.9	21 34.5	8 .2	6 23.3	29 32.8	23 32.9	29 39.9
27	6 19 9.9	4 56.5	22 27.6	5♏17.4	3 45.6	21 8.3	22 20.5	7 59.5	6 24.9	29 33.3	23 34.8	29 40.1
28	6 23 6.5	6 3.0	22 24.6	19 32.2	5 31.0	22 20.1	23 6.5	7 58.7	6 26.6	29 33.7	23 36.6	29 40.3
29	6 27 3.0	7 9.6	22 21.7	4♐49.2	7 16.7	23 32.1	23 52.4	7 57.7	6 28.4	29 34.1	23 38.6	29 40.5
30	6 30 59.6	8 16.1	22 18.7	20 57.1	9 2.7	24 44.5	24 38.1	7 56.5	6 30.3	29 34.4	23 40.4	29 40.6
31	6 34 56.1	9 22.5	22 15.7	7♑24.6	10 49.0	25 57.2	25 23.8	7 55.1	6 32.3	29 34.7	23 42.2	29 40.7
		DECLINATION										
1	4 36 39.4	21S39.8	0N10.4	22S28.9	17S19.8	6S51.6	21S39.9	10N30.7	0S 5.3	1N12.6	17S18.0	16N38.2
4	4 48 29.0	22 7.1	0 10.3	27 46.7	18 45.3	8 .3	21 8.4	10 27.3	0 5.5	1 10.5	17 19.5	16 38.7
7	5 0 18.7	22 30.5	0 10.3	17 52.0	20 4.8	9 8.8	20 34.8	10 24.5	0 5.3	1 8.7	17 21.0	16 39.3
10	5 12 8.4	22 50.0	0 10.2	1 35.8	21 16.6	10 16.8	19 59.2	10 22.3	0 4.7	1 7.0	17 22.5	16 40.0
13	5 23 58.1	23 5.4	0 10.1	14N33.2	22 19.8	11 23.8	19 21.7	10 20.7	0 3.8	1 5.5	17 24.0	16 40.9
16	5 35 47.7	23 16.7	0 10.1	25 54.7	23 13.4	12 29.5	18 42.5	10 19.8	0 2.4	1 4.3	17 25.4	16 41.9
19	5 47 37.4	23 23.8	0 10.0	26 58.6	23 56.6	13 33.6	18 1.4	10 19.5	0 .7	1 3.2	17 26.8	16 43.0
22	5 59 27.1	23 26.7	0 10.0	15 54.5	24 28.7	14 35.6	17 18.8	10 19.8	0N 1.5	1 2.3	17 28.1	16 44.3
25	6 11 16.8	23 25.3	0 9.9	2S31.2	24 49.3	15 35.2	16 34.5	10 20.8	0 4.0	1 1.6	17 29.3	16 45.7
28	6 23 6.5	23 19.7	0 9.8	20 39.4	24 57.5	16 32.0	15 48.8	10 22.4	0 6.8	1 1.1	17 30.6	16 47.1
31	6 34 56.1	23 9.9	0 9.8	28 2.7	24 53.0	17 25.6	15 1.6	10 24.7	0 10.1	1 .8	17 31.7	16 48.7

JANUARY 1968

DAY	EPHEM. SID. TIME	☉	☊	☽	☿	♀	♂	♃	♄	♅	♆	♇
	h m s	° ′	° ′	° ′	° ′	° ′	° ′	° ′	° ′	° ′	° ′	° ′
		LONGITUDE										
1	6 38 52.7	9 ♑ 38.0	23 ♈ 59.5	20 ♑ 56.4	11 ♑ 25.1	28 ♏ 52.7	23 ♒ 26.7	5 ♍ 41.4	6 ♈ 6.5	29 ♍ 12.8	25 ♏ 38.8	22 ♍ 51.1
2	6 42 49.2	10 39.2	23 56.4	4 ♒ 59.4	13 2.1	0 ♐ 4.5	24 13.5	5 R 39.4	6 9.0	29 12.9	25 40.5	22 R 50.8
3	6 46 45.8	11 40.4	23 53.2	18 38.0	14 39.4	1 16.4	25 .4	5 37.3	6 11.6	29 13.0	25 42.2	22 50.6
4	6 50 42.4	12 41.5	23 50.0	1 ♓ 50.7	16 17.1	2 28.3	25 47.2	5 34.9	6 14.3	29 13.1	25 43.9	22 50.3
5	6 54 38.9	13 42.7	23 46.8	14 38.3	17 55.1	3 40.3	26 34.0	5 32.3	6 17.1	29 R 13.0	25 45.5	22 50.0
6	6 58 35.5	14 43.9	23 43.7	27 3.7	19 33.5	4 52.4	27 20.9	5 29.6	6 20.0	29 13.0	25 47.2	22 49.6
7	7 2 32.0	15 45.0	23 40.5	9 ♈ 11.5	21 12.2	6 4.6	28 7.7	5 26.7	6 23.0	29 12.8	25 48.8	22 49.3
8	7 6 28.6	16 46.2	23 37.3	21 6.7	22 51.2	7 16.8	28 54.5	5 23.6	6 26.0	29 12.6	25 50.4	22 48.8
9	7 10 25.2	17 47.3	23 34.1	2 ♉ 55.2	24 30.5	8 29.1	29 41.3	5 20.3	6 29.2	29 12.4	25 51.9	22 48.4
10	7 14 21.7	18 48.5	23 31.0	14 42.5	26 10.1	9 41.4	0 ♓ 28.1	5 16.8	6 32.5	29 12.1	25 53.5	22 47.9
11	7 18 18.3	19 49.6	23 27.8	26 33.7	27 50.0	10 53.9	1 14.9	5 13.1	6 35.9	29 11.7	25 55.0	22 47.4
12	7 22 14.8	20 50.7	23 24.6	8 ♊ 33.3	29 30.1	12 6.3	2 1.7	5 9.3	6 39.3	29 11.3	25 56.5	22 46.9
13	7 26 11.4	21 51.9	23 21.4	20 44.9	1 ♒ 10.4	13 18.9	2 48.5	5 5.3	6 42.9	29 10.9	25 57.9	22 46.3
14	7 30 7.9	22 53.0	23 18.2	3 ♋ 10.9	2 50.8	14 31.5	3 35.2	5 1.1	6 46.6	29 10.3	25 59.4	22 45.7
15	7 34 4.5	23 54.1	23 15.1	15 52.3	4 31.3	15 44.1	4 22.0	4 56.7	6 50.3	29 9.8	26 .8	22 45.1
16	7 38 1.1	24 55.2	23 11.9	28 49.1	6 11.7	16 56.8	5 8.7	4 52.2	6 54.2	29 9.1	26 2.1	22 44.4
17	7 41 57.6	25 56.2	23 8.7	12 ♌ .1	7 51.9	18 9.6	5 55.5	4 47.5	6 58.1	29 8.4	26 3.5	22 43.7
18	7 45 54.2	26 57.3	23 5.5	25 23.4	9 31.8	19 22.4	6 42.2	4 42.7	7 2.1	29 7.7	26 4.8	22 43.0
19	7 49 50.7	27 58.4	23 2.4	8 ♍ 56.9	11 11.4	20 35.4	7 28.9	4 37.7	7 6.3	29 7.0	26 6.1	22 42.3
20	7 53 47.3	28 59.5	22 59.2	22 38.8	12 50.2	21 48.3	8 15.6	4 32.5	7 10.5	29 6.1	26 7.4	22 41.5
21	7 57 43.9	0 ♒ .5	22 56.0	6 ♎ 27.7	14 28.1	23 1.3	9 2.3	4 27.2	7 14.7	29 5.2	26 8.6	22 40.7
22	8 1 40.4	1 1.6	22 52.8	20 23.1	16 4.9	24 14.3	9 48.9	4 21.7	7 19.1	29 4.3	26 9.8	22 39.9
23	8 5 37.0	2 2.6	22 49.7	4 ♏ 24.5	17 40.2	25 27.4	10 35.6	4 16.1	7 23.6	29 3.3	26 11.0	22 39.0
24	8 9 33.5	3 3.7	22 46.5	18 31.6	19 13.6	26 40.5	11 22.2	4 10.3	7 28.1	29 2.2	26 12.2	22 38.1
25	8 13 30.1	4 4.7	22 43.3	2 ♐ 43.5	20 44.8	27 53.6	12 8.8	4 4.4	7 32.7	29 1.1	26 13.3	22 37.2
26	8 17 26.6	5 5.7	22 40.1	16 58.3	22 13.2	29 6.8	12 55.4	3 58.3	7 37.4	28 59.9	26 14.4	22 36.2
27	8 21 23.2	6 6.8	22 37.0	1 ♑ 12.6	23 38.4	0 ♑ 20.1	13 42.0	3 52.1	7 42.2	28 58.7	26 15.4	22 35.3
28	8 25 19.8	7 7.8	22 33.8	15 22.0	24 59.7	1 33.3	14 28.5	3 45.8	7 47.1	28 57.5	26 16.4	22 34.3
29	8 29 16.3	8 8.7	22 30.6	29 21.5	26 16.4	2 46.6	15 15.1	3 39.4	7 52.0	28 56.2	26 17.4	22 33.2
30	8 33 12.9	9 9.7	22 27.4	13 ♒ 6.3	27 27.8	3 60.0	16 1.6	3 32.8	7 57.0	28 54.8	26 18.4	22 32.2
31	8 37 9.4	10 10.7	22 24.2	26 32.6	28 33.2	5 13.3	16 48.1	3 26.1	8 2.1	28 53.4	26 19.3	22 31.1
		LATITUDE										
1	6 38 52.7	0 .0	0 .0	5 S .6	1 S 51.8	2 N 15.4	1 S 6.9	1 N 4.5	2 S 26.3	0 N 45.8	1 N 41.3	15 N 16.2
4	6 50 42.4	0 .0	0 .0	3 59.5	2 .1	2 10.6	1 5.0	1 5.3	2 25.5	0 45.9	1 41.5	15 17.7
7	7 2 32.0	0 .0	0 .0	1 18.1	2 5.5	2 5.2	1 3.0	1 6.1	2 24.8	0 46.0	1 41.6	15 19.3
10	7 14 21.7	0 .0	0 .0	1 N 47.0	2 7.4	1 59.1	1 1.0	1 6.8	2 24.1	0 46.2	1 41.7	15 20.8
13	7 26 11.4	0 .0	0 .0	4 12.3	2 5.2	1 52.3	0 58.9	1 7.6	2 23.4	0 46.3	1 41.8	15 22.3
16	7 38 1.1	0 .0	0 .0	4 58.2	1 58.4	1 45.1	0 56.9	1 8.3	2 22.8	0 46.4	1 42.0	15 23.7
19	7 49 50.7	0 .0	0 .0	3 27.8	1 46.1	1 37.3	0 54.8	1 9.0	2 22.1	0 46.5	1 42.1	15 25.1
22	8 1 40.4	0 .0	0 .0	0 10.5	1 27.7	1 29.2	0 52.7	1 9.7	2 21.5	0 46.6	1 42.3	15 26.5
25	8 13 30.1	0 .0	0 .0	3 S 16.1	1 2.2	1 20.7	0 50.5	1 10.3	2 20.8	0 46.7	1 42.4	15 27.8
28	8 25 19.8	0 .0	0 .0	4 59.1	0 29.1	1 11.9	0 48.4	1 10.9	2 20.3	0 46.8	1 42.6	15 29.1
31	8 37 9.4	0 .0	0 .0	4 6.8	0 N 11.6	1 2.9	0 46.2	1 11.5	2 19.7	0 46.9	1 42.7	15 30.3
		RIGHT ASCENSION										
1	6 38 52.7	10 ♑ 28.9	22 ♈ 12.7	23 ♑ 30.0	12 ♑ 35.4	27 ♏ 10.2	26 ♒ 9.3	7 ♍ 53.5	6 ♈ 34.4	29 ♍ 34.9	23 ♏ 44.0	29 ♍ 40.8
2	6 42 49.2	11 35.2	22 9.7	8 ♒ 38.5	14 22.1	28 23.5	26 54.7	7 R 51.7	6 36.6	29 35.1	23 45.8	29 40.8
3	6 46 45.8	12 41.4	22 6.7	22 34.3	16 8.8	29 37.1	27 40.0	7 49.7	6 38.8	29 35.2	23 47.5	29 40.8
4	6 50 42.4	13 47.6	22 3.7	5 ♓ 19.3	17 55.7	0 ♐ 51.0	28 25.2	7 47.6	6 41.2	29 35.2	23 49.2	29 R 40.7
5	6 54 38.9	14 53.6	22 .7	17 6.5	19 42.6	2 5.2	29 10.3	7 45.3	6 43.7	29 35.2	23 50.9	29 40.7
6	6 58 35.5	15 59.5	21 57.7	28 13.2	21 29.6	3 19.8	29 55.3	7 42.8	6 46.2	29 35.2	23 52.6	29 40.6
7	7 2 32.0	17 5.3	21 54.7	8 ♈ 57.4	23 16.5	4 34.6	0 ♓ 40.2	7 40.1	6 48.9	29 R 35.1	23 54.3	29 40.4
8	7 6 28.6	18 11.0	21 51.7	19 36.3	25 3.3	5 49.7	1 25.0	7 37.3	6 51.6	29 34.9	23 55.9	29 40.3
9	7 10 25.2	19 16.6	21 48.7	0 ♉ 26.2	26 50.0	7 5.0	2 9.7	7 34.3	6 54.4	29 34.7	23 57.5	29 40.1
10	7 14 21.7	20 22.0	21 45.8	11 41.5	28 36.4	8 20.7	2 54.3	7 31.1	6 57.4	29 34.4	23 59.1	29 39.9
11	7 18 18.3	21 27.3	21 42.8	23 34.5	0 ♒ 22.6	9 36.6	3 38.8	7 27.7	7 .4	29 34.1	24 .6	29 39.6
12	7 22 14.8	22 32.4	21 39.8	6 ♊ 12.7	2 8.4	10 52.8	4 23.2	7 24.2	7 3.5	29 33.7	24 2.1	29 39.3
13	7 26 11.4	23 37.4	21 36.8	19 36.2	3 53.7	12 9.3	5 7.5	7 20.5	7 6.6	29 33.3	24 3.6	29 39.0
14	7 30 7.9	24 42.3	21 33.8	3 ♋ 35.7	5 38.5	13 26.0	5 51.6	7 16.6	7 9.9	29 32.9	24 5.1	29 38.7
15	7 34 4.5	25 46.9	21 30.8	17 52.5	7 22.6	14 42.9	6 35.7	7 12.5	7 13.3	29 32.4	24 6.6	29 38.3
16	7 38 1.1	26 51.5	21 27.8	2 ♌ 4.4	9 5.9	16 .1	7 19.7	7 8.4	7 16.7	29 31.8	24 8.0	29 37.9
17	7 41 57.6	27 55.8	21 24.8	15 52.8	10 48.3	17 17.5	8 3.6	7 4.0	7 20.2	29 31.2	24 9.4	29 37.5
18	7 45 54.2	28 60.0	21 21.9	29 8.5	12 29.6	18 35.1	8 47.4	6 59.5	7 23.8	29 30.5	24 10.7	29 37.0
19	7 49 50.7	0 ♒ 4.0	21 18.9	11 ♍ 52.5	14 9.7	19 53.0	9 31.2	6 54.9	7 27.6	29 29.8	24 12.1	29 36.6
20	7 53 47.3	1 7.9	21 15.9	24 14.4	15 48.2	21 11.0	10 14.8	6 50.0	7 31.3	29 29.1	24 13.4	29 36.0
21	7 57 43.9	2 11.5	21 12.9	6 ♎ 28.9	17 25.0	22 29.2	10 58.4	6 45.1	7 35.2	29 28.3	24 14.7	29 35.5
22	8 1 40.4	3 15.0	21 9.9	18 53.5	18 59.9	23 47.6	11 41.8	6 40.0	7 39.1	29 27.4	24 15.9	29 34.9
23	8 5 37.0	4 18.3	21 6.9	1 ♏ 46.7	20 32.4	25 6.1	12 25.2	6 34.7	7 43.1	29 26.5	24 17.1	29 34.3
24	8 9 33.5	5 21.4	21 3.9	15 24.9	22 2.2	26 24.8	13 8.5	6 29.3	7 47.2	29 25.6	24 18.3	29 33.7
25	8 13 30.1	6 24.3	21 1.0	29 58.1	23 29.1	27 43.7	13 51.7	6 23.8	7 51.3	29 24.6	24 19.4	29 33.0
26	8 17 26.6	7 27.0	20 58.0	15 ♐ 23.8	24 52.4	29 2.6	14 34.9	6 18.1	7 55.6	29 23.5	24 20.6	29 32.4
27	8 21 23.2	8 29.5	20 55.0	1 ♑ 22.0	26 11.8	0 ♑ 21.7	15 17.9	6 12.3	7 59.9	29 22.4	24 21.6	29 31.6
28	8 25 19.8	9 31.8	20 52.0	17 19.0	27 26.7	1 40.8	16 .9	6 6.4	8 4.3	29 21.3	24 22.7	29 30.9
29	8 29 16.3	10 33.9	20 49.0	2 ♒ 39.4	28 36.5	3 .0	16 43.9	6 .3	8 8.7	29 20.1	24 23.7	29 30.1
30	8 33 12.9	11 35.9	20 46.0	16 59.8	29 40.6	4 19.3	17 26.7	5 54.2	8 13.3	29 18.9	24 24.7	29 29.3
31	8 37 9.4	12 37.6	20 43.0	0 ♓ 14.0	0 ♓ 38.3	5 38.7	18 9.5	5 47.9	8 17.9	29 17.6	24 25.7	29 28.5
		DECLINATION										
1	6 38 52.7	23 S 5.7	0 N 9.7	26 S 45.7	24 S 48.6	17 S 42.7	14 S 45.6	10 N 25.6	0 N 11.3	1 N .8	17 S 32.1	16 N 49.3
4	6 50 42.4	22 50.4	0 9.7	14 32.8	24 26.4	18 31.5	13 56.8	10 28.7	0 15.0	1 .8	17 33.2	16 51.0
7	7 2 32.0	22 30.9	0 9.6	2 N 26.8	23 50.4	19 16.3	13 6.7	10 32.5	0 19.1	1 1.0	17 34.2	16 52.8
10	7 14 21.7	22 7.5	0 9.6	17 57.5	23 .4	19 56.8	12 15.6	10 36.8	0 23.5	1 1.4	17 35.2	16 54.7
13	7 26 11.4	21 40.2	0 9.5	27 19.1	21 56.3	20 32.7	11 23.5	10 41.7	0 28.3	1 2.0	17 36.1	16 56.7
16	7 38 1.1	21 9.1	0 9.4	25 15.8	20 38.4	21 3.7	10 30.5	10 47.2	0 33.3	1 2.8	17 37.0	16 58.8
19	7 49 50.7	20 34.3	0 9.4	11 25.5	19 7.4	21 29.6	9 36.7	10 53.2	0 38.7	1 3.8	17 37.8	17 .9
22	8 1 40.4	19 56.1	0 9.3	7 S 48.2	17 24.9	21 50.1	8 42.2	10 59.7	0 44.3	1 5.0	17 38.5	17 3.1
25	8 13 30.1	19 14.5	0 9.3	23 54.9	15 33.8	22 5.1	7 47.1	11 6.6	0 50.3	1 6.3	17 39.1	17 5.4
28	8 25 19.8	18 29.7	0 9.2	27 30.7	13 39.0	22 14.3	6 51.4	11 13.9	0 56.5	1 7.8	17 39.7	17 7.7
31	8 37 9.4	17 41.9	0 9.1	16 32.1	11 47.9	22 17.8	5 55.3	11 21.6	1 2.9	1 9.5	17 40.2	17 10.1

FEBRUARY 1968

DAY	EPHEM. SID. TIME	☉	☊	☽	☿	♀	♂	♃	♄	♅	♆	♇
	h m s	° ′	° ′	° ′	° ′	° ′	° ′	° ′	° ′	° ′	° ′	° ′
		LONGITUDE										
1	8 41 6.0	11♒11.6	22♈21.1	9♓38.1	29♒31.7	6♑26.7	17♓34.5	3♍19.3	8♈ 7.3	28♍52.0	26♏20.2	22♍30.0
2	8 45 2.5	12 12.5	22 17.9	22 22.5	0♓22.6	7 40.1	18 21.0	3 R 12.4	8 12.5	28 R 50.5	26 21.1	22 R 28.9
3	8 48 59.1	13 13.4	22 14.7	4♈47.5	1 5.1	8 53.6	19 7.4	3 5.4	8 17.9	28 48.9	26 21.9	22 27.7
4	8 52 55.7	14 14.3	22 11.5	16 56.2	1 38.3	10 7.1	19 53.8	2 58.3	8 23.2	28 47.3	26 22.7	22 26.6
5	8 56 52.2	15 15.2	22 8.4	28 52.9	2 1.6	11 20.5	20 40.2	2 51.1	8 28.7	28 45.7	26 23.5	22 25.4
6	9 0 48.8	16 16.0	22 5.2	10♉42.7	2 14.5	12 34.1	21 26.5	2 43.8	8 34.2	28 44.0	26 24.2	22 24.2
7	9 4 45.3	17 16.8	22 2.0	22 30.9	2 16.6	13 47.6	22 12.8	2 36.5	8 39.8	28 42.3	26 24.9	22 22.9
8	9 8 41.9	18 17.6	21 58.8	4♊23.2	2 R 7.7	15 1.2	22 59.1	2 29.0	8 45.5	28 40.6	26 25.6	22 21.7
9	9 12 38.4	19 18.4	21 55.7	16 24.7	1 47.9	16 14.8	23 45.4	2 21.6	8 51.3	28 38.8	26 26.2	22 20.4
10	9 16 35.0	20 19.1	21 52.5	28 40.0	1 17.7	17 28.4	24 31.6	2 14.0	8 57.1	28 37.0	26 26.8	22 19.1
11	9 20 31.5	21 19.8	21 49.3	11♋12.5	0 37.6	18 42.0	25 17.8	2 6.4	9 2.9	28 35.1	26 27.4	22 17.8
12	9 24 28.1	22 20.5	21 46.1	24 4.6	29♒48.7	19 55.6	26 4.0	1 58.7	9 8.8	28 33.2	26 27.9	22 16.5
13	9 28 24.7	23 21.2	21 42.9	7♌16.8	28 52.4	21 9.3	26 50.1	1 51.0	9 14.8	28 31.3	26 28.4	22 15.1
14	9 32 21.2	24 21.8	21 39.8	20 48.0	27 50.2	22 22.9	27 36.2	1 43.2	9 20.9	28 29.3	26 28.9	22 13.8
15	9 36 17.8	25 22.4	21 36.6	4♍35.7	26 43.9	23 36.6	28 22.2	1 35.4	9 27.0	28 27.2	26 29.3	22 12.4
16	9 40 14.3	26 23.0	21 33.4	18 35.9	25 35.2	24 50.4	29 8.2	1 27.6	9 33.1	28 25.2	26 29.7	22 11.0
17	9 44 10.9	27 23.5	21 30.2	2♎44.4	24 26.1	26 4.1	29 54.2	1 19.7	9 39.3	28 23.1	26 30.1	22 9.6
18	9 48 7.4	28 24.1	21 27.1	16 57.2	23 18.4	27 17.8	0♈40.2	1 11.8	9 45.6	28 21.0	26 30.4	22 8.1
19	9 52 4.0	29 24.6	21 23.9	1♏10.9	22 13.5	28 31.6	1 26.1	1 3.9	9 51.9	28 18.8	26 30.7	22 6.7
20	9 56 .5	0♓25.1	21 20.7	15 22.9	21 13.0	29 45.4	2 11.9	0 56.0	9 58.3	28 16.6	26 31.0	22 5.2
21	9 59 57.1	1 25.6	21 17.5	29 31.6	20 17.8	0♒59.2	2 57.8	0 48.1	10 4.7	28 14.4	26 31.2	22 3.7
22	10 3 53.7	2 26.0	21 14.3	13♐35.5	19 28.9	2 13.0	3 43.6	0 40.2	10 11.2	28 12.2	26 31.4	22 2.2
23	10 7 50.2	3 26.5	21 11.2	27 33.7	18 46.9	3 26.8	4 29.4	0 32.3	10 17.7	28 9.9	26 31.5	22 .7
24	10 11 46.8	4 26.9	21 8.0	11♑24.8	18 12.1	4 40.7	5 15.1	0 24.4	10 24.3	28 7.6	26 31.7	21 59.2
25	10 15 43.3	5 27.3	21 4.8	25 7.1	17 44.7	5 54.5	6 .8	0 16.6	10 30.9	28 5.3	26 31.8	21 57.7
26	10 19 39.9	6 27.6	21 1.6	8♒38.6	17 24.7	7 8.4	6 46.5	0 8.7	10 37.6	28 2.9	26 31.8	21 56.2
27	10 23 36.4	7 28.0	20 58.5	21 57.3	17 11.9	8 22.3	7 32.1	0 .9	10 44.3	28 .5	26 31.8	21 54.6
28	10 27 33.0	8 28.3	20 55.3	5♓ 1.6	17 6.1	9 36.2	8 17.7	29♌53.1	10 51.1	27 58.1	26 31.8	21 53.1
29	10 31 29.5	9 28.5	20 52.1	17 50.3	17 D 7.0	10 50.1	9 3.3	29 45.4	10 57.9	27 55.7	26 31.8	21 51.5
		LATITUDE										
1	8 41 6.0	0 .0	0 .0	3 S 20.9	0 N 26.7	0 N 59.8	0 S 45.5	1 N 11.7	2 S 19.5	0 N 47.0	1 N 42.8	15 N 30.7
4	8 52 55.7	0 .0	0 .0	0 21.5	1 15.5	0 50.6	0 43.3	1 12.2	2 18.9	0 47.1	1 42.9	15 31.8
7	9 4 45.3	0 .0	0 .0	2 N 40.1	2 6.3	0 41.2	0 41.1	1 12.7	2 18.4	0 47.1	1 43.1	15 32.9
10	9 16 35.0	0 .0	0 .0	4 42.4	2 52.8	0 31.9	0 38.9	1 13.2	2 17.9	0 47.2	1 43.3	15 33.9
13	9 28 24.7	0 .0	0 .0	4 51.5	3 27.1	0 22.5	0 36.7	1 13.6	2 17.5	0 47.3	1 43.4	15 34.9
16	9 40 14.3	0 .0	0 .0	2 39.5	3 42.7	0 13.3	0 34.5	1 13.9	2 17.0	0 47.4	1 43.6	15 35.8
19	9 52 4.0	0 .0	0 .0	1 S .8	3 37.4	0 4.2	0 32.3	1 14.2	2 16.6	0 47.4	1 43.8	15 36.6
22	10 3 53.7	0 .0	0 .0	4 9.1	3 14.7	0 S 4.8	0 30.1	1 14.5	2 16.2	0 47.5	1 44.0	15 37.3
25	10 15 43.3	0 .0	0 .0	5 6.9	2 40.7	0 13.5	0 27.9	1 14.7	2 15.8	0 47.6	1 44.1	15 37.9
28	10 27 33.0	0 .0	0 .0	3 36.1	2 1.3	0 21.9	0 25.7	1 14.8	2 15.5	0 47.6	1 44.3	15 38.5
		RIGHT ASCENSION										
1	8 41 6.0	13♒39.1	20♈40.1	12♓28.7	1♓28.9	6♑58.1	18♓52.2	5♍41.5	8♈22.6	29♍16.3	24♏26.6	29♍27.7
2	8 45 2.5	14 40.4	20 37.1	23 57.8	2 11.8	8 17.5	19 34.9	5 R 35.0	8 27.3	29 R 14.9	24 27.5	29 R 26.8
3	8 48 59.1	15 41.5	20 34.1	4♈57.7	2 46.3	9 36.9	20 17.5	5 28.4	8 32.1	29 13.5	24 28.4	29 25.9
4	8 52 55.7	16 42.4	20 31.1	15 44.9	3 11.8	10 56.3	21 .0	5 21.7	8 37.0	29 12.1	24 29.2	29 25.0
5	8 56 52.2	17 43.0	20 28.1	26 35.3	3 27.8	12 15.6	21 42.5	5 14.9	8 41.9	29 10.6	24 30.0	29 24.1
6	9 0 48.8	18 43.5	20 25.2	7♉43.6	3 33.9	13 35.0	22 24.9	5 8.1	8 47.0	29 9.1	24 30.7	29 23.1
7	9 4 45.3	19 43.8	20 22.2	19 22.7	3 R 29.8	14 54.3	23 7.2	5 1.1	8 52.0	29 7.5	24 31.5	29 22.1
8	9 8 41.9	20 43.8	20 19.2	1♊42.1	3 15.5	16 13.5	23 49.5	4 54.1	8 57.2	29 5.9	24 32.2	29 21.1
9	9 12 38.4	21 43.7	20 16.2	14 45.9	2 51.2	17 32.7	24 31.8	4 47.1	9 2.4	29 4.3	24 32.9	29 20.2
10	9 16 35.0	22 43.4	20 13.2	28 29.5	2 17.4	18 51.8	25 14.0	4 39.9	9 7.7	29 2.6	24 33.5	29 19.1
11	9 20 31.5	23 42.8	20 10.2	12♋39.8	1 34.9	20 10.8	25 56.2	4 32.7	9 13.0	29 .9	24 34.1	29 18.0
12	9 24 28.1	24 42.1	20 7.3	26 57.1	0 44.6	21 29.7	26 38.3	4 25.4	9 18.4	28 59.2	24 34.6	29 16.9
13	9 28 24.7	25 41.1	20 4.3	11♌ 1.5	29♒47.9	22 48.4	27 20.3	4 18.1	9 23.8	28 57.4	24 35.2	29 15.8
14	9 32 21.2	26 40.0	20 1.3	24 40.0	28 46.3	24 7.0	28 2.3	4 10.7	9 29.3	28 55.6	24 35.6	29 14.7
15	9 36 17.8	27 38.7	19 58.3	7♍48.9	27 41.4	25 25.5	28 44.3	4 3.3	9 34.9	28 53.7	24 36.1	29 13.6
16	9 40 14.3	28 37.2	19 55.4	20 33.9	26 35.1	26 43.9	29 26.2	3 55.9	9 40.5	28 51.9	24 36.5	29 12.4
17	9 44 10.9	29 35.5	19 52.4	3♎ 6.8	25 28.9	28 2.0	0♈ 8.1	3 48.4	9 46.1	28 50.0	24 36.9	29 11.2
18	9 48 7.4	0♓33.6	19 49.4	15 43.5	24 24.6	29 20.0	0 50.0	3 40.9	9 51.8	28 48.0	24 37.2	29 10.0
19	9 52 4.0	1 31.6	19 46.4	28 40.7	23 23.5	0♒37.8	1 31.8	3 33.4	9 57.6	28 46.0	24 37.6	29 8.8
20	9 56 .5	2 29.4	19 43.4	12♏14.0	22 27.1	1 55.5	2 13.6	3 25.9	10 3.4	28 44.0	24 37.8	29 7.5
21	9 59 57.1	3 27.0	19 40.5	26 33.3	21 36.3	3 12.9	2 55.4	3 18.3	10 9.3	28 42.0	24 38.1	29 6.3
22	10 3 53.7	4 24.5	19 37.5	11♐38.5	20 51.8	4 30.1	3 37.1	3 10.8	10 15.2	28 40.0	24 38.3	29 5.0
23	10 7 50.2	5 21.8	19 34.5	27 14.6	20 14.3	5 47.2	4 18.9	3 3.2	10 21.1	28 37.9	24 38.5	29 3.7
24	10 11 46.8	6 19.0	19 31.5	12♑54.1	19 44.0	7 4.0	5 .6	2 55.7	10 27.1	28 35.8	24 38.6	29 2.4
25	10 15 43.3	7 16.0	19 28.6	28 5.9	19 21.0	8 20.5	5 42.3	2 48.2	10 33.2	28 33.6	24 38.7	29 1.1
26	10 19 39.9	8 12.9	19 25.6	12♒26.9	19 5.3	9 36.9	6 24.0	2 40.7	10 39.3	28 31.5	24 38.8	28 59.8
27	10 23 36.4	9 9.6	19 22.6	25 48.1	18 56.9	10 53.0	7 5.6	2 33.2	10 45.4	28 29.3	24 38.8	28 58.5
28	10 27 33.0	10 6.2	19 19.6	8♓12.9	18 55.3	12 8.8	7 47.3	2 25.8	10 51.6	28 27.1	24 38.8	28 57.1
29	10 31 29.5	11 2.7	19 16.7	19 52.5	19 D .4	13 24.4	8 28.9	2 18.4	10 57.8	28 24.9	24 38.8	28 55.7
		DECLINATION										
1	8 41 6.0	17 S 25.3	0 N 9.1	11 S 3.6	11 S 13.4	22 S 17.6	5 S 36.5	11 N 24.3	1 N 5.1	1 N 10.2	17 S 40.4	17 N 10.9
4	8 52 55.7	16 33.7	0 9.1	6 N 19.5	9 43.1	22 13.2	4 40.0	11 32.4	1 11.9	1 12.1	17 40.8	17 13.3
7	9 4 45.3	15 39.6	0 9.0	20 59.0	8 42.1	22 2.8	3 43.2	11 40.7	1 18.9	1 14.2	17 41.2	17 15.7
10	9 16 35.0	14 43.0	0 8.9	28 8.8	8 19.5	21 46.6	2 46.2	11 49.2	1 26.1	1 16.4	17 41.4	17 18.1
13	9 28 24.7	13 44.3	0 8.9	23 9.0	8 37.8	21 24.6	1 49.2	11 57.8	1 33.6	1 18.7	17 41.6	17 20.6
16	9 40 14.3	12 43.5	0 8.8	6 57.4	9 29.8	20 56.9	0 52.2	12 6.6	1 41.1	1 21.2	17 41.8	17 23.1
19	9 52 4.0	11 40.9	0 8.7	12 S 50.3	10 40.6	20 23.6	0 N 4.6	12 15.3	1 48.9	1 23.8	17 41.8	17 25.5
22	10 3 53.7	10 36.6	0 8.7	26 33.4	11 53.8	19 44.9	1 1.3	12 23.9	1 56.8	1 26.5	17 41.8	17 27.9
25	10 15 43.3	9 30.8	0 8.6	26 8.6	12 58.1	19 1.1	1 57.7	12 32.5	2 4.9	1 29.3	17 41.8	17 30.3
28	10 27 33.0	8 23.8	0 8.6	13 1.2	13 47.2	18 12.2	2 53.9	12 41.0	2 13.1	1 32.2	17 41.6	17 32.7

MARCH 1968

DAY	EPHEM. SID. TIME	☉	☊	☾	☿	♀	♂	♃	♄	♅	♆	♇
		LONGITUDE										
	h m s	° ′	° ′	° ′	° ′	° ′	° ′	° ′	° ′	° ′	° ′	° ′
1	10 35 26.1	10♓28.8	20♈48.9	0♈23.3	17♒14.4	12♒ 4.0	9♈48.8	29♌37.8	11♈ 4.8	27♍53.3	26♏31.8	21♍50.0
2	10 39 22.6	11 29.1	20 45.7	12 41.4	17 27.8	13 17.9	10 34.3	29 R 30.1	11 11.7	27 R 50.8	26 R 31.6	21 R 48.4
3	10 43 19.2	12 29.2	20 42.6	24 46.8	17 46.8	14 31.8	11 19.7	29 22.6	11 18.6	27 48.4	26 31.5	21 46.8
4	10 47 15.8	13 29.4	20 39.4	6♉42.5	18 11.1	15 45.7	12 5.1	29 15.1	11 25.6	27 45.9	26 31.3	21 45.2
5	10 51 12.3	14 29.5	20 36.2	18 32.4	18 40.4	16 59.6	12 50.5	29 7.6	11 32.6	27 43.4	26 31.1	21 43.6
6	10 55 8.9	15 29.6	20 33.0	0♊21.0	19 14.4	18 13.6	13 35.8	29 .3	11 39.6	27 40.8	26 30.9	21 42.0
7	10 59 5.4	16 29.6	20 29.9	12 13.2	19 52.6	19 27.5	14 21.1	28 53.0	11 46.7	27 38.3	26 30.6	21 40.4
8	11 3 2.0	17 29.6	20 26.7	24 14.1	20 34.8	20 41.4	15 6.3	28 45.8	11 53.8	27 35.7	26 30.3	21 38.8
9	11 6 58.5	18 29.6	20 23.5	6♋28.7	21 20.8	21 55.3	15 51.4	28 38.7	12 .9	27 33.2	26 29.9	21 37.2
10	11 10 55.1	19 29.6	20 20.3	19 1.3	22 10.2	23 9.2	16 36.6	28 31.7	12 8.1	27 30.6	26 29.5	21 35.6
11	11 14 51.6	20 29.5	20 17.2	1♌55.6	23 2.9	24 23.2	17 21.6	28 24.9	12 15.3	27 28.0	26 29.1	21 34.0
12	11 18 48.2	21 29.3	20 14.0	15 13.4	23 58.7	25 37.1	18 6.7	28 18.1	12 22.5	27 25.4	26 28.7	21 32.3
13	11 22 44.7	22 29.2	20 10.8	28 55.1	24 57.3	26 51.0	18 51.7	28 11.4	12 29.7	27 22.8	26 28.2	21 30.7
14	11 26 41.3	23 29.0	20 7.6	12♍58.8	25 58.6	28 5.0	19 36.6	28 4.8	12 37.0	27 20.2	26 27.7	21 29.1
15	11 30 37.8	24 28.7	20 4.4	27 20.7	27 2.5	29 18.9	20 21.5	27 58.4	12 44.3	27 17.6	26 27.2	21 27.5
16	11 34 34.4	25 28.5	20 1.3	11♎55.2	28 8.7	0♓32.8	21 6.4	27 52.1	12 51.6	27 15.0	26 26.6	21 25.9
17	11 38 31.0	26 28.2	19 58.1	26 35.8	29 17.2	1 46.8	21 51.2	27 45.8	12 59.0	27 12.4	26 26.0	21 24.3
18	11 42 27.5	27 27.8	19 54.9	11♏16.0	0♓27.8	3 .7	22 35.9	27 39.8	13 6.3	27 9.8	26 25.4	21 22.7
19	11 46 24.1	28 27.5	19 51.7	25 50.3	1 40.5	4 14.7	23 20.6	27 33.8	13 13.7	27 7.2	26 24.7	21 21.1
20	11 50 20.6	29 27.1	19 48.6	10♐14.1	2 55.1	5 28.6	24 5.3	27 28.0	13 21.1	27 4.5	26 24.0	21 19.5
21	11 54 17.2	0♈26.7	19 45.4	24 24.5	4 11.6	6 42.6	24 49.9	27 22.4	13 28.5	27 1.9	26 23.3	21 17.9
22	11 58 13.7	1 26.3	19 42.2	8♑19.9	5 30.0	7 56.6	25 34.5	27 16.9	13 36.0	26 59.4	26 22.6	21 16.3
23	12 2 10.3	2 25.8	19 39.0	21 59.5	6 50.0	9 10.5	26 19.1	27 11.5	13 43.5	26 56.8	26 21.9	21 14.7
24	12 6 6.8	3 25.3	19 35.8	5♒23.7	8 11.8	10 24.5	27 3.6	27 6.3	13 50.9	26 54.2	26 21.1	21 13.2
25	12 10 3.4	4 24.7	19 32.7	18 32.8	9 35.2	11 38.4	27 48.0	27 1.2	13 58.4	26 51.6	26 20.2	21 11.6
26	12 13 59.9	5 24.2	19 29.5	1♓27.7	11 .1	12 52.4	28 32.4	26 56.3	14 5.9	26 49.0	26 19.4	21 10.0
27	12 17 56.5	6 23.6	19 26.3	14 9.1	12 26.7	14 6.3	29 16.8	26 51.6	14 13.4	26 46.4	26 18.5	21 8.5
28	12 21 53.0	7 22.9	19 23.1	26 38.0	13 54.7	15 20.3	0♉ 1.1	26 47.0	14 21.0	26 43.9	26 17.6	21 6.9
29	12 25 49.6	8 22.3	19 20.0	8♈55.3	15 24.3	16 34.2	0 45.3	26 42.5	14 28.5	26 41.3	26 16.6	21 5.4
30	12 29 46.1	9 21.6	19 16.8	21 2.5	16 55.4	17 48.2	1 29.5	26 38.3	14 36.0	26 38.8	26 15.7	21 3.9
31	12 33 42.7	10 20.9	19 13.6	3♉ 1.2	18 27.9	19 2.1	2 13.7	26 34.2	14 43.6	26 36.3	26 14.7	21 2.4
		LATITUDE										
		° ′	° ′	° ′	° ′	° ′	° ′	° ′	° ′	° ′	° ′	° ′
1	10 35 26.1	0 .0	0 .0	1 S 39.9	1 N 34.3	0 S 27.3	0 S 24.2	1 N 14.9	2 S 15.3	0 N 47.6	1 N 44.4	15 N 38.8
4	10 47 15.8	0 .0	0 .0	1 N 34.8	0 54.7	0 35.2	0 22.0	1 15.0	2 15.0	0 47.7	1 44.6	15 39.3
7	10 59 5.4	0 .0	0 .0	4 10.6	0 17.5	0 42.6	0 19.8	1 15.0	2 14.7	0 47.7	1 44.7	15 39.6
10	11 10 55.1	0 .0	0 .0	5 13.2	0 S 16.3	0 49.7	0 17.7	1 15.0	2 14.5	0 47.7	1 44.9	15 39.9
13	11 22 44.7	0 .0	0 .0	4 .4	0 46.5	0 56.2	0 15.5	1 14.9	2 14.3	0 47.7	1 45.1	15 40.1
16	11 34 34.4	0 .0	0 .0	0 37.6	1 12.7	1 2.3	0 13.4	1 14.8	2 14.1	0 47.7	1 45.2	15 40.2
19	11 46 24.1	0 .0	0 .0	3 S 10.5	1 35.0	1 7.9	0 11.2	1 14.7	2 13.9	0 47.7	1 45.4	15 40.2
22	11 58 13.7	0 .0	0 .0	5 10.6	1 53.2	1 12.9	0 9.1	1 14.5	2 13.8	0 47.7	1 45.5	15 40.2
25	12 10 3.4	0 .0	0 .0	4 34.4	2 7.4	1 17.3	0 7.0	1 14.2	2 13.7	0 47.7	1 45.6	15 40.1
28	12 21 53.0	0 .0	0 .0	1 59.1	2 17.5	1 21.1	0 4.9	1 14.0	2 13.6	0 47.6	1 45.8	15 39.8
31	12 33 42.7	0 .0	0 .0	1 N 18.8	2 23.4	1 24.4	0 2.9	1 13.7	2 13.6	0 47.6	1 45.9	15 39.6
		RIGHT ASCENSION										
1	10 35 26.1	11♓59.0	19♈13.7	1♈ 1.1	19♒11.9	14♒39.8	9♈10.6	2♍11.1	11♈ 4.1	28♍22.7	24♏38.8	28♍54.4
2	10 39 22.6	12 55.2	19 10.7	11 53.9	19 29.2	15 54.9	9 52.2	2 R 3.8	11 10.4	28 R 20.5	24 R 38.7	28 R 53.0
3	10 43 19.2	13 51.3	19 7.7	22 45.7	19 52.1	17 9.8	10 33.8	1 56.5	11 16.7	28 18.2	24 38.5	28 51.6
4	10 47 15.8	14 47.2	19 4.8	3♉50.2	20 20.1	18 24.3	11 15.4	1 49.3	11 23.1	28 15.9	24 38.4	28 50.2
5	10 51 12.3	15 43.1	19 1.8	15 19.7	20 52.9	19 38.7	11 57.1	1 42.2	11 29.5	28 13.6	24 38.2	28 48.8
6	10 55 8.9	16 38.8	18 58.8	27 23.6	21 30.2	20 52.7	12 38.7	1 35.1	11 36.0	28 11.3	24 37.9	28 47.4
7	10 59 5.4	17 34.4	18 55.8	10♊ 7.3	22 11.6	22 6.5	13 20.3	1 28.2	11 42.5	28 8.9	24 37.7	28 46.0
8	11 3 2.0	18 29.9	18 52.9	23 29.2	22 56.8	23 20.1	14 1.9	1 21.2	11 49.0	28 6.6	24 37.3	28 44.5
9	11 6 58.5	19 25.3	18 49.9	7♋20.3	23 45.5	24 33.3	14 43.5	1 14.4	11 55.5	28 4.2	24 37.0	28 43.1
10	11 10 55.1	20 20.6	18 46.9	21 25.0	24 37.5	25 46.4	15 25.1	1 7.7	12 2.1	28 1.9	24 36.6	28 41.6
11	11 14 51.6	21 15.8	18 43.9	5♌26.0	25 32.5	26 59.1	16 6.8	1 1.0	12 8.7	27 59.5	24 36.2	28 40.2
12	11 18 48.2	22 10.9	18 41.0	19 9.7	26 30.2	28 11.7	16 48.4	0 54.5	12 15.3	27 57.1	24 35.8	28 38.7
13	11 22 44.7	23 6.0	18 38.0	2♍30.2	27 30.4	29 23.9	17 30.0	0 48.1	12 21.9	27 54.8	24 35.3	28 37.3
14	11 26 41.3	24 1.0	18 35.0	15 30.4	28 33.1	0♓36.0	18 11.7	0 41.7	12 28.6	27 52.4	24 34.8	28 35.8
15	11 30 37.8	24 55.9	18 32.1	28 19.7	29 37.8	1 47.7	18 53.4	0 35.5	12 35.3	27 50.0	24 34.3	28 34.3
16	11 34 34.4	25 50.8	18 29.1	11♎12.3	0♓44.7	2 59.3	19 35.1	0 29.4	12 42.1	27 47.6	24 33.7	28 32.8
17	11 38 31.0	26 45.6	18 26.1	24 24.4	1 53.4	4 10.6	20 16.8	0 23.4	12 48.8	27 45.2	24 33.1	28 31.4
18	11 42 27.5	27 40.4	18 23.1	8♏11.0	3 3.8	5 21.7	20 58.5	0 17.5	12 55.6	27 42.8	24 32.5	28 29.9
19	11 46 24.1	28 35.1	18 20.2	22 41.9	4 15.9	6 32.6	21 40.2	0 11.8	13 2.4	27 40.4	24 31.8	28 28.4
20	11 50 20.6	29 29.8	18 17.2	7♐56.8	5 29.5	7 43.3	22 22.0	0 6.2	13 9.2	27 38.0	24 31.2	28 26.9
21	11 54 17.2	0♈24.5	18 14.2	23 40.8	6 44.5	8 53.7	23 3.8	0 .7	13 16.0	27 35.6	24 30.4	28 25.5
22	11 58 13.7	1 19.1	18 11.3	9♑26.2	8 1.0	10 4.0	23 45.7	29♌55.4	13 22.9	27 33.2	24 29.7	28 24.0
23	12 2 10.3	2 13.8	18 8.3	24 42.2	9 18.7	11 14.1	24 27.6	29 50.1	13 29.8	27 30.8	24 29.0	28 22.6
24	12 6 6.8	3 8.4	18 5.3	9♒ 6.0	10 37.5	12 24.0	25 9.5	29 45.1	13 36.7	27 28.4	24 28.2	28 21.1
25	12 10 3.4	4 3.0	18 2.4	22 28.9	11 57.6	13 33.7	25 51.4	29 40.1	13 43.6	27 26.1	24 27.3	28 19.6
26	12 13 59.9	4 57.5	17 59.4	4♓54.6	13 18.7	14 43.2	26 33.3	29 35.4	13 50.5	27 23.7	24 26.4	28 18.2
27	12 17 56.5	5 52.1	17 56.4	16 34.2	14 41.0	15 52.6	27 15.3	29 30.7	13 57.4	27 21.3	24 25.6	28 16.7
28	12 21 53.0	6 46.7	17 53.5	27 42.0	16 4.2	17 1.8	27 57.4	29 26.3	14 4.3	27 19.0	24 24.6	28 15.2
29	12 25 49.6	7 41.3	17 50.5	8♈32.9	17 28.5	18 10.8	28 39.4	29 22.0	14 11.3	27 16.6	24 23.7	28 13.8
30	12 29 46.1	8 35.9	17 47.5	19 21.4	18 53.8	19 19.7	29 21.5	29 17.8	14 18.2	27 14.3	24 22.7	28 12.3
31	12 33 42.7	9 30.6	17 44.6	0♉20.6	20 20.1	20 28.5	0♉ 3.7	29 13.8	14 25.2	27 12.0	24 21.7	28 10.9
		DECLINATION										
1	10 35 26.1	7 S 38.4	0 N 8.5	1 S 22.4	14 S 10.4	17 S 37.0	3 N 31.1	12 N 46.4	2 N 18.6	1 N 34.1	17 S 41.5	17 N 34.2
4	10 47 15.8	6 29.5	0 8.4	15 N 15.1	14 30.9	16 40.5	4 26.4	12 54.5	2 27.0	1 37.1	17 41.2	17 36.5
7	10 59 5.4	5 19.9	0 8.4	26 24.2	14 34.8	15 39.8	5 21.3	13 2.2	2 35.5	1 40.1	17 40.9	17 38.8
10	11 10 55.1	4 9.6	0 8.3	27 15.7	14 22.9	14 35.1	6 15.5	13 9.6	2 44.0	1 43.2	17 40.5	17 40.9
13	11 22 44.7	2 58.9	0 8.3	15 36.3	13 56.2	13 26.8	7 9.1	13 16.7	2 52.6	1 46.3	17 40.0	17 43.0
16	11 34 34.4	1 47.9	0 8.2	4 S 8.2	13 15.5	12 15.2	8 1.9	13 23.3	3 1.3	1 49.4	17 39.5	17 45.1
19	11 46 24.1	0 36.8	0 8.1	22 18.3	12 21.6	11 .6	8 53.8	13 29.4	3 10.0	1 52.5	17 38.9	17 47.0
22	11 58 13.7	0 N 34.3	0 8.1	28 21.0	11 15.1	9 43.2	9 44.9	13 35.1	3 18.8	1 55.6	17 38.3	17 48.8
25	12 10 3.4	1 45.2	0 8.0	19 37.0	9 56.6	8 23.4	10 35.1	13 40.3	3 27.5	1 58.7	17 37.6	17 50.6
28	12 21 53.0	2 55.8	0 7.9	3 9.6	8 26.7	7 1.6	11 24.3	13 44.9	3 36.3	2 1.7	17 36.9	17 52.2
31	12 33 42.7	4 5.9	0 7.9	13 N 45.4	6 45.7	5 38.0	12 12.3	13 49.0	3 45.1	2 4.7	17 36.1	17 53.8

APRIL 1968

LONGITUDE

DAY	EPHEM. SID. TIME	☉	☊	☾	☿	♀	♂	♃	♄	♅	♆	♇
	h m s	° ′	° ′	° ′	° ′	° ′	° ′	° ′	° ′	° ′	° ′	° ′
1	12 37 39.3	11♈20.1	19♈10.4	14♉53.8	20♓ 1.9	20♓16.1	2♉57.8	26♌30.3	14♈51.1	26♍33.7	26♏13.6	21♍ .9
2	12 41 35.8	12 19.3	19 7.2	26 42.8	21 37.3	21 30.0	3 41.9	26 R 26.5	14 58.7	26 R 31.3	26 R 12.6	20 R 59.4
3	12 45 32.4	13 18.4	19 4.1	8♊31.6	23 14.2	22 43.9	4 25.9	26 22.9	15 6.2	26 28.8	26 11.5	20 57.9
4	12 49 28.9	14 17.6	19 .9	20 24.0	24 52.5	23 57.8	5 9.9	26 19.5	15 13.8	26 26.3	26 10.4	20 56.5
5	12 53 25.5	15 16.6	18 57.7	2♋24.3	26 32.3	25 11.8	5 53.8	26 16.3	15 21.4	26 23.9	26 9.3	20 55.0
6	12 57 22.0	16 15.7	18 54.5	14 36.8	28 13.5	26 25.7	6 37.6	26 13.3	15 28.9	26 21.5	26 8.2	20 53.6
7	13 1 18.6	17 14.7	18 51.4	27 6.0	29 56.2	27 39.6	7 21.5	26 10.4	15 36.5	26 19.1	26 7.0	20 52.2
8	13 5 15.1	18 13.7	18 48.2	9♌56.1	1♈40.4	28 53.5	8 5.2	26 7.8	15 44.0	26 16.7	26 5.8	20 50.8
9	13 9 11.7	19 12.6	18 45.0	23 10.5	3 26.1	0♈ 7.3	8 48.9	26 5.3	15 51.6	26 14.4	26 4.6	20 49.4
10	13 13 8.2	20 11.5	18 41.8	6♍50.9	5 13.2	1 21.2	9 32.6	26 3.0	15 59.1	26 12.0	26 3.4	20 48.0
11	13 17 4.8	21 10.3	18 38.6	20 57.6	7 1.8	2 35.1	10 16.2	26 .8	16 6.7	26 9.7	26 2.1	20 46.7
12	13 21 1.4	22 9.2	18 35.5	5♎28.1	8 52.0	3 49.0	10 59.8	25 58.9	16 14.3	26 7.5	26 .9	20 45.4
13	13 24 57.9	23 8.0	18 32.3	20 17.4	10 43.7	5 2.9	11 43.3	25 57.2	16 21.8	26 5.3	25 59.6	20 44.1
14	13 28 54.5	24 6.7	18 29.1	5♏18.4	12 36.9	6 16.7	12 26.8	25 55.6	16 29.3	26 3.1	25 58.3	20 42.8
15	13 32 51.0	25 5.4	18 25.9	20 22.6	14 31.6	7 30.6	13 10.2	25 54.2	16 36.8	26 .9	25 57.0	20 41.5
16	13 36 47.6	26 4.1	18 22.8	5♐21.1	16 27.8	8 44.4	13 53.6	25 53.0	16 44.3	25 58.7	25 55.6	20 40.3
17	13 40 44.1	27 2.8	18 19.6	20 6.3	18 25.6	9 58.3	14 36.9	25 52.0	16 51.8	25 56.6	25 54.3	20 39.0
18	13 44 40.7	28 1.4	18 16.4	4♑32.4	20 24.8	11 12.1	15 20.1	25 51.2	16 59.3	25 54.5	25 52.9	20 37.8
19	13 48 37.2	29 .0	18 13.2	18 36.2	22 25.5	12 26.0	16 3.4	25 50.5	17 6.8	25 52.4	25 51.5	20 36.6
20	13 52 33.8	29 58.6	18 10.0	2♒16.5	24 27.5	13 39.8	16 46.5	25 50.1	17 14.2	25 50.4	25 50.1	20 35.4
21	13 56 30.3	0♉57.1	18 6.9	15 34.2	26 30.9	14 53.6	17 29.7	25 49.8	17 21.6	25 48.4	25 48.7	20 34.3
22	14 0 26.9	1 55.7	18 3.7	28 31.5	28 35.5	16 7.5	18 12.7	25 49.7	17 29.1	25 46.5	25 47.2	20 33.2
23	14 4 23.5	2 54.2	18 .5	11♓10.9	0♉41.3	17 21.3	18 55.8	25 D 49.8	17 36.5	25 44.5	25 45.7	20 32.0
24	14 8 20.0	3 52.6	17 57.3	23 35.6	2 48.1	18 35.1	19 38.8	25 50.1	17 43.8	25 42.7	25 44.3	20 31.0
25	14 12 16.6	4 51.1	17 54.2	5♈48.4	4 55.7	19 48.9	20 21.7	25 50.6	17 51.2	25 40.8	25 42.8	20 29.9
26	14 16 13.1	5 49.5	17 51.0	17 52.0	7 4.0	21 2.8	21 4.6	25 51.2	17 58.5	25 39.0	25 41.3	20 28.9
27	14 20 9.7	6 47.9	17 47.8	29 48.7	9 12.8	22 16.6	21 47.4	25 52.1	18 5.8	25 37.2	25 39.8	20 27.9
28	14 24 6.2	7 46.2	17 44.6	11♉40.8	11 21.7	23 30.4	22 30.2	25 53.1	18 13.1	25 35.5	25 38.2	20 26.9
29	14 28 2.8	8 44.5	17 41.5	23 30.3	13 30.7	24 44.2	23 13.0	25 54.3	18 20.4	25 33.8	25 36.7	20 25.9
30	14 31 59.3	9 42.8	17 38.3	5♊19.2	15 39.3	25 58.0	23 55.7	25 55.7	18 27.6	25 32.2	25 35.2	20 25.0

LATITUDE

DAY	EPHEM. SID. TIME	☉	☊	☾	☿	♀	♂	♃	♄	♅	♆	♇
1	12 37 39.3	0 .0	0 .0	2N20.5	2S24.4	1S25.3	0S 2.2	1N13.6	2S13.6	0N47.6	1N46.0	15N39.4
4	12 49 28.9	0 .0	0 .0	4 39.7	2 24.5	1 27.8	0 .2	1 13.3	2 13.6	0 47.6	1 46.1	15 39.0
7	13 1 18.6	0 .0	0 .0	5 14.2	2 20.3	1 29.6	0N 1.9	1 12.9	2 13.6	0 47.5	1 46.2	15 38.6
10	13 13 8.2	0 .0	0 .0	3 32.3	2 11.5	1 30.8	0 3.8	1 12.6	2 13.7	0 47.4	1 46.3	15 38.0
13	13 24 57.9	0 .0	0 .0	0S 8.7	1 58.3	1 31.4	0 5.8	1 12.2	2 13.8	0 47.4	1 46.4	15 37.4
16	13 36 47.6	0 .0	0 .0	3 50.9	1 40.4	1 31.3	0 7.8	1 11.8	2 13.9	0 47.3	1 46.5	15 36.8
19	13 48 37.2	0 .0	0 .0	5 17.0	1 18.3	1 30.7	0 9.7	1 11.4	2 14.0	0 47.2	1 46.6	15 36.0
22	14 0 26.9	0 .0	0 .0	4 3.7	0 52.1	1 29.5	0 11.6	1 11.0	2 14.2	0 47.1	1 46.6	15 35.2
25	14 12 16.6	0 .0	0 .0	1 11.0	0 22.6	1 27.6	0 13.4	1 10.5	2 14.4	0 47.1	1 46.7	15 34.4
28	14 24 6.2	0 .0	0 .0	2N 3.3	0N 8.9	1 25.2	0 15.3	1 10.1	2 14.6	0 47.0	1 46.8	15 33.5

RIGHT ASCENSION

DAY	EPHEM. SID. TIME	☉	☊	☾	☿	♀	♂	♃	♄	♅	♆	♇
1	12 37 39.3	10♈25.2	17♈41.6	11♉42.3	21♓47.4	21♓37.1	0♉45.8	29♌10.0	14♈32.2	27♍ 9.7	24♏20.7	28♍ 9.5
2	12 41 35.8	11 19.9	17 38.6	23 35.6	23 15.7	22 45.7	1 28.0	29 R 6.3	14 39.2	27 R 7.4	24 R 19.6	28 R 8.1
3	12 45 32.4	12 14.6	17 35.7	6♊ 5.3	24 45.0	23 54.1	2 10.3	29 2.8	14 46.2	27 5.1	24 18.5	28 6.6
4	12 49 28.9	13 9.3	17 32.7	19 10.5	26 15.2	25 2.4	2 52.6	28 59.5	14 53.1	27 2.8	24 17.4	28 5.2
5	12 53 25.5	14 4.1	17 29.7	2♋43.5	27 46.6	26 10.6	3 34.9	28 56.3	15 .1	27 .6	24 16.3	28 3.8
6	12 57 22.0	14 58.9	17 26.8	16 30.8	29 18.9	27 18.7	4 17.3	28 53.4	15 7.1	26 58.4	24 15.1	28 2.5
7	13 1 18.6	15 53.8	17 23.8	0♌16.7	0♈52.4	28 26.8	4 59.7	28 50.5	15 14.1	26 56.2	24 14.0	28 1.1
8	13 5 15.1	16 48.7	17 20.8	13 48.8	2 27.0	29 34.8	5 42.2	28 47.9	15 21.1	26 54.0	24 12.8	27 59.7
9	13 9 11.7	17 43.6	17 17.9	27 1.0	4 2.7	0♈42.7	6 24.7	28 45.5	15 28.1	26 51.8	24 11.5	27 58.4
10	13 13 8.2	18 38.6	17 14.9	9♍55.3	5 39.6	1 50.6	7 7.3	28 43.2	15 35.1	26 49.7	24 10.3	27 57.0
11	13 17 4.8	19 33.7	17 12.0	22 40.4	7 17.8	2 58.5	7 49.8	28 41.1	15 42.1	26 47.6	24 9.0	27 55.7
12	13 21 1.4	20 28.9	17 9.0	5♎30.1	8 57.2	4 6.4	8 32.5	28 39.2	15 49.1	26 45.5	24 7.8	27 54.4
13	13 24 57.9	21 24.1	17 6.0	18 40.9	10 38.0	5 14.2	9 15.2	28 37.5	15 56.1	26 43.4	24 6.5	27 53.1
14	13 28 54.5	22 19.5	17 3.1	2♏29.5	12 20.2	6 22.0	9 58.0	28 35.9	16 3.1	26 41.4	24 5.2	27 51.8
15	13 32 51.0	23 14.8	17 .1	17 8.6	14 3.8	7 29.9	10 40.7	28 34.5	16 10.1	26 39.4	24 3.8	27 50.6
16	13 36 47.6	24 10.3	16 57.1	2♐40.4	15 48.9	8 37.7	11 23.6	28 33.3	16 17.0	26 37.4	24 2.5	27 49.3
17	13 40 44.1	25 5.9	16 54.2	18 50.7	17 35.5	9 45.6	12 6.5	28 32.3	16 24.0	26 35.4	24 1.1	27 48.1
18	13 44 40.7	26 1.6	16 51.2	5♑ 8.8	19 23.7	10 53.5	12 49.4	28 31.4	16 30.9	26 33.5	23 59.7	27 46.8
19	13 48 37.2	26 57.3	16 48.3	20 57.7	21 13.6	12 1.5	13 32.4	28 30.7	16 37.8	26 31.6	23 58.2	27 45.6
20	13 52 33.8	27 53.2	16 45.3	5♒49.0	23 5.0	13 9.5	14 15.4	28 30.2	16 44.8	26 29.7	23 56.8	27 44.4
21	13 56 30.3	28 49.2	16 42.3	19 31.4	24 58.1	14 17.6	14 58.5	28 29.9	16 51.7	26 27.9	23 55.4	27 43.2
22	14 0 26.9	29 45.3	16 39.4	2♓ 8.5	26 52.8	15 25.8	15 41.7	28 29.8	16 58.6	26 26.1	23 53.9	27 42.1
23	14 4 23.5	0♉41.6	16 36.4	13 52.9	28 49.2	16 34.1	16 24.8	28 29.8	17 5.5	26 24.3	23 52.4	27 40.9
24	14 8 20.0	1 37.9	16 33.5	25 .6	0♉47.2	17 42.4	17 8.1	28 D 30.1	17 12.3	26 22.5	23 50.9	27 39.8
25	14 12 16.6	2 34.4	16 30.5	5♈48.0	2 46.6	18 50.9	17 51.4	28 30.5	17 19.2	26 20.8	23 49.4	27 38.7
26	14 16 13.1	3 30.9	16 27.5	16 30.3	4 47.5	19 59.5	18 34.7	28 31.1	17 26.0	26 19.2	23 47.9	27 37.6
27	14 20 9.7	4 27.6	16 24.6	27 21.9	6 49.7	21 8.2	19 18.1	28 31.8	17 32.8	26 17.5	23 46.3	27 36.6
28	14 24 6.2	5 24.5	16 21.6	8♉34.8	8 52.9	22 17.0	20 1.6	28 32.8	17 39.6	26 15.9	23 44.8	27 35.5
29	14 28 2.8	6 21.4	16 18.7	20 18.7	10 57.1	23 26.0	20 45.1	28 33.9	17 46.4	26 14.4	23 43.2	27 34.5
30	14 31 59.3	7 18.5	16 15.7	2♊38.7	13 2.1	24 35.1	21 28.6	28 35.2	17 53.2	26 12.8	23 41.7	27 33.5

DECLINATION

DAY	EPHEM. SID. TIME	☉	☊	☾	☿	♀	♂	♃	♄	♅	♆	♇
1	12 37 39.3	4N29.1	0N 7.9	18N32.8	6S 9.7	5S 9.8	12N28.1	13N50.3	3N48.0	2N 5.7	17S35.8	17N54.3
4	12 49 28.9	5 38.2	0 7.8	27 44.9	4 14.8	3 44.4	13 14.7	13 53.6	3 56.7	2 8.6	17 34.9	17 55.7
7	13 1 18.6	6 46.4	0 7.7	25 52.7	2 10.2	2 18.1	14 .0	13 56.4	4 5.4	2 11.4	17 34.0	17 57.0
10	13 13 8.2	7 53.6	0 7.7	12 17.0	0N 3.7	0 51.0	14 44.1	13 58.6	4 14.0	2 14.2	17 33.1	17 58.1
13	13 24 57.9	8 59.6	0 7.6	8S 3.9	2 26.1	0N36.5	15 26.8	14 .2	4 22.6	2 16.8	17 32.1	17 59.1
16	13 36 47.6	10 4.2	0 7.5	24 59.2	4 55.7	2 4.0	16 8.2	14 1.2	4 31.1	2 19.3	17 31.1	18 .1
19	13 48 37.2	11 7.3	0 7.5	27 23.2	7 31.1	3 31.3	16 48.1	14 1.7	4 39.6	2 21.8	17 30.0	18 .8
22	14 0 26.9	12 8.8	0 7.4	15 47.7	10 10.0	4 58.1	17 26.6	14 1.6	4 47.9	2 24.1	17 29.0	18 1.5
25	14 12 16.6	13 8.5	0 7.4	1N13.2	12 48.8	6 23.9	18 3.5	14 .9	4 56.1	2 26.2	17 27.9	18 2.0
28	14 24 6.2	14 6.3	0 7.3	17 17.8	15 23.1	7 48.6	18 38.9	13 59.6	5 4.3	2 28.3	17 26.7	18 2.4

MAY 1968

DAY	EPHEM. SID. TIME	☉	☊	☽	☿	♀	♂	♃	♄	♅	♆	♇
	LONGITUDE											
	h m s	° ′	° ′	° ′	° ′	° ′	° ′	° ′	° ′	° ′	° ′	° ′
1	14 35 55.9	10♉41.1	17♈35.1	17♊ 9.9	17♉47.3	27♈11.7	24♉38.3	25♌57.3	18♈34.9	25♍30.6	25♏33.6	20♍24.1
2	14 39 52.4	11 39.3	17 31.9	29 4.9	19 54.4	28 25.5	25 20.9	25 59.1	18 42.0	25 R 29.0	25 R 32.0	20 R 23.2
3	14 43 49.0	12 37.5	17 28.7	11♋ 7.2	22 .3	29 39.3	26 3.5	26 1.0	18 49.2	25 27.5	25 30.5	20 22.4
4	14 47 45.6	13 35.7	17 25.6	23 20.2	24 4.7	0♉53.1	26 46.0	26 3.2	18 56.4	25 26.1	25 28.9	20 21.6
5	14 51 42.1	14 33.8	17 22.4	5♌47.4	26 7.3	2 6.8	27 28.4	26 5.5	19 3.5	25 24.6	25 27.3	20 20.8
6	14 55 38.7	15 31.9	17 19.2	18 32.9	28 7.8	3 20.6	28 10.8	26 7.9	19 10.5	25 23.2	25 25.7	20 20.0
7	14 59 35.2	16 30.0	17 16.0	1♍40.4	0♊ 6.0	4 34.3	28 53.2	26 10.6	19 17.5	25 21.9	25 24.1	20 19.2
8	15 3 31.8	17 28.0	17 12.9	15 12.8	2 1.6	5 48.1	29 35.5	26 13.4	19 24.5	25 20.6	25 22.5	20 18.5
9	15 7 28.3	18 26.0	17 9.7	29 11.8	3 54.5	7 1.8	0♊17.7	26 16.4	19 31.5	25 19.4	25 20.9	20 17.8
10	15 11 24.9	19 24.0	17 6.5	13♎37.2	5 44.6	8 15.5	0 59.9	26 19.6	19 38.4	25 18.2	25 19.3	20 17.2
11	15 15 21.5	20 21.9	17 3.3	28 26.1	7 31.5	9 29.2	1 42.1	26 22.9	19 45.3	25 17.0	25 17.7	20 16.5
12	15 19 18.0	21 19.8	17 .1	13♏32.4	9 15.3	10 42.9	2 24.2	26 26.4	19 52.2	25 15.9	25 16.1	20 15.9
13	15 23 14.6	22 17.7	16 57.0	28 47.5	10 55.9	11 56.6	3 6.2	26 30.1	19 59.0	25 14.9	25 14.4	20 15.4
14	15 27 11.1	23 15.6	16 53.8	14♐ 1.3	12 33.0	13 10.3	3 48.3	26 33.9	20 5.7	25 13.9	25 12.8	20 14.8
15	15 31 7.7	24 13.4	16 50.6	29 3.5	14 6.7	14 24.0	4 30.2	26 37.9	20 12.5	25 12.9	25 11.2	20 14.3
16	15 35 4.2	25 11.2	16 47.4	13♑45.5	15 37.0	15 37.7	5 12.1	26 42.0	20 19.1	25 12.0	25 9.6	20 13.8
17	15 39 .8	26 9.0	16 44.3	28 1.8	17 3.6	16 51.4	5 54.0	26 46.4	20 25.8	25 11.1	25 7.9	20 13.4
18	15 42 57.4	27 6.8	16 41.1	11♒50.0	18 26.7	18 5.1	6 35.8	26 50.8	20 32.4	25 10.3	25 6.3	20 12.9
19	15 46 53.9	28 4.6	16 37.9	25 10.2	19 46.1	19 18.8	7 17.6	26 55.5	20 38.9	25 9.6	25 4.7	20 12.5
20	15 50 50.5	29 2.3	16 34.7	8♓ 5.2	21 1.8	20 32.5	7 59.3	27 .3	20 45.4	25 8.9	25 3.0	20 12.2
21	15 54 47.0	0♊ .0	16 31.6	20 38.8	22 13.7	21 46.2	8 41.0	27 5.2	20 51.9	25 8.2	25 1.4	20 11.8
22	15 58 43.6	0 57.7	16 28.4	2♈55.2	23 21.9	22 59.9	9 22.7	27 10.3	20 58.3	25 7.6	24 59.8	20 11.5
23	16 2 40.1	1 55.4	16 25.2	14 58.9	24 26.1	24 13.6	10 4.3	27 15.6	21 4.7	25 7.0	24 58.2	20 11.3
24	16 6 36.7	2 53.1	16 22.0	26 54.2	25 26.5	25 27.3	10 45.9	27 21.0	21 11.0	25 6.6	24 56.6	20 11.1
25	16 10 33.3	3 50.8	16 18.9	8♉44.4	26 22.8	26 41.0	11 27.4	27 26.6	21 17.3	25 6.1	24 55.0	20 10.9
26	16 14 29.8	4 48.4	16 15.7	20 32.7	27 15.0	27 54.7	12 8.9	27 32.3	21 23.5	25 5.7	24 53.4	20 10.7
27	16 18 26.4	5 46.0	16 12.5	2♊21.6	28 3.2	29 8.4	12 50.3	27 38.2	21 29.7	25 5.4	24 51.8	20 10.5
28	16 22 22.9	6 43.6	16 9.3	14 13.0	28 47.0	0♊22.1	13 31.7	27 44.2	21 35.8	25 5.1	24 50.2	20 10.4
29	16 26 19.5	7 41.2	16 6.1	26 8.6	29 26.6	1 35.7	14 13.1	27 50.3	21 41.8	25 4.9	24 48.6	20 10.3
30	16 30 16.0	8 38.7	16 3.0	8♋10.1	0♋ 1.9	2 49.4	14 54.4	27 56.6	21 47.8	25 4.7	24 47.1	20 10.3
31	16 34 12.6	9 36.3	15 59.8	20 19.2	0 32.6	4 3.1	15 35.6	28 3.0	21 53.7	25 4.5	24 45.5	20 10.3
	LATITUDE											
1	14 35 55.9	0 .0	0 .0	4N28.5	0N40.8	1S22.3	0N17.1	1N 9.7	2S14.8	0N46.9	1N46.8	15N32.5
4	14 47 45.6	0 .0	0 .0	5 12.9	1 11.2	1 18.9	0 18.9	1 9.2	2 15.1	0 46.8	1 46.8	15 31.5
7	14 59 35.2	0 .0	0 .0	3 48.9	1 37.9	1 14.9	0 20.7	1 8.8	2 15.4	0 46.6	1 46.9	15 30.4
10	15 11 24.9	0 .0	0 .0	0 26.5	1 59.4	1 10.5	0 22.4	1 8.4	2 15.8	0 46.5	1 46.9	15 29.3
13	15 23 14.6	0 .0	0 .0	3S22.5	2 14.4	1 5.7	0 24.1	1 7.9	2 16.1	0 46.4	1 46.9	15 28.2
16	15 35 4.2	0 .0	0 .0	5 10.2	2 22.0	1 .5	0 25.8	1 7.5	2 16.5	0 46.3	1 46.9	15 27.1
19	15 46 53.9	0 .0	0 .0	4 8.2	2 21.9	0 54.8	0 27.5	1 7.1	2 16.9	0 46.2	1 46.9	15 25.9
22	15 58 43.6	0 .0	0 .0	1 21.3	2 13.8	0 48.9	0 29.1	1 6.7	2 17.3	0 46.1	1 46.9	15 24.7
25	16 10 33.3	0 .0	0 .0	1N49.5	1 57.6	0 42.6	0 30.7	1 6.3	2 17.8	0 45.9	1 46.8	15 23.4
28	16 22 22.9	0 .0	0 .0	4 16.0	1 33.3	0 36.1	0 32.3	1 5.9	2 18.3	0 45.8	1 46.8	15 22.2
31	16 34 12.6	0 .0	0 .0	5 5.5	1 1.2	0 29.4	0 33.8	1 5.5	2 18.8	0 45.7	1 46.7	15 20.9
	RIGHT ASCENSION											
1	14 35 55.9	8♉15.7	16♈12.7	15♊34.3	15♉ 7.4	25♈44.4	22♉12.2	28♌36.7	17♈59.9	26♍11.3	23♏40.1	27♍32.5
2	14 39 52.4	9 13.1	16 9.8	28 57.6	17 13.0	26 53.8	22 55.9	28 38.3	18 6.6	26 R 9.9	23 R 38.5	27 R 31.6
3	14 43 49.0	10 10.6	16 6.8	12♋35.0	19 18.5	28 3.5	23 39.6	28 40.2	18 13.3	26 8.5	23 36.9	27 30.7
4	14 47 45.6	11 8.3	16 3.9	26 10.2	21 23.5	29 13.3	24 23.3	28 42.2	18 20.0	26 7.2	23 35.3	27 29.8
5	14 51 42.1	12 6.0	16 .9	9♌30.1	23 27.8	0♉23.3	25 7.1	28 44.4	18 26.6	26 5.8	23 33.7	27 28.9
6	14 55 38.7	13 3.9	15 58.0	22 28.0	25 31.1	1 33.5	25 50.9	28 46.7	18 33.2	26 4.6	23 32.1	27 28.0
7	14 59 35.2	14 1.9	15 55.0	5♍ 5.4	27 33.0	2 43.9	26 34.8	28 49.2	18 39.8	26 3.3	23 30.5	27 27.2
8	15 3 31.8	15 .1	15 52.1	17 30.5	29 33.2	3 54.5	27 18.7	28 51.9	18 46.3	26 2.1	23 28.8	27 26.3
9	15 7 28.3	15 58.4	15 49.1	29 57.0	1♊31.5	5 5.4	28 2.6	28 54.8	18 52.8	26 .9	23 27.2	27 25.5
10	15 11 24.9	16 56.8	15 46.1	12♎42.3	3 27.7	6 16.4	28 46.6	28 57.8	18 59.3	25 59.8	23 25.6	27 24.8
11	15 15 21.5	17 55.4	15 43.2	26 5.2	5 21.4	7 27.7	29 30.6	29 .9	19 5.8	25 58.8	23 23.9	27 24.0
12	15 19 18.0	18 54.1	15 40.2	10♏23.1	7 12.4	8 39.2	0♊14.7	29 4.3	19 12.2	25 57.7	23 22.3	27 23.3
13	15 23 14.6	19 53.0	15 37.3	25 45.5	9 .6	9 51.0	0 58.8	29 7.8	19 18.6	25 56.7	23 20.6	27 22.6
14	15 27 11.1	20 52.0	15 34.3	12♐ 5.8	10 45.7	11 3.0	1 42.9	29 11.4	19 24.9	25 55.8	23 18.9	27 21.9
15	15 31 7.7	21 51.1	15 31.4	28 56.0	12 27.6	12 15.3	2 27.1	29 15.2	19 31.2	25 54.9	23 17.3	27 21.3
16	15 35 4.2	22 50.4	15 28.4	15♑32.6	14 6.2	13 27.9	3 11.2	29 19.2	19 37.5	25 54.1	23 15.6	27 20.7
17	15 39 .8	23 49.9	15 25.5	1♒15.4	15 41.2	14 40.7	3 55.5	29 23.3	19 43.7	25 53.3	23 14.0	27 20.1
18	15 42 57.4	24 49.5	15 22.5	15 42.8	17 12.5	15 53.8	4 39.7	29 27.6	19 49.9	25 52.5	23 12.3	27 19.5
19	15 46 53.9	25 49.2	15 19.6	28 53.9	18 40.1	17 7.2	5 24.0	29 32.0	19 56.1	25 51.8	23 10.7	27 19.0
20	15 50 50.5	26 49.1	15 16.6	11♓ .8	20 3.8	18 20.8	6 8.4	29 36.6	20 2.2	25 51.1	23 9.0	27 18.5
21	15 54 47.0	27 49.1	15 13.7	22 21.0	21 23.5	19 34.7	6 52.7	29 41.4	20 8.3	25 50.5	23 7.4	27 18.0
22	15 58 43.6	28 49.2	15 10.7	3♈13.0	22 39.0	20 48.9	7 37.1	29 46.2	20 14.3	25 49.9	23 5.7	27 17.5
23	16 2 40.1	29 49.5	15 7.7	13 54.1	23 50.3	22 3.4	8 21.5	29 51.3	20 20.3	25 49.4	23 4.1	27 17.1
24	16 6 36.7	0♊50.0	15 4.8	24 40.2	24 57.3	23 18.2	9 6.0	29 56.5	20 26.3	25 49.0	23 2.5	27 16.8
25	16 10 33.3	1 50.5	15 1.8	5♉44.8	25 59.8	24 33.3	9 50.5	0♍ 1.8	20 32.2	25 48.5	23 .8	27 16.4
26	16 14 29.8	2 51.2	14 58.9	17 19.2	26 57.7	25 48.6	10 34.9	0 7.3	20 38.0	25 48.1	22 59.2	27 16.0
27	16 18 26.4	3 52.0	14 55.9	29 30.3	27 51.0	27 4.2	11 19.4	0 12.9	20 43.8	25 47.8	22 57.6	27 15.7
28	16 22 22.9	4 52.9	14 53.0	12♊19.0	28 39.5	28 20.1	12 3.9	0 18.6	20 49.6	25 47.5	22 56.0	27 15.4
29	16 26 19.5	5 53.9	14 50.0	25 38.4	29 23.2	29 36.2	12 48.5	0 24.5	20 55.3	25 47.3	22 54.3	27 15.2
30	16 30 16.0	6 55.1	14 47.1	9♋14.6	0♋ 2.0	0♊52.7	13 33.0	0 30.5	21 .9	25 47.1	22 52.7	27 14.9
31	16 34 12.6	7 56.3	14 44.1	22 49.8	0 35.9	2 9.4	14 17.5	0 36.6	21 6.5	25 47.0	22 51.1	27 14.7
	DECLINATION											
1	14 35 55.9	15N 2.0	0N 7.2	27N16.8	17N47.6	9N11.8	19N12.6	13N57.8	5N12.3	2N30.1	17S25.6	18N 2.6
4	14 47 45.6	15 55.4	0 7.2	26 33.9	19 56.8	10 33.1	19 44.7	13 55.4	5 20.1	2 31.8	17 24.5	18 2.7
7	14 59 35.2	16 46.5	0 7.1	14 26.6	21 46.3	11 52.3	20 15.1	13 52.5	5 27.8	2 33.4	17 23.3	18 2.6
10	15 11 24.9	17 35.0	0 7.0	4S58.2	23 13.7	13 9.0	20 43.8	13 49.0	5 35.4	2 34.7	17 22.1	18 2.5
13	15 23 14.6	18 20.9	0 7.0	23 11.2	24 18.4	14 22.8	21 10.7	13 45.0	5 42.8	2 36.0	17 21.0	18 2.2
16	15 35 4.2	19 4.0	0 6.9	27 52.6	25 1.3	15 33.6	21 35.8	13 40.5	5 50.0	2 37.0	17 19.8	18 1.7
19	15 46 53.9	19 44.2	0 6.8	17 1.7	25 24.6	16 40.8	21 59.1	13 35.5	5 57.0	2 37.8	17 18.7	18 1.1
22	15 58 43.6	20 21.4	0 6.8	0 4.9	25 30.4	17 44.3	22 20.5	13 30.0	6 3.9	2 38.5	17 17.5	18 .4
25	16 10 33.3	20 55.5	0 6.7	16N 8.8	25 21.3	18 43.7	22 40.1	13 24.0	6 10.5	2 39.0	17 16.4	17 59.6
28	16 22 22.9	21 26.3	0 6.7	26 44.9	24 59.7	19 38.7	22 57.8	13 17.6	6 16.9	2 39.3	17 15.3	17 58.6
31	16 34 12.6	21 53.8	0 6.6	26 56.5	24 27.9	20 28.9	23 13.7	13 10.7	6 23.1	2 39.4	17 14.2	17 57.5

JUNE 1968

LONGITUDE

DAY	EPHEM. SID. TIME h m s	☉ ° ′	☊ ° ′	☾ ° ′	☿ ° ′	♀ ° ′	♂ ° ′	♃ ° ′	♄ ° ′	♅ ° ′	♆ ° ′	♇ ° ′
1	16 38 9.2	10♊33.8	15♈56.6	2♌37.9	0♋58.9	5♊16.8	16♊16.8	28♌ 9.6	21♈59.6	25♍ 4.5	24♏43.9	20♍10.3
2	16 42 5.7	11 31.3	15 53.4	15 8.8	1 20.6	6 30.5	16 58.0	28 16.3	22 5.4	25R 4.4	24R42.4	20 10.3
3	16 46 2.3	12 28.7	15 50.3	27 54.6	1 37.8	7 44.1	17 39.1	28 23.1	22 11.2	25D 4.5	24 40.9	20D10.4
4	16 49 58.8	13 26.2	15 47.1	10♍58.5	1 50.3	8 57.8	18 20.2	28 30.1	22 16.8	25 4.6	24 39.3	20 10.5
5	16 53 55.4	14 23.6	15 43.9	24 23.5	1 58.1	10 11.5	19 1.2	28 37.2	22 22.5	25 4.7	24 37.8	20 10.7
6	16 57 52.0	15 21.0	15 40.7	8♎12.1	2 1.4	11 25.2	19 42.2	28 44.4	22 28.0	25 4.9	24 36.3	20 10.8
7	17 1 48.5	16 18.4	15 37.6	22 25.4	2R .1	12 38.8	20 23.1	28 51.8	22 33.5	25 5.1	24 34.8	20 11.0
8	17 5 45.1	17 15.8	15 34.4	7♏ 2.4	1 54.4	13 52.5	21 4.0	28 59.3	22 39.0	25 5.4	24 33.3	20 11.3
9	17 9 41.6	18 13.1	15 31.2	21 59.1	1 44.4	15 6.2	21 44.9	29 6.9	22 44.3	25 5.8	24 31.9	20 11.5
10	17 13 38.2	19 10.5	15 28.0	7♐ 8.8	1 30.2	16 19.8	22 25.7	29 14.6	22 49.6	25 6.2	24 30.4	20 11.8
11	17 17 34.8	20 7.8	15 24.9	22 21.8	1 12.2	17 33.5	23 6.5	29 22.5	22 54.9	25 6.6	24 29.0	20 12.2
12	17 21 31.3	21 5.1	15 21.7	7♑27.6	0 50.6	18 47.2	23 47.2	29 30.4	23 .0	25 7.1	24 27.6	20 12.5
13	17 25 27.9	22 2.4	15 18.5	22 16.3	0 25.8	20 .8	24 27.9	29 38.5	23 5.1	25 7.7	24 26.2	20 12.9
14	17 29 24.4	22 59.8	15 15.3	6♒40.6	29♊58.1	21 14.5	25 8.6	29 46.8	23 10.2	25 8.3	24 24.8	20 13.4
15	17 33 21.0	23 57.1	15 12.1	20 36.0	29 28.1	22 28.2	25 49.2	29 55.1	23 15.1	25 9.0	24 23.5	20 13.9
16	17 37 17.5	24 54.3	15 9.0	4♓ 1.7	28 56.2	23 41.9	26 29.8	0♍ 3.5	23 20.0	25 9.7	24 22.1	20 14.3
17	17 41 14.1	25 51.6	15 5.8	16 59.8	28 22.9	24 55.6	27 10.3	0 12.1	23 24.8	25 10.5	24 20.8	20 14.9
18	17 45 10.7	26 48.9	15 2.6	29 34.0	27 48.8	26 9.3	27 50.8	0 20.7	23 29.5	25 11.3	24 19.5	20 15.4
19	17 49 7.2	27 46.1	14 59.4	11♈49.1	27 14.5	27 23.0	28 31.3	0 29.5	23 34.2	25 12.2	24 18.2	20 16.0
20	17 53 3.8	28 43.4	14 56.3	23 50.3	26 40.6	28 36.7	29 11.7	0 38.4	23 38.8	25 13.1	24 16.9	20 16.6
21	17 57 .3	29 40.7	14 53.1	5♉42.8	26 7.6	29 50.4	29 52.1	0 47.3	23 43.3	25 14.1	24 15.6	20 17.2
22	18 0 56.9	0♋37.9	14 49.9	17 31.1	25 36.2	1♋ 4.1	0♋32.4	0 56.4	23 47.7	25 15.1	24 14.4	20 17.9
23	18 4 53.5	1 35.2	14 46.7	29 19.3	25 6.8	2 17.9	1 12.7	1 5.6	23 52.0	25 16.2	24 13.2	20 18.6
24	18 8 50.0	2 32.4	14 43.6	11♊10.5	24 40.0	3 31.6	1 53.0	1 14.9	23 56.3	25 17.4	24 12.0	20 19.4
25	18 12 46.6	3 29.7	14 40.4	23 7.1	24 16.2	4 45.3	2 33.2	1 24.3	24 .5	25 18.5	24 10.8	20 20.1
26	18 16 43.1	4 26.9	14 37.2	5♋10.8	23 55.8	5 59.1	3 13.4	1 33.8	24 4.6	25 19.8	24 9.7	20 20.9
27	18 20 39.7	5 24.1	14 34.0	17 22.8	23 39.3	7 12.8	3 53.6	1 43.4	24 8.6	25 21.1	24 8.5	20 21.7
28	18 24 36.3	6 21.4	14 30.9	29 43.9	23 26.8	8 26.5	4 33.7	1 53.0	24 12.5	25 22.4	24 7.4	20 22.6
29	18 28 32.8	7 18.6	14 27.7	12♌14.9	23 18.7	9 40.3	5 13.8	2 2.8	24 16.4	25 23.8	24 6.3	20 23.5
30	18 32 29.4	8 15.8	14 24.5	24 56.9	23 15.2	10 54.1	5 53.8	2 12.7	24 20.1	25 25.2	24 5.3	20 24.4

LATITUDE

DAY	EPHEM. SID. TIME	☉	☊	☾	☿	♀	♂	♃	♄	♅	♆	♇
1	16 38 9.2	0 .0	0 .0	4N55.0	0N48.8	0S27.1	0N34.4	1N 5.3	2S19.0	0N45.6	1N46.7	15N20.5
4	16 49 58.8	0 .0	0 .0	3 .4	0 7.3	0 20.2	0 35.9	1 5.0	2 19.5	0 45.5	1 46.7	15 19.2
7	17 1 48.5	0 .0	0 .0	0S29.1	0S40.0	0 13.2	0 37.4	1 4.6	2 20.1	0 45.4	1 46.6	15 17.9
10	17 13 38.2	0 .0	0 .0	3 54.4	1 30.6	0 6.0	0 38.8	1 4.3	2 20.7	0 45.2	1 46.5	15 16.6
13	17 25 27.9	0 .0	0 .0	5 1.7	2 21.5	0N 1.1	0 40.2	1 3.9	2 21.3	0 45.1	1 46.4	15 15.3
16	17 37 17.5	0 .0	0 .0	3 23.7	3 8.9	0 8.2	0 41.6	1 3.6	2 21.9	0 45.0	1 46.3	15 14.0
19	17 49 7.2	0 .0	0 .0	0 22.2	3 48.8	0 15.3	0 43.0	1 3.3	2 22.6	0 44.8	1 46.2	15 12.8
22	18 0 56.9	0 .0	0 .0	2N38.9	4 17.7	0 22.3	0 44.4	1 3.0	2 23.3	0 44.7	1 46.1	15 11.5
25	18 12 46.6	0 .0	0 .0	4 38.1	4 33.9	0 29.1	0 45.7	1 2.7	2 24.0	0 44.6	1 46.0	15 10.3
28	18 24 36.3	0 .0	0 .0	4 50.2	4 37.0	0 35.7	0 47.0	1 2.4	2 24.7	0 44.5	1 45.9	15 9.1

RIGHT ASCENSION

DAY	EPHEM. SID. TIME	☉	☊	☾	☿	♀	♂	♃	♄	♅	♆	♇
1	16 38 9.2	8♊57.7	14♈41.2	6♌ 8.4	1♋ 4.6	3♊26.3	15♊ 2.1	0♍42.9	21♈12.1	25♍46.9	22♏49.6	27♍14.6
2	16 42 5.7	9 59.1	14 38.2	19 1.5	1 28.3	4 43.5	15 46.6	0 49.3	21 17.6	25R46.8	22R48.0	27R14.4
3	16 46 2.3	11 .7	14 35.3	1♍28.4	1 46.9	6 1.0	16 31.2	0 55.9	21 23.0	25 46.8	22 46.4	27 14.3
4	16 49 58.8	12 2.3	14 32.3	13 36.3	2 .3	7 18.7	17 15.8	1 2.5	21 28.4	25D46.9	22 44.9	27 14.2
5	16 53 55.4	13 4.0	14 29.4	25 38.0	2 8.6	8 36.7	18 .3	1 9.3	21 33.7	25 47.0	22 43.3	27 14.2
6	16 57 52.0	14 5.8	14 26.4	7♎50.5	2 11.9	9 54.9	18 44.8	1 16.2	21 39.0	25 47.2	22 41.8	27 14.1
7	17 1 48.5	15 7.6	14 23.5	20 33.2	2R10.3	11 13.3	19 29.4	1 23.2	21 44.2	25 47.4	22 40.3	27D14.2
8	17 5 45.1	16 9.6	14 20.6	4♏ 6.1	2 3.8	12 31.9	20 13.9	1 30.4	21 49.3	25 47.6	22 38.8	27 14.2
9	17 9 41.6	17 11.6	14 17.6	18 45.6	1 52.7	13 50.8	20 58.4	1 37.7	21 54.4	25 47.9	22 37.3	27 14.2
10	17 13 38.2	18 13.6	14 14.7	4♐36.5	1 37.2	15 9.8	21 42.9	1 45.0	21 59.5	25 48.3	22 35.8	27 14.3
11	17 17 34.8	19 15.7	14 11.7	21 23.1	1 17.6	16 29.0	22 27.4	1 52.5	22 4.4	25 48.7	22 34.3	27 14.5
12	17 21 31.3	20 17.9	14 8.8	8♑26.5	0 54.3	17 48.5	23 11.9	2 .1	22 9.3	25 49.1	22 32.9	27 14.6
13	17 25 27.9	21 20.1	14 5.8	24 58.1	0 27.6	19 8.0	23 56.4	2 7.9	22 14.2	25 49.6	22 31.5	27 14.8
14	17 29 24.4	22 22.4	14 2.9	10♒21.6	29♊58.0	20 27.8	24 40.9	2 15.7	22 19.0	25 50.2	22 30.1	27 15.0
15	17 33 21.0	23 24.7	13 59.9	24 23.8	29 26.0	21 47.7	25 25.3	2 23.7	22 23.7	25 50.8	22 28.7	27 15.3
16	17 37 17.5	24 27.0	13 57.0	7♓11.2	28 52.0	23 7.8	26 9.7	2 31.7	22 28.3	25 51.5	22 27.3	27 15.5
17	17 41 14.1	25 29.3	13 54.0	19 .3	28 16.8	24 27.9	26 54.1	2 39.9	22 32.9	25 52.1	22 26.0	27 15.8
18	17 45 10.7	26 31.7	13 51.1	0♈10.4	27 40.8	25 48.2	27 38.4	2 48.1	22 37.4	25 52.9	22 24.6	27 16.2
19	17 49 7.2	27 34.1	13 48.1	11 .7	27 4.7	27 8.6	28 22.7	2 56.5	22 41.9	25 53.7	22 23.3	27 16.5
20	17 53 3.8	28 36.5	13 45.2	21 48.4	26 29.1	28 29.0	29 7.0	3 4.9	22 46.2	25 54.5	22 22.0	27 16.9
21	17 57 .3	29 38.9	13 42.3	2♉49.1	25 54.5	29 49.5	29 51.3	3 13.5	22 50.5	25 55.4	22 20.7	27 17.3
22	18 0 56.9	0♋41.3	13 39.3	14 15.8	25 21.6	1♋10.1	0♋35.5	3 22.1	22 54.7	25 56.3	22 19.4	27 17.7
23	18 4 53.5	1 43.7	13 36.4	26 17.8	24 50.9	2 30.7	1 19.7	3 30.9	22 58.9	25 57.3	22 18.2	27 18.2
24	18 8 50.0	2 46.1	13 33.4	8♊58.5	24 22.9	3 51.4	2 3.8	3 39.7	23 3.0	25 58.3	22 16.9	27 18.7
25	18 12 46.6	3 48.5	13 30.5	22 14.0	23 58.0	5 12.0	2 48.0	3 48.6	23 7.0	25 59.4	22 15.7	27 19.2
26	18 16 43.1	4 50.8	13 27.5	5♋51.7	23 36.7	6 32.7	3 32.0	3 57.6	23 10.9	26 .5	22 14.6	27 19.8
27	18 20 39.7	5 53.1	13 24.6	19 33.5	23 19.3	7 53.3	4 16.0	4 6.8	23 14.8	26 1.7	22 13.4	27 20.4
28	18 24 36.3	6 55.4	13 21.6	3♌ 1.4	23 6.2	9 13.9	4 60.0	4 16.0	23 18.5	26 2.9	22 12.3	27 21.0
29	18 28 32.8	7 57.6	13 18.7	16 2.8	22 57.6	10 34.4	5 43.9	4 25.2	23 22.2	26 4.2	22 11.2	27 21.6
30	18 32 29.4	8 59.7	13 15.8	28 34.1	22 53.7	11 54.9	6 27.7	4 34.6	23 25.8	26 5.5	22 10.1	27 22.3

DECLINATION

DAY	EPHEM. SID. TIME	☉	☊	☾	☿	♀	♂	♃	♄	♅	♆	♇
1	16 38 9.2	22N 2.2	0N 6.6	24N21.6	24N15.4	20N44.5	23N18.5	13N 8.3	6N25.2	2N39.3	17S13.8	17N57.1
4	16 49 58.8	22 25.1	0 6.5	10 13.9	23 33.2	21 28.0	23 31.8	13 .8	6 31.0	2 39.2	17 12.8	17 55.9
7	17 1 48.5	22 44.5	0 6.4	9S10.8	22 45.9	22 6.1	23 43.1	12 52.9	6 36.7	2 38.8	17 11.8	17 54.5
10	17 13 38.2	23 .2	0 6.4	25 21.6	21 55.6	22 38.6	23 52.5	12 44.6	6 42.1	2 38.3	17 10.8	17 53.0
13	17 25 27.9	23 12.4	0 6.3	26 33.8	21 5.2	23 5.3	24 .0	12 35.9	6 47.2	2 37.6	17 9.8	17 51.4
16	17 37 17.5	23 20.8	0 6.3	13 11.7	20 17.6	23 26.0	24 5.6	12 26.8	6 52.1	2 36.7	17 9.0	17 49.7
19	17 49 7.2	23 25.6	0 6.2	4N20.0	19 36.3	23 40.5	24 9.3	12 17.3	6 56.7	2 35.6	17 8.1	17 47.8
22	18 0 56.9	23 26.6	0 6.1	19 36.2	19 4.8	23 48.8	24 11.1	12 7.5	7 1.0	2 34.3	17 7.3	17 45.9
25	18 12 46.6	23 24.0	0 6.1	27 53.7	18 45.6	23 50.7	24 11.0	11 57.3	7 5.1	2 32.8	17 6.5	17 43.9
28	18 24 36.3	23 17.6	0 6.0	24 56.2	18 40.3	23 46.2	24 9.0	11 46.7	7 8.8	2 31.2	17 5.8	17 41.8

JULY 1968

DAY	EPHEM. SID. TIME	☉	☊	☽	☿	♀	♂	♃	♄	♅	♆	♇
		LONGITUDE										
	h m s	° ′	° ′	° ′	° ′	° ′	° ′	° ′	° ′	° ′	° ′	° ′
1	18 36 25.9	9♋13.0	14♈21.3	7♍51.2	23♊16.4	12♋ 7.8	6♋33.8	2♍22.6	24♈23.8	25♍26.7	24♏ 4.2	20♍25.3
2	18 40 22.5	10 10.2	14 18.2	20 59.6	23D22.4	13 21.6	7 13.8	2 32.7	24 27.4	25 28.3	24R 3.2	20 26.3
3	18 44 19.0	11 7.4	14 15.0	4♎24.2	23 33.3	14 35.3	7 53.7	2 42.8	24 30.9	25 29.8	24 2.2	20 27.3
4	18 48 15.6	12 4.6	14 11.8	18 7.1	23 49.3	15 49.1	8 33.6	2 53.0	24 34.3	25 31.5	24 1.3	20 28.3
5	18 52 12.2	13 1.9	14 8.6	2♏ 9.5	24 10.3	17 2.9	9 13.5	3 3.4	24 37.7	25 33.2	24 .4	20 29.5
6	18 56 8.7	13 59.1	14 5.4	16 31.4	24 36.3	18 16.7	9 53.3	3 13.8	24 40.9	25 34.9	23 59.5	20 30.5
7	19 0 5.3	14 56.3	14 2.3	1♐10.6	25 7.3	19 30.4	10 33.1	3 24.2	24 44.0	25 36.7	23 58.6	20 31.7
8	19 4 1.8	15 53.4	13 59.1	16 2.4	25 43.2	20 44.2	11 12.9	3 34.8	24 47.1	25 38.5	23 57.7	20 32.8
9	19 7 58.4	16 50.6	13 55.9	0♑59.6	26 24.2	21 58.0	11 52.6	3 45.4	24 50.0	25 40.4	23 56.9	20 34.0
10	19 11 55.0	17 47.8	13 52.7	15 53.1	27 10.0	23 11.8	12 32.2	3 56.1	24 52.9	25 42.3	23 56.1	20 35.2
11	19 15 51.5	18 45.0	13 49.6	0♒34.0	28 .7	24 25.5	13 11.9	4 6.9	24 55.7	25 44.3	23 55.3	20 36.4
12	19 19 48.1	19 42.2	13 46.4	14 54.6	28 56.1	25 39.3	13 51.5	4 17.7	24 58.3	25 46.3	23 54.6	20 37.6
13	19 23 44.6	20 39.4	13 43.2	28 49.7	29 56.4	26 53.1	14 31.1	4 28.6	25 .9	25 48.3	23 53.8	20 38.9
14	19 27 41.2	21 36.6	13 40.0	12♓17.2	1♋ 1.3	28 6.9	15 10.6	4 39.6	25 3.4	25 50.4	23 53.1	20 40.2
15	19 31 37.7	22 33.8	13 36.9	25 17.8	2 10.8	29 20.7	15 50.1	4 50.7	25 5.8	25 52.6	23 52.5	20 41.5
16	19 35 34.3	23 31.0	13 33.7	7♈54.5	3 24.8	0♌34.5	16 29.6	5 1.8	25 8.1	25 54.7	23 51.8	20 42.9
17	19 39 30.9	24 28.3	13 30.5	20 11.5	4 43.4	1 48.4	17 9.0	5 13.0	25 10.3	25 57.0	23 51.2	20 44.3
18	19 43 27.4	25 25.5	13 27.3	2♉14.0	6 6.3	3 2.2	17 48.5	5 24.3	25 12.4	25 59.2	23 50.7	20 45.7
19	19 47 24.0	26 22.8	13 24.2	14 7.5	7 33.4	4 16.0	18 27.9	5 35.6	25 14.4	26 1.5	23 50.1	20 47.1
20	19 51 20.5	27 20.0	13 21.0	25 56.9	9 4.8	5 29.9	19 7.2	5 47.0	25 16.3	26 3.9	23 49.6	20 48.5
21	19 55 17.1	28 17.3	13 17.8	7♊47.2	10 40.2	6 43.7	19 46.5	5 58.5	25 18.1	26 6.3	23 49.1	20 50.0
22	19 59 13.7	29 14.6	13 14.6	19 42.2	12 19.4	7 57.6	20 25.8	6 10.0	25 19.8	26 8.7	23 48.6	20 51.5
23	20 3 10.2	0♌11.9	13 11.4	1♋45.2	14 2.4	9 11.4	21 5.1	6 21.6	25 21.4	26 11.2	23 48.2	20 53.0
24	20 7 6.8	1 9.2	13 8.3	13 58.3	15 48.9	10 25.3	21 44.3	6 33.2	25 22.9	26 13.7	23 47.8	20 54.6
25	20 11 3.3	2 6.5	13 5.1	26 22.9	17 38.6	11 39.2	22 23.5	6 44.9	25 24.3	26 16.3	23 47.5	20 56.1
26	20 14 59.9	3 3.9	13 1.9	8♌59.6	19 31.3	12 53.1	23 2.8	6 56.7	25 25.6	26 18.9	23 47.2	20 57.8
27	20 18 56.4	4 1.3	12 58.7	21 48.1	21 26.7	14 6.9	23 41.9	7 8.5	25 26.8	26 21.5	23 46.9	20 59.4
28	20 22 53.0	4 58.7	12 55.6	4♍48.3	23 24.5	15 20.8	24 21.0	7 20.4	25 27.9	26 24.2	23 46.6	21 1.0
29	20 26 49.6	5 56.0	12 52.4	17 59.8	25 24.4	16 34.7	25 .1	7 32.3	25 28.9	26 26.9	23 46.4	21 2.7
30	20 30 46.1	6 53.4	12 49.2	1♎22.6	27 26.0	17 48.6	25 39.2	7 44.3	25 29.8	26 29.6	23 46.1	21 4.4
31	20 34 42.7	7 50.8	12 46.0	14 57.1	29 29.0	19 2.5	26 18.2	7 56.3	25 30.6	26 32.4	23 46.0	21 6.1
		LATITUDE										
1	18 36 25.9	0 .0	0 .0	2N59.9	4S28.0	0N42.1	0N48.3	1N 2.2	2S25.4	0N44.3	1N45.7	15N 7.9
4	18 48 15.6	0 .0	0 .0	0S20.0	4 8.6	0 48.2	0 49.5	1 1.9	2 26.1	0 44.2	1 45.6	15 6.7
7	19 0 5.3	0 .0	0 .0	3 40.4	3 41.0	0 54.0	0 50.7	1 1.7	2 26.9	0 44.1	1 45.5	15 5.6
10	19 11 55.0	0 .0	0 .0	5 .1	3 7.2	0 59.5	0 51.9	1 1.5	2 27.7	0 44.0	1 45.3	15 4.4
13	19 23 44.6	0 .0	0 .0	3 31.3	2 29.1	1 4.5	0 53.1	1 1.3	2 28.5	0 43.8	1 45.2	15 3.4
16	19 35 34.3	0 .0	0 .0	0 27.6	1 48.6	1 9.2	0 54.3	1 1.1	2 29.3	0 43.7	1 45.0	15 2.3
19	19 47 24.0	0 .0	0 .0	2N36.4	1 7.2	1 13.4	0 55.4	1 .9	2 30.1	0 43.6	1 44.8	15 1.3
22	19 59 13.7	0 .0	0 .0	4 37.6	0 27.0	1 17.1	0 56.5	1 .8	2 30.9	0 43.5	1 44.7	15 .4
25	20 11 3.3	0 .0	0 .0	4 52.4	0N10.4	1 20.3	0 57.6	1 .6	2 31.7	0 43.4	1 44.5	14 59.4
28	20 22 53.0	0 .0	0 .0	3 2.5	0 43.0	1 22.9	0 58.6	1 .5	2 32.5	0 43.3	1 44.3	14 58.6
31	20 34 42.7	0 .0	0 .0	0S17.8	1 9.4	1 25.1	0 59.6	1 .4	2 33.4	0 43.2	1 44.1	14 57.8
		RIGHT ASCENSION										
1	18 36 25.9	10♋ 1.8	13♈12.8	10♍39.8	22♊54.8	13♋15.3	7♋11.5	4♍44.1	23♈29.4	26♍ 6.8	22♏ 9.0	27♍23.0
2	18 40 22.5	11 3.9	13 9.9	22 31.0	23D .8	14 35.6	7 55.3	4 53.6	23 32.8	26 8.2	22R 8.0	27 23.7
3	18 44 19.0	12 5.8	13 6.9	4♎23.2	23 12.0	15 55.8	8 38.9	5 3.2	23 36.2	26 9.6	22 7.0	27 24.5
4	18 48 15.6	13 7.7	13 4.0	16 34.8	23 28.5	17 15.8	9 22.5	5 12.9	23 39.5	26 11.1	22 6.0	27 25.3
5	18 52 12.2	14 9.5	13 1.0	29 25.7	23 50.3	18 35.8	10 6.1	5 22.7	23 42.7	26 12.7	22 5.1	27 26.1
6	18 56 8.7	15 11.2	12 58.1	13♏14.5	24 17.3	19 55.6	10 49.6	5 32.6	23 45.8	26 14.3	22 4.1	27 27.0
7	19 0 5.3	16 12.8	12 55.2	28 13.4	24 49.7	21 15.2	11 33.0	5 42.5	23 48.9	26 15.9	22 3.2	27 27.8
8	19 4 1.8	17 14.3	12 52.2	14♐19.4	25 27.5	22 34.7	12 16.4	5 52.5	23 51.8	26 17.5	22 2.3	27 28.7
9	19 7 58.4	18 15.8	12 49.3	1♑ 7.4	26 10.6	23 53.9	12 59.6	6 2.5	23 54.7	26 19.2	22 1.5	27 29.7
10	19 11 55.0	19 17.1	12 46.3	17 53.8	26 59.0	25 13.0	13 42.8	6 12.6	23 57.5	26 21.0	22 .6	27 30.6
11	19 15 51.5	20 18.3	12 43.4	3♒54.4	27 52.7	26 31.9	14 26.0	6 22.8	24 .2	26 22.8	21 59.8	27 31.6
12	19 19 48.1	21 19.4	12 40.5	18 42.7	28 51.8	27 50.5	15 9.0	6 33.1	24 2.8	26 24.6	21 59.1	27 32.6
13	19 23 44.6	22 20.3	12 37.5	2♓14.3	29 56.1	29 9.0	15 52.0	6 43.4	24 5.3	26 26.5	21 58.3	27 33.6
14	19 27 41.2	23 21.2	12 34.6	14 40.2	1♋ 5.6	0♌27.2	16 34.9	6 53.8	24 7.7	26 28.4	21 57.6	27 34.6
15	19 31 37.7	24 21.9	12 31.6	26 17.9	2 20.4	1 45.1	17 17.7	7 4.3	24 10.1	26 30.3	21 56.9	27 35.7
16	19 35 34.3	25 22.6	12 28.7	7♈26.6	3 40.2	3 2.9	18 .4	7 14.8	24 12.3	26 32.3	21 56.3	27 36.8
17	19 39 30.9	26 23.1	12 25.8	18 24.4	5 5.1	4 20.3	18 43.1	7 25.3	24 14.5	26 34.3	21 55.6	27 37.9
18	19 43 27.4	27 23.4	12 22.8	29 27.7	6 34.9	5 37.5	19 25.6	7 36.0	24 16.6	26 36.4	21 55.0	27 39.1
19	19 47 24.0	28 23.7	12 19.9	10♉50.8	8 9.6	6 54.5	20 8.1	7 46.7	24 18.5	26 38.5	21 54.5	27 40.3
20	19 51 20.5	29 23.8	12 16.9	22 44.8	9 48.9	8 11.1	20 50.5	7 57.4	24 20.4	26 40.7	21 53.9	27 41.5
21	19 55 17.1	0♌23.8	12 14.0	5♊16.0	11 32.8	9 27.5	21 32.9	8 8.2	24 22.2	26 42.8	21 53.4	27 42.7
22	19 59 13.7	1 23.6	12 11.1	18 23.8	13 21.0	10 43.6	22 15.1	8 19.1	24 23.9	26 45.1	21 52.9	27 43.9
23	20 3 10.2	2 23.3	12 8.1	1♋59.1	15 13.2	11 59.5	22 57.2	8 30.0	24 25.5	26 47.3	21 52.5	27 45.2
24	20 7 6.8	3 22.9	12 5.2	15 45.8	17 9.2	13 15.0	23 39.3	8 41.0	24 27.0	26 49.6	21 52.1	27 46.5
25	20 11 3.3	4 22.3	12 2.2	29 25.2	19 8.6	14 30.3	24 21.2	8 52.0	24 28.4	26 51.9	21 51.7	27 47.8
26	20 14 59.9	5 21.6	11 59.3	12♌42.1	21 11.1	15 45.3	25 3.2	9 3.1	24 29.8	26 54.3	21 51.4	27 49.2
27	20 18 56.4	6 20.7	11 56.4	25 29.1	23 16.3	16 59.9	25 44.9	9 14.2	24 31.0	26 56.8	21 51.1	27 50.6
28	20 22 53.0	7 19.7	11 53.4	7♍47.5	25 23.6	18 14.3	26 26.6	9 25.3	24 32.1	26 59.2	21 50.8	27 51.9
29	20 26 49.6	8 18.5	11 50.5	19 45.8	27 32.7	19 28.4	27 8.2	9 36.5	24 33.2	27 1.7	21 50.5	27 53.4
30	20 30 46.1	9 17.2	11 47.6	1♎37.4	29 43.0	20 42.2	27 49.6	9 47.8	24 34.1	27 4.2	21 50.3	27 54.8
31	20 34 42.7	10 15.7	11 44.6	13 39.1	1♌54.2	21 55.7	28 31.0	9 59.1	24 34.9	27 6.7	21 50.1	27 56.2
		DECLINATION										
1	18 36 25.9	23N 7.5	0N 5.9	11N24.4	18N48.8	23N35.5	24N 5.2	11N35.8	7N12.3	2N29.3	17S 5.2	17N39.7
4	18 48 15.6	22 53.8	0 5.9	7S24.9	19 9.7	23 18.4	23 59.6	11 24.7	7 15.4	2 27.3	17 4.6	17 37.4
7	19 0 5.3	22 36.5	0 5.8	23 59.7	19 40.5	22 55.1	23 52.2	11 13.2	7 18.2	2 25.1	17 4.1	17 35.0
10	19 11 55.0	22 15.7	0 5.7	27 27.9	20 17.7	22 25.7	23 43.0	11 1.4	7 20.7	2 22.8	17 3.6	17 32.6
13	19 23 44.6	21 51.4	0 5.7	15 11.0	20 57.6	21 50.5	23 32.1	10 49.3	7 22.9	2 20.3	17 3.2	17 30.2
16	19 35 34.3	21 23.8	0 5.6	2N42.9	21 35.6	21 9.5	23 19.5	10 37.0	7 24.8	2 17.7	17 2.9	17 27.6
19	19 47 24.0	20 52.9	0 5.5	18 34.2	22 6.7	20 23.1	23 5.2	10 24.4	7 26.3	2 14.9	17 2.6	17 25.0
22	19 59 13.7	20 18.9	0 5.5	27 39.5	22 25.6	19 31.4	22 49.3	10 11.6	7 27.5	2 11.9	17 2.4	17 22.4
25	20 11 3.3	19 41.7	0 5.4	25 39.8	22 27.2	18 34.8	22 31.9	9 58.5	7 28.4	2 8.8	17 2.3	17 19.7
28	20 22 53.0	19 1.6	0 5.3	12 34.8	22 7.3	17 33.5	22 12.9	9 45.2	7 28.9	2 5.6	17 2.2	17 17.0
31	20 34 42.7	18 18.7	0 5.3	6S 9.9	21 23.8	16 27.9	21 52.4	9 31.7	7 29.1	2 2.2	17 2.3	17 14.3

AUGUST 1968

LONGITUDE

DAY	EPHEM. SID. TIME h m s	☉ ° ′	☊ ° ′	☽ ° ′	☿ ° ′	♀ ° ′	♂ ° ′	♃ ° ′	♄ ° ′	♅ ° ′	♆ ° ′	♇ ° ′
1	20 38 39.2	8♌48.2	12♈42.9	28♎43.8	1♌33.0	20♌16.3	26♋57.2	8♍ 8.3	25♈31.2	26♍35.2	23♏45.8	21♍ 7.8
2	20 42 35.8	9 45.6	12 39.7	12♏43.0	3 37.8	21 30.2	27 36.1	8 20.5	25 31.8	26 38.1	23 R45.7	21 9.5
3	20 46 32.3	10 43.0	12 36.5	26 54.5	5 42.9	22 44.1	28 15.1	8 32.6	25 32.3	26 41.0	23 45.6	21 11.3
4	20 50 28.9	11 40.5	12 33.3	11♐16.7	7 48.2	23 58.0	28 54.0	8 44.8	25 32.6	26 43.9	23 45.6	21 13.1
5	20 54 25.5	12 37.9	12 30.1	25 46.7	9 53.3	25 11.9	29 32.8	8 57.0	25 32.9	26 46.8	23 45.6	21 14.8
6	20 58 22.0	13 35.4	12 27.0	10♑19.6	11 58.0	26 25.7	0♌11.7	9 9.3	25 33.0	26 49.8	23 45.6	21 16.7
7	21 2 18.6	14 32.8	12 23.8	24 49.3	14 2.0	27 39.6	0 50.5	9 21.6	25 33.1	26 52.8	23 45.6	21 18.5
8	21 6 15.1	15 30.3	12 20.6	9♒ 9.2	16 5.3	28 53.5	1 29.3	9 34.0	25 R33.0	26 55.9	23 D45.7	21 20.3
9	21 10 11.7	16 27.8	12 17.4	23 13.3	18 7.7	0♍ 7.4	2 8.0	9 46.4	25 32.9	26 58.9	23 45.8	21 22.2
10	21 14 8.2	17 25.3	12 14.3	6♓57.1	20 9.0	1 21.2	2 46.7	9 58.8	25 32.6	27 2.0	23 46.0	21 24.1
11	21 18 4.8	18 22.9	12 11.1	20 18.0	22 9.1	2 35.1	3 25.4	10 11.3	25 32.3	27 5.2	23 46.1	21 26.0
12	21 22 1.3	19 20.4	12 7.9	3♈15.8	24 8.0	3 49.0	4 4.1	10 23.8	25 31.8	27 8.3	23 46.3	21 27.9
13	21 25 57.9	20 18.0	12 4.7	15 52.2	26 5.5	5 2.8	4 42.8	10 36.3	25 31.2	27 11.5	23 46.6	21 29.8
14	21 29 54.5	21 15.6	12 1.6	28 10.3	28 1.7	6 16.7	5 21.4	10 48.9	25 30.6	27 14.7	23 46.9	21 31.8
15	21 33 51.0	22 13.3	11 58.4	10♉14.6	29 56.6	7 30.6	5 60.0	11 1.5	25 29.8	27 18.0	23 47.2	21 33.7
16	21 37 47.6	23 11.0	11 55.2	22 9.8	1♍50.0	8 44.5	6 38.6	11 14.2	25 29.0	27 21.3	23 47.5	21 35.8
17	21 41 44.1	24 8.7	11 52.0	4♊ 1.1	3 42.0	9 58.4	7 17.2	11 26.9	25 28.0	27 24.6	23 47.9	21 37.7
18	21 45 40.7	25 6.4	11 48.8	15 53.4	5 32.6	11 12.3	7 55.7	11 39.5	25 26.9	27 27.9	23 48.3	21 39.7
19	21 49 37.2	26 4.1	11 45.7	27 51.5	7 21.8	12 26.1	8 34.2	11 52.3	25 25.7	27 31.3	23 48.7	21 41.8
20	21 53 33.8	27 1.9	11 42.5	9♋59.3	9 9.5	13 40.0	9 12.7	12 5.0	25 24.4	27 34.6	23 49.2	21 43.8
21	21 57 30.3	27 59.7	11 39.3	22 19.9	10 55.9	14 53.9	9 51.1	12 17.8	25 23.0	27 38.0	23 49.7	21 45.8
22	22 1 26.9	28 57.5	11 36.1	4♌55.5	12 40.8	16 7.8	10 29.6	12 30.6	25 21.6	27 41.5	23 50.2	21 47.9
23	22 5 23.5	29 55.3	11 33.0	17 47.0	14 24.4	17 21.7	11 8.0	12 43.4	25 20.0	27 44.9	23 50.8	21 50.0
24	22 9 20.0	0♍53.2	11 29.8	0♍54.3	16 6.6	18 35.5	11 46.3	12 56.2	25 18.3	27 48.4	23 51.4	21 52.0
25	22 13 16.6	1 51.1	11 26.6	14 16.4	17 47.5	19 49.4	12 24.7	13 9.1	25 16.5	27 51.9	23 52.0	21 54.1
26	22 17 13.1	2 49.0	11 23.4	27 51.5	19 27.0	21 3.3	13 3.0	13 21.9	25 14.6	27 55.4	23 52.7	21 56.2
27	22 21 9.7	3 47.0	11 20.3	11♎37.5	21 5.2	22 17.1	13 41.3	13 34.8	25 12.6	27 58.9	23 53.4	21 58.3
28	22 25 6.2	4 44.9	11 17.1	25 32.4	22 42.0	23 31.0	14 19.6	13 47.7	25 10.5	28 2.4	23 54.1	22 .4
29	22 29 2.8	5 42.9	11 13.9	9♏34.3	24 17.6	24 44.8	14 57.9	14 .6	25 8.4	28 6.0	23 54.9	22 2.6
30	22 32 59.3	6 40.9	11 10.7	23 41.5	25 51.9	25 58.7	15 36.1	14 13.6	25 6.1	28 9.6	23 55.6	22 4.7
31	22 36 55.9	7 39.0	11 7.5	7♐52.4	27 24.8	27 12.5	16 14.3	14 26.5	25 3.7	28 13.2	23 56.5	22 6.8

LATITUDE

DAY	SID. TIME	☉	☊	☽	☿	♀	♂	♃	♄	♅	♆	♇
1	20 38 39.2	0 .0	0 .0	1S30.0	1N16.7	1N25.6	0N60.0	1N .4	2S33.6	0N43.2	1N44.1	14N57.5
4	20 50 28.9	0 .0	0 .0	4 23.5	1 33.5	1 27.0	1 1.0	1 .3	2 34.5	0 43.1	1 43.9	14 56.8
7	21 2 18.6	0 .0	0 .0	4 56.2	1 43.1	1 27.8	1 1.9	1 .2	2 35.3	0 43.0	1 43.7	14 56.1
10	21 14 8.2	0 .0	0 .0	2 50.9	1 45.9	1 27.9	1 2.9	1 .2	2 36.1	0 42.9	1 43.5	14 55.4
13	21 25 57.9	0 .0	0 .0	0N27.7	1 42.7	1 27.5	1 3.8	1 .1	2 36.9	0 42.9	1 43.4	14 54.8
16	21 37 47.6	0 .0	0 .0	3 24.6	1 34.4	1 26.4	1 4.7	1 .1	2 37.7	0 42.8	1 43.2	14 54.3
19	21 49 37.2	0 .0	0 .0	5 1.0	1 21.9	1 24.8	1 5.6	1 .1	2 38.5	0 42.7	1 43.0	14 53.8
22	22 1 26.9	0 .0	0 .0	4 40.9	1 5.9	1 22.5	1 6.5	1 .1	2 39.3	0 42.7	1 42.8	14 53.4
25	22 13 16.6	0 .0	0 .0	2 15.2	0 47.1	1 19.7	1 7.3	1 .1	2 40.0	0 42.6	1 42.6	14 53.1
28	22 25 6.2	0 .0	0 .0	1S23.8	0 26.2	1 16.2	1 8.1	1 .2	2 40.7	0 42.5	1 42.5	14 52.8
31	22 36 55.9	0 .0	0 .0	4 24.7	0 3.5	1 12.2	1 8.9	1 .2	2 41.4	0 42.5	1 42.3	14 52.6

RIGHT ASCENSION

DAY	SID. TIME	☉	☊	☽	☿	♀	♂	♃	♄	♅	♆	♇
1	20 38 39.2	11♌14.0	11♈41.7	26♎ 9.1	4♌ 5.8	23♌ 8.8	29♋12.3	10♍10.4	24♈35.7	27♍ 9.3	21♏49.9	27♍57.7
2	20 42 35.8	12 12.2	11 38.7	9♏25.6	6 17.3	24 21.8	29 53.5	10 21.8	24 36.3	27 11.9	21 R49.8	27 59.2
3	20 46 32.3	13 10.3	11 35.8	23 42.4	8 28.3	25 34.4	0♌34.6	10 33.2	24 36.8	27 14.5	21 49.7	28 .7
4	20 50 28.9	14 8.1	11 32.9	9♐ 3.0	10 38.6	26 46.7	1 15.5	10 44.6	24 37.3	27 17.2	21 49.6	28 2.2
5	20 54 25.5	15 5.9	11 29.9	25 13.4	12 47.7	27 58.7	1 56.4	10 56.1	24 37.6	27 19.9	21 49.6	28 3.8
6	20 58 22.0	16 3.4	11 27.0	11♑40.7	14 55.4	29 10.5	2 37.2	11 7.6	24 37.9	27 22.6	21 49.6	28 5.4
7	21 2 18.6	17 .8	11 24.1	27 44.2	17 1.4	0♍22.0	3 17.8	11 19.1	24 38.0	27 25.3	21 49.6	28 6.9
8	21 6 15.1	17 58.1	11 21.1	12♒52.1	19 5.7	1 33.2	3 58.4	11 30.7	24 38.1	27 28.1	21 D49.7	28 8.6
9	21 10 11.7	18 55.2	11 18.2	26 51.2	21 8.0	2 44.2	4 38.9	11 42.3	24 R38.0	27 30.9	21 49.8	28 10.2
10	21 14 8.2	19 52.2	11 15.3	9♓45.3	23 8.3	3 54.9	5 19.2	11 54.0	24 37.9	27 33.8	21 49.9	28 11.8
11	21 18 4.8	20 49.0	11 12.3	21 47.7	25 6.4	5 5.4	5 59.5	12 5.6	24 37.6	27 36.6	21 50.1	28 13.5
12	21 22 1.3	21 45.7	11 9.4	3♈15.6	27 2.4	6 15.6	6 39.6	12 17.3	24 37.3	27 39.5	21 50.3	28 15.2
13	21 25 57.9	22 42.3	11 6.4	14 26.3	28 56.2	7 25.6	7 19.7	12 29.1	24 36.9	27 42.5	21 50.5	28 16.9
14	21 29 54.5	23 38.7	11 3.5	25 36.2	0♍47.9	8 35.4	7 59.6	12 40.8	24 36.3	27 45.4	21 50.8	28 18.6
15	21 33 51.0	24 35.0	11 .6	6♉59.6	2 37.4	9 44.9	8 39.5	12 52.6	24 35.7	27 48.4	21 51.1	28 20.3
16	21 37 47.6	25 31.2	10 57.6	18 48.4	4 24.8	10 54.3	9 19.3	13 4.4	24 35.0	27 51.4	21 51.4	28 22.1
17	21 41 44.1	26 27.3	10 54.7	1♊10.4	6 10.1	12 3.4	9 59.0	13 16.3	24 34.2	27 54.4	21 51.8	28 23.9
18	21 45 40.7	27 23.2	10 51.8	14 7.5	7 53.4	13 12.4	10 38.5	13 28.1	24 33.3	27 57.5	21 52.2	28 25.6
19	21 49 37.2	28 19.0	10 48.8	27 34.4	9 34.7	14 21.1	11 17.9	13 40.0	24 32.2	28 .5	21 52.6	28 27.4
20	21 53 33.8	29 14.7	10 45.9	11♋18.2	11 14.2	15 29.7	11 57.3	13 51.9	24 31.1	28 3.6	21 53.1	28 29.2
21	21 57 30.3	0♍10.2	10 43.0	25 2.0	12 51.7	16 38.1	12 36.5	14 3.8	24 29.9	28 6.7	21 53.6	28 31.1
22	22 1 26.9	1 5.7	10 40.0	8♌30.3	14 27.5	17 46.4	13 15.7	14 15.7	24 28.6	28 9.9	21 54.1	28 32.9
23	22 5 23.5	2 1.0	10 37.1	21 33.1	16 1.6	18 54.5	13 54.7	14 27.6	24 27.2	28 13.0	21 54.6	28 34.7
24	22 9 20.0	2 56.2	10 34.2	4♍ 8.9	17 34.0	20 2.5	14 33.7	14 39.6	24 25.7	28 16.2	21 55.2	28 36.6
25	22 13 16.6	3 51.3	10 31.2	16 23.5	19 4.8	21 10.3	15 12.5	14 51.6	24 24.1	28 19.4	21 55.8	28 38.5
26	22 17 13.1	4 46.3	10 28.3	28 28.1	20 34.1	22 18.0	15 51.2	15 3.6	24 22.5	28 22.6	21 56.5	28 40.4
27	22 21 9.7	5 41.3	10 25.4	10♎37.8	22 1.9	23 25.6	16 29.9	15 15.6	24 20.7	28 25.8	21 57.2	28 42.3
28	22 25 6.2	6 36.1	10 22.4	23 9.2	23 28.2	24 33.1	17 8.4	15 27.6	24 18.8	28 29.1	21 57.9	28 44.2
29	22 29 2.8	7 30.8	10 19.5	6♏19.0	24 53.2	25 40.5	17 46.8	15 39.6	24 16.9	28 32.3	21 58.7	28 46.1
30	22 32 59.3	8 25.4	10 16.6	20 20.5	26 16.7	26 47.8	18 25.1	15 51.6	24 14.8	28 35.6	21 59.4	28 48.0
31	22 36 55.9	9 20.0	10 13.6	5♐18.4	27 39.0	27 55.0	19 3.4	16 3.7	24 12.7	28 38.9	22 .2	28 50.0

DECLINATION

DAY	SID. TIME	☉	☊	☽	☿	♀	♂	♃	♄	♅	♆	♇
1	20 38 39.2	18N 3.8	0N 5.3	12S25.6	21N 4.0	16N 5.1	21N45.2	9N27.2	7N29.1	2N 1.1	17S 2.3	17N13.3
4	20 50 28.9	17 17.3	0 5.2	26 29.1	19 49.8	14 54.2	21 22.8	9 13.4	7 28.8	1 57.6	17 2.4	17 10.6
7	21 2 18.6	16 28.4	0 5.1	26 1.4	18 16.0	13 39.7	20 59.0	8 59.5	7 28.2	1 53.9	17 2.6	17 7.8
10	21 14 8.2	15 37.0	0 5.1	11 36.4	16 26.7	12 21.9	20 33.8	8 45.4	7 27.3	1 50.2	17 2.8	17 4.9
13	21 25 57.9	14 43.4	0 5.0	6N40.3	14 26.1	11 1.2	20 7.4	8 31.2	7 26.0	1 46.3	17 3.2	17 2.1
16	21 37 47.6	13 47.7	0 4.9	21 36.4	12 17.7	9 37.8	19 39.7	8 16.8	7 24.5	1 42.4	17 3.6	16 59.3
19	21 49 37.2	12 49.9	0 4.9	28 26.7	10 4.5	8 12.1	19 10.8	8 2.3	7 22.6	1 38.4	17 4.1	16 56.5
22	22 1 26.9	11 50.4	0 4.8	23 34.8	7 49.0	6 44.4	18 40.7	7 47.6	7 20.4	1 34.2	17 4.6	16 53.7
25	22 13 16.6	10 49.1	0 4.7	8 16.1	5 33.0	5 15.1	18 9.6	7 32.9	7 17.8	1 30.1	17 5.2	16 50.9
28	22 25 6.2	9 46.3	0 4.7	11S10.7	3 17.9	3 44.5	17 37.4	7 18.0	7 15.0	1 25.8	17 5.9	16 48.1
31	22 36 55.9	8 42.1	0 4.6	25 58.8	1 5.0	2 12.9	17 4.2	7 3.1	7 11.9	1 21.5	17 6.6	16 45.4

SEPTEMBER 1968

DAY	EPHEM. SID. TIME	☉	☊	☾	☿	♀	♂	♃	♄	♅	♆	♇
	h m s	° ′	° ′	° ′	° ′	° ′	° ′	° ′	° ′	° ′	° ′	° ′
		LONGITUDE										
1	22 40 52.4	8 ♍ 37.0	11 ♈ 4.4	22 ♐ 5.0	28 ♍ 56.5	28 ♍ 26.3	16 ♌ 52.5	14 ♍ 39.5	25 ♈ 1.3	28 ♍ 16.8	23 ♏ 57.3	22 ♍ 9.0
2	22 44 49.0	9 35.1	11 1.2	6 ♑ 17.1	0 ♎ 26.9	29 40.1	17 30.6	14 52.4	24 R 58.8	28 20.4	23 58.2	22 11.1
3	22 48 45.6	10 33.2	10 58.0	20 26.0	1 55.9	0 ♎ 53.9	18 8.7	15 5.4	24 56.1	28 24.0	23 59.1	22 13.3
4	22 52 42.1	11 31.3	10 54.8	4 ♒ 28.3	3 23.7	2 7.7	18 46.8	15 18.4	24 53.4	28 27.7	24 .0	22 15.5
5	22 56 38.7	12 29.4	10 51.7	18 20.6	4 50.1	3 21.5	19 24.9	15 31.3	24 50.6	28 31.4	24 1.0	22 17.6
6	23 0 35.2	13 27.7	10 48.5	1 ♓ 59.7	6 15.3	4 35.3	20 3.0	15 44.4	24 47.8	28 35.1	24 2.0	22 19.8
7	23 4 31.8	14 25.9	10 45.3	15 22.9	7 39.0	5 49.1	20 41.0	15 57.4	24 44.8	28 38.8	24 3.1	22 22.0
8	23 8 28.3	15 24.1	10 42.1	28 28.7	9 1.4	7 2.9	21 19.0	16 10.4	24 41.7	28 42.5	24 4.1	22 24.2
9	23 12 24.9	16 22.4	10 38.9	11 ♈ 16.5	10 22.3	8 16.6	21 57.0	16 23.4	24 38.6	28 46.2	24 5.2	22 26.4
10	23 16 21.4	17 20.7	10 35.8	23 47.2	11 41.8	9 30.3	22 35.0	16 36.4	24 35.4	28 49.9	24 6.3	22 28.6
11	23 20 18.0	18 19.0	10 32.6	6 ♉ 3.0	12 59.8	10 44.1	23 12.9	16 49.3	24 32.1	28 53.6	24 7.5	22 30.8
12	23 24 14.5	19 17.3	10 29.4	18 6.8	14 16.3	11 57.8	23 50.8	17 2.3	24 28.7	28 57.4	24 8.6	22 33.0
13	23 28 11.1	20 15.7	10 26.2	0 ♊ 2.5	15 31.1	13 11.5	24 28.7	17 15.3	24 25.2	29 1.1	24 9.8	22 35.2
14	23 32 7.6	21 14.2	10 23.1	11 54.4	16 44.3	14 25.2	25 6.6	17 28.3	24 21.7	29 4.9	24 11.1	22 37.4
15	23 36 4.2	22 12.6	10 19.9	23 47.3	17 55.7	15 38.9	25 44.5	17 41.3	24 18.1	29 8.6	24 12.3	22 39.6
16	23 40 .8	23 11.1	10 16.7	5 ♋ 45.8	19 5.3	16 52.6	26 22.3	17 54.3	24 14.4	29 12.4	24 13.6	22 41.8
17	23 43 57.3	24 9.7	10 13.5	17 54.6	20 12.9	18 6.3	27 .1	18 7.2	24 10.7	29 16.2	24 14.9	22 44.0
18	23 47 53.9	25 8.2	10 10.3	0 ♌ 17.8	21 18.4	19 20.0	27 37.9	18 20.2	24 6.9	29 20.0	24 16.3	22 46.2
19	23 51 50.4	26 6.9	10 7.2	12 58.7	22 21.8	20 33.7	28 15.7	18 33.1	24 3.0	29 23.7	24 17.6	22 48.4
20	23 55 47.0	27 5.5	10 4.0	25 59.4	23 22.7	21 47.3	28 53.4	18 46.1	23 59.1	29 27.5	24 19.0	22 50.6
21	23 59 43.5	28 4.2	10 .8	9 ♍ 20.8	24 21.2	23 1.0	29 31.2	18 59.0	23 55.1	29 31.3	24 20.4	22 52.8
22	0 3 40.1	29 2.9	9 57.6	23 2.2	25 17.0	24 14.7	0 ♍ 8.9	19 11.9	23 51.0	29 35.1	24 21.9	22 55.0
23	0 7 36.6	0 ♎ 1.6	9 54.5	7 ♎ 1.2	26 9.8	25 28.3	0 46.6	19 24.8	23 46.9	29 38.9	24 23.4	22 57.2
24	0 11 33.2	1 .4	9 51.3	21 14.2	26 59.5	26 41.9	1 24.2	19 37.7	23 42.8	29 42.7	24 24.9	22 59.4
25	0 15 29.7	1 59.2	9 48.1	5 ♏ 36.6	27 45.8	27 55.5	2 1.9	19 50.6	23 38.5	29 46.5	24 26.4	23 1.5
26	0 19 26.3	2 58.1	9 44.9	20 3.4	28 28.5	29 9.2	2 39.5	20 3.4	23 34.3	29 50.3	24 27.9	23 3.7
27	0 23 22.8	3 57.0	9 41.7	4 ♐ 30.0	29 7.1	0 ♏ 22.8	3 17.1	20 16.3	23 30.0	29 54.1	24 29.5	23 5.9
28	0 27 19.4	4 55.9	9 38.6	18 51.9	29 41.4	1 36.4	3 54.7	20 29.1	23 25.6	29 57.9	24 31.1	23 8.1
29	0 31 16.0	5 54.8	9 35.4	3 ♑ 6.1	0 ♏ 11.0	2 49.9	4 32.2	20 41.8	23 21.2	0 ♎ 1.6	24 32.8	23 10.3
30	0 35 12.5	6 53.8	9 32.2	17 10.1	0 35.6	4 3.5	5 9.7	20 54.6	23 16.8	0 5.4	24 34.4	23 12.4
		LATITUDE										
1	22 40 52.4	0 .0	0 .0	4 S 57.3	0 S 4.3	1 N 10.7	1 N 9.2	1 N .2	2 S 41.6	0 N 42.5	1 N 42.2	14 N 52.5
4	22 52 42.1	0 .0	0 .0	4 44.3	0 28.5	1 6.0	1 10.0	1 .3	2 42.3	0 42.4	1 42.1	14 52.4
7	23 4 31.8	0 .0	0 .0	2 9.4	0 53.3	1 .7	1 10.7	1 .4	2 42.9	0 42.4	1 41.9	14 52.3
10	23 16 21.4	0 .0	0 .0	1 N 17.0	1 18.5	0 54.9	1 11.4	1 .5	2 43.5	0 42.4	1 41.7	14 52.3
13	23 28 11.1	0 .0	0 .0	4 3.1	1 43.4	0 48.6	1 12.2	1 .7	2 44.1	0 42.4	1 41.6	14 52.4
16	23 40 .8	0 .0	0 .0	5 14.9	2 7.8	0 41.9	1 12.9	1 .8	2 44.6	0 42.3	1 41.4	14 52.5
19	23 51 50.4	0 .0	0 .0	4 24.2	2 31.0	0 34.8	1 13.5	1 1.0	2 45.1	0 42.3	1 41.3	14 52.7
22	0 3 40.1	0 .0	0 .0	1 30.5	2 52.4	0 27.3	1 14.2	1 1.1	2 45.5	0 42.3	1 41.1	14 53.0
25	0 15 29.7	0 .0	0 .0	2 S 19.2	3 11.1	0 19.5	1 14.8	1 1.3	2 45.9	0 42.3	1 41.0	14 53.4
28	0 27 19.4	0 .0	0 .0	4 56.5	3 25.9	0 11.4	1 15.4	1 1.6	2 46.2	0 42.3	1 40.8	14 53.8
		RIGHT ASCENSION										
1	22 40 52.4	10 ♍ 14.4	10 ♈ 10.7	21 ♐ 2.8	29 ♍ .0	29 ♍ 2.2	19 ♌ 41.5	16 ♍ 15.7	24 ♈ 10.5	28 ♍ 42.2	22 ♏ 1.1	28 ♍ 51.9
2	22 44 49.0	11 8.8	10 7.8	7 ♑ 7.5	0 ♎ 19.8	0 ♎ 9.3	20 19.5	16 27.8	24 R 8.2	28 45.5	22 2.0	28 53.9
3	22 48 45.6	12 3.1	10 4.8	22 57.6	1 38.3	1 16.4	20 57.4	16 39.8	24 5.8	28 48.8	22 2.9	28 55.8
4	22 52 42.1	12 57.3	10 1.9	8 ♒ 2.5	2 55.6	2 23.4	21 35.3	16 51.9	24 3.3	28 52.2	22 3.8	28 57.8
5	22 56 38.7	13 51.5	9 59.0	22 6.7	4 11.7	3 30.4	22 13.0	17 3.9	24 .8	28 55.6	22 4.8	28 59.8
6	23 0 35.2	14 45.6	9 56.0	5 ♓ 10.2	5 26.7	4 37.5	22 50.7	17 16.0	23 58.2	28 59.0	22 5.8	29 1.8
7	23 4 31.8	15 39.7	9 53.1	17 23.2	6 40.4	5 44.5	23 28.2	17 28.1	23 55.5	29 2.3	22 6.9	29 3.8
8	23 8 28.3	16 33.7	9 50.2	29 .5	7 53.0	6 51.5	24 5.7	17 40.1	23 52.7	29 5.7	22 7.9	29 5.8
9	23 12 24.9	17 27.6	9 47.3	10 ♈ 18.4	9 4.3	7 58.6	24 43.0	17 52.2	23 49.8	29 9.1	22 9.0	29 7.8
10	23 16 21.4	18 21.6	9 44.3	21 32.2	10 14.5	9 5.6	25 20.3	18 4.3	23 46.9	29 12.6	22 10.1	29 9.9
11	23 20 18.0	19 15.5	9 41.4	2 ♉ 55.9	11 23.4	10 12.7	25 57.5	18 16.3	23 43.9	29 16.0	22 11.3	29 11.9
12	23 24 14.5	20 9.3	9 38.5	14 40.9	12 31.0	11 19.9	26 34.5	18 28.4	23 40.8	29 19.4	22 12.4	29 13.9
13	23 28 11.1	21 3.2	9 35.5	26 55.3	13 37.3	12 27.2	27 11.5	18 40.4	23 37.6	29 22.8	22 13.6	29 15.9
14	23 32 7.6	21 57.0	9 32.6	9 ♊ 42.2	14 42.2	13 34.5	27 48.4	18 52.4	23 34.4	29 26.3	22 14.9	29 18.0
15	23 36 4.2	22 50.8	9 29.7	22 57.9	15 45.7	14 41.9	28 25.3	19 4.5	23 31.0	29 29.7	22 16.1	29 20.0
16	23 40 .8	23 44.6	9 26.7	6 ♋ 32.3	16 47.7	15 49.4	29 2.0	19 16.5	23 27.7	29 33.2	22 17.4	29 22.1
17	23 43 57.3	24 38.4	9 23.8	20 10.9	17 48.0	16 57.0	29 38.7	19 28.5	23 24.2	29 36.6	22 18.7	29 24.1
18	23 47 53.9	25 32.2	9 20.9	3 ♌ 39.1	18 46.7	18 4.8	0 ♍ 15.2	19 40.5	23 20.7	29 40.1	22 20.1	29 26.2
19	23 51 50.4	26 26.1	9 17.9	16 46.9	19 43.5	19 12.6	0 51.7	19 52.5	23 17.2	29 43.6	22 21.5	29 28.2
20	23 55 47.0	27 19.9	9 15.0	29 31.4	20 38.3	20 20.6	1 28.1	20 4.5	23 13.5	29 47.0	22 22.9	29 30.3
21	23 59 43.5	28 13.7	9 12.1	11 ♍ 56.5	21 30.9	21 28.8	2 4.4	20 16.4	23 9.8	29 50.5	22 24.3	29 32.3
22	0 3 40.1	29 7.6	9 9.2	24 12.3	22 21.3	22 37.1	2 40.7	20 28.4	23 6.1	29 54.0	22 25.7	29 34.4
23	0 7 36.6	0 ♎ 1.5	9 6.2	6 ♎ 32.4	23 9.1	23 45.6	3 16.8	20 40.3	23 2.3	29 57.5	22 27.2	29 36.5
24	0 11 33.2	0 55.4	9 3.3	19 13.1	23 54.2	24 54.2	3 52.9	20 52.2	22 58.4	0 ♎ .9	22 28.7	29 38.5
25	0 15 29.7	1 49.4	9 .4	2 ♏ 30.4	24 36.3	26 3.1	4 28.9	21 4.1	22 54.5	0 4.4	22 30.3	29 40.6
26	0 19 26.3	2 43.4	8 57.4	16 37.5	25 15.2	27 12.1	5 4.8	21 16.0	22 50.6	0 7.9	22 31.8	29 42.6
27	0 23 22.8	3 37.5	8 54.5	1 ♐ 39.1	25 50.5	28 21.4	5 40.7	21 27.9	22 46.6	0 11.4	22 33.5	29 44.7
28	0 27 19.4	4 31.6	8 51.6	17 25.6	26 21.9	29 30.8	6 16.5	21 39.7	22 42.6	0 14.9	22 35.1	29 46.8
29	0 31 16.0	5 25.7	8 48.7	3 ♑ 31.2	26 49.0	0 ♏ 40.5	6 52.1	21 51.5	22 38.5	0 18.3	22 36.7	29 48.8
30	0 35 12.5	6 19.9	8 45.7	19 21.6	27 11.6	1 50.4	7 27.8	22 3.3	22 34.4	0 21.8	22 38.4	29 50.9
		DECLINATION										
1	22 40 52.4	8 N 20.5	0 N 4.6	28 S 9.3	0 N 21.3	1 N 42.2	16 N 52.9	6 N 58.1	7 N 10.8	1 N 20.0	17 S 6.9	16 N 44.5
4	22 52 42.1	7 14.7	0 4.5	23 44.8	1 S 47.2	0 9.7	16 18.5	6 43.2	7 7.3	1 15.7	17 7.7	16 41.8
7	23 4 31.8	6 7.8	0 4.5	7 45.1	3 51.2	1 S 23.0	15 43.1	6 28.1	7 3.6	1 11.2	17 8.6	16 39.1
10	23 16 21.4	5 .1	0 4.4	10 N 25.6	5 49.8	2 55.6	15 7.0	6 13.1	6 59.6	1 6.8	17 9.6	16 36.5
13	23 28 11.1	3 51.5	0 4.3	24 7.3	7 42.1	4 27.8	14 30.0	5 58.0	6 55.4	1 2.3	17 10.6	16 33.9
16	23 40 .8	2 42.4	0 4.3	28 33.8	9 26.8	5 59.3	13 52.3	5 42.9	6 51.0	0 57.8	17 11.7	16 31.4
19	23 51 50.4	1 32.7	0 4.2	21 8.5	11 2.5	7 29.7	13 13.9	5 27.9	6 46.4	0 53.2	17 12.8	16 29.0
22	0 3 40.1	0 22.7	0 4.1	4 9.0	12 27.5	8 58.8	12 34.8	5 12.8	6 41.6	0 48.7	17 14.0	16 26.6
25	0 15 29.7	0 S 47.4	0 4.1	15 S 34.9	13 39.2	10 26.1	11 55.1	4 57.8	6 36.6	0 44.2	17 15.2	16 24.3
28	0 27 19.4	1 57.6	0 4.0	27 54.1	14 34.5	11 51.4	11 14.9	4 42.9	6 31.6	0 39.7	17 16.5	16 22.1

LONGITUDE

DAY	EPHEM. SID. TIME (h m s)	☉	☊	☾	☿	♀	♂	♃	♄	♅	♆	♇
1	0 39 9.1	7♎52.8	9♈29.0	1♒2.4	0♏54.5	5♏17.0	5♍47.2	21♍7.3	23♈12.3	0♎9.2	24♏36.1	23♍14.6
2	0 43 5.6	8 51.8	9 25.9	14 42.0	1 7.6	6 30.5	6 24.7	21 20.0	23 R 7.7	0 12.9	24 37.7	23 16.7
3	0 47 2.2	9 50.8	9 22.7	28 8.3	1 14.3	7 44.0	7 2.1	21 32.7	23 3.2	0 16.7	24 39.5	23 18.8
4	0 50 58.7	10 49.9	9 19.5	11♓21.1	1 R 14.1	8 57.5	7 39.5	21 45.3	22 58.6	0 20.4	24 41.2	23 21.0
5	0 54 55.3	11 49.0	9 16.3	24 20.2	1 6.8	10 11.0	8 16.9	21 57.9	22 54.0	0 24.2	24 42.9	23 23.1
6	0 58 51.8	12 48.1	9 13.1	7♈5.9	0 51.8	11 24.4	8 54.3	22 10.5	22 49.3	0 27.9	24 44.7	23 25.2
7	1 2 48.4	13 47.3	9 10.0	19 38.5	0 28.9	12 37.9	9 31.7	22 23.0	22 44.6	0 31.6	24 46.5	23 27.3
8	1 6 44.9	14 46.5	9 6.8	1♉58.9	29♎58.1	13 51.3	10 9.0	22 35.5	22 40.0	0 35.3	24 48.3	23 29.4
9	1 10 41.5	15 45.8	9 3.6	14 8.5	29 19.1	15 4.7	10 46.3	22 48.0	22 35.2	0 39.0	24 50.1	23 31.5
10	1 14 38.0	16 45.0	9 .4	26 9.2	28 32.3	16 18.1	11 23.6	23 .4	22 30.5	0 42.7	24 52.0	23 33.5
11	1 18 34.6	17 44.4	8 57.3	8♊3.6	27 38.2	17 31.5	12 .9	23 12.8	22 25.8	0 46.4	24 53.9	23 35.6
12	1 22 31.2	18 43.8	8 54.1	19 55.0	26 37.4	18 44.8	12 38.1	23 25.2	22 21.0	0 50.0	24 55.8	23 37.6
13	1 26 27.7	19 43.1	8 50.9	1♋47.0	25 31.2	19 58.2	13 15.3	23 37.5	22 16.2	0 53.7	24 57.7	23 39.6
14	1 30 24.3	20 42.5	8 47.7	13 44.0	24 20.8	21 11.5	13 52.5	23 49.8	22 11.5	0 57.3	24 59.6	23 41.7
15	1 34 20.8	21 42.0	8 44.5	25 50.4	23 8.1	22 24.8	14 29.7	24 2.0	22 6.7	1 .9	25 1.5	23 43.7
16	1 38 17.4	22 41.5	8 41.4	8♌10.9	21 55.0	23 38.1	15 6.9	24 14.2	22 1.9	1 4.5	25 3.5	23 45.6
17	1 42 13.9	23 41.1	8 38.2	20 49.8	20 43.6	24 51.4	15 44.0	24 26.3	21 57.1	1 8.1	25 5.5	23 47.6
18	1 46 10.5	24 40.7	8 35.0	3♍50.7	19 36.1	26 4.7	16 21.2	24 38.4	21 52.4	1 11.7	25 7.5	23 49.6
19	1 50 7.0	25 40.3	8 31.8	17 16.1	18 34.3	27 18.0	16 58.3	24 50.5	21 47.6	1 15.2	25 9.5	23 51.6
20	1 54 3.6	26 40.0	8 28.7	1♎6.8	17 40.3	28 31.2	17 35.4	25 2.5	21 42.9	1 18.7	25 11.5	23 53.5
21	1 58 .1	27 39.7	8 25.5	15 21.5	16 55.3	29 44.2	18 12.4	25 14.4	21 38.1	1 22.3	25 13.6	23 55.4
22	2 1 56.7	28 39.4	8 22.3	29 56.2	16 20.6	0♐57.6	18 49.4	25 26.3	21 33.4	1 25.7	25 15.6	23 57.3
23	2 5 53.3	29 39.1	8 19.1	14♏44.9	15 56.9	2 10.8	19 26.4	25 38.1	21 28.7	1 29.2	25 17.7	23 59.2
24	2 9 49.8	0♏38.9	8 16.0	29 39.6	15 44.5	3 24.0	20 3.4	25 49.8	21 24.0	1 32.6	25 19.8	24 1.0
25	2 13 46.4	1 38.8	8 12.8	14♐32.2	15 43.5	4 37.2	20 40.3	26 1.6	21 19.3	1 36.1	25 21.9	24 2.9
26	2 17 42.9	2 38.6	8 9.6	29 15.0	15 D 53.5	5 50.3	21 17.2	26 13.2	21 14.7	1 39.4	25 24.0	24 4.7
27	2 21 39.5	3 38.5	8 6.4	13♑42.2	16 14.0	7 3.4	21 54.1	26 24.8	21 10.1	1 42.8	25 26.1	24 6.5
28	2 25 36.0	4 38.4	8 3.2	27 50.3	16 44.4	8 16.5	22 30.9	26 36.3	21 5.5	1 46.2	25 28.2	24 8.3
29	2 29 32.6	5 38.3	8 .1	11♒37.7	17 23.9	9 29.6	23 7.8	26 47.7	21 .9	1 49.5	25 30.4	24 10.1
30	2 33 29.1	6 38.3	7 56.9	25 5.0	18 11.5	10 42.6	23 44.6	26 59.1	20 56.4	1 52.8	25 32.5	24 11.8
31	2 37 25.7	7 38.3	7 53.7	8♓13.8	19 6.5	11 55.6	24 21.3	27 10.4	20 52.0	1 56.0	25 34.7	24 13.5

LATITUDE

DAY	EPHEM. SID. TIME (h m s)	☉	☊	☾	☿	♀	♂	♃	♄	♅	♆	♇
1	0 39 9.1	0 .0	0 .0	4S55.2	3S34.9	0N3.1	1N16.0	1N1.8	2S46.5	0N42.3	1N40.7	14N54.2
4	0 50 58.7	0 .0	0 .0	2 30.5	3 35.8	0S5.5	1 16.6	1 2.0	2 46.7	0 42.3	1 40.5	14 54.8
7	1 2 48.4	0 .0	0 .0	0N55.2	3 25.4	0 14.1	1 17.2	1 2.3	2 46.9	0 42.3	1 40.5	14 55.4
10	1 14 38.0	0 .0	0 .0	3 50.1	3 .4	0 22.9	1 17.7	1 2.6	2 47.0	0 42.4	1 40.3	14 56.1
13	1 26 27.7	0 .0	0 .0	5 13.5	2 19.1	0 31.8	1 18.2	1 2.9	2 47.1	0 42.4	1 40.3	14 56.8
16	1 38 17.4	0 .0	0 .0	4 37.8	1 23.7	0 40.6	1 18.7	1 3.2	2 47.1	0 42.5	1 40.1	14 57.6
19	1 50 7.0	0 .0	0 .0	2 .4	0 22.1	0 49.3	1 19.2	1 3.6	2 47.1	0 42.5	1 40.0	14 58.5
22	2 1 56.7	0 .0	0 .0	1S49.7	0N35.3	0 58.0	1 19.7	1 3.9	2 47.0	0 42.5	1 39.9	14 59.4
25	2 13 46.4	0 .0	0 .0	4 45.1	1 20.6	1 6.5	1 20.1	1 4.3	2 46.8	0 42.6	1 39.8	15 .4
28	2 25 36.0	0 .0	0 .0	4 58.1	1 50.8	1 14.8	1 20.5	1 4.7	2 46.6	0 42.6	1 39.8	15 1.4
31	2 37 25.7	0 .0	0 .0	2 42.9	2 6.8	1 22.6	1 20.9	1 5.1	2 46.3	0 42.7	1 39.8	15 2.5

RIGHT ASCENSION

DAY	EPHEM. SID. TIME (h m s)	☉	☊	☾	☿	♀	♂	♃	♄	♅	♆	♇
1	0 39 9.1	7♎14.2	8♈42.8	4♒26.7	27♎29.1	3♏.5	8♍3.3	22♍15.1	22♈30.2	0♎25.2	22♏40.0	29♍52.9
2	0 43 5.6	8 8.5	8 39.9	18 30.9	27 41.3	4 10.9	8 38.7	22 26.8	22 R26.0	0 28.7	22 41.7	29 55.0
3	0 47 2.2	9 2.9	8 36.9	1♓33.9	27 47.6	5 21.5	9 14.1	22 38.5	22 21.8	0 32.1	22 43.5	29 57.0
4	0 50 58.7	9 57.4	8 34.0	13 45.8	27 47.8	6 32.3	9 49.5	22 50.2	22 17.5	0 35.6	22 45.2	29 59.0
5	0 54 55.3	10 51.9	8 31.1	25 21.4	27 R41.4	7 43.5	10 24.7	23 1.8	22 13.2	0 39.0	22 47.0	0♎1.0
6	0 58 51.8	11 46.6	8 28.2	6♈36.6	27 28.2	8 54.8	10 59.9	23 13.5	22 8.9	0 42.4	22 48.8	0 3.1
7	1 2 48.4	12 41.3	8 25.2	17 46.7	27 7.9	10 6.5	11 35.0	23 25.0	22 4.5	0 45.8	22 50.6	0 5.1
8	1 6 44.9	13 36.2	8 22.3	29 5.5	26 40.5	11 18.4	12 10.1	23 36.6	22 .2	0 49.2	22 52.4	0 7.1
9	1 10 41.5	14 31.1	8 19.4	10♉44.4	26 6.1	12 30.6	12 45.1	23 48.1	21 55.8	0 52.6	22 54.3	0 9.1
10	1 14 38.0	15 26.2	8 16.5	22 51.4	25 24.9	13 43.1	13 20.0	23 59.6	21 51.4	0 56.0	22 56.1	0 11.1
11	1 18 34.6	16 21.4	8 13.5	5♊29.7	24 37.4	14 55.9	13 54.9	24 11.0	21 47.0	0 59.4	22 58.0	0 13.1
12	1 22 31.2	17 16.7	8 10.6	18 36.3	23 44.6	16 9.0	14 29.7	24 22.4	21 42.5	1 2.7	23 .1	0 15.0
13	1 26 27.7	18 12.1	8 7.7	2♋1.5	22 47.3	17 22.4	15 4.5	24 33.8	21 38.1	1 6.1	23 1.9	0 17.0
14	1 30 24.3	19 7.7	8 4.8	15 31.5	21 47.1	18 36.0	15 39.3	24 45.1	21 33.7	1 9.4	23 3.8	0 19.0
15	1 34 20.8	20 3.4	8 1.8	28 52.4	20 45.3	19 50.0	16 13.8	24 56.4	21 29.2	1 12.7	23 5.8	0 20.9
16	1 38 17.4	20 59.3	7 58.9	11♌54.1	19 43.9	21 4.3	16 48.4	25 7.6	21 24.7	1 16.0	23 7.8	0 22.9
17	1 42 13.9	21 55.3	7 56.0	24 33.2	18 44.6	22 18.9	17 22.9	25 18.8	21 20.3	1 19.3	23 9.8	0 24.8
18	1 46 10.5	22 51.5	7 53.1	6♍53.6	17 49.2	23 33.8	17 57.5	25 30.0	21 15.9	1 22.6	23 11.9	0 26.7
19	1 50 7.0	23 47.8	7 50.1	19 4.6	16 59.5	24 49.0	18 31.9	25 41.2	21 11.4	1 25.9	23 13.9	0 28.7
20	1 54 3.6	24 44.3	7 47.2	1♎20.0	16 16.8	26 4.5	19 6.3	25 52.2	21 7.0	1 29.1	23 16.0	0 30.5
21	1 58 .1	25 40.9	7 44.3	13 56.4	15 42.4	27 20.2	19 40.6	26 3.2	21 2.5	1 32.4	23 18.0	0 32.4
22	2 1 56.7	26 37.7	7 41.4	27 11.4	15 17.1	28 36.3	20 14.9	26 14.2	20 58.1	1 35.6	23 20.1	0 34.3
23	2 5 53.3	27 34.6	7 38.4	11♏20.4	15 1.5	29 52.7	20 49.1	26 25.1	20 53.7	1 38.7	23 22.2	0 36.2
24	2 9 49.8	28 31.8	7 35.5	26 31.3	14 55.9	1♐9.3	21 23.3	26 35.9	20 49.3	1 41.9	23 24.3	0 38.0
25	2 13 46.4	29 29.1	7 32.6	12♐36.4	15 D .2	2 26.2	21 57.4	26 46.7	20 44.9	1 45.0	23 26.4	0 39.8
26	2 17 42.9	0♏26.6	7 29.7	29 9.0	15 14.0	3 43.4	22 31.5	26 57.5	20 40.6	1 48.2	23 28.6	0 41.7
27	2 21 39.5	1 24.2	7 26.7	15♑29.3	15 36.9	5 .9	23 5.6	27 8.2	20 36.3	1 51.3	23 30.7	0 43.5
28	2 25 36.0	2 22.1	7 24.1	1♒1.0	16 8.3	6 18.6	23 39.5	27 18.8	20 32.0	1 54.3	23 32.9	0 45.2
29	2 29 32.6	3 20.1	7 20.9	15 24.5	16 47.4	7 36.5	24 13.5	27 29.4	20 27.7	1 57.4	23 35.1	0 47.0
30	2 33 29.1	4 18.3	7 18.0	28 38.7	17 33.7	8 54.7	24 47.4	27 39.9	20 23.5	2 .4	23 37.4	0 48.8
31	2 37 25.7	5 16.7	7 15.0	10♓54.6	18 26.3	10 13.1	25 21.3	27 50.3	20 19.3	2 3.4	23 39.4	0 50.5

DECLINATION

DAY	EPHEM. SID. TIME (h m s)	☉	☊	☾	☿	♀	♂	♃	♄	♅	♆	♇
1	0 39 9.1	3S7.6	0N3.9	24S43.8	15S8.8	13S14.3	10N34.2	4N28.0	6N26.4	0N35.2	17S17.8	16N19.9
4	0 50 58.7	4 17.3	0 3.9	19 37.7	16 16.5	14 34.4	9 53.0	4 13.3	6 21.2	0 30.7	17 19.2	16 17.9
7	1 2 48.4	5 26.5	0 3.8	8N32.2	14 50.9	15 51.5	9 11.4	3 58.6	6 15.9	0 26.3	17 20.5	16 15.9
10	1 14 38.0	6 35.1	0 3.7	23 1.2	13 45.9	17 5.1	8 29.5	3 44.1	6 10.5	0 21.9	17 22.0	16 14.0
13	1 26 27.7	7 42.9	0 3.7	28 39.5	12 1.7	18 14.8	7 47.2	3 29.7	6 5.2	0 17.5	17 23.4	16 12.3
16	1 38 17.4	8 49.8	0 3.6	22 41.6	9 50.1	19 20.5	7 4.6	3 15.5	5 59.9	0 13.3	17 24.9	16 10.6
19	1 50 7.0	9 55.5	0 3.5	6 52.7	7 37.3	20 21.7	6 21.7	3 1.4	5 54.7	0 9.0	17 26.4	16 9.0
22	2 1 56.7	11 0.0	0 3.5	13S9.8	5 53.1	21 18.1	5 38.7	2 47.5	5 49.5	0 4.9	17 28.0	16 7.6
25	2 13 46.4	12 3.0	0 3.4	25 1.1	4 57.0	22 9.4	4 55.5	2 33.8	5 44.4	0 .8	17 29.5	16 6.3
28	2 25 36.0	13 4.3	0 3.3	25 27.9	4 52.5	22 55.3	4 12.2	2 20.4	5 39.4	0S3.1	17 31.1	16 5.1
31	2 37 25.7	14 3.7	0 3.3	11 .2	5 31.6	23 35.4	3 28.9	2 7.2	5 34.6	0 7.0	17 32.7	16 4.0

NOVEMBER 1968

LONGITUDE

DAY	EPHEM. SID. TIME	☉	☊	☾	☿	♀	♂	♃	♄	♅	♆	♇
	h m s	° ′	° ′	° ′	° ′	° ′	° ′	° ′	° ′	° ′	° ′	° ′
1	2 41 22.3	8♏38.3	7♈50.5	21♓ 6.1	20♎ 8.0	13♐ 8.6	24♍58.1	27♍21.7	20♈47.5	1♎59.2	25♏36.9	24♍15.2
2	2 45 18.8	9 38.3	7 47.4	3♈44.4	21 15.2	14 21.5	25 34.8	27 32.8	20 R 43.1	2 2.4	25 39.0	24 16.9
3	2 49 15.4	10 38.4	7 44.2	16 10.9	22 27.3	15 34.4	26 11.5	27 43.9	20 38.8	2 5.6	25 41.2	24 18.6
4	2 53 11.9	11 38.5	7 41.0	28 27.6	23 43.6	16 47.3	26 48.1	27 54.9	20 34.5	2 8.8	25 43.4	24 20.2
5	2 57 8.5	12 38.6	7 37.8	10♉36.0	25 3.5	18 .2	27 24.8	28 5.9	20 30.3	2 11.9	25 45.6	24 21.8
6	3 1 5.0	13 38.8	7 34.6	22 37.6	26 26.5	19 13.0	28 1.4	28 16.7	20 26.1	2 15.0	25 47.8	24 23.4
7	3 5 1.6	14 39.0	7 31.5	4♊33.9	27 52.1	20 25.8	28 37.9	28 27.5	20 21.9	2 18.0	25 50.0	24 25.0
8	3 8 58.1	15 39.2	7 28.3	16 26.6	29 19.8	21 38.6	29 14.5	28 38.3	20 17.9	2 21.1	25 52.3	24 26.6
9	3 12 54.7	16 39.5	7 25.1	28 17.7	0♏49.2	22 51.4	29 51.1	28 48.9	20 13.9	2 24.1	25 54.5	24 28.1
10	3 16 51.3	17 39.8	7 21.9	10♋ 9.8	2 20.1	24 4.1	0♎27.6	28 59.5	20 9.9	2 27.0	25 56.8	24 29.6
11	3 20 47.8	18 40.1	7 18.8	22 5.9	3 52.1	25 16.8	1 4.0	29 9.9	20 6.0	2 29.9	25 59.0	24 31.0
12	3 24 44.4	19 40.4	7 15.6	4♌ 9.9	5 25.1	26 29.4	1 40.5	29 20.3	20 2.2	2 32.8	26 1.2	24 32.5
13	3 28 40.9	20 40.8	7 12.4	16 26.0	6 58.7	27 42.0	2 16.9	29 30.6	19 58.4	2 35.6	26 3.5	24 33.9
14	3 32 37.5	21 41.2	7 9.2	28 58.8	8 33.0	28 54.6	2 53.3	29 40.7	19 54.7	2 38.5	26 5.7	24 35.3
15	3 36 34.0	22 41.7	7 6.1	11♍52.9	10 7.7	0♑ 7.1	3 29.6	29 50.8	19 51.1	2 41.2	26 8.0	24 36.7
16	3 40 30.6	23 42.1	7 2.9	25 12.1	11 42.7	1 19.6	4 5.9	0♎ .8	19 47.5	2 44.0	26 10.2	24 38.0
17	3 44 27.2	24 42.6	6 59.7	8♎59.2	13 17.9	2 32.1	4 42.2	0 10.7	19 44.1	2 46.6	26 12.5	24 39.3
18	3 48 23.7	25 43.2	6 56.5	23 14.8	14 53.2	3 44.5	5 18.5	0 20.5	19 40.7	2 49.3	26 14.7	24 40.6
19	3 52 20.3	26 43.7	6 53.3	7♏56.7	16 28.6	4 56.9	5 54.7	0 30.3	19 37.4	2 51.9	26 17.0	24 41.9
20	3 56 16.8	27 44.3	6 50.2	22 59.0	18 4.1	6 9.3	6 30.9	0 39.9	19 34.1	2 54.5	26 19.3	24 43.1
21	4 0 13.4	28 45.0	6 47.0	8♐13.1	19 39.5	7 21.6	7 7.0	0 49.4	19 31.0	2 57.0	26 21.5	24 44.3
22	4 4 9.9	29 45.6	6 43.8	23 28.3	21 14.8	8 33.9	7 43.1	0 58.7	19 27.9	2 59.5	26 23.8	24 45.5
23	4 8 6.5	0♐46.3	6 40.6	8♑33.7	22 50.1	9 46.1	8 19.2	1 8.0	19 24.9	3 1.9	26 26.0	24 46.6
24	4 12 3.1	1 46.9	6 37.5	23 20.2	24 25.3	10 58.2	8 55.2	1 17.2	19 22.0	3 4.3	26 28.3	24 47.7
25	4 15 59.6	2 47.6	6 34.3	7♒41.8	26 .4	12 10.4	9 31.2	1 26.3	19 19.2	3 6.7	26 30.5	24 48.8
26	4 19 56.2	3 48.4	6 31.1	21 36.2	27 35.3	13 22.4	10 7.2	1 35.2	19 16.5	3 9.0	26 32.8	24 49.8
27	4 23 52.7	4 49.1	6 27.9	5♓ 3.6	29 10.2	14 34.4	10 43.1	1 44.1	19 13.9	3 11.3	26 35.0	24 50.9
28	4 27 49.3	5 49.8	6 24.8	18 6.6	0♐45.0	15 46.4	11 19.0	1 52.8	19 11.4	3 13.5	26 37.2	24 51.8
29	4 31 45.9	6 50.7	6 21.6	0♈49.0	2 19.7	16 58.3	11 54.9	2 1.4	19 9.0	3 15.7	26 39.5	24 52.9
30	4 35 42.4	7 51.4	6 18.4	13 14.9	3 54.2	18 10.1	12 30.6	2 9.9	19 6.7	3 17.9	26 41.7	24 53.8

LATITUDE

DAY	EPHEM. SID. TIME	☉	☊	☾	☿	♀	♂	♃	♄	♅	♆	♇
1	2 41 22.3	0 .0	0 .0	1S39.0	2N 9.5	1S25.2	1N21.1	1N 5.3	2S46.2	0N42.7	1N39.8	15N 2.9
4	2 53 11.9	0 .0	0 .0	1N41.9	2 10.7	1 32.7	1 21.5	1 5.7	2 45.9	0 42.7	1 39.7	15 4.1
7	3 5 1.6	0 .0	0 .0	4 15.5	2 4.1	1 39.8	1 21.8	1 6.2	2 45.5	0 42.8	1 39.7	15 5.3
10	3 16 51.3	0 .0	0 .0	5 9.5	1 52.0	1 46.4	1 22.1	1 6.7	2 45.0	0 42.9	1 39.6	15 6.5
13	3 28 40.9	0 .0	0 .0	4 5.3	1 36.1	1 52.4	1 22.5	1 7.2	2 44.6	0 43.0	1 39.6	15 7.9
16	3 40 30.6	0 .0	0 .0	1 12.6	1 17.8	1 57.9	1 22.7	1 7.7	2 44.0	0 43.0	1 39.6	15 9.2
19	3 52 20.3	0 .0	0 .0	2S30.6	0 58.0	2 2.8	1 23.0	1 8.3	2 43.5	0 43.1	1 39.6	15 10.6
22	4 4 9.9	0 .0	0 .0	4 55.9	0 37.4	2 7.0	1 23.3	1 8.8	2 42.8	0 43.2	1 39.6	15 12.1
25	4 15 59.6	0 .0	0 .0	4 26.2	0 16.6	2 10.4	1 23.5	1 9.4	2 42.2	0 43.3	1 39.6	15 13.5
28	4 27 49.3	0 .0	0 .0	1 44.3	0S 3.9	2 13.1	1 23.7	1 10.0	2 41.5	0 43.4	1 39.6	15 15.1

RIGHT ASCENSION

DAY	EPHEM. SID. TIME	☉	☊	☾	☿	♀	♂	♃	♄	♅	♆	♇
1	2 41 22.3	6♏15.3	7♈12.1	22♓28.7	19♎24.5	11♐31.8	25♍55.1	28♍ .7	20♈15.1	2♎ 6.4	23♏41.7	0♎52.2
2	2 45 18.8	7 14.1	7 9.2	3♈38.4	20 27.6	12 50.6	26 28.9	28 11.0	20 R 11.0	2 9.3	23 43.9	0 53.9
3	2 49 15.4	8 13.1	7 6.3	14 40.3	21 35.0	14 9.6	27 2.6	28 21.2	20 6.9	2 12.2	23 46.1	0 55.6
4	2 53 11.9	9 12.3	7 3.3	25 49.3	22 46.2	15 28.8	27 36.3	28 31.4	20 2.8	2 15.1	23 48.3	0 57.3
5	2 57 8.5	10 11.7	7 .4	7♉17.7	24 .7	16 48.2	28 10.0	28 41.5	19 58.8	2 18.0	23 50.6	0 58.9
6	3 1 5.0	11 11.3	6 57.5	19 14.7	25 17.9	18 7.7	28 43.7	28 51.5	19 54.9	2 20.8	23 52.8	1 .6
7	3 5 1.6	12 11.1	6 54.6	1♊44.3	26 37.6	19 27.3	29 17.3	29 1.5	19 51.0	2 23.6	23 55.1	1 2.2
8	3 8 58.1	13 11.2	6 51.6	14 43.9	27 59.4	20 47.2	29 50.9	29 11.4	19 47.2	2 26.5	23 57.4	1 3.8
9	3 12 54.7	14 11.4	6 48.7	28 4.1	29 22.9	22 7.1	0♎24.4	29 21.2	19 43.4	2 29.2	23 59.6	1 5.4
10	3 16 51.3	15 11.9	6 45.8	11♋30.1	0♏47.9	23 27.1	0 58.0	29 31.0	19 39.7	2 31.9	24 1.9	1 6.9
11	3 20 47.8	16 12.6	6 42.9	24 46.6	2 14.3	24 47.1	1 31.5	29 40.6	19 36.0	2 34.6	24 4.2	1 8.5
12	3 24 44.4	17 13.4	6 40.0	7♌41.9	3 41.9	26 7.3	2 4.9	29 50.2	19 32.3	2 37.3	24 6.5	1 10.0
13	3 28 40.9	18 14.5	6 37.0	20 11.6	5 10.4	27 27.4	2 38.4	29 59.7	19 28.8	2 39.9	24 8.8	1 11.5
14	3 32 37.5	19 15.9	6 34.1	2♍18.4	6 39.9	28 47.6	3 11.8	0♎ 9.1	19 25.3	2 42.5	24 11.1	1 12.9
15	3 36 34.0	20 17.4	6 31.2	14 11.5	8 10.1	0♑ 7.9	3 45.2	0 18.5	19 21.8	2 45.0	24 13.4	1 14.4
16	3 40 30.6	21 19.1	6 28.3	26 4.6	9 41.1	1 28.1	4 18.5	0 27.7	19 18.5	2 47.5	24 15.7	1 15.8
17	3 44 27.2	22 21.1	6 25.4	8♎14.8	11 12.8	2 48.3	4 51.9	0 36.9	19 15.2	2 50.0	24 18.0	1 17.2
18	3 48 23.7	23 23.3	6 22.4	21 1.5	12 45.0	4 8.5	5 25.2	0 45.9	19 12.0	2 52.5	24 20.3	1 18.6
19	3 52 20.3	24 25.7	6 19.5	4♏43.8	14 17.8	5 28.6	5 58.5	0 54.9	19 8.8	2 54.9	24 22.6	1 19.9
20	3 56 16.8	25 28.3	6 16.6	19 36.6	15 51.1	6 48.6	6 31.7	1 3.8	19 5.7	2 57.3	24 24.9	1 21.2
21	4 0 13.4	26 31.1	6 13.7	5♐41.1	17 25.0	8 8.5	7 5.0	1 12.6	19 2.7	2 59.6	24 27.2	1 22.5
22	4 4 9.9	27 34.1	6 10.7	22 36.9	18 59.3	9 28.4	7 38.2	1 21.3	18 59.8	3 1.9	24 29.5	1 23.8
23	4 8 6.5	28 37.3	6 7.8	9♑41.5	20 34.1	10 48.1	8 11.4	1 29.9	18 56.9	3 4.1	24 31.8	1 25.1
24	4 12 3.1	29 40.6	6 4.9	26 6.8	22 9.4	12 7.6	8 44.5	1 38.4	18 54.2	3 6.4	24 34.1	1 26.3
25	4 15 59.6	0♐44.2	6 2.0	11♒20.4	23 45.1	13 27.0	9 17.7	1 46.8	18 51.5	3 8.5	24 36.3	1 27.5
26	4 19 56.2	1 48.0	5 59.1	25 13.8	25 21.3	14 46.2	9 50.8	1 55.1	18 48.9	3 10.7	24 38.6	1 28.7
27	4 23 52.7	2 51.9	5 56.1	7♓56.1	26 57.9	16 5.2	10 23.9	2 3.2	18 46.4	3 12.8	24 40.9	1 29.8
28	4 27 49.3	3 56.0	5 53.2	19 45.0	28 35.0	17 23.9	10 57.0	2 11.3	18 44.0	3 14.8	24 43.2	1 30.9
29	4 31 45.9	5 .4	5 50.3	1♈ .2	0♐12.6	18 42.5	11 30.1	2 19.3	18 41.7	3 16.9	24 45.5	1 32.1
30	4 35 42.4	6 4.8	5 47.4	12 .3	1 50.6	20 .8	12 3.1	2 27.2	18 39.4	3 18.8	24 47.8	1 33.2

DECLINATION

DAY	EPHEM. SID. TIME	☉	☊	☾	☿	♀	♂	♃	♄	♅	♆	♇
1	2 41 22.3	14S23.1	0N 3.3	5S 2.7	5S52.4	23S47.5	3N14.4	2N 2.9	5N33.1	0S 8.3	17S33.2	16N 3.7
4	2 53 11.9	15 19.8	0 3.2	12N30.9	7 11.2	24 19.6	2 31.1	1 50.1	5 28.5	0 12.0	17 34.8	16 2.8
7	3 5 1.6	16 14.2	0 3.1	25 14.5	8 47.2	24 45.5	1 47.7	1 37.5	5 24.2	0 15.6	17 36.4	16 2.0
10	3 16 51.3	17 6.2	0 3.1	28 12.0	10 32.1	25 5.0	1 4.4	1 25.3	5 20.1	0 19.1	17 38.0	16 1.3
13	3 28 40.9	17 55.6	0 3.0	19 48.7	12 20.0	25 18.0	0 21.2	1 13.4	5 16.2	0 22.5	17 39.6	16 .8
16	3 40 30.6	18 42.2	0 2.9	3 1.1	14 7.1	25 24.3	0S21.8	1 1.8	5 12.6	0 25.7	17 41.2	16 .4
19	3 52 20.3	19 25.8	0 2.9	16S32.1	15 50.5	25 23.9	1 4.7	0 50.6	5 9.3	0 28.8	17 42.8	16 .1
22	4 4 9.9	20 6.3	0 2.8	28 12.6	17 28.5	25 16.9	1 47.3	0 39.8	5 6.3	0 31.7	17 44.3	16 .0
25	4 15 59.6	20 43.4	0 2.7	22 38.1	18 59.5	25 3.2	2 29.6	0 29.4	5 3.7	0 34.5	17 45.9	16 .0
28	4 27 49.3	21 17.1	0 2.7	6 18.1	20 22.6	24 43.0	3 11.7	0 19.4	5 1.4	0 37.1	17 47.4	16 .2

DECEMBER 1968

DAY	EPHEM. SID. TIME	☉	☊	☽	☿	♀	♂	♃	♄	♅	♆	♇
	h m s	° ′	° ′	° ′	° ′	° ′	° ′	° ′	° ′	° ′	° ′	° ′
		LONGITUDE										
1	4 39 39.0	8♐52.2	6♈15.2	25♈28.3	5♐28.7	19♑21.9	13♎ 6.4	2♎18.3	19♈ 4.5	3♎19.9	26♏43.9	24♍54.7
2	4 43 35.5	9 53.1	6 12.1	7♉32.8	7 3.1	20 33.6	13 42.1	2 26.5	19R 2.3	3 22.0	26 46.2	24 55.5
3	4 47 32.1	10 53.9	6 8.9	19 31.3	8 37.4	21 45.2	14 17.8	2 34.6	19 .3	3 24.0	26 48.4	24 56.4
4	4 51 28.6	11 54.7	6 5.7	1♊26.1	10 11.7	22 56.7	14 53.4	2 42.6	18 58.4	3 25.9	26 50.5	24 57.2
5	4 55 25.2	12 55.6	6 2.5	13 18.8	11 45.9	24 8.2	15 29.0	2 50.4	18 56.5	3 27.8	26 52.7	24 58.0
6	4 59 21.8	13 56.5	5 59.3	25 11.1	13 20.1	25 19.6	16 4.6	2 58.2	18 54.8	3 29.6	26 54.9	24 58.7
7	5 3 18.3	14 57.4	5 56.2	7♋ 4.0	14 54.3	26 30.9	16 40.1	3 5.8	18 53.2	3 31.4	26 57.1	24 59.4
8	5 7 14.9	15 58.3	5 53.0	18 59.2	16 28.6	27 42.1	17 15.6	3 13.2	18 51.7	3 33.2	26 59.2	25 .1
9	5 11 11.4	16 59.3	5 49.8	0♌58.6	18 2.8	28 53.3	17 51.0	3 20.5	18 50.2	3 34.9	27 1.4	25 .7
10	5 15 8.0	18 .2	5 46.6	13 4.7	19 37.1	0♒ 4.3	18 26.4	3 27.7	18 48.9	3 36.5	27 3.5	25 1.3
11	5 19 4.6	19 1.2	5 43.5	25 20.6	21 11.5	1 15.3	19 1.7	3 34.8	18 47.7	3 38.1	27 5.7	25 1.9
12	5 23 1.1	20 2.2	5 40.3	7♍50.3	22 45.9	2 26.2	19 37.0	3 41.7	18 46.6	3 39.6	27 7.8	25 2.4
13	5 26 57.7	21 3.2	5 37.1	20 37.9	24 20.4	3 37.0	20 12.2	3 48.5	18 45.6	3 41.1	27 9.9	25 3.0
14	5 30 54.2	22 4.2	5 33.9	3♎47.9	25 55.0	4 47.7	20 47.4	3 55.1	18 44.8	3 42.5	27 12.0	25 3.4
15	5 34 50.8	23 5.3	5 30.8	17 23.8	27 29.7	5 58.3	21 22.6	4 1.6	18 44.0	3 43.9	27 14.1	25 3.9
16	5 38 47.4	24 6.3	5 27.6	1♏28.1	29 4.6	7 8.8	21 57.7	4 7.9	18 43.3	3 45.3	27 16.1	25 4.3
17	5 42 43.9	25 7.4	5 24.4	16 .6	0♑39.6	8 19.2	22 32.7	4 14.0	18 42.8	3 46.5	27 18.2	25 4.7
18	5 46 40.5	26 8.5	5 21.2	0♐57.8	2 14.7	9 29.5	23 7.7	4 20.1	18 42.3	3 47.7	27 20.2	25 5.0
19	5 50 37.0	27 9.6	5 18.1	16 12.4	3 49.9	10 39.6	23 42.6	4 25.9	18 42.0	3 48.9	27 22.2	25 5.3
20	5 54 33.6	28 10.8	5 14.9	1♑34.1	5 25.3	11 49.8	24 17.6	4 31.7	18 41.8	3 50.1	27 24.3	25 5.6
21	5 58 30.1	29 11.9	5 11.7	16 50.8	7 .9	12 59.7	24 52.4	4 37.2	18 41.7	3 51.1	27 26.3	25 5.9
22	6 2 26.7	0♑13.0	5 8.5	1♒51.4	8 36.5	14 9.6	25 27.1	4 42.6	18 41.7	3 52.1	27 28.3	25 6.1
23	6 6 23.3	1 14.2	5 5.4	16 27.3	10 12.2	15 19.3	26 1.8	4 47.9	18D41.8	3 53.1	27 30.2	25 6.2
24	6 10 19.8	2 15.3	5 2.2	0♓33.9	11 48.1	16 28.8	26 36.5	4 52.9	18 42.1	3 53.9	27 32.2	25 6.4
25	6 14 16.4	3 16.5	4 59.0	14 10.1	13 24.0	17 38.3	27 11.1	4 57.8	18 42.4	3 54.8	27 34.1	25 6.5
26	6 18 12.9	4 17.6	4 55.8	27 17.8	14 59.9	18 47.5	27 45.6	5 2.6	18 42.9	3 55.5	27 36.0	25 6.5
27	6 22 9.5	5 18.7	4 52.6	10♈ .9	16 35.9	19 56.7	28 20.0	5 7.1	18 43.4	3 56.3	27 37.9	25 6.6
28	6 26 6.1	6 19.9	4 49.5	22 24.4	18 11.7	21 5.6	28 54.4	5 11.5	18 44.1	3 56.9	27 39.7	25 6.6
29	6 30 2.6	7 21.0	4 46.3	4♉33.2	19 47.5	22 14.5	29 28.7	5 15.8	18 44.9	3 57.5	27 41.6	25R 6.5
30	6 33 59.2	8 22.2	4 43.1	16 32.1	21 23.0	23 23.1	0♏ 3.0	5 19.8	18 45.8	3 58.1	27 43.4	25 6.5
31	6 37 55.7	9 23.3	4 39.9	28 25.3	22 58.3	24 31.6	0 37.2	5 23.7	18 46.8	3 58.6	27 45.2	25 6.4
		LATITUDE										
1	4 39 39.0	0 .0	0 .0	1N32.0	0S24.0	2S15.0	1N23.9	1N10.7	2S40.8	0N43.5	1N39.6	15N16.6
4	4 51 28.6	0 .0	0 .0	4 4.3	0 43.1	2 16.0	1 24.0	1 11.3	2 40.1	0 43.6	1 39.7	15 18.2
7	5 3 18.3	0 .0	0 .0	5 1.2	1 1.2	2 16.1	1 24.1	1 12.0	2 39.3	0 43.7	1 39.7	15 19.7
10	5 15 8.0	0 .0	0 .0	4 2.6	1 17.9	2 15.3	1 24.2	1 12.7	2 38.5	0 43.8	1 39.8	15 21.3
13	5 26 57.7	0 .0	0 .0	1 22.0	1 32.9	2 13.5	1 24.3	1 13.4	2 37.7	0 43.9	1 39.8	15 23.0
16	5 38 47.4	0 .0	0 .0	2S 8.8	1 45.9	2 10.7	1 24.3	1 14.1	2 36.9	0 44.0	1 39.9	15 24.6
19	5 50 37.0	0 .0	0 .0	4 42.7	1 56.7	2 6.8	1 24.3	1 14.8	2 36.1	0 44.2	1 39.9	15 26.2
22	6 2 26.7	0 .0	0 .0	4 28.9	2 4.8	2 1.9	1 24.2	1 15.6	2 35.3	0 44.3	1 40.0	15 27.9
25	6 14 16.4	0 .0	0 .0	1 47.9	2 9.7	1 56.0	1 24.2	1 16.3	2 34.4	0 44.4	1 40.1	15 29.5
28	6 26 6.1	0 .0	0 .0	1N30.3	2 11.0	1 48.9	1 24.1	1 17.1	2 33.6	0 44.5	1 40.2	15 31.1
31	6 37 55.7	0 .0	0 .0	4 2.0	2 7.9	1 40.8	1 23.9	1 17.9	2 32.7	0 44.6	1 40.3	15 32.8
		RIGHT ASCENSION										
1	4 39 39.0	7♐ 9.5	5♈44.5	23♈ 2.3	3♐29.1	21♑18.8	12♎36.2	2♎34.9	18♈37.2	3♎20.8	24♏50.1	1♎34.2
2	4 43 35.5	8 14.2	5 41.5	4♉20.3	5 8.0	22 36.5	13 9.2	2 42.6	18R35.2	3 22.6	24 52.3	1 35.2
3	4 47 32.1	9 19.2	5 38.6	16 5.6	6 47.4	23 53.9	13 42.2	2 50.1	18 33.2	3 24.5	24 54.6	1 36.2
4	4 51 28.6	10 24.3	5 35.7	28 24.4	8 27.3	25 11.0	14 15.1	2 57.5	18 31.3	3 26.3	24 56.8	1 37.2
5	4 55 25.2	11 29.5	5 32.8	11♊16.2	10 7.6	26 27.8	14 48.1	3 4.8	18 29.5	3 28.0	24 59.1	1 38.1
6	4 59 21.8	12 34.8	5 29.9	24 33.0	11 48.3	27 44.3	15 21.1	3 12.0	18 27.8	3 29.7	25 1.3	1 39.0
7	5 3 18.3	13 40.3	5 27.0	7♋59.9	13 29.5	29 .4	15 54.0	3 19.0	18 26.2	3 31.4	25 3.5	1 39.9
8	5 7 14.9	14 46.0	5 24.0	21 19.6	15 11.2	0♒16.1	16 26.9	3 26.0	18 24.7	3 33.0	25 5.7	1 40.7
9	5 11 11.4	15 51.7	5 21.1	4♌17.6	16 53.3	1 31.5	16 59.8	3 32.8	18 23.3	3 34.6	25 8.0	1 41.5
10	5 15 8.0	16 57.6	5 18.2	16 46.3	18 35.8	2 46.5	17 32.7	3 39.5	18 22.0	3 36.1	25 10.1	1 42.3
11	5 19 4.6	18 3.5	5 15.3	28 46.5	20 18.7	4 1.1	18 5.6	3 46.0	18 20.8	3 37.5	25 12.3	1 43.1
12	5 23 1.1	19 9.6	5 12.4	10♍25.5	22 2.0	5 15.3	18 38.5	3 52.5	18 19.6	3 39.0	25 14.5	1 43.8
13	5 26 57.7	20 15.8	5 9.4	21 56.0	23 45.7	6 29.2	19 11.3	3 58.8	18 18.6	3 40.4	25 16.7	1 44.5
14	5 30 54.2	21 22.0	5 6.5	3♎34.4	25 29.7	7 42.6	19 44.2	4 4.9	18 17.7	3 41.7	25 18.8	1 45.2
15	5 34 50.8	22 28.4	5 3.6	15 39.8	27 14.1	8 55.6	20 17.0	4 11.0	18 16.9	3 43.0	25 20.9	1 45.8
16	5 38 47.4	23 34.8	5 .7	28 32.9	28 58.8	10 8.2	20 49.8	4 16.9	18 16.2	3 44.2	25 23.1	1 46.4
17	5 42 43.9	24 41.2	4 57.8	12♏33.4	0♑43.7	11 20.4	21 22.6	4 22.6	18 15.5	3 45.4	25 25.2	1 47.0
18	5 46 40.5	25 47.8	4 54.8	27 53.7	2 28.9	12 32.1	21 55.4	4 28.3	18 15.0	3 46.5	25 27.3	1 47.5
19	5 50 37.0	26 54.3	4 51.9	14♐28.4	4 14.3	13 43.4	22 28.2	4 33.7	18 14.6	3 47.6	25 29.3	1 48.0
20	5 54 33.6	28 1.0	4 49.0	1♑46.6	5 59.9	14 54.4	23 1.0	4 39.1	18 14.3	3 48.7	25 31.4	1 48.6
21	5 58 30.1	29 7.6	4 46.1	18 57.2	7 45.5	16 4.8	23 33.7	4 44.3	18 14.1	3 49.6	25 33.5	1 49.0
22	6 2 26.7	0♑14.2	4 43.2	5♒12.3	9 31.1	17 14.8	24 6.4	4 49.4	18 14.0	3 50.6	25 35.5	1 49.4
23	6 6 23.3	1 20.9	4 40.3	20 6.7	11 16.8	18 24.3	24 39.1	4 54.3	18 14.0	3 51.5	25 37.5	1 49.8
24	6 10 19.8	2 27.5	4 37.3	3♓40.1	13 2.3	19 33.4	25 11.8	4 59.0	18D14.1	3 52.3	25 39.5	1 50.2
25	6 14 16.4	3 34.1	4 34.4	16 6.9	14 47.7	20 42.1	25 44.4	5 3.6	18 14.3	3 53.1	25 41.5	1 50.5
26	6 18 12.9	4 40.7	4 31.5	27 47.4	16 32.8	21 50.2	26 17.1	5 8.1	18 14.7	3 53.8	25 43.4	1 50.8
27	6 22 9.5	5 47.2	4 28.6	9♈ 1.9	18 17.6	22 58.0	26 49.7	5 12.4	18 15.1	3 54.5	25 45.4	1 51.1
28	6 26 6.1	6 53.8	4 25.7	20 9.0	20 2.0	24 5.2	27 22.3	5 16.5	18 15.6	3 55.1	25 47.3	1 51.3
29	6 30 2.6	8 .2	4 22.8	1♉25.1	21 45.8	25 12.0	27 54.8	5 20.5	18 16.2	3 55.7	25 49.2	1 51.5
30	6 33 59.2	9 6.6	4 19.8	13 3.2	23 28.9	26 18.3	28 27.4	5 24.3	18 16.9	3 56.2	25 51.1	1 51.7
31	6 37 55.7	10 13.0	4 16.9	25 12.2	25 11.2	27 24.2	28 59.9	5 28.0	18 17.8	3 56.6	25 52.9	1 51.8
		DECLINATION										
1	4 39 39.0	21S47.1	0N 2.6	11N16.8	21S36.9	24S16.4	3S53.3	0N 9.8	4N59.4	0S39.6	17S48.9	16N .5
4	4 51 28.6	22 13.4	0 2.5	24 26.3	22 41.7	23 43.7	4 34.6	0 .8	4 57.8	0 41.9	17 50.4	16 .9
7	5 3 18.3	22 35.8	0 2.5	28 16.2	23 36.3	23 5.0	5 15.5	0S 7.8	4 56.5	0 44.0	17 51.9	16 1.5
10	5 15 8.0	22 54.2	0 2.4	20 46.1	24 20.0	22 20.6	5 55.9	0 15.9	4 55.7	0 45.9	17 53.3	16 2.2
13	5 26 57.7	23 8.6	0 2.3	4 58.2	24 52.3	21 30.7	6 35.8	0 23.5	4 55.1	0 47.6	17 54.7	16 3.0
16	5 38 47.4	23 18.9	0 2.3	14S .0	25 12.5	20 35.8	7 15.2	0 30.6	4 55.0	0 49.1	17 56.0	16 3.9
19	5 50 37.0	23 24.9	0 2.2	27 25.1	25 20.1	19 36.0	7 54.0	0 37.1	4 55.3	0 50.5	17 57.3	16 5.0
22	6 2 26.7	23 26.7	0 2.1	24 7.0	25 14.5	18 31.8	8 32.3	0 43.0	4 56.0	0 51.7	17 58.6	16 6.2
25	6 14 16.4	23 24.3	0 2.1	7 53.5	24 55.8	17 23.5	9 9.8	0 48.3	4 57.0	0 52.6	17 59.8	16 7.5
28	6 26 6.1	23 17.6	0 2.0	10N 7.2	24 22.3	16 11.4	9 46.7	0 53.0	4 58.4	0 53.4	18 1.0	16 9.0
31	6 37 55.7	23 6.8	0 1.9	23 44.6	23 35.4	14 56.0	10 22.9	0 57.1	5 .2	0 53.9	18 2.1	16 10.5

JANUARY 1969

LONGITUDE

DAY	EPHEM. SID. TIME	☉	☊	☾	☿	♀	♂	♃	♄	♅	♆	♇
	h m s	° ′	° ′	° ′	° ′	° ′	° ′	° ′	° ′	° ′	° ′	° ′
1	6 41 52.3	10♑24.4	4♈36.8	10♊16.4	24♑33.1	25♒39.9	1♏11.3	5♎27.4	18♈47.9	3♎59.0	27♏47.0	25♍ 6.2
2	6 45 48.9	11 25.6	4 33.6	22 7.8	26 7.3	26 48.0	1 45.3	5 31.0	18 49.1	3 59.4	27 48.7	25R 6.1
3	6 49 45.4	12 26.7	4 30.4	4♋ 1.6	27 40.9	27 55.9	2 19.3	5 34.3	18 50.4	3 59.7	27 50.5	25 5.9
4	6 53 42.0	13 27.8	4 27.2	15 59.1	29 13.5	29 3.6	2 53.2	5 37.5	18 51.9	3 60.0	27 52.2	25 5.6
5	6 57 38.5	14 29.0	4 24.1	28 1.5	0♒44.9	0♓11.2	3 27.1	5 40.5	18 53.4	4 .2	27 53.9	25 5.4
6	7 1 35.1	15 30.1	4 20.9	10♌ 9.7	2 15.0	1 18.5	4 .9	5 43.3	18 55.1	4 .3	27 55.6	25 5.1
7	7 5 31.6	16 31.3	4 17.7	22 25.0	3 43.3	2 25.6	4 34.6	5 46.0	18 56.9	4 .4	27 57.2	25 4.7
8	7 9 28.2	17 32.4	4 14.5	4♍49.2	5 9.4	3 32.5	5 8.2	5 48.4	18 58.7	4 .5	27 58.8	25 4.4
9	7 13 24.8	18 33.5	4 11.4	17 24.7	6 33.1	4 39.1	5 41.7	5 50.7	19 .7	4R .4	28 .4	25 4.0
10	7 17 21.3	19 34.7	4 8.2	0♎14.6	7 53.7	5 45.6	6 15.3	5 52.8	19 2.8	4 .4	28 2.0	25 3.6
11	7 21 17.9	20 35.8	4 5.0	13 21.9	9 10.7	6 51.8	6 48.7	5 54.7	19 5.0	4 .3	28 3.6	25 3.1
12	7 25 14.4	21 37.0	4 1.8	26 50.1	10 23.6	7 57.7	7 22.0	5 56.5	19 7.3	4 .1	28 5.1	25 2.6
13	7 29 11.0	22 38.1	3 58.7	10♏41.7	11 31.5	9 3.4	7 55.2	5 58.0	19 9.7	3 59.9	28 6.6	25 2.1
14	7 33 7.6	23 39.2	3 55.5	24 57.6	12 33.8	10 8.9	8 28.3	5 59.3	19 12.2	3 59.6	28 8.1	25 1.6
15	7 37 4.1	24 40.4	3 52.3	9♐36.4	13 29.6	11 14.1	9 1.4	6 .5	19 14.8	3 59.2	28 9.5	25 1.0
16	7 41 .7	25 41.5	3 49.1	24 33.3	14 18.1	12 18.9	9 34.3	6 1.4	19 17.5	3 58.8	28 10.9	25 .3
17	7 44 57.2	26 42.6	3 45.9	9♑40.6	14 58.3	13 23.6	10 7.2	6 2.2	19 20.4	3 58.3	28 12.3	24 59.7
18	7 48 53.8	27 43.7	3 42.8	24 48.4	15 29.5	14 27.9	10 40.0	6 2.8	19 23.3	3 57.8	28 13.7	24 59.0
19	7 52 50.3	28 44.8	3 39.6	9♒46.0	15 50.8	15 31.9	11 12.7	6 3.2	19 26.3	3 57.2	28 15.0	24 58.3
20	7 56 46.9	29 45.9	3 36.4	24 24.4	16 1.4	16 35.6	11 45.2	6 3.4	19 29.4	3 56.6	28 16.3	24 57.6
21	8 0 43.5	0♒47.0	3 33.2	8♓37.2	16R .9	17 38.9	12 17.7	6 3.4	19 32.6	3 55.9	28 17.6	24 56.8
22	8 4 40.0	1 48.1	3 30.1	22 21.3	15 48.8	18 42.0	12 50.1	6R 3.2	19 35.9	3 55.2	28 18.8	24 56.0
23	8 8 36.6	2 49.1	3 26.9	5♈37.0	15 25.1	19 44.6	13 22.3	6 2.8	19 39.3	3 54.4	28 20.1	24 55.2
24	8 12 33.1	3 50.2	3 23.7	18 26.7	14 50.1	20 46.9	13 54.5	6 2.2	19 42.8	3 53.5	28 21.2	24 54.3
25	8 16 29.7	4 51.2	3 20.5	0♉54.7	14 4.5	21 48.9	14 26.5	6 1.4	19 46.4	3 52.6	28 22.4	24 53.4
26	8 20 26.2	5 52.2	3 17.4	13 5.9	13 9.5	22 50.4	14 58.4	6 .5	19 50.1	3 51.7	28 23.5	24 52.5
27	8 24 22.8	6 53.2	3 14.2	25 5.5	12 6.5	23 51.5	15 30.3	5 59.3	19 53.9	3 50.7	28 24.6	24 51.6
28	8 28 19.4	7 54.1	3 11.0	6♊58.3	10 57.4	24 52.2	16 2.0	5 58.0	19 57.8	3 49.6	28 25.7	24 50.6
29	8 32 15.9	8 55.1	3 7.8	18 49.0	9 44.3	25 52.4	16 33.6	5 56.4	20 1.8	3 48.5	28 26.7	24 49.6
30	8 36 12.5	9 56.0	3 4.6	0♋41.1	8 29.4	26 52.2	17 5.0	5 54.7	20 5.8	3 47.4	28 27.7	24 48.6
31	8 40 9.0	10 56.9	3 1.5	12 37.9	7 14.9	27 51.6	17 36.4	5 52.8	20 10.0	3 46.2	28 28.7	24 47.6

LATITUDE

DAY	EPHEM. SID. TIME	☉	☊	☾	☿	♀	♂	♃	♄	♅	♆	♇
1	6 41 52.3	0 .0	0 .0	4N33.2	2S 5.8	1S37.8	1N23.9	1N18.2	2S32.5	0N44.7	1N40.3	15N33.3
4	6 53 42.0	0 .0	0 .0	4 52.7	1 55.6	1 28.2	1 23.6	1 19.0	2 31.6	0 44.8	1 40.4	15 34.9
7	7 5 31.6	0 .0	0 .0	3 17.4	1 39.1	1 17.5	1 23.4	1 19.8	2 30.8	0 44.9	1 40.6	15 36.5
10	7 17 21.3	0 .0	0 .0	0 15.3	1 15.0	1 5.6	1 23.1	1 20.6	2 29.9	0 45.0	1 40.7	15 38.0
13	7 29 11.0	0 .0	0 .0	3S 5.1	0 42.5	0 52.6	1 22.7	1 21.4	2 29.1	0 45.1	1 40.8	15 39.6
16	7 41 .7	0 .0	0 .0	4 59.2	0 1.1	0 38.5	1 22.3	1 22.3	2 28.3	0 45.2	1 40.9	15 41.1
19	7 52 50.3	0 .0	0 .0	4 .8	0N48.4	0 23.3	1 21.8	1 23.1	2 27.5	0 45.3	1 41.1	15 42.5
22	8 4 40.0	0 .0	0 .0	0 51.6	1 42.5	0 7.0	1 21.3	1 23.9	2 26.7	0 45.5	1 41.2	15 43.9
25	8 16 29.7	0 .0	0 .0	2N28.0	2 34.6	0N10.4	1 20.7	1 24.7	2 26.0	0 45.6	1 41.4	15 45.3
28	8 28 19.4	0 .0	0 .0	4 37.3	3 15.1	0 28.9	1 20.1	1 25.6	2 25.2	0 45.7	1 41.5	15 46.6
31	8 40 9.0	0 .0	0 .0	4 59.9	3 35.8	0 48.4	1 19.3	1 26.3	2 24.5	0 45.8	1 41.7	15 47.9

RIGHT ASCENSION

DAY	EPHEM. SID. TIME	☉	☊	☾	☿	♀	♂	♃	♄	♅	♆	♇
1	6 41 52.3	11♑19.2	4♈14.0	7♊54.9	26♑52.5	28♒29.6	29♎32.4	5♎31.5	18♈18.7	3♎57.1	25♏54.8	1♎51.9
2	6 45 48.9	12 25.4	4 11.1	21 6.3	28 32.6	29 34.6	0♏ 4.9	5 34.9	18 19.7	3 57.4	25 56.6	1 52.0
3	6 49 45.4	13 31.5	4 8.2	4♋33.6	0♒11.3	0♓39.1	0 37.4	5 38.1	18 20.8	3 57.7	25 58.4	1 52.1
4	6 53 42.0	14 37.6	4 5.3	17 59.5	1 48.3	1 43.1	1 9.8	5 41.1	18 22.1	3 58.0	26 .1	1 52.1
5	6 57 38.5	15 43.5	4 2.3	1♌ 7.4	3 23.5	2 46.7	1 42.3	5 43.9	18 23.4	3 58.2	26 1.9	1 52.1
6	7 1 35.1	16 49.3	3 59.4	13 46.3	4 56.5	3 49.8	2 14.6	5 46.6	18 24.8	3 58.4	26 3.6	1R52.0
7	7 5 31.6	17 55.0	3 56.5	25 53.5	6 27.0	4 52.5	2 47.0	5 49.2	18 26.4	3 58.5	26 5.3	1 51.9
8	7 9 28.2	19 .5	3 53.6	7♍33.8	7 54.6	5 54.7	3 19.4	5 51.5	18 28.0	3 58.5	26 7.0	1 51.8
9	7 13 24.8	20 6.0	3 50.7	18 57.6	9 18.7	6 56.5	3 51.7	5 53.7	18 29.7	3 58.5	26 8.6	1 51.7
10	7 17 21.3	21 11.4	3 47.8	0♎19.5	10 39.1	7 57.9	4 24.0	5 55.8	18 31.6	3 58.5	26 10.3	1 51.5
11	7 21 17.9	22 16.6	3 44.8	11 56.7	11 55.1	8 58.7	4 56.3	5 57.7	18 33.5	3R58.4	26 11.9	1 51.3
12	7 25 14.4	23 21.6	3 41.9	24 8.8	13 6.1	9 59.2	5 28.5	5 59.4	18 35.6	3 58.2	26 13.4	1 51.1
13	7 29 11.0	24 26.5	3 39.0	7♏15.6	14 11.5	10 59.2	6 .7	6 .9	18 37.7	3 58.0	26 15.0	1 50.9
14	7 33 7.6	25 31.3	3 36.1	21 34.0	15 10.5	11 58.7	6 32.9	6 2.2	18 39.9	3 57.8	26 16.5	1 50.6
15	7 37 4.1	26 35.9	3 33.2	7♐10.1	16 2.4	12 57.9	7 5.0	6 3.4	18 42.2	3 57.5	26 18.0	1 50.2
16	7 41 .7	27 40.3	3 30.3	23 50.1	16 46.4	13 56.5	7 37.0	6 4.4	18 44.7	3 57.1	26 19.5	1 49.9
17	7 44 57.2	28 44.6	3 27.3	10♑56.4	17 21.8	14 54.8	8 9.1	6 5.2	18 47.2	3 56.7	26 20.9	1 49.5
18	7 48 53.8	29 48.7	3 24.4	27 39.9	17 47.8	15 52.6	8 41.1	6 5.8	18 49.8	3 56.2	26 22.3	1 49.1
19	7 52 50.3	0♒52.6	3 21.5	13♒21.9	18 3.6	16 50.0	9 13.0	6 6.3	18 52.5	3 55.7	26 23.7	1 48.6
20	7 56 46.9	1 56.3	3 18.6	27 47.1	18 8.6	17 46.9	9 44.9	6 6.6	18 55.3	3 55.1	26 25.0	1 48.2
21	8 0 43.5	2 59.8	3 15.7	11♓ .8	18R 2.5	18 43.4	10 16.7	6 6.7	18 58.2	3 54.5	26 26.3	1 47.7
22	8 4 40.0	4 3.2	3 12.8	23 19.2	17 45.0	19 39.4	10 48.5	6R 6.6	19 1.1	3 53.9	26 27.6	1 47.1
23	8 8 36.6	5 6.3	3 9.8	5♈ 1.8	17 16.2	20 35.0	11 20.2	6 6.4	19 4.2	3 53.1	26 28.9	1 46.6
24	8 12 33.1	6 9.3	3 6.9	16 27.6	16 36.4	21 30.1	11 51.8	6 5.9	19 7.4	3 52.4	26 30.1	1 46.0
25	8 16 29.7	7 12.0	3 4.0	27 53.7	15 46.5	22 24.8	12 23.4	6 5.3	19 10.6	3 51.6	26 31.3	1 45.4
26	8 20 26.2	8 14.6	3 1.1	9♉34.5	14 47.7	23 19.0	12 55.0	6 4.6	19 14.0	3 50.7	26 32.5	1 44.7
27	8 24 22.8	9 16.9	2 58.2	21 40.5	13 41.5	24 12.7	13 26.4	6 3.6	19 17.4	3 49.8	26 33.6	1 44.1
28	8 28 19.4	10 19.1	2 55.3	4♊16.9	12 29.7	25 6.0	13 57.8	6 2.5	19 20.9	3 48.8	26 34.7	1 43.4
29	8 32 15.9	11 21.0	2 52.3	17 22.1	11 14.5	25 58.8	14 29.2	6 1.2	19 24.5	3 47.8	26 35.8	1 42.7
30	8 36 12.5	12 22.7	2 49.4	0♋46.6	9 58.0	26 51.1	15 .4	5 59.7	19 28.2	3 46.8	26 36.8	1 41.9
31	8 40 9.0	13 24.3	2 46.5	14 15.6	8 42.4	27 42.9	15 31.7	5 58.1	19 32.0	3 45.8	26 37.9	1 41.2

DECLINATION

DAY	EPHEM. SID. TIME	☉	☊	☾	☿	♀	♂	♃	♄	♅	♆	♇
1	6 41 52.3	23S 2.2	0N 1.9	26N29.9	23S16.8	14S30.2	10S34.8	0S58.3	5N .9	0S54.0	18S 2.5	16N11.1
4	6 53 42.0	22 45.8	0 1.9	27 19.8	22 12.2	13 10.9	11 10.0	1 1.6	5 3.2	0 54.3	18 3.5	16 12.8
7	7 5 31.6	22 25.4	0 1.8	17 9.2	20 55.8	11 49.1	11 44.4	1 4.2	5 5.8	0 54.4	18 4.5	16 14.6
10	7 17 21.3	22 1.0	0 1.7	0 8.3	19 30.4	10 25.1	12 18.1	1 6.2	5 8.9	0 54.3	18 5.5	16 16.5
13	7 29 11.0	21 32.7	0 1.7	17S57.9	18 .7	8 59.3	12 50.9	1 7.4	5 12.2	0 54.0	18 6.4	16 18.4
16	7 41 .7	21 .7	0 1.6	28 18.9	16 33.7	7 32.1	13 22.9	1 8.0	5 15.9	0 53.4	18 7.2	16 20.5
19	7 52 50.3	20 25.0	0 1.5	21 40.3	15 19.3	6 3.8	13 54.0	1 8.0	5 19.9	0 52.7	18 8.0	16 22.6
22	8 4 40.0	19 45.9	0 1.5	3 49.4	14 28.1	4 34.7	14 24.2	1 7.2	5 24.3	0 51.8	18 8.7	16 24.8
25	8 16 29.7	19 3.4	0 1.4	14N 6.3	14 8.5	3 5.3	14 53.4	1 5.8	5 29.0	0 50.7	18 9.3	16 27.1
28	8 28 19.4	18 17.8	0 1.3	26 2.0	14 21.4	1 35.8	15 21.7	1 3.6	5 33.9	0 49.4	18 9.9	16 29.4
31	8 40 9.0	17 29.3	0 1.3	27 49.3	14 59.0	0 6.7	15 49.1	1 .9	5 39.2	0 47.9	18 10.4	16 31.8

FEBRUARY 1969

LONGITUDE

DAY	EPHEM. SID. TIME (h m s)	☉ (° ′)	☊ (° ′)	☾ (° ′)	☿ (° ′)	♀ (° ′)	♂ (° ′)	♃ (° ′)	♄ (° ′)	♅ (° ′)	♆ (° ′)	♇ (° ′)
1	8 44 5.6	11♒57.8	2♈58.3	24♋41.3	6♒ 2.8	28♓50.4	18♏ 7.7	5♎50.7	20♈14.3	3♎44.9	28♏29.7	24♍46.5
2	8 48 2.1	12 58.7	2 55.1	6♌52.9	4R54.9	29 48.7	18 38.8	5R48.5	20 18.6	3R43.6	28 30.6	24R45.4
3	8 51 58.7	13 59.5	2 51.9	19 13.7	3 52.8	0♈46.5	19 9.8	5 46.0	20 23.0	3 42.3	28 31.5	24 44.3
4	8 55 55.3	15 .3	2 48.8	1♍44.3	2 57.5	1 43.7	19 40.6	5 43.3	20 27.5	3 40.9	28 32.3	24 43.2
5	8 59 51.8	16 1.1	2 45.6	14 25.2	2 9.9	2 40.4	20 11.4	5 40.5	20 32.1	3 39.5	28 33.1	24 42.0
6	9 3 48.4	17 1.9	2 42.4	27 17.2	1 30.5	3 36.5	20 42.0	5 37.5	20 36.7	3 38.0	28 33.9	24 40.8
7	9 7 44.9	18 2.7	2 39.2	10♎21.4	0 59.4	4 32.0	21 12.4	5 34.3	20 41.5	3 36.4	28 34.6	24 39.6
8	9 11 41.5	19 3.5	2 36.1	23 39.0	0 36.7	5 26.9	21 42.7	5 30.9	20 46.3	3 34.9	28 35.4	24 38.4
9	9 15 38.0	20 4.2	2 32.9	7♏11.4	0 22.1	6 21.2	22 12.9	5 27.4	20 51.2	3 33.2	28 36.0	24 37.1
10	9 19 34.6	21 4.9	2 29.7	20 59.8	0 15.4	7 14.8	22 42.9	5 23.6	20 56.2	3 31.6	28 36.7	24 35.9
11	9 23 31.2	22 5.6	2 26.5	5♐ 4.7	0D16.1	8 7.7	23 12.8	5 19.7	21 1.3	3 29.9	28 37.3	24 34.6
12	9 27 27.7	23 6.3	2 23.3	19 25.1	0 23.8	8 59.9	23 42.5	5 15.7	21 6.4	3 28.1	28 37.9	24 33.3
13	9 31 24.3	24 7.0	2 20.2	3♑58.1	0 38.1	9 51.3	24 12.1	5 11.4	21 11.6	3 26.3	28 38.4	24 31.9
14	9 35 20.8	25 7.7	2 17.0	18 39.0	0 58.5	10 42.0	24 41.5	5 7.0	21 16.9	3 24.5	28 38.9	24 30.6
15	9 39 17.4	26 8.3	2 13.8	3♒21.2	1 24.5	11 31.9	25 10.7	5 2.4	21 22.3	3 22.6	28 39.4	24 29.2
16	9 43 13.9	27 8.9	2 10.6	17 57.4	1 55.7	12 21.0	25 39.8	4 57.7	21 27.7	3 20.7	28 39.9	24 27.8
17	9 47 10.5	28 9.5	2 7.5	2♓20.5	2 31.7	13 9.2	26 8.7	4 52.8	21 33.2	3 18.8	28 40.3	24 26.4
18	9 51 7.0	29 10.0	2 4.3	16 24.7	3 12.2	13 56.5	26 37.4	4 47.7	21 38.8	3 16.8	28 40.7	24 25.0
19	9 55 3.6	0♓10.6	2 1.1	0♈ 6.1	3 56.6	14 42.9	27 5.9	4 42.5	21 44.4	3 14.8	28 41.0	24 23.6
20	9 59 .2	1 11.1	1 57.9	13 23.3	4 44.9	15 28.3	27 34.2	4 37.2	21 50.1	3 12.7	28 41.3	24 22.1
21	10 2 56.7	2 11.6	1 54.8	26 17.2	5 36.6	16 12.8	28 2.4	4 31.7	21 56.0	3 10.7	28 41.6	24 20.7
22	10 6 53.3	3 12.0	1 51.6	8♉50.2	6 31.4	16 56.1	28 30.3	4 26.1	22 1.8	3 8.5	28 41.9	24 19.2
23	10 10 49.8	4 12.5	1 48.4	21 5.9	7 29.2	17 38.4	28 58.1	4 20.3	22 7.7	3 6.4	28 42.1	24 17.7
24	10 14 46.4	5 12.8	1 45.2	3♊ 8.9	8 29.8	18 19.5	29 25.6	4 14.4	22 13.7	3 4.2	28 42.3	24 16.2
25	10 18 42.9	6 13.2	1 42.0	15 4.1	9 32.9	18 59.5	29 53.0	4 8.4	22 19.7	3 2.0	28 42.4	24 14.7
26	10 22 39.5	7 13.5	1 38.9	26 56.1	10 38.3	19 38.2	0♐20.1	4 2.2	22 25.8	2 59.8	28 42.5	24 13.2
27	10 26 36.0	8 13.8	1 35.7	8♋49.6	11 46.0	20 15.6	0 47.0	3 55.9	22 32.0	2 57.5	28 42.6	24 11.6
28	10 30 32.6	9 14.0	1 32.5	20 48.7	12 55.8	20 51.7	1 13.7	3 49.5	22 38.2	2 55.2	28 42.6	24 10.1

LATITUDE

DAY	EPHEM. SID. TIME	☉	☊	☾	☿	♀	♂	♃	♄	♅	♆	♇
1	8 44 5.6	0 .0	0 .0	4N41.0	3N37.8	0N55.1	1N19.1	1N26.6	2S24.2	0N45.8	1N41.7	15N48.3
4	8 55 55.3	0 .0	0 .0	2 30.7	3 30.1	1 15.9	1 18.2	1 27.4	2 23.5	0 45.9	1 41.9	15 49.5
7	9 7 44.9	0 .0	0 .0	0S51.0	3 6.9	1 37.7	1 17.3	1 28.1	2 22.8	0 46.0	1 42.0	15 50.6
10	9 19 34.6	0 .0	0 .0	3 58.2	2 34.8	2 .3	1 16.3	1 28.9	2 22.2	0 46.1	1 42.2	15 51.6
13	9 31 24.3	0 .0	0 .0	5 9.9	1 58.8	2 23.9	1 15.2	1 29.6	2 21.5	0 46.1	1 42.4	15 52.6
16	9 43 13.9	0 .0	0 .0	3 31.0	1 22.4	2 48.3	1 13.9	1 30.3	2 20.9	0 46.2	1 42.5	15 53.6
19	9 55 3.6	0 .0	0 .0	0 2.0	0 47.2	3 13.4	1 12.6	1 30.9	2 20.3	0 46.3	1 42.7	15 54.4
22	10 6 53.3	0 .0	0 .0	3N14.9	0 14.3	3 39.2	1 11.2	1 31.5	2 19.7	0 46.4	1 42.9	15 55.2
25	10 18 42.9	0 .0	0 .0	5 2.7	0S15.8	4 5.5	1 9.6	1 32.1	2 19.2	0 46.4	1 43.0	15 55.9
28	10 30 32.6	0 .0	0 .0	4 54.5	0 42.9	4 32.2	1 7.9	1 32.6	2 18.7	0 46.5	1 43.2	15 56.5

RIGHT ASCENSION

DAY	EPHEM. SID. TIME	☉	☊	☾	☿	♀	♂	♃	♄	♅	♆	♇
1	8 44 5.6	14♒25.6	2♈43.6	27♋32.4	7♒29.7	28♓34.2	16♏ 2.8	5♎56.3	19♈35.9	3♎44.6	26♏38.9	1♎40.4
2	8 48 2.1	15 26.7	2 40.7	10♌24.6	6R21.6	29 25.0	16 33.8	5R54.3	19 39.8	3R43.4	26 39.8	1R39.5
3	8 51 58.7	16 27.6	2 37.8	22 46.5	5 19.6	0♈15.3	17 4.8	5 52.1	19 43.8	3 42.2	26 40.7	1 38.7
4	8 55 55.3	17 28.3	2 34.8	4♍40.0	4 24.8	1 5.0	17 35.7	5 49.8	19 47.9	3 40.9	26 41.6	1 37.8
5	8 59 51.8	18 28.8	2 31.9	16 13.2	3 38.1	1 54.2	18 6.4	5 47.3	19 52.1	3 39.6	26 42.5	1 36.9
6	9 3 48.4	19 29.1	2 29.0	27 38.4	2 59.8	2 42.8	18 37.1	5 44.6	19 56.3	3 38.3	26 43.3	1 36.0
7	9 7 44.9	20 29.1	2 26.1	9♎11.0	2 30.2	3 30.9	19 7.8	5 41.8	20 .7	3 36.9	26 44.0	1 35.1
8	9 11 41.5	21 29.0	2 23.2	21 8.1	2 9.2	4 18.3	19 38.3	5 38.8	20 5.1	3 35.4	26 44.8	1 34.1
9	9 15 38.0	22 28.7	2 20.3	3♏47.9	1 56.7	5 5.2	20 8.7	5 35.6	20 9.6	3 34.0	26 45.5	1 33.1
10	9 19 34.6	23 28.3	2 17.4	17 26.3	1 52.3	5 51.5	20 39.0	5 32.3	20 14.1	3 32.4	26 46.2	1 32.1
11	9 23 31.2	24 27.6	2 14.4	2♐12.7	1D55.7	6 37.1	21 9.2	5 28.8	20 18.8	3 30.9	26 46.8	1 31.0
12	9 27 27.7	25 26.7	2 11.5	18 2.1	2 6.3	7 22.1	21 39.2	5 25.2	20 23.5	3 29.3	26 47.4	1 30.0
13	9 31 24.3	26 25.7	2 8.6	4♑30.0	2 23.6	8 6.5	22 9.2	5 21.4	20 28.3	3 27.7	26 48.0	1 28.9
14	9 35 20.8	27 24.4	2 5.7	20 57.3	2 47.3	8 50.1	22 39.0	5 17.4	20 33.1	3 26.0	26 48.5	1 27.8
15	9 39 17.4	28 23.0	2 2.8	6♒45.7	3 16.8	9 33.1	23 8.7	5 13.3	20 38.0	3 24.3	26 49.1	1 26.7
16	9 43 13.9	29 21.4	1 59.9	21 32.2	3 51.7	10 15.3	23 38.2	5 9.0	20 43.0	3 22.5	26 49.5	1 25.5
17	9 47 10.5	0♓19.6	1 56.9	5♓13.5	4 31.5	10 56.7	24 7.7	5 4.6	20 48.1	3 20.8	26 50.0	1 24.4
18	9 51 7.0	1 17.7	1 54.0	17 59.5	5 15.8	11 37.3	24 36.9	5 .1	20 53.2	3 19.0	26 50.4	1 23.2
19	9 55 3.6	2 15.5	1 51.1	0♈ 6.3	6 4.2	12 17.1	25 6.0	4 55.4	20 58.4	3 17.1	26 50.7	1 22.0
20	9 59 .2	3 13.2	1 48.2	11 51.7	6 56.4	12 56.1	25 35.0	4 50.5	21 3.7	3 15.2	26 51.1	1 20.8
21	10 2 56.7	4 10.8	1 45.3	23 32.0	7 52.2	13 34.1	26 3.9	4 45.6	21 9.0	3 13.4	26 51.4	1 19.6
22	10 6 53.3	5 8.2	1 42.4	5♉21.6	8 51.0	14 11.2	26 32.5	4 40.5	21 14.4	3 11.4	26 51.7	1 18.4
23	10 10 49.8	6 5.4	1 39.5	17 31.3	9 52.7	14 47.4	27 1.0	4 35.3	21 19.9	3 9.5	26 51.9	1 17.1
24	10 14 46.4	7 2.4	1 36.5	0♊ 7.3	10 57.0	15 22.5	27 29.2	4 29.9	21 25.4	3 7.5	26 52.1	1 15.8
25	10 18 42.9	7 59.3	1 33.6	13 9.6	12 3.7	15 56.5	27 57.4	4 24.5	21 31.0	3 5.4	26 52.2	1 14.5
26	10 22 39.5	8 56.0	1 30.7	26 31.3	13 12.7	16 29.4	28 25.3	4 18.9	21 36.6	3 3.4	26 52.3	1 13.2
27	10 26 36.0	9 52.6	1 27.8	9♋59.9	14 23.7	17 1.2	28 53.0	4 13.2	21 42.3	3 1.3	26 52.4	1 11.9
28	10 30 32.6	10 49.1	1 24.9	23 20.4	15 36.5	17 31.7	29 20.6	4 7.4	21 48.0	2 59.2	26 52.5	1 10.6

DECLINATION

DAY	EPHEM. SID. TIME	☉	☊	☾	☿	♀	♂	♃	♄	♅	♆	♇
1	8 44 5.6	17S12.5	0N 1.2	25N48.0	15S14.8	0N22.8	15S58.1	0S59.8	5N41.0	0S47.4	18S10.6	16N32.6
4	8 55 55.3	16 20.3	0 1.2	13 12.2	16 5.6	1 50.9	16 24.2	0 56.2	5 46.6	0 45.7	18 11.0	16 35.0
7	9 7, 44.9	15 25.6	0 1.1	4S53.0	16 54.1	3 17.8	16 49.4	0 51.9	5 52.5	0 43.9	18 11.3	16 37.4
10	9 19 34.6	14 28.5	0 1.0	21 50.3	17 34.8	4 43.1	17 13.5	0 47.0	5 58.6	0 41.9	18 11.6	16 39.9
13	9 31 24.3	13 29.2	0 1.0	28 33.0	18 5.1	6 6.6	17 36.8	0 41.5	6 5.0	0 39.7	18 11.8	16 42.3
16	9 43 13.9	12 27.9	0 .9	18 47.8	18 23.8	7 27.8	17 59.0	0 35.5	6 11.5	0 37.4	18 12.0	16 44.8
19	9 55 3.6	11 24.8	0 .8	0N .6	18 30.5	8 46.3	18 20.2	0 28.9	6 18.3	0 35.0	18 12.1	16 47.3
22	10 6 53.3	10 20.1	0 .8	17 31.4	18 25.0	10 1.7	18 40.5	0 21.8	6 25.3	0 32.4	18 12.1	16 49.7
25	10 18 42.9	9 13.9	0 .7	27 37.3	18 7.2	11 13.4	18 59.9	0 14.2	6 32.4	0 29.8	18 12.1	16 52.1
28	10 30 32.6	8 6.6	0 .6	26 41.0	17 37.4	12 20.8	19 18.3	0 6.3	6 39.7	0 27.0	18 11.9	16 54.5

MARCH 1969

LONGITUDE

DAY	EPHEM. SID. TIME h m s	☉ ° ′	☊ ° ′	☽ ° ′	☿ ° ′	♀ ° ′	♂ ° ′	♃ ° ′	♄ ° ′	♅ ° ′	♆ ° ′	♇ ° ′
1	10 34 29.1	10♓14.2	1♈29.3	2♌56.7	14♒ 7.5	21♈26.5	1♐40.2	3♎43.0	22♈44.5	2♎52.9	28♏42.6	24♍ 8.5
2	10 38 25.7	11 14.4	1 26.2	15 16.3	15 21.1	21 59.7	2 6.4	3R36.4	22 50.8	2R50.5	28 42.6	24R 7.0
3	10 42 22.3	12 14.6	1 23.0	27 49.2	16 36.5	22 31.5	2 32.4	3 29.6	22 57.2	2 48.1	28R42.5	24 5.4
4	10 46 18.8	13 14.7	1 19.8	10♍36.4	17 53.5	23 1.7	2 58.2	3 22.8	23 3.6	2 45.8	28 42.4	24 3.8
5	10 50 15.4	14 14.8	1 16.6	23 38.0	19 12.2	23 30.4	3 23.8	3 15.9	23 10.1	2 43.3	28 42.3	24 2.2
6	10 54 11.9	15 14.8	1 13.4	6♎53.5	20 32.4	23 57.3	3 49.1	3 8.9	23 16.6	2 40.9	28 42.1	24 .6
7	10 58 8.5	16 14.9	1 10.3	20 21.9	21 54.0	24 22.6	4 14.1	3 1.8	23 23.2	2 38.5	28 41.9	23 59.0
8	11 2 5.0	17 14.9	1 7.1	4♏ 2.1	23 17.2	24 46.0	4 38.9	2 54.6	23 29.8	2 36.0	28 41.7	23 57.4
9	11 6 1.6	18 14.9	1 3.9	17 52.6	24 41.7	25 7.6	5 3.4	2 47.3	23 36.5	2 33.5	28 41.4	23 55.8
10	11 9 58.1	19 14.8	1 .7	1♐52.1	26 7.6	25 27.3	5 27.7	2 40.0	23 43.2	2 31.0	28 41.1	23 54.2
11	11 13 54.7	20 14.7	0 57.6	15 59.0	27 34.8	25 45.0	5 51.6	2 32.6	23 50.0	2 28.5	28 40.8	23 52.6
12	11 17 51.2	21 14.6	0 54.4	0♑11.4	29 3.3	26 .8	6 15.3	2 25.1	23 56.8	2 25.9	28 40.4	23 50.9
13	11 21 47.8	22 14.5	0 51.2	14 26.9	0♓33.2	26 14.4	6 38.7	2 17.6	24 3.7	2 23.4	28 40.1	23 49.3
14	11 25 44.3	23 14.4	0 48.0	28 43.0	2 4.3	26 25.9	7 1.8	2 10.1	24 10.6	2 20.9	28 39.7	23 47.7
15	11 29 40.9	24 14.2	0 44.8	12♒56.0	3 36.7	26 35.2	7 24.6	2 2.4	24 17.5	2 18.3	28 39.2	23 46.1
16	11 33 37.5	25 14.0	0 41.7	27 2.4	5 10.3	26 42.3	7 47.1	1 54.8	24 24.5	2 15.7	28 38.7	23 44.5
17	11 37 34.0	26 13.7	0 38.5	10♓58.3	6 45.2	26 47.0	8 9.2	1 47.1	24 31.5	2 13.1	28 38.2	23 42.9
18	11 41 30.6	27 13.4	0 35.3	24 40.4	8 21.3	26 49.4	8 31.0	1 39.4	24 38.6	2 10.5	28 37.7	23 41.2
19	11 45 27.1	28 13.1	0 32.1	8♈ 6.1	9 58.6	26 49.4	8 52.4	1 31.6	24 45.7	2 7.9	28 37.1	23 39.6
20	11 49 23.7	29 12.8	0 29.0	21 13.9	11 37.2	26R46.9	9 13.5	1 23.9	24 52.8	2 5.3	28 36.5	23 38.0
21	11 53 20.2	0♈12.4	0 25.8	4♉ 3.3	13 17.1	26 42.0	9 34.2	1 16.1	24 60.0	2 2.7	28 35.8	23 36.4
22	11 57 16.8	1 11.9	0 22.6	16 35.5	14 58.2	26 34.5	9 54.6	1 8.3	25 7.2	2 .1	28 35.1	23 34.8
23	12 1 13.3	2 11.5	0 19.4	28 52.6	16 40.6	26 24.6	10 14.6	1 .5	25 14.4	1 57.5	28 34.4	23 33.2
24	12 5 9.9	3 11.0	0 16.2	10♊57.6	18 24.3	26 12.2	10 34.2	0 52.8	25 21.7	1 54.9	28 33.7	23 31.6
25	12 9 6.4	4 10.5	0 13.1	22 54.4	20 9.3	25 57.3	10 53.4	0 45.0	25 28.9	1 52.3	28 32.9	23 30.0
26	12 13 3.0	5 9.9	0 9.9	4♋47.5	21 55.5	25 40.0	11 12.3	0 37.3	25 36.3	1 49.7	28 32.2	23 28.4
27	12 16 59.5	6 9.3	0 6.7	16 41.4	23 43.1	25 20.2	11 30.7	0 29.5	25 43.6	1 47.1	28 31.3	23 26.8
28	12 20 56.1	7 8.6	0 3.5	28 40.8	25 32.1	24 58.1	11 48.7	0 21.9	25 51.0	1 44.5	28 30.5	23 25.2
29	12 24 52.7	8 7.9	0 .4	10♌50.2	27 22.3	24 33.8	12 6.3	0 14.2	25 58.3	1 41.9	28 29.6	23 23.7
30	12 28 49.2	9 7.2	29♓57.2	23 13.4	29 14.0	24 7.3	12 23.5	0 6.6	26 5.7	1 39.3	28 28.7	23 22.1
31	12 32 45.8	10 6.5	29 54.0	5♍53.7	1♈ 6.9	23 38.9	12 40.2	29♍59.0	26 13.2	1 36.7	28 27.8	23 20.6

LATITUDE

DAY	EPHEM. SID. TIME h m s	☉	☊	☽	☿	♀	♂	♃	♄	♅	♆	♇
1	10 34 29.1	0 .0	0 .0	4N25.0	0S51.2	4N41.2	1N 7.3	1N32.7	2S18.5	0N46.5	1N43.3	15N56.7
4	10 46 18.8	0 .0	0 .0	1 46.2	1 14.1	5 8.1	1 5.3	1 33.2	2 18.0	0 46.5	1 43.4	15 57.2
7	10 58 8.5	0 .0	0 .0	1S49.0	1 33.6	5 34.9	1 3.2	1 33.6	2 17.6	0 46.6	1 43.6	15 57.6
10	11 9 58.1	0 .0	0 .0	4 38.4	1 49.6	6 1.2	1 1.0	1 33.9	2 17.2	0 46.6	1 43.8	15 57.9
13	11 21 47.8	0 .0	0 .0	5 6.9	2 2.1	6 26.5	0 58.5	1 34.2	2 16.8	0 46.6	1 43.9	15 58.2
16	11 33 37.5	0 .0	0 .0	2 53.8	2 10.9	6 50.2	0 55.9	1 34.4	2 16.4	0 46.6	1 44.1	15 58.4
19	11 45 27.1	0 .0	0 .0	0N43.4	2 15.9	7 11.7	0 53.0	1 34.6	2 16.1	0 46.6	1 44.2	15 58.4
22	11 57 16.8	0 .0	0 .0	3 49.5	2 16.9	7 30.0	0 49.9	1 34.7	2 15.7	0 46.6	1 44.4	15 58.4
25	12 9 6.4	0 .0	0 .0	5 14.2	2 13.7	7 44.1	0 46.6	1 34.8	2 15.5	0 46.6	1 44.5	15 58.4
28	12 20 56.1	0 .0	0 .0	4 38.7	2 6.2	7 52.9	0 43.0	1 34.7	2 15.2	0 46.6	1 44.6	15 58.2
31	12 32 45.8	0 .0	0 .0	2 11.0	1 54.2	7 55.3	0 39.1	1 34.7	2 15.0	0 46.6	1 44.8	15 58.0

RIGHT ASCENSION

DAY	EPHEM. SID. TIME h m s	☉	☊	☽	☿	♀	♂	♃	♄	♅	♆	♇
1	10 34 29.1	11♓45.4	1♈22.0	6♌20.6	16♒51.1	18♈ 1.0	29♏47.9	4♎ 1.5	21♈53.8	2♎57.1	26♏52.5	1♎ 9.2
2	10 38 25.7	12 41.6	1 19.0	18 53.9	18 7.2	18 29.0	0♐15.1	3R55.4	21 59.7	2R54.9	26 52.5	1R 7.9
3	10 42 22.3	13 37.6	1 16.1	1♍ .5	19 24.8	18 55.6	0 42.0	3 49.3	22 5.6	2 52.8	26R52.4	1 6.5
4	10 46 18.8	14 33.6	1 13.2	12 46.8	20 43.7	19 20.8	1 8.7	3 43.1	22 11.5	2 50.6	26 52.3	1 5.1
5	10 50 15.4	15 29.4	1 10.3	24 23.7	22 3.9	19 44.6	1 35.2	3 36.8	22 17.5	2 48.4	26 52.2	1 3.7
6	10 54 11.9	16 25.1	1 7.4	6♎ 5.1	23 25.2	20 6.8	2 1.5	3 30.4	22 23.6	2 46.1	26 52.1	1 2.3
7	10 58 8.5	17 20.7	1 4.5	18 6.8	24 47.6	20 27.4	2 27.5	3 24.0	22 29.7	2 43.9	26 51.9	1 .9
8	11 2 5.0	18 16.2	1 1.6	0♏45.2	26 11.0	20 46.3	2 53.3	3 17.4	22 35.8	2 41.6	26 51.6	0 59.5
9	11 6 1.6	19 11.6	0 58.6	14 14.9	27 35.4	21 3.6	3 18.9	3 10.8	22 42.0	2 39.3	26 51.4	0 58.1
10	11 9 58.1	20 7.0	0 55.7	28 44.5	29 .7	21 19.1	3 44.1	3 4.1	22 48.3	2 37.1	26 51.1	0 56.7
11	11 13 54.7	21 2.2	0 52.8	14♐10.5	0♓26.8	21 32.8	4 9.1	2 57.4	22 54.6	2 34.7	26 50.8	0 55.2
12	11 17 51.2	21 57.4	0 49.9	0♑12.9	1 53.7	21 44.6	4 33.9	2 50.6	23 .9	2 32.4	26 50.4	0 53.8
13	11 21 47.8	22 52.5	0 47.0	16 18.5	3 21.4	21 54.5	4 58.3	2 43.7	23 7.3	2 30.1	26 50.0	0 52.3
14	11 25 44.3	23 47.6	0 44.1	1♒53.2	4 49.9	22 2.4	5 22.5	2 36.8	23 13.8	2 27.8	26 49.6	0 50.9
15	11 29 40.9	24 42.6	0 41.1	16 34.5	6 19.1	22 8.3	5 46.3	2 29.9	23 20.2	2 25.4	26 49.2	0 49.4
16	11 33 37.5	25 37.5	0 38.2	0♓16.7	7 49.0	22 12.1	6 9.8	2 22.9	23 26.7	2 23.1	26 48.7	0 48.0
17	11 37 34.0	26 32.3	0 35.3	13 6.8	9 19.6	22 13.7	6 33.0	2 15.8	23 33.3	2 20.7	26 48.2	0 46.5
18	11 41 30.6	27 27.2	0 32.4	25 18.9	10 50.9	22R13.2	6 55.9	2 8.8	23 39.8	2 18.3	26 47.6	0 45.0
19	11 45 27.1	28 21.9	0 29.5	7♈ 9.3	12 22.8	22 10.5	7 18.4	2 1.7	23 46.5	2 15.9	26 47.0	0 43.5
20	11 49 23.7	29 16.7	0 26.6	18 53.8	13 55.5	22 5.6	7 40.5	1 54.6	23 53.1	2 13.5	26 46.4	0 42.1
21	11 53 20.2	0♈11.3	0 23.7	0♉46.2	15 28.9	21 58.5	8 2.3	1 47.5	23 59.8	2 11.1	26 45.8	0 40.6
22	11 57 16.8	1 6.0	0 20.7	12 57.5	17 3.1	21 49.1	8 23.7	1 40.4	24 6.5	2 8.7	26 45.1	0 39.1
23	12 1 13.3	2 .6	0 17.8	25 34.0	18 37.9	21 37.6	8 44.8	1 33.2	24 13.3	2 6.4	26 44.4	0 37.6
24	12 5 9.9	2 55.3	0 14.9	8♊36.1	20 13.6	21 23.8	9 5.4	1 26.1	24 20.1	2 4.0	26 43.6	0 36.2
25	12 9 6.4	3 49.8	0 12.0	21 57.5	21 50.0	21 7.8	9 25.7	1 19.0	24 26.9	2 1.6	26 42.9	0 34.7
26	12 13 3.0	4 44.4	0 9.1	5♋26.2	23 27.2	20 49.7	9 45.5	1 11.9	24 33.7	1 59.2	26 42.1	0 33.2
27	12 16 59.5	5 39.0	0 6.2	18 48.1	25 5.3	20 29.6	10 5.0	1 4.8	24 40.6	1 56.8	26 41.2	0 31.7
28	12 20 56.1	6 33.6	0 3.2	1♌51.0	26 44.3	20 7.5	10 24.0	0 57.8	24 47.5	1 54.4	26 40.4	0 30.3
29	12 24 52.7	7 28.1	0 .3	14 28.0	28 24.2	19 43.6	10 42.5	0 50.7	24 54.4	1 52.0	26 39.5	0 28.8
30	12 28 49.2	8 22.7	29♓57.4	26 39.1	0♈ 5.0	19 17.9	11 .6	0 43.7	25 1.3	1 49.6	26 38.6	0 27.3
31	12 32 45.8	9 17.3	29 54.5	8♍30.1	1 46.8	18 50.6	11 18.3	0 36.8	25 8.3	1 47.3	26 37.6	0 25.9

DECLINATION

DAY	EPHEM. SID. TIME h m s	☉	☊	☽	☿	♀	♂	♃	♄	♅	♆	♇
1	10 34 29.1	7S43.9	0N .6	23N48.1	17S24.8	12N42.3	19S24.2	0S 3.6	6N42.2	0S26.1	18S11.9	16N55.3
4	10 46 18.8	6 35.2	0 .6	9 13.8	16 38.9	13 43.1	19 41.4	0N 4.9	6 49.7	0 23.2	18 11.7	16 57.7
7	10 58 8.5	5 25.7	0 .5	9S38.5	15 41.2	14 38.1	19 57.7	0 13.6	6 57.3	0 20.3	18 11.4	16 60.0
10	11 9 58.1	4 15.5	0 .4	25 5.1	14 31.8	15 26.6	20 13.2	0 22.6	7 5.1	0 17.3	18 11.1	17 2.2
13	11 21 47.8	3 4.8	0 .4	27 44.7	13 11.0	16 7.5	20 27.8	0 31.7	7 12.9	0 14.3	18 10.7	17 4.4
16	11 33 37.5	1 53.7	0 .3	15 13.3	11 38.8	16 39.8	20 41.7	0 41.0	7 20.9	0 11.2	18 10.3	17 6.4
19	11 45 27.1	0 42.5	0 .2	3N52.8	9 55.6	17 2.4	20 54.8	0 50.4	7 28.9	0 8.1	18 9.8	17 8.4
22	11 57 16.8	0N28.6	0 .2	20 27.8	8 1.6	17 13.9	21 7.2	0 59.7	7 37.0	0 5.0	18 9.2	17 10.4
25	12 9 6.4	1 39.6	0 .1	28 29.1	5 57.0	17 13.2	21 18.9	1 9.0	7 45.2	0 1.9	18 8.6	17 12.2
28	12 20 56.1	2 50.2	0 .0	24 58.5	3 42.3	16 59.3	21 30.0	1 18.2	7 53.4	0N 1.2	18 7.9	17 13.9
31	12 32 45.8	4 .2	0 .0	11 22.9	1 18.1	16 31.8	21 40.6	1 27.2	8 1.6	0 4.2	18 7.2	17 15.6

APRIL 1969

LONGITUDE

DAY	EPHEM. SID. TIME (h m s)	☉ (° ′)	☊ (° ′)	☾ (° ′)	☿ (° ′)	♀ (° ′)	♂ (° ′)	♃ (° ′)	♄ (° ′)	♅ (° ′)	♆ (° ′)	♇ (° ′)
1	12 36 42.3	11♈ 5.7	29♓50.8	18♍53.1	3♈ 1.3	23♈ 8.5	12♐56.5	29♍51.5	26♈20.6	1♎34.2	28♏26.8	23♍19.0
2	12 40 38.9	12 4.8	29 47.6	2♎12.5	4 56.9	22 R 36.4	13 12.3	29 R 44.0	26 28.1	1 R 31.6	28 R 25.9	23 R 17.5
3	12 44 35.4	13 3.9	29 44.5	15 51.0	6 53.9	22 2.9	13 27.6	29 36.6	26 35.6	1 29.1	28 24.8	23 16.0
4	12 48 32.0	14 3.1	29 41.3	29 46.6	8 52.2	21 28.0	13 42.6	29 29.3	26 43.1	1 26.6	28 23.9	23 14.5
5	12 52 28.5	15 2.2	29 38.1	13♏55.6	10 51.8	20 52.1	13 57.0	29 22.0	26 50.7	1 24.1	28 22.8	23 13.1
6	12 56 25.1	16 1.2	29 34.9	28 13.6	12 52.6	20 15.2	14 10.9	29 14.8	26 58.2	1 21.6	28 21.7	23 11.6
7	13 0 21.6	17 .2	29 31.8	12♐35.8	14 54.5	19 37.8	14 24.2	29 7.7	27 5.8	1 19.1	28 20.6	23 10.1
8	13 4 18.2	17 59.2	29 28.6	26 57.8	16 57.5	19 .0	14 37.1	29 .6	27 13.3	1 16.6	28 19.5	23 8.7
9	13 8 14.7	18 58.1	29 25.4	11♑15.6	19 1.4	18 22.1	14 49.4	28 53.7	27 20.9	1 14.2	28 18.3	23 7.3
10	13 12 11.3	19 57.0	29 22.2	25 26.3	21 6.2	17 44.4	15 1.1	28 46.8	27 28.5	1 11.7	28 17.2	23 5.8
11	13 16 7.9	20 55.9	29 19.0	9♒27.8	23 11.6	17 7.1	15 12.3	28 40.0	27 36.1	1 9.3	28 16.0	23 4.4
12	13 20 4.4	21 54.8	29 15.9	23 19.0	25 17.5	16 30.4	15 22.9	28 33.4	27 43.7	1 6.9	28 14.8	23 3.1
13	13 24 1.0	22 53.6	29 12.7	6♓59.0	27 23.6	15 54.6	15 33.0	28 26.8	27 51.3	1 4.6	28 13.5	23 1.7
14	13 27 57.5	23 52.4	29 9.5	20 27.3	29 29.8	15 19.8	15 42.4	28 20.3	27 58.9	1 2.2	28 12.3	23 .3
15	13 31 54.1	24 51.2	29 6.3	3♈43.3	1♉35.7	14 46.4	15 51.2	28 14.0	28 6.6	0 59.9	28 11.0	22 59.0
16	13 35 50.6	25 49.9	29 3.2	16 46.6	3 41.1	14 14.5	15 59.4	28 7.8	28 14.2	0 57.6	28 9.7	22 57.7
17	13 39 47.2	26 48.6	28 60.0	29 36.9	5 45.6	13 44.3	16 6.9	28 1.7	28 21.8	0 55.3	28 8.4	22 56.4
18	13 43 43.7	27 47.3	28 56.8	12♉14.0	7 49.0	13 15.9	16 13.8	27 55.7	28 29.5	0 53.1	28 7.0	22 55.1
19	13 47 40.3	28 45.9	28 53.6	24 38.5	9 50.8	12 49.4	16 20.1	27 49.9	28 37.1	0 50.9	28 5.7	22 53.9
20	13 51 36.8	29 44.5	28 50.5	6♊51.4	11 50.8	12 25.0	16 25.7	27 44.2	28 44.8	0 48.7	28 4.3	22 52.6
21	13 55 33.4	0♉43.1	28 47.3	18 54.6	13 48.6	12 2.9	16 30.6	27 38.6	28 52.4	0 46.5	28 2.9	22 51.4
22	13 59 30.0	1 41.6	28 44.1	0♋50.8	15 43.9	11 42.9	16 34.8	27 33.2	29 .0	0 44.4	28 1.5	22 50.2
23	14 3 26.5	2 40.1	28 40.9	12 43.2	17 36.4	11 25.3	16 38.3	27 27.9	29 7.7	0 42.3	28 .1	22 49.1
24	14 7 23.1	3 38.6	28 37.7	24 36.1	19 25.9	11 10.1	16 41.2	27 22.7	29 15.3	0 40.3	27 58.6	22 47.9
25	14 11 19.6	4 37.1	28 34.6	6♌34.0	21 12.1	10 57.4	16 43.4	27 17.8	29 23.0	0 38.3	27 57.2	22 46.9
26	14 15 16.2	5 35.5	28 31.4	18 41.6	22 54.8	10 47.0	16 44.8	27 13.0	29 30.6	0 36.3	27 55.8	22 45.8
27	14 19 12.7	6 33.8	28 28.2	1♍ 3.9	24 33.9	10 39.0	16 45.5	27 8.3	29 38.2	0 34.3	27 54.3	22 44.7
28	14 23 9.3	7 32.2	28 25.0	13 45.1	26 9.0	10 33.5	16 45.5	27 3.7	29 45.8	0 32.4	27 52.8	22 43.6
29	14 27 5.8	8 30.4	28 21.9	26 49.0	27 40.1	10 30.4	16 R 44.7	26 59.4	29 53.4	0 30.5	27 51.3	22 42.6
30	14 31 2.4	9 28.7	28 18.7	10♎17.7	29 7.1	10 29.7	16 43.2	26 55.2	0♉ .9	0 28.7	27 49.8	22 41.6

LATITUDE

DAY	EPHEM. SID. TIME	☉	☊	☾	☿	♀	♂	♃	♄	♅	♆	♇
1	12 36 42.3	0 .0	0 .0	1N 2.7	1S49.2	7N54.5	0N37.7	1N34.6	2S14.9	0N46.6	1N44.8	15N57.9
4	12 48 32.0	0 .0	0 .0	2S35.7	1 31.0	7 46.9	0 33.4	1 34.5	2 14.7	0 46.5	1 44.9	15 57.5
7	13 0 21.6	0 .0	0 .0	5 .5	1 8.3	7 31.5	0 28.7	1 34.3	2 14.6	0 46.5	1 45.1	15 57.1
10	13 12 11.3	0 .0	0 .0	4 45.0	0 41.4	7 8.4	0 23.7	1 34.0	2 14.4	0 46.4	1 45.2	15 56.6
13	13 24 1.0	0 .0	0 .0	2 4.3	0 11.1	6 38.4	0 18.4	1 33.7	2 14.3	0 46.4	1 45.3	15 56.0
16	13 35 50.6	0 .0	0 .0	1N29.7	0N21.4	6 3.0	0 12.6	1 33.3	2 14.2	0 46.3	1 45.4	15 55.4
19	13 47 40.3	0 .0	0 .0	4 14.7	0 54.3	5 23.6	0 6.5	1 32.9	2 14.2	0 46.2	1 45.5	15 54.6
22	13 59 30.0	0 .0	0 .0	5 11.7	1 25.5	4 41.9	0S .1	1 32.4	2 14.2	0 46.2	1 45.5	15 53.9
25	14 11 19.6	0 .0	0 .0	4 9.7	1 53.0	3 59.4	0 7.2	1 31.9	2 14.2	0 46.1	1 45.6	15 53.0
28	14 23 9.3	0 .0	0 .0	1 26.0	2 14.8	3 17.3	0 14.7	1 31.4	2 14.2	0 46.0	1 45.7	15 52.1

RIGHT ASCENSION

DAY	EPHEM. SID. TIME	☉	☊	☾	☿	♀	♂	♃	♄	♅	♆	♇
1	12 36 42.3	10♈11.9	29♓51.6	20♍11.7	3♈29.7	18♈22.0	11♐35.5	0♎29.8	25♈15.3	1♎44.9	26♏36.7	0♎24.4
2	12 40 38.9	11 6.5	29 48.7	1♎57.4	5 13.6	17 R 52.1	11 52.2	0 R 23.0	25 22.3	1 R 42.6	26 R 35.7	0 R 23.0
3	12 44 35.4	12 1.2	29 45.8	14 3.0	6 58.6	17 21.1	12 8.4	0 16.1	25 29.3	1 40.2	26 34.6	0 21.6
4	12 48 32.0	12 55.9	29 42.8	26 45.3	8 44.8	16 49.4	12 24.2	0 9.4	25 36.4	1 38.0	26 33.6	0 20.2
5	12 52 28.5	13 50.7	29 39.9	10♏19.0	10 32.0	16 16.9	12 39.4	0 2.7	25 43.5	1 35.6	26 32.6	0 18.8
6	12 56 25.1	14 45.4	29 37.0	24 53.3	12 20.5	15 44.1	12 54.1	29♍56.1	25 50.6	1 33.3	26 31.5	0 17.3
7	13 0 21.6	15 40.3	29 34.1	10♐24.8	14 10.0	15 11.2	13 8.2	29 49.5	25 57.7	1 31.1	26 30.4	0 15.9
8	13 4 18.2	16 35.2	29 31.2	26 33.2	16 .8	14 38.2	13 21.8	29 43.0	26 4.8	1 28.8	26 29.2	0 14.5
9	13 8 14.7	17 30.1	29 28.3	12♑44.2	17 52.6	14 5.6	13 34.8	29 36.6	26 11.9	1 26.5	26 28.0	0 13.2
10	13 12 11.3	18 25.1	29 25.3	28 22.2	19 45.5	13 33.5	13 47.2	29 30.3	26 19.1	1 24.3	26 26.8	0 11.8
11	13 16 7.9	19 20.2	29 22.4	13♒ 4.0	21 39.4	13 2.2	13 59.0	29 24.0	26 26.2	1 22.1	26 25.6	0 10.4
12	13 20 4.4	20 15.4	29 19.5	26 43.9	23 34.2	12 31.8	14 10.2	29 17.8	26 33.4	1 19.9	26 24.4	0 9.1
13	13 24 1.0	21 10.6	29 16.6	9♓29.4	25 29.7	12 2.5	14 20.8	29 11.8	26 40.6	1 17.7	26 23.1	0 7.7
14	13 27 57.5	22 5.9	29 13.7	21 34.9	27 25.9	11 34.6	14 30.7	29 5.8	26 47.8	1 15.5	26 21.8	0 6.4
15	13 31 54.1	23 1.4	29 10.8	3♈17.3	29 22.5	11 8.2	14 39.9	28 59.9	26 55.0	1 13.4	26 20.5	0 5.1
16	13 35 50.6	23 56.9	29 7.9	14 52.9	1♉19.3	10 43.3	14 48.5	28 54.2	27 2.2	1 11.3	26 19.2	0 3.8
17	13 39 47.2	24 52.4	29 4.9	26 36.5	3 16.1	10 20.3	14 56.4	28 48.5	27 9.4	1 9.2	26 17.9	0 2.5
18	13 43 43.7	25 48.1	29 2.0	8♉39.6	5 12.6	9 59.1	15 3.6	28 43.0	27 16.6	1 7.1	26 16.5	0 1.2
19	13 47 40.3	26 43.9	28 59.1	21 9.5	7 8.5	9 39.9	15 10.1	28 37.6	27 23.8	1 5.1	26 15.1	29♍60.0
20	13 51 36.8	27 39.8	28 56.2	4♊ 7.5	9 3.6	9 22.8	15 15.9	28 32.3	27 31.1	1 3.1	26 13.7	29 58.7
21	13 55 33.4	28 35.8	28 53.3	17 27.6	10 57.4	9 7.7	15 21.0	28 27.1	27 38.3	1 1.1	26 12.3	29 57.5
22	13 59 30.0	29 31.9	28 50.4	0♋57.6	12 49.8	8 54.9	15 25.3	28 22.1	27 45.5	0 59.1	26 10.8	29 56.3
23	14 3 26.5	0♉28.0	28 47.4	14 22.0	14 40.3	8 44.2	15 28.9	28 17.1	27 52.7	0 57.2	26 9.4	29 55.1
24	14 7 23.1	1 24.4	28 44.5	27 27.2	16 28.7	8 35.8	15 31.7	28 12.4	27 60.0	0 55.3	26 7.9	29 53.9
25	14 11 19.6	2 20.8	28 41.6	10♌ 5.0	18 14.8	8 29.6	15 33.8	28 7.7	28 7.2	0 53.5	26 6.5	29 52.8
26	14 15 16.2	3 17.4	28 38.7	22 14.4	19 58.2	8 25.6	15 35.0	28 3.2	28 14.5	0 51.6	26 5.0	29 51.7
27	14 19 12.7	4 14.0	28 35.8	4♍ 1.0	21 38.6	8 23.9	15 35.5	27 58.9	28 21.7	0 49.8	26 3.5	29 50.6
28	14 23 9.3	5 10.8	28 32.9	15 35.2	23 15.8	8 D 24.3	15 R 35.2	27 54.6	28 28.9	0 48.0	26 2.0	29 49.5
29	14 27 5.8	6 7.7	28 30.0	27 11.1	24 49.7	8 26.9	15 34.1	27 50.6	28 36.1	0 46.3	26 .4	29 48.4
30	14 31 2.4	7 4.7	28 27.0	9♎ 5.3	26 19.9	8 31.6	15 32.3	27 46.6	28 43.3	0 44.6	25 58.9	29 47.4

DECLINATION

DAY	EPHEM. SID. TIME	☉	☊	☾	☿	♀	♂	♃	♄	♅	♆	♇
1	12 36 42.3	4N23.5	0S .1	5N21.7	0S28.1	16N19.6	21S44.0	1N30.2	8N 4.4	0N 5.2	18S 6.9	17N16.1
4	12 48 32.0	5 32.6	0 .1	13S49.5	2N 7.4	15 34.5	21 54.0	1 38.9	8 12.6	0 8.2	18 6.2	17 17.6
7	13 0 21.6	6 40.9	0 .2	27 16.7	4 49.5	14 38.1	22 3.5	1 47.3	8 20.9	0 11.2	18 5.3	17 18.9
10	13 12 11.3	7 48.1	0 .3	25 43.5	7 35.8	13 33.1	22 12.7	1 55.4	8 29.1	0 14.1	18 4.5	17 20.2
13	13 24 1.0	8 54.2	0 .3	10 52.4	10 22.5	12 22.9	22 21.5	2 3.0	8 37.4	0 16.9	18 3.6	17 21.3
16	13 35 50.6	9 59.0	0 .4	7N58.5	13 5.0	11 11.3	22 30.0	2 10.3	8 45.6	0 19.6	18 2.6	17 22.3
19	13 47 40.3	11 2.3	0 .5	23 3.0	15 37.7	10 1.8	22 38.2	2 17.0	8 53.7	0 22.2	18 1.7	17 23.2
22	13 59 30.0	12 4.0	0 .5	28 38.2	17 55.1	8 57.3	22 46.3	2 23.2	9 1.8	0 24.7	18 .7	17 23.9
25	14 11 19.6	13 3.8	0 .6	22 39.7	19 52.9	8 .3	22 54.1	2 28.9	9 9.9	0 27.1	17 59.6	17 24.5
28	14 23 9.3	14 1.7	0 .7	7 42.9	21 28.7	7 12.3	23 1.8	2 34.0	9 17.8	0 29.3	17 58.6	17 25.0

MAY 1969

DAY	EPHEM. SID. TIME	LONGITUDE ☉	☊	☾	☿	♀	♂	♃	♄	♅	♆	♇
	h m s	° ′	° ′	° ′	° ′	° ′	° ′	° ′	° ′	° ′	° ′	° ′
1	14 34 59.0	10♉26.9	28♓15.5	24♎11.5	0♊29.9	10♈31.3	16♐41.0	26♍51.1	0♉ 8.5	0♎26.9	27♏48.2	22♍40.6
2	14 38 55.5	11 25.1	28 12.3	8♏28.1	1 48.4	10 D 35.3	16 R 38.0	26 R 47.3	0 16.0	0 R 25.1	27 R 46.7	22 R 39.7
3	14 42 52.1	12 23.3	28 9.1	23 2.9	3 2.4	10 41.5	16 34.3	26 43.5	0 23.6	0 23.4	27 45.2	22 38.8
4	14 46 48.6	13 21.4	28 6.0	7♐48.9	4 11.9	10 49.9	16 29.8	26 40.0	0 31.1	0 21.7	27 43.6	22 37.9
5	14 50 45.2	14 19.5	28 2.8	22 38.3	5 16.8	11 .5	16 24.5	26 36.6	0 38.6	0 20.0	27 42.0	22 37.0
6	14 54 41.7	15 17.6	27 59.6	7♑23.0	6 17.2	11 13.3	16 18.5	26 33.4	0 46.1	0 18.4	27 40.4	22 36.1
7	14 58 38.3	16 15.7	27 56.4	21 56.5	7 12.8	11 28.0	16 11.8	26 30.4	0 53.0	0 16.9	27 38.9	22 35.3
8	15 2 34.8	17 13.7	27 53.3	6♒14.1	8 3.6	11 44.8	16 4.2	26 27.5	1 1.0	0 15.3	27 37.3	22 34.5
9	15 6 31.4	18 11.7	27 50.1	20 13.8	8 49.6	12 3.5	15 55.9	26 24.8	1 8.4	0 13.9	27 35.7	22 33.8
10	15 10 28.0	19 9.7	27 46.9	3♓55.1	9 30.8	12 24.0	15 46.9	26 22.3	1 15.8	0 12.4	27 34.1	22 33.0
11	15 14 24.5	20 7.7	27 43.7	17 19.1	10 7.0	12 46.3	15 37.1	26 20.0	1 23.2	0 11.0	27 32.5	22 32.3
12	15 18 21.1	21 5.7	27 40.6	0♈27.4	10 38.2	13 10.4	15 26.5	26 17.8	1 30.6	0 9.7	27 30.8	22 31.6
13	15 22 17.6	22 3.6	27 37.4	13 22.0	11 4.5	13 36.1	15 15.2	26 15.9	1 37.9	0 8.4	27 29.2	22 31.0
14	15 26 14.2	23 1.5	27 34.2	26 4.5	11 25.7	14 3.4	15 3.2	26 14.1	1 45.3	0 7.1	27 27.6	22 30.4
15	15 30 10.7	23 59.4	27 31.0	8♉36.3	11 41.9	14 32.2	14 50.5	26 12.5	1 52.5	0 5.9	27 26.0	22 29.8
16	15 34 7.3	24 57.3	27 27.8	20 58.4	11 53.1	15 2.6	14 37.2	26 11.1	1 59.9	0 4.8	27 24.4	22 29.3
17	15 38 3.9	25 55.2	27 24.7	3♊11.7	11 59.4	15 34.3	14 23.2	26 9.8	2 7.1	0 3.7	27 22.8	22 28.7
18	15 42 .4	26 53.0	27 21.5	15 17.0	12 .8	16 7.4	14 8.5	26 8.8	2 14.3	0 2.7	27 21.1	22 28.2
19	15 45 57.0	27 50.8	27 18.3	27 15.6	11 R 57.5	16 41.8	13 53.2	26 7.9	2 21.5	0 1.6	27 19.5	22 27.8
20	15 49 53.5	28 48.5	27 15.1	9♋ 9.2	11 49.6	17 17.5	13 37.3	26 7.2	2 28.6	0 .7	27 17.9	22 27.3
21	15 53 50.1	29 46.3	27 12.0	21 .2	11 37.3	17 54.4	13 20.9	26 6.7	2 35.7	29♍59.8	27 16.3	22 26.9
22	15 57 46.6	0♊44.0	27 8.8	2♌51.8	11 20.9	18 32.4	13 3.9	26 6.3	2 42.8	29 58.9	27 14.6	22 26.5
23	16 1 43.2	1 41.7	27 5.6	14 47.9	11 .8	19 11.6	12 46.4	26 6.2	2 49.8	29 58.1	27 13.0	22 26.2
24	16 5 39.8	2 39.3	27 2.4	26 53.0	10 37.2	19 51.8	12 28.5	26 6.2	2 56.8	29 57.3	27 11.4	22 25.9
25	16 9 36.3	3 37.0	26 59.3	9♍12.1	10 10.6	20 33.1	12 10.1	26 D 6.4	3 3.8	29 56.6	27 9.8	22 25.6
26	16 13 32.9	4 34.6	26 56.1	21 50.1	9 41.5	21 15.3	11 51.4	26 6.8	3 10.7	29 55.9	27 8.2	22 25.3
27	16 17 29.4	5 32.2	26 52.9	4♎51.7	9 10.4	21 58.5	11 32.3	26 7.4	3 17.6	29 55.3	27 6.6	22 25.1
28	16 21 26.0	6 29.7	26 49.7	18 20.6	8 37.8	22 42.6	11 12.9	26 8.1	3 24.4	29 54.8	27 4.9	22 24.9
29	16 25 22.5	7 27.3	26 46.6	2♏18.3	8 4.3	23 27.7	10 53.2	26 9.1	3 31.2	29 54.3	27 3.4	22 24.8
30	16 29 19.1	8 24.8	26 43.4	16 44.0	7 30.5	24 13.5	10 33.3	26 10.2	3 38.0	29 53.8	27 1.8	22 24.6
31	16 33 15.7	9 22.3	26 40.2	1♐33.1	6 56.9	25 .3	10 13.2	26 11.5	3 44.7	29 53.4	27 .2	22 24.5

DAY	EPHEM. SID. TIME	LATITUDE ☉	☊	☾	☿	♀	♂	♃	♄	♅	♆	♇
1	14 34 59.0	0 .0	0 .0	2 S 8.5	2 N 29.7	2 N 36.5	0 S 22.6	1 N 30.8	2 S 14.3	0 N 45.9	1 N 45.7	15 N 51.2
4	14 46 48.6	0 .0	0 .0	4 46.5	2 36.5	1 57.8	0 31.0	1 30.2	2 14.4	0 45.8	1 45.8	15 50.2
7	14 58 38.3	0 .0	0 .0	4 44.2	2 34.5	1 21.6	0 39.8	1 29.6	2 14.5	0 45.7	1 45.8	15 49.1
10	15 10 28.0	0 .0	0 .0	2 11.6	2 23.3	0 47.9	0 48.9	1 29.0	2 14.7	0 45.6	1 45.8	15 48.0
13	15 22 17.6	0 .0	0 .0	1 N 15.5	2 2.4	0 17.0	0 58.5	1 28.3	2 14.8	0 45.5	1 45.8	15 46.9
16	15 34 7.3	0 .0	0 .0	4 .6	1 32.0	0 S 11.1	1 8.3	1 27.6	2 15.0	0 45.4	1 45.8	15 45.7
19	15 45 57.0	0 .0	0 .0	5 3.5	0 52.6	0 36.6	1 18.3	1 26.9	2 15.3	0 45.3	1 45.8	15 44.5
22	15 57 46.6	0 .0	0 .0	4 9.5	0 5.9	0 59.6	1 28.5	1 26.2	2 15.5	0 45.1	1 45.8	15 43.3
25	16 9 36.3	0 .0	0 .0	1 37.6	0 S 45.5	1 20.1	1 38.8	1 25.5	2 15.8	0 45.0	1 45.8	15 42.0
28	16 21 26.0	0 .0	0 .0	1 S 46.6	1 37.9	1 38.3	1 48.9	1 24.8	2 16.1	0 44.9	1 45.8	15 40.7
31	16 33 15.7	0 .0	0 .0	4 31.3	2 27.1	1 54.3	1 58.9	1 24.1	2 16.5	0 44.8	1 45.7	15 39.4

DAY	EPHEM. SID. TIME	RIGHT ASCENSION ☉	☊	☾	☿	♀	♂	♃	♄	♅	♆	♇
1	14 34 59.0	8♉ 1.8	28♓24.1	21♎35.7	27♉46.3	8♈38.4	15♐29.5	27♍42.8	28♈50.5	0♎42.9	25♏57.3	29♍46.3
2	14 38 55.5	8 59.1	28 21.2	5♏ .0	29 8.8	8 47.3	15 R 26.0	27 R 39.2	28 57.6	0 R 41.3	25 R 55.7	29 R 45.3
3	14 42 52.1	9 56.5	28 18.3	19 31.3	0♊27.1	8 58.2	15 21.7	27 35.7	29 4.8	0 39.7	25 54.2	29 44.3
4	14 46 48.6	10 54.1	28 15.4	5♐10.6	1 41.1	9 11.0	15 16.5	27 32.4	29 12.0	0 38.1	25 52.6	29 43.3
5	14 50 45.2	11 51.8	28 12.5	21 39.8	2 50.6	9 25.7	15 10.5	27 29.2	29 19.1	0 36.6	25 51.0	29 42.4
6	14 54 41.7	12 49.6	28 9.5	8♑21.6	3 55.6	9 42.2	15 3.7	27 26.2	29 26.2	0 35.1	25 49.3	29 41.5
7	14 58 38.3	13 47.6	28 6.6	24 33.0	4 55.8	10 .5	14 56.0	27 23.3	29 33.4	0 33.7	25 47.7	29 40.5
8	15 2 34.8	14 45.8	28 3.7	9♒43.2	5 51.1	10 20.5	14 47.5	27 20.6	29 40.5	0 32.3	25 46.1	29 39.7
9	15 6 31.4	15 44.0	28 .8	23 42.5	6 41.6	10 42.2	14 38.1	27 18.0	29 47.6	0 30.9	25 44.5	29 38.8
10	15 10 28.0	16 42.5	27 57.9	6♓37.8	7 26.9	11 5.5	14 28.0	27 15.6	29 54.6	0 29.6	25 42.8	29 38.0
11	15 14 24.5	17 41.0	27 55.0	18 44.9	8 7.1	11 30.3	14 17.0	27 13.4	0♉ 1.7	0 28.3	25 41.2	29 37.2
12	15 18 21.1	18 39.8	27 52.1	0♈22.4	8 42.1	11 56.6	14 5.1	27 11.3	0 8.7	0 27.0	25 39.5	29 36.4
13	15 22 17.6	19 38.6	27 49.1	11 48.3	9 11.8	12 24.3	13 52.5	27 9.4	0 15.7	0 25.8	25 37.9	29 35.6
14	15 26 14.2	20 37.6	27 46.2	23 19.0	9 36.2	12 53.3	13 39.1	27 7.7	0 22.7	0 24.6	25 36.2	29 34.9
15	15 30 10.7	21 36.8	27 43.3	5♉ 7.9	9 55.3	13 23.7	13 25.0	27 6.1	0 29.7	0 23.5	25 34.6	29 34.2
16	15 34 7.3	22 36.1	27 40.4	17 24.2	10 9.1	13 55.4	13 10.1	27 4.8	0 36.7	0 22.5	25 32.9	29 33.5
17	15 38 3.9	23 35.6	27 37.5	0♊11.2	10 17.7	14 28.2	12 54.4	27 3.5	0 43.6	0 21.5	25 31.3	29 32.8
18	15 42 .4	24 35.2	27 34.6	13 25.0	10 21.1	15 2.2	12 38.1	27 2.5	0 50.5	0 20.5	25 29.6	29 32.2
19	15 45 57.0	25 34.9	27 31.7	26 53.7	10 R 19.5	15 37.3	12 21.1	27 1.5	0 57.4	0 19.5	25 27.9	29 31.6
20	15 49 53.5	26 34.8	27 28.7	10♋20.9	10 13.2	16 13.5	12 3.4	27 .8	1 4.2	0 18.6	25 26.3	29 31.0
21	15 53 50.1	27 34.8	27 25.8	23 30.4	10 2.3	16 50.7	11 45.1	27 .2	1 11.0	0 17.8	25 24.6	29 30.5
22	15 57 46.6	28 34.9	27 22.9	6♌11.4	9 47.2	17 29.0	11 26.2	26 59.8	1 17.8	0 17.0	25 22.9	29 29.9
23	16 1 43.2	29 35.1	27 20.0	18 20.5	9 28.1	18 8.1	11 6.8	26 59.6	1 24.5	0 16.2	25 21.3	29 29.4
24	16 5 39.8	0♊35.5	27 17.1	0♍ 1.6	9 5.6	18 48.2	10 46.9	26 59.5	1 31.3	0 15.5	25 19.6	29 29.0
25	16 9 36.3	1 36.0	27 14.2	11 24.4	8 40.1	19 29.2	10 26.5	26 D 59.6	1 37.9	0 14.8	25 18.0	29 28.5
26	16 13 32.9	2 36.6	27 11.2	22 42.7	8 12.0	20 11.0	10 5.7	26 59.9	1 44.6	0 14.2	25 16.3	29 28.1
27	16 17 29.4	3 37.4	27 8.3	4♎13.0	7 41.9	20 53.7	9 44.5	27 .3	1 51.2	0 13.6	25 14.7	29 27.7
28	16 21 26.0	4 38.2	27 5.4	16 14.1	7 10.4	21 37.2	9 23.0	27 .9	1 57.8	0 13.1	25 13.0	29 27.3
29	16 25 22.5	5 39.2	27 2.5	29 5.9	6 38.0	22 21.4	9 1.2	27 1.7	2 4.3	0 12.6	25 11.4	29 27.0
30	16 29 19.1	6 40.3	26 59.6	13♏ 6.5	6 5.3	23 6.4	8 39.1	27 2.6	2 10.8	0 12.2	25 9.8	29 26.7
31	16 33 15.7	7 41.4	26 56.7	28 25.8	5 33.0	23 52.2	8 16.8	27 3.7	2 17.3	0 11.8	25 8.1	29 26.4

DAY	EPHEM. SID. TIME	DECLINATION ☉	☊	☾	☿	♀	♂	♃	♄	♅	♆	♇
1	14 34 59.0	14 N 57.5	0 S .7	11 S 22.4	22 N 42.0	6 N 34.0	23 S 9.3	2 N 38.5	9 N 25.7	0 N 31.4	17 S 57.5	17 N 25.3
4	14 46 48.6	15 51.1	0 .8	26 19.8	23 33.2	6 5.7	23 16.5	2 42.3	9 33.5	0 33.4	17 56.5	17 25.5
7	14 58 38.3	16 42.4	0 .9	26 19.9	24 3.6	5 47.3	23 23.3	2 45.6	9 41.1	0 35.2	17 55.4	17 25.5
10	15 10 28.0	17 31.1	0 .9	12 7.0	24 14.6	5 38.2	23 29.9	2 48.2	9 48.7	0 36.9	17 54.3	17 25.4
13	15 22 17.6	18 17.3	0 1.0	6 N 26.2	24 7.7	5 37.8	23 35.9	2 50.1	9 56.1	0 38.4	17 53.2	17 25.2
16	15 34 7.3	19 .6	0 1.1	21 52.1	23 44.3	5 45.4	23 41.3	2 51.4	10 3.5	0 39.7	17 52.1	17 24.8
19	15 45 57.0	19 41.1	0 1.1	28 28.4	23 5.9	6 .0	23 46.1	2 52.1	10 10.6	0 40.9	17 51.0	17 24.3
22	15 57 46.6	20 18.6	0 1.2	23 34.2	22 14.7	6 20.9	23 50.2	2 52.0	10 17.6	0 41.9	17 49.9	17 23.7
25	16 9 36.3	20 52.9	0 1.3	9 37.7	21 13.9	6 47.5	23 53.3	2 51.3	10 24.5	0 42.7	17 48.8	17 22.9
28	16 21 26.0	21 23.9	0 1.3	8 S 50.1	20 8.2	7 18.8	23 55.6	2 50.0	10 31.2	0 43.3	17 47.7	17 22.0
31	16 33 15.7	21 51.7	0 1.4	24 54.2	19 3.5	7 54.5	23 56.9	2 48.0	10 37.7	0 43.7	17 46.7	17 21.0

JUNE 1969

LONGITUDE

DAY	EPHEM. SID. TIME h m s	☉ ° ′	☊ ° ′	☾ ° ′	☿ ° ′	♀ ° ′	♂ ° ′	♃ ° ′	♄ ° ′	♅ ° ′	♆ ° ′	♇ ° ′
1	16 37 12.2	10♊19.8	26♓37.0	16♐38.2	6♊24.2	25♈47.8	9♐53.0	26♍12.9	3♉51.3	29♍53.1	26♏58.6	22♍24.5
2	16 41 8.8	11 17.2	26 33.8	1♑49.3	5R52.8	26 36.0	9R32.6	26 14.6	3 58.0	29R52.8	26R57.0	22R24.4
3	16 45 5.3	12 14.7	26 30.7	16 55.6	5 23.4	27 25.0	9 12.2	26 16.4	4 4.5	29 52.5	26 55.5	22 24.4
4	16 49 1.9	13 12.1	26 27.5	1♒48.0	4 56.5	28 14.7	8 51.8	26 18.4	4 11.1	29 52.3	26 53.9	22D24.5
5	16 52 58.5	14 9.5	26 24.3	16 19.5	4 32.4	29 5.2	8 31.3	26 20.6	4 17.6	29 52.2	26 52.4	22 24.5
6	16 56 55.0	15 7.0	26 21.1	0♓26.8	4 11.5	29 56.3	8 11.0	26 22.9	4 24.0	29 52.1	26 50.9	22 24.7
7	17 0 51.6	16 4.4	26 18.0	14 9.3	3 54.2	0♉48.0	7 50.8	26 25.4	4 30.4	29 52.1	26 49.4	22 24.8
8	17 4 48.1	17 1.8	26 14.8	27 28.6	3 40.8	1 40.3	7 30.7	26 28.1	4 36.8	29 52.1	26 47.9	22 24.9
9	17 8 44.7	17 59.2	26 11.6	10♈27.6	3 31.5	2 33.2	7 10.8	26 31.0	4 43.1	29D52.2	26 46.4	22 25.1
10	17 12 41.3	18 56.6	26 8.4	23 9.7	3 26.4	3 26.7	6 51.2	26 34.0	4 49.3	29 52.3	26 44.9	22 25.4
11	17 16 37.8	19 53.9	26 5.3	5♉38.2	3 25.7	4 20.7	6 31.9	26 37.2	4 55.5	29 52.5	26 43.4	22 25.6
12	17 20 34.4	20 51.3	26 2.1	17 56.0	3D29.5	5 15.2	6 12.9	26 40.5	5 1.6	29 52.7	26 42.0	22 25.9
13	17 24 30.9	21 48.6	25 58.9	0♊ 5.5	3 37.8	6 10.2	5 54.2	26 44.0	5 7.6	29 53.0	26 40.5	22 26.2
14	17 28 27.5	22 46.0	25 55.7	12 8.4	3 50.7	7 5.7	5 36.1	26 47.7	5 13.6	29 53.3	26 39.1	22 26.6
15	17 32 24.0	23 43.3	25 52.6	24 6.2	4 8.2	8 1.7	5 18.3	26 51.6	5 19.6	29 53.7	26 37.7	22 26.9
16	17 36 20.6	24 40.6	25 49.4	6♋ .1	4 30.1	8 58.2	5 1.1	26 55.6	5 25.5	29 54.2	26 36.3	22 27.4
17	17 40 17.2	25 37.9	25 46.2	17 51.6	4 56.6	9 55.0	4 44.5	26 59.8	5 31.3	29 54.7	26 34.9	22 27.8
18	17 44 13.7	26 35.2	25 43.0	29 42.3	5 27.5	10 52.3	4 28.4	27 4.1	5 37.1	29 55.2	26 33.6	22 28.3
19	17 48 10.3	27 32.5	25 39.8	11♌34.6	6 2.7	11 50.0	4 12.9	27 8.6	5 42.8	29 55.8	26 32.2	22 28.8
20	17 52 6.8	28 29.8	25 36.7	23 31.5	6 42.3	12 48.1	3 58.1	27 13.2	5 48.4	29 56.5	26 30.9	22 29.3
21	17 56 3.4	29 27.1	25 33.5	5♍36.6	7 26.1	13 46.5	3 43.9	27 18.0	5 54.0	29 57.2	26 29.6	22 29.9
22	17 59 60.0	0♋24.3	25 30.3	17 54.5	8 14.1	14 45.3	3 30.5	27 23.0	5 59.5	29 58.0	26 28.3	22 30.5
23	18 3 56.5	1 21.6	25 27.1	0♎29.7	9 6.2	15 44.5	3 17.7	27 28.1	6 4.9	29 58.8	26 27.0	22 31.1
24	18 7 53.1	2 18.8	25 24.0	13 27.1	10 2.4	16 44.0	3 5.8	27 33.3	6 10.3	29 59.6	26 25.8	22 31.8
25	18 11 49.6	3 16.0	25 20.8	26 50.9	11 2.5	17 43.9	2 54.5	27 38.7	6 15.6	0♎ .6	26 24.6	22 32.5
26	18 15 46.2	4 13.2	25 17.6	10♏43.7	12 6.5	18 44.1	2 44.1	27 44.3	6 20.8	0 1.5	26 23.4	22 33.2
27	18 19 42.8	5 10.5	25 14.4	25 6.1	13 14.5	19 44.6	2 34.4	27 50.0	6 26.0	0 2.6	26 22.2	22 34.0
28	18 23 39.3	6 7.7	25 11.3	9♐55.0	14 26.2	20 45.4	2 25.6	27 55.9	6 31.1	0 3.7	26 21.1	22 34.8
29	18 27 35.9	7 4.8	25 8.1	25 3.9	15 41.7	21 46.5	2 17.5	28 1.8	6 36.2	0 4.8	26 19.9	22 35.6
30	18 31 32.4	8 2.0	25 4.9	10♑23.0	17 .9	22 47.9	2 10.2	28 8.0	6 41.1	0 6.0	26 18.8	22 36.5

LATITUDE

DAY	SID. TIME	☉	☊	☾	☿	♀	♂	♃	♄	♅	♆	♇
1	16 37 12.2	0 .0	0 .0	4S56.1	2S42.1	1S59.2	2S 2.2	1N23.8	2S16.6	0N44.7	1N45.7	15N39.0
4	16 49 1.9	0 .0	0 .0	4 7.7	3 21.2	2 12.4	2 11.8	1 23.1	2 17.0	0 44.6	1 45.7	15 37.7
7	17 0 51.6	0 .0	0 .0	1 6.3	3 49.7	2 23.7	2 21.0	1 22.4	2 17.4	0 44.5	1 45.6	15 36.3
10	17 12 41.3	0 .0	0 .0	2N14.6	4 6.8	2 33.2	2 29.6	1 21.7	2 17.8	0 44.3	1 45.5	15 35.0
13	17 24 30.9	0 .0	0 .0	4 29.0	4 12.8	2 40.9	2 37.7	1 21.0	2 18.2	0 44.2	1 45.4	15 33.7
16	17 36 20.6	0 .0	0 .0	4 54.6	4 8.6	2 47.1	2 45.1	1 20.3	2 18.7	0 44.1	1 45.3	15 32.4
19	17 48 10.3	0 .0	0 .0	3 27.6	3 55.7	2 51.7	2 51.8	1 19.6	2 19.2	0 43.9	1 45.2	15 31.0
22	17 59 60.0	0 .0	0 .0	0 37.4	3 35.4	2 54.9	2 57.9	1 18.9	2 19.7	0 43.8	1 45.1	15 29.7
25	18 11 49.6	0 .0	0 .0	2S39.9	3 9.1	2 56.7	3 3.2	1 18.2	2 20.3	0 43.7	1 45.0	15 28.4
28	18 23 39.3	0 .0	0 .0	4 51.1	2 37.9	2 57.2	3 7.8	1 17.6	2 20.8	0 43.6	1 44.9	15 27.1

RIGHT ASCENSION

DAY	SID. TIME	☉	☊	☾	☿	♀	♂	♃	♄	♅	♆	♇
1	16 37 12.2	8♊42.7	26♓53.7	14♐55.7	5♊ 1.6	24♈38.6	7♐54.4	27♍ 5.0	2♉23.7	0♎11.4	25♏ 6.5	29♍26.2
2	16 41 8.8	9 44.1	26 50.8	2♑ 3.8	4R31.6	25 25.8	7R31.9	27 6.4	2 30.1	0R11.1	25R 4.9	29R26.0
3	16 45 5.3	10 45.6	26 47.9	19 1.0	4 3.5	26 13.6	7 9.3	27 8.0	2 36.5	0 10.9	25 3.3	29 25.8
4	16 49 1.9	11 47.2	26 45.0	5♒ 3.3	3 37.9	27 2.0	6 46.7	27 9.7	2 42.8	0 10.7	25 1.7	29 25.6
5	16 52 58.5	12 48.9	26 42.1	19 49.2	3 15.0	27 51.2	6 24.1	27 11.6	2 49.0	0 10.6	25 .2	29 25.5
6	16 56 55.0	13 50.7	26 39.2	3♓19.8	2 55.4	28 40.9	6 1.6	27 13.7	2 55.3	0 10.5	24 58.6	29 25.4
7	17 0 51.6	14 52.5	26 36.3	15 50.0	2 39.2	29 31.3	5 39.3	27 15.9	3 1.5	0 10.5	24 57.1	29 25.3
8	17 4 48.1	15 54.5	26 33.3	27 39.6	2 26.8	0♉22.2	5 17.1	27 18.2	3 7.6	0 10.5	24 55.5	29 25.3
9	17 8 44.7	16 56.5	26 30.4	9♈ 8.6	2 18.3	1 13.7	4 55.1	27 20.8	3 13.7	0 10.5	24 54.0	29 25.3
10	17 12 41.3	17 58.5	26 27.5	20 35.0	2 13.9	2 5.8	4 33.4	27 23.4	3 19.7	0D10.6	24 52.5	29 25.3
11	17 16 37.8	19 .7	26 24.6	2♉14.3	2 13.9	2 58.4	4 12.1	27 26.3	3 25.7	0 10.7	24 51.0	29 25.3
12	17 20 34.4	20 2.9	26 21.7	14 18.1	2D18.1	3 51.6	3 51.2	27 29.3	3 31.6	0 10.9	24 49.5	29D25.4
13	17 24 30.9	21 5.1	26 18.8	26 52.3	2 26.8	4 45.2	3 30.6	27 32.4	3 37.5	0 11.2	24 48.0	29 25.5
14	17 28 27.5	22 7.4	26 15.8	9♊55.9	2 39.9	5 39.4	3 10.6	27 35.7	3 43.3	0 11.5	24 46.5	29 25.6
15	17 32 24.0	23 9.7	26 12.9	23 19.5	2 57.5	6 34.1	2 51.1	27 39.1	3 49.1	0 11.8	24 45.1	29 25.8
16	17 36 20.6	24 12.1	26 10.0	6♋47.4	3 19.6	7 29.3	2 32.1	27 42.7	3 54.8	0 12.2	24 43.7	29 26.0
17	17 40 17.2	25 14.5	26 7.1	20 2.0	3 46.1	8 25.0	2 13.8	27 46.4	4 .4	0 12.6	24 42.2	29 26.2
18	17 44 13.7	26 16.9	26 4.2	2♌49.6	4 17.1	9 21.1	1 56.1	27 50.3	4 6.0	0 13.1	24 40.8	29 26.4
19	17 48 10.3	27 19.3	26 1.3	15 3.6	4 52.5	10 17.7	1 39.0	27 54.4	4 11.6	0 13.7	24 39.5	29 26.7
20	17 52 6.8	28 21.7	25 58.3	26 45.3	5 32.3	11 14.8	1 22.7	27 58.5	4 17.0	0 14.3	24 38.1	29 27.0
21	17 56 3.4	29 24.1	25 55.4	8♍ 2.5	6 16.4	12 12.4	1 7.1	28 2.9	4 22.5	0 14.9	24 36.8	29 27.4
22	17 59 60.0	0♋26.5	25 52.5	19 7.5	7 4.9	13 10.4	0 52.3	28 7.3	4 27.8	0 15.6	24 35.4	29 27.7
23	18 3 56.5	1 28.9	25 49.6	0♎15.7	7 57.7	14 8.8	0 38.3	28 11.9	4 33.1	0 16.3	24 34.1	29 28.1
24	18 7 53.1	2 31.3	25 46.7	11 45.0	8 54.8	15 7.7	0 25.1	28 16.6	4 38.3	0 17.1	24 32.9	29 28.5
25	18 11 49.6	3 33.6	25 43.8	23 55.4	9 56.2	16 7.1	0 12.7	28 21.5	4 43.5	0 17.9	24 31.6	29 29.0
26	18 15 46.2	4 35.9	25 40.8	7♏ 7.1	11 1.9	17 6.8	0 1.2	28 26.5	4 48.6	0 18.8	24 30.4	29 29.5
27	18 19 42.8	5 38.2	25 37.9	21 36.6	12 11.9	18 7.1	29♏50.5	28 31.7	4 53.7	0 19.7	24 29.2	29 30.0
28	18 23 39.3	6 40.5	25 35.0	7♐28.4	13 26.2	19 7.8	29 40.7	28 37.0	4 58.7	0 20.7	24 28.0	29 30.6
29	18 27 35.9	7 42.6	25 32.1	24 24.7	14 44.7	20 8.8	29 31.8	28 42.4	5 3.6	0 21.7	24 26.8	29 31.1
30	18 31 32.4	8 44.8	25 29.2	11♑43.1	16 7.5	21 10.4	29 23.8	28 47.9	5 8.4	0 22.8	24 25.7	29 31.7

DECLINATION

DAY	SID. TIME	☉	☊	☾	☿	♀	♂	♃	♄	♅	♆	♇
1	16 37 12.2	22N .2	0S 1.4	27S41.0	18N43.2	8N 7.2	23S57.2	2N47.2	10N39.8	0N43.8	17S46.4	17N20.6
4	16 49 1.9	22 23.3	0 1.5	23 47.2	17 49.7	8 47.5	23 57.3	2 44.4	10 46.1	0 44.0	17 45.3	17 19.4
7	17 0 51.6	22 43.0	0 1.5	7 15.3	17 10.4	9 30.6	23 56.5	2 40.9	10 52.2	0 43.9	17 44.4	17 18.1
10	17 12 41.3	22 59.1	0 1.6	11N 5.1	16 48.5	10 15.9	23 55.1	2 36.9	10 58.1	0 43.7	17 43.4	17 16.7
13	17 24 30.9	23 11.5	0 1.7	24 33.3	16 44.7	11 2.9	23 53.1	2 32.2	11 3.7	0 43.3	17 42.5	17 15.1
16	17 36 20.6	23 20.3	0 1.7	28 12.8	16 58.3	11 51.1	23 50.8	2 27.0	11 9.2	0 42.8	17 41.6	17 13.4
19	17 48 10.3	23 25.3	0 1.8	20 38.3	17 27.1	12 39.9	23 48.4	2 21.2	11 14.4	0 42.0	17 40.8	17 11.7
22	17 59 60.0	23 26.7	0 1.9	5 21.3	18 8.4	13 28.9	23 46.2	2 14.9	11 19.4	0 41.0	17 40.0	17 9.8
25	18 11 49.6	23 24.3	0 1.9	12S50.1	18 59.0	14 17.7	23 44.4	2 8.0	11 24.2	0 39.9	17 39.2	17 7.8
28	18 23 39.3	23 18.2	0 2.0	26 44.4	19 55.4	15 5.9	23 43.1	2 .6	11 28.7	0 38.5	17 38.5	17 5.7

JULY 1969

DAY	EPHEM. SID. TIME	☉	☊	☽	☿	♀	♂	♃	♄	♅	♆	♇
	h m s	° ′	° ′	° ′	° ′	° ′	° ′	° ′	° ′	° ′	° ′	° ′
		LONGITUDE										
1	18 35 29.0	8♋59.2	25♓ 1.7	25♑40.7	18♊23.8	23♉49.6	2♐ 3.8	28♍14.2	6♉46.0	0♎ 7.2	26♏17.7	22♍37.4
2	18 39 25.5	9 56.4	24 58.6	10♒46.2	19 50.4	24 51.6	1 R 58.2	28 20.6	6 50.8	0 8.5	26 R 16.6	22 38.3
3	18 43 22.1	10 53.6	24 55.4	25 30.8	21 20.5	25 53.8	1 53.4	28 27.2	6 55.5	0 9.8	26 15.6	22 39.2
4	18 47 18.7	11 50.8	24 52.2	9♓49.0	22 54.1	26 56.3	1 49.4	28 33.8	7 .1	0 11.2	26 14.6	22 40.2
5	18 51 15.2	12 47.9	24 49.0	23 39.2	24 31.3	27 59.1	1 46.3	28 40.6	7 4.7	0 12.6	26 13.6	22 41.2
6	18 55 11.8	13 45.1	24 45.9	7♈ 2.3	26 11.8	29 2.1	1 44.0	28 47.5	7 9.2	0 14.1	26 12.6	22 42.2
7	18 59 8.3	14 42.3	24 42.7	20 1.3	27 55.6	0♊ 5.4	1 42.5	28 54.6	7 13.6	0 15.6	26 11.6	22 43.2
8	19 3 4.9	15 39.5	24 39.5	2♉40.0	29 42.7	1 8.9	1 41.9	29 1.8	7 17.9	0 17.2	26 10.7	22 44.3
9	19 7 1.5	16 36.8	24 36.3	15 2.6	1♋32.7	2 12.6	1 D 42.1	29 9.1	7 22.2	0 18.8	26 9.8	22 45.4
10	19 10 58.0	17 34.0	24 33.1	27 13.0	3 25.7	3 16.5	1 43.2	29 16.6	7 26.4	0 20.5	26 8.9	22 46.6
11	19 14 54.6	18 31.2	24 30.0	9♊14.9	5 21.4	4 20.7	1 45.0	29 24.1	7 30.4	0 22.2	26 8.1	22 47.7
12	19 18 51.1	19 28.4	24 26.8	21 11.2	7 19.6	5 25.0	1 47.7	29 31.8	7 34.4	0 24.0	26 7.3	22 48.9
13	19 22 47.7	20 25.7	24 23.6	3♋ 4.1	9 20.1	6 29.6	1 51.2	29 39.6	7 38.4	0 25.8	26 6.5	22 50.1
14	19 26 44.3	21 22.9	24 20.4	14 55.5	11 22.6	7 34.3	1 55.5	29 47.6	7 42.2	0 27.6	26 5.7	22 51.4
15	19 30 40.8	22 20.2	24 17.3	26 47.2	13 26.8	8 39.3	2 .7	29 55.6	7 45.9	0 29.5	26 5.0	22 52.7
16	19 34 37.4	23 17.4	24 14.1	8♌40.5	15 32.5	9 44.4	2 6.6	0♎ 3.8	7 49.6	0 31.5	26 4.3	22 54.0
17	19 38 33.9	24 14.7	24 10.9	20 37.3	17 39.2	10 49.8	2 13.3	0 12.1	7 53.1	0 33.5	26 3.6	22 55.3
18	19 42 30.5	25 12.0	24 7.7	2♍39.8	19 46.8	11 55.3	2 20.9	0 20.5	7 56.7	0 35.6	26 3.0	22 56.7
19	19 46 27.0	26 9.3	24 4.6	14 50.6	21 54.9	13 1.0	2 29.2	0 29.1	8 .0	0 37.7	26 2.4	22 58.1
20	19 50 23.6	27 6.5	24 1.4	27 12.9	24 3.1	14 6.8	2 38.2	0 37.7	8 3.3	0 39.8	26 1.8	22 59.5
21	19 54 20.2	28 3.8	23 58.2	9♎50.6	26 11.3	15 12.8	2 48.0	0 46.4	8 6.5	0 42.0	26 1.2	23 .9
22	19 58 16.7	29 1.1	23 55.0	22 47.4	28 19.1	16 19.0	2 58.5	0 55.3	8 9.6	0 44.2	26 .7	23 2.4
23	20 2 13.3	29 58.4	23 51.9	6♏ 7.1	0♌26.4	17 25.3	3 9.8	1 4.2	8 12.6	0 46.4	26 .2	23 3.8
24	20 6 9.8	0♌55.7	23 48.7	19 52.5	2 32.9	18 31.8	3 21.7	1 13.2	8 15.6	0 48.7	25 59.7	23 5.3
25	20 10 6.4	1 53.0	23 45.5	4♐ 4.7	4 38.4	19 38.4	3 34.4	1 22.4	8 18.4	0 51.1	25 59.3	23 6.9
26	20 14 2.9	2 50.3	23 42.3	18 42.0	6 42.8	20 45.2	3 47.7	1 31.6	8 21.1	0 53.5	25 58.9	23 8.4
27	20 17 59.5	3 47.6	23 39.1	3♑39.9	8 45.9	21 52.1	4 1.8	1 41.0	8 23.7	0 55.9	25 58.5	23 10.0
28	20 21 56.1	4 44.9	23 36.0	18 50.4	10 47.7	22 59.2	4 16.4	1 50.4	8 26.3	0 58.4	25 58.1	23 11.6
29	20 25 52.6	5 42.2	23 32.8	4♒ 3.7	12 48.1	24 6.4	4 31.8	1 60.0	8 28.7	1 .9	25 57.8	23 13.2
30	20 29 49.2	6 39.6	23 29.6	19 9.3	14 47.0	25 13.8	4 47.7	2 9.6	8 31.1	1 3.4	25 57.5	23 14.8
31	20 33 45.7	7 36.9	23 26.4	3♓57.9	16 44.4	26 21.3	5 4.3	2 19.4	8 33.3	1 6.0	25 57.3	23 16.5
		LATITUDE										
1	18 35 29.0	0 .0	0 .0	4 S 17.1	2 S 3.3	2 S 56.5	3 S 11.7	1 N 17.0	2 S 21.4	0 N 43.4	1 N 44.8	15 N 25.9
4	18 47 18.7	0 .0	0 .0	1 14.0	1 26.4	2 54.7	3 15.0	1 16.3	2 22.0	0 43.3	1 44.6	15 24.7
7	18 59 8.3	0 .0	0 .0	2 N 14.0	0 48.8	2 51.9	3 17.7	1 15.7	2 22.6	0 43.2	1 44.5	15 23.4
10	19 10 58.0	0 .0	0 .0	4 31.2	0 11.9	2 48.1	3 19.8	1 15.1	2 23.3	0 43.1	1 44.4	15 22.3
13	19 22 47.7	0 .0	0 .0	4 58.2	0 N 22.3	2 43.4	3 21.4	1 14.6	2 23.9	0 42.9	1 44.2	15 21.1
16	19 34 37.4	0 .0	0 .0	3 31.6	0 52.1	2 37.8	3 22.6	1 14.0	2 24.6	0 42.8	1 44.1	15 20.0
19	19 46 27.0	0 .0	0 .0	0 40.8	1 16.1	2 31.5	3 23.3	1 13.5	2 25.3	0 42.7	1 43.9	15 18.9
22	19 58 16.7	0 .0	0 .0	2 S 35.4	1 33.3	2 24.5	3 23.7	1 12.9	2 26.0	0 42.6	1 43.7	15 17.9
25	20 10 6.4	0 .0	0 .0	4 51.7	1 43.6	2 16.8	3 23.7	1 12.4	2 26.7	0 42.5	1 43.6	15 16.9
28	20 21 56.1	0 .0	0 .0	4 34.7	1 47.1	2 8.6	3 23.4	1 12.0	2 27.5	0 42.4	1 43.4	15 16.0
31	20 33 45.7	0 .0	0 .0	1 35.1	1 44.6	1 59.9	3 22.8	1 11.5	2 28.2	0 42.3	1 43.2	15 15.1
		RIGHT ASCENSION										
1	18 35 29.0	9♋46.8	25♓26.3	28♑31.9	17♊34.6	22♉12.3	29♏16.6	28♍53.6	5♉13.2	0♎23.9	24♏24.5	29♍32.4
2	18 39 25.5	10 48.8	25 23.3	14♒13.9	19 5.9	23 14.7	29 R 10.4	28 59.4	5 17.9	0 25.1	24 R 23.4	29 33.0
3	18 43 22.1	11 50.8	25 20.4	28 37.1	20 41.5	24 17.4	29 5.0	29 5.3	5 22.5	0 26.3	24 22.3	29 33.7
4	18 47 18.7	12 52.7	25 17.5	11♓50.1	22 21.2	25 20.6	29 .6	29 11.3	5 27.0	0 27.5	24 21.3	29 34.4
5	18 51 15.2	13 54.5	25 14.6	24 10.9	24 5.2	26 24.3	28 57.0	29 17.5	5 31.5	0 28.8	24 20.3	29 35.2
6	18 55 11.8	14 56.2	25 11.7	6♈ .4	25 53.2	27 28.3	28 54.3	29 23.7	5 35.9	0 30.1	24 19.3	29 35.9
7	18 59 8.3	15 57.8	25 8.7	17 37.8	27 45.3	28 32.7	28 52.6	29 30.1	5 40.2	0 31.5	24 18.3	29 36.7
8	19 3 4.9	16 59.4	25 5.8	29 20.2	29 41.2	29 37.5	28 51.8	29 36.7	5 44.5	0 32.9	24 17.3	29 37.5
9	19 7 1.5	18 .9	25 2.9	11♉20.8	1♋40.8	0♊42.7	28 51.8	29 43.3	5 48.7	0 34.4	24 16.4	29 38.4
10	19 10 58.0	19 2.2	24 60.0	23 48.1	3 43.9	1 48.4	28 D 52.8	29 50.0	5 52.8	0 35.9	24 15.5	29 39.3
11	19 14 54.6	20 3.5	24 57.1	6♊43.8	5 50.2	2 54.3	28 54.6	29 56.9	5 56.8	0 37.5	24 14.6	29 40.2
12	19 18 51.1	21 4.7	24 54.2	20 1.7	7 59.4	4 .7	28 57.4	0♎ 3.9	6 .7	0 39.1	24 13.8	29 41.1
13	19 22 47.7	22 5.7	24 51.2	3♋28.5	10 11.2	5 7.5	29 1.0	0 11.0	6 4.6	0 40.7	24 12.9	29 42.0
14	19 26 44.3	23 6.7	24 48.3	16 47.1	12 25.3	6 14.6	29 5.5	0 18.2	6 8.3	0 42.4	24 12.2	29 43.0
15	19 30 40.8	24 7.5	24 45.4	29 42.6	14 41.1	7 22.0	29 10.9	0 25.5	6 12.0	0 44.1	24 11.4	29 44.0
16	19 34 37.4	25 8.2	24 42.5	12♌ 5.7	16 58.4	8 29.9	29 17.2	0 32.9	6 15.6	0 45.9	24 10.7	29 45.1
17	19 38 33.9	26 8.7	24 39.6	23 55.0	19 16.5	9 38.0	29 24.3	0 40.5	6 19.1	0 47.7	24 10.0	29 46.1
18	19 42 30.5	27 9.2	24 36.6	5♍15.9	21 35.2	10 46.6	29 32.3	0 48.1	6 22.6	0 49.6	24 9.3	29 47.3
19	19 46 27.0	28 9.5	24 33.7	16 18.5	23 53.9	11 55.4	29 41.2	0 55.9	6 26.0	0 51.5	24 8.7	29 48.4
20	19 50 23.6	29 9.7	24 30.8	27 16.6	26 12.1	13 4.6	29 50.8	1 3.7	6 29.2	0 53.5	24 8.1	29 49.5
21	19 54 20.2	0♌ 9.7	24 27.9	8♎26.4	28 29.6	14 14.1	0♐ 1.2	1 11.7	6 32.4	0 55.5	24 7.5	29 50.7
22	19 58 16.7	1 9.5	24 25.0	20 6.0	0♌46.0	15 23.9	0 12.5	1 19.7	6 35.5	0 57.5	24 6.9	29 51.9
23	20 2 13.3	2 9.3	24 22.0	2♏34.7	3 .9	16 34.1	0 24.6	1 27.8	6 38.5	0 59.5	24 6.4	29 53.1
24	20 6 9.8	3 8.8	24 19.1	16 10.6	5 14.1	17 44.5	0 37.4	1 36.1	6 41.4	1 1.6	24 5.9	29 54.3
25	20 10 6.4	4 8.2	24 16.2	1♐ 4.9	7 25.4	18 55.2	0 51.0	1 44.4	6 44.2	1 3.8	24 5.4	29 55.6
26	20 14 2.9	5 7.5	24 13.3	17 13.4	9 34.5	20 6.2	1 5.4	1 52.8	6 46.9	1 5.9	24 5.0	29 56.9
27	20 17 59.5	6 6.6	24 10.4	4♑ 9.1	11 41.4	21 17.5	1 20.4	2 1.3	6 49.5	1 8.2	24 4.6	29 58.2
28	20 21 56.1	7 5.6	24 7.4	21 6.7	13 45.9	22 29.1	1 36.3	2 9.9	6 52.1	1 10.4	24 4.2	29 59.5
29	20 25 52.6	8 4.4	24 4.5	7♒21.9	15 48.0	23 40.9	1 52.8	2 18.6	6 54.5	1 12.7	24 3.9	0♎ .8
30	20 29 49.2	9 3.1	24 1.6	22 29.5	17 47.6	24 53.0	2 10.0	2 27.4	6 56.9	1 15.0	24 3.6	0 2.2
31	20 33 45.7	10 1.6	23 58.7	6♓26.8	19 44.7	26 5.3	2 27.9	2 36.3	6 59.1	1 17.4	24 3.3	0 3.6
		DECLINATION										
1	18 35 29.0	23 N 8.4	0 S 2.1	25 S 13.3	20 N 53.5	15 N 53.0	23 S 42.6	1 N 52.7	11 N 33.0	0 N 37.0	17 S 37.9	17 N 3.6
4	18 47 18.7	22 55.0	0 2.1	9 1.9	21 49.0	16 38.6	23 42.8	1 44.3	11 37.0	0 35.3	17 37.3	17 1.3
7	18 59 8.3	22 38.0	0 2.2	9 N 53.8	22 37.0	17 22.4	23 44.1	1 35.5	11 40.8	0 33.4	17 36.7	16 59.0
10	19 10 58.0	22 17.5	0 2.3	23 56.4	23 12.2	18 4.0	23 46.3	1 26.2	11 44.3	0 31.4	17 36.2	16 56.6
13	19 22 47.7	21 53.5	0 2.3	28 22.7	23 29.3	18 42.9	23 49.5	1 16.5	11 47.6	0 29.1	17 35.8	16 54.1
16	19 34 37.4	21 26.1	0 2.4	21 29.9	23 24.2	19 18.9	23 53.8	1 6.4	11 50.5	0 26.8	17 35.4	16 51.6
19	19 46 27.0	20 55.5	0 2.5	6 35.9	22 54.9	19 51.7	23 59.1	0 55.8	11 53.2	0 24.2	17 35.2	16 49.0
22	19 58 16.7	20 21.6	0 2.5	11 S 16.2	22 1.6	20 20.8	24 5.3	0 44.9	11 55.6	0 21.5	17 34.9	16 46.4
25	20 10 6.4	19 44.7	0 2.6	25 44.5	20 47.0	20 46.0	24 12.3	0 33.7	11 57.7	0 18.7	17 34.8	16 43.7
28	20 21 56.1	19 4.9	0 2.7	26 39.2	19 14.8	21 7.1	24 20.1	0 22.1	11 59.6	0 15.7	17 34.7	16 40.9
31	20 33 45.7	18 22.2	0 2.7	11 32.0	17 29.1	21 23.9	24 28.4	0 10.2	12 1.1	0 12.5	17 34.6	16 38.2

AUGUST 1969

LONGITUDE

DAY	EPHEM. SID. TIME (h m s)	☉ (° ′)	☊ (° ′)	☽ (° ′)	☿ (° ′)	♀ (° ′)	♂ (° ′)	♃ (° ′)	♄ (° ′)	♅ (° ′)	♆ (° ′)	♇ (° ′)
1	20 37 42.3	8♌34.3	23♓23.3	18♓22.8	18♌40.2	27♊29.0	5♐21.5	2♎29.2	8♉35.5	1♎ 8.6	25♏57.0	23♍18.2
2	20 41 38.8	9 31.7	23 20.1	2♈20.4	20 34.4	28 36.8	5 39.3	2 39.1	8 37.5	1 11.3	25 R 56.9	23 19.9
3	20 45 35.4	10 29.1	23 16.9	15 50.4	22 27.0	29 44.8	5 57.6	2 49.1	8 39.5	1 14.0	25 56.7	23 21.6
4	20 49 32.0	11 26.5	23 13.7	28 54.5	24 18.1	0♋52.8	6 16.6	2 59.2	8 41.3	1 16.7	25 56.6	23 23.3
5	20 53 28.5	12 24.0	23 10.6	11♉36.0	26 7.5	2 1.0	6 36.1	3 9.4	8 43.0	1 19.5	25 56.5	23 25.1
6	20 57 25.1	13 21.5	23 7.4	23 59.0	27 55.3	3 9.4	6 56.2	3 19.6	8 44.7	1 22.3	25 56.4	23 26.9
7	21 1 21.6	14 19.0	23 4.2	6♊ 8.1	29 41.6	4 17.9	7 16.8	3 30.0	8 46.2	1 25.1	25 56.4	23 28.7
8	21 5 18.2	15 16.5	23 1.0	18 7.5	1♍26.3	5 26.5	7 38.0	3 40.5	8 47.7	1 28.0	25 56.4	23 30.5
9	21 9 14.7	16 14.1	22 57.8	0♋ 1.1	3 9.4	6 35.2	7 59.7	3 51.0	8 49.0	1 30.9	25 56.4	23 32.4
10	21 13 11.3	17 11.6	22 54.7	11 52.3	4 51.0	7 44.1	8 21.9	4 1.6	8 50.3	1 33.9	25 D 56.5	23 34.2
11	21 17 7.9	18 9.2	22 51.5	23 43.9	6 31.0	8 53.0	8 44.6	4 12.2	8 51.4	1 36.8	25 56.6	23 36.1
12	21 21 4.4	19 6.8	22 48.3	5♌38.4	8 9.5	10 2.1	9 7.8	4 23.0	8 52.4	1 39.9	25 56.7	23 38.0
13	21 25 1.0	20 4.4	22 45.1	17 37.6	9 46.4	11 11.3	9 31.6	4 33.8	8 53.3	1 42.9	25 56.9	23 39.9
14	21 28 57.5	21 2.0	22 42.0	29 43.2	11 21.8	12 20.5	9 55.8	4 44.7	8 54.1	1 46.0	25 57.1	23 41.8
15	21 32 54.1	21 59.7	22 38.8	11♍56.8	12 55.7	13 29.9	10 20.4	4 55.7	8 54.9	1 49.1	25 57.3	23 43.8
16	21 36 50.6	22 57.4	22 35.6	24 20.1	14 28.1	14 39.4	10 45.6	5 6.8	8 55.5	1 52.2	25 57.6	23 45.7
17	21 40 47.2	23 55.1	22 32.4	6♎54.9	15 58.9	15 49.1	11 11.2	5 17.9	8 55.9	1 55.4	25 57.9	23 47.7
18	21 44 43.7	24 52.8	22 29.3	19 43.4	17 28.3	16 58.8	11 37.2	5 29.1	8 56.3	1 58.5	25 58.2	23 49.7
19	21 48 40.3	25 50.5	22 26.1	2♏47.9	18 56.0	18 8.6	12 3.7	5 40.3	8 56.6	2 1.8	25 58.5	23 51.7
20	21 52 36.9	26 48.3	22 22.9	16 10.4	20 22.2	19 18.5	12 30.6	5 51.6	8 56.8	2 5.0	25 58.9	23 53.7
21	21 56 33.4	27 46.1	22 19.7	29 52.7	21 46.8	20 28.5	12 58.0	6 3.0	8 56.9	2 8.3	25 59.3	23 55.7
22	22 0 30.0	28 43.9	22 16.5	13♐55.3	23 9.9	21 38.6	13 25.7	6 14.5	8 R 56.8	2 11.6	25 59.8	23 57.7
23	22 4 26.5	29 41.7	22 13.4	28 17.4	24 31.2	22 48.8	13 53.8	6 26.0	8 56.7	2 14.9	26 .3	23 59.8
24	22 8 23.1	0♍39.5	22 10.2	12♑56.0	25 50.9	23 59.1	14 22.3	6 37.5	8 56.4	2 18.2	26 .8	24 1.9
25	22 12 19.6	1 37.3	22 7.0	27 45.7	27 8.9	25 9.6	14 51.2	6 49.2	8 56.1	2 21.6	26 1.3	24 3.9
26	22 16 16.2	2 35.2	22 3.8	12♒39.8	28 25.1	26 20.1	15 20.5	7 .8	8 55.6	2 25.0	26 1.9	24 6.0
27	22 20 12.7	3 33.1	22 .7	27 30.1	29 39.5	27 30.7	15 50.1	7 12.6	8 55.1	2 28.4	26 2.5	24 8.1
28	22 24 9.3	4 31.0	21 57.5	12♓ 8.8	0♎52.0	28 41.4	16 20.1	7 24.4	8 54.4	2 31.8	26 3.2	24 10.2
29	22 28 5.8	5 29.0	21 54.3	26 29.5	2 2.6	29 52.2	16 50.5	7 36.3	8 53.7	2 35.3	26 3.9	24 12.4
30	22 32 2.4	6 27.0	21 51.1	10♈27.5	3 11.0	1♌ 3.1	17 21.1	7 48.2	8 52.8	2 38.8	26 4.6	24 14.5
31	22 35 59.0	7 25.0	21 47.9	24 .8	4 17.3	2 14.1	17 52.1	8 .1	8 51.8	2 42.3	26 5.4	24 16.7

LATITUDE

DAY	EPHEM. SID. TIME	☉	☊	☽	☿	♀	♂	♃	♄	♅	♆	♇
1	20 37 42.3	0 .0	0 .0	0S18.6	1N42.5	1S56.9	3S22.6	1N11.3	2S28.4	0N42.2	1N43.2	15N14.8
4	20 49 32.0	0 .0	0 .0	3N 7.4	1 33.1	1 47.6	3 21.6	1 10.9	2 29.2	0 42.2	1 43.0	15 14.0
7	21 1 21.6	0 .0	0 .0	4 59.0	1 19.4	1 38.0	3 20.5	1 10.5	2 29.9	0 42.1	1 42.8	15 13.2
10	21 13 11.3	0 .0	0 .0	4 51.5	1 2.0	1 28.1	3 19.2	1 10.1	2 30.7	0 42.0	1 42.6	15 12.5
13	21 25 1.0	0 .0	0 .0	2 53.3	0 41.7	1 18.0	3 17.6	1 9.7	2 31.5	0 41.9	1 42.4	15 11.8
16	21 36 50.6	0 .0	0 .0	0S17.1	0 19.0	1 7.8	3 16.0	1 9.3	2 32.2	0 41.8	1 42.3	15 11.2
19	21 48 40.3	0 .0	0 .0	3 28.8	0S 5.7	0 57.4	3 14.1	1 9.0	2 33.0	0 41.7	1 42.1	15 10.7
22	22 0 30.0	0 .0	0 .0	5 12.0	0 31.8	0 47.0	3 12.2	1 8.6	2 33.7	0 41.7	1 41.9	15 10.2
25	22 12 19.6	0 .0	0 .0	4 13.0	0 59.0	0 36.7	3 10.0	1 8.3	2 34.5	0 41.6	1 41.7	15 9.8
28	22 24 9.3	0 .0	0 .0	0 49.3	1 26.8	0 26.4	3 7.8	1 8.0	2 35.2	0 41.5	1 41.6	15 9.4
31	22 35 59.0	0 .0	0 .0	2N52.1	1 54.8	0 16.2	3 5.5	1 7.7	2 35.9	0 41.5	1 41.4	15 9.1

RIGHT ASCENSION

DAY	EPHEM. SID. TIME	☉	☊	☽	☿	♀	♂	♃	♄	♅	♆	♇
1	20 37 42.3	10♌59.9	23♓55.8	19♓26.3	21♌39.3	27♊17.8	2♐46.5	2♎45.2	7♉ 1.3	1♎19.7	24♏ 3.1	0♎ 5.0
2	20 41 38.8	11 58.1	23 52.8	1♈46.3	23 31.4	28 30.6	3 5.8	2 54.3	7 3.3	1 22.2	24 R 2.9	0 6.5
3	20 45 35.4	12 56.2	23 49.9	13 46.3	25 21.1	29 43.6	3 25.7	3 3.4	7 5.3	1 24.6	24 2.7	0 7.9
4	20 49 32.0	13 54.1	23 47.0	25 43.6	27 8.4	0♋56.8	3 46.2	3 12.6	7 7.2	1 27.1	24 2.5	0 9.4
5	20 53 28.5	14 51.9	23 44.1	7♉52.4	28 53.3	2 10.2	4 7.4	3 21.9	7 9.0	1 29.7	24 2.4	0 10.9
6	20 57 25.1	15 49.5	23 41.2	20 22.6	0♍36.0	3 23.8	4 29.2	3 31.2	7 10.6	1 32.2	24 2.3	0 12.4
7	21 1 21.6	16 47.0	23 38.2	3♊17.8	2 16.4	4 37.5	4 51.6	3 40.7	7 12.2	1 34.8	24 2.3	0 14.0
8	21 5 18.2	17 44.4	23 35.3	16 34.3	3 54.7	5 51.5	5 14.7	3 50.2	7 13.7	1 37.5	24 2.3	0 15.6
9	21 9 14.7	18 41.6	23 32.4	0♋ 1.2	5 30.8	7 5.5	5 38.3	3 59.8	7 15.1	1 40.1	24 2.3	0 17.2
10	21 13 11.3	19 38.6	23 29.5	13 23.6	7 4.9	8 19.7	6 2.5	4 9.5	7 16.4	1 42.8	24 D 2.4	0 18.8
11	21 17 7.9	20 35.5	23 26.6	26 26.4	8 36.9	9 34.0	6 27.3	4 19.2	7 17.5	1 45.5	24 2.5	0 20.4
12	21 21 4.4	21 32.3	23 23.6	8♌59.7	10 7.1	10 48.4	6 52.7	4 29.1	7 18.6	1 48.3	24 2.6	0 22.0
13	21 25 1.0	22 28.9	23 20.7	21 .0	11 35.3	12 2.9	7 18.6	4 39.0	7 19.6	1 51.1	24 2.7	0 23.7
14	21 28 57.5	23 25.4	23 17.8	2♍30.8	13 1.7	13 17.5	7 45.1	4 48.9	7 20.5	1 53.9	24 2.9	0 25.4
15	21 32 54.1	24 21.8	23 14.9	13 40.6	14 26.3	14 32.1	8 12.1	4 58.9	7 21.2	1 56.7	24 3.1	0 27.0
16	21 36 50.6	25 18.0	23 11.9	24 41.2	15 49.1	15 46.8	8 39.6	5 9.0	7 21.9	1 59.6	24 3.4	0 28.8
17	21 40 47.2	26 14.1	23 9.0	5♎47.2	17 10.2	17 1.5	9 7.7	5 19.2	7 22.4	2 2.4	24 3.7	0 30.5
18	21 44 43.7	27 10.0	23 6.1	17 14.8	18 29.7	18 16.3	9 36.3	5 29.4	7 22.9	2 5.4	24 4.0	0 32.2
19	21 48 40.3	28 5.9	23 3.2	29 21.3	19 47.4	19 31.1	10 5.4	5 39.7	7 23.2	2 8.3	24 4.3	0 34.0
20	21 52 36.9	29 1.6	23 .2	12♏23.2	21 3.5	20 45.9	10 35.0	5 50.0	7 23.5	2 11.3	24 4.7	0 35.8
21	21 56 33.4	29 57.1	22 57.3	26 32.8	22 18.0	22 .6	11 5.1	6 .5	7 23.6	2 14.3	24 5.1	0 37.5
22	22 0 30.0	0♍52.6	22 54.4	11♐51.7	23 30.8	23 15.4	11 35.6	6 10.9	7 23.7	2 17.3	24 5.6	0 39.3
23	22 4 26.5	1 47.9	22 51.5	28 3.6	24 42.1	24 30.2	12 6.6	6 21.5	7 R 23.6	2 20.3	24 6.0	0 41.2
24	22 8 23.1	2 43.1	22 48.6	14♑35.0	25 51.6	25 44.9	12 38.1	6 32.0	7 23.5	2 23.4	24 6.6	0 43.0
25	22 12 19.6	3 38.2	22 45.6	0♒45.9	26 59.6	26 59.6	13 10.0	6 42.7	7 23.2	2 26.5	24 7.1	0 44.8
26	22 16 16.2	4 33.2	22 42.7	16 6.7	28 5.8	28 14.2	13 42.3	6 53.4	7 22.9	2 29.6	24 7.7	0 46.7
27	22 20 12.7	5 28.1	22 39.8	0♓26.7	29 10.3	29 28.7	14 15.0	7 4.1	7 22.4	2 32.7	24 8.3	0 48.6
28	22 24 9.3	6 22.9	22 36.9	13 51.3	0♎13.1	0♌43.2	14 48.2	7 14.9	7 21.8	2 35.8	24 8.9	0 50.4
29	22 28 5.8	7 17.7	22 33.9	26 35.0	1 14.2	1 57.7	15 21.8	7 25.8	7 21.2	2 39.0	24 9.7	0 52.4
30	22 32 2.4	8 12.3	22 31.0	8♈55.3	2 13.3	3 12.0	15 55.7	7 36.7	7 20.4	2 42.2	24 10.4	0 54.3
31	22 35 59.0	9 6.8	22 28.1	21 9.1	3 10.5	4 26.2	16 30.1	7 47.7	7 19.6	2 45.4	24 11.1	0 56.2

DECLINATION

DAY	EPHEM. SID. TIME	☉	☊	☽	☿	♀	♂	♃	♄	♅	♆	♇
1	20 37 42.3	18N 7.4	0S 2.7	4S53.0	16N51.5	21N28.4	24S31.3	0N 6.1	12N 1.5	0N11.5	17S34.6	16N37.2
4	20 49 32.0	17 21.2	0 2.8	14N .4	14 53.3	21 38.9	24 40.3	0S 6.2	12 2.7	0 8.2	17 34.7	16 34.4
7	21 1 21.6	16 32.4	0 2.9	26 14.6	12 49.3	21 44.6	24 49.5	0 18.8	12 3.5	0 4.7	17 34.8	16 31.6
10	21 13 11.3	15 41.2	0 2.9	27 45.2	10 41.8	21 45.2	24 59.0	0 31.7	12 4.1	0 1.2	17 35.0	16 28.7
13	21 25 1.0	14 47.7	0 3.0	18 18.2	8 33.0	21 40.7	25 8.5	0 44.9	12 4.3	0S 2.5	17 35.3	16 25.9
16	21 36 50.6	13 52.1	0 3.1	1 59.4	6 24.5	21 31.0	25 17.8	0 58.3	12 4.3	0 6.3	17 35.6	16 23.0
19	21 48 40.3	12 54.5	0 3.1	15S42.7	4 17.6	21 16.0	25 27.0	1 11.9	12 3.9	0 10.1	17 36.0	16 20.1
22	22 0 30.0	11 55.1	0 3.2	27 38.3	2 13.6	20 55.9	25 35.7	1 25.7	12 3.3	0 14.1	17 36.5	16 17.3
25	22 12 19.6	10 54.0	0 3.3	24 48.4	0 13.9	20 30.4	25 43.9	1 39.7	12 2.3	0 18.2	17 37.0	16 14.4
28	22 24 9.3	9 51.4	0 3.3	7 45.9	1S40.3	19 59.9	25 51.5	1 53.9	12 1.1	0 22.3	17 37.6	16 11.6
31	22 35 59.0	8 47.3	0 3.4	11N58.9	3 27.6	19 24.2	25 58.2	2 8.3	11 59.6	0 26.5	17 38.3	16 8.8

SEPTEMBER 1969

LONGITUDE

DAY	EPHEM. SID. TIME h m s	☉ ° ′	☊ ° ′	☽ ° ′	☿ ° ′	♀ ° ′	♂ ° ′	♃ ° ′	♄ ° ′	♅ ° ′	♆ ° ′	♇ ° ′
1	22 39 55.5	8 ♍ 23.0	21 ♓ 44.8	7 ♉ 9.4	5 ♎ 21.4	3 ♌ 25.2	18 ♐ 23.4	8 ♎ 12.1	8 ♉ 50.7	2 ♎ 45.8	26 ♏ 6.1	24 ♍ 18.8
2	22 43 52.1	9 21.1	21 41.6	19 55.3	6 23.1	4 36.4	18 55.0	8 24.2	8 R 49.5	2 49.4	26 6.9	24 21.0
3	22 47 48.6	10 19.2	21 38.4	2 ♊ 21.7	7 22.3	5 47.6	19 27.0	8 36.3	8 48.2	2 52.9	26 7.8	24 23.1
4	22 51 45.2	11 17.3	21 35.2	14 32.6	8 18.8	6 59.0	19 59.2	8 48.4	8 46.9	2 56.5	26 8.6	24 25.3
5	22 55 41.7	12 15.5	21 32.1	26 32.6	9 12.5	8 10.4	20 31.8	9 .6	8 45.4	3 .1	26 9.5	24 27.5
6	22 59 38.3	13 13.7	21 28.9	8 ♋ 26.1	10 3.2	9 22.0	21 4.7	9 12.9	8 43.8	3 3.7	26 10.4	24 29.7
7	23 3 34.8	14 11.9	21 25.7	20 17.5	10 50.7	10 33.6	21 37.8	9 25.1	8 42.1	3 7.3	26 11.4	24 31.8
8	23 7 31.4	15 10.2	21 22.5	2 ♌ 10.7	11 34.7	11 45.3	22 11.3	9 37.5	8 40.3	3 11.0	26 12.4	24 34.0
9	23 11 27.9	16 8.5	21 19.3	14 9.1	12 15.1	12 57.1	22 45.0	9 49.8	8 38.4	3 14.6	26 13.4	24 36.2
10	23 15 24.5	17 6.8	21 16.2	26 15.6	12 51.6	14 9.0	23 19.0	10 2.2	8 36.4	3 18.3	26 14.4	24 38.4
11	23 19 21.0	18 5.2	21 13.0	8 ♍ 32.3	13 23.8	15 20.9	23 53.3	10 14.7	8 34.3	3 22.0	26 15.5	24 40.6
12	23 23 17.6	19 3.5	21 9.8	21 .8	13 51.5	16 32.9	24 27.8	10 27.2	8 32.1	3 25.7	26 16.6	24 42.9
13	23 27 14.2	20 2.0	21 6.6	3 ♎ 42.3	14 14.4	17 45.0	25 2.6	10 39.7	8 29.8	3 29.4	26 17.7	24 45.1
14	23 31 10.7	21 .4	21 3.5	16 37.2	14 32.1	18 57.2	25 37.7	10 52.2	8 27.4	3 33.1	26 18.9	24 47.3
15	23 35 7.3	21 58.9	21 .3	29 45.9	14 44.3	20 9.5	26 13.0	11 4.8	8 24.9	3 36.8	26 20.1	24 49.5
16	23 39 3.8	22 57.4	20 57.1	13 ♏ 8.2	14 50.7	21 21.8	26 48.6	11 17.4	8 22.3	3 40.6	26 21.3	24 51.7
17	23 43 .4	23 55.9	20 53.9	26 43.9	14 50.8	22 34.2	27 24.4	11 30.1	8 19.7	3 44.3	26 22.6	24 53.9
18	23 46 56.9	24 54.5	20 50.8	10 ♐ 32.6	14 R 44.4	23 46.7	28 .5	11 42.8	8 16.9	3 48.0	26 23.8	24 56.2
19	23 50 53.5	25 53.1	20 47.6	24 33.4	14 31.3	24 59.3	28 36.8	11 55.5	8 14.1	3 51.8	26 25.2	24 58.4
20	23 54 50.0	26 51.8	20 44.4	8 ♑ 44.8	14 11.2	26 11.9	29 13.3	12 8.3	8 11.2	3 55.6	26 26.5	25 .7
21	23 58 46.6	27 50.4	20 41.2	23 4.8	13 43.9	27 24.6	29 50.0	12 21.0	8 8.2	3 59.4	26 27.9	25 2.9
22	0 2 43.1	28 49.1	20 38.0	7 ♒ 30.3	13 9.6	28 37.3	0 ♑ 27.0	12 33.8	8 5.1	4 3.2	26 29.2	25 5.1
23	0 6 39.7	29 47.8	20 34.9	21 57.5	12 28.2	29 50.1	1 4.1	12 46.6	8 1.9	4 6.9	26 30.6	25 7.3
24	0 10 36.2	0 ♎ 46.5	20 31.7	6 ♓ 21.7	11 40.3	1 ♍ 3.0	1 41.5	12 59.4	7 58.6	4 10.7	26 32.1	25 9.5
25	0 14 32.8	1 45.3	20 28.5	20 38.1	10 46.3	2 15.9	2 19.0	13 12.2	7 55.3	4 14.5	26 33.5	25 11.7
26	0 18 29.4	2 44.1	20 25.3	4 ♈ 41.9	9 47.2	3 29.0	2 56.8	13 25.1	7 51.9	4 18.3	26 35.0	25 13.9
27	0 22 25.9	3 42.9	20 22.2	18 29.0	8 43.8	4 42.0	3 34.7	13 38.0	7 48.4	4 22.1	26 36.5	25 16.1
28	0 26 22.5	4 41.7	20 19.0	1 ♉ 56.8	7 37.6	5 55.2	4 12.8	13 50.9	7 44.8	4 25.9	26 38.1	25 18.3
29	0 30 19.0	5 40.6	20 15.8	15 4.0	6 30.1	7 8.4	4 51.1	14 3.8	7 41.2	4 29.6	26 39.6	25 20.5
30	0 34 15.6	6 39.6	20 12.6	27 50.9	5 22.9	8 21.7	5 29.6	14 16.7	7 37.4	4 33.4	26 41.2	25 22.7

LATITUDE

DAY	EPHEM. SID. TIME	☉	☊	☽	☿	♀	♂	♃	♄	♅	♆	♇
1	22 39 55.5	0 .0	0 .0	3 N 47.9	2 S 4.0	0 S 12.9	3 S 4.7	1 N 7.7	2 S 36.2	0 N 41.5	1 N 41.3	15 N 9.0
4	22 51 45.2	0 .0	0 .0	5 14.4	2 31.3	0 3.0	3 2.2	1 7.4	2 36.9	0 41.4	1 41.1	15 8.8
7	23 3 34.8	0 .0	0 .0	4 36.6	2 57.2	0 N 6.6	2 59.6	1 7.2	2 37.6	0 41.4	1 41.0	15 8.7
10	23 15 24.5	0 .0	0 .0	2 13.4	3 20.7	0 15.9	2 56.9	1 7.0	2 38.2	0 41.3	1 40.8	15 8.6
13	23 27 14.2	0 .0	0 .0	1 S 9.3	3 40.4	0 24.9	2 54.2	1 6.8	2 38.9	0 41.3	1 40.6	15 8.6
16	23 39 3.8	0 .0	0 .0	4 10.1	3 54.4	0 33.4	2 51.3	1 6.6	2 39.5	0 41.2	1 40.5	15 8.7
19	23 50 53.5	0 .0	0 .0	5 16.3	3 59.8	0 41.6	2 48.4	1 6.4	2 40.1	0 41.2	1 40.3	15 8.8
22	0 2 43.1	0 .0	0 .0	3 38.8	3 53.3	0 49.2	2 45.4	1 6.3	2 40.6	0 41.2	1 40.2	15 9.1
25	0 14 32.8	0 .0	0 .0	0 2.8	3 31.3	0 56.3	2 42.4	1 6.2	2 41.1	0 41.2	1 40.0	15 9.3
28	0 26 22.5	0 .0	0 .0	3 N 26.9	2 52.4	1 2.9	2 39.3	1 6.1	2 41.6	0 41.2	1 39.9	15 9.7

RIGHT ASCENSION

DAY	EPHEM. SID. TIME	☉	☊	☽	☿	♀	♂	♃	♄	♅	♆	♇
1	22 39 55.5	10 ♍ 1.3	22 ♓ 25.2	3 ♉ 30.6	4 ♎ 5.7	5 ♌ 40.4	17 ♐ 4.8	7 ♎ 58.7	7 ♉ 18.6	2 ♎ 48.6	24 ♏ 11.9	0 ♎ 58.1
2	22 43 52.1	10 55.7	22 22.2	16 10.0	4 58.8	6 54.4	17 39.9	8 9.7	7 R 17.5	2 51.9	24 12.7	1 .1
3	22 47 48.6	11 50.0	22 19.3	29 11.6	5 49.7	8 8.3	18 15.4	8 20.8	7 16.3	2 55.1	24 13.5	1 2.0
4	22 51 45.2	12 44.3	22 16.4	12 ♊ 33.0	6 38.2	9 22.1	18 51.2	8 32.0	7 15.1	2 58.4	24 14.4	1 4.0
5	22 55 41.7	13 38.5	22 13.5	26 4.6	7 24.2	10 35.7	19 27.4	8 43.2	7 13.7	3 1.7	24 15.3	1 6.0
6	22 59 38.3	14 32.6	22 10.5	9 ♋ 32.7	8 7.6	11 49.2	20 3.9	8 54.4	7 12.2	3 5.0	24 16.2	1 7.9
7	23 3 34.8	15 26.7	22 7.6	22 43.0	8 48.2	13 2.6	20 40.8	9 5.7	7 10.6	3 8.3	24 17.2	1 9.9
8	23 7 31.4	16 20.8	22 4.7	5 ♌ 25.3	9 25.7	14 15.8	21 18.0	9 17.0	7 9.0	3 11.7	24 18.1	1 11.9
9	23 11 27.9	17 14.8	22 1.8	17 35.7	9 60.0	15 28.9	21 55.5	9 28.3	7 7.2	3 15.0	24 19.2	1 13.9
10	23 15 24.5	18 8.8	21 58.8	29 16.8	10 30.8	16 41.8	22 33.3	9 39.7	7 5.3	3 18.4	24 20.2	1 15.9
11	23 19 21.0	19 2.7	21 55.9	10 ♍ 36.2	10 57.9	17 54.6	23 11.5	9 51.2	7 3.4	3 21.7	24 21.3	1 17.9
12	23 23 17.6	19 56.6	21 53.0	21 44.9	11 21.1	19 7.2	23 50.0	10 2.6	7 1.3	3 25.1	24 22.4	1 20.0
13	23 27 14.2	20 50.5	21 50.1	2 ♎ 56.4	11 40.0	20 19.6	24 28.8	10 14.2	6 59.2	3 28.5	24 23.6	1 22.0
14	23 31 10.7	21 44.3	21 47.1	14 25.8	11 54.3	21 31.9	25 7.8	10 25.7	6 56.9	3 31.9	24 24.7	1 24.0
15	23 35 7.3	22 38.2	21 44.2	26 28.9	12 3.8	22 43.9	25 47.2	10 37.3	6 54.6	3 35.3	24 25.9	1 26.1
16	23 39 3.8	23 32.0	21 41.3	9 ♏ 20.9	12 8.2	23 55.9	26 26.8	10 48.9	6 52.2	3 38.8	24 27.2	1 28.1
17	23 43 .4	24 25.8	21 38.3	23 12.7	12 R 7.2	25 7.6	27 6.7	11 .5	6 49.7	3 42.2	24 28.4	1 30.2
18	23 46 56.9	25 19.6	21 35.4	8 ♐ 6.4	12 .5	26 19.2	27 46.9	11 12.2	6 47.1	3 45.6	24 29.7	1 32.2
19	23 50 53.5	26 13.5	21 32.5	23 49.4	11 48.1	27 30.6	28 27.4	11 23.9	6 44.4	3 49.1	24 31.1	1 34.3
20	23 54 50.0	27 7.3	21 29.6	9 ♑ 53.7	11 29.6	28 41.9	29 8.0	11 35.7	6 41.7	3 52.6	24 32.4	1 36.4
21	23 58 46.6	28 1.1	21 26.6	25 44.8	11 5.1	29 52.9	29 48.9	11 47.4	6 38.8	3 56.0	24 33.8	1 38.4
22	0 2 43.1	28 54.9	21 23.7	10 ♒ 55.0	10 34.6	1 ♍ 3.8	0 ♑ 30.0	11 59.2	6 35.9	3 59.5	24 35.2	1 40.5
23	0 6 39.7	29 48.8	21 20.8	25 11.8	9 58.4	2 14.6	1 11.4	12 11.0	6 32.8	4 3.0	24 36.6	1 42.5
24	0 10 36.2	0 ♎ 42.7	21 17.9	8 ♓ 37.7	9 16.9	3 25.1	1 52.9	12 22.8	6 29.7	4 6.4	24 38.1	1 44.6
25	0 14 32.8	1 36.6	21 14.9	21 24.9	8 30.6	4 35.5	2 34.7	12 34.7	6 26.6	4 9.9	24 39.6	1 46.7
26	0 18 29.4	2 30.5	21 12.0	3 ♈ 49.1	7 40.3	5 45.8	3 16.6	12 46.5	6 23.3	4 13.4	24 41.1	1 48.7
27	0 22 25.9	3 24.5	21 9.1	16 6.9	6 47.0	6 55.9	3 58.8	12 58.4	6 20.0	4 16.8	24 42.6	1 50.8
28	0 26 22.5	4 18.6	21 6.1	28 32.4	5 51.8	8 5.9	4 41.1	13 10.3	6 16.6	4 20.3	24 44.1	1 52.9
29	0 30 19.0	5 12.7	21 3.2	11 ♉ 16.2	4 56.2	9 15.8	5 23.6	13 22.3	6 13.1	4 23.8	24 45.7	1 54.9
30	0 34 15.6	6 6.9	21 .3	24 23.4	4 1.5	10 25.5	6 6.3	13 34.2	6 9.6	4 27.3	24 47.3	1 57.0

DECLINATION

DAY	EPHEM. SID. TIME	☉	☊	☽	☿	♀	♂	♃	♄	♅	♆	♇
1	22 39 55.5	8 N 25.7	0 S 3.4	17 N 29.5	4 S 1.6	19 N 11.2	26 S .2	2 S 13.1	11 N 59.0	0 S 27.9	17 S 38.6	16 N 7.9
4	22 51 45.2	7 20.0	0 3.5	27 45.2	5 36.8	18 29.0	26 5.7	2 27.6	11 57.1	0 32.2	17 39.3	16 5.1
7	23 3 34.8	6 13.2	0 3.6	26 28.2	7 .5	17 42.1	26 10.1	2 42.2	11 55.0	0 36.6	17 40.1	16 2.4
10	23 15 24.5	5 5.5	0 3.6	14 51.5	8 9.6	16 50.5	26 13.3	2 57.0	11 52.5	0 41.0	17 41.0	15 59.7
13	23 27 14.2	3 56.9	0 3.7	2 S 32.0	9 .1	15 54.7	26 15.2	3 11.9	11 49.8	0 45.4	17 41.9	15 57.0
16	23 39 3.8	2 47.8	0 3.8	19 45.4	9 27.1	14 54.7	26 15.7	3 26.8	11 46.9	0 49.9	17 42.9	15 54.5
19	23 50 53.5	1 38.1	0 3.8	28 36.1	9 24.5	13 50.9	26 14.7	3 41.8	11 43.7	0 54.4	17 43.9	15 51.9
22	0 2 43.1	0 28.2	0 3.9	21 55.4	8 46.6	12 43.5	26 12.2	3 56.8	11 40.3	0 58.9	17 45.0	15 49.5
25	0 14 32.8	0 S 41.9	0 4.0	3 45.3	7 30.2	11 32.8	26 7.9	4 11.9	11 36.7	1 3.4	17 46.1	15 47.1
28	0 26 22.5	1 52.0	0 4.0	15 N 23.2	5 40.0	10 19.1	26 1.9	4 27.0	11 32.9	1 7.9	17 47.3	15 44.8

OCTOBER 1969

DAY	EPHEM. SID. TIME	☉	☊	☽	☿	♀	♂	♃	♄	♅	♆	♇
	h m s	° ′	° ′	° ′	° ′	° ′	° ′	° ′	° ′	° ′	° ′	° ′
		LONGITUDE										
1	0 38 12.1	7♎38.5	20♓ 9.4	10♊19.2	4♎17.9	9♍35.0	6♑ 8.2	14♎29.7	7♉33.6	4♎37.2	26♏42.8	25♍24.9
2	0 42 8.7	8 37.6	20 6.3	22 31.9	3 R 16.7	10 48.5	6 47.0	14 42.6	7 R 29.8	4 41.0	26 44.5	25 27.1
3	0 46 5.2	9 36.6	20 3.1	4♋33.0	2 21.1	12 1.9	7 26.0	14 55.6	7 25.9	4 44.8	26 46.1	25 29.3
4	0 50 1.8	10 35.7	19 59.9	16 26.9	1 32.7	13 15.5	8 5.2	15 8.6	7 21.9	4 48.5	26 47.8	25 31.4
5	0 53 58.3	11 34.8	19 56.7	28 18.3	0 52.6	14 29.1	8 44.5	15 21.6	7 17.8	4 52.3	26 49.5	25 33.6
6	0 57 54.9	12 34.0	19 53.6	10♌12.2	0 22.1	15 42.7	9 24.0	15 34.6	7 13.7	4 56.1	26 51.2	25 35.7
7	1 1 51.4	13 33.2	19 50.4	22 12.9	0 1.7	16 56.4	10 3.7	15 47.6	7 9.5	4 59.8	26 52.9	25 37.9
8	1 5 48.0	14 32.4	19 47.2	4♍24.7	29♍51.9	18 10.2	10 43.5	16 .6	7 5.3	5 3.6	26 54.7	25 40.0
9	1 9 44.6	15 31.7	19 44.0	16 50.9	29 D 52.9	19 24.0	11 23.4	16 13.6	7 1.0	5 7.4	26 56.5	25 42.1
10	1 13 41.1	16 31.0	19 40.8	29 33.8	0♎ 4.6	20 37.9	12 3.6	16 26.6	6 56.7	5 11.1	26 58.4	25 44.3
11	1 17 37.7	17 30.4	19 37.7	12♎34.5	0 26.5	21 51.9	12 43.9	16 39.7	6 52.4	5 14.9	27 .2	25 46.4
12	1 21 34.2	18 29.8	19 34.5	25 53.1	0 58.3	23 5.8	13 24.3	16 52.7	6 47.9	5 18.6	27 2.0	25 48.5
13	1 25 30.8	19 29.2	19 31.3	9♏28.0	1 39.3	24 19.9	14 4.9	17 5.7	6 43.5	5 22.3	27 3.9	25 50.6
14	1 29 27.3	20 28.6	19 28.1	23 16.8	2 28.7	25 33.9	14 45.5	17 18.7	6 38.9	5 26.0	27 5.8	25 52.6
15	1 33 23.9	21 28.1	19 25.0	7♐16.3	3 25.8	26 48.0	15 26.4	17 31.7	6 34.4	5 29.7	27 7.7	25 54.7
16	1 37 20.4	22 27.6	19 21.8	21 22.9	4 29.9	28 2.2	16 7.3	17 44.7	6 29.8	5 33.4	27 9.6	25 56.7
17	1 41 17.0	23 27.2	19 18.6	5♑33.4	5 40.0	29 16.4	16 48.4	17 57.7	6 25.2	5 37.0	27 11.5	25 58.8
18	1 45 13.5	24 26.7	19 15.4	19 44.8	6 55.5	0♎30.6	17 29.7	18 10.7	6 20.5	5 40.7	27 13.5	26 .8
19	1 49 10.1	25 26.3	19 12.2	3♒55.0	8 15.5	1 44.9	18 11.0	18 23.7	6 15.8	5 44.3	27 15.5	26 2.8
20	1 53 6.7	26 25.9	19 9.1	18 2.1	9 39.6	2 59.2	18 52.5	18 36.6	6 11.1	5 47.9	27 17.4	26 4.8
21	1 57 3.2	27 25.6	19 5.9	2♓ 4.7	11 6.9	4 13.6	19 34.0	18 49.6	6 6.4	5 51.5	27 19.5	26 6.7
22	2 0 59.8	28 25.3	19 2.7	16 1.2	12 37.1	5 28.0	20 15.7	19 2.5	6 1.6	5 55.1	27 21.5	26 8.7
23	2 4 56.3	29 25.0	18 59.5	29 49.8	14 9.5	6 42.4	20 57.5	19 15.4	5 56.8	5 58.6	27 23.5	26 10.6
24	2 8 52.9	0♏24.7	18 56.4	13♈28.6	15 43.9	7 56.9	21 39.4	19 28.3	5 52.0	6 2.2	27 25.6	26 12.5
25	2 12 49.4	1 24.5	18 53.2	26 55.3	17 19.7	9 11.4	22 21.4	19 41.2	5 47.2	6 5.7	27 27.6	26 14.4
26	2 16 46.0	2 24.3	18 50.0	10♉ 8.0	18 56.7	10 26.0	23 3.5	19 54.1	5 42.4	6 9.2	27 29.7	26 16.3
27	2 20 42.5	3 24.1	18 46.8	23 5.3	20 34.6	11 40.6	23 45.7	20 7.0	5 37.6	6 12.7	27 31.8	26 18.2
28	2 24 39.1	4 24.0	18 43.6	5♊46.4	22 13.2	12 55.2	24 28.0	20 19.8	5 32.8	6 16.2	27 33.9	26 20.0
29	2 28 35.6	5 23.9	18 40.5	18 11.9	23 52.2	14 9.9	25 10.3	20 32.6	5 27.9	6 19.6	27 36.0	26 21.9
30	2 32 32.2	6 23.8	18 37.3	0♋23.5	25 31.6	15 24.6	25 52.8	20 45.4	5 23.1	6 23.0	27 38.1	26 23.7
31	2 36 28.8	7 23.9	18 34.1	12 24.0	27 11.1	16 39.4	26 35.4	20 58.2	5 18.3	6 26.5	27 40.3	26 25.5
		LATITUDE										
1	0 38 12.1	0 .0	0 .0	5N10.0	1S59.0	1N 9.0	2S36.1	1N 6.0	2S42.0	0N41.2	1N39.8	15N10.1
4	0 50 1.8	0 .0	0 .0	4 44.9	0 58.3	1 14.4	2 32.9	1 5.9	2 42.4	0 41.2	1 39.6	15 10.6
7	1 1 51.4	0 .0	0 .0	2 32.1	0N .4	1 19.2	2 29.6	1 5.9	2 42.7	0 41.2	1 39.5	15 11.1
10	1 13 41.1	0 .0	0 .0	0S46.6	0 49.8	1 23.4	2 26.3	1 5.8	2 43.0	0 41.2	1 39.4	15 11.7
13	1 25 30.8	0 .0	0 .0	3 54.4	1 26.3	1 26.9	2 22.9	1 5.8	2 43.3	0 41.2	1 39.3	15 12.4
16	1 37 20.4	0 .0	0 .0	5 11.9	1 49.4	1 29.8	2 19.5	1 5.8	2 43.5	0 41.2	1 39.2	15 13.2
19	1 49 10.1	0 .0	0 .0	3 47.4	2 .8	1 32.0	2 16.0	1 5.9	2 43.6	0 41.2	1 39.1	15 14.0
22	2 0 59.8	0 .0	0 .0	0 25.4	2 2.6	1 33.5	2 12.5	1 5.9	2 43.7	0 41.3	1 39.0	15 14.9
25	2 12 49.4	0 .0	0 .0	3N 3.6	1 57.1	1 34.4	2 9.0	1 6.0	2 43.7	0 41.3	1 38.9	15 15.8
28	2 24 39.1	0 .0	0 .0	4 58.2	1 46.3	1 34.6	2 5.5	1 6.1	2 43.7	0 41.3	1 38.8	15 16.8
31	2 36 28.8	0 .0	0 .0	4 44.7	1 31.7	1 34.2	2 1.9	1 6.2	2 43.6	0 41.4	1 38.8	15 17.9
		RIGHT ASCENSION										
1	0 38 12.1	7♎ 1.1	20♓57.4	7♊51.8	3♎ 9.3	11♍35.0	6♑49.1	13♎46.2	6♉ 6.0	4♎30.7	24♏49.0	1♎59.0
2	0 42 8.7	7 55.4	20 54.4	21 31.9	2 R 21.1	12 44.5	7 32.1	13 58.2	6 R 2.3	4 34.2	24 50.6	2 1.1
3	0 46 5.2	8 49.8	20 51.5	5♋ 9.4	1 38.1	13 53.8	8 15.2	14 10.1	5 58.5	4 37.7	24 52.3	2 3.2
4	0 50 1.8	9 44.3	20 48.6	18 29.2	1 1.8	15 3.1	8 58.5	14 22.2	5 54.7	4 41.2	24 54.0	2 5.2
5	0 53 58.3	10 38.8	20 45.6	1♌20.4	0 33.1	16 12.2	9 42.0	14 34.2	5 50.9	4 44.6	24 55.7	2 7.3
6	0 57 54.9	11 33.5	20 42.7	13 38.6	0 12.9	17 21.2	10 25.6	14 46.2	5 46.9	4 48.1	24 57.5	2 9.3
7	1 1 51.4	12 28.2	20 39.8	25 26.1	0 1.7	18 30.2	11 9.3	14 58.3	5 42.9	4 51.5	24 59.3	2 11.3
8	1 5 48.0	13 23.1	20 36.9	6♍50.5	29♍59.8	19 39.0	11 53.1	15 10.3	5 38.9	4 55.0	25 1.0	2 13.4
9	1 9 44.6	14 18.1	20 33.9	18 3.1	0♎ 7.3	20 47.8	12 37.0	15 22.4	5 34.8	4 58.4	25 2.9	2 15.4
10	1 13 41.1	15 13.2	20 31.0	29 17.4	0 D 24.0	21 56.5	13 21.2	15 34.5	5 30.7	5 1.9	25 4.8	2 17.5
11	1 17 37.7	16 8.4	20 28.1	10♎48.7	0 49.6	23 5.2	14 5.3	15 46.5	5 26.5	5 5.3	25 6.6	2 19.5
12	1 21 34.2	17 3.7	20 25.1	22 53.0	1 23.6	24 13.7	14 49.6	15 58.6	5 22.3	5 8.8	25 8.5	2 21.5
13	1 25 30.8	17 59.1	20 22.2	5♏45.6	2 5.4	25 22.3	15 34.0	16 10.7	5 18.0	5 12.2	25 10.4	2 23.5
14	1 29 27.3	18 54.7	20 19.3	19 37.8	2 54.4	26 30.8	16 18.5	16 22.8	5 13.7	5 15.6	25 12.3	2 25.5
15	1 33 23.9	19 50.4	20 16.3	4♐31.6	3 49.8	27 39.2	17 3.0	16 34.9	5 9.3	5 18.9	25 14.2	2 27.4
16	1 37 20.4	20 46.2	20 13.4	20 14.2	4 51.1	28 47.6	17 47.7	16 47.0	5 4.9	5 22.3	25 16.2	2 29.4
17	1 41 17.0	21 42.2	20 10.5	6♑17.5	5 57.4	29 56.0	18 32.4	16 59.0	5 .5	5 25.7	25 18.2	2 31.4
18	1 45 13.5	22 38.3	20 7.5	22 6.3	7 8.2	1♎ 4.4	19 17.1	17 11.1	4 56.0	5 29.0	25 20.2	2 33.3
19	1 49 10.1	23 34.6	20 4.6	7♒12.3	8 22.8	2 12.8	20 1.9	17 23.2	4 51.5	5 32.4	25 22.2	2 35.3
20	1 53 6.7	24 31.0	20 1.7	21 22.9	9 40.6	3 21.2	20 46.8	17 35.3	4 47.0	5 35.7	25 24.2	2 37.2
21	1 57 3.2	25 27.5	19 58.8	4♓40.7	11 1.2	4 29.7	21 31.7	17 47.3	4 42.4	5 39.0	25 26.3	2 39.1
22	2 0 59.8	26 24.2	19 55.8	17 17.9	12 24.2	5 38.1	22 16.7	17 59.4	4 37.9	5 42.3	25 28.3	2 41.0
23	2 4 56.3	27 21.1	19 52.9	29 31.0	13 49.1	6 46.6	23 1.7	18 11.4	4 33.3	5 45.6	25 30.4	2 42.9
24	2 8 52.9	28 18.2	19 50.0	11♈36.8	15 15.6	7 55.2	23 46.7	18 23.5	4 28.7	5 48.8	25 32.5	2 44.8
25	2 12 49.4	29 15.4	19 47.0	23 50.8	16 43.4	9 3.8	24 31.7	18 35.5	4 24.1	5 52.1	25 34.6	2 46.7
26	2 16 46.0	0♏12.8	19 44.1	6♉25.1	18 12.3	10 12.4	25 16.8	18 47.5	4 19.4	5 55.3	25 36.7	2 48.6
27	2 20 42.5	1 10.4	19 41.2	19 26.5	19 42.0	11 21.2	26 1.8	18 59.5	4 14.8	5 58.5	25 38.8	2 50.4
28	2 24 39.1	2 8.2	19 38.2	2♊54.2	21 12.5	12 30.0	26 46.9	19 11.5	4 10.2	6 1.7	25 41.0	2 52.2
29	2 28 35.6	3 6.1	19 35.3	16 39.5	22 43.6	13 39.0	27 32.0	19 23.5	4 5.5	6 4.9	25 43.1	2 54.1
30	2 32 32.2	4 4.3	19 32.4	0♋26.6	24 15.2	14 48.0	28 17.1	19 35.4	4 .9	6 8.0	25 45.3	2 55.9
31	2 36 28.8	5 2.7	19 29.4	13 58.3	25 47.2	15 57.2	29 2.2	19 47.4	3 56.3	6 11.2	25 47.5	2 57.7
		DECLINATION										
1	0 38 12.1	3S 2.0	0S 4.1	27N 6.7	3S31.7	9N 2.6	25S54.1	4S42.1	11N28.9	1S12.4	17S48.5	15N42.5
4	0 50 1.8	4 11.7	0 4.1	27 8.6	1 30.4	7 43.6	25 44.5	4 57.1	11 24.8	1 16.9	17 49.8	15 40.4
7	1 1 51.4	5 21.0	0 4.2	16 30.4	0 .3	6 22.4	25 33.0	5 12.2	11 20.5	1 21.4	17 51.1	15 38.3
10	1 13 41.1	6 29.7	0 4.3	0S32.3	0N43.9	4 59.4	25 19.6	5 27.2	11 16.0	1 25.8	17 52.5	15 36.3
13	1 25 30.8	7 37.6	0 4.3	18 21.0	0 39.6	3 34.9	25 4.2	5 42.2	11 11.5	1 30.3	17 53.8	15 34.5
16	1 37 20.4	8 44.6	0 4.4	28 21.1	0S 6.9	2 9.2	24 46.8	5 57.1	11 6.9	1 34.6	17 55.2	15 32.7
19	1 49 10.1	9 50.4	0 4.5	22 57.7	1 25.6	0 42.6	24 27.4	6 11.8	11 2.2	1 38.9	17 56.6	15 31.0
22	2 0 59.8	10 55.0	0 4.5	5 54.4	3 6.3	0S44.5	24 6.0	6 26.5	10 57.5	1 43.2	17 58.1	15 29.5
25	2 12 49.4	11 58.0	0 4.6	13N13.8	5 .1	2 11.8	23 42.7	6 41.1	10 52.7	1 47.3	17 59.5	15 28.1
28	2 24 39.1	12 59.4	0 4.7	26 9.9	7 .6	3 39.1	23 17.4	6 55.5	10 48.0	1 51.4	18 1.0	15 26.8
31	2 36 28.8	13 59.0	0 4.7	27 35.4	9 2.8	5 5.9	22 50.2	7 9.8	10 43.3	1 55.5	18 2.5	15 25.5

NOVEMBER 1969

LONGITUDE

DAY	EPHEM. SID. TIME (h m s)	☉ (° ′)	☊ (° ′)	☾ (° ′)	☿ (° ′)	♀ (° ′)	♂ (° ′)	♃ (° ′)	♄ (° ′)	♅ (° ′)	♆ (° ′)	♇ (° ′)
1	2 40 25.3	8♏23.9	18♓30.9	24♋17.1	28♎50.7	17♎54.2	27♑18.1	21♎10.9	5♉13.5	6♎29.8	27♏42.4	26♍27.3
2	2 44 21.9	9 23.9	18 27.8	6♌ 7.3	0♏30.2	19 9.0	28 .8	21 23.7	5R 8.7	6 33.2	27 44.6	26 29.0
3	2 48 18.4	10 24.0	18 24.6	17 59.7	2 9.6	20 23.8	28 43.6	21 36.3	5 3.9	6 36.5	27 46.8	26 30.8
4	2 52 15.0	11 24.1	18 21.4	29 59.6	3 48.8	21 38.7	29 26.5	21 49.0	4 59.1	6 39.8	27 48.9	26 32.5
5	2 56 11.5	12 24.3	18 18.2	12♍12.1	5 27.8	22 53.6	0♒ 9.5	22 1.6	4 54.3	6 43.0	27 51.1	26 34.2
6	3 0 8.1	13 24.5	18 15.1	24 41.8	7 6.6	24 8.5	0 52.6	22 14.2	4 49.5	6 46.3	27 53.3	26 35.8
7	3 4 4.7	14 24.7	18 11.9	7♎32.7	8 45.0	25 23.5	1 35.7	22 26.8	4 44.8	6 49.5	27 55.5	26 37.5
8	3 8 1.2	15 24.9	18 8.7	20 46.8	10 23.2	26 38.5	2 18.9	22 39.3	4 40.1	6 52.7	27 57.7	26 39.1
9	3 11 57.8	16 25.2	18 5.5	4♏24.7	12 1.0	27 53.5	3 2.2	22 51.8	4 35.4	6 55.8	27 59.9	26 40.7
10	3 15 54.3	17 25.5	18 2.3	18 24.3	13 38.6	29 8.5	3 45.6	23 4.2	4 30.7	6 58.9	28 2.2	26 42.3
11	3 19 50.9	18 25.9	17 59.2	2♐41.5	15 15.8	0♏23.6	4 29.0	23 16.6	4 26.1	7 2.0	28 4.4	26 43.8
12	3 23 47.4	19 26.2	17 56.0	17 10.2	16 52.6	1 38.7	5 12.6	23 29.0	4 21.5	7 5.1	28 6.6	26 45.3
13	3 27 44.0	20 26.6	17 52.8	1♑43.7	18 29.2	2 53.8	5 56.1	23 41.3	4 16.9	7 8.1	28 8.9	26 46.8
14	3 31 40.6	21 27.1	17 49.6	16 15.3	20 5.4	4 8.9	6 39.8	23 53.6	4 12.4	7 11.1	28 11.1	26 48.3
15	3 35 37.1	22 27.5	17 46.5	0♒39.8	21 41.4	5 24.0	7 23.5	24 5.8	4 8.0	7 14.0	28 13.3	26 49.7
16	3 39 33.7	23 28.0	17 43.3	14 53.5	23 17.0	6 39.2	8 7.2	24 18.0	4 3.5	7 16.9	28 15.6	26 51.2
17	3 43 30.2	24 28.4	17 40.1	28 54.7	24 52.4	7 54.3	8 51.1	24 30.1	3 59.2	7 19.8	28 17.8	26 52.6
18	3 47 26.8	25 28.9	17 36.9	12♓43.3	26 27.5	9 9.5	9 34.9	24 42.2	3 54.8	7 22.7	28 20.1	26 53.9
19	3 51 23.3	26 29.5	17 33.8	26 19.6	28 2.4	10 24.7	10 18.9	24 54.2	3 50.6	7 25.5	28 22.4	26 55.3
20	3 55 19.9	27 30.0	17 30.6	9♈44.4	29 37.1	11 39.9	11 2.8	25 6.2	3 46.3	7 28.2	28 24.6	26 56.6
21	3 59 16.5	28 30.6	17 27.4	22 58.4	1♐11.5	12 55.2	11 46.9	25 18.1	3 42.2	7 31.0	28 26.9	26 57.9
22	4 3 13.0	29 31.2	17 24.2	6♉ 1.6	2 45.8	14 10.5	12 30.9	25 30.0	3 38.1	7 33.7	28 29.2	26 59.1
23	4 7 9.6	0♐31.8	17 21.1	18 53.9	4 19.8	15 25.7	13 15.0	25 41.8	3 34.1	7 36.4	28 31.4	27 .4
24	4 11 6.1	1 32.5	17 17.9	1♊34.8	5 53.7	16 41.0	13 59.2	25 53.5	3 30.1	7 39.0	28 33.7	27 1.6
25	4 15 2.7	2 33.1	17 14.7	14 4.0	7 27.4	17 56.3	14 43.4	26 5.2	3 26.2	7 41.5	28 35.9	27 2.7
26	4 18 59.2	3 33.8	17 11.5	26 21.5	9 1.0	19 11.6	15 27.6	26 16.8	3 22.4	7 44.1	28 38.2	27 3.9
27	4 22 55.8	4 34.5	17 8.3	8♋28.1	10 34.5	20 26.9	16 11.8	26 28.4	3 18.6	7 46.6	28 40.4	27 5.0
28	4 26 52.4	5 35.2	17 5.2	20 25.6	12 7.8	21 42.3	16 56.1	26 39.9	3 14.9	7 49.0	28 42.7	27 6.1
29	4 30 48.9	6 36.0	17 2.0	2♌16.7	13 41.1	22 57.6	17 40.4	26 51.3	3 11.3	7 51.4	28 44.9	27 7.1
30	4 34 45.5	7 36.8	16 58.8	14 4.9	15 14.3	24 13.0	18 24.8	27 2.7	3 7.7	7 53.8	28 47.1	27 8.1

LATITUDE

DAY	EPHEM. SID. TIME	☉	☊	☾	☿	♀	♂	♃	♄	♅	♆	♇
1	2 40 25.3	0 .0	0 .0	4N14.4	1N26.2	1N33.9	2S .7	1N 6.2	2S43.5	0N41.4	1N38.7	15N18.3
4	2 52 15.0	0 .0	0 .0	1 44.8	1 8.4	1 32.6	1 57.1	1 6.3	2 43.4	0 41.5	1 38.7	15 19.4
7	3 4 4.7	0 .0	0 .0	1S33.4	0 49.1	1 30.7	1 53.5	1 6.5	2 43.2	0 41.5	1 38.6	15 20.6
10	3 15 54.3	0 .0	0 .0	4 20.7	0 29.1	1 28.2	1 49.9	1 6.6	2 42.9	0 41.6	1 38.6	15 21.8
13	3 27 44.0	0 .0	0 .0	4 56.4	0 8.8	1 25.1	1 46.3	1 6.8	2 42.6	0 41.6	1 38.6	15 23.1
16	3 39 33.7	0 .0	0 .0	2 50.2	0S11.4	1 21.5	1 42.6	1 7.0	2 42.2	0 41.7	1 38.5	15 24.5
19	3 51 23.3	0 .0	0 .0	0N39.8	0 31.1	1 17.4	1 39.0	1 7.3	2 41.8	0 41.8	1 38.5	15 25.9
22	4 3 13.0	0 .0	0 .0	3 42.5	0 50.1	1 12.8	1 35.3	1 7.5	2 41.3	0 41.9	1 38.5	15 27.3
25	4 15 2.7	0 .0	0 .0	4 59.7	1 8.0	1 7.7	1 31.7	1 7.8	2 40.7	0 41.9	1 38.5	15 28.8
28	4 26 52.4	0 .0	0 .0	4 12.7	1 24.6	1 2.2	1 28.1	1 8.0	2 40.2	0 42.0	1 38.5	15 30.3

RIGHT ASCENSION

DAY	EPHEM. SID. TIME	☉	☊	☾	☿	♀	♂	♃	♄	♅	♆	♇
1	2 40 25.3	6♏ 1.3	19♓26.5	27♋ .7	27♎19.5	17♎ 6.5	29♑47.3	19♎59.3	3♉51.6	6♎14.3	25♏49.7	2♎59.5
2	2 44 21.9	7 .0	19 23.6	9♌27.1	28 52.0	18 15.9	0♒32.3	20 11.2	3R47.0	6 17.4	25 51.9	3 1.2
3	2 48 18.4	7 59.0	19 20.6	21 18.7	0♏24.9	19 25.5	1 17.4	20 23.1	3 42.4	6 20.4	25 54.2	3 3.0
4	2 52 15.0	8 58.1	19 17.7	2♍42.9	1 57.9	20 35.2	2 2.4	20 34.9	3 37.7	6 23.4	25 56.4	3 4.7
5	2 56 11.5	9 57.5	19 14.8	13 51.1	3 31.1	21 45.0	2 47.5	20 46.8	3 33.1	6 26.5	25 58.6	3 6.4
6	3 0 8.1	10 57.1	19 11.8	24 57.7	5 4.5	22 55.1	3 32.5	20 58.6	3 28.5	6 29.4	26 .9	3 8.1
7	3 4 4.7	11 56.9	19 8.9	6♎18.7	6 38.1	24 5.3	4 17.4	21 10.4	3 24.0	6 32.4	26 3.1	3 9.7
8	3 8 1.2	12 56.9	19 6.0	18 11.4	8 11.9	25 15.7	5 2.4	21 22.1	3 19.4	6 35.3	26 5.4	3 11.4
9	3 11 57.8	13 57.1	19 3.0	0♏53.4	9 45.9	26 26.3	5 47.3	21 33.8	3 14.9	6 38.2	26 7.6	3 13.0
10	3 15 54.3	14 57.6	19 .1	14 39.2	11 20.1	27 37.1	6 32.2	21 45.5	3 10.4	6 41.1	26 9.9	3 14.6
11	3 19 50.9	15 58.2	18 57.2	29 34.9	12 54.6	28 48.2	7 17.0	21 57.2	3 5.9	6 43.9	26 12.2	3 16.2
12	3 23 47.4	16 59.1	18 54.2	15♐30.7	14 29.2	29 59.4	8 1.8	22 8.8	3 1.5	6 46.8	26 14.5	3 17.8
13	3 27 44.0	18 .2	18 51.3	1♑57.4	16 4.1	1♏10.8	8 46.6	22 20.4	2 57.1	6 49.5	26 16.8	3 19.4
14	3 31 40.6	19 1.5	18 48.4	18 14.3	17 39.3	2 22.5	9 31.3	22 32.0	2 52.7	6 52.3	26 19.1	3 20.9
15	3 35 37.1	20 2.9	18 45.4	3♒45.8	19 14.7	3 34.5	10 16.0	22 43.5	2 48.4	6 55.0	26 21.4	3 22.4
16	3 39 33.7	21 4.6	18 42.5	18 14.1	20 50.5	4 46.6	11 .6	22 55.0	2 44.1	6 57.7	26 23.7	3 23.9
17	3 43 30.2	22 6.5	18 39.5	1♓40.2	22 26.5	5 59.0	11 45.2	23 6.4	2 39.9	7 .4	26 26.0	3 25.3
18	3 47 26.8	23 8.6	18 36.6	14 16.9	24 2.8	7 11.7	12 29.7	23 17.8	2 35.7	7 3.0	26 28.3	3 26.8
19	3 51 23.3	24 10.9	18 33.7	26 21.9	25 39.5	8 24.7	13 14.2	23 29.1	2 31.6	7 5.6	26 30.6	3 28.2
20	3 55 19.9	25 13.5	18 30.7	8♈14.0	27 16.6	9 37.9	13 58.6	23 40.4	2 27.5	7 8.1	26 32.9	3 29.6
21	3 59 16.5	26 16.2	18 27.8	20 10.6	28 54.0	10 51.4	14 42.9	23 51.7	2 23.5	7 10.7	26 35.3	3 31.0
22	4 3 13.0	27 19.1	18 24.9	2♉25.8	0♐31.8	12 5.1	15 27.2	24 2.9	2 19.5	7 13.2	26 37.6	3 32.4
23	4 7 9.6	28 22.2	18 21.9	15 9.2	2 9.9	13 19.2	16 11.3	24 14.1	2 15.6	7 15.6	26 39.9	3 33.7
24	4 11 6.1	29 25.5	18 19.0	28 23.7	3 48.4	14 33.5	16 55.4	24 25.2	2 11.8	7 18.0	26 42.2	3 35.0
25	4 15 2.7	0♐29.0	18 16.1	12♊ 3.0	5 27.2	15 48.1	17 39.5	24 36.3	2 8.0	7 20.4	26 44.6	3 36.2
26	4 18 59.2	1 32.7	18 13.1	25 52.6	7 6.5	17 3.1	18 23.4	24 47.3	2 4.2	7 22.7	26 46.9	3 37.5
27	4 22 55.8	2 36.6	18 10.2	9♋33.3	8 46.1	18 18.3	19 7.3	24 58.2	2 .6	7 25.0	26 49.2	3 38.7
28	4 26 52.4	3 40.6	18 7.2	22 47.7	10 26.1	19 33.8	19 51.1	25 9.1	1 57.0	7 27.3	26 51.5	3 39.9
29	4 30 48.9	4 44.9	18 4.3	5♌25.1	12 6.4	20 49.6	20 34.9	25 19.9	1 53.4	7 29.5	26 53.8	3 41.1
30	4 34 45.5	5 49.3	18 1.4	17 23.6	13 47.1	22 5.7	21 18.5	25 30.7	1 50.0	7 31.7	26 56.1	3 42.2

DECLINATION

DAY	EPHEM. SID. TIME	☉	☊	☾	☿	♀	♂	♃	♄	♅	♆	♇
1	2 40 25.3	14S18.4	0S 4.8	25N26.2	9S43.4	5S34.7	22S40.7	7S14.6	10N41.8	1S56.8	18S 3.0	15N25.2
4	2 52 15.0	15 15.3	0 4.8	13 6.7	11 43.2	7 .4	22 10.9	7 28.7	10 37.2	2 .7	18 4.5	15 24.1
7	3 4 4.7	16 10.0	0 4.9	4S25.5	13 38.7	8 24.9	21 39.2	7 42.6	10 32.6	2 4.5	18 6.0	15 23.3
10	3 15 54.3	17 2.2	0 5.0	21 28.9	15 28.5	9 47.8	21 5.8	7 56.3	10 28.2	2 8.1	18 7.6	15 22.5
13	3 27 44.0	17 51.9	0 5.0	28 22.4	17 11.6	11 8.8	20 30.5	8 9.8	10 23.9	2 11.7	18 9.1	15 21.9
16	3 39 33.7	18 38.7	0 5.1	19 5.0	18 47.0	12 27.4	19 53.6	8 23.1	10 19.8	2 15.1	18 10.6	15 21.4
19	3 51 23.3	19 22.5	0 5.1	0 51.1	20 14.1	13 43.4	19 14.9	8 36.1	10 15.9	2 18.4	18 12.1	15 21.0
22	4 3 13.0	20 3.2	0 5.2	17N 1.8	21 32.2	14 56.3	18 34.7	8 48.9	10 12.1	2 21.6	18 13.6	15 20.8
25	4 15 2.7	20 40.5	0 5.3	27 27.2	22 40.7	16 5.9	17 53.0	9 1.4	10 8.6	2 24.6	18 15.1	15 20.7
28	4 26 52.4	21 14.5	0 5.3	26 3.3	23 39.0	17 11.7	17 9.8	9 13.7	10 5.3	2 27.5	18 16.5	15 20.7

DECEMBER 1969

LONGITUDE

DAY	EPHEM. SID. TIME h m s	☉ ° ′	☊ ° ′	☾ ° ′	☿ ° ′	♀ ° ′	♂ ° ′	♃ ° ′	♄ ° ′	♅ ° ′	♆ ° ′	♇ ° ′
1	4 38 42.0	8♐37.6	16♓55.6	25♌55.0	16♐47.4	25♏28.3	19♒ 9.2	27♎14.0	3♉ 4.3	7♎56.1	28♏49.4	27♍ 9.1
2	4 42 38.6	9 38.4	16 52.5	7♍51.8	18 20.4	26 43.7	19 53.6	27 25.2	3R .9	7 58.3	28 51.6	27 10.1
3	4 46 35.1	10 39.2	16 49.3	20 1.1	19 53.4	27 59.1	20 38.1	27 36.3	2 57.6	8 .6	28 53.8	27 11.0
4	4 50 31.7	11 40.1	16 46.1	2♎28.2	21 26.3	29 14.5	21 22.5	27 47.4	2 54.3	8 2.7	28 56.0	27 11.9
5	4 54 28.3	12 41.0	16 42.9	15 18.2	22 59.1	0♐29.9	22 7.1	27 58.4	2 51.2	8 4.9	28 58.2	27 12.7
6	4 58 24.8	13 41.9	16 39.8	28 34.9	24 31.8	1 45.4	22 51.6	28 9.3	2 48.1	8 7.0	29 .4	27 13.6
7	5 2 21.4	14 42.9	16 36.6	12♏20.1	26 4.4	3 .8	23 36.2	28 20.1	2 45.2	8 9.0	29 2.6	27 14.4
8	5 6 17.9	15 43.8	16 33.4	26 33.0	27 36.9	4 16.3	24 20.8	28 30.9	2 42.3	8 11.0	29 4.8	27 15.1
9	5 10 14.5	16 44.8	16 30.2	11♐ 9.4	29 9.3	5 31.7	25 5.4	28 41.5	2 39.5	8 12.9	29 7.0	27 15.9
10	5 14 11.1	17 45.8	16 27.1	26 2.2	0♑41.5	6 47.2	25 50.0	28 52.1	2 36.8	8 14.8	29 9.2	27 16.6
11	5 18 7.6	18 46.8	16 23.9	11♑ 2.3	2 13.5	8 2.6	26 34.7	29 2.6	2 34.2	8 16.7	29 11.3	27 17.2
12	5 22 4.2	19 47.9	16 20.7	25 59.9	3 45.3	9 18.2	27 19.4	29 13.0	2 31.8	8 18.5	29 13.5	27 17.9
13	5 26 .7	20 48.9	16 17.5	10♒46.6	5 16.8	10 33.6	28 4.1	29 23.4	2 29.4	8 20.2	29 15.7	27 18.5
14	5 29 57.3	21 49.9	16 14.3	25 16.3	6 47.8	11 49.1	28 48.8	29 33.6	2 27.1	8 21.9	29 17.8	27 19.1
15	5 33 53.9	22 51.0	16 11.2	9♓26.0	8 18.4	13 4.6	29 33.6	29 43.7	2 24.9	8 23.6	29 19.9	27 19.6
16	5 37 50.4	23 52.0	16 8.0	23 15.0	9 48.4	14 20.1	0♓18.3	29 53.7	2 22.8	8 25.2	29 22.0	27 20.1
17	5 41 47.0	24 53.1	16 4.8	6♈44.5	11 17.7	15 35.5	1 3.0	0♏ 3.6	2 20.8	8 26.7	29 24.1	27 20.6
18	5 45 43.5	25 54.1	16 1.6	19 56.6	12 46.1	16 51.0	1 47.8	0 13.5	2 18.9	8 28.2	29 26.1	27 21.0
19	5 49 40.1	26 55.2	15 58.5	2♉53.8	14 13.5	18 6.5	2 32.6	0 23.2	2 17.1	8 29.6	29 28.2	27 21.4
20	5 53 36.6	27 56.3	15 55.3	15 38.3	15 39.7	19 22.0	3 17.3	0 32.8	2 15.4	8 31.0	29 30.2	27 21.8
21	5 57 33.2	28 57.3	15 52.1	28 11.8	17 4.4	20 37.5	4 2.1	0 42.3	2 13.9	8 32.3	29 32.3	27 22.1
22	6 1 29.8	29 58.4	15 48.9	10♊35.6	18 27.4	21 52.9	4 46.9	0 51.8	2 12.4	8 33.6	29 34.3	27 22.4
23	6 5 26.3	0♑59.5	15 45.8	22 50.5	19 48.4	23 8.4	5 31.6	1 1.1	2 11.0	8 34.8	29 36.3	27 22.6
24	6 9 22.9	2 .6	15 42.6	4♋57.2	21 6.9	24 23.9	6 16.4	1 10.3	2 9.8	8 35.9	29 38.3	27 22.9
25	6 13 19.4	3 1.7	15 39.4	16 56.7	22 22.5	25 39.4	7 1.2	1 19.4	2 8.6	8 37.1	29 40.2	27 23.1
26	6 17 16.0	4 2.8	15 36.2	28 50.0	23 34.7	26 54.9	7 46.0	1 28.3	2 7.6	8 38.1	29 42.2	27 23.2
27	6 21 12.6	5 4.0	15 33.1	10♌39.2	24 43.1	28 10.4	8 30.7	1 37.2	2 6.7	8 39.1	29 44.1	27 23.3
28	6 25 9.1	6 5.1	15 29.9	22 26.8	25 46.9	29 25.9	9 15.5	1 45.9	2 5.8	8 40.0	29 46.0	27 23.4
29	6 29 5.7	7 6.2	15 26.7	4♍16.3	26 45.4	0♑41.4	10 .2	1 54.6	2 5.1	8 40.9	29 47.9	27 23.5
30	6 33 2.2	8 7.3	15 23.5	16 12.0	27 37.9	1 56.9	10 45.0	2 3.1	2 4.5	8 41.8	29 49.8	27 23.5
31	6 36 58.8	9 8.5	15 20.3	28 18.6	28 23.5	3 12.3	11 29.8	2 11.5	2 4.0	8 42.5	29 51.6	27 23.5

LATITUDE

DAY	EPHEM. SID. TIME	☉	☊	☾	☿	♀	♂	♃	♄	♅	♆	♇
1	4 38 42.0	0 .0	0 .0	1N49.8	1S39.6	0N56.3	1S24.5	1N 8.3	2S39.6	0N42.1	1N38.5	15N31.8
4	4 50 31.7	0 .0	0 .0	1S20.2	1 52.6	0 50.2	1 20.9	1 8.7	2 38.9	0 42.2	1 38.6	15 33.4
7	5 2 21.4	0 .0	0 .0	4 7.8	2 3.3	0 43.7	1 17.3	1 9.0	2 38.2	0 42.3	1 38.6	15 35.0
10	5 14 11.1	0 .0	0 .0	4 55.7	2 11.2	0 36.9	1 13.8	1 9.4	2 37.5	0 42.4	1 38.6	15 36.6
13	5 26 .7	0 .0	0 .0	2 53.5	2 15.7	0 30.0	1 10.3	1 9.7	2 36.7	0 42.5	1 38.7	15 38.2
16	5 37 50.4	0 .0	0 .0	0N39.3	2 16.3	0 22.9	1 6.8	1 10.1	2 36.0	0 42.6	1 38.7	15 39.9
19	5 49 40.1	0 .0	0 .0	3 41.5	2 12.1	0 15.7	1 3.3	1 10.6	2 35.2	0 42.7	1 38.8	15 41.5
22	6 1 29.8	0 .0	0 .0	4 59.4	2 2.0	0 8.5	0 59.8	1 11.0	2 34.3	0 42.8	1 38.9	15 43.2
25	6 13 19.4	0 .0	0 .0	4 14.4	1 45.0	0 1.2	0 56.4	1 11.4	2 33.5	0 42.9	1 39.0	15 44.9
28	6 25 9.1	0 .0	0 .0	1 52.3	1 19.5	0S 6.1	0 53.1	1 11.9	2 32.6	0 43.0	1 39.0	15 46.5
31	6 36 58.8	0 .0	0 .0	1S15.4	0 44.4	0 13.3	0 49.7	1 12.4	2 31.8	0 43.2	1 39.1	15 48.2

RIGHT ASCENSION

DAY	EPHEM. SID. TIME	☉	☊	☾	☿	♀	♂	♃	♄	♅	♆	♇
1	4 38 42.0	6♐53.9	17♓58.4	28♌48.5	15♐28.1	23♏22.2	22♒ 2.1	25♎41.4	1♉46.6	7♎33.8	26♏58.4	3♎43.4
2	4 42 38.6	7 58.6	17 55.5	9♍50.5	17 9.4	24 38.9	22 45.6	25 52.1	1R43.3	7 35.9	27 .7	3 44.4
3	4 46 35.1	9 3.5	17 52.6	20 43.7	18 51.0	25 55.9	23 29.1	26 2.6	1 40.0	7 38.0	27 3.0	3 45.5
4	4 50 31.7	10 8.6	17 49.6	1♎44.1	20 32.8	27 13.3	24 12.4	26 13.2	1 36.9	7 40.0	27 5.2	3 46.5
5	4 54 28.3	11 13.8	17 46.7	13 9.8	22 14.8	28 30.9	24 55.7	26 23.6	1 33.8	7 42.0	27 7.5	3 47.6
6	4 58 24.8	12 19.2	17 43.7	25 20.0	23 57.0	29 48.8	25 38.9	26 34.0	1 30.8	7 43.9	27 9.8	3 48.5
7	5 2 21.4	13 24.7	17 40.8	8♏33.2	25 39.2	1♐ 7.0	26 22.1	26 44.3	1 27.9	7 45.8	27 12.0	3 49.5
8	5 6 17.9	14 30.3	17 37.9	23 2.9	27 21.5	2 25.5	27 5.1	26 54.6	1 25.1	7 47.7	27 14.3	3 50.4
9	5 10 14.5	15 36.1	17 34.9	8♐49.3	29 3.8	3 44.3	27 48.1	27 4.7	1 22.4	7 49.5	27 16.5	3 51.3
10	5 14 11.1	16 42.0	17 32.0	25 30.9	0♑46.0	5 3.4	28 31.0	27 14.8	1 19.7	7 51.2	27 18.8	3 52.2
11	5 18 7.6	17 48.0	17 29.0	12♑25.6	2 28.0	6 22.7	29 13.9	27 24.8	1 17.2	7 52.9	27 21.0	3 53.0
12	5 22 4.2	18 54.1	17 26.1	28 47.1	4 9.8	7 42.3	29 56.7	27 34.8	1 14.7	7 54.6	27 23.2	3 53.9
13	5 26 .7	20 .3	17 23.2	14♒ 4.2	5 51.1	9 2.1	0♓39.4	27 44.6	1 12.4	7 56.2	27 25.4	3 54.6
14	5 29 57.3	21 6.5	17 20.2	28 9.6	7 31.9	10 22.2	1 22.0	27 54.4	1 10.1	7 57.8	27 27.6	3 55.4
15	5 33 53.9	22 12.8	17 17.3	11♓13.1	9 12.0	11 42.5	2 4.5	28 4.1	1 7.9	7 59.3	27 29.8	3 56.1
16	5 37 50.4	23 19.2	17 14.3	23 32.6	10 51.3	13 3.0	2 47.0	28 13.7	1 5.8	8 .8	27 32.0	3 56.8
17	5 41 47.0	24 25.6	17 11.4	5♈28.4	12 29.5	14 23.8	3 29.4	28 23.2	1 3.8	8 2.2	27 34.1	3 57.5
18	5 45 43.5	25 32.1	17 8.5	17 19.5	14 6.6	15 44.7	4 11.7	28 32.6	1 1.9	8 3.6	27 36.3	3 58.1
19	5 49 40.1	26 38.6	17 5.5	29 22.4	15 42.2	17 5.9	4 53.9	28 41.9	1 .1	8 4.9	27 38.4	3 58.7
20	5 53 36.6	27 45.1	17 2.6	11♉49.3	17 16.2	18 27.2	5 36.1	28 51.1	0 58.4	8 6.2	27 40.5	3 59.3
21	5 57 33.2	28 51.7	16 59.6	24 46.5	18 48.1	19 48.7	6 18.1	29 .2	0 56.8	8 7.4	27 42.6	3 59.8
22	6 1 29.8	29 58.3	16 56.7	8♊11.7	20 17.7	21 10.3	7 .1	29 9.3	0 55.3	8 8.6	27 44.7	4 .3
23	6 5 26.3	1♑ 4.9	16 53.8	21 54.1	21 44.6	22 32.1	7 42.1	29 18.2	0 53.9	8 9.8	27 46.7	4 .8
24	6 9 22.9	2 11.5	16 50.8	5♋35.8	23 8.4	23 54.1	8 23.9	29 27.0	0 52.6	8 10.8	27 48.8	4 1.2
25	6 13 19.4	3 18.0	16 47.9	18 57.9	24 28.6	25 16.1	9 5.7	29 35.8	0 51.4	8 11.9	27 50.8	4 1.6
26	6 17 16.0	4 24.6	16 44.9	1♌46.2	25 44.6	26 38.2	9 47.4	29 44.4	0 50.4	8 12.8	27 52.8	4 2.0
27	6 21 12.6	5 31.1	16 42.0	13 54.9	26 55.9	28 .5	10 29.1	29 52.9	0 49.4	8 13.8	27 54.8	4 2.4
28	6 25 9.1	6 37.6	16 39.0	25 26.1	28 1.9	29 22.8	11 10.6	0♏ 1.3	0 48.5	8 14.7	27 56.8	4 2.7
29	6 29 5.7	7 44.1	16 36.1	6♍28.2	29 1.7	0♑45.1	11 52.1	0 9.6	0 47.7	8 15.5	27 58.7	4 3.0
30	6 33 2.2	8 50.5	16 33.1	17 13.5	29 54.7	2 7.5	12 33.6	0 17.8	0 47.0	8 16.3	28 .7	4 3.2
31	6 36 58.8	9 56.9	16 30.2	27 57.0	0♒39.9	3 30.0	13 15.0	0 25.9	0 46.5	8 17.0	28 2.6	4 3.4

DECLINATION

DAY	EPHEM. SID. TIME	☉	☊	☾	☿	♀	♂	♃	♄	♅	♆	♇
1	4 38 42.0	21S44.8	0S 5.4	14N36.4	24S26.5	18S13.4	16S25.3	9S25.6	10N 2.3	2S30.2	18S18.0	15N20.9
4	4 50 31.7	22 11.4	0 5.5	2S12.5	25 2.5	18 10.6	15 39.4	9 37.3	9 59.6	2 32.8	18 19.4	15 21.2
7	5 2 21.4	22 34.1	0 5.5	19 28.3	25 26.5	20 3.1	14 52.4	9 48.6	9 57.1	2 35.1	18 20.8	15 21.7
10	5 14 11.1	22 52.9	0 5.6	28 18.7	25 37.8	20 50.5	14 4.1	9 59.6	9 55.0	2 37.3	18 22.1	15 22.3
13	5 26 .7	23 7.6	0 5.7	20 19.0	25 36.0	21 32.5	13 14.8	10 10.3	9 53.1	2 39.4	18 23.5	15 23.0
16	5 37 50.4	23 18.2	0 5.7	2 4.7	25 20.9	22 8.8	12 24.5	10 20.6	9 51.6	2 41.2	18 24.8	15 23.9
19	5 49 40.1	23 24.5	0 5.8	15N56.8	24 52.5	22 39.1	11 33.3	10 30.5	9 50.4	2 42.9	18 26.0	15 24.9
22	6 1 29.8	23 26.7	0 5.9	26 58.7	24 11.3	23 3.3	10 41.3	10 40.1	9 49.6	2 44.3	18 27.3	15 26.0
25	6 13 19.4	23 24.6	0 5.9	26 34.6	23 18.8	23 21.3	9 48.6	10 49.2	9 49.1	2 45.6	18 28.4	15 27.3
28	6 25 9.1	23 18.3	0 6.0	15 48.2	22 17.8	23 32.7	8 55.2	10 57.9	9 49.0	2 46.7	18 29.6	15 28.6
31	6 36 58.8	23 7.8	0 6.1	0S28.8	21 12.8	23 37.7	8 1.2	11 6.3	9 49.2	2 47.6	18 30.7	15 30.1

JANUARY 1970

LONGITUDE

DAY	EPHEM. SID. TIME h m s	☉ ° ′	☊ ° ′	☽ ° ′	☿ ° ′	♀ ° ′	♂ ° ′	♃ ° ′	♄ ° ′	♅ ° ′	♆ ° ′	♇ ° ′
1	6 40 55.4	10♑ 9.6	15♓17.2	10♎41.6	29♑ 1.4	4♑27.8	12♓14.5	2♏19.7	2♉ 3.7	8♎43.3	29♏53.5	27♍23.5
2	6 44 51.9	11 10.8	15 14.0	23 26.1	29 30.6	5 43.4	12 59.3	2 27.9	2R 3.5	8 44.0	29 55.3	27R23.4
3	6 48 48.5	12 12.0	15 10.8	6♏36.6	29 50.3	6 58.9	13 44.0	2 35.9	2 3.3	8 44.6	29 57.1	27 23.3
4	6 52 45.0	13 13.2	15 7.6	20 16.6	29 59.5	8 14.4	14 28.8	2 43.8	2 3.3	8 45.1	29 58.9	27 23.2
5	6 56 41.6	14 14.4	15 4.5	4♐26.8	29R57.6	9 29.9	15 13.5	2 51.5	2 3.3	8 45.6	0♐ .6	27 23.0
6	7 0 38.1	15 15.5	15 1.3	19 4.9	29 44.1	10 45.4	15 58.2	2 59.2	2D 3.5	8 46.1	0 2.4	27 22.8
7	7 4 34.7	16 16.7	14 58.1	4♑ 5.2	29 18.7	12 .9	16 42.9	3 6.6	2 3.8	8 46.4	0 4.1	27 22.5
8	7 8 31.3	17 17.9	14 54.9	19 18.6	28 41.6	13 16.4	17 27.6	3 14.0	2 4.2	8 46.8	0 5.7	27 22.2
9	7 12 27.8	18 19.0	14 51.8	4♒34.2	27 53.3	14 31.9	18 12.3	3 21.2	2 4.8	8 47.0	0 7.4	27 21.9
10	7 16 24.4	19 20.2	14 48.6	19 41.5	26 55.0	15 47.4	18 57.0	3 28.2	2 5.4	8 47.2	0 9.0	27 21.6
11	7 20 20.9	20 21.4	14 45.4	4♓31.4	25 48.2	17 2.9	19 41.7	3 35.2	2 6.1	8 47.4	0 10.6	27 21.2
12	7 24 17.5	21 22.5	14 42.2	18 58.4	24 34.7	18 18.3	20 26.3	3 41.9	2 7.0	8 47.5	0 12.2	27 20.8
13	7 28 14.1	22 23.6	14 39.1	2♈59.9	23 17.1	19 33.8	21 11.0	3 48.6	2 8.0	8 47.5	0 13.8	27 20.3
14	7 32 10.6	23 24.8	14 35.9	16 35.9	21 57.7	20 49.3	21 55.6	3 55.1	2 9.1	8 47.5	0 15.3	27 19.8
15	7 36 7.2	24 25.9	14 32.7	29 48.6	20 39.2	22 4.7	22 40.2	4 1.4	2 10.3	8R47.4	0 16.8	27 19.3
16	7 40 3.7	25 27.0	14 29.5	12♉41.0	19 23.7	23 20.2	23 24.8	4 7.6	2 11.6	8 47.3	0 18.3	27 18.8
17	7 44 .3	26 28.1	14 26.4	25 16.4	18 13.4	24 35.6	24 9.4	4 13.6	2 13.0	8 47.1	0 19.8	27 18.2
18	7 47 56.8	27 29.2	14 23.2	7♊38.4	17 9.9	25 51.1	24 53.9	4 19.5	2 14.5	8 46.8	0 21.2	27 17.6
19	7 51 53.4	28 30.2	14 20.0	19 49.7	16 14.5	27 6.5	25 38.4	4 25.2	2 16.2	8 46.5	0 22.6	27 17.0
20	7 55 50.0	29 31.3	14 16.8	1♋53.0	15 27.9	28 21.9	26 22.9	4 30.8	2 17.9	8 46.2	0 23.9	27 16.3
21	7 59 46.5	0♒32.3	14 13.6	13 50.1	14 50.6	29 37.3	27 7.4	4 36.2	2 19.8	8 45.8	0 25.3	27 15.6
22	8 3 43.1	1 33.3	14 10.5	25 43.0	14 22.6	0♒52.7	27 51.8	4 41.4	2 21.7	8 45.3	0 26.6	27 14.9
23	8 7 39.6	2 34.4	14 7.3	7♌33.2	14 3.8	2 8.1	28 36.3	4 46.6	2 23.8	8 44.8	0 27.9	27 14.2
24	8 11 36.2	3 35.4	14 4.1	19 22.3	13 53.9	3 23.5	29 20.7	4 51.5	2 26.0	8 44.3	0 29.2	27 13.4
25	8 15 32.8	4 36.4	14 .9	1♍12.4	13 52.3	4 38.9	0♈ 5.1	4 56.3	2 28.3	8 43.6	0 30.4	27 12.6
26	8 19 29.3	5 37.4	13 57.8	13 6.0	13D58.6	5 54.3	0 49.4	5 .9	2 30.7	8 42.9	0 31.6	27 11.7
27	8 23 25.9	6 38.3	13 54.6	25 5.9	14 12.2	7 9.7	1 33.7	5 5.3	2 33.2	8 42.2	0 32.8	27 10.8
28	8 27 22.4	7 39.3	13 51.4	7♎15.9	14 32.6	8 25.0	2 18.0	5 9.6	2 35.8	8 41.4	0 33.9	27 9.9
29	8 31 19.0	8 40.2	13 48.2	19 39.8	14 59.1	9 40.4	3 2.3	5 13.6	2 38.5	8 40.6	0 35.0	27 9.0
30	8 35 15.5	9 41.2	13 45.1	2♏22.0	15 31.2	10 55.7	3 46.5	5 17.6	2 41.3	8 39.7	0 36.1	27 8.1
31	8 39 12.1	10 42.1	13 41.9	15 26.5	16 8.5	12 11.1	4 30.7	5 21.3	2 44.2	8 38.7	0 37.2	27 7.1

LATITUDE

DAY	EPHEM. SID. TIME	☉	☊	☽	☿	♀	♂	♃	♄	♅	♆	♇
1	6 40 55.4	0 .0	0 .0	2S17.2	0S30.4	0S15.6	0S48.6	1N12.6	2S31.5	0N43.2	1N39.2	15N48.7
4	6 52 45.0	0 .0	0 .0	4 39.4	0N18.1	0 22.7	0 45.4	1 13.1	2 30.6	0 43.3	1 39.3	15 50.4
7	7 4 34.7	0 .0	0 .0	4 45.5	1 13.9	0 29.5	0 42.1	1 13.6	2 29.7	0 43.4	1 39.4	15 52.0
10	7 16 24.4	0 .0	0 .0	2 2.2	2 10.2	0 36.1	0 38.9	1 14.2	2 28.8	0 43.5	1 39.5	15 53.6
13	7 28 14.1	0 .0	0 .0	1N45.1	2 56.1	0 42.5	0 35.8	1 14.7	2 27.9	0 43.6	1 39.6	15 55.2
16	7 40 3.7	0 .0	0 .0	4 26.0	3 22.4	0 48.6	0 32.7	1 15.3	2 27.0	0 43.7	1 39.7	15 56.7
19	7 51 53.4	0 .0	0 .0	5 5.7	3 26.4	0 54.3	0 29.6	1 15.9	2 26.1	0 43.8	1 39.9	15 58.2
22	8 3 43.1	0 .0	0 .0	3 45.2	3 12.8	0 59.7	0 26.6	1 16.5	2 25.2	0 44.0	1 40.0	15 59.7
25	8 15 32.8	0 .0	0 .0	0 59.4	2 48.0	1 4.7	0 23.6	1 17.1	2 24.4	0 44.1	1 40.1	16 1.1
28	8 27 22.4	0 .0	0 .0	2S12.9	2 17.5	1 9.2	0 20.7	1 17.7	2 23.5	0 44.2	1 40.3	16 2.5
31	8 39 12.1	0 .0	0 .0	4 39.9	1 45.0	1 13.3	0 17.9	1 18.4	2 22.7	0 44.3	1 40.4	16 3.8

RIGHT ASCENSION

DAY	EPHEM. SID. TIME	☉	☊	☽	☿	♀	♂	♃	♄	♅	♆	♇
1	6 40 55.4	11♑ 3.2	16♓27.3	8♎55.5	1♒16.6	4♑52.4	13♓56.3	0♏33.9	0♉46.0	8♎17.7	28♏ 4.5	4♎ 3.6
2	6 44 51.9	12 9.5	16 24.3	20 27.8	1 43.8	6 14.9	14 37.6	0 41.8	0R45.7	8 18.3	28 6.4	4 3.8
3	6 48 48.5	13 15.6	16 21.4	2♏53.1	2 .6	7 37.3	15 18.8	0 49.5	0 45.5	8 18.9	28 8.3	4 4.0
4	6 52 45.0	14 21.7	16 18.4	16 29.4	2 6.4	8 59.7	15 60.0	0 57.1	0 45.3	8 19.4	28 10.1	4 4.1
5	6 56 41.6	15 27.7	16 15.5	1♐27.0	2R .3	10 22.1	16 41.1	1 4.6	0 45.3	8 19.9	28 11.9	4 4.1
6	7 0 38.1	16 33.6	16 12.5	17 39.5	1 42.2	11 44.3	17 22.1	1 12.0	0D45.4	8 20.3	28 13.7	4 4.2
7	7 4 34.7	17 39.3	16 9.6	4♑37.2	1 11.7	13 6.5	18 3.1	1 19.2	0 45.5	8 20.7	28 15.5	4 4.2
8	7 8 31.3	18 45.0	16 6.6	21 33.2	0 29.1	14 28.6	18 44.1	1 26.3	0 45.8	8 21.0	28 17.2	4R 4.1
9	7 12 27.8	19 50.5	16 3.7	7♒44.0	29♑35.2	15 50.6	19 25.0	1 33.3	0 46.2	8 21.3	28 18.9	4 4.1
10	7 16 24.4	20 55.9	16 .8	22 46.5	28 31.1	17 12.4	20 5.9	1 40.1	0 46.7	8 21.5	28 20.6	4 4.0
11	7 20 20.9	22 1.1	15 57.8	6♓40.3	27 18.5	18 34.1	20 46.7	1 46.8	0 47.3	8 21.6	28 22.3	4 3.9
12	7 24 17.5	23 6.2	15 54.9	19 39.4	25 59.5	19 55.7	21 27.4	1 53.4	0 48.1	8 21.7	28 23.9	4 3.7
13	7 28 14.1	24 11.2	15 51.9	2♈ 3.2	24 36.5	21 17.0	22 8.2	1 59.8	0 48.9	8 21.8	28 25.5	4 3.5
14	7 32 10.6	25 16.0	15 49.0	14 11.5	23 12.1	22 38.2	22 48.9	2 6.1	0 49.8	8 21.8	28 27.1	4 3.3
15	7 36 7.2	26 20.6	15 46.0	26 21.8	21 48.8	23 59.2	23 29.5	2 12.3	0 50.9	8R21.7	28 28.7	4 3.1
16	7 40 3.7	27 25.0	15 43.1	8♉48.2	20 29.2	25 20.0	24 10.1	2 18.3	0 52.0	8 21.6	28 30.2	4 2.8
17	7 44 .3	28 29.3	15 40.1	21 38.9	19 15.2	26 40.5	24 50.7	2 24.2	0 53.3	8 21.4	28 31.7	4 2.5
18	7 47 56.8	29 33.4	15 37.2	4♊55.2	18 8.7	28 .9	25 31.2	2 29.9	0 54.6	8 21.2	28 33.2	4 2.2
19	7 51 53.4	0♒37.3	15 34.2	18 29.7	17 10.7	29 20.9	26 52.2	2 40.9	0 57.6	8 20.6	28 36.1	4 1.4
20	7 55 50.0	1 41.0	15 31.3	2♋ 7.8	16 22.2	0♒40.8	27 32.6	2 46.2	0 59.3	8 20.3	28 37.5	4 1.0
21	7 59 46.5	2 44.6	15 28.3	15 32.1	15 43.5	2 .3	28 13.0	2 51.3	1 1.1	8 19.9	28 38.8	4 .5
22	8 3 43.1	3 47.9	15 25.4	28 27.7	15 14.7	3 19.6	28 53.4	2 56.3	1 3.0	8 19.4	28 40.2	4 .1
23	8 7 39.6	4 51.1	15 22.4	10♌46.2	14 55.7	4 38.7	29 33.7	3 1.1	1 5.0	8 18.9	28 41.5	3 59.6
24	8 11 36.2	5 54.1	15 19.5	22 27.0	14 46.1	5 57.5	0♈14.0	3 5.8	1 7.0	8 18.4	28 42.8	3 59.0
25	8 15 32.8	6 56.8	15 16.5	3♍36.1	14 45.5	7 15.9	0 54.3	3 10.3	1 9.2	8 17.8	28 44.1	3 58.5
26	8 19 29.3	7 59.4	15 13.6	14 23.5	14D53.2	8 34.1	1 34.6	3 14.6	1 11.5	8 17.1	28 45.3	3 57.9
27	8 23 25.9	9 1.8	15 10.6	25 2.3	15 8.7	9 52.0	2 14.9	3 18.8	1 13.9	8 16.4	28 46.5	3 57.3
28	8 27 22.4	10 4.0	15 7.7	5♎47.5	15 31.5	11 9.6	2 55.1	3 22.8	1 16.4	8 15.6	28 47.6	3 56.6
29	8 31 19.0	11 6.0	15 4.7	16 55.7	16 .8	12 26.8	3 35.3	3 26.7	1 18.9	8 14.8	28 48.7	3 55.9
30	8 35 15.5	12 7.7	15 1.8	28 44.5	16 36.2	13 43.8	4 15.5	3 30.4	1 21.6	8 13.9	28 49.8	3 55.2
31	8 39 12.1	13 9.3	14 58.8	11♏31.4	17 17.0	15 .5						

DECLINATION

DAY	EPHEM. SID. TIME	☉	☊	☽	☿	♀	♂	♃	♄	♅	♆	♇
1	6 40 55.4	23S 3.4	0S 6.1	6S20.2	20S51.4	23S37.8	7S43.2	11S 8.9	9N49.3	2S47.8	18S31.0	15N30.6
4	6 52 45.0	22 47.3	0 6.1	22 18.2	19 51.8	23 34.0	6 48.5	11 16.7	9 50.0	2 48.5	18 32.1	15 32.2
7	7 4 34.7	22 27.2	0 6.2	28 8.3	19 5.7	23 23.5	5 53.5	11 24.0	9 51.0	2 48.9	18 33.1	15 34.0
10	7 16 24.4	22 3.0	0 6.3	16 50.9	18 39.0	23 6.6	4 58.2	11 30.8	9 52.4	2 49.1	18 34.0	15 35.8
13	7 28 14.1	21 35.0	0 6.3	2N47.9	18 32.5	22 43.2	4 2.7	11 37.1	9 54.1	2 49.1	18 34.9	15 37.7
16	7 40 3.7	21 3.3	0 6.4	19 52.1	18 42.2	22 13.5	3 6.9	11 43.0	9 56.2	2 48.9	18 35.7	15 39.8
19	7 51 53.4	20 27.9	0 6.5	28 8.1	19 2.5	21 37.8	2 11.2	11 48.4	9 58.6	2 48.5	18 36.4	15 41.9
22	8 3 43.1	19 49.1	0 6.5	24 41.6	19 28.5	20 56.3	1 15.4	11 53.2	10 1.3	2 47.9	18 37.1	15 44.0
25	8 15 32.8	19 6.9	0 6.6	11 58.4	19 56.3	20 9.1	0 19.7	11 57.6	10 4.4	2 47.2	18 37.8	15 46.2
28	8 27 22.4	18 21.6	0 6.7	4S55.1	20 22.4	19 16.6	0N35.9	12 1.4	10 7.7	2 46.2	18 38.4	15 48.5
31	8 39 12.1	17 33.3	0 6.7	20 55.6	20 43.9	18 19.1	1 31.2	12 4.7	10 11.4	2 45.1	18 38.9	15 50.9

FEBRUARY 1970

LONGITUDE

DAY	EPHEM. SID. TIME	☉	☊	☽	☿	♀	♂	♃	♄	♅	♆	♇
	h m s	° ′	° ′	° ′	° ′	° ′	° ′	° ′	° ′	° ′	° ′	° ′
1	8 43 8.7	11♒43.0	13♓38.7	28♏56.8	16♑50.4	13♒26.4	5♈14.9	5♏24.9	2♉47.2	8♎37.7	0♐38.2	27♍ 6.1
2	8 47 5.2	12 43.9	13 35.5	12♐54.6	17 36.5	14 41.7	5 59.1	5 28.3	2 50.3	8 R 36.7	0 39.2	27 R 5.0
3	8 51 1.8	13 44.8	13 32.3	27 19.7	18 26.6	15 57.0	6 43.2	5 31.5	2 53.5	8 35.6	0 40.1	27 4.0
4	8 54 58.3	14 45.7	13 29.2	12♑ 8.7	19 20.1	17 12.4	7 27.3	5 34.5	2 56.8	8 34.4	0 41.1	27 2.9
5	8 58 54.9	15 46.5	13 26.0	27 15.1	20 16.9	18 27.7	8 11.4	5 37.4	3 .2	8 33.2	0 41.9	27 1.8
6	9 2 51.4	16 47.4	13 22.8	12♒29.9	21 16.6	19 42.9	8 55.4	5 40.1	3 3.7	8 32.0	0 42.8	27 .6
7	9 6 48.0	17 48.2	13 19.6	27 42.7	22 19.0	20 58.2	9 39.4	5 42.6	3 7.3	8 30.7	0 43.6	26 59.5
8	9 10 44.5	18 49.0	13 16.5	12♓43.7	23 23.8	22 13.5	10 23.4	5 44.9	3 11.0	8 29.3	0 44.4	26 58.3
9	9 14 41.1	19 49.7	13 13.3	27 24.9	24 30.9	23 28.7	11 7.4	5 47.0	3 14.8	8 27.9	0 45.2	26 57.1
10	9 18 37.7	20 50.5	13 10.1	11♈41.0	25 40.1	24 44.0	11 51.3	5 49.0	3 18.7	8 26.5	0 45.9	26 55.9
11	9 22 34.2	21 51.2	13 6.9	25 30.0	26 51.2	25 59.2	12 35.2	5 50.7	3 22.6	8 25.0	0 46.6	26 54.6
12	9 26 30.8	22 51.9	13 3.8	8♉52.1	28 4.2	27 14.4	13 19.1	5 52.3	3 26.7	8 23.5	0 47.3	26 53.4
13	9 30 27.3	23 52.6	13 .6	21 49.6	29 18.9	28 29.7	14 3.0	5 53.7	3 30.9	8 22.0	0 47.9	26 52.1
14	9 34 23.9	24 53.2	12 57.4	4♊25.9	0♒35.1	29 44.8	14 46.8	5 54.9	3 35.1	8 20.3	0 48.5	26 50.8
15	9 38 20.4	25 53.9	12 54.2	16 45.1	1 52.9	0♓60.0	15 30.5	5 55.9	3 39.5	8 18.7	0 49.1	26 49.5
16	9 42 17.0	26 54.4	12 51.0	28 51.2	3 12.1	2 15.1	16 14.2	5 56.8	3 43.9	8 17.0	0 49.6	26 48.1
17	9 46 13.5	27 55.0	12 47.9	10♋48.3	4 32.6	3 30.2	16 57.9	5 57.4	3 48.4	8 15.2	0 50.1	26 46.8
18	9 50 10.1	28 55.5	12 44.7	22 39.8	5 54.4	4 45.4	17 41.6	5 57.8	3 53.0	8 13.4	0 50.6	26 45.4
19	9 54 6.7	29 56.0	12 41.5	4♌28.8	7 17.5	6 .4	18 25.2	5 58.1	3 57.6	8 11.6	0 51.0	26 44.0
20	9 58 3.2	0♓56.5	12 38.3	16 18.0	8 41.8	7 15.5	19 8.7	5 58.2	4 2.4	8 9.7	0 51.4	26 42.6
21	10 1 59.8	1 56.9	12 35.2	28 9.8	10 7.2	8 30.6	19 52.3	5 R 58.1	4 7.2	8 7.8	0 51.7	26 41.1
22	10 5 56.3	2 57.3	12 32.0	10♍ 6.0	11 33.8	9 45.6	20 35.8	5 57.7	4 12.1	8 5.9	0 52.1	26 39.7
23	10 9 52.9	3 57.7	12 28.8	22 8.7	13 1.5	11 .6	21 19.2	5 57.3	4 17.1	8 3.9	0 52.4	26 38.2
24	10 13 49.4	4 58.1	12 25.6	4♎19.8	14 30.3	12 15.6	22 2.6	5 56.6	4 22.2	8 1.9	0 52.6	26 36.7
25	10 17 46.0	5 58.4	12 22.4	16 41.4	16 .2	13 30.6	22 46.0	5 55.7	4 27.4	7 59.9	0 52.8	26 35.2
26	10 21 42.5	6 58.7	12 19.3	29 15.6	17 31.1	14 45.6	23 29.4	5 54.6	4 32.6	7 57.8	0 53.0	26 33.7
27	10 25 39.1	7 59.0	12 16.1	12♏ 4.9	19 3.1	16 .5	24 12.7	5 53.4	4 37.9	7 55.7	0 53.2	26 32.2
28	10 29 35.6	8 59.3	12 12.9	25 11.8	20 36.1	17 15.4	24 55.9	5 52.0	4 43.3	7 53.5	0 53.3	26 30.7

LATITUDE

DAY	EPHEM. SID. TIME	☉	☊	☽	☿	♀	♂	♃	♄	♅	♆	♇
1	8 43 8.7	0 .0	0 .0	5S 5.0	1N34.1	1S14.5	0S16.9	1N18.6	2S22.4	0N44.3	1N40.5	16N 4.3
4	8 54 58.3	0 .0	0 .0	4 31.5	1 1.9	1 17.9	0 14.2	1 19.2	2 21.6	0 44.4	1 40.6	16 5.5
7	9 6 48.0	0 .0	0 .0	1 17.4	0 31.2	1 20.8	0 11.4	1 19.9	2 20.7	0 44.5	1 40.8	16 6.7
10	9 18 37.7	0 .0	0 .0	2N37.0	0 2.5	1 23.2	0 8.7	1 20.5	2 19.9	0 44.6	1 40.9	16 7.8
13	9 30 27.3	0 .0	0 .0	4 56.7	0S24.0	1 25.0	0 6.1	1 21.2	2 19.2	0 44.6	1 41.1	16 8.9
16	9 42 17.0	0 .0	0 .0	5 2.4	0 47.9	1 26.2	0 3.5	1 21.8	2 18.4	0 44.7	1 41.3	16 9.9
19	9 54 6.7	0 .0	0 .0	3 12.3	1 9.1	1 26.9	0 1.0	1 22.4	2 17.7	0 44.8	1 41.4	16 10.8
22	10 5 56.3	0 .0	0 .0	0 9.3	1 27.5	1 27.0	0N 1.4	1 23.1	2 17.0	0 44.9	1 41.6	16 11.6
25	10 17 46.0	0 .0	0 .0	3S 2.0	1 42.9	1 26.5	0 3.9	1 23.7	2 16.3	0 44.9	1 41.8	16 12.4
28	10 29 35.6	0 .0	0 .0	5 4.4	1 55.2	1 25.5	0 6.2	1 24.3	2 15.6	0 45.0	1 41.9	16 13.1

RIGHT ASCENSION

DAY	EPHEM. SID. TIME	☉	☊	☽	☿	♀	♂	♃	♄	♅	♆	♇
1	8 43 8.7	14♒10.7	14♓55.9	25♏30.0	18♑ 2.9	16♒16.8	4♈55.7	3♏33.9	1♉24.4	8♎13.0	28♏50.9	3♎54.5
2	8 47 5.2	15 11.9	14 52.9	10♐43.8	18 53.4	17 32.9	5 35.9	3 37.2	1 27.2	8 R12.1	28 51.9	3 R53.7
3	8 51 1.8	16 12.9	14 50.0	26 58.4	19 48.0	18 48.6	6 16.1	3 40.4	1 30.2	8 11.1	28 52.9	3 52.9
4	8 54 58.3	17 13.6	14 47.0	13♑39.8	20 46.4	20 4.1	6 56.3	3 43.4	1 33.3	8 10.0	28 53.9	3 52.1
5	8 58 54.9	18 14.2	14 44.1	0♒ 5.9	21 48.2	21 19.2	7 36.5	3 46.2	1 36.4	8 8.9	28 54.8	3 51.3
6	9 2 51.4	19 14.6	14 41.1	15 43.9	22 53.1	22 34.0	8 16.7	3 48.9	1 39.7	8 7.8	28 55.7	3 50.4
7	9 6 48.0	20 14.8	14 38.2	0♓21.3	24 .8	23 48.5	8 56.9	3 51.4	1 43.0	8 6.6	28 56.6	3 49.5
8	9 10 44.5	21 14.7	14 35.2	14 3.0	25 11.0	25 2.7	9 37.1	3 53.7	1 46.5	8 5.4	28 57.4	3 48.6
9	9 14 41.1	22 14.5	14 32.3	27 4.0	26 23.6	26 16.6	10 17.3	3 55.8	1 50.0	8 4.1	28 58.2	3 47.7
10	9 18 37.7	23 14.1	14 29.3	9♈42.7	27 38.3	27 30.2	10 57.5	3 57.8	1 53.6	8 2.8	28 59.0	3 46.7
11	9 22 34.2	24 13.5	14 26.4	22 16.4	28 55.0	28 43.5	11 37.7	3 59.5	1 57.3	8 1.4	28 59.7	3 45.8
12	9 26 30.8	25 12.6	14 23.4	4♉59.4	0♒13.4	29 56.5	12 17.9	4 1.1	2 [illegible].1	8 .0	29 .4	3 44.8
13	9 30 27.3	26 11.7	14 20.4	18 1.0	1 33.4	1♓ 9.3	12 58.2	4 2.6	2 5.0	7 58.6	29 1.1	3 43.8
14	9 34 23.9	27 10.5	14 17.5	1♊23.4	2 54.9	2 21.7	13 38.4	4 3.8	2 9.0	7 57.2	29 1.7	3 42.7
15	9 38 20.4	28 9.1	14 14.5	15 1.2	4 17.7	3 33.9	14 18.7	4 4.9	2 13.1	7 55.6	29 2.3	3 41.7
16	9 42 17.0	29 7.5	14 11.6	28 42.1	5 41.8	4 45.8	14 58.9	4 5.7	2 17.2	7 54.1	29 2.9	3 40.6
17	9 46 13.5	0♓ 5.7	14 8.6	12♋10.4	7 7.0	5 57.4	15 39.2	4 6.4	2 21.4	7 52.5	29 3.4	3 39.5
18	9 50 10.1	1 3.7	14 5.7	25 12.0	8 33.2	7 8.8	16 19.5	4 6.9	2 25.7	7 50.9	29 3.9	3 38.3
19	9 54 6.7	2 1.6	14 2.7	7♌38.6	10 .4	8 19.9	16 59.8	4 7.2	2 30.1	7 49.2	29 4.3	3 37.2
20	9 58 3.2	2 59.3	13 59.8	19 28.5	11 28.5	9 30.8	17 40.1	4 7.4	2 34.6	7 47.5	29 4.7	3 36.0
21	10 1 59.8	3 56.8	13 56.8	0♍46.5	12 57.3	10 41.4	18 20.5	4 R 7.3	2 39.2	7 45.7	29 5.1	3 34.8
22	10 5 56.3	4 54.2	13 53.8	11 41.3	14 27.0	11 51.9	19 .8	4 7.1	2 43.8	7 44.0	29 5.5	3 33.6
23	10 9 52.9	5 51.4	13 50.9	22 24.6	15 57.3	13 2.1	19 41.2	4 6.7	2 48.5	7 42.2	29 5.8	3 32.4
24	10 13 49.4	6 48.5	13 47.9	3♎10.0	17 28.3	14 12.1	20 21.6	4 6.1	2 53.3	7 40.3	29 6.1	3 31.2
25	10 17 46.0	7 45.4	13 45.0	14 12.1	18 59.9	15 21.9	21 2.1	4 5.3	2 58.1	7 38.4	29 6.3	3 29.9
26	10 21 42.5	8 42.2	13 42.0	25 46.5	20 32.2	16 31.5	21 42.5	4 4.4	3 3.1	7 36.5	29 6.5	3 28.7
27	10 25 39.1	9 38.8	13 39.1	8♏ 8.6	22 4.9	17 41.0	22 23.0	4 3.3	3 8.1	7 34.6	29 6.7	3 27.4
28	10 29 35.6	10 35.3	13 36.1	21 31.0	23 38.2	18 50.2	23 3.6	4 1.9	3 13.9	7 32.6	29 6.8	3 26.1

DECLINATION

DAY	EPHEM. SID. TIME	☉	☊	☽	☿	♀	♂	♃	♄	♅	♆	♇
1	8 43 8.7	17S16.6	0S 6.7	24S53.2	20S49.7	17S58.9	1N49.6	12S 5.7	10N12.7	2S44.6	18S39.1	15N51.7
4	8 54 58.3	16 24.6	0 6.8	27 23.8	21 1.8	16 55.2	2 44.5	12 8.3	10 16.7	2 43.2	18 39.5	15 54.1
7	9 6 48.0	15 30.0	0 6.9	13 28.9	21 5.0	15 47.2	3 39.1	12 10.4	10 21.1	2 41.7	18 39.9	15 56.5
10	9 18 37.7	14 33.1	0 6.9	7N 1.7	20 58.5	14 35.3	4 33.3	12 11.9	10 25.6	2 40.0	18 40.2	15 59.0
13	9 30 27.3	13 33.9	0 7.0	22 60.0	20 41.4	13 19.7	5 26.9	12 12.8	10 30.5	2 38.1	18 40.4	16 1.4
16	9 42 17.0	12 32.8	0 7.1	28 28.8	20 13.4	12 1.0	6 20.0	12 13.2	10 35.6	2 36.0	18 40.6	16 3.9
19	9 54 6.7	11 29.9	0 7.1	22 15.4	19 34.0	10 39.4	7 12.4	12 13.0	10 40.9	2 33.9	18 40.8	16 6.4
22	10 5 56.3	10 25.3	0 7.2	7 55.7	18 43.2	9 15.3	8 4.1	12 12.3	10 46.5	2 31.6	18 40.8	16 8.9
25	10 17 46.0	9 19.4	0 7.2	9S21.6	17 46.0	7 49.0	8 55.0	12 11.1	10 52.2	2 29.1	18 40.8	16 11.3
28	10 29 35.6	8 12.1	0 7.3	23 59.3	16 26.8	6 20.8	9 45.1	12 9.3	10 58.1	2 26.6	18 40.7	16 13.8

MARCH 1970

DAY	EPHEM. SID. TIME	☉	☊	☽	☿	♀	♂	♃	♄	♅	♆	♇
	h m s	° ′	° ′	° ′	° ′	° ′	° ′	° ′	° ′	° ′	° ′	° ′
		LONGITUDE										
1	10 33 32.2	9♓59.5	12♓ 9.7	8♐38.2	22♒10.2	18♓30.4	25♈39.2	5♏50.3	4♉48.7	7♎51.3	0♐53.4	26♍29.1
2	10 37 28.8	10 59.7	12 6.6	22 25.8	23 45.4	19 45.3	26 22.4	5 R 48.5	4 54.2	7 R 49.1	0 53.4	26 R 27.6
3	10 41 25.3	11 59.9	12 3.4	6♑34.8	25 21.6	21 .1	27 5.5	5 46.5	4 59.8	7 46.9	0 53.5	26 26.0
4	10 45 21.9	13 .1	12 .2	21 3.6	26 58.8	22 15.0	27 48.6	5 44.4	5 5.5	7 44.6	0 R 53.4	26 24.5
5	10 49 18.4	14 .2	11 57.0	5♒48.8	28 37.2	23 29.8	28 31.7	5 42.0	5 11.2	7 42.3	0 53.4	26 22.9
6	10 53 15.0	15 .4	11 53.9	20 44.7	0♓16.6	24 44.7	29 14.8	5 39.5	5 17.0	7 40.1	0 53.4	26 21.3
7	10 57 11.5	16 .4	11 50.7	5♓43.6	1 57.1	25 59.5	29 57.8	5 36.8	5 22.9	7 37.7	0 53.2	26 19.7
8	11 1 8.1	17 .5	11 47.5	20 37.4	3 38.7	27 14.3	0♉40.8	5 33.8	5 28.8	7 35.4	0 53.1	26 18.1
9	11 5 4.6	18 .5	11 44.3	5♈18.1	5 21.4	28 29.1	1 23.7	5 30.8	5 34.8	7 33.0	0 52.9	26 16.5
10	11 9 1.2	19 .5	11 41.1	19 39.1	7 5.2	29 43.8	2 6.6	5 27.5	5 40.9	7 30.6	0 52.7	26 14.9
11	11 12 57.7	20 .4	11 38.0	3♉36.1	8 50.1	0♈58.5	2 49.5	5 24.0	5 47.0	7 28.1	0 52.4	26 13.3
12	11 16 54.3	21 .4	11 34.8	17 7.0	10 36.2	2 13.2	3 32.3	5 20.4	5 53.2	7 25.7	0 52.2	26 11.7
13	11 20 50.9	22 .3	11 31.6	0♊12.2	12 23.5	3 27.9	4 15.1	5 16.6	5 59.4	7 23.2	0 51.9	26 10.1
14	11 24 47.4	23 .1	11 28.4	12 54.2	14 11.9	4 42.5	4 57.8	5 12.7	6 5.7	7 20.7	0 51.5	26 8.4
15	11 28 44.0	23 59.9	11 25.3	25 16.3	16 1.5	5 57.1	5 40.5	5 8.6	6 12.1	7 18.2	0 51.1	26 6.8
16	11 32 40.5	24 59.7	11 22.1	7♋23.0	17 52.3	7 11.7	6 23.2	5 4.3	6 18.5	7 15.7	0 50.7	26 5.2
17	11 36 37.1	25 59.4	11 18.9	19 18.9	19 44.3	8 26.3	7 5.8	4 59.8	6 24.9	7 13.2	0 50.3	26 3.5
18	11 40 33.6	26 59.1	11 15.7	1♌ 8.8	21 37.4	9 40.8	7 48.4	4 55.2	6 31.4	7 10.7	0 49.8	26 1.9
19	11 44 30.2	27 58.7	11 12.5	12 56.9	23 31.7	10 55.3	8 30.9	4 50.5	6 38.0	7 8.1	0 49.3	26 .3
20	11 48 26.7	28 58.4	11 9.4	24 47.4	25 27.2	12 9.8	9 13.4	4 45.6	6 44.6	7 5.5	0 48.8	25 58.6
21	11 52 23.3	29 57.9	11 6.2	6♍43.5	27 23.8	13 24.2	9 55.8	4 40.5	6 51.2	7 3.0	0 48.2	25 57.0
22	11 56 19.8	0♈57.5	11 3.0	18 48.1	29 21.4	14 38.6	10 38.2	4 35.3	6 58.0	7 .4	0 47.6	25 55.4
23	12 0 16.4	1 57.0	10 59.8	1♎ 3.1	1♈20.1	15 53.0	11 20.6	4 30.0	7 4.7	6 57.8	0 47.0	25 53.8
24	12 4 12.9	2 56.5	10 56.7	13 30.2	3 19.8	17 7.4	12 2.9	4 24.5	7 11.5	6 55.2	0 46.3	25 52.1
25	12 8 9.5	3 55.9	10 53.5	26 10.2	5 20.3	18 21.7	12 45.2	4 18.9	7 18.4	6 52.6	0 45.6	25 50.5
26	12 12 6.0	4 55.4	10 50.3	9♏ 3.6	7 21.6	19 36.0	13 27.4	4 13.1	7 25.2	6 50.0	0 44.9	25 48.9
27	12 16 2.6	5 54.7	10 47.1	22 10.6	9 23.4	20 50.3	14 9.6	4 7.2	7 32.2	6 47.4	0 44.2	25 47.3
28	12 19 59.2	6 54.1	10 43.9	5♐31.2	11 25.8	22 4.5	14 51.7	4 1.2	7 39.1	6 44.8	0 43.4	25 45.7
29	12 23 55.7	7 53.4	10 40.8	19 5.4	13 28.3	23 18.8	15 33.8	3 55.1	7 46.2	6 42.2	0 42.6	25 44.1
30	12 27 52.3	8 52.7	10 37.6	2♑53.0	15 30.9	24 33.0	16 15.9	3 48.8	7 53.2	6 39.6	0 41.7	25 42.5
31	12 31 48.8	9 52.0	10 34.4	16 53.7	17 33.3	25 47.2	16 58.0	3 42.5	8 .3	6 37.1	0 40.9	25 41.0
		LATITUDE										
1	10 33 32.2	0 .0	0 .0	5 S 17.2	1 S 58.6	1 S 25.0	0 N 7.0	1 N 24.5	2 S 15.4	0 N 45.0	1 N 42.0	16 N 13.3
4	10 45 21.9	0 .0	0 .0	4 6.3	2 6.4	1 23.1	0 9.3	1 25.1	2 14.7	0 45.0	1 42.1	16 13.9
7	10 57 11.5	0 .0	0 .0	0 33.9	2 10.6	1 20.7	0 11.5	1 25.7	2 14.1	0 45.1	1 42.3	16 14.4
10	11 9 1.2	0 .0	0 .0	3 N 14.9	2 11.0	1 17.7	0 13.7	1 26.2	2 13.5	0 45.1	1 42.5	16 14.8
13	11 20 50.9	0 .0	0 .0	5 10.7	2 7.4	1 14.2	0 15.9	1 26.7	2 12.9	0 45.1	1 42.6	16 15.1
16	11 32 40.5	0 .0	0 .0	4 46.1	1 59.4	1 10.2	0 17.9	1 27.2	2 12.4	0 45.2	1 42.7	16 15.3
19	11 44 30.2	0 .0	0 .0	2 33.3	1 46.8	1 5.6	0 20.0	1 27.7	2 11.9	0 45.2	1 42.9	16 15.5
22	11 56 19.8	0 .0	0 .0	0 S 38.3	1 29.5	1 .6	0 21.9	1 28.1	2 11.4	0 45.2	1 43.0	16 15.5
25	12 8 9.5	0 .0	0 .0	3 40.4	1 7.4	0 55.1	0 23.9	1 28.5	2 10.9	0 45.2	1 43.2	16 15.5
28	12 19 59.2	0 .0	0 .0	5 12.3	0 40.7	0 49.2	0 25.7	1 28.9	2 10.5	0 45.2	1 43.3	16 15.4
31	12 31 48.8	0 .0	0 .0	4 16.3	0 10.0	0 42.9	0 27.6	1 29.1	2 10.1	0 45.2	1 43.5	16 15.2
		RIGHT ASCENSION										
1	10 33 32.2	11♓31.6	13♓33.1	5♐59.1	25♒12.0	19♓59.4	23♈44.1	4♏ .4	3♉18.3	7♎30.6	29♏ 6.9	3♎24.8
2	10 37 28.8	12 27.9	13 30.2	21 25.3	26 46.3	21 8.3	24 24.7	3 R 58.8	3 23.5	7 R 28.6	29 7.0	3 R 23.4
3	10 41 25.3	13 24.0	13 27.2	7♑26.2	28 21.1	22 17.2	25 5.4	3 56.9	3 28.8	7 26.6	29 7.0	3 22.1
4	10 45 21.9	14 20.0	13 24.3	23 28.3	29 56.3	23 25.9	25 46.0	3 54.9	3 34.2	7 24.5	29 7.0	3 20.7
5	10 49 18.4	15 15.9	13 21.3	9♒ .7	1♓32.0	24 34.5	26 26.8	3 52.6	3 39.6	7 22.4	29 7.0	3 19.4
6	10 53 15.0	16 11.7	13 18.3	23 46.4	3 8.3	25 43.0	27 7.6	3 50.3	3 45.2	7 20.3	29 R 6.9	3 18.0
7	10 57 11.5	17 7.3	13 15.4	7♓44.1	4 44.9	26 51.4	27 48.4	3 47.7	3 50.7	7 18.2	29 6.8	3 16.7
8	11 1 8.1	18 2.9	13 12.4	21 4.0	6 22.0	27 59.7	28 29.2	3 45.0	3 56.4	7 16.0	29 6.7	3 15.3
9	11 5 4.6	18 58.4	13 9.5	4♈ 1.7	7 59.6	29 7.9	29 10.1	3 42.1	4 2.1	7 13.8	29 6.5	3 13.8
10	11 9 1.2	19 53.8	13 6.5	16 53.5	9 37.7	0♈16.1	29 51.0	3 39.0	4 7.8	7 11.6	29 6.3	3 12.4
11	11 12 57.7	20 49.1	13 3.5	29 53.5	11 16.3	1 24.2	0♉32.0	3 35.7	4 13.6	7 9.4	29 6.1	3 11.0
12	11 16 54.3	21 44.3	13 .6	13♉11.3	12 55.5	2 32.2	1 13.0	3 32.3	4 19.5	7 7.1	29 5.8	3 9.6
13	11 20 50.9	22 39.4	12 57.6	26 49.5	14 35.2	3 40.2	1 54.1	3 28.7	4 25.5	7 4.8	29 5.5	3 8.2
14	11 24 47.4	23 34.5	12 54.6	10♊42.7	16 15.4	4 48.2	2 35.2	3 24.9	4 31.5	7 2.6	29 5.1	3 6.7
15	11 28 44.0	24 29.4	12 51.7	24 38.4	17 56.3	5 56.2	3 16.4	3 21.0	4 37.5	7 .3	29 4.7	3 5.3
16	11 32 40.5	25 24.3	12 48.7	8♋20.3	19 37.7	7 4.2	3 57.6	3 17.0	4 43.6	6 58.0	29 4.3	3 3.8
17	11 36 37.1	26 19.2	12 45.8	21 34.3	21 19.8	8 12.1	4 38.8	3 12.7	4 49.8	6 55.6	29 3.9	3 2.3
18	11 40 33.6	27 14.0	12 42.8	4♌11.7	23 2.5	9 20.1	5 20.1	3 8.4	4 56.0	6 53.3	29 3.4	3 .9
19	11 44 30.2	28 8.7	12 39.8	16 11.0	24 45.9	10 28.1	6 1.5	3 3.8	5 2.3	6 51.0	29 2.9	2 59.4
20	11 48 26.7	29 3.4	12 36.9	27 36.5	26 30.0	11 36.1	6 42.9	2 59.2	5 8.6	6 48.6	29 2.3	2 57.9
21	11 52 23.3	29 58.1	12 33.9	9♍38.5	28 14.8	12 44.2	7 24.3	2 54.3	5 15.0	6 46.2	29 1.8	2 56.4
22	11 56 19.8	0♈52.7	12 30.9	19 27.3	0♈ .3	13 52.4	8 5.8	2 49.4	5 21.4	6 43.9	29 1.2	2 55.0
23	12 0 16.4	1 47.4	12 28.0	0♎16.5	1 46.4	15 .6	8 47.4	2 44.3	5 27.9	6 41.5	29 .5	2 53.5
24	12 4 12.9	2 41.9	12 25.0	11 20.5	3 33.2	16 8.9	9 29.0	2 39.0	5 34.4	6 39.1	28 59.9	2 52.0
25	12 8 9.5	3 36.5	12 22.0	22 53.9	5 20.7	17 17.3	10 10.6	2 33.7	5 41.0	6 36.7	28 59.2	2 50.5
26	12 12 6.0	4 31.1	12 19.1	5♏10.9	7 8.8	18 25.8	10 52.4	2 28.2	5 47.6	6 34.3	28 58.4	2 49.1
27	12 16 2.6	5 25.6	12 16.1	18 23.0	8 57.4	19 34.4	11 34.1	2 22.6	5 54.2	6 31.9	28 57.7	2 47.6
28	12 19 59.2	6 20.2	12 13.1	2♐34.8	10 46.4	20 43.1	12 15.9	2 16.8	6 .9	6 29.6	28 56.9	2 46.1
29	12 23 55.7	7 14.8	12 10.2	17 39.3	12 35.8	21 51.9	12 57.8	2 11.0	6 7.6	6 27.2	28 56.1	2 44.6
30	12 27 52.3	8 9.3	12 7.2	3♑15.8	14 25.3	23 .9	13 39.7	2 5.0	6 14.4	6 24.8	28 55.2	2 43.1
31	12 31 48.8	9 4.0	12 4.2	18 54.8	16 15.0	24 10.1	14 21.8	1 59.0	6 21.3	6 22.4	28 54.4	2 41.7
		DECLINATION										
1	10 33 32.2	7 S 49.5	0 S 7.3	26 S 58.1	15 S 59.6	5 S 51.0	10 N 1.6	12 S 8.5	11 N .1	2 S 25.7	18 S 40.7	16 N 14.6
4	10 45 21.9	6 40.8	0 7.4	25 51.1	14 30.0	4 20.9	10 50.5	12 6.0	11 6.3	2 23.0	18 40.6	16 16.9
7	10 57 11.5	5 31.2	0 7.5	9 56.4	12 48.9	2 49.7	11 38.5	12 2.9	11 12.7	2 20.2	18 40.4	16 19.3
10	11 9 1.2	4 21.0	0 7.5	10 N 41.7	10 56.3	1 17.7	12 25.5	11 59.3	11 19.2	2 17.4	18 40.1	16 21.5
13	11 20 50.9	3 10.4	0 7.6	25 15.4	8 52.4	0 N 14.6	13 11.4	11 55.3	11 25.8	2 14.5	18 39.8	16 23.8
16	11 32 40.5	1 59.4	0 7.6	27 60.0	6 37.6	1 46.9	13 56.1	11 50.7	11 32.5	2 11.5	18 39.4	16 25.9
19	11 44 30.2	0 48.2	0 7.7	19 22.8	4 12.3	3 19.0	14 39.6	11 45.7	11 39.4	2 8.5	18 39.0	16 28.0
22	11 56 19.8	0 N 22.9	0 7.8	3 50.7	1 37.5	4 50.5	15 21.9	11 40.2	11 46.4	2 5.4	18 38.5	16 30.0
25	12 8 9.5	1 33.8	0 7.8	13 S 31.6	1 N 5.4	6 21.0	16 2.9	11 34.3	11 53.4	2 2.3	18 37.9	16 31.9
28	12 19 59.2	2 44.4	0 7.9	26 21.0	3 53.9	7 50.3	16 42.6	11 28.1	12 .5	1 59.3	18 37.3	16 33.7
31	12 31 48.8	3 54.6	0 8.0	26 36.9	6 44.3	9 18.1	17 20.9	11 21.5	12 7.7	1 56.2	18 36.7	16 35.4

APRIL 1970

LONGITUDE

DAY	EPHEM. SID. TIME	☉	☊	☽	☿	♀	♂	♃	♄	♅	♆	♇
	h m s	° ′	° ′	° ′	° ′	° ′	° ′	° ′	° ′	° ′	° ′	° ′
1	12 35 45.4	10♈51.3	10♓31.2	1♒ 6.2	19♈35.2	27♈ 1.3	17♉40.0	3♏36.0	8♉ 7.5	6♎34.5	0♐40.0	25♍39.4
2	12 39 41.9	11 50.5	10 28.1	15 29.1	21 36.2	28 15.4	18 21.9	3 R29.4	8 14.6	6 R31.9	0 R39.1	25 R37.9
3	12 43 38.5	12 49.6	10 24.9	29 59.3	23 36.0	29 29.5	19 3.8	3 22.7	8 21.8	6 29.3	0 38.2	25 36.3
4	12 47 35.0	13 48.8	10 21.7	14♓32.8	25 34.3	0♉43.6	19 45.7	3 15.9	8 29.1	6 26.7	0 37.2	25 34.8
5	12 51 31.6	14 47.9	10 18.5	29 4.3	27 30.7	1 57.6	20 27.6	3 9.0	8 36.3	6 24.1	0 36.2	25 33.3
6	12 55 28.1	15 47.0	10 15.3	13♈28.2	29 24.8	3 11.6	21 9.4	3 2.1	8 43.6	6 21.6	0 35.2	25 31.8
7	12 59 24.7	16 46.0	10 12.2	27 38.5	1♉16.2	4 25.6	21 51.1	2 55.0	8 50.9	6 19.0	0 34.2	25 30.2
8	13 3 21.2	17 45.1	10 9.0	11♉30.4	3 4.6	5 39.5	22 32.9	2 47.9	8 58.3	6 16.5	0 33.1	25 28.8
9	13 7 17.8	18 44.0	10 5.8	25 .7	4 49.6	6 53.5	23 14.5	2 40.7	9 5.7	6 14.0	0 32.0	25 27.3
10	13 11 14.4	19 43.0	10 2.6	8♊ 8.1	6 30.9	8 7.3	23 56.2	2 33.4	9 13.1	6 11.4	0 30.9	25 25.8
11	13 15 10.9	20 41.9	9 59.5	20 53.0	8 8.2	9 21.2	24 37.8	2 26.1	9 20.5	6 8.9	0 29.7	25 24.4
12	13 19 7.5	21 40.8	9 56.3	3♋18.0	9 41.1	10 35.0	25 19.3	2 18.7	9 28.0	6 6.5	0 28.6	25 22.9
13	13 23 4.0	22 39.6	9 53.1	15 26.7	11 9.5	11 48.8	26 .9	2 11.2	9 35.5	6 4.0	0 27.4	25 21.5
14	13 27 .6	23 38.4	9 49.9	27 23.6	12 33.1	13 2.5	26 42.3	2 3.7	9 43.0	6 1.6	0 26.2	25 20.1
15	13 30 57.1	24 37.1	9 46.7	9♌13.9	13 51.7	14 16.2	27 23.8	1 56.2	9 50.5	5 59.1	0 25.0	25 18.8
16	13 34 53.7	25 35.9	9 43.6	21 2.6	15 5.2	15 29.9	28 5.2	1 48.6	9 58.0	5 56.7	0 23.7	25 17.4
17	13 38 50.2	26 34.5	9 40.4	2♍54.8	16 13.4	16 43.5	28 46.5	1 41.0	10 5.6	5 54.3	0 22.4	25 16.0
18	13 42 46.8	27 33.2	9 37.2	14 55.1	17 16.1	17 57.1	29 27.8	1 33.4	10 13.2	5 52.0	0 21.2	25 14.7
19	13 46 43.3	28 31.8	9 34.0	27 7.3	18 13.3	19 10.7	0♊ 9.1	1 25.8	10 20.7	5 49.6	0 19.8	25 13.4
20	13 50 39.9	29 30.4	9 30.9	9♎34.3	19 4.8	20 24.2	0 50.3	1 18.1	10 28.4	5 47.3	0 18.5	25 12.1
21	13 54 36.5	0♉29.0	9 27.7	22 18.0	19 50.7	21 37.7	1 31.6	1 10.5	10 36.0	5 45.1	0 17.2	25 10.9
22	13 58 33.0	1 27.5	9 24.5	5♏18.7	20 30.7	22 51.2	2 12.7	1 2.8	10 43.7	5 42.8	0 15.9	25 9.6
23	14 2 29.6	2 26.0	9 21.3	18 35.8	21 4.9	24 4.6	2 53.8	0 55.1	10 51.3	5 40.6	0 14.5	25 8.4
24	14 6 26.1	3 24.4	9 18.1	2♐ 7.5	21 33.3	25 17.9	3 34.9	0 47.5	10 59.0	5 38.3	0 13.1	25 7.2
25	14 10 22.7	4 22.8	9 15.0	15 51.3	21 55.8	26 31.3	4 15.9	0 39.8	11 6.6	5 36.2	0 11.7	25 6.0
26	14 14 19.2	5 21.2	9 11.8	29 44.3	22 12.5	27 44.6	4 56.9	0 32.2	11 14.3	5 34.0	0 10.2	25 4.9
27	14 18 15.8	6 19.6	9 8.6	13♑44.1	22 23.4	28 57.9	5 37.9	0 24.6	11 22.0	5 31.9	0 8.8	25 3.7
28	14 22 12.3	7 17.9	9 5.4	27 48.6	22 28.6	0♊11.1	6 18.8	0 17.0	11 29.7	5 29.8	0 7.3	25 2.6
29	14 26 8.9	8 16.2	9 2.3	11♒56.0	22 R28.4	1 24.3	6 59.7	0 9.4	11 37.4	5 27.7	0 5.9	25 1.5
30	14 30 5.5	9 14.5	8 59.1	26 5.1	22 22.8	2 37.5	7 40.6	0 1.9	11 45.1	5 25.7	0 4.4	25 .4

LATITUDE

DAY	EPHEM. SID. TIME	☉	☊	☽	☿	♀	♂	♃	♄	♅	♆	♇
1	12 35 45.4	0 .0	0 .0	3S23.9	0N .9	0S40.7	0N28.2	1N29.2	2S10.0	0N45.2	1N43.5	16N15.1
4	12 47 35.0	0 .0	0 .0	0N16.2	0 35.0	0 34.0	0 29.9	1 29.5	2 9.6	0 45.1	1 43.6	16 14.8
7	12 59 24.7	0 .0	0 .0	3 45.0	1 9.6	0 26.9	0 31.6	1 29.7	2 9.3	0 45.1	1 43.7	16 14.4
10	13 11 14.4	0 .0	0 .0	5 10.2	1 42.4	0 19.5	0 33.3	1 29.8	2 8.9	0 45.1	1 43.9	16 14.0
13	13 23 4.0	0 .0	0 .0	4 16.5	2 11.0	0 12.0	0 34.9	1 29.9	2 8.7	0 45.0	1 44.0	16 13.4
16	13 34 53.7	0 .0	0 .0	1 46.3	2 33.5	0 4.2	0 36.5	1 29.9	2 8.4	0 45.0	1 44.1	16 12.8
19	13 46 43.3	0 .0	0 .0	1S25.8	2 48.1	0N 3.6	0 38.0	1 29.8	2 8.2	0 44.9	1 44.1	16 12.1
22	13 58 33.0	0 .0	0 .0	4 10.0	2 53.3	0 11.6	0 39.5	1 29.7	2 8.0	0 44.8	1 44.2	16 11.4
25	14 10 22.7	0 .0	0 .0	5 4.5	2 48.1	0 19.6	0 40.9	1 29.6	2 7.8	0 44.8	1 44.3	16 10.6
28	14 22 12.3	0 .0	0 .0	3 26.5	2 31.5	0 27.6	0 42.3	1 29.4	2 7.6	0 44.7	1 44.4	16 9.7

RIGHT ASCENSION

DAY	EPHEM. SID. TIME	☉	☊	☽	☿	♀	♂	♃	♄	♅	♆	♇
1	12 35 45.4	9♈58.6	12♓ 1.3	4♒ 8.3	18♈ 4.4	25♈19.4	15♉ 3.8	1♏52.8	6♉28.1	6♎20.0	28♏53.5	2♎40.3
2	12 39 41.9	10 53.3	11 58.3	18 39.9	19 53.4	26 28.9	15 45.9	1 R46.5	6 35.0	6 R17.7	28 R52.5	2 R38.8
3	12 43 38.5	11 48.0	11 55.3	2♓27.5	21 41.7	27 38.5	16 28.1	1 40.1	6 42.0	6 15.3	28 51.6	2 37.3
4	12 47 35.0	12 42.7	11 52.4	15 39.8	23 29.1	28 48.3	17 10.3	1 33.6	6 48.9	6 12.9	28 50.6	2 35.9
5	12 51 31.6	13 37.4	11 49.4	28 31.5	25 15.3	29 58.4	17 52.6	1 27.0	6 56.0	6 10.5	28 49.6	2 34.4
6	12 55 28.1	14 32.3	11 46.4	11♈18.8	26 59.9	1♉ 8.6	18 34.9	1 20.4	7 3.0	6 8.2	28 48.5	2 33.0
7	12 59 24.7	15 27.1	11 43.5	24 16.6	28 42.7	2 19.0	19 17.3	1 13.6	7 10.1	6 5.8	28 47.5	2 31.6
8	13 3 21.2	16 22.0	11 40.5	7♉36.0	0♉23.2	3 29.6	19 59.7	1 6.8	7 17.2	6 3.5	28 46.4	2 30.2
9	13 7 17.8	17 17.0	11 37.5	21 21.0	2 1.1	4 40.5	20 42.2	0 59.9	7 24.3	6 1.2	28 45.2	2 28.7
10	13 11 14.4	18 12.0	11 34.5	5♊27.2	3 36.2	5 51.6	21 24.8	0 53.0	7 31.5	5 58.8	28 44.1	2 27.3
11	13 15 10.9	19 7.1	11 31.6	19 41.0	5 8.1	7 2.9	22 7.4	0 46.0	7 38.6	5 56.5	28 42.9	2 25.9
12	13 19 7.5	20 2.2	11 28.6	3♋43.9	6 36.5	8 14.5	22 50.0	0 38.9	7 45.9	5 54.3	28 41.7	2 24.6
13	13 23 4.0	20 57.5	11 25.6	17 18.5	8 1.2	9 26.3	23 32.7	0 31.8	7 53.1	5 52.0	28 40.5	2 23.2
14	13 27 .6	21 52.7	11 22.7	0♌13.6	9 21.7	10 38.3	24 15.5	0 24.6	8 .4	5 49.7	28 39.3	2 21.8
15	13 30 57.1	22 48.1	11 19.7	12 26.4	10 38.0	11 50.6	24 58.3	0 17.4	8 7.7	5 47.5	28 38.0	2 20.5
16	13 34 53.7	23 43.6	11 16.7	24 1.3	11 49.8	13 3.1	25 41.1	0 10.2	8 15.0	5 45.3	28 36.7	2 19.1
17	13 38 50.2	24 39.1	11 13.8	5♍ 8.0	12 56.8	14 15.9	26 24.0	0 2.9	8 22.3	5 43.1	28 35.4	2 17.8
18	13 42 46.8	25 34.7	11 10.8	15 58.7	13 59.0	15 29.0	27 7.0	29♎55.6	8 29.7	5 40.9	28 34.1	2 16.5
19	13 46 43.3	26 30.5	11 7.8	26 47.5	14 56.0	16 42.3	27 50.0	29 48.3	8 37.0	5 38.7	28 32.8	2 15.2
20	13 50 39.9	27 26.3	11 4.8	7♎49.3	15 47.8	17 55.9	28 33.0	29 41.0	8 44.4	5 36.6	28 31.4	2 13.9
21	13 54 36.5	28 22.3	11 1.9	19 19.8	16 34.2	19 9.8	29 16.1	29 33.7	8 51.9	5 34.5	28 30.1	2 12.7
22	13 58 33.0	29 18.3	10 58.9	1♏33.8	17 15.1	20 24.0	29 59.2	29 26.4	8 59.3	5 32.4	28 28.7	2 11.5
23	14 2 29.6	0♉14.4	10 55.9	14 43.9	17 50.4	21 38.4	0♊42.4	29 19.1	9 6.7	5 30.4	28 27.3	2 10.2
24	14 6 26.1	1 10.7	10 52.9	28 55.6	18 20.2	22 53.0	1 25.6	29 11.8	9 14.2	5 28.3	28 25.8	2 9.0
25	14 10 22.7	2 7.0	10 50.0	14♐ 2.1	18 44.2	24 8.0	2 8.9	29 4.4	9 21.6	5 26.3	28 24.4	2 7.8
26	14 14 19.2	3 3.5	10 47.0	29 42.3	19 2.6	25 23.2	2 52.2	28 57.1	9 29.1	5 24.3	28 22.9	2 6.6
27	14 18 15.8	4 .2	10 44.0	15♑24.4	19 15.4	26 38.7	3 35.5	28 49.9	9 36.6	5 22.4	28 21.4	2 5.4
28	14 22 12.3	4 56.9	10 41.0	0♒38.5	19 22.7	27 54.4	4 18.8	28 42.6	9 44.1	5 20.4	28 19.9	2 4.3
29	14 26 8.9	5 53.8	10 38.1	15 6.5	19 24.7	29 10.4	5 2.3	28 35.4	9 51.6	5 18.5	28 18.4	2 3.2
30	14 30 5.5	6 50.8	10 35.1	28 45.9	19 R21.5	0♊26.7	5 45.7	28 28.2	9 59.1	5 16.7	28 16.9	2 2.1

DECLINATION

DAY	EPHEM. SID. TIME	☉	☊	☽	☿	♀	♂	♃	♄	♅	♆	♇
1	12 35 45.4	4N17.8	0S 8.0	23S14.0	7N40.7	9N46.9	17N33.3	11S19.2	12N10.1	1S55.2	18S36.5	16N36.0
4	12 47 35.0	5 27.1	0 8.0	5 50.2	10 26.0	11 11.9	18 9.7	11 12.2	12 17.3	1 52.1	18 35.8	16 37.5
7	12 59 24.7	6 35.5	0 8.1	14N 8.1	13 .4	12 34.6	18 44.6	11 4.9	12 24.6	1 49.1	18 35.0	16 39.0
10	13 11 14.4	7 42.9	0 8.2	26 46.3	15 18.3	13 54.6	19 18.0	10 57.5	12 31.9	1 46.2	18 34.3	16 40.3
13	13 23 4.0	8 49.1	0 8.2	26 47.9	17 15.3	15 11.6	19 49.7	10 49.8	12 39.2	1 43.3	18 33.4	16 41.6
16	13 34 53.7	9 53.9	0 8.3	16 9.9	18 48.6	16 25.1	20 19.9	10 42.0	12 46.6	1 40.4	18 32.6	16 42.6
19	13 46 43.3	10 57.3	0 8.4	0S10.1	19 56.9	17 34.9	20 48.4	10 34.2	12 53.9	1 37.7	18 31.7	16 43.6
22	13 58 33.0	11 59.0	0 8.4	17 13.2	20 39.9	18 40.6	21 15.3	10 26.3	13 1.2	1 35.0	18 30.8	16 44.4
25	14 10 22.7	12 59.0	0 8.5	27 44.4	20 57.5	19 42.0	21 40.4	10 18.5	13 8.4	1 32.5	18 29.8	16 45.1
28	14 22 12.3	13 57.1	0 8.5	23 58.6	20 50.1	20 38.7	22 3.8	10 10.7	13 15.6	1 30.0	18 28.8	16 45.7

MAY 1970

LONGITUDE

DAY	EPHEM. SID. TIME	☉	☊	☽	☿	♀	♂	♃	♄	♅	♆	♇
	h m s	° ′	° ′	° ′	° ′	° ′	° ′	° ′	° ′	° ′	° ′	° ′
1	14 34 2.0	10♉12.8	8♓55.9	10♓14.7	22♉12.1	3♊50.6	8♊21.4	29♎54.4	11♉52.8	5♎23.7	0♐ 2.9	24♍59.4
2	14 37 58.6	11 11.0	8 52.7	24 23.2	21 R 56.6	5 3.7	9 2.2	29 R 47.0	12 .5	5 R 21.8	0 R 1.4	24 R 58.4
3	14 41 55.1	12 9.3	8 49.6	8♈28.2	21 36.6	6 16.8	9 42.9	29 39.6	12 8.2	5 19.8	29♏59.8	24 57.4
4	14 45 51.7	13 7.4	8 46.4	22 26.6	21 12.6	7 29.8	10 23.6	29 32.2	12 15.9	5 17.9	29 58.3	24 56.4
5	14 49 48.2	14 5.6	8 43.2	6♉15.0	20 45.1	8 42.8	11 4.3	29 25.0	12 23.6	5 16.1	29 56.8	24 55.5
6	14 53 44.8	15 3.7	8 40.0	19 49.8	20 14.5	9 55.8	11 44.9	29 17.8	12 31.3	5 14.3	29 55.2	24 54.6
7	14 57 41.3	16 1.9	8 36.8	3♊ 7.9	19 41.5	11 8.7	12 25.6	29 10.7	12 39.0	5 12.5	29 53.6	24 53.7
8	15 1 37.9	16 59.9	8 33.7	16 7.6	19 6.6	12 21.6	13 6.1	29 3.6	12 46.7	5 10.8	29 52.1	24 52.8
9	15 5 34.5	17 58.0	8 30.5	28 48.3	18 30.5	13 34.4	13 46.7	28 56.7	12 54.4	5 9.1	29 50.5	24 52.0
10	15 9 31.0	18 56.0	8 27.3	11♋11.4	17 53.8	14 47.2	14 27.2	28 49.8	13 2.1	5 7.4	29 48.9	24 51.2
11	15 13 27.6	19 54.0	8 24.1	23 19.5	17 17.3	15 60.0	15 7.6	28 43.0	13 9.7	5 5.8	29 47.3	24 50.4
12	15 17 24.1	20 52.0	8 21.0	5♌16.3	16 41.4	17 12.7	15 48.1	28 36.4	13 17.5	5 4.3	29 45.8	24 49.7
13	15 21 20.7	21 49.9	8 17.8	17 6.5	16 6.9	18 25.4	16 28.5	28 29.8	13 25.1	5 2.8	29 44.2	24 48.9
14	15 25 17.2	22 47.8	8 14.6	28 55.3	15 34.3	19 38.0	17 8.8	28 23.3	13 32.8	5 1.3	29 42.5	24 48.2
15	15 29 13.8	23 45.7	8 11.4	10♍48.3	15 4.1	20 50.6	17 49.2	28 17.0	13 40.4	4 59.9	29 40.9	24 47.6
16	15 33 10.4	24 43.5	8 8.3	22 50.7	14 36.7	22 3.2	18 29.4	28 10.7	13 48.0	4 58.5	29 39.3	24 46.9
17	15 37 6.9	25 41.4	8 5.1	5♎ 7.3	14 12.7	23 15.7	19 9.7	28 4.6	13 55.6	4 57.1	29 37.7	24 46.3
18	15 41 3.5	26 39.1	8 1.9	17 42.3	13 52.4	24 28.1	19 49.9	27 58.6	14 3.2	4 55.8	29 36.1	24 45.8
19	15 45 .0	27 36.9	7 58.7	0♏38.3	13 35.9	25 40.5	20 30.1	27 52.7	14 10.8	4 54.6	29 34.4	24 45.2
20	15 48 56.6	28 34.6	7 55.5	13 56.2	13 23.7	26 52.9	21 10.2	27 46.9	14 18.4	4 53.4	29 32.8	24 44.7
21	15 52 53.1	29 32.3	7 52.4	27 35.0	13 15.7	28 5.2	21 50.3	27 41.3	14 25.9	4 52.2	29 31.2	24 44.2
22	15 56 49.7	0♊30.0	7 49.2	11♐31.8	13 12.2	29 17.4	22 30.4	27 35.8	14 33.4	4 51.1	29 29.6	24 43.7
23	16 0 46.3	1 27.7	7 46.0	25 42.1	13 D 13.2	0♋29.6	23 10.4	27 30.4	14 40.9	4 50.0	29 27.9	24 43.3
24	16 4 42.8	2 25.3	7 42.8	10♑ .5	13 18.7	1 41.8	23 50.4	27 25.2	14 48.4	4 49.0	29 26.3	24 42.9
25	16 8 39.4	3 23.0	7 39.7	24 21.7	13 28.8	2 53.9	24 30.4	27 20.1	14 55.9	4 48.0	29 24.7	24 42.5
26	16 12 35.9	4 20.6	7 36.5	8♒41.1	13 43.4	4 6.0	25 10.4	27 15.2	15 3.3	4 47.1	29 23.1	24 42.2
27	16 16 32.5	5 18.2	7 33.3	22 55.7	14 2.3	5 18.0	25 50.3	27 10.4	15 10.7	4 46.2	29 21.5	24 41.9
28	16 20 29.0	6 15.8	7 30.1	7♓ 3.4	14 25.7	6 30.0	26 30.2	27 5.8	15 18.1	4 45.4	29 19.8	24 41.6
29	16 24 25.6	7 13.3	7 27.0	21 3.3	14 53.3	7 41.9	27 10.0	27 1.3	15 25.5	4 44.7	29 18.2	24 41.4
30	16 28 22.2	8 10.9	7 23.8	4♈55.2	15 25.1	8 53.8	27 49.9	26 57.0	15 32.8	4 43.9	29 16.6	24 41.2
31	16 32 18.7	9 8.4	7 20.6	18 38.6	16 1.0	10 5.7	28 29.7	26 52.8	15 40.1	4 43.3	29 15.0	24 41.0

LATITUDE

DAY	EPHEM. SID. TIME	☉	☊	☽	☿	♀	♂	♃	♄	♅	♆	♇
1	14 34 2.0	0 .0	0 .0	0N .7	2N 3.6	0N35.6	0N43.7	1N29.1	2S 7.5	0N44.6	1N44.4	16N 8.7
4	14 45 51.7	0 .0	0 .0	3 25.7	1 25.0	0 43.4	0 45.0	1 28.8	2 7.4	0 44.5	1 44.5	16 7.7
7	14 57 41.3	0 .0	0 .0	5 .9	0 38.2	0 51.1	0 46.2	1 28.4	2 7.3	0 44.4	1 44.5	16 6.7
10	15 9 31.0	0 .0	0 .0	4 16.8	0S13.4	0 58.6	0 47.5	1 28.0	2 7.3	0 44.3	1 44.6	16 5.6
13	15 21 20.7	0 .0	0 .0	1 52.8	1 5.3	1 5.8	0 48.7	1 27.5	2 7.3	0 44.2	1 44.6	16 4.5
16	15 33 10.4	0 .0	0 .0	1S13.8	1 53.4	1 12.7	0 49.8	1 27.0	2 7.3	0 44.1	1 44.6	16 3.3
19	15 45 .0	0 .0	0 .0	3 58.1	2 34.4	1 19.3	0 50.9	1 26.4	2 7.3	0 44.0	1 44.6	16 2.1
22	15 56 49.7	0 .0	0 .0	5 .1	3 6.3	1 25.5	0 52.0	1 25.8	2 7.4	0 43.9	1 44.6	16 .8
25	16 8 39.4	0 .0	0 .0	3 26.7	3 28.6	1 31.2	0 53.0	1 25.2	2 7.5	0 43.8	1 44.6	15 59.5
28	16 20 29.0	0 .0	0 .0	0 2.2	3 41.5	1 36.4	0 54.0	1 24.5	2 7.6	0 43.7	1 44.5	15 58.2
31	16 32 18.7	0 .0	0 .0	3N19.2	3 45.5	1 41.1	0 55.0	1 23.8	2 7.8	0 43.6	1 44.5	15 56.9

RIGHT ASCENSION

DAY	EPHEM. SID. TIME	☉	☊	☽	☿	♀	♂	♃	♄	♅	♆	♇
1	14 34 2.0	7♉48.0	10♓32.1	11♓45.6	19♉13.4	1♊43.2	6♊29.2	28♎21.0	10♉ 6.7	5♎14.8	28♏15.3	2♎ 1.0
2	14 37 58.6	8 45.2	10 29.1	24 20.9	19 R .7	2 59.9	7 12.7	28 R 13.9	10 14.2	5 R 13.0	28 R 13.8	1 R 59.9
3	14 41 55.1	9 42.7	10 26.2	6♈49.2	18 43.8	4 17.0	7 56.2	28 6.9	10 21.7	5 11.2	28 12.2	1 58.8
4	14 45 51.7	10 40.2	10 23.2	19 27.1	18 23.2	5 34.2	8 39.8	27 59.9	10 29.3	5 9.5	28 10.6	1 57.8
5	14 49 48.2	11 38.0	10 20.2	2♉28.2	17 59.2	6 51.7	9 23.4	27 52.9	10 36.8	5 7.8	28 9.1	1 56.8
6	14 53 44.8	12 35.8	10 17.2	15 60.0	17 32.5	8 9.4	10 7.1	27 46.1	10 44.3	5 6.1	28 7.5	1 55.8
7	14 57 41.3	13 33.8	10 14.3	0♊ 1.3	17 3.6	9 27.3	10 50.7	27 39.3	10 51.9	5 4.5	28 5.9	1 54.8
8	15 1 37.9	14 31.9	10 11.3	14 20.8	16 33.2	10 45.4	11 34.4	27 32.5	10 59.4	5 2.9	28 4.2	1 53.9
9	15 5 34.5	15 30.2	10 8.3	28 39.0	16 1.7	12 3.7	12 18.1	27 25.9	11 7.0	5 1.3	28 2.6	1 53.0
10	15 9 31.0	16 28.6	10 5.3	12♋34.3	15 29.9	13 22.2	13 1.8	27 19.3	11 14.5	4 59.8	28 1.0	1 52.1
11	15 13 27.6	17 27.1	10 2.3	25 50.8	14 58.4	14 40.8	13 45.6	27 12.8	11 22.0	4 58.3	27 59.3	1 51.2
12	15 17 24.1	18 25.9	9 59.4	8♌21.8	14 27.7	15 59.6	14 29.4	27 6.5	11 29.6	4 56.9	27 57.7	1 50.4
13	15 21 20.7	19 24.7	9 56.4	20 9.3	13 58.4	17 18.6	15 13.1	27 .2	11 37.1	4 55.5	27 56.1	1 49.6
14	15 25 17.2	20 23.7	9 53.4	1♍22.2	13 30.9	18 37.6	15 56.9	26 54.0	11 44.7	4 54.1	27 54.4	1 48.8
15	15 29 13.8	21 22.8	9 50.4	12 13.1	13 5.8	19 56.8	16 40.7	26 47.9	11 52.2	4 52.7	27 52.8	1 48.0
16	15 33 10.4	22 22.0	9 47.5	22 56.6	12 43.4	21 16.1	17 24.5	26 41.9	11 59.7	4 51.5	27 51.1	1 47.2
17	15 37 6.9	23 21.4	9 44.5	3♎48.5	12 24.2	22 35.5	18 8.3	26 36.0	12 7.2	4 50.2	27 49.4	1 46.5
18	15 41 3.5	24 20.9	9 41.5	15 5.6	12 8.3	23 54.9	18 52.1	26 30.3	12 14.6	4 49.0	27 47.8	1 45.8
19	15 45 .0	25 20.6	9 38.5	27 4.9	11 56.0	25 14.4	19 35.9	26 24.6	12 22.1	4 47.8	27 46.1	1 45.1
20	15 48 56.6	26 20.4	9 35.5	10♏ 1.5	11 47.6	26 33.9	20 19.7	26 19.1	12 29.5	4 46.7	27 44.4	1 44.5
21	15 52 53.1	27 20.3	9 32.5	24 5.2	11 43.1	27 53.5	21 3.5	26 13.7	12 37.0	4 45.6	27 42.7	1 43.8
22	15 56 49.7	28 20.3	9 29.6	9♐13.9	11 42.6	29 13.1	21 47.2	26 8.4	12 44.4	4 44.6	27 41.1	1 43.2
23	16 0 46.3	29 20.5	9 26.6	25 8.5	11 D 46.1	0♋32.7	22 31.0	26 3.3	12 51.8	4 43.6	27 39.4	1 42.6
24	16 4 42.8	0♊20.9	9 23.6	11♑14.8	11 53.8	1 52.2	23 14.8	25 58.3	12 59.2	4 42.6	27 37.7	1 42.1
25	16 8 39.4	1 21.3	9 20.6	26 56.2	12 5.5	3 11.7	23 58.6	25 53.4	13 6.6	4 41.7	27 36.1	1 41.6
26	16 12 35.9	2 21.9	9 17.6	11♒47.6	12 21.4	4 31.2	24 42.3	25 48.6	13 13.9	4 40.9	27 34.4	1 41.1
27	16 16 32.5	3 22.6	9 14.7	25 42.1	12 41.2	5 50.6	25 26.1	25 44.0	13 21.2	4 40.1	27 32.7	1 40.6
28	16 20 29.0	4 23.4	9 11.7	8♓47.3	13 5.0	7 10.0	26 9.8	25 39.6	13 28.5	4 39.3	27 31.1	1 40.2
29	16 24 25.6	5 24.4	9 8.7	21 18.9	13 32.8	8 29.2	26 53.5	25 35.2	13 35.8	4 38.6	27 29.4	1 39.8
30	16 28 22.2	6 25.5	9 5.7	3♈35.4	14 4.3	9 48.3	27 37.2	25 31.1	13 43.1	4 37.9	27 27.7	1 39.4
31	16 32 18.7	7 26.7	9 2.7	15 55.0	14 39.7	11 7.3	28 20.8	25 27.0	13 50.3	4 37.2	27 26.1	1 39.0

DECLINATION

DAY	EPHEM. SID. TIME	☉	☊	☽	☿	♀	♂	♃	♄	♅	♆	♇
1	14 34 2.0	14N53.1	0S 8.6	7S43.0	20N18.8	21N30.4	22N25.4	10S 3.1	13N22.8	1S27.7	18S27.9	16N46.1
4	14 45 51.7	15 46.9	0 8.7	11N55.0	19 26.1	22 16.8	22 45.3	9 55.6	13 29.9	1 25.5	18 26.9	16 46.4
7	14 57 41.3	16 38.4	0 8.7	25 42.4	18 16.5	22 57.7	23 3.3	9 48.4	13 36.9	1 23.4	18 25.8	16 46.5
10	15 9 31.0	17 27.4	0 8.8	27 14.3	16 57.4	23 32.9	23 19.5	9 41.4	13 43.9	1 21.5	18 24.8	16 46.5
13	15 21 20.7	18 13.7	0 8.9	17 30.1	15 37.3	24 2.0	23 33.9	9 34.8	13 50.8	1 19.7	18 23.8	16 46.3
16	15 33 10.4	18 57.3	0 8.9	1 42.7	14 25.2	24 25.0	23 46.4	9 28.5	13 57.6	1 18.1	18 22.7	16 46.1
19	15 45 .0	19 38.0	0 9.0	15S24.8	13 28.1	24 41.7	23 57.1	9 22.6	14 4.2	1 16.7	18 21.7	16 45.6
22	15 56 49.7	20 15.7	0 9.0	27 7.5	12 50.6	24 52.1	24 5.9	9 17.1	14 10.8	1 15.4	18 20.7	16 45.1
25	16 8 39.4	20 50.2	0 9.1	24 38.5	12 34.2	24 56.0	24 12.8	9 12.1	14 17.3	1 14.3	18 19.7	16 44.4
28	16 20 29.0	21 21.6	0 9.2	8 57.4	12 38.6	24 53.4	24 17.9	9 7.6	14 23.6	1 13.4	18 18.6	16 43.6
31	16 32 18.7	21 49.6	0 9.2	10N22.6	13 2.1	24 44.5	24 21.2	9 3.6	14 29.8	1 12.6	18 17.6	16 42.6

JUNE 1970

DAY	EPHEM. SID. TIME	☉	☊	☽	☿	♀	♂	♃	♄	♅	♆	♇
	LONGITUDE											
	h m s	° ′	° ′	° ′	° ′	° ′	° ′	° ′	° ′	° ′	° ′	° ′
1	16 36 15.3	10♊ 6.0	7♓17.4	2♉12.9	16♉40.9	11♋17.5	29♊ 9.4	26♎48.8	15♉47.4	4♎42.6	29♏13.4	24♍40.9
2	16 40 11.8	11 3.5	7 14.3	15 36.9	17 24.7	12 29.3	29 49.2	26R45.0	15 54.7	4R42.1	29R11.9	24R40.8
3	16 44 8.4	12 1.0	7 11.1	28 49.0	18 12.2	13 40.9	0♋28.9	26 41.3	16 1.9	4 41.6	29 10.3	24 40.7
4	16 48 5.0	12 58.5	7 7.9	11♊47.9	19 3.4	14 52.6	1 8.6	26 37.8	16 9.1	4 41.1	29 8.7	24 40.7
5	16 52 1.5	13 56.0	7 4.7	24 32.3	19 58.1	16 4.2	1 48.3	26 34.4	16 16.2	4 40.7	29 7.2	24 40.6
6	16 55 58.1	14 53.4	7 1.5	7♋ 2.1	20 56.4	17 15.7	2 27.9	26 31.2	16 23.3	4 40.4	29 5.6	24D40.7
7	16 59 54.6	15 50.8	6 58.4	19 17.8	21 58.0	18 27.2	3 7.5	26 28.2	16 30.4	4 40.1	29 4.1	24 40.7
8	17 3 51.2	16 48.3	6 55.2	1♌21.2	23 3.0	19 38.6	3 47.1	26 25.4	16 37.5	4 39.8	29 2.5	24 40.8
9	17 7 47.7	17 45.7	6 52.0	13 15.3	24 11.3	20 50.0	4 26.6	26 22.7	16 44.5	4 39.6	29 1.0	24 40.9
10	17 11 44.3	18 43.0	6 48.8	25 4.0	25 22.8	22 1.3	5 6.2	26 20.3	16 51.4	4 39.5	28 59.5	24 41.0
11	17 15 40.9	19 40.4	6 45.7	6♍51.9	26 37.5	23 12.6	5 45.6	26 17.9	16 58.4	4 39.4	28 58.0	24 41.2
12	17 19 37.4	20 37.8	6 42.5	18 44.2	27 55.3	24 23.7	6 25.1	26 15.8	17 5.2	4 39.3	28 56.5	24 41.4
13	17 23 34.0	21 35.1	6 39.3	0♎46.4	29 16.1	25 34.9	7 4.5	26 13.9	17 12.1	4 39.3	28 55.0	24 41.7
14	17 27 30.5	22 32.4	6 36.1	13 3.8	0♊40.1	26 45.9	7 43.9	26 12.1	17 18.9	4D39.4	28 53.6	24 41.9
15	17 31 27.1	23 29.7	6 33.0	25 41.2	2 7.0	27 56.9	8 23.3	26 10.5	17 25.6	4 39.5	28 52.1	24 42.2
16	17 35 23.7	24 27.0	6 29.8	8♏42.3	3 37.0	29 7.8	9 2.6	26 9.1	17 32.3	4 39.7	28 50.7	24 42.6
17	17 39 20.2	25 24.3	6 26.6	22 9.2	5 9.9	0♌18.7	9 42.0	26 7.8	17 39.0	4 39.9	28 49.3	24 43.0
18	17 43 16.8	26 21.5	6 23.4	6♐ 1.6	6 45.8	1 29.5	10 21.2	26 6.8	17 45.6	4 40.2	28 47.9	24 43.4
19	17 47 13.3	27 18.8	6 20.3	20 16.7	8 24.7	2 40.2	11 .5	26 5.9	17 52.2	4 40.5	28 46.5	24 43.8
20	17 51 9.9	28 16.0	6 17.1	4♑49.2	10 6.4	3 50.8	11 39.7	26 5.2	17 58.7	4 40.9	28 45.1	24 44.3
21	17 55 6.4	29 13.2	6 13.9	19 32.0	11 51.0	5 1.4	12 19.0	26 4.7	18 5.2	4 41.3	28 43.8	24 44.8
22	17 59 3.0	0♋10.5	6 10.7	4♒17.4	13 38.4	6 11.9	12 58.1	26 4.4	18 11.6	4 41.8	28 42.4	24 45.3
23	18 2 59.6	1 7.7	6 7.5	18 58.3	15 28.6	7 22.4	13 37.4	26 4.2	18 18.0	4 42.4	28 41.2	24 45.9
24	18 6 56.1	2 5.0	6 4.4	3♓29.3	17 21.4	8 32.7	14 16.5	26D 4.3	18 24.3	4 43.0	28 39.9	24 46.5
25	18 10 52.7	3 2.2	6 1.2	17 46.6	19 16.8	9 43.0	14 55.6	26 4.5	18 30.6	4 43.6	28 38.6	24 47.1
26	18 14 49.2	3 59.4	5 58.0	1♈48.8	21 14.6	10 53.2	15 34.7	26 4.8	18 36.8	4 44.3	28 37.3	24 47.8
27	18 18 45.8	4 56.6	5 54.8	15 35.3	23 14.8	12 3.3	16 13.8	26 5.4	18 42.9	4 45.1	28 36.1	24 48.4
28	18 22 42.4	5 53.9	5 51.7	29 6.8	25 17.1	13 13.4	16 52.9	26 6.1	18 49.0	4 45.9	28 34.9	24 49.2
29	18 26 38.9	6 51.1	5 48.5	12♉24.2	27 21.3	14 23.4	17 31.9	26 7.1	18 55.0	4 46.7	28 33.7	24 49.9
30	18 30 35.5	7 48.3	5 45.3	25 28.2	29 27.2	15 33.3	18 10.9	26 8.2	19 1.0	4 47.6	28 32.5	24 50.7

DAY	EPHEM. SID. TIME	☉	☊	☽	☿	♀	♂	♃	♄	♅	♆	♇
	LATITUDE											
1	16 36 15.3	0 .0	0 .0	4N 6.6	3S45.0	1N42.5	0N55.3	1N23.6	2S 7.8	0N43.5	1N44.5	15N56.4
4	16 48 5.0	0 .0	0 .0	4 59.1	3 38.6	1 46.4	0 56.2	1 22.9	2 8.0	0 43.4	1 44.4	15 55.1
7	16 59 54.6	0 .0	0 .0	3 40.3	3 25.5	1 49.7	0 57.1	1 22.1	2 8.2	0 43.3	1 44.4	15 53.7
10	17 11 44.3	0 .0	0 .0	0 57.3	3 6.4	1 52.3	0 57.9	1 21.4	2 8.4	0 43.1	1 44.3	15 52.4
13	17 23 34.0	0 .0	0 .0	2S 8.1	2 42.3	1 54.2	0 58.7	1 20.6	2 8.7	0 43.0	1 44.2	15 51.0
16	17 35 23.7	0 .0	0 .0	4 30.1	2 13.9	1 55.3	0 59.5	1 19.8	2 8.9	0 42.9	1 44.2	15 49.6
19	17 47 13.3	0 .0	0 .0	4 52.5	1 42.1	1 55.7	1 .2	1 19.0	2 9.2	0 42.7	1 44.1	15 48.3
22	17 59 3.0	0 .0	0 .0	2 35.0	1 8.1	1 55.3	1 1.0	1 18.1	2 9.5	0 42.6	1 44.0	15 46.9
25	18 10 52.7	0 .0	0 .0	1N 8.9	0 33.1	1 54.1	1 1.6	1 17.3	2 9.9	0 42.5	1 43.9	15 45.5
28	18 22 42.4	0 .0	0 .0	4 8.6	0N 1.3	1 52.0	1 2.3	1 16.5	2 10.3	0 42.4	1 43.8	15 44.2

DAY	EPHEM. SID. TIME	☉	☊	☽	☿	♀	♂	♃	♄	♅	♆	♇
	RIGHT ASCENSION											
1	16 36 15.3	8♊28.0	8♓59.7	28♈33.5	15♉18.7	12♋26.2	29♊ 4.5	25♎23.2	13♉57.5	4♎36.7	27♏24.5	1♎38.7
2	16 40 11.8	9 29.5	8 56.7	11♉41.9	16 1.5	13 44.9	29 48.2	25R19.5	14 4.8	4R36.2	27R22.9	1R38.5
3	16 44 8.4	10 31.0	8 53.8	25 23.6	16 47.8	15 3.5	0♋31.8	25 15.9	14 11.9	4 35.7	27 21.2	1 38.2
4	16 48 5.0	11 32.6	8 50.8	9♊31.8	17 37.6	16 21.8	1 15.3	25 12.5	14 19.1	4 35.2	27 19.6	1 37.9
5	16 52 1.5	12 34.3	8 47.8	23 49.7	18 30.9	17 40.0	1 58.9	25 9.2	14 26.2	4 34.8	27 18.0	1 37.7
6	16 55 58.1	13 36.0	8 44.8	7♋55.1	19 27.6	18 57.9	2 42.4	25 6.2	14 33.2	4 34.5	27 16.4	1 37.5
7	16 59 54.6	14 37.9	8 41.8	21 27.9	20 27.8	20 15.6	3 25.8	25 3.2	14 40.3	4 34.2	27 14.8	1 37.4
8	17 3 51.2	15 39.8	8 38.8	4♌16.4	21 31.4	21 33.0	4 9.3	25 .5	14 47.3	4 33.9	27 13.2	1 37.3
9	17 7 47.7	16 41.8	8 35.8	16 18.6	22 38.4	22 50.2	4 52.6	24 57.8	14 54.2	4 33.7	27 11.7	1 37.2
10	17 11 44.3	17 43.9	8 32.9	27 40.7	23 48.7	24 7.1	5 36.0	24 55.4	15 1.2	4 33.6	27 10.1	1 37.1
11	17 15 40.9	18 46.0	8 29.9	8♍33.8	25 2.5	25 23.7	6 19.3	24 53.1	15 8.0	4 33.5	27 8.6	1 37.1
12	17 19 37.4	19 48.2	8 26.9	19 12.2	26 19.6	26 40.1	7 2.5	24 51.0	15 14.9	4 33.4	27 7.0	1 37.1
13	17 23 34.0	20 50.4	8 23.9	29 51.6	27 40.2	27 56.1	7 45.7	24 49.1	15 21.7	4 33.4	27 5.5	1 37.1
14	17 27 30.5	21 52.6	8 20.9	10♎48.8	29 4.2	29 11.8	8 28.9	24 47.3	15 28.5	4D33.5	27 4.0	1 37.1
15	17 31 27.1	22 54.9	8 17.9	22 21.7	0♊31.8	0♌27.2	9 12.0	24 45.7	15 35.2	4 33.5	27 2.5	1D37.2
16	17 35 23.7	23 57.2	8 14.9	4♏48.0	2 2.8	1 42.3	9 55.0	24 44.3	15 41.9	4 33.7	27 1.0	1 37.3
17	17 39 20.2	24 59.6	8 11.9	18 22.1	3 37.4	2 57.0	10 38.0	24 43.0	15 48.6	4 33.9	26 59.6	1 37.5
18	17 43 16.8	26 1.9	8 9.0	3♐10.0	5 15.5	4 11.4	11 20.9	24 41.9	15 55.2	4 34.1	26 58.1	1 37.6
19	17 47 13.3	27 4.3	8 6.0	19 1.2	6 57.3	5 25.4	12 3.7	24 41.0	16 1.7	4 34.4	26 56.7	1 37.8
20	17 51 9.9	28 6.7	8 3.0	5♑25.9	8 42.6	6 39.1	12 46.5	24 40.2	16 8.2	4 34.7	26 55.3	1 38.1
21	17 55 6.4	29 9.0	7 60.0	21 42.9	10 31.6	7 52.4	13 29.3	24 39.7	16 14.7	4 35.1	26 53.9	1 38.3
22	17 59 3.0	0♋11.4	7 57.0	7♒16.9	12 24.2	9 5.3	14 11.9	24 39.2	16 21.1	4 35.5	26 52.5	1 38.6
23	18 2 59.6	1 13.8	7 54.0	21 51.0	14 20.5	10 17.9	14 54.6	24 39.0	16 27.5	4 36.1	26 51.2	1 39.0
24	18 6 56.1	2 16.2	7 51.0	5♓27.0	16 20.2	11 30.1	15 37.1	24 39.0	16 33.9	4 36.6	26 49.9	1 39.3
25	18 10 52.7	3 18.5	7 48.0	18 18.6	18 23.3	12 41.9	16 19.6	24 39.0	16 40.1	4 37.2	26 48.5	1 39.7
26	18 14 49.2	4 20.9	7 45.0	0♈44.4	20 29.7	13 53.4	17 2.0	24D39.3	16 46.4	4 37.8	26 47.2	1 40.1
27	18 18 45.8	5 23.2	7 42.0	13 3.3	22 39.3	15 4.4	17 44.4	24 39.7	16 52.5	4 38.5	26 46.0	1 40.5
28	18 22 42.4	6 25.4	7 39.0	25 32.7	24 51.7	16 15.1	18 26.6	24 40.3	16 58.6	4 39.2	26 44.7	1 41.0
29	18 26 38.9	7 27.7	7 36.0	8♉25.8	27 6.8	17 25.4	19 8.8	24 41.1	17 4.7	4 39.9	26 43.5	1 41.5
30	18 30 35.5	8 29.8	7 33.0	21 49.2	29 24.1	18 35.3	19 50.9	24 42.0	17 10.7	4 40.8	26 42.2	1 42.0

DAY	EPHEM. SID. TIME	☉	☊	☽	☿	♀	♂	♃	♄	♅	♆	♇
	DECLINATION											
1	16 36 15.3	21N58.2	0S 9.3	16N 6.0	13N13.8	24N40.1	24N21.8	9S 2.3	14N31.8	1S12.4	18S17.3	16N42.3
4	16 48 5.0	22 21.7	0 9.3	27 8.8	13 58.9	24 22.7	24 22.6	8 59.1	14 37.9	1 11.9	18 16.4	16 41.1
7	16 59 54.6	22 41.6	0 9.4	25 41.4	14 57.2	23 59.1	24 21.6	8 56.3	14 43.7	1 11.6	18 15.4	16 39.9
10	17 11 44.3	22 58.0	0 9.4	14 4.1	16 5.7	23 29.5	24 18.7	8 54.2	14 49.4	1 11.5	18 14.5	16 38.5
13	17 23 34.0	23 10.7	0 9.5	2S16.0	17 21.4	22 54.1	24 14.0	8 52.6	14 55.0	1 11.6	18 13.6	16 37.0
16	17 35 23.7	23 19.7	0 9.6	18 39.9	18 41.4	22 13.1	24 7.6	8 51.6	15 .4	1 11.8	18 12.7	16 35.4
19	17 47 13.3	23 25.1	0 9.6	27 57.0	20 1.9	21 26.7	23 59.4	8 51.2	15 5.6	1 12.3	18 11.9	16 33.6
22	17 59 3.0	23 26.7	0 9.7	21 42.0	21 19.0	20 35.3	23 49.4	8 51.4	15 10.6	1 12.9	18 11.1	16 31.8
25	18 10 52.7	23 24.6	0 9.7	3 46.5	22 27.8	19 39.2	23 37.8	8 52.2	15 15.5	1 13.7	18 10.4	16 29.9
28	18 22 42.4	23 18.8	0 9.8	15N 2.0	23 23.0	18 38.6	23 24.5	8 53.6	15 20.1	1 14.7	18 9.7	16 27.8

JULY 1970

LONGITUDE

DAY	EPHEM. SID. TIME h m s	☉ ° ′	☊ ° ′	☽ ° ′	☿ ° ′	♀ ° ′	♂ ° ′	♃ ° ′	♄ ° ′	♅ ° ′	♆ ° ′	♇ ° ′
1	18 34 32.0	8♋45.5	5♓42.1	8♊19.5	1♋34.6	16♌43.1	18♋49.9	26♎ 9.4	19♉ 6.9	4♎48.6	28♏31.4	24♍51.5
2	18 38 28.6	9 42.7	5 39.0	20 58.5	3 43.1	17 52.8	19 28.9	26 10.9	19 12.8	4 49.6	28 R 30.2	24 52.3
3	18 42 25.2	10 40.0	5 35.8	3♋25.6	5 52.6	19 2.5	20 7.8	26 12.5	19 18.6	4 50.7	28 29.1	24 53.2
4	18 46 21.7	11 37.2	5 32.6	15 41.4	8 2.6	20 12.0	20 46.8	26 14.3	19 24.3	4 51.8	28 28.0	24 54.1
5	18 50 18.3	12 34.4	5 29.4	27 46.8	10 13.0	21 21.5	21 25.7	26 16.3	19 30.0	4 52.9	28 27.0	24 55.0
6	18 54 14.8	13 31.6	5 26.3	9♌43.4	12 23.4	22 30.9	22 4.6	26 18.4	19 35.6	4 54.2	28 25.9	24 56.0
7	18 58 11.4	14 28.9	5 23.1	21 33.5	14 33.6	23 40.2	22 43.4	26 20.8	19 41.1	4 55.4	28 24.9	24 57.0
8	19 2 7.9	15 26.1	5 19.9	3♍20.3	16 43.3	24 49.4	23 22.3	26 23.3	19 46.5	4 56.7	28 23.9	24 58.0
9	19 6 4.5	16 23.3	5 16.7	15 7.3	18 52.2	25 58.5	24 1.1	26 26.0	19 51.9	4 58.1	28 23.0	24 59.0
10	19 10 1.1	17 20.5	5 13.6	26 59.2	21 .3	27 7.5	24 39.9	26 28.8	19 57.3	4 59.5	28 22.0	25 .1
11	19 13 57.6	18 17.7	5 10.4	9♎ .6	23 7.2	28 16.4	25 18.7	26 31.8	20 2.5	5 1.0	28 21.1	25 1.2
12	19 17 54.2	19 14.9	5 7.2	21 16.8	25 12.8	29 25.2	25 57.5	26 35.0	20 7.7	5 2.5	28 20.3	25 2.3
13	19 21 50.7	20 12.1	5 4.0	3♏52.6	27 17.0	0♍33.9	26 36.2	26 38.4	20 12.8	5 4.1	28 19.4	25 3.5
14	19 25 47.3	21 9.4	5 .8	16 52.4	29 19.8	1 42.5	27 15.0	26 41.9	20 17.9	5 5.7	28 18.6	25 4.7
15	19 29 43.9	22 6.6	4 57.7	0♐19.2	1♌20.9	2 51.0	27 53.7	26 45.6	20 22.8	5 7.4	28 17.8	25 6.0
16	19 33 40.4	23 3.8	4 54.5	14 14.0	3 20.4	3 59.3	28 32.4	26 49.4	20 27.7	5 9.1	28 17.0	25 7.2
17	19 37 37.0	24 1.0	4 51.3	28 35.2	5 18.1	5 7.5	29 11.1	26 53.5	20 32.5	5 10.9	28 16.3	25 8.5
18	19 41 33.5	24 58.3	4 48.1	13♑18.4	7 14.1	6 15.6	29 49.7	26 57.6	20 37.3	5 12.7	28 15.6	25 9.8
19	19 45 30.1	25 55.5	4 45.0	28 16.5	9 8.3	7 23.6	0♌28.4	27 1.9	20 41.9	5 14.5	28 14.9	25 11.1
20	19 49 26.6	26 52.7	4 41.8	13♒20.8	11 .8	8 31.4	1 7.0	27 6.4	20 46.5	5 16.4	28 14.2	25 12.4
21	19 53 23.2	27 50.0	4 38.6	28 22.2	12 51.4	9 39.2	1 45.6	27 11.1	20 51.0	5 18.3	28 13.6	25 13.8
22	19 57 19.8	28 47.2	4 35.4	13♓12.8	14 40.3	10 46.8	2 24.2	27 15.9	20 55.4	5 20.3	28 13.0	25 15.2
23	20 1 16.3	29 44.5	4 32.3	27 46.5	16 27.3	11 54.2	3 2.8	27 20.8	20 59.7	5 22.4	28 12.4	25 16.6
24	20 5 12.9	0♌41.8	4 29.1	11♈59.7	18 12.6	13 1.5	3 41.3	27 25.9	21 4.0	5 24.4	28 11.8	25 18.1
25	20 9 9.4	1 39.1	4 25.9	25 51.1	19 56.1	14 8.7	4 19.9	27 31.2	21 8.1	5 26.5	28 11.3	25 19.5
26	20 13 6.0	2 36.4	4 22.7	9♉21.0	21 37.8	15 15.8	4 58.4	27 36.6	21 12.2	5 28.7	28 10.8	25 21.0
27	20 17 2.6	3 33.7	4 19.6	22 31.0	23 17.8	16 22.7	5 36.9	27 42.1	21 16.2	5 30.9	28 10.4	25 22.6
28	20 20 59.1	4 31.1	4 16.4	5♊23.2	24 56.0	17 29.4	6 15.4	27 47.8	21 20.1	5 33.2	28 10.0	25 24.1
29	20 24 55.7	5 28.4	4 13.2	17 59.9	26 32.4	18 36.1	6 53.9	27 53.7	21 24.0	5 35.5	28 9.6	25 25.7
30	20 28 52.2	6 25.8	4 10.0	0♋23.3	28 7.1	19 42.5	7 32.4	27 59.7	21 27.7	5 37.8	28 9.2	25 27.3
31	20 32 48.8	7 23.2	4 6.8	12 35.6	29 40.0	20 48.8	8 10.9	28 5.8	21 31.3	5 40.2	28 8.9	25 28.9

LATITUDE

DAY	EPHEM. SID. TIME	☉	☊	☽	☿	♀	♂	♃	♄	♅	♆	♇
1	18 34 32.0	0 .0	0 .0	5N 4.5	0N33.2	1N49.1	1N 2.9	1N15.7	2S10.6	0N42.2	1N43.6	15N42.9
4	18 46 21.7	0 .0	0 .0	3 48.8	1 1.0	1 45.3	1 3.5	1 14.9	2 11.1	0 42.1	1 43.5	15 41.6
7	18 58 11.4	0 .0	0 .0	1 5.0	1 23.0	1 40.6	1 4.1	1 14.1	2 11.5	0 42.0	1 43.4	15 40.3
10	19 10 1.1	0 .0	0 .0	2S 2.9	1 38.6	1 35.0	1 4.6	1 13.3	2 12.0	0 41.9	1 43.2	15 39.1
13	19 21 50.7	0 .0	0 .0	4 29.4	1 47.4	1 28.6	1 5.1	1 12.5	2 12.4	0 41.7	1 43.1	15 37.9
16	19 33 40.4	0 .0	0 .0	5 4.9	1 49.6	1 21.2	1 5.6	1 11.7	2 12.9	0 41.6	1 42.9	15 36.7
19	19 45 30.1	0 .0	0 .0	2 58.7	1 45.8	1 13.0	1 6.0	1 10.9	2 13.4	0 41.5	1 42.8	15 35.5
22	19 57 19.8	0 .0	0 .0	0N54.6	1 36.7	1 3.9	1 6.4	1 10.1	2 14.0	0 41.4	1 42.6	15 34.4
25	20 9 9.4	0 .0	0 .0	4 9.2	1 22.9	0 53.9	1 6.8	1 9.4	2 14.5	0 41.3	1 42.5	15 33.4
28	20 20 59.1	0 .0	0 .0	5 13.1	1 5.0	0 43.0	1 7.2	1 8.6	2 15.1	0 41.2	1 42.3	15 32.4
31	20 32 48.8	0 .0	0 .0	4 1.9	0 43.7	0 31.3	1 7.5	1 7.9	2 15.6	0 41.0	1 42.1	15 31.4

RIGHT ASCENSION

DAY	EPHEM. SID. TIME	☉	☊	☽	☿	♀	♂	♃	♄	♅	♆	♇
1	18 34 32.0	9♋32.0	7♓30.1	5♊40.8	1♋43.5	19♌44.8	20♋33.0	24♎43.1	17♉16.6	4♎41.6	26♏41.1	1♎42.6
2	18 38 28.6	10 34.0	7 27.1	19 48.2	4 4.4	20 54.0	21 15.0	24 44.4	17 22.5	4 42.5	26 R 39.9	1 43.1
3	18 42 25.2	11 36.1	7 24.1	3♋51.9	6 26.6	22 2.7	21 56.9	24 45.8	17 28.3	4 43.5	26 38.7	1 43.8
4	18 46 21.7	12 38.0	7 21.1	17 31.1	8 49.4	23 11.1	22 38.7	24 47.4	17 34.1	4 44.5	26 37.6	1 44.4
5	18 50 18.3	13 39.9	7 18.1	0♌30.9	11 12.6	24 19.1	23 20.4	24 49.2	17 39.8	4 45.6	26 36.5	1 45.1
6	18 54 14.8	14 41.6	7 15.1	12 45.6	13 35.7	25 26.8	24 2.1	24 51.1	17 45.4	4 46.7	26 35.4	1 45.7
7	18 58 11.4	15 43.3	7 12.1	24 17.9	15 58.3	26 34.0	24 43.6	24 53.2	17 51.0	4 47.8	26 34.4	1 46.5
8	19 2 7.9	16 44.9	7 9.1	5♍16.6	18 19.9	27 40.9	25 25.1	24 55.5	17 56.5	4 49.0	26 33.4	1 47.2
9	19 6 4.5	17 46.4	7 6.1	15 54.3	20 40.3	28 47.4	26 6.5	24 57.9	18 1.9	4 50.2	26 32.4	1 48.0
10	19 10 1.1	18 47.8	7 3.1	26 25.2	22 59.1	29 53.6	26 47.8	25 .5	18 7.3	4 51.5	26 31.4	1 48.8
11	19 13 57.6	19 49.1	7 .1	7♎ 5.5	25 16.0	0♍59.4	27 29.1	25 3.3	18 12.6	4 52.8	26 30.5	1 49.6
12	19 17 54.2	20 50.3	6 57.1	18 12.0	27 30.8	2 4.8	28 10.2	25 6.2	18 17.8	4 54.2	26 29.5	1 50.5
13	19 21 50.7	21 51.3	6 54.1	0♏ 2.5	29 43.3	3 9.9	28 51.2	25 9.3	18 22.9	4 55.6	26 28.6	1 51.4
14	19 25 47.3	22 52.3	6 51.1	12 53.7	1♌53.4	4 14.6	29 32.2	25 12.5	18 28.1	4 57.1	26 27.8	1 52.3
15	19 29 43.9	23 53.1	6 48.1	26 57.2	4 .9	5 19.0	0♌13.1	25 15.9	18 33.1	4 58.7	26 27.0	1 53.3
16	19 33 40.4	24 53.8	6 45.1	12♐13.4	6 5.8	6 23.0	0 53.9	25 19.5	18 38.0	5 .2	26 26.2	1 54.2
17	19 37 37.0	25 54.3	6 42.1	28 24.1	8 8.0	7 26.7	1 34.6	25 23.1	18 42.9	5 1.8	26 25.4	1 55.2
18	19 41 33.5	26 54.7	6 39.1	14♑53.8	10 7.4	8 30.1	2 15.2	25 27.0	18 47.7	5 3.4	26 24.7	1 56.3
19	19 45 30.1	27 55.0	6 36.1	1♒ 2.1	12 4.1	9 33.1	2 55.7	25 31.0	18 52.4	5 5.1	26 23.9	1 57.3
20	19 49 26.6	28 55.2	6 33.1	16 20.8	13 58.1	10 35.8	3 36.1	25 35.1	18 57.0	5 6.8	26 23.2	1 58.4
21	19 53 23.2	29 55.2	6 30.1	0♓41.2	15 49.3	11 38.2	4 16.4	25 39.4	19 1.6	5 8.6	26 22.6	1 59.5
22	19 57 19.8	0♌55.1	6 27.1	14 10.7	17 37.9	12 40.2	4 56.6	25 43.9	19 6.0	5 10.4	26 21.9	2 .6
23	20 1 16.3	1 54.8	6 24.1	27 5.6	19 23.8	13 42.0	5 36.8	25 48.5	19 10.4	5 12.3	26 21.3	2 1.7
24	20 5 12.9	2 54.4	6 21.1	9♈44.4	21 7.2	14 43.5	6 16.8	25 53.2	19 14.7	5 14.2	26 20.8	2 2.9
25	20 9 9.4	3 53.9	6 18.1	22 24.7	22 48.0	15 44.6	6 56.8	25 58.1	19 19.0	5 16.1	26 20.2	2 4.1
26	20 13 6.0	4 53.2	6 15.1	5♉20.8	24 26.3	16 45.5	7 36.7	26 3.1	19 23.1	5 18.1	26 19.7	2 5.3
27	20 17 2.6	5 52.3	6 12.1	18 41.1	26 2.1	17 46.2	8 16.4	26 8.3	19 27.2	5 20.1	26 19.2	2 6.6
28	20 20 59.1	6 51.4	6 9.1	2♊25.9	27 35.6	18 46.5	8 56.1	26 13.6	19 31.2	5 22.1	26 18.8	2 7.8
29	20 24 55.7	7 50.3	6 6.1	16 26.5	29 6.7	19 46.6	9 35.7	26 19.0	19 35.0	5 24.2	26 18.4	2 9.1
30	20 28 52.2	8 49.0	6 3.1	0♋26.4	0♍35.5	20 46.4	10 15.2	26 24.6	19 38.9	5 26.3	26 18.0	2 10.5
31	20 32 48.8	9 47.6	6 .1	14 6.7	2 2.0	21 46.0	10 54.7	26 30.3	19 42.6	5 28.5	26 17.6	2 11.8

DECLINATION

DAY	EPHEM. SID. TIME	☉	☊	☽	☿	♀	♂	♃	♄	♅	♆	♇
1	18 34 32.0	23N 9.4	0S 9.9	26N42.5	23N59.4	17N33.8	23N 9.6	8S55.5	15N24.6	1S15.9	18S 9.0	16N25.7
4	18 46 21.7	22 56.2	0 9.9	26 18.6	24 12.9	16 25.1	22 53.1	8 58.1	15 28.9	1 17.3	18 8.4	16 23.5
7	18 58 11.4	22 39.5	0 10.0	15 20.9	24 1.5	15 13.0	22 35.0	9 1.2	15 33.0	1 18.9	18 7.9	16 21.2
10	19 10 1.1	22 19.2	0 10.1	0S40.8	23 25.7	13 57.6	22 15.3	9 4.8	15 36.8	1 20.6	18 7.4	16 18.8
13	19 21 50.7	21 55.5	0 10.1	17 2.0	22 27.8	12 39.4	21 54.2	9 9.0	15 40.5	1 22.5	18 7.0	16 16.3
16	19 33 40.4	21 28.4	0 10.2	27 33.5	21 11.4	11 18.6	21 31.7	9 13.7	15 44.0	1 24.6	18 6.6	16 13.8
19	19 45 30.1	20 58.0	0 10.2	23 25.7	19 40.5	9 55.6	21 7.7	9 18.9	15 47.2	1 26.9	18 6.3	16 11.2
22	19 57 19.8	20 24.5	0 10.3	5 45.5	17 58.6	8 30.7	20 42.4	9 24.6	15 50.2	1 29.3	18 6.0	16 8.6
25	20 9 9.4	19 47.9	0 10.4	13N51.4	16 9.0	7 4.1	20 15.8	9 30.8	15 53.0	1 31.9	18 5.8	16 5.9
28	20 20 59.1	19 8.2	0 10.4	26 20.2	14 14.1	5 36.2	19 47.9	9 37.5	15 55.5	1 34.6	18 5.7	16 3.1
31	20 32 48.8	18 25.8	0 10.5	26 51.7	12 16.4	4 7.3	19 18.7	9 44.6	15 57.9	1 37.5	18 5.6	16 .3

AUGUST 1970

LONGITUDE

DAY	EPHEM. SID. TIME h m s	☉ ° ′	☊ ° ′	☾ ° ′	☿ ° ′	♀ ° ′	♂ ° ′	♃ ° ′	♄ ° ′	♅ ° ′	♆ ° ′	♇ ° ′
1	20 36 45.3	8♌20.6	4♓ 3.7	24♋38.7	1♍11.2	21♍55.0	8♌49.4	28♎12.1	21♉34.9	5♎42.6	28♏ 8.6	25♍30.5
2	20 40 41.9	9 18.0	4 .5	6♌34.6	2 40.5	23 1.0	9 27.8	28 18.5	21 38.4	5 45.0	28R 8.3	25 32.2
3	20 44 38.4	10 15.5	3 57.3	18 25.0	4 8.1	24 6.8	10 6.2	28 25.0	21 41.7	5 47.5	28 8.0	25 33.9
4	20 48 35.0	11 13.0	3 54.1	0♍12.3	5 33.9	25 12.5	10 44.7	28 31.8	21 45.1	5 50.1	28 7.9	25 35.6
5	20 52 31.6	12 10.4	3 51.0	11 58.8	6 57.8	26 18.0	11 23.1	28 38.6	21 48.3	5 52.7	28 7.7	25 37.4
6	20 56 28.1	13 7.9	3 47.8	23 47.4	8 19.9	27 23.3	12 1.5	28 45.6	21 51.3	5 55.3	28 7.6	25 39.1
7	21 0 24.7	14 5.4	3 44.6	5♎41.5	9 40.0	28 28.4	12 39.9	28 52.7	21 54.3	5 58.0	28 7.5	25 40.9
8	21 4 21.2	15 2.9	3 41.4	17 44.8	10 58.2	29 33.3	13 18.3	28 59.9	21 57.2	6 .6	28 7.4	25 42.7
9	21 8 17.8	16 .5	3 38.3	0♏ 1.4	12 14.3	0♎38.0	13 56.6	29 7.3	22 .0	6 3.4	28 7.3	25 44.5
10	21 12 14.3	16 58.0	3 35.1	12 35.7	13 28.5	1 42.5	14 35.0	29 14.8	22 2.8	6 6.1	28 7.3	25 46.3
11	21 16 10.9	17 55.5	3 31.9	25 31.7	14 40.5	2 46.8	15 13.3	29 22.4	22 5.4	6 8.9	28 7.3	25 48.1
12	21 20 7.5	18 53.1	3 28.7	8♐52.6	15 50.3	3 50.9	15 51.6	29 30.1	22 7.9	6 11.8	28D 7.4	25 50.0
13	21 24 4.0	19 50.7	3 25.5	22 40.6	16 57.8	4 54.8	16 29.9	29 38.0	22 10.3	6 14.6	28 7.5	25 51.9
14	21 28 .6	20 48.3	3 22.4	6♑55.7	18 2.9	5 58.4	17 8.2	29 46.0	22 12.6	6 17.5	28 7.6	25 53.8
15	21 31 57.1	21 45.9	3 19.2	21 35.3	19 5.6	7 1.8	17 46.5	29 54.1	22 14.8	6 20.5	28 7.7	25 55.7
16	21 35 53.7	22 43.5	3 16.0	6♒34.2	20 5.7	8 4.9	18 24.8	0♏ 2.3	22 16.9	6 23.4	28 7.9	25 57.6
17	21 39 50.2	23 41.2	3 12.8	21 44.4	21 3.0	9 7.8	19 3.1	0 10.7	22 18.9	6 26.4	28 8.1	25 59.6
18	21 43 46.8	24 38.8	3 9.7	6♓56.8	21 57.5	10 10.4	19 41.3	0 19.1	22 20.8	6 29.5	28 8.3	26 1.5
19	21 47 43.3	25 36.5	3 6.5	22 1.7	22 49.0	11 12.8	20 19.6	0 27.7	22 22.7	6 32.5	28 8.6	26 3.5
20	21 51 39.9	26 34.3	3 3.3	6♈50.9	23 37.4	12 14.8	20 57.8	0 36.4	22 24.4	6 35.6	28 8.9	26 5.5
21	21 55 36.5	27 32.0	3 .1	21 18.4	24 22.4	13 16.6	21 36.1	0 45.1	22 26.0	6 38.7	28 9.3	26 7.5
22	21 59 33.0	28 29.8	2 56.9	5♉20.7	25 3.8	14 18.2	22 14.3	0 54.0	22 27.5	6 41.9	28 9.6	26 9.5
23	22 3 29.6	29 27.6	2 53.8	18 56.8	25 41.5	15 19.4	22 52.5	1 3.1	22 28.9	6 45.1	28 10.0	26 11.6
24	22 7 26.1	0♍25.4	2 50.6	2♊ 8.0	26 15.3	16 20.3	23 30.7	1 12.2	22 30.1	6 48.3	28 10.5	26 13.6
25	22 11 22.7	1 23.3	2 47.4	14 56.9	26 44.8	17 21.0	24 9.0	1 21.4	22 31.4	6 51.6	28 11.0	26 15.7
26	22 15 19.2	2 21.2	2 44.2	27 26.6	27 9.9	18 21.3	24 47.2	1 30.8	22 32.5	6 54.8	28 11.5	26 17.8
27	22 19 15.8	3 19.1	2 41.1	9♋41.0	27 30.2	19 21.2	25 25.4	1 40.2	22 33.4	6 58.1	28 12.0	26 19.9
28	22 23 12.3	4 17.1	2 37.9	21 43.8	27 45.6	20 20.9	26 3.6	1 49.7	22 34.3	7 1.4	28 12.6	26 22.0
29	22 27 8.9	5 15.0	2 34.7	3♌38.3	27 55.7	21 20.1	26 41.8	1 59.4	22 35.1	7 4.8	28 13.2	26 24.1
30	22 31 5.4	6 13.1	2 31.5	15 27.8	28 .3	22 19.1	27 20.0	2 9.1	22 35.7	7 8.1	28 13.8	26 26.2
31	22 35 2.0	7 11.1	2 28.4	27 14.9	27R59.2	23 17.6	27 58.2	2 18.9	22 36.2	7 11.5	28 14.5	26 28.3

LATITUDE

DAY	EPHEM. SID. TIME	☉	☊	☾	☿	♀	♂	♃	♄	♅	♆	♇
1	20 36 45.3	0 .0	0 .0	3N14.8	0N35.9	0N27.2	1N 7.6	1N 7.7	2S15.8	0N41.0	1N42.1	15N31.1
4	20 48 35.0	0 .0	0 .0	0 14.3	0 10.8	0 14.4	1 7.9	1 7.0	2 16.4	0 40.9	1 41.9	15 30.2
7	21 0 24.7	0 .0	0 .0	2S52.0	0S16.7	0 .8	1 8.2	1 6.3	2 17.0	0 40.8	1 41.7	15 29.3
10	21 12 14.3	0 .0	0 .0	4 57.2	0 46.0	0S13.5	1 8.4	1 5.6	2 17.7	0 40.7	1 41.5	15 28.5
13	21 24 4.0	0 .0	0 .0	4 58.2	1 16.6	0 28.6	1 8.7	1 5.0	2 18.3	0 40.6	1 41.3	15 27.8
16	21 35 53.7	0 .0	0 .0	2 20.5	1 48.1	0 44.3	1 8.9	1 4.3	2 18.9	0 40.5	1 41.2	15 27.1
19	21 47 43.3	0 .0	0 .0	1N44.9	2 19.7	1 .7	1 9.1	1 3.7	2 19.6	0 40.5	1 41.0	15 26.5
22	21 59 33.0	0 .0	0 .0	4 42.1	2 50.9	1 17.6	1 9.2	1 3.1	2 20.2	0 40.4	1 40.8	15 25.9
25	22 11 22.7	0 .0	0 .0	5 10.7	3 20.3	1 35.1	1 9.3	1 2.5	2 20.9	0 40.3	1 40.6	15 25.4
28	22 23 12.3	0 .0	0 .0	3 29.2	3 46.7	1 53.1	1 9.4	1 1.9	2 21.5	0 40.2	1 40.5	15 25.0
31	22 35 2.0	0 .0	0 .0	0 31.0	4 7.7	2 11.6	1 9.5	1 1.4	2 22.2	0 40.2	1 40.3	15 24.6

RIGHT ASCENSION

DAY	EPHEM. SID. TIME	☉	☊	☾	☿	♀	♂	♃	♄	♅	♆	♇
1	20 36 45.3	10♌46.0	5♓57.1	27♋12.2	3♍26.3	22♍45.3	11♌34.0	26♎36.2	19♉46.2	5♎30.7	26♏17.3	2♎13.2
2	20 40 41.9	11 44.3	5 54.1	9♌35.3	4 48.5	23 44.4	12 13.2	26 42.2	19 49.7	5 33.0	26R17.0	2 14.5
3	20 44 38.4	12 42.4	5 51.0	21 16.5	6 8.4	24 43.2	12 52.4	26 48.3	19 53.2	5 35.2	26 16.7	2 16.0
4	20 48 35.0	13 40.5	5 48.0	2♍22.4	7 26.3	25 41.9	13 31.5	26 54.7	19 56.6	5 37.6	26 16.6	2 17.4
5	20 52 31.6	14 38.3	5 45.0	13 3.6	8 42.0	26 40.2	14 10.4	27 1.1	19 59.8	5 40.0	26 16.4	2 18.9
6	20 56 28.1	15 36.0	5 42.0	23 33.1	9 55.6	27 38.4	14 49.3	27 7.6	20 3.0	5 42.3	26 16.2	2 20.4
7	21 0 24.7	16 33.5	5 39.0	4♎ 5.1	11 7.0	28 36.3	15 28.1	27 14.3	20 6.0	5 44.8	26 16.1	2 21.8
8	21 4 21.2	17 30.8	5 36.0	14 55.0	12 16.4	29 34.0	16 6.8	27 21.0	20 9.0	5 47.2	26 16.0	2 23.4
9	21 8 17.8	18 28.1	5 33.0	26 18.8	13 23.6	0♎31.5	16 45.4	27 28.0	20 11.9	5 49.7	26 15.9	2 24.9
10	21 12 14.3	19 25.1	5 30.0	8♏32.5	14 28.6	1 28.7	17 23.9	27 35.0	20 14.7	5 52.2	26 15.9	2 26.4
11	21 16 10.9	20 22.1	5 27.0	21 49.4	15 31.5	2 25.8	18 2.3	27 42.2	20 17.3	5 54.8	26 15.9	2 28.0
12	21 20 7.5	21 18.8	5 24.0	6♐15.3	16 32.2	3 22.6	18 40.6	27 49.4	20 19.9	5 57.4	26 15.9	2 29.6
13	21 24 4.0	22 15.5	5 21.0	21 42.9	17 30.5	4 19.2	19 18.9	27 56.8	20 22.4	6 .0	26D16.0	2 31.2
14	21 28 .6	23 11.9	5 18.0	7♑48.2	18 26.6	5 15.6	19 57.0	28 4.4	20 24.8	6 2.7	26 16.1	2 32.9
15	21 31 57.1	24 8.3	5 14.9	23 56.3	19 20.2	6 11.8	20 35.1	28 12.0	20 27.1	6 5.3	26 16.2	2 34.5
16	21 35 53.7	25 4.5	5 11.9	9♒35.2	20 11.4	7 7.8	21 13.1	28 19.8	20 29.3	6 8.1	26 16.4	2 36.2
17	21 39 50.2	26 .6	5 8.9	24 27.2	21 .0	8 3.6	21 51.0	28 27.6	20 31.3	6 10.8	26 16.6	2 37.9
18	21 43 46.8	26 56.5	5 5.9	8♓31.7	21 45.9	8 59.2	22 28.8	28 35.6	20 33.3	6 13.6	26 16.8	2 39.6
19	21 47 43.3	27 52.3	5 2.9	21 59.4	22 29.1	9 54.6	23 6.5	28 43.7	20 35.2	6 16.4	26 17.1	2 41.3
20	21 51 39.9	28 48.0	4 59.9	5♈ 6.5	23 9.3	10 49.8	23 44.2	28 51.9	20 37.0	6 19.2	26 17.4	2 43.0
21	21 55 36.5	29 43.6	4 56.9	18 10.1	23 46.5	11 44.8	24 21.8	29 .2	20 38.6	6 22.1	26 17.7	2 44.8
22	21 59 33.0	0♍39.1	4 53.9	1♉24.3	24 20.4	12 39.6	24 59.3	29 8.7	20 40.2	6 25.0	26 18.1	2 46.5
23	22 3 29.6	1 34.4	4 50.8	14 58.1	24 51.0	13 34.2	25 36.7	29 17.2	20 41.7	6 27.9	26 18.5	2 48.3
24	22 7 26.1	2 29.7	4 47.8	28 52.7	25 18.0	14 28.6	26 14.0	29 25.8	20 43.0	6 30.8	26 18.9	2 50.1
25	22 11 22.7	3 24.9	4 44.8	13♊ .5	25 41.3	15 22.8	26 51.3	29 34.6	20 44.3	6 33.8	26 19.4	2 52.0
26	22 15 19.2	4 19.9	4 41.8	27 6.5	26 .6	16 16.8	27 28.5	29 43.5	20 45.5	6 36.8	26 19.9	2 53.8
27	22 19 15.8	5 14.9	4 38.8	10♋53.0	26 15.7	17 10.6	28 5.6	29 52.4	20 46.5	6 39.8	26 20.5	2 55.6
28	22 23 12.3	6 9.7	4 35.8	24 5.5	26 26.5	18 4.2	28 42.7	0♏ 1.5	20 47.4	6 42.9	26 21.0	2 57.5
29	22 27 8.9	7 4.5	4 32.8	6♌36.2	26 32.7	18 57.6	29 19.7	0 10.6	20 48.2	6 45.9	26 21.6	2 59.4
30	22 31 5.4	7 59.2	4 29.7	18 25.1	26 34.1	19 50.7	29 56.6	0 19.9	20 48.9	6 49.0	26 22.3	3 1.2
31	22 35 2.0	8 53.8	4 26.7	29 38.0	26R30.6	20 43.6	0♍33.4	0 29.2	20 49.5	6 52.1	26 22.9	3 3.1

DECLINATION

DAY	EPHEM. SID. TIME	☉	☊	☾	☿	♀	♂	♃	♄	♅	♆	♇
1	20 36 45.3	18N11.0	0S10.5	24N23.7	11N36.9	3N37.4	19N 8.7	9S47.0	15N58.6	1S38.5	18S 5.6	15N59.4
4	20 48 35.0	17 24.9	0 10.6	11 37.6	9 38.4	2 7.5	18 38.0	9 54.7	16 .6	1 41.5	18 5.6	15 56.5
7	21 0 24.7	16 36.3	0 10.6	4S53.6	7 41.4	0 37.2	18 6.1	10 2.7	16 2.4	1 44.7	18 5.7	15 53.7
10	21 12 14.3	15 45.3	0 10.7	20 20.1	5 47.5	0S53.2	17 33.2	10 11.2	16 4.0	1 48.1	18 5.8	15 50.8
13	21 24 4.0	14 52.0	0 10.7	28 12.3	3 58.4	2 23.4	16 59.2	10 19.9	16 5.3	1 51.5	18 6.0	15 47.9
16	21 35 53.7	13 56.6	0 10.8	20 54.1	2 16.1	3 53.1	16 24.3	10 29.1	16 6.3	1 55.1	18 6.3	15 45.0
19	21 47 43.3	12 59.2	0 10.9	1 33.4	0 42.7	5 22.0	15 48.4	10 38.5	16 7.2	1 58.7	18 6.6	15 42.1
22	21 59 33.0	12 .0	0 10.9	17N44.0	0S39.1	6 50.0	15 11.6	10 48.3	16 7.8	2 2.5	18 7.0	15 39.2
25	22 11 22.7	10 59.0	0 11.0	27 44.4	1 46.2	8 16.7	14 33.9	10 58.3	16 8.1	2 6.4	18 7.5	15 36.3
28	22 23 12.3	9 56.5	0 11.0	25 8.0	2 34.5	9 41.9	13 55.4	11 8.6	16 8.2	2 10.4	18 8.0	15 33.4
31	22 35 2.0	8 52.5	0 11.1	12 55.0	2 59.2	11 5.3	13 16.2	11 19.2	16 8.1	2 14.4	18 8.6	15 30.6

SEPTEMBER 1970

LONGITUDE

DAY	EPHEM. SID. TIME	☉	☊	☾	☿	♀	♂	♃	♄	♅	♆	♇
	h m s	° ′	° ′	° ′	° ′	° ′	° ′	° ′	° ′	° ′	° ′	° ′
1	22 38 58.6	8♍ 9.1	2♓25.2	9♍ 2.1	27♍52.1	24♎15.8	28♌36.3	2♏28.9	22♉36.7	7♎14.9	28♏15.2	26♍30.5
2	22 42 55.1	9 7.2	2 22.0	20 51.8	27 R 38.8	25 13.5	29 14.5	2 38.9	22 37.0	7 18.4	28 15.9	26 32.6
3	22 46 51.7	10 5.4	2 18.8	2♎46.2	27 19.4	26 10.9	29 52.7	2 49.0	22 37.2	7 21.8	28 16.6	26 34.8
4	22 50 48.2	11 3.5	2 15.6	14 47.5	26 53.6	27 7.8	0♍30.8	2 59.2	22 37.3	7 25.3	28 17.4	26 37.0
5	22 54 44.8	12 1.7	2 12.5	26 58.1	26 21.6	28 4.3	1 9.0	3 9.5	22 37.3	7 28.8	28 18.3	26 39.1
6	22 58 41.3	12 59.9	2 9.3	9♏20.8	25 43.7	29 .3	1 47.1	3 19.9	22 R 37.2	7 32.3	28 19.1	26 41.3
7	23 2 37.9	13 58.1	2 6.1	21 58.4	24 60.0	29 55.8	2 25.3	3 30.4	22 37.0	7 35.9	28 20.0	26 43.5
8	23 6 34.4	14 56.3	2 2.9	4♐53.7	24 11.1	0♏50.8	3 3.4	3 40.9	22 36.7	7 39.4	28 20.9	26 45.7
9	23 10 31.0	15 54.6	1 59.8	18 9.6	23 17.8	1 45.3	3 41.5	3 51.5	22 36.3	7 43.0	28 21.8	26 47.9
10	23 14 27.5	16 52.9	1 56.6	1♑48.1	22 20.8	2 39.3	4 19.6	4 2.3	22 35.7	7 46.6	28 22.8	26 50.1
11	23 18 24.1	17 51.2	1 53.4	15 50.4	21 21.2	3 32.7	4 57.8	4 13.1	22 35.1	7 50.2	28 23.8	26 52.3
12	23 22 20.6	18 49.5	1 50.2	0♒15.7	20 20.2	4 25.5	5 35.9	4 23.9	22 34.3	7 53.8	28 24.8	26 54.6
13	23 26 17.2	19 47.9	1 47.0	15 1.1	19 19.1	5 17.7	6 14.0	4 34.9	22 33.5	7 57.4	28 25.9	26 56.8
14	23 30 13.8	20 46.3	1 43.9	0♓ 1.5	18 19.4	6 9.3	6 52.1	4 45.9	22 32.5	8 1.1	28 27.0	26 59.0
15	23 34 10.3	21 44.8	1 40.7	15 9.3	17 22.6	7 .2	7 30.2	4 57.1	22 31.5	8 4.8	28 28.2	27 1.3
16	23 38 6.9	22 43.2	1 37.5	0♈15.3	16 29.9	7 50.5	8 8.3	5 8.3	22 30.3	8 8.5	28 29.3	27 3.5
17	23 42 3.4	23 41.7	1 34.3	15 10.6	15 42.8	8 40.0	8 46.4	5 19.5	22 29.1	8 12.2	28 30.5	27 5.8
18	23 45 60.0	24 40.2	1 31.2	29 47.1	15 2.5	9 28.8	9 24.5	5 30.8	22 27.7	8 15.9	28 31.7	27 8.0
19	23 49 56.5	25 38.8	1 28.0	13♉59.2	14 29.9	10 16.9	10 2.6	5 42.2	22 26.2	8 19.6	28 32.9	27 10.2
20	23 53 53.1	26 37.4	1 24.8	27 43.9	14 6.0	11 4.2	10 40.7	5 53.7	22 24.6	8 23.3	28 34.2	27 12.5
21	23 57 49.6	27 36.0	1 21.6	11♊ 1.0	13 51.4	11 50.7	11 18.8	6 5.2	22 22.9	8 27.0	28 35.5	27 14.7
22	0 1 46.2	28 34.7	1 18.4	23 52.5	13 46.4	12 36.3	11 56.9	6 16.8	22 21.1	8 30.8	28 36.8	27 17.0
23	0 5 42.7	29 33.4	1 15.3	6♋21.8	13 D 51.2	13 21.1	12 34.9	6 28.5	22 19.3	8 34.5	28 38.1	27 19.2
24	0 9 39.3	0♎32.1	1 12.1	18 33.5	14 5.9	14 4.9	13 13.0	6 40.2	22 17.3	8 38.3	28 39.5	27 21.4
25	0 13 35.8	1 30.9	1 8.9	0♌32.3	14 30.4	14 47.9	13 51.1	6 52.0	22 15.2	8 42.0	28 40.9	27 23.7
26	0 17 32.4	2 29.7	1 5.7	12 22.9	15 4.2	15 29.8	14 29.2	7 3.8	22 13.0	8 45.8	28 42.3	27 25.9
27	0 21 28.9	3 28.6	1 2.6	24 9.7	15 46.9	16 10.7	15 7.3	7 15.7	22 10.7	8 49.6	28 43.8	27 28.1
28	0 25 25.5	4 27.5	0 59.4	5♍56.6	16 38.0	16 50.6	15 45.4	7 27.7	22 8.3	8 53.4	28 45.2	27 30.4
29	0 29 22.1	5 26.4	0 56.2	17 46.8	17 36.9	17 29.4	16 23.5	7 39.7	22 5.8	8 57.1	28 46.7	27 32.6
30	0 33 18.6	6 25.4	0 53.0	29 43.1	18 42.9	18 7.0	17 1.6	7 51.8	22 3.2	9 .9	28 48.3	27 34.8

LATITUDE

DAY	EPHEM. SID. TIME	☉	☊	☾	☿	♀	♂	♃	♄	♅	♆	♇
1	22 38 58.6	0 .0	0 .0	0S34.4	4S13.0	2S17.8	1N 9.5	1N 1.2	2S22.4	0N40.1	1N40.2	15N24.5
4	22 50 48.2	0 .0	0 .0	3 32.5	4 22.3	2 36.7	1 9.6	1 .7	2 23.0	0 40.1	1 40.0	15 24.2
7	23 2 37.9	0 .0	0 .0	5 11.3	4 18.6	2 55.9	1 9.6	1 .2	2 23.7	0 40.0	1 39.9	15 24.0
10	23 14 27.5	0 .0	0 .0	4 37.2	3 58.6	3 15.2	1 9.6	0 59.7	2 24.3	0 40.0	1 39.7	15 23.9
13	23 26 17.2	0 .0	0 .0	1 36.8	3 21.5	3 34.7	1 9.6	0 59.2	2 24.9	0 39.9	1 39.5	15 23.8
16	23 38 6.9	0 .0	0 .0	2N26.0	2 30.3	3 54.2	1 9.5	0 58.7	2 25.5	0 39.9	1 39.4	15 23.8
19	23 49 56.5	0 .0	0 .0	4 58.5	1 31.6	4 13.5	1 9.4	0 58.3	2 26.1	0 39.9	1 39.2	15 23.9
22	0 1 46.2	0 .0	0 .0	4 53.4	0 33.1	4 32.6	1 9.3	0 57.9	2 26.7	0 39.8	1 39.1	15 24.0
25	0 13 35.8	0 .0	0 .0	2 47.3	0N18.7	4 51.3	1 9.2	0 57.5	2 27.2	0 39.8	1 38.9	15 24.2
28	0 25 25.5	0 .0	0 .0	0S18.1	0 60.0	5 9.4	1 9.0	0 57.1	2 27.7	0 39.8	1 38.8	15 24.5

RIGHT ASCENSION

DAY	EPHEM. SID. TIME	☉	☊	☾	☿	♀	♂	♃	♄	♅	♆	♇
1	22 38 58.6	9♍48.3	4♓23.7	10♍24.9	26♍21.9	21♎36.3	1♍10.1	0♏38.7	20♉50.0	6♎55.2	26♏23.6	3♎ 5.0
2	22 42 55.1	10 42.7	4 20.7	20 57.6	26 R 8.1	22 28.7	1 46.8	0 48.2	20 50.4	6 58.4	26 24.4	3 7.0
3	22 46 51.7	11 37.1	4 17.7	1♎29.3	25 49.0	23 20.9	2 23.5	0 57.8	20 50.7	7 1.6	26 25.1	3 8.9
4	22 50 48.2	12 31.4	4 14.6	12 13.9	25 24.7	24 12.8	3 .0	1 7.6	20 50.9	7 4.8	26 25.9	3 10.8
5	22 54 44.8	13 25.6	4 11.6	23 25.8	24 55.2	25 4.4	3 36.5	1 17.4	20 50.9	7 8.0	26 26.8	3 12.8
6	22 58 41.3	14 19.8	4 8.6	5♏19.1	24 20.9	25 55.7	4 12.9	1 27.3	20 50.9	7 11.2	26 27.6	3 14.7
7	23 2 37.9	15 13.9	4 5.6	18 5.9	23 42.1	26 46.7	4 49.3	1 37.3	20 R 50.7	7 14.4	26 28.5	3 16.7
8	23 6 34.4	16 7.9	4 2.6	1♐53.0	22 59.2	27 37.4	5 25.6	1 47.4	20 50.5	7 17.7	26 29.4	3 18.7
9	23 10 31.0	17 1.9	3 59.5	16 37.1	22 13.0	28 27.8	6 1.8	1 57.6	20 50.1	7 21.0	26 30.4	3 20.7
10	23 14 27.5	17 55.9	3 56.5	2♑ 2.1	21 24.1	29 17.8	6 38.0	2 7.8	20 49.6	7 24.3	26 31.4	3 22.7
11	23 18 24.1	18 49.8	3 53.5	17 41.4	20 33.6	0♏ 7.4	7 14.1	2 18.2	20 49.0	7 27.6	26 32.4	3 24.7
12	23 22 20.6	19 43.7	3 50.5	3♒ 6.8	19 42.5	0 56.6	7 50.1	2 28.6	20 48.3	7 30.9	26 33.4	3 26.7
13	23 26 17.2	20 37.5	3 47.5	17 58.9	18 52.0	1 45.4	8 26.1	2 39.1	20 47.5	7 34.2	26 34.5	3 28.7
14	23 30 13.8	21 31.3	3 44.4	2♓12.4	18 3.3	2 33.7	9 2.1	2 49.6	20 46.6	7 37.6	26 35.6	3 30.7
15	23 34 10.3	22 25.2	3 41.4	15 53.6	17 17.6	3 21.6	9 38.0	3 .4	20 45.6	7 41.0	26 36.8	3 32.8
16	23 38 6.9	23 19.0	3 38.4	29 16.0	16 36.2	4 9.0	10 13.8	3 11.1	20 44.5	7 44.4	26 38.0	3 34.8
17	23 42 3.4	24 12.7	3 35.4	12♈35.2	16 .1	4 55.9	10 49.6	3 21.9	20 43.3	7 47.8	26 39.1	3 36.9
18	23 45 60.0	25 6.5	3 32.3	26 5.6	15 30.4	5 42.2	11 25.3	3 32.8	20 41.9	7 51.2	26 40.4	3 38.9
19	23 49 56.5	26 .3	3 29.3	9♉56.6	15 8.0	6 27.9	12 1.0	3 43.7	20 40.5	7 54.6	26 41.6	3 41.0
20	23 53 53.1	26 54.1	3 26.3	24 10.0	14 53.5	7 13.0	12 36.7	3 54.8	20 38.9	7 58.0	26 42.9	3 43.0
21	23 57 49.6	27 47.9	3 23.3	8♊37.9	14 47.5	7 57.5	13 12.3	4 5.9	20 37.3	8 1.4	26 44.2	3 45.1
22	0 1 46.2	28 41.7	3 20.2	23 4.3	14 D 50.2	8 41.3	13 47.8	4 17.0	20 35.5	8 4.9	26 45.6	3 47.2
23	0 5 42.7	29 35.6	3 17.2	7♋10.0	15 1.8	9 24.4	14 23.3	4 28.3	20 33.7	8 8.3	26 46.9	3 49.2
24	0 9 39.3	0♎29.5	3 14.2	20 39.2	15 22.1	10 6.8	14 58.8	4 39.6	20 31.7	8 11.8	26 48.3	3 51.3
25	0 13 35.8	1 23.4	3 11.2	3♌23.6	15 51.1	10 48.4	15 34.3	4 51.0	20 29.7	8 15.2	26 49.7	3 53.4
26	0 17 32.4	2 17.4	3 8.1	15 23.1	16 28.3	11 29.1	16 9.7	5 2.4	20 27.5	8 18.7	26 51.2	3 55.4
27	0 21 28.9	3 11.4	3 5.1	26 44.1	17 13.3	12 9.0	16 45.0	5 13.9	20 25.2	8 22.1	26 52.7	3 57.5
28	0 25 25.5	4 5.5	3 2.1	7♍36.9	18 5.6	12 47.9	17 20.3	5 25.5	20 22.9	8 25.6	26 54.2	3 59.6
29	0 29 22.1	4 59.6	2 59.1	18 13.7	19 4.4	13 25.9	17 55.6	5 37.1	20 20.4	8 29.1	26 55.7	4 1.7
30	0 33 18.6	5 53.8	2 56.0	28 47.7	20 9.3	14 2.8	18 30.9	5 48.8	20 17.9	8 32.6	26 57.3	4 3.7

DECLINATION

DAY	EPHEM. SID. TIME	☉	☊	☾	☿	♀	♂	♃	♄	♅	♆	♇
1	22 38 58.6	8N30.9	0S11.1	7N39.2	3S 1.3	11S32.7	13N 2.9	11S22.8	16N 8.0	2S15.8	18S 8.8	15N29.6
4	22 50 48.2	7 25.2	0 11.2	9S 5.6	2 46.6	12 53.3	12 22.7	11 33.6	16 7.5	2 19.9	18 9.5	15 26.8
7	23 2 37.9	6 18.5	0 11.2	23 16.4	1 58.2	14 11.5	11 41.8	11 44.7	16 6.8	2 24.2	18 10.2	15 24.0
10	23 14 27.5	5 10.9	0 11.3	28 3.1	0 37.0	15 27.1	11 .3	11 55.9	16 5.9	2 28.4	18 11.0	15 21.2
13	23 26 17.2	4 2.5	0 11.4	17 52.6	1N 8.3	16 39.6	10 18.3	12 7.3	16 4.7	2 32.8	18 11.9	15 18.5
16	23 38 6.9	2 53.4	0 11.4	2N20.0	3 1.2	17 49.0	9 35.7	12 18.9	16 3.4	2 37.1	18 12.8	15 15.8
19	23 49 56.5	1 43.8	0 11.5	20 47.0	4 41.7	18 54.8	8 52.6	12 30.6	16 1.8	2 41.6	18 13.7	15 13.2
22	0 1 46.2	0 33.9	0 11.5	28 11.3	5 52.4	19 56.9	8 9.0	12 42.4	15 59.9	2 46.0	18 14.7	15 10.7
25	0 13 35.8	0S36.2	0 11.6	22 45.7	6 23.3	20 54.9	7 25.1	12 54.3	15 57.9	2 50.5	18 15.7	15 8.2
28	0 25 25.5	1 46.3	0 11.7	9 3.2	6 11.9	21 48.6	6 40.7	13 6.3	15 55.6	2 54.9	18 16.8	15 5.8

OCTOBER 1970

LONGITUDE

DAY	EPHEM. SID. TIME (h m s)	☉ (° ′)	☊ (° ′)	☽ (° ′)	☿ (° ′)	♀ (° ′)	♂ (° ′)	♃ (° ′)	♄ (° ′)	♅ (° ′)	♆ (° ′)	♇ (° ′)
1	0 37 15.2	7 ♎ 24.4	0 ♓ 49.8	11 ♎ 47.5	19 ♍ 55.3	18 ♏ 43.4	17 ♍ 39.7	8 ♏ 3.9	22 ♉ .6	9 ♎ 4.7	28 ♏ 49.8	27 ♍ 37.0
2	0 41 11.7	8 23.4	0 46.7	24 1.5	21 13.4	19 18.6	18 17.7	8 16.1	21 R 57.8	9 8.5	28 51.4	27 39.3
3	0 45 8.3	9 22.5	0 43.5	6 ♏ 26.2	22 36.5	19 52.4	18 55.8	8 28.3	21 54.9	9 12.3	28 53.0	27 41.5
4	0 49 4.8	10 21.6	0 40.3	19 2.7	24 3.9	20 25.0	19 33.9	8 40.6	21 52.0	9 16.1	28 54.6	27 43.7
5	0 53 1.4	11 20.7	0 37.1	1 ♐ 52.0	25 35.1	20 56.1	20 12.0	8 53.0	21 48.9	9 19.9	28 56.3	27 45.9
6	0 56 57.9	12 19.9	0 34.0	14 55.1	27 9.4	21 25.8	20 50.1	9 5.4	21 45.9	9 23.7	28 58.0	27 48.1
7	1 0 54.5	13 19.1	0 30.8	28 13.1	28 46.3	21 53.9	21 28.2	9 17.8	21 42.7	9 27.5	28 59.7	27 50.3
8	1 4 51.0	14 18.3	0 27.6	11 ♑ 47.3	0 ♎ 25.3	22 20.4	22 6.3	9 30.3	21 39.4	9 31.3	29 1.4	27 52.5
9	1 8 47.6	15 17.5	0 24.4	25 38.7	2 6.0	22 45.3	22 44.3	9 42.8	21 36.0	9 35.0	29 3.1	27 54.6
10	1 12 44.1	16 16.8	0 21.2	9 ♒ 47.6	3 47.9	23 8.5	23 22.4	9 55.4	21 32.6	9 38.8	29 4.9	27 56.8
11	1 16 40.7	17 16.1	0 18.1	24 13.0	5 30.9	23 29.9	24 .5	10 7.9	21 29.0	9 42.6	29 6.6	27 58.9
12	1 20 37.3	18 15.4	0 14.9	8 ♓ 52.3	7 14.5	23 49.4	24 38.5	10 20.6	21 25.4	9 46.3	29 8.4	28 1.1
13	1 24 33.8	19 14.8	0 11.7	23 40.8	8 58.6	24 7.1	25 16.6	10 33.2	21 21.7	9 50.1	29 10.3	28 3.2
14	1 28 30.4	20 14.2	0 8.5	8 ♈ 31.9	10 42.9	24 22.8	25 54.7	10 46.0	21 18.0	9 53.8	29 12.1	28 5.3
15	1 32 26.9	21 13.6	0 5.4	23 17.8	12 27.3	24 36.4	26 32.7	10 58.7	21 14.2	9 57.6	29 14.0	28 7.4
16	1 36 23.5	22 13.1	0 2.2	7 ♉ 50.4	14 11.6	24 48.0	27 10.8	11 11.5	21 10.3	10 1.3	29 15.8	28 9.5
17	1 40 20.0	23 12.5	29 ♒ 59.0	22 3.1	15 55.7	24 57.4	27 48.9	11 24.3	21 6.3	10 5.0	29 17.7	28 11.6
18	1 44 16.6	24 12.1	29 55.8	5 ♊ 51.1	17 39.6	25 4.6	28 27.0	11 37.1	21 2.3	10 8.7	29 19.6	28 13.6
19	1 48 13.1	25 11.6	29 52.6	19 12.5	19 23.1	25 9.6	29 5.0	11 50.0	20 58.2	10 12.4	29 21.6	28 15.7
20	1 52 9.7	26 11.3	29 49.5	2 ♋ 7.9	21 6.2	25 12.3	29 43.1	12 2.9	20 54.0	10 16.1	29 23.5	28 17.7
21	1 56 6.2	27 10.9	29 46.3	14 39.9	22 48.9	25 12.7	0 ♎ 21.2	12 15.8	20 49.8	10 19.8	29 25.5	28 19.8
22	2 0 2.8	28 10.6	29 43.1	26 52.7	24 31.1	25 R 10.7	0 59.3	12 28.8	20 45.6	10 23.4	29 27.5	28 21.8
23	2 3 59.4	29 10.3	29 39.9	8 ♌ 51.5	26 12.8	25 6.4	1 37.4	12 41.8	20 41.2	10 27.1	29 29.5	28 23.8
24	2 7 55.9	0 ♏ 10.0	29 36.8	20 41.6	27 53.9	24 59.6	2 15.5	12 54.8	20 36.9	10 30.7	29 31.5	28 25.7
25	2 11 52.5	1 9.8	29 33.6	2 ♍ 28.3	29 34.5	24 50.4	2 53.6	13 7.8	20 32.4	10 34.3	29 33.5	28 27.7
26	2 15 49.0	2 9.7	29 30.4	14 16.7	1 ♏ 14.6	24 38.8	3 31.7	13 20.9	20 27.9	10 37.9	29 35.5	28 29.7
27	2 19 45.6	3 9.6	29 27.2	26 11.2	2 54.2	24 24.9	4 9.8	13 34.0	20 23.5	10 41.6	29 37.6	28 31.6
28	2 23 42.1	4 9.5	29 24.1	8 ♎ 15.1	4 33.2	24 8.6	4 47.9	13 47.1	20 18.9	10 45.1	29 39.7	28 33.5
29	2 27 38.7	5 9.4	29 20.9	20 31.1	6 11.7	23 49.9	5 26.0	14 .2	20 14.3	10 48.7	29 41.8	28 35.4
30	2 31 35.2	6 9.4	29 17.7	3 ♏ .6	7 49.7	23 29.0	6 4.1	14 13.3	20 9.7	10 52.2	29 43.9	28 37.3
31	2 35 31.8	7 9.4	29 14.5	15 44.1	9 27.2	23 6.0	6 42.2	14 26.5	20 5.0	10 55.7	29 46.0	28 39.2

LATITUDE

DAY	EPHEM. SID. TIME	☉	☊	☽	☿	♀	♂	♃	♄	♅	♆	♇
1	0 37 15.2	0 .0	0 .0	3 S 17.5	1 N 29.4	5 S 26.7	1 N 8.9	0 N 56.7	2 S 28.2	0 N 39.8	1 N 38.6	15 N 24.9
4	0 49 4.8	0 .0	0 .0	5 2.1	1 47.5	5 43.0	1 8.7	0 56.3	2 28.7	0 39.7	1 38.5	15 25.3
7	1 0 54.5	0 .0	0 .0	4 38.4	1 55.6	5 57.9	1 8.4	0 56.0	2 29.1	0 39.7	1 38.4	15 25.8
10	1 12 44.1	0 .0	0 .0	1 57.3	1 55.5	6 11.1	1 8.2	0 55.7	2 29.5	0 39.7	1 38.3	15 26.3
13	1 24 33.8	0 .0	0 .0	1 N 54.5	1 49.1	6 22.2	1 7.9	0 55.4	2 29.9	0 39.7	1 38.1	15 27.0
16	1 36 23.5	0 .0	0 .0	4 41.0	1 37.9	6 30.5	1 7.6	0 55.1	2 30.2	0 39.7	1 38.0	15 27.7
19	1 48 13.1	0 .0	0 .0	4 51.9	1 23.3	6 35.6	1 7.3	0 54.8	2 30.5	0 39.8	1 37.9	15 28.4
22	2 0 2.8	0 .0	0 .0	2 53.2	1 6.3	6 36.7	1 6.9	0 54.6	2 30.7	0 39.8	1 37.8	15 29.3
25	2 11 52.5	0 .0	0 .0	0 S 7.2	0 47.7	6 32.9	1 6.5	0 54.3	2 30.9	0 39.8	1 37.7	15 30.2
28	2 23 42.1	0 .0	0 .0	3 4.5	0 28.0	6 23.7	1 6.1	0 54.1	2 31.0	0 39.8	1 37.7	15 31.1
31	2 35 31.8	0 .0	0 .0	4 52.4	0 7.9	6 8.3	1 5.7	0 53.9	2 31.1	0 39.9	1 37.6	15 32.2

RIGHT ASCENSION

DAY	EPHEM. SID. TIME	☉	☊	☽	☿	♀	♂	♃	♄	♅	♆	♇
1	0 37 15.2	6 ♎ 48.0	2 ♓ 53.0	9 ♎ 32.7	21 ♍ 19.6	14 ♏ 38.7	19 ♍ 6.1	6 ♏ .6	20 ♉ 15.2	8 ♎ 36.1	26 ♏ 58.8	4 ♎ 5.8
2	0 41 11.7	7 42.4	2 50.0	20 42.3	22 34.5	15 13.4	19 41.3	6 12.4	20 R 12.5	8 39.6	27 .5	4 7.9
3	0 45 8.3	8 36.7	2 46.9	2 ♏ 29.8	23 53.4	15 46.9	20 16.5	6 24.3	20 9.7	8 43.0	27 2.1	4 9.9
4	0 49 4.8	9 31.2	2 43.9	15 6.2	25 15.8	16 19.1	20 51.6	6 36.2	20 6.8	8 46.5	27 3.7	4 12.0
5	0 53 1.4	10 25.8	2 40.9	28 37.1	26 41.1	16 50.0	21 26.8	6 48.2	20 3.8	8 50.0	27 5.4	4 14.1
6	0 56 57.9	11 20.4	2 37.8	12 ♐ 59.6	28 8.8	17 19.6	22 1.9	7 .3	20 .7	8 53.5	27 7.2	4 16.2
7	1 0 54.5	12 15.2	2 34.8	27 59.2	29 38.4	17 47.6	22 37.0	7 12.4	19 57.5	8 57.0	27 8.9	4 18.2
8	1 4 51.0	13 10.0	2 31.8	13 ♑ 12.5	1 ♎ 9.5	18 14.1	23 12.0	7 24.5	19 54.3	9 .5	27 10.7	4 20.3
9	1 8 47.6	14 4.9	2 28.7	28 14.5	2 41.8	18 39.0	23 47.0	7 36.7	19 50.9	9 4.0	27 12.4	4 22.3
10	1 12 44.1	14 59.9	2 25.7	12 ♒ 47.5	4 15.0	19 2.2	24 22.0	7 48.9	19 47.5	9 7.5	27 14.2	4 24.4
11	1 16 40.7	15 55.1	2 22.7	26 45.8	5 48.9	19 23.7	24 57.0	8 1.2	19 44.0	9 10.9	27 16.1	4 26.4
12	1 20 37.3	16 50.3	2 19.7	10 ♓ 14.6	7 23.1	19 43.3	25 31.9	8 13.6	19 40.4	9 14.4	27 17.9	4 28.4
13	1 24 33.8	17 45.7	2 16.6	23 26.5	8 57.7	20 1.0	26 6.9	8 25.9	19 36.7	9 17.8	27 19.8	4 30.5
14	1 28 30.4	18 41.2	2 13.6	6 ♈ 37.2	10 32.4	20 16.7	26 41.8	8 38.4	19 33.0	9 21.3	27 21.6	4 32.5
15	1 32 26.9	19 36.8	2 10.5	20 2.0	12 7.1	20 30.4	27 16.7	8 50.8	19 29.2	9 24.7	27 23.5	4 34.5
16	1 36 23.5	20 32.5	2 7.5	3 ♉ 52.7	13 41.8	20 42.0	27 51.7	9 3.3	19 25.3	9 28.2	27 25.5	4 36.5
17	1 40 20.0	21 28.4	2 4.5	18 13.4	15 16.4	20 51.5	28 26.6	9 15.9	19 21.4	9 31.6	27 27.4	4 38.5
18	1 44 16.6	22 24.5	2 1.4	2 ♊ 57.9	16 50.9	20 58.7	29 1.5	9 28.4	19 17.4	9 35.0	27 29.4	4 40.5
19	1 48 13.1	23 20.7	1 58.4	17 49.1	18 25.2	21 3.6	29 36.3	9 41.1	19 13.3	9 38.4	27 31.3	4 42.5
20	1 52 9.7	24 17.1	1 55.4	2 ♋ 24.1	19 59.3	21 6.3	0 ♎ 11.2	9 53.7	19 9.2	9 41.8	27 33.3	4 44.4
21	1 56 6.2	25 13.6	1 52.3	16 22.3	21 33.3	21 6.6	0 46.1	10 6.4	19 5.0	9 45.2	27 35.4	4 46.4
22	2 0 2.8	26 10.3	1 49.3	29 31.5	23 7.0	21 R 4.5	1 21.0	10 19.2	19 .7	9 48.6	27 37.4	4 48.3
23	2 3 59.4	27 7.1	1 46.3	11 ♌ 50.0	24 40.6	21 .1	1 55.9	10 31.9	18 56.4	9 52.0	27 39.4	4 50.3
24	2 7 55.9	28 4.2	1 43.2	23 23.8	26 14.1	20 53.2	2 30.8	10 44.7	18 52.0	9 55.3	27 41.5	4 52.2
25	2 11 52.5	29 1.4	1 40.2	4 ♍ 24.1	27 47.4	20 43.9	3 5.7	10 57.6	18 47.6	9 58.6	27 43.6	4 54.1
26	2 15 49.0	29 58.8	1 37.1	15 4.2	29 20.6	20 32.3	3 40.6	11 10.4	18 43.2	10 2.0	27 45.7	4 56.0
27	2 19 45.6	0 ♏ 56.4	1 34.1	25 38.5	0 ♏ 53.7	20 18.4	4 15.5	11 23.4	18 38.7	10 5.3	27 47.8	4 58.0
28	2 23 42.1	1 54.2	1 31.1	6 ♎ 21.5	2 26.8	20 2.1	4 50.5	11 36.3	18 34.1	10 8.6	27 50.0	4 59.8
29	2 27 38.7	2 52.1	1 28.0	17 28.1	3 59.8	19 43.7	5 25.4	11 49.2	18 29.5	10 11.9	27 52.1	5 1.7
30	2 31 35.2	3 50.3	1 25.0	29 12.1	5 32.8	19 23.0	6 .3	12 2.2	18 24.9	10 15.1	27 54.3	5 3.5
31	2 35 31.8	4 48.6	1 21.9	11 ♏ 45.3	7 5.8	19 .4	6 35.2	12 15.2	18 20.3	10 18.4	27 56.4	5 5.4

DECLINATION

DAY	EPHEM. SID. TIME	☉	☊	☽	☿	♀	♂	♃	♄	♅	♆	♇
1	0 37 15.2	2 S 56.4	0 S 11.7	7 S 41.5	5 N 21.8	22 S 37.6	5 N 56.0	13 S 18.3	15 N 53.2	2 S 59.4	18 S 17.9	15 N 3.5
4	0 49 4.8	4 6.2	0 11.8	22 19.5	4 .1	23 21.5	5 11.1	13 30.5	15 50.6	3 3.9	18 19.1	15 1.2
7	1 0 54.5	5 15.5	0 11.8	28 4.4	2 15.3	24 .0	4 25.9	13 42.6	15 47.8	3 8.4	18 20.3	14 59.1
10	1 12 44.1	6 24.2	0 11.9	19 41.0	0 15.3	24 32.5	3 40.5	13 54.8	15 44.8	3 12.8	18 21.6	14 57.0
13	1 24 33.8	7 32.2	0 11.9	0 45.4	1 S 53.3	24 58.3	2 55.0	14 6.9	15 41.7	3 17.3	18 22.8	14 55.0
16	1 36 23.5	8 39.2	0 12.0	18 N 33.1	4 5.6	25 16.7	2 9.3	14 19.0	15 38.4	3 21.7	18 24.1	14 53.2
19	1 48 13.1	9 45.1	0 12.1	27 51.3	6 18.2	25 27.1	1 23.6	14 31.1	15 35.0	3 26.0	18 25.5	14 51.4
22	2 0 2.8	10 49.7	0 12.1	23 37.1	8 28.5	25 28.4	0 37.8	14 43.2	15 31.5	3 30.3	18 26.8	14 49.8
25	2 11 52.5	11 52.9	0 12.2	10 29.1	10 34.9	25 19.7	0 S 8.0	14 55.2	15 27.9	3 34.6	18 28.2	14 48.2
28	2 23 42.1	12 54.5	0 12.2	6 S 5.9	12 36.1	25 .1	0 53.8	15 7.2	15 24.2	3 38.8	18 29.6	14 46.8
31	2 35 31.8	13 54.3	0 12.3	21 12.8	14 31.2	24 29.1	1 39.4	15 19.0	15 20.4	3 42.9	18 31.0	14 45.5

NOVEMBER 1970

DAY	EPHEM. SID. TIME	☉	☊	☽	☿	♀	♂	♃	♄	♅	♆	♇
	h m s	° ′	° ′	° ′	° ′	° ′	° ′	° ′	° ′	° ′	° ′	° ′
		LONGITUDE										
1	2 39 28.4	8♏ 9.4	29♒11.3	28♏41.2	11♏ 4.2	22♏40.8	7♎20.3	14♏39.6	20♉ .3	10♎59.2	29♏48.1	28♍41.0
2	2 43 24.9	9 9.5	29 8.2	11♐50.9	12 40.7	22 R 13.7	7 58.4	14 52.8	19 R 55.5	11 2.7	29 50.3	28 42.8
3	2 47 21.5	10 9.6	29 5.0	25 12.0	14 16.8	21 44.7	8 36.5	15 6.0	19 50.8	11 6.1	29 52.4	28 44.6
4	2 51 18.0	11 9.7	29 1.8	8♑43.5	15 52.4	21 14.1	9 14.6	15 19.2	19 46.0	11 9.5	29 54.6	28 46.4
5	2 55 14.6	12 9.8	28 58.6	22 24.6	17 27.6	20 42.0	9 52.7	15 32.4	19 41.2	11 12.9	29 56.7	28 48.2
6	2 59 11.1	13 10.0	28 55.5	6♒15.2	19 2.4	20 8.6	10 30.8	15 45.6	19 36.3	11 16.3	29 58.9	28 49.9
7	3 3 7.7	14 10.2	28 52.3	20 15.1	20 36.8	19 34.1	11 8.9	15 58.8	19 31.5	11 19.6	0♐ 1.1	28 51.6
8	3 7 4.2	15 10.4	28 49.1	4♓24.2	22 10.8	18 58.6	11 47.0	16 12.0	19 26.6	11 22.9	0 3.3	28 53.3
9	3 11 .8	16 10.7	28 45.9	18 41.5	23 44.5	18 22.6	12 25.1	16 25.2	19 21.8	11 26.2	0 5.5	28 55.0
10	3 14 57.4	17 10.9	28 42.7	3♈ 4.8	25 17.8	17 46.1	13 3.2	16 38.4	19 16.9	11 29.5	0 7.7	28 56.6
11	3 18 53.9	18 11.2	28 39.6	17 30.4	26 50.8	17 9.5	13 41.3	16 51.7	19 12.0	11 32.7	0 9.9	28 58.2
12	3 22 50.5	19 11.5	28 36.4	1♉53.1	28 23.4	16 33.1	14 19.4	17 4.9	19 7.1	11 35.9	0 12.1	28 59.8
13	3 26 47.0	20 11.9	28 33.2	16 7.1	29 55.8	15 56.9	14 57.5	17 18.1	19 2.2	11 39.1	0 14.3	29 1.4
14	3 30 43.6	21 12.2	28 30.0	0♊ 6.4	1♐27.8	15 21.5	15 35.6	17 31.3	18 57.3	11 42.3	0 16.6	29 3.0
15	3 34 40.1	22 12.6	28 26.9	13 46.3	2 59.6	14 46.8	16 13.7	17 44.5	18 52.5	11 45.4	0 18.8	29 4.5
16	3 38 36.7	23 13.1	28 23.7	27 3.9	4 31.0	14 13.3	16 51.8	17 57.7	18 47.6	11 48.5	0 21.0	29 6.0
17	3 42 33.3	24 13.6	28 20.5	9♋58.5	6 2.3	13 41.1	17 29.9	18 11.0	18 42.8	11 51.6	0 23.3	29 7.5
18	3 46 29.8	25 14.1	28 17.3	22 31.3	7 33.2	13 10.5	18 8.0	18 24.2	18 38.0	11 54.6	0 25.6	29 9.0
19	3 50 26.4	26 14.6	28 14.2	4♌45.4	9 3.8	12 41.5	18 46.1	18 37.3	18 33.1	11 57.6	0 27.8	29 10.4
20	3 54 22.9	27 15.1	28 11.0	16 45.3	10 34.1	12 14.4	19 24.3	18 50.5	18 28.3	12 .5	0 30.1	29 11.8
21	3 58 19.5	28 15.7	28 7.8	28 36.2	12 4.1	11 49.3	20 2.4	19 3.7	18 23.5	12 3.4	0 32.3	29 13.1
22	4 2 16.0	29 16.3	28 4.6	10♍23.6	13 33.8	11 26.3	20 40.5	19 16.8	18 18.8	12 6.3	0 34.6	29 14.5
23	4 6 12.6	0♐17.0	28 1.5	22 13.2	15 3.1	11 5.6	21 18.6	19 29.9	18 14.0	12 9.1	0 36.8	29 15.8
24	4 10 9.2	1 17.6	27 58.3	4♎10.2	16 32.0	10 47.2	21 56.7	19 43.1	18 9.3	12 12.0	0 39.1	29 17.1
25	4 14 5.7	2 18.3	27 55.1	16 19.3	18 .5	10 31.2	22 34.9	19 56.2	18 4.7	12 14.7	0 41.4	29 18.3
26	4 18 2.3	3 19.0	27 51.9	28 43.9	19 28.6	10 17.6	23 13.0	20 9.2	18 .0	12 17.5	0 43.6	29 19.5
27	4 21 58.8	4 19.8	27 48.7	11♏26.4	20 56.2	10 6.5	23 51.1	20 22.3	17 55.4	12 20.1	0 45.9	29 20.7
28	4 25 55.4	5 20.5	27 45.6	24 27.6	22 23.1	9 57.8	24 29.2	20 35.3	17 50.9	12 22.8	0 48.1	29 21.9
29	4 29 52.0	6 21.3	27 42.4	7♐46.5	23 49.4	9 51.7	25 7.3	20 48.4	17 46.4	12 25.4	0 50.4	29 23.0
30	4 33 48.5	7 22.1	27 39.2	21 20.9	25 14.9	9 48.0	25 45.5	21 1.3	17 41.9	12 28.0	0 52.6	29 24.1
		LATITUDE										
1	2 39 28.4	0 .0	0 .0	5 S 2.0	0 N 1.2	6 S 1.7	1 N 5.5	0 N 53.8	2 S 31.1	0 N 39.9	1 N 37.6	15 N 32.5
4	2 51 18.0	0 .0	0 .0	3 55.8	0 S 19.0	5 37.5	1 5.0	0 53.6	2 31.1	0 39.9	1 37.5	15 33.6
7	3 3 7.7	0 .0	0 .0	0 49.9	0 38.8	5 6.7	1 4.5	0 53.5	2 31.1	0 40.0	1 37.4	15 34.8
10	3 14 57.4	0 .0	0 .0	2 N 46.9	0 57.9	4 29.9	1 4.0	0 53.3	2 31.0	0 40.0	1 37.4	15 36.0
13	3 26 47.0	0 .0	0 .0	4 52.8	1 16.0	3 48.4	1 3.4	0 53.2	2 30.8	0 40.1	1 37.4	15 37.3
16	3 38 36.7	0 .0	0 .0	4 24.7	1 32.7	3 3.6	1 2.8	0 53.0	2 30.7	0 40.1	1 37.3	15 38.6
19	3 50 26.4	0 .0	0 .0	2 1.0	1 47.9	2 17.2	1 2.1	0 52.9	2 30.4	0 40.2	1 37.3	15 39.9
22	4 2 16.0	0 .0	0 .0	1 S 3.9	2 1.1	1 31.0	1 1.5	0 52.8	2 30.1	0 40.2	1 37.3	15 41.4
25	4 14 5.7	0 .0	0 .0	3 45.2	2 11.9	0 46.4	1 .7	0 52.8	2 29.8	0 40.3	1 37.3	15 42.8
28	4 25 55.4	0 .0	0 .0	4 59.9	2 19.7	0 4.3	0 60.0	0 52.7	2 29.4	0 40.4	1 37.3	15 44.3
		RIGHT ASCENSION										
1	2 39 28.4	5♏47.1	1♓18.9	25♏14.1	8♏38.9	18♏35.8	7♎10.2	12♏28.2	18♉15.6	10♎21.6	27♏58.6	5♎ 7.2
2	2 43 24.9	6 45.9	1 15.9	9♐35.7	10 12.0	18 R 9.4	7 45.2	12 41.3	18 R 10.8	10 24.8	28 .8	5 9.0
3	2 47 21.5	7 44.8	1 12.8	24 35.1	11 45.2	17 41.5	8 20.1	12 54.3	18 6.1	10 28.0	28 3.0	5 10.8
4	2 51 18.0	8 43.9	1 9.8	9♑47.2	13 18.6	17 12.0	8 55.1	13 7.4	18 1.3	10 31.1	28 5.2	5 12.6
5	2 55 14.6	9 43.2	1 6.7	24 45.2	14 52.1	16 41.4	9 30.1	13 20.5	17 56.5	10 34.3	28 7.5	5 14.3
6	2 59 11.1	10 42.8	1 3.7	9♒10.3	16 25.8	16 9.7	10 5.2	13 33.6	17 51.6	10 37.4	28 9.7	5 16.1
7	3 3 7.7	11 42.5	1 .6	22 55.9	17 59.6	15 37.2	10 40.2	13 46.8	17 46.8	10 40.5	28 11.9	5 17.8
8	3 7 4.2	12 42.4	0 57.6	6♓ 7.3	19 33.7	15 4.1	11 15.2	13 59.9	17 42.0	10 43.5	28 14.2	5 19.5
9	3 11 .8	13 42.6	0 54.6	18 57.5	21 7.9	14 30.7	11 50.3	14 13.0	17 37.1	10 46.6	28 16.5	5 21.2
10	3 14 57.4	14 42.9	0 51.5	1♈43.1	22 42.4	13 57.2	12 25.4	14 26.2	17 32.2	10 49.6	28 18.7	5 22.8
11	3 18 53.9	15 43.5	0 48.5	14 41.3	24 17.1	13 23.9	13 .6	14 39.4	17 27.3	10 52.6	28 21.0	5 24.5
12	3 22 50.5	16 44.3	0 45.4	28 6.8	25 52.1	12 50.9	13 35.7	14 52.6	17 22.5	10 55.5	28 23.3	5 26.1
13	3 26 47.0	17 45.2	0 42.4	12♉ 8.6	27 27.3	12 18.7	14 10.9	15 5.7	17 17.6	10 58.5	28 25.6	5 27.7
14	3 30 43.6	18 46.4	0 39.3	26 45.7	29 2.8	11 47.3	14 46.1	15 18.9	17 12.7	11 1.4	28 27.9	5 29.3
15	3 34 40.1	19 47.8	0 36.3	11♊44.7	0♐38.5	11 17.0	15 21.3	15 32.1	17 7.8	11 4.3	28 30.2	5 30.9
16	3 38 36.7	20 49.4	0 33.2	26 41.5	2 14.5	10 48.0	15 56.6	15 45.3	17 3.0	11 7.1	28 32.5	5 32.4
17	3 42 33.3	21 51.3	0 30.2	11♋10.1	3 50.7	10 20.6	16 32.0	15 58.6	16 58.2	11 10.0	28 34.9	5 34.0
18	3 46 29.8	22 53.4	0 27.1	24 51.1	5 27.1	9 54.8	17 7.3	16 11.8	16 53.3	11 12.8	28 37.2	5 35.5
19	3 50 26.4	23 55.6	0 24.1	7♌37.2	7 3.7	9 30.8	17 42.7	16 25.0	16 48.5	11 15.6	28 39.5	5 37.0
20	3 54 22.9	24 58.1	0 21.1	19 31.6	8 40.4	9 8.7	18 18.1	16 38.2	16 43.7	11 18.3	28 41.8	5 38.5
21	3 58 19.5	26 .7	0 18.0	0♍44.6	10 17.3	8 48.7	18 53.6	16 51.4	16 38.9	11 21.0	28 44.2	5 39.9
22	4 2 16.0	27 3.6	0 15.0	11 29.8	11 54.2	8 30.9	19 29.1	17 4.6	16 34.1	11 23.7	28 46.5	5 41.3
23	4 6 12.6	28 6.7	0 11.9	22 2.7	13 31.2	8 15.3	20 4.6	17 17.8	16 29.4	11 26.3	28 48.8	5 42.7
24	4 10 9.2	29 10.0	0 8.9	2♎38.8	15 8.1	8 2.0	20 40.2	17 31.0	16 24.7	11 28.9	28 51.1	5 44.1
25	4 14 5.7	0♐13.5	0 5.8	13 34.4	16 44.9	7 50.9	21 15.8	17 44.2	16 20.0	11 31.5	28 53.5	5 45.4
26	4 18 2.3	1 17.2	0 2.8	25 5.3	18 21.5	7 42.2	21 51.5	17 57.3	16 15.4	11 34.0	28 55.8	5 46.8
27	4 21 58.8	2 21.0	29♒59.7	7♏25.7	19 57.8	7 35.9	22 27.2	18 10.5	16 10.8	11 36.5	28 58.1	5 48.1
28	4 25 55.4	3 25.1	29 56.6	20 45.7	21 33.7	7 31.9	23 2.9	18 23.6	16 6.2	11 38.9	29 .5	5 49.3
29	4 29 52.0	4 29.3	29 53.6	5♐ 6.2	23 9.0	7 30.2	23 38.7	18 36.8	16 1.7	11 41.4	29 2.8	5 50.6
30	4 33 48.5	5 33.7	29 50.5	20 14.9	24 43.7	7 D 30.8	24 14.6	18 49.9	15 57.2	11 43.7	29 5.1	5 51.8
		DECLINATION										
1	2 39 28.4	14 S 13.8	0 S 12.3	24 S 46.7	15 S 8.1	24 S 16.1	1 S 54.6	15 S 23.0	15 N 19.2	3 S 44.2	18 S 31.5	14 N 45.1
4	2 51 18.0	15 10.9	0 12.4	27 4.8	16 53.9	23 29.7	2 40.1	15 34.7	15 15.4	3 48.2	18 32.9	14 44.0
7	3 3 7.7	16 5.7	0 12.4	15 31.7	18 31.9	22 32.6	3 25.4	15 46.3	15 11.5	3 52.1	18 34.3	14 43.0
10	3 14 57.4	16 58.1	0 12.5	3 N 46.6	20 1.7	21 26.9	4 10.4	15 57.8	15 7.7	3 56.0	18 35.7	14 42.1
13	3 26 47.0	17 47.9	0 12.5	21 20.0	21 22.6	20 15.4	4 55.2	16 9.1	15 3.9	3 59.7	18 37.0	14 41.3
16	3 38 36.7	18 34.9	0 12.6	27 49.4	22 34.1	19 1.8	5 39.7	16 20.3	15 .1	4 3.3	18 38.6	14 40.7
19	3 50 26.4	19 19.0	0 12.7	21 2.2	23 35.5	17 49.7	6 23.8	16 31.3	14 56.4	4 6.8	18 40.0	14 40.2
22	4 2 16.0	19 60.0	0 12.7	6 41.2	24 26.2	16 42.5	7 7.6	16 42.2	14 52.8	4 10.1	18 41.4	14 39.9
25	4 14 5.7	20 37.7	0 12.8	9 S 52.9	25 5.6	15 42.9	7 50.9	16 52.9	14 49.3	4 13.3	18 42.8	14 39.7
28	4 25 55.4	21 11.9	0 12.8	23 43.9	25 33.0	14 52.5	8 33.7	17 3.3	14 45.9	4 16.4	18 44.2	14 39.7

DECEMBER 1970

DAY	EPHEM. SID. TIME	☉	☊	☽	☿	♀	♂	♃	♄	♅	♆	♇
	h m s	° ′	° ′	° ′	° ′	° ′	° ′	° ′	° ′	° ′	° ′	° ′
		LONGITUDE										
1	4 37 45.1	8♐22.9	27♒36.0	5♑ 7.7	26♐39.6	9♏46.8	26♎23.6	21♏14.3	17♉37.5	12♎30.5	0♐54.9	29♍25.2
2	4 41 41.6	9 23.8	27 32.9	19 3.1	28 3.2	9D48.0	27 1.7	21 27.2	17R33.1	12 33.0	0 57.1	29 26.3
3	4 45 38.2	10 24.6	27 29.7	3♒ 4.1	29 25.7	9 51.6	27 39.8	21 40.2	17 28.8	12 35.4	0 59.3	29 27.3
4	4 49 34.7	11 25.5	27 26.5	17 7.8	0♑46.8	9 57.5	28 17.9	21 53.0	17 24.6	12 37.8	1 1.6	29 28.3
5	4 53 31.3	12 26.4	27 23.3	1♓12.8	2 6.4	10 5.7	28 56.0	22 5.9	17 20.4	12 40.2	1 3.8	29 29.2
6	4 57 27.9	13 27.3	27 20.2	15 17.9	3 24.1	10 16.2	29 34.1	22 18.7	17 16.3	12 42.5	1 6.0	29 30.1
7	5 1 24.4	14 28.2	27 17.0	29 22.5	4 39.8	10 28.9	0♏12.2	22 31.4	17 12.2	12 44.8	1 8.2	29 31.0
8	5 5 21.0	15 29.2	27 13.8	13♈25.7	5 53.1	10 43.7	0 50.3	22 44.2	17 8.3	12 47.0	1 10.5	29 31.9
9	5 9 17.5	16 30.1	27 10.6	27 26.0	7 3.5	11 .6	1 28.4	22 56.9	17 4.3	12 49.2	1 12.7	29 32.7
10	5 13 14.1	17 31.1	27 7.5	11♉21.0	8 10.7	11 19.5	2 6.5	23 9.6	17 .5	12 51.3	1 14.9	29 33.5
11	5 17 10.7	18 32.0	27 4.3	25 7.7	9 14.1	11 40.4	2 44.6	23 22.2	16 56.7	12 53.4	1 17.0	29 34.3
12	5 21 7.2	19 33.0	27 1.1	8♊42.8	10 13.2	12 3.1	3 22.7	23 34.8	16 53.0	12 55.5	1 19.2	29 35.0
13	5 25 3.8	20 34.0	26 57.9	22 3.2	11 7.4	12 27.7	4 .8	23 47.3	16 49.3	12 57.4	1 21.4	29 35.7
14	5 29 .3	21 35.0	26 54.7	5♋ 6.5	11 56.0	12 54.1	4 38.9	23 59.8	16 45.8	12 59.4	1 23.5	29 36.4
15	5 32 56.9	22 36.0	26 51.6	17 51.8	12 38.1	13 22.2	5 16.9	24 12.2	16 42.3	13 1.3	1 25.7	29 37.0
16	5 36 53.4	23 37.0	26 48.4	0♌19.5	13 13.0	13 52.0	5 55.0	24 24.6	16 38.9	13 3.1	1 27.8	29 37.6
17	5 40 50.0	24 38.1	26 45.2	12 31.4	13 39.7	14 23.3	6 33.1	24 37.0	16 35.6	13 4.9	1 29.9	29 38.1
18	5 44 46.6	25 39.1	26 42.0	24 30.8	13 57.4	14 56.2	7 11.2	24 49.3	16 32.3	13 6.6	1 32.0	29 38.6
19	5 48 43.1	26 40.2	26 38.9	6♍21.8	14 5.3	15 30.5	7 49.3	25 1.5	16 29.2	13 8.3	1 34.1	29 39.1
20	5 52 39.7	27 41.3	26 35.7	18 9.5	14R 2.5	16 6.3	8 27.3	25 13.7	16 26.1	13 10.0	1 36.2	29 39.6
21	5 56 36.2	28 42.4	26 32.5	29 59.1	13 48.4	16 43.5	9 5.4	25 25.9	16 23.2	13 11.6	1 38.2	29 40.0
22	6 0 32.8	29 43.5	26 29.3	11♎56.1	13 22.6	17 21.9	9 43.5	25 38.0	16 20.3	13 13.1	1 40.3	29 40.4
23	6 4 29.4	0♑44.6	26 26.2	24 5.7	12 45.1	18 1.6	10 21.6	25 50.0	16 17.5	13 14.6	1 42.3	29 40.8
24	6 8 25.9	1 45.7	26 23.0	6♏32.7	11 56.2	18 42.5	10 59.6	26 1.9	16 14.8	13 16.0	1 44.4	29 41.1
25	6 12 22.5	2 46.9	26 19.8	19 20.4	10 57.0	19 24.6	11 37.7	26 13.8	16 12.2	13 17.4	1 46.4	29 41.4
26	6 16 19.0	3 48.0	26 16.6	2♐31.0	9 48.7	20 7.8	12 15.7	26 25.7	16 9.8	13 18.7	1 48.3	29 41.6
27	6 20 15.6	4 49.2	26 13.5	16 4.4	8 33.3	20 52.0	12 53.8	26 37.5	16 7.4	13 20.0	1 50.3	29 41.8
28	6 24 12.2	5 50.4	26 10.3	29 58.8	7 13.3	21 37.3	13 31.8	26 49.2	16 5.1	13 21.2	1 52.3	29 42.0
29	6 28 8.7	6 51.6	26 7.1	14♑10.2	5 51.4	22 23.6	14 9.9	27 .9	16 2.9	13 22.4	1 54.3	29 42.2
30	6 32 5.3	7 52.8	26 3.9	28 33.1	4 30.1	23 10.8	14 47.9	27 12.4	16 .9	13 23.5	1 56.2	29 42.3
31	6 36 1.8	8 53.9	26 .7	13♒ 1.8	3 12.1	23 58.9	15 26.0	27 23.9	15 58.9	13 24.5	1 58.1	29 42.4
		LATITUDE										
1	4 37 45.1	0 .0	0 .0	3S56.9	2S23.9	0N34.3	0N59.2	0N52.6	2S28.9	0N40.5	1N37.3	15N45.8
4	4 49 34.7	0 .0	0 .0	0 50.3	2 23.6	1 9.3	0 58.4	0 52.6	2 28.4	0 40.6	1 37.3	15 47.4
7	5 1 24.4	0 .0	0 .0	2N44.3	2 17.9	1 40.4	0 57.5	0 52.6	2 27.9	0 40.6	1 37.3	15 49.0
10	5 13 14.1	0 .0	0 .0	4 52.2	2 5.4	2 7.6	0 56.6	0 52.6	2 27.3	0 40.7	1 37.4	15 50.6
13	5 25 3.8	0 .0	0 .0	4 31.7	1 44.5	2 31.0	0 55.7	0 52.6	2 26.7	0 40.8	1 37.4	15 52.3
16	5 36 53.4	0 .0	0 .0	2 9.5	1 13.5	2 51.0	0 54.7	0 52.6	2 26.0	0 40.9	1 37.4	15 53.9
19	5 48 43.1	0 .0	0 .0	0S58.9	0 31.2	3 7.7	0 53.6	0 52.6	2 25.3	0 41.0	1 37.5	15 55.6
22	6 0 32.8	0 .0	0 .0	3 43.5	0N21.9	3 21.3	0 52.6	0 52.7	2 24.6	0 41.1	1 37.6	15 57.3
25	6 12 22.5	0 .0	0 .0	5 5.2	1 20.9	3 32.1	0 51.4	0 52.7	2 23.8	0 41.2	1 37.6	15 59.0
28	6 24 12.2	0 .0	0 .0	4 10.9	2 15.8	3 40.5	0 50.2	0 52.8	2 23.1	0 41.3	1 37.7	16 .7
31	6 36 1.8	0 .0	0 .0	1 1.1	2 54.9	3 46.4	0 49.0	0 52.9	2 22.3	0 41.4	1 37.8	16 2.3
		RIGHT ASCENSION										
1	4 37 45.1	6♐38.3	29♒47.5	5♑45.5	26♐17.5	7♏33.6	24♎50.5	19♏ 3.0	15♉52.8	11♎46.1	29♏ 7.4	5♎53.0
2	4 41 41.6	7 43.0	29 44.4	21 6.3	27 50.4	7 38.7	25 26.4	19 16.0	15R48.4	11 48.4	29 9.7	5 54.1
3	4 45 38.2	8 47.9	29 41.4	5♒51.8	29 21.9	7 46.0	26 2 4	19 29.1	15 44.1	11 50.7	29 12.1	5 55.3
4	4 49 34.7	9 53.0	29 38.3	19 50.8	0♑52.0	7 55.5	26 38.4	19 42.1	15 39.8	11 52.9	29 14.4	5 56.4
5	4 53 31.3	10 58.2	29 35.3	3♓ 6.1	2 20.3	8 7.0	27 14.5	19 55.1	15 35.6	11 55.1	29 16.7	5 57.5
6	4 57 27.9	12 3.5	29 32.2	15 50.2	3 46.5	8 20.5	27 50.6	20 8.1	15 31.5	11 57.2	29 19.0	5 58.5
7	5 1 24.4	13 8.9	29 29.2	28 20.2	5 10.2	8 36.1	28 26.8	20 21.0	15 27.4	11 59.3	29 21.3	5 59.6
8	5 5 21.0	14 14.6	29 26.1	10♈54.4	6 31.2	8 53.6	29 3.1	20 34.0	15 23.4	12 1.4	29 23.6	6 .6
9	5 9 17.5	15 20.3	29 23.1	23 49.7	7 48.9	9 13.0	29 39.3	20 46.9	15 19.5	12 3.5	29 25.9	6 1.6
10	5 13 14.1	16 26.1	29 20.0	7♉19.0	9 2.7	9 34.2	0♏15.7	20 59.8	15 15.6	12 5.4	29 28.1	6 2.5
11	5 17 10.7	17 32.0	29 16.9	21 27.3	10 12.2	9 57.1	0 52.1	21 12.6	15 11.8	12 7.4	29 30.4	6 3.5
12	5 21 7.2	18 38.0	29 13.9	6♊ 8.1	11 16.6	10 21.8	1 28.5	21 25.4	15 8.0	12 9.3	29 32.6	6 4.3
13	5 25 3.8	19 44.1	29 10.8	21 2.5	12 15.4	10 48.2	2 5.0	21 38.1	15 4.4	12 11.1	29 34.9	6 5.2
14	5 29 .3	20 50.3	29 7.8	5♋44.1	13 7.7	11 16.2	2 41.6	21 50.9	15 .8	12 12.9	29 37.1	6 6.0
15	5 32 56.9	21 56.6	29 4.7	19 48.4	13 52.6	11 45.7	3 18.2	22 3.5	14 57.3	12 14.7	29 39.3	6 6.8
16	5 36 53.4	23 2.9	29 1.7	3♌ 1.1	14 29.4	12 16.8	3 54.9	22 16.2	14 53.9	12 16.4	29 41.5	6 7.6
17	5 40 50.0	24 9.3	28 58.6	15 19.4	14 57.1	12 49.3	4 31.6	22 28.8	14 50.5	12 18.0	29 43.7	6 8.4
18	5 44 46.6	25 15.8	28 55.5	26 50.2	15 14.8	13 23.3	5 8.5	22 41.3	14 47.2	12 19.7	29 45.9	6 9.1
19	5 48 43.1	26 22.3	28 52.5	7♍45.5	15 21.5	13 58.6	5 45.3	22 53.9	14 44.1	12 21.2	29 48.1	6 9.7
20	5 52 39.7	27 28.8	28 49.4	18 20.0	15R16.6	14 35.3	6 22.3	23 6.3	14 41.0	12 22.8	29 50.2	6 10.4
21	5 56 36.2	28 35.4	28 46.3	28 49.5	14 59.3	15 13.2	6 59.3	23 18.7	14 38.0	12 24.2	29 52.4	6 11.0
22	6 0 32.8	29 42.0	28 43.3	9♎30.3	14 29.5	15 52.4	7 36.3	23 31.1	14 35.1	12 25.7	29 54.5	6 11.6
23	6 4 29.4	0♑48.6	28 40.2	20 39.1	13 47.1	16 32.7	8 13.5	23 43.4	14 32.2	12 27.1	29 56.6	6 12.2
24	6 8 25.9	1 55.3	28 37.2	2♏32.2	12 52.7	17 14.2	8 50.6	23 55.7	14 29.5	12 28.4	29 58.7	6 12.7
25	6 12 22.5	3 1.9	28 34.1	15 23.5	11 47.3	17 56.9	9 27.9	24 7.9	14 26.9	12 29.7	0♐ .8	6 13.2
26	6 16 19.0	4 8.5	28 31.0	29 20.6	10 32.5	18 40.6	10 5.2	24 20.0	14 24.3	12 30.9	0 2.8	6 13.7
27	6 20 15.6	5 15.1	28 28.0	14♐19.1	9 10.6	19 25.3	10 42.6	24 32.1	14 21.9	12 32.1	0 4.9	6 14.1
28	6 24 12.2	6 21.6	28 24.9	29 58.7	7 43.9	20 11.1	11 20.0	24 44.1	14 19.5	12 33.2	0 6.9	6 14.5
29	6 28 8.7	7 28.2	28 21.8	15♑46.7	6 15.6	20 57.9	11 57.6	24 56.2	14 17.3	12 34.4	0 9.0	6 14.9
30	6 32 5.3	8 34.7	28 18.8	1♒10.0	4 48.3	21 45.6	12 35.1	25 8.0	14 15.2	12 35.4	0 11.0	6 15.3
31	6 36 1.8	9 41.1	28 15.7	15 48.0	3 24.8	22 34.2	13 12.8	25 19.9	14 13.2	12 36.4	0 13.0	6 15.6
		DECLINATION										
1	4 37 45.1	21S42.5	0S12.9	27S17.4	25S48.0	14S12.3	9S16.0	17S13.6	14N42.6	4S19.3	18S45.6	14N39.7
4	4 49 34.7	22 9.4	0 12.9	16 30.2	25 50.2	13 42.5	9 57.8	17 23.7	14 39.5	4 22.1	18 46.9	14 40.0
7	5 1 24.4	22 32.5	0 13.0	2N15.8	25 39.6	13 22.8	10 38.9	17 33.5	14 36.5	4 24.7	18 48.3	14 40.3
10	5 13 14.1	22 51.5	0 13.1	19 51.8	25 16.7	13 12.5	11 19.4	17 43.2	14 33.8	4 27.2	18 49.6	14 40.8
13	5 25 3.8	23 6.6	0 13.1	27 43.6	24 42.9	13 10.9	11 59.2	17 52.5	14 31.3	4 29.5	18 50.8	14 41.5
16	5 36 53.4	23 17.5	0 13.2	22 11.6	24 .5	13 17.0	12 38.2	18 1.7	14 29.0	4 31.6	18 52.1	14 42.2
19	5 48 43.1	23 24.2	0 13.2	8 16.0	23 13.0	13 29.7	13 16.5	18 10.5	14 26.9	4 33.6	18 53.3	14 43.1
22	6 0 32.8	23 26.7	0 13.3	8S 8.8	22 24.6	13 47.9	13 54.0	18 19.2	14 25.1	4 35.3	18 54.5	14 44.2
25	6 12 22.5	23 25.0	0 13.3	22 27.3	21 39.0	14 10.8	14 30.6	18 27.5	14 23.5	4 36.9	18 55.6	14 45.3
28	6 24 12.2	23 19.0	0 13.4	27 37.6	20 59.3	14 37.4	15 6.3	18 35.6	14 22.2	4 38.3	18 56.7	14 46.6
31	6 36 1.8	23 8.8	0 13.5	17 53.1	20 29.5	15 6.8	15 41.1	18 43.5	14 21.3	4 39.5	18 57.8	14 48.0

JANUARY 1971

LONGITUDE

DAY	EPHEM. SID. TIME h m s	☉ ° ′	☊ ° ′	☾ ° ′	☿ ° ′	♀ ° ′	♂ ° ′	♃ ° ′	♄ ° ′	♅ ° ′	♆ ° ′	♇ ° ′
1	6 39 58.4	9♑55.1	25♒57.6	27♒30.5	1♑59.7	24♏47.8	16♏ 4.0	27♏35.4	15♉57.0	13♎25.5	1♐60.0	29♍42.4
2	6 43 54.9	10 56.3	25 54.4	11♓54.8	0 R 54.9	25 37.6	16 42.0	27 46.7	15 R 55.2	13 26.5	2 1.8	29 42.4
3	6 47 51.5	11 57.5	25 51.2	26 11.4	29♐58.9	26 28.2	17 20.0	27 58.0	15 53.6	13 27.4	2 3.7	29 42.4
4	6 51 48.1	12 58.6	25 48.0	10♈18.3	29 12.7	27 19.5	17 57.9	28 9.2	15 52.0	13 28.2	2 5.5	29 R 42.3
5	6 55 44.6	13 59.8	25 44.9	24 14.5	28 36.7	28 11.6	18 35.9	28 20.3	15 50.6	13 28.9	2 7.3	29 42.3
6	6 59 41.2	15 .9	25 41.7	7♉59.4	28 10.9	29 4.4	19 13.9	28 31.3	15 49.2	13 29.7	2 9.1	29 42.1
7	7 3 37.7	16 2.1	25 38.5	21 32.7	27 55.1	29 57.9	19 51.8	28 42.3	15 48.0	13 30.3	2 10.8	29 42.0
8	7 7 34.3	17 3.2	25 35.3	4♊54.1	27 48.8	0♐52.0	20 29.8	28 53.2	15 46.9	13 30.9	2 12.6	29 41.8
9	7 11 30.9	18 4.3	25 32.2	18 3.1	27 D 51.5	1 46.8	21 7.7	29 3.9	15 45.9	13 31.5	2 14.3	29 41.5
10	7 15 27.4	19 5.5	25 29.0	0♋59.1	28 2.5	2 42.2	21 45.6	29 14.6	15 45.0	13 32.0	2 16.0	29 41.3
11	7 19 24.0	20 6.6	25 25.8	13 41.8	28 21.2	3 38.2	22 23.5	29 25.2	15 44.2	13 32.4	2 17.6	29 41.0
12	7 23 20.5	21 7.7	25 22.6	26 11.2	28 46.8	4 34.8	23 1.4	29 35.8	15 43.5	13 32.8	2 19.3	29 40.6
13	7 27 17.1	22 8.8	25 19.5	8♌27.9	29 18.7	5 31.9	23 39.3	29 46.2	15 43.0	13 33.1	2 20.9	29 40.3
14	7 31 13.6	23 9.9	25 16.3	20 33.3	29 56.3	6 29.6	24 17.2	29 56.5	15 42.5	13 33.4	2 22.5	29 39.9
15	7 35 10.2	24 11.0	25 13.1	2♍29.5	0♑39.0	7 27.7	24 55.1	0♐ 6.8	15 42.2	13 33.6	2 24.0	29 39.5
16	7 39 6.8	25 12.1	25 9.9	14 19.5	1 26.4	8 26.4	25 33.0	0 16.9	15 41.9	13 33.7	2 25.6	29 39.0
17	7 43 3.3	26 13.2	25 6.7	26 7.0	2 17.8	9 25.6	26 10.9	0 26.9	15 41.8	13 33.8	2 27.1	29 38.5
18	7 46 59.9	27 14.3	25 3.6	7♎56.4	3 13.0	10 25.2	26 48.7	0 36.9	15 41.8	13 33.8	2 28.6	29 38.0
19	7 50 56.4	28 15.4	25 .4	19 52.4	4 11.6	11 25.2	27 26.6	0 46.8	15 D 42.0	13 33.9	2 30.1	29 37.5
20	7 54 53.0	29 16.5	24 57.2	1♏60.0	5 13.1	12 25.7	28 4.5	0 56.5	15 42.2	13 R 33.8	2 31.5	29 36.9
21	7 58 49.5	0♒17.6	24 54.0	14 24.0	6 17.4	13 26.6	28 42.3	1 6.1	15 42.6	13 33.7	2 33.0	29 36.2
22	8 2 46.1	1 18.6	24 50.9	27 8.9	7 24.1	14 27.9	29 20.1	1 15.7	15 43.0	13 33.5	2 34.3	29 35.6
23	8 6 42.7	2 19.7	24 47.7	10♐18.0	8 33.0	15 29.5	29 57.9	1 25.1	15 43.6	13 33.2	2 35.7	29 34.9
24	8 10 39.2	3 20.8	24 44.5	23 53.2	9 44.0	16 31.5	0♐35.7	1 34.4	15 44.3	13 32.9	2 37.0	29 34.2
25	8 14 35.8	4 21.8	24 41.3	7♑54.3	10 56.8	17 33.9	1 13.4	1 43.6	15 45.1	13 32.6	2 38.3	29 33.5
26	8 18 32.3	5 22.8	24 38.2	22 18.4	12 11.3	18 36.6	1 51.2	1 52.7	15 46.0	13 32.2	2 39.6	29 32.7
27	8 22 28.9	6 23.8	24 35.0	7♒ .4	13 27.4	19 39.6	2 28.9	2 1.6	15 47.0	13 31.7	2 40.8	29 31.9
28	8 26 25.4	7 24.8	24 31.8	21 53.3	14 45.0	20 42.9	3 6.6	2 10.5	15 48.1	13 31.2	2 42.0	29 31.0
29	8 30 22.0	8 25.8	24 28.6	6♓49.0	16 3.8	21 46.5	3 44.3	2 19.2	15 49.4	13 30.6	2 43.2	29 30.2
30	8 34 18.6	9 26.8	24 25.5	21 39.7	17 24.0	22 50.4	4 22.0	2 27.8	15 50.7	13 30.0	2 44.4	29 29.3
31	8 38 15.1	10 27.7	24 22.3	6♈18.9	18 45.3	23 54.6	4 59.7	2 36.2	15 52.2	13 29.3	2 45.5	29 28.4

LATITUDE

DAY	SID. TIME	☉	☊	☾	☿	♀	♂	♃	♄	♅	♆	♇
1	6 39 58.4	0 .0	0 .0	0N16.9	3N 3.1	3N47.9	0N48.6	0N52.9	2S22.0	0N41.4	1N37.8	16N 2.9
4	6 51 48.1	0 .0	0 .0	3 43.3	3 13.4	3 51.0	0 47.3	0 53.1	2 21.1	0 41.5	1 37.9	16 4.6
7	7 3 37.7	0 .0	0 .0	5 10.2	3 5.9	3 52.2	0 45.9	0 53.2	2 20.3	0 41.6	1 38.0	16 6.2
10	7 15 27.4	0 .0	0 .0	4 8.8	2 46.8	3 51.7	0 44.5	0 53.3	2 19.4	0 41.7	1 38.1	16 7.9
13	7 27 17.1	0 .0	0 .0	1 22.9	2 21.4	3 49.5	0 43.0	0 53.5	2 18.6	0 41.8	1 38.2	16 9.5
16	7 39 6.8	0 .0	0 .0	1S50.5	1 53.1	3 45.8	0 41.4	0 53.6	2 17.7	0 42.0	1 38.4	16 11.1
19	7 50 56.4	0 .0	0 .0	4 21.5	1 23.9	3 40.9	0 39.8	0 53.8	2 16.8	0 42.1	1 38.5	16 12.7
22	8 2 46.1	0 .0	0 .0	5 14.7	0 55.1	3 34.7	0 38.1	0 54.0	2 15.9	0 42.2	1 38.6	16 14.2
25	8 14 35.8	0 .0	0 .0	3 46.5	0 27.4	3 27.4	0 36.3	0 54.2	2 15.0	0 42.3	1 38.7	16 15.7
28	8 26 25.4	0 .0	0 .0	0 9.6	0 1.2	3 19.2	0 34.5	0 54.4	2 14.1	0 42.4	1 38.9	16 17.1
31	8 38 15.1	0 .0	0 .0	3N35.2	0S23.1	3 10.1	0 32.6	0 54.6	2 13.2	0 42.5	1 39.0	16 18.5

RIGHT ASCENSION

DAY	SID. TIME	☉	☊	☾	☿	♀	♂	♃	♄	♅	♆	♇
1	6 39 58.4	10♑47.5	28♒12.6	29♒36.2	2♑ 7.6	23♏23.7	13♏50.5	25♏31.6	14♉11.2	12♎37.3	0♐14.9	6♎15.8
2	6 43 54.9	11 53.7	28 9.6	12♓43.4	0 R 58.4	24 14.1	14 28.2	25 43.3	14 R 9.4	12 38.2	0 16.8	6 16.1
3	6 47 51.5	12 59.9	28 6.5	25 25.2	29♐58.9	25 5.3	15 6.0	25 54.9	14 7.7	12 39.0	0 18.8	6 16.3
4	6 51 48.1	14 6.0	28 3.4	7♈59.9	29 9.7	25 57.3	15 43.9	26 6.5	14 6.1	12 39.8	0 20.7	6 16.5
5	6 55 44.6	15 12.0	28 .4	20 45.2	28 31.3	26 50.2	16 21.8	26 18.0	14 4.6	12 40.5	0 22.5	6 16.6
6	6 59 41.2	16 17.9	27 57.3	3♉55.6	28 3.9	27 43.8	16 59.8	26 29.4	14 3.1	12 41.2	0 24.4	6 16.7
7	7 3 37.7	17 23.6	27 54.2	17 39.5	27 47.0	28 38.2	17 37.9	26 40.7	14 1.8	12 41.8	0 26.2	6 16.8
8	7 7 34.3	18 29.3	27 51.2	1♊55.8	27 40.2	29 33.3	18 16.0	26 51.9	14 .7	12 42.4	0 28.0	6 16.9
9	7 11 30.9	19 34.8	27 48.1	16 32.0	27 D 43.0	0♐29.2	18 54.2	27 3.0	13 59.6	12 42.9	0 29.8	6 16.9
10	7 15 27.4	20 40.1	27 45.0	1♋ 6.5	27 54.6	1 25.7	19 32.4	27 14.1	13 58.6	12 43.4	0 31.6	6 16.9
11	7 19 24.0	21 45.4	27 42.0	15 15.5	28 14.4	2 23.0	20 10.7	27 25.1	13 57.7	12 43.8	0 33.3	6 16.9
12	7 23 20.5	22 50.5	27 38.9	28 41.3	28 41.7	3 21.0	20 49.1	27 36.0	13 57.0	12 44.2	0 35.0	6 R 16.8
13	7 27 17.1	23 55.4	27 35.8	11♌16.3	29 15.8	4 19.6	21 27.5	27 46.8	13 56.4	12 44.5	0 36.7	6 16.7
14	7 31 13.6	25 .2	27 32.7	23 3.0	29 56.0	5 18.9	22 6.0	27 57.5	13 55.8	12 44.7	0 38.3	6 16.6
15	7 35 10.2	26 4.9	27 29.7	4♍10.4	0♑41.9	6 18.8	22 44.6	28 8.1	13 55.4	12 44.9	0 40.0	6 16.4
16	7 39 6.8	27 9.4	27 26.6	14 51.1	1 32.8	7 19.3	23 23.2	28 18.6	13 55.1	12 45.1	0 41.6	6 16.2
17	7 43 3.3	28 13.7	27 23.5	25 19.3	2 28.3	8 20.5	24 1.9	28 29.0	13 54.9	12 45.2	0 43.2	6 16.0
18	7 46 59.9	29 17.8	27 20.5	5♎50.4	3 27.9	9 22.2	24 40.7	28 39.3	13 54.8	12 45.2	0 44.7	6 15.7
19	7 50 56.4	0♒21.8	27 17.4	16 40.0	4 31.3	10 24.5	25 19.5	28 49.6	13 D 54.9	12 45.3	0 46.3	6 15.5
20	7 54 53.0	1 25.6	27 14.3	28 4.1	5 38.0	11 27.4	25 58.4	28 59.7	13 55.0	12 R 45.2	0 47.8	6 15.2
21	7 58 49.5	2 29.2	27 11.2	10♏17.7	6 47.7	12 30.8	26 37.3	29 9.7	13 55.3	12 45.1	0 49.3	6 14.8
22	8 2 46.1	3 32.7	27 8.2	23 32.4	8 .2	13 34.7	27 16.3	29 19.7	13 55.6	12 44.9	0 50.7	6 14.4
23	8 6 42.7	4 35.9	27 5.1	7♐51.8	9 15.2	14 39.2	27 55.3	29 29.5	13 56.1	12 44.7	0 52.1	6 14.0
24	8 10 39.2	5 39.0	27 2.0	23 6.3	10 32.5	15 44.1	28 34.4	29 39.1	13 56.7	12 44.5	0 53.5	6 13.6
25	8 14 35.8	6 41.8	26 58.9	8♑51.4	11 51.9	16 49.5	29 13.5	29 48.7	13 57.4	12 44.2	0 54.9	6 13.1
26	8 18 32.3	7 44.5	26 55.9	24 34.9	13 13.1	17 55.4	29 52.7	29 58.2	13 58.2	12 43.8	0 56.2	6 12.6
27	8 22 28.9	8 47.0	26 52.8	9♒48.7	14 36.0	19 1.8	0♐32.0	0♐ 7.5	13 59.1	12 43.4	0 57.5	6 12.1
28	8 26 25.4	9 49.2	26 49.7	24 18.7	16 .5	20 8.5	1 11.2	0 16.7	14 .1	12 42.9	0 58.8	6 11.6
29	8 30 22.0	10 51.3	26 46.6	8♓ 5.9	17 26.4	21 15.7	1 50.6	0 25.8	14 1.3	12 42.4	1 .0	6 11.0
30	8 34 18.6	11 53.2	26 43.5	21 21.7	18 53.6	22 23.3	2 29.9	0 34.8	14 2.5	12 41.8	1 1.2	6 10.4
31	8 38 15.1	12 54.8	26 40.5	4♈22.2	20 22.0	23 31.3	3 9.4	0 43.6	14 3.9	12 41.2	1 2.4	6 9.7

DECLINATION

DAY	SID. TIME	☉	☊	☾	☿	♀	♂	♃	♄	♅	♆	♇
1	6 39 58.4	23S 4.4	0S13.5	12S 4.5	20S22.7	15S17.1	15S52.5	18S46.0	14N21.0	4S39.8	18S58.1	14N48.5
4	6 51 48.1	22 48.7	0 13.5	7N30.2	20 13.2	15 48.9	16 25.9	18 53.5	14 20.4	4 40.8	18 59.1	14 50.0
7	7 3 37.7	22 28.9	0 13.6	23 8.4	20 19.9	16 21.8	16 58.3	19 .7	14 20.0	4 41.5	19 .1	14 51.7
10	7 15 27.4	22 5.1	0 13.6	27 35.3	20 39.0	16 55.0	17 29.6	19 7.5	14 20.0	4 42.1	19 1.0	14 53.5
13	7 27 17.1	21 37.4	0 13.7	19 29.1	21 5.2	17 27.9	17 59.9	19 14.1	14 20.2	4 42.4	19 1.8	14 55.3
16	7 39 6.8	21 6.0	0 13.8	4 28.2	21 33.1	17 60.0	18 29.0	19 20.5	14 20.8	4 42.5	19 2.6	14 57.3
19	7 50 56.4	20 30.9	0 13.8	11S48.3	21 58.8	18 30.5	18 56.9	19 26.5	14 21.7	4 42.5	19 3.4	14 59.3
22	8 2 46.1	19 52.3	0 13.9	24 37.6	22 19.3	18 59.1	19 23.6	19 32.2	14 22.8	4 42.3	19 4.1	15 1.5
25	8 14 35.8	19 10.4	0 13.9	26 58.7	22 32.3	19 25.2	19 49.0	19 37.6	14 24.2	4 41.8	19 4.7	15 3.7
28	8 26 25.4	18 25.3	0 14.0	14 22.0	22 36.5	19 48.5	20 13.2	19 42.8	14 26.0	4 41.2	19 5.3	15 5.9
31	8 38 15.1	17 37.2	0 14.0	5N48.0	22 30.9	20 8.4	20 36.1	19 47.6	14 28.0	4 40.4	19 5.8	15 8.2

FEBRUARY 1971

LONGITUDE

DAY	EPHEM. SID. TIME	☉	☊	☽	☿	♀	♂	♃	♄	♅	♆	♇
	h m s	° ′	° ′	° ′	° ′	° ′	° ′	° ′	° ′	° ′	° ′	° ′
1	8 42 11.7	11 ♒ 28.7	24 ♒ 19.1	20 ♈ 41.6	20 ♑ 7.7	24 ♐ 59.1	5 ♐ 37.3	2 ♐ 44.6	15 ♉ 53.8	13 ♎ 28.6	2 ♐ 46.6	29 ♍ 27.4
2	8 46 8.2	12 29.6	24 15.9	4 ♉ 45.3	21 31.2	26 3.8	6 14.9	2 52.8	15 55.5	13 R 27.8	2 47.7	29 R 26.5
3	8 50 4.8	13 30.5	24 12.7	18 29.0	22 55.7	27 8.7	6 52.5	3 .9	15 57.2	13 26.9	2 48.7	29 25.5
4	8 54 1.3	14 31.3	24 9.6	1 ♊ 53.3	24 21.2	28 13.9	7 30.1	3 8.9	15 59.2	13 26.0	2 49.7	29 24.4
5	8 57 57.9	15 32.1	24 6.4	14 59.4	25 47.6	29 19.4	8 7.6	3 16.7	16 1.2	13 25.1	2 50.6	29 23.4
6	9 1 54.5	16 33.0	24 3.2	27 49.2	27 15.0	0 ♑ 25.0	8 45.2	3 24.4	16 3.3	13 24.1	2 51.6	29 22.3
7	9 5 51.0	17 33.7	24 .0	10 ♋ 24.7	28 43.2	1 30.9	9 22.7	3 31.9	16 5.5	13 23.0	2 52.5	29 21.2
8	9 9 47.6	18 34.5	23 56.9	22 47.9	0 ♒ 12.3	2 37.0	10 .1	3 39.3	16 7.9	13 21.9	2 53.4	29 20.1
9	9 13 44.1	19 35.3	23 53.7	5 ♌ .6	1 42.3	3 43.4	10 37.7	3 46.7	16 10.4	13 20.8	2 54.2	29 19.0
10	9 17 40.7	20 36.0	23 50.5	17 4.5	3 13.1	4 49.9	11 15.1	3 53.8	16 12.9	13 19.6	2 55.0	29 17.8
11	9 21 37.2	21 36.7	23 47.3	29 1.3	4 44.8	5 56.6	11 52.5	4 .8	16 15.6	13 18.4	2 55.8	29 16.6
12	9 25 33.8	22 37.4	23 44.2	10 ♍ 53.1	6 17.4	7 3.5	12 29.9	4 7.7	16 18.3	13 17.1	2 56.6	29 15.4
13	9 29 30.3	23 38.0	23 41.0	22 41.9	7 50.7	8 10.6	13 7.3	4 14.4	16 21.2	13 15.7	2 57.3	29 14.1
14	9 33 26.9	24 38.7	23 37.8	4 ♎ 30.4	9 25.0	9 17.8	13 44.7	4 21.0	16 24.1	13 14.3	2 57.9	29 12.9
15	9 37 23.5	25 39.3	23 34.6	16 21.4	11 .1	10 25.3	14 22.0	4 27.4	16 27.2	13 12.9	2 58.6	29 11.6
16	9 41 20.0	26 39.9	23 31.4	28 18.6	12 36.0	11 32.9	14 59.3	4 33.7	16 30.3	13 11.4	2 59.2	29 10.3
17	9 45 16.6	27 40.4	23 28.3	10 ♏ 25.6	14 12.8	12 40.7	15 36.6	4 39.8	16 33.6	13 9.9	2 59.8	29 9.0
18	9 49 13.1	28 41.0	23 25.1	22 46.8	15 50.6	13 48.6	16 13.9	4 45.7	16 36.9	13 8.3	3 .3	29 7.6
19	9 53 9.7	29 41.5	23 21.9	5 ♐ 26.3	17 29.2	14 56.7	16 51.1	4 51.6	16 40.4	13 6.7	3 .8	29 6.3
20	9 57 6.2	0 ♓ 42.0	23 18.7	18 28.0	19 8.7	16 4.9	17 28.3	4 57.2	16 44.0	13 5.1	3 1.3	29 4.9
21	10 1 2.8	1 42.5	23 15.6	1 ♑ 55.1	20 49.1	17 13.3	18 5.5	5 2.7	16 47.6	13 3.4	3 1.7	29 3.5
22	10 4 59.3	2 43.0	23 12.4	15 49.2	22 30.5	18 21.8	18 42.7	5 8.0	16 51.3	13 1.6	3 2.1	29 2.1
23	10 8 55.9	3 43.4	23 9.2	0 ♒ 10.0	24 12.8	19 30.5	19 19.8	5 13.2	16 55.2	12 59.8	3 2.5	29 .6
24	10 12 52.5	4 43.8	23 6.0	14 54.3	25 56.1	20 39.2	19 56.9	5 18.2	16 59.1	12 58.0	3 2.9	28 59.2
25	10 16 49.0	5 44.2	23 2.8	29 56.2	27 40.4	21 48.1	20 33.9	5 23.1	17 3.1	12 56.1	3 3.2	28 57.7
26	10 20 45.6	6 44.6	22 59.7	15 ♓ 7.6	29 25.7	22 57.1	21 10.9	5 27.7	17 7.2	12 54.2	3 3.4	28 56.2
27	10 24 42.1	7 44.9	22 56.5	0 ♈ 18.7	1 ♓ 11.9	24 6.2	21 47.9	5 32.2	17 11.5	12 52.3	3 3.7	28 54.7
28	10 28 38.7	8 45.2	22 53.3	15 20.0	2 59.2	25 15.5	22 24.8	5 36.6	17 15.7	12 50.3	3 3.9	28 53.2

LATITUDE

DAY	EPHEM. SID. TIME	☉	☊	☽	☿	♀	♂	♃	♄	♅	♆	♇
1	8 42 11.7	0 .0	0 .0	4 N 26.3	0 S 30.8	3 N 6.9	0 N 31.9	0 N 54.7	2 S 12.9	0 N 42.5	1 N 39.1	16 N 18.9
4	8 54 1.3	0 .0	0 .0	5 14.0	0 52.4	2 56.8	0 29.9	0 54.9	2 12.1	0 42.6	1 39.2	16 20.2
7	9 5 51.0	0 .0	0 .0	3 37.7	1 11.6	2 46.1	0 27.8	0 55.2	2 11.2	0 42.7	1 39.4	16 21.5
10	9 17 40.7	0 .0	0 .0	0 36.3	1 28.3	2 34.8	0 25.5	0 55.4	2 10.3	0 42.8	1 39.5	16 22.7
13	9 29 30.3	0 .0	0 .0	2 S 34.8	1 42.4	2 23.1	0 23.2	0 55.7	2 9.5	0 42.8	1 39.7	16 23.8
16	9 41 20.0	0 .0	0 .0	4 47.4	1 53.6	2 11.0	0 20.8	0 55.9	2 8.7	0 42.9	1 39.8	16 24.9
19	9 53 9.7	0 .0	0 .0	5 11.0	2 1.7	1 58.6	0 18.3	0 56.2	2 7.8	0 43.0	1 40.0	16 25.9
22	10 4 59.3	0 .0	0 .0	3 15.0	2 6.4	1 46.1	0 15.7	0 56.5	2 7.0	0 43.1	1 40.1	16 26.8
25	10 16 49.0	0 .0	0 .0	0 N 34.8	2 7.5	1 33.4	0 13.0	0 56.8	2 6.2	0 43.1	1 40.3	16 27.6
28	10 28 38.7	0 .0	0 .0	4 8.7	2 4.6	1 20.7	0 10.2	0 57.1	2 5.5	0 43.2	1 40.5	16 28.4

RIGHT ASCENSION

DAY	EPHEM. SID. TIME	☉	☊	☽	☿	♀	♂	♃	♄	♅	♆	♇
1	8 42 11.7	13 ♒ 56.3	26 ♒ 37.4	17 ♈ 24.5	21 ♑ 51.5	24 ♐ 39.7	3 ♐ 48.8	0 ♐ 52.3	14 ♉ 5.4	12 ♎ 40.5	1 ♐ 3.5	6 ♎ 9.1
2	8 46 8.2	14 57.5	26 34.3	0 ♉ 43.1	23 22.0	25 48.4	4 28.3	1 .9	14 7.0	12 R 39.8	1 4.6	6 R 8.4
3	8 50 4.8	15 58.5	26 31.2	14 27.2	24 53.3	26 57.5	5 7.8	1 9.4	14 8.6	12 39.0	1 5.7	6 7.7
4	8 54 1.3	16 59.3	26 28.1	28 37.6	26 25.6	28 6.9	5 47.4	1 17.7	14 10.4	12 38.2	1 6.8	6 6.9
5	8 57 57.9	17 59.9	26 25.1	13 ♊ 5.3	27 58.5	29 16.6	6 27.0	1 25.9	14 12.4	12 37.3	1 7.8	6 6.2
6	9 1 54.5	19 .3	26 22.0	27 32.6	29 32.2	0 ♑ 26.7	7 6.7	1 33.9	14 14.4	12 36.4	1 8.8	6 5.4
7	9 5 51.0	20 .5	26 18.9	11 ♋ 38.6	1 ♒ 6.5	1 37.0	7 46.3	1 41.9	14 16.5	12 35.5	1 9.7	6 4.5
8	9 9 47.6	21 .5	26 15.8	25 6.5	2 41.5	2 47.7	8 26.1	1 49.6	14 18.7	12 34.5	1 10.6	6 3.7
9	9 13 44.1	22 .3	26 12.7	7 ♌ 47.9	4 17.0	3 58.6	9 5.9	1 57.3	14 21.1	12 33.5	1 11.5	6 2.9
10	9 17 40.7	22 59.9	26 9.6	19 43.0	5 53.0	5 9.8	9 45.6	2 4.8	14 23.5	12 32.4	1 12.4	6 2.0
11	9 21 37.2	23 59.3	26 6.5	0 ♍ 58.6	7 29.4	6 21.2	10 25.5	2 12.1	14 26.1	12 31.2	1 13.2	6 1.0
12	9 25 33.8	24 58.5	26 3.5	11 45.6	9 6.3	7 32.8	11 5.3	2 19.3	14 28.7	12 30.0	1 14.0	6 .1
13	9 29 30.3	25 57.5	26 .4	22 16.6	10 43.6	8 44.6	11 45.2	2 26.4	14 31.5	12 28.8	1 14.7	5 59.1
14	9 33 26.9	26 56.3	25 57.3	2 ♎ 45.2	12 21.3	9 56.7	12 25.1	2 33.3	14 34.3	12 27.5	1 15.4	5 58.1
15	9 37 23.5	27 55.0	25 54.2	13 25.5	13 59.4	11 8.9	13 5.0	2 40.0	14 37.3	12 26.2	1 16.1	5 57.1
16	9 41 20.0	28 53.4	25 51.1	24 31.7	15 37.8	12 21.2	13 44.9	2 46.6	14 40.3	12 24.9	1 16.8	5 53.1
17	9 45 16.6	29 51.7	25 48.0	6 ♏ 17.6	17 16.5	13 33.8	14 24.9	2 53.0	14 43.5	12 23.5	1 17.4	5 55.0
18	9 49 13.1	0 ♓ 49.8	25 44.9	18 54.8	18 55.5	14 46.4	15 4.9	2 59.3	14 46.7	12 22.0	1 17.9	5 54.0
19	9 53 9.7	1 47.8	25 41.8	2 ♐ 29.7	20 34.8	15 59.2	15 44.9	3 5.4	14 50.1	12 20.5	1 18.5	5 52.9
20	9 57 6.2	2 45.5	25 38.8	16 59.5	22 14.5	17 12.1	16 24.9	3 11.3	14 53.5	12 19.0	1 19.0	5 51.7
21	10 1 2.8	3 43.1	25 35.7	2 ♑ 9.5	23 54.4	18 25.1	17 4.9	3 17.1	14 57.0	12 17.4	1 19.5	5 50.6
22	10 4 59.3	4 40.6	25 32.6	17 35.2	25 34.6	19 38.2	17 44.9	3 22.7	15 .7	12 15.8	1 19.9	5 49.5
23	10 8 55.9	5 37.9	25 29.5	2 ♒ 50.4	27 15.1	20 51.3	18 25.0	3 28.2	15 4.4	12 14.2	1 20.3	5 48.3
24	10 12 52.5	6 35.0	25 26.4	17 37.0	28 55.9	22 4.4	19 5.0	3 33.4	15 8.2	12 12.5	1 20.7	5 47.1
25	10 16 49.0	7 32.0	25 23.3	1 ♓ 49.4	0 ♓ 36.9	23 17.6	19 45.0	3 38.5	15 12.1	12 10.8	1 21.0	5 45.9
26	10 20 45.6	8 28.8	25 20.2	15 33.3	2 18.3	24 30.9	20 25.0	3 43.4	15 16.1	12 9.1	1 21.3	5 44.6
27	10 24 42.1	9 25.5	25 17.1	29 1.7	3 60.0	25 44.1	21 5.0	3 48.2	15 20.3	12 7.3	1 21.5	5 43.4
28	10 28 38.7	10 22.1	25 14.0	12 ♈ 29.8	5 41.9	26 57.3	21 45.0	3 52.8	15 24.4	12 5.5	1 21.8	5 42.1

DECLINATION

DAY	EPHEM. SID. TIME	☉	☊	☽	☿	♀	♂	♃	♄	♅	♆	♇
1	8 42 11.7	17 S 20.6	0 S 14.1	12 N 11.5	22 S 26.6	20 S 14.2	20 S 43.4	19 S 49.2	14 N 28.7	4 S 40.1	19 S 6.0	15 N 9.0
4	8 54 1.3	16 28.8	0 14.1	25 40.1	22 6.6	20 29.2	21 4.5	19 53.6	14 31.1	4 39.0	19 6.4	15 11.4
7	9 5 51.0	15 34.4	0 14.2	26 39.2	21 35.4	20 40.1	21 24.3	19 57.7	14 33.8	4 37.7	19 6.8	15 13.8
10	9 17 40.7	14 37.7	0 14.2	16 17.9	20 52.4	20 46.7	21 42.7	20 1.6	14 36.7	4 36.3	19 7.2	15 16.3
13	9 29 30.3	13 38.7	0 14.3	0 31.7	19 57.6	20 48.7	21 59.7	20 5.2	14 39.8	4 34.8	19 7.5	15 18.7
16	9 41 20.0	12 37.8	0 14.3	15 S 20.7	18 50.7	20 46.1	22 15.3	20 8.4	14 43.2	4 33.0	19 7.7	15 21.2
19	9 53 9.7	11 35.0	0 14.4	26 18.7	17 31.6	20 38.5	22 29.5	20 11.4	14 46.9	4 31.1	19 7.8	15 23.7
22	10 4 59.3	10 30.5	0 14.4	25 44.1	16 .3	20 26.0	22 42.2	20 14.1	14 50.7	4 29.1	19 7.9	15 26.2
25	10 16 49.0	9 24.6	0 14.5	10 57.2	14 16.7	20 8.6	22 53.6	20 16.4	14 54.8	4 26.9	19 8.0	15 28.7
28	10 28 38.7	8 17.4	0 14.5	9 N 51.7	12 20.8	19 46.1	23 3.5	20 18.5	14 59.1	4 24.6	19 7.9	15 31.2

MARCH 1971

DAY	EPHEM. SID. TIME	☉	☊	☽	☿	♀	♂	♃	♄	♅	♆	♇
	h m s	° ′	° ′	° ′	° ′	° ′	° ′	° ′	° ′	° ′	° ′	° ′
		LONGITUDE										
1	10 32 35.2	9♓45.5	22♒50.1	0♉ 3.2	4♓47.5	26♑24.8	23♐ 1.7	5♐40.8	17♉20.1	12♎48.3	3♐ 4.0	28♍51.7
2	10 36 31.8	10 45.7	22 47.0	14 23.0	6 36.8	27 34.2	23 38.6	5 44.8	17 24.7	12R46.3	3 4.2	28R50.2
3	10 40 28.3	11 45.9	22 43.8	28 16.5	8 27.1	28 43.8	24 15.4	5 48.6	17 29.2	12 44.2	3 4.3	28 48.7
4	10 44 24.9	12 46.1	22 40.6	11♊43.8	10 18.4	29 53.4	24 52.2	5 52.3	17 33.8	12 42.1	3 4.4	28 47.1
5	10 48 21.4	13 46.2	22 37.4	24 46.6	12 10.7	1♒ 3.1	25 28.9	5 55.7	17 38.6	12 40.0	3 4.4	28 45.6
6	10 52 18.0	14 46.3	22 34.2	7♋28.3	14 4.0	2 12.9	26 5.6	5 59.0	17 43.4	12 37.8	3 4.4	28 44.0
7	10 56 14.6	15 46.4	22 31.1	19 52.4	15 58.2	3 22.8	26 42.2	6 2.2	17 48.3	12 35.6	3 4.4	28 42.4
8	11 0 11.1	16 46.4	22 27.9	2♌ 3.0	17 53.2	4 32.7	27 18.8	6 5.1	17 53.2	12 33.4	3R 4.3	28 40.8
9	11 4 7.7	17 46.4	22 24.7	14 3.6	19 49.1	5 42.8	27 55.4	6 7.9	17 58.3	12 31.1	3 4.2	28 39.2
10	11 8 4.2	18 46.4	22 21.5	25 57.6	21 45.8	6 52.9	28 31.9	6 10.4	18 3.4	12 28.9	3 4.1	28 37.6
11	11 12 .8	19 46.3	22 18.4	7♍47.7	23 43.0	8 3.1	29 8.4	6 12.9	18 8.6	12 26.5	3 3.9	28 36.0
12	11 15 57.3	20 46.2	22 15.2	19 36.3	25 40.8	9 13.4	29 44.8	6 15.1	18 13.9	12 24.2	3 3.7	28 34.4
13	11 19 53.9	21 46.0	22 12.0	1♎25.6	27 39.0	10 23.8	0♑21.2	6 17.1	18 19.2	12 21.9	3 3.5	28 32.8
14	11 23 50.4	22 45.8	22 8.8	13 17.5	29 37.3	11 34.3	0 57.5	6 19.0	18 24.7	12 19.5	3 3.2	28 31.1
15	11 27 47.0	23 45.6	22 5.6	25 13.8	1♈35.6	12 44.8	1 33.8	6 20.6	18 30.2	12 17.1	3 2.9	28 29.5
16	11 31 43.5	24 45.4	22 2.5	7♏16.8	3 33.7	13 55.4	2 10.0	6 22.1	18 35.7	12 14.7	3 2.6	28 27.9
17	11 35 40.1	25 45.1	21 59.3	19 28.7	5 31.2	15 6.0	2 46.2	6 23.4	18 41.4	12 12.2	3 2.2	28 26.2
18	11 39 36.6	26 44.8	21 56.1	1♐52.3	7 27.9	16 16.8	3 22.3	6 24.6	18 47.1	12 9.8	3 1.8	28 24.6
19	11 43 33.2	27 44.5	21 52.9	14 30.9	9 23.3	17 27.6	3 58.4	6 25.5	18 52.8	12 7.3	3 1.4	28 22.9
20	11 47 29.7	28 44.2	21 49.8	27 27.6	11 17.1	18 38.4	4 34.5	6 26.2	18 58.7	12 4.8	3 .9	28 21.3
21	11 51 26.3	29 43.8	21 46.6	10♑45.8	13 9.0	19 49.4	5 10.4	6 26.8	19 4.6	12 2.3	3 .4	28 19.7
22	11 55 22.9	0♈43.4	21 43.4	24 28.0	14 58.4	21 .3	5 46.3	6 27.2	19 10.6	11 59.8	2 59.9	28 18.0
23	11 59 19.4	1 43.0	21 40.2	8♒35.6	16 45.1	22 11.4	6 22.2	6 27.4	19 16.6	11 57.3	2 59.4	28 16.4
24	12 3 16.0	2 42.5	21 37.0	23 7.8	18 28.4	23 22.5	6 58.0	6 27.4	19 22.7	11 54.7	2 58.8	28 14.8
25	12 7 12.5	3 42.0	21 33.9	8♓ 1.3	20 7.9	24 33.7	7 33.7	6R27.2	19 28.9	11 52.2	2 58.2	28 13.1
26	12 11 9.1	4 41.5	21 30.7	23 9.9	21 43.2	25 44.9	8 9.3	6 26.8	19 35.1	11 49.6	2 57.6	28 11.5
27	12 15 5.6	5 40.9	21 27.5	8♈24.4	23 14.0	26 56.1	8 44.9	6 26.2	19 41.4	11 47.0	2 56.9	28 9.9
28	12 19 2.2	6 40.3	21 24.3	23 34.5	24 39.8	28 7.4	9 20.4	6 25.4	19 47.7	11 44.4	2 56.2	28 8.3
29	12 22 58.7	7 39.7	21 21.2	8♉30.1	26 .2	29 18.7	9 55.8	6 24.5	19 54.1	11 41.9	2 55.5	28 6.6
30	12 26 55.3	8 39.0	21 18.0	23 3.1	27 14.9	0♓30.1	10 31.1	6 23.3	20 .6	11 39.3	2 54.7	28 5.0
31	12 30 51.8	9 38.3	21 14.8	7♊ 8.3	28 23.7	1 41.5	11 6.4	6 22.0	20 7.1	11 36.7	2 53.9	28 3.4
		LATITUDE										
1	10 32 35.2	0 .0	0 .0	4N50.2	2S 2.7	1N16.4	0N 9.2	0N57.2	2S 5.2	0N43.2	1N40.5	16N28.6
4	10 44 24.9	0 .0	0 .0	5 .5	1 54.0	1 3.7	0 6.2	0 57.5	2 4.5	0 43.3	1 40.7	16 29.3
7	10 56 14.6	0 .0	0 .0	2 55.5	1 40.7	0 51.2	0 3.1	0 57.8	2 3.7	0 43.3	1 40.8	16 29.8
10	11 8 4.2	0 .0	0 .0	0S13.0	1 22.3	0 38.8	0S .1	0 58.1	2 3.0	0 43.3	1 41.0	16 30.3
13	11 19 53.9	0 .0	0 .0	3 12.9	0 58.9	0 26.6	0 3.5	0 58.4	2 2.4	0 43.4	1 41.2	16 30.7
16	11 31 43.5	0 .0	0 .0	5 .2	0 30.4	0 14.8	0 7.0	0 58.6	2 1.7	0 43.4	1 41.3	16 31.0
19	11 43 33.2	0 .0	0 .0	4 50.5	0N 2.4	0 3.3	0 10.7	0 58.9	2 1.1	0 43.4	1 41.5	16 31.2
22	11 55 22.9	0 .0	0 .0	2 29.5	0 38.2	0S 7.8	0 14.5	0 59.2	2 .4	0 43.4	1 41.6	16 31.3
25	12 7 12.5	0 .0	0 .0	1N20.4	1 15.3	0 18.4	0 18.5	0 59.5	1 59.8	0 43.5	1 41.7	16 31.4
28	12 19 2.2	0 .0	0 .0	4 29.8	1 51.2	0 28.5	0 22.7	0 59.8	1 59.3	0 43.5	1 41.9	16 31.3
31	12 30 51.8	0 .0	0 .0	4 58.8	2 23.2	0 38.1	0 27.0	1 .0	1 58.7	0 43.5	1 42.0	16 31.2
		RIGHT ASCENSION										
1	10 32 35.2	11♓18.5	25♒10.9	26♈11.6	7♓24.2	28♑10.5	22♐25.0	3♐57.2	15♉28.7	12♎ 3.6	1♐21.9	5♎40.9
2	10 36 31.8	12 14.8	25 7.8	10♉16.3	9 6.9	29 23.7	23 5.0	4 1.4	15 33.1	12R 1.8	1 22.1	5R39.6
3	10 40 28.3	13 11.0	25 4.7	24 44.4	10 49.8	0♒36.8	23 45.0	4 5.5	15 37.6	11 59.9	1 22.3	5 38.3
4	10 44 24.9	14 7.0	25 1.7	9♊27.1	12 33.0	1 49.8	24 24.9	4 9.3	15 42.1	11 57.9	1 22.3	5 37.0
5	10 48 21.4	15 2.9	24 58.6	24 6.6	14 16.5	3 2.8	25 4.8	4 13.0	15 46.8	11 56.0	1 22.4	5 35.6
6	10 52 18.0	15 58.7	24 55.5	8♋22.5	16 .4	4 15.7	25 44.7	4 16.5	15 51.5	11 54.0	1 22.4	5 34.3
7	10 56 14.6	16 54.3	24 52.4	21 58.5	17 44.6	5 28.5	26 24.6	4 19.7	15 56.3	11 51.9	1 22.4	5 32.9
8	11 0 11.1	17 49.9	24 49.3	4♌46.6	19 29.0	6 41.3	27 4.4	4 22.9	16 1.1	11 49.9	1R22.3	5 31.6
9	11 4 7.7	18 45.4	24 46.2	16 47.5	21 13.7	7 53.9	27 44.2	4 25.8	16 6.1	11 47.8	1 22.2	5 30.2
10	11 8 4.2	19 40.7	24 43.1	28 8.1	22 58.6	9 6.4	28 24.0	4 28.5	16 11.1	11 45.7	1 22.1	5 28.8
11	11 12 .8	20 36.0	24 40.0	8♍59.1	24 43.7	10 18.8	29 3.7	4 31.1	16 16.3	11 43.6	1 21.9	5 27.4
12	11 15 57.3	21 31.2	24 36.9	19 32.6	26 28.9	11 31.1	29 43.4	4 33.4	16 21.4	11 41.4	1 21.7	5 26.0
13	11 19 53.9	22 26.3	24 33.8	0♎ 1.7	28 14.0	12 43.3	0♑23.1	4 35.6	16 26.7	11 39.2	1 21.5	5 24.5
14	11 23 50.4	23 21.4	24 30.7	10 39.5	29 59.1	13 55.3	1 2.7	4 37.5	16 32.1	11 37.0	1 21.2	5 23.1
15	11 27 47.0	24 16.3	24 27.6	21 39.1	1♈43.8	15 7.2	1 42.3	4 39.3	16 37.5	11 34.8	1 20.9	5 21.7
16	11 31 43.5	25 11.3	24 24.5	3♏12.5	3 28.2	16 19.0	2 21.8	4 40.9	16 43.0	11 32.6	1 20.6	5 20.2
17	11 35 40.1	26 6.1	24 21.4	15 30.2	5 11.9	17 30.6	3 1.3	4 42.3	16 48.5	11 30.3	1 20.2	5 18.8
18	11 39 36.6	27 .9	24 18.3	28 37.9	6 54.8	18 42.1	3 40.8	4 43.5	16 54.2	11 28.1	1 19.8	5 17.3
19	11 43 33.2	27 55.7	24 15.2	12♐34.2	8 36.6	19 53.4	4 20.2	4 44.5	16 59.9	11 25.8	1 19.4	5 15.9
20	11 47 29.7	28 50.4	24 12.1	27 8.4	10 17.0	21 4.5	4 59.5	4 45.3	17 5.6	11 23.5	1 18.9	5 14.4
21	11 51 26.3	29 45.1	24 9.0	12♑ 1.3	11 55.7	22 15.5	5 38.7	4 45.9	17 11.5	11 21.2	1 18.4	5 12.9
22	11 55 22.9	0♈39.8	24 5.9	26 51.6	13 32.4	23 26.3	6 17.9	4 46.3	17 17.4	11 18.9	1 17.9	5 11.5
23	11 59 19.4	1 34.5	24 2.8	11♒22.8	15 6.7	24 37.0	6 57.1	4 46.5	17 23.4	11 16.6	1 17.4	5 10.0
24	12 3 16.0	2 29.1	23 59.6	25 28.0	16 38.2	25 47.5	7 36.2	4 46.5	17 29.4	11 14.2	1 16.8	5 8.5
25	12 7 12.5	3 23.7	23 56.5	9♓10.7	18 6.5	26 57.8	8 15.1	4R46.4	17 35.5	11 11.9	1 16.1	5 7.1
26	12 11 9.1	4 18.3	23 53.4	22 41.8	19 31.4	28 7.9	8 54.0	4 46.0	17 41.7	11 9.5	1 15.5	5 5.6
27	12 15 5.6	5 12.9	23 50.3	6♈15.6	20 52.3	29 17.9	9 32.8	4 45.4	17 47.9	11 7.1	1 14.8	5 4.1
28	12 19 2.2	6 7.5	23 47.2	20 6.8	22 9.1	0♓27.7	10 11.5	4 44.6	17 54.2	11 4.7	1 14.1	5 2.6
29	12 22 58.7	7 2.1	23 44.1	4♉25.7	23 21.2	1 37.3	10 50.2	4 43.6	18 .6	11 2.3	1 13.3	5 1.1
30	12 26 55.3	7 56.7	23 41.0	19 14.4	24 28.4	2 46.8	11 28.7	4 42.4	18 7.0	10 60.0	1 12.5	4 59.6
31	12 30 51.8	8 51.3	23 37.9	4♊23.7	25 30.4	3 56.1	12 7.1	4 41.0	18 13.5	10 57.6	1 11.7	4 58.2
		DECLINATION										
1	10 32 35.2	7S54.7	0S14.6	16N 1.0	11S39.6	19S37.5	23S 6.5	20S19.2	15N .5	4S23.8	19S 7.9	15N32.0
4	10 44 24.9	6 46.1	0 14.6	27 9.5	9 27.9	19 8.4	23 14.5	20 20.9	15 5.1	4 21.3	19 7.8	15 34.4
7	10 56 14.6	5 36.7	0 14.7	24 52.0	7 4.9	18 34.5	23 21.1	20 22.3	15 9.8	4 18.7	19 7.7	15 36.8
10	11 8 4.2	4 26.6	0 14.7	12 39.9	4 31.7	17 55.9	23 26.3	20 23.4	15 14.6	4 16.0	19 7.5	15 39.1
13	11 19 53.9	3 16.0	0 14.8	3S31.0	1 50.1	17 12.7	23 30.2	20 24.3	15 19.6	4 13.3	19 7.2	15 41.4
16	11 31 43.5	2 5.0	0 14.8	18 40.1	0N57.1	16 25.0	23 32.7	20 24.9	15 24.8	4 10.5	19 6.9	15 43.6
19	11 43 33.2	0 53.9	0 14.9	27 21.3	3 45.4	15 33.2	23 33.8	20 25.1	15 30.0	4 7.6	19 6.5	15 45.7
22	11 55 22.9	0N17.3	0 14.9	23 41.0	6 29.3	14 37.3	23 33.7	20 25.1	15 35.4	4 4.6	19 6.1	15 47.8
25	12 7 12.5	1 28.3	0 15.0	7 19.2	9 2.0	13 37.6	23 32.2	20 24.9	15 40.9	4 1.6	19 5.6	15 49.7
28	12 19 2.2	2 39.0	0 15.0	13N19.8	11 16.8	12 34.5	23 29.6	20 24.3	15 46.5	3 58.6	19 5.1	15 51.6
31	12 30 51.8	3 49.2	0 15.1	26 24.9	13 8.1	11 28.1	23 25.7	20 23.5	15 52.2	3 55.6	19 4.5	15 53.4

LONGITUDE

DAY	EPHEM. SID. TIME (h m s)	☉	☊	☽	☿	♀	♂	♃	♄	♅	♆	♇
1	12 34 48.4	10♈37.6	21♒11.6	20♊44.1	29♈26.3	2♓52.9	11♑41.6	6♐20.5	20♉13.6	11♎34.1	2♐53.1	28♍1.8
2	12 38 44.9	11 36.8	21 8.4	3♋51.7	0♉22.4	4 4.4	12 16.7	6R18.8	20 20.2	11R31.5	2R52.2	28R .2
3	12 42 41.5	12 35.9	21 5.3	16 34.1	1 11.9	5 15.9	12 51.7	6 16.9	20 26.9	11 28.9	2 51.4	27 58.7
4	12 46 38.1	13 35.1	21 2.1	28 55.9	1 54.5	6 27.5	13 26.6	6 14.8	20 33.6	11 26.3	2 50.5	27 57.1
5	12 50 34.6	14 34.2	20 58.9	11♌2.0	2 30.4	7 39.1	14 1.5	6 12.6	20 40.4	11 23.7	2 49.5	27 55.5
6	12 54 31.2	15 33.2	20 55.7	22 57.4	2 59.2	8 50.7	14 36.2	6 10.1	20 47.2	11 21.1	2 48.6	27 54.0
7	12 58 27.7	16 32.3	20 52.6	4♍46.8	3 21.1	10 2.4	15 10.9	6 7.5	20 54.0	11 18.5	2 47.6	27 52.4
8	13 2 24.3	17 31.2	20 49.4	16 34.1	3 36.1	11 14.0	15 45.5	6 4.8	21 .9	11 15.9	2 46.6	27 50.9
9	13 6 20.8	18 30.2	20 46.2	28 22.6	3 44.2	12 25.8	16 20.0	6 1.8	21 7.8	11 13.4	2 45.6	27 49.4
10	13 10 17.4	19 29.1	20 43.0	10♎14.9	3 45.6	13 37.5	16 54.4	5 58.7	21 14.8	11 10.8	2 44.5	27 47.9
11	13 14 13.9	20 28.0	20 39.9	22 13.1	3R40.5	14 49.3	17 28.7	5 55.3	21 21.8	11 8.2	2 43.4	27 46.4
12	13 18 10.5	21 26.8	20 36.7	4♏18.6	3 29.2	16 1.1	18 2.9	5 51.9	21 28.9	11 5.7	2 42.3	27 44.9
13	13 22 7.0	22 25.7	20 33.5	16 32.5	3 12.1	17 13.0	18 37.1	5 48.3	21 36.0	11 3.2	2 41.2	27 43.5
14	13 26 3.6	23 24.5	20 30.3	28 55.8	2 49.6	18 24.9	19 11.1	5 44.4	21 43.2	11 .7	2 40.1	27 42.1
15	13 30 .1	24 23.2	20 27.1	11♐29.7	2 22.1	19 36.8	19 45.0	5 40.4	21 50.3	10 58.2	2 38.9	27 40.6
16	13 33 56.7	25 22.0	20 24.0	24 15.8	1 50.4	20 48.8	20 18.8	5 36.3	21 57.5	10 55.7	2 37.7	27 39.2
17	13 37 53.3	26 20.7	20 20.8	7♑16.0	1 15.0	22 .8	20 52.5	5 32.0	22 4.8	10 53.2	2 36.5	27 37.8
18	13 41 49.8	27 19.3	20 17.6	20 32.5	0 36.7	23 12.8	21 26.1	5 27.5	22 12.1	10 50.8	2 35.3	27 36.4
19	13 45 46.4	28 18.0	20 14.4	4♒7.6	29♈56.2	24 24.8	21 59.5	5 22.9	22 19.4	10 48.3	2 34.0	27 35.1
20	13 49 42.9	29 16.6	20 11.3	18 2.9	29 14.3	25 36.9	22 32.8	5 18.1	22 26.7	10 45.9	2 32.7	27 33.7
21	13 53 39.5	0♉15.2	20 8.1	2♓19.2	28 31.9	26 48.9	23 6.0	5 13.2	22 34.1	10 43.4	2 31.4	27 32.4
22	13 57 36.0	1 13.7	20 4.9	16 55.0	27 49.6	28 1.1	23 39.1	5 8.1	22 41.5	10 41.1	2 30.1	27 31.1
23	14 1 32.6	2 12.2	20 1.7	1♈46.5	27 8.4	29 13.2	24 12.0	5 2.8	22 48.9	10 38.7	2 28.8	27 29.8
24	14 5 29.1	3 10.7	19 58.5	16 47.0	26 28.7	0♈25.3	24 44.8	4 57.5	22 56.3	10 36.4	2 27.4	27 28.5
25	14 9 25.7	4 9.2	19 55.4	1♉47.8	25 51.4	1 37.5	25 17.4	4 51.9	23 3.8	10 34.1	2 26.0	27 27.3
26	14 13 22.2	5 7.7	19 52.2	16 39.2	25 17.0	2 49.7	25 49.9	4 46.3	23 11.3	10 31.8	2 24.7	27 26.1
27	14 17 18.8	6 6.1	19 49.0	1♊12.5	24 46.0	4 1.9	26 22.2	4 40.5	23 18.9	10 29.5	2 23.3	27 24.9
28	14 21 15.4	7 4.4	19 45.8	15 21.2	24 18.9	5 14.1	26 54.4	4 34.6	23 26.4	10 27.3	2 21.8	27 23.7
29	14 25 11.9	8 2.8	19 42.7	29 1.8	23 55.8	6 26.4	27 26.4	4 28.6	23 34.0	10 25.1	2 20.4	27 22.5
30	14 29 8.5	9 1.1	19 39.5	12♋14.2	23 37.2	7 38.6	27 58.3	4 22.4	23 41.6	10 22.9	2 18.9	27 21.4

LATITUDE

DAY	SID. TIME	☉	☊	☽	☿	♀	♂	♃	♄	♅	♆	♇
1	12 34 48.4	0 .0	0 .0	4N32.1	2N32.5	0S41.2	0S28.5	1N .1	1S58.6	0N43.4	1N42.1	16N31.1
4	12 46 38.1	0 .0	0 .0	2 3.4	2 55.3	0 50.0	0 33.0	1 .3	1 58.0	0 43.4	1 42.2	16 30.9
7	12 58 27.7	0 .0	0 .0	1S 5.9	3 8.5	0 58.2	0 37.8	1 .5	1 57.6	0 43.4	1 42.3	16 30.5
10	13 10 17.4	0 .0	0 .0	3 47.1	3 9.9	1 5.8	0 42.8	1 .7	1 57.1	0 43.4	1 42.4	16 30.1
13	13 22 7.0	0 .0	0 .0	5 2.4	2 58.2	1 12.7	0 47.9	1 .9	1 56.7	0 43.3	1 42.5	16 29.6
16	13 33 56.7	0 .0	0 .0	4 15.0	2 33.0	1 18.9	0 53.3	1 1.0	1 56.2	0 43.3	1 42.6	16 29.0
19	13 45 46.4	0 .0	0 .0	1 29.1	1 55.7	1 24.5	0 58.9	1 1.2	1 55.8	0 43.3	1 42.7	16 28.4
22	13 57 36.0	0 .0	0 .0	2N12.6	1 9.5	1 29.3	1 4.7	1 1.3	1 55.5	0 43.2	1 42.8	16 27.7
25	14 9 25.7	0 .0	0 .0	4 45.6	0 18.9	1 33.3	1 10.8	1 1.3	1 55.1	0 43.1	1 42.9	16 26.9
28	14 21 15.4	0 .0	0 .0	4 33.3	0S31.4	1 36.7	1 17.1	1 1.4	1 54.8	0 43.1	1 43.0	16 26.0

RIGHT ASCENSION

DAY	SID. TIME	☉	☊	☽	☿	♀	♂	♃	♄	♅	♆	♇
1	12 34 48.4	9♈46.0	23♒34.8	19♊33.7	26♈26.9	5♓ 5.2	12♑45.5	4♐39.4	18♉20.0	10♎55.2	1♐10.9	4♎56.7
2	12 38 44.9	10 40.6	23 31.7	4♋20.0	27 17.8	6 14.1	13 23.7	4R37.7	18 26.5	10R52.8	1R10.0	4R55.2
3	12 42 41.5	11 35.3	23 28.6	18 22.6	28 2.7	7 22.9	14 1.8	4 35.7	18 33.2	10 50.4	1 9.1	4 53.7
4	12 46 38.1	12 30.0	23 25.5	1♌31.5	28 41.6	8 31.5	14 39.8	4 33.5	18 39.9	10 48.0	1 8.2	4 52.3
5	12 50 34.6	13 24.7	23 22.4	13 47.0	29 14.3	9 40.0	15 17.8	4 31.2	18 46.6	10 45.6	1 7.2	4 50.8
6	12 54 31.2	14 19.5	23 19.2	25 17.1	29 40.7	10 48.3	15 55.6	4 28.6	18 53.4	10 43.2	1 6.2	4 49.4
7	12 58 27.7	15 14.3	23 16.1	6♍13.5	0♉ .9	11 56.5	16 33.2	4 25.9	19 .2	10 40.8	1 5.2	4 47.9
8	13 2 24.3	16 9.2	23 13.0	16 49.5	0 14.8	13 4.6	17 10.8	4 23.0	19 7.1	10 38.4	1 4.2	4 46.5
9	13 6 20.8	17 4.1	23 9.9	27 18.9	0 22.5	14 12.5	17 48.3	4 19.9	19 14.0	10 36.0	1 3.1	4 45.0
10	13 10 17.4	17 59.1	23 6.8	7♎55.2	0R20.1	15 20.3	18 25.6	4 16.6	19 21.0	10 33.7	1 2.0	4 43.6
11	13 14 13.9	18 54.1	23 3.7	18 51.8	0 10.5	16 28.0	19 2.8	4 13.1	19 28.0	10 31.3	1 .9	4 42.2
12	13 18 10.5	19 49.2	23 .6	0♏20.6	29♈55.8	17 35.5	19 39.9	4 9.5	19 35.0	10 29.0	0 59.8	4 40.8
13	13 22 7.0	20 44.4	22 57.5	12 31.6	29 36.4	18 43.0	20 16.9	4 5.7	19 42.2	10 26.7	0 58.7	4 39.4
14	13 26 3.6	21 39.7	22 54.3	25 29.9	29 24.6	19 50.4	20 53.8	4 1.7	19 49.3	10 24.3	0 57.5	4 38.0
15	13 30 .1	22 35.0	22 51.2	9♐13.9	29 12.8	20 57.6	21 30.5	3 57.5	19 56.5	10 22.0	0 56.3	4 36.6
16	13 33 56.7	23 30.4	22 48.1	23 32.6	28 45.6	22 4.8	22 7.0	3 53.2	20 3.7	10 19.7	0 55.1	4 35.3
17	13 37 53.3	24 26.0	22 45.0	8♑ 7.7	28 15.5	23 11.9	22 43.4	3 48.7	20 11.0	10 17.4	0 53.8	4 33.9
18	13 41 49.8	25 21.6	22 41.9	22 38.6	27 43.1	24 18.9	23 19.7	3 44.0	20 18.3	10 15.1	0 52.5	4 32.6
19	13 45 46.4	26 17.3	22 38.8	6♒49.7	27 9.1	25 25.8	23 55.8	3 39.2	20 25.6	10 12.9	0 51.2	4 31.2
20	13 49 42.9	27 13.1	22 35.6	20 34.5	26 34.3	26 32.7	24 31.7	3 34.1	20 33.0	10 10.6	0 49.9	4 29.9
21	13 53 39.5	28 9.1	22 32.5	3♓56.5	25 59.3	27 39.6	25 7.5	3 29.0	20 40.4	10 8.4	0 48.6	4 28.6
22	13 57 36.0	29 5.1	22 29.4	17 6.2	25 25.0	28 46.4	25 43.1	3 23.6	20 47.8	10 6.2	0 47.2	4 27.3
23	14 1 32.6	0♉ 1.2	22 26.3	0♈18.9	24 51.8	29 53.2	26 18.5	3 18.2	20 55.3	10 4.0	0 45.8	4 26.0
24	14 5 29.1	0 57.5	22 23.2	13 50.4	24 20.4	0♈59.9	26 53.8	3 12.5	21 2.8	10 1.9	0 44.4	4 24.7
25	14 9 25.7	1 53.9	22 20.1	27 58.3	23 51.3	2 6.6	27 28.9	3 6.8	21 10.3	9 59.7	0 43.0	4 23.5
26	14 13 22.2	2 50.4	22 16.9	12♉39.0	23 25.1	3 13.3	28 3.8	3 .9	21 17.9	9 57.6	0 41.6	4 22.3
27	14 17 18.8	3 47.0	22 13.8	27 57.8	23 2.1	4 20.0	28 38.5	2 54.8	21 25.4	9 55.5	0 40.1	4 21.0
28	14 21 15.4	4 43.8	22 10.7	13♊32.5	22 42.6	5 26.7	29 13.0	2 48.6	21 33.0	9 53.4	0 38.6	4 19.8
29	14 25 11.9	5 40.7	22 7.6	28 54.7	22 26.9	6 33.4	29 47.3	2 42.3	21 40.7	9 51.4	0 37.2	4 18.7
30	14 29 8.5	6 37.7	22 4.4	13♋36.8	22 15.1	7 40.1	0♒21.4	2 35.9	21 48.3	9 49.4	0 35.7	4 17.5

DECLINATION

DAY	SID. TIME	☉	☊	☽	☿	♀	♂	♃	♄	♅	♆	♇
1	12 34 48.4	4N12.5	0S15.1	27N38.7	13N39.2	11S 5.4	23S24.2	20S23.2	15N54.1	3S54.6	19S 4.3	15N54.0
4	12 46 38.1	5 21.7	0 15.2	22 23.4	14 52.8	9 55.1	23 18.8	20 22.0	15 59.8	3 51.5	19 3.7	15 55.6
7	12 58 27.7	6 30.2	0 15.2	8 44.3	15 35.2	8 42.3	23 12.4	20 20.5	16 5.7	3 48.5	19 3.0	15 57.2
10	13 10 17.4	7 37.6	0 15.3	7S32.4	15 45.0	7 27.2	23 4.9	20 18.8	16 11.5	3 45.5	19 2.3	15 58.6
13	13 22 7.0	8 43.9	0 15.3	22 14.6	15 22.4	6 10.0	22 56.5	20 16.7	16 17.4	3 42.4	19 1.6	15 59.9
16	13 33 56.7	9 48.8	0 15.4	27 34.0	14 30.4	4 51.1	22 47.2	20 14.6	16 23.3	3 39.7	19 .8	16 1.1
19	13 45 46.4	10 52.3	0 15.4	21 45.0	13 4.3	3 30.7	22 37.1	20 12.1	16 29.3	3 36.9	19 .0	16 2.1
22	13 57 36.0	11 54.3	0 15.5	3 7.8	11 47.1	2 9.2	22 26.2	20 9.4	16 35.2	3 34.1	18 59.1	16 3.1
25	14 9 25.7	12 54.4	0 15.5	16N33.7	10 17.2	0 46.8	22 14.6	20 6.4	16 41.1	3 31.4	18 58.3	16 3.8
28	14 21 15.4	13 52.7	0 15.6	27 10.0	8 56.5	0N36.1	22 2.5	20 3.2	16 47.0	3 28.8	18 57.4	16 4.5

MAY 1971

DAY	EPHEM. SID. TIME	☉	☊	☽	☿	♀	♂	♃	♄	♅	♆	♇
	h m s	° ′	° ′	° ′	° ′	° ′	° ′	° ′	° ′	° ′	° ′	° ′
		LONGITUDE										
1	14 33 5.0	9♉59.4	19♒36.3	25♋ .4	23♈23.2	8♈50.9	28♑30.0	4♐16.1	23♉49.2	10♎20.7	2♐17.5	27♍20.3
2	14 37 1.6	10 57.6	19 33.1	7♌24.5	23 R 13.9	10 3.2	29 1.5	4 R 9.8	23 56.8	10 R 18.6	2 R 16.0	27 R 19.2
3	14 40 58.1	11 55.8	19 29.9	19 31.7	23 9.4	11 15.5	29 32.9	4 3.3	24 4.4	10 16.5	2 14.5	27 18.1
4	14 44 54.7	12 54.0	19 26.8	1♍27.2	23 D 9.8	12 27.8	0♒ 4.1	3 56.7	24 12.1	10 14.5	2 13.0	27 17.1
5	14 48 51.2	13 52.2	19 23.6	13 16.5	23 14.9	13 40.2	0 35.1	3 50.0	24 19.8	10 12.5	2 11.5	27 16.1
6	14 52 47.8	14 50.3	19 20.4	25 4.5	23 24.8	14 52.5	1 5.9	3 43.3	24 27.5	10 10.5	2 10.0	27 15.1
7	14 56 44.4	15 48.4	19 17.2	6♎55.4	23 39.3	16 4.9	1 36.5	3 36.4	24 35.2	10 8.5	2 8.5	27 14.2
8	15 0 40.9	16 46.4	19 14.1	18 52.6	23 58.3	17 17.2	2 6.9	3 29.4	24 42.9	10 6.6	2 6.9	27 13.2
9	15 4 37.5	17 44.4	19 10.9	0♏58.9	24 21.7	18 29.6	2 37.2	3 22.4	24 50.6	10 4.7	2 5.4	27 12.3
10	15 8 34.0	18 42.4	19 7.7	13 15.6	24 49.4	19 42.0	3 7.2	3 15.3	24 58.3	10 2.9	2 3.8	27 11.5
11	15 12 30.6	19 40.4	19 4.5	25 43.7	25 21.3	20 54.5	3 37.1	3 8.1	25 6.1	10 1.1	2 2.2	27 10.6
12	15 16 27.1	20 38.3	19 1.4	8♐23.4	25 57.2	22 6.9	4 6.7	3 .9	25 13.8	9 59.3	2 .6	27 9.8
13	15 20 23.7	21 36.2	18 58.2	21 14.5	26 36.9	23 19.3	4 36.1	2 53.5	25 21.6	9 57.6	1 59.1	27 9.0
14	15 24 20.2	22 34.1	18 55.0	4♑16.8	27 20.4	24 31.8	5 5.3	2 46.2	25 29.3	9 55.9	1 57.5	27 8.2
15	15 28 16.8	23 32.0	18 51.8	17 30.6	28 7.5	25 44.3	5 34.2	2 38.8	25 37.1	9 54.2	1 55.9	27 7.5
16	15 32 13.4	24 29.8	18 48.6	0♒56.3	28 58.0	26 56.8	6 2.9	2 31.3	25 44.8	9 52.6	1 54.2	27 6.7
17	15 36 9.9	25 27.6	18 45.5	14 34.7	29 52.0	28 9.3	6 31.4	2 23.8	25 52.6	9 51.1	1 52.6	27 6.0
18	15 40 6.5	26 25.5	18 42.3	28 26.7	0♉49.1	29 21.8	6 59.6	2 16.2	26 .3	9 49.5	1 51.0	27 5.4
19	15 44 3.0	27 23.2	18 39.1	12♓32.8	1 49.4	0♉34.4	7 27.5	2 8.7	26 8.1	9 48.0	1 49.4	27 4.8
20	15 47 59.6	28 21.0	18 35.9	26 52.4	2 52.8	1 47.0	7 55.2	2 1.1	26 15.9	9 46.6	1 47.8	27 4.2
21	15 51 56.1	29 18.8	18 32.8	11♈23.1	3 59.1	2 59.5	8 22.6	1 53.4	26 23.6	9 45.2	1 46.2	27 3.6
22	15 55 52.7	0♊16.5	18 29.6	26 .7	5 8.2	4 12.1	8 49.7	1 45.8	26 31.4	9 43.8	1 44.5	27 3.1
23	15 59 49.3	1 14.2	18 26.4	10♉39.1	6 20.2	5 24.8	9 16.5	1 38.2	26 39.1	9 42.5	1 42.9	27 2.5
24	16 3 45.8	2 11.9	18 23.2	25 11.1	7 34.9	6 37.4	9 43.1	1 30.5	26 46.9	9 41.3	1 41.3	27 2.1
25	16 7 42.4	3 9.6	18 20.1	9♊29.5	8 52.4	7 50.1	10 9.3	1 22.9	26 54.6	9 40.1	1 39.7	27 1.7
26	16 11 38.9	4 7.3	18 16.9	23 28.2	10 12.4	9 2.7	10 35.2	1 15.3	27 2.4	9 38.9	1 38.1	27 1.3
27	16 15 35.5	5 4.9	18 13.7	7♋ 3.5	11 35.0	10 15.4	11 .7	1 7.6	27 10.1	9 37.8	1 36.4	27 .9
28	16 19 32.1	6 2.5	18 10.5	20 14.0	13 .2	11 28.0	11 26.0	1 .0	27 17.8	9 36.8	1 34.8	27 .5
29	16 23 28.6	7 .1	18 7.4	3♌ .6	14 28.0	12 40.7	11 50.8	0 52.4	27 25.5	9 35.7	1 33.2	27 .2
30	16 27 25.2	7 57.7	18 4.2	15 26.4	15 58.2	13 53.4	12 15.4	0 44.9	27 33.2	9 34.8	1 31.6	26 59.9
31	16 31 21.7	8 55.2	18 1.0	27 35.4	17 31.0	15 6.1	12 39.6	0 37.4	27 40.9	9 33.8	1 30.0	26 59.6
		LATITUDE										
1	14 33 5.0	0 .0	0 .0	2N 8.0	1S17.7	1S39.4	1S23.7	1N 1.4	1S54.5	0N43.0	1N43.0	16N25.1
4	14 44 54.7	0 .0	0 .0	1S .8	1 57.5	1 41.3	1 30.5	1 1.3	1 54.3	0 42.9	1 43.1	16 24.1
7	14 56 44.4	0 .0	0 .0	3 41.3	2 29.6	1 42.5	1 37.7	1 1.3	1 54.0	0 42.8	1 43.1	16 23.1
10	15 8 34.0	0 .0	0 .0	4 58.2	2 53.6	1 43.0	1 45.1	1 1.2	1 53.8	0 42.8	1 43.2	16 22.0
13	15 20 23.7	0 .0	0 .0	4 13.0	3 9.7	1 42.8	1 52.8	1 1.0	1 53.6	0 42.7	1 43.2	16 20.8
16	15 32 13.4	0 .0	0 .0	1 30.1	3 18.4	1 41.9	2 .8	1 .8	1 53.4	0 42.6	1 43.2	16 19.7
19	15 44 3.0	0 .0	0 .0	2N 4.8	3 20.2	1 40.4	2 9.2	1 .6	1 53.3	0 42.5	1 43.2	16 18.4
22	15 55 52.7	0 .0	0 .0	4 39.6	3 15.6	1 38.3	2 17.8	1 .3	1 53.2	0 42.4	1 43.2	16 17.2
25	16 7 42.4	0 .0	0 .0	4 39.5	3 5.1	1 35.5	2 26.9	1 .0	1 53.1	0 42.2	1 43.2	16 15.9
28	16 19 32.1	0 .0	0 .0	2 17.2	2 49.3	1 32.2	2 36.2	0 59.7	1 53.0	0 42.1	1 43.2	16 14.6
31	16 31 21.7	0 .0	0 .0	0S56.0	2 28.5	1 28.3	2 45.9	0 59.3	1 52.9	0 42.0	1 43.2	16 13.2
		RIGHT ASCENSION										
1	14 33 5.0	7♉34.8	22♒ 1.3	27♋22.1	22♈ 7.5	8♈46.8	0♒55.3	2♐29.3	21♉56.0	9♎47.4	0♐34.1	4♎16.4
2	14 37 1.6	8 32.0	21 58.2	10♌ 6.7	22 R 4.0	9 53.6	1 29.0	2 R 22.6	22 3.7	9 R 45.4	0 R 32.6	4 R 15.2
3	14 40 58.1	9 29.4	21 55.1	21 57.4	22 D 4.7	11 .4	2 2.5	2 15.8	22 11.4	9 43.5	0 31.1	4 14.1
4	14 44 54.7	10 27.0	21 52.0	3♍ 6.6	22 9.7	12 7.4	2 35.9	2 9.0	22 19.2	9 41.6	0 29.6	4 13.1
5	14 48 51.2	11 24.6	21 48.8	13 48.9	22 18.8	13 14.3	3 8.9	2 2.0	22 27.0	9 39.7	0 28.0	4 12.0
6	14 52 47.8	12 22.4	21 45.7	24 19.6	22 32.0	14 21.3	3 41.8	1 54.9	22 34.7	9 37.9	0 26.4	4 11.0
7	14 56 44.4	13 20.3	21 42.6	4♎53.4	22 49.2	15 28.4	4 14.4	1 47.7	22 42.5	9 36.1	0 24.8	4 9.9
8	15 0 40.9	14 18.4	21 39.5	15 44.9	23 10.3	16 35.6	4 46.9	1 40.5	22 50.3	9 34.3	0 23.2	4 8.9
9	15 4 37.5	15 16.6	21 36.3	27 7.6	23 35.2	17 42.9	5 19.0	1 33.1	22 58.1	9 32.5	0 21.6	4 7.9
10	15 8 34.0	16 14.9	21 33.2	9♏12.5	24 3.8	18 50.3	5 51.0	1 25.7	23 6.0	9 30.8	0 20.0	4 7.0
11	15 12 30.6	17 13.4	21 30.1	22 6.6	24 35.9	19 57.8	6 22.7	1 18.2	23 13.8	9 29.2	0 18.4	4 6.0
12	15 16 27.1	18 12.0	21 26.9	5♐49.1	25 11.5	21 5.4	6 54.2	1 10.6	23 21.7	9 27.5	0 16.7	4 5.1
13	15 20 23.7	19 10.8	21 23.8	20 9.2	25 50.5	22 13.2	7 25.4	1 3.0	23 29.5	9 25.9	0 15.1	4 4.2
14	15 24 20.2	20 9.7	21 20.7	4♑47.4	26 32.7	23 21.1	7 56.4	0 55.3	23 37.4	9 24.3	0 13.4	4 3.4
15	15 28 16.8	21 8.8	21 17.6	19 20.7	27 18.1	24 29.2	8 27.1	0 47.6	23 45.3	9 22.8	0 11.8	4 2.5
16	15 32 13.4	22 8.0	21 14.4	3♒30.5	28 6.5	25 37.4	8 57.5	0 39.8	23 53.1	9 21.3	0 10.1	4 1.7
17	15 36 9.9	23 7.3	21 11.3	17 8.6	28 57.9	26 45.8	9 27.7	0 31.9	24 1.0	9 19.8	0 8.5	4 .9
18	15 40 6.5	24 6.8	21 8.2	0♓17.2	29 52.2	27 54.4	9 57.6	0 24.1	24 8.9	9 18.4	0 6.8	4 .1
19	15 44 3.0	25 6.5	21 5.0	13 6.7	0♉49.4	29 3.1	10 27.2	0 16.2	24 16.8	9 17.0	0 5.1	3 59.4
20	15 47 59.6	26 6.2	21 1.9	25 52.7	1 49.3	0♉12.1	10 56.5	0 8.2	24 24.7	9 15.7	0 3.4	3 58.6
21	15 51 56.1	27 6.2	20 58.8	8♈52.4	2 52.0	1 21.2	11 25.4	0 .3	24 32.6	9 14.4	0 1.7	3 58.0
22	15 55 52.7	28 6.2	20 55.6	22 22.4	3 57.4	2 30.6	11 54.1	29♏52.3	24 40.5	9 13.1	0 .1	3 57.3
23	15 59 49.3	29 6.4	20 52.5	6♉34.7	5 5.4	3 40.1	12 22.5	29 44.4	24 48.4	9 11.9	29♏58.4	3 56.6
24	16 3 45.8	0♊ 6.8	20 49.4	21 31.9	6 16.1	4 49.9	12 50.5	29 36.4	24 56.3	9 10.7	29 56.7	3 56.0
25	16 7 42.4	1 7.3	20 46.2	7♊ 2.2	7 29.5	5 60.0	13 18.3	29 28.5	25 4.3	9 9.7	29 55.1	3 55.5
26	16 11 38.9	2 7.9	20 43.1	22 39.8	8 45.6	7 10.2	13 45.6	29 20.5	25 12.1	9 8.6	29 53.4	3 54.9
27	16 15 35.5	3 8.6	20 40.0	7♋52.8	10 4.2	8 20.6	14 12.7	29 12.6	25 20.0	9 7.5	29 51.7	3 54.4
28	16 19 32.1	4 9.4	20 36.8	22 15.6	11 25.6	9 31.3	14 39.3	29 4.7	25 27.9	9 6.5	29 50.0	3 53.8
29	16 23 28.6	5 10.4	20 33.7	5♌36.4	12 49.7	10 42.3	15 5.6	28 56.8	25 35.8	9 5.6	29 48.3	3 53.4
30	16 27 25.2	6 11.4	20 30.6	17 56.8	14 16.6	11 53.5	15 31.6	28 48.9	25 43.6	9 4.6	29 46.7	3 52.9
31	16 31 21.7	7 12.6	20 27.4	29 27.3	15 46.2	13 4.9	15 57.2	28 41.1	25 51.5	9 3.8	29 45.0	3 52.5
		DECLINATION										
1	14 33 5.0	14N48.9	0S15.6	23N14.0	7N53.0	1N59.2	21S49.9	19S59.9	16N52.9	3S26.3	18S56.4	16N 5.0
4	14 44 54.7	15 42.9	0 15.7	10 .8	7 11.1	3 22.3	21 36.9	19 56.3	16 58.8	3 23.9	18 55.5	16 5.4
7	14 56 44.4	16 34.5	0 15.8	6S 8.1	6 52.1	4 45.0	21 23.6	19 52.6	17 4.6	3 21.6	18 54.6	16 5.6
10	15 8 34.0	17 23.6	0 15.8	20 33.4	6 55.3	6 7.1	21 10.1	19 48.7	17 10.4	3 19.5	18 53.6	16 5.7
13	15 20 23.7	18 10.1	0 15.9	27 21.8	7 19.0	7 28.2	20 56.5	19 44.7	17 16.1	3 17.5	18 52.7	16 5.6
16	15 32 13.4	18 53.9	0 15.9	21 25.2	8 .9	8 48.1	20 42.9	19 40.5	17 21.7	3 15.7	18 51.7	16 5.4
19	15 44 3.0	19 34.9	0 16.0	4 55.8	8 58.6	10 6.4	20 29.5	19 36.3	17 27.3	3 14.0	18 50.7	16 5.1
22	15 55 52.7	20 12.8	0 16.0	14N23.1	10 9.8	11 22.9	20 16.3	19 32.0	17 32.8	3 12.4	18 49.8	16 4.6
25	16 7 42.4	20 47.6	0 16.1	26 29.0	11 32.1	12 37.1	20 3.6	19 27.7	17 38.2	3 11.0	18 48.8	16 4.0
28	16 19 32.1	21 19.2	0 16.1	24 10.9	13 3.3	13 48.9	19 51.4	19 23.4	17 43.6	3 9.8	18 47.8	16 3.3
31	16 31 21.7	21 47.5	0 16.2	11 26.1	14 41.1	14 57.7	19 39.9	19 19.1	17 48.8	3 8.8	18 46.9	16 2.4

JUNE 1971

LONGITUDE

DAY	EPHEM. SID. TIME (h m s)	☉ (° ′)	☊ (° ′)	☽ (° ′)	☿ (° ′)	♀ (° ′)	♂ (° ′)	♃ (° ′)	♄ (° ′)	♅ (° ′)	♆ (° ′)	♇ (° ′)
1	16 35 18.3	9♊52.7	17♒57.8	9♍32.9	19♉ 6.2	16♉18.8	13♒ 3.4	0♐29.9	27♉48.5	9♎33.0	1♐28.4	26♍59.4
2	16 39 14.8	10 50.2	17 54.6	21 23.9	20 43.9	17 31.5	13 26.8	0R22.4	27 56.2	9R32.1	1R26.8	26R59.2
3	16 43 11.4	11 47.7	17 51.5	3♎13.9	22 24.1	18 44.3	13 49.9	0 15.1	28 3.8	9 31.3	1 25.2	26 59.1
4	16 47 8.0	12 45.1	17 48.3	15 7.8	24 6.8	19 57.0	14 12.6	0 7.7	28 11.4	9 30.6	1 23.6	26 58.9
5	16 51 4.5	13 42.6	17 45.1	27 9.7	25 51.9	21 9.8	14 34.9	0 .5	28 19.0	9 29.9	1 22.0	26 58.8
6	16 55 1.1	14 40.0	17 41.9	9♏23.0	27 39.4	22 22.5	14 56.8	29♏53.2	28 26.5	9 29.3	1 20.4	26 58.8
7	16 58 57.6	15 37.4	17 38.8	21 50.2	29 29.3	23 35.3	15 18.2	29 46.1	28 34.1	9 28.7	1 18.9	26 58.7
8	17 2 54.2	16 34.8	17 35.6	4♐32.4	1♊21.7	24 48.1	15 39.3	29 39.0	28 41.6	9 28.2	1 17.3	26 58.7
9	17 6 50.7	17 32.1	17 32.4	17 29.6	3 16.3	26 .9	15 59.9	29 32.1	28 49.1	9 27.8	1 15.8	26D58.8
10	17 10 47.3	18 29.5	17 29.2	0♑41.2	5 13.2	27 13.7	16 20.1	29 25.2	28 56.6	9 27.3	1 14.2	26 58.8
11	17 14 43.9	19 26.8	17 26.1	14 5.6	7 12.4	28 26.6	16 39.8	29 18.3	29 4.1	9 27.0	1 12.7	26 58.9
12	17 18 40.4	20 24.1	17 22.9	27 41.2	9 13.6	29 39.4	16 59.0	29 11.6	29 11.5	9 26.6	1 11.2	26 59.0
13	17 22 37.0	21 21.5	17 19.7	11♒26.2	11 16.8	0♊52.3	17 17.8	29 5.0	29 18.9	9 26.4	1 9.7	26 59.2
14	17 26 33.5	22 18.8	17 16.5	25 19.4	13 21.8	2 5.2	17 36.0	28 58.5	29 26.3	9 26.2	1 8.2	26 59.4
15	17 30 30.1	23 16.1	17 13.4	9♓19.9	15 28.6	3 18.2	17 53.8	28 52.1	29 33.7	9 26.1	1 6.7	26 59.7
16	17 34 26.7	24 13.4	17 10.2	23 26.5	17 36.7	4 31.1	18 11.1	28 45.8	29 41.0	9 26.0	1 5.3	26 59.9
17	17 38 23.2	25 10.7	17 7.0	7♈38.1	19 46.1	5 44.1	18 27.7	28 39.6	29 48.3	9 25.9	1 3.8	27 .2
18	17 42 19.8	26 8.0	17 3.8	21 53.1	21 56.5	6 57.0	18 43.9	28 33.5	29 55.5	9 25.9	1 2.4	27 .5
19	17 46 16.3	27 5.3	17 .6	6♉ 8.6	24 7.6	8 10.0	18 59.5	28 27.5	0♊ 2.8	9D26.0	1 1.0	27 .9
20	17 50 12.9	28 2.6	16 57.5	20 21.2	26 19.2	9 23.0	19 14.4	28 21.6	0 10.0	9 26.1	0 59.5	27 1.3
21	17 54 9.5	28 59.8	16 54.3	4♊26.4	28 30.9	10 36.0	19 28.8	28 15.9	0 17.1	9 26.2	0 58.1	27 1.7
22	17 58 6.0	29 57.1	16 51.1	18 19.9	0♋42.5	11 49.1	19 42.6	28 10.3	0 24.2	9 26.4	0 56.8	27 2.1
23	18 2 2.6	0♋54.4	16 47.9	1♋57.8	2 53.8	13 2.1	19 55.8	28 4.9	0 31.3	9 26.7	0 55.4	27 2.6
24	18 5 59.1	1 51.6	16 44.8	15 17.3	5 4.4	14 15.2	20 8.4	27 59.6	0 38.4	9 27.0	0 54.1	27 3.1
25	18 9 55.7	2 48.9	16 41.6	28 17.1	7 14.2	15 28.3	20 20.3	27 54.4	0 45.4	9 27.4	0 52.7	27 3.7
26	18 13 52.2	3 46.1	16 38.4	10♌57.6	9 22.8	16 41.4	20 31.6	27 49.4	0 52.3	9 27.8	0 51.4	27 4.3
27	18 17 48.8	4 43.4	16 35.2	23 20.5	11 30.2	17 54.5	20 42.2	27 44.5	0 59.3	9 28.3	0 50.2	27 4.9
28	18 21 45.4	5 40.6	16 32.1	5♍28.9	13 36.2	19 7.7	20 52.1	27 39.8	1 6.1	9 28.8	0 48.9	27 5.5
29	18 25 41.9	6 37.8	16 28.9	17 26.9	15 40.6	20 20.8	21 1.4	27 35.2	1 13.0	9 29.4	0 47.6	27 6.2
30	18 29 38.5	7 35.0	16 25.7	29 19.0	17 43.3	21 34.0	21 10.0	27 30.8	1 19.8	9 30.0	0 46.4	27 6.9

LATITUDE

DAY	EPHEM. SID. TIME	☉	☊	☽	☿	♀	♂	♃	♄	♅	♆	♇
1	16 35 18.3	0 .0	0 .0	1S57.0	2S20.6	1S26.9	2S49.3	0N59.2	1S52.9	0N42.0	1N43.2	16N12.7
4	16 47 8.0	0 .0	0 .0	4 18.8	1 54.3	1 22.3	2 59.4	0 58.8	1 52.9	0 41.9	1 43.1	16 11.4
7	16 58 57.6	0 .0	0 .0	5 2.4	1 24.6	1 17.3	3 10.0	0 58.3	1 52.9	0 41.7	1 43.1	16 10.0
10	17 10 47.3	0 .0	0 .0	3 37.0	0 52.5	1 11.8	3 20.8	0 57.8	1 52.9	0 41.6	1 43.0	16 8.6
13	17 22 37.0	0 .0	0 .0	0 23.4	0 19.4	1 5.9	3 32.1	0 57.3	1 53.0	0 41.5	1 42.9	16 7.2
16	17 34 26.7	0 .0	0 .0	3N 8.1	0N13.3	0 59.7	3 43.6	0 56.8	1 53.1	0 41.4	1 42.9	16 5.7
19	17 46 16.3	0 .0	0 .0	5 3.2	0 43.6	0 53.2	3 55.5	0 56.2	1 53.2	0 41.2	1 42.8	16 4.3
22	17 58 6.0	0 .0	0 .0	4 18.5	1 9.8	0 46.4	4 7.7	0 55.6	1 53.3	0 41.1	1 42.7	16 2.9
25	18 9 55.7	0 .0	0 .0	1 29.8	1 30.4	0 39.4	4 20.1	0 55.0	1 53.4	0 41.0	1 42.6	16 1.5
28	18 21 45.4	0 .0	0 .0	1S48.6	1 44.7	0 32.2	4 32.8	0 54.3	1 53.6	0 40.9	1 42.5	16 .1

RIGHT ASCENSION

DAY	EPHEM. SID. TIME	☉	☊	☽	☿	♀	♂	♃	♄	♅	♆	♇
1	16 35 18.3	8♊13.9	20♒24.3	10♍22.4	17♉18.7	14♉16.6	16♒22.4	28♏33.3	25♉59.3	9♎ 3.0	29♏43.3	3♎52.1
2	16 39 14.8	9 15.2	20 21.2	20 58.0	18 54.1	15 28.6	16 47.2	28R25.5	26 7.1	9R 2.2	29R41.7	3R51.7
3	16 43 11.4	10 16.7	20 18.0	1♎30.2	20 32.4	16 40.8	17 11.6	28 17.9	26 14.9	9 1.4	29 40.0	3 51.3
4	16 47 8.0	11 18.3	20 14.9	12 14.5	22 13.8	17 53.3	17 35.7	28 10.2	26 22.7	9 .8	29 38.4	3 51.0
5	16 51 4.5	12 19.9	20 11.8	23 25.9	23 58.2	19 6.0	17 59.3	28 2.7	26 30.5	9 .1	29 36.7	3 50.7
6	16 55 1.1	13 21.6	20 8.6	5♏17.7	25 45.7	20 19.0	18 22.5	27 55.2	26 38.2	8 59.5	29 35.1	3 50.5
7	16 58 57.6	14 23.4	20 5.5	17 60.0	27 36.4	21 32.3	18 45.3	27 47.8	26 46.0	8 59.0	29 33.5	3 50.2
8	17 2 54.2	15 25.3	20 2.3	1♐35.6	29 30.2	22 45.9	19 7.7	27 40.4	26 53.7	8 58.5	29 31.9	3 50.0
9	17 6 50.7	16 27.2	19 59.2	15 57.2	1♊27.2	23 59.8	19 29.6	27 33.2	27 1.4	8 58.0	29 30.3	3 49.9
10	17 10 47.3	17 29.2	19 56.0	0♑46.2	3 27.4	25 13.9	19 51.1	27 26.0	27 9.1	8 57.6	29 28.7	3 49.7
11	17 14 43.9	18 31.3	19 52.9	15 37.0	5 30.7	26 28.3	20 12.2	27 18.9	27 16.8	8 57.3	29 27.1	3 49.6
12	17 18 40.4	19 33.4	19 49.8	0♒ 6.4	7 37.1	27 43.0	20 32.7	27 11.9	27 24.4	8 57.0	29 25.5	3 49.5
13	17 22 37.0	20 35.6	19 46.6	14 .6	9 46.5	28 58.0	20 52.8	27 5.0	27 32.0	8 56.7	29 23.9	3 49.5
14	17 26 33.5	21 37.8	19 43.5	27 18.3	11 58.7	0♊13.3	21 12.4	26 58.3	27 39.6	8 56.5	29 22.4	3 49.4
15	17 30 30.1	22 40.2	19 40.3	10♓ 8.0	14 13.6	1 28.8	21 31.5	26 51.6	27 47.2	8 56.4	29 20.9	3D49.5
16	17 34 26.7	23 42.5	19 37.2	22 44.3	16 30.8	2 44.6	21 50.0	26 45.1	27 54.7	8 56.3	29 19.4	3 49.5
17	17 38 23.2	24 44.8	19 34.0	5♈24.5	18 50.2	4 .7	22 8.0	26 38.6	28 2.2	8 56.2	29 17.9	3 49.6
18	17 42 19.8	25 47.2	19 30.9	18 26.2	21 11.4	5 17.0	22 25.5	26 32.3	28 9.7	8 56.2	29 16.4	3 49.7
19	17 46 16.3	26 49.6	19 27.8	2♉ 4.1	23 34.0	6 33.6	22 42.4	26 26.1	28 17.2	8 56.2	29 14.9	3 49.8
20	17 50 12.9	27 52.0	19 24.6	16 26.2	25 57.7	7 50.5	22 58.8	26 20.0	28 24.6	8D56.3	29 13.4	3 49.9
21	17 54 9.5	28 54.4	19 21.5	1♊28.7	28 22.1	9 7.5	23 14.5	26 14.1	28 31.9	8 56.4	29 12.0	3 50.1
22	17 58 6.0	29 56.9	19 18.3	16 53.5	0♋46.8	10 24.9	23 29.7	26 8.3	28 39.3	8 56.6	29 10.6	3 50.3
23	18 2 2.6	0♋59.3	19 15.2	2♋11.9	3 11.3	11 42.4	23 44.2	26 2.6	28 46.6	8 56.8	29 9.2	3 50.6
24	18 5 59.1	2 1.7	19 12.0	16 54.8	5 35.2	13 .2	23 58.1	25 57.1	28 53.9	8 57.1	29 7.8	3 50.8
25	18 9 55.7	3 4.1	19 8.9	0♌43.1	7 58.2	14 18.2	24 11.5	25 51.7	29 1.1	8 57.4	29 6.4	3 51.1
26	18 13 52.2	4 6.4	19 5.7	13 31.3	10 19.9	15 36.4	24 24.1	25 46.5	29 8.3	8 57.8	29 5.0	3 51.5
27	18 17 48.8	5 8.7	19 2.6	25 25.3	12 40.0	16 54.8	24 36.1	25 41.4	29 15.5	8 58.2	29 3.7	3 51.8
28	18 21 45.4	6 11.0	18 59.4	6♍37.3	14 58.2	18 13.4	24 47.5	25 36.5	29 22.6	8 58.7	29 2.4	3 52.2
29	18 25 41.9	7 13.2	18 56.3	17 22.2	17 14.3	19 32.1	24 58.2	25 31.8	29 29.6	8 59.2	29 1.1	3 52.6
30	18 29 38.5	8 15.4	18 53.1	27 55.8	19 28.0	20 51.1	25 8.3	25 27.2	29 36.7	8 59.8	28 59.8	3 53.1

DECLINATION

DAY	EPHEM. SID. TIME	☉	☊	☽	☿	♀	♂	♃	♄	♅	♆	♇
1	16 35 18.3	21N56.2	0S16.2	6N11.0	15N14.8	15N20.0	19S36.2	19S17.7	17N50.5	3S 8.5	18S46.6	16N 2.0
4	16 47 8.0	22 19.9	0 16.2	9S56.2	16 57.5	16 24.6	19 25.8	19 13.5	17 55.6	3 7.7	18 45.7	16 1.0
7	16 58 57.6	22 40.1	0 16.3	23 5.5	18 40.1	17 25.6	19 16.4	19 9.4	18 .6	3 7.0	18 44.8	15 59.8
10	17 10 47.3	22 56.8	0 16.3	27 3.6	20 18.9	18 22.8	19 8.1	19 5.4	18 5.4	3 6.6	18 43.9	15 58.5
13	17 22 37.0	23 9.8	0 16.4	17 43.7	21 49.0	19 15.7	19 1.1	19 1.5	18 10.1	3 6.3	18 43.0	15 57.0
16	17 34 26.7	23 19.1	0 16.4	0N16.5	23 5.3	20 4.2	18 55.6	18 57.9	18 14.8	3 6.3	18 42.2	15 55.5
19	17 46 16.3	23 24.8	0 16.5	18 20.0	24 2.4	20 47.9	18 51.6	18 54.5	18 19.3	3 6.4	18 41.4	15 53.8
22	17 58 6.0	23 26.7	0 16.5	27 13.4	24 36.4	21 26.6	18 49.4	18 51.3	18 23.6	3 6.7	18 40.7	15 52.0
25	18 9 55.7	23 24.9	0 16.6	21 58.5	24 45.1	22 .0	18 49.1	18 48.3	18 27.8	3 7.2	18 39.9	15 50.1
28	18 21 45.4	23 19.4	0 16.6	7 49.1	24 29.1	22 27.9	18 50.7	18 45.7	18 31.9	3 7.9	18 39.3	15 48.1

JULY 1971

DAY	EPHEM. SID. TIME	☉	☊	☽	☿	♀	♂	♃	♄	♅	♆	♇
	h m s	° ′	° ′	° ′	° ′	° ′	° ′	° ′	° ′	° ′	° ′	° ′
		LONGITUDE										
1	18 33 35.0	8♋32.2	16♒22.5	11≏10.3	19♋44.2	22♊47.2	21♒17.9	27♏26.5	1♊26.5	9≏30.7	0♐45.2	27♍ 7.6
2	18 37 31.6	9 29.4	16 19.4	23 5.7	21 43.2	24 .4	21 25.1	27R22.4	1 33.2	9 31.5	0R44.0	27 8.4
3	18 41 28.2	10 26.6	16 16.2	5♏ 9.8	23 40.4	25 13.6	21 31.6	27 18.5	1 39.9	9 32.3	0 42.9	27 9.2
4	18 45 24.7	11 23.8	16 13.0	17 26.9	25 35.6	26 26.8	21 37.4	27 14.7	1 46.5	9 33.1	0 41.7	27 10.0
5	18 49 21.3	12 21.0	16 9.8	0♐ .3	27 28.8	27 40.1	21 42.5	27 11.1	1 53.0	9 34.0	0 40.6	27 10.9
6	18 53 17.8	13 18.2	16 6.6	12 52.3	29 20.0	28 53.4	21 46.9	27 7.7	1 59.6	9 35.0	0 39.6	27 11.8
7	18 57 14.4	14 15.4	16 3.5	26 3.5	1♌ 9.2	0♋ 6.7	21 50.5	27 4.4	2 6.0	9 36.0	0 38.5	27 12.7
8	19 1 10.9	15 12.6	16 .3	9♑33.5	2 56.4	1 20.0	21 53.3	27 1.3	2 12.4	9 37.1	0 37.4	27 13.7
9	19 5 7.5	16 9.7	15 57.1	23 20.4	4 41.6	2 33.3	21 55.4	26 58.4	2 18.8	9 38.2	0 36.4	27 14.7
10	19 9 4.1	17 6.9	15 53.9	7♒21.1	6 24.7	3 46.6	21 56.8	26 55.7	2 25.0	9 39.3	0 35.4	27 15.7
11	19 13 .6	18 4.1	15 50.8	21 31.8	8 5.8	5 .0	21 57.4	26 53.1	2 31.3	9 40.5	0 34.4	27 16.7
12	19 16 57.2	19 1.3	15 47.6	5♓48.7	9 44.9	6 13.4	21R57.2	26 50.7	2 37.5	9 41.8	0 33.5	27 17.8
13	19 20 53.7	19 58.5	15 44.4	20 7.9	11 22.0	7 26.8	21 56.3	26 48.4	2 43.6	9 43.1	0 32.6	27 18.9
14	19 24 50.3	20 55.7	15 41.2	4♈26.3	12 57.1	8 40.3	21 54.5	26 46.4	2 49.6	9 44.4	0 31.7	27 20.0
15	19 28 46.9	21 52.9	15 38.1	18 41.0	14 30.1	9 53.7	21 52.0	26 44.5	2 55.7	9 45.8	0 30.8	27 21.2
16	19 32 43.4	22 50.1	15 34.9	2♉49.8	16 1.1	11 7.2	21 48.7	26 42.8	3 1.6	9 47.3	0 30.0	27 22.3
17	19 36 40.0	23 47.4	15 31.7	16 50.6	17 30.0	12 20.7	21 44.7	26 41.3	3 7.5	9 48.8	0 29.1	27 23.5
18	19 40 36.5	24 44.6	15 28.5	0♊41.7	18 56.9	13 34.3	21 39.9	26 40.0	3 13.3	9 50.3	0 28.3	27 24.8
19	19 44 33.1	25 41.9	15 25.4	14 21.5	20 21.6	14 47.8	21 34.3	26 38.8	3 19.1	9 51.9	0 27.6	27 26.0
20	19 48 29.6	26 39.1	15 22.2	27 48.4	21 44.3	16 1.4	21 28.0	26 37.9	3 24.7	9 53.6	0 26.8	27 27.3
21	19 52 26.2	27 36.4	15 19.0	11♋ 1.3	23 4.7	17 15.0	21 20.9	26 37.1	3 30.4	9 55.3	0 26.1	27 28.7
22	19 56 22.8	28 33.7	15 15.8	23 59.3	24 23.0	18 28.6	21 13.1	26 36.5	3 35.9	9 57.0	0 25.5	27 30.0
23	20 0 19.3	29 31.0	15 12.6	6♌42.3	25 39.0	19 42.3	21 4.6	26 36.0	3 41.4	9 58.8	0 24.8	27 31.4
24	20 4 15.9	0♌28.3	15 9.5	19 10.8	26 52.7	20 56.0	20 55.5	26 35.8	3 46.8	10 .7	0 24.2	27 32.8
25	20 8 12.4	1 25.6	15 6.3	1♍26.2	28 4.0	22 9.6	20 45.6	26 35.8	3 52.2	10 2.5	0 23.6	27 34.2
26	20 12 9.0	2 23.0	15 3.1	13 30.5	29 12.9	23 23.4	20 35.2	26D35.9	3 57.5	10 4.5	0 23.0	27 35.6
27	20 16 5.5	3 20.3	14 59.9	25 26.8	0♍19.2	24 37.1	20 24.2	26 36.3	4 2.7	10 6.5	0 22.6	27 37.2
28	20 20 2.1	4 17.7	14 56.8	7≏18.4	1 22.9	25 50.9	20 12.6	26 36.8	4 7.8	10 8.5	0 22.0	27 38.7
29	20 23 58.7	5 15.0	14 53.6	19 9.5	2 23.9	27 4.6	20 .4	26 37.4	4 12.9	10 10.6	0 21.6	27 40.2
30	20 27 55.2	6 12.4	14 50.4	1♏ 4.5	3 22.1	28 18.4	19 47.7	26 38.3	4 17.9	10 12.7	0 21.1	27 41.7
31	20 31 51.8	7 9.8	14 47.2	13 8.1	4 17.3	29 32.2	19 34.5	26 39.4	4 22.8	10 14.8	0 20.7	27 43.3
		LATITUDE										
1	18 33 35.0	0 .0	0 .0	4S18.7	1N52.2	0S24.8	4S45.6	0N53.6	1S53.7	0N40.7	1N42.4	15N58.8
4	18 45 24.7	0 .0	0 .0	5 11.4	1 53.2	0 17.4	4 58.4	0 53.0	1 53.9	0 40.6	1 42.2	15 57.4
7	18 57 14.4	0 .0	0 .0	3 55.0	1 48.1	0 10.0	5 11.2	0 52.3	1 54.2	0 40.5	1 42.1	15 56.1
10	19 9 4.1	0 .0	0 .0	0 40.0	1 37.5	0 2.5	5 23.9	0 51.6	1 54.4	0 40.4	1 42.0	15 54.8
13	19 20 53.7	0 .0	0 .0	3N 2.7	1 21.9	0N 4.9	5 36.4	0 50.9	1 54.7	0 40.2	1 41.8	15 53.5
16	19 32 43.4	0 .0	0 .0	5 8.0	1 1.9	0 12.2	5 48.4	0 50.2	1 54.9	0 40.1	1 41.7	15 52.2
19	19 44 33.1	0 .0	0 .0	4 33.6	0 38.0	0 19.3	5 60.0	0 49.5	1 55.2	0 40.0	1 41.5	15 51.0
22	19 56 22.8	0 .0	0 .0	1 50.9	0 10.6	0 26.3	6 10.7	0 48.7	1 55.6	0 39.9	1 41.4	15 49.8
25	20 8 12.4	0 .0	0 .0	1S32.3	0S19.7	0 33.1	6 20.6	0 48.0	1 55.9	0 39.8	1 41.2	15 48.7
28	20 20 2.1	0 .0	0 .0	4 12.4	0 52.5	0 39.5	6 29.3	0 47.3	1 56.2	0 39.7	1 41.1	15 47.6
31	20 31 51.8	0 .0	0 .0	5 16.8	1 27.2	0 45.7	6 36.8	0 46.6	1 56.6	0 39.5	1 40.9	15 46.6
		RIGHT ASCENSION										
1	18 33 35.0	9♋17.5	18♒50.0	8≏33.9	21♋39.2	22♊10.1	25♒17.6	25♏22.7	29♉43.7	9≏ .4	28♏58.6	3≏53.5
2	18 37 31.6	10 19.6	18 46.8	19 32.0	23 47.8	23 29.4	25 26.3	25R18.5	29 50.6	9 1.1	28R57.3	3 54.0
3	18 41 28.2	11 21.6	18 43.7	1♏ 4.7	25 53.7	24 48.7	25 34.2	25 14.4	29 57.5	9 1.8	28 56.1	3 54.6
4	18 45 24.7	12 23.5	18 40.5	13 24.6	27 56.7	26 8.2	25 41.5	25 10.4	0♊ 4.3	9 2.6	28 54.9	3 55.1
5	18 49 21.3	13 25.3	18 37.4	26 39.1	29 56.8	27 27.8	25 48.0	25 6.7	0 11.1	9 3.4	28 53.8	3 55.7
6	18 53 17.8	14 27.1	18 34.2	10♐46.8	1♌54.1	28 47.5	25 53.9	25 3.1	0 17.9	9 4.3	28 52.7	3 56.4
7	18 57 14.4	15 28.8	18 31.1	25 34.4	3 48.4	0♋ 7.2	25 59.0	24 59.7	0 24.6	9 5.2	28 51.6	3 57.0
8	19 1 10.9	16 30.4	18 27.9	10♑38.5	5 39.8	1 27.1	26 3.3	24 56.5	0 31.2	9 6.1	28 50.5	3 57.7
9	19 5 7.5	17 31.9	18 24.7	25 32.4	7 28.2	2 47.0	26 6.9	24 53.4	0 37.8	9 7.1	28 49.4	3 58.4
10	19 9 4.1	18 33.2	18 21.6	9♒56.1	9 13.8	4 6.9	26 9.7	24 50.5	0 44.3	9 8.2	28 48.4	3 59.1
11	19 13 .6	19 34.5	18 18.4	23 42.0	10 56.5	5 26.9	26 11.7	24 47.8	0 50.8	9 9.3	28 47.4	3 59.9
12	19 16 57.2	20 35.7	18 15.3	6♓54.0	12 36.3	6 46.8	26 13.0	24 45.3	0 57.2	9 10.4	28 46.4	4 .7
13	19 20 53.7	21 36.7	18 12.1	19 44.4	14 13.4	8 6.8	26 13.5	24 42.9	1 3.6	9 11.6	28 45.4	4 1.5
14	19 24 50.3	22 37.7	18 9.0	2♈28.6	15 47.7	9 26.8	26R13.2	24 40.8	1 9.9	9 12.8	28 44.5	4 2.3
15	19 28 46.9	23 38.5	18 5.8	15 24.5	17 19.2	10 46.7	26 12.2	24 38.8	1 16.1	9 14.1	28 43.6	4 3.2
16	19 32 43.4	24 39.3	18 2.6	28 47.0	18 48.0	12 6.7	26 10.3	24 37.0	1 22.3	9 15.4	28 42.7	4 4.1
17	19 36 40.0	25 39.9	17 59.5	12♉46.3	20 14.1	13 26.5	26 7.6	24 35.4	1 28.4	9 16.8	28 41.8	4 5.0
18	19 40 36.5	26 40.3	17 56.3	27 23.2	21 37.5	14 46.3	26 4.2	24 33.9	1 34.5	9 18.2	28 41.0	4 6.0
19	19 44 33.1	27 40.7	17 53.2	12♊26.0	22 58.3	16 6.1	25 59.9	24 32.7	1 40.5	9 19.7	28 40.2	4 7.0
20	19 48 29.6	28 40.9	17 50.0	27 32.3	24 16.4	17 25.7	25 54.9	24 31.6	1 46.4	9 21.2	28 39.4	4 8.0
21	19 52 26.2	29 41.0	17 46.8	12♋15.1	25 31.9	18 45.2	25 49.1	24 30.8	1 52.3	9 22.7	28 38.7	4 9.0
22	19 56 22.8	0♌40.9	17 43.7	26 13.4	26 44.8	20 4.7	25 42.6	24 30.1	1 58.1	9 24.3	28 38.0	4 10.0
23	20 0 19.3	1 40.7	17 40.5	9♌17.3	27 55.0	21 23.9	25 35.3	24 29.6	2 3.8	9 25.9	28 37.3	4 11.1
24	20 4 15.9	2 40.4	17 37.4	21 28.0	29 2.5	22 43.1	25 27.3	24 29.3	2 9.4	9 27.6	28 36.6	4 12.2
25	20 8 12.4	3 39.9	17 34.2	2♍54.3	0♍ 7.4	24 2.1	25 18.6	24 29.2	2 15.0	9 29.3	28 36.0	4 13.4
26	20 12 9.0	4 39.3	17 31.0	13 49.1	1 9.5	25 20.9	25 9.2	24D29.3	2 20.5	9 31.1	28 35.4	4 14.5
27	20 16 5.5	5 38.5	17 27.9	24 26.8	2 9.0	26 39.6	24 59.1	24 29.6	2 26.0	9 32.9	28 34.9	4 15.8
28	20 20 2.1	6 37.6	17 24.7	5≏ 2.2	3 5.5	27 58.1	24 48.4	24 30.1	2 31.3	9 34.8	28 34.4	4 17.0
29	20 23 58.7	7 36.5	17 21.5	15 49.9	3 59.3	29 16.3	24 37.1	24 30.7	2 36.6	9 36.7	28 33.9	4 18.2
30	20 27 55.2	8 35.3	17 18.4	27 4.4	4 50.1	0♌34.4	24 25.2	24 31.5	2 41.8	9 38.6	28 33.4	4 19.5
31	20 31 51.8	9 33.9	17 15.2	8♏58.7	5 37.9	1 52.3	24 12.7	24 32.5	2 46.9	9 40.6	28 33.0	4 20.7
		DECLINATION										
1	18 33 35.0	23N10.2	0S16.7	8S23.2	23N50.6	22N50.1	18S54.4	18S43.3	18N35.8	3S 8.7	18S38.6	15N46.0
4	18 45 24.7	22 57.3	0 16.7	22 1.0	22 52.9	23 6.4	19 .2	18 41.3	18 39.6	3 9.8	18 38.0	15 43.9
7	18 57 14.4	22 40.9	0 16.8	27 18.0	21 39.9	23 16.7	19 8.0	18 39.6	18 43.3	3 11.0	18 37.5	15 41.6
10	19 9 4.1	22 20.9	0 16.8	19 4.9	20 14.9	23 20.9	19 17.8	18 38.3	18 46.8	3 12.5	18 37.0	15 39.2
13	19 20 53.7	21 57.5	0 16.9	1 6.5	18 41.1	23 19.0	19 29.8	18 37.3	18 50.1	3 14.0	18 36.5	15 36.8
16	19 32 43.4	21 30.7	0 16.9	17N16.4	17 1.4	23 10.9	19 43.6	18 36.7	18 53.3	3 15.8	18 36.1	15 34.3
19	19 44 33.1	21 .5	0 17.0	27 3.3	15 18.2	22 56.6	19 59.3	18 36.5	18 56.3	3 17.7	18 35.8	15 31.7
22	19 56 22.8	20 27.2	0 17.0	23 8.1	13 33.8	22 36.3	20 16.4	18 36.7	18 59.1	3 19.9	18 35.5	15 29.0
25	20 8 12.4	19 50.8	0 17.1	9 31.6	11 50.4	22 9.9	20 34.7	18 37.2	19 1.8	3 22.1	18 35.3	15 26.3
28	20 20 2.1	19 11.4	0 17.1	6S45.8	10 10.1	21 37.7	20 53.8	18 38.1	19 4.4	3 24.6	18 35.1	15 23.6
31	20 31 51.8	18 29.1	0 17.2	20 48.7	8 35.2	20 59.8	21 13.1	18 39.4	19 6.8	3 27.2	18 35.0	15 20.8

AUGUST 1971

DAY	EPHEM. SID. TIME	☉	☊	☽	☿	♀	♂	♃	♄	♅	♆	♇
		LONGITUDE										
	h m s	° ′	° ′	° ′	° ′	° ′	° ′	° ′	° ′	° ′	° ′	° ′
1	20 35 48.3	8♌ 7.1	14♒44.1	25♏24.7	5♍ 9.4	0♌46.1	19♒20.9	26♏40.6	4♊27.6	10♎17.0	0♐20.3	27♍44.9
2	20 39 44.9	9 4.5	14 40.9	7♐58.5	5 58.3	1 59.9	19 R 6.9	26 42.0	4 32.3	10 19.3	0 R 20.0	27 46.5
3	20 43 41.4	10 1.9	14 37.7	20 53.0	6 43.8	3 13.8	18 52.5	26 43.6	4 37.0	10 21.6	0 19.7	27 48.1
4	20 47 38.0	10 59.3	14 34.5	4♑10.2	7 25.8	4 27.7	18 37.8	26 45.4	4 41.6	10 23.9	0 19.4	27 49.8
5	20 51 34.6	11 56.7	14 31.3	17 51.0	8 4.0	5 41.6	18 22.8	26 47.3	4 46.1	10 26.3	0 19.1	27 51.5
6	20 55 31.1	12 54.2	14 28.2	1♒54.0	8 38.3	6 55.5	18 7.5	26 49.4	4 50.5	10 28.7	0 18.9	27 53.2
7	20 59 27.7	13 51.6	14 25.0	16 16.1	9 8.6	8 9.4	17 52.1	26 51.7	4 54.9	10 31.1	0 18.7	27 54.9
8	21 3 24.2	14 49.1	14 21.8	0♓52.0	9 34.6	9 23.4	17 36.4	26 54.2	4 59.1	10 33.6	0 18.6	27 56.7
9	21 7 20.8	15 46.6	14 18.6	15 35.6	9 56.1	10 37.4	17 20.7	26 56.9	5 3.3	10 36.1	0 18.4	27 58.4
10	21 11 17.3	16 44.1	14 15.5	0♈20.0	10 12.8	11 51.4	17 4.8	26 59.7	5 7.4	10 38.7	0 18.3	28 .2
11	21 15 13.9	17 41.6	14 12.3	14 58.7	10 24.7	13 5.4	16 48.9	27 2.7	5 11.4	10 41.3	0 18.3	28 2.0
12	21 19 10.4	18 39.2	14 9.1	29 26.5	10 31.6	14 19.5	16 33.0	27 5.8	5 15.3	10 43.9	0 18.2	28 3.9
13	21 23 7.0	19 36.7	14 5.9	13♉39.6	10 33.2	15 33.6	16 17.1	27 9.2	5 19.1	10 46.6	0 18.2	28 5.7
14	21 27 3.6	20 34.3	14 2.8	27 35.9	10 R 29.3	16 47.7	16 1.3	27 12.7	5 22.9	10 49.3	0 D 18.3	28 7.6
15	21 31 .1	21 32.0	13 59.6	11♊14.6	10 20.0	18 1.8	15 45.7	27 16.4	5 26.5	10 52.1	0 18.3	28 9.4
16	21 34 56.7	22 29.6	13 56.4	24 36.2	10 5.2	19 15.9	15 30.2	27 20.2	5 30.1	10 54.9	0 18.4	28 11.3
17	21 38 53.2	23 27.3	13 53.2	7♋41.5	9 44.8	20 30.1	15 15.0	27 24.3	5 33.6	10 57.7	0 18.6	28 13.3
18	21 42 49.8	24 25.0	13 50.0	20 32.0	9 18.8	21 44.3	15 .1	27 28.5	5 37.0	11 .6	0 18.8	28 15.3
19	21 46 46.3	25 22.8	13 46.9	3♌ 9.1	8 47.5	22 58.5	14 45.4	27 32.8	5 40.3	11 3.5	0 19.0	28 17.2
20	21 50 42.9	26 20.5	13 43.7	15 34.2	8 11.2	24 12.8	14 31.2	27 37.3	5 43.4	11 6.4	0 19.2	28 19.2
21	21 54 39.4	27 18.3	13 40.5	27 48.7	7 30.1	25 27.0	14 17.3	27 42.0	5 46.5	11 9.4	0 19.4	28 21.2
22	21 58 36.0	28 16.1	13 37.3	9♍54.3	6 44.9	26 41.3	14 3.9	27 46.8	5 49.5	11 12.4	0 19.7	28 23.2
23	22 2 32.6	29 13.9	13 34.2	21 52.7	5 56.2	27 55.6	13 51.0	27 51.8	5 52.4	11 15.4	0 20.1	28 25.2
24	22 6 29.1	0♍11.7	13 31.0	3♎45.8	5 4.7	29 9.9	13 38.6	27 57.0	5 55.2	11 18.4	0 20.4	28 27.2
25	22 10 25.7	1 9.6	13 27.8	15 36.3	4 11.4	0♍24.2	13 26.8	28 2.3	5 57.9	11 21.5	0 20.8	28 29.3
26	22 14 22.2	2 7.5	13 24.6	27 26.9	3 17.1	1 38.5	13 15.6	28 7.7	6 .5	11 24.7	0 21.2	28 31.3
27	22 18 18.8	3 5.4	13 21.4	9♏21.2	2 23.1	2 52.8	13 5.0	28 13.4	6 3.0	11 27.8	0 21.7	28 33.4
28	22 22 15.3	4 3.3	13 18.3	21 23.1	1 30.4	4 7.2	12 55.1	28 19.1	6 5.4	11 31.0	0 22.2	28 35.5
29	22 26 11.9	5 1.3	13 15.1	3♐36.9	0 40.2	5 21.6	12 45.9	28 25.1	6 7.7	11 34.2	0 22.7	28 37.6
30	22 30 8.4	5 59.2	13 11.9	16 7.0	29♌53.6	6 35.9	12 37.3	28 31.1	6 9.9	11 37.4	0 23.2	28 39.7
31	22 34 5.0	6 57.2	13 8.7	28 57.5	29 11.7	7 50.3	12 29.5	28 37.4	6 12.0	11 40.7	0 23.8	28 41.8
		LATITUDE										
1	20 35 48.3	0 .0	0 .0	5S11.3	1S39.0	0N47.7	6S38.9	0N46.4	1S56.7	0N39.5	1N40.8	15N46.2
4	20 47 38.0	0 .0	0 .0	3 25.7	2 15.2	0 53.4	6 44.3	0 45.7	1 57.1	0 39.4	1 40.7	15 45.3
7	20 59 27.7	0 .0	0 .0	0N 9.6	2 51.2	0 58.8	6 48.1	0 45.0	1 57.5	0 39.3	1 40.5	15 44.3
10	21 11 17.3	0 .0	0 .0	3 47.6	3 26.0	1 3.7	6 50.2	0 44.3	1 57.9	0 39.2	1 40.3	15 43.5
13	21 23 7.0	0 .0	0 .0	5 17.0	3 57.3	1 8.1	6 50.5	0 43.6	1 58.4	0 39.1	1 40.1	15 42.6
16	21 34 56.7	0 .0	0 .0	4 2.9	4 22.7	1 12.1	6 49.0	0 42.9	1 58.8	0 39.0	1 40.0	15 41.9
19	21 46 46.3	0 .0	0 .0	1 2.9	4 38.8	1 15.5	6 45.7	0 42.2	1 59.3	0 38.9	1 39.8	15 41.2
22	21 58 36.0	0 .0	0 .0	2S15.5	4 41.7	1 18.5	6 40.8	0 41.6	1 59.7	0 38.8	1 39.6	15 40.5
25	22 10 25.7	0 .0	0 .0	4 36.3	4 28.4	1 20.9	6 34.3	0 40.9	2 .2	0 38.7	1 39.4	15 40.0
28	22 22 15.3	0 .0	0 .0	5 12.7	3 58.2	1 22.7	6 26.5	0 40.3	2 .7	0 38.7	1 39.2	15 39.4
31	22 34 5.0	0 .0	0 .0	3 44.6	3 13.5	1 24.0	6 17.4	0 39.7	2 1.2	0 38.6	1 39.1	15 39.0
		RIGHT ASCENSION										
1	20 35 48.3	10♌32.3	17♒12.0	21♏42.8	6♍22.5	3♌ 9.9	23♒59.8	24♏33.8	2♊52.0	9♎42.6	28♏32.6	4♎22.0
2	20 39 44.9	11 30.6	17 8.9	5♐20.3	7 4.0	4 27.3	23 R 46.3	24 35.1	2 56.9	9 44.6	28 R 32.2	4 23.4
3	20 43 41.4	12 28.7	17 5.7	19 45.0	7 42.2	5 44.5	23 32.4	24 36.7	3 1.8	9 46.7	28 31.9	4 24.7
4	20 47 38.0	13 26.7	17 2.5	4♑39.9	8 17.0	7 1.4	23 18.1	24 38.5	3 6.6	9 48.9	28 31.6	4 26.1
5	20 51 34.6	14 24.5	16 59.4	19 41.2	8 48.2	8 18.1	23 3.4	24 40.4	3 11.3	9 51.0	28 31.3	4 27.5
6	20 55 31.1	15 22.2	16 56.2	4♒26.0	9 15.7	9 34.5	22 48.4	24 42.5	3 16.0	9 53.2	28 31.0	4 28.9
7	20 59 27.7	16 19.7	16 53.0	18 40.6	9 39.4	10 50.7	22 33.0	24 44.9	3 20.5	9 55.5	28 30.8	4 30.3
8	21 3 24.2	17 17.0	16 49.8	2♓23.0	9 59.1	12 6.7	22 17.5	24 47.3	3 25.0	9 57.8	28 30.6	4 31.8
9	21 7 20.8	18 14.3	16 46.7	15 40.8	10 14.7	13 22.3	22 1.7	24 50.0	3 29.4	10 .1	28 30.5	4 33.3
10	21 11 17.3	19 11.3	16 43.5	28 47.7	10 26.1	14 37.7	21 45.7	24 52.9	3 33.6	10 2.4	28 30.4	4 34.8
11	21 15 13.9	20 8.3	16 40.3	11♈59.3	10 33.0	15 52.9	21 29.6	24 55.9	3 37.8	10 4.8	28 30.3	4 36.3
12	21 19 10.4	21 5.1	16 37.2	25 30.2	10 35.4	17 7.8	21 13.4	24 59.1	3 42.0	10 7.2	28 30.3	4 37.9
13	21 23 7.0	22 1.7	16 34.0	9♉30.7	10 R 33.1	18 22.4	20 57.2	25 2.5	3 46.0	10 9.7	28 30.2	4 39.4
14	21 27 3.6	22 58.3	16 30.8	24 2.7	10 26.0	19 36.8	20 40.9	25 6.0	3 49.9	10 12.2	28 D 30.3	4 41.0
15	21 31 .1	23 54.7	16 27.6	8♊57.5	10 14.2	20 50.9	20 24.8	25 9.7	3 53.7	10 14.7	28 30.3	4 42.6
16	21 34 56.7	24 50.9	16 24.5	23 56.1	9 57.6	22 4.7	20 8.7	25 13.7	3 57.5	10 17.3	28 30.4	4 44.2
17	21 38 53.2	25 47.1	16 21.3	8♋34.8	9 36.2	23 18.3	19 52.9	25 17.8	4 1.2	10 19.9	28 30.6	4 45.9
18	21 42 49.8	26 43.1	16 18.1	22 33.8	9 10.1	24 31.6	19 37.2	25 22.0	4 4.7	10 22.5	28 30.7	4 47.6
19	21 46 46.3	27 39.0	16 14.9	5♌42.4	8 39.6	25 44.7	19 21.7	25 26.5	4 8.1	10 25.2	28 30.9	4 49.3
20	21 50 42.9	28 34.8	16 11.7	18 .3	8 4.9	26 57.5	19 6.6	25 31.0	4 11.5	10 27.9	28 31.1	4 51.0
21	21 54 39.4	29 30.4	16 8.6	29 34.2	7 26.4	28 10.0	18 51.8	25 35.8	4 14.7	10 30.6	28 31.4	4 52.7
22	21 58 36.0	0♍25.9	16 5.4	10♍35.4	6 44.7	29 22.3	18 37.4	25 40.7	4 17.9	10 33.3	28 31.7	4 54.4
23	22 2 32.6	1 21.3	16 2.2	21 16.8	6 .2	0♍34.4	18 23.5	25 45.8	4 20.9	10 36.1	28 32.0	4 56.1
24	22 6 29.1	2 16.6	15 59.0	1♎51.9	5 13.8	1 46.2	18 10.1	25 51.1	4 23.9	10 38.9	28 32.4	4 57.9
25	22 10 25.7	3 11.8	15 55.9	12 34.2	4 26.3	2 57.7	17 57.1	25 56.5	4 26.7	10 41.8	28 32.7	4 59.7
26	22 14 22.2	4 6.9	15 52.7	23 36.7	3 38.5	4 9.1	17 44.8	26 2.1	4 29.5	10 44.6	28 33.2	5 1.5
27	22 18 18.8	5 1.8	15 49.5	5♏11.6	2 51.5	5 20.2	17 33.0	26 7.9	4 32.1	10 47.5	28 33.6	5 3.3
28	22 22 15.3	5 56.7	15 46.3	17 28.8	2 6.2	6 31.1	17 21.9	26 13.8	4 34.6	10 50.4	28 34.1	5 5.1
29	22 26 11.9	6 51.5	15 43.1	0♐33.6	1 23.7	7 41.7	17 11.4	26 19.8	4 37.1	10 53.4	28 34.6	5 7.0
30	22 30 8.4	7 46.1	15 39.9	14 24.1	0 44.9	8 52.2	17 1.6	26 26.1	4 39.4	10 56.4	28 35.2	5 8.8
31	22 34 5.0	8 40.7	15 36.8	28 49.9	0 10.9	10 2.4	16 52.5	26 32.4	4 41.6	10 59.4	28 35.8	5 10.7
		DECLINATION										
1	20 35 48.3	18N14.4	0S17.2	24S 9.1	8N 5.2	20N46.0	21S19.5	18S39.9	19N 7.5	3S28.1	18S35.0	15N19.9
4	20 47 38.0	17 28.6	0 17.2	26 48.3	6 41.5	20 .9	21 38.5	18 41.7	19 9.7	3 30.8	18 34.9	15 17.0
7	20 59 27.7	16 40.2	0 17.3	15 48.7	5 29.8	19 10.6	21 56.6	18 43.9	19 11.6	3 33.8	18 35.0	15 14.1
10	21 11 17.3	15 49.5	0 17.3	3N36.7	4 33.6	18 15.4	22 13.4	18 46.4	19 13.5	3 36.8	18 35.1	15 11.2
13	21 23 7.0	14 56.4	0 17.4	20 58.6	3 56.9	17 15.6	22 28.5	18 49.2	19 15.1	3 40.0	18 35.2	15 8.3
16	21 34 56.7	14 1.1	0 17.4	27 22.8	3 43.8	16 11.3	22 41.5	18 52.4	19 16.6	3 43.3	18 35.4	15 5.4
19	21 46 46.3	13 3.9	0 17.5	20 28.6	3 57.9	15 3.1	22 52.0	18 55.9	19 17.9	3 46.8	18 35.7	15 2.4
22	21 58 36.0	12 4.7	0 17.5	5 45.8	4 40.3	13 51.1	22 59.8	18 59.7	19 19.1	3 50.3	18 36.1	14 59.5
25	22 10 25.7	11 3.9	0 17.6	10S23.3	5 48.3	12 35.6	23 4.6	19 3.8	19 20.0	3 54.0	18 36.5	14 56.5
28	22 22 15.3	10 1.5	0 17.6	23 8.2	7 13.7	11 17.1	23 6.4	19 8.1	19 20.8	3 57.8	18 36.9	14 53.6
31	22 34 5.0	8 57.6	0 17.7	27 11.0	8 43.9	9 55.8	23 5.2	19 12.7	19 21.5	4 1.6	18 37.4	14 50.7

SEPTEMBER 1971

DAY	EPHEM. SID. TIME	☉	☊	☽	☿	♀	♂	♃	♄	♅	♆	♇
	LONGITUDE											
	h m s	° ′	° ′	° ′	° ′	° ′	° ′	° ′	° ′	° ′	° ′	° ′
1	22 38 1.5	7♍55.2	13♒ 5.6	12♑12.0	28♌35.4	9♍ 4.8	12♒22.4	28♏43.7	6♊14.0	11♎44.0	0♐24.4	28♍43.9
2	22 41 58.1	8 53.3	13 2.4	25 52.8	28R 5.6	10 19.2	12R16.1	28 50.2	6 15.8	11 47.3	0 25.1	28 46.1
3	22 45 54.7	9 51.3	12 59.2	10♒ .4	27 43.1	11 33.6	12 10.5	28 56.9	6 17.6	11 50.6	0 25.8	28 48.2
4	22 49 51.2	10 49.4	12 56.0	24 32.7	27 28.4	12 48.1	12 5.7	29 3.7	6 19.3	11 54.0	0 26.5	28 50.4
5	22 53 47.8	11 47.5	12 52.9	9♓24.9	27 22.0	14 2.5	12 1.7	29 10.6	6 20.9	11 57.3	0 27.2	28 52.6
6	22 57 44.3	12 45.7	12 49.7	24 29.6	27D24.2	15 17.0	11 58.4	29 17.7	6 22.3	12 .7	0 28.0	28 54.7
7	23 1 40.9	13 43.9	12 46.5	9♈37.5	27 35.2	16 31.5	11 56.1	29 25.0	6 23.8	12 4.2	0 28.8	28 57.0
8	23 5 37.4	14 42.1	12 43.3	24 39.0	27 55.0	17 46.0	11 54.4	29 32.3	6 25.0	12 7.7	0 29.7	28 59.2
9	23 9 34.0	15 40.3	12 40.1	9♉25.6	28 23.6	19 .5	11 53.5	29 39.8	6 26.2	12 11.1	0 30.5	29 1.4
10	23 13 30.5	16 38.6	12 37.0	23 51.4	29 .7	20 15.1	11 53.5	29 47.4	6 27.2	12 14.6	0 31.4	29 3.6
11	23 17 27.1	17 36.9	12 33.8	7♊53.0	29 46.0	21 29.6	11D54.2	29 55.1	6 28.1	12 18.1	0 32.4	29 5.8
12	23 21 23.6	18 35.3	12 30.6	21 29.8	0♍39.3	22 44.2	11 55.7	0♐ 3.0	6 29.0	12 21.7	0 33.3	29 8.0
13	23 25 20.2	19 33.6	12 27.4	4♋43.2	1 40.1	23 58.7	11 58.1	0 11.0	6 29.7	12 25.2	0 34.3	29 10.3
14	23 29 16.7	20 32.0	12 24.3	17 35.9	2 47.9	25 13.3	12 1.2	0 19.2	6 30.3	12 28.8	0 35.3	29 12.5
15	23 33 13.3	21 30.5	12 21.1	0♌11.3	4 2.1	26 27.9	12 5.1	0 27.4	6 30.8	12 32.4	0 36.4	29 14.7
16	23 37 9.8	22 29.0	12 17.9	12 32.7	5 22.2	27 42.5	12 9.9	0 35.8	6 31.2	12 36.0	0 37.4	29 17.0
17	23 41 6.4	23 27.5	12 14.7	24 43.3	6 47.6	28 57.2	12 15.4	0 44.3	6 31.4	12 39.6	0 38.5	29 19.2
18	23 45 3.0	24 26.0	12 11.5	6♍45.9	8 17.6	0♎11.8	12 21.7	0 52.9	6 31.6	12 43.2	0 39.7	29 21.5
19	23 48 59.5	25 24.6	12 8.4	18 42.7	9 51.7	1 26.4	12 28.8	1 1.7	6 31.7	12 46.9	0 40.8	29 23.7
20	23 52 56.1	26 23.2	12 5.2	0♎35.8	11 29.4	2 41.1	12 36.6	1 10.5	6R31.6	12 50.5	0 42.0	29 26.0
21	23 56 52.6	27 21.9	12 2.0	12 26.7	13 10.0	3 55.7	12 45.2	1 19.5	6 31.5	12 54.2	0 43.3	29 28.3
22	0 0 49.2	28 20.6	11 58.8	24 17.3	14 53.1	5 10.4	12 54.6	1 28.6	6 31.2	12 57.9	0 44.5	29 30.5
23	0 4 45.7	29 19.3	11 55.7	6♏ 9.5	16 38.1	6 25.1	13 4.8	1 37.8	6 30.8	13 1.6	0 45.8	29 32.8
24	0 8 42.3	0♎18.0	11 52.5	18 5.5	18 24.7	7 39.8	13 15.6	1 47.1	6 30.3	13 5.3	0 47.1	29 35.0
25	0 12 38.8	1 16.8	11 49.3	0♐ 8.1	20 12.4	8 54.4	13 27.2	1 56.6	6 29.7	13 9.0	0 48.4	29 37.3
26	0 16 35.4	2 15.6	11 46.1	12 20.8	22 1.0	10 9.1	13 39.5	2 6.1	6 29.0	13 12.8	0 49.8	29 39.5
27	0 20 31.9	3 14.4	11 42.9	24 47.4	23 50.1	11 23.8	13 52.5	2 15.8	6 28.2	13 16.5	0 51.2	29 41.8
28	0 24 28.5	4 13.3	11 39.8	7♑32.1	25 39.6	12 38.6	14 6.3	2 25.6	6 27.3	13 20.3	0 52.6	29 44.1
29	0 28 25.0	5 12.2	11 36.6	20 39.0	27 29.1	13 53.3	14 20.6	2 35.4	6 26.3	13 24.1	0 54.1	29 46.4
30	0 32 21.6	6 11.1	11 33.4	4♒11.5	29 18.4	15 8.0	14 35.7	2 45.4	6 25.2	13 27.8	0 55.5	29 48.6
	LATITUDE											
1	22 38 1.5	0 .0	0 .0	2S48.0	2S56.3	1N24.3	6S14.2	0N39.5	2S 1.3	0N38.6	1N39.0	15N38.9
4	22 49 51.2	0 .0	0 .0	0N55.3	2 .6	1 24.8	6 3.8	0 38.9	2 1.8	0 38.5	1 38.8	15 38.5
7	23 1 40.9	0 .0	0 .0	4 17.3	1 4.0	1 24.8	5 52.6	0 38.3	2 2.3	0 38.4	1 38.7	15 38.2
10	23 13 30.5	0 .0	0 .0	5 7.8	0 11.7	1 24.1	5 40.9	0 37.7	2 2.8	0 38.4	1 38.5	15 38.0
13	23 25 20.2	0 .0	0 .0	3 18.4	0N32.8	1 22.9	5 28.7	0 37.1	2 3.3	0 38.3	1 38.3	15 37.9
16	23 37 9.8	0 .0	0 .0	0 8.7	1 7.3	1 21.0	5 16.2	0 36.6	2 3.8	0 38.3	1 38.2	15 37.8
19	23 48 59.5	0 .0	0 .0	2S56.3	1 31.5	1 18.7	5 3.5	0 36.0	2 4.3	0 38.2	1 38.0	15 37.8
22	0 0 49.2	0 .0	0 .0	4 50.3	1 45.8	1 15.7	4 50.7	0 35.5	2 4.8	0 38.2	1 37.8	15 37.8
25	0 12 38.8	0 .0	0 .0	4 54.3	1 51.4	1 12.3	4 38.0	0 35.0	2 5.2	0 38.2	1 37.7	15 38.0
28	0 24 28.5	0 .0	0 .0	2 59.5	1 49.9	1 8.3	4 25.4	0 34.5	2 5.7	0 38.1	1 37.5	15 38.2
	RIGHT ASCENSION											
1	22 38 1.5	9♍35.2	15♒33.6	13♑32.6	29♌42.5	11♍12.5	16♒44.2	26♏39.0	4♊43.7	11♎ 2.4	28♏36.4	5♎12.6
2	22 41 58.1	10 29.6	15 30.4	28 12.4	29R20.5	12 22.4	16R36.6	26 45.7	4 45.7	11 5.4	28 37.0	5 14.4
3	22 45 54.7	11 24.0	15 27.2	12♒34.0	29 5.5	13 32.1	16 29.7	26 52.5	4 47.6	11 8.5	28 37.7	5 16.3
4	22 49 51.2	12 18.2	15 24.0	26 31.7	28 58.0	14 41.6	16 23.6	26 59.5	4 49.4	11 11.6	28 38.5	5 18.3
5	22 53 47.8	13 12.4	15 20.8	10♓ 9.1	28D58.5	15 51.0	16 18.3	27 6.6	4 51.0	11 14.7	28 39.2	5 20.2
6	22 57 44.3	14 6.6	15 17.7	23 36.7	29 7.2	17 .2	16 13.8	27 13.9	4 52.6	11 17.8	28 40.0	5 22.1
7	23 1 40.9	15 .7	15 14.5	7♈ 8.6	29 24.3	18 9.3	16 10.1	27 21.4	4 54.1	11 21.0	28 40.9	5 24.1
8	23 5 37.4	15 54.7	15 11.3	20 58.6	29 49.6	19 18.2	16 7.2	27 28.9	4 55.4	11 24.2	28 41.7	5 26.1
9	23 9 34.0	16 48.7	15 8.1	5♉16.9	0♍23.1	20 27.0	16 5.1	27 36.6	4 56.7	11 27.4	28 42.6	5 28.0
10	23 13 30.5	17 42.7	15 4.9	20 5.4	1 4.5	21 35.7	16 3.8	27 44.5	4 57.8	11 30.6	28 43.5	5 30.0
11	23 17 27.1	18 36.6	15 1.7	5♊15.2	1 53.6	22 44.3	16 3.3	27 52.5	4 58.8	11 33.9	28 44.4	5 32.0
12	23 21 23.6	19 30.5	14 58.5	20 26.8	2 49.8	23 52.8	16D 3.6	28 .6	4 59.7	11 37.1	28 45.4	5 34.0
13	23 25 20.2	20 24.3	14 55.3	5♋16.5	3 52.8	25 1.3	16 4.8	28 8.8	5 .4	11 40.4	28 46.4	5 36.0
14	23 29 16.7	21 18.2	14 52.1	19 24.3	5 1.9	26 9.6	16 6.7	28 17.2	5 1.1	11 43.7	28 47.5	5 38.0
15	23 33 13.3	22 12.0	14 49.0	2♌39.9	6 16.6	27 17.9	16 9.5	28 25.8	5 1.7	11 47.0	28 48.5	5 40.1
16	23 37 9.8	23 5.8	14 45.8	15 3.2	7 36.4	28 26.1	16 13.0	28 34.4	5 2.1	11 50.3	28 49.6	5 42.1
17	23 41 6.4	23 59.6	14 42.6	26 41.3	9 .4	29 34.3	16 17.4	28 43.2	5 2.4	11 53.6	28 50.8	5 44.1
18	23 45 3.0	24 53.5	14 39.4	7♍45.4	10 28.3	0♎42.5	16 22.6	28 52.2	5 2.6	11 57.0	28 51.9	5 46.2
19	23 48 59.5	25 47.3	14 36.2	18 28.4	11 59.3	1 50.6	16 28.5	29 1.2	5 2.7	12 .3	28 53.1	5 48.2
20	23 52 56.1	26 41.1	14 33.0	29 3.3	13 33.0	2 58.7	16 35.3	29 10.4	5 2.7	12 3.7	28 54.3	5 50.3
21	23 56 52.6	27 34.9	14 29.8	9♎43.0	15 8.7	4 6.8	16 42.8	29 19.7	5R 2.5	12 7.1	28 55.6	5 52.3
22	0 0 49.2	28 28.8	14 26.6	20 39.6	16 46.1	5 14.9	16 51.1	29 29.1	5 2.3	12 10.5	28 56.9	5 54.4
23	0 4 45.7	29 22.6	14 23.4	2♏ 4.3	18 24.7	6 23.1	17 .1	29 38.7	5 1.9	12 13.9	28 58.2	5 56.4
24	0 8 42.3	0♎16.5	14 20.2	14 5.8	20 4.1	7 31.2	17 9.9	29 48.4	5 1.4	12 17.4	28 59.5	5 58.5
25	0 12 38.8	1 10.4	14 17.0	26 49.1	21 44.1	8 39.4	17 20.4	29 58.2	5 .8	12 20.8	29 .9	6 .6
26	0 16 35.4	2 4.4	14 13.8	10♐13.0	23 24.3	9 47.7	17 31.7	0♐ 8.1	5 .1	12 24.2	29 2.3	6 2.7
27	0 20 31.9	2 58.4	14 10.6	24 9.3	25 4.5	10 56.0	17 43.6	0 18.1	4 59.3	12 27.7	29 3.7	6 4.7
28	0 24 28.5	3 52.5	14 7.4	8♑23.6	26 44.7	12 4.4	17 56.3	0 28.3	4 58.4	12 31.2	29 5.2	6 6.9
29	0 28 25.0	4 46.6	14 4.2	22 39.4	28 24.5	13 12.8	18 9.6	0 38.6	4 57.4	12 34.7	29 6.7	6 8.9
30	0 32 21.6	5 40.7	14 1.0	6♒43.4	0♎ 3.9	14 21.4	18 23.5	0 48.9	4 56.2	12 38.1	29 8.2	6 11.0
	DECLINATION											
1	22 38 1.5	8N36.1	0S17.7	25S40.4	9N12.6	9N28.2	23S 4.2	19S14.3	19N21.7	4S 2.9	18S37.6	14N49.7
4	22 49 51.2	7 30.6	0 17.7	12 28.4	10 27.8	8 3.7	22 59.0	19 19.3	19 22.1	4 6.9	18 38.2	14 46.8
7	23 1 40.9	6 24.0	0 17.8	7N45.3	11 18.7	6 37.3	22 51.1	19 24.4	19 22.4	4 11.0	18 38.9	14 44.0
10	23 13 30.5	5 16.4	0 17.8	23 42.4	11 38.3	5 9.1	22 40.6	19 29.8	19 22.4	4 15.1	18 39.6	14 41.2
13	23 25 20.2	4 8.0	0 17.9	26 39.9	11 23.6	3 39.6	22 27.7	19 35.3	19 22.4	4 19.2	18 40.3	14 38.4
16	23 37 9.8	2 59.0	0 17.9	17 11.1	10 35.3	2 9.0	22 12.3	19 41.1	19 22.1	4 23.5	18 41.1	14 35.6
19	23 48 59.5	1 49.5	0 18.0	1 45.8	9 17.1	0 37.8	21 54.7	19 46.9	19 21.7	4 27.8	18 42.0	14 33.0
22	0 0 49.2	0 39.5	0 18.0	13S54.8	7 34.9	0S53.8	21 35.0	19 52.9	19 21.2	4 32.1	18 42.9	14 30.3
25	0 12 38.8	0S30.6	0 18.1	24 58.4	5 35.2	2 25.5	21 13.3	19 59.0	19 20.5	4 36.5	18 43.8	14 27.8
28	0 24 28.5	1 40.7	0 18.1	26 13.1	3 24.4	3 56.8	20 49.8	20 5.3	19 19.6	4 40.9	18 44.8	14 25.3

OCTOBER 1971

DAY	EPHEM. SID. TIME	☉	☊	☽	☿	♀	♂	♃	♄	♅	♆	♇
		LONGITUDE										
	h m s	° ′	° ′	° ′	° ′	° ′	° ′	° ′	° ′	° ′	° ′	° ′
1	0 36 18.1	7♎10.1	11♒30.2	18♒12.1	1♎ 7.5	16♎22.7	14♒51.3	2♐55.4	6♊23.9	13♎31.6	0♐57.0	29♍50.9
2	0 40 14.7	8 9.1	11 27.1	2♓40.4	2 56.2	17 37.4	15 7.7	3 5.6	6R22.6	13 35.3	0 58.5	29 53.1
3	0 44 11.3	9 8.1	11 23.9	17 33.5	4 44.5	18 52.1	15 24.6	3 15.9	6 21.1	13 39.1	1 .1	29 55.3
4	0 48 7.8	10 7.1	11 20.7	2♈44.8	6 32.2	20 6.8	15 42.1	3 26.2	6 19.6	13 42.9	1 1.6	29 57.6
5	0 52 4.4	11 6.2	11 17.5	18 4.5	8 19.2	21 21.5	16 .2	3 36.6	6 17.9	13 46.7	1 3.2	29 59.8
6	0 56 .9	12 5.3	11 14.3	3♉21.4	10 5.6	22 36.2	16 18.9	3 47.2	6 16.1	13 50.5	1 4.8	0♎ 2.0
7	0 59 57.5	13 4.4	11 11.2	18 24.5	11 51.3	23 51.0	16 38.1	3 57.8	6 14.3	13 54.2	1 6.5	0 4.2
8	1 3 54.0	14 3.6	11 8.0	3♊ 5.2	13 36.3	25 5.7	16 57.9	4 8.5	6 12.3	13 58.0	1 8.1	0 6.5
9	1 7 50.6	15 2.8	11 4.8	17 18.0	15 20.5	26 20.4	17 18.2	4 19.3	6 10.2	14 1.8	1 9.8	0 8.7
10	1 11 47.1	16 2.1	11 1.6	1♋ 1.2	17 4.0	27 35.2	17 39.0	4 30.2	6 8.0	14 5.6	1 11.5	0 10.9
11	1 15 43.7	17 1.4	10 58.5	14 16.1	18 46.8	28 49.9	18 .4	4 41.2	6 5.8	14 9.4	1 13.2	0 13.0
12	1 19 40.2	18 .7	10 55.3	27 6.1	20 28.8	0♏ 4.7	18 22.2	4 52.3	6 3.4	14 13.2	1 15.0	0 15.2
13	1 23 36.8	19 .1	10 52.1	9♌35.5	22 10.1	1 19.4	18 44.6	5 3.4	6 .9	14 16.9	1 16.7	0 17.4
14	1 27 33.3	19 59.5	10 48.9	21 49.0	23 50.6	2 34.2	19 7.4	5 14.6	5 58.3	14 20.7	1 18.5	0 19.6
15	1 31 29.9	20 58.9	10 45.7	3♍51.4	25 30.5	3 48.9	19 30.7	5 26.0	5 55.7	14 24.5	1 20.3	0 21.7
16	1 35 26.5	21 58.4	10 42.6	15 46.5	27 9.6	5 3.7	19 54.5	5 37.3	5 52.9	14 28.3	1 22.2	0 23.8
17	1 39 23.0	22 57.9	10 39.4	27 37.9	28 48.0	6 18.5	20 18.7	5 48.8	5 50.1	14 32.0	1 24.0	0 26.0
18	1 43 19.6	23 57.5	10 36.2	9♎28.1	0♏25.8	7 33.2	20 43.4	6 .4	5 47.1	14 35.8	1 25.9	0 28.1
19	1 47 16.1	24 57.1	10 33.0	21 19.3	2 3.0	8 48.1	21 8.6	6 12.0	5 44.1	14 39.6	1 27.8	0 30.2
20	1 51 12.7	25 56.8	10 29.9	3♏12.9	3 39.5	10 2.8	21 34.1	6 23.7	5 41.0	14 43.3	1 29.7	0 32.3
21	1 55 9.2	26 56.4	10 26.7	15 10.2	5 15.4	11 17.6	22 .1	6 35.5	5 37.8	14 47.0	1 31.7	0 34.4
22	1 59 5.8	27 56.1	10 23.5	27 12.5	6 50.7	12 32.4	22 26.4	6 47.3	5 34.5	14 50.8	1 33.6	0 36.5
23	2 3 2.3	28 55.8	10 20.3	9♐21.5	8 25.4	13 47.2	22 53.2	6 59.2	5 31.1	14 54.5	1 35.6	0 38.5
24	2 6 58.9	29 55.6	10 17.1	21 39.1	9 59.5	15 2.0	23 20.3	7 11.2	5 27.7	14 58.2	1 37.5	0 40.6
25	2 10 55.4	0♏55.4	10 14.0	4♑ 8.1	11 33.1	16 16.7	23 47.8	7 23.2	5 24.1	15 1.9	1 39.5	0 42.6
26	2 14 52.0	1 55.2	10 10.8	16 51.7	13 6.1	17 31.5	24 15.7	7 35.3	5 20.5	15 5.5	1 41.5	0 44.6
27	2 18 48.6	2 55.0	10 7.6	29 53.5	14 38.6	18 46.3	24 44.0	7 47.5	5 16.8	15 9.2	1 43.6	0 46.6
28	2 22 45.1	3 54.9	10 4.4	13♒17.2	16 10.5	20 1.0	25 12.5	7 59.7	5 13.0	15 12.8	1 45.6	0 48.6
29	2 26 41.7	4 54.8	10 1.3	27 5.7	17 42.0	21 15.8	25 41.5	8 12.0	5 9.2	15 16.5	1 47.7	0 50.5
30	2 30 38.2	5 54.7	9 58.1	11♓20.3	19 12.9	22 30.6	26 10.7	8 24.4	5 5.3	15 20.1	1 49.7	0 52.5
31	2 34 34.8	6 54.7	9 54.9	25 60.0	20 43.4	23 45.3	26 40.3	8 36.8	5 1.3	15 23.7	1 51.8	0 54.4
		LATITUDE										
1	0 36 18.1	0 .0	0 .0	0N26.9	1N42.6	1N 3.8	4S12.9	0N34.0	2S 6.1	0N38.1	1N37.4	15N38.5
4	0 48 7.8	0 .0	0 .0	3 53.0	1 31.1	0 58.9	4 .6	0 33.5	2 6.6	0 38.1	1 37.3	15 38.8
7	0 59 57.5	0 .0	0 .0	5 2.6	1 16.3	0 53.5	3 48.6	0 33.0	2 7.0	0 38.1	1 37.1	15 39.3
10	1 11 47.1	0 .0	0 .0	3 21.4	0 59.2	0 47.7	3 36.9	0 32.6	2 7.4	0 38.0	1 37.0	15 39.8
13	1 23 36.8	0 .0	0 .0	0 14.4	0 40.4	0 41.6	3 25.4	0 32.1	2 7.7	0 38.0	1 36.9	15 40.3
16	1 35 26.5	0 .0	0 .0	2S47.8	0 20.7	0 35.1	3 14.3	0 31.7	2 8.1	0 38.0	1 36.8	15 41.0
19	1 47 16.1	0 .0	0 .0	4 41.9	0 .3	0 28.3	3 3.5	0 31.3	2 8.4	0 38.0	1 36.7	15 41.7
22	1 59 5.8	0 .0	0 .0	4 48.5	0S20.2	0 21.2	2 53.0	0 30.8	2 8.7	0 38.0	1 36.6	15 42.5
25	2 10 55.4	0 .0	0 .0	2 59.5	0 40.5	0 13.9	2 42.9	0 30.4	2 8.9	0 38.1	1 36.5	15 43.3
28	2 22 45.1	0 .0	0 .0	0N14.7	1 .2	0 6.5	2 33.1	0 30.1	2 9.2	0 38.1	1 36.4	15 44.2
31	2 34 34.8	0 .0	0 .0	3 35.3	1 19.2	0S 1.1	2 23.6	0 29.7	2 9.3	0 38.1	1 36.3	15 45.2
		RIGHT ASCENSION										
1	0 36 18.1	6♎34.9	13♒57.8	20♒29.8	1♎42.8	15♎30.0	18♒38.2	0♐59.4	4♊54.9	12♎41.6	29♏ 9.7	6♎13.1
2	0 40 14.7	7 29.2	13 54.6	4♓ .9	3 21.1	16 38.8	18 53.4	1 10.0	4R53.6	12 45.1	29 11.2	6 15.2
3	0 44 11.3	8 23.5	13 51.4	17 25.9	4 58.9	17 47.6	19 9.2	1 20.7	4 52.1	12 48.6	29 12.8	6 17.3
4	0 48 7.8	9 17.9	13 48.2	0♈58.3	6 36.1	18 56.7	19 25.6	1 31.5	4 50.5	12 52.1	29 14.4	6 19.3
5	0 52 4.4	10 12.4	13 45.0	14 52.7	8 12.6	20 5.8	19 42.6	1 42.4	4 48.8	12 55.6	29 16.1	6 21.4
6	0 56 .9	11 7.0	13 41.8	29 20.8	9 48.6	21 15.1	20 .2	1 53.4	4 46.9	12 59.1	29 17.7	6 23.5
7	0 59 57.5	12 1.6	13 38.6	14♉26.6	11 23.9	22 24.5	20 18.3	2 4.5	4 45.0	13 2.6	29 19.4	6 25.6
8	1 3 54.0	12 56.4	13 35.4	0♊ 1.9	12 58.7	23 34.2	20 36.9	2 15.7	4 43.0	13 6.1	29 21.1	6 27.6
9	1 7 50.6	13 51.3	13 32.2	15 45.3	14 32.9	24 44.0	20 56.0	2 27.0	4 40.8	13 9.6	29 22.8	6 29.7
10	1 11 47.1	14 46.3	13 29.0	1♋ 8.4	16 6.6	25 54.0	21 15.7	2 38.4	4 38.6	13 13.1	29 24.6	6 31.8
11	1 15 43.7	15 41.4	13 25.8	15 46.5	17 39.8	27 4.2	21 35.8	2 49.9	4 36.2	13 16.6	29 26.4	6 33.8
12	1 19 40.2	16 36.6	13 22.6	29 25.9	19 12.6	28 14.6	21 56.4	3 1.5	4 33.8	13 20.1	29 28.2	6 35.9
13	1 23 36.8	17 31.9	13 19.4	12♌ 6.0	20 45.0	29 25.3	22 17.5	3 13.2	4 31.2	13 23.6	29 30.0	6 37.9
14	1 27 33.3	18 27.4	13 16.2	23 54.6	22 16.9	0♏36.1	22 39.1	3 25.0	4 28.6	13 27.1	29 31.8	6 40.0
15	1 31 29.9	19 23.0	13 13.0	5♍ 4.4	23 48.6	1 47.3	23 1.1	3 36.9	4 25.8	13 30.5	29 33.7	6 42.0
16	1 35 26.5	20 18.8	13 9.8	15 49.4	25 19.9	2 58.6	23 23.5	3 48.8	4 23.0	13 34.0	29 35.6	6 44.0
17	1 39 23.0	21 14.7	13 6.6	26 23.8	26 51.0	4 10.2	23 46.3	4 .9	4 20.0	13 37.5	29 37.5	6 46.1
18	1 43 19.6	22 10.8	13 3.4	7♎ 1.1	28 21.8	5 22.1	24 9.6	4 13.0	4 17.0	13 41.0	29 39.4	6 48.1
19	1 47 16.1	23 7.0	13 .2	17 54.0	29 52.5	6 34.2	24 33.3	4 25.3	4 13.9	13 44.5	29 41.4	6 50.1
20	1 51 12.7	24 3.4	12 56.9	29 13.6	1♏23.0	7 46.6	24 57.3	4 37.6	4 10.6	13 48.0	29 43.4	6 52.1
21	1 55 9.2	24 59.9	12 53.7	11♏ 8.5	2 53.3	8 59.3	25 21.8	4 50.0	4 7.3	13 51.4	29 45.4	6 54.1
22	1 59 5.8	25 56.5	12 50.5	23 43.2	4 23.6	10 12.3	25 46.6	5 2.4	4 3.9	13 54.9	29 47.4	6 56.1
23	2 3 2.3	26 53.4	12 47.3	6♐56.1	5 53.8	11 25.5	26 11.7	5 15.0	4 .4	13 58.3	29 49.4	6 58.1
24	2 6 58.9	27 50.4	12 44.1	20 38.7	7 23.9	12 39.0	26 37.2	5 27.6	3 56.8	14 1.7	29 51.4	7 .0
25	2 10 55.4	28 47.5	12 40.9	4♑36.6	8 54.0	13 52.8	27 3.0	5 40.3	3 53.1	14 5.2	29 53.5	7 2.0
26	2 14 52.0	29 44.9	12 37.7	18 33.5	10 24.1	15 7.0	27 29.2	5 53.1	3 49.4	14 8.6	29 55.5	7 3.9
27	2 18 48.6	0♏42.4	12 34.5	2♒16.8	11 54.2	16 21.4	27 55.6	6 5.9	3 45.5	14 11.9	29 57.6	7 5.9
28	2 22 45.1	1 40.1	12 31.3	15 40.9	13 24.3	17 36.1	28 22.4	6 18.8	3 41.6	14 15.3	29 59.7	7 7.8
29	2 26 41.7	2 38.0	12 28.0	28 48.2	14 54.5	18 51.1	28 49.5	6 31.8	3 37.6	14 18.7	0♐ 1.9	7 9.7
30	2 30 38.2	3 36.0	12 24.8	11♓48.0	16 24.7	20 6.5	29 16.8	6 44.9	3 33.6	14 22.0	0 4.0	7 11.6
31	2 34 34.8	4 34.3	12 21.6	24 54.3	17 55.0	21 22.1	29 44.4	6 58.0	3 29.4	14 25.4	0 6.1	7 13.5
		DECLINATION										
1	0 36 18.1	2S50.7	0S18.2	14S57.1	1N 7.3	5S27.6	20S24.5	20S11.6	19N18.6	4S45.3	18S45.9	14N22.9
4	0 48 7.8	4 .5	0 18.2	4N39.3	1S12.1	6 57.3	19 57.5	20 17.9	19 17.5	4 49.7	18 47.0	14 20.5
7	0 59 57.5	5 9.8	0 18.2	22 9.1	3 31.1	8 25.7	19 29.1	20 24.3	19 16.2	4 54.1	18 48.1	14 18.3
10	1 11 47.1	6 18.6	0 18.3	26 47.8	5 47.7	9 52.5	18 59.1	20 30.8	19 14.7	4 58.5	18 49.2	14 16.1
13	1 23 36.8	7 26.6	0 18.3	18 5.1	8 .5	11 17.3	18 27.8	20 37.2	19 13.1	5 2.9	18 50.4	14 14.1
16	1 35 26.5	8 33.7	0 18.4	3 1.9	10 8.6	12 39.7	17 55.1	20 43.6	19 11.4	5 7.3	18 51.6	14 12.1
19	1 47 16.1	9 39.8	0 18.4	12S40.2	12 11.0	13 59.4	17 21.0	20 50.1	19 9.6	5 11.6	18 52.8	14 10.2
22	1 59 5.8	10 44.5	0 18.5	24 13.0	14 7.2	15 16.1	16 45.7	20 56.5	19 7.6	5 16.0	18 54.1	14 8.5
25	2 10 55.4	11 47.9	0 18.5	26 22.2	15 56.6	16 29.3	16 9.1	21 2.8	19 5.6	5 20.2	18 55.4	14 6.8
28	2 22 45.1	12 49.6	0 18.6	16 36.0	17 38.5	17 38.7	15 31.4	21 9.1	19 3.4	5 24.5	18 56.7	14 5.3
31	2 34 34.8	13 49.5	0 18.6	1N42.2	19 12.6	18 44.0	14 52.5	21 15.3	19 1.2	5 28.6	18 58.0	14 3.9

NOVEMBER 1971

LONGITUDE

DAY	EPHEM. SID. TIME h m s	☉ ° ′	☊ ° ′	☾ ° ′	☿ ° ′	♀ ° ′	♂ ° ′	♃ ° ′	♄ ° ′	♅ ° ′	♆ ° ′	♇ ° ′
1	2 38 31.3	7♏54.7	9♒51.7	11♈ .3	22♏13.3	25♏ .1	27♒10.1	8♐49.2	4♊57.2	15♎27.2	1♐53.9	0♎56.3
2	2 42 27.9	8 54.7	9 48.5	26 13.5	23 42.8	26 14.8	27 40.3	9 1.7	4R53.1	15 30.8	1 56.0	0 58.2
3	2 46 24.4	9 54.7	9 45.4	11♉29.2	25 11.7	27 29.6	28 10.7	9 14.3	4 48.9	15 34.3	1 58.1	1 .0
4	2 50 21.0	10 54.8	9 42.2	26 36.0	26 40.1	28 44.3	28 41.4	9 26.9	4 44.7	15 37.9	2 .2	1 1.9
5	2 54 17.6	11 54.9	9 39.0	11♊23.7	28 7.9	29 59.0	29 12.4	9 39.6	4 40.4	15 41.4	2 2.4	1 3.7
6	2 58 14.1	12 55.0	9 35.8	25 45.3	29 35.3	1♐13.8	29 43.7	9 52.3	4 36.1	15 44.9	2 4.5	1 5.5
7	3 2 10.7	13 55.2	9 32.7	9♋37.0	1♐ 2.0	2 28.5	0♓15.2	10 5.0	4 31.7	15 48.3	2 6.7	1 7.3
8	3 6 7.2	14 55.4	9 29.5	22 58.9	2 28.2	3 43.2	0 46.9	10 17.8	4 27.2	15 51.8	2 8.9	1 9.1
9	3 10 3.8	15 55.7	9 26.3	5♌53.4	3 53.7	4 58.0	1 19.0	10 30.7	4 22.7	15 55.2	2 11.1	1 10.8
10	3 14 .3	16 55.9	9 23.1	18 24.7	5 18.5	6 12.8	1 51.2	10 43.6	4 18.2	15 58.6	2 13.3	1 12.6
11	3 17 56.9	17 56.2	9 20.0	0♍38.0	6 42.6	7 27.5	2 23.7	10 56.6	4 13.6	16 2.0	2 15.5	1 14.3
12	3 21 53.4	18 56.6	9 16.8	12 38.6	8 5.9	8 42.2	2 56.4	11 9.6	4 9.0	16 5.3	2 17.7	1 15.9
13	3 25 50.0	19 57.0	9 13.6	24 31.5	9 28.3	9 57.0	3 29.3	11 22.6	4 4.3	16 8.6	2 19.9	1 17.6
14	3 29 46.6	20 57.4	9 10.4	6♎21.3	10 49.7	11 11.7	4 2.5	11 35.6	3 59.6	16 11.9	2 22.1	1 19.2
15	3 33 43.1	21 57.8	9 7.2	18 11.4	12 10.1	12 26.4	4 35.9	11 48.7	3 54.8	16 15.2	2 24.3	1 20.8
16	3 37 39.7	22 58.2	9 4.1	0♏ 4.9	13 29.2	13 41.2	5 9.4	12 1.9	3 50.0	16 18.4	2 26.6	1 22.4
17	3 41 36.2	23 58.7	9 .9	12 3.8	14 47.0	14 55.9	5 43.2	12 15.0	3 45.2	16 21.6	2 28.8	1 23.9
18	3 45 32.8	24 59.3	8 57.7	24 9.5	16 3.3	16 10.6	6 17.2	12 28.2	3 40.4	16 24.8	2 31.0	1 25.5
19	3 49 29.3	25 59.8	8 54.5	6♐22.7	17 17.9	17 25.4	6 51.4	12 41.5	3 35.6	16 28.0	2 33.3	1 27.0
20	3 53 25.9	27 .4	8 51.4	18 44.3	18 30.6	18 40.1	7 25.8	12 54.7	3 30.7	16 31.1	2 35.5	1 28.5
21	3 57 22.5	28 1.0	8 48.2	1♑15.0	19 41.0	19 54.8	8 .3	13 8.0	3 25.8	16 34.2	2 37.8	1 29.9
22	4 1 19.0	29 1.6	8 45.0	13 55.9	20 49.0	21 9.5	8 35.1	13 21.4	3 20.9	16 37.2	2 40.0	1 31.3
23	4 5 15.6	0♐ 2.2	8 41.8	26 48.6	21 54.1	22 24.2	9 10.0	13 34.7	3 16.0	16 40.2	2 42.3	1 32.7
24	4 9 12.1	1 2.9	8 38.7	9♒55.3	22 56.1	23 38.9	9 45.1	13 48.1	3 11.1	16 43.2	2 44.5	1 34.1
25	4 13 8.7	2 3.5	8 35.5	23 18.3	23 54.3	24 53.6	10 20.3	14 1.5	3 6.1	16 46.2	2 46.8	1 35.4
26	4 17 5.2	3 4.2	8 32.3	6♓59.8	24 48.4	26 8.2	10 55.7	14 14.9	3 1.2	16 49.1	2 49.1	1 36.7
27	4 21 1.8	4 4.9	8 29.1	21 1.3	25 37.8	27 22.9	11 31.2	14 28.3	2 56.3	16 51.9	2 51.3	1 38.0
28	4 24 58.4	5 5.7	8 26.0	5♈22.6	26 21.8	28 37.6	12 6.9	14 41.8	2 51.3	16 54.8	2 53.6	1 39.3
29	4 28 54.9	6 6.4	8 22.8	20 1.4	26 59.7	29 52.2	12 42.8	14 55.3	2 46.4	16 57.6	2 55.8	1 40.5
30	4 32 51.5	7 7.2	8 19.6	4♉52.6	27 30.9	1♑ 6.9	13 18.8	15 8.8	2 41.6	17 .4	2 58.1	1 41.7

LATITUDE

DAY	SID. TIME	☉	☊	☾	☿	♀	♂	♃	♄	♅	♆	♇
1	2 38 31.3	0 .0	0 .0	4N22.3	1S25.2	0S 3.6	2S20.5	0N29.6	2S 9.4	0N38.1	1N36.3	15N45.5
4	2 50 21.0	0 .0	0 .0	4 47.2	1 42.5	0 11.3	2 11.4	0 29.2	2 9.5	0 38.1	1 36.2	15 46.6
7	3 2 10.7	0 .0	0 .0	2 29.7	1 58.2	0 18.9	2 2.7	0 28.8	2 9.6	0 38.2	1 36.1	15 47.7
10	3 14 .3	0 .0	0 .0	0S48.2	2 11.8	0 26.6	1 54.3	0 28.5	2 9.7	0 38.2	1 36.1	15 48.9
13	3 25 50.0	0 .0	0 .0	3 34.9	2 22.8	0 34.2	1 46.2	0 28.2	2 9.7	0 38.2	1 36.0	15 50.1
16	3 37 39.7	0 .0	0 .0	4 57.0	2 30.6	0 41.6	1 38.4	0 27.8	2 9.6	0 38.3	1 36.0	15 51.4
19	3 49 29.3	0 .0	0 .0	4 24.8	2 34.4	0 48.9	1 30.8	0 27.5	2 9.5	0 38.3	1 36.0	15 52.8
22	4 1 19.0	0 .0	0 .0	2 1.7	2 33.1	0 55.9	1 23.6	0 27.2	2 9.4	0 38.4	1 35.9	15 54.2
25	4 13 8.7	0 .0	0 .0	1N23.2	2 25.3	1 2.7	1 16.6	0 26.9	2 9.2	0 38.5	1 35.9	15 55.6
28	4 24 58.4	0 .0	0 .0	4 18.1	2 9.2	1 9.1	1 9.8	0 26.6	2 9.0	0 38.5	1 35.9	15 57.1

RIGHT ASCENSION

DAY	SID. TIME	☉	☊	☾	☿	♀	♂	♃	♄	♅	♆	♇
1	2 38 31.3	5♏32.7	12♒18.4	8♈23.2	19♏25.3	22♏38.1	0♓12.3	7♐11.1	3♊25.2	14♎28.7	0♐ 8.3	7♎15.3
2	2 42 27.9	6 31.4	12 15.2	22 30.2	20 55.6	23 54.3	0 40.4	7 24.4	3R20.9	14 32.0	0 10.5	7 17.2
3	2 46 24.4	7 30.2	12 12.0	7♉24.7	22 26.0	25 10.9	1 8.7	7 37.7	3 16.6	14 35.3	0 12.7	7 19.0
4	2 50 21.0	8 29.2	12 8.8	23 4.7	23 56.4	26 27.8	1 37.3	7 51.1	3 12.2	14 38.6	0 14.9	7 20.8
5	2 54 17.6	9 28.5	12 5.5	9♊12.0	25 26.8	27 44.9	2 6.1	8 4.5	3 7.8	14 41.8	0 17.1	7 22.6
6	2 58 14.1	10 27.9	12 2.3	25 15.0	26 57.2	29 2.4	2 35.1	8 18.0	3 3.2	14 45.1	0 19.3	7 24.4
7	3 2 10.7	11 27.6	11 59.1	10♋39.9	28 27.5	0♐20.2	3 4.3	8 31.5	2 58.7	14 48.3	0 21.5	7 26.2
8	3 6 7.2	12 27.5	11 55.9	25 3.9	29 57.6	1 38.3	3 33.8	8 45.1	2 54.1	14 51.5	0 23.8	7 28.0
9	3 10 3.8	13 27.6	11 52.7	8♌20.4	1♐27.7	2 56.7	4 3.4	8 58.8	2 49.4	14 54.7	0 26.1	7 29.8
10	3 14 .3	14 27.9	11 49.4	20 35.4	2 57.4	4 15.3	4 33.3	9 12.6	2 44.7	14 57.8	0 28.4	7 31.5
11	3 17 56.9	15 28.4	11 46.2	2♍ 2.1	4 26.8	5 34.3	5 3.3	9 26.3	2 39.9	15 1.0	0 30.6	7 33.2
12	3 21 53.4	16 29.2	11 43.0	12 56.1	5 55.8	6 53.5	5 33.4	9 40.1	2 35.1	15 4.1	0 32.9	7 34.9
13	3 25 50.0	17 30.1	11 39.8	23 33.4	7 24.3	8 13.0	6 3.8	9 54.0	2 30.3	15 7.2	0 35.2	7 36.5
14	3 29 46.6	18 31.3	11 36.6	4♎ 9.1	8 52.1	9 32.7	6 34.3	10 7.9	2 25.4	15 10.2	0 37.5	7 38.2
15	3 33 43.1	19 32.7	11 33.3	14 57.3	10 19.2	10 52.7	7 5.1	10 21.9	2 20.4	15 13.2	0 39.8	7 39.8
16	3 37 39.7	20 34.3	11 30.1	26 10.8	11 45.3	12 12.9	7 35.9	10 35.9	2 15.5	15 16.3	0 42.1	7 41.4
17	3 41 36.2	21 36.1	11 26.9	7♏59.6	13 10.2	13 33.4	8 6.9	10 49.9	2 10.5	15 19.2	0 44.4	7 43.0
18	3 45 32.8	22 38.2	11 23.7	20 29.7	14 33.7	14 54.0	8 38.1	11 4.0	2 5.5	15 22.2	0 46.8	7 44.6
19	3 49 29.3	23 40.4	11 20.5	3♐40.5	15 55.6	16 14.9	9 9.5	11 18.1	2 .4	15 25.1	0 49.1	7 46.1
20	3 53 25.9	24 42.8	11 17.2	17 23.7	17 15.7	17 35.9	9 40.9	11 32.3	1 55.4	15 28.0	0 51.4	7 47.7
21	3 57 22.5	25 45.5	11 14.0	1♑23.6	18 33.5	18 57.2	10 12.6	11 46.5	1 50.3	15 30.9	0 53.8	7 49.2
22	4 1 19.0	26 48.3	11 10.8	15 21.7	19 48.7	20 18.5	10 44.3	12 .7	1 45.2	15 33.7	0 56.1	7 50.7
23	4 5 15.6	27 51.4	11 7.6	29 2.5	21 .9	21 40.1	11 16.2	12 15.0	1 40.1	15 36.5	0 58.4	7 52.1
24	4 9 12.1	28 54.6	11 4.3	12♒18.4	22 9.6	23 1.7	11 48.2	12 29.3	1 35.0	15 39.3	1 .8	7 53.6
25	4 13 8.7	29 58.0	11 1.1	25 10.4	23 14.3	24 23.5	12 20.3	12 43.6	1 29.9	15 42.1	1 3.1	7 55.0
26	4 17 5.2	1♐ 1.6	10 57.9	7♓47.1	24 14.4	25 45.4	12 52.6	12 58.0	1 24.8	15 44.8	1 5.5	7 56.4
27	4 21 1.8	2 5.4	10 54.7	20 22.5	25 9.3	27 7.3	13 25.0	13 12.4	1 19.7	15 47.4	1 7.8	7 57.7
28	4 24 58.4	3 9.4	10 51.4	3♈13.3	25 58.3	28 29.4	13 57.4	13 26.8	1 14.5	15 50.1	1 10.1	7 59.1
29	4 28 54.9	4 13.6	10 48.2	16 37.2	26 40.5	29 51.4	14 30.0	13 41.2	1 9.4	15 52.7	1 12.5	8 .4
30	4 32 51.5	5 17.9	10 45.0	0♉49.0	27 15.2	1♑13.6	15 2.7	13 55.8	1 4.4	15 55.3	1 14.9	8 1.7

DECLINATION

DAY	SID. TIME	☉	☊	☾	☿	♀	♂	♃	♄	♅	♆	♇
1	2 38 31.3	14S 9.0	0S18.6	8N22.5	19S42.1	19S 4.8	14S39.3	21S17.4	19N .4	5S30.0	18S58.4	14N 3.5
4	2 50 21.0	15 6.2	0 18.7	24 3.0	21 4.6	20 3.9	13 59.1	21 23.5	18 58.0	5 34.0	18 59.7	14 2.2
7	3 2 10.7	16 1.2	0 18.7	25 35.1	22 17.9	20 58.2	13 17.9	21 29.5	18 55.6	5 38.0	19 1.1	14 1.1
10	3 14 .3	16 53.8	0 18.8	14 32.9	23 21.2	21 47.2	12 35.8	21 35.3	18 53.1	5 42.0	19 2.4	14 .1
13	3 25 50.0	17 43.9	0 18.8	1S 6.8	24 13.7	22 30.6	11 52.7	21 41.1	18 50.5	5 45.8	19 3.8	13 59.3
16	3 37 39.7	18 31.2	0 18.8	16 7.9	24 54.9	23 8.2	11 8.8	21 46.7	18 47.9	5 49.5	19 5.1	13 58.5
19	3 49 29.3	19 15.5	0 18.9	25 43.4	25 24.0	23 39.6	10 24.1	21 52.2	18 45.3	5 53.1	19 6.4	13 58.0
22	4 1 19.0	19 56.7	0 18.9	24 43.9	25 40.3	24 4.8	9 38.6	21 57.4	18 42.7	5 56.6	19 7.8	13 57.5
25	4 13 8.7	20 34.7	0 19.0	12 26.6	25 43.4	24 23.4	8 52.5	22 2.6	18 40.1	5 60.0	19 9.1	13 57.2
28	4 24 58.4	21 9.2	0 19.0	6N 5.1	25 32.8	24 35.4	8 5.6	22 7.5	18 37.5	6 3.2	19 10.4	13 57.0

DECEMBER 1971

LONGITUDE

DAY	EPHEM. SID. TIME h m s	☉ ° ′	☊ ° ′	☽ ° ′	☿ ° ′	♀ ° ′	♂ ° ′	♃ ° ′	♄ ° ′	♅ ° ′	♆ ° ′	♇ ° ′
1	4 36 48.0	8♐ 8.0	8♒16.4	19♉48.5	27♐54.5	2♑21.5	13♓54.9	15♐22.3	2♊36.7	17♎ 3.1	3♐ .4	1♎42.9
2	4 40 44.6	9 8.8	8 13.2	4♊40.3	28 9.6	3 36.1	14 31.1	15 35.8	2R31.8	17 5.8	3 2.6	1 44.0
3	4 44 41.2	10 9.6	8 10.1	19 19.1	28 15.5	4 50.7	15 7.5	15 49.3	2 26.9	17 8.5	3 4.9	1 45.1
4	4 48 37.7	11 10.5	8 6.9	3♋37.4	28R11.4	6 5.3	15 44.0	16 2.9	2 22.1	17 11.1	3 7.1	1 46.2
5	4 52 34.3	12 11.3	8 3.7	17 30.5	27 56.7	7 19.9	16 20.5	16 16.4	2 17.3	17 13.6	3 9.4	1 47.2
6	4 56 30.8	13 12.2	8 .5	0♌56.5	27 30.8	8 34.5	16 57.2	16 30.0	2 12.5	17 16.2	3 11.6	1 48.2
7	5 0 27.4	14 13.1	7 57.4	13 56.3	26 53.6	9 49.0	17 34.0	16 43.6	2 7.7	17 18.6	3 13.8	1 49.2
8	5 4 23.9	15 14.0	7 54.2	26 32.8	26 5.4	11 3.6	18 10.9	16 57.1	2 3.0	17 21.1	3 16.0	1 50.2
9	5 8 20.5	16 14.9	7 51.0	8♍50.3	25 6.7	12 18.1	18 48.0	17 10.7	1 58.3	17 23.5	3 18.3	1 51.1
10	5 12 17.1	17 15.9	7 47.8	20 53.7	23 58.9	13 32.6	19 25.1	17 24.3	1 53.6	17 25.8	3 20.5	1 52.0
11	5 16 13.6	18 16.9	7 44.7	2♎48.3	22 43.7	14 47.1	20 2.3	17 37.9	1 49.0	17 28.1	3 22.7	1 52.8
12	5 20 10.2	19 17.9	7 41.5	14 39.1	21 23.3	16 1.7	20 39.6	17 51.5	1 44.4	17 30.4	3 24.9	1 53.6
13	5 24 6.7	20 18.9	7 38.3	26 30.6	20 .5	17 16.1	21 17.1	18 5.1	1 39.8	17 32.6	3 27.0	1 54.4
14	5 28 3.3	21 19.9	7 35.1	8♏26.9	18 37.9	18 30.6	21 54.6	18 18.7	1 35.3	17 34.8	3 29.2	1 55.2
15	5 31 59.9	22 21.0	7 32.0	20 31.0	17 18.5	19 45.1	22 32.2	18 32.3	1 30.9	17 36.9	3 31.4	1 55.9
16	5 35 56.4	23 22.1	7 28.8	2♐45.1	16 4.7	20 59.6	23 9.9	18 45.8	1 26.5	17 39.0	3 33.5	1 56.6
17	5 39 53.0	24 23.1	7 25.6	15 10.7	14 58.5	22 14.0	23 47.6	18 59.4	1 22.1	17 41.0	3 35.7	1 57.2
18	5 43 49.5	25 24.2	7 22.4	27 48.3	14 1.7	23 28.4	24 25.5	19 13.0	1 17.9	17 43.0	3 37.8	1 57.8
19	5 47 46.1	26 25.3	7 19.2	10♑38.0	13 15.3	24 42.8	25 3.5	19 26.5	1 13.6	17 45.0	3 39.9	1 58.4
20	5 51 42.6	27 26.4	7 16.1	23 39.6	12 39.7	25 57.2	25 41.5	19 40.1	1 9.5	17 46.8	3 42.1	1 59.0
21	5 55 39.2	28 27.6	7 12.9	6♒52.8	12 15.2	27 11.6	26 19.6	19 53.7	1 5.4	17 48.7	3 44.2	1 59.5
22	5 59 35.8	29 28.7	7 9.7	20 17.3	12 1.4	28 26.0	26 57.8	20 7.2	1 1.4	17 50.5	3 46.3	2 .0
23	6 3 32.3	0♑29.9	7 6.5	3♓53.2	11 57.8	29 40.3	27 36.1	20 20.7	0 57.4	17 52.2	3 48.4	2 .5
24	6 7 28.9	1 31.0	7 3.4	17 40.7	12D 3.8	0♒54.6	28 14.4	20 34.2	0 53.5	17 53.9	3 50.4	2 .9
25	6 11 25.4	2 32.1	7 .2	1♈39.8	12 18.7	2 8.9	28 52.8	20 47.7	0 49.7	17 55.6	3 52.5	2 1.2
26	6 15 22.0	3 33.2	6 57.0	15 49.6	12 41.6	3 23.1	29 31.2	21 1.1	0 46.0	17 57.1	3 54.5	2 1.6
27	6 19 18.6	4 34.4	6 53.8	0♉ 8.6	13 11.8	4 37.3	0♈ 9.7	21 14.6	0 42.3	17 58.7	3 56.5	2 1.9
28	6 23 15.1	5 35.5	6 50.7	14 33.7	13 48.5	5 51.5	0 48.3	21 28.0	0 38.8	18 .1	3 58.5	2 2.2
29	6 27 11.7	6 36.6	6 47.5	29 .5	14 31.1	7 5.7	1 26.9	21 41.4	0 35.3	18 1.6	4 .5	2 2.4
30	6 31 8.2	7 37.8	6 44.3	13♊23.8	15 18.9	8 19.8	2 5.6	21 54.8	0 31.8	18 2.9	4 2.4	2 2.6
31	6 35 4.8	8 38.9	6 41.1	27 37.9	16 11.3	9 33.9	2 44.3	22 8.1	0 28.5	18 4.3	4 4.4	2 2.8

LATITUDE

DAY	EPHEM. SID. TIME	☉	☊	☽	☿	♀	♂	♃	♄	♅	♆	♇
1	4 36 48.0	0 .0	0 .0	4N56.5	1S42.9	1S15.2	1S 3.4	0N26.3	2S 8.7	0N38.6	1N35.9	15N58.6
4	4 48 37.7	0 .0	0 .0	2 46.7	1 4.4	1 20.9	0 57.2	0 26.1	2 8.4	0 38.6	1 35.9	16 .2
7	5 0 27.4	0 .0	0 .0	0S39.8	0 13.5	1 26.2	0 51.2	0 25.8	2 8.1	0 38.7	1 35.9	16 1.7
10	5 12 17.1	0 .0	0 .0	3 35.6	0N46.0	1 30.9	0 45.4	0 25.5	2 7.7	0 38.8	1 36.0	16 3.4
13	5 24 6.7	0 .0	0 .0	5 3.2	1 44.2	1 35.1	0 39.9	0 25.3	2 7.2	0 38.9	1 36.0	16 5.0
16	5 35 56.4	0 .0	0 .0	4 35.3	2 28.7	1 38.8	0 34.6	0 25.0	2 6.7	0 39.0	1 36.0	16 6.7
19	5 47 46.1	0 .0	0 .0	2 11.4	2 52.8	1 41.8	0 29.5	0 24.8	2 6.2	0 39.0	1 36.1	16 8.3
22	5 59 35.8	0 .0	0 .0	1N19.1	2 57.6	1 44.3	0 24.6	0 24.6	2 5.6	0 39.1	1 36.1	16 10.0
25	6 11 25.4	0 .0	0 .0	4 19.1	2 48.4	1 46.0	0 19.9	0 24.4	2 5.1	0 39.2	1 36.2	16 11.7
28	6 23 15.1	0 .0	0 .0	5 8.5	2 30.3	1 47.1	0 15.3	0 24.1	2 4.4	0 39.3	1 36.3	16 13.5
31	6 35 4.8	0 .0	0 .0	3 12.0	2 7.4	1 47.5	0 11.0	0 23.9	2 3.8	0 39.4	1 36.4	16 15.2

RIGHT ASCENSION

DAY	EPHEM. SID. TIME	☉	☊	☽	☿	♀	♂	♃	♄	♅	♆	♇
1	4 36 48.0	6♐22.4	10♒41.7	15♉55.3	27♐41.4	2♑35.7	15♓35.5	14♐10.2	0♊59.3	15♎57.9	1♐17.2	8♎ 3.0
2	4 40 44.6	7 27.1	10 38.5	1♊48.3	27 58.3	3 57.8	16 8.4	14 24.7	0R54.2	16 .4	1 19.6	8 4.2
3	4 44 41.2	8 31.9	10 35.3	18 2.8	28 5.0	5 19.9	16 41.3	14 39.3	0 49.2	16 2.8	1 21.9	8 5.4
4	4 48 37.7	9 36.9	10 32.0	4♋ 2.0	28R .7	6 42.0	17 14.4	14 53.8	0 44.2	16 5.3	1 24.2	8 6.6
5	4 52 34.3	10 42.0	10 28.8	19 12.7	27 44.7	8 4.0	17 47.5	15 8.4	0 39.1	16 7.7	1 26.5	8 7.8
6	4 56 30.8	11 47.3	10 25.6	3♌16.7	27 16.7	9 26.0	18 20.7	15 22.9	0 34.2	16 10.0	1 28.9	8 8.9
7	5 0 27.4	12 52.7	10 22.4	16 12.5	26 36.5	10 47.8	18 54.0	15 37.5	0 29.2	16 12.3	1 31.2	8 10.0
8	5 4 23.9	13 58.2	10 19.1	28 10.1	25 44.5	12 9.6	19 27.4	15 52.1	0 24.3	16 14.6	1 33.5	8 11.1
9	5 8 20.5	15 3.9	10 15.9	9♍24.8	24 41.5	13 31.3	20 .8	16 6.7	0 19.4	16 16.9	1 35.8	8 12.2
10	5 12 17.1	16 9.7	10 12.7	20 13.3	23 28.9	14 52.8	20 34.3	16 21.4	0 14.6	16 19.1	1 38.1	8 13.2
11	5 16 13.6	17 15.6	10 9.4	0♎52.2	22 8.8	16 14.2	21 7.9	16 36.0	0 9.7	16 21.2	1 40.4	8 14.2
12	5 20 10.2	18 21.6	10 6.2	11 37.0	20 43.6	17 35.4	21 41.6	16 50.6	0 5.0	16 23.3	1 42.7	8 15.2
13	5 24 6.7	19 27.7	10 2.9	22 42.0	19 16.1	18 56.4	22 15.4	17 5.3	0 .2	16 25.4	1 44.9	8 16.1
14	5 28 3.3	20 34.0	9 59.7	4♏19.6	17 49.4	20 17.3	22 49.2	17 19.9	29♉55.6	16 27.4	1 47.2	8 17.0
15	5 31 59.9	21 40.2	9 56.5	16 38.8	16 26.3	21 37.9	23 23.1	17 34.6	29 50.9	16 29.4	1 49.5	8 17.9
16	5 35 56.4	22 46.6	9 53.2	29 42.4	15 9.2	22 58.3	23 57.1	17 49.2	29 46.4	16 31.4	1 51.7	8 18.8
17	5 39 53.0	23 53.0	9 50.0	13♐25.2	14 .5	24 18.5	24 31.2	18 3.9	29 41.9	16 33.3	1 53.9	8 19.6
18	5 43 49.5	24 59.5	9 46.8	27 33.0	13 1.5	25 38.5	25 5.3	18 18.5	29 37.4	16 35.1	1 56.2	8 20.4
19	5 47 46.1	26 6.1	9 43.5	11♑45.6	12 13.3	26 58.2	25 39.5	18 33.1	29 33.0	16 36.9	1 58.4	8 21.1
20	5 51 42.6	27 12.6	9 40.3	25 43.6	11 36.4	28 17.6	26 13.8	18 47.8	29 28.7	16 38.7	2 .6	8 21.9
21	5 55 39.2	28 19.3	9 37.1	9♒14.7	11 10.9	29 36.8	26 48.2	19 2.4	29 24.5	16 40.5	2 2.8	8 22.6
22	5 59 35.8	29 25.9	9 33.8	22 15.8	10 56.3	0♒55.6	27 22.6	19 17.0	29 20.3	16 42.1	2 5.0	8 23.3
23	6 3 32.3	0♑32.5	9 30.6	4♓53.0	10 52.3	2 14.2	27 57.1	19 31.6	29 16.2	16 43.8	2 7.2	8 23.9
24	6 7 28.9	1 39.2	9 27.3	17 18.5	10D58.2	3 32.4	28 31.6	19 46.2	29 12.1	16 45.3	2 9.3	8 24.5
25	6 11 25.4	2 45.8	9 24.1	29 48.2	11 13.2	4 50.3	29 6.2	20 .8	29 8.1	16 46.9	2 11.4	8 25.1
26	6 15 22.0	3 52.4	9 20.8	12♈39.6	11 36.6	6 7.9	29 40.9	20 15.3	29 4.2	16 48.3	2 13.5	8 25.7
27	6 19 18.6	4 58.9	9 17.6	26 9.1	12 7.6	7 25.2	0♈15.6	20 29.9	29 .4	16 49.8	2 15.6	8 26.2
28	6 23 15.1	6 5.5	9 14.4	10♉28.4	12 45.5	8 42.1	0 50.4	20 44.4	28 56.7	16 51.2	2 17.7	8 26.7
29	6 27 11.7	7 12.0	9 11.1	25 38.6	13 29.6	9 58.6	1 25.2	20 58.9	28 53.0	16 52.5	2 19.8	8 27.1
30	6 31 8.2	8 18.4	9 7.9	11♊25.9	14 19.3	11 14.9	2 .1	21 13.3	28 49.5	16 53.8	2 21.8	8 27.6
31	6 35 4.8	9 24.8	9 4.6	27 21.2	15 14.0	12 30.7	2 35.1	21 27.8	28 46.0	16 55.0	2 23.9	8 28.0

DECLINATION

DAY	EPHEM. SID. TIME	☉	☊	☽	☿	♀	♂	♃	♄	♅	♆	♇
1	4 36 48.0	21S40.1	0S19.1	22N26.8	25S 8.6	24S40.6	7S18.2	22S12.3	18N34.9	6S 6.4	19S11.7	13N57.0
4	4 48 37.7	22 7.3	0 19.1	26 10.3	24 30.3	24 39.1	6 30.3	22 16.9	18 32.4	6 9.3	19 13.0	13 57.1
7	5 0 27.4	22 30.7	0 19.1	16 .8	23 37.9	24 30.8	5 41.9	22 21.3	18 30.0	6 12.2	19 14.2	13 57.4
10	5 12 17.1	22 50.1	0 19.2	0 18.3	22 32.5	24 15.8	4 53.2	22 25.4	18 27.6	6 14.8	19 15.5	13 57.8
13	5 24 6.7	23 5.5	0 19.2	14S56.1	21 20.2	23 54.1	4 4.1	22 29.4	18 25.3	6 17.4	19 16.7	13 58.3
16	5 35 56.4	23 16.7	0 19.3	25 12.7	20 15.1	23 25.9	3 14.6	22 33.2	18 23.1	6 19.7	19 17.8	13 59.0
19	5 47 46.1	23 23.8	0 19.3	25 12.1	19 32.2	22 51.4	2 24.9	22 36.7	18 21.0	6 21.9	19 19.0	13 59.8
22	5 59 35.8	23 26.6	0 19.4	13 28.5	19 18.1	22 10.8	1 35.0	22 40.1	18 19.1	6 23.9	19 20.1	14 .7
25	6 11 25.4	23 25.2	0 19.4	4N37.4	19 29.5	21 24.4	0 45.0	22 43.2	18 17.3	6 25.8	19 21.2	14 1.8
28	6 23 15.1	23 19.6	0 19.4	21 7.0	19 58.5	20 32.5	0N 5.2	22 46.1	18 15.7	6 27.4	19 22.3	14 3.0
31	6 35 4.8	23 9.7	0 19.5	26 37.3	20 36.9	19 35.3	0 55.3	22 48.8	18 14.2	6 28.9	19 23.3	14 4.3

JANUARY 1972

LONGITUDE

DAY	EPHEM. SID. TIME h m s	☉ ° ′	☊ ° ′	☽ ° ′	☿ ° ′	♀ ° ′	♂ ° ′	♃ ° ′	♄ ° ′	♅ ° ′	♆ ° ′	♇ ° ′
1	6 39 1.3	9♑40.0	6♒38.0	11♋37.4	17♐ 7.8	10♒48.0	3♈23.0	22♐21.4	0♊25.3	18♎ 5.5	4♐ 6.3	2♎ 2.9
2	6 42 57.9	10 41.2	6 34.8	25 18.4	18 8.0	12 2.0	4 1.8	22 34.7	0R22.1	18 6.7	4 8.2	2 3.0
3	6 46 54.5	11 42.3	6 31.6	8♌38.5	19 11.3	13 16.0	4 40.7	22 48.0	0 19.0	18 7.9	4 10.1	2 3.1
4	6 50 51.0	12 43.5	6 28.4	21 37.1	20 17.6	14 29.9	5 19.5	23 1.2	0 16.1	18 9.0	4 12.0	2 3.1
5	6 54 47.6	13 44.6	6 25.2	4♍15.5	21 26.3	15 43.8	5 58.5	23 14.4	0 13.2	18 10.0	4 13.8	2 3.1
6	6 58 44.1	14 45.8	6 22.1	16 36.2	22 37.4	16 57.7	6 37.4	23 27.6	0 10.4	18 11.0	4 15.6	2 3.1
7	7 2 40.7	15 46.9	6 18.9	28 43.1	23 50.4	18 11.6	7 16.4	23 40.7	0 7.7	18 12.0	4 17.5	2R 3.0
8	7 6 37.3	16 48.1	6 15.7	10♎40.4	25 5.3	19 25.4	7 55.5	23 53.8	0 5.1	18 12.8	4 19.2	2 2.9
9	7 10 33.8	17 49.2	6 12.5	22 32.9	26 21.9	20 39.2	8 34.5	24 6.8	0 2.6	18 13.7	4 21.0	2 2.8
10	7 14 30.4	18 50.4	6 9.4	4♏25.6	27 39.8	21 52.9	9 13.6	24 19.9	0 .2	18 14.4	4 22.8	2 2.6
11	7 18 26.9	19 51.6	6 6.2	16 23.0	28 59.2	23 6.7	9 52.8	24 32.9	29♉57.9	18 15.2	4 24.5	2 2.4
12	7 22 23.5	20 52.7	6 3.0	28 29.4	0♑19.8	24 20.3	10 32.0	24 45.8	29 55.8	18 15.9	4 26.2	2 2.2
13	7 26 20.0	21 53.9	5 59.8	10♐48.3	1 41.4	25 33.9	11 11.2	24 58.7	29 53.7	18 16.5	4 27.9	2 1.9
14	7 30 16.6	22 55.0	5 56.7	23 22.5	3 4.1	26 47.5	11 50.5	25 11.6	29 51.7	18 17.0	4 29.6	2 1.6
15	7 34 13.2	23 56.2	5 53.5	6♑13.4	4 27.8	28 1.0	12 29.8	25 24.4	29 49.8	18 17.5	4 31.2	2 1.2
16	7 38 9.7	24 57.3	5 50.3	19 21.7	5 52.3	29 14.5	13 9.1	25 37.1	29 48.0	18 17.9	4 32.8	2 .9
17	7 42 6.3	25 58.4	5 47.1	2♒46.5	7 17.7	0♓27.9	13 48.4	25 49.8	29 46.4	18 18.3	4 34.4	2 .4
18	7 46 2.8	26 59.6	5 44.0	16 26.2	8 43.8	1 41.3	14 27.8	26 2.5	29 44.8	18 18.6	4 35.9	2 .0
19	7 49 59.4	28 .7	5 40.8	0♓18.3	10 10.7	2 54.6	15 7.1	26 15.1	29 43.3	18 18.9	4 37.5	1 59.5
20	7 53 56.0	29 1.8	5 37.6	14 19.9	11 38.4	4 7.9	15 46.6	26 27.6	29 42.0	18 19.1	4 39.0	1 59.0
21	7 57 52.5	0♒ 2.9	5 34.4	28 27.9	13 6.7	5 21.1	16 26.0	26 40.1	29 40.8	18 19.2	4 40.4	1 58.5
22	8 1 49.1	1 3.9	5 31.2	12♈39.5	14 35.7	6 34.3	17 5.5	26 52.5	29 39.7	18 19.3	4 41.9	1 57.9
23	8 5 45.6	2 5.0	5 28.1	26 52.0	16 5.4	7 47.4	17 44.9	27 4.9	29 38.7	18 19.3	4 43.3	1 57.3
24	8 9 42.2	3 6.0	5 24.9	11♉ 3.0	17 35.7	9 .4	18 24.4	27 17.2	29 37.8	18 19.3	4 44.7	1 56.7
25	8 13 38.7	4 7.1	5 21.7	25 10.3	19 6.7	10 13.4	19 3.9	27 29.5	29 37.0	18R19.2	4 46.1	1 56.0
26	8 17 35.3	5 8.1	5 18.5	9♊11.8	20 38.3	11 26.2	19 43.4	27 41.6	29 36.3	18 19.1	4 47.4	1 55.3
27	8 21 31.9	6 9.0	5 15.4	23 5.5	22 10.5	12 39.1	20 23.0	27 53.8	29 35.8	18 18.9	4 48.7	1 54.6
28	8 25 28.4	7 10.0	5 12.2	6♋49.2	23 43.4	13 51.8	21 2.5	28 5.8	29 35.3	18 18.7	4 50.0	1 53.8
29	8 29 25.0	8 11.0	5 9.0	20 21.0	25 16.9	15 4.5	21 42.0	28 17.8	29 35.0	18 18.4	4 51.2	1 53.0
30	8 33 21.5	9 11.9	5 5.8	3♌39.1	26 51.1	16 17.1	22 21.6	28 29.7	29 34.8	18 18.0	4 52.5	1 52.2
31	8 37 18.1	10 12.8	5 2.7	16 42.4	28 26.0	17 29.6	23 1.2	28 41.6	29 34.7	18 17.6	4 53.7	1 51.3

LATITUDE

DAY	EPHEM. SID. TIME h m s	☉ ° ′	☊ ° ′	☽ ° ′	☿ ° ′	♀ ° ′	♂ ° ′	♃ ° ′	♄ ° ′	♅ ° ′	♆ ° ′	♇ ° ′
1	6 39 1.3	0 .0	0 .0	2N 6.3	1N59.1	1S47.5	0S 9.6	0N23.9	2S 3.5	0N39.4	1N36.4	16N15.7
4	6 50 51.0	0 .0	0 .0	1S28.7	1 33.4	1 46.9	0 5.5	0 23.7	2 2.8	0 39.5	1 36.5	16 17.4
7	7 2 40.7	0 .0	0 .0	4 13.4	1 7.1	1 45.6	0 1.5	0 23.5	2 2.1	0 39.6	1 36.6	16 19.1
10	7 14 30.4	0 .0	0 .0	5 15.5	0 41.2	1 43.5	0N 2.2	0 23.3	2 1.4	0 39.7	1 36.7	16 20.8
13	7 26 20.0	0 .0	0 .0	4 17.3	0 16.1	1 40.7	0 5.9	0 23.1	2 .6	0 39.8	1 36.8	16 22.5
16	7 38 9.7	0 .0	0 .0	1 26.7	0S 7.6	1 37.1	0 9.4	0 22.9	1 59.8	0 39.9	1 36.9	16 24.1
19	7 49 59.4	0 .0	0 .0	2N14.7	0 29.8	1 32.7	0 12.7	0 22.7	1 59.0	0 40.0	1 37.0	16 25.7
22	8 1 49.1	0 .0	0 .0	4 52.8	0 50.3	1 27.6	0 15.9	0 22.5	1 58.2	0 40.1	1 37.1	16 27.3
25	8 13 38.7	0 .0	0 .0	4 58.2	1 8.7	1 21.8	0 18.9	0 22.4	1 57.4	0 40.2	1 37.2	16 28.8
28	8 25 28.4	0 .0	0 .0	2 31.3	1 25.0	1 15.2	0 21.9	0 22.2	1 56.6	0 40.3	1 37.4	16 30.3
31	8 37 18.1	0 .0	0 .0	1S 3.1	1 38.9	1 7.9	0 24.7	0 22.0	1 55.7	0 40.4	1 37.5	16 31.8

RIGHT ASCENSION

DAY	EPHEM. SID. TIME h m s	☉ ° ′	☊ ° ′	☽ ° ′	☿ ° ′	♀ ° ′	♂ ° ′	♃ ° ′	♄ ° ′	♅ ° ′	♆ ° ′	♇ ° ′
1	6 39 1.3	10♑31.1	9♒ 1.4	12♋50.3	16♐13.2	13♒46.2	3♈10.1	21♐42.2	28♉42.6	16♎56.2	2♐25.9	8♎28.3
2	6 42 57.9	11 37.4	8 58.1	27 26.7	17 16.5	15 1.4	3 45.2	21 56.6	28R39.3	16 57.3	2 27.9	8 28.6
3	6 46 54.5	12 43.5	8 54.9	10♌59.1	18 23.4	16 16.2	4 20.3	22 11.0	28 36.1	16 58.4	2 29.8	8 28.9
4	6 50 51.0	13 49.6	8 51.6	23 30.4	19 33.6	17 30.7	4 55.5	22 25.3	28 33.0	16 59.5	2 31.8	8 29.2
5	6 54 47.6	14 55.6	8 48.4	5♍12.1	20 46.8	18 44.7	5 30.7	22 39.6	28 30.0	17 .5	2 33.7	8 29.4
6	6 58 44.1	16 1.5	8 45.2	16 19.5	22 2.6	19 58.5	6 6.0	22 53.9	28 27.0	17 1.4	2 35.6	8 29.6
7	7 2 40.7	17 7.3	8 41.9	27 8.5	23 20.8	21 11.9	6 41.3	23 8.1	28 24.2	17 2.3	2 37.5	8 29.8
8	7 6 37.3	18 13.0	8 38.7	7♎55.0	24 41.3	22 24.9	7 16.8	23 22.3	28 21.5	17 3.1	2 39.4	8 30.0
9	7 10 33.8	19 18.6	8 35.4	18 53.7	26 3.8	23 37.6	7 52.2	23 36.4	28 18.9	17 3.9	2 41.3	8 30.1
10	7 14 30.4	20 24.0	8 32.2	0♏18.2	27 28.0	24 49.9	8 27.8	23 50.6	28 16.3	17 4.6	2 43.1	8 30.2
11	7 18 26.9	21 29.4	8 28.9	12 19.6	28 54.0	26 1.9	9 3.4	24 4.7	28 14.0	17 5.3	2 44.9	8 30.2
12	7 22 23.5	22 34.5	8 25.7	25 4.5	0♑21.5	27 13.5	9 39.0	24 18.7	28 11.7	17 6.0	2 46.7	8 30.3
13	7 26 20.0	23 39.6	8 22.4	8♐32.8	1 50.3	28 24.8	10 14.7	24 32.7	28 9.4	17 6.5	2 48.5	8R30.2
14	7 30 16.6	24 44.4	8 19.2	22 35.3	3 20.4	29 35.8	10 50.5	24 46.7	28 7.3	17 7.1	2 50.2	8 30.2
15	7 34 13.2	25 49.2	8 15.9	6♑54.8	4 51.7	0♓46.4	11 26.4	25 .6	28 5.3	17 7.5	2 51.9	8 30.1
16	7 38 9.7	26 53.7	8 12.7	21 10.9	6 24.1	1 56.8	12 2.3	25 14.4	28 3.5	17 7.9	2 53.6	8 30.0
17	7 42 6.3	27 58.1	8 9.4	5♒ 6.9	7 57.5	3 6.7	12 38.2	25 28.2	28 1.7	17 8.3	2 55.2	8 29.9
18	7 46 2.8	29 2.3	8 6.1	18 34.4	9 31.8	4 16.4	13 14.3	25 41.9	28 .0	17 8.6	2 56.9	8 29.7
19	7 49 59.4	0♒ 6.4	8 2.9	1♓34.8	11 6.9	5 25.8	13 50.4	25 55.6	27 58.5	17 8.9	2 58.5	8 29.5
20	7 53 56.0	1 10.2	7 59.6	14 16.9	12 42.8	6 34.9	14 26.5	26 9.2	27 57.0	17 9.1	3 .0	8 29.2
21	7 57 52.5	2 13.9	7 56.4	26 54.3	14 19.4	7 43.6	15 2.8	26 22.8	27 55.7	17 9.2	3 1.6	8 29.0
22	8 1 49.1	3 17.4	7 53.1	9♈43.0	15 56.6	8 52.1	15 39.0	26 36.3	27 54.5	17 9.3	3 3.1	8 28.7
23	8 5 45.6	4 20.7	7 49.9	22 58.5	17 34.5	10 .3	16 15.4	26 49.7	27 53.4	17 9.3	3 4.6	8 28.3
24	8 9 42.2	5 23.8	7 46.6	6♉53.0	19 13.0	11 8.2	16 51.8	27 3.1	27 52.5	17 9.3	3 6.1	8 28.0
25	8 13 38.7	6 26.7	7 43.4	21 31.2	20 51.9	12 15.8	17 28.3	27 16.4	27 51.6	17 9.3	3 7.5	8 27.6
26	8 17 35.3	7 29.3	7 40.1	6♊45.7	22 31.4	13 23.2	18 4.8	27 29.6	27 50.8	17R 9.2	3 8.9	8 27.2
27	8 21 31.9	8 31.8	7 36.8	22 16.2	24 11.2	14 30.3	18 41.4	27 42.8	27 50.2	17 9.0	3 10.3	8 26.7
28	8 25 28.4	9 34.1	7 33.6	7♋34.3	25 51.5	15 37.2	19 18.1	27 55.9	27 49.7	17 8.8	3 11.6	8 26.2
29	8 29 25.0	10 36.2	7 30.3	22 14.0	27 32.2	16 43.8	19 54.8	28 8.9	27 49.3	17 8.5	3 12.9	8 25.7
30	8 33 21.5	11 38.0	7 27.1	6♌ .1	29 13.2	17 50.2	20 31.6	28 21.9	27 49.0	17 8.2	3 14.2	8 25.2
31	8 37 18.1	12 39.7	7 23.8	18 50.0	0♒54.5	18 56.4	21 8.5	28 34.7	27 48.8	17 7.8	3 15.5	8 24.6

DECLINATION

DAY	EPHEM. SID. TIME h m s	☉ ° ′	☊ ° ′	☽ ° ′	☿ ° ′	♀ ° ′	♂ ° ′	♃ ° ′	♄ ° ′	♅ ° ′	♆ ° ′	♇ ° ′
1	6 39 1.3	23S 5.5	0S19.5	25N 2.0	20S50.7	19S15.1	1N11.9	22S49.6	18N13.8	6S29.4	19S23.6	14N 4.8
4	6 50 51.0	22 50.1	0 19.5	12 54.1	21 32.2	18 11.4	2 1.9	22 52.0	18 12.5	6 30.6	19 24.6	14 6.2
7	7 2 40.7	22 30.7	0 19.6	3S21.8	22 11.0	17 3.3	2 51.8	22 54.2	18 11.5	6 31.7	19 25.5	14 7.8
10	7 14 30.4	22 7.2	0 19.6	17 56.6	22 44.3	15 51.0	3 41.5	22 56.1	18 10.7	6 32.5	19 26.3	14 9.5
13	7 26 20.0	21 39.8	0 19.7	26 18.8	23 9.9	14 34.9	4 31.0	22 57.9	18 10.0	6 33.2	19 27.2	14 11.3
16	7 38 9.7	21 8.6	0 19.7	23 28.5	23 26.5	13 15.4	5 20.2	22 59.4	18 9.6	6 33.6	19 28.0	14 13.2
19	7 49 59.4	20 33.8	0 19.7	9 15.9	23 33.0	11 52.8	6 9.1	23 .8	18 9.4	6 33.9	19 28.7	14 15.2
22	8 1 49.1	19 55.5	0 19.8	9N29.6	23 28.7	10 27.5	6 57.6	23 1.9	18 9.4	6 34.0	19 29.4	14 17.3
25	8 13 38.7	19 13.9	0 19.8	23 52.9	23 13.0	8 59.9	7 45.6	23 2.9	18 9.7	6 33.9	19 30.0	14 19.4
28	8 25 28.4	18 29.0	0 19.9	25 47.2	22 45.4	7 30.3	8 33.0	23 3.6	18 10.1	6 33.6	19 30.6	14 21.6
31	8 37 18.1	17 41.2	0 19.9	14 49.8	22 5.6	5 59.1	9 19.9	23 4.2	18 10.8	6 33.1	19 31.1	14 23.9

FEBRUARY 1972

LONGITUDE

DAY	EPHEM. SID. TIME h m s	☉ ° ′	☊ ° ′	☾ ° ′	☿ ° ′	♀ ° ′	♂ ° ′	♃ ° ′	♄ ° ′	♅ ° ′	♆ ° ′	♇ ° ′
1	8 41 14.6	11 ♒ 13.7	4 ♒ 59.5	29 ♌ 30.3	0 ♒ 1.6	18 ♓ 42.1	23 ♈ 40.8	28 ♐ 53.4	29 ♉ 34.7	18 ♎ 17.2	4 ♐ 54.9	1 ♎ 50.5
2	8 45 11.2	12 14.6	4 56.3	12 ♍ 3.0	1 37.8	19 54.4	24 20.3	29 5.1	29 D 34.9	18 R 16.7	4 56.0	1 R 49.6
3	8 49 7.7	13 15.5	4 53.1	24 21.8	3 14.8	21 6.7	24 59.9	29 16.7	29 35.1	18 16.1	4 57.1	1 48.7
4	8 53 4.3	14 16.3	4 49.9	6 ♎ 28.9	4 52.4	22 18.9	25 39.5	29 28.2	29 35.5	18 15.5	4 58.2	1 47.7
5	8 57 .9	15 17.2	4 46.8	18 27.3	6 30.8	23 31.0	26 19.1	29 39.7	29 35.9	18 14.8	4 59.2	1 46.7
6	9 0 57.4	16 18.0	4 43.6	0 ♏ 20.6	8 9.9	24 43.0	26 58.7	29 51.1	29 36.5	18 14.0	5 .2	1 45.7
7	9 4 54.0	17 18.8	4 40.4	12 13.2	9 49.8	25 54.9	27 38.3	0 ♑ 2.4	29 37.2	18 13.3	5 1.2	1 44.7
8	9 8 50.5	18 19.6	4 37.2	24 9.6	11 30.5	27 6.8	28 17.9	0 13.6	29 38.0	18 12.4	5 2.2	1 43.6
9	9 12 47.1	19 20.4	4 34.1	6 ♐ 14.7	13 11.9	28 18.5	28 57.5	0 24.8	29 38.9	18 11.5	5 3.1	1 42.5
10	9 16 43.6	20 21.1	4 30.9	18 33.0	14 54.2	29 30.2	29 37.1	0 35.8	29 39.9	18 10.6	5 4.0	1 41.4
11	9 20 40.2	21 21.9	4 27.7	1 ♑ 8.7	16 37.2	0 ♈ 41.7	0 ♉ 16.7	0 46.8	29 41.1	18 9.6	5 4.8	1 40.3
12	9 24 36.7	22 22.6	4 24.5	14 4.9	18 21.1	1 53.2	0 56.3	0 57.7	29 42.3	18 8.5	5 5.6	1 39.1
13	9 28 33.3	23 23.3	4 21.4	27 23.8	20 5.8	3 4.5	1 35.9	1 8.5	29 43.7	18 7.4	5 6.4	1 37.9
14	9 32 29.9	24 24.0	4 18.2	11 ♒ 5.4	21 51.4	4 15.8	2 15.6	1 19.2	29 45.2	18 6.3	5 7.2	1 36.7
15	9 36 26.4	25 24.6	4 15.0	25 8.1	23 37.8	5 27.0	2 55.2	1 29.8	29 46.8	18 5.1	5 7.9	1 35.5
16	9 40 23.0	26 25.3	4 11.8	9 ♓ 28.1	25 25.0	6 38.0	3 34.8	1 40.3	29 48.5	18 3.8	5 8.6	1 34.2
17	9 44 19.5	27 25.9	4 8.6	24 .0	27 13.1	7 48.9	4 14.4	1 50.7	29 50.3	18 2.5	5 9.3	1 32.9
18	9 48 16.1	28 26.5	4 5.5	8 ♈ 37.3	29 2.0	8 59.8	4 54.1	2 1.0	29 52.2	18 1.2	5 9.9	1 31.6
19	9 52 12.6	29 27.0	4 2.3	23 13.3	0 ♓ 51.7	10 10.5	5 33.7	2 11.2	29 54.2	17 59.8	5 10.5	1 30.3
20	9 56 9.2	0 ♓ 27.5	3 59.1	7 ♉ 42.3	2 42.1	11 21.0	6 13.3	2 21.3	29 56.4	17 58.4	5 11.0	1 29.0
21	10 0 5.7	1 28.0	3 55.9	21 60.0	4 33.2	12 31.5	6 52.9	2 31.3	29 58.6	17 56.9	5 11.5	1 27.6
22	10 4 2.3	2 28.5	3 52.8	6 ♊ 3.8	6 25.1	13 41.9	7 32.6	2 41.2	0 ♊ 1.0	17 55.4	5 12.1	1 26.3
23	10 7 58.9	3 28.9	3 49.6	19 52.5	8 17.5	14 52.0	8 12.2	2 51.0	0 3.5	17 53.8	5 12.5	1 24.9
24	10 11 55.4	4 29.3	3 46.4	3 ♋ 26.1	10 10.4	16 2.1	8 51.8	3 .6	0 6.0	17 52.2	5 13.0	1 23.5
25	10 15 52.0	5 29.7	3 43.2	16 45.5	12 3.7	17 12.0	9 31.4	3 10.2	0 8.7	17 50.6	5 13.3	1 22.0
26	10 19 48.5	6 30.0	3 40.0	29 51.6	13 57.2	18 21.7	10 10.9	3 19.6	0 11.5	17 48.9	5 13.7	1 20.6
27	10 23 45.1	7 30.3	3 36.9	12 ♌ 45.4	15 50.8	19 31.4	10 50.5	3 28.9	0 14.4	17 47.1	5 14.0	1 19.1
28	10 27 41.6	8 30.6	3 33.7	25 27.6	17 44.2	20 40.8	11 30.0	3 38.1	0 17.3	17 45.4	5 14.3	1 17.6
29	10 31 38.2	9 30.8	3 30.5	7 ♍ 58.9	19 37.4	21 50.1	12 9.6	3 47.2	0 20.4	17 43.5	5 14.5	1 16.2

LATITUDE

DAY	SID. TIME	☉	☊	☾	☿	♀	♂	♃	♄	♅	♆	♇
1	8 41 14.6	0 .0	0 .0	2 S 10.4	1 S 43.0	1 S 5.3	0 N 25.6	0 N 22.0	1 S 55.5	0 N 40.4	1 N 37.6	16 N 32.2
4	8 53 4.3	0 .0	0 .0	4 37.7	1 53.3	0 57.1	0 28.2	0 21.8	1 54.6	0 40.5	1 37.7	16 33.6
7	9 4 54.0	0 .0	0 .0	5 13.9	2 .7	0 48.2	0 30.8	0 21.7	1 53.8	0 40.6	1 37.8	16 34.9
10	9 16 43.6	0 .0	0 .0	3 50.2	2 4.7	0 38.6	0 33.2	0 21.5	1 53.0	0 40.7	1 38.0	16 36.2
13	9 28 33.3	0 .0	0 .0	0 43.2	2 5.2	0 28.5	0 35.5	0 21.4	1 52.1	0 40.8	1 38.1	16 37.4
16	9 40 23.0	0 .0	0 .0	2 N 57.4	2 1.6	0 17.8	0 37.7	0 21.2	1 51.3	0 40.8	1 38.3	16 38.5
19	9 52 12.6	0 .0	0 .0	5 7.2	1 53.7	0 6.6	0 39.8	0 21.1	1 50.5	0 40.9	1 38.4	16 39.6
22	10 4 2.3	0 .0	0 .0	4 28.9	1 40.9	0 N 5.1	0 41.9	0 21.0	1 49.7	0 41.0	1 38.6	16 40.5
25	10 15 52.0	0 .0	0 .0	1 38.4	1 22.9	0 17.1	0 43.8	0 20.8	1 48.9	0 41.0	1 38.8	16 41.5
28	10 27 41.6	0 .0	0 .0	1 S 49.1	0 59.3	0 29.6	0 45.6	0 20.7	1 48.1	0 41.1	1 38.9	16 42.3

RIGHT ASCENSION

DAY	SID. TIME	☉	☊	☾	☿	♀	♂	♃	♄	♅	♆	♇
1	8 41 14.6	13 ♒ 41.2	7 ♒ 20.5	0 ♍ 50.7	2 ♒ 36.1	20 ♓ 2.4	21 ♈ 45.4	28 ♐ 47.6	27 ♉ 48.8	17 ♎ 7.4	3 ♐ 16.7	8 ♎ 24.1
2	8 45 11.2	14 42.5	7 17.3	12 14.2	4 18.0	21 8.2	22 22.4	29 .3	27 D 48.9	17 R 7.0	3 17.9	8 R 23.5
3	8 49 7.7	15 43.5	7 14.0	23 14.7	6 .1	22 13.7	22 59.5	29 12.9	27 49.1	17 6.4	3 19.1	8 22.8
4	8 53 4.3	16 44.4	7 10.8	4 ♎ 6.5	7 42.5	23 19.1	23 36.6	29 25.5	27 49.4	17 5.9	3 20.2	8 22.2
5	8 57 .9	17 45.0	7 7.5	15 3.7	9 25.1	24 24.3	24 13.8	29 38.0	27 49.8	17 5.2	3 21.3	8 21.5
6	9 0 57.4	18 45.5	7 4.2	26 19.2	11 7.8	25 29.3	24 51.0	29 50.3	27 50.3	17 4.6	3 22.4	8 20.7
7	9 4 54.0	19 45.7	7 1.0	8 ♏ 4.2	12 50.8	26 34.2	25 28.3	0 ♑ 2.6	27 51.0	17 3.9	3 23.4	8 20.0
8	9 8 50.5	20 45.8	6 57.7	20 27.0	14 33.9	27 38.9	26 5.7	0 14.8	27 51.8	17 3.1	3 24.4	8 19.2
9	9 12 47.1	21 45.7	6 54.4	3 ♐ 30.6	16 17.2	28 43.5	26 43.2	0 26.9	27 52.6	17 2.3	3 25.4	8 18.4
10	9 16 43.6	22 45.3	6 51.2	17 11.0	18 .6	29 48.0	27 20.7	0 39.0	27 53.6	17 1.4	3 26.3	8 17.6
11	9 20 40.2	23 44.8	6 47.9	1 ♑ 16.6	19 44.1	0 ♈ 52.3	27 58.4	0 50.9	27 54.8	17 .5	3 27.2	8 16.7
12	9 24 36.7	24 44.1	6 44.6	15 30.7	21 27.8	1 56.5	28 36.0	1 2.7	27 56.0	16 59.5	3 28.1	8 15.8
13	9 28 33.3	25 43.2	6 41.4	29 36.8	23 11.6	3 .7	29 13.8	1 14.4	27 57.3	16 58.5	3 28.9	8 14.9
14	9 32 29.9	26 42.1	6 38.1	13 ♒ 23.6	24 55.5	4 4.7	29 51.6	1 26.1	27 58.8	16 57.4	3 29.7	8 14.0
15	9 36 26.4	27 40.8	6 34.8	26 48.1	26 39.5	5 8.6	0 ♉ 29.6	1 37.6	28 .4	16 56.3	3 30.5	8 13.0
16	9 40 23.0	28 39.3	6 31.6	9 ♓ 55.3	28 23.5	6 12.5	1 7.5	1 49.0	28 2.0	16 55.2	3 31.2	8 12.0
17	9 44 19.5	29 37.7	6 28.3	22 55.8	0 ♓ 7.7	7 16.2	1 45.6	2 .3	28 3.9	16 54.0	3 31.9	8 11.0
18	9 48 16.1	0 ♓ 35.9	6 25.0	6 ♈ 3.4	1 51.8	8 20.0	2 23.8	2 11.5	28 5.8	16 52.7	3 32.6	8 10.0
19	9 52 12.6	1 33.9	6 21.8	19 32.2	3 36.0	9 23.6	3 2.0	2 22.6	28 7.8	16 51.5	3 33.2	8 9.0
20	9 56 9.2	2 31.7	6 18.5	3 ♉ 33.2	5 20.2	10 27.2	3 40.3	2 33.6	28 9.9	16 50.1	3 33.8	8 7.9
21	10 0 5.7	3 29.3	6 15.2	18 10.9	7 4.4	11 30.7	4 18.6	2 44.4	28 12.2	16 48.8	3 34.3	8 6.8
22	10 4 2.3	4 26.9	6 11.9	3 ♊ 19.1	8 48.4	12 34.3	4 57.1	2 55.2	28 14.6	16 47.4	3 34.9	8 5.7
23	10 7 58.9	5 24.2	6 8.7	18 40.1	10 32.3	13 37.8	5 35.6	3 5.8	28 17.1	16 45.9	3 35.4	8 4.6
24	10 11 55.4	6 21.3	6 5.4	3 ♋ 49.4	12 16.0	14 41.2	6 14.2	3 16.3	28 19.7	16 44.5	3 35.8	8 3.5
25	10 15 52.0	7 18.3	6 2.1	18 23.7	13 59.4	15 44.6	6 52.9	3 26.7	28 22.3	16 42.9	3 36.2	8 2.3
26	10 19 48.5	8 15.1	5 58.9	2 ♌ 8.6	15 42.4	16 48.0	7 31.6	3 37.0	28 25.1	16 41.4	3 36.6	8 1.1
27	10 23 45.1	9 11.8	5 55.6	15 1.0	17 24.8	17 51.4	8 10.4	3 47.1	28 28.0	16 39.7	3 37.0	7 59.9
28	10 27 41.6	10 8.4	5 52.3	27 6.2	19 6.6	18 54.8	8 49.3	3 57.1	28 31.0	16 38.1	3 37.3	7 58.7
29	10 31 38.2	11 4.8	5 49.0	8 ♍ 35.0	20 47.6	19 58.2	9 28.3	4 7.0	28 34.2	16 36.4	3 37.5	7 57.5

DECLINATION

DAY	SID. TIME	☉	☊	☾	☿	♀	♂	♃	♄	♅	♆	♇
1	8 41 14.6	17 S 24.6	0 S 19.9	9 N 36.7	21 S 49.6	5 S 28.3	9 N 35.5	23 S 4.4	18 N 11.1	6 S 32.9	19 S 31.3	14 N 24.7
4	8 53 4.3	16 33.1	0 20.0	6 S 49.3	20 53.0	3 55.4	10 21.5	23 4.8	18 12.1	6 32.2	19 31.7	14 27.0
7	9 4 54.0	15 38.9	0 20.0	20 28.9	19 43.6	2 21.6	11 6.8	23 5.0	18 13.2	6 31.2	19 32.1	14 29.4
10	9 16 43.6	14 42.4	0 20.0	26 46.3	18 21.3	0 47.3	11 51.4	23 5.0	18 14.6	6 30.1	19 32.5	14 31.9
13	9 28 33.3	13 43.6	0 20.1	21 23.5	16 45.9	0 N 47.2	12 35.3	23 5.0	18 16.2	6 28.9	19 32.8	14 34.3
16	9 40 23.0	12 42.7	0 20.1	5 16.8	14 57.6	2 21.7	13 18.2	23 4.8	18 18.1	6 27.4	19 33.0	14 36.8
19	9 52 12.6	11 40.0	0 20.2	13 N 46.5	12 56.5	3 55.7	14 .3	23 4.5	18 20.1	6 25.8	19 33.2	14 39.3
22	10 4 2.3	10 35.7	0 20.2	25 44.1	10 43.2	5 29.0	14 41.4	23 4.1	18 22.3	6 24.1	19 33.3	14 41.8
25	10 15 52.0	9 29.9	0 20.2	24 1.3	8 18.9	7 1.2	15 21.5	23 3.6	18 24.7	6 22.2	19 33.4	14 44.3
28	10 27 41.6	8 22.8	0 20.3	11 19.4	5 45.5	8 32.1	16 .5	23 3.0	18 27.2	6 20.1	19 33.4	14 46.8

MARCH 1972

LONGITUDE

DAY	EPHEM. SID. TIME h m s	☉ ° ′	☊ ° ′	☽ ° ′	☿ ° ′	♀ ° ′	♂ ° ′	♃ ° ′	♄ ° ′	♅ ° ′	♆ ° ′	♇ ° ′
1	10 35 34.7	10♓31.0	3♒27.3	20♍19.8	21♓29.8	22♈59.2	12♉49.1	3♑56.2	0♊23.6	17♎41.7	5♐14.8	1♎14.6
2	10 39 31.3	11 31.2	3 24.2	2♎31.4	23 21.4	24 8.2	13 28.6	4 5.1	0 26.8	17R39.8	5 14.9	1R13.1
3	10 43 27.8	12 31.4	3 21.0	14 34.6	25 11.7	25 17.0	14 8.1	4 13.8	0 30.2	17 37.9	5 15.1	1 11.6
4	10 47 24.4	13 31.5	3 17.8	26 31.4	27 .3	26 25.7	14 47.6	4 22.4	0 33.7	17 35.9	5 15.2	1 10.1
5	10 51 20.9	14 31.6	3 14.6	8♏24.1	28 46.7	27 34.2	15 27.1	4 30.9	0 37.3	17 33.9	5 15.3	1 8.5
6	10 55 17.5	15 31.6	3 11.4	20 16.0	0♈30.7	28 42.5	16 6.6	4 39.2	0 40.9	17 31.9	5 15.3	1 6.9
7	10 59 14.1	16 31.7	3 8.3	2♐10.9	2 11.5	29 50.6	16 46.1	4 47.5	0 44.7	17 29.8	5 15.4	1 5.4
8	11 3 10.6	17 31.7	3 5.1	14 13.2	3 48.8	0♉58.5	17 25.5	4 55.5	0 48.5	17 27.7	5R15.3	1 3.8
9	11 7 7.2	18 31.7	3 1.9	26 27.8	5 21.9	2 6.3	18 5.0	5 3.5	0 52.5	17 25.5	5 15.3	1 2.2
10	11 11 3.7	19 31.6	2 58.7	8♑59.6	6 50.4	3 13.9	18 44.4	5 11.3	0 56.5	17 23.4	5 15.2	1 .6
11	11 15 .3	20 31.6	2 55.6	21 53.1	8 13.7	4 21.2	19 23.8	5 19.0	1 .6	17 21.2	5 15.1	0 59.0
12	11 18 56.8	21 31.5	2 52.4	5♒12.0	9 31.3	5 28.4	20 3.2	5 26.6	1 4.8	17 19.0	5 14.9	0 57.3
13	11 22 53.4	22 31.3	2 49.2	18 58.4	10 42.7	6 35.4	20 42.6	5 34.0	1 9.1	17 16.7	5 14.7	0 55.7
14	11 26 49.9	23 31.2	2 46.0	3♓11.9	11 47.6	7 42.2	21 22.1	5 41.3	1 13.6	17 14.5	5 14.6	0 54.1
15	11 30 46.5	24 31.0	2 42.8	17 49.2	12 45.3	8 48.8	22 1.5	5 48.4	1 18.1	17 12.2	5 14.3	0 52.5
16	11 34 43.0	25 30.8	2 39.7	2♈44.0	13 35.7	9 55.1	22 40.8	5 55.4	1 22.6	17 9.8	5 14.0	0 50.9
17	11 38 39.6	26 30.6	2 36.5	17 47.5	14 18.3	11 1.2	23 20.2	6 2.2	1 27.3	17 7.5	5 13.7	0 49.2
18	11 42 36.1	27 30.3	2 33.3	2♉49.9	14 53.0	12 7.1	23 59.6	6 8.9	1 32.0	17 5.1	5 13.4	0 47.6
19	11 46 32.7	28 30.0	2 30.1	17 41.9	15 19.6	13 12.7	24 38.9	6 15.4	1 36.8	17 2.7	5 13.0	0 45.9
20	11 50 29.2	29 29.6	2 27.0	2♊16.5	15 38.0	14 18.1	25 18.2	6 21.8	1 41.7	17 .3	5 12.6	0 44.3
21	11 54 25.8	0♈29.2	2 23.8	16 29.2	15 48.3	15 23.2	25 57.5	6 28.0	1 46.7	16 57.9	5 12.1	0 42.6
22	11 58 22.4	1 28.8	2 20.6	0♋18.8	15 50.5	16 28.1	26 36.8	6 34.1	1 51.8	16 55.4	5 11.7	0 41.0
23	12 2 18.9	2 28.3	2 17.4	13 46.0	15R44.8	17 32.6	27 16.1	6 40.0	1 56.9	16 52.9	5 11.1	0 39.3
24	12 6 15.5	3 27.8	2 14.2	26 53.2	15 31.5	18 37.0	27 55.4	6 45.8	2 2.1	16 50.5	5 10.6	0 37.7
25	12 10 12.0	4 27.2	2 11.1	9♌43.3	15 11.1	19 41.0	28 34.6	6 51.4	2 7.4	16 48.0	5 10.0	0 36.0
26	12 14 8.6	5 26.6	2 7.9	22 19.4	14 44.2	20 44.7	29 13.8	6 56.8	2 12.8	16 45.4	5 9.4	0 34.4
27	12 18 5.1	6 26.0	2 4.7	4♍44.2	14 11.2	21 48.1	29 53.0	7 2.1	2 18.2	16 42.9	5 8.8	0 32.7
28	12 22 1.7	7 25.3	2 1.5	16 59.9	13 33.2	22 51.2	0♊32.2	7 7.2	2 23.7	16 40.4	5 8.1	0 31.1
29	12 25 58.2	8 24.6	1 58.4	29 8.4	12 50.8	23 53.9	1 11.4	7 12.2	2 29.3	16 37.8	5 7.5	0 29.5
30	12 29 54.8	9 23.9	1 55.2	11♎10.9	12 5.0	24 56.4	1 50.5	7 16.9	2 35.0	16 35.3	5 6.7	0 27.9
31	12 33 51.3	10 23.1	1 52.0	23 8.5	11 16.9	25 58.5	2 29.7	7 21.6	2 40.7	16 32.7	5 6.0	0 26.2

LATITUDE

DAY	EPHEM. SID. TIME	☉	☊	☽	☿	♀	♂	♃	♄	♅	♆	♇
1	10 35 34.7	0 .0	0 .0	3S41.6	0S40.5	0N38.1	0N46.8	0N20.6	1S47.6	0N41.1	1N39.0	16N42.8
4	10 47 24.4	0 .0	0 .0	5 6.5	0 8.0	0 51.1	0 48.5	0 20.4	1 46.8	0 41.2	1 39.2	16 43.5
7	10 59 14.1	0 .0	0 .0	4 33.8	0N29.0	1 4.3	0 50.1	0 20.3	1 46.0	0 41.2	1 39.3	16 44.1
10	11 11 3.7	0 .0	0 .0	2 12.5	1 8.8	1 17.6	0 51.7	0 20.2	1 45.3	0 41.3	1 39.5	16 44.6
13	11 22 53.4	0 .0	0 .0	1N18.2	1 48.9	1 31.0	0 53.1	0 20.0	1 44.6	0 41.3	1 39.6	16 45.0
16	11 34 43.0	0 .0	0 .0	4 21.7	2 26.2	1 44.5	0 54.5	0 19.9	1 43.9	0 41.4	1 39.8	16 45.4
19	11 46 32.7	0 .0	0 .0	4 56.6	2 57.3	1 57.9	0 55.9	0 19.7	1 43.2	0 41.4	1 39.9	16 45.6
22	11 58 22.4	0 .0	0 .0	2 47.9	3 18.6	2 11.2	0 57.1	0 19.6	1 42.5	0 41.4	1 40.1	16 45.8
25	12 10 12.0	0 .0	0 .0	0S33.1	3 26.9	2 24.3	0 58.3	0 19.4	1 41.9	0 41.4	1 40.2	16 45.8
28	12 22 1.7	0 .0	0 .0	3 29.7	3 19.9	2 37.1	0 59.4	0 19.3	1 41.2	0 41.4	1 40.4	16 45.8
31	12 33 51.3	0 .0	0 .0	4 57.3	2 57.3	2 49.5	1 .5	0 19.1	1 40.6	0 41.4	1 40.5	16 45.7

RIGHT ASCENSION

DAY	EPHEM. SID. TIME	☉	☊	☽	☿	♀	♂	♃	♄	♅	♆	♇
1	10 35 34.7	12♓ 1.1	5♒45.8	19♍39.9	22♓27.4	21♈ 1.6	10♉ 7.3	4♑16.7	28♉37.4	16♎34.7	3♐37.8	7♎56.2
2	10 39 31.3	12 57.2	5 42.5	0♎34.3	24 6.0	22 5.0	10 46.4	4 26.3	28 40.7	16R32.9	3 38.0	7R54.9
3	10 43 27.8	13 53.3	5 39.2	11 30.9	25 43.1	23 8.5	11 25.6	4 35.8	28 44.1	16 31.2	3 38.2	7 53.6
4	10 47 24.4	14 49.2	5 35.9	22 41.5	27 18.2	24 11.9	12 4.8	4 45.2	28 47.6	16 29.3	3 38.3	7 52.3
5	10 51 20.9	15 45.0	5 32.6	4♏16.5	28 51.2	25 15.4	12 44.2	4 54.4	28 51.3	16 27.5	3 38.4	7 51.0
6	10 55 17.5	16 40.7	5 29.4	16 23.4	0♈21.6	26 18.9	13 23.6	5 3.4	28 55.0	16 25.6	3 38.4	7 49.7
7	10 59 14.1	17 36.3	5 26.1	29 5.8	1 49.1	27 22.4	14 3.1	5 12.4	28 58.8	16 23.7	3 38.5	7 48.4
8	11 3 10.6	18 31.8	5 22.8	12♐21.8	3 13.2	28 26.0	14 42.6	5 21.2	29 2.7	16 21.7	3 38.5	7 47.0
9	11 7 7.2	19 27.2	5 19.5	26 3.1	4 33.5	29 29.6	15 22.2	5 29.8	29 6.7	16 19.7	3R38.4	7 45.6
10	11 11 3.7	20 22.5	5 16.2	9♑57.2	5 49.5	0♉33.3	16 2.0	5 38.3	29 10.9	16 17.7	3 38.3	7 44.3
11	11 15 .3	21 17.7	5 13.0	23 50.3	7 .9	1 37.0	16 41.7	5 46.7	29 15.1	16 15.7	3 38.2	7 42.9
12	11 18 56.8	22 12.9	5 9.7	7♒32.2	8 7.1	2 40.7	17 21.6	5 54.9	29 19.4	16 13.6	3 38.1	7 41.5
13	11 22 53.4	23 8.0	5 6.4	20 59.0	9 7.8	3 44.5	18 1.5	6 2.9	29 23.8	16 11.5	3 37.9	7 40.1
14	11 26 49.9	24 3.1	5 3.1	4♓13.7	10 2.7	4 48.4	18 41.6	6 10.8	29 28.3	16 9.5	3 37.7	7 38.7
15	11 30 46.5	24 58.1	4 59.8	17 25.2	10 51.3	5 52.3	19 21.7	6 18.6	29 32.9	16 7.3	3 37.5	7 37.3
16	11 34 43.0	25 53.0	4 56.5	0♈46.1	11 33.2	6 56.2	20 1.9	6 26.1	29 37.6	16 5.2	3 37.2	7 35.8
17	11 38 39.6	26 47.8	4 53.3	14 30.0	12 8.4	8 .2	20 42.1	6 33.6	29 42.3	16 3.0	3 36.8	7 34.4
18	11 42 36.1	27 42.6	4 50.0	28 48.0	12 36.6	9 4.2	21 22.4	6 40.8	29 47.2	16 .8	3 36.5	7 32.9
19	11 46 32.7	28 37.4	4 46.7	13♉44.6	12 57.7	10 8.2	22 2.8	6 47.9	29 52.1	15 58.6	3 36.1	7 31.5
20	11 50 29.2	29 32.1	4 43.4	29 13.0	13 11.5	11 12.2	22 43.3	6 54.8	29 57.1	15 56.3	3 35.7	7 30.0
21	11 54 25.8	0♈26.8	4 40.1	14♊54.1	13 18.3	12 16.3	23 23.8	7 1.6	0♊ 2.2	15 54.1	3 35.2	7 28.5
22	11 58 22.4	1 21.4	4 36.8	0♋20.9	13R18.0	13 20.3	24 4.4	7 8.2	0 7.4	15 51.8	3 34.7	7 27.1
23	12 2 18.9	2 16.0	4 33.6	15 8.8	13 11.0	14 24.4	24 45.1	7 14.6	0 12.7	15 49.5	3 34.2	7 25.6
24	12 6 15.5	3 10.6	4 30.3	29 3.0	12 57.6	15 28.5	25 25.8	7 20.8	0 18.1	15 47.2	3 33.7	7 24.1
25	12 10 12.0	4 5.2	4 27.0	12♌ .6	12 38.1	16 32.5	26 6.6	7 26.9	0 23.5	15 44.9	3 33.1	7 22.6
26	12 14 8.6	4 59.8	4 23.7	24 8.2	12 13.2	17 36.6	26 47.4	7 32.8	0 29.0	15 42.5	3 32.5	7 21.1
27	12 18 5.1	5 54.4	4 20.4	5♍37.1	11 43.5	18 40.5	27 28.4	7 38.5	0 34.6	15 40.2	3 31.8	7 19.7
28	12 22 1.7	6 48.9	4 17.1	16 40.8	11 9.8	19 44.5	28 9.3	7 44.1	0 40.3	15 37.8	3 31.1	7 18.2
29	12 25 58.2	7 43.5	4 13.8	27 32.8	10 32.7	20 48.4	28 50.4	7 49.5	0 46.0	15 35.5	3 30.4	7 16.7
30	12 29 54.8	8 38.1	4 10.5	8♎25.8	9 53.3	21 52.2	29 31.5	7 54.6	0 51.8	15 33.1	3 29.7	7 15.2
31	12 33 51.3	9 32.6	4 7.2	19 31.5	9 12.4	22 55.9	0♊12.6	7 59.7	0 57.7	15 30.7	3 28.9	7 13.7

DECLINATION

DAY	EPHEM. SID. TIME	☉	☊	☽	☿	♀	♂	♃	♄	♅	♆	♇
1	10 35 34.7	7S37.5	0S20.3	0N26.1	3S59.6	9N31.7	16N25.9	23S 2.6	18N29.0	6S18.7	19S33.4	14N48.4
4	10 47 24.4	6 28.7	0 20.3	14S59.4	1 18.8	10 59.6	17 3.1	23 1.9	18 31.9	6 16.4	19 33.3	14 50.9
7	10 59 14.1	5 19.1	0 20.4	25 4.3	1N19.0	12 25.3	17 39.1	23 1.2	18 34.9	6 14.1	19 33.2	14 53.3
10	11 11 3.7	4 8.8	0 20.4	25 20.5	3 46.2	13 48.5	18 13.8	23 .4	18 38.0	6 11.6	19 33.0	14 55.6
13	11 22 53.4	2 58.1	0 20.5	13 54.0	5 54.6	15 9.1	18 47.3	22 59.6	18 41.3	6 9.0	19 32.8	14 57.9
16	11 34 43.0	1 47.0	0 20.5	5N 5.3	7 36.6	16 26.6	19 19.5	22 58.9	18 44.7	6 6.3	19 32.5	15 .2
19	11 46 32.7	0 35.8	0 20.5	21 51.2	8 45.7	17 40.8	19 50.3	22 58.1	18 48.2	6 3.6	19 32.2	15 2.3
22	11 58 22.4	0N35.3	0 20.6	26 14.5	9 17.3	18 51.5	20 19.7	22 57.3	18 51.9	6 .8	19 31.8	15 4.4
25	12 10 12.0	1 46.2	0 20.6	17 17.2	9 9.7	19 58.4	20 47.7	22 56.6	18 55.6	5 57.9	19 31.3	15 6.4
28	12 22 1.7	2 56.8	0 20.6	1 54.9	8 25.1	21 1.2	21 14.2	22 55.9	18 59.4	5 55.0	19 30.9	15 8.4
31	12 33 51.3	4 6.8	0 20.7	13S35.6	7 10.9	21 59.8	21 39.1	22 55.3	19 3.3	5 52.1	19 30.4	15 10.2

APRIL 1972

LONGITUDE

DAY	EPHEM. SID. TIME	☉	☊	☾	☿	♀	♂	♃	♄	♅	♆	♇
	h m s	° ′	° ′	° ′	° ′	° ′	° ′	° ′	° ′	° ′	° ′	° ′
1	12 37 47.9	11♈22.3	1♒48.8	5♏ 2.6	10♈27.4	27♉ .2	3♊ 8.8	7♑26.0	2♊46.5	16♎30.1	5♐ 5.2	0♎24.6
2	12 41 44.4	12 21.5	1 45.6	16 54.6	9R37.5	28 1.6	3 47.9	7 30.3	2 52.3	16R27.6	5R 4.4	0R23.0
3	12 45 41.0	13 20.6	1 42.5	28 46.8	8 48.2	29 2.6	4 27.0	7 34.4	2 58.2	16 25.0	5 3.6	0 21.4
4	12 49 37.5	14 19.7	1 39.3	10♐42.0	8 .6	0♊ 3.2	5 6.1	7 38.4	3 4.3	16 22.4	5 2.8	0 19.9
5	12 53 34.1	15 18.8	1 36.1	22 43.6	7 15.3	1 3.5	5 45.2	7 42.2	3 10.3	16 19.9	5 1.9	0 18.3
6	12 57 30.7	16 17.8	1 32.9	4♑56.0	6 33.1	2 3.3	6 24.2	7 45.8	3 16.4	16 17.3	5 1.0	0 16.7
7	13 1 27.2	17 16.9	1 29.8	17 23.8	5 54.6	3 2.7	7 3.2	7 49.2	3 22.6	16 14.7	5 .0	0 15.1
8	13 5 23.8	18 15.8	1 26.6	0♒11.9	5 20.5	4 1.7	7 42.2	7 52.4	3 28.8	16 12.1	4 59.0	0 13.6
9	13 9 20.3	19 14.8	1 23.4	13 24.9	4 51.0	5 .2	8 21.2	7 55.5	3 35.1	16 9.5	4 58.1	0 12.0
10	13 13 16.9	20 13.7	1 20.2	27 6.1	4 26.4	5 58.3	9 .2	7 58.4	3 41.4	16 6.9	4 57.0	0 10.5
11	13 17 13.4	21 12.6	1 17.0	11♓17.0	4 7.1	6 55.9	9 39.2	8 1.0	3 47.9	16 4.3	4 56.0	0 9.0
12	13 21 10.0	22 11.5	1 13.9	25 55.9	3 53.1	7 53.1	10 18.1	8 3.6	3 54.3	16 1.8	4 54.9	0 7.5
13	13 25 6.5	23 10.3	1 10.7	10♈57.6	3 44.4	8 49.7	10 57.1	8 5.9	4 .8	15 59.2	4 53.8	0 6.0
14	13 29 3.1	24 9.1	1 7.5	26 13.3	3 41.0	9 45.8	11 36.0	8 8.0	4 7.4	15 56.6	4 52.7	0 4.5
15	13 32 59.6	25 7.9	1 4.3	11♉31.8	3D42.9	10 41.4	12 14.9	8 10.0	4 14.0	15 54.1	4 51.6	0 3.0
16	13 36 56.2	26 6.6	1 1.2	26 41.8	3 49.8	11 36.4	12 53.8	8 11.8	4 20.7	15 51.5	4 50.4	0 1.6
17	13 40 52.7	27 5.3	0 58.0	11♊33.4	4 1.8	12 30.9	13 32.7	8 13.4	4 27.4	15 49.0	4 49.2	0 .2
18	13 44 49.3	28 4.0	0 54.8	26 .2	4 18.7	13 24.7	14 11.5	8 14.8	4 34.2	15 46.5	4 48.0	29♍58.7
19	13 48 45.9	29 2.6	0 51.6	9♋59.3	4 40.2	14 17.9	14 50.4	8 16.0	4 41.0	15 44.0	4 46.8	29 57.3
20	13 52 42.4	0♉ 1.2	0 48.4	23 30.8	5 6.1	15 10.5	15 29.2	8 17.0	4 47.9	15 41.5	4 45.5	29 56.0
21	13 56 39.0	0 59.7	0 45.3	6♌37.3	5 36.4	16 2.4	16 8.0	8 17.9	4 54.8	15 39.0	4 44.3	29 54.6
22	14 0 35.5	1 58.2	0 42.1	19 22.6	6 10.8	16 53.6	16 46.8	8 18.5	5 1.7	15 36.6	4 43.0	29 53.3
23	14 4 32.1	2 56.7	0 38.9	1♍50.8	6 49.2	17 44.1	17 25.6	8 19.0	5 8.7	15 34.1	4 41.7	29 51.9
24	14 8 28.6	3 55.2	0 35.7	14 6.1	7 31.3	18 33.9	18 4.3	8 19.2	5 15.7	15 31.7	4 40.3	29 50.6
25	14 12 25.2	4 53.6	0 32.6	26 12.1	8 17.0	19 22.9	18 43.1	8 19.4	5 22.9	15 29.4	4 39.0	29 49.4
26	14 16 21.7	5 52.0	0 29.4	8♎11.7	9 6.2	20 11.0	19 21.9	8R19.3	5 30.0	15 27.0	4 37.7	29 48.1
27	14 20 18.3	6 50.3	0 26.2	20 7.3	9 58.6	20 58.3	20 .6	8 19.0	5 37.1	15 24.6	4 36.3	29 46.9
28	14 24 14.8	7 48.6	0 23.0	2♏ .6	10 54.2	21 44.8	20 39.2	8 18.5	5 44.3	15 22.3	4 34.9	29 45.7
29	14 28 11.4	8 46.9	0 19.9	13 53.2	11 52.9	22 30.3	21 17.9	8 17.9	5 51.5	15 20.0	4 33.5	29 44.5
30	14 32 8.0	9 45.2	0 16.7	25 46.4	12 54.4	23 14.9	21 56.6	8 17.0	5 58.8	15 17.7	4 32.1	29 43.3

LATITUDE

DAY	EPHEM. SID. TIME	☉	☊	☾	☿	♀	♂	♃	♄	♅	♆	♇
1	12 37 47.9	0 .0	0 .0	5S 1.1	2N46.6	2N53.5	1N .8	0N19.1	1S40.4	0N41.4	1N40.5	16N45.7
4	12 49 37.5	0 .0	0 .0	3 56.2	2 7.1	3 5.3	1 1.8	0 18.9	1 39.8	0 41.4	1 40.7	16 45.4
7	13 1 27.2	0 .0	0 .0	1 16.1	1 20.4	3 16.6	1 2.8	0 18.8	1 39.2	0 41.4	1 40.8	16 45.1
10	13 13 16.9	0 .0	0 .0	2N 9.1	0 31.5	3 27.1	1 3.6	0 18.6	1 38.7	0 41.4	1 40.9	16 44.7
13	13 25 6.5	0 .0	0 .0	4 41.4	0S15.4	3 36.9	1 4.5	0 18.4	1 38.2	0 41.4	1 41.0	16 44.3
16	13 36 56.2	0 .0	0 .0	4 30.9	0 57.8	3 45.8	1 5.3	0 18.2	1 37.7	0 41.3	1 41.1	16 43.7
19	13 48 45.9	0 .0	0 .0	1 47.2	1 34.2	3 53.6	1 6.0	0 18.1	1 37.2	0 41.3	1 41.2	16 43.1
22	14 0 35.5	0 .0	0 .0	1S36.9	2 4.1	4 .4	1 6.7	0 17.9	1 36.7	0 41.2	1 41.3	16 42.4
25	14 12 25.2	0 .0	0 .0	4 8.5	2 27.4	4 5.8	1 7.3	0 17.7	1 36.3	0 41.2	1 41.4	16 41.6
28	14 24 14.8	0 .0	0 .0	4 59.3	2 44.2	4 9.8	1 7.9	0 17.5	1 35.8	0 41.1	1 41.4	16 40.7

RIGHT ASCENSION

DAY	EPHEM. SID. TIME	☉	☊	☾	☿	♀	♂	♃	♄	♅	♆	♇
1	12 37 47.9	10♈27.3	4♒ 3.9	0♏59.7	8♈30.8	23♉59.6	0♊53.8	8♑ 4.5	1♊ 3.7	15♎28.3	3♐28.1	7♎12.2
2	12 41 44.4	11 21.9	4 .7	12 57.6	7R49.5	25 3.1	1 35.1	8 9.1	1 9.7	15R25.9	3R27.3	7R10.8
3	12 45 41.0	12 16.6	3 57.4	25 28.1	7 9.3	26 6.5	2 16.5	8 13.6	1 15.8	15 23.5	3 26.4	7 9.3
4	12 49 37.5	13 11.3	3 54.1	8♐29.2	6 31.0	27 9.8	2 57.9	8 17.9	1 22.0	15 21.2	3 25.6	7 7.8
5	12 53 34.1	14 6.1	3 50.8	21 53.1	5 55.3	28 12.9	3 39.3	8 22.0	1 28.3	15 18.8	3 24.6	7 6.4
6	12 57 30.7	15 .9	3 47.5	5♑28.1	5 22.6	29 15.8	4 20.8	8 25.9	1 34.6	15 16.4	3 23.7	7 4.9
7	13 1 27.2	15 55.8	3 44.2	19 2.0	4 53.6	0♊18.6	5 2.4	8 29.6	1 41.0	15 14.0	3 22.7	7 3.4
8	13 5 23.8	16 50.7	3 40.9	2♒25.3	4 28.7	1 21.1	5 44.0	8 33.1	1 47.4	15 11.6	3 21.7	7 2.0
9	13 9 20.3	17 45.7	3 37.6	15 34.9	4 8.1	2 23.4	6 25.6	8 36.4	1 53.9	15 9.2	3 20.7	7 .5
10	13 13 16.9	18 40.7	3 34.3	28 33.8	3 52.0	3 25.4	7 7.3	8 39.6	2 .5	15 6.8	3 19.6	6 59.1
11	13 17 13.4	19 35.9	3 31.0	11♓30.8	3 40.6	4 27.1	7 49.1	8 42.5	2 7.1	15 4.4	3 18.5	6 57.6
12	13 21 10.0	20 31.1	3 27.7	24 39.0	3 34.0	5 28.5	8 30.9	8 45.2	2 13.8	15 2.0	3 17.4	6 56.2
13	13 25 6.5	21 26.3	3 24.4	8♈13.1	3 32.0	6 29.6	9 12.7	8 47.7	2 20.5	14 59.6	3 16.3	6 54.8
14	13 29 3.1	22 21.7	3 21.1	22 27.0	3D34.8	7 30.4	9 54.6	8 50.1	2 27.3	14 57.2	3 15.1	6 53.4
15	13 32 59.6	23 17.1	3 17.8	7♉28.8	3 42.1	8 30.7	10 36.6	8 52.2	2 34.2	14 54.8	3 14.0	6 52.0
16	13 36 56.2	24 12.7	3 14.5	23 15.1	3 53.9	9 30.6	11 18.5	8 54.1	2 41.1	14 52.5	3 12.8	6 50.6
17	13 40 52.7	25 8.3	3 11.2	9♊27.0	4 10.0	10 30.1	12 .5	8 55.8	2 48.1	14 50.1	3 11.5	6 49.2
18	13 44 49.3	26 4.0	3 7.9	25 32.9	4 30.3	11 29.1	12 42.6	8 57.4	2 55.1	14 47.8	3 10.3	6 47.8
19	13 48 45.9	26 59.8	3 4.6	11♋ .8	4 54.5	12 27.5	13 24.7	8 58.7	3 2.2	14 45.4	3 9.0	6 46.5
20	13 52 42.4	27 55.7	3 1.3	25 29.3	5 22.6	13 25.4	14 6.8	8 59.8	3 9.3	14 43.1	3 7.7	6 45.1
21	13 56 39.0	28 51.7	2 58.0	8♌52.5	5 54.3	14 22.7	14 48.9	9 .7	3 16.5	14 40.8	3 6.4	6 43.8
22	14 0 35.5	29 47.8	2 54.7	21 16.7	6 29.6	15 19.3	15 31.1	9 1.4	3 23.7	14 38.6	3 5.0	6 42.5
23	14 4 32.1	0♉44.0	2 51.4	2♍54.6	7 8.1	16 15.3	16 13.3	9 1.9	3 31.0	14 36.3	3 3.7	6 41.2
24	14 8 28.6	1 40.3	2 48.1	14 1.4	7 49.8	17 10.5	16 55.5	9 2.3	3 38.3	14 34.0	3 2.3	6 39.9
25	14 12 25.2	2 36.8	2 44.8	24 52.2	8 34.6	18 5.0	17 37.8	9 2.4	3 45.7	14 31.8	3 1.0	6 38.6
26	14 16 21.7	3 33.4	2 41.5	5♎41.1	9 22.2	18 58.7	18 20.0	9R 2.3	3 53.1	14 29.6	2 59.5	6 37.4
27	14 20 18.3	4 30.1	2 38.2	16 40.9	10 12.6	19 51.5	19 2.3	9 2.0	4 .6	14 27.4	2 58.1	6 36.1
28	14 24 14.8	5 26.9	2 34.9	28 2.3	11 5.7	20 43.4	19 44.6	9 1.5	4 8.0	14 25.3	2 56.7	6 34.9
29	14 28 11.4	6 23.8	2 31.6	9♏53.2	12 1.3	21 34.4	20 26.9	9 .8	4 15.6	14 23.1	2 55.2	6 33.7
30	14 32 8.0	7 20.9	2 28.3	22 17.1	12 59.3	22 24.4	21 9.2	8 59.9	4 23.1	14 21.0	2 53.7	6 32.5

DECLINATION

DAY	EPHEM. SID. TIME	☉	☊	☾	☿	♀	♂	♃	♄	♅	♆	♇
1	12 37 47.9	4N30.0	0S20.7	17S55.7	6N41.6	22N18.4	21N47.1	22S55.1	19N 4.6	5S51.1	19S30.2	15N10.8
4	12 49 37.5	5 39.0	0 20.7	25 57.1	5 7.4	23 11.0	22 10.1	22 54.5	19 8.6	5 48.1	19 29.6	15 12.5
7	13 1 27.2	6 47.3	0 20.8	23 34.2	3 34.7	23 59.1	22 31.4	22 54.1	19 12.6	5 45.2	19 29.0	15 14.0
10	13 13 16.9	7 54.4	0 20.8	10 27.4	2 14.8	24 42.4	22 51.2	22 53.7	19 16.7	5 42.2	19 28.4	15 15.5
13	13 25 6.5	9 .4	0 20.8	8N39.1	1 15.1	25 20.9	23 9.3	22 53.4	19 20.8	5 39.3	19 27.7	15 16.9
16	13 36 56.2	10 5.1	0 20.9	23 48.7	0 38.3	25 54.5	23 25.7	22 53.2	19 25.0	5 36.4	19 27.0	15 18.1
19	13 48 45.9	11 8.2	0 20.9	24 50.9	0 24.9	26 23.2	23 40.5	22 53.2	19 29.2	5 33.5	19 26.2	15 19.2
22	14 0 35.5	12 9.7	0 20.9	13 28.7	0 33.3	26 47.1	23 53.6	22 53.2	19 33.3	5 30.7	19 25.5	15 20.2
25	14 12 25.2	13 9.3	0 21.0	2S17.4	1 1.7	27 6.2	24 4.9	22 53.3	19 37.5	5 28.0	19 24.7	15 21.0
28	14 24 14.8	14 7.0	0 21.0	16 51.0	1 47.9	27 20.6	24 14.6	22 53.6	19 41.7	5 25.3	19 23.8	15 21.7

MAY 1972

LONGITUDE

DAY	EPHEM. SID. TIME	☉	☊	☾	☿	♀	♂	♃	♄	♅	♆	♇
	h m s	° ′	° ′	° ′	° ′	° ′	° ′	° ′	° ′	° ′	° ′	° ′
1	14 36 4.5	10♉43.4	0♒13.5	7♐41.6	13♈58.8	23♊58.6	22♊35.2	8♑16.0	6♊ 6.1	15♎15.4	4♐30.6	29♍42.1
2	14 40 1.1	11 41.6	0 10.3	19 40.9	15 5.8	24 41.2	23 13.8	8 R 14.8	6 13.4	15 R 13.2	4 R 29.2	29 R 41.0
3	14 43 57.6	12 39.8	0 7.1	1♑46.7	16 15.4	25 22.8	23 52.4	8 13.4	6 20.7	15 11.0	4 27.7	29 39.9
4	14 47 54.2	13 37.9	0 4.0	14 2.2	17 27.6	26 3.3	24 31.0	8 11.8	6 28.1	15 8.8	4 26.2	29 38.8
5	14 51 50.7	14 36.0	0 .8	26 31.2	18 42.3	26 42.8	25 9.6	8 10.0	6 35.5	15 6.7	4 24.7	29 37.8
6	14 55 47.3	15 34.1	29♑57.6	9♒17.8	19 59.3	27 21.0	25 48.1	8 8.0	6 43.0	15 4.5	4 23.2	29 36.7
7	14 59 43.8	16 32.2	29 54.4	22 26.3	21 18.6	27 58.0	26 26.7	8 5.9	6 50.5	15 2.4	4 21.7	29 35.7
8	15 3 40.4	17 30.2	29 51.3	6♓ .3	22 40.3	28 33.8	27 5.2	8 3.6	6 58.0	15 .4	4 20.1	29 34.7
9	15 7 37.0	18 28.3	29 48.1	20 2.0	24 4.2	29 8.3	27 43.7	8 1.0	7 5.5	14 58.4	4 18.6	29 33.8
10	15 11 33.5	19 26.3	29 44.9	4♈31.0	25 30.2	29 41.5	28 22.2	7 58.3	7 13.0	14 56.4	4 17.1	29 32.8
11	15 15 30.1	20 24.2	29 41.7	19 24.1	26 58.5	0♋13.3	29 .7	7 55.5	7 20.6	14 54.4	4 15.5	29 31.9
12	15 19 26.6	21 22.2	29 38.5	4♉34.2	28 28.9	0 43.6	29 39.2	7 52.4	7 28.2	14 52.5	4 13.9	29 31.1
13	15 23 23.2	22 20.1	29 35.4	19 51.5	0♉ 1.5	1 12.4	0♋17.7	7 49.2	7 35.8	14 50.6	4 12.3	29 30.2
14	15 27 19.7	23 18.0	29 32.2	5♊ 4.7	1 36.1	1 39.7	0 56.2	7 45.8	7 43.4	14 48.8	4 10.8	29 29.4
15	15 31 16.3	24 15.9	29 29.0	20 3.2	3 12.9	2 5.4	1 34.6	7 42.2	7 51.1	14 46.9	4 9.2	29 28.6
16	15 35 12.9	25 13.8	29 25.8	4♋39.0	4 51.8	2 29.4	2 13.1	7 38.5	7 58.8	14 45.2	4 7.6	29 27.9
17	15 39 9.4	26 11.7	29 22.7	18 47.3	6 32.8	2 51.6	2 51.5	7 34.6	8 6.5	14 43.5	4 6.0	29 27.1
18	15 43 6.0	27 9.5	29 19.5	2♌26.9	8 15.9	3 12.1	3 29.9	7 30.5	8 14.2	14 41.8	4 4.4	29 26.4
19	15 47 2.5	28 7.2	29 16.3	15 39.1	10 1.0	3 30.6	4 8.3	7 26.3	8 21.9	14 40.1	4 2.8	29 25.8
20	15 50 59.1	29 5.0	29 13.1	28 27.3	11 48.3	3 47.3	4 46.7	7 21.8	8 29.6	14 38.5	4 1.2	29 25.1
21	15 54 55.6	0♊ 2.7	29 10.0	10♍55.7	13 37.7	4 1.9	5 25.0	7 17.3	8 37.4	14 36.9	3 59.5	29 24.5
22	15 58 52.2	1 .4	29 6.8	23 9.0	15 29.1	4 14.5	6 3.4	7 12.6	8 45.1	14 35.4	3 57.9	29 23.9
23	16 2 48.7	1 58.1	29 3.6	5♎11.6	17 22.7	4 24.9	6 41.7	7 7.7	8 52.9	14 33.9	3 56.3	29 23.3
24	16 6 45.3	2 55.7	29 .4	17 7.4	19 18.3	4 33.2	7 20.0	7 2.7	9 .6	14 32.5	3 54.7	29 22.8
25	16 10 41.9	3 53.3	28 57.3	28 59.9	21 15.9	4 39.3	7 58.3	6 57.5	9 8.4	14 31.1	3 53.0	29 22.3
26	16 14 38.4	4 50.9	28 54.1	10♏51.9	23 15.5	4 43.1	8 36.6	6 52.2	9 16.2	14 29.7	3 51.4	29 21.9
27	16 18 35.0	5 48.5	28 50.9	22 45.5	25 17.0	4 44.6	9 14.9	6 46.7	9 24.0	14 28.4	3 49.8	29 21.4
28	16 22 31.5	6 46.0	28 47.7	4♐42.4	27 20.3	4 R 43.7	9 53.2	6 41.1	9 31.7	14 27.2	3 48.2	29 21.0
29	16 26 28.1	7 43.6	28 44.5	16 44.1	29 25.3	4 40.4	10 31.4	6 35.4	9 39.5	14 25.9	3 46.6	29 20.6
30	16 30 24.7	8 41.1	28 41.4	28 52.2	1♊31.9	4 34.8	11 9.7	6 29.6	9 47.3	14 24.8	3 44.9	29 20.3
31	16 34 21.2	9 38.6	28 38.2	11♑ 8.3	3 40.0	4 26.7	11 47.9	6 23.6	9 55.1	14 23.7	3 43.3	29 20.0

LATITUDE

DAY	EPHEM. SID. TIME	☉	☊	☾	☿	♀	♂	♃	♄	♅	♆	♇
1	14 36 4.5	0 .0	0 .0	3 S 55.6	2 S 54.7	4 N 12.3	1 N 8.4	0 N 17.2	1 S 35.4	0 N 41.1	1 N 41.5	16 N 39.8
4	14 47 54.2	0 .0	0 .0	1 18.0	2 59.4	4 12.9	1 8.9	0 17.0	1 35.0	0 41.0	1 41.6	16 38.8
7	14 59 43.8	0 .0	0 .0	2 N 1.4	2 58.3	4 11.5	1 9.4	0 16.8	1 34.7	0 40.9	1 41.6	16 37.8
10	15 11 33.5	0 .0	0 .0	4 36.1	2 51.9	4 7.9	1 9.8	0 16.5	1 34.3	0 40.8	1 41.7	16 36.7
13	15 23 23.2	0 .0	0 .0	4 41.6	2 40.4	4 1.8	1 10.2	0 16.3	1 34.0	0 40.8	1 41.7	16 35.6
16	15 35 12.9	0 .0	0 .0	2 .7	2 24.0	3 52.9	1 10.6	0 16.0	1 33.7	0 40.7	1 41.7	16 34.4
19	15 47 2.5	0 .0	0 .0	1 S 33.3	2 3.1	3 40.9	1 10.9	0 15.7	1 33.4	0 40.6	1 41.7	16 33.1
22	15 58 52.2	0 .0	0 .0	4 11.3	1 38.1	3 25.5	1 11.1	0 15.4	1 33.1	0 40.5	1 41.7	16 31.8
25	16 10 41.9	0 .0	0 .0	5 5.0	1 9.8	3 6.4	1 11.4	0 15.1	1 32.9	0 40.4	1 41.7	16 30.5
28	16 22 31.5	0 .0	0 .0	4 2.6	0 38.9	2 43.4	1 11.6	0 14.8	1 32.7	0 40.3	1 41.7	16 29.2
31	16 34 21.2	0 .0	0 .0	1 23.4	0 6.9	2 16.2	1 11.8	0 14.5	1 32.5	0 40.2	1 41.7	16 27.8

RIGHT ASCENSION

DAY	EPHEM. SID. TIME	☉	☊	☾	☿	♀	♂	♃	♄	♅	♆	♇
1	14 36 4.5	8♉18.1	2♒25.0	5♐12.1	13♈59.7	23♊13.4	21♊51.5	8♑58.8	4♊30.7	14♎18.9	2♐52.2	6♎31.3
2	14 40 1.1	9 15.4	2 21.7	18 30.0	15 2.5	24 1.3	22 33.8	8 R 57.4	4 38.4	14 R 16.8	2 R 50.7	6 R 30.2
3	14 43 57.6	10 12.8	2 18.4	1♑58.4	16 7.4	24 48.1	23 16.1	8 55.9	4 46.1	14 14.8	2 49.2	6 29.0
4	14 47 54.2	11 10.5	2 15.1	15 23.6	17 14.5	25 33.6	23 58.5	8 54.2	4 53.8	14 12.7	2 47.6	6 27.9
5	14 51 50.7	12 8.2	2 11.8	28 35.2	18 23.8	26 18.0	24 40.8	8 52.3	5 1.5	14 10.7	2 46.1	6 26.8
6	14 55 47.3	13 6.1	2 8.4	11♒28.9	19 35.2	27 1.0	25 23.1	8 50.2	5 9.3	14 8.8	2 44.5	6 25.7
7	14 59 43.8	14 4.1	2 5.1	24 7.4	20 48.6	27 42.7	26 5.5	8 47.8	5 17.1	14 6.8	2 42.9	6 24.6
8	15 3 40.4	15 2.3	2 1.8	6♓39.3	22 4.2	28 23.0	26 47.8	8 45.3	5 24.9	14 4.9	2 41.3	6 23.6
9	15 7 37.0	16 .7	1 58.5	19 17.7	23 21.8	29 1.9	27 30.2	8 42.6	5 32.8	14 3.0	2 39.7	6 22.6
10	15 11 33.5	16 59.1	1 55.2	2♈18.7	24 41.4	29 39.2	28 12.5	8 39.7	5 40.7	14 1.1	2 38.1	6 21.6
11	15 15 30.1	17 57.8	1 51.9	15 58.9	26 3.2	0♋15.0	28 54.8	8 36.6	5 48.6	13 59.3	2 36.5	6 20.6
12	15 19 26.6	18 56.5	1 48.6	0♉32.0	27 27.0	0 49.1	29 37.1	8 33.3	5 56.6	13 57.5	2 34.8	6 19.6
13	15 23 23.2	19 55.5	1 45.3	16 2.8	28 53.0	1 21.5	0♋19.5	8 29.8	6 4.6	13 55.8	2 33.2	6 18.7
14	15 27 19.7	20 54.5	1 42.0	2♊20.3	0♉21.2	1 52.1	1 1.8	8 26.1	6 12.6	13 54.0	2 31.6	6 17.8
15	15 31 16.3	21 53.7	1 38.7	18 55.2	1 51.6	2 20.8	1 44.0	8 22.2	6 20.6	13 52.4	2 29.9	6 16.9
16	15 35 12.9	22 53.1	1 35.3	5♋ 8.7	3 24.2	2 47.8	2 26.3	8 18.2	6 28.7	13 50.7	2 28.3	6 16.1
17	15 39 9.4	23 52.6	1 32.0	20 28.0	4 59.2	3 12.6	3 8.6	8 14.0	6 36.7	13 49.1	2 26.6	6 15.2
18	15 43 6.0	24 52.2	1 28.7	4♌37.5	6 36.5	3 35.4	3 50.8	8 9.5	6 44.8	13 47.5	2 24.9	6 14.4
19	15 47 2.5	25 52.0	1 25.4	17 38.2	8 16.2	3 56.1	4 33.0	8 4.9	6 52.9	13 46.0	2 23.3	6 13.6
20	15 50 59.1	26 51.9	1 22.1	29 42.0	9 58.5	4 14.6	5 15.1	8 .2	7 1.0	13 44.5	2 21.6	6 12.8
21	15 54 55.6	27 51.9	1 18.8	11♍ 4.7	11 43.3	4 30.8	5 57.3	7 55.2	7 9.1	13 43.0	2 19.9	6 12.1
22	15 58 52.2	28 52.0	1 15.5	22 3.3	13 30.7	4 44.6	6 39.4	7 50.1	7 17.3	13 41.6	2 18.2	6 11.4
23	16 2 48.7	29 52.3	1 12.1	2♎53.6	15 20.8	4 56.1	7 21.4	7 44.8	7 25.4	13 40.2	2 16.5	6 10.7
24	16 6 45.3	0♊52.7	1 8.8	13 50.0	17 13.6	5 5.1	8 3.5	7 39.4	7 33.6	13 38.9	2 14.8	6 10.0
25	16 10 41.9	1 53.2	1 5.5	25 5.0	19 9.2	5 11.6	8 45.5	7 33.8	7 41.8	13 37.6	2 13.1	6 9.4
26	16 14 38.4	2 53.9	1 2.2	6♏48.2	21 7.6	5 15.6	9 27.4	7 28.0	7 50.0	13 36.3	2 11.4	6 8.8
27	16 18 35.0	3 54.6	0 58.9	19 5.3	23 8.8	5 16.9	10 9.3	7 22.1	7 58.1	13 35.1	2 9.7	6 8.2
28	16 22 31.5	4 55.5	0 55.6	1♐56.1	25 12.8	5 R 15.6	10 51.2	7 16.1	8 6.3	13 33.9	2 8.1	6 7.6
29	16 26 28.1	5 56.5	0 52.2	15 13.5	27 19.5	5 11.6	11 33.0	7 9.9	8 14.6	13 32.7	2 6.4	6 7.1
30	16 30 24.7	6 57.6	0 48.9	28 44.7	29 28.8	5 5.0	12 14.8	7 3.5	8 22.8	13 31.6	2 4.7	6 6.6
31	16 34 21.2	7 58.8	0 45.6	12♑14.3	1♊40.6	4 55.7	12 56.5	6 57.0	8 31.0	13 30.6	2 3.0	6 6.1

DECLINATION

DAY	EPHEM. SID. TIME	☉	☊	☾	☿	♀	♂	♃	♄	♅	♆	♇
1	14 36 4.5	15 N 2.6	0 S 21.1	25 S 28.2	2 N 49.8	27 N 30.4	24 N 22.5	22 S 54.0	19 N 45.8	5 S 22.7	19 S 23.0	15 N 22.2
4	14 47 54.2	15 56.0	0 21.1	23 59.8	4 5.5	27 35.9	24 28.7	22 54.5	19 50.0	5 20.2	19 22.1	15 22.7
7	14 59 43.8	16 47.1	0 21.1	12 7.3	5 33.4	27 37.2	24 33.2	22 55.0	19 54.1	5 17.8	19 21.3	15 22.9
10	15 11 33.5	17 35.6	0 21.2	6 N 1.1	7 11.6	27 34.5	24 35.9	22 55.7	19 58.1	5 15.6	19 20.4	15 23.1
13	15 23 23.2	18 21.5	0 21.2	22 13.3	8 58.7	27 28.1	24 36.8	22 56.5	20 2.1	5 13.4	19 19.5	15 23.1
16	15 35 12.9	19 4.6	0 21.2	25 22.3	10 53.0	27 18.1	24 36.1	22 57.4	20 6.1	5 11.4	19 18.6	15 22.9
19	15 47 2.5	19 44.7	0 21.3	14 39.7	12 52.5	27 4.6	24 33.6	22 58.4	20 10.0	5 9.5	19 17.7	15 22.6
22	15 58 52.2	20 21.9	0 21.3	1 S 7.7	14 54.9	26 47.9	24 29.4	22 59.4	20 13.9	5 7.8	19 16.8	15 22.2
25	16 10 41.9	20 55.9	0 21.3	15 52.1	16 57.4	26 28.0	24 23.5	23 .5	20 17.7	5 6.2	19 15.9	15 21.6
28	16 22 31.5	21 26.6	0 21.4	25 3.4	18 56.2	26 4.9	24 15.9	23 1.7	20 21.4	5 4.8	19 15.0	15 20.9
31	16 34 21.2	21 54.1	0 21.4	24 21.7	20 46.6	25 38.3	24 6.7	23 2.9	20 25.0	5 3.5	19 14.1	15 20.0

JUNE 1972

LONGITUDE

DAY	EPHEM. SID. TIME h m s	☉ ° ′	☊ ° ′	☽ ° ′	☿ ° ′	♀ ° ′	♂ ° ′	♃ ° ′	♄ ° ′	♅ ° ′	♆ ° ′	♇ ° ′
1	16 38 17.8	10♊36.1	28♑35.0	23♑34.2	5♊49.3	4♋16.2	12♋26.1	6♑17.5	10♊ 2.9	14♎22.6	3♐41.7	29♍19.7
2	16 42 14.3	11 33.5	28 31.8	6♒12.6	7 59.7	4R 3.3	13 4.3	6R11.3	10 10.7	14R21.5	3R40.1	29R19.5
3	16 46 10.9	12 31.0	28 28.7	19 6.0	10 10.9	3 48.0	13 42.5	6 4.9	10 18.5	14 20.6	3 38.5	29 19.3
4	16 50 7.4	13 28.4	28 25.5	2♓17.4	12 22.7	3 30.4	14 20.7	5 58.5	10 26.3	14 19.6	3 36.9	29 19.1
5	16 54 4.0	14 25.9	28 22.3	15 49.3	14 34.7	3 10.4	14 58.9	5 51.9	10 34.1	14 18.7	3 35.3	29 18.9
6	16 58 .6	15 23.3	28 19.1	29 43.5	16 46.9	2 48.3	15 37.1	5 45.3	10 41.9	14 18.0	3 33.8	29 18.8
7	17 1 57.1	16 20.8	28 16.0	14♈ .0	18 58.8	2 24.0	16 15.3	5 38.5	10 49.7	14 17.2	3 32.2	29 18.8
8	17 5 53.7	17 18.2	28 12.8	28 36.8	21 10.1	1 57.6	16 53.4	5 31.7	10 57.5	14 16.4	3 30.6	29 18.7
9	17 9 50.2	18 15.6	28 9.6	13♉29.0	23 20.7	1 29.4	17 31.6	5 24.7	11 5.2	14 15.8	3 29.0	29 18.7
10	17 13 46.8	19 12.9	28 6.4	28 29.3	25 30.3	0 59.3	18 9.7	5 17.7	11 13.0	14 15.1	3 27.5	29 18.7
11	17 17 43.3	20 10.3	28 3.2	13♊29.0	27 38.6	0 27.7	18 47.8	5 10.6	11 20.7	14 14.5	3 26.0	29 18.7
12	17 21 39.9	21 7.7	28 .1	28 18.9	29 45.5	29♊54.5	19 26.0	5 3.4	11 28.5	14 14.0	3 24.4	29D18.8
13	17 25 36.5	22 5.0	27 56.9	12♋51.2	1♋50.7	29 20.1	20 4.1	4 56.1	11 36.2	14 13.5	3 22.9	29 18.9
14	17 29 33.0	23 2.4	27 53.7	27 .4	3 54.2	28 44.6	20 42.2	4 48.8	11 43.9	14 13.1	3 21.4	29 19.1
15	17 33 29.6	23 59.7	27 50.5	10♌43.7	5 55.8	28 8.2	21 20.3	4 41.4	11 51.6	14 12.7	3 19.9	29 19.2
16	17 37 26.1	24 57.0	27 47.4	24 .9	7 55.4	27 31.2	21 58.4	4 34.0	11 59.3	14 12.4	3 18.4	29 19.5
17	17 41 22.7	25 54.3	27 44.2	6♍53.9	9 52.9	26 53.8	22 36.5	4 26.5	12 6.9	14 12.1	3 16.9	29 19.7
18	17 45 19.3	26 51.6	27 41.0	19 26.1	11 48.2	26 16.2	23 14.6	4 19.0	12 14.6	14 11.9	3 15.5	29 20.0
19	17 49 15.8	27 48.8	27 37.8	1♎41.6	13 41.4	25 38.7	23 52.6	4 11.4	12 22.2	14 11.7	3 14.0	29 20.3
20	17 53 12.4	28 46.1	27 34.7	13 45.1	15 32.3	25 1.4	24 30.7	4 3.8	12 29.8	14 11.6	3 12.6	29 20.6
21	17 57 8.9	29 43.3	27 31.5	25 40.9	17 20.9	24 24.8	25 8.8	3 56.2	12 37.4	14 11.6	3 11.2	29 21.0
22	18 1 5.5	0♋40.6	27 28.3	7♏33.3	19 7.3	23 48.9	25 46.8	3 48.6	12 45.0	14 11.6	3 9.8	29 21.4
23	18 5 2.0	1 37.8	27 25.1	19 26.1	20 51.4	23 14.0	26 24.8	3 40.9	12 52.5	14 11.6	3 8.4	29 21.8
24	18 8 58.6	2 35.0	27 22.0	1♐22.3	22 33.1	22 40.3	27 2.9	3 33.2	13 .0	14D11.7	3 7.0	29 22.3
25	18 12 55.2	3 32.2	27 18.8	13 24.8	24 12.6	22 8.1	27 40.9	3 25.5	13 7.5	14 11.8	3 5.7	29 22.8
26	18 16 51.7	4 29.4	27 15.6	25 35.4	25 49.7	21 37.4	28 18.9	3 17.9	13 15.0	14 12.1	3 4.3	29 23.3
27	18 20 48.3	5 26.6	27 12.4	7♑55.8	27 24.5	21 8.6	28 57.0	3 10.2	13 22.4	14 12.4	3 3.1	29 23.9
28	18 24 44.8	6 23.8	27 9.3	20 27.1	28 56.9	20 41.5	29 35.0	3 2.6	13 29.9	14 12.7	3 1.8	29 24.5
29	18 28 41.4	7 21.0	27 6.1	3♒10.3	0♌27.0	20 16.6	0♌13.0	2 54.9	13 37.2	14 13.0	3 .5	29 25.2
30	18 32 38.0	8 18.2	27 2.9	16 6.4	1 54.7	19 53.7	0 51.0	2 47.3	13 44.6	14 13.4	2 59.2	29 25.8

LATITUDE

DAY	EPHEM. SID. TIME	☉	☊	☽	☿	♀	♂	♃	♄	♅	♆	♇
1	16 38 17.8	0 .0	0 .0	0S17.3	0N 3.8	2N 6.3	1N11.8	0N14.4	1S32.4	0N40.1	1N41.7	16N27.3
4	16 50 7.4	0 .0	0 .0	3N .2	0 34.9	1 33.6	1 11.9	0 14.1	1 32.2	0 40.0	1 41.6	16 25.9
7	17 1 57.1	0 .0	0 .0	5 2.3	1 2.9	0 57.2	1 12.0	0 13.7	1 32.1	0 39.9	1 41.6	16 24.5
10	17 13 46.8	0 .0	0 .0	4 23.3	1 26.4	0 17.6	1 12.1	0 13.3	1 31.9	0 39.8	1 41.5	16 23.1
13	17 25 36.5	0 .0	0 .0	1 12.8	1 43.9	0S24.1	1 12.1	0 13.0	1 31.8	0 39.7	1 41.5	16 21.6
16	17 37 26.1	0 .0	0 .0	2S25.5	1 54.8	1 6.7	1 12.2	0 12.6	1 31.7	0 39.5	1 41.4	16 20.2
19	17 49 15.8	0 .0	0 .0	4 44.7	1 59.0	1 48.5	1 12.1	0 12.2	1 31.6	0 39.4	1 41.3	16 18.7
22	18 1 5.5	0 .0	0 .0	5 7.2	1 56.7	2 28.2	1 12.1	0 11.8	1 31.5	0 39.3	1 41.2	16 17.3
25	18 12 55.2	0 .0	0 .0	3 33.1	1 48.2	3 4.5	1 12.0	0 11.4	1 31.5	0 39.2	1 41.1	16 15.8
28	18 24 44.8	0 .0	0 .0	0 30.6	1 33.9	3 36.3	1 11.9	0 11.0	1 31.5	0 39.0	1 41.0	16 14.4

RIGHT ASCENSION

DAY	EPHEM. SID. TIME	☉	☊	☽	☿	♀	♂	♃	♄	♅	♆	♇
1	16 38 17.8	9♊ .1	0♒42.3	25♑29.1	3♊54.8	4♋43.7	13♋38.2	6♑50.4	8♊39.2	13♎29.6	2♐ 1.3	6♎ 5.7
2	16 42 14.3	10 1.6	0 39.0	8♒22.2	6 11.1	4R29.0	14 19.8	6R43.7	8 47.4	13R28.6	1R59.6	6R 5.2
3	16 46 10.9	11 3.1	0 35.6	20 53.8	8 29.4	4 11.8	15 1.4	6 36.8	8 55.6	13 27.7	1 58.0	6 4.8
4	16 50 7.4	12 4.7	0 32.3	3♓11.1	10 49.2	3 52.0	15 42.9	6 29.8	9 3.9	13 26.8	1 56.3	6 4.5
5	16 54 4.0	13 6.4	0 29.0	15 26.2	13 10.4	3 29.7	16 24.4	6 22.7	9 12.1	13 26.0	1 54.7	6 4.1
6	16 58 .6	14 8.3	0 25.7	27 54.8	15 32.5	3 5.0	17 5.9	6 15.5	9 20.3	13 25.2	1 53.1	6 3.9
7	17 1 57.1	15 10.2	0 22.4	10♈54.1	17 55.2	2 38.1	17 47.3	6 8.1	9 28.6	13 24.5	1 51.4	6 3.6
8	17 5 53.7	16 12.1	0 19.0	24 40.8	20 18.1	2 8.9	18 28.6	6 .7	9 36.8	13 23.8	1 49.8	6 3.3
9	17 9 50.2	17 14.2	0 15.7	9♉26.6	22 40.8	1 37.8	19 9.8	5 53.2	9 45.0	13 23.1	1 48.1	6 3.1
10	17 13 46.8	18 16.3	0 12.4	25 11.1	25 2.9	1 4.8	19 51.0	5 45.5	9 53.2	13 22.5	1 46.5	6 2.9
11	17 17 43.3	19 18.4	0 9.1	11♊36.5	27 24.1	0 30.2	20 32.2	5 37.8	10 1.4	13 22.0	1 44.9	6 2.7
12	17 21 39.9	20 20.6	0 5.7	28 7.7	29 44.0	29♊54.0	21 13.2	5 30.0	10 9.5	13 21.5	1 43.3	6 2.6
13	17 25 36.5	21 22.9	0 2.4	14♋ 5.6	2♋ 2.3	29 16.6	21 54.3	5 22.1	10 17.7	13 21.0	1 41.7	6 2.5
14	17 29 33.0	22 25.2	29♑59.1	29 2.4	4 18.7	28 38.2	22 35.2	5 14.2	10 25.9	13 20.6	1 40.2	6 2.4
15	17 33 29.6	23 27.5	29 55.8	12♌48.8	6 33.1	27 59.0	23 16.1	5 6.1	10 34.0	13 20.2	1 38.6	6 2.4
16	17 37 26.1	24 29.9	29 52.4	25 30.6	8 45.1	27 19.2	23 56.9	4 58.1	10 42.1	13 19.9	1 37.0	6 2.4
17	17 41 22.7	25 32.3	29 49.1	7♍21.8	10 54.6	26 39.1	24 37.6	4 49.9	10 50.3	13 19.7	1 35.5	6 2.4
18	17 45 19.3	26 34.6	29 45.8	18 39.2	13 1.5	25 59.0	25 18.3	4 41.7	10 58.3	13 19.4	1 34.0	6 2.4
19	17 49 15.8	27 37.0	29 42.5	29 39.7	15 5.5	25 19.1	25 58.9	4 33.5	11 6.4	13 19.3	1 32.5	6D 2.5
20	17 53 12.4	28 39.4	29 39.1	10♎38.9	17 6.7	24 39.7	26 39.5	4 25.3	11 14.5	13 19.2	1 31.0	6 2.6
21	17 57 8.9	29 41.8	29 35.8	21 50.6	19 4.9	24 .9	27 19.9	4 17.0	11 22.5	13 19.1	1 29.5	6 2.7
22	18 1 5.5	0♋44.2	29 32.5	3♏26.5	21 .1	23 23.2	28 .3	4 8.7	11 30.5	13 19.1	1 28.0	6 2.9
23	18 5 2.0	1 46.6	29 29.2	15 34.6	22 52.2	22 46.6	28 40.6	4 .4	11 38.5	13 19.1	1 26.6	6 3.1
24	18 8 58.6	2 48.9	29 25.8	28 17.6	24 41.2	22 11.4	29 20.8	3 52.0	11 46.5	13D19.2	1 25.2	6 3.3
25	18 12 55.2	3 51.2	29 22.5	11♐31.7	26 27.1	21 37.9	0♌ 1.0	3 43.7	11 54.5	13 19.3	1 23.8	6 3.5
26	18 16 51.7	4 53.5	29 19.2	25 5.7	28 9.8	21 6.0	0 41.0	3 35.3	12 2.4	13 19.5	1 22.4	6 3.8
27	18 20 48.3	5 55.8	29 15.8	8♑44.4	29 49.5	20 36.2	1 21.1	3 27.0	12 10.3	13 19.7	1 21.0	6 4.2
28	18 24 44.8	6 58.0	29 12.5	22 12.2	1♌26.0	20 8.3	2 1.0	3 18.7	12 18.2	13 20.0	1 19.7	6 4.5
29	18 28 41.4	8 .2	29 9.2	5♒18.6	2 59.3	19 42.7	2 40.9	3 10.4	12 26.0	13 20.3	1 18.4	6 4.9
30	18 32 38.0	9 2.3	29 5.8	18 .5	4 29.5	19 19.3	3 20.6	3 2.1	12 33.9	13 20.7	1 17.1	6 5.2

DECLINATION

DAY	EPHEM. SID. TIME	☉	☊	☽	☿	♀	♂	♃	♄	♅	♆	♇
1	16 38 17.8	22N 2.4	0S21.4	21S40.2	21N20.7	25N28.7	24N 3.2	23S 3.3	20N26.2	5S 3.2	19S13.8	15N19.7
4	16 50 7.4	22 25.3	0 21.4	7 51.3	22 51.5	24 57.4	23 51.8	23 4.5	20 29.8	5 2.1	19 13.0	15 18.7
7	17 1 57.1	22 44.6	0 21.5	10N 9.8	24 1.9	24 22.5	23 38.8	23 5.7	20 33.2	5 1.3	19 12.1	15 17.5
10	17 13 46.8	23 .4	0 21.5	24 6.3	24 48.4	23 44.0	23 24.2	23 6.9	20 36.6	5 .6	19 11.3	15 16.2
13	17 25 36.5	23 12.4	0 21.5	24 1.9	25 9.7	23 2.4	23 8.0	23 8.1	20 39.9	5 .1	19 10.5	15 14.8
16	17 37 26.1	23 20.8	0 21.6	11 13.7	25 7.0	22 18.6	22 50.3	23 9.3	20 43.0	4 59.8	19 9.7	15 13.3
19	17 49 15.8	23 25.5	0 21.6	5S 1.5	24 42.8	21 33.9	22 31.1	23 10.5	20 46.1	4 59.6	19 9.0	15 11.7
22	18 1 5.5	23 26.5	0 21.6	18 52.1	24 .3	20 49.9	22 10.4	23 11.5	20 49.0	4 59.7	19 8.3	15 9.9
25	18 12 55.2	23 23.8	0 21.7	25 56.3	23 3.0	20 8.5	21 48.3	23 12.6	20 51.9	4 59.9	19 7.6	15 8.0
28	18 24 44.8	23 17.4	0 21.7	22 23.5	21 54.3	19 31.2	21 24.8	23 13.6	20 54.7	5 .3	19 6.9	15 6.0

JULY 1972

DAY	EPHEM. SID. TIME	☉	☊	☽	☿	♀	♂	♃	♄	♅	♆	♇
	h m s	° ′	° ′	° ′	° ′	° ′	° ′	° ′	° ′	° ′	° ′	° ′
		LONGITUDE										
1	18 36 34.5	9♋15.4	26♑59.7	29♒16.2	3♌20.0	19♊33.1	1♌28.9	2♑39.7	13♊51.9	14♎13.9	2♐58.0	29♍26.5
2	18 40 31.1	10 12.6	26 56.5	12♓40.4	4 42.8	19R14.8	2 6.9	2R32.1	13 59.2	14 14.4	2R56.8	29 27.2
3	18 44 27.6	11 9.8	26 53.4	26 19.7	6 3.2	18 58.8	2 44.9	2 24.6	14 6.5	14 15.0	2 55.6	29 28.0
4	18 48 24.2	12 7.0	26 50.2	10♈14.2	7 21.1	18 45.2	3 22.9	2 17.1	14 13.7	14 15.6	2 54.4	29 28.8
5	18 52 20.8	13 4.2	26 47.0	24 23.1	8 36.4	18 34.0	4 .9	2 9.6	14 20.9	14 16.3	2 53.3	29 29.6
6	18 56 17.3	14 1.4	26 43.8	8♉44.6	9 49.1	18 25.2	4 38.9	2 2.2	14 28.0	14 17.0	2 52.1	29 30.4
7	19 0 13.9	14 58.6	26 40.7	23 15.6	10 59.1	18 18.8	5 16.9	1 54.9	14 35.1	14 17.8	2 51.0	29 31.3
8	19 4 10.4	15 55.8	26 37.5	7♊51.5	12 6.4	18 14.8	5 54.8	1 47.6	14 42.2	14 18.6	2 49.9	29 32.2
9	19 8 7.0	16 53.0	26 34.3	22 26.6	13 10.8	18 13.2	6 32.8	1 40.4	14 49.3	14 19.5	2 48.9	29 33.2
10	19 12 3.5	17 50.2	26 31.1	6♋54.8	14 12.4	18D13.9	7 10.8	1 33.3	14 56.3	14 20.5	2 47.8	29 34.1
11	19 16 .1	18 47.5	26 28.0	21 10.4	15 10.9	18 16.8	7 48.8	1 26.2	15 3.2	14 21.4	2 46.8	29 35.1
12	19 19 56.7	19 44.7	26 24.8	5♌ 8.6	16 6.3	18 22.0	8 26.8	1 19.2	15 10.1	14 22.5	2 45.8	29 36.1
13	19 23 53.2	20 41.9	26 21.6	18 46.3	16 58.5	18 29.4	9 4.7	1 12.3	15 17.0	14 23.6	2 44.9	29 37.2
14	19 27 49.8	21 39.2	26 18.4	2♍ 1.9	17 47.3	18 38.9	9 42.7	1 5.5	15 23.8	14 24.7	2 43.9	29 38.3
15	19 31 46.3	22 36.4	26 15.3	14 56.0	18 32.6	18 50.5	10 20.7	0 58.8	15 30.6	14 25.9	2 43.0	29 39.4
16	19 35 42.9	23 33.7	26 12.1	27 30.5	19 14.3	19 4.1	10 58.7	0 52.2	15 37.3	14 27.2	2 42.1	29 40.6
17	19 39 39.4	24 30.9	26 8.9	9♎48.3	19 52.2	19 19.6	11 36.7	0 45.7	15 44.0	14 28.5	2 41.3	29 41.7
18	19 43 36.0	25 28.2	26 5.7	21 53.5	20 26.3	19 37.1	12 14.7	0 39.4	15 50.7	14 29.9	2 40.5	29 43.0
19	19 47 32.6	26 25.5	26 2.5	3♏50.4	20 56.2	19 56.4	12 52.6	0 33.1	15 57.3	14 31.2	2 39.7	29 44.2
20	19 51 29.1	27 22.7	25 59.4	15 43.5	21 21.8	20 17.5	13 30.6	0 27.0	16 3.8	14 32.7	2 38.9	29 45.5
21	19 55 25.7	28 20.0	25 56.2	27 37.3	21 43.1	20 40.3	14 8.6	0 21.0	16 10.3	14 34.2	2 38.2	29 46.7
22	19 59 22.2	29 17.2	25 53.0	9♐36.0	21 59.8	21 4.8	14 46.6	0 15.1	16 16.7	14 35.7	2 37.5	29 48.1
23	20 3 18.8	0♌14.5	25 49.8	21 43.3	22 11.9	21 30.9	15 24.5	0 9.3	16 23.1	14 37.3	2 36.8	29 49.4
24	20 7 15.3	1 11.8	25 46.7	4♑ 2.3	22 19.1	21 58.5	16 2.5	0 3.7	16 29.4	14 39.0	2 36.1	29 50.8
25	20 11 11.9	2 9.1	25 43.5	16 35.2	22 21.3	22 27.7	16 40.5	29♐58.2	16 35.7	14 40.6	2 35.5	29 52.2
26	20 15 8.5	3 6.4	25 40.3	29 23.5	22R18.6	22 58.3	17 18.4	29 52.8	16 41.9	14 42.4	2 34.9	29 53.6
27	20 19 5.0	4 3.7	25 37.1	12♒27.7	22 10.8	23 30.3	17 56.4	29 47.6	16 48.0	14 44.2	2 34.3	29 55.0
28	20 23 1.6	5 1.0	25 34.0	25 47.3	21 58.0	24 3.7	18 34.4	29 42.5	16 54.1	14 46.0	2 33.7	29 56.5
29	20 26 58.1	5 58.3	25 30.8	9♓21.4	21 40.1	24 38.4	19 12.4	29 37.6	17 .1	14 47.9	2 33.2	29 58.0
30	20 30 54.7	6 55.7	25 27.6	23 8.0	21 17.4	25 14.3	19 50.4	29 32.9	17 6.1	14 49.8	2 32.7	29 59.5
31	20 34 51.2	7 53.0	25 24.4	7♈ 4.9	20 50.0	25 51.5	20 28.3	29 28.2	17 12.0	14 51.7	2 32.3	0♎ 1.0
		LATITUDE										
1	18 36 34.5	0 .0	0 .0	2N53.4	1N14.3	4S 3.3	1N11.8	0N10.5	1S31.4	0N38.9	1N40.9	16N12.9
4	18 48 24.2	0 .0	0 .0	5 4.1	0 49.8	4 25.3	1 11.6	0 10.1	1 31.5	0 38.8	1 40.8	16 11.5
7	19 0 13.9	0 .0	0 .0	4 41.3	0 21.0	4 42.4	1 11.5	0 9.7	1 31.5	0 38.7	1 40.7	16 10.2
10	19 12 3.5	0 .0	0 .0	1 43.7	0S11.8	4 54.9	1 11.3	0 9.2	1 31.5	0 38.5	1 40.5	16 8.8
13	19 23 53.2	0 .0	0 .0	2S 2.9	0 48.0	5 3.3	1 11.0	0 8.8	1 31.6	0 38.4	1 40.4	16 7.5
16	19 35 42.9	0 .0	0 .0	4 38.7	1 26.9	5 8.1	1 10.8	0 8.4	1 31.6	0 38.3	1 40.2	16 6.1
19	19 47 32.6	0 .0	0 .0	5 14.0	2 7.6	5 9.7	1 10.5	0 7.9	1 31.7	0 38.2	1 40.1	16 4.9
22	19 59 22.2	0 .0	0 .0	3 49.9	2 48.8	5 8.5	1 10.2	0 7.5	1 31.8	0 38.1	1 39.9	16 3.6
25	20 11 11.9	0 .0	0 .0	0 52.2	3 28.6	5 4.8	1 9.9	0 7.0	1 32.0	0 38.0	1 39.8	16 2.5
28	20 23 1.6	0 .0	0 .0	2N37.3	4 4.5	4 59.2	1 9.5	0 6.6	1 32.1	0 37.8	1 39.6	16 1.3
31	20 34 51.2	0 .0	0 .0	4 59.0	4 33.3	4 51.7	1 9.2	0 6.1	1 32.2	0 37.7	1 39.5	16 .2
		RIGHT ASCENSION										
1	18 36 34.5	10♋ 4.4	29♑ 2.5	0♓22.2	5♌56.6	18♊58.3	4♌ .3	2♑53.8	12♊41.6	13♎21.1	1♐15.8	6♎ 5.7
2	18 40 31.1	11 6.4	28 59.2	12 33.7	7 20.5	18R39.6	4 39.9	2R45.6	12 49.4	13 21.5	1R14.5	6 6.1
3	18 44 27.6	12 8.3	28 55.8	24 48.8	8 41.2	18 23.5	5 19.5	2 37.4	12 57.1	13 22.1	1 13.2	6 6.6
4	18 48 24.2	13 10.2	28 52.5	7♈23.8	9 58.8	18 9.8	5 58.9	2 29.2	13 4.8	13 22.6	1 12.0	6 7.1
5	18 52 20.8	14 12.0	28 49.2	20 35.2	11 13.3	17 58.6	6 38.3	2 21.1	13 12.4	13 23.2	1 10.8	6 7.7
6	18 56 17.3	15 13.7	28 45.8	4♉37.0	12 24.5	17 49.9	7 17.6	2 13.1	13 20.0	13 23.9	1 9.6	6 8.2
7	19 0 13.9	16 15.3	28 42.5	19 35.4	13 32.5	17 43.7	7 56.9	2 5.1	13 27.6	13 24.6	1 8.5	6 8.8
8	19 4 10.4	17 16.9	28 39.2	5♊22.8	14 37.3	17 39.9	8 36.0	1 57.1	13 35.1	13 25.4	1 7.3	6 9.5
9	19 8 7.0	18 18.3	28 35.8	21 35.2	15 38.7	17 38.6	9 15.1	1 49.3	13 42.6	13 26.2	1 6.2	6 10.1
10	19 12 3.5	19 19.7	28 32.5	7♋37.7	16 36.8	17D39.6	9 54.1	1 41.5	13 50.1	13 27.0	1 5.1	6 10.8
11	19 16 .1	20 20.9	28 29.1	22 57.8	17 31.6	17 43.0	10 33.0	1 33.8	13 57.5	13 27.9	1 4.1	6 11.5
12	19 19 56.7	21 22.0	28 25.8	7♌17.1	18 22.8	17 48.7	11 11.9	1 26.2	14 4.9	13 28.9	1 3.0	6 12.2
13	19 23 53.2	22 23.1	28 22.5	20 32.9	19 10.6	17 56.6	11 50.6	1 18.7	14 12.2	13 29.9	1 2.0	6 13.0
14	19 27 49.8	23 23.9	28 19.1	2♍54.2	19 54.7	18 6.7	12 29.3	1 11.3	14 19.5	13 30.9	1 1.0	6 13.8
15	19 31 46.3	24 24.7	28 15.8	14 35.3	20 35.1	18 18.9	13 7.9	1 4.1	14 26.7	13 32.0	1 .1	6 14.6
16	19 35 42.9	25 25.4	28 12.5	25 52.0	21 11.8	18 33.1	13 46.4	0 56.9	14 33.9	13 33.1	0 59.2	6 15.5
17	19 39 39.4	26 25.9	28 9.1	6♎59.8	21 44.5	18 49.4	14 24.9	0 49.8	14 41.0	13 34.3	0 58.3	6 16.4
18	19 43 36.0	27 26.3	28 5.8	18 13.1	22 13.3	19 7.7	15 3.3	0 42.9	14 48.1	13 35.6	0 57.4	6 17.3
19	19 47 32.6	28 26.5	28 2.4	29 44.2	22 38.0	19 27.9	15 41.6	0 36.1	14 55.1	13 36.9	0 56.6	6 18.3
20	19 51 29.1	29 26.6	27 59.1	11♏42.8	22 58.4	19 49.9	16 19.8	0 29.4	15 2.1	13 38.2	0 55.8	6 19.2
21	19 55 25.7	0♌26.6	27 55.7	24 14.2	23 14.5	20 13.7	16 58.0	0 22.8	15 9.0	13 39.5	0 55.0	6 20.2
22	19 59 22.2	1 26.4	27 52.4	7♐18.0	23 26.2	20 39.2	17 36.0	0 16.4	15 15.9	13 41.0	0 54.2	6 21.2
23	20 3 18.8	2 26.0	27 49.1	20 46.9	23 33.4	21 6.4	18 14.0	0 10.1	15 22.7	13 42.4	0 53.5	6 22.3
24	20 7 15.3	3 25.5	27 45.7	4♑28.0	23 36.0	21 35.3	18 51.9	0 4.0	15 29.4	13 43.9	0 52.8	6 23.3
25	20 11 11.9	4 24.9	27 42.4	18 6.2	23R33.9	22 5.7	19 29.7	29♐58.0	15 36.1	13 45.5	0 52.1	6 24.4
26	20 15 8.5	5 24.1	27 39.0	1♒28.8	23 27.2	22 37.7	20 7.5	29 52.2	15 42.8	13 47.1	0 51.5	6 25.6
27	20 19 5.0	6 23.2	27 35.7	14 29.4	23 15.8	23 11.1	20 45.2	29 46.5	15 49.3	13 48.7	0 50.9	6 26.7
28	20 23 1.6	7 22.1	27 32.3	27 8.8	22 59.8	23 46.0	21 22.8	29 41.0	15 55.8	13 50.4	0 50.3	6 27.9
29	20 26 58.1	8 20.9	27 29.0	9♓34.0	22 39.2	24 22.3	22 .3	29 35.6	16 2.3	13 52.1	0 49.8	6 29.1
30	20 30 54.7	9 19.5	27 25.6	21 56.7	22 14.3	24 59.9	22 37.8	29 30.4	16 8.7	13 53.9	0 49.3	6 30.3
31	20 34 51.2	10 17.9	27 22.3	4♈31.1	21 45.2	25 38.8	23 15.2	29 25.4	16 15.0	13 55.7	0 48.8	6 31.5
		DECLINATION										
1	18 36 34.5	23N 7.2	0S21.7	9S 1.2	20N37.1	18N59.3	21N .0	23S14.5	20N57.3	5S .9	19S 6.3	15N 3.9
4	18 48 24.2	22 53.5	0 21.8	8N42.7	19 14.4	18 33.7	20 33.9	23 15.3	20 59.9	5 1.7	19 5.7	15 1.8
7	19 0 13.9	22 36.2	0 21.8	23 7.5	17 48.8	18 14.5	20 6.4	23 16.1	21 2.3	5 2.6	19 5.2	14 59.5
10	19 12 3.5	22 15.3	0 21.8	24 59.4	16 22.9	18 1.6	19 37.7	23 16.8	21 4.6	5 3.8	19 4.7	14 57.1
13	19 23 53.2	21 51.0	0 21.9	13 15.2	14 59.3	17 54.5	19 7.9	23 17.5	21 6.8	5 5.1	19 4.3	14 54.7
16	19 35 42.9	21 23.3	0 21.9	3S16.2	13 40.7	17 52.5	18 36.8	23 18.1	21 9.0	5 6.6	19 3.9	14 52.2
19	19 47 32.6	20 52.3	0 21.9	17 43.0	12 30.2	17 54.9	18 4.6	23 18.7	21 11.0	5 8.3	19 3.6	14 49.6
22	19 59 22.2	20 18.2	0 22.0	25 40.9	11 30.9	18 .8	17 31.4	23 19.2	21 12.8	5 10.1	19 3.3	14 46.9
25	20 11 11.9	19 41.1	0 22.0	23 16.7	10 46.3	18 9.4	16 57.1	23 19.6	21 14.6	5 12.1	19 3.1	14 44.2
28	20 23 1.6	19 1.0	0 22.0	10 27.4	10 19.7	18 19.8	16 21.9	23 20.0	21 16.3	5 14.3	19 2.9	14 41.5
31	20 34 51.2	18 18.1	0 22.1	7N23.2	10 13.9	18 31.2	15 45.6	23 20.4	21 17.8	5 16.6	19 2.8	14 38.7

AUGUST 1972

LONGITUDE

DAY	EPHEM. SID. TIME	☉	☊	☽	☿	♀	♂	♃	♄	♅	♆	♇
	h m s	° ′	° ′	° ′	° ′	° ′	° ′	° ′	° ′	° ′	° ′	° ′
1	20 38 47.8	8♌50.4	25♑21.2	21♈10.0	20♌18.2	26♊29.8	21♌ 6.3	29♐23.8	17♊17.9	14♎53.7	2♐31.9	0♎ 2.6
2	20 42 44.4	9 47.8	25 18.1	5♉20.6	19 R 42.4	27 9.3	21 44.3	29 R 19.5	17 23.6	14 55.8	2 R 31.5	0 4.2
3	20 46 40.9	10 45.2	25 14.9	19 34.4	19 3.0	27 49.8	22 22.3	29 15.3	17 29.4	14 57.9	2 31.1	0 5.8
4	20 50 37.5	11 42.7	25 11.7	3♊49.0	18 20.6	28 31.3	23 .4	29 11.4	17 35.0	15 .0	2 30.8	0 7.4
5	20 54 34.0	12 40.2	25 8.5	18 1.8	17 35.9	29 13.9	23 38.4	29 7.6	17 40.6	15 2.2	2 30.5	0 9.1
6	20 58 30.6	13 37.6	25 5.4	2♋10.1	16 49.5	29 57.4	24 16.4	29 3.9	17 46.1	15 4.5	2 30.2	0 10.8
7	21 2 27.1	14 35.1	25 2.2	16 11.1	16 2.2	0♋41.9	24 54.4	29 .5	17 51.5	15 6.7	2 29.9	0 12.5
8	21 6 23.7	15 32.7	24 59.0	0♌ 1.9	15 15.1	1 27.2	25 32.5	28 57.2	17 57.0	15 9.1	2 29.8	0 14.3
9	21 10 20.2	16 30.3	24 55.8	13 39.6	14 28.7	2 13.4	26 10.6	28 54.1	18 2.3	15 11.4	2 29.6	0 16.0
10	21 14 16.8	17 27.8	24 52.7	27 2.1	13 44.2	3 .4	26 48.6	28 51.2	18 7.5	15 13.8	2 29.5	0 17.8
11	21 18 13.4	18 25.4	24 49.5	10♍ 7.8	13 2.4	3 48.2	27 26.7	28 48.4	18 12.6	15 16.3	2 29.3	0 19.6
12	21 22 9.9	19 23.0	24 46.3	22 56.2	12 24.1	4 36.8	28 4.8	28 45.8	18 17.7	15 18.8	2 29.3	0 21.4
13	21 26 6.5	20 20.6	24 43.1	5♎28.0	11 50.1	5 26.0	28 42.8	28 43.4	18 22.7	15 21.3	2 29.2	0 23.2
14	21 30 3.0	21 18.2	24 39.9	17 45.0	11 21.2	6 16.0	29 20.9	28 41.2	18 27.6	15 23.8	2 29.2	0 25.1
15	21 33 59.6	22 15.9	24 36.8	29 49.9	10 57.9	7 6.7	29 59.0	28 39.2	18 32.5	15 26.4	2 29.2	0 26.9
16	21 37 56.1	23 13.6	24 33.6	11♏46.6	10 41.0	7 58.0	0♍37.1	28 37.4	18 37.2	15 29.1	2 D 29.3	0 28.8
17	21 41 52.7	24 11.2	24 30.4	23 39.2	10 30.7	8 50.0	1 15.2	28 35.7	18 41.9	15 31.7	2 29.3	0 30.7
18	21 45 49.2	25 8.9	24 27.2	5♐32.5	10 27.5	9 42.6	1 53.3	28 34.2	18 46.5	15 34.5	2 29.5	0 32.6
19	21 49 45.8	26 6.7	24 24.1	17 31.3	10 D 31.7	10 35.8	2 31.4	28 33.0	18 51.0	15 37.2	2 29.6	0 34.6
20	21 53 42.4	27 4.4	24 20.9	29 40.4	10 43.3	11 29.6	3 9.5	28 31.9	18 55.5	15 40.0	2 29.8	0 36.5
21	21 57 38.9	28 2.2	24 17.7	12♑ 4.0	11 2.7	12 23.9	3 47.6	28 31.0	18 59.8	15 42.8	2 30.0	0 38.5
22	22 1 35.5	28 59.9	24 14.5	24 45.6	11 29.6	13 18.8	4 25.8	28 30.3	19 4.1	15 45.6	2 30.2	0 40.5
23	22 5 32.0	29 57.7	24 11.3	7♒47.5	12 4.2	14 14.2	5 3.9	28 29.7	19 8.3	15 48.5	2 30.5	0 42.5
24	22 9 28.6	0♍55.6	24 8.2	21 10.8	12 46.3	15 10.1	5 42.1	28 29.4	19 12.4	15 51.4	2 30.8	0 44.5
25	22 13 25.1	1 53.4	24 5.0	4♓54.3	13 35.7	16 6.6	6 20.2	28 29.2	19 16.4	15 54.4	2 31.2	0 46.6
26	22 17 21.7	2 51.3	24 1.8	18 55.5	14 32.2	17 3.5	6 58.4	28 D 29.3	19 20.3	15 57.4	2 31.5	0 48.6
27	22 21 18.2	3 49.2	23 58.6	3♈10.1	15 35.6	18 .9	7 36.6	28 29.5	19 24.1	16 .4	2 31.9	0 50.7
28	22 25 14.8	4 47.1	23 55.5	17 32.8	16 45.5	18 58.7	8 14.8	28 29.9	19 27.9	16 3.4	2 32.4	0 52.8
29	22 29 11.3	5 45.1	23 52.3	1♉58.1	18 1.6	19 57.1	8 53.0	28 30.5	19 31.6	16 6.6	2 32.9	0 54.9
30	22 33 7.9	6 43.1	23 49.1	16 21.0	19 23.5	20 55.8	9 31.2	28 31.3	19 35.1	16 9.7	2 33.4	0 57.0
31	22 37 4.4	7 41.1	23 45.9	0♊37.8	20 50.5	21 54.9	10 9.5	28 32.3	19 38.6	16 12.8	2 33.9	0 59.1

LATITUDE

DAY	EPHEM. SID. TIME	☉	☊	☽	☿	♀	♂	♃	♄	♅	♆	♇
1	20 38 47.8	0 .0	0 .0	5N14.8	4S40.6	4S48.9	1N 9.0	0N 6.0	1S32.3	0N37.7	1N39.4	15N59.8
4	20 50 37.5	0 .0	0 .0	4 9.7	4 54.0	4 39.5	1 8.6	0 5.5	1 32.5	0 37.6	1 39.2	15 58.8
7	21 2 27.1	0 .0	0 .0	0 54.0	4 52.1	4 28.9	1 8.2	0 5.1	1 32.7	0 37.5	1 39.1	15 57.8
10	21 14 16.8	0 .0	0 .0	2S42.5	4 33.8	4 17.3	1 7.7	0 4.7	1 32.9	0 37.4	1 38.9	15 56.9
13	21 26 6.5	0 .0	0 .0	4 54.0	4 .4	4 4.8	1 7.3	0 4.2	1 33.1	0 37.3	1 38.7	15 56.0
16	21 37 56.1	0 .0	0 .0	5 1.2	3 15.7	3 51.5	1 6.8	0 3.8	1 33.3	0 37.2	1 38.5	15 55.2
19	21 49 45.8	0 .0	0 .0	3 13.9	2 24.4	3 37.6	1 6.3	0 3.4	1 33.5	0 37.1	1 38.4	15 54.4
22	22 1 35.5	0 .0	0 .0	0 5.4	1 31.2	3 23.2	1 5.7	0 3.0	1 33.8	0 37.0	1 38.2	15 53.7
25	22 13 25.1	0 .0	0 .0	3N16.8	0 40.2	3 8.4	1 5.2	0 2.6	1 34.0	0 36.9	1 38.0	15 53.1
28	22 25 14.8	0 .0	0 .0	5 6.7	0N 5.5	2 53.3	1 4.6	0 2.2	1 34.3	0 36.8	1 37.8	15 52.5
31	22 37 4.4	0 .0	0 .0	4 12.6	0 43.8	2 38.0	1 4.0	0 1.8	1 34.6	0 36.8	1 37.7	15 52.0

RIGHT ASCENSION

DAY	EPHEM. SID. TIME	☉	☊	☽	☿	♀	♂	♃	♄	♅	♆	♇
1	20 38 47.8	11♌16.3	27♑19.0	17♈32.4	21♌12.3	26♊19.0	23♌52.5	29♐20.5	16♊21.2	13♎57.5	0♐48.3	6♎32.8
2	20 42 44.4	12 14.4	27 15.6	1♉13.7	20 R 35.9	27 .4	24 29.8	29 R 15.9	16 27.4	13 59.4	0 R 47.9	6 34.1
3	20 46 40.9	13 12.5	27 12.3	15 42.8	19 56.5	27 43.0	25 7.0	29 11.4	16 33.5	14 1.3	0 47.5	6 35.4
4	20 50 37.5	14 10.4	27 8.9	0♊57.0	19 14.7	28 26.7	25 44.1	29 7.0	16 39.5	14 3.3	0 47.1	6 36.7
5	20 54 34.0	15 8.1	27 5.6	16 39.9	18 31.1	29 11.4	26 21.2	29 2.9	16 45.5	14 5.3	0 46.8	6 38.1
6	20 58 30.6	16 5.7	27 2.2	2♋24.2	17 46.3	29 57.3	26 58.2	28 58.9	16 51.4	14 7.4	0 46.5	6 39.5
7	21 2 27.1	17 3.1	26 58.9	17 40.4	17 1.1	0♋44.1	27 35.1	28 55.1	16 57.2	14 9.4	0 46.3	6 40.9
8	21 6 23.7	18 .5	26 55.5	2♌ 7.9	16 16.5	1 32.0	28 12.1	28 51.6	17 3.0	14 11.6	0 46.1	6 42.3
9	21 10 20.2	18 57.6	26 52.2	15 39.2	15 33.1	2 20.8	28 48.9	28 48.2	17 8.7	14 13.8	0 45.9	6 43.8
10	21 14 16.8	19 54.6	26 48.8	28 18.5	14 51.9	3 10.4	29 25.6	28 45.0	17 14.3	14 16.0	0 45.7	6 45.3
11	21 18 13.4	20 51.5	26 45.5	10♍16.4	14 13.6	4 1.0	0♍ 2.3	28 42.0	17 19.8	14 18.2	0 45.6	6 46.8
12	21 22 9.9	21 48.2	26 42.1	21 46.8	13 39.1	4 52.4	0 39.0	28 39.2	17 25.2	14 20.5	0 45.5	6 48.3
13	21 26 6.5	22 44.8	26 38.8	3♎ 3.9	13 9.2	5 44.5	1 15.6	28 36.6	17 30.6	14 22.9	0 45.4	6 49.8
14	21 30 3.0	23 41.2	26 35.4	14 21.1	12 44.5	6 37.5	1 52.1	28 34.2	17 35.9	14 25.2	0 45.4	6 51.4
15	21 33 59.6	24 37.5	26 32.0	25 50.4	12 25.7	7 31.3	2 28.6	28 32.0	17 41.0	14 27.6	0 45.4	6 52.9
16	21 37 56.1	25 33.7	26 28.7	7♏41.7	12 13.2	8 25.7	3 5.0	28 30.0	17 46.2	14 30.0	0 D 45.5	6 54.5
17	21 41 52.7	26 29.7	26 25.3	20 1.2	12 7.6	9 20.9	3 41.3	28 28.2	17 51.2	14 32.5	0 45.5	6 56.2
18	21 45 49.2	27 25.6	26 22.0	2♐50.7	12 D 9.2	10 16.7	4 17.6	28 26.6	17 56.1	14 35.0	0 45.6	6 57.8
19	21 49 45.8	28 21.4	26 18.6	16 6.2	12 18.2	11 13.2	4 53.9	28 25.2	18 .9	14 37.5	0 45.8	6 59.4
20	21 53 42.4	29 17.0	26 15.3	29 38.2	12 34.8	12 10.3	5 30.1	28 24.0	18 5.7	14 40.1	0 45.9	7 1.1
21	21 57 38.9	0♍12.6	26 11.9	13♑14.3	12 59.1	13 8.1	6 6.2	28 23.0	18 10.4	14 42.7	0 46.2	7 2.8
22	22 1 35.5	1 8.0	26 8.6	26 42.4	13 31.0	14 6.4	6 42.3	28 22.2	18 14.9	14 45.3	0 46.4	7 4.5
23	22 5 32.0	2 3.2	26 5.2	9♒54.8	14 10.6	15 5.3	7 18.4	28 21.6	18 19.4	14 48.0	0 46.7	7 6.2
24	22 9 28.6	2 58.4	26 1.8	22 50.0	14 57.6	16 4.7	7 54.4	28 21.3	18 23.8	14 50.7	0 47.0	7 8.0
25	22 13 25.1	3 53.5	25 58.5	5♓32.5	15 51.8	17 4.6	8 30.4	28 21.1	18 28.1	14 53.4	0 47.3	7 9.7
26	22 17 21.7	4 48.5	25 55.1	18 11.7	16 52.9	18 5.0	9 6.3	28 21.1	18 32.3	14 56.2	0 47.7	7 11.5
27	22 21 18.2	5 43.3	25 51.8	1♈ .1	18 .6	19 5.9	9 42.2	28 D 21.4	18 36.4	14 59.0	0 48.1	7 13.3
28	22 25 14.8	6 38.1	25 48.4	14 11.1	19 14.5	20 7.3	10 18.0	28 21.8	18 40.4	15 1.8	0 48.5	7 15.1
29	22 29 11.3	7 32.8	25 45.0	27 56.8	20 34.2	21 9.2	10 53.9	28 22.5	18 44.4	15 4.7	0 49.1	7 17.0
30	22 33 7.9	8 27.4	25 41.7	12♉24.1	21 59.0	22 11.4	11 29.6	28 23.4	18 48.2	15 7.6	0 49.6	7 18.8
31	22 37 4.4	9 21.9	25 38.3	27 30.8	23 28.6	23 14.0	12 5.4	28 24.4	18 51.9	15 10.5	0 50.1	7 20.6

DECLINATION

DAY	EPHEM. SID. TIME	☉	☊	☽	☿	♀	♂	♃	♄	♅	♆	♇
1	20 38 47.8	18N 3.1	0S22.1	13N 7.1	10N16.8	18N35.1	15N33.3	23S20.6	21N18.3	5S17.4	19S 2.7	14N37.7
4	20 50 37.5	17 16.6	0 22.1	25 .2	10 40.1	18 46.7	14 55.9	23 20.9	21 19.8	5 20.0	19 2.7	14 34.9
7	21 2 27.1	16 27.6	0 22.1	23 21.4	11 22.9	18 57.6	14 17.6	23 21.3	21 21.1	5 22.6	19 2.7	14 32.0
10	21 14 16.8	15 36.2	0 22.2	9 57.4	12 19.9	19 7.4	13 38.4	23 21.7	21 22.3	5 25.5	19 2.8	14 29.0
13	21 26 6.5	14 42.5	0 22.2	6S40.2	13 23.4	19 15.4	12 58.5	23 22.0	21 23.4	5 28.4	19 2.9	14 26.1
16	21 37 56.1	13 46.7	0 22.2	20 8.4	14 25.1	19 21.2	12 17.8	23 22.4	21 24.4	5 31.5	19 3.1	14 23.1
19	21 49 45.8	12 49.0	0 22.2	26 4.6	15 17.1	19 24.3	11 36.5	23 22.7	21 25.3	5 34.7	19 3.3	14 20.1
22	22 1 35.5	11 49.5	0 22.3	21 16.1	15 52.6	19 24.5	10 54.5	23 23.1	21 26.2	5 38.1	19 3.6	14 17.2
25	22 13 25.1	10 48.3	0 22.3	6 39.6	16 6.3	19 21.3	10 11.8	23 23.5	21 26.9	5 41.5	19 4.0	14 14.2
28	22 25 14.8	9 45.5	0 22.3	11N36.5	15 54.3	19 14.4	9 28.6	23 23.9	21 27.5	5 45.1	19 4.4	14 11.2
31	22 37 4.4	8 41.3	0 22.4	24 24.1	15 14.5	19 3.6	8 44.9	23 24.3	21 28.1	5 48.7	19 4.9	14 8.3

SEPTEMBER 1972

DAY	EPHEM. SID. TIME	☉	☊	☽	☿	♀	♂	♃	♄	♅	♆	♇
		LONGITUDE										
	h m s	° ′	° ′	° ′	° ′	° ′	° ′	° ′	° ′	° ′	° ′	° ′
1	22 41 1.0	8♍39.1	23♑42.7	14♊45.8	22♌22.5	22♋54.5	10♍47.7	28♐33.5	19♊42.0	16♎16.0	2♐34.5	1♎ 1.3
2	22 44 57.6	9 37.2	23 39.6	28 43.7	23 58.7	23 54.4	11 26.0	28 34.8	19 45.2	16 19.2	2 35.1	1 3.4
3	22 48 54.1	10 35.3	23 36.4	12♋30.9	25 38.8	24 54.7	12 4.2	28 36.3	19 48.4	16 22.4	2 35.7	1 5.6
4	22 52 50.7	11 33.5	23 33.2	26 7.2	27 22.2	25 55.4	12 42.5	28 38.1	19 51.5	16 25.7	2 36.4	1 7.7
5	22 56 47.2	12 31.7	23 30.0	9♌32.4	29 8.4	26 56.5	13 20.8	28 40.0	19 54.5	16 28.9	2 37.1	1 9.9
6	23 0 43.8	13 29.9	23 26.9	22 46.4	0♍57.0	27 57.9	13 59.1	28 42.1	19 57.4	16 32.2	2 37.8	1 12.1
7	23 4 40.3	14 28.1	23 23.7	5♍48.3	2 47.5	28 59.6	14 37.5	28 44.4	20 .2	16 35.6	2 38.6	1 14.3
8	23 8 36.9	15 26.4	23 20.5	18 37.8	4 39.5	0♌ 1.7	15 15.8	28 46.8	20 2.8	16 38.9	2 39.4	1 16.5
9	23 12 33.4	16 24.7	23 17.3	1♎14.5	6 32.6	1 4.0	15 54.1	28 49.5	20 5.4	16 42.3	2 40.2	1 18.7
10	23 16 30.0	17 23.0	23 14.1	13 38.3	8 26.4	2 6.7	16 32.5	28 52.3	20 7.9	16 45.7	2 41.0	1 20.9
11	23 20 26.5	18 21.4	23 11.0	25 50.3	10 20.7	3 9.7	17 10.9	28 55.3	20 10.3	16 49.1	2 41.9	1 23.1
12	23 24 23.1	19 19.7	23 7.8	7♏52.2	12 15.2	4 13.0	17 49.3	28 58.5	20 12.6	16 52.6	2 42.8	1 25.4
13	23 28 19.6	20 18.2	23 4.6	19 46.6	14 9.6	5 16.5	18 27.7	29 1.9	20 14.7	16 56.0	2 43.8	1 27.6
14	23 32 16.2	21 16.6	23 1.4	1♐37.2	16 3.8	6 20.3	19 6.1	29 5.4	20 16.8	16 59.5	2 44.7	1 29.9
15	23 36 12.7	22 15.1	22 58.3	13 28.3	17 57.5	7 24.5	19 44.5	29 9.1	20 18.8	17 3.0	2 45.7	1 32.1
16	23 40 9.3	23 13.6	22 55.1	25 24.8	19 50.8	8 28.8	20 23.0	29 13.0	20 20.6	17 6.6	2 46.8	1 34.4
17	23 44 5.9	24 12.1	22 51.9	7♑31.8	21 43.3	9 33.5	21 1.4	29 17.1	20 22.4	17 10.1	2 47.8	1 36.6
18	23 48 2.4	25 10.6	22 48.7	19 54.7	23 35.2	10 38.3	21 39.9	29 21.4	20 24.1	17 13.7	2 48.9	1 38.9
19	23 51 59.0	26 9.3	22 45.5	2♒38.2	25 26.2	11 43.5	22 18.4	29 25.8	20 25.6	17 17.3	2 50.1	1 41.2
20	23 55 55.5	27 7.9	22 42.4	15 45.9	27 16.4	12 48.9	22 56.9	29 30.4	20 27.1	17 20.9	2 51.3	1 43.5
21	23 59 52.1	28 6.5	22 39.2	29 19.9	29 5.6	13 54.5	23 35.5	29 35.2	20 28.4	17 24.5	2 52.4	1 45.7
22	0 3 48.6	29 5.2	22 36.0	13♓20.1	0♎54.0	15 .4	24 14.0	29 40.1	20 29.6	17 28.2	2 53.6	1 48.0
23	0 7 45.2	0♎ 3.9	22 32.8	27 43.3	2 41.4	16 6.4	24 52.5	29 45.2	20 30.7	17 31.8	2 54.9	1 50.3
24	0 11 41.7	1 2.6	22 29.7	12♈23.9	4 27.8	17 12.8	25 31.1	29 50.5	20 31.7	17 35.4	2 56.1	1 52.6
25	0 15 38.3	2 1.3	22 26.5	27 13.9	6 13.4	18 19.3	26 9.7	29 55.9	20 32.6	17 39.1	2 57.4	1 54.8
26	0 19 34.8	3 .1	22 23.3	12♉ 4.8	7 57.9	19 26.0	26 48.3	0♑ 1.5	20 33.4	17 42.8	2 58.8	1 57.1
27	0 23 31.4	3 59.0	22 20.1	26 48.4	9 41.5	20 33.0	27 26.9	0 7.2	20 34.1	17 46.5	3 .1	1 59.4
28	0 27 27.9	4 57.8	22 16.9	11♊18.6	11 24.2	21 40.2	28 5.5	0 13.1	20 34.7	17 50.2	3 1.5	2 1.7
29	0 31 24.5	5 56.8	22 13.8	25 31.8	13 6.0	22 47.6	28 44.2	0 19.2	20 35.1	17 53.9	3 2.9	2 3.9
30	0 35 21.0	6 55.7	22 10.6	9♋26.6	14 46.9	23 55.1	29 22.8	0 25.4	20 35.5	17 57.6	3 4.3	2 6.2
		LATITUDE										
1	22 41 1.0	0 .0	0 .0	3N21.2	0N54.6	2S32.9	1N 3.8	0N 1.7	1S34.7	0N36.7	1N37.6	15N51.9
4	22 52 50.7	0 .0	0 .0	0S 4.7	1 20.9	2 17.4	1 3.1	0 1.3	1 34.9	0 36.7	1 37.4	15 51.4
7	23 4 40.3	0 .0	0 .0	3 20.4	1 38.0	2 2.0	1 2.5	0 .9	1 35.2	0 36.6	1 37.3	15 51.1
10	23 16 30.0	0 .0	0 .0	4 59.8	1 46.7	1 46.6	1 1.8	0 .6	1 35.5	0 36.5	1 37.1	15 50.8
13	23 28 19.6	0 .0	0 .0	4 35.9	1 48.1	1 31.4	1 1.1	0 .2	1 35.8	0 36.5	1 36.9	15 50.6
16	23 40 9.3	0 .0	0 .0	2 27.4	1 43.4	1 16.3	1 .3	0S .2	1 36.1	0 36.4	1 36.8	15 50.5
19	23 51 59.0	0 .0	0 .0	0N45.2	1 33.9	1 1.5	0 59.6	0 .5	1 36.4	0 36.4	1 36.6	15 50.4
22	0 3 48.6	0 .0	0 .0	3 50.4	1 20.7	0 47.0	0 58.8	0 .8	1 36.7	0 36.3	1 36.4	15 50.5
25	0 15 38.3	0 .0	0 .0	5 1.5	1 4.6	0 32.9	0 58.0	0 1.2	1 37.0	0 36.3	1 36.3	15 50.5
28	0 27 27.9	0 .0	0 .0	3 22.2	0 46.5	0 19.2	0 57.2	0 1.5	1 37.3	0 36.2	1 36.1	15 50.7
		RIGHT ASCENSION										
1	22 41 1.0	10♍16.4	25♑35.0	13♊ 2.5	25♌ 2.3	24♋17.0	12♍41.1	28♐25.7	18♊55.6	15♎13.4	0♐50.7	7♎22.5
2	22 44 57.6	11 10.8	25 31.6	28 35.3	26 39.6	25 20.3	13 16.7	28 27.2	18 59.1	15 16.3	0 51.3	7 24.4
3	22 48 54.1	12 5.1	25 28.2	13♋43.0	28 19.9	26 23.9	13 52.4	28 28.8	19 2.5	15 19.3	0 51.9	7 26.3
4	22 52 50.7	12 59.3	25 24.9	28 6.4	0♍ 2.7	27 27.9	14 28.0	28 30.7	19 5.8	15 22.3	0 52.6	7 28.2
5	22 56 47.2	13 53.5	25 21.5	11♌37.7	1 47.5	28 32.2	15 3.6	28 32.8	19 9.0	15 25.4	0 53.3	7 30.1
6	23 0 43.8	14 47.7	25 18.2	24 19.7	3 33.7	29 36.7	15 39.2	28 35.1	19 12.1	15 28.4	0 54.1	7 32.0
7	23 4 40.3	15 41.7	25 14.8	6♍21.8	5 21.0	0♌41.5	16 14.7	28 37.6	19 15.1	15 31.5	0 54.8	7 34.0
8	23 8 36.9	16 35.8	25 11.4	17 56.3	7 8.8	1 46.6	16 50.2	28 40.2	19 18.0	15 34.6	0 55.7	7 35.9
9	23 12 33.4	17 29.8	25 8.1	29 16.5	8 56.9	2 51.8	17 25.7	28 43.1	19 20.8	15 37.7	0 56.5	7 37.9
10	23 16 30.0	18 23.7	25 4.7	10♎34.9	10 45.0	3 57.3	18 1.2	28 46.2	19 23.4	15 40.9	0 57.4	7 39.8
11	23 20 26.5	19 17.6	25 1.3	22 2.7	12 32.8	5 2.9	18 36.6	28 49.5	19 26.0	15 44.1	0 58.3	7 41.8
12	23 24 23.1	20 11.5	24 58.0	3♏48.8	14 20.0	6 8.8	19 12.1	28 53.0	19 28.4	15 47.3	0 59.2	7 43.8
13	23 28 19.6	21 5.4	24 54.6	15 59.5	16 6.6	7 14.8	19 47.5	28 56.6	19 30.8	15 50.5	1 .2	7 45.8
14	23 32 16.2	21 59.2	24 51.2	28 36.6	17 52.3	8 20.9	20 22.9	29 .5	19 33.0	15 53.7	1 1.2	7 47.8
15	23 36 12.7	22 53.0	24 47.9	11♐37.4	19 37.1	9 27.2	20 58.3	29 4.6	19 35.1	15 57.0	1 2.2	7 49.8
16	23 40 9.3	23 46.8	24 44.5	24 54.4	21 20.9	10 33.6	21 33.6	29 8.8	19 37.1	16 .2	1 3.3	7 51.8
17	23 44 5.9	24 40.6	24 41.1	8♑17.4	23 3.7	11 40.1	22 9.0	29 13.3	19 39.0	16 3.5	1 4.4	7 53.9
18	23 48 2.4	25 34.4	24 37.8	21 36.3	24 45.4	12 46.7	22 44.3	29 17.9	19 40.8	16 6.8	1 5.5	7 55.9
19	23 51 59.0	26 28.2	24 34.4	4♒44.1	26 26.0	13 53.4	23 19.7	29 22.8	19 42.5	16 10.2	1 6.7	7 58.0
20	23 55 55.5	27 22.0	24 31.0	17 39.1	28 5.6	15 .2	23 55.1	29 27.8	19 44.0	16 13.5	1 7.9	8 .1
21	23 59 52.1	28 15.9	24 27.7	0♓24.9	29 44.1	16 7.1	24 30.4	29 33.0	19 45.5	16 16.9	1 9.1	8 2.1
22	0 3 48.6	29 9.7	24 24.3	13 10.1	1♎21.6	17 14.0	25 5.7	29 38.3	19 46.8	16 20.3	1 10.3	8 4.2
23	0 7 45.2	0♎ 3.5	24 20.9	26 6.4	2 58.1	18 20.9	25 41.0	29 43.9	19 48.0	16 23.6	1 11.6	8 6.2
24	0 11 41.7	0 57.4	24 17.5	9♈27.1	4 33.7	19 27.9	26 16.4	29 49.6	19 49.1	16 27.0	1 12.9	8 8.3
25	0 15 38.3	1 51.3	24 14.2	23 24.2	6 8.3	20 35.0	26 51.7	29 55.5	19 50.0	16 30.4	1 14.2	8 10.4
26	0 19 34.8	2 45.3	24 10.8	8♉ 5.0	7 42.1	21 42.1	27 27.0	0♑ 1.6	19 50.9	16 33.9	1 15.6	8 12.5
27	0 23 31.4	3 39.3	24 7.4	23 27.0	9 15.1	22 49.2	28 2.4	0 7.9	19 51.6	16 37.3	1 17.0	8 14.5
28	0 27 27.9	4 33.4	24 4.1	9♊14.8	10 47.3	23 56.3	28 37.7	0 14.3	19 52.2	16 40.7	1 18.4	8 16.6
29	0 31 24.5	5 27.5	24 .7	25 2.5	12 18.8	25 3.4	29 13.1	0 20.9	19 52.7	16 44.2	1 19.8	8 18.7
30	0 35 21.0	6 21.7	23 57.3	10♋22.1	13 49.6	26 10.6	29 48.4	0 27.7	19 53.1	16 47.6	1 21.3	8 20.8
		DECLINATION										
1	22 41 1.0	8N19.6	0S22.4	25N54.3	14N55.0	18N59.1	8N30.2	23S24.5	21N28.3	5S50.0	19S 5.0	14N 7.3
4	22 52 50.7	7 13.8	0 22.4	20 51.2	13 39.2	18 42.9	7 45.8	23 24.9	21 28.7	5 53.8	19 5.6	14 4.3
7	23 4 40.3	6 6.9	0 22.4	6 16.6	12 .3	18 22.5	7 .9	23 25.4	21 29.1	5 57.6	19 6.2	14 1.4
10	23 16 30.0	4 59.1	0 22.5	9S59.0	10 3.3	17 57.7	6 15.7	23 25.8	21 29.3	6 1.6	19 6.8	13 58.6
13	23 28 19.6	3 50.5	0 22.5	22 6.5	7 53.8	17 28.6	5 30.1	23 26.2	21 29.5	6 5.6	19 7.5	13 55.8
16	23 40 9.3	2 41.4	0 22.5	25 49.1	5 36.4	16 55.1	4 44.1	23 26.7	21 29.7	6 9.7	19 8.2	13 53.0
19	23 51 59.0	1 31.7	0 22.5	18 50.5	3 15.0	16 17.3	3 57.9	23 27.1	21 29.7	6 13.8	19 9.0	13 50.2
22	0 3 48.6	0 21.8	0 22.6	3 .2	0 52.5	15 35.3	3 11.5	23 27.5	21 29.7	6 18.0	19 9.9	13 47.6
25	0 15 38.3	0S48.3	0 22.6	15N10.3	1S28.9	14 49.1	2 24.8	23 27.8	21 29.6	6 22.2	19 10.7	13 45.0
28	0 27 27.9	1 58.4	0 22.6	25 28.6	3 47.9	13 58.9	1 38.0	23 28.1	21 29.5	6 26.5	19 11.7	13 42.4

OCTOBER 1972

LONGITUDE

DAY	EPHEM. SID. TIME h m s	☉ ° ′	☊ ° ′	☽ ° ′	☿ ° ′	♀ ° ′	♂ ° ′	♃ ° ′	♄ ° ′	♅ ° ′	♆ ° ′	♇ ° ′
1	0 39 17.6	7♎54.7	22♑ 7.4	23♋ 3.4	16♎26.9	25♌ 2.9	0♎ 1.5	0♑31.8	20♊35.7	18♎ 1.4	3♐ 5.8	2♎ 8.5
2	0 43 14.2	8 53.7	22 4.2	6♌23.9	18 6.1	26 10.9	0 40.2	0 38.3	20 35.8	18 5.1	3 7.2	2 10.8
3	0 47 10.7	9 52.8	22 1.1	19 30.0	19 44.4	27 19.0	1 19.0	0 45.0	20 35.8	18 8.9	3 8.7	2 13.0
4	0 51 7.3	10 51.9	21 57.9	2♍23.4	21 21.8	28 27.4	1 57.7	0 51.8	20 R 35.7	18 12.6	3 10.3	2 15.3
5	0 55 3.8	11 51.0	21 54.7	15 5.5	22 58.5	29 35.9	2 36.5	0 58.8	20 35.5	18 16.4	3 11.8	2 17.5
6	0 59 .4	12 50.2	21 51.5	27 37.3	24 34.4	0♍44.5	3 15.3	1 5.9	20 35.2	18 20.2	3 13.4	2 19.8
7	1 2 56.9	13 49.4	21 48.3	9♎59.5	26 9.4	1 53.4	3 54.1	1 13.2	20 34.8	18 23.9	3 15.0	2 22.0
8	1 6 53.5	14 48.7	21 45.2	22 12.4	27 43.8	3 2.4	4 32.9	1 20.6	20 34.2	18 27.7	3 16.6	2 24.3
9	1 10 50.0	15 47.9	21 42.0	4♏16.8	29 17.3	4 11.5	5 11.8	1 28.1	20 33.6	18 31.5	3 18.3	2 26.5
10	1 14 46.6	16 47.3	21 38.8	16 13.8	0♏50.2	5 20.9	5 50.7	1 35.9	20 32.9	18 35.3	3 20.0	2 28.8
11	1 18 43.1	17 46.7	21 35.6	28 5.2	2 22.3	6 30.4	6 29.6	1 43.7	20 32.0	18 39.1	3 21.7	2 31.0
12	1 22 39.7	18 46.0	21 32.5	9♐53.7	3 53.6	7 40.0	7 8.5	1 51.7	20 31.0	18 42.9	3 23.4	2 33.2
13	1 26 36.2	19 45.4	21 29.3	21 42.7	5 24.2	8 49.7	7 47.4	1 59.8	20 29.9	18 46.7	3 25.1	2 35.4
14	1 30 32.8	20 44.9	21 26.1	3♑36.6	6 54.2	9 59.6	8 26.3	2 8.1	20 28.7	18 50.5	3 26.9	2 37.6
15	1 34 29.3	21 44.3	21 22.9	15 40.4	8 23.3	11 9.7	9 5.3	2 16.5	20 27.4	18 54.2	3 28.7	2 39.8
16	1 38 25.9	22 43.8	21 19.7	27 59.3	9 51.8	12 19.8	9 44.3	2 25.0	20 26.0	18 58.0	3 30.5	2 42.0
17	1 42 22.5	23 43.4	21 16.6	10♒38.7	11 19.5	13 30.1	10 23.3	2 33.6	20 24.5	19 1.8	3 32.3	2 44.1
18	1 46 19.0	24 42.9	21 13.4	23 43.4	12 46.5	14 40.6	11 2.3	2 42.4	20 22.8	19 5.6	3 34.2	2 46.3
19	1 50 15.6	25 42.5	21 10.2	7♓17.0	14 12.8	15 51.1	11 41.3	2 51.3	20 21.1	19 9.3	3 36.0	2 48.4
20	1 54 12.1	26 42.1	21 7.0	21 20.5	15 38.2	17 1.8	12 20.3	3 .3	20 19.3	19 13.1	3 37.9	2 50.5
21	1 58 8.7	27 41.8	21 3.9	5♈52.3	17 2.9	18 12.7	12 59.4	3 9.4	20 17.3	19 16.8	3 39.8	2 52.7
22	2 2 5.2	28 41.4	21 .7	20 47.0	18 26.7	19 23.6	13 38.5	3 18.7	20 15.3	19 20.6	3 41.7	2 54.8
23	2 6 1.8	29 41.1	20 57.5	5♉56.0	19 49.6	20 34.7	14 17.6	3 28.1	20 13.1	19 24.3	3 43.6	2 56.9
24	2 9 58.3	0♏40.9	20 54.3	21 8.6	21 11.7	21 45.9	14 56.8	3 37.6	20 10.9	19 28.1	3 45.6	2 58.9
25	2 13 54.9	1 40.7	20 51.1	6♊14.1	22 32.7	22 57.2	15 35.9	3 47.2	20 8.5	19 31.8	3 47.6	3 1.0
26	2 17 51.4	2 40.5	20 48.0	21 3.8	23 52.7	24 8.6	16 15.1	3 56.9	20 6.1	19 35.5	3 49.5	3 3.0
27	2 21 48.0	3 40.3	20 44.8	5♋31.6	25 11.6	25 20.1	16 54.3	4 6.8	20 3.5	19 39.2	3 51.5	3 5.1
28	2 25 44.6	4 40.2	20 41.6	19 35.1	26 29.3	26 31.8	17 33.5	4 16.7	20 .9	19 42.9	3 53.6	3 7.1
29	2 29 41.1	5 40.1	20 38.4	3♌14.1	27 45.7	27 43.6	18 12.8	4 26.8	19 58.2	19 46.6	3 55.6	3 9.1
30	2 33 37.7	6 40.1	20 35.3	16 30.8	29 .7	28 55.4	18 52.1	4 37.0	19 55.3	19 50.3	3 57.6	3 11.1
31	2 37 34.2	7 40.1	20 32.1	29 28.1	0♐14.2	0♎ 7.5	19 31.4	4 47.3	19 52.4	19 54.0	3 59.8	3 13.1

LATITUDE

DAY	EPHEM. SID. TIME h m s	☉	☊	☽	☿	♀	♂	♃	♄	♅	♆	♇
1	0 39 17.6	0 .0	0 .0	0 .0	0N26.9	0S 6.1	0N56.3	0S 1.8	1S37.6	0N36.2	1N36.0	15N50.9
4	0 51 7.3	0 .0	0 .0	3S11.9	0 6.4	0N 6.6	0 55.5	0 2.2	1 37.9	0 36.2	1 35.9	15 51.2
7	1 2 56.9	0 .0	0 .0	4 52.8	0S14.6	0 18.6	0 54.6	0 2.5	1 38.2	0 36.1	1 35.7	15 51.6
10	1 14 46.6	0 .0	0 .0	4 33.2	0 35.7	0 30.1	0 53.7	0 2.8	1 38.5	0 36.1	1 35.6	15 52.1
13	1 26 36.2	0 .0	0 .0	2 29.4	0 56.6	0 40.8	0 52.7	0 3.1	1 38.7	0 36.1	1 35.5	15 52.6
16	1 38 25.9	0 .0	0 .0	0N35.5	1 17.0	0 50.9	0 51.7	0 3.4	1 39.0	0 36.1	1 35.4	15 53.2
19	1 50 15.6	0 .0	0 .0	3 37.6	1 36.4	1 .3	0 50.7	0 3.7	1 39.2	0 36.1	1 35.2	15 53.9
22	2 2 5.2	0 .0	0 .0	5 .5	1 54.6	1 8.9	0 49.7	0 4.0	1 39.5	0 36.1	1 35.1	15 54.6
25	2 13 54.9	0 .0	0 .0	3 29.5	2 11.0	1 16.8	0 48.7	0 4.3	1 39.7	0 36.1	1 35.0	15 55.4
28	2 25 44.6	0 .0	0 .0	0 2.4	2 25.3	1 23.8	0 47.6	0 4.5	1 39.8	0 36.1	1 34.9	15 56.3
31	2 37 34.2	0 .0	0 .0	3S12.8	2 36.8	1 30.1	0 46.5	0 4.8	1 40.0	0 36.1	1 34.9	15 57.3

RIGHT ASCENSION

DAY	EPHEM. SID. TIME h m s	☉	☊	☽	☿	♀	♂	♃	♄	♅	♆	♇
1	0 39 17.6	7♎15.9	23♑53.9	24♋53.4	15♎19.8	27♌17.7	0♎23.8	0♑34.6	19♊53.4	16♎51.1	1♐22.8	8♎22.9
2	0 43 14.2	8 10.3	23 50.6	8♌28.7	16 49.4	28 24.8	0 59.2	0 41.7	19 53.5	16 54.6	1 24.3	8 25.0
3	0 47 10.7	9 4.7	23 47.2	21 11.7	18 18.4	29 32.0	1 34.6	0 49.0	19 53.5	16 58.1	1 25.9	8 27.1
4	0 51 7.3	9 59.2	23 43.8	3♍12.5	19 47.0	0♍39.1	2 10.1	0 56.5	19 R 53.4	17 1.6	1 27.5	8 29.1
5	0 55 3.8	10 53.8	23 40.4	14 44.4	21 15.1	1 46.1	2 45.5	1 4.1	19 53.2	17 5.1	1 29.1	8 31.2
6	0 59 .4	11 48.5	23 37.1	26 .8	22 42.7	2 53.2	3 21.0	1 11.8	19 52.9	17 8.6	1 30.7	8 33.3
7	1 2 56.9	12 43.3	23 33.7	7♎14.7	24 10.0	4 .2	3 56.5	1 19.8	19 52.4	17 12.1	1 32.4	8 35.4
8	1 6 53.5	13 38.2	23 30.3	18 37.4	25 36.9	5 7.2	4 32.0	1 27.8	19 51.9	17 15.6	1 34.0	8 37.5
9	1 10 50.0	14 33.1	23 26.9	0♏17.7	27 3.5	6 14.2	5 7.6	1 36.1	19 51.2	17 19.1	1 35.8	8 39.6
10	1 14 46.6	15 28.3	23 23.6	12 21.7	28 29.8	7 21.2	5 43.2	1 44.5	19 50.4	17 22.7	1 37.5	8 41.7
11	1 18 43.1	16 23.5	23 20.2	24 51.0	29 55.8	8 28.1	6 18.8	1 53.1	19 49.5	17 26.2	1 39.3	8 43.8
12	1 22 39.7	17 18.9	23 16.8	7♐42.3	1♏21.6	9 35.0	6 54.4	2 1.8	19 48.4	17 29.7	1 41.1	8 45.8
13	1 26 36.2	18 14.3	23 13.4	20 48.3	2 47.0	10 41.8	7 30.0	2 10.6	19 47.3	17 33.3	1 42.9	8 47.9
14	1 30 32.8	19 9.9	23 10.0	3♑58.8	4 12.3	11 48.6	8 5.7	2 19.6	19 46.0	17 36.8	1 44.7	8 50.0
15	1 34 29.3	20 5.6	23 6.7	17 4.0	5 37.3	12 55.4	8 41.5	2 28.8	19 44.6	17 40.3	1 46.5	8 52.0
16	1 38 25.9	21 1.5	23 3.3	29 57.4	7 2.1	14 2.1	9 17.2	2 38.1	19 43.1	17 43.8	1 48.4	8 54.1
17	1 42 22.5	21 57.5	22 59.9	12♒37.4	8 26.7	15 8.9	9 53.0	2 47.5	19 41.4	17 47.4	1 50.3	8 56.1
18	1 46 19.0	22 53.6	22 56.5	25 8.1	9 51.0	16 15.6	10 28.8	2 57.0	19 39.7	17 50.9	1 52.2	8 58.1
19	1 50 15.6	23 49.9	22 53.1	7♓38.1	11 15.1	17 22.3	11 4.7	3 6.7	19 37.8	17 54.4	1 54.1	9 .2
20	1 54 12.1	24 46.3	22 49.8	20 19.8	12 38.9	18 28.9	11 40.6	3 16.6	19 35.9	17 57.9	1 56.1	9 2.2
21	1 58 8.7	25 42.9	22 46.4	3♈27.7	14 2.4	19 35.6	12 16.6	3 26.5	19 33.8	18 1.4	1 58.1	9 4.2
22	2 2 5.2	26 39.7	22 43.0	17 16.3	15 25.6	20 42.2	12 52.5	3 36.6	19 31.6	18 4.9	2 .0	9 6.2
23	2 6 1.8	27 36.6	22 39.6	1♉56.4	16 48.4	21 48.9	13 28.6	3 46.9	19 29.3	18 8.4	2 2.0	9 8.2
24	2 9 58.3	28 33.7	22 36.2	17 29.4	18 10.7	22 55.5	14 4.7	3 57.2	19 26.9	18 11.9	2 4.1	9 10.2
25	2 13 54.9	29 30.9	22 32.9	3♊42.0	19 32.6	24 2.2	14 40.8	4 7.7	19 24.4	18 15.3	2 6.1	9 12.2
26	2 17 51.4	0♏28.4	22 29.5	20 5.5	20 53.9	25 8.9	15 17.0	4 18.3	19 21.8	18 18.8	2 8.2	9 14.1
27	2 21 48.0	1 26.0	22 26.1	6♋ 4.8	22 14.5	26 15.6	15 53.3	4 29.0	19 19.1	18 22.3	2 10.2	9 16.1
28	2 25 44.6	2 23.9	22 22.7	21 12.1	23 34.4	27 22.3	16 29.6	4 39.9	19 16.3	18 25.7	2 12.3	9 18.0
29	2 29 41.1	3 21.9	22 19.3	5♌15.2	24 53.4	28 29.0	17 6.0	4 50.8	19 13.3	18 29.1	2 14.5	9 20.0
30	2 33 37.7	4 20.1	22 15.9	18 16.3	26 11.3	29 35.8	17 42.4	5 1.9	19 10.3	18 32.6	2 16.6	9 21.9
31	2 37 34.2	5 18.6	22 12.6	0♍26.7	27 28.1	0♎42.7	18 18.9	5 13.2	19 7.2	18 36.0	2 18.8	9 23.9

DECLINATION

DAY	EPHEM. SID. TIME h m s	☉	☊	☽	☿	♀	♂	♃	♄	♅	♆	♇
1	0 39 17.6	3S 8.4	0S22.6	21N28.4	6S 3.2	13N 4.8	0N51.1	23S28.4	21N29.2	6S30.8	19S12.6	13N39.9
4	0 51 7.3	4 18.1	0 22.7	7 38.3	8 14.0	12 6.9	0 4.1	23 28.6	21 28.9	6 35.1	19 13.6	13 37.6
7	1 2 56.9	5 27.3	0 22.7	8S26.6	10 19.7	11 5.7	0S43.0	23 28.8	21 28.6	6 39.4	19 14.6	13 35.2
10	1 14 46.6	6 35.9	0 22.7	21 3.1	12 19.5	10 1.1	1 30.0	23 28.8	21 28.2	6 43.8	19 15.7	13 33.0
13	1 26 36.2	7 43.7	0 22.8	25 40.2	14 12.9	8 53.5	2 17.0	23 28.8	21 27.7	6 48.1	19 16.8	13 30.9
16	1 38 25.9	8 50.6	0 22.8	19 59.3	15 59.4	7 43.2	3 3.9	23 28.7	21 27.2	6 52.4	19 17.9	13 28.9
19	1 50 15.6	9 56.3	0 22.8	5 28.1	17 38.4	6 30.4	3 50.7	23 28.5	21 26.6	6 56.7	19 19.1	13 26.9
22	2 2 5.2	11 .7	0 22.8	12N45.1	19 9.3	5 15.4	4 37.2	23 28.1	21 26.0	7 .9	19 20.2	13 25.1
25	2 13 54.9	12 3.6	0 22.9	24 47.5	20 31.3	3 58.4	5 23.6	23 27.6	21 25.3	7 5.2	19 21.4	13 23.4
28	2 25 44.6	13 4.8	0 22.9	22 3.2	21 43.7	2 39.7	6 9.6	23 27.0	21 24.5	7 9.4	19 22.6	13 21.8
31	2 37 34.2	14 4.3	0 22.9	8 38.9	22 45.5	1 19.7	6 55.4	23 26.2	21 23.7	7 13.5	19 23.9	13 20.3

NOVEMBER 1972

LONGITUDE

DAY	EPHEM. SID. TIME (h m s)	☉ (° ′)	☊ (° ′)	☽ (° ′)	☿ (° ′)	♀ (° ′)	♂ (° ′)	♃ (° ′)	♄ (° ′)	♅ (° ′)	♆ (° ′)	♇ (° ′)
1	2 41 30.8	8♏40.2	20♑28.9	12♍ 9.3	1♐25.9	1♎19.5	20♎10.7	4♑57.7	19♊49.4	19♎57.6	4♐ 1.8	3♎15.0
2	2 45 27.3	9 40.2	20 25.7	24 37.4	2 35.7	2 31.7	20 50.1	5 8.2	19 R 46.3	20 1.2	4 3.9	3 17.0
3	2 49 23.9	10 40.3	20 22.6	6♎55.0	3 43.5	3 44.0	21 29.5	5 18.8	19 43.1	20 4.9	4 6.0	3 18.9
4	2 53 20.4	11 40.5	20 19.4	19 4.2	4 48.8	4 56.3	22 8.9	5 29.5	19 39.8	20 8.5	4 8.1	3 20.8
5	2 57 17.0	12 40.6	20 16.2	1♏ 6.5	5 51.6	6 8.8	22 48.3	5 40.2	19 36.5	20 12.0	4 10.3	3 22.7
6	3 1 13.6	13 40.8	20 13.0	13 3.3	6 51.4	7 21.3	23 27.7	5 51.1	19 33.0	20 15.6	4 12.4	3 24.5
7	3 5 10.1	14 41.1	20 9.8	24 55.7	7 48.0	8 33.9	24 7.2	6 2.1	19 29.5	20 19.1	4 14.5	3 26.3
8	3 9 6.7	15 41.3	20 6.7	6♐45.2	8 40.8	9 46.6	24 46.7	6 13.2	19 25.8	20 22.7	4 16.7	3 28.2
9	3 13 3.2	16 41.6	20 3.5	18 33.8	9 29.6	10 59.4	25 26.2	6 24.4	19 22.1	20 26.2	4 18.9	3 29.9
10	3 16 59.8	17 41.9	20 .3	0♑23.9	10 13.7	12 12.2	26 5.7	6 35.7	19 18.4	20 29.6	4 21.0	3 31.7
11	3 20 56.3	18 42.3	19 57.1	12 18.8	10 52.7	13 25.2	26 45.3	6 47.0	19 14.5	20 33.1	4 23.2	3 33.5
12	3 24 52.9	19 42.6	19 54.0	24 22.6	11 25.9	14 38.2	27 24.8	6 58.5	19 10.6	20 36.5	4 25.4	3 35.2
13	3 28 49.4	20 43.0	19 50.8	6♒39.6	11 52.6	15 51.2	28 4.4	7 10.0	19 6.6	20 39.9	4 27.6	3 36.9
14	3 32 46.0	21 43.4	19 47.6	19 14.9	12 12.2	17 4.4	28 44.0	7 21.6	19 2.5	20 43.3	4 29.8	3 38.6
15	3 36 42.6	22 43.9	19 44.4	2♓13.2	12 24.0	18 17.6	29 23.7	7 33.3	18 58.4	20 46.7	4 32.1	3 40.2
16	3 40 39.1	23 44.3	19 41.3	15 38.6	12 27.1	19 30.9	0♏ 3.3	7 45.1	18 54.2	20 50.0	4 34.3	3 41.9
17	3 44 35.7	24 44.8	19 38.1	29 33.6	12 R 20.9	20 44.2	0 43.0	7 56.9	18 50.0	20 53.3	4 36.5	3 43.5
18	3 48 32.2	25 45.3	19 34.9	13♈58.1	12 4.9	21 57.6	1 22.7	8 8.9	18 45.7	20 56.6	4 38.7	3 45.0
19	3 52 28.8	26 45.8	19 31.7	28 48.8	11 38.5	23 11.1	2 2.5	8 20.9	18 41.3	20 59.9	4 41.0	3 46.6
20	3 56 25.3	27 46.4	19 28.5	13♉58.8	11 1.5	24 24.6	2 42.2	8 33.0	18 36.9	21 3.1	4 43.2	3 48.1
21	4 0 21.9	28 47.0	19 25.4	29 18.2	10 14.2	25 38.2	3 22.0	8 45.2	18 32.5	21 6.4	4 45.5	3 49.7
22	4 4 18.5	29 47.6	19 22.2	14♊35.6	9 16.8	26 51.9	4 1.8	8 57.4	18 27.9	21 9.5	4 47.8	3 51.1
23	4 8 15.0	0♐48.2	19 19.0	29 40.4	8 10.6	28 5.6	4 41.7	9 9.7	18 23.4	21 12.7	4 50.0	3 52.6
24	4 12 11.6	1 48.8	19 15.8	14♋24.4	6 57.0	29 19.3	5 21.5	9 22.1	18 18.8	21 15.8	4 52.3	3 54.0
25	4 16 8.1	2 49.5	19 12.7	28 42.6	5 38.0	0♏33.2	6 1.4	9 34.5	18 14.1	21 18.9	4 54.5	3 55.4
26	4 20 4.7	3 50.2	19 9.5	12♌33.0	4 16.2	1 47.0	6 41.3	9 47.0	18 9.4	21 21.9	4 56.8	3 56.8
27	4 24 1.2	4 50.9	19 6.3	25 56.7	2 54.2	3 1.0	7 21.2	9 59.6	18 4.7	21 24.9	4 59.0	3 58.1
28	4 27 57.8	5 51.7	19 3.1	8♍56.2	1 34.7	4 15.0	8 1.2	10 12.2	17 59.9	21 27.9	5 1.3	3 59.4
29	4 31 54.4	6 52.4	18 60.0	21 35.3	0 20.4	5 29.0	8 41.2	10 24.9	17 55.1	21 30.8	5 3.6	4 .7
30	4 35 50.9	7 53.2	18 56.8	3♎57.9	29♏13.7	6 43.1	9 21.2	10 37.7	17 50.3	21 33.7	5 5.8	4 2.0

LATITUDE

DAY	EPHEM. SID. TIME (h m s)	☉	☊	☽	☿	♀	♂	♃	♄	♅	♆	♇
1	2 41 30.8	0 .0	0 .0	3S59.4	2S39.9	1N32.0	0N46.1	0S 4.9	1S40.0	0N36.1	1N34.8	15N57.6
4	2 53 20.4	0 .0	0 .0	5 1.7	2 46.3	1 37.1	0 45.0	0 5.2	1 40.2	0 36.1	1 34.8	15 58.6
7	3 5 10.1	0 .0	0 .0	4 4.8	2 47.5	1 41.5	0 43.8	0 5.5	1 40.3	0 36.2	1 34.7	15 59.7
10	3 16 59.8	0 .0	0 .0	1 34.9	2 42.1	1 45.0	0 42.6	0 5.7	1 40.4	0 36.2	1 34.6	16 .9
13	3 28 49.4	0 .0	0 .0	1N36.2	2 27.8	1 47.7	0 41.3	0 6.0	1 40.4	0 36.2	1 34.6	16 2.1
16	3 40 39.1	0 .0	0 .0	4 18.3	2 2.4	1 49.6	0 40.1	0 6.3	1 40.4	0 36.2	1 34.5	16 3.4
19	3 52 28.8	0 .0	0 .0	5 1.4	1 23.6	1 50.7	0 38.8	0 6.5	1 40.4	0 36.3	1 34.5	16 4.7
22	4 4 18.5	0 .0	0 .0	2 48.7	0 31.4	1 51.0	0 37.4	0 6.8	1 40.3	0 36.3	1 34.5	16 6.1
25	4 16 8.1	0 .0	0 .0	0S59.5	0N29.1	1 50.5	0 36.1	0 7.1	1 40.3	0 36.4	1 34.5	16 7.5
28	4 27 57.8	0 .0	0 .0	4 2.2	1 27.2	1 49.3	0 34.7	0 7.3	1 40.1	0 36.4	1 34.4	16 9.0

RIGHT ASCENSION

DAY	EPHEM. SID. TIME (h m s)	☉	☊	☽	☿	♀	♂	♃	♄	♅	♆	♇
1	2 41 30.8	6♏17.2	22♑ 9.2	12♍ 1.2	28♏43.4	1♎49.5	18♎55.5	5♑24.5	19♊ 4.0	18♎39.4	2♐20.9	9♎25.8
2	2 45 27.3	7 16.0	22 5.8	23 15.4	29 57.1	2 56.5	19 32.1	5 35.9	19 R .7	18 42.8	2 23.1	9 27.6
3	2 49 23.9	8 15.0	22 2.4	4♎23.7	1♐ 9.0	4 3.4	20 8.8	5 47.5	18 57.3	18 46.2	2 25.3	9 29.5
4	2 53 20.4	9 14.3	21 59.0	15 38.9	2 18.7	5 10.5	20 45.5	5 59.1	18 53.7	18 49.6	2 27.5	9 31.4
5	2 57 17.0	10 13.7	21 55.6	27 11.1	3 25.9	6 17.6	21 22.4	6 10.9	18 50.1	18 52.9	2 29.7	9 33.2
6	3 1 13.6	11 13.4	21 52.2	9♏ 7.4	4 30.3	7 24.8	21 59.2	6 22.7	18 46.4	18 56.2	2 31.9	9 35.0
7	3 5 10.1	12 13.2	21 48.8	21 30.3	5 31.4	8 32.1	22 36.2	6 34.7	18 42.6	18 59.5	2 34.1	9 36.8
8	3 9 6.7	13 13.3	21 45.5	4♐16.9	6 28.9	9 39.4	23 13.2	6 46.8	18 38.8	19 2.8	2 36.4	9 38.6
9	3 13 3.2	14 13.6	21 42.1	17 19.4	7 22.1	10 46.9	23 50.3	6 58.9	18 34.8	19 6.1	2 38.6	9 40.4
10	3 16 59.8	15 14.1	21 38.7	0♑26.4	8 10.4	11 54.4	24 27.5	7 11.2	18 30.8	19 9.4	2 40.9	9 42.2
11	3 20 56.3	16 14.8	21 35.3	13 26.3	8 53.4	13 2.1	25 4.7	7 23.6	18 26.7	19 12.6	2 43.2	9 43.9
12	3 24 52.9	17 15.7	21 31.9	26 11.0	9 30.3	14 9.9	25 42.1	7 36.0	18 22.5	19 15.8	2 45.5	9 45.6
13	3 28 49.4	18 16.8	21 28.5	8♒37.8	10 .3	15 17.8	26 19.5	7 48.6	18 18.2	19 19.0	2 47.8	9 47.3
14	3 32 46.0	19 18.1	21 25.1	20 49.9	10 22.7	16 25.9	26 56.9	8 1.2	18 13.9	19 22.2	2 50.1	9 49.0
15	3 36 42.6	20 19.7	21 21.7	2♓55.5	10 36.7	17 34.0	27 34.5	8 13.9	18 9.4	19 25.3	2 52.4	9 50.7
16	3 40 39.1	21 21.4	21 18.3	15 7.1	10 41.5	18 42.4	28 12.1	8 26.7	18 5.0	19 28.5	2 54.7	9 52.3
17	3 44 35.7	22 23.3	21 15.0	27 40.0	10 R 36.4	19 50.9	28 49.8	8 39.6	18 .4	19 31.6	2 57.0	9 54.0
18	3 48 32.2	23 25.5	21 11.6	10♈50.9	10 20.9	20 59.5	29 27.6	8 52.6	17 55.8	19 34.6	2 59.3	9 55.6
19	3 52 28.8	24 27.8	21 8.2	24 55.6	9 54.5	22 8.4	0♏ 5.5	9 5.7	17 51.2	19 37.7	3 1.7	9 57.2
20	3 56 25.3	25 30.4	21 4.8	10♉ 3.6	9 17.1	23 17.4	0 43.5	9 18.8	17 46.4	19 40.7	3 4.0	9 58.7
21	4 0 21.9	26 33.2	21 1.4	26 11.1	8 28.9	24 26.6	1 21.6	9 32.1	17 41.7	19 43.8	3 6.4	10 .3
22	4 4 18.5	27 36.1	20 58.0	12♊55.5	7 30.5	25 36.1	1 59.8	9 45.4	17 36.9	19 46.7	3 8.7	10 1.9
23	4 8 15.0	28 39.3	20 54.6	29 38.4	6 23.2	26 45.7	2 38.0	9 58.7	17 32.0	19 49.7	3 11.1	10 3.4
24	4 12 11.6	29 42.6	20 51.2	15♋40.6	5 8.7	27 55.5	3 16.3	10 12.2	17 27.1	19 52.6	3 13.4	10 4.8
25	4 16 8.1	0♐46.2	20 47.8	0♌37.3	3 49.1	29 5.5	3 54.8	10 25.7	17 22.1	19 55.5	3 15.8	10 6.3
26	4 20 4.7	1 49.9	20 44.4	14 22.9	2 27.0	0♏15.8	4 33.3	10 39.2	17 17.1	19 58.3	3 18.2	10 7.7
27	4 24 1.2	2 53.9	20 41.0	27 5.8	1 5.2	1 26.3	5 11.9	10 52.9	17 12.0	20 1.2	3 20.5	10 9.1
28	4 27 57.8	3 58.0	20 37.6	9♍ 1.3	29♏46.5	2 37.1	5 50.7	11 6.6	17 6.9	20 4.0	3 22.9	10 10.5
29	4 31 54.4	5 2.3	20 34.2	20 26.6	28 33.3	3 48.1	6 29.5	11 20.4	17 1.8	20 6.7	3 25.2	10 11.9
30	4 35 50.9	6 6.8	20 30.8	1♎38.1	27 27.9	4 59.3	7 8.4	11 34.2	16 56.6	20 9.5	3 27.6	10 13.2

DECLINATION

DAY	EPHEM. SID. TIME (h m s)	☉	☊	☽	☿	♀	♂	♃	♄	♅	♆	♇
1	2 41 30.8	14S23.6	0S22.9	3N18.8	23S 3.5	0N52.7	7S10.6	23S26.0	21N23.5	7S14.9	19S24.3	13N19.9
4	2 53 20.4	15 20.3	0 22.9	12S 7.0	23 49.5	0S28.6	7 55.9	23 25.0	21 22.6	7 19.0	19 25.5	13 18.6
7	3 5 10.1	16 14.8	0 23.0	22 57.5	24 22.1	1 50.5	8 40.7	23 23.8	21 21.7	7 23.0	19 26.7	13 17.4
10	3 16 59.8	17 6.8	0 23.0	25 1.4	24 39.5	3 12.8	9 25.0	23 22.5	21 20.7	7 26.9	19 28.0	13 16.3
13	3 28 49.4	17 56.1	0 23.0	17 3.5	24 39.5	4 34.9	10 8.9	23 21.0	21 19.8	7 30.7	19 29.2	13 15.4
16	3 40 39.1	18 42.7	0 23.0	1 41.4	24 18.9	5 56.7	10 52.1	23 19.3	21 18.7	7 34.5	19 30.5	13 14.6
19	3 52 28.8	19 26.2	0 23.1	15N44.6	23 34.0	7 17.8	11 34.7	23 17.4	21 17.7	7 38.1	19 31.7	13 14.0
22	4 4 18.5	20 6.6	0 23.1	25 20.8	22 21.8	8 37.9	12 16.6	23 15.2	21 16.6	7 41.7	19 33.0	13 13.5
25	4 16 8.1	20 43.7	0 23.1	19 27.1	20 46.2	9 56.5	12 57.8	23 12.9	21 15.5	7 45.2	19 34.2	13 13.1
28	4 27 57.8	21 17.3	0 23.1	4 28.5	19 3.5	11 13.4	13 38.3	23 10.4	21 14.4	7 48.5	19 35.4	13 12.9

DECEMBER 1972

DAY	EPHEM. SID. TIME	☉	☊	☾	☿	♀	♂	♃	♄	♅	♆	♇
	h m s	° ′	° ′	° ′	° ′	° ′	° ′	° ′	° ′	° ′	° ′	° ′
		LONGITUDE										
1	4 39 47.5	8♐54.1	18♑53.6	16♎ 8.0	28♏16.2	7♏57.2	10♏ 1.2	10♑50.5	17♊45.4	21♎36.6	5♐ 8.1	4♎ 3.2
2	4 43 44.0	9 54.9	18 50.4	28 9.0	27 R 29.2	9 11.4	10 41.3	11 3.4	17 R 40.6	21 39.5	5 10.3	4 4.4
3	4 47 40.6	10 55.8	18 47.2	10♏ 3.9	26 53.6	10 25.6	11 21.4	11 16.3	17 35.7	21 42.3	5 12.6	4 5.5
4	4 51 37.1	11 56.7	18 44.1	21 55.3	26 29.4	11 39.8	12 1.5	11 29.3	17 30.8	21 45.0	5 14.8	4 6.7
5	4 55 33.7	12 57.6	18 40.9	3♐45.1	26 16.6	12 54.1	12 41.6	11 42.3	17 25.8	21 47.7	5 17.1	4 7.8
6	4 59 30.3	13 58.5	18 37.7	15 35.3	26 14.7	14 8.5	13 21.8	11 55.4	17 20.9	21 50.4	5 19.3	4 8.8
7	5 3 26.8	14 59.5	18 34.5	27 27.6	26 D 23.0	15 22.8	14 2.0	12 8.6	17 15.9	21 53.1	5 21.5	4 9.9
8	5 7 23.4	16 .4	18 31.4	9♑23.8	26 40.8	16 37.2	14 42.2	12 21.8	17 11.0	21 55.7	5 23.8	4 10.9
9	5 11 19.9	17 1.4	18 28.2	21 26.2	27 7.1	17 51.7	15 22.4	12 35.0	17 6.0	21 58.2	5 26.0	4 11.9
10	5 15 16.5	18 2.4	18 25.0	3♒37.3	27 41.2	19 6.1	16 2.7	12 48.3	17 1.1	22 .8	5 28.2	4 12.8
11	5 19 13.1	19 3.4	18 21.8	16 .2	28 22.2	20 20.6	16 42.9	13 1.6	16 56.1	22 3.2	5 30.4	4 13.7
12	5 23 9.6	20 4.5	18 18.7	28 38.3	29 9.3	21 35.2	17 23.3	13 15.1	16 51.2	22 5.7	5 32.7	4 14.6
13	5 27 6.2	21 5.5	18 15.5	11♓35.2	0♐ 1.8	22 49.7	18 3.6	13 28.5	16 46.3	22 8.1	5 34.9	4 15.5
14	5 31 2.7	22 6.5	18 12.3	24 54.1	0 59.0	24 4.3	18 44.0	13 41.9	16 41.3	22 10.5	5 37.1	4 16.3
15	5 34 59.3	23 7.6	18 9.1	8♈37.6	2 .4	25 18.9	19 24.3	13 55.4	16 36.4	22 12.8	5 39.3	4 17.1
16	5 38 55.8	24 8.6	18 6.0	22 46.5	3 5.4	26 33.5	20 4.7	14 9.0	16 31.5	22 15.0	5 41.4	4 17.8
17	5 42 52.4	25 9.6	18 2.8	7♉19.5	4 13.6	27 48.1	20 45.1	14 22.5	16 26.7	22 17.2	5 43.6	4 18.5
18	5 46 49.0	26 10.7	17 59.6	22 12.4	5 24.6	29 2.8	21 25.6	14 36.1	16 21.8	22 19.4	5 45.7	4 19.2
19	5 50 45.5	27 11.8	17 56.4	7♊18.3	6 38.0	0♐17.5	22 6.0	14 49.8	16 17.0	22 21.5	5 47.9	4 19.8
20	5 54 42.1	28 12.8	17 53.2	22 28.3	7 53.5	1 32.2	22 46.5	15 3.4	16 12.2	22 23.6	5 50.0	4 20.5
21	5 58 38.6	29 13.9	17 50.1	7♋32.5	9 10.9	2 46.9	23 27.0	15 17.1	16 7.4	22 25.6	5 52.1	4 21.0
22	6 2 35.2	0♑15.0	17 46.9	22 22.1	10 29.9	4 1.7	24 7.6	15 30.9	16 2.7	22 27.6	5 54.2	4 21.6
23	6 6 31.8	1 16.1	17 43.7	6♌50.0	11 50.4	5 16.5	24 48.2	15 44.6	15 58.0	22 29.5	5 56.3	4 22.1
24	6 10 28.3	2 17.2	17 40.5	20 52.0	13 12.1	6 31.3	25 28.8	15 58.4	15 53.3	22 31.4	5 58.4	4 22.6
25	6 14 24.9	3 18.3	17 37.4	4♍26.7	14 34.9	7 46.1	26 9.4	16 12.2	15 48.7	22 33.2	6 .4	4 23.0
26	6 18 21.4	4 19.5	17 34.2	17 35.1	15 58.8	9 .9	26 50.0	16 26.0	15 44.2	22 35.0	6 2.5	4 23.4
27	6 22 18.0	5 20.6	17 31.0	0♎19.8	17 23.5	10 15.8	27 30.7	16 39.9	15 39.6	22 36.7	6 4.5	4 23.8
28	6 26 14.5	6 21.7	17 27.8	12 44.7	18 49.1	11 30.7	28 11.4	16 53.7	15 35.2	22 38.4	6 6.5	4 24.1
29	6 30 11.1	7 22.9	17 24.7	24 54.2	20 15.3	12 45.6	28 52.2	17 7.6	15 30.7	22 40.0	6 8.5	4 24.4
30	6 34 7.7	8 24.1	17 21.5	6♏52.7	21 42.3	14 .5	29 32.9	17 21.6	15 26.4	22 41.6	6 10.5	4 24.7
31	6 38 4.2	9 25.2	17 18.3	18 44.4	23 9.9	15 15.4	0♐13.7	17 35.5	15 22.1	22 43.1	6 12.5	4 24.9
		LATITUDE										
1	4 39 47.5	0 .0	0 .0	5S10.0	2N11.1	1N47.4	0N33.2	0S 7.6	1S40.0	0N36.5	1N34.4	16N10.5
4	4 51 37.1	0 .0	0 .0	4 15.7	2 35.7	1 44.8	0 31.8	0 7.9	1 39.8	0 36.5	1 34.4	16 12.0
7	5 3 26.8	0 .0	0 .0	1 44.6	2 42.7	1 41.5	0 30.3	0 8.1	1 39.6	0 36.6	1 34.5	16 13.6
10	5 15 16.5	0 .0	0 .0	1N30.4	2 36.9	1 37.6	0 28.7	0 8.4	1 39.3	0 36.7	1 34.5	16 15.3
13	5 27 6.2	0 .0	0 .0	4 16.9	2 22.6	1 33.2	0 27.2	0 8.7	1 39.0	0 36.7	1 34.5	16 16.9
16	5 38 55.8	0 .0	0 .0	5 13.4	2 3.3	1 28.1	0 25.5	0 8.9	1 38.7	0 36.8	1 34.5	16 18.6
19	5 50 45.5	0 .0	0 .0	3 21.1	1 41.1	1 22.6	0 23.9	0 9.2	1 38.3	0 36.9	1 34.6	16 20.3
22	6 2 35.2	0 .0	0 .0	0S30.9	1 17.5	1 16.7	0 22.2	0 9.5	1 37.9	0 36.9	1 34.6	16 22.0
25	6 14 24.9	0 .0	0 .0	3 54.4	0 53.5	1 10.3	0 20.4	0 9.7	1 37.5	0 37.0	1 34.7	16 23.7
28	6 26 14.5	0 .0	0 .0	5 16.3	0 29.7	1 3.5	0 18.7	0 10.0	1 37.0	0 37.1	1 34.7	16 25.4
31	6 38 4.2	0 .0	0 .0	4 29.4	0 6.7	0 56.5	0 16.8	0 10.3	1 36.5	0 37.2	1 34.8	16 27.1
		RIGHT ASCENSION										
1	4 39 47.5	7♐11.4	20♑27.5	12♎50.4	26♏31.8	6♏10.8	7♏47.4	11♑48.1	16♊51.4	20♎12.1	3♐29.9	10♎14.6
2	4 43 44.0	8 16.2	20 24.1	24 15.9	25 R 46.3	7 22.6	8 26.6	12 2.1	16 R 46.2	20 14.8	3 32.3	10 15.8
3	4 47 40.6	9 21.2	20 20.7	6♏ 3.7	25 11.9	8 34.6	9 5.8	12 16.1	16 41.0	20 17.4	3 34.6	10 17.1
4	4 51 37.1	10 26.3	20 17.3	18 18.8	24 48.7	9 46.9	9 45.1	12 30.2	16 35.7	20 20.0	3 37.0	10 18.3
5	4 55 33.7	11 31.6	20 13.9	1♐ .4	24 36.7	10 59.5	10 24.5	12 44.3	16 30.5	20 22.6	3 39.3	10 19.6
6	4 59 30.3	12 37.0	20 10.5	14 1.9	24 35.3	12 12.3	11 4.1	12 58.5	16 25.2	20 25.1	3 41.7	10 20.7
7	5 3 26.8	13 42.6	20 7.1	27 11.7	24 D 43.9	13 25.4	11 43.7	13 12.7	16 19.9	20 27.6	3 44.0	10 21.9
8	5 7 23.4	14 48.3	20 3.7	10♑16.7	25 1.8	14 38.9	12 23.4	13 27.0	16 14.6	20 30.0	3 46.4	10 23.0
9	5 11 19.9	15 54.1	20 .3	23 6.0	25 28.1	15 52.6	13 3.3	13 41.3	16 9.3	20 32.5	3 48.7	10 24.1
10	5 15 16.5	16 60.0	19 56.9	5♒33.8	26 2.1	17 6.5	13 43.2	13 55.7	16 4.0	20 34.8	3 51.0	10 25.2
11	5 19 13.1	18 6.0	19 53.5	17 40.9	26 42.9	18 20.8	14 23.3	14 10.1	15 58.7	20 37.2	3 53.3	10 26.3
12	5 23 9.6	19 12.1	19 50.1	29 33.7	27 30.1	19 35.4	15 3.5	14 24.7	15 53.5	20 39.5	3 55.7	10 27.3
13	5 27 6.2	20 18.3	19 46.7	11♓23.1	28 22.6	20 50.3	15 43.8	14 39.2	15 48.2	20 41.7	3 58.0	10 28.3
14	5 31 2.7	21 24.5	19 43.3	23 23.5	29 20.2	22 5.5	16 24.1	14 53.7	15 42.9	20 44.0	4 .3	10 29.3
15	5 34 59.3	22 30.9	19 39.9	5♈51.5	0♐22.1	23 20.9	17 4.6	15 8.3	15 37.7	20 46.1	4 2.5	10 30.2
16	5 38 55.8	23 37.2	19 36.5	19 4.4	1 28.0	24 36.7	17 45.2	15 22.9	15 32.4	20 48.2	4 4.8	10 31.1
17	5 42 52.4	24 43.7	19 33.1	3♉17.0	2 37.3	25 52.7	18 25.9	15 37.5	15 27.2	20 50.3	4 7.1	10 32.0
18	5 46 49.0	25 50.1	19 29.7	18 36.1	3 49.9	27 9.0	19 6.7	15 52.2	15 22.0	20 52.4	4 9.3	10 32.8
19	5 50 45.5	26 56.7	19 26.3	4♊53.2	5 5.2	28 25.6	19 47.6	16 6.9	15 16.9	20 54.4	4 11.6	10 33.6
20	5 54 42.1	28 3.2	19 22.9	21 40.0	6 23.1	29 42.5	20 28.6	16 21.7	15 11.8	20 56.3	4 13.8	10 34.4
21	5 58 38.6	29 9.8	19 19.5	8♋15.9	7 43.2	0♐59.7	21 9.7	16 36.4	15 6.7	20 58.2	4 16.0	10 35.2
22	6 2 35.2	0♑16.4	19 16.1	24 4.1	9 5.4	2 17.2	21 51.0	16 51.2	15 1.6	21 .1	4 18.2	10 35.9
23	6 6 31.8	1 22.9	19 12.7	8♌45.1	10 29.5	3 35.0	22 32.3	17 6.0	14 56.6	21 1.9	4 20.4	10 36.6
24	6 10 28.3	2 29.5	19 9.3	22 17.7	11 55.4	4 53.0	23 13.8	17 20.9	14 51.6	21 3.7	4 22.6	10 37.3
25	6 14 24.9	3 36.1	19 5.9	4♍53.0	13 22.8	6 11.3	23 55.3	17 35.7	14 46.7	21 5.4	4 24.7	10 37.9
26	6 18 21.4	4 42.7	19 2.5	16 47.1	14 51.6	7 29.9	24 37.0	17 50.6	14 41.8	21 7.1	4 26.9	10 38.5
27	6 22 18.0	5 49.3	18 59.1	28 16.9	16 21.7	8 48.7	25 18.8	18 5.5	14 36.9	21 8.7	4 29.0	10 39.1
28	6 26 14.5	6 55.8	18 55.7	9♎38.5	17 53.1	10 7.8	26 .7	18 20.4	14 32.2	21 10.3	4 31.1	10 39.6
29	6 30 11.1	8 2.2	18 52.2	21 5.7	19 25.6	11 27.1	26 42.8	18 35.4	14 27.4	21 11.8	4 33.2	10 40.1
30	6 34 7.7	9 8.7	18 48.8	2♏49.5	20 59.2	12 46.7	27 24.9	18 50.3	14 22.8	21 13.3	4 35.3	10 40.6
31	6 38 4.2	10 15.0	18 45.4	14 57.3	22 33.7	14 6.4	28 7.1	19 5.3	14 18.2	21 14.8	4 37.4	10 41.1
		DECLINATION										
1	4 39 47.5	21S47.3	0S23.2	11S 6.7	17S38.9	12S28.1	14S17.8	23S 7.6	21N13.2	7S51.7	19S36.6	13N12.8
4	4 51 37.1	22 13.5	0 23.2	22 21.8	16 50.9	13 40.4	14 56.5	23 4.6	21 12.1	7 54.8	19 37.8	13 12.8
7	5 3 26.8	22 35.9	0 23.2	25 9.7	16 42.6	14 49.9	15 34.3	23 1.4	21 10.9	7 57.7	19 39.0	13 13.0
10	5 15 16.5	22 54.3	0 23.2	17 52.9	17 6.0	15 56.1	16 11.0	22 58.0	21 9.7	8 .5	19 40.2	13 13.3
13	5 27 6.2	23 8.6	0 23.2	3 15.4	17 50.2	16 58.8	16 46.7	22 54.3	21 8.6	8 3.2	19 41.3	13 13.8
16	5 38 55.8	23 18.8	0 23.3	13N42.2	18 45.8	17 57.6	17 21.3	22 50.4	21 7.5	8 5.7	19 42.4	13 14.4
19	5 50 45.5	23 24.8	0 23.3	24 50.3	19 45.6	18 52.1	17 54.7	22 46.2	21 6.4	8 8.1	19 43.5	13 15.2
22	6 2 35.2	23 26.6	0 23.3	21 4.8	20 44.8	19 42.1	18 26.9	22 41.9	21 5.3	8 10.2	19 44.5	13 16.1
25	6 14 24.9	23 24.1	0 23.3	6 14.5	21 40.0	20 27.2	18 57.8	22 37.3	21 4.3	8 12.3	19 45.5	13 17.1
28	6 26 14.5	23 17.4	0 23.4	9S53.1	22 28.7	21 7.1	19 27.4	22 32.4	21 3.3	8 14.1	19 46.5	13 18.2
31	6 38 4.2	23 6.5	0 23.4	21 42.8	23 9.3	21 41.5	19 55.7	22 27.4	21 2.4	8 15.8	19 47.5	13 19.5

JANUARY 1973

LONGITUDE

DAY	EPHEM. SID. TIME	☉	☊	☽	☿	♀	♂	♃	♄	♅	♆	♇
	h m s	° ′	° ′	° ′	° ′	° ′	° ′	° ′	° ′	° ′	° ′	° ′
1	6 42 .8	10♑26.4	17♑15.1	0♐33.4	24♐38.0	16♐30.4	0♐54.5	17♑49.4	15♊17.8	22♎44.6	6♐14.5	4♎25.1
2	6 45 57.3	11 27.6	17 12.0	12 23.0	26 6.7	17 45.4	1 35.4	18 3.4	15R13.7	22 46.1	6 16.4	4 25.3
3	6 49 53.9	12 28.8	17 8.8	24 16.0	27 35.9	19 .4	2 16.3	18 17.4	15 9.5	22 47.4	6 18.4	4 25.4
4	6 53 50.4	13 30.0	17 5.6	6♑14.8	29 5.6	20 15.4	2 57.1	18 31.4	15 5.5	22 48.8	6 20.3	4 25.5
5	6 57 47.0	14 31.2	17 2.4	18 21.4	0♑35.7	21 30.3	3 38.1	18 45.4	15 1.5	22 50.0	6 22.1	4 25.6
6	7 1 43.6	15 32.4	16 59.2	0♒37.2	2 6.3	22 45.3	4 19.0	18 59.4	14 57.6	22 51.2	6 24.0	4 25.6
7	7 5 40.1	16 33.5	16 56.1	13 3.8	3 37.3	24 .4	4 59.9	19 13.4	14 53.7	22 52.4	6 25.8	4 25.6
8	7 9 36.7	17 34.7	16 52.9	25 42.5	5 8.7	25 15.4	5 40.9	19 27.4	14 50.0	22 53.5	6 27.7	4R25.5
9	7 13 33.2	18 35.9	16 49.7	8♓34.5	6 40.6	26 30.4	6 21.9	19 41.5	14 46.3	22 54.5	6 29.4	4 25.4
10	7 17 29.8	19 37.0	16 46.5	21 41.2	8 13.0	27 45.4	7 2.9	19 55.5	14 42.7	22 55.5	6 31.2	4 25.3
11	7 21 26.4	20 38.2	16 43.4	5♈ 4.0	9 45.7	29 .4	7 44.0	20 9.5	14 39.1	22 56.4	6 33.0	4 25.2
12	7 25 22.9	21 39.3	16 40.2	18 43.9	11 18.9	0♑15.5	8 25.1	20 23.5	14 35.7	22 57.3	6 34.7	4 25.0
13	7 29 19.5	22 40.5	16 37.0	2♉41.2	12 52.6	1 30.5	9 6.1	20 37.6	14 32.3	22 58.1	6 36.4	4 24.7
14	7 33 16.0	23 41.6	16 33.8	16 55.2	14 26.7	2 45.5	9 47.3	20 51.6	14 29.1	22 58.9	6 38.1	4 24.5
15	7 37 12.6	24 42.7	16 30.7	1♊24.1	16 1.4	4 .6	10 28.4	21 5.6	14 25.9	22 59.6	6 39.8	4 24.2
16	7 41 9.1	25 43.8	16 27.5	16 4.0	17 36.5	5 15.6	11 9.5	21 19.6	14 22.8	23 .2	6 41.4	4 23.9
17	7 45 5.7	26 44.9	16 24.3	0♋49.7	19 12.1	6 30.7	11 50.7	21 33.6	14 19.8	23 .8	6 43.0	4 23.5
18	7 49 2.3	27 45.9	16 21.1	15 34.6	20 48.2	7 45.7	12 31.9	21 47.6	14 16.9	23 1.4	6 44.6	4 23.1
19	7 52 58.8	28 47.0	16 18.0	0♌11.6	22 24.8	9 .8	13 13.2	22 1.6	14 14.1	23 1.8	6 46.2	4 22.7
20	7 56 55.4	29 48.0	16 14.8	14 34.1	24 2.0	10 15.8	13 54.4	22 15.6	14 11.4	23 2.3	6 47.7	4 22.2
21	8 0 51.9	0♒49.1	16 11.6	28 36.8	25 39.7	11 30.9	14 35.7	22 29.6	14 8.8	23 2.6	6 49.2	4 21.7
22	8 4 48.5	1 50.1	16 8.4	12♍16.3	27 18.1	12 46.0	15 17.0	22 43.5	14 6.3	23 3.0	6 50.7	4 21.2
23	8 8 45.0	2 51.2	16 5.2	25 31.3	28 57.0	14 1.1	15 58.4	22 57.5	14 3.9	23 3.3	6 52.2	4 20.7
24	8 12 41.6	3 52.2	16 2.1	8♎22.6	0♒36.6	15 16.2	16 39.8	23 11.4	14 1.6	23 3.5	6 53.6	4 20.1
25	8 16 38.2	4 53.2	15 58.9	20 52.8	2 16.7	16 31.2	17 21.2	23 25.4	13 59.4	23 3.6	6 55.1	4 19.5
26	8 20 34.7	5 54.2	15 55.7	3♏ 5.6	3 57.5	17 46.3	18 2.6	23 39.2	13 57.3	23 3.7	6 56.4	4 18.9
27	8 24 31.3	6 55.2	15 52.5	15 5.4	5 38.9	19 1.4	18 44.0	23 53.1	13 55.2	23 3.7	6 57.8	4 18.2
28	8 28 27.8	7 56.2	15 49.4	26 57.3	7 21.0	20 16.5	19 25.5	24 7.0	13 53.3	23 3.7	6 59.1	4 17.5
29	8 32 24.4	8 57.1	15 46.2	8♐46.0	9 3.7	21 31.6	20 7.0	24 20.8	13 51.6	23R 3.6	7 .4	4 16.7
30	8 36 20.9	9 58.1	15 43.0	20 36.4	10 47.1	22 46.7	20 48.5	24 34.6	13 49.9	23 3.5	7 1.7	4 15.9
31	8 40 17.5	10 59.0	15 39.8	2♑32.5	12 31.1	24 1.7	21 30.1	24 48.4	13 48.3	23 3.3	7 2.9	4 15.1

LATITUDE

DAY	EPHEM. SID. TIME	☉	☊	☽	☿	♀	♂	♃	♄	♅	♆	♇
1	6 42 .8	0 .0	0 .0	3S49.4	0S .8	0N54.1	0N16.2	0S10.4	1S36.4	0N37.2	1N34.8	16N27.7
4	6 53 50.4	0 .0	0 .0	0 58.2	0 22.4	0 46.7	0 14.3	0 10.6	1 35.8	0 37.3	1 34.9	16 29.4
7	7 5 40.1	0 .0	0 .0	2N21.0	0 42.6	0 39.1	0 12.4	0 10.9	1 35.3	0 37.4	1 35.0	16 31.2
10	7 17 29.8	0 .0	0 .0	4 47.8	1 1.1	0 31.4	0 10.5	0 11.2	1 34.7	0 37.5	1 35.1	16 32.9
13	7 29 19.5	0 .0	0 .0	5 5.4	1 17.8	0 23.5	0 8.4	0 11.5	1 34.1	0 37.6	1 35.2	16 34.6
16	7 41 9.1	0 .0	0 .0	2 42.5	1 32.4	0 15.6	0 6.4	0 11.8	1 33.5	0 37.6	1 35.3	16 36.2
19	7 52 58.8	0 .0	0 .0	1S13.6	1 44.7	0 7.8	0 4.3	0 12.1	1 32.8	0 37.7	1 35.4	16 37.9
22	8 4 48.5	0 .0	0 .0	4 21.0	1 54.4	0S .1	0 2.1	0 12.4	1 32.1	0 37.8	1 35.5	16 39.5
25	8 16 38.2	0 .0	0 .0	5 15.2	2 1.1	0 7.8	0S .1	0 12.7	1 31.5	0 37.9	1 35.7	16 41.0
28	8 28 27.8	0 .0	0 .0	4 1.2	2 4.6	0 15.4	0 2.4	0 13.0	1 30.8	0 38.0	1 35.8	16 42.6
31	8 40 17.5	0 .0	0 .0	1 17.4	2 4.4	0 22.7	0 4.7	0 13.3	1 30.1	0 38.1	1 35.9	16 44.0

RIGHT ASCENSION

DAY	EPHEM. SID. TIME	☉	☊	☽	☿	♀	♂	♃	♄	♅	♆	♇
1	6 42 .8	11♑21.4	18♑42.0	27♏31.5	24♐ 9.2	15♐26.4	28♏49.5	19♑20.3	14♊13.6	21♎16.2	4♐39.4	10♎41.5
2	6 45 57.3	12 27.6	18 38.6	10♐28.7	25 45.5	16 46.7	29 32.0	19 35.3	14R 9.2	21 17.6	4 41.5	10 41.9
3	6 49 53.9	13 33.8	18 35.2	23 39.5	27 22.6	18 7.0	0♐14.5	19 50.3	14 4.8	21 18.8	4 43.5	10 42.3
4	6 53 50.4	14 39.9	18 31.8	6♑51.3	29 .5	19 27.6	0 57.2	20 5.3	14 .4	21 20.1	4 45.5	10 42.6
5	6 57 47.0	15 45.8	18 28.4	19 51.7	0♑39.0	20 48.3	1 39.9	20 20.3	13 56.2	21 21.3	4 47.5	10 42.9
6	7 1 43.6	16 51.7	18 25.0	2♒32.3	2 18.2	22 9.2	2 22.8	20 35.3	13 52.0	21 22.4	4 49.4	10 43.1
7	7 5 40.1	17 57.4	18 21.6	14 50.5	3 58.0	23 30.2	3 5.8	20 50.3	13 47.9	21 23.5	4 51.4	10 43.4
8	7 9 36.7	19 3.0	18 18.2	26 49.6	5 38.4	24 51.3	3 48.8	21 5.3	13 43.8	21 24.6	4 53.3	10 43.5
9	7 13 33.2	20 8.5	18 14.8	8♓38.3	7 19.3	26 12.6	4 32.0	21 20.3	13 39.9	21 25.5	4 55.2	10 43.7
10	7 17 29.8	21 13.8	18 11.4	20 28.5	9 .8	27 33.9	5 15.3	21 35.3	13 36.0	21 26.5	4 57.0	10 43.8
11	7 21 26.4	22 19.0	18 8.0	2♈35.0	10 42.7	28 55.3	5 58.6	21 50.3	13 32.2	21 27.4	4 58.9	10 43.9
12	7 25 22.9	23 24.1	18 4.5	15 13.6	12 25.0	0♑16.8	6 42.1	22 5.3	13 28.6	21 28.2	5 .7	10 44.0
13	7 29 19.5	24 29.0	18 1.1	28 39.6	14 7.7	1 38.4	7 25.7	22 20.3	13 25.0	21 29.0	5 2.5	10 44.0
14	7 33 16.0	25 33.7	17 57.7	13♉ 3.6	15 50.8	2 59.9	8 9.3	22 35.2	13 21.5	21 29.7	5 4.3	10 44.0
15	7 37 12.6	26 38.3	17 54.3	28 26.4	17 34.3	4 21.5	8 53.0	22 50.2	13 18.1	21 30.4	5 6.0	10 44.0
16	7 41 9.1	27 42.7	17 50.9	14♊33.4	19 18.0	5 43.2	9 36.9	23 5.1	13 14.7	21 31.0	5 7.7	10R43.9
17	7 45 5.7	28 46.9	17 47.5	0♋54.7	21 2.1	7 4.8	10 20.8	23 20.1	13 11.5	21 31.6	5 9.4	10 43.9
18	7 49 2.3	29 50.9	17 44.1	16 54.9	22 46.4	8 26.4	11 4.8	23 35.0	13 8.4	21 32.1	5 11.1	10 43.7
19	7 52 58.8	0♒54.8	17 40.7	2♌ 6.4	24 31.0	9 48.0	11 48.9	23 49.9	13 5.4	21 32.5	5 12.7	10 43.6
20	7 56 55.4	1 58.5	17 37.3	16 17.7	26 15.8	11 9.5	12 33.1	24 4.7	13 2.5	21 32.9	5 14.4	10 43.4
21	8 0 51.9	3 2.0	17 33.8	29 31.6	28 .7	12 30.9	13 17.4	24 19.6	12 59.7	21 33.3	5 16.0	10 43.2
22	8 4 48.5	4 5.3	17 30.4	11♍59.5	29 45.9	13 52.3	14 1.7	24 34.4	12 57.0	21 33.6	5 17.5	10 42.9
23	8 8 45.0	5 8.4	17 27.0	23 56.4	1♒31.2	15 13.7	14 46.2	24 49.3	12 54.4	21 33.9	5 19.1	10 42.7
24	8 12 41.6	6 11.4	17 23.6	5♎37.2	3 16.7	16 34.9	15 30.8	25 4.1	12 51.9	21 34.1	5 20.6	10 42.4
25	8 16 38.2	7 14.1	17 20.2	17 16.0	5 2.2	17 56.0	16 15.4	25 18.9	12 49.6	21 34.3	5 22.1	10 42.0
26	8 20 34.7	8 16.6	17 16.8	29 4.2	6 47.8	19 16.9	17 .1	25 33.6	12 47.3	21 34.4	5 23.6	10 41.7
27	8 24 31.3	9 19.0	17 13.4	11♏10.5	8 33.4	20 37.7	17 44.8	25 48.3	12 45.1	21 34.4	5 25.0	10 41.3
28	8 28 27.8	10 21.1	17 9.9	23 39.2	10 19.1	21 58.4	18 29.7	26 3.0	12 43.1	21 34.4	5 26.4	10 40.8
29	8 32 24.4	11 23.1	17 6.5	6♐29.6	12 4.8	23 18.9	19 14.6	26 17.7	12 41.1	21R34.3	5 27.7	10 40.4
30	8 36 20.9	12 24.8	17 3.1	19 35.8	13 50.4	24 39.2	19 59.6	26 32.3	12 39.3	21 34.2	5 29.1	10 39.9
31	8 40 17.5	13 26.4	16 59.7	2♑47.8	15 36.0	25 59.3	20 44.6	26 46.9	12 37.6	21 34.0	5 30.4	10 39.4

DECLINATION

DAY	EPHEM. SID. TIME	☉	☊	☽	☿	♀	♂	♃	♄	♅	♆	♇
1	6 42 .8	23S 2.0	0S23.4	24S .5	23S20.9	21S51.8	20S 4.8	22S25.6	21N 2.1	8S16.3	19S47.8	13N19.9
4	6 53 50.4	22 45.5	0 23.4	24 15.9	23 48.8	22 18.6	20 31.1	22 20.3	21 1.3	8 17.8	19 48.7	13 21.3
7	7 5 40.1	22 25.0	0 23.4	14 38.6	24 6.2	22 39.4	20 55.9	22 14.7	21 .6	8 19.0	19 49.6	13 22.9
10	7 17 29.8	22 .5	0 23.4	1N 6.7	24 12.3	22 54.1	21 19.1	22 8.9	20 59.9	8 20.1	19 50.4	13 24.5
13	7 29 19.5	21 32.2	0 23.5	17 10.9	24 6.7	23 2.6	21 40.8	22 3.0	20 59.4	8 21.0	19 51.1	13 26.3
16	7 41 9.1	21 .1	0 23.5	25 24.5	23 48.7	23 4.7	22 .8	21 56.8	20 58.9	8 21.7	19 51.9	13 28.2
19	7 52 58.8	20 24.4	0 23.5	18 54.9	23 18.0	23 .5	22 19.1	21 50.4	20 58.5	8 22.2	19 52.6	13 30.1
22	8 4 48.5	19 45.3	0 23.5	2 56.1	22 34.3	22 49.9	22 35.8	21 43.9	20 58.3	8 22.5	19 53.2	13 32.2
25	8 16 38.2	19 2.8	0 23.5	13S .9	21 37.3	22 33.0	22 50.6	21 37.2	20 58.2	8 22.7	19 53.8	13 34.3
28	8 28 27.8	18 17.2	0 23.6	23 23.4	20 26.7	22 10.0	23 3.7	21 30.3	20 58.1	8 22.7	19 54.4	13 36.5
31	8 40 17.5	17 28.6	0 23.6	24 42.5	19 2.4	21 40.8	23 14.9	21 23.3	20 58.2	8 22.4	19 54.9	13 38.7

FEBRUARY 1973

LONGITUDE

DAY	EPHEM. SID. TIME h m s	☉ ° ′	☊ ° ′	☽ ° ′	☿ ° ′	♀ ° ′	♂ ° ′	♃ ° ′	♄ ° ′	♅ ° ′	♆ ° ′	♇ ° ′
1	8 44 14.0	11 ♒ 60.0	15 ♑ 36.7	14 ♑ 38.0	14 ♒ 15.8	25 ♑ 16.8	22 ♐ 11.6	25 ♑ 2.2	13 ♊ 46.8	23 ♎ 3.1	7 ♐ 4.1	4 ♎ 14.3
2	8 48 10.6	13 .9	15 33.5	26 55.5	16 1.1	26 31.9	22 53.2	25 15.9	13 R 45.5	23 R 2.8	7 5.3	4 R 13.4
3	8 52 7.2	14 1.8	15 30.3	9 ♒ 27.1	17 47.0	27 47.0	23 34.8	25 29.6	13 44.2	23 2.4	7 6.4	4 12.6
4	8 56 3.7	15 2.6	15 27.1	22 13.5	19 33.5	29 2.1	24 16.4	25 43.3	13 43.1	23 2.0	7 7.5	4 11.6
5	9 0 .3	16 3.5	15 23.9	5 ♓ 14.9	21 20.5	0 ♒ 17.2	24 58.1	25 56.9	13 42.1	23 1.5	7 8.6	4 10.7
6	9 3 56.8	17 4.3	15 20.8	18 30.5	23 8.0	1 32.2	25 39.8	26 10.5	13 41.1	23 1.0	7 9.7	4 9.7
7	9 7 53.4	18 5.1	15 17.6	1 ♈ 58.9	24 55.9	2 47.3	26 21.5	26 24.1	13 40.3	23 .4	7 10.7	4 8.7
8	9 11 49.9	19 5.9	15 14.4	15 38.8	26 44.1	4 2.4	27 3.2	26 37.6	13 39.7	22 59.8	7 11.7	4 7.7
9	9 15 46.5	20 6.7	15 11.2	29 28.6	28 32.6	5 17.4	27 44.9	26 51.1	13 39.1	22 59.1	7 12.7	4 6.6
10	9 19 43.0	21 7.4	15 8.1	13 ♉ 26.8	0 ♓ 21.1	6 32.5	28 26.6	27 4.6	13 38.6	22 58.4	7 13.6	4 5.5
11	9 23 39.6	22 8.1	15 4.9	27 32.2	2 9.5	7 47.5	29 8.4	27 18.0	13 38.3	22 57.6	7 14.5	4 4.4
12	9 27 36.2	23 8.8	15 1.7	11 ♊ 43.5	3 57.7	9 2.5	29 50.2	27 31.4	13 38.1	22 56.7	7 15.4	4 3.3
13	9 31 32.7	24 9.5	14 58.5	25 59.0	5 45.4	10 17.6	0 ♑ 32.1	27 44.7	13 38.0	22 55.9	7 16.2	4 2.2
14	9 35 29.3	25 10.1	14 55.3	10 ♋ 16.3	7 32.3	11 32.6	1 13.9	27 58.0	13 38.0	22 54.9	7 17.0	4 1.0
15	9 39 25.8	26 10.7	14 52.2	24 32.5	9 18.1	12 47.6	1 55.7	28 11.3	13 D 38.1	22 53.9	7 17.8	3 59.8
16	9 43 22.4	27 11.3	14 49.0	8 ♌ 43.7	11 2.5	14 2.6	2 37.6	28 24.4	13 38.3	22 52.9	7 18.5	3 58.6
17	9 47 18.9	28 11.8	14 45.8	22 45.6	12 45.1	15 17.6	3 19.5	28 37.6	13 38.7	22 51.8	7 19.2	3 57.3
18	9 51 15.5	29 12.3	14 42.6	6 ♍ 33.9	14 25.5	16 32.6	4 1.4	28 50.7	13 39.1	22 50.6	7 19.9	3 56.1
19	9 55 12.0	0 ♓ 12.8	14 39.5	20 5.1	16 3.1	17 47.6	4 43.4	29 3.7	13 39.7	22 49.4	7 20.6	3 54.8
20	9 59 8.6	1 13.3	14 36.3	3 ♎ 16.7	17 37.4	19 2.5	5 25.4	29 16.7	13 40.3	22 48.2	7 21.2	3 53.5
21	10 3 5.2	2 13.7	14 33.1	16 7.9	19 7.8	20 17.5	6 7.3	29 29.6	13 41.1	22 46.9	7 21.7	3 52.1
22	10 7 1.7	3 14.2	14 29.9	28 39.8	20 33.7	21 32.5	6 49.4	29 42.5	13 42.0	22 45.6	7 22.3	3 50.8
23	10 10 58.3	4 14.6	14 26.8	10 ♏ 54.6	21 54.6	22 47.4	7 31.4	29 55.4	13 43.0	22 44.2	7 22.8	3 49.4
24	10 14 54.8	5 14.9	14 23.6	22 56.1	23 9.6	24 2.4	8 13.5	0 ♒ 8.1	13 44.2	22 42.7	7 23.2	3 48.0
25	10 18 51.4	6 15.3	14 20.4	4 ♐ 48.8	24 18.3	25 17.3	8 55.5	0 20.8	13 45.4	22 41.3	7 23.7	3 46.6
26	10 22 47.9	7 15.6	14 17.2	16 37.8	25 19.9	26 32.3	9 37.6	0 33.5	13 46.8	22 39.8	7 24.1	3 45.2
27	10 26 44.5	8 15.9	14 14.0	28 28.6	26 14.0	27 47.2	10 19.8	0 46.1	13 48.2	22 38.2	7 24.4	3 43.7
28	10 30 41.0	9 16.2	14 10.9	10 ♑ 26.2	26 59.9	29 2.1	11 1.9	0 58.6	13 49.8	22 36.6	7 24.8	3 42.3

LATITUDE

DAY	EPHEM. SID. TIME h m s	☉ ° ′	☊ ° ′	☽ ° ′	☿ ° ′	♀ ° ′	♂ ° ′	♃ ° ′	♄ ° ′	♅ ° ′	♆ ° ′	♇ ° ′
1	8 44 14.0	0 .0	0 .0	0 S 11.6	2 S 3.4	0 S 25.1	0 S 5.4	0 S 13.4	1 S 29.8	0 N 38.1	1 N 36.0	16 N 44.5
4	8 56 3.7	0 .0	0 .0	3 N 2.5	1 57.6	0 32.2	0 7.8	0 13.7	1 29.1	0 38.2	1 36.1	16 45.9
7	9 7 53.4	0 .0	0 .0	5 2.4	1 47.0	0 39.0	0 10.2	0 14.0	1 28.4	0 38.3	1 36.2	16 47.3
10	9 19 43.0	0 .0	0 .0	4 37.8	1 31.0	0 45.4	0 12.7	0 14.4	1 27.7	0 38.4	1 36.4	16 48.6
13	9 31 32.7	0 .0	0 .0	1 48.4	1 9.1	0 51.5	0 15.2	0 14.7	1 27.0	0 38.4	1 36.5	16 49.8
16	9 43 22.4	0 .0	0 .0	1 S 58.8	0 41.1	0 57.2	0 17.8	0 15.1	1 26.2	0 38.5	1 36.7	16 51.0
19	9 55 12.0	0 .0	0 .0	4 37.7	0 6.9	1 2.4	0 20.5	0 15.4	1 25.5	0 38.6	1 36.8	16 52.1
22	10 7 1.7	0 .0	0 .0	5 .3	0 N 32.7	1 7.2	0 23.2	0 15.8	1 24.8	0 38.7	1 37.0	16 53.1
25	10 18 51.4	0 .0	0 .0	3 21.3	1 15.9	1 11.5	0 25.9	0 16.1	1 24.1	0 38.7	1 37.1	16 54.1
28	10 30 41.0	0 .0	0 .0	0 27.1	2 .0	1 15.3	0 28.7	0 16.5	1 23.3	0 38.8	1 37.3	16 55.0

RIGHT ASCENSION

DAY	EPHEM. SID. TIME h m s	☉ ° ′	☊ ° ′	☽ ° ′	☿ ° ′	♀ ° ′	♂ ° ′	♃ ° ′	♄ ° ′	♅ ° ′	♆ ° ′	♇ ° ′
1	8 44 14.0	14 ♒ 27.7	16 ♑ 56.3	15 ♑ 54.5	17 ♒ 21.5	27 ♑ 19.2	21 ♐ 29.7	27 ♑ 1.4	12 ♊ 36.0	21 ♎ 33.8	5 ♐ 31.6	10 ♎ 38.8
2	8 48 10.6	15 28.8	16 52.9	28 46.7	19 6.9	28 38.9	22 14.9	27 16.0	12 R 34.6	21 R 33.5	5 32.9	10 R 38.3
3	8 52 7.2	16 29.8	16 49.5	11 ♒ 19.9	20 52.1	29 58.4	23 .1	27 30.4	12 33.2	21 33.2	5 34.1	10 37.7
4	8 56 3.7	17 30.5	16 46.0	23 34.9	22 37.0	1 ♒ 17.7	23 45.4	27 44.9	12 32.0	21 32.8	5 35.3	10 37.0
5	9 0 .3	18 31.1	16 42.6	5 ♓ 37.8	24 21.7	2 36.7	24 30.7	27 59.3	12 30.8	21 32.4	5 36.4	10 36.4
6	9 3 56.8	19 31.4	16 39.2	17 38.2	26 6.1	3 55.4	25 16.1	28 13.6	12 29.8	21 31.9	5 37.5	10 35.7
7	9 7 53.4	20 31.5	16 35.8	29 48.5	27 50.0	5 13.9	26 1.5	28 27.9	12 29.0	21 31.4	5 38.6	10 35.0
8	9 11 49.9	21 31.4	16 32.4	12 ♈ 22.4	29 33.5	6 32.1	26 47.0	28 42.2	12 28.2	21 30.8	5 39.7	10 34.2
9	9 15 46.5	22 31.1	16 28.9	25 33.1	1 ♓ 16.3	7 50.1	27 32.5	28 56.4	12 27.6	21 30.2	5 40.7	10 33.5
10	9 19 43.0	23 30.6	16 25.5	9 ♉ 30.6	2 58.4	9 7.8	28 18.1	29 10.6	12 27.0	21 29.5	5 41.7	10 32.7
11	9 23 39.6	24 30.0	16 22.1	24 17.8	4 39.7	10 25.2	29 3.7	29 24.7	12 26.6	21 28.8	5 42.6	10 31.8
12	9 27 36.2	25 29.1	16 18.7	9 ♊ 45.9	6 19.9	11 42.3	29 49.3	29 38.7	12 26.4	21 28.0	5 43.5	10 31.0
13	9 31 32.7	26 28.0	16 15.3	25 33.7	7 58.9	12 59.2	0 ♑ 35.0	29 52.8	12 26.3	21 27.2	5 44.5	10 30.2
14	9 35 29.3	27 26.8	16 11.8	11 ♋ 13.2	9 36.5	14 15.7	1 20.7	0 ♒ 6.8	12 26.2	21 26.3	5 45.3	10 29.3
15	9 39 25.8	28 25.3	16 8.4	26 19.1	11 12.3	15 32.0	2 6.4	0 20.7	12 D 26.3	21 25.4	5 46.1	10 28.4
16	9 43 22.4	29 23.7	16 5.0	10 ♌ 37.1	12 46.2	16 47.9	2 52.2	0 34.5	12 26.5	21 24.4	5 46.9	10 27.4
17	9 47 18.9	0 ♓ 21.8	16 1.6	24 5.1	14 17.8	18 3.6	3 37.9	0 48.3	12 26.9	21 23.4	5 47.7	10 26.5
18	9 51 15.5	1 19.8	15 58.2	6 ♍ 50.3	15 46.6	19 19.0	4 23.7	1 2.0	12 27.3	21 22.3	5 48.4	10 25.5
19	9 55 12.0	2 17.7	15 54.7	19 4.3	17 12.5	20 34.1	5 9.6	1 15.7	12 27.9	21 21.2	5 49.0	10 24.5
20	9 59 8.6	3 15.3	15 51.3	1 ♎ .4	18 34.7	21 48.8	5 55.4	1 29.3	12 28.6	21 20.0	5 49.7	10 23.4
21	10 3 5.2	4 12.8	15 47.9	12 51.1	19 53.0	23 3.3	6 41.2	1 42.8	12 29.4	21 18.8	5 50.3	10 22.4
22	10 7 1.7	5 10.2	15 44.5	24 47.3	21 6.9	24 17.6	7 27.1	1 56.3	12 30.3	21 17.6	5 50.9	10 21.3
23	10 10 58.3	6 7.3	15 41.0	6 ♏ 57.1	22 15.7	25 31.5	8 13.0	2 9.7	12 31.3	21 16.3	5 51.4	10 20.2
24	10 14 54.8	7 4.4	15 37.6	19 25.1	23 19.0	26 45.1	8 58.9	2 23.0	12 32.5	21 15.0	5 51.9	10 19.1
25	10 18 51.4	8 1.3	15 34.2	2 ♐ 11.6	24 16.3	27 58.5	9 44.7	2 36.3	12 33.8	21 13.6	5 52.4	10 17.9
26	10 22 47.9	8 58.0	15 30.8	15 12.2	25 7.0	29 11.6	10 30.6	2 49.5	12 35.2	21 12.2	5 52.8	10 16.8
27	10 26 44.5	9 54.6	15 27.3	28 19.2	25 50.7	0 ♓ 24.4	11 16.5	3 2.6	12 36.7	21 10.7	5 53.2	10 15.6
28	10 30 41.0	10 51.1	15 23.9	11 ♑ 23.5	26 27.0	1 37.0	12 2.4	3 15.7	12 38.3	21 9.2	5 53.6	10 14.4

DECLINATION

DAY	EPHEM. SID. TIME h m s	☉ ° ′	☊ ° ′	☽ ° ′	☿ ° ′	♀ ° ′	♂ ° ′	♃ ° ′	♄ ° ′	♅ ° ′	♆ ° ′	♇ ° ′
1	8 44 14.0	17 S 11.8	0 S 23.6	22 S 49.9	18 S 31.3	21 S 29.8	23 S 18.2	21 S 20.9	20 N 58.3	8 S 22.3	19 S 55.0	13 N 39.5
4	8 56 3.7	16 19.5	0 23.6	11 13.5	16 49.0	20 52.8	23 27.0	21 13.7	20 58.6	8 21.8	19 55.4	13 41.8
7	9 7 53.4	15 24.7	0 23.6	5 N 24.7	14 53.6	20 10.3	23 33.8	21 6.4	20 58.9	8 21.2	19 55.8	13 44.2
10	9 19 43.0	14 27.6	0 23.7	20 17.3	12 46.1	19 22.4	23 38.8	20 58.9	20 59.5	8 20.3	19 56.2	13 46.6
13	9 31 32.7	13 28.3	0 23.7	25 11.3	10 28.4	18 29.5	23 41.8	20 51.4	21 .1	8 19.3	19 56.4	13 49.1
16	9 43 22.4	12 27.0	0 23.7	16 10.2	8 3.6	17 31.8	23 42.9	20 43.8	21 .9	8 18.2	19 56.7	13 51.6
19	9 55 12.0	11 23.9	0 23.7	0 S 19.8	5 36.5	16 29.6	23 42.0	20 36.1	21 1.7	8 16.8	19 56.9	13 54.1
22	10 7 1.7	10 19.2	0 23.7	15 40.4	3 14.4	15 23.2	23 39.2	20 28.3	21 2.8	8 15.3	19 57.0	13 56.6
25	10 18 51.4	9 13.1	0 23.7	24 23.9	1 6.0	14 13.0	23 34.4	20 20.6	21 3.9	8 13.7	19 57.1	13 59.1
28	10 30 41.0	8 5.7	0 23.8	23 29.0	0 N 38.5	12 59.2	23 27.7	20 12.8	21 5.1	8 11.9	19 57.1	14 1.6

MARCH 1973

LONGITUDE

DAY	EPHEM. SID. TIME	☉	☊	☽	☿	♀	♂	♃	♄	♅	♆	♇
	h m s	° ′	° ′	° ′	° ′	° ′	° ′	° ′	° ′	° ′	° ′	° ′
1	10 34 37.6	10♓16.4	14♑ 7.7	22♑35.6	27♓37.2	0♓17.0	11♑44.1	1♒11.0	13♊51.5	22♎34.9	7♐25.1	3♎40.8
2	10 38 34.1	11 16.6	14 4.5	5♒ .7	28 5.5	1 31.9	12 26.2	1 23.4	13 53.3	22 R 33.2	7 25.3	3 R 39.3
3	10 42 30.7	12 16.8	14 1.3	17 44.6	28 24.6	2 46.8	13 8.4	1 35.7	13 55.2	22 31.5	7 25.6	3 37.8
4	10 46 27.2	13 17.0	13 58.2	0♓48.6	28 34.3	4 1.7	13 50.7	1 48.0	13 57.2	22 29.7	7 25.8	3 36.3
5	10 50 23.8	14 17.1	13 55.0	14 12.6	28 34.6	5 16.6	14 32.9	2 .2	13 59.3	22 27.9	7 25.9	3 34.7
6	10 54 20.3	15 17.3	13 51.8	27 54.5	28 R 25.8	6 31.5	15 15.2	2 12.3	14 1.5	22 26.1	7 26.1	3 33.3
7	10 58 16.9	16 17.4	13 48.6	11♈50.8	28 8.1	7 46.4	15 57.4	2 24.3	14 3.9	22 24.2	7 26.2	3 31.7
8	11 2 13.5	17 17.4	13 45.4	25 57.1	27 41.9	9 1.2	16 39.7	2 36.3	14 6.3	22 22.3	7 26.3	3 30.1
9	11 6 10.0	18 17.4	13 42.3	10♉ 8.8	27 8.1	10 16.0	17 22.0	2 48.2	14 8.9	22 20.3	7 26.3	3 28.5
10	11 10 6.6	19 17.4	13 39.1	24 21.9	26 27.4	11 30.9	18 4.3	2 60.0	14 11.5	22 18.3	7 26.3	3 27.0
11	11 14 3.1	20 17.3	13 35.9	8♊33.2	25 40.9	12 45.7	18 46.6	3 11.7	14 14.3	22 16.3	7 26.3	3 25.4
12	11 17 59.7	21 17.2	13 32.7	22 40.7	24 49.7	14 .4	19 28.9	3 23.3	14 17.1	22 14.2	7 R 26.2	3 23.8
13	11 21 56.2	22 17.1	13 29.6	6♋43.3	23 55.0	15 15.2	20 11.3	3 34.8	14 20.1	22 12.1	7 26.1	3 22.1
14	11 25 52.8	23 16.9	13 26.4	20 40.5	22 58.2	16 30.0	20 53.6	3 46.3	14 23.1	22 10.0	7 25.9	3 20.5
15	11 29 49.3	24 16.7	13 23.2	4♌31.7	22 .5	17 44.7	21 36.0	3 57.6	14 26.3	22 7.8	7 25.8	3 18.9
16	11 33 45.9	25 16.4	13 20.0	18 15.7	21 3.3	18 59.4	22 18.4	4 8.9	14 29.5	22 5.6	7 25.6	3 17.3
17	11 37 42.4	26 16.1	13 16.8	1♍51.2	20 7.6	20 14.1	23 .8	4 20.1	14 32.9	22 3.4	7 25.3	3 15.6
18	11 41 39.0	27 15.8	13 13.7	15 16.0	19 14.6	21 28.8	23 43.2	4 31.2	14 36.3	22 1.2	7 25.1	3 14.0
19	11 45 35.5	28 15.5	13 10.5	28 28.2	18 25.1	22 43.5	24 25.7	4 42.2	14 39.9	21 58.9	7 24.8	3 12.3
20	11 49 32.1	29 15.1	13 7.3	11♎25.7	17 40.1	23 58.2	25 8.1	4 53.1	14 43.5	21 56.6	7 24.4	3 10.7
21	11 53 28.6	0♈14.6	13 4.1	24 7.7	17 .0	25 12.8	25 50.6	5 4.0	14 47.2	21 54.3	7 24.1	3 9.0
22	11 57 25.2	1 14.2	13 1.0	6♏34.0	16 25.4	26 27.5	26 33.0	5 14.7	14 51.1	21 51.9	7 23.7	3 7.4
23	12 1 21.8	2 13.7	12 57.8	18 46.1	15 56.6	27 42.1	27 15.5	5 25.3	14 55.0	21 49.6	7 23.2	3 5.7
24	12 5 18.3	3 13.2	12 54.6	0♐46.3	15 33.7	28 56.7	27 58.0	5 35.8	14 59.0	21 47.2	7 22.8	3 4.1
25	12 9 14.9	4 12.6	12 51.4	12 38.4	15 16.8	0♈11.3	28 40.6	5 46.2	15 3.1	21 44.8	7 22.3	3 2.4
26	12 13 11.4	5 12.1	12 48.2	24 27.0	15 6.0	1 25.9	29 23.1	5 56.5	15 7.3	21 42.4	7 21.7	3 .7
27	12 17 8.0	6 11.5	12 45.1	6♑17.1	15 1.1	2 40.5	0♒ 5.7	6 6.8	15 11.6	21 40.0	7 21.2	2 59.1
28	12 21 4.5	7 10.9	12 41.9	18 14.3	15 D 2.0	3 55.1	0 48.3	6 16.9	15 16.0	21 37.5	7 20.7	2 57.5
29	12 25 1.1	8 10.2	12 38.7	0♒24.0	15 8.5	5 9.6	1 30.8	6 26.9	15 20.4	21 35.0	7 20.0	2 55.8
30	12 28 57.6	9 9.5	12 35.5	12 51.4	15 20.4	6 24.2	2 13.4	6 36.8	15 25.0	21 32.5	7 19.4	2 54.2
31	12 32 54.2	10 8.8	12 32.3	25 40.7	15 37.4	7 38.7	2 56.0	6 46.6	15 29.6	21 30.0	7 18.7	2 52.5

LATITUDE

DAY	EPHEM. SID. TIME	☉	☊	☽	☿	♀	♂	♃	♄	♅	♆	♇
1	10 34 37.6	0 .0	0 .0	0N38.2	2N14.3	1S16.4	0S29.6	0S16.6	1S23.1	0N38.8	1N37.3	16N55.2
4	10 46 27.2	0 .0	0 .0	3 38.0	2 53.2	1 19.5	0 32.5	0 17.0	1 22.4	0 38.9	1 37.5	16 56.0
7	10 58 16.9	0 .0	0 .0	5 3.4	3 22.5	1 22.0	0 35.4	0 17.4	1 21.7	0 38.9	1 37.6	16 56.7
10	11 10 6.6	0 .0	0 .0	3 53.5	3 37.4	1 24.0	0 38.4	0 17.8	1 21.0	0 39.0	1 37.8	16 57.3
13	11 21 56.2	0 .0	0 .0	0 40.5	3 34.6	1 25.4	0 41.4	0 18.2	1 20.3	0 39.0	1 37.9	16 57.8
16	11 33 45.9	0 .0	0 .0	2S49.7	3 14.4	1 26.3	0 44.5	0 18.6	1 19.6	0 39.0	1 38.1	16 58.2
19	11 45 35.5	0 .0	0 .0	4 50.5	2 40.1	1 26.5	0 47.6	0 19.1	1 19.0	0 39.1	1 38.2	16 58.5
22	11 57 25.2	0 .0	0 .0	4 36.7	1 57.4	1 26.2	0 50.8	0 19.5	1 18.3	0 39.1	1 38.4	16 58.7
25	12 9 14.9	0 .0	0 .0	2 32.6	1 11.4	1 25.3	0 54.0	0 19.9	1 17.7	0 39.1	1 38.5	16 58.9
28	12 21 4.5	0 .0	0 .0	0N28.8	0 26.4	1 23.8	0 57.3	0 20.4	1 17.0	0 39.1	1 38.6	16 58.9
31	12 32 54.2	0 .0	0 .0	3 26.1	0S15.3	1 21.8	1 .6	0 20.8	1 16.4	0 39.1	1 38.8	16 58.9

RIGHT ASCENSION

DAY	EPHEM. SID. TIME	☉	☊	☽	☿	♀	♂	♃	♄	♅	♆	♇
1	10 34 37.6	11♓47.4	15♑20.5	24♑17.1	26♓55.6	2♓49.3	12♑48.3	3♒28.6	12♊40.1	21♎ 7.7	5♐53.9	10♎13.2
2	10 38 34.1	12 43.6	15 17.1	6♒55.8	27 16.1	4 1.3	13 34.1	3 41.5	12 42.0	21 R 6.1	5 54.2	10 R 12.0
3	10 42 30.7	13 39.7	15 13.6	19 19.8	27 28.4	5 13.1	14 20.0	3 54.4	12 44.0	21 4.5	5 54.4	10 10.7
4	10 46 27.2	14 35.7	15 10.2	1♓34.0	27 32.4	6 24.6	15 5.8	4 7.1	12 46.1	21 2.8	5 54.6	10 9.5
5	10 50 23.8	15 31.6	15 6.8	13 46.7	27 R 28.3	7 36.0	15 51.6	4 19.8	12 48.3	21 1.1	5 54.8	10 8.2
6	10 54 20.3	16 27.4	15 3.4	26 9.2	27 16.3	8 47.1	16 37.4	4 32.4	12 50.7	20 59.4	5 55.0	10 6.9
7	10 58 16.9	17 23.0	14 59.9	8♈53.6	26 56.7	9 57.9	17 23.2	4 44.9	12 53.1	20 57.7	5 55.1	10 5.6
8	11 2 13.5	18 18.6	14 56.5	22 11.9	26 30.1	11 8.6	18 8.9	4 57.3	12 55.7	20 55.9	5 55.2	10 4.3
9	11 6 10.0	19 14.0	14 53.1	6♉12.8	25 57.1	12 19.0	18 54.6	5 9.6	12 58.4	20 54.0	5 55.2	10 3.0
10	11 10 6.6	20 9.4	14 49.7	20 57.9	25 18.6	13 29.2	19 40.3	5 21.8	13 1.2	20 52.1	5 55.2	10 1.6
11	11 14 3.1	21 4.6	14 46.2	6♊18.4	24 35.5	14 39.2	20 25.9	5 34.0	13 4.1	20 50.2	5 55.2	10 .2
12	11 17 59.7	21 59.8	14 42.8	21 54.8	23 49.0	15 49.1	21 11.5	5 46.0	13 7.1	20 48.3	5 R 55.1	9 58.9
13	11 21 56.2	22 54.9	14 39.4	7♋21.5	23 .0	16 58.7	21 57.0	5 58.0	13 10.2	20 46.4	5 55.0	9 57.5
14	11 25 52.8	23 49.9	14 35.9	22 16.1	22 9.9	18 8.2	22 42.5	6 9.8	13 13.4	20 44.4	5 54.9	9 56.1
15	11 29 49.3	24 44.9	14 32.5	6♌25.7	21 19.6	19 17.5	23 28.0	6 21.6	13 16.8	20 42.3	5 54.7	9 54.7
16	11 33 45.9	25 39.7	14 29.1	19 48.4	20 30.4	20 26.7	24 13.4	6 33.3	13 20.2	20 40.3	5 54.5	9 53.3
17	11 37 42.4	26 34.6	14 25.7	2♍30.8	19 43.3	21 35.8	24 58.8	6 44.8	13 23.7	20 38.2	5 54.3	9 51.8
18	11 41 39.0	27 29.4	14 22.2	14 43.9	18 59.0	22 44.7	25 44.1	6 56.3	13 27.4	20 36.1	5 54.0	9 50.4
19	11 45 35.5	28 24.1	14 18.8	26 40.1	18 18.5	23 53.5	26 29.4	7 7.7	13 31.1	20 34.0	5 53.7	9 49.0
20	11 49 32.1	29 18.8	14 15.4	8♎31.4	17 42.3	25 2.2	27 14.6	7 18.9	13 35.0	20 31.8	5 53.4	9 47.5
21	11 53 28.6	0♈13.4	14 11.9	20 28.4	17 10.9	26 10.7	27 59.8	7 30.1	13 38.9	20 29.7	5 53.0	9 46.1
22	11 57 25.2	1 8.1	14 8.5	2♏38.6	16 44.8	27 19.2	28 44.9	7 41.1	13 43.0	20 27.5	5 52.6	9 44.6
23	12 1 21.8	2 2.7	14 5.1	15 6.3	16 24.0	28 27.7	29 30.0	7 52.1	13 47.2	20 25.3	5 52.1	9 43.1
24	12 5 18.3	2 57.3	14 1.6	27 51.5	16 8.8	29 36.0	0♒15.0	8 2.9	13 51.4	20 23.0	5 51.7	9 41.7
25	12 9 14.9	3 51.8	13 58.2	10♐49.5	15 59.2	0♈44.3	0 59.9	8 13.7	13 55.8	20 20.8	5 51.1	9 40.2
26	12 13 11.4	4 46.4	13 54.8	23 52.8	15 55.1	1 52.6	1 44.8	8 24.3	14 .2	20 18.5	5 50.6	9 38.7
27	12 17 8.0	5 41.0	13 51.3	6♑52.5	15 D 56.4	3 .8	2 29.6	8 34.8	14 4.8	20 16.3	5 50.1	9 37.3
28	12 21 4.5	6 35.6	13 47.9	19 41.2	16 2.9	4 9.0	3 14.4	8 45.2	14 9.4	20 14.0	5 49.5	9 35.8
29	12 25 1.1	7 30.2	13 44.5	2♒15.2	16 14.5	5 17.2	3 59.1	8 55.5	14 14.2	20 11.6	5 48.8	9 34.3
30	12 28 57.6	8 24.8	13 41.0	14 35.0	16 30.9	6 25.4	4 43.7	9 5.7	14 19.0	20 9.3	5 48.2	9 32.8
31	12 32 54.2	9 19.4	13 37.6	26 45.8	16 52.0	7 33.5	5 28.2	9 15.7	14 23.9	20 7.0	5 47.5	9 31.3

DECLINATION

DAY	EPHEM. SID. TIME	☉	☊	☽	☿	♀	♂	♃	♄	♅	♆	♇
1	10 34 37.6	7S43.0	0S23.8	20S55.4	1N 6.4	12S34.0	23S25.0	20S10.2	21N 5.5	8S11.2	19S57.1	14N 2.4
4	10 46 27.2	6 34.2	0 23.8	7 47.3	2 4.8	11 16.1	23 15.7	20 2.3	21 6.9	8 9.3	19 57.1	14 4.8
7	10 58 16.9	5 24.6	0 23.8	9N20.1	2 21.3	9 55.5	23 4.5	19 54.5	21 8.4	8 7.2	19 57.0	14 7.3
10	11 10 6.6	4 14.4	0 23.8	22 38.1	1 54.9	8 32.5	22 51.4	19 46.8	21 10.0	8 4.9	19 56.8	14 9.6
13	11 21 56.2	3 3.7	0 23.8	23 56.8	0 52.1	7 7.5	22 36.5	19 39.1	21 11.7	8 2.6	19 56.7	14 12.0
16	11 33 45.9	1 52.7	0 23.9	12 40.0	0S34.1	5 40.8	22 19.7	19 31.5	21 13.4	8 .1	19 56.4	14 14.3
19	11 45 35.5	0 41.6	0 23.9	3S50.0	2 7.4	4 12.7	22 1.1	19 24.0	21 15.2	7 57.6	19 56.2	14 16.5
22	11 57 25.2	0N29.5	0 23.9	18 3.6	3 33.4	2 43.6	21 40.7	19 16.5	21 17.1	7 55.0	19 55.8	14 18.7
25	12 9 14.9	1 40.4	0 23.9	24 50.3	4 42.2	1 13.7	21 18.6	19 9.2	21 19.1	7 52.3	19 55.5	14 20.7
28	12 21 4.5	2 51.0	0 23.9	21 43.5	5 29.5	0N16.6	20 54.8	19 2.1	21 21.2	7 49.6	19 55.1	14 22.7
31	12 32 54.2	4 1.1	0 23.9	9 43.6	5 54.2	1 46.9	20 29.4	18 55.1	21 23.2	7 46.8	19 54.6	14 24.6

APRIL 1973

LONGITUDE

DAY	EPHEM. SID. TIME	☉	☊	☾	☿	♀	♂	♃	♄	♅	♆	♇
	h m s	° ′	° ′	° ′	° ′	° ′	° ′	° ′	° ′	° ′	° ′	° ′
1	12 36 50.7	11♈ 8.0	12♑29.2	8♓54.4	15♓59.4	8♈53.2	3♒38.6	6♒56.2	15♊34.3	21♎27.5	7♐18.0	2♎50.9
2	12 40 47.3	12 7.2	12 26.0	22 33.2	16 26.0	10 7.7	4 21.2	7 5.8	15 39.1	21 R25.0	7 R17.3	2 R49.3
3	12 44 43.8	13 6.4	12 22.8	6♈35.2	16 57.1	11 22.2	5 3.8	7 15.2	15 44.0	21 22.4	7 16.5	2 47.6
4	12 48 40.4	14 5.5	12 19.6	20 56.0	17 32.4	12 36.7	5 46.4	7 24.5	15 48.9	21 19.9	7 15.7	2 46.0
5	12 52 36.9	15 4.6	12 16.5	5♉29.2	18 11.7	13 51.1	6 29.0	7 33.7	15 54.0	21 17.3	7 14.9	2 44.4
6	12 56 33.5	16 3.7	12 13.3	20 7.5	18 54.7	15 5.5	7 11.6	7 42.7	15 59.1	21 14.7	7 14.0	2 42.8
7	13 0 30.0	17 2.7	12 10.1	4♊44.0	19 41.3	16 20.0	7 54.2	7 51.7	16 4.3	21 12.2	7 13.2	2 41.2
8	13 4 26.6	18 1.7	12 6.9	19 12.8	20 31.3	17 34.4	8 36.8	8 .5	16 9.5	21 9.6	7 12.3	2 39.6
9	13 8 23.2	19 .7	12 3.7	3♋30.2	21 24.5	18 48.7	9 19.4	8 9.2	16 14.9	21 7.0	7 11.3	2 38.0
10	13 12 19.7	19 59.6	12 .6	17 34.3	22 20.8	20 3.1	10 2.0	8 17.7	16 20.3	21 4.4	7 10.4	2 36.5
11	13 16 16.3	20 58.5	11 57.4	1♌24.8	23 19.9	21 17.4	10 44.6	8 26.1	16 25.8	21 1.8	7 9.4	2 34.9
12	13 20 12.8	21 57.4	11 54.2	15 2.2	24 21.8	22 31.8	11 27.2	8 34.4	16 31.3	20 59.3	7 8.4	2 33.4
13	13 24 9.4	22 56.2	11 51.0	28 27.2	25 26.3	23 46.1	12 9.8	8 42.6	16 37.0	20 56.7	7 7.4	2 31.8
14	13 28 5.9	23 54.9	11 47.9	11♍40.6	26 33.4	25 .3	12 52.4	8 50.6	16 42.7	20 54.1	7 6.3	2 30.3
15	13 32 2.5	24 53.7	11 44.7	24 42.6	27 42.9	26 14.6	13 35.0	8 58.5	16 48.4	20 51.5	7 5.2	2 28.8
16	13 35 59.0	25 52.4	11 41.5	7♎33.1	28 54.7	27 28.8	14 17.6	9 6.2	16 54.3	20 49.0	7 4.1	2 27.3
17	13 39 55.6	26 51.1	11 38.3	20 12.0	0♈ 8.9	28 43.1	15 .3	9 13.9	17 .2	20 46.4	7 3.0	2 25.9
18	13 43 52.1	27 49.7	11 35.1	2♏38.9	1 25.1	29 57.3	15 42.9	9 21.3	17 6.2	20 43.9	7 1.9	2 24.4
19	13 47 48.7	28 48.3	11 32.0	14 54.3	2 43.5	1♉11.5	16 25.5	9 28.7	17 12.2	20 41.3	7 .7	2 23.0
20	13 51 45.2	29 46.9	11 28.8	26 59.1	4 3.9	2 25.7	17 8.1	9 35.8	17 18.3	20 38.8	6 59.5	2 21.5
21	13 55 41.8	0♉45.4	11 25.6	8♐55.1	5 26.4	3 39.9	17 50.7	9 42.9	17 24.4	20 36.3	6 58.3	2 20.1
22	13 59 38.4	1 43.9	11 22.4	20 45.0	6 50.8	4 54.0	18 33.3	9 49.8	17 30.6	20 33.7	6 57.1	2 18.7
23	14 3 34.9	2 42.4	11 19.3	2♑32.5	8 17.1	6 8.2	19 15.9	9 56.5	17 36.9	20 31.2	6 55.8	2 17.3
24	14 7 31.5	3 40.8	11 16.1	14 21.8	9 45.3	7 22.3	19 58.4	10 3.1	17 43.2	20 28.7	6 54.5	2 16.0
25	14 11 28.0	4 39.3	11 12.9	26 18.1	11 15.4	8 36.4	20 41.0	10 9.5	17 49.6	20 26.2	6 53.2	2 14.6
26	14 15 24.6	5 37.7	11 9.7	8♒26.6	12 47.4	9 50.5	21 23.6	10 15.8	17 56.0	20 23.8	6 51.9	2 13.3
27	14 19 21.1	6 36.0	11 6.6	20 52.7	14 21.2	11 4.5	22 6.1	10 21.9	18 2.5	20 21.3	6 50.6	2 12.0
28	14 23 17.7	7 34.4	11 3.4	3♓41.2	15 56.8	12 18.6	22 48.7	10 27.9	18 9.1	20 18.9	6 49.2	2 10.7
29	14 27 14.2	8 32.7	11 .2	16 55.7	17 34.2	13 32.7	23 31.2	10 33.7	18 15.7	20 16.5	6 47.8	2 9.5
30	14 31 10.8	9 31.0	10 57.0	0♈38.3	19 13.5	14 46.7	24 13.7	10 39.4	18 22.3	20 14.1	6 46.5	2 8.2

LATITUDE

DAY	EPHEM. SID. TIME	☉	☊	☾	☿	♀	♂	♃	♄	♅	♆	♇
1	12 36 50.7	0 .0	0 .0	4N10.9	0S28.2	1S21.0	1S 1.7	0S21.0	1S16.2	0N39.1	1N38.8	16N58.8
4	12 48 40.4	0 .0	0 .0	4 56.7	1 3.4	1 18.2	1 5.1	0 21.5	1 15.6	0 39.1	1 38.9	16 58.7
7	13 0 30.0	0 .0	0 .0	3 .9	1 33.4	1 14.9	1 8.5	0 22.0	1 15.1	0 39.1	1 39.1	16 58.4
10	13 12 19.7	0 .0	0 .0	0S32.5	1 57.9	1 11.2	1 12.0	0 22.5	1 14.5	0 39.1	1 39.2	16 58.1
13	13 24 9.4	0 .0	0 .0	3 41.6	2 17.1	1 6.9	1 15.5	0 23.0	1 13.9	0 39.1	1 39.3	16 57.7
16	13 35 59.0	0 .0	0 .0	5 .6	2 30.9	1 2.2	1 19.0	0 23.5	1 13.4	0 39.1	1 39.4	16 57.2
19	13 47 48.7	0 .0	0 .0	4 8.6	2 39.6	0 57.1	1 22.6	0 24.0	1 12.9	0 39.0	1 39.5	16 56.6
22	13 59 38.4	0 .0	0 .0	1 40.1	2 43.2	0 51.6	1 26.2	0 24.6	1 12.4	0 39.0	1 39.6	16 55.9
25	14 11 28.0	0 .0	0 .0	1N26.6	2 41.8	0 45.7	1 29.8	0 25.1	1 11.9	0 39.0	1 39.7	16 55.2
28	14 23 17.7	0 .0	0 .0	4 6.9	2 35.6	0 39.5	1 33.5	0 25.7	1 11.4	0 38.9	1 39.8	16 54.3

RIGHT ASCENSION

DAY	EPHEM. SID. TIME	☉	☊	☾	☿	♀	♂	♃	♄	♅	♆	♇
1	12 36 50.7	10♈14.1	13♑34.2	8♓56.4	17♓17.3	8♈41.7	6♒12.7	9♒25.6	14♊28.9	20♎ 4.6	5♐46.7	9♎29.8
2	12 40 47.3	11 8.7	13 30.7	21 18.0	17 46.9	9 49.9	6 57.1	9 35.4	14 34.0	20 R 2.2	5 R46.0	9 R28.3
3	12 44 43.8	12 3.4	13 27.3	4♈ 3.7	18 20.2	10 58.2	7 41.4	9 45.1	14 39.2	19 59.9	5 45.2	9 26.8
4	12 48 40.4	12 58.2	13 23.9	17 26.2	18 57.3	12 6.5	8 25.6	9 54.6	14 44.4	19 57.5	5 44.3	9 25.3
5	12 52 36.9	13 53.0	13 20.4	1♉35.2	19 37.8	13 14.9	9 9.8	10 4.1	14 49.8	19 55.1	5 43.5	9 23.9
6	12 56 33.5	14 47.8	13 17.0	16 33.0	20 21.5	14 23.3	9 53.8	10 13.3	14 55.2	19 52.7	5 42.6	9 22.4
7	13 0 30.0	15 42.7	13 13.6	2♊10.5	21 8.3	15 31.8	10 37.8	10 22.5	15 .8	19 50.3	5 41.7	9 20.9
8	13 4 26.6	16 37.6	13 10.1	18 5.9	21 57.9	16 40.4	11 21.7	10 31.5	15 6.4	19 47.8	5 40.8	9 19.4
9	13 8 23.2	17 32.5	13 6.7	3♋50.2	22 50.2	17 49.1	12 5.5	10 40.4	15 12.1	19 45.4	5 39.8	9 17.9
10	13 12 19.7	18 27.6	13 3.3	18 58.0	23 45.0	18 57.9	12 49.2	10 49.2	15 17.8	19 43.0	5 38.8	9 16.5
11	13 16 16.3	19 22.7	12 59.8	3♌15.0	24 42.2	20 6.8	13 32.8	10 57.8	15 23.7	19 40.6	5 37.8	9 15.0
12	13 20 12.8	20 17.8	12 56.4	16 39.4	25 41.7	21 15.8	14 16.4	11 6.3	15 29.6	19 38.2	5 36.7	9 13.6
13	13 24 9.4	21 13.1	12 53.0	29 19.0	26 43.3	22 24.9	14 59.9	11 14.6	15 35.6	19 35.8	5 35.6	9 12.1
14	13 28 5.9	22 8.4	12 49.5	11♍26.0	27 47.0	23 34.2	15 43.2	11 22.8	15 41.7	19 33.3	5 34.5	9 10.7
15	13 32 2.5	23 3.7	12 46.1	23 14.1	28 52.7	24 43.7	16 26.5	11 30.9	15 47.8	19 30.9	5 33.4	9 9.3
16	13 35 59.0	23 59.2	12 42.7	4♎56.5	0♈ .2	25 53.3	17 9.7	11 38.8	15 54.0	19 28.5	5 32.3	9 7.8
17	13 39 55.6	24 54.8	12 39.2	16 44.6	1 9.6	27 3.1	17 52.9	11 46.7	16 .4	19 26.2	5 31.1	9 6.5
18	13 43 52.1	25 50.4	12 35.8	28 47.0	2 20.7	28 13.1	18 35.9	11 54.3	16 6.7	19 23.8	5 29.9	9 5.1
19	13 47 48.7	26 46.2	12 32.3	11♏ 8.7	3 33.4	29 23.3	19 18.8	12 1.8	16 13.2	19 21.4	5 28.7	9 3.7
20	13 51 45.2	27 42.0	12 28.9	23 49.9	4 47.9	0♉33.6	20 1.6	12 9.1	16 19.7	19 19.0	5 27.5	9 2.3
21	13 55 41.8	28 38.0	12 25.5	6♐46.0	6 4.0	1 44.2	20 44.4	12 16.3	16 26.2	19 16.6	5 26.2	9 .9
22	13 59 38.4	29 34.1	12 22.0	19 48.4	7 21.7	2 54.9	21 27.1	12 23.3	16 32.9	19 14.3	5 24.9	8 59.6
23	14 3 34.9	0♉30.2	12 18.6	2♑47.0	8 40.9	4 5.9	22 9.6	12 30.2	16 39.6	19 11.9	5 23.6	8 58.2
24	14 7 31.5	1 26.5	12 15.1	15 33.0	10 1.8	5 17.1	22 52.1	12 36.9	16 46.3	19 9.6	5 22.3	8 56.9
25	14 11 28.0	2 23.0	12 11.7	28 1.5	11 24.3	6 28.6	23 34.5	12 43.5	16 53.1	19 7.3	5 20.9	8 55.6
26	14 15 24.6	3 19.5	12 8.3	10♒12.5	12 48.3	7 40.3	24 16.8	12 49.9	17 .0	19 4.9	5 19.5	8 54.3
27	14 19 21.1	4 16.2	12 4.8	22 11.0	14 14.0	8 52.2	24 59.0	12 56.2	17 7.0	19 2.6	5 18.1	8 53.0
28	14 23 17.7	5 13.0	12 1.4	4♓ 5.8	15 41.3	10 4.4	25 41.1	13 2.3	17 14.0	19 .4	5 16.7	8 51.7
29	14 27 14.2	6 9.9	11 58.0	16 9.1	17 10.3	11 16.9	26 23.1	13 8.2	17 21.0	18 58.1	5 15.3	8 50.4
30	14 31 10.8	7 7.0	11 54.5	28 35.0	18 41.0	12 29.6	27 5.0	13 14.0	17 28.1	18 55.9	5 13.8	8 49.2

DECLINATION

DAY	EPHEM. SID. TIME	☉	☊	☾	☿	♀	♂	♃	♄	♅	♆	♇
1	12 36 50.7	4N24.4	0S23.9	4S21.2	5S57.6	2N17.0	20S20.5	18S52.8	21N23.9	7S45.8	19S54.5	14N25.2
4	12 48 40.4	5 33.5	0 24.0	12N45.0	5 53.9	3 47.0	19 53.0	18 46.1	21 26.1	7 43.0	19 54.0	14 27.0
7	13 0 30.0	6 41.8	0 24.0	24 3.0	5 30.9	5 16.2	19 23.9	18 39.6	21 28.2	7 40.1	19 53.4	14 28.7
10	13 12 19.7	7 49.1	0 24.0	21 45.1	4 50.6	6 44.5	18 53.4	18 33.4	21 30.4	7 37.2	19 52.8	14 30.2
13	13 24 9.4	8 55.1	0 24.0	8 32.8	3 54.6	8 11.4	18 21.5	18 27.4	21 32.6	7 34.3	19 52.2	14 31.6
16	13 35 59.0	9 59.9	0 24.0	7S35.8	2 44.4	9 36.6	17 48.3	18 21.6	21 34.9	7 31.5	19 51.6	14 33.0
19	13 47 48.7	11 3.1	0 24.0	20 16.1	1 21.4	10 59.9	17 13.8	18 16.2	21 37.1	7 28.6	19 50.9	14 34.1
22	13 59 38.4	12 4.7	0 24.0	24 47.1	0N13.2	12 20.8	16 38.0	18 11.1	21 39.3	7 25.8	19 50.3	14 35.2
25	14 11 28.0	13 4.5	0 24.1	19 28.6	1 58.3	13 39.1	16 1.1	18 6.3	21 41.6	7 23.0	19 49.5	14 36.1
28	14 23 17.7	14 2.4	0 24.1	6 19.2	3 52.9	14 54.4	15 23.2	18 1.9	21 43.8	7 20.3	19 48.8	14 36.9

MAY 1973

DAY	EPHEM. SID. TIME h m s	☉ ° '	☊ ° '	☽ ° '	☿ ° '	♀ ° '	♂ ° '	♃ ° '	♄ ° '	♅ ° '	♆ ° '	♇ ° '
		LONGITUDE										
1	14 35 7.3	10♉29.3	10♑53.8	14♈48.2	20♈54.5	16♉ .7	24♒56.2	10♒44.8	18♊29.0	20♎11.7	6♐45.1	2♎ 7.0
2	14 39 3.9	11 27.5	10 50.7	29 21.9	22 37.4	17 14.7	25 38.6	10 50.2	18 35.8	20R 9.3	6R43.6	2R 5.8
3	14 43 .5	12 25.7	10 47.5	14♉12.7	24 22.1	18 28.7	26 21.1	10 55.3	18 42.6	20 7.0	6 42.2	2 4.6
4	14 46 57.0	13 23.9	10 44.3	29 12.2	26 8.6	19 42.7	27 3.5	11 .3	18 49.4	20 4.7	6 40.7	2 3.5
5	14 50 53.6	14 22.1	10 41.1	14♊11.2	27 57.0	20 56.6	27 45.9	11 5.1	18 56.3	20 2.4	6 39.3	2 2.3
6	14 54 50.1	15 20.2	10 38.0	29 1.4	29 47.2	22 10.6	28 28.3	11 9.8	19 3.2	20 .1	6 37.8	2 1.2
7	14 58 46.7	16 18.3	10 34.8	13♋36.5	1♉39.2	23 24.5	29 10.6	11 14.2	19 10.2	19 57.9	6 36.3	2 .2
8	15 2 43.2	17 16.4	10 31.6	27 52.8	3 33.1	24 38.5	29 53.0	11 18.6	19 17.3	19 55.8	6 34.8	1 59.2
9	15 6 39.8	18 14.4	10 28.4	11♌48.8	5 28.8	25 52.3	0♓35.2	11 22.7	19 24.3	19 53.6	6 33.3	1 58.1
10	15 10 36.3	19 12.4	10 25.2	25 24.8	7 26.3	27 6.2	1 17.5	11 26.7	19 31.4	19 51.4	6 31.8	1 57.1
11	15 14 32.9	20 10.4	10 22.1	8♍42.2	9 25.5	28 20.1	1 59.7	11 30.5	19 38.6	19 49.3	6 30.3	1 56.1
12	15 18 29.5	21 8.3	10 18.9	21 42.9	11 26.5	29 33.9	2 41.9	11 34.1	19 45.7	19 47.2	6 28.7	1 55.2
13	15 22 26.0	22 6.2	10 15.7	4♎29.0	13 29.2	0♊47.7	3 24.1	11 37.5	19 52.9	19 45.2	6 27.2	1 54.3
14	15 26 22.6	23 4.1	10 12.5	17 2.3	15 33.4	2 1.5	4 6.2	11 40.7	20 .2	19 43.2	6 25.6	1 53.4
15	15 30 19.1	24 1.9	10 9.4	29 24.3	17 39.2	3 15.3	4 48.3	11 43.8	20 7.5	19 41.2	6 24.0	1 52.5
16	15 34 15.7	24 59.7	10 6.2	11♏36.4	19 46.4	4 29.0	5 30.4	11 46.7	20 14.8	19 39.2	6 22.4	1 51.7
17	15 38 12.2	25 57.5	10 3.0	23 40.0	21 54.8	5 42.8	6 12.4	11 49.4	20 22.1	19 37.3	6 20.9	1 50.9
18	15 42 8.8	26 55.3	9 59.8	5♐36.5	24 4.3	6 56.5	6 54.4	11 51.9	20 29.5	19 35.4	6 19.3	1 50.1
19	15 46 5.3	27 53.1	9 56.7	17 27.5	26 14.6	8 10.2	7 36.4	11 54.3	20 36.9	19 33.6	6 17.7	1 49.3
20	15 50 1.9	28 50.8	9 53.5	29 15.5	28 25.6	9 23.9	8 18.3	11 56.4	20 44.3	19 31.7	6 16.1	1 48.6
21	15 53 58.5	29 48.5	9 50.3	11♑ 3.0	0♊37.1	10 37.6	9 .2	11 58.4	20 51.8	19 30.0	6 14.4	1 47.9
22	15 57 55.0	0♊46.2	9 47.1	22 53.6	2 48.7	11 51.3	9 42.0	12 .2	20 59.3	19 28.2	6 12.8	1 47.2
23	16 1 51.6	1 43.8	9 43.9	4♒51.2	5 .2	13 5.0	10 23.8	12 1.8	21 6.8	19 26.5	6 11.2	1 46.6
24	16 5 48.1	2 41.5	9 40.8	17 .2	7 11.3	14 18.6	11 5.5	12 3.2	21 14.3	19 24.9	6 9.6	1 46.0
25	16 9 44.7	3 39.1	9 37.6	29 25.4	9 21.7	15 32.2	11 47.2	12 4.4	21 21.9	19 23.3	6 8.0	1 45.4
26	16 13 41.2	4 36.8	9 34.4	12♓11.3	11 31.2	16 45.9	12 28.9	12 5.4	21 29.5	19 21.7	6 6.3	1 44.8
27	16 17 37.8	5 34.4	9 31.2	25 21.9	13 39.5	17 59.5	13 10.5	12 6.3	21 37.1	19 20.2	6 4.7	1 44.3
28	16 21 34.4	6 31.9	9 28.1	8♈59.9	15 46.4	19 13.1	13 52.0	12 6.9	21 44.7	19 18.7	6 3.1	1 43.8
29	16 25 30.9	7 29.6	9 24.9	23 6.0	17 51.6	20 26.7	14 33.5	12 7.4	21 52.4	19 17.3	6 1.5	1 43.4
30	16 29 27.5	8 27.1	9 21.7	7♉38.3	19 55.0	21 40.3	15 14.9	12 7.7	22 .1	19 15.9	5 59.9	1 43.0
31	16 33 24.0	9 24.7	9 18.5	22 31.8	21 56.4	22 53.8	15 56.3	12 7.8	22 7.8	19 14.5	5 58.3	1 42.6
		LATITUDE										
1	14 35 7.3	0 .0	0 .0	5N 3.6	2S24.5	0S33.1	1S37.2	0S26.3	1S10.9	0N38.9	1N39.8	16N53.5
4	14 46 57.0	0 .0	0 .0	3 16.4	2 8.8	0 26.4	1 40.9	0 26.9	1 10.5	0 38.8	1 39.9	16 52.5
7	14 58 46.7	0 .0	0 .0	0S25.2	1 48.7	0 19.4	1 44.6	0 27.5	1 10.1	0 38.7	1 39.9	16 51.5
10	15 10 36.3	0 .0	0 .0	3 43.8	1 24.5	0 12.4	1 48.3	0 28.1	1 9.6	0 38.7	1 40.0	16 50.4
13	15 22 26.0	0 .0	0 .0	5 7.2	0 56.8	0 5.2	1 52.1	0 28.7	1 9.2	0 38.6	1 40.0	16 49.3
16	15 34 15.7	0 .0	0 .0	4 18.4	0 26.5	0N 2.1	1 55.8	0 29.3	1 8.9	0 38.5	1 40.0	16 48.1
19	15 46 5.3	0 .0	0 .0	1 49.7	0N 5.1	0 9.4	1 59.6	0 30.0	1 8.5	0 38.4	1 40.1	16 46.8
22	15 57 55.0	0 .0	0 .0	1N20.1	0 36.2	0 16.7	2 3.4	0 30.6	1 8.1	0 38.3	1 40.1	16 45.6
25	16 9 44.7	0 .0	0 .0	4 4.5	1 4.9	0 24.0	2 7.1	0 31.2	1 7.8	0 38.2	1 40.1	16 44.2
28	16 21 34.4	0 .0	0 .0	5 13.0	1 29.5	0 31.1	2 10.8	0 31.9	1 7.5	0 38.1	1 40.1	16 42.9
31	16 33 24.0	0 .0	0 .0	3 43.3	1 48.3	0 38.1	2 14.6	0 32.6	1 7.2	0 38.0	1 40.0	16 41.5
		RIGHT ASCENSION										
1	14 35 7.3	8♉ 4.2	11♑51.1	11♈38.5	20♈13.5	13♉42.6	27♒46.9	13♒19.6	17♊35.3	18♎53.6	5♐12.4	8♎48.0
2	14 39 3.9	9 1.5	11 47.6	25 33.0	21 47.7	14 55.9	28 28.6	13 25.0	17 42.5	18R51.4	5R10.9	8R46.7
3	14 43 .5	9 59.0	11 44.2	10♉26.0	23 23.8	16 9.4	29 10.2	13 30.3	17 49.8	18 49.2	5 9.4	8 45.5
4	14 46 57.0	10 56.6	11 40.8	26 13.1	25 1.8	17 23.2	29 51.7	13 35.4	17 57.1	18 47.1	5 7.9	8 44.4
5	14 50 53.6	11 54.3	11 37.3	12♊34.0	26 41.8	18 37.3	0♓33.1	13 40.3	18 4.5	18 44.9	5 6.3	8 43.2
6	14 54 50.1	12 52.2	11 33.9	28 55.7	28 23.8	19 51.6	1 14.5	13 45.1	18 12.0	18 42.8	5 4.8	8 42.1
7	14 58 46.7	13 50.2	11 30.4	14♋44.1	0♉ 7.8	21 6.3	1 55.7	13 49.6	18 19.4	18 40.7	5 3.2	8 41.0
8	15 2 43.2	14 48.4	11 27.0	29 37.1	1 54.1	22 21.2	2 36.8	13 54.1	18 27.0	18 38.7	5 1.7	8 39.9
9	15 6 39.8	15 46.7	11 23.5	13♌28.4	3 42.5	23 36.4	3 17.9	13 58.3	18 34.6	18 36.7	5 .1	8 38.8
10	15 10 36.3	16 45.2	11 20.1	26 24.7	5 33.3	24 51.9	3 58.8	14 2.4	18 42.2	18 34.6	4 58.5	8 37.8
11	15 14 32.9	17 43.7	11 16.7	8♍39.2	7 26.3	26 7.6	4 39.6	14 6.2	18 49.8	18 32.7	4 56.9	8 36.7
12	15 18 29.5	18 42.4	11 13.2	20 27.4	9 21.7	27 23.6	5 20.3	14 9.9	18 57.5	18 30.7	4 55.3	8 35.7
13	15 22 26.0	19 41.3	11 9.8	2♎ 4.3	11 19.5	28 39.9	6 1.0	14 13.4	19 5.3	18 28.8	4 53.7	8 34.7
14	15 26 22.6	20 40.3	11 6.3	13 43.3	13 19.6	29 56.5	6 41.5	14 16.8	19 13.1	18 26.9	4 52.0	8 33.7
15	15 30 19.1	21 39.4	11 2.9	25 34.8	15 22.1	1♊13.3	7 21.9	14 19.9	19 20.9	18 25.0	4 50.4	8 32.8
16	15 34 15.7	22 38.7	10 59.4	7♏45.9	17 27.0	2 30.4	8 2.3	14 22.9	19 28.7	18 23.2	4 48.7	8 31.8
17	15 38 12.2	23 38.1	10 56.0	20 18.6	19 34.0	3 47.8	8 42.5	14 25.7	19 36.6	18 21.4	4 47.1	8 30.9
18	15 42 8.8	24 37.6	10 52.6	3♐ 9.7	21 43.2	5 5.4	9 22.7	14 28.3	19 44.5	18 19.6	4 45.4	8 30.1
19	15 46 5.3	25 37.3	10 49.1	16 11.0	23 54.4	6 23.2	10 2.8	14 30.7	19 52.5	18 17.9	4 43.7	8 29.2
20	15 50 1.9	26 37.1	10 45.7	29 11.2	26 7.4	7 41.3	10 42.7	14 33.0	20 .5	18 16.2	4 42.1	8 28.4
21	15 53 58.5	27 37.1	10 42.2	11♑59.5	28 21.9	8 59.6	11 22.6	14 35.0	20 8.5	18 14.5	4 40.4	8 27.5
22	15 57 55.0	28 37.2	10 38.8	24 28.7	0♊37.8	10 18.2	12 2.4	14 36.9	20 16.5	18 12.9	4 38.7	8 26.8
23	16 1 51.6	29 37.4	10 35.3	6♒36.6	2 54.7	11 36.9	12 42.1	14 38.5	20 24.6	18 11.3	4 37.0	8 26.0
24	16 5 48.1	0♊37.8	10 31.9	18 26.4	5 12.3	12 55.9	13 21.7	14 40.0	20 32.7	18 9.7	4 35.3	8 25.3
25	16 9 44.7	1 38.3	10 28.5	0♓ 6.1	7 30.2	14 15.1	14 1.2	14 41.3	20 40.8	18 8.2	4 33.6	8 24.5
26	16 13 41.2	2 38.9	10 25.0	11 47.1	9 48.2	15 34.4	14 40.6	14 42.4	20 49.0	18 6.7	4 31.9	8 23.9
27	16 17 37.8	3 39.7	10 21.6	23 43.6	12 5.8	16 54.0	15 19.8	14 43.3	20 57.2	18 5.3	4 30.2	8 23.2
28	16 21 34.4	4 40.6	10 18.1	6♈11.6	14 22.7	18 13.7	15 59.0	14 44.0	21 5.4	18 3.9	4 28.5	8 22.6
29	16 25 30.9	5 41.6	10 14.7	19 27.2	16 38.7	19 33.6	16 38.2	14 44.6	21 13.7	18 2.6	4 26.8	8 22.0
30	16 29 27.5	6 42.8	10 11.2	3♉43.8	18 53.3	20 53.6	17 17.2	14 45.0	21 21.9	18 1.2	4 25.1	8 21.4
31	16 33 24.0	7 44.0	10 7.8	19 6.0	21 6.2	22 13.7	17 56.1	14 45.1	21 30.2	17 60.0	4 23.4	8 20.9
		DECLINATION										
1	14 35 7.3	14N58.2	0S24.1	10N29.8	5N55.8	16N 6.3	14S44.3	17S57.8	21N46.0	7S17.6	19S48.0	14N37.6
4	14 46 57.0	15 51.8	0 24.1	23 10.6	8 5.7	17 14.6	14 4.4	17 54.1	21 48.1	7 15.1	19 47.2	14 38.1
7	14 58 46.7	16 43.0	0 24.1	22 19.8	10 21.0	18 18.9	13 23.7	17 50.9	21 50.3	7 12.6	19 46.4	14 38.4
10	15 10 36.3	17 31.7	0 24.1	9 32.2	12 39.8	19 18.8	12 42.3	17 48.0	21 52.4	7 10.2	19 45.6	14 38.7
13	15 22 26.0	18 17.8	0 24.1	6S28.8	14 59.2	20 14.2	12 .1	17 45.6	21 54.4	7 7.9	19 44.8	14 38.7
16	15 34 15.7	19 1.1	0 24.1	19 24.6	17 15.5	21 4.6	11 17.4	17 43.7	21 56.4	7 5.7	19 44.0	14 38.7
19	15 46 5.3	19 41.5	0 24.2	24 40.3	19 23.8	21 49.7	10 34.0	17 42.2	21 58.3	7 3.7	19 43.2	14 38.5
22	15 57 55.0	20 18.9	0 24.2	20 11.0	21 19.0	22 29.4	9 50.2	17 41.1	22 .2	7 1.7	19 42.3	14 38.1
25	16 9 44.7	20 53.2	0 24.2	7 51.3	22 55.7	23 3.3	9 6.0	17 40.6	22 2.1	6 60.0	19 41.5	14 37.7
28	16 21 34.4	21 24.2	0 24.2	8N21.5	24 9.9	23 31.3	8 21.6	17 40.5	22 3.8	6 58.3	19 40.7	14 37.0
31	16 33 24.0	21 51.9	0 24.2	22 .1	25 .0	23 53.2	7 36.8	17 40.9	22 5.5	6 56.8	19 39.9	14 36.3

JUNE 1973

LONGITUDE

DAY	EPHEM. SID. TIME	☉	☊	☽	☿	♀	♂	♃	♄	♅	♆	♇
	h m s	° ′	° ′	° ′	° ′	° ′	° ′	° ′	° ′	° ′	° ′	° ′
1	16 37 20.6	10♊22.2	9♑15.4	7♊38.9	23♊55.5	24♊ 7.4	16♓37.5	12♒ 7.6	22♊15.5	19♎13.2	5♐56.6	1♎42.2
2	16 41 17.1	11 19.7	9 12.2	22 50.1	25 52.4	25 20.9	17 18.7	12R 7.3	22 23.2	19R11.9	5R55.0	1R41.9
3	16 45 13.7	12 17.2	9 9.0	7♋55.8	27 47.0	26 34.4	17 59.8	12 6.8	22 30.9	19 10.7	5 53.4	1 41.6
4	16 49 10.3	13 14.7	9 5.8	22 47.6	29 39.0	27 48.0	18 40.9	12 6.1	22 38.7	19 9.5	5 51.8	1 41.3
5	16 53 6.8	14 12.1	9 2.7	7♌19.3	1♋28.5	29 1.4	19 21.9	12 5.2	22 46.4	19 8.4	5 50.2	1 41.1
6	16 57 3.4	15 9.6	8 59.5	21 27.2	3 15.5	0♋14.9	20 2.7	12 4.2	22 54.2	19 7.3	5 48.6	1 40.9
7	17 0 59.9	16 7.0	8 56.3	5♍10.4	4 59.9	1 28.4	20 43.5	12 2.9	23 2.0	19 6.3	5 47.0	1 40.7
8	17 4 56.5	17 4.4	8 53.1	18 29.7	6 41.6	2 41.8	21 24.3	12 1.4	23 9.8	19 5.3	5 45.4	1 40.6
9	17 8 53.1	18 1.8	8 49.9	1♎27.3	8 20.6	3 55.2	22 4.9	11 59.8	23 17.6	19 4.4	5 43.8	1 40.5
10	17 12 49.6	18 59.1	8 46.8	14 6.2	9 56.9	5 8.6	22 45.5	11 58.0	23 25.4	19 3.5	5 42.2	1 40.4
11	17 16 46.2	19 56.5	8 43.6	26 29.5	11 30.5	6 22.0	23 25.9	11 55.9	23 33.2	19 2.6	5 40.7	1 40.4
12	17 20 42.7	20 53.8	8 40.4	8♏40.5	13 1.4	7 35.4	24 6.3	11 53.7	23 41.0	19 1.8	5 39.1	1 40.4
13	17 24 39.3	21 51.1	8 37.2	20 41.9	14 29.6	8 48.8	24 46.6	11 51.4	23 48.8	19 1.1	5 37.6	1 40.4
14	17 28 35.8	22 48.4	8 34.1	2♐36.6	15 54.9	10 2.1	25 26.8	11 48.8	23 56.6	19 .4	5 36.0	1 40.4
15	17 32 32.4	23 45.7	8 30.9	14 26.9	17 17.4	11 15.4	26 6.9	11 46.0	24 4.4	18 59.8	5 34.5	1D40.5
16	17 36 29.0	24 43.0	8 27.7	26 15.1	18 37.1	12 28.7	26 46.8	11 43.1	24 12.2	18 59.2	5 33.0	1 40.7
17	17 40 25.5	25 40.2	8 24.5	8♑ 3.4	19 53.9	13 42.0	27 26.7	11 40.0	24 20.0	18 58.7	5 31.5	1 40.8
18	17 44 22.1	26 37.5	8 21.4	19 54.2	21 7.7	14 55.3	28 6.5	11 36.7	24 27.8	18 58.2	5 30.0	1 41.0
19	17 48 18.6	27 34.8	8 18.2	1♒50.0	22 18.6	16 8.6	28 46.3	11 33.3	24 35.7	18 57.8	5 28.6	1 41.3
20	17 52 15.2	28 32.0	8 15.0	13 53.5	23 26.4	17 21.8	29 25.8	11 29.6	24 43.5	18 57.4	5 27.1	1 41.5
21	17 56 11.7	29 29.3	8 11.8	26 8.0	24 31.0	18 35.0	0♈ 5.3	11 25.8	24 51.3	18 57.1	5 25.6	1 41.8
22	18 0 8.3	0♋26.5	8 8.6	8♓36.8	25 32.5	19 48.2	0 44.6	11 21.8	24 59.1	18 56.8	5 24.2	1 42.1
23	18 4 4.9	1 23.7	8 5.5	21 23.5	26 30.6	21 1.4	1 23.8	11 17.7	25 6.9	18 56.6	5 22.8	1 42.5
24	18 8 1.4	2 21.0	8 2.3	4♈31.2	27 25.4	22 14.6	2 2.9	11 13.4	25 14.6	18 56.4	5 21.4	1 42.9
25	18 11 58.0	3 18.2	7 59.1	18 2.6	28 16.7	23 27.8	2 41.9	11 8.9	25 22.4	18 56.3	5 20.0	1 43.3
26	18 15 54.5	4 15.4	7 55.9	1♉59.0	29 4.5	24 40.9	3 20.7	11 4.2	25 30.2	18 56.2	5 18.6	1 43.7
27	18 19 51.1	5 12.7	7 52.8	16 20.0	29 48.5	25 54.1	3 59.4	10 59.4	25 37.9	18 56.2	5 17.2	1 44.2
28	18 23 47.7	6 9.9	7 49.6	1♊ 2.9	0♌28.8	27 7.2	4 37.9	10 54.5	25 45.7	18 56.2	5 15.9	1 44.7
29	18 27 44.2	7 7.1	7 46.4	16 2.1	1 5.1	28 20.3	5 16.3	10 49.3	25 53.4	18D56.3	5 14.6	1 45.3
30	18 31 40.8	8 4.3	7 43.2	1♋10.2	1 37.3	29 33.4	5 54.5	10 44.1	26 1.1	18 56.4	5 13.3	1 45.9

LATITUDE

DAY	EPHEM. SID. TIME	☉	☊	☽	☿	♀	♂	♃	♄	♅	♆	♇
1	16 37 20.6	0 .0	0 .0	2N38.1	1N53.2	0N40.4	2S15.8	0S32.8	1S 7.1	0N38.0	1N40.0	16N41.0
4	16 49 10.3	0 .0	0 .0	1S21.8	2 3.3	0 47.1	2 19.5	0 33.4	1 6.8	0 37.9	1 40.0	16 39.6
7	17 0 59.9	0 .0	0 .0	4 25.9	2 6.5	0 53.6	2 23.2	0 34.1	1 6.5	0 37.8	1 40.0	16 38.2
10	17 12 49.6	0 .0	0 .0	5 13.7	2 2.8	0 59.7	2 26.9	0 34.8	1 6.2	0 37.7	1 39.9	16 36.7
13	17 24 39.3	0 .0	0 .0	3 51.4	1 52.4	1 5.6	2 30.5	0 35.4	1 6.0	0 37.6	1 39.9	16 35.2
16	17 36 29.0	0 .0	0 .0	1 2.6	1 35.6	1 11.0	2 34.0	0 36.1	1 5.7	0 37.5	1 39.8	16 33.7
19	17 48 18.6	0 .0	0 .0	2N10.4	1 12.7	1 16.0	2 37.6	0 36.8	1 5.5	0 37.3	1 39.7	16 32.2
22	18 0 8.3	0 .0	0 .0	4 37.9	0 44.1	1 20.6	2 41.0	0 37.4	1 5.3	0 37.2	1 39.6	16 30.7
25	18 11 58.0	0 .0	0 .0	5 12.5	0 10.3	1 24.7	2 44.5	0 38.1	1 5.1	0 37.1	1 39.5	16 29.2
28	18 23 47.7	0 .0	0 .0	3 9.9	0S28.3	1 28.3	2 47.8	0 38.7	1 4.9	0 37.0	1 39.4	16 27.8

RIGHT ASCENSION

DAY	EPHEM. SID. TIME	☉	☊	☽	☿	♀	♂	♃	♄	♅	♆	♇
1	16 37 20.6	8♊45.3	10♑ 4.3	5♊23.4	23♊17.3	23♊34.0	18♓34.9	14♒45.0	21♊38.5	17♎58.7	4♐21.7	8♎20.3
2	16 41 17.1	9 46.8	10 .9	22 7.1	25 26.2	24 54.3	19 13.6	14R44.8	21 46.8	17R57.5	4R20.0	8R19.8
3	16 45 13.7	10 48.3	9 57.4	8♋38.0	27 32.8	26 14.7	19 52.1	14 44.3	21 55.1	17 56.4	4 18.4	8 19.4
4	16 49 10.3	11 50.0	9 54.0	24 22.2	29 36.8	27 35.2	20 30.6	14 43.7	22 3.5	17 55.3	4 16.7	8 18.9
5	16 53 6.8	12 51.7	9 50.6	9♌ 2.4	1♋38.1	28 55.8	21 9.0	14 42.9	22 11.8	17 54.2	4 15.0	8 18.5
6	16 57 3.4	13 53.5	9 47.1	22 38.8	3 36.5	0♋16.4	21 47.2	14 41.9	22 20.2	17 53.2	4 13.3	8 18.1
7	17 0 59.9	14 55.3	9 43.7	5♍22.4	5 32.0	1 37.0	22 25.4	14 40.7	22 28.6	17 52.2	4 11.6	8 17.8
8	17 4 56.5	15 57.3	9 40.2	17 29.0	7 24.3	2 57.6	23 3.4	14 39.2	22 36.9	17 51.3	4 10.0	8 17.4
9	17 8 53.1	16 59.3	9 36.8	29 15.0	9 13.6	4 18.2	23 41.4	14 37.7	22 45.3	17 50.4	4 8.3	8 17.1
10	17 12 49.6	18 1.3	9 33.3	10♎55.3	10 59.5	5 38.8	24 19.2	14 35.9	22 53.7	17 49.5	4 6.7	8 16.8
11	17 16 46.2	19 3.4	9 29.9	22 42.6	12 42.2	6 59.3	24 57.0	14 33.9	23 2.2	17 48.7	4 5.0	8 16.6
12	17 20 42.7	20 5.6	9 26.4	4♏45.9	14 21.5	8 19.8	25 34.6	14 31.8	23 10.6	17 48.0	4 3.4	8 16.4
13	17 24 39.3	21 7.8	9 23.0	17 9.8	15 57.4	9 40.2	26 12.1	14 29.4	23 19.0	17 47.3	4 1.8	8 16.2
14	17 28 35.8	22 10.0	9 19.5	29 53.9	17 29.8	11 .6	26 49.5	14 26.9	23 27.4	17 46.6	4 .2	8 16.0
15	17 32 32.4	23 12.3	9 16.1	12♐51.7	18 58.7	12 20.8	27 26.9	14 24.2	23 35.8	17 46.0	3 58.6	8 15.9
16	17 36 29.0	24 14.6	9 12.6	25 53.0	20 24.1	13 40.9	28 4.1	14 21.3	23 44.3	17 45.5	3 57.0	8 15.8
17	17 40 25.5	25 17.0	9 9.2	8♑46.1	21 45.9	15 .9	28 41.2	14 18.2	23 52.7	17 44.9	3 55.4	8 15.7
18	17 44 22.1	26 19.3	9 5.7	21 21.6	23 4.1	16 20.8	29 18.1	14 14.9	24 1.1	17 44.5	3 53.8	8 15.7
19	17 48 18.6	27 21.7	9 2.3	3♒34.6	24 18.6	17 40.5	29 55.1	14 11.6	24 9.6	17 44.1	3 52.3	8 15.7
20	17 52 15.2	28 24.1	8 58.8	15 25.8	25 29.4	19 .1	0♈31.8	14 7.9	24 18.0	17 43.7	3 50.8	8D15.8
21	17 56 11.7	29 26.5	8 55.4	27 1.1	26 36.4	20 19.4	1 8.5	14 4.2	24 26.4	17 43.4	3 49.3	8 15.8
22	18 0 8.3	0♋28.9	8 51.9	8♓30.0	27 39.5	21 38.6	1 45.0	14 .2	24 34.8	17 43.1	3 47.8	8 15.9
23	18 4 4.9	1 31.3	8 48.5	20 5.4	28 38.8	22 57.5	2 21.4	13 56.1	24 43.2	17 42.9	3 46.3	8 16.0
24	18 8 1.4	2 33.6	8 45.0	2♈ 2.3	29 34.1	24 16.3	2 57.7	13 51.8	24 51.6	17 42.7	3 44.8	8 16.1
25	18 11 58.0	3 36.0	8 41.6	14 36.7	0♌25.4	25 34.8	3 33.9	13 47.3	25 .0	17 42.6	3 43.3	8 16.3
26	18 15 54.5	4 38.3	8 38.1	28 4.3	1 12.6	26 53.0	4 9.9	13 42.6	25 8.4	17 42.5	3 41.9	8 16.5
27	18 19 51.1	5 40.6	8 34.7	12♉35.9	1 55.6	28 11.1	4 45.9	13 37.8	25 16.8	17 42.5	3 40.5	8 16.7
28	18 23 47.7	6 42.9	8 31.2	28 12.1	2 34.4	29 28.8	5 21.6	13 32.9	25 25.1	17 42.5	3 39.1	8 17.0
29	18 27 44.2	7 45.1	8 27.8	14♊36.6	3 8.8	0♌46.3	5 57.3	13 27.7	25 33.5	17 42.5	3 37.7	8 17.2
30	18 31 40.8	8 47.3	8 24.3	1♋16.9	3 38.8	2 3.6	6 32.8	13 22.5	25 41.8	17D42.7	3 36.3	8 17.6

DECLINATION

DAY	EPHEM. SID. TIME	☉	☊	☽	☿	♀	♂	♃	♄	♅	♆	♇
1	16 37 20.6	22N .4	0S24.2	24N11.3	25N11.3	23N59.1	7S21.9	17S41.1	22N 6.1	6S56.4	19S39.6	14N36.0
4	16 49 10.3	22 23.5	0 24.2	20 10.3	25 29.9	24 12.6	6 37.1	17 42.2	22 7.7	6 55.1	19 38.8	14 35.0
7	17 0 59.9	22 43.1	0 24.2	5 29.3	25 27.3	24 19.7	5 52.2	17 43.7	22 9.2	6 53.9	19 38.0	14 33.9
10	17 12 49.6	22 59.2	0 24.2	10S22.7	25 6.6	24 20.3	5 7.4	17 45.8	22 10.6	6 53.0	19 37.2	14 32.7
13	17 24 39.3	23 11.5	0 24.3	21 38.7	24 31.0	24 14.4	4 22.7	17 48.2	22 12.0	6 52.2	19 36.5	14 31.4
16	17 36 29.0	23 20.2	0 24.3	24 26.0	23 43.6	24 2.1	3 38.1	17 51.2	22 13.3	6 51.6	19 35.7	14 29.9
19	17 48 18.6	23 25.2	0 24.3	17 38.1	22 47.5	23 43.5	2 53.9	17 54.5	22 14.5	6 51.1	19 35.0	14 28.3
22	18 0 8.3	23 26.5	0 24.3	4 2.6	21 45.6	23 18.6	2 10.0	17 58.3	22 15.6	6 50.9	19 34.3	14 26.6
25	18 11 58.0	23 24.1	0 24.3	11N53.3	20 40.6	22 47.7	1 26.5	18 2.5	22 16.6	6 50.8	19 33.7	14 24.8
28	18 23 47.7	23 18.0	0 24.3	23 28.1	19 35.4	22 10.8	0 43.6	18 7.1	22 17.6	6 50.9	19 33.1	14 22.9

JULY 1973

LONGITUDE

DAY	EPHEM. SID. TIME	☉	☊	☽	☿	♀	♂	♃	♄	♅	♆	♇
	h m s	° ′	° ′	° ′	° ′	° ′	° ′	° ′	° ′	° ′	° ′	° ′
1	18 35 37.3	9♋ 1.6	7♑40.1	16♋18.1	2♌ 5.4	0♌46.5	6♈32.6	10♒38.6	26♊ 8.8	18♎56.6	5♐12.0	1♎46.5
2	18 39 33.9	9 58.8	7 36.9	1♌16.8	2 29.2	1 59.6	7 10.5	10R33.1	26 16.5	18 56.9	5R10.7	1 47.1
3	18 43 30.4	10 56.0	7 33.7	15 58.2	2 48.7	3 12.6	7 48.2	10 27.4	26 24.1	18 57.2	5 9.5	1 47.8
4	18 47 27.0	11 53.2	7 30.5	0♍16.7	3 3.6	4 25.6	8 25.8	10 21.5	26 31.8	18 57.5	5 8.2	1 48.5
5	18 51 23.6	12 50.5	7 27.4	14 9.2	3 13.9	5 38.6	9 3.2	10 15.5	26 39.4	18 57.9	5 7.0	1 49.2
6	18 55 20.1	13 47.7	7 24.2	27 35.0	3 19.6	6 51.6	9 40.4	10 9.4	26 47.0	18 58.4	5 5.8	1 50.0
7	18 59 16.7	14 44.9	7 21.0	10♎35.6	3 20.5	8 4.6	10 17.4	10 3.2	26 54.6	18 58.9	5 4.7	1 50.8
8	19 3 13.2	15 42.1	7 17.8	23 14.0	3R16.8	9 17.5	10 54.2	9 56.9	27 2.2	18 59.4	5 3.5	1 51.7
9	19 7 9.8	16 39.3	7 14.6	5♏34.1	3 8.4	10 30.4	11 30.9	9 50.4	27 9.7	19 .1	5 2.4	1 52.5
10	19 11 6.4	17 36.5	7 11.5	17 40.1	2 55.4	11 43.4	12 7.4	9 43.9	27 17.2	19 .8	5 1.4	1 53.5
11	19 15 2.9	18 33.7	7 8.3	29 36.1	2 37.9	12 56.2	12 43.7	9 37.2	27 24.7	19 1.5	5 .3	1 54.4
12	19 18 59.5	19 30.9	7 5.1	11♐26.2	2 16.1	14 9.1	13 19.7	9 30.4	27 32.2	19 2.3	4 59.3	1 55.3
13	19 22 56.0	20 28.1	7 1.9	23 13.8	1 50.3	15 21.9	13 55.6	9 23.5	27 39.6	19 3.1	4 58.2	1 56.3
14	19 26 52.6	21 25.3	6 58.8	5♑ 2.3	1 20.8	16 34.7	14 31.2	9 16.6	27 47.0	19 4.0	4 57.2	1 57.3
15	19 30 49.1	22 22.5	6 55.6	16 54.3	0 48.0	17 47.5	15 6.7	9 9.5	27 54.4	19 4.9	4 56.3	1 58.4
16	19 34 45.7	23 19.7	6 52.4	28 52.1	0 12.4	19 .2	15 41.9	9 2.3	28 1.7	19 5.9	4 55.3	1 59.5
17	19 38 42.3	24 16.9	6 49.2	10♒57.7	29♋34.4	20 12.9	16 16.9	8 55.1	28 9.0	19 6.9	4 54.4	2 .6
18	19 42 38.8	25 14.2	6 46.1	23 13.0	28 54.8	21 25.6	16 51.7	8 47.8	28 16.3	19 8.0	4 53.5	2 1.7
19	19 46 35.4	26 11.4	6 42.9	5♓39.6	28 14.1	22 38.3	17 26.2	8 40.4	28 23.5	19 9.1	4 52.6	2 2.9
20	19 50 31.9	27 8.6	6 39.7	18 19.2	27 33.1	23 50.9	18 .5	8 33.0	28 30.7	19 10.3	4 51.8	2 4.1
21	19 54 28.5	28 5.9	6 36.5	1♈13.7	26 52.4	25 3.6	18 34.5	8 25.5	28 37.9	19 11.5	4 51.0	2 5.3
22	19 58 25.0	29 3.2	6 33.4	14 24.8	26 12.8	26 16.2	19 8.3	8 17.9	28 45.0	19 12.8	4 50.2	2 6.5
23	20 2 21.6	0♌ .4	6 30.2	27 53.9	25 35.1	27 28.7	19 41.8	8 10.3	28 52.1	19 14.2	4 49.4	2 7.8
24	20 6 18.2	0 57.7	6 27.0	11♉42.2	24 59.8	28 41.3	20 15.0	8 2.7	28 59.2	19 15.5	4 48.7	2 9.1
25	20 10 14.7	1 55.1	6 23.8	25 49.9	24 27.7	29 53.8	20 48.0	7 55.0	29 6.2	19 17.0	4 48.0	2 10.4
26	20 14 11.3	2 52.4	6 20.6	10♊15.8	23 59.4	1♍ 6.3	21 20.6	7 47.3	29 13.2	19 18.4	4 47.3	2 11.8
27	20 18 7.8	3 49.7	6 17.5	24 57.0	23 35.4	2 18.8	21 53.0	7 39.5	29 20.1	19 20.0	4 46.6	2 13.2
28	20 22 4.4	4 47.1	6 14.3	9♋48.5	23 16.2	3 31.3	22 25.0	7 31.8	29 27.0	19 21.6	4 46.0	2 14.6
29	20 26 .9	5 44.5	6 11.1	24 43.7	23 2.3	4 43.7	22 56.8	7 24.0	29 33.9	19 23.2	4 45.4	2 16.0
30	20 29 57.5	6 41.9	6 7.9	9♌34.8	22 54.0	5 56.1	23 28.2	7 16.2	29 40.7	19 24.9	4 44.8	2 17.5
31	20 33 54.0	7 39.3	6 4.8	24 13.9	22 51.6	7 8.5	23 59.3	7 8.4	29 47.5	19 26.6	4 44.4	2 19.0

LATITUDE

DAY	EPHEM. SID. TIME	☉	☊	☽	☿	♀	♂	♃	♄	♅	♆	♇
1	18 35 37.3	0 .0	0 .0	0S47.9	1S10.8	1N31.3	2S51.1	0S39.3	1S 4.8	0N36.9	1N39.3	16N26.3
4	18 47 27.0	0 .0	0 .0	4 12.7	1 55.8	1 33.7	2 54.4	0 39.9	1 4.6	0 36.7	1 39.2	16 24.8
7	18 59 16.7	0 .0	0 .0	5 17.2	2 41.8	1 35.5	2 57.5	0 40.5	1 4.5	0 36.6	1 39.1	16 23.4
10	19 11 6.4	0 .0	0 .0	4 3.5	3 26.0	1 36.7	3 .6	0 41.1	1 4.3	0 36.5	1 39.0	16 22.0
13	19 22 56.0	0 .0	0 .0	1 19.4	4 5.3	1 37.2	3 3.6	0 41.7	1 4.2	0 36.4	1 38.9	16 20.6
16	19 34 45.7	0 .0	0 .0	1N54.5	4 35.7	1 37.1	3 6.5	0 42.2	1 4.1	0 36.3	1 38.7	16 19.2
19	19 46 35.4	0 .0	0 .0	4 27.9	4 53.8	1 36.3	3 9.2	0 42.7	1 4.0	0 36.2	1 38.6	16 17.9
22	19 58 25.0	0 .0	0 .0	5 12.9	4 57.0	1 34.8	3 11.9	0 43.2	1 3.9	0 36.0	1 38.4	16 16.6
25	20 10 14.7	0 .0	0 .0	3 29.8	4 44.9	1 32.6	3 14.5	0 43.7	1 3.9	0 35.9	1 38.3	16 15.3
28	20 22 4.4	0 .0	0 .0	0S12.5	4 19.0	1 29.8	3 16.9	0 44.1	1 3.8	0 35.8	1 38.1	16 14.1
31	20 33 54.0	0 .0	0 .0	3 48.5	3 42.2	1 26.2	3 19.2	0 44.5	1 3.8	0 35.7	1 38.0	16 12.9

RIGHT ASCENSION

DAY	EPHEM. SID. TIME	☉	☊	☽	☿	♀	♂	♃	♄	♅	♆	♇
1	18 35 37.3	9♋49.4	8♑20.9	17♋34.6	4♌ 4.4	3♌20.5	7♈ 8.1	13♒17.0	25♊50.1	17♎42.8	3♐35.0	8♎17.9
2	18 39 33.9	10 51.4	8 17.4	3♌ 1.3	4 25.3	4 37.2	7 43.3	13R11.5	25 58.4	17 43.0	3R33.6	8 18.3
3	18 43 30.4	11 53.4	8 14.0	17 25.6	4 41.6	5 53.5	8 18.4	13 5.7	26 6.7	17 43.3	3 32.3	8 18.7
4	18 47 27.0	12 55.3	8 10.5	0♍51.6	4 53.2	7 9.6	8 53.3	12 59.9	26 14.9	17 43.6	3 31.0	8 19.1
5	18 51 23.6	13 57.2	8 7.1	13 32.0	5 .1	8 25.3	9 28.0	12 53.9	26 23.2	17 44.0	3 29.8	8 19.6
6	18 55 20.1	14 58.9	8 3.6	25 42.5	5 2.2	9 40.8	10 2.6	12 47.7	26 31.4	17 44.4	3 28.5	8 20.1
7	18 59 16.7	16 .6	8 .2	7♎38.4	4R59.5	10 55.9	10 37.1	12 41.5	26 39.6	17 44.9	3 27.3	8 20.6
8	19 3 13.2	17 2.1	7 56.7	19 33.4	4 52.2	12 10.7	11 11.3	12 35.1	26 47.7	17 45.4	3 26.1	8 21.2
9	19 7 9.8	18 3.6	7 53.3	1♏38.1	4 40.1	13 25.2	11 45.5	12 28.6	26 55.9	17 45.9	3 24.9	8 21.7
10	19 11 6.4	19 4.9	7 49.8	13 59.2	4 23.6	14 39.4	12 19.4	12 22.0	27 4.1	17 46.6	3 23.8	8 22.4
11	19 15 2.9	20 6.2	7 46.4	26 38.5	4 2.7	15 53.2	12 53.2	12 15.3	27 12.1	17 47.2	3 22.7	8 23.0
12	19 18 59.5	21 7.3	7 42.9	9♐32.5	3 37.6	17 6.7	13 26.8	12 8.4	27 20.2	17 47.9	3 21.6	8 23.7
13	19 22 56.0	22 8.3	7 39.5	22 33.2	3 8.7	18 19.8	14 .3	12 1.5	27 28.2	17 48.7	3 20.5	8 24.4
14	19 26 52.6	23 9.2	7 36.0	5♑30.0	2 36.3	19 32.6	14 33.5	11 54.4	27 36.2	17 49.5	3 19.5	8 25.1
15	19 30 49.1	24 9.9	7 32.6	18 12.9	2 .8	20 45.1	15 6.6	11 47.3	27 44.2	17 50.3	3 18.4	8 25.9
16	19 34 45.7	25 10.6	7 29.1	0♒35.4	1 22.8	21 57.3	15 39.5	11 40.1	27 52.1	17 51.2	3 17.4	8 26.6
17	19 38 42.3	26 11.1	7 25.7	12 35.9	0 42.8	23 9.2	16 12.2	11 32.8	28 .0	17 52.2	3 16.5	8 27.4
18	19 42 38.8	27 11.5	7 22.2	24 17.9	0 1.4	24 20.7	16 44.7	11 25.4	28 7.9	17 53.2	3 15.5	8 28.3
19	19 46 35.4	28 11.7	7 18.8	5♓48.8	29♋19.2	25 31.9	17 17.0	11 17.9	28 15.7	17 54.2	3 14.6	8 29.1
20	19 50 31.9	29 11.8	7 15.3	17 19.4	28 36.9	26 42.9	17 49.1	11 10.4	28 23.5	17 55.3	3 13.7	8 30.0
21	19 54 28.5	0♌11.8	7 11.8	29 2.6	27 55.4	27 53.5	18 20.9	11 2.8	28 31.2	17 56.4	3 12.8	8 30.9
22	19 58 25.0	1 11.7	7 8.4	11♈12.9	27 15.2	29 3.8	18 52.6	10 55.1	28 39.0	17 57.6	3 12.0	8 31.9
23	20 2 21.6	2 11.4	7 4.9	24 4.9	26 37.1	0♍13.8	19 24.0	10 47.4	28 46.6	17 58.8	3 11.2	8 32.9
24	20 6 18.2	3 11.0	7 1.5	7♉50.9	26 1.8	1 23.5	19 55.2	10 39.6	28 54.3	18 .1	3 10.4	8 33.9
25	20 10 14.7	4 10.4	6 58.0	22 36.5	25 30.0	2 32.9	20 26.1	10 31.8	29 1.8	18 1.4	3 9.7	8 34.9
26	20 14 11.3	5 9.7	6 54.6	8♊15.6	25 2.3	3 42.0	20 56.8	10 24.0	29 9.4	18 2.8	3 9.0	8 35.9
27	20 18 7.8	6 8.8	6 51.1	24 27.0	24 39.1	4 50.9	21 27.3	10 16.1	29 16.9	18 4.2	3 8.3	8 37.0
28	20 22 4.4	7 7.8	6 47.7	10♋39.3	24 21.2	5 59.5	21 57.4	10 8.2	29 24.3	18 5.7	3 7.6	8 38.1
29	20 26 .9	8 6.7	6 44.2	26 21.7	24 8.7	7 7.9	22 27.3	10 .3	29 31.7	18 7.2	3 7.0	8 39.2
30	20 29 57.5	9 5.4	6 40.8	11♌15.2	24 2.3	8 16.0	22 56.9	9 52.3	29 39.1	18 8.7	3 6.4	8 40.4
31	20 33 54.0	10 3.9	6 37.3	25 15.3	24 2.0	9 23.9	23 26.3	9 44.4	29 46.4	18 10.4	3 5.9	8 41.6

DECLINATION

DAY	EPHEM. SID. TIME	☉	☊	☽	☿	♀	♂	♃	♄	♅	♆	♇
1	18 35 37.3	23N 8.1	0S24.3	21N39.4	18N32.9	21N28.3	0S 1.3	18S12.0	22N18.5	6S51.1	19S32.5	14N20.9
4	18 47 27.0	22 54.7	0 24.3	7 25.8	17 35.9	20 40.4	0N40.3	18 17.3	22 19.2	6 51.6	19 31.9	14 18.7
7	18 59 16.7	22 37.6	0 24.3	9S 3.2	16 47.3	19 47.3	1 21.2	18 22.8	22 20.0	6 52.2	19 31.4	14 16.5
10	19 11 6.4	22 17.0	0 24.3	20 59.7	16 9.9	18 49.3	2 1.2	18 28.6	22 20.6	6 53.0	19 30.9	14 14.2
13	19 22 56.0	21 53.0	0 24.4	24 35.5	15 46.0	17 46.7	2 40.4	18 34.5	22 21.1	6 54.0	19 30.5	14 11.8
16	19 34 45.7	21 25.6	0 24.4	18 31.3	15 37.0	16 40.0	3 18.6	18 40.7	22 21.6	6 55.2	19 30.1	14 9.3
19	19 46 35.4	20 54.9	0 24.4	5 16.9	15 43.1	15 29.3	3 55.8	18 46.9	22 22.0	6 56.5	19 29.8	14 6.7
22	19 58 25.0	20 21.1	0 24.4	10N29.2	16 2.8	14 14.9	4 32.0	18 53.3	22 22.3	6 58.0	19 29.5	14 4.1
25	20 10 14.7	19 44.2	0 24.4	22 36.8	16 33.3	12 57.3	5 6.9	18 59.7	22 22.5	6 59.7	19 29.2	14 1.4
28	20 22 4.4	19 4.3	0 24.4	22 52.3	17 10.8	11 36.7	5 40.7	19 6.1	22 22.7	7 1.5	19 29.0	13 58.7
31	20 33 54.0	18 21.5	0 24.4	9 51.1	17 51.2	10 13.4	6 13.1	19 12.4	22 22.8	7 3.6	19 28.9	13 55.8

AUGUST 1973

DAY	EPHEM. SID. TIME	☉	☊	☽	☿	♀	♂	♃	♄	♅	♆	♇
	h m s	° ′	° ′	° ′	° ′	° ′	° ′	° ′	° ′	° ′	° ′	° ′
		LONGITUDE										
1	20 37 50.6	8♌36.7	6♑ 1.6	8♍34.0	22♋55.3	8♍20.9	24♈30.1	7♒ .6	29♊54.2	19♎28.4	4♐43.9	2♎20.5
2	20 41 47.2	9 34.1	5 58.4	22 30.5	23D 5.2	9 33.2	25 .5	6R52.8	0♋ .8	19 30.2	4R43.4	2 22.1
3	20 45 43.7	10 31.6	5 55.2	6♎ 1.0	23 21.6	10 45.5	26 30.5	6 45.1	0 7.4	19 32.1	4 42.9	2 23.6
4	20 49 40.3	11 29.0	5 52.1	19 5.6	23 44.4	11 57.7	26 .2	6 37.3	0 14.0	19 34.0	4 42.5	2 25.2
5	20 53 36.8	12 26.5	5 48.9	1♏46.4	24 13.7	13 9.9	26 29.5	6 29.6	0 20.5	19 36.0	4 42.2	2 26.8
6	20 57 33.4	13 24.0	5 45.7	14 7.0	24 49.6	14 22.1	26 58.4	6 21.9	0 26.9	19 38.0	4 41.8	2 28.5
7	21 1 29.9	14 21.4	5 42.5	26 12.1	25 31.8	15 34.3	27 27.0	6 14.2	0 33.3	19 40.0	4 41.5	2 30.1
8	21 5 26.5	15 18.9	5 39.3	8♐ 6.6	26 20.5	16 46.4	27 55.2	6 6.6	0 39.6	19 42.1	4 41.2	2 31.8
9	21 9 23.0	16 16.4	5 36.2	19 55.4	27 15.4	17 58.4	28 22.9	5 59.0	0 45.9	19 44.2	4 40.9	2 33.5
10	21 13 19.6	17 14.0	5 33.0	1♑43.2	28 16.5	19 10.5	28 50.3	5 51.5	0 52.1	19 46.4	4 40.7	2 35.2
11	21 17 16.2	18 11.5	5 29.8	13 34.2	29 23.6	20 22.5	29 17.2	5 44.1	0 58.3	19 48.6	4 40.5	2 37.0
12	21 21 12.7	19 9.1	5 26.6	25 32.0	0♌36.4	21 34.4	29 43.8	5 36.7	1 4.4	19 50.9	4 40.4	2 38.8
13	21 25 9.3	20 6.6	5 23.5	7♒39.4	1 54.8	22 46.3	0♉ 9.8	5 29.3	1 10.4	19 53.2	4 40.2	2 40.5
14	21 29 5.8	21 4.2	5 20.3	19 58.3	3 18.5	23 58.2	0 35.5	5 22.1	1 16.4	19 55.5	4 40.1	2 42.4
15	21 33 2.4	22 1.8	5 17.1	2♓30.0	4 47.2	25 10.0	1 .7	5 14.9	1 22.3	19 57.9	4 40.1	2 44.2
16	21 36 58.9	22 59.5	5 13.9	15 14.8	6 20.6	26 21.8	1 25.4	5 7.8	1 28.2	20 .4	4 40.0	2 46.0
17	21 40 55.5	23 57.1	5 10.7	28 12.9	7 58.4	27 33.6	1 49.6	5 .8	1 34.0	20 2.8	4 40.0	2 47.9
18	21 44 52.0	24 54.8	5 7.6	11♈23.9	9 40.1	28 45.3	2 13.4	4 53.9	1 39.7	20 5.3	4D40.1	2 49.8
19	21 48 48.6	25 52.5	5 4.4	24 47.4	11 25.3	29 57.0	2 36.6	4 47.1	1 45.4	20 7.9	4 40.1	2 51.7
20	21 52 45.1	26 50.3	5 1.2	8♉23.1	13 13.7	1♎ 8.6	2 59.4	4 40.4	1 50.9	20 10.5	4 40.2	2 53.6
21	21 56 41.7	27 48.1	4 58.0	22 11.0	15 4.8	2 20.2	3 21.6	4 33.8	1 56.5	20 13.1	4 40.4	2 55.6
22	22 0 38.3	28 45.9	4 54.9	6♊10.7	16 58.2	3 31.8	3 43.2	4 27.3	2 2.0	20 15.8	4 40.6	2 57.6
23	22 4 34.8	29 43.7	4 51.7	20 21.8	18 53.4	4 43.3	4 4.3	4 21.0	2 7.3	20 18.5	4 40.8	2 59.6
24	22 8 31.4	0♍41.5	4 48.5	4♋43.1	20 50.2	5 54.7	4 24.9	4 14.7	2 12.7	20 21.2	4 41.0	3 1.6
25	22 12 27.9	1 39.4	4 45.3	19 12.0	22 48.0	7 6.2	4 44.8	4 8.6	2 17.9	20 24.0	4 41.3	3 3.6
26	22 16 24.5	2 37.3	4 42.1	3♌44.6	24 46.5	8 17.6	5 4.1	4 2.6	2 23.0	20 26.8	4 41.5	3 5.6
27	22 20 21.0	3 35.3	4 39.0	18 15.5	26 45.5	9 28.9	5 22.8	3 56.7	2 28.1	20 29.7	4 41.9	3 7.6
28	22 24 17.6	4 33.2	4 35.8	2♍38.7	28 44.6	10 40.2	5 40.9	3 51.0	2 33.1	20 32.5	4 42.2	3 9.7
29	22 28 14.1	5 31.2	4 32.6	16 48.0	0♍43.6	11 51.5	5 58.3	3 45.4	2 38.1	20 35.4	4 42.6	3 11.8
30	22 32 10.7	6 29.2	4 29.4	0♎38.2	2 42.3	13 2.7	6 15.1	3 40.0	2 42.9	20 38.4	4 43.0	3 13.9
31	22 36 7.2	7 27.2	4 26.3	14 5.9	4 40.5	14 13.8	6 31.2	3 34.7	2 47.7	20 41.4	4 43.5	3 16.0
		LATITUDE										
1	20 37 50.6	0 .0	0 .0	4S34.3	3S28.1	1N24.9	3S20.0	0S44.6	1S 3.8	0N35.7	1N37.9	16N12.5
4	20 49 40.3	0 .0	0 .0	5 5.8	2 42.4	1 20.4	3 22.1	0 45.0	1 3.7	0 35.6	1 37.7	16 11.4
7	21 1 29.9	0 .0	0 .0	3 25.0	1 54.0	1 15.3	3 24.0	0 45.3	1 3.7	0 35.5	1 37.6	16 10.3
10	21 13 19.6	0 .0	0 .0	0 29.7	1 5.9	1 9.5	3 25.8	0 45.6	1 3.7	0 35.3	1 37.4	16 9.3
13	21 25 9.3	0 .0	0 .0	2N37.7	0 20.7	1 3.0	3 27.4	0 45.9	1 3.7	0 35.2	1 37.2	16 8.4
16	21 36 58.9	0 .0	0 .0	4 46.6	0N19.5	0 56.0	3 28.7	0 46.1	1 3.7	0 35.2	1 37.1	16 7.5
19	21 48 48.6	0 .0	0 .0	4 52.1	0 52.8	0 48.3	3 29.9	0 46.3	1 3.7	0 35.1	1 36.9	16 6.6
22	22 0 38.3	0 .0	0 .0	2 34.9	1 18.1	0 40.1	3 30.8	0 46.5	1 3.7	0 35.0	1 36.7	16 5.8
25	22 12 27.9	0 .0	0 .0	1S 8.6	1 35.2	0 31.4	3 31.4	0 46.7	1 3.8	0 34.9	1 36.5	16 5.1
28	22 24 17.6	0 .0	0 .0	4 14.8	1 44.3	0 22.1	3 31.8	0 46.8	1 3.8	0 34.8	1 36.4	16 4.5
31	22 36 7.2	0 .0	0 .0	5 1.1	1 46.3	0 12.4	3 31.8	0 46.9	1 3.9	0 34.7	1 36.2	16 3.9
		RIGHT ASCENSION										
1	20 37 50.6	11♌ 2.3	6♑33.8	8♍28.8	24♋ 8.3	10♍31.5	23♈55.3	9♒36.5	29♊53.7	18♎12.0	3♐ 5.3	8♎42.8
2	20 41 47.2	12 .6	6 30.4	21 7.9	24D21.1	11 38.8	24 24.0	9R28.5	0♋ .9	18 13.7	3R 4.8	8 44.1
3	20 45 43.7	12 58.7	6 26.9	3♎26.9	24 40.8	12 46.0	24 52.4	9 20.6	0 8.0	18 15.4	3 4.4	8 45.3
4	20 49 40.3	13 56.6	6 23.5	15 38.6	25 7.2	13 52.9	25 20.5	9 12.6	0 15.1	18 17.2	3 3.9	8 46.6
5	20 53 36.8	14 54.4	6 20.0	27 54.0	25 40.6	14 59.6	25 48.2	9 4.8	0 22.1	18 19.0	3 3.5	8 47.9
6	20 57 33.4	15 52.0	6 16.6	10♏20.4	26 20.9	16 6.1	26 15.7	8 56.9	0 29.1	18 20.9	3 3.1	8 49.2
7	21 1 29.9	16 49.4	6 13.1	23 1.0	27 7.9	17 12.4	26 42.7	8 49.0	0 36.0	18 22.8	3 2.8	8 50.6
8	21 5 26.5	17 46.8	6 9.6	5♐54.4	28 1.7	18 18.6	27 9.5	8 41.2	0 42.9	18 24.7	3 2.5	8 51.9
9	21 9 23.0	18 43.9	6 6.2	18 54.5	29 2.1	19 24.5	27 35.8	8 33.5	0 49.6	18 26.7	3 2.2	8 53.3
10	21 13 19.6	19 40.9	6 2.7	1♑52.9	0♌ 8.9	20 30.3	28 1.8	8 25.8	0 56.4	18 28.7	3 2.0	8 54.8
11	21 17 16.2	20 37.8	5 59.3	14 40.6	1 21.8	21 35.9	28 27.4	8 18.1	1 3.0	18 30.7	3 1.8	8 56.2
12	21 21 12.7	21 34.5	5 55.8	27 11.2	2 40.7	22 41.4	28 52.7	8 10.6	1 9.6	18 32.8	3 1.6	8 57.7
13	21 25 9.3	22 31.1	5 52.4	9♒22.1	4 5.2	23 46.8	29 17.5	8 3.0	1 16.2	18 35.0	3 1.4	8 59.1
14	21 29 5.8	23 27.5	5 48.9	21 15.2	5 35.0	24 52.0	29 42.0	7 55.6	1 22.6	18 37.2	3 1.3	9 .6
15	21 33 2.4	24 23.8	5 45.4	2♓56.3	7 9.7	25 57.1	0♉ 6.0	7 48.2	1 29.0	18 39.4	3 1.2	9 2.2
16	21 36 58.9	25 20.0	5 42.0	14 34.4	8 48.8	27 2.0	0 29.5	7 40.9	1 35.4	18 41.6	3 1.2	9 3.7
17	21 40 55.5	26 16.0	5 38.5	26 20.5	10 31.9	28 6.9	0 52.7	7 33.8	1 41.6	18 43.9	3 1.2	9 5.3
18	21 44 52.0	27 12.0	5 35.1	8♈27.4	12 18.5	29 11.7	1 15.4	7 26.6	1 47.8	18 46.3	3 1.2	9 6.9
19	21 48 48.6	28 7.8	5 31.6	21 7.6	14 8.2	0♎16.4	1 37.6	7 19.6	1 53.9	18 48.6	3D 1.3	9 8.5
20	21 52 45.1	29 3.4	5 28.2	4♉32.0	16 .3	1 21.1	1 59.3	7 12.7	1 60.0	18 51.0	3 1.3	9 10.1
21	21 56 41.7	29 59.0	5 24.7	18 46.8	17 54.4	2 25.7	2 20.6	7 6.0	2 6.0	18 53.5	3 1.5	9 11.8
22	22 0 38.3	0♍54.5	5 21.2	3♊48.9	19 50.0	3 30.3	2 41.3	6 59.3	2 11.9	18 56.0	3 1.7	9 13.4
23	22 4 34.8	1 49.8	5 17.8	19 24.2	21 46.6	4 34.8	3 1.5	6 52.7	2 17.7	18 58.5	3 1.9	9 15.1
24	22 8 31.4	2 45.0	5 14.3	5♋ 8.8	23 43.7	5 39.3	3 21.2	6 46.3	2 23.4	19 1.0	3 2.1	9 16.8
25	22 12 27.9	3 40.2	5 10.9	20 36.7	25 41.0	6 43.7	3 40.3	6 40.0	2 29.1	19 3.6	3 2.4	9 18.5
26	22 16 24.5	4 35.2	5 7.4	5♌28.8	27 38.1	7 48.2	3 58.8	6 33.8	2 34.7	19 6.2	3 2.6	9 20.3
27	22 20 21.0	5 30.1	5 3.9	19 37.2	29 34.7	8 52.6	4 16.7	6 27.7	2 40.1	19 8.9	3 3.0	9 22.0
28	22 24 17.6	6 25.0	5 .5	3♍ 4.4	1♍30.6	9 57.1	4 34.1	6 21.8	2 45.6	19 11.6	3 3.3	9 23.8
29	22 28 14.1	7 19.7	4 57.0	15 59.4	3 25.4	11 1.6	4 50.8	6 16.0	2 50.9	19 14.3	3 3.7	9 25.6
30	22 32 10.7	8 14.4	4 53.6	28 34.1	5 19.1	12 6.1	5 6.9	6 10.4	2 56.1	19 17.0	3 4.2	9 27.4
31	22 36 7.2	9 8.9	4 50.1	11♎ .1	7 11.4	13 10.7	5 22.3	6 4.9	3 1.3	19 19.8	3 4.6	9 29.2
		DECLINATION										
1	20 37 50.6	18N 6.7	0S24.4	4N 7.0	18N 4.5	9N45.1	6N23.6	19S14.5	22N22.8	7S 4.3	19S28.9	13N54.9
4	20 49 40.3	17 20.4	0 24.4	12S11.3	18 41.4	8 18.9	6 54.3	19 20.8	22 22.8	7 6.5	19 28.8	13 52.0
7	21 1 29.9	16 31.5	0 24.4	22 37.4	19 10.2	6 50.7	7 23.5	19 26.9	22 22.8	7 8.8	19 28.8	13 49.1
10	21 13 19.6	15 40.3	0 24.4	23 55.6	19 26.0	5 21.0	7 51.3	19 32.8	22 22.7	7 11.4	19 28.8	13 46.2
13	21 25 9.3	14 46.9	0 24.4	15 49.0	19 24.1	3 50.0	8 17.6	19 38.5	22 22.6	7 14.0	19 28.9	13 43.2
16	21 36 58.9	13 51.3	0 24.4	1 24.5	19 .3	2 18.1	8 42.4	19 44.0	22 22.4	7 16.8	19 29.0	13 40.3
19	21 48 48.6	12 53.8	0 24.4	14N 7.6	18 12.1	0 45.5	9 5.6	19 49.3	22 22.2	7 19.7	19 29.2	13 37.3
22	22 0 38.3	11 54.3	0 24.5	23 53.1	16 59.6	0S47.4	9 27.1	19 54.2	22 21.9	7 22.8	19 29.5	13 34.2
25	22 12 27.9	10 53.2	0 24.5	20 56.2	15 25.0	2 20.4	9 47.0	19 58.8	22 21.6	7 26.0	19 29.8	13 31.2
28	22 24 17.6	9 50.5	0 24.5	6 34.1	13 32.5	3 53.1	10 5.1	20 3.1	22 21.3	7 29.2	19 30.1	13 28.2
31	22 36 7.2	8 46.4	0 24.5	10S11.0	11 26.8	5 25.3	10 21.5	20 7.0	22 21.0	7 32.6	19 30.5	13 25.2

SEPTEMBER 1973

LONGITUDE

DAY	EPHEM. SID. TIME	☉	☊	☽	☿	♀	♂	♃	♄	♅	♆	♇
	h m s	° ′	° ′	° ′	° ′	° ′	° ′	° ′	° ′	° ′	° ′	° ′
1	22 40 3.8	8♍25.3	4♑23.1	27♎ 9.9	6♍38.0	15♎24.9	6♉46.7	3♒29.5	2♋52.4	20♎44.4	4♐44.0	3♎18.1
2	22 44 .3	9 23.4	4 19.9	9♏51.2	8 34.8	16 36.0	7 1.4	3R24.5	2 57.0	20 47.4	4 44.5	3 20.2
3	22 47 56.9	10 21.5	4 16.7	22 12.5	10 30.6	17 47.0	7 15.5	3 19.7	3 1.5	20 50.5	4 45.1	3 22.3
4	22 51 53.5	11 19.6	4 13.5	4♐17.9	12 25.5	18 57.9	7 28.8	3 15.1	3 5.9	20 53.6	4 45.6	3 24.5
5	22 55 50.0	12 17.8	4 10.4	16 12.3	14 19.4	20 8.8	7 41.4	3 10.6	3 10.3	20 56.7	4 46.3	3 26.7
6	22 59 46.6	13 16.0	4 7.2	28 1.2	16 12.2	21 19.7	7 53.3	3 6.3	3 14.5	20 59.9	4 46.9	3 28.8
7	23 3 43.1	14 14.2	4 4.0	9♑49.9	18 3.9	22 30.4	8 4.4	3 2.1	3 18.7	21 3.1	4 47.6	3 31.0
8	23 7 39.7	15 12.4	4 .8	21 43.5	19 54.5	23 41.1	8 14.8	2 58.1	3 22.8	21 6.3	4 48.3	3 33.2
9	23 11 36.2	16 10.7	3 57.7	3♒46.6	21 43.9	24 51.8	8 24.4	2 54.3	3 26.8	21 9.5	4 49.0	3 35.4
10	23 15 32.8	17 9.0	3 54.5	16 2.9	23 32.2	26 2.4	8 33.3	2 50.7	3 30.7	21 12.8	4 49.8	3 37.6
11	23 19 29.3	18 7.3	3 51.3	28 35.0	25 19.4	27 12.9	8 41.4	2 47.3	3 34.6	21 16.2	4 50.7	3 39.9
12	23 23 25.9	19 5.7	3 48.1	11♓24.0	27 5.4	28 23.4	8 48.6	2 44.0	3 38.3	21 19.5	4 51.5	3 42.1
13	23 27 22.4	20 4.0	3 44.9	24 29.8	28 50.3	29 33.8	8 55.0	2 40.9	3 42.0	21 22.8	4 52.4	3 44.4
14	23 31 19.0	21 2.4	3 41.8	7♈51.1	0♎34.1	0♏44.1	9 .6	2 38.0	3 45.5	21 26.2	4 53.3	3 46.6
15	23 35 15.5	22 .9	3 38.6	21 25.7	2 16.8	1 54.4	9 5.4	2 35.3	3 49.0	21 29.6	4 54.2	3 48.8
16	23 39 12.1	22 59.3	3 35.4	5♉10.7	3 58.4	3 4.6	9 9.3	2 32.8	3 52.3	21 33.0	4 55.2	3 51.1
17	23 43 8.6	23 57.8	3 32.2	19 3.4	5 38.9	4 14.7	9 12.4	2 30.4	3 55.6	21 36.4	4 56.1	3 53.4
18	23 47 5.2	24 56.4	3 29.1	3♊ 1.8	7 18.4	5 24.7	9 14.5	2 28.3	3 58.7	21 39.9	4 57.2	3 55.6
19	23 51 1.7	25 54.9	3 25.9	17 4.2	8 56.9	6 34.7	9 15.8	2 26.3	4 1.8	21 43.4	4 58.2	3 57.9
20	23 54 58.3	26 53.6	3 22.7	1♋ 9.6	10 34.3	7 44.6	9 16.3	2 24.5	4 4.8	21 46.9	4 59.3	4 .2
21	23 58 54.9	27 52.2	3 19.5	15 17.4	12 10.8	8 54.5	9R15.8	2 22.9	4 7.6	21 50.4	5 .4	4 2.5
22	0 2 51.4	28 50.9	3 16.3	29 26.4	13 46.3	10 4.2	9 14.4	2 21.5	4 10.4	21 54.0	5 1.5	4 4.8
23	0 6 48.0	29 49.6	3 13.2	13♌34.9	15 20.8	11 13.9	9 12.1	2 20.4	4 13.1	21 57.5	5 2.7	4 7.0
24	0 10 44.5	0♎48.4	3 10.0	27 40.2	16 54.4	12 23.6	9 8.9	2 19.4	4 15.6	22 1.1	5 3.9	4 9.3
25	0 14 41.1	1 47.2	3 6.8	11♍38.8	18 27.0	13 33.1	9 4.8	2 18.6	4 18.1	22 4.7	5 5.1	4 11.6
26	0 18 37.6	2 46.0	3 3.6	25 26.6	19 58.7	14 42.6	8 59.9	2 18.0	4 20.5	22 8.3	5 6.4	4 13.9
27	0 22 34.2	3 44.9	3 .5	8♎59.6	21 29.4	15 52.0	8 54.0	2 17.5	4 22.7	22 11.9	5 7.7	4 16.2
28	0 26 30.7	4 43.8	2 57.3	22 14.9	22 59.2	17 1.3	8 47.2	2 17.3	4 24.9	22 15.6	5 9.0	4 18.5
29	0 30 27.3	5 42.7	2 54.1	5♏10.8	24 28.0	18 10.5	8 39.6	2 17.3	4 26.9	22 19.2	5 10.3	4 20.8
30	0 34 23.8	6 41.7	2 50.9	17 47.3	25 56.0	19 19.6	8 31.1	2D17.5	4 28.8	22 22.9	5 11.7	4 23.1

LATITUDE

DAY	EPHEM. SID. TIME	☉	☊	☽	☿	♀	♂	♃	♄	♅	♆	♇
1	22 40 3.8	0 .0	0 .0	4S43.1	1N45.6	0N 9.1	3S31.8	0S46.9	1S 3.9	0N34.7	1N36.1	16N 3.7
4	22 51 53.5	0 .0	0 .0	2 37.4	1 39.9	0S 1.1	3 31.3	0 47.0	1 3.9	0 34.6	1 35.9	16 3.2
7	23 3 43.1	0 .0	0 .0	0N24.3	1 29.6	0 11.7	3 30.4	0 47.0	1 4.0	0 34.5	1 35.8	16 2.8
10	23 15 32.8	0 .0	0 .0	3 18.8	1 15.7	0 22.6	3 29.1	0 47.0	1 4.1	0 34.5	1 35.6	16 2.4
13	23 27 22.4	0 .0	0 .0	4 56.6	0 59.0	0 33.7	3 27.3	0 47.0	1 4.2	0 34.4	1 35.4	16 2.1
16	23 39 12.1	0 .0	0 .0	4 18.3	0 40.3	0 45.0	3 24.9	0 47.0	1 4.2	0 34.3	1 35.3	16 1.9
19	23 51 1.7	0 .0	0 .0	1 27.5	0 19.9	0 56.5	3 22.0	0 46.9	1 4.3	0 34.3	1 35.1	16 1.8
22	0 2 51.4	0 .0	0 .0	2S11.0	0S 1.4	1 8.0	3 18.5	0 46.9	1 4.4	0 34.2	1 34.9	16 1.7
25	0 14 41.1	0 .0	0 .0	4 39.2	0 23.4	1 19.6	3 14.2	0 46.8	1 4.5	0 34.2	1 34.8	16 1.7
28	0 26 30.7	0 .0	0 .0	4 43.6	0 45.7	1 31.0	3 9.3	0 46.7	1 4.6	0 34.1	1 34.6	16 1.8

RIGHT ASCENSION

DAY	EPHEM. SID. TIME	☉	☊	☽	☿	♀	♂	♃	♄	♅	♆	♇
1	22 40 3.8	10♍ 3.4	4♑46.6	23♎27.4	9♍ 2.4	14♎15.3	5♉37.1	5♒59.6	3♋ 6.3	19♎22.6	3♐ 5.1	9♎31.0
2	22 44 .3	10 57.8	4 43.2	6♏ 3.0	10 51.9	15 20.0	5 51.2	5R54.5	3 11.3	19 25.4	3 5.7	9 32.9
3	22 47 56.9	11 52.2	4 39.7	18 50.0	12 39.9	16 24.7	6 4.7	5 49.5	3 16.2	19 28.3	3 6.2	9 34.7
4	22 51 53.5	12 46.4	4 36.3	1♐47.3	14 26.4	17 29.5	6 17.5	5 44.7	3 21.0	19 31.2	3 6.8	9 36.6
5	22 55 50.0	13 40.6	4 32.8	14 49.8	16 11.3	18 34.4	6 29.5	5 40.0	3 25.7	19 34.1	3 7.5	9 38.5
6	22 59 46.6	14 34.7	4 29.3	27 49.9	17 54.8	19 39.4	6 40.9	5 35.5	3 30.3	19 37.1	3 8.1	9 40.4
7	23 3 43.1	15 28.8	4 25.9	10♑39.8	19 36.7	20 44.5	6 51.5	5 31.2	3 34.8	19 40.0	3 8.8	9 42.3
8	23 7 39.7	16 22.8	4 22.4	23 13.9	21 17.2	21 49.6	7 1.4	5 27.1	3 39.2	19 43.0	3 9.5	9 44.2
9	23 11 36.2	17 16.8	4 19.0	5♒30.0	22 56.3	22 54.9	7 10.5	5 23.2	3 43.6	19 46.1	3 10.3	9 46.2
10	23 15 32.8	18 10.7	4 15.5	17 29.8	24 34.0	24 .3	7 18.9	5 19.4	3 47.8	19 49.1	3 11.1	9 48.1
11	23 19 29.3	19 4.7	4 12.0	29 18.8	26 10.4	25 5.9	7 26.5	5 15.9	3 52.0	19 52.2	3 12.0	9 50.1
12	23 23 25.9	19 58.5	4 8.6	11♓ 5.1	27 45.6	26 11.6	7 33.3	5 12.5	3 56.0	19 55.3	3 12.9	9 52.1
13	23 27 22.4	20 52.4	4 5.1	22 59.4	29 19.5	27 17.4	7 39.3	5 9.3	3 59.9	19 58.5	3 13.7	9 54.1
14	23 31 19.0	21 46.2	4 1.7	5♈13.1	0♎52.3	28 23.4	7 44.4	5 6.2	4 3.8	20 1.6	3 14.7	9 56.1
15	23 35 15.5	22 40.0	3 58.2	17 57.8	2 24.1	29 29.5	7 48.8	5 3.4	4 7.5	20 4.8	3 15.6	9 58.1
16	23 39 12.1	23 33.7	3 54.7	1♉23.0	3 54.7	0♏35.8	7 52.3	5 .8	4 11.1	20 8.0	3 16.6	10 .1
17	23 43 8.6	24 27.5	3 51.3	15 33.7	5 24.4	1 42.2	7 55.0	4 58.3	4 14.6	20 11.2	3 17.6	10 2.1
18	23 47 5.2	25 21.3	3 47.8	0♊26.5	6 53.2	2 48.9	7 56.8	4 56.1	4 18.0	20 14.4	3 18.7	10 4.1
19	23 51 1.7	26 15.1	3 44.4	15 47.8	8 21.1	3 55.7	7 57.7	4 54.0	4 21.4	20 17.7	3 19.8	10 6.1
20	23 54 58.3	27 8.9	3 40.9	1♋16.0	9 48.1	5 2.7	7 57.7	4 52.2	4 24.6	20 20.9	3 20.9	10 8.2
21	23 58 54.9	28 2.7	3 37.4	16 28.2	11 14.3	6 9.9	7R56.9	4 50.6	4 27.7	20 24.2	3 22.0	10 10.2
22	0 2 51.4	28 56.6	3 34.0	1♌ 7.2	12 39.8	7 17.3	7 55.1	4 49.1	4 30.7	20 27.5	3 23.2	10 12.3
23	0 6 48.0	29 50.5	3 30.5	15 5.9	14 4.6	8 24.9	7 52.5	4 47.9	4 33.5	20 30.9	3 24.4	10 14.3
24	0 10 44.5	0♎44.4	3 27.0	28 26.7	15 28.7	9 32.7	7 49.0	4 46.8	4 36.3	20 34.2	3 25.7	10 16.4
25	0 14 41.1	1 38.3	3 23.6	11♍18.0	16 52.1	10 40.8	7 44.5	4 46.0	4 39.0	20 37.6	3 26.9	10 18.5
26	0 18 37.6	2 32.3	3 20.1	23 51.0	18 14.9	11 49.0	7 39.2	4 45.3	4 41.5	20 41.0	3 28.2	10 20.6
27	0 22 34.2	3 26.3	3 16.7	6♎17.0	19 37.1	12 57.4	7 33.0	4 44.9	4 43.9	20 44.3	3 29.6	10 22.6
28	0 26 30.7	4 20.4	3 13.2	18 46.0	20 58.7	14 6.1	7 25.9	4 44.7	4 46.3	20 47.8	3 30.9	10 24.7
29	0 30 27.3	5 14.6	3 9.7	1♏24.7	22 19.8	15 15.0	7 17.9	4 44.7	4 48.5	20 51.2	3 32.3	10 26.8
30	0 34 23.8	6 8.8	3 6.3	14 16.1	23 40.2	16 24.1	7 9.1	4D44.9	4 50.6	20 54.6	3 33.7	10 28.9

DECLINATION

DAY	EPHEM. SID. TIME	☉	☊	☽	☿	♀	♂	♃	♄	♅	♆	♇
1	22 40 3.8	8N24.8	0S24.5	14S51.7	10N42.8	5S55.8	10N26.6	20S 8.2	22N20.8	7S33.8	19S30.7	13N24.2
4	22 51 53.5	7 19.1	0 24.5	23 35.0	8 26.2	7 26.8	10 40.6	20 11.7	22 20.5	7 37.3	19 31.1	13 21.3
7	23 3 43.1	6 12.3	0 24.5	22 40.4	6 5.6	8 56.5	10 52.8	20 14.7	22 20.1	7 40.9	19 31.6	13 18.3
10	23 15 32.8	5 4.6	0 24.5	12 51.8	3 43.5	10 24.5	11 3.2	20 17.3	22 19.7	7 44.7	19 32.2	13 15.4
13	23 27 22.4	3 56.1	0 24.5	2N21.1	1 21.9	11 50.7	11 11.8	20 19.6	22 19.3	7 48.5	19 32.8	13 12.5
16	23 39 12.1	2 47.0	0 24.5	17 18.2	0S57.8	13 14.7	11 18.5	20 21.4	22 19.0	7 52.3	19 33.5	13 9.7
19	23 51 1.7	1 37.4	0 24.5	24 16.0	3 14.5	14 36.2	11 23.3	20 22.8	22 18.6	7 56.3	19 34.2	13 6.9
22	0 2 51.4	0 27.5	0 24.5	18 8.1	5 27.4	15 54.9	11 26.3	20 23.9	22 18.2	8 .2	19 34.9	13 4.1
25	0 14 41.1	0S42.6	0 24.5	2 53.4	7 35.7	17 10.4	11 27.3	20 24.5	22 17.9	8 4.3	19 35.7	13 1.5
28	0 26 30.7	1 52.8	0 24.5	13S 2.7	9 38.7	18 22.5	11 26.4	20 24.7	22 17.6	8 8.4	19 36.6	12 58.8

OCTOBER 1973

DAY	EPHEM. SID. TIME	☉	☊	☾	☿	♀	♂	♃	♄	♅	♆	♇
	LONGITUDE											
	h m s	° ′	° ′	° ′	° ′	° ′	° ′	° ′	° ′	° ′	° ′	° ′
1	0 38 20.4	7♎40.7	2♑47.7	0♐ 6.1	27♎22.9	20♏28.6	8♉21.8	2♒17.9	4♋30.7	22♎26.6	5♐13.0	4♎25.4
2	0 42 16.9	8 39.7	2 44.6	12 10.3	28 48.9	21 37.6	8 R 11.7	2 18.5	4 32.4	22 30.3	5 14.5	4 27.7
3	0 46 13.5	9 38.8	2 41.4	24 4.0	0♏14.0	22 46.5	8 .7	2 19.3	4 34.1	22 34.0	5 16.0	4 30.0
4	0 50 10.0	10 37.9	2 38.2	5♑52.5	1 38.0	23 55.2	7 48.9	2 20.3	4 35.6	22 37.7	5 17.4	4 32.3
5	0 54 6.6	11 37.0	2 35.0	17 41.1	3 .9	25 3.8	7 36.4	2 21.5	4 37.0	22 41.4	5 18.9	4 34.6
6	0 58 3.1	12 36.1	2 31.9	29 35.4	4 22.8	26 12.4	7 23.2	2 22.9	4 38.3	22 45.2	5 20.4	4 36.9
7	1 1 59.7	13 35.3	2 28.7	11♒40.6	5 43.6	27 20.8	7 9.2	2 24.4	4 39.4	22 48.9	5 22.0	4 39.2
8	1 5 56.3	14 34.5	2 25.5	24 1.5	7 3.2	28 29.1	6 54.6	2 26.2	4 40.5	22 52.7	5 23.5	4 41.4
9	1 9 52.8	15 33.7	2 22.3	6♓41.6	8 21.6	29 37.2	6 39.3	2 28.2	4 41.5	22 56.4	5 25.1	4 43.7
10	1 13 49.4	16 33.0	2 19.1	19 43.1	9 38.7	0♐45.3	6 23.4	2 30.3	4 42.3	23 .2	5 26.8	4 45.9
11	1 17 45.9	17 32.3	2 16.0	3♈ 6.2	10 54.5	1 53.2	6 6.9	2 32.7	4 43.1	23 3.9	5 28.4	4 48.2
12	1 21 42.5	18 31.6	2 12.8	16 49.3	12 8.8	3 1.0	5 49.8	2 35.2	4 43.7	23 7.7	5 30.1	4 50.4
13	1 25 39.0	19 31.0	2 9.6	0♉49.0	13 21.6	4 8.7	5 32.3	2 37.9	4 44.2	23 11.5	5 31.7	4 52.7
14	1 29 35.6	20 30.4	2 6.4	15 .5	14 32.7	5 16.2	5 14.2	2 40.8	4 44.6	23 15.2	5 33.4	4 54.9
15	1 33 32.1	21 29.8	2 3.3	29 18.6	15 42.0	6 23.6	4 55.8	2 43.9	4 44.9	23 19.0	5 35.2	4 57.1
16	1 37 28.7	22 29.3	2 .1	13♊38.3	16 49.3	7 30.8	4 36.9	2 47.2	4 45.1	23 22.8	5 36.9	4 59.4
17	1 41 25.2	23 28.8	1 56.9	27 55.8	17 54.5	8 38.0	4 17.7	2 50.7	4 45.2	23 26.6	5 38.7	5 1.6
18	1 45 21.8	24 28.3	1 53.7	12♋ 8.4	18 57.5	9 44.9	3 58.2	2 54.4	4 R 45.1	23 30.3	5 40.5	5 3.8
19	1 49 18.3	25 27.9	1 50.5	26 14.7	19 57.8	10 51.7	3 38.4	2 58.2	4 45.0	23 34.1	5 42.3	5 6.0
20	1 53 14.9	26 27.5	1 47.4	10♌13.7	20 55.4	11 58.4	3 18.5	3 2.2	4 44.7	23 37.9	5 44.1	5 8.1
21	1 57 11.4	27 27.2	1 44.2	24 5.0	21 49.9	13 4.9	2 58.3	3 6.4	4 44.3	23 41.7	5 46.0	5 10.3
22	2 1 8.0	28 26.9	1 41.0	7♍47.8	22 41.0	14 11.2	2 38.1	3 10.8	4 43.9	23 45.5	5 47.9	5 12.4
23	2 5 4.6	29 26.7	1 37.8	21 21.2	23 28.3	15 17.4	2 17.9	3 15.4	4 43.3	23 49.3	5 49.8	5 14.6
24	2 9 1.1	0♏26.4	1 34.7	4♎43.5	24 11.5	16 23.4	1 57.6	3 20.2	4 42.6	23 53.0	5 51.7	5 16.8
25	2 12 57.7	1 26.3	1 31.5	17 53.2	24 50.1	17 29.2	1 37.4	3 25.1	4 41.8	23 56.8	5 53.6	5 18.9
26	2 16 54.2	2 26.1	1 28.3	0♏48.9	25 23.5	18 34.8	1 17.3	3 30.2	4 40.8	24 .5	5 55.6	5 21.0
27	2 20 50.8	3 26.0	1 25.1	13 29.6	25 51.4	19 40.2	0 57.4	3 35.5	4 39.8	24 4.3	5 57.5	5 23.1
28	2 24 47.3	4 25.9	1 21.9	25 55.5	26 13.0	20 45.5	0 37.7	3 41.0	4 38.6	24 8.0	5 59.5	5 25.2
29	2 28 43.9	5 25.8	1 18.8	8♐ 7.4	26 27.9	21 50.5	0 18.2	3 46.6	4 37.4	24 11.8	6 1.5	5 27.2
30	2 32 40.4	6 25.8	1 15.6	20 7.7	26 35.3	22 55.3	29♈59.1	3 52.4	4 36.0	24 15.5	6 3.5	5 29.3
31	2 36 37.0	7 25.8	1 12.4	1♑59.3	26 R 34.7	23 59.9	29 40.3	3 58.3	4 34.5	24 19.2	6 5.6	5 31.3
	LATITUDE											
1	0 38 20.4	0 .0	0 .0	2 S 41.9	1 S 7.8	1 S 42.4	3 S 3.5	0 S 46.6	1 S 4.7	0 N 34.1	1 N 34.5	16 N 2.0
4	0 50 10.0	0 .0	0 .0	0 N 18.8	1 29.4	1 53.5	2 56.9	0 46.5	1 4.8	0 34.0	1 34.4	16 2.2
7	1 1 59.7	0 .0	0 .0	3 12.7	1 50.1	2 4.4	2 49.6	0 46.4	1 4.9	0 34.0	1 34.2	16 2.5
10	1 13 49.4	0 .0	0 .0	4 55.0	2 9.5	2 14.9	2 41.4	0 46.3	1 5.0	0 34.0	1 34.1	16 2.9
13	1 25 39.0	0 .0	0 .0	4 23.1	2 27.2	2 25.0	2 32.5	0 46.1	1 5.0	0 34.0	1 34.0	16 3.4
16	1 37 28.7	0 .0	0 .0	1 30.8	2 42.4	2 34.7	2 23.0	0 46.0	1 5.1	0 33.9	1 33.8	16 3.9
19	1 49 18.3	0 .0	0 .0	2 S 10.5	2 54.5	2 43.7	2 12.8	0 45.9	1 5.2	0 33.9	1 33.7	16 4.5
22	2 1 8.0	0 .0	0 .0	4 40.3	3 2.2	2 52.1	2 2.0	0 45.8	1 5.3	0 33.9	1 33.6	16 5.2
25	2 12 57.7	0 .0	0 .0	4 50.3	3 4.0	2 59.7	1 50.9	0 45.6	1 5.3	0 33.9	1 33.5	16 5.9
28	2 24 47.3	0 .0	0 .0	2 51.3	2 58.0	3 6.5	1 39.4	0 45.5	1 5.4	0 33.9	1 33.4	16 6.7
31	2 36 37.0	0 .0	0 .0	0 N 12.1	2 41.6	3 12.4	1 27.8	0 45.4	1 5.4	0 33.9	1 33.3	16 7.6
	RIGHT ASCENSION											
1	0 38 20.4	7♎ 3.0	3♑ 2.8	27♏18.3	25♎ .2	17♏33.4	6♉59.5	4♒45.3	4♋52.5	20♎58.1	3♐35.2	10♎31.0
2	0 42 16.9	7 57.4	2 59.3	10♐25.8	26 19.6	18 42.9	6 R 49.0	4 45.9	4 54.4	21 1.6	3 36.7	10 33.1
3	0 46 13.5	8 51.8	2 55.9	23 30.1	27 38.3	19 52.6	6 37.7	4 46.7	4 56.2	21 5.0	3 38.2	10 35.2
4	0 50 10.0	9 46.3	2 52.4	6♑23.1	28 56.5	21 2.5	6 25.6	4 47.7	4 57.8	21 8.5	3 39.7	10 37.3
5	0 54 6.6	10 40.8	2 49.0	18 58.6	0♏14.1	22 12.7	6 12.8	4 48.9	4 59.3	21 12.0	3 41.2	10 39.4
6	0 58 3.1	11 35.5	2 45.5	1♒14.6	1 31.1	23 23.0	5 59.2	4 50.4	5 .7	21 15.5	3 42.8	10 41.5
7	1 1 59.7	12 30.2	2 42.0	13 13.2	2 47.4	24 33.5	5 44.9	4 52.0	5 2.0	21 19.0	3 44.4	10 43.6
8	1 5 56.3	13 25.0	2 38.6	25 .3	4 3.0	25 44.1	5 29.9	4 53.8	5 3.1	21 22.5	3 46.1	10 45.7
9	1 9 52.8	14 20.0	2 35.1	6♓44.7	5 17.8	26 55.0	5 14.3	4 55.8	5 4.2	21 26.0	3 47.7	10 47.8
10	1 13 49.4	15 15.0	2 31.6	18 37.4	6 31.7	28 6.0	4 58.1	4 58.1	5 5.1	21 29.6	3 49.4	10 49.9
11	1 17 45.9	16 10.1	2 28.2	0♈50.5	7 44.8	29 17.2	4 41.2	5 .5	5 5.9	21 33.1	3 51.1	10 52.0
12	1 21 42.5	17 5.4	2 24.7	13 36.6	8 56.8	0♐28.6	4 23.9	5 3.1	5 6.6	21 36.6	3 52.8	10 54.1
13	1 25 39.0	18 .8	2 21.3	27 6.1	10 7.7	1 40.0	4 6.0	5 5.9	5 7.1	21 40.2	3 54.6	10 56.1
14	1 29 35.6	18 56.3	2 17.8	11♉24.6	11 17.4	2 51.7	3 47.6	5 8.9	5 7.6	21 43.7	3 56.4	10 58.2
15	1 33 32.1	19 52.0	2 14.3	26 28.6	12 25.6	4 3.4	3 28.8	5 12.1	5 7.9	21 47.2	3 58.2	11 .3
16	1 37 28.7	20 47.8	2 10.9	12♊ 3.2	13 32.3	5 15.3	3 9.6	5 15.5	5 8.1	21 50.8	3 60.0	11 2.4
17	1 41 25.2	21 43.7	2 7.4	27 44.4	14 37.3	6 27.3	2 50.1	5 19.1	5 8.2	21 54.3	4 1.8	11 4.4
18	1 45 21.8	22 39.8	2 3.9	13♋ 6.0	15 40.3	7 39.3	2 30.2	5 22.9	5 R 8.1	21 57.9	4 3.7	11 6.5
19	1 49 18.3	23 36.1	2 .5	27 49.2	16 41.0	8 51.5	2 10.1	5 26.9	5 8.0	22 1.4	4 5.6	11 8.6
20	1 53 14.9	24 32.5	1 57.0	11♌46.8	17 39.3	10 3.7	1 49.8	5 31.1	5 7.7	22 5.0	4 7.5	11 10.6
21	1 57 11.4	25 29.1	1 53.6	25 1.7	18 34.7	11 16.0	1 29.3	5 35.4	5 7.3	22 8.5	4 9.4	11 12.6
22	2 1 8.0	26 25.8	1 50.1	7♍43.6	19 27.0	12 28.3	1 8.7	5 40.0	5 6.7	22 12.1	4 11.4	11 14.7
23	2 5 4.6	27 22.8	1 46.6	20 5.2	20 15.7	13 40.7	0 48.1	5 44.7	5 6.1	22 15.7	4 13.4	11 16.8
24	2 9 1.1	28 19.9	1 43.2	2♎19.2	21 .5	14 53.0	0 27.4	5 49.6	5 5.4	22 19.2	4 15.4	11 18.8
25	2 12 57.7	29 17.1	1 39.7	14 36.7	21 40.7	16 5.4	0 6.8	5 54.7	5 4.5	22 22.8	4 17.4	11 20.8
26	2 16 54.2	0♏14.6	1 36.2	27 6.2	22 15.9	17 17.7	29♈46.4	6 .0	5 3.5	22 26.3	4 19.4	11 22.8
27	2 20 50.8	1 12.2	1 32.8	9♏51.7	22 45.5	18 29.9	29 26.0	6 5.5	5 2.3	22 29.8	4 21.5	11 24.8
28	2 24 47.3	2 10.0	1 29.3	22 52.3	23 9.0	19 42.1	29 5.9	6 11.1	5 1.1	22 33.3	4 23.5	11 26.8
29	2 28 43.9	3 8.0	1 25.9	6♐ 2.1	23 25.6	20 54.2	28 46.0	6 16.9	4 59.7	22 36.8	4 25.6	11 28.7
30	2 32 40.4	4 6.2	1 22.4	19 11.4	23 34.8	22 6.2	28 26.5	6 22.9	4 58.2	22 40.3	4 27.7	11 30.7
31	2 36 37.0	5 4.6	1 18.9	2♑ 9.9	23 35.9	23 18.0	28 7.2	6 29.0	4 56.6	22 43.8	4 29.8	11 32.7
	DECLINATION											
1	0 38 20.4	3 S 2.8	0 S 24.5	22 S 48.7	11 S 35.8	19 S 30.9	11 N 23.8	20 S 24.4	22 N 17.3	8 S 12.5	19 S 37.4	12 N 56.3
4	0 50 10.0	4 12.5	0 24.5	22 59.9	13 26.4	20 35.3	11 19.6	20 23.8	22 17.1	8 16.7	19 38.4	12 53.8
7	1 1 59.7	5 21.8	0 24.5	14 11.9	15 9.8	21 35.3	11 13.8	20 22.7	22 16.8	8 20.9	19 39.3	12 51.4
10	1 13 49.4	6 30.4	0 24.5	0 N 27.1	16 45.1	22 30.6	11 6.6	20 21.3	22 16.6	8 25.1	19 40.3	12 49.1
13	1 25 39.0	7 38.2	0 24.5	15 51.8	18 11.4	23 21.2	10 58.3	20 19.4	22 16.5	8 29.3	19 41.3	12 46.9
16	1 37 28.7	8 45.1	0 24.5	23 56.6	19 27.5	24 6.6	10 49.0	20 17.2	22 16.4	8 33.5	19 42.3	12 44.8
19	1 49 18.3	9 50.9	0 24.5	18 46.1	20 32.0	24 46.6	10 39.0	20 14.5	22 16.3	8 37.7	19 43.3	12 42.8
22	2 1 8.0	10 55.5	0 24.5	4 18.5	21 22.8	25 21.2	10 28.7	20 11.5	22 16.3	8 41.9	19 44.4	12 40.8
25	2 12 57.7	11 58.6	0 24.5	11 S 29.2	21 57.2	25 50.2	10 18.4	20 8.0	22 16.3	8 46.0	19 45.5	12 39.0
28	2 24 47.3	12 60.0	0 24.5	22 .8	22 11.5	26 13.3	10 8.5	20 4.2	22 16.3	8 50.2	19 46.6	12 37.3
31	2 36 37.0	13 59.6	0 24.5	23 13.6	22 .7	26 30.6	9 59.3	19 59.9	22 16.4	8 54.3	19 47.7	12 35.8

NOVEMBER 1973

LONGITUDE

DAY	EPHEM. SID. TIME	☉	☊	☽	☿	♀	♂	♃	♄	♅	♆	♇
	h m s	° ′	° ′	° ′	° ′	° ′	° ′	° ′	° ′	° ′	° ′	° ′
1	2 40 33.5	8 ♏ 25.8	1 ♑ 9.2	13 ♑ 46.6	26 ♏ 25.5	25 ♐ 4.2	29 ♈ 22.0	4 ♒ 4.5	4 ♋ 32.9	24 ♎ 22.9	6 ♐ 7.6	5 ♎ 33.3
2	2 44 30.1	9 25.9	1 6.1	25 34.1	26 R 7.3	26 8.3	29 R 4.1	4 10.8	4 R 31.2	24 26.6	6 9.7	5 35.3
3	2 48 26.7	10 25.9	1 2.9	7 ♒ 27.1	25 39.5	27 12.2	28 46.7	4 17.2	4 29.4	24 30.3	6 11.7	5 37.3
4	2 52 23.2	11 26.0	0 59.7	19 31.0	25 2.1	28 15.7	28 29.9	4 23.9	4 27.5	24 33.9	6 13.8	5 39.2
5	2 56 19.8	12 26.2	0 56.5	1 ♓ 50.9	24 15.2	29 19.1	28 13.6	4 30.6	4 25.5	24 37.6	6 15.9	5 41.2
6	3 0 16.3	13 26.3	0 53.4	14 31.3	23 19.1	0 ♑ 22.1	27 57.9	4 37.6	4 23.4	24 41.2	6 18.0	5 43.1
7	3 4 12.9	14 26.5	0 50.2	27 35.7	22 14.9	1 24.8	27 42.8	4 44.7	4 21.2	24 44.8	6 20.1	5 45.0
8	3 8 9.4	15 26.7	0 47.0	11 ♈ 5.8	21 3.7	2 27.2	27 28.4	4 51.9	4 18.8	24 48.5	6 22.3	5 46.9
9	3 12 6.0	16 26.9	0 43.8	25 1.0	19 47.4	3 29.3	27 14.6	4 59.3	4 16.4	24 52.0	6 24.4	5 48.7
10	3 16 2.5	17 27.2	0 40.6	9 ♉ 18.3	18 28.1	4 31.1	27 1.6	5 6.9	4 13.9	24 55.6	6 26.6	5 50.6
11	3 19 59.1	18 27.5	0 37.5	23 52.3	17 8.4	5 32.6	26 49.3	5 14.6	4 11.3	24 59.2	6 28.7	5 52.4
12	3 23 55.7	19 27.8	0 34.3	8 ♊ 36.3	15 50.7	6 33.7	26 37.7	5 22.4	4 8.6	25 2.7	6 30.9	5 54.2
13	3 27 52.2	20 28.2	0 31.1	23 22.8	14 37.7	7 34.4	26 26.9	5 30.4	4 5.8	25 6.3	6 33.1	5 56.0
14	3 31 48.8	21 28.6	0 27.9	8 ♋ 4.8	13 31.6	8 34.8	26 16.8	5 38.6	4 2.9	25 9.8	6 35.3	5 57.7
15	3 35 45.3	22 29.0	0 24.8	22 36.8	12 34.3	9 34.8	26 7.5	5 46.9	3 59.9	25 13.2	6 37.5	5 59.5
16	3 39 41.9	23 29.4	0 21.6	6 ♌ 55.1	11 47.4	10 34.3	25 59.0	5 55.3	3 56.8	25 16.7	6 39.7	6 1.2
17	3 43 38.4	24 29.9	0 18.4	20 57.8	11 11.6	11 33.5	25 51.3	6 3.8	3 53.7	25 20.1	6 41.9	6 2.9
18	3 47 35.0	25 30.4	0 15.2	4 ♍ 44.2	10 47.6	12 32.2	25 44.4	6 12.5	3 50.4	25 23.5	6 44.2	6 4.5
19	3 51 31.6	26 31.0	0 12.0	18 14.6	10 35.2	13 30.5	25 38.2	6 21.4	3 47.0	25 26.9	6 46.4	6 6.2
20	3 55 28.1	27 31.5	0 8.9	1 ♎ 29.7	10 34.2	14 28.3	25 32.9	6 30.3	3 43.6	25 30.3	6 48.6	6 7.8
21	3 59 24.7	28 32.1	0 5.7	14 30.6	10 D 44.0	15 25.7	25 28.4	6 39.4	3 40.1	25 33.6	6 50.9	6 9.4
22	4 3 21.2	29 32.7	0 2.5	27 17.9	11 3.7	16 22.5	25 24.8	6 48.6	3 36.5	25 36.9	6 53.1	6 10.9
23	4 7 17.8	0 ♐ 33.4	29 ♐ 59.3	9 ♏ 52.7	11 32.6	17 18.8	25 21.9	6 58.0	3 32.8	25 40.2	6 55.4	6 12.4
24	4 11 14.3	1 34.1	29 56.2	22 15.5	12 9.8	18 14.6	25 19.9	7 7.5	3 29.0	25 43.4	6 57.6	6 14.0
25	4 15 10.9	2 34.8	29 53.0	4 ♐ 27.5	12 54.3	19 9.9	25 18.6	7 17.1	3 25.2	25 46.7	6 59.9	6 15.4
26	4 19 7.4	3 35.5	29 49.8	16 30.0	13 45.3	20 4.5	25 18.2	7 26.8	3 21.3	25 49.9	7 2.1	6 16.9
27	4 23 4.0	4 36.2	29 46.6	28 24.5	14 42.1	20 58.6	25 D 18.6	7 36.7	3 17.3	25 53.0	7 4.4	6 18.3
28	4 27 .6	5 37.0	29 43.5	10 ♑ 13.6	15 43.8	21 52.0	25 19.8	7 46.7	3 13.2	25 56.2	7 6.6	6 19.7
29	4 30 57.1	6 37.8	29 40.3	21 60.0	16 49.9	22 44.7	25 21.8	7 56.8	3 9.1	25 59.3	7 8.9	6 21.1
30	4 34 53.7	7 38.6	29 37.1	3 ♒ 47.3	17 59.7	23 36.8	25 24.6	8 7.0	3 4.9	26 2.3	7 11.1	6 22.4

LATITUDE

DAY	EPHEM. SID. TIME	☉	☊	☽	☿	♀	♂	♃	♄	♅	♆	♇
1	2 40 33.5	0 .0	0 .0	1 N 15.0	2 S 33.3	3 S 14.2	1 S 23.9	0 S 45.3	1 S 5.4	0 N 33.9	1 N 33.3	16 N 8.0
4	2 52 23.2	0 .0	0 .0	3 56.4	1 58.7	3 18.7	1 12.3	0 45.2	1 5.5	0 33.9	1 33.2	16 8.9
7	3 4 12.9	0 .0	0 .0	5 8.9	1 9.3	3 22.1	1 .9	0 45.1	1 5.5	0 33.9	1 33.1	16 10.0
10	3 16 2.5	0 .0	0 .0	3 57.4	0 9.4	3 24.3	0 49.7	0 44.9	1 5.5	0 33.9	1 33.1	16 11.1
13	3 27 52.2	0 .0	0 .0	0 30.9	0 N 50.8	3 25.2	0 38.9	0 44.8	1 5.5	0 33.9	1 33.0	16 12.3
16	3 39 41.9	0 .0	0 .0	3 S 12.0	1 39.9	3 24.6	0 28.6	0 44.7	1 5.4	0 34.0	1 33.0	16 13.5
19	3 51 31.6	0 .0	0 .0	5 7.2	2 11.8	3 22.5	0 18.7	0 44.6	1 5.4	0 34.0	1 32.9	16 14.8
22	4 3 21.2	0 .0	0 .0	4 35.4	2 26.6	3 18.8	0 9.3	0 44.5	1 5.3	0 34.0	1 32.9	16 16.1
25	4 15 10.9	0 .0	0 .0	2 9.1	2 28.0	3 13.2	0 .5	0 44.4	1 5.2	0 34.1	1 32.9	16 17.5
28	4 27 .6	0 .0	0 .0	1 N 3.7	2 19.9	3 5.8	0 N 7.8	0 44.3	1 5.1	0 34.1	1 32.8	16 19.0

RIGHT ASCENSION

DAY	EPHEM. SID. TIME	☉	☊	☽	☿	♀	♂	♃	♄	♅	♆	♇
1	2 40 33.5	6 ♏ 3.2	1 ♑ 15.5	14 ♑ 49.5	23 ♏ 28.4	24 ♐ 29.7	27 ♈ 48.4	6 ♒ 35.4	4 ♋ 54.9	22 ♎ 47.3	4 ♐ 32.0	11 ♎ 34.6
2	2 44 30.1	7 1.9	1 12.0	27 6.3	23 R 11.8	25 41.1	27 R 30.1	6 41.9	4 R 53.1	22 50.8	4 34.1	11 36.5
3	2 48 26.7	8 .9	1 8.5	9 ♒ 1.5	22 45.9	26 52.4	27 12.2	6 48.5	4 51.1	22 54.3	4 36.3	11 38.4
4	2 52 23.2	9 .1	1 5.1	20 40.6	22 10.5	28 3.4	26 54.8	6 55.4	4 49.1	22 57.7	4 38.5	11 40.3
5	2 56 19.8	9 59.4	1 1.6	2 ♓ 12.8	21 25.8	29 14.2	26 37.9	7 2.3	4 46.9	23 1.2	4 40.7	11 42.2
6	3 0 16.3	10 59.0	0 58.1	13 49.7	20 32.4	0 ♑ 24.7	26 21.7	7 9.5	4 44.6	23 4.6	4 42.9	11 44.1
7	3 4 12.9	11 58.8	0 54.7	25 44.7	19 31.3	1 34.9	26 6.0	7 16.8	4 42.2	23 8.0	4 45.1	11 45.9
8	3 8 9.4	12 58.7	0 51.2	8 ♈ 12.1	18 23.9	2 44.7	25 51.0	7 24.3	4 39.7	23 11.4	4 47.3	11 47.8
9	3 12 6.0	13 58.9	0 47.8	21 25.6	17 12.0	3 54.1	25 36.7	7 31.9	4 37.1	23 14.8	4 49.5	11 49.6
10	3 16 2.5	14 59.3	0 44.3	5 ♉ 35.0	15 57.8	5 3.2	25 23.0	7 39.7	4 34.4	23 18.2	4 51.8	11 51.4
11	3 19 59.1	15 59.9	0 40.8	20 41.8	14 43.7	6 11.9	25 10.0	7 47.6	4 31.6	23 21.5	4 54.1	11 53.2
12	3 23 55.7	17 .7	0 37.4	6 ♊ 34.0	13 32.1	7 20.1	24 57.7	7 55.6	4 28.6	23 24.8	4 56.3	11 55.0
13	3 27 52.2	18 1.8	0 33.9	22 45.7	12 25.4	8 27.9	24 46.2	8 3.9	4 25.7	23 28.2	4 58.7	11 56.8
14	3 31 48.8	19 3.1	0 30.4	8 ♋ 44.5	11 25.5	9 35.1	24 35.4	8 12.3	4 22.5	23 31.5	5 1.0	11 58.5
15	3 35 45.3	20 4.5	0 27.0	24 3.3	10 34.2	10 41.9	24 25.3	8 20.8	4 19.3	23 34.8	5 3.3	12 .3
16	3 39 41.9	21 6.2	0 23.5	8 ♌ 28.7	9 52.7	11 48.0	24 16.0	8 29.4	4 16.0	23 38.1	5 5.6	12 2.0
17	3 43 38.4	22 8.1	0 20.1	22 1.3	9 21.8	12 53.7	24 7.5	8 38.2	4 12.5	23 41.3	5 7.9	12 3.7
18	3 47 35.0	23 10.2	0 16.6	4 ♍ 50.9	9 1.6	13 58.7	23 59.7	8 47.1	4 9.0	23 44.5	5 10.2	12 5.3
19	3 51 31.6	24 12.5	0 13.1	17 11.5	8 52.3	15 3.1	23 52.8	8 56.2	4 5.4	23 47.7	5 12.5	12 7.0
20	3 55 28.1	25 15.0	0 9.7	29 17.7	8 D 53.5	16 6.9	23 46.6	9 5.4	4 1.7	23 50.9	5 14.9	12 8.6
21	3 59 24.7	26 17.8	0 6.2	11 ♎ 23.0	9 4.5	17 9.9	23 41.2	9 14.7	3 57.9	23 54.0	5 17.2	12 10.2
22	4 3 21.2	27 20.7	0 2.7	23 38.0	9 24.8	18 12.3	23 36.6	9 24.1	3 54.0	23 57.2	5 19.6	12 11.8
23	4 7 17.8	28 23.9	29 ♐ 59.3	6 ♏ 9.6	9 53.6	19 14.0	23 32.7	9 33.7	3 50.0	24 .3	5 21.9	12 13.4
24	4 11 14.3	29 27.2	29 55.8	18 59.4	10 30.0	20 14.8	23 29.7	9 43.4	3 45.9	24 3.3	5 24.3	12 14.9
25	4 15 10.9	0 ♐ 30.8	29 52.4	2 ♐ 3.5	11 13.3	21 14.9	23 27.5	9 53.3	3 41.8	24 6.4	5 26.7	12 16.5
26	4 19 7.4	1 34.5	29 48.9	15 12.8	12 2.8	22 14.2	23 26.1	10 3.2	3 37.5	24 9.4	5 29.0	12 18.0
27	4 23 4.0	2 38.4	29 45.4	28 15.9	12 57.8	23 12.6	23 25.4	10 13.3	3 33.2	24 12.4	5 31.4	12 19.4
28	4 27 .6	3 42.5	29 42.0	11 ♑ 2.2	13 57.6	24 10.1	23 D 25.6	10 23.5	3 28.9	24 15.4	5 33.8	12 20.9
29	4 30 57.1	4 46.8	29 38.5	23 24.6	15 1.8	25 6.7	23 26.5	10 33.8	3 24.4	24 18.3	5 36.1	12 22.3
30	4 34 53.7	5 51.2	29 35.0	5 ♒ 21.8	16 9.7	26 2.4	23 28.1	10 44.2	3 19.9	24 21.2	5 38.5	12 23.7

DECLINATION

DAY	EPHEM. SID. TIME	☉	☊	☽	☿	♀	♂	♃	♄	♅	♆	♇
1	2 40 33.5	14 S 19.0	0 S 24.5	21 S 29.2	21 S 50.4	26 S 35.1	9 N 56.5	19 S 58.4	22 N 16.5	8 S 55.6	19 S 48.1	12 N 35.3
4	2 52 23.2	15 15.8	0 24.5	11 13.4	20 56.8	26 44.6	9 48.9	19 53.7	22 16.6	8 59.7	19 49.2	12 33.8
7	3 4 12.9	16 10.4	0 24.5	3 N 46.1	19 27.0	26 48.2	9 42.9	19 48.6	22 16.8	9 3.6	19 50.4	12 32.6
10	3 16 2.5	17 2.6	0 24.5	18 20.6	17 28.7	26 46.1	9 38.5	19 43.1	22 17.1	9 7.6	19 51.5	12 31.4
13	3 27 52.2	17 52.1	0 24.5	23 47.5	15 25.2	26 38.4	9 36.1	19 37.2	22 17.3	9 11.4	19 52.7	12 30.4
16	3 39 41.9	18 38.9	0 24.5	15 26.8	13 47.3	26 25.3	9 35.6	19 31.0	22 17.6	9 15.2	19 53.9	12 29.5
19	3 51 31.6	19 22.7	0 24.5	0 S 3.9	12 54.8	26 6.9	9 37.3	19 24.4	22 17.9	9 18.9	19 55.0	12 28.7
22	4 3 21.2	20 3.4	0 24.5	14 47.4	12 49.5	25 43.6	9 41.1	19 17.4	22 18.3	9 22.5	19 56.2	12 28.1
25	4 15 10.9	20 40.7	0 24.5	23 9.0	13 21.7	25 15.6	9 47.1	19 10.1	22 18.7	9 26.0	19 57.3	12 27.6
28	4 27 .6	21 14.6	0 24.5	21 59.4	14 19.1	24 43.4	9 55.3	19 2.5	22 19.1	9 29.4	19 58.4	12 27.2

DECEMBER 1973

LONGITUDE

DAY	EPHEM. SID. TIME h m s	☉ ° ′	☊ ° ′	☾ ° ′	☿ ° ′	♀ ° ′	♂ ° ′	♃ ° ′	♄ ° ′	♅ ° ′	♆ ° ′	♇ ° ′
1	4 38 50.2	8♐39.4	29♐33.9	15♒39.8	19♏12.7	24♑28.1	25♈28.1	8♒17.3	3♋ .7	26♎ 5.4	7♐13.4	6♎23.7
2	4 42 46.8	9 40.2	29 30.8	27 41.8	20 28.5	25 18.7	25 32.5	8 27.8	2 R 56.4	26 8.4	7 15.7	6 25.0
3	4 46 43.4	10 41.1	29 27.6	9♓58.2	21 46.7	26 8.5	25 37.5	8 38.3	2 52.0	26 11.4	7 17.9	6 26.3
4	4 50 39.9	11 42.0	29 24.4	22 33.8	23 7.0	26 57.5	25 43.4	8 49.0	2 47.6	26 14.3	7 20.2	6 27.5
5	4 54 36.5	12 42.8	29 21.2	5♈32.6	24 28.9	27 45.6	25 49.9	8 59.8	2 43.2	26 17.2	7 22.5	6 28.7
6	4 58 33.0	13 43.7	29 18.0	18 57.7	25 52.4	28 32.9	25 57.2	9 10.7	2 38.6	26 20.1	7 24.7	6 29.9
7	5 2 29.6	14 44.6	29 14.9	2♉50.5	27 17.1	29 19.2	26 5.1	9 21.7	2 34.1	26 22.9	7 27.0	6 31.0
8	5 6 26.1	15 45.5	29 11.7	17 9.9	28 42.9	0♒ 4.5	26 13.7	9 32.7	2 29.5	26 25.7	7 29.2	6 32.1
9	5 10 22.7	16 46.5	29 8.5	1♊52.3	0♐ 9.7	0 48.9	26 23.0	9 43.9	2 24.8	26 28.5	7 31.5	6 33.2
10	5 14 19.3	17 47.4	29 5.3	16 51.2	1 37.2	1 32.1	26 33.0	9 55.2	2 20.1	26 31.2	7 33.7	6 34.2
11	5 18 15.8	18 48.4	29 2.2	1♋58.3	3 5.5	2 14.3	26 43.6	10 6.6	2 15.4	26 33.9	7 35.9	6 35.2
12	5 22 12.4	19 49.3	28 59.0	17 4.3	4 34.3	2 55.4	26 54.8	10 18.0	2 10.6	26 36.5	7 38.1	6 36.2
13	5 26 8.9	20 50.3	28 55.8	2♌ .6	6 3.6	3 35.3	27 6.6	10 29.6	2 5.8	26 39.1	7 40.3	6 37.1
14	5 30 5.5	21 51.3	28 52.6	16 40.0	7 33.4	4 13.9	27 19.0	10 41.3	2 1.0	26 41.7	7 42.6	6 38.0
15	5 34 2.0	22 52.4	28 49.5	0♍58.1	9 3.6	4 51.3	27 32.1	10 53.0	1 56.1	26 44.2	7 44.8	6 38.9
16	5 37 58.6	23 53.4	28 46.3	14 52.7	10 34.2	5 27.4	27 45.7	11 4.8	1 51.2	26 46.6	7 46.9	6 39.7
17	5 41 55.2	24 54.4	28 43.1	28 23.5	12 5.0	6 2.0	27 59.8	11 16.8	1 46.3	26 49.1	7 49.1	6 40.5
18	5 45 51.7	25 55.5	28 39.9	11♎32.3	13 36.2	6 35.3	28 14.5	11 28.8	1 41.4	26 51.5	7 51.3	6 41.3
19	5 49 48.3	26 56.6	28 36.7	24 21.4	15 7.6	7 7.0	28 29.8	11 40.9	1 36.5	26 53.8	7 53.5	6 42.1
20	5 53 44.8	27 57.7	28 33.6	6♏53.8	16 39.3	7 37.3	28 45.6	11 53.0	1 31.5	26 56.1	7 55.6	6 42.8
21	5 57 41.4	28 58.8	28 30.4	19 12.4	18 11.2	8 5.9	29 1.9	12 5.3	1 26.6	26 58.3	7 57.8	6 43.4
22	6 1 37.9	29 59.9	28 27.2	1♐20.2	19 43.3	8 32.8	29 18.7	12 17.6	1 21.6	27 .6	7 59.9	6 44.1
23	6 5 34.5	1♑ 1.1	28 24.0	13 19.6	21 15.7	8 58.0	29 36.0	12 30.0	1 16.6	27 2.7	8 2.0	6 44.7
24	6 9 31.1	2 2.2	28 20.9	25 12.9	22 48.3	9 21.5	29 53.9	12 42.5	1 11.7	27 4.8	8 4.1	6 45.2
25	6 13 27.6	3 3.4	28 17.7	7♑ 2.4	24 21.2	9 43.1	0♉12.2	12 55.2	1 6.7	27 6.9	8 6.3	6 45.8
26	6 17 24.2	4 4.6	28 14.5	18 49.9	25 54.3	10 2.7	0 31.0	13 7.8	1 1.8	27 9.0	8 8.4	6 46.3
27	6 21 20.7	5 5.7	28 11.3	0♒37.7	27 27.6	10 20.3	0 50.2	13 20.5	0 56.8	27 10.9	8 10.4	6 46.8
28	6 25 17.3	6 6.9	28 8.2	12 28.2	29 1.1	10 35.9	1 9.8	13 33.3	0 51.9	27 12.8	8 12.5	6 47.2
29	6 29 13.9	7 8.0	28 5.0	24 24.0	0♑35.0	10 49.3	1 29.9	13 46.2	0 46.9	27 14.7	8 14.5	6 47.6
30	6 33 10.4	8 9.2	28 1.8	6♓28.3	2 9.1	11 .6	1 50.4	13 59.1	0 42.0	27 16.5	8 16.6	6 48.0
31	6 37 7.0	9 10.4	27 58.6	18 44.7	3 43.5	11 9.5	2 11.4	14 12.1	0 37.1	27 18.3	8 18.6	6 48.3

LATITUDE

DAY	EPHEM. SID. TIME	☉	☊	☾	☿	♀	♂	♃	♄	♅	♆	♇
1	4 38 50.2	0 .0	0 .0	3N51.8	2N 5.5	2S56.4	0N15.6	0S44.3	1S 5.0	0N34.1	1N32.8	16N20.4
4	4 50 39.9	0 .0	0 .0	5 15.0	1 47.2	2 44.7	0 22.8	0 44.2	1 4.9	0 34.2	1 32.8	16 22.0
7	5 2 29.6	0 .0	0 .0	4 22.3	1 26.5	2 30.8	0 29.5	0 44.1	1 4.7	0 34.2	1 32.8	16 23.5
10	5 14 19.3	0 .0	0 .0	1 4.7	1 4.6	2 14.4	0 35.6	0 44.1	1 4.5	0 34.3	1 32.8	16 25.1
13	5 26 8.9	0 .0	0 .0	2S55.5	0 42.2	1 55.3	0 41.3	0 44.1	1 4.3	0 34.3	1 32.9	16 26.8
16	5 37 58.6	0 .0	0 .0	5 9.0	0 20.0	1 33.4	0 46.6	0 44.0	1 4.1	0 34.4	1 32.9	16 28.4
19	5 49 48.3	0 .0	0 .0	4 46.6	0S 1.6	1 8.5	0 51.4	0 44.0	1 3.8	0 34.5	1 32.9	16 30.1
22	6 1 37.9	0 .0	0 .0	2 26.1	0 22.4	0 40.4	0 55.9	0 44.0	1 3.5	0 34.5	1 33.0	16 31.8
25	6 13 27.6	0 .0	0 .0	0N46.7	0 42.0	0 9.1	0 60.0	0 44.0	1 3.2	0 34.6	1 33.0	16 33.6
28	6 25 17.3	0 .0	0 .0	3 40.4	1 .2	0N25.5	1 3.7	0 44.0	1 2.9	0 34.7	1 33.1	16 35.3
31	6 37 7.0	0 .0	0 .0	5 12.7	1 16.8	1 3.3	1 7.2	0 44.0	1 2.5	0 34.7	1 33.1	16 37.0

RIGHT ASCENSION

DAY	EPHEM. SID. TIME	☉	☊	☾	☿	♀	♂	♃	♄	♅	♆	♇
1	4 38 50.2	6♐55.8	29♐31.6	16♒57.2	17♏21.0	26♑57.0	23♈30.5	10♒54.8	3♋15.3	24♎24.1	5♐40.9	12♎25.1
2	4 42 46.8	8 .6	29 28.1	28 18.7	18 35.3	27 50.7	23 33.7	11 5.4	3 R 10.6	24 26.9	5 43.2	12 26.5
3	4 46 43.4	9 5.5	29 24.7	9♓37.2	19 52.2	28 43.3	23 37.6	11 16.2	3 5.9	24 29.8	5 45.6	12 27.8
4	4 50 39.9	10 10.6	29 21.2	21 5.9	21 11.4	29 34.8	23 42.3	11 27.1	3 1.2	24 32.6	5 48.0	12 29.2
5	4 54 36.5	11 15.8	29 17.7	2♈59.8	22 32.8	0♒25.2	23 47.6	11 38.0	2 56.4	24 35.3	5 50.4	12 30.4
6	4 58 33.0	12 21.2	29 14.3	15 34.6	23 56.0	1 14.4	23 53.7	11 49.1	2 51.5	24 38.0	5 52.7	12 31.7
7	5 2 29.6	13 26.6	29 10.8	29 4.4	25 20.9	2 2.3	24 .4	12 .3	2 46.6	24 40.7	5 55.1	12 32.9
8	5 6 26.1	14 32.2	29 7.3	13♉38.6	26 47.4	2 49.1	24 7.8	12 11.5	2 41.6	24 43.4	5 57.5	12 34.1
9	5 10 22.7	15 37.9	29 3.9	29 15.2	28 15.2	3 34.5	24 15.8	12 22.9	2 36.5	24 46.0	5 59.8	12 35.3
10	5 14 19.3	16 43.7	29 .4	15♊36.1	29 44.3	4 18.7	24 24.5	12 34.3	2 31.5	24 48.6	6 2.2	12 36.5
11	5 18 15.8	17 49.7	28 57.0	2♋ 8.6	1♐14.6	5 1.5	24 33.9	12 45.9	2 26.3	24 51.1	6 4.5	12 37.6
12	5 22 12.4	18 55.7	28 53.5	18 16.8	2 46.0	5 42.8	24 43.8	12 57.5	2 21.2	24 53.6	6 6.8	12 38.7
13	5 26 8.9	20 1.8	28 50.0	3♌35.0	4 18.5	6 22.8	24 54.4	13 9.2	2 16.0	24 56.1	6 9.2	12 39.8
14	5 30 5.5	21 8.0	28 46.6	17 54.5	5 51.8	7 1.2	25 5.5	13 21.0	2 10.8	24 58.5	6 11.5	12 40.8
15	5 34 2.0	22 14.3	28 43.1	1♍20.3	7 26.1	7 38.1	25 17.3	13 32.9	2 5.5	25 .9	6 13.8	12 41.8
16	5 37 58.6	23 20.7	28 39.6	14 5.3	9 1.2	8 13.4	25 29.6	13 44.9	2 .3	25 3.2	6 16.1	12 42.8
17	5 41 55.2	24 27.1	28 36.2	26 24.8	10 37.1	8 47.1	25 42.5	13 57.0	1 55.0	25 5.5	6 18.4	12 43.8
18	5 45 51.7	25 33.6	28 32.7	8♎33.8	12 13.8	9 19.1	25 55.9	14 9.1	1 49.6	25 7.8	6 20.7	12 44.7
19	5 49 48.3	26 40.1	28 29.3	20 45.0	13 51.1	9 49.5	26 9.9	14 21.3	1 44.3	25 10.0	6 23.0	12 45.6
20	5 53 44.8	27 46.7	28 25.8	3♏ 7.6	15 29.2	10 18.0	26 24.4	14 33.6	1 39.0	25 12.2	6 25.2	12 46.5
21	5 57 41.4	28 53.3	28 22.3	15 46.3	17 7.9	10 44.7	26 39.4	14 46.0	1 33.6	25 14.3	6 27.5	12 47.3
22	6 1 37.9	29 59.9	28 18.9	28 40.5	18 47.3	11 9.5	26 55.0	14 58.4	1 28.2	25 16.4	6 29.7	12 48.1
23	6 5 34.5	1♑ 6.6	28 15.4	11♐43.9	20 27.3	11 32.4	27 11.0	15 10.9	1 22.9	25 18.5	6 32.0	12 48.9
24	6 9 31.1	2 13.2	28 12.0	24 46.5	22 7.8	11 53.3	27 27.6	15 23.5	1 17.5	25 20.5	6 34.2	12 49.6
25	6 13 27.6	3 19.9	28 8.5	7♑37.2	23 49.0	12 12.2	27 44.7	15 36.2	1 12.2	25 22.5	6 36.4	12 50.4
26	6 17 24.2	4 26.5	28 5.0	20 7.2	25 30.6	12 28.9	28 2.2	15 48.9	1 6.8	25 24.4	6 38.6	12 51.1
27	6 21 20.7	5 33.1	28 1.6	2♒12.0	27 12.7	12 43.4	28 20.2	16 1.7	1 1.4	25 26.3	6 40.8	12 51.8
28	6 25 17.3	6 39.6	27 58.1	13 52.4	28 55.4	12 55.8	28 38.7	16 14.5	0 56.1	25 28.1	6 43.0	12 52.4
29	6 29 13.9	7 46.1	27 54.6	25 13.6	0♑38.4	13 5.8	28 57.6	16 27.4	0 50.8	25 29.9	6 45.1	12 53.0
30	6 33 10.4	8 52.5	27 51.2	6♓24.6	2 22.0	13 13.5	29 16.9	16 40.4	0 45.4	25 31.6	6 47.3	12 53.5
31	6 37 7.0	9 58.9	27 47.7	17 36.9	4 5.9	13 18.8	29 36.7	16 53.4	0 40.2	25 33.3	6 49.4	12 54.1

DECLINATION

DAY	EPHEM. SID. TIME	☉	☊	☾	☿	♀	♂	♃	♄	♅	♆	♇
1	4 38 50.2	21S44.9	0S24.5	12S27.0	15S31.0	24S 7.3	10N 5.5	18S54.5	22N19.5	9S32.7	19S59.6	12N27.0
4	4 50 39.9	22 11.5	0 24.5	1N52.3	16 49.5	23 27.7	10 17.8	18 46.1	22 19.9	9 35.9	20 .7	12 27.0
7	5 2 29.6	22 34.2	0 24.5	16 33.8	18 9.1	22 45.2	10 31.9	18 37.4	22 20.4	9 39.0	20 1.8	12 27.1
10	5 14 19.3	22 52.9	0 24.5	23 51.9	19 26.1	22 .2	10 47.8	18 28.4	22 20.8	9 41.9	20 2.9	12 27.3
13	5 26 8.9	23 7.6	0 24.5	16 51.8	20 37.7	21 13.3	11 5.3	18 19.0	22 21.3	9 44.7	20 3.9	12 27.6
16	5 37 58.6	23 18.1	0 24.5	1 12.2	21 42.3	20 25.0	11 24.2	18 9.4	22 21.7	9 47.4	20 4.9	12 28.2
19	5 49 48.3	23 24.4	0 24.5	13S52.9	22 38.4	19 35.9	11 44.5	17 59.4	22 22.2	9 49.9	20 6.0	12 28.8
22	6 1 37.9	23 26.5	0 24.5	22 48.8	23 25.0	18 46.7	12 6.1	17 49.1	22 22.6	9 52.3	20 6.9	12 29.6
25	6 13 27.6	23 24.4	0 24.5	22 28.7	24 1.3	17 57.9	12 28.8	17 38.5	22 23.1	9 54.5	20 7.9	12 30.5
28	6 25 17.3	23 18.1	0 24.5	13 32.2	24 26.5	17 10.4	12 52.6	17 27.6	22 23.5	9 56.6	20 8.8	12 31.5
31	6 37 7.0	23 7.5	0 24.5	0N20.7	24 40.1	16 24.8	13 17.2	17 16.4	22 23.9	9 58.5	20 9.7	12 32.7

JANUARY 1974

LONGITUDE

DAY	EPHEM. SID. TIME	☉	☊	☽	☿	♀	♂	♃	♄	♅	♆	♇
	h m s	° ′	° ′	° ′	° ′	° ′	° ′	° ′	° ′	° ′	° ′	° ′
1	6 41 3.5	10♑11.5	27♐55.5	1♈16.8	5♑18.2	11♒16.2	2♉32.7	14♒25.1	0♋32.3	27♎20.0	8♐20.6	6♎48.6
2	6 45 .1	11 12.7	27 52.3	14 8.5	6 53.2	11 20.5	2 54.4	14 38.2	0 R 27.4	27 21.7	8 22.5	6 48.8
3	6 48 56.6	12 13.8	27 49.1	27 23.4	8 28.5	11 22.3	3 16.5	14 51.4	0 22.6	27 23.3	8 24.5	6 49.1
4	6 52 53.2	13 15.0	27 45.9	11♉ 3.9	10 4.2	11 R 21.7	3 39.0	15 4.6	0 17.8	27 24.9	8 26.4	6 49.2
5	6 56 49.8	14 16.1	27 42.7	25 11.4	11 40.2	11 18.6	4 1.8	15 17.9	0 13.1	27 26.4	8 28.4	6 49.4
6	7 0 46.3	15 17.3	27 39.6	9♊44.5	13 16.6	11 12.9	4 25.0	15 31.2	0 8.4	27 27.9	8 30.3	6 49.5
7	7 4 42.9	16 18.4	27 36.4	24 39.6	14 53.4	11 4.8	4 48.5	15 44.6	0 3.7	27 29.3	8 32.1	6 49.6
8	7 8 39.4	17 19.5	27 33.2	9♋49.8	16 30.6	10 54.0	5 12.3	15 58.0	29♊59.1	27 30.6	8 34.0	6 49.6
9	7 12 36.0	18 20.6	27 30.0	25 6.0	18 8.3	10 40.8	5 36.5	16 11.5	29 54.5	27 31.9	8 35.9	6 49.6
10	7 16 32.5	19 21.8	27 26.9	10♌18.0	19 46.3	10 25.1	6 .9	16 25.1	29 49.9	27 33.2	8 37.7	6 49.6
11	7 20 29.1	20 22.9	27 23.7	25 16.1	21 24.8	10 6.9	6 25.7	16 38.7	29 45.4	27 34.4	8 39.5	6 R 49.5
12	7 24 25.7	21 24.0	27 20.5	9♍52.4	23 3.8	9 46.4	6 50.8	16 52.3	29 41.0	27 35.5	8 41.3	6 49.4
13	7 28 22.2	22 25.1	27 17.3	24 1.9	24 43.2	9 23.6	7 16.1	17 6.0	29 36.6	27 36.6	8 43.0	6 49.3
14	7 32 18.8	23 26.2	27 14.2	7♎42.9	26 23.0	8 58.6	7 41.7	17 19.7	29 32.3	27 37.7	8 44.8	6 49.2
15	7 36 15.3	24 27.4	27 11.0	20 56.2	28 3.4	8 31.7	8 7.7	17 33.5	29 28.1	27 38.7	8 46.5	6 49.0
16	7 40 11.9	25 28.5	27 7.8	3♏44.6	29 44.2	8 2.8	8 33.8	17 47.3	29 23.9	27 39.6	8 48.2	6 48.8
17	7 44 8.4	26 29.6	27 4.6	16 12.1	1♒25.4	7 32.1	9 .3	18 1.2	29 19.7	27 40.5	8 49.9	6 48.5
18	7 48 5.0	27 30.7	27 1.5	28 23.2	3 7.0	6 59.9	9 27.0	18 15.1	29 15.6	27 41.3	8 51.6	6 48.2
19	7 52 1.6	28 31.8	26 58.3	10♐22.4	4 49.1	6 26.3	9 53.9	18 29.0	29 11.6	27 42.0	8 53.2	6 47.9
20	7 55 58.1	29 32.9	26 55.1	22 13.9	6 31.5	5 51.6	10 21.1	18 43.0	29 7.7	27 42.7	8 54.8	6 47.5
21	7 59 54.7	0♒34.0	26 51.9	4♑ 1.5	8 14.2	5 15.9	10 48.5	18 57.0	29 3.8	27 43.4	8 56.4	6 47.1
22	8 3 51.2	1 35.1	26 48.7	15 48.2	9 57.2	4 39.6	11 16.2	19 11.0	29 .0	27 44.0	8 57.9	6 46.6
23	8 7 47.8	2 36.1	26 45.6	27 36.7	11 40.5	4 2.8	11 44.1	19 25.0	28 56.3	27 44.5	8 59.4	6 46.2
24	8 11 44.3	3 37.2	26 42.4	9♒29.0	13 23.8	3 25.9	12 12.2	19 39.1	28 52.7	27 45.0	9 .9	6 45.7
25	8 15 40.9	4 38.2	26 39.2	21 26.8	15 7.1	2 49.0	12 40.5	19 53.3	28 49.1	27 45.4	9 2.4	6 45.1
26	8 19 37.5	5 39.2	26 36.0	3♓31.6	16 50.3	2 12.5	13 9.1	20 7.4	28 45.7	27 45.8	9 3.8	6 44.6
27	8 23 34.0	6 40.2	26 32.9	15 45.2	18 33.3	1 36.5	13 37.8	20 21.6	28 42.3	27 46.1	9 5.3	6 44.0
28	8 27 30.6	7 41.2	26 29.7	28 9.2	20 15.8	1 1.3	14 6.8	20 35.8	28 39.0	27 46.3	9 6.7	6 43.3
29	8 31 27.1	8 42.2	26 26.5	10♈45.8	21 57.5	0 27.2	14 35.9	20 50.0	28 35.8	27 46.5	9 8.0	6 42.7
30	8 35 23.7	9 43.1	26 23.3	23 37.5	23 38.4	29♑54.3	15 5.3	21 4.2	28 32.7	27 46.7	9 9.3	6 42.0
31	8 39 20.2	10 44.1	26 20.2	6♉46.9	25 18.0	29 22.9	15 34.8	21 18.5	28 29.7	27 46.8	9 10.7	6 41.2

LATITUDE

DAY	EPHEM. SID. TIME	☉	☊	☽	☿	♀	♂	♃	♄	♅	♆	♇
1	6 41 3.5	0 .0	0 .0	5N16.9	1S21.9	1N16.6	1N 8.2	0S44.1	1S 2.4	0N34.8	1N33.1	16N37.6
4	6 52 53.2	0 .0	0 .0	3 54.0	1 35.9	1 58.4	1 11.3	0 44.1	1 2.0	0 34.8	1 33.2	16 39.4
7	7 4 42.9	0 .0	0 .0	0 21.7	1 47.6	2 42.6	1 14.0	0 44.2	1 1.6	0 34.9	1 33.3	16 41.1
10	7 16 32.5	0 .0	0 .0	3S30.6	1 56.7	3 28.4	1 16.5	0 44.2	1 1.2	0 35.0	1 33.4	16 42.8
13	7 28 22.2	0 .0	0 .0	5 14.3	2 3.0	4 14.5	1 18.8	0 44.3	1 .8	0 35.1	1 33.5	16 44.5
16	7 40 11.9	0 .0	0 .0	4 17.1	2 5.9	4 59.6	1 20.9	0 44.4	1 .3	0 35.1	1 33.6	16 46.2
19	7 52 1.6	0 .0	0 .0	1 37.5	2 5.0	5 41.8	1 22.8	0 44.5	0 59.8	0 35.2	1 33.7	16 47.9
22	8 3 51.2	0 .0	0 .0	1N33.8	1 59.7	6 19.5	1 24.5	0 44.6	0 59.3	0 35.3	1 33.8	16 49.6
25	8 15 40.9	0 .0	0 .0	4 9.4	1 49.5	6 50.9	1 26.1	0 44.7	0 58.8	0 35.4	1 33.9	16 51.2
28	8 27 30.6	0 .0	0 .0	5 10.1	1 33.6	7 15.1	1 27.5	0 44.8	0 58.3	0 35.5	1 34.0	16 52.8
31	8 39 20.2	0 .0	0 .0	4 .9	1 11.2	7 31.4	1 28.7	0 45.0	0 57.8	0 35.5	1 34.1	16 54.3

RIGHT ASCENSION

DAY	EPHEM. SID. TIME	☉	☊	☽	☿	♀	♂	♃	♄	♅	♆	♇
1	6 41 3.5	11♑ 5.2	27♐44.3	29♓ 4.0	5♑50.2	13♒21.7	29♈56.9	17♒ 6.5	0♋34.9	25♎35.0	6♐51.5	12♎54.6
2	6 45 .1	12 11.5	27 40.8	11♈ .7	7 34.9	13 22.1	0♉17.5	17 19.6	0 R 29.7	25 36.6	6 53.6	12 55.0
3	6 48 56.6	13 17.6	27 37.3	23 42.2	9 19.9	13 R 20.0	0 38.5	17 32.8	0 24.4	25 38.1	6 55.6	12 55.5
4	6 52 53.2	14 23.6	27 33.9	7♉21.5	11 5.3	13 15.4	0 59.8	17 46.0	0 19.3	25 39.6	6 57.7	12 55.9
5	6 56 49.8	15 29.6	27 30.4	22 5.4	12 50.9	13 8.2	1 21.6	17 59.3	0 14.1	25 41.0	6 59.7	12 56.3
6	7 0 46.3	16 35.4	27 27.0	7♊48.6	14 36.8	12 58.4	1 43.8	18 12.6	0 9.0	25 42.4	7 1.7	12 56.6
7	7 4 42.9	17 41.1	27 23.5	24 10.0	16 22.9	12 46.0	2 6.3	18 26.0	0 4.0	25 43.8	7 3.7	12 56.9
8	7 8 39.4	18 46.7	27 20.0	10♋36.7	18 9.2	12 31.2	2 29.1	18 39.4	29♊59.0	25 45.1	7 5.7	12 57.2
9	7 12 36.0	19 52.2	27 16.6	26 35.8	19 55.7	12 13.8	2 52.3	18 52.8	29 54.0	25 46.3	7 7.6	12 57.4
10	7 16 32.5	20 57.5	27 13.1	11♌46.3	21 42.3	11 53.9	3 15.9	19 6.3	29 49.1	25 47.5	7 9.5	12 57.6
11	7 20 29.1	22 2.7	27 9.6	26 2.9	23 29.0	11 31.7	3 39.8	19 19.8	29 44.3	25 48.7	7 11.4	12 57.8
12	7 24 25.7	23 7.8	27 6.2	9♍32.1	25 15.8	11 7.2	4 4.0	19 33.4	29 39.5	25 49.8	7 13.3	12 58.0
13	7 28 22.2	24 12.7	27 2.7	22 26.9	27 2.6	10 40.4	4 28.5	19 47.0	29 34.7	25 50.8	7 15.2	12 58.1
14	7 32 18.8	25 17.5	26 59.3	5♎ 1.3	28 49.5	10 11.6	4 53.4	20 .6	29 30.0	25 51.8	7 17.0	12 58.2
15	7 36 15.3	26 22.1	26 55.8	17 28.7	0♒36.3	9 40.9	5 18.6	20 14.3	29 25.5	25 52.8	7 18.9	12 58.3
16	7 40 11.9	27 26.6	26 52.3	29 59.2	2 23.0	9 8.4	5 44.1	20 28.0	29 20.9	25 53.7	7 20.7	12 58.3
17	7 44 8.4	28 30.9	26 48.9	12♏39.4	4 9.6	8 34.3	6 9.8	20 41.8	29 16.4	25 54.5	7 22.4	12 58.3
18	7 48 5.0	29 35.0	26 45.4	25 30.8	5 55.9	7 58.8	6 35.9	20 55.5	29 12.0	25 55.3	7 24.2	12 58.3
19	7 52 1.6	0♒38.9	26 42.0	8♐30.2	7 42.0	7 22.0	7 2.2	21 9.3	29 7.7	25 56.0	7 25.9	12 R 58.2
20	7 55 58.1	1 42.7	26 38.5	21 30.4	9 27.8	6 44.4	7 28.9	21 23.1	29 3.4	25 56.7	7 27.6	12 58.1
21	7 59 54.7	2 46.3	26 35.0	4♑22.1	11 13.2	6 6.0	7 55.8	21 37.0	28 59.2	25 57.3	7 29.2	12 58.0
22	8 3 51.2	3 49.6	26 31.6	16 57.0	12 58.1	5 27.1	8 23.0	21 50.8	28 55.1	25 57.9	7 30.9	12 57.8
23	8 7 47.8	4 52.8	26 28.1	29 9.6	14 42.4	4 47.9	8 50.5	22 4.7	28 51.1	25 58.4	7 32.5	12 57.6
24	8 11 44.3	5 55.9	26 24.7	10♒58.9	16 26.0	4 8.8	9 18.3	22 18.6	28 47.2	25 58.9	7 34.1	12 57.4
25	8 15 40.9	6 58.7	26 21.2	22 28.2	18 8.8	3 30.0	9 46.3	22 32.6	28 43.3	25 59.3	7 35.6	12 57.1
26	8 19 37.5	8 1.3	26 17.7	3♓44.0	19 50.7	2 51.7	10 14.6	22 46.5	28 39.6	25 59.6	7 37.2	12 56.8
27	8 23 34.0	9 3.7	26 14.3	14 55.8	21 31.4	2 14.1	10 43.1	23 .5	28 35.9	25 59.9	7 38.7	12 56.5
28	8 27 30.6	10 5.9	26 10.8	26 14.9	23 10.8	1 37.6	11 11.9	23 14.4	28 32.4	26 .2	7 40.1	12 56.1
29	8 31 27.1	11 7.9	26 7.4	7♈53.9	24 48.8	1 2.3	11 41.0	23 28.4	28 28.9	26 .4	7 41.6	12 55.8
30	8 35 23.7	12 9.7	26 3.9	20 6.1	26 24.9	0 28.4	12 10.2	23 42.4	28 25.5	26 .5	7 43.0	12 55.3
31	8 39 20.2	13 11.3	26 .4	3♉ 3.9	27 59.0	29♑56.2	12 39.7	23 56.4	28 22.3	26 .6	7 44.4	12 54.9

DECLINATION

DAY	EPHEM. SID. TIME	☉	☊	☽	☿	♀	♂	♃	♄	♅	♆	♇
1	6 41 3.5	23S 3.0	0S24.5	5N21.2	24S42.0	16S10.2	13N25.5	17S12.6	22N24.1	9S59.1	20S10.0	12N33.1
4	6 52 53.2	22 46.9	0 24.5	18 51.2	24 39.2	15 28.5	13 51.1	17 1.1	22 24.5	10 .8	20 10.8	12 34.4
7	7 4 42.9	22 26.8	0 24.5	23 41.7	24 23.6	14 50.6	14 17.3	16 49.3	22 24.9	10 2.3	20 11.7	12 35.9
10	7 16 32.5	22 2.7	0 24.5	14 16.8	23 54.6	14 17.1	14 43.9	16 37.2	22 25.3	10 3.6	20 12.4	12 37.5
13	7 28 22.2	21 34.7	0 24.5	2S26.4	23 12.1	13 48.7	15 10.9	16 25.0	22 25.8	10 4.8	20 13.2	12 39.2
16	7 40 11.9	21 2.9	0 24.5	16 47.6	22 15.6	13 25.8	15 38.2	16 12.4	22 26.2	10 5.7	20 13.9	12 40.9
19	7 52 1.6	20 27.5	0 24.5	23 36.9	21 5.1	13 8.6	16 5.6	15 59.7	22 26.6	10 6.5	20 14.5	12 42.8
22	8 3 51.2	19 48.6	0 24.5	20 57.2	19 40.6	12 57.2	16 33.1	15 46.7	22 27.0	10 7.2	20 15.1	12 44.8
25	8 15 40.9	19 6.4	0 24.5	10 25.0	18 2.8	12 51.5	17 .6	15 33.5	22 27.4	10 7.6	20 15.7	12 46.8
28	8 27 30.6	18 21.0	0 24.5	4N .4	16 12.7	12 51.0	17 28.1	15 20.1	22 27.8	10 7.9	20 16.2	12 49.0
31	8 39 20.2	17 32.7	0 24.5	17 34.1	14 12.5	12 55.1	17 55.3	15 6.6	22 28.3	10 7.9	20 16.7	12 51.2

FEBRUARY 1974

LONGITUDE

DAY	EPHEM. SID. TIME	☉	☊	☽	☿	♀	♂	♃	♄	♅	♆	♇
	h m s	° ′	° ′	° ′	° ′	° ′	° ′	° ′	° ′	° ′	° ′	° ′
1	8 43 16.8	11♒45.0	26♐17.0	20♉16.6	26♒56.0	28♑53.2	16♉ 4.5	21♒32.8	28♊26.7	27♎46.8	9♐11.9	6♎40.5
2	8 47 13.3	12 45.9	26 13.8	4♊ 8.6	28 32.0	28 R 25.3	16 34.4	21 47.1	28 R 23.9	27 R 46.7	9 13.2	6 R 39.7
3	8 51 9.9	13 46.7	26 10.6	18 23.6	0♓ 5.5	27 59.3	17 4.4	22 1.4	28 21.2	27 46.7	9 14.4	6 38.9
4	8 55 6.5	14 47.6	26 7.4	3♋ .5	1 36.1	27 35.5	17 34.6	22 15.7	28 18.5	27 46.5	9 15.6	6 38.0
5	8 59 3.0	15 48.4	26 4.3	17 55.4	3 3.1	27 13.9	18 5.1	22 30.1	28 16.0	27 46.4	9 16.8	6 37.2
6	9 2 59.6	16 49.2	26 1.1	3♌ 1.6	4 26.0	26 54.6	18 35.6	22 44.4	28 13.6	27 46.1	9 17.9	6 36.3
7	9 6 56.1	17 50.0	25 57.9	18 10.3	5 44.0	26 37.7	19 6.2	22 58.8	28 11.3	27 45.8	9 19.0	6 35.4
8	9 10 52.7	18 50.8	25 54.7	3♍11.3	6 56.4	26 23.3	19 37.0	23 13.1	28 9.0	27 45.5	9 20.1	6 34.4
9	9 14 49.2	19 51.5	25 51.6	17 55.4	8 2.5	26 11.3	20 8.0	23 27.5	28 6.9	27 45.0	9 21.1	6 33.4
10	9 18 45.8	20 52.2	25 48.4	2♎15.1	9 1.6	26 1.8	20 39.1	23 41.9	28 4.9	27 44.6	9 22.1	6 32.4
11	9 22 42.3	21 52.9	25 45.2	16 6.3	9 52.9	25 54.8	21 10.3	23 56.3	28 2.9	27 44.0	9 23.1	6 31.4
12	9 26 38.9	22 53.6	25 42.0	29 28.1	10 35.6	25 50.3	21 41.7	24 10.7	28 1.1	27 43.5	9 24.0	6 30.3
13	9 30 35.5	23 54.2	25 38.8	12♏22.2	11 9.2	25 48.4	22 13.1	24 25.0	27 59.4	27 42.8	9 25.0	6 29.2
14	9 34 32.0	24 54.9	25 35.7	24 52.5	11 33.1	25 D 48.8	22 44.7	24 39.4	27 57.8	27 42.2	9 25.8	6 28.1
15	9 38 28.6	25 55.5	25 32.5	7♐ 3.8	11 46.8	25 51.7	23 16.5	24 53.8	27 56.3	27 41.4	9 26.7	6 26.9
16	9 42 25.1	26 56.1	25 29.3	19 1.4	11 50.1	25 56.9	23 48.3	25 8.2	27 54.9	27 40.6	9 27.5	6 25.8
17	9 46 21.7	27 56.7	25 26.1	0♑50.8	11 R 43.0	26 4.5	24 20.3	25 22.6	27 53.6	27 39.8	9 28.3	6 24.6
18	9 50 18.2	28 57.3	25 23.0	12 36.9	11 25.6	26 14.3	24 52.4	25 37.0	27 52.4	27 38.9	9 29.0	6 23.4
19	9 54 14.8	29 57.8	25 19.8	24 24.0	10 58.3	26 26.2	25 24.6	25 51.4	27 51.4	27 37.9	9 29.7	6 22.1
20	9 58 11.3	0♓58.3	25 16.6	6♒15.6	10 21.8	26 40.4	25 57.0	26 5.8	27 50.4	27 36.9	9 30.4	6 20.9
21	10 2 7.9	1 58.8	25 13.4	18 14.5	9 37.1	26 56.5	26 29.4	26 20.1	27 49.6	27 35.9	9 31.1	6 19.6
22	10 6 4.4	2 59.3	25 10.2	0♓22.5	8 45.2	27 14.7	27 1.9	26 34.5	27 48.9	27 34.8	9 31.7	6 18.3
23	10 10 1.0	3 59.7	25 7.1	12 40.6	7 47.7	27 34.8	27 34.6	26 48.9	27 48.3	27 33.6	9 32.3	6 16.9
24	10 13 57.6	5 .1	25 3.9	25 9.4	6 46.0	27 56.8	28 7.3	27 3.2	27 47.8	27 32.5	9 32.8	6 15.6
25	10 17 54.1	6 .5	25 .7	7♈49.3	5 41.7	28 20.6	28 40.2	27 17.5	27 47.4	27 31.2	9 33.3	6 14.2
26	10 21 50.7	7 .9	24 57.5	20 40.3	4 36.6	28 46.1	29 13.2	27 31.9	27 47.2	27 30.0	9 33.9	6 12.9
27	10 25 47.2	8 1.2	24 54.4	3♉43.1	3 32.2	29 13.3	29 46.2	27 46.2	27 47.0	27 28.6	9 34.3	6 11.5
28	10 29 43.8	9 1.5	24 51.2	16 58.5	2 29.9	29 42.0	0♊19.3	28 .5	27 47.0	27 27.2	9 34.7	6 10.1

LATITUDE

DAY	EPHEM. SID. TIME	☉	☊	☽	☿	♀	♂	♃	♄	♅	♆	♇
1	8 43 16.8	0 .0	0 .0	3N 8.6	1S 2.3	7N35.1	1N29.1	0S45.0	0S57.6	0N35.6	1N34.2	16N54.8
4	8 55 6.5	0 .0	0 .0	0S28.8	0 30.7	7 41.1	1 30.1	0 45.2	0 57.1	0 35.6	1 34.3	16 56.3
7	9 6 56.1	0 .0	0 .0	3 58.0	0N 7.9	7 40.2	1 31.1	0 45.4	0 56.5	0 35.7	1 34.4	16 57.7
10	9 18 45.8	0 .0	0 .0	5 5.4	0 52.5	7 33.3	1 31.9	0 45.6	0 56.0	0 35.8	1 34.6	16 59.0
13	9 30 35.5	0 .0	0 .0	3 35.4	1 40.6	7 21.5	1 32.6	0 45.8	0 55.4	0 35.9	1 34.7	17 .3
16	9 42 25.1	0 .0	0 .0	0 41.8	2 28.0	7 5.9	1 33.2	0 46.0	0 54.8	0 35.9	1 34.9	17 1.6
19	9 54 14.8	0 .0	0 .0	2N21.7	3 8.5	6 47.3	1 33.8	0 46.2	0 54.3	0 36.0	1 35.0	17 2.8
22	10 6 4.4	0 .0	0 .0	4 32.1	3 35.4	6 26.5	1 34.2	0 46.4	0 53.7	0 36.1	1 35.1	17 3.8
25	10 17 54.1	0 .0	0 .0	4 55.2	3 43.4	6 4.2	1 34.6	0 46.7	0 53.1	0 36.1	1 35.3	17 4.9
28	10 29 43.8	0 .0	0 .0	3 8.2	3 31.7	5 40.8	1 34.9	0 47.0	0 52.5	0 36.2	1 35.4	17 5.8

RIGHT ASCENSION

DAY	EPHEM. SID. TIME	☉	☊	☽	☿	♀	♂	♃	♄	♅	♆	♇
1	8 43 16.8	14♒12.6	25♐57.0	16♉56.2	29♒30.8	29♑25.8	13♉ 9.5	24♒10.4	28♊19.1	26♎ .6	7♐45.7	12♎54.4
2	8 47 13.3	15 13.8	25 53.5	1♊44.3	0♓59.9	28 R 57.4	13 39.5	24 24.4	28 R 16.0	26 .6	7 47.0	12 R 53.9
3	8 51 9.9	16 14.8	25 50.1	17 18.1	2 25.8	28 31.1	14 9.7	24 38.5	28 13.1	26 R .5	7 48.3	12 53.4
4	8 55 6.5	17 15.5	25 46.6	3♋15.9	3 48.2	28 7.1	14 40.1	24 52.5	28 10.2	26 .4	7 49.6	12 52.8
5	8 59 3.0	18 16.1	25 43.1	19 10.0	5 6.5	27 45.4	15 10.8	25 6.6	28 7.5	26 .3	7 50.9	12 52.3
6	9 2 59.6	19 16.4	25 39.7	4♌36.3	6 20.2	27 26.2	15 41.6	25 20.6	28 4.9	26 .0	7 52.1	12 51.7
7	9 6 56.1	20 16.6	25 36.2	19 21.9	7 28.8	27 9.4	16 12.7	25 34.6	28 2.3	25 59.8	7 53.2	12 51.0
8	9 10 52.7	21 16.5	25 32.8	3♍25.9	8 31.6	26 55.3	16 43.9	25 48.7	27 59.9	25 59.4	7 54.4	12 50.4
9	9 14 49.2	22 16.2	25 29.3	16 55.6	9 28.1	26 43.7	17 15.4	26 2.7	27 57.6	25 59.0	7 55.5	12 49.7
10	9 18 45.8	23 15.8	25 25.8	0♎ 2.1	10 17.6	26 34.7	17 47.0	26 16.7	27 55.4	25 58.6	7 56.5	12 49.0
11	9 22 42.3	24 15.1	25 22.4	12 56.8	10 59.5	26 28.4	18 18.8	26 30.8	27 53.3	25 58.1	7 57.6	12 48.2
12	9 26 38.9	25 14.3	25 18.9	25 49.4	11 33.2	26 24.6	18 50.9	26 44.8	27 51.3	25 57.6	7 58.6	12 47.4
13	9 30 35.5	26 13.2	25 15.5	8♏46.1	11 58.3	26 23.4	19 23.1	26 58.8	27 49.5	25 57.0	7 59.5	12 46.6
14	9 34 32.0	27 12.0	25 12.0	21 48.8	12 14.3	26 D 24.7	19 55.5	27 12.8	27 47.7	25 56.3	8 .5	12 45.8
15	9 38 28.6	28 10.6	25 8.5	4♐55.4	12 21.0	26 28.6	20 28.1	27 26.8	27 46.1	25 55.7	8 1.4	12 44.9
16	9 42 25.1	29 9.1	25 5.1	18 .1	12 R 18.3	26 34.9	21 .9	27 40.8	27 44.6	25 54.9	8 2.2	12 44.1
17	9 46 21.7	0♓ 7.3	25 1.6	0♑55.3	12 6.1	26 43.6	21 33.8	27 54.8	27 43.2	25 54.1	8 3.1	12 43.1
18	9 50 18.2	1 5.4	24 58.2	13 34.1	11 44.8	26 54.6	22 7.0	28 8.8	27 41.9	25 53.3	8 3.9	12 42.2
19	9 54 14.8	2 3.3	24 54.7	25 52.1	11 14.8	27 7.9	22 40.3	28 22.7	27 40.8	25 52.4	8 4.6	12 41.3
20	9 58 11.3	3 1.0	24 51.2	7♒48.5	10 36.9	27 23.4	23 13.8	28 36.7	27 39.8	25 51.5	8 5.3	12 40.3
21	10 2 7.9	3 58.6	24 47.8	19 25.9	9 51.9	27 41.0	23 47.4	28 50.6	27 38.8	25 50.5	8 6.0	12 39.3
22	10 6 4.4	4 56.0	24 44.3	0♓50.2	9 1.1	28 .7	24 21.3	29 4.5	27 38.1	25 49.4	8 6.7	12 38.3
23	10 10 1.0	5 53.3	24 40.9	12 9.5	8 5.7	28 22.4	24 55.3	29 18.4	27 37.4	25 48.4	8 7.3	12 37.2
24	10 13 57.6	6 50.4	24 37.4	23 33.6	7 7.2	28 46.0	25 29.4	29 32.2	27 36.9	25 47.2	8 7.9	12 36.2
25	10 17 54.1	7 47.3	24 33.9	5♈13.5	6 7.1	29 11.4	26 3.8	29 46.1	27 36.4	25 46.1	8 8.5	12 35.1
26	10 21 50.7	8 44.2	24 30.5	17 20.5	5 6.9	29 38.7	26 38.3	29 60.0	27 36.2	25 44.9	8 9.0	12 34.0
27	10 25 47.2	9 40.8	24 27.0	0♉ 4.7	4 7.9	0♒ 7.7	27 13.0	0♓13.8	27 36.0	25 43.6	8 9.5	12 32.9
28	10 29 43.8	10 37.3	24 23.6	13 33.8	3 11.5	0 38.3	27 47.8	0 27.6	27 36.0	25 42.3	8 10.0	12 31.7

DECLINATION

DAY	EPHEM. SID. TIME	☉	☊	☽	☿	♀	♂	♃	♄	♅	♆	♇
1	8 43 16.8	17S15.9	0S24.5	20N50.6	13S30.7	12S57.3	18N 4.3	15S 2.1	22N28.4	10S 7.9	20S16.9	12N52.0
4	8 55 6.5	16 23.9	0 24.5	22 55.7	11 23.1	13 6.3	18 31.1	14 48.3	22 28.8	10 7.8	20 17.3	12 54.2
7	9 6 56.1	15 29.4	0 24.5	11 36.4	9 17.3	13 17.9	18 57.6	14 34.4	22 29.3	10 7.4	20 17.7	12 56.6
10	9 18 45.8	14 32.4	0 24.5	5S33.8	7 22.5	13 31.1	19 23.6	14 20.4	22 29.8	10 6.9	20 18.0	12 59.0
13	9 30 35.5	13 33.3	0 24.5	18 58.0	5 49.9	13 45.0	19 49.1	14 6.2	22 30.2	10 6.2	20 18.3	13 1.4
16	9 42 25.1	12 32.1	0 24.5	23 40.9	4 50.6	13 58.9	20 13.9	13 52.0	22 30.7	10 5.4	20 18.5	13 3.9
19	9 54 14.8	11 29.2	0 24.5	18 54.9	4 32.7	14 11.9	20 38.1	13 37.6	22 31.3	10 4.3	20 18.7	13 6.4
22	10 6 4.4	10 24.6	0 24.5	7 5.6	4 57.5	14 23.4	21 1.6	13 23.2	22 31.8	10 3.2	20 18.9	13 8.8
25	10 17 54.1	9 18.5	0 24.5	7N37.3	5 57.5	14 32.8	21 24.2	13 8.7	22 32.3	10 1.8	20 19.0	13 11.3
28	10 29 43.8	8 11.2	0 24.4	19 54.8	7 17.4	14 39.5	21 46.0	12 54.1	22 32.9	10 .3	20 19.0	13 13.8

MARCH 1974

LONGITUDE

DAY	EPHEM. SID. TIME	☉	☊	☾	☿	♀	♂	♃	♄	♅	♆	♇
	h m s	° ′	° ′	° ′	° ′	° ′	° ′	° ′	° ′	° ′	° ′	° ′
1	10 33 40.3	10♓ 1.7	24♐48.0	0♊27.9	1♓31.0	0♒12.3	0♊52.5	28♒14.7	27♊47.1	27♎25.8	9♐35.1	6♎ 8.6
2	10 37 36.9	11 2.0	24 44.8	14 12.5	0 R 36.7	0 44.1	1 25.8	28 28.9	27 D 47.2	27 R 24.3	9 35.5	6 R 7.2
3	10 41 33.4	12 2.1	24 41.6	28 13.6	29♒47.8	1 17.4	1 59.2	28 43.2	27 47.5	27 22.8	9 35.8	6 5.7
4	10 45 30.0	13 2.3	24 38.5	12♋31.0	29 4.9	1 52.0	2 32.7	28 57.4	27 48.0	27 21.2	9 36.1	6 4.2
5	10 49 26.5	14 2.4	24 35.3	27 3.2	28 28.5	2 27.9	3 6.2	29 11.5	27 48.5	27 19.6	9 36.3	6 2.7
6	10 53 23.1	15 2.5	24 32.1	11♌46.3	27 58.9	3 5.1	3 39.8	29 25.7	27 49.1	27 18.0	9 36.5	6 1.2
7	10 57 19.6	16 2.5	24 28.9	26 34.3	27 36.2	3 43.5	4 13.5	29 39.8	27 49.9	27 16.3	9 36.7	5 59.7
8	11 1 16.2	17 2.5	24 25.8	11♍19.3	27 20.3	4 23.2	4 47.3	29 53.9	27 50.7	27 14.6	9 36.8	5 58.1
9	11 5 12.7	18 2.5	24 22.6	25 53.0	27 11.1	5 3.9	5 21.1	0♓ 7.9	27 51.7	27 12.8	9 37.0	5 56.6
10	11 9 9.3	19 2.5	24 19.4	10♎ 8.0	27 8.4	5 45.8	5 55.0	0 22.0	27 52.8	27 11.0	9 37.0	5 55.0
11	11 13 5.8	20 2.4	24 16.2	23 59.0	27 D 11.9	6 28.7	6 28.9	0 36.0	27 54.0	27 9.1	9 37.1	5 53.4
12	11 17 2.4	21 2.3	24 13.0	7♏23.4	27 21.5	7 12.6	7 2.9	0 49.9	27 55.3	27 7.3	9 37.1	5 51.8
13	11 20 59.0	22 2.1	24 9.9	20 21.6	27 36.6	7 57.5	7 37.0	1 3.9	27 56.7	27 5.3	9 37.1	5 50.2
14	11 24 55.5	23 2.0	24 6.7	2♐55.9	27 57.2	8 43.4	8 11.2	1 17.8	27 58.2	27 3.4	9 R 37.0	5 48.6
15	11 28 52.1	24 1.8	24 3.5	15 10.5	28 22.7	9 30.1	8 45.4	1 31.6	27 59.9	27 1.4	9 36.9	5 47.0
16	11 32 48.6	25 1.5	24 .3	27 10.6	28 53.0	10 17.7	9 19.6	1 45.5	28 1.6	26 59.4	9 36.8	5 45.4
17	11 36 45.2	26 1.3	23 57.2	9♑ 1.6	29 27.7	11 6.1	9 53.9	1 59.3	28 3.5	26 57.3	9 36.6	5 43.8
18	11 40 41.7	27 1.0	23 54.0	20 49.2	0♓ 6.6	11 55.3	10 28.3	2 13.0	28 5.4	26 55.2	9 36.5	5 42.1
19	11 44 38.3	28 .7	23 50.8	2♒38.5	0 49.4	12 45.3	11 2.8	2 26.8	28 7.5	26 53.1	9 36.3	5 40.5
20	11 48 34.8	29 .4	23 47.6	14 34.0	1 35.8	13 35.9	11 37.3	2 40.4	28 9.7	26 51.0	9 36.0	5 38.9
21	11 52 31.4	0 D .0	23 44.4	26 39.4	2 25.6	14 27.3	12 11.9	2 54.1	28 12.0	26 48.8	9 35.7	5 37.2
22	11 56 27.9	0♈59.6	23 41.3	8♓57.2	3 18.7	15 19.4	12 46.5	3 7.7	28 14.4	26 46.6	9 35.4	5 35.6
23	12 0 24.5	1 59.2	23 38.1	21 29.1	4 14.7	16 12.0	13 21.1	3 21.2	28 16.9	26 44.3	9 35.1	5 33.9
24	12 4 21.0	2 58.7	23 34.9	4♈15.3	5 13.7	17 5.3	13 55.8	3 34.7	28 19.5	26 42.1	9 34.7	5 32.2
25	12 8 17.6	3 58.2	23 31.7	17 15.2	6 15.3	17 59.2	14 30.6	3 48.1	28 22.2	26 39.8	9 34.3	5 30.6
26	12 12 14.1	4 57.7	23 28.6	0♉27.6	7 19.5	18 53.7	15 5.4	4 1.5	28 25.0	26 37.5	9 33.8	5 28.9
27	12 16 10.7	5 57.1	23 25.4	13 51.1	8 26.1	19 48.7	15 40.3	4 14.8	28 27.9	26 35.1	9 33.3	5 27.3
28	12 20 7.2	6 56.5	23 22.2	27 24.5	9 35.0	20 44.2	16 15.2	4 28.1	28 30.9	26 32.8	9 32.8	5 25.6
29	12 24 3.8	7 55.8	23 19.0	11♊ 6.8	10 46.1	21 40.2	16 50.1	4 41.3	28 34.0	26 30.4	9 32.3	5 23.9
30	12 28 .3	8 55.1	23 15.8	24 57.6	11 59.3	22 36.7	17 25.1	4 54.5	28 37.2	26 28.0	9 31.7	5 22.3
31	12 31 56.9	9 54.4	23 12.7	8♋57.0	13 14.5	23 33.7	18 .1	5 7.6	28 40.5	26 25.6	9 31.1	5 20.6

LATITUDE

DAY	EPHEM. SID. TIME	☉	☊	☾	☿	♀	♂	♃	♄	♅	♆	♇
1	10 33 40.3	0 .0	0 .0	2N 7.5	3N24.0	5N32.9	1N35.0	0S47.1	0S52.3	0N36.2	1N35.5	17N 6.1
4	10 45 30.0	0 .0	0 .0	1S30.1	2 52.2	5 8.7	1 35.2	0 47.4	0 51.8	0 36.3	1 35.6	17 6.9
7	10 57 19.6	0 .0	0 .0	4 25.0	2 12.4	4 44.2	1 35.3	0 47.7	0 51.2	0 36.3	1 35.8	17 7.7
10	11 9 9.3	0 .0	0 .0	4 49.5	1 29.9	4 19.8	1 35.4	0 48.0	0 50.6	0 36.4	1 35.9	17 8.4
13	11 20 59.0	0 .0	0 .0	2 47.6	0 48.1	3 55.5	1 35.4	0 48.3	0 50.1	0 36.4	1 36.1	17 8.9
16	11 32 48.6	0 .0	0 .0	0N17.3	0 9.1	3 31.5	1 35.4	0 48.7	0 49.5	0 36.4	1 36.2	17 9.4
19	11 44 38.3	0 .0	0 .0	3 9.6	0S26.2	3 8.0	1 35.3	0 49.0	0 49.0	0 36.5	1 36.4	17 9.8
22	11 56 27.9	0 .0	0 .0	4 51.0	0 57.3	2 45.0	1 35.2	0 49.4	0 48.4	0 36.5	1 36.5	17 10.1
25	12 8 17.6	0 .0	0 .0	4 33.6	1 23.9	2 22.6	1 35.0	0 49.8	0 47.9	0 36.5	1 36.7	17 10.3
28	12 20 7.2	0 .0	0 .0	2 7.7	1 46.1	2 .8	1 34.8	0 50.2	0 47.3	0 36.5	1 36.8	17 10.4
31	12 31 56.9	0 .0	0 .0	1S27.4	2 3.9	1 39.8	1 34.6	0 50.6	0 46.8	0 36.6	1 36.9	17 10.5

RIGHT ASCENSION

DAY	EPHEM. SID. TIME	☉	☊	☾	☿	♀	♂	♃	♄	♅	♆	♇
1	10 33 40.3	11♓33.7	24♐20.1	27♉49.3	2♓18.9	1♒10.5	28♉22.7	0♓41.3	27♊36.1	25♎41.0	8♐10.4	12♎30.6
2	10 37 36.9	12 29.9	24 16.7	12♊44.6	1 R 30.9	1 44.2	28 57.8	0 55.0	27 D 36.3	25 R 39.6	8 10.7	12 R 29.4
3	10 41 33.4	13 26.0	24 13.2	28 4.2	0 48.4	2 19.4	29 33.0	1 8.7	27 36.6	25 38.1	8 11.1	12 28.2
4	10 45 30.0	14 22.0	24 9.7	13♋27.1	0 11.9	2 56.0	0♊ 8.4	1 22.4	27 37.0	25 36.7	8 11.4	12 26.9
5	10 49 26.5	15 17.9	24 6.3	28 33.6	29♒41.8	3 34.0	0 43.9	1 36.0	27 37.6	25 35.1	8 11.7	12 25.7
6	10 53 23.1	16 13.6	24 2.8	13♌11.3	29 18.3	4 13.2	1 19.6	1 49.6	27 38.3	25 33.6	8 11.9	12 24.4
7	10 57 19.6	17 9.3	23 59.4	27 16.9	29 1.4	4 53.7	1 55.4	2 3.2	27 39.1	25 32.0	8 12.1	12 23.2
8	11 1 16.2	18 4.8	23 55.9	10♍54.9	28 51.0	5 35.4	2 31.3	2 16.7	27 40.0	25 30.4	8 12.2	12 21.9
9	11 5 12.7	19 .2	23 52.4	24 14.0	28 47.2	6 18.2	3 7.3	2 30.2	27 41.1	25 28.7	8 12.4	12 20.6
10	11 9 9.3	19 55.6	23 49.0	7♎23.9	28 D 49.5	7 2.1	3 43.5	2 43.7	27 42.2	25 27.0	8 12.5	12 19.3
11	11 13 5.8	20 50.8	23 45.5	20 33.2	28 57.8	7 47.1	4 19.7	2 57.1	27 43.5	25 25.2	8 12.5	12 17.9
12	11 17 2.4	21 46.0	23 42.1	3♏47.3	29 11.8	8 33.0	4 56.1	3 10.5	27 44.9	25 23.5	8 12.5	12 16.6
13	11 20 59.0	22 41.1	23 38.6	17 7.4	29 31.2	9 19.9	5 32.7	3 23.9	27 46.5	25 21.6	8 12.5	12 15.2
14	11 24 55.5	23 36.2	23 35.2	0♐30.1	29 55.5	10 7.6	6 9.3	3 37.2	27 48.1	25 19.8	8 12.5	12 13.9
15	11 28 52.1	24 31.1	23 31.7	13 48.9	0♓24.6	10 56.3	6 46.0	3 50.4	27 49.9	25 17.9	8 R 12.4	12 12.5
16	11 32 48.6	25 26.1	23 28.2	26 55.7	0 58.1	11 45.7	7 22.9	4 3.7	27 51.8	25 16.0	8 12.3	12 11.1
17	11 36 45.2	26 20.9	23 24.8	9♑43.6	1 35.6	12 35.9	7 59.9	4 16.9	27 53.8	25 14.1	8 12.1	12 9.7
18	11 40 41.7	27 15.7	23 21.3	22 8.6	2 17.0	13 26.9	8 37.0	4 30.0	27 55.9	25 12.1	8 11.9	12 8.3
19	11 44 38.3	28 10.6	23 17.9	4♒10.3	3 2.0	14 18.5	9 14.2	4 43.1	27 58.2	25 10.1	8 11.7	12 6.9
20	11 48 34.8	29 5.3	23 14.4	15 52.2	3 50.2	15 10.8	9 51.5	4 56.2	28 .5	25 8.1	8 11.5	12 5.5
21	11 52 31.4	0♈ .0	23 11.0	27 20.6	4 41.4	16 3.7	10 28.9	5 9.2	28 3.0	25 6.0	8 11.2	12 4.0
22	11 56 27.9	0 54.7	23 7.5	8♓44.0	5 35.5	16 57.2	11 6.4	5 22.1	28 5.6	25 3.9	8 10.8	12 2.6
23	12 0 24.5	1 49.3	23 4.1	20 12.5	6 32.2	17 51.2	11 44.0	5 35.0	28 8.3	25 1.8	8 10.5	12 1.1
24	12 4 21.0	2 44.0	23 .6	1♈56.8	7 31.3	18 45.7	12 21.7	5 47.9	28 11.1	24 59.7	8 10.1	11 59.7
25	12 8 17.6	3 38.6	22 57.1	14 7.7	8 32.7	19 40.8	12 59.5	6 .7	28 14.0	24 57.5	8 9.6	11 58.2
26	12 12 14.1	4 33.2	22 53.7	26 54.7	9 36.3	20 36.2	13 37.4	6 13.4	28 17.0	24 55.3	8 9.2	11 56.7
27	12 16 10.7	5 27.8	22 50.2	10♉24.2	10 41.8	21 32.2	14 15.4	6 26.1	28 20.2	24 53.1	8 8.7	11 55.2
28	12 20 7.2	6 22.4	22 46.8	24 36.5	11 49.2	22 28.5	14 53.5	6 38.7	28 23.4	24 50.9	8 8.1	11 53.7
29	12 24 3.8	7 17.0	22 43.3	9♊24.0	12 58.3	23 25.2	15 31.6	6 51.3	28 26.8	24 48.6	8 7.6	11 52.3
30	12 28 .3	8 11.6	22 39.9	24 31.2	14 9.0	24 22.3	16 9.9	7 3.8	28 30.2	24 46.3	8 7.0	11 50.8
31	12 31 56.9	9 6.2	22 36.4	9♋38.1	15 21.4	25 19.7	16 48.2	7 16.3	28 33.8	24 44.1	8 6.4	11 49.3

DECLINATION

DAY	EPHEM. SID. TIME	☉	☊	☾	☿	♀	♂	♃	♄	♅	♆	♇
1	10 33 40.3	7S48.5	0S24.4	22N19.7	7S45.5	14S41.1	21N53.1	12S49.3	22N33.1	9S59.8	20S19.0	13N14.7
4	10 45 30.0	6 39.9	0 24.4	21 21.5	9 6.2	14 43.7	22 13.7	12 34.7	22 33.7	9 58.1	20 19.0	13 17.1
7	10 57 19.6	5 30.4	0 24.4	8 30.2	10 14.0	14 42.8	22 33.2	12 20.1	22 34.3	9 56.3	20 19.0	13 19.6
10	11 9 9.3	4 20.3	0 24.4	8S26.9	11 3.4	14 38.0	22 51.7	12 5.6	22 34.9	9 54.3	20 18.9	13 22.0
13	11 20 59.0	3 9.6	0 24.4	20 31.8	11 33.1	14 29.1	23 9.1	11 51.0	22 35.5	9 52.3	20 18.7	13 24.4
16	11 32 48.6	1 58.6	0 24.4	23 7.5	11 43.3	14 16.1	23 25.4	11 36.5	22 36.2	9 50.1	20 18.5	13 26.7
19	11 44 38.3	0 47.4	0 24.4	16 29.6	11 35.5	13 58.6	23 40.5	11 22.0	22 36.8	9 47.8	20 18.3	13 29.0
22	11 56 27.9	0N23.7	0 24.4	3 42.8	11 11.0	13 36.9	23 54.4	11 7.6	22 37.4	9 45.4	20 18.1	13 31.2
25	12 8 17.6	1 34.7	0 24.4	10N59.2	10 31.1	13 10.8	24 7.0	10 53.3	22 38.1	9 43.0	20 17.7	13 33.3
28	12 20 7.2	2 45.3	0 24.4	21 39.3	9 36.9	12 40.4	24 18.3	10 39.2	22 38.7	9 40.4	20 17.4	13 35.3
31	12 31 56.9	3 55.5	0 24.4	21 41.2	8 29.6	12 5.8	24 28.2	10 25.1	22 39.3	9 37.8	20 17.0	13 37.3

APRIL 1974

LONGITUDE

DAY	EPHEM. SID. TIME h m s	☉ ° ′	☊ ° ′	☾ ° ′	☿ ° ′	♀ ° ′	♂ ° ′	♃ ° ′	♄ ° ′	♅ ° ′	♆ ° ′	♇ ° ′
1	12 35 53.5	10♈53.7	23♐ 9.5	23♋ 4.5	14♓31.6	24♒31.1	18♊35.2	5♓20.6	28♊43.9	26♎23.1	9♐30.5	5♎18.9
2	12 39 50.0	11 52.9	23 6.3	7♌19.3	15 50.7	25 29.0	19 10.3	5 33.6	28 47.4	26 R20.7	9 R29.8	5 R17.3
3	12 43 46.6	12 52.0	23 3.1	21 39.1	17 11.6	26 27.3	19 45.5	5 46.5	28 50.9	26 18.2	9 29.1	5 15.6
4	12 47 43.1	13 51.1	22 60.0	6♍ .5	18 34.2	27 26.0	20 20.7	5 59.4	28 54.6	26 15.7	9 28.4	5 14.0
5	12 51 39.7	14 50.2	22 56.8	20 18.7	19 58.6	28 25.1	20 55.9	6 12.2	28 58.4	26 13.2	9 27.6	5 12.4
6	12 55 36.2	15 49.3	22 53.6	4♎28.1	21 24.7	29 24.6	21 31.1	6 24.9	29 2.3	26 10.7	9 26.9	5 10.7
7	12 59 32.8	16 48.3	22 50.4	18 23.5	22 52.4	0♓24.4	22 6.4	6 37.6	29 6.2	26 8.2	9 26.1	5 9.1
8	13 3 29.3	17 47.2	22 47.2	2♏ .4	24 21.8	1 24.7	22 41.7	6 50.1	29 10.3	26 5.6	9 25.2	5 7.5
9	13 7 25.9	18 46.2	22 44.1	15 16.1	25 52.8	2 25.3	23 17.1	7 2.7	29 14.5	26 3.1	9 24.4	5 5.9
10	13 11 22.4	19 45.1	22 40.9	28 10.1	27 25.4	3 26.2	23 52.5	7 15.2	29 18.7	26 .6	9 23.5	5 4.3
11	13 15 19.0	20 44.0	22 37.7	10♐43.4	28 59.6	4 27.4	24 27.9	7 27.5	29 23.0	25 58.0	9 22.6	5 2.7
12	13 19 15.5	21 42.9	22 34.5	22 59.0	0♈35.3	5 29.0	25 3.3	7 39.8	29 27.4	25 55.5	9 21.7	5 1.1
13	13 23 12.1	22 41.7	22 31.4	5♑ 1.0	2 12.7	6 30.8	25 38.8	7 52.1	29 31.9	25 52.9	9 20.7	4 59.6
14	13 27 8.6	23 40.5	22 28.2	16 54.1	3 51.6	7 33.0	26 14.3	8 4.2	29 36.5	25 50.3	9 19.7	4 58.0
15	13 31 5.2	24 39.3	22 25.0	28 43.7	5 32.1	8 35.4	26 49.9	8 16.3	29 41.1	25 47.8	9 18.7	4 56.5
16	13 35 1.7	25 38.0	22 21.8	10♒35.1	7 14.2	9 38.1	27 25.4	8 28.3	29 45.8	25 45.2	9 17.6	4 54.9
17	13 38 58.3	26 36.7	22 18.6	22 33.3	8 57.9	10 41.1	28 1.0	8 40.2	29 50.7	25 42.6	9 16.6	4 53.4
18	13 42 54.9	27 35.4	22 15.5	4♓42.7	10 43.2	11 44.3	28 36.6	8 52.1	29 55.6	25 40.0	9 15.5	4 51.9
19	13 46 51.4	28 34.0	22 12.3	17 7.1	12 30.0	12 47.8	29 12.3	9 3.8	0♋ .5	25 37.5	9 14.3	4 50.4
20	13 50 48.0	29 32.6	22 9.1	29 48.9	14 18.5	13 51.5	29 48.0	9 15.5	0 5.6	25 34.9	9 13.2	4 48.9
21	13 54 44.5	0♉31.2	22 5.9	12♈49.0	16 8.7	14 55.4	0♋23.7	9 27.0	0 10.7	25 32.3	9 12.0	4 47.5
22	13 58 41.1	1 29.8	22 2.8	26 7.3	18 .4	15 59.5	0 59.4	9 38.5	0 15.9	25 29.8	9 10.8	4 46.0
23	14 2 37.6	2 28.3	21 59.6	9♉41.9	19 53.8	17 3.9	1 35.2	9 49.9	0 21.2	25 27.2	9 9.6	4 44.6
24	14 6 34.2	3 26.8	21 56.4	23 30.0	21 48.8	18 8.5	2 11.0	10 1.2	0 26.6	25 24.7	9 8.4	4 43.2
25	14 10 30.7	4 25.3	21 53.2	7♊28.6	23 45.4	19 13.2	2 46.8	10 12.4	0 32.0	25 22.1	9 7.2	4 41.8
26	14 14 27.3	5 23.7	21 50.0	21 34.0	25 43.6	20 18.2	3 22.7	10 23.6	0 37.5	25 19.6	9 5.9	4 40.4
27	14 18 23.8	6 22.1	21 46.9	5♋43.6	27 43.3	21 23.3	3 58.6	10 34.6	0 43.1	25 17.1	9 4.6	4 39.0
28	14 22 20.4	7 20.5	21 43.7	19 54.7	29 44.7	22 28.6	4 34.4	10 45.5	0 48.7	25 14.6	9 3.3	4 37.7
29	14 26 17.0	8 18.8	21 40.5	4♌ 5.6	1♉47.4	23 34.1	5 10.4	10 56.3	0 54.4	25 12.1	9 2.0	4 36.3
30	14 30 13.5	9 17.1	21 37.3	18 14.6	3 51.7	24 39.8	5 46.4	11 7.1	1 .3	25 9.6	9 .7	4 35.1

LATITUDE

DAY	SID. TIME	☉	☊	☾	☿	♀	♂	♃	♄	♅	♆	♇
1	12 35 53.5	0 .0	0 .0	2S35.8	2S 8.8	1N33.0	1N34.5	0S50.8	0S46.6	0N36.6	1N37.0	17N10.4
4	12 47 43.1	0 .0	0 .0	4 51.1	2 20.6	1 13.0	1 34.2	0 51.2	0 46.1	0 36.6	1 37.1	17 10.3
7	12 59 32.8	0 .0	0 .0	4 30.4	2 27.9	0 53.9	1 33.9	0 51.7	0 45.6	0 36.6	1 37.2	17 10.2
10	13 11 22.4	0 .0	0 .0	1 59.4	2 30.8	0 35.7	1 33.5	0 52.2	0 45.1	0 36.6	1 37.3	17 9.9
13	13 23 12.1	0 .0	0 .0	1N13.9	2 29.1	0 18.4	1 33.1	0 52.7	0 44.6	0 36.6	1 37.5	17 9.5
16	13 35 1.7	0 .0	0 .0	3 53.6	2 22.8	0 2.0	1 32.7	0 53.2	0 44.1	0 36.5	1 37.6	17 9.1
19	13 46 51.4	0 .0	0 .0	5 5.8	2 11.9	0S13.4	1 32.2	0 53.7	0 43.7	0 36.5	1 37.7	17 8.5
22	13 58 41.1	0 .0	0 .0	4 9.5	1 56.5	0 27.9	1 31.7	0 54.3	0 43.2	0 36.5	1 37.8	17 7.9
25	14 10 30.7	0 .0	0 .0	1 8.0	1 36.6	0 41.4	1 31.2	0 54.9	0 42.7	0 36.5	1 37.8	17 7.2
28	14 22 20.4	0 .0	0 .0	2S34.3	1 12.6	0 53.9	1 30.7	0 55.5	0 42.3	0 36.4	1 37.9	17 6.4

RIGHT ASCENSION

DAY	SID. TIME	☉	☊	☾	☿	♀	♂	♃	♄	♅	♆	♇
1	12 35 53.5	10♈ .8	22♐33.0	24♋26.9	16♓35.2	26♒17.4	17♊26.6	7♓28.7	28♊37.5	24♎41.8	8♐ 5.7	11♎47.8
2	12 39 50.0	10 55.5	22 29.5	8♌46.9	17 50.4	27 15.4	18 5.0	7 41.0	28 41.3	24 R39.4	8 R 5.0	11 R46.3
3	12 43 46.6	11 50.2	22 26.0	22 36.2	19 7.0	28 13.7	18 43.5	7 53.2	28 45.2	24 37.1	8 4.3	11 44.8
4	12 47 43.1	12 44.9	22 22.6	5♍59.9	20 24.9	29 12.3	19 22.1	8 5.4	28 49.2	24 34.7	8 3.5	11 43.3
5	12 51 39.7	13 39.6	22 19.1	19 7.1	21 44.0	0♓11.1	20 .8	8 17.6	28 53.3	24 32.4	8 2.7	11 41.8
6	12 55 36.2	14 34.4	22 15.7	2♎ 8.4	23 4.4	1 10.1	20 39.5	8 29.6	28 57.4	24 30.0	8 1.9	11 40.3
7	12 59 32.8	15 29.2	22 12.2	15 13.0	24 26.0	2 9.4	21 18.3	8 41.6	29 1.7	24 27.6	8 1.1	11 38.8
8	13 3 29.3	16 24.1	22 8.8	28 27.2	25 48.9	3 8.9	21 57.1	8 53.6	29 6.1	24 25.2	8 .2	11 37.3
9	13 7 25.9	17 19.1	22 5.3	11♏52.9	27 12.9	4 8.6	22 36.0	9 5.5	29 10.7	24 22.9	7 59.4	11 35.9
10	13 11 22.4	18 14.1	22 1.9	25 26.3	28 38.2	5 8.5	23 15.0	9 17.2	29 15.2	24 20.5	7 58.4	11 34.4
11	13 15 19.0	19 9.1	21 58.4	8♐59.5	0♈ 4.6	6 8.5	23 53.9	9 29.0	29 19.9	24 18.0	7 57.5	11 32.9
12	13 19 15.5	20 4.3	21 55.0	22 22.2	1 32.2	7 8.7	24 33.0	9 40.6	29 24.7	24 15.6	7 56.5	11 31.5
13	13 23 12.1	20 59.5	21 51.5	5♑24.9	3 1.0	8 9.0	25 12.0	9 52.2	29 29.5	24 13.2	7 55.5	11 30.0
14	13 27 8.6	21 54.8	21 48.1	18 1.7	4 31.1	9 9.5	25 51.2	10 3.6	29 34.5	24 10.8	7 54.4	11 28.5
15	13 31 5.2	22 50.1	21 44.6	0♒11.3	6 2.5	10 10.1	26 30.3	10 15.1	29 39.5	24 8.3	7 53.3	11 27.1
16	13 35 1.7	23 45.6	21 41.2	11 56.9	7 35.1	11 10.8	27 9.5	10 26.4	29 44.7	24 5.9	7 52.3	11 25.6
17	13 38 58.3	24 41.2	21 37.7	23 25.5	9 9.1	12 11.7	27 48.8	10 37.7	29 49.9	24 3.5	7 51.1	11 24.2
18	13 42 54.9	25 36.9	21 34.2	4♓46.2	10 44.5	13 12.6	28 28.1	10 48.8	29 55.2	24 1.0	7 50.0	11 22.8
19	13 46 51.4	26 32.6	21 30.8	16 10.1	12 21.3	14 13.7	29 7.4	10 59.9	0♋ .6	23 58.6	7 48.8	11 21.3
20	13 50 48.0	27 28.5	21 27.3	27 49.1	13 59.6	15 14.8	29 46.7	11 10.9	0 6.1	23 56.2	7 47.6	11 19.9
21	13 54 44.5	28 24.5	21 23.9	9♈55.4	15 39.5	16 16.1	0♋26.1	11 21.8	0 11.6	23 53.7	7 46.4	11 18.5
22	13 58 41.1	29 20.5	21 20.4	22 40.1	17 20.9	17 17.4	1 5.5	11 32.7	0 17.3	23 51.3	7 45.2	11 17.1
23	14 2 37.6	0♉16.7	21 17.0	6♉11.0	19 4.0	18 18.8	1 45.0	11 43.4	0 23.0	23 48.9	7 43.9	11 15.8
24	14 6 34.2	1 13.0	21 13.5	20 29.7	20 48.8	19 20.2	2 24.4	11 54.1	0 28.8	23 46.5	7 42.6	11 14.4
25	14 10 30.7	2 9.5	21 10.1	5♊28.5	22 35.3	20 21.8	3 3.9	12 4.7	0 34.7	23 44.1	7 41.3	11 13.0
26	14 14 27.3	3 6.0	21 6.6	20 49.8	24 23.7	21 23.4	3 43.4	12 15.1	0 40.7	23 41.7	7 40.0	11 11.7
27	14 18 23.8	4 2.7	21 3.2	6♋10.4	26 13.9	22 25.0	4 22.9	12 25.5	0 46.7	23 39.3	7 38.6	11 10.3
28	14 22 20.4	4 59.4	20 59.7	21 8.8	28 5.9	23 26.8	5 2.5	12 35.8	0 52.8	23 37.0	7 37.2	11 9.0
29	14 26 17.0	5 56.3	20 56.3	5♌32.3	29 59.9	24 28.6	5 42.0	12 46.0	0 59.0	23 34.6	7 35.8	11 7.7
30	14 30 13.5	6 53.4	20 52.8	19 18.2	1♉55.9	25 30.5	6 21.6	12 56.1	1 5.3	23 32.3	7 34.5	11 6.5

DECLINATION

DAY	SID. TIME	☉	☊	☾	☿	♀	♂	♃	♄	♅	♆	♇
1	12 35 53.5	4N18.7	0S24.4	18N54.5	8S 4.3	11S53.3	24N31.3	10S20.4	22N39.6	9S36.9	20S16.9	13N37.9
4	12 47 43.1	5 27.9	0 24.4	4 47.7	6 40.7	11 13.3	24 39.4	10 6.6	22 40.2	9 34.2	20 16.4	13 39.8
7	12 59 32.8	6 36.3	0 24.3	11S22.5	5 5.6	10 29.3	24 46.1	9 52.9	22 40.8	9 31.5	20 16.0	13 41.5
10	13 11 22.4	7 43.6	0 24.3	21 41.6	3 19.8	9 41.6	24 51.4	9 39.4	22 41.3	9 28.8	20 15.5	13 43.1
13	13 23 12.1	8 49.8	0 24.3	22 6.9	1 24.0	8 50.3	24 55.3	9 26.1	22 41.9	9 26.0	20 14.9	13 44.6
16	13 35 1.7	9 54.6	0 24.3	13 50.1	0N41.2	7 55.6	24 57.7	9 13.0	22 42.4	9 23.2	20 14.4	13 46.0
19	13 46 51.4	10 58.0	0 24.3	0 23.5	2 54.9	6 57.9	24 58.6	9 .2	22 42.9	9 20.4	20 13.8	13 47.3
22	13 58 41.1	11 59.8	0 24.3	13N57.5	5 16.1	5 57.3	24 58.0	8 47.6	22 43.3	9 17.6	20 13.2	13 48.5
25	14 10 30.7	12 59.7	0 24.3	22 40.7	7 43.5	4 54.1	24 56.0	8 35.3	22 43.7	9 14.9	20 12.5	13 49.5
28	14 22 20.4	13 57.8	0 24.3	19 25.3	10 15.0	3 48.6	24 52.4	8 23.3	22 44.1	9 12.2	20 11.9	13 50.4

MAY 1974

LONGITUDE

DAY	EPHEM. SID. TIME (h m s)	☉	☊	☾	☿	♀	♂	♃	♄	♅	♆	♇
1	14 34 10.1	10♉15.4	21♐34.2	2♍19.9	5♉57.2	25♓45.6	6♋22.3	11♓17.7	1♋6.1	25♎7.2	8♐59.3	4♎33.8
2	14 38 6.6	11 13.6	21 31.0	16 19.8	8 3.9	26 51.5	6 58.3	11 28.2	1 12.0	25R4.7	8R57.9	4R32.6
3	14 42 3.2	12 11.8	21 27.8	0♎11.8	10 11.7	27 57.7	7 34.3	11 38.6	1 18.0	25 2.3	8 56.5	4 31.3
4	14 45 59.7	13 10.0	21 24.6	13 53.4	12 20.4	29 4.0	8 10.3	11 48.9	1 24.0	24 59.9	8 55.1	4 30.1
5	14 49 56.3	14 8.1	21 21.4	27 22.3	14 29.8	0♈10.4	8 46.3	11 59.1	1 30.1	24 57.5	8 53.7	4 28.9
6	14 53 52.8	15 6.2	21 18.3	10♏36.4	16 39.7	1 17.0	9 22.4	12 9.1	1 36.3	24 55.1	8 52.2	4 27.7
7	14 57 49.4	16 4.2	21 15.1	23 34.2	18 49.9	2 23.7	9 58.5	12 19.1	1 42.5	24 52.8	8 50.8	4 26.6
8	15 1 45.9	17 2.3	21 11.9	6♐15.5	21 .0	3 30.6	10 34.5	12 28.9	1 48.8	24 50.5	8 49.3	4 25.5
9	15 5 42.5	18 .3	21 8.7	18 41.0	23 9.9	4 37.6	11 10.7	12 38.7	1 55.1	24 48.2	8 47.8	4 24.4
10	15 9 39.1	18 58.3	21 5.6	0♑52.6	25 19.2	5 44.7	11 46.8	12 48.3	2 1.5	24 45.9	8 46.3	4 23.3
11	15 13 35.6	19 56.3	21 2.4	12 53.3	27 27.6	6 52.0	12 22.9	12 57.8	2 7.9	24 43.6	8 44.8	4 22.2
12	15 17 32.2	20 54.2	20 59.2	24 46.7	29 34.9	7 59.3	12 59.1	13 7.2	2 14.4	24 41.4	8 43.3	4 21.2
13	15 21 28.7	21 52.1	20 56.0	6♒37.1	1♊40.8	9 6.9	13 35.3	13 16.4	2 21.0	24 39.2	8 41.8	4 20.2
14	15 25 25.3	22 50.0	20 52.9	18 29.4	3 45.0	10 14.5	14 11.5	13 25.6	2 27.6	24 37.0	8 40.2	4 19.2
15	15 29 21.8	23 47.9	20 49.7	0♓28.3	5 47.3	11 22.2	14 47.7	13 34.6	2 34.2	24 34.9	8 38.7	4 18.3
16	15 33 18.4	24 45.8	20 46.5	12 38.6	7 47.4	12 30.1	15 23.9	13 43.5	2 40.9	24 32.8	8 37.1	4 17.4
17	15 37 14.9	25 43.6	20 43.3	25 4.6	9 45.1	13 38.1	16 .2	13 52.2	2 47.7	24 30.7	8 35.5	4 16.5
18	15 41 11.5	26 41.4	20 40.1	7♈49.9	11 40.4	14 46.1	16 36.5	14 .9	2 54.5	24 28.6	8 34.0	4 15.6
19	15 45 8.1	27 39.2	20 37.0	20 56.8	13 33.0	15 54.3	17 12.8	14 9.4	3 1.3	24 26.6	8 32.4	4 14.8
20	15 49 4.6	28 37.0	20 33.8	4♉26.1	15 22.8	17 2.6	17 49.1	14 17.7	3 8.2	24 24.6	8 30.8	4 14.0
21	15 53 1.2	29 34.8	20 30.6	18 16.7	17 9.8	18 11.0	18 25.5	14 26.0	3 15.2	24 22.7	8 29.2	4 13.2
22	15 56 57.7	0♊32.5	20 27.4	2♊18.3	18 53.7	19 19.5	19 1.8	14 34.1	3 22.1	24 20.8	8 27.6	4 12.5
23	16 0 54.3	1 30.2	20 24.3	16 49.1	20 34.7	20 28.0	19 38.2	14 42.1	3 29.2	24 18.9	8 26.0	4 11.8
24	16 4 50.8	2 27.9	20 21.1	1♋21.2	22 12.5	21 36.6	20 14.6	14 49.9	3 36.2	24 17.0	8 24.4	4 11.1
25	16 8 47.4	3 25.6	20 17.9	15 56.1	23 47.2	22 45.4	20 51.0	14 57.5	3 43.3	24 15.2	8 22.8	4 10.4
26	16 12 44.0	4 23.2	20 14.7	0♌28.7	25 18.7	23 54.2	21 27.5	15 5.1	3 50.5	24 13.5	8 21.2	4 9.8
27	16 16 40.5	5 20.9	20 11.6	14 54.2	26 47.0	25 3.0	22 3.9	15 12.4	3 57.6	24 11.7	8 19.6	4 9.2
28	16 20 37.1	6 18.5	20 8.4	29 2.9	28 12.0	26 12.0	22 40.4	15 19.7	4 4.8	24 10.0	8 17.9	4 8.6
29	16 24 33.6	7 16.0	20 5.2	13♍11.6	29 27.1	27 21.0	23 16.8	15 26.8	4 12.1	24 8.4	8 16.3	4 8.1
30	16 28 30.2	8 13.6	20 2.0	26 59.9	0♋52.1	28 30.1	23 53.3	15 33.7	4 19.4	24 6.8	8 14.7	4 7.6
31	16 32 26.7	9 11.1	19 58.8	10♎33.6	2 7.0	29 39.2	24 29.8	15 40.5	4 26.7	24 5.2	8 13.1	4 7.1

LATITUDE

DAY	SID. TIME	☉	☊	☾	☿	♀	♂	♃	♄	♅	♆	♇
1	14 34 10.1	0 .0	0 .0	4S55.5	0S45.0	1S 5.3	1N30.1	0S56.1	0S41.9	0N36.4	1N38.0	17N 5.6
4	14 45 59.7	0 .0	0 .0	0 14.7	1 15.8	1 29.5	0 56.7	0 41.4	0 36.3	1 38.1	17 4.6	
7	14 57 49.4	0 .0	0 .0	2 17.4	0N17.0	1 25.2	1 28.9	0 57.3	0 41.0	0 36.3	1 38.1	17 3.6
10	15 9 39.1	0 .0	0 .0	1N 1.4	0 48.1	1 33.6	1 28.3	0 58.0	0 40.6	0 36.2	1 38.2	17 2.6
13	15 21 28.7	0 .0	0 .0	3 49.9	1 16.8	1 41.1	1 27.7	0 58.7	0 40.2	0 36.1	1 38.2	17 1.5
16	15 33 18.4	0 .0	0 .0	5 12.1	1 41.2	1 47.5	1 27.0	0 59.4	0 39.8	0 36.1	1 38.2	17 .3
19	15 45 8.1	0 .0	0 .0	4 28.7	1 59.8	1 52.9	1 26.3	1 .1	0 39.5	0 36.0	1 38.3	16 59.1
22	15 56 57.7	0 .0	0 .0	1 32.4	2 11.6	1 57.4	1 25.6	1 .8	0 39.1	0 35.9	1 38.3	16 57.8
25	16 8 47.4	0 .0	0 .0	2S21.5	2 16.1	2 .9	1 24.9	1 1.6	0 38.7	0 35.8	1 38.3	16 56.5
28	16 20 37.1	0 .0	0 .0	4 57.0	2 13.3	2 3.5	1 24.2	1 2.3	0 38.4	0 35.7	1 38.3	16 55.1
31	16 32 26.7	0 .0	0 .0	4 55.5	2 2.9	2 5.2	1 23.4	1 3.1	0 38.0	0 35.6	1 38.3	16 53.7

RIGHT ASCENSION

DAY	SID. TIME	☉	☊	☾	☿	♀	♂	♃	♄	♅	♆	♇
1	14 34 10.1	7♉50.6	20♐49.4	2♍32.3	3♉53.8	26♓32.5	7♋1.2	13♓6.1	1♋11.7	23♎30.0	7♐33.0	11♎5.2
2	14 38 6.6	8 47.8	20 45.9	15 25.1	5 53.5	27 34.5	7 40.7	13 16.0	1 18.1	23R27.7	7R31.6	11R3.9
3	14 42 3.2	9 45.2	20 42.5	28 55.1	7 55.1	28 36.6	8 20.3	13 25.8	1 24.6	23 25.4	7 30.1	11 2.7
4	14 45 59.7	10 42.8	20 39.0	10♎55.4	9 58.4	29 38.7	8 59.8	13 35.5	1 31.1	23 23.1	7 28.6	11 1.5
5	14 49 56.3	11 40.5	20 35.6	23 53.1	12 3.3	0♈40.9	9 39.3	13 45.1	1 37.7	23 20.8	7 27.1	11 .3
6	14 53 52.8	12 38.3	20 32.1	7♏6.5	14 9.8	1 43.3	10 18.9	13 54.5	1 44.4	23 18.6	7 25.6	10 59.1
7	14 57 49.4	13 36.2	20 28.7	20 34.4	16 17.5	2 45.7	10 58.4	14 3.9	1 51.1	23 16.4	7 24.1	10 57.9
8	15 1 45.9	14 34.3	20 25.3	4♐9.7	18 26.4	3 48.2	11 37.9	14 13.2	1 57.9	23 14.2	7 22.5	10 56.7
9	15 5 42.5	15 32.6	20 21.8	17 41.2	20 36.1	4 50.8	12 17.4	14 22.3	2 4.8	23 12.0	7 21.0	10 55.6
10	15 9 39.1	16 30.9	20 18.4	0♑56.9	22 46.4	5 53.5	12 56.9	14 31.4	2 11.7	23 9.8	7 19.4	10 54.5
11	15 13 35.6	17 29.5	20 14.9	13 47.4	24 56.9	6 56.3	13 36.4	14 40.3	2 18.7	23 7.7	7 17.8	10 53.4
12	15 17 32.2	18 28.1	20 11.5	26 7.4	27 7.4	7 59.2	14 15.8	14 49.2	2 25.8	23 5.6	7 16.2	10 52.3
13	15 21 28.7	19 27.0	20 8.0	8♒1.0	29 17.6	9 2.2	14 55.3	14 57.9	2 32.9	23 3.5	7 14.6	10 51.3
14	15 25 25.3	20 25.9	20 4.6	19 30.8	1♊27.1	10 5.3	15 34.7	15 6.5	2 40.0	23 1.5	7 13.0	10 50.2
15	15 29 21.8	21 25.1	20 1.1	0♓47.0	3 35.6	11 8.5	16 14.1	15 14.9	2 47.2	22 59.4	7 11.4	10 49.2
16	15 33 18.4	22 24.3	19 57.7	12 .7	5 42.7	12 11.9	16 53.5	15 23.3	2 54.5	22 57.4	7 9.7	10 48.2
17	15 37 14.9	23 23.7	19 54.2	23 24.8	7 48.3	13 15.3	17 32.8	15 31.5	3 1.8	22 55.5	7 8.1	10 47.2
18	15 41 11.5	24 23.3	19 50.8	5♈12.7	9 52.0	14 18.9	18 12.2	15 39.7	3 9.2	22 53.5	7 6.4	10 46.3
19	15 45 8.1	25 23.0	19 47.3	17 37.9	11 53.6	15 22.7	18 51.5	15 47.7	3 16.6	22 51.6	7 4.8	10 45.4
20	15 49 4.6	26 22.8	19 43.9	0♉51.9	13 52.8	16 26.5	19 30.8	15 55.5	3 24.1	22 49.7	7 3.1	10 44.5
21	15 53 1.2	27 22.9	19 40.4	15 .9	15 49.5	17 30.6	20 10.1	16 3.3	3 31.6	22 47.9	7 1.5	10 43.6
22	15 56 57.7	28 23.0	19 37.0	0♊1.8	17 43.4	18 34.7	20 49.3	16 10.9	3 39.2	22 46.1	6 59.8	10 42.8
23	16 0 54.3	29 23.2	19 33.6	15 39.3	19 34.3	19 39.0	21 28.5	16 18.4	3 46.8	22 44.3	6 58.1	10 41.9
24	16 4 50.8	0♊23.6	19 30.1	1♋27.7	21 22.2	20 43.5	22 7.7	16 25.8	3 54.5	22 42.5	6 56.4	10 41.1
25	16 8 47.4	1 24.1	19 26.7	16 59.4	23 6.9	21 48.1	22 46.8	16 33.0	4 2.2	22 40.8	6 54.7	10 40.3
26	16 12 44.0	2 24.7	19 23.2	1♌54.1	24 48.2	22 52.9	23 25.9	16 40.1	4 9.9	22 39.2	6 53.0	10 39.6
27	16 16 40.5	3 25.5	19 19.8	16 4.0	26 26.0	23 57.9	24 4.9	16 47.0	4 17.7	22 37.5	6 51.3	10 38.9
28	16 20 37.1	4 26.3	19 16.3	29 32.6	28 .3	25 3.0	24 43.9	16 53.8	4 25.5	22 35.9	6 49.6	10 38.1
29	16 24 33.6	5 27.3	19 12.9	12♍30.1	29 30.9	26 8.3	25 22.9	17 .5	4 33.3	22 34.3	6 47.9	10 37.5
30	16 28 30.2	6 28.4	19 9.4	25 9.9	0♋57.7	27 13.8	26 1.8	17 7.1	4 41.2	22 32.8	6 46.1	10 36.8
31	16 32 26.7	7 29.6	19 6.0	7♎45.2	2 20.9	28 19.5	26 40.7	17 13.4	4 49.1	22 31.3	6 44.4	10 36.2

DECLINATION

DAY	SID. TIME	☉	☊	☾	☿	♀	♂	♃	♄	♅	♆	♇
1	14 34 10.1	14N53.8	0S24.3	6N 2.6	12N48.0	2S41.1	24N47.4	8S11.7	22N44.4	9S11.7	20S11.2	13N51.7
4	14 45 59.7	15 47.5	0 24.3	9S50.2	15 18.6	1 31.8	24 40.8	8 .3	22 44.6	9 6.9	20 10.5	13 51.7
7	14 57 49.4	16 38.9	0 24.2	20 53.1	17 41.3	0 21.1	24 32.7	7 49.4	22 44.8	9 4.4	20 9.8	13 52.1
10	15 9 39.1	17 27.8	0 24.2	22 25.0	19 52.5	0N50.9	24 23.2	7 38.8	22 45.0	9 1.9	20 9.0	13 52.5
13	15 21 28.7	18 14.1	0 24.2	14 54.5	21 45.3	2 3.9	24 12.1	7 28.6	22 45.1	8 59.5	20 8.3	13 52.7
16	15 33 18.4	18 57.7	0 24.2	2 .4	23 16.5	3 17.4	23 59.6	7 18.9	22 45.1	8 57.2	20 7.5	13 52.7
19	15 45 8.1	19 38.3	0 24.2	12N19.4	24 24.6	4 31.3	23 45.7	7 9.6	22 45.0	8 55.0	20 6.8	13 52.6
22	15 56 57.7	20 16.0	0 24.2	22 9.6	25 9.8	5 45.2	23 30.2	7 .7	22 44.9	8 53.0	20 6.0	13 52.3
25	16 8 47.4	20 50.5	0 24.2	20 9.0	25 33.8	6 58.8	23 13.4	6 52.3	22 44.7	8 51.0	20 5.3	13 51.9
28	16 20 37.1	21 21.8	0 24.2	7 7.6	25 39.0	8 11.8	22 55.1	6 44.5	22 44.4	8 49.2	20 4.5	13 51.4
31	16 32 26.7	21 49.8	0 24.2	8S42.5	25 28.4	9 23.9	22 35.5	6 37.1	22 44.0	8 47.5	20 3.8	13 50.7

JUNE 1974

LONGITUDE

DAY	EPHEM. SID. TIME h m s	☉ ° ′	☊ ° ′	☽ ° ′	☿ ° ′	♀ ° ′	♂ ° ′	♃ ° ′	♄ ° ′	♅ ° ′	♆ ° ′	♇ ° ′
1	16 36 23.3	10♊ 8.6	19♐55.7	23♎52.6	3♋18.6	0♉48.5	25♋ 6.4	15♓47.1	4♋34.0	24♎ 3.7	8♐11.4	4♎ 6.6
2	16 40 19.9	11 6.1	19 52.5	6♏57.2	4 26.6	1 57.9	25 42.9	15 53.6	4 41.4	24R 2.2	8R 9.8	4R 6.2
3	16 44 16.4	12 3.5	19 49.3	19 47.8	5 31.1	3 7.3	26 19.4	15 59.9	4 48.8	24 .7	8 8.2	4 5.8
4	16 48 13.0	13 1.0	19 46.1	2♐25.1	6 31.9	4 16.7	26 56.0	16 6.1	4 56.2	23 59.3	8 6.6	4 5.5
5	16 52 9.5	13 58.4	19 43.0	14 50.0	7 29.0	5 26.3	27 32.6	16 12.1	5 3.7	23 58.0	8 4.9	4 5.2
6	16 56 6.1	14 55.8	19 39.8	27 3.7	8 22.4	6 35.9	28 9.2	16 17.9	5 11.2	23 56.6	8 3.3	4 4.9
7	17 0 2.6	15 53.2	19 36.6	9♑ 7.8	9 11.9	7 45.5	28 45.8	16 23.6	5 18.7	23 55.4	8 1.7	4 4.6
8	17 3 59.2	16 50.6	19 33.4	21 4.4	9 57.5	8 55.3	29 22.4	16 29.1	5 26.2	23 54.1	8 .1	4 4.4
9	17 7 55.8	17 47.9	19 30.3	2♒56.3	10 39.1	10 5.1	29 59.0	16 34.5	5 33.8	23 53.0	7 58.5	4 4.2
10	17 11 52.3	18 45.3	19 27.1	14 46.7	11 16.5	11 15.0	0♌35.7	16 39.7	5 41.3	23 51.8	7 56.9	4 4.0
11	17 15 48.9	19 42.7	19 23.9	26 39.2	11 49.8	12 25.0	1 12.4	16 44.7	5 49.0	23 50.8	7 55.4	4 4.0
12	17 19 45.4	20 40.0	19 20.7	8♓37.8	12 18.7	13 35.0	1 49.1	16 49.6	5 56.6	23 49.8	7 53.8	4 3.9
13	17 23 42.0	21 37.4	19 17.5	20 47.1	12 43.3	14 45.1	2 25.8	16 54.3	6 4.2	23 48.8	7 52.2	4 3.8
14	17 27 38.5	22 34.7	19 14.4	3♈11.3	13 3.5	15 55.2	3 2.5	16 58.8	6 11.9	23 47.8	7 50.7	4 3.8
15	17 31 35.1	23 32.0	19 11.2	15 54.6	13 19.1	17 5.4	3 39.2	17 3.1	6 19.6	23 46.9	7 49.1	4 3.8
16	17 35 31.7	24 29.3	19 8.0	29 .5	13 30.2	18 15.7	4 16.0	17 7.3	6 27.3	23 46.1	7 47.6	4 3.8
17	17 39 28.2	25 26.6	19 4.8	12♉31.3	13 36.7	19 26.0	4 52.8	17 11.3	6 35.0	23 45.3	7 46.0	4D 3.9
18	17 43 24.8	26 23.9	19 1.7	26 27.4	13 38.7	20 36.4	5 29.6	17 15.1	6 42.7	23 44.5	7 44.5	4 4.0
19	17 47 21.3	27 21.2	18 58.5	10♊47.3	13R36.2	21 46.8	6 6.4	17 18.7	6 50.5	23 43.8	7 43.0	4 4.1
20	17 51 17.9	28 18.5	18 55.3	25 27.0	13 29.2	22 57.3	6 43.2	17 22.1	6 58.2	23 43.2	7 41.5	4 4.3
21	17 55 14.4	29 15.8	18 52.1	10♋20.2	13 18.0	24 7.8	7 20.1	17 25.4	7 6.0	23 42.6	7 40.0	4 4.5
22	17 59 11.0	0♋13.1	18 49.0	25 19.1	13 2.6	25 18.4	7 56.9	17 28.5	7 13.7	23 42.1	7 38.5	4 4.7
23	18 3 7.6	1 10.3	18 45.8	10♌15.2	12 43.2	26 29.1	8 33.8	17 31.3	7 21.5	23 41.6	7 37.1	4 5.0
24	18 7 4.1	2 7.6	18 42.6	25 1.0	12 20.3	27 39.7	9 10.7	17 34.0	7 29.3	23 41.1	7 35.6	4 5.3
25	18 11 .7	3 4.8	18 39.4	9♍30.3	11 54.0	28 50.5	9 47.7	17 36.6	7 37.1	23 40.7	7 34.2	4 5.6
26	18 14 57.2	4 2.1	18 36.3	23 39.4	11 24.8	0♊ 1.2	10 24.6	17 38.9	7 44.9	23 40.4	7 32.8	4 6.0
27	18 18 53.8	4 59.3	18 33.1	7♎26.6	10 53.1	1 12.1	11 1.5	17 41.0	7 52.7	23 40.1	7 31.4	4 6.4
28	18 22 50.4	5 56.5	18 29.9	20 52.1	10 19.5	2 23.0	11 38.5	17 43.0	8 .5	23 39.9	7 30.0	4 6.8
29	18 26 46.9	6 53.7	18 26.7	3♏57.6	9 44.5	3 33.9	12 15.5	17 44.7	8 8.3	23 39.7	7 28.6	4 7.3
30	18 30 43.5	7 50.9	18 23.5	16 45.3	9 8.6	4 44.9	12 52.5	17 46.3	8 16.1	23 39.6	7 27.3	4 7.8

LATITUDE

DAY	SID. TIME	☉	☊	☽	☿	♀	♂	♃	♄	♅	♆	♇
1	16 36 23.3	0 .0	0 .0	4S21.4	1N57.8	2S 5.5	1N23.2	1S 3.4	0S37.9	0N35.6	1N38.3	16N53.3
4	16 48 13.0	0 .0	0 .0	1 32.8	1 37.6	2 6.0	1 22.4	1 4.2	0 37.6	0 35.5	1 38.2	16 51.8
7	17 0 2.6	0 .0	0 .0	1N47.4	1 10.3	2 5.7	1 21.6	1 5.0	0 37.3	0 35.4	1 38.2	16 50.4
10	17 11 52.3	0 .0	0 .0	4 21.4	0 36.1	2 4.5	1 20.8	1 5.8	0 37.0	0 35.3	1 38.2	16 48.9
13	17 23 42.0	0 .0	0 .0	5 17.3	0S 4.2	2 2.6	1 19.9	1 6.7	0 36.7	0 35.2	1 38.1	16 47.4
16	17 35 31.7	0 .0	0 .0	4 4.8	0 49.6	1 59.9	1 19.1	1 7.6	0 36.4	0 35.1	1 38.0	16 45.9
19	17 47 21.3	0 .0	0 .0	0 47.8	1 38.4	1 56.5	1 18.2	1 8.4	0 36.1	0 35.0	1 38.0	16 44.3
22	17 59 11.0	0 .0	0 .0	3S 6.0	2 28.0	1 52.5	1 17.4	1 9.3	0 35.8	0 34.9	1 37.9	16 42.8
25	18 11 .7	0 .0	0 .0	5 11.8	3 15.2	1 47.8	1 16.5	1 10.2	0 35.5	0 34.8	1 37.8	16 41.3
28	18 22 50.4	0 .0	0 .0	4 29.9	3 56.0	1 42.6	1 15.6	1 11.1	0 35.3	0 34.7	1 37.7	16 39.7

RIGHT ASCENSION

DAY	SID. TIME	☉	☊	☽	☿	♀	♂	♃	♄	♅	♆	♇
1	16 36 23.3	8♊30.8	19♐ 2.6	20♎27.3	3♋39.6	29♈25.5	27♋19.5	17♓19.7	4♋57.1	22♎29.9	6♐42.7	10♎35.6
2	16 40 19.9	9 32.2	18 59.1	3♏23.4	4 54.6	0♉31.6	27 58.3	17 25.8	5 5.1	22R28.4	6R41.0	10R35.0
3	16 44 16.4	10 33.7	18 55.7	16 35.9	6 5.5	1 37.9	28 37.0	17 31.8	5 13.1	22 27.1	6 39.3	10 34.5
4	16 48 13.0	11 35.2	18 52.2	0♐ .9	7 12.1	2 44.5	29 15.7	17 37.6	5 21.2	22 25.7	6 37.6	10 33.9
5	16 52 9.5	12 36.9	18 48.8	13 29.3	8 14.5	3 51.3	29 54.3	17 43.3	5 29.3	22 24.4	6 35.9	10 33.4
6	16 56 6.1	13 38.6	18 45.4	26 48.9	9 12.4	4 58.3	0♌32.9	17 48.8	5 37.4	22 23.2	6 34.2	10 33.0
7	17 0 2.6	14 40.5	18 41.9	9♑48.2	10 6.0	6 5.6	1 11.4	17 54.2	5 45.5	22 22.0	6 32.5	10 32.5
8	17 3 59.2	15 42.4	18 38.5	22 19.8	10 54.9	7 13.1	1 49.9	17 59.4	5 53.7	22 20.8	6 30.8	10 32.1
9	17 7 55.8	16 44.3	18 35.0	4♒21.5	11 39.3	8 20.8	2 28.3	18 4.5	6 1.9	22 19.7	6 29.2	10 31.8
10	17 11 52.3	17 46.4	18 31.6	15 56.5	12 18.9	9 28.8	3 6.7	18 9.4	6 10.1	22 18.6	6 27.5	10 31.4
11	17 15 48.9	18 48.5	18 28.1	27 12.1	12 53.9	10 37.1	3 45.1	18 14.2	6 18.4	22 17.6	6 25.9	10 31.1
12	17 19 45.4	19 50.7	18 24.7	8♓18.3	13 23.9	11 45.7	4 23.3	18 18.8	6 26.6	22 16.6	6 24.2	10 30.8
13	17 23 42.0	20 52.9	18 21.3	19 27.3	13 49.0	12 54.5	5 1.5	18 23.3	6 34.9	22 15.7	6 22.5	10 30.6
14	17 27 38.5	21 55.2	18 17.8	0♈52.5	14 9.2	14 3.5	5 39.7	18 27.5	6 43.2	22 14.8	6 20.9	10 30.3
15	17 31 35.1	22 57.5	18 14.4	12 48.2	14 24.4	15 12.9	6 17.8	18 31.7	6 51.5	22 13.9	6 19.3	10 30.1
16	17 35 31.7	23 59.8	18 10.9	25 28.1	14 34.7	16 22.5	6 55.9	18 35.6	6 59.9	22 13.1	6 17.6	10 29.9
17	17 39 28.2	25 2.2	18 7.5	9♉ 3.2	14 39.9	17 32.4	7 33.9	18 39.4	7 8.2	22 12.4	6 16.0	10 29.8
18	17 43 24.8	26 4.6	18 4.1	23 37.8	14 40.3	18 42.6	8 11.8	18 43.1	7 16.6	22 11.7	6 14.4	10 29.6
19	17 47 21.3	27 7.0	18 .6	9♊ 4.9	14R35.8	19 53.0	8 49.7	18 46.5	7 25.0	22 11.0	6 12.8	10 29.6
20	17 51 17.9	28 9.4	17 57.2	25 3.8	14 26.7	21 3.8	9 27.5	18 49.8	7 33.4	22 10.4	6 11.3	10 29.5
21	17 55 14.4	29 11.8	17 53.8	11♋ 5.2	14 12.9	22 14.8	10 5.3	18 53.0	7 41.8	22 9.8	6 9.7	10 29.5
22	17 59 11.0	0♋14.3	17 50.3	26 41.0	13 54.9	23 26.1	10 43.0	18 55.9	7 50.2	22 9.3	6 8.1	10 29.5
23	18 3 7.6	1 16.7	17 46.9	11♌33.9	13 32.8	24 37.7	11 20.7	18 58.7	7 58.6	22 8.8	6 6.6	10 29.5
24	18 7 4.1	2 19.1	17 43.4	25 40.3	13 6.9	25 49.5	11 58.3	19 1.3	8 7.0	22 8.4	6 5.1	10 29.5
25	18 11 .7	3 21.4	17 40.0	9♍ 6.9	12 37.7	27 1.7	12 35.9	19 3.8	8 15.5	22 8.0	6 3.6	10D29.6
26	18 14 57.2	4 23.8	17 36.6	22 5.8	12 5.6	28 14.1	13 13.4	19 6.0	8 23.9	22 7.7	6 2.1	10 29.7
27	18 18 53.8	5 26.1	17 33.1	4♎50.3	11 31.0	29 26.8	13 50.8	19 8.1	8 32.3	22 7.4	6 .6	10 29.9
28	18 22 50.4	6 28.3	17 29.7	17 33.1	10 54.5	0♊39.8	14 28.2	19 10.0	8 40.8	22 7.1	5 59.1	10 30.1
29	18 26 46.9	7 30.5	17 26.3	0♏23.2	10 16.8	1 53.0	15 5.5	19 11.8	8 49.2	22 6.9	5 57.7	10 30.3
30	18 30 43.5	8 32.7	17 22.8	13 25.7	9 38.3	3 6.5	15 42.7	19 13.4	8 57.7	22 6.8	5 56.3	10 30.5

DECLINATION

DAY	SID. TIME	☉	☊	☽	☿	♀	♂	♃	♄	♅	♆	♇
1	16 36 23.3	21N58.4	0S24.1	13S18.7	25N21.8	9N47.7	22N28.7	6S34.8	22N43.9	8S46.9	20S 3.5	13N50.5
4	16 48 13.0	22 21.8	0 24.1	22 9.8	24 54.4	10 58.2	22 7.2	6 28.2	22 43.4	8 45.4	20 2.8	13 49.6
7	17 0 2.6	22 41.6	0 24.1	21 20.5	24 17.5	12 7.0	21 44.5	6 22.1	22 42.9	8 44.1	20 2.0	13 48.6
10	17 11 52.3	22 57.9	0 24.1	12 13.9	23 33.8	13 14.0	21 20.4	6 16.6	22 42.2	8 42.9	20 1.3	13 47.5
13	17 23 42.0	23 10.6	0 24.1	1N12.6	22 45.9	14 18.7	20 55.0	6 11.7	22 41.5	8 41.8	20 .6	13 46.2
16	17 35 31.7	23 19.6	0 24.1	14 56.1	21 56.1	15 20.9	20 28.5	6 7.4	22 40.7	8 40.9	19 59.9	13 44.8
19	17 47 21.3	23 24.9	0 24.1	22 51.3	21 6.9	16 20.2	20 .7	6 3.8	22 39.9	8 40.2	19 59.3	13 43.3
22	17 59 11.0	23 26.5	0 24.1	18 1.6	20 20.8	17 16.3	19 31.7	6 .8	22 38.9	8 39.7	19 58.6	13 41.7
25	18 11 .7	23 24.3	0 24.0	3 11.3	19 40.1	18 9.0	19 1.5	5 58.4	22 37.9	8 39.3	19 58.0	13 39.9
28	18 22 50.4	23 18.5	0 24.0	12S18.7	19 7.1	18 57.8	18 30.3	5 56.8	22 36.8	8 39.1	19 57.4	13 38.0

JULY 1974

LONGITUDE

DAY	EPHEM. SID. TIME h m s	☉ ° ′	☊ ° ′	☽ ° ′	☿ ° ′	♀ ° ′	♂ ° ′	♃ ° ′	♄ ° ′	♅ ° ′	♆ ° ′	♇ ° ′
1	18 34 40.0	8♋48.1	18♐20.4	29♏17.9	8♋32.5	5♊55.9	13♌29.5	17♓47.7	8♋23.9	23♎39.5	7♐26.0	4♎ 8.3
2	18 38 36.6	9 45.3	18 17.2	11♐38.1	7 R 56.9	7 7.0	14 6.6	17 48.9	8 31.8	23♎39.5	7 R 24.7	4 8.9
3	18 42 33.1	10 42.5	18 14.0	23 48.2	7 22.2	8 18.1	14 43.6	17 49.9	8 39.6	23 39.5	7 23.4	4 9.5
4	18 46 29.7	11 39.7	18 10.8	5♑50.4	6 49.2	9 29.3	15 20.7	17 50.7	8 47.4	23 D 39.6	7 22.1	4 10.2
5	18 50 26.3	12 36.9	18 7.7	17 46.8	6 18.3	10 40.5	15 57.7	17 51.3	8 55.2	23 39.7	7 20.9	4 10.8
6	18 54 22.8	13 34.1	18 4.5	29 39.3	5 50.2	11 51.8	16 34.8	17 51.7	9 3.0	23 39.9	7 19.6	4 11.5
7	18 58 19.4	14 31.2	18 1.3	11♒29.9	5 25.4	13 3.1	17 11.9	17 51.9	9 10.8	23 40.2	7 18.4	4 12.2
8	19 2 15.9	15 28.4	17 58.1	23 20.8	5 4.2	14 14.5	17 49.1	17 52.0	9 18.6	23 40.5	7 17.2	4 13.0
9	19 6 12.5	16 25.6	17 55.0	5♓14.7	4 47.2	15 25.9	18 26.2	17 R 51.8	9 26.3	23 40.8	7 16.0	4 13.8
10	19 10 9.0	17 22.8	17 51.8	17 14.6	4 34.6	16 37.4	19 3.4	17 51.4	9 34.1	23 41.2	7 14.9	4 14.6
11	19 14 5.6	18 20.0	17 48.6	29 23.8	4 26.7	17 48.9	19 40.6	17 50.9	9 41.9	23 41.6	7 13.7	4 15.4
12	19 18 2.2	19 17.2	17 45.4	11♈46.1	4 23.7	19 .5	20 17.8	17 50.1	9 49.6	23 42.1	7 12.6	4 16.3
13	19 21 58.7	20 14.4	17 42.2	24 25.7	4 D 25.9	20 12.1	20 55.0	17 49.2	9 57.3	23 42.7	7 11.6	4 17.2
14	19 25 55.3	21 11.7	17 39.1	7♉26.4	4 33.4	21 23.8	21 32.3	17 48.0	10 5.1	23 43.3	7 10.5	4 18.2
15	19 29 51.8	22 8.9	17 35.9	20 51.6	4 46.2	22 35.5	22 9.5	17 46.7	10 12.8	23 44.0	7 9.5	4 19.1
16	19 33 48.4	23 6.1	17 32.7	4♊43.3	5 4.5	23 47.3	22 46.8	17 45.2	10 20.5	23 44.7	7 8.4	4 20.1
17	19 37 44.9	24 3.4	17 29.5	19 1.8	5 28.3	24 59.1	23 24.1	17 43.4	10 28.1	23 45.4	7 7.5	4 21.2
18	19 41 41.5	25 .7	17 26.4	3♋44.7	5 57.6	26 10.9	24 1.5	17 41.5	10 35.8	23 46.2	7 6.5	4 22.2
19	19 45 38.1	25 57.9	17 23.2	18 46.5	6 32.3	27 22.8	24 38.8	17 39.4	10 43.4	23 47.1	7 5.5	4 23.3
20	19 49 34.6	26 55.2	17 20.0	3♌58.9	7 12.5	28 34.8	25 16.2	17 37.1	10 51.1	23 48.0	7 4.6	4 24.5
21	19 53 31.2	27 52.5	17 16.8	19 12.0	7 58.1	29 46.8	25 53.6	17 34.6	10 58.7	23 49.0	7 3.7	4 25.6
22	19 57 27.7	28 49.8	17 13.7	4♍15.4	8 49.1	0♋58.8	26 31.0	17 31.9	11 6.2	23 50.0	7 2.9	4 26.8
23	20 1 24.3	29 47.2	17 10.5	19 .5	9 45.4	2 11.0	27 8.5	17 29.1	11 13.9	23 51.1	7 2.1	4 28.1
24	20 5 20.8	0♌44.5	17 7.3	3♎21.2	10 46.9	3 23.1	27 46.0	17 26.0	11 21.4	23 52.3	7 1.3	4 29.3
25	20 9 17.4	1 41.8	17 4.1	17 14.5	11 53.5	4 35.3	28 23.5	17 22.8	11 28.9	23 53.4	7 .5	4 30.6
26	20 13 14.0	2 39.1	17 .9	0♏40.7	13 5.1	5 47.5	29 1.0	17 19.4	11 36.4	23 54.7	6 59.8	4 31.9
27	20 17 10.5	3 36.4	16 57.8	13 41.9	14 21.7	6 59.8	29 38.5	17 15.8	11 43.8	23 55.9	6 59.1	4 33.2
28	20 21 7.1	4 33.7	16 54.6	26 21.7	15 43.1	8 12.1	0♍16.0	17 12.0	11 51.3	23 57.3	6 58.4	4 34.5
29	20 25 3.6	5 31.1	16 51.4	8♐44.2	17 9.2	9 24.4	0 53.6	17 8.0	11 58.7	23 58.6	6 57.7	4 35.9
30	20 29 .2	6 28.4	16 48.2	20 53.5	18 39.8	10 36.8	1 31.2	17 3.9	12 6.0	24 .1	6 57.1	4 37.3
31	20 32 56.7	7 25.8	16 45.1	2♑53.7	20 14.6	11 49.2	2 8.8	16 59.6	12 13.4	24 1.5	6 56.5	4 38.7

LATITUDE

DAY	EPHEM. SID. TIME	☉	☊	☽	☿	♀	♂	♃	♄	♅	♆	♇
1	18 34 40.0	0 .0	0 .0	1 S 48.8	4 S 26.6	1 S 36.8	1 N 14.6	1 S 12.0	0 S 35.0	0 N 34.6	1 N 37.6	16 N 38.2
4	18 46 29.7	0 .0	0 .0	1 N 29.3	4 44.2	1 30.5	1 13.7	1 12.9	0 34.8	0 34.4	1 37.5	16 36.7
7	18 58 19.4	0 .0	0 .0	4 8.1	4 47.8	1 23.8	1 12.8	1 13.8	0 34.5	0 34.3	1 37.4	16 35.2
10	19 10 9.0	0 .0	0 .0	5 12.9	4 37.8	1 16.8	1 11.8	1 14.7	0 34.3	0 34.2	1 37.3	16 33.7
13	19 21 58.7	0 .0	0 .0	4 15.3	4 16.2	1 9.4	1 10.8	1 15.6	0 34.1	0 34.1	1 37.2	16 32.3
16	19 33 48.4	0 .0	0 .0	1 17.5	3 45.4	1 1.7	1 9.8	1 16.5	0 33.8	0 34.0	1 37.0	16 30.8
19	19 45 38.1	0 .0	0 .0	2 S 34.8	3 7.9	0 53.8	1 8.8	1 17.4	0 33.6	0 33.9	1 36.9	16 29.4
22	19 57 27.7	0 .0	0 .0	5 .2	2 26.3	0 45.7	1 7.8	1 18.3	0 33.4	0 33.8	1 36.8	16 28.1
25	20 9 17.4	0 .0	0 .0	4 32.1	1 42.7	0 37.4	1 6.8	1 19.1	0 33.2	0 33.7	1 36.6	16 26.7
28	20 21 7.1	0 .0	0 .0	1 57.3	0 59.1	0 29.1	1 5.7	1 19.9	0 33.0	0 33.5	1 36.5	16 25.4
31	20 32 56.7	0 .0	0 .0	1 N 16.5	0 17.7	0 20.7	1 4.7	1 20.7	0 32.8	0 33.4	1 36.3	16 24.2

RIGHT ASCENSION

DAY	EPHEM. SID. TIME	☉	☊	☽	☿	♀	♂	♃	♄	♅	♆	♇
1	18 34 40.0	9♋34.8	17♐19.4	26♏40.0	8♋59.8	4♊20.4	16♌19.9	19♓14.8	9♋ 6.1	22♎ 6.7	5♐54.9	10♎30.8
2	18 38 36.6	10 36.8	17 15.9	10♐ .2	8 R 21.9	5 34.5	16 57.1	19 16.0	9 14.6	22 6.7	5 R 53.5	10 31.1
3	18 42 33.1	11 38.8	17 12.5	23 16.3	7 45.1	6 48.8	17 34.2	19 17.1	9 23.1	22 6.7	5 52.2	10 31.4
4	18 46 29.7	12 40.7	17 9.1	6♑17.4	7 10.2	8 3.4	18 11.2	19 17.9	9 31.5	22 D 6.8	5 50.8	10 31.8
5	18 50 26.3	13 42.5	17 5.6	18 55.0	6 37.7	9 18.3	18 48.2	19 18.6	9 39.9	22 6.9	5 49.5	10 32.2
6	18 54 22.8	14 44.2	17 2.2	1♒ 4.7	6 8.1	10 33.4	19 25.1	19 19.1	9 48.4	22 7.1	5 48.2	10 32.6
7	18 58 19.4	15 45.9	16 58.8	12 47.1	5 42.1	11 48.8	20 2.0	19 19.4	9 56.8	22 7.3	5 46.9	10 33.0
8	19 2 15.9	16 47.4	16 55.3	24 7.0	5 19.9	13 4.4	20 38.8	19 19.6	10 5.2	22 7.5	5 45.6	10 33.5
9	19 6 12.5	17 48.9	16 51.9	5♓12.5	5 2.1	14 20.3	21 15.5	19 R 19.5	10 13.6	22 7.9	5 44.4	10 34.0
10	19 10 9.0	18 50.3	16 48.5	16 14.2	4 49.0	15 36.3	21 52.2	19 19.3	10 22.0	22 8.2	5 43.2	10 34.5
11	19 14 5.6	19 51.5	16 45.0	27 24.0	4 40.9	16 52.6	22 28.8	19 18.9	10 30.4	22 8.6	5 42.0	10 35.1
12	19 18 2.2	20 52.7	16 41.6	8♈55.1	4 38.1	18 9.1	23 5.4	19 18.3	10 38.7	22 9.1	5 40.8	10 35.7
13	19 21 58.7	21 53.7	16 38.2	21 1.1	4 D 40.7	19 25.9	23 42.0	19 17.6	10 47.1	22 9.6	5 39.7	10 36.3
14	19 25 55.3	22 54.7	16 34.7	3♉54.4	4 48.9	20 42.8	24 18.4	19 16.6	10 55.4	22 10.1	5 38.6	10 36.9
15	19 29 51.8	23 55.5	16 31.3	17 43.8	5 2.8	21 59.9	24 54.9	19 15.5	11 3.8	22 10.7	5 37.5	10 37.6
16	19 33 48.4	24 56.2	16 27.9	2♊30.6	5 22.6	23 17.1	25 31.3	19 14.2	11 12.1	22 11.4	5 36.4	10 38.3
17	19 37 44.9	25 56.8	16 24.4	18 4.2	5 48.3	24 34.6	26 7.6	19 12.7	11 20.4	22 12.1	5 35.4	10 39.1
18	19 41 41.5	26 57.2	16 21.0	4♋ 2.4	6 19.9	25 52.2	26 43.9	19 11.1	11 28.6	22 12.8	5 34.3	10 39.8
19	19 45 38.1	27 57.6	16 17.6	19 57.1	6 57.4	27 9.9	27 20.2	19 9.2	11 36.9	22 13.6	5 33.3	10 40.6
20	19 49 34.6	28 57.7	16 14.1	5♌24.4	7 40.9	28 27.7	27 56.4	19 7.2	11 45.1	22 14.5	5 32.4	10 41.4
21	19 53 31.2	29 57.8	16 10.7	20 11.8	8 30.2	29 45.7	28 32.5	19 5.0	11 53.3	22 15.4	5 31.4	10 42.3
22	19 57 27.7	0♌57.7	16 7.3	4♍18.6	9 25.5	1♋ 3.8	29 8.6	19 2.6	12 1.5	22 16.3	5 30.5	10 43.1
23	20 1 24.3	1 57.5	16 3.8	17 52.5	10 26.5	2 22.0	29 44.7	19 .1	12 9.7	22 17.4	5 29.7	10 44.1
24	20 5 20.8	2 57.1	16 .4	1♎ 5.0	11 33.3	3 40.2	0♍20.8	18 57.4	12 17.8	22 18.4	5 28.8	10 45.0
25	20 9 17.4	3 56.6	15 57.0	14 7.7	12 45.8	4 58.5	0 56.7	18 54.5	12 25.9	22 19.5	5 28.0	10 46.0
26	20 13 14.0	4 55.9	15 53.6	27 10.2	14 3.8	6 16.9	1 32.7	18 51.5	12 34.0	22 20.7	5 27.2	10 47.0
27	20 17 10.5	5 55.1	15 50.1	10♏18.4	15 27.2	7 35.3	2 8.6	18 48.2	12 42.0	22 21.8	5 26.5	10 48.0
28	20 21 7.1	6 54.1	15 46.7	23 33.6	16 55.8	8 53.7	2 44.4	18 44.8	12 50.0	22 23.1	5 25.7	10 49.0
29	20 25 3.6	7 52.9	15 43.3	6♐52.0	18 29.5	10 12.1	3 20.2	18 41.3	12 58.0	22 24.4	5 25.0	10 50.1
30	20 29 .2	8 51.6	15 39.8	20 6.2	20 8.0	11 30.6	3 56.0	18 37.5	13 5.9	22 25.7	5 24.3	10 51.2
31	20 32 56.7	9 50.2	15 36.4	3♑ 7.5	21 51.1	12 49.0	4 31.7	18 33.7	13 13.8	22 27.1	5 23.7	10 52.3

DECLINATION

DAY	EPHEM. SID. TIME	☉	☊	☽	☿	♀	♂	♃	♄	♅	♆	♇
1	18 34 40.0	23 N 9.0	0 S 24.0	21 S 46.4	18 N 44.0	19 N 42.6	17 N 58.0	5 S 55.8	22 N 35.6	8 S 39.0	19 S 56.8	13 N 36.1
4	18 46 29.7	22 55.8	0 24.0	21 49.6	18 32.1	20 23.0	17 24.6	5 55.4	22 34.3	8 39.2	19 56.3	13 34.0
7	18 58 19.4	22 39.0	0 24.0	13 21.4	18 32.3	20 58.8	16 50.2	5 55.8	22 33.0	8 39.5	19 55.8	13 31.8
10	19 10 9.0	22 18.7	0 24.0	0 14.1	18 44.1	21 29.8	16 14.9	5 56.8	22 31.6	8 40.0	19 55.4	13 29.5
13	19 21 58.7	21 55.0	0 24.0	13 N 25.4	19 6.0	21 55.6	15 38.6	5 58.5	22 30.1	8 40.6	19 54.9	13 27.2
16	19 33 48.4	21 27.8	0 23.9	22 21.2	19 35.5	22 16.2	15 1.4	6 .9	22 28.6	8 41.5	19 54.6	13 24.7
19	19 45 38.1	20 57.4	0 23.9	19 34.2	20 9.1	22 31.2	14 23.3	6 3.9	22 27.0	8 42.5	19 54.2	13 22.2
22	19 57 27.7	20 23.8	0 23.9	5 17.1	20 42.9	22 40.6	13 44.4	6 7.7	22 25.4	8 43.6	19 53.9	13 19.6
25	20 9 17.4	19 47.0	0 23.9	10 S 57.5	21 12.3	22 44.3	13 4.7	6 12.0	22 23.6	8 45.0	19 53.7	13 16.9
28	20 21 7.1	19 7.4	0 23.9	21 14.5	21 32.2	22 42.3	12 24.2	6 17.0	22 21.9	8 46.5	19 53.5	13 14.2
31	20 32 56.7	18 24.9	0 23.9	22 8.1	21 37.5	22 34.3	11 43.1	6 22.6	22 20.1	8 48.2	19 53.3	13 11.4

AUGUST 1974

LONGITUDE

DAY	EPHEM. SID. TIME	☉	☊	☾	☿	♀	♂	♃	♄	♅	♆	♇
	h m s	° ′	° ′	° ′	° ′	° ′	° ′	° ′	° ′	° ′	° ′	° ′
1	20 36 53.3	8♌23.2	16♐41.9	14♑48.0	21♋53.6	13♋ 1.7	2♍46.4	16♓55.1	12♋20.7	24♎ 3.1	6♐55.9	4♎40.2
2	20 40 49.8	9 20.5	16 38.7	26 39.3	23 36.4	14 14.2	3 24.0	16R50.4	12 27.9	24 4.6	6R55.3	4 41.7
3	20 44 46.4	10 17.9	16 35.5	8♒29.7	25 22.7	15 26.8	4 1.7	16 45.6	12 35.2	24 6.2	6 54.8	4 43.2
4	20 48 43.0	11 15.3	16 32.4	20 21.3	27 12.4	16 39.4	4 39.4	16 40.7	12 42.4	24 7.9	6 54.3	4 44.7
5	20 52 39.5	12 12.8	16 29.2	2♓15.6	29 4.9	17 52.1	5 17.1	16 35.5	12 49.5	24 9.6	6 53.9	4 46.3
6	20 56 36.1	13 10.2	16 26.0	14 14.2	1♌ .0	19 4.8	5 54.8	16 30.3	12 56.7	24 11.4	6 53.4	4 47.8
7	21 0 32.6	14 7.7	16 22.8	26 19.1	2 57.4	20 17.5	6 32.6	16 24.8	13 3.8	24 13.2	6 53.0	4 49.5
8	21 4 29.2	15 5.2	16 19.6	8♈32.5	4 56.6	21 30.3	7 10.4	16 19.2	13 10.8	24 15.0	6 52.7	4 51.1
9	21 8 25.7	16 2.7	16 16.5	20 57.0	6 57.2	22 43.2	7 48.2	16 13.5	13 17.8	24 16.9	6 52.3	4 52.7
10	21 12 22.3	17 .2	16 13.3	3♉36.0	8 59.0	23 56.1	8 26.0	16 7.6	13 24.8	24 18.9	6 52.0	4 54.4
11	21 16 18.8	17 57.7	16 10.1	16 32.9	11 1.6	25 9.0	9 3.9	16 1.6	13 31.7	24 20.9	6 51.8	4 56.1
12	21 20 15.4	18 55.3	16 6.9	29 51.2	13 4.7	26 22.0	9 41.8	15 55.4	13 38.6	24 22.9	6 51.5	4 57.8
13	21 24 11.9	19 53.0	16 3.8	13♊33.9	15 7.9	27 35.1	10 19.7	15 49.2	13 45.5	24 25.0	6 51.4	4 59.6
14	21 28 8.5	20 50.6	16 .6	27 42.4	17 11.0	28 48.2	10 57.7	15 42.8	13 52.3	24 27.2	6 51.2	5 1.4
15	21 32 5.1	21 48.2	15 57.4	12♋16.3	19 13.8	0♌ 1.3	11 35.6	15 36.3	13 59.1	24 29.3	6 51.0	5 3.2
16	21 36 1.6	22 45.9	15 54.2	27 12.0	21 16.0	1 14.5	12 13.6	15 29.6	14 5.8	24 31.5	6 50.9	5 5.0
17	21 39 58.2	23 43.6	15 51.0	12♌22.5	23 17.5	2 27.7	12 51.6	15 22.8	14 12.4	24 33.8	6 50.8	5 6.8
18	21 43 54.7	24 41.3	15 47.9	27 38.3	25 18.2	3 40.9	13 29.7	15 15.9	14 19.0	24 36.1	6 50.8	5 8.7
19	21 47 51.3	25 39.0	15 44.7	12♍48.3	27 17.8	4 54.2	14 7.8	15 8.9	14 25.6	24 38.4	6 50.8	5 10.5
20	21 51 47.8	26 36.8	15 41.5	27 42.1	29 16.4	6 7.6	14 45.9	15 1.8	14 32.1	24 40.8	6 50.8	5 12.4
21	21 55 44.4	27 34.6	15 38.3	12♎11.9	1♍13.8	7 20.9	15 24.0	14 54.7	14 38.5	24 43.2	6 50.8	5 14.3
22	21 59 40.9	28 32.4	15 35.2	26 13.0	3 10.0	8 34.4	16 2.1	14 47.4	14 44.9	24 45.7	6D50.9	5 16.3
23	22 3 37.5	29 30.2	15 32.0	9♏44.4	5 4.9	9 47.8	16 40.3	14 40.0	14 51.2	24 48.2	6 51.0	5 18.2
24	22 7 34.0	0♍28.0	15 28.8	22 47.8	6 58.5	11 1.3	17 18.5	14 32.6	14 57.5	24 50.7	6 51.2	5 20.2
25	22 11 30.6	1 25.9	15 25.6	5♐27.0	8 50.8	12 14.8	17 56.7	14 25.1	15 3.7	24 53.3	6 51.4	5 22.2
26	22 15 27.2	2 23.8	15 22.5	17 46.8	10 41.8	13 28.4	18 35.0	14 17.5	15 9.9	24 55.9	6 51.6	5 24.2
27	22 19 23.7	3 21.7	15 19.3	29 52.1	12 31.5	14 42.0	19 13.3	14 9.9	15 16.0	24 58.6	6 51.8	5 26.2
28	22 23 20.3	4 19.6	15 16.1	11♑48.0	14 19.8	15 55.7	19 51.6	14 2.2	15 22.0	25 1.3	6 52.1	5 28.2
29	22 27 16.8	5 17.5	15 12.9	23 38.9	16 6.8	17 9.3	20 29.9	13 54.4	15 28.0	25 4.0	6 52.4	5 30.3
30	22 31 13.4	6 15.5	15 9.7	5♒28.6	17 52.6	18 23.1	21 8.3	13 46.6	15 33.9	25 6.8	6 52.8	5 32.3
31	22 35 9.9	7 13.5	15 6.6	17 19.9	19 37.0	19 36.8	21 46.6	13 38.8	15 39.7	25 9.6	6 53.1	5 34.4

LATITUDE

DAY	EPHEM. SID. TIME	☉	☊	☾	☿	♀	♂	♃	♄	♅	♆	♇
1	20 36 53.3	0 .0	0 .0	2N16.5	0S 4.6	0S18.0	1N 4.3	1S21.0	0S32.8	0N33.4	1N36.3	16N23.8
4	20 48 43.0	0 .0	0 .0	4 30.4	0N31.1	0 9.6	1 3.2	1 21.8	0 32.6	0 33.3	1 36.1	16 22.6
7	21 0 32.6	0 .0	0 .0	5 1.5	1 .6	0 1.4	1 2.1	1 22.5	0 32.4	0 33.2	1 35.9	16 21.5
10	21 12 22.3	0 .0	0 .0	3 31.7	1 22.8	0N 6.7	1 1.0	1 23.2	0 32.2	0 33.1	1 35.8	16 20.4
13	21 24 11.9	0 .0	0 .0	0 20.4	1 37.4	0 14.6	0 59.9	1 23.8	0 32.1	0 33.0	1 35.6	16 19.3
16	21 36 1.6	0 .0	0 .0	3S15.2	1 44.6	0 22.3	0 58.7	1 24.4	0 31.9	0 32.9	1 35.4	16 18.3
19	21 47 51.3	0 .0	0 .0	5 1.8	1 45.2	0 29.7	0 57.6	1 25.0	0 31.7	0 32.8	1 35.2	16 17.4
22	21 59 40.9	0 .0	0 .0	3 53.2	1 40.2	0 36.8	0 56.4	1 25.5	0 31.6	0 32.7	1 35.1	16 16.6
25	22 11 30.6	0 .0	0 .0	0 57.5	1 30.4	0 43.6	0 55.2	1 26.0	0 31.4	0 32.6	1 34.9	16 15.8
28	22 23 20.3	0 .0	0 .0	2N10.5	1 16.7	0 49.9	0 54.0	1 26.4	0 31.3	0 32.5	1 34.7	16 15.0
31	22 35 9.9	0 .0	0 .0	4 24.0	0 60.0	0 55.9	0 52.8	1 26.7	0 31.2	0 32.4	1 34.6	16 14.3

RIGHT ASCENSION

DAY	EPHEM. SID. TIME	☉	☊	☾	☿	♀	♂	♃	♄	♅	♆	♇
1	20 36 53.3	10♌48.6	15♐33.0	15♑47.9	23♋38.4	14♋ 7.4	5♍ 7.4	18♓29.6	13♋21.7	22♎28.5	5♐23.1	10♎53.4
2	20 40 49.8	11 46.8	15 29.5	28 2.9	25 29.7	15 25.8	5 43.1	18R25.4	13 29.5	22 29.9	5R22.5	10 54.6
3	20 44 46.4	12 44.9	15 26.1	9♒52.0	27 24.4	16 44.1	6 18.7	18 21.1	13 37.3	22 31.4	5 22.0	10 55.8
4	20 48 43.0	13 42.8	15 22.7	21 18.4	29 22.2	18 2.4	6 54.3	18 16.6	13 45.1	22 33.0	5 21.4	10 57.0
5	20 52 39.5	14 40.6	15 19.3	2♓28.8	1♌22.7	19 20.6	7 29.8	18 11.9	13 52.8	22 34.6	5 20.9	10 58.2
6	20 56 36.1	15 38.2	15 15.8	13 31.7	3 25.3	20 38.7	8 5.4	18 7.1	14 .5	22 36.2	5 20.5	10 59.5
7	21 0 32.6	16 35.7	15 12.4	24 37.5	5 29.7	21 56.8	8 40.9	18 2.1	14 8.1	22 37.9	5 20.1	11 .8
8	21 4 29.2	17 33.0	15 9.0	5♈57.5	7 35.2	23 14.7	9 16.3	17 57.1	14 15.7	22 39.7	5 19.7	11 2.1
9	21 8 25.7	18 30.2	15 5.6	17 43.6	9 41.5	24 32.6	9 51.8	17 51.8	14 23.3	22 41.4	5 19.3	11 3.4
10	21 12 22.3	19 27.3	15 2.1	0♉ 7.1	11 48.1	25 50.3	10 27.2	17 46.5	14 30.8	22 43.3	5 19.0	11 4.8
11	21 16 18.8	20 24.2	14 58.7	13 17.4	13 54.6	27 7.8	11 2.6	17 41.0	14 38.2	22 45.1	5 18.7	11 6.2
12	21 20 15.4	21 21.0	14 55.3	27 18.8	16 .6	28 25.3	11 38.0	17 35.4	14 45.6	22 47.0	5 18.4	11 7.6
13	21 24 11.9	22 17.6	14 51.8	12♊ 7.9	18 5.8	29 42.6	12 13.4	17 29.6	14 53.0	22 49.0	5 18.2	11 9.0
14	21 28 8.5	23 14.2	14 48.4	27 31.1	20 9.9	0♌59.8	12 48.7	17 23.8	15 .3	22 51.0	5 18.0	11 10.5
15	21 32 5.1	24 10.5	14 45.0	13♋ 7.7	22 12.7	2 16.7	13 24.0	17 17.8	15 7.6	22 53.0	5 17.9	11 12.0
16	21 36 1.6	25 6.8	14 41.6	28 35.6	24 13.9	3 33.5	13 59.3	17 11.7	15 14.8	22 55.1	5 17.8	11 13.4
17	21 39 58.2	26 2.9	14 38.1	13♌38.7	26 13.5	4 50.1	14 34.6	17 5.5	15 21.9	22 57.2	5 17.7	11 15.0
18	21 43 54.7	26 58.9	14 34.7	28 10.5	28 11.2	6 6.5	15 9.9	16 59.1	15 29.0	22 59.4	5 17.6	11 16.5
19	21 47 51.3	27 54.7	14 31.3	12♍13.5	0♍ 7.1	7 22.7	15 45.2	16 52.7	15 36.1	23 1.6	5 17.6	11 18.1
20	21 51 47.8	28 50.4	14 27.9	25 55.3	2 1.1	8 38.7	16 20.4	16 46.2	15 43.0	23 3.8	5 17.6	11 19.6
21	21 55 44.4	29 46.1	14 24.4	9♎25.3	3 53.1	9 54.5	16 55.7	16 39.6	15 50.0	23 6.1	5 17.6	11 21.2
22	21 59 40.9	0♍41.5	14 21.0	22 51.8	5 43.1	11 10.1	17 30.9	16 32.9	15 56.8	23 8.4	5D17.7	11 22.9
23	22 3 37.5	1 36.9	14 17.6	6♏20.0	7 31.2	12 25.4	18 6.1	16 26.1	16 3.6	23 10.7	5 17.8	11 24.5
24	22 7 34.0	2 32.2	14 14.2	19 50.8	9 17.4	13 40.6	18 41.3	16 19.3	16 10.4	23 13.1	5 17.9	11 26.1
25	22 11 30.6	3 27.3	14 10.8	3♐21.0	11 1.7	14 55.5	19 16.5	16 12.4	16 17.0	23 15.5	5 18.1	11 27.8
26	22 15 27.2	4 22.3	14 7.3	16 43.8	12 44.2	16 10.1	19 51.8	16 5.4	16 23.6	23 18.0	5 18.3	11 29.5
27	22 19 23.7	5 17.3	14 3.9	29 51.5	14 24.9	17 24.6	20 27.0	15 58.3	16 30.2	23 20.5	5 18.6	11 31.2
28	22 23 20.3	6 12.1	14 .5	12♑37.4	16 3.8	18 38.8	21 2.1	15 51.2	16 36.6	23 23.0	5 18.9	11 33.0
29	22 27 16.8	7 6.8	13 57.1	24 57.8	17 41.1	19 52.8	21 37.3	15 44.0	16 43.1	23 25.6	5 19.2	11 34.7
30	22 31 13.4	8 1.5	13 53.6	6♒52.5	19 16.9	21 6.5	22 12.5	15 36.8	16 49.4	23 28.2	5 19.5	11 36.5
31	22 35 9.9	8 56.0	13 50.2	18 25.1	20 51.0	22 20.0	22 47.7	15 29.6	16 55.7	23 30.8	5 19.9	11 38.2

DECLINATION

DAY	EPHEM. SID. TIME	☉	☊	☾	☿	♀	♂	♃	♄	♅	♆	♇
1	20 36 53.3	18N10.2	0S23.9	20S21.5	21N35.1	22N30.4	11N29.2	6S24.6	22N19.5	8S48.8	19S53.3	13N10.5
4	20 48 43.0	17 24.1	0 23.8	10 25.5	21 13.7	22 14.6	10 47.1	6 30.9	22 17.7	8 50.7	19 53.2	13 7.6
7	21 0 32.6	16 35.5	0 23.8	3N 8.9	20 29.0	21 53.1	10 4.4	6 37.7	22 15.8	8 52.7	19 53.1	13 4.7
10	21 12 22.3	15 44.5	0 23.8	16 2.0	19 20.7	21 25.9	9 21.1	6 45.1	22 13.9	8 54.9	19 53.1	13 1.8
13	21 24 11.9	14 51.2	0 23.8	22 46.1	17 51.0	20 53.1	8 37.2	6 52.8	22 12.0	8 57.2	19 53.2	12 58.8
16	21 36 1.6	13 55.7	0 23.8	17 31.7	16 3.9	20 14.8	7 52.8	7 1.0	22 10.0	8 59.7	19 53.3	12 55.8
19	21 47 51.3	12 58.3	0 23.7	2 6.3	14 3.5	19 31.3	7 7.9	7 9.5	22 8.1	9 2.3	19 53.4	12 52.8
22	21 59 40.9	11 59.0	0 23.7	13S44.4	11 54.1	18 42.8	6 22.5	7 18.3	22 6.2	9 5.1	19 53.6	12 49.8
25	22 11 30.6	10 58.0	0 23.7	22 9.5	9 39.0	17 49.4	5 36.8	7 27.4	22 4.2	9 7.9	19 53.9	12 46.7
28	22 23 20.3	9 55.5	0 23.7	20 45.0	7 20.9	16 51.5	4 50.7	7 36.6	22 2.3	9 10.9	19 54.2	12 43.7
31	22 35 9.9	8 51.5	0 23.7	11 26.7	5 1.9	15 49.3	4 4.2	7 45.9	22 .4	9 14.0	19 54.5	12 40.7

SEPTEMBER 1974

LONGITUDE

DAY	EPHEM. SID. TIME	☉	☊	☽	☿	♀	♂	♃	♄	♅	♆	♇
	h m s	° ′	° ′	° ′	° ′	° ′	° ′	° ′	° ′	° ′	° ′	° ′
1	22 39 6.5	8♍11.5	15♐ 3.4	29♒15.2	21♍20.1	20♌50.6	22♍25.1	13♓31.0	15♋45.5	25♎12.4	6♐53.5	5♎36.5
2	22 43 3.0	9 9.5	15 .2	11♓16.0	23 2.0	22 4.5	23 3.5	13 R 23.1	15 51.2	25 15.3	6 54.0	5 38.6
3	22 46 59.6	10 7.7	14 57.0	23 23.6	24 42.7	23 18.4	23 42.0	13 15.2	15 56.9	25 18.2	6 54.5	5 40.8
4	22 50 56.1	11 5.8	14 53.9	5♈38.7	26 22.2	24 32.3	24 20.5	13 7.3	16 2.5	25 21.2	6 55.0	5 42.9
5	22 54 52.7	12 3.9	14 50.7	18 2.6	28 .4	25 46.3	24 59.0	12 59.3	16 8.0	25 24.1	6 55.5	5 45.0
6	22 58 49.2	13 2.0	14 47.5	0♉36.5	29 37.4	27 .2	25 37.6	12 51.4	16 13.4	25 27.1	6 56.1	5 47.2
7	23 2 45.8	14 .2	14 44.3	13 22.2	1♎13.2	28 14.3	26 16.2	12 43.4	16 18.8	25 30.2	6 56.7	5 49.4
8	23 6 42.3	14 58.5	14 41.1	26 22.2	2 47.8	29 28.3	26 54.8	12 35.5	16 24.1	25 33.2	6 57.3	5 51.5
9	23 10 38.9	15 56.7	14 38.0	9♊39.1	4 21.3	0♍42.5	27 33.5	12 27.6	16 29.3	25 36.3	6 58.0	5 53.7
10	23 14 35.4	16 55.0	14 34.8	23 15.4	5 53.6	1 56.6	28 12.1	12 19.6	16 34.4	25 39.5	6 58.7	5 55.9
11	23 18 32.0	17 53.3	14 31.6	7♋13.0	7 24.8	3 10.8	28 50.9	12 11.8	16 39.5	25 42.6	6 59.4	5 58.2
12	23 22 28.6	18 51.7	14 28.4	21 32.4	8 54.8	4 25.0	29 29.6	12 3.9	16 44.5	25 45.8	7 .2	6 .4
13	23 26 25.1	19 50.1	14 25.2	6♌11.7	10 23.6	5 39.3	0♎ 8.4	11 56.1	16 49.4	25 49.0	7 1.0	6 2.6
14	23 30 21.7	20 48.5	14 22.1	21 6.2	11 51.3	6 53.6	0 47.2	11 48.3	16 54.2	25 52.2	7 1.8	6 4.8
15	23 34 18.2	21 47.0	14 18.9	6♍ 8.3	13 17.8	8 7.9	1 26.1	11 40.6	16 59.0	25 55.5	7 2.6	6 7.1
16	23 38 14.8	22 45.5	14 15.7	21 8.7	14 43.1	9 22.2	2 4.9	11 32.9	17 3.6	25 58.8	7 3.5	6 9.4
17	23 42 11.3	23 44.0	14 12.5	5♎57.6	16 7.1	10 36.6	2 43.8	11 25.3	17 8.2	26 2.1	7 4.4	6 11.6
18	23 46 7.9	24 42.6	14 9.4	20 26.4	17 30.0	11 51.0	3 22.8	11 17.7	17 12.7	26 5.5	7 5.4	6 13.9
19	23 50 4.4	25 41.2	14 6.2	4♏29.5	18 51.5	13 5.5	4 1.8	11 10.2	17 17.1	26 8.8	7 6.4	6 16.2
20	23 54 1.0	26 39.8	14 3.0	18 4.4	20 11.8	14 20.0	4 40.8	11 2.8	17 21.5	26 12.2	7 7.4	6 18.4
21	23 57 57.5	27 38.5	13 59.8	1♐11.6	21 30.7	15 34.5	5 19.8	10 55.5	17 25.7	26 15.6	7 8.4	6 20.7
22	0 1 54.1	28 37.1	13 56.6	13 53.8	22 48.1	16 49.0	5 58.9	10 48.3	17 29.9	26 19.1	7 9.5	6 23.0
23	0 5 50.6	29 35.8	13 53.5	26 15.5	24 4.2	18 3.5	6 38.0	10 41.2	17 33.9	26 22.5	7 10.6	6 25.3
24	0 9 47.2	0♎34.6	13 50.3	8♑21.7	25 18.7	19 18.2	7 17.2	10 34.2	17 38.0	26 26.0	7 11.7	6 27.7
25	0 13 43.7	1 33.4	13 47.1	20 17.7	26 31.5	20 32.8	7 56.3	10 27.3	17 41.8	26 29.5	7 12.9	6 30.0
26	0 17 40.3	2 32.2	13 43.9	2♒ 8.7	27 42.7	21 47.4	8 35.5	10 20.5	17 45.6	26 33.1	7 14.1	6 32.3
27	0 21 36.8	3 31.0	13 40.8	13 59.2	28 52.0	23 2.0	9 14.8	10 13.8	17 49.3	26 36.6	7 15.3	6 34.6
28	0 25 33.4	4 29.8	13 37.6	25 53.1	29 59.4	24 16.7	9 54.0	10 7.2	17 52.9	26 40.1	7 16.5	6 36.9
29	0 29 29.9	5 28.7	13 34.4	7♓53.5	1♏ 4.8	25 31.4	10 33.3	10 .7	17 56.4	26 43.7	7 17.8	6 39.2
30	0 33 26.5	6 27.6	13 31.2	20 2.4	2 7.9	26 46.1	11 12.6	9 54.4	17 59.9	26 47.3	7 19.1	6 41.5

LATITUDE

DAY	EPHEM. SID. TIME	☉	☊	☽	☿	♀	♂	♃	♄	♅	♆	♇
1	22 39 6.5	0 .0	0 .0	4N47.8	0N53.9	0N57.8	0N52.4	1S26.8	0S31.1	0N32.4	1N34.5	16N14.1
4	22 50 56.1	0 .0	0 .0	4 41.0	0 34.0	1 3.1	0 51.2	1 27.1	0 31.0	0 32.3	1 34.3	16 13.6
7	23 2 45.8	0 .0	0 .0	2 36.9	0 12.6	1 8.0	0 49.9	1 27.3	0 30.8	0 32.2	1 34.2	16 13.0
10	23 14 35.4	0 .0	0 .0	0S45.7	0S10.1	1 12.3	0 48.6	1 27.5	0 30.7	0 32.2	1 34.0	16 12.6
13	23 26 25.1	0 .0	0 .0	3 56.8	0 33.6	1 16.1	0 47.3	1 27.5	0 30.6	0 32.1	1 33.8	16 12.2
16	23 38 14.8	0 .0	0 .0	4 58.2	0 57.4	1 19.3	0 46.0	1 27.6	0 30.4	0 32.0	1 33.6	16 11.9
19	23 50 4.4	0 .0	0 .0	3 10.3	1 21.2	1 22.0	0 44.7	1 27.5	0 30.3	0 32.0	1 33.5	16 11.7
22	0 1 54.1	0 .0	0 .0	0N 2.8	1 44.6	1 24.1	0 43.4	1 27.4	0 30.2	0 31.9	1 33.3	16 11.6
25	0 13 43.7	0 .0	0 .0	3 2.7	2 7.2	1 25.6	0 42.0	1 27.3	0 30.1	0 31.9	1 33.2	16 11.5
28	0 25 33.4	0 .0	0 .0	4 49.0	2 28.4	1 26.5	0 40.7	1 27.1	0 29.9	0 31.8	1 33.0	16 11.5

RIGHT ASCENSION

DAY	EPHEM. SID. TIME	☉	☊	☽	☿	♀	♂	♃	♄	♅	♆	♇
1	22 39 6.5	9♍50.5	13♐46.8	29♒41.4	22♍23.8	23♌33.3	23♍23.0	15♓22.3	17♋ 1.9	23♎33.4	5♐20.3	11♎40.0
2	22 43 3.0	10 44.9	13 43.4	10♓49.5	23 55.0	24 46.4	23 58.2	15 R 15.0	17 8.0	23 36.1	5 20.8	11 41.8
3	22 46 59.6	11 39.2	13 40.0	21 58.7	25 25.0	25 59.2	24 33.4	15 7.7	17 14.1	23 38.9	5 21.3	11 43.7
4	22 50 56.1	12 33.5	13 36.5	3♈19.0	26 53.6	27 11.8	25 8.7	15 .3	17 20.1	23 41.7	5 21.8	11 45.6
5	22 54 52.7	13 27.7	13 33.1	15 .7	28 21.0	28 24.2	25 43.9	14 53.0	17 26.0	23 44.5	5 22.4	11 47.4
6	22 58 49.2	14 21.8	13 29.7	27 13.5	29 47.1	29 36.4	26 19.2	14 45.6	17 31.8	23 47.3	5 23.0	11 49.3
7	23 2 45.8	15 15.9	13 26.3	10♉ 5.3	1♎12.1	0♍48.3	26 54.4	14 38.2	17 37.5	23 50.1	5 23.6	11 51.2
8	23 6 42.3	16 9.9	13 22.9	23 39.9	2 36.0	2 .1	27 29.7	14 30.8	17 43.2	23 53.0	5 24.2	11 53.1
9	23 10 38.9	17 3.9	13 19.4	7♊55.2	3 58.8	3 11.6	28 5.0	14 23.4	17 48.8	23 55.9	5 24.9	11 55.0
10	23 14 35.4	17 57.8	13 16.0	22 41.9	5 20.6	4 22.9	28 40.4	14 16.1	17 54.3	23 58.9	5 25.6	11 56.9
11	23 18 32.0	18 51.8	13 12.6	7♋44.7	6 41.4	5 34.1	29 15.7	14 8.7	17 59.7	24 1.9	5 26.4	11 58.8
12	23 22 28.6	19 45.6	13 9.2	22 46.5	8 1.1	6 45.0	29 51.1	14 1.4	18 5.1	24 4.8	5 27.2	12 .8
13	23 26 25.1	20 39.5	13 5.8	7♌33.8	9 19.9	7 55.8	0♎26.5	13 54.1	18 10.3	24 7.9	5 28.0	12 2.7
14	23 30 21.7	21 33.4	13 2.4	21 59.7	10 37.8	9 6.3	1 2.0	13 46.8	18 15.5	24 10.9	5 28.9	12 4.7
15	23 34 18.2	22 27.2	12 58.9	6♍ 4.7	11 54.7	10 16.7	1 37.4	13 39.6	18 20.6	24 14.0	5 29.7	12 6.7
16	23 38 14.8	23 21.0	12 55.5	19 54.6	13 10.6	11 27.0	2 12.9	13 32.5	18 25.6	24 17.1	5 30.7	12 8.7
17	23 42 11.3	24 14.8	12 52.1	3♎37.2	14 25.6	12 37.0	2 48.5	13 25.3	18 30.5	24 20.2	5 31.6	12 10.7
18	23 46 7.9	25 8.7	12 48.7	17 19.9	15 39.7	13 46.9	3 24.0	13 18.3	18 35.3	24 23.4	5 32.6	12 12.7
19	23 50 4.4	26 2.5	12 45.3	1♏ 7.0	16 52.8	14 56.7	3 59.6	13 11.3	18 40.0	24 26.6	5 33.6	12 14.7
20	23 54 1.0	26 56.3	12 41.9	14 58.5	18 4.9	16 6.3	4 35.3	13 4.3	18 44.6	24 29.8	5 34.6	12 16.7
21	23 57 57.5	27 50.1	12 38.4	28 49.7	19 16.0	17 15.8	5 10.9	12 57.5	18 49.2	24 33.0	5 35.7	12 18.8
22	0 1 54.1	28 44.0	12 35.0	12♐32.4	20 26.0	18 25.2	5 46.6	12 50.7	18 53.6	24 36.2	5 36.8	12 20.8
23	0 5 50.6	29 37.8	12 31.6	25 57.4	21 35.0	19 34.4	6 22.4	12 44.0	18 58.0	24 39.5	5 38.0	12 22.9
24	0 9 47.2	0♎31.8	12 28.2	8♑57.4	22 42.8	20 43.6	6 58.2	12 37.5	19 2.3	24 42.8	5 39.2	12 25.0
25	0 13 43.7	1 25.7	12 24.8	21 28.5	23 49.3	21 52.6	7 34.1	12 31.0	19 6.4	24 46.1	5 40.4	12 27.0
26	0 17 40.3	2 19.6	12 21.4	3♒31.1	24 54.4	23 1.5	8 10.0	12 24.6	19 10.5	24 49.4	5 41.6	12 29.1
27	0 21 36.8	3 13.6	12 18.0	15 9.2	25 58.2	24 10.4	8 45.9	12 18.2	19 14.4	24 52.8	5 42.9	12 31.2
28	0 25 33.4	4 7.7	12 14.5	26 29.7	27 .4	25 19.2	9 21.9	12 12.1	19 18.3	24 56.1	5 44.2	12 33.2
29	0 29 29.9	5 1.7	12 11.1	7♓41.2	28 .9	26 27.9	9 57.9	12 6.0	19 22.0	24 59.5	5 45.5	12 35.3
30	0 33 26.5	5 55.9	12 7.7	18 53.3	28 59.6	27 36.6	10 34.0	12 .0	19 25.7	25 2.9	5 46.9	12 37.4

DECLINATION

DAY	EPHEM. SID. TIME	☉	☊	☽	☿	♀	♂	♃	♄	♅	♆	♇
1	22 39 6.5	8N29.9	0S23.7	7S14.2	4N15.6	15N27.7	3N48.7	7S49.0	21N59.8	9S15.1	19S54.6	12N39.7
4	22 50 56.1	7 24.3	0 23.7	6N32.4	1 57.9	14 20.1	3 1.8	7 58.4	21 57.9	9 18.4	19 55.0	12 36.6
7	23 2 45.8	6 17.6	0 23.6	18 20.8	0S17.6	13 9.0	2 14.8	8 7.7	21 56.1	9 21.7	19 55.5	12 33.7
10	23 14 35.4	5 10.0	0 23.6	22 30.6	2 29.8	11 54.6	1 27.5	8 17.0	21 54.4	9 25.2	19 56.0	12 30.7
13	23 26 25.1	4 1.5	0 23.6	14 54.0	4 37.8	10 37.1	0 40.1	8 26.1	21 52.6	9 28.7	19 56.5	12 27.8
16	23 38 14.8	2 52.5	0 23.6	1S 3.6	6 41.0	9 16.9	0S 7.4	8 35.0	21 51.0	9 32.3	19 57.1	12 24.9
19	23 50 4.4	1 42.9	0 23.6	16 .2	8 38.4	7 54.4	0 55.1	8 43.6	21 49.4	9 36.0	19 57.7	12 22.0
22	0 1 54.1	0 33.0	0 23.5	22 25.5	10 29.2	6 29.8	1 42.7	8 51.8	21 47.9	9 39.8	19 58.4	12 19.2
25	0 13 43.7	0S37.1	0 23.5	18 53.8	12 12.5	5 3.5	2 30.4	8 59.7	21 46.5	9 43.6	19 59.1	12 16.5
28	0 25 33.4	1 47.2	0 23.5	8 21.3	13 47.0	3 35.8	3 17.9	9 7.1	21 45.1	9 47.5	19 59.9	12 13.8

OCTOBER 1974

LONGITUDE

DAY	EPHEM. SID. TIME	☉	☊	☾	☿	♀	♂	♃	♄	♅	♆	♇
	h m s	° ′	° ′	° ′	° ′	° ′	° ′	° ′	° ′	° ′	° ′	° ′
1	0 37 23.0	7♎26.6	13♐28.0	2♈21.3	3♏ 8.6	28♍ .9	11♎52.0	9♓48.2	18♋ 3.2	26♎50.9	7♐20.4	6♎43.8
2	0 41 19.6	8 25.6	13 24.9	14 50.8	4 6.8	29 15.6	12 31.4	9 R 42.1	18 6.4	26 54.5	7 21.8	6 46.1
3	0 45 16.2	9 24.6	13 21.7	27 31.0	5 2.2	0♎30.4	13 10.8	9 36.2	18 9.5	26 58.2	7 23.1	6 48.4
4	0 49 12.7	10 23.6	13 18.5	10♉22.0	5 54.5	1 45.3	13 50.3	9 30.4	18 12.6	27 1.8	7 24.5	6 50.8
5	0 53 9.3	11 22.7	13 15.3	23 24.0	6 43.6	3 .1	14 29.8	9 24.8	18 15.5	27 5.5	7 26.0	6 53.1
6	0 57 5.8	12 21.8	13 12.2	6♊37.6	7 29.1	4 15.0	15 9.3	9 19.3	18 18.3	27 9.1	7 27.4	6 55.4
7	1 1 2.4	13 21.0	13 9.0	20 3.5	8 10.6	5 29.8	15 48.9	9 14.0	18 21.0	27 12.8	7 28.9	6 57.7
8	1 4 58.9	14 20.2	13 5.8	3♋42.9	8 47.9	6 44.7	16 28.5	9 8.8	18 23.7	27 16.5	7 30.4	6 60.0
9	1 8 55.5	15 19.4	13 2.6	17 36.6	9 20.5	7 59.7	17 8.2	9 3.8	18 26.2	27 20.2	7 32.0	7 2.3
10	1 12 52.0	16 18.7	12 59.4	1♌44.8	9 48.0	9 14.6	17 47.9	8 59.0	18 28.6	27 23.9	7 33.5	7 4.6
11	1 16 48.6	17 18.0	12 56.3	16 6.4	10 10.0	10 29.6	18 27.6	8 54.3	18 30.9	27 27.7	7 35.1	7 6.8
12	1 20 45.1	18 17.4	12 53.1	0♍38.5	10 25.9	11 44.6	19 7.4	8 49.8	18 33.1	27 31.4	7 36.7	7 9.1
13	1 24 41.7	19 16.7	12 49.9	15 16.2	10 35.3	12 59.6	19 47.2	8 45.5	18 35.2	27 35.1	7 38.3	7 11.4
14	1 28 38.2	20 16.2	12 46.7	29 53.0	10 37.6	14 14.7	20 27.0	8 41.4	18 37.2	27 38.9	7 40.0	7 13.7
15	1 32 34.8	21 15.7	12 43.6	14♎21.8	10 R 32.5	15 29.8	21 6.9	8 37.5	18 39.2	27 42.7	7 41.7	7 16.0
16	1 36 31.3	22 15.2	12 40.4	28 35.7	10 19.3	16 44.8	21 46.8	8 33.7	18 41.0	27 46.4	7 43.4	7 18.2
17	1 40 27.9	23 14.7	12 37.2	12♏29.5	9 57.8	17 59.9	22 26.8	8 30.1	18 42.6	27 50.2	7 45.1	7 20.5
18	1 44 24.4	24 14.3	12 34.0	25 59.9	9 27.8	19 15.0	23 6.8	8 26.7	18 44.2	27 54.0	7 46.9	7 22.7
19	1 48 21.0	25 13.9	12 30.8	9♐ 6.3	8 49.1	20 30.1	23 46.8	8 23.5	18 45.6	27 57.7	7 48.6	7 25.0
20	1 52 17.6	26 13.5	12 27.7	21 50.0	8 2.0	21 45.2	24 26.9	8 20.5	18 47.0	28 1.5	7 50.4	7 27.2
21	1 56 14.1	27 13.1	12 24.5	4♑14.0	7 6.8	23 .4	25 7.0	8 17.7	18 48.2	28 5.3	7 52.2	7 29.4
22	2 0 10.7	28 12.8	12 21.3	16 22.6	6 4.4	24 15.5	25 47.1	8 15.0	18 49.3	28 9.1	7 54.0	7 31.6
23	2 4 7.2	29 12.5	12 18.1	28 20.5	4 56.0	25 30.7	26 27.3	8 12.6	18 50.4	28 12.8	7 55.9	7 33.8
24	2 8 3.8	0♏12.3	12 15.0	10♒12.9	3 43.1	26 45.8	27 7.5	8 10.4	18 51.3	28 16.6	7 57.8	7 36.0
25	2 12 .3	1 12.1	12 11.8	22 4.7	2 27.7	28 1.0	27 47.7	8 8.3	18 52.0	28 20.4	7 59.6	7 38.1
26	2 15 56.9	2 11.9	12 8.6	4♓ .6	1 11.8	29 16.2	28 28.0	8 6.5	18 52.7	28 24.2	8 1.5	7 40.3
27	2 19 53.4	3 11.7	12 5.4	16 4.6	29♎57.8	0♏31.4	29 8.3	8 4.9	18 53.3	28 27.9	8 3.5	7 42.4
28	2 23 50.0	4 11.5	12 2.2	28 19.9	28 47.9	1 46.6	29 48.6	8 3.5	18 53.7	28 31.7	8 5.4	7 44.5
29	2 27 46.5	5 11.4	11 59.1	10♈48.7	27 44.4	3 1.8	0♏29.0	8 2.2	18 54.1	28 35.4	8 7.4	7 46.6
30	2 31 43.1	6 11.3	11 55.9	23 32.3	26 49.1	4 17.0	1 9.5	8 1.2	18 54.3	28 39.2	8 9.3	7 48.7
31	2 35 39.6	7 11.3	11 52.7	6♉30.7	26 3.5	5 32.2	1 49.9	8 .4	18 54.4	28 42.9	8 11.3	7 50.8

LATITUDE

DAY	EPHEM. SID. TIME	☉	☊	☾	☿	♀	♂	♃	♄	♅	♆	♇
1	0 37 23.0	0 .0	0 .0	4N44.4	2S47.6	1N26.7	0N39.3	1S26.8	0S29.8	0N31.8	1N32.9	16N11.6
4	0 49 12.7	0 .0	0 .0	2 39.8	3 4.0	1 26.4	0 37.9	1 26.5	0 29.7	0 31.7	1 32.7	16 11.7
7	1 1 2.4	0 .0	0 .0	0S43.6	3 16.4	1 25.5	0 36.5	1 26.1	0 29.6	0 31.7	1 32.6	16 12.0
10	1 12 52.0	0 .0	0 .0	3 54.5	3 23.2	1 24.0	0 35.0	1 25.7	0 29.5	0 31.6	1 32.4	16 12.3
13	1 24 41.7	0 .0	0 .0	5 5.5	3 22.3	1 22.0	0 33.6	1 25.3	0 29.3	0 31.6	1 32.3	16 12.7
16	1 36 31.3	0 .0	0 .0	3 28.3	3 10.6	1 19.4	0 32.1	1 24.8	0 29.2	0 31.6	1 32.2	16 13.1
19	1 48 21.0	0 .0	0 .0	0 10.6	2 45.1	1 16.2	0 30.6	1 24.3	0 29.1	0 31.5	1 32.1	16 13.7
22	2 0 10.7	0 .0	0 .0	2N59.5	2 3.8	1 12.6	0 29.1	1 23.8	0 28.9	0 31.5	1 32.0	16 14.3
25	2 12 .3	0 .0	0 .0	4 53.5	1 8.4	1 8.4	0 27.6	1 23.2	0 28.8	0 31.5	1 31.9	16 15.0
28	2 23 50.0	0 .0	0 .0	4 56.1	0 6.7	1 3.8	0 26.0	1 22.7	0 28.7	0 31.5	1 31.7	16 15.7
31	2 35 39.6	0 .0	0 .0	2 54.6	0N50.3	0 58.8	0 24.5	1 22.1	0 28.5	0 31.5	1 31.7	16 16.5

RIGHT ASCENSION

DAY	EPHEM. SID. TIME	☉	☊	☾	☿	♀	♂	♃	♄	♅	♆	♇
1	0 37 23.0	6♎50.1	12♐ 4.3	0♈16.2	29♎56.3	28♍45.2	11♎10.1	11♓54.2	19♋29.2	25♎ 6.3	5♐48.2	12♎39.5
2	0 41 19.6	7 44.4	12 .9	12 .0	0♏50.8	29 53.8	11 46.3	11 R 48.4	19 32.7	25 9.7	5 49.6	12 41.6
3	0 45 16.2	8 38.7	11 57.5	24 13.8	1 42.9	1♎ 2.4	12 22.5	11 42.9	19 36.0	25 13.1	5 51.1	12 43.7
4	0 49 12.7	9 33.1	11 54.1	7♉ 4.5	2 32.4	2 10.9	12 58.9	11 37.4	19 39.3	25 16.6	5 52.5	12 45.8
5	0 53 9.3	10 27.7	11 50.7	20 34.8	3 18.9	3 19.5	13 35.2	11 32.1	19 42.4	25 20.1	5 54.0	12 47.9
6	0 57 5.8	11 22.3	11 47.2	4♊41.4	4 2.2	4 28.1	14 11.7	11 26.9	19 45.4	25 23.5	5 55.6	12 50.0
7	1 1 2.4	12 17.0	11 43.8	19 14.6	4 42.0	5 36.7	14 48.2	11 21.8	19 48.3	25 27.0	5 57.1	12 52.1
8	1 4 58.9	13 11.8	11 40.4	3♋59.4	5 17.8	6 45.3	15 24.8	11 16.9	19 51.1	25 30.5	5 58.7	12 54.2
9	1 8 55.5	14 6.7	11 37.0	18 40.3	5 49.4	7 53.9	16 1.4	11 12.2	19 53.8	25 34.0	6 .3	12 56.3
10	1 12 52.0	15 1.7	11 33.6	3♌ 5.5	6 16.2	9 2.6	16 38.1	11 7.6	19 56.4	25 37.5	6 1.9	12 58.4
11	1 16 48.6	15 56.9	11 30.2	17 10.0	6 37.8	10 11.4	17 14.9	11 3.2	19 58.9	25 41.1	6 3.6	13 .5
12	1 20 45.1	16 52.1	11 26.8	0♍55.4	6 53.7	11 20.3	17 51.8	10 58.9	20 1.2	25 44.6	6 5.2	13 2.6
13	1 24 41.7	17 47.5	11 23.4	14 28.3	7 3.5	12 29.2	18 28.7	10 54.8	20 3.5	25 48.1	6 6.9	13 4.7
14	1 28 38.2	18 43.1	11 20.0	27 57.7	7 6.7	13 38.2	19 5.7	10 50.8	20 5.6	25 51.7	6 8.7	13 6.8
15	1 32 34.8	19 38.8	11 16.6	11♎32.3	7 R 2.9	14 47.4	19 42.9	10 47.1	20 7.7	25 55.3	6 10.5	13 9.0
16	1 36 31.3	20 34.6	11 13.2	25 17.8	6 51.6	15 56.6	20 20.1	10 43.5	20 9.6	25 58.9	6 12.3	13 11.1
17	1 40 27.9	21 30.5	11 9.8	9♏15.4	6 32.5	17 5.9	20 57.3	10 40.0	20 11.4	26 2.4	6 14.1	13 13.2
18	1 44 24.4	22 26.6	11 6.4	23 20.3	6 5.5	18 15.4	21 34.7	10 36.8	20 13.1	26 6.0	6 15.9	13 15.2
19	1 48 21.0	23 22.8	11 2.9	7♐22.7	5 30.7	19 25.0	22 12.1	10 33.7	20 14.6	26 9.6	6 17.7	13 17.3
20	1 52 17.6	24 19.2	10 59.5	21 10.5	4 48.3	20 34.7	22 49.7	10 30.8	20 16.1	26 13.2	6 19.6	13 19.4
21	1 56 14.1	25 15.8	10 56.1	4♑32.6	3 58.7	21 44.6	23 27.3	10 28.1	20 17.4	26 16.7	6 21.5	13 21.5
22	2 0 10.7	26 12.5	10 52.7	17 22.5	3 3.0	22 54.7	24 5.0	10 25.5	20 18.6	26 20.3	6 23.4	13 23.5
23	2 4 7.2	27 9.3	10 49.3	29 39.1	2 2.2	24 5.0	24 42.8	10 23.2	20 19.7	26 23.9	6 25.3	13 25.6
24	2 8 3.8	28 6.4	10 45.9	11♒25.9	0 58.0	25 15.4	25 20.6	10 21.0	20 20.6	26 27.5	6 27.3	13 27.6
25	2 12 .3	29 3.5	10 42.5	22 50.4	29♎51.9	26 26.0	25 58.6	10 19.0	20 21.5	26 31.1	6 29.3	13 29.7
26	2 15 56.9	0♏ .9	10 39.1	4♓ 2.0	28 46.2	27 36.8	26 36.7	10 17.2	20 22.2	26 34.7	6 31.3	13 31.7
27	2 19 53.4	0 58.5	10 35.7	15 11.5	27 42.6	28 47.9	27 14.8	10 15.6	20 22.8	26 38.2	6 33.3	13 33.7
28	2 23 50.0	1 56.2	10 32.3	26 30.3	26 43.4	29 59.1	27 53.1	10 14.2	20 23.3	26 41.8	6 35.3	13 35.7
29	2 27 46.5	2 54.1	10 28.9	8♈ 9.9	25 50.3	1♏10.6	28 31.5	10 13.0	20 23.7	26 45.4	6 37.4	13 37.7
30	2 31 43.1	3 52.2	10 25.5	20 20.7	25 4.8	2 22.3	29 9.9	10 12.0	20 23.9	26 48.9	6 39.4	13 39.7
31	2 35 39.6	4 50.5	10 22.1	3♉11.2	24 28.2	3 34.3	29 48.5	10 11.1	20 24.1	26 52.5	6 41.5	13 41.7

DECLINATION

DAY	EPHEM. SID. TIME	☉	☊	☾	☿	♀	♂	♃	♄	♅	♆	♇
1	0 37 23.0	2S57.2	0S23.5	5N17.1	15S11.2	2N 7.0	4S 5.4	9S14.0	21N43.9	9S51.4	20S .6	12N11.2
4	0 49 12.7	4 6.9	0 23.5	17 27.5	16 23.0	0 37.4	4 52.7	9 20.5	21 42.8	9 55.4	20 1.5	12 8.6
7	1 1 2.4	5 16.2	0 23.4	22 20.7	17 19.8	0S52.5	5 39.8	9 26.3	21 41.8	9 59.4	20 2.3	12 6.1
10	1 12 52.0	6 24.9	0 23.4	15 57.6	17 57.8	2 22.6	6 26.7	9 31.6	21 40.9	10 3.4	20 3.2	12 3.8
13	1 24 41.7	7 32.9	0 23.4	1 6.5	18 12.0	3 52.4	7 13.3	9 36.3	21 40.1	10 7.4	20 4.1	12 1.5
16	1 36 31.3	8 39.9	0 23.4	14S13.1	17 55.8	5 21.6	7 59.5	9 40.3	21 39.4	10 11.5	20 5.0	11 59.2
19	1 48 21.0	9 45.8	0 23.4	21 59.6	17 2.7	6 49.9	8 45.4	9 43.6	21 38.9	10 15.6	20 6.0	11 57.1
22	2 0 10.7	10 50.4	0 23.3	19 28.1	15 29.6	8 16.9	9 30.8	9 46.3	21 38.5	10 19.6	20 7.0	11 55.1
25	2 12 .3	11 53.6	0 23.3	9 31.1	13 24.0	9 42.3	10 15.7	9 48.3	21 38.3	10 23.7	20 8.0	11 53.2
28	2 23 50.0	12 55.1	0 23.3	3N51.8	11 9.2	11 5.6	11 .0	9 49.6	21 38.2	10 27.7	20 9.0	11 51.4
31	2 35 39.6	13 54.8	0 23.3	16 26.3	9 17.0	12 26.7	11 43.7	9 50.2	21 38.2	10 31.7	20 10.0	11 49.7

NOVEMBER 1974

LONGITUDE

DAY	EPHEM. SID. TIME (h m s)	☉ (° ′)	☊ (° ′)	☽ (° ′)	☿ (° ′)	♀ (° ′)	♂ (° ′)	♃ (° ′)	♄ (° ′)	♅ (° ′)	♆ (° ′)	♇ (° ′)
1	2 39 36.2	8♏11.3	11♐49.5	19♉43.5	25♎28.6	6♏47.4	2♏30.4	7♓59.8	18♋54.4	28♎46.7	8♐13.3	7♎52.9
2	2 43 32.8	9 11.3	11 46.4	3♊ 9.3	25 R 5.2	8 2.7	3 11.0	7 R 59.4	18 R 54.3	28 50.4	8 15.3	7 54.9
3	2 47 29.3	10 11.3	11 43.2	16 46.6	24 53.4	9 17.9	3 51.5	7 59.2	18 54.1	28 54.1	8 17.4	7 57.0
4	2 51 25.9	11 11.4	11 40.0	0♋33.7	24 53.0	10 33.2	4 32.2	7 59.2	18 53.8	28 57.9	8 19.4	7 59.0
5	2 55 22.4	12 11.5	11 36.8	14 29.1	25 D 3.7	11 48.5	5 12.9	7 D 59.4	18 53.4	29 1.6	8 21.5	8 1.1
6	2 59 19.0	13 11.7	11 33.6	28 31.5	25 24.7	13 3.8	5 53.6	7 59.8	18 52.8	29 5.3	8 23.6	8 3.0
7	3 3 15.5	14 11.9	11 30.5	12♌39.4	25 55.4	14 19.1	6 34.3	8 .5	18 52.2	29 9.0	8 25.7	8 5.0
8	3 7 12.1	15 12.1	11 27.3	26 51.2	26 34.8	15 34.4	7 15.1	8 1.3	18 51.4	29 12.7	8 27.8	8 6.9
9	3 11 8.6	16 12.3	11 24.1	11♍ 4.7	27 22.1	16 49.7	7 56.0	8 2.3	18 50.5	29 16.3	8 29.9	8 8.9
10	3 15 5.2	17 12.6	11 20.9	25 17.1	28 16.4	18 5.0	8 36.8	8 3.5	18 49.5	29 20.0	8 32.1	8 10.8
11	3 19 1.8	18 12.9	11 17.8	9♎25.1	29 16.8	19 20.4	9 17.8	8 4.9	18 48.4	29 23.6	8 34.2	8 12.7
12	3 22 58.3	19 13.3	11 14.6	23 25.0	0♏22.6	20 35.7	9 58.7	8 6.6	18 47.1	29 27.2	8 36.4	8 14.5
13	3 26 54.9	20 13.7	11 11.4	7♏13.0	1 33.0	21 51.0	10 39.7	8 8.4	18 45.8	29 30.8	8 38.5	8 16.4
14	3 30 51.4	21 14.1	11 8.2	20 45.9	2 47.3	23 6.4	11 20.7	8 10.4	18 44.4	29 34.4	8 40.7	8 18.2
15	3 34 48.0	22 14.5	11 5.1	4♐ 1.5	4 5.1	24 21.7	12 1.8	8 12.7	18 42.8	29 38.0	8 42.9	8 20.0
16	3 38 44.5	23 15.0	11 1.9	16 58.7	5 25.7	25 37.1	12 42.9	8 15.1	18 41.2	29 41.5	8 45.1	8 21.8
17	3 42 41.1	24 15.5	10 58.7	29 37.9	6 48.8	26 52.4	13 24.1	8 17.8	18 39.4	29 45.1	8 47.3	8 23.6
18	3 46 37.6	25 16.0	10 55.5	12♑ .7	8 13.8	28 7.8	14 5.3	8 20.6	18 37.5	29 48.6	8 49.5	8 25.3
19	3 50 34.2	26 16.5	10 52.3	24 9.7	9 40.6	29 23.2	14 46.5	8 23.6	18 35.5	29 52.1	8 51.7	8 27.0
20	3 54 30.8	27 17.1	10 49.2	6♒ 8.8	11 8.8	0♐38.5	15 27.8	8 26.9	18 33.4	29 55.5	8 53.9	8 28.7
21	3 58 27.3	28 17.6	10 46.0	18 2.0	12 38.2	1 53.9	16 9.1	8 30.3	18 31.2	29 59.0	8 56.1	8 30.4
22	4 2 23.9	29 18.2	10 42.8	29 54.0	14 8.5	3 9.2	16 50.5	8 33.9	18 29.0	0♏ 2.4	8 58.3	8 32.0
23	4 6 20.4	0♐18.8	10 39.6	11♓49.7	15 39.6	4 24.6	17 31.8	8 37.7	18 26.6	0 5.8	9 .6	8 33.6
24	4 10 17.0	1 19.5	10 36.5	23 53.7	17 11.3	5 40.0	18 13.3	8 41.7	18 24.1	0 9.2	9 2.8	8 35.2
25	4 14 13.5	2 20.1	10 33.3	6♈10.3	18 43.5	6 55.3	18 54.7	8 45.9	18 21.5	0 12.5	9 5.1	8 36.8
26	4 18 10.1	3 20.9	10 30.1	18 43.1	20 16.1	8 10.8	19 36.3	8 50.4	18 18.8	0 15.9	9 7.4	8 38.3
27	4 22 6.7	4 21.6	10 26.9	1♉34.6	21 49.0	9 26.1	20 17.8	8 54.9	18 16.1	0 19.2	9 9.6	8 39.8
28	4 26 3.2	5 22.3	10 23.8	14 46.3	23 22.2	10 41.5	20 59.4	8 59.7	18 13.2	0 22.5	9 11.9	8 41.3
29	4 29 59.8	6 23.0	10 20.6	28 18.0	24 55.5	11 56.8	21 41.0	9 4.6	18 10.2	0 25.7	9 14.1	8 42.8
30	4 33 56.3	7 23.7	10 17.4	12♊ 8.1	26 28.9	13 12.2	22 22.7	9 9.7	18 7.1	0 28.9	9 16.4	8 44.2

LATITUDE

DAY	EPHEM. SID. TIME	☉	☊	☽	☿	♀	♂	♃	♄	♅	♆	♇
1	2 39 36.2	0 .0	0 .0	1N50.8	1N 6.7	0N57.0	0N23.9	1S21.9	0S28.5	0N31.5	1N31.6	16N16.8
4	2 51 25.9	0 .0	0 .0	1S48.1	1 45.2	0 51.5	0 22.3	1 21.2	0 28.3	0 31.5	1 31.5	16 17.8
7	3 3 15.5	0 .0	0 .0	4 37.9	2 7.8	0 45.6	0 20.7	1 20.6	0 28.2	0 31.5	1 31.5	16 18.7
10	3 15 5.2	0 .0	0 .0	5 3.7	2 16.6	0 39.3	0 19.1	1 20.0	0 28.0	0 31.5	1 31.4	16 19.8
13	3 26 54.9	0 .0	0 .0	2 52.1	2 14.9	0 32.8	0 17.5	1 19.4	0 27.9	0 31.5	1 31.3	16 20.9
16	3 38 44.5	0 .0	0 .0	0N37.2	2 5.8	0 26.1	0 15.8	1 18.7	0 27.7	0 31.5	1 31.3	16 22.1
19	3 50 34.2	0 .0	0 .0	3 39.7	1 51.6	0 19.2	0 14.1	1 18.1	0 27.5	0 31.5	1 31.2	16 23.3
22	4 2 23.9	0 .0	0 .0	5 11.6	1 34.1	0 12.2	0 12.4	1 17.4	0 27.3	0 31.5	1 31.2	16 24.6
25	4 14 13.5	0 .0	0 .0	4 45.2	1 14.5	0 5.0	0 10.7	1 16.8	0 27.1	0 31.6	1 31.1	16 26.0
28	4 26 3.2	0 .0	0 .0	2 16.7	0 53.8	0S 2.2	0 8.9	1 16.2	0 26.9	0 31.6	1 31.1	16 27.4

RIGHT ASCENSION

DAY	EPHEM. SID. TIME	☉	☊	☽	☿	♀	♂	♃	♄	♅	♆	♇
1	2 39 36.2	5♏49.0	10♐18.7	16♉44.9	24♎ 1.4	4♏46.5	0♏27.2	10♓10.5	20♋24.1	26♎56.1	6♐43.6	13♎43.7
2	2 43 32.8	6 47.7	10 15.3	0♊58.8	23 R 44.7	5 58.9	1 5.9	10 R 10.0	20 R 24.0	26 59.6	6 45.7	13 45.7
3	2 47 29.3	7 46.5	10 11.9	15 41.7	23 38.3	7 11.7	1 44.8	10 9.7	20 23.7	27 3.1	6 47.9	13 47.6
4	2 51 25.9	8 45.6	10 8.5	0♋36.2	23 D 42.0	8 24.7	2 23.8	10 9.7	20 23.4	27 6.7	6 50.0	13 49.6
5	2 55 22.4	9 45.0	10 5.1	15 23.5	23 55.4	9 38.0	3 3.0	10 D 9.8	20 23.0	27 10.3	6 52.2	13 51.5
6	2 59 19.0	10 44.5	10 1.7	29 49.2	24 18.0	10 51.6	3 42.2	10 10.1	20 22.4	27 13.8	6 54.4	13 53.5
7	3 3 15.5	11 44.2	9 58.3	13♌47.1	24 49.0	12 5.4	4 21.6	10 10.6	20 21.7	27 17.3	6 56.6	13 55.4
8	3 7 12.1	12 44.2	9 54.9	27 19.3	25 27.7	13 19.6	5 1.0	10 11.3	20 20.9	27 20.8	6 58.8	13 57.2
9	3 11 8.6	13 44.3	9 51.5	10♍33.3	26 13.3	14 34.0	5 40.6	10 12.2	20 19.9	27 24.3	7 1.1	13 59.1
10	3 15 5.2	14 44.7	9 48.1	23 39.9	27 5.1	15 48.7	6 20.3	10 13.3	20 18.9	27 27.7	7 3.3	14 1.0
11	3 19 1.8	15 45.3	9 44.7	6♎50.1	28 2.5	17 3.8	7 .1	10 14.5	20 17.7	27 31.2	7 5.5	14 2.8
12	3 22 58.3	16 46.1	9 41.3	20 13.1	29 4.6	18 19.1	7 40.0	10 16.0	20 16.4	27 34.6	7 7.8	14 4.7
13	3 26 54.9	17 47.1	9 37.9	3♏53.5	0♏11.0	19 34.8	8 20.1	10 17.6	20 15.0	27 38.1	7 10.1	14 6.5
14	3 30 51.4	18 48.3	9 34.5	17 50.1	1 21.2	20 50.8	9 .3	10 19.5	20 13.4	27 41.5	7 12.4	14 8.3
15	3 34 48.0	19 49.8	9 31.1	1♐54.9	2 34.5	22 7.0	9 40.6	10 21.5	20 11.8	27 44.9	7 14.6	14 10.1
16	3 38 44.5	20 51.4	9 27.7	15 55.0	3 50.7	23 23.6	10 21.0	10 23.7	20 10.0	27 48.3	7 16.9	14 11.8
17	3 42 41.1	21 53.3	9 24.3	29 36.2	5 9.3	24 40.5	11 1.5	10 26.1	20 8.1	27 51.6	7 19.3	14 13.6
18	3 46 37.6	22 55.4	9 20.9	12♑47.4	6 30.0	25 57.7	11 42.2	10 28.7	20 6.2	27 55.0	7 21.6	14 15.3
19	3 50 34.2	23 57.6	9 17.5	25 23.2	7 52.7	27 15.2	12 23.0	10 31.5	20 4.1	27 58.3	7 23.9	14 17.0
20	3 54 30.8	25 .1	9 14.1	7♒24.5	9 17.0	28 33.0	13 3.9	10 34.4	20 1.8	28 1.6	7 26.2	14 18.7
21	3 58 27.3	26 2.8	9 10.8	18 56.9	10 42.7	29 51.1	13 45.0	10 37.6	19 59.5	28 4.9	7 28.6	14 20.4
22	4 2 23.9	27 5.7	9 7.4	0♓ 9.7	12 9.7	1♐ 9.4	14 26.1	10 40.9	19 57.1	28 8.2	7 30.9	14 22.0
23	4 6 20.4	28 8.7	9 4.0	11 13.9	13 37.9	2 28.1	15 7.4	10 44.4	19 54.5	28 11.4	7 33.3	14 23.6
24	4 10 17.0	29 12.0	9 .6	22 21.9	15 7.2	3 47.1	15 48.9	10 48.1	19 51.9	28 14.7	7 35.6	14 25.2
25	4 14 13.5	0♐15.4	8 57.2	3♈46.3	16 37.3	5 6.3	16 30.4	10 51.9	19 49.1	28 17.9	7 38.0	14 26.8
26	4 18 10.1	1 19.1	8 53.8	15 *40.0	18 8.4	6 25.8	17 12.2	10 56.0	19 46.3	28 21.1	7 40.4	14 28.4
27	4 22 6.7	2 23.0	8 50.4	28 14.0	19 40.3	7 45.6	17 54.0	11 .2	19 43.4	28 24.2	7 42.8	14 30.0
28	4 26 3.2	3 27.0	8 47.0	11♉36.1	21 12.9	9 5.6	18 35.9	11 4.6	19 40.3	28 27.4	7 45.2	14 31.5
29	4 29 59.8	4 31.1	8 43.6	25 47.5	22 46.2	10 25.9	19 18.0	11 9.1	19 37.1	28 30.5	7 47.5	14 33.0
30	4 33 56.3	5 35.5	8 40.2	10♊40.1	24 20.2	11 46.4	20 .2	11 13.9	19 33.9	28 33.5	7 49.9	14 34.5

DECLINATION

DAY	EPHEM. SID. TIME	☉	☊	☽	☿	♀	♂	♃	♄	♅	♆	♇
1	2 39 36.2	14S14.2	0S23.3	19N26.8	8S49.1	12S53.1	11S58.2	9S50.2	21N38.3	10S33.0	20S10.3	11N49.2
4	2 51 25.9	15 11.3	0 23.2	21 38.4	8 .2	14 10.5	12 41.0	9 49.9	21 38.5	10 37.0	20 11.4	11 47.7
7	3 3 15.5	16 6.1	0 23.2	12 33.8	8 1.8	15 24.7	13 23.1	9 48.8	21 38.9	10 40.9	20 12.4	11 46.3
10	3 15 5.2	16 58.4	0 23.2	2S46.4	8 44.0	16 35.3	14 4.4	9 47.1	21 39.4	10 44.8	20 13.5	11 45.0
13	3 26 54.9	17 48.2	0 23.2	16 37.9	9 54.2	17 42.1	14 44.8	9 44.7	21 40.1	10 48.6	20 14.5	11 43.9
16	3 38 44.5	18 35.2	0 23.1	22 11.3	11 21.3	18 44.6	15 24.3	9 41.6	21 40.9	10 52.4	20 15.6	11 42.9
19	3 50 34.2	19 19.3	0 23.1	17 40.5	12 56.9	19 42.5	16 2.8	9 37.8	21 41.8	10 56.1	20 16.7	11 42.0
22	4 2 23.9	20 .2	0 23.1	6 38.5	14 35.2	20 35.4	16 40.3	9 33.3	21 42.9	10 59.7	20 17.7	11 41.3
25	4 14 13.5	20 37.8	0 23.1	6N48.8	16 12.1	21 23.1	17 16.6	9 28.2	21 44.1	11 3.2	20 18.8	11 40.7
28	4 26 3.2	21 12.0	0 23.0	18 26.9	17 45.0	22 5.3	17 51.8	9 22.5	21 45.4	11 6.7	20 19.8	11 40.2

DECEMBER 1974

LONGITUDE

DAY	EPHEM. SID. TIME h m s	☉ ° ′	☊ ° ′	☽ ° ′	☿ ° ′	♀ ° ′	♂ ° ′	♃ ° ′	♄ ° ′	♅ ° ′	♆ ° ′	♇ ° ′
1	4 37 52.9	8♐24.5	10♐14.2	26♊13.4	28♏ 2.5	14♐27.6	23♏ 4.4	9♓15.0	18♋ 4.0	0♏32.1	9♐18.6	8♎45.6
2	4 41 49.4	9 25.3	10 11.0	10♋29.9	29 36.1	15 42.9	23 46.2	9 20.5	18R .7	0 35.3	9 20.9	8 47.0
3	4 45 46.0	10 26.1	10 7.9	24 52.6	1♐ 9.8	16 58.3	24 28.0	9 26.2	17 57.4	0 38.4	9 23.2	8 48.3
4	4 49 42.6	11 27.0	10 4.7	9♌16.9	2 43.5	18 13.7	25 9.8	9 32.0	17 54.0	0 41.5	9 25.4	8 49.6
5	4 53 39.1	12 27.8	10 1.5	23 38.6	4 17.3	19 29.0	25 51.7	9 38.0	17 50.5	0 44.5	9 27.7	8 50.9
6	4 57 35.7	13 28.7	9 58.3	7♍54.0	5 51.0	20 44.4	26 33.6	9 44.1	17 46.9	0 47.6	9 29.9	8 52.2
7	5 1 32.2	14 29.6	9 55.2	22 .6	7 24.8	21 59.8	27 15.6	9 50.5	17 43.3	0 50.6	9 32.2	8 53.4
8	5 5 28.8	15 30.5	9 52.0	5♎56.8	8 58.6	23 15.2	27 57.6	9 57.0	17 39.5	0 53.5	9 34.4	8 54.6
9	5 9 25.3	16 31.5	9 48.8	19 41.5	10 32.4	24 30.5	28 39.7	10 3.7	17 35.7	0 56.5	9 36.7	8 55.7
10	5 13 21.9	17 32.5	9 45.6	3♏14.0	12 6.3	25 45.9	29 21.7	10 10.5	17 31.8	0 59.4	9 38.9	8 56.9
11	5 17 18.5	18 33.5	9 42.5	16 34.0	13 40.2	27 1.3	0♐ 3.9	10 17.5	17 27.8	1 2.2	9 41.2	8 58.0
12	5 21 15.0	19 34.5	9 39.3	29 41.0	15 14.1	28 16.7	0 46.1	10 24.7	17 23.8	1 5.0	9 43.4	8 59.0
13	5 25 11.6	20 35.5	9 36.1	12♐34.9	16 48.1	29 32.1	1 28.3	10 32.0	17 19.7	1 7.8	9 45.6	9 .0
14	5 29 8.1	21 36.5	9 32.9	25 15.7	18 22.2	0♑47.5	2 10.5	10 39.5	17 15.5	1 10.6	9 47.9	9 1.1
15	5 33 4.7	22 37.6	9 29.7	7♑43.8	19 56.4	2 2.8	2 52.8	10 47.1	17 11.3	1 13.3	9 50.1	9 2.0
16	5 37 1.2	23 38.6	9 26.6	20 .0	21 30.6	3 18.2	3 35.2	10 54.9	17 7.0	1 15.9	9 52.3	9 3.0
17	5 40 57.8	24 39.7	9 23.4	2♒ 6.1	23 5.1	4 33.6	4 17.6	11 2.9	17 2.7	1 18.6	9 54.6	9 3.9
18	5 44 54.4	25 40.8	9 20.2	14 4.0	24 39.6	5 49.0	5 .0	11 11.0	16 58.3	1 21.2	9 56.8	9 4.8
19	5 48 50.9	26 41.9	9 17.0	25 56.8	26 14.2	7 4.4	5 42.5	11 19.3	16 53.8	1 23.7	9 58.9	9 5.6
20	5 52 47.5	27 43.0	9 13.9	7♓48.0	27 49.0	8 19.7	6 25.0	11 27.7	16 49.3	1 26.2	10 1.1	9 6.4
21	5 56 44.0	28 44.1	9 10.7	19 41.8	29 24.0	9 35.1	7 7.5	11 36.2	16 44.8	1 28.7	10 3.3	9 7.2
22	6 0 40.6	29 45.2	9 7.5	1♈42.9	0♑59.1	10 50.4	7 50.1	11 44.9	16 40.1	1 31.1	10 5.4	9 7.9
23	6 4 37.1	0♑46.3	9 4.3	13 55.9	2 34.5	12 5.8	8 32.7	11 53.7	16 35.5	1 33.5	10 7.6	9 8.6
24	6 8 33.7	1 47.4	9 1.2	26 25.4	4 10.1	13 21.1	9 15.4	12 2.7	16 30.8	1 35.8	10 9.7	9 9.3
25	6 12 30.3	2 48.5	8 58.0	9♉15.7	5 45.9	14 36.4	9 58.1	12 11.8	16 26.1	1 38.1	10 11.9	9 9.9
26	6 16 26.8	3 49.6	8 54.8	22 29.9	7 21.9	15 51.7	10 40.8	12 21.0	16 21.3	1 40.4	10 14.0	9 10.5
27	6 20 23.4	4 50.7	8 51.6	6♊ 9.7	8 58.2	17 7.0	11 23.6	12 30.4	16 16.5	1 42.5	10 16.1	9 11.1
28	6 24 19.9	5 51.8	8 48.5	20 14.5	10 34.7	18 22.3	12 6.4	12 39.9	16 11.7	1 44.7	10 18.2	9 11.6
29	6 28 16.5	6 53.0	8 45.3	4♋41.3	12 11.5	19 37.6	12 49.3	12 49.5	16 6.9	1 46.8	10 20.2	9 12.1
30	6 32 13.0	7 54.1	8 42.1	19 24.8	13 48.5	20 52.9	13 32.1	12 59.3	16 2.0	1 48.9	10 22.3	9 12.5
31	6 36 9.6	8 55.2	8 38.9	4♌17.4	15 25.8	22 8.2	14 15.1	13 9.1	15 57.1	1 50.9	10 24.3	9 13.0

LATITUDE

DAY	EPHEM. SID. TIME	☉	☊	☽	☿	♀	♂	♃	♄	♅	♆	♇
1	4 37 52.9	0 .0	0 .0	1S27.5	0N32.6	0S 9.4	0N 7.2	1S15.6	0S26.7	0N31.6	1N31.1	16N28.9
4	4 49 42.6	0 .0	0 .0	4 32.2	0 11.5	0 16.6	0 5.4	1 14.9	0 26.5	0 31.7	1 31.1	16 30.4
7	5 1 32.2	0 .0	0 .0	5 10.6	0S 9.3	0 23.7	0 3.6	1 14.4	0 26.3	0 31.7	1 31.1	16 31.9
10	5 13 21.9	0 .0	0 .0	3 11.4	0 29.2	0 30.7	0 1.7	1 13.8	0 26.1	0 31.7	1 31.1	16 33.5
13	5 25 11.6	0 .0	0 .0	0N12.6	0 48.1	0 37.5	0S .1	1 13.2	0 25.8	0 31.8	1 31.1	16 35.1
16	5 37 1.2	0 .0	0 .0	3 22.4	1 5.8	0 44.1	0 2.0	1 12.6	0 25.6	0 31.8	1 31.1	16 36.8
19	5 48 50.9	0 .0	0 .0	5 5.9	1 21.8	0 50.4	0 3.9	1 12.1	0 25.3	0 31.9	1 31.1	16 38.4
22	6 0 40.6	0 .0	0 .0	4 53.4	1 36.1	0 56.5	0 5.8	1 11.6	0 25.0	0 31.9	1 31.2	16 40.1
25	6 12 30.3	0 .0	0 .0	2 42.0	1 48.2	1 2.2	0 7.7	1 11.1	0 24.7	0 32.0	1 31.2	16 41.9
28	6 24 19.9	0 .0	0 .0	0S55.1	1 57.9	1 7.5	0 9.6	1 10.6	0 24.4	0 32.0	1 31.3	16 43.6
31	6 36 9.6	0 .0	0 .0	4 14.1	2 4.8	1 12.4	0 11.6	1 10.1	0 24.1	0 32.1	1 31.3	16 45.3

RIGHT ASCENSION

DAY	EPHEM. SID. TIME	☉	☊	☽	☿	♀	♂	♃	♄	♅	♆	♇
1	4 37 52.9	6♐40.0	8♐36.8	25♊55.8	25♏54.8	13♐ 7.1	20♏42.6	11♓18.8	19♋30.5	28♎36.6	7♐52.3	14♎35.9
2	4 41 49.4	7 44.7	8 33.5	11♋11.6	27 30.1	14 28.0	21 25.0	11 23.8	19R27.1	28 39.6	7 54.7	14 37.4
3	4 45 46.0	8 49.5	8 30.1	26 6.8	29 5.9	15 49.2	22 7.6	11 29.0	19 23.5	28 42.6	7 57.1	14 38.8
4	4 49 42.6	9 54.6	8 26.7	10♌29.1	0♐42.3	17 10.5	22 50.4	11 34.4	19 19.9	28 45.5	7 59.4	14 40.2
5	4 53 39.1	10 59.7	8 23.3	24 16.6	2 19.3	18 32.1	23 33.3	11 40.0	19 16.2	28 48.5	8 1.8	14 41.5
6	4 57 35.7	12 5.0	8 19.9	7♍35.7	3 56.9	19 53.8	24 16.3	11 45.7	19 12.4	28 51.4	8 4.2	14 42.8
7	5 1 32.2	13 10.5	8 16.5	20 37.3	5 35.0	21 15.7	24 59.4	11 51.5	19 8.5	28 54.2	8 6.6	14 44.1
8	5 5 28.8	14 16.1	8 13.1	3♎33.6	7 13.6	22 37.7	25 42.7	11 57.6	19 4.5	28 57.1	8 9.0	14 45.4
9	5 9 25.3	15 21.8	8 9.7	16 36.1	8 52.8	23 59.8	26 26.2	12 3.7	19 .4	28 59.9	8 11.3	14 46.7
10	5 13 21.9	16 27.6	8 6.3	29 53.0	10 32.5	25 22.1	27 9.7	12 10.1	18 56.3	29 2.7	8 13.7	14 47.9
11	5 17 18.5	17 33.5	8 3.0	13♏27.4	12 12.7	26 44.5	27 53.4	12 16.6	18 52.0	29 5.4	8 16.1	14 49.1
12	5 21 15.0	18 39.6	7 59.6	27 15.9	13 53.4	28 6.9	28 37.2	12 23.2	18 47.7	29 8.1	8 18.4	14 50.3
13	5 25 11.6	19 45.7	7 56.2	11♐ 9.0	15 34.5	29 29.4	29 21.2	12 30.0	18 43.4	29 10.8	8 20.8	14 51.4
14	5 29 8.1	20 52.0	7 52.8	24 53.4	17 16.2	0♑52.0	0♐ 5.2	12 36.9	18 38.9	29 13.4	8 23.1	14 52.6
15	5 33 4.7	21 58.3	7 49.4	8♑15.8	18 58.4	2 14.6	0 49.5	12 44.0	18 34.4	29 16.0	8 25.5	14 53.7
16	5 37 1.2	23 4.6	7 46.0	21 7.1	20 41.0	3 37.2	1 33.8	12 51.2	18 29.8	29 18.5	8 27.8	14 54.7
17	5 40 57.8	24 11.1	7 42.7	3♒23.8	22 24.1	4 59.9	2 18.3	12 58.6	18 25.2	29 21.1	8 30.2	14 55.8
18	5 44 54.4	25 17.6	7 39.3	15 8.4	24 7.5	6 22.5	3 2.9	13 6.1	18 20.5	29 23.6	8 32.5	14 56.8
19	5 48 50.9	26 24.1	7 35.9	26 27.5	25 51.4	7 45.0	3 47.6	13 13.8	18 15.8	29 26.0	8 34.8	14 57.8
20	5 52 47.5	27 30.7	7 32.5	7♓30.9	27 35.6	9 7.6	4 32.4	13 21.5	18 10.9	29 28.4	8 37.1	14 58.7
21	5 56 44.0	28 37.3	7 29.1	18 30.0	29 20.3	10 30.0	5 17.4	13 29.5	18 6.1	29 30.8	8 39.4	14 59.7
22	6 0 40.6	29 43.9	7 25.7	29 37.4	1♑ 5.2	11 52.4	6 2.5	13 37.5	18 1.2	29 33.1	8 41.7	15 .5
23	6 4 37.1	0♑50.5	7 22.4	11♈ 6.2	2 50.5	13 14.7	6 47.7	13 45.7	17 56.2	29 35.4	8 44.0	15 1.4
24	6 8 33.7	1 57.0	7 19.0	23 9.3	4 36.1	14 36.8	7 33.0	13 54.0	17 51.2	29 37.6	8 46.2	15 2.2
25	6 12 30.3	3 3.6	7 15.6	5♉58.1	6 21.9	15 58.8	8 18.4	14 2.4	17 46.1	29 39.8	8 48.5	15 3.0
26	6 16 26.8	4 10.2	7 12.2	19 39.5	8 8.0	17 20.7	9 4.0	14 10.9	17 41.1	29 42.0	8 50.7	15 3.8
27	6 20 23.4	5 16.7	7 8.8	4♊12.9	9 54.2	18 42.4	9 49.6	14 19.6	17 35.9	29 44.1	8 52.9	15 4.6
28	6 24 19.9	6 23.2	7 5.5	19 27.3	11 40.6	20 4.0	10 35.4	14 28.4	17 30.8	29 46.2	8 55.1	15 5.3
29	6 28 16.5	7 29.7	7 2.1	5♋ 1.5	13 27.1	21 25.3	11 21.3	14 37.3	17 25.6	29 48.2	8 57.3	15 5.9
30	6 32 13.0	8 36.1	6 58.7	20 30.8	15 13.7	22 46.5	12 7.3	14 46.3	17 20.4	29 50.2	8 59.5	15 6.6
31	6 36 9.6	9 42.5	6 55.3	5♌34.9	17 .3	24 7.4	12 53.4	14 55.5	17 15.2	29 52.1	9 1.7	15 7.2

DECLINATION

DAY	EPHEM. SID. TIME	☉	☊	☽	☿	♀	♂	♃	♄	♅	♆	♇
1	4 37 52.9	21S42.5	0S23.0	21N55.8	19S11.8	22S41.6	18S25.7	9S16.1	21N46.8	11S10.0	20S20.9	11N39.9
4	4 49 42.6	22 9.4	0 23.0	13 33.3	20 31.2	23 11.8	18 58.3	9 9.2	21 48.4	11 13.3	20 21.9	11 39.7
7	5 1 32.2	22 32.4	0 23.0	1S35.3	21 42.1	23 35.7	19 29.5	9 1.6	21 50.0	11 16.4	20 22.9	11 39.7
10	5 13 21.9	22 51.5	0 23.0	15 35.4	22 43.7	23 53.1	19 59.3	8 53.5	21 51.7	11 19.4	20 23.9	11 39.8
13	5 25 11.6	23 6.4	0 22.9	22 5.9	23 35.1	24 4.0	20 27.5	8 44.8	21 53.5	11 22.3	20 24.9	11 40.1
16	5 37 1.2	23 17.3	0 22.9	18 36.9	24 15.8	24 8.1	20 54.3	8 35.6	21 55.4	11 25.1	20 25.8	11 40.4
19	5 48 50.9	23 24.0	0 22.9	8 4.1	24 45.1	24 5.5	21 19.4	8 25.8	21 57.3	11 27.7	20 26.8	11 41.0
22	6 0 40.6	23 26.4	0 22.9	5N10.0	25 2.4	23 56.2	21 42.8	8 15.6	21 59.3	11 30.2	20 27.7	11 41.6
25	6 12 30.3	23 24.7	0 22.8	17 8.4	25 7.1	23 40.3	22 4.4	8 4.8	22 1.3	11 32.6	20 28.6	11 42.4
28	6 24 19.9	23 18.7	0 22.8	22 10.0	24 58.7	23 17.8	22 24.2	7 53.6	22 3.3	11 34.8	20 29.4	11 43.4
31	6 36 9.6	23 8.5	0 22.8	15 4.3	24 36.9	22 48.8	22 42.2	7 42.0	22 5.3	11 36.9	20 30.3	11 44.5

JANUARY 1975

DAY	EPHEM. SID. TIME	☉	☊	☽	☿	♀	♂	♃	♄	♅	♆	♇
		LONGITUDE										
	h m s	° ′	° ′	° ′	° ′	° ′	° ′	° ′	° ′	° ′	° ′	° ′
1	6 40 6.2	9 ♑ 56.3	8 ♐ 35.7	19 ♌ 10.8	17 ♑ 3.3	23 ♑ 23.5	14 ♐ 58.1	13 ♓ 19.1	15 ♋ 52.2	1 ♏ 52.8	10 ♐ 26.4	9 ♎ 13.4
2	6 44 2.7	10 57.5	8 32.6	3 ♍ 56.9	18 41.0	24 38.7	15 41.1	13 29.3	15 R 47.3	1 54.7	10 28.4	9 13.7
3	6 47 59.3	11 58.6	8 29.4	18 29.1	20 19.0	25 54.0	16 24.1	13 39.5	15 42.3	1 56.6	10 30.4	9 14.0
4	6 51 55.8	12 59.8	8 26.2	2 ♎ 43.3	21 57.1	27 9.3	17 7.3	13 49.9	15 37.4	1 58.4	10 32.4	9 14.3
5	6 55 52.4	14 .9	8 23.0	16 37.4	23 35.4	28 24.5	17 50.4	14 .3	15 32.4	2 .2	10 34.3	9 14.6
6	6 59 49.0	15 2.1	8 19.9	0 ♏ 11.5	25 13.8	29 39.7	18 33.6	14 10.9	15 27.4	2 1.9	10 36.3	9 14.8
7	7 3 45.5	16 3.3	8 16.7	13 27.2	26 52.3	0 ♒ 55.0	19 16.9	14 21.7	15 22.5	2 3.6	10 38.3	9 15.0
8	7 7 42.1	17 4.4	8 13.5	26 26.3	28 30.7	2 10.2	20 .1	14 32.5	15 17.5	2 5.2	10 40.2	9 15.1
9	7 11 38.6	18 5.6	8 10.3	9 ♐ 11.3	0 ♒ 9.0	3 25.5	20 43.4	14 43.4	15 12.6	2 6.8	10 42.1	9 15.2
10	7 15 35.2	19 6.7	8 7.2	21 44.3	1 47.0	4 40.7	21 26.8	14 54.4	15 7.6	2 8.3	10 43.9	9 15.3
11	7 19 31.7	20 7.9	8 4.0	4 ♑ 7.1	3 24.7	5 55.9	22 10.2	15 5.6	15 2.7	2 9.7	10 45.8	9 15.3
12	7 23 28.3	21 9.1	8 .8	16 21.2	5 1.9	7 11.1	22 53.6	15 16.8	14 57.8	2 11.1	10 47.6	9 15.3
13	7 27 24.9	22 10.2	7 57.6	28 27.7	6 38.4	8 26.2	23 37.1	15 28.2	14 52.9	2 12.5	10 49.4	9 15.3
14	7 31 21.4	23 11.3	7 54.4	10 ♒ 27.9	8 14.0	9 41.4	24 20.6	15 39.6	14 48.0	2 13.8	10 51.2	9 R 15.2
15	7 35 18.0	24 12.5	7 51.3	22 23.0	9 48.4	10 56.6	25 4.1	15 51.1	14 43.1	2 15.0	10 53.0	9 15.1
16	7 39 14.5	25 13.6	7 48.1	4 ♓ 14.8	11 21.3	12 11.7	25 47.7	16 2.8	14 38.2	2 16.2	10 54.8	9 15.0
17	7 43 11.1	26 14.7	7 44.9	16 5.7	12 52.4	13 26.8	26 31.3	16 14.5	14 33.4	2 17.3	10 56.5	9 14.8
18	7 47 7.6	27 15.8	7 41.7	27 58.6	14 21.2	14 41.9	27 15.0	16 26.3	14 28.6	2 18.4	10 58.2	9 14.6
19	7 51 4.2	28 16.9	7 38.6	9 ♈ 57.3	15 47.3	15 57.0	27 58.7	16 38.3	14 23.9	2 19.4	10 59.9	9 14.3
20	7 55 .7	29 18.0	7 35.4	22 6.0	17 10.2	17 12.1	28 42.4	16 50.3	14 19.2	2 20.4	11 1.5	9 14.1
21	7 58 57.3	0 ♒ 19.1	7 32.2	4 ♉ 29.6	18 29.3	18 27.1	29 26.1	17 2.4	14 14.5	2 21.3	11 3.2	9 13.7
22	8 2 53.9	1 20.2	7 29.0	17 12.9	19 43.9	19 42.2	0 ♑ 10.0	17 14.6	14 9.9	2 22.2	11 4.8	9 13.4
23	8 6 50.4	2 21.2	7 25.9	0 ♊ 20.3	20 53.3	20 57.2	0 53.8	17 26.9	14 5.3	2 23.0	11 6.4	9 13.1
24	8 10 47.0	3 22.2	7 22.7	13 55.5	21 56.7	22 12.2	1 37.7	17 39.2	14 .8	2 23.8	11 8.0	9 12.6
25	8 14 43.5	4 23.2	7 19.5	27 59.9	22 53.3	23 27.2	2 21.6	17 51.6	13 56.3	2 24.5	11 9.5	9 12.2
26	8 18 40.1	5 24.2	7 16.3	12 ♋ 32.4	23 42.2	24 42.1	3 5.5	18 4.1	13 51.8	2 25.1	11 11.0	9 11.7
27	8 22 36.6	6 25.2	7 13.1	27 28.4	24 22.6	25 57.0	3 49.5	18 16.7	13 47.4	2 25.7	11 12.5	9 11.2
28	8 26 33.2	7 26.1	7 10.0	12 ♌ 39.9	24 53.8	27 11.9	4 33.5	18 29.4	13 43.1	2 26.2	11 13.9	9 10.7
29	8 30 29.8	8 27.1	7 6.8	27 56.5	25 14.9	28 26.8	5 17.6	18 42.1	13 38.8	2 26.7	11 15.4	9 10.1
30	8 34 26.3	9 28.0	7 3.6	13 ♍ 6.9	25 25.3	29 41.6	6 1.6	18 54.9	13 34.6	2 27.1	11 16.8	9 9.5
31	8 38 22.9	10 28.9	7 .4	28 1.2	25 R 24.7	0 ♓ 56.5	6 45.8	19 7.7	13 30.5	2 27.5	11 18.1	9 8.8
		LATITUDE										
1	6 40 6.2	0 .0	0 .0	4 S 52.3	2 S 6.4	1 S 14.0	0 S 12.2	1 S 9.9	0 S 24.0	0 N 32.1	1 N 31.3	16 N 45.9
4	6 51 55.8	0 .0	0 .0	4 47.9	2 8.7	1 18.3	0 14.2	1 9.5	0 23.7	0 32.2	1 31.4	16 47.7
7	7 3 45.5	0 .0	0 .0	2 19.0	2 7.1	1 22.1	0 16.2	1 9.1	0 23.4	0 32.2	1 31.4	16 49.4
10	7 15 35.2	0 .0	0 .0	1 N 4.1	2 .7	1 25.4	0 18.2	1 8.6	0 23.0	0 32.3	1 31.5	16 51.2
13	7 27 24.9	0 .0	0 .0	3 52.5	1 48.8	1 28.2	0 20.3	1 8.2	0 22.7	0 32.4	1 31.6	16 52.9
16	7 39 14.5	0 .0	0 .0	5 6.2	1 30.5	1 30.4	0 22.3	1 7.9	0 22.4	0 32.4	1 31.7	16 54.6
19	7 51 4.2	0 .0	0 .0	4 23.6	1 4.9	1 32.0	0 24.4	1 7.5	0 22.0	0 32.5	1 31.8	16 56.3
22	8 2 53.9	0 .0	0 .0	1 53.6	0 31.3	1 33.0	0 26.4	1 7.2	0 21.7	0 32.6	1 31.9	16 58.0
25	8 14 43.5	0 .0	0 .0	1 S 40.7	0 N 10.4	1 33.4	0 28.5	1 6.9	0 21.3	0 32.6	1 32.0	16 59.7
28	8 26 33.2	0 .0	0 .0	4 33.9	0 59.1	1 33.2	0 30.6	1 6.6	0 20.9	0 32.7	1 32.1	17 1.3
31	8 38 22.9	0 .0	0 .0	4 45.9	1 51.4	1 32.4	0 32.7	1 6.3	0 20.5	0 32.8	1 32.2	17 2.9
		RIGHT ASCENSION										
1	6 40 6.2	10 ♑ 48.8	6 ♐ 51.9	20 ♌ 3.6	18 ♑ 46.8	25 ♑ 28.1	13 ♐ 39.6	15 ♓ 4.7	17 ♋ 9.9	29 ♎ 54.0	9 ♐ 3.8	15 ♎ 7.8
2	6 44 2.7	11 55.0	6 48.6	3 ♍ 57.5	20 33.2	26 48.6	14 25.9	15 14.1	17 R 4.6	29 55.8	9 5.9	15 8.4
3	6 47 59.3	13 1.1	6 45.2	17 24.1	22 19.5	28 8.9	15 12.3	15 23.6	16 59.4	29 57.6	9 8.1	15 8.9
4	6 51 55.8	14 7.2	6 41.8	0 ♎ 35.0	24 5.5	29 28.9	15 58.9	15 33.2	16 54.1	29 59.3	9 10.2	15 9.4
5	6 55 52.4	15 13.2	6 38.4	13 41.5	25 51.2	0 ♒ 48.6	16 45.5	15 42.8	16 48.8	0 ♏ 1.0	9 12.2	15 9.8
6	6 59 49.0	16 19.1	6 35.1	26 53.3	27 36.4	2 8.0	17 32.2	15 52.6	16 43.5	0 2.7	9 14.3	15 10.3
7	7 3 45.5	17 24.9	6 31.7	10 ♏ 15.9	29 21.2	3 27.3	18 19.1	16 2.6	16 38.2	0 4.3	9 16.4	15 10.7
8	7 7 42.1	18 30.5	6 28.3	23 49.7	1 ♒ 5.3	4 46.2	19 6.0	16 12.6	16 32.9	0 5.9	9 18.4	15 11.1
9	7 11 38.6	19 36.1	6 24.9	7 ♐ 29.2	2 48.6	6 4.7	19 53.0	16 22.7	16 27.6	0 7.4	9 20.4	15 11.4
10	7 15 35.2	20 41.5	6 21.6	21 4.7	4 31.0	7 23.0	20 40.1	16 32.9	16 22.3	0 8.8	9 22.4	15 11.7
11	7 19 31.7	21 46.8	6 18.2	4 ♑ 25.0	6 12.3	8 41.0	21 27.3	16 43.1	16 17.0	0 10.2	9 24.4	15 12.0
12	7 23 28.3	22 51.9	6 14.8	17 20.4	7 52.3	9 58.7	22 14.6	16 53.5	16 11.7	0 11.6	9 26.3	15 12.2
13	7 27 24.9	23 56.9	6 11.4	29 45.6	9 30.9	11 16.0	23 1.9	17 4.0	16 6.4	0 12.9	9 28.2	15 12.4
14	7 31 21.4	25 1.7	6 8.1	11 ♒ 40.0	11 7.7	12 33.1	23 49.3	17 14.6	16 1.2	0 14.1	9 30.1	15 12.6
15	7 35 18.0	26 6.4	6 4.7	23 7.7	12 42.6	13 49.8	24 36.8	17 25.2	15 56.0	0 15.3	9 32.0	15 12.7
16	7 39 14.5	27 10.9	6 1.3	4 ♓ 15.8	14 15.1	15 6.1	25 24.3	17 36.0	15 50.8	0 16.5	9 33.9	15 12.8
17	7 43 11.1	28 15.2	5 57.9	15 14.0	15 45.0	16 22.2	26 11.9	17 46.8	15 45.6	0 17.6	9 35.7	15 12.9
18	7 47 7.6	29 19.4	5 54.6	26 12.9	17 11.8	17 37.9	26 59.6	17 57.7	15 40.5	0 18.6	9 37.5	15 12.9
19	7 51 4.2	0 ♒ 23.4	5 51.2	7 ♈ 24.4	18 35.1	18 53.3	27 47.3	18 8.7	15 35.4	0 19.6	9 39.3	15 13.0
20	7 55 .7	1 27.1	5 47.8	19 .5	19 54.5	20 8.4	28 35.1	18 19.8	15 30.3	0 20.6	9 41.0	15 R 12.9
21	7 58 57.3	2 30.7	5 44.5	1 ♉ 12.8	21 9.3	21 23.1	29 23.0	18 31.0	15 25.3	0 21.4	9 42.8	15 12.9
22	8 2 53.9	3 34.2	5 41.1	14 11.0	22 19.0	22 37.5	0 ♑ 10.9	18 42.2	15 20.4	0 22.3	9 44.5	15 12.8
23	8 6 50.4	4 37.4	5 37.7	28 .0	23 22.9	23 51.6	0 58.9	18 53.6	15 15.5	0 23.1	9 46.2	15 12.7
24	8 10 47.0	5 40.4	5 34.4	12 ♊ 37.2	24 20.2	25 5.3	1 46.8	19 4.9	15 10.6	0 23.8	9 47.9	15 12.6
25	8 14 43.5	6 43.3	5 31.0	27 50.7	25 10.4	26 18.8	2 34.9	19 16.4	15 5.8	0 24.5	9 49.5	15 12.4
26	8 18 40.1	7 45.9	5 27.6	13 ♋ 20.7	25 52.7	27 31.9	3 22.9	19 27.9	15 1.0	0 25.1	9 51.1	15 12.2
27	8 22 36.6	8 48.3	5 24.2	28 45.5	26 26.4	28 44.7	4 11.0	19 39.5	14 56.3	0 25.7	9 52.7	15 12.0
28	8 26 33.2	9 50.5	5 20.9	13 ♌ 48.8	26 50.7	29 57.1	4 59.1	19 51.2	14 51.7	0 26.2	9 54.2	15 11.7
29	8 30 29.8	10 52.5	5 17.5	28 23.2	27 5.1	1 ♓ 9.3	5 47.3	20 2.9	14 47.1	0 26.7	9 55.7	15 11.4
30	8 34 26.3	11 54.3	5 14.1	12 ♍ 30.3	27 9.2	2 21.2	6 35.5	20 14.7	14 42.6	0 27.1	9 57.2	15 11.0
31	8 38 22.9	12 55.9	5 10.8	26 17.2	27 R 2.7	3 32.8	7 23.7	20 26.5	14 38.1	0 27.4	9 58.7	15 10.7
		DECLINATION										
1	6 40 6.2	23 S 4.1	0 S 22.8	10 N 26.3	24 S 26.5	22 S 37.8	22 S 47.8	7 S 38.0	22 N 6.0	11 S 37.6	20 S 30.5	11 N 44.8
4	6 51 55.8	22 48.4	0 22.7	5 S 29.0	23 46.1	22 .6	23 3.2	7 25.7	22 8.0	11 39.4	20 31.3	11 46.1
7	7 3 45.5	22 28.6	0 22.7	18 5.2	22 51.7	21 17.5	23 16.7	7 13.1	22 10.1	11 41.2	20 32.1	11 47.4
10	7 15 35.2	22 4.8	0 22.7	22 7.1	21 43.5	20 28.7	23 28.1	7 .0	22 12.1	11 42.7	20 32.8	11 48.9
13	7 27 24.9	21 37.0	0 22.7	16 40.5	20 22.1	19 34.5	23 37.5	6 46.6	22 14.1	11 44.1	20 33.5	11 50.5
16	7 39 14.5	21 5.5	0 22.6	5 11.7	18 49.4	18 35.2	23 44.8	6 32.8	22 16.0	11 45.3	20 34.2	11 52.2
19	7 51 4.2	20 30.4	0 22.6	7 N 58.9	17 8.3	17 31.2	23 49.9	6 18.7	22 17.9	11 46.4	20 34.8	11 54.0
22	8 2 53.9	19 51.8	0 22.6	18 47.5	15 23.7	16 22.8	23 52.9	6 4.2	22 19.8	11 47.3	20 35.4	11 55.9
25	8 14 43.5	19 9.9	0 22.6	21 44.9	13 43.5	15 10.4	23 53.7	5 49.5	22 21.5	11 48.0	20 35.9	11 57.9
28	8 26 33.2	18 24.9	0 22.5	12 37.5	12 17.8	13 54.3	23 52.3	5 34.4	22 23.3	11 48.5	20 36.4	11 60.0
31	8 38 22.9	17 36.8	0 22.5	3 S 35.0	11 18.1	12 34.8	23 48.8	5 19.1	22 24.9	11 48.9	20 36.9	12 2.1

FEBRUARY 1975

LONGITUDE

DAY	EPHEM. SID. TIME h m s	☉ ° ′	☊ ° ′	☾ ° ′	☿ ° ′	♀ ° ′	♂ ° ′	♃ ° ′	♄ ° ′	♅ ° ′	♆ ° ′	♇ ° ′
1	8 42 19.4	11 ♒ 29.8	6 ♐ 57.3	12 ♎ 32.3	25 ♒ 12.8	2 ♓ 11.3	7 ♑ 29.9	19 ♓ 20.7	13 ♋ 26.4	2 ♏ 27.8	11 ♐ 19.5	9 ♎ 8.1
2	8 46 16.0	12 30.7	6 54.1	26 36.7	24 R 49.7	3 26.1	8 14.1	19 33.7	13 R 22.4	2 28.0	11 20.8	9 R 7.4
3	8 50 12.5	13 31.5	6 50.9	10 ♏ 14.1	24 15.9	4 40.8	8 58.4	19 46.8	13 18.4	2 28.2	11 22.1	9 6.7
4	8 54 9.1	14 32.4	6 47.7	23 26.4	23 32.0	5 55.6	9 42.7	19 59.9	13 14.6	2 28.3	11 23.3	9 5.9
5	8 58 5.6	15 33.3	6 44.6	6 ♐ 17.1	22 39.2	7 10.3	10 27.0	20 13.1	13 10.8	2 28.4	11 24.6	9 5.1
6	9 2 2.2	16 34.1	6 41.4	18 50.3	21 38.9	8 25.0	11 11.3	20 26.4	13 7.0	2 28.4	11 25.8	9 4.3
7	9 5 58.8	17 34.9	6 38.2	1 ♑ 9.9	20 32.9	9 39.6	11 55.7	20 39.7	13 3.4	2 28.4	11 26.9	9 3.4
8	9 9 55.3	18 35.7	6 35.0	13 19.5	19 23.2	10 54.3	12 40.1	20 53.1	12 59.8	2 R 28.3	11 28.1	9 2.6
9	9 13 51.9	19 36.5	6 31.8	25 21.9	18 11.6	12 8.9	13 24.6	21 6.5	12 56.3	2 28.2	11 29.2	9 1.6
10	9 17 48.4	20 37.2	6 28.7	7 ♒ 19.4	17 .2	13 23.5	14 9.0	21 20.0	12 52.9	2 28.0	11 30.3	9 .7
11	9 21 45.0	21 38.0	6 25.5	19 13.8	15 50.8	14 38.0	14 53.6	21 33.6	12 49.6	2 27.7	11 31.3	8 59.7
12	9 25 41.5	22 38.8	6 22.3	1 ♓ 6.3	14 45.2	15 52.6	15 38.2	21 47.2	12 46.4	2 27.4	11 32.4	8 58.8
13	9 29 38.1	23 39.4	6 19.1	12 58.2	13 44.6	17 7.1	16 22.7	22 .9	12 43.3	2 27.1	11 33.4	8 57.7
14	9 33 34.6	24 40.1	6 16.0	24 51.0	12 50.2	18 21.6	17 7.3	22 14.6	12 40.3	2 26.7	11 34.3	8 56.7
15	9 37 31.2	25 40.8	6 12.8	6 ♈ 46.4	12 2.7	19 36.0	17 52.0	22 28.3	12 37.3	2 26.2	11 35.3	8 55.6
16	9 41 27.7	26 41.4	6 9.6	18 47.1	11 22.7	20 50.4	18 36.6	22 42.1	12 34.5	2 25.7	11 36.2	8 54.5
17	9 45 24.3	27 42.0	6 6.4	0 ♉ 56.2	10 50.4	22 4.8	19 21.3	22 55.9	12 31.7	2 25.1	11 37.0	8 53.4
18	9 49 20.8	28 42.5	6 3.2	13 17.7	10 26.0	23 19.1	20 6.1	23 9.8	12 29.0	2 24.4	11 37.8	8 52.2
19	9 53 17.4	29 43.1	6 .1	25 55.9	10 9.2	24 33.3	20 50.8	23 23.7	12 26.5	2 23.7	11 38.6	8 51.0
20	9 57 14.0	0 ♓ 43.6	5 56.9	8 ♊ 55.6	9 59.9	25 47.6	21 35.6	23 37.7	12 24.0	2 23.0	11 39.4	8 49.8
21	10 1 10.5	1 44.0	5 53.7	22 20.9	9 57.7	27 1.8	22 20.4	23 51.7	12 21.6	2 22.2	11 40.1	8 48.6
22	10 5 7.1	2 44.5	5 50.5	6 ♋ 14.7	10 D 2.4	28 15.9	23 5.2	24 5.7	12 19.4	2 21.4	11 40.8	8 47.3
23	10 9 3.6	3 44.9	5 47.4	20 38.0	10 13.4	29 30.0	23 50.1	24 19.8	12 17.2	2 20.5	11 41.5	8 46.1
24	10 13 .2	4 45.3	5 44.2	5 ♌ 28.1	10 30.5	0 ♈ 44.1	24 35.0	24 33.9	12 15.1	2 19.5	11 42.1	8 44.8
25	10 16 56.7	5 45.6	5 41.0	20 38.8	10 53.2	1 58.1	25 19.9	24 48.0	12 13.2	2 18.5	11 42.7	8 43.4
26	10 20 53.3	6 45.9	5 37.8	6 ♍ .5	11 21.1	3 12.1	26 4.9	25 2.2	12 11.3	2 17.5	11 43.3	8 42.1
27	10 24 49.8	7 46.2	5 34.6	21 21.3	11 53.9	4 26.0	26 49.8	25 16.4	12 9.6	2 16.4	11 43.8	8 40.7
28	10 28 46.4	8 46.5	5 31.5	6 ♎ 29.4	12 31.2	5 39.9	27 34.9	25 30.6	12 8.0	2 15.2	11 44.3	8 39.4

LATITUDE

DAY	EPHEM. SID. TIME	☉	☊	☾	☿	♀	♂	♃	♄	♅	♆	♇
1	8 42 19.4	0 .0	0 .0	4 S 10.8	2 N 8.7	1 S 31.9	0 S 33.4	1 S 6.2	0 S 20.4	0 N 32.8	1 N 32.2	17 N 3.4
4	8 54 9.1	0 .0	0 .0	1 16.3	2 55.7	1 30.2	0 35.5	1 5.9	0 20.0	0 32.9	1 32.4	17 4.9
7	9 5 58.8	0 .0	0 .0	2 N .2	3 28.8	1 27.9	0 37.6	1 5.7	0 19.6	0 32.9	1 32.5	17 6.4
10	9 17 48.4	0 .0	0 .0	4 20.3	3 41.6	1 24.9	0 39.7	1 5.5	0 19.3	0 33.0	1 32.6	17 7.8
13	9 29 38.1	0 .0	0 .0	4 58.3	3 33.4	1 21.3	0 41.8	1 5.3	0 18.9	0 33.1	1 32.8	17 9.2
16	9 41 27.7	0 .0	0 .0	3 42.0	3 9.1	1 17.1	0 43.9	1 5.1	0 18.5	0 33.1	1 32.9	17 10.5
19	9 53 17.4	0 .0	0 .0	0 53.3	2 35.1	1 12.3	0 46.0	1 4.9	0 18.1	0 33.2	1 33.0	17 11.7
22	10 5 7.1	0 .0	0 .0	2 S 32.1	1 56.9	1 6.9	0 48.1	1 4.8	0 17.7	0 33.3	1 33.2	17 12.9
25	10 16 56.7	0 .0	0 .0	4 49.9	1 18.2	1 1.0	0 50.2	1 4.7	0 17.3	0 33.3	1 33.3	17 13.9
28	10 28 46.4	0 .0	0 .0	4 16.6	0 41.1	0 54.6	0 52.3	1 4.6	0 16.9	0 33.4	1 33.5	17 15.0

RIGHT ASCENSION

DAY	EPHEM. SID. TIME	☉	☊	☾	☿	♀	♂	♃	♄	♅	♆	♇
1	8 42 19.4	13 ♒ 57.3	5 ♐ 7.4	9 ♎ 53.1	26 ♒ 45.4	4 ♓ 44.1	8 ♑ 11.9	20 ♓ 38.4	14 ♋ 33.7	0 ♏ 27.7	10 ♐ .1	15 ♎ 10.3
2	8 46 16.0	14 58.6	5 4.0	23 26.5	26 R 17.6	5 55.2	9 .2	20 50.4	14 R 29.4	0 28.0	10 1.5	15 R 9.9
3	8 50 12.5	15 59.6	5 .7	7 ♏ 2.7	25 39.7	7 6.0	9 48.5	21 2.4	14 25.2	0 28.1	10 2.9	15 9.4
4	8 54 9.1	17 .4	4 57.3	20 42.8	24 52.7	8 16.5	10 36.8	21 14.5	14 21.0	0 28.3	10 4.2	15 8.9
5	8 58 5.6	18 1.0	4 54.0	4 ♐ 23.3	23 57.6	9 26.7	11 25.1	21 26.7	14 17.0	0 28.4	10 5.5	15 8.4
6	9 2 2.2	19 1.4	4 50.6	17 57.0	22 55.9	10 36.8	12 13.3	21 38.9	14 13.0	0 28.4	10 6.8	15 7.9
7	9 5 58.8	20 1.6	4 47.2	1 ♑ 15.0	21 49.3	11 46.6	13 1.6	21 51.1	14 9.0	0 28.4	10 8.0	15 7.3
8	9 9 55.3	21 1.6	4 43.9	14 9.9	20 39.6	12 56.1	13 49.9	22 3.4	14 5.2	0 R 28.3	10 9.3	15 6.7
9	9 13 51.9	22 1.5	4 40.5	26 36.9	19 28.8	14 5.5	14 38.2	22 15.8	14 1.5	0 28.2	10 10.4	15 6.1
10	9 17 48.4	23 1.1	4 37.1	8 ♒ 35.4	18 18.7	15 14.6	15 26.5	22 28.2	13 57.8	0 28.0	10 11.6	15 5.4
11	9 21 45.0	24 .5	4 33.8	20 8.6	17 11.2	16 23.5	16 14.8	22 40.7	13 54.3	0 27.7	10 12.7	15 4.8
12	9 25 41.5	24 59.8	4 30.4	1 ♓ 22.2	16 7.8	17 32.3	17 3.1	22 53.2	13 50.9	0 27.5	10 13.8	15 4.1
13	9 29 38.1	25 58.9	4 27.0	12 24.1	15 9.7	18 40.9	17 51.3	23 5.8	13 47.5	0 27.2	10 14.9	15 3.3
14	9 33 34.6	26 57.7	4 23.7	23 23.4	14 18.0	19 49.2	18 39.5	23 18.4	13 44.2	0 26.8	10 15.9	15 2.6
15	9 37 31.2	27 56.4	4 20.3	4 ♈ 30.0	13 33.4	20 57.5	19 27.7	23 31.0	13 41.1	0 26.3	10 16.9	15 1.8
16	9 41 27.7	28 54.9	4 17.0	15 54.1	12 56.5	22 5.5	20 15.8	23 43.7	13 38.0	0 25.8	10 17.8	15 1.0
17	9 45 24.3	29 53.2	4 13.6	27 45.7	12 27.4	23 13.4	21 4.0	23 56.4	13 35.0	0 25.3	10 18.8	15 .1
18	9 49 20.8	0 ♓ 51.3	4 10.2	10 ♉ 13.4	12 6.2	24 21.2	21 52.0	24 9.1	13 32.2	0 24.6	10 19.6	14 59.3
19	9 53 17.4	1 49.2	4 6.9	23 23.1	11 52.8	25 28.9	22 40.1	24 21.9	13 29.4	0 24.0	10 20.5	14 58.4
20	9 57 14.0	2 47.0	4 3.5	7 ♊ 15.6	11 46.9	26 36.4	23 28.1	24 34.7	13 26.8	0 23.3	10 21.3	14 57.5
21	10 1 10.5	3 44.6	4 .2	21 45.4	11 D 48.3	27 43.8	24 16.0	24 47.6	13 24.2	0 22.5	10 22.1	14 56.5
22	10 5 7.1	4 42.0	3 56.8	6 ♋ 40.5	11 56.5	28 51.1	25 4.0	25 .5	13 21.8	0 21.7	10 22.8	14 55.6
23	10 9 3.6	5 39.2	3 53.5	21 45.1	12 11.2	29 58.4	25 51.8	25 13.4	13 19.5	0 20.9	10 23.5	14 54.6
24	10 13 .2	6 36.3	3 50.1	6 ♌ 44.4	12 31.9	1 ♈ 5.6	26 39.6	25 26.4	13 17.3	0 20.0	10 24.2	14 53.6
25	10 16 56.7	7 33.3	3 46.7	21 29.1	12 58.3	2 12.6	27 27.4	25 39.3	13 15.2	0 19.0	10 24.9	14 52.5
26	10 20 53.3	8 30.1	3 43.4	5 ♍ 56.6	13 29.8	3 19.7	28 15.1	25 52.3	13 13.2	0 18.0	10 25.5	14 51.5
27	10 24 49.8	9 26.7	3 40.0	20 10.0	14 6.2	4 26.7	29 2.8	26 5.4	13 11.3	0 17.0	10 26.0	14 50.4
28	10 28 46.4	10 23.2	3 36.7	4 ♎ 15.4	14 47.0	5 33.7	29 50.4	26 18.4	13 9.6	0 15.9	10 26.6	14 49.3

DECLINATION

DAY	EPHEM. SID. TIME	☉	☊	☾	☿	♀	♂	♃	♄	♅	♆	♇
1	8 42 19.4	17 S 20.1	0 S 22.5	8 S 48.1	11 S 5.8	12 S 7.6	23 S 47.1	5 S 14.0	22 N 25.5	11 S 48.9	20 S 37.0	12 N 2.9
4	8 54 9.1	16 28.3	0 22.5	19 51.9	10 54.6	10 44.2	23 40.5	4 58.3	22 27.0	11 49.1	20 37.4	12 5.1
7	9 5 58.8	15 33.9	0 22.4	21 26.0	11 20.3	9 18.2	23 31.8	4 42.5	22 28.5	11 49.0	20 37.8	12 7.4
10	9 17 48.4	14 37.2	0 22.4	14 14.6	12 13.1	7 50.1	23 20.9	4 26.4	22 29.9	11 48.8	20 38.1	12 9.8
13	9 29 38.1	13 38.1	0 22.4	2 5.7	13 17.5	6 20.1	23 7.7	4 10.1	22 31.2	11 48.5	20 38.4	12 12.1
16	9 41 27.7	12 37.1	0 22.3	10 N 46.8	14 20.2	4 48.7	22 52.4	3 53.6	22 32.4	11 47.9	20 38.6	12 14.6
19	9 53 17.4	11 34.3	0 22.3	20 6.2	15 12.7	3 16.2	22 35.0	3 37.0	22 33.6	11 47.2	20 38.8	12 17.0
22	10 5 7.1	10 29.9	0 22.3	20 45.7	15 51.3	1 42.8	22 15.4	3 20.2	22 34.6	11 46.3	20 39.0	12 19.5
25	10 16 56.7	9 24.0	0 22.3	10 1.5	16 14.9	0 9.0	21 53.8	3 3.3	22 35.6	11 45.3	20 39.1	12 22.0
28	10 28 46.4	8 16.9	0 22.2	6 S 30.2	16 23.5	1 N 24.9	21 30.1	2 46.3	22 36.4	11 44.1	20 39.2	12 24.5

MARCH 1975

DAY	EPHEM. SID. TIME	☉	☊	☽	☿	♀	♂	♃	♄	♅	♆	♇
	h m s	° ′	° ′	° ′	° ′	° ′	° ′	° ′	° ′	° ′	° ′	° ′
		LONGITUDE										
1	10 32 42.9	9♓46.7	5♐28.3	21♎15.5	13♒12.6	6♈53.8	28♑19.9	25♓44.9	12♋ 6.4	2♏14.0	11♐44.8	8♎38.0
2	10 36 39.5	10 46.9	5 25.1	5♏33.6	13 57.9	8 7.6	29 5.0	25 59.2	12R 5.0	2R12.8	11 45.2	8R36.6
3	10 40 36.0	11 47.1	5 21.9	19 21.7	14 46.8	9 21.3	29 50.1	26 13.5	12 3.7	2 11.5	11 45.6	8 35.1
4	10 44 32.6	12 47.2	5 18.8	2♐40.9	15 39.1	10 35.0	0♒35.2	26 27.8	12 2.5	2 10.2	11 46.0	8 33.7
5	10 48 29.1	13 47.4	5 15.6	15 34.3	16 34.5	11 48.7	1 20.4	26 42.2	12 1.4	2 8.8	11 46.3	8 32.3
6	10 52 25.7	14 47.5	5 12.4	28 6.5	17 32.7	13 2.3	2 5.6	26 56.6	12 .4	2 7.4	11 46.6	8 30.8
7	10 56 22.3	15 47.6	5 9.2	10♑22.3	18 33.7	14 15.9	2 50.8	27 11.0	11 59.6	2 5.9	11 46.9	8 29.3
8	11 0 18.8	16 47.7	5 6.0	22 26.4	19 37.1	15 29.4	3 36.0	27 25.4	11 58.8	2 4.4	11 47.1	8 27.8
9	11 4 15.4	17 47.7	5 2.9	4♒23.0	20 43.0	16 42.9	4 21.2	27 39.8	11 58.2	2 2.9	11 47.3	8 26.2
10	11 8 11.9	18 47.7	4 59.7	16 15.4	21 51.1	17 56.3	5 6.5	27 54.3	11 57.6	2 1.3	11 47.5	8 24.7
11	11 12 8.5	19 47.7	4 56.5	28 6.6	23 1.3	19 9.7	5 51.8	28 8.7	11 57.2	1 59.6	11 47.6	8 23.1
12	11 16 5.0	20 47.6	4 53.3	9♓58.4	24 13.5	20 23.0	6 37.1	28 23.2	11 56.9	1 57.9	11 47.7	8 21.6
13	11 20 1.6	21 47.5	4 50.2	21 52.5	25 27.7	21 36.2	7 22.5	28 37.7	11 56.7	1 56.2	11 47.8	8 20.0
14	11 23 58.1	22 47.4	4 47.0	3♈50.2	26 43.6	22 49.5	8 7.8	28 52.2	11 56.6	1 54.4	11 47.8	8 18.4
15	11 27 54.7	23 47.2	4 43.8	15 52.6	28 1.3	24 2.6	8 53.2	29 6.7	11 56.6	1 52.6	11 47.8	8 16.8
16	11 31 51.2	24 47.0	4 40.6	28 1.3	29 20.7	25 15.7	9 38.6	29 21.2	11D56.7	1 50.8	11R47.7	8 15.2
17	11 35 47.8	25 46.8	4 37.4	10♉18.3	0♓41.7	26 28.7	10 24.0	29 35.8	11 57.0	1 48.9	11 47.7	8 13.6
18	11 39 44.3	26 46.5	4 34.3	22 46.1	2 4.3	27 41.7	11 9.4	29 50.3	11 57.3	1 47.0	11 47.5	8 12.0
19	11 43 40.9	27 46.2	4 31.1	5♊27.9	3 28.3	28 54.6	11 54.8	0♈ 4.8	11 57.8	1 45.0	11 47.4	8 10.3
20	11 47 37.4	28 45.9	4 27.9	18 27.2	4 53.9	0♉ 7.5	12 40.3	0 19.3	11 58.4	1 43.0	11 47.2	8 8.7
21	11 51 34.0	29 45.5	4 24.7	1♋47.4	6 20.9	1 20.2	13 25.8	0 33.9	11 59.1	1 41.0	11 47.0	8 7.0
22	11 55 30.5	0♈45.1	4 21.6	15 31.5	7 49.4	2 33.0	14 11.3	0 48.4	11 59.9	1 38.9	11 46.8	8 5.4
23	11 59 27.1	1 44.6	4 18.4	29 40.9	9 19.3	3 45.6	14 56.8	1 2.9	12 .8	1 36.9	11 46.5	8 3.7
24	12 3 23.6	2 44.1	4 15.2	14♌14.7	10 50.5	4 58.2	15 42.3	1 17.5	12 1.8	1 34.7	11 46.2	8 2.1
25	12 7 20.2	3 43.6	4 12.0	29 8.8	12 23.1	6 10.7	16 27.8	1 32.0	12 3.0	1 32.6	11 45.9	8 .4
26	12 11 16.7	4 43.1	4 8.8	14♍16.2	13 57.2	7 23.2	17 13.4	1 46.6	12 4.3	1 30.5	11 45.5	7 58.8
27	12 15 13.3	5 42.5	4 5.7	29 27.2	15 32.5	8 35.5	17 58.9	2 1.1	12 5.6	1 28.3	11 45.1	7 57.1
28	12 19 9.9	6 41.8	4 2.5	14♎31.1	17 9.2	9 47.8	18 44.5	2 15.6	12 7.1	1 26.0	11 44.7	7 55.5
29	12 23 6.4	7 41.2	3 59.3	29 18.4	18 47.3	11 .0	19 30.1	2 30.1	12 8.7	1 23.8	11 44.2	7 53.8
30	12 27 3.0	8 40.4	3 56.1	13♏41.9	20 26.8	12 12.2	20 15.7	2 44.6	12 10.3	1 21.5	11 43.7	7 52.1
31	12 30 59.5	9 39.7	3 52.9	27 37.7	22 7.6	13 24.2	21 1.3	2 59.0	12 12.1	1 19.2	11 43.2	7 50.5
		LATITUDE										
1	10 32 42.9	0 .0	0 .0	3S28.2	0N29.3	0S52.3	0S53.0	1S 4.5	0S16.8	0N33.4	1N33.5	17N15.3
4	10 44 32.6	0 .0	0 .0	0 11.3	0S 4.1	0 45.2	0 55.1	1 4.4	0 16.4	0 33.4	1 33.7	17 16.2
7	10 56 22.3	0 .0	0 .0	2N56.1	0 34.2	0 37.6	0 57.2	1 4.4	0 16.0	0 33.5	1 33.8	17 17.0
10	11 8 11.9	0 .0	0 .0	4 45.8	1 .8	0 29.7	0 59.2	1 4.3	0 15.6	0 33.5	1 33.9	17 17.7
13	11 20 1.6	0 .0	0 .0	4 45.8	1 23.7	0 21.3	1 1.3	1 4.3	0 15.2	0 33.6	1 34.1	17 18.4
16	11 31 51.2	0 .0	0 .0	2 54.6	1 42.9	0 12.7	1 3.3	1 4.3	0 14.8	0 33.6	1 34.2	17 18.9
19	11 43 40.9	0 .0	0 .0	0S12.9	1 58.4	0 3.7	1 5.3	1 4.3	0 14.5	0 33.7	1 34.4	17 19.4
22	11 55 30.5	0 .0	0 .0	3 26.2	2 9.9	0N 5.5	1 7.3	1 4.4	0 14.1	0 33.7	1 34.5	17 19.8
25	12 7 20.2	0 .0	0 .0	5 3.8	2 17.6	0 14.9	1 9.2	1 4.4	0 13.7	0 33.7	1 34.6	17 20.1
28	12 19 9.9	0 .0	0 .0	3 46.5	2 21.1	0 24.4	1 11.1	1 4.5	0 13.3	0 33.7	1 34.8	17 20.3
31	12 30 59.5	0 .0	0 .0	0 24.4	2 20.4	0 34.1	1 13.0	1 4.6	0 13.0	0 33.7	1 34.9	17 20.4
		RIGHT ASCENSION										
1	10 32 42.9	11♓19.6	3♐33.3	18♎19.0	15♒31.9	6♈40.6	0♒37.9	26♓31.5	13♋ 7.9	0♏14.8	10♐27.1	14♎48.2
2	10 36 39.5	12 15.9	3 30.0	2♏24.5	16 20.6	7 47.5	1 25.4	26 44.6	13R 6.4	0R13.6	10 27.5	14R47.0
3	10 40 36.0	13 12.0	3 26.6	16 31.4	17 12.7	8 54.5	2 12.8	26 57.7	13 5.0	0 12.3	10 27.9	14 45.9
4	10 44 32.6	14 8.0	3 23.3	0♐34.8	18 8.1	10 1.4	3 .2	27 10.9	13 3.7	0 11.1	10 28.3	14 44.7
5	10 48 29.1	15 4.0	3 19.9	14 26.7	19 6.3	11 8.4	3 47.6	27 24.1	13 2.6	0 9.8	10 28.7	14 43.6
6	10 52 25.7	15 59.8	3 16.5	27 58.2	20 7.2	12 15.4	4 34.8	27 37.3	13 1.6	0 8.4	10 29.1	14 42.3
7	10 56 22.3	16 55.4	3 13.2	11♑ 2.3	21 10.6	13 22.5	5 21.9	27 50.5	13 .6	0 7.0	10 29.3	14 41.1
8	11 0 18.8	17 51.0	3 9.8	23 35.7	22 16.3	14 29.5	6 9.0	28 3.7	12 59.8	0 5.6	10 29.6	14 39.9
9	11 4 15.4	18 46.5	3 6.5	5♒38.9	23 24.0	15 36.7	6 56.0	28 17.0	12 59.1	0 4.1	10 29.8	14 38.6
10	11 8 11.9	19 41.9	3 3.1	17 15.8	24 33.7	16 43.9	7 43.0	28 30.2	12 58.5	0 2.5	10 30.0	14 37.3
11	11 12 8.5	20 37.3	2 59.8	28 32.8	25 45.1	17 51.2	8 29.8	28 43.5	12 58.1	0 1.0	10 30.1	14 36.0
12	11 16 5.0	21 32.5	2 56.4	9♓37.8	26 58.2	18 58.6	9 16.6	28 56.8	12 57.8	29♎59.4	10 30.2	14 34.7
13	11 20 1.6	22 27.7	2 53.1	20 39.7	28 12.8	20 6.1	10 3.3	29 10.1	12 57.6	29 57.7	10 30.3	14 33.4
14	11 23 58.1	23 22.7	2 49.7	1♈47.6	29 28.8	21 13.7	10 49.9	29 23.4	12 57.5	29 56.0	10 30.3	14 32.0
15	11 27 54.7	24 17.8	2 46.4	13 10.6	0♓46.2	22 21.4	11 36.4	29 36.7	12 57.5	29 54.3	10 30.3	14 30.7
16	11 31 51.2	25 12.7	2 43.0	24 57.4	2 4.8	23 29.2	12 22.9	29 50.0	12D57.7	29 52.5	10 30.3	14 29.3
17	11 35 47.8	26 7.6	2 39.7	7♉14.8	3 24.6	24 37.2	13 9.2	0♈ 3.3	12 57.9	29 50.7	10R30.2	14 27.9
18	11 39 44.3	27 2.5	2 36.3	20 7.3	4 45.4	25 45.3	13 55.5	0 16.7	12 58.3	29 48.9	10 30.1	14 26.6
19	11 43 40.9	27 57.2	2 33.0	3♊35.4	6 7.4	26 53.6	14 41.7	0 30.0	12 58.9	29 47.0	10 30.0	14 25.1
20	11 47 37.4	28 52.0	2 29.6	17 34.3	7 30.3	28 2.0	15 27.8	0 43.3	12 59.5	29 45.1	10 29.8	14 23.7
21	11 51 34.0	29 46.7	2 26.3	1♋54.9	8 54.2	29 10.5	16 13.8	0 56.7	13 .3	29 43.2	10 29.6	14 22.3
22	11 55 30.5	0♈41.4	2 23.0	16 25.6	10 19.0	0♉19.3	16 59.7	1 10.0	13 1.1	29 41.2	10 29.3	14 20.9
23	11 59 27.1	1 36.0	2 19.6	0♌55.4	11 44.7	1 28.2	17 45.5	1 23.4	13 2.2	29 39.2	10 29.0	14 19.4
24	12 3 23.6	2 30.6	2 16.3	15 17.3	13 11.3	2 37.2	18 31.2	1 36.7	13 3.3	29 37.2	10 28.7	14 18.0
25	12 7 20.2	3 25.2	2 12.9	29 29.8	14 38.8	3 46.5	19 16.9	1 50.0	13 4.5	29 35.2	10 28.4	14 16.5
26	12 11 16.7	4 19.8	2 9.6	13♍35.9	16 7.1	4 56.0	20 2.5	2 3.4	13 5.9	29 33.1	10 28.0	14 15.1
27	12 15 13.3	5 14.4	2 6.2	27 41.6	17 36.3	6 5.6	20 47.9	2 16.7	13 7.4	29 31.0	10 27.6	14 13.7
28	12 19 9.9	6 8.9	2 2.9	11♎53.2	19 6.4	7 15.5	21 33.3	2 30.0	13 9.0	29 28.9	10 27.2	14 12.2
29	12 23 6.4	7 3.5	1 59.5	26 14.3	20 37.3	8 25.5	22 18.6	2 43.3	13 10.7	29 26.7	10 26.7	14 10.7
30	12 27 3.0	7 58.1	1 56.2	10♏43.9	22 9.1	9 35.8	23 3.8	2 56.6	13 12.5	29 24.5	10 26.1	14 9.2
31	12 30 59.5	8 52.7	1 52.9	25 15.5	23 41.8	10 46.3	23 48.9	3 9.9	13 14.5	29 22.3	10 25.6	14 7.7
		DECLINATION										
1	10 32 42.9	7S54.2	0S22.2	11S30.5	16S23.2	1N56.2	21S21.8	2S40.6	22N36.7	11S43.7	20S39.2	12N25.3
4	10 44 32.6	6 45.6	0 22.2	20 53.0	16 12.7	3 29.8	20 55.4	2 23.5	22 37.4	11 42.3	20 39.2	12 27.8
7	10 56 22.3	5 36.2	0 22.2	20 6.6	15 48.4	5 2.8	20 27.1	2 6.3	22 38.1	11 40.8	20 39.2	12 30.3
10	11 8 11.9	4 26.0	0 22.1	11 24.9	15 11.0	6 34.8	19 57.0	1 49.0	22 38.7	11 39.1	20 39.1	12 32.7
13	11 20 1.6	3 15.4	0 22.1	1N 9.3	14 20.9	8 5.6	19 25.0	1 31.7	22 39.1	11 37.4	20 39.0	12 35.1
16	11 31 51.2	2 4.4	0 22.1	13 29.3	13 18.6	9 34.7	18 51.3	1 14.4	22 39.5	11 35.4	20 38.8	12 37.4
19	11 43 40.9	0 53.2	0 22.0	21 .3	12 4.4	11 1.8	18 15.9	0 57.1	22 39.8	11 33.4	20 38.7	12 39.8
22	11 55 30.5	0N17.9	0 22.0	19 7.4	10 38.7	12 26.7	17 38.8	0 39.8	22 40.0	11 31.3	20 38.4	12 42.0
25	12 7 20.2	1 28.9	0 22.0	7 1.3	9 1.9	13 48.9	17 .2	0 22.5	22 40.1	11 29.1	20 38.2	12 44.2
28	12 19 9.9	2 39.5	0 21.9	9S12.1	7 14.4	15 8.3	16 20.1	0 5.2	22 40.1	11 26.8	20 37.9	12 46.3
31	12 30 59.5	3 49.7	0 21.9	20 1.7	5 16.4	16 24.3	15 38.6	0N12.0	22 40.0	11 24.4	20 37.6	12 48.3

APRIL 1975

DAY	EPHEM. SID. TIME	☉	☊	☽	☿	♀	♂	♃	♄	♅	♆	♇
		LONGITUDE										
	h m s	° ′	° ′	° ′	° ′	° ′	° ′	° ′	° ′	° ′	° ′	° ′
1	12 34 56.1	10♈38.9	3♐49.8	11♐ 4.9	23♓49.8	14♉36.2	21♒46.9	3♈13.5	12♋14.0	1♏16.8	11♐42.6	7♎48.8
2	12 38 52.6	11 38.1	3 46.6	24 5.5	25 33.4	15 48.1	22 32.6	3 28.0	12 16.0	1 R 14.5	11 R 42.1	7 R 47.1
3	12 42 49.2	12 37.3	3 43.4	6♑43.0	27 18.5	16 60.0	23 18.2	3 42.4	12 18.1	1 12.1	11 41.4	7 45.5
4	12 46 45.7	13 36.5	3 40.2	19 1.9	29 4.9	18 11.8	24 3.9	3 56.8	12 20.3	1 9.7	11 40.8	7 43.8
5	12 50 42.3	14 35.6	3 37.1	1♒ 7.1	0♈52.7	19 23.5	24 49.6	4 11.2	12 22.7	1 7.3	11 40.1	7 42.1
6	12 54 38.8	15 34.7	3 33.9	13 3.4	2 42.0	20 35.1	25 35.3	4 25.6	12 25.1	1 4.9	11 39.4	7 40.5
7	12 58 35.4	16 33.7	3 30.7	24 55.2	4 32.7	21 46.6	26 20.9	4 40.0	12 27.6	1 2.4	11 38.7	7 38.8
8	13 2 31.9	17 32.7	3 27.5	6♓46.2	6 24.9	22 58.1	27 6.6	4 54.4	12 30.2	0 60.0	11 37.9	7 37.2
9	13 6 28.5	18 31.7	3 24.3	18 39.5	8 18.5	24 9.4	27 52.3	5 8.7	12 33.0	0 57.5	11 37.1	7 35.5
10	13 10 25.0	19 30.7	3 21.2	0♈37.7	10 13.6	25 20.7	28 38.0	5 23.0	12 35.8	0 55.0	11 36.3	7 33.9
11	13 14 21.6	20 29.6	3 18.0	12 42.4	12 10.1	26 31.9	29 23.7	5 37.3	12 38.7	0 52.5	11 35.4	7 32.3
12	13 18 18.1	21 28.5	3 14.8	24 55.1	14 8.0	27 43.1	0♓ 9.4	5 51.6	12 41.7	0 50.0	11 34.6	7 30.7
13	13 22 14.7	22 27.4	3 11.6	7♉16.9	16 7.4	28 54.1	0 55.1	6 5.8	12 44.9	0 47.4	11 33.6	7 29.1
14	13 26 11.2	23 26.2	3 8.5	19 48.8	18 8.0	0♊ 5.0	1 40.8	6 20.0	12 48.1	0 44.9	11 32.7	7 27.5
15	13 30 7.8	24 25.0	3 5.3	2♊32.0	20 10.0	1 15.9	2 26.5	6 34.2	12 51.4	0 42.4	11 31.8	7 25.9
16	13 34 4.4	25 23.8	3 2.1	15 27.9	22 13.3	2 26.7	3 12.3	6 48.4	12 54.9	0 39.9	11 30.8	7 24.4
17	13 38 .9	26 22.5	2 58.9	28 38.1	24 17.6	3 37.4	3 58.0	7 2.5	12 58.4	0 37.3	11 29.8	7 22.8
18	13 41 57.5	27 21.2	2 55.7	12♋ 4.2	26 23.0	4 47.9	4 43.7	7 16.6	13 2.0	0 34.7	11 28.8	7 21.2
19	13 45 54.0	28 19.9	2 52.6	25 47.7	28 29.2	5 58.4	5 29.4	7 30.6	13 5.7	0 32.2	11 27.7	7 19.7
20	13 49 50.6	29 18.5	2 49.4	9♌49.2	0♉36.2	7 8.8	6 15.0	7 44.6	13 9.5	0 29.6	11 26.6	7 18.2
21	13 53 47.1	0♉17.1	2 46.2	24 7.9	2 43.7	8 19.0	7 .7	7 58.6	13 13.4	0 27.0	11 25.5	7 16.7
22	13 57 43.7	1 15.6	2 43.0	8♍41.2	4 51.5	9 29.1	7 46.4	8 12.5	13 17.4	0 24.5	11 24.4	7 15.2
23	14 1 40.2	2 14.1	2 39.9	23 24.5	6 59.4	10 39.2	8 32.0	8 26.4	13 21.4	0 21.9	11 23.2	7 13.7
24	14 5 36.8	3 12.6	2 36.7	8♎11.4	9 7.1	11 49.1	9 17.7	8 40.3	13 25.6	0 19.4	11 22.1	7 12.2
25	14 9 33.3	4 11.0	2 33.5	22 54.3	11 14.3	12 58.9	10 3.3	8 54.1	13 29.8	0 16.8	11 20.9	7 10.8
26	14 13 29.9	5 9.4	2 30.3	7♏26.0	13 20.7	14 8.6	10 49.0	9 7.9	13 34.1	0 14.2	11 19.7	7 9.3
27	14 17 26.4	6 7.8	2 27.1	21 40.0	15 26.0	15 18.1	11 34.6	9 21.6	13 38.5	0 11.7	11 18.4	7 7.9
28	14 21 23.0	7 6.1	2 24.0	5♐32.1	17 29.9	16 27.6	12 20.2	9 35.3	13 43.0	0 9.1	11 17.2	7 6.5
29	14 25 19.5	8 4.4	2 20.8	19 .1	19 32.0	17 36.9	13 5.8	9 48.9	13 47.6	0 6.6	11 15.9	7 5.2
30	14 29 16.1	9 2.7	2 17.6	2♑ 4.1	21 32.2	18 46.1	13 51.5	10 2.5	13 52.3	0 4.1	11 14.6	7 3.8
		LATITUDE										
1	12 34 56.1	0 .0	0 .0	0N47.8	2S19.2	0N37.3	1S13.6	1S 4.6	0S12.8	0N33.8	1N35.0	17N20.4
4	12 46 45.7	0 .0	0 .0	3 45.1	2 12.8	0 47.0	1 15.4	1 4.7	0 12.5	0 33.8	1 35.1	17 20.3
7	12 58 35.4	0 .0	0 .0	5 5.5	2 1.8	0 56.6	1 17.2	1 4.8	0 12.1	0 33.8	1 35.2	17 20.2
10	13 10 25.0	0 .0	0 .0	4 29.8	1 46.3	1 6.1	1 19.0	1 5.0	0 11.8	0 33.8	1 35.3	17 20.0
13	13 22 14.7	0 .0	0 .0	2 6.6	1 26.2	1 15.4	1 20.6	1 5.1	0 11.4	0 33.8	1 35.4	17 19.7
16	13 34 4.4	0 .0	0 .0	1S16.6	1 1.9	1 24.6	1 22.3	1 5.3	0 11.1	0 33.8	1 35.5	17 19.3
19	13 45 54.0	0 .0	0 .0	4 14.5	0 33.8	1 33.4	1 23.9	1 5.5	0 10.7	0 33.7	1 35.6	17 18.8
22	13 57 43.7	0 .0	0 .0	5 9.9	0 2.9	1 41.9	1 25.4	1 5.8	0 10.4	0 33.7	1 35.7	17 18.2
25	14 9 33.3	0 .0	0 .0	3 13.8	0N29.4	1 50.0	1 26.9	1 6.0	0 10.1	0 33.7	1 35.8	17 17.6
28	14 21 23.0	0 .0	0 .0	0N24.9	1 1.2	1 57.7	1 28.3	1 6.3	0 9.7	0 33.7	1 35.9	17 16.9
		RIGHT ASCENSION										
1	12 34 56.1	9♈47.3	1♐49.5	9♐38.1	25♓15.5	11♉57.0	24♒33.9	3♈23.2	13♋16.5	29♎20.1	10♐25.0	14♎ 6.2
2	12 38 52.6	10 41.9	1 46.2	23 39.4	26 50.1	13 7.9	25 18.8	3 36.5	13 18.7	29 R 17.9	10 R 24.4	14 R 4.8
3	12 42 49.2	11 36.6	1 42.8	7♑ 9.4	28 25.7	14 19.0	26 3.7	3 49.8	13 21.0	29 15.6	10 23.7	14 3.3
4	12 46 45.7	12 31.3	1 39.5	20 3.2	0♈ 2.3	15 30.4	26 48.4	4 3.0	13 23.4	29 13.3	10 23.1	14 1.8
5	12 50 42.3	13 26.0	1 36.2	2♒20.8	1 39.9	16 42.0	27 33.1	4 16.3	13 25.9	29 11.0	10 22.4	14 .3
6	12 54 38.8	14 20.8	1 32.8	14 6.9	3 18.7	17 53.8	28 17.7	4 29.5	13 28.5	29 8.7	10 21.6	13 58.8
7	12 58 35.4	15 15.7	1 29.5	25 29.1	4 58.6	19 5.9	29 2.2	4 42.7	13 31.3	29 6.3	10 20.8	13 57.3
8	13 2 31.9	16 10.6	1 26.1	6♓36.6	6 39.7	20 18.1	29 46.6	4 55.9	13 34.1	29 4.0	10 20.0	13 55.8
9	13 6 28.5	17 5.5	1 22.8	17 39.2	8 22.0	21 30.7	0♓30.9	5 9.1	13 37.0	29 1.6	10 19.2	13 54.3
10	13 10 25.0	18 .6	1 19.5	28 47.0	10 5.6	22 43.4	1 15.1	5 22.2	13 40.1	28 59.2	10 18.3	13 52.8
11	13 14 21.6	18 55.7	1 16.1	10♈ 9.7	11 50.6	23 56.4	1 59.2	5 35.4	13 43.3	28 56.8	10 17.4	13 51.3
12	13 18 18.1	19 50.8	1 12.8	21 56.1	13 36.8	25 9.5	2 43.3	5 48.5	13 46.6	28 54.4	10 16.5	13 49.8
13	13 22 14.7	20 46.0	1 9.4	4♉13.1	15 24.5	26 22.9	3 27.3	6 1.6	13 50.0	28 52.0	10 15.6	13 48.3
14	13 26 11.2	21 41.3	1 6.1	17 4.4	17 13.5	27 36.5	4 11.1	6 14.7	13 53.4	28 49.6	10 14.6	13 46.8
15	13 30 7.8	22 36.7	1 2.8	0♊29.3	19 4.1	28 50.3	4 54.9	6 27.7	13 57.0	28 47.1	10 13.6	13 45.4
16	13 34 4.4	23 32.2	0 59.4	14 22.1	20 56.0	0♊ 4.4	5 38.7	6 40.8	14 .8	28 44.7	10 12.6	13 43.9
17	13 38 .9	24 27.8	0 56.1	28 32.3	22 49.4	1 18.6	6 22.3	6 53.8	14 4.6	28 42.3	10 11.5	13 42.5
18	13 41 57.5	25 23.4	0 52.8	12♋47.6	24 44.2	2 33.0	7 5.8	7 6.8	14 8.5	28 39.9	10 10.4	13 41.0
19	13 45 54.0	26 19.2	0 49.4	26 57.5	26 40.3	3 47.5	7 49.3	7 19.7	14 12.5	28 37.4	10 9.3	13 39.6
20	13 49 50.6	27 15.0	0 46.1	10♌56.0	28 37.7	5 2.2	8 32.7	7 32.6	14 16.6	28 34.9	10 8.2	13 38.1
21	13 53 47.1	28 10.9	0 42.8	24 42.6	0♉36.2	6 17.1	9 16.0	7 45.5	14 20.8	28 32.5	10 7.0	13 36.7
22	13 57 43.7	29 6.9	0 39.4	8♍22.2	2 35.8	7 32.1	9 59.2	7 58.3	14 25.1	28 30.0	10 5.8	13 35.3
23	14 1 40.2	0♉ 3.1	0 36.1	22 2.4	4 36.3	8 47.2	10 42.3	8 11.1	14 29.5	28 27.6	10 4.6	13 33.8
24	14 5 36.8	0 59.3	0 32.8	5♎52.1	6 37.4	10 2.5	11 25.4	8 23.9	14 34.0	28 25.1	10 3.4	13 32.4
25	14 9 33.3	1 55.7	0 29.4	19 57.9	8 39.0	11 17.8	12 8.4	8 36.7	14 38.5	28 22.7	10 2.1	13 31.1
26	14 13 29.9	2 52.1	0 26.1	4♏22.2	10 40.8	12 33.3	12 51.3	8 49.4	14 43.2	28 20.2	10 .8	13 29.7
27	14 17 26.4	3 48.7	0 22.8	19 .6	12 42.5	13 48.9	13 34.2	9 2.0	14 48.0	28 17.8	9 59.5	13 28.3
28	14 21 23.0	4 45.4	0 19.5	3♐42.0	14 43.9	15 4.5	14 16.9	9 14.7	14 52.8	28 15.4	9 58.2	13 26.9
29	14 25 19.5	5 42.3	0 16.1	18 11.0	16 44.6	16 20.2	14 59.7	9 27.3	14 57.8	28 13.0	9 56.8	13 25.6
30	14 29 16.1	6 39.3	0 12.8	2♑12.6	18 44.3	17 35.9	15 42.3	9 39.8	15 2.8	28 10.5	9 55.5	13 24.3
		DECLINATION										
1	12 34 56.1	4N12.9	0S21.9	21S19.1	4S34.9	16N48.9	15S24.5	0N17.7	22N39.9	11S23.6	20S37.4	12N48.9
4	12 46 45.7	5 22.2	0 21.9	18 22.5	2 23.7	18 .1	14 41.2	0 34.8	22 39.7	11 21.1	20 37.1	12 50.8
7	12 58 35.4	6 30.7	0 21.8	8 24.8	0 3.4	19 7.3	13 56.7	0 51.8	22 39.4	11 18.6	20 36.7	12 52.5
10	13 10 25.0	7 38.1	0 21.8	4N22.5	2N25.2	20 10.2	13 11.0	1 8.7	22 39.0	11 16.0	20 36.2	12 54.3
13	13 22 14.7	8 44.4	0 21.8	15 56.3	5 .9	21 8.5	12 24.3	1 25.5	22 38.5	11 13.4	20 35.8	12 55.9
16	13 34 4.4	9 49.4	0 21.7	21 22.8	7 41.7	22 2.0	11 36.6	1 42.1	22 37.8	11 10.7	20 35.3	12 57.4
19	13 45 54.0	10 52.9	0 21.7	16 49.1	10 24.7	22 50.3	10 48.0	1 58.6	22 37.1	11 8.1	20 34.8	12 58.7
22	13 57 43.7	11 54.8	0 21.7	3 31.3	13 5.8	23 33.3	9 58.6	2 14.9	22 36.3	11 5.4	20 34.2	12 60.0
25	14 9 33.3	12 54.9	0 21.6	11S54.3	15 40.1	24 10.6	9 8.4	2 31.1	22 35.4	11 2.7	20 33.6	13 1.1
28	14 21 23.0	13 53.1	0 21.6	20 49.2	18 2.0	24 42.2	8 17.6	2 47.0	22 34.4	11 .1	20 33.0	13 2.0

MAY 1975

DAY	EPHEM. SID. TIME	☉	☊	☾	☿	♀	♂	♃	♄	♅	♆	♇
		LONGITUDE										
	h m s	° ′	° ′	° ′	° ′	° ′	° ′	° ′	° ′	° ′	° ′	° ′
1	14 33 12.7	10♉ 1.0	2♐14.4	14♑46.2	23♉30.0	19♊55.2	14♓37.1	10♈16.1	13♋57.0	0♏ 1.6	11♐13.3	7♎ 2.5
2	14 37 9.2	10 59.2	2 11.3	27 9.6	25 25.3	21 4.2	15 22.6	10 29.6	14 1.8	29♎59.0	11 R 11.9	7 R 1.1
3	14 41 5.8	11 57.4	2 8.1	9♒18.4	27 17.9	22 13.0	16 8.2	10 43.0	14 6.7	29 R 56.5	11 10.6	6 59.8
4	14 45 2.3	12 55.6	2 4.9	21 17.1	29 7.4	23 21.7	16 53.8	10 56.4	14 11.7	29 54.1	11 9.2	6 58.6
5	14 48 58.9	13 53.7	2 1.7	3♓10.4	0♊53.7	24 30.3	17 39.3	11 9.7	14 16.7	29 51.6	11 7.8	6 57.3
6	14 52 55.4	14 51.9	1 58.5	15 2.8	2 36.7	25 38.7	18 24.9	11 23.0	14 21.9	29 49.1	11 6.4	6 56.1
7	14 56 52.0	15 50.0	1 55.4	26 58.5	4 16.3	26 47.1	19 10.4	11 36.3	14 27.1	29 46.7	11 5.0	6 54.9
8	15 0 48.5	16 48.1	1 52.2	9♈ .7	5 52.3	27 55.2	19 55.9	11 49.5	14 32.4	29 44.3	11 3.6	6 53.7
9	15 4 45.1	17 46.2	1 49.0	21 12.5	7 24.6	29 3.2	20 41.4	12 2.6	14 37.7	29 41.9	11 2.1	6 52.5
10	15 8 41.6	18 44.2	1 45.8	3♉36.1	8 53.1	0♋11.1	21 26.8	12 15.6	14 43.2	29 39.5	11 .7	6 51.4
11	15 12 38.2	19 42.2	1 42.7	16 12.8	10 17.8	1 18.8	22 12.2	12 28.6	14 48.7	29 37.2	10 59.2	6 50.3
12	15 16 34.8	20 40.2	1 39.5	29 3.3	11 38.6	2 26.4	22 57.6	12 41.6	14 54.2	29 34.8	10 57.7	6 49.2
13	15 20 31.3	21 38.2	1 36.3	12♊ 7.9	12 55.4	3 33.8	23 43.0	12 54.4	14 59.9	29 32.5	10 56.2	6 48.1
14	15 24 27.9	22 36.1	1 33.1	25 26.2	14 8.2	4 41.1	24 28.4	13 7.2	15 5.6	29 30.2	10 54.7	6 47.0
15	15 28 24.4	23 34.0	1 30.0	8♋57.6	15 16.9	5 48.2	25 13.7	13 20.0	15 11.3	29 27.9	10 53.2	6 46.0
16	15 32 21.0	24 31.9	1 26.8	22 41.3	16 21.5	6 55.1	25 59.0	13 32.6	15 17.2	29 25.7	10 51.6	6 45.0
17	15 36 17.5	25 29.7	1 23.6	6♌36.1	17 21.8	8 1.9	26 44.2	13 45.2	15 23.1	29 23.4	10 50.1	6 44.1
18	15 40 14.1	26 27.6	1 20.4	20 40.6	18 17.8	9 8.4	27 29.4	13 57.7	15 29.0	29 21.2	10 48.5	6 43.1
19	15 44 10.6	27 25.3	1 17.2	4♍53.1	19 9.5	10 14.8	28 14.6	14 10.2	15 35.0	29 19.1	10 47.0	6 42.2
20	15 48 7.2	28 23.1	1 14.1	19 11.2	19 56.8	11 21.0	28 59.8	14 22.5	15 41.1	29 16.9	10 45.4	6 41.3
21	15 52 3.8	29 20.8	1 10.9	3♎31.9	20 39.7	12 27.0	29 44.9	14 34.8	15 47.3	29 14.8	10 43.8	6 40.5
22	15 56 .3	0♊18.5	1 7.7	17 51.7	21 17.9	13 32.8	0♈30.0	14 47.0	15 53.5	29 12.7	10 42.2	6 39.6
23	15 59 56.9	1 16.2	1 4.5	2♏ 6.4	21 51.6	14 38.4	1 15.0	14 59.2	15 59.7	29 10.7	10 40.6	6 38.8
24	16 3 53.4	2 13.9	1 1.4	16 12.0	22 20.6	15 43.7	2 .0	15 11.2	16 6.0	29 8.7	10 39.0	6 38.1
25	16 7 50.0	3 11.5	0 58.2	0♐ 4.5	22 44.9	16 48.9	2 45.0	15 23.2	16 12.4	29 6.7	10 37.4	6 37.3
26	16 11 46.5	4 9.1	0 55.0	13 40.8	23 4.5	17 53.8	3 30.0	15 35.1	16 18.8	29 4.7	10 35.8	6 36.6
27	16 15 43.1	5 6.7	0 51.8	26 58.9	23 19.3	18 58.6	4 14.9	15 46.9	16 25.3	29 2.8	10 34.2	6 35.9
28	16 19 39.7	6 4.3	0 48.7	9♑58.2	23 29.4	20 3.1	4 59.8	15 58.7	16 31.9	29 1.0	10 32.6	6 35.3
29	16 23 36.2	7 1.9	0 45.5	22 38.9	23 34.8	21 7.3	5 44.6	16 10.4	16 38.5	28 59.1	10 31.0	6 34.7
30	16 27 32.8	7 59.4	0 42.3	5♒ 3.1	23 35.6	22 11.3	6 29.4	16 21.9	16 45.1	28 57.3	10 29.4	6 34.1
31	16 31 29.3	8 57.0	0 39.1	17 13.5	23 R 31.8	23 15.1	7 14.2	16 33.4	16 51.8	28 55.6	10 27.7	6 33.5
		LATITUDE										
1	14 33 12.7	0 .0	0 .0	3N38.1	1N30.4	2N 4.8	1S29.7	1S 6.5	0S 9.4	0N33.6	1N36.0	17N16.0
4	14 45 2.3	0 .0	0 .0	5 10.7	1 55.0	2 11.3	1 30.9	1 6.8	0 9.1	0 33.6	1 36.1	17 15.2
7	14 56 52.0	0 .0	0 .0	4 43.7	2 13.6	2 17.2	1 32.2	1 7.1	0 8.8	0 33.5	1 36.1	17 14.2
10	15 8 41.6	0 .0	0 .0	2 25.3	2 25.0	2 22.4	1 33.3	1 7.5	0 8.5	0 33.5	1 36.2	17 13.2
13	15 20 31.3	0 .0	0 .0	1S 1.9	2 28.5	2 26.7	1 34.4	1 7.8	0 8.1	0 33.4	1 36.2	17 12.1
16	15 32 21.0	0 .0	0 .0	4 9.2	2 23.7	2 30.3	1 35.4	1 8.2	0 7.8	0 33.4	1 36.3	17 10.9
19	15 44 10.6	0 .0	0 .0	5 16.2	2 10.4	2 33.0	1 36.3	1 8.6	0 7.5	0 33.3	1 36.3	17 9.7
22	15 56 .3	0 .0	0 .0	3 36.7	1 48.3	2 34.7	1 37.1	1 9.0	0 7.2	0 33.2	1 36.3	17 8.5
25	16 7 50.0	0 .0	0 .0	0 4.7	1 17.6	2 35.4	1 37.8	1 9.4	0 6.9	0 33.2	1 36.3	17 7.1
28	16 19 39.7	0 .0	0 .0	3N19.9	0 38.9	2 35.1	1 38.5	1 9.9	0 6.7	0 33.1	1 36.3	17 5.8
31	16 31 29.3	0 .0	0 .0	5 7.7	0S 6.6	2 33.6	1 39.0	1 10.4	0 6.4	0 33.0	1 36.3	17 4.4
		RIGHT ASCENSION										
1	14 33 12.7	7♉36.4	0♐ 9.5	15♑36.7	20♉42.8	18♊51.6	16♓24.9	9♈52.3	15♋ 7.9	28♎ 8.1	9♐54.1	13♎22.9
2	14 37 9.2	8 33.6	0 6.1	28 19.9	22 39.7	20 7.4	17 7.4	10 4.8	15 13.1	28 R 5.7	9 R 52.7	13 R 21.6
3	14 41 5.8	9 31.0	0 2.8	10♒25.0	24 34.6	21 23.2	17 49.9	10 17.2	15 18.4	28 3.3	9 51.2	13 20.4
4	14 45 2.3	10 28.5	29♏59.5	21 59.2	26 27.5	22 38.9	18 32.3	10 29.6	15 23.8	28 1.0	9 49.8	13 19.1
5	14 48 58.9	11 26.2	29 56.2	3♓12.5	28 17.9	23 54.7	19 14.6	10 41.9	15 29.2	27 58.6	9 48.3	13 17.8
6	14 52 55.4	12 24.0	29 52.8	14 15.8	0♊ 5.7	25 10.4	19 56.9	10 54.2	15 34.7	27 56.3	9 46.8	13 16.6
7	14 56 52.0	13 22.0	29 49.5	25 20.6	1 50.6	26 26.0	20 39.2	11 6.5	15 40.4	27 54.0	9 45.4	13 15.4
8	15 0 48.5	14 20.1	29 46.2	6♈38.1	3 32.4	27 41.6	21 21.4	11 18.7	15 46.1	27 51.7	9 43.9	13 14.2
9	15 4 45.1	15 18.4	29 42.9	18 18.6	5 10.9	28 57.0	22 3.5	11 30.8	15 51.9	27 49.4	9 42.3	13 13.0
10	15 8 41.6	16 16.8	29 39.5	0♉30.9	6 45.9	0♋12.3	22 45.5	11 42.9	15 57.7	27 47.1	9 40.8	13 11.8
11	15 12 38.2	17 15.3	29 36.2	13 20.5	8 17.3	1 27.5	23 27.5	11 55.0	16 3.6	27 44.8	9 39.2	13 10.7
12	15 16 34.8	18 14.0	29 32.9	26 47.8	9 44.9	2 42.6	24 9.5	12 7.0	16 9.6	27 42.6	9 37.7	13 9.5
13	15 20 31.3	19 12.8	29 29.6	10♊47.1	11 8.6	3 57.4	24 51.3	12 18.9	16 15.7	27 40.4	9 36.1	13 8.4
14	15 24 27.9	20 11.8	29 26.3	25 6.6	12 28.3	5 12.1	25 33.2	12 30.7	16 21.8	27 38.2	9 34.5	13 7.3
15	15 28 24.4	21 10.9	29 22.9	9♋31.1	13 43.7	6 26.5	26 15.0	12 42.6	16 28.1	27 36.0	9 32.9	13 6.3
16	15 32 21.0	22 10.1	29 19.6	23 46.8	14 54.8	7 40.7	26 56.7	12 54.3	16 34.3	27 33.8	9 31.2	13 5.2
17	15 36 17.5	23 9.5	29 16.3	7♌45.0	16 1.4	8 54.7	27 38.4	13 6.0	16 40.7	27 31.7	9 29.6	13 4.2
18	15 40 14.1	24 9.0	29 13.0	21 23.9	17 3.5	10 8.4	28 20.0	13 17.6	16 47.1	27 29.6	9 28.0	13 3.2
19	15 44 10.6	25 8.7	29 9.7	4♍47.9	18 .9	11 21.8	29 1.6	13 29.2	16 53.6	27 27.5	9 26.3	13 2.2
20	15 48 7.2	26 8.5	29 6.3	18 5.8	18 53.5	12 34.9	29 43.2	13 40.7	17 .1	27 25.5	9 24.6	13 1.2
21	15 52 3.8	27 8.4	29 3.0	1♎27.9	19 41.2	13 47.7	0♈24.7	13 52.1	17 6.8	27 23.5	9 23.0	13 .3
22	15 56 .3	28 8.4	28 59.7	15 4.2	20 24.0	15 .1	1 6.1	14 3.4	17 13.4	27 21.5	9 21.3	12 59.3
23	15 59 56.9	29 8.6	28 56.4	29 1.2	21 1.6	16 12.2	1 47.5	14 14.7	17 20.2	27 19.5	9 19.6	12 58.4
24	16 3 53.4	0♊ 8.9	28 53.1	13♏19.5	21 34.2	17 23.9	2 28.9	14 26.0	17 26.9	27 17.6	9 17.9	12 57.6
25	16 7 50.0	1 9.3	28 49.8	27 52.7	22 1.6	18 35.2	3 10.3	14 37.1	17 33.8	27 15.7	9 16.2	12 56.7
26	16 11 46.5	2 9.9	28 46.4	12♐27.1	22 23.8	19 46.1	3 51.6	14 48.2	17 40.7	27 13.8	9 14.5	12 55.9
27	16 15 43.1	3 10.5	28 43.1	26 46.1	22 40.7	20 56.6	4 32.9	14 59.2	17 47.7	27 12.0	9 12.8	12 55.1
28	16 19 39.7	4 11.4	28 39.8	10♑34.8	22 52.6	22 6.7	5 14.2	15 10.2	17 54.7	27 10.2	9 11.2	12 54.3
29	16 23 36.2	5 12.3	28 36.5	23 44.4	22 59.2	23 16.2	5 55.4	15 21.0	18 1.8	27 8.5	9 9.5	12 53.6
30	16 27 32.8	6 13.4	28 33.2	6♒13.1	23 .9	24 25.4	6 36.7	15 31.8	18 8.9	27 6.7	9 7.7	12 52.9
31	16 31 29.3	7 14.5	28 29.9	18 5.5	22 R 57.6	25 34.0	7 17.8	15 42.5	18 16.1	27 5.0	9 6.0	12 52.2
		DECLINATION										
1	14 33 12.7	14N49.2	0S21.6	19S .5	20N 6.5	25N 7.9	7S26.1	3N 2.8	22N33.3	10S57.4	20S32.4	13N 2.9
4	14 45 2.3	15 43.2	0 21.6	9 29.8	21 50.1	25 27.6	6 34.2	3 18.3	22 32.1	10 54.8	20 31.8	13 3.6
7	14 56 52.0	16 34.8	0 21.5	3N 8.2	23 11.2	25 41.3	5 41.9	3 33.6	22 30.7	10 52.3	20 31.2	13 4.1
10	15 8 41.6	17 24.0	0 21.5	14 59.6	24 10.2	25 48.8	4 49.2	3 48.6	22 29.3	10 49.8	20 30.5	13 4.5
13	15 20 31.3	18 10.5	0 21.5	21 13.6	24 48.3	25 50.3	3 56.4	4 3.4	22 27.8	10 47.4	20 29.9	13 4.8
16	15 32 21.0	18 54.3	0 21.4	17 26.1	25 7.5	25 45.7	3 3.3	4 17.9	22 26.1	10 45.1	20 29.2	13 5.0
19	15 44 10.6	19 35.2	0 21.4	4 48.7	25 9.9	25 35.2	2 10.3	4 32.0	22 24.4	10 42.8	20 28.5	13 4.9
22	15 56 .3	20 13.0	0 21.3	10S20.7	24 57.4	25 19.0	1 17.2	4 45.9	22 22.5	10 40.6	20 27.8	13 4.8
25	16 7 50.0	20 47.8	0 21.3	20 14.7	24 32.1	24 57.2	0 24.1	4 59.5	22 20.6	10 38.5	20 27.1	13 4.5
28	16 19 39.7	21 19.4	0 21.3	19 44.7	23 55.8	24 30.0	0N28.7	5 12.7	22 18.5	10 36.6	20 26.5	13 4.0
31	16 31 29.3	21 47.6	0 21.2	10 46.9	23 10.4	23 57.7	1 21.4	5 25.6	22 16.3	10 34.8	20 25.8	13 3.4

JUNE 1975

LONGITUDE

DAY	EPHEM. SID. TIME h m s	☉ ° ′	☊ ° ′	☽ ° ′	☿ ° ′	♀ ° ′	♂ ° ′	♃ ° ′	♄ ° ′	♅ ° ′	♆ ° ′	♇ ° ′
1	16 35 25.9	9♊54.5	0♐35.9	29♒13.8	23♊23.6	24♋18.6	7♈58.9	16♈44.8	16♋58.5	28♎53.8	10♐26.1	6♎33.0
2	16 39 22.4	10 52.0	0 32.8	11♓ 8.4	23 R 11.3	25 21.8	8 43.6	16 56.1	17 5.3	28 R 52.1	10 R 24.5	6 R 32.5
3	16 43 19.0	11 49.5	0 29.6	23 1.7	22 54.9	26 24.8	9 28.2	17 7.3	17 12.1	28 50.5	10 22.9	6 32.0
4	16 47 15.6	12 46.9	0 26.4	4♈58.3	22 34.9	27 27.5	10 12.8	17 18.4	17 18.9	28 48.9	10 21.2	6 31.6
5	16 51 12.1	13 44.4	0 23.2	17 2.7	22 11.6	28 29.9	10 57.3	17 29.4	17 25.8	28 47.3	10 19.6	6 31.2
6	16 55 8.7	14 41.8	0 20.1	29 19.0	21 45.3	29 32.1	11 41.8	17 40.3	17 32.8	28 45.7	10 18.0	6 30.8
7	16 59 5.2	15 39.3	0 16.9	11♉50.4	21 16.5	0♌33.9	12 26.2	17 51.1	17 39.8	28 44.3	10 16.4	6 30.4
8	17 3 1.8	16 36.7	0 13.7	24 39.5	20 45.7	1 35.5	13 10.6	18 1.8	17 46.8	28 42.8	10 14.8	6 30.1
9	17 6 58.3	17 34.1	0 10.5	7♊47.4	20 13.4	2 36.7	13 54.9	18 12.4	17 53.9	28 41.4	10 13.2	6 29.8
10	17 10 54.9	18 31.5	0 7.4	21 14.1	19 40.2	3 37.6	14 39.2	18 22.9	18 1.0	28 40.0	10 11.5	6 29.6
11	17 14 51.5	19 28.9	0 4.2	4♋58.1	19 6.6	4 38.2	15 23.4	18 33.2	18 8.1	28 38.7	10 9.9	6 29.4
12	17 18 48.0	20 26.3	0 1.0	18 56.6	18 33.2	5 38.4	16 7.5	18 43.5	18 15.3	28 37.4	10 8.3	6 29.2
13	17 22 44.6	21 23.6	29♏57.8	3♌ 6.0	18 .6	6 38.3	16 51.6	18 53.7	18 22.6	28 36.2	10 6.8	6 29.1
14	17 26 41.1	22 21.0	29 54.6	17 22.0	17 29.3	7 37.8	17 35.6	19 3.7	18 29.8	28 35.0	10 5.2	6 28.9
15	17 30 37.7	23 18.3	29 51.5	1♍40.5	16 59.8	8 36.9	18 19.5	19 13.7	18 37.1	28 33.9	10 3.6	6 28.9
16	17 34 34.2	24 15.6	29 48.3	15 57.8	16 32.7	9 35.7	19 3.4	19 23.5	18 44.4	28 32.8	10 2.0	6 28.8
17	17 38 30.8	25 12.9	29 45.1	0♎10.9	16 8.4	10 34.0	19 47.2	19 33.2	18 51.8	28 31.8	10 .5	6 28.8
18	17 42 27.4	26 10.2	29 41.9	14 17.6	15 47.4	11 31.9	20 31.0	19 42.9	18 59.2	28 30.8	9 59.0	6 D 28.9
19	17 46 23.9	27 7.5	29 38.8	28 16.1	15 29.9	12 29.4	21 14.7	19 52.3	19 6.6	28 29.9	9 57.4	6 28.9
20	17 50 20.5	28 4.8	29 35.6	12♏ 5.1	15 16.3	13 26.4	21 58.3	20 1.7	19 14.0	28 29.0	9 55.9	6 29.0
21	17 54 17.0	29 2.0	29 32.4	25 43.6	15 6.8	14 22.9	22 41.9	20 10.9	19 21.5	28 28.1	9 54.4	6 29.1
22	17 58 13.6	29 59.2	29 29.2	9♐10.5	15 1.7	15 18.9	23 25.3	20 20.0	19 29.0	28 27.3	9 52.9	6 29.2
23	18 2 10.1	0♋56.5	29 26.1	22 24.8	15 1.1	16 14.5	24 8.8	20 29.0	19 36.5	28 26.6	9 51.4	6 29.4
24	18 6 6.7	1 53.7	29 22.9	5♑25.4	15 D 5.1	17 9.5	24 52.1	20 37.9	19 44.0	28 25.9	9 49.9	6 29.6
25	18 10 3.3	2 50.9	29 19.7	18 12.1	15 13.8	18 4.0	25 35.4	20 46.6	19 51.5	28 25.2	9 48.4	6 29.9
26	18 13 59.8	3 48.1	29 16.5	0♒44.8	15 27.3	18 57.9	26 18.5	20 55.2	19 59.1	28 24.6	9 47.0	6 30.2
27	18 17 56.4	4 45.3	29 13.4	13 4.4	15 45.5	19 51.3	27 1.7	21 3.6	20 6.7	28 24.1	9 45.5	6 30.5
28	18 21 52.9	5 42.5	29 10.2	25 12.5	16 8.6	20 44.1	27 44.7	21 12.0	20 14.3	28 23.6	9 44.1	6 30.8
29	18 25 49.5	6 39.7	29 7.0	7♓11.8	16 36.3	21 36.3	28 27.7	21 20.2	20 22.0	28 23.1	9 42.7	6 31.2
30	18 29 46.0	7 36.9	29 3.8	19 5.6	17 8.8	22 27.8	29 10.6	21 28.2	20 29.6	28 22.7	9 41.3	6 31.6

LATITUDE

DAY	SID. TIME	☉	☊	☽	☿	♀	♂	♃	♄	♅	♆	♇
1	16 35 25.9	0 .0	0 .0	5N16.4	0S23.0	2N32.9	1S39.2	1S10.5	0S 6.3	0N33.0	1N36.3	17N 3.9
4	16 47 15.6	0 .0	0 .0	4 22.3	1 14.3	2 29.8	1 39.6	1 11.0	0 6.0	0 32.9	1 36.3	17 2.5
7	16 59 5.2	0 .0	0 .0	1 43.7	2 6.0	2 25.5	1 40.0	1 11.5	0 5.7	0 32.8	1 36.3	17 1.0
10	17 10 54.9	0 .0	0 .0	1S49.6	2 54.1	2 19.8	1 40.2	1 12.1	0 5.4	0 32.7	1 36.2	16 59.5
13	17 22 44.6	0 .0	0 .0	4 38.5	3 34.7	2 12.8	1 40.4	1 12.6	0 5.2	0 32.6	1 36.2	16 58.0
16	17 34 34.2	0 .0	0 .0	5 3.4	4 4.7	2 4.4	1 40.4	1 13.2	0 4.9	0 32.5	1 36.1	16 56.4
19	17 46 23.9	0 .0	0 .0	2 49.1	4 22.4	1 54.5	1 40.3	1 13.8	0 4.6	0 32.4	1 36.1	16 54.9
22	17 58 13.6	0 .0	0 .0	0N45.8	4 27.7	1 43.1	1 40.2	1 14.4	0 4.3	0 32.3	1 36.0	16 53.3
25	18 10 3.3	0 .0	0 .0	3 50.2	4 21.7	1 30.0	1 39.9	1 15.0	0 4.1	0 32.2	1 35.9	16 51.8
28	18 21 52.9	0 .0	0 .0	5 9.6	4 5.9	1 15.3	1 39.5	1 15.7	0 3.8	0 32.1	1 35.8	16 50.2

RIGHT ASCENSION

DAY	SID. TIME	☉	☊	☽	☿	♀	♂	♃	♄	♅	♆	♇
1	16 35 25.9	8♊15.8	28♏26.6	29♒30.1	22♊49.6	26♋42.2	7♈59.0	15♈53.1	18♋23.3	27♎ 3.4	9♐ 4.3	12♎51.5
2	16 39 22.4	9 17.1	28 23.2	10♓37.7	22 R 37.1	27 49.8	8 40.1	16 3.7	18 30.6	27 R 1.8	9 R 2.6	12 R 50.8
3	16 43 19.0	10 18.6	28 19.9	21 40.0	22 20.4	28 56.9	9 21.2	16 14.1	18 37.9	27 .2	9 .9	12 50.2
4	16 47 15.6	11 20.2	28 16.6	2♈49.3	21 59.9	0♌ 3.5	10 2.3	16 24.5	18 45.3	26 58.6	8 59.2	12 49.6
5	16 51 12.1	12 21.9	28 13.3	14 17.3	21 35.8	1 9.6	10 43.3	16 34.8	18 52.7	26 57.1	8 57.4	12 49.0
6	16 55 8.7	13 23.6	28 10.0	26 15.0	21 8.8	2 15.1	11 24.4	16 45.0	19 .1	26 55.6	8 55.7	12 48.5
7	16 59 5.2	14 25.5	28 6.7	8♉50.8	20 39.1	3 20.1	12 5.4	16 55.1	19 7.6	26 54.2	8 54.0	12 48.0
8	17 3 1.8	15 27.4	28 3.4	22 9.0	20 7.4	4 24.4	12 46.4	17 5.1	19 15.2	26 52.8	8 52.3	12 47.5
9	17 6 58.3	16 29.4	28 .1	6♊ 7.1	19 34.3	5 28.2	13 27.3	17 15.0	19 22.8	26 51.5	8 50.6	12 47.0
10	17 10 54.9	17 31.4	27 56.8	20 35.4	19 .2	6 31.4	14 8.2	17 24.9	19 30.4	26 50.2	8 48.9	12 46.6
11	17 14 51.5	18 33.6	27 53.5	5♋17.7	18 25.8	7 34.0	14 49.2	17 34.6	19 38.0	26 48.9	8 47.2	12 46.2
12	17 18 48.0	19 35.7	27 50.1	19 56.3	17 51.7	8 36.0	15 30.0	17 44.2	19 45.7	26 47.7	8 45.5	12 45.8
13	17 22 44.6	20 38.0	27 46.8	4♌17.3	17 18.4	9 37.3	16 10.9	17 53.8	19 53.5	26 46.5	8 43.8	12 45.5
14	17 26 41.1	21 40.2	27 43.5	18 14.3	16 46.5	10 38.0	16 51.8	18 3.2	20 1.2	26 45.4	8 42.2	12 45.2
15	17 30 37.7	22 42.5	27 40.2	1♍48.6	16 16.5	11 38.0	17 32.6	18 12.5	20 9.0	26 44.3	8 40.5	12 44.9
16	17 34 34.2	23 44.9	27 36.9	15 7.4	15 49.0	12 37.3	18 13.4	18 21.7	20 16.9	26 43.2	8 38.9	12 44.6
17	17 38 30.8	24 47.2	27 33.6	28 20.8	15 24.3	13 36.0	18 54.2	18 30.9	20 24.7	26 42.2	8 37.2	12 44.4
18	17 42 27.4	25 49.6	27 30.3	11♎39.9	15 3.0	14 34.0	19 35.0	18 39.9	20 32.7	26 41.3	8 35.6	12 44.2
19	17 46 23.9	26 52.0	27 27.0	25 13.5	14 45.2	15 31.2	20 15.7	18 48.8	20 40.6	26 40.4	8 34.0	12 44.1
20	17 50 20.5	27 54.4	27 23.7	9♏ 6.3	14 31.3	16 27.8	20 56.5	18 57.6	20 48.6	26 39.6	8 32.4	12 43.9
21	17 54 17.0	28 56.8	27 20.4	23 16.8	14 21.7	17 23.6	21 37.2	19 6.3	20 56.5	26 38.7	8 30.8	12 43.8
22	17 58 13.6	29 59.2	27 17.1	7♐36.4	14 16.4	18 18.6	22 17.9	19 14.9	21 4.5	26 38.0	8 29.2	12 43.7
23	18 2 10.1	1♋ 1.5	27 13.8	21 51.4	14 15.6	19 12.9	22 58.6	19 23.3	21 12.6	26 37.2	8 27.6	12 43.7
24	18 6 6.7	2 3.9	27 10.5	5♑46.8	14 D 19.6	20 6.5	23 39.2	19 31.7	21 20.6	26 36.6	8 26.0	12 43.6
25	18 10 3.3	3 6.2	27 7.2	19 10.5	14 28.3	20 59.2	24 19.9	19 39.9	21 28.7	26 35.9	8 24.5	12 43.6
26	18 13 59.8	4 8.5	27 3.9	1♒56.8	14 41.9	21 51.2	25 .6	19 48.0	21 36.8	26 35.4	8 23.0	12 D 43.7
27	18 17 56.4	5 10.8	27 .6	14 6.2	15 .4	22 42.3	25 41.2	19 56.0	21 44.9	26 34.8	8 21.4	12 43.7
28	18 21 52.9	6 13.1	26 57.3	25 44.2	15 23.8	23 32.7	26 21.8	20 3.9	21 53.0	26 34.3	8 19.9	12 43.8
29	18 25 49.5	7 15.3	26 54.0	6♓59.7	15 52.2	24 22.2	27 2.4	20 11.6	22 1.1	26 33.9	8 18.4	12 44.0
30	18 29 46.0	8 17.4	26 50.7	18 3.3	16 25.5	25 10.8	27 43.0	20 19.2	22 9.3	26 33.5	8 17.0	12 44.1

DECLINATION

DAY	SID. TIME	☉	☊	☽	☿	♀	♂	♃	♄	♅	♆	♇
1	16 35 25.9	21N56.3	0S21.2	6S47.7	22N53.6	23N45.8	1N38.8	5N29.8	22N15.6	10S34.2	20S25.5	13N 3.2
4	16 47 15.6	22 20.0	0 21.2	5N59.3	21 59.8	23 7.1	2 31.0	5 42.1	22 13.3	10 32.5	20 24.9	13 2.5
7	16 59 5.2	22 40.1	0 21.2	17 1.9	21 3.5	22 23.9	3 22.8	5 54.1	22 10.8	10 30.9	20 24.2	13 1.5
10	17 10 54.9	22 56.7	0 21.1	21 19.7	20 8.7	21 36.6	4 14.1	6 5.7	22 8.3	10 29.5	20 23.5	13 .5
13	17 22 44.6	23 9.7	0 21.1	14 56.7	19 20.1	20 45.4	5 4.8	6 16.9	22 5.7	10 28.3	20 22.9	12 59.3
16	17 34 34.2	23 19.0	0 21.1	0 52.4	18 42.2	19 50.9	5 54.9	6 27.6	22 3.0	10 27.1	20 22.3	12 58.0
19	17 46 23.9	23 24.6	0 21.0	13S29.4	18 18.2	18 53.3	6 44.2	6 37.9	22 .2	10 26.2	20 21.6	12 56.5
22	17 58 13.6	23 26.5	0 21.0	21 4.4	18 9.9	17 53.1	7 32.8	6 47.8	21 57.3	10 25.4	20 21.1	12 55.0
25	18 10 3.3	23 24.6	0 21.0	18 24.1	18 17.2	16 50.6	8 20.6	6 57.2	21 54.3	10 24.7	20 20.5	12 53.3
28	18 21 52.9	23 19.1	0 20.9	8 15.2	18 38.6	15 46.3	9 7.4	7 6.1	21 51.2	10 24.2	20 19.9	12 51.5

JULY 1975

DAY	EPHEM. SID. TIME	☉	☊	☽	☿	♀	♂	♃	♄	♅	♆	♇
	h m s	° ′	° ′	° ′	° ′	° ′	° ′	° ′	° ′	° ′	° ′	° ′
		LONGITUDE										
1	18 33 42.6	8♋34.1	29♏ .6	0♈58.1	17♊46.0	23♌18.7	29♈53.4	21♈36.1	20♋37.3	28♎22.4	9♐39.9	6♎32.1
2	18 37 39.2	9 31.3	28 57.5	12 53.8	18 27.8	24 8.9	0♉36.1	21 43.9	20 45.0	28 R 22.1	9 R 38.6	6 32.5
3	18 41 35.7	10 28.5	28 54.3	24 57.5	19 14.2	24 58.5	1 18.7	21 51.6	20 52.7	28 21.9	9 37.2	6 33.1
4	18 45 32.3	11 25.7	28 51.1	7♉14.2	20 5.1	25 47.3	2 1.3	21 59.1	21 .4	28 21.7	9 35.9	6 33.6
5	18 49 28.8	12 22.9	28 47.9	19 48.4	21 .4	26 35.4	2 43.7	22 6.4	21 8.1	28 21.5	9 34.6	6 34.2
6	18 53 25.4	13 20.1	28 44.8	2♊43.8	22 .2	27 22.7	3 26.1	22 13.6	21 15.8	28 21.4	9 33.3	6 34.8
7	18 57 21.9	14 17.4	28 41.6	16 2.9	23 4.3	28 9.2	4 8.4	22 20.7	21 23.6	28 21.4	9 32.0	6 35.4
8	19 1 18.5	15 14.6	28 38.4	29 46.2	24 12.6	28 54.8	4 50.5	22 27.5	21 31.3	28 21.4	9 30.8	6 36.1
9	19 5 15.1	16 11.8	28 35.2	13♋52.1	25 25.3	29 39.7	5 32.7	22 34.3	21 39.1	28 D 21.6	9 29.6	6 36.9
10	19 9 11.6	17 9.1	28 32.1	28 16.5	26 42.0	0♍23.6	6 14.6	22 40.9	21 46.9	28 21.7	9 28.4	6 37.6
11	19 13 8.2	18 6.3	28 28.9	12♌53.4	28 2.9	1 6.5	6 56.5	22 47.4	21 54.7	28 21.9	9 27.2	6 38.4
12	19 17 4.7	19 3.5	28 25.7	27 35.4	29 27.8	1 48.5	7 38.3	22 53.6	22 2.4	28 22.1	9 26.1	6 39.2
13	19 21 1.3	20 .8	28 22.5	12♍15.3	0♋56.7	2 29.5	8 20.0	22 59.7	22 10.2	28 22.4	9 24.9	6 40.0
14	19 24 57.8	20 58.0	28 19.3	26 46.8	2 29.4	3 9.4	9 1.5	23 5.7	22 18.0	28 22.7	9 23.8	6 40.9
15	19 28 54.4	21 55.2	28 16.2	11♎ 5.5	4 6.0	3 48.3	9 43.0	23 11.5	22 25.8	28 23.1	9 22.7	6 41.8
16	19 32 51.0	22 52.5	28 13.0	25 8.9	5 46.2	4 26.0	10 24.3	23 17.1	22 33.6	28 23.5	9 21.6	6 42.7
17	19 36 47.5	23 49.7	28 9.8	8♏56.3	7 29.9	5 2.5	11 5.5	23 22.5	22 41.4	28 24.0	9 20.6	6 43.7
18	19 40 44.1	24 46.9	28 6.6	22 28.2	9 16.9	5 37.7	11 46.6	23 27.8	22 49.1	28 24.6	9 19.5	6 44.6
19	19 44 40.6	25 44.2	28 3.5	5♐45.8	11 7.1	6 11.7	12 27.6	23 32.9	22 56.9	28 25.2	9 18.5	6 45.7
20	19 48 37.2	26 41.4	28 .3	18 50.5	13 .3	6 44.3	13 8.5	23 37.9	23 4.7	28 25.8	9 17.6	6 46.7
21	19 52 33.7	27 38.6	27 57.1	1♑43.2	14 56.2	7 15.6	13 49.3	23 42.7	23 12.5	28 26.5	9 16.6	6 47.8
22	19 56 30.3	28 35.9	27 53.9	14 24.7	16 54.5	7 45.4	14 30.0	23 47.3	23 20.2	28 27.3	9 15.7	6 48.9
23	20 0 26.9	29 33.1	27 50.8	26 55.7	18 55.0	8 13.7	15 10.5	23 51.7	23 28.0	28 28.1	9 14.8	6 50.0
24	20 4 23.4	0♌30.4	27 47.6	9♒16.5	20 57.3	8 40.5	15 50.9	23 55.9	23 35.7	28 29.0	9 13.9	6 51.2
25	20 8 20.0	1 27.7	27 44.4	21 27.7	23 1.1	9 5.7	16 31.2	24 .0	23 43.5	28 29.9	9 13.1	6 52.4
26	20 12 16.5	2 25.0	27 41.2	3♓30.5	25 6.0	9 29.2	17 11.4	24 3.9	23 51.2	28 30.8	9 12.3	6 53.6
27	20 16 13.1	3 22.3	27 38.0	15 26.5	27 11.9	9 51.0	17 51.5	24 7.6	23 58.9	28 31.8	9 11.5	6 54.9
28	20 20 9.6	4 19.6	27 34.9	27 18.2	29 18.2	10 11.1	18 31.4	24 11.1	24 6.6	28 32.9	9 10.7	6 56.2
29	20 24 6.2	5 16.9	27 31.7	9♈ 9.0	1♌24.8	10 29.3	19 11.2	24 14.5	24 14.3	28 34.0	9 10.0	6 57.5
30	20 28 2.7	6 14.3	27 28.5	21 2.8	3 31.4	10 45.7	19 50.9	24 17.7	24 22.1	28 35.2	9 9.3	6 58.9
31	20 31 59.3	7 11.7	27 25.3	3♉ 4.4	5 37.7	11 .1	20 30.5	24 20.7	24 29.7	28 36.4	9 8.6	7 .2
		LATITUDE										
1	18 33 42.6	0 .0	0 .0	4N27.4	3S42.1	0N58.8	1S39.0	1S16.3	0S 3.5	0N32.0	1N35.7	16N48.6
4	18 45 32.3	0 .0	0 .0	2 1.7	3 12.0	0 40.5	1 38.4	1 17.0	0 3.3	0 31.9	1 35.6	16 47.1
7	18 57 21.9	0 .0	0 .0	1S24.4	2 37.2	0 20.3	1 37.7	1 17.7	0 3.0	0 31.8	1 35.5	16 45.5
10	19 9 11.6	0 .0	0 .0	4 21.6	1 59.3	0S 1.7	1 36.9	1 18.4	0 2.7	0 31.7	1 35.4	16 44.0
13	19 21 1.3	0 .0	0 .0	4 59.7	1 19.9	0 25.8	1 36.0	1 19.2	0 2.5	0 31.6	1 35.3	16 42.5
16	19 32 51.0	0 .0	0 .0	2 54.0	0 40.5	0 51.9	1 35.0	1 19.9	0 2.2	0 31.5	1 35.2	16 41.0
19	19 44 40.6	0 .0	0 .0	0N33.1	0 2.9	1 20.1	1 33.8	1 20.6	0 2.0	0 31.4	1 35.1	16 39.5
22	19 56 30.3	0 .0	0 .0	3 35.6	0N31.1	1 50.3	1 32.5	1 21.4	0 1.7	0 31.2	1 34.9	16 38.1
25	20 8 20.0	0 .0	0 .0	5 .5	0 59.8	2 22.6	1 31.1	1 22.2	0 1.4	0 31.1	1 34.8	16 36.7
28	20 20 9.6	0 .0	0 .0	4 25.7	1 21.9	2 56.9	1 29.6	1 23.0	0 1.2	0 31.0	1 34.6	16 35.3
31	20 31 59.3	0 .0	0 .0	2 9.5	1 36.8	3 33.0	1 28.0	1 23.8	0 .9	0 30.9	1 34.5	16 34.0
		RIGHT ASCENSION										
1	18 33 42.6	9♋19.6	26♏47.4	29♓ 6.7	17♊ 3.7	25♌58.6	28♈23.6	20♈26.7	22♋17.5	26♎33.2	8♐15.5	12♎44.3
2	18 37 39.2	10 21.6	26 44.1	10♈21.7	17 46.9	26 45.6	29 4.2	20 34.1	22 25.7	26 R 32.9	8 R 14.1	12 44.5
3	18 41 35.7	11 23.6	26 40.8	22 .1	18 35.0	27 31.6	29 44.8	20 41.3	22 33.9	26 32.6	8 12.6	12 44.8
4	18 45 32.3	12 25.5	26 37.5	4♉12.1	19 28.0	28 16.7	0♉25.3	20 48.4	22 42.1	26 32.4	8 11.2	12 45.0
5	18 49 28.8	13 27.4	26 34.2	17 5.5	20 25.8	29 .9	1 5.8	20 55.4	22 50.3	26 32.3	8 9.9	12 45.3
6	18 53 25.4	14 29.2	26 30.9	0♊43.1	21 28.5	29 44.2	1 46.3	21 2.2	22 58.6	26 32.2	8 8.5	12 45.7
7	18 57 21.9	15 30.9	26 27.6	15 .3	22 36.0	0♍26.4	2 26.8	21 8.9	23 6.8	26 32.1	8 7.1	12 46.0
8	19 1 18.5	16 32.5	26 24.3	29 45.2	23 48.4	1 7.7	3 7.3	21 15.4	23 15.1	26 D 32.2	8 5.8	12 46.4
9	19 5 15.1	17 34.1	26 21.0	14♋40.3	25 5.6	1 48.0	3 47.7	21 21.9	23 23.4	26 32.3	8 4.6	12 46.9
10	19 9 11.6	18 35.5	26 17.7	29 28.1	26 27.5	2 27.3	4 28.1	21 28.1	23 31.6	26 32.4	8 3.3	12 47.3
11	19 13 8.2	19 36.8	26 14.4	13♌56.3	27 54.1	3 5.4	5 8.5	21 34.3	23 39.9	26 32.5	8 2.0	12 47.8
12	19 17 4.7	20 38.0	26 11.1	28 .6	29 25.3	3 42.5	5 48.9	21 40.2	23 48.2	26 32.7	8 .8	12 48.3
13	19 21 1.3	21 39.1	26 7.9	11♍43.9	1♋ 1.2	4 18.4	6 29.2	21 46.0	23 56.5	26 33.0	7 59.6	12 48.9
14	19 24 57.8	22 40.1	26 4.6	25 14.1	2 41.5	4 53.1	7 9.4	21 51.7	24 4.7	26 33.3	7 58.4	12 49.4
15	19 28 54.4	23 41.0	26 1.3	8♎40.8	4 26.2	5 26.6	7 49.7	21 57.2	24 13.0	26 33.6	7 57.2	12 50.0
16	19 32 51.0	24 41.7	25 58.0	22 13.0	6 15.1	5 58.9	8 29.9	22 2.6	24 21.3	26 34.1	7 56.1	12 50.7
17	19 36 47.5	25 42.3	25 54.7	5♏56.9	8 8.1	6 30.0	9 10.1	22 7.8	24 29.5	26 34.5	7 55.0	12 51.3
18	19 40 44.1	26 42.7	25 51.4	19 53.4	10 4.9	6 59.7	9 50.2	22 12.8	24 37.8	26 35.0	7 53.9	12 52.0
19	19 44 40.6	27 43.1	25 48.1	3♐58.1	12 5.2	7 28.0	10 30.4	22 17.7	24 46.1	26 35.6	7 52.8	12 52.7
20	19 48 37.2	28 43.2	25 44.8	18 1.1	14 8.7	7 55.0	11 10.4	22 22.5	24 54.3	26 36.2	7 51.8	12 53.5
21	19 52 33.7	29 43.3	25 41.5	1♑50.2	16 15.2	8 20.5	11 50.5	22 27.0	25 2.6	26 36.8	7 50.8	12 54.2
22	19 56 30.3	0♌43.2	25 38.2	15 14.4	18 24.1	8 44.6	12 30.5	22 31.5	25 10.8	26 37.5	7 49.8	12 55.0
23	20 0 26.9	1 42.9	25 35.0	28 6.6	20 35.1	9 7.1	13 10.4	22 35.7	25 19.0	26 38.3	7 48.9	12 55.9
24	20 4 23.4	2 42.5	25 31.7	10♒25.1	22 47.8	9 28.1	13 50.4	22 39.8	25 27.2	26 39.1	7 47.9	12 56.7
25	20 8 20.0	3 42.0	25 28.4	22 12.7	25 1.6	9 47.4	14 30.2	22 43.7	25 35.4	26 39.9	7 47.0	12 57.6
26	20 12 16.5	4 41.3	25 25.1	3♓36.0	27 16.2	10 5.1	15 10.1	22 47.5	25 43.6	26 40.8	7 46.2	12 58.5
27	20 16 13.1	5 40.5	25 21.8	14 43.7	29 31.0	10 21.1	15 49.9	22 51.1	25 51.8	26 41.8	7 45.3	12 59.4
28	20 20 9.6	6 39.5	25 18.5	25 45.9	1♌45.7	10 35.3	16 29.6	22 54.5	25 60.0	26 42.8	7 44.5	13 .4
29	20 24 6.2	7 38.4	25 15.2	6♈53.2	3 59.8	10 47.8	17 9.3	22 57.7	26 8.1	26 43.8	7 43.7	13 1.4
30	20 28 2.7	8 37.2	25 12.0	18 16.4	6 13.0	10 58.5	17 48.9	23 .8	26 16.3	26 45.0	7 43.0	13 2.5
31	20 31 59.3	9 35.8	25 8.7	0♉ 5.7	8 25.0	11 7.2	18 28.5	23 3.7	26 24.4	26 46.1	7 42.3	13 3.5
		DECLINATION										
1	18 33 42.6	23N 9.9	0S20.9	4N28.4	19N11.5	14N40.5	9N53.3	7N14.5	21N48.0	10S23.9	20S19.4	12N49.6
4	18 45 32.3	22 57.0	0 20.8	15 50.7	19 52.8	13 33.6	10 38.2	7 22.4	21 44.8	10 23.8	20 18.9	12 47.6
7	18 57 21.9	22 40.5	0 20.8	21 18.7	20 38.6	12 26.1	11 22.0	7 29.8	21 41.4	10 23.8	20 18.4	12 45.5
10	19 9 11.6	22 20.5	0 20.8	16 14.1	21 24.7	11 18.4	12 4.7	7 36.6	21 38.0	10 24.0	20 18.0	12 43.2
13	19 21 1.3	21 57.0	0 20.7	2 20.6	22 6.4	10 11.2	12 46.1	7 42.9	21 34.5	10 24.3	20 17.6	12 40.9
16	19 32 51.0	21 30.1	0 20.7	12S25.8	22 38.5	9 4.8	13 26.4	7 48.6	21 31.0	10 24.8	20 17.2	12 38.5
19	19 44 40.6	20 59.9	0 20.7	20 43.5	22 55.7	7 59.9	14 5.3	7 53.7	21 27.4	10 25.5	20 16.9	12 36.0
22	19 56 30.3	20 26.6	0 20.6	19 5.3	22 53.2	6 57.2	14 43.0	7 58.3	21 23.7	10 26.4	20 16.6	12 33.4
25	20 8 20.0	19 50.2	0 20.6	9 36.2	22 27.6	5 57.4	15 19.3	8 2.3	21 20.0	10 27.4	20 16.4	12 30.8
28	20 20 9.6	19 10.8	0 20.5	2N59.5	21 38.0	5 1.1	15 54.3	8 5.6	21 16.3	10 28.6	20 16.2	12 28.1
31	20 31 59.3	18 28.5	0 20.5	14 33.9	20 25.8	4 9.3	16 27.8	8 8.4	21 12.5	10 29.9	20 16.0	12 25.3

AUGUST 1975

LONGITUDE

DAY	EPHEM. SID. TIME h m s	☉ ° ′	☊ ° ′	☽ ° ′	☿ ° ′	♀ ° ′	♂ ° ′	♃ ° ′	♄ ° ′	♅ ° ′	♆ ° ′	♇ ° ′
1	20 35 55.9	8♌ 9.1	27♏22.2	15♉18.7	7♌43.4	11♍12.5	21♉ 9.9	24♈23.5	24♋37.4	28♎37.7	9♐ 8.0	7♎ 1.6
2	20 39 52.4	9 6.5	27 19.0	27 51.0	9 48.4	11 22.8	21 49.1	24 26.1	24 45.0	28 39.0	9 R 7.4	7 3.0
3	20 43 49.0	10 3.9	27 15.8	10♊46.0	11 52.5	11 31.1	22 28.2	24 28.5	24 52.6	28 40.4	9 6.8	7 4.5
4	20 47 45.5	11 1.3	27 12.6	24 7.5	13 55.6	11 37.2	23 7.2	24 30.7	25 .2	28 41.8	9 6.2	7 6.0
5	20 51 42.1	11 58.8	27 9.5	7♋57.3	15 57.4	11 41.0	23 46.0	24 32.7	25 7.8	28 43.3	9 5.7	7 7.5
6	20 55 38.6	12 56.3	27 6.3	22 14.8	17 58.0	11 42.7	24 24.6	24 34.6	25 15.4	28 44.8	9 5.2	7 9.0
7	20 59 35.2	13 53.8	27 3.1	6♌55.9	19 57.3	11 R 42.0	25 3.1	24 36.2	25 22.9	28 46.3	9 4.7	7 10.5
8	21 3 31.7	14 51.3	26 59.9	21 53.7	21 55.2	11 39.1	25 41.5	24 37.6	25 30.4	28 47.9	9 4.2	7 12.1
9	21 7 28.3	15 48.8	26 56.7	6♍58.8	23 51.6	11 33.8	26 19.7	24 38.9	25 37.9	28 49.6	9 3.8	7 13.7
10	21 11 24.9	16 46.4	26 53.6	22 1.0	25 46.6	11 26.1	26 57.7	24 39.9	25 45.4	28 51.3	9 3.4	7 15.3
11	21 15 21.4	17 43.9	26 50.4	6♎51.4	27 40.1	11 16.0	27 35.5	24 40.8	25 52.8	28 53.1	9 3.1	7 17.0
12	21 19 18.0	18 41.5	26 47.2	21 23.3	29 32.1	11 3.5	28 13.2	24 41.4	26 .2	28 54.9	9 2.8	7 18.7
13	21 23 14.5	19 39.1	26 44.0	5♏33.3	1♍22.5	10 48.7	28 50.7	24 41.9	26 7.6	28 56.7	9 2.5	7 20.3
14	21 27 11.1	20 36.7	26 40.9	19 20.5	3 11.5	10 31.5	29 28.0	24 42.1	26 14.9	28 58.6	9 2.2	7 22.1
15	21 31 7.6	21 34.3	26 37.7	2♐46.1	4 59.0	10 12.0	0♊ 5.2	24 42.2	26 22.2	29 .5	9 2.0	7 23.8
16	21 35 4.2	22 32.0	26 34.5	15 52.6	6 45.0	9 50.2	0 42.1	24 R 42.0	26 29.5	29 2.5	9 1.8	7 25.6
17	21 39 .7	23 29.6	26 31.3	28 42.9	8 29.5	9 26.3	1 18.9	24 41.7	26 36.8	29 4.5	9 1.7	7 27.4
18	21 42 57.3	24 27.3	26 28.1	11♑19.7	10 12.6	9 .4	1 55.5	24 41.1	26 44.0	29 6.6	9 1.5	7 29.2
19	21 46 53.8	25 25.0	26 25.0	23 45.6	11 54.2	8 32.5	2 31.9	24 40.4	26 51.1	29 8.7	9 1.4	7 31.0
20	21 50 50.4	26 22.7	26 21.8	6♒ 2.3	13 34.4	8 2.8	3 8.2	24 39.5	26 58.3	29 10.9	9 1.4	7 32.9
21	21 54 46.9	27 20.5	26 18.6	18 11.2	15 13.2	7 31.4	3 44.2	24 38.4	27 5.4	29 13.1	9 1.4	7 34.8
22	21 58 43.5	28 18.2	26 15.4	0♓13.6	16 50.5	6 58.6	4 20.1	24 37.0	27 12.5	29 15.4	9 1.4	7 36.6
23	22 2 40.1	29 16.0	26 12.3	12 10.4	18 26.5	6 24.4	4 55.7	24 35.5	27 19.5	29 17.7	9 1.4	7 38.6
24	22 6 36.6	0♍13.8	26 9.1	24 3.1	20 1.1	5 49.2	5 31.2	24 33.8	27 26.5	29 20.0	9 D 1.5	7 40.5
25	22 10 33.2	1 11.6	26 5.9	5♈53.4	21 34.2	5 13.1	6 6.4	24 31.9	27 33.4	29 22.4	9 1.6	7 42.4
26	22 14 29.7	2 9.5	26 2.7	17 43.8	23 6.0	4 36.4	6 41.5	24 29.7	27 40.3	29 24.8	9 1.7	7 44.4
27	22 18 26.3	3 7.4	25 59.5	29 37.4	24 36.4	3 59.3	7 16.3	24 27.4	27 47.2	29 27.2	9 1.9	7 46.4
28	22 22 22.8	4 5.3	25 56.4	11♉38.2	26 5.4	3 22.0	7 50.9	24 24.9	27 54.0	29 29.7	9 2.1	7 48.4
29	22 26 19.4	5 3.2	25 53.2	23 50.8	27 33.0	2 44.8	8 25.2	24 22.2	28 .8	29 32.3	9 2.3	7 50.4
30	22 30 15.9	6 1.2	25 50.0	6♊20.2	28 59.1	2 7.9	8 59.4	24 19.3	28 7.5	29 34.8	9 2.6	7 52.4
31	22 34 12.5	6 59.2	25 46.8	19 11.2	0♎23.9	1 31.6	9 33.3	24 16.2	28 14.2	29 37.4	9 2.9	7 54.5

LATITUDE

DAY	SID. TIME	☉	☊	☽	☿	♀	♂	♃	♄	♅	♆	♇
1	20 35 55.9	0 .0	0 .0	1N 8.1	1N40.2	3S45.3	1S27.4	1S24.0	0S .8	0N30.9	1N34.4	16N33.6
4	20 47 45.5	0 .0	0 .0	2S12.9	1 45.8	4 23.3	1 25.6	1 24.8	0 .6	0 30.8	1 34.3	16 32.3
7	20 59 35.2	0 .0	0 .0	4 41.5	1 45.1	5 2.0	1 23.7	1 25.6	0 .3	0 30.7	1 34.1	16 31.1
10	21 11 24.9	0 .0	0 .0	4 33.8	1 38.9	5 40.8	1 21.7	1 26.4	0 .0	0 30.6	1 33.9	16 29.9
13	21 23 14.5	0 .0	0 .0	1 51.2	1 28.1	6 18.7	1 19.5	1 27.2	0N .2	0 30.5	1 33.8	16 28.8
16	21 35 4.2	0 .0	0 .0	1N37.7	1 13.3	6 54.5	1 17.2	1 28.0	0 .5	0 30.4	1 33.6	16 27.8
19	21 46 53.8	0 .0	0 .0	4 12.1	0 55.4	7 26.6	1 14.7	1 28.7	0 .8	0 30.3	1 33.4	16 26.8
22	21 58 43.5	0 .0	0 .0	4 58.8	0 34.9	7 53.6	1 12.1	1 29.5	0 1.0	0 30.2	1 33.3	16 25.8
25	22 10 33.2	0 .0	0 .0	3 49.6	0 12.3	8 14.1	1 9.4	1 30.3	0 1.3	0 30.1	1 33.1	16 24.9
28	22 22 22.8	0 .0	0 .0	1 11.7	0S11.8	8 27.0	1 6.6	1 31.0	0 1.6	0 30.0	1 32.9	16 24.1
31	22 34 12.5	0 .0	0 .0	2S 3.0	0 37.0	8 31.7	1 3.6	1 31.7	0 1.8	0 29.9	1 32.8	16 23.4

RIGHT ASCENSION

DAY	SID. TIME	☉	☊	☽	☿	♀	♂	♃	♄	♅	♆	♇
1	20 35 55.9	10♌34.2	25♏ 5.4	12♉29.9	10♌35.5	11♍14.0	19♉ 8.0	23♈ 6.4	26♋32.5	26♎47.3	7♐41.6	13♎ 4.6
2	20 39 52.4	11 32.5	25 2.1	25 34.7	12 44.2	11 18.9	19 47.4	23 9.0	26 40.6	26 48.5	7 R 40.9	13 5.7
3	20 43 49.0	12 30.7	24 58.8	9♊20.8	14 51.0	11 21.7	20 26.8	23 11.3	26 48.6	26 49.8	7 40.3	13 6.8
4	20 47 45.5	13 28.7	24 55.5	23 42.4	16 55.7	11 22.5	21 6.0	23 13.5	26 56.7	26 51.2	7 39.7	13 8.0
5	20 51 42.1	14 26.5	24 52.3	8♋27.3	18 58.2	11 R 21.2	21 45.2	23 15.5	27 4.7	26 52.5	7 39.1	13 9.1
6	20 55 38.6	15 24.2	24 49.0	23 20.1	20 58.5	11 17.8	22 24.3	23 17.4	27 12.6	26 54.0	7 38.6	13 10.3
7	20 59 35.2	16 21.8	24 45.7	8♌ 6.6	22 56.5	11 12.3	23 3.4	23 19.0	27 20.6	26 55.4	7 38.1	13 11.6
8	21 3 31.7	17 19.2	24 42.4	22 37.9	24 52.1	11 4.7	23 42.3	23 20.4	27 28.5	26 57.0	7 37.6	13 12.8
9	21 7 28.3	18 16.4	24 39.1	6♍51.9	26 45.4	10 54.9	24 21.1	23 21.7	27 36.4	26 58.5	7 37.2	13 14.1
10	21 11 24.9	19 13.6	24 35.8	20 52.1	28 36.5	10 42.9	24 59.9	23 22.8	27 44.3	27 .1	7 36.8	13 15.4
11	21 15 21.4	20 10.5	24 32.6	4♎45.3	0♍25.3	10 28.8	25 38.5	23 23.7	27 52.1	27 1.8	7 36.4	13 16.7
12	21 19 18.0	21 7.3	24 29.3	18 38.6	2 11.8	10 12.5	26 17.0	23 24.4	27 60.0	27 3.5	7 36.0	13 18.1
13	21 23 14.5	22 4.0	24 26.0	2♏37.0	3 56.2	9 54.2	26 55.4	23 24.9	28 7.7	27 5.2	7 35.7	13 19.4
14	21 27 11.1	23 .5	24 22.7	16 41.7	5 38.4	9 33.7	27 33.7	23 25.2	28 15.5	27 7.0	7 35.4	13 20.8
15	21 31 7.6	23 56.9	24 19.5	0♐48.9	7 18.6	9 11.3	28 11.9	23 25.4	28 23.2	27 8.8	7 35.2	13 22.2
16	21 35 4.2	24 53.2	24 16.2	14 50.9	8 56.8	8 47.0	28 49.9	23 R 25.3	28 30.8	27 10.7	7 35.0	13 23.7
17	21 39 .7	25 49.3	24 12.9	28 37.6	10 33.0	8 20.8	29 27.9	23 25.1	28 38.5	27 12.6	7 34.8	13 25.1
18	21 42 57.3	26 45.3	24 9.6	12♑ .1	12 7.4	7 52.9	0♊ 5.7	23 24.7	28 46.1	27 14.6	7 34.7	13 26.6
19	21 46 53.8	27 41.1	24 6.4	24 52.5	13 39.9	7 23.4	0 43.3	23 24.1	28 53.6	27 16.6	7 34.6	13 28.1
20	21 50 50.4	28 36.9	24 3.1	7♒13.3	15 10.8	6 52.4	1 20.9	23 23.4	29 1.2	27 18.7	7 34.5	13 29.7
21	21 54 46.9	29 32.5	23 59.8	19 4.8	16 39.9	6 20.2	1 58.3	23 22.4	29 8.7	27 20.8	7 34.5	13 31.2
22	21 58 43.5	0♍27.9	23 56.5	0♓32.5	18 7.3	5 46.9	2 35.6	23 21.2	29 16.1	27 22.9	7 34.5	13 32.8
23	22 2 40.1	1 23.3	23 53.3	11 43.9	19 33.2	5 12.6	3 12.7	23 19.9	29 23.5	27 25.1	7 34.5	13 34.4
24	22 6 36.6	2 18.6	23 50.0	22 47.7	20 57.5	4 37.6	3 49.6	23 18.3	29 30.8	27 27.3	7 D 34.6	13 36.0
25	22 10 33.2	3 13.7	23 46.7	3♈53.1	22 20.3	4 2.1	4 26.4	23 16.6	29 38.1	27 29.5	7 34.7	13 37.6
26	22 14 29.7	4 8.7	23 43.4	15 9.4	23 41.6	3 26.3	5 3.0	23 14.7	29 45.4	27 31.8	7 34.8	13 39.3
27	22 18 26.3	5 3.7	23 40.2	26 45.4	25 1.5	2 50.4	5 39.5	23 12.6	29 52.6	27 34.1	7 34.9	13 40.9
28	22 22 22.8	5 58.5	23 36.9	8♉49.1	26 20.0	2 14.7	6 15.7	23 10.4	29 59.7	27 36.5	7 35.1	13 42.6
29	22 26 19.4	6 53.3	23 33.6	21 26.1	27 37.1	1 39.4	6 51.8	23 7.9	0♌ 6.8	27 38.9	7 35.4	13 44.3
30	22 30 15.9	7 48.0	23 30.4	4♊38.8	28 52.8	1 4.7	7 27.7	23 5.3	0 13.9	27 41.3	7 35.6	13 46.1
31	22 34 12.5	8 42.6	23 27.1	18 25.1	0♎ 7.2	0 30.9	8 3.4	23 2.5	0 20.9	27 43.8	7 35.9	13 47.8

DECLINATION

DAY	SID. TIME	☉	☊	☽	☿	♀	♂	♃	♄	♅	♆	♇
1	20 35 55.9	18N13.8	0S20.5	17N30.8	19N57.2	3N53.2	16N38.7	8N 9.2	21N11.2	10S30.4	20S15.9	12N24.4
4	20 47 45.5	17 27.9	0 20.5	21 5.9	18 20.3	3 8.7	17 10.4	8 11.1	21 7.4	10 31.9	20 15.8	12 21.6
7	20 59 35.2	16 39.5	0 20.4	13 59.8	16 29.5	2 31.0	17 40.6	8 12.3	21 3.5	10 33.6	20 15.8	12 18.7
10	21 11 24.9	15 48.6	0 20.4	1S 1.6	14 28.8	2 1.1	18 9.3	8 12.9	20 59.7	10 35.5	20 15.7	12 15.7
13	21 23 14.5	14 55.5	0 20.3	15 7.3	12 21.5	1 40.0	18 36.6	8 12.9	20 55.8	10 37.5	20 15.8	12 12.8
16	21 35 4.2	14 .3	0 20.3	21 4.4	10 10.2	1 28.6	19 2.4	8 12.2	20 51.9	10 39.7	20 15.8	12 9.8
19	21 46 53.8	13 3.0	0 20.3	17 12.7	7 57.1	1 27.5	19 26.8	8 10.9	20 48.0	10 41.9	20 15.9	12 6.8
22	21 58 43.5	12 3.9	0 20.2	6 43.6	5 43.9	1 36.7	19 49.8	8 9.0	20 44.2	10 44.4	20 16.1	12 3.7
25	22 10 33.2	11 3.1	0 20.2	5N51.1	3 31.9	1 55.6	20 11.3	8 6.4	20 40.3	10 46.9	20 16.3	12 .7
28	22 22 22.8	10 .7	0 20.2	16 27.8	1 22.5	2 23.0	20 31.5	8 3.2	20 36.5	10 49.6	20 16.5	11 57.6
31	22 34 12.5	8 56.8	0 20.1	20 57.4	0S43.5	2 57.1	20 50.3	7 59.4	20 32.8	10 52.4	20 16.8	11 54.6

SEPTEMBER 1975

LONGITUDE

DAY	EPHEM. SID. TIME	☉	☊	☽	☿	♀	♂	♃	♄	♅	♆	♇
	h m s	° ′	° ′	° ′	° ′	° ′	° ′	° ′	° ′	° ′	° ′	° ′
1	22 38 9.0	7♍57.2	25♏43.7	2♋28.4	1♎47.1	0♍56.1	10♊ 7.0	24♈12.9	28♋20.8	29♎40.1	9♐ 3.2	7♎56.5
2	22 42 5.6	8 55.3	25 40.5	16 14.8	3 8.9	0 R 21.6	10 40.4	24 R 9.5	28 27.4	29 42.8	9 3.5	7 58.6
3	22 46 2.1	9 53.4	25 37.3	0♌31.0	4 29.2	29♌48.4	11 13.6	24 5.8	28 33.9	29 45.5	9 3.9	8 .7
4	22 49 58.7	10 51.5	25 34.1	15 14.4	5 47.9	29 16.5	11 46.6	24 2.0	28 40.4	29 48.2	9 4.3	8 2.8
5	22 53 55.2	11 49.7	25 30.9	0♍18.9	7 5.0	28 46.3	12 19.2	23 57.9	28 46.8	29 51.0	9 4.8	8 4.9
6	22 57 51.8	12 47.9	25 27.8	15 35.1	8 20.4	28 17.7	12 51.6	23 53.7	28 53.1	29 53.9	9 5.3	8 7.1
7	23 1 48.3	13 46.1	25 24.6	0♎51.7	9 34.1	27 51.1	13 23.8	23 49.3	28 59.4	29 56.7	9 5.8	8 9.2
8	23 5 44.9	14 44.3	25 21.4	15 57.8	10 46.0	27 26.5	13 55.6	23 44.8	29 5.7	29 59.6	9 6.4	8 11.4
9	23 9 41.5	15 42.6	25 18.2	0♏44.7	11 56.0	27 3.9	14 27.2	23 40.0	29 11.9	0♏ 2.6	9 7.0	8 13.6
10	23 13 38.0	16 41.0	25 15.1	15 6.9	13 4.1	26 43.7	14 58.5	23 35.2	29 18.0	0 5.6	9 7.6	8 15.8
11	23 17 34.6	17 39.3	25 11.9	29 2.2	14 10.0	26 25.6	15 29.5	23 30.1	29 24.1	0 8.6	9 8.3	8 18.0
12	23 21 31.1	18 37.6	25 8.7	12♐31.2	15 13.7	26 9.9	16 .2	23 24.9	29 30.1	0 11.6	9 9.0	8 20.2
13	23 25 27.7	19 36.0	25 5.5	25 36.6	16 15.0	25 56.5	16 30.6	23 19.5	29 36.0	0 14.7	9 9.7	8 22.5
14	23 29 24.2	20 34.4	25 2.3	8♑21.9	17 13.9	25 45.5	17 .7	23 13.9	29 41.9	0 17.7	9 10.4	8 24.7
15	23 33 20.8	21 32.8	24 59.2	20 50.9	18 10.0	25 36.9	17 30.5	23 8.2	29 47.7	0 20.9	9 11.2	8 26.9
16	23 37 17.3	22 31.3	24 56.0	3♒ 7.3	19 3.3	25 30.8	18 .0	23 2.4	29 53.4	0 24.0	9 12.0	8 29.2
17	23 41 13.9	23 29.8	24 52.8	15 14.2	19 53.6	25 27.0	18 29.2	22 56.4	29 59.1	0 27.2	9 12.8	8 31.4
18	23 45 10.4	24 28.3	24 49.6	27 14.4	20 40.5	25 25.7	18 58.0	22 50.2	0♌ 4.7	0 30.4	9 13.7	8 33.7
19	23 49 7.0	25 26.8	24 46.5	9♓10.0	21 23.9	25 D 26.7	19 26.5	22 43.9	0 10.3	0 33.6	9 14.6	8 36.0
20	23 53 3.5	26 25.4	24 43.3	21 2.7	22 3.5	25 30.0	19 54.7	22 37.5	0 15.7	0 36.9	9 15.5	8 38.3
21	23 57 .1	27 24.0	24 40.1	2♈54.0	22 38.9	25 35.6	20 22.5	22 31.0	0 21.1	0 40.2	9 16.5	8 40.5
22	0 0 56.6	28 22.7	24 36.9	14 45.5	23 9.9	25 43.5	20 49.9	22 24.3	0 26.4	0 43.5	9 17.5	8 42.8
23	0 4 53.2	29 21.3	24 33.7	26 39.1	23 36.1	25 53.6	21 17.0	22 17.5	0 31.7	0 46.8	9 18.5	8 45.1
24	0 8 49.7	0♎20.0	24 30.6	8♉37.1	23 57.2	26 5.8	21 43.8	22 10.6	0 36.9	0 50.2	9 19.6	8 47.4
25	0 12 46.3	1 18.8	24 27.4	20 42.3	24 12.7	26 20.1	22 10.1	22 3.6	0 42.0	0 53.5	9 20.6	8 49.7
26	0 16 42.8	2 17.6	24 24.2	2♊58.2	24 22.2	26 36.5	22 36.1	21 56.4	0 47.0	0 57.0	9 21.8	8 52.1
27	0 20 39.4	3 16.4	24 21.0	15 28.7	24 25.4	26 54.8	23 1.6	21 49.2	0 51.9	1 .4	9 22.9	8 54.4
28	0 24 35.9	4 15.2	24 17.8	28 18.1	24 R 21.9	27 15.0	23 26.8	21 41.9	0 56.8	1 3.8	9 24.1	8 56.7
29	0 28 32.5	5 14.1	24 14.7	11♋30.4	24 11.3	27 37.1	23 51.6	21 34.5	1 1.6	1 7.3	9 25.3	8 59.0
30	0 32 29.0	6 13.1	24 11.5	25 8.7	23 53.4	28 .9	24 15.9	21 26.9	1 6.3	1 10.8	9 26.5	9 1.3

LATITUDE

DAY	EPHEM. SID. TIME	☉	☊	☽	☿	♀	♂	♃	♄	♅	♆	♇
1	22 38 9.0	0 .0	0 .0	3S 3.4	0S45.6	8S31.4	1S 2.5	1S31.9	0N 1.9	0N29.9	1N32.7	16N23.1
4	22 49 58.7	0 .0	0 .0	4 57.5	1 11.7	8 25.4	0 59.3	1 32.6	0 2.2	0 29.8	1 32.5	16 22.5
7	23 1 48.3	0 .0	0 .0	4 3.5	1 37.9	8 12.1	0 55.9	1 33.2	0 2.5	0 29.7	1 32.4	16 21.9
10	23 13 38.0	0 .0	0 .0	0 48.2	2 3.8	7 52.7	0 52.4	1 33.8	0 2.8	0 29.7	1 32.2	16 21.3
13	23 25 27.7	0 .0	0 .0	2N39.1	2 28.8	7 28.4	0 48.7	1 34.3	0 3.0	0 29.6	1 32.0	16 20.9
16	23 37 17.3	0 .0	0 .0	4 44.2	2 52.3	7 .5	0 44.8	1 34.8	0 3.3	0 29.5	1 31.9	16 20.5
19	23 49 7.0	0 .0	0 .0	4 52.8	3 13.3	6 30.1	0 40.7	1 35.3	0 3.6	0 29.5	1 31.7	16 20.2
22	0 0 56.6	0 .0	0 .0	3 9.7	3 30.6	5 58.3	0 36.4	1 35.7	0 3.9	0 29.4	1 31.5	16 20.0
25	0 12 46.3	0 .0	0 .0	0 11.6	3 42.4	5 25.9	0 31.9	1 36.0	0 4.2	0 29.3	1 31.4	16 19.8
28	0 24 35.9	0 .0	0 .0	2S59.4	3 46.3	4 53.3	0 27.2	1 36.3	0 4.5	0 29.3	1 31.2	16 19.7

RIGHT ASCENSION

DAY	EPHEM. SID. TIME	☉	☊	☽	☿	♀	♂	♃	♄	♅	♆	♇
1	22 38 9.0	9♍37.1	23♏23.8	2♋38.1	1♎20.2	29♌58.0	8♊38.9	22♈59.5	0♌27.8	27♎46.3	7♐36.3	13♎49.6
2	22 42 5.6	10 31.5	23 20.5	17 7.4	2 31.8	29 R 26.4	9 14.2	22 R 56.3	0 34.7	27 48.9	7 36.6	13 51.3
3	22 46 2.1	11 25.9	23 17.3	1♌41.9	3 42.1	28 56.1	9 49.2	22 52.9	0 41.5	27 51.5	7 37.0	13 53.1
4	22 49 58.7	12 20.2	23 14.0	16 13.0	4 50.9	28 27.5	10 24.1	22 49.4	0 48.3	27 54.1	7 37.5	13 54.9
5	22 53 55.2	13 14.4	23 10.7	0♍37.0	5 58.4	28 .5	10 58.7	22 45.7	0 55.0	27 56.7	7 37.9	13 56.7
6	22 57 51.8	14 8.6	23 7.5	14 54.7	7 4.4	27 35.5	11 33.0	22 41.8	1 1.7	27 59.4	7 38.5	13 58.6
7	23 1 48.3	15 2.7	23 4.2	29 10.4	8 8.9	27 12.3	12 7.1	22 37.8	1 8.3	28 2.1	7 39.0	14 .4
8	23 5 44.9	15 56.8	23 .9	13♎29.0	9 11.8	26 51.3	12 41.0	22 33.6	1 14.8	28 4.9	7 39.6	14 2.3
9	23 9 41.5	16 50.8	22 57.7	27 53.8	10 13.1	26 32.4	13 14.5	22 29.2	1 21.3	28 7.7	7 40.2	14 4.2
10	23 13 38.0	17 44.8	22 54.4	12♏24.3	11 12.8	26 15.8	13 47.9	22 24.7	1 27.8	28 10.6	7 40.9	14 6.1
11	23 17 34.6	18 38.8	22 51.2	26 54.9	12 10.6	26 1.4	14 20.9	22 20.0	1 34.1	28 13.4	7 41.5	14 8.0
12	23 21 31.1	19 32.7	22 47.9	11♐16.6	13 6.6	25 49.3	14 53.7	22 15.2	1 40.4	28 16.3	7 42.3	14 10.0
13	23 25 27.7	20 26.5	22 44.6	25 18.7	14 .5	25 39.6	15 26.1	22 10.2	1 46.6	28 19.2	7 43.0	14 11.9
14	23 29 24.2	21 20.4	22 41.4	8♑52.1	14 52.3	25 32.2	15 58.3	22 5.1	1 52.7	28 22.1	7 43.8	14 13.8
15	23 33 20.8	22 14.2	22 38.1	21 51.8	15 41.7	25 27.2	16 30.2	21 59.8	1 58.8	28 25.1	7 44.6	14 15.8
16	23 37 17.3	23 8.0	22 34.8	4♒17.3	16 28.7	25 24.6	17 1.7	21 54.4	2 4.8	28 28.1	7 45.4	14 17.8
17	23 41 13.9	24 1.7	22 31.6	16 11.9	17 13.0	25 24.4	17 33.0	21 48.8	2 10.7	28 31.1	7 46.3	14 19.7
18	23 45 10.4	24 55.5	22 28.3	27 41.9	17 54.4	25 D 26.5	18 3.9	21 43.1	2 16.6	28 34.2	7 47.2	14 21.7
19	23 49 7.0	25 49.3	22 25.1	8♓55.2	18 32.7	25 30.8	18 34.5	21 37.3	2 22.4	28 37.3	7 48.1	14 23.7
20	23 53 3.5	26 43.1	22 21.8	20 .3	19 7.7	25 37.5	19 4.7	21 31.3	2 28.1	28 40.4	7 49.1	14 25.7
21	23 57 .1	27 36.9	22 18.5	1♈ 6.1	19 38.9	25 46.3	19 34.6	21 25.2	2 33.7	28 43.5	7 50.1	14 27.8
22	0 0 56.6	28 30.7	22 15.3	12 21.1	20 6.3	25 57.4	20 4.1	21 19.0	2 39.3	28 46.6	7 51.2	14 29.8
23	0 4 53.2	29 24.5	22 12.0	23 53.2	20 29.3	26 10.5	20 33.3	21 12.7	2 44.8	28 49.8	7 52.2	14 31.8
24	0 8 49.7	0♎18.4	22 8.8	5♉48.9	20 47.8	26 25.7	21 2.1	21 6.3	2 50.2	28 53.0	7 53.3	14 33.9
25	0 12 46.3	1 12.3	22 5.5	18 12.9	21 1.3	26 42.9	21 30.5	20 59.8	2 55.5	28 56.3	7 54.5	14 35.9
26	0 16 42.8	2 6.2	22 2.2	1♊ 6.5	21 9.4	27 2.0	21 58.5	20 53.1	3 .7	28 59.5	7 55.6	14 38.0
27	0 20 39.4	3 .2	21 59.0	14 27.8	21 12.0	27 23.1	22 26.1	20 46.4	3 5.9	29 2.8	7 56.8	14 40.1
28	0 24 35.9	3 54.2	21 55.7	28 11.4	21 R 8.6	27 45.9	22 53.3	20 39.6	3 11.0	29 6.1	7 58.0	14 42.1
29	0 28 32.5	4 48.3	21 52.5	12♋ 9.5	20 58.9	28 10.5	23 20.0	20 32.7	3 16.0	29 9.4	7 59.3	14 44.2
30	0 32 29.0	5 42.5	21 49.2	26 14.0	20 42.8	28 36.7	23 46.3	20 25.7	3 20.9	29 12.7	8 .6	14 46.3

DECLINATION

DAY	EPHEM. SID. TIME	☉	☊	☽	☿	♀	♂	♃	♄	♅	♆	♇
1	22 38 9.0	8N35.3	0S20.1	20N21.7	1S24.5	3N 9.6	20N56.2	7N58.0	20N31.5	10S53.4	20S16.9	11N53.6
4	22 49 58.7	7 29.7	0 20.1	11 31.4	3 24.0	3 49.3	21 13.3	7 53.3	20 27.8	10 56.3	20 17.3	11 50.5
7	23 1 48.3	6 23.1	0 20.0	4S 4.0	5 17.5	4 30.6	21 29.0	7 48.1	20 24.2	10 59.4	20 17.7	11 47.5
10	23 13 38.0	5 15.5	0 20.0	17 8.4	7 3.6	5 11.3	21 43.6	7 42.4	20 20.6	11 2.5	20 18.1	11 44.5
13	23 25 27.7	4 7.1	0 19.9	20 43.1	8 40.8	5 49.8	21 57.0	7 36.1	20 17.1	11 5.8	20 18.6	11 41.5
16	23 37 17.3	2 58.1	0 19.9	14 50.9	10 7.0	6 24.5	22 9.4	7 29.3	20 13.7	11 9.1	20 19.1	11 38.6
19	23 49 7.0	1 48.6	0 19.9	3 36.4	11 19.8	6 54.5	22 20.7	7 22.1	20 10.5	11 12.6	20 19.6	11 35.7
22	0 0 56.6	0 38.7	0 19.8	8N43.8	12 15.7	7 19.0	22 31.1	7 14.4	20 7.3	11 16.1	20 20.2	11 32.8
25	0 12 46.3	0S31.3	0 19.8	18 7.0	12 50.0	7 37.5	22 40.7	7 6.4	20 4.2	11 19.6	20 20.9	11 30.0
28	0 24 35.9	1 41.5	0 19.7	20 26.4	12 57.0	7 49.8	22 49.5	6 58.1	20 1.3	11 23.3	20 21.5	11 27.3

OCTOBER 1975

LONGITUDE

DAY	EPHEM. SID. TIME h m s	☉ ° ′	☊ ° ′	☾ ° ′	☿ ° ′	♀ ° ′	♂ ° ′	♃ ° ′	♄ ° ′	♅ ° ′	♆ ° ′	♇ ° ′
1	0 36 25.6	7 ♎ 12.1	24 ♏ 8.3	9 ♌ 14.6	23 ♎ 27.9	28 ♌ 26.6	24 ♊ 39.8	21 ♈ 19.4	1 ♌ 10.9	1 ♏ 14.3	9 ♐ 27.8	9 ♎ 3.7
2	0 40 22.2	8 11.1	24 5.1	23 47.1	22 R 54.8	28 53.8	25 3.3	21 R 11.7	1 15.5	1 17.9	9 29.1	9 6.0
3	0 44 18.7	9 10.1	24 2.0	8 ♍ 41.9	22 14.0	29 22.7	25 26.3	21 4.0	1 19.9	1 21.4	9 30.4	9 8.4
4	0 48 15.3	10 9.2	23 58.8	23 51.8	21 26.1	29 53.1	25 48.8	20 56.2	1 24.3	1 25.0	9 31.7	9 10.7
5	0 52 11.8	11 8.3	23 55.6	9 ♎ 6.9	20 31.3	0 ♍ 25.0	26 10.8	20 48.3	1 28.6	1 28.6	9 33.1	9 13.0
6	0 56 8.4	12 7.5	23 52.4	24 16.6	19 30.7	0 58.3	26 32.4	20 40.4	1 32.8	1 32.2	9 34.5	9 15.3
7	1 0 4.9	13 6.7	23 49.2	9 ♏ 11.0	18 25.2	1 33.0	26 53.4	20 32.4	1 36.9	1 35.8	9 35.9	9 17.7
8	1 4 1.5	14 5.9	23 46.1	23 43.1	17 16.3	2 9.0	27 14.0	20 24.4	1 40.9	1 39.4	9 37.3	9 20.0
9	1 7 58.0	15 5.1	23 42.9	7 ♐ 48.5	16 5.6	2 46.3	27 34.0	20 16.4	1 44.8	1 43.1	9 38.8	9 22.3
10	1 11 54.6	16 4.4	23 39.7	21 26.3	14 55.0	3 24.9	27 53.5	20 8.3	1 48.6	1 46.7	9 40.3	9 24.6
11	1 15 51.1	17 3.7	23 36.5	4 ♑ 37.7	13 46.4	4 4.6	28 12.5	20 .2	1 52.3	1 50.4	9 41.8	9 27.0
12	1 19 47.7	18 3.1	23 33.4	17 25.9	12 41.9	4 45.5	28 30.9	19 52.1	1 56.0	1 54.1	9 43.4	9 29.3
13	1 23 44.2	19 2.4	23 30.2	29 54.6	11 43.2	5 27.4	28 48.8	19 44.0	1 59.5	1 57.7	9 45.0	9 31.6
14	1 27 40.8	20 1.8	23 27.0	12 ♒ 8.3	10 52.1	6 10.5	29 6.1	19 35.9	2 3.0	2 1.5	9 46.6	9 33.9
15	1 31 37.3	21 1.2	23 23.8	24 11.0	10 10.0	6 54.5	29 22.8	19 27.8	2 6.3	2 5.2	9 48.2	9 36.2
16	1 35 33.9	22 .7	23 20.6	6 ♓ 6.7	9 37.8	7 39.6	29 39.0	19 19.7	2 9.6	2 8.9	9 49.8	9 38.5
17	1 39 30.4	23 .2	23 17.5	17 58.6	9 16.5	8 25.6	29 54.5	19 11.7	2 12.7	2 12.6	9 51.5	9 40.7
18	1 43 27.0	23 59.7	23 14.3	29 49.7	9 6.2	9 12.5	0 ♋ 9.4	19 3.6	2 15.8	2 16.3	9 53.2	9 43.0
19	1 47 23.5	24 59.3	23 11.1	11 ♈ 42.2	9 D 7.0	10 .4	0 23.7	18 55.6	2 18.8	2 20.1	9 54.9	9 45.3
20	1 51 20.1	25 58.8	23 7.9	23 38.2	9 18.7	10 49.1	0 37.4	18 47.6	2 21.6	2 23.8	9 56.6	9 47.5
21	1 55 16.7	26 58.5	23 4.8	5 ♉ 39.3	9 40.9	11 38.6	0 50.4	18 39.7	2 24.4	2 27.6	9 58.4	9 49.8
22	1 59 13.2	27 58.2	23 1.6	17 47.4	10 13.0	12 29.0	1 2.9	18 31.8	2 27.1	2 31.4	10 .2	9 52.1
23	2 3 9.8	28 57.8	22 58.4	0 ♊ 4.2	10 54.1	13 20.1	1 14.5	18 24.0	2 29.6	2 35.1	10 2.0	9 54.3
24	2 7 6.3	29 57.6	22 55.2	12 31.7	11 43.4	14 12.0	1 25.6	18 16.2	2 32.1	2 38.9	10 3.8	9 56.5
25	2 11 2.9	0 ♏ 57.3	22 52.0	25 12.1	12 40.2	15 4.6	1 35.9	18 8.5	2 34.4	2 42.7	10 5.6	9 58.7
26	2 14 59.4	1 57.1	22 48.9	8 ♋ 8.1	13 43.5	15 57.9	1 45.4	18 .8	2 36.7	2 46.4	10 7.5	10 .9
27	2 18 56.0	2 56.9	22 45.7	21 22.1	14 52.7	16 51.8	1 54.3	17 53.3	2 38.8	2 50.2	10 9.4	10 3.1
28	2 22 52.5	3 56.8	22 42.5	4 ♌ 56.1	16 6.9	17 46.4	2 2.4	17 45.8	2 40.8	2 54.0	10 11.3	10 5.3
29	2 26 49.1	4 56.7	22 39.3	18 51.3	17 25.3	18 41.7	2 9.7	17 38.4	2 42.8	2 57.7	10 13.2	10 7.5
30	2 30 45.6	5 56.7	22 36.2	3 ♍ 7.6	18 47.5	19 37.5	2 16.3	17 31.1	2 44.6	3 1.5	10 15.1	10 9.6
31	2 34 42.2	6 56.6	22 33.0	17 42.5	20 12.8	20 34.0	2 22.1	17 23.8	2 46.3	3 5.3	10 17.1	10 11.8

LATITUDE

DAY	SID. TIME	☉	☊	☾	☿	♀	♂	♃	♄	♅	♆	♇
1	0 36 25.6	0 .0	0 .0	5 S .4	3 S 39.0	4 S 21.1	0 S 22.3	1 S 36.6	0 N 4.8	0 N 29.2	1 N 31.1	16 N 19.7
4	0 48 15.3	0 .0	0 .0	4 24.3	3 17.1	3 49.6	0 17.2	1 36.7	0 5.1	0 29.2	1 30.9	16 19.8
7	1 0 4.9	0 .0	0 .0	1 10.7	2 38.5	3 19.0	0 11.8	1 36.8	0 5.4	0 29.1	1 30.8	16 20.0
10	1 11 54.6	0 .0	0 .0	2 N 32.2	1 45.2	2 49.5	0 6.1	1 36.8	0 5.7	0 29.1	1 30.6	16 20.2
13	1 23 44.2	0 .0	0 .0	4 48.9	0 44.1	2 21.2	0 .2	1 36.8	0 6.0	0 29.0	1 30.5	16 20.5
16	1 35 33.9	0 .0	0 .0	5 3.2	0 N 14.8	1 54.2	0 N 6.0	1 36.6	0 6.3	0 29.0	1 30.4	16 20.9
19	1 47 23.5	0 .0	0 .0	3 22.6	1 3.4	1 28.5	0 12.4	1 36.5	0 6.7	0 29.0	1 30.3	16 21.3
22	1 59 13.2	0 .0	0 .0	0 22.1	1 37.9	1 4.2	0 19.2	1 36.2	0 7.0	0 28.9	1 30.1	16 21.9
25	2 11 2.9	0 .0	0 .0	2 S 54.0	1 58.4	0 41.2	0 26.2	1 35.9	0 7.3	0 28.9	1 30.0	16 22.5
28	2 22 52.5	0 .0	0 .0	5 2.5	2 6.8	0 19.6	0 33.6	1 35.5	0 7.7	0 28.9	1 29.9	16 23.2
31	2 34 42.2	0 .0	0 .0	4 44.7	2 5.9	0 N .6	0 41.2	1 35.0	0 8.0	0 28.9	1 29.8	16 23.9

RIGHT ASCENSION

DAY	SID. TIME	☉	☊	☾	☿	♀	♂	♃	♄	♅	♆	♇
1	0 36 25.6	6 ♎ 36.7	21 ♏ 46.0	10 ♌ 19.3	20 ♎ 20.1	29 ♌ 4.7	24 ♊ 12.2	20 ♈ 18.7	3 ♌ 25.7	29 ♎ 16.1	8 ♐ 2.0	14 ♎ 48.4
2	0 40 22.2	7 31.0	21 42.7	24 23.2	19 R 50.8	29 34.1	24 37.6	20 R 11.5	3 30.5	29 19.5	8 3.3	14 50.5
3	0 44 18.7	8 25.4	21 39.5	8 ♍ 27.6	19 15.1	0 ♍ 5.1	25 2.5	20 4.3	3 35.1	29 22.9	8 4.7	14 52.6
4	0 48 15.3	9 19.9	21 36.2	22 37.4	18 33.3	0 37.4	25 26.9	19 57.0	3 39.7	29 26.3	8 6.1	14 54.7
5	0 52 11.8	10 14.4	21 33.0	6 ♎ 58.2	17 46.0	1 11.2	25 50.8	19 49.7	3 44.1	29 29.7	8 7.5	14 56.8
6	0 56 8.4	11 9.0	21 29.7	21 33.9	16 54.0	1 46.2	26 14.1	19 42.3	3 48.5	29 33.1	8 9.0	14 58.9
7	1 0 4.9	12 3.7	21 26.5	6 ♏ 24.0	15 58.3	2 22.5	26 37.0	19 34.9	3 52.8	29 36.6	8 10.5	15 1.0
8	1 4 1.5	12 58.5	21 23.2	21 22.2	15 .2	3 .0	26 59.3	19 27.5	3 57.0	29 40.1	8 12.0	15 3.2
9	1 7 58.0	13 53.4	21 20.0	6 ♐ 16.2	14 1.3	3 38.7	27 21.1	19 20.0	4 1.0	29 43.6	8 13.5	15 5.3
10	1 11 54.6	14 48.5	21 16.7	20 51.3	13 3.0	4 18.5	27 42.3	19 12.5	4 5.0	29 47.1	8 15.1	15 7.4
11	1 15 51.1	15 43.6	21 13.5	4 ♑ 54.8	12 7.2	4 59.3	28 2.9	19 4.9	4 8.9	29 50.6	8 16.7	15 9.5
12	1 19 47.7	16 38.8	21 10.2	18 18.8	11 15.4	5 41.1	28 22.9	18 57.4	4 12.7	29 54.1	8 18.3	15 11.6
13	1 23 44.2	17 34.2	21 7.0	1 ♒ 2.0	10 29.3	6 23.9	28 42.4	18 49.8	4 16.4	29 57.6	8 20.0	15 13.7
14	1 27 40.8	18 29.7	21 3.7	13 8.3	9 50.1	7 7.6	29 1.2	18 42.2	4 20.0	0 ♏ 1.2	8 21.6	15 15.8
15	1 31 37.3	19 25.3	21 .5	24 44.9	9 19.0	7 52.2	29 19.5	18 34.7	4 23.5	0 4.7	8 23.3	15 17.9
16	1 35 33.9	20 21.0	20 57.2	6 ♓ 1.1	8 56.8	8 37.7	29 37.1	18 27.1	4 26.9	0 8.3	8 25.1	15 20.1
17	1 39 30.4	21 16.9	20 54.0	17 6.9	8 44.0	9 24.0	29 54.0	18 19.6	4 30.2	0 11.8	8 26.8	15 22.2
18	1 43 27.0	22 12.9	20 50.7	28 12.0	8 40.9	10 11.0	0 ♋ 10.3	18 12.1	4 33.4	0 15.4	8 28.6	15 24.3
19	1 47 23.5	23 9.0	20 47.5	9 ♈ 25.8	8 D 47.5	10 58.8	0 25.9	18 4.6	4 36.5	0 19.0	8 30.4	15 26.4
20	1 51 20.1	24 5.4	20 44.2	20 56.6	9 3.5	11 47.3	0 40.9	17 57.2	4 39.5	0 22.6	8 32.2	15 28.5
21	1 55 16.7	25 1.8	20 41.0	2 ♉ 51.0	9 28.4	12 36.5	0 55.1	17 49.7	4 42.3	0 26.2	8 34.1	15 30.5
22	1 59 13.2	25 58.5	20 37.8	15 13.2	10 1.8	13 26.4	1 8.7	17 42.4	4 45.2	0 29.8	8 36.0	15 32.7
23	2 3 9.8	26 55.3	20 34.5	28 3.6	10 42.9	14 16.8	1 21.5	17 35.1	4 47.8	0 33.5	8 37.9	15 34.8
24	2 7 6.3	27 52.3	20 31.3	11 ♊ 19.2	11 31.0	15 7.9	1 33.5	17 27.8	4 50.4	0 37.1	8 39.8	15 36.8
25	2 11 2.9	28 49.4	20 28.0	24 53.1	12 25.4	15 59.5	1 44.8	17 20.6	4 52.9	0 40.7	8 41.7	15 38.9
26	2 14 59.4	29 46.8	20 24.8	8 ♋ 36.5	13 25.4	16 51.7	1 55.3	17 13.4	4 55.2	0 44.3	8 43.7	15 41.0
27	2 18 56.0	0 ♏ 44.3	20 21.5	22 21.3	14 30.4	17 44.5	2 5.1	17 6.3	4 57.4	0 47.9	8 45.7	15 43.0
28	2 22 52.5	1 42.0	20 18.3	6 ♌ 1.9	15 39.6	18 37.7	2 14.0	16 59.3	4 59.6	0 51.5	8 47.7	15 45.1
29	2 26 49.1	2 39.9	20 15.1	19 37.6	16 52.6	19 31.4	2 22.1	16 52.4	5 1.6	0 55.1	8 49.7	15 47.1
30	2 30 45.6	3 37.9	20 11.8	3 ♍ 11.6	18 8.7	20 25.5	2 29.3	16 45.6	5 3.5	0 58.8	8 51.7	15 49.1
31	2 34 42.2	4 36.2	20 8.6	16 50.7	19 27.6	21 20.1	2 35.7	16 38.8	5 5.3	1 2.4	8 53.8	15 51.2

DECLINATION

DAY	SID. TIME	☉	☊	☾	☿	♀	♂	♃	♄	♅	♆	♇
1	0 36 25.6	2 S 51.5	0 S 19.7	13 N 6.7	12 S 30.1	7 N 55.8	22 N 57.7	6 N 49.5	19 N 58.5	11 S 27.0	20 S 22.2	11 N 24.6
4	0 48 15.3	4 1.3	0 19.7	1 S 36.5	11 24.1	7 55.6	23 5.3	6 40.7	19 55.9	11 30.7	20 23.0	11 21.9
7	1 0 4.9	5 10.6	0 19.6	15 40.4	9 39.8	7 49.4	23 12.5	6 31.7	19 53.4	11 34.5	20 23.7	11 19.4
10	1 11 54.6	6 19.4	0 19.6	20 38.0	7 29.6	7 37.2	23 19.3	6 22.6	19 51.1	11 38.3	20 24.5	11 16.9
13	1 23 44.2	7 27.4	0 19.5	15 27.7	5 18.7	7 19.2	23 25.9	6 13.5	19 48.9	11 42.1	20 25.3	11 14.6
16	1 35 33.9	8 34.5	0 19.5	4 34.1	3 35.3	6 55.8	23 32.4	6 4.5	19 47.0	11 46.0	20 26.2	11 12.3
19	1 47 23.5	9 40.4	0 19.4	7 N 44.1	2 38.5	6 27.1	23 38.9	5 55.6	19 45.2	11 49.9	20 27.0	11 10.1
22	1 59 13.2	10 45.2	0 19.4	17 29.4	2 32.7	5 53.3	23 45.4	5 46.8	19 43.7	11 53.8	20 27.9	11 8.0
25	2 11 2.9	11 48.4	0 19.4	20 27.3	3 11.3	5 14.8	23 52.1	5 38.2	19 42.3	11 57.7	20 28.8	11 6.0
28	2 22 52.5	12 50.1	0 19.3	14 8.2	4 23.2	4 31.9	23 59.1	5 30.0	19 41.2	12 1.6	20 29.7	11 4.1
31	2 34 42.2	13 50.0	0 19.3	0 29.2	5 57.3	3 44.8	24 6.4	5 22.0	19 40.3	12 5.4	20 30.7	11 2.3

NOVEMBER 1975

DAY	EPHEM. SID. TIME	☉	☊	☽	☿	♀	♂	♃	♄	♅	♆	♇
		LONGITUDE										
	h m s	° ′	° ′	° ′	° ′	° ′	° ′	° ′	° ′	° ′	° ′	° ′
1	2 38 38.7	7♏56.6	22♏29.8	2♎31.5	21♎40.6	21♍30.9	2♋27.1	17♈16.7	2♌47.9	3♏ 9.0	10♐19.0	10♎13.9
2	2 42 35.3	8 56.7	22 26.6	17 27.9	23 10.6	22 28.5	2 31.3	17R 9.7	2 49.3	3 12.8	10 21.0	10 16.0
3	2 46 31.9	9 56.8	22 23.4	2♏23.8	24 42.3	23 26.5	2 34.7	17 2.9	2 50.7	3 16.5	10 23.0	10 18.1
4	2 50 28.4	10 56.9	22 20.3	17 10.7	26 15.5	24 25.1	2 37.2	16 56.1	2 52.0	3 20.3	10 25.0	10 20.2
5	2 54 25.0	11 57.0	22 17.1	1♐41.4	27 49.8	25 24.1	2 38.9	16 49.5	2 53.1	3 24.0	10 27.1	10 22.2
6	2 58 21.5	12 57.2	22 13.9	15 50.2	29 24.9	26 23.6	2 39.7	16 43.0	2 54.2	3 27.8	10 29.1	10 24.3
7	3 2 18.1	13 57.4	22 10.7	29 34.2	1♏ .7	27 23.6	2 39.7	16 36.6	2 55.1	3 31.5	10 31.2	10 26.3
8	3 6 14.6	14 57.6	22 7.6	12♑52.6	2 37.0	28 24.0	2R38.9	16 30.4	2 55.9	3 35.2	10 33.2	10 28.3
9	3 10 11.2	15 57.9	22 4.4	25 46.8	4 13.7	29 24.8	2 37.1	16 24.3	2 56.6	3 38.9	10 35.3	10 30.3
10	3 14 7.7	16 58.2	22 1.2	8♒19.9	5 50.5	0♎26.1	2 34.5	16 18.4	2 57.2	3 42.6	10 37.4	10 32.3
11	3 18 4.3	17 58.5	21 58.0	20 35.6	7 27.5	1 27.7	2 31.1	16 12.6	2 57.7	3 46.3	10 39.6	10 34.2
12	3 22 .8	18 58.8	21 54.8	2♓38.5	9 4.6	2 29.8	2 26.8	16 7.0	2 58.1	3 50.0	10 41.7	10 36.2
13	3 25 57.4	19 59.2	21 51.7	14 33.1	10 41.6	3 32.2	2 21.6	16 1.6	2 58.4	3 53.7	10 43.9	10 38.1
14	3 29 54.0	20 59.6	21 48.5	26 23.9	12 18.6	4 34.9	2 15.5	15 56.3	2 58.5	3 57.4	10 46.0	10 40.0
15	3 33 50.5	21 60.0	21 45.3	8♈15.0	13 55.4	5 38.1	2 8.5	15 51.2	2 58.5	4 1.0	10 48.2	10 41.9
16	3 37 47.1	23 .4	21 42.1	20 10.0	15 32.1	6 41.5	2 .7	15 46.2	2 58.5	4 4.6	10 50.3	10 43.8
17	3 41 43.6	24 .8	21 39.0	2♉11.8	17 8.6	7 45.4	1 52.0	15 41.4	2R58.3	4 8.2	10 52.5	10 45.6
18	3 45 40.2	25 1.3	21 35.8	14 22.8	18 44.9	8 49.5	1 42.5	15 36.8	2 57.9	4 11.8	10 54.7	10 47.4
19	3 49 36.7	26 1.8	21 32.6	26 44.9	20 21.1	9 53.9	1 32.1	15 32.4	2 57.5	4 15.4	10 56.9	10 49.2
20	3 53 33.3	27 2.3	21 29.4	9♊19.1	21 57.0	10 58.7	1 20.8	15 28.2	2 57.0	4 18.9	10 59.1	10 51.0
21	3 57 29.9	28 2.9	21 26.3	22 6.3	23 32.8	12 3.8	1 8.7	15 24.1	2 56.3	4 22.5	11 1.3	10 52.7
22	4 1 26.4	29 3.4	21 23.1	5♋ 6.8	25 8.3	13 9.1	0 55.8	15 20.2	2 55.6	4 26.0	11 3.5	10 54.4
23	4 5 23.0	0♐ 4.0	21 19.9	18 20.7	26 43.6	14 14.8	0 42.1	15 16.6	2 54.7	4 29.5	11 5.7	10 56.1
24	4 9 19.5	1 4.7	21 16.7	1♌48.0	28 18.8	15 20.7	0 27.5	15 13.1	2 53.7	4 33.0	11 8.0	10 57.8
25	4 13 16.1	2 5.3	21 13.5	15 28.6	29 53.8	16 26.8	0 12.2	15 9.8	2 52.7	4 36.4	11 10.2	10 59.4
26	4 17 12.6	3 6.0	21 10.4	29 22.0	1♐28.7	17 33.3	29♊56.2	15 6.7	2 51.5	4 39.9	11 12.4	11 1.0
27	4 21 9.2	4 6.7	21 7.2	13♍27.4	3 3.4	18 40.0	29 39.3	15 3.8	2 50.1	4 43.3	11 14.7	11 2.6
28	4 25 5.7	5 7.4	21 4.0	27 43.4	4 37.9	19 46.9	29 21.8	15 1.1	2 48.7	4 46.7	11 16.9	11 4.2
29	4 29 2.3	6 8.2	21 .8	12♎ 7.5	6 12.4	20 54.1	29 3.6	14 58.6	2 47.2	4 50.1	11 19.2	11 5.7
30	4 32 58.9	7 9.0	20 57.7	26 36.3	7 46.7	22 1.5	28 44.7	14 56.3	2 45.6	4 53.4	11 21.4	11 7.2
		LATITUDE										
1	2 38 38.7	0 .0	0 .0	4S .1	2N 4.0	0N 7.0	0N43.9	1S34.9	0N 8.1	0N28.9	1N29.8	16N24.2
4	2 50 28.4	0 .0	0 .0	0 25.4	1 54.3	0 25.3	0 51.9	1 34.3	0 8.4	0 28.9	1 29.7	16 25.0
7	3 2 18.1	0 .0	0 .0	3N14.8	1 40.3	0 42.3	1 .2	1 33.8	0 8.8	0 28.9	1 29.6	16 26.0
10	3 14 7.7	0 .0	0 .0	5 8.8	1 23.3	0 57.9	1 8.8	1 33.1	0 9.1	0 28.9	1 29.5	16 27.0
13	3 25 57.4	0 .0	0 .0	4 53.0	1 4.5	1 12.2	1 17.6	1 32.4	0 9.5	0 28.9	1 29.5	16 28.0
16	3 37 47.1	0 .0	0 .0	2 46.9	0 44.5	1 25.0	1 26.6	1 31.7	0 9.8	0 28.9	1 29.4	16 29.2
19	3 49 36.7	0 .0	0 .0	0S27.4	0 24.0	1 36.6	1 35.6	1 30.9	0 10.2	0 28.9	1 29.4	16 30.3
22	4 1 26.4	0 .0	0 .0	3 37.9	0 3.5	1 46.8	1 44.8	1 30.1	0 10.6	0 28.9	1 29.3	16 31.6
25	4 13 16.1	0 .0	0 .0	5 15.0	0S16.6	1 55.8	1 53.9	1 29.3	0 10.9	0 28.9	1 29.3	16 32.9
28	4 25 5.7	0 .0	0 .0	4 16.6	0 36.2	2 3.5	2 2.9	1 28.5	0 11.3	0 28.9	1 29.2	16 34.3
		RIGHT ASCENSION										
1	2 38 38.7	5♏34.7	20♏ 5.4	0♎43.3	20♎48.8	22♍15.2	2♋41.2	16♈32.1	5♌ 6.9	1♏ 6.0	8♐55.8	15♎53.2
2	2 42 35.3	6 33.4	20 2.1	14 56.8	22 11.9	23 10.6	2 45.9	16R25.6	5 8.5	1 9.6	8 57.9	15 55.2
3	2 46 31.9	7 32.3	19 58.9	29 35.1	23 36.7	24 6.4	2 49.6	16 19.1	5 10.0	1 13.2	9 .0	15 57.2
4	2 50 28.4	8 31.4	19 55.6	14♏35.3	25 3.0	25 2.6	2 52.4	16 12.8	5 11.3	1 16.8	9 2.2	15 59.1
5	2 54 25.0	9 30.7	19 52.4	29 46.6	26 30.4	25 59.2	2 54.4	16 6.6	5 12.5	1 20.4	9 4.3	16 1.1
6	2 58 21.5	10 30.2	19 49.2	14♐51.8	27 58.9	26 56.1	2 55.3	16 .5	5 13.6	1 24.0	9 6.5	16 3.1
7	3 2 18.1	11 29.9	19 45.9	29 32.5	29 28.2	27 53.3	2 55.4	15 54.5	5 14.6	1 27.6	9 8.6	16 5.0
8	3 6 14.6	12 29.8	19 42.7	13♑34.4	0♏58.3	28 50.9	2R54.5	15 48.6	5 15.5	1 31.2	9 10.8	16 7.0
9	3 10 11.2	13 29.9	19 39.5	26 50.8	2 29.0	29 48.8	2 52.7	15 42.9	5 16.2	1 34.8	9 13.0	16 8.9
10	3 14 7.7	14 30.2	19 36.2	9♒22.9	4 .3	0♎47.0	2 49.9	15 37.3	5 16.9	1 38.3	9 15.2	16 10.8
11	3 18 4.3	15 30.7	19 33.0	21 17.3	5 32.1	1 45.4	2 46.1	15 31.9	5 17.4	1 41.9	9 17.5	16 12.7
12	3 22 .8	16 31.5	19 29.8	2♓43.8	7 4.4	2 44.3	2 41.5	15 26.6	5 17.8	1 45.5	9 19.8	16 14.6
13	3 25 57.4	17 32.5	19 26.5	13 53.5	8 37.1	3 43.4	2 35.8	15 21.5	5 18.1	1 49.0	9 22.0	16 16.5
14	3 29 54.0	18 33.6	19 23.3	24 57.8	10 10.2	4 42.7	2 29.2	15 16.5	5 18.3	1 52.5	9 24.3	16 18.3
15	3 33 50.5	19 35.0	19 20.1	6♈ 7.7	11 43.7	5 42.4	2 21.6	15 11.7	5 18.4	1 56.0	9 26.6	16 20.1
16	3 37 47.1	20 36.5	19 16.8	17 33.3	13 17.6	6 42.3	2 13.0	15 7.0	5R18.3	1 59.5	9 28.9	16 22.0
17	3 41 43.6	21 38.3	19 13.6	29 22.9	14 51.8	7 42.5	2 3.5	15 2.5	5 18.1	2 3.0	9 31.2	16 23.7
18	3 45 40.2	22 40.3	19 10.4	11♉42.4	16 26.4	8 43.0	1 53.0	14 58.1	5 17.8	2 6.4	9 33.5	16 25.5
19	3 49 36.7	23 42.5	19 7.2	24 33.6	18 1.3	9 43.7	1 41.6	14 53.9	5 17.4	2 9.9	9 35.8	16 27.3
20	3 53 33.3	24 44.9	19 3.9	7♊53.6	19 36.6	10 44.8	1 29.2	14 49.9	5 16.9	2 13.3	9 38.1	16 29.0
21	3 57 29.9	25 47.5	19 .7	21 34.5	21 12.3	11 46.1	1 15.9	14 46.0	5 16.3	2 16.7	9 40.4	16 30.8
22	4 1 26.4	26 50.3	18 57.5	5♋25.3	22 48.4	12 47.6	1 1.6	14 42.4	5 15.5	2 20.1	9 42.8	16 32.5
23	4 5 23.0	27 53.3	18 54.3	19 14.7	24 24.8	13 49.4	0 46.5	14 38.8	5 14.7	2 23.5	9 45.1	16 34.2
24	4 9 19.5	28 56.5	18 51.0	2♌54.5	26 1.7	14 51.5	0 30.4	14 35.5	5 13.7	2 26.9	9 47.5	16 35.8
25	4 13 16.1	29 59.9	18 47.8	16 21.6	27 38.9	15 53.9	0 13.5	14 32.4	5 12.6	2 30.2	9 49.9	16 37.5
26	4 17 12.6	1♐ 3.5	18 44.6	29 38.6	29 16.6	16 56.5	29♊55.7	14 29.4	5 11.4	2 33.5	9 52.2	16 39.1
27	4 21 9.2	2 7.3	18 41.4	12♍52.4	0♐54.6	17 59.4	29 37.1	14 26.6	5 10.0	2 36.8	9 54.6	16 40.7
28	4 25 5.7	3 11.3	18 38.1	26 12.6	2 33.1	19 2.6	29 17.7	14 24.0	5 8.6	2 40.1	9 57.0	16 42.3
29	4 29 2.3	4 15.5	18 34.9	9♎49.3	4 12.0	20 6.0	28 57.5	14 21.5	5 7.0	2 43.4	9 59.4	16 43.9
30	4 32 58.9	5 19.9	18 31.7	23 50.9	5 51.3	21 9.7	28 36.6	14 19.3	5 5.4	2 46.6	10 1.7	16 45.4
		DECLINATION										
1	2 38 38.7	14S 9.5	0S19.3	4S40.5	6S32.0	3N28.3	24N 8.9	5N19.5	19N40.0	12S 6.7	20S31.0	11N 1.7
4	2 50 28.4	15 6.7	0 19.2	17 22.2	8 21.6	2 36.3	24 16.8	5 12.1	19 39.4	12 10.6	20 31.9	11 .1
7	3 2 18.1	16 1.7	0 19.2	20 11.6	10 15.6	1 41.0	24 25.1	5 5.2	19 39.0	12 14.4	20 32.9	10 58.6
10	3 14 7.7	16 54.3	0 19.1	13 12.5	12 9.6	0 42.8	24 33.8	4 58.8	19 38.9	12 18.1	20 33.8	10 57.3
13	3 25 57.4	17 44.3	0 19.1	1 34.5	14 .7	0S18.1	24 42.8	4 53.0	19 38.9	12 21.9	20 34.8	10 56.0
16	3 37 47.1	18 31.5	0 19.1	10N27.4	15 47.0	1 21.3	24 52.1	4 47.7	19 39.3	12 25.6	20 35.8	10 54.9
19	3 49 36.7	19 15.8	0 19.0	18 59.2	17 27.0	2 26.4	25 1.5	4 43.1	19 39.8	12 29.2	20 36.7	10 53.9
22	4 1 26.4	19 57.0	0 19.0	19 42.8	18 59.6	3 33.1	25 11.0	4 39.2	19 40.6	12 32.8	20 37.7	10 53.1
25	4 13 16.1	20 34.8	0 18.9	11 10.5	20 24.0	4 41.1	25 20.3	4 35.9	19 41.6	12 36.3	20 38.6	10 52.3
28	4 25 5.7	21 9.3	0 18.9	3S 1.1	21 39.5	5 49.9	25 29.2	4 33.4	19 42.9	12 39.7	20 39.6	10 51.8

DECEMBER 1975

LONGITUDE

DAY	EPHEM. SID. TIME	☉	☊	☽	☿	♀	♂	♃	♄	♅	♆	♇
	h m s	° ′	° ′	° ′	° ′	° ′	° ′	° ′	° ′	° ′	° ′	° ′
1	4 36 55.4	8♐ 9.8	20♏54.5	11♏ 5.3	9♐21.0	23♎ 9.1	28♊25.2	14♈54.2	2♌43.8	4♏56.7	11♐23.7	11♎ 8.7
2	4 40 52.0	9 10.7	20 51.3	25 29.5	10 55.1	24 16.9	28R 5.2	14R52.3	2R42.0	5 .0	11 26.0	11 10.2
3	4 44 48.5	10 11.6	20 48.1	9♐43.5	12 29.3	25 25.0	27 44.6	14 50.7	2 40.0	5 3.3	11 28.3	11 11.7
4	4 48 45.1	11 12.4	20 45.0	23 42.3	14 3.4	26 33.2	27 23.5	14 49.2	2 38.0	5 6.6	11 30.5	11 13.0
5	4 52 41.6	12 13.3	20 41.8	7♑22.1	15 37.4	27 41.6	27 1.9	14 47.9	2 35.8	5 9.8	11 32.8	11 14.4
6	4 56 38.2	13 14.2	20 38.6	20 40.7	17 11.4	28 50.2	26 39.9	14 46.9	2 33.5	5 12.9	11 35.0	11 15.8
7	5 0 34.8	14 15.2	20 35.4	3♒37.6	18 45.5	29 58.9	26 17.6	14 46.1	2 31.2	5 16.1	11 37.3	11 17.1
8	5 4 31.3	15 16.1	20 32.2	16 14.0	20 19.5	1♏ 7.9	25 54.9	14 45.4	2 28.7	5 19.2	11 39.6	11 18.4
9	5 8 27.9	16 17.1	20 29.1	28 32.6	21 53.6	2 17.0	25 32.0	14 45.0	2 26.1	5 22.3	11 41.8	11 19.6
10	5 12 24.4	17 18.0	20 25.9	10♓37.2	23 27.6	3 26.2	25 8.8	14 44.8	2 23.5	5 25.3	11 44.1	11 20.8
11	5 16 21.0	18 19.0	20 22.7	22 32.3	25 1.7	4 35.7	24 45.5	14 44.8	2 20.7	5 28.4	11 46.3	11 22.0
12	5 20 17.5	19 20.0	20 19.5	4♈22.8	26 35.9	5 45.2	24 22.1	14D45.0	2 17.8	5 31.4	11 48.6	11 23.2
13	5 24 14.1	20 21.0	20 16.4	16 13.8	28 10.1	6 55.0	23 58.7	14 45.4	2 14.9	5 34.3	11 50.8	11 24.3
14	5 28 10.7	21 22.0	20 13.2	28 10.0	29 44.3	8 4.8	23 35.2	14 46.0	2 11.8	5 37.2	11 53.1	11 25.4
15	5 32 7.2	22 23.0	20 10.0	10♉15.8	1♑18.6	9 14.8	23 11.7	14 46.9	2 8.7	5 40.1	11 55.3	11 26.4
16	5 36 3.8	23 24.0	20 6.8	22 34.8	2 52.9	10 25.0	22 48.3	14 47.9	2 5.5	5 42.9	11 57.5	11 27.5
17	5 40 .3	24 25.0	20 3.7	5♊ 9.8	4 27.3	11 35.3	22 25.1	14 49.2	2 2.2	5 45.8	11 59.7	11 28.5
18	5 43 56.9	25 26.1	20 .5	18 2.2	6 1.6	12 45.7	22 2.1	14 50.6	1 58.8	5 48.5	12 1.9	11 29.4
19	5 47 53.4	26 27.1	19 57.3	1♋12.2	7 35.9	13 56.2	21 39.3	14 52.3	1 55.3	5 51.3	12 4.2	11 30.4
20	5 51 50.0	27 28.2	19 54.1	14 38.8	9 10.2	15 6.9	21 16.7	14 54.1	1 51.7	5 54.0	12 6.4	11 31.3
21	5 55 46.6	28 29.2	19 50.9	28 19.7	10 44.3	16 17.7	20 54.5	14 56.2	1 48.1	5 56.6	12 8.5	11 32.1
22	5 59 43.1	29 30.3	19 47.8	12♌12.0	12 18.4	17 28.6	20 32.6	14 58.5	1 44.4	5 59.2	12 10.7	11 33.0
23	6 3 39.7	0♑31.4	19 44.6	26 12.4	13 52.2	18 39.7	20 11.2	15 1.0	1 40.6	6 1.8	12 12.9	11 33.8
24	6 7 36.2	1 32.6	19 41.4	10♍17.8	15 25.7	19 50.9	19 50.2	15 3.7	1 36.7	6 4.4	12 15.1	11 34.6
25	6 11 32.8	2 33.7	19 38.2	24 25.5	16 58.9	21 2.1	19 29.6	15 6.5	1 32.8	6 6.9	12 17.3	11 35.3
26	6 15 29.3	3 34.8	19 35.1	8♎33.6	18 31.5	22 13.5	19 9.6	15 9.6	1 28.8	6 9.3	12 19.4	11 36.0
27	6 19 25.9	4 35.9	19 31.9	22 40.6	20 3.6	23 25.0	18 50.1	15 12.9	1 24.7	6 11.7	12 21.5	11 36.7
28	6 23 22.5	5 37.1	19 28.7	6♏45.2	21 34.8	24 36.5	18 31.3	15 16.3	1 20.6	6 14.1	12 23.7	11 37.3
29	6 27 19.0	6 38.2	19 25.5	20 46.1	23 5.1	25 48.2	18 13.0	15 20.0	1 16.4	6 16.4	12 25.8	11 37.9
30	6 31 15.6	7 39.4	19 22.4	4♐41.4	24 34.2	26 59.9	17 55.4	15 23.9	1 12.1	6 18.7	12 27.9	11 38.4
31	6 35 12.1	8 40.6	19 19.2	18 28.9	26 1.8	28 11.8	17 38.4	15 27.9	1 7.7	6 20.9	12 29.9	11 39.0

LATITUDE

DAY	EPHEM. SID. TIME	☉	☊	☽	☿	♀	♂	♃	♄	♅	♆	♇
1	4 36 55.4	0 .0	0 .0	0S58.9	0S54.7	2N 9.9	2N11.6	1S27.6	0N11.6	0N28.9	1N29.2	16N35.7
4	4 48 45.1	0 .0	0 .0	2N47.2	1 12.1	2 15.2	2 20.1	1 26.7	0 12.0	0 28.9	1 29.2	16 37.1
7	5 0 34.8	0 .0	0 .0	4 59.4	1 27.9	2 19.3	2 28.0	1 25.8	0 12.4	0 29.0	1 29.2	16 38.7
10	5 12 24.4	0 .0	0 .0	4 57.3	1 42.0	2 22.2	2 35.5	1 24.9	0 12.7	0 29.0	1 29.2	16 40.2
13	5 24 14.1	0 .0	0 .0	3 1.9	1 54.0	2 24.0	2 42.3	1 23.9	0 13.1	0 29.0	1 29.2	16 41.8
16	5 36 3.8	0 .0	0 .0	0S 5.4	2 3.5	2 24.8	2 48.4	1 23.0	0 13.5	0 29.1	1 29.2	16 43.4
19	5 47 53.4	0 .0	0 .0	3 19.3	2 10.0	2 24.5	2 53.7	1 22.1	0 13.8	0 29.1	1 29.2	16 45.1
22	5 59 43.1	0 .0	0 .0	5 6.5	2 13.1	2 23.3	2 58.2	1 21.2	0 14.2	0 29.1	1 29.2	16 46.8
25	6 11 32.8	0 .0	0 .0	4 19.1	2 12.0	2 21.1	3 2.0	1 20.2	0 14.6	0 29.2	1 29.3	16 48.5
28	6 23 22.5	0 .0	0 .0	1 16.5	2 6.0	2 18.0	3 5.0	1 19.3	0 14.9	0 29.2	1 29.3	16 50.2
31	6 35 12.1	0 .0	0 .0	2N22.7	1 54.2	2 14.2	3 7.2	1 18.4	0 15.3	0 29.3	1 29.3	16 52.0

RIGHT ASCENSION

DAY	EPHEM. SID. TIME	☉	☊	☽	☿	♀	♂	♃	♄	♅	♆	♇
1	4 36 55.4	6♐24.4	18♏28.5	8♏20.6	7♐31.1	22♎13.7	28♊15.0	14♈17.3	5♌ 3.6	2♏49.8	10♐ 4.1	16♎46.9
2	4 40 52.0	7 29.1	18 25.2	23 14.4	9 11.3	23 17.9	27R52.7	14R15.4	5R 1.7	2 53.0	10 6.5	16 48.4
3	4 44 48.5	8 34.0	18 22.0	8♐19.5	10 51.9	24 22.5	27 29.8	14 13.8	4 59.8	2 56.2	10 9.0	16 50.0
4	4 48 45.1	9 39.0	18 18.8	23 17.1	12 33.0	25 27.2	27 6.3	14 12.3	4 57.7	2 59.3	10 11.4	16 51.4
5	4 52 41.6	10 44.2	18 15.6	7♑48.1	14 14.4	26 32.3	26 42.4	14 11.0	4 55.5	3 2.4	10 13.7	16 52.8
6	4 56 38.2	11 49.5	18 12.4	21 38.9	15 56.2	27 37.6	26 17.9	14 9.9	4 53.1	3 5.5	10 16.1	16 54.2
7	5 0 34.8	12 54.9	18 9.1	4♒44.2	17 38.4	28 43.2	25 53.0	14 9.0	4 50.7	3 8.5	10 18.5	16 55.6
8	5 4 31.3	14 .5	18 5.9	17 6.3	19 21.0	29 49.1	25 27.8	14 8.3	4 48.2	3 11.6	10 20.9	16 57.0
9	5 8 27.9	15 6.2	18 2.7	28 52.8	21 3.9	0♏55.2	25 2.2	14 7.8	4 45.5	3 14.6	10 23.3	16 58.3
10	5 12 24.4	16 12.0	17 59.5	10♓14.2	22 47.1	2 1.7	24 36.5	14 7.5	4 42.8	3 17.5	10 25.7	16 59.6
11	5 16 21.0	17 17.9	17 56.3	21 22.4	24 30.7	3 8.4	24 10.5	14 7.4	4 40.0	3 20.4	10 28.1	17 .9
12	5 20 17.5	18 23.9	17 53.1	2♈29.3	26 14.5	4 15.4	23 44.4	14D 7.5	4 37.0	3 23.3	10 30.5	17 2.1
13	5 24 14.1	19 30.0	17 49.8	13 46.4	27 58.5	5 22.7	23 18.2	14 7.7	4 34.0	3 26.2	10 32.8	17 3.4
14	5 28 10.7	20 36.2	17 46.6	25 24.0	29 42.7	6 30.4	22 52.0	14 8.2	4 30.9	3 29.0	10 35.2	17 4.6
15	5 32 7.2	21 42.4	17 43.4	7♉30.8	1♑27.0	7 38.3	22 25.9	14 8.8	4 27.7	3 31.8	10 37.6	17 5.7
16	5 36 3.8	22 48.7	17 40.2	20 11.9	3 11.4	8 46.5	21 59.8	14 9.7	4 24.3	3 34.6	10 39.9	17 6.9
17	5 40 .3	23 55.1	17 37.0	3♊27.8	4 55.9	9 55.0	21 33.9	14 10.7	4 20.9	3 37.3	10 42.3	17 8.0
18	5 43 56.9	25 1.5	17 33.8	17 13.0	6 40.3	11 3.9	21 8.2	14 11.9	4 17.5	3 40.0	10 44.6	17 9.1
19	5 47 53.4	26 8.0	17 30.6	1♋16.8	8 24.6	12 13.0	20 42.8	14 13.4	4 13.9	3 42.6	10 47.0	17 10.1
20	5 51 50.0	27 14.5	17 27.3	15 25.4	10 8.7	13 22.5	20 17.7	14 15.0	4 10.2	3 45.2	10 49.3	17 11.2
21	5 55 46.6	28 21.1	17 24.1	29 26.5	11 52.6	14 32.3	19 52.9	14 16.8	4 6.5	3 47.8	10 51.6	17 12.2
22	5 59 43.1	29 27.6	17 20.9	13♌12.2	13 36.0	15 42.4	19 28.5	14 18.7	4 2.6	3 50.4	10 54.0	17 13.1
23	6 3 39.7	0♑34.2	17 17.7	26 41.3	15 18.9	16 52.9	19 4.6	14 20.9	3 58.7	3 52.9	10 56.3	17 14.1
24	6 7 36.2	1 40.9	17 14.5	9♍57.9	17 1.3	18 3.7	18 41.3	14 23.3	3 54.8	3 55.4	10 58.6	17 15.0
25	6 11 32.8	2 47.5	17 11.3	23 10.3	18 42.8	19 14.8	18 18.4	14 25.8	3 50.7	3 57.8	11 .9	17 15.9
26	6 15 29.3	3 54.1	17 8.1	6♎28.6	20 23.4	20 26.2	17 56.1	14 28.6	3 46.6	4 .2	11 3.2	17 16.8
27	6 19 25.9	5 .6	17 4.9	20 2.6	22 2.8	21 37.9	17 34.5	14 31.5	3 42.4	4 2.5	11 5.4	17 17.6
28	6 23 22.5	6 7.2	17 1.7	3♏59.2	23 41.0	22 50.0	17 13.5	14 34.6	3 38.1	4 4.8	11 7.7	17 18.4
29	6 27 19.0	7 13.7	16 58.5	18 19.6	25 17.5	24 2.3	16 53.2	14 37.8	3 33.8	4 7.1	11 9.9	17 19.2
30	6 31 15.6	8 20.2	16 55.2	2♐58.1	26 52.2	25 15.0	16 33.6	14 41.3	3 29.3	4 9.3	11 12.1	17 19.9
31	6 35 12.1	9 26.6	16 52.0	17 41.7	28 24.7	26 28.0	16 14.8	14 44.9	3 24.9	4 11.4	11 14.4	17 20.6

DECLINATION

DAY	EPHEM. SID. TIME	☉	☊	☽	☿	♀	♂	♃	♄	♅	♆	♇
1	4 36 55.4	21S40.2	0S18.8	16S 5.3	22S45.3	6S59.1	25N37.5	4N31.5	19N44.4	12S43.0	20S40.5	10N51.4
4	4 48 45.1	22 7.4	0 18.8	20 30.4	23 40.9	8 8.5	25 44.9	4 30.4	19 46.1	12 46.3	20 41.5	10 51.0
7	5 0 34.8	22 30.7	0 18.7	14 29.3	24 25.5	9 17.5	25 51.3	4 30.1	19 48.0	12 49.4	20 42.4	10 50.9
10	5 12 24.4	22 50.0	0 18.7	2 59.8	24 58.6	10 25.9	25 56.5	4 30.4	19 50.1	12 52.5	20 43.3	10 50.9
13	5 24 14.1	23 5.4	0 18.7	9N10.9	25 19.6	11 33.3	26 .3	4 31.5	19 52.4	12 55.4	20 44.2	10 51.0
16	5 36 3.8	23 16.6	0 18.6	18 19.8	25 28.0	12 39.2	26 2.8	4 33.3	19 54.8	12 58.3	20 45.1	10 51.3
19	5 47 53.4	23 23.6	0 18.6	20 6.8	25 23.1	13 43.4	26 4.0	4 35.9	19 57.5	13 1.0	20 45.9	10 51.8
22	5 59 43.1	23 26.4	0 18.5	12 13.8	25 4.7	14 45.4	26 4.0	4 39.1	20 .3	13 3.6	20 46.8	10 52.3
25	6 11 32.8	23 25.0	0 18.5	1S45.1	24 32.6	15 44.9	26 2.9	4 43.1	20 3.2	13 6.1	20 47.6	10 53.0
28	6 23 22.5	23 19.3	0 18.4	14 58.5	23 47.0	16 41.4	26 1.0	4 47.7	20 6.3	13 8.4	20 48.4	10 53.8
31	6 35 12.1	23 9.4	0 18.4	20 34.3	22 48.8	17 34.7	25 58.3	4 53.0	20 9.4	13 10.6	20 49.1	10 54.8

JANUARY 1976

LONGITUDE

DAY	EPHEM. SID. TIME (h m s)	☉ (° ′)	☊ (° ′)	☽ (° ′)	☿ (° ′)	♀ (° ′)	♂ (° ′)	♃ (° ′)	♄ (° ′)	♅ (° ′)	♆ (° ′)	♇ (° ′)
1	6 39 8.7	9♑41.8	19♏16.0	2♑ 5.6	27♑27.6	29♏23.7	17♊22.2	15♈32.1	1♌ 3.4	6♏23.1	12♐32.0	11♎39.5
2	6 43 5.2	10 42.9	19 12.8	15 29.1	28 51.3	0♐35.7	17R 6.7	15 36.6	0R58.9	6 25.3	12 34.1	11 39.9
3	6 47 1.8	11 44.1	19 9.7	28 37.0	0♒12.5	1 47.7	16 51.9	15 41.2	0 54.4	6 27.3	12 36.1	11 40.3
4	6 50 58.4	12 45.3	19 6.5	11♒27.9	1 30.7	2 59.9	16 37.9	15 46.0	0 49.9	6 29.4	12 38.1	11 40.7
5	6 54 54.9	13 46.5	19 3.3	24 1.7	2 45.4	4 12.1	16 24.7	15 51.0	0 45.3	6 31.4	12 40.1	11 41.0
6	6 58 51.5	14 47.6	19 .1	6♓19.6	3 55.9	5 24.4	16 12.3	15 56.2	0 40.7	6 33.3	12 42.1	11 41.4
7	7 2 48.0	15 48.8	18 56.9	18 24.1	5 1.6	6 36.7	16 .7	16 1.5	0 36.0	6 35.2	12 44.1	11 41.6
8	7 6 44.6	16 50.0	18 53.8	0♈19.0	6 1.7	7 49.1	15 49.9	16 7.1	0 31.3	6 37.1	12 46.1	11 41.9
9	7 10 41.1	17 51.1	18 50.6	12 8.7	6 55.4	9 1.6	15 39.9	16 12.8	0 26.5	6 38.9	12 48.0	11 42.1
10	7 14 37.7	18 52.3	18 47.4	23 58.3	7 41.9	10 14.1	15 30.7	16 18.7	0 21.8	6 40.6	12 49.9	11 42.2
11	7 18 34.3	19 53.4	18 44.2	5♉53.4	8 20.2	11 26.7	15 22.4	16 24.7	0 17.0	6 42.3	12 51.8	11 42.4
12	7 22 30.8	20 54.5	18 41.1	17 59.2	8 49.5	12 39.3	15 14.9	16 31.0	0 12.1	6 44.0	12 53.7	11 42.5
13	7 26 27.4	21 55.6	18 37.9	0♊20.8	9 8.8	13 52.0	15 8.2	16 37.4	0 7.3	6 45.6	12 55.6	11 42.5
14	7 30 23.9	22 56.8	18 34.7	13 2.2	9 17.6	15 4.8	15 2.4	16 44.0	0 2.5	6 47.2	12 57.4	11 42.6
15	7 34 20.5	23 57.9	18 31.5	26 6.2	9R15.0	16 17.6	14 57.4	16 50.7	29♋57.6	6 48.7	12 59.3	11 42.6
16	7 38 17.0	24 59.0	18 28.4	9♋33.8	9 .7	17 30.5	14 53.1	16 57.6	29 52.7	6 50.1	13 1.1	11R42.5
17	7 42 13.6	26 .1	18 25.2	23 23.7	8 34.6	18 43.4	14 49.7	17 4.7	29 47.7	6 51.5	13 2.8	11 42.5
18	7 46 10.2	27 1.1	18 22.0	7♌32.4	7 57.1	19 56.4	14 47.1	17 11.9	29 42.8	6 52.8	13 4.6	11 42.3
19	7 50 6.7	28 2.2	18 18.8	21 54.3	7 8.9	21 9.4	14 45.2	17 19.3	29 37.9	6 54.1	13 6.3	11 42.2
20	7 54 3.3	29 3.3	18 15.6	6♍23.1	6 11.0	22 22.4	14 44.1	17 26.8	29 32.9	6 55.4	13 8.1	11 42.0
21	7 57 59.8	0♒ 4.3	18 12.5	20 52.3	5 5.2	23 35.5	14 43.8	17 34.5	29 28.0	6 56.5	13 9.7	11 41.8
22	8 1 56.4	1 5.3	18 9.3	5♎16.5	3 53.3	24 48.7	14D44.3	17 42.3	29 23.1	6 57.7	13 11.4	11 41.5
23	8 5 52.9	2 6.4	18 6.1	19 32.0	2 37.7	26 1.9	14 45.5	17 50.3	29 18.1	6 58.7	13 13.1	11 41.2
24	8 9 49.5	3 7.4	18 2.9	3♏36.8	1 20.6	27 15.1	14 47.5	17 58.4	29 13.2	6 59.7	13 14.7	11 40.9
25	8 13 46.0	4 8.4	17 59.8	17 30.2	0 4.4	28 28.4	14 50.2	18 6.7	29 8.3	7 .7	13 16.3	11 40.6
26	8 17 42.6	5 9.4	17 56.6	1♐12.8	28♑51.3	29 41.7	14 53.6	18 15.1	29 3.4	7 1.6	13 17.8	11 40.2
27	8 21 39.2	6 10.5	17 53.4	14 44.8	27 43.0	0♑55.0	14 57.7	18 23.7	28 58.5	7 2.5	13 19.4	11 39.7
28	8 25 35.7	7 11.4	17 50.2	28 6.8	26 41.2	2 8.4	15 2.5	18 32.4	28 53.6	7 3.3	13 20.9	11 39.3
29	8 29 32.3	8 12.4	17 47.1	11♑18.5	25 46.9	3 21.8	15 8.0	18 41.3	28 48.7	7 4.0	13 22.4	11 38.8
30	8 33 28.8	9 13.4	17 43.9	24 19.4	25 .8	4 35.3	15 14.3	18 50.3	28 43.9	7 4.7	13 23.9	11 38.3
31	8 37 25.4	10 14.4	17 40.7	7♒ 8.7	24 23.4	5 48.7	15 21.1	18 59.4	28 39.1	7 5.3	13 25.3	11 37.7

LATITUDE

DAY	EPHEM. SID. TIME	☉	☊	☽	☿	♀	♂	♃	♄	♅	♆	♇
1	6 39 8.7	0 .0	0 .0	3N22.9	1S48.7	2N12.7	3N 7.8	1S18.1	0N15.4	0N29.3	1N29.4	16N52.6
4	6 50 58.4	0 .0	0 .0	5 2.3	1 27.3	2 7.8	3 9.1	1 17.2	0 15.8	0 29.3	1 29.4	16 54.3
7	7 2 48.0	0 .0	0 .0	4 29.6	0 57.3	2 2.2	3 9.7	1 16.4	0 16.1	0 29.4	1 29.5	16 56.1
10	7 14 37.7	0 .0	0 .0	2 14.4	0 18.0	1 56.0	3 9.8	1 15.5	0 16.5	0 29.4	1 29.6	16 57.8
13	7 26 27.4	0 .0	0 .0	0S55.4	0N30.4	1 49.2	3 9.3	1 14.7	0 16.8	0 29.5	1 29.6	16 59.6
16	7 38 17.0	0 .0	0 .0	3 52.2	1 25.1	1 41.9	3 8.5	1 13.9	0 17.1	0 29.6	1 29.7	17 1.3
19	7 50 6.7	0 .0	0 .0	5 1.8	2 19.7	1 34.1	3 7.3	1 13.1	0 17.5	0 29.6	1 29.8	17 3.1
22	8 1 56.4	0 .0	0 .0	3 28.8	3 4.2	1 25.9	3 5.7	1 12.3	0 17.8	0 29.7	1 29.9	17 4.8
25	8 13 46.0	0 .0	0 .0	0 6.3	3 29.5	1 17.4	3 4.0	1 11.5	0 18.1	0 29.7	1 30.0	17 6.5
28	8 25 35.7	0 .0	0 .0	3N12.3	3 32.6	1 8.6	3 2.0	1 10.8	0 18.4	0 29.8	1 30.1	17 8.1
31	8 37 25.4	0 .0	0 .0	4 54.6	3 17.4	0 59.6	2 59.8	1 10.0	0 18.7	0 29.8	1 30.2	17 9.7

RIGHT ASCENSION

DAY	EPHEM. SID. TIME	☉	☊	☽	☿	♀	♂	♃	♄	♅	♆	♇
1	6 39 8.7	10♑33.0	16♏48.8	2♑13.5	29♑54.8	27♏41.4	15♊56.8	14♈48.7	3♌20.3	4♏13.6	11♐16.5	17♎21.3
2	6 43 5.2	11 39.2	16 45.6	16 17.8	1♒21.9	28 55.0	15R39.6	14 52.7	3R15.7	4 15.6	11 18.7	17 21.9
3	6 47 1.8	12 45.5	16 42.4	29 44.3	2 45.8	0♐ 8.9	15 23.3	14 56.9	3 11.1	4 17.7	11 20.9	17 22.5
4	6 50 58.4	13 51.6	16 39.2	12♒30.1	4 5.8	1 23.2	15 7.8	15 1.2	3 6.4	4 19.7	11 23.0	17 23.1
5	6 54 54.9	14 57.6	16 36.0	24 38.3	5 21.5	2 37.7	14 53.1	15 5.7	3 1.7	4 21.6	11 25.2	17 23.6
6	6 58 51.5	16 3.5	16 32.8	6♓16.5	6 32.3	3 52.5	14 39.4	15 10.4	2 56.9	4 23.5	11 27.3	17 24.2
7	7 2 48.0	17 9.3	16 29.6	17 34.9	7 37.4	5 7.6	14 26.6	15 15.3	2 52.0	4 25.4	11 29.4	17 24.6
8	7 6 44.6	18 15.0	16 26.4	28 44.3	8 36.1	6 23.0	14 14.6	15 20.3	2 47.2	4 27.2	11 31.5	17 25.1
9	7 10 41.1	19 20.6	16 23.2	9♈56.1	9 27.7	7 38.7	14 3.6	15 25.5	2 42.2	4 28.9	11 33.5	17 25.5
10	7 14 37.7	20 26.0	16 20.0	21 21.1	10 11.4	8 54.6	13 53.5	15 30.8	2 37.3	4 30.6	11 35.6	17 25.9
11	7 18 34.3	21 31.3	16 16.8	3♉ 9.3	10 46.3	10 10.8	13 44.4	15 36.3	2 32.3	4 32.3	11 37.6	17 26.2
12	7 22 30.8	22 36.4	16 13.6	15 28.4	11 11.6	11 27.3	13 36.1	15 42.0	2 27.3	4 33.9	11 39.6	17 26.6
13	7 26 27.4	23 41.4	16 10.4	28 23.0	11 26.5	12 44.0	13 28.8	15 47.8	2 22.3	4 35.4	11 41.6	17 26.9
14	7 30 23.9	24 46.3	16 7.2	11♊52.7	11 30.4	14 1.0	13 22.4	15 53.9	2 17.3	4 37.0	11 43.6	17 27.2
15	7 34 20.5	25 50.9	16 4.0	25 51.0	11R22.7	15 18.2	13 16.9	16 .0	2 12.2	4 38.4	11 45.5	17 27.4
16	7 38 17.0	26 55.4	16 .8	10♋ 6.7	11 3.3	16 35.7	13 12.3	16 6.3	2 7.1	4 39.9	11 47.4	17 27.6
17	7 42 13.6	27 59.8	15 57.6	24 26.6	10 32.0	17 53.3	13 8.5	16 12.8	2 2.0	4 41.2	11 49.3	17 27.7
18	7 46 10.2	29 3.9	15 54.4	8♌39.2	9 49.3	19 11.2	13 5.7	16 19.4	1 56.9	4 42.5	11 51.2	17 27.9
19	7 50 6.7	0♒ 7.9	15 51.2	22 37.7	8 56.0	20 29.2	13 3.7	16 26.1	1 51.8	4 43.8	11 53.0	17 28.0
20	7 54 3.3	1 11.7	15 48.0	6♍21.8	7 53.5	21 47.5	13 2.6	16 33.0	1 46.6	4 45.0	11 54.9	17 28.0
21	7 57 59.8	2 15.4	15 44.8	19 55.8	6 43.3	23 5.9	13 2.3	16 40.1	1 41.5	4 46.1	11 56.7	17 28.1
22	8 1 56.4	3 18.8	15 41.6	3♎27.4	5 27.4	24 24.5	13D 2.9	16 47.2	1 36.4	4 47.2	11 58.4	17 28.1
23	8 5 52.9	4 22.1	15 38.4	17 4.9	4 8.2	25 43.2	13 4.3	16 54.6	1 31.2	4 48.3	12 .2	17R28.0
24	8 9 49.5	5 25.2	15 35.2	0♏54.9	2 48.0	27 2.1	13 6.6	17 2.0	1 26.1	4 49.3	12 1.9	17 28.0
25	8 13 46.0	6 28.0	15 32.0	15 .5	1 29.1	28 21.1	13 9.6	17 9.6	1 21.0	4 50.2	12 3.6	17 27.9
26	8 17 42.6	7 30.7	15 28.8	29 19.2	0 13.7	29 40.2	13 13.4	17 17.4	1 15.9	4 51.1	12 5.3	17 27.8
27	8 21 39.2	8 33.2	15 25.7	13♐42.9	29♑ 3.6	0♑59.4	13 18.1	17 25.2	1 10.8	4 51.9	12 6.9	17 27.6
28	8 25 35.7	9 35.5	15 22.5	27 59.5	28 .5	2 18.7	13 23.5	17 33.3	1 5.7	4 52.7	12 8.5	17 27.4
29	8 29 32.3	10 37.6	15 19.3	11♑56.3	27 5.3	3 38.1	13 29.6	17 41.4	1 .6	4 53.4	12 10.1	17 27.2
30	8 33 28.8	11 39.5	15 16.1	25 23.3	26 18.8	4 57.6	13 36.5	17 49.7	0 55.6	4 54.1	12 11.7	17 26.9
31	8 37 25.4	12 41.2	15 12.9	8♒16.0	25 41.4	6 17.0	13 44.2	17 58.1	0 50.6	4 54.7	12 13.2	17 26.7

DECLINATION

DAY	EPHEM. SID. TIME	☉	☊	☽	☿	♀	♂	♃	♄	♅	♆	♇
1	6 39 8.7	23S 5.2	0S18.4	20S 2.6	22S26.8	17S51.7	25N57.4	4N54.9	20N10.5	13S11.3	20S49.4	10N55.1
4	6 50 58.4	22 49.7	0 18.3	12 29.8	21 14.6	18 40.1	25 54.2	5 1.0	20 13.8	13 13.3	20 50.1	10 56.3
7	7 2 48.0	22 30.2	0 18.3	0 27.0	19 56.3	19 24.4	25 51.0	5 7.8	20 17.1	13 15.2	20 50.8	10 57.6
10	7 14 37.7	22 6.7	0 18.2	11N23.0	18 38.2	20 4.3	25 47.8	5 15.1	20 20.5	13 16.9	20 51.5	10 58.9
13	7 26 27.4	21 39.3	0 18.2	19 19.3	17 28.8	20 39.5	25 44.9	5 23.1	20 24.0	13 18.5	20 52.1	11 .4
16	7 38 17.0	21 8.2	0 18.1	19 14.2	16 38.2	21 9.8	25 42.3	5 31.6	20 27.4	13 19.9	20 52.7	11 2.0
19	7 50 6.7	20 33.3	0 18.1	9 26.5	16 14.0	21 34.8	25 40.2	5 40.6	20 30.8	13 21.2	20 53.3	11 3.8
22	8 1 56.4	19 55.0	0 18.1	5S17.3	16 17.8	21 54.5	25 38.6	5 50.1	20 34.2	13 22.3	20 53.8	11 5.6
25	8 13 46.0	19 13.4	0 18.0	17 9.4	16 43.4	22 8.5	25 37.5	6 .1	20 37.6	13 23.2	20 54.3	11 7.5
28	8 25 35.7	18 28.5	0 18.0	20 13.3	17 20.4	22 16.8	25 36.9	6 10.6	20 41.0	13 24.0	20 54.8	11 9.5
31	8 37 25.4	17 40.7	0 17.9	13 43.9	18 .1	22 19.2	25 36.8	6 21.4	20 44.2	13 24.6	20 55.2	11 11.6

FEBRUARY 1976

DAY	EPHEM. SID. TIME	☉	☊	☾	☿	♀	♂	♃	♄	♅	♆	♇
	h m s	° ′	° ′	° ′	° ′	° ′	° ′	° ′	° ′	° ′	° ′	° ′
		LONGITUDE										
1	8 41 21.9	11♒15.3	17♏37.5	19♒45.5	23♑54.8	7♑ 2.2	15♊28.7	19♈ 8.7	28♋34.3	7♏ 5.9	13♐26.7	11♎37.1
2	8 45 18.5	12 16.2	17 34.3	2♓ 9.6	23 R 34.9	8 15.8	15 36.8	19 18.1	28 R 29.6	7 6.4	13 28.1	11 R 36.5
3	8 49 15.0	13 17.1	17 31.2	14 21.5	23 23.4	9 29.3	15 45.7	19 27.6	28 24.9	7 6.9	13 29.5	11 35.8
4	8 53 11.6	14 18.0	17 28.0	26 22.5	23 19.9	10 42.9	15 55.1	19 37.3	28 20.3	7 7.3	13 30.8	11 35.2
5	8 57 8.2	15 18.9	17 24.8	8♈15.3	23 D 24.0	11 56.5	16 5.2	19 47.0	28 15.6	7 7.7	13 32.1	11 34.5
6	9 1 4.7	16 19.7	17 21.6	20 3.4	23 35.1	13 10.1	16 15.8	19 56.9	28 11.1	7 8.0	13 33.4	11 33.7
7	9 5 1.3	17 20.6	17 18.5	1♉51.3	23 52.8	14 23.8	16 27.0	20 7.0	28 6.5	7 8.2	13 34.6	11 32.9
8	9 8 57.8	18 21.3	17 15.3	13 44.0	24 16.5	15 37.4	16 38.8	20 17.1	28 2.0	7 8.4	13 35.9	11 32.1
9	9 12 54.4	19 22.1	17 12.1	25 47.2	24 45.8	16 51.1	16 51.2	20 27.4	27 57.6	7 8.5	13 37.0	11 31.3
10	9 16 50.9	20 22.8	17 8.9	8♊ 6.3	25 20.2	18 4.8	17 4.1	20 37.7	27 53.2	7 8.6	13 38.2	11 30.4
11	9 20 47.5	21 23.6	17 5.7	20 46.6	25 59.3	19 18.5	17 17.5	20 48.2	27 48.9	7 8.6	13 39.3	11 29.5
12	9 24 44.0	22 24.2	17 2.6	3♋52.3	26 42.6	20 32.2	17 31.4	20 58.8	27 44.6	7 R 8.5	13 40.4	11 28.6
13	9 28 40.6	23 24.9	16 59.4	17 25.7	27 29.9	21 45.9	17 45.8	21 9.5	27 40.4	7 8.5	13 41.5	11 27.6
14	9 32 37.1	24 25.5	16 56.2	1♌26.9	28 20.8	22 59.7	18 .8	21 20.3	27 36.3	7 8.3	13 42.5	11 26.6
15	9 36 33.7	25 26.1	16 53.0	15 52.8	29 15.0	24 13.4	18 16.2	21 31.2	27 32.2	7 8.1	13 43.5	11 25.6
16	9 40 30.3	26 26.7	16 49.9	0♍37.4	0♒12.3	25 27.2	18 32.0	21 42.2	27 28.2	7 7.8	13 44.5	11 24.6
17	9 44 26.8	27 27.3	16 46.7	15 32.2	1 12.4	26 41.0	18 48.4	21 53.3	27 24.3	7 7.5	13 45.4	11 23.5
18	9 48 23.4	28 27.8	16 43.5	0♎28.2	2 15.1	27 54.9	19 5.1	22 4.5	27 20.4	7 7.1	13 46.3	11 22.4
19	9 52 19.9	29 28.3	16 40.3	15 16.7	3 20.2	29 8.7	19 22.3	22 15.9	27 16.6	7 6.7	13 47.2	11 21.3
20	9 56 16.5	0♓28.8	16 37.1	29 51.3	4 27.5	0♒22.5	19 39.9	22 27.3	27 12.9	7 6.2	13 48.0	11 20.2
21	10 0 13.0	1 29.3	16 34.0	14♏ 8.2	5 36.9	1 36.4	19 58.0	22 38.8	27 9.2	7 5.7	13 48.8	11 19.0
22	10 4 9.6	2 29.7	16 30.8	28 5.8	6 48.3	2 50.3	20 16.4	22 50.4	27 5.7	7 5.1	13 49.6	11 17.8
23	10 8 6.1	3 30.2	16 27.6	11♐44.6	8 1.6	4 4.2	20 35.2	23 2.1	27 2.2	7 4.5	13 50.4	11 16.6
24	10 12 2.7	4 30.6	16 24.4	25 6.2	9 16.5	5 18.1	20 54.5	23 13.8	26 58.8	7 3.8	13 51.1	11 15.4
25	10 15 59.2	5 31.0	16 21.3	8♑12.5	10 33.2	6 32.1	21 14.1	23 25.7	26 55.5	7 3.1	13 51.8	11 14.2
26	10 19 55.8	6 31.4	16 18.1	21 5.4	11 51.4	7 46.0	21 34.1	23 37.7	26 52.3	7 2.3	13 52.4	11 12.9
27	10 23 52.3	7 31.7	16 14.9	3♒46.5	13 11.0	8 59.9	21 54.4	23 49.7	26 49.1	7 1.5	13 53.0	11 11.6
28	10 27 48.9	8 32.0	16 11.7	16 16.8	14 32.1	10 13.9	22 15.1	24 1.9	26 46.1	7 .6	13 53.6	11 10.2
29	10 31 45.4	9 32.3	16 8.5	28 37.1	15 54.6	11 27.9	22 36.2	24 14.1	26 43.1	6 59.6	13 54.2	11 8.9
		LATITUDE										
1	8 41 21.9	0 .0	0 .0	4 N 59.7	3 N 9.4	0 N 56.6	2 N 59.0	1 S 9.8	0 N 18.8	0 N 29.9	1 N 30.2	17 N 10.3
4	8 53 11.6	0 .0	0 .0	3 53.5	2 39.9	0 47.4	2 56.7	1 9.1	0 19.1	0 29.9	1 30.3	17 11.8
7	9 5 1.3	0 .0	0 .0	1 19.0	2 6.1	0 38.1	2 54.2	1 8.4	0 19.4	0 30.0	1 30.5	17 13.4
10	9 16 50.9	0 .0	0 .0	1 S 49.7	1 31.2	0 28.8	2 51.7	1 7.8	0 19.7	0 30.0	1 30.6	17 14.8
13	9 28 40.6	0 .0	0 .0	4 23.1	0 57.2	0 19.6	2 49.2	1 7.1	0 19.9	0 30.1	1 30.7	17 16.2
16	9 40 30.3	0 .0	0 .0	4 51.3	0 24.9	0 10.4	2 46.6	1 6.5	0 20.2	0 30.2	1 30.8	17 17.6
19	9 52 19.9	0 .0	0 .0	2 33.3	0 S 4.9	0 1.4	2 44.0	1 5.9	0 20.4	0 30.2	1 31.0	17 18.9
22	10 4 9.6	0 .0	0 .0	1 N 5.8	0 32.0	0 S 7.4	2 41.4	1 5.4	0 20.7	0 30.3	1 31.1	17 20.1
25	10 15 59.2	0 .0	0 .0	4 1.3	0 56.2	0 16.0	2 38.8	1 4.8	0 20.9	0 30.3	1 31.2	17 21.3
28	10 27 48.9	0 .0	0 .0	5 2.2	1 17.5	0 24.3	2 36.2	1 4.3	0 21.2	0 30.4	1 31.4	17 22.3
		RIGHT ASCENSION										
1	8 41 21.9	13♒42.7	15♏ 9.7	20♒34.8	25♑13.2	7♑36.5	13♊52.6	18♈ 6.6	0♌45.6	4♏55.3	12♐14.7	17♎26.3
2	8 45 18.5	14 44.0	15 6.5	2♓24.4	24 R 54.2	8 56.1	14 1.7	18 15.3	0 R 40.7	4 55.8	12 16.2	17 R 26.0
3	8 49 15.0	15 45.1	15 3.3	13 52.4	24 44.0	10 15.6	14 11.5	18 24.1	0 35.8	4 56.3	12 17.7	17 25.6
4	8 53 11.6	16 46.0	15 .1	25 7.7	24 42.2	11 35.1	14 22.0	18 33.0	0 31.0	4 56.7	12 19.1	17 25.3
5	8 57 8.2	17 46.7	14 56.9	6♈19.9	24 D 48.4	12 54.6	14 33.2	18 42.0	0 26.1	4 57.0	12 20.5	17 24.8
6	9 1 4.7	18 47.2	14 53.7	17 38.7	25 2.0	14 14.0	14 45.0	18 51.2	0 21.4	4 57.3	12 21.9	17 24.4
7	9 5 1.3	19 47.4	14 50.6	29 13.1	25 22.5	15 33.4	14 57.4	19 .4	0 16.6	4 57.6	12 23.2	17 23.9
8	9 8 57.8	20 47.5	14 47.4	11♉11.3	25 49.3	16 52.7	15 10.5	19 9.8	0 11.9	4 57.8	12 24.5	17 23.3
9	9 12 54.4	21 47.3	14 44.2	23 39.1	26 22.1	18 11.9	15 24.2	19 19.3	0 7.3	4 57.9	12 25.7	17 22.8
10	9 16 50.9	22 47.0	14 41.0	6♊39.3	27 .1	19 31.1	15 38.5	19 28.9	0 2.7	4 58.0	12 27.0	17 22.2
11	9 20 47.5	23 46.4	14 37.8	20 10.3	27 43.2	20 50.1	15 53.4	19 38.6	29♋58.2	4 58.0	12 28.2	17 21.6
12	9 24 44.0	24 45.7	14 34.6	4♋ 6.2	28 30.6	22 9.0	16 8.9	19 48.4	29 53.8	4 R 57.9	12 29.3	17 21.0
13	9 28 40.6	25 44.7	14 31.4	18 17.8	29 22.2	23 27.7	16 24.9	19 58.3	29 49.4	4 57.9	12 30.5	17 20.3
14	9 32 37.1	26 43.6	14 28.3	2♌34.9	0♒17.5	24 46.4	16 41.4	20 8.4	29 45.0	4 57.7	12 31.6	17 19.6
15	9 36 33.7	27 42.2	14 25.1	16 49.4	1 16.2	26 4.9	16 58.5	20 18.5	29 40.8	4 57.5	12 32.6	17 18.9
16	9 40 30.3	28 40.7	14 21.9	0♍57.5	2 18.1	27 23.2	17 16.1	20 28.7	29 36.6	4 57.3	12 33.7	17 18.1
17	9 44 26.8	29 39.0	14 18.7	14 59.8	3 22.7	28 41.3	17 34.2	20 39.0	29 32.5	4 57.0	12 34.7	17 17.4
18	9 48 23.4	0♓37.2	14 15.5	29 .3	4 29.9	29 59.3	17 52.9	20 49.5	29 28.4	4 56.6	12 35.6	17 16.6
19	9 52 19.9	1 35.1	14 12.3	13♎ 4.4	5 39.5	1♒17.1	18 11.9	20 60.0	29 24.5	4 56.2	12 36.6	17 15.7
20	9 56 16.5	2 32.9	14 9.2	27 16.6	6 51.2	2 34.7	18 31.5	21 10.6	29 20.6	4 55.8	12 37.5	17 14.9
21	10 0 13.0	3 30.5	14 6.0	11♏38.2	8 4.9	3 52.1	18 51.5	21 21.3	29 16.7	4 55.2	12 38.3	17 14.0
22	10 4 9.6	4 28.0	14 2.8	26 6.1	9 20.4	5 9.3	19 12.0	21 32.1	29 13.0	4 54.7	12 39.2	17 13.1
23	10 8 6.1	5 25.3	13 59.6	10♐32.6	10 37.6	6 26.3	19 32.9	21 43.0	29 9.4	4 54.1	12 40.0	17 12.2
24	10 12 2.7	6 22.5	13 56.4	24 47.5	11 56.2	7 43.0	19 54.2	21 54.0	29 5.8	4 53.4	12 40.7	17 11.2
25	10 15 59.2	7 19.5	13 53.3	8♑40.4	13 16.3	8 59.6	20 16.0	22 5.1	29 2.4	4 52.7	12 41.5	17 10.3
26	10 19 55.8	8 16.4	13 50.1	22 3.5	14 37.7	10 15.8	20 38.2	22 16.3	28 59.0	4 52.0	12 42.2	17 9.3
27	10 23 52.3	9 13.1	13 46.9	4♒53.8	16 .2	11 31.9	21 .8	22 27.5	28 55.7	4 51.2	12 42.9	17 8.3
28	10 27 48.9	10 9.7	13 43.7	17 12.2	17 23.7	12 47.7	21 23.8	22 38.8	28 52.5	4 50.3	12 43.5	17 7.2
29	10 31 45.4	11 6.1	13 40.5	29 3.4	18 48.3	14 3.2	21 47.1	22 50.2	28 49.4	4 49.4	12 44.1	17 6.2
		DECLINATION										
1	8 41 21.9	17 S 24.1	0 S 17.9	10 S 8.6	18 S 12.9	22 S 18.7	25 N 36.9	6 N 25.2	20 N 45.3	13 S 24.8	20 S 55.3	11 N 12.3
4	8 53 11.6	16 32.4	0 17.8	2 N 7.9	18 47.8	22 13.2	25 37.5	6 36.6	20 48.4	13 25.2	20 55.7	11 14.5
7	9 5 1.3	15 38.3	0 17.8	13 21.2	19 15.6	22 1.9	25 38.4	6 48.4	20 51.5	13 25.4	20 56.1	11 16.7
10	9 16 50.9	14 41.7	0 17.8	19 51.3	19 34.6	21 44.6	25 39.6	7 .6	20 54.4	13 25.5	20 56.4	11 19.0
13	9 28 40.6	13 42.9	0 17.7	17 57.4	19 43.7	21 21.5	25 41.1	7 13.1	20 57.2	13 25.4	20 56.6	11 21.4
16	9 40 30.3	12 42.1	0 17.7	6 42.4	19 42.1	20 52.8	25 42.7	7 25.8	20 59.9	13 25.1	20 56.9	11 23.8
19	9 52 19.9	11 39.5	0 17.6	8 S 22.4	19 29.4	20 18.5	25 44.4	7 38.9	21 2.4	13 24.7	20 57.1	11 26.2
22	10 4 9.6	10 35.2	0 17.6	18 40.1	19 5.3	19 38.8	25 46.0	7 52.2	21 4.8	13 24.1	20 57.2	11 28.6
25	10 15 59.2	9 29.3	0 17.5	19 10.4	18 29.7	18 53.9	25 47.5	8 5.8	21 7.0	13 23.4	20 57.3	11 31.1
28	10 27 48.9	8 22.2	0 17.5	11 8.8	17 42.5	18 4.2	25 48.8	8 19.6	21 9.0	13 22.5	20 57.4	11 33.6

MARCH 1976

LONGITUDE

DAY	EPHEM. SID. TIME h m s	☉ ° ′	☊ ° ′	☽ ° ′	☿ ° ′	♀ ° ′	♂ ° ′	♃ ° ′	♄ ° ′	♅ ° ′	♆ ° ′	♇ ° ′
1	10 35 42.0	10♓32.5	16♏ 5.4	10♓48.1	17♒18.4	12♒41.8	22♊57.5	24♈26.4	26♋40.3	6♏58.6	13♐54.7	11♎ 7.5
2	10 39 38.6	11 32.7	16 2.2	22 50.6	18 43.5	13 55.8	23 19.3	24 38.7	26 R 37.5	6 R 57.6	13 55.2	11 R 6.1
3	10 43 35.1	12 32.9	15 59.0	4♈45.8	20 9.9	15 9.7	23 41.3	24 51.2	26 34.8	6 56.5	13 55.6	11 4.7
4	10 47 31.7	13 33.1	15 55.8	16 35.6	21 37.5	16 23.7	24 3.7	25 3.7	26 32.2	6 55.3	13 56.0	11 3.3
5	10 51 28.2	14 33.2	15 52.7	28 22.5	23 6.3	17 37.7	24 26.3	25 16.2	26 29.7	6 54.1	13 56.4	11 1.9
6	10 55 24.8	15 33.3	15 49.5	10♉ 9.9	24 36.3	18 51.7	24 49.3	25 28.9	26 27.3	6 52.9	13 56.7	11 .4
7	10 59 21.3	16 33.4	15 46.3	22 2.1	26 7.4	20 5.7	25 12.6	25 41.6	26 25.0	6 51.6	13 57.0	10 58.9
8	11 3 17.9	17 33.4	15 43.1	4♊ 3.7	27 39.8	21 19.6	25 36.1	25 54.4	26 22.9	6 50.3	13 57.3	10 57.4
9	11 7 14.4	18 33.4	15 39.9	16 20.0	29 13.3	22 33.6	25 59.9	26 7.3	26 20.8	6 48.9	13 57.6	10 55.9
10	11 11 11.0	19 33.3	15 36.8	28 56.2	0♓47.9	23 47.6	26 24.0	26 20.2	26 18.8	6 47.4	13 57.8	10 54.4
11	11 15 7.5	20 33.2	15 33.6	11♋57.0	2 23.8	25 1.6	26 48.4	26 33.2	26 16.9	6 46.0	13 57.9	10 52.9
12	11 19 4.1	21 33.1	15 30.4	25 26.0	4 .7	26 15.6	27 13.0	26 46.2	26 15.2	6 44.5	13 58.1	10 51.3
13	11 23 .6	22 33.0	15 27.2	9♌24.6	5 38.9	27 29.5	27 37.8	26 59.3	26 13.5	6 42.9	13 58.2	10 49.7
14	11 26 57.2	23 32.8	15 24.1	23 51.7	7 18.2	28 43.5	28 3.0	27 12.5	26 11.9	6 41.3	13 58.3	10 48.2
15	11 30 53.7	24 32.5	15 20.9	8♍42.5	8 58.7	29 57.5	28 28.3	27 25.7	26 10.5	6 39.7	13 58.3	10 46.6
16	11 34 50.3	25 32.3	15 17.7	23 49.3	10 40.4	1♓11.5	28 53.9	27 39.0	26 9.1	6 38.0	13 58.3	10 45.0
17	11 38 46.8	26 32.0	15 14.5	9♎ 2.2	12 23.4	2 25.5	29 19.7	27 52.3	26 7.9	6 36.3	13 58.3	10 43.4
18	11 42 43.4	27 31.7	15 11.3	24 10.9	14 7.5	3 39.5	29 45.7	28 5.7	26 6.8	6 34.5	13 58.3	10 41.8
19	11 46 39.9	28 31.3	15 8.2	9♏ 6.3	15 52.9	4 53.5	0♋11.9	28 19.1	26 5.8	6 32.7	13 R 58.2	10 40.2
20	11 50 36.5	29 30.9	15 5.0	23 41.7	17 39.5	6 7.5	0 38.4	28 32.6	26 4.9	6 30.9	13 58.0	10 38.6
21	11 54 33.0	0♈30.5	15 1.8	7♐53.6	19 27.3	7 21.5	1 5.0	28 46.1	26 4.1	6 29.0	13 57.9	10 36.9
22	11 58 29.6	1 30.1	14 58.6	21 41.0	21 16.5	8 35.5	1 31.9	28 59.7	26 3.4	6 27.1	13 57.7	10 35.3
23	12 2 26.1	2 29.6	14 55.5	5♑ 5.0	23 6.9	9 49.5	1 58.9	29 13.3	26 2.8	6 25.2	13 57.5	10 33.6
24	12 6 22.7	3 29.1	14 52.3	18 7.8	24 58.6	11 3.5	2 26.1	29 27.0	26 2.3	6 23.2	13 57.2	10 32.0
25	12 10 19.3	4 28.5	14 49.1	0♒52.5	26 51.6	12 17.5	2 53.6	29 40.7	26 1.9	6 21.2	13 56.9	10 30.3
26	12 14 15.8	5 28.0	14 45.9	13 21.9	28 45.8	13 31.5	3 21.2	29 54.4	26 1.7	6 19.1	13 56.6	10 28.6
27	12 18 12.4	6 27.4	14 42.7	25 39.1	0♈41.4	14 45.5	3 49.0	0♉ 8.2	26 1.6	6 17.0	13 56.2	10 27.0
28	12 22 8.9	7 26.7	14 39.6	7♓46.4	2 38.2	15 59.4	4 17.0	0 22.0	26 1.5	6 14.9	13 55.8	10 25.3
29	12 26 5.5	8 26.1	14 36.4	19 46.1	4 36.2	17 13.4	4 45.1	0 35.9	26 D 1.6	6 12.8	13 55.4	10 23.6
30	12 30 2.0	9 25.4	14 33.2	1♈40.0	6 35.3	18 27.4	5 13.4	0 49.8	26 1.8	6 10.6	13 55.0	10 21.9
31	12 33 58.6	10 24.7	14 30.0	13 29.9	8 35.6	19 41.4	5 41.9	1 3.7	26 2.1	6 8.4	13 54.5	10 20.3

LATITUDE

DAY	EPHEM. SID. TIME	☉	☊	☽	☿	♀	♂	♃	♄	♅	♆	♇
1	10 35 42.0	0 .0	0 .0	4N31.9	1S29.9	0S29.6	2N34.5	1S 3.9	0N21.3	0N30.4	1N31.5	17N23.0
4	10 47 31.7	0 .0	0 .0	2 21.5	1 45.8	0 37.3	2 31.9	1 3.5	0 21.5	0 30.5	1 31.6	17 24.0
7	10 59 21.3	0 .0	0 .0	0S42.6	1 58.4	0 44.6	2 29.3	1 3.0	0 21.8	0 30.5	1 31.8	17 24.8
10	11 11 11.0	0 .0	0 .0	3 37.3	2 7.5	0 51.5	2 26.8	1 2.5	0 22.0	0 30.5	1 31.9	17 25.6
13	11 23 .6	0 .0	0 .0	5 6.3	2 12.8	0 57.9	2 24.3	1 2.1	0 22.2	0 30.6	1 32.0	17 26.3
16	11 34 50.3	0 .0	0 .0	3 55.1	2 14.4	1 3.8	2 21.9	1 1.7	0 22.4	0 30.6	1 32.2	17 26.9
19	11 46 39.9	0 .0	0 .0	0 22.9	2 11.8	1 9.2	2 19.5	1 1.3	0 22.5	0 30.7	1 32.3	17 27.4
22	11 58 29.6	0 .0	0 .0	3N13.0	2 5.0	1 14.0	2 17.1	1 .9	0 22.7	0 30.7	1 32.4	17 27.8
25	12 10 19.3	0 .0	0 .0	5 3.4	1 53.6	1 18.2	2 14.7	1 .6	0 22.9	0 30.7	1 32.6	17 28.2
28	12 22 8.9	0 .0	0 .0	4 42.5	1 37.7	1 21.9	2 12.4	1 .2	0 23.1	0 30.7	1 32.7	17 28.4
31	12 33 58.6	0 .0	0 .0	2 32.9	1 17.0	1 25.0	2 10.1	0 59.9	0 23.3	0 30.8	1 32.8	17 28.5

RIGHT ASCENSION

DAY	EPHEM. SID. TIME	☉	☊	☽	☿	♀	♂	♃	♄	♅	♆	♇
1	10 35 42.0	12♓ 2.4	13♏37.4	10♓33.9	20♒13.9	15♒18.5	22♊10.9	23♈ 1.7	28♋46.4	4♏48.4	12♐44.6	17♎ 5.1
2	10 39 38.6	12 58.6	13 34.2	21 51.7	21 40.3	16 33.5	22 35.0	23 13.3	28 R 43.5	4 R 47.4	12 45.1	17 R 4.0
3	10 43 35.1	13 54.7	13 31.0	3♈ 5.2	23 7.5	17 48.3	22 59.5	23 24.9	28 40.7	4 46.3	12 45.6	17 2.8
4	10 47 31.7	14 50.6	13 27.8	14 22.5	24 35.4	19 2.8	23 24.3	23 36.7	28 38.0	4 45.2	12 46.0	17 1.7
5	10 51 28.2	15 46.5	13 24.7	25 51.3	26 4.1	20 17.0	23 49.5	23 48.5	28 35.4	4 44.1	12 46.4	17 .5
6	10 55 24.8	16 42.2	13 21.5	7♉38.3	27 33.5	21 31.0	24 15.0	24 .3	28 32.9	4 42.9	12 46.8	16 59.3
7	10 59 21.3	17 37.8	13 18.3	19 48.6	29 3.6	22 44.7	24 40.8	24 12.3	28 30.5	4 41.6	12 47.2	16 58.1
8	11 3 17.9	18 33.3	13 15.1	2♊24.9	0♓34.3	23 58.2	25 7.0	24 24.3	28 28.2	4 40.3	12 47.5	16 56.9
9	11 7 14.4	19 28.7	13 12.0	15 27.2	2 5.6	25 11.4	25 33.4	24 36.4	28 26.0	4 39.0	12 47.7	16 55.7
10	11 11 11.0	20 24.0	13 8.8	28 52.3	3 37.5	26 24.3	26 .2	24 48.5	28 23.9	4 37.6	12 47.9	16 54.4
11	11 15 7.5	21 19.3	13 5.6	12♋34.8	5 10.0	27 37.0	26 27.3	25 .7	28 22.0	4 36.2	12 48.1	16 53.1
12	11 19 4.1	22 14.4	13 2.5	26 28.4	6 43.1	28 49.4	26 54.6	25 13.0	28 20.1	4 34.7	12 48.3	16 51.8
13	11 23 .6	23 9.5	12 59.3	10♌27.6	8 16.7	0♓ 1.6	27 22.2	25 25.3	28 18.4	4 33.2	12 48.4	16 50.5
14	11 26 57.2	24 4.5	12 56.1	24 29.6	9 51.0	1 13.6	27 50.1	25 37.7	28 16.8	4 31.6	12 48.5	16 49.2
15	11 30 53.7	24 59.4	12 52.9	8♍34.9	11 25.9	2 25.3	28 18.2	25 50.2	28 15.2	4 30.1	12 48.5	16 47.9
16	11 34 50.3	25 54.3	12 49.8	22 46.6	13 1.4	3 36.7	28 46.6	26 2.7	28 13.8	4 28.4	12 48.5	16 46.5
17	11 38 46.8	26 49.1	12 46.6	7♎ 9.0	14 37.6	4 48.0	29 15.3	26 15.3	28 12.6	4 26.8	12 48.6	16 45.2
18	11 42 43.4	27 43.9	12 43.4	21 45.3	16 14.4	5 59.0	29 44.1	26 28.0	28 11.4	4 25.1	12 R 48.5	16 43.8
19	11 46 39.9	28 38.6	12 40.3	6♏35.2	17 51.8	7 9.8	0♋13.2	26 40.7	28 10.3	4 23.4	12 48.4	16 42.5
20	11 50 36.5	29 33.3	12 37.1	21 33.4	19 30.0	8 20.4	0 42.6	26 53.4	28 9.4	4 21.6	12 48.3	16 41.1
21	11 54 33.0	0♈28.0	12 33.9	6♐29.3	21 8.9	9 30.8	1 12.1	27 6.2	28 8.6	4 19.8	12 48.1	16 39.7
22	11 58 29.6	1 22.6	12 30.8	21 9.7	22 48.5	10 41.0	1 41.9	27 19.0	28 7.8	4 17.9	12 47.9	16 38.2
23	12 2 26.1	2 17.2	12 27.6	5♑22.3	24 29.0	11 51.0	2 11.9	27 31.9	28 7.2	4 16.0	12 47.7	16 36.8
24	12 6 22.7	3 11.8	12 24.4	18 59.1	26 10.2	13 .8	2 42.0	27 44.9	28 6.7	4 14.1	12 47.4	16 35.4
25	12 10 19.3	4 6.4	12 21.3	1♒57.3	27 52.3	14 10.5	3 12.4	27 57.9	28 6.4	4 12.1	12 47.1	16 33.9
26	12 14 15.8	5 1.0	12 18.1	14 19.5	29 35.3	15 19.9	3 43.0	28 10.9	28 6.1	4 10.2	12 46.8	16 32.5
27	12 18 12.4	5 55.6	12 14.9	26 11.6	1♈19.1	16 29.2	4 13.8	28 24.0	28 6.0	4 8.1	12 46.4	16 31.0
28	12 22 8.9	6 50.2	12 11.8	7♓41.5	3 3.9	17 38.4	4 44.7	28 37.2	28 5.9	4 6.1	12 46.0	16 29.5
29	12 26 5.5	7 44.8	12 8.6	18 58.0	4 49.7	18 47.4	5 15.9	28 50.3	28 D 6.0	4 4.0	12 45.6	16 28.1
30	12 30 2.0	8 39.5	12 5.5	0♈ 9.9	6 36.4	19 56.2	5 47.2	29 3.6	28 6.3	4 1.9	12 45.1	16 26.6
31	12 33 58.6	9 34.1	12 2.3	11 25.3	8 24.0	21 5.0	6 18.7	29 16.8	28 6.6	3 59.8	12 44.6	16 25.1

DECLINATION

DAY	EPHEM. SID. TIME	☉	☊	☽	☿	♀	♂	♃	♄	♅	♆	♇
1	10 35 42.0	7S36.9	0S17.4	3S19.2	17S 4.5	17S28.4	25N49.5	8N28.9	21N10.3	13S21.9	20S57.4	11N35.2
4	10 47 31.7	6 28.0	0 17.4	8N42.0	15 58.0	16 31.0	25 50.2	8 43.0	21 12.0	13 20.8	20 57.5	11 37.7
7	10 59 21.3	5 18.4	0 17.3	17 35.5	14 40.0	15 29.5	25 50.5	8 57.2	21 13.6	13 19.5	20 57.4	11 40.2
10	11 11 11.0	4 8.1	0 17.3	19 48.9	13 10.6	14 24.0	25 50.3	9 11.6	21 15.0	13 18.1	20 57.4	11 42.6
13	11 23 .6	2 57.4	0 17.2	12 58.3	11 29.9	13 15.0	25 49.5	9 26.1	21 16.2	13 16.6	20 57.3	11 45.0
16	11 34 50.3	1 46.4	0 17.2	1S 8.7	9 38.2	12 2.7	25 48.0	9 40.7	21 17.2	13 14.9	20 57.2	11 47.4
19	11 46 39.9	0 35.3	0 17.1	14 53.5	7 35.6	10 47.5	25 45.9	9 55.4	21 18.0	13 13.2	20 57.0	11 49.7
22	11 58 29.6	0N35.8	0 17.1	19 58.2	5 22.4	9 29.5	25 43.0	10 10.1	21 18.7	13 11.3	20 56.8	11 51.9
25	12 10 19.3	1 46.7	0 17.1	15 1.4	2 59.2	8 9.3	25 39.2	10 24.9	21 19.1	13 9.3	20 56.6	11 54.1
28	12 22 8.9	2 57.3	0 17.0	4 16.9	0 26.7	6 47.0	25 34.6	10 39.7	21 19.3	13 7.2	20 56.3	11 56.2
31	12 33 58.6	4 7.3	0 17.0	7N40.5	2N13.7	5 23.1	25 29.0	10 54.5	21 19.4	13 5.1	20 56.1	11 58.3

APRIL 1976

LONGITUDE

DAY	EPHEM. SID. TIME h m s	☉ ° ′	☊ ° ′	☽ ° ′	☿ ° ′	♀ ° ′	♂ ° ′	♃ ° ′	♄ ° ′	♅ ° ′	♆ ° ′	♇ ° ′
1	12 37 55.1	11♈23.9	14♏26.8	25♈17.7	10♈37.0	20♓55.4	6♋10.6	1♉17.7	26♋ 2.5	6♏ 6.2	13♐54.0	10♎18.6
2	12 41 51.7	12 23.1	14 23.7	7♉ 5.5	12 39.3	22 9.4	6 39.4	1 31.7	26 3.0	6R 3.9	13R53.4	10R16.9
3	12 45 48.2	13 22.3	14 20.5	18 55.9	14 42.4	23 23.3	7 8.4	1 45.7	26 3.7	6 1.6	13 52.9	10 15.2
4	12 49 44.8	14 21.4	14 17.3	0♊51.9	16 46.2	24 37.3	7 37.5	1 59.8	26 4.4	5 59.3	13 52.2	10 13.6
5	12 53 41.3	15 20.5	14 14.1	12 57.0	18 50.6	25 51.2	8 6.8	2 13.9	26 5.3	5 57.0	13 51.6	10 11.9
6	12 57 37.9	16 19.6	14 11.0	25 15.1	20 55.3	27 5.2	8 36.3	2 28.0	26 6.2	5 54.7	13 50.9	10 10.2
7	13 1 34.4	17 18.6	14 7.8	7♋50.7	23 .1	28 19.2	9 5.9	2 42.1	26 7.3	5 52.4	13 50.3	10 8.6
8	13 5 31.0	18 17.6	14 4.6	20 47.5	25 4.7	29 33.1	9 35.6	2 56.3	26 8.5	5 50.0	13 49.6	10 7.0
9	13 9 27.5	19 16.5	14 1.4	4♌ 9.3	27 8.8	0♈47.0	10 5.5	3 10.5	26 9.8	5 47.6	13 48.8	10 5.3
10	13 13 24.1	20 15.5	13 58.2	17 58.3	29 12.3	2 .9	10 35.4	3 24.7	26 11.2	5 45.1	13 48.0	10 3.7
11	13 17 20.6	21 14.3	13 55.1	2♍14.6	1♉14.6	3 14.9	11 5.6	3 38.9	26 12.7	5 42.7	13 47.2	10 2.0
12	13 21 17.2	22 13.1	13 51.9	16 55.8	3 15.5	4 28.8	11 35.8	3 53.1	26 14.3	5 40.2	13 46.4	10 .4
13	13 25 13.7	23 11.9	13 48.7	1♎56.5	5 14.7	5 42.6	12 6.2	4 7.3	26 16.1	5 37.8	13 45.5	9 58.8
14	13 29 10.3	24 10.7	13 45.5	17 8.6	7 11.7	6 56.5	12 36.6	4 21.6	26 17.9	5 35.3	13 44.6	9 57.1
15	13 33 6.8	25 9.4	13 42.4	2♏22.5	9 6.3	8 10.4	13 7.2	4 35.9	26 19.8	5 32.8	13 43.7	9 55.5
16	13 37 3.4	26 8.1	13 39.2	17 28.1	10 58.1	9 24.3	13 37.9	4 50.2	26 21.8	5 30.3	13 42.8	9 53.9
17	13 40 60.0	27 6.8	13 36.0	2♐17.2	12 46.8	10 38.2	14 8.8	5 4.5	26 24.0	5 27.8	13 41.8	9 52.4
18	13 44 56.5	28 5.4	13 32.8	16 43.4	14 32.2	11 52.0	14 39.7	5 18.8	26 26.2	5 25.2	13 40.8	9 50.8
19	13 48 53.1	29 4.0	13 29.6	0♑43.6	16 13.9	13 5.9	15 10.7	5 33.1	26 28.6	5 22.7	13 39.8	9 49.2
20	13 52 49.6	0♉ 2.6	13 26.5	14 17.0	17 51.7	14 19.8	15 41.9	5 47.4	26 31.0	5 20.2	13 38.7	9 47.7
21	13 56 46.2	1 1.1	13 23.3	27 25.1	19 25.4	15 33.6	16 13.1	6 1.8	26 33.5	5 17.6	13 37.7	9 46.1
22	14 0 42.7	1 59.6	13 20.1	10♒10.6	20 54.9	16 47.5	16 44.5	6 16.1	26 36.2	5 15.1	13 36.6	9 44.6
23	14 4 39.3	2 58.1	13 16.9	22 37.2	22 19.9	18 1.4	17 16.0	6 30.5	26 38.9	5 12.5	13 35.4	9 43.1
24	14 8 35.8	3 56.6	13 13.8	4♓48.8	23 40.4	19 15.2	17 47.5	6 44.8	26 41.8	5 10.0	13 34.3	9 41.6
25	14 12 32.4	4 55.0	13 10.6	16 49.3	24 56.3	20 29.1	18 19.2	6 59.2	26 44.7	5 7.4	13 33.1	9 40.1
26	14 16 28.9	5 53.5	13 7.4	28 42.3	26 7.3	21 42.9	18 51.0	7 13.6	26 47.8	5 4.8	13 32.0	9 38.6
27	14 20 25.5	6 51.8	13 4.2	10♈31.1	27 13.4	22 56.7	19 22.8	7 27.9	26 50.9	5 2.3	13 30.7	9 37.2
28	14 24 22.0	7 50.2	13 1.0	22 18.6	28 14.7	24 10.6	19 54.9	7 42.3	26 54.2	4 59.8	13 29.6	9 35.8
29	14 28 18.6	8 48.6	12 57.9	4♉ 7.2	29 10.8	25 24.4	20 26.9	7 56.7	26 57.5	4 57.2	13 28.3	9 34.4
30	14 32 15.2	9 46.9	12 54.7	15 59.2	0♊ 1.8	26 38.3	20 59.1	8 11.1	27 .9	4 54.7	13 27.0	9 33.0

LATITUDE

DAY	EPHEM. SID. TIME	☉	☊	☽	☿	♀	♂	♃	♄	♅	♆	♇
1	12 37 55.1	0 .0	0 .0	1N33.8	1S 9.1	1S25.8	2N 9.3	0S59.8	0N23.3	0N30.8	1N32.9	17N28.5
4	12 49 44.8	0 .0	0 .0	1S38.4	0 42.6	1 28.1	2 7.1	0 59.5	0 23.5	0 30.8	1 33.0	17 28.6
7	13 1 34.4	0 .0	0 .0	4 18.8	0 12.3	1 29.7	2 4.8	0 59.2	0 23.6	0 30.8	1 33.1	17 28.5
10	13 13 24.1	0 .0	0 .0	5 14.0	0N20.5	1 30.8	2 2.6	0 59.0	0 23.8	0 30.8	1 33.2	17 28.3
13	13 25 13.7	0 .0	0 .0	3 26.0	0 54.1	1 31.2	2 .5	0 58.7	0 24.0	0 30.8	1 33.4	17 28.0
16	13 37 3.4	0 .0	0 .0	0N27.3	1 26.4	1 31.0	1 58.3	0 58.5	0 24.1	0 30.8	1 33.5	17 27.6
19	13 48 53.1	0 .0	0 .0	3 56.5	1 55.2	1 30.1	1 56.2	0 58.3	0 24.3	0 30.8	1 33.6	17 27.2
22	14 0 42.7	0 .0	0 .0	5 16.9	2 18.6	1 28.7	1 54.2	0 58.1	0 24.4	0 30.7	1 33.7	17 26.7
25	14 12 32.4	0 .0	0 .0	4 22.5	2 34.9	1 26.8	1 52.1	0 57.9	0 24.6	0 30.7	1 33.8	17 26.0
28	14 24 22.0	0 .0	0 .0	1 50.0	2 42.9	1 24.2	1 50.0	0 57.8	0 24.7	0 30.7	1 33.8	17 25.3

RIGHT ASCENSION

DAY	EPHEM. SID. TIME	☉	☊	☽	☿	♀	♂	♃	♄	♅	♆	♇
1	12 37 55.1	10♈28.8	11♏59.1	22♈51.5	10♈12.6	22♓13.6	6♋50.3	29♈30.1	28♋ 7.0	3♏57.6	12♐44.0	16♎23.6
2	12 41 51.7	11 23.4	11 56.0	4♉34.6	12 2.1	23 22.1	7 22.1	29 43.5	28 7.6	3R55.5	12R43.5	16R22.1
3	12 45 48.2	12 18.2	11 52.8	16 38.4	13 52.5	24 30.5	7 54.1	29 56.8	28 8.3	3 53.2	12 42.9	16 20.6
4	12 49 44.8	13 12.9	11 49.6	29 4.6	15 43.7	25 38.8	8 26.2	0♉10.3	28 9.1	3 51.0	12 42.2	16 19.1
5	12 53 41.3	14 7.7	11 46.5	11♊52.2	17 35.7	26 47.0	8 58.5	0 23.7	28 10.0	3 48.8	12 41.5	16 17.6
6	12 57 37.9	15 2.5	11 43.3	24 57.8	19 28.3	27 55.1	9 30.9	0 37.2	28 11.0	3 46.5	12 40.8	16 16.1
7	13 1 34.4	15 57.5	11 40.2	8♋16.3	21 21.4	29 3.2	10 3.5	0 50.8	28 12.2	3 44.3	12 40.2	16 14.7
8	13 5 31.0	16 52.4	11 37.0	21 42.5	23 14.8	0♈11.2	10 36.2	1 4.3	28 13.5	3 41.9	12 39.4	16 13.2
9	13 9 27.5	17 47.4	11 33.9	5♌13.0	25 8.3	1 19.1	11 9.0	1 17.9	28 14.8	3 39.6	12 38.6	16 11.7
10	13 13 24.1	18 42.4	11 30.7	18 46.9	27 1.7	2 27.1	11 41.9	1 31.5	28 16.3	3 37.3	12 37.8	16 10.2
11	13 17 20.6	19 37.5	11 27.5	2♍26.6	28 54.7	3 34.9	12 14.9	1 45.1	28 17.9	3 34.9	12 36.9	16 8.7
12	13 21 17.2	20 32.7	11 24.4	16 17.1	0♉47.2	4 42.8	12 48.1	1 58.8	28 19.6	3 32.5	12 36.0	16 7.2
13	13 25 13.7	21 27.9	11 21.2	0♎24.8	2 38.7	5 50.6	13 21.3	2 12.4	28 21.4	3 30.1	12 35.1	16 5.7
14	13 29 10.3	22 23.2	11 18.1	14 55.5	4 29.0	6 58.5	13 54.7	2 26.1	28 23.4	3 27.7	12 34.2	16 4.2
15	13 33 6.8	23 18.6	11 14.9	29 51.3	6 17.7	8 6.4	14 28.1	2 39.9	28 25.4	3 25.3	12 33.2	16 2.7
16	13 37 3.4	24 14.1	11 11.8	15♏ 8.3	8 4.6	9 14.3	15 1.6	2 53.6	28 27.6	3 22.9	12 32.2	16 1.2
17	13 40 60.0	25 9.7	11 8.6	0♐34.8	9 49.3	10 22.2	15 35.3	3 7.4	28 29.8	3 20.5	12 31.2	15 59.7
18	13 44 56.5	26 5.4	11 5.5	15 53.4	11 31.5	11 30.2	16 9.0	3 21.2	28 32.2	3 18.0	12 30.1	15 58.3
19	13 48 53.1	27 1.2	11 2.3	0♑46.2	13 11.0	12 38.2	16 42.8	3 35.0	28 34.7	3 15.6	12 29.0	15 56.8
20	13 52 49.6	27 57.1	10 59.2	14 59.3	14 47.3	13 46.3	17 16.7	3 48.8	28 37.3	3 13.1	12 27.9	15 55.3
21	13 56 46.2	28 53.1	10 56.0	28 26.9	16 20.4	14 54.4	17 50.6	4 2.7	28 40.0	3 10.6	12 26.8	15 53.9
22	14 0 42.7	29 49.2	10 52.9	11♒10.1	17 49.9	16 2.7	18 24.7	4 16.5	28 42.8	3 8.2	12 25.6	15 52.4
23	14 4 39.3	0♉45.4	10 49.7	23 15.4	19 15.7	17 11.0	18 58.8	4 30.4	28 45.7	3 5.7	12 24.5	15 51.0
24	14 8 35.8	1 41.8	10 46.6	4♓52.1	20 37.4	18 19.4	19 33.0	4 44.3	28 48.7	3 3.2	12 23.2	15 49.6
25	14 12 32.4	2 38.3	10 43.4	16 10.5	21 54.9	19 28.0	20 7.2	4 58.2	28 51.8	3 .7	12 22.0	15 48.2
26	14 16 28.9	3 34.9	10 40.3	27 21.1	23 8.0	20 36.7	20 41.5	5 12.1	28 55.0	2 58.3	12 20.8	15 46.8
27	14 20 25.5	4 31.6	10 37.1	8♈33.5	24 16.6	21 45.5	21 15.9	5 26.0	28 58.3	2 55.8	12 19.5	15 45.4
28	14 24 22.0	5 28.5	10 34.0	19 56.2	25 20.5	22 54.5	21 50.4	5 40.0	29 1.8	2 53.4	12 18.2	15 44.0
29	14 28 18.6	6 25.5	10 30.8	1♉35.8	26 19.5	24 3.5	22 24.9	5 54.0	29 5.3	2 50.9	12 16.9	15 42.7
30	14 32 15.2	7 22.6	10 27.7	13 37.0	27 13.6	25 12.8	22 59.5	6 7.9	29 8.9	2 48.4	12 15.6	15 41.3

DECLINATION

DAY	EPHEM. SID. TIME	☉	☊	☽	☿	♀	♂	♃	♄	♅	♆	♇
1	12 37 55.1	4N30.5	0S16.9	11N14.5	3N 8.6	4S54.8	25N27.0	10N59.4	21N19.4	13S 4.3	20S56.0	11N58.9
4	12 49 44.8	5 39.6	0 16.9	18 43.6	5 56.1	3 29.1	25 20.1	11 14.2	21 19.2	13 2.1	20 55.6	12 .9
7	13 1 34.4	6 47.9	0 16.8	18 54.1	8 45.1	2 2.4	25 12.2	11 29.0	21 18.8	12 59.8	20 55.3	12 2.7
10	13 13 24.1	7 55.0	0 16.8	10 27.5	11 30.7	0 35.2	25 3.3	11 43.7	21 18.2	12 57.4	20 54.9	12 4.4
13	13 25 13.7	9 .9	0 16.7	3S55.3	14 7.2	0N52.4	24 53.4	11 58.3	21 17.5	12 54.9	20 54.5	12 6.0
16	13 37 3.4	10 5.5	0 16.7	16 36.6	16 29.2	2 20.0	24 42.3	12 12.9	21 16.5	12 52.4	20 54.0	12 7.5
19	13 48 53.1	11 8.6	0 16.6	19 29.8	18 31.9	3 47.3	24 30.1	12 27.4	21 15.4	12 49.9	20 53.6	12 8.9
22	14 0 42.7	12 10.0	0 16.6	12 36.1	20 12.7	5 14.0	24 16.8	12 41.8	21 14.1	12 47.4	20 53.1	12 10.2
25	14 12 32.4	13 9.7	0 16.5	1 10.3	21 30.4	6 39.7	24 2.3	12 56.0	21 12.6	12 44.9	20 52.6	12 11.3
28	14 24 22.0	14 7.4	0 16.5	10N23.2	22 25.0	8 4.2	23 46.6	13 10.2	21 10.9	12 42.3	20 52.1	12 12.3

MAY 1976

LONGITUDE

DAY	EPHEM. SID. TIME (h m s)	☉	☊	☽	☿	♀	♂	♃	♄	♅	♆	♇
1	14 36 11.7	10♉45.1	12♏51.5	27♉56.9	0♊47.7	27♈52.1	21♋31.3	8♉25.4	27♋4.5	4♏52.1	13♐25.8	9♎31.6
2	14 40 8.3	11 43.4	12 48.3	10♊2.2	1 28.3	29 5.9	22 3.7	8 39.8	27 8.1	4 R49.6	13 R24.4	9 R30.2
3	14 44 4.8	12 41.6	12 45.2	22 17.4	2 3.6	0♉19.7	22 36.1	8 54.1	27 11.8	4 47.1	13 23.1	9 28.9
4	14 48 1.4	13 39.8	12 42.0	4♋45.0	2 33.6	1 33.5	23 8.6	9 8.4	27 15.6	4 44.5	13 21.8	9 27.6
5	14 51 57.9	14 37.9	12 38.8	17 27.5	2 58.2	2 47.3	23 41.2	9 22.7	27 19.5	4 42.0	13 20.4	9 26.3
6	14 55 54.5	15 36.0	12 35.6	0♌27.4	3 17.6	4 1.0	24 13.9	9 37.1	27 23.4	4 39.5	13 19.0	9 25.0
7	14 59 51.0	16 34.1	12 32.4	13 47.1	3 31.6	5 14.8	24 46.6	9 51.4	27 27.5	4 37.0	13 17.6	9 23.7
8	15 3 47.6	17 32.1	12 29.3	27 28.3	3 40.4	6 28.6	25 19.4	10 5.6	27 31.6	4 34.6	13 16.2	9 22.5
9	15 7 44.1	18 30.1	12 26.1	11♍31.7	3 44.0	7 42.3	25 52.3	10 19.9	27 35.9	4 32.1	13 14.8	9 21.3
10	15 11 40.7	19 28.1	12 22.9	25 56.3	3 R42.5	8 56.0	26 25.3	10 34.2	27 40.2	4 29.6	13 13.3	9 20.1
11	15 15 37.2	20 26.1	12 19.7	10♎39.2	3 36.2	10 9.8	26 58.4	10 48.4	27 44.6	4 27.2	13 11.9	9 18.9
12	15 19 33.8	21 24.0	12 16.6	25 35.1	3 25.2	11 23.5	27 31.5	11 2.6	27 49.1	4 24.8	13 10.4	9 17.8
13	15 23 30.4	22 21.9	12 13.4	10♏36.9	3 9.8	12 37.2	28 4.7	11 16.8	27 53.6	4 22.4	13 8.9	9 16.7
14	15 27 26.9	23 19.7	12 10.2	25 36.4	2 50.4	13 51.0	28 38.0	11 31.0	27 58.3	4 20.0	13 7.4	9 15.6
15	15 31 23.5	24 17.6	12 7.0	10♐25.1	2 27.2	15 4.7	29 11.3	11 45.2	28 3.0	4 17.7	13 5.9	9 14.5
16	15 35 20.0	25 15.4	12 3.9	24 55.7	2 .9	16 18.4	29 44.7	11 59.3	28 7.8	4 15.3	13 4.4	9 13.5
17	15 39 16.6	26 13.2	12 .7	9♑3.1	1 31.7	17 32.1	0♌18.2	12 13.4	28 12.7	4 13.0	13 2.9	9 12.5
18	15 43 13.1	27 11.0	11 57.5	22 44.4	1 .4	18 45.8	0 51.7	12 27.5	28 17.7	4 10.7	13 1.3	9 11.5
19	15 47 9.7	28 8.8	11 54.3	5♒59.4	0 27.4	19 59.6	1 25.4	12 41.6	28 22.7	4 8.5	12 59.8	9 10.6
20	15 51 6.2	29 6.5	11 51.1	18 49.6	29♉53.2	21 13.3	1 59.0	12 55.7	28 27.8	4 6.3	12 58.3	9 9.6
21	15 55 2.8	0♊4.2	11 48.0	1♓18.5	29 18.6	22 27.0	2 32.8	13 9.7	28 33.0	4 4.0	12 56.7	9 8.7
22	15 58 59.4	1 1.9	11 44.8	13 30.0	28 44.1	23 40.7	3 6.6	13 23.7	28 38.3	4 1.8	12 55.1	9 7.8
23	16 2 55.9	1 59.6	11 41.6	25 28.9	28 10.3	24 54.4	3 40.4	13 37.7	28 43.6	3 59.7	12 53.5	9 7.0
24	16 6 52.5	2 57.3	11 38.4	7♈19.9	27 37.8	26 8.1	4 14.3	13 51.6	28 49.0	3 57.5	12 51.9	9 6.2
25	16 10 49.0	3 55.0	11 35.3	19 7.2	27 7.2	27 21.8	4 48.3	14 5.5	28 54.5	3 55.4	12 50.3	9 5.4
26	16 14 45.6	4 52.6	11 32.1	0♉55.3	26 38.9	28 35.5	5 22.4	14 19.3	29 .0	3 53.4	12 48.7	9 4.6
27	16 18 42.1	5 50.2	11 28.9	12 47.3	26 13.3	29 49.2	5 56.5	14 33.2	29 5.6	3 51.3	12 47.1	9 3.8
28	16 22 38.7	6 47.8	11 25.7	24 46.3	25 51.0	1♊2.9	6 30.7	14 47.0	29 11.3	3 49.3	12 45.5	9 3.1
29	16 26 35.3	7 45.4	11 22.5	6♊54.5	25 32.2	2 16.6	7 4.9	15 .7	29 17.0	3 47.3	12 43.9	9 2.5
30	16 30 31.8	8 42.9	11 19.4	19 13.8	25 17.1	3 30.3	7 39.2	15 14.5	29 22.8	3 45.4	12 42.3	9 1.8
31	16 34 28.4	9 40.5	11 16.2	1♋45.3	25 6.2	4 44.0	8 13.6	15 28.1	29 28.7	3 43.4	12 40.7	9 1.2

LATITUDE

DAY	EPHEM. SID. TIME (h m s)	☉	☊	☽	☿	♀	♂	♃	♄	♅	♆	♇
1	14 36 11.7	0 .0	0 .0	1S24.8	2N41.7	1S21.2	1N48.0	0S57.7	0N24.9	0N30.7	1N33.9	17N24.5
4	14 48 1.4	0 .0	0 .0	4 11.5	2 30.5	1 17.6	1 46.0	0 57.5	0 25.0	0 30.6	1 34.0	17 23.7
7	14 59 51.0	0 .0	0 .0	5 17.7	2 9.0	1 13.5	1 44.1	0 57.4	0 25.2	0 30.6	1 34.0	17 22.7
10	15 11 40.7	0 .0	0 .0	3 51.2	1 37.2	1 9.0	1 42.1	0 57.3	0 25.3	0 30.5	1 34.1	17 21.7
13	15 23 30.4	0 .0	0 .0	0 56.1	1 4.0	1 4.0	1 40.2	0 57.2	0 25.5	0 30.5	1 34.1	17 20.6
16	15 35 20.0	0 .0	0 .0	3N34.1	0 7.9	0 58.7	1 38.3	0 57.2	0 25.6	0 30.4	1 34.2	17 19.5
19	15 47 9.7	0 .0	0 .0	4 10.0	0S44.3	0 53.0	1 36.4	0 57.1	0 25.8	0 30.4	1 34.2	17 18.3
22	15 58 59.4	0 .0	0 .0	4 31.4	1 36.3	0 46.9	1 34.5	0 57.1	0 25.9	0 30.3	1 34.2	17 17.0
25	16 10 49.0	0 .0	0 .0	2 23.7	2 23.7	0 40.6	1 32.6	0 57.1	0 26.1	0 30.3	1 34.2	17 15.7
28	16 22 38.7	0 .0	0 .0	1S 7.0	3 3.3	0 34.1	1 30.7	0 57.1	0 26.2	0 30.2	1 34.3	17 14.3
31	16 34 28.4	0 .0	0 .0	3 58.3	3 33.3	0 27.5	1 28.8	0 57.1	0 26.4	0 30.1	1 34.2	17 12.9

RIGHT ASCENSION

DAY	EPHEM. SID. TIME (h m s)	☉	☊	☽	☿	♀	♂	♃	♄	♅	♆	♇
1	14 36 11.7	8♉19.8	10♏24.5	26♉1.3	28♉2.5	26♈22.2	23♋34.1	6♉21.9	29♋12.6	2♏46.0	12♐14.2	15♎40.0
2	14 40 8.3	9 17.2	10 21.4	8♊46.9	28 46.1	27 31.8	24 8.7	6 35.8	29 16.4	2 R43.5	12 R12.8	15 R38.6
3	14 44 4.8	10 14.7	10 18.2	21 49.0	29 24.5	28 41.5	24 43.4	6 49.8	29 20.3	2 41.1	12 11.4	15 37.3
4	14 48 1.4	11 12.3	10 15.1	5♋5.5	29 57.5	29 51.5	25 18.1	7 3.8	29 24.3	2 38.6	12 10.0	15 36.0
5	14 51 57.9	12 10.1	10 12.0	18 16.4	0♊25.0	1♉1.6	25 52.9	7 17.7	29 28.4	2 36.2	12 8.5	15 34.7
6	14 55 54.5	13 8.0	10 8.8	1♌30.4	0 47.2	2 11.9	26 27.7	7 31.7	29 32.6	2 33.8	12 7.1	15 33.4
7	14 59 51.0	14 6.1	10 5.7	14 42.0	1 3.8	3 22.5	27 2.6	7 45.6	29 36.9	2 31.4	12 5.6	15 32.2
8	15 3 47.6	15 4.3	10 2.5	27 53.8	1 15.1	4 33.2	27 37.5	7 59.6	29 41.2	2 29.0	12 4.1	15 30.9
9	15 7 44.1	16 2.6	9 59.4	11♍11.8	1 21.2	5 44.2	28 12.4	8 13.6	29 45.7	2 26.6	12 2.6	15 29.7
10	15 11 40.7	17 1.1	9 56.2	24 44.6	1 22.0	6 55.4	28 47.3	8 27.5	29 50.2	2 24.2	12 1.0	15 28.5
11	15 15 37.2	17 59.7	9 53.1	8♎41.1	1 R18.0	8 6.9	29 22.2	8 41.5	29 54.9	2 21.9	11 59.5	15 27.3
12	15 19 33.8	18 58.4	9 50.0	23 8.4	1 9.2	9 18.6	29 57.2	8 55.4	29 59.6	2 19.5	11 57.9	15 26.2
13	15 23 30.4	19 57.3	9 46.8	8♏11.7	0 55.9	10 30.5	0♌32.2	9 9.3	0♌4.4	2 17.2	11 56.4	15 25.0
14	15 27 26.9	20 56.3	9 43.7	23 34.3	0 38.7	11 42.7	1 7.2	9 23.2	0 9.3	2 14.9	11 54.8	15 23.9
15	15 31 23.5	21 55.5	9 40.5	9♐11.1	0 17.7	12 55.2	1 42.2	9 37.1	0 14.3	2 12.6	11 53.2	15 22.8
16	15 35 20.0	22 54.8	9 37.4	24 37.2	29♉53.6	14 7.9	2 17.2	9 51.0	0 19.3	2 10.4	11 51.5	15 21.7
17	15 39 16.6	23 54.2	9 34.3	9♑32.0	29 26.8	15 20.9	2 52.2	10 4.9	0 24.4	2 8.1	11 49.9	15 20.6
18	15 43 13.1	24 53.8	9 31.1	23 41.8	28 57.9	16 34.1	3 27.3	10 18.8	0 29.6	2 5.9	11 48.3	15 19.6
19	15 47 9.7	25 53.6	9 28.0	7♒2.0	28 27.4	17 47.7	4 2.4	10 32.7	0 35.0	2 3.8	11 46.7	15 18.6
20	15 51 6.2	26 53.5	9 24.9	19 36.3	27 56.0	19 1.5	4 37.4	10 46.5	0 40.3	2 1.6	11 45.0	15 17.6
21	15 55 2.8	27 53.5	9 21.7	1♓33.1	27 24.1	20 15.6	5 12.5	11 .4	0 45.8	1 59.5	11 43.4	15 16.6
22	15 58 59.4	28 53.7	9 18.6	13 3.6	26 52.5	21 30.0	5 47.6	11 14.2	0 51.3	1 57.3	11 41.7	15 15.6
23	16 2 55.9	29 54.0	9 15.5	24 19.3	26 21.6	22 44.7	6 22.7	11 28.0	0 56.9	1 55.3	11 40.0	15 14.7
24	16 6 52.5	0♊54.4	9 12.3	5♈31.5	25 52.1	23 59.6	6 57.7	11 41.7	1 2.6	1 53.2	11 38.3	15 13.7
25	16 10 49.0	1 55.0	9 9.2	16 50.4	25 24.4	25 14.8	7 32.8	11 55.5	1 8.3	1 51.1	11 36.6	15 12.8
26	16 14 45.6	2 55.7	9 6.1	28 24.7	24 59.0	26 30.3	8 7.9	12 9.2	1 14.1	1 49.1	11 34.9	15 12.0
27	16 18 42.1	3 56.5	9 2.9	10♉20.8	24 36.2	27 46.1	8 43.0	12 22.9	1 20.0	1 47.2	11 33.2	15 11.1
28	16 22 38.7	4 57.4	8 59.8	22 42.0	24 16.5	29 2.2	9 18.1	12 36.6	1 25.9	1 45.2	11 31.5	15 10.3
29	16 26 35.3	5 58.4	8 56.7	5♊27.7	24 .2	0♊18.5	9 53.1	12 50.2	1 31.9	1 43.3	11 29.8	15 9.5
30	16 30 31.8	6 59.6	8 53.5	18 33.4	23 47.4	1 35.1	10 28.2	13 3.8	1 38.0	1 41.4	11 28.1	15 8.7
31	16 34 28.4	8 .9	8 50.4	1♋51.4	23 38.5	2 52.0	11 3.3	13 17.4	1 44.2	1 39.5	11 26.4	15 8.0

DECLINATION

DAY	EPHEM. SID. TIME (h m s)	☉	☊	☽	☿	♀	♂	♃	♄	♅	♆	♇
1	14 36 11.7	15N 3.1	0S16.4	18N19.6	22N57.2	9N27.2	23N29.8	13N24.2	21N 9.1	12S39.8	20S51.6	12N13.2
4	14 48 1.4	15 56.4	0 16.4	16 10.0	23 0.0	10 48.2	23 11.9	13 38.0	21 7.1	12 37.3	20 51.0	12 14.0
7	14 59 51.0	16 47.4	0 16.3	11 36.7	22 58.2	12 7.0	22 52.7	13 51.7	21 4.9	12 34.8	20 50.4	12 14.6
10	15 11 40.7	17 35.9	0 16.3	1S55.3	22 29.1	13 23.2	22 32.4	14 5.2	21 2.5	12 32.4	20 49.9	12 15.0
13	15 23 30.4	18 21.7	0 16.3	15 10.7	21 42.5	14 36.6	22 11.0	14 18.5	21 0.0	12 30.0	20 49.3	12 15.4
16	15 35 20.0	19 4.8	0 16.2	19 40.7	20 45.6	15 46.7	21 48.4	14 31.6	20 57.3	12 27.7	20 48.7	12 15.4
19	15 47 9.7	19 44.9	0 16.1	13 41.4	19 31.5	16 53.4	21 24.6	14 44.5	20 54.4	12 25.4	20 48.1	12 15.5
22	15 58 59.4	20 22.0	0 16.1	2 18.5	18 18.8	17 56.1	20 59.7	14 57.1	20 51.4	12 23.2	20 47.5	12 15.5
25	16 10 49.0	20 56.0	0 16.0	9N25.5	17 11.0	18 54.7	20 33.7	15 9.6	20 48.3	12 21.1	20 46.8	12 15.2
28	16 22 38.7	21 26.7	0 16.0	17 52.7	16 15.0	19 48.9	20 6.6	15 21.8	20 44.9	12 19.1	20 46.2	12 14.8
31	16 34 28.4	21 54.1	0 15.9	19 27.5	15 35.7	20 38.2	19 38.4	15 33.8	20 41.5	12 17.2	20 45.6	12 14.3

LONGITUDE

DAY	EPHEM. SID. TIME (h m s)	☉	☊	☽	☿	♀	♂	♃	♄	♅	♆	♇
1	16 38 24.9	10♊38.0	11♏13.0	14♋29.8	24♉59.4	5♊57.7	8♌48.0	15♉41.8	29♋34.6	3♏41.6	12♐39.0	9♎ .6
2	16 42 21.5	11 35.5	11 9.8	27 28.0	24R56.9	7 11.4	9 22.5	15 55.4	29 40.6	3R39.7	12R37.4	9R .0
3	16 46 18.0	12 33.0	11 6.7	10♌40.3	24D58.9	8 25.1	9 57.0	16 8.9	29 46.7	3 37.9	12 35.8	8 59.5
4	16 50 14.6	13 30.5	11 3.5	24 7.1	25 5.4	9 38.8	10 31.6	16 22.4	29 52.8	3 36.1	12 34.1	8 59.0
5	16 54 11.2	14 27.9	11 .3	7♍48.7	25 16.3	10 52.5	11 6.3	16 35.9	29 59.0	3 34.4	12 32.5	8 58.6
6	16 58 7.7	15 25.3	10 57.1	21 45.1	25 31.8	12 6.2	11 41.0	16 49.3	0♌ 5.2	3 32.7	12 30.9	8 58.1
7	17 2 4.3	16 22.7	10 54.0	5♎55.8	25 51.7	13 19.9	12 15.7	17 2.7	0 11.5	3 31.1	12 29.3	8 57.7
8	17 6 .8	17 20.1	10 50.8	20 19.2	26 15.9	14 33.6	12 50.5	17 16.0	0 17.8	3 29.5	12 27.7	8 57.4
9	17 9 57.4	18 17.5	10 47.6	4♏52.8	26 44.6	15 47.3	13 25.4	17 29.3	0 24.2	3 27.9	12 26.1	8 57.1
10	17 13 53.9	19 14.9	10 44.4	19 32.1	27 17.5	17 1.0	14 .3	17 42.5	0 30.7	3 26.4	12 24.5	8 56.8
11	17 17 50.5	20 12.2	10 41.3	4♐11.8	27 54.5	18 14.6	14 35.3	17 55.7	0 37.2	3 24.9	12 22.9	8 56.5
12	17 21 47.0	21 9.5	10 38.1	18 45.4	28 35.7	19 28.3	15 10.3	18 8.8	0 43.7	3 23.5	12 21.3	8 56.3
13	17 25 43.6	22 6.8	10 34.9	3♑ 6.3	29 20.9	20 42.0	15 45.3	18 21.8	0 50.3	3 22.1	12 19.7	8 56.1
14	17 29 40.2	23 4.1	10 31.7	17 9.1	0♊10.0	21 55.7	16 20.4	18 34.8	0 56.9	3 20.7	12 18.1	8 55.9
15	17 33 36.7	24 1.4	10 28.5	0♒49.6	1 3.1	23 9.4	16 55.6	18 47.8	1 3.6	3 19.4	12 16.5	8 55.8
16	17 37 33.3	24 58.7	10 25.4	14 6.0	1 59.9	24 23.1	17 30.8	19 .6	1 10.4	3 18.1	12 14.9	8 55.6
17	17 41 29.8	25 55.9	10 22.2	26 58.6	3 .4	25 36.8	18 6.0	19 13.5	1 17.1	3 16.9	12 13.3	8 55.6
18	17 45 26.4	26 53.2	10 19.0	9♓29.6	4 4.6	26 50.5	18 41.3	19 26.2	1 24.0	3 15.7	12 11.8	8 55.5
19	17 49 23.0	27 50.5	10 15.8	21 42.2	5 12.4	28 4.2	19 16.7	19 38.9	1 30.8	3 14.6	12 10.2	8 55.5
20	17 53 19.5	28 47.7	10 12.7	3♈42.2	6 23.8	29 17.9	19 52.0	19 51.5	1 37.7	3 13.5	12 8.7	8 55.5
21	17 57 16.1	29 45.0	10 9.5	15 33.4	7 38.6	0♋31.6	20 27.5	20 3.1	1 44.7	3 12.4	12 7.1	8D55.6
22	18 1 12.6	0♋42.2	10 6.3	27 21.5	8 56.9	1 45.3	21 3.0	20 16.6	1 51.7	3 11.4	12 5.6	8 55.7
23	18 5 9.2	1 39.5	10 3.1	9♉11.4	10 18.6	2 59.0	21 38.5	20 29.0	1 58.7	3 10.5	12 4.1	8 55.8
24	18 9 5.7	2 36.7	9 60.0	21 7.6	11 43.8	4 12.8	22 14.1	20 41.4	2 5.8	3 9.6	12 2.6	8 56.0
25	18 13 2.3	3 34.0	9 56.8	3♊14.1	13 12.2	5 26.5	22 49.8	20 53.7	2 12.9	3 8.7	12 1.1	8 56.2
26	18 16 58.9	4 31.2	9 53.6	15 33.9	14 44.0	6 40.2	23 25.5	21 5.9	2 20.0	3 7.9	11 59.6	8 56.4
27	18 20 55.4	5 28.5	9 50.4	28 8.7	16 19.0	7 54.0	24 1.2	21 18.1	2 27.2	3 7.2	11 58.2	8 56.7
28	18 24 52.0	6 25.7	9 47.2	10♋59.4	17 57.3	9 7.7	24 37.0	21 30.1	2 34.4	3 6.5	11 56.7	8 56.9
29	18 28 48.5	7 22.9	9 44.1	24 5.7	19 38.7	10 21.5	25 12.8	21 42.1	2 41.7	3 5.8	11 55.3	8 57.3
30	18 32 45.1	8 20.2	9 40.9	7♌26.3	21 23.3	11 35.3	25 48.8	21 54.1	2 49.0	3 5.3	11 53.9	8 57.7

LATITUDE

DAY	SID. TIME	☉	☊	☽	☿	♀	♂	♃	♄	♅	♆	♇
1	16 38 24.9	0 .0	0 .0	4S37.2	3S40.5	0S25.0	1N28.3	0S57.1	0N26.5	0N30.1	1N34.2	17N12.5
4	16 50 14.6	0 .0	0 .0	5 6.2	3 56.0	0 18.0	1 26.5	0 57.1	0 26.6	0 30.0	1 34.2	17 11.0
7	17 2 4.3	0 .0	0 .0	3 5.0	4 1.2	0 11.0	1 24.6	0 57.2	0 26.8	0 29.9	1 34.2	17 9.5
10	17 13 53.9	0 .0	0 .0	0N40.3	3 57.4	0 3.8	1 22.8	0 57.3	0 27.0	0 29.8	1 34.2	17 8.0
13	17 25 43.6	0 .0	0 .0	4 1.9	3 45.5	0N 3.3	1 21.1	0 57.4	0 27.1	0 29.8	1 34.1	17 6.5
16	17 37 33.3	0 .0	0 .0	5 9.4	3 26.8	0 10.4	1 19.3	0 57.4	0 27.3	0 29.7	1 34.1	17 4.9
19	17 49 23.0	0 .0	0 .0	3 56.9	3 2.3	0 17.5	1 17.5	0 57.5	0 27.5	0 29.6	1 34.0	17 3.3
22	18 1 12.6	0 .0	0 .0	1 15.9	2 33.5	0 23.4	1 15.7	0 57.6	0 27.7	0 29.5	1 34.0	17 1.7
25	18 13 2.3	0 .0	0 .0	1S54.3	2 .5	0 28.1	1 13.9	0 57.8	0 27.9	0 29.4	1 33.9	17 .1
28	18 24 52.0	0 .0	0 .0	4 24.4	1 24.4	0 31.2	1 12.0	0 57.9	0 28.1	0 29.3	1 33.8	16 58.5

RIGHT ASCENSION

DAY	SID. TIME	☉	☊	☽	☿	♀	♂	♃	♄	♅	♆	♇
1	16 38 24.9	9♊ 2.2	8♏47.3	15♋12.9	23♉33.5	4♊ 9.1	11♌38.3	13♉31.0	1♌50.4	1♏37.7	11♐24.7	15♎ 7.3
2	16 42 21.5	10 3.7	8 44.1	28 30.5	23R32.6	5 26.5	12 13.4	13 44.5	1 56.7	1R35.9	11R22.9	15R 6.6
3	16 46 18.0	11 5.3	8 41.0	11♌40.4	23D35.9	6 44.1	12 48.4	13 58.0	2 3.0	1 34.2	11 21.2	15 5.9
4	16 50 14.6	12 6.9	8 37.9	24 43.2	23 43.3	8 2.0	13 23.5	14 11.4	2 9.4	1 32.5	11 19.5	15 5.3
5	16 54 11.2	13 8.6	8 34.8	7♍43.8	23 55.0	9 20.1	13 58.5	14 24.9	2 15.8	1 30.8	11 17.8	15 4.6
6	16 58 7.7	14 10.4	8 31.6	20 50.4	24 11.0	10 38.5	14 33.5	14 38.2	2 22.4	1 29.2	11 16.0	15 4.0
7	17 2 4.3	15 12.3	8 28.5	4♎13.1	24 31.1	11 57.0	15 8.5	14 51.6	2 28.9	1 27.6	11 14.3	15 3.5
8	17 6 .8	16 14.2	8 25.4	18 1.4	24 55.5	13 15.8	15 43.5	15 4.9	2 35.5	1 26.0	11 12.6	15 2.9
9	17 9 57.4	17 16.3	8 22.2	2♏24.2	25 24.1	14 34.8	16 18.5	15 18.2	2 42.3	1 24.5	11 10.9	15 2.5
10	17 13 53.9	18 18.4	8 19.1	17 16.5	25 56.7	15 54.0	16 53.4	15 31.4	2 49.0	1 23.1	11 9.2	15 2.0
11	17 17 50.5	19 20.5	8 16.0	2♐35.7	26 33.5	17 13.3	17 28.4	15 44.6	2 55.8	1 21.6	11 7.5	15 1.6
12	17 21 47.0	20 22.6	8 12.9	18 3.1	27 14.3	18 32.9	18 3.3	15 57.7	3 2.6	1 20.2	11 5.8	15 1.1
13	17 25 43.6	21 24.9	8 9.7	3♑19.0	27 59.1	19 52.6	18 38.2	16 10.8	3 9.5	1 18.8	11 4.1	15 .7
14	17 29 40.2	22 27.1	8 6.6	17 58.1	28 47.9	21 12.4	19 13.0	16 23.8	3 16.4	1 17.5	11 2.4	15 .4
15	17 33 36.7	23 29.4	8 3.5	1♒54.2	29 40.7	22 32.4	19 47.9	16 36.8	3 23.4	1 16.2	11 .7	15 .0
16	17 37 33.3	24 31.7	8 .4	15 2.9	0♊37.4	23 52.5	20 22.7	16 49.7	3 30.4	1 15.0	10 59.1	14 59.7
17	17 41 29.8	25 34.1	7 57.3	27 28.6	1 38.0	25 12.7	20 57.6	17 2.6	3 37.5	1 13.8	10 57.4	14 59.4
18	17 45 26.4	26 36.4	7 54.1	9♓20.5	2 42.5	26 33.0	21 32.4	17 15.4	3 44.6	1 12.7	10 55.7	14 59.2
19	17 49 23.0	27 38.8	7 51.0	20 49.8	3 50.9	27 53.5	22 7.1	17 28.2	3 51.7	1 11.6	10 54.1	14 59.0
20	17 53 19.5	28 41.2	7 47.9	2♈ 8.2	5 3.2	29 14.0	22 41.9	17 40.9	3 58.9	1 10.5	10 52.5	14 58.8
21	17 57 16.1	29 43.6	7 44.8	13 26.8	6 19.3	0♋34.5	23 16.7	17 53.6	4 6.2	1 9.5	10 50.8	14 58.6
22	18 1 12.6	0♋46.0	7 41.7	24 55.8	7 39.4	1 55.1	23 51.4	18 6.2	4 13.4	1 8.5	10 49.2	14 58.5
23	18 5 9.2	1 48.4	7 38.5	6♉43.6	9 3.5	3 15.8	24 26.1	18 18.7	4 20.7	1 7.6	10 47.6	14 58.3
24	18 9 5.7	2 50.8	7 35.4	18 56.0	10 31.4	4 36.4	25 .8	18 31.2	4 28.1	1 6.7	10 46.0	14 58.3
25	18 13 2.3	3 53.2	7 32.3	1♊37.1	12 3.3	5 57.1	25 35.5	18 43.6	4 35.5	1 5.9	10 44.4	14 58.2
26	18 16 58.9	4 55.5	7 29.2	14 39.3	13 39.2	7 17.7	26 10.2	18 56.0	4 42.9	1 5.1	10 42.9	14 58.2
27	18 20 55.4	5 57.8	7 26.1	28 2.4	15 19.0	8 38.3	26 44.9	19 8.2	4 50.4	1 4.4	10 41.3	14 58.2
28	18 24 52.0	7 .1	7 22.9	11♋34.1	17 2.7	9 58.9	27 19.5	19 20.5	4 57.9	1 3.7	10 39.8	14D58.3
29	18 28 48.5	8 2.3	7 19.8	25 6.1	18 50.3	11 19.4	27 54.1	19 32.6	5 5.4	1 3.0	10 38.2	14 58.3
30	18 32 45.1	9 4.5	7 16.7	8♌31.0	20 41.9	12 39.9	28 28.8	19 44.7	5 13.0	1 2.5	10 36.8	14 58.5

DECLINATION

DAY	SID. TIME	☉	☊	☽	☿	♀	♂	♃	♄	♅	♆	♇
1	16 38 24.9	22N 2.5	0S15.9	18N 3.4	15N26.8	20N53.5	19N28.8	15N37.7	20N40.3	12S16.6	20S45.4	12N14.1
4	16 50 14.6	22 25.3	0 15.9	8 39.8	15 13.2	21 36.0	18 59.2	15 49.3	20 36.6	12 14.8	20 44.8	12 13.3
7	17 2 4.3	22 44.6	0 15.8	5S11.2	15 13.1	22 13.1	18 28.5	16 .7	20 32.8	12 13.2	20 44.2	12 12.5
10	17 13 53.9	23 .3	0 15.8	16 58.2	15 42.1	22 44.6	17 56.9	16 11.8	20 28.9	12 11.7	20 43.6	12 11.5
13	17 25 43.6	23 12.3	0 15.7	19 22.4	16 20.4	23 10.2	17 24.2	16 22.6	20 24.8	12 10.3	20 43.0	12 10.3
16	17 37 33.3	23 20.7	0 15.7	11 39.4	17 11.0	23 29.7	16 50.6	16 33.2	20 20.6	12 9.0	20 42.5	12 9.0
19	17 49 23.0	23 25.4	0 15.6	0N20.5	18 10.7	23 43.0	16 16.1	16 43.4	20 16.2	12 7.9	20 41.9	12 7.6
22	18 1 12.6	23 26.3	0 15.5	11 42.8	19 16.1	23 50.1	15 40.6	16 53.4	20 11.8	12 6.9	20 41.4	12 6.1
25	18 13 2.3	23 23.5	0 15.5	18 56.1	20 23.5	23 50.8	15 4.3	17 3.1	20 7.2	12 6.1	20 40.9	12 4.5
28	18 24 52.0	23 17.0	0 15.4	18 35.6	21 28.7	23 45.2	14 27.1	17 12.4	20 2.5	12 5.4	20 40.4	12 2.7

JULY 1976

LONGITUDE

DAY	EPHEM. SID. TIME h m s	☉ ° ′	☊ ° ′	☽ ° ′	☿ ° ′	♀ ° ′	♂ ° ′	♃ ° ′	♄ ° ′	♅ ° ′	♆ ° ′	♇ ° ′
1	18 36 41.6	9♋17.4	9♏37.7	20♌59.5	23♊10.9	12♋49.0	26♌24.7	22♉ 5.9	2♌56.3	3♏ 4.7	11♐52.5	8♎58.1
2	18 40 38.2	10 14.6	9 34.5	4♍43.1	25 1.3	14 2.8	27 .7	22 17.7	3 3.6	3R 4.2	11R51.1	8 58.5
3	18 44 34.8	11 11.8	9 31.4	18 35.4	26 54.6	15 16.6	27 36.7	22 29.3	3 11.0	3 3.8	11 49.8	8 59.0
4	18 48 31.3	12 9.1	9 28.2	2♎34.9	28 50.5	16 30.3	28 12.8	22 40.9	3 18.4	3 3.4	11 48.4	8 59.5
5	18 52 27.9	13 6.3	9 25.0	16 40.4	0♋48.9	17 44.1	28 48.9	22 52.4	3 25.8	3 3.0	11 47.1	8 60.0
6	18 56 24.4	14 3.4	9 21.8	0♏50.8	2 49.5	18 57.9	29 25.0	23 3.8	3 33.2	3 2.7	11 45.8	9 .5
7	19 0 21.0	15 .6	9 18.7	15 4.9	4 52.3	20 11.6	0♍ 1.2	23 15.1	3 40.7	3 2.5	11 44.5	9 1.1
8	19 4 17.5	15 57.8	9 15.5	29 20.7	6 56.8	21 25.4	0 37.5	23 26.4	3 48.2	3 2.3	11 43.2	9 1.8
9	19 8 14.1	16 55.0	9 12.3	13♐35.4	9 2.8	22 39.2	1 13.8	23 37.5	3 55.7	3 2.1	11 41.9	9 2.4
10	19 12 10.7	17 52.2	9 9.1	27 45.0	11 10.1	23 53.0	1 50.1	23 48.6	4 3.2	3 2.0	11 40.7	9 3.1
11	19 16 7.2	18 49.4	9 5.9	11♑45.3	13 18.3	25 6.7	2 26.5	23 59.5	4 10.8	3 2.0	11 39.5	9 3.8
12	19 20 3.8	19 46.6	9 2.8	25 31.7	15 27.1	26 20.5	3 2.9	24 10.4	4 18.3	3 2.0	11 38.3	9 4.6
13	19 24 .3	20 43.8	8 59.6	9♒ .6	17 36.3	27 34.3	3 39.3	24 21.1	4 25.9	3D 2.1	11 37.1	9 5.3
14	19 27 56.9	21 41.0	8 56.4	22 9.7	19 45.6	28 48.1	4 15.8	24 31.8	4 33.5	3 2.2	11 36.0	9 6.2
15	19 31 53.4	22 38.2	8 53.2	4♓58.2	21 54.6	0♌ 1.9	4 52.4	24 42.3	4 41.2	3 2.4	11 34.8	9 7.0
16	19 35 50.0	23 35.4	8 50.1	17 27.3	24 3.2	1 15.7	5 29.0	24 52.8	4 48.8	3 2.6	11 33.7	9 7.9
17	19 39 46.5	24 32.6	8 46.9	29 39.6	26 11.0	2 29.5	6 5.6	25 3.2	4 56.4	3 2.9	11 32.6	9 8.8
18	19 43 43.1	25 29.9	8 43.7	11♈39.0	28 18.0	3 43.3	6 42.3	25 13.4	5 4.1	3 3.2	11 31.6	9 9.7
19	19 47 39.7	26 27.1	8 40.5	23 30.3	0♌23.9	4 57.1	7 19.0	25 23.5	5 11.8	3 3.6	11 30.5	9 10.7
20	19 51 36.2	27 24.4	8 37.4	5♉18.8	2 28.6	6 10.9	7 55.8	25 33.6	5 19.5	3 4.0	11 29.5	9 11.7
21	19 55 32.8	28 21.7	8 34.2	17 10.0	4 32.0	7 24.8	8 32.6	25 43.6	5 27.2	3 4.5	11 28.6	9 12.8
22	19 59 29.3	29 19.0	8 31.0	29 9.1	6 34.0	8 38.6	9 9.5	25 53.4	5 34.9	3 5.1	11 27.6	9 13.9
23	20 3 25.9	0♌16.3	8 27.8	11♊20.9	8 34.4	9 52.5	9 46.4	26 3.1	5 42.6	3 5.7	11 26.7	9 15.0
24	20 7 22.4	1 13.6	8 24.6	23 49.3	10 33.2	11 6.3	10 23.4	26 12.7	5 50.4	3 6.3	11 25.8	9 16.1
25	20 11 19.0	2 10.9	8 21.5	6♋37.0	12 30.5	12 20.2	11 .3	26 22.1	5 58.1	3 7.0	11 24.9	9 17.2
26	20 15 15.5	3 8.2	8 18.3	19 45.0	14 26.0	13 34.0	11 37.4	26 31.5	6 5.8	3 7.8	11 24.0	9 18.4
27	20 19 12.1	4 5.6	8 15.1	3♌12.8	16 20.0	14 47.9	12 14.5	26 40.7	6 13.6	3 8.6	11 23.2	9 19.6
28	20 23 8.7	5 3.0	8 11.9	16 57.7	18 12.2	16 1.7	12 51.6	26 49.8	6 21.3	3 9.4	11 22.4	9 20.9
29	20 27 5.2	6 .3	8 8.8	0♍56.2	20 2.8	17 15.6	13 28.8	26 58.8	6 29.0	3 10.3	11 21.6	9 22.1
30	20 31 1.8	6 57.7	8 5.6	15 3.8	21 51.7	18 29.5	14 6.0	27 7.6	6 36.8	3 11.3	11 20.8	9 23.4
31	20 34 58.3	7 55.1	8 2.4	29 16.0	23 38.9	19 43.3	14 43.3	27 16.3	6 44.5	3 12.3	11 20.1	9 24.8

LATITUDE

DAY	SID. TIME	☉	☊	☽	☿	♀	♂	♃	♄	♅	♆	♇
1	18 36 41.6	0 .0	0 .0	5S .2	0S48.9	0N44.0	1N10.4	0S58.1	0N28.3	0N29.2	1N33.7	16N56.9
4	18 48 31.3	0 .0	0 .0	3 8.1	0 12.9	0 50.1	1 8.7	0 58.3	0 28.5	0 29.1	1 33.6	16 55.3
7	19 0 21.0	0 .0	0 .0	0N24.5	0N20.9	0 55.8	1 6.9	0 58.4	0 28.7	0 29.0	1 33.5	16 53.7
10	19 12 10.7	0 .0	0 .0	3 43.8	0 50.7	1 1.1	1 5.2	0 58.6	0 28.9	0 28.9	1 33.4	16 52.2
13	19 24 .3	0 .0	0 .0	5 2.3	1 15.0	1 6.1	1 3.5	0 58.9	0 29.1	0 28.8	1 33.3	16 50.6
16	19 35 50.0	0 .0	0 .0	3 58.7	1 32.8	1 10.6	1 1.7	0 59.1	0 29.3	0 28.7	1 33.2	16 49.1
19	19 47 39.7	0 .0	0 .0	1 22.5	1 43.7	1 14.6	1 .0	0 59.3	0 29.5	0 28.6	1 33.1	16 47.6
22	19 59 29.3	0 .0	0 .0	1S43.8	1 47.9	1 18.2	0 58.3	0 59.6	0 29.8	0 28.5	1 32.9	16 46.1
25	20 11 19.0	0 .0	0 .0	4 15.0	1 46.0	1 21.3	0 56.5	0 59.9	0 30.0	0 28.4	1 32.8	16 44.6
28	20 23 8.7	0 .0	0 .0	4 57.3	1 38.6	1 23.8	0 54.8	1 .1	0 30.3	0 28.3	1 32.6	16 43.2
31	20 34 58.3	0 .0	0 .0	3 8.7	1 26.5	1 25.7	0 53.1	1 .4	0 30.5	0 28.2	1 32.5	16 41.9

RIGHT ASCENSION

DAY	SID. TIME	☉	☊	☽	☿	♀	♂	♃	♄	♅	♆	♇
1	18 36 41.6	10♋ 6.6	7♏13.6	21♌45.7	22♊37.2	14♋ .2	29♌ 3.4	19♉56.7	5♌20.6	1♏ 2.0	10♐35.3	14♎58.6
2	18 40 38.2	11 8.6	7 10.5	4♍52.2	24 36.1	15 20.5	29 38.0	20 8.6	5 28.2	1R 1.5	10R33.8	14 58.8
3	18 44 34.8	12 10.5	7 7.4	17 56.5	26 38.6	16 40.6	0♍12.6	20 20.5	5 35.8	1 1.0	10 32.4	14 59.0
4	18 48 31.3	13 12.4	7 4.3	1♎ 7.2	28 44.4	18 .6	0 47.1	20 32.2	5 43.5	1 .6	10 30.9	14 59.2
5	18 52 27.9	14 14.2	7 1.1	14 33.9	0♋53.3	19 20.5	1 21.6	20 43.9	5 51.2	1 .3	10 29.5	14 59.4
6	18 56 24.4	15 15.9	6 58.0	28 24.9	3 5.0	20 40.2	1 56.2	20 55.5	5 58.9	0 60.0	10 28.1	14 59.7
7	19 0 21.0	16 17.5	6 54.9	12♏44.5	5 19.2	21 59.7	2 30.7	21 7.0	6 6.6	0 59.7	10 26.7	15 .0
8	19 4 17.5	17 19.0	6 51.8	27 30.8	7 35.6	23 19.0	3 5.2	21 18.4	6 14.3	0 59.5	10 25.4	15 .4
9	19 8 14.1	18 20.4	6 48.7	12♐33.7	9 53.8	24 38.2	3 39.6	21 29.8	6 22.1	0 59.4	10 24.1	15 .8
10	19 12 10.7	19 21.7	6 45.6	27 36.9	12 13.3	25 57.1	4 14.1	21 41.0	6 29.9	0 59.3	10 22.7	15 1.2
11	19 16 7.2	20 22.9	6 42.5	12♑22.0	14 33.7	27 15.9	4 48.5	21 52.2	6 37.7	0 59.2	10 21.4	15 1.6
12	19 20 3.8	21 24.0	6 39.4	26 33.9	16 54.5	28 34.4	5 23.0	22 3.3	6 45.5	0 59.2	10 20.2	15 2.0
13	19 24 .3	22 25.0	6 36.2	10♒ 4.9	19 15.4	29 52.7	5 57.4	22 14.3	6 53.4	0D59.3	10 18.9	15 2.5
14	19 27 56.9	23 25.8	6 33.1	22 54.6	21 35.8	1♌10.8	6 31.8	22 25.1	7 1.2	0 59.4	10 17.7	15 3.1
15	19 31 53.4	24 26.5	6 30.0	5♓ 8.3	23 55.5	2 28.6	7 6.2	22 35.9	7 9.1	0 59.5	10 16.5	15 3.6
16	19 35 50.0	25 27.1	6 26.9	16 54.7	26 14.1	3 46.1	7 40.6	22 46.6	7 17.0	0 59.8	10 15.3	15 4.2
17	19 39 46.5	26 27.6	6 23.8	28 24.1	28 31.1	5 3.4	8 15.0	22 57.2	7 24.9	1 .0	10 14.2	15 4.8
18	19 43 43.1	27 28.0	6 20.7	9♈47.2	0♌46.4	6 20.5	8 49.4	23 7.7	7 32.8	1 .3	10 13.0	15 5.4
19	19 47 39.7	28 28.2	6 17.6	21 14.2	2 59.7	7 37.2	9 23.8	23 18.1	7 40.7	1 .7	10 11.9	15 6.1
20	19 51 36.2	29 28.3	6 14.5	2♉54.2	5 10.8	8 53.7	9 58.2	23 28.4	7 48.6	1 1.1	10 10.8	15 6.8
21	19 55 32.8	0♌28.3	6 11.4	14 54.5	7 19.7	10 10.0	10 32.6	23 38.6	7 56.6	1 1.6	10 9.8	15 7.6
22	19 59 29.3	1 28.1	6 8.3	27 19.9	9 26.0	11 25.9	11 7.0	23 48.7	8 4.6	1 2.1	10 8.8	15 8.3
23	20 3 25.9	2 27.8	6 5.2	10♊11.6	11 29.9	12 41.6	11 41.3	23 58.6	8 12.5	1 2.6	10 7.8	15 9.1
24	20 7 22.4	3 27.4	6 2.1	23 26.8	13 31.1	13 56.9	12 15.7	24 8.4	8 20.5	1 3.2	10 6.8	15 9.9
25	20 11 19.0	4 26.8	5 59.0	6♋58.9	15 29.8	15 12.0	12 50.1	24 18.2	8 28.4	1 3.9	10 5.9	15 10.7
26	20 15 15.5	5 26.0	5 55.9	20 39.2	17 25.8	16 26.8	13 24.5	24 27.8	8 36.4	1 4.6	10 5.0	15 11.6
27	20 19 12.1	6 25.1	5 52.8	4♌19.3	19 19.3	17 41.2	13 58.9	24 37.2	8 44.3	1 5.4	10 4.1	15 12.5
28	20 23 8.7	7 24.1	5 49.7	17 53.4	21 10.2	18 55.4	14 33.2	24 46.6	8 52.3	1 6.2	10 3.2	15 13.4
29	20 27 5.2	8 22.9	5 46.6	1♍20.1	22 58.5	20 9.3	15 7.6	24 55.8	9 .2	1 7.0	10 2.4	15 14.4
30	20 31 1.8	9 21.5	5 43.5	14 41.8	24 44.4	21 22.9	15 42.0	25 5.0	9 8.2	1 7.9	10 1.6	15 15.3
31	20 34 58.3	10 20.0	5 40.3	28 4.6	26 27.8	22 36.2	16 16.5	25 13.9	9 16.2	1 8.9	10 .8	15 16.3

DECLINATION

DAY	SID. TIME	☉	☊	☽	☿	♀	♂	♃	♄	♅	♆	♇
1	18 36 41.6	23N 6.9	0S15.4	9N45.2	22N27.0	23N33.2	13N49.0	17N21.5	19N57.7	12S 4.9	20S39.9	12N .8
4	18 48 31.3	22 53.1	0 15.3	3S54.2	23 13.2	23 14.9	13 10.2	17 30.2	19 52.7	12 4.5	20 39.4	11 58.8
7	19 0 21.0	22 35.7	0 15.3	15 58.2	23 41.9	22 50.5	12 30.6	17 38.6	19 47.7	12 4.3	20 39.0	11 56.7
10	19 12 10.7	22 14.8	0 15.2	19 41.5	23 48.8	22 20.0	11 50.2	17 46.7	19 42.6	12 4.3	20 38.6	11 54.5
13	19 24 .3	21 50.5	0 15.2	13 8.3	23 31.3	21 43.6	11 9.2	17 54.5	19 37.5	12 4.4	20 38.3	11 52.2
16	19 35 50.0	21 22.8	0 15.1	1 17.5	22 49.4	21 1.6	10 27.5	18 1.9	19 32.2	12 4.7	20 37.9	11 49.9
19	19 47 39.7	20 51.8	0 15.1	10N24.3	21 45.3	20 14.2	9 45.2	18 9.1	19 26.8	12 5.1	20 37.6	11 47.4
22	19 59 29.3	20 17.7	0 15.0	18 16.8	20 22.4	19 21.5	9 2.2	18 15.9	19 21.4	12 5.7	20 37.4	11 44.8
25	20 11 19.0	19 40.5	0 15.0	19 1.8	18 44.8	18 24.0	8 18.6	18 22.3	19 15.9	12 6.5	20 37.1	11 42.2
28	20 23 8.7	19 .3	0 14.9	11 1.5	16 56.2	17 21.9	7 34.6	18 28.4	19 10.4	12 7.4	20 36.9	11 39.5
31	20 34 58.3	18 17.3	0 14.9	2S35.6	14 59.9	16 15.5	6 50.0	18 34.2	19 4.8	12 8.4	20 36.8	11 36.8

AUGUST 1976

LONGITUDE

DAY	EPHEM. SID. TIME h m s	☉ ° ′	☊ ° ′	☽ ° ′	☿ ° ′	♀ ° ′	♂ ° ′	♃ ° ′	♄ ° ′	♅ ° ′	♆ ° ′	♇ ° ′
1	20 38 54.9	8♌52.5	7♏59.2	13♎29.2	25♌24.4	20♌57.2	15♍20.6	27♉24.9	6♌52.3	3♏13.3	11♐19.4	9♎26.1
2	20 42 51.4	9 49.9	7 56.1	27 40.7	27 8.3	22 11.0	15 58.0	27 33.4	6 60.0	3 14.4	11 R 18.8	9 27.5
3	20 46 48.0	10 47.4	7 52.9	11♏48.8	28 50.5	23 24.9	16 35.4	27 41.7	7 7.7	3 15.6	11 18.1	9 28.9
4	20 50 44.5	11 44.8	7 49.7	25 52.5	0♍31.1	24 38.8	17 12.8	27 49.9	7 15.5	3 16.8	11 17.5	9 30.4
5	20 54 41.1	12 42.2	7 46.5	9♐51.1	2 10.0	25 52.6	17 50.3	27 58.0	7 23.2	3 18.1	11 16.9	9 31.8
6	20 58 37.7	13 39.7	7 43.3	23 43.6	3 47.3	27 6.5	18 27.8	28 5.9	7 30.9	3 19.4	11 16.4	9 33.3
7	21 2 34.2	14 37.2	7 40.2	7♑28.6	5 23.0	28 20.3	19 5.4	28 13.7	7 38.6	3 20.7	11 15.9	9 34.8
8	21 6 30.8	15 34.6	7 37.0	21 4.0	6 57.1	29 34.2	19 43.0	28 21.3	7 46.3	3 22.1	11 15.4	9 36.4
9	21 10 27.3	16 32.1	7 33.8	4♒27.6	8 29.5	0♍48.0	20 20.7	28 28.8	7 54.0	3 23.6	11 14.9	9 37.9
10	21 14 23.9	17 29.7	7 30.6	17 37.3	10 .3	2 1.9	20 58.4	28 36.2	8 1.6	3 25.1	11 14.5	9 39.5
11	21 18 20.4	18 27.2	7 27.5	0♓31.3	11 29.5	3 15.7	21 36.2	28 43.4	8 9.3	3 26.7	11 14.1	9 41.2
12	21 22 17.0	19 24.8	7 24.3	13 8.9	12 57.0	4 29.6	22 14.0	28 50.5	8 17.0	3 28.3	11 13.8	9 42.8
13	21 26 13.5	20 22.4	7 21.1	25 30.8	14 22.8	5 43.4	22 51.8	28 57.4	8 24.6	3 29.9	11 13.4	9 44.5
14	21 30 10.1	21 20.0	7 17.9	7♈38.7	15 46.9	6 57.3	23 29.7	29 4.1	8 32.2	3 31.6	11 13.1	9 46.2
15	21 34 6.6	22 17.6	7 14.7	19 35.6	17 9.3	8 11.1	24 7.6	29 10.7	8 39.9	3 33.4	11 12.9	9 47.9
16	21 38 3.2	23 15.3	7 11.6	1♉25.6	18 30.0	9 24.9	24 45.6	29 17.2	8 47.4	3 35.2	11 12.6	9 49.6
17	21 41 59.8	24 12.9	7 8.4	13 13.4	19 48.9	10 38.8	25 23.6	29 23.5	8 55.0	3 37.0	11 12.4	9 51.4
18	21 45 56.3	25 10.6	7 5.2	25 4.2	21 5.9	11 52.6	26 1.6	29 29.6	9 2.6	3 38.9	11 12.2	9 53.2
19	21 49 52.9	26 8.4	7 2.0	7♊ 3.6	22 21.1	13 6.4	26 39.8	29 35.6	9 10.1	3 40.8	11 12.1	9 55.0
20	21 53 49.4	27 6.1	6 58.9	19 16.8	23 34.3	14 20.3	27 17.9	29 41.4	9 17.6	3 42.8	11 12.0	9 56.8
21	21 57 46.0	28 3.9	6 55.7	1♋48.5	24 45.4	15 34.1	27 56.1	29 47.1	9 25.1	3 44.8	11 11.9	9 58.6
22	22 1 42.5	29 1.7	6 52.5	14 42.5	25 54.5	16 47.9	28 34.4	29 52.5	9 32.5	3 46.9	11 11.9	10 .5
23	22 5 39.1	29 59.5	6 49.3	28 .7	27 1.4	18 1.8	29 12.7	29 57.8	9 40.0	3 49.0	11 11.8	10 2.4
24	22 9 35.6	0♍57.4	6 46.1	11♌43.2	28 6.0	19 15.6	29 51.0	0♊ 3.0	9 47.4	3 51.1	11 D 11.9	10 4.3
25	22 13 32.2	1 55.3	6 43.0	25 47.6	29 8.2	20 29.4	0♎29.4	0 8.0	9 54.8	3 53.3	11 11.9	10 6.2
26	22 17 28.7	2 53.2	6 39.8	10♍ 9.3	0♎ 7.9	21 43.2	1 7.9	0 12.7	10 2.1	3 55.6	11 12.0	10 8.2
27	22 21 25.3	3 51.1	6 36.6	24 42.0	1 4.9	22 57.1	1 46.3	0 17.4	10 9.5	3 57.9	11 12.1	10 10.1
28	22 25 21.8	4 49.1	6 33.4	9♎19.0	1 59.1	24 10.9	2 24.9	0 21.8	10 16.8	4 .2	11 12.2	10 12.1
29	22 29 18.4	5 47.1	6 30.3	23 53.9	2 50.3	25 24.7	3 3.5	0 26.1	10 24.0	4 2.5	11 12.4	10 14.1
30	22 33 14.9	6 45.1	6 27.1	8♏21.7	3 38.3	26 38.5	3 42.1	0 30.2	10 31.3	4 4.9	11 12.6	10 16.1
31	22 37 11.5	7 43.1	6 23.9	22 38.9	4 23.0	27 52.3	4 20.8	0 34.1	10 38.5	4 7.4	11 12.9	10 18.2

LATITUDE

DAY	EPHEM. SID. TIME	☉	☊	☽	☿	♀	♂	♃	♄	♅	♆	♇
1	20 38 54.9	0 .0	0 .0	2S 4.9	1N21.5	1N26.3	0N52.5	1S .5	0N30.6	0N28.2	1N32.4	16N41.4
4	20 50 44.5	0 .0	0 .0	1N34.2	1 4.2	1 27.5	0 50.8	1 .8	0 30.9	0 28.1	1 32.3	16 40.1
7	21 2 34.2	0 .0	0 .0	4 20.9	0 43.6	1 28.1	0 49.1	1 1.1	0 31.1	0 28.0	1 32.1	16 38.8
10	21 14 23.9	0 .0	0 .0	4 55.9	0 20.4	1 28.1	0 47.3	1 1.5	0 31.4	0 27.9	1 32.0	16 37.6
13	21 26 13.5	0 .0	0 .0	3 18.7	0S 5.0	1 27.5	0 45.6	1 1.8	0 31.7	0 27.8	1 31.8	16 36.4
16	21 38 3.2	0 .0	0 .0	0 26.1	0 32.1	1 26.2	0 43.9	1 2.1	0 32.0	0 27.7	1 31.7	16 35.3
19	21 49 52.9	0 .0	0 .0	2S36.1	1 .4	1 24.4	0 42.2	1 2.5	0 32.3	0 27.6	1 31.5	16 34.2
22	22 1 42.5	0 .0	0 .0	4 43.1	1 29.5	1 21.9	0 40.4	1 2.9	0 32.6	0 27.5	1 31.3	16 33.2
25	22 13 32.2	0 .0	0 .0	4 45.3	1 59.0	1 18.9	0 38.7	1 3.2	0 32.9	0 27.4	1 31.2	16 32.3
28	22 25 21.8	0 .0	0 .0	2 13.9	2 28.1	1 15.3	0 37.0	1 3.6	0 33.2	0 27.3	1 31.0	16 31.4
31	22 37 11.5	0 .0	0 .0	1N32.2	2 56.1	1 11.1	0 35.2	1 4.0	0 33.5	0 27.2	1 30.8	16 30.6

RIGHT ASCENSION

DAY	EPHEM. SID. TIME	☉	☊	☽	☿	♀	♂	♃	♄	♅	♆	♇
1	20 38 54.9	11♌18.3	5♏37.2	11♎35.7	28♌ 8.8	23♌49.2	16♍50.9	25♉22.8	9♌24.1	1♏ 9.9	10♐ .1	15♎17.4
2	20 42 51.4	12 16.5	5 34.1	25 22.4	29 47.6	25 1.9	17 25.3	25 31.5	9 32.0	1 10.9	9 R 59.4	15 18.4
3	20 46 48.0	13 14.6	5 31.0	9♏29.3	1♍24.0	26 14.4	17 59.7	25 40.1	9 40.0	1 12.0	9 58.7	15 19.5
4	20 50 44.5	14 12.4	5 27.9	23 56.3	2 58.3	27 26.5	18 34.2	25 48.5	9 47.9	1 13.2	9 58.0	15 20.6
5	20 54 41.1	15 10.1	5 24.8	8♐37.3	4 30.3	28 38.4	19 8.6	25 56.9	9 55.8	1 14.4	9 57.4	15 21.8
6	20 58 37.7	16 7.7	5 21.7	23 21.0	6 .3	29 50.0	19 43.1	26 5.0	10 3.7	1 15.6	9 56.8	15 22.9
7	21 2 34.2	17 5.1	5 18.6	7♑52.9	7 28.2	1♍ 1.3	20 17.6	26 13.1	10 11.6	1 16.9	9 56.3	15 24.1
8	21 6 30.8	18 2.4	5 15.6	22 .0	8 54.1	2 12.4	20 52.1	26 21.0	10 19.5	1 18.3	9 55.7	15 25.3
9	21 10 27.3	18 59.5	5 12.5	5♒34.0	10 18.1	3 23.2	21 26.6	26 28.7	10 27.4	1 19.7	9 55.3	15 26.6
10	21 14 23.9	19 56.4	5 9.4	18 32.1	11 40.1	4 33.7	22 1.1	26 36.3	10 35.2	1 21.1	9 54.8	15 27.8
11	21 18 20.4	20 53.3	5 6.3	0♓57.1	13 .2	5 44.0	22 35.7	26 43.8	10 43.1	1 22.6	9 54.4	15 29.1
12	21 22 17.0	21 50.0	5 3.2	12 55.0	14 18.5	6 54.1	23 10.3	26 51.1	10 50.9	1 24.2	9 54.0	15 30.5
13	21 26 13.5	22 46.5	5 .1	24 34.1	15 34.9	8 3.9	23 44.9	26 58.3	10 58.7	1 25.7	9 53.7	15 31.8
14	21 30 10.1	23 42.9	4 57.0	6♈ 3.3	16 49.4	9 13.5	24 19.5	27 5.3	11 6.5	1 27.4	9 53.3	15 33.1
15	21 34 6.6	24 39.2	4 53.9	17 31.5	18 2.1	10 22.9	24 54.1	27 12.1	11 14.3	1 29.0	9 53.0	15 34.5
16	21 38 3.2	25 35.3	4 50.8	29 7.3	19 13.0	11 32.1	25 28.8	27 18.8	11 22.0	1 30.7	9 52.8	15 35.9
17	21 41 59.8	26 31.3	4 47.7	10♉57.7	20 22.1	12 41.1	26 3.5	27 25.3	11 29.8	1 32.5	9 52.5	15 37.4
18	21 45 56.3	27 27.2	4 44.6	23 8.1	21 29.3	13 49.9	26 38.2	27 31.7	11 37.5	1 34.3	9 52.4	15 38.8
19	21 49 52.9	28 23.0	4 41.5	5♊41.6	22 34.7	14 58.5	27 13.0	27 37.9	11 45.2	1 36.1	9 52.2	15 40.3
20	21 53 49.4	29 18.6	4 38.4	18 38.2	23 38.1	16 6.9	27 47.8	27 43.9	11 52.8	1 38.0	9 52.1	15 41.8
21	21 57 46.0	0♍14.2	4 35.3	1♋54.7	24 39.6	17 15.2	28 22.6	27 49.8	12 .5	1 40.0	9 52.0	15 43.3
22	22 1 42.5	1 9.6	4 32.2	15 25.5	25 39.2	18 23.3	28 57.5	27 55.5	12 8.1	1 41.9	9 51.9	15 44.8
23	22 5 39.1	2 4.9	4 29.1	29 4.1	26 36.7	19 31.3	29 32.4	28 1.0	12 15.6	1 44.0	9 51.9	15 46.4
24	22 9 35.6	3 .1	4 26.0	12♌45.2	27 32.0	20 39.2	0♎ 7.4	28 6.3	12 23.2	1 46.0	9 51.9	15 48.0
25	22 13 32.2	3 55.2	4 23.0	26 25.7	28 25.2	21 46.9	0 42.4	28 11.5	12 30.7	1 48.1	9 51.9	15 49.6
26	22 17 28.7	4 50.2	4 19.9	10♍ 6.0	29 16.0	22 54.5	1 17.4	28 16.5	12 38.2	1 50.3	9 D 52.0	15 51.2
27	22 21 25.3	5 45.1	4 16.8	23 49.3	0♎ 4.4	24 2.0	1 52.5	28 21.3	12 45.7	1 52.5	9 52.1	15 52.8
28	22 25 21.8	6 40.0	4 13.7	7♎40.6	0 50.3	25 9.4	2 27.6	28 25.9	12 53.1	1 54.7	9 52.3	15 54.5
29	22 29 18.4	7 34.7	4 10.6	21 44.9	1 33.5	26 16.7	3 2.8	28 30.4	13 .5	1 57.0	9 52.5	15 56.2
30	22 33 14.9	8 29.3	4 7.5	6♏ 4.8	2 13.9	27 23.9	3 38.0	28 34.6	13 7.8	1 59.3	9 52.7	15 57.9
31	22 37 11.5	9 23.8	4 4.4	20 39.2	2 51.3	28 31.1	4 13.3	28 38.7	13 15.2	2 1.6	9 52.9	15 59.6

DECLINATION

DAY	EPHEM. SID. TIME	☉	☊	☽	☿	♀	♂	♃	♄	♅	♆	♇
1	20 38 54.9	18N 2.4	0S14.8	7S14.4	14N19.9	15N52.5	6N35.0	18N36.1	19N 3.0	12S 8.8	20S36.7	11N35.8
4	20 50 44.5	17 15.9	0 14.8	17 42.1	12 17.4	14 40.9	5 49.8	18 41.4	18 57.3	12 10.1	20 36.6	11 33.0
7	21 2 34.2	16 26.9	0 14.7	18 53.2	10 12.8	13 25.7	5 4.2	18 46.4	18 51.7	12 11.5	20 36.6	11 30.1
10	21 14 23.9	15 35.5	0 14.7	10 51.1	8 8.0	12 7.4	4 18.2	18 51.0	18 46.0	12 13.1	20 36.5	11 27.2
13	21 26 13.5	14 41.8	0 14.6	1N15.4	6 4.3	10 46.1	3 31.9	18 55.3	18 40.3	12 14.8	20 36.5	11 24.2
16	21 38 3.2	13 46.1	0 14.6	12 22.7	4 3.4	9 22.3	2 45.2	18 59.2	18 34.6	12 16.7	20 36.6	11 21.2
19	21 49 52.9	12 48.3	0 14.5	18 55.4	2 6.6	7 56.2	1 58.3	19 2.8	18 28.9	12 18.7	20 36.7	11 18.2
22	22 1 42.5	11 48.7	0 14.5	17 56.3	0 15.4	6 28.2	1 11.1	19 6.1	18 23.2	12 20.8	20 36.8	11 15.2
25	22 13 32.2	10 47.5	0 14.4	8 26.5	1S28.5	4 58.6	0 23.8	19 8.9	18 17.6	12 23.1	20 37.0	11 12.1
28	22 25 21.8	9 44.7	0 14.4	5S44.6	3 3.2	3 27.8	0S23.7	19 11.5	18 12.0	12 25.5	20 37.2	11 9.0
31	22 37 11.5	8 40.5	0 14.3	16 56.9	4 26.2	1 56.0	1 11.3	19 13.7	18 6.4	12 28.0	20 37.5	11 6.0

SEPTEMBER 1976

LONGITUDE

DAY	EPHEM. SID. TIME h m s	☉ ° ′	☊ ° ′	☾ ° ′	☿ ° ′	♀ ° ′	♂ ° ′	♃ ° ′	♄ ° ′	♅ ° ′	♆ ° ′	♇ ° ′
1	22 41 8.0	8 ♍ 41.2	6 ♏ 20.7	6 ♐ 43.9	5 ♎ 4.1	29 ♍ 6.1	4 ♎ 59.5	0 ♊ 37.8	10 ♌ 45.7	4 ♏ 9.9	11 ♐ 13.2	10 ♎ 20.3
2	22 45 4.6	9 39.3	6 17.5	20 35.8	5 41.3	0 ♎ 19.8	5 38.3	0 41.4	10 52.8	4 12.5	11 13.5	10 22.3
3	22 49 1.2	10 37.4	6 14.4	4 ♑ 14.7	6 14.5	1 33.6	6 17.1	0 44.7	10 59.9	4 15.0	11 13.9	10 24.4
4	22 52 57.7	11 35.5	6 11.2	17 40.8	6 43.2	2 47.4	6 56.0	0 47.9	11 6.9	4 17.6	11 14.2	10 26.5
5	22 56 54.3	12 33.7	6 8.0	0 ♒ 54.4	7 7.4	4 1.1	7 34.9	0 50.9	11 13.9	4 20.3	11 14.6	10 28.6
6	23 0 50.8	13 31.8	6 4.8	13 55.3	7 26.5	5 14.8	8 13.8	0 53.7	11 20.9	4 22.9	11 15.1	10 30.8
7	23 4 47.4	14 30.0	6 1.7	26 43.5	7 40.5	6 28.5	8 52.8	0 56.3	11 27.8	4 25.7	11 15.6	10 32.9
8	23 8 43.9	15 28.2	5 58.5	9 ♓ 19.0	7 48.8	7 42.2	9 31.9	0 58.7	11 34.7	4 28.4	11 16.1	10 35.0
9	23 12 40.5	16 26.5	5 55.3	21 41.8	7 51.3	8 55.9	10 10.9	1 .9	11 41.6	4 31.2	11 16.6	10 37.2
10	23 16 37.0	17 24.8	5 52.1	3 ♈ 53.0	7 R 47.7	10 9.6	10 50.1	1 2.9	11 48.4	4 34.0	11 17.2	10 39.4
11	23 20 33.6	18 23.1	5 48.9	15 53.8	7 37.7	11 23.3	11 29.3	1 4.8	11 55.1	4 36.9	11 17.8	10 41.6
12	23 24 30.1	19 21.5	5 45.8	27 46.6	7 21.1	12 37.0	12 8.5	1 6.4	12 1.8	4 39.7	11 18.4	10 43.8
13	23 28 26.7	20 19.8	5 42.6	9 ♉ 34.5	6 57.7	13 50.6	12 47.8	1 7.9	12 8.5	4 42.7	11 19.1	10 46.0
14	23 32 23.2	21 18.3	5 39.4	21 21.3	6 27.7	15 4.3	13 27.1	1 9.1	12 15.1	4 45.6	11 19.8	10 48.2
15	23 36 19.8	22 16.7	5 36.2	3 ♊ 11.4	5 51.0	16 17.9	14 6.5	1 10.2	12 21.7	4 48.6	11 20.5	10 50.5
16	23 40 16.3	23 15.2	5 33.0	15 9.8	5 7.9	17 31.5	14 45.9	1 11.0	12 28.2	4 51.6	11 21.3	10 52.7
17	23 44 12.9	24 13.7	5 29.9	27 21.6	4 18.8	18 45.2	15 25.4	1 11.7	12 34.6	4 54.7	11 22.1	10 55.0
18	23 48 9.4	25 12.3	5 26.7	9 ♋ 51.6	3 24.5	19 58.8	16 4.9	1 12.1	12 41.1	4 57.8	11 22.9	10 57.2
19	23 52 6.0	26 10.9	5 23.5	22 44.4	2 25.7	21 12.4	16 44.5	1 12.4	12 47.4	5 .9	11 23.7	10 59.5
20	23 56 2.5	27 9.5	5 20.3	6 ♌ 3.1	1 23.6	22 26.0	17 24.1	1 12.4	12 53.7	5 4.0	11 24.6	11 1.8
21	23 59 59.1	28 8.2	5 17.2	19 49.0	0 19.3	23 39.6	18 3.8	1 R 12.3	12 59.9	5 7.2	11 25.5	11 4.1
22	0 3 55.6	29 6.9	5 14.0	4 ♍ 1.1	29 ♍ 14.5	24 53.2	18 43.6	1 11.9	13 6.2	5 10.4	11 26.5	11 6.4
23	0 7 52.2	0 ♎ 5.7	5 10.8	18 35.5	28 10.5	26 6.8	19 23.4	1 11.4	13 12.3	5 13.7	11 27.5	11 8.7
24	0 11 48.7	1 4.4	5 7.6	3 ♎ 26.1	27 9.2	27 20.3	20 3.2	1 10.6	13 18.4	5 16.9	11 28.5	11 11.1
25	0 15 45.3	2 3.2	5 4.4	18 24.6	26 12.0	28 33.9	20 43.1	1 9.7	13 24.3	5 20.2	11 29.6	11 13.4
26	0 19 41.8	3 2.1	5 1.3	3 ♏ 22.6	25 20.5	29 47.4	21 23.0	1 8.5	13 30.3	5 23.5	11 30.6	11 15.7
27	0 23 38.4	4 1.0	4 58.1	18 12.3	24 36.1	1 ♏ 1.0	22 3.0	1 7.1	13 36.2	5 26.8	11 31.7	11 18.0
28	0 27 35.0	4 59.9	4 54.9	2 ♐ 47.5	23 59.9	2 14.5	22 43.0	1 5.5	13 42.0	5 30.2	11 32.9	11 20.4
29	0 31 31.5	5 58.8	4 51.7	17 4.3	23 32.9	3 28.0	23 23.1	1 3.8	13 47.7	5 33.6	11 34.0	11 22.7
30	0 35 28.1	6 57.7	4 48.6	1 ♑ 1.0	23 15.8	4 41.5	24 3.3	1 1.8	13 53.4	5 37.0	11 35.2	11 25.0

LATITUDE

DAY	EPHEM. SID. TIME	☉	☊	☾	☿	♀	♂	♃	♄	♅	♆	♇
1	22 41 8.0	0 .0	0 .0	2N40.8	3S 5.1	1N 9.6	0N34.6	1S 4.1	0N33.6	0N27.2	1N30.8	16N30.3
4	22 52 57.7	0 .0	0 .0	4 52.8	3 30.0	1 4.6	0 32.9	1 4.5	0 34.0	0 27.1	1 30.6	16 29.6
7	23 4 47.4	0 .0	0 .0	4 44.6	3 50.8	0 59.2	0 31.2	1 4.8	0 34.3	0 27.0	1 30.4	16 28.9
10	23 16 37.0	0 .0	0 .0	2 36.7	4 5.1	0 53.2	0 29.4	1 5.2	0 34.7	0 27.0	1 30.2	16 28.3
13	23 28 26.7	0 .0	0 .0	0S29.1	4 9.7	0 46.8	0 27.7	1 5.6	0 35.0	0 26.9	1 30.1	16 27.8
16	23 40 16.3	0 .0	0 .0	3 24.4	4 1.1	0 40.0	0 25.9	1 5.9	0 35.4	0 26.8	1 29.9	16 27.4
19	23 52 6.0	0 .0	0 .0	5 5.5	3 36.2	0 32.7	0 24.1	1 6.3	0 35.8	0 26.8	1 29.8	16 27.0
22	0 3 55.6	0 .0	0 .0	4 30.3	2 54.4	0 25.1	0 22.4	1 6.6	0 36.2	0 26.7	1 29.6	16 26.7
25	0 15 45.3	0 .0	0 .0	1 23.3	1 59.4	0 17.1	0 20.6	1 7.0	0 36.6	0 26.6	1 29.4	16 26.5
28	0 27 35.0	0 .0	0 .0	2N32.8	0 59.0	0 8.9	0 18.9	1 7.3	0 37.0	0 26.6	1 29.3	16 26.4

RIGHT ASCENSION

DAY	EPHEM. SID. TIME	☉	☊	☾	☿	♀	♂	♃	♄	♅	♆	♇
1	22 41 8.0	10 ♍ 18.3	4 ♏ 1.3	5 ♐ 21.9	3 ♎ 25.5	29 ♍ 38.2	4 ♎ 48.7	28 ♉ 42.6	13 ♌ 22.5	2 ♏ 4.1	9 ♐ 53.3	16 ♎ 1.4
2	22 45 4.6	11 12.7	3 58.2	20 2.5	3 56.3	0 ♎ 45.3	5 24.1	28 46.3	13 29.7	2 6.5	9 53.6	16 3.1
3	22 49 1.2	12 7.0	3 55.2	4 ♑ 28.6	4 23.4	1 52.3	5 59.5	28 49.8	13 36.9	2 8.9	9 53.9	16 4.9
4	22 52 57.7	13 1.2	3 52.1	18 29.5	4 46.8	2 59.2	6 35.0	28 53.1	13 44.1	2 11.4	9 54.3	16 6.7
5	22 56 54.3	13 55.4	3 49.0	1 ♒ 58.7	5 6.0	4 6.2	7 10.5	28 56.3	13 51.2	2 14.0	9 54.7	16 8.5
6	23 0 50.8	14 49.5	3 45.9	14 54.3	5 20.9	5 13.2	7 46.1	28 59.2	13 58.3	2 16.6	9 55.2	16 10.3
7	23 4 47.4	15 43.5	3 42.8	27 19.0	5 31.2	6 20.1	8 21.8	29 1.9	14 5.3	2 19.2	9 55.7	16 12.1
8	23 8 43.9	16 37.5	3 39.7	9 ♓ 18.5	5 36.7	7 27.1	8 57.5	29 4.4	14 12.3	2 21.8	9 56.2	16 14.0
9	23 12 40.5	17 31.4	3 36.6	21 .0	5 37.1	8 34.1	9 33.3	29 6.8	14 19.3	2 24.5	9 56.8	16 15.8
10	23 16 37.0	18 25.4	3 33.6	2 ♈ 31.5	5 R 32.2	9 41.2	10 9.1	29 8.9	14 26.1	2 27.2	9 57.4	16 17.7
11	23 20 33.6	19 19.2	3 30.5	14 .7	5 21.8	10 48.3	10 45.0	29 10.8	14 33.0	2 30.0	9 58.0	16 19.6
12	23 24 30.1	20 13.1	3 27.4	25 34.8	5 5.9	11 55.4	11 21.0	29 12.6	14 39.8	2 32.7	9 58.7	16 21.5
13	23 28 26.7	21 6.9	3 24.3	7 ♉ 20.0	4 44.3	13 2.6	11 57.1	29 14.1	14 46.5	2 35.5	9 59.4	16 23.4
14	23 32 23.2	22 .7	3 21.2	19 20.7	4 17.1	14 9.9	12 33.2	29 15.4	14 53.2	2 38.4	10 .1	16 25.4
15	23 36 19.8	22 54.5	3 18.1	1 ♊ 39.8	3 44.4	15 17.3	13 9.4	29 16.5	14 59.9	2 41.3	10 .9	16 27.3
16	23 40 16.3	23 48.3	3 15.1	14 17.6	3 6.6	16 24.8	13 45.7	29 17.4	15 6.5	2 44.2	10 1.7	16 29.3
17	23 44 12.9	24 42.1	3 12.0	27 12.6	2 24.1	17 32.5	14 22.0	29 18.1	15 13.0	2 47.1	10 2.5	16 31.2
18	23 48 9.4	25 35.9	3 8.9	10 ♋ 21.5	1 37.5	18 40.2	14 58.5	29 18.6	15 19.5	2 50.1	10 3.4	16 33.2
19	23 52 6.0	26 29.7	3 5.8	23 40.5	0 47.6	19 48.1	15 35.0	29 18.9	15 25.9	2 53.1	10 4.3	16 35.2
20	23 56 2.5	27 23.6	3 2.7	7 ♌ 6.5	29 ♍ 55.4	20 56.1	16 11.6	29 19.0	15 32.3	2 56.1	10 5.2	16 37.2
21	23 59 59.1	28 17.4	2 59.7	20 37.9	29 2.0	22 4.3	16 48.3	29 R 18.9	15 38.6	2 59.2	10 6.1	16 39.2
22	0 3 55.6	29 11.3	2 56.6	4 ♍ 16.0	28 8.8	23 12.6	17 25.2	29 18.6	15 44.9	3 2.3	10 7.2	16 41.3
23	0 7 52.2	0 ♎ 5.2	2 53.5	18 3.8	27 17.1	24 21.2	18 2.1	29 18.0	15 51.1	3 5.4	10 8.2	16 43.3
24	0 11 48.7	0 59.1	2 50.4	2 ♎ 6.0	26 28.1	25 29.8	18 39.0	29 17.2	15 57.2	3 8.6	10 9.3	16 45.4
25	0 15 45.3	1 53.1	2 47.4	16 26.9	25 43.3	26 38.7	19 16.1	29 16.3	16 3.3	3 11.7	10 10.4	16 47.4
26	0 19 41.8	2 47.1	2 44.3	1 ♏ 8.3	25 4.0	27 47.8	19 53.2	29 15.1	16 9.3	3 14.9	10 11.5	16 49.5
27	0 23 38.4	3 41.1	2 41.2	16 7.3	24 31.3	28 57.1	20 30.5	29 13.7	16 15.2	3 18.1	10 12.7	16 51.5
28	0 27 35.0	4 35.2	2 38.1	1 ♐ 15.4	24 6.1	0 ♏ 6.6	21 7.8	29 12.1	16 21.1	3 21.4	10 13.8	16 53.6
29	0 31 31.5	5 29.4	2 35.1	16 19.3	23 49.2	1 16.3	21 45.3	29 10.3	16 26.9	3 24.6	10 15.1	16 55.7
30	0 35 28.1	6 23.6	2 32.0	1 ♑ 4.3	23 41.0	2 26.3	22 22.8	29 8.2	16 32.6	3 27.9	10 16.3	16 57.8

DECLINATION

DAY	EPHEM. SID. TIME	☉	☊	☾	☿	♀	♂	♃	♄	♅	♆	♇
1	22 41 8.0	8N18.8	0S14.3	18S47.5	4S50.7	1N25.3	1S27.2	19N14.3	18N 4.5	12S28.9	20S37.6	11N 4.9
4	22 52 57.7	7 13.0	0 14.2	17 26.0	5 52.9	0S 7.2	2 14.9	19 16.0	17 59.0	12 31.6	20 37.9	11 1.9
7	23 4 47.4	6 6.1	0 14.2	8 8.5	6 34.7	1 39.9	3 2.6	19 17.4	17 53.6	12 34.3	20 38.2	10 58.8
10	23 16 37.0	4 58.4	0 14.1	3N56.4	6 50.6	3 12.5	3 50.2	19 18.4	17 48.2	12 37.2	20 38.6	10 55.8
13	23 28 26.7	3 49.9	0 14.1	14 13.2	6 35.1	4 44.6	4 37.8	19 19.0	17 43.0	12 40.2	20 39.0	10 52.8
16	23 40 16.3	2 40.7	0 14.0	19 13.7	5 43.6	6 15.9	5 25.2	19 19.3	17 37.8	12 43.3	20 39.5	10 49.8
19	23 52 6.0	1 31.1	0 13.9	16 29.9	4 16.3	7 46.1	6 12.5	19 19.2	17 32.7	12 46.4	20 40.0	10 46.9
22	0 3 55.6	0 21.1	0 13.9	5 50.1	2 21.9	9 14.9	6 59.5	19 18.8	17 27.7	12 49.7	20 40.5	10 44.0
25	0 15 45.3	0S49.0	0 13.8	8S30.0	0 19.0	10 41.9	7 46.3	19 18.0	17 22.9	12 53.0	20 41.1	10 41.2
28	0 27 35.0	1 59.1	0 13.8	18 13.2	1N28.9	12 6.8	8 32.7	19 16.9	17 18.3	12 56.4	20 41.7	10 38.4

OCTOBER 1976

DAY	EPHEM. SID. TIME	☉	☊	☽	☿	♀	♂	♃	♄	♅	♆	♇
	h m s	° ′	° ′	° ′	° ′	° ′	° ′	° ′	° ′	° ′	° ′	° ′
		LONGITUDE										
1	0 39 24.6	7♎56.7	4♏45.4	14♑37.3	23♍ 8.9	5♏54.9	24♎43.4	0♊59.6	13♌59.0	5♏40.4	11♐36.4	11♎27.4
2	0 43 21.2	8 55.7	4 42.2	27 54.4	23D12.4	7 8.4	25 23.7	0R57.3	14 4.5	5 43.8	11 37.7	11 29.7
3	0 47 17.7	9 54.8	4 39.0	10♒53.9	23 26.3	8 21.8	26 3.9	0 54.7	14 10.0	5 47.3	11 38.9	11 32.0
4	0 51 14.3	10 53.9	4 35.8	23 37.8	23 50.2	9 35.2	26 44.3	0 51.9	14 15.4	5 50.8	11 40.2	11 34.4
5	0 55 10.8	11 53.0	4 32.7	6♓ 8.0	24 23.7	10 48.6	27 24.6	0 49.0	14 20.7	5 54.3	11 41.6	11 36.7
6	0 59 7.4	12 52.1	4 29.5	18 26.5	25 6.3	12 2.0	28 5.1	0 45.8	14 25.9	5 57.8	11 42.9	11 39.1
7	1 3 3.9	13 51.3	4 26.3	0♈35.0	25 57.3	13 15.4	28 45.5	0 42.5	14 31.1	6 1.3	11 44.3	11 41.4
8	1 7 .5	14 50.5	4 23.1	12 35.1	26 56.0	14 28.7	29 26.1	0 39.0	14 36.2	6 4.9	11 45.7	11 43.8
9	1 10 57.0	15 49.7	4 20.0	24 28.7	28 1.6	15 42.0	0♏ 6.6	0 35.3	14 41.2	6 8.5	11 47.1	11 46.1
10	1 14 53.6	16 49.0	4 16.8	6♉17.8	29 13.4	16 55.3	0 47.3	0 31.4	14 46.1	6 12.1	11 48.6	11 48.4
11	1 18 50.1	17 48.3	4 13.6	18 4.8	0♎30.6	18 8.6	1 27.9	0 27.3	14 51.0	6 15.7	11 50.1	11 50.8
12	1 22 46.7	18 47.6	4 10.4	29 52.5	1 52.6	19 21.9	2 8.7	0 23.0	14 55.8	6 19.3	11 51.6	11 53.1
13	1 26 43.2	19 47.0	4 7.2	11♊44.2	3 18.7	20 35.2	2 49.5	0 18.6	15 .5	6 23.0	11 53.2	11 55.5
14	1 30 39.8	20 46.5	4 4.1	23 43.6	4 48.1	21 48.4	3 30.3	0 14.0	15 5.1	6 26.6	11 54.7	11 57.8
15	1 34 36.3	21 45.9	4 .9	5♋54.9	6 20.4	23 1.7	4 11.2	0 9.2	15 9.7	6 30.3	11 56.3	12 .1
16	1 38 32.9	22 45.4	3 57.7	18 22.4	7 55.0	24 14.9	4 52.1	0 4.2	15 14.1	6 34.0	11 57.9	12 2.4
17	1 42 29.4	23 44.9	3 54.5	1♌10.3	9 31.6	25 28.1	5 33.1	29♉59.1	15 18.5	6 37.6	11 59.6	12 4.7
18	1 46 26.0	24 44.5	3 51.4	14 22.3	11 9.7	26 41.2	6 14.2	29 53.8	15 22.8	6 41.3	12 1.2	12 7.0
19	1 50 22.6	25 44.1	3 48.2	28 .9	12 49.0	27 54.4	6 55.3	29 48.3	15 27.0	6 45.0	12 2.9	12 9.3
20	1 54 19.1	26 43.8	3 45.0	12♍ 7.0	14 29.2	29 7.6	7 36.4	29 42.6	15 31.1	6 48.8	12 4.6	12 11.6
21	1 58 15.7	27 43.4	3 41.8	26 38.8	16 10.0	0♐20.7	8 17.6	29 36.8	15 35.1	6 52.5	12 6.3	12 13.9
22	2 2 12.2	28 43.2	3 38.6	11♎31.8	17 51.2	1 33.8	8 58.9	29 30.9	15 39.0	6 56.2	12 8.1	12 16.2
23	2 6 8.8	29 42.9	3 35.5	26 38.9	19 32.7	2 46.9	9 40.2	29 24.8	15 42.8	6 59.9	12 9.8	12 18.4
24	2 10 5.3	0♏42.7	3 32.3	11♏51.2	21 14.2	3 60.0	10 21.6	29 18.6	15 46.6	7 3.7	12 11.6	12 20.7
25	2 14 1.9	1 42.5	3 29.1	26 58.9	22 55.8	5 13.0	11 3.0	29 12.2	15 50.2	7 7.4	12 13.4	12 22.9
26	2 17 58.4	2 42.4	3 25.9	11♐53.3	24 37.2	6 26.1	11 44.5	29 5.6	15 53.7	7 11.2	12 15.3	12 25.2
27	2 21 55.0	3 42.3	3 22.8	26 27.5	26 18.5	7 39.1	12 26.0	28 59.0	15 57.2	7 14.9	12 17.1	12 27.4
28	2 25 51.5	4 42.2	3 19.6	10♑37.2	27 59.4	8 52.1	13 7.5	28 52.2	16 .5	7 18.7	12 19.0	12 29.6
29	2 29 48.1	5 42.1	3 16.4	24 21.0	29 40.1	10 5.0	13 49.2	28 45.3	16 3.8	7 22.5	12 20.9	12 31.8
30	2 33 44.6	6 42.1	3 13.2	7♒39.4	1♏20.4	11 17.9	14 30.8	28 38.3	16 6.9	7 26.2	12 22.8	12 34.0
31	2 37 41.2	7 42.1	3 10.0	20 34.8	3 .3	12 30.8	15 12.6	28 31.2	16 10.0	7 30.0	12 24.7	12 36.2
		LATITUDE										
1	0 39 24.6	0 .0	0 .0	4N57.3	0S 1.5	0N .5	0N17.1	1S 7.6	0N37.4	0N26.5	1N29.1	16N26.3
4	0 51 14.3	0 .0	0 .0	4 56.1	0N46.6	0S 8.1	0 15.3	1 7.9	0 37.8	0 26.5	1 29.0	16 26.3
7	1 3 3.9	0 .0	0 .0	2 52.1	1 22.4	0 16.9	0 13.6	1 8.1	0 38.2	0 26.4	1 28.8	16 26.4
10	1 14 53.6	0 .0	0 .0	0S15.5	1 45.5	0 25.8	0 11.8	1 8.4	0 38.7	0 26.4	1 28.7	16 26.6
13	1 26 43.2	0 .0	0 .0	3 16.6	1 57.3	0 34.7	0 10.0	1 8.6	0 39.1	0 26.3	1 28.6	16 26.8
16	1 38 32.9	0 .0	0 .0	5 6.7	1 59.8	0 43.5	0 8.2	1 8.8	0 39.6	0 26.3	1 28.4	16 27.2
19	1 50 22.6	0 .0	0 .0	4 49.5	1 55.0	0 52.3	0 6.4	1 8.9	0 40.1	0 26.2	1 28.3	16 27.6
22	2 2 12.2	0 .0	0 .0	1 59.5	1 44.9	1 1.0	0 4.6	1 9.0	0 40.5	0 26.2	1 28.2	16 28.1
25	2 14 1.9	0 .0	0 .0	2N 6.9	1 31.0	1 9.5	0 2.8	1 9.1	0 41.0	0 26.2	1 28.1	16 28.6
28	2 25 51.5	0 .0	0 .0	4 53.2	1 14.3	1 17.7	0 1.1	1 9.1	0 41.5	0 26.2	1 28.0	16 29.3
31	2 37 41.2	0 .0	0 .0	5 4.3	0 55.9	1 25.6	0S .7	1 9.1	0 42.0	0 26.1	1 27.9	16 30.0
		RIGHT ASCENSION										
1	0 39 24.6	7♎17.8	2♏28.9	15♑18.5	23♍42.0	3♏36.5	23♎ .5	29♉ 6.0	16♌38.3	3♏31.2	10♐17.6	16♎59.8
2	0 43 21.2	8 12.2	2 25.8	28 55.2	23D52.0	4 46.9	23 38.2	29R 3.6	16 43.8	3 34.6	10 18.9	17 1.9
3	0 47 17.7	9 6.6	2 22.8	11♒53.9	24 11.1	5 57.6	24 16.1	29 .9	16 49.4	3 37.9	10 20.2	17 4.0
4	0 51 14.3	10 1.0	2 19.7	24 18.5	24 39.0	7 8.5	24 54.0	28 58.1	16 54.8	3 41.3	10 21.6	17 6.1
5	0 55 10.8	10 55.6	2 16.6	6♓16.1	25 15.1	8 19.7	25 32.1	28 55.0	17 .2	3 44.7	10 23.0	17 8.3
6	0 59 7.4	11 50.3	2 13.5	17 54.9	25 59.0	9 31.1	26 10.2	28 51.8	17 5.5	3 48.1	10 24.4	17 10.4
7	1 3 3.9	12 45.0	2 10.5	29 23.5	26 50.0	10 42.8	26 48.5	28 48.4	17 10.7	3 51.5	10 25.9	17 12.5
8	1 7 .5	13 39.9	2 7.4	10♈50.1	27 47.5	11 54.8	27 26.9	28 44.7	17 15.8	3 54.9	10 27.4	17 14.6
9	1 10 57.0	14 34.8	2 4.3	22 21.6	28 50.8	13 7.1	28 5.4	28 40.9	17 20.9	3 58.4	10 28.9	17 16.7
10	1 14 53.6	15 29.9	2 1.3	4♉ 3.7	29 59.2	14 19.7	28 44.0	28 36.9	17 25.9	4 1.9	10 30.4	17 18.8
11	1 18 50.1	16 25.1	1 58.2	16 .3	1♎12.1	15 32.6	29 22.7	28 32.7	17 30.8	4 5.4	10 32.0	17 20.9
12	1 22 46.7	17 20.4	1 55.1	28 12.8	2 28.8	16 45.7	0♏ 1.6	28 28.3	17 35.6	4 8.9	10 33.6	17 23.1
13	1 26 43.2	18 15.8	1 52.1	10♊41.0	3 48.9	17 59.2	0 40.6	28 23.7	17 40.4	4 12.4	10 35.3	17 25.2
14	1 30 39.8	19 11.4	1 49.0	23 22.3	5 11.6	19 13.0	1 19.7	28 19.0	17 45.0	4 16.0	10 36.9	17 27.4
15	1 34 36.3	20 7.1	1 45.9	6♋13.3	6 36.6	20 27.0	1 58.9	28 14.0	17 49.6	4 19.5	10 38.6	17 29.5
16	1 38 32.9	21 3.0	1 42.9	19 10.6	8 3.5	21 41.4	2 38.3	28 8.9	17 54.1	4 23.1	10 40.3	17 31.6
17	1 42 29.4	21 59.0	1 39.8	2♌12.1	9 32.0	22 56.0	3 17.7	28 3.6	17 58.5	4 26.6	10 42.0	17 33.7
18	1 46 26.0	22 55.1	1 36.7	15 17.9	11 1.6	24 11.0	3 57.3	27 58.1	18 2.8	4 30.2	10 43.8	17 35.8
19	1 50 22.6	23 51.4	1 33.7	28 30.6	12 32.2	25 26.2	4 37.1	27 52.4	18 7.1	4 33.8	10 45.5	17 37.9
20	1 54 19.1	24 47.9	1 30.6	11♍55.5	14 3.6	26 41.7	5 17.0	27 46.6	18 11.2	4 37.4	10 47.3	17 40.1
21	1 58 15.7	25 44.5	1 27.5	25 39.4	15 35.6	27 57.6	5 57.0	27 40.6	18 15.2	4 41.0	10 49.2	17 42.2
22	2 2 12.2	26 41.3	1 24.5	9♎49.0	17 8.0	29 13.7	6 37.1	27 34.5	18 19.2	4 44.7	10 51.0	17 44.3
23	2 6 8.8	27 38.3	1 21.4	24 29.3	18 40.7	0♐30.1	7 17.4	27 28.2	18 23.1	4 48.3	10 52.9	17 46.4
24	2 10 5.3	28 35.5	1 18.3	9♏39.6	20 13.7	1 46.8	7 57.8	27 21.8	18 26.8	4 51.9	10 54.8	17 48.5
25	2 14 1.9	29 32.8	1 15.3	25 12.0	21 46.8	3 3.8	8 38.3	27 15.2	18 30.5	4 55.6	10 56.7	17 50.6
26	2 17 58.4	0♏30.3	1 12.2	10♐50.7	23 20.0	4 21.0	9 19.0	27 8.5	18 34.1	4 59.2	10 58.6	17 52.6
27	2 21 55.0	1 28.0	1 9.1	26 15.6	24 53.3	5 38.5	9 59.8	27 1.6	18 37.6	5 2.8	11 .6	17 54.7
28	2 25 51.5	2 25.8	1 6.1	11♑ 8.5	26 26.7	6 56.3	10 40.7	26 54.6	18 41.0	5 6.5	11 2.6	17 56.8
29	2 29 48.1	3 23.9	1 3.0	25 17.9	28 .1	8 14.2	11 21.8	26 47.5	18 44.3	5 10.2	11 4.6	17 58.8
30	2 33 44.6	4 22.1	0 60.0	8♒40.7	29 33.6	9 32.5	12 3.1	26 40.3	18 47.5	5 13.8	11 6.6	18 .9
31	2 37 41.2	5 20.5	0 56.9	21 20.7	1♏ 7.0	10 50.9	12 44.4	26 32.9	18 50.6	5 17.5	11 8.6	18 2.9
		DECLINATION										
1	0 39 24.6	3S 9.1	0S13.7	17S42.7	2N41.8	13S29.2	9S18.7	19N15.4	17N13.8	12S59.8	20S42.3	10N35.7
4	0 51 14.3	4 18.8	0 13.7	8 58.8	3 9.7	14 48.8	10 4.3	19 13.5	17 9.4	13 3.3	20 43.0	10 33.0
7	1 3 3.9	5 28.0	0 13.6	2N51.8	2 52.1	16 5.2	10 49.4	19 11.3	17 5.2	13 6.8	20 43.7	10 30.4
10	1 14 53.6	6 36.5	0 13.6	13 22.6	1 55.3	17 18.2	11 33.9	19 8.8	17 1.3	13 10.4	20 44.4	10 27.9
13	1 26 43.2	7 44.3	0 13.5	18 56.8	0 28.6	18 27.3	12 17.8	19 5.9	16 57.5	13 14.0	20 45.1	10 25.5
16	1 38 32.9	8 51.1	0 13.4	17 6.9	1S18.4	19 32.3	13 1.0	19 2.8	16 53.9	13 17.7	20 45.9	10 23.1
19	1 50 22.6	9 56.8	0 13.4	7 37.9	3 17.8	20 32.7	13 43.4	18 59.3	16 50.5	13 21.4	20 46.6	10 20.9
22	2 2 12.2	11 1.2	0 13.3	6S23.6	5 23.3	21 28.2	14 25.1	18 55.5	16 47.4	13 25.0	20 47.4	10 18.7
25	2 14 1.9	12 4.1	0 13.3	17 25.6	7 30.4	22 18.6	15 5.9	18 51.4	16 44.5	13 28.7	20 48.2	10 16.7
28	2 25 51.5	13 5.4	0 13.2	18 8.6	9 36.2	23 3.5	15 45.8	18 47.1	16 41.9	13 32.4	20 49.1	10 14.7
31	2 37 41.2	14 4.7	0 13.2	9 49.0	11 38.3	23 42.7	16 24.6	18 42.5	16 39.6	13 36.1	20 49.9	10 12.9

NOVEMBER 1976

LONGITUDE

DAY	EPHEM. SID. TIME (h m s)	☉ (° ′)	☊ (° ′)	☽ (° ′)	☿ (° ′)	♀ (° ′)	♂ (° ′)	♃ (° ′)	♄ (° ′)	♅ (° ′)	♆ (° ′)	♇ (° ′)
1	2 41 37.7	8♏42.1	3♏ 6.9	3♓10.3	4♏39.9	13♐43.7	15♏54.3	28♉23.9	16♌13.0	7♏33.7	12♐26.7	12♎38.3
2	2 45 34.3	9 42.1	3 3.7	15 29.7	6 19.0	14 56.6	16 36.1	28 R 16.6	16 15.8	7 37.5	12 28.6	12 40.5
3	2 49 30.9	10 42.2	3 .5	27 36.6	7 57.7	16 9.4	17 18.1	28 9.2	16 18.6	7 41.3	12 30.6	12 42.7
4	2 53 27.4	11 42.3	2 57.3	9♈34.4	9 36.0	17 22.2	17 60.0	28 1.7	16 21.3	7 45.1	12 32.6	12 44.8
5	2 57 24.0	12 42.5	2 54.2	21 26.3	11 13.9	18 35.0	18 42.0	27 54.1	16 23.8	7 48.8	12 34.7	12 46.9
6	3 1 20.5	13 42.6	2 51.0	3♉14.8	12 51.3	19 47.7	19 24.0	27 46.4	16 26.3	7 52.6	12 36.7	12 49.0
7	3 5 17.1	14 42.8	2 47.8	15 2.5	14 28.4	21 .4	20 6.1	27 38.6	16 28.6	7 56.3	12 38.7	12 51.0
8	3 9 13.6	15 43.0	2 44.6	26 51.6	16 5.1	22 13.0	20 48.2	27 30.8	16 30.8	8 .0	12 40.8	12 53.1
9	3 13 10.2	16 43.2	2 41.4	8♊44.0	17 41.4	23 25.6	21 30.4	27 22.9	16 33.0	8 3.8	12 42.8	12 55.1
10	3 17 6.7	17 43.5	2 38.3	20 42.0	19 17.3	24 38.2	22 12.6	27 15.0	16 35.0	8 7.5	12 44.9	12 57.2
11	3 21 3.3	18 43.8	2 35.1	2♋47.9	20 52.9	25 50.7	22 54.9	27 7.0	16 36.9	8 11.2	12 47.0	12 59.2
12	3 24 59.9	19 44.2	2 31.9	15 4.3	22 28.2	27 3.2	23 37.2	26 58.9	16 38.7	8 14.9	12 49.1	13 1.1
13	3 28 56.4	20 44.5	2 28.7	27 34.1	24 3.1	28 15.7	24 19.6	26 50.8	16 40.4	8 18.6	12 51.2	13 3.1
14	3 32 53.0	21 44.9	2 25.6	10♌20.3	25 37.8	29 28.1	25 2.1	26 42.7	16 42.0	8 22.3	12 53.4	13 5.0
15	3 36 49.5	22 45.4	2 22.4	23 26.1	27 12.1	0♑40.5	25 44.6	26 34.6	16 43.5	8 26.0	12 55.5	13 7.0
16	3 40 46.1	23 45.8	2 19.2	6♍54.3	28 46.2	1 52.9	26 27.2	26 26.4	16 44.9	8 29.7	12 57.7	13 8.9
17	3 44 42.6	24 46.3	2 16.0	20 46.6	0♐20.1	3 5.2	27 9.8	26 18.2	16 46.1	8 33.3	12 59.8	13 10.8
18	3 48 39.2	25 46.9	2 12.8	5♎ 3.4	1 53.7	4 17.5	27 52.4	26 10.0	16 47.3	8 37.0	13 2.0	13 12.6
19	3 52 35.7	26 47.4	2 9.7	19 42.9	3 27.1	5 29.7	28 35.1	26 1.8	16 48.3	8 40.6	13 4.2	13 14.5
20	3 56 32.3	27 48.0	2 6.5	4♏40.7	5 .3	6 41.9	29 17.9	25 53.6	16 49.3	8 44.2	13 6.4	13 16.3
21	4 0 28.8	28 48.6	2 3.3	19 49.6	6 33.3	7 54.1	0♐ .7	25 45.5	16 50.1	8 47.8	13 8.6	13 18.1
22	4 4 25.4	29 49.2	2 .1	5♐ .7	8 6.2	9 6.2	0 43.6	25 37.3	16 50.8	8 51.4	13 10.8	13 19.8
23	4 8 22.0	0♐49.9	1 57.0	20 4.1	9 38.8	10 18.2	1 26.5	25 29.2	16 51.4	8 55.0	13 13.0	13 21.6
24	4 12 18.5	1 50.6	1 53.8	4♑50.6	11 11.3	11 30.3	2 9.6	25 21.1	16 51.9	8 58.6	13 15.3	13 23.4
25	4 16 15.1	2 51.3	1 50.6	19 13.4	12 43.6	12 42.2	2 52.6	25 13.1	16 52.3	9 2.1	13 17.5	13 25.0
26	4 20 11.6	3 52.1	1 47.4	3♒ 8.5	14 15.7	13 54.1	3 35.7	25 5.1	16 52.5	9 5.6	13 19.7	13 26.7
27	4 24 8.2	4 52.8	1 44.3	16 35.0	15 47.7	15 6.0	4 18.8	24 57.1	16 52.6	9 9.1	13 22.0	13 28.4
28	4 28 4.7	5 53.6	1 41.1	29 34.4	17 19.5	16 17.7	5 2.0	24 49.2	16 52.7	9 12.6	13 24.2	13 30.0
29	4 32 1.3	6 54.3	1 37.9	12♓10.0	18 51.1	17 29.4	5 45.2	24 41.4	16 R 52.6	9 16.0	13 26.5	13 31.6
30	4 35 57.9	7 55.1	1 34.7	24 26.5	20 22.6	18 41.1	6 28.5	24 33.6	16 52.4	9 19.4	13 28.7	13 33.1

LATITUDE

DAY	EPHEM. SID. TIME	☉	☊	☽	☿	♀	♂	♃	♄	♅	♆	♇
1	2 41 37.7	0 .0	0 .0	4N36.8	0N49.4	1S28.2	0S 1.3	1S 9.0	0N42.2	0N26.1	1N27.8	16N30.2
4	2 53 27.4	0 .0	0 .0	2 9.7	0 29.6	1 35.6	0 3.1	1 9.0	0 42.7	0 26.1	1 27.8	16 31.0
7	3 5 17.1	0 .0	0 .0	1S 3.1	0 9.4	1 42.6	0 4.9	1 8.8	0 43.2	0 26.1	1 27.7	16 31.9
10	3 17 6.7	0 .0	0 .0	3 52.5	0S10.8	1 49.2	0 6.7	1 8.6	0 43.7	0 26.1	1 27.6	16 32.9
13	3 28 56.4	0 .0	0 .0	5 14.6	0 30.6	1 55.1	0 8.5	1 8.4	0 44.2	0 26.1	1 27.5	16 33.9
16	3 40 46.1	0 .0	0 .0	4 23.9	0 49.7	2 .5	0 10.3	1 8.1	0 44.7	0 26.1	1 27.4	16 35.0
19	3 52 35.7	0 .0	0 .0	1 15.2	1 7.9	2 5.2	0 12.1	1 7.8	0 45.3	0 26.1	1 27.4	16 36.1
22	4 4 25.4	0 .0	0 .0	2N45.1	1 24.8	2 9.3	0 13.9	1 7.4	0 45.8	0 26.1	1 27.3	16 37.3
25	4 16 15.1	0 .0	0 .0	5 4.3	1 40.2	2 12.6	0 15.7	1 7.0	0 46.3	0 26.1	1 27.3	16 38.6
28	4 28 4.7	0 .0	0 .0	4 40.8	1 53.6	2 15.1	0 17.5	1 6.5	0 46.9	0 26.1	1 27.2	16 39.9

RIGHT ASCENSION

DAY	EPHEM. SID. TIME	☉	☊	☽	☿	♀	♂	♃	♄	♅	♆	♇
1	2 41 37.7	6♏19.1	0♏53.8	3♓26.2	2♏40.6	12♐ 9.5	13♏25.9	26♉25.5	18♌53.6	5♏21.1	11♐10.7	18♎ 5.0
2	2 45 34.3	7 17.9	0 50.8	15 7.2	4 14.2	13 28.4	14 7.6	26 R 17.9	18 56.5	5 24.8	11 12.7	18 7.0
3	2 49 30.9	8 17.0	0 47.7	26 34.1	5 47.9	14 47.4	14 49.4	26 10.3	18 59.3	5 28.5	11 14.9	18 9.1
4	2 53 27.4	9 16.2	0 44.7	7♈56.6	7 21.6	16 6.6	15 31.4	26 2.6	19 2.0	5 32.1	11 17.0	18 11.1
5	2 57 24.0	10 15.6	0 41.6	19 23.2	8 55.5	17 26.0	16 13.4	25 54.7	19 4.6	5 35.8	11 19.1	18 13.1
6	3 1 20.5	11 15.2	0 38.5	1♉ .8	10 29.4	18 45.4	16 55.7	25 46.8	19 7.1	5 39.4	11 21.3	18 15.1
7	3 5 17.1	12 15.0	0 35.5	12 53.9	12 3.6	20 5.1	17 38.0	25 38.8	19 9.4	5 43.1	11 23.4	18 17.0
8	3 9 13.6	13 15.0	0 32.4	25 4.2	13 37.9	21 24.8	18 20.6	25 30.8	19 11.7	5 46.7	11 25.6	18 19.0
9	3 13 10.2	14 15.3	0 29.4	7♊30.7	15 12.4	22 44.6	19 3.2	25 22.6	19 13.9	5 50.4	11 27.8	18 20.9
10	3 17 6.7	15 15.7	0 26.3	20 10.0	16 47.1	24 4.6	19 46.0	25 14.5	19 16.0	5 54.0	11 30.0	18 22.9
11	3 21 3.3	16 16.4	0 23.3	2♋56.9	18 22.0	25 24.5	20 29.0	25 6.2	19 17.9	5 57.6	11 32.2	18 24.8
12	3 24 59.9	17 17.3	0 20.2	15 46.2	19 57.2	26 44.6	21 12.1	24 58.0	19 19.8	6 1.2	11 34.5	18 26.7
13	3 28 56.4	18 18.4	0 17.2	28 34.3	21 32.7	28 4.7	21 55.4	24 49.7	19 21.5	6 4.8	11 36.7	18 28.6
14	3 32 53.0	19 19.7	0 14.1	11♌20.4	23 8.4	29 24.8	22 38.8	24 41.3	19 23.2	6 8.4	11 39.0	18 30.5
15	3 36 49.5	20 21.2	0 11.0	24 7.0	24 44.4	0♑44.8	23 22.3	24 32.9	19 24.7	6 12.0	11 41.2	18 32.4
16	3 40 46.1	21 23.0	0 8.0	6♍59.9	26 20.8	2 4.9	24 6.1	24 24.6	19 26.1	6 15.6	11 43.5	18 34.2
17	3 44 42.6	22 24.9	0 4.9	20 7.2	27 57.5	3 25.0	24 49.9	24 16.2	19 27.4	6 19.2	11 45.8	18 36.0
18	3 48 39.2	23 27.1	0 1.9	3♎38.6	29 34.5	4 45.0	25 33.9	24 7.7	19 28.6	6 22.7	11 48.1	18 37.9
19	3 52 35.7	24 29.5	29♎58.8	17 43.2	1♐11.8	6 4.9	26 18.1	23 59.3	19 29.7	6 26.3	11 50.4	18 39.7
20	3 56 32.3	25 32.1	29 55.8	2♏26.7	2 49.5	7 24.8	27 2.4	23 50.9	19 30.7	6 29.8	11 52.8	18 41.4
21	4 0 28.8	26 34.9	29 52.7	17 47.8	4 27.5	8 44.5	27 46.9	23 42.5	19 31.6	6 33.3	11 55.1	18 43.2
22	4 4 25.4	27 37.9	29 49.7	3♐35.6	6 5.8	10 4.1	28 31.5	23 34.2	19 32.3	6 36.8	11 57.4	18 45.0
23	4 8 22.0	28 41.1	29 46.6	19 29.7	7 44.4	11 23.6	29 16.2	23 25.8	19 33.0	6 40.3	11 59.8	18 46.7
24	4 12 18.5	29 44.6	29 43.6	5♑ 6.0	9 23.4	12 43.0	0♐ 1.2	23 17.6	19 33.5	6 43.8	12 2.2	18 48.4
25	4 16 15.1	0♐48.2	29 40.5	20 3.7	11 2.7	14 2.2	0 46.2	23 9.3	19 34.0	6 47.3	12 4.6	18 50.1
26	4 20 11.6	1 51.9	29 37.5	4♒11.8	12 42.1	15 21.1	1 31.4	23 1.1	19 34.3	6 50.7	12 6.9	18 51.8
27	4 24 8.2	2 55.9	29 34.4	17 29.1	14 21.9	16 39.8	2 16.7	22 52.9	19 34.5	6 54.1	12 9.3	18 53.5
28	4 28 4.7	4 .0	29 31.4	0♓ 1.8	16 1.8	17 58.3	3 2.2	22 44.8	19 34.5	6 57.5	12 11.7	18 55.1
29	4 32 1.3	5 4.3	29 28.3	12 .3	17 41.8	19 16.6	3 47.8	22 36.8	19 34.5	7 .9	12 14.1	18 56.7
30	4 35 57.9	6 8.8	29 25.3	23 36.2	19 22.0	20 34.6	4 33.5	22 28.8	19 R 34.4	7 4.2	12 16.5	18 58.3

DECLINATION

DAY	EPHEM. SID. TIME	☉	☊	☽	☿	♀	♂	♃	♄	♅	♆	♇
1	2 41 37.7	14S24.1	0S13.1	6S 2.2	12S18.0	23S54.5	16S37.3	18N40.9	16N38.8	13S37.3	20S50.2	10N12.3
4	2 53 27.4	15 20.8	0 13.1	5N46.8	14 13.2	24 25.6	17 14.7	18 36.1	16 36.8	13 41.0	20 51.0	10 10.6
7	3 5 17.1	16 15.1	0 13.0	15 20.6	16 1.9	24 50.5	17 50.9	18 31.1	16 35.1	13 44.7	20 51.9	10 9.1
10	3 17 6.7	17 7.1	0 13.0	19 14.9	17 43.3	25 8.9	18 25.8	18 25.9	16 33.7	13 48.3	20 52.8	10 7.6
13	3 28 56.4	17 56.4	0 12.9	15 30.2	19 16.8	25 20.8	18 59.5	18 20.6	16 32.5	13 51.9	20 53.6	10 6.3
16	3 40 46.1	18 42.9	0 12.9	4 53.3	20 41.7	25 26.1	19 31.7	18 15.2	16 31.7	13 55.4	20 54.5	10 5.2
19	3 52 35.7	19 26.4	0 12.8	8S52.3	21 57.4	25 24.7	20 2.5	18 9.8	16 31.1	13 59.0	20 55.4	10 4.1
22	4 4 25.4	20 6.8	0 12.7	18 25.6	23 3.3	25 16.6	20 31.8	18 4.5	16 30.9	14 2.4	20 56.2	10 3.2
25	4 16 15.1	20 43.8	0 12.7	17 2.3	23 58.8	25 1.9	20 59.5	17 59.1	16 31.0	14 5.8	20 57.1	10 2.4
28	4 28 4.7	21 17.4	0 12.6	7 14.0	24 43.3	24 40.8	21 25.5	17 53.8	16 31.4	14 9.1	20 58.0	10 1.8

DECEMBER 1976

DAY	EPHEM. SID. TIME	LONGITUDE ☉	☊	☽	☿	♀	♂	♃	♄	♅	♆	♇
	h m s	° ′	° ′	° ′	° ′	° ′	° ′	° ′	° ′	° ′	° ′	° ′
1	4 39 54.4	8♐55.9	1♏31.5	6♈28.6	21♐53.8	19♑52.6	7♐11.8	24♉25.9	16♌52.1	9♏22.8	13♐31.0	13♎34.7
2	4 43 51.0	9 56.7	1 28.4	18 21.2	23 24.7	21 4.1	7 55.2	24R 18.3	16R 51.6	9 26.2	13 33.2	13 36.2
3	4 47 47.5	10 57.6	1 25.2	0♉ 8.8	24 55.4	22 15.5	8 38.6	24 10.8	16 51.1	9 29.6	13 35.5	13 37.7
4	4 51 44.1	11 58.4	1 22.0	11 55.5	26 25.9	23 26.9	9 22.1	24 3.3	16 50.5	9 32.9	13 37.8	13 39.1
5	4 55 40.6	12 59.3	1 18.8	23 44.5	27 55.9	24 38.1	10 5.6	23 56.0	16 49.7	9 36.2	13 40.0	13 40.6
6	4 59 37.2	14 .2	1 15.7	5♊38.5	29 25.5	25 49.3	10 49.2	23 48.8	16 48.8	9 39.5	13 42.3	13 42.0
7	5 3 33.8	15 1.1	1 12.5	17 39.5	0♑54.7	27 .4	11 32.8	23 41.6	16 47.8	9 42.7	13 44.5	13 43.3
8	5 7 30.3	16 2.0	1 9.3	29 48.9	2 23.3	28 11.4	12 16.5	23 34.6	16 46.8	9 46.0	13 46.8	13 44.7
9	5 11 26.9	17 2.9	1 6.1	12♋ 8.0	3 51.2	29 22.3	13 .2	23 27.7	16 45.6	9 49.2	13 49.1	13 46.0
10	5 15 23.4	18 3.9	1 3.0	24 37.6	5 18.4	0♒33.1	13 43.9	23 21.0	16 44.2	9 52.3	13 51.3	13 47.3
11	5 19 20.0	19 4.8	0 59.8	7♌18.7	6 44.6	1 43.8	14 27.8	23 14.3	16 42.8	9 55.5	13 53.6	13 48.5
12	5 23 16.5	20 5.8	0 56.6	20 12.6	8 9.7	2 54.5	15 11.6	23 7.8	16 41.3	9 58.6	13 55.8	13 49.7
13	5 27 13.1	21 6.8	0 53.4	3♍20.8	9 33.6	4 5.0	15 55.6	23 1.5	16 39.7	10 1.6	13 58.1	13 50.9
14	5 31 9.7	22 7.9	0 50.2	16 44.9	10 55.9	5 15.4	16 39.5	22 55.2	16 37.9	10 4.7	14 .3	13 52.1
15	5 35 6.2	23 8.9	0 47.1	0♎26.7	12 16.4	6 25.8	17 23.6	22 49.2	16 36.1	10 7.7	14 2.6	13 53.3
16	5 39 2.8	24 10.0	0 43.9	14 27.1	13 34.9	7 36.0	18 7.7	22 43.3	16 34.2	10 10.7	14 4.8	13 54.4
17	5 42 59.3	25 11.1	0 40.7	28 46.3	14 50.8	8 46.1	18 51.8	22 37.5	16 32.1	10 13.7	14 7.1	13 55.4
18	5 46 55.9	26 12.2	0 37.5	13♏22.5	16 3.9	9 56.1	19 36.0	22 31.9	16 30.0	10 16.6	14 9.3	13 56.4
19	5 50 52.4	27 13.3	0 34.4	28 11.6	17 13.7	11 6.0	20 20.2	22 26.4	16 27.7	10 19.4	14 11.5	13 57.4
20	5 54 49.0	28 14.4	0 31.2	13♐ 7.3	18 19.5	12 15.7	21 4.5	22 21.1	16 25.3	10 22.3	14 13.7	13 58.4
21	5 58 45.6	29 15.5	0 28.0	28 1.2	19 20.9	13 25.4	21 48.8	22 16.0	16 22.9	10 25.1	14 15.9	13 59.3
22	6 2 42.1	0♑16.6	0 24.8	12♑44.5	20 17.0	14 34.9	22 33.2	22 11.1	16 20.3	10 27.8	14 18.1	14 .2
23	6 6 38.7	1 17.8	0 21.7	27 9.3	21 7.3	15 44.2	23 17.6	22 6.3	16 17.6	10 30.6	14 20.3	14 1.1
24	6 10 35.2	2 18.9	0 18.5	11♒ 9.5	21 50.7	16 53.5	24 2.0	22 1.7	16 14.9	10 33.2	14 22.5	14 1.9
25	6 14 31.8	3 20.0	0 15.3	24 42.3	22 26.5	18 2.5	24 46.5	21 57.3	16 12.0	10 35.9	14 24.7	14 2.7
26	6 18 28.3	4 21.2	0 12.1	7♓47.6	22 53.8	19 11.5	25 31.1	21 53.1	16 9.1	10 38.5	14 26.8	14 3.5
27	6 22 24.9	5 22.3	0 8.9	20 27.6	23 11.6	20 20.2	26 15.7	21 49.1	16 6.0	10 41.0	14 29.0	14 4.2
28	6 26 21.5	6 23.5	0 5.8	2♈46.4	23 19.0	21 28.8	27 .3	21 45.2	16 2.9	10 43.6	14 31.1	14 4.9
29	6 30 18.0	7 24.6	0 2.6	14 49.2	23R 15.5	22 37.2	27 45.0	21 41.6	15 59.7	10 46.0	14 33.2	14 5.6
30	6 34 14.6	8 25.8	29♎59.4	26 41.3	23 .3	23 45.5	28 29.7	21 38.1	15 56.4	10 48.5	14 35.3	14 6.2
31	6 38 11.1	9 26.9	29 56.2	8♉28.4	22 33.3	24 53.5	29 14.5	21 34.9	15 53.0	10 50.9	14 37.4	14 6.8

LATITUDE

DAY	SID. TIME	☉	☊	☽	☿	♀	♂	♃	♄	♅	♆	♇
1	4 39 54.4	0 .0	0 .0	2N20.8	2S 4.8	2S16.7	0S19.3	1S 6.0	0N47.4	0N26.1	1N27.2	16N41.3
4	4 51 44.1	0 .0	0 .0	0S47.6	2 13.2	2 17.5	0 21.1	1 5.5	0 47.9	0 26.1	1 27.2	16 42.8
7	5 3 33.8	0 .0	0 .0	3 37.9	2 18.4	2 17.4	0 22.8	1 4.9	0 48.5	0 26.1	1 27.2	16 44.3
10	5 15 23.4	0 .0	0 .0	5 5.3	2 19.5	2 16.3	0 24.6	1 4.2	0 49.0	0 26.1	1 27.2	16 45.8
13	5 27 13.1	0 .0	0 .0	4 24.3	2 15.8	2 14.2	0 26.4	1 3.6	0 49.5	0 26.2	1 27.2	16 47.4
16	5 39 2.8	0 .0	0 .0	1 34.4	2 6.1	2 11.1	0 28.1	1 2.9	0 50.1	0 26.2	1 27.2	16 49.0
19	5 50 52.4	0 .0	0 .0	2N14.7	1 49.1	2 6.9	0 29.8	1 2.1	0 50.6	0 26.2	1 27.2	16 50.6
22	6 2 42.1	0 .0	0 .0	4 48.3	1 23.4	2 1.7	0 31.6	1 1.4	0 51.1	0 26.2	1 27.2	16 52.3
25	6 14 31.8	0 .0	0 .0	4 40.2	0 47.5	1 55.4	0 33.3	1 .6	0 51.6	0 26.3	1 27.2	16 54.0
28	6 26 21.5	0 .0	0 .0	2 25.8	0 .9	1 48.0	0 35.0	0 59.8	0 52.1	0 26.3	1 27.3	16 55.7
31	6 38 11.1	0 .0	0 .0	0S38.7	0N54.4	1 39.4	0 36.7	0 59.0	0 52.6	0 26.3	1 27.3	16 57.5

RIGHT ASCENSION

DAY	SID. TIME	☉	☊	☽	☿	♀	♂	♃	♄	♅	♆	♇
1	4 39 54.4	7♐13.4	29♎22.2	5♈ .9	21♐ 2.3	21♑52.3	5♐19.4	22♉21.0	19♌34.1	7♏ 7.6	12♐18.9	18♎59.8
2	4 43 51.0	8 18.2	29 19.2	16 24.9	22 42.5	23 9.7	6 5.4	22R 13.2	19R 33.7	7 10.9	12 21.3	19 1.4
3	4 47 47.5	9 23.1	29 16.2	27 57.1	24 22.7	24 26.9	6 51.6	22 5.4	19 33.3	7 14.2	12 23.7	19 2.9
4	4 51 44.1	10 28.2	29 13.1	9♉44.2	26 2.7	25 43.6	7 37.8	21 57.8	19 32.7	7 17.4	12 26.1	19 4.4
5	4 55 40.6	11 33.5	29 10.1	21 50.1	27 42.4	27 .1	8 24.2	21 50.3	19 32.0	7 20.7	12 28.5	19 5.9
6	4 59 37.2	12 38.8	29 7.0	4♊15.1	29 21.8	28 16.2	9 10.8	21 42.9	19 31.2	7 23.9	12 30.9	19 7.3
7	5 3 33.8	13 44.3	29 4.0	16 56.5	1♑ .7	29 32.0	9 57.4	21 35.6	19 30.3	7 27.1	12 33.3	19 8.7
8	5 7 30.3	14 50.0	29 .9	29 48.3	2 39.0	0♒47.4	10 44.2	21 28.4	19 29.2	7 30.2	12 35.7	19 10.1
9	5 11 26.9	15 55.7	28 57.9	12♋43.7	4 16.5	2 2.4	11 31.1	21 21.4	19 28.1	7 33.3	12 38.1	19 11.5
10	5 15 23.4	17 1.6	28 54.8	25 36.4	5 53.0	3 17.0	12 18.2	21 14.5	19 26.8	7 36.5	12 40.5	19 12.9
11	5 19 20.0	18 7.5	28 51.8	8♌22.8	7 28.4	4 31.3	13 5.3	21 7.7	19 25.5	7 39.5	12 42.9	19 14.2
12	5 23 16.5	19 13.6	28 48.8	21 2.8	9 2.5	5 45.1	13 52.6	21 1.0	19 24.0	7 42.6	12 45.3	19 15.5
13	5 27 13.1	20 19.7	28 45.7	3♍40.4	10 34.9	6 58.5	14 40.0	20 54.5	19 22.5	7 45.6	12 47.7	19 16.8
14	5 31 9.7	21 26.0	28 42.7	16 22.8	12 5.3	8 11.5	15 27.5	20 48.1	19 20.8	7 48.6	12 50.1	19 18.0
15	5 35 6.2	22 32.4	28 39.6	29 19.7	13 33.6	9 24.2	16 15.2	20 41.9	19 19.0	7 51.6	12 52.5	19 19.3
16	5 39 2.8	23 38.8	28 36.6	12♎41.4	14 59.2	10 36.3	17 3.0	20 35.8	19 17.2	7 54.5	12 54.9	19 20.5
17	5 42 59.3	24 45.2	28 33.6	26 37.6	16 21.7	11 48.1	17 50.8	20 29.9	19 15.2	7 57.4	12 57.2	19 21.6
18	5 46 55.9	25 51.7	28 30.5	11♏13.8	17 40.7	12 59.4	18 38.7	20 24.2	19 13.1	8 .2	12 59.6	19 22.8
19	5 50 52.4	26 58.3	28 27.5	26 28.1	18 55.7	14 10.2	19 26.8	20 18.6	19 10.9	8 3.0	13 2.0	19 23.9
20	5 54 49.0	28 4.9	28 24.4	12♐ 8.6	20 6.0	15 20.6	20 15.0	20 13.1	19 8.6	8 5.8	13 4.3	19 25.0
21	5 58 45.6	29 11.5	28 21.4	27 54.5	21 11.0	16 30.6	21 3.2	20 7.9	19 6.2	8 8.6	13 6.7	19 26.0
22	6 2 42.1	0♑18.1	28 18.4	13♑21.9	22 10.0	17 40.1	21 51.5	20 2.8	19 3.7	8 11.3	13 9.0	19 27.1
23	6 6 38.7	1 24.7	28 15.3	28 11.3	23 2.1	18 49.2	22 40.0	19 57.9	19 1.1	8 14.0	13 11.3	19 28.1
24	6 10 35.2	2 31.4	28 12.3	12♒12.5	23 46.6	19 57.8	23 28.5	19 53.2	18 58.4	8 16.6	13 13.7	19 29.0
25	6 14 31.8	3 38.0	28 9.2	25 25.3	24 22.6	21 6.0	24 17.1	19 48.7	18 55.6	8 19.2	13 16.0	19 30.0
26	6 18 28.3	4 44.6	28 6.2	7♓56.3	24 49.0	22 13.6	25 5.7	19 44.3	18 52.7	8 21.8	13 18.3	19 30.9
27	6 22 24.9	5 51.1	28 3.2	19 55.5	25 5.1	23 20.9	25 54.5	19 40.2	18 49.7	8 24.3	13 20.6	19 31.7
28	6 26 21.5	6 57.7	28 .1	1♈34.7	25 10.0	24 27.6	26 43.3	19 36.2	18 46.7	8 26.8	13 22.8	19 32.6
29	6 30 18.0	8 4.1	27 57.1	13 5.0	25R 3.0	25 33.9	27 32.2	19 32.5	18 43.5	8 29.2	13 25.1	19 33.4
30	6 34 14.6	9 10.5	27 54.1	24 36.8	24 43.7	26 39.7	28 21.1	19 28.9	18 40.3	8 31.6	13 27.4	19 34.2
31	6 38 11.1	10 16.9	27 51.0	6♉18.6	24 11.8	27 45.1	29 10.1	19 25.5	18 37.0	8 33.9	13 29.6	19 34.9

DECLINATION

DAY	SID. TIME	☉	☊	☽	☿	♀	♂	♃	♄	♅	♆	♇
1	4 39 54.4	21S47.4	0S12.6	4N43.6	25S16.1	24S13.3	21S49.7	17N48.7	16N32.0	14S12.4	20S58.8	10N 1.3
4	4 51 44.1	22 13.6	0 12.5	14 39.5	25 36.7	23 39.7	22 12.2	17 43.7	16 33.0	14 15.6	20 59.6	10 .9
7	5 3 33.8	22 35.9	0 12.5	19 15.0	25 44.6	23 .2	22 32.7	17 39.0	16 34.3	14 18.7	21 .5	10 .7
10	5 15 23.4	22 54.2	0 12.4	16 11.4	25 39.4	22 15.0	22 51.4	17 34.5	16 35.9	14 21.7	21 1.3	10 .7
13	5 27 13.1	23 8.5	0 12.3	6 10.1	25 21.1	21 24.5	23 8.0	17 30.2	16 37.8	14 24.6	21 2.1	10 .7
16	5 39 2.8	23 18.7	0 12.3	7S 8.9	24 50.2	20 28.9	23 22.6	17 26.3	16 40.0	14 27.4	21 2.9	10 .9
19	5 50 52.4	23 24.6	0 12.2	17 34.1	24 8.0	19 28.6	23 35.0	17 22.8	16 42.5	14 30.1	21 3.6	10 1.3
22	3 2 42.1	23 26.4	0 12.2	18 2.8	23 16.9	18 23.9	23 45.3	17 19.6	16 45.2	14 32.7	21 4.4	10 1.8
25	6 14 31.8	23 23.9	0 12.1	8 52.8	22 21.2	17 15.2	23 53.5	17 16.8	16 48.1	14 35.2	21 5.1	10 2.4
28	6 26 21.5	23 17.1	0 12.0	3N19.9	21 26.5	16 2.8	23 59.3	17 14.5	16 51.3	14 37.6	21 5.8	10 3.2
31	6 38 11.1	23 6.2	0 12.0	13 43.1	20 39.5	14 47.1	24 2.9	17 12.6	16 54.8	14 39.8	21 6.5	10 4.1

JANUARY 1977

LONGITUDE

DAY	EPHEM. SID. TIME	☉	☊	☾	☿	♀	♂	♃	♄	♅	♆	♇
	h m s	° ′	° ′	° ′	° ′	° ′	° ′	° ′	° ′	° ′	° ′	° ′
1	6 42 7.7	10♑28.1	29♎53.1	20♉15.6	21♑54.5	26♒ 1.4	29♐59.3	21♉31.8	15♌49.5	10♏53.2	14♐39.5	14♎ 7.3
2	6 46 4.2	11 29.2	29 49.9	2♊ 7.3	21 R 4.5	27 9.1	0♑44.1	21 R 29.0	15 R 46.0	10 55.5	14 41.6	14 7.8
3	6 50 .8	12 30.3	29 46.7	14 7.1	20 4.4	28 16.6	1 29.0	21 26.3	15 42.4	10 57.8	14 43.7	14 8.3
4	6 53 57.4	13 31.5	29 43.5	26 17.8	18 55.7	29 23.8	2 13.9	21 23.9	15 38.7	11 .0	14 45.7	14 8.8
5	6 57 53.9	14 32.7	29 40.4	8♋41.0	17 40.5	0♓30.9	2 58.9	21 21.6	15 34.9	11 2.2	14 47.8	14 9.2
6	7 1 50.5	15 33.8	29 37.2	21 17.3	16 21.2	1 37.7	3 44.0	21 19.6	15 31.1	11 4.3	14 49.8	14 9.6
7	7 5 47.0	16 34.9	29 34.0	4♌ 6.4	15 .4	2 44.3	4 29.0	21 17.7	15 27.2	11 6.4	14 51.8	14 9.9
8	7 9 43.6	17 36.0	29 30.8	17 7.6	13 40.7	3 50.7	5 14.1	21 16.1	15 23.2	11 8.5	14 53.8	14 10.2
9	7 13 40.1	18 37.2	29 27.7	0♍20.0	12 24.5	4 56.8	5 59.3	21 14.7	15 19.1	11 10.4	14 55.7	14 10.5
10	7 17 36.7	19 38.3	29 24.5	13 42.9	11 14.0	6 2.7	6 44.5	21 13.4	15 15.0	11 12.4	14 57.7	14 10.7
11	7 21 33.2	20 39.4	29 21.3	27 15.9	10 10.9	7 8.3	7 29.7	21 12.4	15 10.8	11 14.3	14 59.6	14 10.9
12	7 25 29.8	21 40.5	29 18.1	10♎59.2	9 16.3	8 13.6	8 15.0	21 11.6	15 6.6	11 16.1	15 1.5	14 11.1
13	7 29 26.4	22 41.7	29 14.9	24 53.2	8 31.1	9 18.7	9 .3	21 11.0	15 2.3	11 17.9	15 3.4	14 11.2
14	7 33 22.9	23 42.8	29 11.8	8♏58.2	7 55.6	10 23.5	9 45.7	21 10.6	14 57.9	11 19.6	15 5.3	14 11.3
15	7 37 19.5	24 43.9	29 8.6	23 13.6	7 29.8	11 28.0	10 31.1	21 10.4	14 53.5	11 21.3	15 7.1	14 11.4
16	7 41 16.0	25 45.0	29 5.4	7♐37.8	7 13.5	12 32.2	11 16.5	21 10.4	14 49.0	11 23.0	15 9.0	14 11.4
17	7 45 12.6	26 46.2	29 2.2	22 7.1	7 6.3	13 36.1	12 2.0	21 D 10.6	14 44.5	11 24.5	15 10.8	14 11.4
18	7 49 9.1	27 47.3	28 59.1	6♑36.5	7 D 7.7	14 39.7	12 47.5	21 11.0	14 39.9	11 26.1	15 12.6	14 R 11.3
19	7 53 5.7	28 48.4	28 55.9	20 59.4	7 17.1	15 42.9	13 33.1	21 11.7	14 35.3	11 27.6	15 14.3	14 11.2
20	7 57 2.3	29 49.5	28 52.7	5♒ 9.3	7 33.8	16 45.8	14 18.7	21 12.5	14 30.7	11 29.0	15 16.1	14 11.1
21	8 0 58.8	0♒50.5	28 49.5	19 .6	7 57.2	17 48.4	15 4.3	21 13.6	14 26.0	11 30.4	15 17.8	14 10.9
22	8 4 55.4	1 51.6	28 46.4	2♓29.4	8 26.8	18 50.6	15 50.0	21 14.8	14 21.3	11 31.7	15 19.5	14 10.7
23	8 8 51.9	2 52.7	28 43.2	15 34.1	9 2.0	19 52.4	16 35.7	21 16.3	14 16.6	11 33.0	15 21.2	14 10.5
24	8 12 48.5	3 53.7	28 40.0	28 15.7	9 42.2	20 53.8	17 21.4	21 17.9	14 11.8	11 34.2	15 22.8	14 10.2
25	8 16 45.0	4 54.7	28 36.8	10♈36.9	10 26.9	21 54.8	18 7.2	21 19.8	14 7.0	11 35.4	15 24.5	14 9.9
26	8 20 41.6	5 55.8	28 33.6	22 41.9	11 15.9	22 55.5	18 53.0	21 21.9	14 2.2	11 36.5	15 26.1	14 9.7
27	8 24 38.1	6 56.8	28 30.5	4♉35.8	12 8.5	23 55.6	19 38.9	21 24.2	13 57.4	11 37.6	15 27.7	14 9.3
28	8 28 34.7	7 57.7	28 27.3	16 24.1	13 4.6	24 55.3	20 24.7	21 26.7	13 52.5	11 38.6	15 29.2	14 8.9
29	8 32 31.3	8 58.7	28 24.1	28 12.5	14 3.7	25 54.5	21 10.6	21 29.3	13 47.6	11 39.5	15 30.8	14 8.4
30	8 36 27.8	9 59.6	28 20.9	10♊ 6.3	15 5.6	26 53.2	21 56.5	21 32.2	13 42.7	11 40.4	15 32.3	14 8.0
31	8 40 24.4	11 .5	28 17.8	22 10.2	16 10.1	27 51.4	22 42.5	21 35.3	13 37.8	11 41.3	15 33.7	14 7.5

LATITUDE

DAY	EPHEM. SID. TIME	☉	☊	☾	☿	♀	♂	♃	♄	♅	♆	♇
1	6 42 7.7	0 .0	0 .0	1 S 39.7	1 N 13.9	1 S 36.3	0 S 37.2	0 S 58.7	0 N 52.8	0 N 26.3	1 N 27.3	16 N 58.0
4	6 53 57.4	0 .0	0 .0	4 8.9	2 10.4	1 26.3	0 38.9	0 57.9	0 53.3	0 26.4	1 27.4	16 59.8
7	7 5 47.0	0 .0	0 .0	5 .1	2 54.7	1 15.0	0 40.5	0 57.1	0 53.7	0 26.4	1 27.4	17 1.6
10	7 17 36.7	0 .0	0 .0	3 37.3	3 18.2	1 2.7	0 42.2	0 56.3	0 54.2	0 26.5	1 27.5	17 3.3
13	7 29 26.4	0 .0	0 .0	0 24.7	3 20.1	0 49.2	0 43.8	0 55.4	0 54.6	0 26.5	1 27.6	17 5.1
16	7 41 16.0	0 .0	0 .0	3 N 6.7	3 5.8	0 34.5	0 45.4	0 54.6	0 55.0	0 26.5	1 27.6	17 6.8
19	7 53 5.7	0 .0	0 .0	4 57.4	2 41.6	0 18.7	0 46.9	0 53.8	0 55.4	0 26.6	1 27.7	17 8.6
22	8 4 55.4	0 .0	0 .0	4 9.5	2 12.5	0 1.8	0 48.4	0 52.9	0 55.8	0 26.7	1 27.8	17 10.3
25	8 16 45.0	0 .0	0 .0	1 31.2	1 41.5	0 N 16.2	0 50.0	0 52.1	0 56.2	0 26.7	1 27.9	17 12.0
28	8 28 34.7	0 .0	0 .0	1 S 35.6	1 10.5	0 35.3	0 51.4	0 51.3	0 56.5	0 26.8	1 28.0	17 13.7
31	8 40 24.4	0 .0	0 .0	4 5.6	0 40.6	0 55.5	0 52.9	0 50.5	0 56.9	0 26.8	1 28.1	17 15.3

RIGHT ASCENSION

DAY	EPHEM. SID. TIME	☉	☊	☾	☿	♀	♂	♃	♄	♅	♆	♇
1	6 42 7.7	11♑23.1	27♎48.0	18♉16.8	23♑27.6	28♒49.9	29♐59.2	19♉22.4	18♌33.5	8♏36.3	13♐31.8	19♎35.7
2	6 46 4.2	12 29.3	27 45.0	0♊34.7	22 R 31.7	29 54.3	0♑48.3	19 R 19.4	18 R 30.1	8 38.5	13 34.0	19 36.4
3	6 50 .8	13 35.4	27 41.9	13 12.1	21 25.4	0♓58.3	1 37.5	19 16.7	18 26.5	8 40.8	13 36.2	19 37.0
4	6 53 57.4	14 41.4	27 38.9	26 5.3	20 10.3	2 1.7	2 26.7	19 14.1	18 22.8	8 42.9	13 38.4	19 37.7
5	6 57 53.9	15 47.4	27 35.9	9♋ 7.8	18 48.8	3 4.8	3 16.0	19 11.8	18 19.2	8 45.1	13 40.6	19 38.3
6	7 1 50.5	16 53.2	27 32.8	22 12.4	17 23.3	4 7.3	4 5.3	19 9.7	18 15.4	8 47.2	13 42.8	19 38.9
7	7 5 47.0	17 58.9	27 29.8	5♌12.8	15 56.5	5 9.4	4 54.6	19 7.7	18 11.5	8 49.3	13 44.9	19 39.4
8	7 9 43.6	19 4.4	27 26.8	18 5.9	14 31.3	6 11.0	5 44.0	19 6.0	18 7.6	8 51.3	13 47.0	19 39.9
9	7 13 40.1	20 9.9	27 23.7	0♍52.2	13 10.1	7 12.1	6 33.4	19 4.5	18 3.5	8 53.2	13 49.1	19 40.4
10	7 17 36.7	21 15.2	27 20.7	13 36.2	11 55.2	8 12.8	7 22.8	19 3.1	17 59.5	8 55.1	13 51.2	19 40.8
11	7 21 33.2	22 20.3	27 17.7	26 25.1	10 48.2	9 13.0	8 12.3	19 2.0	17 55.3	8 57.0	13 53.2	19 41.2
12	7 25 29.8	23 25.4	27 14.7	9♎27.9	9 50.4	10 12.8	9 1.7	19 1.1	17 51.1	8 58.8	13 55.3	19 41.6
13	7 29 26.4	24 30.2	27 11.6	22 54.1	9 2.7	11 12.1	9 51.2	19 .4	17 46.9	9 .6	13 57.3	19 42.0
14	7 33 22.9	25 35.0	27 8.6	6♏51.2	8 25.2	12 10.9	10 40.7	18 59.9	17 42.6	9 2.3	13 59.3	19 42.3
15	7 37 19.5	26 39.6	27 5.6	21 22.0	7 58.2	13 9.3	11 30.2	18 59.7	17 38.2	9 3.9	14 1.2	19 42.6
16	7 41 16.0	27 44.0	27 2.5	6♐22.4	7 41.3	14 7.3	12 19.8	18 59.6	17 33.8	9 5.6	14 3.2	19 42.8
17	7 45 12.6	28 48.2	26 59.5	21 40.3	7 34.0	15 4.8	13 9.3	18 D 59.7	17 29.3	9 7.1	14 5.1	19 43.0
18	7 49 9.1	29 52.3	26 56.5	6♑57.2	7 D 36.0	16 1.8	13 58.8	19 .1	17 24.8	9 8.6	14 7.0	19 43.2
19	7 53 5.7	0♒56.2	26 53.5	21 54.0	7 46.4	16 58.4	14 48.3	19 .7	17 20.2	9 10.1	14 8.9	19 43.4
20	7 57 2.3	1 59.9	26 50.4	6♒16.2	8 4.8	17 54.5	15 37.8	19 1.4	17 15.6	9 11.5	14 10.8	19 43.5
21	8 0 58.8	3 3.4	26 47.4	19 57.1	8 30.4	18 50.1	16 27.3	19 2.4	17 10.9	9 12.9	14 12.6	19 43.6
22	8 4 55.4	4 6.8	26 44.4	2♓57.5	9 2.6	19 45.3	17 16.8	19 3.6	17 6.2	9 14.2	14 14.4	19 43.6
23	8 8 51.9	5 9.9	26 41.4	15 23.6	9 40.9	20 40.0	18 6.2	19 5.0	17 1.5	9 15.5	14 16.2	19 43.6
24	8 12 48.5	6 12.9	26 38.3	27 24.3	10 24.7	21 34.2	18 55.6	19 6.6	16 56.8	9 16.7	14 18.0	19 43.6
25	8 16 45.0	7 15.6	26 35.3	9♈ 9.5	11 13.4	22 28.0	19 45.0	19 8.4	16 52.0	9 17.8	14 19.7	19 43.6
26	8 20 41.6	8 18.2	26 32.3	20 49.0	12 6.7	23 21.3	20 34.4	19 10.5	16 47.2	9 19.0	14 21.5	19 43.6
27	8 24 38.1	9 20.5	26 29.3	2♉31.5	13 4.0	24 14.0	21 23.7	19 12.7	16 42.4	9 20.0	14 23.2	19 R 43.4
28	8 28 34.7	10 22.7	26 26.2	14 24.5	14 5.0	25 6.3	22 13.0	19 15.1	16 37.6	9 21.0	14 24.9	19 43.3
29	8 32 31.3	11 24.6	26 23.2	26 33.1	15 9.4	25 58.0	23 2.2	19 17.8	16 32.7	9 21.9	14 26.5	19 43.1
30	8 36 27.8	12 26.3	26 20.2	8♊59.7	16 16.8	26 49.2	23 51.4	19 20.6	16 27.8	9 22.8	14 28.1	19 42.9
31	8 40 24.4	13 27.8	26 17.2	21 43.8	17 26.9	27 39.9	24 40.6	19 23.6	16 22.9	9 23.7	14 29.7	19 42.7

DECLINATION

DAY	EPHEM. SID. TIME	☉	☊	☾	☿	♀	♂	♃	♄	♅	♆	♇
1	6 42 7.7	23 S 1.6	0 S 12.0	16 N 12.5	20 S 26.5	14 S 21.3	24 S 3.6	17 N 12.0	16 N 56.0	14 S 40.5	21 S 6.7	10 N 4.4
4	6 53 57.4	22 45.2	0 11.9	19 14.5	19 57.0	13 1.8	24 4.2	17 10.8	16 59.7	14 42.6	21 7.3	10 5.5
7	7 5 47.0	22 24.7	0 11.9	14 21.9	19 42.1	11 39.9	24 2.4	17 10.0	17 3.5	14 44.5	21 8.0	10 6.7
10	7 17 36.7	22 .2	0 11.8	3 3.6	19 40.4	10 15.9	23 58.2	17 9.7	17 7.5	14 46.3	21 8.6	10 8.0
13	7 29 26.4	21 31.8	0 11.7	10 S 1.2	19 50.2	8 50.3	23 51.7	17 9.8	17 11.7	14 48.0	21 9.1	10 9.4
16	7 41 16.0	20 59.7	0 11.7	18 30.8	20 9.0	7 23.2	23 42.9	17 10.5	17 16.0	14 49.5	21 9.7	10 11.0
19	7 53 5.7	20 24.0	0 11.6	16 54.1	20 33.0	5 55.2	23 31.7	17 11.6	17 20.4	14 50.9	21 10.2	10 12.7
22	8 4 55.4	19 44.8	0 11.6	6 42.2	20 58.0	4 26.5	23 18.2	17 13.3	17 24.9	14 52.1	21 10.6	10 14.4
25	8 16 45.0	19 2.3	0 11.5	5 N 36.1	21 20.5	2 57.6	23 2.3	17 15.3	17 29.4	14 53.2	21 11.1	10 16.3
28	8 28 34.7	18 16.7	0 11.4	15 12.9	21 37.7	1 28.7	22 44.2	17 17.9	17 33.9	14 54.2	21 11.5	10 18.2
31	8 40 24.4	17 28.1	0 11.4	19 7.3	21 47.4	0 .2	22 23.8	17 20.9	17 38.5	14 54.9	21 11.9	10 20.3

FEBRUARY 1977

LONGITUDE

DAY	EPHEM. SID. TIME h m s	☉ ° ′	☊ ° ′	☽ ° ′	☿ ° ′	♀ ° ′	♂ ° ′	♃ ° ′	♄ ° ′	♅ ° ′	♆ ° ′	♇ ° ′
1	8 44 20.9	12♒ 1.4	28♎14.6	4♋27.8	17♑16.9	28♓49.0	23♑28.5	21♉38.5	13♌32.9	11♏42.0	15♐35.2	14♎ 6.9
2	8 48 17.5	13 2.3	28 11.4	17 1.8	18 25.8	29 46.2	24 14.5	21 41.9	13 R 28.0	11 42.8	15 36.6	14 R 6.4
3	8 52 14.0	14 3.1	28 8.2	29 53.4	19 36.8	0♈42.7	25 .6	21 45.6	13 23.1	11 43.4	15 38.0	14 5.8
4	8 56 10.6	15 3.9	28 5.0	13♌ 2.2	20 49.5	1 38.7	25 46.7	21 49.4	13 18.2	11 44.1	15 39.4	14 5.1
5	9 0 7.1	16 4.7	28 1.9	26 26.6	22 4.0	2 34.0	26 32.8	21 53.4	13 13.3	11 44.6	15 40.7	14 4.5
6	9 4 3.7	17 5.5	27 58.7	10♍ 4.1	23 20.0	3 28.7	27 18.9	21 57.6	13 8.4	11 45.1	15 42.0	14 3.8
7	9 8 .2	18 6.3	27 55.5	23 51.6	24 37.5	4 22.8	28 5.1	22 2.0	13 3.5	11 45.6	15 43.3	14 3.0
8	9 11 56.8	19 7.0	27 52.3	7♎46.3	25 56.4	5 16.2	28 51.3	22 6.5	12 58.7	11 46.0	15 44.6	14 2.3
9	9 15 53.4	20 7.8	27 49.2	21 45.9	27 16.6	6 8.8	29 37.5	22 11.3	12 53.8	11 46.3	15 45.8	14 1.5
10	9 19 49.9	21 8.5	27 46.0	5♏48.7	28 38.1	7 .8	0♒23.8	22 16.2	12 49.0	11 46.6	15 47.0	14 .7
11	9 23 46.5	22 9.2	27 42.8	19 53.6	0♒ .8	7 52.0	1 10.1	22 21.3	12 44.2	11 46.8	15 48.2	13 59.8
12	9 27 43.0	23 9.9	27 39.6	4♐ .0	1 24.6	8 42.4	1 56.4	22 26.6	12 39.4	11 47.0	15 49.3	13 59.0
13	9 31 39.6	24 10.5	27 36.4	18 6.7	2 49.5	9 32.0	2 42.7	22 32.0	12 34.6	11 47.1	15 50.4	13 58.0
14	9 35 36.1	25 11.2	27 33.3	2♑12.2	4 15.5	10 20.8	3 29.1	22 37.6	12 29.9	11 47.2	15 51.5	13 57.1
15	9 39 32.7	26 11.8	27 30.1	16 13.8	5 42.5	11 8.7	4 15.5	22 43.4	12 25.2	11 47.2	15 52.5	13 56.1
16	9 43 29.2	27 12.5	27 26.9	0♒ 8.3	7 10.6	11 55.8	5 2.0	22 49.4	12 20.5	11 47.2	15 53.6	13 55.2
17	9 47 25.8	28 13.0	27 23.7	13 52.1	8 39.7	12 41.9	5 48.4	22 55.6	12 15.9	11 R 47.1	15 54.6	13 54.2
18	9 51 22.3	29 13.6	27 20.6	27 21.5	10 9.7	13 27.0	6 34.9	23 1.9	12 11.3	11 47.0	15 55.5	13 53.1
19	9 55 18.9	0♓14.1	27 17.4	10♓33.9	11 40.7	14 11.1	7 21.4	23 8.3	12 6.8	11 46.7	15 56.4	13 52.0
20	9 59 15.4	1 14.6	27 14.2	23 27.3	13 12.7	14 54.1	8 7.9	23 14.9	12 2.2	11 46.5	15 57.3	13 50.9
21	10 3 12.0	2 15.1	27 11.0	6♈ 3.3	14 45.7	15 36.0	8 54.4	23 21.7	11 57.8	11 46.2	15 58.2	13 49.8
22	10 7 8.6	3 15.6	27 7.8	18 21.9	16 19.5	16 16.8	9 41.0	23 28.7	11 53.4	11 45.8	15 59.0	13 48.7
23	10 11 5.1	4 16.0	27 4.7	0♉26.5	17 54.4	16 56.4	10 27.5	23 35.8	11 49.0	11 45.3	15 59.8	13 47.5
24	10 15 1.7	5 16.4	27 1.5	12 21.1	19 30.2	17 34.7	11 14.1	23 43.0	11 44.7	11 44.9	16 .5	13 46.3
25	10 18 58.2	6 16.7	26 58.3	24 10.4	21 7.0	18 11.7	12 .7	23 50.4	11 40.5	11 44.3	16 1.3	13 45.1
26	10 22 54.8	7 17.0	26 55.1	5♊59.5	22 44.8	18 47.4	12 47.3	23 58.0	11 36.3	11 43.7	16 2.0	13 43.8
27	10 26 51.3	8 17.3	26 52.0	17 53.8	24 23.6	19 21.7	13 34.0	24 5.6	11 32.2	11 43.1	16 2.6	13 42.5
28	10 30 47.9	9 17.6	26 48.8	29 58.5	26 3.3	19 54.6	14 20.6	24 13.5	11 28.1	11 42.4	16 3.2	13 41.2

LATITUDE

DAY	SID. TIME	☉	☊	☽	☿	♀	♂	♃	♄	♅	♆	♇
1	8 44 20.9	0 .0	0 .0	4S37.3	0N30.9	1N 2.4	0S53.3	0S50.2	0N57.0	0N26.8	1N28.1	17N15.9
4	8 56 10.6	0 .0	0 .0	4 50.1	0 3.2	1 24.0	0 54.7	0 49.4	0 57.3	0 26.9	1 28.2	17 17.5
7	9 8 .2	0 .0	0 .0	2 44.6	0S22.3	1 46.6	0 56.1	0 48.6	0 57.5	0 26.9	1 28.4	17 19.0
10	9 19 49.9	0 .0	0 .0	0N49.1	0 45.6	2 10.1	0 57.4	0 47.9	0 57.8	0 27.0	1 28.5	17 20.5
13	9 31 39.6	0 .0	0 .0	3 59.2	1 6.4	2 34.5	0 58.7	0 47.1	0 58.0	0 27.0	1 28.6	17 22.0
16	9 43 29.2	0 .0	0 .0	5 3.7	1 24.6	2 59.8	0 59.9	0 46.4	0 58.3	0 27.1	1 28.7	17 23.3
19	9 55 18.9	0 .0	0 .0	3 36.8	1 39.9	3 25.8	1 1.1	0 45.6	0 58.5	0 27.1	1 28.8	17 24.7
22	10 7 8.6	0 .0	0 .0	0 38.1	1 52.3	3 52.5	1 2.3	0 44.9	0 58.6	0 27.2	1 29.0	17 25.9
25	10 18 58.2	0 .0	0 .0	2S28.8	2 1.5	4 19.7	1 3.4	0 44.2	0 58.8	0 27.2	1 29.1	17 27.1
28	10 30 47.9	0 .0	0 .0	4 39.4	2 7.3	4 47.3	1 4.5	0 43.5	0 58.9	0 27.3	1 29.2	17 28.2

RIGHT ASCENSION

DAY	SID. TIME	☉	☊	☽	☿	♀	♂	♃	♄	♅	♆	♇
1	8 44 20.9	14♒29.1	26♎14.1	4♋41.9	18♑39.6	28♓30.1	25♑29.7	19♉26.8	16♌18.0	9♏24.4	14♐31.2	19♎42.4
2	8 48 17.5	15 30.2	26 11.1	17 48.6	19 54.6	29 19.7	26 18.7	19 30.2	16 R 13.1	9 25.2	14 32.7	19 R 42.1
3	8 52 14.0	16 31.1	26 8.1	0♌58.2	21 11.6	0♈ 8.7	27 7.7	19 33.8	16 8.2	9 25.8	14 34.2	19 41.8
4	8 56 10.6	17 31.8	26 5.1	14 6.0	22 30.5	0 57.1	27 56.6	19 37.6	16 3.3	9 26.4	14 35.7	19 41.5
5	9 0 7.1	18 32.3	26 2.1	27 10.3	23 51.2	1 45.0	28 45.5	19 41.6	15 58.4	9 27.0	14 37.1	19 41.1
6	9 4 3.7	19 32.5	25 59.0	10♍12.5	25 13.4	2 32.2	29 34.3	19 45.8	15 53.5	9 27.5	14 38.5	19 40.7
7	9 8 .2	20 32.6	25 56.0	23 16.7	26 37.0	3 18.8	0♒23.0	19 50.2	15 48.7	9 28.0	14 39.9	19 40.2
8	9 11 56.8	21 32.5	25 53.0	6♎29.3	28 2.0	4 4.8	1 11.7	19 54.7	15 43.8	9 28.4	14 41.2	19 39.7
9	9 15 53.4	22 32.2	25 50.0	19 57.4	29 28.2	4 50.1	2 .3	19 59.5	15 38.9	9 28.7	14 42.5	19 39.2
10	9 19 49.9	23 31.7	25 47.0	3♏46.9	0♒55.4	5 34.8	2 48.8	20 4.4	15 34.1	9 29.0	14 43.8	19 38.7
11	9 23 46.5	24 31.0	25 43.9	18 .7	2 23.7	6 18.7	3 37.3	20 9.5	15 29.2	9 29.2	14 45.1	19 38.1
12	9 27 43.0	25 30.1	25 40.9	2♐36.7	3 52.9	7 2.0	4 25.7	20 14.8	15 24.4	9 29.4	14 46.3	19 37.5
13	9 31 39.6	26 29.0	25 37.9	17 27.1	5 22.9	7 44.5	5 14.0	20 20.2	15 19.6	9 29.5	14 47.5	19 36.9
14	9 35 36.1	27 27.8	25 34.9	2♑19.2	6 53.7	8 26.3	6 2.2	20 25.9	15 14.9	9 29.6	14 48.6	19 36.3
15	9 39 32.7	28 26.3	25 31.9	16 58.4	8 25.2	9 7.2	6 50.3	20 31.7	15 10.2	9 29.6	14 49.7	19 35.6
16	9 43 29.2	29 24.8	25 28.8	1♒12.7	9 57.5	9 47.4	7 38.5	20 37.7	15 5.5	9 29.6	14 50.9	19 34.9
17	9 47 25.8	0♓23.0	25 25.8	14 54.9	11 30.3	10 26.7	8 26.4	20 43.9	15 .9	9 R 29.5	14 51.9	19 34.2
18	9 51 22.3	1 21.0	25 22.8	28 3.4	13 3.7	11 5.2	9 14.3	20 50.2	14 56.3	9 29.4	14 53.0	19 33.4
19	9 55 18.9	2 18.9	25 19.8	10♓41.5	14 37.6	11 42.7	10 2.1	20 56.7	14 51.7	9 29.2	14 53.9	19 32.7
20	9 59 15.4	3 16.6	25 16.8	22 55.5	16 12.0	12 19.2	10 49.9	21 3.4	14 47.1	9 28.9	14 54.9	19 31.8
21	10 3 12.0	4 14.1	25 13.8	4♈52.9	17 46.9	12 54.8	11 37.5	21 10.2	14 42.7	9 28.6	14 55.8	19 31.0
22	10 7 8.6	5 11.5	25 10.7	16 41.8	19 22.2	13 29.3	12 25.0	21 17.2	14 38.2	9 28.2	14 56.7	19 30.1
23	10 11 5.1	6 8.7	25 7.7	28 29.6	20 58.0	14 2.8	13 12.5	21 24.4	14 33.8	9 27.8	14 57.5	19 29.3
24	10 15 1.7	7 5.7	25 4.7	10♉22.8	22 34.2	14 35.1	13 59.8	21 31.7	14 29.5	9 27.3	14 58.3	19 28.3
25	10 18 58.2	8 2.6	25 1.7	22 26.3	24 10.7	15 6.2	14 47.0	21 39.2	14 25.2	9 26.8	14 59.1	19 27.4
26	10 22 54.8	8 59.3	24 58.7	4♊43.1	25 47.7	15 36.1	15 34.2	21 46.8	14 21.0	9 26.2	14 59.9	19 26.4
27	10 26 51.3	9 55.9	24 55.7	17 14.1	27 25.0	16 4.7	16 21.2	21 54.6	14 16.9	9 25.6	15 .6	19 25.4
28	10 30 47.9	10 52.4	24 52.7	29 58.4	29 2.7	16 32.0	17 8.2	22 2.5	14 12.8	9 24.9	15 1.2	19 24.4

DECLINATION

DAY	SID. TIME	☉	☊	☽	☿	♀	♂	♃	♄	♅	♆	♇
1	8 44 20.9	17S11.3	0S11.4	18N44.7	21S48.7	0N29.1	22S16.5	17N22.0	17N40.0	14S55.2	21S12.0	10N21.0
4	8 56 10.6	16 19.0	0 11.3	12 15.8	21 46.4	1 56.3	21 53.2	17 25.6	17 44.5	14 55.7	21 12.3	10 23.1
7	9 8 .2	15 24.3	0 11.2	0S 4.9	21 33.9	3 22.3	21 27.7	17 29.6	17 49.0	14 56.2	21 12.6	10 25.3
10	9 19 49.9	14 27.1	0 11.2	12 41.2	21 10.7	4 46.5	21 .1	17 34.0	17 53.4	14 56.4	21 12.9	10 27.6
13	9 31 39.6	13 27.8	0 11.1	18 56.3	20 36.3	6 8.7	20 30.4	17 38.7	17 57.7	14 56.5	21 13.1	10 29.9
16	9 43 29.2	12 26.5	0 11.1	15 10.4	19 50.5	7 28.5	19 58.7	17 43.9	18 1.8	14 56.5	21 13.3	10 32.2
19	9 55 18.9	11 23.4	0 11.0	4 15.6	18 53.0	8 45.3	19 25.1	17 49.3	18 5.9	14 56.3	21 13.5	10 34.6
22	10 7 8.6	10 18.6	0 10.9	7N47.2	17 43.7	9 58.6	18 49.6	17 55.1	18 9.8	14 56.0	21 13.7	10 37.1
25	10 18 58.2	9 12.5	0 10.9	16 24.6	16 22.7	11 8.0	18 12.3	18 1.2	18 13.6	14 55.5	21 13.8	10 39.5
28	10 30 47.9	8 5.1	0 10.8	18 47.0	14 49.8	12 12.9	17 33.4	18 7.5	18 17.1	14 54.9	21 13.8	10 42.0

MARCH 1977

LONGITUDE

DAY	EPHEM. SID. TIME	☉	☊	☽	☿	♀	♂	♃	♄	♅	♆	♇
	h m s	° ′	° ′	° ′	° ′	° ′	° ′	° ′	° ′	° ′	° ′	° ′
1	10 34 44.4	10♓17.8	26♎45.6	12♋18.1	27♒44.1	20♈25.9	15♒ 7.3	24♉21.5	11♌24.1	11♏41.6	16♐ 3.8	13♎39.9
2	10 38 41.0	11 18.0	26 42.4	24 56.4	29 25.9	20 55.6	15 53.9	24 29.6	11 R 20.2	11 R 40.8	16 4.4	13 R 38.6
3	10 42 37.5	12 18.2	26 39.2	7♌55.9	1♓ 8.8	21 23.8	16 40.6	24 37.9	11 16.4	11 40.0	16 4.9	13 37.2
4	10 46 34.1	13 18.3	26 36.1	21 17.2	2 52.7	21 50.2	17 27.3	24 46.3	11 12.6	11 39.1	16 5.4	13 35.9
5	10 50 30.6	14 18.4	26 32.9	4♍59.5	4 37.7	22 14.9	18 14.0	24 54.8	11 8.9	11 38.1	16 5.9	13 34.5
6	10 54 27.2	15 18.4	26 29.7	18 59.6	6 23.7	22 37.7	19 .7	25 3.5	11 5.3	11 37.1	16 6.3	13 33.0
7	10 58 23.7	16 18.5	26 26.5	3♎13.5	8 10.9	22 58.7	19 47.5	25 12.3	11 1.7	11 36.1	16 6.7	13 31.6
8	11 2 20.3	17 18.5	26 23.4	17 35.9	9 59.1	23 17.7	20 34.2	25 21.2	10 58.3	11 35.0	16 7.0	13 30.2
9	11 6 16.8	18 18.5	26 20.2	2♏ 1.8	11 48.6	23 34.8	21 21.0	25 30.3	10 54.9	11 33.9	16 7.4	13 28.7
10	11 10 13.4	19 18.4	26 17.0	16 26.4	13 39.1	23 49.8	22 7.8	25 39.5	10 51.6	11 32.7	16 7.7	13 27.3
11	11 14 9.9	20 18.3	26 13.8	0♐46.1	15 30.7	24 2.7	22 54.6	25 48.8	10 48.4	11 31.5	16 8.0	13 25.8
12	11 18 6.5	21 18.2	26 10.6	14 58.4	17 23.4	24 13.4	23 41.4	25 58.2	10 45.3	11 30.2	16 8.2	13 24.2
13	11 22 3.0	22 18.1	26 7.5	29 1.6	19 17.2	24 21.8	24 28.2	26 7.7	10 42.2	11 28.8	16 8.4	13 22.7
14	11 25 59.6	23 17.9	26 4.3	12♑54.4	21 12.1	24 28.0	25 15.0	26 17.4	10 39.2	11 27.5	16 8.5	13 21.2
15	11 29 56.2	24 17.7	26 1.1	26 36.1	23 8.1	24 31.9	26 1.8	26 27.2	10 36.4	11 26.0	16 8.6	13 19.6
16	11 33 52.7	25 17.5	25 57.9	10♒ 5.8	25 5.0	24 33.4	26 48.6	26 37.1	10 33.6	11 24.6	16 8.7	13 18.0
17	11 37 49.3	26 17.2	25 54.8	23 22.9	27 2.8	24 R 32.5	27 35.5	26 47.1	10 30.9	11 23.1	16 8.8	13 16.5
18	11 41 45.8	27 16.9	25 51.6	6♓26.7	29 1.5	24 29.1	28 22.3	26 57.2	10 28.3	11 21.5	16 8.8	13 14.9
19	11 45 42.4	28 16.6	25 48.4	19 16.6	1♈ 1.0	24 23.3	29 9.1	27 7.4	10 25.8	11 19.9	16 8.8	13 13.3
20	11 49 38.9	29 16.3	25 45.2	1♈52.7	3 1.0	24 15.0	29 56.0	27 17.7	10 23.4	11 18.3	16 R 8.7	13 11.7
21	11 53 35.5	0♈15.9	25 42.0	14 15.3	5 1.5	24 4.2	0♓42.8	27 28.2	10 21.1	11 16.6	16 8.7	13 10.0
22	11 57 32.0	1 15.5	25 38.9	26 25.8	7 2.3	23 50.9	1 29.7	27 38.7	10 18.9	11 14.9	16 8.6	13 8.4
23	12 1 28.6	2 15.0	25 35.7	8♉26.1	9 3.2	23 35.2	2 16.5	27 49.4	10 16.9	11 13.1	16 8.4	13 6.8
24	12 5 25.1	3 14.5	25 32.5	20 19.1	11 4.0	23 17.0	3 3.3	28 .1	10 14.9	11 11.3	16 8.2	13 5.1
25	12 9 21.7	4 14.0	25 29.3	2♊ 8.2	13 4.3	22 56.5	3 50.2	28 11.0	10 13.0	11 9.5	16 8.0	13 3.5
26	12 13 18.2	5 13.5	25 26.1	13 57.4	15 3.8	22 33.6	4 37.0	28 21.9	10 11.2	11 7.6	16 7.8	13 1.8
27	12 17 14.8	6 12.9	25 23.0	25 51.4	17 2.3	22 8.6	5 23.8	28 32.9	10 9.5	11 5.7	16 7.5	13 .1
28	12 21 11.3	7 12.2	25 19.8	7♋55.0	18 59.3	21 41.5	6 10.6	28 44.1	10 7.9	11 3.7	16 7.2	12 58.5
29	12 25 7.9	8 11.5	25 16.6	20 12.8	20 54.5	21 12.3	6 57.5	28 55.3	10 6.4	11 1.8	16 6.8	12 56.8
30	12 29 4.4	9 10.9	25 13.4	2♌49.3	22 47.6	20 41.5	7 44.3	29 6.6	10 5.1	10 59.8	16 6.5	12 55.2
31	12 33 1.0	10 10.1	25 10.3	15 48.1	24 37.9	20 8.9	8 31.1	29 18.0	10 3.9	10 57.8	16 6.1	12 53.5

LATITUDE

DAY	EPHEM. SID. TIME	☉	☊	☽	☿	♀	♂	♃	♄	♅	♆	♇
1	10 34 44.4	0 .0	0 .0	5S 1.2	2S 8.5	4N56.5	1S 4.8	0S43.3	0N59.0	0N27.3	1N29.3	17N28.6
4	10 46 34.1	0 .0	0 .0	4 37.7	2 9.4	5 24.2	1 5.8	0 42.7	0 59.1	0 27.3	1 29.4	17 29.6
7	10 58 23.7	0 .0	0 .0	1 54.4	2 6.3	5 51.6	1 6.7	0 42.0	0 59.2	0 27.3	1 29.5	17 30.6
10	11 10 13.4	0 .0	0 .0	1N55.8	1 58.9	6 18.3	1 7.6	0 41.4	0 59.3	0 27.4	1 29.7	17 31.4
13	11 22 3.0	0 .0	0 .0	4 41.9	1 47.0	6 43.7	1 8.4	0 40.8	0 59.3	0 27.4	1 29.8	17 32.2
16	11 33 52.7	0 .0	0 .0	5 1.6	1 30.2	7 7.2	1 9.2	0 40.2	0 59.4	0 27.5	1 30.0	17 32.8
19	11 45 42.4	0 .0	0 .0	3 1.0	1 8.5	7 27.7	1 9.9	0 39.6	0 59.4	0 27.5	1 30.1	17 33.4
22	11 57 32.0	0 .0	0 .0	0S11.5	0 42.1	7 44.4	1 10.5	0 39.0	0 59.5	0 27.5	1 30.2	17 33.9
25	12 9 21.7	0 .0	0 .0	3 13.9	0 11.3	7 56.1	1 11.1	0 38.5	0 59.5	0 27.5	1 30.3	17 34.3
28	12 21 11.3	0 .0	0 .0	5 3.5	0N22.7	8 1.6	1 11.6	0 38.0	0 59.5	0 27.6	1 30.5	17 34.6
31	12 33 1.0	0 .0	0 .0	4 54.9	0 58.2	8 .1	1 12.0	0 37.4	0 59.5	0 27.6	1 30.6	17 34.8

RIGHT ASCENSION

DAY	EPHEM. SID. TIME	☉	☊	☽	☿	♀	♂	♃	♄	♅	♆	♇
1	10 34 44.4	11♓48.7	24♎49.7	12♋53.1	0♓40.8	16♈58.0	17♒55.0	22♉10.6	14♌ 8.8	9♏24.2	15♐ 1.9	19♎23.4
2	10 38 41.0	12 44.9	24 46.6	25 54.9	2 19.3	17 22.4	18 41.8	22 18.9	14 R 4.8	9 R 23.4	15 2.5	19 R 22.4
3	10 42 37.5	13 40.9	24 43.6	9♌ 1.0	3 58.2	17 45.4	19 28.4	22 27.2	14 .9	9 22.6	15 3.0	19 21.3
4	10 46 34.1	14 36.9	24 40.6	22 10.0	5 37.4	18 6.8	20 15.0	22 35.8	13 57.1	9 21.7	15 3.6	19 20.2
5	10 50 30.6	15 32.7	24 37.6	5♍22.5	7 17.1	18 26.6	21 1.4	22 44.4	13 53.4	9 20.8	15 4.1	19 19.1
6	10 54 27.2	16 28.4	24 34.6	18 41.7	8 57.3	18 44.7	21 47.8	22 53.2	13 49.7	9 19.8	15 4.5	19 17.9
7	10 58 23.7	17 24.0	24 31.6	2♎12.0	10 37.8	19 1.1	22 34.0	23 2.2	13 46.1	9 18.7	15 4.9	19 16.8
8	11 2 20.3	18 19.5	24 28.6	15 58.6	12 18.8	19 15.7	23 20.2	23 11.3	13 42.6	9 17.7	15 5.3	19 15.6
9	11 6 16.8	19 15.0	24 25.6	0♏ 5.2	14 .4	19 28.5	24 6.3	23 20.5	13 39.2	9 16.6	15 5.7	19 14.4
10	11 10 13.4	20 10.3	24 22.6	14 32.7	15 42.3	19 39.3	24 52.3	23 29.9	13 35.9	9 15.4	15 6.1	19 13.2
11	11 14 9.9	21 5.5	24 19.5	29 17.1	17 24.8	19 48.2	25 38.2	23 39.4	13 32.6	9 14.2	15 6.3	19 12.0
12	11 18 6.5	22 .7	24 16.5	14♐ 9.8	19 7.8	19 55.1	26 23.9	23 49.0	13 29.5	9 12.9	15 6.6	19 10.7
13	11 22 3.0	22 55.8	24 13.5	28 58.5	20 51.3	19 60.0	27 9.6	23 58.7	13 26.4	9 11.6	15 6.8	19 9.5
14	11 25 59.6	23 50.8	24 10.5	13♑30.5	22 35.4	20 2.8	27 55.2	24 8.6	13 23.4	9 10.3	15 7.0	19 8.2
15	11 29 56.2	24 45.8	24 7.5	27 35.8	24 19.9	20 3.4	28 40.7	24 18.6	13 20.5	9 8.9	15 7.1	19 6.9
16	11 33 52.7	25 40.7	24 4.5	11♒ 9.5	26 5.0	20 R 1.9	29 26.1	24 28.7	13 17.7	9 7.4	15 7.2	19 5.6
17	11 37 49.3	26 35.6	24 1.5	24 11.4	27 50.6	19 58.2	0♓11.4	24 38.9	13 14.9	9 6.0	15 7.3	19 4.3
18	11 41 45.8	27 30.4	23 58.5	6♓45.5	29 36.7	19 52.3	0 56.6	24 49.3	13 12.3	9 4.4	15 7.3	19 2.9
19	11 45 42.4	28 25.2	23 55.5	18 57.7	1♈23.2	19 44.2	1 41.7	24 59.7	13 9.8	9 2.9	15 7.3	19 1.6
20	11 49 38.9	29 19.9	23 52.5	0♈55.4	3 10.0	19 33.8	2 26.8	25 10.3	13 7.4	9 1.2	15 R 7.2	19 .2
21	11 53 35.5	0♈14.6	23 49.5	12 45.7	4 57.1	19 21.3	3 11.7	25 21.0	13 5.0	8 59.6	15 7.1	18 58.8
22	11 57 32.0	1 9.3	23 46.5	24 35.1	6 44.4	19 6.6	3 56.5	25 31.9	13 2.8	8 57.9	15 7.0	18 57.4
23	12 1 28.6	2 3.9	23 43.5	6♉28.9	8 31.8	18 49.8	4 41.3	25 42.8	13 .7	8 56.2	15 6.9	18 56.0
24	12 5 25.1	2 58.5	23 40.5	18 31.0	10 19.0	18 30.9	5 26.0	25 53.8	12 58.7	8 54.4	15 6.7	18 54.6
25	12 9 21.7	3 53.1	23 37.5	0♊43.2	12 5.9	18 10.0	6 10.5	26 5.0	12 56.7	8 52.6	15 6.5	18 53.2
26	12 13 18.2	4 47.7	23 34.5	13 6.1	13 52.4	17 47.2	6 55.0	26 16.2	12 54.9	8 50.8	15 6.2	18 51.7
27	12 17 14.8	5 42.3	23 31.4	25 38.3	15 38.0	17 22.6	7 39.4	26 27.6	12 53.2	8 48.9	15 5.9	18 50.3
28	12 21 11.3	6 36.9	23 28.4	8♋18.1	17 22.6	16 56.3	8 23.7	26 39.0	12 51.6	8 47.0	15 5.6	18 48.8
29	12 25 7.9	7 31.5	23 25.4	21 3.2	19 5.9	16 28.6	9 7.9	26 50.6	12 50.1	8 45.0	15 5.2	18 47.4
30	12 29 4.4	8 26.1	23 22.4	3♌52.6	20 47.6	15 59.5	9 52.1	27 2.3	12 48.8	8 43.1	15 4.9	18 45.9
31	12 33 1.0	9 20.7	23 19.4	16 46.5	22 27.2	15 29.2	10 36.2	27 14.0	12 47.5	8 41.1	15 4.5	18 44.5

DECLINATION

DAY	EPHEM. SID. TIME	☉	☊	☽	☿	♀	♂	♃	♄	♅	♆	♇
1	10 34 44.4	7S42.4	0S10.8	17N52.3	14S16.2	12N33.3	17S20.0	18N 9.6	18N18.3	14S54.6	21S13.9	10N42.8
4	10 46 34.1	6 33.7	0 10.7	10 1.1	12 27.5	13 30.9	16 38.8	18 16.3	18 21.6	14 53.8	21 13.9	10 45.3
7	10 58 23.7	5 24.2	0 10.7	3S 1.9	10 27.2	14 22.1	15 56.1	18 23.2	18 24.7	14 52.8	21 13.9	10 47.7
10	11 10 13.4	4 14.0	0 10.6	14 54.2	8 15.5	15 6.0	15 12.0	18 30.3	18 27.5	14 51.8	21 13.8	10 50.1
13	11 22 3.0	3 3.3	0 10.6	18 44.3	5 52.8	15 41.6	14 26.4	18 37.5	18 30.2	14 50.5	21 13.8	10 52.5
16	11 33 52.7	1 52.3	0 10.5	12 52.1	3 20.0	16 7.6	13 39.6	18 44.9	18 32.6	14 49.2	21 13.7	10 54.9
19	11 45 42.4	0 41.1	0 10.4	1 28.1	0 38.6	16 22.8	12 51.6	18 52.4	18 34.7	14 47.7	21 13.6	10 57.2
22	11 57 32.0	0N30.0	0 10.4	10N 1.2	2N 9.0	16 26.1	12 2.5	19 .1	18 36.6	14 46.1	21 13.4	10 59.5
25	12 9 21.7	1 41.0	0 10.3	17 25.3	4 59.3	16 16.4	11 12.4	19 7.8	18 38.3	14 44.4	21 13.2	11 1.8
28	12 21 11.3	2 51.5	0 10.3	18 9.2	7 47.2	15 53.1	10 21.3	19 15.6	18 39.6	14 42.6	21 13.0	11 3.9
31	12 33 1.0	4 1.6	0 10.2	11 24.1	10 26.7	15 16.3	9 29.4	19 23.5	18 40.7	14 40.8	21 12.8	11 6.0

LONGITUDE

DAY	EPHEM. SID. TIME (h m s)	☉	☊	☽	☿	♀	♂	♃	♄	♅	♆	♇
1	12 36 57.5	11♈9.3	25♎7.1	29♌11.5	26♈25.3	19♈34.9	9♓17.9	29♉29.5	10♌2.7	10♏55.7	16♐5.7	12♎51.8
2	12 40 54.1	12 8.5	25 3.9	13♍.0	28 9.2	18R59.6	10 4.7	29 41.1	10R1.7	10R53.6	16R5.2	12R50.1
3	12 44 50.6	13 7.6	25 .7	27 12.1	29 49.3	18 23.3	10 51.5	29 52.7	10 .7	10 51.4	16 4.7	12 48.5
4	12 48 47.2	14 6.7	24 57.5	11♎43.9	1♉25.2	17 46.2	11 38.2	0♊4.4	9 59.9	10 49.3	16 4.2	12 46.8
5	12 52 43.7	15 5.8	24 54.4	26 29.4	2 56.7	17 8.6	12 25.0	0 16.2	9 59.1	10 47.1	16 3.6	12 45.1
6	12 56 40.3	16 4.8	24 51.2	11♏21.5	4 23.3	16 30.7	13 11.7	0 28.1	9 58.5	10 44.9	16 3.0	12 43.4
7	13 0 36.8	17 3.8	24 48.0	26 12.5	5 44.9	15 52.7	13 58.5	0 40.0	9 58.0	10 42.6	16 2.4	12 41.7
8	13 4 33.4	18 2.8	24 44.8	10♐55.6	7 1.1	15 15.1	14 45.2	0 52.1	9 57.6	10 40.4	16 1.7	12 40.1
9	13 8 29.9	19 1.7	24 41.7	25 25.1	8 11.9	14 37.9	15 31.9	1 4.1	9 57.3	10 38.1	16 1.1	12 38.4
10	13 12 26.5	20 .6	24 38.5	9♑37.4	9 16.9	14 1.4	16 18.6	1 16.3	9 57.1	10 35.8	16 .4	12 36.7
11	13 16 23.1	20 59.5	24 35.3	23 30.7	10 16.0	13 25.9	17 5.3	1 28.6	9 57.1	10 33.4	15 59.6	12 35.1
12	13 20 19.6	21 58.4	24 32.1	7♒4.6	11 9.2	12 51.6	17 52.0	1 40.9	9 57.1	10 31.1	15 58.9	12 33.4
13	13 24 16.2	22 57.2	24 28.9	20 20.0	11 56.2	12 18.7	18 38.7	1 53.2	9D57.2	10 28.7	15 58.1	12 31.8
14	13 28 12.7	23 56.0	24 25.8	3♓18.3	12 37.0	11 47.4	19 25.4	2 5.7	9 57.5	10 26.3	15 57.2	12 30.1
15	13 32 9.3	24 54.8	24 22.6	16 1.3	13 11.6	11 17.8	20 12.0	2 18.2	9 57.8	10 23.9	15 56.4	12 28.5
16	13 36 5.8	25 53.5	24 19.4	28 31.0	13 39.9	10 50.1	20 58.6	2 30.7	9 58.3	10 21.4	15 55.5	12 26.8
17	13 40 2.4	26 52.2	24 16.2	10♈49.0	14 1.9	10 24.4	21 45.2	2 43.4	9 58.9	10 19.0	15 54.6	12 25.2
18	13 43 58.9	27 50.9	24 13.1	22 57.4	14 17.6	10 .9	22 31.8	2 56.0	9 59.6	10 16.5	15 53.7	12 23.6
19	13 47 55.5	28 49.5	24 9.9	4♉57.7	14 27.1	9 39.6	23 18.4	3 8.8	10 .4	10 14.1	15 52.7	12 22.0
20	13 51 52.0	29 48.2	24 6.7	16 52.0	14 30.7	9 20.7	24 5.0	3 21.6	10 1.3	10 11.6	15 51.8	12 20.5
21	13 55 48.6	0♉46.8	24 3.5	28 42.2	14R28.3	9 4.0	24 51.5	3 34.5	10 2.3	10 9.1	15 50.8	12 18.9
22	13 59 45.1	1 45.3	24 .3	10♊31.0	14 20.2	8 49.8	25 38.0	3 47.4	10 3.4	10 6.6	15 49.7	12 17.3
23	14 3 41.7	2 43.8	23 57.2	22 21.2	14 6.7	8 38.0	26 24.5	4 .4	10 4.7	10 4.1	15 48.7	12 15.8
24	14 7 38.2	3 42.3	23 54.0	4♋16.0	13 48.3	8 28.6	27 10.9	4 13.4	10 6.0	10 1.6	15 47.6	12 14.2
25	14 11 34.8	4 40.8	23 50.8	16 19.4	13 25.2	8 21.6	27 57.3	4 26.4	10 7.4	9 59.0	15 46.5	12 12.7
26	14 15 31.3	5 39.2	23 47.6	28 35.3	12 58.0	8 17.1	28 43.7	4 39.5	10 9.0	9 56.5	15 45.3	12 11.2
27	14 19 27.9	6 37.5	23 44.5	11♌8.1	12 27.2	8 14.9	29 30.1	4 52.7	10 10.6	9 53.9	15 44.2	12 9.7
28	14 23 24.5	7 35.9	23 41.3	24 1.6	11 54.3	8D15.1	0♈16.4	5 5.9	10 12.4	9 51.4	15 43.0	12 8.2
29	14 27 21.0	8 34.2	23 38.1	7♍19.3	11 17.3	8 17.7	1 2.7	5 19.1	10 14.2	9 48.9	15 41.8	12 6.7
30	14 31 17.6	9 32.4	23 34.9	21 3.4	10 39.5	8 22.5	1 49.0	5 32.4	10 16.2	9 46.3	15 40.6	12 5.3

LATITUDE

DAY	EPHEM. SID. TIME (h m s)	☉	☊	☽	☿	♀	♂	♃	♄	♅	♆	♇
1	12 36 57.5	0 .0	0 .0	4S20.2	1N10.0	7N57.8	1S12.2	0S37.3	0N59.5	0N27.6	1N30.6	17N34.9
4	12 48 47.2	0 .0	0 .0	1 9.3	1 44.1	7 45.8	1 12.5	0 36.8	0 59.4	0 27.6	1 30.8	17 35.0
7	13 0 36.8	0 .0	0 .0	2N48.1	2 14.4	7 24.8	1 12.8	0 36.3	0 59.4	0 27.6	1 30.9	17 34.9
10	13 12 26.5	0 .0	0 .0	5 7.3	2 38.6	6 58.5	1 13.0	0 35.8	0 59.4	0 27.6	1 31.0	17 34.8
13	13 24 16.2	0 .0	0 .0	4 45.8	2 54.6	6 25.1	1 13.1	0 35.3	0 59.3	0 27.6	1 31.1	17 34.6
16	13 36 5.8	0 .0	0 .0	2 18.8	3 .7	5 47.2	1 13.2	0 34.9	0 59.3	0 27.6	1 31.2	17 34.3
19	13 47 55.5	0 .0	0 .0	0S58.6	2 55.5	5 6.3	1 13.2	0 34.5	0 59.2	0 27.6	1 31.3	17 33.9
22	13 59 45.1	0 .0	0 .0	3 49.2	2 38.2	4 24.1	1 13.1	0 34.1	0 59.2	0 27.6	1 31.4	17 33.5
25	14 11 34.8	0 .0	0 .0	5 14.0	2 8.3	3 42.0	1 13.0	0 33.6	0 59.1	0 27.6	1 31.5	17 32.9
28	14 23 24.5	0 .0	0 .0	4 35.4	1 28.3	3 .8	1 12.7	0 33.2	0 59.1	0 27.5	1 31.6	17 32.2

RIGHT ASCENSION

DAY	EPHEM. SID. TIME (h m s)	☉	☊	☽	☿	♀	♂	♃	♄	♅	♆	♇
1	12 36 57.5	10♈15.3	23♎16.4	29♌47.4	24♈4.6	14♈57.9	11♓20.1	27♉25.9	12♌46.3	8♏39.1	15♐4.0	18♎43.0
2	12 40 54.1	11 10.0	23 13.4	13♍59.5	25 39.2	14R25.8	12 4.0	27 37.8	12R45.2	8R37.0	15R3.5	18R41.5
3	12 44 50.6	12 4.6	23 10.4	26 28.4	27 10.8	13 53.2	12 47.9	27 49.8	12 44.3	8 34.9	15 3.0	18 40.0
4	12 48 47.2	12 59.3	23 7.4	10♎20.0	28 39.0	13 20.3	13 31.6	28 2.0	12 43.4	8 32.8	15 2.4	18 38.5
5	12 52 43.7	13 54.1	23 4.4	24 38.0	0♉3.5	12 47.3	14 15.3	28 14.2	12 42.7	8 30.6	15 1.8	18 37.0
6	12 56 40.3	14 48.8	23 1.4	9♏25.3	1 24.0	12 14.4	14 58.9	28 26.5	12 42.1	8 28.5	15 1.2	18 35.5
7	13 0 36.8	15 43.7	22 58.4	24 34.6	2 40.2	11 41.9	15 42.5	28 38.8	12 41.5	8 26.3	15 .5	18 34.0
8	13 4 33.4	16 38.6	22 55.4	9♐55.1	3 51.9	11 10.0	16 25.9	28 51.3	12 41.1	8 24.0	14 59.8	18 32.5
9	13 8 29.9	17 33.5	22 52.4	25 10.6	4 58.7	10 38.9	17 9.3	29 3.8	12 40.8	8 21.8	14 59.1	18 31.0
10	13 12 26.5	18 28.5	22 49.4	10♑4.9	6 .4	10 8.9	17 52.7	29 16.5	12 40.6	8 19.5	14 58.4	18 29.5
11	13 16 23.1	19 23.6	22 46.4	24 25.9	6 56.9	9 40.0	18 36.0	29 29.2	12 40.5	8 17.2	14 57.6	18 28.0
12	13 20 19.6	20 18.8	22 43.4	8♒8.1	7 48.0	9 12.6	19 19.2	29 42.0	12D40.6	8 14.9	14 56.8	18 26.5
13	13 24 16.2	21 14.1	22 40.4	21 12.3	8 33.5	8 46.7	20 2.4	29 54.8	12 40.7	8 12.6	14 55.9	18 25.0
14	13 28 12.7	22 9.4	22 37.4	3♓44.2	9 13.3	8 22.6	20 45.5	0♊7.8	12 41.0	8 10.2	14 55.1	18 23.5
15	13 32 9.3	23 4.8	22 34.5	15 51.6	9 47.2	8 .2	21 28.6	0 20.8	12 41.3	8 7.8	14 54.1	18 22.0
16	13 36 5.8	24 .3	22 31.5	27 43.1	10 14.7	7 39.8	22 11.6	0 33.9	12 41.8	8 5.5	14 53.2	18 20.5
17	13 40 2.4	24 55.9	22 28.5	9♈27.3	10 37.6	7 21.4	22 54.5	0 47.0	12 42.4	8 3.1	14 52.3	18 19.0
18	13 43 58.9	25 51.6	22 25.5	21 11.3	10 54.0	7 5.1	23 37.4	1 .2	12 43.1	8 .6	14 51.3	18 17.5
19	13 47 55.5	26 47.4	22 22.5	3♉.9	11 4.6	6 51.0	24 20.3	1 13.5	12 43.9	7 58.2	14 50.2	18 16.0
20	13 51 52.0	27 43.4	22 19.5	14 59.8	11 9.5	6 39.1	25 3.1	1 26.9	12 44.8	7 55.8	14 49.2	18 14.6
21	13 55 48.6	28 39.4	22 16.5	27 9.5	11R8.9	6 29.3	25 45.9	1 40.4	12 45.8	7 53.4	14 48.2	18 13.1
22	13 59 45.1	29 35.5	22 13.5	9♊29.3	11 3.1	6 21.8	26 28.6	1 53.9	12 47.0	7 50.9	14 47.1	18 11.6
23	14 3 41.7	0♉31.7	22 10.5	21 56.8	10 52.3	6 16.6	27 11.2	2 7.4	12 48.2	7 48.4	14 45.9	18 10.2
24	14 7 38.2	1 28.0	22 7.5	4♋28.9	10 36.9	6 13.5	27 53.9	2 21.0	12 49.6	7 45.9	14 44.8	18 8.7
25	14 11 34.8	2 24.4	22 4.5	17 2.5	10 17.2	6 12.7	28 36.5	2 34.7	12 51.0	7 43.5	14 43.6	18 7.3
26	14 15 31.3	3 21.0	22 1.5	29 36.1	9 54.1	6D14.0	29 19.0	2 48.4	12 52.6	7 41.0	14 42.4	18 5.9
27	14 19 27.9	4 17.7	21 58.5	12♌10.3	9 27.7	6 17.5	0♈1.5	3 2.2	12 54.2	7 38.5	14 41.2	18 4.4
28	14 23 24.5	5 14.5	21 55.5	24 48.0	8 58.8	6 23.1	0 44.0	3 16.0	12 56.0	7 36.0	14 39.9	18 3.0
29	14 27 21.0	6 11.4	21 52.5	7♍35.0	8 27.9	6 30.8	1 26.4	3 29.9	12 57.9	7 33.5	14 38.7	18 1.6
30	14 31 17.6	7 8.4	21 49.5	20 38.5	7 55.9	6 40.5	2 8.8	3 43.9	12 59.9	7 31.0	14 37.4	18 .2

DECLINATION

DAY	EPHEM. SID. TIME (h m s)	☉	☊	☽	☿	♀	♂	♃	♄	♅	♆	♇
1	12 36 57.5	4N24.8	0S10.2	7N41.3	11N16.9	15N1.2	9S11.9	19N26.2	18N41.0	14S40.1	21S12.7	11N6.7
4	12 48 47.2	5 33.9	0 10.1	5S42.1	13 35.7	14 8.1	8 19.0	19 34.1	18 41.8	14 38.1	21 12.4	11 8.6
7	13 0 36.8	6 42.2	0 10.1	16 34.8	15 33.0	13 5.7	7 25.5	19 42.0	18 42.4	14 36.0	21 12.1	11 10.5
10	13 12 26.5	7 49.4	0 10.0	17 58.9	17 5.5	11 57.1	6 31.4	19 49.9	18 42.4	14 33.9	21 11.8	11 12.3
13	13 24 16.2	8 55.5	0 9.9	10 11.2	18 11.1	10 46.1	5 36.8	19 57.8	18 42.4	14 31.7	21 11.4	11 14.0
16	13 36 5.8	10 .2	0 9.9	1N31.9	18 48.8	9 36.4	4 41.9	20 5.6	18 42.0	14 29.4	21 11.1	11 15.8
19	13 47 55.5	11 3.4	0 9.8	13 18.0	18 58.1	8 31.1	3 46.7	20 13.4	18 41.4	14 27.1	21 10.7	11 17.0
22	13 59 45.1	12 5.1	0 9.8	18 14.6	18 39.4	7 32.7	2 51.3	20 21.1	18 40.5	14 24.8	21 10.3	11 18.4
25	14 11 34.8	13 4.9	0 9.7	17 14.8	17 54.7	6 42.8	1 55.7	20 28.7	18 39.4	14 22.4	21 9.8	11 19.6
28	14 23 24.5	14 2.7	0 9.6	9 10.7	16 48.2	6 2.5	1 .2	20 36.3	18 38.0	14 20.0	21 9.4	11 20.7

MAY 1977

LONGITUDE

DAY	EPHEM. SID. TIME	☉	☊	☽	☿	♀	♂	♃	♄	♅	♆	♇
	h m s	° ′	° ′	° ′	° ′	° ′	° ′	° ′	° ′	° ′	° ′	° ′
1	14 35 14.1	10♉30.7	23♎31.7	5♎14.2	10♉ .8	8♈29.6	2♈35.2	5♊45.7	10♌18.3	9♏43.8	15♐39.3	12♎ 3.9
2	14 39 10.7	11 28.9	23 28.6	19 49.7	9 R 21.9	8 38.8	3 21.4	5 59.0	10 20.4	9 R 41.2	15 R 38.1	12 R 2.5
3	14 43 7.2	12 27.0	23 25.4	4♏45.0	8 43.4	8 50.2	4 7.6	6 12.4	10 22.7	9 38.7	15 36.8	12 1.1
4	14 47 3.8	13 25.2	23 22.2	19 52.8	8 6.0	9 3.7	4 53.8	6 25.9	10 25.1	9 36.1	15 35.5	11 59.7
5	14 51 .3	14 23.3	23 19.0	5♐ 3.7	7 30.4	9 19.2	5 39.9	6 39.3	10 27.5	9 33.6	15 34.2	11 58.3
6	14 54 56.9	15 21.4	23 15.9	20 8.1	6 57.1	9 36.7	6 26.0	6 52.8	10 30.1	9 31.1	15 32.9	11 57.0
7	14 58 53.4	16 19.5	23 12.7	4♑57.5	6 26.7	9 56.1	7 12.0	7 6.3	10 32.8	9 28.5	15 31.5	11 55.7
8	15 2 50.0	17 17.5	23 9.5	19 25.3	5 59.5	10 17.3	7 58.1	7 19.9	10 35.5	9 26.0	15 30.1	11 54.4
9	15 6 46.6	18 15.5	23 6.3	3♒27.9	5 36.1	10 40.3	8 44.1	7 33.5	10 38.4	9 23.5	15 28.7	11 53.1
10	15 10 43.1	19 13.5	23 3.1	17 4.6	5 16.6	11 5.0	9 30.0	7 47.1	10 41.3	9 21.0	15 27.3	11 51.8
11	15 14 39.7	20 11.5	22 60.0	0♓16.4	5 1.4	11 31.4	10 16.0	8 .8	10 44.4	9 18.5	15 26.0	11 50.7
12	15 18 36.2	21 9.5	22 56.8	13 6.2	4 50.6	11 59.3	11 1.9	8 14.5	10 47.6	9 16.1	15 24.5	11 49.4
13	15 22 32.8	22 7.4	22 53.6	25 37.5	4 44.3	12 28.7	11 47.7	8 28.2	10 50.8	9 13.6	15 23.1	11 48.3
14	15 26 29.3	23 5.3	22 50.4	7♈54.0	4 42.6	12 59.7	12 33.6	8 41.9	10 54.1	9 11.1	15 21.6	11 47.1
15	15 30 25.9	24 3.2	22 47.3	19 59.3	4 D 45.6	13 32.0	13 19.3	8 55.7	10 57.6	9 8.7	15 20.1	11 45.9
16	15 34 22.4	25 1.1	22 44.1	1♉56.7	4 53.1	14 5.6	14 5.1	9 9.4	11 1.1	9 6.3	15 18.6	11 44.8
17	15 38 19.0	25 58.9	22 40.9	13 49.0	5 5.2	14 40.6	14 50.8	9 23.2	11 4.7	9 3.9	15 17.1	11 43.7
18	15 42 15.5	26 56.7	22 37.7	25 38.6	5 21.8	15 16.8	15 36.4	9 37.0	11 8.4	9 1.5	15 15.6	11 42.7
19	15 46 12.1	27 54.5	22 34.5	7♊27.5	5 42.8	15 54.2	16 22.0	9 50.9	11 12.2	8 59.1	15 14.1	11 41.6
20	15 50 8.7	28 52.3	22 31.4	19 17.9	6 8.2	16 32.7	17 7.6	10 4.7	11 16.1	8 56.8	15 12.6	11 40.6
21	15 54 5.2	29 50.1	22 28.2	1♋11.5	6 37.7	17 12.4	17 53.1	10 18.6	11 20.0	8 54.4	15 11.0	11 39.6
22	15 58 1.8	0♊47.8	22 25.0	13 10.5	7 11.3	17 53.1	18 38.6	10 32.5	11 24.1	8 52.1	15 9.5	11 38.7
23	16 1 58.3	1 45.5	22 21.8	25 17.6	7 48.9	18 34.8	19 24.0	10 46.4	11 28.2	8 49.8	15 7.9	11 37.7
24	16 5 54.9	2 43.2	22 18.7	7♌35.4	8 30.3	19 17.5	20 9.4	11 .3	11 32.5	8 47.6	15 6.3	11 36.8
25	16 9 51.4	3 40.8	22 15.5	20 7.5	9 15.4	20 1.1	20 54.7	11 14.2	11 36.8	8 45.3	15 4.7	11 36.0
26	16 13 48.0	4 38.4	22 12.3	2♍57.2	10 4.2	20 45.6	21 40.0	11 28.1	11 41.2	8 43.1	15 3.1	11 35.1
27	16 17 44.5	5 36.0	22 9.1	16 8.1	10 56.5	21 31.0	22 25.3	11 42.0	11 45.6	8 40.9	15 1.5	11 34.3
28	16 21 41.1	6 33.6	22 6.0	29 43.2	11 52.2	22 17.3	23 10.4	11 56.0	11 50.2	8 38.8	14 59.9	11 33.5
29	16 25 37.7	7 31.2	22 2.8	13♎44.4	12 51.2	23 4.3	23 55.6	12 9.9	11 54.8	8 36.6	14 58.3	11 32.7
30	16 29 34.2	8 28.7	21 59.6	28 11.5	13 53.5	23 52.1	24 40.7	12 23.9	11 59.5	8 34.5	14 56.7	11 32.0
31	16 33 30.8	9 26.2	21 56.4	13♏ 1.7	14 58.9	24 40.7	25 25.7	12 37.8	12 4.3	8 32.5	14 55.1	11 31.3

LATITUDE

DAY	EPHEM. SID. TIME	☉	☊	☽	☿	♀	♂	♃	♄	♅	♆	♇
1	14 35 14.1	0 .0	0 .0	1 S 43.8	0 N 40.2	2 N 21.4	1 S 12.4	0 S 32.9	0 N 59.0	0 N 27.5	1 N 31.7	17 N 31.5
4	14 47 3.8	0 .0	0 .0	2 N 16.6	0 S 11.5	1 44.2	1 12.0	0 32.5	0 58.9	0 27.5	1 31.7	17 30.7
7	14 58 53.4	0 .0	0 .0	4 57.6	1 2.3	1 9.5	1 11.6	0 32.1	0 58.9	0 27.5	1 31.8	17 29.8
10	15 10 43.1	0 .0	0 .0	4 50.2	1 48.2	0 37.4	1 11.0	0 31.8	0 58.8	0 27.4	1 31.9	17 28.8
13	15 22 32.8	0 .0	0 .0	2 30.6	2 26.8	0 8.0	1 10.4	0 31.4	0 58.8	0 27.4	1 31.9	17 27.8
16	15 34 22.4	0 .0	0 .0	0 S 42.4	2 56.8	0 S 18.8	1 9.7	0 31.1	0 58.7	0 27.3	1 32.0	17 26.7
19	15 46 12.1	0 .0	0 .0	3 34.5	3 17.8	0 43.0	1 9.0	0 30.8	0 58.7	0 27.3	1 32.0	17 25.5
22	15 58 1.8	0 .0	0 .0	5 5.4	3 30.1	1 4.8	1 8.1	0 30.5	0 58.6	0 27.2	1 32.0	17 24.2
25	16 9 51.4	0 .0	0 .0	4 37.9	3 34.4	1 24.2	1 7.2	0 30.2	0 58.6	0 27.2	1 32.0	17 23.0
28	16 21 41.1	0 .0	0 .0	2 5.6	3 31.4	1 41.4	1 6.2	0 29.9	0 58.6	0 27.1	1 32.0	17 21.6
31	16 33 30.8	0 .0	0 .0	1 N 43.5	3 21.7	1 56.5	1 5.1	0 29.6	0 58.6	0 27.1	1 32.1	17 20.2

RIGHT ASCENSION

DAY	EPHEM. SID. TIME	☉	☊	☽	☿	♀	♂	♃	♄	♅	♆	♇
1	14 35 14.1	8♉ 5.6	21♎46.6	4♎ 7.2	7♉23.1	6♈52.1	2♈51.2	3♊57.9	13♌ 2.0	7♏28.5	14♐36.0	17♎58.8
2	14 39 10.7	9 2.9	21 43.6	18 8.8	6 R 50.5	7 5.7	3 33.5	4 11.9	13 4.2	7 R 26.0	14 R 34.7	17 R 57.5
3	14 43 7.2	10 .3	21 40.6	2♏48.3	6 18.5	7 21.1	4 15.9	4 26.0	13 6.5	7 23.5	14 33.3	17 56.1
4	14 47 3.8	10 57.9	21 37.6	18 4.1	5 47.7	7 38.4	4 58.2	4 40.1	13 8.9	7 21.0	14 32.0	17 54.8
5	14 51 .3	11 55.6	21 34.6	3♐46.3	5 18.7	7 57.4	5 40.5	4 54.3	13 11.4	7 18.5	14 30.6	17 53.4
6	14 54 56.9	12 53.5	21 31.6	19 36.5	4 52.1	8 18.0	6 22.7	5 8.5	13 14.0	7 16.1	14 29.1	17 52.1
7	14 58 53.4	13 51.5	21 28.6	5♑12.4	4 28.1	8 40.4	7 5.0	5 22.8	13 16.7	7 13.6	14 27.7	17 50.8
8	15 2 50.0	14 49.6	21 25.6	20 14.5	4 7.3	9 4.3	7 47.2	5 37.1	13 19.5	7 11.1	14 26.2	17 49.5
9	15 6 46.6	15 47.9	21 22.6	4♒31.8	3 49.8	9 29.7	8 29.5	5 51.4	13 22.3	7 8.7	14 24.8	17 48.3
10	15 10 43.1	16 46.3	21 19.7	18 2.2	3 36.0	9 56.6	9 11.7	6 5.8	13 25.3	7 6.2	14 23.3	17 47.0
11	15 14 39.7	17 45.0	21 16.7	0♓50.7	3 26.1	10 24.9	9 53.9	6 20.3	13 28.5	7 3.8	14 21.8	17 45.8
12	15 18 36.2	18 43.7	21 13.7	13 6.2	3 20.1	10 54.6	10 36.2	6 34.7	13 31.7	7 1.4	14 20.3	17 44.6
13	15 22 32.8	19 42.6	21 10.7	24 59.3	3 18.1	11 25.5	11 18.3	6 49.2	13 34.9	6 59.0	14 18.7	17 43.4
14	15 26 29.3	20 41.6	21 7.7	6♈40.4	3 D 20.2	11 57.7	12 .5	7 3.7	13 38.3	6 56.5	14 17.2	17 42.2
15	15 30 25.9	21 40.8	21 4.7	18 18.5	3 26.3	12 31.1	12 42.7	7 18.3	13 41.8	6 54.2	14 15.6	17 41.0
16	15 34 22.4	22 40.1	21 1.7	0♉ 1.3	3 36.6	13 5.6	13 24.9	7 32.9	13 45.3	6 51.8	14 14.0	17 39.9
17	15 38 19.0	23 39.5	20 58.7	11 54.0	3 50.9	13 41.2	14 7.1	7 47.5	13 49.0	6 49.4	14 12.4	17 38.7
18	15 42 15.5	24 39.1	20 55.8	23 59.1	4 9.1	14 17.9	14 49.3	8 2.2	13 52.7	6 47.1	14 10.8	17 37.6
19	15 46 12.1	25 38.9	20 52.8	6♊16.5	4 31.3	14 55.6	15 31.5	8 16.8	13 56.6	6 44.8	14 9.2	17 36.5
20	15 50 8.7	26 38.8	20 49.8	18 43.3	4 57.2	15 34.3	16 13.6	8 31.5	14 .5	6 42.5	14 7.5	17 35.5
21	15 54 5.2	27 38.8	20 46.8	1♋15.2	5 26.9	16 13.9	16 55.8	8 46.3	14 4.5	6 40.2	14 5.9	17 34.4
22	15 58 1.8	28 38.9	20 43.8	13 47.3	6 .3	16 54.4	17 38.0	9 1.0	14 8.6	6 37.9	14 4.2	17 33.4
23	16 1 58.3	29 39.2	20 40.8	26 16.3	6 37.2	17 35.8	18 20.2	9 15.8	14 12.8	6 35.7	14 2.6	17 32.4
24	16 5 54.9	0♊39.6	20 37.9	8♌40.8	7 17.5	18 18.0	19 2.4	9 30.6	14 17.1	6 33.5	14 .9	17 31.4
25	16 9 51.4	1 40.1	20 34.9	21 2.7	8 1.3	19 1.0	19 44.6	9 45.4	14 21.4	6 31.3	13 59.2	17 30.5
26	16 13 48.0	2 40.8	20 31.9	3♍27.0	8 48.4	19 44.8	20 26.8	10 .2	14 25.9	6 29.1	13 57.5	17 29.5
27	16 17 44.5	3 41.5	20 28.9	16 1.1	9 38.7	20 29.3	21 9.0	10 15.0	14 30.4	6 27.0	13 55.8	17 28.6
28	16 21 41.1	4 42.4	20 25.9	28 54.6	10 32.3	21 14.6	21 51.3	10 29.9	14 35.0	6 24.8	13 54.1	17 27.7
29	16 25 37.7	5 43.4	20 22.9	12♎18.0	11 29.0	22 .6	22 33.5	10 44.8	14 39.6	6 22.8	13 52.4	17 26.8
30	16 29 34.2	6 44.5	20 20.0	26 20.3	12 28.8	22 47.3	23 15.8	10 59.6	14 44.4	6 20.7	13 50.7	17 26.0
31	16 33 30.8	7 45.7	20 17.0	11♏ 6.9	13 31.8	23 34.6	23 58.0	11 14.5	14 49.2	6 18.7	13 49.0	17 25.2

DECLINATION

DAY	EPHEM. SID. TIME	☉	☊	☽	☿	♀	♂	♃	♄	♅	♆	♇
1	14 35 14.1	14 N 58.5	0 S 9.6	3 S 40.1	15 N 27.3	5 N 32.0	0 S 4.7	20 N 43.7	18 N 36.4	14 S 17.6	21 S 8.9	11 N 21.7
4	14 47 3.8	15 52.0	0 9.5	15 30.9	14 1.6	5 11.3	0 N 50.6	20 51.0	18 34.5	14 15.2	21 8.4	11 22.5
7	14 58 53.4	16 43.2	0 9.4	18 23.4	12 41.3	5 .0	1 45.7	20 58.1	18 32.3	14 12.9	21 7.9	11 23.2
10	15 10 43.1	17 31.9	0 9.4	11 6.2	11 34.8	4 57.6	2 40.6	21 5.1	18 29.9	14 10.5	21 7.4	11 23.7
13	15 22 32.8	18 18.0	0 9.3	0 N 34.0	10 47.7	5 3.2	3 35.0	21 12.0	18 27.3	14 8.2	21 6.9	11 24.1
16	15 34 22.4	19 1.3	0 9.3	11 29.2	10 22.4	5 16.2	4 29.0	21 18.7	18 24.4	14 5.9	21 6.4	11 24.4
19	15 46 12.1	19 41.7	0 9.2	18 1.6	10 18.9	5 35.7	5 22.5	21 25.2	18 21.3	14 3.7	21 5.9	11 24.6
22	15 58 1.8	20 19.0	0 9.1	17 43.3	10 36.0	6 1.1	6 15.3	21 31.5	18 18.0	14 1.5	21 5.3	11 24.5
25	16 9 51.4	20 53.3	0 9.1	10 22.6	11 11.3	6 31.6	7 7.5	21 37.7	18 14.4	13 59.4	21 4.8	11 24.4
28	16 21 41.1	21 24.3	0 9.0	1 S 48.5	12 2.5	7 6.4	7 58.8	21 43.6	18 10.7	13 57.3	21 4.3	11 24.1
31	16 33 30.8	21 52.0	0 9.0	14 6.3	13 6.9	7 45.1	8 49.4	21 49.4	18 6.7	13 55.4	21 3.7	11 23.6

JUNE 1977

LONGITUDE

DAY	EPHEM. SID. TIME	☉	☊	☽	☿	♀	♂	♃	♄	♅	♆	♇
	h m s	° ′	° ′	° ′	° ′	° ′	° ′	° ′	° ′	° ′	° ′	° ′
1	16 37 27.3	10♊23.8	21♎53.2	28♏ 9.2	16♉ 7.5	25♈30.0	26♈10.7	12♊51.8	12♌ 9.2	8♏30.5	14♐53.6	11♎30.7
2	16 41 23.9	11 21.2	21 50.1	13♐25.3	17 19.0	26 20.0	26 55.6	13 5.8	12 14.2	8 R 28.5	14 R 51.9	11 R 30.0
3	16 45 20.4	12 18.7	21 46.9	28 39.3	18 33.5	27 10.7	27 40.5	13 19.7	12 19.2	8 26.5	14 50.3	11 29.4
4	16 49 17.0	13 16.1	21 43.7	13♑40.9	19 51.0	28 2.0	28 25.4	13 33.7	12 24.3	8 24.6	14 48.7	11 28.9
5	16 53 13.6	14 13.5	21 40.5	28 21.2	21 11.3	28 54.0	29 10.1	13 47.6	12 29.4	8 22.6	14 47.1	11 28.3
6	16 57 10.1	15 11.0	21 37.4	12♒34.5	22 34.5	29 46.5	29 54.9	14 1.6	12 34.6	8 20.8	14 45.4	11 27.8
7	17 1 6.7	16 8.4	21 34.2	26 18.4	24 .5	0♉39.7	0♉39.5	14 15.5	12 39.9	8 18.9	14 43.8	11 27.3
8	17 5 3.2	17 5.7	21 31.0	9♓33.7	25 29.3	1 33.3	1 24.2	14 29.5	12 45.3	8 17.1	14 42.2	11 26.8
9	17 8 59.8	18 3.1	21 27.8	22 23.2	27 .9	2 27.6	2 8.7	14 43.4	12 50.7	8 15.4	14 40.6	11 26.4
10	17 12 56.3	19 .5	21 24.7	4♈51.2	28 35.3	3 22.3	2 53.2	14 57.3	12 56.3	8 13.6	14 38.9	11 26.0
11	17 16 52.9	19 57.9	21 21.5	17 2.4	0♊12.4	4 17.6	3 37.7	15 11.3	13 1.8	8 11.9	14 37.3	11 25.7
12	17 20 49.5	20 55.2	21 18.3	29 1.8	1 52.2	5 13.3	4 22.1	15 25.2	13 7.5	8 10.3	14 35.7	11 25.3
13	17 24 46.0	21 52.6	21 15.1	10♉53.7	3 34.7	6 9.5	5 6.4	15 39.1	13 13.2	8 8.7	14 34.1	11 25.0
14	17 28 42.6	22 49.9	21 11.9	22 42.2	5 19.9	7 6.2	5 50.7	15 53.0	13 18.9	8 7.1	14 32.5	11 24.8
15	17 32 39.1	23 47.3	21 8.8	4♊30.4	7 7.7	8 3.2	6 34.9	16 6.8	13 24.8	8 5.6	14 30.9	11 24.5
16	17 36 35.7	24 44.6	21 5.6	16 20.9	8 58.1	9 .7	7 19.1	16 20.7	13 30.7	8 4.1	14 29.3	11 24.3
17	17 40 32.2	25 41.9	21 2.4	28 15.7	10 51.1	9 58.6	8 3.2	16 34.6	13 36.6	8 2.6	14 27.7	11 24.2
18	17 44 28.8	26 39.2	20 59.2	10♋16.3	12 46.5	10 56.9	8 47.2	16 48.4	13 42.6	8 1.2	14 26.1	11 24.0
19	17 48 25.4	27 36.5	20 56.1	22 24.0	14 44.3	11 55.5	9 31.1	17 2.2	13 48.7	7 59.9	14 24.5	11 23.9
20	17 52 21.9	28 33.8	20 52.9	4♌40.1	16 44.4	12 54.6	10 15.0	17 16.0	13 54.8	7 58.5	14 23.0	11 23.9
21	17 56 18.5	29 31.1	20 49.7	17 6.2	18 46.5	13 53.9	10 58.9	17 29.8	14 1.0	7 57.3	14 21.4	11 23.9
22	18 0 15.0	0♋28.4	20 46.5	29 44.3	20 50.7	14 53.7	11 42.7	17 43.6	14 7.3	7 56.1	14 19.9	11 23.9
23	18 4 11.6	1 25.6	20 43.4	12♍36.6	22 56.5	15 53.7	12 26.4	17 57.3	14 13.6	7 54.9	14 18.4	11 23.9
24	18 8 8.1	2 22.9	20 40.2	25 46.0	25 3.9	16 54.0	13 10.0	18 11.1	14 20.0	7 53.8	14 16.8	11 D 24.0
25	18 12 4.7	3 20.1	20 37.0	9♎15.1	27 12.6	17 54.7	13 53.6	18 24.7	14 26.4	7 52.7	14 15.3	11 24.1
26	18 16 1.3	4 17.3	20 33.8	23 6.1	29 22.2	18 55.6	14 37.0	18 38.4	14 32.8	7 51.6	14 13.8	11 24.2
27	18 19 57.8	5 14.5	20 30.6	7♏20.2	1♋32.7	19 56.8	15 20.5	18 52.0	14 39.3	7 50.7	14 12.3	11 24.4
28	18 23 54.4	6 11.7	20 27.5	21 56.0	3 43.6	20 58.4	16 3.8	19 5.6	14 45.9	7 49.7	14 10.8	11 24.6
29	18 27 50.9	7 8.9	20 24.3	6♐50.0	5 54.6	22 .2	16 47.1	19 19.2	14 52.4	7 48.8	14 9.4	11 24.9
30	18 31 47.5	8 6.1	20 21.1	21 55.2	8 5.6	23 2.2	17 30.3	19 32.8	14 59.1	7 48.0	14 7.9	11 25.1

LATITUDE

DAY	EPHEM. SID. TIME	☉	☊	☽	☿	♀	♂	♃	♄	♅	♆	♇
1	16 37 27.3	0 .0	0 .0	2N55.9	3S17.2	2S 1.1	1S 4.8	0S29.5	0N58.6	0N27.0	1N32.1	17N19.7
4	16 49 17.0	0 .0	0 .0	5 3.2	2 59.8	2 13.6	1 3.6	0 29.2	0 58.5	0 27.0	1 32.0	17 18.3
7	17 1 6.7	0 .0	0 .0	4 16.9	2 37.4	2 24.2	1 2.3	0 29.0	0 58.5	0 26.9	1 32.0	17 16.8
10	17 12 56.3	0 .0	0 .0	1 35.2	2 10.7	2 33.1	1 1.0	0 28.7	0 58.5	0 26.8	1 32.0	17 15.3
13	17 24 46.0	0 .0	0 .0	1S35.2	1 40.5	2 40.3	0 59.6	0 28.4	0 58.5	0 26.7	1 32.0	17 13.7
16	17 36 35.7	0 .0	0 .0	4 5.5	1 7.8	2 46.0	0 58.2	0 28.2	0 58.6	0 26.7	1 31.9	17 12.2
19	17 48 25.4	0 .0	0 .0	5 2.7	0 33.8	2 50.2	0 56.7	0 28.0	0 58.6	0 26.6	1 31.9	17 10.6
22	18 0 15.0	0 .0	0 .0	3 58.5	0 .0	2 53.0	0 55.1	0 27.7	0 58.6	0 26.5	1 31.8	17 9.0
25	18 12 4.7	0 .0	0 .0	1 4.2	0N31.8	2 54.5	0 53.4	0 27.5	0 58.7	0 26.4	1 31.7	17 7.3
28	18 23 54.4	0 .0	0 .0	2N34.3	0 59.8	2 54.7	0 51.7	0 27.3	0 58.7	0 26.3	1 31.7	17 5.7

RIGHT ASCENSION

DAY	EPHEM. SID. TIME	☉	☊	☽	☿	♀	♂	♃	♄	♅	♆	♇
1	16 37 27.3	8♊47.0	20♎14.0	26♏35.1	14♉37.8	24♈22.7	24♈40.4	11♊29.5	14♌54.2	6♏16.7	13♐47.3	17♎24.4
2	16 41 23.9	9 48.4	20 11.0	12♐31.9	15 46.9	25 11.3	25 22.7	11 44.4	14 59.2	6 R 14.8	13 R 45.6	17 R 23.7
3	16 45 20.4	10 49.9	20 8.0	28 35.1	16 59.0	26 .6	26 5.0	11 59.3	15 4.2	6 12.8	13 43.9	17 22.9
4	16 49 17.0	11 51.5	20 5.1	14♑19.1	18 14.2	26 50.5	26 47.4	12 14.2	15 9.4	6 10.9	13 42.1	17 22.2
5	16 53 13.6	12 53.2	20 2.1	29 23.8	19 32.5	27 41.0	27 29.8	12 29.1	15 14.6	6 9.1	13 40.4	17 21.5
6	16 57 10.1	13 55.0	19 59.1	13♒39.0	20 53.9	28 32.0	28 12.2	12 44.0	15 19.8	6 7.2	13 38.7	17 20.9
7	17 1 6.7	14 56.8	19 56.1	27 4.6	22 18.5	29 23.6	28 54.6	12 59.0	15 25.2	6 5.4	13 36.9	17 20.2
8	17 5 3.2	15 58.8	19 53.2	9♓47.7	23 46.2	0♉15.8	29 37.0	13 13.9	15 30.6	6 3.6	13 35.2	17 19.6
9	17 8 59.8	17 .8	19 50.2	21 58.9	25 17.1	1 8.5	0♉19.5	13 28.8	15 36.1	6 1.9	13 33.5	17 19.0
10	17 12 56.3	18 2.8	19 47.2	3♈49.5	26 51.3	2 1.7	1 2.0	13 43.8	15 41.6	6 .2	13 31.8	17 18.5
11	17 16 52.9	19 5.0	19 44.2	15 30.4	28 28.8	2 55.4	1 44.6	13 58.7	15 47.2	5 58.6	13 30.0	17 17.9
12	17 20 49.5	20 7.2	19 41.2	27 11.0	0♊ 9.6	3 49.7	2 27.1	14 13.6	15 52.9	5 56.9	13 28.3	17 17.4
13	17 24 46.0	21 9.4	19 38.3	8♉58.7	1 53.8	4 44.4	3 9.7	14 28.5	15 58.6	5 55.4	13 26.6	17 16.9
14	17 28 42.6	22 11.7	19 35.3	20 58.3	3 41.4	5 39.6	3 52.3	14 43.5	16 4.4	5 53.8	13 24.9	17 16.5
15	17 32 39.1	23 14.0	19 32.3	3♊11.4	5 32.5	6 35.3	4 34.9	14 58.4	16 10.3	5 52.3	13 23.2	17 16.1
16	17 36 35.7	24 16.4	19 29.3	15 36.7	7 26.9	7 31.5	5 17.6	15 13.3	16 16.2	5 50.9	13 21.5	17 15.7
17	17 40 32.2	25 18.8	19 26.4	28 10.2	9 24.7	8 28.1	6 .2	15 28.1	16 22.2	5 49.4	13 19.8	17 15.3
18	17 44 28.8	26 21.2	19 23.4	10♋46.4	11 25.9	9 25.2	6 42.9	15 43.0	16 28.3	5 48.1	13 18.1	17 15.0
19	17 48 25.4	27 23.6	19 20.4	23 20.1	13 30.4	10 22.8	7 25.7	15 57.9	16 34.4	5 46.7	13 16.4	17 14.7
20	17 52 21.9	28 26.0	19 17.4	5♌47.7	15 38.0	11 20.7	8 8.4	16 12.7	16 40.5	5 45.4	13 14.7	17 14.4
21	17 56 18.5	29 28.5	19 14.5	18 8.8	17 48.7	12 19.1	8 51.2	16 27.5	16 46.7	5 44.2	13 13.1	17 14.2
22	18 0 15.0	0♋30.9	19 11.5	0♍26.0	20 2.2	13 18.0	9 34.0	16 42.4	16 53.1	5 43.0	13 11.5	17 14.0
23	18 4 11.6	1 33.3	19 8.5	12 45.1	22 18.2	14 17.3	10 16.8	16 57.2	16 59.4	5 41.9	13 9.8	17 13.8
24	18 8 8.1	2 35.7	19 5.5	25 14.6	24 36.5	15 17.0	10 59.7	17 12.0	17 5.7	5 40.8	13 8.2	17 13.7
25	18 12 4.7	3 38.0	19 2.6	8♎ 4.6	26 56.8	16 17.2	11 42.6	17 26.7	17 12.2	5 39.7	13 6.6	17 13.5
26	18 16 1.3	4 40.4	18 59.6	21 25.8	29 18.6	17 17.7	12 25.4	17 41.4	17 18.6	5 38.7	13 5.0	17 13.4
27	18 19 57.8	5 42.6	18 56.6	5♏27.0	1♋41.7	18 18.7	13 8.3	17 56.1	17 25.1	5 37.7	13 3.4	17 13.4
28	18 23 54.4	6 44.9	18 53.7	20 12.4	4 5.5	19 20.1	13 51.3	18 10.8	17 31.7	5 36.7	13 1.8	17 13.3
29	18 27 50.9	7 47.1	18 50.7	5♐37.8	6 29.6	20 21.9	14 34.2	18 25.5	17 38.3	5 35.9	13 .3	17 13.3
30	18 31 47.5	8 49.2	18 47.7	21 29.1	8 53.7	21 24.1	15 17.2	18 40.1	17 45.0	5 35.0	12 58.7	17 13.3

DECLINATION

DAY	EPHEM. SID. TIME	☉	☊	☽	☿	♀	♂	♃	♄	♅	♆	♇
1	16 37 27.3	22N .4	0S 8.9	16S53.4	13N30.8	7N58.8	9N 6.1	21N51.2	18N 5.3	13S54.8	21S 3.6	11N23.4
4	16 49 17.0	22 23.5	0 8.9	17 42.5	14 48.8	8 41.7	9 55.4	21 56.7	18 1.0	13 52.9	21 3.0	11 22.8
7	17 1 6.7	22 43.1	0 8.8	8 43.0	16 13.9	9 27.0	10 43.8	22 1.9	17 56.6	13 51.2	21 2.5	11 22.0
10	17 12 56.3	22 59.1	0 8.7	3N23.1	17 43.2	10 14.3	11 31.1	22 6.9	17 52.0	13 49.6	21 2.0	11 21.1
13	17 24 46.0	23 11.4	0 8.7	13 35.2	19 13.4	11 3.0	12 17.2	22 11.7	17 47.2	13 48.0	21 1.5	11 20.1
16	17 36 35.7	23 20.1	0 8.6	18 40.2	20 40.7	11 52.6	13 2.2	22 16.3	17 42.1	13 46.6	21 1.0	11 18.9
19	17 48 25.4	23 25.1	0 8.6	16 35.9	22 .4	12 42.7	13 46.0	22 20.6	17 37.0	13 45.4	21 .5	11 17.6
22	18 0 15.0	23 26.3	0 8.5	7 50.3	23 7.5	13 32.9	14 28.5	22 24.8	17 31.6	13 44.2	20 60.0	11 16.1
25	18 12 4.7	23 23.8	0 8.4	4S39.0	23 56.4	14 22.5	15 9.6	22 28.6	17 26.1	13 43.2	20 59.5	11 14.6
28	18 23 54.4	23 17.7	0 8.4	15 45.9	24 23.0	15 11.4	15 49.3	22 32.3	17 20.5	13 42.3	20 59.1	11 12.9

JULY 1977

DAY	EPHEM. SID. TIME h m s	☉ ° ′	☊ ° ′	☽ ° ′	☿ ° ′	♀ ° ′	♂ ° ′	♃ ° ′	♄ ° ′	♅ ° ′	♆ ° ′	♇ ° ′
		LONGITUDE										
1	18 35 44.0	9♋ 3.3	20♎17.9	7♑ 2.5	10♋16.2	24♉ 4.6	18♉13.4	19♊46.3	15♌ 5.8	7♏47.2	14♐ 6.5	11♎25.4
2	18 39 40.6	10 .5	20 14.8	22 1.7	12 26.2	25 7.2	18 56.5	19 59.8	15 12.5	7R46.4	14R 5.1	11 25.8
3	18 43 37.2	10 57.7	20 11.6	6♒43.4	14 35.4	26 10.0	19 39.5	20 13.2	15 19.3	7 45.7	14 3.7	11 26.1
4	18 47 33.7	11 54.9	20 8.4	21 .5	16 43.5	27 13.1	20 22.4	20 26.6	15 26.1	7 45.0	14 2.3	11 26.5
5	18 51 30.3	12 52.0	20 5.2	4♓49.1	18 50.4	28 16.4	21 5.3	20 40.0	15 33.0	7 44.4	14 .9	11 27.0
6	18 55 26.8	13 49.2	20 2.1	18 8.7	20 55.9	29 20.0	21 48.1	20 53.3	15 39.9	7 43.9	13 59.5	11 27.4
7	18 59 23.4	14 46.4	19 58.9	1♈ 1.3	22 59.9	0♊23.8	22 30.8	21 6.7	15 46.8	7 43.4	13 58.2	11 27.9
8	19 3 19.9	15 43.6	19 55.7	13 30.9	25 2.3	1 27.8	23 13.5	21 19.9	15 53.8	7 42.9	13 56.8	11 28.5
9	19 7 16.5	16 40.8	19 52.5	25 42.4	27 3.0	2 32.0	23 56.0	21 33.2	16 .8	7 42.5	13 55.5	11 29.1
10	19 11 13.0	17 38.1	19 49.4	7♉41.2	29 2.0	3 36.5	24 38.5	21 46.3	16 7.8	7 42.2	13 54.3	11 29.7
11	19 15 9.6	18 35.3	19 46.2	19 32.4	0♌59.1	4 41.1	25 20.9	21 59.5	16 14.9	7 41.9	13 53.0	11 30.3
12	19 19 6.2	19 32.5	19 43.0	1♊20.8	2 54.4	5 45.9	26 3.3	22 12.6	16 22.1	7 41.6	13 51.7	11 31.0
13	19 23 2.7	20 29.8	19 39.8	13 10.7	4 48.0	6 51.0	26 45.6	22 25.7	16 29.3	7 41.5	13 50.6	11 31.7
14	19 26 59.3	21 27.0	19 36.6	25 5.1	6 39.6	7 56.2	27 27.8	22 38.7	16 36.5	7 41.3	13 49.3	11 32.4
15	19 30 55.8	22 24.3	19 33.5	7♋ 6.7	8 29.3	9 1.6	28 9.9	22 51.7	16 43.7	7 41.2	13 48.2	11 33.2
16	19 34 52.4	23 21.5	19 30.3	19 17.1	10 17.1	10 7.2	28 51.9	23 4.6	16 50.9	7 41.2	13 47.0	11 34.0
17	19 38 48.9	24 18.8	19 27.1	1♌37.2	12 3.1	11 12.9	29 33.8	23 17.4	16 58.2	7 41.2	13 45.8	11 34.8
18	19 42 45.5	25 16.1	19 23.9	14 7.6	13 47.2	12 18.9	0♊15.7	23 30.2	17 5.5	7 41.2	13 44.7	11 35.7
19	19 46 42.1	26 13.4	19 20.8	26 48.5	15 29.4	13 24.9	0 57.5	23 43.0	17 12.9	7D41.4	13 43.6	11 36.6
20	19 50 38.6	27 10.6	19 17.6	9♍40.6	17 9.7	14 31.2	1 39.1	23 55.7	17 20.2	7 41.5	13 42.6	11 37.5
21	19 54 35.2	28 7.9	19 14.4	22 44.4	18 48.2	15 37.5	2 20.7	24 8.3	17 27.6	7 41.7	13 41.5	11 38.5
22	19 58 31.7	29 5.2	19 11.2	6♎ 1.4	20 24.8	16 44.1	3 2.2	24 20.9	17 35.0	7 42.0	13 40.5	11 39.4
23	20 2 28.3	0♌ 2.5	19 8.1	19 32.9	21 59.5	17 50.8	3 43.6	24 33.4	17 42.5	7 42.3	13 39.5	11 40.5
24	20 6 24.8	0 59.8	19 4.9	3♏20.3	23 32.3	18 57.6	4 25.0	24 45.9	17 49.9	7 42.7	13 38.5	11 41.5
25	20 10 21.4	1 57.1	19 1.7	17 24.6	25 3.3	20 4.6	5 6.2	24 58.3	17 57.4	7 43.1	13 37.5	11 42.6
26	20 14 17.9	2 54.4	18 58.5	1♐45.3	26 32.3	21 11.7	5 47.3	25 10.7	18 4.9	7 43.6	13 36.6	11 43.7
27	20 18 14.5	3 51.7	18 55.3	16 20.0	27 59.5	22 19.0	6 28.4	25 22.9	18 12.4	7 44.2	13 35.7	11 44.8
28	20 22 11.1	4 49.1	18 52.2	1♑ 4.3	29 24.6	23 26.4	7 9.4	25 35.1	18 20.0	7 44.8	13 34.9	11 46.0
29	20 26 7.6	5 46.4	18 49.0	15 51.4	0♍47.8	24 33.9	7 50.2	25 47.3	18 27.5	7 45.4	13 34.0	11 47.2
30	20 30 4.2	6 43.7	18 45.8	0♒33.4	2 9.1	25 41.6	8 31.0	25 59.4	18 35.1	7 46.1	13 33.2	11 48.4
31	20 34 .7	7 41.1	18 42.6	15 2.1	3 28.2	26 49.4	9 11.7	26 11.4	18 42.6	7 46.8	13 32.4	11 49.7
		LATITUDE										
1	18 35 44.0	0 .0	0 .0	4N52.5	1N22.4	2S53.8	0S49.8	0S27.1	0N58.8	0N26.2	1N31.6	17N 4.1
4	18 47 33.7	0 .0	0 .0	4 20.0	1 38.6	2 51.7	0 48.0	0 26.9	0 58.8	0 26.2	1 31.5	17 2.4
7	18 59 23.4	0 .0	0 .0	1 40.1	1 48.2	2 48.7	0 46.0	0 26.7	0 58.9	0 26.1	1 31.4	17 .8
10	19 11 13.0	0 .0	0 .0	1S30.9	1 51.1	2 44.7	0 44.0	0 26.5	0 59.0	0 26.0	1 31.3	16 59.2
13	19 23 2.7	0 .0	0 .0	4 1.2	1 47.9	2 39.9	0 42.0	0 26.3	0 59.1	0 25.9	1 31.2	16 57.6
16	19 34 52.4	0 .0	0 .0	4 60.0	1 39.2	2 34.2	0 39.8	0 26.1	0 59.2	0 25.8	1 31.1	16 56.0
19	19 46 42.1	0 .0	0 .0	3 57.4	1 25.6	2 27.8	0 37.6	0 26.0	0 59.3	0 25.7	1 31.0	16 54.5
22	19 58 31.7	0 .0	0 .0	1 5.9	1 7.6	2 20.7	0 35.4	0 25.8	0 59.5	0 25.6	1 30.8	16 52.9
25	20 10 21.4	0 .0	0 .0	2N26.5	0 45.9	2 13.0	0 33.0	0 25.6	0 59.6	0 25.5	1 30.7	16 51.4
28	20 22 11.1	0 .0	0 .0	4 48.5	0 21.0	2 4.7	0 30.6	0 25.5	0 59.8	0 25.4	1 30.6	16 49.9
31	20 34 .7	0 .0	0 .0	4 28.9	0S 6.6	1 56.0	0 28.2	0 25.3	0 60.0	0 25.3	1 30.4	16 48.5
		RIGHT ASCENSION										
1	18 35 44.0	9♋51.3	18♎44.7	7♑23.7	11♋17.3	22♉26.7	16♉ .2	18♊54.7	17♌51.7	5♏34.2	12♐57.2	17♎13.4
2	18 39 40.6	10 53.3	18 41.8	22 57.4	13 40.0	23 29.7	16 43.3	19 9.2	17 58.4	5R33.5	12R55.7	17D13.5
3	18 43 37.2	11 55.2	18 38.8	7♒52.1	16 1.5	24 33.2	17 26.3	19 23.7	18 5.2	5 32.8	12 54.2	17 13.6
4	18 47 33.7	12 57.1	18 35.8	21 59.5	18 21.4	25 37.0	18 9.4	19 38.2	18 12.0	5 32.1	12 52.7	17 13.7
5	18 51 30.3	13 58.9	18 32.9	5♓20.6	20 39.5	26 41.2	18 52.5	19 52.7	18 18.9	5 31.5	12 51.2	17 13.9
6	18 55 26.8	15 .6	18 29.9	18 2.9	22 55.5	27 45.9	19 35.6	20 7.1	18 25.8	5 31.0	12 49.8	17 14.1
7	18 59 23.4	16 2.2	18 26.9	0♈16.5	25 9.2	28 50.9	20 18.7	20 21.5	18 32.7	5 30.5	12 48.3	17 14.3
8	19 3 19.9	17 3.8	18 23.9	12 12.3	27 20.4	29 56.3	21 1.9	20 35.8	18 39.7	5 30.0	12 46.9	17 14.6
9	19 7 16.5	18 5.2	18 21.0	24 .5	29 29.1	1♊ 2.2	21 45.0	20 50.1	18 46.7	5 29.6	12 45.5	17 14.9
10	19 11 13.0	19 6.6	18 18.0	5♉49.9	1♌35.1	2 8.3	22 28.2	21 4.4	18 53.7	5 29.3	12 44.1	17 15.2
11	19 15 9.6	20 7.8	18 15.0	17 47.0	3 38.3	3 14.9	23 11.4	21 18.6	19 .8	5 29.0	12 42.8	17 15.5
12	19 19 6.2	21 9.0	18 12.1	29 55.8	5 38.7	4 21.8	23 54.6	21 32.8	19 7.9	5 28.7	12 41.5	17 15.9
13	19 23 2.7	22 10.1	18 9.1	12♊17.3	7 36.4	5 29.2	24 37.9	21 47.0	19 15.1	5 28.6	12 40.2	17 16.4
14	19 26 59.3	23 11.0	18 6.1	24 49.5	9 31.2	6 36.8	25 21.1	22 1.1	19 22.3	5 28.4	12 38.9	17 16.8
15	19 30 55.8	24 11.8	18 3.2	7♋28.1	11 23.2	7 44.9	26 4.3	22 15.1	19 29.5	5 28.3	12 37.6	17 17.3
16	19 34 52.4	25 12.5	18 .2	20 8.1	13 12.4	8 53.2	26 47.6	22 29.1	19 36.7	5 28.2	12 36.4	17 17.8
17	19 38 48.9	26 13.0	17 57.2	2♌44.6	14 58.8	10 1.9	27 30.8	22 43.0	19 44.0	5 28.2	12 35.2	17 18.3
18	19 42 45.5	27 13.5	17 54.3	15 15.2	16 42.6	11 10.9	28 14.0	22 56.9	19 51.3	5D28.3	12 34.0	17 18.9
19	19 46 42.1	28 13.8	17 51.3	27 39.8	18 23.6	12 20.3	28 57.2	23 10.7	19 58.6	5 28.4	12 32.8	17 19.5
20	19 50 38.6	29 13.9	17 48.3	10♍ 2.0	20 2.0	13 30.0	29 40.5	23 24.5	20 5.9	5 28.5	12 31.7	17 20.1
21	19 54 35.2	0♌13.9	17 45.4	22 27.8	21 37.9	14 39.9	0♊23.7	23 38.2	20 13.3	5 28.8	12 30.5	17 20.7
22	19 58 31.7	1 13.8	17 42.4	5♎ 5.6	23 11.1	15 50.2	1 6.9	23 51.8	20 20.6	5 29.0	12 29.4	17 21.4
23	20 2 28.3	2 13.5	17 39.4	18 4.6	24 41.9	17 .8	1 50.0	24 5.4	20 28.0	5 29.3	12 28.4	17 22.1
24	20 6 24.8	3 13.1	17 36.5	1♏33.7	26 10.1	18 11.7	2 33.2	24 18.9	20 35.4	5 29.7	12 27.3	17 22.8
25	20 10 21.4	4 12.5	17 33.5	15 39.3	27 36.0	19 22.8	3 16.4	24 32.4	20 42.9	5 30.1	12 26.3	17 23.6
26	20 14 17.9	5 11.7	17 30.5	0♐22.6	28 59.4	20 34.3	3 59.5	24 45.8	20 50.3	5 30.5	12 25.3	17 24.4
27	20 18 14.5	6 10.8	17 27.6	15 36.9	0♍20.4	21 46.0	4 42.6	24 59.1	20 57.8	5 31.0	12 24.4	17 25.2
28	20 22 11.1	7 9.8	17 24.6	1♑ 7.6	1 39.1	22 57.9	5 25.7	25 12.3	21 5.3	5 31.6	12 23.4	17 26.1
29	20 26 7.6	8 8.6	17 21.6	16 35.0	2 55.4	24 10.2	6 8.8	25 25.5	21 12.8	5 32.2	12 22.5	17 26.9
30	20 30 4.2	9 7.2	17 18.7	1♒39.9	4 9.4	25 22.6	6 51.8	25 38.6	21 20.3	5 32.9	12 21.6	17 27.9
31	20 34 .7	10 5.7	17 15.7	16 9.4	5 21.0	26 35.3	7 34.9	25 51.7	21 27.8	5 33.6	12 20.8	17 28.8
		DECLINATION										
1	18 35 44.0	23N 7.8	0S 8.3	18S23.1	24N24.7	15N59.0	16N27.5	22N35.7	17N14.7	13S41.6	20S58.7	11N11.1
4	18 47 33.7	22 54.3	0 8.2	10 23.1	24 1.5	16 45.0	17 4.2	22 38.9	17 8.7	13 41.0	20 58.2	11 9.2
7	18 59 23.4	22 37.2	0 8.2	1N56.2	23 15.4	17 29.0	17 39.5	22 41.9	17 2.6	13 40.5	20 57.9	11 7.1
10	19 11 13.0	22 16.6	0 8.1	12 38.4	22 9.9	18 10.7	18 13.1	22 44.6	16 56.4	13 40.2	20 57.5	11 5.0
13	19 23 2.7	21 52.5	0 8.1	18 23.5	20 48.6	18 49.6	18 45.1	22 47.1	16 50.1	13 40.1	20 57.2	11 2.7
16	19 34 52.4	21 25.1	0 8.0	17 6.1	19 15.3	19 25.5	19 15.5	22 49.4	16 43.6	13 40.1	20 56.9	11 .4
19	19 46 42.1	20 54.4	0 7.9	8 51.3	17 33.2	19 57.9	19 44.2	22 51.5	16 37.1	13 40.2	20 56.6	10 58.0
22	19 58 31.7	20 20.5	0 7.9	3S24.1	15 45.2	20 26.7	20 11.2	22 53.4	16 30.5	13 40.5	20 56.3	10 55.5
25	20 10 21.4	19 43.5	0 7.8	14 41.1	13 53.5	20 51.5	20 36.5	22 55.0	16 23.7	13 41.0	20 56.1	10 52.9
28	20 22 11.1	19 3.6	0 7.7	18 37.6	12 .4	21 12.0	21 .1	22 56.5	16 16.9	13 41.6	20 55.9	10 50.3
31	20 34 .7	18 20.9	0 7.7	12 2.2	10 7.9	21 28.1	21 21.9	22 57.8	16 10.0	13 42.3	20 55.8	10 47.6

AUGUST 1977

DAY	EPHEM. SID. TIME	☉	☊	☾	☿	♀	♂	♃	♄	♅	♆	♇
	h m s	° ′	° ′	° ′	° ′	° ′	° ′	° ′	° ′	° ′	° ′	° ′
		LONGITUDE										
1	20 37 57.3	8♌38.5	18♎39.5	29♒11.0	4♍45.3	27♊57.4	9♊52.3	26♊23.3	18♌50.2	7♏47.6	13♐31.6	11♎51.0
2	20 41 53.8	9 35.9	18 36.3	12♓55.7	6 .3	29 5.4	10 32.9	26 35.2	18 57.8	7 48.5	13R30.9	11 52.3
3	20 45 50.4	10 33.3	18 33.1	26 14.5	7 13.1	0♋13.7	11 13.3	26 47.0	19 5.5	7 49.4	13 30.2	11 53.7
4	20 49 46.9	11 30.7	18 29.9	9♈ 8.3	8 23.6	1 22.1	11 53.7	26 58.7	19 13.1	7 50.4	13 29.6	11 55.0
5	20 53 43.5	12 28.2	18 26.7	21 39.8	9 31.7	2 30.5	12 33.9	27 10.4	19 20.8	7 51.3	13 28.9	11 56.4
6	20 57 40.1	13 25.6	18 23.6	3♉53.4	10 37.5	3 39.1	13 14.0	27 21.9	19 28.4	7 52.4	13 28.3	11 57.9
7	21 1 36.6	14 23.1	18 20.4	15 53.9	11 40.7	4 47.8	13 54.1	27 33.4	19 36.1	7 53.5	13 27.7	11 59.3
8	21 5 33.2	15 20.6	18 17.2	27 46.7	12 41.2	5 56.7	14 34.0	27 44.8	19 43.7	7 54.6	13 27.1	12 .8
9	21 9 29.7	16 18.2	18 14.0	9♊37.0	13 39.1	7 5.6	15 13.9	27 56.2	19 51.4	7 55.8	13 26.6	12 2.3
10	21 13 26.3	17 15.7	18 10.9	21 29.4	14 34.0	8 14.7	15 53.6	28 7.4	19 59.1	7 57.1	13 26.1	12 3.8
11	21 17 22.8	18 13.3	18 7.7	3♋28.1	15 26.0	9 23.9	16 33.3	28 18.6	20 6.8	7 58.4	13 25.6	12 5.4
12	21 21 19.4	19 10.9	18 4.5	15 36.4	16 14.8	10 33.2	17 12.8	28 29.6	20 14.4	7 59.7	13 25.2	12 7.0
13	21 25 15.9	20 8.5	18 1.3	27 56.6	17 .2	11 42.6	17 52.2	28 40.6	20 22.1	8 1.1	13 24.8	12 8.6
14	21 29 12.5	21 6.1	17 58.1	10♌30.1	17 42.1	12 52.1	18 31.6	28 51.5	20 29.8	8 2.6	13 24.4	12 10.2
15	21 33 9.0	22 3.8	17 55.0	23 17.1	18 20.3	14 1.7	19 10.8	29 2.3	20 37.5	8 4.1	13 24.0	12 11.9
16	21 37 5.6	23 1.5	17 51.8	6♍17.4	18 54.7	15 11.4	19 49.9	29 13.0	20 45.2	8 5.6	13 23.7	12 13.5
17	21 41 2.1	23 59.2	17 48.6	19 30.1	19 24.8	16 21.3	20 28.9	29 23.6	20 52.8	8 7.2	13 23.4	12 15.2
18	21 44 58.7	24 56.9	17 45.4	2♎54.2	19 50.6	17 31.2	21 7.8	29 34.1	21 .5	8 8.9	13 23.2	12 17.0
19	21 48 55.3	25 54.6	17 42.3	16 29.0	20 11.9	18 41.2	21 46.5	29 44.5	21 8.2	8 10.6	13 22.9	12 18.7
20	21 52 51.8	26 52.4	17 39.1	0♏13.8	20 28.3	19 51.3	22 25.2	29 54.9	21 15.8	8 12.3	13 22.7	12 20.5
21	21 56 48.4	27 50.2	17 35.9	14 8.3	20 39.6	21 1.5	23 3.7	0♋ 5.1	21 23.5	8 14.1	13 22.6	12 22.3
22	22 0 44.9	28 48.0	17 32.7	28 11.9	20 45.6	22 11.8	23 42.1	0 15.2	21 31.1	8 15.9	13 22.5	12 24.1
23	22 4 41.5	29 45.8	17 29.5	12♐23.7	20 46.1	23 22.2	24 20.4	0 25.2	21 38.7	8 17.8	13 22.4	12 26.0
24	22 8 38.0	0♍43.7	17 26.4	26 42.1	20R41.0	24 32.8	24 58.7	0 35.1	21 46.4	8 19.8	13 22.3	12 27.9
25	22 12 34.6	1 41.5	17 23.2	11♑ 3.9	20 29.9	25 43.3	25 36.7	0 44.9	21 54.0	8 21.8	13 22.3	12 29.7
26	22 16 31.1	2 39.4	17 20.0	25 25.0	20 12.9	26 54.0	26 14.7	0 54.6	22 1.6	8 23.8	13 22.3	12 31.7
27	22 20 27.7	3 37.3	17 16.8	9♒40.5	19 50.0	28 4.8	26 52.5	1 4.1	22 9.2	8 25.8	13D22.4	12 33.6
28	22 24 24.2	4 35.2	17 13.7	23 45.2	19 21.1	29 15.6	27 30.2	1 13.6	22 16.8	8 27.9	13 22.4	12 35.5
29	22 28 20.8	5 33.1	17 10.5	7♓34.3	18 46.5	0♌26.6	28 7.8	1 22.9	22 24.3	8 30.1	13 22.5	12 37.5
30	22 32 17.3	6 31.1	17 7.3	21 4.6	18 6.4	1 37.6	28 45.2	1 32.1	22 31.9	8 32.3	13 22.6	12 39.5
31	22 36 13.9	7 29.1	17 4.1	4♈14.2	17 21.3	2 48.8	29 22.5	1 41.2	22 39.4	8 34.5	13 22.8	12 41.5
		LATITUDE										
1	20 37 57.3	0 .0	0 .0	3N47.0	0S16.4	1S53.0	0S27.4	0S25.3	1N .0	0N25.3	1N30.4	16N48.0
4	20 49 46.9	0 .0	0 .0	0 44.2	0 46.9	1 43.8	0 24.8	0 25.1	1 .2	0 25.2	1 30.2	16 46.6
7	21 1 36.6	0 .0	0 .0	2S25.8	1 19.1	1 34.2	0 22.2	0 25.0	1 .4	0 25.1	1 30.1	16 45.3
10	21 13 26.3	0 .0	0 .0	4 34.7	1 52.3	1 24.3	0 19.6	0 24.8	1 .6	0 25.0	1 29.9	16 44.0
13	21 25 15.9	0 .0	0 .0	4 59.1	2 25.8	1 14.3	0 16.8	0 24.7	1 .8	0 24.9	1 29.8	16 42.8
16	21 37 5.6	0 .0	0 .0	3 17.6	2 58.8	1 4.1	0 14.0	0 24.5	1 1.1	0 24.8	1 29.6	16 41.6
19	21 48 55.3	0 .0	0 .0	0N 1.1	3 29.9	0 53.8	0 11.2	0 24.4	1 1.3	0 24.7	1 29.4	16 40.4
22	22 0 44.9	0 .0	0 .0	3 26.6	3 57.4	0 43.5	0 8.2	0 24.3	1 1.6	0 24.6	1 29.3	16 39.3
25	22 12 34.6	0 .0	0 .0	5 7.5	4 18.7	0 33.3	0 5.2	0 24.1	1 1.9	0 24.6	1 29.1	16 38.3
28	22 24 24.2	0 .0	0 .0	4 4.3	4 30.5	0 23.1	0 2.2	0 24.0	1 2.1	0 24.5	1 29.0	16 37.3
31	22 36 13.9	0 .0	0 .0	1 1.8	4 29.1	0 13.1	0N 1.0	0 23.9	1 2.4	0 24.4	1 28.8	16 36.4
		RIGHT ASCENSION										
1	20 37 57.3	11♌ 4.1	17♎12.8	29♒58.6	6♍30.3	27♊48.2	8♊17.9	26♊ 4.6	21♌35.3	5♏34.4	12♐20.0	17♎29.7
2	20 41 53.8	12 2.3	17 9.8	13♓ 9.6	7 37.3	29 1.4	9 .8	26 17.5	21 42.9	5 35.2	12R19.2	17 30.7
3	20 45 50.4	13 .4	17 6.8	25 49.3	8 41.9	0♋14.7	9 43.8	26 30.4	21 50.5	5 36.1	12 18.5	17 31.8
4	20 49 46.9	13 58.3	17 3.9	8♈ 6.3	9 44.1	1 28.3	10 26.7	26 43.1	21 58.0	5 37.0	12 17.7	17 32.8
5	20 53 43.5	14 56.0	17 .9	20 9.9	10 43.8	2 42.0	11 9.6	26 55.7	22 5.6	5 37.9	12 17.1	17 33.9
6	20 57 40.1	15 53.6	16 57.9	2♉ 8.6	11 41.0	3 55.9	11 52.4	27 8.3	22 13.1	5 39.0	12 16.4	17 35.0
7	21 1 36.6	16 51.1	16 55.0	14 9.4	12 35.7	5 9.9	12 35.2	27 20.8	22 20.7	5 40.0	12 15.7	17 36.1
8	21 5 33.2	17 48.4	16 52.0	26 17.3	13 27.8	6 24.1	13 17.9	27 33.2	22 28.3	5 41.1	12 15.1	17 37.2
9	21 9 29.7	18 45.6	16 49.1	8♊35.0	14 17.2	7 38.4	14 .5	27 45.5	22 35.9	5 42.3	12 14.6	17 38.4
10	21 13 26.3	19 42.6	16 46.1	21 2.8	15 3.8	8 52.9	14 43.2	27 57.7	22 43.5	5 43.5	12 14.0	17 39.6
11	21 17 22.8	20 39.5	16 43.1	3♋38.6	15 47.5	10 7.4	15 25.7	28 9.8	22 51.1	5 44.8	12 13.5	17 40.8
12	21 21 19.4	21 36.3	16 40.2	16 19.1	16 28.2	11 22.1	16 8.2	28 21.8	22 58.7	5 46.1	12 13.0	17 42.1
13	21 25 15.9	22 32.9	16 37.2	29 .3	17 5.8	12 36.8	16 50.6	28 33.7	23 6.2	5 47.4	12 12.6	17 43.4
14	21 29 12.5	23 29.4	16 34.3	11♌39.5	17 40.1	13 51.6	17 33.0	28 45.6	23 13.8	5 48.8	12 12.2	17 44.7
15	21 33 9.0	24 25.7	16 31.3	24 15.5	18 11.0	15 6.5	18 15.3	28 57.3	23 21.4	5 50.3	12 11.8	17 46.0
16	21 37 5.6	25 21.9	16 28.3	6♍49.9	18 38.3	16 21.4	18 57.5	29 8.9	23 29.0	5 51.8	12 11.5	17 47.3
17	21 41 2.1	26 18.0	16 25.4	19 26.6	19 1.9	17 36.3	19 39.6	29 20.5	23 36.6	5 53.3	12 11.1	17 48.7
18	21 44 58.7	27 13.9	16 22.4	2♎11.5	19 21.6	18 51.3	20 21.6	29 31.9	23 44.1	5 54.9	12 10.9	17 50.1
19	21 48 55.3	28 9.8	16 19.5	15 11.7	19 37.1	20 6.2	21 3.6	29 43.2	23 51.7	5 56.5	12 10.6	17 51.5
20	21 52 51.8	29 5.4	16 16.5	28 34.4	19 48.4	21 21.2	21 45.4	29 54.4	23 59.2	5 58.2	12 10.4	17 53.0
21	21 56 48.4	0♍ 1.0	16 13.5	12♏24.9	19 55.2	22 36.1	22 27.2	0♋ 5.5	24 6.8	5 60.0	12 10.2	17 54.4
22	22 0 44.9	0 56.5	16 10.6	26 44.8	19 57.3	23 51.0	23 8.9	0 16.5	24 14.3	6 1.7	12 10.1	17 55.9
23	22 4 41.5	1 51.8	16 7.6	11♐30.4	19R54.7	25 5.9	23 50.5	0 27.3	24 21.8	6 3.6	12 10.0	17 57.4
24	22 8 38.0	2 47.0	16 4.7	26 32.0	19 47.2	26 20.8	24 32.0	0 38.1	24 29.4	6 5.5	12 10.0	17 59.0
25	22 12 34.6	3 42.1	16 1.7	11♑35.1	19 34.6	27 35.6	25 13.3	0 48.8	24 36.9	6 7.4	12 9.9	18 .5
26	22 16 31.1	4 37.1	15 58.8	26 24.9	19 17.0	28 50.3	25 54.6	0 59.3	24 44.3	6 9.3	12 9.9	18 2.1
27	22 20 27.7	5 32.0	15 55.8	10♒49.5	18 54.3	0♌ 5.0	26 35.7	1 9.7	24 51.8	6 11.3	12 9.9	18 3.7
28	22 24 24.2	6 26.8	15 52.8	24 42.6	18 26.8	1 19.6	27 16.8	1 20.0	24 59.2	6 13.4	12D10.0	18 5.3
29	22 28 20.8	7 21.5	15 49.9	8♓ 3.9	17 54.6	2 34.1	27 57.7	1 30.1	25 6.7	6 15.5	12 10.1	18 6.9
30	22 32 17.3	8 16.1	15 46.9	20 57.1	17 17.9	3 48.5	28 38.5	1 40.1	25 14.1	6 17.6	12 10.2	18 8.6
31	22 36 13.9	9 10.6	15 44.0	3♈28.7	16 37.4	5 2.7	29 19.2	1 50.0	25 21.5	6 19.8	12 10.4	18 10.3
		DECLINATION										
1	20 37 57.3	18N 6.1	0S 7.7	8S12.6	9N30.8	21N32.4	21N28.8	22N58.2	16N 7.7	13S42.6	20S55.7	10N46.6
4	20 49 46.9	17 19.8	0 7.6	4N17.9	7 41.9	21 42.2	21 48.3	22 59.2	16 .8	13 43.6	20 55.6	10 43.8
7	21 1 36.6	16 30.9	0 7.5	14 16.2	5 57.9	21 47.0	22 6.1	23 .1	15 53.7	13 44.7	20 55.5	10 41.0
10	21 13 26.3	15 39.7	0 7.5	18 35.9	4 20.9	21 46.8	22 22.1	23 .8	15 46.7	13 46.0	20 55.5	10 38.1
13	21 25 15.9	14 46.2	0 7.4	15 41.1	2 53.6	21 41.4	22 36.4	23 1.3	15 39.6	13 47.4	20 55.5	10 35.1
16	21 37 5.6	13 50.5	0 7.3	6 8.5	1 38.7	21 30.8	22 49.0	23 1.7	15 32.5	13 48.9	20 55.5	10 32.1
19	21 48 55.3	12 52.9	0 7.3	6S27.8	0 39.9	21 14.9	22 59.9	23 2.0	15 25.3	13 50.6	20 55.6	10 29.1
22	22 0 44.9	11 53.5	0 7.2	16 24.0	0 1.4	20 53.7	23 9.2	23 2.1	15 18.2	13 52.4	20 55.7	10 26.1
25	22 12 34.6	10 52.4	0 7.1	17 52.3	0S12.0	20 27.3	23 16.8	23 2.1	15 11.0	13 54.3	20 55.9	10 23.0
28	22 24 24.2	9 49.7	0 7.1	9 45.4	0N 4.0	19 55.8	23 22.8	23 2.0	15 3.9	13 56.4	20 56.0	10 19.9
31	22 36 13.9	8 45.7	0 7.0	2N37.8	0 51.8	19 19.1	23 27.3	23 1.9	14 56.8	13 58.6	20 56.2	10 16.9

SEPTEMBER 1977

LONGITUDE

DAY	EPHEM. SID. TIME	☉	☊	☽	☿	♀	♂	♃	♄	♅	♆	♇
	h m s	° ′	° ′	° ′	° ′	° ′	° ′	° ′	° ′	° ′	° ′	° ′
1	22 40 10.4	8♍27.1	17♎ .9	17♈ 3.1	16♍31.8	4♌ .0	29♊59.8	1♋50.2	22♌46.9	8♏36.8	13♐23.0	12♎43.5
2	22 44 7.0	9 25.2	16 57.8	29 33.0	15 R 38.6	5 11.3	0♋36.8	1 59.1	22 54.4	8 39.1	13 23.2	12 45.5
3	22 48 3.5	10 23.3	16 54.6	11♉46.8	14 42.6	6 22.7	1 13.8	2 7.8	23 1.8	8 41.4	13 23.5	12 47.6
4	22 52 .1	11 21.4	16 51.4	23 48.5	13 44.9	7 34.2	1 50.6	2 16.5	23 9.3	8 43.8	13 23.8	12 49.6
5	22 55 56.6	12 19.5	16 48.2	5♊42.8	12 46.6	8 45.8	2 27.3	2 24.9	23 16.7	8 46.3	13 24.1	12 51.7
6	22 59 53.2	13 17.7	16 45.1	17 34.4	11 49.0	9 57.5	3 3.8	2 33.3	23 24.1	8 48.7	13 24.5	12 53.8
7	23 3 49.8	14 15.9	16 41.9	29 28.3	10 53.4	11 9.2	3 40.2	2 41.5	23 31.4	8 51.3	13 24.9	12 55.9
8	23 7 46.3	15 14.2	16 38.7	11♋29.2	10 1.1	12 21.1	4 16.5	2 49.6	23 38.8	8 53.8	13 25.3	12 58.0
9	23 11 42.9	16 12.5	16 35.5	23 41.2	9 13.3	13 33.0	4 52.6	2 57.6	23 46.1	8 56.4	13 25.8	13 .2
10	23 15 39.4	17 10.8	16 32.3	6♌ 7.7	8 31.3	14 45.0	5 28.6	3 5.4	23 53.4	8 59.0	13 26.2	13 2.3
11	23 19 36.0	18 9.1	16 29.2	18 51.0	7 56.0	15 57.1	6 4.4	3 13.1	24 .6	9 1.7	13 26.8	13 4.5
12	23 23 32.5	19 7.5	16 26.0	1♍52.2	7 28.4	17 9.2	6 40.1	3 20.7	24 7.8	9 4.4	13 27.3	13 6.7
13	23 27 29.1	20 5.9	16 22.8	15 11.2	7 9.1	18 21.4	7 15.7	3 28.1	24 15.0	9 7.2	13 27.9	13 8.9
14	23 31 25.6	21 4.4	16 19.6	28 46.7	6 58.8	19 33.8	7 51.1	3 35.4	24 22.2	9 10.0	13 28.6	13 11.2
15	23 35 22.2	22 2.9	16 16.5	12♎36.1	6 57.6	20 46.2	8 26.3	3 42.5	24 29.4	9 12.8	13 29.2	13 13.4
16	23 39 18.7	23 1.4	16 13.3	26 36.7	7D 5.9	21 58.6	9 1.3	3 49.5	24 36.5	9 15.7	13 29.9	13 15.6
17	23 43 15.3	23 60.0	16 10.1	10♏45.0	7 23.5	23 11.1	9 36.2	3 56.3	24 43.5	9 18.6	13 30.6	13 17.9
18	23 47 11.8	24 58.5	16 6.9	24 58.0	7 50.5	24 23.7	10 10.9	4 2.9	24 50.5	9 21.5	13 31.4	13 20.1
19	23 51 8.4	25 57.1	16 3.7	9♐12.8	8 26.5	25 36.3	10 45.5	4 9.5	24 57.5	9 24.4	13 32.2	13 22.4
20	23 55 4.9	26 55.7	16 .6	23 26.6	9 11.1	26 49.1	11 19.9	4 15.8	25 4.4	9 27.4	13 33.0	13 24.7
21	23 59 1.5	27 54.4	15 57.4	7♑37.4	10 3.9	28 1.8	11 54.1	4 22.0	25 11.3	9 30.4	13 33.8	13 26.9
22	0 2 58.0	28 53.0	15 54.2	21 42.8	11 4.3	29 14.7	12 28.1	4 28.0	25 18.2	9 33.5	13 34.7	13 29.2
23	0 6 54.6	29 51.7	15 51.0	5♒40.7	12 11.8	0♍27.6	13 2.0	4 33.9	25 25.0	9 36.5	13 35.6	13 31.5
24	0 10 51.1	0♎50.5	15 47.8	19 29.0	13 25.6	1 40.6	13 35.7	4 39.7	25 31.7	9 39.6	13 36.5	13 33.8
25	0 14 47.7	1 49.2	15 44.7	3♓ 5.8	14 45.2	2 53.6	14 9.2	4 45.2	25 38.4	9 42.8	13 37.5	13 36.2
26	0 18 44.2	2 48.0	15 41.5	16 29.1	16 9.8	4 6.7	14 42.5	4 50.6	25 45.1	9 45.9	13 38.5	13 38.5
27	0 22 40.8	3 46.8	15 38.3	29 37.7	17 38.9	5 19.9	15 15.7	4 55.8	25 51.7	9 49.1	13 39.5	13 40.8
28	0 26 37.3	4 45.7	15 35.1	12♈30.7	19 11.8	6 33.1	15 48.6	5 .9	25 58.3	9 52.4	13 40.6	13 43.1
29	0 30 33.9	5 44.6	15 32.0	25 8.3	20 48.0	7 46.4	16 21.4	5 5.8	26 4.8	9 55.6	13 41.7	13 45.5
30	0 34 30.4	6 43.5	15 28.8	7♉31.4	22 26.8	8 59.8	16 54.0	5 10.5	26 11.3	9 58.9	13 42.8	13 47.8

LATITUDE

DAY	EPHEM. SID. TIME	☉	☊	☽	☿	♀	♂	♃	♄	♅	♆	♇
1	22 40 10.4	0 .0	0 .0	0S 7.6	4S25.2	0S 9.8	0N 2.0	0S23.8	1N 2.5	0N24.4	1N28.7	16N36.2
4	22 52 .1	0 .0	0 .0	3 13.3	4 1.7	0 .1	0 5.2	0 23.7	1 2.9	0 24.3	1 28.6	16 35.3
7	23 3 49.8	0 .0	0 .0	5 .4	3 21.7	0N 9.4	0 8.5	0 23.6	1 3.2	0 24.2	1 28.4	16 34.6
10	23 15 39.4	0 .0	0 .0	4 53.0	2 29.3	0 18.6	0 11.9	0 23.5	1 3.5	0 24.1	1 28.2	16 33.9
13	23 27 29.1	0 .0	0 .0	2 38.0	1 31.0	0 27.4	0 15.4	0 23.3	1 3.9	0 24.1	1 28.1	16 33.3
16	23 39 18.7	0 .0	0 .0	1N 2.0	0 34.0	0 35.7	0 18.9	0 23.2	1 4.3	0 24.0	1 27.9	16 32.8
19	23 51 8.4	0 .0	0 .0	4 15.2	0N16.4	0 43.7	0 22.6	0 23.1	1 4.7	0 23.9	1 27.7	16 32.3
22	0 2 58.0	0 .0	0 .0	5 13.8	0 56.8	0 51.2	0 26.3	0 23.0	1 5.1	0 23.9	1 27.6	16 32.0
25	0 14 47.7	0 .0	0 .0	3 32.5	1 26.0	0 58.1	0 30.1	0 22.8	1 5.5	0 23.8	1 27.4	16 31.6
28	0 26 37.3	0 .0	0 .0	0 15.0	1 44.3	1 4.5	0 34.0	0 22.7	1 5.9	0 23.7	1 27.3	16 31.4

RIGHT ASCENSION

DAY	EPHEM. SID. TIME	☉	☊	☽	☿	♀	♂	♃	♄	♅	♆	♇
1	22 40 10.4	10♍ 5.1	15♎41.0	15♈46.0	15♍53.4	6♌16.9	29♊59.7	1♋59.8	25♌28.8	6♏22.0	12♐10.6	18♎11.9
2	22 44 7.0	10 59.5	15 38.1	27 55.8	15R 6.7	7 31.0	0♋40.2	2 9.4	25 36.2	6 24.2	12 10.8	18 13.7
3	22 48 3.5	11 53.8	15 35.1	10♉ 4.1	14 18.1	8 44.9	1 20.5	2 18.9	25 43.5	6 26.5	12 11.1	18 15.4
4	22 52 .1	12 48.0	15 32.1	22 15.5	13 28.7	9 58.7	2 .6	2 28.3	25 50.8	6 28.8	12 11.4	18 17.1
5	22 55 56.6	13 42.2	15 29.2	4♊32.7	12 39.3	11 12.4	2 40.6	2 37.5	25 58.1	6 31.2	12 11.8	18 18.9
6	22 59 53.2	14 36.3	15 26.2	16 56.7	11 51.1	12 25.9	3 20.5	2 46.6	26 5.3	6 33.6	12 12.1	18 20.7
7	23 3 49.8	15 30.4	15 23.3	29 26.7	11 5.3	13 39.3	4 .2	2 55.5	26 12.5	6 36.1	12 12.5	18 22.5
8	23 7 46.3	16 24.5	15 20.3	12♋ 1.2	10 22.9	14 52.6	4 39.8	3 4.3	26 19.7	6 38.6	12 13.0	18 24.3
9	23 11 42.9	17 18.4	15 17.4	24 38.0	9 45.1	16 5.6	5 19.2	3 13.0	26 26.9	6 41.1	12 13.5	18 26.1
10	23 15 39.4	18 12.4	15 14.4	7♌15.7	9 12.9	17 18.5	5 58.5	3 21.5	26 34.0	6 43.7	12 14.0	18 27.9
11	23 19 36.0	19 6.3	15 11.5	19 54.0	8 47.1	18 31.3	6 37.6	3 29.8	26 41.2	6 46.3	12 14.5	18 29.8
12	23 23 32.5	20 .2	15 8.5	2♍34.5	8 28.6	19 43.9	7 16.5	3 38.0	26 48.2	6 48.9	12 15.1	18 31.7
13	23 27 29.1	20 54.1	15 5.6	15 20.5	8 17.8	20 56.3	7 55.3	3 46.1	26 55.3	6 51.6	12 15.7	18 33.6
14	23 31 25.6	21 48.0	15 2.6	28 17.0	8 15.4	22 8.6	8 33.9	3 54.0	27 2.3	6 54.3	12 16.4	18 35.5
15	23 35 22.2	22 41.8	14 59.7	11♎29.7	8D21.4	23 20.7	9 12.3	4 1.7	27 9.3	6 57.1	12 17.1	18 37.4
16	23 39 18.7	23 35.7	14 56.7	25 3.9	8 36.1	24 32.6	9 50.5	4 9.3	27 16.2	6 59.9	12 17.8	18 39.4
17	23 43 15.3	24 29.5	14 53.7	9♏ 3.2	8 59.3	25 44.3	10 28.5	4 16.7	27 23.1	7 2.7	12 18.6	18 41.3
18	23 47 11.8	25 23.3	14 50.8	23 27.5	9 31.0	26 55.9	11 6.4	4 23.9	27 30.0	7 5.5	12 19.4	18 43.3
19	23 51 8.4	26 17.1	14 47.8	8♐12.0	10 10.7	28 7.2	11 44.0	4 31.0	27 36.8	7 8.4	12 20.2	18 45.2
20	23 55 4.9	27 10.9	14 44.9	23 6.9	10 58.1	29 18.4	12 21.4	4 37.9	27 43.6	7 11.3	12 21.1	18 47.2
21	23 59 1.5	28 4.7	14 41.9	7♑59.1	11 52.7	0♍29.5	12 58.7	4 44.6	27 50.3	7 14.3	12 21.9	18 49.2
22	0 2 58.0	28 58.6	14 39.0	22 35.9	12 53.9	1 40.3	13 35.7	4 51.2	27 57.0	7 17.2	12 22.9	18 51.2
23	0 6 54.6	29 52.4	14 36.0	6♒48.0	14 1.1	2 51.0	14 12.5	4 57.6	28 3.7	7 20.2	12 23.8	18 53.2
24	0 10 51.1	0♎46.3	14 33.1	20 30.9	15 13.7	4 1.6	14 49.1	5 3.8	28 10.3	7 23.3	12 24.8	18 55.3
25	0 14 47.7	1 40.2	14 30.1	3♓45.0	16 31.0	5 12.0	15 25.6	5 9.8	28 16.9	7 26.3	12 25.8	18 57.3
26	0 18 44.2	2 34.2	14 27.2	16 34.6	17 52.5	6 22.2	16 1.8	5 15.7	28 23.4	7 29.4	12 26.9	18 59.3
27	0 22 40.8	3 28.2	14 24.2	29 5.6	19 17.4	7 32.3	16 37.7	5 21.4	28 29.8	7 32.6	12 28.0	19 1.4
28	0 26 37.3	4 22.2	14 21.3	11♈24.6	20 45.3	8 42.2	17 13.5	5 26.9	28 36.2	7 35.7	12 29.1	19 3.4
29	0 30 33.9	5 16.3	14 18.3	23 37.8	22 15.6	9 52.0	17 49.0	5 32.2	28 42.6	7 38.9	12 30.2	19 5.5
30	0 34 30.4	6 10.5	14 15.4	5♉50.2	23 47.8	11 1.7	18 24.3	5 37.3	28 48.9	7 42.1	12 31.4	19 7.6

DECLINATION

DAY	EPHEM. SID. TIME	☉	☊	☽	☿	♀	♂	♃	♄	♅	♆	♇
1	22 40 10.4	8N24.0	0S 7.0	6N34.9	1N14.6	19N 5.8	23N28.4	23N 1.8	14N54.4	13S59.3	20S56.3	10N15.9
4	22 52 .1	7 18.3	0 6.9	15 36.2	2 40.2	18 22.6	23 30.9	23 1.5	14 47.4	14 1.7	20 56.6	10 12.8
7	23 3 49.8	6 11.5	0 6.9	18 25.9	4 22.2	17 34.7	23 31.9	23 1.2	14 40.4	14 4.1	20 56.9	10 9.7
10	23 15 39.4	5 3.8	0 6.8	14 .3	6 4.0	16 42.3	23 31.5	23 .8	14 33.5	14 6.7	20 57.2	10 6.7
13	23 27 29.1	3 55.3	0 6.7	3 24.5	7 28.6	15 45.6	23 29.8	23 .3	14 26.6	14 9.3	20 57.6	10 3.6
16	23 39 18.7	2 46.2	0 6.7	9S18.1	8 22.8	14 44.8	23 26.9	22 59.9	14 19.8	14 12.1	20 58.0	10 .6
19	23 51 8.4	1 36.6	0 6.6	17 37.7	8 39.5	13 40.3	23 22.8	22 59.4	14 13.1	14 14.9	20 58.4	9 57.7
22	0 2 58.0	0 26.6	0 6.6	16 31.4	8 17.4	12 32.1	23 17.5	22 58.9	14 6.5	14 17.9	20 58.9	9 54.7
25	0 14 47.7	0S43.4	0 6.5	7 3.9	7 19.6	11 20.7	23 11.2	22 58.5	14 .1	14 20.9	20 59.4	9 51.8
28	0 26 37.3	1 53.5	0 6.4	5N10.4	5 52.5	10 6.4	23 4.0	22 58.0	13 53.7	14 23.9	20 59.9	9 49.0

OCTOBER 1977

DAY	EPHEM. SID. TIME	☉	☊	☽	☿	♀	♂	♃	♄	♅	♆	♇
	h m s	° ′	° ′	° ′	° ′	° ′	° ′	° ′	° ′	° ′	° ′	° ′
LONGITUDE												
1	0 38 27.0	7♎42.4	15♎25.6	19♉41.9	24♍ 7.8	10♍13.2	17♋26.4	5♋15.1	26♌17.7	10♏ 2.2	13♐43.9	13♎50.1
2	0 42 23.5	8 41.4	15 22.4	1♊42.5	25 50.6	11 26.7	17 58.6	5 19.4	26 24.1	10 5.5	13 45.1	13 52.5
3	0 46 20.1	9 40.5	15 19.2	13 36.6	27 34.7	12 40.2	18 30.6	5 23.6	26 30.4	10 8.8	13 46.3	13 54.8
4	0 50 16.7	10 39.5	15 16.1	25 28.1	29 19.8	13 53.8	19 2.3	5 27.6	26 36.6	10 12.2	13 47.5	13 57.2
5	0 54 13.2	11 38.7	15 12.9	7♋21.7	1♎ 5.7	15 7.5	19 34.0	5 31.5	26 42.9	10 15.6	13 48.8	13 59.6
6	0 58 9.8	12 37.8	15 9.7	19 21.8	2 52.0	16 21.2	20 5.3	5 35.2	26 49.0	10 19.1	13 50.1	14 2.0
7	1 2 6.3	13 37.0	15 6.5	1♌33.0	4 38.5	17 35.0	20 36.4	5 38.7	26 55.1	10 22.5	13 51.4	14 4.3
8	1 6 2.9	14 36.3	15 3.4	13 59.7	6 25.1	18 48.9	21 7.3	5 42.0	27 1.1	10 26.0	13 52.8	14 6.7
9	1 9 59.4	15 35.5	15 .2	26 45.6	8 11.5	20 2.7	21 38.0	5 45.1	27 7.1	10 29.4	13 54.1	14 9.0
10	1 13 56.0	16 34.8	14 57.0	9♍53.1	9 57.7	21 16.7	22 8.5	5 48.0	27 13.0	10 32.9	13 55.5	14 11.4
11	1 17 52.5	17 34.2	14 53.8	23 23.5	11 43.6	22 30.7	22 38.7	5 50.7	27 18.8	10 36.5	13 57.0	14 13.7
12	1 21 49.1	18 33.5	14 50.6	7♎16.2	13 29.1	23 44.7	23 8.6	5 53.2	27 24.6	10 40.0	13 58.4	14 16.1
13	1 25 45.6	19 32.9	14 47.5	21 28.5	15 14.1	24 58.8	23 38.3	5 55.6	27 30.3	10 43.5	13 59.9	14 18.4
14	1 29 42.2	20 32.4	14 44.3	5♏56.0	16 58.5	26 12.9	24 7.8	5 57.7	27 35.9	10 47.1	14 1.4	14 20.8
15	1 33 38.7	21 31.8	14 41.1	20 32.9	18 42.4	27 27.1	24 37.0	5 59.7	27 41.5	10 50.7	14 2.9	14 23.1
16	1 37 35.3	22 31.4	14 37.9	5♐12.8	20 25.7	28 41.3	25 5.9	6 1.4	27 47.0	10 54.3	14 4.5	14 25.5
17	1 41 31.8	23 30.9	14 34.8	19 49.3	22 8.3	29 55.6	25 34.6	6 3.0	27 52.4	10 57.9	14 6.0	14 27.8
18	1 45 28.4	24 30.5	14 31.6	4♑17.1	23 50.4	1♎ 9.9	26 3.0	6 4.4	27 57.8	11 1.5	14 7.6	14 30.2
19	1 49 24.9	25 30.0	14 28.4	18 32.3	25 31.8	2 24.2	26 31.1	6 5.6	28 3.1	11 5.2	14 9.3	14 32.5
20	1 53 21.5	26 29.7	14 25.2	2♒32.4	27 12.5	3 38.6	26 58.9	6 6.5	28 8.3	11 8.8	14 10.9	14 34.8
21	1 57 18.0	27 29.3	14 22.0	16 16.6	28 52.7	4 53.0	27 26.5	6 7.3	28 13.4	11 12.5	14 12.6	14 37.1
22	2 1 14.6	28 29.0	14 18.9	29 44.9	0♏32.2	6 7.4	27 53.7	6 7.9	28 18.5	11 16.2	14 14.3	14 39.4
23	2 5 11.2	29 28.7	14 15.7	12♓57.9	2 11.1	7 21.9	28 20.7	6 8.3	28 23.4	11 19.9	14 16.0	14 41.7
24	2 9 7.7	0♏28.4	14 12.5	25 56.8	3 49.4	8 36.4	28 47.4	6 8.4	28 28.3	11 23.6	14 17.7	14 44.0
25	2 13 4.3	1 28.2	14 9.3	8♈42.5	5 27.2	9 51.0	29 13.7	6 8.4	28 33.1	11 27.3	14 19.5	14 46.3
26	2 17 .8	2 28.0	14 6.2	21 16.2	7 4.4	11 5.6	29 39.8	6R 8.2	28 37.9	11 31.0	14 21.3	14 48.6
27	2 20 57.4	3 27.9	14 3.0	3♉38.8	8 41.1	12 20.3	0♌ 5.5	6 7.8	28 42.6	11 34.8	14 23.1	14 50.9
28	2 24 53.9	4 27.7	13 59.8	15 51.5	10 17.2	13 34.9	0 31.0	6 7.2	28 47.2	11 38.5	14 24.9	14 53.1
29	2 28 50.5	5 27.6	13 56.6	27 55.7	11 52.8	14 49.6	0 56.0	6 6.4	28 51.7	11 42.2	14 26.8	14 55.4
30	2 32 47.0	6 27.6	13 53.4	9♊53.1	13 27.9	16 4.4	1 20.8	6 5.4	28 56.1	11 46.0	14 28.7	14 57.6
31	2 36 43.6	7 27.5	13 50.3	21 45.9	15 2.5	17 19.1	1 45.2	6 4.1	29 .4	11 49.7	14 30.5	14 59.8
LATITUDE												
1	0 38 27.0	0 .0	0 .0	2S59.8	1N53.0	1N10.3	0N38.0	0S22.6	1N 6.4	0N23.7	1N27.1	16N31.3
4	0 50 16.7	0 .0	0 .0	4 58.7	1 53.6	1 15.5	0 42.2	0 22.4	1 6.8	0 23.6	1 27.0	16 31.2
7	1 2 6.3	0 .0	0 .0	5 4.7	1 47.9	1 20.1	0 46.4	0 22.3	1 7.3	0 23.6	1 26.8	16 31.2
10	1 13 56.0	0 .0	0 .0	3 4.1	1 37.3	1 24.1	0 50.8	0 22.1	1 7.8	0 23.5	1 26.7	16 31.3
13	1 25 45.6	0 .0	0 .0	0N34.3	1 23.3	1 27.4	0 55.2	0 22.0	1 8.3	0 23.5	1 26.5	16 31.5
16	1 37 35.3	0 .0	0 .0	4 2.9	1 6.6	1 30.1	0 59.8	0 21.8	1 8.8	0 23.4	1 26.4	16 31.7
19	1 49 24.9	0 .0	0 .0	5 16.3	0 48.2	1 32.1	1 4.6	0 21.7	1 9.4	0 23.4	1 26.3	16 32.0
22	2 1 14.6	0 .0	0 .0	3 46.2	0 28.7	1 33.5	1 9.5	0 21.5	1 9.9	0 23.3	1 26.2	16 32.4
25	2 13 4.3	0 .0	0 .0	0 36.3	0 8.6	1 34.1	1 14.5	0 21.3	1 10.5	0 23.3	1 26.0	16 32.9
28	2 24 53.9	0 .0	0 .0	2S40.7	0S11.7	1 34.2	1 19.7	0 21.1	1 11.0	0 23.3	1 25.9	16 33.5
31	2 36 43.6	0 .0	0 .0	4 48.6	0 31.8	1 33.5	1 25.0	0 20.9	1 11.6	0 23.2	1 25.8	16 34.1
RIGHT ASCENSION												
1	0 38 27.0	7♎ 4.7	14♎12.4	18♉ 5.2	25♍21.5	12♍11.2	18♋59.4	5♋42.2	28♌55.2	7♏45.3	12♐32.6	19♎ 9.7
2	0 42 23.5	7 59.0	14 9.5	0♊24.4	26 56.4	13 20.7	19 34.2	5 47.0	29 1.4	7 48.5	12 33.9	19 11.8
3	0 46 20.1	8 53.4	14 6.5	12 47.9	28 32.1	14 30.0	20 8.8	5 51.5	29 7.6	7 51.8	12 35.1	19 13.9
4	0 50 16.7	9 47.8	14 3.6	25 14.6	0♎ 8.3	15 39.2	20 43.2	5 55.9	29 13.7	7 55.1	12 36.4	19 16.0
5	0 54 13.2	10 42.4	14 .6	7♋42.6	1 45.0	16 48.3	21 17.3	6 .1	29 19.8	7 58.5	12 37.8	19 18.1
6	0 58 9.8	11 37.1	13 57.7	20 10.5	3 21.7	17 57.3	21 51.1	6 4.1	29 25.8	8 1.8	12 39.2	19 20.2
7	1 2 6.3	12 31.8	13 54.8	2♌37.8	4 58.4	19 6.2	22 24.7	6 7.9	29 31.7	8 5.2	12 40.6	19 22.3
8	1 6 2.9	13 26.7	13 51.8	15 5.6	6 35.0	20 15.1	22 58.0	6 11.4	29 37.6	8 8.6	12 42.0	19 24.4
9	1 9 59.4	14 21.6	13 48.9	27 36.8	8 11.4	21 23.8	23 31.1	6 14.8	29 43.4	8 12.0	12 43.4	19 26.6
10	1 13 56.0	15 16.7	13 45.9	10♍15.9	9 47.5	22 32.5	24 3.9	6 18.0	29 49.2	8 15.4	12 44.9	19 28.7
11	1 17 52.5	16 11.9	13 43.0	23 9.1	11 23.4	23 41.1	24 36.4	6 20.9	29 54.8	8 18.9	12 46.4	19 30.8
12	1 21 49.1	17 7.2	13 40.0	6♎23.0	12 58.9	24 49.7	25 8.6	6 23.7	0♍ .5	8 22.3	12 48.0	19 32.9
13	1 25 45.6	18 2.7	13 37.1	20 3.8	14 34.0	25 58.2	25 40.5	6 26.2	0 6.0	8 25.8	12 49.5	19 35.1
14	1 29 42.2	18 58.2	13 34.1	4♏15.3	16 8.8	27 6.7	26 12.1	6 28.6	0 11.5	8 29.3	12 51.1	19 37.2
15	1 33 38.7	19 53.9	13 31.2	18 57.0	17 43.2	28 15.2	26 43.4	6 30.7	0 17.0	8 32.8	12 52.7	19 39.3
16	1 37 35.3	20 49.8	13 28.2	4♐ 2.4	19 17.2	29 23.6	27 14.4	6 32.6	0 22.3	8 36.4	12 54.4	19 41.5
17	1 41 31.8	21 45.8	13 25.3	19 18.7	20 51.0	0♎32.1	27 45.2	6 34.3	0 27.6	8 39.9	12 56.0	19 43.6
18	1 45 28.4	22 41.9	13 22.3	4♑29.5	22 24.4	1 40.5	28 15.5	6 35.8	0 32.8	8 43.5	12 57.7	19 45.7
19	1 49 24.9	23 38.1	13 19.4	19 19.5	23 57.6	2 48.9	28 45.6	6 37.1	0 38.0	8 47.1	12 59.5	19 47.9
20	1 53 21.5	24 34.6	13 16.5	3♒38.1	25 30.5	3 57.4	29 15.4	6 38.1	0 43.1	8 50.7	13 1.2	19 50.0
21	1 57 18.0	25 31.1	13 13.5	17 21.2	27 3.2	5 5.8	29 44.8	6 39.0	0 48.1	8 54.3	13 3.0	19 52.1
22	2 1 14.6	26 27.9	13 10.6	0♓30.9	28 35.7	6 14.3	0♌13.9	6 39.6	0 53.0	8 57.9	13 4.8	19 54.2
23	2 5 11.2	27 24.8	13 7.6	13 12.9	0♏ 8.0	7 22.8	0 42.7	6 40.0	0 57.9	9 1.5	13 6.6	19 56.4
24	2 9 7.7	28 21.8	13 4.7	25 35.1	1 40.2	8 31.4	1 11.1	6 40.2	1 2.6	9 5.1	13 8.5	19 58.5
25	2 13 4.3	29 19.0	13 1.7	7♈45.6	3 12.4	9 40.1	1 39.2	6 40.2	1 7.3	9 8.8	13 10.3	20 .6
26	2 17 .8	0♏16.5	12 58.8	19 51.7	4 44.5	10 48.8	2 7.0	6R40.0	1 12.0	9 12.5	13 12.3	20 2.7
27	2 20 57.4	1 14.1	12 55.8	1♉59.1	6 16.5	11 57.6	2 34.4	6 39.6	1 16.6	9 16.1	13 14.2	20 4.8
28	2 24 53.9	2 11.9	12 52.9	14 11.4	7 48.5	13 6.5	3 1.5	6 38.9	1 21.0	9 19.8	13 16.1	20 6.9
29	2 28 50.5	3 9.8	12 50.0	26 30.0	9 20.6	14 15.5	3 28.1	6 38.0	1 25.4	9 23.5	13 18.1	20 9.0
30	2 32 47.0	4 8.0	12 47.0	8♊54.1	10 52.7	15 24.6	3 54.4	6 36.9	1 29.7	9 27.2	13 20.1	20 11.1
31	2 36 43.6	5 6.3	12 44.1	21 21.0	12 24.9	16 33.9	4 20.4	6 35.6	1 33.9	9 30.8	13 22.1	20 13.2
DECLINATION												
1	0 38 27.0	3S 3.5	0S 6.4	14N46.4	4N 3.6	8N49.3	22N55.9	22N57.6	13N47.6	14S27.1	21S .5	9N46.2
4	0 50 16.7	4 13.2	0 6.3	18 23.2	2 .2	7 29.8	22 47.0	22 57.2	13 41.5	14 30.3	21 1.0	9 43.5
7	1 2 6.3	5 22.4	0 6.2	14 51.6	0S11.7	6 8.2	22 37.4	22 56.9	13 35.7	14 33.6	21 1.6	9 40.9
10	1 13 56.0	6 31.1	0 6.2	5 1.2	2 27.2	4 44.8	22 27.3	22 56.6	13 30.0	14 36.9	21 2.3	9 38.3
13	1 25 45.6	7 38.9	0 6.1	7S50.6	4 43.2	3 20.0	22 16.7	22 56.5	13 24.5	14 40.2	21 2.9	9 35.8
16	1 37 35.3	8 45.9	0 6.0	17 11.1	6 57.1	1 54.0	22 5.7	22 56.4	13 19.2	14 43.6	21 3.6	9 33.4
19	1 49 24.9	9 51.6	0 6.0	16 56.0	9 7.3	0 27.2	21 54.4	22 56.3	13 14.1	14 47.0	21 4.3	9 31.1
22	2 1 14.6	10 56.1	0 5.9	8 1.6	11 12.7	1S .1	21 43.0	22 56.4	13 9.3	14 50.5	21 5.0	9 28.8
25	2 13 4.3	11 59.1	0 5.8	4N .5	13 12.3	2 27.5	21 31.6	22 56.5	13 4.7	14 53.9	21 5.7	9 26.7
28	2 24 53.9	13 .5	0 5.8	14 1.2	15 5.4	3 54.8	21 20.2	22 56.8	13 .4	14 57.4	21 6.4	9 24.7
31	2 36 43.6	14 .0	0 5.7	18 22.9	16 51.3	5 21.6	21 9.1	22 57.1	12 56.3	15 .9	21 7.2	9 22.7

NOVEMBER 1977

LONGITUDE

DAY	EPHEM. SID. TIME	☉	☊	☽	☿	♀	♂	♃	♄	♅	♆	♇
	h m s	° ′	° ′	° ′	° ′	° ′	° ′	° ′	° ′	° ′	° ′	° ′
1	2 40 40.1	8♏27.5	13♎47.1	3♋36.9	16♏36.7	18♎33.9	2♌ 9.2	6♋ 2.7	29♌ 4.6	11♏53.4	14♐32.4	15♎ 2.1
2	2 44 36.7	9 27.6	13 43.9	15 29.4	18 10.4	19 48.8	2 32.9	6R 1.1	29 8.8	11 57.2	14 34.3	15 4.3
3	2 48 33.2	10 27.6	13 40.7	27 27.4	19 43.7	21 3.7	2 56.2	5 59.3	29 12.8	12 .9	14 36.3	15 6.4
4	2 52 29.8	11 27.7	13 37.6	9♌35.2	21 16.6	22 18.6	3 19.1	5 57.2	29 16.8	12 4.7	14 38.2	15 8.6
5	2 56 26.3	12 27.9	13 34.4	21 57.5	22 49.1	23 33.5	3 41.6	5 55.0	29 20.7	12 8.4	14 40.2	15 10.8
6	3 0 22.9	13 28.0	13 31.2	4♍38.7	24 21.2	24 48.4	4 3.8	5 52.6	29 24.5	12 12.2	14 42.2	15 12.9
7	3 4 19.5	14 28.2	13 28.0	17 43.0	25 52.9	26 3.4	4 25.5	5 50.0	29 28.2	12 16.0	14 44.2	15 15.0
8	3 8 16.0	15 28.5	13 24.8	1♎13.2	27 24.2	27 18.4	4 46.8	5 47.2	29 31.8	12 19.7	14 46.2	15 17.2
9	3 12 12.6	16 28.8	13 21.7	15 10.7	28 55.2	28 33.5	5 7.7	5 44.2	29 35.3	12 23.5	14 48.3	15 19.3
10	3 16 9.1	17 29.1	13 18.5	29 34.1	0♐25.7	29 48.5	5 28.2	5 41.0	29 38.7	12 27.2	14 50.3	15 21.3
11	3 20 5.7	18 29.4	13 15.3	14♏19.4	1 55.9	1♏ 3.6	5 48.2	5 37.6	29 42.0	12 30.9	14 52.4	15 23.4
12	3 24 2.2	19 29.8	13 12.1	29 19.6	3 25.7	2 18.7	6 7.8	5 34.0	29 45.2	12 34.7	14 54.5	15 25.4
13	3 27 58.8	20 30.1	13 9.0	14♐25.8	4 55.2	3 33.9	6 26.9	5 30.2	29 48.3	12 38.4	14 56.5	15 27.5
14	3 31 55.3	21 30.6	13 5.8	29 28.1	6 24.2	4 49.0	6 45.5	5 26.2	29 51.3	12 42.1	14 58.6	15 29.5
15	3 35 51.9	22 31.0	13 2.6	14♑17.7	7 52.7	6 4.2	7 3.6	5 22.1	29 54.3	12 45.9	15 .8	15 31.5
16	3 39 48.5	23 31.5	12 59.4	28 48.1	9 20.9	7 19.4	7 21.3	5 17.8	29 57.1	12 49.6	15 2.9	15 33.5
17	3 43 45.0	24 32.0	12 56.2	12♒55.3	10 48.6	8 34.6	7 38.5	5 13.3	29 59.8	12 53.3	15 5.1	15 35.4
18	3 47 41.6	25 32.5	12 53.1	26 38.4	12 15.7	9 49.8	7 55.1	5 8.6	0♍ 2.4	12 57.0	15 7.2	15 37.4
19	3 51 38.1	26 33.0	12 49.9	9♓58.4	13 42.3	11 5.0	8 11.3	5 3.8	0 4.9	13 .7	15 9.4	15 39.3
20	3 55 34.7	27 33.6	12 46.7	22 57.9	15 8.2	12 20.2	8 26.9	4 58.7	0 7.3	13 4.4	15 11.6	15 41.2
21	3 59 31.2	28 34.2	12 43.5	5♈40.1	16 33.4	13 35.5	8 41.9	4 53.6	0 9.6	13 8.0	15 13.7	15 43.0
22	4 3 27.8	29 34.7	12 40.4	18 8.3	17 57.9	14 50.8	8 56.5	4 48.2	0 11.8	13 11.7	15 15.9	15 44.9
23	4 7 24.3	0♐35.3	12 37.2	0♉25.4	19 21.5	16 6.0	9 10.4	4 42.7	0 13.9	13 15.3	15 18.1	15 46.7
24	4 11 20.9	1 36.0	12 34.0	12 34.0	20 44.2	17 21.3	9 23.8	4 37.0	0 15.9	13 18.9	15 20.3	15 48.5
25	4 15 17.5	2 36.6	12 30.8	24 36.1	22 5.7	18 36.6	9 36.6	4 31.2	0 17.8	13 22.5	15 22.6	15 50.3
26	4 19 14.0	3 37.3	12 27.7	6♊33.4	23 25.9	19 51.9	9 48.8	4 25.2	0 19.5	13 26.1	15 24.8	15 52.0
27	4 23 10.6	4 38.0	12 24.5	18 27.4	24 44.8	21 7.3	10 .4	4 19.1	0 21.2	13 29.7	15 27.0	15 53.7
28	4 27 7.1	5 38.7	12 21.3	0♋19.4	26 1.9	22 22.6	10 11.4	4 12.8	0 22.7	13 33.2	15 29.2	15 55.4
29	4 31 3.7	6 39.5	12 18.1	12 11.2	27 17.2	23 38.0	10 21.8	4 6.4	0 24.2	13 36.8	15 31.5	15 57.1
30	4 35 .2	7 40.2	12 14.9	24 4.8	28 30.4	24 53.3	10 31.5	3 59.9	0 25.5	13 40.3	15 33.7	15 58.8

LATITUDE

DAY	EPHEM. SID. TIME	☉	☊	☽	☿	♀	♂	♃	♄	♅	♆	♇
1	2 40 40.1	0 .0	0 .0	5S 7.9	0S38.4	1N33.2	1N26.8	0S20.9	1N11.8	0N23.2	1N25.8	16N34.3
4	2 52 29.8	0 .0	0 .0	4 45.5	0 57.8	1 31.7	1 32.4	0 20.7	1 12.4	0 23.2	1 25.7	16 35.1
7	3 4 19.5	0 .0	0 .0	2 24.0	1 16.3	1 29.7	1 38.2	0 20.4	1 13.0	0 23.2	1 25.6	16 35.9
10	3 16 9.1	0 .0	0 .0	1N18.8	1 33.5	1 27.0	1 44.2	0 20.2	1 13.6	0 23.2	1 25.5	16 36.8
13	3 27 58.8	0 .0	0 .0	4 28.5	1 49.2	1 23.8	1 50.3	0 20.0	1 14.3	0 23.2	1 25.4	16 37.7
16	3 39 48.5	0 .0	0 .0	5 1.2	2 2.9	1 20.1	1 56.7	0 19.7	1 14.9	0 23.1	1 25.4	16 38.7
19	3 51 38.1	0 .0	0 .0	2 56.5	2 14.3	1 15.8	2 3.2	0 19.4	1 15.6	0 23.1	1 25.3	16 39.8
22	4 3 27.8	0 .0	0 .0	0S19.3	2 22.7	1 11.0	2 10.0	0 19.2	1 16.2	0 23.1	1 25.3	16 41.0
25	4 15 17.5	0 .0	0 .0	3 18.6	2 27.6	1 5.9	2 16.9	0 18.9	1 16.9	0 23.1	1 25.2	16 42.2
28	4 27 7.1	0 .0	0 .0	4 57.0	2 27.9	1 .3	2 24.1	0 18.5	1 17.5	0 23.1	1 25.2	16 43.5

RIGHT ASCENSION

DAY	EPHEM. SID. TIME	☉	☊	☽	☿	♀	♂	♃	♄	♅	♆	♇
1	2 40 40.1	6♏ 4.9	12♎41.1	3♋47.5	13♏57.2	17♎43.2	4♌45.9	6♋34.0	1♍38.1	9♏34.5	13♐24.1	20♎15.2
2	2 44 36.7	7 3.6	12 38.2	16 10.7	15 29.7	18 52.7	5 11.0	6R32.3	1 42.1	9 38.2	13 26.1	20 17.3
3	2 48 33.2	8 2.6	12 35.3	28 29.2	17 2.2	20 2.4	5 35.8	6 30.3	1 46.1	9 41.9	13 28.2	20 19.3
4	2 52 29.8	9 1.8	12 32.3	10♌43.6	18 34.9	21 12.2	6 .1	6 28.1	1 50.0	9 45.6	13 30.2	20 21.4
5	2 56 26.3	10 1.1	12 29.4	22 57.2	20 7.8	22 22.1	6 24.0	6 25.7	1 53.8	9 49.3	13 32.3	20 23.4
6	3 0 22.9	11 .7	12 26.4	5♍15.5	21 40.9	23 32.3	6 47.5	6 23.1	1 57.5	9 53.0	13 34.5	20 25.4
7	3 4 19.5	12 .5	12 23.5	17 46.0	23 14.1	24 42.6	7 10.6	6 20.2	2 1.1	9 56.7	13 36.6	20 27.5
8	3 8 16.0	13 .5	12 20.5	0♎37.4	24 47.5	25 53.1	7 33.2	6 17.2	2 4.7	10 .4	13 38.7	20 29.5
9	3 12 12.6	14 .8	12 17.6	13 58.9	26 21.1	27 3.9	7 55.4	6 13.9	2 8.1	10 4.1	13 40.9	20 31.5
10	3 16 9.1	15 1.2	12 14.7	27 58.1	27 54.9	28 14.8	8 17.1	6 10.5	2 11.4	10 7.8	13 43.1	20 33.4
11	3 20 5.7	16 1.9	12 11.7	12♏38.4	29 28.8	29 25.9	8 38.3	6 6.8	2 14.7	10 11.5	13 45.3	20 35.4
12	3 24 2.2	17 2.7	12 8.8	27 56.2	1♐ 2.8	0♏37.3	8 59.1	6 2.9	2 17.9	10 15.2	13 47.5	20 37.4
13	3 27 58.8	18 3.8	12 5.9	13♐38.9	2 37.0	1 48.9	9 19.4	5 58.8	2 20.9	10 18.9	13 49.7	20 39.3
14	3 31 55.3	19 5.1	12 2.9	29 26.5	4 11.2	3 .7	9 39.2	5 54.5	2 23.9	10 22.5	13 52.0	20 41.2
15	3 35 51.9	20 6.6	11 60.0	14♑56.7	5 45.4	4 12.8	9 58.4	5 50.0	2 26.8	10 26.2	13 54.2	20 43.1
16	3 39 48.5	21 8.4	11 57.0	29 52.1	7 19.7	5 25.2	10 17.3	5 45.4	2 29.6	10 29.9	13 56.5	20 45.1
17	3 43 45.0	22 10.3	11 54.1	14♒ 4.0	8 53.9	6 37.7	10 35.5	5 40.5	2 32.2	10 33.6	13 58.8	20 47.0
18	3 47 41.6	23 12.4	11 51.2	27 32.4	10 27.9	7 50.5	10 53.2	5 35.4	2 34.8	10 37.2	14 1.1	20 48.8
19	3 51 38.1	24 14.7	11 48.2	10♓23.7	12 1.8	9 3.6	11 10.4	5 30.1	2 37.3	10 40.9	14 3.4	20 50.7
20	3 55 34.7	25 17.2	11 45.3	22 47.2	13 35.3	10 17.0	11 27.1	5 24.7	2 39.7	10 44.5	14 5.7	20 52.5
21	3 59 31.2	26 19.9	11 42.3	4♈53.1	15 8.4	11 30.6	11 43.2	5 19.0	2 42.0	10 48.1	14 8.0	20 54.3
22	4 3 27.8	27 22.8	11 39.4	16 51.1	16 40.9	12 44.6	11 58.7	5 13.2	2 44.2	10 51.7	14 10.4	20 56.1
23	4 7 24.3	28 26.0	11 36.5	28 49.0	18 12.8	13 58.8	12 13.7	5 7.2	2 46.2	10 55.3	14 12.7	20 57.9
24	4 11 20.9	29 29.3	11 33.5	10♉52.6	19 43.8	15 13.3	12 28.1	5 1.1	2 48.2	10 58.9	14 15.0	20 59.7
25	4 15 17.5	0♐32.7	11 30.6	23 4.7	21 13.9	16 28.1	12 41.8	4 54.8	2 50.1	11 2.5	14 17.4	21 1.4
26	4 19 14.0	1 36.4	11 27.7	5♊25.4	22 42.7	17 43.1	12 55.0	4 48.3	2 51.9	11 6.0	14 19.8	21 3.2
27	4 23 10.6	2 40.3	11 24.7	17 52.1	24 10.1	18 58.5	13 7.6	4 41.6	2 53.5	11 9.5	14 22.1	21 4.9
28	4 27 7.1	3 44.4	11 21.8	0♋20.4	25 35.7	20 14.2	13 19.5	4 34.8	2 55.1	11 13.1	14 24.5	21 6.6
29	4 31 3.7	4 48.6	11 18.9	12 45.5	26 59.3	21 30.2	13 30.8	4 27.9	2 56.6	11 16.6	14 26.9	21 8.2
30	4 35 .2	5 53.0	11 15.9	25 3.8	28 20.5	22 46.5	13 41.5	4 20.8	2 57.9	11 20.1	14 29.3	21 9.9

DECLINATION

DAY	EPHEM. SID. TIME	☉	☊	☽	☿	♀	♂	♃	♄	♅	♆	♇
1	2 40 40.1	14S19.4	0S 5.7	18N15.6	17S25.0	5S50.4	21N 5.4	22N57.2	12N55.0	15S 2.1	21S 7.4	9N22.1
4	2 52 29.8	15 16.3	0 5.6	13 15.6	19 .6	7 15.9	20 54.8	22 57.7	12 51.3	15 5.5	21 8.2	9 20.4
7	3 4 19.5	16 10.8	0 5.6	2 38.7	20 27.7	8 40.2	20 44.6	22 58.2	12 47.9	15 9.0	21 8.9	9 18.7
10	3 16 9.1	17 3.0	0 5.5	10S 5.4	21 45.9	10 2.8	20 35.1	22 58.9	12 44.8	15 12.4	21 9.7	9 17.2
13	3 27 58.8	17 52.5	0 5.4	18 5.1	22 54.4	11 23.4	20 26.5	22 59.6	12 42.0	15 15.8	21 10.4	9 15.8
16	3 39 48.5	18 39.3	0 5.4	15 29.0	23 52.7	12 41.7	20 18.7	23 .3	12 39.5	15 19.3	21 11.2	9 14.5
19	3 51 38.1	19 23.0	0 5.3	5 6.2	24 40.0	13 57.1	20 12.1	23 1.1	12 37.3	15 22.6	21 12.0	9 13.3
22	4 3 27.8	20 3.6	0 5.2	6N48.9	25 15.8	15 9.5	20 6.7	23 2.0	12 35.5	15 25.9	21 12.8	9 12.3
25	4 15 17.5	20 41.0	0 5.2	15 42.5	25 39.5	16 18.5	20 2.6	23 2.9	12 34.0	15 29.2	21 13.5	9 11.4
28	4 27 7.1	21 14.8	0 5.1	18 29.3	25 50.6	17 23.6	20 .1	23 3.8	12 32.9	15 32.4	21 14.3	9 10.7

DECEMBER 1977

LONGITUDE

DAY	EPHEM. SID. TIME h m s	☉ ° ′	☊ ° ′	☽ ° ′	☿ ° ′	♀ ° ′	♂ ° ′	♃ ° ′	♄ ° ′	♅ ° ′	♆ ° ′	♇ ° ′
1	4 38 56.8	8♐41.0	12♎11.8	6♌ 3.1	29♐41.0	26♏ 8.7	10♌40.6	3♋53.2	0♍26.7	13♏43.8	15♐36.0	16♎ .4
2	4 42 53.3	9 41.8	12 8.6	18 9.5	0♑48.8	27 24.1	10 49.0	3R46.5	0 27.9	13 47.3	15 38.2	16 2.0
3	4 46 49.9	10 42.7	12 5.4	0♍27.9	1 53.4	28 39.5	10 56.7	3 39.5	0 28.9	13 50.7	15 40.5	16 3.6
4	4 50 46.5	11 43.5	12 2.2	13 2.8	2 54.2	29 54.9	11 3.7	3 32.5	0 29.7	13 54.2	15 42.7	16 5.1
5	4 54 43.0	12 44.4	11 59.1	25 58.9	3 50.7	1♐10.4	11 10.0	3 25.4	0 30.5	13 57.6	15 45.0	16 6.6
6	4 58 39.6	13 45.3	11 55.9	9♎20.2	4 42.3	2 25.8	11 15.6	3 18.1	0 31.2	14 1.0	15 47.2	16 8.1
7	5 2 36.1	14 46.3	11 52.7	23 9.8	5 28.4	3 41.3	11 20.5	3 10.8	0 31.8	14 4.4	15 49.5	16 9.6
8	5 6 32.7	15 47.2	11 49.5	7♏28.6	6 8.0	4 56.7	11 24.6	3 3.4	0 32.2	14 7.7	15 51.8	16 11.0
9	5 10 29.2	16 48.2	11 46.4	22 14.4	6 40.6	6 12.2	11 28.0	2 55.9	0 32.6	14 11.0	15 54.1	16 12.4
10	5 14 25.8	17 49.2	11 43.2	7♐21.5	7 5.2	7 27.7	11 30.5	2 48.2	0 32.8	14 14.3	15 56.3	16 13.8
11	5 18 22.4	18 50.2	11 40.0	22 40.8	7 20.9	8 43.1	11 32.4	2 40.5	0 32.9	14 17.6	15 58.6	16 15.2
12	5 22 18.9	19 51.2	11 36.8	8♑ .7	7 26.9	9 58.6	11 33.4	2 32.8	0 32.9	14 20.8	16 .9	16 16.5
13	5 26 15.5	20 52.2	11 33.6	23 9.7	7R22.5	11 14.1	11 33.6	2 24.9	0R32.8	14 24.1	16 3.1	16 17.8
14	5 30 12.0	21 53.3	11 30.5	7♒58.2	7 6.9	12 29.6	11R33.0	2 17.0	0 32.5	14 27.2	16 5.4	16 19.0
15	5 34 8.6	22 54.3	11 27.3	22 19.8	6 39.9	13 45.1	11 31.7	2 9.1	0 32.2	14 30.4	16 7.6	16 20.2
16	5 38 5.1	23 55.4	11 24.1	6♓12.1	6 1.2	15 .6	11 29.5	2 1.1	0 31.7	14 33.5	16 9.9	16 21.4
17	5 42 1.7	24 56.4	11 20.9	19 35.8	5 11.3	16 16.1	11 26.5	1 53.1	0 31.1	14 36.6	16 12.1	16 22.6
18	5 45 58.3	25 57.5	11 17.8	2♈33.8	4 11.1	17 31.5	11 22.7	1 45.0	0 30.5	14 39.7	16 14.4	16 23.7
19	5 49 54.8	26 58.6	11 14.6	15 10.4	3 1.8	18 47.0	11 18.0	1 36.9	0 29.7	14 42.7	16 16.6	16 24.8
20	5 53 51.4	27 59.7	11 11.4	27 30.2	1 45.6	20 2.5	11 12.6	1 28.8	0 28.8	14 45.7	16 18.8	16 25.8
21	5 57 47.9	29 .7	11 8.2	9♉37.9	0 24.8	21 18.0	11 6.3	1 20.6	0 27.8	14 48.6	16 21.0	16 26.9
22	6 1 44.5	0♑ 1.8	11 5.1	21 37.4	29♐ 2.1	22 33.5	10 59.1	1 12.5	0 26.6	14 51.6	16 23.2	16 27.9
23	6 5 41.0	1 2.9	11 1.9	3♊32.0	27 40.2	23 49.0	10 51.2	1 4.3	0 25.4	14 54.5	16 25.5	16 28.8
24	6 9 37.6	2 4.0	10 58.7	15 24.4	26 21.9	25 4.5	10 42.4	0 56.2	0 24.1	14 57.3	16 27.7	16 29.7
25	6 13 34.2	3 5.1	10 55.5	27 16.4	25 9.5	26 20.0	10 32.8	0 48.0	0 22.6	15 .1	16 29.8	16 30.6
26	6 17 30.7	4 6.2	10 52.3	9♋ 9.6	24 5.0	27 35.5	10 22.4	0 39.9	0 21.1	15 2.9	16 32.0	16 31.5
27	6 21 27.3	5 7.3	10 49.2	21 5.0	23 9.8	28 51.0	10 11.1	0 31.8	0 19.4	15 5.7	16 34.2	16 32.3
28	6 25 23.8	6 8.5	10 46.0	3♌ 4.0	22 24.7	0♑ 6.5	9 59.1	0 23.8	0 17.7	15 8.4	16 36.4	16 33.2
29	6 29 20.4	7 9.6	10 42.8	15 8.0	21 50.1	1 22.0	9 46.3	0 15.7	0 15.8	15 11.1	16 38.6	16 33.9
30	6 33 16.9	8 10.8	10 39.6	27 19.3	21 26.1	2 37.5	9 32.7	0 7.7	0 13.9	15 13.7	16 40.7	16 34.6
31	6 37 13.5	9 11.9	10 36.5	9♍40.4	21 12.4	3 53.0	9 18.2	29♊59.7	0 11.8	15 16.3	16 42.8	16 35.3

LATITUDE

DAY	EPHEM. SID. TIME	☉	☊	☽	☿	♀	♂	♃	♄	♅	♆	♇
1	4 38 56.8	0 .0	0 .0	4S42.3	2S22.6	0N54.4	2N31.4	0S18.2	1N18.2	0N23.1	1N25.1	16N44.8
4	4 50 46.5	0 .0	0 .0	2 34.6	2 10.4	0 48.1	2 39.0	0 17.9	1 18.9	0 23.1	1 25.1	16 46.2
7	5 2 36.1	0 .0	0 .0	0N52.2	1 49.3	0 41.6	2 46.7	0 17.5	1 19.6	0 23.1	1 25.1	16 47.6
10	5 14 25.8	0 .0	0 .0	4 6.3	1 17.7	0 34.8	2 54.6	0 17.2	1 20.3	0 23.1	1 25.1	16 49.1
13	5 26 15.5	0 .0	0 .0	4 57.4	0 34.1	0 27.8	3 2.6	0 16.8	1 21.0	0 23.1	1 25.0	16 50.6
16	5 38 5.1	0 .0	0 .0	2 59.0	0N20.4	0 20.7	3 10.6	0 16.4	1 21.6	0 23.2	1 25.0	16 52.2
19	5 49 54.8	0 .0	0 .0	0S15.4	1 20.2	0 13.5	3 18.7	0 16.0	1 22.3	0 23.2	1 25.0	16 53.8
22	6 1 44.5	0 .0	0 .0	3 12.1	2 14.1	0 6.2	3 26.7	0 15.6	1 23.0	0 23.2	1 25.1	16 55.5
25	6 13 34.2	0 .0	0 .0	4 50.4	2 50.9	0S 1.0	3 34.6	0 15.1	1 23.7	0 23.2	1 25.1	16 57.2
28	6 25 23.8	0 .0	0 .0	4 37.5	3 6.2	0 8.3	3 42.3	0 14.7	1 24.3	0 23.2	1 25.1	16 58.9
31	6 37 13.5	0 .0	0 .0	2 34.3	3 3.1	0 15.4	3 49.7	0 14.2	1 25.0	0 23.3	1 25.1	17 .6

RIGHT ASCENSION

DAY	EPHEM. SID. TIME	☉	☊	☽	☿	♀	♂	♃	♄	♅	♆	♇
1	4 38 56.8	6♐57.6	11♎13.0	7♌13.8	29♐38.9	24♏ 3.1	13♌51.5	4♋13.6	2♍59.2	11♏23.5	14♐31.7	21♎11.5
2	4 42 53.3	8 2.3	11 10.0	19 17.0	0♑54.2	25 20.0	14 .8	4R 6.2	3 .3	11 27.0	14 34.1	21 13.1
3	4 46 49.9	9 7.2	11 7.1	1♍17.7	2 5.7	26 37.2	14 9.4	3 58.7	3 1.4	11 30.4	14 36.5	21 14.7
4	4 50 46.5	10 12.3	11 4.2	13 23.1	3 13.0	27 54.7	14 17.3	3 51.1	3 2.3	11 33.8	14 38.9	21 16.3
5	4 54 43.0	11 17.5	11 1.2	25 42.4	4 15.4	29 12.5	14 24.5	3 43.3	3 3.1	11 37.2	14 41.3	21 17.8
6	4 58 39.6	12 22.9	10 58.3	8♎26.2	5 12.2	0♐30.5	14 31.0	3 35.4	3 3.9	11 40.6	14 43.7	21 19.3
7	5 2 36.1	13 28.4	10 55.4	21 45.5	6 2.7	1 49.0	14 36.8	3 27.5	3 4.5	11 44.0	14 46.2	21 20.9
8	5 6 32.7	14 34.1	10 52.4	5♏49.0	6 46.0	3 7.6	14 41.8	3 19.4	3 5.0	11 47.3	14 48.6	21 22.4
9	5 10 29.2	15 39.8	10 49.5	20 40.6	7 21.2	4 26.6	14 46.0	3 11.2	3 5.4	11 50.6	14 51.0	21 23.8
10	5 14 25.8	16 45.7	10 46.6	6♐15.7	7 47.5	5 45.8	14 49.4	3 3.0	3 5.7	11 53.8	14 53.4	21 25.2
11	5 18 22.4	17 51.7	10 43.6	22 18.3	8 4.0	7 5.2	14 52.1	2 54.6	3 5.9	11 57.1	14 55.8	21 26.6
12	5 22 18.9	18 57.8	10 40.7	8♑24.2	8 9.7	8 25.0	14 53.9	2 46.1	3 6.0	12 .3	14 58.2	21 28.0
13	5 26 15.5	20 3.9	10 37.8	24 7.8	8R 3.9	9 45.0	14 54.9	2 37.6	3R 5.9	12 3.5	15 .7	21 29.3
14	5 30 12.0	21 10.2	10 34.8	9♒10.6	7 45.9	11 5.2	14 55.2	2 29.0	3 5.8	12 6.6	15 3.1	21 30.7
15	5 34 8.6	22 16.5	10 31.9	23 24.6	7 15.4	12 25.6	14R54.6	2 20.4	3 5.5	12 9.8	15 5.5	21 32.0
16	5 38 5.1	23 22.9	10 29.0	6♓51.8	6 32.4	13 46.3	14 53.1	2 11.7	3 5.2	12 12.9	15 7.9	21 33.2
17	5 42 1.7	24 29.3	10 26.0	19 40.2	5 37.4	15 7.2	14 50.9	2 3.0	3 4.7	12 16.0	15 10.3	21 34.5
18	5 45 58.3	25 35.8	10 23.1	2♈ .7	4 31.5	16 28.2	14 47.8	1 54.2	3 4.2	12 19.0	15 12.7	21 35.7
19	5 49 54.8	26 42.3	10 20.2	14 4.3	3 16.2	17 49.5	14 43.8	1 45.4	3 3.5	12 22.0	15 15.0	21 36.9
20	5 53 51.4	27 48.8	10 17.2	26 1.0	1 53.7	19 10.9	14 39.0	1 36.6	3 2.7	12 25.0	15 17.4	21 38.0
21	5 57 47.9	28 55.4	10 14.3	7♉59.0	0 26.6	20 32.5	14 33.4	1 27.7	3 1.8	12 27.9	15 19.8	21 39.2
22	6 1 44.5	0♑ 2.0	10 11.4	20 3.7	28♐57.9	21 54.2	14 26.9	1 18.8	3 .8	12 30.8	15 22.2	21 40.3
23	6 5 41.0	1 8.6	10 8.4	2♊17.6	27 30.4	23 16.1	14 19.5	1 10.0	2 59.7	12 33.7	15 24.5	21 41.4
24	6 9 37.6	2 15.2	10 5.5	14 40.2	26 7.1	24 38.1	14 11.3	1 1.1	2 58.5	12 36.5	15 26.9	21 42.4
25	6 13 34.2	3 21.7	10 2.6	27 8.0	24 50.2	26 .2	14 2.2	0 52.3	2 57.2	12 39.4	15 29.2	21 43.4
26	6 17 30.7	4 28.3	9 59.6	9♋36.4	23 41.8	27 22.4	13 52.2	0 43.4	2 55.8	12 42.1	15 31.5	21 44.4
27	6 21 27.3	5 34.8	9 56.7	22 .1	22 43.3	28 44.7	13 41.4	0 34.6	2 54.3	12 44.9	15 33.8	21 45.4
28	6 25 23.8	6 41.4	9 53.8	4♌15.5	21 55.6	0♑ 7.1	13 29.8	0 25.9	2 52.7	12 47.6	15 36.2	21 46.3
29	6 29 20.4	7 47.8	9 50.9	16 21.5	21 19.0	1 29.5	13 17.3	0 17.1	2 51.0	12 50.3	15 38.5	21 47.2
30	6 33 16.9	8 54.2	9 47.9	28 19.8	20 53.4	2 51.9	13 4.0	0 8.4	2 49.2	12 52.9	15 40.8	21 48.1
31	6 37 13.5	10 .6	9 45.0	10♍15.4	20 38.7	4 14.4	12 49.8	29♊59.7	2 47.3	12 55.5	15 43.1	21 49.0

DECLINATION

DAY	EPHEM. SID. TIME	☉	☊	☽	☿	♀	♂	♃	♄	♅	♆	♇
1	4 38 56.8	21S45.0	0S 5.0	14N11.8	25S49.0	18S24.5	19N59.2	23N 4.7	12N32.1	15S35.5	21S15.0	9N10.1
4	4 50 46.5	22 11.5	0 5.0	4 16.7	25 34.8	19 21.0	20 .0	23 5.7	12 31.6	15 38.6	21 15.8	9 9.6
7	5 2 36.1	22 34.2	0 4.9	8S11.6	25 8.8	20 12.6	20 2.8	23 6.6	12 31.6	15 41.7	21 16.5	9 9.3
10	5 14 25.8	22 52.9	0 4.9	17 29.3	24 32.5	20 59.0	20 7.5	23 7.4	12 31.9	15 44.6	21 17.2	9 9.1
13	5 26 15.5	23 7.5	0 4.8	16 33.8	23 48.1	21 40.0	20 14.3	23 8.3	12 32.5	15 47.5	21 18.0	9 9.0
16	5 38 5.1	23 18.0	0 4.7	6 27.7	22 57.7	22 15.2	20 23.2	23 9.1	12 33.5	15 50.3	21 18.6	9 9.1
19	5 49 54.8	23 24.3	0 4.7	5N44.3	22 4.1	22 44.5	20 34.1	23 9.8	12 34.9	15 52.9	21 19.3	9 9.4
22	6 1 44.5	23 26.4	0 4.6	15 4.6	21 12.0	23 7.6	20 47.1	23 10.5	12 36.6	15 55.5	21 20.0	9 9.8
25	6 13 34.2	23 24.2	0 4.5	18 34.4	20 30.3	23 24.4	21 2.0	23 11.1	12 38.6	15 58.0	21 20.6	9 10.3
28	6 25 23.8	23 17.8	0 4.5	14 58.1	20 7.5	23 34.6	21 18.7	23 11.6	12 41.0	16 .4	21 21.3	9 10.9
31	6 37 13.5	23 7.2	0 4.4	5 33.6	20 6.2	23 38.4	21 36.9	23 12.1	12 43.7	16 2.7	21 21.9	9 11.7

JANUARY 1978

LONGITUDE

DAY	EPHEM. SID. TIME (h m s)	☉ (° ′)	☊ (° ′)	☽ (° ′)	☿ (° ′)	♀ (° ′)	♂ (° ′)	♃ (° ′)	♄ (° ′)	♅ (° ′)	♆ (° ′)	♇ (° ′)
1	6 41 10.1	10♑13.0	10≏33.3	22♍14.9	21♐ 8.5	5♑ 8.5	9♌ 3.1	29♊51.8	0♍ 9.6	15♏18.8	16♐44.9	16≏36.0
2	6 45 6.6	11 14.2	10 30.1	5≏ 6.7	21 D 13.8	6 24.0	8 R 47.1	29 R 44.0	0 R 7.3	15 21.4	16 47.1	16 36.6
3	6 49 3.2	12 15.3	10 26.9	18 19.8	21 27.5	7 39.5	8 30.5	29 36.2	0 5.0	15 23.8	16 49.1	16 37.2
4	6 52 59.7	13 16.5	10 23.8	1♏57.6	21 48.9	8 55.0	8 13.1	29 28.4	0 2.5	15 26.2	16 51.2	16 37.7
5	6 56 56.3	14 17.7	10 20.6	16 2.5	22 17.4	10 10.5	7 55.0	29 20.8	29♌59.9	15 28.6	16 53.3	16 38.2
6	7 0 52.8	15 18.8	10 17.4	0♐34.2	22 52.2	11 26.0	7 36.3	29 13.2	29 57.3	15 31.0	16 55.3	16 38.7
7	7 4 49.4	16 20.0	10 14.2	15 29.4	23 32.6	12 41.5	7 17.0	29 5.7	29 54.5	15 33.3	16 57.4	16 39.2
8	7 8 46.0	17 21.2	10 11.0	0♑41.0	24 18.1	13 57.0	6 57.0	28 58.3	29 51.6	15 35.5	16 59.4	16 39.6
9	7 12 42.5	18 22.3	10 7.9	15 59.1	25 8.2	15 12.5	6 36.5	28 51.0	29 48.7	15 37.7	17 1.4	16 39.9
10	7 16 39.1	19 23.5	10 4.7	1♒11.9	26 2.3	16 28.0	6 15.4	28 43.8	29 45.6	15 39.9	17 3.4	16 40.3
11	7 20 35.6	20 24.7	10 1.5	16 8.7	26 60.0	17 43.5	5 53.9	28 36.7	29 42.5	15 42.0	17 5.4	16 40.6
12	7 24 32.2	21 25.8	9 58.3	0♓41.0	28 .9	18 58.9	5 31.9	28 29.7	29 39.3	15 44.0	17 7.3	16 40.8
13	7 28 28.7	22 27.0	9 55.2	14 44.3	29 4.8	20 14.4	5 9.5	28 22.9	29 36.0	15 46.1	17 9.3	16 41.1
14	7 32 25.3	23 28.1	9 52.0	28 17.3	0♑11.2	21 29.9	4 46.7	28 16.1	29 32.6	15 48.0	17 11.2	16 41.2
15	7 36 21.8	24 29.2	9 48.8	11♈22.1	1 20.0	22 45.3	4 23.7	28 9.5	29 29.2	15 49.9	17 13.1	16 41.4
16	7 40 18.4	25 30.3	9 45.6	24 2.3	2 30.9	24 .8	4 .3	28 3.0	29 25.6	15 51.8	17 14.9	16 41.5
17	7 44 15.0	26 31.4	9 42.5	6♉23.0	3 43.7	25 16.2	3 36.7	27 56.7	29 22.0	15 53.6	17 16.8	16 41.6
18	7 48 11.5	27 32.6	9 39.3	18 29.3	4 58.3	26 31.7	3 13.0	27 50.6	29 18.3	15 55.5	17 18.7	16 41.7
19	7 52 8.1	28 33.6	9 36.1	0♊26.1	6 14.4	27 47.2	2 49.1	27 44.5	29 14.6	15 57.2	17 20.5	16 41.7
20	7 56 4.6	29 34.7	9 32.9	12 18.0	7 31.9	29 2.6	2 25.1	27 38.6	29 10.7	15 58.8	17 22.3	16 41.7
21	8 0 1.2	0♒35.7	9 29.7	24 8.6	8 50.8	0♒18.0	2 1.0	27 32.9	29 6.8	16 .5	17 24.1	16 R 41.6
22	8 3 57.7	1 36.8	9 26.6	6♋ .9	10 11.0	1 33.4	1 37.0	27 27.3	29 2.8	16 2.0	17 25.8	16 41.5
23	8 7 54.3	2 37.8	9 23.4	17 57.0	11 32.2	2 48.8	1 13.0	27 21.8	28 58.8	16 3.6	17 27.6	16 41.4
24	8 11 50.9	3 38.8	9 20.2	29 58.6	12 54.6	4 4.2	0 49.1	27 16.6	28 54.7	16 5.0	17 29.3	16 41.2
25	8 15 47.4	4 39.8	9 17.0	12♌ 6.6	14 18.0	5 19.6	0 25.4	27 11.5	28 50.5	16 6.5	17 31.0	16 41.0
26	8 19 44.0	5 40.7	9 13.9	24 22.0	15 42.3	6 34.9	0 1.8	27 6.5	28 46.3	16 7.8	17 32.6	16 40.8
27	8 23 40.5	6 41.7	9 10.7	6♍45.7	17 7.6	7 50.3	29♋38.5	27 1.8	28 42.0	16 9.1	17 34.3	16 40.5
28	8 27 37.1	7 42.7	9 7.5	19 19.1	18 33.7	9 5.7	29 15.4	26 57.2	28 37.7	16 10.4	17 35.9	16 40.2
29	8 31 33.6	8 43.6	9 4.3	2≏ 3.8	20 .7	10 21.0	28 52.7	26 52.8	28 33.3	16 11.6	17 37.5	16 39.9
30	8 35 30.2	9 44.5	9 1.2	15 2.3	21 28.5	11 36.3	28 30.3	26 48.5	28 28.9	16 12.8	17 39.0	16 39.5
31	8 39 26.7	10 45.4	8 58.0	28 16.9	22 57.1	12 51.7	28 8.3	26 44.5	28 24.4	16 13.9	17 40.6	16 39.1

LATITUDE

DAY	EPHEM. SID. TIME	☉	☊	☽	☿	♀	♂	♃	♄	♅	♆	♇
1	6 41 10.1	0 .0	0 .0	1S34.0	2N59.0	0S17.8	3N52.1	0S14.1	1N25.2	0N23.3	1N25.2	17N 1.2
4	6 52 59.7	0 .0	0 .0	1N51.6	2 40.6	0 24.8	3 58.9	0 13.6	1 25.8	0 23.3	1 25.2	17 2.9
7	7 4 49.4	0 .0	0 .0	4 33.5	2 16.5	0 31.5	4 5.2	0 13.2	1 26.5	0 23.3	1 25.2	17 4.7
10	7 16 39.1	0 .0	0 .0	4 39.3	1 49.6	0 38.1	4 10.8	0 12.7	1 27.1	0 23.4	1 25.3	17 6.4
13	7 28 28.7	0 .0	0 .0	2 5.1	1 21.7	0 44.4	4 15.6	0 12.2	1 27.6	0 23.4	1 25.4	17 8.2
16	7 40 18.4	0 .0	0 .0	1S18.5	0 54.1	0 50.4	4 19.6	0 11.7	1 28.2	0 23.4	1 25.4	17 10.0
19	7 52 8.1	0 .0	0 .0	3 57.1	0 27.4	0 56.0	4 22.6	0 11.3	1 28.8	0 23.5	1 25.5	17 11.7
22	8 3 57.7	0 .0	0 .0	5 1.5	0 2.0	1 1.3	4 24.7	0 10.8	1 29.3	0 23.5	1 25.6	17 13.5
25	8 15 47.4	0 .0	0 .0	4 10.4	0S21.7	1 6.1	4 25.8	0 10.3	1 29.8	0 23.5	1 25.7	17 15.2
28	8 27 37.1	0 .0	0 .0	1 35.4	0 43.5	1 10.5	4 25.9	0 9.8	1 30.3	0 23.6	1 25.8	17 16.9
31	8 39 26.7	0 .0	0 .0	1N49.2	1 3.2	1 14.5	4 25.1	0 9.3	1 30.7	0 23.6	1 25.8	17 18.6

RIGHT ASCENSION

DAY	EPHEM. SID. TIME	☉	☊	☽	☿	♀	♂	♃	♄	♅	♆	♇
1	6 41 10.1	11♑ 6.9	9≏42.1	22♍15.8	20♐34.3	5♑36.8	12♌34.8	29♊51.1	2♍45.3	12♏58.0	15♐45.3	21≏49.8
2	6 45 6.6	12 13.1	9 39.1	4≏30.6	20 D 39.5	6 59.2	12 R 19.0	29 R 42.5	2 R 43.2	13 .5	15 47.6	21 50.5
3	6 49 3.2	13 19.2	9 36.2	17 10.5	20 53.7	8 21.7	12 2.4	29 34.1	2 41.0	13 3.0	15 49.8	21 51.3
4	6 52 59.7	14 25.3	9 33.3	0♏26.4	21 16.0	9 44.0	11 45.0	29 25.6	2 38.7	13 5.4	15 52.1	21 52.0
5	6 56 56.3	15 31.2	9 30.3	14 26.9	21 45.9	11 6.3	11 26.9	29 17.3	2 36.3	13 7.7	15 54.3	21 52.7
6	7 0 52.8	16 37.1	9 27.4	29 15.2	22 22.5	12 28.6	11 8.0	29 9.1	2 33.8	13 10.1	15 56.5	21 53.4
7	7 4 49.4	17 42.8	9 24.5	14♐45.9	23 5.2	13 50.7	10 48.4	29 .9	2 31.3	13 12.4	15 58.6	21 54.0
8	7 8 46.0	18 48.5	9 21.6	0♑43.1	23 53.5	15 12.8	10 28.2	28 52.8	2 28.6	13 14.6	16 .8	21 54.6
9	7 12 42.5	19 54.0	9 18.6	16 43.3	24 46.7	16 34.7	10 7.3	28 44.9	2 25.8	13 16.8	16 2.9	21 55.1
10	7 16 39.1	20 59.4	9 15.7	2♒22.2	25 44.5	17 56.4	9 45.8	28 37.1	2 23.0	13 19.0	16 5.1	21 55.7
11	7 20 35.6	22 4.6	9 12.8	17 22.6	26 46.3	19 18.1	9 23.7	28 29.3	2 20.0	13 21.1	16 7.2	21 56.2
12	7 24 32.2	23 9.7	9 9.8	1♓37.3	27 51.7	20 39.5	9 1.1	28 21.7	2 17.0	13 23.1	16 9.3	21 56.6
13	7 28 28.7	24 14.6	9 6.9	15 8.3	29 .4	22 .8	8 38.0	28 14.3	2 13.9	13 25.1	16 11.3	21 57.0
14	7 32 25.3	25 19.4	9 4.0	28 3.2	0♑12.1	23 21.9	8 14.5	28 7.0	2 10.8	13 27.1	16 13.4	21 57.4
15	7 36 21.8	26 24.0	9 1.1	10♈31.8	1 26.5	24 42.8	7 50.6	27 59.8	2 7.5	13 29.0	16 15.4	21 57.8
16	7 40 18.4	27 28.5	8 58.1	22 44.6	2 43.3	26 3.5	7 26.3	27 52.7	2 4.2	13 30.9	16 17.4	21 58.1
17	7 44 15.0	28 32.7	8 55.2	4♉50.5	4 2.4	27 23.9	7 1.7	27 45.8	2 .7	13 32.7	16 19.4	21 58.4
18	7 48 11.5	29 36.9	8 52.3	16 56.7	5 23.5	28 44.2	6 36.9	27 39.1	1 57.3	13 34.5	16 21.4	21 58.8
19	7 52 8.1	0♒40.8	8 49.3	29 8.0	6 46.4	0♒ 4.1	6 11.8	27 32.5	1 53.7	13 36.2	16 23.4	21 59.0
20	7 56 4.6	1 44.5	8 46.4	11♊26.3	8 10.9	1 23.8	5 46.6	27 26.1	1 50.1	13 37.9	16 25.3	21 59.2
21	8 0 1.2	2 48.0	8 43.5	23 50.8	9 37.0	2 43.2	5 21.3	27 19.9	1 46.4	13 39.5	16 27.2	21 59.4
22	8 3 57.7	3 51.4	8 40.6	6♋18.6	11 4.4	4 2.4	4 55.9	27 13.8	1 42.7	13 41.1	16 29.1	21 59.5
23	8 7 54.3	4 54.5	8 37.6	18 45.6	12 33.2	5 21.3	4 30.5	27 7.9	1 38.8	13 42.6	16 30.9	21 59.6
24	8 11 50.9	5 57.5	8 34.7	1♌ 7.8	14 3.1	6 39.9	4 5.1	27 2.1	1 34.9	13 44.1	16 32.8	21 59.7
25	8 15 47.4	7 .2	8 31.8	13 22.6	15 34.1	7 58.2	3 39.8	26 56.6	1 31.0	13 45.5	16 34.6	21 59.7
26	8 19 44.0	8 2.8	8 28.9	25 29.8	17 6.0	9 16.2	3 14.7	26 51.2	1 27.0	13 46.9	16 36.4	21 59.8
27	8 23 40.5	9 5.2	8 25.9	7♍31.7	18 38.9	10 33.9	2 49.7	26 46.0	1 22.9	13 48.2	16 38.1	21 R 59.7
28	8 27 37.1	10 7.3	8 23.0	19 33.5	20 12.6	11 51.3	2 25.0	26 41.0	1 18.8	13 49.5	16 39.8	21 59.7
29	8 31 33.6	11 9.3	8 20.1	1≏42.2	21 47.1	13 8.5	2 .6	26 36.2	1 14.6	13 50.7	16 41.5	21 59.6
30	8 35 30.2	12 11.0	8 17.1	14 6.5	23 22.2	14 25.3	1 36.5	26 31.6	1 10.4	13 51.8	16 43.2	21 59.5
31	8 39 26.7	13 12.6	8 14.2	26 55.8	24 58.0	15 41.8	1 12.8	26 27.2	1 6.1	13 52.9	16 44.9	21 59.3

DECLINATION

DAY	EPHEM. SID. TIME	☉	☊	☽	☿	♀	♂	♃	♄	♅	♆	♇
1	6 41 10.1	23S 2.8	0S 4.4	1N38.1	20S10.0	23S38.1	21N43.3	23N12.3	12N44.7	16S 3.4	21S22.0	9N12.0
4	6 52 59.7	22 46.6	0 4.3	10S24.5	20 30.9	23 33.1	22 3.2	23 12.7	12 47.8	16 5.5	21 22.6	9 13.0
7	7 4 49.4	22 26.4	0 4.2	18 7.0	21 .6	23 21.4	22 24.0	23 13.0	12 51.2	16 7.6	21 23.2	9 14.1
10	7 16 39.1	22 2.2	0 4.2	15 20.8	21 33.3	23 3.3	22 45.3	23 13.3	12 54.9	16 9.4	21 23.7	9 15.3
13	7 28 28.7	21 34.2	0 4.1	4 5.2	22 4.5	22 38.7	23 6.5	23 13.6	12 58.8	16 11.2	21 24.2	9 16.6
16	7 40 18.4	21 2.4	0 4.0	8N 6.5	22 30.9	22 8.0	23 27.3	23 13.8	13 3.0	16 12.8	21 24.7	9 18.1
19	7 52 8.1	20 26.9	0 4.0	16 22.6	22 50.2	21 31.2	23 47.3	23 14.0	13 7.4	16 14.3	21 25.1	9 19.6
22	8 3 57.7	19 48.1	0 3.9	18 16.9	23 .9	20 48.5	24 5.9	23 14.1	13 12.0	16 15.7	21 25.5	9 21.3
25	8 15 47.4	19 5.9	0 3.9	13 9.2	23 1.9	20 .4	24 23.1	23 14.3	13 16.8	16 16.9	21 25.9	9 23.1
28	8 27 37.1	18 20.5	0 3.8	2 45.9	22 52.3	19 6.9	24 38.3	23 14.5	13 21.7	16 18.0	21 26.3	9 24.9
31	8 39 26.7	17 32.2	0 3.7	9S 9.8	22 31.6	18 8.5	24 51.6	23 14.6	13 26.8	16 19.0	21 26.6	9 26.9

FEBRUARY 1978

LONGITUDE

DAY	EPHEM. SID. TIME	☉	☊	☽	☿	♀	♂	♃	♄	♅	♆	♇
	h m s	° ′	° ′	° ′	° ′	° ′	° ′	° ′	° ′	° ′	° ′	° ′
1	8 43 23.3	11♒46.3	8♎54.8	11♏50.4	24♑26.5	14♒ 7.0	27♋46.7	26♊40.6	28♌19.9	16♏14.9	17♐42.1	16♎38.6
2	8 47 19.8	12 47.2	8 51.6	25 44.4	25 56.7	15 22.3	27 R 25.6	26 R 37.0	28 R 15.3	16 15.9	17 43.6	16 R 38.2
3	8 51 16.4	13 48.1	8 48.4	9♐59.4	27 27.7	16 37.6	27 5.0	26 33.5	28 10.7	16 16.8	17 45.0	16 37.7
4	8 55 13.0	14 49.0	8 45.3	24 33.7	28 59.4	17 52.9	26 45.0	26 30.2	28 6.0	16 17.7	17 46.5	16 37.1
5	8 59 9.5	15 49.8	8 42.1	9♑22.9	0♒31.9	19 8.2	26 25.5	26 27.1	28 1.4	16 18.5	17 47.9	16 36.5
6	9 3 6.1	16 50.7	8 38.9	24 20.1	2 5.1	20 23.5	26 6.6	26 24.1	27 56.6	16 19.3	17 49.3	16 35.9
7	9 7 2.6	17 51.5	8 35.7	9♒16.5	3 39.2	21 38.8	25 48.4	26 21.4	27 51.9	16 20.0	17 50.6	16 35.3
8	9 10 59.2	18 52.3	8 32.6	24 2.8	5 14.0	22 54.1	25 30.9	26 18.9	27 47.2	16 20.7	17 52.0	16 34.7
9	9 14 55.7	19 53.1	8 29.4	8♓31.0	6 49.6	24 9.4	25 14.0	26 16.6	27 42.4	16 21.4	17 53.3	16 33.9
10	9 18 52.3	20 53.8	8 26.2	22 35.3	8 25.9	25 24.6	24 57.8	26 14.5	27 37.6	16 21.9	17 54.5	16 33.2
11	9 22 48.8	21 54.6	8 23.0	6♈13.1	10 3.1	26 39.8	24 42.3	26 12.6	27 32.8	16 22.4	17 55.8	16 32.4
12	9 26 45.4	22 55.3	8 19.8	19 24.2	11 41.0	27 55.0	24 27.6	26 10.9	27 27.9	16 22.8	17 57.0	16 31.6
13	9 30 41.9	23 55.9	8 16.7	2♉10.9	13 19.8	29 10.2	24 13.6	26 9.3	27 23.1	16 23.2	17 58.2	16 30.8
14	9 34 38.5	24 56.6	8 13.5	14 36.9	14 59.4	0♓25.4	24 .4	26 8.0	27 18.2	16 23.6	17 59.3	16 30.0
15	9 38 35.0	25 57.2	8 10.3	26 46.9	16 39.9	1 40.5	23 48.0	26 6.9	27 13.4	16 23.8	18 .4	16 29.1
16	9 42 31.6	26 57.8	8 7.1	8♊45.8	18 21.3	2 55.7	23 36.4	26 6.0	27 8.5	16 24.1	18 1.5	16 28.1
17	9 46 28.2	27 58.4	8 4.0	20 38.7	20 3.5	4 10.8	23 25.6	26 5.3	27 3.6	16 24.2	18 2.6	16 27.2
18	9 50 24.7	28 58.9	8 .8	2♋30.0	21 46.6	5 25.9	23 15.5	26 4.8	26 58.8	16 24.3	18 3.6	16 26.2
19	9 54 21.3	29 59.4	7 57.6	14 23.8	23 30.6	6 41.0	23 6.3	26 4.4	26 53.9	16 24.4	18 4.6	16 25.2
20	9 58 17.8	0♓59.9	7 54.4	26 23.4	25 15.5	7 56.0	22 57.8	26 4.3	26 49.1	16 24.4	18 5.6	16 24.2
21	10 2 14.4	2 .3	7 51.2	8♌31.4	27 1.4	9 11.1	22 50.2	26 D 4.4	26 44.3	16 R 24.3	18 6.5	16 23.1
22	10 6 10.9	3 .7	7 48.1	20 49.4	28 48.2	10 26.1	22 43.3	26 4.7	26 39.4	16 24.2	18 7.4	16 22.0
23	10 10 7.5	4 1.1	7 44.9	3♍18.7	0♓36.0	11 41.1	22 37.3	26 5.2	26 34.6	16 24.0	18 8.3	16 20.9
24	10 14 4.0	5 1.5	7 41.7	15 59.8	2 24.7	12 56.1	22 32.0	26 5.9	26 29.8	16 23.8	18 9.1	16 19.8
25	10 18 .6	6 1.8	7 38.5	28 52.8	4 14.3	14 11.1	22 27.5	26 6.8	26 25.1	16 23.6	18 9.9	16 18.6
26	10 21 57.1	7 2.1	7 35.4	11♎57.9	6 4.9	15 26.0	22 23.8	26 7.9	26 20.3	16 23.2	18 10.7	16 17.5
27	10 25 53.7	8 2.4	7 32.2	25 15.3	7 56.3	16 41.0	22 20.8	26 9.1	26 15.6	16 22.8	18 11.4	16 16.2
28	10 29 50.2	9 2.6	7 29.0	8♏45.1	9 48.7	17 55.9	22 18.7	26 10.6	26 10.9	16 22.4	18 12.1	16 15.0

LATITUDE

DAY	EPHEM. SID. TIME	☉	☊	☽	☿	♀	♂	♃	♄	♅	♆	♇
1	8 43 23.3	0 .0	0 .0	2N53.5	1S 9.3	1S15.7	4N24.6	0S 9.2	1N30.8	0N23.6	1N25.9	17N19.1
4	8 55 13.0	0 .0	0 .0	4 58.8	1 26.0	1 18.9	4 22.6	0 8.7	1 31.3	0 23.7	1 26.0	17 20.7
7	9 7 2.6	0 .0	0 .0	4 19.5	1 40.1	1 21.7	4 19.8	0 8.2	1 31.6	0 23.7	1 26.1	17 22.3
10	9 18 52.3	0 .0	0 .0	1 15.4	1 51.4	1 23.9	4 16.3	0 7.8	1 32.0	0 23.7	1 26.2	17 23.9
13	9 30 41.9	0 .0	0 .0	2S13.7	1 59.8	1 25.5	4 12.1	0 7.3	1 32.3	0 23.8	1 26.3	17 25.4
16	9 42 31.6	0 .0	0 .0	4 34.4	2 4.9	1 26.6	4 7.5	0 6.9	1 32.6	0 23.8	1 26.4	17 26.8
19	9 54 21.3	0 .0	0 .0	5 7.4	2 6.5	1 27.1	4 2.5	0 6.4	1 32.8	0 23.9	1 26.5	17 28.2
22	10 6 10.9	0 .0	0 .0	3 41.8	2 4.1	1 27.1	3 57.2	0 6.0	1 33.0	0 23.9	1 26.7	17 29.5
25	10 18 .6	0 .0	0 .0	0 39.1	1 57.5	1 26.4	3 51.6	0 5.5	1 33.2	0 23.9	1 26.8	17 30.7
28	10 29 50.2	0 .0	0 .0	2N50.0	1 46.3	1 25.1	3 45.9	0 5.1	1 33.4	0 24.0	1 26.9	17 31.9

RIGHT ASCENSION

DAY	EPHEM. SID. TIME	☉	☊	☽	☿	♀	♂	♃	♄	♅	♆	♇
1	8 43 23.3	14♒14.0	8♎11.3	10♏18.7	26♑34.4	16♒57.9	0♌49.5	26♊23.0	1♍ 1.8	13♏54.0	16♐46.5	21♎59.2
2	8 47 19.8	15 15.1	8 8.4	24 20.9	28 11.4	18 13.8	0 R 26.6	26 R 19.0	0 R 57.5	13 55.0	16 48.1	21 R 58.9
3	8 51 16.4	16 16.1	8 5.4	9♐ 2.9	29 48.8	19 29.4	0 4.3	26 15.2	0 53.1	13 55.9	16 49.7	21 58.7
4	8 55 13.0	17 16.9	8 2.5	24 17.4	1♒26.7	20 44.6	29♋42.5	26 11.6	0 48.7	13 56.8	16 51.2	21 58.4
5	8 59 9.5	18 17.4	7 59.6	9♑49.9	3 5.1	21 59.6	29 21.3	26 8.2	0 44.2	13 57.6	16 52.7	21 58.1
6	9 3 6.1	19 17.8	7 56.7	25 20.8	4 43.8	23 14.2	29 .7	26 5.0	0 39.7	13 58.4	16 54.2	21 57.8
7	9 7 2.6	20 18.0	7 53.7	10♒32.0	6 22.9	24 28.6	28 40.7	26 2.1	0 35.2	13 59.1	16 55.6	21 57.4
8	9 10 59.2	21 18.0	7 50.8	25 11.2	8 2.4	25 42.7	28 21.5	25 59.4	0 30.7	13 59.8	16 57.1	21 57.1
9	9 14 55.7	22 17.7	7 47.9	9♓13.8	9 42.1	26 56.4	28 3.0	25 56.8	0 26.1	14 .5	16 58.5	21 56.6
10	9 18 52.3	23 17.3	7 45.0	22 41.9	11 22.2	28 9.8	27 45.2	25 54.5	0 21.5	14 1.0	16 59.8	21 56.2
11	9 22 48.8	24 16.7	7 42.0	5♈41.5	13 2.5	29 23.0	27 28.1	25 52.4	0 16.9	14 1.5	17 1.2	21 55.7
12	9 26 45.4	25 15.9	7 39.1	18 20.6	14 43.0	0♓35.8	27 11.9	25 50.5	0 12.2	14 2.0	17 2.5	21 55.2
13	9 30 41.9	26 14.8	7 36.2	0♉46.8	16 23.9	1 48.4	26 56.4	25 48.9	0 7.6	14 2.3	17 3.7	21 54.6
14	9 34 38.5	27 13.6	7 33.3	13 7.0	18 4.9	3 .7	26 41.8	25 47.4	0 2.9	14 2.7	17 5.0	21 54.0
15	9 38 35.0	28 12.2	7 30.3	25 26.1	19 46.2	4 12.7	26 28.0	25 46.2	29♌58.3	14 3.0	17 6.2	21 53.4
16	9 42 31.6	29 10.6	7 27.4	7♊47.2	21 27.7	5 24.5	26 15.0	25 45.2	29 53.6	14 3.2	17 7.3	21 52.8
17	9 46 28.2	0♓ 8.9	7 24.5	20 11.3	23 9.4	6 35.9	26 2.9	25 44.4	29 48.9	14 3.3	17 8.5	21 52.1
18	9 50 24.7	1 6.9	7 21.6	2♋37.3	24 51.3	7 47.2	25 51.7	25 43.9	29 44.2	14 3.5	17 9.6	21 51.5
19	9 54 21.3	2 4.8	7 18.6	15 3.3	26 33.5	8 58.2	25 41.3	25 43.5	29 39.6	14 3.5	17 10.6	21 50.7
20	9 58 17.8	3 2.5	7 15.7	27 26.9	28 15.8	10 8.9	25 31.8	25 43.4	29 34.9	14 3.5	17 11.7	21 50.0
21	10 2 14.4	4 .0	7 12.8	9♌46.3	29 58.4	11 19.5	25 23.1	25 D 43.5	29 30.3	14 3.5	17 12.7	21 49.2
22	10 6 10.9	4 57.4	7 9.9	22 1.0	1♓41.1	12 29.8	25 15.3	25 43.8	29 25.6	14 R 3.4	17 13.6	21 48.4
23	10 10 7.5	5 54.6	7 6.9	4♍12.8	3 24.1	13 39.9	25 8.4	25 44.4	29 21.0	14 3.2	17 14.6	21 47.6
24	10 14 4.0	6 51.6	7 4.0	16 24.9	5 7.3	14 49.8	25 2.3	25 45.1	29 16.4	14 3.0	17 15.5	21 46.7
25	10 18 .6	7 48.5	7 1.1	28 42.8	6 50.7	15 59.5	24 57.1	25 46.1	29 11.8	14 2.7	17 16.3	21 45.9
26	10 21 57.1	8 45.3	6 58.2	11♎12.9	8 34.3	17 9.0	24 52.7	25 47.2	29 7.2	14 2.4	17 17.2	21 45.0
27	10 25 53.7	9 41.9	6 55.2	24 2.4	10 18.1	18 18.3	24 49.1	25 48.6	29 2.7	14 2.0	17 17.9	21 44.1
28	10 29 50.2	10 38.4	6 52.3	7♏17.6	12 2.1	19 27.5	24 46.4	25 50.2	28 58.1	14 1.6	17 18.7	21 43.1

DECLINATION

DAY	EPHEM. SID. TIME	☉	☊	☽	☿	♀	♂	♃	♄	♅	♆	♇
1	8 43 23.3	17S15.4	0S 3.7	12S38.1	22S22.1	17S48.0	24N55.6	23N14.7	13N28.5	16S19.3	21S26.7	9N27.6
4	8 55 13.0	16 23.4	0 3.6	18 21.1	21 45.8	16 43.5	25 6.0	23 14.9	13 33.6	16 20.0	21 27.0	9 29.6
7	9 7 2.6	15 28.8	0 3.6	13 45.7	20 57.5	15 34.7	25 14.2	23 15.1	13 38.9	16 20.7	21 27.3	9 31.8
10	9 18 52.3	14 31.8	0 3.5	1 47.2	19 56.9	14 22.0	25 20.2	23 15.4	13 44.2	16 21.2	21 27.5	9 34.0
13	9 30 41.9	13 32.6	0 3.4	10N 8.3	18 43.9	13 5.9	25 24.3	23 15.7	13 49.5	16 21.5	21 27.8	9 36.2
16	9 42 31.6	12 31.5	0 3.4	17 14.6	17 18.4	11 46.6	25 26.3	23 16.1	13 54.8	16 21.7	21 27.9	9 38.5
19	9 54 21.3	11 28.5	0 3.3	17 34.0	15 40.3	10 24.5	25 26.6	23 16.5	14 .0	16 21.8	21 28.1	9 40.9
22	10 6 10.9	10 24.0	0 3.2	11 2.8	13 49.7	8 59.9	25 25.3	23 16.9	14 5.2	16 21.7	21 28.2	9 43.3
25	10 18 .6	9 18.0	0 3.2	0S 9.1	11 46.8	7 33.1	25 22.5	23 17.4	14 10.3	16 21.5	21 28.3	9 45.7
28	10 29 50.2	8 10.7	0 3.1	11 44.0	9 31.8	6 4.6	25 18.4	23 18.0	14 15.3	16 21.1	21 28.4	9 48.1

MARCH 1978

LONGITUDE

DAY	EPHEM. SID. TIME	☉	☊	☽	☿	♀	♂	♃	♄	♅	♆	♇
	h m s	° ′	° ′	° ′	° ′	° ′	° ′	° ′	° ′	° ′	° ′	° ′
1	10 33 46.8	10♓ 2.9	7♎25.8	22♏27.6	11♓41.9	19♓10.8	22♋17.3	26♊12.3	26♌ 6.3	16♏22.0	18♐12.8	16♎13.8
2	10 37 43.3	11 3.1	7 22.6	6♐22.8	13 35.8	20 25.7	22 R 16.6	26 14.2	26 R 1.7	16 R 21.4	18 13.5	16 R 12.5
3	10 41 39.9	12 3.3	7 19.5	20 30.0	15 30.5	21 40.6	22 D 16.7	26 16.3	25 57.1	16 20.8	18 14.1	16 11.2
4	10 45 36.4	13 3.5	7 16.3	4♑47.8	17 25.8	22 55.4	22 17.5	26 18.5	25 52.6	16 20.2	18 14.7	16 9.9
5	10 49 33.0	14 3.6	7 13.1	19 13.4	19 21.6	24 10.2	22 19.0	26 20.9	25 48.1	16 19.5	18 15.2	16 8.6
6	10 53 29.6	15 3.7	7 9.9	3♒42.6	21 17.7	25 25.0	22 21.2	26 23.6	25 43.6	16 18.7	18 15.7	16 7.2
7	10 57 26.1	16 3.8	7 6.8	18 10.3	23 14.1	26 39.8	22 24.2	26 26.4	25 39.2	16 17.9	18 16.2	16 5.8
8	11 1 22.7	17 3.8	7 3.6	2♓30.8	25 10.5	27 54.6	22 27.8	26 29.4	25 34.8	16 17.1	18 16.6	16 4.4
9	11 5 19.2	18 3.8	7 .4	16 38.6	27 6.7	29 9.3	22 32.1	26 32.6	25 30.5	16 16.2	18 17.0	16 3.0
10	11 9 15.8	19 3.8	6 57.2	0♈29.1	29 2.3	0♈24.1	22 37.1	26 36.0	25 26.3	16 15.2	18 17.4	16 1.5
11	11 13 12.3	20 3.8	6 54.0	13 59.4	0♈57.2	1 38.8	22 42.8	26 39.5	25 22.1	16 14.2	18 17.7	16 .1
12	11 17 8.9	21 3.7	6 50.9	27 8.3	2 51.0	2 53.4	22 49.1	26 43.3	25 17.9	16 13.2	18 18.0	15 58.6
13	11 21 5.4	22 3.6	6 47.7	9♉56.3	4 43.3	4 8.1	22 56.1	26 47.2	25 13.8	16 12.1	18 18.3	15 57.1
14	11 25 2.0	23 3.4	6 44.5	22 25.5	6 33.6	5 22.7	23 3.7	26 51.3	25 9.8	16 10.9	18 18.5	15 55.6
15	11 28 58.5	24 3.2	6 41.3	4♊39.0	8 21.7	6 37.3	23 11.9	26 55.6	25 5.9	16 9.7	18 18.7	15 54.1
16	11 32 55.1	25 3.0	6 38.1	16 41.0	10 6.9	7 51.9	23 20.7	27 .1	25 2.0	16 8.5	18 18.9	15 52.5
17	11 36 51.6	26 2.8	6 35.0	28 36.0	11 48.8	9 6.4	23 30.2	27 4.7	24 58.2	16 7.2	18 19.1	15 51.0
18	11 40 48.2	27 2.5	6 31.8	10♋28.6	13 27.0	10 20.9	23 40.2	27 9.5	24 54.4	16 5.9	18 19.2	15 49.4
19	11 44 44.7	28 2.1	6 28.6	22 23.5	15 .9	11 35.4	23 50.7	27 14.5	24 50.8	16 4.5	18 19.2	15 47.9
20	11 48 41.3	29 1.7	6 25.4	4♌25.0	16 30.2	12 49.8	24 1.8	27 19.6	24 47.2	16 3.1	18 19.3	15 46.3
21	11 52 37.8	0♈ 1.3	6 22.3	16 36.9	17 54.2	14 4.3	24 13.5	27 25.0	24 43.7	16 1.6	18 19.3	15 44.7
22	11 56 34.4	1 .9	6 19.1	29 2.3	19 12.7	15 18.7	24 25.7	27 30.5	24 40.3	16 .1	18 19.3	15 43.1
23	12 0 30.9	2 .5	6 15.9	11♍43.2	20 25.3	16 33.1	24 38.4	27 36.1	24 36.9	15 58.6	18 R 19.2	15 41.5
24	12 4 27.5	2 59.9	6 12.7	24 40.8	21 31.4	17 47.4	24 51.6	27 41.9	24 33.7	15 57.0	18 19.1	15 39.9
25	12 8 24.0	3 59.4	6 9.5	7♎55.2	22 31.0	19 1.7	25 5.3	27 47.9	24 30.5	15 55.3	18 19.0	15 38.2
26	12 12 20.6	4 58.8	6 6.4	21 25.4	23 23.6	20 16.0	25 19.5	27 54.0	24 27.4	15 53.7	18 18.8	15 36.6
27	12 16 17.1	5 58.2	6 3.2	5♏ 9.5	24 9.2	21 30.2	25 34.2	28 .2	24 24.3	15 52.0	18 18.6	15 34.9
28	12 20 13.7	6 57.5	6 .0	19 5.1	24 47.4	22 44.4	25 49.3	28 6.7	24 21.4	15 50.2	18 18.4	15 33.3
29	12 24 10.2	7 56.8	5 56.8	3♐ 9.4	25 18.2	23 58.6	26 4.9	28 13.2	24 18.6	15 48.4	18 18.1	15 31.6
30	12 28 6.8	8 56.1	5 53.7	17 19.4	25 41.6	25 12.8	26 20.9	28 19.9	24 15.8	15 46.6	18 17.8	15 29.9
31	12 32 3.3	9 55.4	5 50.5	1♑32.3	25 57.5	26 26.9	26 37.3	28 26.8	24 13.1	15 44.7	18 17.5	15 28.3

LATITUDE

DAY	EPHEM. SID. TIME	☉	☊	☽	☿	♀	♂	♃	♄	♅	♆	♇
1	10 33 46.8	0 .0	0 .0	3N47.8	1S41.5	1S24.6	3N44.0	0S 5.0	1N33.4	0N24.0	1N27.0	17N32.3
4	10 45 36.4	0 .0	0 .0	5 14.3	1 23.5	1 22.6	3 38.2	0 4.6	1 33.6	0 24.0	1 27.1	17 33.4
7	10 57 26.1	0 .0	0 .0	3 53.4	1 .3	1 20.0	3 32.3	0 4.2	1 33.6	0 24.1	1 27.2	17 34.4
10	11 9 15.8	0 .0	0 .0	0 29.7	0 31.9	1 16.9	3 26.4	0 3.8	1 33.7	0 24.1	1 27.3	17 35.3
13	11 21 5.4	0 .0	0 .0	2S57.4	0N 1.1	1 13.2	3 20.6	0 3.4	1 33.7	0 24.1	1 27.5	17 36.1
16	11 32 55.1	0 .0	0 .0	4 59.0	0 37.8	1 9.0	3 14.8	0 3.0	1 33.7	0 24.1	1 27.6	17 36.9
19	11 44 44.7	0 .0	0 .0	5 3.8	1 16.0	1 4.3	3 9.2	0 2.6	1 33.7	0 24.2	1 27.7	17 37.5
22	11 56 34.4	0 .0	0 .0	3 10.4	1 53.5	0 59.1	3 3.7	0 2.2	1 33.6	0 24.2	1 27.9	17 38.1
25	12 8 24.0	0 .0	0 .0	0N11.3	2 27.3	0 53.5	2 58.2	0 1.9	1 33.5	0 24.2	1 28.0	17 38.6
28	12 20 13.7	0 .0	0 .0	3 37.4	2 54.6	0 47.5	2 53.0	0 1.5	1 33.4	0 24.2	1 28.1	17 39.0
31	12 32 3.3	0 .0	0 .0	5 16.1	3 12.3	0 41.0	2 47.8	0 1.2	1 33.3	0 24.3	1 28.2	17 39.2

RIGHT ASCENSION

DAY	EPHEM. SID. TIME	☉	☊	☽	☿	♀	♂	♃	♄	♅	♆	♇
1	10 33 46.8	11♓34.8	6♎49.4	21♏ 3.2	13♓46.2	20♓36.6	24♋44.5	25♊52.1	28♌53.7	14♏ 1.2	17♐19.5	21♎42.2
2	10 37 43.3	12 31.0	6 46.5	5♐19.7	15 30.4	21 45.5	24 R 43.4	25 54.1	28 R 49.2	14 R .6	17 20.2	21 R 41.2
3	10 41 39.9	13 27.1	6 43.5	20 2.5	17 14.7	22 54.2	24 43.2	25 56.3	28 44.8	14 .0	17 20.8	21 40.2
4	10 45 36.4	14 23.1	6 40.6	5♑ 1.6	18 59.0	24 2.8	24 D 43.7	25 58.8	28 40.4	13 59.4	17 21.4	21 39.1
5	10 49 33.0	15 19.0	6 37.7	20 3.3	20 43.3	25 11.4	24 44.9	26 1.4	28 36.0	13 58.7	17 22.0	21 38.1
6	10 53 29.6	16 14.7	6 34.8	4♒54.1	22 27.4	26 19.8	24 47.0	26 4.3	28 31.7	13 57.9	17 22.6	21 37.0
7	10 57 26.1	17 10.4	6 31.9	19 23.4	24 11.2	27 28.1	24 49.9	26 7.4	28 27.4	13 57.1	17 23.1	21 35.9
8	11 1 22.7	18 6.0	6 28.9	3♓26.1	25 54.7	28 36.4	24 53.4	26 10.6	28 23.2	13 56.3	17 23.6	21 34.7
9	11 5 19.2	19 1.4	6 26.0	17 2.0	27 37.6	29 44.5	24 57.8	26 14.1	28 19.0	13 55.4	17 24.0	21 33.6
10	11 9 15.8	19 56.8	6 23.1	0♈14.9	29 19.8	0♈52.6	25 2.9	26 17.8	28 14.9	13 54.5	17 24.4	21 32.4
11	11 13 12.3	20 52.1	6 20.2	13 10.0	1♈ 1.0	2 .7	25 8.6	26 21.7	28 10.8	13 53.5	17 24.8	21 31.2
12	11 17 8.9	21 47.3	6 17.2	25 53.0	2 41.0	3 8.7	25 15.1	26 25.7	28 6.8	13 52.4	17 25.1	21 30.0
13	11 21 5.4	22 42.5	6 14.3	8♉29.1	4 19.5	4 16.7	25 22.3	26 30.0	28 2.8	13 51.3	17 25.4	21 28.8
14	11 25 2.0	23 37.5	6 11.4	21 1.7	5 56.2	5 24.7	25 30.2	26 34.5	27 58.9	13 50.2	17 25.7	21 27.6
15	11 28 58.5	24 32.5	6 8.5	3♊32.9	7 30.8	6 32.6	25 38.7	26 39.2	27 55.1	13 49.0	17 25.9	21 26.3
16	11 32 55.1	25 27.4	6 5.6	16 3.2	9 2.8	7 40.6	25 47.9	26 44.0	27 51.3	13 47.7	17 26.1	21 25.0
17	11 36 51.6	26 22.3	6 2.6	28 31.9	10 32.0	8 48.6	25 57.7	26 49.0	27 47.6	13 46.5	17 26.2	21 23.7
18	11 40 48.2	27 17.1	5 59.7	10♋57.7	11 57.8	9 56.5	26 8.2	26 54.3	27 43.9	13 45.1	17 26.3	21 22.4
19	11 44 44.7	28 11.8	5 56.8	23 19.4	13 20.0	11 4.6	26 19.2	26 59.7	27 40.4	13 43.7	17 26.4	21 21.1
20	11 48 41.3	29 6.6	5 53.9	5♌36.6	14 38.0	12 12.6	26 30.9	27 5.3	27 36.9	13 42.3	17 26.4	21 19.8
21	11 52 37.8	0♈ 1.2	5 50.9	17 50.4	15 51.5	13 20.7	26 43.1	27 11.1	27 33.4	13 40.9	17 26.4	21 18.4
22	11 56 34.4	0 55.9	5 48.0	0♍ 3.1	17 .2	14 28.9	26 55.9	27 17.1	27 30.1	13 39.4	17 26.5	21 17.1
23	12 0 30.9	1 50.5	5 45.1	12 18.7	18 3.7	15 37.2	27 9.2	27 23.2	27 26.8	13 37.9	17 R 26.4	21 15.7
24	12 4 27.5	2 45.1	5 42.2	24 42.5	19 1.6	16 45.5	27 23.1	27 29.5	27 23.6	13 36.3	17 26.3	21 14.3
25	12 8 24.0	3 39.7	5 39.3	7♎20.9	19 53.6	17 53.9	27 37.4	27 36.0	27 20.5	13 34.6	17 26.2	21 12.9
26	12 12 20.6	4 34.2	5 36.3	20 20.0	20 39.6	19 2.5	27 52.3	27 42.7	27 17.5	13 33.0	17 26.0	21 11.5
27	12 16 17.1	5 28.8	5 33.4	3♏45.1	21 19.2	20 11.1	28 7.7	27 49.5	27 14.5	13 31.3	17 25.8	21 10.1
28	12 20 13.7	6 23.4	5 30.5	17 39.0	21 52.4	21 19.9	28 23.5	27 56.5	27 11.7	13 29.5	17 25.5	21 8.7
29	12 24 10.2	7 17.9	5 27.6	2♐ .5	22 19.1	22 28.8	28 39.9	28 3.6	27 8.9	13 27.7	17 25.3	21 7.2
30	12 28 6.8	8 12.5	5 24.7	16 43.3	22 39.0	23 37.8	28 56.6	28 11.0	27 6.2	13 25.9	17 25.0	21 5.8
31	12 32 3.3	9 7.1	5 21.7	1♑36.7	22 52.4	24 47.0	29 13.9	28 18.4	27 3.6	13 24.0	17 24.6	21 4.3

DECLINATION

DAY	EPHEM. SID. TIME	☉	☊	☽	☿	♀	♂	♃	♄	♅	♆	♇
1	10 33 46.8	7S48.0	0S 3.1	14S42.8	8S44.3	5S34.8	25N16.7	23N18.1	14N16.9	16S21.0	21S28.4	9N48.9
4	10 45 36.4	6 39.4	0 3.0	18 7.0	6 14.9	4 4.4	25 10.9	23 18.7	14 21.7	16 20.4	21 28.4	9 51.3
7	10 57 26.1	5 29.9	0 3.0	11 40.7	3 36.6	2 33.0	25 4.0	23 19.4	14 26.3	16 19.7	21 28.4	9 53.8
10	11 9 15.8	4 19.7	0 2.9	0N38.9	0 52.3	1 1.0	24 56.1	23 20.0	14 30.7	16 18.9	21 28.4	9 56.2
13	11 21 5.4	3 9.0	0 2.8	11 59.2	1N53.6	0N31.4	24 47.1	23 20.7	14 34.9	16 18.0	21 28.4	9 58.6
16	11 32 55.1	1 58.0	0 2.8	17 48.8	4 35.1	2 3.8	24 37.2	23 21.4	14 38.9	16 16.9	21 28.3	10 1.0
19	11 44 44.7	0 46.9	0 2.7	16 34.9	7 5.0	3 35.8	24 26.4	23 22.1	14 42.7	16 15.8	21 28.2	10 3.3
22	11 56 34.4	0N24.2	0 2.6	8 49.9	9 16.3	5 7.2	24 14.7	23 22.7	14 46.1	16 14.5	21 28.1	10 5.6
25	12 8 24.0	1 35.2	0 2.6	2S58.2	11 2.4	6 37.6	24 2.2	23 23.4	14 49.3	16 13.1	21 27.9	10 7.9
28	12 20 13.7	2 45.7	0 2.5	14 .4	12 18.4	8 6.6	23 48.8	23 24.1	14 52.3	16 11.6	21 27.7	10 10.0
31	12 32 3.3	3 55.9	0 2.4	18 9.7	13 .7	9 34.0	23 34.5	23 24.7	14 54.9	16 10.0	21 27.5	10 12.2

APRIL 1978

LONGITUDE

DAY	EPHEM. SID. TIME	☉	☊	☽	☿	♀	♂	♃	♄	♅	♆	♇
	h m s	° ′	° ′	° ′	° ′	° ′	° ′	° ′	° ′	° ′	° ′	° ′
1	12 35 59.9	10♈54.6	5♎47.3	15♑45.6	26♈ 6.0	27♈41.0	26♋54.2	28♊33.8	24♌10.6	15♏42.8	18♐17.2	15♎26.6
2	12 39 56.5	11 53.8	5 44.1	29 56.7	26 7.2	28 55.1	27 11.5	28 41.0	24R 8.1	15R40.9	18R16.8	15R24.9
3	12 43 53.0	12 53.0	5 40.9	14♒ 3.3	26R 1.5	0♉ 9.2	27 29.2	28 48.3	24 5.7	15 38.9	18 16.3	15 23.2
4	12 47 49.6	13 52.1	5 37.8	28 3.3	25 49.0	1 23.2	27 47.3	28 55.7	24 3.4	15 36.9	18 15.9	15 21.6
5	12 51 46.1	14 51.3	5 34.6	11♓54.3	25 30.1	2 37.2	28 5.8	29 3.3	24 1.2	15 34.9	18 15.4	15 19.9
6	12 55 42.7	15 50.3	5 31.4	25 34.2	25 5.5	3 51.1	28 24.7	29 11.0	23 59.1	15 32.8	18 14.9	15 18.2
7	12 59 39.2	16 49.4	5 28.2	9♈ 1.0	24 35.6	5 5.1	28 43.9	29 18.9	23 57.1	15 30.7	18 14.3	15 16.5
8	13 3 35.8	17 48.4	5 25.1	22 13.1	24 1.0	6 19.0	29 3.5	29 26.9	23 55.2	15 28.6	18 13.8	15 14.8
9	13 7 32.3	18 47.4	5 21.9	5♉ 9.6	23 22.6	7 32.9	29 23.5	29 35.0	23 53.5	15 26.4	18 13.2	15 13.1
10	13 11 28.9	19 46.3	5 18.7	17 50.4	22 41.2	8 46.7	29 43.9	29 43.2	23 51.8	15 24.2	18 12.5	15 11.4
11	13 15 25.4	20 45.2	5 15.5	0♊16.3	21 57.5	10 .5	0♌ 4.6	29 51.6	23 50.2	15 22.0	18 11.8	15 9.8
12	13 19 22.0	21 44.2	5 12.3	12 29.1	21 12.6	11 14.3	0 25.6	0♋ .2	23 48.8	15 19.8	18 11.2	15 8.1
13	13 23 18.5	22 43.0	5 9.2	24 31.6	20 27.1	12 28.1	0 47.0	0 8.8	23 47.4	15 17.5	18 10.5	15 6.5
14	13 27 15.1	23 41.8	5 6.0	6♋27.1	19 42.0	13 41.8	1 8.6	0 17.6	23 46.1	15 15.3	18 9.7	15 4.8
15	13 31 11.6	24 40.6	5 2.8	18 19.9	18 58.1	14 55.4	1 30.6	0 26.4	23 44.9	15 13.0	18 8.9	15 3.1
16	13 35 8.2	25 39.3	4 59.6	0♌14.4	18 16.2	16 9.1	1 52.9	0 35.4	23 43.9	15 10.6	18 8.1	15 1.5
17	13 39 4.7	26 38.0	4 56.4	12 15.4	17 37.0	17 22.6	2 15.5	0 44.5	23 42.9	15 8.3	18 7.3	14 59.8
18	13 43 1.3	27 36.7	4 53.3	24 27.5	17 1.0	18 36.2	2 38.4	0 53.8	23 42.1	15 5.9	18 6.4	14 58.2
19	13 46 57.8	28 35.3	4 50.1	6♍55.0	16 28.7	19 49.7	3 1.5	1 3.1	23 41.3	15 3.5	18 5.5	14 56.6
20	13 50 54.4	29 33.9	4 46.9	19 41.5	16 .6	21 3.2	3 25.0	1 12.5	23 40.7	15 1.1	18 4.6	14 55.0
21	13 54 50.9	0♉32.4	4 43.7	2♎49.5	15 37.1	22 16.6	3 48.7	1 22.1	23 40.1	14 58.7	18 3.7	14 53.3
22	13 58 47.5	1 30.9	4 40.6	16 19.9	15 18.2	23 30.0	4 12.7	1 31.7	23 39.7	14 56.3	18 2.7	14 51.7
23	14 2 44.1	2 29.4	4 37.4	0♏11.8	15 4.3	24 43.4	4 36.9	1 41.5	23 39.4	14 53.8	18 1.7	14 50.2
24	14 6 40.6	3 27.8	4 34.2	14 22.4	14 55.4	25 56.7	5 1.4	1 51.4	23 39.2	14 51.3	18 .7	14 48.6
25	14 10 37.2	4 26.3	4 31.0	28 46.9	14 51.5	27 10.0	5 26.1	2 1.3	23 39.1	14 48.9	17 59.6	14 47.0
26	14 14 33.7	5 24.7	4 27.8	13♐19.5	14D52.6	28 23.3	5 51.1	2 11.4	23 39.1	14 46.4	17 58.5	14 45.5
27	14 18 30.3	6 23.0	4 24.7	27 53.7	14 58.6	29 36.5	6 16.3	2 21.6	23D39.2	14 43.9	17 57.5	14 43.9
28	14 22 26.8	7 21.4	4 21.5	12♑23.8	15 9.5	0♊49.7	6 41.7	2 31.8	23 39.4	14 41.4	17 56.3	14 42.4
29	14 26 23.4	8 19.7	4 18.3	26 45.0	15 25.1	2 2.8	7 7.4	2 42.2	23 39.7	14 38.9	17 55.2	14 40.9
30	14 30 19.9	9 18.0	4 15.1	10♒54.3	15 45.3	3 15.9	7 33.3	2 52.6	23 40.2	14 36.3	17 54.0	14 39.4

LATITUDE

DAY	EPHEM. SID. TIME	☉	☊	☽	☿	♀	♂	♃	♄	♅	♆	♇
1	12 35 59.9	0 .0	0 .0	5N12.4	3N15.7	0S38.8	2N46.1	0S 1.0	1N33.2	0N24.3	1N28.3	17N39.3
4	12 47 49.6	0 .0	0 .0	3 14.8	3 16.9	0 31.9	2 41.1	0 .7	1 33.1	0 24.3	1 28.4	17 39.5
7	12 59 39.2	0 .0	0 .0	0S17.1	3 3.8	0 24.8	2 36.2	0 .4	1 32.9	0 24.3	1 28.5	17 39.5
10	13 11 28.9	0 .0	0 .0	3 31.5	2 36.6	0 17.3	2 31.5	0 .0	1 32.7	0 24.3	1 28.6	17 39.5
13	13 23 18.5	0 .0	0 .0	5 9.4	1 57.3	0 9.7	2 26.9	0N .3	1 32.5	0 24.3	1 28.7	17 39.4
16	13 35 8.2	0 .0	0 .0	4 47.1	1 10.2	0 1.9	2 22.4	0 .6	1 32.3	0 24.3	1 28.8	17 39.1
19	13 46 57.8	0 .0	0 .0	2 32.4	0 20.1	0N 6.1	2 18.1	0 .9	1 32.1	0 24.3	1 29.0	17 38.8
22	13 58 47.5	0 .0	0 .0	0N57.5	0S28.6	0 14.1	2 13.8	0 1.2	1 31.9	0 24.3	1 29.0	17 38.4
25	14 10 37.2	0 .0	0 .0	4 10.3	1 12.7	0 22.1	2 9.7	0 1.6	1 31.6	0 24.3	1 29.1	17 37.9
28	14 22 26.8	0 .0	0 .0	5 10.1	1 50.4	0 30.2	2 5.7	0 1.9	1 31.4	0 24.2	1 29.2	17 37.3

RIGHT ASCENSION

DAY	EPHEM. SID. TIME	☉	☊	☽	☿	♀	♂	♃	♄	♅	♆	♇
1	12 35 59.9	10♈ 1.7	5♎18.8	16♑27.6	22♈59.3	25♈56.4	29♋31.5	28♊26.1	27♌ 1.0	13♏22.2	17♐24.2	21♎ 2.8
2	12 39 56.5	10 56.4	5 15.9	1♒ 3.9	22 59.7	27 5.9	29 49.6	28 33.9	26R58.6	13R20.2	17R23.8	21R 1.4
3	12 43 53.0	11 51.1	5 13.0	15 17.6	22R54.1	28 15.6	0♌ 8.1	28 41.8	26 56.3	13 18.3	17 23.4	20 59.9
4	12 47 49.6	12 45.8	5 10.0	29 5.5	22 42.6	29 25.5	0 27.1	28 49.9	26 54.0	13 16.3	17 22.9	20 58.4
5	12 51 46.1	13 40.6	5 7.1	12♓29.3	22 25.7	0♉35.6	0 46.4	28 58.2	26 51.9	13 14.2	17 22.4	20 56.9
6	12 55 42.7	14 35.4	5 4.2	25 33.4	22 3.9	1 46.0	1 6.1	29 6.6	26 49.8	13 12.2	17 21.8	20 55.4
7	12 59 39.2	15 30.3	5 1.3	8♈23.7	21 37.7	2 56.5	1 26.2	29 15.2	26 47.8	13 10.1	17 21.2	20 53.9
8	13 3 35.8	16 25.2	4 58.4	21 6.0	21 7.8	4 7.2	1 46.6	29 23.9	26 46.0	13 8.0	17 20.6	20 52.4
9	13 7 32.3	17 20.2	4 55.4	3♉45.0	20 34.9	5 18.2	2 7.4	29 32.7	26 44.2	13 5.8	17 20.0	20 50.9
10	13 11 28.9	18 15.2	4 52.5	16 23.4	19 59.8	6 29.4	2 28.6	29 41.7	26 42.5	13 3.6	17 19.3	20 49.4
11	13 15 25.4	19 10.3	4 49.6	29 2.2	19 23.1	7 40.8	2 50.1	29 50.9	26 41.0	13 1.4	17 18.6	20 47.9
12	13 19 22.0	20 5.5	4 46.7	11♊40.4	18 45.8	8 52.5	3 12.0	0♋ .2	26 39.5	12 59.3	17 17.9	20 46.4
13	13 23 18.5	21 .7	4 43.8	24 15.7	18 8.5	10 4.4	3 34.1	0 9.6	26 38.2	12 57.0	17 17.1	20 44.9
14	13 27 15.1	21 56.0	4 40.8	6♋45.5	17 32.0	11 16.6	3 56.6	0 19.1	26 36.9	12 54.7	17 16.3	20 43.4
15	13 31 11.6	22 51.4	4 37.9	19 7.9	16 57.0	12 29.0	4 19.4	0 28.8	26 35.7	12 52.4	17 15.5	20 41.9
16	13 35 8.2	23 46.9	4 35.0	1♌22.4	16 24.1	13 41.6	4 42.4	0 38.6	26 34.7	12 50.1	17 14.6	20 40.4
17	13 39 4.7	24 42.5	4 32.1	13 30.3	15 53.9	14 54.6	5 5.7	0 48.5	26 33.7	12 47.8	17 13.7	20 38.9
18	13 43 1.3	25 38.1	4 29.2	25 35.0	15 26.8	16 7.7	5 29.4	0 58.6	26 32.9	12 45.4	17 12.8	20 37.4
19	13 46 57.8	26 33.8	4 26.3	7♍41.8	15 3.3	17 21.2	5 53.2	1 8.8	26 32.1	12 43.0	17 11.9	20 35.9
20	13 50 54.4	27 29.7	4 23.3	19 57.2	14 43.6	18 34.9	6 17.4	1 19.1	26 31.4	12 40.7	17 10.9	20 34.4
21	13 54 50.9	28 25.6	4 20.4	2♎29.0	14 28.0	19 48.9	6 41.8	1 29.5	26 30.9	12 38.2	17 9.9	20 32.9
22	13 58 47.5	29 21.6	4 17.5	15 25.0	14 16.7	21 3.1	7 6.4	1 40.0	26 30.5	12 35.8	17 8.8	20 31.4
23	14 2 44.1	0♉17.8	4 14.6	28 52.1	14 9.7	22 17.6	7 31.3	1 50.6	26 30.1	12 33.4	17 7.8	20 29.9
24	14 6 40.6	1 14.1	4 11.7	12♏54.2	14 7.2	23 32.4	7 56.4	2 1.4	26 29.9	12 30.9	17 6.7	20 28.4
25	14 10 37.2	2 10.4	4 8.7	27 30.2	14D 9.0	24 47.5	8 21.7	2 12.3	26 29.8	12 28.5	17 5.6	20 27.0
26	14 14 33.7	3 6.9	4 5.8	12♐32.6	14 15.2	26 2.8	8 47.2	2 23.2	26 29.7	12 26.0	17 4.4	20 25.5
27	14 18 30.3	4 3.6	4 2.9	27 47.6	14 25.6	27 18.4	9 12.9	2 34.3	26D29.8	12 23.5	17 3.2	20 24.1
28	14 22 26.8	5 .3	3 60.0	12♑58.2	14 40.2	28 34.2	9 38.8	2 45.5	26 30.0	12 21.0	17 2.1	20 22.6
29	14 26 23.4	5 57.2	3 57.1	27 49.1	14 58.9	29 50.3	10 5.0	2 56.8	26 30.3	12 18.5	17 .8	20 21.2
30	14 30 19.9	6 54.2	3 54.2	12♒10.1	15 21.5	1♊ 6.7	10 31.3	3 8.2	26 30.7	12 16.0	16 59.6	20 19.7

DECLINATION

DAY	EPHEM. SID. TIME	☉	☊	☽	☿	♀	♂	♃	♄	♅	♆	♇
1	12 35 59.9	4N19.1	0S 2.4	17S20.2	13N 6.9	10N 2.7	23N29.6	23N24.9	14N55.7	16S 9.4	21S27.5	10N12.8
4	12 47 49.6	5 28.3	0 2.3	9 6.0	13 1.8	11 27.4	23 14.1	23 25.4	14 58.0	16 7.7	21 27.2	10 14.9
7	12 59 39.2	6 36.7	0 2.3	3N18.7	12 22.6	12 49.7	22 57.8	23 25.9	14 59.9	16 5.9	21 27.0	10 16.8
10	13 11 28.9	7 44.0	0 2.2	13 45.8	11 14.8	14 9.1	22 40.5	23 26.3	15 1.5	16 4.0	21 26.7	10 18.6
13	13 23 18.5	8 50.2	0 2.1	18 10.4	9 48.0	15 25.5	22 22.3	23 26.7	15 2.8	16 2.1	21 26.4	10 20.4
16	13 35 8.2	9 55.0	0 2.1	15 25.3	8 14.7	16 38.4	22 3.2	23 26.9	15 3.7	16 .1	21 26.1	10 22.0
19	13 46 57.8	10 58.4	0 2.0	6 36.7	6 47.3	17 47.5	21 43.2	23 27.1	15 4.4	15 58.0	21 25.8	10 23.5
22	13 58 47.5	12 .1	0 1.9	5S32.3	5 35.2	18 52.6	21 22.3	23 27.1	15 4.7	15 55.9	21 25.4	10 25.0
25	14 10 37.2	13 .0	0 1.9	15 48.9	4 44.2	19 53.1	21 .4	23 27.0	15 4.7	15 53.7	21 25.1	10 26.3
28	14 22 26.8	13 58.0	0 1.8	17 42.9	4 16.4	20 48.9	20 37.6	23 26.8	15 4.3	15 51.5	21 24.7	10 27.4

MAY 1978

DAY	EPHEM. SID. TIME	☉	☊	☾	☿	♀	♂	♃	♄	♅	♆	♇
	h m s	° ′	° ′	° ′	° ′	° ′	° ′	° ′	° ′	° ′	° ′	° ′
		LONGITUDE										
1	14 34 16.5	10♉16.2	4♎12.0	24♒49.9	16♈10.0	4♊29.0	7♌59.4	3♋ 3.2	23♌40.7	14♏33.8	17♐52.8	14♎37.9
2	14 38 13.0	11 14.5	4 8.8	8♓31.6	16 38.9	5 42.0	8 25.7	3 13.8	23 41.3	14 R 31.3	17 R 51.6	14 R 36.4
3	14 42 9.6	12 12.7	4 5.6	21 59.6	17 12.1	6 55.1	8 52.3	3 24.6	23 42.1	14 28.8	17 50.5	14 35.0
4	14 46 6.1	13 10.9	4 2.4	5♈14.5	17 49.1	8 8.0	9 19.1	3 35.4	23 43.0	14 26.3	17 49.2	14 33.6
5	14 50 2.7	14 9.1	3 59.2	18 17.0	18 30.0	9 21.0	9 46.1	3 46.3	23 43.9	14 23.7	17 47.9	14 32.2
6	14 53 59.3	15 7.2	3 56.1	1♉ 7.5	19 14.6	10 33.9	10 13.2	3 57.3	23 45.0	14 21.2	17 46.6	14 30.8
7	14 57 55.8	16 5.3	3 52.9	13 46.4	20 2.6	11 46.7	10 40.6	4 8.4	23 46.2	14 18.6	17 45.3	14 29.4
8	15 1 52.4	17 3.4	3 49.7	26 14.1	20 54.1	12 59.5	11 8.2	4 19.5	23 47.4	14 16.1	17 44.0	14 28.0
9	15 5 48.9	18 1.5	3 46.5	8♊31.2	21 48.8	14 12.3	11 35.9	4 30.8	23 48.8	14 13.6	17 42.7	14 26.7
10	15 9 45.5	18 59.5	3 43.4	20 38.7	22 46.6	15 25.0	12 3.9	4 42.1	23 50.3	14 11.0	17 41.3	14 25.4
11	15 13 42.0	19 57.5	3 40.2	2♋38.2	23 47.5	16 37.7	12 32.0	4 53.5	23 51.9	14 8.5	17 39.9	14 24.1
12	15 17 38.6	20 55.4	3 37.0	14 32.2	24 51.2	17 50.4	13 .3	5 4.9	23 53.6	14 6.0	17 38.5	14 22.8
13	15 21 35.1	21 53.4	3 33.8	26 23.7	25 57.8	19 3.0	13 28.8	5 16.4	23 55.4	14 3.5	17 37.1	14 21.6
14	15 25 31.7	22 51.3	3 30.7	8♌16.7	27 7.2	20 15.5	13 57.5	5 28.1	23 57.3	14 1.0	17 35.7	14 20.3
15	15 29 28.2	23 49.2	3 27.5	20 15.5	28 19.2	21 28.1	14 26.3	5 39.7	23 59.3	13 58.5	17 34.2	14 19.1
16	15 33 24.8	24 47.0	3 24.3	2♍25.2	29 33.8	22 40.5	14 55.3	5 51.5	24 1.4	13 56.0	17 32.8	14 17.9
17	15 37 21.4	25 44.9	3 21.1	14 50.6	0♉51.0	23 52.9	15 24.5	6 3.3	24 3.6	13 53.5	17 31.3	14 16.8
18	15 41 17.9	26 42.6	3 17.9	27 36.4	2 10.6	25 5.3	15 53.8	6 15.1	24 5.9	13 51.1	17 29.8	14 15.7
19	15 45 14.5	27 40.4	3 14.8	10♎46.6	3 32.7	26 17.6	16 23.2	6 27.1	24 8.3	13 48.6	17 28.3	14 14.5
20	15 49 11.0	28 38.2	3 11.6	24 23.5	4 57.2	27 29.9	16 52.9	6 39.1	24 10.8	13 46.2	17 26.8	14 13.5
21	15 53 7.6	29 35.9	3 8.4	8♏27.4	6 24.1	28 42.1	17 22.6	6 51.1	24 13.4	13 43.8	17 25.3	14 12.4
22	15 57 4.1	0♊33.6	3 5.2	22 55.7	7 53.4	29 54.3	17 52.5	7 3.3	24 16.1	13 41.4	17 23.8	14 11.4
23	16 1 .7	1 31.2	3 2.1	7♐42.9	9 25.0	1♋ 6.4	18 22.6	7 15.4	24 18.9	13 39.0	17 22.2	14 10.4
24	16 4 57.2	2 28.9	2 58.9	22 41.0	10 59.0	2 18.5	18 52.8	7 27.7	24 21.8	13 36.7	17 20.7	14 9.4
25	16 8 53.8	3 26.6	2 55.7	7♑40.6	12 35.2	3 30.6	19 23.2	7 40.0	24 24.8	13 34.4	17 19.2	14 8.5
26	16 12 50.4	4 24.2	2 52.5	22 32.8	14 13.8	4 42.5	19 53.6	7 52.3	24 27.8	13 32.0	17 17.6	14 7.5
27	16 16 46.9	5 21.8	2 49.3	7♒10.1	15 54.7	5 54.5	20 24.2	8 4.7	24 31.0	13 29.7	17 16.0	14 6.6
28	16 20 43.5	6 19.3	2 46.2	21 27.9	17 37.8	7 6.4	20 55.0	8 17.2	24 34.2	13 27.5	17 14.4	14 5.8
29	16 24 40.0	7 16.9	2 43.0	5♓24.3	19 23.3	8 18.2	21 25.9	8 29.7	24 37.6	13 25.2	17 12.8	14 4.9
30	16 28 36.6	8 14.5	2 39.8	18 59.4	21 11.1	9 30.0	21 56.9	8 42.2	24 41.0	13 23.0	17 11.3	14 4.1
31	16 32 33.1	9 12.0	2 36.6	2♈15.2	23 1.1	10 41.7	22 28.0	8 54.8	24 44.6	13 20.8	17 9.6	14 3.3
		LATITUDE										
1	14 34 16.5	0 .0	0 .0	3N23.7	2S20.8	0N38.1	2N 1.8	0N 2.1	1N31.1	0N24.2	1N29.3	17N36.6
4	14 46 6.1	0 .0	0 .0	0 1.5	2 43.8	0 46.0	1 58.0	0 2.4	1 30.9	0 24.2	1 29.4	17 35.9
7	14 57 55.8	0 .0	0 .0	3S12.5	2 59.6	0 53.6	1 54.2	0 2.7	1 30.6	0 24.2	1 29.4	17 35.0
10	15 9 45.5	0 .0	0 .0	4 58.5	3 8.5	1 1.1	1 50.6	0 3.0	1 30.3	0 24.1	1 29.5	17 34.1
13	15 21 35.1	0 .0	0 .0	4 46.4	3 11.0	1 8.3	1 47.1	0 3.3	1 30.1	0 24.1	1 29.6	17 33.1
16	15 33 24.8	0 .0	0 .0	2 44.6	3 7.5	1 15.1	1 43.6	0 3.6	1 29.8	0 24.1	1 29.6	17 32.0
19	15 45 14.5	0 .0	0 .0	0N32.9	2 58.3	1 21.6	1 40.2	0 3.9	1 29.6	0 24.1	1 29.6	17 30.9
22	15 57 4.1	0 .0	0 .0	3 48.8	2 43.9	1 27.7	1 36.9	0 4.1	1 29.3	0 24.0	1 29.7	17 29.7
25	16 8 53.8	0 .0	0 .0	5 3.9	2 24.7	1 33.4	1 33.7	0 4.4	1 29.1	0 24.0	1 29.7	17 28.4
28	16 20 43.5	0 .0	0 .0	3 25.7	2 1.1	1 38.5	1 30.5	0 4.7	1 28.8	0 23.9	1 29.7	17 27.1
31	16 32 33.1	0 .0	0 .0	0 8.1	1 33.7	1 43.0	1 27.4	0 5.0	1 28.6	0 23.8	1 29.7	17 25.7
		RIGHT ASCENSION										
1	14 34 16.5	7♉51.4	3♎51.2	25♒58.1	15♈47.9	2♊23.3	10♌57.8	3♋19.7	26♌31.1	12♏13.5	16♐58.3	20♎18.3
2	14 38 13.0	8 48.7	3 48.3	9♓15.9	16 17.9	3 40.1	11 24.5	3 31.3	26 31.7	12 R 11.0	16 R 57.0	20 R 16.9
3	14 42 9.6	9 46.2	3 45.4	22 10.0	16 51.6	4 57.3	11 51.4	3 43.0	26 32.5	12 8.5	16 55.8	20 15.6
4	14 46 6.1	10 43.8	3 42.5	4♈48.1	17 28.5	6 14.6	12 18.5	3 54.8	26 33.3	12 6.0	16 54.4	20 14.2
5	14 50 2.7	11 41.5	3 39.6	17 18.2	18 8.7	7 32.1	12 45.7	4 6.7	26 34.2	12 3.5	16 53.1	20 12.8
6	14 53 59.3	12 39.3	3 36.6	29 46.7	18 52.0	8 49.9	13 13.1	4 18.7	26 35.2	12 .9	16 51.7	20 11.5
7	14 57 55.8	13 37.3	3 33.7	12♉17.9	19 38.4	10 7.9	13 40.7	4 30.7	26 36.3	11 58.4	16 50.3	20 10.1
8	15 1 52.4	14 35.5	3 30.8	24 53.5	20 27.6	11 26.0	14 8.4	4 42.9	26 37.5	11 55.9	16 48.9	20 8.8
9	15 5 48.9	15 33.8	3 27.9	7♊32.4	21 19.7	12 44.4	14 36.2	4 55.1	26 38.9	11 53.4	16 47.5	20 7.5
10	15 9 45.5	16 32.2	3 25.0	20 11.3	22 14.4	14 2.9	15 4.2	5 7.4	26 40.3	11 50.9	16 46.0	20 6.2
11	15 13 42.0	17 30.7	3 22.1	2♋46.0	23 11.8	15 21.6	15 32.4	5 19.8	26 41.8	11 48.4	16 44.5	20 4.9
12	15 17 38.6	18 29.5	3 19.1	15 12.4	24 11.8	16 40.4	16 .6	5 32.3	26 43.4	11 45.9	16 43.0	20 3.6
13	15 21 35.1	19 28.3	3 16.2	27 28.3	25 14.3	17 59.4	16 29.1	5 44.9	26 45.1	11 43.4	16 41.5	20 2.4
14	15 25 31.7	20 27.3	3 13.3	9♌33.3	26 19.3	19 18.5	16 57.6	5 57.5	26 47.0	11 40.9	16 40.0	20 1.1
15	15 29 28.2	21 26.4	3 10.4	21 30.2	27 26.7	20 37.6	17 26.3	6 10.2	26 48.9	11 38.4	16 38.5	19 59.9
16	15 33 24.8	22 25.7	3 7.5	3♍24.0	28 36.5	21 56.9	17 55.1	6 23.0	26 50.9	11 35.9	16 36.9	19 58.7
17	15 37 21.4	23 25.1	3 4.6	15 22.1	29 48.7	23 16.3	18 24.0	6 35.9	26 53.0	11 33.5	16 35.3	19 57.5
18	15 41 17.9	24 24.6	3 1.6	27 33.2	1♉ 3.3	24 35.7	18 53.0	6 48.8	26 55.2	11 31.0	16 33.7	19 56.3
19	15 45 14.5	25 24.3	2 58.7	10♎ 7.2	2 20.3	25 55.2	19 22.1	7 1.8	26 57.6	11 28.6	16 32.2	19 55.2
20	15 49 11.0	26 24.1	2 55.8	23 13.9	3 39.6	27 14.7	19 51.3	7 14.8	26 60.0	11 26.2	16 30.5	19 54.1
21	15 53 7.6	27 24.0	2 52.9	7♏ .9	5 1.5	28 34.2	20 20.6	7 27.9	27 2.5	11 23.8	16 28.9	19 53.0
22	15 57 4.1	28 24.1	2 50.0	21 31.6	6 25.7	29 53.7	20 50.0	7 41.1	27 5.1	11 21.4	16 27.3	19 51.9
23	16 1 .7	29 24.3	2 47.1	6♐42.1	7 52.5	1♋13.2	21 19.5	7 54.4	27 7.7	11 19.1	16 25.6	19 50.8
24	16 4 57.2	0♊24.7	2 44.1	22 19.3	9 21.8	2 32.8	21 49.2	8 7.7	27 10.6	11 16.8	16 24.0	19 49.8
25	16 8 53.8	1 25.1	2 41.2	8♑ 3.0	10 53.6	3 52.2	22 18.9	8 21.1	27 13.4	11 14.4	16 22.4	19 48.8
26	16 12 50.4	2 25.7	2 38.3	23 31.4	12 28.1	5 11.6	22 48.7	8 34.5	27 16.4	11 12.1	16 20.7	19 47.8
27	16 16 46.9	3 26.4	2 35.4	8♒27.5	14 5.3	6 30.9	23 18.5	8 48.0	27 19.4	11 9.9	16 19.0	19 46.8
28	16 20 43.5	4 27.3	2 32.5	22 43.4	15 45.2	7 50.1	23 48.5	9 1.5	27 22.6	11 7.6	16 17.3	19 45.9
29	16 24 40.0	5 28.3	2 29.6	6♓19.5	17 27.9	9 9.2	24 18.5	9 15.1	27 25.8	11 5.4	16 15.6	19 44.9
30	16 28 36.6	6 29.3	2 26.6	19 22.2	19 13.5	10 28.1	24 48.6	9 28.7	27 29.1	11 3.1	16 13.9	19 44.0
31	16 32 33.1	7 30.5	2 23.7	2♈ .8	21 2.0	11 47.0	25 18.8	9 42.4	27 32.5	11 1.0	16 12.2	19 43.1
		DECLINATION										
1	14 34 16.5	14N54.0	0S 1.7	10S 2.6	4N11.5	21N39.7	20N13.8	23N26.4	15N 3.7	15S49.3	21S24.3	10N28.5
4	14 46 6.1	15 47.7	0 1.7	2N 6.3	4 28.1	22 25.2	19 49.1	23 25.9	15 2.7	15 47.1	21 23.9	10 29.4
7	14 57 55.8	16 39.1	0 1.6	12 54.6	5 3.8	23 5.1	19 23.4	23 25.2	15 1.4	15 44.9	21 23.5	10 30.2
10	15 9 45.5	17 28.1	0 1.5	18 8.8	5 56.4	23 39.2	18 56.7	23 24.4	14 59.7	15 42.7	21 23.0	10 30.8
13	15 21 35.1	18 14.3	0 1.5	16 11.1	7 3.7	24 7.3	18 29.1	23 23.4	14 57.8	15 40.5	21 22.6	10 31.3
16	15 33 24.8	18 57.8	0 1.4	8 3.0	8 23.5	24 29.2	18 .6	23 22.2	14 55.6	15 38.3	21 22.2	10 31.7
19	15 45 14.5	19 38.5	0 1.4	3S45.6	9 54.0	24 44.9	17 31.1	23 20.8	14 53.0	15 36.1	21 21.7	10 31.9
22	15 57 4.1	20 16.1	0 1.3	14 48.7	11 33.2	24 54.1	17 .7	23 19.2	14 50.2	15 34.0	21 21.3	10 32.0
25	16 8 53.8	20 50.6	0 1.2	18 9.6	13 19.0	24 56.9	16 29.4	23 17.5	14 47.0	15 31.9	21 20.8	10 31.9
28	16 20 43.5	21 21.8	0 1.2	11 6.0	15 9.2	24 53.2	15 57.2	23 15.5	14 43.6	15 29.9	21 20.3	10 31.7
31	16 32 33.1	21 49.8	0 1.1	1N 1.2	17 .9	24 43.2	15 24.1	23 13.3	14 40.0	15 28.0	21 19.9	10 31.4

JUNE 1978

LONGITUDE

DAY	EPHEM. SID. TIME	☉	☊	☽	☿	♀	♂	♃	♄	♅	♆	♇
	h m s	° ′	° ′	° ′	° ′	° ′	° ′	° ′	° ′	° ′	° ′	° ′
1	16 36 29.7	10♊ 9.5	2♎33.5	15♈14.0	24♉53.4	11♋53.4	22♌59.3	9♋ 7.5	24♌48.2	13♏18.6	17♐ 8.0	14♎ 2.6
2	16 40 26.2	11 7.0	2 30.3	27 58.6	26 47.9	13 5.0	23 30.7	9 20.2	24 51.9	13R16.4	17R 6.4	14R 1.8
3	16 44 22.8	12 4.5	2 27.1	10♉31.2	28 44.6	14 16.6	24 2.2	9 32.9	24 55.7	13 14.3	17 4.8	14 1.1
4	16 48 19.4	13 2.0	2 23.9	22 53.7	0♊43.4	15 28.1	24 33.8	9 45.7	24 59.5	13 12.2	17 3.2	14 .5
5	16 52 15.9	13 59.5	2 20.8	5♊ 7.8	2 44.3	16 39.6	25 5.6	9 58.5	25 3.5	13 10.1	17 1.6	13 59.8
6	16 56 12.5	14 56.9	2 17.6	17 14.4	4 47.1	17 51.0	25 37.5	10 11.4	25 7.6	13 8.1	16 59.9	13 59.2
7	17 0 9.0	15 54.4	2 14.4	29 14.7	6 51.7	19 2.4	26 9.5	10 24.3	25 11.7	13 6.1	16 58.3	13 58.6
8	17 4 5.6	16 51.8	2 11.2	11♋ 9.9	8 58.0	20 13.7	26 41.6	10 37.2	25 15.9	13 4.1	16 56.7	13 58.1
9	17 8 2.1	17 49.2	2 8.0	23 1.6	11 5.8	21 24.9	27 13.8	10 50.2	25 20.2	13 2.2	16 55.1	13 57.6
10	17 11 58.7	18 46.6	2 4.9	4♌52.0	13 14.9	22 36.1	27 46.2	11 3.2	25 24.6	13 .3	16 53.4	13 57.1
11	17 15 55.3	19 44.0	2 1.7	16 44.3	15 25.1	23 47.2	28 18.6	11 16.2	25 29.1	12 58.4	16 51.8	13 56.7
12	17 19 51.8	20 41.3	1 58.5	28 42.0	17 36.2	24 58.3	28 51.2	11 29.3	25 33.6	12 56.6	16 50.2	13 56.2
13	17 23 48.4	21 38.7	1 55.3	10♍49.6	19 47.8	26 9.2	29 23.9	11 42.4	25 38.2	12 54.8	16 48.6	13 55.8
14	17 27 44.9	22 36.1	1 52.2	23 12.0	21 59.9	27 20.2	29 56.7	11 55.6	25 43.0	12 53.1	16 47.0	13 55.5
15	17 31 41.5	23 33.4	1 49.0	5♎54.1	24 11.8	28 31.1	0♍29.6	12 8.7	25 47.7	12 51.4	16 45.4	13 55.2
16	17 35 38.0	24 30.7	1 45.8	19 .8	26 23.6	29 41.8	1 2.6	12 21.9	25 52.6	12 49.7	16 43.8	13 54.9
17	17 39 34.6	25 28.0	1 42.6	2♏35.4	28 34.8	0♌52.6	1 35.6	12 35.2	25 57.5	12 48.0	16 42.2	13 54.7
18	17 43 31.2	26 25.2	1 39.5	16 39.8	0♋45.3	2 3.2	2 8.8	12 48.4	26 2.5	12 46.4	16 40.6	13 54.5
19	17 47 27.7	27 22.5	1 36.3	1♐12.7	2 54.8	3 13.8	2 42.1	13 1.7	26 7.6	12 44.9	16 39.0	13 54.3
20	17 51 24.3	28 19.7	1 33.1	16 9.2	5 3.1	4 24.2	3 15.5	13 14.9	26 12.7	12 43.3	16 37.4	13 54.1
21	17 55 20.8	29 17.0	1 29.9	1♑21.1	7 10.0	5 34.6	3 48.9	13 28.2	26 17.9	12 41.8	16 35.8	13 54.0
22	17 59 17.4	0♋14.2	1 26.7	16 37.7	9 15.4	6 45.0	4 22.5	13 41.6	26 23.2	12 40.4	16 34.3	13 53.9
23	18 3 13.9	1 11.4	1 23.6	1♒47.9	11 19.1	7 55.2	4 56.2	13 54.9	26 28.5	12 39.0	16 32.7	13 53.8
24	18 7 10.5	2 8.6	1 20.4	16 42.0	13 20.9	9 5.4	5 29.9	14 8.3	26 34.0	12 37.6	16 31.2	13 53.8
25	18 11 7.1	3 5.9	1 17.2	1♓13.1	15 20.9	10 15.5	6 3.8	14 21.7	26 39.4	12 36.3	16 29.6	13 53.8
26	18 15 3.6	4 3.1	1 14.0	15 18.0	17 18.9	11 25.5	6 37.7	14 35.1	26 45.0	12 35.1	16 28.1	13D53.9
27	18 19 .2	5 .3	1 10.9	28 56.5	19 14.9	12 35.5	7 11.7	14 48.5	26 50.6	12 33.8	16 26.6	13 54.0
28	18 22 56.7	5 57.5	1 7.7	12♈10.5	21 8.9	13 45.3	7 45.8	15 1.9	26 56.3	12 32.6	16 25.0	13 54.1
29	18 26 53.3	6 54.7	1 4.5	25 3.4	23 .8	14 55.1	8 20.0	15 15.3	27 2.0	12 31.5	16 23.5	13 54.2
30	18 30 49.8	7 52.0	1 1.3	7♉38.9	24 50.5	16 4.8	8 54.3	15 28.8	27 7.8	12 30.4	16 22.0	13 54.4

LATITUDE

DAY	EPHEM. SID. TIME	☉	☊	☽	☿	♀	♂	♃	♄	♅	♆	♇
1	16 36 29.7	0 .0	0 .0	1S .6	1S23.9	1N44.4	1N26.4	0N 5.1	1N28.5	0N23.8	1N29.7	17N25.2
4	16 48 19.4	0 .0	0 .0	3 49.6	0 52.8	1 48.2	1 23.4	0 5.3	1 28.3	0 23.7	1 29.7	17 23.8
7	17 0 9.0	0 .0	0 .0	5 .3	0 20.3	1 51.3	1 20.4	0 5.6	1 28.1	0 23.7	1 29.7	17 22.3
10	17 11 58.7	0 .0	0 .0	4 14.6	0N12.0	1 53.7	1 17.5	0 5.9	1 27.9	0 23.6	1 29.7	17 20.8
13	17 23 48.4	0 .0	0 .0	1 50.4	0 42.4	1 55.4	1 14.6	0 6.2	1 27.7	0 23.6	1 29.7	17 19.3
16	17 35 38.0	0 .0	0 .0	1N28.0	1 9.1	1 56.4	1 11.8	0 6.4	1 27.5	0 23.5	1 29.6	17 17.7
19	17 47 27.7	0 .0	0 .0	4 18.9	1 30.4	1 56.5	1 9.0	0 6.7	1 27.3	0 23.4	1 29.6	17 16.1
22	17 59 17.4	0 .0	0 .0	4 50.0	1 45.4	1 55.9	1 6.3	0 7.0	1 27.2	0 23.3	1 29.5	17 14.5
25	18 11 7.1	0 .0	0 .0	2 30.4	1 53.8	1 54.4	1 3.6	0 7.2	1 27.0	0 23.3	1 29.5	17 12.8
28	18 22 56.7	0 .0	0 .0	0S58.8	1 55.5	1 52.1	1 1.0	0 7.5	1 26.9	0 23.2	1 29.4	17 11.2

RIGHT ASCENSION

DAY	EPHEM. SID. TIME	☉	☊	☽	☿	♀	♂	♃	♄	♅	♆	♇
1	16 36 29.7	8♊31.8	2♎20.8	14♈25.2	22♉53.5	13♋ 5.7	25♌49.0	9♋56.2	27♌36.0	10♏58.8	16♐10.5	19♎42.3
2	16 40 26.2	9 33.3	2 17.9	26 44.1	24 48.0	14 24.2	26 19.4	10 9.9	27 39.6	10R56.7	16R 8.8	19R41.4
3	16 44 22.8	10 34.8	2 15.0	9♉ 4.3	26 45.5	15 42.5	26 49.8	10 23.8	27 43.3	10 54.6	16 7.0	19 40.6
4	16 48 19.4	11 36.4	2 12.1	21 29.8	28 46.0	17 .7	27 20.3	10 37.6	27 47.0	10 52.5	16 5.3	19 39.8
5	16 52 15.9	12 38.1	2 9.2	4♊ 1.5	0♊49.5	18 18.6	27 50.8	10 51.5	27 50.9	10 50.4	16 3.6	19 39.1
6	16 56 12.5	13 39.9	2 6.2	16 37.1	2 55.9	19 36.3	28 21.4	11 5.5	27 54.8	10 48.4	16 1.8	19 38.3
7	17 0 9.0	14 41.8	2 3.3	29 12.4	5 5.2	20 53.8	28 52.1	11 19.5	27 58.8	10 46.4	16 .1	19 37.6
8	17 4 5.6	15 43.7	2 .4	11♋42.3	7 17.2	22 11.0	29 22.9	11 33.5	28 2.8	10 44.5	15 58.4	19 36.9
9	17 8 2.1	16 45.7	1 57.5	24 2.1	9 31.7	23 28.0	29 53.7	11 47.6	28 7.0	10 42.5	15 56.6	19 36.3
10	17 11 58.7	17 47.8	1 54.6	6♌ 9.5	11 48.6	24 44.7	0♍24.6	12 1.7	28 11.2	10 40.6	15 54.9	19 35.6
11	17 15 55.3	18 49.9	1 51.7	18 5.0	14 7.6	26 1.1	0 55.5	12 15.8	28 15.5	10 38.8	15 53.2	19 35.0
12	17 19 51.8	19 52.1	1 48.7	29 51.9	16 28.4	27 17.1	1 26.5	12 30.0	28 19.9	10 37.0	15 51.4	19 34.4
13	17 23 48.4	20 54.3	1 45.8	11♍36.3	18 50.6	28 32.9	1 57.6	12 44.2	28 24.4	10 35.2	15 49.7	19 33.9
14	17 27 44.9	21 56.6	1 42.9	23 26.7	21 13.9	29 48.4	2 28.7	12 58.5	28 29.0	10 33.5	15 48.0	19 33.4
15	17 31 41.5	22 58.9	1 40.0	5♎33.0	23 37.9	1♌ 3.6	2 59.9	13 12.7	28 33.6	10 31.8	15 46.3	19 32.9
16	17 35 38.0	24 1.3	1 37.1	18 6.2	26 2.1	2 18.3	3 31.1	13 27.0	28 38.3	10 30.1	15 44.6	19 32.4
17	17 39 34.6	25 3.6	1 34.2	1♏17.1	28 26.3	3 32.8	4 2.4	13 41.3	28 43.0	10 28.5	15 42.9	19 32.0
18	17 43 31.2	26 6.0	1 31.3	15 14.0	0♋49.9	4 46.9	4 33.7	13 55.6	28 47.8	10 26.9	15 41.2	19 31.6
19	17 47 27.7	27 8.3	1 28.3	29 60.0	3 12.7	6 .6	5 5.1	14 9.9	28 52.7	10 25.3	15 39.5	19 31.2
20	17 51 24.3	28 10.7	1 25.4	15♐29.1	5 34.3	7 14.0	5 36.5	14 24.3	28 57.7	10 23.8	15 37.8	19 30.9
21	17 55 20.8	29 13.1	1 22.5	1♑25.1	7 54.3	8 26.9	6 7.9	14 38.7	29 2.7	10 22.3	15 36.1	19 30.5
22	17 59 17.4	0♋15.5	1 19.6	17 24.4	10 12.4	9 39.6	6 39.4	14 53.1	29 7.8	10 20.9	15 34.4	19 30.2
23	18 3 13.9	1 17.8	1 16.7	3♒ 3.1	12 28.5	10 51.8	7 11.0	15 7.5	29 13.0	10 19.5	15 32.7	19 30.0
24	18 7 10.5	2 20.2	1 13.8	18 4.1	14 42.3	12 3.7	7 42.6	15 21.9	29 18.2	10 18.2	15 31.1	19 29.7
25	18 11 7.1	3 22.5	1 10.8	2♓21.1	16 53.6	13 15.1	8 14.2	15 36.4	29 23.5	10 16.8	15 29.4	19 29.5
26	18 15 3.6	4 24.9	1 7.9	15 56.2	19 2.2	14 26.2	8 45.9	15 50.8	29 28.8	10 15.6	15 27.8	19 29.3
27	18 19 .2	5 27.1	1 5.0	28 57.4	21 8.1	15 36.9	9 17.6	16 5.3	29 34.2	10 14.4	15 26.1	19 29.2
28	18 22 56.7	6 29.4	1 2.1	11♈34.8	23 11.2	16 47.3	9 49.4	16 19.8	29 39.7	10 13.2	15 24.5	19 29.1
29	18 26 53.3	7 31.6	0 59.2	23 58.5	25 11.3	17 57.2	10 21.2	16 34.3	29 45.2	10 12.1	15 22.9	19 29.0
30	18 30 49.8	8 33.8	0 56.3	6♉17.2	27 8.6	19 6.8	10 53.1	16 48.8	29 50.8	10 11.0	15 21.3	19 28.9

DECLINATION

DAY	EPHEM. SID. TIME	☉	☊	☽	☿	♀	♂	♃	♄	♅	♆	♇
1	16 36 29.7	21N58.4	0S 1.1	5N 4.0	17N38.0	24N38.4	15N12.9	23N12.6	14N38.7	15S27.3	21S19.7	10N31.2
4	16 48 19.4	22 21.7	0 1.0	14 47.5	19 26.4	24 20.0	14 38.6	23 10.1	14 34.6	15 25.5	21 19.3	10 30.7
7	17 0 9.0	22 41.6	0 .9	18 25.9	21 7.3	23 55.4	14 3.5	23 7.5	14 30.4	15 23.7	21 18.8	10 30.0
10	17 11 58.7	22 57.9	0 .9	14 55.6	22 35.3	23 24.8	13 27.6	23 4.6	14 25.8	15 22.0	21 18.4	10 29.2
13	17 23 48.4	23 10.5	0 .8	5 48.2	23 45.1	22 48.5	12 50.9	23 1.5	14 21.0	15 20.4	21 17.9	10 28.3
16	17 35 38.0	23 19.5	0 .7	6S 5.3	24 32.5	22 6.6	12 13.3	22 58.3	14 16.0	15 18.9	21 17.5	10 27.1
19	17 47 27.7	23 24.8	0 .7	16 10.5	24 54.8	21 19.4	11 35.1	22 54.8	14 10.7	15 17.5	21 17.1	10 25.9
22	17 59 17.4	23 26.3	0 .6	17 36.4	24 52.1	20 27.3	10 56.1	22 51.0	14 5.2	15 16.3	21 16.6	10 24.6
25	18 11 7.1	23 24.2	0 .5	8 41.9	24 26.4	19 30.5	10 16.4	22 47.1	13 59.5	15 15.1	21 16.2	10 23.1
28	18 22 56.7	23 18.3	0 .5	3N54.6	23 40.7	18 29.2	9 36.0	22 43.0	13 53.6	15 14.1	21 15.8	10 21.5

JULY 1978

LONGITUDE

DAY	EPHEM. SID. TIME	☉	☊	☽	☿	♀	♂	♃	♄	♅	♆	♇
	h m s	° ′	° ′	° ′	° ′	° ′	° ′	° ′	° ′	° ′	° ′	° ′
1	18 34 46.4	8♋49.2	0♎58.2	20♉ .8	26♋38.2	17♌14.4	9♍28.7	15♋42.3	27♌13.6	12♏29.4	16♐20.6	13♎54.6
2	18 38 43.0	9 46.4	0 55.0	2♊12.3	28 23.7	18 23.9	10 3.2	15 55.7	27 19.6	12 R 28.4	16 R 19.1	13 54.8
3	18 42 39.5	10 43.6	0 51.8	14 16.1	0♌ 7.1	19 33.4	10 37.8	16 9.2	27 25.5	12 27.4	16 17.7	13 55.1
4	18 46 36.1	11 40.9	0 48.6	26 14.4	1 48.4	20 42.7	11 12.4	16 22.7	27 31.6	12 26.5	16 16.2	13 55.4
5	18 50 32.6	12 38.1	0 45.5	8♋ 8.8	3 27.6	21 52.0	11 47.2	16 36.3	27 37.7	12 25.7	16 14.9	13 55.8
6	18 54 29.2	13 35.4	0 42.3	20 .8	5 4.5	23 1.2	12 22.1	16 49.8	27 43.9	12 24.9	16 13.5	13 56.2
7	18 58 25.7	14 32.6	0 39.1	1♌51.8	6 39.4	24 10.2	12 57.0	17 3.3	27 50.1	12 24.2	16 12.1	13 56.6
8	19 2 22.3	15 29.8	0 35.9	13 43.5	8 12.1	25 19.2	13 32.0	17 16.8	27 56.3	12 23.5	16 10.7	13 57.1
9	19 6 18.9	16 27.0	0 32.7	25 38.1	9 42.6	26 28.0	14 7.1	17 30.3	28 2.6	12 22.8	16 9.3	13 57.5
10	19 10 15.4	17 24.3	0 29.6	7♍38.4	11 10.9	27 36.8	14 42.2	17 43.8	28 9.0	12 22.2	16 8.0	13 58.1
11	19 14 12.0	18 21.5	0 26.4	19 47.9	12 37.0	28 45.4	15 17.5	17 57.3	28 15.4	12 21.6	16 6.7	13 58.6
12	19 18 8.5	19 18.7	0 23.2	2♎10.7	14 .8	29 54.0	15 52.8	18 10.8	28 21.8	12 21.1	16 5.4	13 59.2
13	19 22 5.1	20 15.9	0 20.0	14 51.3	15 22.4	1♍ 2.4	16 28.2	18 24.3	28 28.4	12 20.7	16 4.1	13 59.8
14	19 26 1.6	21 13.2	0 16.9	27 54.0	16 41.7	2 10.7	17 3.7	18 37.8	28 34.9	12 20.3	16 2.9	14 .4
15	19 29 58.2	22 10.4	0 13.7	11♏22.8	17 58.6	3 18.9	17 39.3	18 51.3	28 41.5	12 19.9	16 1.6	14 1.1
16	19 33 54.7	23 7.6	0 10.5	25 20.1	19 13.1	4 26.9	18 14.9	19 4.8	28 48.1	12 19.6	16 .4	14 1.8
17	19 37 51.3	24 4.8	0 7.3	9♐45.9	20 25.1	5 34.9	18 50.6	19 18.3	28 54.8	12 19.4	15 59.2	14 2.6
18	19 41 47.9	25 2.1	0 4.2	24 37.0	21 34.6	6 42.7	19 26.4	19 31.7	29 1.6	12 19.2	15 58.0	14 3.4
19	19 45 44.4	25 59.3	0 1.0	9♑46.7	22 41.4	7 50.3	20 2.3	19 45.2	29 8.3	12 19.0	15 56.9	14 4.2
20	19 49 41.0	26 56.5	29♍57.8	25 5.1	23 45.6	8 57.9	20 38.2	19 58.6	29 15.1	12 18.9	15 55.8	14 5.0
21	19 53 37.5	27 53.8	29 54.6	10♒21.1	24 46.9	10 5.3	21 14.2	20 12.0	29 22.0	12 18.9	15 54.6	14 5.9
22	19 57 34.1	28 51.0	29 51.4	25 24.0	25 45.4	11 12.5	21 50.3	20 25.5	29 28.9	12 18.9	15 53.6	14 6.8
23	20 1 30.6	29 48.3	29 48.3	10♓ 5.3	26 40.8	12 19.6	22 26.5	20 38.9	29 35.8	12 D 19.0	15 52.5	14 7.7
24	20 5 27.2	0♌45.6	29 45.1	24 20.0	27 33.1	13 26.6	23 2.7	20 52.2	29 42.8	12 19.1	15 51.5	14 8.7
25	20 9 23.7	1 42.9	29 41.9	8♈ 6.4	28 22.1	14 33.4	23 39.0	21 5.6	29 49.8	12 19.2	15 50.4	14 9.7
26	20 13 20.3	2 40.2	29 38.7	21 25.7	29 7.8	15 40.2	24 15.4	21 19.0	29 56.9	12 19.5	15 49.5	14 10.8
27	20 17 16.9	3 37.6	29 35.6	4♉20.5	29 49.9	16 46.7	24 51.9	21 32.4	0♍ 3.9	12 19.8	15 48.5	14 11.8
28	20 21 13.4	4 34.9	29 32.4	16 55.1	0♍28.3	17 53.0	25 28.4	21 45.7	0 11.0	12 20.1	15 47.6	14 12.9
29	20 25 10.0	5 32.3	29 29.2	29 13.6	1 2.8	18 59.3	26 5.1	21 59.0	0 18.2	12 20.4	15 46.7	14 14.0
30	20 29 6.5	6 29.6	29 26.0	11♊20.2	1 33.2	20 5.3	26 41.7	22 12.2	0 25.3	12 20.9	15 45.8	14 15.2
31	20 33 3.1	7 27.0	29 22.8	23 18.7	1 59.4	21 11.2	27 18.5	22 25.5	0 32.5	12 21.3	15 44.9	14 16.4

LATITUDE

DAY	EPHEM. SID. TIME	☉	☊	☽	☿	♀	♂	♃	♄	♅	♆	♇
1	18 34 46.4	0 .0	0 .0	3 S 48.2	1 N 51.0	1 N 48.9	0 N 58.4	0 N 7.8	1 N 26.8	0 N 23.1	1 N 29.3	17 N 9.5
4	18 46 36.1	0 .0	0 .0	4 59.5	1 40.7	1 44.9	0 55.8	0 8.1	1 26.7	0 23.0	1 29.2	17 7.9
7	18 58 25.7	0 .0	0 .0	4 15.0	1 25.2	1 39.9	0 53.3	0 8.3	1 26.6	0 22.9	1 29.2	17 6.2
10	19 10 15.4	0 .0	0 .0	1 52.3	1 4.9	1 34.0	0 50.8	0 8.6	1 26.5	0 22.9	1 29.1	17 4.5
13	19 22 5.1	0 .0	0 .0	1 N 21.9	0 40.4	1 27.3	0 48.3	0 8.9	1 26.4	0 22.8	1 29.0	17 2.9
16	19 33 54.7	0 .0	0 .0	4 12.7	0 12.1	1 19.6	0 45.9	0 9.2	1 26.4	0 22.7	1 28.8	17 1.3
19	19 45 44.4	0 .0	0 .0	4 58.2	0 S 19.5	1 11.0	0 43.4	0 9.5	1 26.3	0 22.6	1 28.7	16 59.7
22	19 57 34.1	0 .0	0 .0	2 46.7	0 53.9	1 1.5	0 41.1	0 9.8	1 26.3	0 22.5	1 28.6	16 58.1
25	20 9 23.7	0 .0	0 .0	0 S 52.0	1 30.5	0 51.2	0 38.7	0 10.1	1 26.3	0 22.4	1 28.5	16 56.5
28	20 21 13.4	0 .0	0 .0	3 50.3	2 8.5	0 39.9	0 36.4	0 10.4	1 26.3	0 22.3	1 28.4	16 55.0
31	20 33 3.1	0 .0	0 .0	5 5.4	2 46.8	0 27.9	0 34.0	0 10.7	1 26.3	0 22.3	1 28.2	16 53.5

RIGHT ASCENSION

DAY	EPHEM. SID. TIME	☉	☊	☽	☿	♀	♂	♃	♄	♅	♆	♇
1	18 34 46.4	9♋35.9	0♎53.4	18♉37.2	29♋ 2.8	20♌15.9	11♍25.0	17♋ 3.3	29♌56.5	10♏ 9.9	15♐19.8	19♎28.9
2	18 38 43.0	10 38.0	0 50.4	1♊ 1.8	0♌54.0	21 24.7	11 57.0	17 17.8	0♍ 2.2	10 R 8.9	15 R 18.2	19 28.9
3	18 42 39.5	11 40.0	0 47.5	13 31.3	2 42.3	22 33.1	12 29.0	17 32.3	0 8.0	10 8.0	15 16.6	19 28.9
4	18 46 36.1	12 41.9	0 44.6	26 3.1	4 27.5	23 41.1	13 1.1	17 46.8	0 13.8	10 7.1	15 15.1	19 D 29.0
5	18 50 32.6	13 43.8	0 41.7	8♋32.9	6 9.8	24 48.8	13 33.2	18 1.4	0 19.7	10 6.3	15 13.6	19 29.1
6	18 54 29.2	14 45.6	0 38.8	20 55.8	7 49.1	25 56.1	14 5.4	18 15.9	0 25.6	10 5.5	15 12.1	19 29.2
7	18 58 25.7	15 47.3	0 35.9	3♌ 7.9	9 25.5	27 3.0	14 37.6	18 30.4	0 31.6	10 4.7	15 10.7	19 29.4
8	19 2 22.3	16 48.9	0 33.0	15 7.6	10 58.9	28 9.5	15 9.9	18 44.9	0 37.6	10 4.0	15 9.2	19 29.5
9	19 6 18.9	17 50.4	0 30.0	26 56.1	12 29.4	29 15.7	15 42.2	18 59.4	0 43.7	10 3.4	15 7.8	19 29.8
10	19 10 15.4	18 51.8	0 27.1	8♍37.3	13 57.1	0♍21.4	16 14.5	19 13.9	0 49.8	10 2.8	15 6.3	19 30.0
11	19 14 12.0	19 53.1	0 24.2	20 17.8	15 21.8	1 26.9	16 46.9	19 28.4	0 56.0	10 2.2	15 4.9	19 30.3
12	19 18 8.5	20 54.2	0 21.3	2♎ 6.1	16 43.6	2 31.9	17 19.4	19 42.9	1 2.2	10 1.7	15 3.5	19 30.6
13	19 22 5.1	21 55.3	0 18.4	14 12.3	18 2.6	3 36.6	17 51.9	19 57.4	1 8.4	10 1.2	15 2.2	19 30.9
14	19 26 1.6	22 56.2	0 15.5	26 47.4	19 18.7	4 40.9	18 24.4	20 11.9	1 14.7	10 .8	15 .8	19 31.3
15	19 29 58.2	23 57.0	0 12.6	10♏ 1.5	20 32.0	5 44.9	18 57.0	20 26.3	1 21.1	10 .5	14 59.5	19 31.6
16	19 33 54.7	24 57.7	0 9.6	24 2.2	21 42.3	6 48.6	19 29.7	20 40.8	1 27.5	10 .2	14 58.2	19 32.1
17	19 37 51.3	25 58.3	0 6.7	8♐51.1	22 49.8	7 51.9	20 2.3	20 55.2	1 33.9	9 59.9	14 56.9	19 32.5
18	19 41 47.9	26 58.7	0 3.8	24 21.1	23 54.3	8 54.8	20 35.1	21 9.6	1 40.4	9 59.7	14 55.6	19 33.0
19	19 45 44.4	27 59.0	0 .9	10♑15.3	24 55.8	9 57.4	21 7.8	21 24.0	1 46.9	9 59.6	14 54.4	19 33.5
20	19 49 41.0	28 59.1	29♍58.0	26 10.6	25 54.4	10 59.7	21 40.7	21 38.3	1 53.4	9 59.5	14 53.2	19 34.0
21	19 53 37.5	29 59.1	29 55.1	11♒44.8	26 49.8	12 1.7	22 13.5	21 52.7	1 60.0	9 59.4	14 52.0	19 34.6
22	19 57 34.1	0♌59.0	29 52.1	26 43.2	27 42.2	13 3.4	22 46.5	22 7.0	2 6.6	9 59.4	14 50.9	19 35.2
23	20 1 30.6	1 58.7	29 49.2	11♓ .4	28 31.3	14 4.7	23 19.4	22 21.3	2 13.3	9 59.4	14 49.7	19 35.8
24	20 5 27.2	2 58.3	29 46.3	24 39.3	29 17.3	15 5.8	23 52.5	22 35.6	2 19.9	9 D 59.5	14 48.6	19 36.5
25	20 9 23.7	3 57.7	29 43.4	7♈47.3	29 59.8	16 6.5	24 25.6	22 49.9	2 26.7	9 59.7	14 47.5	19 37.2
26	20 13 20.3	4 57.1	29 40.5	20 33.5	0♍39.0	17 7.0	24 58.8	23 4.2	2 33.5	9 60.0	14 46.5	19 37.9
27	20 17 16.9	5 56.2	29 37.6	3♉ 6.7	1 14.5	18 7.2	25 32.0	23 18.4	2 40.2	10 .2	14 45.5	19 38.7
28	20 21 13.4	6 55.2	29 34.7	15 34.3	1 46.4	19 7.1	26 5.2	23 32.6	2 47.1	10 .5	14 44.5	19 39.5
29	20 25 10.0	7 54.1	29 31.7	28 1.1	2 14.5	20 6.8	26 38.5	23 46.7	2 53.9	10 .9	14 43.5	19 40.3
30	20 29 6.5	8 52.8	29 28.8	10♊29.5	2 38.8	21 6.1	27 11.9	24 .9	3 .8	10 1.3	14 42.5	19 41.1
31	20 33 3.1	9 51.4	29 25.9	22 59.2	2 58.9	22 5.2	27 45.4	24 15.0	3 7.7	10 1.7	14 41.6	19 41.9

DECLINATION

DAY	EPHEM. SID. TIME	☉	☊	☽	☿	♀	♂	♃	♄	♅	♆	♇
1	18 34 46.4	23 N 8.7	0 S .4	14 N 4.6	22 N 38.6	17 N 23.8	8 N 55.0	22 N 38.7	13 N 47.5	15 S 13.1	21 S 15.5	10 N 19.8
4	18 46 36.1	22 55.5	0 .3	18 23.8	21 23.7	16 14.7	8 13.4	22 34.1	13 41.3	15 12.4	21 15.1	10 17.9
7	18 58 25.7	22 38.7	0 .3	15 36.0	19 59.0	15 2.1	7 31.1	22 29.4	13 34.8	15 11.7	21 14.8	10 15.9
10	19 10 15.4	22 18.4	0 .2	6 58.0	18 27.7	13 46.4	6 48.2	22 24.4	13 28.1	15 11.2	21 14.5	10 13.9
13	19 22 5.1	21 54.6	0 .1	4 S 35.6	16 52.2	12 27.9	6 4.9	22 19.3	13 21.3	15 10.8	21 14.2	10 11.7
16	19 33 54.7	21 27.5	0 .1	15 .3	15 15.1	11 6.8	5 21.0	22 14.0	13 14.4	15 10.6	21 13.9	10 9.5
19	19 45 44.4	20 57.0	0 .0	18 7.3	13 38.6	9 43.7	4 36.7	22 8.5	13 7.3	15 10.5	21 13.6	10 7.1
22	19 57 34.1	20 23.4	0 N .1	10 26.2	12 5.3	8 18.6	3 52.0	22 2.9	13 .0	15 10.5	21 13.4	10 4.7
25	20 9 23.7	19 46.7	0 .1	2 N 25.2	10 37.5	6 52.0	3 6.8	21 57.1	12 52.7	15 10.7	21 13.2	10 2.1
28	20 21 13.4	19 7.0	0 .2	13 12.4	9 18.1	5 24.1	2 21.3	21 51.1	12 45.2	15 11.0	21 13.1	9 59.5
31	20 33 3.1	18 24.5	0 .3	18 11.2	8 10.1	3 55.3	1 35.5	21 45.0	12 37.6	15 11.5	21 12.9	9 56.9

AUGUST 1978

LONGITUDE

DAY	EPHEM. SID. TIME (h m s)	☉ (° ′)	☊ (° ′)	☾ (° ′)	☿ (° ′)	♀ (° ′)	♂ (° ′)	♃ (° ′)	♄ (° ′)	♅ (° ′)	♆ (° ′)	♇ (° ′)
1	20 36 59.6	8♌24.4	29♍19.7	5♋12.4	2♍21.2	22♍16.9	27♍55.3	22♋38.7	0♍39.8	12♏21.9	15♐44.1	14♎17.6
2	20 40 56.2	9 21.9	29 16.5	17 3.8	2 38.4	23 22.5	28 32.3	22 51.9	0 47.0	12 22.5	15R43.3	14 18.8
3	20 44 52.7	10 19.3	29 13.3	28 55.2	2 50.8	24 27.8	29 9.2	23 5.1	0 54.3	12 23.1	15 42.5	14 20.1
4	20 48 49.3	11 16.8	29 10.1	10♌48.4	2 58.2	25 33.0	29 46.3	23 18.2	1 1.6	12 23.8	15 41.8	14 21.4
5	20 52 45.9	12 14.2	29 7.0	22 44.9	3 .6	26 38.0	0♎23.4	23 31.4	1 8.9	12 24.5	15 41.0	14 22.7
6	20 56 42.4	13 11.7	29 3.8	4♍46.5	2R57.8	27 42.8	1 .6	23 44.4	1 16.3	12 25.3	15 40.3	14 24.1
7	21 0 39.0	14 9.2	29 .6	16 55.2	2 49.6	28 47.4	1 37.9	23 57.5	1 23.7	12 26.1	15 39.7	14 25.4
8	21 4 35.5	15 6.7	28 57.4	29 13.2	2 36.2	29 51.8	2 15.2	24 10.5	1 31.1	12 27.0	15 39.0	14 26.9
9	21 8 32.1	16 4.3	28 54.3	11♎43.5	2 17.4	0♎56.0	2 52.7	24 23.5	1 38.5	12 28.0	15 38.4	14 28.3
10	21 12 28.6	17 1.8	28 51.1	24 29.1	1 53.4	1 60.0	3 30.2	24 36.4	1 45.9	12 29.0	15 37.9	14 29.8
11	21 16 25.2	17 59.4	28 47.9	7♏33.3	1 24.2	3 3.7	4 7.7	24 49.3	1 53.4	12 30.0	15 37.3	14 31.3
12	21 20 21.7	18 57.0	28 44.7	20 59.2	0 50.3	4 7.2	4 45.3	25 2.2	2 .8	12 31.1	15 36.8	14 32.8
13	21 24 18.3	19 54.5	28 41.5	4♐48.7	0 11.9	5 10.5	5 23.0	25 15.0	2 8.3	12 32.3	15 36.3	14 34.3
14	21 28 14.8	20 52.2	28 38.4	19 2.5	29♌29.6	6 13.5	6 .8	25 27.8	2 15.8	12 33.5	15 35.9	14 35.9
15	21 32 11.4	21 49.8	28 35.2	3♑38.6	28 43.9	7 16.3	6 38.6	25 40.6	2 23.3	12 34.7	15 35.4	14 37.5
16	21 36 7.9	22 47.5	28 32.0	18 32.5	27 55.5	8 18.8	7 16.6	25 53.3	2 30.9	12 36.1	15 35.1	14 39.2
17	21 40 4.5	23 45.1	28 28.8	3♒36.7	27 5.2	9 21.0	7 54.5	26 6.0	2 38.5	12 37.4	15 34.7	14 40.8
18	21 44 1.1	24 42.8	28 25.7	18 42.4	26 14.0	10 22.9	8 32.5	26 18.6	2 46.0	12 38.8	15 34.4	14 42.5
19	21 47 57.6	25 40.5	28 22.5	3♓39.9	25 22.7	11 24.6	9 10.6	26 31.1	2 53.6	12 40.2	15 34.1	14 44.2
20	21 51 54.2	26 38.2	28 19.3	18 20.8	24 32.5	12 25.9	9 48.8	26 43.7	3 1.1	12 41.7	15 33.8	14 45.9
21	21 55 50.7	27 35.9	28 16.1	2♈39.0	23 44.3	13 27.0	10 27.0	26 56.1	3 8.7	12 43.3	15 33.6	14 47.6
22	21 59 47.3	28 33.7	28 12.9	16 31.1	22 59.2	14 27.7	11 5.3	27 8.5	3 16.3	12 44.9	15 33.4	14 49.4
23	22 3 43.8	29 31.5	28 9.8	29 56.5	22 18.2	15 28.1	11 43.7	27 20.9	3 23.9	12 46.5	15 33.2	14 51.2
24	22 7 40.4	0♍29.3	28 6.6	12♉56.8	21 42.1	16 28.2	12 22.1	27 33.2	3 31.5	12 48.2	15 33.0	14 53.0
25	22 11 36.9	1 27.2	28 3.4	25 35.0	21 11.8	17 28.0	13 .6	27 45.5	3 39.1	12 49.9	15 32.9	14 54.8
26	22 15 33.5	2 25.1	28 .2	7♊55.2	20 48.0	18 27.4	13 39.2	27 57.7	3 46.7	12 51.7	15 32.8	14 56.7
27	22 19 30.0	3 23.0	27 57.1	20 1.8	20 31.3	19 26.4	14 17.8	28 9.8	3 54.3	12 53.5	15 32.8	14 58.6
28	22 23 26.6	4 20.9	27 53.9	1♋59.2	20 22.2	20 25.1	14 56.5	28 21.9	4 1.9	12 55.4	15 32.8	15 .4
29	22 27 23.1	5 18.9	27 50.7	13 51.6	20 21.0	21 23.4	15 35.3	28 33.9	4 9.5	12 57.3	15 32.8	15 2.4
30	22 31 19.7	6 16.9	27 47.5	25 42.7	20D27.9	22 21.3	16 14.2	28 45.9	4 17.1	12 59.3	15D32.9	15 4.3
31	22 35 16.2	7 14.9	27 44.3	7♌35.7	20 43.2	23 18.8	16 53.1	28 57.8	4 24.7	13 1.3	15 32.9	15 6.3

LATITUDE

DAY	EPHEM. SID. TIME	☉	☊	☾	☿	♀	♂	♃	♄	♅	♆	♇
1	20 36 59.6	0 .0	0 .0	5S 4.1	2S59.4	0N23.6	0N33.3	0N10.8	1N26.3	0N22.2	1N28.2	16N53.0
4	20 48 49.3	0 .0	0 .0	3 44.4	3 35.7	0 10.5	0 31.0	0 11.1	1 26.4	0 22.1	1 28.0	16 51.5
7	21 0 39.0	0 .0	0 .0	0 56.1	4 7.9	0S 3.5	0 28.7	0 11.4	1 26.5	0 22.1	1 27.9	16 50.1
10	21 12 28.6	0 .0	0 .0	2N22.2	4 33.0	0 18.2	0 26.5	0 11.7	1 26.5	0 22.0	1 27.7	16 48.8
13	21 24 18.3	0 .0	0 .0	4 47.7	4 47.1	0 33.7	0 24.3	0 12.0	1 26.6	0 21.9	1 27.6	16 47.4
16	21 36 7.9	0 .0	0 .0	4 50.2	4 46.8	0 49.9	0 22.1	0 12.4	1 26.8	0 21.8	1 27.4	16 46.2
19	21 47 57.6	0 .0	0 .0	2 4.0	4 29.8	1 6.7	0 19.9	0 12.7	1 26.9	0 21.7	1 27.3	16 45.0
22	21 59 47.3	0 .0	0 .0	1S45.3	3 56.7	1 24.1	0 17.8	0 13.0	1 27.0	0 21.6	1 27.1	16 43.8
25	22 11 36.9	0 .0	0 .0	4 28.4	3 10.7	1 42.1	0 15.6	0 13.4	1 27.2	0 21.6	1 26.9	16 42.7
28	22 23 26.6	0 .0	0 .0	5 13.2	2 17.2	2 .6	0 13.5	0 13.7	1 27.4	0 21.5	1 26.8	16 41.6
31	22 35 16.2	0 .0	0 .0	3 58.7	1 21.7	2 19.5	0 11.4	0 14.1	1 27.6	0 21.4	1 26.6	16 40.7

RIGHT ASCENSION

DAY	EPHEM. SID. TIME	☉	☊	☾	☿	♀	♂	♃	♄	♅	♆	♇
1	20 36 59.6	10♌49.8	29♍23.0	5♋27.7	3♍14.9	23♍4.1	28♍18.9	24♋29.0	3♍14.6	10♏2.2	14♐40.7	19♎42.8
2	20 40 56.2	11 48.1	29 20.1	17 51.6	3 26.7	24 2.7	28 52.4	24 43.0	3 21.5	10 2.8	14R39.9	19 43.7
3	20 44 52.7	12 46.2	29 17.2	0♌7.3	3 34.0	25 1.0	29 26.1	24 57.0	3 28.5	10 3.4	14 39.0	19 44.7
4	20 48 49.3	13 44.2	29 14.3	12 12.6	3 36.7	25 59.1	29 59.8	25 11.0	3 35.5	10 4.1	14 38.2	19 45.7
5	20 52 45.9	14 42.0	29 11.3	24 7.3	3R34.9	26 57.0	0♎33.5	25 24.9	3 42.5	10 4.8	14 37.4	19 46.7
6	20 56 42.4	15 39.7	29 8.4	5♍53.6	3 28.4	27 54.6	1 7.4	25 38.8	3 49.6	10 5.6	14 36.7	19 47.7
7	21 0 39.0	16 37.2	29 5.5	17 36.1	3 17.1	28 52.0	1 41.3	25 52.6	3 56.6	10 6.4	14 36.0	19 48.7
8	21 4 35.5	17 34.6	29 2.6	29 21.2	3 1.1	29 49.2	2 15.2	26 6.4	4 3.7	10 7.3	14 35.3	19 49.8
9	21 8 32.1	18 31.8	28 59.7	11♎17.2	2 40.5	0♎46.1	2 49.3	26 20.2	4 10.8	10 8.2	14 34.6	19 50.9
10	21 12 28.6	19 28.9	28 56.8	23 33.2	2 15.4	1 42.8	3 23.4	26 33.9	4 17.9	10 9.2	14 34.0	19 52.1
11	21 16 25.2	20 25.8	28 53.8	6♏18.6	1 45.9	2 39.3	3 57.6	26 47.5	4 25.0	10 10.2	14 33.4	19 53.2
12	21 20 21.7	21 22.6	28 50.9	19 41.3	1 12.3	3 35.6	4 31.8	27 1.2	4 32.2	10 11.3	14 32.9	19 54.4
13	21 24 18.3	22 19.2	28 48.0	3♐46.0	0 35.1	4 31.6	5 6.1	27 14.7	4 39.3	10 12.4	14 32.3	19 55.6
14	21 28 14.8	23 15.7	28 45.1	18 31.5	29♌54.6	5 27.4	5 40.5	27 28.2	4 46.5	10 13.6	14 31.9	19 56.8
15	21 32 11.4	24 12.0	28 42.2	3♑49.2	29 11.5	6 23.0	6 15.0	27 41.7	4 53.7	10 14.8	14 31.4	19 58.1
16	21 36 7.9	25 8.3	28 39.3	19 23.3	28 26.4	7 18.4	6 49.6	27 55.1	5 .9	10 16.1	14 31.0	19 59.4
17	21 40 4.5	26 4.3	28 36.4	4♒54.8	27 40.1	8 13.6	7 24.2	28 8.5	5 8.1	10 17.4	14 30.6	20 .7
18	21 44 1.1	27 .3	28 33.4	20 6.8	26 53.4	9 8.5	7 58.9	28 21.8	5 15.3	10 18.8	14 30.3	20 2.1
19	21 47 57.6	27 56.1	28 30.5	4♓49.1	26 7.2	10 3.2	8 33.7	28 35.0	5 22.6	10 20.2	14 29.9	20 3.4
20	21 51 54.2	28 51.8	28 27.6	18 58.7	25 22.5	10 57.7	9 8.6	28 48.2	5 29.8	10 21.7	14 29.6	20 4.8
21	21 55 50.7	29 47.3	28 24.7	2♈38.2	24 40.1	11 51.9	9 43.6	29 1.3	5 37.0	10 23.2	14 29.4	20 6.2
22	21 59 47.3	0♍42.8	28 21.8	15 53.8	24 1.1	12 46.0	10 18.6	29 14.4	5 44.2	10 24.8	14 29.1	20 7.6
23	22 3 43.8	1 38.1	28 18.9	28 52.2	23 26.3	13 39.8	10 53.7	29 27.4	5 51.5	10 26.4	14 29.0	20 9.1
24	22 7 40.4	2 33.4	28 15.9	11♉39.7	22 56.6	14 33.4	11 28.9	29 40.4	5 58.7	10 28.0	14 28.8	20 10.6
25	22 11 36.9	3 28.5	28 13.0	24 20.9	22 32.7	15 26.7	12 4.2	29 53.2	6 6.0	10 29.7	14 28.7	20 12.1
26	22 15 33.5	4 23.5	28 10.1	6♊58.7	22 15.2	16 19.8	12 39.6	0♌6.0	6 13.2	10 31.5	14 28.6	20 13.6
27	22 19 30.0	5 18.5	28 7.2	19 33.7	22 4.8	17 12.7	13 15.1	0 18.8	6 20.5	10 33.3	14 28.5	20 15.1
28	22 23 26.6	6 13.3	28 4.3	2♋5.0	22 1.8	18 5.4	13 50.7	0 31.5	6 27.7	10 35.1	14 28.5	20 16.7
29	22 27 23.1	7 8.1	28 1.4	14 30.5	22D 6.6	18 57.8	14 26.4	0 44.1	6 35.0	10 37.0	14 28.5	20 18.3
30	22 31 19.7	8 2.7	27 58.4	26 48.4	22 19.4	19 49.9	15 2.2	0 56.6	6 42.2	10 38.9	14D28.6	20 19.9
31	22 35 16.2	8 57.3	27 55.5	8♌57.2	22 40.2	20 41.8	15 38.1	1 9.1	6 49.5	10 40.9	14 28.6	20 21.5

DECLINATION

DAY	EPHEM. SID. TIME	☉	☊	☾	☿	♀	♂	♃	♄	♅	♆	♇
1	20 36 59.6	18N 9.7	0N .3	18N16.3	7N50.6	3N25.5	1N20.1	21N42.9	12N35.0	15S11.7	21S12.9	9N55.9
4	20 48 49.3	17 23.6	0 .3	13 55.4	7 3.5	1 55.7	0 33.9	21 36.6	12 27.3	15 12.4	21 12.8	9 53.2
7	21 0 39.0	16 34.9	0 .4	4 18.2	6 36.5	0 25.7	0S12.6	21 30.2	12 19.5	15 13.2	21 12.7	9 50.4
10	21 12 28.6	15 43.9	0 .5	7S17.0	6 33.0	1S 4.5	0 59.2	21 23.6	12 11.6	15 14.1	21 12.6	9 47.5
13	21 24 18.3	14 50.6	0 .5	16 22.8	6 55.2	2 34.3	1 46.0	21 17.0	12 3.7	15 15.2	21 12.6	9 44.6
16	21 36 7.9	13 55.1	0 .6	17 21.8	7 42.2	4 3.7	2 33.0	21 10.3	11 55.7	15 16.4	21 12.7	9 41.6
19	21 47 57.6	12 57.7	0 .7	8 14.2	8 49.3	5 32.2	3 19.9	21 3.5	11 47.6	15 17.8	21 12.7	9 38.6
22	21 59 47.3	11 58.5	0 .7	4N52.4	10 7.4	6 59.7	4 6.9	20 56.6	11 39.5	15 19.3	21 12.8	9 35.6
25	22 11 36.9	10 57.5	0 .8	14 48.5	11 25.3	8 25.8	4 53.9	20 49.7	11 31.4	15 20.9	21 12.9	9 32.5
28	22 23 26.6	9 54.9	0 .9	18 12.3	12 31.7	9 50.3	5 40.8	20 42.8	11 23.3	15 22.6	21 13.1	9 29.5
31	22 35 16.2	8 50.9	0 .9	14 31.4	13 17.7	11 13.0	6 27.5	20 35.8	11 15.1	15 24.4	21 13.2	9 26.4

SEPTEMBER 1978

LONGITUDE

DAY	EPHEM. SID. TIME (h m s)	☉ (° ′)	☊ (° ′)	☾ (° ′)	☿ (° ′)	♀ (° ′)	♂ (° ′)	♃ (° ′)	♄ (° ′)	♅ (° ′)	♆ (° ′)	♇ (° ′)
1	22 39 12.8	8 ♍ 13.0	27 ♍ 41.2	19 ♌ 33.2	21 ♌ 6.8	24 ♎ 15.9	17 ♎ 32.1	29 ♋ 9.6	4 ♍ 32.3	13 ♏ 3.3	15 ♐ 33.1	15 ♎ 8.2
2	22 43 9.3	9 11.1	27 38.0	1 ♍ 37.5	21 38.6	25 12.5	18 11.1	29 21.4	4 39.9	13 5.4	15 33.2	15 10.2
3	22 47 5.9	10 9.2	27 34.8	13 50.2	22 18.6	26 8.7	18 50.3	29 33.1	4 47.5	13 7.6	15 33.4	15 12.2
4	22 51 2.5	11 7.3	27 31.6	26 12.8	23 6.4	27 4.4	19 29.5	29 44.7	4 55.1	13 9.7	15 33.6	15 14.3
5	22 54 59.0	12 5.5	27 28.4	8 ♎ 46.7	24 1.8	27 59.7	20 8.7	29 56.2	5 2.7	13 12.0	15 33.8	15 16.3
6	22 58 55.6	13 3.7	27 25.3	21 33.1	25 4.4	28 54.4	20 48.1	0 ♌ 7.8	5 10.3	13 14.3	15 34.2	15 18.4
7	23 2 52.1	14 1.9	27 22.1	4 ♏ 33.2	26 13.7	29 48.7	21 27.5	0 19.2	5 17.8	13 16.6	15 34.5	15 20.5
8	23 6 48.7	15 .2	27 18.9	17 48.3	27 29.4	0 ♏ 42.3	22 7.0	0 30.5	5 25.4	13 19.0	15 34.8	15 22.6
9	23 10 45.2	15 58.5	27 15.7	1 ♐ 19.6	28 50.8	1 35.4	22 46.5	0 41.8	5 32.9	13 21.3	15 35.2	15 24.7
10	23 14 41.8	16 56.8	27 12.6	15 7.6	0 ♍ 17.5	2 27.9	23 26.1	0 52.9	5 40.4	13 23.8	15 35.6	15 26.9
11	23 18 38.3	17 55.1	27 9.4	29 12.3	1 48.9	3 19.8	24 5.8	1 4.0	5 47.9	13 26.3	15 36.1	15 29.0
12	23 22 34.9	18 53.4	27 6.2	13 ♑ 32.3	3 24.4	4 11.0	24 45.5	1 15.0	5 55.4	13 28.8	15 36.5	15 31.2
13	23 26 31.4	19 51.8	27 3.0	28 4.6	5 3.6	5 1.6	25 25.3	1 26.0	6 2.9	13 31.3	15 37.0	15 33.4
14	23 30 28.0	20 50.2	26 59.8	12 ♒ 44.8	6 45.8	5 51.5	26 5.1	1 36.8	6 10.3	13 33.9	15 37.6	15 35.5
15	23 34 24.5	21 48.6	26 56.7	27 27.0	8 30.5	6 40.7	26 45.0	1 47.6	6 17.8	13 36.5	15 38.2	15 37.7
16	23 38 21.1	22 47.1	26 53.5	12 ♓ 4.7	10 17.4	7 29.1	27 25.0	1 58.2	6 25.2	13 39.2	15 38.8	15 40.0
17	23 42 17.6	23 45.6	26 50.3	26 31.3	12 5.9	8 16.8	28 5.1	2 8.8	6 32.6	13 41.9	15 39.4	15 42.2
18	23 46 14.2	24 44.1	26 47.1	10 ♈ 41.2	13 55.6	9 3.6	28 45.2	2 19.3	6 39.9	13 44.6	15 40.1	15 44.4
19	23 50 10.7	25 42.6	26 44.0	24 30.4	15 46.3	9 49.6	29 25.3	2 29.7	6 47.3	13 47.4	15 40.8	15 46.7
20	23 54 7.3	26 41.2	26 40.8	7 ♉ 56.7	17 37.5	10 34.8	0 ♏ 5.6	2 40.0	6 54.6	13 50.2	15 41.5	15 48.9
21	23 58 3.8	27 39.8	26 37.6	21 .0	19 29.0	11 19.0	0 45.9	2 50.2	7 1.9	13 53.1	15 42.3	15 51.2
22	0 2 .4	28 38.5	26 34.4	3 ♊ 41.8	21 20.7	12 2.4	1 26.3	3 .3	7 9.2	13 55.9	15 43.1	15 53.5
23	0 5 56.9	29 37.2	26 31.2	16 5.1	23 12.2	12 44.7	2 6.7	3 10.4	7 16.4	13 58.9	15 43.9	15 55.8
24	0 9 53.5	0 ♎ 35.9	26 28.1	28 13.7	25 3.4	13 26.1	2 47.2	3 20.3	7 23.6	14 1.8	15 44.8	15 58.1
25	0 13 50.0	1 34.7	26 24.9	10 ♋ 12.0	26 54.2	14 6.4	3 27.8	3 30.1	7 30.8	14 4.8	15 45.6	16 .4
26	0 17 46.6	2 33.5	26 21.7	22 4.6	28 44.5	14 45.7	4 8.4	3 39.8	7 38.0	14 7.8	15 46.6	16 2.7
27	0 21 43.1	3 32.4	26 18.5	3 ♌ 56.2	0 ♎ 34.2	15 23.8	4 49.2	3 49.4	7 45.2	14 10.9	15 47.6	16 5.0
28	0 25 39.7	4 31.3	26 15.4	15 50.9	2 23.2	16 .8	5 30.0	3 58.9	7 52.2	14 13.9	15 48.5	16 7.4
29	0 29 36.2	5 30.2	26 12.2	27 52.8	4 11.5	16 36.5	6 10.8	4 8.3	7 59.3	14 17.0	15 49.6	16 9.7
30	0 33 32.8	6 29.1	26 9.0	10 ♍ 4.9	5 59.0	17 11.0	6 51.8	4 17.6	8 6.3	14 20.2	15 50.6	16 12.0

LATITUDE

DAY	EPHEM. SID. TIME	☉	☊	☾	☿	♀	♂	♃	♄	♅	♆	♇
1	22 39 12.8	0 .0	0 .0	3 S 11.0	1 S 3.7	2 S 25.9	0 N 10.7	0 N 14.2	1 N 27.7	0 N 21.4	1 N 26.6	16 N 40.4
4	22 51 2.5	0 .0	0 .0	0 2.8	0 13.0	2 45.3	0 8.6	0 14.6	1 27.9	0 21.3	1 26.4	16 39.5
7	23 2 52.1	0 .0	0 .0	3 N 14.5	0 N 30.3	3 5.0	0 6.6	0 14.9	1 28.2	0 21.2	1 26.2	16 38.6
10	23 14 41.8	0 .0	0 .0	5 10.5	1 4.5	3 24.9	0 4.5	0 15.3	1 28.4	0 21.1	1 26.1	16 37.9
13	23 26 31.4	0 .0	0 .0	4 31.0	1 28.7	3 44.9	0 2.5	0 15.7	1 28.7	0 21.1	1 25.9	16 37.2
16	23 38 21.1	0 .0	0 .0	1 20.5	1 43.4	4 4.8	0 .5	0 16.1	1 29.0	0 21.0	1 25.7	16 36.6
19	23 50 10.7	0 .0	0 .0	2 S 28.2	1 49.7	4 24.7	0 S 1.5	0 16.5	1 29.4	0 20.9	1 25.6	16 36.0
22	0 2 .4	0 .0	0 .0	4 52.1	1 48.8	4 44.3	0 3.5	0 16.9	1 29.7	0 20.9	1 25.4	16 35.5
25	0 13 50.0	0 .0	0 .0	5 8.7	1 42.1	5 3.4	0 5.4	0 17.3	1 30.1	0 20.8	1 25.3	16 35.2
28	0 25 39.7	0 .0	0 .0	3 28.1	1 31.1	5 21.8	0 7.4	0 17.7	1 30.5	0 20.7	1 25.1	16 34.8

RIGHT ASCENSION

DAY	EPHEM. SID. TIME	☉	☊	☾	☿	♀	♂	♃	♄	♅	♆	♇
1	22 39 12.8	9 ♍ 51.8	27 ♍ 52.6	20 ♌ 57.1	23 ♌ 9.1	21 ♎ 33.4	16 ♎ 14.1	1 ♌ 21.5	6 ♍ 56.7	10 ♏ 42.9	14 ♐ 28.8	20 ♎ 23.1
2	22 43 9.3	10 46.2	27 49.7	2 ♍ 49.9	23 45.8	22 24.7	16 50.2	1 33.8	7 3.9	10 45.0	14 28.9	20 24.8
3	22 47 5.9	11 40.6	27 46.8	14 39.3	24 30.4	23 15.7	17 26.4	1 46.0	7 11.1	10 47.1	14 29.1	20 26.5
4	22 51 2.5	12 34.9	27 43.9	26 30.4	25 22.3	24 6.4	18 2.7	1 58.2	7 18.4	10 49.3	14 29.3	20 28.2
5	22 54 59.0	13 29.1	27 40.9	8 ♎ 29.9	26 21.3	24 56.8	18 39.1	2 10.3	7 25.6	10 51.5	14 29.6	20 29.9
6	22 58 55.6	14 23.3	27 38.0	20 45.2	27 27.0	25 46.9	19 15.7	2 22.3	7 32.8	10 53.7	14 29.9	20 31.7
7	23 2 52.1	15 17.4	27 35.1	3 ♏ 23.5	28 38.7	26 36.6	19 52.4	2 34.2	7 40.0	10 56.0	14 30.2	20 33.4
8	23 6 48.7	16 11.5	27 32.2	16 31.3	29 56.1	27 25.9	20 29.1	2 46.1	7 47.2	10 58.3	14 30.6	20 35.2
9	23 10 45.2	17 5.5	27 29.3	0 ♐ 12.6	1 ♍ 18.5	28 14.8	21 6.0	2 57.8	7 54.3	11 .7	14 31.0	20 37.0
10	23 14 41.8	17 59.4	27 26.4	14 27.4	2 45.3	29 3.3	21 42.9	3 9.5	8 1.5	11 3.1	14 31.4	20 38.8
11	23 18 38.3	18 53.4	27 23.4	29 10.0	4 16.0	29 51.4	22 20.0	3 21.0	8 8.6	11 5.5	14 31.9	20 40.7
12	23 22 34.9	19 47.2	27 20.5	14 ♑ 10.2	5 50.0	0 ♏ 39.0	22 57.2	3 32.5	8 15.7	11 8.0	14 32.4	20 42.5
13	23 26 31.4	20 41.1	27 17.6	29 14.1	7 26.7	1 26.1	23 34.6	3 43.9	8 22.8	11 10.6	14 32.9	20 44.4
14	23 30 28.0	21 34.9	27 14.7	14 ♒ 8.7	9 5.6	2 12.7	24 12.0	3 55.2	8 29.9	11 13.1	14 33.5	20 46.2
15	23 34 24.5	22 28.7	27 11.8	28 44.6	10 46.1	2 58.8	24 49.5	4 6.4	8 37.0	11 15.7	14 34.1	20 48.1
16	23 38 21.1	23 22.5	27 8.9	12 ♓ 57.6	12 27.9	3 44.2	25 27.2	4 17.5	8 44.0	11 18.3	14 34.8	20 50.0
17	23 42 17.6	24 16.3	27 5.9	26 48.0	14 10.5	4 29.1	26 5.0	4 28.5	8 51.0	11 21.0	14 35.4	20 51.9
18	23 46 14.2	25 10.0	27 3.0	10 ♈ 19.5	15 53.7	5 13.4	26 43.0	4 39.4	8 58.0	11 23.7	14 36.1	20 53.9
19	23 50 10.7	26 3.8	27 .1	23 36.6	17 37.0	5 56.9	27 21.0	4 50.2	9 5.0	11 26.5	14 36.9	20 55.8
20	23 54 7.3	26 57.6	26 57.2	6 ♉ 43.7	19 20.3	6 39.8	27 59.2	5 .9	9 11.9	11 29.2	14 37.7	20 57.8
21	23 58 3.8	27 51.4	26 54.3	19 43.9	21 3.3	7 22.0	28 37.5	5 11.5	9 18.9	11 32.0	14 38.5	20 59.7
22	0 2 .4	28 45.2	26 51.3	2 ♊ 38.5	22 45.9	8 3.3	29 16.0	5 22.0	9 25.8	11 34.9	14 39.3	21 1.7
23	0 5 56.9	29 39.1	26 48.4	15 27.2	24 28.0	8 43.9	29 54.5	5 32.4	9 32.6	11 37.8	14 40.2	21 3.7
24	0 9 53.5	0 ♎ 33.0	26 45.5	28 8.6	26 9.4	9 23.6	0 ♏ 33.3	5 42.6	9 39.5	11 40.7	14 41.1	21 5.7
25	0 13 50.0	1 26.9	26 42.6	10 ♋ 40.9	27 50.1	10 2.4	1 12.1	5 52.8	9 46.3	11 43.6	14 42.0	21 7.7
26	0 17 46.6	2 20.8	26 39.7	23 2.7v	29 30.1	10 40.3	1 51.1	6 2.9	9 53.1	11 46.6	14 43.0	21 9.7
27	0 21 43.1	3 14.9	26 36.8	5 ♌ 13.8	1 ♎ 9.3	11 17.2	2 30.3	6 12.8	9 59.9	11 49.7	14 44.1	21 11.8
28	0 25 39.7	4 9.0	26 33.8	17 15.2	2 47.6	11 53.0	3 9.6	6 22.7	10 6.6	11 52.7	14 45.1	21 13.9
29	0 29 36.2	5 3.1	26 30.9	29 9.8	4 25.2	12 27.7	3 49.0	6 32.4	10 13.3	11 55.8	14 46.2	21 15.9
30	0 33 32.8	5 57.3	26 28.0	11 ♍ 1.9	6 2.0	13 1.3	4 28.6	6 42.0	10 20.0	11 58.9	14 47.3	21 18.0

DECLINATION

DAY	EPHEM. SID. TIME	☉	☊	☾	☿	♀	♂	♃	♄	♅	♆	♇
1	22 39 12.8	8 N 29.3	0 N 1.0	11 N 55.8	13 N 27.3	11 S 40.1	6 S 43.1	20 N 33.5	11 N 12.4	15 S 25.1	21 S 13.3	9 N 25.4
4	22 51 2.5	7 23.7	0 1.0	1 27.8	13 36.6	12 60.0	7 29.6	20 26.5	11 4.3	15 27.1	21 13.5	9 22.3
7	23 2 52.1	6 16.9	0 1.1	9 S 59.0	13 15.0	14 17.4	8 15.9	20 19.5	10 56.2	15 29.2	21 13.8	9 19.2
10	23 14 41.8	5 9.3	0 1.2	17 28.0	12 22.5	15 32.0	9 1.9	20 12.6	10 48.1	15 31.4	21 14.1	9 16.1
13	23 26 31.4	4 .9	0 1.2	16 7.1	11 1.9	16 43.6	9 47.6	20 5.8	10 40.1	15 33.8	21 14.4	9 13.1
16	23 38 21.1	2 51.8	0 1.3	5 47.4	9 18.3	17 51.8	10 32.8	19 59.0	10 32.1	15 36.2	21 14.7	9 10.1
19	23 50 10.7	1 42.3	0 1.4	7 N 11.9	7 17.7	18 56.4	11 17.5	19 52.2	10 24.2	15 38.7	21 15.1	9 7.1
22	0 2 .4	0 32.4	0 1.4	16 6.4	5 5.9	19 57.2	12 1.7	19 45.6	10 16.4	15 41.3	21 15.5	9 4.1
25	0 13 50.0	0 S 37.7	0 1.5	17 55.1	2 47.6	20 53.7	12 45.3	19 39.2	10 8.6	15 44.0	21 15.9	9 1.2
28	0 25 39.7	1 47.8	0 1.6	12 46.3	0 26.6	21 45.6	13 28.3	19 32.8	10 1.0	15 46.8	21 16.4	8 58.3

OCTOBER 1978

DAY	EPHEM. SID. TIME	☉	☊	☽	☿	♀	♂	♃	♄	♅	♆	♇
	h m s	° ′	° ′	° ′	° ′	° ′	° ′	° ′	° ′	° ′	° ′	° ′
		LONGITUDE										
1	0 37 29.4	7♎28.1	26♍ 5.8	22♍29.7	7♎45.7	17♏44.1	7♏32.7	4♌26.7	8♍13.3	14♏23.3	15♐51.7	16♎14.4
2	0 41 25.9	8 27.2	26 2.6	5♎ 8.9	9 31.6	18 15.9	8 13.8	4 35.8	8 20.3	14 26.5	15 52.8	16 16.7
3	0 45 22.5	9 26.2	25 59.5	18 3.3	11 16.6	18 46.2	8 54.9	4 44.7	8 27.2	14 29.7	15 53.9	16 19.1
4	0 49 19.0	10 25.3	25 56.3	1♏12.6	13 .8	19 15.1	9 36.1	4 53.5	8 34.0	14 33.0	15 55.1	16 21.5
5	0 53 15.6	11 24.4	25 53.1	14 36.3	14 44.2	19 42.4	10 17.3	5 2.2	8 40.9	14 36.2	15 56.3	16 23.8
6	0 57 12.1	12 23.6	25 49.9	28 12.9	16 26.7	20 8.1	10 58.6	5 10.7	8 47.6	14 39.5	15 57.5	16 26.2
7	1 1 8.7	13 22.8	25 46.7	12♐ .8	18 8.4	20 32.2	11 40.0	5 19.2	8 54.4	14 42.9	15 58.7	16 28.5
8	1 5 5.2	14 22.0	25 43.6	25 58.2	19 49.3	20 54.5	12 21.5	5 27.5	9 1.1	14 46.2	16 .0	16 30.9
9	1 9 1.8	15 21.2	25 40.4	10♑ 3.3	21 29.5	21 15.0	13 3.0	5 35.6	9 7.7	14 49.6	16 1.3	16 33.3
10	1 12 58.3	16 20.5	25 37.2	24 14.2	23 8.8	21 33.6	13 44.5	5 43.7	9 14.3	14 52.9	16 2.6	16 35.7
11	1 16 54.9	17 19.8	25 34.0	8♒28.7	24 47.4	21 50.4	14 26.2	5 51.6	9 20.9	14 56.4	16 4.0	16 38.0
12	1 20 51.4	18 19.1	25 30.9	22 44.6	26 25.2	22 5.1	15 7.9	5 59.4	9 27.4	14 59.8	16 5.4	16 40.4
13	1 24 48.0	19 18.5	25 27.7	6♓59.0	28 2.3	22 17.7	15 49.6	6 7.0	9 33.8	15 3.2	16 6.8	16 42.8
14	1 28 44.5	20 17.9	25 24.5	21 8.9	29 38.7	22 28.3	16 31.4	6 14.5	9 40.2	15 6.7	16 8.2	16 45.1
15	1 32 41.1	21 17.3	25 21.3	5♈10.6	1♏14.4	22 36.7	17 13.3	6 21.9	9 46.6	15 10.2	16 9.7	16 47.5
16	1 36 37.6	22 16.7	25 18.1	19 .6	2 49.4	22 42.8	17 55.2	6 29.2	9 52.9	15 13.7	16 11.2	16 49.9
17	1 40 34.2	23 16.2	25 15.0	2♉35.6	4 23.8	22 46.7	18 37.2	6 36.2	9 59.1	15 17.2	16 12.7	16 52.2
18	1 44 30.7	24 15.8	25 11.8	15 53.5	5 57.6	22 48.3	19 19.4	6 43.2	10 5.4	15 20.8	16 14.3	16 54.6
19	1 48 27.3	25 15.3	25 8.6	28 52.7	7 30.7	22 R 47.5	20 1.5	6 50.0	10 11.5	15 24.4	16 15.9	16 57.0
20	1 52 23.8	26 14.9	25 5.4	11♊33.5	9 3.2	22 44.3	20 43.7	6 56.7	10 17.5	15 28.0	16 17.5	16 59.3
21	1 56 20.4	27 14.6	25 2.3	23 57.2	10 35.0	22 38.7	21 25.9	7 3.2	10 23.6	15 31.6	16 19.1	17 1.7
22	2 0 17.0	28 14.2	24 59.1	6♋ 6.6	12 6.3	22 30.7	22 8.3	7 9.6	10 29.5	15 35.2	16 20.7	17 4.0
23	2 4 13.5	29 13.9	24 55.9	18 5.2	13 37.0	22 20.3	22 50.7	7 15.8	10 35.4	15 38.8	16 22.4	17 6.3
24	2 8 10.1	0♏13.7	24 52.7	29 57.7	15 7.0	22 7.5	23 33.1	7 21.8	10 41.2	15 42.4	16 24.1	17 8.7
25	2 12 6.6	1 13.5	24 49.5	11♌48.7	16 36.5	21 52.3	24 15.6	7 27.7	10 47.0	15 46.1	16 25.8	17 11.0
26	2 16 3.2	2 13.3	24 46.4	23 43.4	18 5.4	21 34.8	24 58.2	7 33.4	10 52.7	15 49.7	16 27.5	17 13.3
27	2 19 59.7	3 13.1	24 43.2	5♍46.6	19 33.7	21 15.0	25 40.9	7 39.0	10 58.3	15 53.4	16 29.2	17 15.6
28	2 23 56.3	4 13.0	24 40.0	18 3.0	21 1.4	20 53.0	26 23.6	7 44.4	11 3.9	15 57.1	16 31.0	17 17.9
29	2 27 52.8	5 12.9	24 36.8	0♎36.2	22 28.5	20 28.9	27 6.4	7 49.6	11 9.4	16 .8	16 32.8	17 20.2
30	2 31 49.4	6 12.9	24 33.7	13 28.9	23 54.9	20 2.8	27 49.2	7 54.7	11 14.8	16 4.5	16 34.6	17 22.5
31	2 35 45.9	7 12.9	24 30.5	26 42.2	25 20.7	19 34.7	28 32.1	7 59.6	11 20.2	16 8.2	16 36.5	17 24.7
		LATITUDE										
1	0 37 29.4	0 .0	0 .0	0S23.8	1N16.7	5S39.4	0S 9.3	0N18.2	1N30.9	0N20.7	1N25.0	16N34.6
4	0 49 19.0	0 .0	0 .0	2N59.1	0 59.9	5 55.8	0 11.2	0 18.6	1 31.3	0 20.6	1 24.8	16 34.4
7	1 1 8.7			5 5.4	0 41.3	6 10.7	0 13.1	0 19.1	1 31.7	0 20.6	1 24.7	16 34.4
10	1 12 58.3			4 39.8	0 21.5	6 23.7	0 14.9	0 19.5	1 32.2	0 20.5	1 24.5	16 34.4
13	1 24 48.0			1 46.5	0 1.0	6 34.2	0 16.8	0 20.0	1 32.7	0 20.5	1 24.4	16 34.4
16	1 36 37.6			1S59.6	0S19.7	6 41.6	0 18.6	0 20.5	1 33.2	0 20.4	1 24.3	16 34.6
19	1 48 27.3			4 37.3	0 40.3	6 45.3	0 20.4	0 21.0	1 33.7	0 20.4	1 24.1	16 34.8
22	2 0 17.0			5 8.0	1 .5	6 44.4	0 22.2	0 21.5	1 34.2	0 20.3	1 24.0	16 35.1
25	2 12 6.6			3 39.1	1 19.9	6 38.1	0 24.0	0 22.0	1 34.8	0 20.3	1 23.9	16 35.5
28	2 23 56.3			0 44.9	1 38.2	6 25.7	0 25.7	0 22.5	1 35.4	0 20.3	1 23.8	16 36.0
31	2 35 45.9			2N37.4	1 55.1	6 6.7	0 27.4	0 23.1	1 36.0	0 20.2	1 23.7	16 36.6
		RIGHT ASCENSION										
1	0 37 29.4	6♎51.5	26♍25.1	22♍57.1	7♎38.0	13♏33.6	5♏ 8.3	6♌51.4	10♍26.6	12♏ 2.0	14♐48.4	21♎20.1
2	0 41 25.9	7 45.8	26 22.2	5♎ 1.9	9 13.2	14 4.6	5 48.2	7 .8	10 33.2	12 5.2	14 49.6	21 22.1
3	0 45 22.5	8 40.2	26 19.3	17 23.0	10 47.8	14 34.4	6 28.2	7 10.0	10 39.7	12 8.4	14 50.8	21 24.2
4	0 49 19.0	9 34.7	26 16.3	0♏ 7.2	12 21.7	15 2.6	7 8.3	7 19.1	10 46.2	12 11.6	14 52.0	21 26.3
5	0 53 15.6	10 29.3	26 13.4	13 19.3	13 54.9	15 29.5	7 48.6	7 28.1	10 52.7	12 14.8	14 53.3	21 28.4
6	0 57 12.1	11 23.9	26 10.5	27 1.9	15 27.6	15 54.7	8 29.1	7 36.9	10 59.1	12 18.1	14 54.6	21 30.5
7	1 1 8.7	12 18.6	26 7.6	11♐13.1	16 59.7	16 18.4	9 9.7	7 45.6	11 5.5	12 21.4	14 55.9	21 32.6
8	1 5 5.2	13 13.5	26 4.7	25 46.7	18 31.2	16 40.3	9 50.5	7 54.2	11 11.9	12 24.7	14 57.3	21 34.7
9	1 9 1.8	14 8.4	26 1.7	10♑32.0	20 2.3	17 .5	10 31.4	8 2.6	11 18.2	12 28.0	14 58.7	21 36.9
10	1 12 58.3	15 3.4	25 58.8	25 17.0	21 33.0	17 18.9	11 12.4	8 10.9	11 24.4	12 31.4	15 .1	21 39.0
11	1 16 54.9	15 58.5	25 55.9	9♒50.9	23 3.3	17 35.3	11 53.7	8 19.1	11 30.6	12 34.8	15 1.5	21 41.1
12	1 20 51.4	16 53.8	25 53.0	24 6.9	24 33.2	17 49.7	12 35.0	8 27.1	11 36.8	12 38.2	15 3.0	21 43.2
13	1 24 48.0	17 49.2	25 50.1	8♓ 2.6	26 2.9	18 2.1	13 16.6	8 35.0	11 42.9	12 41.6	15 4.5	21 45.4
14	1 28 44.5	18 44.7	25 47.1	21 40.1	27 32.2	18 12.4	13 58.2	8 42.7	11 49.0	12 45.1	15 6.1	21 47.5
15	1 32 41.1	19 40.3	25 44.2	5♈ 3.5	29 1.3	18 20.5	14 40.1	8 50.3	11 55.0	12 48.5	15 7.6	21 49.7
16	1 36 37.6	20 36.1	25 41.3	18 18.0	0♏30.2	18 26.4	15 22.1	8 57.7	12 1.0	12 52.0	15 9.2	21 51.8
17	1 40 34.2	21 32.0	25 38.4	1♉27.9	1 58.9	18 30.0	16 4.2	9 5.0	12 6.9	12 55.5	15 10.8	21 53.9
18	1 44 30.7	22 28.0	25 35.5	14 35.9	3 27.5	18 31.3	16 46.6	9 12.3	12 12.8	12 59.1	15 12.5	21 56.1
19	1 48 27.3	23 24.2	25 32.6	27 42.0	4 55.9	18 R 30.2	17 29.0	9 19.3	12 18.6	13 2.6	15 14.2	21 58.3
20	1 52 23.8	24 20.6	25 29.6	10♊44.4	6 24.2	18 26.8	18 11.7	9 26.1	12 24.4	13 6.2	15 15.9	22 .4
21	1 56 20.4	25 17.1	25 26.7	23 39.8	7 52.4	18 21.0	18 54.5	9 32.8	12 30.1	13 9.8	15 17.6	22 2.5
22	2 0 17.0	26 13.8	25 23.8	6♋24.3	9 20.5	18 12.8	19 37.4	9 39.3	12 35.7	13 13.4	15 19.3	22 4.7
23	2 4 13.5	27 10.7	25 20.9	18 55.2	10 48.6	18 2.3	20 20.5	9 45.7	12 41.3	13 17.0	15 21.1	22 6.8
24	2 8 10.1	28 7.7	25 18.0	1♌11.2	12 16.6	17 49.4	21 3.8	9 51.9	12 46.8	13 20.6	15 22.9	22 8.9
25	2 12 6.6	29 4.9	25 15.0	13 13.8	13 44.6	17 34.2	21 47.3	9 58.0	12 52.3	13 24.2	15 24.7	22 11.1
26	2 16 3.2	0♏ 2.3	25 12.1	25 6.1	15 12.5	17 16.8	22 30.9	10 3.9	12 57.7	13 27.9	15 26.6	22 13.2
27	2 19 59.7	0 59.9	25 9.2	6♍53.6	16 40.3	16 57.3	23 14.6	10 9.6	13 3.0	13 31.5	15 28.4	22 15.3
28	2 23 56.3	1 57.6	25 6.3	18 43.1	18 8.1	16 35.7	23 58.6	10 15.2	13 8.3	13 35.2	15 30.3	22 17.4
29	2 27 52.8	2 55.6	25 3.4	0♎42.5	19 35.8	16 12.1	24 42.7	10 20.6	13 13.5	13 38.9	15 32.2	22 19.6
30	2 31 49.4	3 53.7	25 .4	13 .1	21 3.3	15 46.7	25 26.9	10 25.8	13 18.7	13 42.6	15 34.2	22 21.7
31	2 35 45.9	4 52.1	24 57.5	25 43.8	22 30.7	15 19.7	26 11.4	10 30.9	13 23.8	13 46.3	15 36.1	22 23.8
		DECLINATION										
1	0 37 29.4	2S57.8	0N 1.6	2N36.8	1S54.3	22S32.6	14S10.5	19N26.6	9N53.5	15S49.6	21S16.9	8N55.5
4	0 49 19.0	4 7.6	0 1.7	9S 5.7	4 13.2	23 14.2	14 51.9	19 20.6	9 46.1	15 52.5	21 17.4	8 52.7
7	1 1 8.7	5 16.9	0 1.8	17 11.1	6 28.7	23 49.9	15 32.5	19 14.9	9 38.9	15 55.5	21 17.9	8 50.0
10	1 12 58.3	6 25.6	0 1.8	16 40.5	8 39.8	24 19.1	16 12.1	19 9.3	9 31.8	15 58.5	21 18.4	8 47.4
13	1 24 48.0	7 33.5	0 1.9	7 17.9	10 45.6	24 41.1	16 50.7	19 4.0	9 24.8	16 1.5	21 19.0	8 44.8
16	1 36 37.6	8 40.4	0 2.0	5N36.0	12 45.6	24 54.9	17 28.2	18 59.0	9 18.1	16 4.6	21 19.6	8 42.4
19	1 48 27.3	9 46.3	0 2.0	15 23.8	14 39.1	24 59.7	18 4.5	18 54.2	9 11.5	16 7.8	21 20.2	8 39.9
22	2 0 17.0	10 50.9	0 2.1	18 10.3	16 25.7	24 54.4	18 39.7	18 49.8	9 5.2	16 11.0	21 20.8	8 37.6
25	2 12 6.6	11 54.0	0 2.2	13 44.2	18 4.6	24 38.1	19 13.4	18 45.6	8 59.1	16 14.2	21 21.4	8 35.4
28	2 23 56.3	12 55.5	0 2.2	4 2.2	19 35.5	24 10.1	19 45.8	18 41.9	8 53.2	16 17.4	21 22.0	8 33.3
31	2 35 45.9	13 55.2	0 2.3	7S51.0	20 57.7	23 30.2	20 16.8	18 38.4	8 47.5	16 20.6	21 22.7	8 31.3

NOVEMBER 1978

LONGITUDE

DAY	EPHEM. SID. TIME	☉	☊	☽	☿	♀	♂	♃	♄	♅	♆	♇
	h m s	° ′	° ′	° ′	° ′	° ′	° ′	° ′	° ′	° ′	° ′	° ′
1	2 39 42.5	8♏12.9	24♍27.3	10♏15.6	26♏45.7	19♏ 5.0	29♏15.1	8♌ 4.4	11♍25.4	16♏11.9	16♐38.3	17♎27.0
2	2 43 39.0	9 13.0	24 24.1	24 6.8	28 10.0	18R33.7	29 58.1	8 8.9	11 30.6	16 15.6	16 40.2	17 29.2
3	2 47 35.6	10 13.1	24 20.9	8♐12.0	29 33.5	18 .9	0♐41.2	8 13.3	11 35.8	16 19.3	16 42.1	17 31.5
4	2 51 32.1	11 13.2	24 17.8	22 26.3	0♐56.2	17 27.0	1 24.4	8 17.5	11 40.8	16 23.1	16 44.0	17 33.7
5	2 55 28.7	12 13.3	24 14.6	6♑44.8	2 18.0	16 52.1	2 7.6	8 21.6	11 45.8	16 26.8	16 45.9	17 35.9
6	2 59 25.3	13 13.5	24 11.4	21 2.9	3 38.7	16 16.4	2 50.9	8 25.4	11 50.7	16 30.5	16 47.9	17 38.1
7	3 3 21.8	14 13.7	24 8.2	5♒17.1	4 58.4	15 40.2	3 34.2	8 29.1	11 55.5	16 34.3	16 49.8	17 40.3
8	3 7 18.4	15 13.9	24 5.1	19 25.0	6 17.0	15 3.8	4 17.6	8 32.7	12 .3	16 38.1	16 51.9	17 42.5
9	3 11 14.9	16 14.2	24 1.9	3♓25.4	7 34.1	14 27.2	5 1.1	8 36.0	12 5.0	16 41.8	16 53.9	17 44.6
10	3 15 11.5	17 14.4	23 58.7	17 17.7	8 49.9	13 50.9	5 44.6	8 39.1	12 9.6	16 45.6	16 55.9	17 46.8
11	3 19 8.0	18 14.7	23 55.5	1♈ 1.3	10 4.0	13 15.1	6 28.2	8 42.1	12 14.1	16 49.3	16 57.9	17 48.9
12	3 23 4.6	19 15.0	23 52.3	14 35.9	11 16.3	12 40.0	7 11.8	8 44.8	12 18.5	16 53.1	16 60.0	17 51.0
13	3 27 1.1	20 15.4	23 49.2	28 .4	12 26.5	12 5.8	7 55.5	8 47.4	12 22.8	16 56.8	17 2.0	17 53.1
14	3 30 57.7	21 15.7	23 46.0	11♉13.7	13 34.5	11 32.8	8 39.2	8 49.8	12 27.0	17 .5	17 4.1	17 55.2
15	3 34 54.3	22 16.1	23 42.8	24 14.5	14 39.9	11 1.2	9 23.0	8 52.0	12 31.2	17 4.3	17 6.2	17 57.2
16	3 38 50.8	23 16.6	23 39.6	7♊ 1.6	15 42.4	10 31.2	10 6.9	8 54.0	12 35.3	17 8.0	17 8.3	17 59.2
17	3 42 47.4	24 17.0	23 36.5	19 34.5	16 41.6	10 3.0	10 50.8	8 55.8	12 39.2	17 11.7	17 10.4	18 1.3
18	3 46 43.9	25 17.5	23 33.3	1♋53.7	17 37.1	9 36.7	11 34.8	8 57.5	12 43.1	17 15.4	17 12.5	18 3.3
19	3 50 40.5	26 18.0	23 30.1	14 .6	18 28.4	9 12.4	12 18.8	8 58.9	12 46.9	17 19.1	17 14.7	18 5.2
20	3 54 37.0	27 18.5	23 26.9	25 57.8	19 15.0	8 50.4	13 2.9	9 .2	12 50.6	17 22.9	17 16.8	18 7.2
21	3 58 33.6	28 19.1	23 23.8	7♌48.8	19 56.2	8 30.6	13 47.1	9 1.2	12 54.2	17 26.6	17 19.0	18 9.1
22	4 2 30.1	29 19.7	23 20.6	19 38.0	20 31.5	8 13.2	14 31.3	9 2.1	12 57.8	17 30.2	17 21.1	18 11.0
23	4 6 26.7	0♐20.3	23 17.4	1♍30.4	21 .0	7 58.2	15 15.5	9 2.7	13 1.2	17 33.9	17 23.3	18 12.9
24	4 10 23.3	1 20.9	23 14.2	13 31.6	21 21.1	7 45.7	15 59.9	9 3.2	13 4.5	17 37.6	17 25.5	18 14.8
25	4 14 19.8	2 21.6	23 11.0	25 46.8	21 33.9	7 35.6	16 44.3	9 3.5	13 7.8	17 41.3	17 27.7	18 16.7
26	4 18 16.4	3 22.3	23 7.9	8♎21.2	21 37.7	7 28.1	17 28.7	9 3.5	13 10.9	17 44.9	17 29.9	18 18.5
27	4 22 12.9	4 23.0	23 4.7	21 18.9	21R31.7	7 23.0	18 13.2	9R 3.4	13 13.9	17 48.5	17 32.1	18 20.3
28	4 26 9.5	5 23.8	23 1.5	4♏42.3	21 15.4	7 20.5	18 57.8	9 3.1	13 16.9	17 52.2	17 34.3	18 22.1
29	4 30 6.0	6 24.6	22 58.3	18 31.9	20 48.2	7 20.4	19 42.4	9 2.6	13 19.7	17 55.8	17 36.6	18 23.9
30	4 34 2.6	7 25.4	22 55.2	2♐45.1	20 10.0	7D22.7	20 27.1	9 1.8	13 22.5	17 59.4	17 38.8	18 25.6

LATITUDE

DAY	EPHEM. SID. TIME	☉	☊	☽	☿	♀	♂	♃	♄	♅	♆	♇
1	2 39 42.5	0 .0	0 .0	3N35.4	2S .3	5S58.9	0S28.0	0N23.3	1N36.2	0N20.2	1N23.6	16N36.8
4	2 51 32.1	0 .0	0 .0	5 7.6	2 14.6	5 30.9	0 29.7	0 23.8	1 36.8	0 20.2	1 23.5	16 37.4
7	3 3 21.8	0 .0	0 .0	3 57.5	2 26.4	4 56.6	0 31.3	0 24.4	1 37.4	0 20.2	1 23.4	16 38.2
10	3 15 11.5	0 .0	0 .0	0 44.6	2 34.9	4 16.9	0 33.0	0 24.9	1 38.1	0 20.1	1 23.3	16 39.0
13	3 27 1.1	0 .0	0 .0	2S44.7	2 39.4	3 33.3	0 34.6	0 25.5	1 38.7	0 20.1	1 23.3	16 39.8
16	3 38 50.8	0 .0	0 .0	4 49.3	2 38.6	2 47.5	0 36.2	0 26.1	1 39.4	0 20.1	1 23.2	16 40.8
19	3 50 40.5	0 .0	0 .0	4 46.8	2 31.2	2 1.1	0 37.7	0 26.7	1 40.1	0 20.1	1 23.1	16 41.8
22	4 2 30.1	0 .0	0 .0	2 53.8	2 15.1	1 15.7	0 39.2	0 27.3	1 40.8	0 20.1	1 23.1	16 42.9
25	4 14 19.8	0 .0	0 .0	0N 7.9	1 48.1	0 32.5	0 40.7	0 27.9	1 41.5	0 20.1	1 23.0	16 44.0
28	4 26 9.5	0 .0	0 .0	3 17.0	1 8.3	0N 7.7	0 42.2	0 28.5	1 42.3	0 20.0	1 22.9	16 45.3

RIGHT ASCENSION

DAY	EPHEM. SID. TIME	☉	☊	☽	☿	♀	♂	♃	♄	♅	♆	♇
1	2 39 42.5	5♏50.6	24♍54.6	8♏59.8	23♏57.9	14♏51.2	26♏55.9	10♌35.7	13♍28.8	13♏50.0	15♐38.1	22♎25.9
2	2 43 39.0	6 49.4	24 51.7	22 51.1	25 24.8	14R21.4	27 40.7	10 40.4	13 33.7	13 53.7	15 40.1	22 28.0
3	2 47 35.6	7 48.3	24 48.8	7♐15.4	26 51.4	13 50.5	28 25.6	10 45.0	13 38.6	13 57.4	15 42.1	22 30.0
4	2 51 32.1	8 47.4	24 45.8	22 4.5	28 17.7	13 18.7	29 10.7	10 49.3	13 43.4	14 1.1	15 44.2	22 32.1
5	2 55 28.7	9 46.8	24 42.9	7♑ 4.7	29 43.4	12 46.2	29 55.9	10 53.5	13 48.1	14 4.8	15 46.2	22 34.2
6	2 59 25.3	10 46.3	24 40.0	22 .5	1♐ 8.6	12 13.2	0♐41.3	10 57.5	13 52.8	14 8.6	15 48.3	22 36.2
7	3 3 21.8	11 46.0	24 37.1	6♒38.8	2 33.0	11 40.1	1 26.8	11 1.3	13 57.4	14 12.3	15 50.4	22 38.3
8	3 7 18.4	12 46.0	24 34.2	20 51.9	3 56.7	11 7.0	2 12.5	11 4.9	14 2.0	14 16.1	15 52.6	22 40.4
9	3 11 14.9	13 46.2	24 31.2	4♓38.2	5 19.3	10 34.2	2 58.4	11 8.3	14 6.4	14 19.8	15 54.7	22 42.4
10	3 15 11.5	14 46.5	24 28.3	18 1.3	6 40.7	10 1.9	3 44.3	11 11.6	14 10.8	14 23.6	15 56.8	22 44.4
11	3 19 8.0	15 47.1	24 25.4	1♈ 7.8	8 .7	9 30.3	4 30.5	11 14.6	14 15.0	14 27.3	15 59.0	22 46.4
12	3 23 4.6	16 47.9	24 22.5	14 5.2	9 19.1	8 59.7	5 16.8	11 17.5	14 19.2	14 31.1	16 1.2	22 48.4
13	3 27 1.1	17 48.9	24 19.6	27 .1	10 35.5	8 30.3	6 3.2	11 20.2	14 23.4	14 34.8	16 3.4	22 50.4
14	3 30 57.7	18 50.0	24 16.6	9♉57.3	11 49.8	8 2.3	6 49.7	11 22.7	14 27.4	14 38.5	16 5.6	22 52.4
15	3 34 54.3	19 51.4	24 13.7	22 58.5	13 1.5	7 35.9	7 36.5	11 25.0	14 31.4	14 42.3	16 7.8	22 54.3
16	3 38 50.8	20 53.1	24 10.8	6♊ 2.3	14 10.1	7 11.1	8 23.3	11 27.1	14 35.3	14 46.0	16 10.1	22 56.3
17	3 42 47.4	21 54.9	24 7.9	19 4.5	15 15.4	6 48.3	9 10.3	11 29.0	14 39.1	14 49.7	16 12.3	22 58.2
18	3 46 43.9	22 56.9	24 5.0	1♋59.4	16 16.8	6 27.4	9 57.5	11 30.7	14 42.8	14 53.5	16 14.6	23 .1
19	3 50 40.5	23 59.2	24 2.0	14 41.4	17 13.6	6 8.6	10 44.7	11 32.2	14 46.4	14 57.2	16 16.9	23 2.0
20	3 54 37.0	25 1.6	23 59.1	27 6.9	18 5.4	5 52.0	11 32.1	11 33.6	14 50.0	15 .9	16 19.2	23 3.9
21	3 58 33.6	26 4.3	23 56.2	9♌14.7	18 51.3	5 37.6	12 19.7	11 34.7	14 53.4	15 4.6	16 21.5	23 5.8
22	4 2 30.1	27 7.2	23 53.3	21 7.1	19 30.8	5 25.6	13 7.4	11 35.6	14 56.8	15 8.3	16 23.8	23 7.6
23	4 6 26.7	28 10.2	23 50.4	2♍48.9	20 2.8	5 15.8	13 55.2	11 36.3	15 .1	15 12.0	16 26.1	23 9.5
24	4 10 23.3	29 13.5	23 47.4	14 27.2	20 26.7	5 8.4	14 43.1	11 36.9	15 3.3	15 15.7	16 28.5	23 11.3
25	4 14 19.8	0♐17.0	23 44.5	26 10.8	20 41.6	5 3.3	15 31.2	11 37.2	15 6.4	15 19.3	16 30.8	23 13.1
26	4 18 16.4	1 20.7	23 41.6	8♎ 9.6	20 46.6	5 .6	16 19.3	11 37.3	15 9.4	15 23.0	16 33.2	23 14.9
27	4 22 12.9	2 24.5	23 38.7	20 33.9	20R41.0	5 .2	17 7.6	11R37.2	15 12.3	15 26.6	16 35.5	23 16.7
28	4 26 9.5	3 28.6	23 35.7	3♏33.1	20 24.1	5D 2.0	17 56.1	11 36.9	15 15.2	15 30.3	16 37.9	23 18.4
29	4 30 6.0	4 32.9	23 32.8	17 14.1	19 55.6	5 6.2	18 44.6	11 36.5	15 17.9	15 33.9	16 40.3	23 20.2
30	4 34 2.6	5 37.3	23 29.9	1♐38.6	19 15.4	5 12.5	19 33.3	11 35.8	15 20.6	15 37.5	16 42.7	23 21.9

DECLINATION

DAY	EPHEM. SID. TIME	☉	☊	☽	☿	♀	♂	♃	♄	♅	♆	♇
1	2 39 42.5	14S14.7	0N 2.3	11S29.1	21S23.0	23S14.3	20S26.7	18N37.4	8N45.7	16S21.7	21S22.9	8N30.7
4	2 51 32.1	15 11.7	0 2.4	18 6.3	22 32.5	22 19.5	20 55.6	18 34.5	8 40.4	16 24.9	21 23.6	8 28.8
7	3 3 21.8	16 6.5	0 2.4	15 6.3	23 31.6	21 15.4	21 22.8	18 32.0	8 35.4	16 28.1	21 24.2	8 27.1
10	3 15 11.5	16 58.8	0 2.5	4 20.0	24 19.4	20 4.7	21 48.3	18 30.0	8 30.6	16 31.4	21 24.9	8 25.4
13	3 27 1.1	17 48.6	0 2.6	8N12.1	24 55.3	18 50.8	22 12.0	18 28.3	8 26.2	16 34.6	21 25.6	8 23.9
16	3 38 50.8	18 35.5	0 2.6	16 43.7	25 18.1	17 37.6	22 33.8	18 27.1	8 22.0	16 37.8	21 26.3	8 22.6
19	3 50 40.5	19 19.5	0 2.7	17 56.8	25 27.0	16 28.5	22 53.6	18 26.4	8 18.2	16 40.9	21 26.9	8 21.3
22	4 2 30.1	20 .4	0 2.8	12 10.6	25 20.8	15 26.4	23 11.5	18 26.2	8 14.7	16 44.0	21 27.6	8 20.2
25	4 14 19.8	20 38.0	0 2.8	1 47.8	24 58.1	14 33.4	23 27.2	18 26.4	8 11.5	16 47.1	21 28.3	8 19.2
28	4 26 9.5	21 12.1	0 2.9	9S59.7	24 17.2	13 50.5	23 40.9	18 27.1	8 8.7	16 50.2	21 28.9	8 18.4

DECEMBER 1978

LONGITUDE

DAY	EPHEM. SID. TIME h m s	☉ ° ′	☊ ° ′	☽ ° ′	☿ ° ′	♀ ° ′	♂ ° ′	♃ ° ′	♄ ° ′	♅ ° ′	♆ ° ′	♇ ° ′
1	4 37 59.1	8♐26.2	22♍52.0	17♐17.0	19♐21.0	7♏27.4	21♐11.8	9♌ .9	13♍25.1	18♏ 3.0	17♐41.1	18♎27.3
2	4 41 55.7	9 27.1	22 48.8	2♑ .1	18 R 21.9	7 34.4	21 56.6	8 R 59.8	13 27.6	18 6.6	17 43.3	18 29.0
3	4 45 52.3	10 27.9	22 45.6	16 46.3	17 13.8	7 43.7	22 41.5	8 58.4	13 30.1	18 10.1	17 45.6	18 30.6
4	4 49 48.8	11 28.8	22 42.5	1♒27.6	15 58.5	7 55.1	23 26.3	8 56.9	13 32.4	18 13.6	17 47.8	18 32.3
5	4 53 45.4	12 29.7	22 39.3	15 58.0	14 38.1	8 8.8	24 11.3	8 55.2	13 34.6	18 17.1	17 50.1	18 33.9
6	4 57 41.9	13 30.6	22 36.1	0♓13.6	13 15.3	8 24.6	24 56.3	8 53.2	13 36.7	18 20.6	17 52.3	18 35.4
7	5 1 38.5	14 31.5	22 32.9	14 12.6	11 53.0	8 42.4	25 41.3	8 51.1	13 38.7	18 24.1	17 54.6	18 37.0
8	5 5 35.0	15 32.4	22 29.7	27 55.4	10 33.8	9 2.1	26 26.4	8 48.8	13 40.6	18 27.5	17 56.8	18 38.5
9	5 9 31.6	16 33.4	22 26.6	11♈23.2	9 20.3	9 23.9	27 11.5	8 46.3	13 42.4	18 30.9	17 59.1	18 40.0
10	5 13 28.2	17 34.3	22 23.4	24 37.4	8 14.7	9 47.4	27 56.7	8 43.6	13 44.1	18 34.3	18 1.4	18 41.4
11	5 17 24.7	18 35.3	22 20.2	7♉39.7	7 18.7	10 12.8	28 42.0	8 40.7	13 45.7	18 37.7	18 3.6	18 42.9
12	5 21 21.3	19 36.2	22 17.0	20 30.9	6 33.1	10 39.9	29 27.2	8 37.6	13 47.1	18 41.1	18 5.9	18 44.3
13	5 25 17.8	20 37.2	22 13.9	3♊11.7	5 58.8	11 8.7	0♑12.6	8 34.4	13 48.5	18 44.4	18 8.2	18 45.6
14	5 29 14.4	21 38.2	22 10.7	15 42.2	5 35.7	11 39.1	0 57.9	8 30.9	13 49.7	18 47.7	18 10.4	18 47.0
15	5 33 10.9	22 39.2	22 7.5	28 2.4	5 23.5	12 11.1	1 43.4	8 27.3	13 50.9	18 51.0	18 12.7	18 48.3
16	5 37 7.5	23 40.2	22 4.3	10♋12.8	5 21.9	12 44.6	2 28.9	8 23.5	13 51.9	18 54.2	18 14.9	18 49.6
17	5 41 4.1	24 41.3	22 1.2	22 14.1	5 D 30.0	13 19.5	3 14.4	8 19.5	13 52.8	18 57.5	18 17.2	18 50.8
18	5 45 .6	25 42.3	21 58.0	4♌ 8.1	5 47.2	13 55.8	3 59.9	8 15.3	13 53.7	19 .7	18 19.4	18 52.1
19	5 48 57.2	26 43.4	21 54.8	15 57.1	6 12.5	14 33.5	4 45.6	8 10.9	13 54.4	19 3.8	18 21.7	18 53.2
20	5 52 53.7	27 44.5	21 51.6	27 44.7	6 45.3	15 12.5	5 31.3	8 6.4	13 55.0	19 7.0	18 24.0	18 54.4
21	5 56 50.3	28 45.6	21 48.4	9♍35.2	7 24.7	15 52.8	6 17.0	8 1.7	13 55.5	19 10.1	18 26.2	18 55.6
22	6 0 46.8	29 46.7	21 45.3	21 33.4	8 9.9	16 34.2	7 2.8	7 56.9	13 55.9	19 13.2	18 28.4	18 56.7
23	6 4 43.4	0♑47.8	21 42.1	3♎44.9	9 .3	17 16.7	7 48.6	7 51.8	13 56.1	19 16.2	18 30.7	18 57.7
24	6 8 40.0	1 48.9	21 38.9	16 15.1	9 55.3	18 .4	8 34.4	7 46.6	13 56.3	19 19.3	18 32.9	18 58.7
25	6 12 36.5	2 50.0	21 35.7	29 9.1	10 54.4	18 45.1	9 20.3	7 41.3	13 56.3	19 22.2	18 35.1	18 59.7
26	6 16 33.1	3 51.2	21 32.6	12♏31.0	11 57.0	19 30.8	10 6.3	7 35.7	13 R 56.2	19 25.2	18 37.3	19 .7
27	6 20 29.6	4 52.3	21 29.4	26 22.6	13 2.8	20 17.5	10 52.3	7 30.1	13 56.0	19 28.1	18 39.5	19 1.6
28	6 24 26.2	5 53.5	21 26.2	10♐43.0	14 11.4	21 5.1	11 38.3	7 24.2	13 55.7	19 31.0	18 41.7	19 2.5
29	6 28 22.7	6 54.7	21 23.0	25 28.1	15 22.4	21 53.6	12 24.4	7 18.3	13 55.3	19 33.8	18 43.9	19 3.4
30	6 32 19.3	7 55.8	21 19.9	10♑30.1	16 35.6	22 43.0	13 10.5	7 12.1	13 54.8	19 36.6	18 46.0	19 4.2
31	6 36 15.9	8 57.0	21 16.7	25 39.1	17 50.7	23 33.2	13 56.6	7 5.9	13 54.2	19 39.4	18 48.2	19 5.0

LATITUDE

DAY	SID. TIME	☉	☊	☽	☿	♀	♂	♃	♄	♅	♆	♇
1	4 37 59.1	0 .0	0 .0	4N59.3	0S15.9	0N44.3	0S43.6	0N29.1	1N43.0	0N20.0	1N22.9	16N46.5
4	4 49 48.8	0 .0	0 .0	3 57.0	0N44.5	1 17.2	0 45.0	0 29.7	1 43.8	0 20.0	1 22.9	16 47.9
7	5 1 38.5	0 .0	0 .0	0 46.5	1 41.8	1 46.2	0 46.4	0 30.3	1 44.6	0 20.0	1 22.8	16 49.3
10	5 13 28.2	0 .0	0 .0	2S38.6	2 24.4	2 11.6	0 47.7	0 30.9	1 45.3	0 20.0	1 22.8	16 50.7
13	5 25 17.8	0 .0	0 .0	4 43.0	2 46.8	2 33.5	0 49.0	0 31.5	1 46.1	0 20.0	1 22.8	16 52.2
16	5 37 7.5	0 .0	0 .0	4 44.5	2 51.0	2 52.0	0 50.2	0 32.1	1 46.9	0 20.0	1 22.8	16 53.7
19	5 48 57.2	0 .0	0 .0	2 54.8	2 42.2	3 7.4	0 51.4	0 32.7	1 47.7	0 20.0	1 22.8	16 55.3
22	6 0 46.8	0 .0	0 .0	0N 2.0	2 25.2	3 20.0	0 52.6	0 33.3	1 48.5	0 20.0	1 22.8	16 56.9
25	6 12 36.5	0 .0	0 .0	3 6.8	2 3.5	3 30.0	0 53.7	0 33.9	1 49.3	0 20.1	1 22.8	16 58.6
28	6 24 26.2	0 .0	0 .0	4 57.1	1 39.4	3 37.6	0 54.7	0 34.5	1 50.0	0 20.1	1 22.8	17 .2
31	6 36 15.9	0 .0	0 .0	4 6.4	1 14.3	3 42.9	0 55.8	0 35.0	1 50.8	0 20.1	1 22.8	17 1.9

RIGHT ASCENSION

DAY	SID. TIME	☉	☊	☽	☿	♀	♂	♃	♄	♅	♆	♇
1	4 37 59.1	6♐41.9	23♍27.0	16♐40.7	18♐23.7	5♏21.0	20♐22.0	11♌34.9	15♍23.1	15♏41.1	16♐45.1	23♎23.6
2	4 41 55.7	7 46.6	23 24.1	2♑ 6.1	17 R 21.4	5 31.6	21 10.9	11 R 33.8	15 25.6	15 44.7	16 47.5	23 25.3
3	4 45 52.3	8 51.5	23 21.1	17 35.0	16 9.9	5 44.2	21 59.8	11 32.5	15 27.9	15 48.3	16 49.9	23 26.9
4	4 49 48.8	9 56.5	23 18.2	2♒47.6	14 51.2	5 58.9	22 48.8	11 31.0	15 30.2	15 51.8	16 52.3	23 28.5
5	4 53 45.4	11 1.7	23 15.3	17 29.8	13 27.5	6 15.5	23 38.0	11 29.3	15 32.4	15 55.3	16 54.7	23 30.1
6	4 57 41.9	12 7.1	23 12.4	1♓36.4	12 1.8	6 34.0	24 27.2	11 27.4	15 34.4	15 58.8	16 57.1	23 31.7
7	5 1 38.5	13 12.5	23 9.4	15 9.4	10 36.9	6 54.3	25 16.5	11 25.3	15 36.4	16 2.3	16 59.6	23 33.3
8	5 5 35.0	14 18.1	23 6.5	28 16.0	9 15.7	7 16.4	26 5.9	11 23.0	15 38.3	16 5.8	17 2.0	23 34.8
9	5 9 31.6	15 23.8	23 3.6	11♈ 5.5	8 .7	7 40.2	26 55.3	11 20.5	15 40.0	16 9.2	17 4.4	23 36.3
10	5 13 28.2	16 29.6	23 .7	23 47.1	6 53.9	8 5.8	27 44.8	11 17.8	15 41.7	16 12.6	17 6.8	23 37.8
11	5 17 24.7	17 35.5	22 57.8	6♉28.3	5 57.0	8 32.9	28 34.4	11 14.9	15 43.3	16 16.0	17 9.2	23 39.3
12	5 21 21.3	18 41.5	22 54.8	19 14.1	5 10.9	9 1.6	29 24.1	11 11.9	15 44.7	16 19.4	17 11.7	23 40.8
13	5 25 17.8	19 47.6	22 51.9	2♊ 6.0	4 36.1	9 31.8	0♑13.8	11 8.6	15 46.1	16 22.8	17 14.1	23 42.2
14	5 29 14.4	20 53.8	22 49.0	15 1.8	4 12.7	10 3.5	1 3.6	11 5.1	15 47.4	16 26.1	17 16.5	23 43.6
15	5 33 10.9	22 .1	22 46.1	27 56.5	4 .4	10 36.7	1 53.4	11 1.5	15 48.5	16 29.4	17 18.9	23 44.9
16	5 37 7.5	23 6.4	22 43.1	10♋43.6	3 58.6	11 11.2	2 43.3	10 57.6	15 49.6	16 32.6	17 21.3	23 46.3
17	5 41 4.1	24 12.8	22 40.2	23 17.2	4 D 6.7	11 47.0	3 33.2	10 53.6	15 50.6	16 35.9	17 23.8	23 47.6
18	5 45 .6	25 19.2	22 37.3	5♌33.3	4 24.0	12 24.2	4 23.1	10 49.4	15 51.4	16 39.1	17 26.2	23 48.9
19	5 48 57.2	26 25.7	22 34.4	17 31.2	4 49.6	13 2.6	5 13.1	10 45.0	15 52.2	16 42.3	17 28.6	23 50.2
20	5 52 53.7	27 32.3	22 31.4	29 13.6	5 22.8	13 42.3	6 3.2	10 40.5	15 52.9	16 45.5	17 31.0	23 51.4
21	5 56 50.3	28 38.9	22 28.5	10♍45.7	6 2.8	14 23.0	6 53.3	10 35.8	15 53.4	16 48.6	17 33.4	23 52.7
22	6 0 46.8	29 45.5	22 25.6	22 15.5	6 48.9	15 4.9	7 43.4	10 30.8	15 53.9	16 51.7	17 35.8	23 53.8
23	6 4 43.4	0♑52.1	22 22.7	3♎52.6	7 40.6	15 48.0	8 33.5	10 25.8	15 54.2	16 54.8	17 38.2	23 55.0
24	6 8 40.0	1 58.7	22 19.7	15 48.0	8 37.2	16 32.0	9 23.7	10 20.5	15 54.5	16 57.8	17 40.6	23 56.1
25	6 12 36.5	3 5.3	22 16.8	28 12.9	9 38.2	17 17.1	10 13.8	10 15.1	15 54.6	17 .8	17 42.9	23 57.2
26	6 16 33.1	4 11.9	22 13.9	11♏17.8	10 43.1	18 3.2	11 4.0	10 9.5	15 54.6	17 3.8	17 45.3	23 58.3
27	6 20 29.6	5 18.5	22 11.0	25 10.2	11 51.6	18 50.3	11 54.2	10 3.7	15 54.6	17 6.8	17 47.6	23 59.3
28	6 24 26.2	6 25.0	22 8.1	9♐51.6	13 3.3	19 38.3	12 44.4	9 57.8	15 R 54.4	17 9.7	17 50.0	24 .4
29	6 28 22.7	7 31.5	22 5.1	25 14.6	14 17.9	20 27.2	13 34.5	9 51.8	15 54.1	17 12.5	17 52.3	24 1.3
30	6 32 19.3	8 38.0	22 2.2	11♑ 1.8	15 35.1	21 16.9	14 24.7	9 45.6	15 53.7	17 15.4	17 54.7	24 2.3
31	6 36 15.9	9 44.4	21 59.3	26 50.2	16 54.6	22 7.6	15 14.9	9 39.2	15 53.2	17 18.1	17 57.0	24 3.2

DECLINATION

DAY	SID. TIME	☉	☊	☽	☿	♀	♂	♃	♄	♅	♆	♇
1	4 37 59.1	21S42.7	0N 3.0	17S51.9	23S16.5	13S18.1	23S52.3	18N28.2	8N 6.2	16S53.2	21S29.6	8N17.6
4	4 49 48.8	22 9.5	0 3.0	15 58.7	21 57.8	12 55.9	24 1.5	18 29.9	8 4.1	16 56.2	21 30.2	8 17.0
7	5 1 38.5	22 32.5	0 3.1	5 29.9	20 31.9	12 43.5	24 8.5	18 32.0	8 2.4	16 59.1	21 30.9	8 16.6
10	5 13 28.2	22 51.5	0 3.2	7N 4.8	19 18.3	12 40.0	24 13.1	18 34.5	8 1.0	17 1.9	21 31.5	8 16.3
13	5 25 17.8	23 6.4	0 3.2	16 9.8	18 34.0	12 44.4	24 15.3	18 37.5	8 .0	17 4.7	21 32.1	8 16.2
16	5 37 7.5	23 17.3	0 3.3	18 19.0	18 23.5	12 55.8	24 15.2	18 41.0	7 59.4	17 7.4	21 32.7	8 16.1
19	5 48 57.2	23 23.9	0 3.4	13 16.3	18 40.9	13 13.2	24 12.6	18 44.8	7 59.2	17 10.0	21 33.3	8 16.3
22	6 0 46.8	23 26.3	0 3.4	3 22.7	19 16.7	13 35.6	24 7.6	18 49.0	7 59.4	17 12.5	21 33.9	8 16.5
25	6 12 36.5	23 24.5	0 3.5	8S15.5	20 2.5	14 2.0	24 .2	18 53.6	7 59.9	17 15.0	21 34.4	8 16.9
28	6 24 26.2	23 18.5	0 3.6	17 9.0	20 51.5	14 31.7	23 50.3	18 58.5	8 .9	17 17.3	21 35.0	8 17.5
31	6 36 15.9	23 8.2	0 3.6	16 58.4	21 39.0	15 3.7	23 38.0	19 3.7	8 2.2	17 19.6	21 35.5	8 18.1

JANUARY 1979

LONGITUDE

DAY	EPHEM. SID. TIME h m s	☉ ° ′	☊ ° ′	☽ ° ′	☿ ° ′	♀ ° ′	♂ ° ′	♃ ° ′	♄ ° ′	♅ ° ′	♆ ° ′	♇ ° ′
1	6 40 12.4	9♑58.2	21♍13.5	10♒44.7	19♐ 7.5	24♏24.1	14♑42.8	6♌59.5	13♍53.4	19♏42.1	18♐50.3	19♎ 5.7
2	6 44 9.0	10 59.4	21 10.3	25 37.6	20 25.8	25 15.8	15 29.1	6 R 53.0	13 R 52.6	19 44.8	18 52.5	19 6.5
3	6 48 5.5	12 .5	21 7.1	10♓11.4	21 45.5	26 8.3	16 15.3	6 46.3	13 51.6	19 47.5	18 54.6	19 7.1
4	6 52 2.1	13 1.7	21 4.0	24 22.6	23 6.4	27 1.4	17 1.7	6 39.6	13 50.5	19 50.1	18 56.7	19 7.8
5	6 55 58.6	14 2.9	21 .8	8♈10.5	24 28.4	27 55.2	17 48.0	6 32.7	13 49.4	19 52.6	18 58.8	19 8.4
6	6 59 55.2	15 4.0	20 57.6	21 36.4	25 51.4	28 49.7	18 34.4	6 25.7	13 48.1	19 55.2	19 .9	19 9.0
7	7 3 51.7	16 5.2	20 54.4	4♉42.8	27 15.4	29 44.8	19 20.8	6 18.6	13 46.7	19 57.7	19 3.0	19 9.5
8	7 7 48.3	17 6.3	20 51.3	17 32.6	28 40.1	0♐40.5	20 7.2	6 11.4	13 45.2	20 .1	19 5.0	19 10.0
9	7 11 44.9	18 7.4	20 48.1	0♊ 8.6	0♑ 5.7	1 36.7	20 53.7	6 4.2	13 43.6	20 2.5	19 7.1	19 10.5
10	7 15 41.4	19 8.6	20 44.9	12 33.3	1 32.1	2 33.6	21 40.3	5 56.8	13 41.9	20 4.9	19 9.1	19 11.0
11	7 19 38.0	20 9.7	20 41.7	24 48.5	2 59.1	3 31.0	22 26.8	5 49.4	13 40.1	20 7.2	19 11.1	19 11.4
12	7 23 34.5	21 10.9	20 38.6	6♋55.7	4 26.7	4 28.9	23 13.4	5 41.8	13 38.2	20 9.5	19 13.1	19 11.8
13	7 27 31.1	22 12.0	20 35.4	18 56.1	5 55.0	5 27.2	24 .0	5 34.2	13 36.2	20 11.7	19 15.1	19 12.1
14	7 31 27.6	23 13.1	20 32.2	0♌51.0	7 23.9	6 26.1	24 46.7	5 26.6	13 34.1	20 13.9	19 17.1	19 12.4
15	7 35 24.2	24 14.2	20 29.0	12 41.7	8 53.3	7 25.5	25 33.3	5 18.8	13 31.8	20 16.1	19 19.0	19 12.6
16	7 39 20.8	25 15.3	20 25.8	24 30.1	10 23.4	8 25.3	26 20.0	5 11.0	13 29.5	20 18.2	19 20.9	19 12.9
17	7 43 17.3	26 16.3	20 22.7	6♍18.6	11 54.0	9 25.5	27 6.8	5 3.2	13 27.1	20 20.2	19 22.8	19 13.0
18	7 47 13.9	27 17.4	20 19.5	18 10.4	13 25.2	10 26.2	27 53.5	4 55.3	13 24.6	20 22.2	19 24.7	19 13.2
19	7 51 10.4	28 18.5	20 16.3	0♎ 9.4	14 56.9	11 27.3	28 40.3	4 47.4	13 22.0	20 24.2	19 26.6	19 13.3
20	7 55 7.0	29 19.6	20 13.1	12 20.1	16 29.2	12 28.7	29 27.2	4 39.4	13 19.3	20 26.1	19 28.4	19 13.4
21	7 59 3.5	0♒20.6	20 10.0	24 47.2	18 2.1	13 30.5	0♒14.0	4 31.4	13 16.5	20 27.9	19 30.3	19 13.4
22	8 3 .1	1 21.7	20 6.8	7♏35.6	19 35.5	14 32.7	1 .9	4 23.4	13 13.6	20 29.7	19 32.1	19 13.4
23	8 6 56.6	2 22.7	20 3.6	20 49.8	21 9.5	15 35.3	1 47.8	4 15.4	13 10.7	20 31.5	19 33.9	19 13.4
24	8 10 53.2	3 23.8	20 .4	4♐32.6	22 44.1	16 38.2	2 34.7	4 7.3	13 7.6	20 33.2	19 35.6	19 R 13.3
25	8 14 49.8	4 24.8	19 57.3	18 45.0	24 19.3	17 41.4	3 21.7	3 59.3	13 4.5	20 34.9	19 37.4	19 13.2
26	8 18 46.3	5 25.8	19 54.1	3♑24.8	25 55.1	18 44.9	4 8.7	3 51.2	13 1.2	20 36.5	19 39.1	19 13.1
27	8 22 42.9	6 26.9	19 50.9	18 26.5	27 31.5	19 48.7	4 55.7	3 43.2	12 57.9	20 38.0	19 40.8	19 12.9
28	8 26 39.4	7 27.9	19 47.7	3♒41.2	29 8.6	20 52.8	5 42.7	3 35.2	12 54.5	20 39.5	19 42.5	19 12.7
29	8 30 36.0	8 28.8	19 44.5	18 58.4	0♒46.3	21 57.2	6 29.8	3 27.2	12 51.1	20 41.0	19 44.1	19 12.5
30	8 34 32.5	9 29.8	19 41.4	4♓ 7.3	2 24.6	23 1.8	7 16.9	3 19.2	12 47.5	20 42.4	19 45.7	19 12.2
31	8 38 29.1	10 30.8	19 38.2	18 59.1	4 3.7	24 6.8	8 4.0	3 11.3	12 43.9	20 43.8	19 47.4	19 11.9

LATITUDE

DAY	EPHEM. SID. TIME	☉	☊	☽	☿	♀	♂	♃	♄	♅	♆	♇
1	6 40 12.4	0 .0	0 .0	3N12.2	1N 5.9	3N44.2	0S56.1	0N35.2	1N51.1	0N20.1	1N22.9	17N 2.5
4	6 52 2.1	0 .0	0 .0	0S23.6	0 40.8	3 46.8	0 57.1	0 35.7	1 51.9	0 20.1	1 22.9	17 4.2
7	7 3 51.7	0 .0	0 .0	3 34.9	0 16.5	3 47.6	0 58.0	0 36.3	1 52.6	0 20.1	1 22.9	17 6.0
10	7 15 41.4	0 .0	0 .0	5 1.6	0S 6.7	3 46.7	0 58.9	0 36.8	1 53.4	0 20.1	1 23.0	17 7.7
13	7 27 31.1	0 .0	0 .0	4 24.1	0 28.5	3 44.3	0 59.7	0 37.2	1 54.1	0 20.2	1 23.0	17 9.5
16	7 39 20.8	0 .0	0 .0	2 5.6	0 48.6	3 40.4	1 .4	0 37.7	1 54.8	0 20.2	1 23.1	17 11.3
19	7 51 10.4	0 .0	0 .0	1N 2.4	1 7.0	3 35.3	1 1.1	0 38.1	1 55.5	0 20.2	1 23.2	17 13.0
22	8 3 .1	0 .0	0 .0	3 54.0	1 23.2	3 29.1	1 1.8	0 38.5	1 56.2	0 20.2	1 23.2	17 14.8
25	8 14 49.8	0 .0	0 .0	5 9.3	1 37.2	3 21.7	1 2.4	0 38.9	1 56.9	0 20.3	1 23.3	17 16.5
28	8 26 39.4	0 .0	0 .0	3 37.2	1 48.6	3 13.5	1 2.9	0 39.3	1 57.5	0 20.3	1 23.4	17 18.2
31	8 38 29.1	0 .0	0 .0	0S 5.7	1 57.3	3 4.4	1 3.4	0 39.6	1 58.1	0 20.3	1 23.5	17 19.9

RIGHT ASCENSION

DAY	EPHEM. SID. TIME	☉	☊	☽	☿	♀	♂	♃	♄	♅	♆	♇
1	6 40 12.4	10♑50.8	21♍56.4	12♒17.8	18♐16.2	22♏59.0	16♑ 5.0	9♌32.7	15♍52.6	17♏20.9	17♐59.3	24♎ 4.1
2	6 44 9.0	11 57.0	21 53.4	27 10.3	19 39.7	23 51.3	16 55.2	9 R 26.1	15 R 51.9	17 23.6	18 1.6	24 5.0
3	6 48 5.5	13 3.2	21 50.5	11♓23.1	21 5.0	24 44.3	17 45.3	9 19.3	15 51.2	17 26.3	18 3.8	24 5.8
4	6 52 2.1	14 9.3	21 47.6	24 59.7	22 31.9	25 38.1	18 35.4	9 12.5	15 50.3	17 28.9	18 6.1	24 6.6
5	6 55 58.6	15 15.3	21 44.6	8♈ 8.2	24 .3	26 32.6	19 25.4	9 5.5	15 49.3	17 31.5	18 8.3	24 7.4
6	6 59 55.2	16 21.1	21 41.7	20 58.4	25 30.0	27 27.9	20 15.4	8 58.4	15 48.2	17 34.1	18 10.6	24 8.1
7	7 3 51.7	17 26.9	21 38.8	3♉39.6	27 1.0	28 23.9	21 5.4	8 51.1	15 47.0	17 36.6	18 12.8	24 8.8
8	7 7 48.3	18 32.5	21 35.9	16 18.9	28 33.1	29 20.5	21 55.4	8 43.8	15 45.7	17 39.1	18 15.0	24 9.5
9	7 11 44.9	19 38.0	21 32.9	29 .8	0♑ 6.2	0♐17.9	22 45.3	8 36.4	15 44.3	17 41.5	18 17.2	24 10.1
10	7 15 41.4	20 43.5	21 30.0	11♊46.3	1 40.4	1 16.0	23 35.2	8 28.9	15 42.8	17 43.9	18 19.4	24 10.8
11	7 19 38.0	21 48.7	21 27.1	24 33.1	3 15.5	2 14.6	24 24.9	8 21.3	15 41.2	17 46.3	18 21.6	24 11.4
12	7 23 34.5	22 53.8	21 24.2	7♋16.8	4 51.4	3 14.0	25 14.7	8 13.6	15 39.5	17 48.6	18 23.7	24 11.9
13	7 27 31.1	23 58.7	21 21.2	19 51.5	6 28.0	4 13.9	26 4.4	8 5.8	15 37.8	17 50.8	18 25.8	24 12.5
14	7 31 27.6	25 3.5	21 18.3	2♌12.6	8 5.4	5 14.5	26 54.0	7 57.9	15 35.9	17 53.0	18 27.9	24 12.9
15	7 35 24.2	26 8.1	21 15.4	14 17.2	9 43.5	6 15.6	27 43.6	7 50.0	15 33.9	17 55.2	18 30.0	24 13.4
16	7 39 20.8	27 12.6	21 12.5	26 5.3	11 22.2	7 17.3	28 33.1	7 42.0	15 31.8	17 57.3	18 32.1	24 13.8
17	7 43 17.3	28 16.9	21 9.5	7♍40.0	13 1.5	8 19.6	29 22.5	7 34.0	15 29.7	17 59.4	18 34.1	24 14.2
18	7 47 13.9	29 21.0	21 6.6	19 6.8	14 41.3	9 22.5	0♒11.9	7 25.9	15 27.4	18 1.4	18 36.2	24 14.6
19	7 51 10.4	0♒25.0	21 3.7	0♎33.5	16 21.6	10 25.9	1 1.2	7 17.8	15 25.1	18 3.4	18 38.2	24 14.9
20	7 55 7.0	1 28.7	21 .7	12 9.4	18 2.4	11 29.8	1 50.4	7 9.6	15 22.7	18 5.3	18 40.1	24 15.2
21	7 59 3.5	2 32.3	20 57.8	24 5.2	19 43.6	12 34.3	2 39.5	7 1.4	15 20.2	18 7.2	18 42.1	24 15.4
22	8 3 .1	3 35.8	20 54.9	6♏31.4	21 25.2	13 39.2	3 28.6	6 53.1	15 17.6	18 9.0	18 44.0	24 15.7
23	8 6 56.6	4 39.0	20 52.0	19 38.1	23 7.2	14 44.7	4 17.6	6 44.9	15 14.9	18 10.8	18 46.0	24 15.9
24	8 10 53.2	5 42.0	20 49.0	3♐31.8	24 49.5	15 50.6	5 6.5	6 36.6	15 12.1	18 12.6	18 47.9	24 16.0
25	8 14 49.8	6 44.9	20 46.1	18 13.4	26 32.1	16 56.9	5 55.3	6 28.3	15 9.3	18 14.2	18 49.7	24 16.2
26	8 18 46.3	7 47.5	20 43.2	3♑35.1	28 15.0	18 3.7	6 44.1	6 20.1	15 6.3	18 15.9	18 51.6	24 16.3
27	8 22 42.9	8 50.0	20 40.2	19 20.3	29 58.1	19 11.0	7 32.7	6 11.8	15 3.3	18 17.4	18 53.4	24 16.3
28	8 26 39.4	9 52.2	20 37.3	5♒ 7.2	1♒41.5	20 18.6	8 21.3	6 3.5	15 .3	18 19.0	18 55.2	24 16.4
29	8 30 36.0	10 54.3	20 34.4	20 35.8	3 25.1	21 26.7	9 9.7	5 55.3	14 57.1	18 20.4	18 57.0	24 16.4
30	8 34 32.5	11 56.1	20 31.4	5♓33.0	5 8.8	22 35.1	9 58.1	5 47.0	14 53.9	18 21.9	18 58.7	24 R 16.3
31	8 38 29.1	12 57.8	20 28.5	19 54.7	6 52.8	23 44.0	10 46.4	5 38.9	14 50.6	18 23.3	19 .5	24 16.3

DECLINATION

DAY	EPHEM. SID. TIME	☉	☊	☽	☿	♀	♂	♃	♄	♅	♆	♇
1	6 40 12.4	23S 3.9	0N 3.6	14S27.3	21S54.0	15S14.8	23S33.4	19N 5.5	8N 2.7	17S20.3	21S35.6	8N18.4
4	6 52 2.1	22 48.1	0 3.7	2 35.7	22 34.8	15 48.7	23 17.9	19 11.1	8 4.5	17 22.4	21 36.1	8 19.2
7	7 3 51.7	22 28.2	0 3.8	9N42.9	23 8.1	16 23.3	23 .0	19 16.8	8 6.7	17 24.4	21 36.6	8 20.2
10	7 15 41.4	22 4.3	0 3.8	17 18.9	23 32.5	16 58.0	22 39.8	19 22.7	8 9.3	17 26.4	21 37.1	8 21.3
13	7 27 31.1	21 36.6	0 3.9	17 44.5	23 46.9	17 32.0	22 17.3	19 28.8	8 12.2	17 28.2	21 37.5	8 22.6
16	7 39 20.8	21 5.1	0 4.0	11 22.8	23 50.4	18 4.8	21 52.5	19 34.9	8 15.4	17 29.9	21 37.9	8 23.9
19	7 51 10.4	20 30.0	0 4.0	0 53.5	23 42.6	18 36.0	21 25.4	19 41.0	8 18.9	17 31.4	21 38.3	8 25.4
22	8 3 .1	19 51.4	0 4.1	10S21.2	23 22.9	19 4.9	20 56.2	19 47.2	8 22.8	17 32.9	21 38.6	8 26.9
25	8 14 49.8	19 9.4	0 4.2	17 49.5	22 50.8	19 31.3	20 24.9	19 53.3	8 26.9	17 34.2	21 39.0	8 28.6
28	8 26 39.4	18 24.3	0 4.2	15 48.4	22 6.1	19 54.5	19 51.6	19 59.3	8 31.3	17 35.4	21 39.3	8 30.4
31	8 38 29.1	17 36.1	0 4.3	4 26.7	21 8.4	20 14.3	19 16.3	20 5.2	8 35.9	17 36.5	21 39.6	8 32.2

FEBRUARY 1979

LONGITUDE

DAY	EPHEM. SID. TIME h m s	☉ ° ′	☊ ° ′	☽ ° ′	☿ ° ′	♀ ° ′	♂ ° ′	♃ ° ′	♄ ° ′	♅ ° ′	♆ ° ′	♇ ° ′
1	8 42 25.6	11 ♒ 31.7	19 ♍ 35.0	3 ♈ 27.5	5 ♒ 43.4	25 ♐ 11.9	8 ♒ 51.1	3 ♌ 3.4	12 ♍ 40.2	20 ♏ 45.1	19 ♐ 49.0	19 ♎ 11.6
2	8 46 22.2	12 32.7	19 31.8	17 29.5	7 23.8	26 17.3	9 38.3	2 R 55.5	12 R 36.4	20 46.3	19 50.5	19 R 11.2
3	8 50 18.8	13 33.5	19 28.7	1 ♉ 4.9	9 5.0	27 22.9	10 25.4	2 47.7	12 32.6	20 47.5	19 52.0	19 10.8
4	8 54 15.3	14 34.4	19 25.5	14 15.5	10 46.8	28 28.7	11 12.6	2 40.0	12 28.7	20 48.7	19 53.5	19 10.3
5	8 58 11.9	15 35.3	19 22.3	27 4.5	12 29.4	29 34.7	11 59.8	2 32.3	12 24.7	20 49.7	19 55.0	19 9.8
6	9 2 8.4	16 36.1	19 19.1	9 ♊ 35.4	14 12.8	0 ♑ 41.0	12 47.0	2 24.7	12 20.7	20 50.8	19 56.4	19 9.3
7	9 6 5.0	17 36.9	19 15.9	21 51.9	15 56.9	1 47.4	13 34.2	2 17.2	12 16.6	20 51.8	19 57.9	19 8.8
8	9 10 1.5	18 37.6	19 12.8	3 ♋ 57.7	17 41.7	2 54.1	14 21.4	2 9.7	12 12.4	20 52.7	19 59.3	19 8.2
9	9 13 58.1	19 38.4	19 9.6	15 55.7	19 27.3	4 .9	15 8.6	2 2.3	12 8.2	20 53.5	20 .6	19 7.6
10	9 17 54.6	20 39.1	19 6.4	27 48.6	21 13.7	5 7.9	15 55.8	1 55.1	12 4.0	20 54.4	20 2.0	19 6.9
11	9 21 51.2	21 39.8	19 3.2	9 ♌ 38.7	23 .8	6 15.1	16 43.1	1 47.9	11 59.6	20 55.1	20 3.3	19 6.2
12	9 25 47.7	22 40.5	19 .1	21 27.9	24 48.7	7 22.5	17 30.4	1 40.8	11 55.3	20 55.8	20 4.5	19 5.5
13	9 29 44.3	23 41.1	18 56.9	3 ♍ 18.3	26 37.2	8 30.1	18 17.6	1 33.8	11 50.9	20 56.5	20 5.8	19 4.8
14	9 33 40.9	24 41.8	18 53.7	15 11.7	28 26.4	9 37.8	19 4.9	1 26.9	11 46.4	20 57.1	20 7.0	19 4.0
15	9 37 37.4	25 42.4	18 50.5	27 10.4	0 ♓ 16.2	10 45.7	19 52.2	1 20.2	11 41.9	20 57.6	20 8.2	19 3.2
16	9 41 34.0	26 42.9	18 47.3	9 ♎ 16.9	2 6.5	11 53.7	20 39.5	1 13.5	11 37.4	20 58.1	20 9.4	19 2.3
17	9 45 30.5	27 43.5	18 44.2	21 34.2	3 57.3	13 1.9	21 26.8	1 7.0	11 32.8	20 58.5	20 10.5	19 1.5
18	9 49 27.1	28 44.1	18 41.0	4 ♏ 5.6	5 48.5	14 10.2	22 14.1	1 .6	11 28.2	20 58.9	20 11.6	19 .6
19	9 53 23.6	29 44.6	18 37.8	16 54.6	7 39.8	15 18.7	23 1.5	0 54.3	11 23.6	20 59.2	20 12.7	18 59.7
20	9 57 20.2	0 ♓ 45.1	18 34.6	0 ♐ 4.6	9 31.3	16 27.3	23 48.8	0 48.2	11 18.9	20 59.5	20 13.7	18 58.7
21	10 1 16.7	1 45.6	18 31.5	13 38.3	11 22.7	17 36.1	24 36.2	0 42.3	11 14.2	20 59.8	20 14.8	18 57.8
22	10 5 13.3	2 46.1	18 28.3	27 37.0	13 13.7	18 45.0	25 23.5	0 36.4	11 9.5	20 59.9	20 15.7	18 56.8
23	10 9 9.8	3 46.5	18 25.1	12 ♑ .4	15 4.1	19 54.0	26 10.9	0 30.7	11 4.8	21 .0	20 16.7	18 55.7
24	10 13 6.4	4 46.9	18 21.9	26 45.4	16 53.7	21 3.2	26 58.2	0 25.2	11 .0	21 .1	20 17.6	18 54.7
25	10 17 2.9	5 47.3	18 18.7	11 ♒ 46.2	18 42.0	22 12.4	27 45.6	0 19.8	10 55.2	21 R .0	20 18.5	18 53.6
26	10 20 59.5	6 47.7	18 15.6	26 54.9	20 28.8	23 21.7	28 32.9	0 14.5	10 50.4	20 60.0	20 19.3	18 52.4
27	10 24 56.0	7 48.0	18 12.4	12 ♓ 2.1	22 13.5	24 31.2	29 20.3	0 9.4	10 45.6	20 59.9	20 20.1	18 51.3
28	10 28 52.6	8 48.3	18 9.2	26 58.6	23 55.7	25 40.7	0 ♓ 7.7	0 4.5	10 40.8	20 59.7	20 20.9	18 50.1

LATITUDE

DAY	EPHEM. SID. TIME h m s	☉	☊	☽	☿	♀	♂	♃	♄	♅	♆	♇
1	8 42 25.6	0 .0	0 .0	1 S 23.7	1 S 59.5	3 N 1.2	1 S 3.6	0 N 39.7	1 N 58.3	0 N 20.3	1 N 23.5	17 N 20.5
4	8 54 15.3	0 .0	0 .0	4 20.4	2 4.0	2 51.1	1 4.0	0 40.0	1 58.8	0 20.4	1 23.6	17 22.1
7	9 6 5.0	0 .0	0 .0	5 12.1	2 4.9	2 40.4	1 4.3	0 40.3	1 59.4	0 20.4	1 23.7	17 23.7
10	9 17 54.6	0 .0	0 .0	3 59.8	2 1.9	2 29.3	1 4.6	0 40.5	1 59.9	0 20.4	1 23.8	17 25.3
13	9 29 44.3	0 .0	0 .0	1 17.4	1 54.5	2 17.6	1 4.8	0 40.7	2 .3	0 20.4	1 23.9	17 26.9
16	9 41 34.0	0 .0	0 .0	1 N 57.6	1 42.1	2 5.7	1 5.0	0 40.9	2 .8	0 20.5	1 24.0	17 28.3
19	9 53 23.6	0 .0	0 .0	4 32.7	1 24.5	1 53.4	1 5.1	0 41.1	2 1.1	0 20.5	1 24.1	17 29.8
22	10 5 13.3	0 .0	0 .0	5 11.9	1 1.1	1 41.0	1 5.1	0 41.2	2 1.5	0 20.5	1 24.2	17 31.1
25	10 17 2.9	0 .0	0 .0	3 5.4	0 31.9	1 28.5	1 5.1	0 41.3	2 1.8	0 20.6	1 24.4	17 32.4
28	10 28 52.6	0 .0	0 .0	0 S 52.7	0 N 2.7	1 15.9	1 5.0	0 41.4	2 2.1	0 20.6	1 24.5	17 33.7

RIGHT ASCENSION

DAY	EPHEM. SID. TIME h m s	☉	☊	☽	☿	♀	♂	♃	♄	♅	♆	♇
1	8 42 25.6	13 ♒ 59.3	20 ♍ 25.6	3 ♈ 43.6	8 ♒ 36.9	24 ♐ 53.1	11 ♒ 34.6	5 ♌ 30.7	14 ♍ 47.2	18 ♏ 24.6	19 ♐ 2.2	24 ♎ 16.2
2	8 46 22.2	15 .5	20 22.7	17 6.7	10 21.1	26 2.6	12 22.7	5 R 22.6	14 R 43.8	18 25.9	19 3.8	24 R 16.1
3	8 50 18.8	16 1.5	20 19.7	0 ♉ 12.0	12 5.4	27 12.4	13 10.6	5 14.6	14 40.2	18 27.1	19 5.5	24 15.9
4	8 54 15.3	17 2.3	20 16.8	13 6.8	13 49.8	28 22.6	13 58.5	5 6.5	14 36.7	18 28.2	19 7.1	24 15.7
5	8 58 11.9	18 2.9	20 13.9	25 56.4	15 34.3	29 33.0	14 46.3	4 58.6	14 33.0	18 29.3	19 8.7	24 15.5
6	9 2 8.4	19 3.3	20 10.9	8 ♊ 43.7	17 18.9	0 ♑ 43.7	15 33.9	4 50.7	14 29.3	18 30.4	19 10.2	24 15.2
7	9 6 5.0	20 3.5	20 8.0	21 28.8	19 3.5	1 54.7	16 21.5	4 42.9	14 25.6	18 31.4	19 11.7	24 15.0
8	9 10 1.5	21 3.5	20 5.1	4 ♋ 9.5	20 48.1	3 6.0	17 8.9	4 35.2	14 21.7	18 32.3	19 13.2	24 14.6
9	9 13 58.1	22 3.3	20 2.1	16 42.5	22 32.8	4 17.5	17 56.3	4 27.6	14 17.9	18 33.2	19 14.7	24 14.3
10	9 17 54.6	23 2.9	19 59.2	29 4.1	24 17.4	5 29.3	18 43.5	4 20.0	14 14.0	18 34.0	19 16.1	24 13.9
11	9 21 51.2	24 2.3	19 56.3	11 ♌ 11.9	26 2.0	6 41.2	19 30.7	4 12.5	14 10.0	18 34.8	19 17.5	24 13.5
12	9 25 47.7	25 1.4	19 53.3	23 5.2	27 46.6	7 53.4	20 17.7	4 5.2	14 6.0	18 35.5	19 18.9	24 13.1
13	9 29 44.3	26 .4	19 50.4	4 ♍ 45.7	29 31.0	9 5.8	21 4.6	3 57.9	14 1.9	18 36.1	19 20.3	24 12.6
14	9 33 40.9	26 59.3	19 47.5	16 17.3	1 ♓ 15.3	10 18.3	21 51.4	3 50.8	13 57.8	18 36.8	19 21.6	24 12.1
15	9 37 37.4	27 57.9	19 44.5	27 45.5	2 59.5	11 31.0	22 38.1	3 43.8	13 53.6	18 37.3	19 22.8	24 11.6
16	9 41 34.0	28 56.3	19 41.6	9 ♎ 17.9	4 43.3	12 43.9	23 24.7	3 36.9	13 49.5	18 37.8	19 24.1	24 11.0
17	9 45 30.5	29 54.6	19 38.7	21 2.8	6 26.9	13 56.9	24 11.2	3 30.1	13 45.2	18 38.2	19 25.3	24 10.4
18	9 49 27.1	0 ♓ 52.7	19 35.7	3 ♏ 9.2	8 10.0	15 10.0	24 57.6	3 23.4	13 41.0	18 38.6	19 26.5	24 9.8
19	9 53 23.6	1 50.6	19 32.8	15 45.9	9 52.7	16 23.2	25 43.9	3 16.9	13 36.7	18 39.0	19 27.6	24 9.2
20	9 57 20.2	2 48.4	19 29.9	29 .0	11 34.7	17 36.5	26 30.1	3 10.5	13 32.4	18 39.2	19 28.8	24 8.5
21	10 1 16.7	3 46.0	19 26.9	12 ♐ 55.4	13 16.0	18 49.9	27 16.3	3 4.3	13 28.1	18 39.5	19 29.9	24 7.8
22	10 5 13.3	4 43.5	19 24.0	27 30.1	14 56.2	20 3.4	28 2.3	2 58.3	13 23.7	18 39.6	19 31.0	24 7.1
23	10 9 9.8	5 40.7	19 21.1	12 ♑ 35.8	16 35.4	21 16.9	28 48.2	2 52.3	13 19.3	18 39.8	19 32.0	24 6.3
24	10 13 6.4	6 37.9	19 18.1	27 58.3	18 13.1	22 30.4	29 33.9	2 46.5	13 14.9	18 39.8	19 33.0	24 5.6
25	10 17 2.9	7 34.8	19 15.2	13 ♒ 20.8	19 49.2	23 43.9	0 ♓ 19.6	2 40.9	13 10.4	18 39.8	19 33.9	24 4.7
26	10 20 59.5	8 31.7	19 12.3	28 29.1	21 23.4	24 57.5	1 5.2	2 35.4	13 6.0	18 R 39.7	19 34.8	24 3.9
27	10 24 56.0	9 28.4	19 9.3	13 ♓ 14.5	22 55.3	26 11.0	1 50.7	2 30.1	13 1.5	18 39.6	19 35.7	24 3.0
28	10 28 52.6	10 24.9	19 6.4	27 34.5	24 24.5	27 24.5	2 36.1	2 25.0	12 57.0	18 39.4	19 36.5	24 2.2

DECLINATION

DAY	EPHEM. SID. TIME h m s	☉	☊	☽	☿	♀	♂	♃	♄	♅	♆	♇
1	8 42 25.6	17 S 19.5	0 N 4.3	0 N 5.7	20 S 46.3	20 S 20.1	19 S 4.1	20 N 7.1	8 N 37.5	17 S 36.9	21 S 39.7	8 N 32.9
4	8 54 15.3	16 27.6	0 4.4	11 58.2	19 31.1	20 34.7	18 26.3	20 12.8	8 42.5	17 37.8	21 39.9	8 34.9
7	9 6 5.0	15 33.2	0 4.4	17 59.9	18 2.6	20 45.2	17 46.7	20 18.2	8 47.6	17 38.6	21 40.1	8 36.9
10	9 17 54.6	14 36.5	0 4.5	16 40.8	16 20.9	20 51.3	17 5.4	20 23.5	8 52.9	17 39.2	21 40.3	8 39.1
13	9 29 44.3	13 37.5	0 4.6	9 5.5	14 26.1	20 52.6	16 22.4	20 28.4	8 58.3	17 39.8	21 40.5	8 41.3
16	9 41 34.0	12 36.5	0 4.6	1 S 52.6	12 18.8	20 49.2	15 38.0	20 33.1	9 3.9	17 40.2	21 40.7	8 43.5
19	9 53 23.6	11 33.7	0 4.7	12 31.6	10 .1	20 40.9	14 52.0	20 37.4	9 9.5	17 40.4	21 40.8	8 45.8
22	10 5 13.3	10 29.2	0 4.8	18 13.2	7 31.9	20 27.6	14 4.7	20 41.5	9 15.2	17 40.6	21 40.9	8 48.1
25	10 17 2.9	9 23.3	0 4.8	14 17.2	4 57.6	20 9.2	13 16.2	20 45.2	9 20.9	17 40.6	21 41.0	8 50.5
28	10 28 52.6	8 16.1	0 4.9	2 .5	2 22.2	19 45.8	12 26.5	20 48.5	9 26.6	17 40.5	21 41.1	8 52.9

MARCH 1979

LONGITUDE

DAY	EPHEM. SID. TIME h m s	☉ ° ′	☊ ° ′	☽ ° ′	☿ ° ′	♀ ° ′	♂ ° ′	♃ ° ′	♄ ° ′	♅ ° ′	♆ ° ′	♇ ° ′
1	10 32 49.1	9♓48.6	18♍ 6.0	11♈36.4	25♓34.9	26♑50.4	0♓55.0	29♋59.8	10♍36.0	20♏59.5	20♐21.7	18♎48.9
2	10 36 45.7	10 48.8	18 2.9	25 50.2	27 10.6	28 .1	1 42.4	29 R 55.2	10 R 31.2	20 R 59.2	20 22.4	18 R 47.7
3	10 40 42.3	11 49.0	17 59.7	9♉37.4	28 42.2	29 9.9	2 29.7	29 50.8	10 26.4	20 58.8	20 23.1	18 46.5
4	10 44 38.8	12 49.2	17 56.5	22 57.7	0♈ 9.1	0♒19.8	3 17.0	29 46.5	10 21.6	20 58.5	20 23.7	18 45.2
5	10 48 35.4	13 49.3	17 53.3	5♊53.1	1 30.8	1 29.8	4 4.4	29 42.5	10 16.8	20 58.0	20 24.4	18 43.9
6	10 52 31.9	14 49.4	17 50.1	18 26.8	2 46.6	2 39.9	4 51.7	29 38.6	10 12.0	20 57.5	20 24.9	18 42.6
7	10 56 28.5	15 49.5	17 47.0	0♋43.0	3 56.1	3 50.1	5 39.0	29 34.9	10 7.2	20 57.0	20 25.5	18 41.3
8	11 0 25.0	16 49.5	17 43.8	12 46.1	4 58.6	5 .3	6 26.3	29 31.4	10 2.5	20 56.4	20 26.0	18 39.9
9	11 4 21.6	17 49.5	17 40.6	24 40.3	5 53.7	6 10.6	7 13.6	29 28.0	9 57.7	20 55.7	20 26.5	18 38.6
10	11 8 18.1	18 49.5	17 37.4	6♌29.7	6 41.1	7 21.0	8 .9	29 24.9	9 53.0	20 55.0	20 27.0	18 37.2
11	11 12 14.7	19 49.4	17 34.3	18 18.0	7 20.3	8 31.4	8 48.1	29 21.9	9 48.3	20 54.3	20 27.4	18 35.8
12	11 16 11.2	20 49.3	17 31.1	0♍ 8.2	7 51.0	9 42.0	9 35.4	29 19.2	9 43.6	20 53.4	20 27.8	18 34.3
13	11 20 7.8	21 49.2	17 27.9	12 3.1	8 13.1	10 52.6	10 22.6	29 16.6	9 38.9	20 52.6	20 28.1	18 32.9
14	11 24 4.3	22 49.0	17 24.7	24 4.9	8 26.6	12 3.3	11 9.9	29 14.2	9 34.4	20 51.7	20 28.5	18 31.5
15	11 28 .9	23 48.8	17 21.5	6♎15.4	8 31.3	13 14.0	11 57.1	29 12.0	9 29.8	20 50.8	20 28.8	18 30.0
16	11 31 57.4	24 48.6	17 18.4	18 36.1	8 R 27.5	14 24.9	12 44.3	29 10.0	9 25.2	20 49.8	20 29.0	18 28.5
17	11 35 54.0	25 48.3	17 15.2	1♏ 8.5	8 15.4	15 35.7	13 31.5	29 8.1	9 20.7	20 48.7	20 29.3	18 27.0
18	11 39 50.5	26 48.0	17 12.0	13 54.1	7 55.4	16 46.7	14 18.7	29 6.5	9 16.2	20 47.6	20 29.4	18 25.5
19	11 43 47.1	27 47.7	17 8.8	26 54.2	7 28.2	17 57.7	15 5.9	29 5.0	9 11.8	20 46.5	20 29.6	18 23.9
20	11 47 43.6	28 47.3	17 5.7	10♐10.2	6 54.4	19 8.7	15 53.1	29 3.8	9 7.4	20 45.3	20 29.7	18 22.4
21	11 51 40.2	29 47.0	17 2.5	23 43.2	6 14.7	20 19.8	16 40.2	29 2.7	9 3.0	20 44.0	20 29.8	18 20.8
22	11 55 36.7	0♈46.5	16 59.3	7♑33.8	5 30.2	21 31.0	17 27.3	29 1.9	8 58.7	20 42.7	20 29.8	18 19.2
23	11 59 33.3	1 46.1	16 56.1	21 42.0	4 41.9	22 42.2	18 14.4	29 1.2	8 54.5	20 41.4	20 29.9	18 17.6
24	12 3 29.8	2 45.6	16 52.9	6♒ 6.3	3 50.9	23 53.5	19 1.5	29 .7	8 50.3	20 40.0	20 R 29.8	18 16.0
25	12 7 26.4	3 45.1	16 49.8	20 43.7	2 58.2	25 4.8	19 48.6	29 .4	8 46.2	20 38.6	20 29.8	18 14.4
26	12 11 22.9	4 44.6	16 46.6	5♓29.5	2 5.1	26 16.2	20 35.6	29 .3	8 42.1	20 37.1	20 29.7	18 12.8
27	12 15 19.5	5 44.0	16 43.4	20 17.5	1 12.6	27 27.6	21 22.7	29 D .4	8 38.1	20 35.6	20 29.6	18 11.1
28	12 19 16.0	6 43.4	16 40.2	5♈ .7	0 21.7	28 39.1	22 9.7	29 .7	8 34.1	20 34.1	20 29.5	18 9.5
29	12 23 12.6	7 42.8	16 37.0	19 31.8	29♓33.3	29 50.6	22 56.7	29 1.1	8 30.2	20 32.5	20 29.3	18 7.8
30	12 27 9.2	8 42.1	16 33.9	3♉44.8	28 48.2	1♓ 2.1	23 43.6	29 1.8	8 26.4	20 30.8	20 29.1	18 6.2
31	12 31 5.7	9 41.4	16 30.7	17 35.3	28 7.2	2 13.7	24 30.6	29 2.7	8 22.6	20 29.2	20 28.8	18 4.5

LATITUDE

DAY	EPHEM. SID. TIME	☉	☊	☽	☿	♀	♂	♃	♄	♅	♆	♇
1	10 32 49.1	0 .0	0 .0	2S10.3	0N15.3	1N11.8	1S 5.0	0N41.4	2N 2.1	0N20.6	1N24.5	17N34.1
4	10 44 38.8	0 .0	0 .0	4 49.4	0 55.5	0 59.3	1 4.8	0 41.5	2 2.3	0 20.6	1 24.6	17 35.2
7	10 56 28.5	0 .0	0 .0	5 9.5	1 37.4	0 46.9	1 4.5	0 41.5	2 2.5	0 20.7	1 24.8	17 36.3
10	11 8 18.1	0 .0	0 .0	3 28.9	2 17.9	0 34.7	1 4.2	0 41.5	2 2.6	0 20.7	1 24.9	17 37.3
13	11 20 7.8	0 .0	0 .0	0 30.3	2 53.2	0 22.8	1 3.9	0 41.5	2 2.7	0 20.7	1 25.0	17 38.2
16	11 31 57.4	0 .0	0 .0	2N44.3	3 19.1	0 11.2	1 3.4	0 41.5	2 2.8	0 20.7	1 25.1	17 39.0
19	11 43 47.1	0 .0	0 .0	4 57.1	3 31.8	0S .1	1 2.9	0 41.5	2 2.8	0 20.7	1 25.3	17 39.7
22	11 55 36.7	0 .0	0 .0	4 57.7	3 28.4	0 10.9	1 2.3	0 41.5	2 2.7	0 20.8	1 25.4	17 40.4
25	12 7 26.4	0 .0	0 .0	2 22.8	3 8.4	0 21.3	1 1.7	0 41.4	2 2.6	0 20.8	1 25.5	17 40.9
28	12 19 16.0	0 .0	0 .0	1S35.5	2 34.2	0 31.2	1 1.0	0 41.3	2 2.5	0 20.8	1 25.6	17 41.4
31	12 31 5.7	0 .0	0 .0	4 33.7	1 50.8	0 40.6	1 .3	0 41.3	2 2.4	0 20.8	1 25.8	17 41.7

RIGHT ASCENSION

DAY	EPHEM. SID. TIME	☉	☊	☽	☿	♀	♂	♃	♄	♅	♆	♇
1	10 32 49.1	11♓21.3	19♍ 3.5	11♈31.3	25♓50.6	28♑38.0	3♓21.4	2♌20.0	12♍52.6	18♏39.2	19♐37.4	24♎ 1.2
2	10 36 45.7	12 17.6	19 .5	25 9.6	27 13.3	29 51.4	4 6.6	2 R 15.2	12 R 48.1	18 R 38.9	19 38.1	24 R .3
3	10 40 42.3	13 13.8	18 57.6	8♉34.2	28 32.0	1♒ 4.8	4 51.7	2 10.6	12 43.6	18 38.6	19 38.9	23 59.4
4	10 44 38.8	14 9.8	18 54.7	21 49.0	29 46.3	2 18.1	5 36.7	2 6.2	12 39.1	18 38.2	19 39.6	23 58.4
5	10 48 35.4	15 5.7	18 51.7	4♊56.0	0♈55.7	3 31.3	6 21.6	2 2.0	12 34.6	18 37.8	19 40.2	23 57.4
6	10 52 31.9	16 1.5	18 48.8	17 55.2	1 59.7	4 44.5	7 6.4	1 57.9	12 30.2	18 37.3	19 40.9	23 56.3
7	10 56 28.5	16 57.2	18 45.9	0♋45.1	2 57.9	5 57.5	7 51.1	1 54.0	12 25.7	18 36.7	19 41.5	23 55.3
8	11 0 25.0	17 52.7	18 42.9	13 23.6	3 49.9	7 10.4	8 35.8	1 50.3	12 21.2	18 36.1	19 42.0	23 54.2
9	11 4 21.6	18 48.2	18 40.0	25 48.5	4 35.2	8 23.3	9 20.3	1 46.9	12 16.8	18 35.4	19 42.6	23 53.1
10	11 8 18.1	19 43.6	18 37.0	7♌58.9	5 13.5	9 36.0	10 4.8	1 43.6	12 12.4	18 34.7	19 43.1	23 52.0
11	11 12 14.7	20 38.9	18 34.1	19 55.1	5 44.6	10 48.5	10 49.1	1 40.5	12 8.0	18 34.0	19 43.5	23 50.8
12	11 16 11.2	21 34.1	18 31.2	1♍39.3	6 8.2	12 1.0	11 33.4	1 37.5	12 3.6	18 33.1	19 43.9	23 49.7
13	11 20 7.8	22 29.2	18 28.2	13 15.3	6 24.3	13 13.3	12 17.6	1 34.8	11 59.2	18 32.3	19 44.3	23 48.5
14	11 24 4.3	23 24.3	18 25.3	24 48.5	6 32.8	14 25.5	13 1.8	1 32.4	11 55.0	18 31.4	19 44.7	23 47.4
15	11 28 .9	24 19.3	18 22.4	6♎25.1	6 33.6	15 37.6	13 45.8	1 30.1	11 50.7	18 30.5	19 45.0	23 46.1
16	11 31 57.4	25 14.2	18 19.4	18 12.3	6 R 27.2	16 49.4	14 29.8	1 27.9	11 46.4	18 29.4	19 45.3	23 44.9
17	11 35 54.0	26 9.0	18 16.5	0♏17.3	6 13.7	18 1.1	15 13.7	1 26.0	11 42.1	18 28.4	19 45.5	23 43.7
18	11 39 50.5	27 3.8	18 13.5	12 47.1	5 53.6	19 12.7	15 57.5	1 24.3	11 37.9	18 27.3	19 45.7	23 42.4
19	11 43 47.1	27 58.6	18 10.6	25 47.1	5 27.5	20 24.1	16 41.3	1 22.8	11 33.8	18 26.1	19 45.9	23 41.1
20	11 47 43.6	28 53.3	18 7.7	9♐20.3	4 56.0	21 35.3	17 24.9	1 21.4	11 29.6	18 24.9	19 46.0	23 39.8
21	11 51 40.2	29 48.0	18 4.7	23 25.2	4 20.0	22 46.4	18 8.6	1 20.3	11 25.5	18 23.6	19 46.1	23 38.5
22	11 55 36.7	0♈42.7	18 1.8	7♑56.3	3 40.2	23 57.3	18 52.1	1 19.4	11 21.5	18 22.3	19 46.2	23 37.2
23	11 59 33.3	1 37.3	17 58.8	22 43.5	2 57.8	25 8.0	19 35.6	1 18.7	11 17.5	18 21.0	19 46.2	23 35.8
24	12 3 29.8	2 32.0	17 55.9	7♒35.2	2 13.5	26 18.6	20 19.0	1 18.2	11 13.5	18 19.6	19 46.2	23 34.5
25	12 7 26.4	3 26.6	17 53.0	22 20.9	1 28.6	27 29.0	21 2.4	1 17.9	11 9.6	18 18.2	19 R 46.1	23 33.1
26	12 11 22.9	4 21.2	17 50.0	6♓53.7	0 43.8	28 39.2	21 45.7	1 17.8	11 5.8	18 16.7	19 46.1	23 31.7
27	12 15 19.5	5 15.8	17 47.1	21 10.9	0 .1	29 49.2	22 29.0	1 D 17.9	11 2.0	18 15.1	19 45.9	23 30.3
28	12 19 16.0	6 10.4	17 44.1	5♈13.8	29♓18.5	0♓59.0	23 12.2	1 18.1	10 58.2	18 13.6	19 45.8	23 28.9
29	12 23 12.6	7 5.0	17 41.2	19 5.4	28 39.6	2 8.7	23 55.4	1 18.6	10 54.6	18 12.0	19 45.6	23 27.5
30	12 27 9.2	7 59.6	17 38.3	2♉48.8	28 4.0	3 18.2	24 38.5	1 19.3	10 50.9	18 10.3	19 45.4	23 26.0
31	12 31 5.7	8 54.3	17 35.3	16 26.2	27 32.5	4 27.6	25 21.5	1 20.2	10 47.4	18 8.6	19 45.1	23 24.6

DECLINATION

DAY	EPHEM. SID. TIME	☉	☊	☽	☿	♀	♂	♃	♄	♅	♆	♇
1	10 32 49.1	7S53.5	0N 4.9	2N35.5	1S31.3	19S36.9	12S 9.6	20N49.5	9N28.5	17S40.4	21S41.1	8N53.7
4	10 44 38.8	6 44.9	0 5.0	13 50.6	0N54.6	19 6.9	11 18.5	20 52.4	9 34.2	17 40.1	21 41.1	8 56.1
7	10 56 28.5	5 35.4	0 5.1	18 16.7	3 3.6	18 32.1	10 26.4	20 54.9	9 39.8	17 39.7	21 41.1	8 58.5
10	11 8 18.1	4 25.3	0 5.1	15 16.6	4 45.9	17 52.5	9 33.4	20 57.0	9 45.3	17 39.2	21 41.1	9 .9
13	11 20 7.8	3 14.7	0 5.2	6 34.5	5 54.7	17 8.3	8 39.7	20 58.8	9 50.7	17 38.5	21 41.0	9 3.3
16	11 31 57.4	2 3.7	0 5.3	4S45.3	6 24.2	16 19.7	7 45.3	21 .1	9 56.0	17 37.7	21 41.0	9 5.7
19	11 43 47.1	0 52.6	0 5.3	14 38.7	6 12.4	15 27.0	6 50.3	21 1.1	10 1.0	17 36.9	21 40.9	9 8.0
22	11 55 36.7	0N18.5	0 5.4	18 16.2	5 22.4	14 30.3	5 54.8	21 1.7	10 5.9	17 35.8	21 40.8	9 10.3
25	12 7 26.4	1 29.5	0 5.4	12 19.6	4 3.7	13 29.8	4 58.9	21 2.0	10 10.6	17 34.7	21 40.7	9 12.6
28	12 19 16.0	2 40.2	0 5.5	0N31.8	2 30.1	12 25.9	4 2.7	21 1.9	10 15.0	17 33.5	21 40.5	9 14.8
31	12 31 5.7	3 50.3	0 5.6	12 41.8	0 56.8	11 18.8	3 6.2	21 1.4	10 19.2	17 32.2	21 40.3	9 16.9

LONGITUDE

DAY	EPHEM. SID. TIME (h m s)	☉	☊	☽	☿	♀	♂	♃	♄	♅	♆	♇
1	12 35 2.3	10♈40.7	16♍27.5	1♊1.1	27♓30.7	3♓25.3	25♓17.5	29♋3.7	8♍18.9	20♏27.5	20♐28.5	18♎2.9
2	12 38 58.8	11 39.9	16 24.3	14 2.3	26 R59.3	4 36.9	26 4.3	29 5.0	8 R15.3	20 R25.7	20 R28.2	18 R 1.2
3	12 42 55.4	12 39.1	16 21.2	26 40.9	26 33.1	5 48.6	26 51.2	29 6.4	8 11.8	20 23.9	20 27.9	17 59.5
4	12 46 51.9	13 38.3	16 18.0	9♋.1	26 12.4	7 .4	27 38.1	29 8.1	8 8.4	20 22.1	20 27.5	17 57.9
5	12 50 48.5	14 37.4	16 14.8	21 4.5	25 57.3	8 12.1	28 24.9	29 9.9	8 5.0	20 20.3	20 27.1	17 56.2
6	12 54 45.0	15 36.5	16 11.6	2♌36.5	25 47.8	9 23.9	29 11.6	29 11.9	8 1.7	20 18.4	20 26.7	17 54.5
7	12 58 41.6	16 35.5	16 8.4	14 47.7	25 43.9	10 35.7	29 58.4	29 14.1	7 58.4	20 16.4	20 26.2	17 52.8
8	13 2 38.1	17 34.5	16 5.3	26 36.4	25 D45.4	11 47.5	0♈45.1	29 16.4	7 55.3	20 14.5	20 25.7	17 51.1
9	13 6 34.7	18 33.4	16 2.1	8♍29.0	25 52.2	12 59.3	1 31.7	29 19.0	7 52.2	20 12.5	20 25.2	17 49.4
10	13 10 31.2	19 32.4	15 58.9	20 29.5	26 4.2	14 11.2	2 18.4	29 21.7	7 49.3	20 10.4	20 24.6	17 47.8
11	13 14 27.8	20 31.2	15 55.7	2♎40.7	26 21.1	15 23.1	3 5.0	29 24.6	7 46.4	20 8.4	20 24.0	17 46.1
12	13 18 24.3	21 30.1	15 52.6	15 4.9	26 42.9	16 35.1	3 51.5	29 27.7	7 43.6	20 6.3	20 23.4	17 44.4
13	13 22 20.9	22 28.9	15 49.4	27 43.4	27 9.2	17 47.1	4 38.1	29 30.9	7 40.9	20 4.2	20 22.8	17 42.7
14	13 26 17.4	23 27.7	15 46.2	10♏36.5	27 39.8	18 59.1	5 24.6	29 34.3	7 38.2	20 2.0	20 22.1	17 41.0
15	13 30 14.0	24 26.4	15 43.0	23 44.0	28 14.6	20 11.1	6 11.1	29 37.9	7 35.7	19 59.8	20 21.4	17 39.3
16	13 34 10.5	25 25.2	15 39.8	7♐4.9	28 53.4	21 23.2	6 57.5	29 41.7	7 33.3	19 57.6	20 20.6	17 37.7
17	13 38 7.1	26 23.9	15 36.7	20 38.1	29 36.0	22 35.2	7 43.9	29 45.6	7 30.9	19 55.4	20 19.9	17 36.0
18	13 42 3.6	27 22.5	15 33.5	4♑22.3	0♈22.1	23 47.4	8 30.3	29 49.7	7 28.7	19 53.2	20 19.1	17 34.3
19	13 46 .2	28 21.1	15 30.3	18 16.4	1 11.7	24 59.5	9 16.6	29 54.0	7 26.5	19 50.9	20 18.2	17 32.7
20	13 49 56.7	29 19.8	15 27.1	2♒19.3	2 4.5	26 11.7	10 2.9	29 58.5	7 24.4	19 48.6	20 17.4	17 31.0
21	13 53 53.3	0♉18.3	15 24.0	16 29.9	3 .4	27 23.9	10 49.2	0♌3.1	7 22.5	19 46.3	20 16.5	17 29.4
22	13 57 49.9	1 16.9	15 20.8	0♓46.6	3 59.3	28 36.1	11 35.5	0 7.8	7 20.6	19 43.9	20 15.6	17 27.8
23	14 1 46.4	2 15.4	15 17.6	15 7.4	5 1.1	29 48.3	12 21.7	0 12.8	7 18.8	19 41.6	20 14.7	17 26.1
24	14 5 43.0	3 13.9	15 14.4	29 29.0	6 5.6	1♈.6	13 7.8	0 17.9	7 17.2	19 39.2	20 13.7	17 24.5
25	14 9 39.5	4 12.4	15 11.2	13♈47.7	7 12.7	2 12.9	13 54.0	0 23.2	7 15.6	19 36.8	20 12.8	17 23.0
26	14 13 36.1	5 10.9	15 8.1	27 58.1	8 22.3	3 25.2	14 40.1	0 28.6	7 14.2	19 34.4	20 11.8	17 21.4
27	14 17 32.6	6 9.3	15 4.9	11♉8.9	9 34.4	4 37.5	15 26.1	0 34.1	7 12.8	19 32.0	20 10.7	17 19.8
28	14 21 29.2	7 7.7	15 1.7	25 36.7	10 48.8	5 49.8	16 12.1	0 39.9	7 11.5	19 29.5	20 9.7	17 18.2
29	14 25 25.7	8 6.0	14 58.5	8♊57.5	12 5.5	7 2.1	16 58.1	0 45.7	7 10.4	19 27.1	20 8.6	17 16.7
30	14 29 22.3	9 4.3	14 55.4	21 57.1	13 24.4	8 14.5	17 44.0	0 51.8	7 9.3	19 24.6	20 7.5	17 15.1

LATITUDE

DAY	SID. TIME	☉	☊	☽	☿	♀	♂	♃	♄	♅	♆	♇
1	12 35 2.3	0 .0	0 .0	5S 2.4	1N35.2	0S43.6	1S .0	0N41.3	2N 2.3	0N20.8	1N25.8	17N41.8
4	12 46 51.9	0 .0	0 .0	4 52.4	0 47.4	0 52.2	0 59.2	0 41.2	2 2.1	0 20.8	1 25.9	17 42.0
7	12 58 41.6	0 .0	0 .0	2 49.0	0 1.3	1 2.2	0 58.3	0 41.1	2 1.9	0 20.8	1 26.0	17 42.2
10	13 10 31.2	0 .0	0 .0	0N17.6	0S40.7	1 7.5	0 57.3	0 41.0	2 1.7	0 20.8	1 26.1	17 42.2
13	13 22 20.9	0 .0	0 .0	3 22.9	1 17.2	1 14.1	0 56.3	0 41.0	2 1.4	0 20.8	1 26.2	17 42.0
16	13 34 10.5	0 .0	0 .0	5 6.0	1 47.8	1 20.1	0 55.2	0 40.9	2 1.1	0 20.8	1 26.3	17 42.0
19	13 46 .2	0 .0	0 .0	4 24.7	2 12.3	1 25.4	0 54.1	0 40.8	2 .8	0 20.8	1 26.4	17 41.8
22	13 57 49.9	0 .0	0 .0	1 25.2	2 30.8	1 30.0	0 52.9	0 40.7	2 .4	0 20.8	1 26.5	17 41.4
25	14 9 39.5	0 .0	0 .0	2S21.1	2 43.5	1 33.9	0 51.7	0 40.6	2 .1	0 20.8	1 26.6	17 41.0
28	14 21 29.2	0 .0	0 .0	4 47.3	2 50.5	1 37.0	0 50.4	0 40.5	1 59.7	0 20.8	1 26.7	17 40.4

RIGHT ASCENSION

DAY	SID. TIME	☉	☊	☽	☿	♀	♂	♃	♄	♅	♆	♇
1	12 35 2.3	9♈48.9	17♍32.4	29♉57.3	27♓5.2	5♓36.7	26♓4.5	1♌21.3	10♍43.9	18♏6.9	19♐44.8	23♎23.1
2	12 38 58.8	10 43.6	17 29.4	13♊20.1	26 R42.7	6 45.7	26 47.5	1 22.6	10 R40.5	18 R5.1	19 R44.5	23 R21.7
3	12 42 55.4	11 38.2	17 26.5	26 31.2	26 25.0	7 54.5	27 30.4	1 24.1	10 37.1	18 3.3	19 44.1	23 20.2
4	12 46 51.9	12 33.0	17 23.6	9♋27.0	26 12.3	9 3.3	28 13.3	1 25.9	10 33.9	18 1.5	19 43.8	23 18.8
5	12 50 48.5	13 27.7	17 20.6	22 4.8	26 4.7	10 11.8	28 56.1	1 27.8	10 30.6	17 59.6	19 43.3	23 17.3
6	12 54 45.0	14 22.5	17 17.7	4♌23.6	26 2.1	11 20.2	29 38.9	1 29.9	10 27.5	17 57.7	19 42.9	23 15.8
7	12 58 41.6	15 17.4	17 14.7	16 24.8	26 D4.4	12 28.4	0♈21.7	1 32.1	10 24.4	17 55.8	19 42.3	23 14.3
8	13 2 38.1	16 12.2	17 11.8	28 11.5	26 11.5	13 36.5	1 4.4	1 34.6	10 21.4	17 53.8	19 41.8	23 12.8
9	13 6 34.7	17 7.2	17 8.8	9♍48.7	26 23.4	14 44.4	1 47.1	1 37.2	10 18.5	17 51.7	19 41.2	23 11.3
10	13 10 31.2	18 2.1	17 5.9	21 22.7	26 39.8	15 52.2	2 29.7	1 40.1	10 15.7	17 49.7	19 40.6	23 9.8
11	13 14 27.8	18 57.2	17 3.0	3♎.6	27 .4	16 60.0	3 12.4	1 43.1	10 12.9	17 47.6	19 40.0	23 8.3
12	13 18 24.3	19 52.3	17 .1	14 49.8	27 25.2	18 7.5	3 55.0	1 46.3	10 10.2	17 45.5	19 39.3	23 6.8
13	13 22 20.9	20 47.5	16 57.1	26 57.8	27 54.0	19 15.0	4 37.6	1 49.7	10 7.7	17 43.4	19 38.6	23 5.3
14	13 26 17.4	21 42.7	16 54.1	9♏31.0	28 26.4	20 22.4	5 20.1	1 53.3	10 5.1	17 41.2	19 37.9	23 3.8
15	13 30 14.0	22 38.0	16 51.2	22 34.2	29 2.4	21 29.7	6 2.7	1 57.1	10 2.7	17 39.0	19 37.2	23 2.3
16	13 34 10.5	23 33.5	16 48.2	6♐8.6	29 41.8	22 36.9	6 45.2	2 1.0	10 .4	17 36.8	19 36.4	23 .8
17	13 38 7.1	24 29.0	16 45.3	20 11.5	0♈24.4	23 44.0	7 27.7	2 5.1	9 58.1	17 34.5	19 35.5	22 59.2
18	13 42 3.6	25 24.7	16 42.3	4♑35.5	1 9.9	24 51.1	8 10.2	2 9.4	9 56.0	17 32.2	19 34.7	22 57.7
19	13 46 .2	26 20.4	16 39.4	19 10.2	1 58.4	25 58.1	8 52.7	2 13.9	9 53.9	17 29.9	19 33.8	22 56.2
20	13 49 56.7	27 16.2	16 36.5	3♒44.4	2 49.5	27 5.0	9 35.2	2 18.5	9 51.9	17 27.6	19 32.9	22 54.7
21	13 53 53.3	28 12.2	16 33.5	18 9.3	3 43.3	28 11.9	10 17.7	2 23.3	9 50.0	17 25.3	19 32.0	22 53.2
22	13 57 49.9	29 8.2	16 30.6	2♓19.2	4 39.5	29 18.8	11 .2	2 28.3	9 48.2	17 23.0	19 31.0	22 51.7
23	14 1 46.4	0♉4.4	16 27.6	16 14.8	5 38.0	0♈25.6	11 42.6	2 33.5	9 46.5	17 20.5	19 30.0	22 50.2
24	14 5 43.0	1 .6	16 24.7	29 58.9	6 38.9	1 32.4	12 25.1	2 38.8	9 44.8	17 18.1	19 29.0	22 48.7
25	14 9 39.5	1 57.1	16 21.7	13♈36.4	7 41.9	2 39.2	13 7.6	2 44.3	9 43.4	17 15.8	19 28.0	22 47.3
26	14 13 36.1	2 53.6	16 18.8	27 12.0	8 47.0	3 46.0	13 50.1	2 49.9	9 41.9	17 13.3	19 26.9	22 45.8
27	14 17 32.6	3 50.2	16 15.8	10♉48.9	9 54.1	4 52.8	14 32.6	2 55.7	9 40.6	17 10.9	19 25.8	22 44.3
28	14 21 29.2	4 47.0	16 12.9	24 27.2	11 3.2	5 59.5	15 15.1	3 1.7	9 39.3	17 8.4	19 24.7	22 42.9
29	14 25 25.7	5 43.9	16 9.9	8♊4.0	12 14.2	7 6.3	15 57.6	3 7.8	9 38.2	17 5.9	19 23.5	22 41.4
30	14 29 22.3	6 40.9	16 7.0	21 33.7	13 27.1	8 13.1	16 40.1	3 14.1	9 37.2	17 3.5	19 22.3	22 39.9

DECLINATION

DAY	SID. TIME	☉	☊	☽	☿	♀	♂	♃	♄	♅	♆	♇
1	12 35 2.3	4N13.6	0N 5.6	15N25.7	0N28.0	10S55.8	2S47.4	21N 1.2	10N20.5	17S31.8	21S40.3	9N17.6
4	12 46 51.9	5 22.9	0 5.7	18 16.3	0S46.9	9 44.8	1 50.7	20 58.9	10 23.1	17 30.2	21 40.1	9 19.3
7	12 58 41.6	6 31.3	0 5.7	13 42.0	1 40.4	8 31.4	0 54.1	20 56.6	10 25.7	17 28.6	21 39.9	9 21.0
10	13 10 31.2	7 38.7	0 5.8	4N 2.4	2 11.1	7 15.6	0N 2.4	20 54.3	10 28.3	17 27.0	21 39.7	9 22.7
13	13 22 20.9	8 45.0	0 5.9	7S30.3	2 18.8	6 2.4	0 58.9	20 52.0	10 30.9	17 25.4	21 39.4	9 24.4
16	13 34 10.5	9 49.9	0 5.9	15 27.7	2 4.7	4 38.5	1 55.0	20 49.7	10 33.5	17 23.8	21 39.1	9 26.1
19	13 46 .2	10 53.3	0 6.0	17 49.2	1 33.2	3 18.1	2 51.0	20 47.4	10 36.1	17 22.1	21 38.8	9 27.8
22	13 57 49.9	11 55.2	0 6.0	9 52.2	0 43.0	1 56.2	3 46.2	20 45.1	10 38.7	17 20.5	21 38.5	9 29.4
25	14 9 39.5	12 55.3	0 6.1	3N16.4	0N22.0	0 33.1	4 41.1	20 42.8	10 41.3	17 18.8	21 38.2	9 31.1
28	14 21 29.2	13 53.5	0 6.2	14 30.6	1 40.5	0N49.8	5 35.8	20 40.5	10 44.0	17 16.2	21 38.0	9 32.7

MAY 1979

DAY	EPHEM. SID. TIME	☉	☊	☾	☿	♀	♂	♃	♄	♅	♆	♇
		LONGITUDE										
	h m s	° ′	° ′	° ′	° ′	° ′	° ′	° ′	° ′	° ′	° ′	° ′
1	14 33 18.8	10♉ 2.6	14♍52.2	4♋35.9	14♈45.5	9♈26.9	18♈29.8	0♌57.9	7♍ 8.4	19♏22.1	20♐ 6.3	17♎13.6
2	14 37 15.4	11 .9	14 49.0	16 56.2	16 8.7	10 39.2	19 15.7	1 4.3	7R 7.5	19R19.7	20R 5.2	17R12.1
3	14 41 11.9	11 59.1	14 45.8	29 1.5	17 34.0	11 51.6	20 1.4	1 10.7	7 6.8	19 17.2	20 4.0	17 10.6
4	14 45 8.5	12 57.3	14 42.6	10♌56.3	19 1.4	13 4.0	20 47.2	1 17.3	7 6.1	19 14.6	20 2.8	17 9.1
5	14 49 5.1	13 55.4	14 39.5	22 45.8	20 30.7	14 16.4	21 32.8	1 24.1	7 5.6	19 12.1	20 1.6	17 7.7
6	14 53 1.6	14 53.5	14 36.3	4♍35.2	22 2.1	15 28.9	22 18.5	1 31.0	7 5.2	19 9.6	20 .4	17 6.2
7	14 56 58.2	15 51.6	14 33.1	16 29.8	23 35.5	16 41.3	23 4.1	1 38.0	7 4.9	19 7.1	19 59.1	17 4.8
8	15 0 54.7	16 49.7	14 29.9	28 34.4	25 10.9	17 53.8	23 49.6	1 45.1	7 4.6	19 4.6	19 57.8	17 3.4
9	15 4 51.3	17 47.7	14 26.8	10♎53.2	26 48.2	19 6.2	24 35.1	1 52.4	7 4.5	19 2.1	19 56.5	17 2.0
10	15 8 47.8	18 45.7	14 23.6	23 29.2	28 27.6	20 18.7	25 20.5	1 59.8	7 4.5	18 59.5	19 55.2	17 .6
11	15 12 44.4	19 43.6	14 20.4	6♏24.1	0♉ 8.9	21 31.2	26 5.9	2 7.4	7D 4.6	18 57.0	19 53.9	16 59.2
12	15 16 40.9	20 41.6	14 17.2	19 38.2	1 52.1	22 43.7	26 51.3	2 15.1	7 4.8	18 54.5	19 52.5	16 57.9
13	15 20 37.5	21 39.5	14 14.0	3♐10.0	3 37.4	23 56.2	27 36.6	2 22.9	7 5.1	18 51.9	19 51.1	16 56.6
14	15 24 34.0	22 37.4	14 10.9	16 56.7	5 24.6	25 8.8	28 21.8	2 30.8	7 5.5	18 49.4	19 49.8	16 55.3
15	15 28 30.6	23 35.2	14 7.7	0♑54.7	7 13.8	26 21.3	29 7.0	2 38.9	7 6.0	18 46.9	19 48.4	16 54.0
16	15 32 27.2	24 33.1	14 4.5	15 .1	9 5.1	27 33.9	29 52.2	2 47.1	7 6.7	18 44.4	19 47.0	16 52.8
17	15 36 23.7	25 30.9	14 1.3	29 9.0	10 58.2	28 46.5	0♉37.3	2 55.4	7 7.4	18 41.9	19 45.6	16 51.6
18	15 40 20.3	26 28.7	13 58.2	13♒18.8	12 53.4	29 59.1	1 22.4	3 3.8	7 8.3	18 39.4	19 44.1	16 50.4
19	15 44 16.8	27 26.5	13 55.0	27 27.5	14 50.4	1♉11.7	2 7.4	3 12.3	7 9.2	18 36.9	19 42.6	16 49.2
20	15 48 13.4	28 24.3	13 51.8	11♓33.8	16 49.4	2 24.3	2 52.4	3 21.0	7 10.2	18 34.5	19 41.2	16 48.0
21	15 52 9.9	29 22.0	13 48.6	25 36.9	18 50.2	3 37.0	3 37.3	3 29.7	7 11.4	18 32.0	19 39.7	16 46.9
22	15 56 6.5	0♊19.8	13 45.4	9♈35.6	20 52.9	4 49.7	4 22.2	3 38.6	7 12.6	18 29.5	19 38.2	16 45.8
23	16 0 3.0	1 17.5	13 42.3	23 28.6	22 57.2	6 2.3	5 7.0	3 47.6	7 13.9	18 27.1	19 36.7	16 44.7
24	16 3 59.6	2 15.2	13 39.1	7♉13.6	25 3.1	7 15.0	5 51.7	3 56.6	7 15.4	18 24.6	19 35.1	16 43.7
25	16 7 56.2	3 12.8	13 35.9	20 48.2	27 10.5	8 27.7	6 36.5	4 5.8	7 16.9	18 22.2	19 33.6	16 42.6
26	16 11 52.7	4 10.5	13 32.7	4♊ 9.6	29 19.2	9 40.4	7 21.1	4 15.1	7 18.6	18 19.8	19 32.1	16 41.6
27	16 15 49.3	5 8.1	13 29.6	17 15.4	1♊29.0	10 53.1	8 5.7	4 24.6	7 20.3	18 17.4	19 30.5	16 40.6
28	16 19 45.8	6 5.7	13 26.4	0♋ 4.5	3 39.7	12 5.9	8 50.2	4 34.1	7 22.2	18 15.0	19 28.9	16 39.7
29	16 23 42.4	7 3.3	13 23.2	12 36.6	5 51.2	13 18.6	9 34.7	4 43.7	7 24.2	18 12.7	19 27.4	16 38.8
30	16 27 38.9	8 .9	13 20.0	24 52.9	8 3.0	14 31.4	10 19.2	4 53.4	7 26.2	18 10.4	19 25.8	16 37.9
31	16 31 35.5	8 58.5	13 16.9	6♌56.1	10 15.0	15 44.1	11 3.5	5 3.2	7 28.4	18 8.0	19 24.2	16 37.0
		LATITUDE										
1	14 33 18.8	0 .0	0 .0	4S50.8	2S52.1	1S39.5	0S49.0	0N40.5	1N59.3	0N20.8	1N26.8	17N39.8
4	14 45 8.5	0 .0	0 .0	2 55.8	2 48.5	1 41.2	0 47.6	0 40.4	1 58.9	0 20.8	1 26.9	17 39.1
7	14 56 58.2	0 .0	0 .0	0N 3.9	2 39.8	1 42.2	0 46.2	0 40.3	1 58.5	0 20.7	1 26.9	17 38.3
10	15 8 47.8	0 .0	0 .0	3 7.2	2 26.2	1 42.5	0 44.7	0 40.3	1 58.0	0 20.7	1 27.0	17 37.5
13	15 20 37.5	0 .0	0 .0	4 56.4	2 8.0	1 42.1	0 43.2	0 40.2	1 57.6	0 20.7	1 27.1	17 36.5
16	15 32 27.2	0 .0	0 .0	4 22.0	1 45.5	1 41.1	0 41.6	0 40.2	1 57.2	0 20.6	1 27.1	17 35.5
19	15 44 16.8	0 .0	0 .0	1 29.6	1 19.2	1 39.4	0 39.9	0 40.1	1 56.7	0 20.6	1 27.2	17 34.4
22	15 56 6.5	0 .0	0 .0	2S 8.6	0 49.9	1 37.1	0 38.3	0 40.1	1 56.3	0 20.6	1 27.2	17 33.2
25	16 7 56.2	0 .0	0 .0	4 36.6	0 18.6	1 34.2	0 36.6	0 40.0	1 55.8	0 20.5	1 27.2	17 32.0
28	16 19 45.8	0 .0	0 .0	4 48.7	0N13.2	1 30.7	0 34.8	0 40.0	1 55.4	0 20.5	1 27.2	17 30.7
31	16 31 35.5	0 .0	0 .0	2 59.0	0 43.6	1 26.7	0 33.0	0 40.0	1 55.0	0 20.4	1 27.2	17 29.4
		RIGHT ASCENSION										
1	14 33 18.8	7♉38.0	16♍ 4.0	4♋49.9	14♈41.9	9♈20.0	17♈22.6	3♌20.5	9♍36.2	17♏ 1.0	19♐21.1	22♎38.5
2	14 37 15.4	8 35.3	16 1.1	17 47.0	15 58.5	10 26.8	18 5.1	3 27.1	9R35.4	16R58.4	19R19.8	22R37.0
3	14 41 11.9	9 32.7	15 58.2	0♌21.7	17 17.0	11 33.7	18 47.6	3 33.8	9 34.6	16 55.9	19 18.6	22 35.6
4	14 45 8.5	10 30.2	15 55.2	12 33.9	18 37.3	12 40.7	19 30.1	3 40.7	9 33.9	16 53.4	19 17.3	22 34.2
5	14 49 5.1	11 27.9	15 52.3	24 26.5	19 59.5	13 47.8	20 12.7	3 47.7	9 33.4	16 50.9	19 16.0	22 32.8
6	14 53 1.6	12 25.7	15 49.3	6♍ 4.8	21 23.5	14 54.9	20 55.2	3 54.9	9 32.9	16 48.3	19 14.7	22 31.4
7	14 56 58.2	13 23.6	15 46.4	17 36.0	22 49.5	16 2.1	21 37.8	4 2.2	9 32.6	16 45.8	19 13.3	22 30.0
8	15 0 54.7	14 21.7	15 43.4	29 8.5	24 17.4	17 9.4	22 20.4	4 9.6	9 32.3	16 43.2	19 12.0	22 28.6
9	15 4 51.3	15 19.9	15 40.5	10♎51.4	25 47.3	18 16.8	23 3.0	4 17.2	9 32.2	16 40.7	19 10.6	22 27.3
10	15 8 47.8	16 18.3	15 37.5	22 53.7	27 19.2	19 24.3	23 45.7	4 24.9	9 32.1	16 38.2	19 9.2	22 25.9
11	15 12 44.4	17 16.8	15 34.6	5♏23.5	28 53.1	20 31.9	24 28.3	4 32.8	9 32.1	16 35.6	19 7.7	22 24.6
12	15 16 40.9	18 15.4	15 31.6	18 27.1	0♉29.2	21 39.7	25 11.0	4 40.7	9D32.3	16 33.1	19 6.3	22 23.3
13	15 20 37.5	19 14.2	15 28.7	2♐ 6.9	2 7.5	22 47.6	25 53.7	4 48.8	9 32.5	16 30.5	19 4.8	22 22.0
14	15 24 34.0	20 13.1	15 25.7	16 20.0	3 48.0	23 55.6	26 36.5	4 57.0	9 32.8	16 28.0	19 3.3	22 20.7
15	15 28 30.6	21 12.1	15 22.8	0♑57.5	5 30.9	25 3.8	27 19.3	5 5.4	9 33.3	16 25.4	19 1.8	22 19.4
16	15 32 27.2	22 11.4	15 19.8	15 46.2	7 16.1	26 12.2	28 2.1	5 13.9	9 33.8	16 23.0	19 .4	22 18.2
17	15 36 23.7	23 10.8	15 16.9	0♒31.0	9 3.8	27 20.7	28 44.9	5 22.5	9 34.5	16 20.4	18 58.8	22 17.0
18	15 40 20.3	24 10.3	15 13.9	15 .3	10 54.0	28 29.5	29 27.8	5 31.2	9 35.2	16 17.9	18 57.3	22 15.8
19	15 44 16.8	25 9.9	15 11.0	29 7.9	12 46.7	29 38.4	0♉10.7	5 40.1	9 36.0	16 15.4	18 55.7	22 14.6
20	15 48 13.4	26 9.7	15 8.0	12♓53.5	14 42.1	0♉47.5	0 53.7	5 49.0	9 36.9	16 12.9	18 54.1	22 13.4
21	15 52 9.9	27 9.6	15 5.1	26 21.7	16 40.0	1 56.8	1 36.7	5 58.1	9 37.9	16 10.4	18 52.5	22 12.2
22	15 56 6.5	28 9.7	15 2.1	9♈39.5	18 40.6	3 6.3	2 19.7	6 7.2	9 39.1	16 7.9	18 50.9	22 11.1
23	16 0 3.0	29 9.9	14 59.2	22 54.4	20 43.8	4 16.0	3 2.7	6 16.5	9 40.3	16 5.5	18 49.3	22 9.9
24	16 3 59.6	0♊10.3	14 56.2	6♉12.6	22 49.6	5 25.9	3 45.8	6 25.9	9 41.6	16 3.0	18 47.7	22 8.8
25	16 7 56.2	1 10.7	14 53.3	19 37.2	24 57.8	6 36.1	4 29.0	6 35.4	9 43.0	16 .6	18 46.0	22 7.8
26	16 11 52.7	2 11.3	14 50.3	3♊ 7.6	27 8.5	7 46.5	5 12.1	6 45.0	9 44.5	15 58.2	18 44.4	22 6.7
27	16 15 49.3	3 12.1	14 47.3	16 39.2	29 21.4	8 57.2	5 55.3	6 54.7	9 46.1	15 55.7	18 42.7	22 5.6
28	16 19 45.8	4 12.9	14 44.4	0♋ 4.7	1♊36.3	10 8.0	6 38.6	7 4.5	9 47.8	15 53.4	18 41.0	22 4.6
29	16 23 42.4	5 13.9	14 41.4	13 16.0	3 53.1	11 19.2	7 21.9	7 14.4	9 49.6	15 51.0	18 39.3	22 3.6
30	16 27 38.9	6 14.9	14 38.5	26 6.6	6 11.3	12 30.5	8 5.2	7 24.4	9 51.5	15 48.6	18 37.6	22 2.7
31	16 31 35.5	7 16.1	14 35.5	8♌33.0	8 30.9	13 42.2	8 48.5	7 34.5	9 53.4	15 46.3	18 35.9	22 1.7
		DECLINATION										
1	14 33 18.8	14N49.7	0N 6.2	18N31.0	3N10.2	2N13.2	6N29.6	20N36.1	10N44.1	17S14.3	21S37.7	9N33.8
4	14 45 8.5	15 43.6	0 6.3	14 40.0	4 51.0	3 36.4	7 22.7	20 31.8	10 44.6	17 12.2	21 37.3	9 34.8
7	14 56 58.2	16 35.2	0 6.4	5 23.4	6 41.1	4 59.2	8 15.1	20 27.1	10 44.6	17 10.2	21 37.0	9 35.7
10	15 8 47.8	17 24.3	0 6.4	6S13.2	8 38.9	6 21.2	9 6.5	20 22.2	10 44.4	17 8.2	21 36.6	9 36.4
13	15 20 37.5	18 10.7	0 6.5	15 56.4	10 43.0	7 42.3	9 57.1	20 16.9	10 43.8	17 6.1	21 36.3	9 37.0
16	15 32 27.2	18 54.5	0 6.6	18 15.4	12 51.4	9 2.1	10 46.7	20 11.3	10 42.8	17 4.1	21 35.9	9 37.4
19	15 44 16.8	19 35.3	0 6.6	10 57.1	15 1.6	10 20.2	11 35.2	20 5.4	10 41.4	17 2.1	21 35.5	9 37.8
22	15 56 6.5	20 13.2	0 6.7	1N49.8	17 10.4	11 36.4	12 22.6	19 59.3	10 39.7	17 .1	21 35.2	9 37.9
25	16 7 56.2	20 47.9	0 6.8	13 30.3	19 13.6	12 50.3	13 8.8	19 52.8	10 37.7	16 58.1	21 34.8	9 38.0
28	16 19 45.8	21 19.5	0 6.8	18 37.7	21 6.0	14 1.6	13 53.7	19 46.0	10 35.4	16 56.1	21 34.4	9 37.9
31	16 31 35.5	21 47.7	0 6.9	15 39.1	22 42.4	15 10.0	14 37.4	19 39.0	10 32.7	16 54.2	21 34.0	9 37.6

JUNE 1979

LONGITUDE

DAY	EPHEM. SID. TIME h m s	☉ ° ′	☊ ° ′	☽ ° ′	☿ ° ′	♀ ° ′	♂ ° ′	♃ ° ′	♄ ° ′	♅ ° ′	♆ ° ′	♇ ° ′
1	16 35 32.0	9♊56.0	13♍13.7	18♌49.8	12♊27.0	16♉56.9	11♉47.9	5♌13.1	7♍30.6	18♏ 5.8	19♐22.6	16♎36.2
2	16 39 28.6	10 53.5	13 10.5	0♍38.6	14 38.5	18 9.7	12 32.1	5 23.1	7 33.0	18R 3.5	19R21.0	16R35.3
3	16 43 25.2	11 51.0	13 7.3	12 27.7	16 49.4	19 22.5	13 16.3	5 33.2	7 35.4	18 1.2	19 19.4	16 34.6
4	16 47 21.7	12 48.4	13 4.1	24 22.6	18 59.4	20 35.3	14 .5	5 43.3	7 37.9	17 59.0	19 17.8	16 33.8
5	16 51 18.3	13 45.9	13 1.0	6♎28.7	21 8.2	21 48.1	14 44.6	5 53.6	7 40.6	17 56.8	19 16.2	16 33.1
6	16 55 14.8	14 43.3	12 57.8	18 51.0	23 15.7	23 .9	15 28.6	6 4.0	7 43.4	17 54.7	19 14.6	16 32.4
7	16 59 11.4	15 40.7	12 54.6	1♏33.5	25 21.6	24 13.8	16 12.6	6 14.4	7 46.2	17 52.6	19 13.0	16 31.8
8	17 3 7.9	16 38.1	12 51.4	14 39.0	27 25.7	25 26.6	16 56.5	6 25.0	7 49.1	17 50.4	19 11.4	16 31.2
9	17 7 4.5	17 35.5	12 48.3	28 8.4	29 27.9	26 39.5	17 40.4	6 35.6	7 52.1	17 48.4	19 9.7	16 30.6
10	17 11 1.1	18 32.8	12 45.1	12♐ .1	1♋28.0	27 52.4	18 24.2	6 46.2	7 55.2	17 46.3	19 8.1	16 30.0
11	17 14 57.6	19 30.2	12 41.9	26 10.6	3 26.1	29 5.2	19 7.9	6 57.0	7 58.4	17 44.3	19 6.5	16 29.4
12	17 18 54.2	20 27.5	12 38.7	10♑34.4	5 21.9	0♊18.1	19 51.6	7 7.8	8 1.7	17 42.3	19 4.9	16 28.9
13	17 22 50.7	21 24.8	12 35.6	25 5.2	7 15.4	1 31.1	20 35.2	7 18.7	8 5.1	17 40.3	19 3.2	16 28.5
14	17 26 47.3	22 22.1	12 32.4	9♒36.5	9 6.6	2 44.0	21 18.8	7 29.7	8 8.5	17 38.4	19 1.6	16 28.0
15	17 30 43.8	23 19.4	12 29.2	24 3.1	10 55.4	3 57.0	22 2.3	7 40.8	8 12.1	17 36.5	19 .0	16 27.6
16	17 34 40.4	24 16.7	12 26.0	8♓21.5	12 41.8	5 9.9	22 45.7	7 51.9	8 15.7	17 34.6	18 58.4	16 27.2
17	17 38 37.0	25 14.0	12 22.8	22 29.4	14 25.7	6 22.9	23 29.1	8 3.1	8 19.4	17 32.8	18 56.8	16 26.9
18	17 42 33.5	26 11.3	12 19.7	6♈26.1	16 7.3	7 35.9	24 12.5	8 14.4	8 23.3	17 31.0	18 55.2	16 26.6
19	17 46 30.1	27 8.6	12 16.5	20 11.4	17 46.4	8 49.0	24 55.8	8 25.8	8 27.1	17 29.3	18 53.6	16 26.3
20	17 50 26.6	28 5.9	12 13.3	3♉45.6	19 23.0	10 2.0	25 39.0	8 37.2	8 31.1	17 27.5	18 52.0	16 26.0
21	17 54 23.2	29 3.1	12 10.1	17 8.6	20 57.1	11 15.1	26 22.1	8 48.7	8 35.2	17 25.9	18 50.4	16 25.8
22	17 58 19.7	0♋ .4	12 7.0	0♊19.9	22 28.8	12 28.2	27 5.2	9 .2	8 39.3	17 24.2	18 48.8	16 25.6
23	18 2 16.3	0 57.7	12 3.8	13 19.2	23 57.9	13 41.3	27 48.3	9 11.8	8 43.6	17 22.6	18 47.2	16 25.5
24	18 6 12.9	1 54.9	12 .6	26 5.6	25 24.5	14 54.4	28 31.3	9 23.5	8 47.9	17 21.0	18 45.6	16 25.4
25	18 10 9.4	2 52.2	11 57.4	8♋38.8	26 48.5	16 7.5	29 14.2	9 35.2	8 52.2	17 19.5	18 44.1	16 25.3
26	18 14 6.0	3 49.4	11 54.3	20 59.0	28 9.9	17 20.6	29 57.0	9 47.0	8 56.7	17 18.0	18 42.5	16 25.2
27	18 18 2.5	4 46.7	11 51.1	3♌ 7.2	29 28.8	18 33.9	0♊39.9	9 58.9	9 1.3	17 16.6	18 41.0	16D25.3
28	18 21 59.1	5 44.0	11 47.9	15 5.2	0♌44.9	19 47.0	1 22.6	10 10.8	9 5.9	17 15.2	18 39.5	16 25.3
29	18 25 55.6	6 41.2	11 44.7	26 55.9	1 58.2	21 .2	2 5.3	10 22.8	9 10.6	17 13.9	18 37.9	16 25.3
30	18 29 52.2	7 38.4	11 41.6	8♍43.0	3 8.8	22 13.4	2 47.9	10 34.8	9 15.4	17 12.6	18 36.4	16 25.4

LATITUDE

DAY	EPHEM. SID. TIME	☉	☊	☽	☿	♀	♂	♃	♄	♅	♆	♇
1	16 35 32.0	0 .0	0 .0	2S 4.7	0N53.2	1S25.2	0S32.4	0N40.0	1N54.8	0N20.4	1N27.2	17N28.9
4	16 47 21.7	0 .0	0 .0	0N59.6	1 18.9	1 20.5	0 30.6	0 39.9	1 54.4	0 20.4	1 27.3	17 27.5
7	16 59 11.4	0 .0	0 .0	3 46.9	1 39.4	1 15.4	0 28.7	0 39.9	1 54.0	0 20.3	1 27.2	17 26.0
10	17 11 1.1	0 .0	0 .0	5 .9	1 53.5	1 9.8	0 26.8	0 39.9	1 53.6	0 20.3	1 27.2	17 24.5
13	17 22 50.7	0 .0	0 .0	3 40.4	2 .8	1 3.9	0 24.8	0 39.9	1 53.2	0 20.2	1 27.2	17 23.0
16	17 34 40.4	0 .0	0 .0	0 18.0	2 1.4	0 57.6	0 22.8	0 40.0	1 52.8	0 20.1	1 27.2	17 21.4
19	17 46 30.1	0 .0	0 .0	3S 9.0	1 55.4	0 51.0	0 20.8	0 40.0	1 52.4	0 20.1	1 27.1	17 19.8
22	17 58 19.7	0 .0	0 .0	4 56.7	1 43.3	0 44.2	0 18.8	0 40.0	1 52.0	0 20.0	1 27.1	17 18.2
25	18 10 9.4	0 .0	0 .0	4 27.8	1 25.3	0 37.1	0 16.7	0 40.1	1 51.7	0 19.9	1 27.0	17 16.5
28	18 21 59.1	0 .0	0 .0	2 10.7	1 1.9	0 29.9	0 14.6	0 40.1	1 51.3	0 19.9	1 27.0	17 14.9

RIGHT ASCENSION

DAY	EPHEM. SID. TIME	☉	☊	☽	☿	♀	♂	♃	♄	♅	♆	♇
1	16 35 32.0	8♊17.4	14♍32.6	20♌35.7	10♊51.3	14♉54.0	9♉31.9	7♌44.7	9♍55.5	15♏44.0	18♐34.2	22♎ .8
2	16 39 28.6	9 18.8	14 29.6	2♍18.7	13 12.3	16 6.2	10 15.4	7 55.0	9 57.7	15R41.7	18R32.5	21R59.9
3	16 43 25.2	10 20.3	14 26.7	13 48.6	15 33.5	17 18.6	10 58.9	8 5.4	9 59.9	15 39.5	18 30.8	21 59.0
4	16 47 21.7	11 21.8	14 23.7	25 14.0	17 54.5	18 31.3	11 42.4	8 15.9	10 2.3	15 37.2	18 29.1	21 58.1
5	16 51 18.3	12 23.5	14 20.8	6♎44.6	20 14.9	19 44.2	12 25.9	8 26.4	10 4.7	15 35.0	18 27.3	21 57.3
6	16 55 14.8	13 25.2	14 17.8	18 31.1	22 34.5	20 57.5	13 9.6	8 37.1	10 7.2	15 32.9	18 25.7	21 56.5
7	16 59 11.4	14 27.1	14 14.9	0♏43.6	24 52.8	22 11.0	13 53.2	8 47.8	10 9.9	15 30.7	18 23.9	21 55.7
8	17 3 7.9	15 28.9	14 11.9	13 31.4	27 9.6	23 24.8	14 36.9	8 58.6	10 12.6	15 28.6	18 22.2	21 55.0
9	17 7 4.5	16 30.9	14 8.9	27 .5	29 24.5	24 38.8	15 20.6	9 9.5	10 15.3	15 26.5	18 20.4	21 54.2
10	17 11 1.1	17 32.9	14 6.0	11♐11.9	1♋37.3	25 53.2	16 4.3	9 20.4	10 18.2	15 24.5	18 18.7	21 53.5
11	17 14 57.6	18 35.0	14 3.0	25 59.0	3 47.9	27 7.8	16 48.1	9 31.4	10 21.2	15 22.4	18 17.0	21 52.9
12	17 18 54.2	19 37.1	14 .1	11♑ 7.9	5 56.0	28 22.7	17 32.0	9 42.5	10 24.2	15 20.4	18 15.2	21 52.2
13	17 22 50.7	20 39.3	13 57.1	26 20.2	8 1.4	29 37.8	18 15.8	9 53.7	10 27.3	15 18.4	18 13.5	21 51.6
14	17 26 47.3	21 41.5	13 54.2	11♒18.3	10 4.0	0♊53.3	18 59.8	10 4.9	10 30.5	15 16.5	18 11.8	21 51.0
15	17 30 43.8	22 43.8	13 51.2	25 50.6	12 3.7	2 9.0	19 43.7	10 16.3	10 33.8	15 14.6	18 10.0	21 50.4
16	17 34 40.4	23 46.1	13 48.3	9♓53.0	14 .5	3 25.0	20 27.7	10 27.6	10 37.2	15 12.7	18 8.3	21 49.9
17	17 38 37.0	24 48.4	13 45.3	23 28.7	15 54.1	4 41.2	21 11.7	10 39.1	10 40.7	15 10.9	18 6.6	21 49.3
18	17 42 33.5	25 50.8	13 42.3	6♈44.7	17 44.7	5 57.7	21 55.8	10 50.6	10 44.2	15 9.1	18 4.8	21 48.8
19	17 46 30.1	26 53.2	13 39.4	19 50.1	19 32.1	7 14.5	22 39.9	11 2.2	10 47.8	15 7.3	18 3.1	21 48.4
20	17 50 26.6	27 55.6	13 36.4	2♉53.3	21 16.3	8 31.5	23 24.1	11 13.8	10 51.5	15 5.6	18 1.4	21 48.0
21	17 54 23.2	28 58.0	13 33.5	16 .4	22 57.2	9 48.7	24 8.3	11 25.5	10 55.3	15 3.9	17 59.7	21 47.5
22	17 58 19.7	0♋ .4	13 30.5	29 14.4	24 35.0	11 6.2	24 52.5	11 37.3	10 59.1	15 2.2	17 58.0	21 47.2
23	18 2 16.3	1 2.9	13 27.5	12♊33.8	26 9.4	12 24.0	25 36.7	11 49.1	11 3.1	15 .6	17 56.3	21 46.8
24	18 6 12.9	2 5.3	13 24.6	25 53.7	27 40.5	13 41.9	26 21.0	12 .9	11 7.1	14 59.0	17 54.6	21 46.5
25	18 10 9.4	3 7.6	13 21.6	9♋ 6.3	29 8.4	15 .0	27 5.3	12 12.9	11 11.1	14 57.5	17 52.9	21 46.2
26	18 14 6.0	4 10.0	13 18.7	22 3.9	0♌32.9	16 18.4	27 49.6	12 24.9	11 15.3	14 56.0	17 51.2	21 45.9
27	18 18 2.5	5 12.4	13 15.7	4♌40.5	1 54.1	17 37.0	28 34.1	12 36.9	11 19.6	14 54.6	17 49.6	21 45.8
28	18 21 59.1	6 14.7	13 12.7	16 53.5	3 11.9	18 55.7	29 18.4	12 49.0	11 23.9	14 53.2	17 48.0	21 45.6
29	18 25 55.6	7 16.9	13 9.8	28 44.0	4 26.3	20 14.6	0♊ 2.8	13 1.2	11 28.2	14 51.8	17 46.3	21 45.4
30	18 29 52.2	8 19.1	13 6.8	10♍16.7	5 37.2	21 33.6	0 47.3	13 13.3	11 32.7	14 50.5	17 44.7	21 45.2

DECLINATION

DAY	EPHEM. SID. TIME	☉	☊	☽	☿	♀	♂	♃	♄	♅	♆	♇
1	16 35 32.0	21N56.4	0N 6.9	13N12.2	23N10.0	15N32.2	14N51.6	19N36.6	10N31.7	16S53.6	21S33.9	9N37.5
4	16 47 21.7	22 20.0	0 7.0	3 8.8	24 17.6	16 36.2	15 33.4	19 29.2	10 28.5	16 51.8	21 33.5	9 37.1
7	16 59 11.4	22 40.2	0 7.0	8S27.9	25 .8	17 36.7	16 13.8	19 21.5	10 25.1	16 50.1	21 33.1	9 36.5
10	17 11 1.1	22 56.7	0 7.1	17 15.4	25 19.3	18 33.1	16 52.6	19 13.5	10 21.3	16 48.4	21 32.7	9 35.7
13	17 22 50.7	23 9.7	0 7.2	17 30.2	25 15.1	19 25.3	17 29.9	19 5.2	10 17.2	16 46.7	21 32.4	9 34.9
16	17 34 40.4	23 18.9	0 7.2	8 9.5	24 50.9	20 13.0	18 5.7	18 56.7	10 12.9	16 45.2	21 32.0	9 33.9
19	17 46 30.1	23 24.5	0 7.3	4N58.3	24 10.0	20 55.9	18 39.8	18 48.0	10 8.2	16 43.8	21 31.6	9 32.8
22	17 58 19.7	23 26.3	0 7.3	15 23.0	23 15.8	21 33.6	19 12.2	18 39.0	10 3.3	16 42.4	21 31.3	9 31.5
25	18 10 9.4	23 24.5	0 7.4	18 42.2	22 11.4	22 6.1	19 42.9	18 29.7	9 58.1	16 41.2	21 30.9	9 30.1
28	18 21 59.1	23 18.9	0 7.5	14 13.7	20 59.9	22 33.0	20 11.9	18 20.2	9 52.7	16 40.0	21 30.6	9 28.6

JULY 1979

LONGITUDE

DAY	EPHEM. SID. TIME	☉	☊	☽	☿	♀	♂	♃	♄	♅	♆	♇
	h m s	° ′	° ′	° ′	° ′	° ′	° ′	° ′	° ′	° ′	° ′	° ′
1	18 33 48.8	8♋35.6	11♍38.4	20♍31.1	4♌16.4	23♊26.7	3♊30.4	10♌46.9	9♍20.2	17♏11.3	18♐34.9	16♎25.5
2	18 37 45.3	9 32.8	11 35.2	2♎25.2	5 21.2	24 39.9	4 12.9	10 59.0	9 25.2	17 R 10.1	18 R 33.4	16 25.7
3	18 41 41.9	10 30.0	11 32.0	14 30.6	6 22.9	25 53.2	4 55.3	11 11.1	9 30.1	17 8.9	18 31.9	16 25.9
4	18 45 38.4	11 27.2	11 28.8	26 52.5	7 21.5	27 6.4	5 37.6	11 23.3	9 35.2	17 7.8	18 30.5	16 26.1
5	18 49 35.0	12 24.4	11 25.7	9♏35.7	8 16.8	28 19.7	6 19.9	11 35.6	9 40.3	17 6.7	18 29.0	16 26.4
6	18 53 31.5	13 21.6	11 22.5	22 43.9	8 8.9	29 33.0	7 2.1	11 47.9	9 45.5	17 5.7	18 27.6	16 26.6
7	18 57 28.1	14 18.8	11 19.3	6♐19.0	9 57.5	0♋46.4	7 44.2	12 .3	9 50.8	17 4.7	18 26.1	16 27.0
8	19 1 24.7	15 16.0	11 16.1	20 20.7	10 42.5	1 59.7	8 26.3	12 12.6	9 56.1	17 3.7	18 24.7	16 27.3
9	19 5 21.2	16 13.1	11 13.0	4♑45.7	11 23.8	3 13.1	9 8.3	12 25.1	10 1.5	17 2.8	18 23.3	16 27.7
10	19 9 17.8	17 10.3	11 9.8	19 28.5	12 1.3	4 26.4	9 50.2	12 37.5	10 7.0	17 2.0	18 22.0	16 28.1
11	19 13 14.3	18 7.5	11 6.6	4♒21.2	12 34.8	5 39.8	10 32.1	12 50.1	10 12.5	17 1.2	18 20.6	16 28.6
12	19 17 10.9	19 4.7	11 3.4	19 15.5	13 4.2	6 53.3	11 14.0	13 2.6	10 18.1	17 .4	18 19.3	16 29.1
13	19 21 7.4	20 1.9	11 .3	4♓3.6	13 29.4	8 6.7	11 55.7	13 15.2	10 23.8	16 59.7	18 17.9	16 29.6
14	19 25 4.0	20 59.1	10 57.1	18 39.4	13 50.2	9 20.2	12 37.4	13 27.8	10 29.5	16 59.1	18 16.6	16 30.2
15	19 29 .5	21 56.3	10 53.9	2♈58.9	14 6.5	10 33.7	13 19.1	13 40.5	10 35.3	16 58.5	18 15.3	16 30.7
16	19 32 57.1	22 53.5	10 50.7	17 .3	14 18.2	11 47.2	14 .6	13 53.2	10 41.1	16 57.9	18 14.1	16 31.4
17	19 36 53.7	23 50.8	10 47.5	0♉43.2	14 25.1	13 .7	14 42.1	14 5.9	10 47.0	16 57.4	18 12.8	16 32.0
18	19 40 50.2	24 48.1	10 44.4	14 8.5	14 27.3	14 14.3	15 23.6	14 18.7	10 53.0	16 57.0	18 11.6	16 32.8
19	19 44 46.8	25 45.3	10 41.2	27 17.4	14 R 24.6	15 27.9	16 5.0	14 31.5	10 59.0	16 56.6	18 10.4	16 33.5
20	19 48 43.3	26 42.6	10 38.0	10♊11.4	14 17.0	16 41.5	16 46.3	14 44.3	11 5.0	16 56.2	18 9.3	16 34.2
21	19 52 39.9	27 39.9	10 34.8	22 51.9	14 4.6	17 55.2	17 27.6	14 57.1	11 11.2	16 55.9	18 8.1	16 35.0
22	19 56 36.4	28 37.2	10 31.7	5♋20.2	13 47.4	19 8.8	18 8.7	15 10.0	11 17.3	16 55.7	18 6.9	16 35.8
23	20 0 33.0	29 34.5	10 28.5	17 37.4	13 25.6	20 22.5	18 49.8	15 22.9	11 23.6	16 55.5	18 5.8	16 36.7
24	20 4 29.6	0♌31.8	10 25.3	29 44.6	12 59.4	21 36.2	19 30.9	15 35.8	11 29.8	16 55.3	18 4.7	16 37.6
25	20 8 26.1	1 29.1	10 22.1	11♌43.3	12 29.0	22 49.9	20 11.8	15 48.8	11 36.2	16 55.2	18 3.6	16 38.5
26	20 12 22.7	2 26.4	10 19.0	23 35.3	11 55.0	24 3.6	20 52.7	16 1.7	11 42.5	16 55.2	18 2.6	16 39.4
27	20 16 19.2	3 23.8	10 15.8	5♍23.0	11 17.6	25 17.4	21 33.6	16 14.7	11 48.9	16 55.2	18 1.6	16 40.4
28	20 20 15.8	4 21.1	10 12.6	17 9.1	10 37.4	26 31.2	22 14.3	16 27.7	11 55.4	16 55.2	18 .6	16 41.4
29	20 24 12.3	5 18.5	10 9.4	28 57.4	9 55.1	27 45.0	22 55.0	16 40.7	12 1.9	16 D 55.3	17 59.6	16 42.5
30	20 28 8.9	6 15.8	10 6.2	10♎51.8	9 11.4	28 58.8	23 35.6	16 53.8	12 8.5	16 55.5	17 58.6	16 43.5
31	20 32 5.4	7 13.2	10 3.1	22 56.9	8 26.9	0♌12.6	24 16.2	17 6.8	12 15.1	16 55.7	17 57.7	16 44.6

LATITUDE

DAY	EPHEM. SID. TIME	☉	☊	☽	☿	♀	♂	♃	♄	♅	♆	♇
1	18 33 48.8	0 .0	0 .0	0N54.3	0N33.6	0S22.6	0S12.5	0N40.2	1N51.0	0N19.8	1N26.9	17N13.2
4	18 45 38.4	0 .0	0 .0	3 42.9	0 .7	0 15.1	0 10.4	0 40.2	1 50.7	0 19.7	1 26.8	17 11.5
7	18 57 28.1	0 .0	0 .0	5 5.6	0S36.2	0 7.7	0 8.2	0 40.3	1 50.4	0 19.7	1 26.8	17 9.8
10	19 9 17.8	0 .0	0 .0	3 56.1	1 16.4	0 .3	0 6.0	0 40.4	1 50.1	0 19.6	1 26.7	17 8.1
13	19 21 7.4	0 .0	0 .0	0 29.3	1 58.8	0N 7.1	0 3.8	0 40.5	1 49.9	0 19.5	1 26.6	17 6.5
16	19 32 57.1	0 .0	0 .0	3S 8.8	2 42.1	0 14.3	0 1.5	0 40.6	1 49.6	0 19.4	1 26.5	17 4.8
19	19 44 46.8	0 .0	0 .0	5 2.6	3 24.2	0 21.4	0N .7	0 40.7	1 49.4	0 19.4	1 26.4	17 3.1
22	19 56 36.4	0 .0	0 .0	4 38.0	4 2.3	0 28.3	0 3.0	0 40.9	1 49.2	0 19.3	1 26.2	17 1.5
25	20 8 26.1	0 .0	0 .0	2 22.1	4 33.0	0 35.0	0 5.3	0 41.0	1 49.0	0 19.2	1 26.1	16 59.9
28	20 20 15.8	0 .0	0 .0	0N45.9	4 52.4	0 41.4	0 7.7	0 41.2	1 48.8	0 19.1	1 26.0	16 58.3
31	20 32 5.4	0 .0	0 .0	3 39.1	4 57.4	0 47.5	0 10.0	0 41.3	1 48.7	0 19.0	1 25.9	16 56.8

RIGHT ASCENSION

DAY	EPHEM. SID. TIME	☉	☊	☽	☿	♀	♂	♃	♄	♅	♆	♇
1	18 33 48.8	9♋21.2	13♍3.9	21♍38.7	6♌44.7	22♊52.8	1♊31.7	13♌25.6	11♍37.2	14♏49.2	17♐43.1	21♎45.1
2	18 37 45.3	10 23.3	13 .9	2♎59.2	7 48.7	24 12.2	2 16.2	13 37.8	11 41.8	14 R 48.0	17 R 41.5	21 R 45.0
3	18 41 41.9	11 25.3	12 57.9	14 28.3	8 49.1	25 31.6	3 .6	13 50.1	11 46.4	14 46.8	17 39.9	21 45.0
4	18 45 38.4	12 27.2	12 55.0	26 17.1	9 45.9	26 51.2	3 45.1	14 2.5	11 51.1	14 45.7	17 38.3	21 45.0
5	18 49 35.0	13 29.0	12 52.0	8♏36.6	10 39.0	28 10.9	4 29.6	14 14.9	11 55.9	14 44.6	17 36.8	21 45.0
6	18 53 31.5	14 30.8	12 49.1	21 36.0	11 28.4	29 30.6	5 14.1	14 27.3	12 .7	14 43.6	17 35.2	21 45.0
7	18 57 28.1	15 32.4	12 46.1	5♐21.5	12 14.0	0♋50.5	5 58.6	14 39.8	12 5.6	14 42.6	17 33.7	21 D 45.1
8	19 1 24.7	16 34.0	12 43.1	19 52.6	12 55.6	2 10.4	6 43.2	14 52.3	12 10.6	14 41.6	17 32.2	21 45.2
9	19 5 21.2	17 35.5	12 40.2	5♑ .8	13 33.3	3 30.3	7 27.7	15 4.8	12 15.6	14 40.7	17 30.7	21 45.3
10	19 9 17.8	18 36.8	12 37.2	20 29.2	14 6.9	4 50.3	8 12.2	15 17.4	12 20.7	14 39.8	17 29.2	21 45.5
11	19 13 14.3	19 38.1	12 34.2	5♒57.2	14 36.3	6 10.3	8 56.8	15 30.0	12 25.9	14 39.0	17 27.8	21 45.7
12	19 17 10.9	20 39.3	12 31.3	21 6.5	15 1.4	7 30.3	9 41.3	15 42.6	12 31.1	14 38.3	17 26.3	21 45.9
13	19 21 7.4	21 40.3	12 28.3	5♓46.1	15 22.3	8 50.3	10 25.9	15 55.2	12 36.3	14 37.6	17 24.9	21 46.1
14	19 25 4.0	22 41.3	12 25.3	19 53.7	15 38.6	10 10.3	11 10.4	16 7.9	12 41.7	14 36.9	17 23.5	21 46.4
15	19 29 .5	23 42.1	12 22.4	3♈33.3	15 50.5	11 30.2	11 55.0	16 20.6	12 47.0	14 36.3	17 22.1	21 46.7
16	19 32 57.1	24 42.8	12 19.4	16 52.8	15 57.8	12 50.1	12 39.5	16 33.4	12 52.5	14 35.7	17 20.8	21 47.0
17	19 36 53.7	25 43.4	12 16.5	0♉1.0	16 .4	14 10.0	13 24.0	16 46.1	12 58.0	14 35.2	17 19.4	21 47.4
18	19 40 50.2	26 43.9	12 13.5	13 5.7	15 R 58.4	15 29.8	14 8.6	16 59.0	13 3.5	14 34.8	17 18.2	21 47.9
19	19 44 46.8	27 44.3	12 10.5	26 11.7	15 51.7	16 49.5	14 53.1	17 11.8	13 9.1	14 34.4	17 16.9	21 48.3
20	19 48 43.3	28 44.5	12 7.6	9♊20.8	15 40.3	18 9.1	15 37.6	17 24.6	13 14.8	14 34.0	17 15.6	21 48.7
21	19 52 39.9	29 44.5	12 4.6	22 30.9	15 24.4	19 28.6	16 22.1	17 37.5	13 20.5	14 33.7	17 14.3	21 49.2
22	19 56 36.4	0♌44.5	12 1.6	5♋37.0	15 4.0	20 48.0	17 6.5	17 50.4	13 26.2	14 33.4	17 13.1	21 49.8
23	20 0 33.0	1 44.3	11 58.7	18 32.6	14 39.4	22 7.2	17 50.9	18 3.3	13 32.0	14 33.2	17 11.9	21 50.3
24	20 4 29.6	2 43.9	11 55.7	1♌11.7	14 10.7	23 26.3	18 35.3	18 16.2	13 37.9	14 33.1	17 10.7	21 50.9
25	20 8 26.1	3 43.4	11 52.7	13 30.1	13 38.3	24 45.2	19 19.7	18 29.1	13 43.8	14 33.0	17 9.6	21 51.5
26	20 12 22.7	4 42.8	11 49.7	25 27.2	13 2.6	26 4.0	20 4.0	18 42.0	13 49.7	14 32.9	17 8.5	21 52.1
27	20 16 19.2	5 42.0	11 46.8	7♍5.1	12 24.0	27 22.5	20 48.3	18 55.0	13 55.7	14 32.9	17 7.4	21 52.8
28	20 20 15.8	6 41.1	11 43.8	18 28.8	11 43.1	28 40.9	21 32.5	19 7.9	14 1.7	14 32.9	17 6.3	21 53.5
29	20 24 12.3	7 40.0	11 40.8	29 45.7	11 .5	29 59.1	22 16.8	19 20.9	14 7.8	14 D 33.0	17 5.2	21 54.2
30	20 28 8.9	8 38.7	11 37.9	11♎4.6	10 16.8	1♌17.1	23 .9	19 33.9	14 13.9	14 33.2	17 4.2	21 55.0
31	20 32 5.4	9 37.3	11 34.9	22 35.3	9 32.8	2 34.8	23 45.0	19 46.9	14 20.0	14 33.4	17 3.2	21 55.8

DECLINATION

DAY	EPHEM. SID. TIME	☉	☊	☽	☿	♀	♂	♃	♄	♅	♆	♇
1	18 33 48.8	23N 9.6	0N 7.5	4N35.3	19N44.0	22N54.1	20N39.0	18N10.4	9N47.0	16S39.0	21S30.3	9N26.9
4	18 45 38.4	22 56.7	0 7.6	6S53.4	18 26.6	23 9.3	21 4.4	18 .5	9 41.0	16 38.0	21 30.0	9 25.2
7	18 57 28.1	22 40.2	0 7.7	16 20.6	17 10.3	23 18.5	21 27.9	17 50.3	9 34.8	16 37.2	21 29.7	9 23.3
10	19 9 17.8	22 20.2	0 7.7	18 7.8	15 57.9	23 21.6	21 49.6	17 39.9	9 28.5	16 36.5	21 29.5	9 21.3
13	19 21 7.4	21 56.7	0 7.8	9 33.9	14 52.5	23 18.5	22 9.4	17 29.3	9 21.8	16 36.0	21 29.2	9 19.2
16	19 32 57.1	21 29.8	0 7.9	3N46.4	13 57.1	23 9.3	22 27.4	17 18.5	9 15.0	16 35.5	21 29.0	9 17.1
19	19 44 46.8	20 59.6	0 7.9	14 38.4	13 14.9	22 53.9	22 43.5	17 7.5	9 8.0	16 35.2	21 28.8	9 14.7
22	19 56 36.4	20 26.2	0 8.0	18 42.1	12 48.9	22 32.4	22 57.6	16 56.3	9 .8	16 35.1	21 28.6	9 12.4
25	20 8 26.1	19 49.7	0 8.0	14 59.7	12 41.3	22 4.9	23 9.9	16 44.9	8 53.5	16 35.0	21 28.4	9 9.9
28	20 20 15.8	19 10.3	0 8.1	5 46.7	12 52.7	21 31.7	23 20.4	16 33.4	8 46.0	16 35.1	21 28.3	9 7.4
31	20 32 5.4	18 28.0	0 8.2	5S31.8	13 21.7	20 52.7	23 28.9	16 21.7	8 38.3	16 35.3	21 28.1	9 4.7

AUGUST 1979

LONGITUDE

DAY	EPHEM. SID. TIME	☉	☊	☽	☿	♀	♂	♃	♄	♅	♆	♇
	h m s	° ′	° ′	° ′	° ′	° ′	° ′	° ′	° ′	° ′	° ′	° ′
1	20 36 2.0	8♌10.6	9♍59.9	5♏17.4	7♌42.5	1♌26.5	24♊56.7	17♌19.9	12♍21.8	16♏56.0	17♐56.8	16♎45.8
2	20 39 58.6	9 8.0	9 56.7	17 58.1	6 R 58.9	2 40.3	25 37.1	17 33.0	12 28.4	16 56.3	17 R 55.9	16 46.9
3	20 43 55.1	10 5.4	9 53.5	1♐ 2.9	6 17.1	3 54.2	26 17.4	17 46.1	12 35.2	16 56.7	17 55.1	16 48.1
4	20 47 51.7	11 2.8	9 50.4	14 34.8	5 37.8	5 8.1	26 57.6	17 59.2	12 41.9	16 57.1	17 54.3	16 49.3
5	20 51 48.2	12 .3	9 47.2	28 34.8	5 1.7	6 22.0	27 37.8	18 12.3	12 48.7	16 57.6	17 53.5	16 50.6
6	20 55 44.8	12 57.7	9 44.0	13♑ 1.2	4 29.6	7 36.0	28 17.9	18 25.4	12 55.6	16 58.1	17 52.7	16 51.9
7	20 59 41.3	13 55.1	9 40.8	27 49.6	4 2.2	8 49.9	28 58.0	18 38.6	13 2.5	16 58.7	17 52.0	16 53.2
8	21 3 37.9	14 52.7	9 37.6	12♒53.0	3 40.0	10 4.0	29 38.0	18 51.7	13 9.4	16 59.4	17 51.3	16 54.6
9	21 7 34.4	15 50.2	9 34.5	28 2.5	3 23.6	11 18.0	0♋17.9	19 4.9	13 16.4	17 .0	17 50.7	16 55.9
10	21 11 31.0	16 47.7	9 31.3	13♓ 8.6	3 13.3	12 32.0	0 57.8	19 18.0	13 23.4	17 .8	17 50.0	16 57.3
11	21 15 27.5	17 45.2	9 28.1	28 2.8	3 9.5	13 46.0	1 37.5	19 31.2	13 30.4	17 1.6	17 49.4	16 58.8
12	21 19 24.1	18 42.7	9 24.9	12♈38.8	3 D 12.5	15 .1	2 17.2	19 44.3	13 37.5	17 2.4	17 48.8	17 .2
13	21 23 20.6	19 40.3	9 21.8	26 52.3	3 22.5	16 14.2	2 56.8	19 57.5	13 44.5	17 3.3	17 48.2	17 1.7
14	21 27 17.2	20 37.9	9 18.6	10♉41.9	3 39.6	17 28.3	3 36.4	20 10.6	13 51.6	17 4.2	17 47.7	17 3.2
15	21 31 13.8	21 35.5	9 15.4	24 7.8	4 3.9	18 42.4	4 15.9	20 23.8	13 58.8	17 5.2	17 47.2	17 4.7
16	21 35 10.3	22 33.2	9 12.2	7♊12.0	4 35.3	19 56.6	4 55.3	20 37.0	14 6.0	17 6.3	17 46.7	17 6.3
17	21 39 6.9	23 30.8	9 9.0	19 56.9	5 13.8	21 10.8	5 34.6	20 50.1	14 13.2	17 7.3	17 46.3	17 7.9
18	21 43 3.4	24 28.5	9 5.9	2♋25.5	5 59.4	22 25.0	6 13.9	21 3.3	14 20.4	17 8.5	17 45.9	17 9.5
19	21 46 60.0	25 26.3	9 2.7	14 40.8	6 51.8	23 39.2	6 53.0	21 16.4	14 27.6	17 9.7	17 45.5	17 11.1
20	21 50 56.5	26 24.0	8 59.5	26 45.5	7 50.9	24 53.4	7 32.1	21 29.5	14 34.9	17 10.9	17 45.1	17 12.8
21	21 54 53.1	27 21.8	8 56.3	8♌42.3	8 56.5	26 7.7	8 11.2	21 42.7	14 42.2	17 12.2	17 44.8	17 14.4
22	21 58 49.6	28 19.6	8 53.2	20 33.5	10 8.3	27 21.9	8 50.1	21 55.8	14 49.5	17 13.6	17 44.5	17 16.1
23	22 2 46.2	29 17.4	8 50.0	2♍21.4	11 25.9	28 36.2	9 29.0	22 8.9	14 56.9	17 14.9	17 44.3	17 17.9
24	22 6 42.7	0♍15.3	8 46.8	14 8.1	12 49.1	29 50.5	10 7.8	22 22.0	15 4.2	17 16.4	17 44.1	17 19.6
25	22 10 39.3	1 13.1	8 43.6	25 56.2	14 17.5	1♍ 4.9	10 46.5	22 35.1	15 11.6	17 17.9	17 43.9	17 21.4
26	22 14 35.8	2 11.0	8 40.4	7♎48.1	15 50.6	2 19.2	11 25.1	22 48.1	15 19.0	17 19.4	17 43.7	17 23.2
27	22 18 32.4	3 8.9	8 37.3	19 46.8	17 28.0	3 33.5	12 3.7	23 1.2	15 26.4	17 21.0	17 43.6	17 25.0
28	22 22 28.9	4 6.9	8 34.1	1♏55.5	19 9.3	4 47.9	12 42.1	23 14.2	15 33.8	17 22.6	17 43.5	17 26.9
29	22 26 25.5	5 4.9	8 30.9	14 17.9	20 54.0	6 2.3	13 20.6	23 27.3	15 41.3	17 24.4	17 43.5	17 28.8
30	22 30 22.1	6 2.8	8 27.7	26 57.7	22 41.5	7 16.7	13 58.9	23 40.3	15 48.8	17 26.1	17 43.4	17 30.7
31	22 34 18.6	7 .9	8 24.6	9♐58.3	24 31.6	8 31.1	14 37.1	23 53.3	15 56.2	17 27.9	17 43.4	17 32.6

LATITUDE

DAY	EPHEM. SID. TIME	☉	☊	☽	☿	♀	♂	♃	♄	♅	♆	♇
1	20 36 2.0	0 .0	0 .0	4N22.1	4S55.6	0N49.4	0N10.8	0N41.4	1N48.6	0N19.0	1N25.8	16N56.2
4	20 47 51.7	0 .0	0 .0	5 12.6	4 39.3	0 55.0	0 13.2	0 41.5	1 48.5	0 18.9	1 25.7	16 54.7
7	20 59 41.3	0 .0	0 .0	3 25.9	4 8.5	1 .2	0 15.6	0 41.7	1 48.4	0 18.9	1 25.6	16 53.3
10	21 11 31.0	0 .0	0 .0	0S25.5	3 26.7	1 5.0	0 18.0	0 41.9	1 48.3	0 18.8	1 25.4	16 51.8
13	21 23 20.6	0 .0	0 .0	3 56.5	2 38.0	1 9.3	0 20.4	0 42.1	1 48.2	0 18.7	1 25.3	16 50.5
16	21 35 10.3	0 .0	0 .0	5 16.4	1 46.8	1 13.1	0 22.9	0 42.3	1 48.2	0 18.6	1 25.1	16 49.1
19	21 46 60.0	0 .0	0 .0	4 15.9	0 56.5	1 16.5	0 25.4	0 42.6	1 48.2	0 18.6	1 25.0	16 47.8
22	21 58 49.6	0 .0	0 .0	1 37.7	0 10.2	1 19.3	0 27.9	0 42.8	1 48.2	0 18.5	1 24.8	16 46.6
25	22 10 39.3	0 .0	0 .0	1N35.8	0N29.8	1 21.5	0 30.4	0 43.1	1 48.2	0 18.4	1 24.6	16 45.4
28	22 22 28.9	0 .0	0 .0	4 15.8	1 1.9	1 23.2	0 32.9	0 43.3	1 48.2	0 18.3	1 24.5	16 44.3
31	22 34 18.6	0 .0	0 .0	5 18.0	1 25.3	1 24.3	0 35.5	0 43.6	1 48.3	0 18.3	1 24.3	16 43.2

RIGHT ASCENSION

DAY	EPHEM. SID. TIME	☉	☊	☽	☿	♀	♂	♃	♄	♅	♆	♇
1	20 36 2.0	10♌35.8	11♍31.9	4♏28.4	8♌49.3	3♌52.3	24♊29.1	19♌59.8	14♍26.2	14♏33.7	17♐ 2.2	21♎56.6
2	20 39 58.6	11 34.0	11 29.0	16 54.2	8 R 7.0	5 9.6	25 13.1	20 12.8	14 32.4	14 34.0	17 R 1.3	21 57.4
3	20 43 55.1	12 32.2	11 26.0	0♐ .9	7 26.7	6 26.7	25 57.1	20 25.8	14 38.7	14 34.3	17 .4	21 58.3
4	20 47 51.7	13 30.1	11 23.0	13 53.6	6 49.2	7 43.5	26 41.0	20 38.8	14 45.0	14 34.8	16 59.5	21 59.2
5	20 51 48.2	14 28.0	11 20.1	28 30.4	6 15.3	9 .1	27 24.8	20 51.8	14 51.3	14 35.2	16 58.7	22 .1
6	20 55 44.8	15 25.6	11 17.1	13♑42.1	5 45.6	10 16.4	28 8.6	21 4.8	14 57.7	14 35.8	16 57.8	22 1.1
7	20 59 41.3	16 23.1	11 14.1	29 12.0	5 20.9	11 32.4	28 52.3	21 17.8	15 4.1	14 36.3	16 57.1	22 2.0
8	21 3 37.9	17 20.5	11 11.1	14♒40.9	5 1.7	12 48.3	29 36.0	21 30.9	15 10.6	14 37.0	16 56.3	22 3.1
9	21 7 34.4	18 17.8	11 8.2	29 52.5	4 48.4	14 3.8	0♋19.6	21 43.9	15 17.1	14 37.7	16 55.6	22 4.1
10	21 11 31.0	19 14.8	11 5.2	14♓37.7	4 41.5	15 19.1	1 3.1	21 56.9	15 23.6	14 38.4	16 54.9	22 5.2
11	21 15 27.5	20 11.7	11 2.2	28 54.6	4 41.4	16 34.1	1 46.5	22 9.9	15 30.1	14 39.2	16 54.2	22 6.3
12	21 19 24.1	21 8.5	10 59.2	12♈47.1	4 D 48.3	17 48.8	2 29.9	22 22.9	15 36.7	14 40.0	16 53.6	22 7.4
13	21 23 20.6	22 5.2	10 56.3	26 21.9	5 2.4	19 3.3	3 13.2	22 35.8	15 43.3	14 40.9	16 53.0	22 8.5
14	21 27 17.2	23 1.7	10 53.3	9♉45.4	5 23.9	20 17.5	3 56.4	22 48.8	15 49.9	14 41.8	16 52.4	22 9.7
15	21 31 13.8	23 58.1	10 50.3	23 3.2	5 52.7	21 31.5	4 39.6	23 1.8	15 56.5	14 42.8	16 51.9	22 10.9
16	21 35 10.3	24 54.3	10 47.3	6♊17.6	6 28.9	22 45.1	5 22.6	23 14.7	16 3.2	14 43.8	16 51.4	22 12.1
17	21 39 6.9	25 50.5	10 44.4	19 28.5	7 12.4	23 58.6	6 5.6	23 27.7	16 9.9	14 44.9	16 50.9	22 13.4
18	21 43 3.4	26 46.5	10 41.4	2♋33.0	8 3.0	25 11.7	6 48.4	23 40.6	16 16.6	14 46.1	16 50.4	22 14.6
19	21 46 60.0	27 42.3	10 38.4	15 26.7	9 .5	26 24.6	7 31.2	23 53.5	16 23.3	14 47.2	16 50.0	22 15.9
20	21 50 56.5	28 38.1	10 35.4	28 5.2	10 4.8	27 37.3	8 13.9	24 6.4	16 30.1	14 48.5	16 49.7	22 17.3
21	21 54 53.1	29 33.7	10 32.5	10♌25.2	11 15.4	28 49.7	8 56.5	24 19.3	16 36.9	14 49.8	16 49.3	22 18.6
22	21 58 49.6	0♍29.2	10 29.5	22 25.6	12 32.2	0♍ 1.8	9 39.0	24 32.2	16 43.7	14 51.1	16 49.0	22 20.0
23	22 2 46.2	1 24.6	10 26.5	4♍ 7.8	13 54.5	1 13.7	10 21.3	24 45.0	16 50.5	14 52.5	16 48.7	22 21.4
24	22 6 42.7	2 19.9	10 23.5	15 35.5	15 22.1	2 25.4	11 3.6	24 57.9	16 57.4	14 53.9	16 48.5	22 22.8
25	22 10 39.3	3 15.1	10 20.6	26 54.3	16 54.5	3 36.8	11 45.8	25 10.7	17 4.2	14 55.4	16 48.3	22 24.2
26	22 14 35.8	4 10.2	10 17.6	8♎11.5	18 31.0	4 48.0	12 27.8	25 23.5	17 11.1	14 56.9	16 48.1	22 25.7
27	22 18 32.4	5 5.2	10 14.6	19 35.2	20 11.3	5 59.0	13 9.8	25 36.3	17 18.0	14 58.5	16 48.0	22 27.2
28	22 22 28.9	6 .0	10 11.6	1♏14.4	21 54.7	7 9.8	13 51.6	25 49.0	17 24.9	15 .2	16 47.8	22 28.7
29	22 26 25.5	6 54.8	10 8.6	13 18.0	23 40.8	8 20.4	14 33.3	26 1.8	17 31.8	15 1.9	16 47.8	22 30.3
30	22 30 22.1	7 49.5	10 5.7	25 54.1	25 29.0	9 30.7	15 14.9	26 14.5	17 38.8	15 3.6	16 47.8	22 31.8
31	22 34 18.6	8 44.1	10 2.7	9♐ 8.6	27 18.7	10 40.8	15 56.4	26 27.1	17 45.7	15 5.4	16 47.8	22 33.4

DECLINATION

DAY	EPHEM. SID. TIME	☉	☊	☽	☿	♀	♂	♃	♄	♅	♆	♇
1	20 36 2.0	18N13.3	0N 8.2	9S 9.8	13N34.6	20N38.5	23N31.4	16N17.8	8N35.7	16S35.4	21S28.1	9N 3.8
4	20 47 51.7	17 27.4	0 8.3	17 22.3	14 20.9	19 52.4	23 37.4	16 6.0	8 27.8	16 35.8	21 28.0	9 1.1
7	20 59 41.3	16 39.0	0 8.3	17 13.9	15 13.2	19 1.2	23 41.7	15 54.0	8 19.8	16 36.3	21 27.9	8 58.4
10	21 11 31.0	15 48.2	0 8.4	7 .9	16 5.0	18 5.0	23 44.1	15 41.8	8 11.7	16 37.0	21 27.9	8 55.5
13	21 23 20.6	14 55.0	0 8.4	6N40.7	16 50.3	17 4.3	23 44.8	15 29.6	8 3.5	16 37.8	21 27.9	8 52.6
16	21 35 10.3	13 59.8	0 8.5	16 18.5	17 23.2	15 59.3	23 43.7	15 17.3	7 55.2	16 38.7	21 27.9	8 49.7
19	21 46 60.0	13 2.5	0 8.6	18 23.4	17 38.7	14 50.3	23 41.0	15 4.9	7 46.8	16 39.7	21 28.0	8 46.7
22	21 58 49.6	12 3.3	0 8.6	13 5.6	17 32.4	13 37.6	23 36.5	14 52.4	7 38.3	16 40.9	21 28.0	8 43.7
25	22 10 39.3	11 2.5	0 8.7	3 4.9	17 1.1	12 21.6	23 30.4	14 39.9	7 29.8	16 42.2	21 28.1	8 40.7
28	22 22 28.9	10 .0	0 8.8	8S 8.3	16 3.5	11 2.5	23 22.8	14 27.3	7 21.2	16 43.6	21 28.2	8 37.7
31	22 34 18.6	8 56.2	0 8.8	16 42.1	14 41.2	9 40.7	23 13.6	14 14.7	7 12.6	16 45.1	21 28.4	8 34.6

SEPTEMBER 1979

LONGITUDE

DAY	EPHEM. SID. TIME (h m s)	☉ (° ′)	☊ (° ′)	☾ (° ′)	☿ (° ′)	♀ (° ′)	♂ (° ′)	♃ (° ′)	♄ (° ′)	♅ (° ′)	♆ (° ′)	♇ (° ′)
1	22 38 15.2	7♍58.9	8♍21.4	23♐22.9	26♌23.6	9♍45.5	15♋15.2	24♌ 6.2	16♍ 3.7	17♏29.7	17♐43.5	17♎34.5
2	22 42 11.7	8 56.9	8 18.2	7♑13.2	28 17.2	10 60.0	15 53.3	24 19.2	16 11.2	17 31.6	17D43.6	17 36.5
3	22 46 8.3	9 55.0	8 15.0	21 29.4	0♍12.1	12 14.4	16 31.2	24 32.1	16 18.7	17 33.5	17 43.7	17 38.5
4	22 50 4.8	10 53.1	8 11.8	6♒ 9.2	2 7.8	13 28.8	17 9.1	24 44.9	16 26.2	17 35.4	17 43.8	17 40.5
5	22 54 1.4	11 51.2	8 8.7	21 7.8	4 4.0	14 43.3	17 46.9	24 57.8	16 33.7	17 37.4	17 44.0	17 42.5
6	22 57 57.9	12 49.3	8 5.5	6♓17.7	6 .4	15 57.8	18 24.6	25 10.6	16 41.2	17 39.5	17 44.2	17 44.5
7	23 1 54.5	13 47.5	8 2.3	21 29.8	7 56.9	17 12.3	19 2.3	25 23.4	16 48.7	17 41.6	17 44.4	17 46.5
8	23 5 51.0	14 45.7	7 59.1	6♈34.7	9 53.1	18 26.8	19 39.8	25 36.2	16 56.2	17 43.7	17 44.6	17 48.6
9	23 9 47.6	15 44.0	7 56.0	21 23.6	11 48.9	19 41.3	20 17.3	25 48.9	17 3.7	17 45.9	17 44.9	17 50.7
10	23 13 44.1	16 42.2	7 52.8	5♉50.2	13 44.2	20 55.8	20 54.6	26 1.6	17 11.3	17 48.1	17 45.3	17 52.8
11	23 17 40.7	17 40.5	7 49.6	19 50.6	15 38.8	22 10.3	21 31.9	26 14.3	17 18.8	17 50.4	17 45.6	17 54.9
12	23 21 37.2	18 38.9	7 46.4	3♊23.6	17 32.6	23 24.9	22 9.1	26 27.0	17 26.3	17 52.7	17 46.0	17 57.0
13	23 25 33.8	19 37.2	7 43.2	16 30.6	19 25.6	24 39.4	22 46.2	26 39.6	17 33.8	17 55.0	17 46.5	17 59.2
14	23 29 30.3	20 35.6	7 40.1	29 14.2	21 17.6	25 54.0	23 23.3	26 52.1	17 41.4	17 57.4	17 46.9	18 1.3
15	23 33 26.9	21 34.1	7 36.9	11♋38.3	23 8.7	27 8.6	24 .2	27 4.7	17 48.9	17 59.8	17 47.4	18 3.5
16	23 37 23.4	22 32.6	7 33.7	23 47.0	24 58.8	28 23.2	24 37.1	27 17.2	17 56.4	18 2.3	17 47.9	18 5.7
17	23 41 20.0	23 31.1	7 30.5	5♌44.7	26 47.9	29 37.8	25 13.8	27 29.6	18 3.9	18 4.8	17 48.5	18 7.9
18	23 45 16.5	24 29.6	7 27.4	17 35.4	28 36.0	0♎52.4	25 50.5	27 42.0	18 11.4	18 7.4	17 49.1	18 10.1
19	23 49 13.1	25 28.2	7 24.2	29 22.6	0♎23.1	2 7.1	26 27.1	27 54.4	18 18.9	18 10.0	17 49.8	18 12.4
20	23 53 9.6	26 26.9	7 21.0	11♍ 9.4	2 9.1	3 21.7	27 3.5	28 6.7	18 26.4	18 12.6	17 50.4	18 14.6
21	23 57 6.2	27 25.5	7 17.8	22 58.6	3 54.1	4 36.3	27 39.9	28 19.0	18 33.9	18 15.3	17 51.1	18 16.9
22	0 1 2.8	28 24.2	7 14.6	4♎52.4	5 38.1	5 51.0	28 16.1	28 31.2	18 41.4	18 18.0	17 51.8	18 19.1
23	0 4 59.3	29 22.9	7 11.5	16 52.8	7 21.0	7 5.7	28 52.3	28 43.4	18 48.8	18 20.7	17 52.6	18 21.4
24	0 8 55.9	0♎21.7	7 8.3	29 1.5	9 3.0	8 20.3	29 28.3	28 55.5	18 56.3	18 23.5	17 53.4	18 23.7
25	0 12 52.4	1 20.4	7 5.1	11♏20.6	10 44.0	9 35.0	0♌ 4.3	29 7.6	19 3.7	18 26.3	17 54.2	18 26.0
26	0 16 49.0	2 19.2	7 1.9	23 51.7	12 24.1	10 49.7	0 40.1	29 19.6	19 11.1	18 29.1	17 55.0	18 28.3
27	0 20 45.5	3 18.1	6 58.7	6♐37.1	14 3.2	12 4.4	1 15.9	29 31.5	19 18.5	18 32.0	17 55.9	18 30.6
28	0 24 42.1	4 16.9	6 55.6	19 38.9	15 41.4	13 19.0	1 51.5	29 43.4	19 25.9	18 34.9	17 56.8	18 32.9
29	0 28 38.6	5 15.8	6 52.4	2♑59.2	17 18.6	14 33.7	2 27.0	29 55.3	19 33.2	18 37.8	17 57.7	18 35.2
30	0 32 35.2	6 14.7	6 49.2	16 39.8	18 55.0	15 48.4	3 2.4	0♍ 7.0	19 40.5	18 40.8	17 58.7	18 37.6

LATITUDE

DAY	EPHEM. SID. TIME	☉	☊	☾	☿	♀	♂	♃	♄	♅	♆	♇
1	22 38 15.2	0 .0	0 .0	5N 7.5	1N31.1	1N24.6	0N36.4	0N43.7	1N48.3	0N18.2	1N24.3	16N42.9
4	22 50 4.8	0 .0	0 .0	2 50.4	1 43.0	1 24.9	0 39.0	0 44.0	1 48.4	0 18.2	1 24.1	16 41.9
7	23 1 54.5	0 .0	0 .0	1S11.8	1 47.3	1 24.7	0 41.6	0 44.3	1 48.5	0 18.1	1 23.9	16 41.0
10	23 13 44.1	0 .0	0 .0	4 27.8	1 45.1	1 23.8	0 44.2	0 44.6	1 48.7	0 18.0	1 23.8	16 40.1
13	23 25 33.8	0 .0	0 .0	5 14.4	1 37.6	1 22.4	0 46.9	0 45.0	1 48.8	0 18.0	1 23.6	16 39.4
16	23 37 23.4	0 .0	0 .0	3 43.5	1 26.0	1 20.4	0 49.6	0 45.3	1 49.0	0 17.9	1 23.5	16 38.7
19	23 49 13.1	0 .0	0 .0	0 50.4	1 11.1	1 17.9	0 52.4	0 45.7	1 49.2	0 17.8	1 23.3	16 38.0
22	0 1 2.8	0 .0	0 .0	2N20.6	0 53.7	1 14.8	0 55.2	0 46.1	1 49.4	0 17.8	1 23.1	16 37.5
25	0 12 52.4	0 .0	0 .0	4 40.6	0 34.6	1 11.2	0 58.0	0 46.4	1 49.7	0 17.7	1 23.0	16 37.0
28	0 24 42.1	0 .0	0 .0	5 8.2	0 14.2	1 7.1	1 .8	0 46.9	1 50.0	0 17.6	1 22.8	16 36.6

RIGHT ASCENSION

DAY	EPHEM. SID. TIME	☉	☊	☾	☿	♀	♂	♃	♄	♅	♆	♇
1	22 38 15.2	9♍38.6	9♍59.7	23♐ 3.7	29♌ 9.6	11♍50.8	16♋37.7	26♌39.8	17♍52.7	15♏ 7.2	16♐47.8	22♎35.0
2	22 42 11.7	10 33.0	9 56.7	7♑35.7	1♍ 1.2	13 .6	17 18.9	26 52.4	17 59.6	15 9.1	16D47.9	22 36.6
3	22 46 8.3	11 27.4	9 53.8	22 35.2	2 53.0	14 10.2	17 60.0	27 4.9	18 6.6	15 11.0	16 48.0	22 38.2
4	22 50 4.8	12 21.6	9 50.8	7♒48.1	4 44.8	15 19.6	18 40.9	27 17.5	18 13.5	15 12.9	16 48.1	22 39.9
5	22 54 1.4	13 15.8	9 47.8	22 59.8	6 36.3	16 28.8	19 21.7	27 30.0	18 20.5	15 14.9	16 48.3	22 41.6
6	22 57 57.9	14 10.0	9 44.8	7♓58.9	8 27.2	17 38.0	20 2.4	27 42.5	18 27.5	15 17.0	16 48.5	22 43.3
7	23 1 54.5	15 4.0	9 41.8	22 39.7	10 17.4	18 46.9	20 43.0	27 54.9	18 34.5	15 19.1	16 48.8	22 45.0
8	23 5 51.0	15 58.1	9 38.8	7♈ 1.7	12 6.6	19 55.8	21 23.4	28 7.3	18 41.5	15 21.2	16 49.0	22 46.7
9	23 9 47.6	16 52.0	9 35.9	21 7.6	13 54.7	21 4.5	22 3.7	28 19.7	18 48.5	15 23.4	16 49.3	22 48.5
10	23 13 44.1	17 46.0	9 32.9	5♉ 1.6	15 41.7	22 13.1	22 43.9	28 32.0	18 55.4	15 25.6	16 49.7	22 50.2
11	23 17 40.7	18 39.9	9 29.9	18 46.8	17 27.5	23 21.7	23 23.9	28 44.3	19 2.4	15 27.9	16 50.1	22 52.0
12	23 21 37.2	19 33.8	9 26.9	2♊24.6	19 12.1	24 30.1	24 3.7	28 56.6	19 9.4	15 30.2	16 50.5	22 53.8
13	23 25 33.8	20 27.6	9 23.9	15 53.9	20 55.3	25 38.5	24 43.5	29 8.8	19 16.4	15 32.5	16 50.9	22 55.6
14	23 29 30.3	21 21.5	9 20.9	29 11.9	22 37.4	26 46.7	25 23.1	29 21.0	19 23.4	15 34.9	16 51.4	22 57.5
15	23 33 26.9	22 15.3	9 18.0	12♋14.7	24 18.1	27 55.0	26 2.5	29 33.1	19 30.4	15 37.3	16 52.0	22 59.3
16	23 37 23.4	23 9.1	9 15.0	24 59.1	25 57.7	29 3.2	26 41.8	29 45.2	19 37.4	15 39.8	16 52.5	23 1.2
17	23 41 20.0	24 2.9	9 12.0	7♌23.0	27 36.1	0♎11.3	27 21.0	29 57.3	19 44.3	15 42.3	16 53.1	23 3.1
18	23 45 16.5	24 56.7	9 9.0	19 26.5	29 13.3	1 19.4	27 60.0	0♍ 9.3	19 51.3	15 44.9	16 53.7	23 5.0
19	23 49 13.1	25 50.6	9 6.0	1♍11.7	0♎49.4	2 27.6	28 38.8	0 21.2	19 58.3	15 47.5	16 54.4	23 6.9
20	23 53 9.6	26 44.4	9 3.0	12 42.5	2 24.5	3 35.7	29 17.5	0 33.1	20 5.3	15 50.1	16 55.1	23 8.9
21	23 57 6.2	27 38.2	9 .0	24 4.5	3 58.5	4 43.7	29 56.1	0 45.0	20 12.2	15 52.8	16 55.9	23 10.8
22	0 1 2.8	28 32.1	8 57.1	5♎24.1	5 31.6	5 51.8	0♌34.4	0 56.8	20 19.2	15 55.5	16 56.6	23 12.8
23	0 4 59.3	29 26.0	8 54.1	16 48.7	7 3.8	6 60.0	1 12.6	1 8.5	20 26.1	15 58.3	16 57.4	23 14.7
24	0 8 55.9	0♎19.9	8 51.1	28 25.9	8 35.1	8 8.1	1 50.7	1 20.2	20 33.0	16 1.0	16 58.3	23 16.7
25	0 12 52.4	1 13.8	8 48.1	10♏23.0	10 5.5	9 16.3	2 28.5	1 31.8	20 39.9	16 3.8	16 59.1	23 18.7
26	0 16 49.0	2 7.8	8 45.1	22 46.6	11 35.3	10 24.6	3 6.3	1 43.4	20 46.8	16 6.7	17 .0	23 20.7
27	0 20 45.5	3 1.8	8 42.1	5♐41.6	13 4.3	11 32.9	3 43.8	1 54.9	20 53.6	16 9.6	17 1.0	23 22.7
28	0 24 42.1	3 55.8	8 39.1	19 9.5	14 32.6	12 41.3	4 21.2	2 6.4	21 .5	16 12.5	17 1.9	23 24.8
29	0 28 38.6	4 49.9	8 36.1	3♑ 8.5	16 .3	13 49.8	4 58.4	2 17.7	21 7.3	16 15.5	17 2.9	23 26.8
30	0 32 35.2	5 44.0	8 33.2	17 32.1	17 27.4	14 58.4	5 35.4	2 29.1	21 14.1	16 18.4	17 4.0	23 28.9

DECLINATION

DAY	EPHEM. SID. TIME	☉	☊	☾	☿	♀	♂	♃	♄	♅	♆	♇
1	22 38 15.2	8N34.6	0N 8.8	18S 9.4	14N 8.8	9N12.9	23N10.2	14N10.5	7N 9.7	16S45.7	21S28.5	8N33.5
4	22 50 4.8	7 29.1	0 8.9	15 58.9	12 19.2	7 48.0	22 59.0	13 57.8	7 1.0	16 47.3	21 28.6	8 30.5
7	23 1 54.5	6 22.5	0 9.0	4 28.3	10 14.9	6 21.2	22 46.4	13 45.2	6 52.4	16 49.1	21 28.9	8 27.4
10	23 13 44.1	5 14.9	0 9.0	9N15.2	8 .8	4 52.8	22 32.5	13 32.6	6 43.7	16 51.0	21 29.1	8 24.3
13	23 25 33.8	4 6.6	0 9.1	17 32.5	5 41.0	3 23.0	22 17.3	13 20.0	6 35.0	16 53.0	21 29.4	8 21.3
16	23 37 23.4	2 57.5	0 9.1	17 40.6	3 18.6	1 52.3	22 .9	13 7.4	6 26.4	16 55.1	21 29.7	8 18.2
19	23 49 13.1	1 48.0	0 9.2	10 54.2	0 56.0	0 20.9	21 43.2	12 54.9	6 17.7	16 57.3	21 30.0	8 15.2
22	0 1 2.8	0 38.1	0 9.3	0 12.9	1S25.0	1S10.7	21 24.5	12 42.5	6 9.2	16 59.6	21 30.3	8 12.2
25	0 12 52.4	0S32.0	0 9.3	10S47.0	3 43.1	2 42.3	21 4.8	12 30.2	6 .6	17 1.9	21 30.7	8 9.3
28	0 24 42.1	1 42.1	0 9.4	17 54.8	5 57.4	4 13.6	20 44.1	12 18.0	5 52.2	17 4.4	21 31.1	8 6.4

OCTOBER 1979

LONGITUDE

DAY	EPHEM. SID. TIME	☉	☊	☾	☿	♀	♂	♃	♄	♅	♆	♇
	h m s	° ′	° ′	° ′	° ′	° ′	° ′	° ′	° ′	° ′	° ′	° ′
1	0 36 31.7	7♎13.7	6♍46.0	0♒41.6	20♎30.5	17♎ 3.1	3♌37.7	0♍18.8	19♍47.8	18♏43.8	17♐59.7	18♎39.9
2	0 40 28.3	8 12.7	6 42.9	15 4.2	22 5.2	18 17.8	4 12.9	0 30.4	19 55.1	18 46.9	18 .7	18 42.2
3	0 44 24.8	9 11.7	6 39.7	29 45.2	23 39.0	19 32.5	4 48.0	0 42.0	20 2.4	18 49.9	18 1.8	18 44.6
4	0 48 21.4	10 10.7	6 36.5	14♓40.1	25 12.0	20 47.2	5 23.0	0 53.5	20 9.6	18 53.0	18 2.9	18 47.0
5	0 52 17.9	11 9.8	6 33.3	29 41.9	26 44.1	22 1.9	5 57.8	1 5.0	20 16.8	18 56.1	18 4.0	18 49.3
6	0 56 14.5	12 8.9	6 30.1	14♈42.2	28 15.4	23 16.6	6 32.6	1 16.3	20 24.0	18 59.3	18 5.2	18 51.7
7	1 0 11.0	13 8.0	6 27.0	29 32.2	29 45.9	24 31.3	7 7.2	1 27.7	20 31.2	19 2.5	18 6.3	18 54.1
8	1 4 7.6	14 7.2	6 23.8	14♉ 3.8	1♏15.6	25 46.0	7 41.7	1 38.9	20 38.3	19 5.7	18 7.5	18 56.4
9	1 8 4.1	15 6.4	6 20.6	28 11.4	2 44.5	27 .7	8 16.1	1 50.1	20 45.4	19 8.9	18 8.8	18 58.8
10	1 12 .7	16 5.7	6 17.4	11♊51.7	4 12.6	28 15.4	8 50.4	2 1.2	20 52.5	19 12.2	18 10.1	19 1.2
11	1 15 57.2	17 5.0	6 14.3	25 4.3	5 39.8	29 30.2	9 24.6	2 12.2	20 59.6	19 15.5	18 11.4	19 3.6
12	1 19 53.8	18 4.3	6 11.1	7♋51.4	7 6.2	0♏44.9	9 58.6	2 23.2	21 6.6	19 18.8	18 12.7	19 6.0
13	1 23 50.3	19 3.7	6 7.9	20 16.4	8 31.8	1 59.6	10 32.5	2 34.1	21 13.5	19 22.1	18 14.1	19 8.4
14	1 27 46.9	20 3.1	6 4.7	2♌24.2	9 56.5	3 14.3	11 6.3	2 44.8	21 20.5	19 25.5	18 15.4	19 10.8
15	1 31 43.4	21 2.5	6 1.5	14 19.8	11 20.3	4 29.1	11 39.9	2 55.5	21 27.4	19 28.9	18 16.8	19 13.1
16	1 35 40.0	22 2.0	5 58.4	26 8.4	12 43.1	5 43.8	12 13.4	3 6.2	21 34.2	19 32.3	18 18.3	19 15.5
17	1 39 36.6	23 1.5	5 55.2	7♍54.8	14 5.0	6 58.5	12 46.8	3 16.7	21 41.0	19 35.7	18 19.7	19 17.9
18	1 43 33.1	24 1.1	5 52.0	19 43.1	15 25.9	8 13.3	13 20.1	3 27.1	21 47.8	19 39.2	18 21.2	19 20.3
19	1 47 29.7	25 .7	5 48.8	1♎37.0	16 45.7	9 28.0	13 53.2	3 37.5	21 54.6	19 42.6	18 22.7	19 22.7
20	1 51 26.2	26 .3	5 45.7	13 39.3	18 4.3	10 42.8	14 26.1	3 47.7	22 1.3	19 46.1	18 24.2	19 25.0
21	1 55 22.8	26 59.9	5 42.5	25 51.8	19 21.7	11 57.5	14 58.9	3 57.9	22 7.9	19 49.6	18 25.8	19 27.4
22	1 59 19.3	27 59.6	5 39.3	8♏15.8	20 37.8	13 12.2	15 31.6	4 8.0	22 14.5	19 53.1	18 27.4	19 29.8
23	2 3 15.9	28 59.4	5 36.1	20 51.8	21 52.5	14 27.0	16 4.1	4 17.9	22 21.1	19 56.7	18 29.0	19 32.1
24	2 7 12.4	29 59.1	5 32.9	3♐40.1	23 5.7	15 41.7	16 36.4	4 27.8	22 27.6	20 .2	18 30.6	19 34.5
25	2 11 9.0	0♏58.9	5 29.8	16 40.5	24 17.2	16 56.5	17 8.6	4 37.6	22 34.0	20 3.8	18 32.3	19 36.8
26	2 15 5.5	1 58.7	5 26.6	29 53.4	25 26.8	18 11.2	17 40.7	4 47.3	22 40.4	20 7.4	18 33.9	19 39.2
27	2 19 2.1	2 58.6	5 23.4	13♑18.9	26 34.4	19 26.0	18 12.6	4 56.8	22 46.8	20 11.0	18 35.6	19 41.5
28	2 22 58.6	3 58.4	5 20.2	26 57.7	27 39.8	20 40.7	18 44.3	5 6.3	22 53.1	20 14.6	18 37.4	19 43.9
29	2 26 55.2	4 58.3	5 17.1	10♒50.3	28 42.8	21 55.4	19 15.8	5 15.6	22 59.4	20 18.2	18 39.1	19 46.2
30	2 30 51.7	5 58.3	5 13.9	24 57.0	29 43.0	23 10.2	19 47.2	5 24.9	23 5.6	20 21.9	18 40.9	19 48.5
31	2 34 48.3	6 58.3	5 10.7	9♓17.2	0♐40.3	24 24.9	20 18.5	5 34.1	23 11.8	20 25.6	18 42.7	19 50.8

LATITUDE

DAY	EPHEM. SID. TIME	☉	☊	☾	☿	♀	♂	♃	♄	♅	♆	♇
1	0 36 31.7	0 .0	0 .0	3N11.6	0S 6.9	1N 2.5	1N 3.7	0N47.3	1N50.3	0N17.6	1N22.7	16N36.3
4	0 48 21.4	0 .0	0 .0	0S35.3	0 28.4	0 57.4	1 6.6	0 47.7	1 50.6	0 17.5	1 22.5	16 36.0
7	1 0 11.0	0 .0	0 .0	4 4.2	0 49.9	0 51.9	1 9.6	0 48.2	1 50.9	0 17.5	1 22.4	16 35.8
10	1 12 .7	0 .0	0 .0	5 10.6	1 11.1	0 46.0	1 12.6	0 48.6	1 51.3	0 17.4	1 22.3	16 35.7
13	1 23 50.3	0 .0	0 .0	3 49.7	1 31.5	0 39.7	1 15.7	0 49.1	1 51.7	0 17.4	1 22.1	16 35.7
16	1 35 40.0	0 .0	0 .0	1 2.7	1 50.9	0 33.1	1 18.8	0 49.6	1 52.1	0 17.3	1 22.0	16 35.8
19	1 47 29.7	0 .0	0 .0	2N 5.4	2 8.8	0 26.2	1 21.9	0 50.1	1 52.5	0 17.3	1 21.8	16 36.0
22	1 59 19.3	0 .0	0 .0	4 28.1	2 24.7	0 19.1	1 25.2	0 50.7	1 53.0	0 17.2	1 21.7	16 36.2
25	2 11 9.0	0 .0	0 .0	5 1.7	2 38.0	0 11.7	1 28.5	0 51.2	1 53.5	0 17.2	1 21.6	16 36.5
28	2 22 58.6	0 .0	0 .0	3 16.2	2 48.0	0 4.2	1 31.8	0 51.8	1 54.0	0 17.2	1 21.5	16 36.9
31	2 34 48.3	0 .0	0 .0	0S13.9	2 53.6	0S 3.4	1 35.2	0 52.4	1 54.5	0 17.1	1 21.4	16 37.3

RIGHT ASCENSION

DAY	EPHEM. SID. TIME	☉	☊	☾	☿	♀	♂	♃	♄	♅	♆	♇
1	0 36 31.7	6♎38.2	8♍30.2	2♒10.9	18♎53.9	16♎ 7.1	6♌12.3	2♍40.3	21♍20.9	16♏21.5	17♐ 5.0	23♎30.9
2	0 40 28.3	7 32.5	8 27.2	16 54.6	20 19.9	17 15.8	6 49.0	2 51.5	21 27.7	16 24.5	17 6.1	23 33.0
3	0 44 24.8	8 26.8	8 24.2	1♓34.7	21 45.4	18 24.8	7 25.5	3 2.6	21 34.4	16 27.6	17 7.3	23 35.0
4	0 48 21.4	9 21.3	8 21.2	16 6.5	23 10.5	19 33.8	8 1.9	3 13.7	21 41.2	16 30.7	17 8.4	23 37.1
5	0 52 17.9	10 15.7	8 18.2	0♈29.1	24 35.1	20 43.0	8 38.0	3 24.7	21 47.9	16 33.8	17 9.6	23 39.2
6	0 56 14.5	11 10.3	8 15.2	14 44.3	25 59.4	21 52.4	9 14.0	3 35.6	21 54.5	16 37.0	17 10.9	23 41.3
7	1 0 11.0	12 5.0	8 12.2	28 54.9	27 23.2	23 1.9	9 49.9	3 46.5	22 1.2	16 40.2	17 12.1	23 43.4
8	1 4 7.6	12 59.8	8 9.2	13♉ 2.7	28 46.7	24 11.6	10 25.5	3 57.2	22 7.8	16 43.4	17 13.4	23 45.5
9	1 8 4.1	13 54.6	8 6.2	27 7.0	0♏ 9.7	25 21.5	11 1.0	4 8.0	22 14.4	16 46.7	17 14.7	23 47.6
10	1 12 .7	14 49.7	8 3.3	11♊ 4.4	1 32.5	26 31.6	11 36.4	4 18.6	22 21.0	16 50.0	17 16.1	23 49.8
11	1 15 57.2	15 44.8	8 .3	24 49.5	2 54.9	27 41.9	12 11.5	4 29.2	22 27.6	16 53.3	17 17.5	23 51.9
12	1 19 53.8	16 40.0	7 57.3	8♋16.3	4 16.9	28 52.4	12 46.5	4 39.7	22 34.1	16 56.6	17 18.9	23 54.1
13	1 23 50.3	17 35.4	7 54.3	21 19.9	5 38.5	0♏ 3.1	13 21.2	4 50.1	22 40.5	16 60.0	17 20.3	23 56.2
14	1 27 46.9	18 30.8	7 51.3	3♌57.9	6 59.8	1 14.1	13 55.8	5 .4	22 47.0	17 3.4	17 21.8	23 58.3
15	1 31 43.4	19 26.5	7 48.3	16 10.7	8 20.6	2 25.3	14 30.2	5 10.6	22 53.4	17 6.8	17 23.3	24 .5
16	1 35 40.0	20 22.2	7 45.3	28 1.4	9 41.0	3 36.8	15 4.4	5 20.8	22 59.8	17 10.2	17 24.8	24 2.6
17	1 39 36.6	21 18.1	7 42.3	9♍35.0	11 .9	4 48.5	15 38.5	5 30.8	23 6.1	17 13.7	17 26.4	24 4.8
18	1 43 33.1	22 14.2	7 39.3	20 58.4	12 20.2	6 .4	16 12.3	5 40.8	23 12.4	17 17.1	17 28.0	24 6.9
19	1 47 29.7	23 10.4	7 36.3	2♎18.9	13 38.9	7 12.7	16 45.9	5 50.7	23 18.7	17 20.6	17 29.6	24 9.1
20	1 51 26.2	24 6.7	7 33.3	13 44.4	14 57.0	8 25.2	17 19.4	6 .5	23 24.9	17 24.1	17 31.2	24 11.2
21	1 55 22.8	25 3.3	7 30.3	25 22.7	16 14.3	9 38.0	17 52.6	6 10.2	23 31.1	17 27.7	17 32.9	24 13.4
22	1 59 19.3	25 59.9	7 27.3	7♏21.1	17 30.7	10 51.0	18 25.7	6 19.8	23 37.3	17 31.2	17 34.6	24 15.5
23	2 3 15.9	26 56.8	7 24.3	19 45.4	18 46.1	12 4.4	18 58.5	6 29.3	23 43.4	17 34.8	17 36.3	24 17.7
24	2 7 12.4	27 53.8	7 21.3	2♐39.2	20 .4	13 18.1	19 31.2	6 38.8	23 49.4	17 38.4	17 38.0	24 19.8
25	2 11 9.0	28 51.0	7 18.3	16 3.0	21 13.4	14 32.0	20 3.6	6 48.1	23 55.4	17 42.0	17 39.8	24 22.0
26	2 15 5.5	29 48.3	7 15.3	29 53.0	22 24.9	15 46.3	20 35.9	6 57.3	24 1.4	17 45.6	17 41.6	24 24.1
27	2 19 2.1	0♏45.9	7 12.3	14♑ 2.1	23 34.8	17 .8	21 7.9	7 6.4	24 7.3	17 49.2	17 43.4	24 26.3
28	2 22 58.6	1 43.6	7 9.3	28 20.7	24 42.6	18 15.7	21 39.8	7 15.5	24 13.2	17 52.9	17 45.2	24 28.4
29	2 26 55.2	2 41.5	7 6.3	12♒39.7	25 48.3	19 30.9	22 11.4	7 24.4	24 19.0	17 56.6	17 47.1	24 30.5
30	2 30 51.7	3 39.5	7 3.3	26 52.7	26 51.5	20 46.3	22 42.8	7 33.2	24 24.8	18 .2	17 49.0	24 32.7
31	2 34 48.3	4 37.8	7 .3	10♓57.3	27 51.9	22 2.1	23 14.1	7 41.9	24 30.6	18 4.0	17 51.0	24 34.8

DECLINATION

DAY	EPHEM. SID. TIME	☉	☊	☾	☿	♀	♂	♃	♄	♅	♆	♇
1	0 36 31.7	2S52.1	0N 9.5	16S52.9	8S 7.1	5S44.2	20N22.5	12N 6.0	5N43.8	17S 6.9	21S31.5	8N 3.5
4	0 48 21.4	4 1.9	0 9.5	6 34.8	10 11.5	7 13.7	20 .0	11 54.1	5 35.5	17 9.4	21 31.9	8 .7
7	1 0 11.0	5 11.2	0 9.6	7N29.8	12 10.1	8 41.9	19 36.9	11 42.3	5 27.4	17 12.1	21 32.4	7 58.0
10	1 12 .7	6 19.9	0 9.6	17 4.7	14 2.3	10 8.4	19 13.0	11 30.8	5 19.3	17 14.8	21 32.8	7 55.3
13	1 23 50.3	7 27.9	0 9.7	18 7.4	15 47.4	11 32.7	18 48.5	11 19.4	5 11.4	17 17.5	21 33.3	7 52.7
16	1 35 40.0	8 34.9	0 9.8	11 49.3	17 24.9	12 54.7	18 23.5	11 8.3	5 3.6	17 20.3	21 33.8	7 50.1
19	1 47 29.7	9 40.9	0 9.8	1 16.5	18 54.1	14 13.9	17 58.1	10 57.4	4 56.0	17 23.2	21 34.3	7 47.7
22	1 59 19.3	10 45.6	0 9.9	10S 1.6	20 14.0	15 30.0	17 32.2	10 46.8	4 48.5	17 26.0	21 34.9	7 45.3
25	2 11 9.0	11 48.9	0 9.9	17 46.1	21 23.7	16 42.5	17 6.1	10 36.6	4 41.2	17 28.9	21 35.4	7 43.0
28	2 22 58.6	12 50.6	0 10.0	17 33.3	22 22.0	17 51.2	16 39.8	10 26.6	4 34.1	17 31.9	21 36.0	7 40.8
31	2 34 48.3	13 50.5	0 10.1	8 18.2	23 7.2	18 55.8	16 13.3	10 16.9	4 27.3	17 34.8	21 36.5	7 38.7

NOVEMBER 1979

LONGITUDE

DAY	EPHEM. SID. TIME	☉	☊	☾	☿	♀	♂	♃	♄	♅	♆	♇
	h m s	° ′	° ′	° ′	° ′	° ′	° ′	° ′	° ′	° ′	° ′	° ′
1	2 38 44.9	7♏58.2	5♍ 7.5	23♓48.6	1♐34.1	25♏39.7	20♌49.6	5♍43.1	23♍17.8	20♏29.2	18♐44.5	19♎53.1
2	2 42 41.4	8 58.2	5 4.3	8♈27.4	2 24.1	26 54.4	21 20.4	5 52.0	23 23.9	20 32.9	18 46.3	19 55.4
3	2 46 38.0	9 58.3	5 1.2	23 7.8	3 10.0	28 9.1	21 51.1	6 .8	23 29.8	20 36.6	18 48.2	19 57.7
4	2 50 34.5	10 58.3	4 58.0	7♉42.8	3 51.2	29 23.8	22 21.7	6 9.5	23 35.7	20 40.3	18 50.1	19 60.0
5	2 54 31.1	11 58.4	4 54.8	22 5.1	4 27.2	0♐38.5	22 52.0	6 18.0	23 41.6	20 44.0	18 51.9	20 2.2
6	2 58 27.6	12 58.6	4 51.6	6♊ 8.4	4 57.5	1 53.2	23 22.2	6 26.5	23 47.4	20 47.7	18 53.8	20 4.5
7	3 2 24.2	13 58.7	4 48.5	19 48.4	5 21.3	3 7.9	23 52.1	6 34.8	23 53.1	20 51.4	18 55.8	20 6.7
8	3 6 20.7	14 58.9	4 45.3	3♋ 2.9	5 38.1	4 22.6	24 21.9	6 43.0	23 58.8	20 55.1	18 57.7	20 8.9
9	3 10 17.3	15 59.1	4 42.1	15 52.6	5 47.2	5 37.3	24 51.5	6 51.0	24 4.3	20 58.8	18 59.7	20 11.1
10	3 14 13.8	16 59.4	4 38.9	28 20.1	5 47.8	6 52.0	25 20.9	6 58.9	24 9.9	21 2.6	19 1.6	20 13.3
11	3 18 10.4	17 59.7	4 35.7	10♌29.6	5R39.4	8 6.7	25 50.1	7 6.8	24 15.3	21 6.3	19 3.6	20 15.5
12	3 22 7.0	19 .0	4 32.6	22 26.0	5 21.4	9 21.4	26 19.1	7 14.4	24 20.7	21 10.0	19 5.6	20 17.6
13	3 26 3.5	20 .4	4 29.4	4♍14.9	4 53.3	10 36.1	26 47.8	7 22.0	24 26.0	21 13.8	19 7.7	20 19.8
14	3 30 .1	21 .8	4 26.2	16 2.0	4 15.2	11 50.7	27 16.4	7 29.4	24 31.3	21 17.5	19 9.7	20 21.9
15	3 33 56.6	22 1.2	4 23.0	27 52.4	3 26.9	13 5.4	27 44.7	7 36.6	24 36.5	21 21.2	19 11.8	20 24.0
16	3 37 53.2	23 1.6	4 19.9	9♎50.7	2 29.2	14 20.1	28 12.8	7 43.8	24 41.6	21 25.0	19 13.8	20 26.1
17	3 41 49.7	24 2.1	4 16.7	22 .8	1 23.0	15 34.8	28 40.7	7 50.7	24 46.6	21 28.7	19 15.9	20 28.2
18	3 45 46.3	25 2.6	4 13.5	4♏25.2	0 9.7	16 49.5	29 8.3	7 57.6	24 51.5	21 32.4	19 18.0	20 30.2
19	3 49 42.8	26 3.2	4 10.3	17 5.4	28♏51.4	18 4.2	29 35.7	8 4.3	24 56.4	21 36.2	19 20.1	20 32.3
20	3 53 39.4	27 3.7	4 7.1	0♐ 1.5	27 30.4	19 18.8	0♍ 2.8	8 10.8	25 1.2	21 39.9	19 22.2	20 34.3
21	3 57 36.0	28 4.4	4 4.0	13 12.4	26 9.3	20 33.6	0 29.8	8 17.3	25 6.0	21 43.6	19 24.4	20 36.4
22	4 1 32.5	29 5.0	4 .8	26 36.1	24 50.9	21 48.2	0 56.4	8 23.5	25 10.6	21 47.4	19 26.6	20 38.3
23	4 5 29.1	0♐ 5.6	3 57.6	10♑10.5	23 37.6	23 2.9	1 22.8	8 29.6	25 15.1	21 51.1	19 28.7	20 40.3
24	4 9 25.6	1 6.3	3 54.4	23 53.5	22 31.9	24 17.5	1 48.9	8 35.5	25 19.6	21 54.8	19 30.9	20 42.2
25	4 13 22.2	2 6.9	3 51.3	7♒43.4	21 35.5	25 32.2	2 14.7	8 41.3	25 24.0	21 58.5	19 33.1	20 44.2
26	4 17 18.7	3 7.6	3 48.1	21 39.3	20 49.7	26 46.8	2 40.3	8 46.9	25 28.3	22 2.2	19 35.3	20 46.1
27	4 21 15.3	4 8.3	3 44.9	5♓40.8	20 15.).	28 1.4	3 5.6	8 52.4	25 32.5	22 5.8	19 37.4	20 47.9
28	4 25 11.8	5 9.1	3 41.7	19 47.3	19 52.3	29 16.0	3 30.5	8 57.7	25 36.6	22 9.5	19 39.7	20 49.8
29	4 29 8.4	6 9.8	3 38.6	3♈58.2	19 41.0	0♑30.6	3 55.2	9 2.8	25 40.6	22 13.2	19 41.9	20 51.6
30	4 33 5.0	7 10.6	3 35.4	18 11.7	19 40.7	1 45.2	4 19.6	9 7.8	25 44.6	22 16.8	19 44.1	20 53.4

LATITUDE

DAY	EPHEM. SID. TIME	☉	☊	☾	☿	♀	♂	♃	♄	♅	♆	♇
1	2 38 44.9	0 .0	0 .0	1S30.3	2S54.3	0S 5.9	1N36.4	0N52.6	1N54.7	0N17.1	1N21.3	16N37.5
4	2 50 34.5	0 .0	0 .0	4 26.6	2 51.7	0 13.6	1 39.9	0 53.2	1 55.3	0 17.1	1 21.2	16 38.1
7	3 2 24.2	0 .0	0 .0	4 54.3	2 40.6	0 21.3	1 43.5	0 53.8	1 55.9	0 17.0	1 21.1	16 38.7
10	3 14 13.8	0 .0	0 .0	3 4.1	2 18.6	0 29.0	1 47.1	0 54.4	1 56.5	0 17.0	1 21.0	16 39.5
13	3 26 3.5	0 .0	0 .0	0 6.6	1 43.0	0 36.6	1 50.9	0 55.1	1 57.1	0 17.0	1 21.0	16 40.3
16	3 37 53.2	0 .0	0 .0	2N51.6	0 53.3	0 44.0	1 54.7	0 55.8	1 57.7	0 17.0	1 20.9	16 41.1
19	3 49 42.8	0 .0	0 .0	4 46.3	0N 6.5	0 51.2	1 58.7	0 56.5	1 58.4	0 16.9	1 20.8	16 42.1
22	4 1 32.5	0 .0	0 .0	4 38.1	1 6.3	0 58.2	2 2.7	0 57.2	1 59.1	0 16.9	1 20.7	16 43.1
25	4 13 22.2	0 .0	0 .0	2 13.4	1 54.2	1 4.9	2 6.8	0 57.9	1 59.8	0 16.9	1 20.7	16 44.2
28	4 25 11.8	0 .0	0 .0	1S23.3	2 23.9	1 11.3	2 11.1	0 58.6	2 .5	0 16.9	1 20.6	16 45.3

RIGHT ASCENSION

DAY	EPHEM. SID. TIME	☉	☊	☾	☿	♀	♂	♃	♄	♅	♆	♇
1	2 38 44.9	5♏36.3	6♍57.3	24♓54.8	28♏48.9	23♏18.2	23♌45.1	7♍50.5	24♍36.3	18♏ 7.7	17♐52.9	24♎37.0
2	2 42 41.4	6 34.9	6 54.3	8♈49.5	29 42.3	24 34.6	24 15.9	7 59.0	24 41.9	18 11.4	17 54.8	24 39.1
3	2 46 38.0	7 33.8	6 51.3	22 46.3	0♐31.4	25 51.3	24 46.4	8 7.4	24 47.4	18 15.1	17 56.8	24 41.2
4	2 50 34.5	8 32.8	6 48.3	6♉48.9	1 15.9	27 8.3	25 16.8	8 15.7	24 53.0	18 18.8	17 58.8	24 43.3
5	2 54 31.1	9 32.1	6 45.3	20 58.0	1 55.0	28 25.6	25 46.9	8 23.8	24 58.4	18 22.6	18 .8	24 45.4
6	2 58 27.6	10 31.5	6 42.3	5♊10.3	2 28.2	29 43.2	26 16.9	8 31.8	25 3.8	18 26.3	18 2.9	24 47.5
7	3 2 24.2	11 31.2	6 39.3	19 18.3	2 54.8	1♐ 1.1	26 46.6	8 39.8	25 9.2	18 30.1	18 4.9	24 49.5
8	3 6 20.7	12 31.1	6 36.3	3♋12.8	3 14.0	2 19.3	27 16.1	8 47.6	25 14.4	18 33.8	18 7.0	24 51.6
9	3 10 17.3	13 31.1	6 33.3	16 44.6	3 25.1	3 37.8	27 45.3	8 55.2	25 19.7	18 37.6	18 9.1	24 53.7
10	3 14 13.8	14 31.5	6 30.3	29 47.8	3 27.5	4 56.6	28 14.4	9 2.8	25 24.8	18 41.4	18 11.2	24 55.7
11	3 18 10.4	15 32.0	6 27.3	12♌20.3	3R20.5	6 15.6	28 43.2	9 10.2	25 29.9	18 45.1	18 13.4	24 57.8
12	3 22 7.0	16 32.7	6 24.3	24 24.4	3 3.5	7 34.9	29 11.7	9 17.5	25 35.0	18 48.9	18 15.5	24 59.8
13	3 26 3.5	17 33.7	6 21.3	6♍ 5.2	2 36.3	8 54.5	29 40.1	9 24.7	25 39.9	18 52.7	18 17.7	25 1.8
14	3 30 .1	18 34.8	6 18.3	17 30.5	1 58.6	10 14.3	0♍ 8.2	9 31.8	25 44.8	18 56.5	18 19.9	25 3.9
15	3 33 56.6	19 36.2	6 15.3	28 49.0	1 10.9	11 34.4	0 36.0	9 38.7	25 49.7	19 .3	18 22.1	25 5.9
16	3 37 53.2	20 37.8	6 12.3	10♎10.2	0 13.7	12 54.7	1 3.6	9 45.5	25 54.5	19 4.1	18 24.3	25 7.8
17	3 41 49.7	21 39.6	6 9.3	21 43.5	29♏ 8.2	14 15.2	1 31.0	9 52.1	25 59.2	19 7.8	18 26.5	25 9.8
18	3 45 46.3	22 41.7	6 6.3	3♏37.7	27 56.1	15 36.0	1 58.0	9 58.6	26 3.8	19 11.6	18 28.8	25 11.8
19	3 49 42.8	23 43.9	6 3.3	16 .4	26 39.3	16 56.9	2 24.9	10 5.0	26 8.4	19 15.4	18 31.0	25 13.7
20	3 53 39.4	24 46.4	6 .3	28 56.3	25 20.4	18 18.0	2 51.5	10 11.3	26 12.9	19 19.2	18 33.3	25 15.7
21	3 57 36.0	25 49.1	5 57.3	12♐26.1	24 1.9	19 39.3	3 17.8	10 17.4	26 17.3	19 23.0	18 35.6	25 17.6
22	4 1 32.5	26 51.9	5 54.3	26 25.3	22 46.5	21 .7	3 43.8	10 23.4	26 21.7	19 26.8	18 37.9	25 19.5
23	4 5 29.1	27 55.0	5 51.3	10♑44.5	21 36.5	22 22.3	4 9.6	10 29.2	26 26.0	19 30.5	18 40.2	25 21.4
24	4 9 25.6	28 58.2	5 48.3	25 10.9	20 34.2	23 44.0	4 35.1	10 34.8	26 30.2	19 34.3	18 42.6	25 23.3
25	4 13 22.2	0♐ 1.6	5 45.3	9♒32.5	19 41.1	25 5.8	5 .3	10 40.3	26 34.3	19 38.1	18 44.9	25 25.2
26	4 17 18.7	1 5.3	5 42.3	23 40.6	18 58.3	26 27.7	5 25.2	10 45.7	26 38.3	19 41.8	18 47.2	25 27.0
27	4 21 15.3	2 9.1	5 39.2	7♓32.3	18 26.4	27 49.6	5 49.8	10 50.9	26 42.3	19 45.5	18 49.6	25 28.8
28	4 25 11.8	3 13.0	5 36.2	21 9.8	18 5.7	29 11.7	6 14.2	10 56.0	26 46.2	19 49.3	18 52.0	25 30.6
29	4 29 8.4	4 17.2	5 33.2	4♈39.0	17 56.0	0♑33.7	6 38.2	11 .9	26 50.0	19 53.0	18 54.3	25 32.4
30	4 33 5.0	5 21.5	5 30.2	18 7.6	17D56.8	1 55.8	7 2.0	11 5.7	26 53.7	19 56.7	18 56.7	25 34.2

DECLINATION

DAY	EPHEM. SID. TIME	☉	☊	☾	☿	♀	♂	♃	♄	♅	♆	♇
1	2 38 44.9	14S10.0	0N10.1	3S50.4	23S19.1	19S16.3	16N 4.5	10N13.8	4N25.0	17S35.8	21S36.7	7N38.1
4	2 50 34.5	15 7.1	0 10.1	9N52.6	23 43.8	20 14.6	15 38.0	10 4.6	4 18.4	17 38.8	21 37.3	7 36.1
7	3 2 24.2	16 2.1	0 10.2	18 9.5	23 49.7	21 8.0	15 11.5	9 55.8	4 12.1	17 41.7	21 37.8	7 34.3
10	3 14 13.8	16 54.6	0 10.3	17 29.3	23 32.8	21 56.0	14 45.2	9 47.4	4 6.0	17 44.7	21 38.4	7 32.6
13	3 26 3.5	17 44.6	0 10.3	9 51.0	22 48.0	22 38.4	14 19.1	9 39.5	4 .2	17 47.6	21 39.0	7 31.0
16	3 37 53.2	18 31.8	0 10.4	1S16.2	21 31.8	23 14.9	13 53.3	9 32.0	3 54.6	17 50.6	21 39.6	7 29.5
19	3 49 42.8	19 16.0	0 10.5	12 21.5	19 47.9	23 45.2	13 27.9	9 25.0	3 49.3	17 53.5	21 40.1	7 28.2
22	4 1 32.5	19 57.2	0 10.5	18 45.8	17 54.5	24 9.3	13 3.1	9 18.4	3 44.3	17 56.4	21 40.7	7 26.9
25	4 13 22.2	20 35.1	0 10.6	16 11.3	16 19.4	24 26.7	12 38.9	9 12.4	3 39.7	17 59.3	21 41.3	7 25.9
28	4 25 11.8	21 9.5	0 10.6	5 19.2	15 23.7	24 37.6	12 15.4	9 7.0	3 35.3	18 2.2	21 41.8	7 24.9

DECEMBER 1979

LONGITUDE

DAY	EPHEM. SID. TIME h m s	☉ ° ′	☊ ° ′	☾ ° ′	☿ ° ′	♀ ° ′	♂ ° ′	♃ ° ′	♄ ° ′	♅ ° ′	♆ ° ′	♇ ° ′
1	4 37 1.5	8♐11.3	3♍32.2	2♉24.8	19♏50.8	2♑59.8	4♍43.7	9♍12.6	25♍48.5	22♏20.4	19♐46.3	20♎55.2
2	4 40 58.1	9 12.1	3 29.0	16 33.6	20 D 10.5	4 14.4	5 7.5	9 17.2	25 52.2	22 24.1	19 48.5	20 57.0
3	4 44 54.6	10 12.9	3 25.8	0♊33.1	20 38.9	5 28.9	5 31.0	9 21.7	25 55.9	22 27.7	19 50.8	20 58.7
4	4 48 51.2	11 13.8	3 22.7	14 18.6	21 15.2	6 43.5	5 54.2	9 26.0	25 59.5	22 31.3	19 53.0	21 .4
5	4 52 47.7	12 14.6	3 19.5	27 46.1	21 58.5	7 58.0	6 17.0	9 30.1	26 3.0	22 34.8	19 55.2	21 2.1
6	4 56 44.3	13 15.5	3 16.3	10♋53.2	22 48.0	9 12.5	6 39.5	9 34.1	26 6.4	22 38.4	19 57.5	21 3.7
7	5 0 40.9	14 16.4	3 13.1	23 39.4	23 42.9	10 27.0	7 1.7	9 37.8	26 9.7	22 42.0	19 59.8	21 5.4
8	5 4 37.4	15 17.3	3 10.0	6♌ 6.0	24 42.6	11 41.5	7 23.5	9 41.4	26 12.9	22 45.5	20 2.0	21 7.0
9	5 8 34.0	16 18.2	3 6.8	18 15.8	25 46.5	12 56.0	7 44.9	9 44.9	26 16.0	22 49.0	20 4.3	21 8.6
10	5 12 30.5	17 19.1	3 3.6	0♍13.1	26 53.9	14 10.5	8 6.0	9 48.1	26 19.0	22 52.5	20 6.5	21 10.1
11	5 16 27.1	18 20.1	3 .4	12 2.8	28 4.5	15 24.9	8 26.7	9 51.2	26 21.9	22 56.0	20 8.8	21 11.6
12	5 20 23.6	19 21.1	2 57.3	23 50.5	29 17.9	16 39.4	8 47.1	9 54.1	26 24.8	22 59.5	20 11.1	21 13.2
13	5 24 20.2	20 22.1	2 54.1	5♎41.7	0♐33.6	17 53.8	9 7.0	9 56.8	26 27.5	23 2.9	20 13.4	21 14.6
14	5 28 16.8	21 23.2	2 50.9	17 41.8	1 51.3	19 8.3	9 26.5	9 59.3	26 30.1	23 6.3	20 15.6	21 16.1
15	5 32 13.3	22 24.2	2 47.7	29 55.5	3 10.9	20 22.7	9 45.6	10 1.6	26 32.6	23 9.7	20 17.9	21 17.5
16	5 36 9.9	23 25.3	2 44.5	12♏26.7	4 31.9	21 37.1	10 4.3	10 3.8	26 35.1	23 13.1	20 20.2	21 18.8
17	5 40 6.4	24 26.3	2 41.4	25 17.9	5 54.3	22 51.4	10 22.6	10 5.7	26 37.4	23 16.4	20 22.4	21 20.2
18	5 44 3.0	25 27.4	2 38.2	8♐29.7	7 17.9	24 5.8	10 40.4	10 7.5	26 39.6	23 19.7	20 24.7	21 21.5
19	5 47 59.5	26 28.5	2 35.0	22 1.3	8 42.5	25 20.1	10 57.8	10 9.0	26 41.7	23 23.0	20 26.9	21 22.8
20	5 51 56.1	27 29.6	2 31.8	5♑49.6	10 8.0	26 34.5	11 14.7	10 10.4	26 43.7	23 26.3	20 29.2	21 24.0
21	5 55 52.7	28 30.7	2 28.7	19 50.9	11 34.2	27 48.8	11 31.1	10 11.6	26 45.5	23 29.5	20 31.4	21 25.2
22	5 59 49.2	29 31.8	2 25.5	4♒ .5	13 1.2	29 3.0	11 47.1	10 12.6	26 47.3	23 32.7	20 33.7	21 26.4
23	6 3 45.8	0♑33.0	2 22.3	18 13.9	14 28.8	0♒17.3	12 2.6	10 13.4	26 49.0	23 35.9	20 35.9	21 27.6
24	6 7 42.3	1 34.1	2 19.1	2♓27.6	15 57.0	1 31.5	12 17.5	10 14.0	26 50.6	23 39.0	20 38.2	21 28.7
25	6 11 38.9	2 35.2	2 16.0	16 39.0	17 25.7	2 45.7	12 32.0	10 14.4	26 52.0	23 42.2	20 40.4	21 29.8
26	6 15 35.4	3 36.4	2 12.8	0♈46.4	18 54.8	3 59.9	12 46.0	10 14.6	26 53.4	23 45.3	20 42.6	21 30.9
27	6 19 32.0	4 37.5	2 9.6	14 48.9	20 24.4	5 14.1	12 59.4	10 14.6	26 54.6	23 48.3	20 44.8	21 31.9
28	6 23 28.6	5 38.6	2 6.4	28 45.7	21 54.3	6 28.2	13 12.3	10 R 14.4	26 55.7	23 51.3	20 47.0	21 32.9
29	6 27 25.1	6 39.8	2 3.3	12♉35.7	23 24.7	7 42.3	13 24.6	10 14.1	26 56.8	23 54.3	20 49.2	21 33.8
30	6 31 21.7	7 40.9	2 .1	26 17.5	24 55.4	8 56.3	13 36.4	10 13.5	26 57.7	23 57.3	20 51.4	21 34.8
31	6 35 18.2	8 42.0	1 56.9	9♊49.3	26 26.5	10 10.3	13 47.6	10 12.7	26 58.5	24 .2	20 53.6	21 35.6

LATITUDE

DAY	SID. TIME	☉	☊	☾	☿	♀	♂	♃	♄	♅	♆	♇
1	4 37 1.5	0 .0	0 .0	4S17.7	2N35.9	1S17.3	2N15.4	0N59.4	2N 1.3	0N16.9	1N20.6	16N46.5
4	4 48 51.2	0 .0	0 .0	4 54.8	2 34.2	1 22.9	2 19.9	1 .1	2 2.0	0 16.9	1 20.5	16 47.8
7	5 0 40.9	0 .0	0 .0	3 9.8	2 23.2	1 28.1	2 24.5	1 .9	2 2.8	0 16.8	1 20.5	16 49.1
10	5 12 30.5	0 .0	0 .0	0 11.3	2 6.4	1 32.7	2 29.2	1 1.7	2 3.6	0 16.8	1 20.5	16 50.5
13	5 24 20.2	0 .0	0 .0	2N47.6	1 46.1	1 36.8	2 34.1	1 2.5	2 4.4	0 16.8	1 20.4	16 52.0
16	5 36 9.9	0 .0	0 .0	4 45.6	1 23.8	1 40.3	2 39.1	1 3.3	2 5.2	0 16.8	1 20.4	16 53.4
19	5 47 59.5	0 .0	0 .0	4 43.9	1 .7	1 43.2	2 44.2	1 4.1	2 6.0	0 16.8	1 20.4	16 55.0
22	5 59 49.2	0 .0	0 .0	2 19.0	0 37.5	1 45.5	2 49.5	1 4.9	2 6.9	0 16.8	1 20.4	16 56.5
25	6 11 38.9	0 .0	0 .0	1S22.9	0 14.8	1 47.1	2 54.8	1 5.8	2 7.7	0 16.8	1 20.4	16 58.2
28	6 23 28.6	0 .0	0 .0	4 19.6	0S 7.2	1 48.0	3 .3	1 6.6	2 8.6	0 16.8	1 20.4	16 59.8
31	6 35 18.2	0 .0	0 .0	5 2.4	0 28.1	1 48.2	3 5.9	1 7.4	2 9.4	0 16.8	1 20.4	17 1.5

RIGHT ASCENSION

DAY	SID. TIME	☉	☊	☾	☿	♀	♂	♃	♄	♅	♆	♇
1	4 37 1.5	6♐26.0	5♍27.2	1♉42.8	18♏ 7.5	3♑17.9	7♍25.4	11♍10.3	26♍57.4	20♏ .4	18♐59.1	25♎35.9
2	4 40 58.1	7 30.7	5 24.2	15 29.6	18 27.4	4 40.0	7 48.5	11 14.7	27 .9	20 4.1	19 1.5	25 37.7
3	4 44 54.6	8 35.5	5 21.2	29 28.4	18 55.6	6 2.0	8 11.4	11 19.0	27 4.4	20 7.7	19 3.9	25 39.4
4	4 48 51.2	9 40.5	5 18.2	13♊34.6	19 31.4	7 24.0	8 33.9	11 23.1	27 7.8	20 11.4	19 6.3	25 41.1
5	4 52 47.7	10 45.6	5 15.2	27 38.9	20 14.1	8 45.9	8 56.1	11 27.1	27 11.1	20 15.0	19 8.7	25 42.7
6	4 56 44.3	11 50.8	5 12.2	11♋29.9	21 2.9	10 7.8	9 17.9	11 30.9	27 14.3	20 18.7	19 11.1	25 44.4
7	5 0 40.9	12 56.2	5 9.1	24 57.2	21 57.1	11 29.6	9 39.5	11 34.5	27 17.5	20 22.3	19 13.5	25 46.0
8	5 4 37.4	14 1.8	5 6.1	7♌53.9	22 56.2	12 51.2	10 .6	11 38.0	27 20.5	20 25.9	19 15.9	25 47.6
9	5 8 34.0	15 7.4	5 3.1	20 18.5	23 59.5	14 12.8	10 21.5	11 41.3	27 23.5	20 29.4	19 18.4	25 49.2
10	5 12 30.5	16 13.2	5 .1	2♍13.8	25 6.8	15 34.2	10 42.0	11 44.5	27 26.4	20 33.0	19 20.8	25 50.8
11	5 16 27.1	17 19.1	4 57.1	13 46.4	26 17.4	16 55.4	11 2.1	11 47.4	27 29.1	20 36.5	19 23.2	25 52.3
12	5 20 23.6	18 25.2	4 54.1	25 5.1	27 31.1	18 16.6	11 21.9	11 50.3	27 31.9	20 40.1	19 25.7	25 53.9
13	5 24 20.2	19 31.3	4 51.1	6♎20.0	28 47.4	19 37.4	11 41.3	11 52.9	27 34.5	20 43.6	19 28.1	25 55.4
14	5 28 16.8	20 37.5	4 48.1	17 41.8	0♐ 6.2	20 58.1	12 .3	11 55.4	27 37.0	20 47.1	19 30.5	25 56.8
15	5 32 13.3	21 43.8	4 45.0	29 21.4	1 27.2	22 18.6	12 18.9	11 57.6	27 39.4	20 50.5	19 33.0	25 58.3
16	5 36 9.9	22 50.1	4 42.0	11♏28.6	2 50.2	23 38.9	12 37.1	11 59.7	27 41.7	20 53.9	19 35.4	25 59.7
17	5 40 6.4	23 56.5	4 39.0	24 11.6	4 15.0	24 58.9	12 54.9	12 1.7	27 44.0	20 57.3	19 37.8	26 1.1
18	5 44 3.0	25 3.0	4 36.0	7♐34.8	5 41.3	26 18.6	13 12.3	12 3.4	27 46.1	21 .7	19 40.3	26 2.4
19	5 47 59.5	26 9.5	4 33.0	21 36.8	7 9.2	27 38.1	13 29.2	12 5.0	27 48.1	21 4.1	19 42.7	26 3.8
20	5 51 56.1	27 16.1	4 30.0	6♑ 9.2	8 38.5	28 57.4	13 45.7	12 6.4	27 50.1	21 7.4	19 45.1	26 5.1
21	5 55 52.7	28 22.7	4 27.0	20 57.7	10 9.0	0♒16.3	14 1.8	12 7.6	27 51.9	21 10.7	19 47.5	26 6.4
22	5 59 49.2	29 29.3	4 23.9	5♒45.6	11 40.6	1 34.9	14 17.4	12 8.6	27 53.7	21 14.0	19 49.9	26 7.7
23	6 3 45.8	0♑35.9	4 20.9	20 18.6	13 13.3	2 53.3	14 32.6	12 9.5	27 55.3	21 17.2	19 52.3	26 8.9
24	6 7 42.3	1 42.6	4 17.9	4♓28.8	14 47.1	4 11.3	14 47.3	12 10.1	27 56.9	21 20.5	19 54.7	26 10.1
25	6 11 38.9	2 49.2	4 14.9	18 15.4	16 21.8	5 29.0	15 1.5	12 10.6	27 58.3	21 23.6	19 57.1	26 11.3
26	6 15 35.4	3 55.8	4 11.9	1♈43.3	17 57.3	6 46.4	15 15.3	12 10.9	27 59.7	21 26.8	19 59.5	26 12.4
27	6 19 32.0	5 2.3	4 8.8	15 .6	19 33.7	8 3.4	15 28.5	12 11.0	28 .9	21 29.9	20 1.9	26 13.5
28	6 23 28.6	6 8.9	4 5.8	28 16.6	21 10.8	9 20.1	15 41.3	12 11.0	28 2.1	21 33.0	20 4.3	26 14.6
29	6 27 25.1	7 15.3	4 2.8	11♉38.9	22 48.7	10 36.4	15 53.6	12 R 10.7	28 3.1	21 36.1	20 6.6	26 15.7
30	6 31 21.7	8 21.8	3 59.8	25 12.3	24 27.3	11 52.4	16 5.3	12 10.3	28 4.1	21 39.1	20 9.0	26 16.7
31	6 35 18.2	9 28.2	3 56.8	8♊56.9	26 6.6	13 8.0	16 16.5	12 9.7	28 4.9	21 42.1	20 11.3	26 17.7

DECLINATION

DAY	SID. TIME	☉	☊	☾	☿	♀	♂	♃	♄	♅	♆	♇
1	4 37 1.5	21S40.4	0N10.7	8N16.5	15S11.8	24S41.6	11N52.6	9N 2.0	3N31.3	18S 5.0	21S42.4	7N24.1
4	4 48 51.2	22 7.5	0 10.8	17 38.2	15 35.5	24 38.9	11 30.8	8 57.7	3 27.6	18 7.8	21 42.9	7 23.4
7	5 0 40.9	22 30.7	0 10.8	18 15.0	16 23.3	24 29.5	11 10.0	8 53.9	3 24.3	18 10.5	21 43.5	7 22.8
10	5 12 30.5	22 50.1	0 10.9	11 13.1	17 24.8	24 13.3	10 50.3	8 50.8	3 21.3	18 13.2	21 44.0	7 22.4
13	5 24 20.2	23 5.4	0 10.9	0 18.2	18 32.3	23 50.5	10 31.9	8 48.2	3 18.6	18 15.8	21 44.5	7 22.2
16	5 36 9.9	23 16.5	0 11.0	11S 2.0	19 40.4	23 21.2	10 14.8	8 46.4	3 16.4	18 18.4	21 45.0	7 22.0
19	5 47 59.5	23 23.5	0 11.1	18 28.5	20 45.3	22 45.7	9 59.2	8 45.1	3 14.5	18 20.9	21 45.5	7 22.0
22	5 59 49.2	23 26.3	0 11.1	17 .1	21 44.4	22 4.1	9 45.2	8 44.5	3 13.0	18 23.3	21 46.0	7 22.2
25	6 11 38.9	23 24.8	0 11.2	6 32.5	22 36.0	21 16.7	9 32.9	8 44.6	3 11.9	18 25.6	21 46.5	7 22.5
28	6 23 28.6	23 19.1	0 11.2	6N59.2	23 18.7	20 23.9	9 22.4	8 45.3	3 11.2	18 27.9	21 46.9	7 22.9
31	6 35 18.2	23 9.2	0 11.3	16 56.2	23 51.6	19 25.8	9 14.0	8 46.7	3 10.9	18 30.1	21 47.3	7 23.5

JANUARY 1980

DAY	EPHEM. SID. TIME	☉	☊	☾	☿	♀	♂	♃	♄	♅	♆	♇
		LONGITUDE										
	h m s	° ′	° ′	° ′	° ′	° ′	° ′	° ′	° ′	° ′	° ′	° ′
1	6 39 14.8	9♑43.2	1♍53.7	23♊ 9.0	27♐58.0	11♒24.3	13♍58.3	10♍11.8	26♍59.2	24♏ 3.1	20♐55.8	21♎36.5
2	6 43 11.3	10 44.3	1 50.5	6♋14.7	29 29.8	12 38.3	14 8.4	10R10.7	26 59.8	24 6.0	20 58.0	21 37.4
3	6 47 7.9	11 45.5	1 47.4	19 5.1	1♑ 2.0	13 52.2	14 17.8	10 9.4	27 .3	24 8.8	21 .1	21 38.2
4	6 51 4.5	12 46.6	1 44.2	1♌39.8	2 34.5	15 6.1	14 26.7	10 7.8	27 .7	24 11.6	21 2.3	21 38.9
5	6 55 1.0	13 47.7	1 41.0	13 59.4	4 7.4	16 19.9	14 34.9	10 6.1	27 .9	24 14.4	21 4.4	21 39.6
6	6 58 57.6	14 48.9	1 37.8	26 5.7	5 40.6	17 33.7	14 42.5	10 4.2	27 1.1	24 17.1	21 6.5	21 40.3
7	7 2 54.1	15 50.0	1 34.7	8♍ 1.8	7 14.2	18 47.5	14 49.4	10 2.1	27 1.1	24 19.8	21 8.6	21 41.0
8	7 6 50.7	16 51.1	1 31.5	19 51.4	8 48.2	20 1.2	14 55.7	9 59.8	27 1.1	24 22.4	21 10.7	21 41.6
9	7 10 47.2	17 52.3	1 28.3	1♎39.0	10 22.5	21 14.9	15 1.3	9 57.3	27R .9	24 25.0	21 12.8	21 42.1
10	7 14 43.8	18 53.4	1 25.1	13 29.9	11 57.3	22 28.5	15 6.2	9 54.6	27 .6	24 27.5	21 14.9	21 42.7
11	7 18 40.3	19 54.6	1 22.0	25 29.1	13 32.6	23 42.1	15 10.5	9 51.7	27 .2	24 30.1	21 16.9	21 43.2
12	7 22 36.9	20 55.7	1 18.8	7♏41.8	15 8.2	24 55.7	15 14.0	9 48.7	26 59.7	24 32.5	21 18.9	21 43.7
13	7 26 33.5	21 56.9	1 15.6	20 12.8	16 44.3	26 9.2	15 16.8	9 45.5	26 59.1	24 35.0	21 21.0	21 44.1
14	7 30 30.0	22 58.0	1 12.4	3♐ 5.7	18 20.9	27 22.6	15 18.8	9 42.0	26 58.4	24 37.4	21 23.0	21 44.5
15	7 34 26.6	23 59.1	1 9.2	16 22.9	19 57.9	28 36.0	15 20.2	9 38.4	26 57.5	24 39.7	21 25.0	21 44.8
16	7 38 23.1	25 .3	1 6.1	0♑ 4.6	21 35.5	29 49.4	15 20.7	9 34.7	26 56.6	24 42.0	21 26.9	21 45.2
17	7 42 19.7	26 1.4	1 2.9	14 9.0	23 13.5	1♓ 2.7	15R20.5	9 30.7	26 55.5	24 44.3	21 28.9	21 45.5
18	7 46 16.2	27 2.5	0 59.7	28 31.9	24 52.1	2 16.0	15 19.6	9 26.6	26 54.4	24 46.5	21 30.8	21 45.7
19	7 50 12.8	28 3.6	0 56.5	13♒ 7.5	26 31.2	3 29.2	15 17.8	9 22.3	26 53.1	24 48.6	21 32.7	21 45.9
20	7 54 9.4	29 4.7	0 53.4	27 49.0	28 10.8	4 42.4	15 15.3	9 17.8	26 51.7	24 50.8	21 34.6	21 46.1
21	7 58 5.9	0♒ 5.8	0 50.2	12♓29.7	29 51.0	5 55.5	15 12.0	9 13.1	26 50.3	24 52.8	21 36.5	21 46.2
22	8 2 2.5	1 6.9	0 47.0	27 3.8	1♒31.9	7 8.5	15 8.0	9 8.4	26 48.7	24 54.9	21 38.4	21 46.4
23	8 5 59.0	2 8.0	0 43.8	11♈26.9	3 13.2	8 21.5	15 3.1	9 3.4	26 47.1	24 56.9	21 40.2	21 46.5
24	8 9 55.6	3 9.0	0 40.7	25 36.3	4 55.1	9 34.4	14 57.4	8 58.3	26 45.3	24 58.8	21 42.0	21 46.5
25	8 13 52.1	4 10.1	0 37.5	9♉30.7	6 37.6	10 47.2	14 51.0	8 53.0	26 43.4	25 .7	21 43.8	21 46.5
26	8 17 48.7	5 11.1	0 34.3	23 9.7	8 20.6	11 60.0	14 43.7	8 47.5	26 41.4	25 2.6	21 45.6	21 46.5
27	8 21 45.2	6 12.1	0 31.1	6♊33.6	10 4.1	13 12.7	14 35.7	8 42.0	26 39.3	25 4.3	21 47.4	21R46.4
28	8 25 41.8	7 13.0	0 27.9	19 43.1	11 48.2	14 25.3	14 26.8	8 36.2	26 37.1	25 6.1	21 49.1	21 46.3
29	8 29 38.4	8 14.0	0 24.8	2♋38.7	13 32.8	15 37.8	14 17.2	8 30.4	26 34.9	25 7.8	21 50.8	21 46.1
30	8 33 34.9	9 14.9	0 21.6	15 21.3	15 17.9	16 50.2	14 6.8	8 24.4	26 32.5	25 9.4	21 52.5	21 45.9
31	8 37 31.5	10 15.8	0 18.4	27 51.4	17 3.3	18 2.6	13 55.6	8 18.2	26 30.0	25 11.0	21 54.1	21 45.7
		LATITUDE										
1	6 39 14.8	0 .0	0 .0	4S42.9	0S34.8	1S48.1	3N 7.8	1N 7.7	2N 9.7	0N16.8	1N20.5	17N 2.0
4	6 51 4.5	0 .0	0 .0	2 27.1	0 53.8	1 47.3	3 13.5	1 8.5	2 10.5	0 16.8	1 20.4	17 3.7
7	7 2 54.1	0 .0	0 .0	0N43.5	1 11.1	1 45.8	3 19.4	1 9.3	2 11.4	0 16.8	1 20.5	17 5.4
10	7 14 43.8	0 .0	0 .0	3 34.5	1 26.5	1 43.5	3 25.3	1 10.1	2 12.2	0 16.8	1 20.5	17 7.2
13	7 26 33.5	0 .0	0 .0	5 6.9	1 39.8	1 40.4	3 31.2	1 10.9	2 13.1	0 16.8	1 20.6	17 8.9
16	7 38 23.1	0 .0	0 .0	4 29.1	1 50.6	1 36.6	3 37.1	1 11.6	2 13.9	0 16.8	1 20.6	17 10.7
19	7 50 12.8	0 .0	0 .0	1 28.5	1 58.7	1 32.0	3 42.9	1 12.4	2 14.7	0 16.9	1 20.7	17 12.4
22	8 2 2.5	0 .0	0 .0	2S25.8	2 3.7	1 26.6	3 48.7	1 13.1	2 15.5	0 16.9	1 20.7	17 14.2
25	8 13 52.1	0 .0	0 .0	4 55.8	2 5.2	1 20.5	3 54.2	1 13.8	2 16.3	0 16.9	1 20.8	17 15.9
28	8 25 41.8	0 .0	0 .0	4 55.4	2 2.8	1 13.6	3 59.6	1 14.4	2 17.0	0 16.9	1 20.9	17 17.7
31	8 37 31.5	0 .0	0 .0	2 44.9	1 56.0	1 6.1	4 4.6	1 15.1	2 17.8	0 16.9	1 21.0	17 19.4
		RIGHT ASCENSION										
1	6 39 14.8	10♑34.5	3♍53.8	22♊47.8	27♐46.4	14♒23.3	16♍27.2	12♍ 8.9	28♍ 5.7	21♏45.0	20♐13.7	26♎18.7
2	6 43 11.3	11 40.8	3 50.7	6♋35.7	29 27.0	15 38.3	16 37.3	12R 8.0	28 6.4	21 48.0	20 16.0	26 19.7
3	6 47 7.9	12 46.9	3 47.7	20 9.7	1♑ 8.0	16 52.8	16 46.9	12 6.9	28 6.9	21 50.9	20 18.3	26 20.6
4	6 51 4.5	13 53.0	3 44.7	3♌20.3	2 49.5	18 7.0	16 55.9	12 5.5	28 7.4	21 53.7	20 20.6	26 21.5
5	6 55 1.0	14 59.0	3 41.7	16 1.8	4 31.6	19 20.9	17 4.3	12 4.0	28 7.7	21 56.6	20 22.9	26 22.4
6	6 58 57.6	16 4.8	3 38.6	28 13.1	6 14.1	20 34.4	17 12.2	12 2.3	28 8.0	21 59.3	20 25.2	26 23.2
7	7 2 54.1	17 10.6	3 35.6	9♍57.8	7 57.0	21 47.5	17 19.4	12 .4	28 8.1	22 2.1	20 27.5	26 24.0
8	7 6 50.7	18 16.3	3 32.6	21 22.4	9 40.4	23 .3	17 26.0	11 58.4	28 8.2	22 4.8	20 29.7	26 24.8
9	7 10 47.2	19 21.8	3 29.6	2♎35.9	11 24.1	24 12.7	17 32.0	11 56.2	28R 8.1	22 7.4	20 31.9	26 25.5
10	7 14 43.8	20 27.2	3 26.5	13 48.5	13 8.2	25 24.7	17 37.4	11 53.8	28 8.0	22 10.0	20 34.2	26 26.2
11	7 18 40.3	21 32.5	3 23.5	25 11.2	14 52.7	26 36.5	17 42.1	11 51.2	28 7.7	22 12.6	20 36.4	26 26.9
12	7 22 36.9	22 37.7	3 20.5	6♏55.0	16 37.4	27 47.8	17 46.1	11 48.4	28 7.4	22 15.1	20 38.6	26 27.5
13	7 26 33.5	23 42.7	3 17.5	19 10.3	18 22.5	28 58.9	17 49.5	11 45.5	28 6.9	22 17.6	20 40.7	26 28.1
14	7 30 30.0	24 47.5	3 14.4	2♐ 5.3	20 7.7	0♓ 9.6	17 52.2	11 42.4	28 6.4	22 20.1	20 42.9	26 28.7
15	7 34 26.6	25 52.2	3 11.4	15 44.3	21 53.2	1 20.0	17 54.2	11 39.1	28 5.7	22 22.5	20 45.0	26 29.2
16	7 38 23.1	26 56.8	3 8.4	0♑ 4.8	23 38.9	2 30.0	17 55.5	11 35.6	28 5.0	22 24.8	20 47.1	26 29.7
17	7 42 19.7	28 1.2	3 5.4	14 57.0	25 24.8	3 39.8	17 56.1	11 32.0	28 4.1	22 27.2	20 49.2	26 30.2
18	7 46 16.2	29 5.4	3 2.3	0♒ 4.6	27 10.8	4 49.2	17R56.0	11 28.2	28 3.2	22 29.4	20 51.3	26 30.6
19	7 50 12.8	0♒ 9.4	2 59.3	15 9.4	28 57.0	5 58.3	17 55.1	11 24.3	28 2.1	22 31.6	20 53.4	26 31.1
20	7 54 9.4	1 13.3	2 56.3	29 56.7	0♒43.2	7 7.2	17 53.6	11 20.2	28 .9	22 33.8	20 55.4	26 31.4
21	7 58 5.9	2 16.9	2 53.3	14♓19.0	2 29.4	8 15.7	17 51.2	11 15.9	27 59.7	22 35.9	20 57.4	26 31.8
22	8 2 2.5	3 20.5	2 50.2	28 16.3	4 15.8	9 24.0	17 48.2	11 11.5	27 58.4	22 38.1	20 59.5	26 32.1
23	8 5 59.0	4 23.7	2 47.2	11♈53.8	6 2.0	10 31.9	17 44.4	11 7.0	27 57.0	22 40.1	21 1.5	26 32.4
24	8 9 55.6	5 26.8	2 44.2	25 19.6	7 48.3	11 39.6	17 39.9	11 2.2	27 55.4	22 42.1	21 3.4	26 32.7
25	8 13 52.1	6 29.7	2 41.1	8♉41.9	9 34.4	12 47.0	17 34.6	10 57.4	27 53.8	22 44.0	21 5.3	26 32.9
26	8 17 48.7	7 32.4	2 38.1	22 6.9	11 20.5	13 54.2	17 28.5	10 52.3	27 52.1	22 45.9	21 7.2	26 33.1
27	8 21 45.2	8 34.9	2 35.1	5♊37.6	13 6.3	15 1.0	17 21.7	10 47.2	27 50.3	22 47.7	21 9.1	26 33.2
28	8 25 41.8	9 37.1	2 32.0	19 12.9	14 52.0	16 7.7	17 14.2	10 41.9	27 48.4	22 49.5	21 11.0	26 33.3
29	8 29 38.4	10 39.2	2 29.0	2♋47.4	16 37.4	17 14.1	17 5.9	10 36.5	27 46.4	22 51.3	21 12.8	26 33.4
30	8 33 34.9	11 41.1	2 26.0	16 13.3	18 22.5	18 20.3	16 56.8	10 30.9	27 44.3	22 52.9	21 14.6	26 33.5
31	8 37 31.5	12 42.7	2 23.0	29 22.3	20 7.1	19 26.2	16 47.0	10 25.2	27 42.1	22 54.6	21 16.4	26 33.5
		DECLINATION										
1	6 39 14.8	23S 5.0	0N11.3	18N33.2	24S .2	19S 5.4	9N11.6	8N47.3	3N10.9	18S30.8	21S47.5	7N23.7
4	6 51 4.5	22 49.6	0 11.4	17 23.9	24 18.7	18 .9	9 5.9	8 49.6	3 11.1	18 32.9	21 47.9	7 24.4
7	7 2 54.1	22 30.0	0 11.4	9 13.9	24 25.5	16 52.0	9 2.5	8 52.5	3 11.7	18 34.9	21 48.3	7 25.3
10	7 14 43.8	22 6.5	0 11.5	2S 1.9	24 20.3	15 39.1	9 1.4	8 56.1	3 12.7	18 36.8	21 48.7	7 26.3
13	7 26 33.5	21 39.1	0 11.5	12 51.9	24 2.5	14 22.4	9 2.7	9 .3	3 14.0	18 38.6	21 49.0	7 27.4
16	7 38 23.1	21 7.9	0 11.6	18 57.2	23 31.7	13 2.4	9 6.6	9 5.1	3 15.8	18 40.3	21 49.4	7 28.6
19	7 50 12.8	20 33.0	0 11.7	15 27.8	22 47.5	11 39.4	9 13.1	9 10.4	3 17.9	18 41.9	21 49.7	7 30.0
22	8 2 2.5	19 54.6	0 11.7	3 23.8	21 49.8	10 13.7	9 22.2	9 16.3	3 20.4	18 43.4	21 50.0	7 31.4
25	8 13 52.1	19 13.0	0 11.8	9N58.8	20 38.2	8 45.8	9 34.0	9 22.8	3 23.2	18 44.8	21 50.2	7 33.0
28	8 25 41.8	18 28.1	0 11.8	18 7.9	19 12.9	7 15.9	9 48.3	9 29.7	3 26.4	18 46.1	21 50.5	7 34.7
31	8 37 31.5	17 40.2	0 11.9	17 53.7	17 33.9	5 44.4	10 5.0	9 37.0	3 29.9	18 47.2	21 50.7	7 36.5

FEBRUARY 1980

LONGITUDE

DAY	EPHEM. SID. TIME h m s	☉ ° ′	☊ ° ′	☽ ° ′	☿ ° ′	♀ ° ′	♂ ° ′	♃ ° ′	♄ ° ′	♅ ° ′	♆ ° ′	♇ ° ′
1	8 41 28.0	11♒16.7	0♍15.2	10♌10.1	18♒49.1	19♓14.9	13♍43.6	8♍12.0	26♍27.4	25♏12.5	21♐55.8	21♎45.5
2	8 45 24.6	12 17.6	0 12.1	22 18.4	20 35.2	20 27.1	13 R 30.9	8 R 5.6	26 R 24.8	25 14.0	21 57.4	21 R 45.2
3	8 49 21.1	13 18.5	0 8.9	4♍17.9	22 21.4	21 39.2	13 17.4	7 59.1	26 22.0	25 15.5	21 59.0	21 44.9
4	8 53 17.7	14 19.3	0 5.7	16 10.8	24 7.7	22 51.2	13 3.1	7 52.4	26 19.2	25 16.9	22 .5	21 44.5
5	8 57 14.2	15 20.1	0 2.5	27 59.6	25 53.9	24 3.1	12 48.2	7 45.7	26 16.3	25 18.2	22 2.1	21 44.1
6	9 1 10.8	16 21.0	29♌59.3	9♎47.6	27 39.8	25 15.0	12 32.5	7 38.9	26 13.3	25 19.5	22 3.6	21 43.7
7	9 5 7.3	17 21.7	29 56.2	21 38.7	29 25.2	26 26.7	12 16.1	7 31.9	26 10.2	25 20.7	22 5.1	21 43.3
8	9 9 3.9	18 22.5	29 53.0	3♏37.2	1♓ 9.8	27 38.4	11 59.0	7 24.9	26 7.0	25 21.9	22 6.5	21 42.8
9	9 13 .5	19 23.3	29 49.8	15 47.7	2 53.4	28 49.9	11 41.2	7 17.7	26 3.7	25 23.0	22 7.9	21 42.2
10	9 16 57.0	20 24.0	29 46.6	28 14.7	4 35.7	0♈ 1.4	11 22.8	7 10.5	26 .4	25 24.1	22 9.3	21 41.7
11	9 20 53.6	21 24.8	29 43.5	11♐ 2.6	6 16.2	1 12.7	11 3.8	7 3.2	25 57.0	25 25.1	22 10.7	21 41.1
12	9 24 50.1	22 25.5	29 40.3	24 14.9	7 54.6	2 24.0	10 44.3	6 55.8	25 53.5	25 26.1	22 12.1	21 40.5
13	9 28 46.7	23 26.2	29 37.1	7♑53.8	9 30.2	3 35.2	10 24.1	6 48.4	25 50.0	25 27.0	22 13.4	21 39.9
14	9 32 43.2	24 26.9	29 33.9	21 59.3	11 2.6	4 46.2	10 3.4	6 40.8	25 46.3	25 27.9	22 14.7	21 39.2
15	9 36 39.8	25 27.6	29 30.7	6♒29.1	12 31.3	5 57.2	9 42.2	6 33.2	25 42.6	25 28.7	22 16.0	21 38.5
16	9 40 36.3	26 28.2	29 27.6	21 18.4	13 55.5	7 8.0	9 20.6	6 25.6	25 38.8	25 29.4	22 17.2	21 37.7
17	9 44 32.9	27 28.8	29 24.4	6♓19.8	15 14.6	8 18.7	8 58.5	6 17.9	25 35.0	25 30.1	22 18.4	21 36.9
18	9 48 29.4	28 29.4	29 21.2	21 24.6	16 27.9	9 29.3	8 36.1	6 10.1	25 31.0	25 30.7	22 19.6	21 36.1
19	9 52 26.0	29 29.9	29 18.0	6♈24.0	17 34.7	10 39.7	8 13.4	6 2.3	25 27.1	25 31.3	22 20.7	21 35.3
20	9 56 22.5	0♓30.5	29 14.9	21 10.2	18 34.4	11 50.1	7 50.3	5 54.5	25 23.0	25 31.9	22 21.9	21 34.4
21	10 0 19.1	1 31.0	29 11.7	5♉37.4	19 26.3	13 .3	7 27.0	5 46.7	25 18.9	25 32.3	22 22.9	21 33.5
22	10 4 15.7	2 31.4	29 8.5	19 42.3	20 9.7	14 10.3	7 3.5	5 38.8	25 14.8	25 32.7	22 24.0	21 32.6
23	10 8 12.2	3 31.9	29 5.3	3♊23.8	20 44.2	15 20.2	6 39.9	5 30.9	25 10.6	25 33.1	22 25.0	21 31.6
24	10 12 8.8	4 32.3	29 2.1	16 42.8	21 9.3	16 30.0	6 16.1	5 23.0	25 6.3	25 33.4	22 26.0	21 30.6
25	10 16 5.3	5 32.6	28 59.0	29 41.2	21 24.7	17 39.6	5 52.3	5 15.1	25 2.0	25 33.7	22 27.0	21 29.6
26	10 20 1.9	6 33.0	28 55.8	12♋21.7	21 30.3	18 49.1	5 28.4	5 7.2	24 57.7	25 33.9	22 27.9	21 28.5
27	10 23 58.4	7 33.3	28 52.6	24 47.4	21 R 25.9	19 58.4	5 4.6	4 59.4	24 53.3	25 34.0	22 28.8	21 27.5
28	10 27 55.0	8 33.5	28 49.4	7♌ 1.0	21 11.9	21 7.6	4 40.9	4 51.5	24 48.8	25 34.1	22 29.6	21 26.4
29	10 31 51.5	9 33.8	28 46.3	19 5.3	20 48.7	22 16.6	4 17.2	4 43.6	24 44.4	25 34.1	22 30.5	21 25.2

LATITUDE

DAY	EPHEM. SID. TIME	☉	☊	☽	☿	♀	♂	♃	♄	♅	♆	♇
1	8 41 28.0	0 .0	0 .0	1S43.6	1S52.6	1S 3.4	4N 6.2	1N15.3	2N18.0	0N16.9	1N21.0	17N19.9
4	8 53 17.7	0 .0	0 .0	1N32.6	1 38.8	0 54.9	4 10.6	1 15.9	2 18.7	0 16.9	1 21.1	17 21.6
7	9 5 7.3	0 .0	0 .0	4 11.7	1 19.2	0 45.7	4 14.6	1 16.4	2 19.4	0 17.0	1 21.2	17 23.2
10	9 16 57.0	0 .0	0 .0	5 17.6	0 53.2	0 35.9	4 17.9	1 16.9	2 20.1	0 17.0	1 21.2	17 24.8
13	9 28 46.7	0 .0	0 .0	4 8.6	0 20.7	0 25.5	4 20.5	1 17.4	2 20.7	0 17.0	1 21.3	17 26.4
16	9 40 36.3	0 .0	0 .0	0 44.2	0N18.1	0 14.6	4 22.2	1 17.8	2 21.3	0 17.0	1 21.4	17 27.9
19	9 52 26.0	0 .0	0 .0	3S12.3	1 1.7	0 3.2	4 23.2	1 18.1	2 21.8	0 17.0	1 21.6	17 29.4
22	10 4 15.7	0 .0	0 .0	5 13.6	1 47.7	0N 8.8	4 23.1	1 18.4	2 22.3	0 17.1	1 21.7	17 30.8
25	10 16 5.3	0 .0	0 .0	4 34.4	2 32.0	0 21.1	4 22.2	1 18.7	2 22.8	0 17.1	1 21.8	17 32.2
28	10 27 55.0	0 .0	0 .0	2 .9	3 9.4	0 33.9	4 20.3	1 18.9	2 23.2	0 17.1	1 21.9	17 33.5

RIGHT ASCENSION

DAY	EPHEM. SID. TIME	☉	☊	☽	☿	♀	♂	♃	♄	♅	♆	♇
1	8 41 28.0	13♒44.2	2♍19.9	12♌ 7.9	21♒51.3	20♓32.0	16♍36.5	10♍19.4	27♍39.9	22♏56.2	21♐18.2	26♎33.5
2	8 45 24.6	14 45.4	2 16.9	24 27.2	23 35.0	21 37.5	16 R 25.2	10 R 13.5	27 R 37.5	22 57.7	21 19.9	26 R 33.4
3	8 49 21.1	15 46.4	2 13.8	6♍20.9	25 18.0	22 42.8	16 13.1	10 7.4	27 35.1	22 59.2	21 21.6	26 33.4
4	8 53 17.7	16 47.3	2 10.8	17 53.0	27 .2	23 48.0	16 .4	10 1.2	27 32.6	23 .6	21 23.3	26 33.3
5	8 57 14.2	17 47.9	2 7.8	29 10.3	28 41.4	24 53.0	15 46.9	9 55.0	27 30.0	23 2.0	21 24.9	26 33.1
6	9 1 10.8	18 48.3	2 4.7	10♎21.1	0♓21.6	25 57.8	15 32.7	9 48.6	27 27.3	23 3.3	21 26.6	26 32.9
7	9 5 7.3	19 48.6	2 1.7	21 34.7	2 .5	27 2.5	15 17.9	9 42.1	27 24.6	23 4.5	21 28.2	26 32.7
8	9 9 3.9	20 48.6	1 58.7	3♏ 1.3	3 37.8	28 7.0	15 2.3	9 35.6	27 21.7	23 5.7	21 29.7	26 32.5
9	9 13 .5	21 48.5	1 55.6	14 50.8	5 13.5	29 11.3	14 46.1	9 28.9	27 18.8	23 6.9	21 31.3	26 32.2
10	9 16 57.0	22 48.1	1 52.6	27 12.7	6 47.0	0♈15.6	14 29.2	9 22.1	27 15.8	23 8.0	21 32.8	26 31.9
11	9 20 53.6	23 47.6	1 49.6	10♐13.8	8 18.2	1 19.7	14 11.8	9 15.3	27 12.8	23 9.0	21 34.3	26 31.6
12	9 24 50.1	24 46.9	1 46.5	23 57.3	9 46.7	2 23.7	13 53.7	9 8.4	27 9.7	23 10.1	21 35.8	26 31.3
13	9 28 46.7	25 46.0	1 43.5	8♑20.1	11 12.0	3 27.6	13 35.1	9 1.4	27 6.5	23 11.0	21 37.2	26 30.9
14	9 32 43.2	26 44.9	1 40.4	23 12.7	12 33.7	4 31.4	13 15.9	8 54.4	27 3.2	23 11.9	21 38.6	26 30.5
15	9 36 39.8	27 43.6	1 37.4	8♒20.2	13 51.4	5 35.1	12 56.1	8 47.3	26 59.9	23 12.7	21 39.9	26 30.0
16	9 40 36.3	28 42.1	1 34.4	23 26.8	15 4.4	6 38.8	12 35.9	8 40.1	26 56.5	23 13.5	21 41.3	26 29.6
17	9 44 32.9	29 40.5	1 31.3	8♓20.1	16 12.3	7 42.3	12 15.3	8 32.9	26 53.0	23 14.2	21 42.6	26 29.0
18	9 48 29.4	0♓38.6	1 28.3	22 54.1	17 14.5	8 45.8	11 54.2	8 25.6	26 49.5	23 14.9	21 43.8	26 28.5
19	9 52 26.0	1 36.6	1 25.3	7♈ 8.6	18 10.4	9 49.2	11 32.8	8 18.3	26 45.9	23 15.5	21 45.1	26 27.9
20	9 56 22.5	2 34.5	1 22.2	21 7.7	18 59.5	10 52.6	11 11.0	8 10.9	26 42.3	23 16.0	21 46.3	26 27.3
21	10 0 19.1	3 32.1	1 19.2	4♉57.2	19 41.3	11 55.9	10 49.0	8 3.6	26 38.6	23 16.5	21 47.4	26 26.7
22	10 4 15.7	4 29.6	1 16.1	18 42.0	20 15.3	12 59.2	10 26.7	7 56.2	26 34.8	23 16.9	21 48.6	26 26.0
23	10 8 12.2	5 26.9	1 13.1	2♊25.0	20 41.0	14 2.5	10 4.1	7 48.7	26 31.0	23 17.3	21 49.7	26 25.4
24	10 12 8.8	6 24.0	1 10.0	16 5.5	20 58.3	15 5.7	9 41.5	7 41.3	26 27.1	23 17.6	21 50.7	26 24.6
25	10 16 5.3	7 21.0	1 7.0	29 40.2	21 6.8	16 8.9	9 18.6	7 33.9	26 23.3	23 17.9	21 51.8	26 23.9
26	10 20 1.9	8 17.9	1 4.0	13♋ 3.4	21 R 6.6	17 12.1	8 55.8	7 26.4	26 19.3	23 18.1	21 52.8	26 23.1
27	10 23 58.4	9 14.6	1 .9	26 9.3	20 57.7	18 15.2	8 32.8	7 19.0	26 15.3	23 18.2	21 53.7	26 22.3
28	10 27 55.0	10 11.1	0 57.9	8♌53.0	20 40.4	19 18.4	8 9.9	7 11.6	26 11.3	23 18.3	21 54.7	26 21.5
29	10 31 51.5	11 7.5	0 54.8	21 12.6	20 15.1	20 21.5	7 47.0	7 4.1	26 7.2	23 18.3	21 55.6	26 20.7

DECLINATION

DAY	EPHEM. SID. TIME	☉	☊	☽	☿	♀	♂	♃	♄	♅	♆	♇
1	8 41 28.0	17S23.6	0N11.9	16N 2.0	16S58.0	5S13.7	10N11.1	9N39.5	3N31.2	18S47.6	21S50.8	7N37.1
4	8 53 17.7	16 32.0	0 12.0	6 52.5	15 1.9	3 40.6	10 30.8	9 47.4	3 35.1	18 48.6	21 51.0	7 39.0
7	9 5 7.3	15 37.9	0 12.0	4S32.6	12 54.7	2 6.8	10 52.6	9 55.5	3 39.3	18 49.5	21 51.2	7 40.9
10	9 16 57.0	14 41.3	0 12.1	14 36.3	10 39.1	0 32.4	11 16.1	10 4.0	3 43.8	18 50.3	21 51.3	7 43.0
13	9 28 46.7	13 42.4	0 12.2	19 4.1	8 19.5	1N 2.1	11 41.0	10 12.6	3 48.5	18 51.0	21 51.5	7 45.1
16	9 40 36.3	12 41.6	0 12.2	13 42.1	6 2.8	2 36.5	12 6.8	10 21.5	3 53.5	18 51.5	21 51.6	7 47.3
19	9 52 26.0	11 38.9	0 12.3	0 24.1	3 57.7	4 10.3	12 33.1	10 30.4	3 58.6	18 52.0	21 51.7	7 49.5
22	10 4 15.7	10 34.5	0 12.3	12N37.5	2 14.8	5 43.4	12 59.3	10 39.4	4 4.0	18 52.3	21 51.8	7 51.8
25	10 16 5.3	9 28.7	0 12.4	18 51.9	1 4.6	7 15.4	13 25.1	10 48.3	4 9.5	18 52.5	21 51.8	7 54.1
28	10 27 55.0	8 21.7	0 12.4	16 34.1	0 35.3	8 46.0	13 49.8	10 57.2	4 15.1	18 52.6	21 51.9	7 56.4

MARCH 1980

DAY	EPHEM. SID. TIME	☉	☊	☽	☿	♀	♂	♃	♄	♅	♆	♇
		LONGITUDE										
	h m s	° ′	° ′	° ′	° ′	° ′	° ′	° ′	° ′	° ′	° ′	° ′
1	10 35 48.1	10♓34.0	28♌43.1	1♍ 2.5	20♓16.8	23♈25.4	3♍53.8	4♍35.8	24♍39.9	25♏34.1	22♐31.3	21♎24.1
2	10 39 44.6	11 34.2	28 39.9	12 55.0	19 R 37.0	24 34.1	3 R 30.5	4 R 28.0	24 R 35.3	25 R 34.0	22 32.0	21 R 22.9
3	10 43 41.2	12 34.3	28 36.7	24 44.6	18 50.5	25 42.5	3 7.4	4 20.3	24 30.7	25 33.9	22 32.8	21 21.7
4	10 47 37.7	13 34.5	28 33.5	6♎33.5	17 58.3	26 50.9	2 44.7	4 12.6	24 26.2	25 33.8	22 33.5	21 20.5
5	10 51 34.3	14 34.6	28 30.4	18 23.9	17 1.9	27 59.0	2 22.3	4 4.9	24 21.6	25 33.5	22 34.2	21 19.3
6	10 55 30.8	15 34.6	28 27.2	0♏18.3	16 2.5	29 6.9	2 .2	3 57.3	24 16.9	25 33.2	22 34.8	21 18.0
7	10 59 27.4	16 34.7	28 24.0	12 19.6	15 1.7	0♉14.7	1 38.6	3 49.7	24 12.2	25 32.9	22 35.4	21 16.7
8	11 3 23.9	17 34.7	28 20.8	24 31.1	14 .9	1 22.2	1 17.3	3 42.2	24 7.5	25 32.5	22 36.0	21 15.4
9	11 7 20.5	18 34.7	28 17.7	6♐56.4	13 1.5	2 29.6	0 56.5	3 34.8	24 2.8	25 32.1	22 36.5	21 14.1
10	11 11 17.0	19 34.6	28 14.5	19 39.5	12 4.6	3 36.7	0 36.3	3 27.4	23 58.1	25 31.6	22 37.1	21 12.7
11	11 15 13.6	20 34.5	28 11.3	2♑43.9	11 11.3	4 43.7	0 16.5	3 20.2	23 53.4	25 31.0	22 37.5	21 11.4
12	11 19 10.2	21 34.4	28 8.1	16 12.9	10 22.5	5 50.4	29♌57.4	3 13.0	23 48.6	25 30.4	22 38.0	21 10.0
13	11 23 6.7	22 34.3	28 4.9	0♒ 8.2	9 38.9	6 56.9	29 38.8	3 5.9	23 43.9	25 29.8	22 38.4	21 8.5
14	11 27 3.3	23 34.1	28 1.8	14 30.0	9 1.1	8 3.2	29 20.8	2 58.8	23 39.1	25 29.0	22 38.7	21 7.1
15	11 30 59.8	24 34.0	27 58.6	29 15.6	8 29.3	9 9.3	29 3.5	2 51.9	23 34.3	25 28.3	22 39.1	21 5.7
16	11 34 56.4	25 33.7	27 55.4	14♓19.5	8 3.8	10 15.1	28 46.9	2 45.1	23 29.6	25 27.5	22 39.4	21 4.2
17	11 38 52.9	26 33.5	27 52.2	29 33.4	7 44.7	11 20.7	28 30.9	2 38.4	23 24.8	25 26.6	22 39.6	21 2.7
18	11 42 49.5	27 33.2	27 49.1	14♈47.5	7 32.0	12 26.1	28 15.7	2 31.8	23 20.1	25 25.7	22 39.9	21 1.2
19	11 46 46.0	28 32.9	27 45.9	29 51.5	7 25.4	13 31.2	28 1.2	2 25.3	23 15.4	25 24.7	22 40.1	20 59.7
20	11 50 42.6	29 32.5	27 42.7	14♉36.5	7 25.0	14 36.0	27 47.4	2 18.9	23 10.7	25 23.7	22 40.2	20 58.1
21	11 54 39.1	0♈32.1	27 39.5	28 56.6	7 D 30.3	15 40.6	27 34.4	2 12.7	23 6.0	25 22.7	22 40.4	20 56.6
22	11 58 35.7	1 31.7	27 36.3	12♊48.6	7 41.3	16 44.9	27 22.1	2 6.6	23 1.3	25 21.6	22 40.5	20 55.0
23	12 2 32.2	2 31.2	27 33.2	26 12.6	7 57.6	17 48.9	27 10.7	2 .6	22 56.6	25 20.4	22 40.5	20 53.5
24	12 6 28.8	3 30.7	27 30.0	9♋10.7	8 19.0	18 52.6	26 60.0	1 54.8	22 52.0	25 19.2	22 40.6	20 51.9
25	12 10 25.3	4 30.2	27 26.8	21 46.6	8 45.2	19 56.0	26 50.1	1 49.1	22 47.4	25 18.0	22 40.6	20 50.3
26	12 14 21.9	5 29.6	27 23.6	4♌ 4.7	9 15.9	20 59.1	26 41.0	1 43.6	22 42.8	25 16.7	22 40.6	20 48.7
27	12 18 18.4	6 29.0	27 20.4	16 9.4	9 51.0	22 1.8	26 32.7	1 38.2	22 38.3	25 15.4	22 R 40.5	20 47.1
28	12 22 15.0	7 28.4	27 17.3	28 5.0	10 30.0	23 4.2	26 25.2	1 32.9	22 33.8	25 14.0	22 40.4	20 45.5
29	12 26 11.5	8 27.7	27 14.1	9♍55.2	11 12.9	24 6.3	26 18.4	1 27.8	22 29.3	25 12.6	22 40.3	20 43.8
30	12 30 8.1	9 26.9	27 10.9	21 43.4	11 59.4	25 7.9	26 12.5	1 22.8	22 24.8	25 11.1	22 40.1	20 42.2
31	12 34 4.6	10 26.2	27 7.7	3♎32.0	12 49.2	26 9.3	26 7.3	1 18.0	22 20.4	25 9.6	22 39.9	20 40.5
		LATITUDE										
1	10 35 48.1	0 .0	0 .0	0N 9.5	3N27.6	0N42.5	4N18.6	1N19.0	2N23.5	0N17.1	1N22.0	17N34.3
4	10 47 37.7	0 .0	0 .0	3 12.0	3 41.0	0 55.7	4 15.2	1 19.1	2 23.8	0 17.1	1 22.1	17 35.5
7	10 59 27.4	0 .0	0 .0	5 2.5	3 35.6	1 9.2	4 10.9	1 19.2	2 24.1	0 17.1	1 22.2	17 36.6
10	11 11 17.0	0 .0	0 .0	4 55.9	3 12.7	1 22.7	4 6.0	1 19.2	2 24.4	0 17.2	1 22.3	17 37.6
13	11 23 6.7	0 .0	0 .0	2 33.3	2 36.9	1 36.4	4 .3	1 19.1	2 24.6	0 17.2	1 22.4	17 38.5
16	11 34 56.4	0 .0	0 .0	1S22.5	1 54.2	1 50.0	3 54.1	1 19.1	2 24.7	0 17.2	1 22.6	17 39.4
19	11 46 46.0	0 .0	0 .0	4 33.9	1 9.6	2 3.6	3 47.5	1 18.9	2 24.8	0 17.2	1 22.7	17 40.2
22	11 58 35.7	0 .0	0 .0	5 3.9	0 26.4	2 17.1	3 40.5	1 18.7	2 24.9	0 17.2	1 22.8	17 40.8
25	12 10 25.3	0 .0	0 .0	3 8.9	0S13.2	2 30.3	3 33.2	1 18.5	2 24.9	0 17.2	1 22.9	17 41.4
28	12 22 15.0	0 .0	0 .0	0 4.3	0 48.4	2 43.3	3 25.8	1 18.3	2 24.8	0 17.2	1 23.0	17 41.9
31	12 34 4.6	0 .0	0 .0	2N57.0	1 18.8	2 55.9	3 18.3	1 18.0	2 24.8	0 17.2	1 23.1	17 42.3
		RIGHT ASCENSION										
1	10 35 48.1	12♓ 3.8	0♍51.8	3♍ 8.5	19♓42.6	21♈24.6	7♍24.3	6♍56.7	26♍ 3.1	23♏18.3	21♐56.4	26♎19.8
2	10 39 44.6	12 59.9	0 48.7	14 44.0	19 R 3.5	22 27.8	7 R 1.6	6 R 49.4	25 R 59.0	23 R 18.2	21 57.2	26 R 18.9
3	10 43 41.2	13 56.0	0 45.7	26 4.6	18 19.0	23 31.0	6 39.1	6 42.0	25 54.9	23 18.1	21 58.0	26 18.0
4	10 47 37.7	14 51.9	0 42.6	7♎17.2	17 30.1	24 34.2	6 16.9	6 34.8	25 50.7	23 18.0	21 58.8	26 17.1
5	10 51 34.3	15 47.7	0 39.6	18 29.5	16 38.0	25 37.4	5 54.9	6 27.5	25 46.5	23 17.7	21 59.6	26 16.1
6	10 55 30.8	16 43.4	0 36.5	29 49.8	15 44.1	26 40.6	5 33.2	6 20.3	25 42.3	23 17.4	22 .3	26 15.1
7	10 59 27.4	17 39.0	0 33.5	11♏26.8	14 49.6	27 43.8	5 11.8	6 13.1	25 38.0	23 17.1	22 .9	26 14.1
8	11 3 23.9	18 34.5	0 30.4	23 28.3	13 55.7	28 47.1	4 50.8	6 6.0	25 33.7	23 16.7	22 1.5	26 13.0
9	11 7 20.5	19 29.9	0 27.4	6♐ 1.1	13 3.7	29 50.4	4 30.1	5 58.9	25 29.4	23 16.2	22 2.1	26 12.0
10	11 11 17.0	20 25.2	0 24.3	19 9.2	12 14.6	0♉53.7	4 10.0	5 51.9	25 25.1	23 15.7	22 2.6	26 10.9
11	11 15 13.6	21 20.5	0 21.3	2♑52.9	11 29.3	1 57.0	3 50.2	5 45.0	25 20.8	23 15.2	22 3.2	26 9.8
12	11 19 10.2	22 15.6	0 18.2	17 7.9	10 48.6	3 .4	3 31.0	5 38.1	25 16.4	23 14.5	22 3.6	26 8.7
13	11 23 6.7	23 10.7	0 15.2	1♒45.2	10 13.0	4 3.8	3 12.4	5 31.4	25 12.1	23 13.9	22 4.1	26 7.5
14	11 27 3.3	24 5.7	0 12.1	16 33.8	9 42.9	5 7.3	2 54.2	5 24.7	25 7.7	23 13.1	22 4.5	26 6.3
15	11 30 59.8	25 .7	0 9.1	1♓23.1	9 18.7	6 10.8	2 36.7	5 18.1	25 3.4	23 12.4	22 4.8	26 5.2
16	11 34 56.4	25 55.6	0 6.0	16 5.7	9 .4	7 14.3	2 19.8	5 11.6	24 59.0	23 11.5	22 5.2	26 4.0
17	11 38 52.9	26 50.5	0 3.0	0♈39.1	8 48.1	8 17.8	2 3.6	5 5.2	24 54.6	23 10.6	22 5.4	26 2.7
18	11 42 49.5	27 45.3	29♌59.9	15 4.1	8 41.7	9 21.4	1 48.0	4 58.9	24 50.3	23 9.7	22 5.7	26 1.5
19	11 46 46.0	28 40.1	29 56.9	29 23.5	8 41.1	10 24.9	1 33.1	4 52.7	24 46.0	23 8.7	22 5.9	26 .2
20	11 50 42.6	29 34.8	29 53.8	13♉40.0	8 D 46.2	11 28.5	1 18.9	4 46.6	24 41.6	23 7.7	22 6.1	25 58.9
21	11 54 39.1	0♈29.5	29 50.8	27 53.8	8 56.6	12 32.1	1 5.4	4 40.6	24 37.3	23 6.6	22 6.2	25 57.6
22	11 58 35.7	1 24.1	29 47.7	12♊ 2.4	9 12.1	13 35.6	0 52.6	4 34.8	24 33.0	23 5.5	22 6.4	25 56.3
23	12 2 32.2	2 18.8	29 44.7	26 .6	9 32.6	14 39.2	0 40.6	4 29.1	24 28.7	23 4.3	22 6.4	25 55.0
24	12 6 28.8	3 13.4	29 41.6	9♋41.8	9 57.6	15 42.7	0 29.3	4 23.5	24 24.4	23 3.1	22 6.5	25 53.7
25	12 10 25.3	4 8.0	29 38.6	23 .2	10 27.0	16 46.2	0 18.9	4 18.1	24 20.2	23 1.8	22 6.5	25 52.4
26	12 14 21.9	5 2.6	29 35.5	5♌51.7	11 .5	17 49.6	0 9.1	4 12.7	24 16.0	23 .5	22 6.5	25 51.0
27	12 18 18.4	5 57.2	29 32.4	18 15.6	11 37.8	18 53.0	0 .1	4 7.5	24 11.8	22 59.1	22 R 6.4	25 49.6
28	12 22 15.0	6 51.7	29 29.4	0♍13.7	12 18.6	19 56.3	29♌51.9	4 2.5	24 7.7	22 57.7	22 6.3	25 48.2
29	12 26 11.5	7 46.3	29 26.3	11 50.4	13 2.8	20 59.5	29 44.4	3 57.6	24 3.5	22 56.3	22 6.2	25 46.8
30	12 30 8.1	8 40.9	29 23.3	23 11.8	13 50.1	22 2.6	29 37.7	3 52.8	23 59.4	22 54.8	22 6.0	25 45.4
31	12 34 4.6	9 35.5	29 20.2	4♎24.9	14 40.3	23 5.7	29 31.8	3 48.2	23 55.3	22 53.2	22 5.8	25 44.0
		DECLINATION										
1	10 35 48.1	7S36.3	0N12.5	11N15.1	0S40.2	9N45.4	14N 5.5	11N 3.0	4N18.9	18S52.6	21S51.9	7N58.0
4	10 47 37.7	6 27.5	0 12.5	0 20.1	1 21.8	11 12.9	14 27.6	11 11.6	4 24.6	18 52.5	21 51.9	8 .4
7	10 59 27.4	5 17.9	0 12.6	10S43.8	2 34.9	12 38.2	14 47.7	11 20.0	4 30.4	18 52.3	21 51.9	8 2.7
10	11 11 17.0	4 7.6	0 12.7	18 7.2	4 3.7	14 1.0	15 5.4	11 28.1	4 36.3	18 51.9	21 51.9	8 5.1
13	11 23 6.7	2 56.9	0 12.7	17 37.4	5 31.7	15 21.1	15 20.6	11 35.9	4 42.1	18 51.5	21 51.8	8 7.5
16	11 34 56.4	1 45.8	0 12.8	7 26.3	6 46.8	16 38.0	15 33.2	11 43.4	4 47.9	18 50.9	21 51.7	8 9.8
19	11 46 46.0	0 34.7	0 12.8	7N 8.8	7 42.5	17 51.7	15 43.0	11 50.4	4 53.6	18 50.3	21 51.7	8 12.2
22	11 58 35.7	0N36.5	0 12.9	17 18.5	8 16.6	19 1.8	15 50.1	11 56.9	4 59.3	18 49.5	21 51.6	8 14.5
25	12 10 25.3	1 47.4	0 12.9	18 34.1	8 29.5	20 8.1	15 54.3	12 3.0	5 4.8	18 48.6	21 51.5	8 16.7
28	12 22 15.0	2 57.9	0 13.0	12 4.4	8 22.6	21 10.4	15 56.0	12 8.6	5 10.1	18 47.7	21 51.3	8 18.9
31	12 34 4.6	4 7.9	0 13.1	1 18.2	7 57.6	22 8.4	15 55.1	12 13.6	5 15.3	18 46.6	21 51.2	8 21.0

APRIL 1980

LONGITUDE

DAY	EPHEM. SID. TIME	☉	☊	☽	☿	♀	♂	♃	♄	♅	♆	♇
	h m s	° ′	° ′	° ′	° ′	° ′	° ′	° ′	° ′	° ′	° ′	° ′
1	12 38 1.2	11♈25.4	27♌ 4.6	15♎23.4	13♓42.3	27♉10.2	26♌ 2.9	1♍13.4	22♍16.1	25♏ 8.1	22♐39.7	20♎38.9
2	12 41 57.7	12 24.5	27 1.4	27 19.1	14 38.5	28 10.8	25 R 59.2	1 R 8.9	22 R 11.8	25 R 6.5	22 R 39.4	20 R 37.2
3	12 45 54.3	13 23.7	26 58.2	9♏20.9	15 37.5	29 10.9	25 56.4	1 4.6	22 7.5	25 4.8	22 39.1	20 35.5
4	12 49 50.8	14 22.7	26 55.0	21 30.4	16 39.2	0♊10.7	25 54.2	1 .5	22 3.3	25 3.2	22 38.8	20 33.9
5	12 53 47.4	15 21.8	26 51.8	3♐49.3	17 43.6	1 10.0	25 52.9	0 56.5	21 59.1	25 1.5	22 38.4	20 32.2
6	12 57 44.0	16 20.9	26 48.7	16 19.8	18 50.4	2 8.9	25 52.2	0 52.7	21 55.0	24 59.7	22 38.0	20 30.5
7	13 1 40.5	17 19.9	26 45.5	29 4.4	19 59.7	3 7.3	25 D 52.4	0 49.1	21 50.9	24 57.9	22 37.6	20 28.8
8	13 5 37.1	18 18.8	26 42.3	12♑ 6.1	21 11.2	4 5.3	25 53.2	0 45.6	21 46.9	24 56.1	22 37.2	20 27.1
9	13 9 33.6	19 17.8	26 39.1	25 27.7	22 24.9	5 2.8	25 54.7	0 42.3	21 43.0	24 54.2	22 36.7	20 25.4
10	13 13 30.2	20 16.7	26 36.0	9♒11.5	23 40.7	5 59.8	25 57.0	0 39.2	21 39.1	24 52.3	22 36.2	20 23.7
11	13 17 26.7	21 15.6	26 32.8	23 19.1	24 58.5	6 56.3	25 60.0	0 36.3	21 35.3	24 50.4	22 35.6	20 22.0
12	13 21 23.3	22 14.4	26 29.6	7♓49.8	26 18.4	7 52.3	26 3.6	0 33.5	21 31.5	24 48.5	22 35.0	20 20.4
13	13 25 19.8	23 13.3	26 26.4	22 40.7	27 40.1	8 47.7	26 8.0	0 30.9	21 27.8	24 46.5	22 34.4	20 18.7
14	13 29 16.4	24 12.1	26 23.2	7♈45.8	29 3.7	9 42.6	26 13.0	0 28.6	21 24.2	24 44.4	22 33.8	20 17.0
15	13 33 12.9	25 10.9	26 20.1	22 56.4	0♈29.3	10 36.9	26 18.7	0 26.4	21 20.7	24 42.4	22 33.2	20 15.3
16	13 37 9.5	26 9.6	26 16.9	8♉ 2.3	1 56.5	11 30.6	26 25.1	0 24.4	21 17.3	24 40.3	22 32.5	20 13.7
17	13 41 6.0	27 8.3	26 13.7	22 53.5	3 25.6	12 23.7	26 32.1	0 22.5	21 13.9	24 38.2	22 31.8	20 12.0
18	13 45 2.6	28 7.0	26 10.5	7♊22.0	4 56.4	13 16.1	26 39.7	0 20.9	21 10.5	24 36.1	22 31.0	20 10.3
19	13 48 59.1	29 5.6	26 7.4	21 22.7	6 28.9	14 7.8	26 47.9	0 19.4	21 7.3	24 33.9	22 30.2	20 8.6
20	13 52 55.7	0♉ 4.2	26 4.2	4♋53.9	8 3.1	14 58.9	26 56.8	0 18.2	21 4.1	24 31.7	22 29.4	20 7.0
21	13 56 52.2	1 2.8	26 1.0	17 56.9	9 39.1	15 49.2	27 6.3	0 17.1	21 1.1	24 29.5	22 28.6	20 5.3
22	14 0 48.8	2 1.3	25 57.8	0♌35.0	11 16.8	16 38.8	27 16.3	0 16.2	20 58.1	24 27.2	22 27.7	20 3.7
23	14 4 45.3	2 59.8	25 54.6	12 52.8	12 56.1	17 27.6	27 26.9	0 15.5	20 55.1	24 25.0	22 26.8	20 2.0
24	14 8 41.9	3 58.3	25 51.5	24 55.6	14 37.2	18 15.5	27 38.1	0 14.9	20 52.3	24 22.7	22 25.9	20 .4
25	14 12 38.5	4 56.7	25 48.3	6♍48.7	16 20.0	19 2.6	27 49.8	0 14.6	20 49.6	24 20.4	22 24.9	19 58.8
26	14 16 35.0	5 55.1	25 45.1	18 36.9	18 4.5	19 48.9	28 2.1	0 14.4	20 46.9	24 18.0	22 24.0	19 57.2
27	14 20 31.6	6 53.4	25 41.9	0♎24.5	19 50.7	20 34.2	28 14.9	0 D 14.5	20 44.4	24 15.7	22 23.0	19 55.6
28	14 24 28.1	7 51.7	25 38.8	12 15.1	21 38.6	21 18.6	28 28.2	0 14.7	20 41.9	24 13.3	22 21.9	19 54.0
29	14 28 24.7	8 50.0	25 35.6	24 11.4	23 28.3	22 2.0	28 42.1	0 15.1	20 39.5	24 10.9	22 20.9	19 52.4
30	14 32 21.2	9 48.3	25 32.4	6♏15.3	25 19.8	22 44.4	28 56.4	0 15.7	20 37.2	24 8.5	22 19.8	19 50.8

LATITUDE

DAY	EPHEM. SID. TIME	☉	☊	☽	☿	♀	♂	♃	♄	♅	♆	♇
1	12 38 1.2	0 .0	0 .0	3N45.4	1S27.8	2N60.0	3N15.8	1N17.9	2N24.7	0N17.2	1N23.2	17N42.4
4	12 49 50.8	0 .0	0 .0	5 5.8	1 51.5	3 11.9	3 8.2	1 17.6	2 24.6	0 17.2	1 23.3	17 42.7
7	13 1 40.5	0 .0	0 .0	4 24.0	2 10.2	3 23.2	3 .7	1 17.2	2 24.4	0 17.2	1 23.4	17 42.9
10	13 13 30.2	0 .0	0 .0	1 39.2	2 24.1	3 33.8	2 53.3	1 16.8	2 24.2	0 17.2	1 23.5	17 43.0
13	13 25 19.8	0 .0	0 .0	2S 8.8	2 33.1	3 43.6	2 46.0	1 16.4	2 23.9	0 17.2	1 23.6	17 43.0
16	13 37 9.5	0 .0	0 .0	4 47.6	2 37.3	3 52.4	2 38.9	1 16.0	2 23.6	0 17.2	1 23.7	17 42.8
19	13 48 59.1	0 .0	0 .0	4 38.3	2 36.7	4 .2	2 31.9	1 15.6	2 23.3	0 17.2	1 23.8	17 42.6
22	14 0 48.8	0 .0	0 .0	2 16.2	2 31.3	4 6.9	2 25.1	1 15.1	2 22.9	0 17.2	1 23.9	17 42.3
25	14 12 38.5	0 .0	0 .0	0N52.1	2 21.3	4 12.2	2 18.5	1 14.6	2 22.5	0 17.2	1 24.0	17 41.9
28	14 24 28.1	0 .0	0 .0	3 36.0	2 6.7	4 16.0	2 12.0	1 14.2	2 22.1	0 17.2	1 24.1	17 41.4

RIGHT ASCENSION

DAY	EPHEM. SID. TIME	☉	☊	☽	☿	♀	♂	♃	♄	♅	♆	♇
1	12 38 1.2	10♈30.1	29♌17.2	15♎37.3	15♓33.3	24♉ 8.5	29♌26.6	3♍43.7	23♍51.3	22♏51.6	22♐ 5.5	25♎42.5
2	12 41 57.7	11 24.8	29 14.1	26 56.9	16 28.8	25 11.3	29 R 22.1	3 R 39.4	23 R 47.3	22 R 50.0	22 R 5.2	25 R 41.1
3	12 45 54.3	12 19.4	29 11.0	8♏31.1	17 26.7	26 13.8	29 18.4	3 35.2	23 43.4	22 48.3	22 4.9	25 39.6
4	12 49 50.8	13 14.2	29 8.0	20 26.6	18 26.9	27 16.2	29 15.5	3 31.2	23 39.5	22 46.6	22 4.6	25 38.2
5	12 53 47.4	14 8.9	29 4.9	2♐48.8	19 29.2	28 18.4	29 13.2	3 27.4	23 35.6	22 44.9	22 4.2	25 36.7
6	12 57 44.0	15 3.7	29 1.9	15 40.4	20 33.5	29 20.4	29 11.7	3 23.7	23 31.8	22 43.1	22 3.8	25 35.2
7	13 1 40.5	15 58.6	28 58.8	29 1.4	21 39.7	0♊22.1	29 10.9	3 20.2	23 28.0	22 41.2	22 3.3	25 33.7
8	13 5 37.1	16 53.5	28 55.7	12♑48.0	22 47.8	1 23.6	29 10.9	3 16.8	23 24.3	22 39.4	22 2.8	25 32.2
9	13 9 33.6	17 48.5	28 52.7	26 53.7	23 57.5	2 24.8	29 D 11.5	3 13.6	23 20.6	22 37.5	22 2.3	25 30.7
10	13 13 30.2	18 43.6	28 49.6	11♒10.3	25 8.9	3 25.7	29 12.8	3 10.6	23 17.0	22 35.5	22 1.8	25 29.2
11	13 17 26.7	19 38.7	28 46.5	25 30.6	26 22.0	4 26.3	29 14.9	3 7.7	23 13.5	22 33.6	22 1.2	25 27.7
12	13 21 23.3	20 33.9	28 43.5	9♓50.1	27 36.5	5 26.5	29 17.6	3 5.1	23 10.0	22 31.5	22 .6	25 26.2
13	13 25 19.8	21 29.2	28 40.4	24 7.7	28 52.6	6 26.3	29 20.9	3 2.6	23 6.5	22 29.5	21 59.9	25 24.7
14	13 29 16.4	22 24.5	28 37.4	8♈25.4	0♈10.1	7 25.8	29 25.0	3 .2	23 3.1	22 27.4	21 59.2	25 23.2
15	13 33 12.9	23 20.0	28 34.3	22 46.7	1 29.1	8 24.8	29 29.7	2 58.1	22 59.9	22 25.4	21 58.6	25 21.7
16	13 37 9.5	24 15.6	28 31.2	7♉14.4	2 49.5	9 23.3	29 35.0	2 56.1	22 56.6	22 23.2	21 57.8	25 20.2
17	13 41 6.0	25 11.2	28 28.2	21 48.6	4 11.2	10 21.2	29 41.0	2 54.3	22 53.5	22 21.1	21 57.0	25 18.7
18	13 45 2.6	26 6.9	28 25.1	6♊25.2	5 34.4	11 18.7	29 47.6	2 52.7	22 50.4	22 18.9	21 56.2	25 17.1
19	13 48 59.1	27 2.8	28 22.0	20 56.0	6 59.0	12 15.5	29 54.7	2 51.2	22 47.3	22 16.6	21 55.4	25 15.6
20	13 52 55.7	27 58.7	28 19.0	5♋10.8	8 25.0	13 11.7	0♍ 2.5	2 49.9	22 44.4	22 14.4	21 54.5	25 14.1
21	13 56 52.2	28 54.7	28 15.9	18 59.7	9 52.5	14 7.3	0 10.9	2 48.8	22 41.5	22 12.1	21 53.6	25 12.6
22	14 0 48.8	29 50.8	28 12.8	2♌16.4	11 21.4	15 2.1	0 19.8	2 47.9	22 38.6	22 9.8	21 52.7	25 11.1
23	14 4 45.3	0♉47.0	28 9.8	14 58.8	12 51.8	15 56.2	0 29.3	2 47.2	22 35.9	22 7.5	21 51.7	25 9.6
24	14 8 41.9	1 43.4	28 6.7	27 8.9	14 23.8	16 49.4	0 39.4	2 46.6	22 33.2	22 5.2	21 50.7	25 8.1
25	14 12 38.5	2 39.8	28 3.6	8♍52.3	15 57.4	17 41.9	0 49.9	2 46.2	22 30.7	22 2.8	21 49.7	25 6.6
26	14 16 35.0	3 36.4	28 .6	20 16.2	17 32.5	18 33.4	1 1.0	2 46.0	22 28.2	22 .4	21 48.7	25 5.1
27	14 20 31.6	4 33.1	27 57.5	1♎29.3	19 9.4	19 24.0	1 12.6	2 46.0	22 25.7	21 58.0	21 47.6	25 3.6
28	14 24 28.1	5 29.9	27 54.4	12 40.3	20 47.9	20 13.7	1 24.7	2 D 46.1	22 23.4	21 55.6	21 46.5	25 2.1
29	14 28 24.7	6 26.9	27 51.3	23 58.0	22 28.3	21 2.3	1 37.3	2 46.5	22 21.1	21 53.1	21 45.4	25 .6
30	14 32 21.2	7 23.9	27 48.3	5♏30.5	24 10.6	21 49.8	1 50.3	2 47.0	22 19.0	21 50.7	21 44.2	24 59.1

DECLINATION

DAY	EPHEM. SID. TIME	☉	☊	☽	☿	♀	♂	♃	♄	♅	♆	♇
1	12 38 1.2	4N31.1	0N13.1	2S35.6	7S45.5	22N26.7	15N54.2	12N15.2	5N17.0	18S46.2	21S51.1	8N21.7
4	12 49 50.8	5 40.2	0 13.1	13 12.8	6 58.8	23 18.8	15 50.1	12 19.5	5 21.9	18 45.0	21 51.0	8 23.8
7	13 1 40.5	6 48.3	0 13.2	19 2.2	5 57.5	24 6.2	15 43.7	12 23.2	5 26.7	18 43.8	21 50.8	8 25.8
10	13 13 30.2	7 55.5	0 13.2	16 21.7	4 42.9	24 49.0	15 35.1	12 26.4	5 31.1	18 42.4	21 50.6	8 27.7
13	13 25 19.8	9 1.4	0 13.3	4 52.7	3 16.1	25 26.9	15 24.5	12 28.9	5 35.3	18 41.0	21 50.4	8 29.5
16	13 37 9.5	10 6.0	0 13.4	9N38.9	1 37.9	26 .0	15 11.9	12 30.8	5 39.2	18 39.5	21 50.2	8 31.2
19	13 48 59.1	11 9.1	0 13.4	18 31.9	0N10.5	26 28.3	14 57.5	12 32.2	5 42.8	18 38.0	21 50.0	8 32.8
22	14 0 48.8	12 10.6	0 13.5	17 48.5	2 8.4	26 51.8	14 41.4	12 32.9	5 46.1	18 36.3	21 49.7	8 34.3
25	14 12 38.5	13 10.2	0 13.5	9 49.1	4 14.9	27 10.6	14 23.5	12 33.0	5 49.1	18 34.7	21 49.5	8 35.7
28	14 24 28.1	14 7.9	0 13.6	1S31.6	6 28.7	27 24.7	14 4.2	12 32.6	5 51.8	18 33.0	21 49.2	8 37.0

MAY 1980

LONGITUDE

DAY	EPHEM. SID. TIME	☉	☊	☽	☿	♀	♂	♃	♄	♅	♆	♇
	h m s	° ′	° ′	° ′	° ′	° ′	° ′	° ′	° ′	° ′	° ′	° ′
1	14 36 17.8	10♉46.5	25♌29.2	18♏28.1	27♈12.9	23♊25.7	29♌11.2	0♍16.4	20♍35.0	24♏ 6.1	22♐18.7	19♎49.3
2	14 40 14.3	11 44.7	25 26.0	0♐50.6	29 7.9	24 5.9	29 26.4	0 17.4	20 R32.9	24 R 3.7	22 R17.6	19 R47.7
3	14 44 10.9	12 42.8	25 22.9	13 23.4	1♉ 4.5	24 45.0	29 42.2	0 18.5	20 30.9	24 1.2	22 16.5	19 46.2
4	14 48 7.4	13 41.0	25 19.7	26 7.0	3 2.8	25 22.9	29 58.4	0 19.8	20 29.0	23 58.8	22 15.3	19 44.7
5	14 52 4.0	14 39.1	25 16.5	9♑ 2.4	5 2.9	25 59.6	0♍15.0	0 21.3	20 27.2	23 56.3	22 14.1	19 43.2
6	14 56 .5	15 37.2	25 13.3	22 11.0	7 4.6	26 35.0	0 32.1	0 23.0	20 25.5	23 53.9	22 13.0	19 41.7
7	14 59 57.1	16 35.3	25 10.2	5♒34.1	9 7.9	27 9.1	0 49.6	0 24.8	20 23.9	23 51.4	22 11.7	19 40.3
8	15 3 53.7	17 33.3	25 7.0	19 13.7	11 12.6	27 41.8	1 7.5	0 26.9	20 22.3	23 48.9	22 10.5	19 38.8
9	15 7 50.2	18 31.4	25 3.8	3♓11.1	13 18.8	28 13.1	1 25.9	0 29.1	20 20.9	23 46.4	22 9.2	19 37.4
10	15 11 46.8	19 29.3	25 .6	17 26.6	15 26.2	28 43.0	1 44.6	0 31.4	20 19.6	23 43.9	22 7.9	19 36.0
11	15 15 43.3	20 27.3	24 57.4	1♈58.9	17 34.7	29 11.3	2 3.7	0 34.0	20 18.3	23 41.4	22 6.6	19 34.6
12	15 19 39.9	21 25.3	24 54.3	16 44.1	19 44.3	29 38.1	2 23.3	0 36.7	20 17.2	23 38.9	22 5.3	19 33.2
13	15 23 36.4	22 23.2	24 51.1	1♉36.1	21 54.5	0♋ 3.2	2 43.2	0 39.6	20 16.2	23 36.3	22 4.0	19 31.9
14	15 27 33.0	23 21.1	24 47.9	16 27.0	24 5.3	0 26.6	3 3.5	0 42.7	20 15.3	23 33.8	22 2.6	19 30.5
15	15 31 29.5	24 19.0	24 44.7	1♊ 7.8	26 16.4	0 48.3	3 24.1	0 45.9	20 14.4	23 31.3	22 1.2	19 29.2
16	15 35 26.1	25 16.9	24 41.6	15 30.7	28 27.5	1 8.2	3 45.1	0 49.4	20 13.7	23 28.8	21 59.8	19 27.9
17	15 39 22.7	26 14.7	24 38.4	29 29.8	0♊38.4	1 26.2	4 6.5	0 52.9	20 13.1	23 26.3	21 58.4	19 26.6
18	15 43 19.2	27 12.5	24 35.2	13♋ 2.1	2 48.7	1 42.2	4 28.2	0 56.7	20 12.6	23 23.8	21 57.0	19 25.4
19	15 47 15.8	28 10.3	24 32.0	26 7.6	4 58.2	1 56.2	4 50.3	1 .6	20 12.2	23 21.2	21 55.6	19 24.2
20	15 51 12.3	29 8.1	24 28.9	8♌48.5	7 6.6	2 8.2	5 12.7	1 4.7	20 11.9	23 18.7	21 54.1	19 23.0
21	15 55 8.9	0♊ 5.8	24 25.7	21 8.8	9 13.7	2 18.1	5 35.4	1 8.9	20 11.7	23 16.2	21 52.6	19 21.8
22	15 59 5.4	1 3.5	24 22.5	3♍13.3	11 19.1	2 25.7	5 58.4	1 13.3	20 11.6	23 13.8	21 51.1	19 20.6
23	16 3 2.0	2 1.2	24 19.3	15 7.6	13 22.7	2 31.1	6 21.8	1 17.9	20 11.6	23 11.3	21 49.6	19 19.5
24	16 6 58.5	2 58.8	24 16.1	26 57.0	15 24.3	2 34.3	6 45.4	1 22.6	20 D11.7	23 8.8	21 48.1	19 18.4
25	16 10 55.1	3 56.4	24 13.0	8♎46.5	17 23.7	2 35.1	7 9.4	1 27.5	20 11.9	23 6.3	21 46.6	19 17.3
26	16 14 51.7	4 54.0	24 9.8	20 40.5	19 20.8	2 R33.5	7 33.6	1 32.5	20 12.2	23 3.9	21 45.1	19 16.3
27	16 18 48.2	5 51.7	24 6.6	2♏42.6	21 15.4	2 29.6	7 58.2	1 37.7	20 12.7	23 1.5	21 43.6	19 15.3
28	16 22 44.8	6 49.2	24 3.4	14 55.3	23 7.4	2 23.2	8 23.0	1 43.1	20 13.2	22 59.1	21 42.1	19 14.3
29	16 26 41.3	7 46.7	24 .3	27 20.3	24 56.8	2 14.3	8 48.0	1 48.5	20 13.8	22 56.7	21 40.5	19 13.3
30	16 30 37.9	8 44.3	23 57.1	9♐58.3	26 43.5	2 3.1	9 13.4	1 54.2	20 14.5	22 54.3	21 38.9	19 12.4
31	16 34 34.4	9 41.8	23 53.9	22 49.0	28 27.4	1 49.4	9 38.9	1 59.9	20 15.4	22 51.9	21 37.4	19 11.4

LATITUDE

DAY	EPHEM. SID. TIME	☉	☊	☽	☿	♀	♂	♃	♄	♅	♆	♇
1	14 36 17.8	0 .0	0 .0	4N58.3	1S47.5	4N18.1	2N 5.8	1N13.7	2N21.6	0N17.2	1N24.2	17N40.9
4	14 48 7.4	0 .0	0 .0	4 20.0	1 24.2	4 18.2	1 59.8	1 13.2	2 21.1	0 17.2	1 24.2	17 40.2
7	14 59 57.1	0 .0	0 .0	1 42.9	0 57.2	4 16.3	1 53.9	1 12.7	2 20.6	0 17.1	1 24.3	17 39.4
10	15 11 46.8	0 .0	0 .0	1S53.8	0 27.4	4 11.9	1 48.3	1 12.2	2 20.1	0 17.1	1 24.4	17 38.6
13	15 23 36.4	0 .0	0 .0	4 36.0	0N 4.0	4 4.9	1 42.8	1 11.7	2 19.6	0 17.1	1 24.4	17 37.7
16	15 35 26.1	0 .0	0 .0	4 40.9	0 35.3	3 54.9	1 37.5	1 11.3	2 19.0	0 17.1	1 24.5	17 36.7
19	15 47 15.8	0 .0	0 .0	2 22.4	1 4.6	3 41.6	1 32.3	1 10.8	2 18.4	0 17.0	1 24.5	17 35.6
22	15 59 5.4	0 .0	0 .0	0N48.1	1 29.9	3 24.7	1 27.4	1 10.3	2 17.9	0 17.0	1 24.6	17 34.5
25	16 10 55.1	0 .0	0 .0	3 33.1	1 49.8	3 3.9	1 22.5	1 9.8	2 17.3	0 17.0	1 24.6	17 33.2
28	16 22 44.8	0 .0	0 .0	4 57.6	2 3.3	2 38.9	1 17.9	1 9.4	2 16.7	0 16.9	1 24.6	17 32.0
31	16 34 34.4	0 .0	0 .0	4 21.7	2 9.8	2 9.6	1 13.3	1 8.9	2 16.1	0 16.9	1 24.6	17 30.6

RIGHT ASCENSION

DAY	EPHEM. SID. TIME	☉	☊	☽	☿	♀	♂	♃	♄	♅	♆	♇
1	14 36 17.8	8♉21.1	27♌45.2	17♏24.9	25♈54.7	22♊36.1	2♍ 3.9	2♍47.6	22♍16.9	21♏48.2	21♐43.1	24♎57.7
2	14 40 14.3	9 18.5	27 42.1	29 46.1	27 40.9	23 21.3	2 17.8	2 48.5	22 R14.9	21 R45.7	21 R41.9	24 R56.2
3	14 44 10.9	10 15.9	27 39.1	12♐36.3	29 29.0	24 5.3	2 32.2	2 49.5	22 12.9	21 43.2	21 40.6	24 54.8
4	14 48 7.4	11 13.6	27 36.0	25 54.2	1♉19.3	24 47.9	2 47.1	2 50.7	22 11.1	21 40.7	21 39.4	24 53.3
5	14 52 4.0	12 11.3	27 32.9	9♑34.5	3 11.7	25 29.2	3 2.3	2 52.1	22 9.4	21 38.2	21 38.1	24 51.9
6	14 56 .5	13 9.3	27 29.8	23 29.3	5 6.3	26 9.1	3 18.0	2 53.7	22 7.7	21 35.7	21 36.9	24 50.5
7	14 59 57.1	14 7.3	27 26.8	7♒29.7	7 3.1	26 47.5	3 34.1	2 55.4	22 6.2	21 33.2	21 35.6	24 49.1
8	15 3 53.7	15 5.5	27 23.7	21 28.5	9 2.1	27 24.4	3 50.6	2 57.2	22 4.7	21 30.6	21 34.2	24 47.7
9	15 7 50.2	16 3.8	27 20.6	5♓22.3	11 3.3	27 59.7	4 7.4	2 59.3	22 3.3	21 28.0	21 32.9	24 46.3
10	15 11 46.8	17 2.3	27 17.5	19 11.7	13 6.6	28 33.3	4 24.6	3 1.5	22 2.0	21 25.5	21 31.5	24 45.0
11	15 15 43.3	18 .9	27 14.5	3♈ .8	15 11.9	29 5.2	4 42.2	3 3.9	22 .8	21 22.9	21 30.1	24 43.6
12	15 19 39.9	18 59.7	27 11.4	16 55.9	17 19.2	29 35.3	5 .2	3 6.4	21 59.7	21 20.3	21 28.6	24 42.3
13	15 23 36.4	19 58.7	27 8.3	1♉ 3.1	19 28.4	0♋ 3.6	5 18.5	3 9.2	21 58.7	21 17.8	21 27.2	24 40.9
14	15 27 33.0	20 57.7	27 5.2	15 25.9	21 39.2	0 29.9	5 37.2	3 12.0	21 57.7	21 15.2	21 25.7	24 39.6
15	15 31 29.5	21 56.9	27 2.2	0♊ 3.2	23 51.4	0 54.3	5 56.2	3 15.1	21 56.9	21 12.6	21 24.3	24 38.3
16	15 35 26.1	22 56.3	26 59.1	14 48.0	26 4.8	1 16.6	6 15.5	3 18.3	21 56.2	21 10.1	21 22.8	24 37.0
17	15 39 22.7	23 55.8	26 56.0	29 28.1	28 19.0	1 36.7	6 35.2	3 21.7	21 55.5	21 7.5	21 21.2	24 35.8
18	15 43 19.2	24 55.4	26 52.9	13♋49.2	0♊33.9	1 54.7	6 55.2	3 25.2	21 55.0	21 4.9	21 19.7	24 34.5
19	15 47 15.8	25 55.2	26 49.8	27 39.6	2 49.0	2 10.3	7 15.5	3 28.9	21 54.5	21 2.4	21 18.2	24 33.3
20	15 51 12.3	26 55.1	26 46.8	10♌52.3	5 4.1	2 23.7	7 36.0	3 32.7	21 54.2	20 59.8	21 16.6	24 32.1
21	15 55 8.9	27 55.1	26 43.7	23 26.7	7 18.8	2 34.6	7 56.9	3 36.7	21 53.9	20 57.2	21 15.0	24 30.9
22	15 59 5.4	28 55.3	26 40.6	5♍27.0	9 32.7	2 43.0	8 18.1	3 40.9	21 53.7	20 54.7	21 13.4	24 29.7
23	16 3 2.0	29 55.6	26 37.5	17 .8	11 45.5	2 48.9	8 39.5	3 45.2	21 53.7	20 52.2	21 11.8	24 28.5
24	16 6 58.5	0♊56.0	26 34.4	28 17.6	13 57.0	2 52.3	9 1.2	3 49.6	21 53.7	20 49.6	21 10.2	24 27.4
25	16 10 55.1	1 56.5	26 31.4	9♎27.5	16 6.8	2 53.0	9 23.2	3 54.2	21 D53.8	20 47.1	21 8.6	24 26.2
26	16 14 51.7	2 57.2	26 28.3	20 41.0	18 14.6	2 R51.1	9 45.4	3 58.9	21 54.0	20 44.6	21 6.9	24 25.1
27	16 18 48.2	3 58.0	26 25.2	2♏ 7.7	20 20.4	2 46.5	10 8.0	4 3.9	21 54.4	20 42.2	21 5.3	24 24.1
28	16 22 44.8	4 58.9	26 22.1	13 56.5	22 23.7	2 39.2	10 30.7	4 8.9	21 54.8	20 39.7	21 3.7	24 23.0
29	16 26 41.3	5 59.9	26 19.0	26 14.1	24 24.4	2 29.2	10 53.7	4 14.1	21 55.3	20 37.3	21 2.0	24 22.0
30	16 30 37.9	7 1.0	26 15.9	9♐ 4.1	26 22.3	2 16.5	11 16.9	4 19.4	21 55.9	20 34.8	21 .3	24 21.0
31	16 34 34.4	8 2.2	26 12.9	22 25.7	28 17.4	2 1.2	11 40.3	4 24.8	21 56.6	20 32.4	20 58.6	24 20.0

DECLINATION

DAY	EPHEM. SID. TIME	☉	☊	☽	☿	♀	♂	♃	♄	♅	♆	♇
1	14 36 17.8	15N 3.5	0N13.6	12S32.5	8N48.5	27N34.3	13N43.3	12N31.5	5N54.0	18S31.2	21S49.0	8N38.1
4	14 48 7.4	15 56.8	0 13.7	19 3.1	11 12.5	27 39.6	13 21.0	12 29.8	5 56.0	18 29.4	21 48.7	8 39.1
7	14 59 57.1	16 47.8	0 13.8	17 12.9	13 38.1	27 40.7	12 57.3	12 27.6	5 57.5	18 27.6	21 48.4	8 40.0
10	15 11 46.8	17 36.2	0 13.8	6 42.5	16 1.6	27 37.9	12 32.4	12 24.8	5 58.7	18 25.8	21 48.1	8 40.8
13	15 23 36.4	18 22.0	0 13.9	7N42.7	18 18.5	27 31.3	12 6.2	12 21.4	5 59.6	18 23.9	21 47.9	8 41.4
16	15 35 26.1	19 5.1	0 13.9	17 59.8	20 23.4	27 21.0	11 38.7	12 17.5	6 .1	18 22.1	21 47.6	8 42.0
19	15 47 15.8	19 45.2	0 14.0	18 35.5	22 11.1	27 7.1	11 10.1	12 13.1	6 .1	18 20.2	21 47.3	8 42.3
22	15 59 5.4	20 22.3	0 14.0	11 4.3	23 37.3	26 49.7	10 40.4	12 8.1	5 59.9	18 18.4	21 47.0	8 42.5
25	16 10 55.1	20 56.2	0 14.1	0S12.8	24 39.9	26 28.7	10 9.6	12 2.6	5 59.2	18 16.6	21 46.7	8 42.6
28	16 22 44.8	21 27.0	0 14.1	11 34.0	25 18.8	26 4.0	9 37.8	11 56.6	5 58.2	18 14.8	21 46.3	8 42.5
31	16 34 34.4	21 54.3	0 14.2	18 53.4	25 35.6	25 35.2	9 5.0	11 50.2	5 56.8	18 13.0	21 46.0	8 42.3

JUNE 1980

LONGITUDE

DAY	EPHEM. SID. TIME h m s	☉ ° ′	☊ ° ′	☾ ° ′	☿ ° ′	♀ ° ′	♂ ° ′	♃ ° ′	♄ ° ′	♅ ° ′	♆ ° ′	♇ ° ′
1	16 38 31.0	10♊39.2	23♌50.7	5♑52.0	0♋ 8.5	1♋33.3	10♍ 4.8	2♍ 5.9	20♍16.3	22♏49.5	21♐35.8	19♎10.5
2	16 42 27.6	11 36.7	23 47.5	19 6.4	1 46.7	1 R 14.9	10 30.9	2 11.9	20 17.3	22 R 47.2	21 R 34.2	19 R 9.7
3	16 46 24.1	12 34.1	23 44.4	2♒31.6	3 22.1	0 54.2	10 57.2	2 18.1	20 18.5	22 44.9	21 32.6	19 8.8
4	16 50 20.7	13 31.6	23 41.2	16 7.5	4 54.6	0 31.3	11 23.8	2 24.4	20 19.7	22 42.6	21 31.0	19 8.0
5	16 54 17.2	14 29.0	23 38.0	29 53.9	6 24.1	0 6.2	11 50.7	2 30.9	20 21.0	22 40.3	21 29.4	19 7.2
6	16 58 13.8	15 26.4	23 34.8	13♓51.1	7 50.7	29♊39.2	12 17.7	2 37.5	20 22.5	22 38.0	21 27.8	19 6.5
7	17 2 10.3	16 23.8	23 31.7	27 59.0	9 14.3	29 10.2	12 45.0	2 44.3	20 24.0	22 35.8	21 26.2	19 5.8
8	17 6 6.9	17 21.2	23 28.5	12♈16.4	10 34.9	28 39.6	13 12.6	2 51.2	20 25.6	22 33.6	21 24.5	19 5.1
9	17 10 3.4	18 18.6	23 25.3	26 41.0	11 52.4	28 7.3	13 40.3	2 58.2	20 27.4	22 31.4	21 22.9	19 4.4
10	17 14 .0	19 16.0	23 22.1	11♉ 8.9	13 6.8	27 33.7	14 8.3	3 5.3	20 29.2	22 29.2	21 21.3	19 3.8
11	17 17 56.6	20 13.4	23 19.0	25 34.8	14 18.1	26 58.9	14 36.5	3 12.6	20 31.1	22 27.1	21 19.7	19 3.2
12	17 21 53.1	21 10.7	23 15.8	9♊52.6	15 26.1	26 23.1	15 4.9	3 20.0	20 33.1	22 25.0	21 18.1	19 2.6
13	17 25 49.7	22 8.1	23 12.6	23 56.4	16 30.9	25 46.5	15 33.6	3 27.6	20 35.3	22 22.9	21 16.4	19 2.1
14	17 29 46.2	23 5.4	23 9.4	7♋41.5	17 32.3	25 9.3	16 2.4	3 35.2	20 37.5	22 20.9	21 14.8	19 1.6
15	17 33 42.8	24 2.7	23 6.3	21 4.8	18 30.2	24 31.9	16 31.5	3 43.0	20 39.8	22 18.8	21 13.2	19 1.1
16	17 37 39.3	25 .1	23 3.1	4♌ 5.5	19 24.6	23 54.3	17 .7	3 50.9	20 42.2	22 16.8	21 11.6	19 .7
17	17 41 35.9	25 57.4	22 59.9	16 44.7	20 15.5	23 16.9	17 30.2	3 59.0	20 44.8	22 14.9	21 10.0	19 .3
18	17 45 32.5	26 54.7	22 56.7	29 5.2	21 2.6	22 39.9	17 59.9	4 7.1	20 47.4	22 13.0	21 8.4	18 60.0
19	17 49 29.0	27 52.0	22 53.5	11♍11.0	21 45.9	22 3.5	18 29.7	4 15.4	20 50.1	22 11.1	21 6.8	18 59.6
20	17 53 25.6	28 49.2	22 50.4	23 6.9	22 25.3	21 28.0	18 59.7	4 23.7	20 52.9	22 9.3	21 5.2	18 59.3
21	17 57 22.1	29 46.5	22 47.2	4♎58.0	23 .6	20 53.5	19 29.9	4 32.2	20 55.8	22 7.5	21 3.6	18 59.0
22	18 1 18.7	0♋43.7	22 44.0	16 49.5	23 31.8	20 20.4	20 .3	4 40.8	20 58.8	22 5.7	21 2.0	18 58.8
23	18 5 15.2	1 41.0	22 40.8	28 46.2	23 58.7	19 48.6	20 30.9	4 49.5	21 1.8	22 3.9	21 .4	18 58.6
24	18 9 11.8	2 38.2	22 37.7	10♏52.5	24 21.3	19 18.5	21 1.6	4 58.3	21 5.0	22 2.2	20 58.8	18 58.4
25	18 13 8.4	3 35.4	22 34.5	23 11.9	24 39.4	18 50.2	21 32.5	5 7.2	21 8.2	22 .5	20 57.2	18 58.3
26	18 17 4.9	4 32.6	22 31.3	5♐46.7	24 53.1	18 23.8	22 3.6	5 16.3	21 11.6	21 58.9	20 55.6	18 58.2
27	18 21 1.5	5 29.8	22 28.1	18 38.3	25 2.1	17 59.5	22 34.9	5 25.4	21 15.0	21 57.3	20 54.1	18 58.1
28	18 24 58.0	6 27.0	22 25.0	1♑46.8	25 6.6	17 37.3	23 6.3	5 34.6	21 18.5	21 55.7	20 52.5	18 58.0
29	18 28 54.6	7 24.2	22 21.8	15 10.9	25 R 6.4	17 17.4	23 37.8	5 43.9	21 22.1	21 54.2	20 51.0	18 58.0
30	18 32 51.1	8♋21.3	22 18.6	28♑48.7	25♋ 1.7	16♊59.8	24 9.6	5♍53.4	21 25.8	21♏52.8	20♐49.5	18♎58.0

LATITUDE

DAY	EPHEM. SID. TIME	☉	☊	☾	☿	♀	♂	♃	♄	♅	♆	♇
1	16 38 31.0	0 .0	0 .0	3N41.0	2N10.3	1N58.9	1N11.8	1N 8.8	2N15.9	0N16.9	1N24.6	17N30.2
4	16 50 20.7	0 .0	0 .0	0 34.3	2 7.3	1 24.2	1 7.5	1 8.4	2 15.3	0 16.8	1 24.6	17 28.8
7	17 2 10.3	0 .0	0 .0	2S56.7	1 57.3	0 46.0	1 3.2	1 7.9	2 14.8	0 16.8	1 24.6	17 27.3
10	17 14 .0	0 .0	0 .0	4 58.1	1 40.5	0 5.1	0 59.1	1 7.5	2 14.2	0 16.7	1 24.6	17 25.8
13	17 25 49.7	0 .0	0 .0	4 18.1	1 17.1	0S37.2	0 55.1	1 7.1	2 13.6	0 16.7	1 24.6	17 24.3
16	17 37 39.3	0 .0	0 .0	1 32.4	0 47.5	1 19.5	0 51.3	1 6.7	2 13.0	0 16.6	1 24.6	17 22.7
19	17 49 29.0	0 .0	0 .0	1N43.5	0 12.1	2 .3	0 47.5	1 6.4	2 12.5	0 16.6	1 24.5	17 21.1
22	18 1 18.7	0 .0	0 .0	4 13.2	0S28.4	2 38.3	0 43.8	1 6.0	2 11.9	0 16.5	1 24.5	17 19.5
25	18 13 8.4	0 .0	0 .0	5 7.4	1 13.0	3 12.3	0 40.2	1 5.7	2 11.4	0 16.5	1 24.4	17 17.8
28	18 24 58.0	0 .0	0 .0	3 53.6	2 .2	3 41.6	0 36.7	1 5.3	2 10.8	0 16.4	1 24.4	17 16.1

RIGHT ASCENSION

DAY	EPHEM. SID. TIME	☉	☊	☾	☿	♀	♂	♃	♄	♅	♆	♇
1	16 38 31.0	9♊ 3.6	26♌ 9.8	6♑13.0	0♋ 9.4	1♋43.3	12♍ 4.0	4♍30.4	21♍57.3	20♏30.0	20♐56.9	24♎19.0
2	16 42 27.6	10 5.0	26 6.7	20 16.1	1 58.3	1 R 22.8	12 27.8	4 36.1	21 58.2	20 R 27.6	20 R 55.2	24 R 18.1
3	16 46 24.1	11 6.5	26 3.6	4♒23.3	3 43.9	0 59.8	12 51.9	4 42.0	21 59.2	20 25.2	20 53.5	24 17.1
4	16 50 20.7	12 8.1	26 .5	18 24.3	5 26.2	0 34.4	13 16.2	4 48.0	22 .2	20 22.9	20 51.8	24 16.2
5	16 54 17.2	13 9.8	25 57.4	2♓13.5	7 5.0	0 6.8	13 40.7	4 54.1	22 1.4	20 20.6	20 50.1	24 15.4
6	16 58 13.8	14 11.6	25 54.4	15 50.4	8 40.4	29♊37.1	14 5.4	5 .4	22 2.6	20 18.3	20 48.3	24 14.5
7	17 2 10.3	15 13.5	25 51.3	29 19.3	10 12.2	29 5.4	14 30.4	5 6.7	22 4.0	20 16.0	20 46.6	24 13.7
8	17 6 6.9	16 15.5	25 48.2	12♈47.9	11 40.4	28 32.0	14 55.5	5 13.2	22 5.4	20 13.7	20 44.9	24 12.9
9	17 10 3.4	17 17.5	25 45.1	26 24.7	13 4.9	27 56.9	15 20.8	5 19.8	22 6.9	20 11.5	20 43.1	24 12.1
10	17 14 .0	18 19.6	25 42.0	10♉17.2	14 25.6	27 20.5	15 46.3	5 26.6	22 8.5	20 9.3	20 41.4	24 11.3
11	17 17 56.6	19 21.8	25 38.9	24 29.1	15 42.6	26 42.9	16 12.0	5 33.5	22 10.3	20 7.1	20 39.6	24 10.6
12	17 21 53.1	20 24.0	25 35.8	8♊58.4	16 55.7	26 4.3	16 37.8	5 40.5	22 12.1	20 5.0	20 37.9	24 9.9
13	17 25 49.7	21 26.2	25 32.7	23 36.5	18 4.8	25 25.1	17 3.9	5 47.6	22 13.9	20 2.8	20 36.1	24 9.2
14	17 29 46.2	22 28.5	25 29.6	8♋ 9.4	19 9.9	24 45.4	17 30.1	5 54.8	22 15.9	20 .7	20 34.4	24 8.6
15	17 33 42.8	23 30.9	25 26.6	22 21.9	20 11.0	24 5.5	17 56.6	6 2.1	22 18.0	19 58.7	20 32.7	24 8.0
16	17 37 39.3	24 33.2	25 23.5	6♌ 2.1	21 7.9	23 25.6	18 23.1	6 9.6	22 20.1	19 56.7	20 30.9	24 7.4
17	17 41 35.9	25 35.7	25 20.4	19 3.8	22 .7	22 46.2	18 49.9	6 17.2	22 22.4	19 54.7	20 29.2	24 6.8
18	17 45 32.5	26 38.1	25 17.3	1♍27.4	22 49.1	22 7.2	19 16.9	6 24.9	22 24.8	19 52.8	20 27.5	24 6.3
19	17 49 29.0	27 40.5	25 14.2	13 18.1	23 33.1	21 29.0	19 44.0	6 32.7	22 27.2	19 50.8	20 25.8	24 5.8
20	17 53 25.6	28 42.9	25 11.1	24 44.7	24 12.7	20 51.9	20 11.2	6 40.6	22 29.7	19 48.9	20 24.0	24 5.3
21	17 57 22.1	29 45.3	25 8.0	5♎57.5	24 47.7	20 16.0	20 38.6	6 48.6	22 32.3	19 47.1	20 22.3	24 4.8
22	18 1 18.7	0♋47.7	25 4.9	17 7.5	25 18.1	19 41.6	21 6.2	6 56.7	22 34.9	19 45.3	20 20.6	24 4.4
23	18 5 15.2	1 50.0	25 1.8	28 25.7	25 43.8	19 8.8	21 33.9	7 4.8	22 37.7	19 43.5	20 18.9	24 4.0
24	18 9 11.8	2 52.4	24 58.7	10♏ 2.8	26 4.8	18 37.8	22 1.8	7 13.1	22 40.5	19 41.7	20 17.2	24 3.6
25	18 13 8.4	3 54.7	24 55.6	22 7.7	26 21.0	18 8.8	22 29.8	7 21.5	22 43.5	19 40.0	20 15.5	24 3.3
26	18 17 4.9	4 57.0	24 52.5	4♐47.1	26 32.3	17 41.8	22 57.9	7 30.0	22 46.5	19 38.4	20 13.8	24 3.0
27	18 21 1.5	5 59.2	24 49.4	18 3.3	26 38.8	17 17.0	23 26.2	7 38.6	22 49.6	19 36.7	20 12.1	24 2.7
28	18 24 58.0	7 1.4	24 46.3	1♑53.0	26 40.4	16 54.6	23 54.7	7 47.3	22 52.7	19 35.1	20 10.5	24 2.5
29	18 28 54.6	8 3.6	24 43.2	16 6.9	26 R 37.2	16 34.5	24 23.2	7 56.1	22 56.0	19 33.6	20 8.8	24 2.2
30	18 32 51.1	9♋ 5.7	24 40.1	0♒31.6	26♋29.3	16♊16.8	24 52.0	8 4.9	22 59.3	19♏32.1	20♐ 7.2	24♎ 2.0

DECLINATION

DAY	EPHEM. SID. TIME	☉	☊	☾	☿	♀	♂	♃	♄	♅	♆	♇
1	16 38 31.0	22N 2.7	0N14.2	19S37.8	25N36.7	25N24.8	8N53.9	11N47.9	5N56.2	18S12.4	21S45.9	8N42.2
4	16 50 20.7	22 25.4	0 14.3	15 27.5	25 28.2	24 50.5	8 19.8	11 40.8	5 54.3	18 10.7	21 45.6	8 41.9
7	17 2 10.3	22 44.7	0 14.3	3 30.2	25 4.1	24 12.2	7 44.9	11 33.3	5 52.1	18 9.0	21 45.3	8 41.3
10	17 14 .0	23 .3	0 14.4	10N26.8	24 27.6	23 30.1	7 9.1	11 25.3	5 49.5	18 7.4	21 45.0	8 40.7
13	17 25 49.7	23 12.4	0 14.4	19 .2	23 41.6	22 45.1	6 32.4	11 16.9	5 46.6	18 5.8	21 44.7	8 39.9
16	17 37 39.3	23 20.7	0 14.5	17 44.2	22 49.1	21 58.5	5 55.0	11 8.0	5 43.3	18 4.3	21 44.4	8 38.9
19	17 49 29.0	23 25.4	0 14.5	8 58.0	21 52.8	21 12.0	5 16.7	10 58.8	5 39.7	18 2.9	21 44.2	8 37.8
22	18 1 18.7	23 26.3	0 14.6	2S42.7	20 55.4	20 27.4	4 37.8	10 49.1	5 35.8	18 1.6	21 43.9	8 36.6
25	18 13 8.4	23 23.5	0 14.6	13 36.5	19 59.7	19 46.6	3 58.2	10 39.1	5 31.6	18 .3	21 43.6	8 35.3
28	18 24 58.0	23 17.0	0 14.7	19 32.1	19 8.4	19 11.1	3 18.0	10 28.8	5 27.0	17 59.1	21 43.4	8 33.8

JULY 1980

LONGITUDE

DAY	EPHEM. SID. TIME h m s	☉ ° ′	☊ ° ′	☽ ° ′	☿ ° ′	♀ ° ′	♂ ° ′	♃ ° ′	♄ ° ′	♅ ° ′	♆ ° ′	♇ ° ′
1	18 36 47.7	9♋18.5	22♌15.4	12♒37.9	24♋52.4	16♊44.5	24♍41.5	6♍ 2.9	21♍29.5	21♏51.3	20♐47.9	18♎58.1
2	18 40 44.3	10 15.7	22 12.2	26 35.8	24R38.7	16R31.6	25 13.5	6 12.5	21 33.4	21R49.9	20R46.4	18D58.2
3	18 44 40.8	11 12.9	22 9.1	10♓40.0	24 20.8	16 21.2	25 45.7	6 22.2	21 37.3	21 48.6	20 44.9	18 58.3
4	18 48 37.4	12 10.1	22 5.9	24 48.6	23 58.8	16 13.1	26 18.0	6 32.0	21 41.3	21 47.3	20 43.4	18 58.5
5	18 52 33.9	13 7.3	22 2.7	8♈59.7	23 33.2	16 7.5	26 50.5	6 41.9	21 45.4	21 46.0	20 42.0	18 58.7
6	18 56 30.5	14 4.5	21 59.5	23 11.6	23 4.1	16 4.2	27 23.2	6 51.9	21 49.6	21 44.8	20 40.5	18 58.9
7	19 0 27.0	15 1.7	21 56.4	7♉22.1	22 32.2	16 3.3	27 56.0	7 1.9	21 53.8	21 43.6	20 39.1	18 59.2
8	19 4 23.6	15 58.9	21 53.2	21 28.9	21 57.8	16D 4.8	28 29.0	7 12.1	21 58.2	21 42.5	20 37.7	18 59.5
9	19 8 20.2	16 56.2	21 50.0	5♊29.1	21 21.4	16 8.5	29 2.0	7 22.4	22 2.6	21 41.4	20 36.3	18 59.8
10	19 12 16.7	17 53.4	21 46.8	19 19.7	20 43.6	16 14.4	29 35.3	7 32.7	22 7.1	21 40.4	20 34.9	19 .2
11	19 16 13.3	18 50.6	21 43.7	2♋57.5	20 5.1	16 22.5	0♎ 8.7	7 43.1	22 11.7	21 39.4	20 33.5	19 .6
12	19 20 9.8	19 47.8	21 40.5	16 20.1	19 26.5	16 32.7	0 42.2	7 53.6	22 16.3	21 38.5	20 32.1	19 1.0
13	19 24 6.4	20 45.1	21 37.3	29 25.8	18 48.6	16 45.0	1 15.8	8 4.2	22 21.0	21 37.6	20 30.7	19 1.5
14	19 28 2.9	21 42.3	21 34.1	12♌14.0	18 11.8	16 59.3	1 49.6	8 14.8	22 25.8	21 36.7	20 29.4	19 2.0
15	19 31 59.5	22 39.6	21 30.9	24 45.4	17 37.0	17 15.5	2 23.6	8 25.6	22 30.7	21 35.9	20 28.1	19 2.5
16	19 35 56.1	23 36.8	21 27.8	7♍ 1.7	17 4.7	17 33.6	2 57.6	8 36.4	22 35.6	21 35.2	20 26.8	19 3.1
17	19 39 52.6	24 34.1	21 24.6	19 5.8	16 35.5	17 53.6	3 31.8	8 47.2	22 40.6	21 34.5	20 25.5	19 3.7
18	19 43 49.2	25 31.3	21 21.4	1♎ 1.5	16 10.0	18 15.3	4 6.2	8 58.2	22 45.7	21 33.8	20 24.3	19 4.3
19	19 47 45.7	26 28.6	21 18.2	12 53.1	15 48.7	18 38.6	4 40.6	9 9.2	22 50.8	21 33.2	20 23.0	19 5.0
20	19 51 42.3	27 25.9	21 15.1	24 45.1	15 31.9	19 3.7	5 15.2	9 20.3	22 56.0	21 32.7	20 21.8	19 5.7
21	19 55 38.8	28 23.1	21 11.9	6♏42.5	15 20.1	19 30.3	5 49.9	9 31.5	23 1.3	21 32.2	20 20.6	19 6.4
22	19 59 35.4	29 20.4	21 8.7	18 49.8	15 13.5	19 58.5	6 24.8	9 42.7	23 6.7	21 31.7	20 19.4	19 7.2
23	20 3 32.0	0♌17.7	21 5.5	1♐11.3	15 12.5	20 28.1	6 59.7	9 54.0	23 12.1	21 31.3	20 18.3	19 8.0
24	20 7 28.5	1 15.0	21 2.4	13 50.5	15D17.1	20 59.2	7 34.8	10 5.3	23 17.5	21 30.9	20 17.2	19 8.8
25	20 11 25.1	2 12.3	20 59.2	26 49.9	15 27.6	21 31.6	8 10.0	10 16.8	23 23.1	21 30.6	20 16.0	19 9.6
26	20 15 21.6	3 9.6	20 56.0	10♑10.4	15 44.1	22 5.4	8 45.3	10 28.2	23 28.7	21 30.4	20 15.0	19 10.5
27	20 19 18.2	4 6.9	20 52.8	23 51.6	16 6.5	22 40.4	9 20.7	10 39.8	23 34.3	21 30.2	20 13.9	19 11.5
28	20 23 14.7	5 4.2	20 49.6	7♒51.2	16 35.0	23 16.7	9 56.3	10 51.4	23 40.0	21 30.0	20 12.9	19 12.4
29	20 27 11.3	6 1.6	20 46.5	22 5.7	17 9.7	23 54.3	10 32.0	11 3.1	23 45.8	21 30.0	20 11.9	19 13.5
30	20 31 7.8	6 58.9	20 43.3	6♓30.3	17 50.3	24 32.9	11 7.7	11 14.8	23 51.7	21 30.0	20 10.9	19 14.5
31	20 35 4.4	7 56.3	20 40.1	20 59.9	18 36.8	25 12.7	11 43.6	11 26.5	23 57.5	21 30.0	20 9.9	19 15.5

LATITUDE

DAY	EPHEM. SID. TIME	☉	☊	☽	☿	♀	♂	♃	♄	♅	♆	♇
1	18 36 47.7	0 .0	0 .0	0N43.9	2S47.8	4S 6.1	0N33.3	1N 5.0	2N10.3	0N16.3	1N24.3	17N14.5
4	18 48 37.4	0 .0	0 .0	2S54.6	3 32.5	4 25.7	0 30.0	1 4.7	2 9.8	0 16.3	1 24.2	17 12.8
7	19 0 27.0	0 .0	0 .0	5 3.0	4 10.8	4 40.7	0 26.7	1 4.4	2 9.3	0 16.2	1 24.2	17 11.1
10	19 12 16.7	0 .0	0 .0	4 33.3	4 38.8	4 51.4	0 23.6	1 4.2	2 8.9	0 16.1	1 24.1	17 9.3
13	19 24 6.4	0 .0	0 .0	1 52.0	4 53.4	4 58.4	0 20.5	1 3.9	2 8.4	0 16.1	1 24.0	17 7.6
16	19 35 56.1	0 .0	0 .0	1N30.5	4 53.2	5 1.9	0 17.4	1 3.7	2 8.0	0 16.0	1 23.9	17 6.0
19	19 47 45.7	0 .0	0 .0	4 10.1	4 38.6	5 2.6	0 14.5	1 3.5	2 7.6	0 15.9	1 23.8	17 4.3
22	19 59 35.4	0 .0	0 .0	5 14.9	4 11.7	5 .8	0 11.6	1 3.3	2 7.2	0 15.9	1 23.7	17 2.6
25	20 11 25.1	0 .0	0 .0	4 13.5	3 35.3	4 56.7	0 8.7	1 3.1	2 6.8	0 15.8	1 23.6	17 1.0
28	20 23 14.7	0 .0	0 .0	1 7.7	2 52.8	4 50.8	0 6.0	1 2.9	2 6.4	0 15.7	1 23.4	16 59.3
31	20 35 4.4	0 .0	0 .0	2S42.4	2 7.0	4 43.2	0 3.2	1 2.7	2 6.1	0 15.7	1 23.3	16 57.7

RIGHT ASCENSION

DAY	EPHEM. SID. TIME	☉	☊	☽	☿	♀	♂	♃	♄	♅	♆	♇
1	18 36 47.7	10♋ 7.8	24♌37.0	14♒52.9	26♋16.8	16♊ 1.5	25♍20.8	8♍13.9	23♍ 2.7	19♏30.6	20♐ 5.5	24♎ 1.9
2	18 40 44.3	11 9.7	24 33.9	29 .5	25R59.7	15R48.7	25 49.8	8 22.9	23 6.2	19R29.2	20R 3.9	24R 1.7
3	18 44 40.8	12 11.7	24 30.8	12♓50.2	25 38.5	15 38.5	26 18.9	8 32.0	23 9.7	19 27.8	20 2.3	24 1.6
4	18 48 37.4	13 13.5	24 27.7	26 23.6	25 13.2	15 30.7	26 48.2	8 41.2	23 13.4	19 26.5	20 .7	24 1.6
5	18 52 33.9	14 15.3	24 24.6	9♈47.3	24 44.3	15 25.4	27 17.6	8 50.5	23 17.1	19 25.2	19 59.1	24 1.5
6	18 56 30.5	15 17.0	24 21.5	23 10.1	24 12.1	15 22.5	27 47.1	8 59.9	23 20.9	19 24.0	19 57.5	24 1.5
7	19 0 27.0	16 18.6	24 18.4	6♉40.9	23 37.1	15 22.0	28 16.8	9 9.4	23 24.7	19 22.8	19 56.0	24 1.5
8	19 4 23.6	17 20.2	24 15.3	20 26.6	22 59.8	15D24.0	28 46.7	9 18.9	23 28.7	19 21.7	19 54.5	24D 1.6
9	19 8 20.2	18 21.7	24 12.2	4♊29.7	22 20.8	15 28.2	29 16.6	9 28.6	23 32.7	19 20.6	19 53.0	24 1.7
10	19 12 16.7	19 23.0	24 9.1	18 46.6	21 40.6	15 34.7	29 46.7	9 38.2	23 36.8	19 19.5	19 51.5	24 1.8
11	19 16 13.3	20 24.2	24 6.0	3♋ 8.0	20 59.8	15 43.4	0♎16.9	9 48.0	23 40.9	19 18.5	19 50.0	24 1.9
12	19 20 9.8	21 25.4	24 2.9	17 20.5	20 19.3	15 54.3	0 47.2	9 57.9	23 45.1	19 17.5	19 48.5	24 2.1
13	19 24 6.4	22 26.4	23 59.8	1♌10.7	19 39.5	16 7.3	1 17.7	10 7.8	23 49.4	19 16.6	19 47.0	24 2.3
14	19 28 2.9	23 27.3	23 56.7	14 28.9	19 1.3	16 22.4	1 48.3	10 17.7	23 53.8	19 15.7	19 45.6	24 2.5
15	19 31 59.5	24 28.0	23 53.6	27 11.1	18 25.3	16 39.4	2 19.1	10 27.8	23 58.2	19 14.9	19 44.2	24 2.8
16	19 35 56.1	25 28.7	23 50.5	9♍19.0	17 52.0	16 58.3	2 49.9	10 37.9	24 2.7	19 14.2	19 42.8	24 3.0
17	19 39 52.6	26 29.2	23 47.4	20 58.5	17 22.2	17 19.2	3 20.9	10 48.1	24 7.2	19 13.4	19 41.4	24 3.4
18	19 43 49.2	27 29.5	23 44.3	2♎18.2	16 56.3	17 41.8	3 52.1	10 58.4	24 11.8	19 12.8	19 40.1	24 3.7
19	19 47 45.7	28 29.8	23 41.2	13 28.5	16 34.9	18 6.2	4 23.3	11 8.7	24 16.5	19 12.1	19 38.7	24 4.1
20	19 51 42.3	29 29.9	23 38.1	24 40.1	16 18.3	18 32.3	4 54.7	11 19.0	24 21.2	19 11.6	19 37.4	24 4.5
21	19 55 38.8	0♌29.8	23 35.0	6♏ 4.1	16 7.1	19 .0	5 26.2	11 29.5	24 26.0	19 11.1	19 36.1	24 4.9
22	19 59 35.4	1 29.6	23 31.9	17 50.8	16 1.4	19 29.4	5 57.8	11 40.0	24 30.9	19 10.6	19 34.9	24 5.4
23	20 3 32.0	2 29.3	23 28.8	0♐ 9.0	16D 1.6	20 .3	6 29.6	11 50.5	24 35.8	19 10.2	19 33.6	24 5.9
24	20 7 28.5	3 28.8	23 25.7	13 4.8	16 7.9	20 32.7	7 1.5	12 1.1	24 40.8	19 9.8	19 32.4	24 6.4
25	20 11 25.1	4 28.2	23 22.5	26 39.3	16 20.4	21 6.5	7 33.5	12 11.8	24 45.9	19 9.5	19 31.2	24 7.0
26	20 15 21.6	5 27.4	23 19.4	10♑47.5	16 39.3	21 41.8	8 5.6	12 22.5	24 51.0	19 9.2	19 30.1	24 7.6
27	20 19 18.2	6 26.4	23 16.3	25 18.6	17 4.6	22 18.4	8 37.9	12 33.3	24 56.1	19 9.0	19 28.9	24 8.2
28	20 23 14.7	7 25.3	23 13.2	9♒57.8	17 36.5	22 56.4	9 10.3	12 44.1	25 1.3	19 8.9	19 27.8	24 8.9
29	20 27 11.3	8 24.1	23 10.1	24 31.1	18 14.9	23 35.6	9 42.8	12 55.0	25 6.6	19 8.8	19 26.8	24 9.6
30	20 31 7.8	9 22.7	23 7.0	8♓48.9	18 59.7	24 16.1	10 15.5	13 6.0	25 11.9	19 8.8	19 25.7	24 10.3
31	20 35 4.4	10 21.2	23 3.9	22 48.1	19 51.0	24 57.8	10 48.3	13 16.9	25 17.3	19 8.8	19 24.7	24 11.0

DECLINATION

DAY	EPHEM. SID. TIME	☉	☊	☽	☿	♀	♂	♃	♄	♅	♆	♇
1	18 36 47.7	23N 6.8	0N14.8	16S18.9	18N24.2	18N41.8	2N37.1	10N18.0	5N22.2	17S58.0	21S43.1	8N32.2
4	18 48 37.4	22 53.0	0 14.8	4 44.0	17 49.4	18 19.2	1 55.8	10 7.0	5 17.1	17 57.1	21 42.9	8 30.5
7	19 0 27.0	22 35.6	0 14.9	9N11.5	17 25.9	18 3.4	1 13.9	9 55.6	5 11.7	17 56.2	21 42.7	8 28.7
10	19 12 16.7	22 14.6	0 14.9	18 28.2	17 14.8	17 53.8	0 31.5	9 43.9	5 6.0	17 55.4	21 42.4	8 26.7
13	19 24 6.4	21 50.3	0 15.0	18 26.7	17 16.5	17 49.9	0S11.4	9 31.9	5 .1	17 54.7	21 42.2	8 24.7
16	19 35 56.1	21 22.5	0 15.0	10 19.9	17 30.0	17 50.8	0 54.6	9 19.6	4 53.9	17 54.2	21 42.1	8 22.5
19	19 47 45.7	20 51.5	0 15.1	1S14.9	17 53.5	17 55.7	1 38.2	9 7.1	4 47.5	17 53.7	21 41.9	8 20.3
22	19 59 35.4	20 17.4	0 15.1	12 22.3	18 24.2	18 3.7	2 22.1	8 54.3	4 40.9	17 53.4	21 41.8	8 18.0
25	20 11 25.1	19 40.2	0 15.2	19 10.6	18 58.7	18 14.0	3 6.3	8 41.2	4 34.0	17 53.2	21 41.6	8 15.5
28	20 23 14.7	19 .0	0 15.2	17 12.9	19 33.1	18 25.8	3 50.7	8 27.9	4 27.0	17 53.1	21 41.5	8 13.0
31	20 35 4.4	18 17.0	0 15.3	6 3.4	20 3.0	18 38.2	4 35.3	8 14.4	4 19.7	17 53.2	21 41.4	8 10.4

LONGITUDE

DAY	EPHEM. SID. TIME (h m s)	☉	☊	☽	☿	♀	♂	♃	♄	♅	♆	♇
1	20 39 1.0	8♌53.7	20♌36.9	5♈29.5	19♋29.3	25♊53.5	12♎19.6	11♍38.4	24♍3.5	21♏30.0	20♐9.0	19♎16.6
2	20 42 57.5	9 51.1	20 33.8	19 54.5	20 27.6	26 35.4	12 55.7	11 50.2	24 9.5	21 D30.1	20 R8.1	19 17.7
3	20 46 54.1	10 48.5	20 30.6	4♉11.6	21 31.7	27 18.2	13 32.0	12 2.1	24 15.5	21 30.3	20 7.2	19 18.9
4	20 50 50.6	11 45.9	20 27.4	18 18.0	22 41.2	28 2.0	14 8.3	12 14.1	24 21.6	21 30.5	20 6.3	19 20.0
5	20 54 47.2	12 43.4	20 24.2	2♊12.1	23 56.2	28 46.7	14 44.7	12 26.1	24 27.8	21 30.8	20 5.5	19 21.2
6	20 58 43.7	13 40.9	20 21.1	15 52.7	25 16.5	29 32.3	15 21.3	12 38.2	24 34.0	21 31.1	20 4.7	19 22.5
7	21 2 40.3	14 38.4	20 17.9	29 19.5	26 41.7	0♋18.7	15 58.0	12 50.3	24 40.2	21 31.4	20 3.9	19 23.7
8	21 6 36.8	15 35.9	20 14.7	12♋32.1	28 11.8	1 6.0	16 34.7	13 2.5	24 46.6	21 31.9	20 3.2	19 25.0
9	21 10 33.4	16 33.4	20 11.5	25 30.6	29 46.3	1 54.0	17 11.6	13 14.7	24 52.9	21 32.3	20 2.5	19 26.3
10	21 14 29.9	17 31.0	20 8.3	8♌15.4	1♌25.1	2 42.8	17 48.6	13 27.0	24 59.3	21 32.9	20 1.8	19 27.7
11	21 18 26.5	18 28.6	20 5.2	20 46.9	3 7.8	3 32.3	18 25.7	13 39.3	25 5.8	21 33.4	20 1.1	19 29.1
12	21 22 23.1	19 26.2	20 2.0	3♍6.2	4 54.0	4 22.6	19 2.9	13 51.6	25 12.2	21 34.1	20 .5	19 30.5
13	21 26 19.6	20 23.8	19 58.8	15 14.8	6 43.4	5 13.5	19 40.3	14 4.0	25 18.8	21 34.7	19 59.9	19 31.9
14	21 30 16.2	21 21.4	19 55.6	27 14.6	8 35.5	6 5.0	20 17.7	14 16.4	25 25.4	21 35.5	19 59.3	19 33.4
15	21 34 12.7	22 19.1	19 52.5	9♎8.2	10 30.0	6 57.2	20 55.2	14 28.8	25 32.0	21 36.3	19 58.7	19 34.8
16	21 38 9.3	23 16.8	19 49.3	20 58.9	12 26.5	7 50.0	21 32.8	14 41.3	25 38.6	21 37.1	19 58.2	19 36.4
17	21 42 5.8	24 14.5	19 46.1	2♏50.4	14 24.6	8 43.3	22 10.6	14 53.8	25 45.4	21 38.0	19 57.7	19 37.9
18	21 46 2.4	25 12.2	19 42.9	14 46.7	16 23.9	9 37.3	22 48.4	15 6.4	25 52.1	21 38.9	19 57.3	19 39.5
19	21 49 58.9	26 10.0	19 39.7	26 52.3	18 24.1	10 31.8	23 26.4	15 19.0	25 58.9	21 40.0	19 56.9	19 41.1
20	21 53 55.5	27 7.7	19 36.6	9♐11.7	20 24.8	11 26.8	24 4.4	15 31.6	26 5.7	21 41.0	19 56.5	19 42.7
21	21 57 52.0	28 5.5	19 33.4	21 49.2	22 25.7	12 22.4	24 42.5	15 44.3	26 12.6	21 42.1	19 56.1	19 44.4
22	22 1 48.6	29 3.3	19 30.2	4♑48.4	24 26.5	13 18.4	25 20.7	15 56.9	26 19.5	21 43.2	19 55.7	19 46.1
23	22 5 45.1	0♍1.1	19 27.0	18 11.8	26 27.1	14 14.9	25 59.1	16 9.6	26 26.4	21 44.4	19 55.5	19 47.8
24	22 9 41.7	0 58.9	19 23.9	2♒.5	28 27.2	15 12.0	26 37.5	16 22.4	26 33.3	21 45.7	19 55.2	19 49.5
25	22 13 38.2	1 56.7	19 20.7	16 13.2	0♍26.7	16 9.4	27 16.0	16 35.1	26 40.3	21 47.0	19 55.0	19 51.2
26	22 17 34.8	2 54.6	19 17.5	0♓46.5	2 25.4	17 7.4	27 54.6	16 47.9	26 47.3	21 48.3	19 54.8	19 53.0
27	22 21 31.4	3 52.5	19 14.3	15 34.6	4 23.2	18 5.7	28 33.3	17 .7	26 54.4	21 49.7	19 54.6	19 54.8
28	22 25 27.9	4 50.4	19 11.1	0♈30.2	6 20.0	19 4.5	29 12.2	17 13.5	27 1.4	21 51.1	19 54.4	19 56.6
29	22 29 24.5	5 48.4	19 8.0	15 24.9	8 15.7	20 3.7	29 50.9	17 26.3	27 8.5	21 52.6	19 54.4	19 58.4
30	22 33 21.0	6 46.4	19 4.8	0♉11.1	10 10.3	21 3.3	0♏29.9	17 39.2	27 15.7	21 54.1	19 54.3	20 .3
31	22 37 17.6	7 44.4	19 1.6	14 42.6	12 3.8	22 3.3	1 8.9	17 52.0	27 22.8	21 55.7	19 54.2	20 2.2

LATITUDE

DAY	EPHEM. SID. TIME (h m s)	☉	☊	☽	☿	♀	♂	♃	♄	♅	♆	♇
1	20 39 1.0	0 .0	0 .0	3S45.4	1S51.4	4S40.3	0N 2.4	1N 2.7	2N 6.0	0N15.6	1N23.3	16N57.2
4	20 50 50.6	0 .0	0 .0	5 16.7	1 5.3	4 30.9	0S .3	1 2.5	2 5.7	0 15.6	1 23.1	16 55.7
7	21 2 40.3	0 .0	0 .0	4 6.2	0 21.5	4 20.3	0 2.9	1 2.4	2 5.4	0 15.5	1 23.0	16 54.1
10	21 14 29.9	0 .0	0 .0	1 5.8	0N17.7	4 8.7	0 5.4	1 2.3	2 5.1	0 15.4	1 22.9	16 52.7
13	21 26 19.6	0 .0	0 .0	2N14.6	0 50.7	3 56.3	0 7.9	1 2.2	2 4.9	0 15.4	1 22.7	16 51.2
16	21 38 9.3	0 .0	0 .0	4 37.0	1 16.1	3 43.2	0 10.3	1 2.2	2 4.6	0 15.3	1 22.6	16 49.8
19	21 49 58.9	0 .0	0 .0	5 15.0	1 33.6	3 29.5	0 12.7	1 2.1	2 4.3	0 15.2	1 22.4	16 48.5
22	22 1 48.6	0 .0	0 .0	3 46.0	1 43.3	3 15.4	0 15.0	1 2.1	2 4.1	0 15.1	1 22.1	16 47.2
25	22 13 38.2	0 .0	0 .0	0 22.2	1 46.0	3 .8	0 17.3	1 2.0	2 4.0	0 15.0	1 22.0	16 46.0
28	22 25 27.9	0 .0	0 .0	3S24.7	1 42.6	2 46.0	0 19.5	1 2.1	2 3.9	0 14.9	1 21.8	16 44.8
31	22 37 17.6	0 .0	0 .0	5 14.3	1 34.2	2 31.0	0 21.7	1 2.1	2 3.9	0 14.9	1 21.8	16 43.7

RIGHT ASCENSION

DAY	EPHEM. SID. TIME (h m s)	☉	☊	☽	☿	♀	♂	♃	♄	♅	♆	♇
1	20 39 1.0	11♌19.5	23♌ .8	6♈31.7	20♋48.6	25♊40.6	11♎21.2	13♍27.9	25♍22.7	19♏ 8.8	19♐23.7	24♎11.8
2	20 42 57.5	12 17.7	22 57.6	20 6.3	21 52.5	26 24.5	11 54.2	13 39.0	25 28.2	19D 8.9	19R22.7	24 12.6
3	20 46 54.1	13 15.7	22 54.5	3♉40.0	23 2.4	27 9.6	12 27.4	13 50.1	25 33.7	19 9.1	19 21.7	24 13.4
4	20 50 50.6	14 13.5	22 51.4	17 20.1	24 18.3	27 55.6	13 .7	14 1.3	25 39.3	19 9.3	19 20.8	24 14.3
5	20 54 47.2	15 11.3	22 48.3	1♊10.7	25 39.9	28 42.7	13 34.1	14 12.5	25 44.9	19 9.5	19 19.9	24 15.1
6	20 58 43.7	16 8.8	22 45.2	15 11.6	27 6.9	29 30.8	14 7.7	14 23.7	25 50.6	19 9.9	19 19.0	24 16.0
7	21 2 40.3	17 6.3	22 42.1	29 17.2	28 39.2	0♋19.8	14 41.4	14 35.0	25 56.3	19 10.2	19 18.2	24 17.0
8	21 6 36.8	18 3.6	22 39.0	13♋18.0	0♌16.3	1 9.7	15 15.2	14 46.3	26 2.1	19 10.6	19 17.4	24 17.9
9	21 10 33.4	19 .7	22 35.8	27 3.1	1 57.8	2 .4	15 49.2	14 57.7	26 7.9	19 11.1	19 16.6	24 18.9
10	21 14 29.9	19 57.7	22 32.7	10♌22.8	3 43.5	2 52.0	16 23.3	15 9.1	26 13.7	19 11.6	19 15.9	24 20.0
11	21 18 26.5	20 54.6	22 29.6	23 11.6	5 32.7	3 44.5	16 57.6	15 20.5	26 19.6	19 12.2	19 15.1	24 21.0
12	21 22 23.1	21 51.3	22 26.5	5♍28.7	7 25.2	4 37.6	17 32.0	15 32.0	26 25.5	19 12.9	19 14.5	24 22.1
13	21 26 19.6	22 47.9	22 23.4	17 17.5	9 20.3	5 31.6	18 6.5	15 43.5	26 31.5	19 13.5	19 13.8	24 23.2
14	21 30 16.2	23 44.3	22 20.2	28 44.5	11 17.7	6 26.3	18 41.2	15 55.0	26 37.5	19 14.3	19 13.2	24 24.3
15	21 34 12.7	24 40.6	22 17.1	9♎57.8	13 16.7	7 21.6	19 16.0	16 6.6	26 43.6	19 15.1	19 12.6	24 25.5
16	21 38 9.3	25 36.8	22 14.0	21 .7	15 16.9	8 17.7	19 51.0	16 18.1	26 49.7	19 15.9	19 12.0	24 26.6
17	21 42 5.8	26 32.8	22 10.9	2♏22.4	17 17.8	9 14.4	20 26.1	16 29.8	26 55.8	19 16.8	19 11.5	24 27.8
18	21 46 2.4	27 28.7	22 7.8	13 53.4	19 19.1	10 11.7	21 1.3	16 41.4	27 2.0	19 17.7	19 11.0	24 29.1
19	21 49 58.9	28 24.5	22 4.6	25 49.5	21 20.3	11 9.6	21 36.7	16 53.1	27 8.2	19 18.8	19 10.6	24 30.4
20	21 53 55.5	29 20.2	22 1.5	8♐17.9	23 21.1	12 8.1	22 12.3	17 4.8	27 14.5	19 19.8	19 10.2	24 31.7
21	21 57 52.0	0♍15.7	21 58.3	21 23.3	25 21.1	13 7.2	22 48.0	17 16.6	27 20.7	19 20.9	19 9.8	24 33.0
22	22 1 48.6	1 11.1	21 55.3	5♑5.5	27 20.1	14 6.8	23 23.8	17 28.3	27 27.0	19 22.1	19 9.4	24 34.3
23	22 5 45.1	2 6.4	21 52.1	19 18.8	29 17.9	15 6.9	23 59.7	17 40.1	27 33.4	19 23.3	19 9.1	24 35.7
24	22 9 41.7	3 1.6	21 49.0	3♒52.5	1♍14.3	16 7.5	24 35.9	17 51.9	27 39.7	19 24.6	19 8.8	24 37.1
25	22 13 38.2	3 56.6	21 45.9	18 33.7	3 9.3	17 8.5	25 12.1	18 3.7	27 46.1	19 25.9	19 8.5	24 38.5
26	22 17 34.8	4 51.6	21 42.8	3♓10.8	5 2.6	18 10.1	25 48.5	18 15.5	27 52.6	19 27.2	19 8.3	24 39.9
27	22 21 31.4	5 46.4	21 39.6	17 36.4	6 54.2	19 12.0	26 25.1	18 27.3	27 59.0	19 28.6	19 8.0	24 41.3
28	22 25 27.9	6 41.2	21 36.5	1♈49.2	8 44.2	20 14.4	27 1.8	18 39.2	28 5.5	19 30.1	19 8.0	24 42.8
29	22 29 24.5	7 35.9	21 33.4	15 51.9	10 32.4	21 17.2	27 38.6	18 51.1	28 12.0	19 31.6	19 7.8	24 44.3
30	22 33 21.0	8 30.5	21 30.3	29 50.1	12 19.0	22 20.3	28 15.7	19 3.0	28 18.5	19 33.1	19 7.8	24 45.8
31	22 37 17.6	9 25.0	21 27.1	13♉49.1	14 3.8	23 23.9	28 52.8	19 14.9	28 25.1	19 34.7	19 7.7	24 47.4

DECLINATION

DAY	EPHEM. SID. TIME (h m s)	☉	☊	☽	☿	♀	♂	♃	♄	♅	♆	♇
1	20 39 1.0	18N 2.1	0N15.3	1S16.1	20N11.1	18N42.4	4S50.1	8N 9.8	4N17.3	17S53.2	21S41.4	8N 9.5
4	20 50 50.6	17 15.6	0 15.4	12N12.1	19 27.5	18 54.6	5 34.4	7 56.1	4 9.8	17 53.4	21 41.3	8 6.9
7	21 2 40.3	16 26.5	0 15.4	19 20.1	20 27.9	19 6.1	6 19.6	7 42.1	4 2.1	17 53.5	21 41.3	8 4.1
10	21 14 29.9	15 35.1	0 15.5	17 8.5	20 7.9	19 16.0	7 4.3	7 27.9	3 54.3	17 54.1	21 41.3	8 1.3
13	21 26 19.6	14 41.4	0 15.5	7 52.9	19 24.6	19 24.1	7 49.0	7 13.6	3 46.4	17 54.7	21 41.3	7 58.5
16	21 38 9.3	13 45.6	0 15.6	3S54.4	18 17.3	19 29.7	8 33.6	6 59.1	3 38.3	17 55.4	21 41.4	7 55.6
19	21 49 58.9	12 47.8	0 15.6	14 20.8	16 47.8	19 32.4	9 18.0	6 44.5	3 30.0	17 56.2	21 41.4	7 52.6
22	22 1 48.6	11 48.2	0 15.7	19 35.3	14 59.9	19 32.1	10 2.2	6 29.7	3 21.7	17 57.1	21 41.4	7 49.6
25	22 13 38.2	10 47.0	0 15.7	15 37.3	12 58.0	19 28.2	10 46.2	6 14.9	3 13.3	17 58.1	21 41.5	7 46.6
28	22 25 27.9	9 44.2	0 15.8	2S55.8	10 46.6	19 20.6	11 29.7	5 59.9	3 4.8	17 59.3	21 41.6	7 43.6
31	22 37 17.6	8 40.0	0 15.8	11N14.4	8 29.2	19 9.0	12 12.8	5 44.9	2 56.2	18 .5	21 41.8	7 40.5

SEPTEMBER 1980

LONGITUDE

DAY	EPHEM. SID. TIME h m s	☉ ° ′	☊ ° ′	☽ ° ′	☿ ° ′	♀ ° ′	♂ ° ′	♃ ° ′	♄ ° ′	♅ ° ′	♆ ° ′	♇ ° ′
1	22 41 14.1	8♍42.4	18♌58.4	28♉55.3	13♍56.0	23♋ 3.7	1♏48.1	18♍ 4.9	27♍30.0	21♏57.4	19♐54.2	20♎ 4.1
2	22 45 10.7	9 40.5	18 55.3	12♊47.2	15 47.1	24 4.4	2 27.3	18 17.8	27 37.2	21 59.0	19D54.3	20 6.0
3	22 49 7.2	10 38.6	18 52.1	26 18.2	17 36.9	25 5.5	3 6.7	18 30.7	27 44.4	22 .8	19 54.3	20 7.9
4	22 53 3.8	11 36.8	18 48.9	9♋29.6	19 25.6	26 7.0	3 46.1	18 43.7	27 51.6	22 2.5	19 54.4	20 9.9
5	22 57 .3	12 34.9	18 45.7	22 23.6	21 13.0	27 8.8	4 25.7	18 56.6	27 58.9	22 4.3	19 54.5	20 11.9
6	23 0 56.9	13 33.1	18 42.5	5♌ 2.4	22 59.2	28 10.9	5 5.3	19 9.5	28 6.2	22 6.2	19 54.7	20 13.9
7	23 4 53.4	14 31.4	18 39.4	17 28.5	24 44.2	29 13.3	5 45.0	19 22.5	28 13.5	22 8.1	19 54.8	20 15.9
8	23 8 50.0	15 29.6	18 36.2	29 43.9	26 28.1	0♌16.0	6 24.8	19 35.5	28 20.8	22 10.1	19 55.1	20 17.9
9	23 12 46.5	16 28.0	18 33.0	11♍50.8	28 10.8	1 19.1	7 4.8	19 48.5	28 28.2	22 12.1	19 55.4	20 20.0
10	23 16 43.1	17 26.3	18 29.8	23 50.7	29 52.3	2 22.4	7 44.7	20 1.5	28 35.5	22 14.2	19 55.6	20 22.1
11	23 20 39.6	18 24.7	18 26.6	5♎45.5	1♎32.7	3 26.0	8 24.8	20 14.5	28 42.9	22 16.3	19 56.0	20 24.2
12	23 24 36.2	19 23.1	18 23.5	17 36.9	3 12.0	4 29.9	9 5.0	20 27.5	28 50.3	22 18.4	19 56.3	20 26.3
13	23 28 32.7	20 21.5	18 20.3	29 27.1	4 50.1	5 34.1	9 45.3	20 40.5	28 57.7	22 20.6	19 56.7	20 28.4
14	23 32 29.3	21 20.0	18 17.1	11♏18.7	6 27.2	6 38.5	10 25.6	20 53.5	29 5.1	22 22.8	19 57.1	20 30.6
15	23 36 25.8	22 18.4	18 13.9	23 14.7	8 3.2	7 43.1	11 6.0	21 6.5	29 12.5	22 25.0	19 57.5	20 32.7
16	23 40 22.4	23 16.9	18 10.8	5♐18.8	9 38.1	8 48.1	11 46.6	21 19.5	29 19.9	22 27.3	19 58.0	20 34.9
17	23 44 19.0	24 15.5	18 7.6	17 34.9	11 12.0	9 53.2	12 27.2	21 32.4	29 27.3	22 29.7	19 58.5	20 37.1
18	23 48 15.5	25 14.0	18 4.4	0♑ 7.5	12 44.8	10 58.6	13 7.9	21 45.4	29 34.7	22 32.1	19 59.1	20 39.3
19	23 52 12.1	26 12.6	18 1.2	13 .8	14 16.6	12 4.2	13 48.6	21 58.4	29 42.2	22 34.5	19 59.7	20 41.5
20	23 56 8.6	27 11.2	17 58.0	26 18.5	15 47.4	13 10.1	14 29.5	22 11.4	29 49.6	22 37.0	20 .3	20 43.7
21	0 0 5.2	28 9.9	17 54.9	10♒ 3.5	17 17.1	14 16.2	15 10.4	22 24.3	29 57.1	22 39.5	20 .9	20 46.0
22	0 4 1.7	29 8.5	17 51.7	24 16.3	18 45.8	15 22.5	15 51.5	22 37.3	0♎ 4.5	22 42.0	20 1.6	20 48.2
23	0 7 58.3	0♎ 7.2	17 48.5	8♓55.0	20 13.4	16 29.0	16 32.6	22 50.2	0 11.9	22 44.6	20 2.3	20 50.5
24	0 11 54.8	1 6.0	17 45.3	23 54.7	21 40.0	17 35.7	17 13.7	23 3.2	0 19.4	22 47.2	20 3.0	20 52.8
25	0 15 51.4	2 4.7	17 42.2	9♈ 7.2	23 5.5	18 42.7	17 55.0	23 16.1	0 26.8	22 49.9	20 3.8	20 55.0
26	0 19 47.9	3 3.5	17 39.0	24 22.3	24 29.9	19 49.8	18 36.3	23 29.0	0 34.3	22 52.6	20 4.6	20 57.3
27	0 23 44.5	4 2.4	17 35.8	9♉29.4	25 53.3	20 57.2	19 17.8	23 41.9	0 41.7	22 55.3	20 5.4	20 59.6
28	0 27 41.0	5 1.2	17 32.6	24 19.2	27 15.4	22 4.7	19 59.3	23 54.8	0 49.1	22 58.1	20 6.3	21 2.0
29	0 31 37.6	6 .1	17 29.4	8♊45.2	28 36.4	23 12.5	20 40.9	24 7.6	0 56.6	23 .8	20 7.2	21 4.3
30	0 35 34.1	6 59.1	17 26.3	22 44.2	29 56.3	24 20.5	21 22.6	24 20.5	1 4.0	23 3.7	20 8.2	21 6.7

LATITUDE

DAY	EPHEM. SID. TIME	☉	☊	☽	☿	♀	♂	♃	♄	♅	♆	♇
1	22 41 14.1	0 .0	0 .0	5S12.0	1N30.4	2S25.9	0S22.5	1N 2.1	2N 3.9	0N14.9	1N21.8	16N43.3
4	22 53 3.8	0 .0	0 .0	3 25.8	1 16.8	2 10.8	0 24.6	1 2.1	2 3.8	0 14.9	1 21.6	16 42.3
7	23 4 53.4	0 .0	0 .0	0 14.8	1 .3	1 55.6	0 26.7	1 2.1	2 3.7	0 14.8	1 21.4	16 41.3
10	23 16 43.1	0 .0	0 .0	2N54.3	0 41.5	1 40.5	0 28.7	1 2.2	2 3.7	0 14.7	1 21.3	16 40.4
13	23 28 32.7	0 .0	0 .0	4 52.5	0 21.0	1 25.5	0 30.7	1 2.3	2 3.7	0 14.7	1 21.1	16 39.6
16	23 40 22.4	0 .0	0 .0	5 .3	0S .7	1 10.8	0 32.6	1 2.4	2 3.8	0 14.6	1 21.0	16 38.8
19	23 52 12.1	0 .0	0 .0	3 6.3	0 23.2	0 56.3	0 34.5	1 2.5	2 3.8	0 14.6	1 20.8	16 38.1
22	0 4 1.7	0 .0	0 .0	0S25.0	0 46.0	0 42.1	0 36.3	1 2.7	2 3.9	0 14.5	1 20.7	16 37.5
25	0 15 51.4	0 .0	0 .0	3 55.7	1 8.8	0 28.3	0 38.1	1 2.8	2 4.0	0 14.4	1 20.5	16 36.9
28	0 27 41.0	0 .0	0 .0	5 7.2	1 31.2	0 15.0	0 39.9	1 3.0	2 4.1	0 14.4	1 20.4	16 36.5

RIGHT ASCENSION

DAY	EPHEM. SID. TIME	☉	☊	☽	☿	♀	♂	♃	♄	♅	♆	♇
1	22 41 14.1	10♍19.4	21♌24.0	27♉52.3	15♍47.0	24♋27.7	29♎30.2	19♍26.8	28♍31.6	19♏36.4	19♐ 7.7	24♎48.9
2	22 45 10.7	11 13.8	21 20.9	11♊59.3	17 28.6	25 31.9	0♏ 7.7	19 38.7	28 38.2	19 38.1	19 7.7	24 50.5
3	22 49 7.2	12 8.1	21 17.7	26 5.8	19 8.6	26 36.4	0 45.3	19 50.7	28 44.8	19 39.8	19D 7.8	24 52.1
4	22 53 3.8	13 2.4	21 14.6	10♋ 4.2	20 47.1	27 41.2	1 23.1	20 2.6	28 51.5	19 41.6	19 7.8	24 53.8
5	22 57 .3	13 56.5	21 11.5	23 45.7	22 24.2	28 46.2	2 1.1	20 14.6	28 58.1	19 43.5	19 8.0	24 55.4
6	23 0 56.9	14 50.7	21 8.4	7♌ 2.6	23 59.8	29 51.5	2 39.2	20 26.5	29 4.8	19 45.3	19 8.1	24 57.1
7	23 4 53.4	15 44.8	21 5.2	19 50.5	25 34.1	0♌57.0	3 17.5	20 38.5	29 11.5	19 47.3	19 8.3	24 58.8
8	23 8 50.0	16 38.8	21 2.1	2♍ 8.8	27 7.1	2 2.7	3 56.0	20 50.5	29 18.2	19 49.3	19 8.5	25 .5
9	23 12 46.5	17 32.8	20 59.0	14 .3	28 38.9	3 8.7	4 34.7	21 2.5	29 25.0	19 51.3	19 8.9	25 2.2
10	23 16 43.1	18 26.8	20 55.8	25 30.2	0♎ 9.4	4 14.8	5 13.5	21 14.5	29 31.7	19 53.4	19 9.2	25 4.0
11	23 20 39.6	19 20.7	20 52.7	6♎45.9	1 38.9	5 21.1	5 52.5	21 26.5	29 38.5	19 55.5	19 9.5	25 5.8
12	23 24 36.2	20 14.6	20 49.6	17 55.3	3 7.3	6 27.5	6 31.6	21 38.5	29 45.3	19 57.7	19 9.9	25 7.5
13	23 28 32.7	21 8.5	20 46.4	29 7.1	4 34.6	7 34.0	7 11.0	21 50.5	29 52.0	19 59.9	19 10.3	25 9.3
14	23 32 29.3	22 2.3	20 43.3	10♏29.8	6 1.0	8 40.7	7 50.4	22 2.5	29 58.8	20 2.2	19 10.7	25 11.2
15	23 36 25.8	22 56.1	20 40.1	22 11.5	7 26.4	9 47.5	8 30.1	22 14.5	0♎ 5.6	20 4.4	19 11.2	25 13.0
16	23 40 22.4	23 49.9	20 37.0	4♐19.0	8 50.9	10 54.4	9 9.9	22 26.5	0 12.5	20 6.8	19 11.7	25 14.8
17	23 44 19.0	24 43.7	20 33.9	16 57.2	10 14.6	12 1.4	9 49.9	22 38.5	0 19.3	20 9.2	19 12.2	25 16.7
18	23 48 15.5	25 37.5	20 30.7	0♑ 7.9	11 37.4	13 8.5	10 30.1	22 50.4	0 26.1	20 11.6	19 12.8	25 18.6
19	23 52 12.1	26 31.3	20 27.6	13 49.1	12 59.5	14 15.6	11 10.4	23 2.4	0 32.9	20 14.1	19 13.4	25 20.5
20	23 56 8.6	27 25.1	20 24.5	27 54.5	14 20.7	15 22.8	11 50.9	23 14.4	0 39.8	20 16.6	19 14.1	25 22.4
21	0 0 5.2	28 19.0	20 21.3	12♒15.6	15 41.2	16 30.1	12 31.6	23 26.3	0 46.6	20 19.1	19 14.8	25 24.3
22	0 4 1.7	29 12.8	20 18.2	26 43.1	17 1.0	17 37.4	13 12.5	23 38.3	0 53.4	20 21.7	19 15.5	25 26.3
23	0 7 58.3	0♎ 6.6	20 15.0	11♓10.3	18 20.1	18 44.7	13 53.5	23 50.2	1 .3	20 24.3	19 16.2	25 28.2
24	0 11 54.8	1 .5	20 11.9	25 34.1	19 38.4	19 52.0	14 34.7	24 2.1	1 7.1	20 27.0	19 17.0	25 30.2
25	0 15 51.4	1 54.5	20 8.8	9♈55.4	20 56.0	20 59.4	15 16.1	24 14.0	1 14.0	20 29.7	19 17.8	25 32.2
26	0 19 47.9	2 48.4	20 5.6	24 17.3	22 12.9	22 6.8	15 57.6	24 25.9	1 20.8	20 32.4	19 18.7	25 34.2
27	0 23 44.5	3 42.4	20 2.5	8♉43.2	23 29.0	23 14.2	16 39.4	24 37.8	1 27.6	20 35.2	19 19.6	25 36.2
28	0 27 41.0	4 36.5	19 59.3	23 14.6	24 44.4	24 21.6	17 21.3	24 49.7	1 34.5	20 38.0	19 20.5	25 38.2
29	0 31 37.6	5 30.6	19 56.2	7♊49.1	25 59.0	25 29.0	18 3.4	25 1.5	1 41.3	20 40.8	19 21.5	25 40.2
30	0 35 34.1	6 24.8	19 53.1	22 20.3	27 12.9	26 36.5	18 45.7	25 13.4	1 48.2	20 43.8	19 22.5	25 42.3

DECLINATION

DAY	EPHEM. SID. TIME	☉	☊	☽	☿	♀	♂	♃	♄	♅	♆	♇
1	22 41 14.1	8N18.3	0N15.9	14N50.5	7N42.7	19N 4.2	12S27.1	5N39.9	2N53.3	18S 1.0	21S41.8	7N39.5
4	22 53 3.8	7 12.5	0 15.9	19 40.8	5 21.8	18 47.1	13 9.6	5 24.7	2 44.6	18 2.4	21 42.0	7 36.4
7	23 4 53.4	6 5.6	0 16.0	15 21.7	3 .8	18 25.7	13 51.5	5 9.5	2 35.9	18 3.9	21 42.2	7 33.4
10	23 16 43.1	4 57.8	0 16.0	5 6.7	0 41.1	17 59.9	14 32.8	4 54.3	2 27.1	18 5.5	21 42.4	7 30.3
13	23 28 32.7	3 49.2	0 16.1	6S42.8	1S36.0	17 29.8	15 13.3	4 39.0	2 18.3	18 7.2	21 42.6	7 27.2
16	23 40 22.4	2 40.0	0 16.1	16 15.6	3 49.7	16 55.3	15 53.1	4 23.8	2 9.5	18 9.0	21 42.9	7 24.2
19	23 52 12.1	1 30.4	0 16.2	19 42.8	5 59.1	16 16.4	16 32.0	4 8.5	2 .7	18 10.9	21 43.2	7 21.2
22	0 4 1.7	0 20.5	0 16.2	13 49.5	8 3.6	15 33.3	17 10.0	3 53.3	1 51.9	18 12.8	21 43.5	7 18.2
25	0 15 51.4	0S49.6	0 16.3	0N .2	10 2.4	14 46.1	17 46.9	3 38.1	1 43.1	18 14.9	21 43.8	7 15.2
28	0 27 41.0	1 59.7	0 16.3	13 53.0	11 54.9	13 54.8	18 22.7	3 22.9	1 34.3	18 17.0	21 44.1	7 12.3

OCTOBER 1980

LONGITUDE

DAY	EPHEM. SID. TIME h m s	☉ ° ′	☊ ° ′	☽ ° ′	☿ ° ′	♀ ° ′	♂ ° ′	♃ ° ′	♄ ° ′	♅ ° ′	♆ ° ′	♇ ° ′
1	0 39 30.7	7 ♎ 58.1	17 ♌ 23.1	6 ♋ 15.9	1 ♏ 14.8	25 ♌ 28.6	22 ♏ 4.3	24 ♍ 33.3	1 ♎ 11.5	23 ♏ 6.6	20 ♐ 9.1	21 ♎ 9.0
2	0 43 27.2	8 57.1	17 19.9	19 22.5	2 32.0	26 36.9	22 46.2	24 46.1	1 18.9	23 9.5	20 10.1	21 11.3
3	0 47 23.8	9 56.2	17 16.7	2 ♌ 7.4	3 47.8	27 45.4	23 28.1	24 58.9	1 26.3	23 12.4	20 11.1	21 13.7
4	0 51 20.3	10 55.3	17 13.6	14 34.6	5 2.2	28 54.1	24 10.1	25 11.7	1 33.7	23 15.4	20 12.2	21 16.1
5	0 55 16.9	11 54.4	17 10.4	26 48.3	6 15.0	0 ♍ 2.9	24 52.2	25 24.4	1 41.0	23 18.4	20 13.2	21 18.4
6	0 59 13.4	12 53.6	17 7.2	8 ♍ 52.2	7 26.1	1 11.9	25 34.3	25 37.1	1 48.4	23 21.4	20 14.3	21 20.8
7	1 3 10.0	13 52.8	17 4.0	20 49.5	8 35.4	2 21.0	26 16.6	25 49.8	1 55.7	23 24.5	20 15.5	21 23.2
8	1 7 6.5	14 52.1	17 .8	2 ♎ 42.7	9 42.9	3 30.3	26 58.9	26 2.4	2 3.1	23 27.6	20 16.6	21 25.5
9	1 11 3.1	15 51.4	16 57.7	14 33.9	10 48.2	4 39.8	27 41.3	26 15.1	2 10.4	23 30.7	20 17.8	21 27.9
10	1 14 59.7	16 50.7	16 54.5	26 24.8	11 51.3	5 49.4	28 23.8	26 27.6	2 17.7	23 33.9	20 19.1	21 30.3
11	1 18 56.2	17 50.0	16 51.3	8 ♏ 16.9	12 52.0	6 59.1	29 6.4	26 40.2	2 25.0	23 37.0	20 20.3	21 32.7
12	1 22 52.8	18 49.4	16 48.1	20 11.8	13 49.9	8 9.0	29 49.0	26 52.7	2 32.2	23 40.2	20 21.6	21 35.1
13	1 26 49.3	19 48.8	16 44.9	2 ♐ 11.3	14 45.0	9 19.1	0 ♐ 31.7	27 5.2	2 39.5	23 43.5	20 22.9	21 37.5
14	1 30 45.9	20 48.3	16 41.8	14 17.8	15 36.9	10 29.2	1 14.5	27 17.6	2 46.7	23 46.7	20 24.2	21 39.9
15	1 34 42.4	21 47.7	16 38.6	26 34.4	16 25.2	11 39.5	1 57.4	27 30.0	2 53.9	23 50.0	20 25.6	21 42.3
16	1 38 39.0	22 47.2	16 35.4	9 ♑ 4.6	17 9.7	12 50.0	2 40.3	27 42.4	3 1.1	23 53.3	20 27.0	21 44.7
17	1 42 35.5	23 46.8	16 32.2	21 52.4	17 49.9	14 .5	3 23.3	27 54.7	3 8.2	23 56.6	20 28.4	21 47.1
18	1 46 32.1	24 46.3	16 29.1	5 ♒ 1.9	18 25.4	15 11.2	4 6.4	28 7.0	3 15.3	23 60.0	20 29.9	21 49.5
19	1 50 28.6	25 45.9	16 25.9	18 36.6	18 55.8	16 22.0	4 49.5	28 19.2	3 22.4	24 3.4	20 31.3	21 51.9
20	1 54 25.2	26 45.6	16 22.7	2 ♓ 38.8	19 20.5	17 32.9	5 32.8	28 31.4	3 29.5	24 6.8	20 32.8	21 54.2
21	1 58 21.7	27 45.2	16 19.5	17 8.7	19 39.1	18 44.0	6 16.1	28 43.6	3 36.6	24 10.2	20 34.4	21 56.7
22	2 2 18.3	28 44.9	16 16.3	2 ♈ 3.2	19 50.9	19 55.2	6 59.5	28 55.7	3 43.6	24 13.7	20 36.0	21 59.1
23	2 6 14.8	29 44.6	16 13.2	17 15.6	19 55.4	21 6.4	7 42.9	29 7.8	3 50.5	24 17.1	20 37.5	22 1.4
24	2 10 11.4	0 ♏ 44.4	16 10.0	2 ♉ 36.1	19 R 52.0	22 17.8	8 26.4	29 19.7	3 57.4	24 20.6	20 39.1	22 3.8
25	2 14 7.9	1 44.2	16 6.8	17 53.1	19 40.2	23 29.3	9 10.0	29 31.7	4 4.3	24 24.1	20 40.7	22 6.2
26	2 18 4.5	2 44.0	16 3.6	2 ♊ 55.4	19 19.6	24 40.9	9 53.6	29 43.6	4 11.2	24 27.6	20 42.4	22 8.5
27	2 22 1.1	3 43.8	16 .5	17 34.2	18 49.8	25 52.7	10 37.3	29 55.4	4 18.0	24 31.1	20 44.1	22 10.9
28	2 25 57.6	4 43.7	15 57.3	1 ♋ 44.1	18 10.9	27 4.5	11 21.1	0 ♎ 7.2	4 24.8	24 34.7	20 45.7	22 13.3
29	2 29 54.2	5 43.6	15 54.1	15 23.6	17 22.9	28 16.4	12 5.0	0 18.9	4 31.6	24 38.3	20 47.5	22 15.6
30	2 33 50.7	6 43.5	15 50.9	28 34.2	16 26.3	29 28.5	12 48.9	0 30.5	4 38.3	24 41.8	20 49.2	22 17.9
31	2 37 47.3	7 43.5	15 47.7	11 ♌ 19.4	15 22.1	0 ♎ 40.6	13 32.9	0 42.1	4 45.0	24 45.4	20 50.9	22 20.3

LATITUDE

DAY	SID. TIME	☉	☊	☽	☿	♀	♂	♃	♄	♅	♆	♇
1	0 39 30.7	0 .0	0 .0	3 S 30.0	1 S 52.8	0 S 2.1	0 S 41.6	1 N 3.2	2 N 4.3	0 N 14.3	1 N 20.2	16 N 36.1
4	0 51 20.3	0 .0	0 .0	0 24.3	2 13.3	0 N 10.2	0 43.3	1 3.4	2 4.5	0 14.3	1 20.1	16 35.8
7	1 3 10.0	0 .0	0 .0	2 N 41.7	2 31.9	0 22.0	0 44.9	1 3.6	2 4.7	0 14.2	1 19.9	16 35.5
10	1 14 59.7	0 .0	0 .0	4 41.5	2 48.2	0 33.1	0 46.4	1 3.9	2 4.9	0 14.2	1 19.8	16 35.4
13	1 26 49.3	0 .0	0 .0	4 54.2	3 1.2	0 43.6	0 47.9	1 4.1	2 5.2	0 14.1	1 19.6	16 35.3
16	1 38 39.0	0 .0	0 .0	3 10.2	3 9.7	0 53.4	0 49.4	1 4.4	2 5.5	0 14.1	1 19.5	16 35.3
19	1 50 28.6	0 .0	0 .0	0 S 5.0	3 12.1	1 2.4	0 50.8	1 4.7	2 5.8	0 14.0	1 19.4	16 35.4
22	2 2 18.3	0 .0	0 .0	3 32.3	3 6.1	1 10.8	0 52.2	1 5.0	2 6.2	0 14.0	1 19.2	16 35.6
25	2 14 7.9	0 .0	0 .0	5 1.2	2 48.9	1 18.3	0 53.5	1 5.4	2 6.5	0 14.0	1 19.1	16 35.8
28	2 25 57.6	0 .0	0 .0	3 33.5	2 17.6	1 25.1	0 54.7	1 5.7	2 6.9	0 13.9	1 19.0	16 36.1
31	2 37 47.3	0 .0	0 .0	0 27.5	1 30.9	1 31.1	0 55.9	1 6.1	2 7.4	0 13.9	1 18.9	16 36.5

RIGHT ASCENSION

DAY	SID. TIME	☉	☊	☽	☿	♀	♂	♃	♄	♅	♆	♇
1	0 39 30.7	7 ♎ 19.1	19 ♌ 49.9	6 ♋ 38.9	28 ♎ 25.8	27 ♌ 43.9	19 ♏ 28.1	25 ♍ 25.2	1 ♎ 55.0	20 ♏ 46.7	19 ♐ 23.5	25 ♎ 44.3
2	0 43 27.2	8 13.4	19 46.8	20 35.2	29 37.9	28 51.3	20 10.7	25 37.0	2 1.8	20 49.6	19 24.6	25 46.4
3	0 47 23.8	9 7.9	19 43.6	4 ♌ 1.8	0 ♏ 49.0	29 58.6	20 53.5	25 48.8	2 8.6	20 52.6	19 25.7	25 48.5
4	0 51 20.3	10 2.4	19 40.5	16 55.2	1 59.0	1 ♍ 5.9	21 36.5	26 .5	2 15.4	20 55.7	19 26.8	25 50.5
5	0 55 16.9	10 57.0	19 37.3	29 16.0	3 7.8	2 13.2	22 19.7	26 12.3	2 22.2	20 58.7	19 27.9	25 52.6
6	0 59 13.4	11 51.7	19 34.2	11 ♍ 8.2	4 15.5	3 20.5	23 3.0	26 24.0	2 29.0	21 1.8	19 29.1	25 54.7
7	1 3 10.0	12 46.5	19 31.0	22 38.2	5 21.7	4 27.7	23 46.6	26 35.6	2 35.8	21 4.9	19 30.3	25 56.8
8	1 7 6.5	13 41.3	19 27.9	3 ♎ 53.4	6 26.4	5 34.9	24 30.3	26 47.3	2 42.5	21 8.1	19 31.6	25 58.9
9	1 11 3.1	14 36.3	19 24.7	15 2.0	7 29.5	6 42.1	25 14.1	26 58.9	2 49.3	21 11.2	19 32.9	26 1.1
10	1 14 59.7	15 31.5	19 21.6	26 12.3	8 30.7	7 49.2	25 58.2	27 10.5	2 56.0	21 14.5	19 34.2	26 3.2
11	1 18 56.2	16 26.7	19 18.4	7 ♏ 32.0	9 29.8	8 56.3	26 42.4	27 22.1	3 2.7	21 17.7	19 35.5	26 5.3
12	1 22 52.8	17 22.0	19 15.3	19 8.3	10 26.6	10 3.3	27 26.8	27 33.6	3 9.4	21 21.0	19 36.9	26 7.4
13	1 26 49.3	18 17.5	19 12.1	1 ♐ 6.7	11 20.8	11 10.3	28 11.4	27 45.1	3 16.1	21 24.3	19 38.3	26 9.6
14	1 30 45.9	19 13.1	19 9.0	13 31.1	12 12.1	12 17.3	28 56.2	27 56.6	3 22.8	21 27.6	19 39.7	26 11.7
15	1 34 42.4	20 8.8	19 5.8	26 22.5	13 .2	13 24.2	29 41.1	28 8.0	3 29.4	21 30.9	19 41.2	26 13.9
16	1 38 39.0	21 4.7	19 2.7	9 ♑ 38.9	13 44.7	14 31.1	0 ♐ 26.2	28 19.4	3 36.0	21 34.3	19 42.7	26 16.0
17	1 42 35.5	22 .7	18 59.5	23 15.5	14 25.2	15 38.0	1 11.5	28 30.7	3 42.6	21 37.7	19 44.2	26 18.2
18	1 46 32.1	22 56.9	18 56.4	7 ♒ 6.0	15 1.2	16 44.8	1 56.9	28 42.0	3 49.2	21 41.1	19 45.8	26 20.3
19	1 50 28.6	23 53.2	18 53.2	21 4.1	15 32.3	17 51.7	2 42.5	28 53.3	3 55.7	21 44.6	19 47.3	26 22.5
20	1 54 25.2	24 49.6	18 50.1	5 ♓ 5.5	15 57.9	18 58.5	3 28.3	29 4.5	4 2.2	21 48.0	19 48.9	26 24.6
21	1 58 21.7	25 46.3	18 46.9	19 9.2	16 17.6	20 5.3	4 14.3	29 15.8	4 8.8	21 51.6	19 50.6	26 26.8
22	2 2 18.3	26 43.0	18 43.8	3 ♈ 17.5	16 30.6	21 12.1	5 .4	29 26.9	4 15.2	21 55.1	19 52.3	26 29.0
23	2 6 14.8	27 39.9	18 40.6	17 34.5	16 36.4	22 18.8	5 46.6	29 38.0	4 21.7	21 58.6	19 54.0	26 31.2
24	2 10 11.4	28 37.1	18 37.5	2 ♉ 5.1	16 R 34.6	23 25.6	6 33.0	29 49.0	4 28.1	22 2.2	19 55.7	26 33.3
25	2 14 7.9	29 34.3	18 34.3	16 51.3	16 24.6	24 32.4	7 19.6	0 ♎ .0	4 34.5	22 5.8	19 57.4	26 35.5
26	2 18 4.5	0 ♏ 31.8	18 31.2	1 ♊ 50.7	16 6.1	25 39.2	8 6.3	0 11.0	4 40.8	22 9.4	19 59.2	26 37.6
27	2 22 1.1	1 29.4	18 28.0	16 54.9	15 38.8	26 46.0	8 53.1	0 21.9	4 47.1	22 13.0	20 1.0	26 39.8
28	2 25 57.6	2 27.3	18 24.8	1 ♋ 50.5	15 2.7	27 52.8	9 40.2	0 32.7	4 53.4	22 16.6	20 2.8	26 41.9
29	2 29 54.2	3 25.3	18 21.7	16 23.2	14 18.2	28 59.7	10 27.3	0 43.5	4 59.6	22 20.2	20 4.6	26 44.1
30	2 33 50.7	4 23.5	18 18.5	0 ♌ 21.3	13 25.7	0 ♎ 6.6	11 14.6	0 54.3	5 5.9	22 23.9	20 6.5	26 46.2
31	2 37 47.3	5 21.9	18 15.4	13 38.9	12 26.3	1 13.5	12 2.1	1 5.0	5 12.0	22 27.6	20 8.4	26 48.4

DECLINATION

DAY	SID. TIME	☉	☊	☽	☿	♀	♂	♃	♄	♅	♆	♇
1	0 39 30.7	3 S 9.7	0 N 16.4	19 N 47.7	13 S 40.2	12 N 59.7	18 S 57.4	3 N 7.8	1 N 25.6	18 S 19.2	21 S 44.5	7 N 9.4
4	0 51 20.3	4 19.3	0 16.4	16 4.4	15 17.6	12 1.0	19 30.8	2 52.8	1 17.0	18 21.5	21 44.9	7 6.6
7	1 3 10.0	5 28.6	0 16.5	6 6.8	16 45.8	10 58.8	20 2.8	2 37.8	1 8.4	18 23.8	21 45.2	7 3.8
10	1 14 59.7	6 37.1	0 16.5	5 S 48.9	18 3.5	9 53.4	20 33.5	2 23.0	0 59.9	18 26.2	21 45.6	7 1.1
13	1 26 49.3	7 44.9	0 16.6	15 47.4	19 8.8	8 45.0	21 2.6	2 8.4	0 51.5	18 28.6	21 46.1	6 58.5
16	1 38 39.0	8 51.8	0 16.6	19 58.0	19 59.4	7 33.9	21 30.1	1 53.8	0 43.2	18 31.1	21 46.5	6 56.0
19	1 50 28.6	9 57.4	0 16.7	15 19.7	20 31.7	6 20.3	21 56.0	1 39.5	0 35.0	18 33.6	21 46.9	6 53.5
22	2 2 18.3	11 1.8	0 16.7	2 25.8	20 41.2	5 4.6	22 20.1	1 25.2	0 26.9	18 36.2	21 47.4	6 51.1
25	2 14 7.9	12 4.7	0 16.8	12 N 20.2	20 21.7	3 47.0	22 42.4	1 11.2	0 19.0	18 38.8	21 47.8	6 48.8
28	2 25 57.6	13 5.9	0 16.8	19 52.3	19 26.8	2 27.9	23 2.7	0 57.5	0 11.3	18 41.4	21 48.3	6 46.5
31	2 37 47.3	14 5.2	0 16.9	16 56.4	17 53.6	1 7.4	23 21.1	0 43.9	0 3.7	18 44.0	21 48.7	6 44.4

NOVEMBER 1980

LONGITUDE

DAY	EPHEM. SID. TIME	☉	☊	☽	☿	♀	♂	♃	♄	♅	♆	♇
	h m s	° ′	° ′	° ′	° ′	° ′	° ′	° ′	° ′	° ′	° ′	° ′
1	2 41 43.8	8♏43.6	15♌44.6	23♌44.0	14♏11.5	1♎52.8	14♐17.0	0♎53.7	4♎51.6	24♏49.0	20♐52.7	22♎22.6
2	2 45 40.4	9 43.6	15 41.4	5♍53.1	12 R56.1	3 5.2	15 1.1	1 5.1	4 58.2	24 52.7	20 54.5	22 24.9
3	2 49 36.9	10 43.7	15 38.2	17 51.7	11 38.2	4 17.6	15 45.3	1 16.5	5 4.7	24 56.3	20 56.3	22 27.2
4	2 53 33.5	11 43.9	15 35.0	29 44.1	10 20.1	5 30.1	16 29.6	1 27.9	5 11.2	24 59.9	20 58.2	22 29.5
5	2 57 30.0	12 44.0	15 31.9	11♎34.1	9 4.2	6 42.7	17 13.9	1 39.1	5 17.6	25 3.6	21 .0	22 31.8
6	3 1 26.6	13 44.2	15 28.7	23 24.4	7 53.0	7 55.4	17 58.3	1 50.3	5 24.0	25 7.3	21 1.9	22 34.1
7	3 5 23.2	14 44.4	15 25.5	5♏17.3	6 48.6	9 8.2	18 42.8	2 1.4	5 30.4	25 10.9	21 3.8	22 36.3
8	3 9 19.7	15 44.7	15 22.3	17 14.3	5 53.1	10 21.0	19 27.3	2 12.5	5 36.7	25 14.6	21 5.7	22 38.6
9	3 13 16.3	16 45.0	15 19.2	29 16.5	5 7.8	11 33.9	20 11.9	2 23.5	5 42.9	25 18.3	21 7.7	22 40.8
10	3 17 12.8	17 45.3	15 16.0	11♐24.9	4 33.6	12 46.9	20 56.6	2 34.3	5 49.1	25 22.0	21 9.6	22 43.0
11	3 21 9.4	18 45.7	15 12.8	23 40.7	4 11.1	14 .0	21 41.4	2 45.2	5 55.3	25 25.8	21 11.7	22 45.3
12	3 25 5.9	19 46.1	15 9.6	6♑ 5.4	4 .2	15 13.2	22 26.2	2 55.9	6 1.4	25 29.5	21 13.6	22 47.5
13	3 29 2.5	20 46.4	15 6.4	18 41.4	4D .7	16 26.4	23 11.0	3 6.6	6 7.4	25 33.2	21 15.6	22 49.7
14	3 32 59.0	21 46.9	15 3.3	1♒31.2	4 12.1	17 39.6	23 55.9	3 17.1	6 13.3	25 36.9	21 17.7	22 51.8
15	3 36 55.6	22 47.3	15 .1	14 38.1	4 33.5	18 53.0	24 40.9	3 27.6	6 19.2	25 40.6	21 19.7	22 54.0
16	3 40 52.1	23 47.8	14 56.9	28 5.2	5 4.2	20 6.4	25 25.9	3 38.0	6 25.1	25 44.3	21 21.8	22 56.1
17	3 44 48.7	24 48.2	14 53.7	11♓55.2	5 43.3	21 19.8	26 11.0	3 48.3	6 30.9	25 48.1	21 23.8	22 58.3
18	3 48 45.3	25 48.7	14 50.6	26 9.2	6 29.9	22 33.3	26 56.2	3 58.5	6 36.6	25 51.8	21 25.9	23 .4
19	3 52 41.8	26 49.3	14 47.4	10♈46.1	7 23.0	23 46.9	27 41.4	4 8.6	6 42.2	25 55.5	21 28.0	23 2.4
20	3 56 38.4	27 49.8	14 44.2	25 41.6	8 22.0	25 .5	28 26.6	4 18.6	6 47.8	25 59.2	21 30.1	23 4.5
21	4 0 34.9	28 50.4	14 41.0	10♉48.3	9 26.0	26 14.2	29 11.9	4 28.5	6 53.4	26 2.9	21 32.2	23 6.5
22	4 4 31.5	29 51.0	14 37.8	25 56.5	10 34.4	27 28.0	29 57.3	4 38.3	6 58.8	26 6.7	21 34.3	23 8.6
23	4 8 28.0	0♐51.6	14 34.7	10♊55.7	11 46.5	28 41.8	0♑42.7	4 48.1	7 4.2	26 10.4	21 36.5	23 10.6
24	4 12 24.6	1 52.2	14 31.5	25 36.2	13 1.9	29 55.6	1 28.2	4 57.7	7 9.5	26 14.1	21 38.6	23 12.6
25	4 16 21.2	2 52.9	14 28.3	9♋51.4	14 20.0	1♏ 9.5	2 13.7	5 7.2	7 14.8	26 17.8	21 40.8	23 14.5
26	4 20 17.7	3 53.6	14 25.1	23 37.7	15 40.5	2 23.5	2 59.3	5 16.6	7 20.0	26 21.5	21 43.0	23 16.5
27	4 24 14.3	4 54.3	14 22.0	6♌55.2	17 3.0	3 37.5	3 44.9	5 25.9	7 25.1	26 25.2	21 45.1	23 18.4
28	4 28 10.8	5 55.0	14 18.8	19 46.1	18 27.2	4 51.6	4 30.6	5 35.1	7 30.1	26 28.9	21 47.3	23 20.3
29	4 32 7.4	6 55.8	14 15.6	2♍14.6	19 52.8	6 5.7	5 16.3	5 44.2	7 35.1	26 32.6	21 49.5	23 22.2
30	4 36 3.9	7 56.6	14 12.4	14 25.7	21 19.6	7 19.8	6 2.1	5 53.2	7 39.9	26 36.2	21 51.7	23 24.0

LATITUDE

DAY	EPHEM. SID. TIME	☉	☊	☽	☿	♀	♂	♃	♄	♅	♆	♇
1	2 41 43.8	0 .0	0 .0	0N38.1	1S12.4	1N32.9	0S56.3	1N 6.3	2N 7.5	0N13.9	1N18.9	16N36.7
4	2 53 33.5	0 .0	0 .0	3 27.0	0 11.6	1 37.8	0 57.5	1 6.7	2 8.0	0 13.8	1 18.8	16 37.2
7	3 5 23.2	0 .0	0 .0	4 54.3	0N47.9	1 41.9	0 58.5	1 7.1	2 8.5	0 13.8	1 18.7	16 37.8
10	3 17 12.8	0 .0	0 .0	4 28.7	1 35.5	1 45.1	0 59.5	1 7.5	2 9.0	0 13.8	1 18.6	16 38.5
13	3 29 2.5	0 .0	0 .0	2 12.4	2 6.4	1 47.6	1 .5	1 8.0	2 9.5	0 13.7	1 18.5	16 39.2
16	3 40 52.1	0 .0	0 .0	1S10.7	2 21.1	1 49.2	1 1.4	1 8.5	2 10.1	0 13.7	1 18.4	16 40.0
19	3 52 41.8	0 .0	0 .0	4 11.1	2 23.0	1 50.1	1 2.3	1 9.0	2 10.6	0 13.7	1 18.3	16 40.9
22	4 4 31.5	0 .0	0 .0	4 54.6	2 15.8	1 50.2	1 3.1	1 9.5	2 11.2	0 13.7	1 18.2	16 41.9
25	4 16 21.2	0 .0	0 .0	2 48.1	2 2.4	1 49.5	1 3.8	1 10.1	2 11.9	0 13.6	1 18.2	16 42.9
28	4 28 10.8	0 .0	0 .0	0N33.7	1 45.0	1 48.1	1 4.5	1 10.6	2 12.5	0 13.6	1 18.1	16 44.0

RIGHT ASCENSION

DAY	EPHEM. SID. TIME	☉	☊	☽	☿	♀	♂	♃	♄	♅	♆	♇
1	2 41 43.8	6♏20.6	18♌12.2	26♌16.2	11♏21.3	2♎20.5	12♐49.7	1♎15.6	5♎18.2	22♏31.3	20♐10.3	26♎50.5
2	2 45 40.4	7 19.4	18 9.1	8♍18.0	10 R12.5	3 27.5	13 37.5	1 26.2	5 24.3	22 35.0	20 12.2	26 52.7
3	2 49 36.9	8 18.4	18 5.9	19 52.2	9 1.8	4 34.6	14 25.4	1 36.7	5 30.3	22 38.7	20 14.1	26 54.8
4	2 53 33.5	9 17.7	18 2.7	1♎ 7.9	7 51.4	5 41.8	15 13.4	1 47.1	5 36.4	22 42.4	20 16.1	26 56.9
5	2 57 30.0	10 17.1	17 59.6	12 14.8	6 43.7	6 49.0	16 1.5	1 57.5	5 42.3	22 46.2	20 18.1	26 59.0
6	3 1 26.6	11 16.8	17 56.4	23 22.3	5 40.8	7 56.3	16 49.8	2 7.8	5 48.3	22 49.9	20 20.1	27 1.1
7	3 5 23.2	12 16.6	17 53.3	4♏39.1	4 44.6	9 3.7	17 38.2	2 18.1	5 54.1	22 53.7	20 22.2	27 3.2
8	3 9 19.7	13 16.7	17 50.1	16 12.7	3 56.7	10 11.2	18 26.8	2 28.3	5 60.0	22 57.5	20 24.2	27 5.3
9	3 13 16.3	14 17.0	17 46.9	28 8.9	3 18.4	11 18.8	19 15.4	2 38.4	6 5.8	23 1.3	20 26.3	27 7.4
10	3 17 12.8	15 17.5	17 43.8	10♐30.9	2 50.3	12 26.5	20 4.2	2 48.5	6 11.5	23 5.1	20 28.4	27 9.5
11	3 21 9.4	16 18.3	17 40.6	23 18.7	2 32.8	13 34.3	20 53.1	2 58.5	6 17.3	23 8.9	20 30.6	27 11.6
12	3 25 5.9	17 19.2	17 37.4	6♑28.8	2 25.9	14 42.3	21 42.1	3 8.4	6 22.9	23 12.7	20 32.7	27 13.7
13	3 29 2.5	18 20.3	17 34.3	19 55.0	2D29.3	15 50.3	22 31.2	3 18.2	6 28.5	23 16.5	20 34.9	27 15.7
14	3 32 59.0	19 21.7	17 31.1	3♒29.6	2 42.4	16 58.5	23 20.4	3 28.0	6 34.1	23 20.3	20 37.0	27 17.8
15	3 36 55.6	20 23.2	17 27.9	17 6.0	3 4.6	18 6.8	24 9.7	3 37.6	6 39.6	23 24.1	20 39.2	27 19.8
16	3 40 52.1	21 24.9	17 24.8	0♓40.5	3 35.2	19 15.3	24 59.1	3 47.2	6 45.0	23 28.0	20 41.4	27 21.8
17	3 44 48.7	22 26.9	17 21.6	14 13.2	4 13.4	20 24.0	25 48.5	3 56.7	6 50.4	23 31.8	20 43.6	27 23.8
18	3 48 45.3	23 29.1	17 18.4	27 48.2	4 58.4	21 32.8	26 38.1	4 6.2	6 55.7	23 35.6	20 45.9	27 25.8
19	3 52 41.8	24 31.4	17 15.3	11♈32.2	5 49.5	22 41.8	27 27.7	4 15.5	7 1.0	23 39.4	20 48.1	27 27.8
20	3 56 38.4	25 34.0	17 12.1	25 33.3	6 46.0	23 50.9	28 17.4	4 24.8	7 6.2	23 43.3	20 50.4	27 29.8
21	4 0 34.9	26 36.7	17 8.9	9♉58.1	7 47.3	25 .3	29 7.2	4 34.0	7 11.3	23 47.1	20 52.7	27 31.7
22	4 4 31.5	27 39.7	17 5.8	24 48.8	8 52.8	26 9.9	29 57.0	4 43.0	7 16.4	23 50.9	20 54.9	27 33.6
23	4 8 28.0	28 42.9	17 2.6	10♊ .6	10 2.0	27 19.6	0♑46.9	4 52.0	7 21.5	23 54.7	20 57.2	27 35.6
24	4 12 24.6	29 46.2	16 59.4	25 20.5	11 14.4	28 29.6	1 36.9	5 .9	7 26.4	23 58.5	20 59.6	27 37.5
25	4 16 21.2	0♐49.8	16 56.3	10♋30.1	12 29.8	29 39.8	2 26.9	5 9.8	7 31.3	24 2.4	21 1.9	27 39.4
26	4 20 17.7	1 53.5	16 53.1	25 10.9	13 47.6	0♏50.3	3 17.0	5 18.5	7 36.2	24 6.2	21 4.2	27 41.2
27	4 24 14.3	2 57.4	16 49.9	9♌ 9.8	15 7.7	2 .9	4 7.1	5 27.1	7 41.0	24 10.0	21 6.6	27 43.1
28	4 28 10.8	4 1.6	16 46.8	22 21.9	16 29.8	3 11.9	4 57.2	5 35.6	7 45.7	24 13.8	21 8.9	27 45.0
29	4 32 7.4	5 5.9	16 43.6	4♍49.7	17 53.6	4 23.0	5 47.4	5 44.0	7 50.3	24 17.6	21 11.3	27 46.8
30	4 36 3.9	6 10.3	16 40.4	16 40.8	19 19.0	5 34.5	6 37.7	5 52.4	7 54.9	24 21.3	21 13.7	27 48.6

DECLINATION

DAY	EPHEM. SID. TIME	☉	☊	☽	☿	♀	♂	♃	♄	♅	♆	♇
1	2 41 43.8	14S24.6	0N16.9	14N12.5	17S15.0	0N40.3	23S26.8	0N39.4	0N 1.2	18S44.9	21S48.9	6N43.7
4	2 53 33.5	15 21.2	0 16.9	3 16.2	15 6.2	0S41.4	23 42.4	0 26.2	0S 6.2	18 47.6	21 49.4	6 41.8
7	3 5 23.2	16 15.6	0 17.0	8S39.4	13 2.1	2 3.6	23 55.9	0 13.3	0 13.3	18 50.3	21 49.9	6 39.9
10	3 17 12.8	17 7.6	0 17.0	17 42.8	11 32.5	3 26.1	24 7.2	0 .6	0 20.2	18 52.9	21 50.3	6 38.1
13	3 29 2.5	17 56.9	0 17.1	19 57.1	10 52.4	4 48.5	24 16.3	0S11.8	0 27.0	18 55.6	21 50.8	6 36.5
16	3 40 52.1	18 43.3	0 17.1	13 14.6	10 59.7	6 10.4	24 23.1	0 23.8	0 33.5	18 58.3	21 51.3	6 35.0
19	3 52 41.8	19 26.8	0 17.2	0N24.6	11 43.3	7 31.5	24 27.5	0 35.5	0 39.7	19 1.0	21 51.8	6 33.6
22	4 4 31.5	20 7.1	0 17.2	14 28.0	12 50.6	8 51.4	24 29.5	0 46.8	0 45.7	19 3.6	21 52.2	6 32.3
25	4 16 21.2	20 44.1	0 17.3	20 16.8	14 11.5	10 9.9	24 29.1	0 57.7	0 51.4	19 6.3	21 52.7	6 31.2
28	4 28 10.8	21 17.7	0 17.3	15 25.3	15 38.3	11 26.6	24 26.2	1 8.3	0 56.8	19 8.9	21 53.2	6 30.1

DECEMBER 1980

LONGITUDE

DAY	EPHEM. SID. TIME	☉	☊	☽	☿	♀	♂	♃	♄	♅	♆	♇
	h m s	° ′	° ′	° ′	° ′	° ′	° ′	° ′	° ′	° ′	° ′	° ′
1	4 40 .5	8♐57.4	14♌ 9.3	26♍24.8	22♏47.4	8♏34.0	6♑48.0	6♎ 2.1	7♎44.8	26♏39.9	21♐54.0	23♎25.9
2	4 43 57.0	9 58.3	14 6.1	8♎17.0	24 16.1	9 48.3	7 33.9	6 10.9	7 49.5	26 43.6	21 56.2	23 27.7
3	4 47 53.6	10 59.1	14 2.9	20 6.9	25 45.5	11 2.6	8 19.9	6 19.5	7 54.2	26 47.3	21 58.5	23 29.5
4	4 51 50.2	12 .0	13 59.7	1♏58.4	27 15.4	12 17.0	9 5.9	6 28.0	7 58.8	26 50.9	22 .7	23 31.3
5	4 55 46.7	13 .9	13 56.5	13 54.7	28 45.9	13 31.3	9 51.9	6 36.4	8 3.2	26 54.5	22 2.9	23 33.0
6	4 59 43.3	14 1.8	13 53.4	25 58.0	0♐16.7	14 45.7	10 38.0	6 44.7	8 7.6	26 58.1	22 5.2	23 34.7
7	5 3 39.8	15 2.8	13 50.2	8♐ 9.8	1 48.0	16 .2	11 24.2	6 52.8	8 12.0	27 1.7	22 7.4	23 36.4
8	5 7 36.4	16 3.7	13 47.0	20 31.0	3 19.5	17 14.6	12 10.4	7 .8	8 16.2	27 5.3	22 9.7	23 38.1
9	5 11 32.9	17 4.7	13 43.8	3♑ 2.1	4 51.2	18 29.1	12 56.6	7 8.7	8 20.4	27 8.9	22 11.9	23 39.7
10	5 15 29.5	18 5.7	13 40.7	15 43.4	6 23.2	19 43.7	13 42.9	7 16.5	8 24.4	27 12.4	22 14.2	23 41.3
11	5 19 26.1	19 6.7	13 37.5	28 35.4	7 55.4	20 58.2	14 29.2	7 24.1	8 28.4	27 16.0	22 16.5	23 42.9
12	5 23 22.6	20 7.7	13 34.3	11♒39.0	9 27.7	22 12.8	15 15.6	7 31.6	8 32.3	27 19.5	22 18.7	23 44.4
13	5 27 19.2	21 8.7	13 31.1	24 55.4	11 .2	23 27.4	16 2.0	7 38.9	8 36.1	27 23.0	22 21.0	23 46.0
14	5 31 15.7	22 9.8	13 28.0	8♓26.2	12 32.9	24 42.0	16 48.4	7 46.1	8 39.8	27 26.4	22 23.3	23 47.4
15	5 35 12.3	23 10.8	13 24.8	22 12.6	14 5.7	25 56.7	17 34.9	7 53.2	8 43.4	27 29.9	22 25.5	23 48.9
16	5 39 8.8	24 11.8	13 21.6	6♈15.4	15 38.6	27 11.4	18 21.4	8 .1	8 46.9	27 33.3	22 27.8	23 50.3
17	5 43 5.4	25 12.9	13 18.4	20 33.9	17 11.6	28 26.1	19 8.0	8 6.9	8 50.4	27 36.8	22 30.1	23 51.7
18	5 47 2.0	26 14.0	13 15.3	5♉ 5.8	18 44.8	29 40.8	19 54.6	8 13.6	8 53.7	27 40.1	22 32.3	23 53.1
19	5 50 58.5	27 15.0	13 12.1	19 46.5	20 18.1	0♐55.5	20 41.2	8 20.1	8 56.9	27 43.5	22 34.6	23 54.5
20	5 54 55.1	28 16.1	13 8.9	4♊29.5	21 51.6	2 10.3	21 27.9	8 26.4	9 .1	27 46.9	22 36.8	23 55.8
21	5 58 51.6	29 17.2	13 5.7	19 7.3	23 25.3	3 25.0	22 14.6	8 32.6	9 3.1	27 50.2	22 39.1	23 57.1
22	6 2 48.2	0♑18.2	13 2.5	3♋32.5	24 59.1	4 39.8	23 1.4	8 38.7	9 6.1	27 53.5	22 41.3	23 58.3
23	6 6 44.7	1 19.4	12 59.4	17 38.8	26 33.2	5 54.7	23 48.2	8 44.6	9 9.0	27 56.8	22 43.6	23 59.6
24	6 10 41.3	2 20.5	12 56.2	1♌22.2	28 7.4	7 9.6	24 35.0	8 50.3	9 11.8	28 .0	22 45.9	24 .8
25	6 14 37.9	3 21.6	12 53.0	14 40.9	29 41.9	8 24.4	25 21.8	8 55.9	9 14.4	28 3.3	22 48.1	24 1.9
26	6 18 34.4	4 22.7	12 49.8	27 35.6	1♑16.6	9 39.3	26 8.7	9 1.4	9 17.0	28 6.5	22 50.3	24 3.0
27	6 22 31.0	5 23.8	12 46.7	10♍ 8.9	2 51.5	10 54.2	26 55.6	9 6.6	9 19.4	28 9.6	22 52.6	24 4.1
28	6 26 27.5	6 24.9	12 43.5	22 24.4	4 26.7	12 9.1	27 42.5	9 11.7	9 21.8	28 12.7	22 54.8	24 5.2
29	6 30 24.1	7 26.1	12 40.3	4♎27.0	6 2.2	13 24.1	28 29.5	9 16.7	9 24.1	28 15.9	22 57.0	24 6.2
30	6 34 20.7	8 27.2	12 37.1	16 21.4	7 38.0	14 39.0	29 16.5	9 21.5	9 26.2	28 18.9	22 59.2	24 7.2
31	6 38 17.2	9 28.4	12 34.0	28 12.8	9 14.1	15 54.0	0♒ 3.5	9 26.1	9 28.3	28 22.0	23 1.4	24 8.2

LATITUDE

DAY	EPHEM. SID. TIME	☉	☊	☽	☿	♀	♂	♃	♄	♅	♆	♇
1	4 40 .5	0 .0	0 .0	3N28.0	1N25.1	1N46.0	1S 5.1	1N11.2	2N13.2	0N13.6	1N18.1	16N45.2
4	4 51 50.2	0 .0	0 .0	4 57.9	1 3.9	1 43.2	1 5.6	1 11.8	2 13.9	0 13.6	1 18.0	16 46.4
7	5 3 39.8	0 .0	0 .0	4 34.1	0 42.2	1 39.8	1 6.1	1 12.5	2 14.6	0 13.6	1 18.0	16 47.7
10	5 15 29.5	0 .0	0 .0	2 16.2	0 20.4	1 35.8	1 6.6	1 13.1	2 15.4	0 13.5	1 17.9	16 49.0
13	5 27 19.2	0 .0	0 .0	1S 9.0	0S .9	1 31.2	1 6.9	1 13.8	2 16.1	0 13.5	1 17.9	16 50.4
16	5 39 8.8	0 .0	0 .0	4 10.4	0 21.5	1 26.0	1 7.2	1 14.5	2 16.9	0 13.5	1 17.9	16 51.8
19	5 50 58.5	0 .0	0 .0	5 5.2	0 41.0	1 20.4	1 7.5	1 15.2	2 17.7	0 13.5	1 17.9	16 53.3
22	6 2 48.2	0 .0	0 .0	3 10.4	0 59.2	1 14.4	1 7.7	1 15.9	2 18.5	0 13.5	1 17.9	16 54.9
25	6 14 37.9	0 .0	0 .0	0N18.1	1 15.8	1 7.9	1 7.8	1 16.6	2 19.3	0 13.5	1 17.9	16 56.4
28	6 26 27.5	0 .0	0 .0	3 25.1	1 30.7	1 1.1	1 7.8	1 17.4	2 20.1	0 13.5	1 17.9	16 58.1
31	6 38 17.2	0 .0	0 .0	5 4.1	1 43.4	0 54.0	1 7.8	1 18.1	2 21.0	0 13.5	1 17.9	16 59.7

RIGHT ASCENSION

DAY	EPHEM. SID. TIME	☉	☊	☽	☿	♀	♂	♃	♄	♅	♆	♇
1	4 40 .5	7♐15.0	16♌37.2	28♍ 5.3	20♏45.9	6♏46.1	7♑27.9	6♎ .6	7♎59.4	24♏25.1	21♐16.0	27♎50.4
2	4 43 57.0	8 19.8	16 34.1	9♎14.7	22 14.1	7 58.1	8 18.3	6 8.8	8 3.9	24 28.9	21 18.5	27 52.2
3	4 47 53.6	9 24.8	16 30.9	20 19.9	23 43.4	9 10.3	9 8.6	6 16.8	8 8.2	24 32.7	21 20.9	27 53.9
4	4 51 50.2	10 29.9	16 27.7	1♏31.6	25 13.8	10 22.8	9 59.0	6 24.7	8 12.5	24 36.4	21 23.3	27 55.7
5	4 55 46.7	11 35.2	16 24.5	12 59.2	26 45.2	11 35.6	10 49.3	6 32.5	8 16.7	24 40.2	21 25.7	27 57.4
6	4 59 43.3	12 40.6	16 21.4	24 50.5	28 17.6	12 48.6	11 39.7	6 40.1	8 20.9	24 43.9	21 28.1	27 59.1
7	5 3 39.8	13 46.2	16 18.2	7♐10.0	29 50.8	14 2.0	12 30.1	6 47.7	8 24.9	24 47.6	21 30.5	28 .8
8	5 7 36.4	14 51.8	16 15.0	19 59.0	1♐24.8	15 15.6	13 20.4	6 55.1	8 28.9	24 51.3	21 32.9	28 2.4
9	5 11 32.9	15 57.6	16 11.8	3♑13.7	2 59.6	16 29.5	14 10.8	7 2.5	8 32.8	24 55.0	21 35.4	28 4.0
10	5 15 29.5	17 3.5	16 8.7	16 46.6	4 35.1	17 43.7	15 1.2	7 9.7	8 36.7	24 58.6	21 37.8	28 5.6
11	5 19 26.1	18 9.5	16 5.5	0♒27.3	6 11.4	18 58.1	15 51.5	7 16.8	8 40.4	25 2.3	21 40.2	28 7.2
12	5 23 22.6	19 15.6	16 2.3	14 6.0	7 48.3	20 12.9	16 41.9	7 23.7	8 44.1	25 5.9	21 42.7	28 8.8
13	5 27 19.2	20 21.8	15 59.1	27 36.3	9 25.9	21 28.0	17 32.2	7 30.6	8 47.7	25 9.5	21 45.1	28 10.3
14	5 31 15.7	21 28.1	15 55.9	10♓56.5	11 4.1	22 43.3	18 22.5	7 37.3	8 51.2	25 13.1	21 47.5	28 11.8
15	5 35 12.3	22 34.4	15 52.8	24 9.8	12 42.8	23 59.0	19 12.7	7 43.9	8 54.6	25 16.6	21 50.0	28 13.3
16	5 39 8.8	23 40.8	15 49.6	7♈23.7	14 22.2	25 14.9	20 2.9	7 50.4	8 58.0	25 20.2	21 52.4	28 14.8
17	5 43 5.4	24 47.2	15 46.4	20 47.8	16 2.2	26 31.2	20 53.1	7 56.7	9 1.2	25 23.7	21 54.9	28 16.2
18	5 47 2.0	25 53.7	15 43.2	4♉32.0	17 42.6	27 47.7	21 43.3	8 2.9	9 4.4	25 27.2	21 57.3	28 17.6
19	5 50 58.5	27 .2	15 40.0	18 43.9	19 23.7	29 4.5	22 33.4	8 9.0	9 7.5	25 30.7	21 59.7	28 19.0
20	5 54 55.1	28 6.7	15 36.9	3♊25.7	21 5.2	0♐21.6	23 23.4	8 14.9	9 10.5	25 34.2	22 2.1	28 20.4
21	5 58 51.6	29 13.3	15 33.7	18 31.3	22 47.2	1 39.0	24 13.4	8 20.7	9 13.4	25 37.6	22 4.6	28 21.7
22	6 2 48.2	0♑19.9	15 30.5	3♋46.1	24 29.8	2 56.7	25 3.3	8 26.3	9 16.2	25 41.0	22 7.0	28 23.0
23	6 6 44.7	1 26.5	15 27.3	18 50.0	26 12.8	4 14.7	25 53.3	8 31.9	9 19.0	25 44.4	22 9.5	28 24.4
24	6 10 41.3	2 33.1	15 24.1	3♌23.7	27 56.2	5 32.9	26 43.1	8 37.3	9 21.6	25 47.8	22 11.9	28 25.6
25	6 14 37.9	3 39.7	15 20.9	17 14.3	29 40.1	6 51.4	27 32.9	8 42.5	9 24.2	25 51.1	22 14.3	28 26.8
26	6 18 34.4	4 46.2	15 17.8	0♍17.9	1♑24.3	8 10.1	28 22.6	8 47.6	9 26.6	25 54.4	22 16.7	28 28.0
27	6 22 31.0	5 52.7	15 14.6	12 38.0	3 9.0	9 29.1	29 12.2	8 52.6	9 29.0	25 57.7	22 19.1	28 29.2
28	6 26 27.5	6 59.2	15 11.4	24 23.1	4 54.0	10 48.3	0♒ 1.7	8 57.4	9 31.3	26 .9	22 21.5	28 30.4
29	6 30 24.1	8 5.7	15 8.2	5♎44.1	6 39.3	12 7.8	0 51.2	9 2.0	9 33.5	26 4.1	22 23.9	28 31.5
30	6 34 20.7	9 12.1	15 5.0	16 53.0	8 24.9	13 27.5	1 40.6	9 6.5	9 35.6	26 7.3	22 26.2	28 32.6
31	6 38 17.2	10 18.5	15 1.8	28 1.5	10 10.9	14 47.4	2 30.0	9 10.8	9 37.6	26 10.5	22 28.6	28 33.6

DECLINATION

DAY	EPHEM. SID. TIME	☉	☊	☽	☿	♀	♂	♃	♄	♅	♆	♇
1	4 40 .5	21S47.6	0N17.4	4N36.4	17S 5.8	12S41.1	24S20.9	1S18.4	1S 2.0	19S11.4	21S53.6	6N29.3
4	4 51 50.2	22 13.8	0 17.4	7S29.7	18 30.6	13 53.0	24 13.1	1 28.1	1 6.9	19 14.0	21 54.1	6 28.5
7	5 3 39.8	22 36.1	0 17.5	17 9.4	19 50.0	15 2.1	24 2.9	1 37.3	1 11.4	19 16.5	21 54.5	6 27.9
10	5 15 29.5	22 54.4	0 17.5	20 15.6	21 2.4	16 7.8	23 50.2	1 46.1	1 15.6	19 19.0	21 54.9	6 27.4
13	5 27 19.2	23 8.7	0 17.6	14 17.9	22 6.5	17 10.0	23 35.1	1 54.3	1 19.5	19 21.4	21 55.3	6 27.1
16	5 39 8.8	23 18.8	0 17.6	1 21.0	23 1.3	18 8.1	23 17.5	2 2.0	1 23.1	19 23.7	21 55.7	6 26.9
19	5 50 58.5	23 24.7	0 17.7	12N46.6	23 46.0	19 1.9	22 57.5	2 9.2	1 26.3	19 26.0	21 56.1	6 26.8
22	6 2 48.2	23 26.4	0 17.7	20 13.2	24 19.8	19 51.1	22 35.2	2 15.9	1 29.1	19 28.3	21 56.5	6 26.9
25	6 14 37.9	23 23.8	0 17.7	16 43.1	24 42.2	20 35.4	22 10.6	2 22.0	1 31.7	19 30.5	21 56.9	6 27.1
28	6 26 27.5	23 17.1	0 17.8	6 9.2	24 52.5	21 14.4	21 43.7	2 27.5	1 33.8	19 32.6	21 57.2	6 27.5
31	6 38 17.2	23 6.1	0 17.8	6S 6.0	24 50.3	21 47.9	21 14.6	2 32.5	1 35.5	19 34.7	21 57.6	6 28.0

JANUARY 1981

DAY	EPHEM. SID. TIME	☉	☊	☽	☿	♀	♂	♃	♄	♅	♆	♇
		LONGITUDE										
	h m s	° ′	° ′	° ′	° ′	° ′	° ′	° ′	° ′	° ′	° ′	° ′
1	6 42 13.8	10♑29.6	12♌30.8	10♏ 5.8	10♑50.5	17♐ 8.9	0♒50.5	9♎30.5	9♎30.2	28♏25.0	23♐ 3.6	24♎ 9.1
2	6 46 10.3	11 30.7	12 27.6	22 4.6	12 27.2	18 23.9	1 37.6	9 34.8	9 32.1	28 28.0	23 5.8	24 10.0
3	6 50 6.9	12 31.9	12 24.4	4♐12.7	14 4.3	19 38.9	2 24.7	9 38.9	9 33.8	28 30.9	23 7.9	24 10.8
4	6 54 3.4	13 33.1	12 21.2	16 32.7	15 41.8	20 54.0	3 11.9	9 42.8	9 35.4	28 33.8	23 10.1	24 11.6
5	6 57 60.0	14 34.2	12 18.1	29 6.1	17 19.6	22 9.0	3 59.0	9 46.6	9 37.0	28 36.7	23 12.2	24 12.4
6	7 1 56.6	15 35.4	12 14.9	11♑53.9	18 57.8	23 24.0	4 46.2	9 50.1	9 38.4	28 39.5	23 14.4	24 13.2
7	7 5 53.1	16 36.6	12 11.7	24 55.9	20 36.4	24 39.1	5 33.4	9 53.5	9 39.7	28 42.3	23 16.5	24 13.9
8	7 9 49.7	17 37.8	12 8.5	8♒11.3	22 15.3	25 54.1	6 20.7	9 56.8	9 40.9	28 45.1	23 18.6	24 14.6
9	7 13 46.2	18 38.9	12 5.4	21 39.1	23 54.6	27 9.2	7 7.9	9 59.8	9 42.0	28 47.8	23 20.7	24 15.2
10	7 17 42.8	19 40.1	12 2.2	5♓18.1	25 34.2	28 24.2	7 55.2	10 2.7	9 43.0	28 50.5	23 22.8	24 15.8
11	7 21 39.3	20 41.2	11 59.0	19 6.8	27 14.2	29 39.3	8 42.5	10 5.3	9 43.8	28 53.2	23 24.9	24 16.4
12	7 25 35.9	21 42.4	11 55.8	3♈ 4.2	28 54.5	0♑54.3	9 29.8	10 7.8	9 44.6	28 55.8	23 26.9	24 16.9
13	7 29 32.4	22 43.6	11 52.7	17 9.0	0♒35.1	2 9.5	10 17.1	10 10.2	9 45.3	28 58.4	23 29.0	24 17.5
14	7 33 29.0	23 44.7	11 49.5	1♉19.5	2 16.0	3 24.5	11 4.5	10 12.3	9 45.9	29 .9	23 31.0	24 17.9
15	7 37 25.6	24 45.8	11 46.3	15 33.8	3 57.0	4 39.6	11 51.8	10 14.2	9 46.3	29 3.4	23 33.0	24 18.3
16	7 41 22.1	25 46.9	11 43.1	29 49.3	5 38.1	5 54.7	12 39.2	10 16.0	9 46.7	29 5.9	23 35.0	24 18.7
17	7 45 18.7	26 48.0	11 39.9	14♊ 2.6	7 19.3	7 9.7	13 26.5	10 17.6	9 46.9	29 8.3	23 37.0	24 19.1
18	7 49 15.2	27 49.0	11 36.8	28 9.8	9 .4	8 24.8	14 13.9	10 18.9	9 47.0	29 10.7	23 39.0	24 19.4
19	7 53 11.8	28 50.1	11 33.6	12♋ 7.0	10 41.4	9 39.9	15 1.3	10 20.1	9 47.0	29 13.0	23 40.9	24 19.7
20	7 57 8.3	29 51.1	11 30.4	25 50.7	12 22.0	10 55.0	15 48.7	10 21.1	9 R 46.9	29 15.3	23 42.8	24 19.9
21	8 1 4.9	0♒52.2	11 27.2	9♌17.8	14 2.1	12 10.1	16 36.1	10 21.9	9 46.7	29 17.5	23 44.7	24 20.2
22	8 5 1.5	1 53.2	11 24.1	22 26.7	15 41.5	13 25.1	17 23.5	10 22.6	9 46.4	29 19.7	23 46.6	24 20.3
23	8 8 58.0	2 54.2	11 20.9	5♍17.1	17 20.0	14 40.2	18 10.9	10 23.0	9 46.0	29 21.8	23 48.5	24 20.5
24	8 12 54.6	3 55.2	11 17.7	17 49.8	18 57.2	15 55.3	18 58.4	10 23.2	9 45.5	29 24.0	23 50.3	24 20.6
25	8 16 51.1	4 56.2	11 14.5	0♎ 7.1	20 32.9	17 10.4	19 45.8	10 23.3	9 44.8	29 26.0	23 52.2	24 20.6
26	8 20 47.7	5 57.2	11 11.4	12 12.1	22 6.6	18 25.5	20 33.3	10 R 23.2	9 44.1	29 28.0	23 54.0	24 20.7
27	8 24 44.2	6 58.1	11 8.2	24 8.7	23 37.9	19 40.6	21 20.7	10 22.8	9 43.2	29 30.0	23 55.7	24 20.7
28	8 28 40.8	7 59.1	11 5.0	6♏ 1.3	25 6.2	20 55.7	22 8.2	10 22.3	9 42.3	29 31.9	23 57.5	24 R 20.6
29	8 32 37.3	9 .1	11 1.8	17 54.8	26 31.2	22 10.8	22 55.6	10 21.6	9 41.2	29 33.8	23 59.2	24 20.5
30	8 36 33.9	10 1.0	10 58.6	29 53.8	27 52.0	23 25.9	23 43.1	10 20.7	9 40.1	29 35.6	24 1.0	24 20.4
31	8 40 30.5	11 1.9	10 55.5	12♐ 2.7	29 8.0	24 41.0	24 30.6	10 19.6	9 38.8	29 37.4	24 2.6	24 20.3
		LATITUDE										
1	6 42 13.8	0 .0	0 .0	5N12.2	1S47.2	0N51.6	1S 7.8	1N18.4	2N21.2	0N13.5	1N17.9	17N .3
4	6 54 3.4	0 .0	0 .0	4 15.1	1 56.7	0 44.2	1 7.7	1 19.2	2 22.1	0 13.5	1 17.9	17 1.9
7	7 5 53.1	0 .0	0 .0	1 26.8	2 3.3	0 36.6	1 7.5	1 20.0	2 23.0	0 13.5	1 18.0	17 3.6
10	7 17 42.8	0 .0	0 .0	2S10.3	2 6.7	0 28.8	1 7.3	1 20.8	2 23.8	0 13.5	1 18.0	17 5.4
13	7 29 32.4	0 .0	0 .0	4 48.9	2 6.3	0 21.0	1 7.0	1 21.6	2 24.7	0 13.5	1 18.0	17 7.1
16	7 41 22.1	0 .0	0 .0	4 58.9	2 1.5	0 13.2	1 6.6	1 22.4	2 25.5	0 13.5	1 18.1	17 8.8
19	7 53 11.8	0 .0	0 .0	2 32.4	1 51.7	0 5.3	1 6.2	1 23.2	2 26.4	0 13.5	1 18.1	17 10.6
22	8 5 1.5	0 .0	0 .0	1N 3.8	1 36.0	0S 2.4	1 5.7	1 24.0	2 27.3	0 13.5	1 18.2	17 12.3
25	8 16 51.1	0 .0	0 .0	4 .5	1 13.8	0 10.1	1 5.2	1 24.8	2 28.1	0 13.5	1 18.2	17 14.0
28	8 28 40.8	0 .0	0 .0	5 16.1	0 44.3	0 17.6	1 4.6	1 25.6	2 28.9	0 13.5	1 18.3	17 15.8
31	8 40 30.5	0 .0	0 .0	4 31.7	0 7.3	0 24.9	1 3.9	1 26.4	2 29.8	0 13.5	1 18.4	17 17.5
		RIGHT ASCENSION										
1	6 42 13.8	11♑24.8	14♌58.6	9♏20.8	11♑57.0	16♐ 7.5	3♒19.2	9♎15.0	9♎39.5	26♏13.6	22♐30.9	28♎34.7
2	6 46 10.3	12 31.0	14 55.4	21 .8	13 43.4	17 27.9	4 8.4	9 19.1	9 41.3	26 16.7	22 33.3	28 35.7
3	6 50 6.9	13 37.1	14 52.3	3♐ 9.2	15 30.0	18 48.4	4 57.4	9 23.0	9 43.0	26 19.7	22 35.6	28 36.6
4	6 54 3.4	14 43.1	14 49.1	15 50.0	17 16.7	20 9.1	5 46.4	9 26.7	9 44.6	26 22.7	22 38.0	28 37.6
5	6 57 60.0	15 49.1	14 45.9	29 2.8	19 3.6	21 29.9	6 35.3	9 30.2	9 46.1	26 25.7	22 40.3	28 38.5
6	7 1 56.6	16 54.9	14 42.7	12♑41.5	20 50.5	22 50.9	7 24.2	9 33.6	9 47.5	26 28.6	22 42.6	28 39.4
7	7 5 53.1	18 .7	14 39.5	26 35.6	22 37.4	24 12.0	8 12.9	9 36.9	9 48.8	26 31.5	22 44.8	28 40.2
8	7 9 49.7	19 6.3	14 36.3	10♒32.4	24 24.3	25 33.2	9 1.5	9 39.9	9 50.1	26 34.4	22 47.1	28 41.0
9	7 13 46.2	20 11.7	14 33.1	24 21.2	26 11.2	26 54.6	9 50.0	9 42.8	9 51.2	26 37.2	22 49.4	28 41.8
10	7 17 42.8	21 17.1	14 29.9	7♓56.0	27 57.9	28 16.0	10 38.4	9 45.6	9 52.2	26 40.0	22 51.6	28 42.6
11	7 21 39.3	22 22.3	14 26.7	21 16.6	29 44.5	29 37.5	11 26.8	9 48.1	9 53.1	26 42.8	22 53.9	28 43.3
12	7 25 35.9	23 27.3	14 23.5	4♈28.1	1♒30.8	0♑59.1	12 15.0	9 50.5	9 53.9	26 45.5	22 56.1	28 44.0
13	7 29 32.4	24 32.2	14 20.3	17 39.0	3 16.8	2 20.7	13 3.1	9 52.8	9 54.7	26 48.2	22 58.3	28 44.7
14	7 33 29.0	25 37.0	14 17.1	0♉59.5	5 2.4	3 42.4	13 51.1	9 54.9	9 55.3	26 50.8	23 .5	28 45.3
15	7 37 25.6	26 41.5	14 13.9	14 39.0	6 47.5	5 4.0	14 39.0	9 56.8	9 55.8	26 53.4	23 2.7	28 45.9
16	7 41 22.1	27 45.9	14 10.7	28 43.9	8 32.0	6 25.7	15 26.8	9 58.5	9 56.3	26 56.0	23 4.8	28 46.5
17	7 45 18.7	28 50.1	14 7.5	13♊14.3	10 15.8	7 47.3	16 14.5	10 .0	9 56.6	26 58.5	23 6.9	28 47.0
18	7 49 15.2	29 54.1	14 4.3	28 3.1	11 58.7	9 8.9	17 2.0	10 1.4	9 56.8	27 .9	23 9.0	28 47.5
19	7 53 11.8	0♒58.0	14 1.2	12♋55.5	13 40.7	10 30.5	17 49.5	10 2.6	9 56.9	27 3.3	23 11.1	28 48.0
20	7 57 8.3	2 1.6	13 58.0	27 33.7	15 21.6	11 52.0	18 36.8	10 3.6	9 57.0	27 5.7	23 13.2	28 48.4
21	8 1 4.9	3 5.1	13 54.8	11♌41.6	17 1.1	13 13.5	19 24.1	10 4.5	9 R 56.9	27 8.0	23 15.3	28 48.8
22	8 5 1.5	4 8.4	13 51.6	25 9.6	18 39.1	14 34.9	20 11.2	10 5.2	9 56.7	27 10.3	23 17.3	28 49.2
23	8 8 58.0	5 11.5	13 48.4	7♍55.5	20 15.3	15 56.1	20 58.2	10 5.7	9 56.4	27 12.5	23 19.3	28 49.5
24	8 12 54.6	6 14.4	13 45.2	20 3.7	21 49.4	17 17.3	21 45.1	10 6.0	9 56.1	27 14.7	23 21.3	28 49.8
25	8 16 51.1	7 17.1	13 42.0	1♎42.3	23 21.1	18 38.3	22 31.9	10 6.2	9 55.6	27 16.8	23 23.3	28 50.1
26	8 20 47.7	8 19.6	13 38.8	13 1.8	24 50.1	19 59.2	23 18.6	10 R 6.1	9 55.0	27 18.9	23 25.2	28 50.3
27	8 24 44.2	9 21.9	13 35.5	24 13.3	26 16.0	21 20.0	24 5.2	10 5.9	9 54.3	27 21.0	23 27.1	28 50.5
28	8 28 40.8	10 24.1	13 32.3	5♏28.1	27 38.3	22 40.6	24 51.6	10 5.6	9 53.6	27 23.0	23 29.0	28 50.7
29	8 32 37.3	11 26.0	13 29.1	16 56.8	28 56.4	24 1.0	25 38.0	10 5.0	9 52.7	27 24.9	23 30.9	28 50.8
30	8 36 33.9	12 27.7	13 25.9	28 48.6	0♓10.0	25 21.2	26 24.3	10 4.3	9 51.8	27 26.8	23 32.7	28 50.9
31	8 40 30.5	13 29.3	13 22.7	11♐10.6	1 18.3	26 41.3	27 10.4	10 3.4	9 50.7	27 28.6	23 34.6	28 51.0
		DECLINATION										
1	6 42 13.8	23S 1.5	0N17.9	9S54.0	24S46.6	21S57.8	21S 4.4	2S34.0	1S36.1	19S35.3	21S57.7	6N28.2
4	6 54 3.4	22 45.0	0 17.9	18 31.8	24 26.9	22 23.6	20 32.4	2 38.1	1 37.3	19 37.3	21 58.0	6 28.8
7	7 5 53.1	22 24.4	0 17.9	19 43.2	23 53.5	22 43.4	19 58.4	2 41.6	1 38.2	19 39.1	21 58.3	6 29.6
10	7 17 42.8	21 59.9	0 18.0	11 35.3	23 6.2	22 57.0	19 22.3	2 44.4	1 38.7	19 40.9	21 58.6	6 30.6
13	7 29 32.4	21 31.5	0 18.0	2N17.1	22 4.8	23 4.3	18 44.4	2 46.6	1 38.8	19 42.7	21 58.8	6 31.6
16	7 41 22.1	20 59.4	0 18.1	15 14.6	20 49.5	23 5.3	18 4.6	2 48.1	1 38.6	19 44.3	21 59.1	6 32.8
19	7 53 11.8	20 23.6	0 18.1	20 21.4	19 20.7	22 59.9	17 23.1	2 49.0	1 37.9	19 45.8	21 59.3	6 34.1
22	8 5 1.5	19 44.4	0 18.2	15 2.2	17 39.6	22 48.2	16 40.0	2 49.2	1 36.9	19 47.3	21 59.5	6 35.5
25	8 16 51.1	19 1.9	0 18.2	3 37.8	15 48.4	22 30.2	15 55.2	2 48.8	1 35.5	19 48.6	21 59.7	6 37.0
28	8 28 40.8	18 16.3	0 18.3	8S33.2	13 51.0	22 6.0	15 9.0	2 47.6	1 33.7	19 49.9	21 59.9	6 38.6
31	8 40 30.5	17 27.7	0 18.3	17 44.7	11 53.4	21 35.8	14 21.4	2 45.8	1 31.6	19 51.1	22 .1	6 40.3

FEBRUARY 1981

LONGITUDE

DAY	EPHEM. SID. TIME (h m s)	☉ (° ′)	☊ (° ′)	☽ (° ′)	☿ (° ′)	♀ (° ′)	♂ (° ′)	♃ (° ′)	♄ (° ′)	♅ (° ′)	♆ (° ′)	♇ (° ′)
1	8 44 27.0	12♒ 2.8	10♌52.3	24♐25.6	0♓18.6	25♑56.1	25♒18.1	10♎18.3	9♎37.4	29♏39.1	24♐ 4.3	24♎20.1
2	8 48 23.6	13 3.8	10 49.1	7♑ 5.6	1 22.9	27 11.2	26 5.5	10 R 16.8	9 R 36.0	29 40.8	24 6.0	24 R 19.9
3	8 52 20.1	14 4.7	10 45.9	20 4.9	2 20.1	28 26.4	26 53.1	10 15.2	9 34.4	29 42.4	24 7.6	24 19.7
4	8 56 16.7	15 5.6	10 42.8	3♒23.9	3 9.5	29 41.5	27 40.5	10 13.3	9 32.8	29 44.0	24 9.2	24 19.4
5	9 0 13.2	16 6.4	10 39.6	17 2.1	3 50.2	0♒56.6	28 28.0	10 11.3	9 31.0	29 45.5	24 10.8	24 19.0
6	9 4 9.8	17 7.2	10 36.4	0♓57.2	4 21.6	2 11.7	29 15.5	10 9.1	9 29.1	29 47.0	24 12.3	24 18.7
7	9 8 6.3	18 8.1	10 33.2	15 5.5	4 43.0	3 26.7	0♓ 2.9	10 6.6	9 27.1	29 48.4	24 13.9	24 18.3
8	9 12 2.9	19 8.8	10 30.1	29 22.8	4 54.0	4 41.8	0 50.4	10 4.0	9 25.0	29 49.8	24 15.4	24 17.9
9	9 15 59.4	20 9.6	10 26.9	13♈44.4	4 54.1	5 56.9	1 37.9	10 1.2	9 22.9	29 51.1	24 16.8	24 17.4
10	9 19 56.0	21 10.3	10 23.7	28 5.8	4 R 43.5	7 12.0	2 25.3	9 58.3	9 20.6	29 52.4	24 18.3	24 16.9
11	9 23 52.6	22 11.1	10 20.5	12♉23.1	4 22.1	8 27.0	3 12.7	9 55.1	9 18.2	29 53.6	24 19.7	24 16.4
12	9 27 49.1	23 11.7	10 17.3	26 33.6	3 50.5	9 42.1	4 .2	9 51.8	9 15.8	29 54.7	24 21.1	24 15.8
13	9 31 45.7	24 12.4	10 14.2	10♊35.1	3 9.5	10 57.1	4 47.6	9 48.3	9 13.2	29 55.8	24 22.4	24 15.2
14	9 35 42.2	25 13.0	10 11.0	24 26.3	2 20.0	12 12.1	5 35.0	9 44.6	9 10.6	29 56.9	24 23.8	24 14.6
15	9 39 38.8	26 13.6	10 7.8	8♋ 6.5	1 23.5	13 27.2	6 22.4	9 40.7	9 7.8	29 57.9	24 25.1	24 13.9
16	9 43 35.3	27 14.2	10 4.6	21 34.9	0 21.5	14 42.2	7 9.7	9 36.7	9 5.0	29 58.8	24 26.3	24 13.2
17	9 47 31.9	28 14.7	10 1.5	4♌51.1	29♒15.6	15 57.2	7 57.1	9 32.5	9 2.1	29 59.7	24 27.6	24 12.5
18	9 51 28.4	29 15.2	9 58.3	17 54.6	28 7.8	17 12.2	8 44.5	9 28.1	8 59.1	0♐ .6	24 28.8	24 11.7
19	9 55 25.0	0♓15.7	9 55.1	0♍45.2	26 59.7	18 27.2	9 31.8	9 23.6	8 56.1	0 1.3	24 30.0	24 10.9
20	9 59 21.5	1 16.2	9 51.9	13 22.7	25 53.2	19 42.2	10 19.1	9 18.9	8 52.9	0 2.1	24 31.1	24 10.1
21	10 3 18.1	2 16.6	9 48.7	25 47.7	24 49.7	20 57.1	11 6.4	9 14.1	8 49.7	0 2.7	24 32.3	24 9.3
22	10 7 14.6	3 17.0	9 45.6	8♎ 1.1	23 50.5	22 12.1	11 53.7	9 9.1	8 46.4	0 3.4	24 33.4	24 8.4
23	10 11 11.2	4 17.4	9 42.4	20 4.8	22 56.6	23 27.1	12 41.0	9 4.0	8 43.0	0 3.9	24 34.4	24 7.5
24	10 15 7.8	5 17.8	9 39.2	2♏ 1.4	22 9.1	24 42.1	13 28.3	8 58.7	8 39.6	0 4.5	24 35.5	24 6.6
25	10 19 4.3	6 18.2	9 36.0	13 54.1	21 28.2	25 57.0	14 15.5	8 53.3	8 36.1	0 5.0	24 36.5	24 5.6
26	10 23 .9	7 18.5	9 32.9	25 46.8	20 54.4	27 12.0	15 2.7	8 47.7	8 32.5	0 5.4	24 37.5	24 4.6
27	10 26 57.4	8 18.8	9 29.7	7♐44.1	20 27.9	28 26.9	15 49.9	8 42.0	8 28.8	0 5.7	24 38.4	24 3.6
28	10 30 54.0	9 19.0	9 26.5	19 50.6	20 8.6	29 41.9	16 37.1	8 36.1	8 25.0	0 6.0	24 39.3	24 2.6

LATITUDE

DAY	EPHEM. SID. TIME	☉	☊	☽	☿	♀	♂	♃	♄	♅	♆	♇
1	8 44 27.0	0 .0	0 .0	3N50.3	0N 6.6	0S27.3	1S 3.7	1N26.7	2N30.0	0N13.5	1N18.4	17N18.0
4	8 56 16.7	0 .0	0 .0	0 41.6	0 52.6	0 34.2	1 2.9	1 27.5	2 30.8	0 13.5	1 18.5	17 19.7
7	9 8 6.3	0 .0	0 .0	2S58.3	1 42.4	0 40.9	1 2.1	1 28.3	2 31.6	0 13.5	1 18.6	17 21.4
10	9 19 56.0	0 .0	0 .0	5 8.8	2 31.3	0 47.2	1 1.3	1 29.0	2 32.3	0 13.5	1 18.7	17 23.0
13	9 31 45.7	0 .0	0 .0	4 35.0	3 12.2	0 53.2	1 .4	1 29.7	2 33.1	0 13.5	1 18.7	17 24.6
16	9 43 35.3	0 .0	0 .0	1 44.9	3 37.6	0 58.7	0 59.4	1 30.4	2 33.8	0 13.5	1 18.8	17 26.1
19	9 55 25.0	0 .0	0 .0	1N47.2	3 42.9	1 3.8	0 58.4	1 31.1	2 34.4	0 13.5	1 18.9	17 27.6
22	10 7 14.6	0 .0	0 .0	4 24.3	3 28.4	1 8.4	0 57.3	1 31.7	2 35.1	0 13.6	1 19.0	17 29.0
25	10 19 4.3	0 .0	0 .0	5 13.2	2 59.1	1 12.6	0 56.1	1 32.3	2 35.7	0 13.6	1 19.1	17 30.4
28	10 30 54.0	0 .0	0 .0	4 3.0	2 21.4	1 16.2	0 55.0	1 32.9	2 36.2	0 13.6	1 19.3	17 31.7

RIGHT ASCENSION

DAY	EPHEM. SID. TIME	☉	☊	☽	☿	♀	♂	♃	♄	♅	♆	♇
1	8 44 27.0	14♒30.6	13♌19.5	24♐ 6.0	2♓20.7	28♑ 1.1	27♒56.5	10♎ 2.3	9♎49.5	27♏30.4	23♐36.4	28♎51.1
2	8 48 23.6	15 31.7	13 16.3	7♑33.4	3 16.7	29 20.7	28 42.4	10 R 1.0	9 R 48.3	27 32.2	23 38.1	28 51.1
3	8 52 20.1	16 32.7	13 13.1	21 25.8	4 5.5	0♒40.1	29 28.3	9 59.6	9 47.0	27 33.9	23 39.9	28 51.1
4	8 56 16.7	17 33.4	13 9.9	5♒32.0	4 46.5	1 59.3	0♓14.0	9 58.0	9 45.5	27 35.5	23 41.7	28 R 51.0
5	9 0 13.2	18 33.9	13 6.7	19 39.8	5 19.0	3 18.2	0 59.6	9 56.3	9 44.0	27 37.1	23 43.4	28 50.9
6	9 4 9.8	19 34.2	13 3.5	3♓39.5	5 42.4	4 36.8	1 45.1	9 54.3	9 42.4	27 38.6	23 45.0	28 50.8
7	9 8 6.3	20 34.3	13 .3	17 26.1	5 56.4	5 55.2	2 30.6	9 52.2	9 40.7	27 40.1	23 46.7	28 50.7
8	9 12 2.9	21 34.3	12 57.1	1♈ .5	6 .6	7 13.3	3 15.9	9 49.9	9 38.9	27 41.5	23 48.3	28 50.5
9	9 15 59.4	22 34.0	12 53.9	14 28.0	5 R 54.8	8 31.2	4 1.1	9 47.4	9 37.0	27 42.9	23 49.9	28 50.3
10	9 19 56.0	23 33.5	12 50.7	27 56.5	5 39.0	9 48.7	4 46.2	9 44.7	9 35.0	27 44.2	23 51.4	28 50.0
11	9 23 52.6	24 32.8	12 47.5	11♉34.5	5 13.5	11 6.0	5 31.2	9 41.9	9 32.9	27 45.5	23 52.9	28 49.7
12	9 27 49.1	25 31.9	12 44.2	25 28.3	4 38.8	12 23.0	6 16.1	9 39.0	9 30.7	27 46.7	23 54.4	28 49.4
13	9 31 45.7	26 30.8	12 41.0	9♊40.2	3 55.8	13 39.7	7 1.0	9 35.8	9 28.5	27 47.8	23 55.9	28 49.1
14	9 35 42.2	27 29.5	12 37.8	24 6.7	3 5.5	14 56.1	7 45.7	9 32.5	9 26.1	27 48.9	23 57.3	28 48.7
15	9 39 38.8	28 28.1	12 34.6	8♋38.4	2 9.2	16 12.2	8 30.3	9 29.1	9 23.7	27 50.0	23 58.7	28 48.3
16	9 43 35.3	29 26.4	12 31.4	23 1.8	1 8.4	17 28.0	9 14.8	9 25.5	9 21.2	27 50.9	24 .1	28 47.9
17	9 47 31.9	0♓24.6	12 28.2	7♌ 3.4	0 4.7	18 43.6	9 59.3	9 21.7	9 18.7	27 51.9	24 1.5	28 47.4
18	9 51 28.4	1 22.6	12 25.0	20 33.4	28♒59.9	19 58.8	10 43.6	9 17.8	9 16.0	27 52.7	24 2.8	28 46.9
19	9 55 25.0	2 20.4	12 21.8	3♍27.4	27 55.5	21 13.7	11 27.9	9 13.7	9 13.3	27 53.6	24 4.0	28 46.4
20	9 59 21.5	3 18.0	12 18.5	15 46.8	26 53.0	22 28.4	12 12.1	9 9.5	9 10.5	27 54.3	24 5.3	28 45.8
21	10 3 18.1	4 15.5	12 15.3	27 37.0	25 54.0	23 42.7	12 56.2	9 5.1	9 7.6	27 55.0	24 6.5	28 45.2
22	10 7 14.6	5 12.8	12 12.1	9♎ 6.1	24 59.6	24 56.8	13 40.2	9 .6	9 4.6	27 55.7	24 7.7	28 44.6
23	10 11 11.2	6 10.0	12 8.9	20 23.4	24 10.7	26 10.6	14 24.1	8 56.0	9 1.6	27 56.3	24 8.8	28 44.0
24	10 15 7.8	7 7.1	12 5.7	1♏38.7	23 28.1	27 24.1	15 8.0	8 51.2	8 58.5	27 56.8	24 10.0	28 43.4
25	10 19 4.3	8 3.9	12 2.5	13 1.6	22 52.2	28 37.4	15 51.8	8 46.3	8 55.4	27 57.3	24 11.1	28 42.7
26	10 23 .9	9 .7	11 59.2	24 41.0	22 23.4	29 50.3	16 35.5	8 41.2	8 52.1	27 57.7	24 12.1	28 41.9
27	10 26 57.4	9 57.3	11 56.0	6♐44.3	22 1.8	1♓ 3.0	17 19.2	8 36.0	8 48.8	27 58.1	24 13.2	28 41.2
28	10 30 54.0	10 53.7	11 52.8	19 16.7	21 47.2	2 15.4	18 2.7	8 30.7	8 45.5	27 58.4	24 14.1	28 40.4

DECLINATION

DAY	EPHEM. SID. TIME	☉	☊	☽	☿	♀	♂	♃	♄	♅	♆	♇
1	8 44 27.0	17S10.9	0N18.3	19S29.2	11S15.6	21S24.4	14S 5.3	2S45.1	1S30.8	19S51.4	22S .1	6N40.9
4	8 56 16.7	16 18.6	0 18.4	18 43.3	9 31.8	20 46.4	13 15.9	2 42.4	1 28.2	19 52.5	22 .2	6 42.7
7	9 8 6.3	15 23.7	0 18.4	8 36.8	8 11.5	20 2.9	12 25.5	2 39.1	1 25.3	19 53.4	22 .4	6 44.6
10	9 19 56.0	14 26.6	0 18.5	5N59.2	7 25.8	19 14.0	11 33.9	2 35.1	1 22.1	19 54.2	22 .5	6 46.6
13	9 31 45.7	13 27.2	0 18.5	17 29.8	7 21.5	18 20.2	10 41.4	2 30.5	1 18.5	19 55.0	22 .6	6 48.6
16	9 43 35.3	12 25.9	0 18.6	19 59.0	7 57.0	17 21.6	9 48.0	2 25.3	1 14.6	19 55.6	22 .6	6 50.8
19	9 55 25.0	11 22.8	0 18.6	12 52.7	9 1.2	16 18.5	8 53.9	2 19.6	1 10.5	19 56.1	22 .7	6 52.9
22	10 7 14.6	10 18.1	0 18.6	0 52.1	10 17.7	15 11.4	7 59.0	2 13.3	1 6.1	19 56.5	22 .7	6 55.2
25	10 19 4.3	9 12.0	0 18.7	11S 1.5	11 31.1	14 .5	7 3.5	2 6.5	1 1.5	19 56.9	22 .7	6 57.4
28	10 30 54.0	8 4.6	0 18.7	19 .8	12 32.0	12 46.1	6 7.6	1 59.3	0 56.7	19 57.1	22 .7	6 59.7

MARCH 1981

LONGITUDE

DAY	EPHEM. SID. TIME	☉	☊	☽	☿	♀	♂	♃	♄	♅	♆	♇
	h m s	° ′	° ′	° ′	° ′	° ′	° ′	° ′	° ′	° ′	° ′	° ′
1	10 34 50.5	10♓19.3	9♌23.3	2♑11.3	19♒56.4	0♓56.8	17♓24.3	8♎30.1	8♎21.2	0♐ 6.3	24♐40.2	24♎ 1.5
2	10 38 47.1	11 19.5	9 20.1	14 50.5	19 R 51.1	2 11.7	18 11.4	8 R 24.0	8 R 17.4	0 6.4	24 41.1	24 R .4
3	10 42 43.6	12 19.7	9 17.0	27 52.1	19 D 52.5	3 26.6	18 58.5	8 17.8	8 13.4	0 6.6	24 41.9	23 59.3
4	10 46 40.2	13 19.8	9 13.8	11♒18.3	20 .1	4 41.5	19 45.6	8 11.4	8 9.4	0 6.7	24 42.7	23 58.1
5	10 50 36.7	14 20.0	9 10.6	25 9.8	20 13.7	5 56.4	20 32.7	8 4.9	8 5.4	0 6.7	24 43.4	23 56.9
6	10 54 33.3	15 20.1	9 7.4	9♓24.7	20 32.8	7 11.3	21 19.7	7 58.3	8 1.3	0 R 6.6	24 44.1	23 55.7
7	10 58 29.8	16 20.2	9 4.3	23 58.5	20 57.3	8 26.1	22 6.8	7 51.6	7 57.1	0 6.6	24 44.8	23 54.5
8	11 2 26.4	17 20.2	9 1.1	8♈44.7	21 26.6	9 41.0	22 53.8	7 44.8	7 52.9	0 6.4	24 45.5	23 53.2
9	11 6 22.9	18 20.2	8 57.9	23 35.3	22 .5	10 55.8	23 40.7	7 37.9	7 48.7	0 6.2	24 46.1	23 52.0
10	11 10 19.5	19 20.2	8 54.7	8♉22.0	22 38.7	12 10.7	24 27.7	7 31.0	7 44.4	0 6.0	24 46.7	23 50.7
11	11 14 16.0	20 20.1	8 51.5	22 57.9	23 20.8	13 25.5	25 14.6	7 23.9	7 40.0	0 5.7	24 47.2	23 49.3
12	11 18 12.6	21 20.0	8 48.4	7♊18.1	24 6.7	14 40.3	26 1.5	7 16.7	7 35.7	0 5.3	24 47.7	23 48.0
13	11 22 9.1	22 19.9	8 45.2	21 19.9	24 56.1	15 55.1	26 48.3	7 9.5	7 31.2	0 4.9	24 48.2	23 46.6
14	11 26 5.7	23 19.7	8 42.0	5♋ 2.7	25 48.7	17 9.8	27 35.1	7 2.2	7 26.8	0 4.5	24 48.7	23 45.2
15	11 30 2.3	24 19.5	8 38.8	18 27.4	26 44.4	18 24.6	28 21.9	6 54.8	7 22.3	0 4.0	24 49.1	23 43.8
16	11 33 58.8	25 19.3	8 35.6	1♌35.9	27 42.9	19 39.3	29 8.7	6 47.4	7 17.8	0 3.4	24 49.5	23 42.4
17	11 37 55.4	26 19.0	8 32.5	14 30.1	28 44.2	20 54.1	29 55.4	6 39.9	7 13.3	0 2.8	24 49.9	23 41.0
18	11 41 51.9	27 18.7	8 29.3	27 11.9	29 48.0	22 8.8	0♈42.1	6 32.4	7 8.7	0 2.2	24 50.2	23 39.6
19	11 45 48.5	28 18.4	8 26.1	9♍43.1	0♓54.1	23 23.5	1 28.7	6 24.8	7 4.1	0 1.4	24 50.5	23 38.1
20	11 49 45.0	29 18.0	8 22.9	22 4.8	2 2.6	24 38.1	2 15.4	6 17.2	6 59.5	0 .7	24 50.7	23 36.6
21	11 53 41.6	0♈17.5	8 19.8	4♎18.0	3 13.2	25 52.8	3 1.9	6 9.5	6 54.9	29♏59.9	24 50.9	23 35.1
22	11 57 38.1	1 17.1	8 16.6	16 23.7	4 25.8	27 7.4	3 48.5	6 1.9	6 50.2	29 59.0	24 51.1	23 33.6
23	12 1 34.7	2 16.6	8 13.4	28 23.1	5 40.5	28 22.1	4 35.0	5 54.1	6 45.5	29 58.1	24 51.3	23 32.0
24	12 5 31.2	3 16.1	8 10.2	10♏17.7	6 57.1	29 36.7	5 21.5	5 46.4	6 40.9	29 57.1	24 51.4	23 30.5
25	12 9 27.8	4 15.5	8 7.0	22 9.6	8 15.4	0♈51.3	6 7.9	5 38.7	6 36.2	29 56.1	24 51.5	23 28.9
26	12 13 24.3	5 14.9	8 3.9	4♐ 1.8	9 35.6	2 5.9	6 54.3	5 30.9	6 31.5	29 55.0	24 51.5	23 27.4
27	12 17 20.9	6 14.3	8 .7	15 57.7	10 57.5	3 20.5	7 40.7	5 23.2	6 26.8	29 53.9	24 51.5	23 25.8
28	12 21 17.4	7 13.7	7 57.5	28 1.7	12 21.0	4 35.0	8 27.0	5 15.4	6 22.1	29 52.8	24 51.5	23 24.2
29	12 25 14.0	8 13.0	7 54.3	10♑18.6	13 46.1	5 49.6	9 13.3	5 7.7	6 17.4	29 51.6	24 51.5	23 22.6
30	12 29 10.5	9 12.3	7 51.2	22 53.2	15 12.9	7 4.1	9 59.5	4 59.9	6 12.7	29 50.3	24 R 51.4	23 20.9
31	12 33 7.1	10 11.6	7 48.0	5♒50.4	16 41.2	8 18.7	10 45.7	4 52.2	6 8.1	29 49.1	24 51.3	23 19.3

LATITUDE

DAY	EPHEM. SID. TIME	☉	☊	☽	☿	♀	♂	♃	♄	♅	♆	♇
1	10 34 50.5	0 .0	0 .0	3N15.0	2N 7.9	1S17.3	0S54.5	1N33.1	2N36.4	0N13.6	1N19.3	17N32.1
4	10 46 40.2	0 .0	0 .0	0S 3.7	1 26.9	1 20.3	0 53.3	1 33.6	2 36.9	0 13.6	1 19.4	17 33.4
7	10 58 29.8	0 .0	0 .0	3 34.1	0 47.0	1 22.6	0 52.0	1 34.0	2 37.4	0 13.6	1 19.5	17 34.5
10	11 10 19.5	0 .0	0 .0	5 9.9	0 9.8	1 24.4	0 50.7	1 34.4	2 37.8	0 13.6	1 19.6	17 35.6
13	11 22 9.1	0 .0	0 .0	3 53.5	0S23.8	1 25.7	0 49.3	1 34.8	2 38.2	0 13.6	1 19.7	17 36.6
16	11 33 58.8	0 .0	0 .0	0 46.1	0 53.6	1 26.3	0 47.9	1 35.0	2 38.5	0 13.6	1 19.8	17 37.5
19	11 45 48.5	0 .0	0 .0	2N32.5	1 19.3	1 26.4	0 46.4	1 35.3	2 38.8	0 13.6	1 20.0	17 38.4
22	11 57 38.1	0 .0	0 .0	4 40.9	1 40.9	1 25.9	0 44.9	1 35.4	2 39.0	0 13.6	1 20.1	17 39.1
25	12 9 27.8	0 .0	0 .0	4 57.5	1 58.4	1 24.8	0 43.3	1 35.5	2 39.1	0 13.6	1 20.2	17 39.8
28	12 21 17.4	0 .0	0 .0	3 20.6	2 11.7	1 23.2	0 41.7	1 35.6	2 39.2	0 13.6	1 20.3	17 40.4
31	12 33 7.1	0 .0	0 .0	0 16.6	2 20.8	1 21.0	0 40.1	1 35.6	2 39.3	0 13.6	1 20.4	17 40.8

RIGHT ASCENSION

DAY	EPHEM. SID. TIME	☉	☊	☽	☿	♀	♂	♃	♄	♅	♆	♇
1	10 34 50.5	11♓50.1	11♌49.6	2♑19.6	21♒39.7	3♓27.6	18♓46.2	8♎25.3	8♎42.0	27♏58.7	24♐15.1	28♎39.6
2	10 38 47.1	12 46.3	11 46.4	15 50.6	21 R 38.9	4 39.5	19 29.7	8 R 19.7	8 R 38.6	27 58.9	24 16.0	28 R 38.8
3	10 42 43.6	13 42.4	11 43.1	29 42.8	21 D 44.6	5 51.2	20 13.0	8 14.0	8 35.0	27 59.0	24 16.9	28 37.9
4	10 46 40.2	14 38.3	11 39.9	13♒46.9	21 56.5	7 2.6	20 56.4	8 8.3	8 31.4	27 59.1	24 17.7	28 37.0
5	10 50 36.7	15 34.2	11 36.7	27 53.6	22 14.1	8 13.8	21 39.6	8 2.4	8 27.8	27 59.1	24 18.5	28 36.1
6	10 54 33.3	16 29.9	11 33.5	11♓56.5	22 37.1	9 24.8	22 22.8	7 56.4	8 24.1	27 59.1	24 19.3	28 35.2
7	10 58 29.8	17 25.6	11 30.3	25 53.3	23 5.2	10 35.5	23 6.0	7 50.3	8 20.3	27 R 59.0	24 20.0	28 34.2
8	11 2 26.4	18 21.1	11 27.0	9♈46.1	23 38.0	11 46.1	23 49.0	7 44.1	8 16.5	27 58.9	24 20.8	28 33.2
9	11 6 22.9	19 16.6	11 23.8	23 39.8	24 15.2	12 56.4	24 32.1	7 37.8	8 12.6	27 58.7	24 21.4	28 32.2
10	11 10 19.5	20 11.9	11 20.6	7♉40.4	24 56.4	14 6.5	25 15.0	7 31.4	8 8.7	27 58.4	24 22.1	28 31.2
11	11 14 16.0	21 7.2	11 17.4	21 52.6	25 41.4	15 16.4	25 58.0	7 25.0	8 4.8	27 58.1	24 22.6	28 30.2
12	11 18 12.6	22 2.4	11 14.1	6♊17.1	26 29.8	16 26.2	26 40.9	7 18.4	8 .8	27 57.7	24 23.2	28 29.1
13	11 22 9.1	22 57.5	11 10.9	20 50.0	27 21.4	17 35.8	27 23.7	7 11.8	7 56.8	27 57.3	24 23.7	28 28.0
14	11 26 5.7	23 52.5	11 7.7	5♋22.5	28 15.9	18 45.2	28 6.5	7 5.1	7 52.8	27 56.8	24 24.2	28 26.9
15	11 30 2.3	24 47.5	11 4.4	19 42.8	29 13.2	19 54.5	28 49.2	6 58.4	7 48.7	27 56.3	24 24.7	28 25.7
16	11 33 58.8	25 42.3	11 1.2	3♌39.7	0♓13.0	21 3.6	29 31.9	6 51.6	7 44.6	27 55.7	24 25.1	28 24.6
17	11 37 55.4	26 37.2	10 58.0	17 5.2	1 15.2	22 12.6	0♈14.6	6 44.8	7 40.5	27 55.1	24 25.5	28 23.4
18	11 41 51.9	27 32.0	10 54.8	29 56.3	2 19.5	23 21.5	0 57.3	6 37.9	7 36.3	27 54.4	24 25.9	28 22.2
19	11 45 48.5	28 26.7	10 51.5	12♍14.6	3 25.8	24 30.2	1 39.9	6 31.0	7 32.1	27 53.7	24 26.2	28 21.0
20	11 49 45.0	29 21.4	10 48.3	24 5.3	4 34.0	25 38.8	2 22.4	6 24.0	7 27.9	27 52.9	24 26.4	28 19.8
21	11 53 41.6	0♈16.1	10 45.1	5♎35.7	5 43.9	26 47.4	3 5.0	6 17.0	7 23.7	27 52.0	24 26.7	28 18.5
22	11 57 38.1	1 10.7	10 41.8	16 54.3	6 55.5	27 55.8	3 47.5	6 10.0	7 19.5	27 51.1	24 26.9	28 17.3
23	12 1 34.7	2 5.3	10 38.6	28 9.6	8 8.6	29 4.2	4 30.0	6 2.9	7 15.2	27 50.2	24 27.0	28 16.0
24	12 5 31.2	2 59.9	10 35.4	9♏30.0	9 23.2	0♈12.5	5 12.4	5 55.8	7 11.0	27 49.2	24 27.2	28 14.7
25	12 9 27.8	3 54.5	10 32.2	21 3.4	10 39.1	1 20.8	5 54.9	5 48.7	7 6.7	27 48.1	24 27.2	28 13.3
26	12 13 24.3	4 49.1	10 28.9	2♐56.0	11 56.3	2 29.0	6 37.3	5 41.6	7 2.4	27 47.0	24 27.3	28 12.0
27	12 17 20.9	5 43.6	10 25.7	15 12.3	13 14.8	3 37.2	7 19.7	5 34.5	6 58.1	27 45.9	24 27.3	28 10.7
28	12 21 17.4	6 38.2	10 22.5	27 54.3	14 34.5	4 45.4	8 2.1	5 27.4	6 53.8	27 44.7	24 27.3	28 9.3
29	12 25 14.0	7 32.8	10 19.2	11♑ .7	15 55.3	5 53.6	8 44.5	5 20.3	6 49.5	27 43.4	24 27.3	28 7.9
30	12 29 10.5	8 27.4	10 16.0	24 27.5	17 17.2	7 1.8	9 26.9	5 13.2	6 45.2	27 42.1	24 R 27.2	28 6.5
31	12 33 7.1	9 22.0	10 12.7	8♒ 8.4	18 40.2	8 10.0	10 9.3	5 6.1	6 40.9	27 40.8	24 27.0	28 5.1

DECLINATION

DAY	EPHEM. SID. TIME	☉	☊	☽	☿	♀	♂	♃	♄	♅	♆	♇
1	10 34 50.5	7S41.9	0N18.7	20S10.4	12S48.6	12S20.6	5S48.8	1S56.7	0S55.0	19S57.1	22S .7	7N .5
4	10 46 40.2	6 33.1	0 18.8	17 26.8	13 26.4	11 2.1	4 52.3	1 48.9	0 49.9	19 57.2	22 .7	7 2.8
7	10 58 29.8	5 23.5	0 18.8	5 40.1	13 46.2	9 41.0	3 55.5	1 40.7	0 44.6	19 57.2	22 .7	7 5.1
10	11 10 19.5	4 13.3	0 18.9	9N23.9	13 48.8	8 17.6	2 58.5	1 32.2	0 39.2	19 57.0	22 .7	7 7.5
13	11 22 9.1	3 2.6	0 18.9	19 16.4	13 35.1	6 52.2	2 1.4	1 23.4	0 33.7	19 56.8	22 .6	7 9.8
16	11 33 58.8	1 51.6	0 19.0	19 3.4	13 6.4	5 25.2	1 4.3	1 14.4	0 28.1	19 56.5	22 .6	7 12.2
19	11 45 48.5	0 40.4	0 19.0	10 16.7	12 23.4	3 56.8	0 7.3	1 5.3	0 22.5	19 56.1	22 .5	7 14.4
22	11 57 38.1	0N30.7	0 19.1	2S 7.4	11 27.1	2 27.4	0N49.6	0 56.1	0 16.8	19 55.5	22 .4	7 16.7
25	12 9 27.8	1 41.6	0 19.1	13 30.8	10 18.2	0 57.4	1 46.3	0 46.8	0 11.1	19 54.9	22 .3	7 19.0
28	12 21 17.4	2 52.1	0 19.1	20 4.9	8 57.3	0N32.9	2 42.7	0 37.6	0 5.5	19 54.2	22 .2	7 21.2
31	12 33 7.1	4 2.2	0 19.2	18 32.7	7 25.0	2 3.3	3 38.7	0 28.4	0N .1	19 53.4	22 .1	7 23.3

APRIL 1981

LONGITUDE

DAY	EPHEM. SID. TIME	☉	☊	☽	☿	♀	♂	♃	♄	♅	♆	♇
	h m s	° ′	° ′	° ′	° ′	° ′	° ′	° ′	° ′	° ′	° ′	° ′
1	12 37 3.6	11♈10.8	7♌44.8	19♒14.1	18♓11.0	9♈33.2	11♈31.9	4♎44.5	6♎ 3.4	29♏47.7	24♐51.1	23♎17.7
2	12 41 .2	12 10.0	7 41.6	3♓ 6.4	19 42.4	10 47.7	12 18.1	4 R 36.9	5 R 58.7	29 R 46.3	24 R 50.9	23 R 16.0
3	12 44 56.7	13 9.2	7 38.4	17 27.2	21 15.3	12 2.2	13 4.2	4 29.2	5 54.1	29 44.9	24 50.7	23 14.4
4	12 48 53.3	14 8.3	7 35.3	2♈13.0	22 49.6	13 16.6	13 50.2	4 21.7	5 49.4	29 43.4	24 50.5	23 12.7
5	12 52 49.8	15 7.4	7 32.1	17 16.8	24 25.5	14 31.1	14 36.2	4 14.1	5 44.8	29 41.9	24 50.2	23 11.0
6	12 56 46.4	16 6.5	7 28.9	2♉29.0	26 2.8	15 45.5	15 22.2	4 6.6	5 40.3	29 40.4	24 49.9	23 9.3
7	13 0 43.0	17 5.6	7 25.7	17 38.7	27 41.6	16 60.0	16 8.2	3 59.3	5 35.7	29 38.8	24 49.6	23 7.7
8	13 4 39.5	18 4.6	7 22.6	2♊35.8	29 21.9	18 14.4	16 54.1	3 51.9	5 31.2	29 37.2	24 49.2	23 6.0
9	13 8 36.1	19 3.6	7 19.4	17 12.7	1♈ 3.7	19 28.8	17 39.9	3 44.6	5 26.7	29 35.5	24 48.8	23 4.3
10	13 12 32.6	20 2.5	7 16.2	1♋25.0	2 46.9	20 43.1	18 25.7	3 37.4	5 22.2	29 33.8	24 48.4	23 2.6
11	13 16 29.2	21 1.4	7 13.0	15 11.6	4 31.7	21 57.5	19 11.4	3 30.2	5 17.8	29 32.1	24 47.9	23 1.0
12	13 20 25.7	22 .2	7 9.8	28 33.8	6 18.0	23 11.8	19 57.1	3 23.2	5 13.4	29 30.3	24 47.4	22 59.3
13	13 24 22.3	22 59.1	7 6.7	11♌34.3	8 5.8	24 26.1	20 42.8	3 16.2	5 9.0	29 28.5	24 46.8	22 57.6
14	13 28 18.8	23 57.8	7 3.5	24 16.9	9 55.1	25 40.4	21 28.4	3 9.3	5 4.7	29 26.6	24 46.3	22 55.9
15	13 32 15.4	24 56.6	7 .3	6♍45.2	11 46.0	26 54.7	22 14.0	3 2.6	5 .4	29 24.7	24 45.7	22 54.2
16	13 36 11.9	25 55.3	6 57.1	19 2.4	13 38.4	28 8.9	22 59.5	2 55.9	4 56.2	29 22.8	24 45.1	22 52.5
17	13 40 8.5	26 53.9	6 53.9	1♎11.2	15 32.3	29 23.1	23 44.9	2 49.3	4 52.0	29 20.8	24 44.4	22 50.8
18	13 44 5.0	27 52.6	6 50.8	13 13.9	17 27.9	0♉37.3	24 30.3	2 42.8	4 47.9	29 18.8	24 43.7	22 49.1
19	13 48 1.6	28 51.2	6 47.6	25 11.9	19 24.9	1 51.5	25 15.7	2 36.5	4 43.8	29 16.8	24 43.0	22 47.4
20	13 51 58.1	29 49.8	6 44.4	7♏ 6.7	21 23.5	3 5.7	26 1.0	2 30.2	4 39.8	29 14.8	24 42.3	22 45.8
21	13 55 54.7	0♉48.3	6 41.2	18 59.4	23 23.5	4 19.9	26 46.3	2 24.1	4 35.8	29 12.7	24 41.5	22 44.1
22	13 59 51.2	1 46.8	6 38.1	0♐51.7	25 25.0	5 34.0	27 31.5	2 18.1	4 31.9	29 10.6	24 40.7	22 42.4
23	14 3 47.8	2 45.3	6 34.9	12 45.3	27 27.9	6 48.1	28 16.7	2 12.2	4 28.1	29 8.5	24 39.9	22 40.7
24	14 7 44.4	3 43.7	6 31.7	24 43.0	29 32.1	8 2.3	29 1.8	2 6.5	4 24.3	29 6.3	24 39.0	22 39.1
25	14 11 40.9	4 42.1	6 28.5	6♑47.9	1♉37.5	9 16.4	29 46.9	2 .9	4 20.6	29 4.1	24 38.2	22 37.4
26	14 15 37.5	5 40.5	6 25.4	19 4.2	3 44.0	10 30.4	0♉31.9	1 55.4	4 16.9	29 1.9	24 37.3	22 35.8
27	14 19 34.0	6 38.9	6 22.2	1♒36.2	5 51.5	11 44.5	1 16.9	1 50.1	4 13.3	28 59.7	24 36.3	22 34.2
28	14 23 30.6	7 37.3	6 19.0	14 28.8	7 59.8	12 58.6	2 1.9	1 45.0	4 9.8	28 57.4	24 35.4	22 32.6
29	14 27 27.1	8 35.6	6 15.8	27 46.1	10 8.7	14 12.6	2 46.8	1 39.9	4 6.4	28 55.2	24 34.4	22 31.0
30	14 31 23.7	9 33.9	6 12.6	11♓31.6	12 17.9	15 26.7	3 31.6	1 35.0	4 3.0	28 52.9	24 33.4	22 29.4

LATITUDE

DAY	EPHEM. SID. TIME	☉	☊	☽	☿	♀	♂	♃	♄	♅	♆	♇
1	12 37 3.6	0 .0	0 .0	0S54.6	2S22.9	1S20.2	0S39.6	1N35.5	2N39.3	0N13.6	1N20.5	17N41.0
4	12 48 53.3	0 .0	0 .0	4 3.9	2 26.3	1 17.3	0 37.9	1 35.4	2 39.3	0 13.6	1 20.6	17 41.3
7	13 0 43.0	0 .0	0 .0	4 58.3	2 25.3	1 13.9	0 36.3	1 35.3	2 39.2	0 13.6	1 20.7	17 41.6
10	13 12 32.6	0 .0	0 .0	3 .7	2 19.8	1 9.9	0 34.5	1 35.1	2 39.1	0 13.6	1 20.8	17 41.7
13	13 24 22.3	0 .0	0 .0	0N19.5	2 9.8	1 5.6	0 32.8	1 34.8	2 39.0	0 13.6	1 20.9	17 41.8
16	13 36 11.9	0 .0	0 .0	3 19.2	1 55.3	1 .7	0 31.0	1 34.5	2 38.8	0 13.6	1 21.0	17 41.8
19	13 48 1.6	0 .0	0 .0	4 53.2	1 36.2	0 55.5	0 29.2	1 34.1	2 38.5	0 13.6	1 21.1	17 41.6
22	13 59 51.2	0 .0	0 .0	4 33.5	1 12.9	0 49.9	0 27.4	1 33.7	2 38.2	0 13.6	1 21.2	17 41.4
25	14 11 40.9	0 .0	0 .0	2 28.1	0 45.8	0 43.9	0 25.6	1 33.2	2 37.9	0 13.6	1 21.3	17 41.1
28	14 23 30.6	0 .0	0 .0	0S44.2	0 15.8	0 37.6	0 23.7	1 32.7	2 37.5	0 13.6	1 21.3	17 40.7

RIGHT ASCENSION

DAY	EPHEM. SID. TIME	☉	☊	☽	☿	♀	♂	♃	♄	♅	♆	♇
1	12 37 3.6	10♈16.7	10♌ 9.5	21♒57.1	20♓ 4.3	9♈18.2	10♈51.7	4♎59.0	6♎36.6	27♏39.4	24♐26.9	28♎ 3.7
2	12 41 .2	11 11.3	10 6.3	5♓49.0	21 29.4	10 26.4	11 34.1	4 R 52.0	6 R 32.4	27 R 38.0	24 R 26.7	28 R 2.3
3	12 44 56.7	12 6.0	10 3.0	19 42.3	22 55.6	11 34.7	12 16.4	4 45.0	6 28.1	27 36.5	24 26.5	28 .9
4	12 48 53.3	13 .8	9 59.8	3♈39.0	24 22.8	12 43.1	12 58.8	4 38.0	6 23.9	27 35.0	24 26.2	27 59.4
5	12 52 49.8	13 55.6	9 56.6	17 43.6	25 51.1	13 51.5	13 41.2	4 31.1	6 19.6	27 33.4	24 25.9	27 57.9
6	12 56 46.4	14 50.4	9 53.3	2♉ 1.5	27 20.4	14 59.9	14 23.5	4 24.2	6 15.4	27 31.8	24 25.6	27 56.5
7	13 0 43.0	15 45.3	9 50.1	16 36.4	28 50.9	16 8.5	15 6.0	4 17.4	6 11.3	27 30.2	24 25.2	27 55.1
8	13 4 39.5	16 40.3	9 46.8	1♊27.9	0♈22.3	17 17.2	15 48.4	4 10.6	6 7.1	27 28.5	24 24.8	27 53.6
9	13 8 36.1	17 35.3	9 43.6	16 30.0	1 55.0	18 25.9	16 30.7	4 3.9	6 2.9	27 26.8	24 24.4	27 52.1
10	13 12 32.6	18 30.3	9 40.4	1♋30.6	3 28.7	19 34.8	17 13.1	3 57.2	5 58.8	27 25.0	24 23.9	27 50.6
11	13 16 29.2	19 25.4	9 37.1	16 15.2	5 3.7	20 43.8	17 55.6	3 50.7	5 54.7	27 23.2	24 23.4	27 49.1
12	13 20 25.7	20 20.6	9 33.9	0♌30.3	6 39.9	21 52.9	18 38.0	3 44.1	5 50.7	27 21.3	24 22.9	27 47.6
13	13 24 22.3	21 15.8	9 30.6	14 7.6	8 17.4	23 2.1	19 20.4	3 37.7	5 46.7	27 19.4	24 22.3	27 46.1
14	13 28 18.8	22 11.1	9 27.4	27 4.6	9 56.2	24 11.5	20 2.9	3 31.4	5 42.7	27 17.5	24 21.7	27 44.6
15	13 32 15.4	23 6.5	9 24.2	9♍24.6	11 36.3	25 21.0	20 45.3	3 25.1	5 38.7	27 15.5	24 21.1	27 43.0
16	13 36 11.9	24 2.0	9 20.9	21 14.1	13 17.9	26 30.8	21 27.8	3 18.9	5 34.8	27 13.5	24 20.4	27 41.5
17	13 40 8.5	24 57.6	9 17.7	2♎41.8	15 1.0	27 40.6	22 10.3	3 12.8	5 30.9	27 11.5	24 19.7	27 40.0
18	13 44 5.0	25 53.2	9 14.4	13 56.8	16 45.6	28 50.7	22 52.8	3 6.9	5 27.1	27 9.4	24 18.9	27 38.5
19	13 48 1.6	26 49.0	9 11.2	25 8.4	18 31.8	0♉ 1.0	23 35.4	3 1.0	5 23.3	27 7.3	24 18.2	27 37.0
20	13 51 58.1	27 44.8	9 7.9	6♏25.1	20 19.6	1 11.4	24 18.0	2 55.2	5 19.6	27 5.2	24 17.4	27 35.4
21	13 55 54.7	28 40.8	9 4.7	17 54.2	22 9.1	2 22.1	25 .6	2 49.5	5 15.9	27 3.1	24 16.6	27 33.9
22	13 59 51.2	29 36.9	9 1.4	29 41.6	24 .3	3 33.0	25 43.2	2 44.0	5 12.3	27 .9	24 15.7	27 32.4
23	14 3 47.8	0♉33.0	8 58.2	11♐51.0	25 53.2	4 44.1	26 25.9	2 38.5	5 8.7	26 58.6	24 14.8	27 30.9
24	14 7 44.4	1 29.4	8 55.0	24 23.1	27 47.8	5 55.5	27 8.6	2 33.2	5 5.2	26 56.4	24 13.9	27 29.4
25	14 11 40.9	2 25.8	8 51.7	7♑16.1	29 44.2	7 7.1	27 51.3	2 28.0	5 1.8	26 54.1	24 13.0	27 27.8
26	14 15 37.5	3 22.3	8 48.5	20 25.4	1♉42.2	8 18.9	28 34.0	2 22.9	4 58.3	26 51.8	24 12.0	27 26.3
27	14 19 34.0	4 19.0	8 45.2	3♒45.2	3 41.8	9 31.0	29 16.8	2 18.0	4 55.0	26 49.5	24 11.0	27 24.8
28	14 23 30.6	5 15.8	8 42.0	17 10.2	5 43.1	10 43.3	29 59.7	2 13.2	4 51.8	26 47.2	24 10.0	27 23.3
29	14 27 27.1	6 12.8	8 38.7	0♓36.8	7 45.7	11 55.9	0♉42.6	2 8.5	4 48.5	26 44.9	24 8.9	27 21.8
30	14 31 23.7	7 9.8	8 35.5	14 5.3	9 49.6	13 8.8	1 25.5	2 3.9	4 45.4	26 42.5	24 7.9	27 20.3

DECLINATION

DAY	EPHEM. SID. TIME	☉	☊	☽	☿	♀	♂	♃	♄	♅	♆	♇
1	12 37 3.6	4N25.4	0N19.2	15S55.2	6S51.8	2N33.4	3N57.2	0S25.4	0N 2.0	19S53.1	22S .0	7N24.0
4	12 48 53.3	5 34.6	0 19.2	2 50.9	5 5.2	4 3.3	4 52.6	0 16.4	0 7.5	19 52.2	21 59.9	7 26.1
7	13 0 43.0	6 42.9	0 19.3	12N19.1	3 8.3	5 32.5	5 47.4	0 7.7	0 12.8	19 51.3	21 59.7	7 28.1
10	13 12 32.6	7 50.1	0 19.3	20 25.3	1 1.9	7 .6	6 41.5	0N .8	0 18.1	19 50.2	21 59.6	7 30.0
13	13 24 22.3	8 56.2	0 19.4	17 37.5	1N13.4	8 27.3	7 34.9	0 9.0	0 23.2	19 49.0	21 59.4	7 31.9
16	13 36 11.9	10 .9	0 19.4	7 23.4	3 36.7	9 52.2	8 27.5	0 16.8	0 28.0	19 47.8	21 59.3	7 33.6
19	13 48 1.6	11 4.0	0 19.5	5S11.9	6 6.8	11 15.1	9 19.2	0 24.1	0 32.7	19 46.6	21 59.1	7 35.3
22	13 59 51.2	12 5.6	0 19.5	15 52.2	8 41.9	12 35.6	10 10.0	0 31.0	0 37.2	19 45.2	21 58.9	7 36.8
25	14 11 40.9	13 5.4	0 19.5	20 48.0	11 19.4	13 53.4	10 59.8	0 37.4	0 41.3	19 43.8	21 58.7	7 38.3
28	14 23 30.6	14 3.2	0 19.6	17 11.6	13 55.6	15 8.2	11 48.5	0 43.3	0 45.2	19 42.4	21 58.5	7 39.6

MAY 1981

DAY	EPHEM. SID. TIME	☉	☊	☽	☿	♀	♂	♃	♄	♅	♆	♇
	h m s	° ′	° ′	° ′	° ′	° ′	° ′	° ′	° ′	° ′	° ′	° ′
		LONGITUDE										
1	14 35 20.2	10♉32.2	6♌ 9.5	25♓46.5	14♉27.2	16♉40.7	4♉16.4	1♎30.3	3♎59.7	28♏50.5	24♐32.4	22♎27.8
2	14 39 16.8	11 30.4	6 6.3	10♈28.8	16 36.4	17 54.7	5 1.2	1R25.7	3R56.4	28R48.2	24R31.3	22R26.2
3	14 43 13.3	12 28.6	6 3.1	25 33.3	18 45.1	19 8.7	5 45.8	1 21.3	3 53.3	28 45.8	24 30.3	22 24.6
4	14 47 9.9	13 26.8	5 59.9	10♉50.8	20 53.1	20 22.6	6 30.5	1 17.0	3 50.2	28 43.4	24 29.2	22 23.1
5	14 51 6.4	14 25.0	5 56.8	26 10.1	23 .1	21 36.6	7 15.1	1 12.9	3 47.2	28 41.0	24 28.0	22 21.5
6	14 55 3.0	15 23.1	5 53.6	11♊19.8	25 5.8	22 50.5	7 59.6	1 9.0	3 44.3	28 38.6	24 26.9	22 20.0
7	14 58 59.6	16 21.2	5 50.4	26 10.1	27 9.8	24 4.4	8 44.1	1 5.2	3 41.5	28 36.2	24 25.7	22 18.5
8	15 2 56.1	17 19.3	5 47.2	10♋34.7	29 11.9	25 18.3	9 28.5	1 1.6	3 38.7	28 33.8	24 24.5	22 17.0
9	15 6 52.7	18 17.3	5 44.0	24 30.8	1♊11.9	26 32.2	10 12.9	0 58.2	3 36.1	28 31.3	24 23.3	22 15.5
10	15 10 49.2	19 15.3	5 40.9	7♌58.7	3 9.6	27 46.1	10 57.2	0 54.9	3 33.5	28 28.9	24 22.0	22 14.0
11	15 14 45.8	20 13.3	5 37.7	21 1.2	5 4.6	28 59.9	11 41.5	0 51.9	3 31.0	28 26.4	24 20.8	22 12.6
12	15 18 42.3	21 11.2	5 34.5	3♍42.1	6 56.9	0♊13.7	12 25.7	0 48.9	3 28.6	28 23.9	24 19.5	22 11.2
13	15 22 38.9	22 9.1	5 31.3	16 5.8	8 46.3	1 27.5	13 9.9	0 46.2	3 26.3	28 21.4	24 18.2	22 9.8
14	15 26 35.4	23 7.0	5 28.2	28 16.7	10 32.7	2 41.3	13 54.0	0 43.6	3 24.1	28 18.9	24 16.9	22 8.4
15	15 30 32.0	24 4.9	5 25.0	10♎18.7	12 15.9	3 55.1	14 38.0	0 41.3	3 22.0	28 16.4	24 15.6	22 7.0
16	15 34 28.6	25 2.7	5 21.8	22 15.0	13 55.9	5 8.8	15 22.0	0 39.1	3 19.9	28 13.9	24 14.2	22 5.6
17	15 38 25.1	26 .5	5 18.6	4♏ 8.3	15 32.6	6 22.6	16 5.9	0 37.0	3 18.0	28 11.4	24 12.8	22 4.3
18	15 42 21.7	26 58.3	5 15.4	16 .7	17 5.9	7 36.3	16 49.8	0 35.2	3 16.1	28 8.9	24 11.5	22 3.0
19	15 46 18.2	27 56.1	5 12.3	27 53.7	18 35.8	8 50.0	17 33.7	0 33.6	3 14.4	28 6.5	24 10.1	22 1.7
20	15 50 14.8	28 53.8	5 9.1	9♐48.8	20 2.2	10 3.7	18 17.5	0 32.1	3 12.8	28 4.0	24 8.7	22 .5
21	15 54 11.3	29 51.5	5 5.9	21 47.5	21 25.1	11 17.4	19 1.2	0 30.8	3 11.2	28 1.5	24 7.3	21 59.2
22	15 58 7.9	0♊49.2	5 2.7	3♑51.6	22 44.4	12 31.0	19 44.9	0 29.6	3 9.8	27 59.0	24 5.8	21 58.0
23	16 2 4.4	1 46.8	4 59.6	16 3.4	24 .0	13 44.7	20 28.5	0 28.7	3 8.4	27 56.5	24 4.3	21 56.8
24	16 6 1.0	2 44.5	4 56.4	28 25.6	25 12.0	14 58.3	21 12.1	0 27.9	3 7.1	27 54.0	24 2.9	21 55.6
25	16 9 57.6	3 42.1	4 53.2	11♒ 1.6	26 20.3	16 11.9	21 55.6	0 27.3	3 6.0	27 51.5	24 1.4	21 54.5
26	16 13 54.1	4 39.7	4 50.0	23 55.2	27 24.8	17 25.5	22 39.1	0 26.9	3 4.9	27 49.0	23 59.9	21 53.3
27	16 17 50.7	5 37.3	4 46.9	7♓ 9.9	28 25.5	18 39.1	23 22.5	0 26.7	3 3.9	27 46.5	23 58.4	21 52.2
28	16 21 47.2	6 34.9	4 43.7	20 48.8	29 22.2	19 52.6	24 5.8	0 26.7	3 3.0	27 44.0	23 56.9	21 51.2
29	16 25 43.8	7 32.5	4 40.5	4♈53.6	0♋15.0	21 6.2	24 49.1	0D26.8	3 2.3	27 41.6	23 55.3	21 50.1
30	16 29 40.3	8 30.0	4 37.3	19 23.5	1 3.7	22 19.7	25 32.4	0 27.1	3 1.6	27 39.1	23 53.8	21 49.1
31	16 33 36.9	9 27.6	4 34.1	4♉15.0	1 48.3	23 33.3	26 15.6	0 27.6	3 1.0	27 36.7	23 52.2	21 48.1
		LATITUDE										
1	14 35 20.2	0 .0	0 .0	3S50.4	0N16.0	0S31.1	0S21.9	1N32.1	2N37.0	0N13.5	1N21.4	17N40.1
4	14 47 9.9	0 .0	0 .0	4 59.2	0 47.6	0 24.3	0 20.0	1 31.6	2 36.6	0 13.5	1 21.5	17 39.5
7	14 58 59.6	0 .0	0 .0	3 9.6	1 17.0	0 17.3	0 18.1	1 30.9	2 36.1	0 13.5	1 21.6	17 38.8
10	15 10 49.2	0 .0	0 .0	0N16.2	1 42.4	0 10.2	0 16.2	1 30.3	2 35.6	0 13.5	1 21.6	17 38.1
13	15 22 38.9	0 .0	0 .0	3 19.8	2 2.2	0 2.9	0 14.3	1 29.6	2 35.0	0 13.5	1 21.7	17 37.2
16	15 34 28.6	0 .0	0 .0	4 54.9	2 15.2	0N 4.4	0 12.3	1 29.0	2 34.4	0 13.4	1 21.7	17 36.3
19	15 46 18.2	0 .0	0 .0	4 36.1	2 20.9	0 11.7	0 10.4	1 28.3	2 33.8	0 13.4	1 21.8	17 35.3
22	15 58 7.9	0 .0	0 .0	2 30.5	2 18.8	0 19.0	0 8.5	1 27.5	2 33.2	0 13.4	1 21.8	17 34.2
25	16 9 57.6	0 .0	0 .0	0S40.8	2 8.9	0 26.2	0 6.5	1 26.8	2 32.6	0 13.3	1 21.8	17 33.0
28	16 21 47.2	0 .0	0 .0	3 45.9	1 51.0	0 33.4	0 4.6	1 26.1	2 31.9	0 13.3	1 21.9	17 31.8
31	16 33 36.9	0 .0	0 .0	5 5.8	1 25.3	0 40.3	0 2.6	1 25.3	2 31.3	0 13.3	1 21.9	17 30.5
		RIGHT ASCENSION										
1	14 35 20.2	8♉ 7.1	8♌32.2	27♓39.1	11♉54.6	14♉21.9	2♉ 8.5	1♎59.5	4♎42.3	26♏40.1	24♐ 6.8	27♎18.9
2	14 39 16.8	9 4.4	8 29.0	11♈24.5	14 .5	15 35.3	2 51.5	1R55.2	4R39.3	26R37.6	24R 5.6	27R17.4
3	14 43 13.3	10 1.9	8 25.7	25 29.3	16 7.0	16 49.0	3 34.5	1 51.1	4 36.3	26 35.2	24 4.4	27 15.9
4	14 47 9.9	10 59.5	8 22.5	10♉ .0	18 13.9	18 3.0	4 17.6	1 47.1	4 33.4	26 32.7	24 3.3	27 14.4
5	14 51 6.4	11 57.3	8 19.2	24 59.2	20 20.8	19 17.2	5 .7	1 43.3	4 30.6	26 30.2	24 2.0	27 13.0
6	14 55 3.0	12 55.2	8 16.0	10♊22.1	22 27.6	20 31.7	5 43.9	1 39.6	4 27.9	26 27.7	24 .8	27 11.5
7	14 58 59.6	13 53.2	8 12.7	25 55.4	24 33.8	21 46.5	6 27.1	1 36.0	4 25.2	26 25.2	23 59.5	27 10.1
8	15 2 56.1	14 51.4	8 9.4	11♋19.7	26 39.1	23 1.6	7 10.3	1 32.6	4 22.6	26 22.7	23 58.3	27 8.6
9	15 6 52.7	15 49.7	8 6.2	26 15.3	28 43.3	24 16.9	7 53.6	1 29.4	4 20.1	26 20.1	23 56.9	27 7.2
10	15 10 49.2	16 48.1	8 2.9	10♌28.1	0♊46.0	25 32.5	8 36.9	1 26.3	4 17.7	26 17.6	23 55.6	27 5.8
11	15 14 45.8	17 46.7	7 59.7	23 52.5	2 46.9	26 48.4	9 20.3	1 23.4	4 15.3	26 15.0	23 54.3	27 4.4
12	15 18 42.3	18 45.4	7 56.4	6♍30.8	4 45.8	28 4.6	10 3.7	1 20.7	4 13.1	26 12.5	23 52.9	27 3.0
13	15 22 38.9	19 44.3	7 53.2	18 30.6	6 42.5	29 21.0	10 47.2	1 18.1	4 10.9	26 9.9	23 51.5	27 1.7
14	15 26 35.4	20 43.3	7 49.9	0♎ 2.2	8 36.6	0♊37.7	11 30.7	1 15.6	4 8.8	26 7.3	23 50.1	27 .3
15	15 30 32.0	21 42.4	7 46.7	11 16.5	10 28.0	1 54.7	12 14.2	1 13.3	4 6.7	26 4.7	23 48.6	26 59.0
16	15 34 28.6	22 41.7	7 43.4	22 24.4	12 16.5	3 11.9	12 57.8	1 11.2	4 4.8	26 2.2	23 47.2	26 57.6
17	15 38 25.1	23 41.1	7 40.1	3♏35.9	14 1.9	4 29.4	13 41.5	1 9.3	4 2.9	25 59.6	23 45.7	26 56.3
18	15 42 21.7	24 40.7	7 36.9	14 59.6	15 44.0	5 47.2	14 25.1	1 7.5	4 1.2	25 57.0	23 44.2	26 55.0
19	15 46 18.2	25 40.5	7 33.6	26 42.2	17 22.8	7 5.2	15 8.9	1 5.9	3 59.5	25 54.4	23 42.8	26 53.8
20	15 50 14.8	26 40.3	7 30.4	8♐47.8	18 58.0	8 23.4	15 52.7	1 4.4	3 57.9	25 51.8	23 41.2	26 52.5
21	15 54 11.3	27 40.3	7 27.1	21 17.2	20 29.5	9 41.8	16 36.5	1 3.1	3 56.4	25 49.2	23 39.7	26 51.3
22	15 58 7.9	28 40.4	7 23.8	4♑ 7.7	21 57.2	11 .5	17 20.4	1 2.0	3 55.0	25 46.6	23 38.1	26 50.0
23	16 2 4.4	29 40.6	7 20.6	17 13.4	23 21.1	12 19.4	18 4.3	1 1.1	3 53.7	25 44.1	23 36.6	26 48.8
24	16 6 1.0	0♊41.0	7 17.3	0♒26.7	24 40.9	13 38.4	18 48.3	1 .3	3 52.4	25 41.5	23 35.0	26 47.6
25	16 9 57.6	1 41.5	7 14.1	13 40.7	25 56.7	14 57.7	19 32.3	0 59.6	3 51.3	25 38.9	23 33.4	26 46.4
26	16 13 54.1	2 42.1	7 10.8	26 51.0	27 8.2	16 17.1	20 16.4	0 59.1	3 50.2	25 36.3	23 31.8	26 45.3
27	16 17 50.7	3 42.9	7 7.5	9♓57.2	28 15.4	17 36.8	21 .5	0 58.8	3 49.2	25 33.8	23 30.1	26 44.1
28	16 21 47.2	4 43.8	7 4.3	23 3.1	29 18.3	18 56.5	21 44.6	0 58.7	3 48.3	25 31.2	23 28.5	26 43.0
29	16 25 43.8	5 44.8	7 1.0	6♈16.2	0♋16.6	20 16.5	22 28.8	0 58.7	3 47.5	25 28.6	23 26.8	26 41.9
30	16 29 40.3	6 45.9	6 57.7	19 46.3	1 10.3	21 36.5	23 13.1	0D58.9	3 46.8	25 26.1	23 25.2	26 40.8
31	16 33 36.9	7 47.1	6 54.5	3♉43.6	1 59.3	22 56.7	23 57.4	0 59.3	3 46.2	25 23.6	23 23.5	26 39.8
		DECLINATION										
1	14 35 20.2	14N59.0	0N19.6	5S12.2	16N25.8	16N19.5	12N36.1	0N48.6	0N48.9	19S40.9	21S58.3	7N40.8
4	14 47 9.9	15 52.5	0 19.7	10N20.2	18 44.5	17 27.1	13 22.5	0 53.4	0 52.2	19 39.4	21 58.1	7 41.9
7	14 58 59.6	16 43.7	0 19.7	20 13.6	20 46.5	18 30.7	14 7.6	0 57.5	0 55.2	19 37.8	21 57.9	7 42.9
10	15 10 49.2	17 32.4	0 19.7	18 32.0	22 27.9	19 29.9	14 51.4	1 1.0	0 57.9	19 36.2	21 57.7	7 43.8
13	15 22 38.9	18 18.4	0 19.8	8 33.1	23 46.6	20 24.4	15 33.8	1 3.9	1 .3	19 34.6	21 57.4	7 44.5
16	15 34 28.6	19 1.7	0 19.8	4S 5.9	24 42.7	21 13.8	16 14.8	1 6.1	1 2.3	19 32.9	21 57.2	7 45.1
19	15 46 18.2	19 42.0	0 19.9	15 12.3	25 17.4	21 58.0	16 54.3	1 7.6	1 3.9	19 31.3	21 57.0	7 45.5
22	15 58 7.9	20 19.4	0 19.9	20 52.5	25 33.1	22 36.7	17 32.3	1 8.5	1 5.2	19 29.6	21 56.8	7 45.8
25	16 9 57.6	20 53.6	0 19.9	18 7.1	25 32.2	23 9.6	18 8.7	1 8.8	1 6.1	19 28.0	21 56.5	7 46.0
28	16 21 47.2	21 24.5	0 20.0	7 6.0	25 17.3	23 36.5	18 43.4	1 8.4	1 6.6	19 26.4	21 56.3	7 46.0
31	16 33 36.9	21 52.2	0 20.0	8N 8.0	24 50.9	23 57.3	19 16.5	1 7.3	1 6.8	19 24.7	21 56.1	7 45.9

JUNE 1981

LONGITUDE

DAY	EPHEM. SID. TIME h m s	☉ ° ′	☊ ° ′	☽ ° ′	☿ ° ′	♀ ° ′	♂ ° ′	♃ ° ′	♄ ° ′	♅ ° ′	♆ ° ′	♇ ° ′
1	16 37 33.5	10♊25.1	4♌31.0	19♉21.2	2♋28.7	24♊46.8	26♉58.7	0♎28.3	3♎ .6	27♏34.2	23♐50.7	21♎47.1
2	16 41 30.0	11 22.6	4 27.8	4♊32.7	3 4.8	26 .3	27 41.8	0 29.2	3R .2	27R31.8	23R49.1	21R46.1
3	16 45 26.6	12 20.1	4 24.6	19 39.2	3 36.5	27 13.8	28 24.9	0 30.2	2 59.9	27 29.4	23 47.5	21 45.2
4	16 49 23.1	13 17.6	4 21.4	4♋30.8	4 3.8	28 27.3	29 7.9	0 31.4	2 59.8	27 27.0	23 45.9	21 44.3
5	16 53 19.7	14 15.1	4 18.3	19 .1	4 26.6	29 40.7	29 50.8	0 32.8	2 59.7	27 24.7	23 44.3	21 43.5
6	16 57 16.2	15 12.5	4 15.1	3♌ 2.8	4 44.8	0♋54.2	0♊33.7	0 34.4	2D59.8	27 22.3	23 42.7	21 42.6
7	17 1 12.8	16 9.9	4 11.9	16 37.6	4 58.5	2 7.6	1 16.5	0 36.1	2 59.9	27 20.0	23 41.1	21 41.8
8	17 5 9.4	17 7.3	4 8.7	29 45.8	5 7.5	3 21.0	1 59.3	0 38.1	3 .2	27 17.7	23 39.5	21 41.1
9	17 9 5.9	18 4.8	4 5.6	12♍30.6	5 12.0	4 34.5	2 42.0	0 40.2	3 .6	27 15.4	23 38.0	21 40.4
10	17 13 2.5	19 2.1	4 2.4	24 56.1	5 12.0	5 47.9	3 24.7	0 42.5	3 1.0	27 13.2	23 36.3	21 39.6
11	17 16 59.0	19 59.5	3 59.2	7♎ 6.9	5R 7.4	7 1.2	4 7.2	0 44.9	3 1.6	27 10.9	23 34.7	21 39.0
12	17 20 55.6	20 56.8	3 56.0	19 7.4	4 58.5	8 14.6	4 49.8	0 47.6	3 2.2	27 8.7	23 33.1	21 38.3
13	17 24 52.1	21 54.1	3 52.8	1♏ 1.8	4 45.4	9 27.9	5 32.3	0 50.4	3 3.0	27 6.5	23 31.5	21 37.7
14	17 28 48.7	22 51.4	3 49.7	12 53.8	4 28.3	10 41.2	6 14.7	0 53.3	3 3.8	27 4.3	23 29.9	21 37.1
15	17 32 45.3	23 48.7	3 46.5	24 46.3	4 7.6	11 54.5	6 57.1	0 56.4	3 4.8	27 2.2	23 28.2	21 36.5
16	17 36 41.8	24 46.0	3 43.3	6♐42.0	3 43.5	13 7.7	7 39.4	0 59.7	3 5.8	27 .0	23 26.6	21 36.0
17	17 40 38.4	25 43.3	3 40.1	18 42.6	3 16.4	14 21.0	8 21.6	1 3.2	3 7.0	26 57.9	23 25.0	21 35.5
18	17 44 34.9	26 40.5	3 37.0	0♑49.9	2 46.7	15 34.2	9 3.8	1 6.8	3 8.2	26 55.9	23 23.4	21 35.0
19	17 48 31.5	27 37.8	3 33.8	13 5.2	2 15.0	16 47.4	9 46.0	1 10.6	3 9.6	26 53.8	23 21.8	21 34.6
20	17 52 28.0	28 35.0	3 30.6	25 30.0	1 41.7	18 .6	10 28.1	1 14.5	3 11.0	26 51.8	23 20.2	21 34.2
21	17 56 24.6	29 32.2	3 27.4	8♒ 6.0	1 7.4	19 13.8	11 10.2	1 18.6	3 12.6	26 49.8	23 18.5	21 33.8
22	18 0 21.2	0♋29.5	3 24.3	20 54.8	0 32.7	20 27.0	11 52.1	1 22.9	3 14.2	26 47.9	23 16.9	21 33.5
23	18 4 17.7	1 26.7	3 21.1	3♓58.4	29♊58.2	21 40.1	12 34.1	1 27.3	3 16.0	26 46.0	23 15.3	21 33.2
24	18 8 14.3	2 23.9	3 17.9	17 19.0	29 24.5	22 53.2	13 16.0	1 31.9	3 17.8	26 44.1	23 13.7	21 32.9
25	18 12 10.8	3 21.2	3 14.7	0♈58.1	28 52.2	24 6.4	13 57.8	1 36.6	3 19.8	26 42.2	23 12.1	21 32.7
26	18 16 7.4	4 18.4	3 11.6	14 56.4	28 21.7	25 19.5	14 39.6	1 41.5	3 21.8	26 40.4	23 10.5	21 32.5
27	18 20 3.9	5 15.6	3 8.4	29 13.6	27 53.7	26 32.6	15 21.4	1 46.5	3 23.9	26 38.6	23 9.0	21 32.3
28	18 24 .5	6 12.8	3 5.2	13♉47.1	27 28.7	27 45.6	16 3.0	1 51.7	3 26.2	26 36.9	23 7.4	21 32.2
29	18 27 57.1	7 10.1	3 2.0	28 32.3	27 7.0	28 58.7	16 44.7	1 57.1	3 28.5	26 35.2	23 5.8	21 32.0
30	18 31 53.6	8 7.3	2 58.8	13♊22.8	26 49.0	0♌11.8	17 26.3	2 2.6	3 30.9	26 33.6	23 4.3	21 32.0

LATITUDE

DAY	EPHEM. SID. TIME	☉	☊	☽	☿	♀	♂	♃	♄	♅	♆	♇
1	16 37 33.5	0 .0	0 .0	4S53.7	1N15.0	0N42.6	0S 1.9	1N25.1	2N31.0	0N13.3	1N21.9	17N30.0
4	16 49 23.1	0 .0	0 .0	2 25.4	0 39.4	0 49.2	0 .0	1 24.3	2 30.3	0 13.2	1 21.9	17 28.7
7	17 1 12.8	0 .0	0 .0	1N14.9	0S 2.8	0 55.7	0N 2.0	1 23.6	2 29.7	0 13.2	1 21.9	17 27.2
10	17 13 2.5	0 .0	0 .0	4 5.0	0 50.3	1 1.7	0 4.0	1 22.8	2 29.0	0 13.1	1 21.9	17 25.8
13	17 24 52.1	0 .0	0 .0	5 9.2	1 40.8	1 7.5	0 5.9	1 22.1	2 28.3	0 13.1	1 21.9	17 24.2
16	17 36 41.8	0 .0	0 .0	4 15.5	2 31.2	1 12.8	0 7.9	1 21.4	2 27.6	0 13.0	1 21.9	17 22.7
19	17 48 31.5	0 .0	0 .0	1 40.9	3 17.8	1 17.8	0 9.8	1 20.6	2 26.9	0 13.0	1 21.8	17 21.1
22	18 0 21.2	0 .0	0 .0	1S42.1	3 56.5	1 22.2	0 11.8	1 19.9	2 26.2	0 12.9	1 21.8	17 19.5
25	18 12 10.8	0 .0	0 .0	4 28.9	4 24.0	1 26.2	0 13.8	1 19.2	2 25.5	0 12.9	1 21.7	17 17.8
28	18 24 .5	0 .0	0 .0	5 6.9	4 38.4	1 29.6	0 15.7	1 18.5	2 24.8	0 12.8	1 21.7	17 16.1

RIGHT ASCENSION

DAY	EPHEM. SID. TIME	☉	☊	☽	☿	♀	♂	♃	♄	♅	♆	♇
1	16 37 33.5	8♊48.5	6♌51.2	18♉15.8	2♋43.6	24♊17.0	24♉41.7	0♎59.8	3♎45.7	25♏21.1	23♐21.8	26♎38.7
2	16 41 30.0	9 49.9	6 47.9	3♊24.6	3 23.0	25 37.3	25 26.1	1 .5	3R45.3	25R18.6	23R20.1	26R37.7
3	16 45 26.6	10 51.5	6 44.7	19 2.0	3 57.5	26 57.8	26 10.5	1 1.3	3 44.9	25 16.1	23 18.4	26 36.7
4	16 49 23.1	11 53.1	6 41.4	4♋49.8	4 27.0	28 18.3	26 54.9	1 2.4	3 44.7	25 13.6	23 16.7	26 35.8
5	16 53 19.7	12 54.8	6 38.1	20 23.5	4 51.4	29 38.9	27 39.4	1 3.5	3 44.6	25 11.2	23 15.0	26 34.8
6	16 57 16.2	13 56.6	6 34.9	5♌20.9	5 10.8	0♋59.5	28 23.9	1 4.9	3 44.5	25 8.7	23 13.3	26 33.9
7	17 1 12.8	14 58.5	6 31.6	19 28.4	5 25.1	2 20.1	29 8.4	1 6.4	3 44.5	25 6.3	23 11.6	26 33.0
8	17 5 9.4	16 .5	6 28.3	2♍42.8	5 34.3	3 40.7	29 53.0	1 8.1	3D44.7	25 3.9	23 9.8	26 32.1
9	17 9 5.9	17 2.5	6 25.1	15 9.5	5 38.5	5 1.3	0♊37.7	1 10.0	3 45.0	25 1.6	23 8.2	26 31.3
10	17 13 2.5	18 4.6	6 21.8	26 58.6	5R37.7	6 21.9	1 22.3	1 11.9	3 45.3	24 59.3	23 6.4	26 30.5
11	17 16 59.0	19 6.7	6 18.5	8♎22.3	5 32.1	7 42.4	2 7.0	1 14.1	3 45.7	24 56.9	23 4.7	26 29.7
12	17 20 55.6	20 8.9	6 15.3	19 32.9	5 21.8	9 2.8	2 51.7	1 16.4	3 46.2	24 54.6	23 2.9	26 28.9
13	17 24 52.1	21 11.1	6 12.0	0♏42.1	5 7.0	10 23.2	3 36.4	1 18.9	3 46.8	24 52.4	23 1.2	26 28.1
14	17 28 48.7	22 13.3	6 8.7	12 .4	4 48.1	11 43.4	4 21.1	1 21.5	3 47.5	24 50.1	22 59.4	26 27.4
15	17 32 45.3	23 15.6	6 5.4	23 36.5	4 25.3	13 3.6	5 5.9	1 24.2	3 48.3	24 47.9	22 57.7	26 26.7
16	17 36 41.8	24 17.9	6 2.2	5♐36.4	3 59.0	14 23.6	5 50.7	1 27.2	3 49.1	24 45.7	22 56.0	26 26.1
17	17 40 38.4	25 20.3	5 58.9	18 2.6	3 29.6	15 43.5	6 35.5	1 30.2	3 50.1	24 43.5	22 54.2	26 25.4
18	17 44 34.9	26 22.6	5 55.6	0♑53.3	2 57.6	17 3.3	7 20.3	1 33.5	3 51.2	24 41.4	22 52.5	26 24.8
19	17 48 31.5	27 25.0	5 52.4	14 2.5	2 23.5	18 22.8	8 5.2	1 36.8	3 52.3	24 39.3	22 50.7	26 24.2
20	17 52 28.0	28 27.4	5 49.1	27 21.3	1 47.9	19 42.2	8 50.0	1 40.4	3 53.6	24 37.2	22 49.0	26 23.6
21	17 56 24.6	29 29.8	5 45.8	10♒40.3	1 11.4	21 1.5	9 34.9	1 44.0	3 54.9	24 35.2	22 47.3	26 23.1
22	18 0 21.2	0♋32.1	5 42.5	23 52.1	0 34.6	22 20.5	10 19.8	1 47.8	3 56.3	24 33.2	22 45.5	26 22.6
23	18 4 17.7	1 34.5	5 39.3	6♓54.0	29♊58.1	23 39.3	11 4.7	1 51.8	3 57.8	24 31.2	22 43.8	26 22.1
24	18 8 14.3	2 36.9	5 36.0	19 47.9	29 22.5	24 57.8	11 49.6	1 55.9	3 59.4	24 29.2	22 42.1	26 21.7
25	18 12 10.8	3 39.2	5 32.7	2♈40.4	28 48.4	26 16.2	12 34.5	2 .2	4 1.1	24 27.3	22 40.4	26 21.2
26	18 16 7.4	4 41.5	5 29.4	15 41.2	28 16.4	27 34.3	13 19.5	2 4.5	4 2.9	24 25.5	22 38.6	26 20.9
27	18 20 3.9	5 43.8	5 26.1	29 1.7	27 47.0	28 52.1	14 4.4	2 9.1	4 4.7	24 23.6	22 36.9	26 20.5
28	18 24 .5	6 46.1	5 22.9	12♉52.9	27 20.7	0♌ 9.7	14 49.3	2 13.7	4 6.7	24 21.8	22 35.3	26 20.2
29	18 27 57.1	7 48.3	5 19.6	27 22.1	26 57.9	1 27.0	15 34.2	2 18.5	4 8.7	24 20.1	22 33.6	26 19.8
30	18 31 53.6	8 50.5	5 16.3	12♊29.2	26 39.0	2 44.1	16 19.2	2 23.5	4 10.9	24 18.4	22 31.9	26 19.6

DECLINATION

DAY	EPHEM. SID. TIME	☉	☊	☽	☿	♀	♂	♃	♄	♅	♆	♇
1	16 37 33.5	22N .7	0N20.0	12N51.1	24N40.0	24N 2.8	19N27.1	1N 6.8	1N 6.8	19S24.2	21S56.0	7N45.9
4	16 49 23.1	22 23.7	0 20.1	20 56.4	24 2.0	24 15.1	19 57.9	1 4.9	1 6.5	19 22.6	21 55.8	7 45.6
7	17 1 12.8	22 43.3	0 20.1	17 2.6	23 18.0	24 21.0	20 26.9	1 2.3	1 5.8	19 21.0	21 55.6	7 45.1
10	17 13 2.5	22 59.3	0 20.2	5 45.6	22 30.0	24 20.5	20 54.1	0 59.1	1 4.7	19 19.5	21 55.3	7 44.6
13	17 24 52.1	23 11.6	0 20.2	6S59.9	21 40.6	24 13.5	21 19.5	0 55.3	1 3.3	19 18.0	21 55.1	7 43.8
16	17 36 41.8	23 20.2	0 20.2	17 13.8	20 52.1	24 .0	21 43.0	0 50.9	1 1.5	19 16.6	21 54.9	7 43.0
19	17 48 31.5	23 25.1	0 20.3	21 7.4	20 7.5	23 40.3	22 4.7	0 45.9	0 59.4	19 15.2	21 54.7	7 42.0
22	18 0 21.2	23 26.4	0 20.3	16 8.2	19 29.9	23 14.3	22 24.4	0 40.4	0 56.9	19 13.9	21 54.5	7 40.9
25	18 12 10.8	23 23.9	0 20.3	3 43.6	19 2.1	22 42.3	22 42.3	0 34.3	0 54.1	19 12.7	21 54.3	7 39.7
28	18 24 .5	23 17.6	0 20.4	11N 5.4	18 46.6	22 4.4	22 58.2	0 27.6	0 50.9	19 11.5	21 54.1	7 38.3

JULY 1981

LONGITUDE

DAY	EPHEM. SID. TIME h m s	☉ ° ′	☊ ° ′	☽ ° ′	☿ ° ′	♀ ° ′	♂ ° ′	♃ ° ′	♄ ° ′	♅ ° ′	♆ ° ′	♇ ° ′
1	18 35 50.2	9♋ 4.6	2♌55.7	28♊11.0	26♊35.2	1♌24.8	18♊ 7.8	2♎ 8.2	3♎33.5	26♏31.9	23♐ 2.8	21♎32.0
2	18 39 46.7	10 1.8	2 52.5	12♋49.0	26 R 25.6	2 37.8	18 49.3	2 14.0	3 36.1	26 R 30.3	23 R 1.2	21 32.0
3	18 43 43.3	10 59.0	2 49.3	27 10.3	26 20.7	3 50.8	19 30.7	2 19.9	3 38.8	26 28.8	22 59.7	21 32.0
4	18 47 39.8	11 56.2	2 46.1	11♌10.0	26 20.5	5 3.8	20 12.1	2 26.0	3 41.5	26 27.3	22 58.2	21 D 32.1
5	18 51 36.4	12 53.4	2 43.0	24 45.7	26 D 25.2	6 16.7	20 53.4	2 32.2	3 44.4	26 25.8	22 56.7	21 32.2
6	18 55 33.0	13 50.7	2 39.8	7♍56.9	26 35.0	7 29.6	21 34.6	2 38.5	3 47.4	26 24.4	22 55.2	21 32.3
7	18 59 29.5	14 47.9	2 36.6	20 45.5	26 49.8	8 42.5	22 15.8	2 45.0	3 50.5	26 23.0	22 53.7	21 32.5
8	19 3 26.1	15 45.1	2 33.4	3♎14.4	27 9.7	9 55.4	22 57.0	2 51.7	3 53.6	26 21.7	22 52.2	21 32.7
9	19 7 22.6	16 42.3	2 30.3	15 27.6	27 34.7	11 8.3	23 38.1	2 58.4	3 56.8	26 20.4	22 50.8	21 32.9
10	19 11 19.2	17 39.5	2 27.1	27 29.4	28 4.9	12 21.1	24 19.1	3 5.3	4 .2	26 19.1	22 49.4	21 33.2
11	19 15 15.7	18 36.7	2 23.9	9♏24.3	28 40.2	13 33.9	25 .1	3 12.3	4 3.6	26 17.9	22 47.9	21 33.5
12	19 19 12.3	19 33.9	2 20.7	21 16.9	29 20.5	14 46.7	25 41.0	3 19.5	4 7.1	26 16.7	22 46.5	21 33.8
13	19 23 8.9	20 31.1	2 17.5	3♐10.9	0♋ 5.8	15 59.5	26 21.9	3 26.7	4 10.7	26 15.6	22 45.1	21 34.2
14	19 27 5.4	21 28.3	2 14.4	15 10.0	0 56.2	17 12.2	27 2.7	3 34.1	4 14.3	26 14.5	22 43.8	21 34.6
15	19 31 2.0	22 25.5	2 11.2	27 17.1	1 51.4	18 24.9	27 43.5	3 41.7	4 18.1	26 13.5	22 42.4	21 35.0
16	19 34 58.5	23 22.7	2 8.0	9♑34.4	2 51.6	19 37.6	28 24.2	3 49.3	4 21.9	26 12.5	22 41.1	21 35.5
17	19 38 55.1	24 19.9	2 4.8	22 3.7	3 56.5	20 50.2	29 4.8	3 57.1	4 25.8	26 11.6	22 39.7	21 36.0
18	19 42 51.6	25 17.2	2 1.7	4♒46.0	5 6.2	22 2.8	29 45.4	4 5.0	4 29.8	26 10.7	22 38.4	21 36.5
19	19 46 48.2	26 14.4	1 58.5	17 42.0	6 20.5	23 15.4	0♋26.0	4 13.0	4 33.9	26 9.8	22 37.1	21 37.1
20	19 50 44.8	27 11.6	1 55.3	0♓51.7	7 39.4	24 28.0	1 6.5	4 21.1	4 38.0	26 9.0	22 35.9	21 37.7
21	19 54 41.3	28 8.9	1 52.1	14 15.0	9 2.8	25 40.6	1 47.0	4 29.4	4 42.3	26 8.3	22 34.7	21 38.4
22	19 58 37.9	29 6.2	1 49.0	27 51.6	10 30.6	26 53.1	2 27.4	4 37.7	4 46.6	26 7.6	22 33.4	21 39.1
23	20 2 34.4	0♌ 3.5	1 45.8	11♈40.8	12 2.5	28 5.6	3 7.7	4 46.2	4 51.0	26 7.0	22 32.2	21 39.8
24	20 6 31.0	1 .8	1 42.6	25 41.5	13 38.6	29 18.1	3 48.0	4 54.8	4 55.5	26 6.4	22 31.0	21 40.5
25	20 10 27.5	1 58.1	1 39.4	9♉52.4	15 18.5	0♍30.5	4 28.3	5 3.4	5 .0	26 5.8	22 29.9	21 41.3
26	20 14 24.1	2 55.4	1 36.2	24 11.1	17 2.2	1 42.9	5 8.5	5 12.2	5 4.6	26 5.3	22 28.7	21 42.1
27	20 18 20.6	3 52.7	1 33.1	8♊34.7	18 49.3	2 55.3	5 48.7	5 21.1	5 9.3	26 4.9	22 27.6	21 42.9
28	20 22 17.2	4 50.1	1 29.9	22 59.5	20 39.6	4 7.7	6 28.8	5 30.1	5 14.1	26 4.5	22 26.5	21 43.8
29	20 26 13.8	5 47.5	1 26.7	7♋21.1	22 32.9	5 20.0	7 8.8	5 39.3	5 18.9	26 4.1	22 25.4	21 44.7
30	20 30 10.3	6 44.9	1 23.5	21 35.0	24 28.8	6 32.3	7 48.8	5 48.5	5 23.8	26 3.8	22 24.4	21 45.6
31	20 34 6.9	7 42.3	1 20.4	5♌36.6	26 26.9	7 44.6	8 28.7	5 57.8	5 28.8	26 3.5	22 23.4	21 46.6

LATITUDE

DAY	EPHEM. SID. TIME	☉	☊	☽	☿	♀	♂	♃	♄	♅	♆	♇
1	18 35 50.2	0 .0	0 .0	2S54.1	4S39.5	1N32.4	0N17.7	1N17.9	2N24.1	0N12.8	1N21.6	17N14.4
4	18 47 39.8	0 .0	0 .0	0N51.9	4 28.4	1 34.7	0 19.6	1 17.2	2 23.5	0 12.7	1 21.6	17 12.7
7	18 59 29.5	0 .0	0 .0	3 58.6	4 6.9	1 36.3	0 21.6	1 16.5	2 22.8	0 12.7	1 21.5	17 11.0
10	19 11 19.2	0 .0	0 .0	5 15.0	3 37.3	1 37.4	0 23.5	1 15.9	2 22.2	0 12.6	1 21.4	17 9.3
13	19 23 8.9	0 .0	0 .0	4 29.8	3 1.7	1 37.7	0 25.4	1 15.3	2 21.6	0 12.6	1 21.3	17 7.6
16	19 34 58.5	0 .0	0 .0	1 59.4	2 22.2	1 37.4	0 27.4	1 14.7	2 21.0	0 12.5	1 21.2	17 5.8
19	19 46 48.2	0 .0	0 .0	1S27.7	1 40.6	1 36.4	0 29.3	1 14.1	2 20.4	0 12.5	1 21.2	17 4.1
22	19 58 37.9	0 .0	0 .0	4 23.6	0 58.8	1 34.7	0 31.2	1 13.5	2 19.8	0 12.4	1 21.0	17 2.4
25	20 10 27.5	0 .0	0 .0	5 13.8	0 18.6	1 32.3	0 33.1	1 13.0	2 19.2	0 12.3	1 20.9	17 .8
28	20 22 17.2	0 .0	0 .0	3 18.6	0N18.2	1 29.2	0 35.0	1 12.4	2 18.7	0 12.3	1 20.8	16 59.1
31	20 34 6.9	0 .0	0 .0	0N21.6	0 49.7	1 25.5	0 36.9	1 11.9	2 18.2	0 12.2	1 20.7	16 57.5

RIGHT ASCENSION

DAY	EPHEM. SID. TIME	☉	☊	☽	☿	♀	♂	♃	♄	♅	♆	♇
1	18 35 50.2	9♋52.6	5♌13.0	28♊ 3.7	26♊24.4	4♌ .9	17♊ 4.1	2♎28.6	4♎13.1	24♏16.7	22♐30.3	26♎19.4
2	18 39 46.7	10 54.7	5 9.7	13♋45.1	26 R 14.3	5 17.3	17 49.0	2 33.8	4 15.4	24 R 15.1	22 R 28.6	26 R 19.1
3	18 43 43.3	11 56.6	5 6.5	29 8.4	26 9.0	6 33.5	18 33.9	2 39.2	4 17.8	24 13.5	22 27.0	26 19.0
4	18 47 39.8	12 58.6	5 3.2	13♌52.4	26 8.7	7 49.3	19 18.8	2 44.6	4 20.3	24 11.9	22 25.3	26 18.8
5	18 51 36.4	14 .4	4 59.9	27 45.8	26 D 13.5	9 4.9	20 3.6	2 50.2	4 22.8	24 10.4	22 23.7	26 18.7
6	18 55 33.0	15 2.1	4 56.6	10♍47.8	26 23.6	10 20.1	20 48.5	2 56.0	4 25.5	24 8.9	22 22.1	26 18.6
7	18 59 29.5	16 3.8	4 53.3	23 5.1	26 39.0	11 35.0	21 33.3	3 1.8	4 28.2	24 7.5	22 20.5	26 18.5
8	19 3 26.1	17 5.3	4 50.1	4♎48.7	26 59.8	12 49.6	22 18.1	3 7.8	4 31.0	24 6.1	22 18.9	26 18.5
9	19 7 22.6	18 6.8	4 46.8	16 11.1	27 26.1	14 3.8	23 2.8	3 14.0	4 33.9	24 4.7	22 17.4	26 18.5
10	19 11 19.2	19 8.1	4 43.5	27 24.7	27 57.9	15 17.7	23 47.6	3 20.2	4 36.8	24 3.4	22 15.8	26 18.5
11	19 15 15.7	20 9.4	4 40.2	8♏41.3	28 35.2	16 31.3	24 32.3	3 26.5	4 39.9	24 2.2	22 14.3	26 18.5
12	19 19 12.3	21 10.5	4 36.9	20 11.2	29 18.0	17 44.6	25 16.9	3 33.0	4 43.0	24 1.0	22 12.8	26 D 18.6
13	19 23 8.9	22 11.5	4 33.6	2♐ 2.6	0♋ 6.2	18 57.5	26 1.5	3 39.6	4 46.2	23 59.8	22 11.3	26 18.7
14	19 27 5.4	23 12.4	4 30.3	14 20.7	0 60.0	20 10.1	26 46.1	3 46.3	4 49.5	23 58.7	22 9.8	26 18.9
15	19 31 2.0	24 13.1	4 27.1	27 6.4	1 59.1	21 22.4	27 30.7	3 53.1	4 52.9	23 57.6	22 8.3	26 19.1
16	19 34 58.5	25 13.7	4 23.8	10♑15.8	3 3.7	22 34.4	28 15.2	4 .1	4 56.3	23 56.6	22 6.9	26 19.3
17	19 38 55.1	26 14.2	4 20.5	23 40.9	4 13.6	23 46.0	28 59.6	4 7.1	4 59.8	23 55.6	22 5.5	26 19.5
18	19 42 51.6	27 14.6	4 17.2	7♒11.1	5 28.8	24 57.3	29 44.1	4 14.3	5 3.4	23 54.7	22 4.1	26 19.8
19	19 46 48.2	28 14.9	4 13.9	20 36.6	6 49.3	26 8.3	0♋28.4	4 21.6	5 7.0	23 53.9	22 2.7	26 20.1
20	19 50 44.8	29 15.0	4 10.6	3♓51.1	8 14.8	27 19.0	1 12.7	4 28.9	5 10.8	23 53.0	22 1.3	26 20.4
21	19 54 41.3	0♌15.0	4 7.3	16 53.4	9 45.4	28 29.4	1 57.1	4 36.5	5 14.6	23 52.3	22 .0	26 20.8
22	19 58 37.9	1 14.8	4 4.0	29 47.3	11 20.9	29 39.5	2 41.3	4 44.1	5 18.5	23 51.6	21 58.7	26 21.2
23	20 2 34.4	2 14.5	4 .7	12♈40.7	13 1.0	0♍49.2	3 25.4	4 51.8	5 22.4	23 50.9	21 57.4	26 21.6
24	20 6 31.0	3 14.1	3 57.4	25 44.0	14 45.6	1 58.7	4 9.5	4 59.6	5 26.5	23 50.3	21 56.1	26 22.0
25	20 10 27.5	4 13.5	3 54.2	9♉ 8.4	16 34.5	3 7.9	4 53.5	5 7.5	5 30.6	23 49.7	21 54.8	26 22.5
26	20 14 24.1	5 12.7	3 50.9	23 3.0	18 27.3	4 16.9	5 37.5	5 15.5	5 34.7	23 49.2	21 53.6	26 23.0
27	20 18 20.6	6 11.9	3 47.6	7♊32.4	20 23.8	5 25.5	6 21.4	5 23.6	5 38.9	23 48.7	21 52.4	26 23.6
28	20 22 17.2	7 10.9	3 44.3	22 33.3	22 23.5	6 33.9	7 5.3	5 31.8	5 43.2	23 48.3	21 51.2	26 24.1
29	20 26 13.8	8 9.7	3 41.0	7♋52.6	24 26.1	7 42.0	7 49.0	5 40.1	5 47.6	23 47.9	21 50.1	26 24.7
30	20 30 10.3	9 8.4	3 37.7	23 10.0	26 31.1	8 49.9	8 32.7	5 48.4	5 52.0	23 47.6	21 48.9	26 25.4
31	20 34 6.9	10 6.9	3 34.4	8♌ 4.1	28 38.2	9 57.5	9 16.3	5 56.9	5 56.5	23 47.3	21 47.8	26 26.0

DECLINATION

DAY	EPHEM. SID. TIME	☉	☊	☽	☿	♀	♂	♃	♄	♅	♆	♇
1	18 35 50.2	23N 7.8	0N20.4	20N31.6	18N44.3	21N20.9	23N12.2	0N20.4	0N47.4	19S10.4	21S53.9	7N36.8
4	18 47 39.8	22 54.2	0 20.5	18 15.3	18 55.1	20 32.0	23 24.3	0 12.8	0 43.6	19 9.3	21 53.8	7 35.2
7	18 59 29.5	22 37.1	0 20.5	7 19.0	19 17.3	19 38.0	23 34.4	0 4.6	0 39.5	19 8.4	21 53.6	7 33.4
10	19 11 19.2	22 16.5	0 20.5	5S40.5	19 48.3	18 39.2	23 42.6	0S 4.0	0 35.0	19 7.5	21 53.4	7 31.6
13	19 23 8.9	21 52.4	0 20.6	16 22.7	20 24.7	17 35.9	23 48.8	0 13.1	0 30.3	19 6.8	21 53.3	7 29.6
16	19 34 58.5	21 25.0	0 20.6	21 6.6	21 2.4	16 28.4	23 53.2	0 22.6	0 25.3	19 6.1	21 53.2	7 27.6
19	19 46 48.2	20 54.2	0 20.7	16 55.2	21 36.8	15 17.0	23 55.7	0 32.5	0 20.0	19 5.5	21 53.0	7 25.4
22	19 58 37.9	20 20.3	0 20.7	4 52.8	22 2.8	14 2.1	23 56.2	0 42.9	0 14.4	19 5.1	21 52.9	7 23.1
25	20 10 27.5	19 43.3	0 20.7	9N48.4	22 15.3	12 43.9	23 55.0	0 53.6	0 8.6	19 4.7	21 52.9	7 20.8
28	20 22 17.2	19 3.4	0 20.8	19 57.0	22 9.1	11 22.9	23 51.9	1 4.6	0 2.6	19 4.5	21 52.8	7 18.3
31	20 34 6.9	18 20.7	0 20.8	19 13.1	21 40.7	9 59.2	23 47.0	1 16.1	0S 3.7	19 4.3	21 52.7	7 15.8

AUGUST 1981

DAY	EPHEM. SID. TIME	☉	☊	☽	☿	♀	♂	♃	♄	♅	♆	♇
	h m s	° ′	° ′	° ′	° ′	° ′	° ′	° ′	° ′	° ′	° ′	° ′
		LONGITUDE										
1	20 38 3.4	8♌39.7	1♌17.2	19♌22.2	28♋27.0	8♍56.9	9♋ 8.6	6♎ 7.2	5♎33.8	26♏ 3.3	22♐22.4	21♎47.6
2	20 41 60.0	9 37.1	1 14.0	2♍49.2	0♌28.8	10 9.1	9 48.5	6 16.7	5 38.9	26R 3.2	22R21.4	21 48.6
3	20 45 56.5	10 34.5	1 10.8	15 56.3	2 31.7	11 21.3	10 28.3	6 26.3	5 44.1	26 3.1	22 20.4	21 49.7
4	20 49 53.1	11 32.0	1 7.7	28 43.9	4 35.6	12 33.4	11 8.0	6 36.0	5 49.3	26 3.1	22 19.5	21 50.7
5	20 53 49.6	12 29.5	1 4.5	11♎13.4	6 40.1	13 45.5	11 47.7	6 45.8	5 54.6	26 3.1	22 18.6	21 51.9
6	20 57 46.2	13 26.9	1 1.3	23 27.8	8 44.8	14 57.6	12 27.3	6 55.7	5 60.0	26 3.1	22 17.7	21 53.0
7	21 1 42.8	14 24.4	0 58.1	5♏30.6	10 49.5	16 9.7	13 6.9	7 5.7	6 5.4	26D 3.2	22 16.9	21 54.2
8	21 5 39.3	15 21.9	0 54.9	17 26.0	12 54.0	17 21.7	13 46.4	7 15.8	6 10.9	26 3.4	22 16.1	21 55.4
9	21 9 35.9	16 19.4	0 51.8	29 18.8	14 57.9	18 33.6	14 25.8	7 25.9	6 16.5	26 3.6	22 15.3	21 56.7
10	21 13 32.4	17 17.0	0 48.6	11♐13.5	17 1.2	19 45.6	15 5.3	7 36.2	6 22.1	26 3.9	22 14.5	21 57.9
11	21 17 29.0	18 14.6	0 45.4	23 14.6	19 3.7	20 57.5	15 44.7	7 46.6	6 27.8	26 4.2	22 13.8	21 59.3
12	21 21 25.5	19 12.1	0 42.2	5♑26.2	21 5.2	22 9.3	16 24.0	7 57.0	6 33.5	26 4.6	22 13.1	22 .6
13	21 25 22.1	20 9.7	0 39.1	17 51.7	23 5.5	23 21.1	17 3.2	8 7.5	6 39.3	26 5.0	22 12.5	22 2.0
14	21 29 18.6	21 7.3	0 35.9	0♒33.7	25 4.7	24 32.9	17 42.4	8 18.0	6 45.2	26 5.5	22 11.8	22 3.3
15	21 33 15.2	22 4.9	0 32.7	13 33.6	27 2.6	25 44.6	18 21.6	8 28.7	6 51.1	26 6.0	22 11.2	22 4.8
16	21 37 11.7	23 2.6	0 29.5	26 51.6	28 59.2	26 56.3	19 .6	8 39.4	6 57.0	26 6.6	22 10.6	22 6.2
17	21 41 8.3	24 .2	0 26.3	10♓26.7	0♍54.5	28 7.9	19 39.7	8 50.2	7 3.0	26 7.2	22 10.0	22 7.7
18	21 45 4.9	24 57.9	0 23.2	24 16.5	2 48.4	29 19.5	20 18.7	9 1.1	7 9.1	26 7.9	22 9.5	22 9.2
19	21 49 1.4	25 55.6	0 20.0	8♈17.9	4 40.9	0♎31.0	20 57.6	9 12.0	7 15.2	26 8.7	22 9.0	22 10.7
20	21 52 58.0	26 53.3	0 16.8	22 27.2	6 32.0	1 42.5	21 36.5	9 23.0	7 21.4	26 9.4	22 8.5	22 12.2
21	21 56 54.5	27 51.1	0 13.6	6♉40.8	8 21.7	2 54.0	22 15.4	9 34.1	7 27.6	26 10.3	22 8.1	22 13.8
22	22 0 51.1	28 48.9	0 10.5	20 55.4	10 10.0	4 5.4	22 54.2	9 45.3	7 33.8	26 11.2	22 7.7	22 15.4
23	22 4 47.6	29 46.7	0 7.3	5♊ 8.2	11 56.9	5 16.8	23 32.9	9 56.5	7 40.1	26 12.1	22 7.3	22 17.1
24	22 8 44.2	0♍44.5	0 4.1	19 16.9	13 42.5	6 28.1	24 11.6	10 7.8	7 46.5	26 13.1	22 7.0	22 18.7
25	22 12 40.7	1 42.4	0 .9	3♋19.9	15 26.7	7 39.4	24 50.2	10 19.2	7 52.9	26 14.1	22 6.6	22 20.4
26	22 16 37.3	2 40.3	29♋57.7	17 15.6	17 9.6	8 50.6	25 28.8	10 30.6	7 59.3	26 15.2	22 6.4	22 22.1
27	22 20 33.8	3 38.2	29 54.6	1♌ 2.3	18 51.1	10 1.8	26 7.4	10 42.1	8 5.8	26 16.3	22 6.1	22 23.8
28	22 24 30.4	4 36.2	29 51.4	14 38.6	20 31.3	11 12.9	26 45.8	10 53.7	8 12.3	26 17.5	22 5.9	22 25.6
29	22 28 26.9	5 34.2	29 48.2	28 2.5	22 10.3	12 24.0	27 24.3	11 5.3	8 18.9	26 18.8	22 5.7	22 27.4
30	22 32 23.5	6 32.2	29 45.0	11♍12.7	23 47.9	13 35.1	28 2.7	11 17.0	8 25.5	26 20.1	22 5.5	22 29.2
31	22 36 20.0	7 30.2	29 41.9	24 8.0	25 24.2	14 46.1	28 41.0	11 28.7	8 32.2	26 21.4	22 5.4	22 31.0
		LATITUDE										
1	20 38 3.4	0 .0	0 .0	1N36.3	0N58.8	1N24.1	0N37.5	1N11.8	2N18.0	0N12.2	1N20.7	16N56.9
4	20 49 53.1	0 .0	0 .0	4 25.7	1 21.4	1 19.4	0 39.4	1 11.3	2 17.5	0 12.1	1 20.5	16 55.3
7	21 1 42.8	0 .0	0 .0	5 15.5	1 36.5	1 14.0	0 41.3	1 10.8	2 17.0	0 12.1	1 20.4	16 53.7
10	21 13 32.4	0 .0	0 .0	4 3.9	1 44.3	1 8.0	0 43.2	1 10.4	2 16.6	0 12.0	1 20.3	16 52.2
13	21 25 22.1	0 .0	0 .0	1 15.6	1 45.5	1 1.3	0 45.1	1 9.9	2 16.2	0 11.9	1 20.1	16 50.7
16	21 37 11.7	0 .0	0 .0	2S14.1	1 41.0	0 54.1	0 46.9	1 9.5	2 15.8	0 11.9	1 20.0	16 49.3
19	21 49 1.4	0 .0	0 .0	4 48.3	1 31.6	0 46.2	0 48.8	1 9.1	2 15.4	0 11.8	1 19.9	16 47.9
22	22 0 51.1	0 .0	0 .0	4 55.6	1 18.2	0 37.8	0 50.7	1 8.7	2 15.0	0 11.8	1 19.7	16 46.5
25	22 12 40.7	0 .0	0 .0	2 27.9	1 1.5	0 28.8	0 52.5	1 8.4	2 14.7	0 11.7	1 19.6	16 45.2
28	22 24 30.4	0 .0	0 .0	1N11.3	0 42.3	0 19.4	0 54.4	1 8.0	2 14.4	0 11.6	1 19.4	16 43.9
31	22 36 20.0	0 .0	0 .0	4 7.7	0 21.1	0 9.5	0 56.2	1 7.7	2 14.1	0 11.6	1 19.3	16 42.8
		RIGHT ASCENSION										
1	20 38 3.4	11♌ 5.3	3♌31.1	22♌18.8	0♌46.7	11♍ 4.9	9♋59.9	6♎ 5.5	6♎ 1.1	23♏47.1	21♐46.8	26♎26.7
2	20 41 60.0	12 3.5	3 27.8	5♍47.0	2 56.3	12 12.1	10 43.3	6 14.2	6 5.7	23R47.0	21R45.7	26 27.4
3	20 45 56.5	13 1.6	3 24.5	18 30.2	5 6.4	13 19.1	11 26.7	6 23.0	6 10.4	23 46.9	21 44.7	26 28.2
4	20 49 53.1	13 59.5	3 21.2	0♎36.1	7 16.7	14 25.8	12 10.0	6 31.8	6 15.1	23 46.8	21 43.7	26 29.0
5	20 53 49.6	14 57.3	3 17.9	12 15.0	9 26.7	15 32.3	12 53.2	6 40.8	6 19.9	23 46.8	21 42.7	26 29.8
6	20 57 46.2	15 54.9	3 14.6	23 38.7	11 36.1	16 38.6	13 36.3	6 49.8	6 24.8	23D46.9	21 41.8	26 30.6
7	21 1 42.8	16 52.4	3 11.3	4♏58.7	13 44.5	17 44.8	14 19.3	6 58.9	6 29.7	23 47.0	21 40.9	26 31.5
8	21 5 39.3	17 49.7	3 8.0	16 25.7	15 51.7	18 50.7	15 2.2	7 8.1	6 34.7	23 47.1	21 40.0	26 32.3
9	21 9 35.9	18 46.9	3 4.7	28 9.0	17 57.4	19 56.5	15 45.0	7 17.4	6 39.7	23 47.4	21 39.1	26 33.3
10	21 13 32.4	19 43.9	3 1.4	10♐15.5	20 1.3	21 2.1	16 27.8	7 26.7	6 44.8	23 47.6	21 38.3	26 34.2
11	21 17 29.0	20 40.8	2 58.1	22 49.2	22 3.5	22 7.6	17 10.4	7 36.2	6 50.0	23 48.0	21 37.6	26 35.2
12	21 21 25.5	21 37.5	2 54.8	5♑49.2	24 3.6	23 12.9	17 53.0	7 45.7	6 55.2	23 48.4	21 36.8	26 36.2
13	21 25 22.1	22 34.1	2 51.5	19 10.5	26 1.7	24 18.1	18 35.4	7 55.3	7 .5	23 48.8	21 36.1	26 37.3
14	21 29 18.6	23 30.5	2 48.2	2♒44.5	27 57.7	25 23.2	19 17.7	8 5.0	7 5.8	23 49.3	21 35.4	26 38.3
15	21 33 15.2	24 26.8	2 44.9	16 21.1	29 51.6	26 28.1	19 60.0	8 14.7	7 11.2	23 49.8	21 34.7	26 39.4
16	21 37 11.7	25 23.0	2 41.6	29 52.0	1♍43.4	27 32.9	20 42.1	8 24.5	7 16.6	23 50.4	21 34.0	26 40.5
17	21 41 8.3	26 19.0	2 38.3	13♓12.9	3 33.1	28 37.6	21 24.1	8 34.4	7 22.0	23 51.1	21 33.4	26 41.7
18	21 45 4.9	27 14.9	2 35.0	26 24.1	5 20.7	29 42.3	22 6.0	8 44.3	7 27.5	23 51.8	21 32.9	26 42.8
19	21 49 1.4	28 10.7	2 31.7	9♈30.9	7 6.3	0♎46.8	22 47.8	8 54.4	7 33.1	23 52.5	21 32.3	26 44.0
20	21 52 58.0	29 6.3	2 28.4	22 41.2	8 49.9	1 51.3	23 29.5	9 4.5	7 38.7	23 53.3	21 31.8	26 45.2
21	21 56 54.5	0♍ 1.9	2 25.1	6♉ 4.5	10 31.5	2 55.8	24 11.1	9 14.6	7 44.4	23 54.2	21 31.3	26 46.5
22	22 0 51.1	0 57.3	2 21.8	19 49.4	12 11.3	4 .2	24 52.6	9 24.8	7 50.1	23 55.1	21 30.9	26 47.8
23	22 4 47.6	1 52.7	2 18.5	4♊ 1.0	13 49.3	5 4.6	25 34.0	9 35.1	7 55.8	23 56.0	21 30.5	26 49.1
24	22 8 44.2	2 47.9	2 15.2	18 38.5	15 25.5	6 8.9	26 15.2	9 45.5	8 1.6	23 57.0	21 30.1	26 50.4
25	22 12 40.7	3 43.0	2 11.9	3♋33.9	17 .1	7 13.2	26 56.4	9 55.9	8 7.4	23 58.1	21 29.8	26 51.7
26	22 16 37.3	4 38.0	2 8.5	18 31.9	18 33.0	8 17.6	27 37.4	10 6.4	8 13.3	23 59.2	21 29.4	26 53.1
27	22 20 33.8	5 32.9	2 5.2	3♌15.1	20 4.4	9 21.9	28 18.3	10 16.9	8 19.2	24 .4	21 29.2	26 54.5
28	22 24 30.4	6 27.8	2 1.9	17 28.3	21 34.2	10 26.2	28 59.1	10 27.6	8 25.2	24 1.6	21 28.9	26 55.9
29	22 28 26.9	7 22.5	1 58.6	1♍ 2.7	23 2.6	11 30.6	29 39.8	10 38.2	8 31.2	24 2.9	21 28.7	26 57.3
30	22 32 23.5	8 17.2	1 55.3	13 56.9	24 29.6	12 35.0	0♌20.3	10 48.9	8 37.2	24 4.2	21 28.6	26 58.8
31	22 36 20.0	9 11.7	1 52.0	26 15.5	25 55.3	13 39.5	1 .8	10 59.7	8 43.3	24 5.6	21 28.4	27 .3
		DECLINATION										
1	20 38 3.4	18N 5.8	0N20.8	16N32.2	21N25.9	9N30.8	23N45.0	1S19.9	0S 5.9	19S 4.3	21S52.7	7N15.0
4	20 49 53.1	17 19.5	0 20.8	4 34.0	20 25.9	8 4.2	23 37.7	1 31.8	0 12.5	19 4.3	21 52.7	7 12.3
7	21 1 42.8	16 30.6	0 20.9	8S23.7	19 3.9	6 35.8	23 28.8	1 43.9	0 19.3	19 4.4	21 52.7	7 9.7
10	21 13 32.4	15 39.3	0 20.9	18 5.9	17 23.5	5 5.9	23 18.1	1 56.4	0 26.3	19 4.6	21 52.7	7 6.9
13	21 25 22.1	14 45.8	0 21.0	20 59.9	15 28.9	3 34.7	23 5.9	2 9.1	0 33.5	19 4.9	21 52.7	7 4.1
16	21 37 11.7	13 50.2	0 21.0	14 39.6	13 24.3	2 2.7	22 52.0	2 22.1	0 40.8	19 5.4	21 52.7	7 1.2
19	21 49 1.4	12 52.6	0 21.0	1 7.5	11 12.9	0 30.0	22 36.6	2 35.3	0 48.4	19 5.9	21 52.8	6 58.3
22	22 0 51.1	11 53.2	0 21.1	13N13.9	8 57.8	1S 2.9	22 19.7	2 48.7	0 56.0	19 6.5	21 52.8	6 55.4
25	22 12 40.7	10 52.1	0 21.1	20 56.0	6 41.0	2 35.8	22 1.4	3 2.3	1 3.8	19 7.3	21 52.9	6 52.4
28	22 24 30.4	9 49.4	0 21.1	17 34.7	4 24.2	4 8.4	21 41.6	3 16.1	1 11.8	19 8.1	21 53.0	6 49.4
31	22 36 20.0	8 45.3	0 21.2	6 7.1	2 8.9	5 40.5	21 20.5	3 30.1	1 19.8	19 9.1	21 53.1	6 46.4

SEPTEMBER 1981

LONGITUDE

DAY	EPHEM. SID. TIME h m s	☉ ° ′	☊ ° ′	☾ ° ′	☿ ° ′	♀ ° ′	♂ ° ′	♃ ° ′	♄ ° ′	♅ ° ′	♆ ° ′	♇ ° ′
1	22 40 16.6	8♍28.4	29♋38.7	6♎48.1	26♍59.4	15♎57.1	29♋19.3	11♎40.5	8♎38.9	26♏22.8	22♐ 5.4	22♎32.9
2	22 44 13.2	9 26.4	29 35.5	19 13.3	28 33.2	17 8.0	29 57.5	11 52.4	8 45.7	26 24.3	22R 5.3	22 34.8
3	22 48 9.7	10 24.6	29 32.3	1♏25.4	0♎ 5.7	18 18.8	0♌35.6	12 4.3	8 52.4	26 25.8	22 5.3	22 36.6
4	22 52 6.3	11 22.7	29 29.1	13 26.8	1 37.0	19 29.6	1 13.7	12 16.2	8 59.2	26 27.3	22 5.3	22 38.6
5	22 56 2.8	12 20.9	29 26.0	25 21.1	3 7.0	20 40.3	1 51.8	12 28.2	9 6.0	26 28.9	22 5.3	22 40.5
6	22 59 59.4	13 19.1	29 22.8	7♐12.5	4 35.8	21 51.0	2 29.8	12 40.3	9 12.9	26 30.5	22D 5.4	22 42.4
7	23 3 55.9	14 17.3	29 19.6	19 5.7	6 3.3	23 1.6	3 7.7	12 52.4	9 19.8	26 32.2	22 5.5	22 44.4
8	23 7 52.5	15 15.5	29 16.4	1♑ 5.8	7 29.5	24 12.1	3 45.6	13 4.5	9 26.7	26 33.9	22 5.6	22 46.4
9	23 11 49.0	16 13.8	29 13.3	13 17.8	8 54.4	25 22.6	4 23.4	13 16.7	9 33.7	26 35.7	22 5.8	22 48.4
10	23 15 45.6	17 12.1	29 10.1	25 46.4	10 17.9	26 33.0	5 1.1	13 29.0	9 40.7	26 37.5	22 6.0	22 50.5
11	23 19 42.1	18 10.4	29 6.9	8♒35.4	11 40.1	27 43.3	5 38.8	13 41.2	9 47.7	26 39.4	22 6.2	22 52.5
12	23 23 38.7	19 8.7	29 3.7	21 47.3	13 1.0	28 53.6	6 16.5	13 53.6	9 54.7	26 41.3	22 6.5	22 54.6
13	23 27 35.2	20 7.1	29 .5	5♓23.0	14 20.4	0♏ 3.7	6 54.1	14 5.9	10 1.8	26 43.2	22 6.8	22 56.7
14	23 31 31.8	21 5.5	28 57.4	19 21.1	15 38.3	1 13.9	7 31.6	14 18.3	10 8.9	26 45.2	22 7.1	22 58.8
15	23 35 28.3	22 3.9	28 54.2	3♈37.9	16 54.7	2 23.9	8 9.1	14 30.8	10 16.0	26 47.3	22 7.5	23 .9
16	23 39 24.9	23 2.4	28 51.0	18 7.7	18 9.5	3 33.9	8 46.5	14 43.2	10 23.1	26 49.3	22 7.9	23 3.0
17	23 43 21.4	24 .9	28 47.8	2♉43.8	19 22.7	4 43.8	9 23.9	14 55.8	10 30.3	26 51.5	22 8.3	23 5.2
18	23 47 18.0	24 59.5	28 44.7	17 19.3	20 34.1	5 53.6	10 1.2	15 8.3	10 37.5	26 53.6	22 8.8	23 7.3
19	23 51 14.5	25 58.0	28 41.5	1♊48.3	21 43.7	7 3.4	10 38.5	15 20.9	10 44.7	26 55.9	22 9.3	23 9.5
20	23 55 11.1	26 56.6	28 38.3	16 6.4	22 51.3	8 13.0	11 15.7	15 33.5	10 51.9	26 58.1	22 9.8	23 11.7
21	23 59 7.6	27 55.3	28 35.1	0♋11.4	23 56.9	9 22.6	11 52.8	15 46.2	10 59.1	27 .4	22 10.4	23 13.9
22	0 3 4.2	28 54.0	28 31.9	14 2.5	25 .3	10 32.2	12 30.0	15 58.9	11 6.4	27 2.8	22 11.0	23 16.2
23	0 7 .8	29 52.7	28 28.8	27 39.9	26 1.4	11 41.6	13 7.0	16 11.6	11 13.7	27 5.2	22 11.6	23 18.4
24	0 10 57.3	0♎51.5	28 25.6	11♌ 4.5	26 59.9	12 51.0	13 44.0	16 24.3	11 21.0	27 7.6	22 12.3	23 20.7
25	0 14 53.9	1 50.3	28 22.4	24 17.1	27 55.8	14 .3	14 20.9	16 37.1	11 28.3	27 10.1	22 13.0	23 22.9
26	0 18 50.4	2 49.1	28 19.2	7♍18.3	28 48.7	15 9.5	14 57.7	16 49.9	11 35.6	27 12.6	22 13.7	23 25.2
27	0 22 47.0	3 48.0	28 16.1	20 8.3	29 38.4	16 18.6	15 34.5	17 2.7	11 42.9	27 15.1	22 14.5	23 27.5
28	0 26 43.5	4 46.9	28 12.9	2♎47.1	0♏24.8	17 27.6	16 11.3	17 15.5	11 50.2	27 17.7	22 15.3	23 29.8
29	0 30 40.1	5 45.8	28 9.7	15 14.7	1 7.4	18 36.6	16 47.9	17 28.4	11 57.6	27 20.3	22 16.1	23 32.1
30	0 34 36.6	6 44.8	28 6.5	27 31.2	1 46.0	19 45.4	17 24.5	17 41.3	12 4.9	27 23.0	22 16.9	23 34.4

LATITUDE

DAY	EPHEM. SID. TIME	☉	☊	☾	☿	♀	♂	♃	♄	♅	♆	♇
1	22 40 16.6	0 .0	0 .0	4N42.5	0N13.6	0N 6.1	0N56.8	1N 7.6	2N14.0	0N11.6	1N19.2	16N42.4
4	22 52 6.3	0 .0	0 .0	5 2.4	0S 9.6	0S 4.4	0 58.7	1 7.3	2 13.8	0 11.5	1 19.1	16 41.3
7	23 3 55.9	0 .0	0 .0	3 26.5	0 33.7	0 15.1	1 .5	1 7.0	2 13.5	0 11.5	1 18.9	16 40.2
10	23 15 45.6	0 .0	0 .0	0 27.4	0 58.3	0 26.2	1 2.4	1 6.8	2 13.3	0 11.4	1 18.7	16 39.2
13	23 27 35.2	0 .0	0 .0	2S54.9	1 23.1	0 37.5	1 4.2	1 6.5	2 13.2	0 11.3	1 18.6	16 38.3
16	23 39 24.9	0 .0	0 .0	4 58.9	1 47.6	0 49.0	1 6.0	1 6.3	2 13.0	0 11.3	1 18.4	16 37.5
19	23 51 14.5	0 .0	0 .0	4 20.4	2 11.3	1 .6	1 7.9	1 6.1	2 12.9	0 11.2	1 18.3	16 36.7
22	0 3 4.2	0 .0	0 .0	1 24.4	2 33.8	1 12.3	1 9.7	1 5.9	2 12.8	0 11.2	1 18.1	16 36.0
25	0 14 53.9	0 .0	0 .0	2N 5.7	2 54.2	1 23.9	1 11.6	1 5.8	2 12.8	0 11.1	1 18.0	16 35.3
28	0 26 43.5	0 .0	0 .0	4 30.1	3 11.8	1 35.5	1 13.4	1 5.6	2 12.7	0 11.1	1 17.8	16 34.8

RIGHT ASCENSION

DAY	EPHEM. SID. TIME	☉	☊	☾	☿	♀	♂	♃	♄	♅	♆	♇
1	22 40 16.6	10♍ 6.3	1♌48.7	8♎ 6.3	27♍19.6	14♎44.0	1♌41.1	11♎10.6	8♎49.5	24♏ 7.0	21♐28.4	27♎ 1.9
2	22 44 13.2	11 .7	1 45.4	19 39.3	28 42.7	15 48.6	2 21.3	11 21.5	8 55.6	24 8.5	21R28.3	27 3.4
3	22 48 9.7	11 55.0	1 42.1	1♏ 4.5	0♎ 4.6	16 53.2	3 1.4	11 32.4	9 1.8	24 10.0	21 28.3	27 4.9
4	22 52 6.3	12 49.3	1 38.7	12 31.9	1 25.2	17 57.9	3 41.3	11 43.4	9 8.0	24 11.6	21 28.3	27 6.5
5	22 56 2.8	13 43.5	1 35.4	24 10.3	2 44.7	19 2.6	4 21.1	11 54.5	9 14.3	24 13.2	21 28.3	27 8.1
6	22 59 59.4	14 37.6	1 32.1	6♐ 6.8	4 3.0	20 7.5	5 .8	12 5.5	9 20.6	24 14.9	21D28.4	27 9.7
7	23 3 55.9	15 31.7	1 28.8	18 26.4	5 20.1	21 12.5	5 40.3	12 16.7	9 26.9	24 16.6	21 28.5	27 11.4
8	23 7 52.5	16 25.7	1 25.5	1♑10.4	6 36.2	22 17.5	6 19.8	12 27.9	9 33.2	24 18.4	21 28.6	27 13.0
9	23 11 49.0	17 19.7	1 22.2	14 16.8	7 51.1	23 22.7	6 59.1	12 39.1	9 39.6	24 20.2	21 28.8	27 14.7
10	23 15 45.6	18 13.6	1 18.9	27 40.0	9 4.9	24 28.0	7 38.2	12 50.4	9 46.0	24 22.1	21 29.0	27 16.4
11	23 19 42.1	19 7.5	1 15.5	11♒12.4	10 17.6	25 33.5	8 17.3	13 1.7	9 52.4	24 24.0	21 29.3	27 18.2
12	23 23 38.7	20 1.4	1 12.2	24 46.7	11 29.2	26 39.0	8 56.2	13 13.1	9 58.9	24 26.0	21 29.6	27 19.9
13	23 27 35.2	20 55.2	1 8.9	8♓17.6	12 39.5	27 44.7	9 35.0	13 24.5	10 5.3	24 28.0	21 29.9	27 21.6
14	23 31 31.8	21 49.0	1 5.6	21 43.9	13 48.7	28 50.6	10 13.6	13 35.9	10 11.8	24 30.0	21 30.2	27 23.4
15	23 35 28.3	22 42.8	1 2.3	5♈ 8.4	14 56.7	29 56.6	10 52.2	13 47.4	10 18.4	24 32.1	21 30.6	27 25.2
16	23 39 24.9	23 36.6	0 59.0	18 37.0	16 3.4	1♏ 2.8	11 30.6	13 58.9	10 24.9	24 34.3	21 31.0	27 27.0
17	23 43 21.4	24 30.4	0 55.6	2♉17.1	17 8.7	2 9.1	12 8.9	14 10.4	10 31.5	24 36.4	21 31.5	27 28.9
18	23 47 18.0	25 24.1	0 52.3	16 15.7	18 12.7	3 15.6	12 47.0	14 22.0	10 38.1	24 38.7	21 32.0	27 30.7
19	23 51 14.5	26 17.9	0 49.0	0♊36.5	19 15.1	4 22.3	13 25.1	14 33.7	10 44.7	24 41.0	21 32.5	27 32.6
20	23 55 11.1	27 11.7	0 45.7	15 18.0	20 16.0	5 29.2	14 3.0	14 45.3	10 51.3	24 43.3	21 33.1	27 34.5
21	23 59 7.6	28 5.6	0 42.4	0♋12.2	21 15.2	6 36.2	14 40.7	14 57.0	10 58.0	24 45.6	21 33.7	27 36.3
22	0 3 4.2	28 59.5	0 39.0	15 5.4	22 12.6	7 43.6	15 18.4	15 8.8	11 4.7	24 48.1	21 34.4	27 38.3
23	0 7 .8	29 53.3	0 35.7	29 41.9	23 8.0	8 51.0	15 56.0	15 20.6	11 11.3	24 50.6	21 35.1	27 40.2
24	0 10 57.3	0♎47.2	0 32.4	13♌48.8	24 1.3	9 58.7	16 33.4	15 32.3	11 18.0	24 53.1	21 35.8	27 42.2
25	0 14 53.9	1 41.2	0 29.1	27 18.7	24 52.2	11 6.6	17 10.6	15 44.2	11 24.8	24 55.6	21 36.5	27 44.1
26	0 18 50.4	2 35.2	0 25.7	10♍10.6	25 40.6	12 14.6	17 47.8	15 56.0	11 31.5	24 58.2	21 37.3	27 46.1
27	0 22 47.0	3 29.2	0 22.4	22 28.8	26 26.3	13 22.9	18 24.8	16 7.9	11 38.2	25 .8	21 38.1	27 48.1
28	0 26 43.5	4 23.3	0 19.1	4♎20.7	27 8.9	14 31.4	19 1.7	16 19.8	11 45.0	25 3.4	21 38.9	27 50.1
29	0 30 40.1	5 17.5	0 15.8	15 55.3	27 48.3	15 40.1	19 38.4	16 31.7	11 51.7	25 6.1	21 39.8	27 52.1
30	0 34 36.6	6 11.7	0 12.5	27 21.6	28 24.0	16 49.0	20 15.1	16 43.7	11 58.5	25 8.9	21 40.7	27 54.1

DECLINATION

DAY	EPHEM. SID. TIME	☉	☊	☾	☿	♀	♂	♃	♄	♅	♆	♇
1	22 40 16.6	8N23.6	0N21.2	1N37.5	1N24.3	6S11.0	21N13.2	3S34.8	1S22.6	19S 9.5	21S53.2	6N45.4
4	22 52 6.3	7 17.9	0 21.2	11S 3.8	0S47.4	7 41.7	20 50.4	3 49.0	1 30.8	19 10.6	21 53.3	6 42.3
7	23 3 55.9	6 11.1	0 21.3	19 33.8	2 55.2	9 11.1	20 26.4	4 3.3	1 39.1	19 11.7	21 53.5	6 39.3
10	23 15 45.6	5 3.3	0 21.3	20 32.6	4 58.3	10 38.9	20 1.3	4 17.8	1 47.4	19 13.0	21 53.7	6 36.2
13	23 27 35.2	3 54.9	0 21.3	12 14.9	6 55.8	12 4.8	19 35.0	4 32.3	1 55.9	19 14.4	21 53.9	6 33.2
16	23 39 24.9	2 45.8	0 21.4	2N30.1	8 46.7	13 28.4	19 7.7	4 46.9	2 4.3	19 15.9	21 54.1	6 30.1
19	23 51 14.5	1 36.2	0 21.4	16 16.2	10 29.8	14 49.4	18 39.4	5 1.6	2 12.9	19 17.4	21 54.4	6 27.1
22	0 3 4.2	0 26.2	0 21.4	21 18.1	12 3.8	16 7.6	18 10.2	5 16.4	2 21.4	19 19.1	21 54.6	6 24.1
25	0 14 53.9	0S43.9	0 21.5	15 24.1	13 26.9	17 22.7	17 40.1	5 31.2	2 30.0	19 20.8	21 54.9	6 21.1
28	0 26 43.5	1 54.0	0 21.5	3 1.4	14 36.5	18 34.2	17 9.2	5 46.1	2 38.6	19 22.6	21 55.2	6 18.2

OCTOBER 1981

LONGITUDE

DAY	EPHEM. SID. TIME h m s	☉ ° ′	☊ ° ′	☽ ° ′	☿ ° ′	♀ ° ′	♂ ° ′	♃ ° ′	♄ ° ′	♅ ° ′	♆ ° ′	♇ ° ′
1	0 38 33.2	7♎43.8	28♋ 3.3	9♏37.5	2♏20.2	20♏54.1	18♌ 1.1	17♎54.2	12♎12.3	27♏25.6	22♐17.8	23♎36.7
2	0 42 29.7	8 42.8	28 .2	21 35.3	2 49.6	22 2.8	18 37.5	18 7.1	12 19.6	27 28.4	22 18.7	23 39.1
3	0 46 26.3	9 41.9	27 57.0	3♐26.9	3 13.9	23 11.3	19 13.9	18 20.0	12 27.0	27 31.1	22 19.7	23 41.4
4	0 50 22.8	10 41.0	27 53.8	15 16.0	3 32.5	24 19.7	19 50.3	18 33.0	12 34.4	27 33.9	22 20.6	23 43.8
5	0 54 19.4	11 40.1	27 50.6	27 6.6	3 45.2	25 28.0	20 26.5	18 45.9	12 41.7	27 36.8	22 21.6	23 46.1
6	0 58 15.9	12 39.3	27 47.4	9♑ 3.7	3 51.2	26 36.2	21 2.7	18 58.9	12 49.1	27 39.6	22 22.7	23 48.5
7	1 2 12.5	13 38.4	27 44.3	21 12.6	3R50.4	27 44.3	21 38.9	19 11.9	12 56.5	27 42.5	22 23.7	23 50.9
8	1 6 9.0	14 37.6	27 41.1	3♒38.7	3 42.1	28 52.2	22 14.9	19 24.9	13 3.8	27 45.5	22 24.8	23 53.2
9	1 10 5.6	15 36.9	27 37.9	16 26.9	3 26.1	0♐ .1	22 50.9	19 37.9	13 11.2	27 48.4	22 26.0	23 55.6
10	1 14 2.1	16 36.2	27 34.7	29 41.3	3 2.0	1 7.8	23 26.9	19 50.9	13 18.6	27 51.4	22 27.1	23 58.0
11	1 17 58.7	17 35.5	27 31.6	13♓24.0	2 29.8	2 15.3	24 2.7	20 3.9	13 25.9	27 54.4	22 28.3	24 .4
12	1 21 55.3	18 34.8	27 28.4	27 34.6	1 49.3	3 22.7	24 38.5	20 16.9	13 33.3	27 57.5	22 29.5	24 2.8
13	1 25 51.8	19 34.2	27 25.2	12♈ 9.7	1 .9	4 30.0	25 14.3	20 30.0	13 40.7	28 .6	22 30.8	24 5.2
14	1 29 48.4	20 33.6	27 22.0	27 2.6	0 5.1	5 37.2	25 49.9	20 43.0	13 48.0	28 3.7	22 32.1	24 7.6
15	1 33 44.9	21 33.0	27 18.8	12♉ 4.2	29♎ 2.7	6 44.1	26 25.5	20 56.0	13 55.3	28 6.9	22 33.4	24 10.0
16	1 37 41.5	22 32.5	27 15.7	27 4.6	27 54.9	7 51.0	27 1.0	21 9.0	14 2.6	28 10.1	22 34.7	24 12.4
17	1 41 38.0	23 32.0	27 12.5	11♊55.0	26 43.2	8 57.6	27 36.5	21 22.1	14 10.0	28 13.3	22 36.0	24 14.8
18	1 45 34.6	24 31.6	27 9.3	26 28.7	25 29.5	10 4.1	28 11.8	21 35.1	14 17.3	28 16.5	22 37.4	24 17.2
19	1 49 31.1	25 31.1	27 6.1	10♋41.9	24 15.8	11 10.5	28 47.1	21 48.1	14 24.5	28 19.7	22 38.8	24 19.6
20	1 53 27.7	26 30.8	27 3.0	24 33.6	23 4.3	12 16.6	29 22.4	22 1.1	14 31.8	28 23.0	22 40.3	24 22.0
21	1 57 24.2	27 30.4	26 59.8	8♌ 4.8	21 57.1	13 22.6	29 57.5	22 14.1	14 39.1	28 26.3	22 41.7	24 24.4
22	2 1 20.8	28 30.1	26 56.6	21 17.5	20 56.2	14 28.4	0♍32.6	22 27.2	14 46.3	28 29.6	22 43.2	24 26.8
23	2 5 17.3	29 29.9	26 53.4	4♍14.4	20 3.4	15 34.1	1 7.6	22 40.1	14 53.5	28 33.0	22 44.7	24 29.2
24	2 9 13.9	0♏29.6	26 50.2	16 57.9	19 20.2	16 39.5	1 42.5	22 53.1	15 .7	28 36.3	22 46.3	24 31.6
25	2 13 10.4	1 29.4	26 47.1	29 30.2	18 47.6	17 44.7	2 17.3	23 6.1	15 7.9	28 39.7	22 47.8	24 34.0
26	2 17 7.0	2 29.3	26 43.9	11♎52.8	18 26.2	18 49.8	2 52.1	23 19.1	15 15.1	28 43.2	22 49.4	24 36.4
27	2 21 3.6	3 29.2	26 40.7	24 6.7	18 16.2	19 54.6	3 26.7	23 32.0	15 22.2	28 46.6	22 51.0	24 38.8
28	2 25 .1	4 29.1	26 37.5	6♏12.7	18D17.5	20 59.2	4 1.3	23 45.0	15 29.3	28 50.0	22 52.7	24 41.2
29	2 28 56.7	5 29.0	26 34.4	18 11.9	18 29.8	22 3.6	4 35.8	23 57.9	15 36.4	28 53.5	22 54.3	24 43.6
30	2 32 53.2	6 29.0	26 31.2	0♐ 5.3	18 52.5	23 7.8	5 10.2	24 10.8	15 43.5	28 57.0	22 56.0	24 45.9
31	2 36 49.8	7 29.0	26 28.0	11 54.7	19 24.9	24 11.7	5 44.5	24 23.7	15 50.6	29 .5	22 57.7	24 48.3

LATITUDE

DAY	SID. TIME	☉	☊	☽	☿	♀	♂	♃	♄	♅	♆	♇
1	0 38 33.2	0 .0	0 .0	4N56.8	3S25.1	1S46.9	1N15.3	1N 5.5	2N12.7	0N11.0	1N17.7	16N34.3
4	0 50 22.8	0 .0	0 .0	3 28.1	3 32.5	1 58.2	1 17.1	1 5.4	2 12.7	0 11.0	1 17.5	16 33.9
7	1 2 12.5	0 .0	0 .0	0 38.7	3 31.4	2 9.1	1 19.0	1 5.3	2 12.8	0 10.9	1 17.4	16 33.6
10	1 14 2.1	0 .0	0 .0	2S37.0	3 18.7	2 19.7	1 20.9	1 5.2	2 12.9	0 10.9	1 17.2	16 33.3
13	1 25 51.8	0 .0	0 .0	4 49.1	2 51.2	2 29.9	1 22.7	1 5.1	2 13.0	0 10.8	1 17.1	16 33.2
16	1 37 41.5	0 .0	0 .0	4 21.7	2 7.4	2 39.5	1 24.6	1 5.1	2 13.1	0 10.8	1 17.0	16 33.1
19	1 49 31.1	0 .0	0 .0	1 26.3	1 10.5	2 48.6	1 26.5	1 5.1	2 13.3	0 10.8	1 16.8	16 33.1
22	2 1 20.8	0 .0	0 .0	2N 3.3	0 8.8	2 56.9	1 28.4	1 5.1	2 13.5	0 10.7	1 16.7	16 33.1
25	2 13 10.4	0 .0	0 .0	4 26.7	0N47.1	3 4.5	1 30.4	1 5.1	2 13.7	0 10.7	1 16.6	16 33.3
28	2 25 .1	0 .0	0 .0	4 55.2	1 29.7	3 11.2	1 32.3	1 5.1	2 13.9	0 10.6	1 16.5	16 33.5
31	2 36 49.8	0 .0	0 .0	3 28.6	1 57.0	3 17.0	1 34.3	1 5.2	2 14.2	0 10.6	1 16.4	16 33.8

RIGHT ASCENSION

DAY	SID. TIME	☉	☊	☽	☿	♀	♂	♃	♄	♅	♆	♇
1	0 38 33.2	7♎ 5.9	0♌ 9.1	8♏48.7	28♎55.8	17♏58.1	20♌51.5	16♎55.7	12♎ 5.3	25♏11.6	21♐41.7	27♎56.1
2	0 42 29.7	8 .3	0 5.8	20 24.4	29 23.2	19 7.5	21 27.9	17 7.6	12 12.1	25 14.5	21 42.6	27 58.2
3	0 46 26.3	8 54.7	0 2.5	2♐14.9	29 45.9	20 17.0	22 4.1	17 19.7	12 18.8	25 17.3	21 43.7	28 .2
4	0 50 22.8	9 49.2	29♋59.1	14 24.5	0♏ 3.5	21 26.7	22 40.2	17 31.7	12 25.6	25 20.2	21 44.7	28 2.3
5	0 54 19.4	10 43.7	29 55.8	26 54.8	0 15.5	22 36.6	23 16.2	17 43.7	12 32.4	25 23.1	21 45.8	28 4.3
6	0 58 15.9	11 38.4	29 52.5	9♑44.3	0 21.6	23 46.7	23 52.0	17 55.8	12 39.2	25 26.1	21 46.9	28 6.4
7	1 2 12.5	12 33.1	29 49.2	22 49.2	0R21.3	24 56.9	24 27.8	18 7.9	12 46.0	25 29.1	21 48.0	28 8.5
8	1 6 9.0	13 28.0	29 45.8	6♒ 4.1	0 14.2	26 7.4	25 3.3	18 20.0	12 52.8	25 32.1	21 49.2	28 10.6
9	1 10 5.6	14 22.9	29 42.5	19 23.6	0 .1	27 18.0	25 38.8	18 32.1	12 59.7	25 35.1	21 50.4	28 12.7
10	1 14 2.1	15 18.0	29 39.2	2♓44.2	29♎38.7	28 28.7	26 14.1	18 44.2	13 6.5	25 38.2	21 51.7	28 14.8
11	1 17 58.7	16 13.1	29 35.8	16 5.3	29 10.0	29 39.6	26 49.3	18 56.3	13 13.3	25 41.4	21 52.9	28 16.9
12	1 21 55.3	17 8.4	29 32.5	29 29.9	28 34.1	0♐50.7	27 24.4	19 8.5	13 20.1	25 44.5	21 54.2	28 19.1
13	1 25 51.8	18 3.8	29 29.2	13♈ 3.8	27 51.3	2 1.9	27 59.4	19 20.7	13 26.9	25 47.8	21 55.6	28 21.2
14	1 29 48.4	18 59.4	29 25.9	26 54.4	27 2.2	3 13.2	28 34.3	19 32.8	13 33.7	25 51.0	21 57.0	28 23.4
15	1 33 44.9	19 55.0	29 22.5	11♉ 8.4	26 7.6	4 24.6	29 9.0	19 45.0	13 40.5	25 54.2	21 58.4	28 25.5
16	1 37 41.5	20 50.9	29 19.2	25 49.4	25 8.7	5 36.2	29 43.5	19 57.2	13 47.2	25 57.5	21 59.8	28 27.7
17	1 41 38.0	21 46.8	29 15.9	10♊54.8	24 7.0	6 47.8	0♍18.0	20 9.3	13 54.0	26 .8	22 1.2	28 29.8
18	1 45 34.6	22 42.9	29 12.5	26 14.2	23 4.0	7 59.4	0 52.4	20 21.5	14 .8	26 4.1	22 2.7	28 32.0
19	1 49 31.1	23 39.2	29 9.2	11♋30.7	22 1.7	9 11.2	1 26.6	20 33.7	14 7.5	26 7.5	22 4.2	28 34.1
20	1 53 27.7	24 35.6	29 5.9	26 26.0	21 2.0	10 23.0	2 .7	20 45.9	14 14.3	26 10.9	22 5.8	28 36.3
21	1 57 24.2	25 32.2	29 2.5	10♌45.4	20 6.5	11 34.8	2 34.6	20 58.1	14 21.0	26 14.3	22 7.3	28 38.5
22	2 1 20.8	26 28.9	28 59.2	24 21.6	19 17.2	12 46.6	3 8.5	21 10.2	14 27.7	26 17.7	22 8.9	28 40.6
23	2 5 17.3	27 25.8	28 55.9	7♍15.0	18 35.3	13 58.5	3 42.2	21 22.4	14 34.4	26 21.2	22 10.6	28 42.8
24	2 9 13.9	28 22.9	28 52.5	19 31.1	18 2.1	15 10.3	4 15.8	21 34.6	14 41.1	26 24.7	22 12.2	28 45.0
25	2 13 10.4	29 20.2	28 49.2	1♎19.0	17 38.3	16 22.1	4 49.3	21 46.8	14 47.8	26 28.2	22 13.9	28 47.1
26	2 17 7.0	0♏17.7	28 45.8	12 48.5	17 24.4	17 33.8	5 22.7	21 59.0	14 54.4	26 31.7	22 15.6	28 49.3
27	2 21 3.6	1 15.3	28 42.5	24 9.9	17 20.6	18 45.5	5 55.9	22 11.1	15 1.0	26 35.3	22 17.3	28 51.5
28	2 25 .1	2 13.1	28 39.2	5♏32.2	17D26.6	19 57.1	6 29.0	22 23.3	15 7.7	26 38.9	22 19.1	28 53.7
29	2 28 56.7	3 11.1	28 35.8	17 3.3	17 42.2	21 8.5	7 2.0	22 35.4	15 14.3	26 42.5	22 20.9	28 55.8
30	2 32 53.2	4 9.4	28 32.5	28 49.3	18 6.7	22 19.8	7 34.8	22 47.6	15 20.8	26 46.1	22 22.7	28 58.0
31	2 36 49.8	5 7.7	28 29.2	10♐53.6	18 39.6	23 31.0	8 7.5	22 59.7	15 27.4	26 49.7	22 24.5	29 .1

DECLINATION

DAY	SID. TIME	☉	☊	☽	☿	♀	♂	♃	♄	♅	♆	♇
1	0 38 33.2	3S 4.0	0N21.5	10S .0	15S29.5	19S42.0	16N37.5	6S .9	2S47.2	19S24.4	21S55.4	6N15.3
4	0 50 22.8	4 13.7	0 21.6	19 10.7	16 1.5	20 45.8	16 5.2	6 15.7	2 55.8	19 26.4	21 55.8	6 12.5
7	1 2 12.5	5 23.0	0 21.6	21 7.9	16 6.6	21 45.2	15 32.2	6 30.6	3 4.3	19 28.4	21 56.1	6 9.7
10	1 14 2.1	6 31.6	0 21.6	14 1.9	15 38.0	22 39.9	14 58.6	6 45.4	3 12.8	19 30.4	21 56.4	6 6.9
13	1 25 51.8	7 39.4	0 21.7	0N22.2	14 30.0	23 29.8	14 24.5	7 .1	3 21.3	19 32.5	21 56.8	6 4.3
16	1 37 41.5	8 46.3	0 21.7	15 15.5	12 42.9	24 14.6	13 49.9	7 14.8	3 29.6	19 34.7	21 57.1	6 1.7
19	1 49 31.1	9 52.1	0 21.7	21 34.5	10 30.0	24 54.0	13 14.9	7 29.4	3 37.9	19 36.9	21 57.5	5 59.1
22	2 1 20.8	10 56.6	0 21.8	16 21.0	8 18.5	25 27.9	12 39.6	7 43.9	3 46.2	19 39.1	21 57.8	5 56.7
25	2 13 10.4	11 59.6	0 21.8	4 16.5	6 38.2	25 56.2	12 4.0	7 58.3	3 54.3	19 41.3	21 58.2	5 54.3
28	2 25 .1	13 1.0	0 21.8	8S56.6	5 47.3	26 18.8	11 28.1	8 12.6	4 2.3	19 43.6	21 58.6	5 52.1
31	2 36 49.8	14 .5	0 21.8	18 46.3	5 47.6	26 35.6	10 52.0	8 26.7	4 10.2	19 46.0	21 59.0	5 49.9

NOVEMBER 1981

DAY	EPHEM. SID. TIME	☉	☊	☾	☿	♀	♂	♃	♄	♅	♆	♇
	h m s	° ′	° ′	° ′	° ′	° ′	° ′	° ′	° ′	° ′	° ′	° ′
		LONGITUDE										
1	2 40 46.3	8♏29.0	26♋24.8	23♐42.5	20♎ 6.0	25♐15.4	6♍18.7	24♎36.5	15♎57.6	29♏ 4.0	22♐59.4	24♎50.6
2	2 44 42.9	9 29.1	26 21.6	5♑32.2	20 55.1	26 18.8	6 52.9	24 49.4	16 4.6	29 7.6	23 1.2	24 53.0
3	2 48 39.4	10 29.2	26 18.5	17 27.7	21 51.4	27 21.9	7 27.0	25 2.2	16 11.6	29 11.2	23 3.0	24 55.4
4	2 52 36.0	11 29.3	26 15.3	29 33.8	22 53.8	28 24.8	8 .9	25 15.0	16 18.5	29 14.8	23 4.8	24 57.7
5	2 56 32.5	12 29.5	26 12.1	11♒55.6	24 1.6	29 27.3	8 34.7	25 27.8	16 25.4	29 18.4	23 6.6	25 .0
6	3 0 29.1	13 29.6	26 8.9	24 38.5	25 14.2	0♑29.6	9 8.5	25 40.5	16 32.2	29 22.0	23 8.4	25 2.3
7	3 4 25.7	14 29.8	26 5.8	7♓47.3	26 30.8	1 31.5	9 42.1	25 53.2	16 39.0	29 25.6	23 10.3	25 4.6
8	3 8 22.2	15 30.0	26 2.6	21 25.3	27 50.8	2 33.1	10 15.7	26 5.9	16 45.8	29 29.2	23 12.2	25 6.9
9	3 12 18.8	16 30.3	25 59.4	5♈33.9	29 13.7	3 34.3	10 49.2	26 18.6	16 52.6	29 32.8	23 14.1	25 9.2
10	3 16 15.3	17 30.5	25 56.2	20 11.1	0♏39.0	4 35.2	11 22.5	26 31.2	16 59.3	29 36.5	23 16.0	25 11.5
11	3 20 11.9	18 30.8	25 53.1	5♉11.5	2 6.4	5 35.7	11 55.8	26 43.7	17 5.9	29 40.1	23 17.9	25 13.7
12	3 24 8.4	19 31.2	25 49.9	20 26.0	3 35.4	6 35.8	12 28.9	26 56.3	17 12.6	29 43.8	23 19.8	25 16.0
13	3 28 5.0	20 31.5	25 46.7	5♊43.8	5 5.8	7 35.6	13 2.0	27 8.8	17 19.1	29 47.5	23 21.8	25 18.2
14	3 32 1.5	21 31.9	25 43.5	20 53.6	6 37.4	8 34.9	13 34.9	27 21.3	17 25.7	29 51.1	23 23.8	25 20.4
15	3 35 58.1	22 32.3	25 40.3	5♋46.2	8 9.8	9 33.8	14 7.8	27 33.7	17 32.2	29 54.8	23 25.8	25 22.6
16	3 39 54.7	23 32.7	25 37.2	20 15.5	9 42.9	10 32.2	14 40.5	27 46.1	17 38.6	29 58.5	23 27.8	25 24.8
17	3 43 51.2	24 33.2	25 34.0	4♌18.7	11 16.6	11 30.2	15 13.1	27 58.4	17 45.0	0♐ 2.2	23 29.8	25 27.0
18	3 47 47.8	25 33.7	25 30.8	17 55.7	12 50.7	12 27.7	15 45.6	28 10.7	17 51.4	0 5.9	23 31.9	25 29.1
19	3 51 44.3	26 34.2	25 27.6	1♍ 8.7	14 25.1	13 24.8	16 18.0	28 23.0	17 57.7	0 9.6	23 33.9	25 31.3
20	3 55 40.9	27 34.8	25 24.5	14 .9	15 59.7	14 21.3	16 50.3	28 35.2	18 4.0	0 13.3	23 36.0	25 33.4
21	3 59 37.4	28 35.4	25 21.3	26 36.0	17 34.5	15 17.3	17 22.5	28 47.3	18 10.2	0 17.0	23 38.1	25 35.5
22	4 3 34.0	29 36.0	25 18.1	8♎57.5	19 9.3	16 12.7	17 54.5	28 59.5	18 16.4	0 20.8	23 40.2	25 37.6
23	4 7 30.5	0♐36.6	25 14.9	21 8.4	20 44.2	17 7.6	18 26.4	29 11.5	18 22.5	0 24.5	23 42.3	25 39.7
24	4 11 27.1	1 37.4	25 11.8	3♏11.5	22 19.2	18 2.0	18 58.2	29 23.6	18 28.6	0 28.2	23 44.5	25 41.8
25	4 15 23.7	2 38.1	25 8.6	15 8.6	23 54.1	18 55.6	19 29.9	29 35.5	18 34.6	0 31.9	23 46.6	25 43.8
26	4 19 20.2	3 38.8	25 5.4	27 1.6	25 28.9	19 48.7	20 1.4	29 47.4	18 40.5	0 35.7	23 48.8	25 45.8
27	4 23 16.8	4 39.5	25 2.2	8♐52.0	27 3.7	20 41.0	20 32.8	29 59.3	18 46.4	0 39.4	23 50.9	25 47.8
28	4 27 13.3	5 40.3	24 59.0	20 41.2	28 38.4	21 32.7	21 4.0	0♏11.0	18 52.2	0 43.1	23 53.1	25 49.8
29	4 31 9.9	6 41.1	24 55.9	2♑31.3	0♐13.1	22 23.7	21 35.1	0 22.8	18 58.0	0 46.8	23 55.3	25 51.7
30	4 35 6.4	7 41.9	24 52.7	14 24.5	1 47.6	23 13.8	22 6.1	0 34.4	19 3.7	0 50.5	23 57.5	25 53.7
		LATITUDE										
1	2 40 46.3	0 .0	0 .0	2N39.6	2N 2.8	3S18.7	1N34.9	1N 5.2	2N14.3	0N10.6	1N16.3	16N34.0
4	2 52 36.0	0 .0	0 .0	0S22.0	2 12.0	3 23.1	1 36.9	1 5.3	2 14.6	0 10.5	1 16.2	16 34.4
7	3 4 25.7	0 .0	0 .0	3 25.1	2 11.1	3 26.3	1 38.9	1 5.4	2 14.9	0 10.5	1 16.1	16 34.9
10	3 16 15.3	0 .0	0 .0	5 1.7	2 2.9	3 28.3	1 40.9	1 5.5	2 15.3	0 10.5	1 16.0	16 35.5
13	3 28 5.0	0 .0	0 .0	3 48.8	1 49.5	3 28.8	1 42.9	1 5.6	2 15.7	0 10.4	1 15.9	16 36.1
16	3 39 54.7	0 .0	0 .0	0 21.9	1 32.8	3 27.9	1 45.0	1 5.8	2 16.1	0 10.4	1 15.8	16 36.9
19	3 51 44.3	0 .0	0 .0	3N 3.7	1 13.9	3 25.4	1 47.1	1 6.0	2 16.6	0 10.4	1 15.8	16 37.7
22	4 3 34.0	0 .0	0 .0	4 55.0	0 53.7	3 21.2	1 49.2	1 6.2	2 17.0	0 10.4	1 15.7	16 38.5
25	4 15 23.7	0 .0	0 .0	4 44.8	0 32.9	3 15.1	1 51.3	1 6.4	2 17.5	0 10.3	1 15.6	16 39.5
28	4 27 13.3	0 .0	0 .0	2 46.0	0 12.0	3 7.0	1 53.4	1 6.6	2 18.1	0 10.3	1 15.6	16 40.5
		RIGHT ASCENSION										
1	2 40 46.3	6♏ 6.3	28♋25.8	23♐17.0	19♎20.2	24♐41.9	8♍40.1	23♎11.8	15♎33.9	26♏53.4	22♐26.4	29♎ 2.3
2	2 44 42.9	7 5.1	28 22.5	5♑57.2	20 7.6	25 52.7	9 12.6	23 23.9	15 40.4	26 57.1	22 28.3	29 4.5
3	2 48 39.4	8 4.2	28 19.1	18 49.6	21 1.2	27 3.3	9 45.0	23 36.0	15 46.9	27 .8	22 30.2	29 6.7
4	2 52 36.0	9 3.3	28 15.8	1♒48.5	22 .2	28 13.5	10 17.2	23 48.1	15 53.4	27 4.5	22 32.1	29 8.8
5	2 56 32.5	10 2.7	28 12.5	14 48.7	23 3.9	29 23.5	10 49.3	24 .1	15 59.8	27 8.2	22 34.1	29 10.9
6	3 0 29.1	11 2.3	28 9.1	27 47.6	24 11.9	0♑33.1	11 21.3	24 12.1	16 6.2	27 11.9	22 36.1	29 13.1
7	3 4 25.7	12 2.1	28 5.8	10♓45.7	25 23.5	1 42.4	11 53.1	24 24.1	16 12.5	27 15.7	22 38.1	29 15.2
8	3 8 22.2	13 2.1	28 2.4	23 47.3	26 38.2	2 51.3	12 24.8	24 36.1	16 18.9	27 19.5	22 40.1	29 17.3
9	3 12 18.8	14 2.3	27 59.1	6♈59.6	27 55.7	3 59.8	12 56.4	24 48.0	16 25.2	27 23.2	22 42.1	29 19.5
10	3 16 15.3	15 2.7	27 55.8	20 32.2	29 15.5	5 7.9	13 27.9	24 60.0	16 31.4	27 27.0	22 44.2	29 21.6
11	3 20 11.9	16 3.3	27 52.4	4♉34.7	0♏37.4	6 15.6	13 59.2	25 11.9	16 37.7	27 30.8	22 46.2	29 23.7
12	3 24 8.4	17 4.1	27 49.1	19 14.3	2 1.0	7 22.7	14 30.4	25 23.7	16 43.8	27 34.6	22 48.3	29 25.8
13	3 28 5.0	18 5.2	27 45.7	4♊31.7	3 26.1	8 29.4	15 1.5	25 35.6	16 50.0	27 38.4	22 50.5	29 27.8
14	3 32 1.5	19 6.4	27 42.4	20 17.7	4 52.5	9 35.5	15 32.5	25 47.4	16 56.1	27 42.2	22 52.6	29 29.9
15	3 35 58.1	20 7.9	27 39.0	6♋12.6	6 20.2	10 41.0	16 3.3	25 59.2	17 2.2	27 46.1	22 54.7	29 32.0
16	3 39 54.7	21 9.6	27 35.7	21 51.4	7 48.8	11 46.0	16 34.1	26 10.9	17 8.2	27 49.9	22 56.9	29 34.0
17	3 43 51.2	22 11.5	27 32.3	6♌52.0	9 18.4	12 50.3	17 4.7	26 22.7	17 14.2	27 53.8	22 59.1	29 36.1
18	3 47 47.8	23 13.6	27 29.0	21 1.5	10 48.8	13 54.0	17 35.1	26 34.3	17 20.2	27 57.6	23 1.3	29 38.1
19	3 51 44.3	24 15.9	27 25.6	4♍18.1	12 20.0	14 57.1	18 5.5	26 46.0	17 26.1	28 1.5	23 3.5	29 40.1
20	3 55 40.9	25 18.4	27 22.3	16 47.7	13 51.8	15 59.4	18 35.7	26 57.6	17 32.0	28 5.3	23 5.7	29 42.2
21	3 59 37.4	26 21.2	27 19.0	28 40.9	15 24.3	17 1.0	19 5.7	27 9.2	17 37.8	28 9.2	23 8.0	29 44.2
22	4 3 34.0	27 24.1	27 15.6	10♎ 9.8	16 57.4	18 1.9	19 35.7	27 20.7	17 43.6	28 13.0	23 10.3	29 46.1
23	4 7 30.5	28 27.3	27 12.3	21 26.5	18 31.0	19 1.9	20 5.5	27 32.2	17 49.3	28 16.9	23 12.5	29 48.1
24	4 11 27.1	29 30.7	27 8.9	2♏42.0	20 5.3	20 1.2	20 35.2	27 43.7	17 55.0	28 20.8	23 14.9	29 50.1
25	4 15 23.7	0♐34.2	27 5.6	14 5.7	21 40.0	20 59.6	21 4.7	27 55.1	18 .7	28 24.7	23 17.2	29 52.1
26	4 19 20.2	1 38.0	27 2.2	25 45.0	23 15.2	21 57.2	21 34.1	28 6.4	18 6.3	28 28.5	23 19.5	29 54.0
27	4 23 16.8	2 41.9	26 58.9	7♐44.2	24 51.0	22 53.8	22 3.4	28 17.7	18 11.8	28 32.4	23 21.8	29 55.9
28	4 27 13.3	3 46.0	26 55.5	20 4.4	26 27.2	23 49.4	22 32.5	28 28.9	18 17.3	28 36.3	23 24.1	29 57.8
29	4 31 9.9	4 50.3	26 52.2	2♑42.7	28 3.9	24 44.1	23 1.4	28 40.1	18 22.7	28 40.1	23 26.5	29 59.7
30	4 35 6.4	5 54.7	26 48.8	15 33.1	29 41.1	25 37.7	23 30.3	28 51.3	18 28.0	28 44.0	23 28.9	0♏ 1.5
		DECLINATION										
1	2 40 46.3	14S19.9	0N21.9	20S38.0	5S57.7	26S39.9	10N40.0	8S31.4	4S12.8	19S46.7	21S59.1	5N49.2
4	2 52 36.0	15 16.8	0 21.9	20 36.1	6 51.5	26 48.9	10 3.7	8 45.4	4 20.5	19 49.1	21 59.5	5 47.1
7	3 4 25.7	16 11.3	0 21.9	11 49.1	8 11.4	26 52.2	9 27.5	8 59.2	4 28.0	19 51.5	21 59.8	5 45.2
10	3 16 15.3	17 3.5	0 22.0	3N13.7	9 46.9	26 49.8	8 51.2	9 12.8	4 35.4	19 53.8	22 .2	5 43.3
13	3 28 5.0	17 52.9	0 22.0	17 30.4	11 30.0	26 41.9	8 15.0	9 26.2	4 42.6	19 56.2	22 .6	5 41.6
16	3 39 54.7	18 39.6	0 22.0	21 33.1	13 15.4	26 28.6	7 38.9	9 39.4	4 49.7	19 58.6	22 1.0	5 40.0
19	3 51 44.3	19 23.4	0 22.0	13 55.6	14 59.3	26 10.2	7 3.0	9 52.3	4 56.5	20 1.0	22 1.4	5 38.5
22	4 3 34.0	20 4.0	0 22.1	0 58.2	16 39.1	25 47.1	6 27.3	10 5.1	5 3.1	20 3.3	22 1.7	5 37.2
25	4 15 23.7	20 41.3	0 22.1	11S50.1	18 13.1	25 19.4	5 51.8	10 17.6	5 9.6	20 5.7	22 2.1	5 35.9
28	4 27 13.3	21 15.1	0 22.1	20 21.2	19 39.7	24 47.6	5 16.7	10 29.8	5 15.7	20 8.0	22 2.5	5 34.8

DECEMBER 1981

LONGITUDE

DAY	EPHEM. SID. TIME h m s	☉ ° ′	☊ ° ′	☾ ° ′	☿ ° ′	♀ ° ′	♂ ° ′	♃ ° ′	♄ ° ′	♅ ° ′	♆ ° ′	♇ ° ′
1	4 39 3.0	8♐42.7	24♋49.5	26♑23.7	3♐22.1	24♑ 3.2	22♍36.9	0♏46.0	19♎ 9.3	0♐54.2	23♐59.7	25♎55.6
2	4 42 59.6	9 43.5	24 46.3	8♒32.4	4 56.5	24 51.8	23 7.5	0 57.5	19 14.9	0 57.8	24 1.9	25 57.4
3	4 46 56.1	10 44.4	24 43.2	20 54.7	6 30.9	25 39.5	23 38.1	1 9.0	19 20.4	1 1.5	24 4.1	25 59.3
4	4 50 52.7	11 45.3	24 40.0	3♓34.9	8 5.2	26 26.3	24 8.4	1 20.4	19 25.8	1 5.2	24 6.3	26 1.1
5	4 54 49.2	12 46.1	24 36.8	16 37.5	9 39.4	27 12.2	24 38.6	1 31.7	19 31.2	1 8.9	24 8.5	26 3.0
6	4 58 45.8	13 47.0	24 33.6	0♈ 5.9	11 13.6	27 57.1	25 8.7	1 42.9	19 36.5	1 12.5	24 10.8	26 4.7
7	5 2 42.3	14 47.9	24 30.5	14 2.5	12 47.8	28 40.9	25 38.5	1 54.1	19 41.7	1 16.1	24 13.0	26 6.5
8	5 6 38.9	15 48.9	24 27.3	28 27.1	14 22.0	29 23.7	26 8.3	2 5.2	19 46.9	1 19.8	24 15.3	26 8.2
9	5 10 35.5	16 49.8	24 24.1	13♉16.5	15 56.2	0♒ 5.4	26 37.8	2 16.2	19 52.0	1 23.4	24 17.5	26 9.9
10	5 14 32.0	17 50.7	24 20.9	28 24.1	17 30.5	0 45.9	27 7.2	2 27.1	19 57.0	1 27.0	24 19.8	26 11.6
11	5 18 28.6	18 51.7	24 17.7	13♊40.9	19 4.8	1 25.2	27 36.4	2 38.0	20 1.9	1 30.6	24 22.0	26 13.3
12	5 22 25.1	19 52.7	24 14.6	28 55.9	20 39.1	2 3.3	28 5.5	2 48.8	20 6.8	1 34.2	24 24.3	26 14.9
13	5 26 21.7	20 53.6	24 11.4	13♋59.1	22 13.5	2 40.1	28 34.4	2 59.5	20 11.6	1 37.7	24 26.5	26 16.5
14	5 30 18.2	21 54.6	24 8.2	28 42.0	23 48.0	3 15.5	29 3.0	3 10.1	20 16.3	1 41.3	24 28.8	26 18.1
15	5 34 14.8	22 55.7	24 5.0	12♌59.3	25 22.7	3 49.5	29 31.6	3 20.7	20 21.0	1 44.9	24 31.1	26 19.7
16	5 38 11.4	23 56.7	24 1.9	26 48.9	26 57.4	4 22.0	29 59.9	3 31.1	20 25.6	1 48.4	24 33.4	26 21.2
17	5 42 7.9	24 57.8	23 58.7	10♍11.2	28 32.3	4 53.0	0♎28.1	3 41.4	20 30.0	1 51.9	24 35.6	26 22.7
18	5 46 4.5	25 58.8	23 55.5	23 8.7	0♑ 7.3	5 22.5	0 56.0	3 51.7	20 34.4	1 55.3	24 37.9	26 24.2
19	5 50 1.0	26 59.9	23 52.3	5♎44.9	1 42.4	5 50.3	1 23.7	4 1.9	20 38.8	1 58.8	24 40.2	26 25.6
20	5 53 57.6	28 1.0	23 49.2	18 4.0	3 17.8	6 16.4	1 51.2	4 11.9	20 43.0	2 2.2	24 42.4	26 27.0
21	5 57 54.1	29 2.1	23 46.0	0♏10.2	4 53.2	6 40.7	2 18.5	4 21.9	20 47.1	2 5.7	24 44.7	26 28.4
22	6 1 50.7	0♑ 3.2	23 42.8	12 7.4	6 28.9	7 3.2	2 45.6	4 31.8	20 51.2	2 9.1	24 47.0	26 29.7
23	6 5 47.3	1 4.4	23 39.6	23 59.3	8 4.7	7 23.9	3 12.5	4 41.5	20 55.2	2 12.4	24 49.2	26 31.1
24	6 9 43.8	2 5.5	23 36.4	5♐48.7	9 40.7	7 42.6	3 39.2	4 51.2	20 59.1	2 15.8	24 51.5	26 32.3
25	6 13 40.4	3 6.6	23 33.3	17 38.3	11 16.8	7 59.2	4 5.6	5 .8	21 2.9	2 19.1	24 53.7	26 33.6
26	6 17 36.9	4 7.8	23 30.1	29 30.2	12 53.1	8 13.8	4 31.7	5 10.2	21 6.6	2 22.4	24 56.0	26 34.8
27	6 21 33.5	5 8.9	23 26.9	11♑26.4	14 29.5	8 26.2	4 57.7	5 19.6	21 10.2	2 25.7	24 58.2	26 36.0
28	6 25 30.1	6 10.1	23 23.7	23 28.5	16 6.0	8 36.4	5 23.4	5 28.8	21 13.8	2 29.0	25 .5	26 37.1
29	6 29 26.6	7 11.3	23 20.6	5♒38.5	17 42.6	8 44.4	5 48.8	5 38.0	21 17.2	2 32.2	25 2.7	26 38.3
30	6 33 23.2	8 12.4	23 17.4	17 58.5	19 19.1	8 50.0	6 14.0	5 47.0	21 20.5	2 35.4	25 4.9	26 39.4
31	6 37 19.7	9 13.6	23 14.2	0♓30.7	20 55.7	8 53.2	6 38.9	5 55.9	21 23.8	2 38.6	25 7.1	26 40.4

LATITUDE

DAY	EPHEM. SID. TIME	☉	☊	☾	☿	♀	♂	♃	♄	♅	♆	♇
1	4 39 3.0	0 .0	0 .0	0S17.7	0S 8.5	2S56.9	1N55.6	1N 6.9	2N18.6	0N10.3	1N15.5	16N41.6
4	4 50 52.7	0 .0	0 .0	3 22.0	0 28.4	2 44.4	1 57.9	1 7.1	2 19.2	0 10.3	1 15.4	16 42.8
7	5 2 42.3	0 .0	0 .0	5 7.3	0 47.4	2 29.5	2 .1	1 7.4	2 19.8	0 10.2	1 15.4	16 44.0
10	5 14 32.0	0 .0	0 .0	4 13.8	1 5.1	2 11.9	2 2.4	1 7.7	2 20.4	0 10.2	1 15.4	16 45.2
13	5 26 21.7	0 .0	0 .0	0 47.6	1 21.4	1 51.6	2 4.7	1 8.0	2 21.1	0 10.2	1 15.3	16 46.6
16	5 38 11.4	0 .0	0 .0	2N56.3	1 35.9	1 28.2	2 7.1	1 8.4	2 21.7	0 10.2	1 15.3	16 47.9
19	5 50 1.0	0 .0	0 .0	5 .7	1 48.4	1 1.7	2 9.5	1 8.8	2 22.4	0 10.2	1 15.3	16 49.4
22	6 1 50.7	0 .0	0 .0	4 56.6	1 58.4	0 32.0	2 11.9	1 9.1	2 23.1	0 10.1	1 15.3	16 50.9
25	6 13 40.4	0 .0	0 .0	3 .4	2 5.7	0N 1.1	2 14.4	1 9.5	2 23.9	0 10.1	1 15.3	16 52.4
28	6 25 30.1	0 .0	0 .0	0S 5.9	2 9.8	0 37.6	2 16.9	1 9.9	2 24.6	0 10.1	1 15.3	16 53.9
31	6 37 19.7	0 .0	0 .0	3 15.9	2 10.0	1 17.4	2 19.5	1 10.4	2 25.4	0 10.1	1 15.3	16 55.5

RIGHT ASCENSION

DAY	EPHEM. SID. TIME	☉	☊	☾	☿	♀	♂	♃	♄	♅	♆	♇
1	4 39 3.0	6♐59.4	26♋45.5	28♑28.2	1♐18.7	26♑30.3	23♍58.9	29♎ 2.4	18♎33.3	28♏47.8	23♐31.2	0♏ 3.4
2	4 42 59.6	8 4.1	26 42.1	11♒20.7	2 56.9	27 21.8	24 27.4	29 13.4	18 38.6	28 51.7	23 33.6	0 5.2
3	4 46 56.1	9 9.1	26 38.8	24 6.5	4 35.5	28 12.2	24 55.8	29 24.4	18 43.8	28 55.5	23 36.0	0 7.0
4	4 50 52.7	10 14.1	26 35.4	6♓44.9	6 14.6	29 1.4	25 24.0	29 35.3	18 48.9	28 59.3	23 38.4	0 8.8
5	4 54 49.2	11 19.4	26 32.1	19 20.0	7 54.1	29 49.3	25 52.1	29 46.1	18 54.0	29 3.1	23 40.8	0 10.6
6	4 58 45.8	12 24.7	26 28.7	1♈59.6	9 34.1	0♒36.1	26 20.0	29 56.9	18 59.0	29 6.9	23 43.2	0 12.3
7	5 2 42.3	13 30.2	26 25.3	14 54.4	11 14.6	1 21.5	26 47.8	0♏ 7.6	19 3.9	29 10.7	23 45.6	0 14.1
8	5 6 38.9	14 35.8	26 22.0	28 16.9	12 55.6	2 5.5	27 15.4	0 18.3	19 8.8	29 14.5	23 48.0	0 15.8
9	5 10 35.5	15 41.5	26 18.6	12♉18.7	14 37.0	2 48.2	27 42.9	0 28.8	19 13.6	29 18.3	23 50.4	0 17.5
10	5 14 32.0	16 47.4	26 15.3	27 7.9	16 18.8	3 29.5	28 10.1	0 39.3	19 18.4	29 22.1	23 52.9	0 19.1
11	5 18 28.6	17 53.3	26 11.9	12♊43.3	18 1.1	4 9.3	28 37.3	0 49.8	19 23.0	29 25.8	23 55.3	0 20.8
12	5 22 25.1	18 59.3	26 8.6	28 51.3	19 43.8	4 47.5	29 4.3	1 .1	19 27.7	29 29.5	23 57.7	0 22.4
13	5 26 21.7	20 5.4	26 5.2	15♋ 5.8	21 26.9	5 24.2	29 31.1	1 10.4	19 32.2	29 33.3	24 .2	0 24.0
14	5 30 18.2	21 11.6	26 1.9	0♌56.7	23 10.4	5 59.3	29 57.7	1 20.7	19 36.7	29 37.0	24 2.6	0 25.6
15	5 34 14.8	22 18.0	25 58.5	15 59.9	24 54.3	6 32.7	0♎24.2	1 30.8	19 41.1	29 40.7	24 5.1	0 27.2
16	5 38 11.4	23 24.3	25 55.1	0♍ 4.4	26 38.6	7 4.4	0 50.5	1 40.9	19 45.5	29 44.4	24 7.5	0 28.7
17	5 42 7.9	24 30.8	25 51.8	13 11.7	28 23.2	7 34.4	1 16.6	1 50.9	19 49.7	29 48.0	24 10.0	0 30.2
18	5 46 4.5	25 37.2	25 48.4	25 31.1	0♑ 8.0	8 2.5	1 42.6	2 .8	19 53.9	29 51.7	24 12.4	0 31.7
19	5 50 1.0	26 43.8	25 45.1	7♎15.6	1 53.2	8 28.7	2 8.3	2 10.6	19 58.0	29 55.3	24 14.9	0 33.2
20	5 53 57.6	27 50.3	25 41.7	18 39.0	3 38.6	8 53.1	2 33.9	2 20.3	20 2.0	29 58.9	24 17.3	0 34.6
21	5 57 54.1	28 56.9	25 38.3	29 54.4	5 24.2	9 15.4	2 59.2	2 30.0	20 6.0	0♐ 2.5	24 19.8	0 36.0
22	6 1 50.7	0♑ 3.5	25 35.0	11♏13.3	7 9.9	9 35.7	3 24.4	2 39.5	20 9.9	0 6.0	24 22.2	0 37.4
23	6 5 47.3	1 10.1	25 31.6	22 45.2	8 55.8	9 53.9	3 49.4	2 49.0	20 13.7	0 9.5	24 24.6	0 38.8
24	6 9 43.8	2 16.8	25 28.3	4♐37.0	10 41.7	10 10.0	4 14.2	2 58.3	20 17.4	0 13.1	24 27.1	0 40.1
25	6 13 40.4	3 23.4	25 24.9	16 51.6	12 27.7	10 23.9	4 38.7	3 7.6	20 21.0	0 16.5	24 29.5	0 41.4
26	6 17 36.9	4 30.0	25 21.5	29 28.0	14 13.6	10 35.5	5 3.1	3 16.8	20 24.6	0 20.0	24 31.9	0 42.7
27	6 21 33.5	5 36.6	25 18.2	12♑20.7	15 59.3	10 44.8	5 27.2	3 25.8	20 28.1	0 23.4	24 34.3	0 43.9
28	6 25 30.1	6 43.1	25 14.8	25 20.9	17 44.9	10 51.7	5 51.1	3 34.8	20 31.4	0 26.8	24 36.7	0 45.2
29	6 29 26.6	7 49.6	25 11.5	8♒19.5	19 30.1	10 56.2	6 14.8	3 43.7	20 34.7	0 30.2	24 39.1	0 46.4
30	6 33 23.2	8 56.0	25 8.1	21 9.0	21 15.0	10 58.3	6 38.2	3 52.4	20 38.0	0 33.6	24 41.5	0 47.5
31	6 37 19.7	10 2.4	25 4.7	3♓46.1	22 59.4	10R57.8	7 1.4	4 1.1	20 41.1	0 36.9	24 43.9	0 48.7

DECLINATION

DAY	EPHEM. SID. TIME	☉	☊	☾	☿	♀	♂	♃	♄	♅	♆	♇
1	4 39 3.0	21S45.4	0N22.2	21S 9.9	20S58.1	24S12.1	4N42.1	10S41.8	5S21.7	20S10.3	22S 2.8	5N33.8
4	4 50 52.7	22 11.8	0 22.2	13 19.8	22 7.5	23 33.4	4 7.9	10 53.5	5 27.4	20 12.6	22 3.2	5 33.0
7	5 2 42.3	22 34.5	0 22.2	0N48.9	23 7.0	22 51.8	3 34.2	11 4.8	5 32.8	20 14.9	22 3.5	5 32.3
10	5 14 32.0	22 53.1	0 22.3	15 40.7	23 56.0	22 8.0	3 1.0	11 15.9	5 38.0	20 17.1	22 3.8	5 31.7
13	5 26 21.7	23 7.7	0 22.3	21 55.0	24 34.0	21 22.5	2 28.5	11 26.6	5 42.8	20 19.3	22 4.2	5 31.3
16	5 38 11.4	23 18.1	0 22.3	15 20.2	25 .2	20 35.8	1 56.6	11 37.0	5 47.5	20 21.5	22 4.5	5 30.9
19	5 50 1.0	23 24.4	0 22.3	2 19.1	25 14.1	19 48.6	1 25.5	11 47.1	5 51.8	20 23.6	22 4.8	5 30.8
22	6 1 50.7	23 26.4	0 22.4	10S45.9	25 15.2	19 1.5	0 55.2	11 56.8	5 55.7	20 25.6	22 5.0	5 30.7
25	6 13 40.4	23 24.2	0 22.4	19 52.3	25 3.0	18 15.2	0 25.8	12 6.1	5 59.4	20 27.6	22 5.3	5 30.8
28	6 25 30.1	23 17.8	0 22.4	21 29.8	24 37.0	17 30.3	0S 2.7	12 15.0	6 2.8	20 29.6	22 5.6	5 31.1
31	6 37 19.7	23 7.2	0 22.5	14 20.7	23 57.1	16 47.6	0 30.2	12 23.5	6 5.8	20 31.5	22 5.8	5 31.5

JANUARY 1982

DAY	EPHEM. SID. TIME	☉	☊	☽	☿	♀	♂	♃	♄	♅	♆	♇
	h m s	° ′	° ′	° ′	° ′	° ′	° ′	° ′	° ′	° ′	° ′	° ′
		LONGITUDE										
1	6 41 16.3	10♑14.8	23♋11.0	13♓17.7	22♑32.1	8♒54.0	7♎ 3.5	6♏ 4.7	21♎26.9	2♐41.7	25♐ 9.3	26♎41.4
2	6 45 12.8	11 15.9	23 7.9	26 22.2	24 8.3	8 R 52.3	7 27.9	6 13.3	21 30.0	2 44.8	25 11.5	26 42.4
3	6 49 9.4	12 17.1	23 4.7	9♈46.4	25 44.2	8 48.1	7 52.0	6 21.9	21 33.0	2 47.9	25 13.7	26 43.4
4	6 53 6.0	13 18.2	23 1.5	23 32.3	27 19.6	8 41.4	8 15.8	6 30.3	21 35.8	2 51.0	25 15.9	26 44.3
5	6 57 2.5	14 19.4	22 58.3	7♉40.1	28 54.6	8 32.2	8 39.4	6 38.6	21 38.7	2 54.0	25 18.1	26 45.2
6	7 0 59.1	15 20.6	22 55.2	22 8.6	0♒28.7	8 20.4	9 2.6	6 46.8	21 41.3	2 57.0	25 20.3	26 46.1
7	7 4 55.6	16 21.7	22 52.0	6♊54.2	2 1.8	8 6.1	9 25.6	6 54.8	21 43.9	2 60.0	25 22.4	26 46.9
8	7 8 52.2	17 22.8	22 48.8	21 51.0	3 33.8	7 49.3	9 48.2	7 2.8	21 46.4	3 2.9	25 24.6	26 47.7
9	7 12 48.7	18 23.9	22 45.6	6♋51.4	5 4.3	7 30.1	10 10.5	7 10.5	21 48.8	3 5.8	25 26.7	26 48.4
10	7 16 45.3	19 25.1	22 42.4	21 46.7	6 32.9	7 8.6	10 32.5	7 18.2	21 51.0	3 8.6	25 28.8	26 49.1
11	7 20 41.9	20 26.2	22 39.3	6♌28.9	7 59.3	6 44.8	10 54.2	7 25.7	21 53.2	3 11.5	25 30.9	26 49.8
12	7 24 38.4	21 27.3	22 36.1	20 51.2	9 23.0	6 18.9	11 15.6	7 33.1	21 55.3	3 14.2	25 33.0	26 50.4
13	7 28 35.0	22 28.4	22 32.9	4♍49.3	10 43.5	5 51.0	11 36.6	7 40.4	21 57.3	3 17.0	25 35.1	26 51.0
14	7 32 31.5	23 29.5	22 29.7	18 21.2	12 .3	5 21.2	11 57.2	7 47.5	21 59.1	3 19.7	25 37.2	26 51.6
15	7 36 28.1	24 30.6	22 26.6	1♎27.4	13 12.6	4 49.8	12 17.5	7 54.4	22 .9	3 22.4	25 39.2	26 52.1
16	7 40 24.6	25 31.7	22 23.4	14 10.1	14 19.9	4 16.9	12 37.5	8 1.3	22 2.6	3 25.0	25 41.2	26 52.6
17	7 44 21.2	26 32.8	22 20.2	26 33.0	15 21.2	3 42.7	12 57.0	8 7.9	22 4.1	3 27.6	25 43.2	26 53.1
18	7 48 17.8	27 33.9	22 17.0	8♏40.3	16 15.8	3 7.5	13 16.2	8 14.5	22 5.6	3 30.2	25 45.2	26 53.5
19	7 52 14.3	28 35.0	22 13.9	20 36.9	17 2.9	2 31.5	13 35.0	8 20.9	22 6.9	3 32.7	25 47.2	26 53.9
20	7 56 10.9	29 36.0	22 10.7	2♐27.2	17 41.4	1 54.9	13 53.4	8 27.1	22 8.2	3 35.1	25 49.2	26 54.3
21	8 0 7.4	0♒37.1	22 7.5	14 15.7	18 10.7	1 18.0	14 11.4	8 33.2	22 9.3	3 37.6	25 51.2	26 54.6
22	8 4 4.0	1 38.2	22 4.3	26 6.3	18 29.8	0 41.1	14 28.9	8 39.1	22 10.3	3 40.0	25 53.1	26 54.8
23	8 8 .5	2 39.2	22 1.1	8♑ 2.3	18 38.2	0 4.4	14 46.0	8 44.9	22 11.3	3 42.3	25 55.0	26 55.1
24	8 11 57.1	3 40.3	21 58.0	20 6.4	18 R 35.3	29♑28.1	15 2.7	8 50.5	22 12.1	3 44.6	25 56.9	26 55.3
25	8 15 53.6	4 41.3	21 54.8	2♒20.8	18 20.9	28 52.5	15 18.9	8 56.0	22 12.8	3 46.9	25 58.8	26 55.5
26	8 19 50.2	5 42.4	21 51.6	14 46.9	17 55.1	28 18.0	15 34.8	9 1.4	22 13.4	3 49.1	26 .7	26 55.6
27	8 23 46.8	6 43.4	21 48.4	27 25.6	17 18.2	27 44.5	15 50.1	9 6.5	22 13.9	3 51.3	26 2.5	26 55.7
28	8 27 43.3	7 44.4	21 45.3	10♓17.4	16 31.1	27 12.4	16 4.9	9 11.5	22 14.3	3 53.4	26 4.3	26 55.8
29	8 31 39.9	8 45.4	21 42.1	23 22.7	15 34.9	26 41.9	16 19.2	9 16.3	22 14.6	3 55.5	26 6.1	26 55.8
30	8 35 36.4	9 46.3	21 38.9	6♈41.5	14 31.2	26 13.0	16 33.0	9 20.9	22 14.8	3 57.6	26 7.9	26 55.8
31	8 39 33.0	10 47.2	21 35.7	20 14.0	13 21.9	25 46.1	16 46.4	9 25.4	22 14.8	3 59.5	26 9.6	26 55.8
		LATITUDE										
1	6 41 16.3	0 .0	0 .0	4S 6.3	2S 9.1	1N31.3	2N20.4	1N10.5	2N25.6	0N10.1	1N15.3	16N56.1
4	6 53 6.0	0 .0	0 .0	5 17.3	2 3.2	2 14.7	2 23.0	1 11.0	2 26.4	0 10.1	1 15.3	16 57.7
7	7 4 55.6	0 .0	0 .0	3 47.0	1 51.7	3 .2	2 25.6	1 11.5	2 27.2	0 10.1	1 15.3	16 59.4
10	7 16 45.3	0 .0	0 .0	0 3.7	1 33.5	3 46.6	2 28.4	1 12.0	2 28.0	0 10.1	1 15.3	17 1.1
13	7 28 35.0	0 .0	0 .0	3N34.5	1 7.8	4 32.5	2 31.1	1 12.5	2 28.8	0 10.1	1 15.4	17 2.8
16	7 40 24.6	0 .0	0 .0	5 14.5	0 33.7	5 16.3	2 33.9	1 13.0	2 29.6	0 10.1	1 15.4	17 4.5
19	7 52 14.3	0 .0	0 .0	4 40.3	0N 9.1	5 56.0	2 36.7	1 13.5	2 30.5	0 10.1	1 15.5	17 6.2
22	8 4 4.0	0 .0	0 .0	2 21.4	0 59.4	6 30.1	2 39.5	1 14.1	2 31.3	0 10.0	1 15.5	17 8.0
25	8 15 53.6	0 .0	0 .0	0S54.3	1 53.2	6 57.2	2 42.4	1 14.6	2 32.1	0 10.0	1 15.6	17 9.7
28	8 27 43.3	0 .0	0 .0	3 54.6	2 43.6	7 16.8	2 45.2	1 15.2	2 33.0	0 10.0	1 15.6	17 11.4
31	8 39 33.0	0 .0	0 .0	5 15.5	3 21.0	7 28.7	2 48.1	1 15.8	2 33.8	0 10.0	1 15.7	17 13.1
		RIGHT ASCENSION										
1	6 41 16.3	11♑ 8.7	25♋ 1.4	16♓12.3	24♑43.2	10♒54.8	7♎24.4	4♏ 9.6	20♎44.1	0♐40.2	24♐46.3	0♏49.8
2	6 45 12.8	12 15.0	24 58.0	28 33.8	26 26.2	10 R 49.3	7 47.1	4 18.0	20 47.1	0 43.4	24 48.7	0 50.9
3	6 49 9.4	13 21.1	24 54.6	11♈ .4	28 8.3	10 41.1	8 9.6	4 26.3	20 49.9	0 46.7	24 51.0	0 51.9
4	6 53 6.0	14 27.1	24 51.3	23 44.4	29 49.4	10 30.4	8 31.8	4 34.5	20 52.7	0 49.9	24 53.4	0 52.9
5	6 57 2.5	15 33.1	24 47.9	6♉59.3	1♒29.3	10 17.2	8 53.8	4 42.7	20 55.5	0 53.1	24 55.8	0 54.0
6	7 0 59.1	16 39.0	24 44.5	20 56.8	3 7.6	10 1.3	9 15.5	4 50.6	20 58.0	0 56.2	24 58.1	0 54.9
7	7 4 55.6	17 44.7	24 41.2	5♊44.1	4 44.3	9 42.9	9 36.9	4 58.5	21 .5	0 59.3	25 .4	0 55.9
8	7 8 52.2	18 50.3	24 37.8	21 18.3	6 18.9	9 22.1	9 58.1	5 6.2	21 3.0	1 2.4	25 2.7	0 56.8
9	7 12 48.7	19 55.7	24 34.4	7♋23.2	7 51.3	8 58.8	10 19.0	5 13.8	21 5.3	1 5.4	25 5.0	0 57.6
10	7 16 45.3	21 1.0	24 31.1	23 31.3	9 21.0	8 33.3	10 39.6	5 21.3	21 7.5	1 8.4	25 7.3	0 58.5
11	7 20 41.9	22 6.2	24 27.7	9♌12.6	10 47.7	8 5.6	10 59.9	5 28.6	21 9.6	1 11.3	25 9.6	0 59.3
12	7 24 38.4	23 11.3	24 24.3	24 5.3	12 10.9	7 35.8	11 19.9	5 35.9	21 11.7	1 14.3	25 11.8	1 .0
13	7 28 35.0	24 16.2	24 21.0	8♍ .6	13 30.1	7 4.1	11 39.6	5 43.0	21 13.6	1 17.1	25 14.1	1 .8
14	7 32 31.5	25 20.9	24 17.6	21 1.6	14 44.8	6 30.7	11 58.9	5 49.9	21 15.5	1 20.0	25 16.3	1 1.5
15	7 36 28.1	26 25.5	24 14.2	3♎18.4	15 54.4	5 55.7	12 18.0	5 56.7	21 17.2	1 22.8	25 18.5	1 2.2
16	7 40 24.6	27 29.9	24 10.9	15 4.2	16 58.1	5 19.5	12 36.7	6 3.4	21 18.9	1 25.5	25 20.7	1 2.8
17	7 44 21.2	28 34.2	24 7.5	26 32.7	17 55.3	4 42.1	12 55.1	6 10.0	21 20.4	1 28.3	25 22.9	1 3.5
18	7 48 17.8	29 38.3	24 4.1	7♏56.5	18 45.2	4 3.8	13 13.2	6 16.4	21 21.9	1 30.9	25 25.0	1 4.0
19	7 52 14.3	0♒42.2	24 .7	19 26.9	19 27.0	3 24.9	13 30.9	6 22.7	21 23.3	1 33.6	25 27.2	1 4.6
20	7 56 10.9	1 45.9	23 57.4	1♐12.8	20 .1	2 45.7	13 48.2	6 28.8	21 24.5	1 36.2	25 29.3	1 5.1
21	8 0 7.4	2 49.5	23 54.0	13 19.8	20 23.6	2 6.3	14 5.1	6 34.8	21 25.7	1 38.7	25 31.4	1 5.6
22	8 4 4.0	3 52.9	23 50.6	25 49.8	20 36.9	1 27.1	14 21.7	6 40.6	21 26.7	1 41.2	25 33.5	1 6.1
23	8 8 .5	4 56.1	23 47.2	8♑39.8	20 39.5	0 48.3	14 37.9	6 46.3	21 27.7	1 43.7	25 35.6	1 6.5
24	8 11 57.1	5 59.1	23 43.9	21 43.1	20 R 30.9	0 10.1	14 53.6	6 51.8	21 28.6	1 46.1	25 37.6	1 6.9
25	8 15 53.6	7 1.9	23 40.5	4♒50.1	20 11.2	29♑32.8	15 9.0	6 57.2	21 29.3	1 48.5	25 39.6	1 7.2
26	8 19 50.2	8 4.5	23 37.1	17 51.8	19 40.4	28 56.7	15 24.0	7 2.5	21 30.1	1 50.9	25 41.7	1 7.6
27	8 23 46.8	9 6.9	23 33.8	0♓41.9	18 59.0	28 21.9	15 38.5	7 7.6	21 30.6	1 53.2	25 43.7	1 7.9
28	8 27 43.3	10 9.1	23 30.4	13 18.7	18 8.0	27 48.6	15 52.6	7 12.5	21 31.1	1 55.4	25 45.6	1 8.2
29	8 31 39.9	11 11.1	23 27.0	25 45.2	17 8.5	27 17.1	16 6.2	7 17.2	21 31.4	1 57.6	25 47.5	1 8.4
30	8 35 36.4	12 12.9	23 23.6	8♈ 8.9	16 2.2	26 47.4	16 19.3	7 21.8	21 31.7	1 59.7	25 49.5	1 8.6
31	8 39 33.0	13 14.4	23 20.2	20 39.9	14 50.9	26 19.8	16 32.0	7 26.3	21 31.9	2 1.8	25 51.3	1 8.7
		DECLINATION										
1	6 41 16.3	23S 2.7	0N22.5	10S21.2	23S40.8	16S34.0	0S39.2	12S26.3	6S 6.8	20S32.1	22S 5.9	5N31.6
4	6 53 6.0	22 46.5	0 22.5	4N13.3	22 42.5	15 55.3	1 5.2	12 34.3	6 9.3	20 33.9	22 6.1	5 32.2
7	7 4 55.6	22 26.3	0 22.5	17 44.0	21 31.3	15 20.4	1 30.2	12 41.8	6 11.6	20 35.6	22 6.3	5 32.8
10	7 16 45.3	22 2.1	0 22.5	21 37.1	20 8.8	14 49.9	1 53.9	12 49.0	6 13.5	20 37.3	22 6.5	5 33.7
13	7 28 35.0	21 34.0	0 22.6	13 4.2	18 38.0	14 24.3	2 16.4	12 55.7	6 15.0	20 38.9	22 6.7	5 34.6
16	7 40 24.6	21 2.2	0 22.6	0S45.2	17 4.2	14 3.9	2 37.5	13 1.9	6 16.2	20 40.5	22 6.8	5 35.7
19	7 52 14.3	20 26.7	0 22.6	13 23.9	15 34.9	13 48.9	2 57.2	13 7.7	6 17.1	20 41.9	22 7.0	5 36.8
22	8 4 4.0	19 47.8	0 22.7	21 1.7	14 20.6	13 39.1	3 15.4	13 13.0	6 17.6	20 43.3	22 7.1	5 38.1
25	8 15 53.6	19 5.5	0 22.7	20 31.2	13 32.0	13 34.4	3 32.0	13 17.9	6 17.7	20 44.6	22 7.3	5 39.5
28	8 27 43.3	18 20.1	0 22.7	11 19.7	13 17.1	13 34.3	3 47.0	13 22.2	6 17.5	20 45.9	22 7.4	5 41.0
31	8 39 33.0	17 31.7	0 22.7	3N 2.0	13 35.8	13 38.3	4 .2	13 26.1	6 16.9	20 47.0	22 7.4	5 42.6

FEBRUARY 1982

LONGITUDE

DAY	EPHEM. SID. TIME h m s	☉ ° ′	☊ ° ′	☽ ° ′	☿ ° ′	♀ ° ′	♂ ° ′	♃ ° ′	♄ ° ′	♅ ° ′	♆ ° ′	♇ ° ′
1	8 43 29.5	11♒48.2	21♋32.6	3♉59.9	12♒ 9.1	25♑21.3	16♎59.2	9♏29.7	22♎14.8	4♐ 1.5	26♐11.3	26♎55.7
2	8 47 26.1	12 49.0	21 29.4	17 59.0	10R54.9	24R58.5	17 11.5	9 33.9	22R14.6	4 3.4	26 13.1	26R55.6
3	8 51 22.6	13 49.9	21 26.2	2♊10.3	9 41.4	24 38.0	17 23.2	9 37.8	22 14.4	4 5.2	26 14.7	26 55.4
4	8 55 19.2	14 50.7	21 23.0	16 32.0	8 30.7	24 19.9	17 34.4	9 41.6	22 14.0	4 7.0	26 16.4	26 55.2
5	8 59 15.8	15 51.6	21 19.8	1♋ 1.3	7 24.3	24 4.1	17 45.1	9 45.2	22 13.6	4 8.8	26 18.0	26 55.0
6	9 3 12.3	16 52.4	21 16.7	15 34.2	6 23.8	23 50.8	17 55.1	9 48.7	22 13.0	4 10.5	26 19.6	26 54.7
7	9 7 8.9	17 53.1	21 13.5	0♌ 5.5	5 30.2	23 40.0	18 4.7	9 52.0	22 12.3	4 12.1	26 21.2	26 54.4
8	9 11 5.4	18 53.9	21 10.3	14 29.5	4 44.2	23 31.7	18 13.6	9 55.0	22 11.5	4 13.7	26 22.8	26 54.1
9	9 15 2.0	19 54.6	21 7.1	28 40.6	4 6.2	23 25.8	18 21.9	9 58.0	22 10.6	4 15.3	26 24.3	26 53.7
10	9 18 58.5	20 55.3	21 4.0	12♍33.8	3 36.5	23 22.5	18 29.6	10 .7	22 9.6	4 16.8	26 25.8	26 53.3
11	9 22 55.1	21 56.0	21 .8	26 5.9	3 14.9	23 21.6	18 36.7	10 3.3	22 8.6	4 18.2	26 27.3	26 52.9
12	9 26 51.6	22 56.7	20 57.6	9♎15.2	3 1.3	23D23.2	18 43.2	10 5.6	22 7.4	4 19.6	26 28.7	26 52.4
13	9 30 48.2	23 57.3	20 54.4	22 2.4	2 55.4	23 27.1	18 49.0	10 7.8	22 6.1	4 21.0	26 30.2	26 51.9
14	9 34 44.7	24 58.0	20 51.2	4♏29.4	2D56.9	23 33.4	18 54.1	10 9.8	22 4.7	4 22.3	26 31.6	26 51.4
15	9 38 41.3	25 58.6	20 48.1	16 39.7	3 5.1	23 42.0	18 58.6	10 11.7	22 3.2	4 23.5	26 32.9	26 50.8
16	9 42 37.9	26 59.2	20 44.9	28 37.9	3 19.9	23 52.9	19 2.4	10 13.4	22 1.6	4 24.8	26 34.3	26 50.3
17	9 46 34.4	27 59.8	20 41.7	10♐28.8	3 40.6	24 5.9	19 5.5	10 14.8	21 59.9	4 25.9	26 35.6	26 49.6
18	9 50 31.0	29 .3	20 38.5	22 17.7	4 6.9	24 21.0	19 7.9	10 16.1	21 58.1	4 27.0	26 36.9	26 49.0
19	9 54 27.5	0♓ .9	20 35.4	4♑ 9.4	4 38.2	24 38.2	19 9.6	10 17.2	21 56.2	4 28.0	26 38.2	26 48.3
20	9 58 24.1	1 1.4	20 32.2	16 8.7	5 14.3	24 57.3	19 10.5	10 18.1	21 54.2	4 29.0	26 39.4	26 47.5
21	10 2 20.6	2 1.8	20 29.0	28 19.5	5 54.8	25 18.3	19 10.8	10 18.8	21 52.1	4 29.9	26 40.6	26 46.8
22	10 6 17.2	3 2.3	20 25.8	10♒45.0	6 39.3	25 41.2	19R10.2	10 19.3	21 49.9	4 30.8	26 41.8	26 46.0
23	10 10 13.7	4 2.7	20 22.6	23 27.2	7 27.5	26 5.9	19 9.0	10 19.6	21 47.7	4 31.6	26 42.9	26 45.2
24	10 14 10.3	5 3.1	20 19.5	6♓26.6	8 19.1	26 32.2	19 6.9	10 19.7	21 45.3	4 32.4	26 44.0	26 44.3
25	10 18 6.8	6 3.5	20 16.3	19 42.8	9 14.0	27 .3	19 4.1	10 19.7	21 42.8	4 33.1	26 45.1	26 43.4
26	10 22 3.4	7 3.9	20 13.1	3♈14.0	10 11.7	27 29.8	19 .5	10R19.4	21 40.3	4 33.8	26 46.2	26 42.5
27	10 25 59.9	8 4.2	20 9.9	16 57.6	11 12.2	28 .9	18 56.2	10 19.0	21 37.6	4 34.4	26 47.2	26 41.6
28	10 29 56.5	9 4.5	20 6.8	0♉50.8	12 15.3	28 33.5	18 51.1	10 18.4	21 34.9	4 34.9	26 48.2	26 40.6

LATITUDE

DAY	SID. TIME	☉	☊	☽	☿	♀	♂	♃	♄	♅	♆	♇
1	8 43 29.5	0 .0	0 .0	5S 9.2	3N29.2	7N31.0	2N49.1	1N16.0	2N34.1	0N10.0	1N15.7	17N13.7
4	8 55 19.2	0 .0	0 .0	3 4.9	3 39.0	7 33.3	2 51.9	1 16.6	2 34.9	0 10.0	1 15.8	17 15.4
7	9 7 8.9	0 .0	0 .0	0N42.4	3 28.3	7 29.5	2 54.7	1 17.2	2 35.7	0 10.0	1 15.8	17 17.0
10	9 18 58.5	0 .0	0 .0	4 1.4	3 2.9	7 20.4	2 57.5	1 17.8	2 36.5	0 10.0	1 15.9	17 18.6
13	9 30 48.2	0 .0	0 .0	5 12.7	2 29.4	7 7.1	3 .2	1 18.4	2 37.3	0 10.0	1 16.0	17 20.2
16	9 42 37.9	0 .0	0 .0	4 10.9	1 52.6	6 50.5	3 2.8	1 19.0	2 38.1	0 10.0	1 16.1	17 21.8
19	9 54 27.5	0 .0	0 .0	1 35.7	1 15.7	6 31.5	3 5.2	1 19.6	2 38.8	0 10.0	1 16.2	17 23.3
22	10 6 17.2	0 .0	0 .0	1S40.2	0 40.3	6 10.7	3 7.5	1 20.2	2 39.6	0 10.0	1 16.3	17 24.8
25	10 18 6.8	0 .0	0 .0	4 21.8	0 7.4	5 48.6	3 9.5	1 20.8	2 40.2	0 10.0	1 16.4	17 26.2
28	10 29 56.5	0 .0	0 .0	5 3.6	0S22.5	5 25.7	3 11.3	1 21.4	2 40.9	0 10.0	1 16.5	17 27.6

RIGHT ASCENSION

DAY	SID. TIME	☉	☊	☽	☿	♀	♂	♃	♄	♅	♆	♇
1	8 43 29.5	14♒15.8	23♋16.9	3♉30.5	13♒36.7	25♑54.4	16♎44.3	7♏30.5	21♎31.9	2♐ 3.9	25♐53.2	1♏ 8.9
2	8 47 26.1	15 17.0	23 13.5	16 52.5	12R21.6	25R31.3	16 56.0	7 34.6	21 31.9	2 5.8	25 55.0	1 9.0
3	8 51 22.6	16 17.9	23 10.1	0♊55.3	11 7.9	25 10.6	17 7.2	7 38.6	21R31.8	2 7.8	25 56.9	1 9.0
4	8 55 19.2	17 18.6	23 6.7	15 42.0	9 57.2	24 52.3	17 18.0	7 42.3	21 31.5	2 9.7	25 58.6	1 9.1
5	8 59 15.8	18 19.2	23 3.4	1♋ 5.9	8 51.4	24 36.6	17 28.2	7 45.9	21 31.2	2 11.5	26 .4	1R 9.0
6	9 3 12.3	19 19.5	22 60.0	16 49.0	7 51.7	24 23.4	17 37.9	7 49.4	21 30.8	2 13.3	26 2.1	1 9.0
7	9 7 8.9	20 19.6	22 56.6	2♌26.3	6 59.3	24 12.8	17 47.1	7 52.6	21 30.2	2 15.0	26 3.8	1 8.9
8	9 11 5.4	21 19.5	22 53.2	17 33.8	6 14.7	24 4.9	17 55.7	7 55.7	21 29.6	2 16.7	26 5.5	1 8.8
9	9 15 2.0	22 19.3	22 49.8	1♍56.3	5 38.4	23 59.5	18 3.8	7 58.6	21 28.9	2 18.3	26 7.2	1 8.7
10	9 18 58.5	23 18.8	22 46.5	15 29.3	5 10.7	23 56.7	18 11.3	8 1.4	21 28.0	2 19.9	26 8.8	1 8.5
11	9 22 55.1	24 18.1	22 43.1	28 17.3	4 51.3	23 56.5	18 18.2	8 3.9	21 27.1	2 21.4	26 10.4	1 8.3
12	9 26 51.6	25 17.2	22 39.7	10♎30.0	4 40.2	23D58.8	18 24.5	8 6.3	21 26.1	2 22.9	26 12.0	1 8.1
13	9 30 48.2	26 16.2	22 36.3	22 19.3	4 37.0	24 3.6	18 30.2	8 8.5	21 25.0	2 24.3	26 13.5	1 7.9
14	9 34 44.7	27 15.0	22 32.9	3♏57.1	4D41.3	24 10.9	18 35.3	8 10.6	21 23.8	2 25.7	26 15.0	1 7.6
15	9 38 41.3	28 13.6	22 29.5	15 34.6	4 52.6	24 20.5	18 39.8	8 12.4	21 22.5	2 27.0	26 16.5	1 7.2
16	9 42 37.9	29 12.0	22 26.2	27 21.2	5 10.7	24 32.5	18 43.7	8 14.1	21 21.1	2 28.3	26 18.0	1 6.9
17	9 46 34.4	0♓10.2	22 22.8	9♐23.8	5 34.8	24 46.7	18 46.9	8 15.6	21 19.6	2 29.5	26 19.4	1 6.5
18	9 50 31.0	1 8.3	22 19.4	21 46.2	6 4.6	25 3.1	18 49.4	8 16.9	21 18.0	2 30.7	26 20.8	1 6.1
19	9 54 27.5	2 6.2	22 16.0	4♑28.5	6 39.6	25 21.6	18 51.3	8 18.0	21 16.4	2 31.8	26 22.2	1 5.7
20	9 58 24.1	3 3.9	22 12.6	17 26.6	7 19.5	25 42.2	18 52.4	8 19.0	21 14.6	2 32.8	26 23.5	1 5.2
21	10 2 20.6	4 1.5	22 9.2	0♒33.5	8 3.8	26 4.8	18 52.9	8 19.7	21 12.7	2 33.8	26 24.8	1 4.7
22	10 6 17.2	4 58.9	22 5.9	13 41.1	8 52.1	26 29.2	18R52.7	8 20.3	21 10.8	2 34.7	26 26.1	1 4.2
23	10 10 13.7	5 56.1	22 2.5	26 42.5	9 44.1	26 55.5	18 51.8	8 20.7	21 8.7	2 35.5	26 27.3	1 3.6
24	10 14 10.3	6 53.2	21 59.1	9♓34.1	10 39.5	27 23.6	18 50.2	8 20.9	21 6.6	2 36.4	26 28.5	1 3.0
25	10 18 6.8	7 50.2	21 55.7	22 16.4	11 38.0	27 53.4	18 47.8	8 20.9	21 4.4	2 37.1	26 29.7	1 2.4
26	10 22 3.4	8 47.0	21 52.3	4♈54.3	12 39.4	28 24.8	18 44.7	8R20.7	21 2.1	2 37.8	26 30.8	1 1.7
27	10 25 59.9	9 43.6	21 48.9	17 35.4	13 43.3	28 57.8	18 40.9	8 20.3	20 59.7	2 38.4	26 31.9	1 1.0
28	10 29 56.5	10 40.1	21 45.5	0♉29.8	14 49.7	29 32.3	18 36.4	8 19.8	20 57.3	2 39.0	26 32.9	1 .3

DECLINATION

DAY	SID. TIME	☉	☊	☽	☿	♀	♂	♃	♄	♅	♆	♇
1	8 43 29.5	17S15.0	0N22.7	7N59.9	13S48.2	13S40.4	4S 4.2	13S27.3	6S16.6	20S47.4	22S 7.5	5N43.2
4	8 55 19.2	16 22.9	0 22.8	19 41.6	14 36.6	13 48.5	4 14.9	13 30.4	6 15.6	20 48.4	22 7.5	5 44.9
7	9 7 8.9	15 28.3	0 22.8	20 49.3	15 31.6	13 58.9	4 23.8	13 33.1	6 14.2	20 49.4	22 7.6	5 46.7
10	9 18 58.5	14 31.4	0 22.8	10 33.6	16 22.9	14 10.7	4 30.7	13 35.3	6 12.5	20 50.2	22 7.7	5 48.6
13	9 30 48.2	13 32.2	0 22.8	3S44.7	17 4.9	14 23.1	4 35.5	13 37.0	6 10.4	20 51.0	22 7.7	5 50.6
16	9 42 37.9	12 31.0	0 22.9	15 46.5	17 35.1	14 35.2	4 38.2	13 38.1	6 8.1	20 51.7	22 7.7	5 52.6
19	9 54 27.5	11 28.1	0 22.9	21 46.9	17 52.8	14 46.4	4 38.6	13 38.7	6 5.4	20 52.3	22 7.7	5 54.7
22	10 6 17.2	10 23.4	0 22.9	19 8.8	17 57.6	14 55.9	4 36.8	13 38.8	6 2.4	20 52.8	22 7.7	5 56.9
25	10 18 6.8	9 17.4	0 22.9	8 5.1	17 49.6	15 3.2	4 32.6	13 38.4	5 59.1	20 53.2	22 7.7	5 59.1
28	10 29 56.5	8 10.1	0 23.0	7N 1.3	17 29.0	15 7.9	4 26.0	13 37.4	5 55.5	20 53.6	22 7.7	6 1.3

MARCH 1982

LONGITUDE

DAY	EPHEM. SID. TIME h m s	☉ ° ′	☊ ° ′	☾ ° ′	☿ ° ′	♀ ° ′	♂ ° ′	♃ ° ′	♄ ° ′	♅ ° ′	♆ ° ′	♇ ° ′
1	10 33 53.1	10♓ 4.7	20♋ 3.6	14♉50.7	13♒20.7	29♑ 7.5	18♎45.2	10♏17.6	21♎32.1	4♐35.4	26♐49.1	26♎39.6
2	10 37 49.6	11 4.9	20 .4	28 55.0	14 28.3	29 42.8	18 R38.5	10 R16.6	21 R29.2	4 35.9	26 50.0	26 R38.6
3	10 41 46.2	12 5.1	19 57.2	13♊ 1.7	15 38.1	0♒19.4	18 31.1	10 15.4	21 26.2	4 36.3	26 50.9	26 37.5
4	10 45 42.7	13 5.3	19 54.0	27 9.6	16 49.8	0 57.2	18 22.9	10 14.0	21 23.1	4 36.6	26 51.8	26 36.4
5	10 49 39.3	14 5.4	19 50.9	11♋17.4	18 3.4	1 36.3	18 13.9	10 12.4	21 20.0	4 36.9	26 52.6	26 35.3
6	10 53 35.8	15 5.5	19 47.7	25 23.8	19 18.8	2 16.5	18 4.1	10 10.7	21 16.8	4 37.1	26 53.4	26 34.2
7	10 57 32.4	16 5.5	19 44.5	9♌26.7	20 35.9	2 57.8	17 53.6	10 8.7	21 13.5	4 37.3	26 54.2	26 33.0
8	11 1 28.9	17 5.5	19 41.3	23 23.5	21 54.6	3 40.2	17 42.4	10 6.6	21 10.1	4 37.4	26 54.9	26 31.8
9	11 5 25.5	18 5.6	19 38.2	7♍11.1	23 14.9	4 23.6	17 30.4	10 4.4	21 6.7	4 37.5	26 55.7	26 30.7
10	11 9 22.0	19 5.5	19 35.0	20 46.1	24 36.7	5 8.0	17 17.6	10 1.9	21 3.2	4 37.5	26 56.3	26 29.4
11	11 13 18.6	20 5.4	19 31.8	4♎ 5.5	25 60.0	5 53.4	17 4.1	9 59.2	20 59.6	4 37.5	26 57.0	26 28.2
12	11 17 15.1	21 5.3	19 28.6	17 7.3	27 24.7	6 39.6	16 49.9	9 56.4	20 56.0	4 R37.4	26 57.6	26 26.9
13	11 21 11.7	22 5.1	19 25.4	29 50.8	28 50.7	7 26.8	16 35.0	9 53.4	20 52.3	4 37.2	26 58.1	26 25.6
14	11 25 8.2	23 5.0	19 22.3	12♏16.8	0♓18.2	8 14.8	16 19.4	9 50.2	20 48.5	4 37.0	26 58.7	26 24.3
15	11 29 4.8	24 4.8	19 19.1	24 27.4	1 46.9	9 3.6	16 3.1	9 46.8	20 44.7	4 36.8	26 59.2	26 22.9
16	11 33 1.3	25 4.5	19 15.9	6♐26.0	3 17.0	9 53.2	15 46.1	9 43.3	20 40.8	4 36.5	26 59.6	26 21.6
17	11 36 57.9	26 4.3	19 12.7	18 17.2	4 48.4	10 43.5	15 28.5	9 39.6	20 36.8	4 36.1	27 .1	26 20.2
18	11 40 54.4	27 4.0	19 9.6	0♑ 6.0	6 21.1	11 34.6	15 10.3	9 35.7	20 32.8	4 35.7	27 .5	26 18.8
19	11 44 51.0	28 3.6	19 6.4	11 57.9	7 55.1	12 26.3	14 51.5	9 31.6	20 28.7	4 35.2	27 .8	26 17.3
20	11 48 47.6	29 3.3	19 3.2	23 58.2	9 30.3	13 18.7	14 32.2	9 27.4	20 24.6	4 34.7	27 1.2	26 15.9
21	11 52 44.1	0♈ 2.9	19 .0	6♒12.0	11 6.9	14 11.7	14 12.3	9 23.1	20 20.4	4 34.1	27 1.5	26 14.4
22	11 56 40.7	1 2.5	18 56.8	18 43.8	12 44.7	15 5.4	13 51.9	9 18.5	20 16.2	4 33.5	27 1.7	26 13.0
23	12 0 37.2	2 2.1	18 53.7	1♓36.6	14 23.8	15 59.6	13 31.0	9 13.8	20 12.0	4 32.8	27 2.0	26 11.5
24	12 4 33.8	3 1.6	18 50.5	14 51.9	16 4.1	16 54.4	13 9.7	9 9.0	20 7.7	4 32.1	27 2.2	26 10.0
25	12 8 30.3	4 1.1	18 47.3	28 29.2	17 45.8	17 49.7	12 48.0	9 4.0	20 3.3	4 31.3	27 2.3	26 8.4
26	12 12 26.9	5 .6	18 44.1	12♈25.8	19 28.8	18 45.6	12 26.0	8 58.8	19 59.0	4 30.5	27 2.5	26 6.9
27	12 16 23.4	5 60.0	18 41.0	26 37.2	21 13.1	19 41.9	12 3.6	8 53.5	19 54.6	4 29.6	27 2.6	26 5.3
28	12 20 20.0	6 59.4	18 37.8	10♉57.7	22 58.7	20 38.7	11 41.0	8 48.1	19 50.1	4 28.7	27 2.6	26 3.8
29	12 24 16.5	7 58.7	18 34.6	25 21.5	24 45.7	21 36.0	11 18.2	8 42.5	19 45.6	4 27.7	27 2.7	26 2.2
30	12 28 13.1	8 58.1	18 31.4	9♊43.4	26 34.1	22 33.8	10 55.2	8 36.8	19 41.2	4 26.8	27 2.7	26 .6
31	12 32 9.6	9 57.4	18 28.2	23 59.7	28 23.7	23 31.9	10 32.1	8 31.0	19 36.7	4 25.7	27 2.7	25 59.0

LATITUDE

DAY	SID. TIME	☉	☊	☾	☿	♀	♂	♃	♄	♅	♆	♇
1	10 33 53.1	0 .0	0 .0	4S42.3	0S31.8	5N17.9	3N11.8	1N21.6	2N41.1	0N10.0	1N16.5	17N28.0
4	10 45 42.7	0 .0	0 .0	2 5.6	0 57.5	4 54.4	3 13.1	1 22.2	2 41.8	0 10.0	1 16.6	17 29.3
7	10 57 32.4	0 .0	0 .0	1N36.4	1 19.8	4 30.7	3 14.0	1 22.7	2 42.3	0 10.0	1 16.7	17 30.5
10	11 9 22.0	0 .0	0 .0	4 23.8	1 38.7	4 6.9	3 14.5	1 23.3	2 42.9	0 10.0	1 16.8	17 31.6
13	11 21 11.7	0 .0	0 .0	4 59.9	1 54.0	3 43.4	3 14.4	1 23.8	2 43.4	0 10.0	1 16.9	17 32.7
16	11 33 1.3	0 .0	0 .0	3 30.4	2 5.7	3 20.2	3 13.8	1 24.3	2 43.9	0 10.0	1 17.0	17 33.7
19	11 44 51.0	0 .0	0 .0	0 42.5	2 13.6	2 57.4	3 12.4	1 24.7	2 44.3	0 10.0	1 17.1	17 34.6
22	11 56 40.7	0 .0	0 .0	2S26.6	2 17.6	2 35.1	3 10.4	1 25.2	2 44.7	0 10.0	1 17.3	17 35.4
25	12 8 30.3	0 .0	0 .0	4 41.5	2 17.6	2 13.4	3 7.7	1 25.6	2 45.0	0 10.0	1 17.4	17 36.1
28	12 20 20.0	0 .0	0 .0	4 39.4	2 13.3	1 52.3	3 4.3	1 25.9	2 45.3	0 10.0	1 17.5	17 36.8
31	12 32 9.6	0 .0	0 .0	2 6.4	2 4.5	1 32.0	3 .2	1 26.3	2 45.5	0 10.0	1 17.6	17 37.3

RIGHT ASCENSION

DAY	SID. TIME	☉	☊	☾	☿	♀	♂	♃	♄	♅	♆	♇
1	10 33 53.1	11♓36.5	21♋42.1	13♉47.6	15♒58.2	0♒ 8.2	18♎31.1	8♏19.0	20♎54.7	2♐39.5	26♐34.0	0♏59.6
2	10 37 49.6	12 32.7	21 38.8	27 36.9	17 8.7	0 45.5	18 R25.1	8 R18.1	20 R52.1	2 40.0	26 35.0	0 R58.8
3	10 41 46.2	13 28.8	21 35.4	12♊ 1.4	18 21.0	1 24.2	18 18.4	8 17.0	20 49.4	2 40.4	26 35.9	0 58.0
4	10 45 42.7	14 24.8	21 32.0	26 57.2	19 35.1	2 4.1	18 10.9	8 15.7	20 46.6	2 40.8	26 36.9	0 57.2
5	10 49 39.3	15 20.6	21 28.6	12♋11.8	20 50.7	2 45.2	18 2.8	8 14.3	20 43.8	2 41.1	26 37.8	0 56.4
6	10 53 35.8	16 16.4	21 25.2	27 26.0	22 7.7	3 27.5	17 53.8	8 12.6	20 40.8	2 41.3	26 38.6	0 55.5
7	10 57 32.4	17 12.0	21 21.8	12♌20.1	23 26.1	4 10.9	17 44.2	8 10.8	20 37.8	2 41.5	26 39.4	0 54.6
8	11 1 28.9	18 7.6	21 18.4	26 39.4	24 45.7	4 55.4	17 33.8	8 8.8	20 34.8	2 41.6	26 40.2	0 53.7
9	11 5 25.5	19 3.0	21 15.0	10♍17.4	26 6.6	5 41.0	17 22.8	8 6.7	20 31.7	2 41.7	26 41.0	0 52.8
10	11 9 22.0	19 58.4	21 11.6	23 15.7	27 28.4	6 27.4	17 11.1	8 4.3	20 28.5	2 41.7	26 41.8	0 51.8
11	11 13 18.6	20 53.6	21 8.2	5♎41.1	28 51.3	7 14.9	16 58.6	8 1.8	20 25.2	2 41.7	26 42.4	0 50.8
12	11 17 15.1	21 48.8	21 4.8	17 43.1	0♓15.2	8 3.2	16 45.4	7 59.0	20 21.9	2 R41.6	26 43.1	0 49.8
13	11 21 11.7	22 43.9	21 1.5	29 32.1	1 39.9	8 52.3	16 31.6	7 56.1	20 18.5	2 41.4	26 43.7	0 48.7
14	11 25 8.2	23 38.9	20 58.1	11♏17.9	3 5.6	9 42.3	16 17.1	7 53.1	20 15.0	2 41.2	26 44.3	0 47.7
15	11 29 4.8	24 33.9	20 54.7	23 9.0	4 32.0	10 33.0	16 2.0	7 49.9	20 11.5	2 40.9	26 44.8	0 46.6
16	11 33 1.3	25 28.8	20 51.3	5♐12.1	5 59.3	11 24.4	15 46.2	7 46.5	20 7.9	2 40.6	26 45.3	0 45.5
17	11 36 57.9	26 23.7	20 47.9	17 31.0	7 27.4	12 16.6	15 29.8	7 42.9	20 4.3	2 40.2	26 45.8	0 44.4
18	11 40 54.4	27 18.5	20 44.5	0♑ 6.5	8 56.2	13 9.4	15 12.8	7 39.2	20 .6	2 39.8	26 46.2	0 43.2
19	11 44 51.0	28 13.2	20 41.1	12 56.2	10 25.7	14 2.8	14 55.3	7 35.3	19 56.9	2 39.3	26 46.6	0 42.0
20	11 48 47.6	29 8.0	20 37.7	25 55.2	11 56.0	14 56.8	14 37.2	7 31.2	19 53.1	2 38.8	26 47.0	0 40.8
21	11 52 44.1	0♈ 2.7	20 34.3	8♒57.4	13 27.1	15 51.3	14 18.6	7 27.0	19 49.3	2 38.2	26 47.3	0 39.6
22	11 56 40.7	0 57.4	20 30.9	21 57.2	14 58.9	16 46.4	13 59.5	7 22.6	19 45.4	2 37.5	26 47.6	0 38.4
23	12 0 37.2	1 52.0	20 27.5	4♓51.7	16 31.4	17 41.9	13 39.9	7 18.1	19 41.5	2 36.8	26 47.9	0 37.2
24	12 4 33.8	2 46.6	20 24.1	17 41.0	18 4.8	18 37.9	13 20.0	7 13.4	19 37.6	2 36.0	26 48.1	0 35.9
25	12 8 30.3	3 41.3	20 20.7	0♈29.0	19 38.9	19 34.3	12 59.6	7 8.6	19 33.6	2 35.2	26 48.2	0 34.6
26	12 12 26.9	4 35.9	20 17.3	13 22.4	21 13.7	20 31.1	12 38.9	7 3.6	19 29.5	2 34.4	26 48.4	0 33.3
27	12 16 23.4	5 30.5	20 13.9	26 30.0	22 49.5	21 28.4	12 17.9	6 58.5	19 25.5	2 33.4	26 48.5	0 32.0
28	12 20 20.0	6 25.1	20 10.5	10♉ .6	24 26.0	22 25.9	11 56.6	6 53.2	19 21.4	2 32.5	26 48.6	0 30.7
29	12 24 16.5	7 19.7	20 7.1	24 1.1	26 3.5	23 23.8	11 35.1	6 47.8	19 17.2	2 31.4	26 48.6	0 29.3
30	12 28 13.1	8 14.3	20 3.7	8♊33.9	27 41.9	24 22.0	11 13.4	6 42.3	19 13.1	2 30.4	26 48.7	0 28.0
31	12 32 9.6	9 8.9	20 .3	23 33.7	29 21.2	25 20.5	10 51.6	6 36.7	19 9.0	2 29.3	26 R48.6	0 26.6

DECLINATION

DAY	SID. TIME	☉	☊	☾	☿	♀	♂	♃	♄	♅	♆	♇
1	10 33 53.1	7S47.4	0N23.0	11N47.4	17S19.4	15S 8.8	4S23.3	13S37.0	5S54.3	20S53.7	22S 7.7	6N 2.0
4	10 45 42.7	6 38.7	0 23.0	21 19.0	16 42.4	15 9.3	4 13.7	13 35.3	5 50.4	20 53.9	22 7.6	6 4.3
7	10 57 32.4	5 29.2	0 23.0	19 26.4	15 53.2	15 6.2	4 1.8	13 33.1	5 46.2	20 54.0	22 7.6	6 6.6
10	11 9 22.0	4 19.0	0 23.1	7 41.9	14 52.1	14 59.4	3 47.7	13 30.5	5 41.9	20 54.0	22 7.5	6 8.9
13	11 21 11.7	3 8.4	0 23.1	6S44.1	13 39.4	14 48.5	3 31.5	13 27.3	5 37.3	20 54.0	22 7.5	6 11.2
16	11 33 1.3	1 57.4	0 23.1	17 55.7	12 15.3	14 33.4	3 13.5	13 23.7	5 32.6	20 53.9	22 7.4	6 13.5
19	11 44 51.0	0 46.3	0 23.1	22 11.8	10 40.0	14 14.0	2 53.7	13 19.6	5 27.7	20 53.6	22 7.3	6 15.8
22	11 56 40.7	0N24.9	0 23.1	17 32.1	8 53.7	13 50.3	2 32.6	13 15.0	5 22.7	20 53.3	22 7.2	6 18.0
25	12 8 30.3	1 35.8	0 23.2	4 54.4	6 56.8	13 22.4	2 10.4	13 10.0	5 17.6	20 52.9	22 7.1	6 20.3
28	12 20 20.0	2 46.5	0 23.2	10N41.2	4 49.6	12 50.1	1 47.5	13 4.6	5 12.4	20 52.5	22 7.0	6 22.5
31	12 32 9.6	3 56.6	0 23.2	21 12.0	2 32.6	12 13.7	1 24.5	12 58.9	5 7.1	20 51.9	22 6.9	6 24.6

APRIL 1982

LONGITUDE

DAY	EPHEM. SID. TIME h m s	☉ ° ′	☊ ° ′	☾ ° ′	☿ ° ′	♀ ° ′	♂ ° ′	♃ ° ′	♄ ° ′	♅ ° ′	♆ ° ′	♇ ° ′
1	12 36 6.2	10♈56.6	18♋25.1	8♋ 8.1	0♈14.8	24♒30.5	10♎ 8.9	8♏25.0	19♎32.1	4♐24.6	27♐ 2.6	25♎57.4
2	12 40 2.7	11 55.8	18 21.9	22 7.5	2 7.2	25 29.4	9 R 45.6	8 R 18.9	19 R 27.6	4 R 23.4	27 R 2.5	25 R 55.8
3	12 43 59.3	12 55.0	18 18.7	5♌57.9	4 1.0	26 28.8	9 22.4	8 12.7	19 23.0	4 22.2	27 2.4	25 54.1
4	12 47 55.8	13 54.1	18 15.5	19 39.3	5 56.1	27 28.5	8 59.2	8 6.4	19 18.4	4 21.0	27 2.2	25 52.5
5	12 51 52.4	14 53.2	18 12.4	3♍11.4	7 52.7	28 28.5	8 36.1	7 60.0	19 13.8	4 19.7	27 2.0	25 50.9
6	12 55 48.9	15 52.2	18 9.2	16 33.7	9 50.5	29 29.0	8 13.1	7 53.4	19 9.2	4 18.3	27 1.8	25 49.2
7	12 59 45.5	16 51.2	18 6.0	29 45.1	11 49.7	0♓29.7	7 50.3	7 46.8	19 4.5	4 17.0	27 1.5	25 47.5
8	13 3 42.0	17 50.2	18 2.8	12♎44.2	13 50.1	1 30.8	7 27.7	7 40.0	18 59.9	4 15.5	27 1.2	25 45.9
9	13 7 38.6	18 49.2	17 59.6	25 30.1	15 51.7	2 32.3	7 5.4	7 33.2	18 55.3	4 14.1	27 .9	25 44.2
10	13 11 35.2	19 48.1	17 56.5	8♏ 2.1	17 54.5	3 34.0	6 43.4	7 26.3	18 50.6	4 12.6	27 .5	25 42.5
11	13 15 31.7	20 47.0	17 53.3	20 20.5	19 58.3	4 36.0	6 21.8	7 19.3	18 46.0	4 11.0	27 .1	25 40.8
12	13 19 28.3	21 45.8	17 50.1	2♐26.6	22 3.0	5 38.3	6 .5	7 12.2	18 41.4	4 9.4	26 59.7	25 39.1
13	13 23 24.8	22 44.6	17 46.9	14 22.9	24 8.5	6 40.9	5 39.6	7 5.0	18 36.8	4 7.8	26 59.2	25 37.4
14	13 27 21.4	23 43.4	17 43.8	26 12.8	26 14.6	7 43.8	5 19.2	6 57.8	18 32.1	4 6.1	26 58.7	25 35.7
15	13 31 17.9	24 42.2	17 40.6	8♑ .8	28 21.1	8 46.9	4 59.2	6 50.5	18 27.5	4 4.4	26 58.2	25 34.0
16	13 35 14.5	25 40.9	17 37.4	19 51.8	0♉27.8	9 50.3	4 39.8	6 43.2	18 23.0	4 2.7	26 57.7	25 32.4
17	13 39 11.0	26 39.6	17 34.2	1♒51.3	2 34.3	10 53.9	4 20.9	6 35.7	18 18.4	4 .9	26 57.1	25 30.7
18	13 43 7.6	27 38.3	17 31.0	14 4.8	4 40.5	11 57.8	4 2.7	6 28.3	18 13.8	3 59.1	26 56.5	25 29.0
19	13 47 4.1	28 36.9	17 27.9	26 37.3	6 46.1	13 1.9	3 45.0	6 20.8	18 9.3	3 57.2	26 55.9	25 27.3
20	13 51 .7	29 35.6	17 24.7	9♓33.3	8 50.7	14 6.2	3 28.0	6 13.3	18 4.9	3 55.4	26 55.2	25 25.6
21	13 54 57.2	0♉34.2	17 21.5	22 55.3	10 53.9	15 10.7	3 11.6	6 5.7	18 .4	3 53.5	26 54.5	25 23.9
22	13 58 53.8	1 32.7	17 18.3	6♈43.9	12 55.5	16 15.5	2 55.8	5 58.1	17 55.9	3 51.5	26 53.8	25 22.2
23	14 2 50.3	2 31.2	17 15.2	20 56.9	14 55.2	17 20.4	2 40.8	5 50.4	17 51.5	3 49.5	26 53.1	25 20.6
24	14 6 46.9	3 29.7	17 12.0	5♉29.3	16 52.6	18 25.5	2 26.5	5 42.8	17 47.1	3 47.5	26 52.3	25 18.9
25	14 10 43.5	4 28.2	17 8.8	20 14.2	18 47.4	19 30.8	2 13.0	5 35.1	17 42.8	3 45.4	26 51.5	25 17.2
26	14 14 40.0	5 26.6	17 5.6	5♊ 3.1	20 39.4	20 36.2	2 .2	5 27.4	17 38.5	3 43.4	26 50.6	25 15.6
27	14 18 36.6	6 25.0	17 2.4	19 48.4	22 28.3	21 41.9	1 48.1	5 19.8	17 34.2	3 41.3	26 49.8	25 13.9
28	14 22 33.1	7 23.4	16 59.3	4♋23.5	24 13.9	22 47.7	1 36.9	5 12.1	17 30.0	3 39.1	26 48.9	25 12.2
29	14 26 29.7	8 21.7	16 56.1	18 44.3	25 56.0	23 53.6	1 26.4	5 4.4	17 25.8	3 37.0	26 48.0	25 10.6
30	14 30 26.2	9 20.0	16 52.9	2♌48.6	27 34.4	24 59.7	1 16.8	4 56.8	17 21.6	3 34.8	26 47.0	25 9.0

LATITUDE

DAY	SID. TIME	☉	☊	☾	☿	♀	♂	♃	♄	♅	♆	♇
1	12 36 6.2	0 .0	0 .0	0 S 55.3	2 S .6	1 N 25.4	2 N 58.6	1 N 26.4	2 N 45.6	0 N 10.0	1 N 17.6	17 N 37.5
4	12 47 55.8	0 .0	0 .0	2 N 36.1	1 45.9	1 6.0	2 53.5	1 26.6	2 45.7	0 10.0	1 17.7	17 37.9
7	12 59 45.5	0 .0	0 .0	4 44.9	1 26.5	0 47.5	2 47.8	1 26.8	2 45.8	0 10.0	1 17.8	17 38.2
10	13 11 35.2	0 .0	0 .0	4 41.3	1 2.7	0 29.9	2 41.5	1 27.0	2 45.9	0 10.0	1 17.9	17 38.5
13	13 23 24.8	0 .0	0 .0	2 43.4	0 34.9	0 13.1	2 34.7	1 27.1	2 45.9	0 9.9	1 18.0	17 38.6
16	13 35 14.5	0 .0	0 .0	0 S 15.3	0 4.1	0 S 2.8	2 27.5	1 27.2	2 45.8	0 9.9	1 18.1	17 38.6
19	13 47 4.1	0 .0	0 .0	3 13.8	0 N 28.6	0 17.7	2 19.9	1 27.2	2 45.7	0 9.9	1 18.2	17 38.6
22	13 58 53.8	0 .0	0 .0	4 57.4	1 1.0	0 31.7	2 12.2	1 27.2	2 45.5	0 9.9	1 18.3	17 38.4
25	14 10 43.5	0 .0	0 .0	4 10.2	1 31.3	0 44.7	2 4.2	1 27.1	2 45.3	0 9.9	1 18.4	17 38.2
28	14 22 33.1	0 .0	0 .0	1 .1	1 57.2	0 56.8	1 56.2	1 26.9	2 45.0	0 9.9	1 18.5	17 37.8

RIGHT ASCENSION

DAY	SID. TIME	☉	☊	☾	☿	♀	♂	♃	♄	♅	♆	♇
1	12 36 6.2	10♈ 3.6	19♋56.9	8♋47.6	1♈ 1.6	26♒19.3	10♎29.7	6♏30.9	19♎ 4.8	2♐28.1	26♐48.5	0♏25.2
2	12 40 2.7	10 58.2	19 53.5	23 57.3	2 42.9	27 18.3	10 R 7.7	6 R 25.0	19 R .5	2 R 26.9	26 R 48.4	0 R 23.8
3	12 43 59.3	11 52.9	19 50.1	8♌44.2	4 25.3	28 17.6	9 45.6	6 19.0	18 56.3	2 25.6	26 48.3	0 22.4
4	12 47 55.8	12 47.6	19 46.7	22 55.5	6 8.8	29 17.0	9 23.6	6 12.9	18 52.0	2 24.3	26 48.1	0 21.0
5	12 51 52.4	13 42.4	19 43.3	6♍26.3	7 53.5	0♓16.7	9 1.7	6 6.7	18 47.8	2 23.0	26 47.9	0 19.6
6	12 55 48.9	14 37.2	19 39.9	19 18.7	9 39.4	1 16.6	8 39.8	6 .4	18 43.5	2 21.6	26 47.6	0 18.1
7	12 59 45.5	15 32.0	19 36.5	1♎39.9	11 26.4	2 16.7	8 18.1	5 54.0	18 39.2	2 20.1	26 47.4	0 16.7
8	13 3 42.0	16 26.9	19 33.1	13 39.2	13 14.7	3 17.0	7 56.6	5 47.4	18 34.9	2 18.6	26 47.0	0 15.2
9	13 7 38.6	17 21.8	19 29.7	25 26.9	15 4.2	4 17.4	7 35.3	5 40.8	18 30.6	2 17.1	26 46.7	0 13.7
10	13 11 35.2	18 16.8	19 26.3	7♏12.2	16 54.9	5 17.9	7 14.3	5 34.1	18 26.3	2 15.5	26 46.3	0 12.3
11	13 15 31.7	19 11.9	19 22.9	19 3.2	18 46.9	6 18.6	6 53.5	5 27.4	18 22.0	2 13.8	26 45.9	0 10.8
12	13 19 28.3	20 7.0	19 19.5	1♐ 5.9	20 40.0	7 19.5	6 33.1	5 20.5	18 17.7	2 12.2	26 45.4	0 9.3
13	13 23 24.8	21 2.2	19 16.1	13 23.3	22 34.2	8 20.5	6 13.0	5 13.6	18 13.5	2 10.5	26 44.9	0 7.8
14	13 27 21.4	21 57.5	19 12.7	25 55.8	24 29.5	9 21.5	5 53.3	5 6.6	18 9.2	2 8.7	26 44.4	0 6.3
15	13 31 17.9	22 52.9	19 9.3	8♑40.3	26 25.6	10 22.7	5 34.1	4 59.5	18 4.9	2 6.9	26 43.8	0 4.8
16	13 35 14.5	23 48.4	19 5.9	21 32.0	28 22.6	11 24.0	5 15.3	4 52.4	18 .6	2 5.1	26 43.3	0 3.2
17	13 39 11.0	24 43.9	19 2.5	4♒25.1	0♉20.2	12 25.4	4 57.0	4 45.3	17 56.4	2 3.2	26 42.6	0 1.7
18	13 43 7.6	25 39.6	18 59.1	17 15.0	2 18.1	13 26.9	4 39.2	4 38.0	17 52.2	2 1.3	26 42.0	0 .2
19	13 47 4.1	26 35.4	18 55.7	29 59.5	4 16.3	14 28.4	4 22.0	4 30.8	17 47.9	1 59.3	26 41.3	29♎58.7
20	13 51 .7	27 31.3	18 52.3	12♓39.6	6 14.4	15 30.1	4 5.4	4 23.5	17 43.8	1 57.4	26 40.6	29 57.2
21	13 54 57.2	28 27.3	18 48.8	25 20.1	8 12.1	16 31.8	3 49.3	4 16.2	17 39.6	1 55.4	26 39.9	29 55.7
22	13 58 53.8	29 23.4	18 45.4	8♈ 8.4	10 9.2	17 33.6	3 33.8	4 8.8	17 35.5	1 53.3	26 39.1	29 54.1
23	14 2 50.3	0♉19.6	18 42.0	21 14.1	12 5.3	18 35.4	3 19.0	4 1.5	17 31.3	1 51.2	26 38.3	29 52.6
24	14 6 46.9	1 15.9	18 38.6	4♉47.4	14 .2	19 37.3	3 4.9	3 54.1	17 27.3	1 49.1	26 37.4	29 51.1
25	14 10 43.5	2 12.3	18 35.2	18 56.4	15 53.5	20 39.3	2 51.4	3 46.7	17 23.2	1 47.0	26 36.6	29 49.5
26	14 14 40.0	3 8.9	18 31.8	3♊44.3	17 44.9	21 41.3	2 38.6	3 39.2	17 19.2	1 44.8	26 35.7	29 48.0
27	14 18 36.6	4 5.5	18 28.4	19 5.6	19 34.1	22 43.4	2 26.5	3 31.8	17 15.2	1 42.6	26 34.7	29 46.5
28	14 22 33.1	5 2.3	18 25.0	4♋44.9	21 20.9	23 45.5	2 15.1	3 24.4	17 11.2	1 40.3	26 33.8	29 45.0
29	14 26 29.7	5 59.2	18 21.6	20 19.8	23 4.9	24 47.7	2 4.5	3 17.0	17 7.3	1 38.1	26 32.8	29 43.4
30	14 30 26.2	6 56.3	18 18.2	5♌27.7	24 46.0	25 49.9	1 54.5	3 9.6	17 3.5	1 35.8	26 31.8	29 41.9

DECLINATION

DAY	SID. TIME	☉	☊	☾	☿	♀	♂	♃	♄	♅	♆	♇
1	12 36 6.2	4 N 19.9	0 N 23.2	22 N 16.3	1 S 44.8	12 S .7	1 S 16.8	12 S 56.9	5 S 5.3	20 S 51.7	22 S 6.9	6 N 25.3
4	12 47 55.8	5 29.1	0 23.2	17 23.6	0 N 44.2	11 19.0	0 54.2	12 50.7	5 .0	20 51.1	22 6.8	6 27.4
7	12 59 45.5	6 37.4	0 23.3	4 27.3	3 21.0	10 33.4	0 32.4	12 44.1	4 54.7	20 50.3	22 6.6	6 29.4
10	13 11 35.2	7 44.7	0 23.3	9 S 44.8	6 3.6	9 44.1	0 11.8	12 37.4	4 49.4	20 49.5	22 6.5	6 31.3
13	13 23 24.8	8 50.8	0 23.3	19 49.2	8 49.3	8 51.4	0 N 7.1	12 30.4	4 44.2	20 48.6	22 6.4	6 33.2
16	13 35 14.5	9 55.6	0 23.3	22 13.4	11 34.3	7 55.4	0 24.2	12 23.2	4 39.0	20 47.7	22 6.3	6 35.0
19	13 47 4.1	10 59.0	0 23.4	15 40.6	14 13.5	6 56.4	0 39.0	12 15.8	4 34.0	20 46.7	22 6.1	6 36.7
22	13 58 53.8	12 .7	0 23.4	1 52.8	16 41.3	5 54.6	0 51.4	12 8.4	4 29.0	20 45.6	22 6.0	6 38.3
25	14 10 43.5	13 .7	0 23.4	13 N 47.1	18 52.5	4 50.3	1 1.1	12 .9	4 24.2	20 44.5	22 5.8	6 39.8
28	14 22 33.1	13 58.7	0 23.4	22 22.0	20 43.4	3 43.7	1 8.1	11 53.5	4 19.6	20 43.4	22 5.7	6 41.2

MAY 1982

DAY	EPHEM. SID. TIME	☉	☊	☽	☿	♀	♂	♃	♄	♅	♆	♇
	h m s	° ′	° ′	° ′	° ′	° ′	° ′	° ′	° ′	° ′	° ′	° ′
		LONGITUDE										
1	14 34 22.8	10♉18.3	16♋49.7	16♌36.3	29♉ 9.0	26♓ 6.0	1♎ 7.9	4♏49.2	17♎17.6	3♐32.6	26♐46.0	25♎ 7.3
2	14 38 19.3	11 16.5	16 46.6	0♍ 7.9	0♊39.7	27 12.4	0 R59.8	4 R41.6	17 R13.5	3 R30.3	26 R45.0	25 R 5.7
3	14 42 15.9	12 14.7	16 43.4	13 24.8	2 6.3	28 18.9	0 52.6	4 34.0	17 9.6	3 28.1	26 44.0	25 4.1
4	14 46 12.4	13 12.9	16 40.2	26 28.2	3 28.7	29 25.6	0 46.1	4 26.5	17 5.6	3 25.8	26 43.0	25 2.5
5	14 50 9.0	14 11.0	16 37.0	9♎19.1	4 46.9	0♈32.5	0 40.4	4 19.0	17 1.8	3 23.5	26 41.9	25 .9
6	14 54 5.6	15 9.1	16 33.8	21 58.3	6 .8	1 39.4	0 35.5	4 11.6	16 57.9	3 21.2	26 40.8	24 59.4
7	14 58 2.1	16 7.2	16 30.7	4♏26.3	7 10.4	2 46.5	0 31.5	4 4.2	16 54.2	3 18.9	26 39.7	24 57.8
8	15 1 58.7	17 5.2	16 27.5	16 43.6	8 15.4	3 53.8	0 28.2	3 56.9	16 50.5	3 16.5	26 38.6	24 56.3
9	15 5 55.2	18 3.2	16 24.3	28 51.0	9 16.0	5 1.1	0 25.7	3 49.6	16 46.9	3 14.1	26 37.4	24 54.8
10	15 9 51.8	19 1.2	16 21.1	10♐49.8	10 11.9	6 8.6	0 23.9	3 42.4	16 43.3	3 11.8	26 36.2	24 53.2
11	15 13 48.3	19 59.2	16 18.0	22 41.9	11 3.3	7 16.2	0 23.0	3 35.3	16 39.9	3 9.4	26 35.1	24 51.8
12	15 17 44.9	20 57.2	16 14.8	4♑29.9	11 49.8	8 24.0	0 22.8	3 28.3	16 36.5	3 7.0	26 33.8	24 50.3
13	15 21 41.4	21 55.1	16 11.6	16 17.4	12 31.7	9 31.8	0 D23.3	3 21.3	16 33.1	3 4.6	26 32.6	24 48.9
14	15 25 38.0	22 53.0	16 8.4	28 8.3	13 8.7	10 39.7	0 24.6	3 14.4	16 29.8	3 2.1	26 31.3	24 47.4
15	15 29 34.6	23 50.9	16 5.2	10♒ 7.5	13 40.8	11 47.8	0 26.7	3 7.6	16 26.6	2 59.7	26 30.0	24 46.0
16	15 33 31.1	24 48.7	16 2.1	22 19.9	14 8.1	12 55.9	0 29.4	3 .9	16 23.5	2 57.2	26 28.7	24 44.6
17	15 37 27.7	25 46.6	15 58.9	4♓50.8	14 30.4	14 4.2	0 32.9	2 54.3	16 20.5	2 54.7	26 27.4	24 43.2
18	15 41 24.2	26 44.4	15 55.7	17 44.6	14 47.7	15 12.6	0 37.1	2 47.7	16 17.5	2 52.3	26 26.1	24 41.8
19	15 45 20.8	27 42.2	15 52.5	1♈ 5.0	15 .2	16 21.0	0 42.0	2 41.3	16 14.6	2 49.8	26 24.7	24 40.4
20	15 49 17.3	28 39.9	15 49.4	14 53.7	15 7.8	17 29.6	0 47.6	2 35.0	16 11.8	2 47.3	26 23.3	24 39.1
21	15 53 13.9	29 37.7	15 46.2	29 10.1	15 10.5	18 38.2	0 53.9	2 28.8	16 9.0	2 44.8	26 21.9	24 37.8
22	15 57 10.4	0♊35.4	15 43.0	13♉50.3	15 R 8.6	19 46.9	1 .9	2 22.8	16 6.4	2 42.3	26 20.5	24 36.5
23	16 1 7.0	1 33.1	15 39.8	28 47.6	15 2.1	20 55.7	1 8.5	2 16.8	16 3.8	2 39.8	26 19.1	24 35.2
24	16 5 3.6	2 30.8	15 36.7	13♊53.3	14 51.2	22 4.6	1 16.9	2 11.0	16 1.4	2 37.3	26 17.7	24 34.0
25	16 9 .1	3 28.5	15 33.5	28 58.0	14 36.2	23 13.6	1 25.8	2 5.3	15 59.0	2 34.8	26 16.2	24 32.8
26	16 12 56.7	4 26.2	15 30.3	13♋52.8	14 17.4	24 22.6	1 35.4	1 59.8	15 56.7	2 32.3	26 14.7	24 31.6
27	16 16 53.2	5 23.8	15 27.1	28 31.1	13 55.0	25 31.8	1 45.6	1 54.4	15 54.5	2 29.8	26 13.3	24 30.4
28	16 20 49.8	6 21.4	15 23.9	12♌48.7	13 29.5	26 41.0	1 56.5	1 49.1	15 52.3	2 27.3	26 11.8	24 29.2
29	16 24 46.3	7 19.0	15 20.8	26 43.8	13 1.4	27 50.2	2 8.0	1 44.0	15 50.3	2 24.8	26 10.3	24 28.1
30	16 28 42.9	8 16.5	15 17.6	10♍16.8	12 31.0	28 59.5	2 20.0	1 39.0	15 48.4	2 22.4	26 8.7	24 27.0
31	16 32 39.5	9 14.1	15 14.4	23 29.1	11 59.1	0♉ 8.9	2 32.6	1 34.1	15 46.5	2 19.9	26 7.2	24 25.9
		LATITUDE										
1	14 34 22.8	0 .0	0 .0	2N36.6	2N17.2	1S 7.8	1N48.3	1N26.7	2N44.7	0N 9.8	1N18.6	17N37.4
4	14 46 12.4	0 .0	0 .0	4 47.5	2 29.9	1 17.9	1 40.3	1 26.4	2 44.4	0 9.8	1 18.6	17 36.9
7	14 58 2.1	0 .0	0 .0	4 47.0	2 34.6	1 26.9	1 32.5	1 26.1	2 44.0	0 9.8	1 18.7	17 36.2
10	15 9 51.8	0 .0	0 .0	2 50.5	2 30.5	1 35.0	1 24.8	1 25.7	2 43.5	0 9.8	1 18.8	17 35.5
13	15 21 41.4	0 .0	0 .0	0S 9.7	2 17.2	1 42.1	1 17.4	1 25.3	2 43.1	0 9.8	1 18.8	17 34.7
16	15 33 31.1	0 .0	0 .0	3 9.8	1 54.5	1 48.2	1 10.1	1 24.9	2 42.5	0 9.7	1 18.9	17 33.9
19	15 45 20.8	0 .0	0 .0	5 .6	1 22.6	1 53.3	1 3.0	1 24.4	2 42.0	0 9.7	1 18.9	17 32.9
22	15 57 10.4	0 .0	0 .0	4 28.7	0 42.1	1 57.4	0 56.2	1 23.8	2 41.4	0 9.7	1 19.0	17 31.9
25	16 9 .1	0 .0	0 .0	1 20.2	0S 5.2	2 .7	0 49.7	1 23.2	2 40.8	0 9.7	1 19.0	17 30.7
28	16 20 49.8	0 .0	0 .0	2N31.1	0 56.8	2 3.0	0 43.4	1 22.6	2 40.1	0 9.6	1 19.0	17 29.6
31	16 32 39.5	0 .0	0 .0	4 52.6	1 49.0	2 4.4	0 37.3	1 21.9	2 39.5	0 9.6	1 19.0	17 28.3
		RIGHT ASCENSION										
1	14 34 22.8	7♉53.4	18♋14.8	19♌53.1	26♉23.9	26♓52.2	1♎45.3	3♏ 2.3	16♎59.6	1♐33.4	26♐30.7	29♎40.4
2	14 38 19.3	8 50.7	18 11.4	3♍30.6	27 58.4	27 54.5	1 R36.9	2 R54.9	16 R55.8	1 R31.1	26 R29.6	29 R38.9
3	14 42 15.9	9 48.1	18 7.9	16 23.4	29 29.3	28 57.0	1 29.2	2 47.6	16 52.1	1 28.7	26 28.5	29 37.4
4	14 46 12.4	10 45.7	18 4.5	28 40.3	0♊56.4	29 59.4	1 22.2	2 40.4	16 48.4	1 26.3	26 27.4	29 35.9
5	14 50 9.0	11 43.4	18 1.1	10♎32.5	2 19.5	1♈ 2.0	1 16.0	2 33.1	16 44.8	1 23.9	26 26.3	29 34.4
6	14 54 5.6	12 41.2	17 57.7	22 11.5	3 38.5	2 4.6	1 10.4	2 25.9	16 41.2	1 21.5	26 25.1	29 33.0
7	14 58 2.1	13 39.2	17 54.3	3♏48.1	4 53.2	3 7.3	1 5.7	2 18.8	16 37.7	1 19.0	26 23.9	29 31.5
8	15 1 58.7	14 37.3	17 50.9	15 31.2	6 3.5	4 10.1	1 1.6	2 11.7	16 34.2	1 16.6	26 22.6	29 30.0
9	15 5 55.2	15 35.5	17 47.5	27 27.4	7 9.3	5 13.0	0 58.3	2 4.7	16 30.8	1 14.1	26 21.4	29 28.6
10	15 9 51.8	16 33.9	17 44.1	9♐40.3	8 10.4	6 16.0	0 55.7	1 57.7	16 27.5	1 11.6	26 20.1	29 27.1
11	15 13 48.3	17 32.5	17 40.7	22 9.7	9 6.7	7 19.1	0 53.8	1 50.9	16 24.2	1 9.1	26 18.9	29 25.7
12	15 17 44.9	18 31.2	17 37.2	4♑52.1	9 58.0	8 22.3	0 52.7	1 44.1	16 21.0	1 6.6	26 17.6	29 24.3
13	15 21 41.4	19 30.0	17 33.8	17 41.3	10 44.4	9 25.5	0 52.2	1 37.3	16 17.9	1 4.0	26 16.2	29 22.9
14	15 25 38.0	20 29.0	17 30.4	0♒30.1	11 25.6	10 28.9	0 D52.4	1 30.7	16 14.8	1 1.5	26 14.8	29 21.5
15	15 29 34.6	21 28.1	17 27.0	13 12.6	12 1.7	11 32.4	0 53.3	1 24.1	16 11.7	0 58.9	26 13.5	29 20.1
16	15 33 31.1	22 27.4	17 23.6	25 45.9	12 32.5	12 36.0	0 54.9	1 17.6	16 8.8	0 56.3	26 12.1	29 18.8
17	15 37 27.7	23 26.8	17 20.2	8♓10.9	12 58.0	13 39.7	0 57.1	1 11.2	16 5.9	0 53.7	26 10.6	29 17.4
18	15 41 24.2	24 26.4	17 16.8	20 32.7	13 18.3	14 43.6	1 .0	1 4.9	16 3.0	0 51.1	26 9.2	29 16.1
19	15 45 20.8	25 26.1	17 13.3	2♈59.4	13 33.3	15 47.5	1 3.6	0 58.7	16 .3	0 48.5	26 7.7	29 14.7
20	15 49 17.3	26 25.9	17 9.9	15 42.1	13 43.1	16 51.7	1 7.9	0 52.6	15 57.6	0 45.9	26 6.2	29 13.4
21	15 53 13.9	27 25.9	17 6.5	28 53.3	13 47.7	17 55.9	1 12.7	0 46.6	15 55.0	0 43.3	26 4.7	29 12.1
22	15 57 10.4	28 26.0	17 3.1	12♉44.6	13 R47.4	19 .3	1 18.2	0 40.8	15 52.5	0 40.7	26 3.2	29 10.8
23	16 1 7.0	29 26.3	16 59.7	27 24.1	13 42.2	20 4.9	1 24.4	0 35.0	15 50.0	0 38.1	26 1.7	29 9.5
24	16 5 3.6	0♊26.7	16 56.3	12♊51.2	13 32.4	21 9.6	1 31.1	0 29.4	15 47.7	0 35.5	26 .1	29 8.3
25	16 9 .1	1 27.2	16 52.9	28 53.1	13 18.2	22 14.5	1 38.5	0 23.9	15 45.4	0 32.8	25 58.5	29 7.1
26	16 12 56.7	2 27.8	16 49.4	15♋ 4.4	13 .1	23 19.5	1 46.5	0 18.5	15 43.2	0 30.2	25 57.0	29 5.8
27	16 16 53.2	3 28.6	16 46.0	0♌55.4	12 38.3	24 24.7	1 55.0	0 13.2	15 41.0	0 27.6	25 55.4	29 4.7
28	16 20 49.8	4 29.4	16 42.6	16 1.8	12 13.4	25 30.1	2 4.1	0 8.1	15 39.0	0 25.0	25 53.8	29 3.5
29	16 24 46.3	5 30.4	16 39.2	0♍12.4	11 45.7	26 35.7	2 13.8	0 3.1	15 37.0	0 22.4	25 52.1	29 2.3
30	16 28 42.9	6 31.5	16 35.8	13 28.0	11 15.9	27 41.5	2 24.1	29♎58.3	15 35.2	0 19.8	25 50.5	29 1.2
31	16 32 39.5	7 32.7	16 32.3	25 57.6	10 44.4	28 47.4	2 34.9	29 53.6	15 33.4	0 17.2	25 48.9	29 .1
		DECLINATION										
1	14 34 22.8	14N54.7	0N23.4	18N20.9	22N12.0	2S35.3	1N12.3	11S46.0	4S15.2	20S42.1	22S 5.6	6N42.5
4	14 46 12.4	15 48.4	0 23.5	5 48.0	23 18.2	1 25.1	1 13.7	11 38.7	4 11.0	20 40.9	22 5.4	6 43.6
7	14 58 2.1	16 39.7	0 23.5	8S29.5	24 2.9	0 13.5	1 12.4	11 31.5	4 7.0	20 39.6	22 5.3	6 44.7
10	15 9 51.8	17 28.6	0 23.5	19 15.4	24 27.6	0N59.2	1 8.3	11 24.5	4 3.3	20 38.2	22 5.1	6 45.6
13	15 21 41.4	18 14.8	0 23.5	22 36.5	24 34.0	2 12.7	1 1.7	11 17.8	3 59.8	20 36.9	22 4.9	6 46.4
16	15 33 31.1	18 58.3	0 23.5	17 3.5	24 23.6	3 26.8	0 52.6	11 11.3	3 56.6	20 35.5	22 4.8	6 47.1
19	15 45 20.8	19 38.9	0 23.6	4 9.9	23 57.9	4 41.2	0 41.1	11 5.1	3 53.7	20 34.1	22 4.6	6 47.6
22	15 57 10.4	20 16.5	0 23.6	11N42.9	23 18.7	5 55.5	0 27.4	10 59.3	3 51.1	20 32.6	22 4.5	6 48.0
25	16 9 .1	20 51.0	0 23.6	22 6.0	22 28.0	7 9.4	0 11.4	10 53.9	3 48.9	20 31.2	22 4.3	6 48.3
28	16 20 49.8	21 22.3	0 23.6	19 22.9	21 28.8	8 22.7	0S 6.6	10 48.9	3 46.9	20 29.8	22 4.2	6 48.4
31	16 32 39.5	21 50.2	0 23.6	7 3.8	20 25.6	9 35.0	0 26.5	10 44.3	3 45.3	20 28.3	22 4.0	6 48.4

JUNE 1982

LONGITUDE

DAY	EPHEM. SID. TIME	☉	☊	☽	☿	♀	♂	♃	♄	♅	♆	♇
	h m s	° ′	° ′	° ′	° ′	° ′	° ′	° ′	° ′	° ′	° ′	° ′
1	16 36 36.0	10♊11.6	15♋11.2	6♎23.1	11♊26.0	1♉18.4	2♎45.9	1♏29.5	15♎44.8	2♐17.5	26♐ 5.7	24♎24.9
2	16 40 32.6	11 9.1	15 8.1	19 1.2	10 R 52.4	2 28.0	2 59.6	1 R 25.0	15 R 43.2	2 R 15.0	26 R 4.2	24 R 23.9
3	16 44 29.1	12 6.6	15 4.9	1♏26.0	10 18.8	3 37.6	3 13.9	1 20.6	15 41.6	2 12.6	26 2.6	24 22.9
4	16 48 25.7	13 4.0	15 1.7	13 39.6	9 45.9	4 47.3	3 28.8	1 16.4	15 40.1	2 10.1	26 1.1	24 21.9
5	16 52 22.2	14 1.4	14 58.5	25 44.2	9 14.2	5 57.0	3 44.1	1 12.3	15 38.8	2 7.7	25 59.5	24 21.0
6	16 56 18.8	14 58.8	14 55.4	7♐41.5	8 44.2	7 6.8	3 60.0	1 8.4	15 37.5	2 5.3	25 57.9	24 20.1
7	17 0 15.4	15 56.2	14 52.2	19 33.5	8 16.4	8 16.6	4 16.4	1 4.7	15 36.3	2 2.9	25 56.3	24 19.2
8	17 4 11.9	16 53.6	14 49.0	1♑22.2	7 51.4	9 26.6	4 33.2	1 1.1	15 35.2	2 .5	25 54.7	24 18.3
9	17 8 8.5	17 51.0	14 45.8	13 9.8	7 29.4	10 36.6	4 50.6	0 57.7	15 34.2	1 58.1	25 53.1	24 17.5
10	17 12 5.0	18 48.3	14 42.7	24 59.0	7 10.9	11 46.6	5 8.4	0 54.4	15 33.3	1 55.7	25 51.5	24 16.7
11	17 16 1.6	19 45.7	14 39.5	6♒52.9	6 56.2	12 56.7	5 26.7	0 51.4	15 32.6	1 53.4	25 49.9	24 15.9
12	17 19 58.1	20 43.0	14 36.3	18 55.1	6 45.5	14 6.9	5 45.4	0 48.5	15 31.9	1 51.1	25 48.3	24 15.2
13	17 23 54.7	21 40.4	14 33.1	1♓ 9.6	6 39.1	15 17.1	6 4.6	0 45.7	15 31.3	1 48.8	25 46.7	24 14.5
14	17 27 51.3	22 37.7	14 29.9	13 40.5	6 37.0	16 27.4	6 24.2	0 43.2	15 30.8	1 46.5	25 45.1	24 13.8
15	17 31 47.8	23 35.0	14 26.8	26 32.0	6 D 39.4	17 37.8	6 44.3	0 40.8	15 30.4	1 44.2	25 43.5	24 13.1
16	17 35 44.4	24 32.3	14 23.6	9♈47.5	6 46.3	18 48.2	7 4.8	0 38.6	15 30.1	1 42.0	25 41.8	24 12.5
17	17 39 40.9	25 29.6	14 20.4	23 29.6	6 57.9	19 58.7	7 25.7	0 36.6	15 29.9	1 39.8	25 40.2	24 11.9
18	17 43 37.5	26 26.9	14 17.2	7♉38.8	7 14.0	21 9.2	7 47.0	0 34.7	15 29.8	1 37.6	25 38.6	24 11.3
19	17 47 34.0	27 24.2	14 14.1	22 13.0	7 34.8	22 19.8	8 8.7	0 33.0	15 29.8	1 35.4	25 37.0	24 10.8
20	17 51 30.6	28 21.5	14 10.9	7♊ 7.7	8 .1	23 30.4	8 30.8	0 31.5	15 D 29.9	1 33.3	25 35.3	24 10.3
21	17 55 27.2	29 18.8	14 7.7	22 15.5	8 29.9	24 41.1	8 53.3	0 30.2	15 30.1	1 31.1	25 33.7	24 9.9
22	17 59 23.7	0♋16.1	14 4.5	7♋27.3	9 4.2	25 51.9	9 16.2	0 29.1	15 30.5	1 29.1	25 32.2	24 9.5
23	18 3 20.3	1 13.3	14 1.4	22 33.4	9 42.9	27 2.7	9 39.5	0 28.2	15 30.9	1 27.0	25 30.5	24 9.1
24	18 7 16.8	2 10.6	13 58.2	7♌25.3	10 25.9	28 13.5	10 3.1	0 27.4	15 31.4	1 25.0	25 28.9	24 8.7
25	18 11 13.4	3 7.8	13 55.0	21 56.6	11 13.2	29 24.4	10 27.1	0 26.8	15 32.0	1 23.0	25 27.3	24 8.4
26	18 15 10.0	4 5.1	13 51.8	6♍ 3.3	12 4.7	0♊35.3	10 51.4	0 26.4	15 32.7	1 21.0	25 25.7	24 8.1
27	18 19 6.5	5 2.3	13 48.6	19 44.0	13 .3	1 46.3	11 16.1	0 26.2	15 33.5	1 19.1	25 24.1	24 7.8
28	18 23 3.1	5 59.5	13 45.5	2♎59.7	14 .0	2 57.3	11 41.1	0 26.2	15 34.5	1 17.2	25 22.5	24 7.6
29	18 26 59.6	6 56.8	13 42.3	15 52.5	15 3.7	4 8.3	12 6.5	0 D 26.3	15 35.5	1 15.3	25 21.0	24 7.4
30	18 30 56.2	7 54.0	13 39.1	28 25.8	16 11.5	5 19.4	12 32.2	0 26.6	15 36.6	1 13.5	25 19.4	24 7.2

LATITUDE

DAY	EPHEM. SID. TIME	☉	☊	☽	☿	♀	♂	♃	♄	♅	♆	♇
1	16 36 36.0	0 .0	0 .0	5N 9.4	2S 5.8	2S 4.7	0N35.3	1N21.7	2N39.2	0N 9.6	1N19.0	17N27.9
4	16 48 25.7	0 .0	0 .0	4 30.7	2 52.3	2 4.9	0 29.5	1 21.0	2 38.5	0 9.5	1 19.1	17 26.6
7	17 0 15.4	0 .0	0 .0	2 7.3	3 30.3	2 4.4	0 24.0	1 20.3	2 37.8	0 9.5	1 19.1	17 25.2
10	17 12 5.0	0 .0	0 .0	1S 3.5	3 57.4	2 3.0	0 18.7	1 19.5	2 37.1	0 9.5	1 19.1	17 23.7
13	17 23 54.7	0 .0	0 .0	3 54.0	4 12.8	2 .9	0 13.5	1 18.8	2 36.4	0 9.4	1 19.0	17 22.2
16	17 35 44.4	0 .0	0 .0	5 15.4	4 16.9	1 58.1	0 8.6	1 18.0	2 35.6	0 9.4	1 19.0	17 20.7
19	17 47 34.0	0 .0	0 .0	4 6.7	4 10.7	1 54.5	0 3.9	1 17.2	2 34.8	0 9.3	1 19.0	17 19.1
22	17 59 23.7	0 .0	0 .0	0 32.5	3 55.7	1 50.3	0S .6	1 16.4	2 34.1	0 9.3	1 19.0	17 17.5
25	18 11 13.4	0 .0	0 .0	3N18.3	3 33.4	1 45.5	0 4.9	1 15.6	2 33.3	0 9.3	1 18.9	17 15.9
28	18 23 3.1	0 .0	0 .0	5 12.3	3 5.2	1 40.2	0 9.1	1 14.8	2 32.5	0 9.2	1 18.9	17 14.2

RIGHT ASCENSION

DAY	EPHEM. SID. TIME	☉	☊	☽	☿	♀	♂	♃	♄	♅	♆	♇
1	16 36 36.0	8♊34.1	16♋28.9	7♎54.1	10♊11.9	29♈53.6	2♎46.2	29♎49.1	15♎31.7	0♐14.7	25♐47.2	28♎59.0
2	16 40 32.6	9 35.5	16 25.5	19 30.9	9 R 38.8	1♉ .0	2 58.1	29 R 44.7	15 R 30.1	0 R 12.1	25 R 45.6	28 R 57.9
3	16 44 29.1	10 36.9	16 22.1	1♏ .9	9 5.9	2 6.6	3 10.4	29 40.4	15 28.6	0 9.5	25 43.9	28 56.9
4	16 48 25.7	11 38.5	16 18.7	12 34.8	8 33.7	3 13.4	3 23.3	29 36.3	15 27.1	0 7.0	25 42.2	28 55.8
5	16 52 22.2	12 40.2	16 15.3	24 21.4	8 2.7	4 20.5	3 36.7	29 32.4	15 25.7	0 4.4	25 40.5	28 54.8
6	16 56 18.8	13 41.9	16 11.8	6♐25.8	7 33.5	5 27.7	3 50.5	29 28.5	15 24.5	0 1.9	25 38.8	28 53.8
7	17 0 15.4	14 43.7	16 8.4	18 49.3	7 6.5	6 35.3	4 4.8	29 24.9	15 23.3	29♏59.4	25 37.1	28 52.9
8	17 4 11.9	15 45.6	16 5.0	1♑28.9	6 42.2	7 43.0	4 19.6	29 21.4	15 22.2	29 56.9	25 35.4	28 51.9
9	17 8 8.5	16 47.6	16 1.6	14 18.0	6 21.0	8 51.0	4 34.8	29 18.1	15 21.2	29 54.4	25 33.7	28 51.0
10	17 12 5.0	17 49.7	15 58.2	27 7.9	6 3.2	9 59.3	4 50.5	29 14.9	15 20.3	29 51.9	25 31.9	28 50.1
11	17 16 1.6	18 51.8	15 54.7	9♒50.5	5 49.1	11 7.8	5 6.6	29 11.9	15 19.5	29 49.5	25 30.2	28 49.2
12	17 19 58.1	19 53.9	15 51.3	22 20.7	5 39.0	12 16.6	5 23.1	29 9.0	15 18.7	29 47.0	25 28.5	28 48.4
13	17 23 54.7	20 56.1	15 47.9	4♓37.6	5 33.0	13 25.7	5 40.1	29 6.3	15 18.1	29 44.6	25 26.7	28 47.6
14	17 27 51.3	21 58.4	15 44.5	16 44.7	5 31.3	14 35.0	5 57.5	29 3.8	15 17.5	29 42.2	25 25.0	28 46.8
15	17 31 47.8	23 .7	15 41.0	28 49.7	5 D 33.9	15 44.6	6 15.2	29 1.4	15 17.1	29 39.9	25 23.2	28 46.0
16	17 35 44.4	24 3.0	15 37.6	11♈ 3.7	5 41.1	16 54.4	6 33.4	28 59.2	15 16.7	29 37.5	25 21.5	28 45.2
17	17 39 40.9	25 5.4	15 34.2	23 39.8	5 52.9	18 4.6	6 52.0	28 57.2	15 16.4	29 35.2	25 19.7	28 44.5
18	17 43 37.5	26 7.8	15 30.8	6♉52.1	6 9.1	19 15.0	7 11.0	28 55.3	15 16.2	29 32.9	25 18.0	28 43.8
19	17 47 34.0	27 10.2	15 27.4	20 53.6	6 30.0	20 25.7	7 30.4	28 53.6	15 16.2	29 30.6	25 16.2	28 43.2
20	17 51 30.6	28 12.6	15 23.9	5♊51.3	6 55.5	21 36.7	7 50.1	28 52.1	15 16.2	29 28.4	25 14.5	28 42.5
21	17 55 27.2	29 15.0	15 20.5	21 41.4	7 25.5	22 48.0	8 10.2	28 50.8	15 16.2	29 26.2	25 12.7	28 41.9
22	17 59 23.7	0♋17.5	15 17.1	8♋ 5.0	8 .1	23 59.6	8 30.8	28 49.7	15 D 16.5	29 24.1	25 11.0	28 41.4
23	18 3 20.3	1 19.9	15 13.7	24 30.5	8 39.2	25 11.5	8 51.6	28 48.6	15 16.8	29 21.9	25 9.3	28 40.8
24	18 7 16.8	2 22.3	15 10.2	10♌25.0	9 22.8	26 23.6	9 12.8	28 47.8	15 17.1	29 19.8	25 7.6	28 40.3
25	18 11 13.4	3 24.7	15 6.8	25 25.8	10 10.9	27 36.0	9 34.4	28 47.2	15 17.6	29 17.7	25 5.8	28 39.8
26	18 15 10.0	4 27.0	15 3.4	9♍25.5	11 3.5	28 48.7	9 56.3	28 46.7	15 18.2	29 15.6	25 4.1	28 39.3
27	18 19 6.5	5 29.4	14 60.0	22 29.2	12 .5	0♊ 1.6	10 18.6	28 46.4	15 18.8	29 13.6	25 2.4	28 38.9
28	18 23 3.1	6 31.6	14 56.5	4♎49.0	13 1.9	1 14.9	10 41.1	28 46.2	15 19.6	29 11.6	25 .7	28 38.5
29	18 26 59.6	7 33.8	14 53.1	16 39.4	14 7.8	2 28.4	11 4.0	28 D 46.3	15 20.4	29 9.6	24 59.0	28 38.1
30	18 30 56.2	8 36.0	14 49.7	28 14.5	15 18.1	3 42.2	11 27.3	28 46.5	15 21.3	29 7.7	24 57.3	28 37.7

DECLINATION

DAY	EPHEM. SID. TIME	☉	☊	☽	☿	♀	♂	♃	♄	♅	♆	♇
1	16 36 36.0	21N58.7	0N23.6	2N12.1	20N 4.6	9N58.8	0S33.6	10S43.0	3S44.9	20S27.9	22S 4.0	6N48.3
4	16 48 25.7	22 22.1	0 23.7	11S37.9	19 4.5	11 9.3	0 55.9	10 39.1	3 43.7	20 26.4	22 3.8	6 48.1
7	17 0 15.4	22 41.9	0 23.7	20 54.9	18 13.5	12 18.2	1 19.9	10 35.7	3 42.9	20 25.0	22 3.7	6 47.8
10	17 12 5.0	22 58.1	0 23.7	22 10.6	17 36.4	13 25.0	1 45.4	10 32.9	3 42.4	20 23.7	22 3.5	6 47.3
13	17 23 54.7	23 10.7	0 23.7	14 42.3	17 16.0	14 29.5	2 12.4	10 30.6	3 42.3	20 22.3	22 3.4	6 46.7
16	17 35 44.4	23 19.7	0 23.7	0 57.4	17 13.2	15 31.5	2 40.7	10 28.8	3 42.6	20 21.0	22 3.3	6 46.0
19	17 47 34.0	23 24.9	0 23.8	14N20.9	17 27.1	16 30.5	3 10.2	10 27.6	3 43.2	20 19.7	22 3.1	6 45.1
22	17 59 23.7	23 26.4	0 23.8	22 41.4	17 55.7	17 26.2	3 41.0	10 27.0	3 44.1	20 18.5	22 3.0	6 44.1
25	18 11 13.4	23 24.2	0 23.8	17 19.2	18 36.1	18 18.4	4 12.8	10 27.0	3 45.4	20 17.3	22 2.9	6 42.9
28	18 23 3.1	23 18.3	0 23.8	3 35.2	19 25.0	19 6.7	4 45.6	10 27.5	3 47.1	20 16.1	22 2.8	6 41.6

JULY 1982

LONGITUDE

DAY	EPHEM. SID. TIME h m s	☉ ° ′	☊ ° ′	☽ ° ′	☿ ° ′	♀ ° ′	♂ ° ′	♃ ° ′	♄ ° ′	♅ ° ′	♆ ° ′	♇ ° ′
1	18 34 52.7	8♋51.2	13♋35.9	10♏43.1	17♊23.1	6♊30.6	12♎58.2	0♏27.1	15♎37.8	1♐11.7	25♐17.8	24♎ 7.1
2	18 38 49.3	9 48.3	13 32.8	22 48.2	18 38.6	7 41.8	13 24.5	0 27.8	15 39.1	1 R 9.9	25 R 16.3	24 R 7.0
3	18 42 45.9	10 45.5	13 29.6	4♐44.7	19 57.9	8 53.0	13 51.1	0 28.6	15 40.5	1 8.2	25 14.7	24 6.9
4	18 46 42.4	11 42.7	13 26.4	16 35.5	21 21.0	10 4.3	14 18.0	0 29.7	15 42.0	1 6.5	25 13.2	24 6.9
5	18 50 39.0	12 39.9	13 23.2	28 23.8	22 47.8	11 15.6	14 45.3	0 30.9	15 43.6	1 4.8	25 11.6	24 6.9
6	18 54 35.5	13 37.1	13 20.1	10♑11.9	24 18.3	12 27.0	15 12.8	0 32.3	15 45.3	1 3.2	25 10.1	24 6.9
7	18 58 32.1	14 34.3	13 16.9	22 2.2	25 52.5	13 38.4	15 40.5	0 33.8	15 47.1	1 1.6	25 8.6	24 D 7.0
8	19 2 28.6	15 31.4	13 13.7	3♒57.1	27 30.1	14 49.9	16 8.6	0 35.6	15 49.0	1 .1	25 7.1	24 7.1
9	19 6 25.2	16 28.6	13 10.5	15 58.7	29 11.2	16 1.4	16 36.9	0 37.5	15 50.9	0 58.6	25 5.6	24 7.2
10	19 10 21.8	17 25.8	13 7.4	28 9.4	0♋55.6	17 13.0	17 5.5	0 39.6	15 53.0	0 57.1	25 4.1	24 7.4
11	19 14 18.3	18 23.0	13 4.2	10♓31.8	2 43.3	18 24.6	17 34.4	0 41.8	15 55.2	0 55.7	25 2.7	24 7.6
12	19 18 14.9	19 20.2	13 1.0	23 8.5	4 34.0	19 36.3	18 3.5	0 44.3	15 57.4	0 54.3	25 1.2	24 7.8
13	19 22 11.4	20 17.5	12 57.8	6♈ 2.4	6 27.6	20 48.1	18 32.9	0 46.9	15 59.9	0 53.0	24 59.9	24 8.1
14	19 26 8.0	21 14.7	12 54.6	19 16.0	8 23.9	21 59.8	19 2.6	0 49.7	16 2.3	0 51.7	24 58.4	24 8.5
15	19 30 4.5	22 11.9	12 51.5	2♉51.4	10 22.7	23 11.6	19 32.5	0 52.7	16 4.8	0 50.4	24 57.0	24 8.8
16	19 34 1.1	23 9.1	12 48.3	16 49.6	12 23.6	24 23.5	20 2.6	0 55.8	16 7.5	0 49.2	24 55.7	24 9.2
17	19 37 57.7	24 6.4	12 45.1	1♊10.1	14 26.4	25 35.4	20 33.0	0 59.0	16 10.2	0 48.1	24 54.3	24 9.6
18	19 41 54.2	25 3.7	12 41.9	15 50.5	16 30.9	26 47.4	21 3.6	1 2.5	16 13.0	0 47.0	24 52.9	24 10.0
19	19 45 50.8	26 .9	12 38.8	0♋45.8	18 36.6	27 59.4	21 34.4	1 6.1	16 15.9	0 45.9	24 51.6	24 10.5
20	19 49 47.3	26 58.2	12 35.6	15 49.3	20 43.4	29 11.4	22 5.5	1 9.9	16 18.9	0 44.9	24 50.3	24 11.0
21	19 53 43.9	27 55.5	12 32.4	0♌52.4	22 50.8	0♋23.5	22 36.9	1 13.8	16 22.0	0 43.9	24 49.0	24 11.5
22	19 57 40.4	28 52.8	12 29.2	15 46.5	24 58.6	1 35.7	23 8.4	1 17.9	16 25.2	0 42.9	24 47.7	24 12.1
23	20 1 37.0	29 50.1	12 26.1	0♍23.6	27 6.5	2 47.8	23 40.2	1 22.2	16 28.4	0 42.0	24 46.4	24 12.7
24	20 5 33.6	0♌47.4	12 22.9	14 38.0	29 14.1	4 .0	24 12.2	1 26.6	16 31.8	0 41.2	24 45.2	24 13.4
25	20 9 30.1	1 44.7	12 19.7	28 26.4	1♌21.3	5 12.3	24 44.4	1 31.2	16 35.2	0 40.4	24 44.0	24 14.1
26	20 13 26.7	2 42.0	12 16.5	11♎47.9	3 27.9	6 24.6	25 16.8	1 36.0	16 38.7	0 39.7	24 42.8	24 14.8
27	20 17 23.2	3 39.4	12 13.3	24 44.0	5 33.6	7 36.9	25 49.5	1 40.9	16 42.3	0 39.0	24 41.6	24 15.5
28	20 21 19.8	4 36.7	12 10.2	7♏17.8	7 38.3	8 49.3	26 22.3	1 45.9	16 46.0	0 38.3	24 40.5	24 16.3
29	20 25 16.3	5 34.1	12 7.0	19 33.4	9 41.8	10 1.8	26 55.3	1 51.2	16 49.8	0 37.7	24 39.3	24 17.1
30	20 29 12.9	6 31.4	12 3.8	1♐35.4	11 44.1	11 14.2	27 28.6	1 56.5	16 53.6	0 37.2	24 38.2	24 17.9
31	20 33 9.4	7 28.8	12 .6	13 28.3	13 45.0	12 26.7	28 2.0	2 2.0	16 57.5	0 36.7	24 37.1	24 18.8

LATITUDE

DAY	EPHEM. SID. TIME	☉	☊	☽	☿	♀	♂	♃	♄	♅	♆	♇
1	18 34 52.7	0 .0	0 .0	4N42.2	2S32.6	1S34.3	0S13.1	1N14.0	2N31.8	0N 9.2	1N18.8	17N12.5
4	18 46 42.4	0 .0	0 .0	2 23.3	1 56.7	1 28.0	0 16.9	1 13.1	2 31.0	0 9.1	1 18.8	17 10.8
7	18 58 32.1	0 .0	0 .0	0S48.1	1 18.9	1 21.2	0 20.6	1 12.3	2 30.2	0 9.1	1 18.7	17 9.1
10	19 10 21.8	0 .0	0 .0	3 44.1	0 40.8	1 14.1	0 24.2	1 11.5	2 29.5	0 9.0	1 18.6	17 7.4
13	19 22 11.4	0 .0	0 .0	5 14.9	0 4.1	1 6.7	0 27.6	1 10.7	2 28.7	0 9.0	1 18.6	17 5.6
16	19 34 1.1	0 .0	0 .0	4 24.9	0N29.5	0 59.0	0 30.8	1 9.9	2 28.0	0 8.9	1 18.5	17 3.9
19	19 45 50.8	0 .0	0 .0	1 9.3	0 58.2	0 51.0	0 34.0	1 9.1	2 27.3	0 8.9	1 18.4	17 2.1
22	19 57 40.4	0 .0	0 .0	2N50.1	1 20.7	0 42.9	0 37.0	1 8.3	2 26.6	0 8.8	1 18.3	17 .4
25	20 9 30.1	0 .0	0 .0	5 5.5	1 36.2	0 34.7	0 39.9	1 7.6	2 25.9	0 8.8	1 18.2	16 58.7
28	20 21 19.8	0 .0	0 .0	4 48.4	1 44.8	0 26.4	0 42.7	1 6.8	2 25.2	0 8.7	1 18.1	16 57.0
31	20 33 9.4	0 .0	0 .0	2 36.9	1 46.8	0 18.1	0 45.4	1 6.1	2 24.5	0 8.7	1 18.0	16 55.3

RIGHT ASCENSION

DAY	EPHEM. SID. TIME	☉	☊	☽	☿	♀	♂	♃	♄	♅	♆	♇
1	18 34 52.7	9♋38.1	14♋46.3	9♏47.3	16♊32.8	4♊56.2	11♎50.8	28♎46.9	15♎22.3	29♏ 5.8	24♐55.6	28♎37.4
2	18 38 49.3	10 40.1	14 42.8	21 28.4	17 51.9	6 10.5	12 14.6	28 47.4	15 23.4	29 R 4.0	24 R 53.9	28 R 37.1
3	18 42 45.9	11 42.1	14 39.4	3♐25.2	19 15.4	7 25.1	12 38.8	28 48.1	15 24.6	29 2.2	24 52.2	28 36.8
4	18 46 42.4	12 43.9	14 36.0	15 41.4	20 43.3	8 40.0	13 3.2	28 49.0	15 25.9	29 .4	24 50.6	28 36.6
5	18 50 39.0	13 45.8	14 32.5	28 16.2	22 15.5	9 55.1	13 28.0	28 50.1	15 27.3	28 58.7	24 48.9	28 36.4
6	18 54 35.5	14 47.5	14 29.1	11♑ 4.1	23 52.1	11 10.4	13 53.0	28 51.3	15 28.8	28 57.0	24 47.3	28 36.2
7	18 58 32.1	15 49.1	14 25.7	23 56.7	25 32.9	12 26.0	14 18.3	28 52.7	15 30.3	28 55.3	24 45.6	28 36.0
8	19 2 28.6	16 50.7	14 22.3	6♒44.6	27 18.0	13 41.8	14 43.9	28 54.3	15 32.0	28 53.7	24 44.0	28 35.9
9	19 6 25.2	17 52.1	14 18.8	19 20.2	29 7.2	14 57.9	15 9.8	28 56.0	15 33.7	28 52.1	24 42.4	28 35.8
10	19 10 21.8	18 53.5	14 15.4	1♓39.9	1♋ .3	16 14.2	15 35.9	28 57.9	15 35.5	28 50.6	24 40.8	28 35.8
11	19 14 18.3	19 54.7	14 12.0	13 44.9	2 57.3	17 30.7	16 2.4	28 59.9	15 37.5	28 49.1	24 39.3	28 35.7
12	19 18 14.9	20 55.9	14 8.5	25 40.9	4 57.9	18 47.4	16 29.1	29 2.2	15 39.5	28 47.7	24 37.7	28 35.7
13	19 22 11.4	21 56.9	14 5.1	7♈37.3	7 2.0	20 4.3	16 56.1	29 4.6	15 41.6	28 46.3	24 36.2	28 D 35.8
14	19 26 8.0	22 57.9	14 1.7	19 46.4	9 9.0	21 21.4	17 23.3	29 7.2	15 43.7	28 45.0	24 34.7	28 35.9
15	19 30 4.5	23 58.7	13 58.3	2♉22.1	11 18.9	22 38.7	17 50.8	29 9.9	15 46.0	28 43.7	24 33.2	28 36.0
16	19 34 1.1	24 59.4	13 54.8	15 38.7	13 31.1	23 56.2	18 18.6	29 12.7	15 48.3	28 42.4	24 31.7	28 36.1
17	19 37 57.7	25 59.9	13 51.4	29 47.8	15 45.3	25 13.8	18 46.6	29 15.8	15 50.8	28 41.2	24 30.2	28 36.2
18	19 41 54.2	27 .4	13 48.0	14♊54.0	18 1.1	26 31.5	19 14.9	29 19.0	15 53.3	28 40.0	24 28.7	28 36.4
19	19 45 50.8	28 .7	13 44.5	0♋49.5	20 18.0	27 49.4	19 43.5	29 22.3	15 55.9	28 38.9	24 27.3	28 36.6
20	19 49 47.3	29 .9	13 41.1	17 11.6	22 35.5	29 7.4	20 12.3	29 25.9	15 58.6	28 37.8	24 25.9	28 36.9
21	19 53 43.9	0♌ .9	13 37.7	3♌27.7	24 53.2	0♋25.5	20 41.4	29 29.5	16 1.3	28 36.8	24 24.5	28 37.1
22	19 57 40.4	1 .8	13 34.2	19 7.4	27 10.8	1 43.7	21 10.7	29 33.4	16 4.2	28 35.8	24 23.1	28 37.5
23	20 1 37.0	2 .6	13 30.8	3♍52.6	29 27.7	3 2.0	21 40.3	29 37.4	16 7.1	28 34.9	24 21.8	28 37.8
24	20 5 33.6	3 .2	13 27.4	17 39.7	1♌43.6	4 20.3	22 10.1	29 41.5	16 10.1	28 34.0	24 20.4	28 38.2
25	20 9 30.1	3 59.7	13 23.9	0♎36.0	3 58.2	5 38.7	22 40.2	29 45.8	16 13.2	28 33.2	24 19.1	28 38.6
26	20 13 26.7	4 59.0	13 20.5	12 54.1	6 11.2	6 57.2	23 10.5	29 50.2	16 16.4	28 32.4	24 17.8	28 39.0
27	20 17 23.2	5 58.1	13 17.1	24 48.3	8 22.3	8 15.7	23 41.0	29 54.8	16 19.6	28 31.7	24 16.5	28 39.4
28	20 21 19.8	6 57.1	13 13.6	6♏32.1	10 31.4	9 34.2	24 11.8	29 59.6	16 22.9	28 31.0	24 15.3	28 39.9
29	20 25 16.3	7 56.0	13 10.2	18 17.2	12 38.4	10 52.7	24 42.8	0♏ 4.5	16 26.3	28 30.4	24 14.1	28 40.5
30	20 29 12.9	8 54.7	13 6.8	0♐12.9	14 43.0	12 11.2	25 14.1	0 9.5	16 29.8	28 29.8	24 12.9	28 41.0
31	20 33 9.4	9 53.2	13 3.3	12 25.0	16 45.3	13 29.7	25 45.6	0 14.7	16 33.4	28 29.3	24 11.7	28 41.6

DECLINATION

DAY	EPHEM. SID. TIME	☉	☊	☽	☿	♀	♂	♃	♄	♅	♆	♇
1	18 34 52.7	23N 8.7	0N23.8	10S34.1	20N18.7	19N50.9	5S19.4	10S28.6	3S49.0	20S15.0	22S 2.6	6N40.2
4	18 46 42.4	22 55.5	0 23.8	20 23.3	21 13.1	20 30.6	5 53.9	10 30.2	3 51.4	20 14.0	22 2.5	6 38.7
7	18 58 32.1	22 38.6	0 23.9	22 25.8	22 3.7	21 5.7	6 29.2	10 32.5	3 54.0	20 13.1	22 2.4	6 37.1
10	19 10 21.8	22 18.3	0 23.9	15 37.0	22 45.4	21 35.8	7 5.2	10 35.2	3 57.0	20 12.2	22 2.3	6 35.3
13	19 22 11.4	21 54.5	0 23.9	2 25.2	23 12.9	22 .8	7 41.7	10 38.5	4 .3	20 11.4	22 2.3	6 33.4
16	19 34 1.1	21 27.3	0 23.9	12N37.7	23 21.2	22 20.4	8 18.7	10 42.3	4 3.9	20 10.7	22 2.2	6 31.5
19	19 45 50.8	20 56.8	0 23.9	22 17.0	23 6.5	22 34.5	8 56.2	10 46.7	4 7.8	20 10.0	22 2.1	6 29.4
22	19 57 40.4	20 23.1	0 23.9	18 48.8	22 27.6	22 43.0	9 34.0	10 51.5	4 12.0	20 9.5	22 2.1	6 27.2
25	20 9 30.1	19 46.4	0 23.9	5 17.5	21 25.4	22 45.6	10 12.1	10 56.8	4 16.5	20 9.0	22 2.0	6 24.9
28	20 21 19.8	19 6.7	0 24.0	9S24.0	20 3.0	22 42.5	10 50.5	11 2.6	4 21.2	20 8.6	22 2.0	6 22.6
31	20 33 9.4	18 24.1	0 24.0	19 49.3	18 24.2	22 33.5	11 28.9	11 8.8	4 26.2	20 8.3	22 2.0	6 20.1

AUGUST 1982

DAY	EPHEM. SID. TIME	☉	☊	☽	☿	♀	♂	♃	♄	♅	♆	♇
	h m s	° ′	° ′	° ′	° ′	° ′	° ′	° ′	° ′	° ′	° ′	° ′
		LONGITUDE										
1	20 37 6.0	8♌26.1	11♋57.5	25♐16.6	15♌44.4	13♋39.3	28♎35.6	2♏ 7.7	17♎ 1.5	0♐36.2	24♐36.1	24♎19.7
2	20 41 2.6	9 23.5	11 54.3	7♑ 4.2	17 42.4	14 51.9	29 9.5	2 13.5	17 5.6	0 R 35.8	24 R 35.0	24 20.7
3	20 44 59.1	10 21.0	11 51.1	18 54.8	19 38.9	16 4.6	29 43.5	2 19.5	17 9.8	0 35.5	24 34.1	24 21.7
4	20 48 55.7	11 18.4	11 47.9	0♒51.0	21 33.8	17 17.2	0♏17.7	2 25.6	17 14.1	0 35.2	24 33.1	24 22.7
5	20 52 52.2	12 15.8	11 44.8	12 55.3	23 27.1	18 30.0	0 52.0	2 31.8	17 18.4	0 35.0	24 32.1	24 23.7
6	20 56 48.8	13 13.3	11 41.6	25 9.3	25 18.8	19 42.8	1 26.6	2 38.2	17 22.8	0 34.8	24 31.2	24 24.8
7	21 0 45.3	14 10.7	11 38.4	7♓34.5	27 9.0	20 55.6	2 1.3	2 44.7	17 27.3	0 34.7	24 30.3	24 25.9
8	21 4 41.9	15 8.2	11 35.2	20 11.9	28 57.6	22 8.4	2 36.2	2 51.3	17 31.8	0 34.6	24 29.4	24 27.0
9	21 8 38.4	16 5.7	11 32.0	3♈ 2.3	0♍44.6	23 21.3	3 11.2	2 58.1	17 36.4	0 34.5	24 28.5	24 28.2
10	21 12 35.0	17 3.2	11 28.9	16 6.7	2 30.1	24 34.3	3 46.5	3 5.0	17 41.1	0 34.5	24 27.7	24 29.4
11	21 16 31.6	18 .7	11 25.7	29 25.8	4 14.1	25 47.3	4 21.9	3 12.1	17 45.9	0 D 34.6	24 26.9	24 30.6
12	21 20 28.1	18 58.3	11 22.5	13♉ .6	5 56.5	27 .3	4 57.4	3 19.3	17 50.7	0 34.7	24 26.1	24 31.8
13	21 24 24.7	19 55.9	11 19.3	26 51.5	7 37.3	28 13.4	5 33.2	3 26.6	17 55.6	0 34.9	24 25.4	24 33.1
14	21 28 21.2	20 53.5	11 16.2	10♊58.6	9 16.7	29 26.6	6 9.1	3 34.1	18 .5	0 35.1	24 24.7	24 34.4
15	21 32 17.8	21 51.2	11 13.0	25 20.9	10 54.6	0♌39.8	6 45.1	3 41.6	18 5.6	0 35.3	24 24.0	24 35.7
16	21 36 14.3	22 48.8	11 9.8	9♋55.9	12 31.0	1 53.0	7 21.3	3 49.3	18 10.7	0 35.7	24 23.3	24 37.1
17	21 40 10.9	23 46.5	11 6.6	24 39.4	14 5.9	3 6.3	7 57.7	3 57.2	18 15.8	0 36.0	24 22.7	24 38.5
18	21 44 7.4	24 44.2	11 3.4	9♌25.6	15 39.3	4 19.6	8 34.3	4 5.1	18 21.1	0 36.5	24 22.1	24 39.9
19	21 48 4.0	25 42.0	11 .3	24 7.4	17 11.2	5 32.9	9 11.0	4 13.2	18 26.4	0 36.9	24 21.5	24 41.4
20	21 52 .5	26 39.7	10 57.1	8♍37.5	18 41.7	6 46.3	9 47.8	4 21.4	18 31.7	0 37.5	24 20.9	24 42.9
21	21 55 57.1	27 37.5	10 53.9	22 49.4	20 10.6	7 59.7	10 24.9	4 29.7	18 37.2	0 38.0	24 20.4	24 44.4
22	21 59 53.7	28 35.3	10 50.7	6♎38.3	21 38.0	9 13.2	11 2.0	4 38.1	18 42.6	0 38.7	24 19.9	24 45.9
23	22 3 50.2	29 33.1	10 47.6	20 2.1	23 3.9	10 26.7	11 39.3	4 46.7	18 48.2	0 39.4	24 19.5	24 47.5
24	22 7 46.8	0♍31.0	10 44.4	3♏ .8	24 28.3	11 40.3	12 16.9	4 55.4	18 53.8	0 40.1	24 19.1	24 49.1
25	22 11 43.3	1 28.9	10 41.2	15 36.5	25 51.1	12 53.9	12 54.5	5 4.2	18 59.5	0 40.9	24 18.7	24 50.7
26	22 15 39.9	2 26.8	10 38.0	27 52.9	27 12.3	14 7.5	13 32.2	5 13.1	19 5.2	0 41.8	24 18.3	24 52.3
27	22 19 36.4	3 24.7	10 34.8	9♐54.6	28 31.8	15 21.2	14 10.1	5 22.0	19 11.0	0 42.6	24 18.0	24 54.0
28	22 23 33.0	4 22.6	10 31.7	21 46.9	29 49.6	16 34.9	14 48.1	5 31.2	19 16.8	0 43.6	24 17.7	24 55.7
29	22 27 29.5	5 20.5	10 28.5	3♑35.0	1♎ 5.7	17 48.6	15 26.3	5 40.4	19 22.7	0 44.6	24 17.4	24 57.4
30	22 31 26.1	6 18.5	10 25.3	15 23.9	2 20.0	19 2.4	16 4.6	5 49.7	19 28.7	0 45.6	24 17.2	24 59.2
31	22 35 22.6	7 16.5	10 22.1	27 18.0	3 32.5	20 16.2	16 43.1	5 59.1	19 34.7	0 46.7	24 17.0	25 .9
		LATITUDE										
1	20 37 6.0	0 .0	0 .0	1N37.5	1N46.1	0S15.3	0S46.3	1N 5.8	2N24.3	0N 8.7	1N17.9	16N54.8
4	20 48 55.7	0 .0	0 .0	1S35.1	1 40.4	0 7.1	0 48.8	1 5.1	2 23.7	0 8.6	1 17.8	16 53.1
7	21 0 45.3	0 .0	0 .0	4 14.5	1 29.8	0N 1.1	0 51.3	1 4.4	2 23.0	0 8.6	1 17.7	16 51.5
10	21 12 35.0	0 .0	0 .0	5 11.4	1 15.2	0 9.1	0 53.6	1 3.7	2 22.4	0 8.5	1 17.6	16 49.9
13	21 24 24.7	0 .0	0 .0	3 44.3	0 57.3	0 16.9	0 55.9	1 3.0	2 21.9	0 8.5	1 17.4	16 48.4
16	21 36 14.3	0 .0	0 .0	0 15.6	0 36.5	0 24.5	0 58.0	1 2.4	2 21.3	0 8.4	1 17.3	16 46.9
19	21 48 4.0	0 .0	0 .0	3N25.1	0 13.5	0 31.8	1 .1	1 1.7	2 20.7	0 8.4	1 17.2	16 45.4
22	21 59 53.7	0 .0	0 .0	5 7.0	0S11.3	0 38.8	1 2.0	1 1.1	2 20.2	0 8.3	1 17.0	16 44.0
25	22 11 43.3	0 .0	0 .0	4 17.7	0 37.4	0 45.4	1 3.9	1 .5	2 19.7	0 8.3	1 16.9	16 42.6
28	22 23 33.0	0 .0	0 .0	1 47.4	1 4.3	0 51.6	1 5.7	0 59.9	2 19.3	0 8.2	1 16.7	16 41.3
31	22 35 22.6	0 .0	0 .0	1S20.8	1 31.8	0 57.4	1 7.4	0 59.3	2 18.8	0 8.2	1 16.6	16 40.0
		RIGHT ASCENSION										
1	20 37 6.0	10♌51.6	12♋59.9	24♐54.9	18♌45.1	14♋48.2	26♎17.4	0♏20.0	16♎37.0	28♏28.8	24♐10.6	28♎42.2
2	20 41 2.6	11 49.8	12 56.5	7♑40.0	20 42.5	16 6.6	26 49.3	0 25.5	16 40.7	28 R 28.4	24 R 9.5	28 42.8
3	20 44 59.1	12 47.9	12 53.0	20 33.4	22 37.4	17 25.0	27 21.6	0 31.2	16 44.5	28 28.1	24 8.4	28 43.5
4	20 48 55.7	13 45.8	12 49.6	3♒26.1	24 29.9	18 43.3	27 54.0	0 36.9	16 48.4	28 27.7	24 7.3	28 44.2
5	20 52 52.2	14 43.6	12 46.1	16 9.9	26 20.0	20 1.5	28 26.6	0 42.8	16 52.3	28 27.5	24 6.3	28 45.0
6	20 56 48.8	15 41.2	12 42.7	28 39.2	28 7.7	21 19.7	28 59.5	0 48.8	16 56.3	28 27.3	24 5.3	28 45.7
7	21 0 45.3	16 38.7	12 39.3	10♓52.7	29 53.1	22 37.7	29 32.6	0 55.0	17 .3	28 27.1	24 4.3	28 46.5
8	21 4 41.9	17 36.0	12 35.8	22 53.8	1♍36.2	23 55.6	0♏ 5.9	1 1.3	17 4.5	28 27.0	24 3.4	28 47.3
9	21 8 38.4	18 33.2	12 32.4	4♈49.5	3 17.2	25 13.5	0 39.5	1 7.7	17 8.7	28 27.0	24 2.4	28 48.2
10	21 12 35.0	19 30.2	12 29.0	16 50.2	4 55.9	26 31.1	1 13.3	1 14.3	17 12.9	28 27.0	24 1.5	28 49.0
11	21 16 31.6	20 27.1	12 25.5	29 8.2	6 32.6	27 48.7	1 47.3	1 21.0	17 17.3	28 27.0	24 .7	28 50.0
12	21 20 28.1	21 23.9	12 22.1	11♉56.6	8 7.3	29 6.1	2 21.5	1 27.8	17 21.7	28 D 27.1	23 59.8	28 50.9
13	21 24 24.7	22 20.5	12 18.7	25 27.4	9 40.0	0♌23.3	2 56.0	1 34.7	17 26.1	28 27.3	23 59.0	28 51.8
14	21 28 21.2	23 17.0	12 15.2	9♊48.6	11 10.8	1 40.4	3 30.7	1 41.8	17 30.7	28 27.5	23 58.2	28 52.8
15	21 32 17.8	24 13.4	12 11.8	24 59.4	12 39.8	2 57.3	4 5.6	1 49.0	17 35.3	28 27.8	23 57.5	28 53.8
16	21 36 14.3	25 9.6	12 8.3	10♋47.0	14 6.9	4 14.0	4 40.7	1 56.4	17 39.9	28 28.1	23 56.8	28 54.9
17	21 40 10.9	26 5.7	12 4.9	26 47.1	15 32.4	5 30.6	5 16.1	2 3.8	17 44.7	28 28.5	23 56.1	28 56.0
18	21 44 7.4	27 1.7	12 1.5	12♌31.3	16 56.1	6 46.9	5 51.7	2 11.4	17 49.4	28 28.9	23 55.4	28 57.1
19	21 48 4.0	27 57.5	11 58.0	27 36.9	18 18.1	8 3.0	6 27.5	2 19.1	17 54.3	28 29.4	23 54.8	28 58.2
20	21 52 .5	28 53.2	11 54.6	11♍53.0	19 38.5	9 19.0	7 3.6	2 26.9	17 59.2	28 30.0	23 54.2	28 59.3
21	21 55 57.1	29 48.8	11 51.1	25 20.3	20 57.3	10 34.7	7 39.9	2 34.8	18 4.2	28 30.6	23 53.6	29 .5
22	21 59 53.7	0♍44.3	11 47.7	8♎ 7.1	22 14.5	11 50.2	8 16.4	2 42.9	18 9.2	28 31.2	23 53.1	29 1.7
23	22 3 50.2	1 39.7	11 44.3	20 25.3	23 30.1	13 5.4	8 53.1	2 51.1	18 14.3	28 31.9	23 52.6	29 2.9
24	22 7 46.8	2 35.0	11 40.8	2♏27.5	24 44.2	14 20.5	9 30.1	2 59.4	18 19.5	28 32.8	23 52.2	29 4.2
25	22 11 43.3	3 30.1	11 37.4	14 25.0	25 56.7	15 35.3	10 7.3	3 7.8	18 24.7	28 33.6	23 51.8	29 5.5
26	22 15 39.9	4 25.2	11 33.9	26 27.5	27 7.7	16 49.9	10 44.6	3 16.3	18 29.9	28 34.4	23 51.4	29 6.8
27	22 19 36.4	5 20.1	11 30.5	8♐41.6	28 17.1	18 4.3	11 22.3	3 24.9	18 35.2	28 35.4	23 51.0	29 8.2
28	22 23 33.0	6 14.9	11 27.0	21 10.4	29 24.9	19 18.4	12 .1	3 33.6	18 40.6	28 36.3	23 50.7	29 9.5
29	22 27 29.5	7 9.6	11 23.6	3♑52.9	0♎31.1	20 32.3	12 38.1	3 42.5	18 46.0	28 37.4	23 50.4	29 10.9
30	22 31 26.1	8 4.3	11 20.2	16 44.7	1 35.6	21 45.9	13 16.4	3 51.4	18 51.5	28 38.4	23 50.2	29 12.3
31	22 35 22.6	8 58.8	11 16.7	29 38.6	2 38.5	22 59.3	13 54.9	4 .4	18 57.0	28 39.6	23 49.9	29 13.8
		DECLINATION										
1	20 37 6.0	18N 9.3	0N24.0	21S43.9	17N48.4	22N29.2	11S41.8	11S11.0	4S28.0	20S 8.2	22S 2.0	6N19.3
4	20 48 55.7	17 23.2	0 24.0	21 31.0	15 54.1	22 12.4	12 20.3	11 17.8	4 33.4	20 8.1	22 2.0	6 16.7
7	21 0 45.3	16 34.6	0 24.0	12 39.7	13 52.1	21 49.8	12 58.7	11 25.0	4 38.9	20 8.0	22 2.0	6 14.1
10	21 12 35.0	15 43.5	0 24.0	1N32.7	11 45.2	21 21.5	13 37.0	11 32.6	4 44.8	20 8.0	22 2.0	6 11.4
13	21 24 24.7	14 50.2	0 24.0	15 49.0	9 35.8	20 47.7	14 15.1	11 40.6	4 50.8	20 8.2	22 2.0	6 8.7
16	21 36 14.3	13 54.7	0 24.1	22 48.6	7 25.6	20 8.4	14 52.9	11 48.9	4 57.1	20 8.4	22 2.1	6 5.9
19	21 48 4.0	12 57.3	0 24.1	16 42.2	5 16.1	19 23.9	15 30.3	11 57.5	5 3.5	20 8.7	22 2.2	6 3.0
22	21 59 53.7	11 58.0	0 24.1	2 3.8	3 8.7	18 34.4	16 7.3	12 6.5	5 10.1	20 9.1	22 2.2	6 .1
25	22 11 43.3	10 56.9	0 24.1	12S24.1	1 4.6	17 40.1	16 43.7	12 15.7	5 17.0	20 9.6	22 2.3	5 57.2
28	22 23 33.0	9 54.4	0 24.1	21 24.0	0S54.9	16 41.3	17 19.6	12 25.3	5 23.9	20 10.2	22 2.4	5 54.2
31	22 35 22.6	8 50.4	0 24.1	22 1.3	2 48.7	15 38.3	17 54.6	12 35.1	5 31.1	20 10.9	22 2.6	5 51.2

SEPTEMBER 1982

LONGITUDE

DAY	EPHEM. SID. TIME h m s	☉ ° ′	☊ ° ′	☽ ° ′	☿ ° ′	♀ ° ′	♂ ° ′	♃ ° ′	♄ ° ′	♅ ° ′	♆ ° ′	♇ ° ′
1	22 39 19.2	8♍14.5	10♋19.0	9♒21.2	4♎43.0	21♌30.0	17♏21.6	6♏ 8.6	19♎40.7	0♐47.8	24♐16.8	25♎ 2.7
2	22 43 15.7	9 12.6	10 15.8	21 36.3	5 51.4	22 43.9	18 .3	6 18.2	19 46.8	0 49.0	24R16.7	25 4.5
3	22 47 12.3	10 10.6	10 12.6	4♓ 5.2	6 57.7	23 57.8	18 39.1	6 27.9	19 52.9	0 50.3	24 16.6	25 6.3
4	22 51 8.8	11 8.7	10 9.4	16 48.7	8 1.8	25 11.8	19 18.1	6 37.8	19 59.1	0 51.6	24 16.5	25 8.2
5	22 55 5.4	12 6.8	10 6.2	29 46.6	9 3.6	26 25.8	19 57.2	6 47.7	20 5.4	0 52.9	24 16.5	25 10.1
6	22 59 2.0	13 5.0	10 3.1	12♈58.1	10 2.8	27 39.8	20 36.4	6 57.7	20 11.6	0 54.3	24 16.5	25 12.0
7	23 2 58.5	14 3.2	9 59.9	26 21.7	10 59.4	28 53.8	21 15.7	7 7.8	20 18.0	0 55.7	24 16.5	25 13.9
8	23 6 55.1	15 1.4	9 56.7	9♉56.2	11 53.1	0♍ 7.9	21 55.1	7 17.9	20 24.3	0 57.2	24 16.5	25 15.8
9	23 10 51.6	15 59.7	9 53.5	23 40.3	12 43.9	1 22.1	22 34.7	7 28.2	20 30.8	0 58.7	24D16.6	25 17.8
10	23 14 48.2	16 57.9	9 50.4	7♊33.3	13 31.4	2 36.3	23 14.4	7 38.6	20 37.2	1 .3	24 16.7	25 19.8
11	23 18 44.7	17 56.3	9 47.2	21 34.5	14 15.5	3 50.5	23 54.2	7 49.0	20 43.7	1 1.9	24 16.9	25 21.8
12	23 22 41.3	18 54.6	9 44.0	5♋43.3	14 55.9	5 4.7	24 34.2	7 59.6	20 50.3	1 3.6	24 17.1	25 23.8
13	23 26 37.8	19 53.0	9 40.8	19 58.9	15 32.4	6 19.0	25 14.2	8 10.2	20 56.8	1 5.3	24 17.3	25 25.8
14	23 30 34.4	20 51.5	9 37.6	4♌19.1	16 4.7	7 33.4	25 54.5	8 21.0	21 3.5	1 7.2	24 17.6	25 28.0
15	23 34 30.9	21 50.0	9 34.5	18 40.8	16 32.3	8 47.7	26 34.8	8 31.8	21 10.2	1 9.0	24 17.9	25 30.0
16	23 38 27.5	22 48.4	9 31.3	2♍59.5	16 55.1	10 2.1	27 15.2	8 42.6	21 16.9	1 10.8	24 18.2	25 32.1
17	23 42 24.0	23 47.0	9 28.1	17 10.1	17 12.6	11 16.5	27 55.7	8 53.6	21 23.6	1 12.7	24 18.5	25 34.2
18	23 46 20.6	24 45.5	9 24.9	1♎ 7.0	17 24.6	12 31.0	28 36.4	9 4.6	21 30.4	1 14.7	24 18.9	25 36.4
19	23 50 17.1	25 44.1	9 21.8	14 45.9	17 30.6	13 45.4	29 17.2	9 15.7	21 37.2	1 16.7	24 19.3	25 38.5
20	23 54 13.7	26 42.8	9 18.6	28 3.7	17R30.3	14 59.9	29 58.0	9 26.9	21 44.0	1 18.7	24 19.8	25 40.7
21	23 58 10.2	27 41.4	9 15.4	10♏59.4	17 23.4	16 14.5	0♐39.0	9 38.2	21 50.9	1 20.8	24 20.3	25 42.9
22	0 2 6.8	28 40.1	9 12.2	23 34.0	17 9.5	17 29.0	1 20.1	9 49.5	21 57.7	1 23.0	24 20.8	25 45.0
23	0 6 3.3	29 38.8	9 9.0	5♐50.1	16 48.6	18 43.6	2 1.4	10 .9	22 4.7	1 25.1	24 21.3	25 47.3
24	0 9 59.9	0♎37.6	9 5.9	17 51.8	16 20.4	19 58.2	2 42.7	10 12.4	22 11.6	1 27.3	24 21.9	25 49.5
25	0 13 56.5	1 36.3	9 2.7	29 44.1	15 45.0	21 12.8	3 24.1	10 23.9	22 18.6	1 29.6	24 22.5	25 51.7
26	0 17 53.0	2 35.1	8 59.5	11♑32.3	15 2.5	22 27.5	4 5.6	10 35.5	22 25.6	1 31.9	24 23.2	25 54.0
27	0 21 49.6	3 33.9	8 56.3	23 22.0	14 13.3	23 42.1	4 47.3	10 47.2	22 32.6	1 34.2	24 23.9	25 56.2
28	0 25 46.1	4 32.8	8 53.2	5♒18.5	13 18.0	24 56.8	5 29.0	10 58.9	22 39.7	1 36.6	24 24.6	25 58.5
29	0 29 42.7	5 31.7	8 50.0	17 26.5	12 17.5	26 11.5	6 10.8	11 10.7	22 46.7	1 39.0	24 25.3	26 .8
30	0 33 39.2	6 30.6	8 46.8	29 49.9	11 12.8	27 26.3	6 52.8	11 22.6	22 53.8	1 41.5	24 26.1	26 3.1

LATITUDE

DAY	SID. TIME	☉	☊	☽	☿	♀	♂	♃	♄	♅	♆	♇
1	22 39 19.2	0 .0	0 .0	2S20.9	1S40.9	0N59.3	1S 8.0	0N59.1	2N18.7	0N 8.1	1N16.5	16N39.6
4	22 51 8.8	0 .0	0 .0	4 36.3	2 8.2	1 4.5	1 9.6	0 58.6	2 18.3	0 8.1	1 16.4	16 38.5
7	23 2 58.5	0 .0	0 .0	4 53.4	2 34.7	1 9.2	1 11.1	0 58.0	2 17.9	0 8.0	1 16.2	16 37.3
10	23 14 48.2	0 .0	0 .0	2 47.9	2 59.6	1 13.3	1 12.5	0 57.5	2 17.5	0 8.0	1 16.1	16 36.3
13	23 26 37.8	0 .0	0 .0	0N48.0	3 22.0	1 17.0	1 13.8	0 57.0	2 17.2	0 7.9	1 15.9	16 35.3
16	23 38 27.5	0 .0	0 .0	3 59.4	3 40.4	1 20.0	1 15.1	0 56.5	2 16.9	0 7.9	1 15.8	16 34.3
19	23 50 17.1	0 .0	0 .0	5 .5	3 52.7	1 22.5	1 16.2	0 56.1	2 16.6	0 7.8	1 15.6	16 33.5
22	0 2 6.8	0 .0	0 .0	3 38.3	3 56.1	1 24.4	1 17.3	0 55.6	2 16.3	0 7.8	1 15.5	16 32.7
25	0 13 56.5	0 .0	0 .0	0 51.9	3 47.3	1 25.7	1 18.4	0 55.2	2 16.1	0 7.7	1 15.3	16 32.0
28	0 25 46.1	0 .0	0 .0	2S11.9	3 22.8	1 26.5	1 19.3	0 54.8	2 15.9	0 7.7	1 15.2	16 31.3

RIGHT ASCENSION

DAY	SID. TIME	☉	☊	☽	☿	♀	♂	♃	♄	♅	♆	♇
1	22 39 19.2	9♍53.3	11♋13.3	12♒27.2	3♎39.6	24♌12.5	14♏33.6	4♏ 9.6	19♎ 2.6	28♏40.8	23♐49.8	29♎15.2
2	22 43 15.7	10 47.7	11 9.8	25 4.7	4 38.9	25 25.4	15 12.5	4 18.8	19 8.2	28 42.0	23R49.6	29 16.7
3	22 47 12.3	11 42.0	11 6.4	7♓28.7	5 36.3	26 38.1	15 51.6	4 28.2	19 13.8	28 43.3	23 49.5	29 18.2
4	22 51 8.8	12 36.2	11 2.9	19 40.8	6 31.7	27 50.6	16 31.0	4 37.6	19 19.5	28 44.6	23 49.4	29 19.7
5	22 55 5.4	13 30.4	10 59.5	1♈46.4	7 25.1	29 2.9	17 10.5	4 47.1	19 25.3	28 46.0	23 49.4	29 21.3
6	22 59 2.0	14 24.5	10 56.1	13 53.8	8 16.3	0♍15.0	17 50.3	4 56.8	19 31.1	28 47.5	23 49.3	29 22.8
7	23 2 58.5	15 18.6	10 52.6	26 13.6	9 5.1	1 26.8	8 30.3	5 6.5	19 36.9	28 49.0	23D49.4	29 24.4
8	23 6 55.1	16 12.6	10 49.2	8♉57.2	9 51.5	2 38.4	19 10.5	5 16.3	19 42.8	28 50.5	23 49.4	29 26.0
9	23 10 51.6	17 6.6	10 45.7	22 15.0	10 35.2	3 49.9	19 50.9	5 26.3	19 48.8	28 52.1	23 49.5	29 27.7
10	23 14 48.2	18 .5	10 42.3	6♊14.5	11 16.2	5 1.1	20 31.5	5 36.3	19 54.7	28 53.7	23 49.6	29 29.3
11	23 18 44.7	18 54.4	10 38.8	20 56.6	11 54.1	6 12.1	21 12.4	5 46.4	20 .7	28 55.4	23 49.8	29 31.0
12	23 22 41.3	19 48.3	10 35.4	6♋12.7	12 28.7	7 23.0	21 53.4	5 56.6	20 6.8	28 57.2	23 50.0	29 32.7
13	23 26 37.8	20 42.2	10 31.9	21 44.8	12 59.9	8 33.6	22 34.7	6 6.9	20 12.9	28 59.0	23 50.2	29 34.4
14	23 30 34.4	21 36.1	10 28.5	7♌ 9.8	13 27.4	9 44.1	23 16.2	6 17.3	20 19.1	29 .9	23 50.6	29 36.2
15	23 34 30.9	22 29.9	10 25.1	22 7.3	13 50.8	10 54.5	23 57.9	6 27.7	20 25.2	29 2.7	23 50.9	29 37.9
16	23 38 27.5	23 23.7	10 21.6	6♍25.2	14 9.9	12 4.6	24 39.8	6 38.3	20 31.4	29 4.7	23 51.2	29 39.7
17	23 42 24.0	24 17.6	10 18.2	20 1.0	14 24.3	13 14.6	25 22.0	6 48.9	20 37.7	29 6.7	23 51.6	29 41.5
18	23 46 20.6	25 11.4	10 14.7	3♎ .1	14 33.9	14 24.4	26 4.3	6 59.6	20 44.0	29 8.7	23 52.0	29 43.3
19	23 50 17.1	26 5.2	10 11.3	15 31.7	14 38.2	15 34.1	26 46.9	7 10.4	20 50.3	29 10.8	23 52.4	29 45.1
20	23 54 13.7	26 59.0	10 7.8	27 46.8	14R37.1	16 43.6	27 29.6	7 21.3	20 56.6	29 12.9	23 52.9	29 47.0
21	23 58 10.2	27 52.8	10 4.4	9♏55.7	14 30.1	17 53.1	28 12.6	7 32.2	21 3.0	29 15.1	23 53.4	29 48.8
22	0 2 6.8	28 46.7	10 .9	22 7.2	14 17.2	19 2.4	28 55.7	7 43.2	21 9.4	29 17.3	23 54.0	29 50.7
23	0 6 3.3	29 40.6	9 57.5	4♐27.5	13 58.2	20 11.5	29 39.1	7 54.3	21 15.8	29 19.6	23 54.6	29 52.6
24	0 9 59.9	0♎34.5	9 54.0	16 59.5	13 32.9	21 20.6	0♐22.7	8 5.5	21 22.3	29 21.9	23 55.2	29 54.5
25	0 13 56.5	1 28.4	9 50.6	29 42.8	13 1.7	22 29.6	1 6.4	8 16.8	21 28.8	29 24.2	23 55.9	29 56.4
26	0 17 53.0	2 22.3	9 47.1	12♑33.6	12 24.5	23 38.5	1 50.4	8 28.1	21 35.3	29 26.6	23 56.5	29 58.4
27	0 21 49.6	3 16.3	9 43.7	25 26.3	11 41.9	24 47.3	2 34.5	8 39.5	21 41.8	29 29.1	23 57.3	0♏ .3
28	0 25 46.1	4 10.4	9 40.2	8♒14.3	10 54.5	25 56.1	3 18.9	8 50.9	21 48.4	29 31.6	23 58.0	0 2.3
29	0 29 42.7	5 4.5	9 36.8	20 53.0	10 3.1	27 4.8	4 3.4	9 2.5	21 55.0	29 34.1	23 58.8	0 4.3
30	0 33 39.2	5 58.6	9 33.3	3♓20.3	9 8.7	28 13.4	4 48.1	9 14.1	22 1.6	29 36.7	23 59.7	0 6.3

DECLINATION

DAY	SID. TIME	☉	☊	☽	☿	♀	♂	♃	♄	♅	♆	♇
1	22 39 19.2	8N28.8	0N24.1	20S10.6	3S25.1	15N16.4	18S 6.2	12S38.4	5S33.5	20S11.2	22S 2.6	5N50.2
4	22 51 8.8	7 23.2	0 24.1	9 26.8	5 8.9	14 8.1	18 40.1	12 48.5	5 40.8	20 12.0	22 2.7	5 47.2
7	23 2 58.5	6 16.5	0 24.2	5N36.8	6 43.2	12 56.3	19 13.2	12 58.8	5 48.2	20 12.9	22 2.9	5 44.2
10	23 14 48.2	5 8.8	0 24.2	18 48.7	8 5.7	11 41.2	19 45.2	13 9.3	5 55.7	20 13.9	22 3.0	5 41.2
13	23 26 37.8	4 .4	0 24.2	22 44.8	9 13.4	10 23.2	20 16.2	13 19.9	6 3.4	20 15.0	22 3.2	5 38.1
16	23 38 27.5	2 51.3	0 24.2	14 7.6	10 2.3	9 2.5	20 45.9	13 30.8	6 11.1	20 16.2	22 3.4	5 35.1
19	23 50 17.1	1 41.7	0 24.2	1S11.8	10 27.3	7 39.5	21 14.4	13 41.8	6 19.0	20 17.4	22 3.6	5 32.1
22	0 2 6.8	0 31.8	0 24.2	15 8.4	10 22.4	6 14.5	21 41.5	13 52.8	6 26.8	20 18.7	22 3.8	5 29.1
25	0 13 56.5	0S38.3	0 24.2	22 34.5	9 41.5	4 47.8	22 7.1	14 4.0	6 34.8	20 20.1	22 4.0	5 26.1
28	0 25 46.1	1 48.4	0 24.2	21 4.5	8 21.8	3 19.8	22 31.2	14 15.3	6 42.8	20 21.6	22 4.3	5 23.2

LONGITUDE

DAY	EPHEM. SID. TIME (h m s)	☉	☊	☽	☿	♀	♂	♃	♄	♅	♆	♇
1	0 37 35.8	7♎29.6	8♋43.6	12♓31.4	10♎5.5	28♍41.0	7♐34.8	11♏34.5	23♎.9	1♐44.0	24♐26.9	26♎5.4
2	0 41 32.3	8 28.5	8 40.4	25 31.9	8R57.0	29 55.8	8 16.9	11 46.4	23 8.1	1 46.5	24 27.7	26 7.7
3	0 45 28.9	9 27.5	8 37.3	8♈51.1	7 49.1	1♎10.6	8 59.1	11 58.5	23 15.2	1 49.1	24 28.6	26 10.0
4	0 49 25.4	10 26.6	8 34.1	22 26.8	6 43.7	2 25.5	9 41.5	12 10.6	23 22.4	1 51.7	24 29.5	26 12.3
5	0 53 22.0	11 25.7	8 30.9	6♉15.9	5 42.6	3 40.4	10 23.9	12 22.7	23 29.6	1 54.4	24 30.5	26 14.7
6	0 57 18.5	12 24.8	8 27.7	20 14.4	4 47.4	4 55.2	11 6.4	12 34.9	23 36.8	1 57.1	24 31.4	26 17.1
7	1 1 15.1	13 24.0	8 24.6	4♊18.6	3 59.8	6 10.1	11 49.0	12 47.2	23 44.0	1 59.8	24 32.4	26 19.4
8	1 5 11.6	14 23.2	8 21.4	18 25.5	3 20.9	7 25.0	12 31.7	12 59.5	23 51.2	2 2.6	24 33.4	26 21.8
9	1 9 8.2	15 22.4	8 18.2	2♋32.8	2 51.8	8 40.0	13 14.5	13 11.8	23 58.5	2 5.4	24 34.5	26 24.2
10	1 13 4.7	16 21.7	8 15.0	16 39.3	2 33.2	9 54.9	13 57.3	13 24.2	24 5.7	2 8.2	24 35.6	26 26.5
11	1 17 1.3	17 21.0	8 11.8	0♌44.0	2 25.4	11 9.9	14 40.3	13 36.6	24 13.0	2 11.1	24 36.7	26 28.9
12	1 20 57.9	18 20.3	8 8.7	14 46.2	2D28.4	12 24.9	15 23.4	13 49.1	24 20.3	2 14.0	24 37.8	26 31.3
13	1 24 54.4	19 19.7	8 5.5	28 44.7	2 42.1	13 39.9	16 6.5	14 1.6	24 27.5	2 16.9	24 39.0	26 33.7
14	1 28 51.0	20 19.2	8 2.3	12♍37.6	3 6.1	14 55.0	16 49.8	14 14.2	24 34.8	2 19.9	24 40.2	26 36.1
15	1 32 47.5	21 18.6	7 59.1	26 22.2	3 39.8	16 10.0	17 33.1	14 26.8	24 42.1	2 22.8	24 41.4	26 38.5
16	1 36 44.1	22 18.1	7 56.0	9♎55.6	4 22.6	17 25.1	18 16.5	14 39.5	24 49.4	2 25.9	24 42.7	26 40.9
17	1 40 40.6	23 17.7	7 52.8	23 14.8	5 13.6	18 40.2	19 0.0	14 52.2	24 56.7	2 28.9	24 44.0	26 43.3
18	1 44 37.2	24 17.2	7 49.6	6♏17.6	6 12.1	19 55.3	19 43.6	15 4.9	25 4.0	2 32.0	24 45.3	26 45.7
19	1 48 33.7	25 16.8	7 46.4	19 2.9	7 17.2	21 10.4	20 27.3	15 17.7	25 11.3	2 35.1	24 46.6	26 48.1
20	1 52 30.3	26 16.5	7 43.2	1♐30.9	8 28.2	22 25.5	21 11.0	15 30.5	25 18.6	2 38.3	24 48.0	26 50.6
21	1 56 26.8	27 16.1	7 40.1	13 43.3	9 44.3	23 40.7	21 54.9	15 43.3	25 25.9	2 41.4	24 49.4	26 53.0
22	2 0 23.4	28 15.8	7 36.9	25 43.1	11 4.9	24 55.8	22 38.8	15 56.2	25 33.2	2 44.6	24 50.8	26 55.4
23	2 4 19.9	29 15.5	7 33.7	7♑34.3	12 29.1	26 11.0	23 22.8	16 9.1	25 40.5	2 47.8	24 52.3	26 57.8
24	2 8 16.5	0♏15.3	7 30.5	19 21.7	13 56.6	27 26.2	24 6.8	16 22.0	25 47.8	2 51.1	24 53.7	27 .2
25	2 12 13.0	1 15.1	7 27.4	1♒10.8	15 26.6	28 41.3	24 51.0	16 35.0	25 55.1	2 54.4	24 55.2	27 2.6
26	2 16 9.6	2 14.9	7 24.2	13 7.1	16 58.9	29 56.6	25 35.3	16 48.0	26 2.4	2 57.7	24 56.8	27 5.1
27	2 20 6.2	3 14.8	7 21.0	25 15.7	18 32.9	1♏11.8	26 19.6	17 1.0	26 9.7	3 1.0	24 58.4	27 7.5
28	2 24 2.7	4 14.6	7 17.8	7♓41.6	20 8.2	2 27.0	27 3.9	17 14.1	26 16.9	3 4.4	24 60.0	27 9.9
29	2 27 59.3	5 14.6	7 14.6	20 28.5	21 44.7	3 42.2	27 48.4	17 27.1	26 24.2	3 7.7	25 1.6	27 12.3
30	2 31 55.8	6 14.4	7 11.5	3♈38.6	23 22.0	4 57.4	28 32.9	17 40.2	26 31.4	3 11.1	25 3.2	27 14.7
31	2 35 52.4	7 14.4	7 8.3	17 12.4	24 60.0	6 12.8	29 17.5	17 53.3	26 38.6	3 14.5	25 4.8	27 17.0

LATITUDE

DAY	EPHEM. SID. TIME (h m s)	☉	☊	☽	☿	♀	♂	♃	♄	♅	♆	♇
1	0 37 35.8	0 .0	0 .0	4S29.0	2S41.5	1N26.6	1S20.1	0N54.3	2N15.7	0N7.7	1N15.0	16N30.7
4	0 49 25.4	0 .0	0 .0	4 51.6	1 46.4	1 26.1	1 20.9	0 54.0	2 15.6	0 7.6	1 14.9	16 30.3
7	1 1 15.1	0 .0	0 .0	2 48.3	0 45.3	1 25.0	1 21.6	0 53.6	2 15.4	0 7.6	1 14.7	16 29.8
10	1 13 4.7	0 .0	0 .0	0N45.4	0N12.4	1 23.4	1 22.2	0 53.2	2 15.3	0 7.5	1 14.6	16 29.5
13	1 24 54.4	0 .0	0 .0	3 54.3	0 59.8	1 21.2	1 22.7	0 52.9	2 15.2	0 7.5	1 14.5	16 29.2
16	1 36 44.1	0 .0	0 .0	5 .9	1 33.6	1 18.4	1 23.2	0 52.6	2 15.2	0 7.4	1 14.3	16 29.1
19	1 48 33.7	0 .0	0 .0	3 44.4	1 54.1	1 15.1	1 23.6	0 52.3	2 15.1	0 7.4	1 14.2	16 29.0
22	2 0 23.4	0 .0	0 .0	0 57.7	2 3.1	1 11.3	1 23.9	0 52.0	2 15.3	0 7.4	1 14.1	16 29.0
25	2 12 13.0	0 .0	0 .0	2S7.4	2 2.9	1 7.0	1 24.1	0 51.7	2 15.3	0 7.3	1 14.0	16 29.0
28	2 24 2.7	0 .0	0 .0	4 27.1	1 45.8	1 2.3	1 24.2	0 51.5	2 15.3	0 7.3	1 13.8	16 29.2
31	2 35 52.4	0 .0	0 .0	4 59.0	1 43.9	0 57.2	1 24.3	0 51.2	2 15.5	0 7.3	1 13.7	16 29.4

RIGHT ASCENSION

DAY	EPHEM. SID. TIME (h m s)	☉	☊	☽	☿	♀	♂	♃	♄	♅	♆	♇
1	0 37 35.8	6♎52.8	9♋29.9	15♓37.9	8♎12.6	29♍22.0	5♐33.0	9♏25.7	22♎8.2	29♏39.3	24♐.5	0♏8.3
2	0 41 32.3	7 47.1	9 26.4	27 50.5	7R16.2	0♎30.6	6 18.1	9 37.4	22 14.9	29 41.9	24 1.4	0 10.3
3	0 45 28.9	8 41.4	9 23.0	10♈6.0	6 21.0	1 39.1	7 3.4	9 49.2	22 21.5	29 44.6	24 2.4	0 12.3
4	0 49 25.4	9 35.9	9 19.6	22 34.2	5 28.5	2 47.7	7 48.8	10 1.1	22 28.2	29 47.3	24 3.3	0 14.4
5	0 53 22.0	10 30.4	9 16.1	5♉25.5	4 40.3	3 56.3	8 34.5	10 13.0	22 35.0	29 50.1	24 4.4	0 16.5
6	0 57 18.5	11 25.0	9 12.7	18 49.5	3 57.7	5 4.9	9 20.2	10 25.0	22 41.7	29 53.0	24 5.4	0 18.5
7	1 1 15.1	12 19.7	9 9.2	2♊52.5	3 22.0	6 13.4	10 6.2	10 37.0	22 48.4	29 55.8	24 6.5	0 20.6
8	1 5 11.6	13 14.6	9 5.8	17 34.4	2 54.3	7 22.1	10 52.3	10 49.1	22 55.2	29 58.7	24 7.6	0 22.7
9	1 9 8.2	14 9.5	9 2.3	2♋45.9	2 35.3	8 30.8	11 38.6	11 1.3	23 2.0	0♐1.6	24 8.7	0 24.8
10	1 13 4.7	15 4.5	8 58.9	18 9.6	2 25.5	9 39.5	12 25.1	11 13.5	23 8.8	0 4.6	24 9.9	0 26.9
11	1 17 1.3	15 59.7	8 55.4	3♌23.9	2D25.2	10 48.3	13 11.7	11 25.7	23 15.5	0 7.5	24 11.1	0 29.0
12	1 20 57.9	16 54.9	8 51.9	18 10.2	2 34.2	11 57.2	13 58.5	11 38.0	23 22.4	0 10.6	24 12.3	0 31.1
13	1 24 54.4	17 50.3	8 48.5	2♍52.5	2 52.5	13 6.1	14 45.4	11 50.4	23 29.2	0 13.6	24 13.6	0 33.2
14	1 28 51.0	18 45.9	8 45.0	15 46.5	3 19.6	14 15.2	15 32.5	12 2.8	23 36.0	0 16.7	24 14.8	0 35.3
15	1 32 47.5	19 41.5	8 41.6	28 38.0	3 55.0	15 24.3	16 19.8	12 15.3	23 42.8	0 19.9	24 16.2	0 37.5
16	1 36 44.1	20 37.3	8 38.1	11♎5.4	4 38.1	16 33.6	17 7.2	12 27.8	23 49.7	0 23.0	24 17.5	0 39.6
17	1 40 40.6	21 33.3	8 34.7	23 18.1	5 28.2	17 43.0	17 54.7	12 40.3	23 56.5	0 26.2	24 18.9	0 41.8
18	1 44 37.2	22 29.4	8 31.2	5♏26.3	6 24.6	18 52.5	18 42.4	12 52.9	24 3.4	0 29.4	24 20.3	0 43.9
19	1 48 33.7	23 25.6	8 27.8	17 38.7	7 26.6	20 2.2	19 30.2	13 5.6	24 10.2	0 32.7	24 21.8	0 46.1
20	1 52 30.3	24 22.0	8 24.3	0♐1.1	8 33.4	21 12.0	20 18.2	13 18.3	24 17.1	0 36.0	24 23.2	0 48.3
21	1 56 26.8	25 18.6	8 20.9	12 44.6	9 44.6	22 22.0	21 6.3	13 31.0	24 24.0	0 39.3	24 24.8	0 50.4
22	2 0 23.4	26 15.3	8 17.4	25 22.1	10 59.4	23 32.2	21 54.5	13 43.8	24 30.8	0 42.6	24 26.3	0 52.6
23	2 4 19.9	27 12.2	8 14.0	8♑14.9	12 17.4	24 42.5	22 42.8	13 56.6	24 37.7	0 46.0	24 27.8	0 54.8
24	2 8 16.5	28 9.2	8 10.5	21 8.0	13 38.0	25 53.1	23 31.2	14 9.5	24 44.5	0 49.4	24 29.4	0 57.0
25	2 12 13.0	29 6.4	8 7.1	3♒36.6	15 .9	27 3.8	24 19.8	14 22.3	24 51.4	0 52.8	24 31.1	0 59.1
26	2 16 9.6	0♏3.9	8 3.6	16 30.0	16 25.7	28 14.8	25 8.5	14 35.3	24 58.3	0 56.3	24 32.8	1 1.3
27	2 20 6.2	1 1.4	8 .2	29 12.3	17 52.0	29 25.9	25 57.2	14 48.3	25 5.1	0 59.8	24 34.4	1 3.5
28	2 24 2.7	1 59.2	7 56.7	11♓4.5	19 19.6	0♏37.3	26 46.1	15 1.3	25 12.0	1 3.3	24 36.1	1 5.7
29	2 27 59.3	2 57.1	7 53.3	23 11.3	20 48.3	1 48.9	27 35.0	15 14.3	25 18.8	1 6.9	24 37.9	1 7.9
30	2 31 55.8	3 55.2	7 49.8	5♈29.7	22 17.8	3 .7	28 24.0	15 27.3	25 25.6	1 10.4	24 39.6	1 10.1
31	2 35 52.4	4 53.5	7 46.4	17 46.0	23 48.1	4 12.8	29 13.2	15 40.4	25 32.5	1 14.0	24 41.4	1 12.2

DECLINATION

DAY	EPHEM. SID. TIME (h m s)	☉	☊	☽	☿	♀	♂	♃	♄	♅	♆	♇
1	0 37 35.8	2S58.4	0N24.2	11S.0	6S28.3	1N50.8	22S53.6	14N26.7	6S50.8	20S23.1	22S4.5	5N20.3
4	0 49 25.4	4 8.1	0 24.3	4N13.3	4 18.0	0 21.1	23 14.3	14 38.1	6 58.8	20 24.7	22 4.8	5 17.4
7	1 1 15.1	5 17.4	0 24.3	18 15.0	2 16.9	1S8.9	23 33.2	14 49.5	7 6.9	20 26.4	22 5.0	5 14.6
10	1 13 4.7	6 26.0	0 24.3	23 9.3	0N49.5	2 39.0	23 50.2	15 1.0	7 14.9	20 28.1	22 5.3	5 11.9
13	1 24 54.4	7 34.0	0 24.3	15 34.2	0N9.6	4 8.8	24 5.3	15 12.5	7 22.9	20 29.8	22 5.6	5 9.2
16	1 36 44.1	8 41.0	0 24.3	0 40.9	0 18.4	5 37.9	24 18.3	15 24.0	7 30.9	20 31.6	22 5.9	5 6.5
19	1 48 33.7	9 46.9	0 24.3	13S53.1	1 8.7	7 6.0	24 29.2	15 35.4	7 38.9	20 33.5	22 6.1	5 4.0
22	2 0 23.4	10 51.5	0 24.3	22 24.6	2 29.8	8 32.8	24 38.0	15 46.8	7 46.8	20 35.4	22 6.4	5 1.5
25	2 12 13.0	11 54.6	0 24.3	21 58.1	4 11.4	9 57.9	24 44.5	15 58.2	7 54.7	20 37.3	22 6.7	4 59.1
28	2 24 2.7	12 56.1	0 24.3	12 49.2	6 4.9	11 20.9	24 48.7	16 9.5	8 2.5	20 39.3	22 7.0	4 56.7
31	2 35 52.4	13 55.8	0 24.3	2N9.0	8 4.6	12 41.6	24 50.6	16 20.7	8 10.2	20 41.3	22 7.3	4 54.5

NOVEMBER 1982

DAY	EPHEM. SID. TIME	☉	☊	☽	☿	♀	♂	♃	♄	♅	♆	♇
	h m s	° ′	° ′	° ′	° ′	° ′	° ′	° ′	° ′	° ′	° ′	° ′
		LONGITUDE										
	2 39 48.9	8♏14.4	7♋ 5.1	1♉ 7.7	26♎38.4	7♏27.9	0♑ 2.1	18♏ 6.4	26♎45.8	3♐18.0	25♐ 6.5	27♎19.4
2	2 43 45.5	9 14.4	7 1.9	15 20.7	28 17.0	8 43.1	0 46.8	18 19.5	26 53.0	3 21.4	25 8.2	27 21.8
3	2 47 42.0	10 14.4	6 58.8	29 45.9	29 55.8	9 58.3	1 31.6	18 32.7	27 .2	3 24.9	25 9.9	27 24.2
4	2 51 38.6	11 14.5	6 55.6	14♊16.9	1♏34.7	11 13.6	2 16.5	18 45.9	27 7.4	3 28.3	25 11.7	27 26.5
5	2 55 35.2	12 14.6	6 52.4	28 47.8	3 13.5	12 28.9	3 1.4	18 59.0	27 14.5	3 31.8	25 13.4	27 28.9
6	2 59 31.7	13 14.8	6 49.2	13♋13.9	4 52.3	13 44.1	3 46.4	19 12.2	27 21.6	3 35.4	25 15.2	27 31.2
7	3 3 28.3	14 14.9	6 46.0	27 31.6	6 30.8	14 59.4	4 31.4	19 25.4	27 28.7	3 38.9	25 17.0	27 33.6
8	3 7 24.8	15 15.1	6 42.9	11♌38.9	8 9.2	16 14.7	5 16.5	19 38.7	27 35.8	3 42.5	25 18.8	27 35.9
9	3 11 21.4	16 15.4	6 39.7	25 35.0	9 47.4	17 30.0	6 1.7	19 51.9	27 42.9	3 46.0	25 20.7	27 38.2
10	3 15 17.9	17 15.7	6 36.5	9♍19.4	11 25.2	18 45.3	6 46.9	20 5.1	27 49.9	3 49.6	25 22.5	27 40.5
11	3 19 14.5	18 16.0	6 33.3	22 52.2	13 2.8	20 .7	7 32.2	20 18.4	27 56.9	3 53.2	25 24.4	27 42.8
12	3 23 11.0	19 16.3	6 30.2	6♎13.0	14 40.2	21 16.0	8 17.6	20 31.6	28 3.9	3 56.8	25 26.3	27 45.1
13	3 27 7.6	20 16.7	6 27.0	19 21.6	16 17.2	22 31.3	9 3.0	20 44.9	28 10.9	4 .4	25 28.3	27 47.4
14	3 31 4.2	21 17.1	6 23.8	2♏17.4	17 54.0	23 46.7	9 48.5	20 58.1	28 17.8	4 4.0	25 30.2	27 49.6
15	3 35 .7	22 17.6	6 20.6	15 .0	19 30.4	25 2.0	10 34.0	21 11.4	28 24.7	4 7.7	25 32.2	27 51.9
16	3 38 57.3	23 18.1	6 17.5	27 29.4	21 6.6	26 17.4	11 19.7	21 24.7	28 31.6	4 11.4	25 34.2	27 54.2
17	3 42 53.8	24 18.6	6 14.3	9♐46.0	22 42.5	27 32.8	12 5.4	21 38.0	28 38.5	4 15.0	25 36.2	27 56.4
18	3 46 50.4	25 19.1	6 11.1	21 51.0	24 18.2	28 48.1	12 51.1	21 51.2	28 45.3	4 18.7	25 38.2	27 58.6
19	3 50 46.9	26 19.6	6 7.9	3♑46.7	25 53.6	0♐ 3.5	13 36.8	22 4.5	28 52.0	4 22.4	25 40.2	28 .8
20	3 54 43.5	27 20.2	6 4.7	15 35.9	27 28.7	1 18.8	14 22.7	22 17.7	28 58.8	4 26.0	25 42.3	28 3.0
21	3 58 40.0	28 20.8	6 1.6	27 22.3	29 3.6	2 34.2	15 8.5	22 31.0	29 5.5	4 29.7	25 44.3	28 5.1
22	4 2 36.6	29 21.4	5 58.4	9♒10.4	0♐38.3	3 49.6	15 54.5	22 44.2	29 12.1	4 33.4	25 46.4	28 7.3
23	4 6 33.2	0♐22.0	5 55.2	21 5.0	2 12.8	5 4.9	16 40.4	22 57.4	29 18.8	4 37.1	25 48.5	28 9.4
24	4 10 29.7	1 22.7	5 52.0	3♓11.3	3 47.2	6 20.3	17 26.4	23 10.6	29 25.3	4 40.8	25 50.6	28 11.5
25	4 14 26.3	2 23.3	5 48.9	15 34.3	5 21.3	7 35.6	18 12.5	23 23.8	29 31.9	4 44.5	25 52.7	28 13.6
26	4 18 22.8	3 24.0	5 45.7	28 18.5	6 55.4	8 51.0	18 58.6	23 37.0	29 38.4	4 48.2	25 54.8	28 15.7
27	4 22 19.4	4 24.7	5 42.5	11♈27.6	8 29.2	10 6.4	19 44.8	23 50.1	29 44.8	4 51.9	25 56.9	28 17.7
28	4 26 15.9	5 25.5	5 39.3	25 3.3	10 3.0	11 21.7	20 31.0	24 3.3	29 51.2	4 55.6	25 59.1	28 19.8
29	4 30 12.5	6 26.2	5 36.2	9♉ 5.4	11 36.7	12 37.1	21 17.2	24 16.4	29 57.6	4 59.3	26 1.2	28 21.8
30	4 34 9.1	7 27.0	5 33.0	23 31.1	13 10.2	13 52.4	22 3.5	24 29.5	0♏ 3.9	5 3.0	26 3.4	28 23.8
		LATITUDE										
1	2 39 48.9	0 .0	0 .0	4S36.0	1N39.1	0N55.4	1S24.3	0N51.1	2N15.5	0N 7.2	1N13.7	16N29.5
4	2 51 38.6	0 .0	0 .0	1 51.5	1 22.7	0 49.7	1 24.2	0 50.9	2 15.7	0 7.2	1 13.6	16 29.8
7	3 3 28.3	0 .0	0 .0	1N55.8	1 4.4	0 43.7	1 24.1	0 50.7	2 15.8	0 7.2	1 13.5	16 30.2
10	3 15 17.9	0 .0	0 .0	4 36.9	0 44.8	0 37.4	1 23.9	0 50.5	2 16.0	0 7.1	1 13.4	16 30.7
13	3 27 7.6	0 .0	0 .0	4 59.0	0 24.6	0 30.8	1 23.7	0 50.3	2 16.3	0 7.1	1 13.3	16 31.3
16	3 38 57.3	0 .0	0 .0	3 8.1	0 4.2	0 24.0	1 23.3	0 50.2	2 16.5	0 7.1	1 13.2	16 31.9
19	3 50 46.9	0 .0	0 .0	0 4.8	0S15.9	0 17.1	1 22.9	0 50.0	2 16.8	0 7.1	1 13.1	16 32.6
22	4 2 36.6	0 .0	0 .0	2S57.6	0 35.5	0 10.0	1 22.4	0 49.9	2 17.1	0 7.0	1 13.0	16 33.4
25	4 14 26.3	0 .0	0 .0	4 56.2	0 54.2	0 2.8	1 21.9	0 49.8	2 17.5	0 7.0	1 13.0	16 34.3
28	4 26 15.9	0 .0	0 .0	4 53.8	1 11.8	0S 4.4	1 21.2	0 49.7	2 17.8	0 7.0	1 12.9	16 35.2
		RIGHT ASCENSION										
1	2 39 48.9	5♏52.0	7♋42.9	0♉36.2	25♎19.0	5♏25.1	0♑ 2.3	15♏53.5	25♎39.3	1♐17.6	24♐43.2	1♏14.4
2	2 43 45.5	6 50.7	7 39.5	14 3.1	26 50.4	6 37.7	0 51.6	16 6.7	25 46.1	1 21.2	24 45.0	1 16.6
3	2 47 42.0	7 49.6	7 36.0	28 14.5	28 22.2	7 50.6	1 40.9	16 19.8	25 52.8	1 24.8	24 46.9	1 18.8
4	2 51 38.6	8 48.7	7 32.5	13♊10.7	29 54.4	9 3.7	2 30.3	16 33.0	25 59.6	1 28.5	24 48.7	1 20.9
5	2 55 35.2	9 48.0	7 29.1	28 41.7	1♏27.0	10 17.2	3 19.8	16 46.2	26 6.4	1 32.1	24 50.6	1 23.1
6	2 59 31.7	10 47.5	7 25.6	14♋26.9	2 59.8	11 30.9	4 9.3	16 59.5	26 13.1	1 35.8	24 52.6	1 25.2
7	3 3 28.3	11 47.3	7 22.2	0♌ .5	4 32.9	12 44.9	4 58.9	17 12.7	26 19.8	1 39.5	24 54.5	1 27.4
8	3 7 24.8	12 47.2	7 18.7	15 .3	6 6.2	13 59.2	5 48.5	17 26.0	26 26.6	1 43.3	24 56.5	1 29.5
9	3 11 21.4	13 47.4	7 15.3	29 14.0	7 39.8	15 13.7	6 38.2	17 39.3	26 33.2	1 47.0	24 58.5	1 31.7
10	3 15 17.9	14 47.8	7 11.8	12♍40.6	9 13.6	16 28.6	7 27.9	17 52.6	26 39.9	1 50.8	25 .5	1 33.8
11	3 19 14.5	15 48.4	7 8.4	25 27.0	10 47.7	17 43.8	8 17.6	18 5.9	26 46.6	1 54.5	25 2.5	1 36.0
12	3 23 11.0	16 49.2	7 4.9	7♎44.4	12 22.0	18 59.3	9 7.4	18 19.3	26 53.2	1 58.3	25 4.6	1 38.1
13	3 27 7.6	17 50.2	7 1.5	19 45.3	13 56.6	20 15.2	9 57.2	18 32.6	26 59.8	2 2.1	25 6.6	1 40.2
14	3 31 4.2	18 51.4	6 58.0	1♏41.6	15 31.4	21 31.3	10 47.0	18 46.0	27 6.4	2 5.9	25 8.7	1 42.3
15	3 35 .7	19 52.9	6 54.6	13 43.2	17 6.5	22 47.7	11 36.9	18 59.4	27 12.9	2 9.8	25 10.8	1 44.4
16	3 38 57.3	20 54.6	6 51.1	25 57.4	18 42.0	24 4.5	12 26.8	19 12.8	27 19.5	2 13.6	25 13.0	1 46.6
17	3 42 53.8	21 56.5	6 47.6	8♐27.4	20 17.7	25 21.6	13 16.7	19 26.2	27 26.0	2 17.5	25 15.2	1 48.6
18	3 46 50.4	22 58.6	6 44.2	21 12.3	21 53.7	26 38.9	14 6.6	19 39.6	27 32.5	2 21.3	25 17.3	1 50.7
19	3 50 46.9	24 .9	6 40.7	4♑ 6.9	23 30.0	27 56.6	14 56.4	19 53.1	27 38.9	2 25.2	25 19.5	1 52.8
20	3 54 43.5	25 3.4	6 37.3	17 2.9	25 6.7	29 14.5	15 46.3	20 6.5	27 45.3	2 29.1	25 21.7	1 54.8
21	3 58 40.0	26 6.1	6 33.8	29 51.8	26 43.7	0♐32.8	16 36.2	20 19.9	27 51.7	2 32.9	25 23.9	1 56.9
22	4 2 36.6	27 9.0	6 30.4	12♒26.7	28 21.1	1 51.3	17 26.0	20 33.3	27 58.1	2 36.8	25 26.2	1 58.9
23	4 6 33.2	28 12.1	6 26.9	24 44.6	29 58.9	3 10.1	18 15.9	20 46.7	28 4.4	2 40.7	25 28.4	2 .9
24	4 10 29.7	29 15.3	6 23.5	6♓47.0	1♐37.1	4 29.2	19 5.7	21 .1	28 10.7	2 44.6	25 30.7	2 2.9
25	4 14 26.3	0♐18.8	6 20.0	18 39.5	3 15.6	5 48.6	19 55.5	21 13.5	28 16.9	2 48.5	25 33.0	2 4.9
26	4 18 22.8	1 22.5	6 16.5	0♈31.2	4 54.5	7 8.2	20 45.2	21 26.9	28 23.1	2 52.4	25 35.2	2 6.9
27	4 22 19.4	2 26.3	6 13.1	12 33.7	6 33.8	8 28.1	21 34.9	21 40.3	28 29.3	2 56.3	25 37.5	2 8.8
28	4 26 15.9	3 30.3	6 9.6	25 .6	8 13.5	9 48.3	22 24.6	21 53.7	28 35.4	3 .2	25 39.9	2 10.8
29	4 30 12.5	4 34.5	6 6.2	8♉ 5.7	9 53.5	11 8.7	23 14.2	22 7.1	28 41.5	3 4.1	25 42.2	2 12.7
30	4 34 9.1	5 38.9	6 2.7	22 1.2	11 34.0	12 29.3	24 3.8	22 20.5	28 47.5	3 8.0	25 44.5	2 14.6
		DECLINATION										
1	2 39 48.9	14S15.3	0N24.3	7N33.0	8S44.1	13S 7.8	24S50.8	16S24.4	8S12.7	20S41.9	22S 7.4	4N53.8
4	2 51 38.6	15 12.2	0 24.4	20 40.1	10 43.8	14 24.7	24 49.5	16 35.4	8 20.3	20 43.9	22 7.7	4 51.7
7	3 3 28.3	16 6.9	0 24.4	22 33.0	12 40.7	15 38.3	24 45.9	16 46.4	8 27.8	20 46.0	22 8.0	4 49.7
10	3 15 17.9	16 59.3	0 24.4	12 20.8	14 32.9	16 48.3	24 39.9	16 57.2	8 35.1	20 48.0	22 8.3	4 47.8
13	3 27 7.6	17 49.0	0 24.4	2S57.8	16 19.1	17 54.4	24 31.4	17 8.0	8 42.4	20 50.1	22 8.6	4 46.0
16	3 38 57.3	18 36.0	0 24.4	16 32.8	17 58.2	18 56.1	24 20.5	17 18.5	8 49.5	20 52.1	22 8.9	4 44.3
19	3 50 46.9	19 20.0	0 24.4	23 18.4	19 29.3	19 53.2	24 7.2	17 28.9	8 56.4	20 54.2	22 9.2	4 42.7
22	4 2 36.6	20 .9	0 24.4	20 48.9	20 51.9	20 45.2	23 51.4	17 39.2	9 3.2	20 56.3	22 9.4	4 41.3
25	4 14 26.3	20 38.4	0 24.4	10 14.1	22 5.1	21 31.9	23 33.3	17 49.2	9 9.8	20 58.3	22 9.7	4 40.0
28	4 26 15.9	21 12.5	0 24.4	5N 8.2	23 8.5	22 13.1	23 12.8	17 59.1	9 16.2	21 .3	22 10.0	4 38.8

DECEMBER 1982

DAY	EPHEM. SID. TIME	☉	☊	☾	☿	♀	♂	♃	♄	♅	♆	♇
		LONGITUDE										
	h m s	° ′	° ′	° ′	° ′	° ′	° ′	° ′	° ′	° ′	° ′	° ′
1	4 38 5.6	8♐27.7	5♋29.8	8♊15.0	14♐43.7	15♐ 7.8	22♑49.8	24♏42.6	0♏10.2	5♐ 6.7	26♐ 5.6	28♎25.7
2	4 42 2.2	9 28.5	5 26.6	23 9.6	16 17.2	16 23.1	23 36.1	24 55.7	0 16.4	5 10.4	26 7.8	28 27.7
3	4 45 58.7	10 29.3	5 23.4	8♋ 6.7	17 50.5	17 38.5	24 22.5	25 8.8	0 22.5	5 14.1	26 9.9	28 29.6
4	4 49 55.3	11 30.2	5 20.3	22 58.5	19 23.9	18 53.9	25 8.9	25 21.8	0 28.7	5 17.8	26 12.1	28 31.5
5	4 53 51.8	12 31.0	5 17.1	7♌38.1	20 57.1	20 9.2	25 55.4	25 34.8	0 34.7	5 21.4	26 14.4	28 33.4
6	4 57 48.4	13 31.9	5 13.9	22 1.1	22 30.4	21 24.6	26 41.9	25 47.7	0 40.7	5 25.1	26 16.6	28 35.3
7	5 1 45.0	14 32.9	5 10.7	6♍ 4.9	24 3.6	22 40.0	27 28.5	26 .7	0 46.7	5 28.8	26 18.9	28 37.2
8	5 5 41.5	15 33.8	5 7.6	19 48.7	25 36.8	23 55.3	28 15.0	26 13.7	0 52.6	5 32.5	26 21.1	28 39.0
9	5 9 38.1	16 34.7	5 4.4	3♎13.0	27 9.9	25 10.7	29 1.6	26 26.5	0 58.5	5 36.2	26 23.3	28 40.8
10	5 13 34.6	17 35.7	5 1.2	16 19.3	28 42.9	26 26.1	29 48.3	26 39.4	1 4.2	5 39.8	26 25.6	28 42.5
11	5 17 31.2	18 36.7	4 58.0	29 9.5	0♑15.9	27 41.4	0♒34.9	26 52.2	1 10.0	5 43.4	26 27.8	28 44.3
12	5 21 27.7	19 37.7	4 54.9	11♏45.4	1 48.7	28 56.8	1 21.6	27 5.0	1 15.6	5 47.1	26 30.1	28 46.0
13	5 25 24.3	20 38.7	4 51.7	24 8.9	3 21.4	0♑12.2	2 8.4	27 17.7	1 21.2	5 50.7	26 32.3	28 47.7
14	5 29 20.9	21 39.8	4 48.5	6♐21.6	4 53.9	1 27.6	2 55.1	27 30.5	1 26.8	5 54.3	26 34.6	28 49.3
15	5 33 17.4	22 40.8	4 45.3	18 25.4	6 26.2	2 42.9	3 41.9	27 43.1	1 32.2	5 57.9	26 36.8	28 51.0
16	5 37 14.0	23 41.9	4 42.1	0♑21.7	7 58.2	3 58.3	4 28.8	27 55.8	1 37.6	6 1.5	26 39.1	28 52.6
17	5 41 10.5	24 43.0	4 39.0	12 12.6	9 29.8	5 13.6	5 15.6	28 8.3	1 43.0	6 5.0	26 41.4	28 54.2
18	5 45 7.1	25 44.0	4 35.8	24 .2	11 .9	6 29.0	6 2.5	28 20.9	1 48.2	6 8.6	26 43.6	28 55.7
19	5 49 3.7	26 45.1	4 32.6	5♒47.1	12 31.5	7 44.4	6 49.4	28 33.4	1 53.4	6 12.1	26 45.9	28 57.2
20	5 53 .2	27 46.2	4 29.4	17 36.4	14 1.3	8 59.7	7 36.3	28 45.8	1 58.6	6 15.6	26 48.2	28 58.7
21	5 56 56.8	28 47.3	4 26.3	29 31.6	15 30.3	10 15.1	8 23.2	28 58.2	2 3.6	6 19.1	26 50.5	29 .2
22	6 0 53.3	29 48.5	4 23.1	11♓36.9	16 58.2	11 30.4	9 10.2	29 10.6	2 8.6	6 22.6	26 52.7	29 1.6
23	6 4 49.9	0♑49.6	4 19.9	23 56.6	18 24.9	12 45.7	9 57.2	29 22.8	2 13.5	6 26.1	26 55.0	29 3.0
24	6 8 46.4	1 50.7	4 16.7	6♈35.0	19 50.1	14 1.0	10 44.2	29 35.1	2 18.4	6 29.5	26 57.2	29 4.4
25	6 12 43.0	2 51.8	4 13.6	19 36.0	21 13.4	15 16.4	11 31.2	29 47.3	2 23.1	6 32.9	26 59.5	29 5.7
26	6 16 39.6	3 52.9	4 10.4	3♉ 3.0	22 34.6	16 31.7	12 18.2	29 59.4	2 27.8	6 36.3	27 1.8	29 7.0
27	6 20 36.1	4 54.0	4 7.2	16 57.6	23 53.3	17 47.0	13 5.2	0♐11.4	2 32.4	6 39.7	27 4.0	29 8.3
28	6 24 32.7	5 55.2	4 4.0	1♊19.2	25 9.0	19 2.3	13 52.3	0 23.5	2 37.0	6 43.1	27 6.3	29 9.6
29	6 28 29.2	6 56.3	4 .9	16 4.6	26 21.2	20 17.6	14 39.4	0 35.4	2 41.5	6 46.4	27 8.6	29 10.8
30	6 32 25.8	7 57.5	3 57.7	1♋ 7.7	27 29.2	21 32.8	15 26.4	0 47.3	2 45.8	6 49.7	27 10.8	29 12.0
31	6 36 22.3	8 58.6	3 54.5	16 20.2	28 32.5	22 48.1	16 13.5	0 59.1	2 50.1	6 53.0	27 13.0	29 13.2
		LATITUDE										
1	4 38 5.6	0 .0	0 .0	2S18.8	1S27.9	0S11.7	1S20.5	0N49.6	2N18.2	0N 6.9	1N12.8	16N36.2
4	4 49 55.3	0 .0	0 .0	1N41.1	1 42.4	0 18.8	1 19.7	0 49.5	2 18.6	0 6.9	1 12.8	16 37.3
7	5 1 45.0	0 .0	0 .0	4 38.5	1 54.8	0 25.9	1 18.9	0 49.4	2 19.1	0 6.9	1 12.7	16 38.5
10	5 13 34.6	0 .0	0 .0	5 9.4	2 4.7	0 32.9	1 18.0	0 49.4	2 19.6	0 6.9	1 12.7	16 39.7
13	5 25 24.3	0 .0	0 .0	3 24.3	2 11.7	0 39.6	1 17.0	0 49.3	2 20.1	0 6.8	1 12.6	16 40.9
16	5 37 14.0	0 .0	0 .0	0 21.4	2 15.3	0 46.2	1 16.0	0 49.3	2 20.6	0 6.8	1 12.6	16 42.2
19	5 49 3.7	0 .0	0 .0	2S46.7	2 14.8	0 52.4	1 14.9	0 49.3	2 21.1	0 6.8	1 12.6	16 43.6
22	6 0 53.3	0 .0	0 .0	4 53.7	2 9.3	0 58.4	1 13.7	0 49.3	2 21.7	0 6.8	1 12.6	16 45.0
25	6 12 43.0	0 .0	0 .0	5 6.9	1 57.8	1 4.0	1 12.5	0 49.3	2 22.3	0 6.8	1 12.6	16 46.5
28	6 24 32.7	0 .0	0 .0	2 53.4	1 39.0	1 9.2	1 11.2	0 49.3	2 22.9	0 6.7	1 12.5	16 48.0
31	6 36 22.3	0 .0	0 .0	1N 6.6	1 11.8	1 14.0	1 9.9	0 49.4	2 23.5	0 6.7	1 12.5	16 49.5
		RIGHT ASCENSION										
1	4 38 5.6	6♐43.4	5♋59.3	6♊53.2	13♐14.7	13♐50.1	24♑53.3	22♏33.8	28♎53.5	3♐11.9	25♐46.9	2♏16.5
2	4 42 2.2	7 48.1	5 55.8	22 36.5	14 55.9	15 11.2	25 42.8	22 47.2	28 59.4	3 15.8	25 49.2	2 18.4
3	4 45 58.7	8 53.0	5 52.3	8♋51.3	16 37.4	16 32.5	26 32.2	23 .5	29 5.3	3 19.6	25 51.6	2 20.2
4	4 49 55.3	9 58.0	5 48.9	25 6.4	18 19.2	17 53.9	27 21.6	23 13.8	29 11.2	3 23.5	25 54.0	2 22.1
5	4 53 51.8	11 3.2	5 45.4	10♌50.4	20 1.2	19 15.5	28 10.9	23 27.1	29 17.0	3 27.4	25 56.4	2 23.9
6	4 57 48.4	12 8.5	5 42.0	25 42.5	21 43.5	20 37.3	29 .1	23 40.4	29 22.8	3 31.3	25 58.8	2 25.7
7	5 1 45.0	13 14.0	5 38.5	9♍36.9	23 26.1	21 59.3	29 49.3	23 53.7	29 28.5	3 35.2	26 1.2	2 27.6
8	5 5 41.5	14 19.6	5 35.1	22 39.6	25 8.9	23 21.4	0♒38.4	24 6.9	29 34.2	3 39.1	26 3.6	2 29.3
9	5 9 38.1	15 25.3	5 31.6	5♎ 2.8	26 51.7	24 43.6	1 27.4	24 20.1	29 39.8	3 42.9	26 6.0	2 31.1
10	5 13 34.6	16 31.1	5 28.1	17 1.1	28 34.6	26 5.9	2 16.3	24 33.3	29 45.3	3 46.8	26 8.5	2 32.8
11	5 17 31.2	17 37.1	5 24.7	28 48.7	0♑17.6	27 28.3	3 5.2	24 46.5	29 50.8	3 50.6	26 10.9	2 34.5
12	5 21 27.7	18 43.1	5 21.2	10♏38.0	2 .4	28 50.8	3 54.0	24 59.6	29 56.3	3 54.4	26 13.3	2 36.2
13	5 25 24.3	19 49.3	5 17.8	22 38.7	3 43.2	0♑13.3	4 42.7	25 12.7	0♏ 1.7	3 58.3	26 15.7	2 37.9
14	5 29 20.9	20 55.5	5 14.3	4♐56.6	5 25.7	1 35.9	5 31.3	25 25.8	0 7.0	4 2.1	26 18.2	2 39.5
15	5 33 17.4	22 1.8	5 10.9	17 32.8	7 7.8	2 58.5	6 19.8	25 38.8	0 12.3	4 5.9	26 20.6	2 41.2
16	5 37 14.0	23 8.2	5 7.4	0♑23.6	8 49.5	4 21.2	7 8.3	25 51.8	0 17.5	4 9.6	26 23.1	2 42.8
17	5 41 10.5	24 14.6	5 3.9	13 20.7	10 30.7	5 43.8	7 56.6	26 4.8	0 22.6	4 13.4	26 25.5	2 44.3
18	5 45 7.1	25 21.1	5 .5	26 13.7	12 11.1	7 6.4	8 44.9	26 17.7	0 27.7	4 17.1	26 28.0	2 45.9
19	5 49 3.7	26 27.7	4 57.0	8♒53.3	13 50.6	8 28.9	9 33.0	26 30.6	0 32.7	4 20.9	26 30.4	2 47.4
20	5 53 .2	27 34.2	4 53.6	21 13.5	15 29.0	9 51.4	10 21.1	26 43.4	0 37.7	4 24.6	26 32.9	2 48.9
21	5 56 56.8	28 40.8	4 50.1	3♓13.3	17 6.1	11 13.8	11 9.0	26 56.2	0 42.6	4 28.3	26 35.3	2 50.4
22	6 0 53.3	29 47.4	4 46.7	14 56.6	18 41.7	12 36.1	11 56.9	27 9.0	0 47.4	4 32.0	26 37.8	2 51.9
23	6 4 49.9	0♑54.0	4 43.2	26 31.1	20 15.5	13 58.3	12 44.6	27 21.7	0 52.1	4 35.6	26 40.2	2 53.3
24	6 8 46.4	2 .6	4 39.7	8♈ 8.3	21 47.2	15 20.4	13 32.3	27 34.4	0 56.8	4 39.3	26 42.6	2 54.7
25	6 12 43.0	3 7.2	4 36.3	20 1.6	23 16.5	16 42.4	14 19.8	27 47.0	1 1.4	4 42.9	26 45.1	2 56.1
26	6 16 39.6	4 13.8	4 32.8	2♉26.3	24 42.9	18 4.2	15 7.3	27 59.5	1 6.0	4 46.5	26 47.5	2 57.4
27	6 20 36.1	5 20.3	4 29.4	15 37.8	26 6.1	19 25.8	15 54.6	28 12.0	1 10.4	4 50.0	26 50.0	2 58.8
28	6 24 32.7	6 26.9	4 25.9	29 48.7	27 25.5	20 47.3	16 41.8	28 24.5	1 14.9	4 53.6	26 52.4	3 .1
29	6 28 29.2	7 33.4	4 22.4	15♊ 3.8	28 40.6	22 8.5	17 28.9	28 36.9	1 19.2	4 57.2	26 54.9	3 1.4
30	6 32 25.8	8 39.8	4 19.0	1♋13.6	29 50.8	23 29.6	18 15.9	28 49.3	1 23.5	5 .7	26 57.3	3 2.6
31	6 36 22.3	9 46.1	4 15.5	17 51.9	0♒55.3	24 50.4	19 2.8	29 1.5	1 27.6	5 4.1	26 59.7	3 3.9
		DECLINATION										
1	4 38 5.6	21S43.0	0N24.4	19N24.0	24S 1.4	22S48.3	22S49.9	18S 8.8	9S22.4	21S 2.4	22S10.2	4N37.7
4	4 49 55.3	22 9.8	0 24.4	23 8.7	24 43.1	23 17.4	22 24.8	18 18.3	9 28.5	21 4.4	22 10.5	4 36.7
7	5 1 45.0	22 32.7	0 24.4	13 35.5	25 13.1	23 40.1	21 57.4	18 27.5	9 34.3	21 6.4	22 10.7	4 35.9
10	5 13 34.6	22 51.7	0 24.4	1S39.4	25 30.8	23 56.4	21 27.8	18 36.6	9 39.9	21 8.3	22 10.9	4 35.2
13	5 25 24.3	23 6.7	0 24.5	15 30.5	25 35.6	24 6.1	20 56.1	18 45.4	9 45.3	21 10.2	22 11.1	4 34.7
16	5 37 14.0	23 17.5	0 24.5	23 5.1	25 27.2	24 9.0	20 22.3	18 54.0	9 50.5	21 12.1	22 11.3	4 34.3
19	5 49 3.7	23 24.1	0 24.5	21 31.1	25 5.3	24 5.2	19 46.6	19 2.3	9 55.4	21 14.0	22 11.5	4 34.0
22	6 0 53.3	23 26.5	0 24.5	11 43.8	24 30.1	23 54.7	19 8.9	19 10.4	10 .1	21 15.8	22 11.7	4 33.9
25	6 12 43.0	23 24.6	0 24.5	2N55.9	23 42.3	23 37.6	18 29.4	19 18.2	10 4.5	21 17.6	22 11.9	4 33.9
28	6 24 32.7	23 18.5	0 24.5	17 35.8	22 43.7	23 13.9	17 48.1	19 25.8	10 8.6	21 19.3	22 12.0	4 34.0
31	6 36 22.3	23 8.2	0 24.5	23 32.6	21 37.5	22 43.8	17 5.2	19 33.2	10 12.5	21 21.0	22 12.2	4 34.3

JANUARY 1983

LONGITUDE

DAY	EPHEM. SID. TIME	☉	☊	☽	☿	♀	♂	♃	♄	♅	♆	♇
	h m s	° ′	° ′	° ′	° ′	° ′	° ′	° ′	° ′	° ′	° ′	° ′
1	6 40 18.9	9♑59.7	3♋51.3	1♌32.4	29♑30.4	24♑ 3.4	17♒ .6	1♐10.9	2♏54.3	6♐56.3	27♐15.3	29♎14.3
2	6 44 15.5	11 .8	3 48.1	16 34.6	0♒21.9	25 18.6	17 47.7	1 22.6	2 58.5	6 59.5	27 17.5	29 15.4
3	6 48 12.0	12 2.0	3 45.0	1♍18.8	1 6.3	26 33.8	18 34.8	1 34.2	3 2.5	7 2.7	27 19.7	29 16.4
4	6 52 8.6	13 3.1	3 41.8	15 39.6	1 42.6	27 49.1	19 21.9	1 45.8	3 6.4	7 5.9	27 21.9	29 17.4
5	6 56 5.1	14 4.3	3 38.6	29 34.2	2 10.0	29 4.3	20 9.0	1 57.2	3 10.3	7 9.1	27 24.1	29 18.4
6	7 0 1.7	15 5.4	3 35.4	13♎ 2.6	2 27.5	0♒19.5	20 56.1	2 8.6	3 14.1	7 12.2	27 26.3	29 19.4
7	7 3 58.3	16 6.6	3 32.3	26 6.5	2 34.4	1 34.7	21 43.2	2 20.0	3 17.8	7 15.3	27 28.4	29 20.3
8	7 7 54.8	17 7.7	3 29.1	8♏49.0	2R30.1	2 49.9	22 30.3	2 31.2	3 21.4	7 18.3	27 30.6	29 21.2
9	7 11 51.4	18 8.9	3 25.9	21 13.8	2 14.0	4 5.1	23 17.5	2 42.4	3 24.9	7 21.4	27 32.8	29 22.0
10	7 15 47.9	19 10.0	3 22.7	3♐24.6	1 46.1	5 20.3	24 4.6	2 53.5	3 28.4	7 24.4	27 34.9	29 22.8
11	7 19 44.5	20 11.2	3 19.6	15 25.2	1 6.5	6 35.5	24 51.8	3 4.5	3 31.7	7 27.3	27 37.1	29 23.6
12	7 23 41.0	21 12.4	3 16.4	27 18.8	0 16.1	7 50.7	25 38.9	3 15.4	3 34.9	7 30.3	27 39.2	29 24.4
13	7 27 37.6	22 13.5	3 13.2	9♑ 8.2	29♑16.0	9 5.8	26 26.1	3 26.3	3 38.1	7 33.2	27 41.3	29 25.1
14	7 31 34.2	23 14.7	3 10.0	20 55.8	28 7.9	10 20.9	27 13.2	3 37.0	3 41.1	7 36.1	27 43.4	29 25.7
15	7 35 30.7	24 15.8	3 6.9	2♒43.8	26 53.9	11 36.1	28 .3	3 47.7	3 44.1	7 38.9	27 45.5	29 26.4
16	7 39 27.3	25 16.9	3 3.7	14 34.1	25 36.2	12 51.2	28 47.5	3 58.3	3 47.0	7 41.7	27 47.5	29 27.0
17	7 43 23.8	26 18.0	3 .5	26 28.8	24 17.4	14 6.3	29 34.6	4 8.8	3 49.7	7 44.4	27 49.6	29 27.5
18	7 47 20.4	27 19.2	2 57.3	8♓30.0	22 59.9	15 21.4	0♓21.8	4 19.2	3 52.4	7 47.2	27 51.7	29 28.1
19	7 51 16.9	28 20.3	2 54.1	20 40.2	21 45.9	16 36.5	1 8.9	4 29.5	3 55.0	7 49.9	27 53.7	29 28.6
20	7 55 13.5	29 21.4	2 51.0	3♈ 2.2	20 37.4	17 51.5	1 56.0	4 39.7	3 57.5	7 52.6	27 55.7	29 29.0
21	7 59 10.1	0♒22.5	2 47.8	15 39.2	19 35.8	19 6.5	2 43.1	4 49.8	3 59.8	7 55.2	27 57.7	29 29.5
22	8 3 6.6	1 23.5	2 44.6	28 34.4	18 42.4	20 21.6	3 30.2	4 59.8	4 2.1	7 57.7	27 59.7	29 29.8
23	8 7 3.2	2 24.6	2 41.4	11♉51.2	17 57.7	21 36.5	4 17.3	5 9.7	4 4.3	8 .3	28 1.6	29 30.2
24	8 10 59.7	3 25.6	2 38.3	25 32.0	17 22.2	22 51.5	5 4.4	5 19.5	4 6.4	8 2.8	28 3.6	29 30.5
25	8 14 56.3	4 26.6	2 35.1	9♊38.3	16 55.9	24 6.4	5 51.4	5 29.2	4 8.3	8 5.2	28 5.5	29 30.8
26	8 18 52.8	5 27.6	2 31.9	24 9.4	16 38.6	25 21.4	6 38.4	5 38.7	4 10.2	8 7.6	28 7.4	29 31.0
27	8 22 49.4	6 28.6	2 28.7	9♋ 2.1	16 29.9	26 36.2	7 25.5	5 48.2	4 12.0	8 10.0	28 9.3	29 31.2
28	8 26 45.9	7 29.5	2 25.6	24 10.3	16 29.4	27 51.1	8 12.5	5 57.6	4 13.6	8 12.3	28 11.1	29 31.4
29	8 30 42.5	8 30.4	2 22.4	9♌25.2	16D36.7	29 6.0	8 59.5	6 6.8	4 15.2	8 14.6	28 13.0	29 31.5
30	8 34 39.1	9 31.4	2 19.2	24 36.6	16 51.0	0♓20.8	9 46.4	6 15.9	4 16.7	8 16.8	28 14.8	29 31.6
31	8 38 35.6	10 32.3	2 16.0	9♍34.4	17 11.9	1 35.6	10 33.4	6 25.0	4 18.0	8 19.0	28 16.6	29 31.7

LATITUDE

DAY	EPHEM. SID. TIME	☉	☊	☽	☿	♀	♂	♃	♄	♅	♆	♇
1	6 40 18.9	0 .0	0 .0	2N26.0	1S .6	1S15.5	1S 9.4	0N49.4	2N23.8	0N 6.7	1N12.5	16N50.1
4	6 52 8.6	0 .0	0 .0	5 1.2	0 20.3	1 19.7	1 8.0	0 49.4	2 24.4	0 6.7	1 12.6	16 51.7
7	7 3 58.3	0 .0	0 .0	4 54.8	0N29.6	1 23.4	1 6.6	0 49.5	2 25.1	0 6.7	1 12.6	16 53.3
10	7 15 47.9	0 .0	0 .0	2 43.1	1 25.7	1 26.6	1 5.1	0 49.6	2 25.8	0 6.7	1 12.6	16 54.9
13	7 27 37.6	0 .0	0 .0	0S26.7	2 20.7	1 29.2	1 3.6	0 49.7	2 26.5	0 6.6	1 12.6	16 56.6
16	7 39 27.3	0 .0	0 .0	3 24.4	3 3.8	1 31.2	1 2.0	0 49.8	2 27.2	0 6.6	1 12.6	16 58.3
19	7 51 16.9	0 .0	0 .0	5 5.9	3 26.3	1 32.7	1 .3	0 49.9	2 28.0	0 6.6	1 12.7	16 60.0
22	8 3 6.6	0 .0	0 .0	4 45.8	3 26.9	1 33.5	0 58.7	0 50.0	2 28.7	0 6.6	1 12.7	17 1.7
25	8 14 56.3	0 .0	0 .0	2 9.6	3 10.7	1 33.7	0 56.9	0 50.2	2 29.5	0 6.6	1 12.8	17 3.4
28	8 26 45.9	0 .0	0 .0	1N48.3	2 44.1	1 33.3	0 55.2	0 50.3	2 30.2	0 6.6	1 12.8	17 5.1
31	8 38 35.6	0 .0	0 .0	4 44.1	2 12.5	1 32.3	0 53.4	0 50.5	2 31.0	0 6.6	1 12.9	17 6.8

RIGHT ASCENSION

DAY	EPHEM. SID. TIME	☉	☊	☽	☿	♀	♂	♃	♄	♅	♆	♇
1	6 40 18.9	10♑52.4	4♋12.1	4♌21.7	1♒53.6	26♑11.0	19♒49.6	29♏13.8	1♏31.7	5♐ 7.6	27♐ 2.1	3♏ 5.0
2	6 44 15.5	11 58.6	4 8.6	20 10.0	2 44.7	27 31.3	20 36.2	29 25.9	1 35.7	5 11.0	27 4.5	3 6.2
3	6 48 12.0	13 4.8	4 5.1	4♍58.7	3 27.9	28 51.4	21 22.8	29 38.0	1 39.7	5 14.4	27 6.9	3 7.3
4	6 52 8.6	14 10.8	4 1.7	18 46.4	4 2.2	0♒11.2	22 9.2	29 50.0	1 43.5	5 17.8	27 9.2	3 8.4
5	6 56 5.1	15 16.8	3 58.2	1♎42.6	4 26.9	1 30.8	22 55.5	0♐ 2.0	1 47.3	5 21.1	27 11.6	3 9.5
6	7 0 1.7	16 22.7	3 54.8	14 1.9	4 41.1	2 50.1	23 41.8	0 13.8	1 51.0	5 24.4	27 14.0	3 10.6
7	7 3 58.3	17 28.4	3 51.3	25 59.9	4 44.0	4 9.1	24 27.9	0 25.7	1 54.6	5 27.7	27 16.3	3 11.6
8	7 7 54.8	18 34.1	3 47.8	7♏50.9	4R35.1	5 27.8	25 13.9	0 37.4	1 58.1	5 30.9	27 18.7	3 12.6
9	7 11 51.4	19 39.6	3 44.4	19 46.7	4 14.1	6 46.2	25 59.8	0 49.0	2 1.6	5 34.2	27 21.0	3 13.5
10	7 15 47.9	20 45.0	3 40.9	1♐55.8	3 40.9	8 4.3	26 45.6	1 .6	2 4.9	5 37.3	27 23.3	3 14.4
11	7 19 44.5	21 50.3	3 37.5	14 22.3	2 56.0	9 22.1	27 31.3	1 12.1	2 8.2	5 40.5	27 25.6	3 15.3
12	7 23 41.0	22 55.4	3 34.0	27 5.2	2 .0	10 39.6	28 16.8	1 23.6	2 11.4	5 43.6	27 27.9	3 16.2
13	7 27 37.6	24 .4	3 30.5	9♑58.5	0 54.4	11 56.8	29 2.3	1 34.9	2 14.5	5 46.7	27 30.2	3 17.0
14	7 31 34.2	25 5.2	3 27.1	22 52.9	29♑40.9	13 13.6	29 47.7	1 46.1	2 17.5	5 49.7	27 32.5	3 17.8
15	7 35 30.7	26 9.9	3 23.6	5♒37.8	28 21.7	14 30.1	0♓32.9	1 57.3	2 20.4	5 52.7	27 34.7	3 18.6
16	7 39 27.3	27 14.4	3 20.2	18 5.2	26 59.1	15 46.3	1 18.1	2 8.4	2 23.2	5 55.7	27 36.9	3 19.3
17	7 43 23.8	28 18.7	3 16.7	0♓11.1	25 35.7	17 2.2	2 3.2	2 19.4	2 25.9	5 58.6	27 39.2	3 20.0
18	7 47 20.4	29 22.9	3 13.2	11 56.6	24 14.2	18 17.7	2 48.2	2 30.3	2 28.6	6 1.5	27 41.4	3 20.7
19	7 51 16.9	0♒26.9	3 9.8	23 27.2	22 56.6	19 32.9	3 33.0	2 41.1	2 31.2	6 4.4	27 43.6	3 21.4
20	7 55 13.5	1 30.7	3 6.3	4♈52.2	21 44.9	20 47.8	4 17.8	2 51.8	2 33.6	6 7.2	27 45.8	3 22.0
21	7 59 10.1	2 34.3	3 2.9	16 23.5	20 40.8	22 2.3	5 2.4	3 2.4	2 36.0	6 10.0	27 47.9	3 22.6
22	8 3 6.6	3 37.7	2 59.4	28 15.3	19 45.3	23 16.5	5 47.0	3 12.9	2 38.2	6 12.7	27 50.1	3 23.1
23	8 7 3.2	4 40.9	2 55.9	10♉42.6	18 59.2	24 30.4	6 31.4	3 23.3	2 40.4	6 15.4	27 52.2	3 23.6
24	8 10 59.7	5 43.9	2 52.5	24 .3	18 22.8	25 44.0	7 15.8	3 33.5	2 42.5	6 18.0	27 54.3	3 24.1
25	8 14 56.3	6 46.7	2 49.0	8♊19.0	17 56.1	26 57.2	8 .0	3 43.7	2 44.4	6 20.6	27 56.3	3 24.5
26	8 18 52.8	7 49.3	2 45.6	23 40.6	17 38.9	28 10.1	8 44.2	3 53.8	2 46.3	6 23.2	27 58.4	3 25.0
27	8 22 49.4	8 51.7	2 42.1	9♋52.0	17 31.0	29 22.7	9 28.3	4 3.7	2 48.1	6 25.7	28 .4	3 25.3
28	8 26 45.9	9 53.9	2 38.6	26 24.6	17D31.7	0♓35.0	10 12.3	4 13.6	2 49.8	6 28.1	28 2.4	3 25.7
29	8 30 42.5	10 55.9	2 35.2	12♌43.0	17 40.6	1 47.0	10 56.2	4 23.3	2 51.4	6 30.6	28 4.4	3 26.0
30	8 34 39.1	11 57.7	2 31.7	28 18.5	17 57.1	2 58.7	11 40.0	4 32.9	2 52.9	6 32.9	28 6.4	3 26.3
31	8 38 35.6	12 59.3	2 28.2	12♍57.5	18 20.6	4 10.2	12 23.7	4 42.4	2 54.2	6 35.3	28 8.3	3 26.5

DECLINATION

DAY	EPHEM. SID. TIME	☉	☊	☽	☿	♀	♂	♃	♄	♅	♆	♇
1	6 40 18.9	23S 3.9	0N24.5	22N11.4	21S14.6	22S32.4	16S50.5	19S35.5	10S13.7	21S21.6	22S12.2	4N34.4
4	6 52 8.6	22 48.0	0 24.5	10 16.7	20 6.6	21 54.1	16 5.5	19 42.5	10 17.2	21 23.2	22 12.4	4 34.8
7	7 3 58.3	22 28.1	0 24.5	5S30.0	19 6.4	21 9.9	15 19.0	19 49.2	10 20.4	21 24.8	22 12.5	4 35.4
10	7 15 47.9	22 4.2	0 24.5	18 10.2	18 22.5	20 20.1	14 31.2	19 55.7	10 23.3	21 26.3	22 12.6	4 36.1
13	7 27 37.6	21 36.5	0 24.5	23 34.2	18 .6	19 25.0	13 42.1	20 1.9	10 25.9	21 27.8	22 12.7	4 36.9
16	7 39 27.3	21 4.9	0 24.5	19 43.1	18 .7	18 24.8	12 51.8	20 7.8	10 28.2	21 29.2	22 12.7	4 37.9
19	7 51 16.9	20 29.7	0 24.5	8 22.9	18 17.2	17 20.0	12 .4	20 13.4	10 30.2	21 30.5	22 12.8	4 38.9
22	8 3 6.6	19 51.1	0 24.5	6N30.8	18 43.1	16 10.8	11 8.1	20 18.8	10 31.9	21 31.8	22 12.9	4 40.1
25	8 14 56.3	19 9.1	0 24.5	19 45.7	19 12.9	14 57.6	10 14.8	20 23.8	10 33.2	21 33.0	22 12.9	4 41.4
28	8 26 45.9	18 23.9	0 24.5	23 3.4	19 42.5	13 40.8	9 20.8	20 28.6	10 34.3	21 34.1	22 12.9	4 42.8
31	8 38 35.6	17 35.8	0 24.5	12 21.8	20 8.6	12 20.7	8 26.0	20 33.2	10 35.0	21 35.2	22 12.9	4 44.3

FEBRUARY 1983

LONGITUDE

DAY	EPHEM. SID. TIME	☉	☊	☽	☿	♀	♂	♃	♄	♅	♆	♇
	h m s	° ′	° ′	° ′	° ′	° ′	° ′	° ′	° ′	° ′	° ′	° ′
1	8 42 32.2	11 ♒ 33.2	2 ♋ 12.8	24 ♍ 10.2	17 ♑ 38.8	2 ♓ 50.3	11 ♓ 20.3	6 ♐ 33.9	4 ♏ 19.3	8 ♐ 21.2	28 ♐ 18.4	29 ♎ 31.7
2	8 46 28.7	12 34.0	2 9.7	8 ♎ 18.6	18 11.3	4 5.1	12 7.2	6 42.6	4 20.4	8 23.3	28 20.1	29 31.7
3	8 50 25.3	13 34.9	2 6.5	21 57.6	18 48.7	5 19.8	12 54.1	6 51.3	4 21.5	8 25.3	28 21.9	29 R 31.6
4	8 54 21.8	14 35.8	2 3.3	5 ♏ 7.9	19 30.8	6 34.5	13 41.0	6 59.9	4 22.4	8 27.3	28 23.6	29 31.5
5	8 58 18.4	15 36.6	2 .1	17 52.4	20 17.1	7 49.2	14 27.9	7 8.3	4 23.2	8 29.3	28 25.3	29 31.4
6	9 2 14.9	16 37.4	1 57.0	0 ♐ 15.6	21 7.1	9 3.8	15 14.7	7 16.6	4 24.0	8 31.2	28 26.9	29 31.2
7	9 6 11.5	17 38.2	1 53.8	12 22.3	22 .7	10 18.4	16 1.5	7 24.7	4 24.6	8 33.1	28 28.6	29 31.0
8	9 10 8.1	18 39.1	1 50.6	24 17.7	22 57.4	11 33.1	16 48.4	7 32.8	4 25.2	8 35.0	28 30.3	29 30.9
9	9 14 4.6	19 39.8	1 47.4	6 ♑ 6.4	23 57.1	12 47.6	17 35.2	7 40.7	4 25.6	8 36.8	28 31.8	29 30.6
10	9 18 1.2	20 40.6	1 44.2	17 52.5	24 59.4	14 2.2	18 21.9	7 48.5	4 25.9	8 38.5	28 33.4	29 30.3
11	9 21 57.7	21 41.3	1 41.1	29 39.7	26 4.1	15 16.7	19 8.6	7 56.1	4 26.1	8 40.2	28 35.0	29 30.0
12	9 25 54.3	22 42.1	1 37.9	11 ♒ 30.6	27 11.2	16 31.2	19 55.4	8 3.6	4 26.2	8 41.8	28 36.5	29 29.6
13	9 29 50.8	23 42.7	1 34.7	23 27.4	28 20.3	17 45.6	20 42.0	8 11.0	4 26.2	8 43.4	28 38.0	29 29.2
14	9 33 47.4	24 43.4	1 31.5	5 ♓ 31.7	29 31.4	19 .0	21 28.7	8 18.2	4 R 26.1	8 44.9	28 39.4	29 28.7
15	9 37 43.9	25 44.1	1 28.4	17 44.5	0 ♒ 44.3	20 14.4	22 15.3	8 25.3	4 25.8	8 46.4	28 40.9	29 28.3
16	9 41 40.5	26 44.7	1 25.2	0 ♈ 6.9	1 59.0	21 28.7	23 1.9	8 32.2	4 25.5	8 47.8	28 42.3	29 27.8
17	9 45 37.1	27 45.3	1 22.0	12 40.0	3 15.2	22 43.0	23 48.5	8 39.0	4 25.1	8 49.2	28 43.7	29 27.2
18	9 49 33.6	28 45.8	1 18.8	25 25.1	4 32.9	23 57.3	24 35.0	8 45.6	4 24.5	8 50.5	28 45.0	29 26.6
19	9 53 30.2	29 46.4	1 15.7	8 ♉ 23.9	5 52.1	25 11.5	25 21.5	8 52.1	4 23.9	8 51.8	28 46.3	29 26.0
20	9 57 26.7	0 ♓ 46.9	1 12.5	21 38.5	7 12.7	26 25.7	26 8.0	8 58.5	4 23.2	8 53.0	28 47.6	29 25.4
21	10 1 23.3	1 47.4	1 9.3	5 ♊ 11.1	8 34.6	27 39.8	26 54.5	9 4.7	4 22.3	8 54.2	28 48.9	29 24.7
22	10 5 19.8	2 47.8	1 6.1	19 3.3	9 57.8	28 53.9	27 40.9	9 10.7	4 21.4	8 55.3	28 50.2	29 24.0
23	10 9 16.4	3 48.2	1 2.9	3 ♋ 16.0	11 22.2	0 ♈ 8.0	28 27.2	9 16.6	4 20.3	8 56.4	28 51.4	29 23.3
24	10 13 12.9	4 48.6	0 59.8	17 48.3	12 47.8	1 22.0	29 13.6	9 22.3	4 19.2	8 57.4	28 52.6	29 22.5
25	10 17 9.5	5 48.9	0 56.6	2 ♌ 36.7	14 14.5	2 36.0	0 ♈ -.1	9 27.9	4 17.9	8 58.3	28 53.7	29 21.7
26	10 21 6.0	6 49.2	0 53.4	17 35.4	15 42.4	3 49.9	0 46.2	9 33.3	4 16.6	8 59.3	28 54.8	29 20.9
27	10 25 2.6	7 49.5	0 50.2	2 ♍ 36.1	17 11.4	5 3.8	1 32.4	9 38.5	4 15.1	9 .1	28 55.9	29 20.0
28	10 28 59.1	8 49.8	0 47.1	17 29.2	18 41.5	6 17.6	2 18.6	9 43.6	4 13.6	9 .9	28 57.0	29 19.1

LATITUDE

DAY	EPHEM. SID. TIME	☉	☊	☽	☿	♀	♂	♃	♄	♅	♆	♇
1	8 42 32.2	0 .0	0 .0	5 N 6.9	2 N 1.5	1 S 31.8	0 S 52.8	0 N 50.5	2 N 31.3	0 N 6.6	1 N 12.9	17 N 7.4
4	8 54 21.8	0 .0	0 .0	4 25.1	1 28.3	1 29.9	0 51.0	0 50.7	2 32.0	0 6.5	1 13.0	17 9.0
7	9 6 11.5	0 .0	0 .0	1 52.2	0 55.8	1 27.4	0 49.1	0 50.9	2 32.8	0 6.5	1 13.0	17 10.7
10	9 18 1.2	0 .0	0 .0	1 S 17.0	0 24.9	1 24.2	0 47.3	0 51.1	2 33.6	0 6.5	1 13.1	17 12.4
13	9 29 50.8	0 .0	0 .0	3 56.0	0 S 3.7	1 20.4	0 45.4	0 51.3	2 34.3	0 6.5	1 13.2	17 14.0
16	9 41 40.5	0 .0	0 .0	5 5.2	0 30.0	1 16.0	0 43.4	0 51.5	2 35.1	0 6.5	1 13.2	17 15.5
19	9 53 30.2	0 .0	0 .0	4 7.6	0 53.5	1 11.1	0 41.5	0 51.7	2 35.9	0 6.5	1 13.3	17 17.1
22	10 5 19.8	0 .0	0 .0	1 10.3	1 14.3	1 5.5	0 39.5	0 51.9	2 36.6	0 6.5	1 13.4	17 18.6
25	10 17 9.5	0 .0	0 .0	2 N 34.2	1 32.2	0 59.4	0 37.6	0 52.1	2 37.3	0 6.5	1 13.5	17 20.0
28	10 28 59.1	0 .0	0 .0	4 53.4	1 46.9	0 52.8	0 35.6	0 52.4	2 38.0	0 6.4	1 13.6	17 21.4

RIGHT ASCENSION

DAY	EPHEM. SID. TIME	☉	☊	☽	☿	♀	♂	♃	♄	♅	♆	♇
1	8 42 32.2	14 ♒ .7	2 ♋ 24.8	26 ♍ 41.2	18 ♑ 50.5	5 ♓ 21.3	13 ♓ 7.3	4 ♐ 51.8	2 ♏ 55.5	6 ♐ 37.6	28 ♐ 10.2	3 ♏ 26.7
2	8 46 28.7	15 1.9	2 21.3	9 ♎ 40.1	19 26.4	6 32.2	13 50.9	5 1.1	2 56.7	6 39.8	28 12.1	3 26.9
3	8 50 25.3	16 2.9	2 17.9	22 8.4	20 7.6	7 42.8	14 34.3	5 10.2	2 57.8	6 42.0	28 14.0	3 27.1
4	8 54 21.8	17 3.7	2 14.4	4 ♏ 20.3	20 53.7	8 53.1	15 17.7	5 19.2	2 58.8	6 44.1	28 15.9	3 27.2
5	8 58 18.4	18 4.3	2 10.9	16 28.6	21 44.3	10 3.2	16 1.1	5 28.1	2 59.7	6 46.2	28 17.7	3 27.3
6	9 2 14.9	19 4.7	2 7.5	28 42.9	22 38.9	11 13.1	16 44.3	5 36.8	3 .5	6 48.2	28 19.5	3 27.3
7	9 6 11.5	20 4.9	2 4.0	11 ♐ 9.4	23 37.2	12 22.7	17 27.5	5 45.5	3 1.2	6 50.2	28 21.3	3 27.3
8	9 10 8.1	21 4.9	2 .5	23 49.5	24 38.9	13 32.2	18 10.7	5 54.0	3 1.8	6 52.2	28 23.1	3 27.4
9	9 14 4.6	22 4.8	1 57.1	6 ♑ 39.8	25 43.6	14 41.4	18 53.7	6 2.4	3 2.3	6 54.1	28 24.8	3 R 27.3
10	9 18 1.2	23 4.4	1 53.6	19 33.2	26 51.1	15 50.3	19 36.7	6 10.6	3 2.7	6 55.9	28 26.5	3 27.2
11	9 21 57.7	24 3.8	1 50.2	2 ♒ 20.7	28 1.1	16 59.1	20 19.6	6 18.6	3 2.9	6 57.7	28 28.2	3 27.1
12	9 25 54.3	25 3.0	1 46.7	14 54.2	29 13.3	18 7.7	21 2.5	6 26.6	3 3.1	6 59.5	28 29.8	3 27.0
13	9 29 50.8	26 2.0	1 43.2	27 8.5	0 ♒ 27.7	19 16.1	21 45.3	6 34.4	3 3.2	7 1.1	28 31.4	3 26.8
14	9 33 47.4	27 .9	1 39.8	9 ♓ 2.7	1 44.0	20 24.4	22 28.0	6 42.0	3 3.2	7 2.8	28 33.0	3 26.6
15	9 37 43.9	27 59.6	1 36.3	20 40.2	3 2.0	21 32.5	23 10.7	6 49.5	3 R 3.0	7 4.3	28 34.5	3 26.3
16	9 41 40.5	28 58.0	1 32.8	2 ♈ 8.0	4 21.5	22 40.4	23 53.3	6 56.8	3 2.8	7 5.9	28 36.1	3 26.1
17	9 45 37.1	29 56.3	1 29.4	13 36.1	5 42.6	23 48.2	24 35.9	7 4.0	3 2.5	7 7.3	28 37.6	3 25.8
18	9 49 33.6	0 ♓ 54.4	1 25.9	25 16.5	7 4.9	24 55.9	25 18.4	7 11.0	3 2.0	7 8.7	28 39.0	3 25.4
19	9 53 30.2	1 52.4	1 22.5	7 ♉ 22.3	8 28.5	26 3.5	26 .9	7 17.9	3 1.5	7 10.1	28 40.5	3 25.0
20	9 57 26.7	2 50.1	1 19.0	20 6.9	9 53.2	27 10.9	26 43.3	7 24.6	3 .9	7 11.4	28 41.9	3 24.6
21	10 1 23.3	3 47.7	1 15.5	3 ♊ 41.6	11 18.9	28 18.2	27 25.7	7 31.2	3 .2	7 12.6	28 43.2	3 24.2
22	10 5 19.8	4 45.1	1 12.1	18 12.1	12 45.6	29 25.5	28 8.1	7 37.6	2 59.3	7 13.8	28 44.6	3 23.8
23	10 9 16.4	5 42.4	1 8.6	3 ♋ 33.8	14 13.1	0 ♈ 32.6	28 50.4	7 43.8	2 58.4	7 15.0	28 45.9	3 23.3
24	10 13 12.9	6 39.5	1 5.1	19 29.3	15 41.5	1 39.7	29 32.6	7 49.9	2 57.4	7 16.0	28 47.2	3 22.7
25	10 17 9.5	7 36.4	1 1.7	5 ♌ 31.3	17 10.6	2 46.7	0 ♈ 14.8	7 55.8	2 56.3	7 17.1	28 48.4	3 22.2
26	10 21 6.0	8 33.2	0 58.2	21 12.0	18 40.4	3 53.7	0 57.0	8 1.6	2 55.1	7 18.0	28 49.6	3 21.6
27	10 25 2.6	9 29.8	0 54.7	6 ♍ 12.1	20 10.8	5 .6	1 39.2	8 7.1	2 53.7	7 18.9	28 50.8	3 21.0
28	10 28 59.1	10 26.3	0 51.3	20 25.3	21 41.9	6 7.5	2 21.3	8 12.6	2 52.3	7 19.8	28 51.9	3 20.4

DECLINATION

DAY	EPHEM. SID. TIME	☉	☊	☽	☿	♀	♂	♃	♄	♅	♆	♇
1	8 42 32.2	17 S 19.2	0 N 24.5	7 N .6	20 S 16.1	11 S 53.4	8 S 7.6	20 S 34.6	10 S 35.2	21 S 35.6	22 S 12.9	4 N 44.8
4	8 54 21.8	16 27.3	0 24.5	9 S 3.9	20 34.0	10 29.5	7 12.1	20 38.8	10 35.5	21 36.5	22 12.9	4 46.4
7	9 6 11.5	15 32.9	0 24.5	20 25.5	20 43.5	9 3.1	6 16.1	20 42.7	10 35.5	21 37.5	22 12.9	4 48.1
10	9 18 1.2	14 36.1	0 24.5	23 31.1	20 43.6	7 34.6	5 19.6	20 46.4	10 35.2	21 38.3	22 12.9	4 49.9
13	9 29 50.8	13 37.1	0 24.5	17 24.7	20 33.4	6 4.3	4 22.9	20 49.8	10 34.6	21 39.1	22 12.9	4 51.8
16	9 41 40.5	12 36.0	0 24.5	4 37.2	20 12.4	4 32.6	3 25.9	20 52.9	10 33.7	21 39.8	22 12.9	4 53.8
19	9 53 30.2	11 33.2	0 24.5	10 N 23.7	19 40.2	2 59.9	2 28.8	20 55.8	10 32.4	21 40.4	22 12.8	4 55.8
22	10 5 19.8	10 28.7	0 24.5	21 49.3	18 56.7	1 26.4	1 31.6	20 58.4	10 30.9	21 41.0	22 12.8	4 57.8
25	10 17 9.5	9 22.8	0 24.5	22 4.8	18 1.7	0 N 7.5	0 34.5	21 .8	10 29.1	21 41.4	22 12.7	4 60.0
28	10 28 59.1	8 15.6	0 24.5	9 26.7	16 55.1	1 41.5	0 N 22.5	21 2.9	10 26.9	21 41.9	22 12.6	5 2.1

MARCH 1983

LONGITUDE

DAY	EPHEM. SID. TIME h m s	☉ ° ′	☊ ° ′	☽ ° ′	☿ ° ′	♀ ° ′	♂ ° ′	♃ ° ′	♄ ° ′	♅ ° ′	♆ ° ′	♇ ° ′
1	10 32 55.7	9♓50.1	0♋43.9	2♎ 6.0	20♒12.7	7♈31.4	3♈ 4.8	9♐48.6	4♏12.0	9♐ 1.7	28♐58.1	29♎18.3
2	10 36 52.2	10 50.3	0 40.7	16 19.2	21 45.0	8 45.1	3 50.9	9 53.4	4R10.2	9 2.4	28 59.1	29R17.3
3	10 40 48.8	11 50.4	0 37.5	0♏ 4.8	23 18.4	9 58.8	4 37.0	9 58.0	4 8.4	9 3.0	29 .0	29 16.3
4	10 44 45.4	12 50.6	0 34.3	13 21.8	24 52.8	11 12.4	5 23.0	10 2.4	4 6.4	9 3.6	29 1.0	29 15.3
5	10 48 41.9	13 50.7	0 31.2	26 11.8	26 28.3	12 26.0	6 9.0	10 6.7	4 4.4	9 4.2	29 1.9	29 14.3
6	10 52 38.5	14 50.8	0 28.0	8♐38.7	28 5.0	13 39.5	6 55.0	10 10.8	4 2.3	9 4.7	29 2.8	29 13.2
7	10 56 35.0	15 50.9	0 24.8	20 47.4	29 42.7	14 53.0	7 40.9	10 14.7	4 .1	9 5.1	29 3.6	29 12.2
8	11 0 31.6	16 50.9	0 21.6	2♑43.3	1♓21.5	16 6.4	8 26.8	10 18.4	3 57.8	9 5.5	29 4.4	29 11.0
9	11 4 28.1	17 50.9	0 18.5	14 31.9	3 1.4	17 19.8	9 12.7	10 22.0	3 55.4	9 5.8	29 5.2	29 9.9
10	11 8 24.7	18 50.9	0 15.3	26 18.5	4 42.4	18 33.1	9 58.5	10 25.4	3 52.9	9 6.0	29 5.9	29 8.7
11	11 12 21.2	19 50.9	0 12.1	8♒ 7.6	6 24.5	19 46.4	10 44.3	10 28.6	3 50.3	9 6.2	29 6.7	29 7.5
12	11 16 17.8	20 50.8	0 8.9	20 3.0	8 7.8	20 59.6	11 30.0	10 31.6	3 47.6	9 6.4	29 7.3	29 6.3
13	11 20 14.3	21 50.7	0 5.7	2♓ 7.5	9 52.3	22 12.8	12 15.7	10 34.5	3 44.9	9 6.5	29 8.0	29 5.1
14	11 24 10.9	22 50.6	0 2.6	14 23.1	11 37.9	23 25.9	13 1.4	10 37.2	3 42.1	9 6.6	29 8.6	29 3.8
15	11 28 7.4	23 50.4	29♊59.4	26 50.7	13 24.7	24 39.0	13 47.0	10 39.7	3 39.2	9 6.6	29 9.2	29 2.5
16	11 32 4.0	24 50.2	29 56.2	9♈30.3	15 12.7	25 52.0	14 32.6	10 42.0	3 36.2	9R 6.5	29 9.7	29 1.2
17	11 36 .5	25 50.0	29 53.0	22 21.8	17 1.9	27 4.9	15 18.1	10 44.1	3 33.1	9 6.4	29 10.2	28 59.9
18	11 39 57.1	26 49.7	29 49.9	5♉24.6	18 52.2	28 17.8	16 3.6	10 46.1	3 29.9	9 6.2	29 10.7	28 58.6
19	11 43 53.7	27 49.4	29 46.7	18 38.4	20 43.8	29 30.6	16 49.1	10 47.8	3 26.7	9 6.0	29 11.2	28 57.2
20	11 47 50.2	28 49.1	29 43.5	2♊ 3.4	22 36.6	0♉43.3	17 34.5	10 49.4	3 23.4	9 5.7	29 11.6	28 55.8
21	11 51 46.8	29 48.7	29 40.3	15 40.0	24 30.6	1 56.0	18 19.8	10 50.8	3 20.1	9 5.4	29 12.0	28 54.4
22	11 55 43.3	0♈48.3	29 37.1	29 29.1	26 25.9	3 8.7	19 5.2	10 52.1	3 16.7	9 5.1	29 12.4	28 53.0
23	11 59 39.9	1 47.9	29 34.0	13♋31.2	28 22.2	4 21.2	19 50.4	10 53.1	3 13.1	9 4.7	29 12.7	28 51.6
24	12 3 36.4	2 47.4	29 30.8	27 46.1	0♈19.7	5 33.7	20 35.6	10 53.9	3 9.6	9 4.2	29 13.0	28 50.1
25	12 7 33.0	3 46.9	29 27.6	12♌12.1	2 18.3	6 46.1	21 20.8	10 54.6	3 5.9	9 3.6	29 13.2	28 48.6
26	12 11 29.5	4 46.3	29 24.4	26 46.0	4 17.9	7 58.4	22 5.9	10 55.0	3 2.2	9 3.1	29 13.4	28 47.1
27	12 15 26.1	5 45.7	29 21.2	11♍22.2	6 18.4	9 10.6	22 51.0	10 55.3	2 58.5	9 2.4	29 13.6	28 45.6
28	12 19 22.6	6 45.0	29 18.1	25 54.1	8 19.7	10 22.8	23 36.0	10 55.4	2 54.6	9 1.8	29 13.8	28 44.1
29	12 23 19.2	7 44.4	29 14.9	10♎14.4	10 21.8	11 34.9	24 21.0	10R55.3	2 50.8	9 1.0	29 13.9	28 42.5
30	12 27 15.7	8 43.7	29 11.7	24 16.8	12 24.4	12 46.9	25 5.9	10 55.0	2 46.8	9 .2	29 13.9	28 41.0
31	12 31 12.3	9 42.9	29 8.5	7♏56.9	14 27.4	13 58.8	25 50.8	10 54.5	2 42.8	8 59.4	29 14.0	28 39.4

LATITUDE

DAY	SID. TIME	☉	☊	☽	☿	♀	♂	♃	♄	♅	♆	♇
1	10 32 55.7	0 .0	0 .0	5N 2.7	1S51.1	0S50.4	0S34.9	0N52.4	2N38.2	0N 6.4	1N13.6	17N21.9
4	10 44 45.4	0 .0	0 .0	3 45.4	2 1.6	0 43.2	0 32.9	0 52.7	2 38.9	0 6.4	1 13.7	17 23.2
7	10 56 35.0	0 .0	0 .0	0 54.9	2 8.6	0 35.5	0 30.9	0 52.9	2 39.6	0 6.4	1 13.8	17 24.4
10	11 8 24.7	0 .0	0 .0	2S 9.2	2 11.8	0 27.3	0 28.9	0 53.1	2 40.2	0 6.4	1 13.9	17 25.6
13	11 20 14.3	0 .0	0 .0	4 24.1	2 11.2	0 18.9	0 26.8	0 53.4	2 40.8	0 6.4	1 14.0	17 26.7
16	11 32 4.0	0 .0	0 .0	4 55.9	2 6.5	0 10.0	0 24.8	0 53.6	2 41.4	0 6.4	1 14.1	17 27.8
19	11 43 53.7	0 .0	0 .0	3 17.6	1 57.3	0 .9	0 22.8	0 53.8	2 41.9	0 6.4	1 14.2	17 28.7
22	11 55 43.3	0 .0	0 .0	0N .3	1 43.6	0N 8.4	0 20.7	0 54.1	2 42.4	0 6.4	1 14.3	17 29.6
25	12 7 33.0	0 .0	0 .0	3 25.4	1 25.0	0 17.9	0 18.7	0 54.3	2 42.8	0 6.3	1 14.4	17 30.4
28	12 19 22.6	0 .0	0 .0	5 .1	1 1.8	0 27.6	0 16.6	0 54.5	2 43.2	0 6.3	1 14.5	17 31.1
31	12 31 12.3	0 .0	0 .0	3 52.5	0 34.2	0 37.3	0 14.6	0 54.7	2 43.6	0 6.3	1 14.6	17 31.7

RIGHT ASCENSION

DAY	SID. TIME	☉	☊	☽	☿	♀	♂	♃	♄	♅	♆	♇
1	10 32 55.7	11♓22.8	0♋47.8	3♎56.1	23♒13.7	7♈14.4	3♈ 3.4	8♐17.8	2♏50.9	7♐20.6	28♐53.1	3♏19.7
2	10 36 52.2	12 19.0	0 44.4	16 54.6	24 45.9	8 21.3	3 45.5	8 22.9	2R49.3	7 21.4	28 54.2	3R19.0
3	10 40 48.8	13 15.1	0 40.9	29 33.3	26 18.8	9 28.2	4 27.5	8 27.8	2 47.6	7 22.0	28 55.2	3 18.3
4	10 44 45.4	14 11.1	0 37.4	12♏ 3.8	27 52.1	10 35.1	5 9.5	8 32.5	2 45.8	7 22.7	28 56.3	3 17.6
5	10 48 41.9	15 7.0	0 34.0	24 35.5	29 26.0	11 42.0	5 51.5	8 37.0	2 44.0	7 23.2	28 57.2	3 16.8
6	10 52 38.5	16 2.8	0 30.5	7♐14.5	1♓ .3	12 49.0	6 33.5	8 41.4	2 42.0	7 23.8	28 58.2	3 16.0
7	10 56 35.0	16 58.5	0 27.0	20 2.8	2 35.2	13 56.0	7 15.5	8 45.5	2 40.0	7 24.2	28 59.1	3 15.1
8	11 0 31.6	17 54.0	0 23.6	2♑58.1	4 10.5	15 3.0	7 57.5	8 49.5	2 37.8	7 24.6	28 60.0	3 14.3
9	11 4 28.1	18 49.5	0 20.1	15 54.9	5 46.4	16 10.1	8 39.4	8 53.3	2 35.6	7 24.9	29 .8	3 13.4
10	11 8 24.7	19 44.9	0 16.6	28 45.6	7 22.8	17 17.3	9 21.3	8 56.9	2 33.3	7 25.2	29 1.6	3 12.5
11	11 12 21.2	20 40.2	0 13.2	11♒23.3	8 59.7	18 24.6	10 3.3	9 .4	2 30.9	7 25.5	29 2.4	3 11.6
12	11 16 17.8	21 35.5	0 9.7	23 43.3	10 37.1	19 32.0	10 45.2	9 3.6	2 28.4	7 25.6	29 3.1	3 10.6
13	11 20 14.3	22 30.6	0 6.3	5♓44.6	12 15.1	20 39.4	11 27.1	9 6.7	2 25.9	7 25.7	29 3.8	3 9.6
14	11 24 10.9	23 25.7	0 2.8	17 30.1	13 53.6	21 47.0	12 9.1	9 9.5	2 23.2	7 25.8	29 4.5	3 8.6
15	11 28 7.4	24 20.7	29♊59.3	29 5.7	15 32.7	22 54.7	12 51.0	9 12.2	2 20.5	7 25.8	29 5.1	3 7.6
16	11 32 4.0	25 15.7	29 55.9	10♈40.3	17 12.4	24 2.5	13 32.9	9 14.6	2 17.7	7R25.7	29 5.7	3 6.5
17	11 36 .5	26 10.6	29 52.4	22 24.3	18 52.7	25 10.5	14 14.8	9 16.9	2 14.9	7 25.6	29 6.3	3 5.4
18	11 39 57.1	27 5.4	29 48.9	4♉29.3	20 33.7	26 18.6	14 56.8	9 19.0	2 11.9	7 25.4	29 6.8	3 4.3
19	11 43 53.7	28 .2	29 45.5	17 7.0	22 15.4	27 26.9	15 38.7	9 20.9	2 8.9	7 25.2	29 7.3	3 3.2
20	11 47 50.2	28 54.9	29 42.0	0♊27.1	23 57.8	28 35.3	16 20.7	9 22.6	2 5.8	7 24.9	29 7.7	3 2.1
21	11 51 46.8	29 49.6	29 38.5	14 34.5	25 40.8	29 43.8	17 2.6	9 24.1	2 2.6	7 24.6	29 8.1	3 .9
22	11 55 43.3	0♈44.4	29 35.1	29 26.3	27 24.7	0♉52.6	17 44.6	9 25.4	1 59.4	7 24.2	29 8.6	2 59.8
23	11 59 39.9	1 39.0	29 31.6	14♋49.3	29 9.3	2 1.5	18 26.6	9 26.5	1 56.1	7 23.7	29 8.9	2 58.6
24	12 3 36.4	2 33.6	29 28.2	0♌21.9	0♈54.6	3 10.6	19 8.6	9 27.4	1 52.8	7 23.2	29 9.2	2 57.4
25	12 7 33.0	3 28.2	29 24.7	15 41.2	2 40.7	4 19.9	19 50.6	9 28.1	1 49.4	7 22.7	29 9.5	2 56.1
26	12 11 29.5	4 22.8	29 21.2	0♍29.6	4 27.5	5 29.4	20 32.6	9 28.6	1 45.9	7 22.1	29 9.7	2 54.9
27	12 15 26.1	5 17.3	29 17.8	14 39.9	6 15.1	6 39.0	21 14.7	9 28.9	1 42.3	7 21.4	29 9.9	2 53.6
28	12 19 22.6	6 11.9	29 14.3	28 14.0	8 3.4	7 48.9	21 56.8	9 29.0	1 38.7	7 20.7	29 10.1	2 52.3
29	12 23 19.2	7 6.4	29 10.8	11♎20.1	9 52.3	8 58.9	22 38.8	9R28.9	1 35.1	7 19.9	29 10.2	2 51.0
30	12 27 15.7	8 1.0	29 7.4	24 9.0	11 41.8	10 9.2	23 21.0	9 28.6	1 31.4	7 19.1	29 10.3	2 49.7
31	12 31 12.3	8 55.6	29 3.9	6♏51.4	13 31.8	11 19.7	24 3.1	9 28.1	1 27.6	7 18.2	29 10.3	2 48.3

DECLINATION

DAY	SID. TIME	☉	☊	☽	☿	♀	♂	♃	♄	♅	♆	♇
1	10 32 55.7	7S52.9	0N24.5	3N47.6	16S30.3	2N12.8	0N41.5	21S 3.6	10S26.2	21S42.0	22S12.6	5N 2.8
4	10 44 45.4	6 44.3	0 24.5	12S15.9	15 8.3	3 46.3	1 38.1	21 5.3	10 23.7	21 42.3	22 12.6	5 5.0
7	10 56 35.0	5 34.9	0 24.5	22 12.6	13 34.8	5 19.2	2 34.5	21 6.9	10 21.0	21 42.5	22 12.5	5 7.3
10	11 8 24.7	4 24.8	0 24.5	23 .4	11 49.8	6 51.0	3 30.5	21 8.2	10 18.0	21 42.7	22 12.4	5 9.5
13	11 20 14.3	3 14.1	0 24.5	14 49.5	9 53.6	8 21.5	4 26.1	21 9.3	10 14.7	21 42.8	22 12.3	5 11.8
16	11 32 4.0	2 3.1	0 24.5	0 46.1	7 46.3	9 50.3	5 21.1	21 10.1	10 11.3	21 42.8	22 12.2	5 14.0
19	11 43 53.7	0 51.9	0 24.5	14N12.3	5 28.3	11 17.1	6 15.5	21 10.7	10 7.6	21 42.7	22 12.1	5 16.3
22	11 55 43.3	0N19.2	0 24.5	23 26.7	3 .2	12 41.7	7 9.3	21 11.0	10 3.7	21 42.6	22 12.0	5 18.5
25	12 7 33.0	1 30.2	0 24.5	20 25.3	0 23.0	14 3.5	8 2.2	21 11.2	9 59.7	21 42.4	22 11.9	5 20.7
28	12 19 22.6	2 40.8	0 24.5	6 13.1	2N21.4	15 22.3	8 54.4	21 11.1	9 55.5	21 42.1	22 11.8	5 22.9
31	12 31 12.3	3 51.0	0 24.5	10S29.4	5 10.5	16 37.8	9 45.6	21 10.7	9 51.1	21 41.8	22 11.7	5 25.0

APRIL 1983

LONGITUDE

DAY	EPHEM. SID. TIME h m s	☉ ° ′	☊ ° ′	☽ ° ′	☿ ° ′	♀ ° ′	♂ ° ′	♃ ° ′	♄ ° ′	♅ ° ′	♆ ° ′	♇ ° ′
1	12 35 8.8	10♈42.1	29♊ 5.4	21♏12.3	16♈30.6	15♉10.7	26♈35.6	10♐53.9	2♏38.8	8♐58.5	29♐14.0	28♎37.8
2	12 39 5.4	11 41.3	29 2.2	4♐ 3.6	18 33.7	16 22.5	27 20.4	10 R 53.0	2 R 34.7	8 R 57.6	29 14.0	28 R 36.2
3	12 43 1.9	12 40.5	28 59.0	16 32.9	20 36.5	17 34.2	28 5.1	10 52.0	2 30.6	8 56.6	29 R 13.9	28 34.6
4	12 46 58.5	13 39.6	28 55.8	28 44.4	22 38.6	18 45.8	28 49.8	10 50.8	2 26.4	8 55.6	29 13.9	28 33.0
5	12 50 55.0	14 38.7	28 52.6	10♑42.8	24 39.8	19 57.3	29 34.4	10 49.4	2 22.2	8 54.5	29 13.7	28 31.4
6	12 54 51.6	15 37.8	28 49.5	22 33.7	26 39.7	21 8.8	0♉19.0	10 47.8	2 17.9	8 53.4	29 13.6	28 29.7
7	12 58 48.2	16 36.9	28 46.3	4♒22.3	28 37.9	22 20.2	1 3.6	10 46.0	2 13.6	8 52.3	29 13.4	28 28.1
8	13 2 44.7	17 35.9	28 43.1	16 14.1	0♉34.0	23 31.5	1 48.1	10 44.0	2 9.3	8 51.1	29 13.2	28 26.4
9	13 6 41.3	18 34.9	28 39.9	28 13.5	2 27.8	24 42.7	2 32.5	10 41.9	2 4.9	8 49.8	29 12.9	28 24.8
10	13 10 37.8	19 33.8	28 36.8	10♓24.5	4 18.8	25 53.8	3 16.9	10 39.5	2 .5	8 48.5	29 12.7	28 23.1
11	13 14 34.4	20 32.7	28 33.6	22 49.7	6 6.6	27 4.9	4 1.3	10 37.0	1 56.1	8 47.2	29 12.3	28 21.4
12	13 18 30.9	21 31.7	28 30.4	5♈30.7	7 51.1	28 15.8	4 45.6	10 34.4	1 51.7	8 45.8	29 12.0	28 19.8
13	13 22 27.5	22 30.5	28 27.2	18 27.8	9 31.7	29 26.7	5 29.9	10 31.5	1 47.2	8 44.4	29 11.7	28 18.1
14	13 26 24.0	23 29.4	28 24.0	1♉40.0	11 8.3	0♊37.5	6 14.1	10 28.5	1 42.7	8 42.9	29 11.3	28 16.4
15	13 30 20.6	24 28.2	28 20.9	15 5.7	12 40.6	1 48.1	6 58.3	10 25.2	1 38.2	8 41.4	29 10.8	28 14.7
16	13 34 17.1	25 26.9	28 17.7	28 42.6	14 8.4	2 58.7	7 42.4	10 21.8	1 33.6	8 39.9	29 10.3	28 13.0
17	13 38 13.7	26 25.7	28 14.5	12♊28.7	15 31.4	4 9.2	8 26.4	10 18.3	1 29.1	8 38.3	29 9.8	28 11.3
18	13 42 10.2	27 24.3	28 11.3	26 22.1	16 49.6	5 19.6	9 10.4	10 14.5	1 24.5	8 36.6	29 9.3	28 9.6
19	13 46 6.8	28 23.0	28 8.2	10♋21.6	18 2.7	6 29.8	9 54.4	10 10.6	1 20.0	8 35.0	29 8.7	28 7.9
20	13 50 3.3	29 21.6	28 5.0	24 26.2	19 10.6	7 40.0	10 38.3	10 6.6	1 15.4	8 33.2	29 8.2	28 6.3
21	13 53 59.9	0♉20.2	28 1.8	8♌34.9	20 13.1	8 50.0	11 22.1	10 2.3	1 10.8	8 31.5	29 7.5	28 4.6
22	13 57 56.5	1 18.7	27 58.6	22 46.4	21 10.3	9 60.0	12 5.9	9 57.9	1 6.2	8 29.7	29 6.9	28 2.9
23	14 1 53.0	2 17.2	27 55.4	6♍58.7	22 1.9	11 9.8	12 49.7	9 53.4	1 1.6	8 27.9	29 6.2	28 1.2
24	14 5 49.6	3 15.7	27 52.3	21 8.8	22 48.0	12 19.5	13 33.4	9 48.7	0 57.1	8 26.0	29 5.5	27 59.5
25	14 9 46.1	4 14.1	27 49.1	5♎12.9	23 28.5	13 29.1	14 17.0	9 43.8	0 52.5	8 24.2	29 4.7	27 57.8
26	14 13 42.7	5 12.5	27 45.9	19 6.7	24 3.2	14 38.5	15 .6	9 38.8	0 47.9	8 22.2	29 4.0	27 56.1
27	14 17 39.2	6 10.9	27 42.7	2♏46.4	24 32.3	15 47.8	15 44.2	9 33.7	0 43.4	8 20.3	29 3.2	27 54.4
28	14 21 35.8	7 9.2	27 39.6	16 8.9	24 55.6	16 57.0	16 27.6	9 28.4	0 38.8	8 18.3	29 2.4	27 52.8
29	14 25 32.3	8 7.5	27 36.4	29 12.2	25 13.2	18 6.1	17 11.1	9 23.0	0 34.3	8 16.3	29 1.5	27 51.1
30	14 29 28.9	9 5.8	27 33.2	11♐56.2	25 25.2	19 15.1	17 54.5	9 17.4	0 29.8	8 14.2	29 .6	27 49.4

LATITUDE

DAY	EPHEM. SID. TIME	☉	☊	☽	☿	♀	♂	♃	♄	♅	♆	♇
1	12 35 8.8	0 .0	0 .0	3N 2.2	0S 24.1	0N 40.5	0S 13.9	0N 54.8	2N 43.7	0N 6.3	1N 14.7	17N 31.9
4	12 46 58.5	0 .0	0 .0	0S 3.4	0N 8.3	0 50.3	0 11.9	0 55.0	2 44.0	0 6.3	1 14.8	17 32.4
7	12 58 48.2	0 .0	0 .0	3 .1	0 42.4	0 59.9	0 9.9	0 55.2	2 44.3	0 6.3	1 14.9	17 32.8
10	13 10 37.8	0 .0	0 .0	4 49.0	1 16.4	1 9.5	0 7.9	0 55.3	2 44.5	0 6.3	1 15.0	17 33.1
13	13 22 27.5	0 .0	0 .0	4 42.3	1 48.0	1 18.9	0 5.9	0 55.5	2 44.6	0 6.2	1 15.1	17 33.3
16	13 34 17.1	0 .0	0 .0	2 23.7	2 14.9	1 28.0	0 3.9	0 55.6	2 44.7	0 6.2	1 15.2	17 33.5
19	13 46 6.8	0 .0	0 .0	1N 12.3	2 35.3	1 36.9	0 1.9	0 55.7	2 44.8	0 6.2	1 15.2	17 33.5
22	13 57 56.5	0 .0	0 .0	4 14.3	2 47.6	1 45.4	0 .0	0 55.8	2 44.8	0 6.2	1 15.3	17 33.4
25	14 9 46.1	0 .0	0 .0	5 2.4	2 50.4	1 53.4	0N 2.0	0 55.8	2 44.7	0 6.2	1 15.4	17 33.2
28	14 21 35.8	0 .0	0 .0	3 17.2	2 42.8	2 1.0	0 3.9	0 55.9	2 44.6	0 6.1	1 15.5	17 33.0

RIGHT ASCENSION

DAY	EPHEM. SID. TIME	☉	☊	☽	☿	♀	♂	♃	♄	♅	♆	♇
1	12 35 8.8	9♈50.2	29♊ .4	19♏36.0	15♈22.1	12♉30.4	24♈45.3	9♐27.4	1♏23.8	7♐17.2	29♐10.3	2♏47.0
2	12 39 5.4	10 44.9	28 57.0	2♐28.4	17 12.6	13 41.3	25 27.4	9 R 26.5	1 R 19.9	7 R 16.2	29 10.3	2 R 45.6
3	12 43 1.9	11 39.5	28 53.5	15 29.9	19 3.1	14 52.5	26 9.7	9 25.4	1 16.0	7 15.2	29 R 10.2	2 44.2
4	12 46 58.5	12 34.2	28 50.1	28 37.6	20 53.5	16 3.8	26 51.9	9 24.2	1 12.1	7 14.1	29 10.0	2 42.8
5	12 50 55.0	13 29.0	28 46.6	11♑45.0	22 43.4	17 15.4	27 34.2	9 22.7	1 8.1	7 13.0	29 10.0	2 41.4
6	12 54 51.6	14 23.8	28 43.1	24 44.4	24 32.6	18 27.2	28 16.6	9 21.0	1 4.1	7 11.8	29 9.9	2 40.0
7	12 58 48.2	15 18.6	28 39.7	7♒28.6	26 20.9	19 39.3	28 58.9	9 19.1	0 60.0	7 10.6	29 9.7	2 38.6
8	13 2 44.7	16 13.5	28 36.2	19 53.3	28 7.8	20 51.6	29 41.3	9 17.0	0 55.9	7 9.3	29 9.5	2 37.1
9	13 6 41.3	17 8.5	28 32.7	1♓58.2	29 53.2	22 4.0	0♉23.8	9 14.8	0 51.7	7 7.9	29 9.2	2 35.7
10	13 10 37.8	18 3.5	28 29.3	13 46.6	1♉36.6	23 16.8	1 6.3	9 12.3	0 47.6	7 6.6	29 8.9	2 34.2
11	13 14 34.4	18 58.6	28 25.8	25 24.9	3 17.7	24 29.7	1 48.8	9 9.6	0 43.4	7 5.1	29 8.5	2 32.7
12	13 18 30.9	19 53.8	28 22.3	7♈ 2.2	4 56.4	25 42.9	2 31.4	9 6.8	0 39.2	7 3.7	29 8.2	2 31.3
13	13 22 27.5	20 49.0	28 18.9	18 49.3	6 32.0	26 56.2	3 14.0	9 3.8	0 35.0	7 2.2	29 7.8	2 29.8
14	13 26 24.0	21 44.3	28 15.4	0♉57.6	8 4.5	28 9.8	3 56.7	9 .6	0 30.7	7 .6	29 7.4	2 28.3
15	13 30 20.6	22 39.7	28 12.0	13 38.7	9 33.4	29 23.6	4 39.4	8 57.2	0 26.4	6 59.0	29 6.9	2 26.8
16	13 34 17.1	23 35.2	28 8.5	27 1.8	10 58.6	0♊37.5	5 22.1	8 53.6	0 22.1	6 57.4	29 6.4	2 25.3
17	13 38 13.7	24 30.7	28 5.0	11♊11.1	12 19.7	1 51.6	6 4.9	8 49.8	0 17.8	6 55.7	29 5.8	2 23.8
18	13 42 10.2	25 26.4	28 1.6	26 2.7	13 36.6	3 6.0	6 47.7	8 45.8	0 13.4	6 53.9	29 5.3	2 22.3
19	13 46 6.8	26 22.1	27 58.1	11♋22.3	14 49.0	4 20.4	7 30.6	8 41.7	0 9.1	6 52.1	29 4.7	2 20.7
20	13 50 3.3	27 18.0	27 54.6	26 48.3	15 56.8	5 35.1	8 13.5	8 37.4	0 4.8	6 50.3	29 4.0	2 19.2
21	13 53 59.9	28 13.9	27 51.2	11♌57.8	16 59.6	6 49.8	8 56.4	8 32.9	0 .4	6 48.5	29 3.4	2 17.7
22	13 57 56.5	29 9.9	27 47.7	26 34.4	17 57.5	8 4.7	9 39.5	8 28.2	29♎56.0	6 46.6	29 2.6	2 16.1
23	14 1 53.0	0♉ 6.1	27 44.3	10♍31.9	18 50.2	9 19.8	10 22.5	8 23.4	29 51.7	6 44.6	29 1.9	2 14.6
24	14 5 49.6	1 2.3	27 40.8	23 53.1	19 37.5	10 34.9	11 5.6	8 18.4	29 47.3	6 42.7	29 1.1	2 13.1
25	14 9 46.1	1 58.7	27 37.3	6♎47.1	20 19.5	11 50.2	11 48.7	8 13.3	29 43.0	6 40.7	29 .3	2 11.5
26	14 13 42.7	2 55.2	27 33.9	19 25.3	20 55.9	13 5.5	12 31.9	8 8.0	29 38.6	6 38.6	28 59.5	2 10.0
27	14 17 39.2	3 51.8	27 30.4	1♏59.4	21 26.8	14 20.9	13 15.2	8 2.6	29 34.3	6 36.6	28 58.7	2 8.5
28	14 21 35.8	4 48.5	27 26.9	14 39.2	21 52.1	15 36.4	13 58.5	7 57.0	29 30.0	6 34.5	28 57.8	2 6.9
29	14 25 32.3	5 45.3	27 23.5	27 30.9	22 11.8	16 51.9	14 41.8	7 51.2	29 25.7	6 32.3	28 56.9	2 5.4
30	14 29 28.9	6 42.3	27 20.0	10♐36.5	22 25.9	18 7.4	15 25.2	7 45.3	29 21.4	6 30.1	28 55.9	2 3.9

DECLINATION

DAY	EPHEM. SID. TIME	☉	☊	☽	☿	♀	♂	♃	♄	♅	♆	♇
1	12 35 8.8	4N 14.2	0N 24.5	15S 7.9	6N 7.3	17N 2.1	10N 2.5	21S 10.6	9S 49.7	21S 41.6	22S 11.7	5N 25.7
4	12 46 58.5	5 23.5	0 24.5	23 29.5	8 56.3	18 12.7	10 52.4	21 10.0	9 45.2	21 41.2	22 11.6	5 27.8
7	12 58 48.2	6 31.9	0 24.5	22 5.0	11 39.0	19 19.3	11 41.3	21 9.1	9 40.6	21 40.7	22 11.5	5 29.8
10	13 10 37.8	7 39.3	0 24.5	12 7.2	14 9.4	20 21.4	12 29.1	21 8.0	9 35.9	21 40.1	22 11.4	5 31.8
13	13 22 27.5	8 45.6	0 24.5	2N 53.0	16 22.3	21 19.0	13 15.8	21 6.8	9 31.2	21 39.5	22 11.3	5 33.7
16	13 34 17.1	9 50.6	0 24.5	17 32.2	18 13.8	22 11.7	14 1.2	21 5.3	9 26.5	21 38.8	22 11.2	5 35.5
19	13 46 6.8	10 54.0	0 24.5	24 14.4	19 41.5	22 59.2	14 45.3	21 3.5	9 21.7	21 38.1	22 11.1	5 37.2
22	13 57 56.5	11 55.9	0 24.5	17 55.7	20 44.8	23 41.3	15 28.1	21 1.6	9 17.0	21 37.3	22 11.0	5 38.9
25	14 9 46.1	12 56.0	0 24.5	2 33.4	21 23.5	24 17.8	16 9.5	20 59.5	9 12.3	21 36.4	22 10.9	5 40.4
28	14 21 35.8	13 54.1	0 24.5	13S 31.2	21 38.0	24 48.5	16 49.4	20 57.2	9 7.7	21 35.5	22 10.8	5 41.8

MAY 1983

DAY	EPHEM. SID. TIME	☉	☊	☾	☿	♀	♂	♃	♄	♅	♆	♇
	LONGITUDE											
	h m s	° ′	° ′	° ′	° ′	° ′	° ′	° ′	° ′	° ′	° ′	° ′
1	14 33 25.4	10♉ 4.1	27♊30.0	24♐22.3	25♉31.7	20♊23.9	18♉37.8	9♐11.7	0♏25.3	8♐12.2	28♐59.7	27♎47.8
2	14 37 22.0	11 2.3	27 26.9	6♑33.1	25 32.7	21 32.6	19 21.1	9R 5.9	0R20.8	8R10.1	28R58.8	27R46.2
3	14 41 18.6	12 .5	27 23.7	18 32.4	25R28.5	22 41.2	20 4.4	8 60.0	0 16.4	8 8.0	28 57.9	27 44.6
4	14 45 15.1	12 58.7	27 20.5	0♒24.7	25 19.2	23 49.6	20 47.6	8 53.9	0 12.0	8 5.8	28 56.9	27 42.9
5	14 49 11.7	13 56.9	27 17.3	12 15.0	25 5.1	24 57.9	21 30.7	8 47.7	0 7.6	8 3.7	28 55.9	27 41.3
6	14 53 8.2	14 55.0	27 14.1	24 8.4	24 46.6	26 6.0	22 13.8	8 41.4	0 3.3	8 1.5	28 54.9	27 39.7
7	14 57 4.8	15 53.1	27 11.0	6♓ 9.8	24 24.1	27 14.0	22 56.8	8 34.9	29♎58.9	7 59.2	28 53.8	27 38.1
8	15 1 1.3	16 51.2	27 7.8	18 23.8	23 57.9	28 21.8	23 39.8	8 28.4	29 54.7	7 57.0	28 52.7	27 36.5
9	15 4 57.9	17 49.2	27 4.6	0♈54.1	23 28.6	29 29.5	24 22.8	8 21.8	29 50.4	7 54.7	28 51.6	27 35.0
10	15 8 54.4	18 47.3	27 1.4	13 43.2	22 56.8	0♋37.1	25 5.7	8 15.1	29 46.2	7 52.4	28 50.5	27 33.4
11	15 12 51.0	19 45.3	26 58.3	26 52.5	22 23.0	1 44.4	25 48.5	8 8.2	29 42.0	7 50.1	28 49.4	27 31.9
12	15 16 47.6	20 43.3	26 55.1	10♉21.6	21 47.8	2 51.7	26 31.3	8 1.3	29 37.9	7 47.8	28 48.2	27 30.3
13	15 20 44.1	21 41.2	26 51.9	24 8.5	21 11.9	3 58.7	27 14.1	7 54.3	29 33.8	7 45.4	28 47.0	27 28.8
14	15 24 40.7	22 39.1	26 48.7	8♊10.1	20 35.9	5 5.6	27 56.8	7 47.2	29 29.8	7 43.1	28 45.8	27 27.3
15	15 28 37.2	23 37.1	26 45.5	22 22.3	20 .4	6 12.3	28 39.4	7 40.1	29 25.8	7 40.7	28 44.5	27 25.9
16	15 32 33.8	24 34.9	26 42.4	6♋40.8	19 26.0	7 18.9	29 22.0	7 32.9	29 21.9	7 38.3	28 43.3	27 24.4
17	15 36 30.3	25 32.8	26 39.2	21 1.5	18 53.4	8 25.2	0♊ 4.6	7 25.6	29 18.0	7 35.9	28 42.0	27 22.9
18	15 40 26.9	26 30.6	26 36.0	5♌20.8	18 23.0	9 31.4	0 47.1	7 18.2	29 14.2	7 33.5	28 40.7	27 21.5
19	15 44 23.4	27 28.4	26 32.8	19 36.0	17 55.3	10 37.4	1 29.5	7 10.8	29 10.4	7 31.0	28 39.4	27 20.1
20	15 48 20.0	28 26.2	26 29.7	3♍44.7	17 30.7	11 43.1	2 11.9	7 3.4	29 6.7	7 28.6	28 38.1	27 18.7
21	15 52 16.6	29 23.9	26 26.5	17 45.3	17 9.7	12 48.7	2 54.2	6 55.9	29 3.1	7 26.1	28 36.7	27 17.3
22	15 56 13.1	0♊21.6	26 23.3	1♎36.2	16 52.5	13 54.0	3 36.5	6 48.4	28 59.5	7 23.7	28 35.3	27 16.0
23	16 0 9.7	1 19.3	26 20.1	15 16.0	16 39.3	14 59.2	4 18.8	6 40.8	28 56.0	7 21.2	28 34.0	27 14.7
24	16 4 6.2	2 17.0	26 17.0	28 43.4	16 30.3	16 4.1	5 1.0	6 33.3	28 52.6	7 18.8	28 32.6	27 13.4
25	16 8 2.8	3 14.6	26 13.8	11♏57.1	16 25.7	17 8.8	5 43.2	6 25.7	28 49.2	7 16.3	28 31.2	27 12.1
26	16 11 59.3	4 12.3	26 10.6	24 56.5	16 25.6	18 13.2	6 25.2	6 18.1	28 45.9	7 13.8	28 29.8	27 10.8
27	16 15 55.9	5 9.8	26 7.4	7♐41.2	16D30.0	19 17.4	7 7.3	6 10.4	28 42.7	7 11.3	28 28.3	27 9.6
28	16 19 52.5	6 7.4	26 4.2	20 11.6	16 38.8	20 21.4	7 49.3	6 2.8	28 39.5	7 8.9	28 26.9	27 8.4
29	16 23 49.0	7 5.0	26 1.1	2♑28.7	16 52.2	21 25.0	8 31.2	5 55.2	28 36.4	7 6.4	28 25.4	27 7.2
30	16 27 45.6	8 2.5	25 57.9	14 34.5	17 10.0	22 28.5	9 13.1	5 47.5	28 33.4	7 3.9	28 23.9	27 6.0
31	16 31 42.1	9 .0	25 54.7	26 31.7	17 32.3	23 31.7	9 55.0	5 39.9	28 30.5	7 1.4	28 22.4	27 4.8
	LATITUDE											
1	14 33 25.4	0 .0	0 .0	0N 8.0	2N24.2	2N 8.1	0N 5.8	0N55.9	2N44.5	0N 6.1	1N15.6	17N32.6
4	14 45 15.1	0 .0	0 .0	2S56.3	1 54.4	2 14.5	0 7.7	0 55.8	2 44.3	0 6.1	1 15.6	17 32.1
7	14 57 4.8	0 .0	0 .0	4 52.4	1 14.5	2 20.2	0 9.6	0 55.8	2 44.0	0 6.1	1 15.7	17 31.6
10	15 8 54.4	0 .0	0 .0	4 55.3	0 26.8	2 25.3	0 11.5	0 55.7	2 43.7	0 6.1	1 15.8	17 30.9
13	15 20 44.1	0 .0	0 .0	2 41.9	0S25.2	2 29.5	0 13.3	0 55.6	2 43.4	0 6.0	1 15.8	17 30.2
16	15 32 33.8	0 .0	0 .0	1N 1.9	1 17.0	2 32.9	0 15.1	0 55.4	2 43.0	0 6.0	1 15.9	17 29.4
19	15 44 23.4	0 .0	0 .0	4 14.9	2 4.5	2 35.4	0 16.9	0 55.2	2 42.5	0 6.0	1 15.9	17 28.5
22	15 56 13.1	0 .0	0 .0	5 12.0	2 44.6	2 36.9	0 18.7	0 55.0	2 42.0	0 6.0	1 16.0	17 27.5
25	16 8 2.8	0 .0	0 .0	3 35.5	3 15.3	2 37.4	0 20.5	0 54.7	2 41.5	0 5.9	1 16.0	17 26.5
28	16 19 52.5	0 .0	0 .0	0 26.9	3 36.1	2 36.7	0 22.2	0 54.4	2 41.0	0 5.9	1 16.0	17 25.4
31	16 31 42.1	0 .0	0 .0	2S45.3	3 47.2	2 34.9	0 24.0	0 54.1	2 40.4	0 5.9	1 16.1	17 24.2
	RIGHT ASCENSION											
1	14 33 25.4	7♉39.4	27♊16.6	23♐52.5	22♉34.6	19♊22.9	16♉ 8.6	7♐39.3	29♎17.1	6♐27.9	28♐54.9	2♏ 2.3
2	14 37 22.0	8 36.7	27 13.1	7♑11.2	22 37.9	20 38.5	16 52.1	7R33.1	29R12.8	6R25.7	28R53.9	2R .8
3	14 41 18.6	9 34.1	27 9.6	20 22.7	22R36.1	21 54.1	17 35.7	7 26.9	29 8.6	6 23.5	28 52.9	1 59.3
4	14 45 15.1	10 31.7	27 6.2	3♒17.7	22 29.3	23 9.6	18 19.3	7 20.5	29 4.4	6 21.2	28 51.9	1 57.8
5	14 49 11.7	11 29.3	27 2.7	15 50.1	22 17.9	24 25.1	19 2.9	7 13.9	29 .2	6 18.9	28 50.8	1 56.3
6	14 53 8.2	12 27.1	26 59.2	27 58.8	22 2.3	25 40.5	19 46.6	7 7.2	28 56.1	6 16.6	28 49.7	1 54.8
7	14 57 4.8	13 25.1	26 55.8	9♓47.0	21 42.7	26 55.8	20 30.4	7 .4	28 52.0	6 14.2	28 48.5	1 53.3
8	15 1 1.3	14 23.2	26 52.3	21 21.7	21 19.8	28 11.0	21 14.1	6 53.5	28 47.8	6 11.8	28 47.4	1 51.8
9	15 4 57.9	15 21.4	26 48.9	2♈52.8	20 53.9	29 26.2	21 58.0	6 46.5	28 43.8	6 9.4	28 46.2	1 50.4
10	15 8 54.4	16 19.8	26 45.4	14 32.1	20 25.7	0♋41.1	22 41.9	6 39.4	28 39.8	6 7.0	28 45.0	1 48.9
11	15 12 51.0	17 18.4	26 41.9	26 32.5	19 55.8	1 56.0	23 25.8	6 32.2	28 35.8	6 4.5	28 43.7	1 47.4
12	15 16 47.6	18 17.1	26 38.5	9♉ 7.2	19 24.7	3 10.6	24 9.8	6 24.9	28 31.8	6 2.0	28 42.5	1 46.0
13	15 20 44.1	19 15.9	26 35.0	22 27.6	18 53.0	4 25.1	24 53.8	6 17.5	28 27.9	5 59.5	28 41.2	1 44.5
14	15 24 40.7	20 14.9	26 31.6	6♊40.3	18 21.4	5 39.4	25 37.9	6 10.0	28 24.0	5 57.0	28 39.9	1 43.1
15	15 28 37.2	21 14.0	26 28.1	21 42.7	17 50.5	6 53.4	26 22.0	6 2.4	28 20.2	5 54.5	28 38.5	1 41.6
16	15 32 33.8	22 13.2	26 24.6	7♋19.9	17 20.7	8 7.2	27 6.1	5 54.8	28 16.5	5 52.0	28 37.2	1 40.2
17	15 36 30.3	23 12.6	26 21.2	23 6.7	16 52.7	9 20.7	27 50.3	5 47.1	28 12.7	5 49.4	28 35.8	1 38.8
18	15 40 26.9	24 12.2	26 17.7	8♌35.4	16 26.8	10 34.0	28 34.5	5 39.4	28 9.1	5 46.8	28 34.4	1 37.4
19	15 44 23.4	25 11.8	26 14.3	23 25.4	16 3.5	11 46.9	29 18.8	5 31.6	28 5.5	5 44.3	28 33.0	1 36.1
20	15 48 20.0	26 11.6	26 10.8	7♍28.3	15 43.2	12 59.5	0♊ 3.1	5 23.7	28 1.9	5 41.7	28 31.5	1 34.7
21	15 52 16.6	27 11.6	26 7.3	20 47.3	15 26.2	14 11.8	0 47.4	5 15.8	27 58.4	5 39.1	28 30.1	1 33.4
22	15 56 13.1	28 11.6	26 3.9	3♎32.5	15 12.7	15 23.7	1 31.8	5 7.9	27 55.0	5 36.5	28 28.6	1 32.0
23	16 0 9.7	29 11.8	26 .4	15 57.3	15 2.9	16 35.3	2 16.2	4 59.9	27 51.6	5 33.9	28 27.1	1 30.7
24	16 4 6.2	0♊12.2	25 57.0	28 15.3	14 57.1	17 46.5	3 .7	4 52.0	27 48.3	5 31.3	28 25.7	1 29.5
25	16 8 2.8	1 12.6	25 53.5	10♏38.3	14 55.2	18 57.2	3 45.1	4 44.0	27 45.1	5 28.7	28 24.1	1 28.2
26	16 11 59.3	2 13.2	25 50.0	23 15.3	14D57.4	20 7.5	4 29.6	4 35.9	27 41.9	5 26.0	28 22.6	1 26.9
27	16 15 55.9	3 13.9	25 46.6	6♐10.4	15 3.7	21 17.4	5 14.2	4 27.9	27 38.8	5 23.4	28 21.0	1 25.7
28	16 19 52.5	4 14.7	25 43.1	19 22.0	15 14.2	22 26.8	5 58.7	4 19.9	27 35.7	5 20.8	28 19.4	1 24.4
29	16 23 49.0	5 15.6	25 39.7	2♑42.9	15 28.7	23 35.7	6 43.3	4 11.8	27 32.7	5 18.1	28 17.9	1 23.2
30	16 27 45.6	6 16.6	25 36.2	16 2.0	15 47.3	24 44.2	7 27.9	4 3.8	27 29.8	5 15.5	28 16.3	1 22.0
31	16 31 42.1	7 17.8	25 32.7	29 7.4	16 10.0	25 52.1	8 12.5	3 55.7	27 27.0	5 12.9	28 14.6	1 20.8
	DECLINATION											
1	14 33 25.4	14N50.2	0N24.5	23S11.3	21N28.6	25N13.4	17N27.8	20S54.7	9S 3.1	21S34.6	22S10.7	5N43.2
4	14 45 15.1	15 44.1	0 24.5	22 55.9	20 56.7	25 32.2	18 4.7	20 52.0	8 58.7	21 33.6	22 10.6	5 44.4
7	14 57 4.8	16 35.7	0 24.5	13 46.6	20 4.6	25 45.0	18 39.9	20 49.1	8 54.4	21 32.5	22 10.5	5 45.5
10	15 8 54.4	17 24.8	0 24.5	0N52.6	18 56.6	25 51.7	19 13.6	20 46.1	8 50.2	21 31.5	22 10.4	5 46.5
13	15 20 44.1	18 11.3	0 24.5	16 11.5	17 39.4	25 52.3	19 45.5	20 42.9	8 46.2	21 30.4	22 10.3	5 47.4
16	15 32 33.8	18 55.0	0 24.5	24 18.2	16 21.3	25 47.0	20 15.8	20 39.6	8 42.4	21 29.2	22 10.2	5 48.1
19	15 44 23.4	19 35.9	0 24.5	18 58.2	15 10.8	25 35.9	20 44.3	20 36.2	8 38.8	21 28.1	22 10.1	5 48.7
22	15 56 13.1	20 13.7	0 24.5	4 7.9	14 14.8	25 19.0	21 11.0	20 32.7	8 35.4	21 26.9	22 10.1	5 49.2
25	16 8 2.8	20 48.4	0 24.5	12S .1	13 37.8	24 56.6	21 35.9	20 29.1	8 32.3	21 25.7	22 10.0	5 49.5
28	16 19 52.5	21 19.9	0 24.5	22 37.9	13 21.6	24 28.9	21 58.9	20 25.5	8 29.4	21 24.5	22 9.9	5 49.8
31	16 31 42.1	21 48.1	0 24.5	23 33.2	13 25.7	23 56.1	22 20.1	20 21.9	8 26.8	21 23.3	22 9.8	5 49.8

JUNE 1983

LONGITUDE

DAY	EPHEM. SID. TIME	☉	☊	☽	☿	♀	♂	♃	♄	♅	♆	♇
	h m s	° ′	° ′	° ′	° ′	° ′	° ′	° ′	° ′	° ′	° ′	° ′
1	16 35 38.7	9♊57.5	25♊51.5	8♒23.7	17♉58.8	24♋34.6	10♊36.8	5♐32.3	28♎27.6	6♐58.9	28♐20.9	27♎ 3.7
2	16 39 35.2	10 55.0	25 48.4	20 14.3	18 29.5	25 37.2	11 18.5	5 R 24.7	28 R 24.8	6 R 56.4	28 R 19.4	27 R 2.6
3	16 43 31.8	11 52.5	25 45.2	2♓ 8.0	19 4.4	26 39.5	12 .3	5 17.1	28 22.1	6 54.0	28 17.8	27 1.5
4	16 47 28.4	12 50.0	25 42.0	14 9.4	19 43.3	27 41.6	12 41.9	5 9.6	28 19.5	6 51.5	28 16.3	27 .5
5	16 51 24.9	13 47.4	25 38.8	26 23.0	20 26.2	28 43.3	13 23.5	5 2.1	28 17.0	6 49.0	28 14.7	26 59.5
6	16 55 21.5	14 44.9	25 35.7	8♈53.3	21 12.9	29 44.7	14 5.1	4 54.6	28 14.6	6 46.6	28 13.2	26 58.5
7	16 59 18.0	15 42.3	25 32.5	21 43.8	22 3.3	0♌45.8	14 46.7	4 47.2	28 12.2	6 44.1	28 11.6	26 57.5
8	17 3 14.6	16 39.7	25 29.3	4♉57.1	22 57.4	1 46.6	15 28.1	4 39.8	28 9.9	6 41.7	28 10.0	26 56.6
9	17 7 11.1	17 37.1	25 26.1	18 34.3	23 55.0	2 47.1	16 9.6	4 32.5	28 7.7	6 39.2	28 8.5	26 55.6
10	17 11 7.7	18 34.5	25 23.0	2♊34.4	24 56.2	3 47.2	16 51.0	4 25.3	28 5.6	6 36.8	28 6.9	26 54.8
11	17 15 4.3	19 31.9	25 19.8	16 54.5	26 .8	4 46.9	17 32.3	4 18.1	28 3.6	6 34.4	28 5.3	26 53.9
12	17 19 .8	20 29.3	25 16.6	1♋29.8	27 8.7	5 46.3	18 13.6	4 11.0	28 1.7	6 32.0	28 3.7	26 53.1
13	17 22 57.4	21 26.7	25 13.4	16 13.9	28 20.0	6 45.3	18 54.9	4 3.9	27 59.9	6 29.6	28 2.1	26 52.3
14	17 26 53.9	22 24.1	25 10.2	1♌ .2	29 34.5	7 44.0	19 36.2	3 57.0	27 58.2	6 27.3	28 .5	26 51.5
15	17 30 50.5	23 21.4	25 7.1	15 41.6	0♊52.2	8 42.2	20 17.3	3 50.2	27 56.5	6 25.0	27 58.9	26 50.8
16	17 34 47.1	24 18.7	25 3.9	0♍12.8	2 13.1	9 39.9	20 58.5	3 43.4	27 55.0	6 22.6	27 57.3	26 50.1
17	17 38 43.6	25 16.0	25 .7	14 29.5	3 37.1	10 37.3	21 39.5	3 36.7	27 53.5	6 20.3	27 55.7	26 49.4
18	17 42 40.2	26 13.3	24 57.5	28 29.3	5 4.2	11 34.1	22 20.6	3 30.1	27 52.2	6 18.0	27 54.0	26 48.8
19	17 46 36.7	27 10.6	24 54.4	12♎11.3	6 34.3	12 30.5	23 1.5	3 23.6	27 50.9	6 15.7	27 52.4	26 48.1
20	17 50 33.3	28 7.8	24 51.2	25 35.6	8 7.6	13 26.4	23 42.5	3 17.3	27 49.7	6 13.5	27 50.8	26 47.6
21	17 54 29.8	29 5.1	24 48.0	8♏43.1	9 43.8	14 21.8	24 23.4	3 11.0	27 48.7	6 11.3	27 49.2	26 47.0
22	17 58 26.4	0♋ 2.3	24 44.8	21 35.2	11 23.1	15 16.7	25 4.2	3 4.9	27 47.7	6 9.1	27 47.5	26 46.5
23	18 2 23.0	0 59.5	24 41.7	4♐13.4	13 5.3	16 11.0	25 45.0	2 58.8	27 46.8	6 6.9	27 45.9	26 46.0
24	18 6 19.5	1 56.7	24 38.5	16 39.3	14 50.5	17 4.8	26 25.8	2 52.9	27 46.0	6 4.7	27 44.3	26 45.5
25	18 10 16.1	2 54.0	24 35.3	28 54.5	16 38.4	17 58.0	27 6.5	2 47.2	27 45.4	6 2.6	27 42.7	26 45.1
26	18 14 12.6	3 51.2	24 32.1	11♑ .7	18 29.2	18 50.6	27 47.1	2 41.5	27 44.8	6 .5	27 41.1	26 44.7
27	18 18 9.2	4 48.4	24 29.0	22 59.5	20 22.7	19 42.6	28 27.8	2 36.0	27 44.3	5 58.4	27 39.5	26 44.3
28	18 22 5.8	5 45.6	24 25.8	4♒53.1	22 18.7	20 33.9	29 8.3	2 30.6	27 43.9	5 56.3	27 37.9	26 44.0
29	18 26 2.3	6 42.8	24 22.6	16 43.9	24 17.1	21 24.6	29 48.9	2 25.4	27 43.6	5 54.3	27 36.3	26 43.7
30	18 29 58.9	7 39.9	24 19.4	28 34.7	26 17.9	22 14.5	0♋29.4	2 20.3	27 43.4	5 52.3	27 34.7	26 43.4

LATITUDE

DAY	EPHEM. SID. TIME	☉	☊	☽	☿	♀	♂	♃	♄	♅	♆	♇
1	16 35 38.7	0 .0	0 .0	3 S 37.2	3 S 48.9	2 N 34.1	0 N 24.5	0 N 53.9	2 N 40.2	0 N 5.8	1 N 16.1	17 N 23.7
4	16 47 28.4	0 .0	0 .0	5 10.8	3 48.3	2 30.6	0 26.2	0 53.6	2 39.5	0 5.8	1 16.1	17 22.5
7	16 59 18.0	0 .0	0 .0	4 43.3	3 40.0	2 25.9	0 27.9	0 53.1	2 38.9	0 5.8	1 16.1	17 21.1
10	17 11 7.7	0 .0	0 .0	2 1.6	3 25.0	2 19.9	0 29.6	0 52.7	2 38.2	0 5.8	1 16.1	17 19.7
13	17 22 57.4	0 .0	0 .0	1 N 54.7	3 4.2	2 12.4	0 31.2	0 52.2	2 37.5	0 5.7	1 16.1	17 18.3
16	17 34 47.1	0 .0	0 .0	4 48.0	2 38.4	2 3.5	0 32.8	0 51.7	2 36.8	0 5.7	1 16.1	17 16.8
19	17 46 36.7	0 .0	0 .0	5 3.3	2 8.6	1 53.0	0 34.4	0 51.2	2 36.0	0 5.6	1 16.1	17 15.2
22	17 58 26.4	0 .0	0 .0	2 55.5	1 35.7	1 40.9	0 36.0	0 50.6	2 35.2	0 5.6	1 16.0	17 13.6
25	18 10 16.1	0 .0	0 .0	0 S 21.0	1 .9	1 27.2	0 37.5	0 50.0	2 34.5	0 5.6	1 16.0	17 12.0
28	18 22 5.8	0 .0	0 .0	3 22.8	0 25.6	1 11.7	0 39.1	0 49.4	2 33.7	0 5.5	1 16.0	17 10.3

RIGHT ASCENSION

DAY	EPHEM. SID. TIME	☉	☊	☽	☿	♀	♂	♃	♄	♅	♆	♇
1	16 35 38.7	8♊19.0	25♊29.3	11♒49.8	16♉36.6	26♋59.5	8♊57.1	3♐47.7	27♎24.2	5♐10.2	28♐13.0	1♏19.7
2	16 39 35.2	9 20.4	25 25.8	24 5.4	17 7.2	28 6.5	9 41.8	3 R 39.7	27 R 21.5	5 R 7.6	28 R 11.4	1 R 18.5
3	16 43 31.8	10 21.9	25 22.4	5♓55.4	17 41.6	29 12.8	10 26.5	3 31.8	27 18.9	5 5.0	28 9.7	1 17.4
4	16 47 28.4	11 23.5	25 18.9	17 26.1	18 19.9	0♌18.7	11 11.2	3 23.8	27 16.3	5 2.3	28 8.0	1 16.3
5	16 51 24.9	12 25.1	25 15.4	28 47.2	19 1.9	1 23.9	11 55.9	3 15.9	27 13.9	4 59.7	28 6.4	1 15.3
6	16 55 21.5	13 26.9	25 12.0	10♈10.9	19 47.6	2 28.6	12 40.6	3 8.1	27 11.5	4 57.1	28 4.7	1 14.2
7	16 59 18.0	14 28.7	25 8.5	21 51.2	20 36.9	3 32.7	13 25.4	3 .3	27 9.2	4 54.5	28 3.0	1 13.2
8	17 3 14.6	15 30.6	25 5.1	4♉ 2.8	21 29.9	4 36.2	14 10.1	2 52.5	27 6.9	4 51.9	28 1.3	1 12.2
9	17 7 11.1	16 32.6	25 1.6	17 .5	22 26.4	5 39.1	14 54.9	2 44.8	27 4.8	4 49.4	27 59.6	1 11.2
10	17 11 7.7	17 34.7	24 58.2	0♊55.5	23 26.5	6 41.4	15 39.6	2 37.2	27 2.7	4 46.8	27 57.9	1 10.2
11	17 15 4.3	18 36.8	24 54.7	15 51.3	24 30.1	7 43.1	16 24.4	2 29.6	27 .7	4 44.2	27 56.1	1 9.3
12	17 19 .8	19 39.0	24 51.2	1♋38.3	25 37.2	8 44.1	17 9.2	2 22.2	26 58.8	4 41.7	27 54.4	1 8.3
13	17 22 57.4	20 41.3	24 47.8	17 51.5	26 47.9	9 44.4	17 53.9	2 14.8	26 57.0	4 39.2	27 52.7	1 7.5
14	17 26 53.9	21 43.6	24 44.3	3♌57.6	28 2.1	10 44.2	18 38.7	2 7.5	26 55.3	4 36.7	27 51.0	1 6.6
15	17 30 50.5	22 45.9	24 40.9	19 26.7	29 19.8	11 43.1	19 23.5	2 .3	26 53.7	4 34.3	27 49.3	1 5.8
16	17 34 47.1	23 48.2	24 37.4	4♍ 2.9	0♊41.0	12 41.4	20 8.2	1 53.2	26 52.2	4 31.8	27 47.5	1 5.0
17	17 38 43.6	24 50.6	24 33.9	17 45.3	2 5.8	13 39.0	20 52.9	1 46.1	26 50.7	4 29.3	27 45.8	1 4.2
18	17 42 40.2	25 53.0	24 30.5	0♎43.2	3 34.2	14 35.9	21 37.6	1 39.2	26 49.3	4 26.9	27 44.0	1 3.4
19	17 46 36.7	26 55.3	24 27.0	13 10.8	5 6.3	15 32.0	22 22.3	1 32.4	26 48.0	4 24.5	27 42.3	1 2.7
20	17 50 33.3	27 57.7	24 23.6	25 23.4	6 42.0	16 27.3	23 7.0	1 25.7	26 46.8	4 22.1	27 40.5	1 1.9
21	17 54 29.8	29 .1	24 20.1	7♏35.0	8 21.4	17 21.9	23 51.6	1 19.2	26 45.7	4 19.8	27 38.8	1 1.3
22	17 58 26.4	0♋ 2.5	24 16.7	19 57.1	10 4.4	18 15.7	24 36.3	1 12.7	26 44.7	4 17.4	27 37.0	1 .6
23	18 2 23.0	1 4.9	24 13.2	2♐36.6	11 51.2	19 8.8	25 20.9	1 6.4	26 43.8	4 15.1	27 35.3	0 60.0
24	18 6 19.5	2 7.2	24 9.8	15 35.2	13 41.7	20 1.0	26 5.4	1 .2	26 43.0	4 12.8	27 33.5	0 59.4
25	18 10 16.1	3 9.6	24 6.3	28 48.5	15 35.8	20 52.4	26 50.0	0 54.1	26 42.2	4 10.6	27 31.8	0 58.8
26	18 14 12.6	4 11.9	24 2.8	12♑ 6.3	17 33.5	21 42.9	27 34.5	0 48.2	26 41.6	4 8.4	27 30.0	0 58.2
27	18 18 9.2	5 14.2	23 59.4	25 16.3	19 34.7	22 32.6	28 19.0	0 42.4	26 41.0	4 6.2	27 28.3	0 57.7
28	18 22 5.8	6 16.4	23 55.9	8♒ 6.7	21 39.4	23 21.4	29 3.4	0 36.7	26 40.6	4 4.0	27 26.6	0 57.2
29	18 26 2.3	7 18.6	23 52.5	20 30.5	23 47.2	24 9.4	29 47.8	0 31.2	26 40.2	4 1.9	27 24.9	0 56.7
30	18 29 58.9	8 20.8	23 49.0	2♓26.0	25 58.0	24 56.5	0♋32.2	0 25.9	26 39.9	3 59.7	27 23.1	0 56.3

DECLINATION

DAY	EPHEM. SID. TIME	☉	☊	☽	☿	♀	♂	♃	♄	♅	♆	♇
1	16 35 38.7	21 N 56.7	0 N 24.5	21 S 39.6	13 N 31.4	23 N 44.1	22 N 26.7	20 S 20.7	8 S 25.9	21 S 22.9	22 S 9.8	5 N 49.8
4	16 47 28.4	22 20.3	0 24.5	11 .7	14 .1	23 5.1	22 45.4	20 17.0	8 23.7	21 21.7	22 9.7	5 49.7
7	16 59 18.0	22 40.4	0 24.5	4 N 5.2	14 44.3	22 21.7	23 2.1	20 13.4	8 21.7	21 20.5	22 9.7	5 49.5
10	17 11 7.7	22 57.0	0 24.5	18 41.3	15 41.1	21 34.3	23 16.9	20 9.9	8 20.0	21 19.3	22 9.6	5 49.1
13	17 22 57.4	23 9.9	0 24.5	24 21.2	16 47.8	20 43.3	23 29.8	20 6.4	8 18.6	21 18.1	22 9.5	5 48.6
16	17 34 47.1	23 19.1	0 24.5	15 53.1	18 1.1	19 48.9	23 40.8	20 3.1	8 17.6	21 16.9	22 9.5	5 47.9
19	17 46 36.7	23 24.7	0 24.4	0 S 9.7	19 17.8	18 51.6	23 49.8	19 59.9	8 16.8	21 15.8	22 9.4	5 47.2
22	17 58 26.4	23 26.5	0 24.4	15 20.1	20 34.1	17 51.8	23 56.9	19 56.9	8 16.4	21 14.7	22 9.4	5 46.2
25	18 10 16.1	23 24.6	0 24.4	23 47.2	21 45.7	16 49.8	24 2.1	19 54.0	8 16.3	21 13.6	22 9.3	5 45.2
28	18 22 5.8	23 19.0	0 24.4	22 19.5	22 47.6	15 46.2	24 5.4	19 51.4	8 16.5	21 12.5	22 9.3	5 44.0

JULY 1983

LONGITUDE

DAY	EPHEM. SID. TIME h m s	☉ ° ′	☊ ° ′	☽ ° ′	☿ ° ′	♀ ° ′	♂ ° ′	♃ ° ′	♄ ° ′	♅ ° ′	♆ ° ′	♇ ° ′
1	18 33 55.4	8♋37.1	24♊16.2	10♓28.7	28♊20.7	23♌ 3.8	1♋ 9.8	2♐15.3	27♎43.3	5♐50.4	27♐33.1	26♎43.2
2	18 37 52.0	9 34.3	24 13.1	22 29.8	0♋25.3	23 52.3	1 50.3	2 R 10.5	27 43.3	5 R 48.4	27 R 31.5	26 R 43.0
3	18 41 48.5	10 31.5	24 9.9	4♈42.1	2 31.6	24 40.1	2 30.6	2 5.8	27 D 43.4	5 46.5	27 30.0	26 42.8
4	18 45 45.1	11 28.7	24 6.7	17 9.6	4 39.2	25 27.1	3 11.0	2 1.3	27 43.6	5 44.7	27 28.4	26 42.7
5	18 49 41.7	12 26.0	24 3.5	29 56.7	6 48.0	26 13.3	3 51.3	1 57.0	27 44.0	5 42.9	27 26.9	26 42.7
6	18 53 38.2	13 23.2	24 .4	13♉ 6.8	8 57.5	26 58.6	4 31.6	1 52.8	27 44.4	5 41.1	27 25.3	26 42.6
7	18 57 34.8	14 20.4	23 57.2	26 42.5	11 7.4	27 43.1	5 11.8	1 48.8	27 44.9	5 39.3	27 23.8	26 42.6
8	19 1 31.3	15 17.6	23 54.0	10♊44.5	13 17.6	28 26.6	5 52.0	1 44.9	27 45.5	5 37.6	27 22.3	26 42.6
9	19 5 27.9	16 14.9	23 50.8	25 11.5	15 27.7	29 9.2	6 32.1	1 41.2	27 46.1	5 35.9	27 20.8	26 42.6
10	19 9 24.4	17 12.1	23 47.7	9♋59.3	17 37.4	29 50.8	7 12.2	1 37.7	27 46.9	5 34.3	27 19.2	26 D 42.7
11	19 13 21.0	18 9.3	23 44.5	25 1.2	19 46.5	0♍31.4	7 52.3	1 34.3	27 47.8	5 32.6	27 17.8	26 42.8
12	19 17 17.6	19 6.6	23 41.3	10♌ 8.4	21 54.8	1 10.9	8 32.3	1 31.1	27 48.8	5 31.1	27 16.3	26 42.9
13	19 21 14.1	20 3.8	23 38.1	25 11.5	24 2.1	1 49.4	9 12.3	1 28.1	27 49.9	5 29.5	27 14.8	26 43.1
14	19 25 10.7	21 1.0	23 35.0	10♍ 1.9	26 8.3	2 26.6	9 52.3	1 25.3	27 51.1	5 28.0	27 13.4	26 43.3
15	19 29 7.2	21 58.3	23 31.8	24 32.9	28 13.1	3 2.7	10 32.2	1 22.6	27 52.4	5 26.6	27 11.9	26 43.6
16	19 33 3.8	22 55.5	23 28.6	8♎40.3	0♌16.4	3 37.5	11 12.0	1 20.1	27 53.8	5 25.2	27 10.5	26 43.8
17	19 37 .3	23 52.7	23 25.4	22 23.0	2 18.3	4 11.0	11 51.8	1 17.8	27 55.3	5 23.8	27 9.1	26 44.1
18	19 40 56.9	24 50.0	23 22.2	5♏41.6	4 18.5	4 43.2	12 31.6	1 15.6	27 56.8	5 22.5	27 7.7	26 44.5
19	19 44 53.5	25 47.2	23 19.1	18 38.6	6 17.1	5 14.0	13 11.4	1 13.7	27 58.5	5 21.2	27 6.3	26 44.9
20	19 48 50.0	26 44.5	23 15.9	1♐17.1	8 13.9	5 43.3	13 51.1	1 11.9	28 .3	5 19.9	27 5.0	26 45.3
21	19 52 46.6	27 41.7	23 12.7	13 40.5	10 9.1	6 11.1	14 30.7	1 10.3	28 2.1	5 18.7	27 3.6	26 45.7
22	19 56 43.1	28 39.0	23 9.5	25 52.2	12 2.4	6 37.3	15 10.4	1 8.9	28 4.1	5 17.6	27 2.3	26 46.2
23	20 0 39.7	29 36.2	23 6.4	7♑55.2	13 54.0	7 1.9	15 49.9	1 7.7	28 6.2	5 16.5	27 1.0	26 46.7
24	20 4 36.2	0♌33.5	23 3.2	19 52.1	15 43.9	7 24.8	16 29.5	1 6.6	28 8.3	5 15.4	26 59.7	26 47.3
25	20 8 32.8	1 30.8	23 .0	1♒45.1	17 32.0	7 46.0	17 9.0	1 5.7	28 10.5	5 14.4	26 58.4	26 47.9
26	20 12 29.4	2 28.1	22 56.8	13 36.2	19 18.3	8 5.5	17 48.5	1 5.1	28 12.9	5 13.4	26 57.2	26 48.5
27	20 16 25.9	3 25.4	22 53.7	25 27.1	21 2.9	8 23.0	18 27.9	1 4.6	28 15.3	5 12.5	26 56.0	26 49.2
28	20 20 22.5	4 22.7	22 50.5	7♓19.8	22 45.7	8 38.6	19 7.4	1 4.3	28 17.8	5 11.6	26 54.8	26 49.9
29	20 24 19.0	5 20.0	22 47.3	19 16.6	24 26.8	8 52.2	19 46.7	1 4.1	28 20.4	5 10.8	26 53.6	26 50.6
30	20 28 15.6	6 17.4	22 44.1	1♈20.0	26 6.1	9 3.8	20 26.1	1 D 4.2	28 23.1	5 10.0	26 52.4	26 51.3
31	20 32 12.1	7 14.7	22 40.9	13 33.1	27 43.7	9 13.4	21 5.4	1 4.4	28 25.9	5 9.3	26 51.3	26 52.1

LATITUDE

DAY	EPHEM. SID. TIME	☉	☊	☽	☿	♀	♂	♃	♄	♅	♆	♇
1	18 33 55.4	0 .0	0 .0	5S 6.0	0N 8.6	0N54.4	0N40.6	0N48.8	2N32.9	0N 5.5	1N15.9	17N 8.7
4	18 45 45.1	0 .0	0 .0	4 52.7	0 39.8	0 35.2	0 42.0	0 48.2	2 32.1	0 5.5	1 15.9	17 7.0
7	18 57 34.8	0 .0	0 .0	2 30.1	1 6.4	0 14.1	0 43.5	0 47.6	2 31.3	0 5.4	1 15.8	17 5.2
10	19 9 24.4	0 .0	0 .0	1N21.4	1 27.0	0S 9.0	0 44.9	0 46.9	2 30.5	0 5.4	1 15.7	17 3.5
13	19 21 14.1	0 .0	0 .0	4 32.8	1 40.9	0 34.2	0 46.4	0 46.2	2 29.7	0 5.3	1 15.7	17 1.8
16	19 33 3.8	0 .0	0 .0	5 4.6	1 48.0	1 1.6	0 47.8	0 45.6	2 28.9	0 5.3	1 15.6	17 .0
19	19 44 53.5	0 .0	0 .0	3 5.3	1 48.7	1 31.1	0 49.1	0 44.9	2 28.1	0 5.3	1 15.5	16 58.3
22	19 56 43.1	0 .0	0 .0	0S 5.6	1 43.6	2 2.7	0 50.5	0 44.2	2 27.3	0 5.2	1 15.4	16 56.5
25	20 8 32.8	0 .0	0 .0	3 7.3	1 33.3	2 36.4	0 51.8	0 43.5	2 26.5	0 5.2	1 15.3	16 54.8
28	20 20 22.5	0 .0	0 .0	4 55.7	1 18.5	3 12.1	0 53.1	0 42.8	2 25.7	0 5.1	1 15.2	16 53.0
31	20 32 12.1	0 .0	0 .0	4 51.7	0 59.9	3 49.4	0 54.4	0 42.1	2 25.0	0 5.1	1 15.1	16 51.3

RIGHT ASCENSION

DAY	EPHEM. SID. TIME	☉	☊	☽	☿	♀	♂	♃	♄	♅	♆	♇
1	18 33 55.4	9♋22.9	23♊45.6	13♓57.3	28♊11.6	25♌42.6	1♋16.5	0♐20.7	26♎39.7	3♐57.7	27♐21.4	0♍55.9
2	18 37 52.0	10 24.9	23 42.1	25 12.3	0♋27.7	26 27.8	2 .8	0 R 15.6	26 39.7	3 R 55.6	27 R 19.7	0 R 55.5
3	18 41 48.5	11 26.9	23 38.6	6♈22.4	2 45.9	27 12.1	2 45.0	0 10.7	26 39.7	3 53.6	27 18.0	0 55.2
4	18 45 45.1	12 28.8	23 35.2	17 41.1	5 5.8	27 55.3	3 29.2	0 6.0	26 39.7	3 51.6	27 16.3	0 54.8
5	18 49 41.7	13 30.7	23 31.7	29 23.3	7 27.1	28 37.7	4 13.4	0 1.4	26 D 40.0	3 49.8	27 14.7	0 54.6
6	18 53 38.2	14 32.5	23 28.3	11♉44.9	9 49.2	29 19.0	4 57.5	29♏57.0	26 40.3	3 47.9	27 13.0	0 54.3
7	18 57 34.8	15 34.2	23 24.8	25 .7	12 11.8	29 59.2	5 41.6	29 52.8	26 40.6	3 46.0	27 11.4	0 54.1
8	19 1 31.3	16 35.8	23 21.4	9♊21.0	14 34.5	0♍38.4	6 25.5	29 48.7	26 41.1	3 44.2	27 9.7	0 53.9
9	19 5 27.9	17 37.3	23 17.9	24 45.7	16 56.8	1 16.4	7 9.5	29 44.8	26 41.7	3 42.4	27 8.1	0 53.7
10	19 9 24.4	18 38.8	23 14.5	10♋58.7	19 18.2	1 53.4	7 53.3	29 41.1	26 42.3	3 40.6	27 6.5	0 53.6
11	19 13 21.0	19 40.1	23 11.0	27 28.8	21 38.6	2 29.2	8 37.1	29 37.5	26 43.1	3 38.9	27 4.9	0 53.5
12	19 17 17.6	20 41.3	23 7.5	13♌39.6	23 57.4	3 3.8	9 20.9	29 34.2	26 43.9	3 37.3	27 3.3	0 53.4
13	19 21 14.1	21 42.4	23 4.1	29 3.9	26 14.5	3 37.2	10 4.6	29 31.0	26 44.8	3 35.6	27 1.7	0 53.3
14	19 25 10.7	22 43.3	23 .6	13♍31.0	28 29.6	4 9.3	10 48.2	29 28.0	26 45.9	3 34.1	27 .1	0 53.3
15	19 29 7.2	23 44.2	22 57.2	27 4.8	0♌42.4	4 40.2	11 31.7	29 25.1	26 47.0	3 32.5	26 58.5	0 53.3
16	19 33 3.8	24 44.9	22 53.7	9♎57.9	2 52.9	5 9.7	12 15.1	29 22.5	26 48.2	3 31.0	26 57.0	0 53.3
17	19 37 .3	25 45.5	22 50.3	22 25.6	5 .8	5 37.8	12 58.5	29 20.0	26 49.5	3 29.6	26 55.5	0 D 53.4
18	19 40 56.9	26 46.0	22 46.8	4♏43.3	7 6.2	6 4.5	13 41.8	29 17.8	26 50.9	3 28.2	26 54.0	0 53.5
19	19 44 53.5	27 46.3	22 43.4	17 3.8	9 8.8	6 29.8	14 25.0	29 15.7	26 52.4	3 26.8	26 52.5	0 53.6
20	19 48 50.0	28 46.4	22 39.9	29 36.4	11 8.8	6 53.5	15 8.2	29 13.8	26 53.9	3 25.5	26 51.0	0 53.8
21	19 52 46.6	29 46.5	22 36.5	12♐25.6	13 6.1	7 15.7	15 51.2	29 12.1	26 55.6	3 24.2	26 49.6	0 54.0
22	19 56 43.1	0♌46.4	22 33.0	25 29.8	15 .7	7 36.3	16 34.2	29 10.5	26 57.4	3 23.0	26 48.2	0 54.2
23	20 0 39.7	1 46.1	22 29.6	8♑42.0	16 52.6	7 55.2	17 17.1	29 9.2	26 59.2	3 21.8	26 46.7	0 54.5
24	20 4 36.2	2 45.7	22 26.1	21 51.0	18 41.8	8 12.5	17 59.9	29 8.1	27 1.1	3 20.7	26 45.4	0 54.8
25	20 8 32.8	3 45.2	22 22.7	4♒45.2	20 28.4	8 28.0	18 42.6	29 7.1	27 3.2	3 19.6	26 44.0	0 55.1
26	20 12 29.4	4 44.5	22 19.2	17 15.7	22 12.5	8 41.7	19 25.3	29 6.4	27 5.3	3 18.6	26 42.7	0 55.5
27	20 16 25.9	5 43.7	22 15.7	29 18.4	23 54.0	8 53.6	20 7.8	29 5.8	27 7.5	3 17.7	26 41.4	0 55.8
28	20 20 22.5	6 42.7	22 12.3	10♓54.8	25 33.1	9 3.7	20 50.2	29 5.4	27 9.8	3 16.7	26 40.1	0 56.3
29	20 24 19.0	7 41.6	22 8.8	22 10.7	27 9.8	9 11.8	21 32.6	29 5.2	27 12.1	3 15.8	26 38.8	0 56.7
30	20 28 15.6	8 40.3	22 5.4	3♈15.6	28 44.1	9 17.9	22 14.9	29 5.2	27 14.6	3 15.0	26 37.5	0 57.2
31	20 32 12.1	9 38.9	22 1.9	14 21.4	0♍16.0	9 22.0	22 57.0	29 D 5.4	27 17.1	3 14.2	26 36.3	0 57.7

DECLINATION

DAY	EPHEM. SID. TIME	☉	☊	☽	☿	♀	♂	♃	♄	♅	♆	♇
1	18 33 55.4	23N 9.7	0N24.4	12S21.2	23N34.5	14N41.2	24N 6.7	19S49.0	8S17.0	21S11.5	22S 9.2	5N42.7
4	18 45 45.1	22 56.7	0 24.4	2N13.9	24 1.4	13 35.4	24 6.2	19 46.9	8 17.9	21 10.6	22 9.2	5 41.3
7	18 57 34.8	22 40.2	0 24.4	16 59.3	24 4.7	12 29.2	24 3.8	19 45.0	8 19.1	21 9.7	22 9.2	5 39.7
10	19 9 24.4	22 20.1	0 24.4	24 25.1	23 43.1	11 23.1	23 59.6	19 43.4	8 20.6	21 8.8	22 9.1	5 38.1
13	19 21 14.1	21 56.5	0 24.4	17 24.1	22 57.6	10 17.6	23 53.6	19 42.1	8 22.4	21 8.0	22 9.1	5 36.3
16	19 33 3.8	21 29.6	0 24.4	1 13.7	21 51.1	9 13.3	23 45.7	19 41.2	8 24.5	21 7.3	22 9.1	5 34.4
19	19 44 53.5	20 59.4	0 24.4	14S24.2	20 27.5	8 10.9	23 36.2	19 40.5	8 26.9	21 6.6	22 9.1	5 32.4
22	19 56 43.1	20 26.0	0 24.4	23 28.2	18 50.5	7 10.9	23 24.9	19 40.2	8 29.7	21 6.0	22 9.1	5 30.3
25	20 8 32.8	19 49.5	0 24.4	22 48.8	17 3.6	6 14.2	23 11.9	19 40.3	8 32.7	21 5.5	22 9.1	5 28.2
28	20 20 22.5	19 10.0	0 24.3	13 23.4	15 10.0	5 21.6	22 57.3	19 40.6	8 36.0	21 5.1	22 9.1	5 25.9
31	20 32 12.1	18 27.7	0 24.3	0N52.1	13 12.0	4 34.1	22 41.0	19 41.3	8 39.6	21 4.7	22 9.2	5 23.5

AUGUST 1983

LONGITUDE

DAY	EPHEM. SID. TIME h m s	☉ ° ′	☊ ° ′	☽ ° ′	☿ ° ′	♀ ° ′	♂ ° ′	♃ ° ′	♄ ° ′	♅ ° ′	♆ ° ′	♇ ° ′
1	20 36 8.7	8♌12.1	22♊37.8	25♈59.4	29♌19.6	9♍20.8	21♋44.6	1♐ 4.8	28♎28.8	5♐ 8.6	26♐50.2	26♎52.9
2	20 40 5.3	9 9.5	22 34.6	8♉42.7	0♍53.8	9 26.0	22 23.8	1 5.4	28 31.8	5R 7.9	26R49.1	26 53.8
3	20 44 1.8	10 6.9	22 31.4	21 46.9	2 26.3	9 29.0	23 3.0	1 6.2	28 34.8	5 7.3	26 48.0	26 54.6
4	20 47 58.4	11 4.3	22 28.2	5♊15.3	3 57.0	9 29.7	23 42.2	1 7.1	28 37.9	5 6.8	26 47.0	26 55.5
5	20 51 54.9	12 1.8	22 25.1	19 10.2	5 25.9	9R28.1	24 21.3	1 8.3	28 41.2	5 6.3	26 45.9	26 56.5
6	20 55 51.5	12 59.3	22 21.9	3♋32.1	6 53.1	9 24.2	25 .4	1 9.6	28 44.5	5 5.9	26 44.9	26 57.5
7	20 59 48.0	13 56.8	22 18.7	18 18.4	8 18.6	9 18.0	25 39.5	1 11.1	28 47.9	5 5.5	26 44.0	26 58.5
8	21 3 44.6	14 54.3	22 15.5	3♌23.7	9 42.2	9 9.4	26 18.5	1 12.8	28 51.3	5 5.1	26 43.0	26 59.5
9	21 7 41.1	15 51.8	22 12.4	18 39.4	11 4.0	8 58.4	26 57.5	1 14.6	28 54.9	5 4.8	26 42.1	27 .6
10	21 11 37.7	16 49.4	22 9.2	3♍54.8	12 23.9	8 45.0	27 36.5	1 16.7	28 58.5	5 4.6	26 41.2	27 1.7
11	21 15 34.3	17 46.9	22 6.0	18 59.2	13 41.9	8 29.3	28 15.4	1 18.9	29 2.3	5 4.4	26 40.3	27 2.8
12	21 19 30.8	18 44.5	22 2.8	3♎43.5	14 57.9	8 11.3	28 54.3	1 21.3	29 6.1	5 4.3	26 39.5	27 4.0
13	21 23 27.4	19 42.1	21 59.6	18 1.6	16 11.9	7 51.0	29 33.1	1 23.9	29 10.0	5 4.2	26 38.6	27 5.2
14	21 27 23.9	20 39.7	21 56.5	1♏50.8	17 23.9	7 28.5	0♌12.0	1 26.6	29 13.9	5 4.1	26 37.9	27 6.4
15	21 31 20.5	21 37.3	21 53.3	15 11.5	18 33.6	7 3.9	0 50.7	1 29.5	29 18.0	5 4.1	26 37.1	27 7.7
16	21 35 17.0	22 35.0	21 50.1	28 6.6	19 41.2	6 37.3	1 29.5	1 32.7	29 22.2	5D 4.3	26 36.4	27 9.0
17	21 39 13.6	23 32.7	21 46.9	10♐40.0	20 46.3	6 8.8	2 8.2	1 36.0	29 26.4	5 4.4	26 35.7	27 10.3
18	21 43 10.1	24 30.4	21 43.8	22 56.3	21 49.0	5 38.5	2 46.9	1 39.4	29 30.7	5 4.5	26 35.0	27 11.7
19	21 47 6.7	25 28.1	21 40.6	5♑ .3	22 49.2	5 6.6	3 25.6	1 43.0	29 35.0	5 4.8	26 34.4	27 13.0
20	21 51 3.2	26 25.8	21 37.4	16 56.3	23 46.6	4 33.2	4 4.2	1 46.8	29 39.4	5 5.0	26 33.8	27 14.4
21	21 54 59.8	27 23.5	21 34.2	28 47.8	24 41.2	3 58.7	4 42.7	1 50.8	29 43.9	5 5.4	26 33.2	27 15.9
22	21 58 56.4	28 21.2	21 31.0	10♒37.9	25 32.8	3 23.1	5 21.3	1 54.9	29 48.5	5 5.7	26 32.6	27 17.3
23	22 2 52.9	29 19.0	21 27.9	22 29.0	26 21.3	2 46.7	5 59.8	1 59.2	29 53.2	5 6.2	26 32.1	27 18.8
24	22 6 49.5	0♍16.8	21 24.7	4♓22.9	27 6.4	2 9.8	6 38.3	2 3.6	29 57.9	5 6.6	26 31.6	27 20.3
25	22 10 46.0	1 14.6	21 21.5	16 20.9	27 48.0	1 32.5	7 16.7	2 8.2	0♏ 2.7	5 7.2	26 31.1	27 21.9
26	22 14 42.6	2 12.5	21 18.3	28 24.6	28 25.8	0 55.1	7 55.1	2 13.0	0 7.5	5 7.8	26 30.7	27 23.4
27	22 18 39.1	3 10.4	21 15.2	10♈35.2	28 59.7	0 18.0	8 33.5	2 17.9	0 12.4	5 8.4	26 30.3	27 25.0
28	22 22 35.7	4 8.3	21 12.0	22 54.7	29 29.3	29♌41.2	9 11.9	2 23.0	0 17.4	5 9.1	26 29.9	27 26.6
29	22 26 32.2	5 6.2	21 8.8	5♉25.4	29 54.4	29 5.1	9 50.2	2 28.3	0 22.5	5 9.8	26 29.5	27 28.3
30	22 30 28.8	6 4.2	21 5.6	18 9.9	0♎14.8	28 29.8	10 28.5	2 33.7	0 27.6	5 10.6	26 29.2	27 30.0
31	22 34 25.3	7 2.2	21 2.4	1♊11.6	0 30.1	27 55.7	11 6.8	2 39.2	0 32.8	5 11.4	26 28.9	27 31.7

LATITUDE

DAY	EPHEM. SID. TIME	☉	☊	☽	☿	♀	♂	♃	♄	♅	♆	♇
1	20 36 8.7	0 .0	0 .0	4S22.7	0N53.0	4S 2.1	0N54.8	0N41.9	2N24.7	0N 5.1	1N15.1	16N50.8
4	20 47 58.4	0 .0	0 .0	1 40.0	0 30.1	4 41.0	0 56.1	0 41.2	2 24.0	0 5.0	1 15.0	16 49.1
7	20 59 48.0	0 .0	0 .0	2N 6.6	0 4.7	5 20.2	0 57.4	0 40.6	2 23.2	0 5.0	1 14.8	16 47.4
10	21 11 37.7	0 .0	0 .0	4 48.0	0S22.8	5 59.0	0 58.6	0 39.9	2 22.5	0 4.9	1 14.7	16 45.8
13	21 23 27.4	0 .0	0 .0	4 38.4	0 51.9	6 36.1	0 59.8	0 39.2	2 21.8	0 4.9	1 14.6	16 44.2
16	21 35 17.0	0 .0	0 .0	2 10.8	1 22.2	7 10.2	1 1.0	0 38.6	2 21.1	0 4.9	1 14.5	16 42.7
19	21 47 6.7	0 .0	0 .0	1S 2.0	1 53.2	7 39.7	1 2.1	0 37.9	2 20.5	0 4.8	1 14.3	16 41.1
22	21 58 56.4	0 .0	0 .0	3 43.9	2 24.2	8 3.2	1 3.3	0 37.3	2 19.8	0 4.8	1 14.2	16 39.7
25	22 10 46.0	0 .0	0 .0	4 59.8	2 54.5	8 19.3	1 4.4	0 36.6	2 19.2	0 4.7	1 14.1	16 38.2
28	22 22 35.7	0 .0	0 .0	4 19.2	3 22.9	8 27.4	1 5.5	0 36.0	2 18.6	0 4.7	1 13.9	16 36.9
31	22 34 25.3	0 .0	0 .0	1 46.8	3 47.9	8 27.3	1 6.6	0 35.4	2 18.0	0 4.7	1 13.8	16 35.5

RIGHT ASCENSION

DAY	EPHEM. SID. TIME	☉	☊	☽	☿	♀	♂	♃	♄	♅	♆	♇
1	20 36 8.7	10♌37.3	21♊58.5	25♈41.7	1♍45.8	9♍24.1	23♋39.1	29♏ 5.8	27♎19.8	3♐13.5	26♐35.1	0♏58.2
2	20 40 5.3	11 35.6	21 55.0	7♉31.6	3 13.3	9 24.2	24 21.1	29 6.4	27 22.5	3R12.8	26R33.9	0 58.7
3	20 44 1.8	12 33.7	21 51.6	20 6.2	4 38.6	9R22.1	25 3.0	29 7.1	27 25.3	3 12.2	26 32.7	0 59.3
4	20 47 58.4	13 31.7	21 48.1	3♊38.5	6 1.8	9 17.9	25 44.8	29 8.1	27 28.1	3 11.6	26 31.6	0 60.0
5	20 51 54.9	14 29.5	21 44.7	18 15.7	7 22.9	9 11.5	26 26.5	29 9.2	27 31.1	3 11.1	26 30.5	1 .6
6	20 55 51.5	15 27.2	21 41.2	3♋52.6	8 41.9	9 3.0	27 8.1	29 10.5	27 34.1	3 10.6	26 29.4	1 1.3
7	20 59 48.0	16 24.8	21 37.8	20 8.6	9 58.9	8 52.4	27 49.6	29 12.0	27 37.3	3 10.2	26 28.4	1 2.0
8	21 3 44.6	17 22.2	21 34.3	6♌31.0	11 13.8	8 39.5	28 31.0	29 13.7	27 40.5	3 9.8	26 27.3	1 2.7
9	21 7 41.1	18 19.4	21 30.9	22 27.3	12 26.7	8 24.5	29 12.2	29 15.6	27 43.8	3 9.5	26 26.3	1 3.5
10	21 11 37.7	19 16.5	21 27.4	7♍36.5	13 37.5	8 7.4	29 53.4	29 17.7	27 47.1	3 9.3	26 25.4	1 4.3
11	21 15 34.3	20 13.5	21 24.0	21 53.4	14 46.3	7 48.2	0♌34.5	29 19.9	27 50.6	3 9.1	26 24.4	1 5.1
12	21 19 30.8	21 10.3	21 20.5	5♎24.7	15 53.1	7 27.0	1 15.5	29 22.4	27 54.1	3 8.9	26 23.5	1 6.0
13	21 23 27.4	22 7.0	21 17.1	18 23.6	16 57.8	7 3.8	1 56.3	29 25.0	27 57.7	3 8.8	26 22.6	1 6.9
14	21 27 23.9	23 3.5	21 13.6	1♏ 4.4	18 .3	6 38.6	2 37.1	29 27.8	28 1.4	3 8.8	26 21.8	1 7.8
15	21 31 20.5	23 59.9	21 10.2	13 40.5	19 .7	6 11.7	3 17.7	29 30.9	28 5.1	3 8.8	26 20.9	1 8.7
16	21 35 17.0	24 56.2	21 6.7	26 22.0	19 59.0	5 43.1	3 58.3	29 34.1	28 9.0	3D 8.9	26 20.2	1 9.7
17	21 39 13.6	25 52.3	21 3.3	9♐14.5	20 54.9	5 12.9	4 38.8	29 37.4	28 12.9	3 9.0	26 19.4	1 10.7
18	21 43 10.1	26 48.2	20 59.8	22 18.8	21 48.5	4 41.3	5 19.1	29 41.0	28 16.9	3 9.2	26 18.7	1 11.8
19	21 47 6.7	27 44.1	20 56.4	5♑29.8	22 39.6	4 8.4	5 59.3	29 44.7	28 20.9	3 9.4	26 18.0	1 12.8
20	21 51 3.2	28 39.8	20 52.9	18 38.6	23 28.3	3 34.5	6 39.4	29 48.6	28 25.1	3 9.7	26 17.3	1 13.9
21	21 54 59.8	29 35.4	20 49.5	1♒35.0	24 14.3	2 59.7	7 19.4	29 52.7	28 29.3	3 10.0	26 16.7	1 15.0
22	21 58 56.4	0♍30.9	20 46.0	14 10.2	24 57.6	2 24.3	7 59.3	29 56.9	28 33.5	3 10.4	26 16.1	1 16.2
23	22 2 52.9	1 26.2	20 42.6	26 19.5	25 38.0	1 48.3	8 39.0	0♐ 1.4	28 37.8	3 10.9	26 15.5	1 17.3
24	22 6 49.5	2 21.5	20 39.1	8♓ 2.8	26 15.3	1 12.2	9 18.7	0 6.0	28 42.2	3 11.4	26 15.0	1 18.5
25	22 10 46.0	3 16.6	20 35.7	19 24.4	26 49.5	0 36.0	9 58.3	0 10.7	28 46.7	3 11.9	26 14.5	1 19.7
26	22 14 42.6	4 11.6	20 32.2	0♈32.1	27 20.3	0 .1	10 37.7	0 15.6	28 51.3	3 12.6	26 14.0	1 21.0
27	22 18 39.1	5 6.5	20 28.8	11 36.0	27 47.5	29♌24.6	11 17.1	0 20.7	28 55.9	3 13.2	26 13.5	1 22.2
28	22 22 35.7	6 1.4	20 25.3	22 48.2	28 11.0	28 49.7	11 56.3	0 26.0	29 .5	3 13.9	26 13.1	1 23.5
29	22 26 32.2	6 56.1	20 21.9	4♉21.8	28 30.5	28 15.8	12 35.5	0 31.5	29 5.3	3 14.7	26 12.8	1 24.9
30	22 30 28.8	7 50.8	20 18.4	16 30.4	28 45.9	27 43.0	13 14.5	0 37.1	29 10.1	3 15.5	26 12.4	1 26.2
31	22 34 25.3	8 45.4	20 15.0	29 26.8	28 56.8	27 11.4	13 53.4	0 42.8	29 14.9	3 16.4	26 12.1	1 27.6

DECLINATION

DAY	EPHEM. SID. TIME	☉	☊	☽	☿	♀	♂	♃	♄	♅	♆	♇
1	20 36 8.7	18N13.0	0N24.3	5N57.4	12N32.1	4N19.5	22N35.3	19S41.6	8S40.8	21S 4.6	22S 9.2	5N22.7
4	20 47 58.4	17 27.1	0 24.3	19 32.4	10 31.8	4 40.1	22 17.0	19 42.8	8 44.7	21 4.3	22 9.2	5 20.2
7	20 59 48.0	16 38.6	0 24.3	24 16.8	8 31.7	3 8.0	21 57.2	19 44.2	8 48.9	21 4.1	22 9.3	5 17.7
10	21 11 37.7	15 47.7	0 24.3	14 32.5	6 33.5	2 44.2	21 35.9	19 46.0	8 53.4	21 4.0	22 9.3	5 15.1
13	21 23 27.4	14 54.6	0 24.3	2S46.8	4 38.9	2 29.6	21 13.3	19 48.2	8 58.0	21 3.9	22 9.4	5 12.4
16	21 35 17.0	13 59.3	0 24.3	17 37.0	2 49.4	2 24.8	20 49.2	19 50.6	9 3.0	21 4.0	22 9.4	5 9.6
19	21 47 6.7	13 2.0	0 24.3	24 22.8	1 7.0	2 30.0	20 23.9	19 53.3	9 8.1	21 4.1	22 9.5	5 6.8
22	21 58 56.4	12 2.8	0 24.3	21 9.6	0S26.2	2 44.9	19 57.3	19 56.3	9 13.4	21 4.4	22 9.6	5 4.0
25	22 10 46.0	11 2.0	0 24.3	9 59.3	1 47.6	3 8.4	19 29.5	19 59.6	9 18.9	21 4.7	22 9.7	5 1.1
28	22 22 35.7	9 59.6	0 24.2	4N53.7	2 53.9	3 39.1	19 .6	20 3.1	9 24.6	21 5.0	22 9.8	4 58.2
31	22 34 25.3	8 55.7	0 24.2	18 39.5	3 41.0	4 14.8	18 30.5	20 6.8	9 30.5	21 5.5	22 9.9	4 55.3

SEPTEMBER 1983

DAY	EPHEM. SID. TIME	☉	☊	☽	☿	♀	♂	♃	♄	♅	♆	♇
		LONGITUDE										
	h m s	° ′	° ′	° ′	° ′	° ′	° ′	° ′	° ′	° ′	° ′	° ′
1	22 38 21.9	8 ♍ .2	20 ♊ 59.3	14 ♊ 33.7	0 ♎ 40.1	27 ♌ 22.8	11 ♌ 45.0	2 ♐ 44.9	0 ♏ 38.1	5 ♐ 12.3	26 ♐ 28.7	27 ♎ 33.4
2	22 42 18.4	8 58.3	20 56.1	28 18.9	0 44.6	26 R 51.4	12 23.2	2 50.8	0 43.4	5 13.3	26 R 28.5	27 35.1
3	22 46 15.0	9 56.3	20 52.9	12 ♋ 28.7	0 R 43.3	26 21.7	13 1.4	2 56.8	0 48.8	5 14.2	26 28.3	27 36.9
4	22 50 11.6	10 54.5	20 49.7	27 2.5	0 35.9	25 53.9	13 39.5	3 3.0	0 54.2	5 15.3	26 28.1	27 38.7
5	22 54 8.1	11 52.6	20 46.6	11 ♌ 56.8	0 22.3	25 27.9	14 17.6	3 9.3	0 59.7	5 16.4	26 28.0	27 40.5
6	22 58 4.7	12 50.9	20 43.4	27 4.7	0 2.3	25 4.1	14 55.8	3 15.8	1 5.3	5 17.6	26 27.9	27 42.4
7	23 2 1.2	13 49.1	20 40.2	12 ♍ 16.6	29 ♍ 36.0	24 42.4	15 33.8	3 22.4	1 10.9	5 18.8	26 27.9	27 44.3
8	23 5 57.8	14 47.3	20 37.0	27 21.8	29 3.3	24 22.9	16 11.8	3 29.2	1 16.6	5 20.0	26 27.9	27 46.1
9	23 9 54.3	15 45.6	20 33.8	12 ♎ 10.3	28 24.5	24 5.7	16 49.8	3 36.1	1 22.4	5 21.3	26 27.9	27 48.0
10	23 13 50.9	16 43.9	20 30.7	26 34.3	27 39.9	23 50.8	17 27.8	3 43.1	1 28.1	5 22.6	26 27.9	27 50.0
11	23 17 47.4	17 42.2	20 27.5	10 ♏ 29.6	26 50.0	23 38.3	18 5.7	3 50.3	1 34.0	5 24.0	26 D 28.0	27 51.9
12	23 21 44.0	18 40.6	20 24.3	23 55.5	25 55.6	23 28.3	18 43.6	3 57.6	1 39.9	5 25.5	26 28.1	27 53.9
13	23 25 40.5	19 39.0	20 21.1	6 ♐ 53.7	24 57.5	23 20.6	19 21.4	4 5.1	1 45.8	5 27.0	26 28.2	27 55.9
14	23 29 37.1	20 37.4	20 18.0	19 28.3	23 56.8	23 15.3	19 59.3	4 12.6	1 51.8	5 28.5	26 28.4	27 57.9
15	23 33 33.6	21 35.8	20 14.8	1 ♑ 44.0	22 54.8	23 12.4	20 37.0	4 20.4	1 57.9	5 30.1	26 28.6	27 59.9
16	23 37 30.2	22 34.3	20 11.6	13 46.3	21 52.9	23 11.9	21 14.8	4 28.2	2 4.0	5 31.7	26 28.8	28 2.0
17	23 41 26.7	23 32.8	20 8.4	25 40.2	20 52.4	23 D 13.7	21 52.5	4 36.2	2 10.1	5 33.4	26 29.1	28 4.0
18	23 45 23.3	24 31.3	20 5.2	7 ♒ 30.3	19 55.0	23 17.8	22 30.2	4 44.3	2 16.3	5 35.1	26 29.4	28 6.1
19	23 49 19.8	25 29.8	20 2.1	19 20.6	19 2.1	23 24.2	23 7.9	4 52.5	2 22.6	5 36.9	26 29.7	28 8.2
20	23 53 16.4	26 28.4	19 58.9	1 ♓ 14.2	18 15.0	23 32.8	23 45.5	5 .9	2 28.9	5 38.7	26 30.1	28 10.4
21	23 57 13.0	27 27.0	19 55.7	13 13.4	17 35.0	23 43.5	24 23.1	5 9.4	2 35.2	5 40.6	26 30.5	28 12.5
22	0 1 9.5	28 25.6	19 52.5	25 19.8	17 3.1	23 56.4	25 .7	5 18.0	2 41.6	5 42.5	26 30.9	28 14.6
23	0 5 6.1	29 24.3	19 49.4	7 ♈ 34.4	16 40.0	24 11.4	25 38.2	5 26.7	2 48.0	5 44.4	26 31.4	28 16.8
24	0 9 2.6	0 ♎ 23.0	19 46.2	19 57.8	16 26.5	24 28.3	26 15.7	5 35.5	2 54.4	5 46.4	26 31.9	28 19.0
25	0 12 59.2	1 21.8	19 43.0	2 ♉ 30.7	16 22.9	24 47.2	26 53.2	5 44.5	3 .9	5 48.5	26 32.4	28 21.2
26	0 16 55.7	2 20.5	19 39.8	15 13.8	16 D 29.3	25 8.0	27 30.6	5 53.5	3 7.4	5 50.5	26 33.0	28 23.4
27	0 20 52.3	3 19.4	19 36.6	28 8.6	16 45.7	25 30.7	28 8.1	6 2.8	3 14.1	5 52.7	26 33.7	28 25.7
28	0 24 48.8	4 18.2	19 33.5	11 ♊ 16.6	17 11.8	25 55.1	28 45.5	6 12.1	3 20.7	5 54.9	26 34.3	28 27.9
29	0 28 45.4	5 17.1	19 30.3	24 40.0	17 47.3	26 21.2	29 22.8	6 21.5	3 27.3	5 57.1	26 34.9	28 30.2
30	0 32 41.9	6 16.0	19 27.1	8 ♋ 20.7	18 31.6	26 48.9	0 ♍ .2	6 31.0	3 34.0	5 59.4	26 35.6	28 32.4
		LATITUDE										
1	22 38 21.9	0 .0	0 .0	0 S 38.2	3 S 55.1	8 S 25.5	1 N 7.0	0 N 35.2	2 N 17.8	0 N 4.6	1 N 13.7	16 N 35.1
4	22 50 11.6	0 .0	0 .0	2 N 54.9	4 12.1	8 15.3	1 8.1	0 34.6	2 17.3	0 4.6	1 13.6	16 33.8
7	23 2 1.2	0 .0	0 .0	4 56.8	4 19.4	7 58.6	1 9.1	0 34.0	2 16.8	0 4.6	1 13.4	16 32.7
10	23 13 50.9	0 .0	0 .0	4 4.4	4 13.4	7 36.7	1 10.2	0 33.5	2 16.3	0 4.5	1 13.3	16 31.5
13	23 25 40.5	0 .0	0 .0	1 11.7	3 51.0	7 10.9	1 11.2	0 32.9	2 15.8	0 4.5	1 13.2	16 30.4
16	23 37 30.2	0 .0	0 .0	1 S 59.4	3 11.7	6 42.2	1 12.2	0 32.4	2 15.3	0 4.4	1 13.0	16 29.4
19	23 49 19.8	0 .0	0 .0	4 18.0	2 18.7	6 11.7	1 13.2	0 31.8	2 14.9	0 4.4	1 12.9	16 28.5
22	0 1 9.5	0 .0	0 .0	4 58.3	1 19.3	5 40.2	1 14.1	0 31.3	2 14.5	0 4.4	1 12.7	16 27.6
25	0 12 59.2	0 .0	0 .0	3 38.8	0 21.2	5 8.4	1 15.1	0 30.8	2 14.1	0 4.3	1 12.6	16 26.8
28	0 24 48.8	0 .0	0 .0	0 40.0	0 N 29.1	4 36.7	1 16.0	0 30.3	2 13.7	0 4.3	1 12.4	16 26.1
		RIGHT ASCENSION										
1	22 38 21.9	9 ♍ 39.9	20 ♊ 11.5	13 ♊ 19.5	29 ♍ 3.1	26 ♌ 41.3	14 ♌ 32.2	0 ♐ 48.7	29 ♎ 19.8	3 ♐ 17.3	26 ♐ 11.8	1 ♏ 29.0
2	22 42 18.4	10 34.3	20 8.1	28 9.3	29 4.6	26 R 12.9	15 10.9	0 54.8	29 24.8	3 18.3	26 R 11.6	1 30.4
3	22 46 15.0	11 28.6	20 4.6	13 ♋ 44.7	29 R 1.1	25 46.2	15 49.5	1 1.1	29 29.9	3 19.4	26 11.4	1 31.8
4	22 50 11.6	12 22.9	20 1.2	29 42.3	28 52.5	25 21.5	16 28.0	1 7.5	29 35.0	3 20.5	26 11.2	1 33.3
5	22 54 8.1	13 17.2	19 57.7	15 ♌ 33.6	28 38.5	24 58.8	17 6.4	1 14.0	29 40.2	3 21.6	26 11.1	1 34.8
6	22 58 4.7	14 11.4	19 54.3	0 ♍ 55.1	28 19.2	24 38.2	17 44.8	1 20.8	29 45.4	3 22.9	26 11.0	1 36.4
7	23 2 1.2	15 5.5	19 50.8	15 35.0	27 54.6	24 19.9	18 23.0	1 27.7	29 50.7	3 24.1	26 11.0	1 37.9
8	23 5 57.8	15 59.6	19 47.4	29 34.0	27 24.8	24 3.7	19 1.0	1 34.7	29 56.1	3 25.4	26 10.9	1 39.4
9	23 9 54.3	16 53.6	19 44.0	13 ♎ .9	26 50.0	23 49.9	19 39.0	1 41.9	0 ♏ 1.5	3 26.8	26 10.9	1 41.0
10	23 13 50.9	17 47.6	19 40.5	26 7.8	26 10.7	23 38.4	20 16.9	1 49.2	0 6.9	3 28.2	26 D 11.0	1 42.6
11	23 17 47.4	18 41.5	19 37.1	9 ♏ 6.9	25 27.2	23 29.3	20 54.6	1 56.7	0 12.4	3 29.7	26 11.1	1 44.3
12	23 21 44.0	19 35.4	19 33.6	22 7.9	24 40.3	23 22.6	21 32.3	2 4.4	0 18.0	3 31.2	26 11.2	1 45.9
13	23 25 40.5	20 29.3	19 30.2	5 ♐ 16.5	23 50.8	23 18.2	22 9.8	2 12.1	0 23.6	3 32.8	26 11.3	1 47.6
14	23 29 37.1	21 23.1	19 26.7	18 33.4	22 59.6	23 16.2	22 47.3	2 20.0	0 29.3	3 34.4	26 11.5	1 49.3
15	23 33 33.6	22 16.9	19 23.3	1 ♑ 54.2	22 8.0	23 D 16.6	23 24.6	2 28.1	0 35.0	3 36.0	26 11.7	1 51.0
16	23 37 30.2	23 10.7	19 19.8	15 10.9	21 17.0	23 19.3	24 1.9	2 36.3	0 40.7	3 37.8	26 12.0	1 52.7
17	23 41 26.7	24 4.5	19 16.4	28 14.0	20 28.0	23 24.2	24 39.0	2 44.6	0 46.6	3 39.5	26 12.3	1 54.5
18	23 45 23.3	24 58.3	19 12.9	10 ♒ 55.5	19 42.2	23 31.4	25 16.0	2 53.1	0 52.4	3 41.3	26 12.6	1 56.2
19	23 49 19.8	25 52.0	19 9.5	23 11.1	19 .9	23 40.8	25 53.0	3 1.7	0 58.3	3 43.2	26 13.0	1 58.0
20	23 53 16.4	26 45.8	19 6.1	5 ♓ .8	18 25.1	23 52.4	26 29.8	3 10.5	1 4.3	3 45.1	26 13.4	1 59.8
21	23 57 13.0	27 39.6	19 2.6	16 28.6	17 56.0	24 6.1	27 6.6	3 19.4	1 10.3	3 47.1	26 13.8	2 1.6
22	0 1 9.5	28 33.4	18 59.2	27 41.8	17 34.4	24 21.8	27 43.2	3 28.4	1 16.3	3 49.1	26 14.3	2 3.5
23	0 5 6.1	29 27.3	18 55.7	8 ♈ 49.8	17 20.8	24 39.5	28 19.8	3 37.5	1 22.4	3 51.2	26 14.8	2 5.3
24	0 9 2.6	0 ♎ 21.1	18 52.3	20 3.5	17 15.9	24 59.1	28 56.2	3 46.8	1 28.5	3 53.3	26 15.3	2 7.2
25	0 12 59.2	1 15.0	18 48.8	1 ♉ 35.0	17 D 19.8	25 20.6	29 32.6	3 56.2	1 34.7	3 55.4	26 15.9	2 9.1
26	0 16 55.7	2 8.9	18 45.4	13 36.3	17 32.7	25 43.9	0 ♍ 8.9	4 5.7	1 40.9	3 57.6	26 16.5	2 11.0
27	0 20 52.3	3 3.0	18 42.0	26 18.6	17 54.5	26 9.0	0 45.1	4 15.4	1 47.2	3 59.9	26 17.2	2 13.0
28	0 24 48.8	3 57.0	18 38.5	9 ♊ 49.4	18 24.7	26 35.7	1 21.2	4 25.2	1 53.4	4 2.2	26 17.9	2 14.9
29	0 28 45.4	4 51.1	18 35.1	24 10.0	19 3.2	27 4.1	1 57.2	4 35.1	1 59.8	4 4.5	26 18.6	2 16.8
30	0 32 41.9	5 45.2	18 31.6	9 ♋ 12.0	19 49.4	27 34.0	2 33.2	4 45.1	2 6.1	4 6.9	26 19.3	2 18.8
		DECLINATION										
1	22 38 21.9	8 N 34.1	0 N 24.2	21 N 55.0	3 S 51.6	4 N 27.4	18 N 20.3	20 S 8.2	9 S 32.5	21 S 5.7	22 S 10.0	4 N 54.3
4	22 50 11.6	7 28.6	0 24.2	23 36.6	4 5.5	5 6.4	17 48.8	20 12.2	9 38.6	21 6.2	22 10.1	4 51.3
7	23 2 1.2	6 21.9	0 24.2	11 31.4	3 48.4	5 45.4	17 16.3	20 16.5	9 44.9	21 6.9	22 10.3	4 48.3
10	23 13 50.9	5 14.3	0 24.2	6 S 27.0	2 56.8	6 22.7	16 42.9	20 21.0	9 51.3	21 7.6	22 10.4	4 45.3
13	23 25 40.5	4 5.9	0 24.2	20 17.1	1 31.9	6 56.8	16 8.6	20 25.6	9 57.8	21 8.4	22 10.6	4 42.3
16	23 37 30.2	2 56.9	0 24.2	24 42.5	0 N 17.1	7 26.7	15 33.5	20 30.4	10 4.5	21 9.3	22 10.7	4 39.3
19	23 49 19.8	1 47.4	0 24.2	19 6.1	2 12.7	7 51.7	14 57.6	20 35.4	10 11.2	21 10.3	22 10.9	4 36.3
22	0 1 9.5	0 37.5	0 24.1	6 25.1	3 53.9	8 11.1	14 21.0	20 40.4	10 18.1	21 11.3	22 11.1	4 33.3
25	0 12 59.2	0 S 32.5	0 24.1	8 N 55.1	5 2.9	8 24.7	13 43.7	20 45.6	10 25.0	21 12.4	22 11.3	4 30.4
28	0 24 48.8	1 42.6	0 24.1	21 28.4	5 30.3	8 32.2	13 5.7	20 50.9	10 32.0	21 13.5	22 11.5	4 27.4

OCTOBER 1983

DAY	EPHEM. SID. TIME	☉	☊	☾	☿	♀	♂	♃	♄	♅	♆	♇
	h m s	° ′	° ′	° ′	° ′	° ′	° ′	° ′	° ′	° ′	° ′	° ′
		LONGITUDE										
1	0 36 38.5	7♎15.0	19♊23.9	22♋20.2	19♍24.3	27♌18.3	0♍37.4	6♐40.6	3♏40.7	6♐ 1.6	26♐36.4	28♎34.7
2	0 40 35.0	8 14.0	19 20.8	6♌38.4	20 24.6	27 49.1	1 14.7	6 50.4	3 47.5	6 4.0	26 37.1	28 37.0
3	0 44 31.6	9 13.0	19 17.6	21 13.6	21 31.8	28 21.5	1 51.9	7 .2	3 54.2	6 6.4	26 37.9	28 39.3
4	0 48 28.1	10 12.1	19 14.4	6♍ 1.0	22 45.3	28 55.3	2 29.1	7 10.1	4 1.1	6 8.8	26 38.7	28 41.6
5	0 52 24.7	11 11.2	19 11.2	20 53.8	24 4.2	29 30.4	3 6.3	7 20.2	4 7.9	6 11.2	26 39.6	28 43.9
6	0 56 21.2	12 10.4	19 8.0	5♎43.5	25 27.9	0♍ 6.8	3 43.5	7 30.3	4 14.8	6 13.7	26 40.5	28 46.3
7	1 0 17.8	13 9.6	19 4.9	20 21.3	26 55.8	0 44.6	4 20.6	7 40.6	4 21.7	6 16.3	26 41.4	28 48.6
8	1 4 14.4	14 8.8	19 1.7	4♏39.6	28 27.2	1 23.5	4 57.6	7 50.9	4 28.6	6 18.9	26 42.3	28 51.0
9	1 8 10.9	15 8.0	18 58.5	18 33.5	0♎ 1.6	2 3.6	5 34.7	8 1.4	4 35.6	6 21.5	26 43.3	28 53.3
10	1 12 7.5	16 7.3	18 55.3	2♐ .8	1 38.4	2 44.8	6 11.6	8 11.9	4 42.5	6 24.1	26 44.3	28 55.7
11	1 16 4.0	17 6.6	18 52.2	15 1.9	3 17.1	3 27.1	6 48.6	8 22.5	4 49.5	6 26.8	26 45.4	28 58.1
12	1 20 .6	18 6.0	18 49.0	27 39.7	4 57.4	4 10.5	7 25.5	8 33.3	4 56.6	6 29.5	26 46.4	29 .5
13	1 23 57.1	19 5.4	18 45.8	9♑58.1	6 38.9	4 54.9	8 2.4	8 44.1	5 3.6	6 32.3	26 47.5	29 2.8
14	1 27 53.7	20 4.8	18 42.6	22 2.2	8 21.3	5 40.2	8 39.3	8 55.0	5 10.7	6 35.1	26 48.7	29 5.2
15	1 31 50.2	21 4.2	18 39.4	3♒57.2	10 4.3	6 26.5	9 16.1	9 6.0	5 17.7	6 37.9	26 49.8	29 7.6
16	1 35 46.8	22 3.7	18 36.3	15 48.3	11 47.7	7 13.7	9 52.9	9 17.0	5 24.8	6 40.8	26 51.0	29 10.0
17	1 39 43.3	23 3.1	18 33.1	27 40.1	13 31.3	8 1.7	10 29.6	9 28.2	5 32.0	6 43.7	26 52.2	29 12.4
18	1 43 39.9	24 2.7	18 29.9	9♓36.7	15 15.0	8 50.7	11 6.4	9 39.5	5 39.1	6 46.6	26 53.5	29 14.9
19	1 47 36.4	25 2.3	18 26.7	21 41.4	16 58.5	9 40.4	11 43.0	9 50.8	5 46.3	6 49.6	26 54.8	29 17.3
20	1 51 33.0	26 1.9	18 23.6	3♈56.4	18 41.9	10 30.9	12 19.7	10 2.2	5 53.4	6 52.6	26 56.1	29 19.7
21	1 55 29.6	27 1.5	18 20.4	16 23.2	20 25.0	11 22.2	12 56.3	10 13.7	6 .6	6 55.6	26 57.4	29 22.1
22	1 59 26.1	28 1.1	18 17.2	29 2.4	22 7.8	12 14.2	13 32.8	10 25.2	6 7.8	6 58.7	26 58.8	29 24.5
23	2 3 22.7	29 .8	18 14.0	11♉53.9	23 50.1	13 7.0	14 9.4	10 36.8	6 15.0	7 1.7	27 .2	29 27.0
24	2 7 19.2	0♏ .5	18 10.8	24 57.3	25 32.1	14 .4	14 45.8	10 48.5	6 22.2	7 4.8	27 1.6	29 29.4
25	2 11 15.8	1 .3	18 7.7	8♊12.0	27 13.6	14 54.5	15 22.3	11 .3	6 29.4	7 8.0	27 3.0	29 31.8
26	2 15 12.3	2 .1	18 4.5	21 37.8	28 54.6	15 49.2	15 58.7	11 12.1	6 36.6	7 11.1	27 4.5	29 34.2
27	2 19 8.9	2 59.9	18 1.3	5♋14.5	0♏35.1	16 44.6	16 35.1	11 24.0	6 43.8	7 14.3	27 6.0	29 36.6
28	2 23 5.4	3 59.7	17 58.1	19 2.1	2 15.0	17 40.5	17 11.5	11 36.0	6 51.1	7 17.5	27 7.5	29 39.0
29	2 27 2.0	4 59.6	17 55.0	3♌ .7	3 54.5	18 37.1	17 47.8	11 48.1	6 58.3	7 20.8	27 9.0	29 41.5
30	2 30 58.5	5 59.6	17 51.8	17 9.6	5 33.5	19 34.2	18 24.0	12 .2	7 5.5	7 24.1	27 10.6	29 43.9
31	2 34 55.1	6 59.6	17 48.6	1♍27.5	7 12.0	20 31.8	19 .3	12 12.4	7 12.8	7 27.3	27 12.2	29 46.3
		LATITUDE										
1	0 36 38.5	0 .0	0 .0	2N47.8	1N 8.3	4S 5.5	1N17.0	0N29.8	2N13.4	0N 4.2	1N12.3	16N25.4
4	0 48 28.1	0 .0	0 .0	4 55.3	1 35.4	3 35.0	1 17.9	0 29.3	2 13.1	0 4.2	1 12.1	16 24.9
7	1 0 17.8	0 .0	0 .0	4 16.3	1 51.1	3 5.6	1 18.8	0 28.9	2 12.8	0 4.2	1 12.0	16 24.3
10	1 12 7.5	0 .0	0 .0	1 23.0	1 57.1	2 37.2	1 19.7	0 28.4	2 12.6	0 4.1	1 11.9	16 23.9
13	1 23 57.1	0 .0	0 .0	1S56.0	1 55.3	2 10.0	1 20.6	0 28.0	2 12.4	0 4.1	1 11.7	16 23.6
16	1 35 46.8	0 .0	0 .0	4 20.0	1 47.5	1 44.0	1 21.4	0 27.5	2 12.2	0 4.1	1 11.6	16 23.3
19	1 47 36.4	0 .0	0 .0	5 4.8	1 35.3	1 19.3	1 22.3	0 27.1	2 12.0	0 4.0	1 11.5	16 23.1
22	1 59 26.1	0 .0	0 .0	3 47.6	1 19.9	0 55.9	1 23.1	0 26.7	2 11.9	0 4.0	1 11.3	16 23.0
25	2 11 15.8	0 .0	0 .0	0 45.5	1 2.4	0 33.8	1 23.9	0 26.3	2 11.7	0 4.0	1 11.2	16 23.0
28	2 23 5.4	0 .0	0 .0	2N46.3	0 43.4	0 13.1	1 24.7	0 25.9	2 11.7	0 3.9	1 11.1	16 23.0
31	2 34 55.1	0 .0	0 .0	4 59.4	0 23.6	0N 6.3	1 25.5	0 25.5	2 11.6	0 3.9	1 11.0	16 23.2
		RIGHT ASCENSION										
1	0 36 38.5	6♎39.4	18♊28.2	24♋37.4	20♍42.6	28♌ 5.3	3♍ 9.0	4♐55.2	2♏12.5	4♐ 9.3	26♐20.1	2♏20.8
2	0 40 35.0	7 33.7	18 24.7	10♌ 2.7	21 42.3	28 38.1	3 44.8	5 5.4	2 18.9	4 11.8	26 20.9	2 22.8
3	0 44 31.6	8 28.1	18 21.3	25 7.4	22 47.9	29 12.3	4 20.4	5 15.8	2 25.4	4 14.3	26 21.8	2 24.8
4	0 48 28.1	9 22.5	18 17.9	9♍39.7	23 58.6	29 47.8	4 56.0	5 26.3	2 31.9	4 16.9	26 22.6	2 26.8
5	0 52 24.7	10 17.1	18 14.4	23 38.2	25 13.8	0♍24.6	5 31.5	5 36.9	2 38.4	4 19.5	26 23.6	2 28.8
6	0 56 21.2	11 11.7	18 11.0	7♎ 9.6	26 32.9	1 2.5	6 6.9	5 47.6	2 45.0	4 22.1	26 24.5	2 30.9
7	1 0 17.8	12 6.4	18 7.5	20 24.5	27 55.2	1 41.6	6 42.2	5 58.4	2 51.6	4 24.8	26 25.5	2 32.9
8	1 4 14.4	13 1.2	18 4.1	3♏34.3	29 20.3	2 21.8	7 17.5	6 9.3	2 58.2	4 27.5	26 26.5	2 35.0
9	1 8 10.9	13 56.1	18 .7	16 48.5	0♎47.6	3 3.0	7 52.6	6 20.3	3 4.8	4 30.3	26 27.6	2 37.1
10	1 12 7.5	14 51.2	17 57.2	0♐12.7	2 16.8	3 45.2	8 27.7	6 31.5	3 11.5	4 33.1	26 28.7	2 39.2
11	1 16 4.0	15 46.3	17 53.8	13 47.0	3 47.4	4 28.4	9 2.7	6 42.7	3 18.2	4 35.9	26 29.8	2 41.3
12	1 20 .6	16 41.5	17 50.3	27 26.0	5 19.2	5 12.5	9 37.6	6 54.0	3 24.9	4 38.8	26 31.0	2 43.4
13	1 23 57.1	17 36.9	17 46.9	11♑ .2	6 51.8	5 57.5	10 12.4	7 5.5	3 31.6	4 41.7	26 32.1	2 45.5
14	1 27 53.7	18 32.4	17 43.5	24 18.8	8 25.1	6 43.3	10 47.2	7 17.0	3 38.4	4 44.7	26 33.4	2 47.6
15	1 31 50.2	19 28.0	17 40.0	7♒13.0	9 58.8	7 29.9	11 21.9	7 28.6	3 45.2	4 47.7	26 34.6	2 49.7
16	1 35 46.8	20 23.7	17 36.6	19 38.1	11 32.8	8 17.2	11 56.5	7 40.4	3 52.0	4 50.7	26 35.9	2 51.9
17	1 39 43.3	21 19.6	17 33.1	1♓34.6	13 6.9	9 5.3	12 31.0	7 52.2	3 58.8	4 53.7	26 37.2	2 54.0
18	1 43 39.9	22 15.7	17 29.7	13 7.0	14 41.2	9 54.2	13 5.5	8 4.1	4 5.7	4 56.9	26 38.6	2 56.2
19	1 47 36.4	23 11.9	17 26.3	24 23.3	16 15.4	10 43.7	13 39.9	8 16.2	4 12.5	5 .0	26 40.0	2 58.4
20	1 51 33.0	24 8.2	17 22.8	5♈33.3	17 49.6	11 33.8	14 14.2	8 28.2	4 19.4	5 3.2	26 41.4	3 .5
21	1 55 29.6	25 4.7	17 19.4	16 48.5	19 23.7	12 24.5	14 48.4	8 40.4	4 26.3	5 6.4	26 42.8	3 2.7
22	1 59 26.1	26 1.3	17 16.0	28 21.0	20 57.7	13 15.8	15 22.6	8 52.7	4 33.2	5 9.6	26 44.3	3 4.9
23	2 3 22.7	26 58.1	17 12.5	10♉23.0	22 31.5	14 7.7	15 56.7	9 5.0	4 40.1	5 12.9	26 45.8	3 7.0
24	2 7 19.2	27 55.1	17 9.1	23 5.1	24 5.3	15 .1	16 30.7	9 17.5	4 47.1	5 16.2	26 47.3	3 9.2
25	2 11 15.8	28 52.3	17 5.6	6♊34.5	25 38.9	15 53.1	17 4.7	9 30.0	4 54.0	5 19.5	26 48.8	3 11.4
26	2 15 12.3	29 49.6	17 2.2	20 51.5	27 12.4	16 46.5	17 38.6	9 42.6	5 .9	5 22.8	26 50.4	3 13.6
27	2 19 8.9	0♏47.1	16 58.8	5♋46.9	28 45.9	17 40.4	18 12.5	9 55.3	5 7.9	5 26.2	26 52.0	3 15.8
28	2 23 5.4	1 44.8	16 55.3	21 2.2	0♏19.2	18 34.8	18 46.2	10 8.0	5 14.9	5 29.6	26 53.7	3 17.9
29	2 27 2.0	2 42.7	16 51.9	6♌14.4	1 52.6	19 29.6	19 20.0	10 20.9	5 21.8	5 33.0	26 55.3	3 20.1
30	2 30 58.5	3 40.8	16 48.5	21 3.6	3 25.8	20 24.8	19 53.6	10 33.8	5 28.8	5 36.5	26 57.0	3 22.3
31	2 34 55.1	4 39.1	16 45.0	5♍19.3	4 59.1	21 20.5	20 27.2	10 46.8	5 35.8	5 40.0	26 58.7	3 24.5
		DECLINATION										
1	0 36 38.5	2S52.7	0N24.1	24N20.9	5N14.5	8N33.8	12N27.2	20S56.2	10S39.1	21S14.8	22S11.7	4N24.5
4	0 48 28.1	4 2.4	0 24.1	13 52.5	4 20.2	8 29.3	11 48.1	21 1.6	10 46.2	21 16.0	22 11.9	4 21.6
7	1 0 17.8	5 11.8	0 24.1	3S59.7	2 55.2	8 19.0	11 8.5	21 7.1	10 53.4	21 17.4	22 12.1	4 18.8
10	1 12 7.5	6 20.5	0 24.1	19 12.7	1 8.3	8 3.0	10 28.5	21 12.6	11 .6	21 18.7	22 12.3	4 16.1
13	1 23 57.1	7 28.5	0 24.1	24 59.7	0S52.5	7 41.6	9 48.0	21 18.0	11 7.8	21 20.2	22 12.5	4 13.3
16	1 35 46.8	8 35.6	0 24.0	20 14.1	3 .9	7 14.8	9 7.3	21 23.5	11 15.0	21 21.6	22 12.7	4 10.7
19	1 47 36.4	9 41.6	0 24.0	7 57.7	5 12.1	6 43.1	8 26.2	21 29.0	11 22.2	21 23.2	22 12.9	4 8.1
22	1 59 26.1	10 46.2	0 24.0	7N35.1	7 22.9	6 6.6	7 44.9	21 34.4	11 29.4	21 24.7	22 13.1	4 5.6
25	2 11 15.8	11 49.5	0 24.0	20 55.7	9 31.0	5 25.5	7 3.3	21 39.7	11 36.6	21 26.3	22 13.4	4 3.1
28	2 23 5.4	12 51.1	0 24.0	24 50.0	11 34.6	4 40.2	6 21.6	21 45.0	11 43.7	21 27.9	22 13.6	4 .8
31	2 34 55.1	13 51.0	0 24.0	15 36.8	13 32.7	3 51.0	5 39.8	21 50.2	11 50.8	21 29.6	22 13.8	3 58.5

NOVEMBER 1983

LONGITUDE

DAY	EPHEM. SID. TIME (h m s)	☉	☊	☽	☿	♀	♂	♃	♄	♅	♆	♇
1	2 38 51.7	7♏59.6	17♊45.4	15♍51.3	8♏50.0	21♍30.0	19♍36.5	12♐24.6	7♏20.0	7♐30.7	27♐13.8	29♎48.7
2	2 42 48.2	8 59.6	17 42.2	0♎17.1	10 27.6	22 28.7	20 12.6	12 36.9	7 27.2	7 34.0	27 15.4	29 51.1
3	2 46 44.8	9 59.7	17 39.1	14 39.6	12 4.6	23 27.8	20 48.7	12 49.3	7 34.5	7 37.4	27 17.1	29 53.5
4	2 50 41.3	10 59.8	17 35.9	28 53.0	13 41.3	24 27.5	21 24.8	13 1.7	7 41.7	7 40.7	27 18.8	29 55.8
5	2 54 37.9	11 60.0	17 32.7	12♏52.1	15 17.4	25 27.5	22 .8	13 14.2	7 48.9	7 44.1	27 20.5	29 58.2
6	2 58 34.4	13 .1	17 29.5	26 32.6	16 53.2	26 28.1	22 36.8	13 26.7	7 56.2	7 47.6	27 22.2	0♏.6
7	3 2 31.0	14 .3	17 26.4	9♐52.3	18 28.6	27 29.0	23 12.8	13 39.3	8 3.4	7 51.0	27 24.0	0 3.0
8	3 6 27.5	15 .6	17 23.2	22 50.4	20 3.6	28 30.4	23 48.7	13 52.0	8 10.6	7 54.5	27 25.8	0 5.4
9	3 10 24.1	16 .9	17 20.0	5♑28.1	21 38.2	29 32.1	24 24.5	14 4.7	8 17.8	7 58.0	27 27.6	0 7.7
10	3 14 20.7	17 1.2	17 16.8	17 48.2	23 12.4	0♎34.2	25 .3	14 17.4	8 25.0	8 1.5	27 29.4	0 10.1
11	3 18 17.2	18 1.5	17 13.7	29 54.3	24 46.3	1 36.7	25 36.1	14 30.2	8 32.2	8 5.0	27 31.3	0 12.4
12	3 22 13.8	19 1.8	17 10.5	11♒51.2	26 19.9	2 39.6	26 11.8	14 43.0	8 39.4	8 8.5	27 33.1	0 14.7
13	3 26 10.3	20 2.2	17 7.3	23 43.4	27 53.2	3 42.8	26 47.4	14 55.9	8 46.5	8 12.1	27 35.0	0 17.0
14	3 30 6.9	21 2.6	17 4.1	5♓36.1	29 26.1	4 46.3	27 23.1	15 8.8	8 53.7	8 15.6	27 36.9	0 19.3
15	3 34 3.4	22 3.0	17 .9	17 33.9	0♐58.6	5 50.2	27 58.6	15 21.8	9 .8	8 19.2	27 38.8	0 21.6
16	3 37 60.0	23 3.4	16 57.8	29 41.0	2 31.2	6 54.4	28 34.1	15 34.8	9 7.9	8 22.8	27 40.8	0 23.9
17	3 41 56.5	24 3.8	16 54.6	12♈ 1.0	4 3.3	7 58.8	29 9.6	15 47.9	9 15.0	8 26.4	27 42.7	0 26.2
18	3 45 53.1	25 4.3	16 51.4	24 36.5	5 35.2	9 3.7	29 45.0	16 1.0	9 22.0	8 30.0	27 44.7	0 28.4
19	3 49 49.7	26 4.8	16 48.2	7♉28.9	7 6.8	10 8.8	0♎20.3	16 14.1	9 29.1	8 33.6	27 46.7	0 30.7
20	3 53 46.2	27 5.3	16 45.1	20 38.5	8 38.2	11 14.1	0 55.6	16 27.2	9 36.1	8 37.2	27 48.7	0 32.9
21	3 57 42.8	28 5.9	16 41.9	4♊4.6	10 9.3	12 19.8	1 30.9	16 40.4	9 43.1	8 40.9	27 50.7	0 35.1
22	4 1 39.3	29 6.5	16 38.7	17 45.3	11 40.1	13 25.7	2 6.1	16 53.7	9 50.1	8 44.5	27 52.7	0 37.3
23	4 5 35.9	0♐7.1	16 35.5	1♋38.0	13 10.7	14 32.0	2 41.3	17 6.9	9 57.0	8 48.2	27 54.8	0 39.5
24	4 9 32.4	1 7.7	16 32.4	15 39.9	14 41.0	15 38.4	3 16.4	17 20.2	10 4.0	8 51.8	27 56.8	0 41.6
25	4 13 29.0	2 8.3	16 29.2	29 48.0	16 10.9	16 45.1	3 51.4	17 33.5	10 10.9	8 55.5	27 58.9	0 43.8
26	4 17 25.6	3 9.0	16 26.0	13♌59.5	17 40.6	17 52.1	4 26.4	17 46.9	10 17.8	8 59.2	28 1.0	0 45.9
27	4 21 22.1	4 9.7	16 22.8	28 11.9	19 9.9	18 59.3	5 1.4	18 .2	10 24.6	9 2.8	28 3.1	0 48.0
28	4 25 18.7	5 10.5	16 19.6	12♍22.9	20 38.8	20 6.7	5 36.3	18 13.7	10 31.4	9 6.5	28 5.2	0 50.1
29	4 29 15.2	6 11.3	16 16.5	26 30.4	22 7.3	21 14.4	6 11.1	18 27.1	10 38.2	9 10.3	28 7.4	0 52.2
30	4 33 11.8	7 12.1	16 13.3	10♎32.1	23 35.3	22 22.3	6 45.9	18 40.6	10 45.0	9 13.9	28 9.6	0 54.3

LATITUDE

DAY	EPHEM. SID. TIME (h m s)	☉	☊	☽	☿	♀	♂	♃	♄	♅	♆	♇
1	2 38 51.7	0 .0	0 .0	5N10.1	0N16.9	0N12.5	1N25.8	0N25.4	2N11.6	0N 3.9	1N10.9	16N23.2
4	2 50 41.3	0 .0	0 .0	3 49.1	0S 3.3	0 30.1	1 26.6	0 25.0	2 11.6	0 3.8	1 10.8	16 23.5
7	3 2 31.0	0 .0	0 .0	0 34.2	0 23.4	0 46.4	1 27.3	0 24.7	2 11.6	0 3.8	1 10.7	16 23.8
10	3 14 20.7	0 .0	0 .0	2S44.8	0 43.0	1 1.4	1 28.1	0 24.3	2 11.6	0 3.8	1 10.6	16 24.2
13	3 26 10.3	0 .0	0 .0	4 50.2	1 1.8	1 15.0	1 28.8	0 24.0	2 11.7	0 3.8	1 10.5	16 24.7
16	3 37 60.0	0 .0	0 .0	5 5.4	1 19.5	1 27.3	1 29.5	0 23.6	2 11.7	0 3.7	1 10.4	16 25.2
19	3 49 49.7	0 .0	0 .0	3 16.2	1 35.8	1 38.4	1 30.2	0 23.3	2 11.9	0 3.7	1 10.3	16 25.8
22	4 1 39.3	0 .0	0 .0	0N10.2	1 50.4	1 48.1	1 30.9	0 23.0	2 12.0	0 3.7	1 10.3	16 26.5
25	4 13 29.0	0 .0	0 .0	3 39.5	2 2.9	1 56.7	1 31.6	0 22.7	2 12.2	0 3.6	1 10.2	16 27.3
28	4 25 18.7	0 .0	0 .0	5 15.9	2 13.8	2 3.3	1 32.3	0 22.4	2 12.4	0 3.6	1 10.1	16 28.2

RIGHT ASCENSION

DAY	EPHEM. SID. TIME (h m s)	☉	☊	☽	☿	♀	♂	♃	♄	♅	♆	♇
1	2 38 51.7	5♏37.6	16♊41.6	19♍.9	6♏32.4	22♍16.5	21♍.7	10♐59.8	5♏42.8	5♐43.5	27♐.5	3♏26.7
2	2 42 48.2	6 36.3	16 38.2	2♎15.8	8 5.8	23 12.9	21 34.2	11 12.9	5 49.8	5 47.0	27 2.3	3 28.9
3	2 46 44.8	7 35.1	16 34.7	15 15.5	9 39.2	24 9.6	22 7.6	11 26.1	5 56.8	5 50.6	27 4.1	3 31.1
4	2 50 41.3	8 34.2	16 31.3	28 12.7	11 12.8	25 6.7	22 41.0	11 39.4	6 3.8	5 54.2	27 5.9	3 33.3
5	2 54 37.9	9 33.5	16 27.9	11♏18.3	12 46.4	26 4.1	23 14.3	11 52.7	6 10.8	5 57.8	27 7.7	3 35.4
6	2 58 34.4	10 33.1	16 24.4	24 39.9	14 20.2	27 1.9	23 47.5	12 6.1	6 17.8	6 1.4	27 9.6	3 37.6
7	3 2 31.0	11 32.8	16 21.0	8♐18.8	15 54.2	27 59.9	24 20.7	12 19.6	6 24.7	6 5.1	27 11.5	3 39.8
8	3 6 27.5	12 32.7	16 17.6	22 10.0	17 28.4	28 58.3	24 53.9	12 33.2	6 31.8	6 8.8	27 13.5	3 42.0
9	3 10 24.1	13 32.9	16 14.1	6♑ 2.1	19 2.8	29 56.9	25 26.9	12 46.8	6 38.8	6 12.5	27 15.4	3 44.2
10	3 14 20.7	14 33.2	16 10.7	19 41.3	20 37.4	0♎55.8	25 59.9	13 .4	6 45.7	6 16.2	27 17.4	3 46.3
11	3 18 17.2	15 33.7	16 7.3	2♒55.1	22 12.1	1 55.0	26 32.9	13 14.1	6 52.7	6 19.9	27 19.4	3 48.5
12	3 22 13.8	16 34.5	16 3.8	15 36.2	23 47.3	2 54.5	27 5.8	13 27.9	6 59.6	6 23.7	27 21.4	3 50.6
13	3 26 10.3	17 35.5	16 .4	27 43.4	25 22.6	3 54.2	27 38.6	13 41.7	7 6.6	6 27.4	27 23.4	3 52.8
14	3 30 6.9	18 36.6	15 57.0	9♓21.2	26 58.2	4 54.2	28 11.4	13 55.5	7 13.5	6 31.2	27 25.4	3 54.9
15	3 34 3.4	19 38.0	15 53.6	20 37.8	28 34.1	5 54.5	28 44.1	14 9.4	7 20.4	6 35.0	27 27.5	3 57.1
16	3 37 60.0	20 39.6	15 50.1	1♈44.4	0♐10.2	6 55.0	29 16.8	14 23.4	7 27.3	6 38.8	27 29.6	3 59.2
17	3 41 56.5	21 41.4	15 46.7	12 53.3	1 46.6	7 55.8	29 49.4	14 37.4	7 34.2	6 42.6	27 31.7	4 1.3
18	3 45 53.1	22 43.4	15 43.3	24 18.1	3 23.3	8 56.8	0♎22.0	14 51.5	7 41.1	6 46.5	27 33.8	4 3.4
19	3 49 49.7	23 45.6	15 39.8	6♉12.6	5 .2	9 58.1	0 54.6	15 5.6	7 48.0	6 50.3	27 36.0	4 5.5
20	3 53 46.2	24 48.0	15 36.4	18 49.4	6 37.4	10 59.6	1 27.0	15 19.7	7 54.8	6 54.1	27 38.1	4 7.6
21	3 57 42.8	25 50.6	15 33.0	2♊18.0	8 14.7	12 1.4	1 59.5	15 33.9	8 1.6	6 58.0	27 40.3	4 9.7
22	4 1 39.3	26 53.4	15 29.5	16 40.4	9 52.3	13 3.5	2 31.9	15 48.1	8 8.5	7 1.9	27 42.5	4 11.7
23	4 5 35.9	27 56.5	15 26.1	1♋48.0	11 30.0	14 5.8	3 4.2	16 2.4	8 15.2	7 5.8	27 44.7	4 13.8
24	4 9 32.4	28 59.7	15 22.7	17 20.0	13 7.8	15 8.4	3 36.5	16 16.7	8 22.0	7 9.7	27 47.0	4 15.8
25	4 13 29.0	0♐3.1	15 19.3	2♌48.9	14 45.7	16 11.2	4 8.7	16 31.0	8 28.7	7 13.6	27 49.2	4 17.8
26	4 17 25.6	1 6.7	15 15.8	17 50.4	16 23.5	17 14.3	4 40.9	16 45.4	8 35.4	7 17.5	27 51.5	4 19.9
27	4 21 22.1	2 10.5	15 12.4	2♍10.6	18 1.3	18 17.6	5 13.1	16 59.8	8 42.1	7 21.4	27 53.7	4 21.9
28	4 25 18.7	3 14.5	15 9.0	15 48.4	19 39.0	19 21.2	5 45.2	17 14.3	8 48.8	7 25.3	27 56.0	4 23.9
29	4 29 15.2	4 18.7	15 5.6	28 51.8	21 16.5	20 25.1	6 17.3	17 28.8	8 55.5	7 29.3	27 58.4	4 25.9
30	4 33 11.8	5 23.1	15 2.1	11♎33.8	22 53.6	21 29.2	6 49.3	17 43.3	9 2.1	7 33.2	28 .7	4 27.8

DECLINATION

DAY	EPHEM. SID. TIME (h m s)	☉	☊	☽	☿	♀	♂	♃	♄	♅	♆	♇
1	2 38 51.7	14S10.5	0N24.0	10N20.3	14S10.7	3N33.8	5N25.8	21S51.9	11S53.2	21S30.1	22S13.9	3N57.7
4	2 50 41.3	15 7.7	0 23.9	7S30.4	16 .1	2 39.8	4 43.8	21 57.0	12 .2	21 31.8	22 14.1	3 55.6
7	3 2 31.0	16 2.6	0 23.9	14 22.1	17 42.2	1 42.6	4 1.9	22 2.0	12 7.2	21 33.5	22 14.3	3 53.5
10	3 14 20.7	16 55.2	0 23.9	24 58.8	19 16.2	0 42.7	3 19.9	22 6.9	12 14.0	21 35.2	22 14.5	3 51.5
13	3 26 10.3	17 45.2	0 23.9	18 10.5	20 41.7	0S19.7	2 38.0	22 11.6	12 20.8	21 36.9	22 14.7	3 49.7
16	3 37 60.0	18 32.3	0 23.9	4 47.7	21 58.0	1 24.3	1 56.3	22 16.2	12 27.5	21 38.6	22 14.9	3 47.9
19	3 49 49.7	19 16.5	0 23.9	10N54.9	23 4.5	2 30.6	1 14.7	22 20.6	12 34.1	21 40.4	22 15.1	3 46.3
22	4 1 39.3	19 57.6	0 23.8	23 2.8	24 .6	3 38.4	0 33.3	22 24.9	12 40.5	21 42.1	22 15.2	3 44.8
25	4 13 29.0	20 35.5	0 23.8	23 46.2	24 47.3	4 47.3	0S 7.9	22 29.0	12 46.8	21 43.8	22 15.4	3 43.4
28	4 25 18.7	21 9.9	0 23.8	11 46.6	25 19.3	5 56.9	0 48.9	22 32.9	12 53.0	21 45.5	22 15.6	3 42.1

DECEMBER 1983

DAY	EPHEM. SID. TIME	☉	☊	☾	☿	♀	♂	♃	♄	♅	♆	♇
	h m s	° ′	° ′	° ′	° ′	° ′	° ′	° ′	° ′	° ′	° ′	° ′
		LONGITUDE										
1	4 37 8.3	8♐12.9	16♊10.1	24♎26.0	25♐ 2.7	23♎30.3	7♎20.6	18♐54.1	10♏51.7	9♐17.6	28♐11.7	0♏56.3
2	4 41 4.9	9 13.7	16 6.9	8♏ 9.8	26 29.4	24 38.6	7 55.3	19 7.5	10 58.4	9 21.3	28 13.9	0 58.4
3	4 45 1.5	10 14.6	16 3.8	21 41.4	27 55.4	25 47.1	8 29.8	19 21.1	11 5.0	9 25.0	28 16.1	1 .4
4	4 48 58.0	11 15.5	16 .6	4♐59.0	29 20.5	26 55.7	9 4.4	19 34.6	11 11.7	9 28.7	28 18.2	1 2.3
5	4 52 54.6	12 16.4	15 57.4	18 1.4	0♑44.6	28 4.5	9 38.8	19 48.1	11 18.2	9 32.4	28 20.4	1 4.3
6	4 56 51.1	13 17.3	15 54.2	0♑48.0	2 7.5	29 13.5	10 13.2	20 1.7	11 24.8	9 36.1	28 22.6	1 6.2
7	5 0 47.7	14 18.2	15 51.1	13 19.3	3 29.1	0♏22.7	10 47.5	20 15.3	11 31.2	9 39.8	28 24.8	1 8.1
8	5 4 44.3	15 19.2	15 47.9	25 36.7	4 49.0	1 32.0	11 21.8	20 28.9	11 37.7	9 43.4	28 27.1	1 10.0
9	5 8 40.8	16 20.1	15 44.7	7♒42.3	6 7.1	2 41.5	11 55.9	20 42.5	11 44.1	9 47.1	28 29.3	1 11.9
10	5 12 37.4	17 21.1	15 41.5	19 39.5	7 23.1	3 51.1	12 30.0	20 56.1	11 50.4	9 50.8	28 31.5	1 13.7
11	5 16 33.9	18 22.1	15 38.4	1♓32.0	8 36.5	5 .9	13 4.1	21 9.7	11 56.8	9 54.4	28 33.8	1 15.5
12	5 20 30.5	19 23.1	15 35.2	13 24.1	9 47.0	6 10.8	13 38.0	21 23.3	12 3.0	9 58.1	28 36.0	1 17.3
13	5 24 27.0	20 24.1	15 32.0	25 20.5	10 54.2	7 20.8	14 11.9	21 36.9	12 9.2	10 1.8	28 38.2	1 19.1
14	5 28 23.6	21 25.1	15 28.8	7♈25.9	11 57.5	8 31.0	14 45.7	21 50.6	12 15.4	10 5.4	28 40.5	1 20.8
15	5 32 20.2	22 26.1	15 25.6	19 44.8	12 56.3	9 41.4	15 19.4	22 4.2	12 21.5	10 9.0	28 42.8	1 22.5
16	5 36 16.7	23 27.1	15 22.5	2♉21.4	13 49.9	10 51.8	15 53.1	22 17.8	12 27.6	10 12.6	28 45.0	1 24.2
17	5 40 13.3	24 28.2	15 19.3	15 18.7	14 37.7	12 2.4	16 26.6	22 31.4	12 33.6	10 16.2	28 47.3	1 25.9
18	5 44 9.8	25 29.2	15 16.1	28 38.5	15 18.8	13 13.1	17 .1	22 45.1	12 39.5	10 19.8	28 49.5	1 27.5
19	5 48 6.4	26 30.3	15 12.9	12♊21.0	15 52.4	14 23.9	17 33.5	22 58.7	12 45.4	10 23.4	28 51.8	1 29.1
20	5 52 2.9	27 31.4	15 9.8	26 24.4	16 17.7	15 34.9	18 6.9	23 12.4	12 51.3	10 27.1	28 54.1	1 30.7
21	5 55 59.5	28 32.5	15 6.6	10♋44.9	16 33.5	16 46.0	18 40.2	23 26.0	12 57.1	10 30.6	28 56.4	1 32.3
22	5 59 56.1	29 33.6	15 3.4	25 17.2	16 39.2	17 57.1	19 13.3	23 39.6	13 2.8	10 34.2	28 58.7	1 33.8
23	6 3 52.6	0♑34.7	15 .2	9♌54.8	16R34.0	19 8.4	19 46.4	23 53.2	13 8.5	10 37.7	29 .9	1 35.3
24	6 7 49.2	1 35.8	14 57.1	24 31.4	16 17.3	20 19.8	20 19.4	24 6.8	13 14.1	10 41.2	29 3.2	1 36.8
25	6 11 45.7	2 36.9	14 53.9	9♍ 1.2	15 48.8	21 31.3	20 52.3	24 20.4	13 19.7	10 44.7	29 5.5	1 38.2
26	6 15 42.3	3 38.0	14 50.7	23 19.8	15 8.7	22 42.9	21 25.1	24 33.9	13 25.2	10 48.2	29 7.7	1 39.6
27	6 19 38.9	4 39.1	14 47.5	7♎24.4	14 17.3	23 54.6	21 57.8	24 47.5	13 30.6	10 51.6	29 10.0	1 41.0
28	6 23 35.4	5 40.3	14 44.4	21 13.9	13 15.9	25 6.4	22 30.5	25 1.0	13 35.9	10 55.1	29 12.2	1 42.3
29	6 27 32.0	6 41.4	14 41.2	4♏48.1	12 5.9	26 18.2	23 3.0	25 14.5	13 41.2	10 58.5	29 14.5	1 43.6
30	6 31 28.5	7 42.6	14 38.0	18 7.5	10 49.4	27 30.2	23 35.4	25 28.1	13 46.5	11 1.9	29 16.8	1 44.9
31	6 35 25.1	8 43.8	14 34.8	1♐13.3	9 28.9	28 42.2	24 7.8	25 41.5	13 51.6	11 5.3	29 19.0	1 46.1
		LATITUDE										
1	4 37 8.3	0 .0	0 .0	4N 8.0	2S19.8	2N10.0	1N32.9	0N22.1	2N12.6	0N 3.6	1N10.1	16N29.1
4	4 48 58.0	0 .0	0 .0	1 .2	2 22.9	2 14.9	1 33.5	0 21.8	2 12.9	0 3.6	1 10.0	16 30.1
7	5 0 47.7	0 .0	0 .0	2S26.3	2 21.5	2 18.6	1 34.2	0 21.5	2 13.1	0 3.5	1 9.9	16 31.1
10	5 12 37.4	0 .0	0 .0	4 44.6	2 14.3	2 21.2	1 34.8	0 21.2	2 13.4	0 3.5	1 9.9	16 32.3
13	5 24 27.0	0 .0	0 .0	5 12.8	2 .1	2 22.7	1 35.3	0 21.0	2 13.8	0 3.5	1 9.8	16 33.5
16	5 36 16.7	0 .0	0 .0	3 38.8	1 37.4	2 23.2	1 35.9	0 20.7	2 14.1	0 3.4	1 9.8	16 34.7
19	5 48 6.4	0 .0	0 .0	0 20.0	1 4.3	2 22.7	1 36.4	0 20.4	2 14.5	0 3.4	1 9.8	16 36.0
22	5 59 56.1	0 .0	0 .0	3N20.7	0 20.0	2 21.2	1 37.0	0 20.2	2 14.9	0 3.4	1 9.8	16 37.3
25	6 11 45.7	0 .0	0 .0	5 13.4	0N34.3	2 18.9	1 37.5	0 19.9	2 15.3	0 3.4	1 9.7	16 38.7
28	6 23 35.4	0 .0	0 .0	4 17.4	1 33.3	2 15.6	1 37.9	0 19.7	2 15.8	0 3.3	1 9.7	16 40.2
31	6 35 25.1	0 .0	0 .0	1 19.9	2 26.2	2 11.6	1 38.4	0 19.5	2 16.3	0 3.3	1 9.7	16 41.7
		RIGHT ASCENSION										
1	4 37 8.3	6♐27.6	14♊58.7	24♎ 9.1	24♐30.3	22♎33.6	7♎21.3	17♐57.8	9♏ 8.7	7♐37.1	28♐ 3.0	4♏29.8
2	4 41 4.9	7 32.4	14 55.3	6♏51.4	26 6.4	23 38.3	7 53.2	18 12.4	9 15.2	7 41.0	28 5.4	4 31.7
3	4 45 1.5	8 37.2	14 51.9	19 51.3	27 41.7	24 43.2	8 25.1	18 27.0	9 21.7	7 45.0	28 7.7	4 33.6
4	4 48 58.0	9 42.3	14 48.4	3♐14.0	29 16.2	25 48.3	8 56.9	18 41.6	9 28.2	7 48.9	28 10.1	4 35.5
5	4 52 54.6	10 47.4	14 45.0	16 57.7	0♑49.5	26 53.8	9 28.7	18 56.2	9 34.6	7 52.8	28 12.4	4 37.4
6	4 56 51.1	11 52.8	14 41.6	0♑52.9	2 21.5	27 59.5	10 .4	19 10.9	9 41.0	7 56.7	28 14.8	4 39.3
7	5 0 47.7	12 58.2	14 38.2	14 44.4	3 52.0	29 5.5	10 32.1	19 25.5	9 47.4	8 .7	28 17.2	4 41.1
8	5 4 44.3	14 3.8	14 34.7	28 16.2	5 20.5	0♏11.7	11 3.7	19 40.2	9 53.7	8 4.6	28 19.6	4 43.0
9	5 8 40.8	15 9.5	14 31.3	11♒16.1	6 46.9	1 18.3	11 35.3	19 54.9	10 .0	8 8.5	28 22.0	4 44.8
10	5 12 37.4	16 15.3	14 27.9	23 39.0	8 10.7	2 25.1	12 6.9	20 9.6	10 6.3	8 12.4	28 24.4	4 46.6
11	5 16 33.9	17 21.2	14 24.5	5♓26.6	9 31.5	3 32.2	12 38.3	20 24.4	10 12.5	8 16.3	28 26.8	4 48.3
12	5 20 30.5	18 27.3	14 21.0	16 46.1	10 48.9	4 39.6	13 9.8	20 39.1	10 18.6	8 20.2	28 29.2	4 50.1
13	5 24 27.0	19 33.4	14 17.6	27 48.2	12 2.3	5 47.3	13 41.1	20 53.8	10 24.8	8 24.1	28 31.7	4 51.8
14	5 28 23.6	20 39.6	14 14.2	8♈45.9	13 11.1	6 55.3	14 12.5	21 8.6	10 30.8	8 28.0	28 34.1	4 53.5
15	5 32 20.2	21 45.8	14 10.8	19 53.5	14 14.7	8 3.5	14 43.7	21 23.3	10 36.9	8 31.8	28 36.5	4 55.2
16	5 36 16.7	22 52.2	14 7.4	1♉26.2	15 12.4	9 12.1	15 15.0	21 38.1	10 42.8	8 35.7	28 39.0	4 56.9
17	5 40 13.3	23 58.5	14 3.9	13 39.3	16 3.3	10 21.0	15 46.1	21 52.9	10 48.8	8 39.5	28 41.4	4 58.5
18	5 44 9.8	25 5.0	14 .5	26 46.3	16 46.6	11 30.2	16 17.3	22 7.6	10 54.6	8 43.4	28 43.9	5 .1
19	5 48 6.4	26 11.5	13 57.1	10♊55.2	17 21.5	12 39.7	16 48.3	22 22.4	11 .5	8 47.2	28 46.3	5 1.7
20	5 52 2.9	27 18.1	13 53.7	26 3.4	17 47.0	13 49.6	17 19.4	22 37.2	11 6.3	8 51.1	28 48.8	5 3.4
21	5 55 59.5	28 24.6	13 50.3	11♋53.2	18 2.2	14 59.7	17 50.4	22 52.0	11 12.0	8 54.9	28 51.3	5 4.9
22	5 59 56.1	29 31.2	13 46.8	27 54.7	18 6.2	16 10.1	18 21.3	23 6.7	11 17.7	8 58.6	28 53.7	5 6.4
23	6 3 52.6	0♑37.8	13 43.4	13♌35.3	17R58.3	17 20.9	18 52.2	23 21.5	11 23.3	9 2.4	28 56.2	5 7.9
24	6 7 49.2	1 44.4	13 40.0	28 32.1	17 38.0	18 32.0	19 23.0	23 36.2	11 28.8	9 6.2	28 58.6	5 9.4
25	6 11 45.7	2 51.0	13 36.6	12♍37.6	17 5.0	19 43.4	19 53.7	23 50.9	11 34.3	9 9.9	29 1.1	5 10.9
26	6 15 42.3	3 57.5	13 33.2	25 57.2	16 19.7	20 55.2	20 24.4	24 5.7	11 39.7	9 13.6	29 3.5	5 12.3
27	6 19 38.9	5 4.1	13 29.7	8♎44.0	15 22.5	22 7.2	20 55.1	24 20.4	11 45.1	9 17.3	29 6.0	5 13.7
28	6 23 35.4	6 10.7	13 26.3	21 13.7	14 14.7	23 19.6	21 25.6	24 35.1	11 50.4	9 21.0	29 8.4	5 15.1
29	6 27 32.0	7 17.2	13 22.9	3♏42.1	12 58.1	24 32.3	21 56.2	24 49.8	11 55.7	9 24.6	29 10.8	5 16.4
30	6 31 28.5	8 23.6	13 19.5	16 22.1	11 35.0	25 45.3	22 26.6	25 4.4	12 .8	9 28.3	29 13.3	5 17.8
31	6 35 25.1	9 30.1	13 16.1	29 22.8	10 7.9	26 58.6	22 57.0	25 19.1	12 6.0	9 31.9	29 15.7	5 19.1
		DECLINATION										
1	4 37 8.3	21S40.7	0N23.8	5S37.4	25S40.6	7S 6.9	1S29.5	22S36.7	12S59.1	21S47.3	22S15.7	3N40.9
4	4 48 58.0	22 7.8	0 23.8	20 8.6	25 49.3	8 16.9	2 9.8	22 40.2	13 5.0	21 49.0	22 15.9	3 39.9
7	5 0 47.7	22 31.1	0 23.8	25 12.1	25 45.2	9 26.5	2 49.7	22 43.6	13 10.7	21 50.6	22 16.0	3 39.0
10	5 12 37.4	22 50.4	0 23.7	19 25.2	25 28.3	10 35.3	3 29.1	22 46.7	13 16.3	21 52.3	22 16.1	3 38.2
13	5 24 27.0	23 5.7	0 23.7	6 38.1	24 59.4	11 42.9	4 8.1	22 49.7	13 21.7	21 53.9	22 16.2	3 37.6
16	5 36 16.7	23 16.8	0 23.7	8N52.0	24 20.2	12 49.0	4 46.5	22 52.4	13 26.9	21 55.5	22 16.3	3 37.1
19	5 48 6.4	23 23.7	0 23.7	21 56.8	23 33.7	13 53.3	5 24.4	22 54.9	13 31.9	21 57.1	22 16.4	3 36.7
22	5 59 56.1	23 26.4	0 23.7	24 22.2	22 44.1	14 55.2	6 1.8	22 57.2	13 36.7	21 58.7	22 16.5	3 36.4
25	6 11 45.7	23 24.9	0 23.7	13 1.5	21 56.2	15 54.6	6 38.5	22 59.3	13 41.3	22 .2	22 16.6	3 36.3
28	6 23 35.4	23 19.2	0 23.6	4S18.2	21 14.0	16 50.9	7 14.6	23 1.2	13 45.7	22 1.7	22 16.6	3 36.4
31	6 35 25.1	23 9.2	0 23.6	19 6.2	20 40.4	17 43.9	7 50.1	23 2.9	13 49.9	22 3.2	22 16.7	3 36.5

JANUARY 1984

DAY	EPHEM. SID. TIME	☉	☊	☽	☿	♀	♂	♃	♄	♅	♆	♇
	h m s	° ′	° ′	° ′	° ′	° ′	° ′	° ′	° ′	° ′	° ′	° ′
		LONGITUDE										
1	6 39 21.6	9♑45.0	14♊31.6	14♐ 6.2	8♑ 7.1	29♏54.4	24♎40.0	25♐55.0	13♏56.7	11♐ 8.6	29♐21.2	1♏47.4
2	6 43 18.2	10 46.1	14 28.5	26 47.2	6R46.7	1♐ 6.6	25 12.1	26 8.5	14 1.7	11 12.0	29 23.5	1 48.5
3	6 47 14.8	11 47.3	14 25.3	9♑17.0	5 30.1	2 18.8	25 44.1	26 21.9	14 6.7	11 15.3	29 25.7	1 49.7
4	6 51 11.3	12 48.5	14 22.1	21 36.5	4 19.6	3 31.2	26 16.0	26 35.3	14 11.5	11 18.6	29 27.9	1 50.8
5	6 55 7.9	13 49.7	14 18.9	3♒46.4	3 16.9	4 43.6	26 47.8	26 48.7	14 16.3	11 21.9	29 30.2	1 51.9
6	6 59 4.4	14 50.9	14 15.8	15 48.3	2 23.1	5 56.0	27 19.4	27 2.0	14 21.0	11 25.1	29 32.4	1 52.9
7	7 3 1.0	15 52.0	14 12.6	27 43.8	1 39.2	7 8.5	27 51.0	27 15.3	14 25.7	11 28.3	29 34.6	1 53.9
8	7 6 57.6	16 53.2	14 9.4	9♓35.5	1 5.4	8 21.1	28 22.4	27 28.6	14 30.3	11 31.5	29 36.8	1 54.9
9	7 10 54.1	17 54.4	14 6.2	21 26.6	0 41.6	9 33.8	28 53.7	27 41.9	14 34.7	11 34.7	29 38.9	1 55.9
10	7 14 50.7	18 55.6	14 3.1	3♈20.9	0 27.6	10 46.5	29 24.9	27 55.1	14 39.2	11 37.8	29 41.2	1 56.8
11	7 18 47.2	19 56.7	13 59.9	15 22.8	0 23.0	11 59.3	29 55.9	28 8.3	14 43.5	11 40.9	29 43.3	1 57.7
12	7 22 43.8	20 57.9	13 56.7	27 37.0	0D27.1	13 12.1	0♏26.8	28 21.5	14 47.8	11 44.0	29 45.5	1 58.6
13	7 26 40.3	21 59.0	13 53.5	10♉ 8.3	0 39.2	14 24.9	0 57.6	28 34.6	14 51.9	11 47.0	29 47.6	1 59.4
14	7 30 36.9	23 .1	13 50.4	23 1.3	0 58.8	15 37.8	1 28.3	28 47.6	14 56.0	11 50.0	29 49.7	2 .1
15	7 34 33.5	24 1.2	13 47.2	6♊19.6	1 25.1	16 50.8	1 58.8	29 .7	15 .0	11 53.0	29 51.8	2 .9
16	7 38 30.0	25 2.3	13 44.0	20 5.4	1 57.6	18 3.8	2 29.2	29 13.7	15 3.9	11 56.0	29 53.9	2 1.6
17	7 42 26.6	26 3.4	13 40.8	4♋18.4	2 35.6	19 16.8	2 59.4	29 26.6	15 7.8	11 58.9	29 56.0	2 2.2
18	7 46 23.1	27 4.5	13 37.6	18 55.7	3 18.6	20 29.9	3 29.5	29 39.5	15 11.5	12 1.8	29 58.1	2 2.9
19	7 50 19.7	28 5.6	13 34.5	3♌51.1	4 6.1	21 43.1	3 59.5	29 52.4	15 15.2	12 4.6	0♑ .2	2 3.5
20	7 54 16.2	29 6.6	13 31.3	18 56.0	4 57.7	22 56.2	4 29.3	0♑ 5.2	15 18.7	12 7.4	0 2.2	2 4.0
21	7 58 12.8	0♒ 7.7	13 28.1	4♍ .6	5 52.9	24 9.5	4 58.9	0 17.9	15 22.2	12 10.2	0 4.2	2 4.5
22	8 2 9.4	1 8.7	13 24.9	18 55.4	6 51.4	25 22.7	5 28.4	0 30.6	15 25.6	12 12.9	0 6.3	2 5.0
23	8 6 5.9	2 9.8	13 21.8	3♎32.8	7 52.9	26 36.0	5 57.8	0 43.3	15 28.9	12 15.6	0 8.3	2 5.5
24	8 10 2.5	3 10.8	13 18.6	17 48.3	8 57.0	27 49.4	6 27.0	0 55.9	15 32.2	12 18.3	0 10.3	2 5.9
25	8 13 59.0	4 11.8	13 15.4	1♏39.9	10 3.6	29 2.8	6 56.0	1 8.5	15 35.3	12 20.9	0 12.2	2 6.3
26	8 17 55.6	5 12.8	13 12.2	15 8.3	11 12.4	0♑16.2	7 24.9	1 20.9	15 38.3	12 23.5	0 14.2	2 6.7
27	8 21 52.1	6 13.8	13 9.1	28 15.8	12 23.3	1 29.7	7 53.5	1 33.4	15 41.2	12 26.1	0 16.1	2 7.0
28	8 25 48.7	7 14.8	13 5.9	11♐ 5.3	13 36.0	2 43.2	8 22.1	1 45.8	15 44.1	12 28.6	0 18.0	2 7.2
29	8 29 45.3	8 15.8	13 2.7	23 40.2	14 50.4	3 56.7	8 50.4	1 58.1	15 46.8	12 31.0	0 19.9	2 7.5
30	8 33 41.8	9 16.8	12 59.5	6♑ 3.4	16 6.3	5 10.3	9 18.5	2 10.3	15 49.5	12 33.5	0 21.8	2 7.7
31	8 37 38.4	10 17.7	12 56.3	18 17.4	17 23.7	6 23.8	9 46.4	2 22.5	15 52.0	12 35.9	0 23.6	2 7.8
		LATITUDE										
1	6 39 21.6	0 .0	0 .0	0N 9.9	2N40.4	2N10.1	1N38.5	0N19.4	2N16.4	0N 3.3	1N 9.7	16N42.2
4	6 51 11.3	0 .0	0 .0	3S 3.4	3 8.7	2 5.1	1 38.9	0 19.2	2 16.9	0 3.3	1 9.7	16 43.7
7	7 3 1.0	0 .0	0 .0	4 57.0	3 15.4	1 59.4	1 39.3	0 18.9	2 17.4	0 3.3	1 9.7	16 45.3
10	7 14 50.7	0 .0	0 .0	4 56.6	3 5.1	1 53.0	1 39.7	0 18.7	2 18.0	0 3.2	1 9.7	16 46.9
13	7 26 40.3	0 .0	0 .0	2 60.0	2 44.1	1 46.2	1 40.0	0 18.5	2 18.5	0 3.2	1 9.8	16 48.5
16	7 38 30.0	0 .0	0 .0	0N25.5	2 17.4	1 38.8	1 40.3	0 18.3	2 19.1	0 3.2	1 9.8	16 50.2
19	7 50 19.7	0 .0	0 .0	3 51.9	1 48.2	1 31.0	1 40.5	0 18.1	2 19.7	0 3.2	1 9.8	16 51.8
22	8 2 9.4	0 .0	0 .0	5 7.2	1 18.6	1 22.8	1 40.7	0 17.9	2 20.3	0 3.2	1 9.8	16 53.5
25	8 13 59.0	0 .0	0 .0	3 30.7	0 49.4	1 14.2	1 40.9	0 17.6	2 20.9	0 3.1	1 9.8	16 55.2
28	8 25 48.7	0 .0	0 .0	0 19.7	0 21.6	1 5.4	1 40.9	0 17.4	2 21.6	0 3.1	1 9.9	16 56.9
31	8 37 38.4	0 .0	0 .0	2S49.5	0S 4.5	0 56.4	1 41.0	0 17.2	2 22.2	0 3.1	1 9.9	16 58.5
		RIGHT ASCENSION										
1	6 39 21.6	10♑36.4	13♊12.7	12♐46.5	8♑39.8	28♏12.3	23♎27.3	25♐33.7	12♏11.0	9♐35.5	29♐18.1	5♏20.3
2	6 43 18.2	11 42.7	13 9.2	26 28.3	7R13.5	29 26.2	23 57.6	25 48.3	12 16.0	9 39.0	29 20.5	5 21.6
3	6 47 14.8	12 48.9	13 5.8	10♑15.8	5 51.5	0♐40.5	24 27.7	26 2.9	12 20.9	9 42.6	29 23.0	5 22.8
4	6 51 11.3	13 55.0	13 2.4	23 52.9	4 36.3	1 55.0	24 57.8	26 17.5	12 25.7	9 46.1	29 25.4	5 24.0
5	6 55 7.9	15 1.1	12 59.0	7♒ 4.6	3 29.4	3 9.9	25 27.9	26 32.0	12 30.5	9 49.6	29 27.7	5 25.1
6	6 59 4.4	16 7.0	12 55.6	19 ⇃1.6	2 32.3	4 25.0	25 57.8	26 46.5	12 35.2	9 53.0	29 30.1	5 26.2
7	7 3 1.0	17 12.8	12 52.2	1♓41.6	1 45.5	5 40.4	26 27.7	27 1.0	12 39.8	9 56.5	29 32.5	5 27.3
8	7 6 57.6	18 18.5	12 48.7	13 8.8	1 9.5	6 56.1	26 57.5	27 15.4	12 44.4	9 59.9	29 34.9	5 28.4
9	7 10 54.1	19 24.1	12 45.3	24 11.7	0 44.3	8 12.1	27 27.2	27 29.8	12 48.9	10 3.3	29 37.2	5 29.4
10	7 14 50.7	20 29.6	12 41.9	5♈ 2.3	0 29.4	9 28.3	27 56.8	27 44.2	12 53.3	10 6.6	29 39.6	5 30.5
11	7 18 47.2	21 34.8	12 38.5	15 54.0	0 24.5	10 44.8	28 26.3	27 58.6	12 57.6	10 10.0	29 42.0	5 31.5
12	7 22 43.8	22 40.0	12 35.1	27 1.8	0D28.9	12 1.6	28 55.8	28 12.9	13 1.9	10 13.2	29 44.3	5 32.4
13	7 26 40.3	23 45.0	12 31.7	8♉41.5	0 41.9	13 18.6	29 25.1	28 27.1	13 6.0	10 16.5	29 46.6	5 33.3
14	7 30 36.9	24 49.8	12 28.3	21 8.7	1 2.8	14 35.8	29 54.4	28 41.3	13 10.1	10 19.7	29 48.9	5 34.2
15	7 34 33.5	25 54.5	12 24.8	4♊36.5	1 31.1	15 53.2	0♏23.5	28 55.5	13 14.1	10 22.9	29 51.2	5 35.0
16	7 38 30.0	26 59.0	12 21.4	19 11.0	2 6.0	17 10.9	0 52.6	29 9.6	13 18.0	10 26.0	29 53.5	5 35.9
17	7 42 26.6	28 3.3	12 18.0	4♋45.2	2 46.9	18 28.8	1 21.6	29 23.7	13 21.9	10 29.2	29 55.7	5 36.7
18	7 46 23.1	29 7.5	12 14.6	20 56.0	3 33.3	19 46.9	1 50.4	29 37.7	13 25.6	10 32.2	29 58.0	5 37.4
19	7 50 19.7	0♒11.5	12 11.2	7♌ 9.3	4 24.6	21 5.2	2 19.2	29 51.7	13 29.3	10 35.3	0♑ .2	5 38.1
20	7 54 16.2	1 15.3	12 7.8	22 52.8	5 20.4	22 23.6	2 47.9	0♑ 5.6	13 32.9	10 38.3	0 2.4	5 38.8
21	7 58 12.8	2 18.9	12 4.4	7♍47.5	6 20.2	23 42.2	3 16.4	0 19.5	13 36.4	10 41.3	0 4.6	5 39.5
22	8 2 9.4	3 22.3	12 1.0	21 50.7	7 23.6	25 1.0	3 44.8	0 33.3	13 39.8	10 44.2	0 6.8	5 40.1
23	8 6 5.9	4 25.6	11 57.6	5♎11.2	8 30.4	26 20.0	4 13.1	0 47.1	13 43.1	10 47.1	0 8.9	5 40.7
24	8 10 2.5	5 28.7	11 54.1	18 3.7	9 40.2	27 39.0	4 41.3	1 .8	13 46.4	10 49.9	0 11.1	5 41.3
25	8 13 59.0	6 31.5	11 50.7	0♏44.0	10 52.6	28 58.2	5 9.4	1 14.4	13 49.5	10 52.8	0 13.2	5 41.8
26	8 17 55.6	7 34.2	11 47.3	13 26.3	12 7.6	0♑17.5	5 37.4	1 28.0	13 52.6	10 55.5	0 15.3	5 42.3
27	8 21 52.1	8 36.7	11 43.9	26 21.4	13 24.7	1 36.9	6 5.2	1 41.6	13 55.5	10 58.3	0 17.4	5 42.8
28	8 25 48.7	9 39.0	11 40.5	9♐34.4	14 43.9	2 56.4	6 32.8	1 55.0	13 58.4	11 .9	0 19.5	5 43.2
29	8 29 45.3	10 41.1	11 37.1	23 3.9	16 4.9	4 15.9	7 .3	2 8.4	14 1.2	11 3.6	0 21.5	5 43.6
30	8 33 41.8	11 43.0	11 33.7	6♑41.5	17 27.6	5 35.5	7 27.7	2 21.7	14 3.8	11 6.2	0 23.5	5 44.0
31	8 37 38.4	12 44.7	11 30.3	20 14.0	18 51.9	6 55.1	7 54.9	2 35.0	14 6.4	11 8.7	0 25.5	5 44.3
		DECLINATION										
1	6 39 21.6	23S 5.0	0N23.6	22S19.9	20S31.5	18S .8	8S 1.7	23S 3.4	13S51.3	22S 3.6	22S16.7	3N36.6
4	6 51 11.3	22 49.5	0 23.6	24 43.5	20 13.7	18 48.8	8 36.1	23 4.7	13 55.2	22 5.0	22 16.7	3 36.9
7	7 3 1.0	22 29.9	0 23.6	16 54.2	20 10.5	19 32.6	9 9.8	23 5.9	13 58.8	22 6.4	22 16.8	3 37.4
10	7 14 50.7	22 6.3	0 23.6	3 12.3	20 21.4	20 11.9	9 42.7	23 6.8	14 2.2	22 7.7	22 16.8	3 38.0
13	7 26 40.3	21 38.8	0 23.5	12N .6	20 42.3	20 46.4	10 14.8	23 7.6	14 5.4	22 9.0	22 16.8	3 38.7
16	7 38 30.0	21 7.6	0 23.5	23 29.8	21 8.3	21 15.9	10 46.0	23 8.1	14 8.3	22 10.2	22 16.7	3 39.5
19	7 50 19.7	20 32.7	0 23.5	23 2.8	21 34.5	21 40.2	11 16.4	23 8.4	14 11.0	22 11.3	22 16.7	3 40.5
22	8 2 9.4	19 54.3	0 23.5	9 5.5	21 57.4	21 58.9	11 45.9	23 8.6	14 13.4	22 12.5	22 16.7	3 41.5
25	8 13 59.0	19 12.6	0 23.4	8S45.4	22 14.3	22 12.1	12 14.5	23 8.6	14 15.6	22 13.6	22 16.7	3 42.7
28	8 25 48.7	18 27.7	0 23.4	21 47.0	22 23.3	22 19.4	12 42.1	23 8.4	14 17.5	22 14.6	22 16.6	3 44.0
31	8 37 38.4	17 39.8	0 23.4	24 59.5	22 23.1	22 20.9	13 8.8	23 8.0	14 19.2	22 15.6	22 16.6	3 45.4

FEBRUARY 1984

LONGITUDE

DAY	EPHEM. SID. TIME	☉	☊	☽	☿	♀	♂	♃	♄	♅	♆	♇
	h m s	° ′	° ′	° ′	° ′	° ′	° ′	° ′	° ′	° ′	° ′	° ′
1	8 41 34.9	11 ♒ 18.7	12 ♊ 53.2	0 ♒ 24.1	18 ♑ 42.5	7 ♑ 37.4	10 ♏ 14.2	2 ♑ 34.7	15 ♏ 54.5	12 ♐ 38.2	0 ♑ 25.5	2 ♏ 7.9
2	8 45 31.5	12 19.6	12 50.0	12 25.1	20 2.6	8 51.1	10 41.7	2 46.7	15 56.8	12 40.5	0 27.3	2 8.0
3	8 49 28.0	13 20.5	12 46.8	24 21.5	21 23.9	10 4.7	11 9.1	2 58.7	15 59.1	12 42.8	0 29.1	2 8.1
4	8 53 24.6	14 21.4	12 43.6	6 ♓ 14.7	22 46.3	11 18.4	11 36.2	3 10.6	16 1.2	12 45.0	0 30.8	2 8.1
5	8 57 21.1	15 22.3	12 40.5	18 6.1	24 9.8	12 32.1	12 3.1	3 22.5	16 3.3	12 47.1	0 32.6	2 8.1
6	9 1 17.7	16 23.1	12 37.3	29 57.7	25 34.3	13 45.8	12 29.8	3 34.2	16 5.2	12 49.3	0 34.3	2 R 8.0
7	9 5 14.3	17 24.0	12 34.1	11 ♈ 52.2	26 59.8	14 59.5	12 56.3	3 45.9	16 7.1	12 51.4	0 36.0	2 7.9
8	9 9 10.8	18 24.8	12 30.9	23 52.9	28 26.3	16 13.3	13 22.5	3 57.5	16 8.8	12 53.4	0 37.7	2 7.8
9	9 13 7.4	19 25.5	12 27.8	6 ♉ 3.9	29 53.8	17 27.0	13 48.5	4 9.1	16 10.5	12 55.4	0 39.3	2 7.6
10	9 17 3.9	20 26.3	12 24.6	18 29.8	1 ♒ 22.2	18 40.9	14 14.4	4 20.6	16 12.1	12 57.4	0 41.0	2 7.5
11	9 21 .5	21 27.0	12 21.4	1 ♊ 15.4	2 51.5	19 54.7	14 39.9	4 32.0	16 13.5	12 59.3	0 42.6	2 7.2
12	9 24 57.0	22 27.7	12 18.2	14 25.3	4 21.6	21 8.5	15 5.2	4 43.3	16 14.9	13 1.1	0 44.2	2 7.0
13	9 28 53.6	23 28.4	12 15.0	28 3.3	5 52.6	22 22.3	15 30.2	4 54.5	16 16.1	13 2.9	0 45.7	2 6.7
14	9 32 50.1	24 29.0	12 11.9	12 ♋ 11.2	7 24.6	23 36.1	15 55.0	5 5.6	16 17.3	13 4.7	0 47.3	2 6.3
15	9 36 46.7	25 29.7	12 8.7	26 47.8	8 57.3	24 50.0	16 19.6	5 16.6	16 18.3	13 6.4	0 48.8	2 5.9
16	9 40 43.3	26 30.2	12 5.5	11 ♌ 48.7	10 31.0	26 3.8	16 43.9	5 27.6	16 19.2	13 8.0	0 50.3	2 5.5
17	9 44 39.8	27 30.8	12 2.3	27 5.4	12 5.6	27 17.7	17 7.9	5 38.4	16 20.1	13 9.6	0 51.7	2 5.1
18	9 48 36.4	28 31.3	11 59.2	12 ♍ 27.0	13 41.0	28 31.6	17 31.6	5 49.2	16 20.8	13 11.2	0 53.1	2 4.6
19	9 52 32.9	29 31.9	11 56.0	27 41.5	15 17.3	29 45.5	17 55.0	5 59.9	16 21.4	13 12.7	0 54.5	2 4.1
20	9 56 29.5	0 ♓ 32.3	11 52.8	12 ♎ 38.5	16 54.6	0 ♒ 59.4	18 18.2	6 10.5	16 21.9	13 14.1	0 55.9	2 3.5
21	10 0 26.0	1 32.8	11 49.6	27 10.5	18 32.7	2 13.3	18 41.1	6 20.9	16 22.4	13 15.5	0 57.2	2 3.0
22	10 4 22.6	2 33.3	11 46.4	11 ♏ 14.0	20 11.8	3 27.3	19 3.6	6 31.3	16 22.7	13 16.9	0 58.5	2 2.4
23	10 8 19.1	3 33.7	11 43.3	24 48.8	21 51.8	4 41.3	19 25.9	6 41.6	16 22.9	13 18.2	0 59.8	2 1.7
24	10 12 15.7	4 34.1	11 40.1	7 ♐ 57.1	23 32.8	5 55.2	19 47.8	6 51.8	16 23.0	13 19.5	1 1.1	2 1.0
25	10 16 12.2	5 34.4	11 36.9	20 42.8	25 14.7	7 9.2	20 9.4	7 1.9	16 23.0	13 20.7	1 2.3	2 .3
26	10 20 8.8	6 34.8	11 33.7	3 ♑ 10.4	26 57.7	8 23.2	20 30.7	7 11.8	16 R 22.9	13 21.8	1 3.5	1 59.6
27	10 24 5.4	7 35.1	11 30.6	15 24.3	28 41.6	9 37.2	20 51.6	7 21.7	16 22.7	13 22.9	1 4.7	1 58.8
28	10 28 1.9	8 35.4	11 27.4	27 28.5	0 ♓ 26.5	10 51.2	21 12.2	7 31.5	16 22.4	13 24.0	1 5.8	1 58.0
29	10 31 58.5	9 35.7	11 24.2	9 ♒ 26.3	2 12.5	12 5.2	21 32.4	7 41.1	16 22.0	13 25.0	1 6.9	1 57.2

LATITUDE

DAY	EPHEM. SID. TIME	☉	☊	☽	☿	♀	♂	♃	♄	♅	♆	♇
1	8 41 34.9	0 .0	0 .0	3 S 38.9	0 S 12.8	0 N 53.4	1 N 41.0	0 N 17.2	2 N 22.4	0 N 3.0	1 N 9.9	16 N 59.1
4	8 53 24.6	0 .0	0 .0	5 .2	0 36.2	0 44.3	1 40.9	0 17.0	2 23.1	0 3.0	1 10.0	17 .8
7	9 5 14.3	0 .0	0 .0	4 26.8	0 57.4	0 35.0	1 40.8	0 16.8	2 23.8	0 3.0	1 10.1	17 2.4
10	9 17 3.9	0 .0	0 .0	2 7.6	1 16.2	0 25.8	1 40.7	0 16.6	2 24.5	0 3.0	1 10.1	17 4.1
13	9 28 53.6	0 .0	0 .0	1 N 17.7	1 32.5	0 16.7	1 40.4	0 16.4	2 25.1	0 3.0	1 10.2	17 5.7
16	9 40 43.3	0 .0	0 .0	4 18.1	1 45.9	0 7.6	1 40.1	0 16.2	2 25.8	0 2.9	1 10.3	17 7.3
19	9 52 32.9	0 .0	0 .0	4 50.4	1 56.4	0 S 1.3	1 39.6	0 16.0	2 26.5	0 2.9	1 10.3	17 8.8
22	10 4 22.6	0 .0	0 .0	2 35.3	2 3.7	0 10.0	1 39.1	0 15.8	2 27.2	0 2.9	1 10.4	17 10.3
25	10 16 12.2	0 .0	0 .0	0 S 45.5	2 7.5	0 18.5	1 38.4	0 15.6	2 27.9	0 2.9	1 10.5	17 11.8
28	10 28 1.9	0 .0	0 .0	3 34.9	2 7.6	0 26.6	1 37.6	0 15.4	2 28.5	0 2.9	1 10.6	17 13.2

RIGHT ASCENSION

DAY	EPHEM. SID. TIME	☉	☊	☽	☿	♀	♂	♃	♄	♅	♆	♇
1	8 41 34.9	13 ♒ 46.2	11 ♊ 26.9	3 ♒ 27.2	20 ♑ 17.5	8 ♑ 14.7	8 ♏ 22.0	2 ♑ 48.2	14 ♏ 8.9	11 ♐ 11.3	0 ♑ 27.5	5 ♏ 44.6
2	8 45 31.5	14 47.5	11 23.5	16 10.6	21 44.4	9 34.4	8 48.9	3 1.3	14 11.3	11 13.7	0 29.5	5 44.9
3	8 49 28.0	15 48.5	11 20.1	28 19.3	23 12.5	10 54.0	9 15.6	3 14.3	14 13.6	11 16.1	0 31.4	5 45.1
4	8 53 24.6	16 49.4	11 16.7	9 ♓ 54.6	24 41.6	12 13.6	9 42.1	3 27.3	14 15.8	11 18.5	0 33.3	5 45.3
5	8 57 21.1	17 50.1	11 13.3	21 2.9	26 11.7	13 33.2	10 8.5	3 40.2	14 17.9	11 20.8	0 35.2	5 45.5
6	9 1 17.7	18 50.5	11 9.8	1 ♈ 53.8	27 42.7	14 52.7	10 34.7	3 53.0	14 19.9	11 23.1	0 37.1	5 45.6
7	9 5 14.3	19 50.8	11 6.4	12 39.0	29 14.5	16 12.1	11 .7	4 5.7	14 21.8	11 25.3	0 38.9	5 45.7
8	9 9 10.8	20 50.9	11 3.0	23 31.9	0 ♒ 47.1	17 31.5	11 26.5	4 18.3	14 23.6	11 27.5	0 40.7	5 45.8
9	9 13 7.4	21 50.7	10 59.6	4 ♉ 46.9	2 20.4	18 50.8	11 52.1	4 30.8	14 25.3	11 29.7	0 42.5	5 45.9
10	9 17 3.9	22 50.4	10 56.2	16 38.7	3 54.3	20 10.0	12 17.5	4 43.3	14 26.9	11 31.8	0 44.3	5 45.9
11	9 21 .5	23 49.8	10 52.8	29 21.4	5 28.8	21 29.1	12 42.7	4 55.7	14 28.4	11 33.8	0 46.0	5 45.9
12	9 24 57.0	24 49.1	10 49.4	13 ♊ 5.1	7 3.8	22 48.0	13 7.7	5 8.0	14 29.8	11 35.8	0 47.7	5 R 45.8
13	9 28 53.6	25 48.1	10 46.0	27 51.6	8 39.3	24 6.8	13 32.5	5 20.2	14 31.1	11 37.7	0 49.4	5 45.7
14	9 32 50.1	26 47.0	10 42.6	13 ♋ 29.5	10 15.3	25 25.4	13 57.0	5 32.2	14 32.3	11 39.6	0 51.1	5 45.6
15	9 36 46.7	27 45.7	10 39.2	29 33.9	11 51.7	26 43.9	14 21.3	5 44.2	14 33.4	11 41.4	0 52.7	5 45.4
16	9 40 43.3	28 44.1	10 35.8	15 ♌ 33.3	13 28.5	28 2.2	14 45.4	5 56.1	14 34.4	11 43.2	0 54.3	5 45.2
17	9 44 39.8	29 42.4	10 32.4	1 ♍ 1.6	15 5.7	29 20.4	15 9.2	6 7.9	14 35.3	11 44.9	0 55.9	5 45.0
18	9 48 36.4	0 ♓ 40.6	10 29.0	15 46.3	16 43.3	0 ♒ 38.3	15 32.8	6 19.6	14 36.1	11 46.6	0 57.4	5 44.7
19	9 52 32.9	1 38.5	10 25.6	29 48.7	18 21.2	1 56.1	15 56.1	6 31.2	14 36.7	11 48.2	0 58.9	5 44.5
20	9 56 29.5	2 36.3	10 22.2	13 ♎ 18.9	19 59.4	3 13.7	16 19.2	6 42.7	14 37.3	11 49.8	1 .4	5 44.1
21	10 0 26.0	3 33.9	10 18.8	26 30.7	21 38.0	4 31.0	16 42.0	6 54.1	14 37.8	11 51.3	1 1.8	5 43.8
22	10 4 22.6	4 31.3	10 15.4	9 ♏ 37.6	23 16.9	5 48.2	17 4.5	7 5.3	14 38.2	11 52.7	1 3.2	5 43.4
23	10 8 19.1	5 28.6	10 12.0	22 50.3	24 56.2	7 5.1	17 26.7	7 16.5	14 38.5	11 54.1	1 4.6	5 43.0
24	10 12 15.7	6 25.8	10 8.6	6 ♐ 14.6	26 35.7	8 21.8	17 48.6	7 27.6	14 38.6	11 55.5	1 6.0	5 42.5
25	10 16 12.2	7 22.8	10 5.2	19 50.2	28 15.5	9 38.2	18 10.2	7 38.5	14 38.7	11 56.8	1 7.3	5 42.1
26	10 20 8.8	8 19.6	10 1.8	3 ♑ 30.4	29 55.7	10 54.4	18 31.5	7 49.3	14 38.7	11 58.0	1 8.6	5 41.6
27	10 24 5.4	9 16.3	9 58.4	17 4.0	1 ♓ 36.2	12 10.4	18 52.5	8 .0	14 R 38.5	11 59.2	1 9.9	5 41.0
28	10 28 1.9	10 12.9	9 55.0	0 ♒ 18.9	3 17.0	13 26.1	19 13.1	8 10.6	14 38.3	12 .3	1 11.1	5 40.5
29	10 31 58.5	11 9.4	9 51.6	13 5.2	4 58.1	14 41.6	19 33.3	8 21.1	14 37.9	12 1.4	1 12.3	5 39.9

DECLINATION

DAY	EPHEM. SID. TIME	☉	☊	☽	☿	♀	♂	♃	♄	♅	♆	♇
1	8 41 34.9	17 S 23.2	0 N 23.4	23 S 37.7	22 S 20.8	22 S 20.0	13 S 17.5	23 S 7.9	14 S 19.7	22 S 15.9	22 S 16.5	3 N 45.8
4	8 53 24.6	16 31.6	0 23.4	13 52.0	22 6.9	22 13.5	13 42.9	23 7.3	14 21.0	22 16.8	22 16.5	3 47.4
7	9 5 14.3	15 37.3	0 23.4	0 N 35.9	21 42.0	22 1.1	14 7.3	23 6.6	14 22.0	22 17.6	22 16.4	3 49.0
10	9 17 3.9	14 40.7	0 23.3	15 17.3	21 5.8	21 42.8	14 30.6	23 5.7	14 22.8	22 18.4	22 16.3	3 50.7
13	9 28 53.6	13 41.8	0 23.3	24 43.4	20 17.9	21 18.7	14 53.0	23 4.7	14 23.3	22 19.1	22 16.2	3 52.5
16	9 40 43.3	12 41.0	0 23.3	21 22.6	19 18.1	20 48.9	15 14.3	23 3.6	14 23.5	22 19.7	22 16.1	3 54.3
19	9 52 32.9	11 38.3	0 23.3	5 21.4	18 6.4	20 13.5	15 34.7	23 2.4	14 23.5	22 20.3	22 16.0	3 56.2
22	10 4 22.6	10 33.9	0 23.2	12 S 44.4	16 42.5	19 32.8	15 54.0	23 1.1	14 23.2	22 20.9	22 15.9	3 58.2
25	10 16 12.2	9 28.1	0 23.2	23 52.4	15 6.5	18 47.0	16 12.3	22 59.7	14 22.6	22 21.4	22 15.8	4 .3
28	10 28 1.9	8 21.0	0 23.2	24 10.7	13 18.4	17 56.3	16 29.5	22 58.3	14 21.8	22 21.8	22 15.7	4 2.3

MARCH 1984

LONGITUDE

DAY	EPHEM. SID. TIME h m s	☉ ° ′	☊ ° ′	☾ ° ′	☿ ° ′	♀ ° ′	♂ ° ′	♃ ° ′	♄ ° ′	♅ ° ′	♆ ° ′	♇ ° ′
1	10 35 55.0	10♓36.0	11♊21.0	21♒20.4	3♓59.4	13♒19.3	21♏52.2	7♑50.7	16♏21.4	13♐25.9	1♑ 8.0	1♏56.3
2	10 39 51.6	11 36.2	11 17.8	3♓12.7	5 47.5	14 33.3	22 11.7	8 .1	16R20.9	13 26.8	1 9.1	1R55.5
3	10 43 48.1	12 36.4	11 14.7	15 4.7	7 36.6	15 47.4	22 30.8	8 9.4	16 20.2	13 27.7	1 10.1	1 54.5
4	10 47 44.7	13 36.6	11 11.5	26 57.6	9 26.7	17 1.4	22 49.5	8 18.6	16 19.3	13 28.5	1 11.1	1 53.6
5	10 51 41.2	14 36.7	11 8.3	8♈52.8	11 17.8	18 15.4	23 7.7	8 27.7	16 18.4	13 29.2	1 12.0	1 52.6
6	10 55 37.8	15 36.8	11 5.1	20 52.0	13 10.0	19 29.5	23 25.6	8 36.6	16 17.4	13 29.9	1 13.0	1 51.6
7	10 59 34.3	16 36.9	11 2.0	2♉57.2	15 3.1	20 43.5	23 43.0	8 45.5	16 16.3	13 30.5	1 13.8	1 50.6
8	11 3 30.9	17 36.9	10 58.8	15 11.4	16 57.3	21 57.5	24 .0	8 54.2	16 15.0	13 31.0	1 14.7	1 49.5
9	11 7 27.4	18 36.9	10 55.6	27 38.0	18 52.4	23 11.6	24 16.6	9 2.7	16 13.7	13 31.6	1 15.5	1 48.4
10	11 11 24.0	19 36.8	10 52.4	10♊21.3	20 48.3	24 25.6	24 32.7	9 11.2	16 12.3	13 32.0	1 16.3	1 47.3
11	11 15 20.5	20 36.8	10 49.2	23 25.3	22 45.1	25 39.7	24 48.3	9 19.5	16 10.8	13 32.4	1 17.1	1 46.1
12	11 19 17.1	21 36.7	10 46.1	6♋53.9	24 42.6	26 53.7	25 3.5	9 27.7	16 9.1	13 32.8	1 17.8	1 45.0
13	11 23 13.7	22 36.5	10 42.9	20 50.0	26 40.7	28 7.7	25 18.3	9 35.7	16 7.4	13 33.1	1 18.5	1 43.8
14	11 27 10.2	23 36.3	10 39.7	5♌14.0	28 39.3	29 21.8	25 32.5	9 43.7	16 5.6	13 33.3	1 19.2	1 42.6
15	11 31 6.8	24 36.1	10 36.5	20 3.5	0♈38.2	0♓35.8	25 46.2	9 51.5	16 3.7	13 33.5	1 19.8	1 41.3
16	11 35 3.3	25 35.8	10 33.4	5♍12.2	2 37.2	1 49.8	25 59.5	9 59.1	16 1.7	13 33.7	1 20.4	1 40.0
17	11 38 59.9	26 35.5	10 30.2	20 30.8	4 36.2	3 3.8	26 12.2	10 6.6	15 59.7	13 33.7	1 21.0	1 38.8
18	11 42 56.4	27 35.2	10 27.0	5♎47.8	6 34.7	4 17.9	26 24.4	10 14.0	15 57.5	13 33.8	1 21.5	1 37.5
19	11 46 53.0	28 34.8	10 23.8	20 52.0	8 32.6	5 31.9	26 36.1	10 21.2	15 55.2	13 33.8	1 22.0	1 36.1
20	11 50 49.5	29 34.4	10 20.6	5♏34.2	10 29.6	6 45.9	26 47.2	10 28.3	15 52.9	13R33.7	1 22.4	1 34.8
21	11 54 46.1	0♈34.0	10 17.5	19 48.8	12 25.2	7 60.0	26 57.8	10 35.3	15 50.4	13 33.6	1 22.9	1 33.4
22	11 58 42.6	1 33.5	10 14.3	3♐33.7	14 19.0	9 14.0	27 7.8	10 42.1	15 47.9	13 33.4	1 23.3	1 32.0
23	12 2 39.2	2 33.1	10 11.1	16 49.9	16 10.8	10 28.1	27 17.2	10 48.8	15 45.3	13 33.2	1 23.7	1 30.6
24	12 6 35.7	3 32.6	10 7.9	29 40.5	17 60.0	11 42.1	27 26.0	10 55.3	15 42.7	13 32.9	1 24.0	1 29.2
25	12 10 32.3	4 32.0	10 4.8	12♑10.0	19 46.1	12 56.1	27 34.2	11 1.6	15 39.9	13 32.6	1 24.3	1 27.8
26	12 14 28.8	5 31.5	10 1.6	24 23.2	21 28.9	14 10.2	27 41.8	11 7.8	15 37.0	13 32.2	1 24.6	1 26.3
27	12 18 25.4	6 30.8	9 58.4	6♒24.9	23 7.8	15 24.2	27 48.7	11 13.8	15 34.1	13 31.8	1 24.8	1 24.8
28	12 22 21.9	7 30.2	9 55.2	18 19.6	24 42.4	16 38.2	27 55.0	11 19.7	15 31.1	13 31.3	1 25.0	1 23.3
29	12 26 18.5	8 29.5	9 52.0	0♓10.9	26 12.4	17 52.3	28 .6	11 25.5	15 28.0	13 30.7	1 25.2	1 21.8
30	12 30 15.1	9 28.8	9 48.9	12 1.8	27 37.4	19 6.3	28 5.6	11 31.0	15 24.8	13 30.1	1 25.3	1 20.3
31	12 34 11.6	10 28.1	9 45.7	23 54.8	28 57.0	20 20.3	28 9.8	11 36.4	15 21.6	13 29.5	1 25.4	1 18.7

LATITUDE

DAY	EPHEM. SID. TIME h m s	☉	☊	☾	☿	♀	♂	♃	♄	♅	♆	♇
1	10 35 55.0	0 .0	0 .0	4S41.0	2S 5.5	0S31.9	1N37.0	0N15.3	2N29.0	0N 2.8	1N10.6	17N14.1
4	10 47 44.7	0 .0	0 .0	4 47.4	1 58.7	0 39.4	1 35.9	0 15.1	2 29.6	0 2.8	1 10.7	17 15.5
7	10 59 34.3	0 .0	0 .0	3 2.7	1 47.3	0 46.6	1 34.7	0 14.9	2 30.2	0 2.8	1 10.8	17 16.7
10	11 11 24.0	0 .0	0 .0	0N 1.1	1 31.0	0 53.3	1 33.4	0 14.7	2 30.9	0 2.8	1 10.9	17 17.9
13	11 23 13.7	0 .0	0 .0	3 17.5	1 9.8	0 59.5	1 31.8	0 14.6	2 31.5	0 2.8	1 11.0	17 19.1
16	11 35 3.3	0 .0	0 .0	5 .2	0 43.5	1 5.2	1 30.0	0 14.4	2 32.0	0 2.7	1 11.1	17 20.1
19	11 46 53.0	0 .0	0 .0	3 45.9	0 12.7	1 10.4	1 28.0	0 14.2	2 32.6	0 2.7	1 11.2	17 21.1
22	11 58 42.6	0 .0	0 .0	0 29.0	0N21.8	1 15.1	1 25.7	0 14.0	2 33.1	0 2.7	1 11.3	17 22.0
25	12 10 32.3	0 .0	0 .0	2S46.8	0 58.2	1 19.1	1 23.1	0 13.8	2 33.6	0 2.7	1 11.4	17 22.9
28	12 22 21.9	0 .0	0 .0	4 44.5	1 34.5	1 22.6	1 20.3	0 13.6	2 34.1	0 2.6	1 11.5	17 23.6
31	12 34 11.6	0 .0	0 .0	4 52.4	2 7.9	1 25.5	1 17.1	0 13.3	2 34.5	0 2.6	1 11.6	17 24.3

RIGHT ASCENSION

DAY	EPHEM. SID. TIME h m s	☉	☊	☾	☿	♀	♂	♃	♄	♅	♆	♇
1	10 35 55.0	12♓ 5.7	9♊48.2	25♒18.5	6♓39.6	15♒56.8	19♏53.3	8♑31.4	14♏37.5	12♐ 2.4	1♑13.5	5♏39.3
2	10 39 51.6	13 1.9	9 44.8	6♓59.3	8 21.4	17 11.8	20 12.8	8 41.7	14R37.0	12 3.4	1 14.6	5R38.6
3	10 43 48.1	13 58.0	9 41.4	18 12.7	10 3.6	18 26.5	20 32.0	8 51.8	14 36.3	12 4.3	1 15.7	5 38.0
4	10 47 44.7	14 53.9	9 38.0	29 7.3	11 46.2	19 40.9	20 50.8	9 1.7	14 35.6	12 5.1	1 16.8	5 37.2
5	10 51 41.2	15 49.7	9 34.6	9♈53.3	13 29.1	20 55.1	21 9.2	9 11.6	14 34.7	12 5.9	1 17.8	5 36.5
6	10 55 37.8	16 45.4	9 31.2	20 42.6	15 12.4	22 9.0	21 27.2	9 21.3	14 33.8	12 6.6	1 18.8	5 35.7
7	10 59 34.3	17 41.1	9 27.8	1♉47.8	16 56.0	23 22.6	21 44.7	9 30.8	14 32.7	12 7.3	1 19.8	5 34.9
8	11 3 30.9	18 36.6	9 24.4	13 22.0	18 40.1	24 36.0	22 1.8	9 40.3	14 31.6	12 7.9	1 20.7	5 34.1
9	11 7 27.4	19 32.0	9 21.0	25 37.4	20 24.4	25 49.1	22 18.5	9 49.6	14 30.3	12 8.4	1 21.6	5 33.3
10	11 11 24.0	20 27.3	9 17.6	8♊44.2	22 9.1	27 1.9	22 34.8	9 58.7	14 29.0	12 8.9	1 22.4	5 32.4
11	11 15 20.5	21 22.5	9 14.2	22 46.3	23 54.2	28 14.5	22 50.6	10 7.7	14 27.5	12 9.4	1 23.3	5 31.5
12	11 19 17.1	22 17.7	9 10.8	7♋38.6	25 39.4	29 26.9	23 5.9	10 16.6	14 26.0	12 9.7	1 24.1	5 30.6
13	11 23 13.7	23 12.7	9 7.4	23 4.8	27 24.9	0♓39.0	23 20.8	10 25.3	14 24.4	12 10.1	1 24.8	5 29.6
14	11 27 10.2	24 7.7	9 4.0	8♌40.8	29 10.5	1 50.9	23 35.1	10 33.9	14 22.6	12 10.3	1 25.5	5 28.7
15	11 31 6.8	25 2.7	9 .7	24 2.6	0♈56.1	3 2.5	23 49.0	10 42.3	14 20.8	12 10.5	1 26.2	5 27.7
16	11 35 3.3	25 57.5	8 57.3	8♍55.1	2 41.6	4 13.9	24 2.4	10 50.6	14 18.9	12 10.7	1 26.8	5 26.6
17	11 38 59.9	26 52.4	8 53.9	23 14.4	4 26.8	5 25.0	24 15.2	10 58.7	14 16.9	12 10.8	1 27.5	5 25.6
18	11 42 56.4	27 47.1	8 50.5	7♎ 6.2	6 11.7	6 35.9	24 27.5	11 6.7	14 14.8	12 10.8	1 28.0	5 24.5
19	11 46 53.0	28 41.8	8 47.1	20 41.6	7 55.9	7 46.7	24 39.3	11 14.5	14 12.6	12 10.8	1 28.6	5 23.4
20	11 50 49.5	29 36.5	8 43.7	4♏12.9	9 39.2	8 57.2	24 50.5	11 22.2	14 10.4	12R10.7	1 29.1	5 22.3
21	11 54 46.1	0♈31.2	8 40.3	17 50.0	11 21.4	10 7.5	25 1.1	11 29.7	14 8.0	12 10.6	1 29.5	5 21.2
22	11 58 42.6	1 25.8	8 36.9	1♐38.5	13 2.2	11 17.6	25 11.1	11 37.1	14 5.6	12 10.4	1 30.0	5 20.0
23	12 2 39.2	2 20.5	8 33.5	15 37.2	14 41.3	12 27.6	25 20.6	11 44.3	14 3.1	12 10.2	1 30.4	5 18.9
24	12 6 35.7	3 15.1	8 30.1	29 38.5	16 18.2	13 37.3	25 29.5	11 51.4	14 .5	12 9.9	1 30.8	5 17.7
25	12 10 32.3	4 9.7	8 26.7	13♑30.3	17 52.7	14 46.9	25 37.6	11 58.2	13 57.8	12 9.5	1 31.1	5 16.5
26	12 14 28.8	5 4.2	8 23.3	26 59.8	19 24.4	15 56.3	25 45.2	12 4.9	13 55.0	12 9.1	1 31.4	5 15.3
27	12 18 25.4	5 58.8	8 20.0	9♒57.4	20 52.9	17 5.5	25 52.1	12 11.5	13 52.2	12 8.6	1 31.6	5 14.0
28	12 22 21.9	6 53.4	8 16.6	22 18.9	22 17.9	18 14.6	25 58.3	12 17.8	13 49.2	12 8.1	1 31.8	5 12.8
29	12 26 18.5	7 48.0	8 13.2	4♓ 5.6	23 38.9	19 23.6	26 3.8	12 24.0	13 46.2	12 7.5	1 32.0	5 11.5
30	12 30 15.1	8 42.7	8 9.8	15 23.5	24 55.7	20 32.4	26 8.7	12 30.1	13 43.2	12 6.9	1 32.1	5 10.2
31	12 34 11.6	9 37.3	8 6.4	26 21.3	26 7.9	21 41.1	26 12.8	12 35.9	13 40.0	12 6.2	1 32.3	5 8.8

DECLINATION

DAY	EPHEM. SID. TIME h m s	☉	☊	☾	☿	♀	♂	♃	♄	♅	♆	♇
1	10 35 55.0	7S35.6	0N23.2	18S49.2	11S59.7	17S20.0	16S40.5	22S57.3	14S21.1	22S22.1	22S15.6	4N 3.7
4	10 47 44.7	6 26.7	0 23.2	5 36.2	9 51.7	16 21.7	16 56.0	22 55.8	14 19.9	22 22.4	22 15.5	4 5.9
7	10 59 34.3	5 17.1	0 23.1	9N38.0	7 32.3	15 19.3	17 10.5	22 54.3	14 18.4	22 22.7	22 15.4	4 8.1
10	11 11 24.0	4 6.8	0 23.1	22 1.4	5 2.4	14 13.1	17 23.9	22 52.7	14 16.7	22 22.9	22 15.3	4 10.2
13	11 23 13.7	2 56.0	0 23.1	25 4.7	2 23.3	13 3.4	17 36.4	22 51.2	14 14.7	22 23.0	22 15.2	4 12.5
16	11 35 3.3	1 45.0	0 23.1	14 15.3	0N22.6	11 50.4	17 47.8	22 49.7	14 12.6	22 23.1	22 15.0	4 14.7
19	11 46 53.0	0 33.9	0 23.0	4S39.3	3 11.7	10 34.5	17 58.3	22 48.2	14 10.2	22 23.2	22 14.9	4 16.9
22	11 58 42.6	0N37.2	0 23.0	20 23.7	5 58.8	9 16.1	18 7.7	22 46.7	14 7.6	22 23.1	22 14.8	4 19.1
25	12 10 32.3	1 48.1	0 23.0	25 39.2	8 37.9	7 55.3	18 16.2	22 45.4	14 4.8	22 23.1	22 14.7	4 21.2
28	12 22 21.9	2 58.7	0 23.0	19 50.6	11 2.2	6 32.6	18 23.7	22 44.0	14 1.8	22 22.9	22 14.6	4 23.4
31	12 34 11.6	4 8.7	0 23.0	6 53.4	13 5.7	5 8.3	18 30.1	22 42.8	13 58.7	22 22.7	22 14.5	4 25.5

APRIL 1984

LONGITUDE

DAY	EPHEM. SID. TIME h m s	☉ ° ′	☊ ° ′	☾ ° ′	☿ ° ′	♀ ° ′	♂ ° ′	♃ ° ′	♄ ° ′	♅ ° ′	♆ ° ′	♇ ° ′
1	12 38 8.2	11♈27.4	9♊42.5	5♈51.6	0♉11.0	21♓34.3	28♏13.4	11♑41.7	15♏18.3	13♐28.8	1♑25.5	1♏17.1
2	12 42 4.7	12 26.6	9 39.3	17 53.5	1 19.1	22 48.3	28 16.3	11 46.7	15R14.9	13R28.1	1 25.5	1R15.6
3	12 46 1.3	13 25.7	9 36.2	0♉ 1.9	2 21.0	24 2.3	28 18.5	11 51.7	15 11.4	13 27.3	1 25.5	1 14.0
4	12 49 57.8	14 24.9	9 33.0	12 17.9	3 16.6	25 16.3	28 20.0	11 56.4	15 7.9	13 26.4	1 25.5	1 12.4
5	12 53 54.4	15 24.0	9 29.8	24 43.3	4 5.7	26 30.3	28 20.7	12 1.0	15 4.3	13 25.5	1R25.4	1 10.8
6	12 57 50.9	16 23.0	9 26.6	7♊20.2	4 48.2	27 44.3	28 20.7	12 5.4	15 .7	13 24.6	1 25.3	1 9.2
7	13 1 47.5	17 22.0	9 23.4	20 10.9	5 24.0	28 58.3	28R20.0	12 9.6	14 57.0	13 23.6	1 25.1	1 7.5
8	13 5 44.0	18 21.0	9 20.3	3♋18.4	5 53.0	0♈12.2	28 18.5	12 13.7	14 53.2	13 22.6	1 25.0	1 5.9
9	13 9 40.6	19 20.0	9 17.1	16 45.3	6 15.2	1 26.2	28 16.3	12 17.6	14 49.4	13 21.5	1 24.8	1 4.2
10	13 13 37.1	20 18.9	9 13.9	0♌33.7	6 30.7	2 40.1	28 13.3	12 21.3	14 45.5	13 20.4	1 24.5	1 2.6
11	13 17 33.7	21 17.8	9 10.7	14 44.4	6 39.5	3 54.1	28 9.6	12 24.8	14 41.6	13 19.2	1 24.3	1 .9
12	13 21 30.2	22 16.6	9 7.6	29 16.0	6 41.7	5 8.0	28 5.1	12 28.2	14 37.6	13 18.0	1 24.0	0 59.3
13	13 25 26.8	23 15.4	9 4.4	14♍ 4.6	6R37.6	6 22.0	27 59.9	12 31.4	14 33.6	13 16.8	1 23.7	0 57.6
14	13 29 23.4	24 14.2	9 1.2	29 3.6	6 27.4	7 35.9	27 53.9	12 34.4	14 29.5	13 15.5	1 23.3	0 55.9
15	13 33 19.9	25 12.9	8 58.0	14♎ 4.2	6 11.5	8 49.8	27 47.2	12 37.3	14 25.4	13 14.1	1 22.9	0 54.3
16	13 37 16.5	26 11.6	8 54.8	28 57.3	5 50.2	10 3.7	27 39.7	12 39.9	14 21.3	13 12.7	1 22.5	0 52.6
17	13 41 13.0	27 10.3	8 51.7	13♏34.4	5 24.1	11 17.6	27 31.4	12 42.4	14 17.1	13 11.3	1 22.1	0 50.9
18	13 45 9.6	28 8.9	8 48.5	27 49.0	4 53.7	12 31.5	27 22.4	12 44.7	14 12.8	13 9.8	1 21.6	0 49.2
19	13 49 6.1	29 7.5	8 45.3	11♐37.8	4 19.7	13 45.4	27 12.6	12 46.8	14 8.6	13 8.3	1 21.1	0 47.5
20	13 53 2.7	0♉ 6.0	8 42.1	24 59.8	3 42.7	14 59.3	27 2.1	12 48.7	14 4.2	13 6.8	1 20.5	0 45.8
21	13 56 59.2	1 4.6	8 39.0	7♑56.6	3 3.5	16 13.2	26 50.8	12 50.4	13 59.9	13 5.2	1 19.9	0 44.1
22	14 0 55.8	2 3.1	8 35.8	20 31.5	2 22.7	17 27.0	26 38.8	12 52.0	13 55.5	13 3.5	1 19.3	0 42.4
23	14 4 52.3	3 1.6	8 32.6	2♒48.6	1 41.3	18 40.9	26 26.1	12 53.4	13 51.1	13 1.9	1 18.7	0 40.7
24	14 8 48.9	4 .0	8 29.4	14 52.7	0 59.9	19 54.8	26 12.6	12 54.6	13 46.7	13 .2	1 18.0	0 39.0
25	14 12 45.5	4 58.5	8 26.2	26 48.4	0 19.3	21 8.6	25 58.5	12 55.5	13 42.3	12 58.4	1 17.3	0 37.3
26	14 16 42.0	5 56.9	8 23.1	8♓40.3	29♈40.2	22 22.5	25 43.6	12 56.3	13 37.8	12 56.6	1 16.6	0 35.6
27	14 20 38.6	6 55.2	8 19.9	20 32.2	29 3.3	23 36.4	25 28.2	12 57.0	13 33.3	12 54.8	1 15.9	0 33.9
28	14 24 35.1	7 53.6	8 16.7	2♈27.8	28 29.0	24 50.2	25 12.0	12 57.4	13 28.8	12 53.0	1 15.1	0 32.3
29	14 28 31.7	8 51.9	8 13.5	14 29.6	27 58.1	26 4.1	24 55.3	12 57.6	13 24.3	12 51.1	1 14.3	0 30.6
30	14 32 28.2	9 50.2	8 10.4	26 39.8	27 30.7	27 17.9	24 38.0	12 57.7	13 19.8	12 49.2	1 13.4	0 28.9

LATITUDE

DAY	EPHEM. SID. TIME	☉	☊	☾	☿	♀	♂	♃	♄	♅	♆	♇
1	12 38 8.2	0 .0	0 .0	4S29.1	2N18.0	1S26.3	1N15.9	0N13.3	2N34.7	0N 2.6	1N11.6	17N24.5
4	12 49 57.8	0 .0	0 .0	2 11.6	2 43.9	1 28.4	1 12.3	0 13.1	2 35.1	0 2.6	1 11.7	17 25.0
7	13 1 47.5	0 .0	0 .0	1N 7.0	3 1.3	1 29.8	1 8.2	0 12.8	2 35.4	0 2.6	1 11.8	17 25.4
10	13 13 37.1	0 .0	0 .0	4 6.2	3 8.2	1 30.7	1 3.8	0 12.6	2 35.7	0 2.5	1 11.9	17 25.8
13	13 25 26.8	0 .0	0 .0	5 6.2	3 2.8	1 30.9	0 58.9	0 12.4	2 36.0	0 2.5	1 12.0	17 26.1
16	13 37 16.5	0 .0	0 .0	3 11.6	2 44.2	1 30.5	0 53.6	0 12.1	2 36.2	0 2.5	1 12.1	17 26.2
19	13 49 6.1	0 .0	0 .0	0S24.8	2 12.8	1 29.6	0 47.8	0 11.9	2 36.4	0 2.5	1 12.2	17 26.3
22	14 0 55.8	0 .0	0 .0	3 34.6	1 30.7	1 28.0	0 41.6	0 11.7	2 36.5	0 2.4	1 12.2	17 26.2
25	14 12 45.5	0 .0	0 .0	5 6.8	0 41.7	1 25.9	0 34.9	0 11.4	2 36.6	0 2.4	1 12.3	17 26.1
28	14 24 35.1	0 .0	0 .0	4 41.6	0S 9.5	1 23.2	0 27.8	0 11.1	2 36.6	0 2.4	1 12.4	17 25.9

RIGHT ASCENSION

DAY	EPHEM. SID. TIME	☉	☊	☾	☿	♀	♂	♃	♄	♅	♆	♇
1	12 38 8.2	10♈31.9	8♊ 3.0	7♈ 9.3	27♈15.2	22♓49.7	26♏16.2	12♑41.6	13♏36.8	12♐ 5.5	1♑32.3	5♏ 7.5
2	12 42 4.7	11 26.6	7 59.6	17 59.2	28 17.4	23 58.1	26 18.9	12 47.1	13R33.5	12R 4.7	1 32.4	5R 6.2
3	12 46 1.3	12 21.4	7 56.2	29 2.9	29 14.2	25 6.5	26 20.9	12 52.4	13 30.1	12 3.8	1R32.3	5 4.8
4	12 49 57.8	13 16.1	7 52.9	10♉32.6	0♉ 5.4	26 14.8	26 22.1	12 57.5	13 26.7	12 2.9	1 32.3	5 3.4
5	12 53 54.4	14 10.9	7 49.5	22 39.4	0 50.7	27 22.9	26 22.6	13 2.4	13 23.2	12 2.0	1 32.2	5 2.0
6	12 57 50.9	15 5.7	7 46.1	5♊32.0	1 30.1	28 31.1	26R22.2	13 7.2	13 19.6	12 1.0	1 32.1	5 .6
7	13 1 47.5	16 .6	7 42.7	19 13.7	2 3.4	29 39.1	26 21.2	13 11.8	13 16.0	11 59.9	1 32.0	4 59.2
8	13 5 44.0	16 55.6	7 39.3	3♋39.9	2 30.6	0♈47.1	26 19.3	13 16.2	13 12.3	11 58.8	1 31.8	4 57.8
9	13 9 40.6	17 50.5	7 35.9	18 36.8	2 51.6	1 55.1	26 16.7	13 20.4	13 8.6	11 57.6	1 31.6	4 56.3
10	13 13 37.1	18 45.6	7 32.5	3♌43.9	3 6.4	3 3.0	26 13.3	13 24.4	13 4.8	11 56.4	1 31.3	4 54.9
11	13 17 33.7	19 40.7	7 29.2	18 41.0	3 15.1	4 10.9	26 9.1	13 28.2	13 1.0	11 55.2	1 31.0	4 53.4
12	13 21 30.2	20 35.9	7 25.8	3♍14.3	3 17.9	5 18.7	26 4.1	13 31.9	12 57.1	11 53.9	1 30.7	4 51.9
13	13 25 26.8	21 31.2	7 22.4	17 19.8	3R15.1	6 26.7	25 58.4	13 35.4	12 53.2	11 52.6	1 30.4	4 50.5
14	13 29 23.4	22 26.5	7 19.0	1♎ 2.5	3 6.7	7 34.5	25 51.8	13 38.6	12 49.2	11 51.2	1 30.0	4 49.0
15	13 33 19.9	23 21.9	7 15.6	14 32.9	2 53.2	8 42.4	25 44.4	13 41.7	12 45.2	11 49.7	1 29.6	4 47.5
16	13 37 16.5	24 17.4	7 12.3	28 3.4	2 35.1	9 50.4	25 36.3	13 44.5	12 41.1	11 48.2	1 29.1	4 46.0
17	13 41 13.0	25 13.0	7 8.9	11♏45.2	2 12.7	10 58.3	25 27.3	13 47.2	12 37.0	11 46.7	1 28.6	4 44.5
18	13 45 9.6	26 8.7	7 5.5	25 45.1	1 46.7	12 6.3	25 17.6	13 49.7	12 32.9	11 45.1	1 28.1	4 43.0
19	13 49 6.1	27 4.5	7 2.1	10♐ 2.5	1 17.7	13 14.4	25 7.0	13 52.0	12 28.7	11 43.5	1 27.6	4 41.5
20	13 53 2.7	28 .4	6 58.7	24 28.9	0 46.3	14 22.5	24 55.7	13 54.1	12 24.5	11 41.8	1 27.0	4 39.9
21	13 56 59.2	28 56.4	6 55.4	8♑49.5	0 13.3	15 30.8	24 43.6	13 55.9	12 20.2	11 40.1	1 26.3	4 38.4
22	14 0 55.8	29 52.5	6 52.0	22 47.6	29♈39.2	16 39.1	24 30.8	13 57.6	12 16.0	11 38.3	1 25.7	4 36.9
23	14 4 52.3	0♉48.7	6 48.6	6♒10.1	29 4.9	17 47.5	24 17.2	13 59.1	12 11.7	11 36.5	1 25.0	4 35.3
24	14 8 48.9	1 45.1	6 45.2	18 51.0	28 31.0	18 56.0	24 2.8	14 .4	12 7.3	11 34.7	1 24.3	4 33.8
25	14 12 45.5	2 41.5	6 41.8	0♓51.2	27 58.1	20 4.6	23 47.7	14 1.5	12 3.0	11 32.8	1 23.5	4 32.3
26	14 16 42.0	3 38.1	6 38.5	12 17.2	27 26.8	21 13.4	23 31.9	14 2.3	11 58.6	11 30.9	1 22.7	4 30.7
27	14 20 38.6	4 34.9	6 35.1	23 18.7	26 57.8	22 22.2	23 15.5	14 3.0	11 54.2	11 29.0	1 21.9	4 29.2
28	14 24 35.1	5 31.7	6 31.7	4♈ 7.6	26 31.3	23 31.3	22 58.3	14 3.5	11 49.8	11 27.0	1 21.1	4 27.6
29	14 28 31.7	6 28.7	6 28.3	14 56.2	26 8.0	24 40.5	22 40.6	14 3.7	11 45.4	11 25.0	1 20.2	4 26.1
30	14 32 28.2	7 25.8	6 25.0	25 57.5	25 48.0	25 49.8	22 22.2	14 3.8	11 40.9	11 22.9	1 19.3	4 24.5

DECLINATION

DAY	EPHEM. SID. TIME	☉	☊	☾	☿	♀	♂	♃	♄	♅	♆	♇
1	12 38 8.2	4N31.9	0N22.9	1S47.5	13N41.5	4S39.9	18S32.0	22S42.4	13S57.6	22S22.7	22S14.5	4N26.2
4	12 49 57.8	5 41.0	0 22.9	13N26.4	15 10.5	3 13.9	18 37.0	22 41.4	13 54.2	22 22.4	22 14.4	4 28.2
7	13 1 47.5	6 49.2	0 22.9	24 11.6	16 10.2	1 47.0	18 40.9	22 40.4	13 50.8	22 22.1	22 14.3	4 30.2
10	13 13 37.1	7 56.3	0 22.9	24 2.3	16 39.0	0 19.5	18 43.8	22 39.5	13 47.1	22 21.7	22 14.2	4 32.2
13	13 25 26.8	9 2.3	0 22.8	10 58.3	16 36.3	1N 8.2	18 45.6	22 38.8	13 43.4	22 21.3	22 14.1	4 34.0
16	13 37 16.5	10 6.8	0 22.8	8S 7.1	16 2.9	2 35.9	18 46.2	22 38.3	13 39.6	22 20.8	22 14.0	4 35.8
19	13 49 6.1	11 9.9	0 22.8	22 35.5	15 2.8	4 3.2	18 45.8	22 37.8	13 35.7	22 20.3	22 14.0	4 37.5
22	14 0 55.8	12 11.3	0 22.8	25 24.5	13 43.2	5 29.8	18 44.1	22 37.6	13 31.8	22 19.7	22 13.9	4 39.2
25	14 12 45.5	13 10.9	0 22.8	17 22.8	12 14.2	6 55.4	18 41.2	22 37.5	13 27.8	22 19.1	22 13.8	4 40.7
28	14 24 35.1	14 8.6	0 22.7	3 19.6	10 47.3	8 19.7	18 37.0	22 37.6	13 23.8	22 18.4	22 13.8	4 42.2

MAY 1984

LONGITUDE

DAY	EPHEM. SID. TIME	☉	☊	☾	☿	♀	♂	♃	♄	♅	♆	♇
	h m s	° ′	° ′	° ′	° ′	° ′	° ′	° ′	° ′	° ′	° ′	° ′
1	14 36 24.8	10♉48.5	8♊ 7.2	9♉ .0	27♈ 7.4	28♈31.7	24♏20.1	12♑57.5	13♏15.3	12♐47.2	1♑12.6	0♏27.2
2	14 40 21.3	11 46.7	8 4.0	21 31.3	26 R 48.4	29 45.6	24 R 1.7	12 R 57.2	13 R 10.7	12 R 45.2	1 R 11.7	0 R 25.6
3	14 44 17.9	12 44.9	8 .8	4♊14.3	26 33.9	0♉59.4	23 42.8	12 56.7	13 6.2	12 43.2	1 10.8	0 23.9
4	14 48 14.4	13 43.1	7 57.7	17 9.8	26 24.1	2 13.2	23 23.5	12 56.0	13 1.7	12 41.2	1 9.9	0 22.3
5	14 52 11.0	14 41.3	7 54.5	0♋18.4	26 18.9	3 27.1	23 3.7	12 55.1	12 57.2	12 39.1	1 8.9	0 20.7
6	14 56 7.6	15 39.4	7 51.3	13 40.7	26 18.5	4 40.9	22 43.5	12 54.0	12 52.6	12 37.0	1 7.9	0 19.1
7	15 0 4.1	16 37.5	7 48.1	27 17.3	26 D 22.8	5 54.6	22 23.0	12 52.7	12 48.1	12 34.9	1 6.9	0 17.5
8	15 4 .7	17 35.5	7 44.9	11♌ 8.4	26 31.9	7 8.4	22 2.2	12 51.3	12 43.6	12 32.8	1 5.8	0 15.9
9	15 7 57.2	18 33.5	7 41.8	25 13.7	26 45.5	8 22.2	21 41.2	12 49.6	12 39.1	12 30.6	1 4.8	0 14.3
10	15 11 53.8	19 31.5	7 38.6	9♍31.6	27 3.7	9 36.0	21 19.9	12 47.8	12 34.6	12 28.4	1 3.7	0 12.7
11	15 15 50.3	20 29.5	7 35.4	23 59.5	27 26.3	10 49.7	20 58.5	12 45.8	12 30.1	12 26.2	1 2.6	0 11.1
12	15 19 46.9	21 27.4	7 32.2	8♎33.1	27 53.1	12 3.5	20 36.9	12 43.6	12 25.7	12 23.9	1 1.4	0 9.6
13	15 23 43.5	22 25.3	7 29.1	23 7.1	28 24.2	13 17.2	20 15.3	12 41.2	12 21.3	12 21.7	1 .3	0 8.0
14	15 27 40.0	23 23.1	7 25.9	7♏35.6	28 59.2	14 30.9	19 53.6	12 38.7	12 16.8	12 19.4	0 59.1	0 6.5
15	15 31 36.6	24 21.0	7 22.7	21 52.8	29 38.2	15 44.7	19 31.9	12 35.9	12 12.5	12 17.1	0 57.9	0 5.0
16	15 35 33.1	25 18.8	7 19.5	5♐53.5	0♉21.0	16 58.4	19 10.3	12 33.0	12 8.1	12 14.8	0 56.6	0 3.5
17	15 39 29.7	26 16.6	7 16.4	19 34.3	1 7.3	18 12.1	18 48.8	12 29.9	12 3.8	12 12.4	0 55.4	0 2.0
18	15 43 26.2	27 14.4	7 13.2	2♑53.5	1 57.2	19 25.8	18 27.4	12 26.7	11 59.5	12 10.1	0 54.1	0 .5
19	15 47 22.8	28 12.1	7 10.0	15 50.9	2 50.5	20 39.6	18 6.1	12 23.2	11 55.2	12 7.7	0 52.9	29♎59.1
20	15 51 19.3	29 9.8	7 6.8	28 28.4	3 47.1	21 53.3	17 45.1	12 19.6	11 51.0	12 5.3	0 51.5	29 57.7
21	15 55 15.9	0♊ 7.5	7 3.6	10♒48.7	4 46.9	23 7.0	17 24.4	12 15.8	11 46.8	12 2.9	0 50.2	29 56.3
22	15 59 12.5	1 5.2	7 .5	22 55.7	5 49.8	24 20.7	17 3.9	12 11.9	11 42.6	12 .5	0 48.9	29 54.9
23	16 3 9.0	2 2.9	6 57.3	4♓53.6	6 55.7	25 34.4	16 43.8	12 7.8	11 38.5	11 58.1	0 47.5	29 53.5
24	16 7 5.6	3 .6	6 54.1	16 46.9	8 4.5	26 48.2	16 24.1	12 3.5	11 34.4	11 55.6	0 46.2	29 52.1
25	16 11 2.1	3 58.3	6 50.9	28 40.4	9 16.3	28 1.9	16 4.9	11 59.1	11 30.5	11 53.2	0 44.8	29 50.9
26	16 14 58.7	4 55.9	6 47.8	10♈38.1	10 30.8	29 15.6	15 46.1	11 54.5	11 26.5	11 50.8	0 43.4	29 49.5
27	16 18 55.2	5 53.5	6 44.6	22 44.1	11 48.0	0♊29.3	15 27.7	11 49.7	11 22.6	11 48.3	0 42.0	29 48.3
28	16 22 51.8	6 51.1	6 41.4	5♉ 1.4	13 8.0	1 43.1	15 10.0	11 44.8	11 18.7	11 45.9	0 40.5	29 47.0
29	16 26 48.4	7 48.7	6 38.2	17 32.7	14 30.6	2 56.8	14 52.8	11 39.7	11 14.9	11 43.4	0 39.1	29 45.7
30	16 30 44.9	8 46.2	6 35.1	0♊19.5	15 55.8	4 10.5	14 36.2	11 34.5	11 11.1	11 40.9	0 37.6	29 44.5
31	16 34 41.5	9 43.8	6 31.9	13 22.4	17 23.6	5 24.2	14 20.2	11 29.2	11 7.4	11 38.4	0 36.1	29 43.3

LATITUDE

DAY	EPHEM. SID. TIME	☉	☊	☾	☿	♀	♂	♃	♄	♅	♆	♇
1	14 36 24.8	0 .0	0 .0	2S25.7	0S58.7	1S20.0	0N20.3	0N10.9	2N36.6	0N 2.4	1N12.5	17N25.6
4	14 48 14.4	0 .0	0 .0	0N57.7	1 42.4	1 16.3	0 12.5	0 10.6	2 36.5	0 2.3	1 12.6	17 25.2
7	15 0 4.1	0 .0	0 .0	4 3.9	2 18.8	1 12.1	0 4.4	0 10.3	2 36.4	0 2.3	1 12.6	17 24.7
10	15 11 53.8	0 .0	0 .0	5 14.9	2 47.1	1 7.4	0S 4.0	0 10.0	2 36.2	0 2.3	1 12.7	17 24.1
13	15 23 43.5	0 .0	0 .0	3 37.4	3 7.0	1 2.3	0 12.5	0 9.7	2 36.0	0 2.3	1 12.7	17 23.4
16	15 35 33.1	0 .0	0 .0	0 3.6	3 19.1	0 56.9	0 21.1	0 9.4	2 35.8	0 2.2	1 12.8	17 22.6
19	15 47 22.8	0 .0	0 .0	3S20.8	3 23.9	0 51.1	0 29.7	0 9.1	2 35.5	0 2.2	1 12.8	17 21.7
22	15 59 12.5	0 .0	0 .0	5 7.8	3 21.8	0 45.0	0 38.1	0 8.7	2 35.1	0 2.2	1 12.9	17 20.8
25	16 11 2.1	0 .0	0 .0	4 53.6	3 13.5	0 38.6	0 46.4	0 8.4	2 34.7	0 2.1	1 12.9	17 19.8
28	16 22 51.8	0 .0	0 .0	2 46.2	2 59.4	0 32.0	0 54.4	0 8.1	2 34.3	0 2.1	1 12.9	17 18.7
31	16 34 41.5	0 .0	0 .0	0N37.5	2 40.3	0 25.2	1 2.1	0 7.7	2 33.8	0 2.1	1 13.0	17 17.5

RIGHT ASCENSION

DAY	EPHEM. SID. TIME	☉	☊	☾	☿	♀	♂	♃	♄	♅	♆	♇
1	14 36 24.8	8♉23.1	6♊21.6	7♉24.2	25♈31.7	26♈59.3	22♏ 3.3	14♑ 3.7	11♏36.5	11♐20.8	1♑18.4	4♏23.0
2	14 40 21.3	9 20.4	6 18.2	19 28.1	25 R 19.3	28 9.0	21 R 43.8	14 R 3.3	11 R 32.0	11 R 18.7	1 R 17.4	4 R 21.5
3	14 44 17.9	10 18.0	6 14.8	2♊17.9	25 10.9	29 18.9	21 23.8	14 2.8	11 27.6	11 16.5	1 16.4	4 19.9
4	14 48 14.4	11 15.7	6 11.5	15 57.1	25 6.7	0♉29.0	21 3.4	14 2.1	11 23.2	11 14.4	1 15.5	4 18.5
5	14 52 11.0	12 13.5	6 8.1	0♋20.4	25 6.6	1 39.3	20 42.5	14 1.1	11 18.7	11 12.2	1 14.4	4 16.9
6	14 56 7.6	13 11.4	6 4.7	15 12.9	25 D 10.6	2 49.7	20 21.2	13 59.9	11 14.3	11 9.9	1 13.3	4 15.4
7	15 0 4.1	14 9.4	6 1.3	0♌13.2	25 18.8	4 .4	19 59.6	13 58.6	11 9.8	11 7.6	1 12.2	4 13.9
8	15 4 .7	15 7.6	5 58.0	14 60.0	25 31.1	5 11.3	19 37.7	13 57.0	11 5.4	11 5.3	1 11.1	4 12.4
9	15 7 57.2	16 6.0	5 54.6	29 19.1	25 47.3	6 22.5	19 15.5	13 55.2	11 1.0	11 3.0	1 9.9	4 10.9
10	15 11 53.8	17 4.5	5 51.2	13♍ 6.9	26 7.5	7 33.8	18 53.1	13 53.3	10 56.6	11 .6	1 8.8	4 9.4
11	15 15 50.3	18 3.1	5 47.9	26 29.0	26 31.5	8 45.4	18 30.6	13 51.1	10 52.2	10 58.3	1 7.6	4 7.9
12	15 19 46.9	19 1.8	5 44.5	9♎36.8	26 59.2	9 57.3	18 7.9	13 48.7	10 47.8	10 55.8	1 6.3	4 6.4
13	15 23 43.5	20 .7	5 41.1	22 44.3	27 30.5	11 9.4	17 45.2	13 46.2	10 43.4	10 53.4	1 5.1	4 5.0
14	15 27 40.0	20 59.8	5 37.7	6♏ 5.1	28 5.4	12 21.7	17 22.5	13 43.4	10 39.1	10 51.0	1 3.8	4 3.5
15	15 31 36.6	21 58.9	5 34.4	19 49.3	28 43.6	13 34.3	16 59.7	13 40.5	10 34.8	10 48.5	1 2.5	4 2.1
16	15 35 33.1	22 58.2	5 31.0	4♐ .6	29 25.2	14 47.2	16 37.0	13 37.4	10 30.5	10 46.0	1 1.2	4 .6
17	15 39 29.7	23 57.7	5 27.6	18 33.3	0♉ 9.9	16 .4	16 14.4	13 34.0	10 26.2	10 43.5	0 59.8	3 59.2
18	15 43 26.2	24 57.3	5 24.3	3♑12.4	0 57.8	17 13.8	15 52.0	13 30.5	10 22.0	10 41.0	0 58.5	3 57.8
19	15 47 22.8	25 57.0	5 20.9	17 37.9	1 48.8	18 27.5	15 29.8	13 26.8	10 17.8	10 38.4	0 57.1	3 56.4
20	15 51 19.3	26 56.9	5 17.5	1♒30.8	2 42.7	19 41.5	15 7.8	13 22.9	10 13.6	10 35.9	0 55.7	3 55.0
21	15 55 15.9	27 56.9	5 14.2	14 39.9	3 39.5	20 55.7	14 46.0	13 18.9	10 9.5	10 33.3	0 54.2	3 53.6
22	15 59 12.5	28 57.1	5 10.8	27 2.4	4 39.3	22 10.3	14 24.6	13 14.6	10 5.4	10 30.7	0 52.8	3 52.3
23	16 3 9.0	29 57.4	5 7.4	8♓43.6	5 41.8	23 25.1	14 3.6	13 10.2	10 1.4	10 28.1	0 51.3	3 50.9
24	16 7 5.6	0♊57.8	5 4.1	19 53.3	6 47.2	24 40.2	13 43.0	13 5.6	9 57.3	10 25.5	0 49.8	3 49.6
25	16 11 2.1	1 58.4	5 .7	0♈44.1	7 55.4	25 55.6	13 22.8	13 .8	9 53.4	10 23.0	0 48.4	3 48.3
26	16 14 58.7	2 59.1	4 57.3	11 29.4	9 6.2	27 11.3	13 3.2	12 55.9	9 49.5	10 20.3	0 46.9	3 47.0
27	16 18 55.2	3 59.9	4 54.0	22 23.6	10 19.9	28 27.3	12 44.0	12 50.7	9 45.6	10 17.7	0 45.3	3 45.7
28	16 22 51.8	5 .9	4 50.6	3♉41.0	11 36.3	29 43.5	12 25.4	12 45.4	9 41.8	10 15.1	0 43.8	3 44.4
29	16 26 48.4	6 1.9	4 47.3	15 35.0	12 55.5	0♊60.0	12 7.4	12 40.0	9 38.0	10 12.4	0 42.2	3 43.2
30	16 30 44.9	7 3.1	4 43.9	28 17.1	14 17.5	2 16.7	11 50.0	12 34.4	9 34.3	10 9.8	0 40.6	3 42.0
31	16 34 41.5	8 4.4	4 40.5	11♊53.2	15 42.3	3 33.8	11 33.3	12 28.6	9 30.6	10 7.1	0 39.0	3 40.7

DECLINATION

DAY	EPHEM. SID. TIME	☉	☊	☾	☿	♀	♂	♃	♄	♅	♆	♇
1	14 36 24.8	15N 4.2	0N22.7	12N11.8	9N32.2	9N42.4	18S31.7	22S37.8	13S19.8	22S17.7	22S13.7	4N43.5
4	14 48 14.4	15 57.5	0 22.7	23 46.8	8 35.8	11 3.2	18 25.3	22 38.3	13 15.8	22 17.0	22 13.7	4 44.7
7	15 0 4.1	16 48.5	0 22.6	24 41.3	8 1.4	12 21.6	18 17.9	22 38.9	13 11.8	22 16.2	22 13.6	4 45.9
10	15 11 53.8	17 36.9	0 22.6	21 51.3	7 49.7	13 37.4	18 9.6	22 39.6	13 7.9	22 15.4	22 13.6	4 46.9
13	15 23 43.5	18 22.7	0 22.6	5S37.1	7 59.6	14 50.3	18 .7	22 40.6	13 4.1	22 14.5	22 13.6	4 47.8
16	15 35 33.1	19 5.7	0 22.6	21 13.9	8 29.1	15 59.9	17 51.4	22 41.6	13 .4	22 13.6	22 13.6	4 48.5
19	15 47 22.8	19 45.7	0 22.5	25 49.4	9 15.9	17 5.9	17 41.9	22 42.9	12 56.8	22 12.7	22 13.5	4 49.2
22	15 59 12.5	20 22.8	0 22.5	18 43.0	10 17.5	18 7.9	17 32.5	22 44.2	12 53.3	22 11.8	22 13.5	4 49.7
25	16 11 2.1	20 56.7	0 22.5	5 1.0	11 31.6	19 5.8	17 23.5	22 45.7	12 49.9	22 10.9	22 13.5	4 50.1
28	16 22 51.8	21 27.4	0 22.4	10N35.2	12 55.8	19 59.1	17 15.2	22 47.3	12 46.8	22 9.9	22 13.5	4 50.3
31	16 34 41.5	21 54.7	0 22.4	23 1.6	14 27.7	20 47.6	17 7.8	22 49.1	12 43.7	22 9.0	22 13.5	4 50.5

JUNE 1984

LONGITUDE

DAY	EPHEM. SID. TIME	☉	☊	☾	☿	♀	♂	♃	♄	♅	♆	♇
	h m s	° ′	° ′	° ′	° ′	° ′	° ′	° ′	° ′	° ′	° ′	° ′
1	16 38 38.0	10♊41.3	6♊28.7	26♊41.1	18♉54.1	6♊37.9	14♏ 4.9	11♑23.7	11♏ 3.7	11♐36.0	0♑34.7	29♎42.2
2	16 42 34.6	11 38.8	6 25.5	10♋14.5	20 27.0	7 51.6	13 R 50.3	11 R 18.0	11 R .2	11 R 33.5	0 R 33.1	29 R 41.0
3	16 46 31.2	12 36.3	6 22.3	24 .9	22 2.6	9 5.3	13 36.4	11 12.3	10 56.6	11 31.0	0 31.6	29 39.9
4	16 50 27.7	13 33.7	6 19.2	7♌57.9	23 40.6	10 19.0	13 23.3	11 6.4	10 53.2	11 28.5	0 30.1	29 38.8
5	16 54 24.3	14 31.2	6 16.0	22 3.1	25 21.2	11 32.7	13 10.9	11 .3	10 49.8	11 26.0	0 28.6	29 37.7
6	16 58 20.8	15 28.6	6 12.8	6♍13.9	27 4.4	12 46.4	12 59.3	10 54.2	10 46.5	11 23.6	0 27.0	29 36.7
7	17 2 17.4	16 26.0	6 9.6	20 27.8	28 50.0	14 .1	12 48.5	10 47.9	10 43.2	11 21.1	0 25.5	29 35.6
8	17 6 13.9	17 23.4	6 6.5	4♎42.3	0♊38.1	15 13.8	12 38.4	10 41.6	10 40.0	11 18.6	0 23.9	29 34.6
9	17 10 10.5	18 20.8	6 3.3	18 54.7	2 28.6	16 27.5	12 29.2	10 35.1	10 36.9	11 16.2	0 22.3	29 33.7
10	17 14 7.1	19 18.1	6 .1	3♏ 2.5	4 21.6	17 41.2	12 20.8	10 28.5	10 33.9	11 13.7	0 20.8	29 32.7
11	17 18 3.6	20 15.5	5 56.9	17 2.9	6 16.9	18 54.9	12 13.2	10 21.8	10 30.9	11 11.3	0 19.2	29 31.8
12	17 22 .2	21 12.8	5 53.8	0♐53.2	8 14.5	20 8.6	12 6.5	10 15.0	10 28.0	11 8.9	0 17.6	29 30.9
13	17 25 56.7	22 10.1	5 50.6	14 30.8	10 14.3	21 22.3	12 .5	10 8.1	10 25.2	11 6.4	0 16.0	29 30.1
14	17 29 53.3	23 7.4	5 47.4	27 53.8	12 16.1	22 35.9	11 55.4	10 1.2	10 22.5	11 4.0	0 14.4	29 29.3
15	17 33 49.9	24 4.7	5 44.2	11♑ .6	14 20.0	23 49.7	11 51.1	9 54.2	10 19.9	11 1.7	0 12.8	29 28.5
16	17 37 46.4	25 2.0	5 41.1	23 50.6	16 25.6	25 3.4	11 47.7	9 47.0	10 17.3	10 59.3	0 11.2	29 27.7
17	17 41 43.0	25 59.2	5 37.9	6♒24.5	18 32.8	26 17.1	11 45.0	9 39.8	10 14.9	10 56.9	0 9.6	29 27.0
18	17 45 39.5	26 56.5	5 34.7	18 43.7	20 41.4	27 30.8	11 43.2	9 32.6	10 12.5	10 54.6	0 8.0	29 26.3
19	17 49 36.1	27 53.8	5 31.5	0♓50.7	22 51.1	28 44.5	11 42.1	9 25.2	10 10.1	10 52.2	0 6.4	29 25.6
20	17 53 32.6	28 51.0	5 28.3	12 49.0	25 1.7	29 58.2	11 41.9	9 17.8	10 7.9	10 49.9	0 4.7	29 25.0
21	17 57 29.2	29 48.2	5 25.2	24 42.6	27 12.9	1♋11.9	11 D 42.5	9 10.4	10 5.8	10 47.6	0 3.1	29 24.3
22	18 1 25.8	0♋45.5	5 22.0	6♈36.1	29 24.4	2 25.6	11 43.9	9 2.9	10 3.7	10 45.3	0 1.5	29 23.8
23	18 5 22.3	1 42.7	5 18.8	18 34.1	1♋36.0	3 39.3	11 46.1	8 55.3	10 1.7	10 43.1	29♐59.9	29 23.2
24	18 9 18.9	2 40.0	5 15.6	0♉41.3	3 47.3	4 53.1	11 49.1	8 47.8	9 59.9	10 40.8	29 58.3	29 22.7
25	18 13 15.4	3 37.2	5 12.5	13 2.2	5 58.2	6 6.8	11 52.9	8 40.1	9 58.1	10 38.6	29 56.6	29 22.2
26	18 17 12.0	4 34.4	5 9.3	25 40.3	8 8.3	7 20.5	11 57.4	8 32.5	9 56.4	10 36.4	29 55.0	29 21.7
27	18 21 8.6	5 31.7	5 6.1	8♊38.5	10 17.5	8 34.3	12 2.8	8 24.8	9 54.8	10 34.2	29 53.4	29 21.3
28	18 25 5.1	6 28.9	5 2.9	21 58.1	12 25.5	9 48.0	12 8.9	8 17.2	9 53.2	10 32.1	29 51.8	29 20.9
29	18 29 1.7	7 26.1	4 59.8	5♋38.6	14 32.1	11 1.8	12 15.7	8 9.5	9 51.8	10 29.9	29 50.2	29 20.5
30	18 32 58.2	8♋23.4	4 56.6	19♋37.9	16♋37.3	12♋15.5	12♏23.3	8♑ 1.8	9♏50.5	10♐27.8	29♐48.6	29♎20.2

LATITUDE

DAY	EPHEM. SID. TIME	☉	☊	☾	☿	♀	♂	♃	♄	♅	♆	♇
1	16 38 38.0	0 .0	0 .0	1N49.0	2S32.9	0S22.9	1S 4.5	0N 7.6	2N33.7	0N 2.1	1N13.0	17N17.1
4	16 50 27.7	0 .0	0 .0	4 38.0	2 7.8	0 15.9	1 11.7	0 7.2	2 33.1	0 2.0	1 13.0	17 15.9
7	17 2 17.4	0 .0	0 .0	5 7.1	1 39.0	0 8.8	1 18.6	0 6.8	2 32.6	0 2.0	1 13.0	17 14.6
10	17 14 7.1	0 .0	0 .0	2 55.0	1 7.5	0 1.6	1 24.9	0 6.5	2 32.0	0 2.0	1 13.0	17 13.2
13	17 25 56.7	0 .0	0 .0	0S43.6	0 34.4	0N 5.5	1 30.9	0 6.1	2 31.4	0 1.9	1 13.0	17 11.8
16	17 37 46.4	0 .0	0 .0	3 51.6	0 1.1	0 12.6	1 36.5	0 5.7	2 30.7	0 1.9	1 13.0	17 10.3
19	17 49 36.1	0 .0	0 .0	5 12.8	0N30.6	0 19.6	1 41.6	0 5.3	2 30.0	0 1.9	1 13.0	17 8.7
22	18 1 25.8	0 .0	0 .0	4 31.7	0 58.8	0 26.5	1 46.3	0 4.9	2 29.3	0 1.8	1 12.9	17 7.2
25	18 13 15.4	0 .0	0 .0	2 4.7	1 21.9	0 33.2	1 50.6	0 4.5	2 28.6	0 1.8	1 12.9	17 5.6
28	18 25 5.1	0 .0	0 .0	1N24.0	1 38.9	0 39.7	1 54.5	0 4.0	2 27.9	0 1.8	1 12.9	17 3.9

RIGHT ASCENSION

DAY	EPHEM. SID. TIME	☉	☊	☾	☿	♀	♂	♃	♄	♅	♆	♇
1	16 38 38.0	9♊ 5.7	4♊37.2	26♊20.2	17♉10.0	4♊51.1	11♏17.2	12♑22.7	9♏27.0	10♐ 4.5	0♑37.4	3♏39.6
2	16 42 34.6	10 7.2	4 33.8	11♋23.5	18 40.7	6 8.6	11 R 1.9	12 R 16.6	9 R 23.5	10 R 1.8	0 R 35.8	3 R 38.4
3	16 46 31.2	11 8.8	4 30.4	26 38.9	20 14.2	7 26.4	10 47.3	12 10.3	9 20.0	9 59.2	0 34.2	3 37.2
4	16 50 27.7	12 10.4	4 27.1	11♌40.5	21 50.8	8 44.4	10 33.4	12 4.0	9 16.6	9 56.5	0 32.5	3 36.1
5	16 54 24.3	13 12.2	4 23.7	26 9.7	23 30.5	10 2.7	10 20.4	11 57.5	9 13.2	9 53.9	0 30.9	3 35.0
6	16 58 20.8	14 14.0	4 20.4	10♍ .2	25 13.2	11 21.2	10 8.1	11 50.8	9 9.9	9 51.2	0 29.2	3 33.9
7	17 2 17.4	15 15.9	4 17.0	23 16.3	26 59.1	12 39.9	9 56.6	11 44.1	9 6.7	9 48.6	0 27.5	3 32.8
8	17 6 13.9	16 17.8	4 13.6	6♎ 9.8	28 48.3	13 58.8	9 45.9	11 37.2	9 3.5	9 45.9	0 25.8	3 31.7
9	17 10 10.5	17 19.8	4 10.3	18 55.9	0♊40.6	15 17.9	9 36.1	11 30.2	9 .5	9 43.3	0 24.1	3 30.7
10	17 14 7.1	18 21.9	4 6.9	1♏50.3	2 36.2	16 37.2	9 27.0	11 23.1	8 57.4	9 40.7	0 22.4	3 29.7
11	17 18 3.6	19 24.0	4 3.6	15 6.0	4 35.0	17 56.7	9 18.8	11 15.8	8 54.5	9 38.1	0 20.7	3 28.7
12	17 22 .2	20 26.2	4 .2	28 51.4	6 37.1	19 16.3	9 11.5	11 8.5	8 51.6	9 35.5	0 19.0	3 27.8
13	17 25 56.7	21 28.4	3 56.9	13♐ 6.3	8 42.2	20 36.1	9 4.9	11 1.0	8 48.8	9 32.9	0 17.3	3 26.8
14	17 29 53.3	22 30.7	3 53.5	27 40.4	10 50.5	21 56.0	8 59.2	10 53.5	8 46.1	9 30.3	0 15.5	3 25.9
15	17 33 49.9	23 33.0	3 50.1	12♑14.8	13 1.6	23 16.1	8 54.4	10 45.9	8 43.5	9 27.8	0 13.8	3 25.1
16	17 37 46.4	24 35.3	3 46.8	26 27.5	15 15.5	24 36.3	8 50.4	10 38.2	8 40.9	9 25.3	0 12.1	3 24.2
17	17 41 43.0	25 37.7	3 43.4	10♒ 1.3	17 31.9	25 56.6	8 47.2	10 30.4	8 38.5	9 22.7	0 10.4	3 23.4
18	17 45 39.5	26 40.0	3 40.1	22 48.1	19 50.6	27 17.0	8 44.8	10 22.6	8 36.0	9 20.2	0 8.6	3 22.5
19	17 49 36.1	27 42.4	3 36.7	4♓48.9	22 11.1	28 37.5	8 43.2	10 14.6	8 33.7	9 17.7	0 6.9	3 21.8
20	17 53 32.6	28 44.8	3 33.4	16 11.5	24 33.3	29 58.0	8 42.5	10 6.6	8 31.5	9 15.2	0 5.1	3 21.0
21	17 57 29.2	29 47.2	3 30.0	27 7.6	26 56.7	1♋18.6	8 D 42.6	9 58.6	8 29.3	9 12.8	0 3.4	3 20.3
22	18 1 25.8	0♋49.6	3 26.7	7♈51.1	29 20.9	2 39.2	8 43.5	9 50.4	8 27.2	9 10.3	0 1.6	3 19.5
23	18 5 22.3	1 52.0	3 23.3	18 36.4	1♋45.5	3 59.9	8 45.2	9 42.3	8 25.2	9 7.9	29♐59.9	3 18.9
24	18 9 18.9	2 54.3	3 20.0	29 39.0	4 10.0	5 20.5	8 47.7	9 34.1	8 23.3	9 5.5	29 58.1	3 18.2
25	18 13 15.4	3 56.7	3 16.6	11♉13.9	6 34.2	6 41.2	8 51.0	9 25.8	8 21.5	9 3.1	29 56.4	3 17.6
26	18 17 12.0	4 59.0	3 13.3	23 35.1	8 57.5	8 1.8	8 55.1	9 17.5	8 19.8	9 .8	29 54.6	3 17.0
27	18 21 8.6	6 1.3	3 9.9	6♊52.9	11 19.6	9 22.4	8 60.0	9 9.2	8 18.2	8 58.5	29 52.9	3 16.4
28	18 25 5.1	7 3.6	3 6.6	21 9.8	13 40.3	10 43.0	9 5.6	9 .9	8 16.6	8 56.2	29 51.1	3 15.8
29	18 29 1.7	8 5.8	3 3.2	6♋16.1	15 59.1	12 3.4	9 12.1	8 52.6	8 15.1	8 53.9	29 49.4	3 15.3
30	18 32 58.2	9♋ 7.9	2 59.9	21♋48.9	18♋15.8	13♋23.8	9♏19.2	8♑44.2	8♏13.8	8♐51.6	29♐47.7	3♏14.8

DECLINATION

DAY	EPHEM. SID. TIME	☉	☊	☾	☿	♀	♂	♃	♄	♅	♆	♇
1	16 38 38.0	22N 3.1	0N22.4	25N13.0	14N59.6	21N 2.6	17S 5.6	22S49.6	12S42.8	22S 8.6	22S13.5	4N50.5
4	16 50 27.7	22 25.9	0 22.4	22 45.0	16 37.9	21 44.2	16 60.0	22 51.5	12 40.0	22 7.6	22 13.5	4 50.4
7	17 2 17.4	22 45.1	0 22.3	8 28.9	18 17.4	22 20.3	16 55.9	22 53.4	12 37.5	22 6.7	22 13.5	4 50.2
10	17 14 7.1	23 .7	0 22.3	9S47.1	19 54.7	22 50.7	16 53.5	22 55.3	12 35.2	22 5.7	22 13.5	4 49.9
13	17 25 56.7	23 12.7	0 22.3	23 15.9	21 25.2	23 15.2	16 52.9	22 57.2	12 33.1	22 4.7	22 13.5	4 49.4
16	17 37 46.4	23 20.9	0 22.3	25 8.3	22 43.9	23 33.6	16 54.2	22 59.2	12 31.2	22 3.7	22 13.5	4 48.8
19	17 49 36.1	23 25.5	0 22.2	16 2.7	23 45.5	23 45.8	16 57.4	23 1.2	12 29.7	22 2.8	22 13.6	4 48.1
22	18 1 25.8	23 26.4	0 22.2	1 32.3	24 25.2	23 51.7	17 2.4	23 3.1	12 28.3	22 1.8	22 13.6	4 47.2
25	18 13 15.4	23 23.6	0 22.2	13N46.2	24 40.3	23 51.2	17 9.3	23 5.1	12 27.2	22 .9	22 13.6	4 46.2
28	18 25 5.1	23 17.0	0 22.1	24 35.8	24 30.1	23 44.4	17 18.0	23 6.9	12 26.4	22 .0	22 13.7	4 45.1

JULY 1984

LONGITUDE

DAY	EPHEM. SID. TIME (h m s)	☉ (° ′)	☊ (° ′)	☽ (° ′)	☿ (° ′)	♀ (° ′)	♂ (° ′)	♃ (° ′)	♄ (° ′)	♅ (° ′)	♆ (° ′)	♇ (° ′)
1	18 36 54.8	9♋20.6	4♊53.4	3♌52.0	18♋40.9	13♋29.3	12♏31.6	7♑54.1	9♏49.3	10♐25.8	29♐47.0	29♎19.9
2	18 40 51.3	10 17.8	4 50.2	18 15.8	20 42.8	14 43.1	12 40.7	7R46.4	9R48.1	10R23.7	29R45.4	29R19.7
3	18 44 47.9	11 15.0	4 47.1	2♍43.7	22 42.9	15 56.8	12 50.5	7 38.7	9 47.1	10 21.7	29 43.8	29 19.4
4	18 48 44.5	12 12.2	4 43.9	17 10.1	24 41.1	17 10.6	13 1.0	7 31.0	9 46.1	10 19.7	29 42.2	29 19.2
5	18 52 41.0	13 9.4	4 40.7	1♎30.7	26 37.4	18 24.3	13 12.2	7 23.4	9 45.3	10 17.8	29 40.7	29 19.1
6	18 56 37.6	14 6.7	4 37.5	15 42.4	28 31.8	19 38.2	13 24.1	7 15.9	9 44.6	10 15.9	29 39.2	29 19.0
7	19 0 34.1	15 3.9	4 34.3	29 43.1	0♌24.3	20 51.9	13 36.6	7 8.3	9 43.9	10 14.0	29 37.6	29 18.9
8	19 4 30.7	16 1.1	4 31.2	13♏32.1	2 14.7	22 5.7	13 49.8	7 .7	9 43.4	10 12.2	29 36.1	29 18.8
9	19 8 27.3	16 58.3	4 28.0	27 9.1	4 3.2	23 19.5	14 3.6	6 53.3	9 42.9	10 10.3	29 34.5	29 18.8
10	19 12 23.8	17 55.5	4 24.8	10♐34.3	5 49.7	24 33.2	14 18.0	6 45.8	9 42.5	10 8.6	29 33.0	29 18.8
11	19 16 20.4	18 52.6	4 21.6	23 47.6	7 34.2	25 47.0	14 33.1	6 38.4	9 42.3	10 6.8	29 31.5	29D18.9
12	19 20 16.9	19 49.8	4 18.5	6♑48.8	9 16.7	27 .8	14 48.8	6 31.1	9 42.1	10 5.1	29 30.0	29 18.9
13	19 24 13.5	20 47.0	4 15.3	19 37.9	10 57.2	28 14.6	15 5.0	6 23.9	9 42.0	10 3.4	29 28.5	29 19.0
14	19 28 10.0	21 44.2	4 12.1	2♒14.6	12 35.8	29 28.3	15 21.9	6 16.7	9 42.0	10 1.8	29 27.1	29 19.2
15	19 32 6.6	22 41.4	4 8.9	14 39.2	14 12.3	0♌42.1	15 39.3	6 9.5	9D42.2	10 .2	29 25.6	29 19.4
16	19 36 3.2	23 38.6	4 5.8	26 52.6	15 46.9	1 55.9	15 57.2	6 2.5	9 42.4	9 58.6	29 24.1	29 19.6
17	19 39 59.7	24 35.9	4 2.6	8♓56.2	17 19.5	3 9.7	16 15.7	5 55.6	9 42.7	9 57.1	29 22.7	29 19.8
18	19 43 56.3	25 33.1	3 59.4	20 52.5	18 50.1	4 23.5	16 34.8	5 48.7	9 43.1	9 55.6	29 21.3	29 20.1
19	19 47 52.8	26 30.3	3 56.2	2♈44.6	20 18.6	5 37.3	16 54.4	5 41.9	9 43.6	9 54.1	29 19.9	29 20.4
20	19 51 49.4	27 27.6	3 53.1	14 36.6	21 45.2	6 51.1	17 14.5	5 35.2	9 44.2	9 52.7	29 18.5	29 20.8
21	19 55 45.9	28 24.8	3 49.9	26 32.9	23 9.6	8 4.9	17 35.1	5 28.7	9 45.0	9 51.4	29 17.1	29 21.1
22	19 59 42.5	29 22.1	3 46.7	8♉38.5	24 32.0	9 18.7	17 56.2	5 22.2	9 45.8	9 50.0	29 15.8	29 21.6
23	20 3 39.1	0♌19.4	3 43.5	20 58.6	25 52.3	10 32.5	18 17.8	5 15.8	9 46.7	9 48.8	29 14.5	29 22.0
24	20 7 35.6	1 16.7	3 40.3	3♊37.9	27 10.3	11 46.4	18 39.8	5 9.6	9 47.7	9 47.5	29 13.1	29 22.5
25	20 11 32.2	2 14.0	3 37.2	16 40.3	28 26.2	13 .2	19 2.4	5 3.5	9 48.8	9 46.3	29 11.8	29 23.0
26	20 15 28.7	3 11.4	3 34.0	0♋ 8.6	29 39.8	14 14.0	19 25.4	4 57.5	9 50.0	9 45.2	29 10.6	29 23.6
27	20 19 25.3	4 8.8	3 30.8	14 3.2	0♍51.1	15 27.9	19 49.0	4 51.6	9 51.3	9 44.1	29 9.4	29 24.2
28	20 23 21.8	5 6.1	3 27.6	28 22.0	1 59.9	16 41.7	20 12.9	4 45.9	9 52.7	9 43.1	29 8.1	29 24.8
29	20 27 18.4	6 3.5	3 24.5	12♌60.0	3 6.3	17 55.6	20 37.3	4 40.3	9 54.2	9 42.0	29 6.9	29 25.5
30	20 31 15.0	7 .9	3 21.3	27 49.8	4 10.0	19 9.4	21 2.1	4 34.8	9 55.8	9 41.1	29 5.7	29 26.2
31	20 35 11.5	7 58.3	3 18.1	12♍42.9	5 11.1	20 23.3	21 27.4	4 29.5	9 57.4	9 40.1	29 4.5	29 26.9

LATITUDE

DAY	EPHEM. SID. TIME	☉	☊	☽	☿	♀	♂	♃	♄	♅	♆	♇
1	18 36 54.8	0 .0	0 .0	4N23.0	1N49.2	0N45.9	1S58.1	0N 3.6	2N27.1	0N 1.7	1N12.8	17N 2.2
4	18 48 44.5	0 .0	0 .0	5 5.1	1 52.9	0 51.9	2 1.3	0 3.2	2 26.4	0 1.7	1 12.8	17 .5
7	19 0 34.1	0 .0	0 .0	3 4.3	1 50.3	0 57.5	2 4.3	0 2.8	2 25.6	0 1.7	1 12.7	16 58.8
10	19 12 23.8	0 .0	0 .0	0S24.6	1 42.0	1 2.7	2 7.0	0 2.4	2 24.8	0 1.6	1 12.7	16 57.1
13	19 24 13.5	0 .0	0 .0	3 33.3	1 28.5	1 7.6	2 9.3	0 1.9	2 24.0	0 1.6	1 12.6	16 55.3
16	19 36 3.2	0 .0	0 .0	5 3.3	1 10.5	1 12.0	2 11.5	0 1.5	2 23.2	0 1.6	1 12.5	16 53.6
19	19 47 52.8	0 .0	0 .0	4 32.2	0 48.4	1 15.9	2 13.4	0 1.1	2 22.4	0 1.5	1 12.4	16 51.8
22	19 59 42.5	0 .0	0 .0	2 17.0	0 22.8	1 19.3	2 15.0	0 .7	2 21.6	0 1.5	1 12.4	16 50.1
25	20 11 32.2	0 .0	0 .0	1N 1.6	0S 5.9	1 22.2	2 16.5	0 .3	2 20.8	0 1.5	1 12.3	16 48.3
28	20 23 21.8	0 .0	0 .0	4 4.6	0 37.1	1 24.6	2 17.7	0S .1	2 20.0	0 1.4	1 12.2	16 46.6
31	20 35 11.5	0 .0	0 .0	5 .2	1 10.4	1 26.4	2 18.8	0 .6	2 19.2	0 1.4	1 12.1	16 44.9

RIGHT ASCENSION

DAY	EPHEM. SID. TIME	☉	☊	☽	☿	♀	♂	♃	♄	♅	♆	♇
1	18 36 54.8	10♋10.0	2♊56.5	7♌18.5	20♋30.3	14♋44.1	9♏27.2	8♑35.9	8♏12.5	8♐49.4	29♐46.0	3♏14.4
2	18 40 51.3	11 12.0	2 53.2	22 19.0	22 42.3	16 4.3	9 35.8	8R27.5	8R11.3	8R47.3	29R44.2	3R13.9
3	18 44 47.9	12 14.0	2 49.8	6♍36.8	24 51.7	17 24.4	9 45.3	8 19.2	8 10.2	8 45.1	29 42.5	3 13.5
4	18 48 44.5	13 15.9	2 46.5	20 12.2	26 58.4	18 44.3	9 55.4	8 10.9	8 9.2	8 43.0	29 40.8	3 13.2
5	18 52 41.0	14 17.7	2 43.1	3♎15.0	29 2.3	20 4.1	10 6.2	8 2.6	8 8.3	8 40.9	29 39.1	3 12.8
6	18 56 37.6	15 19.4	2 39.8	16 .2	1♌ 3.4	21 23.8	10 17.8	7 54.4	8 7.5	8 38.9	29 37.5	3 12.5
7	19 0 34.1	16 21.0	2 36.4	28 44.1	3 1.6	22 43.2	10 30.1	7 46.2	8 6.8	8 36.9	29 35.8	3 12.3
8	19 4 30.7	17 22.5	2 33.1	11♏41.5	4 56.9	24 2.4	10 43.0	7 38.0	8 6.2	8 34.9	29 34.2	3 12.0
9	19 8 27.3	18 23.9	2 29.7	25 3.5	6 49.3	25 21.5	10 56.5	7 29.9	8 5.6	8 33.0	29 32.5	3 11.8
10	19 12 23.8	19 25.2	2 26.4	8♐54.4	8 38.8	26 40.3	11 10.8	7 21.8	8 5.2	8 31.1	29 30.9	3 11.6
11	19 16 20.4	20 26.4	2 23.0	23 9.5	10 25.4	27 58.9	11 25.6	7 13.8	8 4.9	8 29.2	29 29.2	3 11.4
12	19 20 16.9	21 27.5	2 19.7	7♑34.2	12 9.1	29 17.3	11 41.1	7 5.8	8 4.6	8 27.3	29 27.6	3 11.3
13	19 24 13.5	22 28.5	2 16.4	21 48.8	13 50.1	0♌35.5	11 57.2	6 58.0	8 4.4	8 25.6	29 26.0	3 11.2
14	19 28 10.0	23 29.3	2 13.0	5♒33.7	15 28.3	1 53.4	12 13.9	6 50.2	8 4.4	8 23.8	29 24.4	3 11.1
15	19 32 6.6	24 30.0	2 9.7	18 36.6	17 3.7	3 11.1	12 31.3	6 42.4	8 4.4	8 22.1	29 22.8	3 11.1
16	19 36 3.2	25 30.6	2 6.3	0♓54.0	18 36.5	4 28.5	12 49.2	6 34.8	8D 4.5	8 20.4	29 21.3	3 11.0
17	19 39 59.7	26 31.1	2 3.0	12 30.1	20 6.5	5 45.6	13 7.6	6 27.2	8 4.8	8 18.8	29 19.7	3D11.1
18	19 43 56.3	27 31.4	1 59.6	23 34.4	21 34.0	7 2.5	13 26.7	6 19.8	8 5.1	8 17.2	29 18.2	3 11.1
19	19 47 52.8	28 31.6	1 56.3	4♈19.3	22 58.8	8 19.1	13 46.3	6 12.4	8 5.5	8 15.7	29 16.7	3 11.2
20	19 51 49.4	29 31.7	1 53.0	14 58.7	24 21.0	9 35.4	14 6.5	6 5.1	8 6.0	8 14.1	29 15.2	3 11.3
21	19 55 45.9	0♌31.6	1 49.6	25 47.4	25 40.6	10 51.4	14 27.2	5 58.0	8 6.6	8 12.7	29 13.7	3 11.4
22	19 59 42.5	1 31.5	1 46.3	7♉ .6	26 57.7	12 7.2	14 48.5	5 51.0	8 7.3	8 11.3	29 12.3	3 11.6
23	20 3 39.1	2 31.1	1 42.9	18 53.2	28 12.2	13 22.7	15 10.3	5 44.0	8 8.1	8 9.9	29 10.8	3 11.8
24	20 7 35.6	3 30.6	1 39.6	1♊38.6	29 24.2	14 37.8	15 32.6	5 37.2	8 9.0	8 8.6	29 9.4	3 12.0
25	20 11 32.2	4 30.0	1 36.3	15 24.6	0♍33.6	15 52.7	15 55.5	5 30.6	8 10.0	8 7.3	29 8.0	3 12.3
26	20 15 28.7	5 29.3	1 32.9	0♋ 9.5	1 40.4	17 7.3	16 18.8	5 24.1	8 11.1	8 6.1	29 6.6	3 12.6
27	20 19 25.3	6 28.4	1 29.6	15 38.1	2 44.6	18 21.7	16 42.8	5 17.7	8 12.3	8 5.0	29 5.3	3 13.0
28	20 23 21.8	7 27.4	1 26.2	1♌22.9	3 46.2	19 35.7	17 7.1	5 11.5	8 13.5	8 3.8	29 4.0	3 13.3
29	20 27 18.4	8 26.2	1 22.9	16 53.8	4 45.1	20 49.4	17 32.0	5 5.4	8 14.9	8 2.7	29 2.6	3 13.7
30	20 31 15.0	9 24.8	1 19.6	1♍49.1	5 41.3	22 2.8	17 57.4	4 59.4	8 16.3	8 1.7	29 1.3	3 14.1
31	20 35 11.5	10 23.3	1 16.2	16 1.0	6 34.7	23 15.9	18 23.2	4 53.6	8 17.9	8 .7	29 .1	3 14.6

DECLINATION

DAY	EPHEM. SID. TIME	☉	☊	☽	☿	♀	♂	♃	♄	♅	♆	♇
1	18 36 54.8	23N 6.8	0N22.1	23N32.8	23N56.5	23N31.2	17S28.4	23S 8.8	12S25.9	21S59.1	22S13.7	4N43.9
4	18 48 44.5	22 52.9	0 22.1	9 44.9	23 2.5	23 11.8	17 40.5	23 10.5	12 25.7	21 58.3	22 13.7	4 42.5
7	19 0 34.1	22 35.5	0 22.1	8S29.9	21 51.7	22 46.2	17 54.1	23 12.2	12 25.7	21 57.5	22 13.8	4 41.0
10	19 12 23.8	22 14.5	0 22.0	22 26.4	20 27.8	22 14.6	18 9.1	23 13.8	12 26.0	21 56.8	22 13.8	4 39.4
13	19 24 13.5	21 50.1	0 22.0	25 31.3	18 54.2	21 37.1	18 25.4	23 15.3	12 26.6	21 56.0	22 13.9	4 37.7
16	19 36 3.2	21 22.4	0 22.0	17 18.0	17 13.7	20 54.1	18 42.8	23 16.8	12 27.5	21 55.4	22 13.9	4 35.9
19	19 47 52.8	20 51.3	0 21.9	3 4.3	15 29.0	20 5.6	19 1.1	23 18.1	12 28.6	21 54.7	22 14.0	4 34.0
22	19 59 42.5	20 17.1	0 21.9	12N13.2	13 42.2	19 12.1	19 20.3	23 19.3	12 30.1	21 54.2	22 14.1	4 31.9
25	20 11 32.2	19 39.9	0 21.9	23 47.8	11 55.6	18 13.7	19 40.2	23 20.5	12 31.8	21 53.7	22 14.1	4 29.8
28	20 23 21.8	18 59.7	0 21.8	24 28.9	10 11.2	17 10.7	20 .7	23 21.5	12 33.8	21 53.2	22 14.2	4 27.6
31	20 35 11.5	18 16.6	0 21.8	11 24.4	8 31.2	16 3.5	20 21.6	23 22.5	12 36.0	21 52.8	22 14.3	4 25.3

LONGITUDE

DAY	EPHEM. SID. TIME (h m s)	☉	☊	☽	☿	♀	♂	♃	♄	⛢	♆	♇
1	20 39 8.1	8♌55.7	3♊14.9	27♍30.8	6♍ 9.4	21♌37.1	21♏53.0	4♑24.3	9♏59.2	9♐39.3	29♐ 3.4	29♎27.6
2	20 43 4.6	9 53.1	3 11.8	12♎ 6.5	7 4.7	22 51.0	22 19.1	4R19.2	10 1.1	9R38.4	29R 2.2	29 28.4
3	20 47 1.2	10 50.6	3 8.6	26 25.4	7 57.0	24 4.8	22 45.6	4 14.4	10 3.0	9 37.7	29 1.1	29 29.2
4	20 50 57.7	11 48.0	3 5.4	10♏25.3	8 46.1	25 18.6	23 12.5	4 9.6	10 5.1	9 36.9	29 .0	29 30.1
5	20 54 54.3	12 45.4	3 2.2	24 6.2	9 31.8	26 32.5	23 39.8	4 5.1	10 7.3	9 36.3	28 59.0	29 31.0
6	20 58 50.8	13 42.9	2 59.0	7♐29.5	10 14.1	27 46.3	24 7.4	4 .7	10 9.5	9 35.6	28 57.9	29 31.9
7	21 2 47.4	14 40.4	2 55.9	20 37.0	10 52.6	29 .1	24 35.4	3 56.4	10 11.8	9 35.0	28 56.9	29 32.8
8	21 6 44.0	15 37.9	2 52.7	3♑30.8	11 27.2	0♍13.9	25 3.8	3 52.3	10 14.3	9 34.5	28 55.9	29 33.8
9	21 10 40.5	16 35.4	2 49.5	16 12.8	11 57.7	1 27.8	25 32.5	3 48.4	10 16.8	9 34.0	28 55.0	29 34.8
10	21 14 37.1	17 32.9	2 46.3	28 44.2	12 23.9	2 41.6	26 1.5	3 44.7	10 19.4	9 33.6	28 54.0	29 35.9
11	21 18 33.6	18 30.4	2 43.2	11♒ 6.2	12 45.7	3 55.4	26 30.9	3 41.1	10 22.1	9 33.2	28 53.1	29 37.0
12	21 22 30.2	19 28.0	2 40.0	23 19.4	13 2.7	5 9.2	27 .6	3 37.7	10 24.9	9 32.9	28 52.2	29 38.1
13	21 26 26.7	20 25.6	2 36.8	5♓24.6	13 14.8	6 23.0	27 30.7	3 34.5	10 27.7	9 32.6	28 51.4	29 39.2
14	21 30 23.3	21 23.1	2 33.6	17 23.0	13 21.8	7 36.8	28 1.1	3 31.4	10 30.7	9 32.3	28 50.6	29 40.4
15	21 34 19.8	22 20.8	2 30.4	29 16.1	13 23.4	8 50.6	28 31.7	3 28.5	10 33.7	9 32.1	28 49.7	29 41.6
16	21 38 16.4	23 18.4	2 27.3	11♈ 6.4	13R19.7	10 4.4	29 2.7	3 25.8	10 36.9	9 32.0	28 49.0	29 42.8
17	21 42 13.0	24 16.1	2 24.1	22 56.9	13 10.4	11 18.3	29 34.0	3 23.4	10 40.1	9 32.0	28 48.3	29 44.1
18	21 46 9.5	25 13.8	2 20.9	4♉51.6	12 55.3	12 32.1	0♐ 5.6	3 21.0	10 43.4	9 31.9	28 47.5	29 45.4
19	21 50 6.1	26 11.5	2 17.7	16 55.0	12 34.6	13 45.8	0 37.5	3 18.9	10 46.8	9D32.0	28 46.9	29 46.7
20	21 54 2.6	27 9.3	2 14.6	29 12.2	12 8.3	14 59.6	1 9.7	3 16.9	10 50.3	9 32.0	28 46.2	29 48.1
21	21 57 59.2	28 7.0	2 11.4	11♊48.5	11 36.6	16 13.4	1 42.1	3 15.1	10 53.8	9 32.1	28 45.6	29 49.4
22	22 1 55.7	29 4.8	2 8.2	24 48.6	10 59.7	17 27.2	2 14.8	3 13.5	10 57.5	9 32.3	28 44.9	29 50.9
23	22 5 52.3	0♍ 2.7	2 5.0	8♋16.4	10 17.9	18 41.0	2 47.8	3 12.1	11 1.2	9 32.5	28 44.4	29 52.3
24	22 9 48.8	1 .5	2 1.9	22 13.7	9 31.9	19 54.8	3 21.1	3 10.9	11 5.0	9 32.8	28 43.8	29 53.8
25	22 13 45.4	1 58.4	1 58.7	6♌39.6	8 42.3	21 8.6	3 54.6	3 9.8	11 8.9	9 33.1	28 43.3	29 55.2
26	22 17 41.9	2 56.3	1 55.5	21 29.6	7 49.9	22 22.3	4 28.4	3 9.0	11 12.9	9 33.5	28 42.8	29 56.8
27	22 21 38.5	3 54.3	1 52.3	6♍35.9	6 55.5	23 36.1	5 2.5	3 8.3	11 16.9	9 34.0	28 42.4	29 58.3
28	22 25 35.1	4 52.2	1 49.1	21 48.5	6 .3	24 49.9	5 36.8	3 7.9	11 21.0	9 34.4	28 41.9	29 59.9
29	22 29 31.6	5 50.2	1 46.0	6♎56.3	5 5.3	26 3.6	6 11.4	3 7.6	11 25.2	9 35.0	28 41.5	0♏ 1.5
30	22 33 28.2	6 48.2	1 42.8	21 49.9	4 11.7	27 17.4	6 46.2	3 7.5	11 29.5	9 35.6	28 41.2	0 3.1
31	22 37 24.7	7 46.3	1 39.6	6♏22.7	3 20.6	28 31.1	7 21.3	3D 7.6	11 33.8	9 36.2	28 40.9	0 4.8

LATITUDE

DAY	EPHEM. SID. TIME (h m s)	☉	☊	☽	☿	♀	♂	♃	♄	⛢	♆	♇
1	20 39 8.1	0 .0	0 .0	4N39.0	1S21.8	1N26.9	2S19.1	0S .7	2N18.9	0N 1.4	1N12.0	16N44.3
4	20 50 57.7	0 .0	0 .0	2 2.6	1 56.9	1 27.9	2 19.9	0 1.1	2 18.1	0 1.4	1 11.9	16 42.6
7	21 2 47.4	0 .0	0 .0	1S26.3	2 32.4	1 28.3	2 20.6	0 1.5	2 17.4	0 1.3	1 11.8	16 40.9
10	21 14 37.1	0 .0	0 .0	4 6.7	3 7.3	1 28.1	2 21.1	0 1.9	2 16.6	0 1.3	1 11.7	16 39.3
13	21 26 26.7	0 .0	0 .0	5 .0	3 40.0	1 27.4	2 21.5	0 2.3	2 15.8	0 1.3	1 11.6	16 37.6
16	21 38 16.4	0 .0	0 .0	3 56.2	4 8.3	1 26.0	2 21.7	0 2.6	2 15.1	0 1.2	1 11.5	16 36.0
19	21 50 6.1	0 .0	0 .0	1 21.4	4 29.3	1 23.9	2 21.8	0 3.0	2 14.4	0 1.2	1 11.3	16 34.5
22	22 1 55.7	0 .0	0 .0	1N55.1	4 39.4	1 21.3	2 21.8	0 3.4	2 13.6	0 1.2	1 11.2	16 33.0
25	22 13 45.4	0 .0	0 .0	4 31.3	4 35.0	1 18.1	2 21.6	0 3.7	2 12.9	0 1.1	1 11.1	16 31.5
28	22 25 35.1	0 .0	0 .0	4 42.1	4 13.3	1 14.3	2 21.3	0 4.1	2 12.3	0 1.1	1 10.9	16 30.1
31	22 37 24.7	0 .0	0 .0	2 7.6	3 36.1	1 9.9	2 20.9	0 4.4	2 11.6	0 1.1	1 10.8	16 28.7

RIGHT ASCENSION

DAY	EPHEM. SID. TIME (h m s)	☉	☊	☽	☿	♀	♂	♃	♄	⛢	♆	♇
1	20 39 8.1	11♌21.6	1♊12.9	29♍34.4	7♍25.2	24♌28.7	18♏49.5	4♑48.0	8♏19.5	7♐59.8	28♐58.8	3♏15.1
2	20 43 4.6	12 19.8	1 9.6	12♎41.7	8 12.8	25 41.3	19 16.3	4R42.5	8 21.3	7R58.9	28R57.6	3 15.6
3	20 47 1.2	13 17.8	1 6.2	25 38.4	8 57.4	26 53.5	19 43.6	4 37.2	8 23.1	7 58.1	28 56.4	3 16.1
4	20 50 57.7	14 15.7	1 2.9	8♏39.7	9 38.8	28 5.5	20 11.3	4 32.0	8 25.0	7 57.3	28 55.2	3 16.7
5	20 54 54.3	15 13.4	0 59.6	21 42.4	10 17.0	29 17.2	20 39.4	4 27.1	8 27.0	7 56.6	28 54.1	3 17.3
6	20 58 50.8	16 10.9	0 56.2	5♐ 3.4	10 51.8	0♍28.6	21 8.0	4 22.3	8 29.1	7 55.9	28 53.0	3 17.9
7	21 2 47.4	17 8.3	0 52.9	19 40.6	11 23.1	1 39.7	21 37.0	4 17.7	8 31.3	7 55.3	28 51.9	3 18.6
8	21 6 44.0	18 5.6	0 49.6	3♑54.1	11 50.8	2 50.6	22 6.4	4 13.2	8 33.6	7 54.7	28 50.8	3 19.3
9	21 10 40.5	19 2.7	0 46.2	18 2.2	12 14.7	4 1.3	22 36.2	4 9.0	8 36.0	7 54.2	28 49.8	3 20.0
10	21 14 37.1	19 59.6	0 42.9	1♒47.2	12 34.6	5 11.6	23 6.5	4 4.9	8 38.4	7 53.7	28 48.8	3 20.7
11	21 18 33.6	20 56.4	0 39.6	14 55.6	12 50.5	6 21.8	23 37.1	4 1.0	8 41.0	7 53.3	28 47.8	3 21.5
12	21 22 30.2	21 53.1	0 36.2	27 21.6	13 2.0	7 31.7	24 8.2	3 57.3	8 43.6	7 52.9	28 46.8	3 22.3
13	21 26 26.7	22 49.6	0 32.9	9♓ 6.9	13 9.2	8 41.3	24 39.6	3 53.8	8 46.3	7 52.6	28 45.9	3 23.2
14	21 30 23.3	23 46.0	0 29.6	20 18.6	13 11.4	9 50.5	25 11.4	3 50.5	8 49.1	7 52.4	28 45.0	3 24.0
15	21 34 19.8	24 42.3	0 26.2	1♈ 7.1	13R 9.7	11 .0	25 43.6	3 47.3	8 52.0	7 52.2	28 44.1	3 24.9
16	21 38 16.4	25 38.4	0 22.9	11 45.0	13 2.9	12 9.1	26 16.2	3 44.4	8 55.0	7 52.0	28 43.3	3 25.9
17	21 42 13.0	26 34.5	0 19.6	22 25.6	12 51.2	13 17.9	26 49.2	3 41.7	8 58.1	7 51.9	28 42.5	3 26.9
18	21 46 9.5	27 30.3	0 16.2	3♉22.8	12 34.7	14 26.6	27 22.5	3 39.2	9 1.2	7 51.9	28 41.7	3 27.8
19	21 50 6.1	28 26.1	0 12.9	14 51.0	12 13.3	15 35.1	27 56.2	3 36.8	9 4.4	7D52.0	28 41.0	3 28.8
20	21 54 2.6	29 21.7	0 9.6	27 3.4	11 47.2	16 43.4	28 30.3	3 34.7	9 7.8	7 52.0	28 40.3	3 29.9
21	21 57 59.2	0♍17.2	0 6.3	10♊ 4.5	11 16.6	17 51.5	29 4.7	3 32.7	9 11.1	7 52.2	28 39.6	3 31.0
22	22 1 55.7	1 12.7	0 2.9	24 15.8	10 41.7	18 59.5	29 39.4	3 31.0	9 14.6	7 52.3	28 38.9	3 32.0
23	22 5 52.3	2 8.0	29♉59.6	9♋12.7	10 3.0	20 7.4	0♐14.5	3 29.4	9 18.2	7 52.6	28 38.3	3 33.2
24	22 9 48.8	3 3.2	29 56.3	24 41.9	9 21.0	21 15.1	0 50.0	3 28.1	9 21.8	7 52.9	28 37.7	3 34.3
25	22 13 45.4	3 58.2	29 53.0	10♌16.8	8 36.2	22 22.7	1 25.8	3 27.0	9 25.5	7 53.2	28 37.2	3 35.5
26	22 17 41.9	4 53.2	29 49.6	25 32.5	7 49.4	23 30.2	2 1.9	3 26.1	9 29.3	7 53.6	28 36.6	3 36.7
27	22 21 38.5	5 48.1	29 46.3	10♍ 7.1	7 1.5	24 37.6	2 38.4	3 25.4	9 33.2	7 54.1	28 36.1	3 37.9
28	22 25 35.1	6 42.9	29 43.0	24 20.7	6 13.3	25 44.9	3 15.2	3 24.8	9 37.1	7 54.6	28 35.7	3 39.2
29	22 29 31.6	7 37.6	29 39.7	7♎59.1	5 26.0	26 52.1	3 52.3	3 24.6	9 41.2	7 55.2	28 35.2	3 40.5
30	22 33 28.2	8 32.3	29 36.3	21 22.9	4 40.4	27 59.2	4 29.7	3 24.5	9 45.3	7 55.8	28 34.9	3 41.8
31	22 37 24.7	9 26.8	29 33.0	4♏46.1	3 57.7	29 6.3	5 7.5	3D24.6	9 49.5	7 56.5	28 34.5	3 43.1

DECLINATION

DAY	EPHEM. SID. TIME (h m s)	☉	☊	☽	☿	♀	♂	♃	♄	⛢	♆	♇
1	20 39 8.1	18N 1.7	0N21.8	5N15.3	7N59.2	16N40.3	20S28.7	23S22.8	12S36.8	21S52.7	22S14.3	4N24.5
4	20 50 57.7	17 15.1	0 21.8	13S .5	6 28.6	14 27.9	20 50.0	23 23.7	12 39.4	21 52.4	22 14.4	4 22.1
7	21 2 47.4	16 26.0	0 21.7	24 32.7	5 8.2	13 12.1	21 11.5	23 24.5	12 42.2	21 52.1	22 14.5	4 19.6
10	21 14 37.1	15 34.6	0 21.7	24 26.3	4 1.4	11 53.2	21 32.9	23 25.2	12 45.3	21 51.9	22 14.6	4 17.0
13	21 26 26.7	14 40.9	0 21.7	13 11.8	3 11.8	10 31.4	21 54.2	23 25.9	12 48.6	21 51.8	22 14.7	4 14.4
16	21 38 16.4	13 45.1	0 21.6	0N46.3	2 43.8	9 7.1	22 15.2	23 26.5	12 52.2	21 51.8	22 14.8	4 11.7
19	21 50 6.1	12 47.3	0 21.6	15 35.4	2 41.4	7 40.7	22 35.7	23 27.1	12 55.9	21 51.8	22 14.9	4 8.9
22	22 1 55.7	11 47.7	0 21.6	25 15.4	3 7.9	6 12.3	22 55.7	23 27.6	12 59.9	21 51.9	22 15.0	4 6.1
25	22 13 45.4	10 46.4	0 21.5	22 59.1	4 3.2	4 42.5	23 15.1	23 28.0	13 4.1	21 52.0	22 15.1	4 3.3
28	22 25 35.1	9 43.6	0 21.5	7 34.0	5 22.5	3 11.4	23 33.7	23 28.4	13 8.4	21 52.3	22 15.2	4 .4
31	22 37 24.7	8 39.4	0 21.5	11S38.4	6 55.2	1 39.5	23 51.4	23 28.7	13 13.0	21 52.6	22 15.4	3 57.5

SEPEMBER 1984

DAY	EPHEM. SID. TIME	☉	☊	☽	☿	♀	♂	♃	♄	♅	♆	♇
	h m s	° ′	° ′	° ′	° ′	° ′	° ′	° ′	° ′	° ′	° ′	° ′
		LONGITUDE										
1	22 41 21.3	8♍44.3	1♊36.4	20♏31.0	2♍33.4	29♍44.9	7♐56.6	3♑ 7.9	11♏38.2	9♐36.9	28♐40.6	0♏ 6.4
2	22 45 17.8	9 42.4	1 33.3	4♐14.4	1 R 50.9	0♎58.6	8 32.1	3 8.4	11 42.7	9 37.6	28 R 40.3	0 8.1
3	22 49 14.4	10 40.5	1 30.1	17 34.6	1 14.3	2 12.3	9 7.8	3 9.1	11 47.3	9 38.4	28 40.1	0 9.9
4	22 53 10.9	11 38.6	1 26.9	0♑34.5	0 44.4	3 26.0	9 43.8	3 10.0	11 51.9	9 39.3	28 39.8	0 11.6
5	22 57 7.5	12 36.8	1 23.7	13 17.3	0 22.0	4 39.7	10 20.0	3 11.0	11 56.7	9 40.2	28 39.7	0 13.4
6	23 1 4.0	13 34.9	1 20.5	25 46.4	0 7.6	5 53.4	10 56.4	3 12.3	12 1.4	9 41.1	28 39.5	0 15.2
7	23 5 .6	14 33.2	1 17.4	8♒ 4.8	0 1.9	7 7.1	11 33.0	3 13.8	12 6.3	9 42.1	28 39.5	0 17.1
8	23 8 57.1	15 31.4	1 14.2	20 14.5	0 D 4.9	8 20.7	12 9.8	3 15.4	12 11.2	9 43.2	28 39.4	0 18.9
9	23 12 53.7	16 29.7	1 11.0	2♓17.5	0 16.8	9 34.4	12 46.8	3 17.2	12 16.2	9 44.3	28 39.4	0 20.8
10	23 16 50.3	17 28.0	1 7.8	14 15.2	0 37.7	10 48.0	13 24.0	3 19.2	12 21.3	9 45.4	28 39.4	0 22.7
11	23 20 46.8	18 26.3	1 4.7	26 8.9	1 7.5	12 1.6	14 1.4	3 21.3	12 26.4	9 46.6	28 39.4	0 24.6
12	23 24 43.4	19 24.6	1 1.5	8♈ .0	1 45.9	13 15.3	14 39.0	3 23.7	12 31.6	9 47.9	28 39.4	0 26.5
13	23 28 39.9	20 23.0	0 58.3	19 50.3	2 32.6	14 28.9	15 16.8	3 26.3	12 36.8	9 49.2	28 D 39.5	0 28.5
14	23 32 36.5	21 21.4	0 55.1	1♉42.0	3 27.3	15 42.4	15 54.7	3 29.0	12 42.1	9 50.5	28 39.6	0 30.5
15	23 36 33.0	22 19.8	0 51.9	13 38.2	4 29.4	16 56.0	16 32.8	3 31.9	12 47.5	9 51.9	28 39.8	0 32.4
16	23 40 29.6	23 18.3	0 48.8	25 42.5	5 38.4	18 9.6	17 11.2	3 35.0	12 52.9	9 53.3	28 40.0	0 34.5
17	23 44 26.1	24 16.8	0 45.6	7♊59.2	6 53.7	19 23.1	17 49.6	3 38.2	12 58.4	9 54.8	28 40.2	0 36.5
18	23 48 22.7	25 15.4	0 42.4	20 33.1	8 14.7	20 36.7	18 28.3	3 41.7	13 3.9	9 56.4	28 40.5	0 38.6
19	23 52 19.2	26 14.0	0 39.2	3♋28.9	9 40.9	21 50.2	19 7.1	3 45.3	13 9.5	9 58.0	28 40.7	0 40.6
20	23 56 15.8	27 12.6	0 36.1	16 50.7	11 11.6	23 3.8	19 46.1	3 49.1	13 15.2	9 59.6	28 41.1	0 42.7
21	0 0 12.3	28 11.3	0 32.9	0♌41.3	12 46.2	24 17.3	20 25.3	3 53.1	13 20.9	10 1.3	28 41.4	0 44.8
22	0 4 8.9	29 10.0	0 29.7	15 1.2	14 24.1	25 30.8	21 4.6	3 57.2	13 26.7	10 3.0	28 41.8	0 47.0
23	0 8 5.4	0♎ 8.7	0 26.5	29 47.6	16 4.8	26 44.3	21 44.1	4 1.6	13 32.5	10 4.8	28 42.2	0 49.1
24	0 12 2.0	1 7.5	0 23.3	14♍54.2	17 47.8	27 57.8	22 23.7	4 6.1	13 38.4	10 6.6	28 42.7	0 51.3
25	0 15 58.5	2 6.3	0 20.2	0♎11.5	19 32.6	29 11.3	23 3.6	4 10.7	13 44.3	10 8.4	28 43.2	0 53.4
26	0 19 55.1	3 5.1	0 17.0	15 28.6	21 18.8	0♏24.7	23 43.5	4 15.6	13 50.3	10 10.4	28 43.7	0 55.6
27	0 23 51.7	4 4.0	0 13.8	0♏34.4	23 6.1	1 38.2	24 23.7	4 20.6	13 56.3	10 12.3	28 44.2	0 57.8
28	0 27 48.2	5 2.9	0 10.6	15 20.3	24 54.2	2 51.7	25 4.0	4 25.8	14 2.5	10 14.4	28 44.9	1 .1
29	0 31 44.8	6 1.9	0 7.5	29 40.8	26 42.7	4 5.1	25 44.4	4 31.2	14 8.6	10 16.4	28 45.5	1 2.3
30	0 35 41.3	7 .8	0 4.3	13♐33.7	28 31.4	5 18.5	26 25.0	4 36.7	14 14.8	10 18.5	28 46.1	1 4.6
		LATITUDE										
1	22 41 21.3	0 .0	0 .0	0 N 56.7	3 S 20.5	1 N 8.4	2 S 20.7	0 S 4.5	2 N 11.4	0 N 1.1	1 N 10.7	16 N 28.3
4	22 53 10.9	0 .0	0 .0	2 S 28.2	2 27.4	1 3.2	2 20.2	0 4.9	2 10.7	0 1.0	1 10.6	16 27.0
7	23 5 .6	0 .0	0 .0	4 37.4	1 30.1	0 57.6	2 19.5	0 5.2	2 10.1	0 1.0	1 10.5	16 25.7
10	23 16 50.3	0 .0	0 .0	4 52.0	0 34.7	0 51.5	2 18.7	0 5.5	2 9.5	0 1.0	1 10.3	16 24.5
13	23 28 39.9	0 .0	0 .0	3 14.6	0 N 14.2	0 44.9	2 17.8	0 5.8	2 8.9	0 .9	1 10.2	16 23.4
16	23 40 29.6	0 .0	0 .0	0 20.8	0 53.8	0 37.9	2 16.8	0 6.1	2 8.4	0 .9	1 10.0	16 22.4
19	23 52 19.2	0 .0	0 .0	2 N 50.4	1 22.8	0 30.6	2 15.8	0 6.4	2 7.9	0 .9	1 9.9	16 21.4
22	0 4 8.9	0 .0	0 .0	4 55.1	1 41.4	0 22.8	2 14.6	0 6.7	2 7.3	0 .8	1 9.8	16 20.4
25	0 15 58.5	0 .0	0 .0	4 21.1	1 50.6	0 14.7	2 13.3	0 7.0	2 6.8	0 .8	1 9.6	16 19.6
28	0 27 48.2	0 .0	0 .0	1 11.3	1 51.9	0 6.4	2 11.9	0 7.3	2 6.4	0 .8	1 9.5	16 18.8
		RIGHT ASCENSION										
1	22 41 21.3	10♍21.2	29♉29.7	18♏20.4	3♍18.9	0♎13.3	5♐45.6	3♑24.9	9♏53.7	7♐57.2	28♐34.2	3♏44.5
2	22 45 17.8	11 15.6	29 26.4	2♐12.4	2 R 44.9	1 20.3	6 23.9	3 25.4	9 58.0	7 58.0	28 R 33.9	3 45.9
3	22 49 14.4	12 9.9	29 23.0	16 21.3	2 16.7	2 27.2	7 2.6	3 26.2	10 2.4	7 58.8	28 33.6	3 47.3
4	22 53 10.9	13 4.1	29 19.7	0♑38.3	1 55.0	3 34.2	7 41.6	3 27.1	10 6.9	7 59.7	28 33.4	3 48.7
5	22 57 7.5	13 58.3	29 16.4	14 48.5	1 40.5	4 41.1	8 20.8	3 28.3	10 11.4	8 .7	28 33.2	3 50.2
6	23 1 4.0	14 52.4	29 13.1	28 35.7	1 33.7	5 48.0	9 .3	3 29.7	10 16.1	8 1.7	28 33.1	3 51.6
7	23 5 .6	15 46.5	29 9.8	11♒47.5	1 D 35.0	6 54.9	9 40.2	3 31.3	10 20.8	8 2.8	28 33.0	3 53.2
8	23 8 57.1	16 40.4	29 6.4	24 17.8	1 44.6	8 1.9	10 20.3	3 33.0	10 25.5	8 3.9	28 32.9	3 54.7
9	23 12 53.7	17 34.4	29 3.1	6♓ 7.9	2 2.6	9 8.9	11 .6	3 35.0	10 30.4	8 5.1	28 32.9	3 56.3
10	23 16 50.3	18 28.3	28 59.8	17 24.1	2 28.9	10 15.9	11 41.2	3 37.2	10 35.2	8 6.3	28 32.9	3 57.8
11	23 20 46.8	19 22.2	28 56.5	28 15.9	3 3.5	11 22.9	12 22.1	3 39.6	10 40.2	8 7.6	28 32.9	3 59.4
12	23 24 43.4	20 16.0	28 53.2	8♈54.7	3 45.9	12 30.1	13 3.2	3 42.1	10 45.2	8 8.9	28 D 33.0	4 1.1
13	23 28 39.9	21 9.8	28 49.9	19 32.6	4 36.0	13 37.3	13 44.6	3 44.9	10 50.3	8 10.3	28 33.1	4 2.7
14	23 32 36.5	22 3.6	28 46.5	0♉22.4	5 33.1	14 44.6	14 26.2	3 47.9	10 55.4	8 11.7	28 33.2	4 4.4
15	23 36 33.0	22 57.4	28 43.2	11 36.8	6 36.8	15 51.9	15 8.0	3 51.1	11 .6	8 13.2	28 33.4	4 6.0
16	23 40 29.6	23 51.2	28 39.9	23 27.8	7 46.6	16 59.4	15 50.1	3 54.4	11 5.9	8 14.7	28 33.6	4 7.7
17	23 44 26.1	24 45.0	28 36.6	6♊ 5.4	9 1.7	18 7.1	16 32.4	3 58.0	11 11.2	8 16.3	28 33.8	4 9.5
18	23 48 22.7	25 38.8	28 33.3	19 34.6	10 21.7	19 14.8	17 15.0	4 1.8	11 16.6	8 17.9	28 34.1	4 11.2
19	23 52 19.2	26 32.6	28 30.0	3♋52.6	11 45.8	20 22.7	17 57.7	4 5.7	11 22.0	8 19.6	28 34.4	4 13.0
20	23 56 15.8	27 26.4	28 26.6	18 46.9	13 13.5	21 30.7	18 40.7	4 9.9	11 27.5	8 21.4	28 34.7	4 14.7
21	0 0 12.3	28 20.2	28 23.3	3♌57.2	14 44.3	22 38.9	19 23.9	4 14.2	11 33.1	8 23.1	28 35.1	4 16.5
22	0 4 8.9	29 14.1	28 20.0	19 1.7	16 17.4	23 47.2	20 7.3	4 18.7	11 38.7	8 25.0	28 35.5	4 18.4
23	0 8 5.4	0♎ 8.0	28 16.7	3♍44.7	17 52.6	24 55.8	20 50.9	4 23.5	11 44.4	8 26.9	28 36.0	4 20.2
24	0 12 2.0	1 1.9	28 13.4	18 1.0	19 29.2	26 4.5	21 34.8	4 28.4	11 50.1	8 28.8	28 36.5	4 22.0
25	0 15 58.5	1 55.9	28 10.1	1♎54.6	21 7.0	27 13.4	22 18.8	4 33.5	11 55.9	8 30.8	28 37.0	4 23.9
26	0 19 55.1	2 49.9	28 6.8	15 36.3	22 45.5	28 22.5	23 3.0	4 38.7	12 1.7	8 32.8	28 37.5	4 25.8
27	0 23 51.7	3 43.9	28 3.5	29 18.9	24 24.5	29 31.9	23 47.4	4 44.2	12 7.6	8 34.9	28 38.1	4 27.7
28	0 27 48.2	4 38.0	28 .2	13♏13.9	26 3.8	0♏41.4	24 32.1	4 49.9	12 13.6	8 37.1	28 38.8	4 29.7
29	0 31 44.8	5 32.2	27 56.8	27 27.9	27 43.0	1 51.2	25 16.8	4 55.7	12 19.6	8 39.3	28 39.5	4 31.6
30	0 35 41.3	6 26.4	27 53.5	11♐59.8	29 22.1	3 1.2	26 1.7	5 1.8	12 25.6	8 41.5	28 40.2	4 33.6
		DECLINATION										
1	22 41 21.3	8 N 17.7	0 N 21.5	16 S 58.3	7 N 26.7	1 N 8.7	23 S 57.0	23 S 28.9	13 S 14.6	21 S 52.7	22 S 15.4	3 N 56.6
4	22 53 10.9	7 11.8	0 21.4	25 54.7	8 54.8	0 S 23.9	24 13.3	23 29.1	13 19.3	21 53.1	22 15.6	3 53.6
7	23 5 .6	6 4.9	0 21.4	22 42.7	10 3.4	1 56.6	24 28.5	23 29.4	13 24.3	21 53.5	22 15.7	3 50.7
10	23 16 50.3	4 57.2	0 21.4	10 41.1	10 42.7	3 29.1	24 42.3	23 29.6	13 29.4	21 54.0	22 15.8	3 47.7
13	23 28 39.9	3 48.6	0 21.3	4 N 45.3	10 47.4	5 1.1	24 54.8	23 29.7	13 34.6	21 54.6	22 16.0	3 44.7
16	23 40 29.6	2 39.5	0 21.3	18 51.1	10 16.7	6 32.3	25 5.7	23 29.8	13 40.0	21 55.3	22 16.1	3 41.8
19	23 52 19.2	1 29.9	0 21.2	26 14.1	9 13.1	8 2.3	25 15.1	23 29.8	13 45.5	21 56.0	22 16.3	3 38.8
22	0 4 8.9	0 19.9	0 21.2	21 1.8	7 42.0	9 30.8	25 22.8	23 29.7	13 51.1	21 56.8	22 16.4	3 35.8
25	0 15 58.5	0 S 50.2	0 21.2	3 54.9	5 50.2	10 57.4	25 28.8	23 29.6	13 56.8	21 57.6	22 16.6	3 32.9
28	0 27 48.2	2 .4	0 21.1	15 S 18.0	3 44.2	12 22.0	25 32.9	23 29.4	14 2.6	21 58.5	22 16.7	3 30.0

OCTOBER 1984

LONGITUDE

DAY	EPHEM. SID. TIME	☉	☊	☽	☿	♀	♂	♃	♄	♅	♆	♇
	h m s	° ′	° ′	° ′	° ′	° ′	° ′	° ′	° ′	° ′	° ′	° ′
1	0 39 37.9	7♎59.8	0♊ 1.1	26♐59.6	0♎20.1	6♏31.9	27♐ 5.7	4♑42.4	14♏21.0	10♐20.6	28♐46.8	1♏ 6.8
2	0 43 34.4	8 58.8	29♉57.9	10♑ 1.2	2 8.7	7 45.3	27 46.5	4 48.2	14 27.3	10 22.8	28 47.5	1 9.1
3	0 47 31.0	9 57.9	29 54.7	22 42.0	3 56.9	8 58.7	28 27.5	4 54.2	14 33.6	10 25.0	28 48.3	1 11.4
4	0 51 27.5	10 57.0	29 51.6	5♒ 6.2	5 44.8	10 12.0	29 8.6	5 .4	14 39.9	10 27.3	28 49.0	1 13.7
5	0 55 24.1	11 56.1	29 48.4	17 17.7	7 32.2	11 25.3	29 49.8	5 6.7	14 46.3	10 29.6	28 49.8	1 16.0
6	0 59 20.6	12 55.2	29 45.2	29 20.0	9 19.1	12 38.6	0♑31.2	5 13.1	14 52.7	10 31.9	28 50.7	1 18.3
7	1 3 17.2	13 54.4	29 42.0	11♓16.3	11 5.3	13 51.9	1 12.7	5 19.8	14 59.2	10 34.3	28 51.6	1 20.7
8	1 7 13.7	14 53.6	29 38.9	23 9.1	12 50.9	15 5.2	1 54.3	5 26.5	15 5.7	10 36.7	28 52.5	1 23.0
9	1 11 10.3	15 52.8	29 35.7	5♈ .5	14 35.9	16 18.4	2 36.0	5 33.4	15 12.3	10 39.2	28 53.4	1 25.3
10	1 15 6.9	16 52.1	29 32.5	16 52.2	16 20.1	17 31.7	3 17.8	5 40.5	15 18.9	10 41.7	28 54.4	1 27.7
11	1 19 3.4	17 51.4	29 29.3	28 45.9	18 3.6	18 44.9	3 59.8	5 47.7	15 25.5	10 44.2	28 55.4	1 30.1
12	1 22 60.0	18 50.7	29 26.1	10♉43.4	19 46.4	19 58.1	4 41.8	5 55.1	15 32.1	10 46.8	28 56.4	1 32.4
13	1 26 56.5	19 50.1	29 23.0	22 46.8	21 28.4	21 11.2	5 24.0	6 2.6	15 38.8	10 49.4	28 57.4	1 34.8
14	1 30 53.1	20 49.5	29 19.8	4♊58.6	23 9.8	22 24.4	6 6.3	6 10.2	15 45.5	10 52.0	28 58.5	1 37.2
15	1 34 49.6	21 48.9	29 16.6	17 21.7	24 50.4	23 37.5	6 48.6	6 18.0	15 52.3	10 54.7	28 59.6	1 39.6
16	1 38 46.2	22 48.4	29 13.4	29 59.5	26 30.4	24 50.6	7 31.1	6 25.9	15 59.1	10 57.5	29 .8	1 42.0
17	1 42 42.7	23 47.9	29 10.3	12♋55.5	28 9.7	26 3.7	8 13.7	6 34.0	16 5.9	11 .2	29 2.0	1 44.4
18	1 46 39.3	24 47.5	29 7.1	26 13.1	29 48.3	27 16.8	8 56.4	6 42.2	16 12.7	11 3.0	29 3.2	1 46.8
19	1 50 35.8	25 47.2	29 3.9	9♌54.9	1♏26.3	28 29.9	9 39.2	6 50.6	16 19.6	11 5.9	29 4.4	1 49.2
20	1 54 32.4	26 46.8	29 .7	24 1.8	3 3.7	29 43.0	10 22.1	6 59.0	16 26.5	11 8.7	29 5.7	1 51.7
21	1 58 28.9	27 46.5	28 57.5	8♍32.8	4 40.4	0♐56.0	11 5.1	7 7.6	16 33.4	11 11.6	29 7.0	1 54.1
22	2 2 25.5	28 46.2	28 54.4	23 23.9	6 16.6	2 9.0	11 48.2	7 16.3	16 40.4	11 14.5	29 8.3	1 56.5
23	2 6 22.1	29 45.9	28 51.2	8♎28.3	7 52.1	3 22.0	12 31.4	7 25.2	16 47.4	11 17.5	29 9.7	1 58.9
24	2 10 18.6	0♏45.7	28 48.0	23 37.1	9 27.1	4 35.0	13 14.7	7 34.2	16 54.3	11 20.5	29 11.0	2 1.3
25	2 14 15.2	1 45.5	28 44.8	8♏40.4	11 1.5	5 47.9	13 58.1	7 43.3	17 1.3	11 23.5	29 12.4	2 3.8
26	2 18 11.7	2 45.4	28 41.7	23 29.2	12 35.5	7 .9	14 41.5	7 52.5	17 8.4	11 26.6	29 13.9	2 6.2
27	2 22 8.3	3 45.3	28 38.5	7♐56.6	14 8.8	8 13.8	15 25.1	8 1.9	17 15.4	11 29.6	29 15.3	2 8.6
28	2 26 4.8	4 45.2	28 35.3	21 58.4	15 41.7	9 26.6	16 8.7	8 11.4	17 22.5	11 32.7	29 16.8	2 11.0
29	2 30 1.4	5 45.1	28 32.1	5♑33.1	17 14.1	10 39.5	16 52.5	8 20.9	17 29.6	11 35.9	29 18.3	2 13.5
30	2 33 57.9	6 45.1	28 28.9	18 41.8	18 46.0	11 52.3	17 36.3	8 30.7	17 36.7	11 39.0	29 19.8	2 15.9
31	2 37 54.5	7 45.1	28 25.8	1♒27.1	20 17.4	13 5.1	18 20.2	8 40.5	17 43.8	11 42.2	29 21.4	2 18.3

LATITUDE

DAY	EPHEM. SID. TIME	☉	☊	☽	☿	♀	♂	♃	♄	♅	♆	♇
1	0 39 37.9	0 .0	0 .0	2S26.0	1N46.9	0S 2.2	2S10.5	0S 7.6	2N 5.9	0N .8	1N 9.3	16N18.1
4	0 51 27.5	0 .0	0 .0	4 42.3	1 36.9	0 10.9	2 9.0	0 7.8	2 5.5	0 .7	1 9.2	16 17.4
7	1 3 17.2	0 .0	0 .0	5 .1	1 23.3	0 19.7	2 7.3	0 8.1	2 5.1	0 .7	1 9.1	16 16.9
10	1 15 6.9	0 .0	0 .0	3 23.6	1 7.0	0 28.7	2 5.6	0 8.4	2 4.7	0 .7	1 8.9	16 16.4
13	1 26 56.5	0 .0	0 .0	0 27.3	0 48.9	0 37.6	2 3.8	0 8.6	2 4.4	0 .6	1 8.8	16 16.0
16	1 38 46.2	0 .0	0 .0	2N46.7	0 29.5	0 46.5	2 2.0	0 8.9	2 4.1	0 .6	1 8.7	16 15.6
19	1 50 35.8	0 .0	0 .0	4 57.7	0 9.4	0 55.3	2 .0	0 9.1	2 3.8	0 .6	1 8.5	16 15.4
22	2 2 25.5	0 .0	0 .0	4 42.2	0S11.1	1 4.0	1 58.0	0 9.4	2 3.5	0 .5	1 8.4	16 15.2
25	2 14 15.2	0 .0	0 .0	1 41.8	0 31.4	1 12.5	1 56.0	0 9.6	2 3.3	0 .5	1 8.3	16 15.1
28	2 26 4.8	0 .0	0 .0	2S10.6	0 51.3	1 20.7	1 53.8	0 9.9	2 3.0	0 .5	1 8.2	16 15.1
31	2 37 54.5	0 .0	0 .0	4 43.4	1 10.6	1 28.6	1 51.6	0 10.1	2 2.8	0 .5	1 8.0	16 15.2

RIGHT ASCENSION

DAY	EPHEM. SID. TIME	☉	☊	☽	☿	♀	♂	♃	♄	♅	♆	♇
1	0 39 37.9	7♎20.7	27♉50.2	26♐39.7	1♎ .9	4♏11.5	26♐46.8	5♑ 7.9	12♏31.7	8♐43.8	28♐40.9	4♏35.5
2	0 43 34.4	8 15.0	27 46.9	11♑11.1	2 39.4	5 21.9	27 32.1	5 14.3	12 37.9	8 46.1	28 41.7	4 37.5
3	0 47 31.0	9 9.4	27 43.6	25 16.2	4 17.4	6 32.7	28 17.5	5 20.8	12 44.0	8 48.5	28 42.5	4 39.5
4	0 51 27.5	10 3.9	27 40.3	8♒41.8	5 54.9	7 43.7	29 3.0	5 27.5	12 50.3	8 50.9	28 43.3	4 41.5
5	0 55 24.1	10 58.5	27 37.0	21 22.3	7 31.9	8 54.9	29 48.7	5 34.4	12 56.5	8 53.3	28 44.2	4 43.5
6	0 59 20.6	11 53.1	27 33.7	3♓19.2	9 8.4	10 6.5	0♑34.6	5 41.5	13 2.8	8 55.8	28 45.1	4 45.5
7	1 3 17.2	12 47.9	27 30.4	14 39.7	10 44.3	11 18.3	1 20.5	5 48.7	13 9.2	8 58.4	28 46.0	4 47.6
8	1 7 13.7	13 42.7	27 27.1	25 34.0	12 19.7	12 30.3	2 6.6	5 56.1	13 15.6	9 .9	28 47.0	4 49.6
9	1 11 10.3	14 37.7	27 23.8	6♈13.7	13 54.5	13 42.7	2 52.7	6 3.6	13 22.0	9 3.6	28 48.0	4 51.7
10	1 15 6.9	15 32.7	27 20.5	16 51.0	15 28.9	14 55.3	3 39.0	6 11.3	13 28.5	9 6.2	28 49.1	4 53.8
11	1 19 3.4	16 27.9	27 17.2	27 38.2	17 2.7	16 8.3	4 25.4	6 19.2	13 35.0	9 8.9	28 50.1	4 55.9
12	1 22 60.0	17 23.2	27 13.9	8♉47.5	18 36.1	17 21.5	5 11.9	6 27.2	13 41.5	9 11.7	28 51.3	4 58.0
13	1 26 56.5	18 18.7	27 10.6	20 30.0	20 9.2	18 35.0	5 58.5	6 35.3	13 48.1	9 14.5	28 52.4	5 .1
14	1 30 53.1	19 14.2	27 7.3	2♊54.4	21 41.8	19 48.8	6 45.2	6 43.7	13 54.7	9 17.3	28 53.6	5 2.2
15	1 34 49.6	20 9.9	27 4.0	16 5.1	23 14.1	21 2.9	7 32.0	6 52.2	14 1.4	9 20.2	28 54.8	5 4.3
16	1 38 46.2	21 5.8	27 .7	29 59.4	24 46.0	22 17.4	8 18.8	7 .8	14 8.0	9 23.1	28 56.0	5 6.5
17	1 42 42.7	22 1.8	26 57.4	14♋26.5	26 17.7	23 32.1	9 5.7	7 9.6	14 14.7	9 26.0	28 57.3	5 8.6
18	1 46 39.3	22 57.9	26 54.1	29 8.9	27 49.2	24 47.1	9 52.7	7 18.5	14 21.5	9 29.0	28 58.6	5 10.7
19	1 50 35.8	23 54.3	26 50.8	13♌47.9	29 20.5	26 2.4	10 39.9	7 27.6	14 28.3	9 32.1	28 60.0	5 12.9
20	1 54 32.4	24 50.8	26 47.5	28 9.4	0♏51.6	27 18.0	11 27.0	7 36.8	14 35.1	9 35.1	29 1.3	5 15.1
21	1 58 28.9	25 47.4	26 44.2	12♍ 8.5	2 22.6	28 33.9	12 14.2	7 46.2	14 41.9	9 38.2	29 2.7	5 17.3
22	2 2 25.5	26 44.2	26 40.9	25 48.7	3 53.5	29 50.1	13 1.4	7 55.7	14 48.8	9 41.3	29 4.1	5 19.4
23	2 6 22.1	27 41.2	26 37.6	9♎20.4	5 24.3	1♐ 6.6	13 48.7	8 5.3	14 55.7	9 44.5	29 5.6	5 21.6
24	2 10 18.6	28 38.3	26 34.3	22 56.7	6 55.1	2 23.3	14 36.0	8 15.1	15 2.6	9 47.7	29 7.1	5 23.8
25	2 14 15.2	29 35.6	26 31.0	6♏50.9	8 25.8	3 40.3	15 23.4	8 25.0	15 9.5	9 50.9	29 8.6	5 26.0
26	2 18 11.7	0♏33.1	26 27.7	21 11.8	9 56.5	4 57.6	16 10.8	8 35.1	15 16.5	9 54.2	29 10.1	5 28.2
27	2 22 8.3	1 30.8	26 24.4	6♐ .5	11 27.3	6 15.1	16 58.3	8 45.2	15 23.5	9 57.5	29 11.7	5 30.4
28	2 26 4.8	2 28.7	26 21.1	21 7.0	12 58.1	7 32.9	17 45.7	8 55.5	15 30.5	10 .8	29 13.3	5 32.6
29	2 30 1.4	3 26.7	26 17.8	6♑12.0	14 29.0	8 50.9	18 33.2	9 6.0	15 37.5	10 4.2	29 14.9	5 34.8
30	2 33 57.9	4 25.0	26 14.5	20 52.5	15 59.9	10 9.1	19 20.7	9 16.5	15 44.5	10 7.5	29 16.6	5 37.0
31	2 37 54.5	5 23.4	26 11.2	4♒50.1	17 31.0	11 27.6	20 8.2	9 27.2	15 51.6	10 10.9	29 18.3	5 39.2

DECLINATION

DAY	EPHEM. SID. TIME	☉	☊	☽	☿	♀	♂	♃	♄	♅	♆	♇
1	0 39 37.9	3S10.4	0N21.1	25S50.5	1N30.0	13S44.0	25S35.1	23S29.1	14S 8.5	21S59.4	22S16.9	3N27.1
4	0 51 27.5	4 20.0	0 21.1	23 33.3	0S48.0	15 3.1	25 35.3	23 28.7	14 14.4	22 .4	22 17.1	3 24.3
7	1 3 17.2	5 29.2	0 21.0	11 57.6	3 6.6	16 19.0	25 33.6	23 28.2	14 20.4	22 1.4	22 17.2	3 21.4
10	1 15 6.9	6 37.7	0 21.0	3N29.7	5 23.6	17 31.4	25 29.7	23 27.6	14 26.4	22 2.5	22 17.4	3 18.7
13	1 26 56.5	7 45.5	0 21.0	18 1.7	7 37.1	18 39.8	25 23.7	23 26.9	14 32.5	22 3.6	22 17.5	3 16.0
16	1 38 46.2	8 52.3	0 20.9	26 13.2	9 46.1	19 44.0	25 15.5	23 26.0	14 38.6	22 4.8	22 17.7	3 13.3
19	1 50 35.8	9 57.9	0 20.9	22 32.4	11 49.8	20 43.7	25 5.2	23 25.1	14 44.8	22 6.0	22 17.8	3 10.7
22	2 2 25.5	11 2.3	0 20.9	6 56.3	13 47.3	21 38.4	24 52.7	23 23.9	14 50.9	22 7.2	22 18.0	3 8.2
25	2 14 15.2	12 5.2	0 20.8	12S47.2	15 38.1	22 27.9	24 37.9	23 22.6	14 57.0	22 8.5	22 18.1	3 5.8
28	2 26 4.8	13 6.5	0 20.8	25 22.3	17 21.6	23 12.0	24 21.0	23 21.2	15 3.2	22 9.8	22 18.3	3 3.4
31	2 37 54.5	14 5.8	0 20.7	24 26.5	18 57.2	23 50.2	24 1.8	23 19.6	15 9.3	22 11.1	22 18.4	3 1.1

NOVEMBER 1984

LONGITUDE

DAY	EPHEM. SID. TIME h m s	☉ ° ′	☊ ° ′	☽ ° ′	☿ ° ′	♀ ° ′	♂ ° ′	♃ ° ′	♄ ° ′	♅ ° ′	♆ ° ′	♇ ° ′
1	2 41 51.1	8♏45.1	28♉22.6	13♒53.0	21♏48.4	14♐17.9	19♑ 4.1	8♑50.4	17♏50.9	11♐45.4	29♐23.0	2♏20.7
2	2 45 47.6	9 45.2	28 19.4	26 3.8	23 18.8	15 30.6	19 48.1	9 .5	17 58.0	11 48.7	29 24.6	2 23.1
3	2 49 44.2	10 45.2	28 16.2	8♓ 3.7	24 48.8	16 43.3	20 32.2	9 10.6	18 5.2	11 51.9	29 26.2	2 25.5
4	2 53 40.7	11 45.3	28 13.1	19 57.2	26 18.3	17 56.0	21 16.4	9 20.9	18 12.3	11 55.2	29 27.9	2 27.9
5	2 57 37.3	12 45.5	28 9.9	1♈47.9	27 47.4	19 8.6	22 .7	9 31.2	18 19.5	11 58.5	29 29.6	2 30.3
6	3 1 33.8	13 45.6	28 6.7	13 39.1	29 15.9	20 21.2	22 45.0	9 41.7	18 26.6	12 1.9	29 31.3	2 32.7
7	3 5 30.4	14 45.8	28 3.5	25 33.6	0♐44.0	21 33.8	23 29.3	9 52.3	18 33.8	12 5.2	29 33.0	2 35.1
8	3 9 26.9	15 46.0	28 .4	7♉33.7	2 11.5	22 46.3	24 13.7	10 3.0	18 41.0	12 8.6	29 34.7	2 37.5
9	3 13 23.5	16 46.3	27 57.2	19 41.2	3 38.5	23 58.9	24 58.3	10 13.8	18 48.2	12 12.1	29 36.5	2 39.9
10	3 17 20.1	17 46.6	27 54.0	1♊57.7	5 4.9	25 11.3	25 42.8	10 24.7	18 55.4	12 15.5	29 38.3	2 42.3
11	3 21 16.6	18 46.9	27 50.8	14 24.6	6 30.7	26 23.7	26 27.4	10 35.6	19 2.6	12 18.9	29 40.1	2 44.6
12	3 25 13.2	19 47.2	27 47.6	27 3.2	7 55.8	27 36.1	27 12.1	10 46.7	19 9.7	12 22.4	29 42.0	2 47.0
13	3 29 9.7	20 47.6	27 44.5	9♋55.1	9 20.2	28 48.4	27 56.8	10 57.9	19 16.9	12 25.8	29 43.8	2 49.3
14	3 33 6.3	21 48.0	27 41.3	23 1.6	10 43.8	0♑ .7	28 41.6	11 9.1	19 24.1	12 29.3	29 45.7	2 51.6
15	3 37 2.8	22 48.4	27 38.1	6♌24.1	12 6.5	1 13.0	29 26.4	11 20.5	19 31.3	12 32.8	29 47.6	2 53.9
16	3 40 59.4	23 48.8	27 34.9	20 3.8	13 28.3	2 25.2	0♒11.3	11 31.9	19 38.5	12 36.3	29 49.5	2 56.2
17	3 44 55.9	24 49.3	27 31.8	4♍ .9	14 49.0	3 37.3	0 56.2	11 43.4	19 45.6	12 39.9	29 51.4	2 58.5
18	3 48 52.5	25 49.9	27 28.6	18 15.0	16 8.5	4 49.4	1 41.2	11 55.0	19 52.8	12 43.4	29 53.4	3 .8
19	3 52 49.1	26 50.4	27 25.4	2♎43.7	17 26.6	6 1.5	2 26.2	12 6.7	19 59.9	12 47.0	29 55.3	3 3.1
20	3 56 45.6	27 51.0	27 22.2	17 23.3	18 43.2	7 13.5	3 11.3	12 18.5	20 7.1	12 50.6	29 57.3	3 5.3
21	4 0 42.2	28 51.6	27 19.1	2♏ 8.3	19 58.1	8 25.5	3 56.4	12 30.3	20 14.2	12 54.2	29 59.3	3 7.6
22	4 4 38.7	29 52.2	27 15.9	16 52.1	21 11.1	9 37.5	4 41.6	12 42.3	20 21.4	12 57.8	0♑ 1.3	3 9.8
23	4 8 35.3	0♐52.9	27 12.7	1♐27.6	22 21.7	10 49.4	5 26.8	12 54.3	20 28.5	13 1.4	0 3.3	3 12.0
24	4 12 31.8	1 53.6	27 9.5	15 48.5	23 29.9	12 1.2	6 12.0	13 6.4	20 35.6	13 5.0	0 5.4	3 14.2
25	4 16 28.4	2 54.3	27 6.3	29 49.5	24 35.1	13 13.0	6 57.3	13 18.5	20 42.7	13 8.6	0 7.5	3 16.4
26	4 20 25.0	3 55.0	27 3.2	13♑27.5	25 37.1	14 24.7	7 42.7	13 30.8	20 49.7	13 12.3	0 9.5	3 18.6
27	4 24 21.5	4 55.8	26 60.0	26 41.5	26 35.2	15 36.3	8 28.1	13 43.1	20 56.8	13 15.9	0 11.6	3 20.7
28	4 28 18.1	5 56.5	26 56.8	9♒32.3	27 29.1	16 47.9	9 13.5	13 55.5	21 3.8	13 19.5	0 13.7	3 22.8
29	4 32 14.6	6 57.3	26 53.6	22 2.6	28 18.0	17 59.4	9 58.9	14 7.9	21 10.8	13 23.2	0 15.8	3 25.0
30	4 36 11.2	7 58.2	26 50.5	4♓16.0	29 1.5	19 10.9	10 44.5	14 20.5	21 17.9	13 26.9	0 18.0	3 27.1

LATITUDE

DAY	EPHEM. SID. TIME	☉	☊	☽	☿	♀	♂	♃	♄	♅	♆	♇
1	2 41 51.1	0 .0	0 .0	5S 6.6	1S16.7	1S31.2	1S50.9	0S10.2	2N 2.8	0N .5	1N 8.0	16N15.2
4	2 53 40.7	0 .0	0 .0	4 51.9	1 34.5	1 38.6	1 48.6	0 10.4	2 2.6	0 .4	1 7.9	16 15.4
7	3 5 30.4	0 .0	0 .0	2 47.3	1 50.7	1 45.5	1 46.3	0 10.7	2 2.5	0 .4	1 7.8	16 15.6
10	3 17 20.1	0 .0	0 .0	0N25.3	2 5.1	1 51.9	1 43.9	0 10.9	2 2.4	0 .4	1 7.7	16 16.0
13	3 29 9.7	0 .0	0 .0	3 34.7	2 17.1	1 57.8	1 41.5	0 11.1	2 2.3	0 .3	1 7.6	16 16.4
16	3 40 59.4	0 .0	0 .0	5 14.8	2 26.2	2 3.1	1 39.0	0 11.4	2 2.2	0 .3	1 7.5	16 16.9
19	3 52 49.1	0 .0	0 .0	4 19.3	2 31.7	2 7.7	1 36.4	0 11.6	2 2.2	0 .3	1 7.4	16 17.4
22	4 4 38.7	0 .0	0 .0	0 58.4	2 32.6	2 11.6	1 33.9	0 11.8	2 2.2	0 .3	1 7.3	16 18.1
25	4 16 28.4	0 .0	0 .0	2S50.3	2 27.8	2 14.7	1 31.3	0 12.1	2 2.2	0 .2	1 7.3	16 18.8
28	4 28 18.1	0 .0	0 .0	5 1.8	2 15.8	2 17.0	1 28.7	0 12.3	2 2.2	0 .2	1 7.2	16 19.6

RIGHT ASCENSION

DAY	EPHEM. SID. TIME	☉	☊	☽	☿	♀	♂	♃	♄	♅	♆	♇
1	2 41 51.1	6♏22.0	26♉ 7.9	17♒55.8	19♏ 2.1	12♐46.2	20♑55.7	9♑38.0	15♏58.6	10♐14.4	29♐20.0	5♏41.4
2	2 45 47.6	7 20.9	26 4.6	0♓10.6	20 33.3	14 5.1	21 43.2	9 48.9	16 5.7	10 17.8	29 21.7	5 43.6
3	2 49 44.2	8 19.9	26 1.3	11 42.1	22 4.5	15 24.1	22 30.7	9 60.0	16 12.8	10 21.3	29 23.5	5 45.8
4	2 53 40.7	9 19.1	25 58.0	22 41.8	23 35.9	16 43.3	23 18.1	10 11.1	16 19.9	10 24.9	29 25.3	5 47.9
5	2 57 37.3	10 18.5	25 54.7	3♈22.9	25 7.3	18 2.6	24 5.6	10 22.4	16 27.0	10 28.4	29 27.1	5 50.1
6	3 1 33.8	11 18.1	25 51.5	13 58.8	26 38.7	19 22.0	24 53.0	10 33.8	16 34.2	10 32.0	29 28.9	5 52.3
7	3 5 30.4	12 18.0	25 48.2	24 42.9	28 10.1	20 41.6	25 40.4	10 45.3	16 41.3	10 35.6	29 30.8	5 54.5
8	3 9 26.9	13 18.0	25 44.9	5♉48.1	29 41.5	22 1.3	26 27.8	10 56.8	16 48.4	10 39.2	29 32.7	5 56.7
9	3 13 23.5	14 18.3	25 41.6	17 26.3	1♐12.9	23 21.1	27 15.2	11 8.6	16 55.6	10 42.9	29 34.6	5 58.9
10	3 17 20.1	15 18.8	25 38.3	29 46.5	2 44.2	24 41.0	28 2.5	11 20.4	17 2.8	10 46.5	29 36.6	6 1.1
11	3 21 16.6	16 19.4	25 35.0	12♊53.3	4 15.2	26 .9	28 49.7	11 32.3	17 9.9	10 50.2	29 38.5	6 3.3
12	3 25 13.2	17 20.3	25 31.7	26 43.5	5 46.0	27 20.8	29 37.0	11 44.3	17 17.1	10 53.9	29 40.5	6 5.5
13	3 29 9.7	18 21.4	25 28.4	11♋ 5.3	7 16.5	28 40.8	0♒24.1	11 56.4	17 24.3	10 57.6	29 42.5	6 7.6
14	3 33 6.3	19 22.7	25 25.1	25 40.0	8 46.5	0♑ .8	1 11.2	12 8.6	17 31.4	11 1.3	29 44.5	6 9.8
15	3 37 2.8	20 24.3	25 21.9	10♌ 7.7	10 16.0	1 20.7	1 58.3	12 20.9	17 38.6	11 5.1	29 46.6	6 11.9
16	3 40 59.4	21 26.0	25 18.6	24 13.7	11 44.8	2 40.7	2 45.3	12 33.3	17 45.8	11 8.9	29 48.6	6 14.1
17	3 44 55.9	22 28.0	25 15.3	7♍52.8	13 12.8	4 .6	3 32.3	12 45.8	17 53.0	11 12.7	29 50.7	6 16.2
18	3 48 52.5	23 30.2	25 12.0	21 9.1	14 39.8	5 20.4	4 19.2	12 58.4	18 .1	11 16.5	29 52.8	6 18.3
19	3 52 49.1	24 32.6	25 8.7	4♎13.3	16 5.5	6 40.2	5 6.0	13 11.0	18 7.3	11 20.3	29 54.9	6 20.5
20	3 56 45.6	25 35.2	25 5.4	17 20.1	17 29.8	7 59.9	5 52.8	13 23.8	18 14.4	11 24.1	29 57.1	6 22.6
21	4 0 42.2	26 38.0	25 2.2	0♏45.1	18 52.5	9 19.4	6 39.5	13 36.6	18 21.6	11 28.0	29 59.2	6 24.7
22	4 4 38.7	27 41.0	24 58.9	14 41.3	20 13.1	10 38.8	7 26.2	13 49.5	18 28.7	11 31.8	0♑ 1.4	6 26.8
23	4 8 35.3	28 44.2	24 55.6	29 15.7	21 31.4	11 58.1	8 12.7	14 2.5	18 35.9	11 35.7	0 3.6	6 28.9
24	4 12 31.8	29 47.6	24 52.3	14♐23.7	22 47.0	13 17.2	8 59.2	14 15.6	18 43.0	11 39.6	0 5.8	6 30.9
25	4 16 28.4	0♐51.2	24 49.0	29 48.3	23 59.4	14 36.1	9 45.7	14 28.8	18 50.1	11 43.5	0 8.1	6 33.0
26	4 20 25.0	1 55.0	24 45.7	15♑ 2.8	25 8.2	15 54.8	10 32.0	14 42.0	18 57.2	11 47.4	0 10.3	6 35.0
27	4 24 21.5	2 59.0	24 42.5	29 40.9	26 12.8	17 13.3	11 18.3	14 55.3	19 4.3	11 51.3	0 12.6	6 37.1
28	4 28 18.1	4 3.1	24 39.2	13♒25.7	27 12.6	18 31.6	12 4.5	15 8.7	19 11.4	11 55.2	0 14.8	6 39.1
29	4 32 14.6	5 7.5	24 35.9	26 12.5	28 7.0	19 49.5	12 50.6	15 22.2	19 18.4	11 59.1	0 17.1	6 41.1
30	4 36 11.2	6 12.0	24 32.6	8♓ 7.0	28 55.2	21 7.3	13 36.7	15 35.7	19 25.5	12 3.1	0 19.5	6 43.1

DECLINATION

DAY	EPHEM. SID. TIME	☉	☊	☽	☿	♀	♂	♃	♄	♅	♆	♇
1	2 41 51.1	14S25.2	0N20.7	21S33.0	19S27.3	24S 1.7	23S54.9	23S19.0	15S11.3	22S11.5	22S18.5	3N .4
4	2 53 40.7	15 21.8	0 20.7	8 27.1	20 51.6	24 31.8	23 32.9	23 17.2	15 17.4	22 12.9	22 18.6	2 58.2
7	3 5 30.4	16 16.1	0 20.7	7N17.2	22 6.7	24 55.7	23 8.7	23 15.1	15 23.4	22 14.2	22 18.7	2 56.1
10	3 17 20.1	17 8.0	0 20.6	20 58.2	23 12.0	25 13.2	22 42.3	23 12.9	15 29.3	22 15.6	22 18.8	2 54.1
13	3 29 9.7	17 57.3	0 20.6	26 38.4	24 6.7	25 24.0	22 13.9	23 10.5	15 35.2	22 17.0	22 18.9	2 52.3
16	3 40 59.4	18 43.7	0 20.5	19 46.1	24 50.3	25 28.3	21 43.5	23 7.8	15 41.1	22 18.4	22 19.0	2 50.5
19	3 52 49.1	19 27.2	0 20.5	2 52.9	25 22.0	25 25.9	21 11.0	23 5.0	15 46.8	22 19.8	22 19.1	2 48.8
22	4 4 38.7	20 7.6	0 20.5	15S56.7	25 41.3	25 16.8	20 36.7	23 1.9	15 52.5	22 21.1	22 19.2	2 47.3
25	4 16 28.4	20 44.6	0 20.4	26 16.8	25 47.6	25 1.2	20 .5	22 58.6	15 58.1	22 22.5	22 19.3	2 45.8
28	4 28 18.1	21 18.1	0 20.4	22 42.6	25 40.9	24 39.1	19 22.5	22 55.1	16 3.6	22 23.9	22 19.4	2 44.5

DECEMBER 1984

LONGITUDE

DAY	EPHEM. SID. TIME	☉	☊	☽	☿	♀	♂	♃	♄	♅	♆	♇
	h m s	° ′	° ′	° ′	° ′	° ′	° ′	° ′	° ′	° ′	° ′	° ′
1	4 40 7.8	8♐59.0	26♉47.3	16♓16.9	29♐38.6	20♑22.3	11♒30.0	14♑33.1	21♏24.9	13♐30.6	0♑20.1	3♏29.2
2	4 44 4.3	9 59.8	26 44.1	28 10.0	0♑ 8.7	21 33.6	12 15.5	14 45.7	21 31.8	13 34.3	0 22.3	3 31.2
3	4 48 .9	11 .6	26 40.9	10♈ .2	0 31.0	22 44.8	13 1.1	14 58.4	21 38.7	13 37.9	0 24.5	3 33.3
4	4 51 57.4	12 1.5	26 37.8	21 52.0	0 44.5	23 55.9	13 46.6	15 11.2	21 45.6	13 41.6	0 26.6	3 35.3
5	4 55 54.0	13 2.4	26 34.6	3♉49.3	0 48.5	25 7.0	14 32.3	15 24.0	21 52.5	13 45.3	0 28.8	3 37.3
6	4 59 50.5	14 3.3	26 31.4	15 55.8	0 R 42.3	26 17.9	15 17.9	15 36.9	21 59.4	13 48.9	0 31.0	3 39.3
7	5 3 47.1	15 4.2	26 28.2	28 14.1	0 25.1	27 28.8	16 3.5	15 49.9	22 6.2	13 52.6	0 33.2	3 41.2
8	5 7 43.7	16 5.1	26 25.1	10♊46.0	29♐56.7	28 39.5	16 49.2	16 2.9	22 13.0	13 56.3	0 35.4	3 43.1
9	5 11 40.2	17 6.0	26 21.9	23 32.6	29 16.9	29 50.2	17 34.9	16 15.9	22 19.7	13 60.0	0 37.6	3 45.0
10	5 15 36.8	18 7.0	26 18.7	6♋33.9	28 26.1	1♒ .8	18 20.6	16 29.0	22 26.5	14 3.6	0 39.8	3 46.9
11	5 19 33.3	19 7.9	26 15.5	19 49.5	27 25.0	2 11.3	19 6.3	16 42.2	22 33.2	14 7.3	0 42.1	3 48.8
12	5 23 29.9	20 8.9	26 12.3	3♌18.1	26 15.1	3 21.6	19 52.0	16 55.4	22 39.8	14 11.0	0 44.3	3 50.6
13	5 27 26.5	21 9.9	26 9.2	16 58.3	24 58.4	4 31.9	20 37.8	17 8.6	22 46.4	14 14.6	0 46.5	3 52.4
14	5 31 23.0	22 10.9	26 6.0	0♍48.6	23 37.1	5 42.0	21 23.5	17 21.9	22 53.0	14 18.3	0 48.8	3 54.2
15	5 35 19.6	23 12.0	26 2.8	14 47.5	22 14.1	6 52.1	22 9.3	17 35.3	22 59.6	14 21.9	0 51.0	3 56.0
16	5 39 16.1	24 13.0	25 59.6	28 53.5	20 52.1	8 2.0	22 55.1	17 48.7	23 6.1	14 25.6	0 53.3	3 57.7
17	5 43 12.7	25 14.1	25 56.5	13♎ 5.1	19 33.8	9 11.8	23 40.9	18 2.1	23 12.6	14 29.2	0 55.6	3 59.4
18	5 47 9.2	26 15.2	25 53.3	27 20.4	18 21.7	10 21.5	24 26.7	18 15.6	23 19.0	14 32.8	0 57.8	4 1.1
19	5 51 5.8	27 16.3	25 50.1	11♏37.1	17 17.8	11 31.0	25 12.5	18 29.1	23 25.4	14 36.4	1 .1	4 2.8
20	5 55 2.4	28 17.4	25 46.9	25 52.0	16 23.4	12 40.4	25 58.4	18 42.7	23 31.7	14 40.0	1 2.3	4 4.4
21	5 58 58.9	29 18.6	25 43.8	10♐ 1.5	15 39.5	13 49.8	26 44.3	18 56.3	23 38.1	14 43.7	1 4.7	4 6.1
22	6 2 55.5	0♑19.7	25 40.6	24 1.5	15 6.4	14 58.9	27 30.1	19 9.9	23 44.4	14 47.3	1 6.9	4 7.7
23	6 6 52.0	1 20.8	25 37.4	7♑47.9	14 44.2	16 7.9	28 16.0	19 23.6	23 50.6	14 50.8	1 9.2	4 9.2
24	6 10 48.6	2 22.0	25 34.2	21 17.4	14 32.5	17 16.8	29 1.8	19 37.3	23 56.7	14 54.4	1 11.5	4 10.7
25	6 14 45.2	3 23.1	25 31.1	4♒27.8	14 30.8	18 25.5	29 47.7	19 51.0	24 2.8	14 57.9	1 13.7	4 12.2
26	6 18 41.7	4 24.3	25 27.9	17 18.5	14 D 38.5	19 34.0	0♓33.6	20 4.8	24 8.9	15 1.5	1 16.0	4 13.7
27	6 22 38.3	5 25.5	25 24.7	29 50.2	14 54.7	20 42.4	1 19.5	20 18.6	24 14.9	15 5.0	1 18.3	4 15.1
28	6 26 34.8	6 26.6	25 21.5	12♓ 5.3	15 18.8	21 50.6	2 5.3	20 32.4	24 20.9	15 8.5	1 20.5	4 16.5
29	6 30 31.4	7 27.8	25 18.4	24 7.3	15 49.9	22 58.6	2 51.2	20 46.2	24 26.8	15 11.9	1 22.8	4 17.9
30	6 34 27.9	8 28.9	25 15.2	6♈ .7	16 27.4	24 6.4	3 37.0	21 .1	24 32.6	15 15.4	1 25.1	4 19.2
31	6 38 24.5	9 30.1	25 12.0	17 50.3	17 10.5	25 14.1	4 22.9	21 14.0	24 38.4	15 18.8	1 27.3	4 20.5

LATITUDE

DAY	EPHEM. SID. TIME	☉	☊	☽	☿	♀	♂	♃	♄	♅	♆	♇
1	4 40 7.8	0 .0	0 .0	4S59.9	1S54.5	2S18.5	1S26.0	0S12.5	2N 2.3	0N .2	1N 7.1	16N20.4
4	4 51 57.4	0 .0	0 .0	3 4.5	1 22.1	2 19.0	1 23.3	0 12.8	2 2.4	0 .1	1 7.1	16 21.3
7	5 3 47.1	0 .0	0 .0	0N 4.2	0 37.2	2 18.6	1 20.6	0 13.0	2 2.5	0 .1	1 7.0	16 22.3
10	5 15 36.8	0 .0	0 .0	3 19.1	0N18.8	2 17.2	1 17.9	0 13.3	2 2.7	0 .1	1 6.9	16 23.4
13	5 27 26.5	0 .0	0 .0	5 9.1	1 19.0	2 14.9	1 15.1	0 13.5	2 2.8	0 .1	1 6.9	16 24.5
16	5 39 16.1	0 .0	0 .0	4 27.3	2 11.7	2 11.5	1 12.3	0 13.7	2 3.0	0 .0	1 6.9	16 25.7
19	5 51 5.8	0 .0	0 .0	1 24.5	2 46.2	2 7.0	1 9.6	0 14.0	2 3.2	0 .0	1 6.8	16 26.9
22	6 2 55.5	0 .0	0 .0	2S21.1	2 59.8	2 1.4	1 6.8	0 14.2	2 3.5	0 .0	1 6.8	16 28.2
25	6 14 45.2	0 .0	0 .0	4 47.1	2 56.3	1 54.7	1 4.0	0 14.5	2 3.7	0 .0	1 6.8	16 29.6
28	6 26 34.8	0 .0	0 .0	4 59.2	2 41.4	1 46.9	1 1.2	0 14.7	2 4.0	0S .1	1 6.8	16 31.0
31	6 38 24.5	0 .0	0 .0	3 14.6	2 19.9	1 37.9	0 58.4	0 15.0	2 4.3	0 .1	1 6.8	16 32.4

RIGHT ASCENSION

DAY	EPHEM. SID. TIME	☉	☊	☽	☿	♀	♂	♃	♄	♅	♆	♇
1	4 40 7.8	7♐16.6	24♉29.4	19♓20.7	29♐36.3	22♑24.7	14♒22.6	15♑49.3	19♏32.5	12♐ 7.0	0♑21.8	6♏45.1
2	4 44 4.3	8 21.4	24 26.1	0♈ 7.7	0♑ 9.6	23 41.9	15 8.4	16 3.0	19 39.5	12 11.0	0 24.1	6 47.1
3	4 48 .9	9 26.4	24 22.8	10 43.2	0 34.2	24 58.7	15 54.2	16 16.7	19 46.5	12 14.9	0 26.4	6 49.0
4	4 51 57.4	10 31.5	24 19.5	21 22.0	0 49.0	26 15.2	16 39.9	16 30.5	19 53.4	12 18.9	0 28.8	6 51.0
5	4 55 54.0	11 36.7	24 16.3	2♉18.6	0 53.4	27 31.3	17 25.4	16 44.3	20 .4	12 22.8	0 31.1	6 52.9
6	4 59 50.5	12 42.1	24 13.0	13 46.8	0 R 46.4	28 47.1	18 10.9	16 58.2	20 7.3	12 26.8	0 33.5	6 54.8
7	5 3 47.1	13 47.6	24 9.7	25 58.1	0 27.5	0♒ 2.5	18 56.2	17 12.1	20 14.1	12 30.7	0 35.9	6 56.7
8	5 7 43.7	14 53.3	24 6.4	8♊59.5	29♐56.4	1 17.5	19 41.5	17 26.1	20 21.0	12 34.7	0 38.3	6 58.5
9	5 11 40.2	15 59.0	24 3.2	22 50.5	29 13.0	2 32.2	20 26.7	17 40.2	20 27.8	12 38.6	0 40.7	7 .4
10	5 15 36.8	17 4.9	23 59.9	7♋20.0	28 17.9	3 46.4	21 11.8	17 54.3	20 34.6	12 42.5	0 43.1	7 2.2
11	5 19 33.3	18 10.9	23 56.6	22 7.5	27 11.9	5 .3	21 56.8	18 8.5	20 41.4	12 46.5	0 45.5	7 4.0
12	5 23 29.9	19 16.9	23 53.3	6♌49.0	25 56.8	6 13.7	22 41.6	18 22.7	20 48.1	12 50.4	0 47.9	7 5.8
13	5 27 26.5	20 23.1	23 50.1	21 5.1	24 34.7	7 26.7	23 26.4	18 36.9	20 54.8	12 54.4	0 50.3	7 7.6
14	5 31 23.0	21 29.3	23 46.8	4♍47.1	23 8.1	8 39.3	24 11.1	18 51.2	21 1.5	12 58.3	0 52.7	7 9.3
15	5 35 19.6	22 35.7	23 43.5	17 57.2	21 40.0	9 51.5	24 55.7	19 5.5	21 8.1	13 2.2	0 55.2	7 11.0
16	5 39 16.1	23 42.0	23 40.3	0♎45.6	20 13.4	11 3.2	25 40.2	19 19.9	21 14.7	13 6.1	0 57.6	7 12.7
17	5 43 12.7	24 48.5	23 37.0	13 27.4	18 51.1	12 14.5	26 24.6	19 34.3	21 21.2	13 10.0	1 .0	7 14.4
18	5 47 9.2	25 55.0	23 33.7	26 19.5	17 35.5	13 25.4	27 9.0	19 48.8	21 27.8	13 13.9	1 2.5	7 16.1
19	5 51 5.8	27 1.6	23 30.4	9♏37.8	16 28.5	14 35.8	27 53.2	20 3.3	21 34.2	13 17.8	1 4.9	7 17.7
20	5 55 2.4	28 8.2	23 27.2	23 34.3	15 31.7	15 45.7	28 37.3	20 17.8	21 40.7	13 21.7	1 7.4	7 19.4
21	5 58 58.9	29 14.8	23 23.9	8♐12.2	14 45.8	16 55.3	29 21.4	20 32.5	21 47.1	13 25.6	1 9.9	7 21.0
22	6 2 55.5	0♑21.5	23 20.6	23 22.4	14 11.2	18 4.3	0♓ 5.4	20 47.1	21 53.5	13 29.5	1 12.3	7 22.6
23	6 6 52.0	1 28.1	23 17.4	8♑42.7	13 47.8	19 12.9	0 49.2	21 1.7	21 59.8	13 33.3	1 14.8	7 24.1
24	6 10 48.6	2 34.7	23 14.1	23 44.4	13 35.3	20 21.0	1 33.0	21 16.4	22 6.0	13 37.1	1 17.3	7 25.6
25	6 14 45.2	3 41.4	23 10.8	8♒ 2.7	13 33.3	21 28.6	2 16.7	21 31.0	22 12.2	13 40.9	1 19.7	7 27.1
26	6 18 41.7	4 48.0	23 7.6	21 24.5	13 D 40.9	22 35.8	3 .3	21 45.8	22 18.4	13 44.7	1 22.2	7 28.6
27	6 22 38.3	5 54.5	23 4.3	3♓49.3	13 57.4	23 42.5	3 43.8	22 .5	22 24.5	13 48.5	1 24.6	7 30.1
28	6 26 34.8	7 1.1	23 1.1	15 25.4	14 22.1	24 48.7	4 27.2	22 15.3	22 30.6	13 52.3	1 27.1	7 31.5
29	6 30 31.4	8 7.6	22 57.8	26 26.0	14 54.3	25 54.5	5 10.5	22 30.0	22 36.6	13 56.0	1 29.5	7 32.9
30	6 34 27.9	9 14.0	22 54.5	7♈ 6.1	15 33.2	26 59.8	5 53.7	22 44.8	22 42.5	13 59.7	1 31.9	7 34.3
31	6 38 24.5	10 20.3	22 51.3	17 41.4	16 18.1	28 4.6	6 36.9	22 59.6	22 48.4	14 3.4	1 34.4	7 35.6

DECLINATION

DAY	EPHEM. SID. TIME	☉	☊	☽	☿	♀	♂	♃	♄	♅	♆	♇
1	4 40 7.8	21S48.0	0N20.4	10S 1.0	25S21.0	24S10.7	18S42.7	22S51.3	16S 9.0	22S25.3	22S19.4	2N43.3
4	4 51 57.4	22 14.1	0 20.3	5N40.0	24 48.5	23 36.3	18 1.4	22 47.4	16 14.2	22 26.7	22 19.5	2 42.2
7	5 3 47.1	22 36.4	0 20.3	19 50.3	24 3.7	22 55.9	17 18.4	22 43.1	16 19.3	22 28.0	22 19.5	2 41.3
10	5 15 36.8	22 54.7	0 20.2	26 35.6	23 7.2	22 10.0	16 34.0	22 38.7	16 24.3	22 29.4	22 19.5	2 40.5
13	5 27 26.5	23 8.9	0 20.2	20 39.3	22 1.9	21 18.8	15 48.2	22 34.0	16 29.2	22 30.7	22 19.5	2 39.8
16	5 39 16.1	23 19.0	0 20.2	4 31.6	20 56.3	20 22.6	15 1.1	22 29.0	16 33.9	22 32.0	22 19.5	2 39.2
19	5 51 5.8	23 24.9	0 20.1	13S58.8	20 4.7	19 21.8	14 12.7	22 23.9	16 38.5	22 33.3	22 19.5	2 38.8
22	6 2 55.5	23 26.5	0 20.1	25 39.5	19 37.9	18 16.6	13 23.2	22 18.4	16 43.0	22 34.5	22 19.5	2 38.5
25	6 14 45.2	23 24.0	0 20.0	23 47.5	19 37.5	17 7.5	12 32.6	22 12.8	16 47.2	22 35.7	22 19.4	2 38.3
28	6 26 34.8	23 17.2	0 20.0	11 38.0	19 57.5	15 54.8	11 41.1	22 6.9	16 51.3	22 36.9	22 19.4	2 38.3
31	6 38 24.5	23 6.1	0 20.0	4N .1	20 30.1	14 38.9	10 48.7	22 .8	16 55.3	22 38.1	22 19.3	2 38.4

JANUARY 1985

LONGITUDE

DAY	EPHEM. SID. TIME h m s	☉ ° ′	☊ ° ′	☽ ° ′	☿ ° ′	♀ ° ′	♂ ° ′	♃ ° ′	♄ ° ′	♅ ° ′	♆ ° ′	♇ ° ′
1	6 42 21.1	10 ♑ 31.3	25 ♉ 8.8	29 ♈ 41.6	17 ♐ 58.6	26 ♒ 21.5	5 ♓ 8.8	21 ♑ 27.9	24 ♏ 44.1	15 ♐ 22.3	1 ♑ 29.6	4 ♏ 21.8
2	6 46 17.6	11 32.4	25 5.6	11 ♉ 39.6	18 51.3	27 28.7	5 54.6	21 41.8	24 49.8	15 25.7	1 31.8	4 23.0
3	6 50 14.2	12 33.6	25 2.5	23 49.0	19 47.9	28 35.7	6 40.4	21 55.7	24 55.4	15 29.1	1 34.1	4 24.2
4	6 54 10.7	13 34.7	24 59.3	6 ♊ 14.2	20 48.1	29 42.5	7 26.2	22 9.7	25 1.0	15 32.4	1 36.3	4 25.4
5	6 58 7.3	14 35.8	24 56.1	18 57.9	21 51.4	0 ♓ 49.0	8 12.0	22 23.7	25 6.5	15 35.7	1 38.5	4 26.6
6	7 2 3.9	15 37.0	24 52.9	2 ♋ 1.9	22 57.6	1 55.3	8 57.8	22 37.7	25 11.9	15 39.1	1 40.7	4 27.7
7	7 6 .4	16 38.1	24 49.8	15 26.1	24 6.2	3 1.4	9 43.6	22 51.7	25 17.2	15 42.4	1 42.9	4 28.7
8	7 9 57.0	17 39.2	24 46.6	29 8.6	25 17.0	4 7.2	10 29.4	23 5.7	25 22.5	15 45.6	1 45.1	4 29.8
9	7 13 53.5	18 40.4	24 43.4	13 ♌ 6.1	26 29.9	5 12.7	11 15.1	23 19.7	25 27.8	15 48.9	1 47.3	4 30.8
10	7 17 50.1	19 41.5	24 40.2	27 14.0	27 44.6	6 18.0	12 .9	23 33.7	25 33.0	15 52.1	1 49.5	4 31.8
11	7 21 46.6	20 42.7	24 37.1	11 ♍ 27.7	29 .9	7 23.0	12 46.7	23 47.8	25 38.1	15 55.3	1 51.8	4 32.8
12	7 25 43.2	21 43.8	24 33.9	25 42.5	0 ♑ 18.7	8 27.7	13 32.4	24 1.9	25 43.1	15 58.5	1 53.9	4 33.7
13	7 29 39.8	22 44.9	24 30.7	9 ♎ 55.2	1 37.8	9 32.1	14 18.1	24 15.9	25 48.1	16 1.6	1 56.1	4 34.6
14	7 33 36.3	23 46.1	24 27.5	24 3.4	2 58.1	10 36.3	15 3.7	24 30.0	25 53.0	16 4.7	1 58.2	4 35.4
15	7 37 32.9	24 47.2	24 24.4	8 ♏ 5.8	4 19.6	11 40.0	15 49.4	24 44.1	25 57.8	16 7.8	2 .4	4 36.2
16	7 41 29.4	25 48.3	24 21.2	22 1.8	5 42.1	12 43.5	16 35.1	24 58.1	26 2.5	16 10.8	2 2.5	4 37.0
17	7 45 26.0	26 49.4	24 18.0	5 ♐ 51.0	7 5.6	13 46.7	17 20.7	25 12.2	26 7.2	16 13.9	2 4.6	4 37.7
18	7 49 22.6	27 50.5	24 14.8	19 32.6	8 30.0	14 49.5	18 6.3	25 26.3	26 11.8	16 16.9	2 6.7	4 38.4
19	7 53 19.1	28 51.6	24 11.6	3 ♑ 5.6	9 55.3	15 51.9	18 51.9	25 40.3	26 16.3	16 19.8	2 8.8	4 39.1
20	7 57 15.7	29 52.7	24 8.5	16 28.2	11 21.4	16 54.0	19 37.5	25 54.4	26 20.8	16 22.7	2 10.8	4 39.7
21	8 1 12.2	0 ♒ 53.8	24 5.3	29 38.7	12 48.3	17 55.7	20 23.0	26 8.5	26 25.1	16 25.6	2 12.9	4 40.3
22	8 5 8.8	1 54.9	24 2.1	12 ♒ 35.3	14 15.9	18 57.0	21 8.6	26 22.5	26 29.4	16 28.5	2 14.9	4 40.8
23	8 9 5.3	2 56.0	23 58.9	25 16.8	15 44.2	19 57.9	21 54.1	26 36.6	26 33.6	16 31.3	2 16.9	4 41.4
24	8 13 1.9	3 57.0	23 55.8	7 ♓ 43.3	17 13.3	20 58.4	22 39.6	26 50.6	26 37.7	16 34.1	2 19.0	4 41.8
25	8 16 58.5	4 58.0	23 52.6	19 55.7	18 43.0	21 58.4	23 25.0	27 4.6	26 41.8	16 36.8	2 20.9	4 42.3
26	8 20 55.0	5 59.1	23 49.4	1 ♈ 56.4	20 13.4	22 58.0	24 10.5	27 18.6	26 45.7	16 39.5	2 22.9	4 42.7
27	8 24 51.6	7 .1	23 46.2	13 48.8	21 44.5	23 57.0	24 55.9	27 32.6	26 49.6	16 42.2	2 24.9	4 43.1
28	8 28 48.1	8 1.0	23 43.1	25 37.2	23 16.3	24 55.6	25 41.3	27 46.6	26 53.4	16 44.9	2 26.8	4 43.4
29	8 32 44.7	9 2.0	23 39.9	7 ♉ 26.7	24 48.7	25 53.7	26 26.6	28 .5	26 57.1	16 47.4	2 28.7	4 43.7
30	8 36 41.2	10 2.9	23 36.7	19 22.8	26 21.8	26 51.3	27 12.0	28 14.5	27 .7	16 50.0	2 30.6	4 44.0
31	8 40 37.8	11 3.9	23 33.5	1 ♊ 31.1	27 55.6	27 48.3	27 57.3	28 28.4	27 4.2	16 52.5	2 32.5	4 44.2

LATITUDE

DAY	SID. TIME	☉	☊	☽	☿	♀	♂	♃	♄	♅	♆	♇
1	6 42 21.1	0 .0	0 .0	2 S 20.7	2 N 11.9	1 S 34.7	0 S 57.5	0 S 15.1	2 N 4.4	0 S .1	1 N 6.7	16 N 32.9
4	6 54 10.7	0 .0	0 .0	0 N 51.7	1 46.3	1 24.1	0 54.7	0 15.4	2 4.8	0 .1	1 6.7	16 34.4
7	7 6 .4	0 .0	0 .0	3 51.8	1 19.7	1 12.4	0 51.9	0 15.6	2 5.1	0 .2	1 6.7	16 35.9
10	7 17 50.1	0 .0	0 .0	5 5.6	0 53.2	0 59.6	0 49.1	0 15.9	2 5.5	0 .2	1 6.8	16 37.5
13	7 29 39.8	0 .0	0 .0	3 39.6	0 27.4	0 45.5	0 46.4	0 16.2	2 5.9	0 .2	1 6.8	16 39.1
16	7 41 29.4	0 .0	0 .0	0 19.6	0 2.7	0 30.3	0 43.6	0 16.4	2 6.3	0 .3	1 6.8	16 40.7
19	7 53 19.1	0 .0	0 .0	3 S 5.4	0 S 20.4	0 13.9	0 40.9	0 16.7	2 6.8	0 .3	1 6.8	16 42.3
22	8 5 8.8	0 .0	0 .0	4 55.0	0 41.8	0 N 3.6	0 38.2	0 17.0	2 7.2	0 .3	1 6.8	16 43.9
25	8 16 58.5	0 .0	0 .0	4 33.1	1 1.3	0 22.3	0 35.5	0 17.3	2 7.7	0 .3	1 6.9	16 45.6
28	8 28 48.1	0 .0	0 .0	2 25.5	1 18.6	0 42.1	0 32.8	0 17.6	2 8.2	0 .4	1 6.9	16 47.3
31	8 40 37.8	0 .0	0 .0	0 N 38.8	1 33.6	1 3.0	0 30.2	0 17.9	2 8.7	0 .4	1 6.9	16 48.9

RIGHT ASCENSION

DAY	SID. TIME	☉	☊	☽	☿	♀	♂	♃	♄	♅	♆	♇
1	6 42 21.1	11 ♑ 26.6	22 ♉ 48.0	28 ♈ 27.2	17 ♐ 8.6	29 ♒ 8.9	7 ♓ 19.9	23 ♑ 14.5	22 ♏ 54.2	14 ♐ 7.1	1 ♑ 36.8	7 ♏ 36.9
2	6 46 17.6	12 32.8	22 44.7	9 ♉ 38.9	18 3.9	0 ♓ 12.7	8 2.9	23 29.3	23 .0	14 10.8	1 39.2	7 38.2
3	6 50 14.2	13 38.9	22 41.5	21 30.2	19 3.6	1 16.1	8 45.8	23 44.2	23 5.7	14 14.4	1 41.7	7 39.5
4	6 54 10.7	14 44.9	22 38.2	4 ♊ 12.2	20 7.3	2 18.9	9 28.6	23 59.0	23 11.4	14 18.0	1 44.1	7 40.7
5	6 58 7.3	15 50.8	22 35.0	17 49.3	21 14.6	3 21.3	10 11.3	24 13.9	23 17.0	14 21.6	1 46.5	7 41.9
6	7 2 3.9	16 56.6	22 31.7	2 ♋ 15.9	22 25.0	4 23.3	10 54.0	24 28.8	23 22.6	14 25.2	1 48.9	7 43.1
7	7 6 .4	18 2.3	22 28.4	17 14.5	23 38.4	5 24.7	11 36.5	24 43.7	23 28.0	14 28.8	1 51.3	7 44.2
8	7 9 57.0	19 7.9	22 25.2	2 ♌ 19.3	24 54.4	6 25.7	12 19.0	24 58.6	23 33.4	14 32.3	1 53.6	7 45.3
9	7 13 53.5	20 13.3	22 21.9	17 5.0	26 12.8	7 26.1	13 1.4	25 13.4	23 38.8	14 35.8	1 56.0	7 46.4
10	7 17 50.1	21 18.6	22 18.7	1 ♍ 15.7	27 33.4	8 26.1	13 43.8	25 28.3	23 44.1	14 39.2	1 58.4	7 47.5
11	7 21 46.6	22 23.8	22 15.4	14 48.2	28 56.0	9 25.7	14 26.1	25 43.3	23 49.3	14 42.7	2 .8	7 48.5
12	7 25 43.2	23 28.8	22 12.1	27 49.4	0 ♑ 20.3	10 24.8	15 8.3	25 58.2	23 54.5	14 46.1	2 3.1	7 49.5
13	7 29 39.8	24 33.7	22 8.9	10 ♎ 33.2	1 46.2	11 23.3	15 50.4	26 13.1	23 59.6	14 49.5	2 5.5	7 50.5
14	7 33 36.3	25 38.4	22 5.6	23 15.9	3 13.7	12 21.5	16 32.5	26 28.0	24 4.6	14 52.9	2 7.8	7 51.5
15	7 37 32.9	26 43.0	22 2.4	6 ♏ 14.3	4 42.5	13 19.1	17 14.5	26 42.9	24 9.5	14 56.2	2 10.1	7 52.4
16	7 41 29.4	27 47.4	21 59.1	19 42.1	6 12.6	14 16.2	17 56.4	26 57.8	24 14.4	14 59.5	2 12.4	7 53.2
17	7 45 26.0	28 51.7	21 55.9	3 ♐ 47.1	7 43.8	15 12.9	18 38.3	27 12.6	24 19.2	15 2.7	2 14.6	7 54.1
18	7 49 22.6	29 55.7	21 52.6	18 26.9	9 16.1	16 9.1	19 20.1	27 27.5	24 23.9	15 5.9	2 16.9	7 54.9
19	7 53 19.1	0 ♒ 59.6	21 49.4	3 ♑ 27.1	10 49.3	17 4.9	20 1.9	27 42.4	24 28.5	15 9.1	2 19.2	7 55.7
20	7 57 15.7	2 3.3	21 46.1	18 23.8	12 23.5	18 .1	20 43.6	27 57.2	24 33.1	15 12.3	2 21.4	7 56.4
21	8 1 12.2	3 6.9	21 42.9	2 ♒ 51.6	13 58.4	18 54.9	21 25.3	28 12.0	24 37.5	15 15.4	2 23.6	7 57.1
22	8 5 8.8	4 10.2	21 39.6	16 32.5	15 34.2	19 49.1	22 6.9	28 26.9	24 41.9	15 18.5	2 25.8	7 57.8
23	8 9 5.3	5 13.4	21 36.4	29 19.6	17 10.6	20 42.9	22 48.5	28 41.7	24 46.3	15 21.5	2 28.0	7 58.5
24	8 13 1.9	6 16.3	21 33.1	11 ♓ 16.4	18 47.6	21 36.1	23 30.0	28 56.4	24 50.5	15 24.5	2 30.2	7 59.1
25	8 16 58.5	7 19.1	21 29.9	22 32.9	20 25.3	22 28.9	24 11.4	29 11.2	24 54.6	15 27.5	2 32.3	7 59.7
26	8 20 55.0	8 21.6	21 26.6	3 ♈ 22.3	22 3.5	23 21.1	24 52.9	29 25.9	24 58.7	15 30.4	2 34.5	8 .2
27	8 24 51.6	9 23.9	21 23.4	13 59.1	23 42.2	24 12.8	25 34.3	29 40.7	25 2.7	15 33.3	2 36.6	8 .7
28	8 28 48.1	10 26.1	21 20.1	24 38.3	25 21.3	25 3.9	26 15.6	29 55.3	25 6.6	15 36.1	2 38.7	8 1.2
29	8 32 44.7	11 28.0	21 16.9	5 ♉ 34.7	27 .9	25 54.6	26 56.9	0 ♒ 10.0	25 10.4	15 38.9	2 40.7	8 1.7
30	8 36 41.2	12 29.7	21 13.6	17 2.9	28 40.8	26 44.6	27 38.2	0 24.6	25 14.1	15 41.7	2 42.8	8 2.1
31	8 40 37.8	13 31.2	21 10.4	29 15.7	0 ♒ 21.2	27 34.1	28 19.4	0 39.2	25 17.7	15 44.4	2 44.8	8 2.5

DECLINATION

DAY	SID. TIME	☉	☊	☽	☿	♀	♂	♃	♄	♅	♆	♇
1	6 42 21.1	23 S 1.6	0 N 20.0	9 N 10.2	20 S 42.6	14 S 12.9	10 S 31.0	21 S 58.7	16 S 56.5	22 S 38.5	22 S 19.3	2 N 38.4
4	6 54 10.7	22 45.0	0 19.9	22 12.1	21 21.4	12 53.3	9 37.6	21 52.3	17 .2	22 39.6	22 19.2	2 38.7
7	7 6 .4	22 24.4	0 19.9	26 23.2	21 59.0	11 31.4	8 43.5	21 45.7	17 3.8	22 40.7	22 19.1	2 39.1
10	7 17 50.1	21 59.8	0 19.8	17 12.7	22 32.2	10 7.4	7 48.8	21 38.9	17 7.1	22 41.8	22 19.1	2 39.6
13	7 29 39.8	21 31.4	0 19.8	0 S 33.8	22 58.6	8 41.9	6 53.6	21 31.8	17 10.3	22 42.8	22 18.9	2 40.2
16	7 41 29.4	20 59.2	0 19.8	17 57.8	23 16.4	7 15.1	5 58.0	21 24.6	17 13.2	22 43.8	22 18.8	2 41.0
19	7 53 19.1	20 23.5	0 19.7	26 29.7	23 24.6	5 47.4	5 2.0	21 17.2	17 16.0	22 44.7	22 18.7	2 41.9
22	8 5 8.8	19 44.2	0 19.7	21 44.6	23 22.3	4 19.1	4 5.8	21 9.5	17 18.6	22 45.6	22 18.6	2 42.9
25	8 16 58.5	19 1.6	0 19.6	8 10.4	23 8.8	2 50.6	3 9.4	21 1.8	17 20.9	22 46.5	22 18.5	2 44.0
28	8 28 48.1	18 15.9	0 19.6	7 N 38.8	22 43.7	1 22.3	2 13.0	20 53.8	17 23.1	22 47.3	22 18.3	2 45.2
31	8 40 37.8	17 27.3	0 19.5	21 6.1	22 6.5	0 N 5.4	1 16.5	20 45.7	17 25.1	22 48.1	22 18.2	2 46.5

FEBRUARY 1985

LONGITUDE

DAY	EPHEM. SID. TIME	☉	☊	☽	☿	♀	♂	♃	♄	♅	♆	♇
	h m s	° ′	° ′	° ′	° ′	° ′	° ′	° ′	° ′	° ′	° ′	° ′
1	8 44 34.3	12♒ 4.8	23♉30.3	13♊56.8	29♑30.1	28♓44.7	28♓42.6	28♑42.4	27♏ 7.7	16♐55.1	2♑34.4	4♏44.4
2	8 48 30.9	13 5.7	23 27.2	26 44.4	1♒ 5.3	29 40.6	29 27.8	28 56.2	27 11.0	16 57.5	2 36.2	4 44.6
3	8 52 27.5	14 6.5	23 24.0	9♋56.8	2 41.2	0♈35.8	0♈13.0	29 10.1	27 14.3	16 59.9	2 38.1	4 44.7
4	8 56 24.0	15 7.4	23 20.8	23 35.1	4 17.8	1 30.3	0 58.2	29 23.9	27 17.5	17 2.3	2 39.9	4 44.8
5	9 0 20.6	16 8.2	23 17.6	7♌37.7	5 55.1	2 24.2	1 43.3	29 37.7	27 20.5	17 4.6	2 41.6	4 44.8
6	9 4 17.1	17 9.0	23 14.5	22 .4	7 33.2	3 17.4	2 28.4	29 51.5	27 23.5	17 6.8	2 43.4	4 44.8
7	9 8 13.7	18 9.8	23 11.3	6♍36.7	9 12.0	4 9.9	3 13.5	0♒ 5.3	27 26.4	17 9.1	2 45.1	4 44.8
8	9 12 10.2	19 10.5	23 8.1	21 18.9	10 51.6	5 1.7	3 58.5	0 19.0	27 29.2	17 11.3	2 46.8	4 R 44.7
9	9 16 6.8	20 11.2	23 4.9	5♎59.3	12 32.0	5 52.6	4 43.5	0 32.7	27 31.9	17 13.4	2 48.5	4 44.6
10	9 20 3.4	21 12.0	23 1.8	20 31.5	14 13.2	6 42.8	5 28.5	0 46.3	27 34.5	17 15.5	2 50.2	4 44.5
11	9 23 59.9	22 12.7	22 58.6	4♏51.1	15 55.2	7 32.2	6 13.4	0 59.9	27 37.0	17 17.6	2 51.8	4 44.3
12	9 27 56.5	23 13.3	22 55.4	18 56.2	17 38.1	8 20.7	6 58.3	1 13.5	27 39.4	17 19.6	2 53.4	4 44.1
13	9 31 53.0	24 14.0	22 52.2	2♐46.2	19 21.8	9 8.3	7 43.2	1 27.1	27 41.8	17 21.5	2 55.0	4 43.9
14	9 35 49.6	25 14.7	22 49.0	16 21.9	21 6.4	9 55.0	8 28.0	1 40.6	27 44.0	17 23.5	2 56.6	4 43.6
15	9 39 46.1	26 15.3	22 45.9	29 44.6	22 51.8	10 40.8	9 12.8	1 54.1	27 46.1	17 25.3	2 58.1	4 43.3
16	9 43 42.7	27 15.9	22 42.7	12♑55.3	24 38.1	11 25.5	9 57.6	2 7.5	27 48.1	17 27.2	2 59.7	4 43.0
17	9 47 39.2	28 16.5	22 39.5	25 54.8	26 25.2	12 9.3	10 42.3	2 20.9	27 50.1	17 28.9	3 1.1	4 42.6
18	9 51 35.8	29 17.0	22 36.3	8♒43.4	28 13.3	12 52.0	11 27.0	2 34.3	27 51.9	17 30.7	3 2.6	4 42.2
19	9 55 32.3	0♓17.6	22 33.2	21 21.0	0♓ 2.1	13 33.5	12 11.6	2 47.6	27 53.6	17 32.3	3 4.0	4 41.7
20	9 59 28.9	1 18.1	22 30.0	3♓47.5	1 51.9	14 13.9	12 56.3	3 .9	27 55.3	17 34.0	3 5.4	4 41.2
21	10 3 25.5	2 18.6	22 26.8	16 3.1	3 42.4	14 53.1	13 40.9	3 14.1	27 56.8	17 35.6	3 6.8	4 40.7
22	10 7 22.0	3 19.1	22 23.6	28 8.3	5 33.7	15 31.1	14 25.4	3 27.3	27 58.3	17 37.1	3 8.2	4 40.2
23	10 11 18.6	4 19.5	22 20.4	10♈ 4.7	7 25.8	16 7.7	15 10.0	3 40.4	27 59.6	17 38.6	3 9.6	4 39.6
24	10 15 15.1	5 19.9	22 17.3	21 54.7	9 18.4	16 43.0	15 54.4	3 53.5	28 .8	17 40.0	3 10.9	4 39.0
25	10 19 11.7	6 20.3	22 14.1	3♉41.7	11 11.7	17 16.9	16 38.8	4 6.5	28 1.9	17 41.4	3 12.1	4 38.4
26	10 23 8.2	7 20.6	22 10.9	15 29.8	13 5.5	17 49.3	17 23.2	4 19.4	28 2.9	17 42.8	3 13.4	4 37.7
27	10 27 4.8	8 20.9	22 7.7	27 23.9	14 59.6	18 20.1	18 7.6	4 32.3	28 3.9	17 44.0	3 14.6	4 37.0
28	10 31 1.3	9 21.2	22 4.6	9♊29.5	16 53.9	18 49.4	18 51.9	4 45.2	28 4.7	17 45.3	3 15.7	4 36.2

LATITUDE

DAY	EPHEM. SID. TIME	☉	☊	☽	☿	♀	♂	♃	♄	♅	♆	♇
1	8 44 34.3	0 .0	0 .0	1N42.7	1S38.1	1N10.3	0S29.3	0S18.0	2N 8.9	0S .4	1N 7.0	16N49.5
4	8 56 24.0	0 .0	0 .0	4 20.0	1 49.6	1 32.6	0 26.7	0 18.4	2 9.4	0 .4	1 7.0	16 51.1
7	9 8 13.7	0 .0	0 .0	4 52.2	1 58.2	1 56.0	0 24.1	0 18.7	2 9.9	0 .5	1 7.1	16 52.8
10	9 20 3.4	0 .0	0 .0	2 41.6	2 3.7	2 20.4	0 21.5	0 19.0	2 10.4	0 .5	1 7.1	16 54.4
13	9 31 53.0	0 .0	0 .0	0S52.4	2 5.7	2 45.7	0 19.0	0 19.3	2 11.0	0 .5	1 7.2	16 56.0
16	9 43 42.7	0 .0	0 .0	3 51.7	2 3.9	3 11.9	0 16.5	0 19.7	2 11.5	0 .6	1 7.2	16 57.6
19	9 55 32.3	0 .0	0 .0	4 59.8	1 57.8	3 38.8	0 14.0	0 20.0	2 12.1	0 .6	1 7.3	16 59.1
22	10 7 22.0	0 .0	0 .0	4 1.4	1 47.1	4 6.4	0 11.6	0 20.4	2 12.7	0 .6	1 7.4	17 .6
25	10 19 11.7	0 .0	0 .0	1 30.8	1 31.3	4 34.6	0 9.2	0 20.8	2 13.2	0 .6	1 7.5	17 2.1
28	10 31 1.3	0 .0	0 .0	1N36.5	1 10.2	5 3.0	0 6.8	0 21.1	2 13.8	0 .7	1 7.5	17 3.5

RIGHT ASCENSION

DAY	EPHEM. SID. TIME	☉	☊	☽	☿	♀	♂	♃	♄	♅	♆	♇
1	8 44 34.3	14♒32.6	21♉ 7.1	12♊21.8	2♒ 1.9	28♓23.0	29♓ .6	0♒53.9	25♏21.3	15♐47.1	2♑46.9	8♏ 2.9
2	8 48 30.9	15 33.7	21 3.9	26 22.3	3 42.8	29 11.3	29 41.8	1 8.4	25 24.8	15 49.8	2 48.9	8 3.2
3	8 52 27.5	16 34.6	21 .6	11♋ 7.4	5 24.0	29 59.0	0♈22.9	1 22.9	25 28.2	15 52.4	2 50.8	8 3.5
4	8 56 24.0	17 35.2	20 57.4	26 16.1	7 5.5	0♈46.0	1 4.0	1 37.4	25 31.4	15 54.9	2 52.8	8 3.7
5	9 0 20.6	18 35.7	20 54.1	11♌22.5	8 47.3	1 32.4	1 45.1	1 51.8	25 34.6	15 57.4	2 54.7	8 4.0
6	9 4 17.1	19 36.0	20 50.9	26 4.8	10 29.2	2 18.2	2 26.1	2 6.3	25 37.7	15 59.9	2 56.6	8 4.1
7	9 8 13.7	20 36.1	20 47.6	10♍12.5	12 11.4	3 3.2	3 7.1	2 20.6	25 40.7	16 2.3	2 58.4	8 4.3
8	9 12 10.2	21 35.9	20 44.4	23 46.5	13 53.7	3 47.6	3 48.1	2 34.9	25 43.6	16 4.6	3 .3	8 4.4
9	9 16 6.8	22 35.6	20 41.2	6♎57.0	15 36.3	4 31.2	4 29.1	2 49.2	25 46.4	16 7.0	3 2.1	8 4.5
10	9 20 3.4	23 35.1	20 37.9	19 58.4	17 19.0	5 14.1	5 10.0	3 3.5	25 49.1	16 9.2	3 3.9	8 4.6
11	9 23 59.9	24 34.4	20 34.7	3♏ 6.4	19 1.9	5 56.3	5 51.0	3 17.7	25 51.7	16 11.4	3 5.7	8 4.6
12	9 27 56.5	25 33.5	20 31.4	16 34.7	20 44.9	6 37.6	6 31.9	3 31.8	25 54.2	16 13.6	3 7.4	8 4.6
13	9 31 53.0	26 32.4	20 28.2	0♐31.8	22 28.1	7 18.2	7 12.9	3 46.0	25 56.6	16 15.7	3 9.1	8 R 4.5
14	9 35 49.6	27 31.2	20 24.9	14 57.9	24 11.5	7 57.9	7 53.8	4 .0	25 58.9	16 17.8	3 10.8	8 4.5
15	9 39 46.1	28 29.7	20 21.7	29 42.8	25 54.9	8 36.7	8 34.7	4 14.0	26 1.2	16 19.8	3 12.5	8 4.3
16	9 43 42.7	29 28.1	20 18.5	14♑27.4	27 38.5	9 14.6	9 15.6	4 28.0	26 3.3	16 21.8	3 14.1	8 4.2
17	9 47 39.2	0♓26.3	20 15.2	28 49.6	29 22.3	9 51.6	9 56.5	4 41.9	26 5.3	16 23.7	3 15.7	8 4.0
18	9 51 35.8	1 24.3	20 12.0	12♒31.9	1♓ 6.1	10 27.6	10 37.4	4 55.8	26 7.2	16 25.6	3 17.3	8 3.8
19	9 55 32.3	2 22.2	20 8.7	25 25.6	2 50.0	11 2.6	11 18.3	5 9.6	26 9.0	16 27.4	3 18.9	8 3.6
20	9 59 28.9	3 19.9	20 5.5	7♓31.6	4 34.0	11 36.6	11 59.3	5 23.3	26 10.7	16 29.2	3 20.4	8 3.3
21	10 3 25.5	4 17.4	20 2.3	18 57.3	6 18.1	12 9.4	12 40.2	5 37.0	26 12.3	16 30.9	3 21.9	8 3.0
22	10 7 22.0	5 14.8	19 59.0	29 53.7	8 2.2	12 41.2	13 21.2	5 50.7	26 13.9	16 32.6	3 23.4	8 2.7
23	10 11 18.6	6 12.0	19 55.8	10♈33.8	9 46.2	13 11.7	14 2.1	6 4.3	26 15.3	16 34.2	3 24.8	8 2.3
24	10 15 15.1	7 9.1	19 52.6	21 10.9	11 30.2	13 40.9	14 43.0	6 17.8	26 16.6	16 35.7	3 26.2	8 1.9
25	10 19 11.7	8 6.0	19 49.3	1♉58.8	13 14.1	14 8.9	15 24.0	6 31.3	26 17.8	16 37.2	3 27.6	8 1.5
26	10 23 8.2	9 2.7	19 46.1	13 10.7	14 57.8	14 35.5	16 5.0	6 44.6	26 18.8	16 38.6	3 28.9	8 1.1
27	10 27 4.8	9 59.3	19 42.9	24 59.0	16 41.2	15 .7	16 45.9	6 58.0	26 19.8	16 40.0	3 30.2	8 .6
28	10 31 1.3	10 55.8	19 39.6	7♊33.3	18 24.3	15 24.5	17 26.9	7 11.2	26 20.7	16 41.4	3 31.5	8 .0

DECLINATION

DAY	EPHEM. SID. TIME	☉	☊	☽	☿	♀	♂	♃	♄	♅	♆	♇
1	8 44 34.3	17S10.4	0N19.5	24N10.6	21S51.4	0N34.5	0S57.7	20S43.0	17S25.7	22S48.4	22S18.1	2N47.0
4	8 56 24.0	16 18.1	0 19.5	25 39.0	20 57.7	2 .9	0 1.3	20 34.7	17 27.4	22 49.1	22 18.0	2 48.4
7	9 8 13.7	15 23.3	0 19.4	13 36.3	19 51.4	3 25.8	0N54.9	20 26.3	17 28.9	22 49.8	22 17.8	2 49.9
10	9 20 3.4	14 26.1	0 19.4	5S31.3	18 32.3	4 48.9	1 50.8	20 17.8	17 30.2	22 50.4	22 17.6	2 51.6
13	9 31 53.0	13 26.8	0 19.4	21 34.4	17 .3	6 9.6	2 46.4	20 9.2	17 31.3	22 51.0	22 17.5	2 53.3
16	9 43 42.7	12 25.4	0 19.3	26 39.5	15 15.5	7 27.7	3 41.6	20 .5	17 32.2	22 51.6	22 17.3	2 55.1
19	9 55 32.3	11 22.2	0 19.3	19 6.8	13 17.9	8 42.6	4 36.3	19 51.8	17 32.8	22 52.1	22 17.1	2 56.9
22	10 7 22.0	10 17.5	0 19.2	4 25.8	11 8.0	9 53.8	5 30.6	19 43.0	17 33.3	22 52.6	22 17.0	2 58.8
25	10 19 11.7	9 11.3	0 19.2	11N19.6	8 46.6	11 .7	6 24.2	19 34.1	17 33.6	22 53.0	22 16.8	3 .8
28	10 31 1.3	8 3.8	0 19.2	23 28.0	6 15.1	12 2.5	7 17.1	19 25.3	17 33.6	22 53.4	22 16.6	3 2.8

MARCH 1985

LONGITUDE

DAY	EPHEM. SID. TIME	☉	☊	☾	☿	♀	♂	♃	♄	♅	♆	♇
	h m s	° ′	° ′	° ′	° ′	° ′	° ′	° ′	° ′	° ′	° ′	° ′
1	10 34 57.9	10♓21.4	22♉ 1.4	21♊52.0	18♓48.2	19♈17.0	19♈36.1	4♒57.9	28♏ 5.4	17♐46.4	3♑16.9	4♏35.4
2	10 38 54.4	11 21.6	21 58.2	4♋36.6	20 42.3	19 43.0	20 20.4	5 10.6	28 6.0	17 47.6	3 18.0	4R34.6
3	10 42 51.0	12 21.8	21 55.0	17 47.5	22 36.0	20 7.1	21 4.5	5 23.3	28 6.5	17 48.6	3 19.1	4 33.8
4	10 46 47.6	13 21.9	21 51.8	1♌27.3	24 29.0	20 29.4	21 48.7	5 35.9	28 6.9	17 49.7	3 20.2	4 32.9
5	10 50 44.1	14 22.0	21 48.7	15 35.9	26 20.9	20 49.8	22 32.7	5 48.4	28 7.2	17 50.6	3 21.2	4 32.0
6	10 54 40.7	15 22.1	21 45.5	0♍10.1	28 11.4	21 8.2	23 16.8	6 .9	28 7.4	17 51.6	3 22.2	4 31.1
7	10 58 37.2	16 22.1	21 42.3	15 3.6	0♈ .1	21 24.6	24 .8	6 13.3	28 7.5	17 52.4	3 23.2	4 30.1
8	11 2 33.8	17 22.1	21 39.1	0♎ 7.4	1 46.5	21 38.9	24 44.7	6 25.6	28 7.5	17 53.2	3 24.1	4 29.2
9	11 6 30.3	18 22.1	21 36.0	15 11.8	3 30.2	21 51.0	25 28.6	6 37.8	28R 7.4	17 54.0	3 25.0	4 28.1
10	11 10 26.9	19 22.0	21 32.8	0♏ 7.4	5 10.7	22 .9	26 12.5	6 50.0	28 7.2	17 54.7	3 25.9	4 27.1
11	11 14 23.4	20 21.9	21 29.6	14 47.3	6 47.4	22 8.6	26 56.3	7 2.1	28 6.9	17 55.4	3 26.7	4 26.0
12	11 18 20.0	21 21.8	21 26.4	29 7.1	8 19.9	22 14.0	27 40.1	7 14.2	28 6.5	17 56.0	3 27.5	4 24.9
13	11 22 16.5	22 21.7	21 23.2	13♐ 5.0	9 47.6	22 17.0	28 23.8	7 26.1	28 6.0	17 56.5	3 28.3	4 23.8
14	11 26 13.1	23 21.5	21 20.1	26 41.5	11 10.0	22 17.6	29 7.5	7 38.0	28 5.3	17 57.0	3 29.0	4 22.7
15	11 30 9.6	24 21.4	21 16.9	9♑58.4	12 26.6	22R15.9	29 51.2	7 49.9	28 4.7	17 57.5	3 29.8	4 21.6
16	11 34 6.2	25 21.1	21 13.7	22 57.9	13 37.1	22 11.6	0♉34.8	8 1.6	28 3.9	17 57.9	3 30.5	4 20.4
17	11 38 2.7	26 20.9	21 10.5	5♒42.4	14 40.8	22 4.9	1 18.4	8 13.2	28 3.0	17 58.2	3 31.1	4 19.1
18	11 41 59.3	27 20.6	21 7.4	18 14.3	15 37.6	21 55.7	2 1.9	8 24.8	28 1.9	17 58.5	3 31.7	4 17.9
19	11 45 55.9	28 20.3	21 4.2	0♓35.2	16 27.0	21 44.0	2 45.4	8 36.2	28 .8	17 58.7	3 32.3	4 16.6
20	11 49 52.4	29 19.9	21 1.0	12 46.7	17 8.8	21 29.8	3 28.8	8 47.6	27 59.6	17 58.9	3 32.9	4 15.3
21	11 53 49.0	0♈19.6	20 57.8	24 50.2	17 42.8	21 13.2	4 12.2	8 58.9	27 58.3	17 59.0	3 33.4	4 14.0
22	11 57 45.5	1 19.2	20 54.6	6♈46.7	18 8.9	20 54.2	4 55.6	9 10.1	27 56.9	17 59.1	3 33.8	4 12.7
23	12 1 42.1	2 18.7	20 51.5	18 38.0	18 27.0	20 32.9	5 38.9	9 21.2	27 55.4	17 59.1	3 34.3	4 11.3
24	12 5 38.6	3 18.2	20 48.3	0♉25.8	18 37.1	20 9.3	6 22.2	9 32.3	27 53.8	17 59.1	3 34.7	4 9.9
25	12 9 35.2	4 17.7	20 45.1	12 12.8	18 39.3	19 43.5	7 5.4	9 43.2	27 52.1	17R59.0	3 35.1	4 8.6
26	12 13 31.7	5 17.2	20 41.9	24 2.0	18R33.9	19 15.7	7 48.5	9 54.0	27 50.3	17 58.8	3 35.4	4 7.1
27	12 17 28.3	6 16.6	20 38.8	5♊57.2	18 21.1	18 46.0	8 31.7	10 4.7	27 48.5	17 58.6	3 35.7	4 5.7
28	12 21 24.8	7 15.9	20 35.6	18 2.9	18 1.4	18 14.6	9 14.8	10 15.3	27 46.5	17 58.4	3 36.0	4 4.2
29	12 25 21.4	8 15.3	20 32.4	0♋23.8	17 35.3	17 41.5	9 57.8	10 25.9	27 44.4	17 58.1	3 36.3	4 2.8
30	12 29 17.9	9 14.6	20 29.2	13 4.7	17 3.4	17 7.1	10 40.8	10 36.3	27 42.3	17 57.8	3 36.5	4 1.3
31	12 33 14.5	10 13.8	20 26.0	26 10.1	16 26.4	16 31.5	11 23.7	10 46.6	27 40.0	17 57.3	3 36.7	3 59.8

LATITUDE

DAY	EPHEM. SID. TIME	☉	☊	☾	☿	♀	♂	♃	♄	♅	♆	♇
1	10 34 57.9	0 .0	0 .0	2N36.2	1S 2.0	5N12.6	0S 6.0	0S21.3	2N14.0	0S .7	1N 7.6	17N 4.0
4	10 46 47.6	0 .0	0 .0	4 46.2	0 33.6	5 41.0	0 3.7	0 21.7	2 14.6	0 .7	1 7.6	17 5.3
7	10 58 37.2	0 .0	0 .0	4 35.6	0 .1	6 8.9	0 1.4	0 22.1	2 15.1	0 .7	1 7.7	17 6.6
10	11 10 26.9	0 .0	0 .0	1 43.9	0N37.3	6 35.8	0N .8	0 22.5	2 15.7	0 .8	1 7.8	17 7.9
13	11 22 16.5	0 .0	0 .0	2S .6	1 16.9	7 1.0	0 3.0	0 22.9	2 16.2	0 .8	1 7.9	17 9.0
16	11 34 6.2	0 .0	0 .0	4 33.2	1 56.0	7 23.7	0 5.2	0 23.3	2 16.7	0 .8	1 8.0	17 10.2
19	11 45 55.9	0 .0	0 .0	5 .3	2 31.7	7 42.9	0 7.3	0 23.8	2 17.3	0 .9	1 8.1	17 11.2
22	11 57 45.5	0 .0	0 .0	3 27.1	3 .5	7 57.4	0 9.4	0 24.2	2 17.8	0 .9	1 8.2	17 12.2
25	12 9 35.2	0 .0	0 .0	0 35.8	3 19.1	8 6.1	0 11.5	0 24.7	2 18.3	0 .9	1 8.3	17 13.0
28	12 21 24.8	0 .0	0 .0	2N32.0	3 24.6	8 7.9	0 13.5	0 25.1	2 18.7	0 1.0	1 8.4	17 13.8
31	12 33 14.5	0 .0	0 .0	4 47.4	3 14.9	8 2.0	0 15.5	0 25.6	2 19.2	0 1.0	1 8.4	17 14.6

RIGHT ASCENSION

DAY	EPHEM. SID. TIME	☉	☊	☾	☿	♀	♂	♃	♄	♅	♆	♇
1	10 34 57.9	11♓52.1	19♉36.4	20♊58.1	20♓ 6.8	15♈46.7	18♈ 7.9	7♒24.4	26♏21.5	16♐42.6	3♑32.8	7♏59.5
2	10 38 54.4	12 48.3	19 33.2	5♋ 9.6	21 48.6	16 7.4	18 49.0	7 37.5	26 22.1	16 43.8	3 34.0	7R58.9
3	10 42 51.0	13 44.3	19 29.9	19 54.1	23 29.6	16 26.4	19 30.0	7 50.5	26 22.7	16 45.0	3 35.1	7 58.3
4	10 46 47.6	14 40.3	19 26.7	4♌51.0	25 9.5	16 43.8	20 11.1	8 3.5	26 23.1	16 46.1	3 36.3	7 57.7
5	10 50 44.1	15 36.1	19 23.5	19 39.2	26 48.1	16 59.3	20 52.2	8 16.4	26 23.5	16 47.2	3 37.4	7 57.0
6	10 54 40.7	16 31.8	19 20.2	4♍ 4.4	28 25.0	17 13.1	21 33.3	8 29.2	26 23.7	16 48.1	3 38.5	7 56.3
7	10 58 37.2	17 27.4	19 17.0	18 2.7	0♈ .1	17 25.0	22 14.4	8 41.9	26 23.9	16 49.1	3 39.5	7 55.6
8	11 2 33.8	18 22.9	19 13.8	1♎39.7	1 32.9	17 34.9	22 55.6	8 54.6	26 23.9	16 50.0	3 40.5	7 54.8
9	11 6 30.3	19 18.3	19 10.5	15 7.0	3 3.2	17 42.9	23 36.7	9 7.2	26 23.9	16 50.8	3 41.5	7 54.0
10	11 10 26.9	20 13.6	19 7.3	28 38.7	4 30.3	17 48.9	24 18.0	9 19.7	26R23.7	16 51.5	3 42.4	7 53.2
11	11 14 23.4	21 8.9	19 4.1	12♏27.9	5 54.1	17 52.7	24 59.2	9 32.1	26 23.4	16 52.3	3 43.3	7 52.4
12	11 18 20.0	22 4.0	19 .9	26 42.7	7 14.0	17 54.5	25 40.5	9 44.4	26 23.1	16 52.9	3 44.2	7 51.5
13	11 22 16.5	22 59.1	18 57.6	11♐23.0	8 29.6	17R54.2	26 21.8	9 56.7	26 22.6	16 53.5	3 45.0	7 50.7
14	11 26 13.1	23 54.2	18 54.4	26 18.6	9 40.4	17 51.6	27 3.2	10 8.9	26 22.0	16 54.0	3 45.9	7 49.8
15	11 30 9.6	24 49.2	18 51.2	11♑10.8	10 46.2	17 47.0	27 44.6	10 21.0	26 21.3	16 54.6	3 46.7	7 48.9
16	11 34 6.2	25 44.1	18 47.9	25 38.1	11 46.4	17 40.1	28 26.0	10 33.0	26 20.6	16 55.0	3 47.4	7 47.9
17	11 38 2.7	26 38.9	18 44.7	9♒24.0	12 40.7	17 30.9	29 7.5	10 44.9	26 19.7	16 55.3	3 48.1	7 46.9
18	11 41 59.3	27 33.8	18 41.5	22 20.7	13 28.9	17 19.6	29 49.0	10 56.7	26 18.7	16 55.6	3 48.8	7 45.9
19	11 45 55.9	28 28.5	18 38.3	4♓29.3	14 10.5	17 6.2	0♉30.6	11 8.4	26 17.6	16 55.9	3 49.4	7 44.9
20	11 49 52.4	29 23.3	18 35.0	15 57.1	14 45.4	16 50.5	1 12.2	11 20.0	26 16.4	16 56.1	3 50.0	7 43.8
21	11 53 49.0	0♈18.0	18 31.8	26 55.0	15 13.4	16 32.8	1 53.8	11 31.6	26 15.1	16 56.2	3 50.5	7 42.7
22	11 57 45.5	1 12.6	18 28.6	7♈35.3	15 34.5	16 13.1	2 35.5	11 43.0	26 13.7	16 56.3	3 51.0	7 41.6
23	12 1 42.1	2 7.3	18 25.4	18 10.8	15 48.5	15 51.5	3 17.2	11 54.3	26 12.2	16 56.3	3 51.5	7 40.5
24	12 5 38.6	3 1.9	18 22.2	28 54.1	15 55.5	15 27.9	3 59.0	12 5.5	26 10.6	16 56.3	3 52.0	7 39.3
25	12 9 35.2	3 56.5	18 18.9	9♉57.5	15 55.7	15 2.7	4 40.9	12 16.7	26 8.9	16R56.2	3 52.4	7 38.2
26	12 13 31.7	4 51.1	18 15.7	21 32.1	15R49.3	14 35.9	5 22.7	12 27.7	26 7.1	16 56.0	3 52.8	7 37.0
27	12 17 28.3	5 45.7	18 12.5	3♊46.6	15 36.6	14 7.6	6 4.7	12 38.6	26 5.2	16 55.8	3 53.1	7 35.8
28	12 21 24.8	6 40.3	18 9.3	16 45.5	15 18.1	13 38.0	6 46.6	12 49.4	26 3.3	16 55.5	3 53.4	7 34.6
29	12 25 21.4	7 34.9	18 6.1	0♋26.7	14 54.2	13 7.4	7 28.6	13 .1	26 1.2	16 55.2	3 53.7	7 33.3
30	12 29 17.9	8 29.5	18 2.8	14 40.3	14 25.6	12 35.8	8 10.7	13 10.7	25 59.0	16 54.8	3 53.9	7 32.0
31	12 33 14.5	9 24.1	17 59.6	29 10.1	13 53.1	12 3.5	8 52.8	13 21.2	25 56.8	16 54.4	3 54.1	7 30.8

DECLINATION

DAY	EPHEM. SID. TIME	☉	☊	☾	☿	♀	♂	♃	♄	♅	♆	♇
1	10 34 57.9	7S41.1	0N19.1	25N47.5	5S22.9	12N21.9	7N34.6	19S22.3	17S33.6	22S53.5	22S16.6	3N 3.5
4	10 46 47.6	6 32.4	0 19.1	24 29.2	2 42.3	13 15.8	8 26.6	19 13.4	17 33.4	22 53.8	22 16.4	3 5.5
7	10 58 37.2	5 22.8	0 19.1	10 7.2	0 .1	14 2.6	9 17.7	19 4.6	17 33.0	22 54.1	22 16.3	3 7.6
10	11 10 26.9	4 12.6	0 19.0	9S53.7	2N37.7	14 41.3	10 7.9	18 55.8	17 32.4	22 54.4	22 16.1	3 9.8
13	11 22 16.5	3 1.9	0 19.0	24 22.0	5 3.5	15 10.7	10 57.2	18 47.0	17 31.6	22 54.6	22 16.0	3 11.9
16	11 34 6.2	1 50.8	0 18.9	25 58.5	7 9.4	15 29.6	11 45.5	18 38.3	17 30.6	22 54.7	22 15.8	3 14.0
19	11 45 55.9	0 39.7	0 18.9	15 56.6	8 48.1	15 36.8	12 32.7	18 29.7	17 29.4	22 54.8	22 15.7	3 16.2
22	11 57 45.5	0N31.5	0 18.8	0 28.7	9 53.9	15 31.2	13 18.8	18 21.2	17 28.0	22 54.9	22 15.6	3 18.3
25	12 9 35.2	1 42.4	0 18.8	14N56.1	10 22.7	15 12.2	14 3.7	18 12.9	17 26.5	22 54.9	22 15.4	3 20.5
28	12 21 24.8	2 53.0	0 18.7	25 25.8	10 13.2	14 39.6	14 47.4	18 4.7	17 24.8	22 54.9	22 15.3	3 22.6
31	12 33 14.5	4 3.1	0 18.7	25 37.3	9 27.7	13 54.1	15 29.8	17 56.7	17 22.9	22 54.8	22 15.2	3 24.7

APRIL 1985

LONGITUDE

DAY	EPHEM. SID. TIME h m s	☉ ° ′	☊ ° ′	☽ ° ′	☿ ° ′	♀ ° ′	♂ ° ′	♃ ° ′	♄ ° ′	♅ ° ′	♆ ° ′	♇ ° ′
1	12 37 11.0	11♈13.0	20♉22.9	9♌43.1	15♈45.2	15♈55.0	12♉ 6.6	10♒56.8	27♏37.7	17♐56.9	3♑36.8	3♏58.3
2	12 41 7.6	12 12.2	20 19.7	23 45.2	15R .7	15R17.7	12 49.5	11 6.9	27R35.3	17R56.4	3 36.9	3R56.7
3	12 45 4.2	13 11.4	20 16.5	8♍15.0	14 13.8	14 40.0	13 32.3	11 16.9	27 32.8	17 55.8	3 37.0	3 55.2
4	12 49 .7	14 10.5	20 13.3	23 8.2	13 25.5	14 2.0	14 15.0	11 26.8	27 30.2	17 55.2	3 37.0	3 53.6
5	12 52 57.3	15 9.6	20 10.2	8♎17.2	12 36.8	13 24.2	14 57.8	11 36.6	27 27.6	17 54.6	3 37.1	3 52.1
6	12 56 53.8	16 8.6	20 7.0	23 32.3	11 48.6	12 46.6	15 40.4	11 46.2	27 24.9	17 53.9	3 37.1	3 50.5
7	13 0 50.4	17 7.6	20 3.8	8♏43.2	11 1.8	12 9.6	16 23.1	11 55.8	27 22.1	17 53.2	3R37.0	3 48.9
8	13 4 46.9	18 6.6	20 .6	23 40.6	10 17.3	11 33.4	17 5.6	12 5.2	27 19.2	17 52.4	3 36.9	3 47.3
9	13 8 43.5	19 5.5	19 57.4	8♐17.6	9 35.7	10 58.3	17 48.1	12 14.5	27 16.2	17 51.5	3 36.8	3 45.7
10	13 12 40.0	20 4.4	19 54.3	22 30.2	8 57.7	10 24.4	18 30.6	12 23.7	27 13.1	17 50.6	3 36.7	3 44.1
11	13 16 36.6	21 3.3	19 51.1	6♑17.0	8 23.8	9 52.0	19 13.1	12 32.8	27 10.0	17 49.7	3 36.5	3 42.4
12	13 20 33.1	22 2.1	19 47.9	19 38.9	7 54.4	9 21.2	19 55.4	12 41.7	27 6.8	17 48.7	3 36.3	3 40.8
13	13 24 29.7	23 1.0	19 44.7	2♒38.0	7 29.9	8 52.3	20 37.8	12 50.5	27 3.6	17 47.6	3 36.0	3 39.1
14	13 28 26.2	23 59.7	19 41.6	15 17.7	7 10.5	8 25.3	21 20.1	12 59.2	27 .2	17 46.6	3 35.7	3 37.4
15	13 32 22.8	24 58.5	19 38.4	27 41.3	6 56.3	8 .4	22 2.4	13 7.8	26 56.8	17 45.4	3 35.4	3 35.8
16	13 36 19.4	25 57.2	19 35.2	9♓52.2	6 47.3	7 37.7	22 44.6	13 16.2	26 53.3	17 44.2	3 35.1	3 34.1
17	13 40 15.9	26 55.9	19 32.0	21 53.6	6 43.5	7 17.2	23 26.8	13 24.5	26 49.8	17 43.0	3 34.7	3 32.4
18	13 44 12.5	27 54.6	19 28.9	3♈48.0	6D44.9	6 59.1	24 8.9	13 32.7	26 46.2	17 41.8	3 34.3	3 30.7
19	13 48 9.0	28 53.3	19 25.7	15 38.1	6 51.5	6 43.4	24 51.0	13 40.7	26 42.5	17 40.4	3 33.9	3 29.0
20	13 52 5.6	29 51.9	19 22.5	27 26.0	7 3.0	6 30.1	25 33.1	13 48.6	26 38.8	17 39.1	3 33.4	3 27.3
21	13 56 2.1	0♉50.5	19 19.3	9♉13.9	7 19.3	6 19.2	26 15.1	13 56.4	26 35.0	17 37.7	3 32.9	3 25.6
22	13 59 58.7	1 49.0	19 16.1	21 3.9	7 40.2	6 10.8	26 57.0	14 4.0	26 31.2	17 36.3	3 32.3	3 24.0
23	14 3 55.2	2 47.5	19 13.0	2♊58.4	8 5.7	6 4.8	27 38.9	14 11.4	26 27.3	17 34.8	3 31.8	3 22.3
24	14 7 51.8	3 46.0	19 9.8	15 .1	8 35.4	6 1.2	28 20.8	14 18.8	26 23.4	17 33.3	3 31.2	3 20.6
25	14 11 48.3	4 44.4	19 6.6	27 12.0	9 9.3	6 .0	29 2.7	14 25.9	26 19.4	17 31.7	3 30.6	3 18.9
26	14 15 44.9	5 42.9	19 3.4	9♋37.5	9 47.2	6D 1.2	29 44.5	14 33.0	26 15.4	17 30.1	3 30.0	3 17.2
27	14 19 41.5	6 41.3	19 .3	22 20.0	10 28.8	6 4.7	0♊26.2	14 39.9	26 11.4	17 28.5	3 29.3	3 15.5
28	14 23 38.0	7 39.6	18 57.1	5♌22.9	11 14.0	6 10.4	1 7.9	14 46.6	26 7.2	17 26.8	3 28.6	3 13.8
29	14 27 34.6	8 37.9	18 53.9	18 49.3	12 2.7	6 18.4	1 49.6	14 53.2	26 3.1	17 25.1	3 27.8	3 12.1
30	14 31 31.1	9 36.2	18 50.7	2♍40.8	12 54.7	6 28.5	2 31.2	14 59.6	25 58.9	17 23.4	3 27.1	3 10.4

LATITUDE

DAY	SID. TIME	☉	☊	☽	☿	♀	♂	♃	♄	♅	♆	♇
1	12 37 11.0	0 .0	0 .0	5N 7.5	3N 8.2	7N58.2	0N16.1	0S25.8	2N19.3	0S 1.0	1N 8.5	17N14.8
4	12 49 .7	0 .0	0 .0	4 17.0	2 38.7	7 41.5	0 18.0	0 26.3	2 19.7	0 1.0	1 8.6	17 15.4
7	13 0 50.4	0 .0	0 .0	0 53.0	1 57.8	7 17.0	0 19.9	0 26.8	2 20.1	0 1.1	1 8.7	17 15.9
10	13 12 40.0	0 .0	0 .0	2S56.2	1 10.2	6 45.9	0 21.7	0 27.3	2 20.5	0 1.1	1 8.7	17 16.3
13	13 24 29.7	0 .0	0 .0	5 2.5	0 21.0	6 9.7	0 23.5	0 27.8	2 20.8	0 1.1	1 8.8	17 16.6
16	13 36 19.4	0 .0	0 .0	4 52.7	0S25.9	5 30.0	0 25.3	0 28.4	2 21.1	0 1.2	1 8.9	17 16.9
19	13 48 9.0	0 .0	0 .0	2 50.0	1 7.8	4 48.4	0 27.0	0 28.9	2 21.4	0 1.2	1 9.0	17 17.0
22	13 59 58.7	0 .0	0 .0	0N16.1	1 43.5	4 6.4	0 28.7	0 29.5	2 21.6	0 1.2	1 9.1	17 17.1
25	14 11 48.3	0 .0	0 .0	3 19.9	2 12.4	3 25.0	0 30.4	0 30.1	2 21.8	0 1.3	1 9.2	17 17.0
28	14 23 38.0	0 .0	0 .0	5 9.4	2 34.6	2 44.9	0 32.0	0 30.7	2 21.9	0 1.3	1 9.2	17 16.8

RIGHT ASCENSION

DAY	SID. TIME	☉	☊	☽	☿	♀	♂	♃	♄	♅	♆	♇
1	12 37 11.0	10♈18.7	17♉56.4	13♌38.6	13♈17.3	11♈30.8	9♉35.0	13♒31.5	25♏54.4	16♐53.9	3♑54.2	7♏29.5
2	12 41 7.6	11 13.4	17 53.2	27 52.3	12R39.1	10R57.8	10 17.2	13 41.8	25R52.0	16R53.3	3 54.4	7R28.2
3	12 45 4.2	12 8.0	17 50.0	11♍46.2	11 59.3	10 24.8	10 59.5	13 51.9	25 49.5	16 52.7	3 54.4	7 26.8
4	12 49 .7	13 2.8	17 46.7	25 24.1	11 18.9	9 52.1	11 41.8	14 1.9	25 46.9	16 52.1	3 54.5	7 25.5
5	12 52 57.3	13 57.5	17 43.5	8♎56.2	10 38.8	9 19.8	12 24.2	14 11.9	25 44.3	16 51.4	3 54.5	7 24.2
6	12 56 53.8	14 52.3	17 40.3	22 36.2	9 59.5	8 48.1	13 6.6	14 21.7	25 41.5	16 50.7	3 54.5	7 22.8
7	13 0 50.4	15 47.2	17 37.1	6♏37.6	9 22.0	8 17.3	13 49.1	14 31.3	25 38.7	16 49.9	3 54.5	7 21.4
8	13 4 46.9	16 42.1	17 33.9	21 10.0	8 46.9	7 47.6	14 31.6	14 40.9	25 35.7	16 49.0	3R54.4	7 20.0
9	13 8 43.5	17 37.0	17 30.7	6♐14.2	8 14.8	7 19.2	15 14.1	14 50.3	25 32.7	16 48.1	3 54.2	7 18.6
10	13 12 40.0	18 32.1	17 27.5	21 39.2	7 46.2	6 52.3	15 56.8	14 59.6	25 29.7	16 47.1	3 54.1	7 17.1
11	13 16 36.6	19 27.1	17 24.2	7♑ 3.1	7 21.5	6 26.9	16 39.4	15 8.8	25 26.5	16 46.1	3 53.9	7 15.7
12	13 20 33.1	20 22.3	17 21.0	22 .2	7 1.0	6 3.4	17 22.2	15 17.8	25 23.3	16 45.0	3 53.6	7 14.3
13	13 24 29.7	21 17.6	17 17.8	6♒10.4	6 44.9	5 41.7	18 4.9	15 26.7	25 20.0	16 43.9	3 53.4	7 12.8
14	13 28 26.2	22 12.9	17 14.6	19 24.6	6 33.3	5 22.0	18 47.8	15 35.5	25 16.6	16 42.7	3 53.1	7 11.3
15	13 32 22.8	23 8.3	17 11.4	1♓44.2	6 26.4	5 4.3	19 30.7	15 44.2	25 13.1	16 41.5	3 52.7	7 9.8
16	13 36 19.4	24 3.8	17 8.2	13 17.7	6 24.2	4 48.8	20 13.6	15 52.7	25 9.6	16 40.2	3 52.4	7 8.3
17	13 40 15.9	24 59.4	17 5.0	24 17.5	6D26.5	4 35.5	20 56.6	16 1.1	25 6.0	16 38.9	3 51.9	7 6.8
18	13 44 12.5	25 55.1	17 1.8	4♈56.9	6 33.3	4 24.4	21 39.7	16 9.3	25 2.4	16 37.5	3 51.5	7 5.3
19	13 48 9.0	26 50.9	16 58.6	15 29.7	6 44.6	4 15.5	22 22.8	16 17.4	24 58.7	16 36.1	3 51.0	7 3.8
20	13 52 5.6	27 46.8	16 55.4	26 8.7	7 .2	4 8.9	23 5.9	16 25.4	24 54.9	16 34.6	3 50.5	7 2.3
21	13 56 2.1	28 42.8	16 52.1	7♉ 6.4	7 19.9	4 4.5	23 49.1	16 33.2	24 51.1	16 33.1	3 50.0	7 .8
22	13 59 58.7	29 39.0	16 48.9	18 33.5	7 43.5	4 2.4	24 32.4	16 40.9	24 47.2	16 31.6	3 49.4	6 59.2
23	14 3 55.2	0♉35.2	16 45.7	0♊38.6	8 11.0	4 2.4	25 15.7	16 48.4	24 43.3	16 30.0	3 48.8	6 57.7
24	14 7 51.8	1 31.5	16 42.5	13 25.6	8 42.1	4D 4.6	25 59.0	16 55.8	24 39.3	16 28.3	3 48.2	6 56.2
25	14 11 48.3	2 28.0	16 39.3	26 52.2	9 16.8	4 9.0	26 42.4	17 3.1	24 35.3	16 26.6	3 47.5	6 54.6
26	14 15 44.9	3 24.6	16 36.1	10♋48.5	9 54.8	4 15.5	27 25.9	17 10.2	24 31.2	16 24.9	3 46.8	6 53.1
27	14 19 41.5	4 21.3	16 32.9	24 59.0	10 35.9	4 24.0	28 9.4	17 17.2	24 27.1	16 23.2	3 46.1	6 51.6
28	14 23 38.0	5 18.1	16 29.7	9♌ 6.9	11 20.2	4 34.5	28 52.9	17 23.9	24 22.9	16 21.4	3 45.3	6 50.0
29	14 27 34.6	6 15.0	16 26.5	22 59.8	12 7.3	4 47.0	29 36.5	17 30.6	24 18.7	16 19.5	3 44.5	6 48.5
30	14 31 31.1	7 12.1	16 23.3	6♍32.9	12 57.2	5 1.3	0♊20.1	17 37.1	24 14.5	16 17.6	3 43.7	6 46.9

DECLINATION

DAY	SID. TIME	☉	☊	☽	☿	♀	♂	♃	♄	♅	♆	♇
1	12 37 11.0	4N26.3	0N18.7	22N45.1	9N 5.7	13N36.4	15N43.7	17S54.0	17S22.3	22S54.8	22S15.2	3N25.4
4	12 49 .7	5 35.4	0 18.6	6 39.4	7 44.2	12 36.9	16 24.3	17 46.3	17 20.2	22 54.7	22 15.1	3 27.4
7	13 0 50.4	6 43.7	0 18.6	13S34.4	6 10.3	11 30.3	17 3.5	17 38.7	17 18.0	22 54.5	22 15.0	3 29.4
10	13 12 40.0	7 50.9	0 18.6	26 9.7	4 37.7	10 20.2	17 41.2	17 31.4	17 15.6	22 54.3	22 14.9	3 31.3
13	13 24 29.7	8 56.9	0 18.5	24 28.7	3 17.9	9 10.6	18 17.4	17 24.3	17 13.2	22 54.1	22 14.8	3 33.2
16	13 36 19.4	10 1.6	0 18.5	12 22.9	2 18.0	8 4.6	18 52.1	17 17.5	17 10.6	22 53.8	22 14.8	3 35.0
19	13 48 9.0	11 4.8	0 18.4	3N32.4	1 41.1	7 5.0	19 25.2	17 11.0	17 7.8	22 53.5	22 14.7	3 36.7
22	13 59 58.7	12 6.4	0 18.4	18 17.2	1 27.5	6 13.4	19 56.7	17 4.9	17 5.0	22 53.1	22 14.7	3 38.4
25	14 11 48.3	13 6.2	0 18.3	26 44.7	1 36.0	5 31.2	20 26.5	16 59.0	17 2.1	22 52.7	22 14.7	3 39.9
28	14 23 38.0	14 4.1	0 18.3	23 55.3	2 4.4	4 58.6	20 54.7	16 53.5	16 59.2	22 52.3	22 14.6	3 41.4

MAY 1985

LONGITUDE

DAY	EPHEM. SID. TIME (h m s)	☉ (° ′)	☊ (° ′)	☾ (° ′)	☿ (° ′)	♀ (° ′)	♂ (° ′)	♃ (° ′)	♄ (° ′)	♅ (° ′)	♆ (° ′)	♇ (° ′)
1	14 35 27.7	10♉34.4	18♉47.5	16♍57.4	13♈49.9	6♈40.7	3♊12.8	15♒ 5.9	25♏54.7	17♐21.6	3♑26.3	3♏ 8.8
2	14 39 24.2	11 32.7	18 44.4	1♎36.9	14 48.2	6 54.9	3 54.3	15 12.0	25 R 50.4	17 R 19.8	3 R 25.4	3 R 7.1
3	14 43 20.8	12 30.8	18 41.2	16 34.4	15 49.4	7 11.2	4 35.8	15 18.0	25 46.1	17 17.9	3 24.6	3 5.4
4	14 47 17.3	13 29.0	18 38.0	1♏42.4	16 53.4	7 29.4	5 17.2	15 23.8	25 41.8	17 16.0	3 23.7	3 3.7
5	14 51 13.9	14 27.1	18 34.8	16 52.1	18 .2	7 49.4	5 58.6	15 29.5	25 37.4	17 14.1	3 22.8	3 2.1
6	14 55 10.5	15 25.2	18 31.7	1♐54.1	19 9.6	8 11.3	6 39.9	15 34.9	25 33.1	17 12.2	3 21.9	3 .4
7	14 59 7.0	16 23.2	18 28.5	16 40.1	20 21.6	8 34.9	7 21.2	15 40.3	25 28.7	17 10.2	3 20.9	2 58.8
8	15 3 3.6	17 21.3	18 25.3	1♑ 3.7	21 36.1	9 .2	8 2.5	15 45.4	25 24.3	17 8.2	3 19.9	2 57.2
9	15 7 .1	18 19.3	18 22.1	15 1.5	22 53.0	9 27.1	8 43.7	15 50.4	25 19.8	17 6.1	3 18.9	2 55.5
10	15 10 56.7	19 17.2	18 19.0	28 32.2	24 12.3	9 55.6	9 24.9	15 55.2	25 15.4	17 4.1	3 17.9	2 53.9
11	15 14 53.2	20 15.2	18 15.8	11♒37.2	25 33.9	10 25.6	10 6.0	15 59.9	25 10.9	17 2.0	3 16.9	2 52.3
12	15 18 49.8	21 13.2	18 12.6	24 19.2	26 57.8	10 57.1	10 47.1	16 4.4	25 6.4	16 59.8	3 15.8	2 50.7
13	15 22 46.3	22 11.1	18 9.4	6♓41.8	28 23.9	11 29.9	11 28.2	16 8.7	25 2.0	16 57.7	3 14.7	2 49.1
14	15 26 42.9	23 9.0	18 6.2	18 49.5	29 52.3	12 4.1	12 9.2	16 12.8	24 57.5	16 55.5	3 13.5	2 47.6
15	15 30 39.5	24 6.9	18 3.1	0♈46.3	1♉22.9	12 39.6	12 50.2	16 16.8	24 53.0	16 53.3	3 12.4	2 46.0
16	15 34 36.0	25 4.7	17 59.9	12 36.6	2 55.7	13 16.3	13 31.2	16 20.6	24 48.5	16 51.1	3 11.2	2 44.5
17	15 38 32.6	26 2.6	17 56.7	24 23.9	4 30.6	13 54.2	14 12.1	16 24.2	24 44.0	16 48.9	3 10.1	2 43.0
18	15 42 29.1	27 .4	17 53.5	6♉11.6	6 7.7	14 33.2	14 53.0	16 27.7	24 39.5	16 46.6	3 8.9	2 41.5
19	15 46 25.7	27 58.2	17 50.4	18 2.5	7 47.0	15 13.3	15 33.9	16 30.9	24 35.0	16 44.4	3 7.6	2 40.0
20	15 50 22.2	28 56.0	17 47.2	29 59.1	9 28.4	15 54.5	16 14.7	16 34.0	24 30.6	16 42.1	3 6.4	2 38.5
21	15 54 18.8	29 53.7	17 44.0	12♊ 3.4	11 11.9	16 36.6	16 55.4	16 36.9	24 26.1	16 39.7	3 5.1	2 37.1
22	15 58 15.4	0♊51.5	17 40.8	24 17.2	12 57.6	17 19.7	17 36.2	16 39.6	24 21.6	16 37.4	3 3.8	2 35.6
23	16 2 11.9	1 49.2	17 37.7	6♋42.2	14 45.5	18 3.8	18 16.8	16 42.1	24 17.2	16 35.1	3 2.5	2 34.2
24	16 6 8.5	2 46.8	17 34.5	19 20.1	16 35.5	18 48.7	18 57.5	16 44.4	24 12.7	16 32.7	3 1.2	2 32.8
25	16 10 5.0	3 44.5	17 31.3	2♌12.7	18 27.6	19 34.5	19 38.1	16 46.6	24 8.3	16 30.3	2 59.8	2 31.4
26	16 14 1.6	4 42.1	17 28.1	15 21.4	20 21.8	20 21.1	20 18.7	16 48.5	24 3.9	16 27.9	2 58.4	2 30.0
27	16 17 58.1	5 39.7	17 24.9	28 47.8	22 18.1	21 8.5	20 59.2	16 50.3	23 59.6	16 25.5	2 57.1	2 28.7
28	16 21 54.7	6 37.3	17 21.8	12♍33.0	24 16.4	21 56.6	21 39.7	16 51.9	23 55.2	16 23.1	2 55.7	2 27.3
29	16 25 51.3	7 34.9	17 18.6	26 37.1	26 16.7	22 45.5	22 20.1	16 53.3	23 50.9	16 20.7	2 54.2	2 26.0
30	16 29 47.8	8 32.4	17 15.4	10♎59.2	28 18.9	23 35.1	23 .5	16 54.5	23 46.7	16 18.2	2 52.8	2 24.7
31	16 33 44.4	9 29.9	17 12.2	25 36.8	0♊23.0	24 25.3	23 40.9	16 55.5	23 42.4	16 15.8	2 51.4	2 23.5

LATITUDE

DAY	EPHEM. SID. TIME	☉	☊	☾	☿	♀	♂	♃	♄	♅	♆	♇
1	14 35 27.7	0 .0	0 .0	4N38.4	2S50.1	2N 6.9	0N33.6	0S31.3	2N22.0	0S 1.3	1N 9.3	17N16.6
4	14 47 17.3	0 .0	0 .0	1 30.3	2 59.3	1 31.2	0 35.1	0 31.9	2 22.1	0 1.4	1 9.4	17 16.3
7	14 59 7.0	0 .0	0 .0	2S31.9	3 2.5	0 58.1	0 36.6	0 32.5	2 22.1	0 1.4	1 9.4	17 15.8
10	15 10 56.7	0 .0	0 .0	4 59.3	3 .0	0 27.5	0 38.0	0 33.2	2 22.1	0 1.4	1 9.5	17 15.3
13	15 22 46.3	0 .0	0 .0	5 1.3	2 52.1	0S .4	0 39.5	0 33.8	2 22.0	0 1.5	1 9.5	17 14.7
16	15 34 36.0	0 .0	0 .0	3 5.2	2 39.0	0 25.9	0 40.9	0 34.5	2 21.9	0 1.5	1 9.6	17 14.0
19	15 46 25.7	0 .0	0 .0	0 1.1	2 21.2	0 48.8	0 42.2	0 35.1	2 21.7	0 1.5	1 9.6	17 13.2
22	15 58 15.4	0 .0	0 .0	3N 6.7	1 58.9	1 9.5	0 43.5	0 35.8	2 21.5	0 1.6	1 9.7	17 12.4
25	16 10 5.0	0 .0	0 .0	5 4.0	1 32.8	1 27.9	0 44.8	0 36.5	2 21.3	0 1.6	1 9.7	17 11.4
28	16 21 54.7	0 .0	0 .0	4 47.7	1 3.5	1 44.2	0 46.1	0 37.2	2 21.0	0 1.6	1 9.8	17 10.4
31	16 33 44.4	0 .0	0 .0	2 1.1	0 32.0	1 58.5	0 47.3	0 37.9	2 20.7	0 1.7	1 9.8	17 9.3

RIGHT ASCENSION

DAY	EPHEM. SID. TIME	☉	☊	☾	☿	♀	♂	♃	♄	♅	♆	♇
1	14 35 27.7	8♉ 9.3	16♉20.1	19♍49.8	13♈49.8	5♈17.5	1♊ 3.7	17♒43.4	24♏10.2	16♐15.7	3♑42.8	6♏45.4
2	14 39 24.2	9 6.6	16 16.9	3♎ .8	14 45.0	5 35.5	1 47.4	17 49.6	24 R 5.9	16 R 13.7	3 R 41.9	6 R 43.8
3	14 43 20.8	10 4.0	16 13.7	16 20.4	15 42.7	5 55.2	2 31.1	17 55.6	24 1.5	16 11.7	3 41.0	6 42.3
4	14 47 17.3	11 1.6	16 10.5	0♏ 4.4	16 42.8	6 16.5	3 14.8	18 1.4	23 57.1	16 9.7	3 40.1	6 40.8
5	14 51 13.9	11 59.3	16 7.3	14 26.3	17 45.3	6 39.5	3 58.6	18 7.1	23 52.7	16 7.6	3 39.1	6 39.2
6	14 55 10.5	12 57.2	16 4.1	29 31.9	18 50.1	7 4.0	4 42.4	18 12.6	23 48.3	16 5.5	3 38.1	6 37.7
7	14 59 7.0	13 55.2	16 .9	15♐14.3	19 57.1	7 30.0	5 26.3	18 18.0	23 43.8	16 3.4	3 37.1	6 36.2
8	15 3 3.6	14 53.3	15 57.7	1♑11.4	21 6.3	7 57.4	6 10.2	18 23.2	23 39.3	16 1.2	3 36.0	6 34.6
9	15 7 .1	15 51.6	15 54.5	16 51.8	22 17.7	8 26.3	6 54.1	18 28.3	23 34.8	15 59.0	3 34.9	6 33.1
10	15 10 56.7	16 50.1	15 51.3	1♒46.5	23 31.3	8 56.5	7 38.0	18 33.1	23 30.3	15 56.8	3 33.8	6 31.6
11	15 14 53.2	17 48.6	15 48.1	15 39.2	24 47.0	9 27.9	8 22.0	18 37.8	23 25.8	15 54.5	3 32.7	6 30.1
12	15 18 49.8	18 47.4	15 44.9	28 27.9	26 4.9	10 .6	9 6.0	18 42.4	23 21.2	15 52.2	3 31.5	6 28.6
13	15 22 46.3	19 46.3	15 41.7	10♓20.9	27 25.0	10 34.5	9 50.0	18 46.7	23 16.7	15 49.9	3 30.3	6 27.1
14	15 26 42.9	20 45.3	15 38.5	21 31.8	28 47.2	11 9.5	10 34.1	18 50.9	23 12.1	15 47.5	3 29.1	6 25.6
15	15 30 39.5	21 44.5	15 35.3	2♈15.8	0♉11.6	11 45.6	11 18.2	18 54.9	23 7.6	15 45.2	3 27.8	6 24.1
16	15 34 36.0	22 43.8	15 32.1	12 48.1	1 38.2	12 22.7	12 2.2	18 58.8	23 3.0	15 42.8	3 26.6	6 22.6
17	15 38 32.6	23 43.3	15 28.9	23 23.3	3 7.2	13 .9	12 46.4	19 2.5	22 58.5	15 40.4	3 25.3	6 21.2
18	15 42 29.1	24 42.9	15 25.8	4♉14.9	4 38.4	13 40.0	13 30.5	19 6.0	22 53.9	15 37.9	3 24.0	6 19.8
19	15 46 25.7	25 42.7	15 22.6	15 35.1	6 12.0	14 20.0	14 14.7	19 9.3	22 49.4	15 35.5	3 22.7	6 18.3
20	15 50 22.2	26 42.5	15 19.4	27 33.4	7 48.0	15 .9	14 58.8	19 12.4	22 44.8	15 33.0	3 21.3	6 16.9
21	15 54 18.8	27 42.6	15 16.2	10♊14.8	9 26.6	15 42.6	15 43.0	19 15.3	22 40.3	15 30.5	3 20.0	6 15.5
22	15 58 15.4	28 42.7	15 13.0	23 37.6	11 7.6	16 25.2	16 27.2	19 18.1	22 35.7	15 28.0	3 18.6	6 14.1
23	16 2 11.9	29 43.0	15 9.8	7♋31.5	12 51.3	17 8.6	17 11.3	19 20.6	22 31.2	15 25.4	3 17.1	6 12.7
24	16 6 8.5	0♊43.4	15 6.6	21 39.8	14 37.6	17 52.7	17 55.5	19 23.0	22 26.7	15 22.9	3 15.7	6 11.3
25	16 10 5.0	1 44.0	15 3.4	5♌43.8	16 26.6	18 37.5	18 39.7	19 25.2	22 22.2	15 20.3	3 14.2	6 9.9
26	16 14 1.6	2 44.6	15 .2	19 28.9	18 18.5	19 23.1	19 23.9	19 27.3	22 17.8	15 17.7	3 12.8	6 8.6
27	16 17 58.1	3 45.4	14 57.0	2♍49.0	20 13.1	20 9.4	20 8.1	19 29.1	22 13.4	15 15.1	3 11.3	6 7.3
28	16 21 54.7	4 46.3	14 53.9	15 46.8	22 10.6	20 56.3	20 52.2	19 30.7	22 8.9	15 12.5	3 9.8	6 5.9
29	16 25 51.3	5 47.3	14 50.7	28 32.4	24 11.0	21 43.9	21 36.4	19 32.2	22 4.6	15 9.9	3 8.2	6 4.6
30	16 29 47.8	6 48.4	14 47.5	11♎20.7	26 14.1	22 32.1	22 20.5	19 33.5	22 .2	15 7.3	3 6.7	6 3.4
31	16 33 44.4	7 49.6	14 44.3	24 29.0	28 20.1	23 20.9	23 4.7	19 34.6	21 55.9	15 4.6	3 5.1	6 2.1

DECLINATION

DAY	EPHEM. SID. TIME	☉	☊	☾	☿	♀	♂	♃	♄	♅	♆	♇
1	14 35 27.7	14N59.8	0N18.2	9N25.3	2N50.7	4N35.7	21N21.1	16S48.5	16S56.2	22S51.9	22S14.6	3N42.8
4	14 47 17.3	15 53.3	0 18.2	10S39.4	3 52.6	4 22.2	21 45.7	16 43.8	16 53.1	22 51.4	22 14.6	3 44.1
7	14 59 7.0	16 44.4	0 18.1	25 17.6	5 8.2	4 17.6	22 8.5	16 39.5	16 50.0	22 50.8	22 14.6	3 45.2
10	15 10 56.7	17 33.1	0 18.1	25 20.3	6 35.8	4 21.3	22 29.6	16 35.7	16 46.9	22 50.3	22 14.6	3 46.3
13	15 22 46.3	18 19.1	0 18.1	13 42.9	8 13.5	4 32.5	22 48.8	16 32.3	16 43.8	22 49.7	22 14.7	3 47.3
16	15 34 36.0	19 2.3	0 18.0	2N 8.3	9 59.8	4 50.6	23 6.1	16 29.3	16 40.7	22 49.1	22 14.7	3 48.1
19	15 46 25.7	19 42.7	0 18.0	17 11.5	11 52.8	5 14.7	23 21.6	16 26.9	16 37.6	22 48.4	22 14.7	3 48.8
22	15 58 15.4	20 20.0	0 17.9	26 25.7	13 50.5	5 44.1	23 35.2	16 24.9	16 34.6	22 47.8	22 14.8	3 49.4
25	16 10 5.0	20 54.2	0 17.9	24 36.1	15 50.3	6 18.2	23 47.0	16 23.4	16 31.6	22 47.1	22 14.8	3 49.8
28	16 21 54.7	21 25.1	0 17.8	11 16.7	17 49.0	6 56.3	23 56.8	16 22.5	16 28.7	22 46.4	22 14.9	3 50.2
31	16 33 44.4	21 52.7	0 17.8	8S 1.3	19 42.8	7 37.8	24 4.7	16 22.1	16 25.8	22 45.7	22 15.0	3 50.4

JUNE 1985

LONGITUDE

DAY	EPHEM. SID. TIME	☉	☊	☽	☿	♀	♂	♃	♄	♅	♆	♇
	h m s	° ′	° ′	° ′	° ′	° ′	° ′	° ′	° ′	° ′	° ′	° ′
1	16 37 40.9	10♊27.4	17♉ 9.1	10♏25.2	2♊28.7	25♈16.3	24♊21.3	16♒56.3	23♏38.2	16♐13.3	2♑49.9	2♏22.2
2	16 41 37.5	11 24.9	17 5.9	25 18.4	4 35.9	26 7.8	25 1.6	16 57.0	23 R 34.0	16 R 10.9	2 R 48.4	2 R 21.0
3	16 45 34.1	12 22.3	17 2.7	10♐ 8.9	6 44.6	27 .0	25 41.8	16 57.4	23 29.9	16 8.4	2 47.0	2 19.8
4	16 49 30.6	13 19.8	16 59.5	24 49.2	8 54.4	27 52.8	26 22.1	16 57.7	23 25.8	16 5.9	2 45.5	2 18.6
5	16 53 27.2	14 17.2	16 56.4	9♑12.3	11 5.1	28 46.1	27 2.2	16 57.8	23 21.7	16 3.5	2 44.0	2 17.5
6	16 57 23.7	15 14.6	16 53.2	23 13.1	13 16.6	29 40.0	27 42.4	16 R 57.6	23 17.7	16 1.0	2 42.4	2 16.4
7	17 1 20.3	16 12.0	16 50.0	6♒48.7	15 28.6	0♉34.5	28 22.6	16 57.4	23 13.8	15 58.6	2 41.0	2 15.3
8	17 5 16.8	17 9.4	16 46.8	19 58.6	17 40.7	1 29.4	29 2.7	16 56.9	23 9.9	15 56.1	2 39.4	2 14.2
9	17 9 13.4	18 6.8	16 43.7	2♓44.3	19 52.7	2 24.9	29 42.7	16 56.2	23 6.0	15 53.6	2 37.9	2 13.2
10	17 13 10.0	19 4.1	16 40.5	15 9.2	22 4.4	3 20.8	0♋22.8	16 55.3	23 2.2	15 51.2	2 36.3	2 12.2
11	17 17 6.5	20 1.5	16 37.3	27 17.5	24 15.4	4 17.2	1 2.8	16 54.2	22 58.5	15 48.7	2 34.7	2 11.2
12	17 21 3.1	20 58.8	16 34.1	9♈13.9	26 25.5	5 14.0	1 42.7	16 53.0	22 54.8	15 46.3	2 33.2	2 10.2
13	17 24 59.6	21 56.2	16 30.9	21 3.4	28 34.6	6 11.3	2 22.7	16 51.5	22 51.1	15 43.8	2 31.6	2 9.3
14	17 28 56.2	22 53.5	16 27.8	2♉50.9	0♋42.3	7 9.0	3 2.6	16 49.9	22 47.5	15 41.3	2 30.0	2 8.4
15	17 32 52.8	23 50.8	16 24.6	14 40.6	2 48.5	8 7.0	3 42.4	16 48.0	22 44.0	15 38.9	2 28.4	2 7.5
16	17 36 49.3	24 48.2	16 21.4	26 36.5	4 53.0	9 5.5	4 22.3	16 46.0	22 40.5	15 36.5	2 26.8	2 6.6
17	17 40 45.9	25 45.5	16 18.2	8♊41.7	6 55.8	10 4.3	5 2.1	16 43.8	22 37.1	15 34.0	2 25.2	2 5.8
18	17 44 42.4	26 42.8	16 15.1	20 58.4	8 56.6	11 3.5	5 41.9	16 41.4	22 33.8	15 31.6	2 23.6	2 5.0
19	17 48 39.0	27 40.1	16 11.9	3♋28.3	10 55.4	12 3.0	6 21.6	16 38.8	22 30.5	15 29.2	2 22.0	2 4.2
20	17 52 35.5	28 37.3	16 8.7	16 11.9	12 52.1	13 2.9	7 1.3	16 36.1	22 27.3	15 26.8	2 20.3	2 3.5
21	17 56 32.1	29 34.6	16 5.5	29 9.4	14 46.7	14 3.1	7 41.0	16 33.1	22 24.2	15 24.5	2 18.7	2 2.8
22	18 0 28.7	0♋31.9	16 2.4	12♌20.4	16 39.1	15 3.5	8 20.7	16 30.0	22 21.2	15 22.1	2 17.1	2 2.1
23	18 4 25.2	1 29.1	15 59.2	25 44.3	18 29.3	16 4.3	9 .3	16 26.7	22 18.2	15 19.8	2 15.5	2 1.5
24	18 8 21.8	2 26.4	15 56.0	9♍20.5	20 17.3	17 5.4	9 39.9	16 23.2	22 15.3	15 17.4	2 13.9	2 .9
25	18 12 18.3	3 23.6	15 52.8	23 8.5	22 3.0	18 6.8	10 19.5	16 19.5	22 12.5	15 15.1	2 12.2	2 .3
26	18 16 14.9	4 20.9	15 49.7	7♎ 7.7	23 46.5	19 8.4	10 59.0	16 15.7	22 9.7	15 12.8	2 10.6	1 59.7
27	18 20 11.5	5 18.1	15 46.5	21 17.3	25 27.7	20 10.4	11 38.5	16 11.7	22 7.0	15 10.6	2 9.0	1 59.2
28	18 24 8.0	6 15.3	15 43.3	5♏36.1	27 6.7	21 12.6	12 18.0	16 7.5	22 4.5	15 8.3	2 7.4	1 58.8
29	18 28 4.6	7 12.5	15 40.1	20 1.8	28 43.4	22 15.0	12 57.4	16 3.2	22 2,0	15 6.1	2 5.8	1 58.3
30	18 32 1.1	8 9.7	15 36.9	4♐31.1	0♌17.8	23 17.7	13 36.9	15 58.7	21 59.6	15 3.9	2 4.2	1 57.9

LATITUDE

DAY	EPHEM. SID. TIME	☉	☊	☽	☿	♀	♂	♃	♄	♅	♆	♇
1	16 37 40.9	0 .0	0 .0	0N42.4	0S21.3	2S 2.9	0N47.7	0S38.1	2N20.6	0S 1.7	1N 9.8	17N 8.9
4	16 49 30.6	0 .0	0 .0	3S 8.3	0N10.8	2 14.6	0 48.8	0 38.8	2 20.2	0 1.7	1 9.8	17 7.7
7	17 1 20.3	0 .0	0 .0	5 7.8	0 41.4	2 24.6	0 50.0	0 39.5	2 19.8	0 1.7	1 9.8	17 6.4
10	17 13 10.0	0 .0	0 .0	4 38.6	1 8.5	2 32.9	0 51.1	0 40.3	2 19.3	0 1.8	1 9.8	17 5.1
13	17 24 59.6	0 .0	0 .0	2 21.4	1 30.5	2 39.6	0 52.1	0 41.0	2 18.8	0 1.8	1 9.8	17 3.7
16	17 36 49.3	0 .0	0 .0	0N47.5	1 46.3	2 44.8	0 53.2	0 41.7	2 18.3	0 1.8	1 9.8	17 2.3
19	17 48 39.0	0 .0	0 .0	3 42.4	1 55.6	2 48.6	0 54.2	0 42.4	2 17.8	0 1.8	1 9.8	17 .8
22	18 0 28.7	0 .0	0 .0	5 7.8	1 58.1	2 51.0	0 55.2	0 43.1	2 17.2	0 1.9	1 9.8	16 59.3
25	18 12 18.3	0 .0	0 .0	4 10.3	1 54.2	2 52.2	0 56.1	0 43.8	2 16.6	0 1.9	1 9.8	16 57.7
28	18 24 8.0	0 .0	0 .0	1 2.0	1 44.3	2 52.2	0 57.0	0 44.5	2 15.9	0 1.9	1 9.7	16 56.1

RIGHT ASCENSION

DAY	EPHEM. SID. TIME	☉	☊	☽	☿	♀	♂	♃	♄	♅	♆	♇
1	16 37 40.9	8♊50.9	14♉41.1	8♏13.9	0♊28.8	24♈10.4	23♊48.8	19♒35.5	21♏51.6	15♐ 2.0	3♑ 3.6	6♏ .8
2	16 41 37.5	9 52.3	14 37.9	22 47.8	2 40.1	25 .4	24 32.9	19 36.2	21 R 47.4	14 R 59.3	3 R 2.0	5 R 59.6
3	16 45 34.1	10 53.8	14 34.7	8♐12.3	4 53.9	25 51.0	25 17.0	19 36.7	21 43.2	14 56.7	3 .4	5 58.4
4	16 49 30.6	11 55.4	14 31.6	24 13.2	7 9.9	26 42.1	26 1.0	19 37.0	21 39.0	14 54.0	2 58.8	5 57.2
5	16 53 27.2	12 57.1	14 28.4	10♑20.0	9 28.0	27 33.8	26 45.1	19 37.2	21 34.9	14 51.3	2 57.1	5 56.0
6	16 57 23.7	13 58.9	14 25.2	25 57.0	11 47.8	28 26.0	27 29.1	19 R 37.1	21 30.8	14 48.7	2 55.5	5 54.9
7	17 1 20.3	15 .8	14 22.0	10♒36.6	14 9.0	29 18.8	28 13.1	19 37.0	21 26.8	14 46.1	2 53.9	5 53.8
8	17 5 16.8	16 2.7	14 18.8	24 8.0	16 31.3	0♉12.1	28 57.1	19 36.5	21 22.8	14 43.4	2 52.2	5 52.7
9	17 9 13.4	17 4.7	14 15.6	6♓34.7	18 54.3	1 5.9	29 41.1	19 35.9	21 18.9	14 40.7	2 50.5	5 51.6
10	17 13 10.0	18 6.8	14 12.5	18 9.2	21 17.7	2 .2	0♋25.0	19 35.1	21 15.0	14 38.1	2 48.9	5 50.5
11	17 17 6.5	19 8.9	14 9.3	29 7.4	23 41.0	2 54.9	1 8.8	19 34.1	21 11.2	14 35.4	2 47.2	5 49.4
12	17 21 3.1	20 11.1	14 6.1	9♈45.9	26 3.8	3 50.2	1 52.7	19 32.9	21 7.4	14 32.8	2 45.5	5 48.4
13	17 24 59.6	21 13.3	14 2.9	20 20.6	28 25.8	4 45.9	2 36.5	19 31.6	21 3.7	14 30.1	2 43.8	5 47.4
14	17 28 56.2	22 15.6	13 59.7	1♉ 6.7	0♋46.7	5 42.0	3 20.3	19 30.0	21 .0	14 27.5	2 42.0	5 46.4
15	17 32 52.8	23 17.9	13 56.6	12 18.2	3 6.0	6 38.6	4 4.0	19 28.3	20 56.4	14 24.8	2 40.3	5 45.5
16	17 36 49.3	24 20.3	13 53.4	24 6.5	5 23.6	7 35.7	4 47.7	19 26.3	20 52.9	14 22.2	2 38.6	5 44.5
17	17 40 45.9	25 22.7	13 50.2	6♊39.4	7 39.1	8 33.2	5 31.3	19 24.2	20 49.4	14 19.6	2 36.9	5 43.6
18	17 44 42.4	26 25.1	13 47.0	19 57.8	9 52.4	9 31.1	6 14.9	19 21.9	20 46.0	14 17.0	2 35.1	5 42.7
19	17 48 39.0	27 27.5	13 43.9	3♋53.5	12 3.2	10 29.5	6 58.5	19 19.4	20 42.7	14 14.4	2 33.4	5 41.9
20	17 52 35.5	28 29.9	13 40.7	18 9.7	14 11.4	11 28.3	7 42.0	19 16.7	20 39.4	14 11.8	2 31.6	5 41.0
21	17 56 32.1	29 32.3	13 37.5	2♌25.1	16 16.8	12 27.5	8 25.4	19 13.9	20 36.2	14 9.3	2 29.9	5 40.2
22	18 0 28.7	0♋34.8	13 34.3	16 21.2	18 19.4	13 27.2	9 8.8	19 10.8	20 33.1	14 6.7	2 28.1	5 39.4
23	18 4 25.2	1 37.2	13 31.2	29 47.9	20 19.0	14 27.2	9 52.1	19 7.6	20 30.0	14 4.2	2 26.4	5 38.7
24	18 8 21.8	2 39.5	13 28.0	12♍45.3	22 15.7	15 27.7	10 35.4	19 4.2	20 27.1	14 1.7	2 24.6	5 37.9
25	18 12 18.3	3 41.9	13 24.8	25 21.7	24 9.3	16 28.5	11 18.6	19 .6	20 24.2	13 59.2	2 22.9	5 37.2
26	18 16 14.9	4 44.2	13 21.6	7♎51.3	25 59.8	17 29.8	12 1.7	18 56.9	20 21.3	13 56.7	2 21.1	5 36.6
27	18 20 11.5	5 46.5	13 18.5	20 31.1	27 47.3	18 31.4	12 44.8	18 53.0	20 18.6	13 54.3	2 19.4	5 35.9
28	18 24 8.0	6 48.8	13 15.3	3♏39.1	29 31.7	19 33.6	13 27.8	18 48.9	20 16.0	13 51.9	2 17.7	5 35.3
29	18 28 4.6	7 51.0	13 12.1	17 30.8	1♌13.0	20 36.0	14 10.8	18 44.7	20 13.4	13 49.5	2 15.9	5 34.7
30	18 32 1.1	8 53.1	13 9.0	2♐14.7	2 51.1	21 38.9	14 53.6	18 40.3	20 10.9	13 47.1	2 14.2	5 34.2

DECLINATION

DAY	EPHEM. SID. TIME	☉	☊	☽	☿	♀	♂	♃	♄	♅	♆	♇
1	16 37 40.9	22N 1.1	0N17.8	14S16.6	20N18.7	7N52.3	24N 7.0	16S22.0	16S24.9	22S45.4	22S15.0	3N50.4
4	16 49 30.6	22 24.2	0 17.7	26 28.7	21 58.0	8 37.5	24 12.4	16 22.3	16 22.2	22 44.7	22 15.0	3 50.5
7	17 1 20.3	22 43.7	0 17.7	23 31.9	23 20.2	9 24.9	24 15.9	16 23.1	16 19.7	22 44.0	22 15.1	3 50.3
10	17 13 10.0	22 59.6	0 17.6	10 7.8	24 20.7	10 14.1	24 17.6	16 24.4	16 17.2	22 43.2	22 15.2	3 50.1
13	17 24 59.6	23 11.8	0 17.6	6N 2.0	24 56.6	11 4.4	24 17.4	16 26.2	16 14.9	22 42.5	22 15.3	3 49.7
16	17 36 49.3	23 20.4	0 17.5	20 10.3	25 7.4	11 55.4	24 15.4	16 28.5	16 12.8	22 41.7	22 15.4	3 49.2
19	17 48 39.0	23 25.3	0 17.5	27 6.1	24 54.8	12 46.6	24 11.5	16 31.4	16 10.8	22 41.0	22 15.5	3 48.6
22	18 0 28.7	23 26.5	0 17.4	22 1.1	24 21.5	13 37.7	24 5.9	16 34.7	16 9.0	22 40.2	22 15.6	3 47.8
25	18 12 18.3	23 24.0	0 17.4	6 33.2	23 31.0	14 28.2	23 58.4	16 38.5	16 7.4	22 39.5	22 15.7	3 47.0
28	18 24 8.0	23 17.7	0 17.3	12S25.0	22 26.7	15 17.6	23 49.2	16 42.8	16 6.0	22 38.8	22 15.8	3 45.9

JULY 1985

DAY	EPHEM. SID. TIME	☉	☊	☾	☿	♀	♂	♃	♄	♅	♆	♇
	h m s	° ′	° ′	° ′	° ′	° ′	° ′	° ′	° ′	° ′	° ′	° ′
	LONGITUDE											
1	18 35 57.7	9♋ 6.9	15♉33.8	18♐59.2	1♌49.8	24♉20.6	14♋16.2	15♒54.0	21♏57.2	15♐ 1.7	2♑ 2.6	1♏57.5
2	18 39 54.3	10 4.1	15 30.6	3♑20.8	3 19.6	25 23.8	14 55.6	15 R 49.2	21 R 55.0	14 R 59.6	2 R 1.0	1 R 57.1
3	18 43 50.8	11 1.3	15 27.4	17 30.0	4 47.0	26 27.2	15 34.9	15 44.2	21 52.8	14 57.4	1 59.4	1 56.8
4	18 47 47.4	11 58.4	15 24.2	1♒21.9	6 12.0	27 30.8	16 14.2	15 39.1	21 50.7	14 55.3	1 57.8	1 56.5
5	18 51 43.9	12 55.6	15 21.1	14 52.8	7 34.7	28 34.7	16 53.5	15 33.8	21 48.7	14 53.2	1 56.2	1 56.3
6	18 55 40.5	13 52.8	15 17.9	28 1.0	8 54.9	29 38.8	17 32.7	15 28.4	21 46.8	14 51.2	1 54.6	1 56.0
7	18 59 37.0	14 50.0	15 14.7	10♓46.9	10 12.7	0♊43.1	18 11.9	15 22.8	21 45.0	14 49.1	1 53.1	1 55.8
8	19 3 33.6	15 47.2	15 11.5	23 12.5	11 27.9	1 47.6	18 51.1	15 17.1	21 43.2	14 47.1	1 51.5	1 55.7
9	19 7 30.2	16 44.4	15 8.4	5♈21.5	12 40.6	2 52.3	19 30.3	15 11.3	21 41.6	14 45.2	1 50.0	1 55.5
10	19 11 26.7	17 41.6	15 5.2	17 18.4	13 50.7	3 57.2	20 9.5	15 5.3	21 40.0	14 43.2	1 48.4	1 55.5
11	19 15 23.3	18 38.8	15 2.0	29 8.4	14 58.0	5 2.3	20 48.6	14 59.2	21 38.6	14 41.3	1 46.9	1 55.4
12	19 19 19.8	19 36.0	14 58.8	10♉56.8	16 2.6	6 7.5	21 27.7	14 52.9	21 37.2	14 39.4	1 45.3	1 55.4
13	19 23 16.4	20 33.2	14 55.7	22 48.9	17 4.2	7 13.0	22 6.8	14 46.6	21 35.9	14 37.6	1 43.8	1 55.4
14	19 27 13.0	21 30.5	14 52.5	4♊49.4	18 3.0	8 18.6	22 45.8	14 40.1	21 34.7	14 35.8	1 42.3	1 55.4
15	19 31 9.5	22 27.7	14 49.3	17 2.4	18 58.6	9 24.4	23 24.9	14 33.5	21 33.6	14 34.0	1 40.8	1 D 55.5
16	19 35 6.1	23 25.0	14 46.1	29 31.0	19 51.0	10 30.4	24 3.9	14 26.8	21 32.6	14 32.2	1 39.3	1 55.6
17	19 39 2.6	24 22.2	14 42.9	12♋16.9	20 40.1	11 36.5	24 42.9	14 20.0	21 31.7	14 30.5	1 37.9	1 55.8
18	19 42 59.2	25 19.5	14 39.8	25 20.6	21 25.8	12 42.8	25 21.8	14 13.1	21 30.9	14 28.8	1 36.4	1 55.9
19	19 46 55.7	26 16.8	14 36.6	8♌41.1	22 7.9	13 49.3	26 .8	14 6.1	21 30.3	14 27.3	1 35.0	1 56.2
20	19 50 52.3	27 14.1	14 33.4	22 16.1	22 46.3	14 55.9	26 39.7	13 59.0	21 29.7	14 25.7	1 33.6	1 56.4
21	19 54 48.9	28 11.4	14 30.2	6♍ 2.9	23 20.7	16 2.7	27 18.6	13 51.9	21 29.1	14 24.1	1 32.2	1 56.7
22	19 58 45.4	29 8.7	14 27.1	19 58.2	23 51.0	17 9.5	27 57.5	13 44.6	21 28.7	14 22.6	1 30.8	1 57.0
23	20 2 42.0	0♌ 6.0	14 23.9	3♎59.5	24 17.2	18 16.6	28 36.3	13 37.3	21 28.4	14 21.1	1 29.4	1 57.4
24	20 6 38.5	1 3.3	14 20.7	18 4.3	24 38.9	19 23.7	29 15.2	13 29.9	21 28.2	14 19.7	1 28.1	1 57.8
25	20 10 35.1	2 .6	14 17.5	2♏11.3	24 56.1	20 31.0	29 54.0	13 22.4	21 28.1	14 18.3	1 26.7	1 58.2
26	20 14 31.6	2 57.9	14 14.4	16 19.4	25 8.6	21 38.5	0♌32.8	13 14.9	21 28.0	14 16.9	1 25.4	1 58.7
27	20 18 28.2	3 55.2	14 11.2	0♐27.5	25 16.3	22 46.0	1 11.5	13 7.3	21 D 28.1	14 15.6	1 24.1	1 59.1
28	20 22 24.8	4 52.6	14 8.0	14 34.2	25 18.9	23 53.8	1 50.2	12 59.7	21 28.3	14 14.3	1 22.8	1 59.7
29	20 26 21.3	5 49.9	14 4.8	28 37.3	25 R 16.6	25 1.6	2 29.0	12 52.0	21 28.5	14 13.1	1 21.5	2 .2
30	20 30 17.9	6 47.2	14 1.7	12♑33.9	25 9.1	26 9.5	3 7.6	12 44.3	21 28.9	14 11.9	1 20.3	2 .8
31	20 34 14.4	7 44.6	13 58.5	26 20.4	24 56.4	27 17.6	3 46.3	12 36.6	21 29.3	14 10.8	1 19.0	2 1.4
	LATITUDE											
1	18 35 57.7	0 .0	0 .0	2 S 42.6	1 N 28.8	2 S 51.0	0 N 57.9	0 S 45.2	2 N 15.3	0 S 2.0	1 N 9.7	16 N 54.4
4	18 47 47.4	0 .0	0 .0	4 54.8	1 8.3	2 48.8	0 58.8	0 45.8	2 14.6	0 2.0	1 9.6	16 52.7
7	18 59 37.0	0 .0	0 .0	4 38.5	0 43.1	2 45.5	0 59.6	0 46.5	2 13.9	0 2.0	1 9.6	16 51.0
10	19 11 26.7	0 .0	0 .0	2 28.3	0 13.7	2 41.4	1 .4	0 47.1	2 13.2	0 2.0	1 9.5	16 49.3
13	19 23 16.4	0 .0	0 .0	0 N 35.3	0 S 19.3	2 36.4	1 1.2	0 47.7	2 12.5	0 2.1	1 9.5	16 47.6
16	19 35 6.1	0 .0	0 .0	3 29.1	0 55.5	2 30.6	1 1.9	0 48.3	2 11.7	0 2.1	1 9.4	16 45.8
19	19 46 55.7	0 .0	0 .0	4 59.8	1 34.1	2 24.1	1 2.6	0 48.8	2 11.0	0 2.1	1 9.3	16 44.1
22	19 58 45.4	0 .0	0 .0	4 8.1	2 14.2	2 16.9	1 3.3	0 49.4	2 10.2	0 2.1	1 9.3	16 42.3
25	20 10 35.1	0 .0	0 .0	1 6.9	2 54.6	2 9.2	1 4.0	0 49.9	2 9.4	0 2.2	1 9.2	16 40.5
28	20 22 24.8	0 .0	0 .0	2 S 30.1	3 33.4	2 .9	1 4.6	0 50.4	2 8.7	0 2.2	1 9.1	16 38.8
31	20 34 14.4	0 .0	0 .0	4 45.8	4 8.0	1 52.2	1 5.2	0 50.8	2 7.9	0 2.2	1 9.0	16 37.0
	RIGHT ASCENSION											
1	18 35 57.7	9♋55.2	13♉ 5.8	17♐46.5	4♌26.2	22♉42.2	15♋36.4	18♒35.7	20♏ 8.5	13♐44.8	2♑12.5	5♏33.6
2	18 39 54.3	10 57.2	13 2.6	3♑45.1	5 58.2	23 45.8	16 19.1	18 R 31.0	20 R 6.2	13 R 42.4	2 R 10.7	5 R 33.1
3	18 43 50.8	11 59.1	12 59.4	19 36.6	7 27.1	24 49.9	17 1.8	18 26.1	20 3.9	13 40.1	2 9.0	5 32.6
4	18 47 47.4	13 1.0	12 56.3	4♒47.3	8 52.9	25 54.3	17 44.4	18 21.0	20 1.8	13 37.9	2 7.3	5 32.2
5	18 51 43.9	14 2.7	12 53.1	18 56.5	10 15.6	26 59.2	18 26.8	18 15.8	19 59.7	13 35.6	2 5.6	5 31.7
6	18 55 40.5	15 4.4	12 49.9	1♓59.4	11 35.2	28 4.4	19 9.3	18 10.5	19 57.7	13 33.4	2 3.9	5 31.3
7	18 59 37.0	16 6.1	12 46.8	14 3.6	12 51.8	29 10.0	19 51.6	18 5.0	19 55.8	13 31.2	2 2.2	5 31.0
8	19 3 33.6	17 7.6	12 43.6	25 23.2	14 5.3	0♊16.0	20 33.8	17 59.3	19 54.0	13 29.1	2 .5	5 30.6
9	19 7 30.2	18 9.0	12 40.4	6♈14.6	15 15.6	1 22.3	21 16.0	17 53.6	19 52.3	13 26.9	1 58.8	5 30.3
10	19 11 26.7	19 10.4	12 37.3	16 54.1	16 22.8	2 29.1	21 58.1	17 47.6	19 50.6	13 24.8	1 57.1	5 30.1
11	19 15 23.3	20 11.6	12 34.1	27 37.7	17 26.9	3 36.2	22 40.1	17 41.6	19 49.1	13 22.8	1 55.5	5 29.8
12	19 19 19.8	21 12.7	12 30.9	8♉40.3	18 27.7	4 43.6	23 22.1	17 35.4	19 47.7	13 20.7	1 53.8	5 29.6
13	19 23 16.4	22 13.8	12 27.8	20 15.3	19 25.2	5 51.4	24 3.9	17 29.1	19 46.3	13 18.8	1 52.2	5 29.4
14	19 27 13.0	23 14.7	12 24.6	2♊33.0	20 19.5	6 59.6	24 45.7	17 22.7	19 45.1	13 16.8	1 50.5	5 29.2
15	19 31 9.5	24 15.5	12 21.4	15 38.3	21 10.4	8 8.1	25 27.3	17 16.1	19 43.9	13 14.9	1 48.9	5 29.1
16	19 35 6.1	25 16.1	12 18.3	29 27.5	21 57.8	9 17.0	26 8.9	17 9.5	19 42.8	13 13.0	1 47.3	5 29.0
17	19 39 2.6	26 16.7	12 15.1	13♋46.9	22 41.7	10 26.1	26 50.4	17 2.7	19 41.9	13 11.2	1 45.7	5 28.9
18	19 42 59.2	27 17.1	12 12.0	28 15.6	23 21.9	11 35.7	27 31.8	16 55.9	19 41.0	13 9.4	1 44.2	5 28.9
19	19 46 55.7	28 17.4	12 8.8	12♌31.8	23 58.5	12 45.5	28 13.2	16 48.9	19 40.3	13 7.7	1 42.7	5 28.9
20	19 50 52.3	29 17.6	12 5.6	26 20.3	24 31.3	13 55.7	28 54.4	16 41.9	19 39.6	13 5.9	1 41.1	5 D 29.0
21	19 54 48.9	0♌17.6	12 2.5	9♍36.5	25 .1	15 6.1	29 35.6	16 34.7	19 39.0	13 4.3	1 39.6	5 29.0
22	19 58 45.4	1 17.4	11 59.3	22 25.3	25 24.9	16 16.9	0♌16.6	16 27.5	19 38.5	13 2.6	1 38.1	5 29.1
23	20 2 42.0	2 17.1	11 56.2	4♎58.7	25 45.5	17 27.9	0 57.5	16 20.2	19 38.1	13 1.0	1 36.6	5 29.2
24	20 6 38.5	3 16.7	11 53.0	17 32.4	26 1.9	18 39.2	1 38.4	16 12.8	19 37.8	12 59.5	1 35.1	5 29.4
25	20 10 35.1	4 16.1	11 49.8	0♏23.9	26 13.9	19 50.8	2 19.1	16 5.4	19 37.6	12 58.0	1 33.7	5 29.6
26	20 14 31.6	5 15.4	11 46.7	13 49.1	26 21.4	21 2.6	2 59.8	15 57.8	19 37.5	12 56.5	1 32.3	5 29.8
27	20 18 28.2	6 14.5	11 43.5	27 59.4	26 24.3	22 14.7	3 40.3	15 50.3	19 37.5	12 55.1	1 30.9	5 30.0
28	20 22 24.8	7 13.4	11 40.4	12♐56.4	26 R 22.6	23 27.1	4 20.8	15 42.7	19 D 37.6	12 53.8	1 29.5	5 30.3
29	20 26 21.3	8 12.2	11 37.2	28 27.4	26 16.3	24 39.7	5 1.2	15 35.0	19 37.8	12 52.4	1 28.1	5 30.6
30	20 30 17.9	9 10.9	11 34.1	14♑ 6.1	26 5.2	25 52.5	5 41.4	15 27.3	19 38.1	12 51.2	1 26.7	5 30.9
31	20 34 14.4	10 9.3	11 30.9	29 21.0	25 49.5	27 5.5	6 21.6	15 19.5	19 38.5	12 49.9	1 25.4	5 31.3
	DECLINATION											
1	18 35 57.7	23 N 7.8	0 N 17.3	25 S 41.2	21 N 11.9	16 N 5.7	23 N 38.3	16 S 47.5	16 S 4.7	22 S 38.1	22 S 15.9	3 N 44.8
4	18 47 47.4	22 54.2	0 17.2	24 38.8	19 49.6	16 52.0	23 25.7	16 52.5	16 3.7	22 37.4	22 16.1	3 43.5
7	18 59 37.0	22 37.0	0 17.2	11 48.9	18 22.7	17 36.2	23 11.4	16 58.0	16 2.9	22 36.7	22 16.2	3 42.1
10	19 11 26.7	22 16.4	0 17.1	4 N 30.8	16 53.6	18 17.9	22 55.5	17 3.8	16 2.4	22 36.1	22 16.3	3 40.6
13	19 23 16.4	21 52.2	0 17.1	19 2.8	15 24.9	18 56.8	22 38.0	17 9.8	16 2.0	22 35.5	22 16.4	3 39.0
16	19 35 6.1	21 24.7	0 17.0	26 55.6	13 59.1	19 32.5	22 19.0	17 16.2	16 1.9	22 34.9	22 16.5	3 37.3
19	19 46 55.7	20 53.9	0 17.0	22 54.6	12 39.1	20 4.7	21 58.4	17 22.7	16 2.0	22 34.3	22 16.7	3 35.5
22	19 58 45.4	20 20.0	0 16.9	7 46.5	11 27.6	20 33.1	21 36.4	17 29.5	16 2.3	22 33.8	22 16.8	3 33.5
25	20 10 35.1	19 42.9	0 16.9	11 S 11.3	10 28.1	20 57.4	21 13.0	17 36.4	16 2.9	22 33.3	22 16.9	3 31.5
28	20 22 24.8	19 3.0	0 16.8	25 2.1	9 44.0	21 17.3	20 48.2	17 43.3	16 3.7	22 32.9	22 17.1	3 29.4
31	20 34 14.4	18 20.2	0 16.8	25 33.7	9 18.7	21 32.7	20 22.1	17 50.3	16 4.7	22 32.5	22 17.2	3 27.1

AUGUST 1985

DAY	EPHEM. SID. TIME	☉	☊	☽	☿	♀	♂	♃	♄	♅	♆	♇
	h m s	° ′	° ′	° ′	° ′	° ′	° ′	° ′	° ′	° ′	° ′	° ′
		LONGITUDE										
1	20 38 11.0	8♌42.0	13♉55.3	9♒53.5	24♌38.7	28♊25.9	4♌25.0	12♒28.8	21♏29.9	14♐ 9.7	1♑17.8	2♏ 2.1
2	20 42 7.5	9 39.3	13 52.1	23 10.0	24 R 16.0	29 34.2	5 3.6	12 R 21.1	21 30.6	14 R 8.6	1 R 16.7	2 2.8
3	20 46 4.1	10 36.7	13 48.9	6♓ 8.2	23 48.5	0♋42.7	5 42.2	12 13.3	21 31.3	14 7.6	1 15.5	2 3.5
4	20 50 .7	11 34.2	13 45.8	18 47.7	23 16.5	1 51.3	6 20.8	12 5.5	21 32.2	14 6.7	1 14.3	2 4.3
5	20 53 57.2	12 31.6	13 42.6	1♈ 9.6	22 40.3	2 60.0	6 59.4	11 57.7	21 33.1	14 5.8	1 13.2	2 5.1
6	20 57 53.8	13 29.1	13 39.4	13 16.6	22 .4	4 8.8	7 37.9	11 49.9	21 34.1	14 4.9	1 12.1	2 5.9
7	21 1 50.3	14 26.5	13 36.2	25 12.6	21 17.4	5 17.7	8 16.5	11 42.1	21 35.3	14 4.1	1 11.1	2 6.7
8	21 5 46.9	15 24.0	13 33.1	7♉ 2.2	20 31.8	6 26.8	8 55.0	11 34.3	21 36.5	14 3.3	1 10.0	2 7.6
9	21 9 43.4	16 21.6	13 29.9	18 50.8	19 44.6	7 36.0	9 33.6	11 26.6	21 37.9	14 2.6	1 9.0	2 8.6
10	21 13 40.0	17 19.1	13 26.7	0♊43.7	18 56.3	8 45.3	10 12.1	11 18.8	21 39.3	14 2.0	1 8.0	2 9.5
11	21 17 36.5	18 16.7	13 23.5	12 46.3	18 8.0	9 54.7	10 50.6	11 11.1	21 40.8	14 1.3	1 7.0	2 10.5
12	21 21 33.1	19 14.3	13 20.4	25 3.6	17 20.6	11 4.2	11 29.0	11 3.4	21 42.4	14 .7	1 6.1	2 11.5
13	21 25 29.7	20 11.9	13 17.2	7♋39.6	16 35.0	12 13.9	12 7.5	10 55.8	21 44.1	14 .2	1 5.2	2 12.6
14	21 29 26.2	21 9.5	13 14.0	20 37.0	15 52.0	13 23.6	12 45.9	10 48.2	21 46.0	13 59.7	1 4.3	2 13.7
15	21 33 22.8	22 7.2	13 10.8	3♌56.6	15 12.7	14 33.4	13 24.3	10 40.6	21 47.9	13 59.3	1 3.4	2 14.8
16	21 37 19.3	23 4.9	13 7.6	17 37.5	14 37.8	15 43.3	14 2.7	10 33.2	21 49.8	13 58.9	1 2.5	2 15.9
17	21 41 15.9	24 2.6	13 4.5	1♍36.5	14 8.1	16 53.3	14 41.1	10 25.8	21 51.9	13 58.6	1 1.7	2 17.1
18	21 45 12.4	25 .3	13 1.3	15 48.9	13 44.2	18 3.5	15 19.5	10 18.4	21 54.1	13 58.3	1 .9	2 18.3
19	21 49 9.0	25 58.0	12 58.1	0♎ 9.2	13 26.7	19 13.7	15 57.9	10 11.1	21 56.4	13 58.1	1 .2	2 19.5
20	21 53 5.5	26 55.8	12 54.9	14 32.2	13 16.1	20 24.0	16 36.2	10 3.9	21 58.7	13 57.9	0 59.4	2 20.8
21	21 57 2.1	27 53.6	12 51.8	28 53.2	13 12.8	21 34.4	17 14.5	9 56.8	22 1.2	13 57.8	0 58.7	2 22.1
22	22 0 58.7	28 51.4	12 48.6	13♏ 9.0	13 D 17.0	22 44.8	17 52.8	9 49.8	22 3.7	13 57.7	0 58.0	2 23.4
23	22 4 55.2	29 49.2	12 45.4	27 17.7	13 28.9	23 55.4	18 31.1	9 42.9	22 6.4	13 57.7	0 57.4	2 24.8
24	22 8 51.8	0♍47.0	12 42.2	11♐18.3	13 48.7	25 6.1	19 9.4	9 36.1	22 9.1	13 57.7	0 56.8	2 26.2
25	22 12 48.3	1 44.9	12 39.0	25 10.2	14 16.2	26 16.8	19 47.7	9 29.4	22 11.9	13 D 57.8	0 56.2	2 27.6
26	22 16 44.9	2 42.7	12 35.9	8♑53.1	14 51.5	27 27.7	20 25.9	9 22.8	22 14.8	13 57.9	0 55.6	2 29.0
27	22 20 41.4	3 40.6	12 32.7	22 26.1	15 34.5	28 38.6	21 4.1	9 16.3	22 17.8	13 58.1	0 55.1	2 30.5
28	22 24 38.0	4 38.6	12 29.5	5♒48.3	16 24.9	29 49.6	21 42.3	9 9.9	22 20.9	13 58.3	0 54.6	2 32.0
29	22 28 34.5	5 36.5	12 26.3	18 58.2	17 22.5	1♌ .7	22 20.5	9 3.7	22 24.1	13 58.6	0 54.1	2 33.5
30	22 32 31.1	6 34.5	12 23.2	1♓54.7	18 27.0	2 12.0	22 58.8	8 57.6	22 27.4	13 59.0	0 53.7	2 35.1
31	22 36 27.6	7 32.5	12 20.0	14 36.7	19 37.9	3 23.2	23 36.9	8 51.7	22 30.7	13 59.4	0 53.3	2 36.7
		LATITUDE										
1	20 38 11.0	0 .0	0 .0	4S59.6	4S18.1	1S49.2	1N 5.4	0S51.0	2N 7.6	0S 2.2	1N 9.0	16N36.5
4	20 50 .7	0 .0	0 .0	4 6.7	4 41.9	1 39.9	1 6.0	0 51.4	2 6.9	0 2.3	1 8.9	16 34.7
7	21 1 50.3	0 .0	0 .0	1 35.1	4 53.4	1 30.4	1 6.5	0 51.7	2 6.1	0 2.3	1 8.7	16 33.0
10	21 13 40.0	0 .0	0 .0	1N30.2	4 49.4	1 20.6	1 7.0	0 52.0	2 5.3	0 2.3	1 8.6	16 31.3
13	21 25 29.7	0 .0	0 .0	4 5.6	4 28.8	1 10.6	1 7.5	0 52.3	2 4.6	0 2.3	1 8.5	16 29.7
16	21 37 19.3	0 .0	0 .0	4 59.8	3 53.4	1 .4	1 8.0	0 52.6	2 3.8	0 2.4	1 8.4	16 28.1
19	21 49 9.0	0 .0	0 .0	3 22.7	3 6.9	0 50.2	1 8.5	0 52.8	2 3.1	0 2.4	1 8.3	16 26.5
22	22 0 58.7	0 .0	0 .0	0S 5.6	2 14.4	0 40.1	1 8.9	0 53.0	2 2.3	0 2.4	1 8.2	16 24.9
25	22 12 48.3	0 .0	0 .0	3 27.8	1 20.7	0 29.9	1 9.3	0 53.2	2 1.6	0 2.4	1 8.0	16 23.4
28	22 24 38.0	0 .0	0 .0	5 1.2	0 29.9	0 19.9	1 9.6	0 53.3	2 .9	0 2.4	1 7.9	16 21.9
31	22 36 27.6	0 .0	0 .0	4 13.4	0N14.9	0 10.0	1 10.0	0 53.4	2 .2	0 2.5	1 7.8	16 20.5
		RIGHT ASCENSION										
1	20 38 11.0	11♌ 7.7	11♉27.7	13♒47.0	25♌29.3	28♊18.8	7♌ 1.7	15♒11.8	19♏39.0	12♐48.8	1♑24.1	5♏31.7
2	20 42 7.5	12 5.9	11 24.6	27 12.7	25 R 4.6	29 32.2	7 41.6	15 R 4.0	19 39.6	12 R 47.6	1 R 22.8	5 32.1
3	20 46 4.1	13 3.9	11 21.4	9♓40.1	24 35.7	0♋45.9	8 21.5	14 56.1	19 40.3	12 46.5	1 21.6	5 32.6
4	20 50 .7	14 1.8	11 18.3	21 19.4	24 2.9	1 59.7	9 1.3	14 48.3	19 41.1	12 45.5	1 20.3	5 33.1
5	20 53 57.2	14 59.5	11 15.1	2♈25.0	23 26.5	3 13.8	9 41.0	14 40.5	19 41.9	12 44.5	1 19.1	5 33.6
6	20 57 53.8	15 57.1	11 12.0	13 12.3	22 47.1	4 27.9	10 20.6	14 32.6	19 42.9	12 43.6	1 17.9	5 34.1
7	21 1 50.3	16 54.5	11 8.8	23 56.7	22 5.1	5 42.3	11 .1	14 24.8	19 44.0	12 42.7	1 16.8	5 34.7
8	21 5 46.9	17 51.8	11 5.7	4♉53.1	21 21.2	6 56.7	11 39.5	14 17.0	19 45.2	12 41.9	1 15.6	5 35.3
9	21 9 43.4	18 49.0	11 2.5	16 15.1	20 36.1	8 11.3	12 18.8	14 9.2	19 46.5	12 41.2	1 14.6	5 36.0
10	21 13 40.0	19 46.0	10 59.4	28 14.4	19 50.6	9 26.0	12 58.0	14 1.4	19 47.8	12 40.4	1 13.5	5 36.7
11	21 17 36.5	20 42.9	10 56.2	10♊58.6	19 5.5	10 40.8	13 37.2	13 53.6	19 49.3	12 39.7	1 12.4	5 37.4
12	21 21 33.1	21 39.7	10 53.1	24 28.7	18 21.6	11 55.7	14 16.2	13 45.9	19 50.8	12 39.1	1 11.4	5 38.1
13	21 25 29.7	22 36.3	10 49.9	8♋36.3	17 39.9	13 10.7	14 55.1	13 38.2	19 52.5	12 38.6	1 10.4	5 38.9
14	21 29 26.2	23 32.7	10 46.8	23 4.7	17 1.2	14 25.7	15 34.0	13 30.5	19 54.2	12 38.0	1 9.4	5 39.7
15	21 33 22.8	24 29.0	10 43.6	7♌32.5	16 26.3	15 40.8	16 12.7	13 22.9	19 56.1	12 37.6	1 8.5	5 40.5
16	21 37 19.3	25 25.2	10 40.5	21 41.6	15 56.1	16 55.9	16 51.4	13 15.3	19 58.0	12 37.2	1 7.6	5 41.4
17	21 41 15.9	26 21.3	10 37.3	5♍22.5	15 31.2	18 11.0	17 29.9	13 7.8	20 .1	12 36.8	1 6.7	5 42.2
18	21 45 12.4	27 17.3	10 34.2	18 35.5	15 12.2	19 26.1	18 8.4	13 .4	20 2.2	12 36.5	1 5.8	5 43.1
19	21 49 9.0	28 13.1	10 31.0	1♎29.2	14 59.8	20, 41.3	18 46.8	12 53.0	20 4.4	12 36.3	1 5.0	5 44.1
20	21 53 5.5	29 8.7	10 27.9	14 17.4	14 54.3	21 56.4	19 25.1	12 45.7	20 6.7	12 36.1	1 4.2	5 45.1
21	21 57 2.1	0♍ 4.3	10 24.7	27 15.9	14 D 56.1	23 11.5	20 3.3	12 38.5	20 9.1	12 35.9	1 3.5	5 46.1
22	22 0 58.7	0 59.7	10 21.6	10♏40.1	15 5.5	24 26.5	20 41.4	12 31.4	20 11.6	12 35.8	1 2.7	5 47.1
23	22 4 55.2	1 55.1	10 18.4	24 41.2	15 22.5	25 41.6	21 19.4	12 24.4	20 14.2	12 35.8	1 2.0	5 48.1
24	22 8 51.8	2 50.3	10 15.3	9♐22.7	15 47.4	26 56.5	21 57.3	12 17.5	20 16.9	12 35.8	1 1.4	5 49.2
25	22 12 48.3	3 45.4	10 12.2	24 35.8	16 20.0	28 11.4	22 35.1	12 10.7	20 19.7	12 D 35.9	1 .7	5 50.3
26	22 16 44.9	4 40.4	10 9.0	9♑59.3	17 .3	29 26.3	23 12.8	12 4.0	20 22.5	12 36.1	1 .1	5 51.5
27	22 20 41.4	5 35.2	10 5.9	25 5.8	17 48.0	0♌41.0	23 50.5	11 57.4	20 25.5	12 36.3	0 59.5	5 52.6
28	22 24 38.0	6 30.0	10 2.7	9♒31.4	18 43.0	1 55.7	24 28.1	11 50.9	20 28.5	12 36.5	0 59.0	5 53.8
29	22 28 34.5	7 24.7	9 59.6	23 3.0	19 44.8	3 10.2	25 5.5	11 44.6	20 31.6	12 36.8	0 58.5	5 55.0
30	22 32 31.1	8 19.4	9 56.4	5♓39.7	20 53.3	4 24.7	25 43.0	11 38.4	20 34.9	12 37.2	0 58.1	5 56.3
31	22 36 27.6	9 13.9	9 53.3	17 28.9	22 7.7	5 39.1	26 20.3	11 32.3	20 38.2	12 37.6	0 57.6	5 57.6
		DECLINATION										
1	20 38 11.0	18N 5.3	0N16.8	22S34.7	9N15.0	21N36.8	20N13.1	17S52.6	16S 5.1	22S32.4	22S17.2	3N26.4
4	20 50 .7	17 19.0	0 16.7	8 12.9	9 19.2	21 45.9	19 45.2	17 59.6	16 6.4	22 32.1	22 17.4	3 24.1
7	21 1 50.3	16 30.1	0 16.7	8N16.8	9 46.2	21 49.9	19 16.2	18 6.5	16 8.0	22 31.8	22 17.5	3 21.7
10	21 13 40.0	15 38.8	0 16.6	21 46.6	10 33.6	21 48.8	18 45.9	18 13.2	16 9.8	22 31.6	22 17.7	3 19.2
13	21 25 29.7	14 45.2	0 16.6	27 18.5	11 35.5	21 42.6	18 14.5	18 19.9	16 11.7	22 31.4	22 17.8	3 16.6
16	21 37 19.3	13 49.6	0 16.5	20 18.4	12 43.4	21 31.0	17 42.1	18 26.3	16 13.9	22 31.3	22 17.9	3 14.0
19	21 49 9.0	12 51.9	0 16.5	3 2.3	13 48.1	21 14.1	17 8.6	18 32.5	16 16.3	22 31.2	22 18.1	3 11.3
22	22 0 58.7	11 52.4	0 16.4	15S52.7	14 41.2	20 51.9	16 34.1	18 38.4	16 18.9	22 31.2	22 18.2	3 8.6
25	22 12 48.3	10 51.3	0 16.4	26 48.9	15 15.8	20 24.5	15 58.6	18 44.0	16 21.7	22 31.2	22 18.4	3 5.8
28	22 24 38.0	9 48.6	0 16.3	23 41.0	15 26.6	19 52.0	15 22.3	18 49.3	16 24.7	22 31.3	22 18.5	3 3.0
31	22 36 27.6	8 44.5	0 16.3	9 57.2	15 10.0	19 14.4	14 45.1	18 54.3	16 27.8	22 31.4	22 18.6	3 .2

SEPTEMBER 1985

LONGITUDE

DAY	EPHEM. SID. TIME	☉	☊	☽	☿	♀	♂	♃	♄	♅	♆	♇
	h m s	° ′	° ′	° ′	° ′	° ′	° ′	° ′	° ′	° ′	° ′	° ′
1	22 40 24.2	8 ♍ 30.5	12 ♉ 16.8	27 ♓ 4.2	20 ♌ 55.0	4 ♌ 34.6	24 ♌ 15.1	8 ♒ 45.8	22 ♏ 34.1	13 ♐ 59.8	0 ♑ 52.9	2 ♏ 38.3
2	22 44 20.8	9 28.6	12 13.6	9 ♈ 18.1	22 17.8	5 46.1	24 53.3	8 R 40.1	22 37.6	14 .3	0 R 52.6	2 39.9
3	22 48 17.3	10 26.7	12 10.4	21 20.1	23 45.8	6 57.6	25 31.4	8 34.5	22 41.2	14 .9	0 52.3	2 41.6
4	22 52 13.9	11 24.8	12 7.3	3 ♉ 13.2	25 18.5	8 9.2	26 9.5	8 29.1	22 44.8	14 1.4	0 52.0	2 43.2
5	22 56 10.4	12 22.9	12 4.1	15 1.3	26 55.4	9 20.9	26 47.6	8 23.8	22 48.6	14 2.1	0 51.7	2 44.9
6	23 0 7.0	13 21.1	12 .9	26 48.8	28 35.9	10 32.7	27 25.7	8 18.7	22 52.4	14 2.8	0 51.5	2 46.7
7	23 4 3.5	14 19.3	11 57.7	8 ♊ 41.0	0 ♍ 19.6	11 44.6	28 3.8	8 13.7	22 56.3	14 3.5	0 51.3	2 48.4
8	23 8 .1	15 17.5	11 54.6	20 43.0	2 6.0	12 56.6	28 41.9	8 8.9	23 .3	14 4.3	0 51.2	2 50.2
9	23 11 56.6	16 15.8	11 51.4	3 ♋ .3	3 54.6	14 8.6	29 20.0	8 4.3	23 4.3	14 5.2	0 51.1	2 52.0
10	23 15 53.2	17 14.1	11 48.2	15 37.4	5 44.9	15 20.7	29 58.1	7 59.8	23 8.5	14 6.1	0 51.0	2 53.8
11	23 19 49.7	18 12.5	11 45.0	28 38.1	7 36.6	16 32.9	0 ♍ 36.1	7 55.5	23 12.7	14 7.0	0 50.9	2 55.7
12	23 23 46.3	19 10.8	11 41.8	12 ♌ 4.6	9 29.2	17 45.2	1 14.2	7 51.3	23 17.0	14 8.0	0 50.9	2 57.6
13	23 27 42.8	20 9.3	11 38.7	25 56.7	11 22.5	18 57.5	1 52.2	7 47.3	23 21.3	14 9.1	0 50.9	2 59.5
14	23 31 39.4	21 7.7	11 35.5	10 ♍ 11.8	13 16.2	20 10.0	2 30.3	7 43.5	23 25.8	14 10.2	0 50.9	3 1.4
15	23 35 35.9	22 6.2	11 32.3	24 44.9	15 9.9	21 22.4	3 8.3	7 39.9	23 30.3	14 11.3	0 D 51.0	3 3.3
16	23 39 32.5	23 4.7	11 29.1	9 ♎ 29.1	17 3.6	22 35.0	3 46.3	7 36.5	23 34.9	14 12.5	0 51.1	3 5.3
17	23 43 29.1	24 3.2	11 26.0	24 16.7	18 56.9	23 47.6	4 24.3	7 33.2	23 39.5	14 13.8	0 51.2	3 7.3
18	23 47 25.6	25 1.8	11 22.8	9 ♏ .6	20 49.9	25 .3	5 2.3	7 30.2	23 44.3	14 15.1	0 51.4	3 9.3
19	23 51 22.2	26 .4	11 19.6	23 34.9	22 42.2	26 13.1	5 40.2	7 27.3	23 49.1	14 16.4	0 51.6	3 11.3
20	23 55 18.7	26 59.0	11 16.4	7 ♐ 55.6	24 33.9	27 25.9	6 18.2	7 24.6	23 54.0	14 17.9	0 51.9	3 13.4
21	23 59 15.3	27 57.7	11 13.2	22 .5	26 24.9	28 38.8	6 56.2	7 22.1	23 58.9	14 19.3	0 52.2	3 15.4
22	0 3 11.8	28 56.4	11 10.1	5 ♑ 48.9	28 15.0	29 51.8	7 34.1	7 19.8	24 3.9	14 20.8	0 52.5	3 17.5
23	0 7 8.4	29 55.1	11 6.9	19 21.1	0 ♎ 4.3	1 ♍ 4.8	8 12.1	7 17.7	24 9.0	14 22.4	0 52.8	3 19.6
24	0 11 4.9	0 ♎ 53.8	11 3.7	2 ♒ 38.0	1 52.7	2 17.8	8 50.0	7 15.8	24 14.1	14 23.9	0 53.2	3 21.7
25	0 15 1.5	1 52.6	11 .5	15 40.4	3 40.2	3 31.0	9 27.9	7 14.1	24 19.3	14 25.6	0 53.6	3 23.9
26	0 18 58.0	2 51.4	10 57.4	28 29.4	5 26.8	4 44.2	10 5.8	7 12.5	24 24.6	14 27.3	0 54.0	3 26.0
27	0 22 54.6	3 50.2	10 54.2	11 ♓ 5.6	7 12.5	5 57.4	10 43.7	7 11.2	24 29.9	14 29.0	0 54.5	3 28.2
28	0 26 51.1	4 49.0	10 51.0	23 29.9	8 57.2	7 10.7	11 21.5	7 10.0	24 35.3	14 30.8	0 55.0	3 30.4
29	0 30 47.7	5 47.9	10 47.8	5 ♈ 43.2	10 41.1	8 24.1	11 59.4	7 9.1	24 40.7	14 32.6	0 55.5	3 32.6
30	0 34 44.3	6 46.8	10 44.6	17 46.8	12 24.0	9 37.6	12 37.3	7 8.3	24 46.2	14 34.5	0 56.1	3 34.8

LATITUDE

DAY	EPHEM. SID. TIME	☉	☊	☽	☿	♀	♂	♃	♄	♅	♆	♇
1	22 40 24.2	0 .0	0 .0	3 S 31.3	0 N 28.1	0 S 6.7	1 N 10.1	0 S 53.4	1 N 60.0	0 S 2.5	1 N 7.7	16 N 20.0
4	22 52 13.9	0 .0	0 .0	0 40.5	1 1.7	0 N 2.9	1 10.4	0 53.4	1 59.3	0 2.5	1 7.6	16 18.7
7	23 4 3.5	0 .0	0 .0	2 N 24.1	1 26.1	0 12.2	1 10.7	0 53.4	1 58.6	0 2.5	1 7.5	16 17.4
10	23 15 53.2	0 .0	0 .0	4 38.4	1 41.3	0 21.2	1 11.0	0 53.4	1 58.0	0 2.5	1 7.3	16 16.1
13	23 27 42.8	0 .0	0 .0	4 56.0	1 48.1	0 29.8	1 11.3	0 53.4	1 57.3	0 2.6	1 7.2	16 14.9
16	23 39 32.5	0 .0	0 .0	2 37.2	1 47.8	0 38.0	1 11.5	0 53.3	1 56.7	0 2.6	1 7.0	16 13.8
19	23 51 22.2	0 .0	0 .0	1 S 13.2	1 41.8	0 45.7	1 11.7	0 53.2	1 56.1	0 2.6	1 6.9	16 12.7
22	0 3 11.8	0 .0	0 .0	4 17.2	1 31.3	0 53.0	1 11.9	0 53.1	1 55.5	0 2.6	1 6.8	16 11.7
25	0 15 1.5	0 .0	0 .0	5 9.0	1 17.2	0 59.8	1 12.0	0 53.0	1 55.0	0 2.7	1 6.6	16 10.8
28	0 26 51.1	0 .0	0 .0	3 44.4	1 .6	1 6.0	1 12.1	0 52.9	1 54.4	0 2.7	1 6.5	16 9.9

RIGHT ASCENSION

DAY	EPHEM. SID. TIME	☉	☊	☽	☿	♀	♂	♃	♄	♅	♆	♇
1	22 40 24.2	10 ♍ 8.3	9 ♉ 50.2	28 ♓ 42.9	23 ♌ 27.8	6 ♌ 53.3	26 ♌ 57.5	11 ♒ 26.4	20 ♏ 41.6	12 ♐ 38.1	0 ♑ 57.2	5 ♏ 58.9
2	22 44 20.8	11 2.7	9 47.0	9 ♈ 35.7	24 52.9	8 7.4	27 34.7	11 R 20.5	20 45.0	12 38.6	0 R 56.8	6 .2
3	22 48 17.3	11 57.0	9 43.9	20 21.4	26 22.6	9 21.4	28 11.7	11 14.9	20 48.6	12 39.2	0 56.5	6 1.5
4	22 52 13.9	12 51.2	9 40.7	1 ♉ 14.0	27 56.2	10 35.2	28 48.7	11 9.3	20 52.2	12 39.9	0 56.2	6 2.9
5	22 56 10.4	13 45.4	9 37.6	12 26.4	29 33.2	11 48.9	29 25.7	11 3.9	20 56.0	12 40.5	0 55.9	6 4.3
6	23 0 7.0	14 39.5	9 34.5	24 9.9	1 ♍ 13.1	13 2.4	0 ♍ 2.5	10 58.7	20 59.8	12 41.3	0 55.7	6 5.7
7	23 4 3.5	15 33.6	9 31.3	6 ♊ 32.9	2 55.3	14 15.8	0 39.3	10 53.6	21 3.6	12 42.1	0 55.5	6 7.2
8	23 8 .1	16 27.6	9 28.2	19 38.5	4 39.2	15 29.1	1 16.0	10 48.7	21 7.6	12 42.9	0 55.3	6 8.7
9	23 11 56.6	17 21.6	9 25.1	3 ♋ 22.7	6 24.4	16 42.1	1 52.6	10 44.0	21 11.6	12 43.9	0 55.2	6 10.2
10	23 15 53.2	18 15.5	9 21.9	17 33.3	8 10.6	17 55.1	2 29.1	10 39.4	21 15.8	12 44.8	0 55.1	6 11.7
11	23 19 49.7	19 9.4	9 18.8	1 ♌ 53.1	9 57.2	19 7.8	3 5.6	10 35.0	21 20.0	12 45.8	0 55.0	6 13.2
12	23 23 46.3	20 3.3	9 15.7	16 4.7	11 44.0	20 20.4	3 42.0	10 30.7	21 24.2	12 46.9	0 55.0	6 14.8
13	23 27 42.8	20 57.2	9 12.5	29 56.6	13 30.7	21 32.8	4 18.4	10 26.6	21 28.6	12 48.0	0 55.0	6 16.4
14	23 31 39.4	21 51.0	9 9.4	13 ♍ 25.9	15 17.1	22 45.0	4 54.7	10 22.8	21 33.0	12 49.2	0 55.0	6 18.0
15	23 35 35.9	22 44.9	9 6.2	26 38.1	17 2.9	23 57.1	5 30.9	10 19.1	21 37.5	12 50.5	0 D 55.1	6 19.6
16	23 39 32.5	23 38.7	9 3.1	9 ♎ 44.7	18 48.0	25 9.0	6 7.0	10 15.5	21 42.1	12 51.8	0 55.2	6 21.3
17	23 43 29.1	24 32.5	8 60.0	23 .1	20 32.4	26 20.7	6 43.1	10 12.2	21 46.8	12 53.1	0 55.4	6 22.9
18	23 47 25.6	25 26.3	8 56.8	6 ♏ 38.9	22 15.8	27 32.2	7 19.1	10 9.0	21 51.5	12 54.5	0 55.6	6 24.6
19	23 51 22.2	26 20.1	8 53.7	20 52.4	23 58.4	28 43.5	7 55.0	10 6.1	21 56.3	12 55.9	0 55.8	6 26.3
20	23 55 18.7	27 14.0	8 50.6	5 ♐ 43.6	25 39.9	29 54.8	8 31.0	10 3.4	22 1.3	12 57.5	0 56.1	6 28.1
21	23 59 15.3	28 7.8	8 47.5	21 4.0	27 20.5	1 ♍ 5.8	9 6.8	10 .8	22 6.2	12 59.1	0 56.4	6 29.9
22	0 3 11.8	29 1.6	8 44.3	6 ♑ 32.8	29 .0	2 16.6	9 42.5	9 58.4	22 11.2	13 .7	0 56.7	6 31.7
23	0 7 8.4	29 55.5	8 41.2	21 43.2	0 ♎ 38.6	3 27.3	10 18.2	9 56.2	22 16.3	13 2.3	0 57.1	6 33.5
24	0 11 4.9	0 ♎ 49.4	8 38.1	6 ♒ 11.8	2 16.1	4 37.8	10 53.9	9 54.3	22 21.5	13 4.0	0 57.5	6 35.3
25	0 15 1.5	1 43.3	8 34.9	19 46.1	3 52.8	5 48.1	11 29.5	9 52.5	22 26.7	13 5.8	0 57.9	6 37.1
26	0 18 58.0	2 37.2	8 31.8	2 ♓ 25.0	5 28.5	6 58.3	12 5.0	9 50.9	22 32.0	13 7.6	0 58.4	6 38.9
27	0 22 54.6	3 31.2	8 28.7	14 16.0	7 3.4	8 8.4	12 40.5	9 49.5	22 37.3	13 9.5	0 58.9	6 40.8
28	0 26 51.1	4 25.3	8 25.6	25 31.1	8 37.4	9 18.3	13 15.9	9 48.3	22 42.7	13 11.4	0 59.5	6 42.7
29	0 30 47.7	5 19.4	8 22.4	6 ♈ 23.8	10 10.7	10 28.1	13 51.3	9 47.3	22 48.2	13 13.3	1 .0	6 44.6
30	0 34 44.3	6 13.5	8 19.3	17 7.9	11 43.2	11 37.7	14 26.6	9 46.5	22 53.7	13 15.3	1 .7	6 46.5

DECLINATION

DAY	EPHEM. SID. TIME	☉	☊	☽	☿	♀	♂	♃	♄	♅	♆	♇
1	22 40 24.2	8 N 22.8	0 N 16.3	4 S 23.8	14 N 58.1	19 N .7	14 N 32.5	18 S 55.8	16 S 28.9	22 S 31.5	22 S 18.7	2 N 59.2
4	22 52 13.9	7 17.1	0 16.2	11 N 57.3	14 3.4	18 16.6	13 54.3	19 .3	16 32.3	22 31.7	22 18.8	2 56.4
7	23 4 3.5	6 10.3	0 16.2	24 7.6	12 42.1	17 27.8	13 15.3	19 4.3	16 35.8	22 32.0	22 19.0	2 53.4
10	23 15 53.2	5 2.6	0 16.1	27 8.2	10 58.4	16 34.5	12 35.6	19 7.9	16 39.5	22 32.3	22 19.1	2 50.5
13	23 27 42.8	3 54.1	0 16.1	17 30.6	8 57.9	15 36.9	11 55.2	19 11.1	16 43.3	22 32.7	22 19.2	2 47.6
16	23 39 32.5	2 44.9	0 16.0	1 S 21.0	6 46.0	14 35.2	11 14.2	19 13.8	16 47.2	22 33.1	22 19.4	2 44.7
19	23 51 22.2	1 35.3	0 16.0	19 51.1	4 27.3	13 29.8	10 32.7	19 16.1	16 51.3	22 33.6	22 19.5	2 41.7
22	0 3 11.8	0 25.3	0 15.9	27 35.9	2 5.5	12 21.0	9 50.6	19 17.9	16 55.5	22 34.1	22 19.7	2 38.8
25	0 15 1.5	0 S 44.8	0 15.8	21 3.1	0 S 16.7	11 8.9	9 8.0	19 19.3	16 59.8	22 34.7	22 19.8	2 35.9
28	0 26 51.1	1 54.9	0 15.8	6 .9	2 37.3	9 53.8	8 25.1	19 20.1	17 4.2	22 35.3	22 19.9	2 33.0

OCTOBER 1985

DAY	EPHEM. SID. TIME	☉	☊	☾	☿	♀	♂	♃	♄	♅	♆	♇
	h m s	° ′	° ′	° ′	° ′	° ′	° ′	° ′	° ′	° ′	° ′	° ′
		LONGITUDE										
1	0 38 40.8	7♎45.8	10♉41.5	29♈42.3	14♎ 6.0	10♍51.1	13♍15.1	7♒ 7.8	24♏51.8	14♐36.4	0♑56.7	3♏37.0
2	0 42 37.4	8 44.8	10 38.3	11♉32.0	15 47.2	12 4.6	13 52.9	7R 7.4	24 57.4	14 38.3	0 57.3	3 39.2
3	0 46 33.9	9 43.8	10 35.1	23 18.8	17 27.5	13 18.2	14 30.8	7 7.2	25 3.0	14 40.3	0 58.0	3 41.5
4	0 50 30.5	10 42.9	10 31.9	5♊ 6.1	19 6.9	14 31.9	15 8.6	7D 7.3	25 8.8	14 42.4	0 58.7	3 43.7
5	0 54 27.0	11 42.0	10 28.8	16 58.1	20 45.5	15 45.6	15 46.4	7 7.5	25 14.5	14 44.5	0 59.4	3 46.0
6	0 58 23.6	12 41.1	10 25.6	28 59.3	22 23.3	16 59.4	16 24.3	7 7.9	25 20.4	14 46.6	1 .2	3 48.3
7	1 2 20.1	13 40.3	10 22.4	11♋14.5	24 .3	18 13.3	17 2.1	7 8.6	25 26.3	14 48.8	1 1.0	3 50.6
8	1 6 16.7	14 39.5	10 19.2	23 48.4	25 36.6	19 27.2	17 39.9	7 9.4	25 32.2	14 51.0	1 1.8	3 52.9
9	1 10 13.2	15 38.7	10 16.1	6♌45.3	27 12.1	20 41.1	18 17.7	7 10.4	25 38.2	14 53.3	1 2.7	3 55.3
10	1 14 9.8	16 38.0	10 12.9	20 8.4	28 46.8	21 55.1	18 55.5	7 11.6	25 44.2	14 55.6	1 3.6	3 57.6
11	1 18 6.3	17 37.4	10 9.7	3♍59.1	0♏20.8	23 9.2	19 33.3	7 13.1	25 50.3	14 58.0	1 4.5	3 60.0
12	1 22 2.9	18 36.8	10 6.5	18 16.5	1 54.1	24 23.3	20 11.1	7 14.7	25 56.5	15 .3	1 5.5	4 2.3
13	1 25 59.4	19 36.2	10 3.3	2♎57.1	3 26.7	25 37.4	20 48.8	7 16.5	26 2.7	15 2.8	1 6.5	4 4.7
14	1 29 56.0	20 35.6	10 .2	17 54.5	4 58.6	26 51.6	21 26.6	7 18.5	26 8.9	15 5.2	1 7.5	4 7.1
15	1 33 52.6	21 35.1	9 57.0	3♏ .4	6 29.8	28 5.9	22 4.3	7 20.7	26 15.1	15 7.7	1 8.5	4 9.4
16	1 37 49.1	22 34.6	9 53.8	18 5.6	8 .3	29 20.1	22 42.1	7 23.1	26 21.5	15 10.3	1 9.6	4 11.8
17	1 41 45.7	23 34.1	9 50.6	3♐ 1.6	9 30.1	0♎34.5	23 19.8	7 25.7	26 27.8	15 12.8	1 10.7	4 14.2
18	1 45 42.2	24 33.7	9 47.5	17 41.4	10 59.2	1 48.8	23 57.5	7 28.5	26 34.2	15 15.5	1 11.8	4 16.6
19	1 49 38.8	25 33.3	9 44.3	2♑ .4	12 27.6	3 3.2	24 35.2	7 31.4	26 40.6	15 18.1	1 13.0	4 19.0
20	1 53 35.3	26 32.9	9 41.1	15 56.3	13 55.4	4 17.6	25 12.9	7 34.6	26 47.1	15 20.8	1 14.2	4 21.4
21	1 57 31.9	27 32.6	9 37.9	29 29.2	15 22.4	5 32.1	25 50.6	7 38.0	26 53.6	15 23.5	1 15.4	4 23.8
22	2 1 28.4	28 32.3	9 34.7	12♒40.2	16 48.7	6 46.6	26 28.3	7 41.5	27 .2	15 26.3	1 16.7	4 26.2
23	2 5 25.0	29 32.0	9 31.6	25 31.8	18 14.2	8 1.1	27 5.9	7 45.2	27 6.8	15 29.1	1 17.9	4 28.7
24	2 9 21.5	0♏31.7	9 28.4	8♓ 6.6	19 39.0	9 15.7	27 43.6	7 49.1	27 13.4	15 31.9	1 19.2	4 31.1
25	2 13 18.1	1 31.5	9 25.2	20 27.5	21 2.9	10 30.3	28 21.2	7 53.2	27 20.0	15 34.8	1 20.6	4 33.5
26	2 17 14.7	2 31.3	9 22.0	2♈37.2	22 26.0	11 45.0	28 58.9	7 57.5	27 26.7	15 37.7	1 21.9	4 35.9
27	2 21 11.2	3 31.1	9 18.9	14 38.1	23 48.2	12 59.6	29 36.5	8 2.0	27 33.4	15 40.6	1 23.3	4 38.4
28	2 25 7.8	4 31.0	9 15.7	26 32.5	25 9.5	14 14.3	0♎14.1	8 6.6	27 40.2	15 43.5	1 24.7	4 40.8
29	2 29 4.3	5 30.9	9 12.5	8♉22.5	26 29.7	15 29.1	0 51.8	8 11.4	27 46.9	15 46.5	1 26.2	4 43.2
30	2 33 .9	6 30.8	9 9.3	20 10.3	27 48.9	16 43.9	1 29.4	8 16.4	27 53.7	15 49.5	1 27.7	4 45.6
31	2 36 57.4	7 30.7	9 6.1	1♊58.0	29 6.8	17 58.7	2 7.0	8 21.6	28 .6	15 52.6	1 29.2	4 48.1
		LATITUDE										
1	0 38 40.8	0 .0	0 .0	0S52.7	0N42.1	1N11.6	1N12.3	0S52.7	1N53.9	0S 2.7	1N 6.4	16N 9.1
4	0 50 30.5	0 .0	0 .0	2N16.9	0 22.3	1 16.6	1 12.3	0 52.6	1 53.4	0 2.7	1 6.2	16 8.4
7	1 2 20.1	0 .0	0 .0	4 37.9	0 1.8	1 21.0	1 12.4	0 52.4	1 52.9	0 2.7	1 6.1	16 7.8
10	1 14 9.8	0 .0	0 .0	5 9.7	0S19.2	1 24.8	1 12.4	0 52.2	1 52.4	0 2.8	1 6.0	16 7.2
13	1 25 59.4	0 .0	0 .0	3 7.2	0 40.2	1 27.9	1 12.5	0 52.0	1 52.0	0 2.8	1 5.8	16 6.7
16	1 37 49.1	0 .0	0 .0	0S49.1	1 .8	1 30.4	1 12.4	0 51.8	1 51.6	0 2.8	1 5.7	16 6.3
19	1 49 38.8	0 .0	0 .0	4 12.7	1 20.8	1 32.2	1 12.4	0 51.6	1 51.2	0 2.8	1 5.6	16 5.9
22	2 1 28.4	0 .0	0 .0	5 16.6	1 39.8	1 33.3	1 12.3	0 51.4	1 50.8	0 2.8	1 5.4	16 5.6
25	2 13 18.1	0 .0	0 .0	3 58.9	1 57.4	1 33.8	1 12.3	0 51.2	1 50.4	0 2.9	1 5.3	16 5.5
28	2 25 7.8	0 .0	0 .0	1 9.7	2 13.1	1 33.7	1 12.1	0 51.0	1 50.1	0 2.9	1 5.2	16 5.4
31	2 36 57.4	0 .0	0 .0	2N 3.4	2 26.6	1 32.9	1 12.0	0 50.8	1 49.8	0 2.9	1 5.1	16 5.3
		RIGHT ASCENSION										
1	0 38 40.8	7♎ 7.7	8♉16.2	27♈56.6	13♎15.1	12♍47.2	15♍ 1.9	9♒46.0	22♏59.3	13♐17.4	1♑ 1.3	6♏48.4
2	0 42 37.4	8 2.0	8 13.0	9♉ 2.1	14 46.3	13 56.6	15 37.1	9R45.6	23 5.0	13 19.5	1 2.0	6 50.4
3	0 46 33.9	8 56.4	8 9.9	20 35.1	16 16.8	15 5.9	16 12.3	9 45.4	23 10.7	13 21.7	1 2.7	6 52.4
4	0 50 30.5	9 50.9	8 6.8	2♊43.2	17 46.9	16 15.0	16 47.5	9 45.4	23 16.5	13 23.9	1 3.5	6 54.3
5	0 54 27.0	10 45.4	8 3.7	15 29.7	19 16.4	17 24.1	17 22.6	9D45.6	23 22.3	13 26.1	1 4.2	6 56.3
6	0 58 23.6	11 40.1	8 .6	28 51.8	20 45.5	18 33.1	17 57.7	9 46.0	23 28.2	13 28.4	1 5.1	6 58.3
7	1 2 20.1	12 34.8	7 57.4	12♋39.8	22 14.1	19 42.0	18 32.7	9 46.7	23 34.1	13 30.8	1 5.9	7 .4
8	1 6 16.7	13 29.7	7 54.3	26 39.3	23 42.4	20 50.8	19 7.7	9 47.5	23 40.1	13 33.1	1 6.8	7 2.4
9	1 10 13.2	14 24.6	7 51.2	10♌35.1	25 10.2	21 59.5	19 42.7	9 48.5	23 46.2	13 35.6	1 7.7	7 4.4
10	1 14 9.8	15 19.7	7 48.1	24 16.5	26 37.8	23 8.2	20 17.6	9 49.8	23 52.3	13 38.0	1 8.7	7 6.5
11	1 18 6.3	16 14.9	7 44.9	7♍40.1	28 5.1	24 16.9	20 52.5	9 51.2	23 58.5	13 40.6	1 9.8	7 8.6
12	1 22 2.9	17 10.2	7 41.8	20 50.1	29 32.1	25 25.5	21 27.4	9 52.9	24 4.7	13 43.2	1 10.8	7 10.7
13	1 25 59.4	18 5.7	7 38.7	3♎56.9	0♏58.9	26 34.0	22 2.2	9 54.7	24 11.0	13 45.8	1 11.8	7 12.8
14	1 29 56.0	19 1.2	7 35.6	17 14.9	2 25.4	27 42.5	22 37.0	9 56.7	24 17.3	13 48.4	1 12.9	7 14.9
15	1 33 52.6	19 56.9	7 32.5	0♏59.5	3 51.7	28 51.0	23 11.8	9 59.0	24 23.6	13 51.1	1 14.1	7 17.0
16	1 37 49.1	20 52.8	7 29.3	15 23.5	5 17.8	29 59.4	23 46.6	10 1.4	24 30.0	13 53.9	1 15.2	7 19.1
17	1 41 45.7	21 48.8	7 26.2	0♐32.0	6 43.8	1♎ 7.8	24 21.3	10 4.0	24 36.5	13 56.7	1 16.4	7 21.2
18	1 45 42.2	22 44.9	7 23.1	16 17.0	8 9.5	2 16.3	24 56.0	10 6.9	24 43.0	13 59.5	1 17.6	7 23.4
19	1 49 38.8	23 41.2	7 20.0	2♑15.5	9 35.1	3 24.7	25 30.6	10 9.9	24 49.5	14 2.3	1 18.9	7 25.5
20	1 53 35.3	24 37.6	7 16.9	17 56.2	11 .5	4 33.2	26 5.3	10 13.1	24 56.1	14 5.2	1 20.2	7 27.7
21	1 57 31.9	25 34.2	7 13.8	2♒50.9	12 25.7	5 41.7	26 39.9	10 16.5	25 2.7	14 8.2	1 21.5	7 29.8
22	2 1 28.4	26 30.9	7 10.6	16 44.4	13 50.7	6 50.2	27 14.5	10 20.1	25 9.4	14 11.1	1 22.9	7 32.0
23	2 5 25.0	27 27.8	7 7.5	29 35.3	15 15.5	7 58.8	27 49.1	10 23.9	25 16.1	14 14.1	1 24.2	7 34.2
24	2 9 21.5	28 24.9	7 4.4	11♓32.2	16 40.0	9 7.5	28 23.6	10 27.9	25 22.8	14 17.2	1 25.7	7 36.3
25	2 13 18.1	29 22.1	7 1.3	22 48.7	18 4.2	10 16.2	28 58.1	10 32.1	25 29.6	14 20.3	1 27.1	7 38.5
26	2 17 14.7	0♏19.6	6 58.2	3♈39.5	19 28.0	11 24.9	29 32.7	10 36.4	25 36.4	14 23.4	1 28.6	7 40.7
27	2 21 11.2	1 17.2	6 55.1	14 19.6	20 51.4	12 33.8	0♎ 7.2	10 41.0	25 43.2	14 26.5	1 30.1	7 42.9
28	2 25 7.8	2 14.9	6 52.0	25 2.7	22 14.4	13 42.8	0 41.7	10 45.7	25 50.1	14 29.7	1 31.6	7 45.1
29	2 29 4.3	3 12.9	6 48.8	6♉ 1.4	23 36.7	14 51.8	1 16.2	10 50.6	25 57.0	14 32.9	1 33.2	7 47.3
30	2 33 .9	4 11.1	6 45.7	17 26.5	24 58.4	16 1.0	1 50.6	10 55.7	26 3.9	14 36.2	1 34.8	7 49.5
31	2 36 57.4	5 9.4	6 42.6	29 25.6	26 19.4	17 10.3	2 25.1	11 .9	26 10.9	14 39.5	1 36.4	7 51.7
		DECLINATION										
1	0 38 40.8	3S 4.8	0N15.7	10N32.9	4S54.9	8N36.2	7N41.7	19S20.6	17S 8.7	22S36.0	22S20.0	2N30.1
4	0 50 30.5	4 14.5	0 15.7	23 23.8	7 8.5	7 16.1	6 58.0	19 20.5	17 13.2	22 36.7	22 20.2	2 27.3
7	1 2 20.1	5 23.7	0 15.6	27 34.9	9 17.2	5 54.1	6 14.0	19 20.0	17 17.8	22 37.4	22 20.3	2 24.5
10	1 14 9.8	6 32.3	0 15.6	19 39.8	11 20.5	4 30.3	5 29.6	19 19.1	17 22.5	22 38.2	22 20.4	2 21.8
13	1 25 59.4	7 40.2	0 15.5	1 41.4	13 17.7	3 5.1	4 45.1	19 17.7	17 27.2	22 39.0	22 20.5	2 19.0
16	1 37 49.1	8 47.1	0 15.5	18S .5	15 8.3	1 38.8	4 .4	19 15.8	17 32.0	22 39.9	22 20.6	2 16.4
19	1 49 38.8	9 52.9	0 15.4	27 38.3	16 51.7	0 11.7	3 15.5	19 13.4	17 36.8	22 40.8	22 20.7	2 13.8
22	2 1 28.4	10 57.4	0 15.4	22 3.9	18 27.3	1S15.7	2 30.6	19 10.7	17 41.6	22 41.7	22 20.8	2 11.3
25	2 13 18.1	12 .4	0 15.3	7 26.4	19 54.5	2 43.2	1 45.6	19 7.4	17 46.5	22 42.6	22 20.9	2 8.8
28	2 25 7.8	13 1.7	0 15.3	9N 9.4	21 12.6	4 10.6	1 .6	19 3.8	17 51.3	22 43.6	22 20.9	2 6.4
31	2 36 57.4	14 1.2	0 15.2	22 34.4	22 20.8	5 37.3	0 15.6	18 59.7	17 56.2	22 44.6	22 21.0	2 4.1

NOVEMBER 1985

DAY	EPHEM. SID. TIME	☉	☊	☾	☿	♀	♂	♃	♄	♅	♆	♇
	h m s	° ′	° ′	° ′	° ′	° ′	° ′	° ′	° ′	° ′	° ′	° ′
		LONGITUDE										
1	2 40 54.0	8♏30.8	9♉ 3.0	13♊48.3	0♐23.5	19♎13.5	2♎44.6	8♒27.0	28♏ 7.5	15♐55.7	1♑30.7	4♏50.5
2	2 44 50.5	9 30.8	8 59.8	25 43.9	1 38.8	20 28.4	3 22.2	8 32.5	28 14.3	15 58.8	1 32.3	4 52.9
3	2 48 47.1	10 30.9	8 56.6	7♋47.9	2 52.4	21 43.3	3 59.8	8 38.2	28 21.2	16 1.9	1 33.8	4 55.4
4	2 52 43.7	11 30.9	8 53.4	20 3.9	4 4.4	22 58.2	4 37.3	8 44.0	28 28.2	16 5.1	1 35.4	4 57.8
5	2 56 40.2	12 31.1	8 50.3	2♌35.8	5 14.4	24 13.2	5 14.9	8 50.0	28 35.1	16 8.3	1 37.1	5 .2
6	3 0 36.8	13 31.2	8 47.1	15 27.3	6 22.3	25 28.2	5 52.5	8 56.2	28 42.1	16 11.5	1 38.7	5 2.6
7	3 4 33.3	14 31.4	8 43.9	28 41.8	7 27.9	26 43.2	6 30.0	9 2.6	28 49.1	16 14.7	1 40.4	5 5.0
8	3 8 29.9	15 31.7	8 40.7	12♍22.0	8 30.7	27 58.2	7 7.6	9 9.1	28 56.1	16 18.0	1 42.1	5 7.4
9	3 12 26.4	16 31.9	8 37.6	26 28.7	9 30.6	29 13.3	7 45.1	9 15.8	29 3.1	16 21.3	1 43.8	5 9.8
10	3 16 23.0	17 32.2	8 34.4	11♎ .7	10 27.2	0♏28.4	8 22.6	9 22.6	29 10.1	16 24.6	1 45.5	5 12.2
11	3 20 19.6	18 32.6	8 31.2	25 54.1	11 20.0	1 43.5	9 .1	9 29.6	29 17.2	16 27.9	1 47.3	5 14.6
12	3 24 16.1	19 32.9	8 28.0	11♏ 2.2	12 8.5	2 58.6	9 37.6	9 36.7	29 24.2	16 31.3	1 49.1	5 16.9
13	3 28 12.7	20 33.3	8 24.8	26 16.1	12 52.3	4 13.8	10 15.1	9 44.1	29 31.3	16 34.6	1 50.9	5 19.3
14	3 32 9.2	21 33.7	8 21.7	11♐26.1	13 30.8	5 28.9	10 52.6	9 51.5	29 38.4	16 38.0	1 52.7	5 21.7
15	3 36 5.8	22 34.2	8 18.5	26 22.6	14 3.3	6 44.1	11 30.1	9 59.1	29 45.5	16 41.4	1 54.5	5 24.0
16	3 40 2.3	23 34.6	8 15.3	10♑58.1	14 29.2	7 59.3	12 7.5	10 6.9	29 52.6	16 44.9	1 56.4	5 26.4
17	3 43 58.9	24 35.1	8 12.1	25 7.8	14 47.7	9 14.6	12 45.0	10 14.8	29 59.7	16 48.3	1 58.3	5 28.7
18	3 47 55.5	25 35.6	8 9.0	8♒49.8	14 58.1	10 29.8	13 22.4	10 22.9	0♐ 6.9	16 51.8	2 .2	5 31.0
19	3 51 52.0	26 36.2	8 5.8	22 4.8	14 59.6	11 45.0	13 59.8	10 31.1	0 14.0	16 55.3	2 2.1	5 33.3
20	3 55 48.6	27 36.7	8 2.6	4♓55.2	14R51.6	13 .3	14 37.2	10 39.5	0 21.1	16 58.8	2 4.0	5 35.6
21	3 59 45.1	28 37.3	7 59.4	17 24.9	14 33.5	14 15.6	15 14.6	10 47.9	0 28.3	17 2.3	2 6.0	5 37.9
22	4 3 41.7	29 37.9	7 56.3	29 38.1	14 4.9	15 30.9	15 52.0	10 56.6	0 35.5	17 5.9	2 8.0	5 40.2
23	4 7 38.2	0♐38.6	7 53.1	11♈39.1	13 25.5	16 46.2	16 29.4	11 5.4	0 42.6	17 9.4	2 10.0	5 42.4
24	4 11 34.8	1 39.2	7 49.9	23 32.1	12 35.7	18 1.5	17 6.7	11 14.3	0 49.8	17 13.0	2 12.0	5 44.7
25	4 15 31.4	2 39.9	7 46.7	5♉20.6	11 36.0	19 16.8	17 44.1	11 23.3	0 56.9	17 16.5	2 14.0	5 46.9
26	4 19 27.9	3 40.5	7 43.5	17 7.8	10 27.7	20 32.1	18 21.4	11 32.5	1 4.0	17 20.1	2 16.1	5 49.1
27	4 23 24.5	4 41.2	7 40.4	28 56.4	9 12.3	21 47.5	18 58.7	11 41.8	1 11.2	17 23.7	2 18.1	5 51.3
28	4 27 21.0	5 41.9	7 37.2	10♊48.6	7 52.2	23 2.8	19 36.0	11 51.2	1 18.3	17 27.3	2 20.2	5 53.5
29	4 31 17.6	6 42.7	7 34.0	22 46.2	6 29.8	24 18.2	20 13.3	12 .8	1 25.4	17 30.9	2 22.3	5 55.7
30	4 35 14.1	7 43.4	7 30.8	4♋50.8	5 7.9	25 33.6	20 50.6	12 10.4	1 32.5	17 34.5	2 24.4	5 57.8
		LATITUDE										
1	2 40 54.0	0 .0	0 .0	3N 1.0	2S30.4	1N32.5	1N12.0	0S50.7	1N49.7	0S 2.9	1N 5.1	16N 5.3
4	2 52 43.7	0 .0	0 .0	5 .4	2 39.8	1 30.9	1 11.8	0 50.5	1 49.4	0 2.9	1 4.9	16 5.4
7	3 4 33.3	0 .0	0 .0	4 59.7	2 44.9	1 28.6	1 11.6	0 50.3	1 49.1	0 3.0	1 4.8	16 5.6
10	3 16 23.0	0 .0	0 .0	2 30.4	2 44.7	1 25.8	1 11.3	0 50.1	1 48.9	0 3.0	1 4.7	16 5.8
13	3 28 12.7	0 .0	0 .0	1S33.3	2 37.5	1 22.5	1 11.1	0 50.0	1 48.7	0 3.0	1 4.6	16 6.1
16	3 40 2.3	0 .0	0 .0	4 39.3	2 21.3	1 18.6	1 10.8	0 49.8	1 48.5	0 3.0	1 4.5	16 6.5
19	3 51 52.0	0 .0	0 .0	5 8.5	1 53.5	1 14.2	1 10.5	0 49.6	1 48.3	0 3.1	1 4.5	16 7.0
22	4 3 41.7	0 .0	0 .0	3 21.5	1 12.4	1 9.3	1 10.1	0 49.4	1 48.2	0 3.1	1 4.4	16 7.5
25	4 15 31.4	0 .0	0 .0	0 21.2	0 18.3	1 4.0	1 9.7	0 49.3	1 48.1	0 3.1	1 4.3	16 8.2
28	4 27 21.0	0 .0	0 .0	2N45.2	0N42.6	0 58.4	1 9.3	0 49.1	1 48.0	0 3.1	1 4.2	16 8.9
		RIGHT ASCENSION										
1	2 40 54.0	6♏ 8.0	6♉39.5	12♊ 2.0	27♏39.4	18♎19.8	2♎59.6	11♒ 6.4	26♏17.9	14♐42.8	1♑38.1	7♏54.0
2	2 44 50.5	7 6.8	6 36.4	25 12.5	28 58.4	19 29.4	3 34.1	11 12.0	26 25.0	14 46.2	1 39.7	7 56.2
3	2 48 47.1	8 5.7	6 33.3	8♋47.4	0♐16.1	20 39.1	4 8.6	11 17.8	26 32.0	14 49.5	1 41.4	7 58.4
4	2 52 43.7	9 4.9	6 30.2	22 32.0	1 32.4	21 49.0	4 43.0	11 23.7	26 39.1	14 53.0	1 43.2	8 .6
5	2 56 40.2	10 4.3	6 27.1	6♌11.5	2 47.0	22 59.0	5 17.5	11 29.9	26 46.2	14 56.4	1 44.9	8 2.8
6	3 0 36.8	11 3.9	6 24.0	19 35.0	3 59.7	24 9.3	5 51.9	11 36.1	26 53.3	14 59.9	1 46.7	8 5.0
7	3 4 33.3	12 3.7	6 20.9	2♍39.1	5 10.2	25 19.7	6 26.4	11 42.6	27 .5	15 3.3	1 48.5	8 7.2
8	3 8 29.9	13 3.7	6 17.8	15 28.0	6 18.1	26 30.4	7 .9	11 49.2	27 7.7	15 6.9	1 50.3	8 9.4
9	3 12 26.4	14 3.9	6 14.7	28 12.1	7 23.1	27 41.2	7 35.3	11 56.0	27 14.9	15 10.4	1 52.2	8 11.6
10	3 16 23.0	15 4.4	6 11.5	11♎ 6.2	8 24.6	28 52.2	8 9.8	12 2.9	27 22.1	15 14.0	1 54.1	8 13.8
11	3 20 19.6	16 5.0	6 8.4	24 27.8	9 22.3	0♏ 3.5	8 44.3	12 10.0	27 29.3	15 17.6	1 56.0	8 16.0
12	3 24 16.1	17 5.9	6 5.3	8♏33.3	10 15.7	1 15.0	9 18.7	12 17.3	27 36.6	15 21.2	1 57.9	8 18.2
13	3 28 12.7	18 7.0	6 2.2	23 33.9	11 4.0	2 26.7	9 53.2	12 24.7	27 43.8	15 24.8	1 59.8	8 20.4
14	3 32 9.2	19 8.3	5 59.1	9♐28.0	11 46.6	3 38.7	10 27.7	12 32.3	27 51.1	15 28.5	2 1.8	8 22.6
15	3 36 5.8	20 9.8	5 56.0	25 55.9	12 22.9	4 50.9	11 2.2	12 40.0	27 58.4	15 32.2	2 3.8	8 24.7
16	3 40 2.3	21 11.5	5 52.9	12♑21.6	12 52.1	6 3.4	11 36.7	12 47.9	28 5.7	15 35.9	2 5.8	8 26.9
17	3 43 58.9	22 13.4	5 49.8	28 6.7	13 13.3	7 16.1	12 11.2	12 55.9	28 13.0	15 39.6	2 7.9	8 29.1
18	3 47 55.5	23 15.6	5 46.7	12♒45.8	13 25.8	8 29.1	12 45.8	13 4.1	28 20.4	15 43.3	2 9.9	8 31.2
19	3 51 52.0	24 17.9	5 43.6	26 12.2	13 28.9	9 42.3	13 20.3	13 12.4	28 27.7	15 47.1	2 12.0	8 33.4
20	3 55 48.6	25 20.4	5 40.5	8♓33.1	13R21.6	10 55.9	13 54.8	13 20.8	28 35.0	15 50.9	2 14.1	8 35.5
21	3 59 45.1	26 23.2	5 37.4	20 3.4	13 3.6	12 9.7	14 29.4	13 29.4	28 42.4	15 54.7	2 16.2	8 37.7
22	4 3 41.7	27 26.1	5 34.3	1♈ .2	12 34.5	13 23.8	15 4.0	13 38.2	28 49.8	15 58.5	2 18.4	8 39.8
23	4 7 38.2	28 29.3	5 31.2	11 40.0	11 54.1	14 38.2	15 38.6	13 47.0	28 57.1	16 2.4	2 20.6	8 41.9
24	4 11 34.8	29 32.6	5 28.1	22 18.7	11 2.9	15 52.8	16 13.2	13 56.0	29 4.5	16 6.2	2 22.7	8 44.0
25	4 15 31.4	0♐36.1	5 25.0	3♉10.2	10 1.5	17 7.8	16 47.9	14 5.1	29 11.9	16 10.1	2 24.9	8 46.1
26	4 19 27.9	1 39.8	5 21.9	14 26.9	8 51.4	18 23.1	17 22.5	14 14.4	29 19.2	16 13.9	2 27.1	8 48.2
27	4 23 24.5	2 43.7	5 18.8	26 18.0	7 34.5	19 38.6	17 57.2	14 23.8	29 26.6	16 17.8	2 29.3	8 50.3
28	4 27 21.0	3 47.7	5 15.7	8♊47.9	6 13.0	20 54.5	18 31.9	14 33.3	29 34.0	16 21.7	2 31.6	8 52.4
29	4 31 17.6	4 52.0	5 12.6	21 54.4	4 49.6	22 10.6	19 6.6	14 42.9	29 41.3	16 25.6	2 33.8	8 54.4
30	4 35 14.1	5 56.4	5 9.5	5♋27.6	3 27.3	23 27.1	19 41.4	14 52.6	29 48.7	16 29.5	2 36.1	8 56.4
		DECLINATION										
1	2 40 54.0	14S20.6	0N15.2	25N27.3	22S41.2	6S 6.0	0N .6	18S58.2	17S57.8	22S44.9	22S21.0	2N 3.3
4	2 52 43.7	15 17.4	0 15.1	26 53.6	23 34.8	7 31.5	0S44.3	18 53.5	18 2.6	22 45.9	22 21.1	2 1.1
7	3 4 33.3	16 11.9	0 15.1	16 36.3	24 16.2	8 55.6	1 29.1	18 48.5	18 7.4	22 46.9	22 21.1	1 59.0
10	3 16 23.0	17 4.0	0 15.0	2S 3.1	24 44.1	10 18.0	2 13.8	18 42.9	18 12.2	22 47.9	22 21.2	1 57.0
13	3 28 12.7	17 53.5	0 15.0	20 49.9	24 57.0	11 38.3	2 58.2	18 37.0	18 16.9	22 49.0	22 21.2	1 55.1
16	3 40 2.3	18 40.2	0 14.9	27 37.8	24 52.8	12 56.1	3 42.4	18 30.7	18 21.6	22 50.0	22 21.2	1 53.2
19	3 51 52.0	19 24.0	0 14.9	19 .6	24 28.7	14 11.1	4 26.3	18 24.0	18 26.2	22 51.1	22 21.2	1 51.5
22	4 3 41.7	20 4.5	0 14.8	3 13.5	23 41.5	15 23.0	5 10.0	18 16.8	18 30.8	22 52.1	22 21.2	1 49.9
25	4 15 31.4	20 41.8	0 14.8	12N58.4	22 28.9	16 31.3	5 53.2	18 9.3	18 35.3	22 53.2	22 21.2	1 48.4
28	4 27 21.0	21 15.5	0 14.7	24 47.7	20 55.4	17 35.7	6 36.0	18 1.4	18 39.8	22 54.2	22 21.1	1 47.0

DECEMBER 1985

DAY	EPHEM. SID. TIME	☉	☊	☽	☿	♀	♂	♃	♄	♅	♆	♇
	h m s	° ′	° ′	° ′	° ′	° ′	° ′	° ′	° ′	° ′	° ′	° ′
		LONGITUDE										
1	4 39 10.7	8♐44.2	7♉27.7	17♋ 4.4	3♐49.2	26♏49.0	21♎27.8	12♒20.2	1♐39.6	17♐38.1	2♑26.5	5♏60.0
2	4 43 7.3	9 45.0	7 24.5	29 28.6	2 R 36.5	28 4.4	22 5.1	12 30.1	1 46.8	17 41.8	2 28.6	6 2.1
3	4 47 3.8	10 45.9	7 21.3	12♌ 5.6	1 31.7	29 19.8	22 42.3	12 40.2	1 53.8	17 45.4	2 30.7	6 4.2
4	4 51 .4	11 46.7	7 18.1	24 57.8	0 36.5	0♐35.2	23 19.6	12 50.3	2 .9	17 49.1	2 32.9	6 6.2
5	4 54 56.9	12 47.6	7 15.0	8♍ 7.7	29♏52.1	1 50.6	23 56.8	13 .6	2 8.0	17 52.7	2 35.0	6 8.3
6	4 58 53.5	13 48.5	7 11.8	21 37.7	29 19.1	3 6.1	24 34.0	13 11.0	2 15.0	17 56.4	2 37.2	6 10.3
7	5 2 50.1	14 49.4	7 8.6	5♎29.4	28 57.5	4 21.5	25 11.2	13 21.5	2 22.1	18 .0	2 39.4	6 12.3
8	5 6 46.6	15 50.4	7 5.4	19 43.6	28 47.1	5 37.0	25 48.3	13 32.1	2 29.1	18 3.7	2 41.6	6 14.3
9	5 10 43.2	16 51.3	7 2.3	4♏18.9	28 D 47.3	6 52.5	26 25.5	13 42.8	2 36.1	18 7.4	2 43.8	6 16.3
10	5 14 39.7	17 52.3	6 59.1	19 11.6	28 57.6	8 7.9	27 2.6	13 53.6	2 43.1	18 11.0	2 46.0	6 18.3
11	5 18 36.3	18 53.3	6 55.9	4♐15.4	29 17.0	9 23.4	27 39.8	14 4.6	2 50.1	18 14.7	2 48.2	6 20.2
12	5 22 32.8	19 54.3	6 52.7	19 21.6	29 44.7	10 38.9	28 16.9	14 15.6	2 57.0	18 18.3	2 50.4	6 22.1
13	5 26 29.4	20 55.4	6 49.6	4♑20.8	0♐20.0	11 54.5	28 54.0	14 26.8	3 4.0	18 22.1	2 52.7	6 24.0
14	5 30 26.0	21 56.4	6 46.4	19 3.6	1 1.8	13 9.9	29 31.1	14 38.1	3 10.9	18 25.7	2 54.9	6 25.9
15	5 34 22.5	22 57.5	6 43.2	3♒23.1	1 49.6	14 25.4	0♏ 8.1	14 49.4	3 17.8	18 29.4	2 57.2	6 27.7
16	5 38 19.1	23 58.5	6 40.0	17 14.9	2 42.5	15 40.9	0 45.1	15 .8	3 24.7	18 33.0	2 59.4	6 29.5
17	5 42 15.6	24 59.6	6 36.8	0♓37.9	3 40.1	16 56.4	1 22.1	15 12.4	3 31.5	18 36.7	3 1.7	6 31.3
18	5 46 12.2	26 .7	6 33.7	13 33.6	4 41.6	18 11.9	1 59.1	15 24.0	3 38.3	18 40.3	3 3.9	6 33.1
19	5 50 8.8	27 1.8	6 30.5	26 5.4	5 46.7	19 27.4	2 36.1	15 35.7	3 45.1	18 44.0	3 6.2	6 34.8
20	5 54 5.3	28 2.9	6 27.3	8♈18.1	6 54.8	20 42.9	3 13.0	15 47.5	3 51.8	18 47.6	3 8.4	6 36.5
21	5 58 1.9	29 3.9	6 24.1	20 16.9	8 5.7	21 58.4	3 49.9	15 59.4	3 58.5	18 51.2	3 10.7	6 38.2
22	6 1 58.4	0♑ 5.0	6 21.0	2♉ 7.1	9 18.9	23 13.9	4 26.8	16 11.4	4 5.2	18 54.8	3 13.0	6 39.9
23	6 5 55.0	1 6.1	6 17.8	13 53.5	10 34.2	24 29.4	5 3.7	16 23.5	4 11.8	18 58.4	3 15.2	6 41.5
24	6 9 51.6	2 7.2	6 14.6	25 40.8	11 51.3	25 44.9	5 40.5	16 35.6	4 18.4	19 2.0	3 17.5	6 43.1
25	6 13 48.1	3 8.3	6 11.4	7♊32.4	13 10.0	27 .4	6 17.4	16 47.9	4 25.0	19 5.6	3 19.8	6 44.7
26	6 17 44.7	4 9.5	6 8.3	19 31.2	14 30.2	28 15.9	6 54.2	17 .2	4 31.5	19 9.2	3 22.0	6 46.2
27	6 21 41.2	5 10.6	6 5.1	1♋39.2	15 51.6	29 31.4	7 31.0	17 12.6	4 38.0	19 12.7	3 24.3	6 47.7
28	6 25 37.8	6 11.7	6 1.9	13 57.6	17 14.1	0♑46.9	8 7.7	17 25.0	4 44.5	19 16.3	3 26.6	6 49.2
29	6 29 34.3	7 12.8	5 58.7	26 27.1	18 37.6	2 2.4	8 44.5	17 37.6	4 50.9	19 19.8	3 28.8	6 50.7
30	6 33 30.9	8 13.9	5 55.6	9♌ 7.8	20 2.1	3 17.9	9 21.2	17 50.2	4 57.3	19 23.3	3 31.1	6 52.1
31	6 37 27.5	9 15.1	5 52.4	21 60.0	21 27.3	4 33.4	9 57.9	18 2.9	5 3.6	19 26.9	3 33.4	6 53.5
		LATITUDE										
1	4 39 10.7	0 .0	0 .0	4N50.4	1N38.9	0N52.4	1N 8.8	0S49.0	1N47.9	0S 3.2	1N 4.2	16N 9.6
4	4 51 .4	0 .0	0 .0	4 60.0	2 19.6	0 46.0	1 8.4	0 48.9	1 47.8	0 3.2	1 4.1	16 10.5
7	5 2 50.1	0 .0	0 .0	2 51.2	2 40.6	0 39.4	1 7.8	0 48.7	1 47.8	0 3.2	1 4.0	16 11.4
10	5 14 39.7	0 .0	0 .0	0S56.9	2 44.6	0 32.6	1 7.2	0 48.6	1 47.8	0 3.3	1 4.0	16 12.3
13	5 26 29.4	0 .0	0 .0	4 16.3	2 36.4	0 25.6	1 6.6	0 48.5	1 47.8	0 3.3	1 3.9	16 13.4
16	5 38 19.1	0 .0	0 .0	5 5.1	2 20.4	0 18.5	1 6.0	0 48.4	1 47.8	0 3.3	1 3.9	16 14.5
19	5 50 8.8	0 .0	0 .0	3 26.9	1 59.9	0 11.3	1 5.3	0 48.4	1 47.9	0 3.3	1 3.8	16 15.6
22	6 1 58.4	0 .0	0 .0	0 31.9	1 36.9	0 4.0	1 4.6	0 48.3	1 48.0	0 3.4	1 3.8	16 16.9
25	6 13 48.1	0 .0	0 .0	2N31.5	1 12.9	0S 3.3	1 3.8	0 48.2	1 48.1	0 3.4	1 3.8	16 18.1
28	6 25 37.8	0 .0	0 .0	4 38.9	0 48.6	0 10.5	1 2.9	0 48.2	1 48.2	0 3.4	1 3.8	16 19.5
31	6 37 27.5	0 .0	0 .0	4 53.3	0 24.7	0 17.6	1 2.0	0 48.2	1 48.3	0 3.5	1 3.7	16 20.8
		RIGHT ASCENSION										
1	4 39 10.7	7♐ 1.0	5♉ 6.4	19♋11.7	2♐ 8.6	24♏43.8	20♎16.1	15♒ 2.5	29♏56.0	16♐33.4	2♑38.4	8♏58.5
2	4 43 7.3	8 5.7	5 3.3	2♌49.3	0 R 56.2	26 .9	20 50.9	15 12.5	0♐ 3.4	16 37.3	2 40.7	9 .5
3	4 47 3.8	9 10.6	5 .2	16 7.3	29♏52.0	27 18.3	21 25.7	15 22.6	0 10.7	16 41.3	2 43.0	9 2.5
4	4 51 .4	10 15.7	4 57.1	29 .2	28 57.7	28 35.9	22 .6	15 32.8	0 18.0	16 45.2	2 45.3	9 4.5
5	4 54 56.9	11 20.9	4 54.1	11♍31.0	28 14.1	29 53.9	22 35.5	15 43.1	0 25.3	16 49.2	2 47.6	9 6.4
6	4 58 53.5	12 26.3	4 51.0	23 49.4	27 41.8	1♐12.1	23 10.4	15 53.6	0 32.6	16 53.1	2 50.0	9 8.4
7	5 2 50.1	13 31.8	4 47.9	6♎10.2	27 20.8	2 30.7	23 45.3	16 4.1	0 39.9	16 57.1	2 52.3	9 10.3
8	5 6 46.6	14 37.4	4 44.8	18 51.3	27 10.8	3 49.5	24 20.3	16 14.7	0 47.2	17 1.0	2 54.7	9 12.2
9	5 10 43.2	15 43.1	4 41.7	2♏11.6	27 D 11.4	5 8.6	24 55.3	16 25.5	0 54.5	17 5.0	2 57.1	9 14.1
10	5 14 39.7	16 49.0	4 38.6	16 28.0	27 21.8	6 28.0	25 30.3	16 36.3	1 1.7	17 8.9	2 59.4	9 16.0
11	5 18 36.3	17 55.0	4 35.5	1♐49.3	27 41.3	7 47.6	26 5.4	16 47.3	1 9.0	17 12.9	3 1.8	9 17.9
12	5 22 32.8	19 1.1	4 32.4	18 7.6	28 9.0	9 7.5	26 40.5	16 58.4	1 16.2	17 16.9	3 4.2	9 19.7
13	5 26 29.4	20 7.3	4 29.3	4♑53.6	28 44.3	10 27.6	27 15.7	17 9.6	1 23.4	17 20.9	3 6.7	9 21.6
14	5 30 26.0	21 13.6	4 26.2	21 24.0	29 26.3	11 48.0	27 50.8	17 20.8	1 30.6	17 24.9	3 9.1	9 23.4
15	5 34 22.5	22 19.9	4 23.1	6♒59.7	0♐14.3	13 8.6	28 26.0	17 32.2	1 37.7	17 28.8	3 11.5	9 25.2
16	5 38 19.1	23 26.3	4 20.1	21 20.6	1 7.7	14 29.4	29 1.2	17 43.6	1 44.8	17 32.8	3 14.0	9 27.0
17	5 42 15.6	24 32.7	4 17.0	4♓26.3	2 6.0	15 50.4	29 36.4	17 55.1	1 51.9	17 36.7	3 16.4	9 28.7
18	5 46 12.2	25 39.2	4 13.9	16 29.3	3 8.6	17 11.6	0♏11.7	18 6.7	1 59.0	17 40.7	3 18.8	9 30.4
19	5 50 8.8	26 45.8	4 10.8	27 47.1	4 15.0	18 32.9	0 47.0	18 18.4	2 6.1	17 44.6	3 21.3	9 32.1
20	5 54 5.3	27 52.3	4 7.7	8♈38.0	5 24.8	19 54.5	1 22.4	18 30.2	2 13.1	17 48.5	3 23.7	9 33.8
21	5 58 1.9	28 58.9	4 4.6	19 19.5	6 37.8	21 16.2	1 57.8	18 42.0	2 20.0	17 52.4	3 26.2	9 35.5
22	6 1 58.4	0♑ 5.5	4 1.5	0♉ 7.5	7 53.5	22 38.0	2 33.2	18 54.0	2 27.0	17 56.4	3 28.6	9 37.1
23	6 5 55.0	1 12.1	3 58.4	11 16.2	9 11.7	23 60.0	3 8.6	19 6.0	2 33.9	18 .3	3 31.1	9 38.7
24	6 9 51.6	2 18.7	3 55.4	22 57.1	10 32.2	25 22.0	3 44.1	19 18.1	2 40.8	18 4.2	3 33.5	9 40.3
25	6 13 48.1	3 25.2	3 52.3	5♊17.5	11 54.7	26 44.2	4 19.6	19 30.2	2 47.6	18 8.0	3 36.0	9 41.9
26	6 17 44.7	4 31.8	3 49.2	18 18.2	13 19.1	28 6.5	4 55.2	19 42.5	2 54.5	18 11.9	3 38.4	9 43.4
27	6 21 41.2	5 38.3	3 46.1	1♋51.6	14 45.1	29 28.8	5 30.8	19 54.8	3 1.2	18 15.8	3 40.9	9 45.0
28	6 25 37.8	6 44.8	3 43.0	15 42.2	16 12.7	0♑51.2	6 6.4	20 7.1	3 8.0	18 19.6	3 43.3	9 46.5
29	6 29 34.3	7 51.3	3 39.9	29 30.9	17 41.8	2 13.6	6 42.1	20 19.6	3 14.7	18 23.4	3 45.8	9 47.9
30	6 33 30.9	8 57.7	3 36.9	13♌ .7	19 12.1	3 36.1	7 17.8	20 32.1	3 21.3	18 27.2	3 48.2	9 49.4
31	6 37 27.5	10 4.0	3 33.8	26 2.1	20 43.7	4 58.5	7 53.5	20 44.6	3 27.9	18 31.0	3 50.7	9 50.8
		DECLINATION										
1	4 39 10.7	21S45.7	0N14.7	27N 9.1	19S17.9	18S35.9	7S18.4	17S53.2	18S44.1	22S55.2	22S21.1	1N45.7
4	4 51 .4	22 12.2	0 14.6	17 54.5	18 .3	19 31.6	8 .3	17 44.5	18 48.4	22 56.3	22 21.0	1 44.6
7	5 2 50.1	22 34.8	0 14.6	0 26.3	17 19.0	20 22.3	8 41.7	17 35.5	18 52.6	22 57.3	22 21.0	1 43.6
10	5 14 39.7	22 53.4	0 14.5	18S26.2	17 15.1	21 7.8	9 22.5	17 26.2	18 56.7	22 58.3	22 20.9	1 42.7
13	5 26 29.4	23 7.9	0 14.4	27 38.5	17 40.5	21 47.8	10 2.8	17 16.4	19 .6	22 59.3	22 20.8	1 41.9
16	5 38 19.1	23 18.4	0 14.4	20 30.4	18 24.5	22 22.0	10 42.4	17 6.4	19 4.5	23 .3	22 20.7	1 41.2
19	5 50 8.8	23 24.6	0 14.3	4 43.1	19 18.3	22 50.2	11 21.3	16 56.0	19 8.3	23 1.2	22 20.6	1 40.7
22	6 1 58.4	23 26.6	0 14.3	11N42.7	20 15.2	23 12.2	11 59.5	16 45.3	19 11.9	23 2.2	22 20.4	1 40.3
25	6 13 48.1	23 24.3	0 14.2	24 3.7	21 10.6	23 27.8	12 36.9	16 34.2	19 15.5	23 3.1	22 20.3	1 40.0
28	6 25 37.8	23 17.9	0 14.2	27 20.0	22 1.4	23 36.9	13 13.6	16 22.9	19 18.9	23 4.0	22 20.2	1 39.9
31	6 37 27.5	23 7.2	0 14.1	18 47.9	22 45.4	23 39.4	13 49.4	16 11.3	19 22.2	23 4.9	22 20.0	1 39.9

JANUARY 1986

DAY	EPHEM. SID. TIME	☉	☊	☾	☿	♀	♂	♃	♄	♅	♆	♇
	h m s	° ′	° ′	° ′	° ′	° ′	° ′	° ′	° ′	° ′	° ′	° ′
		LONGITUDE										
1	6 41 24.0	10♑16.2	5♉49.2	5♍ 3.8	22♐53.3	5♑48.9	10♏34.6	18♒15.6	5♐ 9.9	19♐30.3	3♑35.6	6♏54.9
2	6 45 20.6	11 17.4	5 46.0	18 20.1	24 20.0	7 4.4	11 11.2	18 28.4	5 16.2	19 33.8	3 37.9	6 56.2
3	6 49 17.1	12 18.6	5 42.8	1♎49.8	25 47.4	8 19.9	11 47.9	18 41.4	5 22.4	19 37.3	3 40.2	6 57.5
4	6 53 13.7	13 19.7	5 39.7	15 33.9	27 15.4	9 35.4	12 24.5	18 54.3	5 28.6	19 40.8	3 42.4	6 58.8
5	6 57 10.3	14 20.9	5 36.5	29 33.5	28 43.9	10 50.9	13 1.0	19 7.4	5 34.7	19 44.2	3 44.7	7 .1
6	7 1 6.8	15 22.0	5 33.3	13♏48.7	0♑12.9	12 6.4	13 37.6	19 20.5	5 40.7	19 47.6	3 46.9	7 1.3
7	7 5 3.4	16 23.2	5 30.1	28 17.9	1 42.4	13 22.0	14 14.1	19 33.6	5 46.7	19 51.0	3 49.1	7 2.4
8	7 8 59.9	17 24.4	5 27.0	12♐57.9	3 12.5	14 37.4	14 50.6	19 46.8	5 52.7	19 54.3	3 51.4	7 3.6
9	7 12 56.5	18 25.5	5 23.8	27 43.1	4 43.0	15 52.9	15 27.0	20 .1	5 58.6	19 57.7	3 53.6	7 4.7
10	7 16 53.0	19 26.7	5 20.6	12♑26.1	6 14.0	17 8.4	16 3.5	20 13.4	6 4.4	20 1.0	3 55.8	7 5.8
11	7 20 49.6	20 27.9	5 17.4	26 58.8	7 45.5	18 23.9	16 39.9	20 26.8	6 10.2	20 4.3	3 58.0	7 6.8
12	7 24 46.2	21 29.0	5 14.3	11♒14.0	9 17.4	19 39.4	17 16.2	20 40.3	6 16.0	20 7.5	4 .2	7 7.8
13	7 28 42.7	22 30.2	5 11.1	25 6.0	10 49.8	20 54.9	17 52.5	20 53.7	6 21.7	20 10.8	4 2.4	7 8.8
14	7 32 39.3	23 31.3	5 7.9	8♓31.9	12 22.7	22 10.4	18 28.8	21 7.3	6 27.3	20 14.0	4 4.5	7 9.7
15	7 36 35.8	24 32.5	5 4.7	21 31.7	13 56.1	23 25.8	19 5.0	21 20.9	6 32.8	20 17.2	4 6.7	7 10.6
16	7 40 32.4	25 33.6	5 1.6	4♈ 7.4	15 29.9	24 41.3	19 41.2	21 34.5	6 38.3	20 20.4	4 8.9	7 11.5
17	7 44 29.0	26 34.7	4 58.4	16 23.0	17 4.3	25 56.8	20 17.4	21 48.2	6 43.8	20 23.5	4 11.0	7 12.3
18	7 48 25.5	27 35.8	4 55.2	28 23.5	18 39.1	27 12.2	20 53.5	22 1.9	6 49.1	20 26.6	4 13.1	7 13.1
19	7 52 22.1	28 36.9	4 52.0	10♉14.6	20 14.5	28 27.6	21 29.6	22 15.7	6 54.4	20 29.7	4 15.2	7 13.9
20	7 56 18.6	29 37.9	4 48.8	22 1.7	21 50.4	29 43.1	22 5.7	22 29.5	6 59.7	20 32.7	4 17.3	7 14.6
21	8 0 15.2	0♒39.0	4 45.7	3♊50.3	23 26.8	0♒58.5	22 41.7	22 43.4	7 4.9	20 35.8	4 19.4	7 15.3
22	8 4 11.7	1 40.0	4 42.5	15 45.1	25 3.8	2 13.9	23 17.7	22 57.2	7 10.0	20 38.8	4 21.5	7 16.0
23	8 8 8.3	2 41.1	4 39.3	27 50.1	26 41.4	3 29.3	23 53.6	23 11.2	7 15.0	20 41.7	4 23.6	7 16.6
24	8 12 4.9	3 42.1	4 36.1	10♋ 8.0	28 19.6	4 44.7	24 29.6	23 25.2	7 20.0	20 44.7	4 25.6	7 17.2
25	8 16 1.4	4 43.1	4 33.0	22 40.4	29 58.4	6 .1	25 5.4	23 39.2	7 24.9	20 47.6	4 27.7	7 17.8
26	8 19 58.0	5 44.1	4 29.8	5♌27.9	1♒37.8	7 15.5	25 41.2	23 53.2	7 29.8	20 50.4	4 29.7	7 18.3
27	8 23 54.5	6 45.1	4 26.6	18 29.7	3 17.9	8 30.8	26 17.0	24 7.3	7 34.5	20 53.3	4 31.7	7 18.8
28	8 27 51.1	7 46.0	4 23.4	1♍44.5	4 58.6	9 46.2	26 52.7	24 21.3	7 39.2	20 56.1	4 33.7	7 19.2
29	8 31 47.6	8 46.9	4 20.3	15 10.3	6 39.9	11 1.5	27 28.4	24 35.5	7 43.8	20 58.8	4 35.6	7 19.6
30	8 35 44.2	9 47.9	4 17.1	28 45.5	8 22.0	12 16.9	28 4.1	24 49.6	7 48.4	21 1.5	4 37.6	7 20.0
31	8 39 40.8	10 48.8	4 13.9	12♎28.8	10 4.7	13 32.2	28 39.7	25 3.8	7 52.8	21 4.2	4 39.5	7 20.3
		LATITUDE										
1	6 41 24.0	0 .0	0 .0	4N27.9	0N16.9	0S19.9	1N 1.7	0S48.1	1N48.4	0S 3.5	1N 3.7	16N21.3
4	6 53 13.7	0 .0	0 .0	1 50.0	0S 5.8	0 26.8	1 .8	0 48.1	1 48.6	0 3.5	1 3.7	16 22.7
7	7 5 3.4	0 .0	0 .0	1S52.2	0 27.2	0 33.6	0 59.8	0 48.1	1 48.7	0 3.5	1 3.7	16 24.2
10	7 16 53.0	0 .0	0 .0	4 35.9	0 47.2	0 40.0	0 58.7	0 48.1	1 48.9	0 3.6	1 3.7	16 25.7
13	7 28 42.7	0 .0	0 .0	4 44.5	1 5.4	0 46.3	0 57.5	0 48.2	1 49.2	0 3.6	1 3.7	16 27.2
16	7 40 32.4	0 .0	0 .0	2 37.4	1 21.6	0 52.1	0 56.3	0 48.2	1 49.4	0 3.6	1 3.7	16 28.8
19	7 52 22.1	0 .0	0 .0	0N25.9	1 35.7	0 57.7	0 55.1	0 48.2	1 49.7	0 3.7	1 3.8	16 30.3
22	8 4 11.7	0 .0	0 .0	3 16.3	1 47.4	1 2.8	0 53.7	0 48.3	1 50.0	0 3.7	1 3.8	16 31.9
25	8 16 1.4	0 .0	0 .0	4 53.3	1 56.4	1 7.5	0 52.3	0 48.4	1 50.3	0 3.7	1 3.8	16 33.6
28	8 27 51.1	0 .0	0 .0	4 25.8	2 2.3	1 11.8	0 50.8	0 48.5	1 50.6	0 3.8	1 3.8	16 35.2
31	8 39 40.8	0 .0	0 .0	1 49.3	2 4.9	1 15.6	0 49.2	0 48.6	1 50.9	0 3.8	1 3.9	16 36.8
		RIGHT ASCENSION										
1	6 41 24.0	11♑10.3	3♉30.7	8♍34.8	22♐16.4	6♑21.0	8♏29.3	20♒57.3	3♐34.5	18♐34.8	3♑53.1	9♏52.2
2	6 45 20.6	12 16.5	3 27.6	20 46.4	23 50.1	7 43.4	9 5.1	21 10.0	3 41.0	18 38.6	3 55.5	9 53.5
3	6 49 17.1	13 22.7	3 24.5	2♎50.1	25 24.9	9 5.9	9 41.0	21 22.8	3 47.6	18 42.4	3 58.0	9 54.9
4	6 53 13.7	14 28.7	3 21.5	15 2.7	27 .4	10 28.2	10 16.9	21 35.6	3 54.0	18 46.1	4 .5	9 56.2
5	6 57 10.3	15 34.7	3 18.4	27 42.9	28 36.9	11 50.5	10 52.8	21 48.4	4 .4	18 49.8	4 2.9	9 57.5
6	7 1 6.8	16 40.6	3 15.3	11♏ 9.4	0♑14.1	13 12.7	11 28.8	22 1.4	4 6.7	18 53.5	4 5.3	9 58.8
7	7 5 3.4	17 46.3	3 12.2	25 36.3	1 52.0	14 34.8	12 4.8	22 14.3	4 13.0	18 57.2	4 7.7	9 60.0
8	7 8 59.9	18 51.9	3 9.1	11♐ 6.9	3 30.7	15 56.8	12 40.8	22 27.4	4 19.2	19 .8	4 10.1	10 1.2
9	7 12 56.5	19 57.4	3 6.1	27 26.2	5 9.9	17 18.7	13 16.9	22 40.4	4 25.4	19 4.4	4 12.5	10 2.3
10	7 16 53.0	21 2.8	3 3.0	13♑59.7	6 49.8	18 40.4	13 53.0	22 53.5	4 31.5	19 8.0	4 14.9	10 3.5
11	7 20 49.6	22 8.1	2 59.9	0♒ 5.2	8 30.2	20 1.9	14 29.1	23 6.7	4 37.6	19 11.6	4 17.3	10 4.6
12	7 24 46.2	23 13.2	2 56.8	15 10.4	10 11.1	21 23.3	15 5.3	23 19.9	4 43.6	19 15.1	4 19.6	10 5.7
13	7 28 42.7	24 18.1	2 53.8	29 2.7	11 52.5	22 44.5	15 41.5	23 33.2	4 49.5	19 18.7	4 22.0	10 6.7
14	7 32 39.3	25 22.9	2 50.7	11♓46.6	13 34.4	24 5.5	16 17.7	23 46.5	4 55.4	19 22.2	4 24.3	10 7.7
15	7 36 35.8	26 27.5	2 47.6	23 36.4	15 16.7	25 26.3	16 53.9	23 59.8	5 1.3	19 25.6	4 26.7	10 8.7
16	7 40 32.4	27 31.9	2 44.5	4♈49.5	16 59.3	26 46.9	17 30.2	24 13.2	5 7.0	19 29.0	4 29.0	10 9.7
17	7 44 29.0	28 36.2	2 41.5	15 43.8	18 42.3	28 7.2	18 6.5	24 26.6	5 12.7	19 32.5	4 31.3	10 10.6
18	7 48 25.5	29 40.3	2 38.4	26 35.9	20 25.6	29 27.3	18 42.8	24 40.1	5 18.4	19 35.8	4 33.6	10 11.5
19	7 52 22.1	0♒44.2	2 35.3	7♉41.3	22 9.3	0♒47.1	19 19.1	24 53.5	5 23.9	19 39.2	4 35.9	10 12.4
20	7 56 18.6	1 47.9	2 32.2	19 12.9	23 53.1	2 6.7	19 55.5	25 7.0	5 29.4	19 42.5	4 38.2	10 13.2
21	8 0 15.2	2 51.5	2 29.2	1♊20.5	25 37.3	3 26.0	20 31.9	25 20.6	5 34.9	19 45.8	4 40.4	10 14.0
22	8 4 11.7	3 54.8	2 26.1	14 8.6	27 21.6	4 45.0	21 8.3	25 34.2	5 40.2	19 49.0	4 42.6	10 14.8
23	8 8 8.3	4 58.0	2 23.0	27 34.0	29 6.2	6 3.7	21 44.8	25 47.7	5 45.5	19 52.2	4 44.9	10 15.5
24	8 12 4.9	6 1.0	2 19.9	11♋24.8	0♒51.0	7 22.3	22 21.3	26 1.4	5 50.8	19 55.4	4 47.1	10 16.2
25	8 16 1.4	7 3.7	2 16.9	25 22.9	2 35.9	8 40.4	22 57.7	26 15.1	5 56.0	19 58.6	4 49.3	10 16.9
26	8 19 58.0	8 6.3	2 13.8	9♌ 9.5	4 20.9	9 58.3	23 34.3	26 28.7	6 1.0	20 1.7	4 51.5	10 17.5
27	8 23 54.5	9 8.6	2 10.7	22 31.1	6 6.0	11 15.8	24 10.8	26 42.4	6 6.1	20 4.7	4 53.6	10 18.1
28	8 27 51.1	10 10.8	2 7.7	5♍23.1	7 51.2	12 33.1	24 47.3	26 56.1	6 11.0	20 7.8	4 55.8	10 18.7
29	8 31 47.6	11 12.7	2 4.6	17 49.4	9 36.5	13 50.0	25 23.9	27 9.9	6 15.8	20 10.8	4 57.9	10 19.3
30	8 35 44.2	12 14.5	2 1.5	0♎ .6	11 21.8	15 6.7	26 .5	27 23.6	6 20.6	20 13.7	5 .0	10 19.8
31	8 39 40.8	13 16.0	1 58.5	12 11.4	13 7.1	16 23.0	26 37.1	27 37.4	6 25.3	20 16.6	5 2.1	10 20.2
		DECLINATION										
1	6 41 24.0	23S 2.7	0N14.1	13N48.4	22S58.2	23S38.8	14S 1.2	16S 7.3	19S23.2	23S 5.1	22S19.9	1N39.9
4	6 53 13.7	22 46.5	0 14.0	4S26.2	23 30.6	23 32.5	14 35.9	15 55.3	19 26.3	23 6.0	22 19.8	1 40.1
7	7 5 3.4	22 26.3	0 14.0	21 36.4	23 53.1	23 19.7	15 9.7	15 43.0	19 29.3	23 6.8	22 19.6	1 40.3
10	7 16 53.0	22 2.0	0 13.9	27 26.4	24 4.9	23 .4	15 42.6	15 30.4	19 32.2	23 7.6	22 19.4	1 40.8
13	7 28 42.7	21 33.9	0 13.9	17 37.1	24 5.2	22 34.7	16 14.4	15 17.6	19 34.9	23 8.4	22 19.2	1 41.3
16	7 40 32.4	21 2.0	0 13.8	0 46.2	23 53.7	22 2.7	16 45.3	15 4.5	19 37.4	23 9.1	22 19.0	1 41.9
19	7 52 22.1	20 26.5	0 13.8	15N18.2	23 29.7	21 24.8	17 15.2	14 51.2	19 39.9	23 9.8	22 18.8	1 42.7
22	8 4 11.7	19 47.5	0 13.7	25 56.0	22 53.0	20 41.1	17 44.0	14 37.7	19 42.1	23 10.5	22 18.5	1 43.6
25	8 16 1.4	19 5.2	0 13.7	26 21.3	22 3.2	19 51.9	18 11.7	14 23.9	19 44.3	23 11.1	22 18.3	1 44.6
28	8 27 51.1	18 19.8	0 13.6	14 59.5	21 .2	18 57.5	18 38.3	14 10.0	19 46.3	23 11.7	22 18.1	1 45.7
31	8 39 40.8	17 31.4	0 13.5	3S15.2	19 43.6	17 58.2	19 3.8	13 55.9	19 48.1	23 12.3	22 17.8	1 46.9

FEBRUARY 1986

LONGITUDE

DAY	EPHEM. SID. TIME	☉	☊	☽	☿	♀	♂	♃	♄	♅	♆	♇
	h m s	° ′	° ′	° ′	° ′	° ′	° ′	° ′	° ′	° ′	° ′	° ′
1	8 43 37.3	11 ♒ 49.7	4 ♉ 10.7	26 ♎ 19.6	11 ♒ 48.1	14 ♒ 47.5	29 ♏ 15.2	25 ♒ 18.0	7 ♐ 57.2	21 ♐ 6.9	4 ♑ 41.4	7 ♏ 20.6
2	8 47 33.9	12 50.6	4 7.5	10 ♏ 17.4	13 32.1	16 2.9	29 50.7	25 32.2	8 1.5	21 9.5	4 43.3	7 20.9
3	8 51 30.4	13 51.5	4 4.4	24 22.3	15 16.9	17 18.2	0 ♐ 26.2	25 46.4	8 5.7	21 12.1	4 45.2	7 21.1
4	8 55 27.0	14 52.3	4 1.2	8 ♐ 33.5	17 2.3	18 33.5	1 1.6	26 .7	8 9.9	21 14.6	4 47.0	7 21.3
5	8 59 23.5	15 53.2	3 58.0	22 49.6	18 48.4	19 48.8	1 37.0	26 15.0	8 14.0	21 17.1	4 48.8	7 21.4
6	9 3 20.1	16 54.0	3 54.8	7 ♑ 7.5	20 35.1	21 4.0	2 12.3	26 29.3	8 17.9	21 19.6	4 50.6	7 21.5
7	9 7 16.6	17 54.8	3 51.7	21 23.0	22 22.4	22 19.3	2 47.5	26 43.6	8 21.8	21 22.0	4 52.4	7 21.6
8	9 11 13.2	18 55.6	3 48.5	5 ♒ 31.0	24 10.2	23 34.6	3 22.7	26 58.0	8 25.7	21 24.3	4 54.2	7 21.6
9	9 15 9.8	19 56.4	3 45.3	19 26.2	25 58.5	24 49.8	3 57.8	27 12.3	8 29.4	21 26.7	4 55.9	7 21.6
10	9 19 6.3	20 57.2	3 42.1	3 ♓ 3.9	27 47.3	26 5.1	4 32.9	27 26.7	8 33.0	21 29.0	4 57.7	7 21.6
11	9 23 2.9	21 57.9	3 39.0	16 21.1	29 36.3	27 20.3	5 7.9	27 41.1	8 36.6	21 31.2	4 59.4	7 R 21.5
12	9 26 59.4	22 58.6	3 35.8	29 16.7	1 ♓ 25.6	28 35.5	5 42.8	27 55.5	8 40.1	21 33.4	5 1.0	7 21.4
13	9 30 56.0	23 59.3	3 32.6	11 ♈ 51.4	3 14.8	29 50.7	6 17.7	28 9.9	8 43.5	21 35.6	5 2.7	7 21.3
14	9 34 52.5	25 .0	3 29.4	24 8.0	5 4.0	1 ♓ 5.9	6 52.6	28 24.3	8 46.8	21 37.7	5 4.4	7 21.2
15	9 38 49.1	26 .7	3 26.2	6 ♉ 10.1	6 52.9	2 21.0	7 27.3	28 38.7	8 50.0	21 39.8	5 6.0	7 21.0
16	9 42 45.6	27 1.3	3 23.1	18 2.7	8 41.1	3 36.2	8 2.0	28 53.1	8 53.1	21 41.8	5 7.5	7 20.7
17	9 46 42.2	28 1.8	3 19.9	29 51.2	10 28.6	4 51.3	8 36.6	29 7.5	8 56.2	21 43.8	5 9.1	7 20.4
18	9 50 38.8	29 2.4	3 16.7	11 ♊ 41.1	12 14.8	6 6.4	9 11.1	29 22.0	8 59.1	21 45.8	5 10.6	7 20.1
19	9 54 35.3	0 ♓ 2.9	3 13.5	23 37.6	13 59.5	7 21.5	9 45.6	29 36.4	9 1.9	21 47.6	5 12.1	7 19.8
20	9 58 31.9	1 3.4	3 10.4	5 ♋ 45.5	15 42.3	8 36.5	10 20.0	29 50.8	9 4.7	21 49.5	5 13.6	7 19.4
21	10 2 28.4	2 3.8	3 7.2	18 8.9	17 22.6	9 51.6	10 54.3	0 ♓ 5.2	9 7.3	21 51.3	5 15.0	7 19.0
22	10 6 25.0	3 4.3	3 4.0	0 ♌ 50.5	19 .0	11 6.6	11 28.6	0 19.6	9 9.9	21 53.0	5 16.4	7 18.5
23	10 10 21.5	4 4.7	3 .8	13 51.6	20 34.0	12 21.6	12 2.7	0 34.0	9 12.4	21 54.7	5 17.8	7 18.0
24	10 14 18.1	5 5.0	2 57.7	27 11.7	22 3.9	13 36.6	12 36.8	0 48.4	9 14.8	21 56.4	5 19.2	7 17.5
25	10 18 14.6	6 5.4	2 54.5	10 ♍ 49.1	23 29.1	14 51.6	13 10.9	1 2.8	9 17.0	21 58.0	5 20.5	7 16.9
26	10 22 11.2	7 5.7	2 51.3	24 40.6	24 49.0	16 6.5	13 44.8	1 17.2	9 19.2	21 59.5	5 21.8	7 16.3
27	10 26 7.8	8 6.0	2 48.1	8 ♎ 42.4	26 3.1	17 21.4	14 18.7	1 31.6	9 21.3	22 1.0	5 23.1	7 15.7
28	10 30 4.3	9 6.2	2 44.9	22 50.6	27 10.5	18 36.3	14 52.5	1 45.9	9 23.3	22 2.5	5 24.4	7 15.1

LATITUDE

DAY	EPHEM. SID. TIME	☉	☊	☽	☿	♀	♂	♃	♄	♅	♆	♇
1	8 43 37.3	0 .0	0 .0	0 N 38.6	2 S 4.9	1 S 16.8	0 N 48.7	0 S 48.6	1 N 51.0	0 S 3.8	1 N 3.9	16 N 37.3
4	8 55 27.0	0 .0	0 .0	2 S 53.5	2 2.4	1 19.9	0 47.0	0 48.7	1 51.4	0 3.8	1 3.9	16 39.0
7	9 7 16.6	0 .0	0 .0	4 54.8	1 55.4	1 22.5	0 45.2	0 48.8	1 51.7	0 3.9	1 4.0	16 40.6
10	9 19 6.3	0 .0	0 .0	4 20.4	1 43.6	1 24.5	0 43.3	0 49.0	1 52.1	0 3.9	1 4.0	16 42.2
13	9 30 56.0	0 .0	0 .0	1 46.4	1 26.3	1 26.0	0 41.3	0 49.2	1 52.5	0 3.9	1 4.1	16 43.8
16	9 42 45.6	0 .0	0 .0	1 N 23.3	1 3.1	1 26.9	0 39.3	0 49.3	1 52.9	0 4.0	1 4.1	16 45.4
19	9 54 35.3	0 .0	0 .0	3 58.8	0 33.7	1 27.3	0 37.1	0 49.5	1 53.3	0 4.0	1 4.2	16 46.9
22	10 6 25.0	0 .0	0 .0	5 4.4	0 N 1.5	1 27.0	0 34.7	0 49.7	1 53.7	0 4.1	1 4.2	16 48.4
25	10 18 14.6	0 .0	0 .0	3 55.9	0 41.6	1 26.2	0 32.3	0 49.9	1 54.1	0 4.1	1 4.3	16 49.9
28	10 30 4.3	0 .0	0 .0	0 44.3	1 24.7	1 24.8	0 29.7	0 50.2	1 54.5	0 4.1	1 4.4	16 51.3

RIGHT ASCENSION

DAY	EPHEM. SID. TIME	☉	☊	☽	☿	♀	♂	♃	♄	♅	♆	♇
1	8 43 37.3	14 ♒ 17.4	1 ♉ 55.4	24 ♎ 39.1	14 ♒ 52.5	17 ♒ 39.0	27 ♏ 13.7	27 ♒ 51.2	6 ♐ 29.9	20 ♐ 19.5	5 ♑ 4.1	10 ♏ 20.7
2	8 47 33.9	15 18.5	1 52.3	7 ♏ 41.1	16 37.8	18 54.7	27 50.3	28 5.0	6 34.5	20 22.3	5 6.2	10 21.1
3	8 51 30.4	16 19.5	1 49.3	21 32.2	18 23.1	20 10.1	28 26.9	28 18.8	6 38.9	20 25.1	5 8.2	10 21.5
4	8 55 27.0	17 20.3	1 46.2	6 ♐ 19.7	20 8.2	21 25.2	29 3.5	28 32.6	6 43.3	20 27.9	5 10.2	10 21.8
5	8 59 23.5	18 20.8	1 43.1	21 57.4	21 53.3	22 40.0	29 40.2	28 46.5	6 47.6	20 30.6	5 12.2	10 22.1
6	9 3 20.1	19 21.2	1 40.1	8 ♑ 1.9	23 38.2	23 54.5	0 ♐ 16.8	29 .3	6 51.8	20 33.3	5 14.1	10 22.4
7	9 7 16.6	20 21.3	1 37.0	23 58.2	25 22.9	25 8.6	0 53.5	29 14.2	6 55.9	20 35.9	5 16.1	10 22.6
8	9 11 13.2	21 21.3	1 33.9	9 ♒ 13.1	27 7.3	26 22.5	1 30.1	29 28.0	6 59.9	20 38.5	5 18.0	10 22.8
9	9 15 9.8	22 21.1	1 30.9	23 27.1	28 51.3	27 36.1	2 6.7	29 41.9	7 3.9	20 41.0	5 19.8	10 23.0
10	9 19 6.3	23 20.6	1 27.8	6 ♓ 37.3	0 ♓ 35.0	28 49.4	2 43.3	29 55.8	7 7.7	20 43.5	5 21.7	10 23.1
11	9 23 2.9	24 20.0	1 24.7	18 52.2	2 18.2	0 ♓ 2.3	3 19.9	0 ♓ 9.6	7 11.5	20 45.9	5 23.5	10 23.2
12	9 26 59.4	25 19.2	1 21.7	0 ♈ 26.3	4 .8	1 15.1	3 56.5	0 23.5	7 15.2	20 48.3	5 25.3	10 23.3
13	9 30 56.0	26 18.2	1 18.6	11 35.8	5 42.6	2 27.5	4 33.1	0 37.4	7 18.7	20 50.7	5 27.1	10 23.4
14	9 34 52.5	27 17.0	1 15.5	22 36.7	7 23.6	3 39.7	5 9.7	0 51.3	7 22.3	20 53.0	5 28.9	10 23.4
15	9 38 49.1	28 15.6	1 12.5	3 ♉ 43.9	9 3.5	4 51.5	5 46.3	1 5.2	7 25.7	20 55.3	5 30.7	10 23.4
16	9 42 45.6	29 14.0	1 9.4	15 10.6	10 42.2	6 3.1	6 22.8	1 19.0	7 29.0	20 57.5	5 32.4	10 R 23.3
17	9 46 42.2	0 ♓ 12.3	1 6.4	27 7.3	12 19.4	7 14.5	6 59.3	1 32.9	7 32.2	20 59.6	5 34.0	10 23.2
18	9 50 38.8	1 10.3	1 3.3	9 ♊ 40.6	13 54.9	8 25.6	7 35.7	1 46.7	7 35.3	21 1.7	5 35.7	10 23.1
19	9 54 35.3	2 8.2	1 .2	22 50.6	15 28.3	9 36.5	8 12.2	2 .6	7 38.3	21 3.8	5 37.3	10 22.9
20	9 58 31.9	3 5.9	0 57.2	6 ♋ 29.8	16 59.3	10 47.1	8 48.6	2 14.4	7 41.2	21 5.8	5 38.9	10 22.8
21	10 2 28.4	4 3.4	0 54.1	20 24.1	18 27.6	11 57.5	9 25.0	2 28.3	7 44.0	21 7.7	5 40.4	10 22.5
22	10 6 25.0	5 .8	0 51.1	4 ♌ 16.2	19 52.8	13 7.7	10 1.3	2 42.1	7 46.7	21 9.6	5 42.0	10 22.3
23	10 10 21.5	5 58.0	0 48.0	17 51.5	21 14.3	14 17.7	10 37.7	2 55.9	7 49.3	21 11.5	5 43.5	10 22.0
24	10 14 18.1	6 55.0	0 44.9	1 ♍ 2.3	22 31.8	15 27.5	11 13.9	3 9.7	7 51.9	21 13.3	5 44.9	10 21.7
25	10 18 14.6	7 51.9	0 41.9	13 49.0	23 44.7	16 37.1	11 50.2	3 23.4	7 54.3	21 15.0	5 46.4	10 21.3
26	10 22 11.2	8 48.7	0 38.8	26 19.4	24 52.5	17 46.5	12 26.4	3 37.2	7 56.6	21 16.7	5 47.8	10 20.9
27	10 26 7.8	9 45.3	0 35.8	8 ♎ 46.1	25 54.7	18 55.7	13 2.6	3 50.9	7 58.8	21 18.3	5 49.2	10 20.5
28	10 30 4.3	10 41.8	0 32.7	21 24.4	26 50.8	20 4.8	13 38.7	4 4.7	8 .9	21 19.9	5 50.5	10 20.1

DECLINATION

DAY	EPHEM. SID. TIME	☉	☊	☽	☿	♀	♂	♃	♄	♅	♆	♇
1	8 43 37.3	17 S 14.7	0 N 13.5	9 S 33.8	19 S 15.1	17 S 37.4	19 S 12.1	13 S 51.2	19 S 48.7	23 S 12.5	22 S 17.8	1 N 47.3
4	8 55 27.0	16 22.6	0 13.5	24 35.4	17 40.5	16 32.0	19 36.1	13 36.8	19 50.4	23 13.1	22 17.5	1 48.6
7	9 7 16.6	15 27.9	0 13.4	26 35.6	15 52.5	15 22.4	19 58.9	13 22.3	19 51.9	23 13.6	22 17.3	1 50.1
10	9 19 6.3	14 30.9	0 13.4	14 25.5	13 51.8	14 9.1	20 20.6	13 7.7	19 53.3	23 14.1	22 17.0	1 51.6
13	9 30 56.0	13 31.6	0 13.3	3 N 3.4	11 39.4	12 52.2	20 41.0	12 52.9	19 54.5	23 14.5	22 16.8	1 53.2
16	9 42 45.6	12 30.4	0 13.2	18 32.5	9 17.3	11 32.3	21 .3	12 38.1	19 55.6	23 15.0	22 16.6	1 54.9
19	9 54 35.3	11 27.4	0 13.2	27 15.9	6 49.1	10 9.6	21 18.4	12 23.1	19 56.5	23 15.4	22 16.3	1 56.6
22	10 6 25.0	10 22.8	0 13.1	24 55.3	4 19.9	8 44.5	21 35.3	12 8.0	19 57.3	23 15.7	22 16.1	1 58.4
25	10 18 14.6	9 16.8	0 13.1	11 8.8	1 57.0	7 17.4	21 51.0	11 52.9	19 58.0	23 16.1	22 15.9	2 .3
28	10 30 4.3	8 9.5	0 13.0	8 S 12.0	0 N 10.4	5 48.5	22 5.6	11 37.8	19 58.5	23 16.4	22 15.6	2 2.2

MARCH 1986

LONGITUDE

DAY	EPHEM. SID. TIME h m s	☉ ° ′	☊ ° ′	☽ ° ′	☿ ° ′	♀ ° ′	♂ ° ′	♃ ° ′	♄ ° ′	♅ ° ′	♆ ° ′	♇ ° ′
1	10 34 .9	10♓ 6.5	2♉41.8	7♏ 1.7	28♓10.9	19♓51.2	15♐26.2	2♓ .3	9♐25.2	22♐ 3.9	5♑25.6	7♏14.4
2	10 37 57.4	11 6.7	2 38.6	21 13.1	29 3.6	21 6.1	15 59.8	2 14.6	9 27.0	22 5.3	5 26.8	7 R 13.7
3	10 41 54.0	12 6.8	2 35.4	5♐22.9	29 48.1	22 20.9	16 33.4	2 28.9	9 28.7	22 6.6	5 28.0	7 12.9
4	10 45 50.5	13 7.0	2 32.2	19 29.6	0♈24.1	23 35.8	17 6.8	2 43.3	9 30.3	22 7.8	5 29.1	7 12.1
5	10 49 47.1	14 7.1	2 29.1	3♑32.0	0 51.2	24 50.6	17 40.1	2 57.6	9 31.8	22 9.0	5 30.2	7 11.3
6	10 53 43.6	15 7.2	2 25.9	17 28.9	1 9.1	26 5.4	18 13.4	3 11.8	9 33.2	22 10.2	5 31.3	7 10.5
7	10 57 40.2	16 7.4	2 22.7	1♒18.3	1 17.9	27 20.2	18 46.6	3 26.1	9 34.5	22 11.3	5 32.4	7 9.7
8	11 1 36.7	17 7.4	2 19.5	14 58.1	1 R 17.5	28 34.9	19 19.7	3 40.4	9 35.7	22 12.4	5 33.4	7 8.8
9	11 5 33.3	18 7.4	2 16.3	28 26.1	1 8.0	29 49.7	19 52.6	3 54.6	9 36.8	22 13.4	5 34.3	7 7.8
10	11 9 29.8	19 7.4	2 13.2	11♓40.0	0 50.0	1♈ 4.4	20 25.4	4 8.8	9 37.8	22 14.3	5 35.3	7 6.9
11	11 13 26.4	20 7.4	2 10.0	24 38.3	0 23.8	2 19.1	20 58.2	4 22.9	9 38.7	22 15.2	5 36.2	7 5.9
12	11 17 23.0	21 7.3	2 6.8	7♈20.4	29♓50.2	3 33.7	21 30.8	4 37.1	9 39.5	22 16.1	5 37.1	7 4.9
13	11 21 19.5	22 7.2	2 3.6	19 46.7	29 10.0	4 48.3	22 3.3	4 51.2	9 40.2	22 16.9	5 38.0	7 3.8
14	11 25 16.1	23 7.1	2 .5	1♉58.7	28 24.2	6 2.9	22 35.6	5 5.3	9 40.8	22 17.6	5 38.8	7 2.7
15	11 29 12.6	24 6.9	1 57.3	13 59.2	27 33.9	7 17.5	23 7.9	5 19.3	9 41.3	22 18.3	5 39.6	7 1.6
16	11 33 9.2	25 6.7	1 54.1	25 51.8	26 40.3	8 32.1	23 40.0	5 33.3	9 41.6	22 18.9	5 40.3	7 .5
17	11 37 5.7	26 6.5	1 50.9	7♊40.8	25 44.6	9 46.6	24 12.0	5 47.3	9 41.9	22 19.5	5 41.0	6 59.4
18	11 41 2.3	27 6.2	1 47.7	19 31.0	24 48.1	11 1.1	24 43.9	6 1.3	9 42.1	22 20.0	5 41.7	6 58.2
19	11 44 58.8	28 5.9	1 44.6	1♋27.4	23 52.0	12 15.6	25 15.7	6 15.2	9 42.2	22 20.5	5 42.4	6 57.0
20	11 48 55.4	29 5.5	1 41.4	13 35.1	22 57.5	13 30.0	25 47.3	6 29.1	9 42.2	22 20.9	5 43.0	6 55.8
21	11 52 51.9	0♈ 5.1	1 38.2	25 58.7	22 5.5	14 44.4	26 18.8	6 42.9	9 R 42.0	22 21.3	5 43.6	6 54.5
22	11 56 48.5	1 4.7	1 35.0	8♌42.1	21 17.1	15 58.8	26 50.2	6 56.7	9 41.8	22 21.6	5 44.2	6 53.3
23	12 0 45.0	2 4.2	1 31.9	21 47.9	20 32.9	17 13.1	27 21.4	7 10.5	9 41.5	22 21.8	5 44.7	6 52.0
24	12 4 41.6	3 3.7	1 28.7	5♍17.2	19 53.5	18 27.4	27 52.5	7 24.2	9 41.1	22 22.1	5 45.2	6 50.6
25	12 8 38.2	4 3.1	1 25.5	19 9.1	19 19.4	19 41.7	28 23.4	7 37.9	9 40.6	22 22.2	5 45.7	6 49.3
26	12 12 34.7	5 2.6	1 22.3	3♎20.6	18 51.0	20 56.0	28 54.2	7 51.5	9 39.9	22 22.3	5 46.1	6 47.9
27	12 16 31.3	6 1.9	1 19.1	17 47.0	18 28.4	22 10.2	29 24.8	8 5.1	9 39.2	22 22.4	5 46.5	6 46.6
28	12 20 27.8	7 1.3	1 16.0	2♏22.6	18 11.8	23 24.4	29 55.4	8 18.7	9 38.5	22 22.4	5 46.9	6 45.2
29	12 24 24.4	8 .7	1 12.8	17 .9	18 1.0	24 38.6	0♑25.7	8 32.2	9 37.5	22 22.4	5 47.2	6 43.8
30	12 28 20.9	8 60.0	1 9.6	1♐36.3	17 56.1	25 52.7	0 55.9	8 45.6	9 36.5	22 R 22.3	5 47.5	6 42.4
31	12 32 17.5	9 59.2	1 6.4	16 3.8	17 D 56.8	27 6.8	1 25.9	8 59.0	9 35.4	22 22.1	5 47.8	6 40.9

LATITUDE

DAY	EPHEM. SID. TIME h m s	☉ ° ′	☊ ° ′	☽ ° ′	☿ ° ′	♀ ° ′	♂ ° ′	♃ ° ′	♄ ° ′	♅ ° ′	♆ ° ′	♇ ° ′
1	10 34 .9	0 .0	0 .0	0 S 31.9	1 N 39.3	1 S 24.2	0 N 28.8	0 S 50.3	1 N 54.7	0 S 4.2	1 N 4.4	16 N 51.8
4	10 45 50.5	0 .0	0 .0	3 50.9	2 21.6	1 22.0	0 26.0	0 50.5	1 55.1	0 4.2	1 4.5	16 53.2
7	10 57 40.2	0 .0	0 .0	5 8.3	2 58.4	1 19.3	0 23.1	0 50.8	1 55.5	0 4.2	1 4.6	16 54.5
10	11 9 29.8	0 .0	0 .0	3 53.2	3 24.9	1 16.0	0 20.1	0 51.1	1 56.0	0 4.3	1 4.6	16 55.8
13	11 21 19.5	0 .0	0 .0	0 57.3	3 36.8	1 12.1	0 16.8	0 51.4	1 56.4	0 4.3	1 4.7	16 57.0
16	11 33 9.2	0 .0	0 .0	2 N 14.8	3 31.1	1 7.8	0 13.5	0 51.7	1 56.8	0 4.4	1 4.8	16 58.1
19	11 44 58.8	0 .0	0 .0	4 34.1	3 8.5	1 2.9	0 9.9	0 52.0	1 57.3	0 4.4	1 4.9	16 59.2
22	11 56 48.5	0 .0	0 .0	5 9.7	2 32.6	0 57.6	0 6.1	0 52.3	1 57.7	0 4.4	1 5.0	17 .2
25	12 8 38.2	0 .0	0 .0	3 26.0	1 48.7	0 51.8	0 2.1	0 52.7	1 58.1	0 4.5	1 5.0	17 1.1
28	12 20 27.8	0 .0	0 .0	0 S 12.9	1 2.2	0 45.7	0 S 2.1	0 53.1	1 58.5	0 4.5	1 5.1	17 2.0
31	12 32 17.5	0 .0	0 .0	3 47.3	0 17.0	0 39.1	0 6.5	0 53.5	1 58.9	0 4.6	1 5.2	17 2.8

RIGHT ASCENSION

DAY	EPHEM. SID. TIME h m s	☉ ° ′	☊ ° ′	☽ ° ′	☿ ° ′	♀ ° ′	♂ ° ′	♃ ° ′	♄ ° ′	♅ ° ′	♆ ° ′	♇ ° ′
1	10 34 .9	11♓38.1	0♉29.6	4♏30.4	27♓40.4	21♓13.7	14♐14.7	4♓18.4	8♐ 2.9	21♐21.4	5♑51.8	10♏19.6
2	10 37 57.4	12 34.3	0 26.6	18 17.7	28 23.0	22 22.5	14 50.7	4 32.1	8 4.8	21 22.9	5 53.1	10 R 19.1
3	10 41 54.0	13 30.4	0 23.5	2♐53.7	28 58.2	23 31.2	15 26.7	4 45.7	8 6.6	21 24.3	5 54.4	10 18.6
4	10 45 50.5	14 26.4	0 20.5	18 13.9	29 25.7	24 39.8	16 2.6	4 59.4	8 8.4	21 25.7	5 55.6	10 18.0
5	10 49 47.1	15 22.3	0 17.4	3♑59.3	29 45.3	25 48.2	16 38.4	5 13.0	8 9.9	21 27.0	5 56.8	10 17.4
6	10 53 43.6	16 18.0	0 14.4	19 40.3	29 56.9	26 56.6	17 14.1	5 26.6	8 11.4	21 28.2	5 58.0	10 16.8
7	10 57 40.2	17 13.8	0 11.3	4♒46.9	0♈ .4	28 4.9	17 49.9	5 40.2	8 12.9	21 29.5	5 59.1	10 16.2
8	11 1 36.7	18 9.3	0 8.3	18 59.9	29♓55.9	29 13.1	18 25.5	5 53.8	8 14.2	21 30.6	6 .2	10 15.5
9	11 5 33.3	19 4.8	0 5.2	2♓14.1	29 R 43.7	0♈21.2	19 1.0	6 7.3	8 15.3	21 31.7	6 1.3	10 14.8
10	11 9 29.8	20 .2	0 2.2	14 35.7	29 24.2	1 29.3	19 36.4	6 20.8	8 16.4	21 32.8	6 2.3	10 14.0
11	11 13 26.4	20 55.5	29♈59.1	26 17.0	28 57.9	2 37.3	20 11.7	6 34.2	8 17.4	21 33.7	6 3.3	10 13.3
12	11 17 23.0	21 50.7	29 56.0	7♈32.5	28 25.5	3 45.3	20 47.0	6 47.7	8 18.2	21 34.6	6 4.2	10 12.5
13	11 21 19.5	22 45.8	29 53.0	18 37.3	27 47.8	4 53.3	21 22.1	7 1.1	8 19.0	21 35.5	6 5.2	10 11.7
14	11 25 16.1	23 40.9	29 49.9	29 45.1	27 5.8	6 1.2	21 57.1	7 14.4	8 19.6	21 36.3	6 6.1	10 10.8
15	11 29 12.6	24 35.9	29 46.9	11♉ 8.7	26 20.4	7 9.1	22 32.0	7 27.7	8 20.1	21 37.0	6 6.9	10 9.9
16	11 33 9.2	25 30.8	29 43.8	22 58.0	25 32.8	8 17.1	23 6.9	7 41.0	8 20.6	21 37.7	6 7.7	10 9.0
17	11 37 5.7	26 25.7	29 40.8	5♊19.6	24 44.1	9 25.1	23 41.6	7 54.3	8 20.9	21 38.3	6 8.5	10 8.1
18	11 41 2.3	27 20.5	29 37.7	18 14.9	23 55.3	10 33.0	24 16.2	8 7.5	8 21.1	21 38.9	6 9.2	10 7.2
19	11 44 58.8	28 15.3	29 34.7	1♋38.7	23 7.6	11 41.1	24 50.6	8 20.7	8 21.2	21 39.4	6 10.0	10 6.2
20	11 48 55.4	29 10.0	29 31.6	15 19.6	22 21.8	12 49.2	25 25.0	8 33.8	8 21.2	21 39.9	6 10.6	10 5.2
21	11 52 51.9	0♈ 4.7	29 28.6	29 3.2	21 38.9	13 57.3	25 59.2	8 46.9	8 R 21.1	21 40.3	6 11.3	10 4.2
22	11 56 48.5	0 59.3	29 25.6	12♌35.8	20 59.6	15 5.5	26 33.3	8 59.9	8 20.9	21 40.6	6 11.9	10 3.1
23	12 0 45.0	1 53.9	29 22.5	25 49.5	20 24.4	16 13.8	27 7.2	9 12.9	8 20.6	21 40.9	6 12.4	10 2.0
24	12 4 41.6	2 48.5	29 19.5	8♍43.2	19 54.0	17 22.1	27 41.1	9 25.9	8 20.2	21 41.1	6 13.0	10 .9
25	12 8 38.2	3 43.1	29 16.4	21 23.0	19 28.6	18 30.6	28 14.7	9 38.8	8 19.6	21 41.3	6 13.5	9 59.8
26	12 12 34.7	4 37.7	29 13.4	4♎ .3	19 8.4	19 39.2	28 48.3	9 51.7	8 19.0	21 41.4	6 13.9	9 58.7
27	12 16 31.3	5 32.3	29 10.3	16 49.5	18 53.7	20 47.9	29 21.7	10 4.5	8 18.3	21 41.5	6 14.4	9 57.5
28	12 20 27.8	6 26.9	29 7.3	0♏ 6.6	18 44.4	21 56.7	29 54.9	10 17.3	8 17.5	21 41.5	6 14.8	9 56.4
29	12 24 24.4	7 21.4	29 4.2	14 5.4	18 40.5	23 5.7	0♑28.0	10 30.0	8 16.5	21 41.5	6 15.2	9 55.2
30	12 28 20.9	8 16.0	29 1.2	28 53.2	18 D 41.8	24 14.8	1 .9	10 42.7	8 15.5	21 R 41.3	6 15.5	9 54.0
31	12 32 17.5	9 10.6	28 58.1	14♐25.5	18 48.3	25 24.1	1 33.7	10 55.3	8 14.4	21 41.2	6 15.8	9 52.7

DECLINATION

DAY	EPHEM. SID. TIME h m s	☉ ° ′	☊ ° ′	☽ ° ′	☿ ° ′	♀ ° ′	♂ ° ′	♃ ° ′	♄ ° ′	♅ ° ′	♆ ° ′	♇ ° ′
1	10 34 .9	7 S 46.8	0 N 13.0	14 S 21.9	0 N 47.7	5 S 18.6	22 S 10.2	11 S 32.7	19 S 58.6	23 S 16.5	22 S 15.6	2 N 2.9
4	10 45 50.5	6 38.1	0 12.9	26 51.8	2 19.5	3 47.9	22 23.2	11 17.5	19 59.0	23 16.8	22 15.4	2 4.9
7	10 57 40.2	5 28.5	0 12.9	24 52.8	3 14.7	2 16.3	22 35.1	11 2.2	19 59.2	23 17.0	22 15.1	2 6.9
10	11 9 29.8	4 18.3	0 12.8	10 46.8	3 27.9	0 44.1	22 45.8	10 47.0	19 59.2	23 17.2	22 14.9	2 8.9
13	11 21 19.5	3 7.6	0 12.8	6 N 51.2	2 59.0	0 N 48.4	22 55.5	10 31.8	19 59.1	23 17.4	22 14.8	2 11.0
16	11 33 9.2	1 56.6	0 12.7	21 24.5	1 54.3	2 20.8	23 4.1	10 16.6	19 58.9	23 17.6	22 14.6	2 13.1
19	11 44 58.8	0 45.4	0 12.7	28 .2	0 27.0	3 52.8	23 11.6	10 1.5	19 58.6	23 17.7	22 14.4	2 15.2
22	11 56 48.5	0 N 25.7	0 12.6	23 3.9	1 S 7.1	5 24.1	23 18.2	9 46.4	19 58.1	23 17.8	22 14.2	2 17.3
25	12 8 38.2	1 36.7	0 12.5	7 27.1	2 33.6	6 54.3	23 23.9	9 31.4	19 57.5	23 17.9	22 14.1	2 19.4
28	12 20 27.8	2 47.3	0 12.5	12 S 30.1	3 42.8	8 23.2	23 28.7	9 16.5	19 56.8	23 17.9	22 14.0	2 21.4
31	12 32 17.5	3 57.4	0 12.4	26 28.9	4 30.3	9 50.3	23 32.6	9 1.8	19 56.0	23 18.0	22 13.8	2 23.5

APRIL 1986

LONGITUDE

DAY	EPHEM. SID. TIME h m s	☉ ° ′	☊ ° ′	☾ ° ′	☿ ° ′	♀ ° ′	♂ ° ′	♃ ° ′	♄ ° ′	♅ ° ′	♆ ° ′	♇ ° ′
1	12 36 14.0	10♈58.4	1♉ 3.3	0♑20.0	18♓ 3.2	28♈20.9	1♑55.7	9♓12.3	9♐34.2	22♐21.9	5♑48.0	6♏39.4
2	12 40 10.6	11 57.7	1 .1	14 22.7	18 14.8	29 35.0	2 25.4	9 25.6	9R32.9	22R21.6	5 48.2	6R38.0
3	12 44 7.1	12 56.8	0 56.9	28 10.7	18 31.6	0♉49.0	2 54.9	9 38.8	9 31.5	22 21.3	5 48.4	6 36.5
4	12 48 3.7	13 56.0	0 53.7	11♒43.8	18 53.3	2 3.0	3 24.2	9 52.0	9 30.0	22 20.9	5 48.5	6 34.9
5	12 52 .2	14 55.1	0 50.5	25 2.0	19 19.7	3 16.9	3 53.3	10 5.1	9 28.4	22 20.5	5 48.6	6 33.4
6	12 55 56.8	15 54.2	0 47.4	8♓ 5.9	19 50.5	4 30.8	4 22.2	10 18.2	9 26.8	22 20.1	5 48.7	6 31.8
7	12 59 53.3	16 53.2	0 44.2	20 55.8	20 25.5	5 44.7	4 50.9	10 31.2	9 25.0	22 19.5	5 48.7	6 30.3
8	13 3 49.9	17 52.2	0 41.0	3♈32.6	21 4.4	6 58.6	5 19.4	10 44.2	9 23.1	22 19.0	5 48.7	6 28.7
9	13 7 46.5	18 51.2	0 37.8	15 57.1	21 47.2	8 12.4	5 47.6	10 57.0	9 21.2	22 18.4	5R48.6	6 27.1
10	13 11 43.0	19 50.2	0 34.7	28 10.3	22 33.5	9 26.2	6 15.7	11 9.8	9 19.1	22 17.7	5 48.6	6 25.5
11	13 15 39.6	20 49.1	0 31.5	10♉13.9	23 23.2	10 40.0	6 43.5	11 22.6	9 17.0	22 17.0	5 48.5	6 23.9
12	13 19 36.1	21 48.0	0 28.3	22 9.9	24 16.2	11 53.7	7 11.2	11 35.3	9 14.8	22 16.2	5 48.3	6 22.3
13	13 23 32.7	22 46.8	0 25.1	4♊ .6	25 12.2	13 7.4	7 38.5	11 47.9	9 12.5	22 15.4	5 48.2	6 20.6
14	13 27 29.2	23 45.7	0 21.9	15 49.4	26 11.2	14 21.1	8 5.7	12 .4	9 10.1	22 14.5	5 48.0	6 19.0
15	13 31 25.8	24 44.4	0 18.8	27 39.9	27 12.9	15 34.7	8 32.6	12 12.9	9 7.6	22 13.6	5 47.7	6 17.4
16	13 35 22.3	25 43.2	0 15.6	9♋36.0	28 17.3	16 48.3	8 59.2	12 25.3	9 5.0	22 12.6	5 47.5	6 15.7
17	13 39 18.9	26 41.9	0 12.4	21 42.4	29 24.3	18 1.9	9 25.6	12 37.6	9 2.4	22 11.6	5 47.2	6 14.0
18	13 43 15.4	27 40.6	0 9.2	4♌ 3.5	0♈33.7	19 15.4	9 51.8	12 49.9	8 59.7	22 10.6	5 46.9	6 12.4
19	13 47 12.0	28 39.2	0 6.1	16 43.5	1 45.5	20 28.9	10 17.7	13 2.0	8 56.9	22 9.5	5 46.5	6 10.7
20	13 51 8.6	29 37.8	0 2.9	29 46.2	2 59.5	21 42.4	10 43.3	13 14.1	8 54.0	22 8.4	5 46.1	6 9.1
21	13 55 5.1	0♉36.4	29♈59.7	13♍14.2	4 15.8	22 55.7	11 8.6	13 26.1	8 51.1	22 7.2	5 45.7	6 7.4
22	13 59 1.7	1 34.9	29 56.5	27 8.3	5 34.2	24 9.1	11 33.7	13 38.0	8 48.1	22 6.0	5 45.2	6 5.7
23	14 2 58.2	2 33.4	29 53.3	11♎27.3	6 54.7	25 22.4	11 58.4	13 49.9	8 45.0	22 4.7	5 44.7	6 4.0
24	14 6 54.8	3 31.8	29 50.2	26 7.2	8 17.2	26 35.7	12 22.9	14 1.6	8 41.8	22 3.4	5 44.2	6 2.3
25	14 10 51.3	4 30.3	29 47.0	11♏ 2.1	9 41.7	27 48.9	12 47.1	14 13.3	8 38.6	22 2.0	5 43.7	6 .6
26	14 14 47.9	5 28.6	29 43.8	26 3.8	11 8.2	29 2.1	13 11.0	14 24.9	8 35.2	22 .6	5 43.1	5 58.9
27	14 18 44.4	6 27.0	29 40.6	11♐ 3.9	12 36.6	0♊15.3	13 34.5	14 36.4	8 31.9	21 59.2	5 42.5	5 57.2
28	14 22 41.0	7 25.3	29 37.5	25 54.3	14 6.9	1 28.4	13 57.7	14 47.8	8 28.4	21 57.7	5 41.9	5 55.5
29	14 26 37.5	8 23.6	29 34.3	10♑28.4	15 39.1	2 41.5	14 20.6	14 59.1	8 24.9	21 56.2	5 41.2	5 53.8
30	14 30 34.1	9 21.9	29 31.1	24 41.9	17 13.2	3 54.5	14 43.2	15 10.3	8 21.4	21 54.6	5 40.5	5 52.1

LATITUDE

DAY	SID. TIME	☉	☊	☾	☿	♀	♂	♃	♄	♅	♆	♇
1	12 36 14.0	0 .0	0 .0	4S34.3	0N 2.7	0S36.9	0S 8.0	0S53.6	1N59.0	0S 4.6	1N 5.2	17N 3.0
4	12 48 3.7	0 .0	0 .0	5 9.3	0S37.3	0 29.9	0 12.8	0 54.0	1 59.4	0 4.6	1 5.3	17 3.7
7	12 59 53.3	0 .0	0 .0	3 19.5	1 12.0	0 22.6	0 17.8	0 54.5	1 59.7	0 4.6	1 5.4	17 4.2
10	13 11 43.0	0 .0	0 .0	0 9.7	1 41.3	0 15.1	0 23.0	0 54.9	2 .1	0 4.7	1 5.5	17 4.7
13	13 23 32.7	0 .0	0 .0	2N58.1	2 4.9	0 7.3	0 28.5	0 55.4	2 .4	0 4.7	1 5.6	17 5.1
16	13 35 22.3	0 .0	0 .0	4 57.7	2 23.0	0N .5	0 34.4	0 55.9	2 .7	0 4.8	1 5.7	17 5.4
19	13 47 12.0	0 .0	0 .0	5 4.1	2 35.8	0 8.5	0 40.5	0 56.4	2 1.0	0 4.8	1 5.7	17 5.6
22	13 59 1.7	0 .0	0 .0	2 52.5	2 43.2	0 16.6	0 47.0	0 56.9	2 1.2	0 4.9	1 5.8	17 5.7
25	14 10 51.3	0 .0	0 .0	1S 1.0	2 45.6	0 24.7	0 53.8	0 57.5	2 1.4	0 4.9	1 5.9	17 5.8
28	14 22 41.0	0 .0	0 .0	4 22.9	2 42.9	0 32.7	1 1.0	0 58.0	2 1.6	0 4.9	1 6.0	17 5.7

RIGHT ASCENSION

DAY	SID. TIME	☉	☊	☾	☿	♀	♂	♃	♄	♅	♆	♇
1	12 36 14.0	10♈ 5.3	28♈55.1	0♑22.6	18♓59.8	26♈33.5	2♑ 6.3	11♓ 7.9	8♐13.1	21♐40.9	6♑16.0	9♏51.5
2	12 40 10.6	10 59.9	28 52.1	16 13.4	19 16.0	27 43.1	2 38.6	11 20.4	8R11.8	21R40.6	6 16.2	9R50.2
3	12 44 7.1	11 54.6	28 49.0	1♒27.1	19 36.7	28 52.9	3 10.8	11 32.8	8 10.3	21 40.3	6 16.4	9 48.9
4	12 48 3.7	12 49.3	28 46.0	15 44.0	20 1.8	0♉ 2.9	3 42.8	11 45.2	8 8.8	21 39.9	6 16.5	9 47.6
5	12 52 .2	13 44.1	28 42.9	28 59.5	20 30.9	1 13.1	4 14.6	11 57.6	8 7.1	21 39.5	6 16.6	9 46.3
6	12 55 56.8	14 38.9	28 39.9	11♓20.2	21 3.9	2 23.5	4 46.2	12 9.9	8 5.4	21 38.9	6 16.7	9 44.9
7	12 59 53.3	15 33.8	28 36.8	22 59.1	21 40.5	3 34.1	5 17.6	12 22.1	8 3.5	21 38.4	6 16.7	9 43.6
8	13 3 49.9	16 28.7	28 33.8	4♈11.1	22 20.6	4 44.9	5 48.8	12 34.2	8 1.6	21 37.8	6 16.7	9 42.2
9	13 7 46.5	17 23.7	28 30.8	15 11.3	23 3.8	5 56.0	6 19.7	12 46.3	7 59.5	21 37.1	6 16.7	9 40.8
10	13 11 43.0	18 18.8	28 27.7	26 13.6	23 50.1	7 7.3	6 50.4	12 58.4	7 57.4	21 36.4	6R16.6	9 39.4
11	13 15 39.6	19 13.9	28 24.7	7♉30.5	24 39.3	8 18.8	7 20.8	13 10.3	7 55.2	21 35.6	6 16.5	9 38.0
12	13 19 36.1	20 9.0	28 21.6	19 12.1	25 31.1	9 30.6	7 51.1	13 22.2	7 52.9	21 34.7	6 16.3	9 36.6
13	13 23 32.7	21 4.3	28 18.6	1♊24.6	26 25.5	10 42.6	8 21.0	13 34.0	7 50.5	21 33.9	6 16.1	9 35.1
14	13 27 29.2	21 59.6	28 15.6	14 9.5	27 22.4	11 54.8	8 50.7	13 45.8	7 48.0	21 32.9	6 15.9	9 33.7
15	13 31 25.8	22 55.0	28 12.5	27 21.9	28 21.5	13 7.4	9 20.2	13 57.5	7 45.4	21 31.9	6 15.7	9 32.2
16	13 35 22.3	23 50.5	28 9.5	10♋51.1	29 22.7	14 20.2	9 49.4	14 9.1	7 42.7	21 30.9	6 15.4	9 30.7
17	13 39 18.9	24 46.1	28 6.5	24 23.0	0♈26.1	15 33.2	10 18.3	14 20.7	7 39.9	21 29.8	6 15.1	9 29.2
18	13 43 15.4	25 41.8	28 3.4	7♌44.9	1 31.5	16 46.6	10 47.0	14 32.2	7 37.2	21 28.7	6 14.7	9 27.8
19	13 47 12.0	26 37.6	28 .4	20 48.5	2 38.7	18 .1	11 15.3	14 43.6	7 34.2	21 27.5	6 14.4	9 26.3
20	13 51 8.6	27 33.4	27 57.3	3♍32.7	3 47.9	19 14.0	11 43.4	14 54.9	7 31.2	21 26.3	6 13.9	9 24.8
21	13 55 5.1	28 29.4	27 54.3	16 3.3	4 58.8	20 28.1	12 11.1	15 6.1	7 28.1	21 25.0	6 13.5	9 23.3
22	13 59 1.7	29 25.4	27 51.3	28 31.2	6 11.4	21 42.4	12 38.6	15 17.3	7 25.0	21 23.6	6 13.0	9 21.8
23	14 2 58.2	0♉21.6	27 48.2	11♎11.5	7 25.8	22 57.1	13 5.8	15 28.4	7 21.7	21 22.2	6 12.4	9 20.2
24	14 6 54.8	1 17.9	27 45.2	24 21.2	8 41.8	24 12.0	13 32.6	15 39.4	7 18.4	21 20.8	6 11.9	9 18.7
25	14 10 51.3	2 14.3	27 42.2	8♏16.7	9 59.5	25 27.1	13 59.2	15 50.3	7 15.0	21 19.3	6 11.3	9 17.2
26	14 14 47.9	3 10.8	27 39.1	23 9.2	11 18.9	26 42.5	14 25.4	16 1.1	7 11.6	21 17.8	6 10.7	9 15.6
27	14 18 44.4	4 7.4	27 36.1	8♐57.7	12 40.0	27 58.2	14 51.2	16 11.9	7 8.0	21 16.2	6 10.0	9 14.1
28	14 22 41.0	5 4.2	27 33.1	25 23.1	14 2.7	29 14.2	15 16.7	16 22.6	7 4.4	21 14.6	6 9.3	9 12.5
29	14 26 37.5	6 1.1	27 30.0	11♑50.1	15 27.0	0♊30.4	15 41.9	16 33.1	7 .8	21 13.0	6 8.6	9 11.0
30	14 30 34.1	6 58.1	27 27.0	27 40.2	16 53.1	1 46.8	16 6.7	16 43.6	6 57.1	21 11.3	6 7.9	9 9.4

DECLINATION

DAY	SID. TIME	☉	☊	☾	☿	♀	♂	♃	♄	♅	♆	♇
1	12 36 14.0	4N20.6	0N12.4	28S .9	4S41.0	10N18.9	23S33.8	8S56.9	19S55.7	23S18.0	22S13.8	2N24.1
4	12 48 3.7	5 29.8	0 12.3	22 13.1	4 58.1	11 43.2	23 36.7	8 42.3	19 54.7	23 17.9	22 13.7	2 26.2
7	12 59 53.3	6 38.2	0 12.3	6 39.0	4 53.9	13 5.0	23 39.0	8 27.8	19 53.6	23 17.9	22 13.6	2 28.1
10	13 11 43.0	7 45.5	0 12.2	10N40.5	4 30.2	14 24.0	23 40.7	8 13.6	19 52.4	23 17.8	22 13.5	2 30.0
13	13 23 32.7	8 51.7	0 12.2	23 52.1	3 49.0	15 39.8	23 41.9	7 59.5	19 51.1	23 17.7	22 13.5	2 31.9
16	13 35 22.3	9 56.5	0 12.1	28 2.7	2 52.1	16 52.1	23 42.6	7 45.7	19 49.7	23 17.6	22 13.4	2 33.7
19	13 47 12.0	10 59.9	0 12.1	20 39.2	1 41.0	18 .6	23 43.0	7 32.1	19 48.2	23 17.5	22 13.4	2 35.4
22	13 59 1.7	12 1.6	0 12.0	3 46.6	0 17.1	19 4.9	23 43.2	7 18.7	19 46.6	23 17.3	22 13.3	2 37.1
25	14 10 51.3	13 1.5	0 11.9	16S 6.4	1N18.2	20 4.6	23 43.3	7 5.6	19 44.9	23 17.1	22 13.3	2 38.7
28	14 22 41.0	13 59.4	0 11.9	27 45.6	3 3.9	20 59.6	23 43.4	6 52.8	19 43.1	23 16.9	22 13.3	2 40.2

MAY 1986

LONGITUDE

DAY	EPHEM. SID. TIME h m s	☉ ° ′	☊ ° ′	☽ ° ′	☿ ° ′	♀ ° ′	♂ ° ′	♃ ° ′	♄ ° ′	♅ ° ′	♆ ° ′	♇ ° ′
1	14 34 30.7	10♉20.2	29♈27.9	8♒32.9	18♈49.1	5♊ 7.5	15♑ 5.4	15♓21.5	8♐17.7	21♐53.0	5♑39.8	5♏50.4
2	14 38 27.2	11 18.4	29 24.8	22 1.3	20 26.9	6 20.5	15 27.2	15 32.5	8 R 14.1	21 R 51.4	5 R 39.0	5 R 48.7
3	14 42 23.8	12 16.6	29 21.6	5♓ 8.7	22 6.6	7 33.4	15 48.7	15 43.4	8 10.3	21 49.7	5 38.2	5 47.0
4	14 46 20.3	13 14.8	29 18.4	17 57.4	23 48.1	8 46.3	16 9.7	15 54.3	8 6.5	21 48.0	5 37.4	5 45.4
5	14 50 16.9	14 13.0	29 15.2	0♈30.2	25 31.5	9 59.2	16 30.4	16 5.0	8 2.7	21 46.2	5 36.6	5 43.7
6	14 54 13.4	15 11.1	29 12.0	12 49.8	27 16.7	11 12.0	16 50.7	16 15.6	7 58.8	21 44.4	5 35.7	5 42.0
7	14 58 10.0	16 9.2	29 8.9	24 58.9	29 3.8	12 24.8	17 10.5	16 26.2	7 54.8	21 42.6	5 34.8	5 40.3
8	15 2 6.6	17 7.3	29 5.7	6♉59.8	0♉52.8	13 37.5	17 30.0	16 36.6	7 50.8	21 40.7	5 33.9	5 38.7
9	15 6 3.1	18 5.4	29 2.5	18 54.9	2 43.7	14 50.3	17 49.0	16 47.0	7 46.8	21 38.9	5 33.0	5 37.1
10	15 9 59.7	19 3.4	28 59.3	0♊46.0	4 36.4	16 2.9	18 7.6	16 57.2	7 42.8	21 37.0	5 32.1	5 35.4
11	15 13 56.2	20 1.4	28 56.2	12 35.2	6 31.0	17 15.6	18 25.7	17 7.3	7 38.6	21 35.0	5 31.1	5 33.8
12	15 17 52.8	20 59.4	28 53.0	24 24.7	8 27.4	18 28.1	18 43.3	17 17.2	7 34.5	21 33.0	5 30.0	5 32.2
13	15 21 49.3	21 57.4	28 49.8	6♋17.1	10 25.7	19 40.7	19 .5	17 27.1	7 30.3	21 31.0	5 29.0	5 30.6
14	15 25 45.9	22 55.3	28 46.6	18 15.2	12 25.7	20 53.1	19 17.1	17 36.9	7 26.1	21 29.0	5 27.9	5 29.0
15	15 29 42.4	23 53.2	28 43.5	0♌22.4	14 27.5	22 5.6	19 33.3	17 46.5	7 21.8	21 26.9	5 26.8	5 27.4
16	15 33 39.0	24 51.0	28 40.3	12 42.2	16 30.9	23 18.0	19 49.0	17 56.0	7 17.5	21 24.8	5 25.7	5 25.8
17	15 37 35.6	25 48.9	28 37.1	25 18.7	18 36.0	24 30.3	20 4.2	18 5.4	7 13.2	21 22.7	5 24.6	5 24.2
18	15 41 32.1	26 46.7	28 33.9	8♍15.7	20 42.5	25 42.6	20 18.8	18 14.7	7 8.8	21 20.6	5 23.4	5 22.7
19	15 45 28.7	27 44.4	28 30.7	21 36.6	22 50.3	26 54.8	20 32.9	18 23.8	7 4.5	21 18.4	5 22.2	5 21.1
20	15 49 25.2	28 42.2	28 27.6	5♎23.7	24 59.4	28 7.0	20 46.5	18 32.9	7 .1	21 16.2	5 21.0	5 19.6
21	15 53 21.8	29 39.9	28 24.4	19 37.7	27 9.4	29 19.1	20 59.6	18 41.8	6 55.7	21 14.0	5 19.8	5 18.1
22	15 57 18.3	0♊37.6	28 21.2	4♏16.8	29 20.2	0♋31.2	21 12.0	18 50.5	6 51.3	21 11.7	5 18.6	5 16.6
23	16 1 14.9	1 35.3	28 18.0	19 16.2	1♊31.6	1 43.3	21 23.9	18 59.2	6 46.9	21 9.5	5 17.3	5 15.1
24	16 5 11.5	2 32.9	28 14.9	4♐28.3	3 43.2	2 55.2	21 35.2	19 7.7	6 42.4	21 7.2	5 16.0	5 13.7
25	16 9 8.0	3 30.5	28 11.7	19 43.4	5 55.0	4 7.1	21 46.0	19 16.1	6 38.0	21 4.9	5 14.7	5 12.2
26	16 13 4.6	4 28.1	28 8.5	4♑51.2	8 6.4	5 19.0	21 56.1	19 24.3	6 33.5	21 2.6	5 13.4	5 10.8
27	16 17 1.1	5 25.7	28 5.3	19 42.3	10 17.4	6 30.8	22 5.5	19 32.4	6 29.1	21 .3	5 12.1	5 9.4
28	16 20 57.7	6 23.3	28 2.2	4♒ 9.9	12 27.6	7 42.6	22 14.4	19 40.4	6 24.6	20 57.9	5 10.7	5 8.0
29	16 24 54.3	7 20.9	27 59.0	18 10.3	14 36.7	8 54.3	22 22.6	19 48.2	6 20.1	20 55.5	5 9.3	5 6.6
30	16 28 50.8	8 18.5	27 55.8	1♓42.7	16 44.6	10 6.0	22 30.2	19 56.0	6 15.7	20 53.2	5 8.0	5 5.3
31	16 32 47.4	9 16.0	27 52.6	14 48.9	18 50.9	11 17.6	22 37.0	20 3.5	6 11.2	20 50.8	5 6.6	5 4.0

LATITUDE

DAY	EPHEM. SID. TIME	☉	☊	☽	☿	♀	♂	♃	♄	♅	♆	♇
1	14 34 30.7	0 .0	0 .0	5S13.5	2S35.2	0N40.7	1S 8.6	0S58.6	2N 1.8	0S 5.0	1N 6.0	17N 5.5
4	14 46 20.3	0 .0	0 .0	3 32.4	2 22.8	0 48.6	1 16.6	0 59.2	2 1.9	0 5.0	1 6.1	17 5.3
7	14 58 10.0	0 .0	0 .0	0 27.8	2 5.7	0 56.2	1 24.9	0 59.8	2 2.0	0 5.0	1 6.2	17 4.9
10	15 9 59.7	0 .0	0 .0	2N41.7	1 44.3	1 3.6	1 33.7	1 .4	2 2.1	0 5.1	1 6.2	17 4.5
13	15 21 49.3	0 .0	0 .0	4 48.3	1 19.0	1 10.8	1 42.9	1 1.1	2 2.1	0 5.1	1 6.3	17 3.9
16	15 33 39.0	0 .0	0 .0	5 6.2	0 50.4	1 17.6	1 52.6	1 1.8	2 2.1	0 5.2	1 6.3	17 3.3
19	15 45 28.7	0 .0	0 .0	3 14.1	0 19.6	1 24.0	2 2.8	1 2.5	2 2.0	0 5.2	1 6.4	17 2.6
22	15 57 18.3	0 .0	0 .0	0S24.9	0N12.1	1 30.0	2 13.4	1 3.2	2 2.0	0 5.2	1 6.4	17 1.8
25	16 9 8.0	0 .0	0 .0	3 59.5	0 42.8	1 35.5	2 24.4	1 3.9	2 1.8	0 5.3	1 6.4	17 .9
28	16 20 57.7	0 .0	0 .0	5 10.2	1 10.5	1 40.5	2 35.9	1 4.6	2 1.7	0 5.3	1 6.5	16 60.0
31	16 32 47.4	0 .0	0 .0	3 38.5	1 33.7	1 44.9	2 47.8	1 5.4	2 1.5	0 5.3	1 6.5	16 58.9

RIGHT ASCENSION

DAY	EPHEM. SID. TIME	☉	☊	☽	☿	♀	♂	♃	♄	♅	♆	♇
1	14 34 30.7	7♉55.3	27♈24.0	12♒27.3	18♈20.9	3♊ 3.5	16♑31.1	16♓54.0	6♐53.3	21♐ 9.5	6♑ 7.1	9♏ 7.9
2	14 38 27.2	8 52.6	27 20.9	26 3.6	19 50.4	4 20.5	16 55.1	17 4.4	6 R 49.4	21 R 7.7	6 R 6.3	9 R 6.3
3	14 42 23.8	9 50.0	27 17.9	8♓36.1	21 21.8	5 37.6	17 18.7	17 14.6	6 45.5	21 5.9	6 5.4	9 4.8
4	14 46 20.3	10 47.6	27 14.9	20 19.2	22 55.0	6 55.0	17 41.9	17 24.7	6 41.5	21 4.0	6 4.5	9 3.2
5	14 50 16.9	11 45.3	27 11.9	1♈29.9	24 30.1	8 12.7	18 4.7	17 34.7	6 37.5	21 2.1	6 3.6	9 1.6
6	14 54 13.4	12 43.2	27 8.8	12 24.6	26 7.1	9 30.5	18 27.0	17 44.7	6 33.4	21 .2	6 2.7	9 .1
7	14 58 10.0	13 41.2	27 5.8	23 19.0	27 46.1	10 48.5	18 48.9	17 54.5	6 29.3	20 58.2	6 1.7	8 58.5
8	15 2 6.6	14 39.3	27 2.8	4♉26.3	29 27.3	12 6.7	19 10.3	18 4.3	6 25.1	20 56.2	6 .8	8 57.0
9	15 6 3.1	15 37.7	26 59.7	15 57.7	1♉10.5	13 25.2	19 31.4	18 13.9	6 20.9	20 54.2	5 59.8	8 55.5
10	15 9 59.7	16 36.1	26 56.7	28 .6	2 56.0	14 43.7	19 51.9	18 23.5	6 16.7	20 52.1	5 58.7	8 54.0
11	15 13 56.2	17 34.7	26 53.7	10♊37.0	4 43.7	16 2.4	20 11.9	18 32.9	6 12.4	20 50.0	5 57.7	8 52.4
12	15 17 52.8	18 33.4	26 50.7	23 42.6	6 33.7	17 21.3	20 31.5	18 42.2	6 8.0	20 47.8	5 56.6	8 50.9
13	15 21 49.3	19 32.3	26 47.6	7♋ 6.2	8 26.1	18 40.3	20 50.5	18 51.5	6 3.6	20 45.6	5 55.4	8 49.4
14	15 25 45.9	20 31.3	26 44.6	20 33.0	10 21.0	19 59.4	21 9.0	19 .6	5 59.2	20 43.4	5 54.3	8 47.9
15	15 29 42.4	21 30.4	26 41.6	3♌48.5	12 18.2	21 18.6	21 27.0	19 9.6	5 54.7	20 41.2	5 53.1	8 46.3
16	15 33 39.0	22 29.7	26 38.6	16 43.2	14 17.9	22 37.8	21 44.5	19 18.5	5 50.2	20 38.9	5 51.9	8 44.8
17	15 37 35.6	23 29.1	26 35.5	29 14.8	16 20.0	23 57.2	22 1.4	19 27.2	5 45.7	20 36.6	5 50.7	8 43.4
18	15 41 32.1	24 28.7	26 32.5	11♍28.3	18 24.6	25 16.6	22 17.8	19 35.9	5 41.2	20 34.3	5 49.4	8 41.9
19	15 45 28.7	25 28.4	26 29.5	23 34.5	20 31.5	26 36.0	22 33.7	19 44.4	5 36.6	20 31.9	5 48.1	8 40.4
20	15 49 25.2	26 28.2	26 26.5	5♎48.5	22 40.6	27 55.5	22 48.9	19 52.9	5 32.0	20 29.5	5 46.8	8 38.9
21	15 53 21.8	27 28.2	26 23.4	18 28.1	24 51.8	29 15.0	23 3.6	20 1.2	5 27.4	20 27.1	5 45.5	8 37.5
22	15 57 18.3	28 28.2	26 20.4	1♏52.6	27 4.9	0♋34.4	23 17.7	20 9.4	5 22.8	20 24.7	5 44.2	8 36.0
23	16 1 14.9	29 28.5	26 17.4	16 18.8	29 19.7	1 53.9	23 31.1	20 17.5	5 18.2	20 22.2	5 42.8	8 34.6
24	16 5 11.5	0♊28.8	26 14.4	1♐54.2	1♊36.0	3 13.2	23 44.0	20 25.4	5 13.5	20 19.7	5 41.4	8 33.2
25	16 9 8.0	1 29.3	26 11.4	18 28.6	3 53.4	4 32.6	23 56.2	20 33.3	5 8.9	20 17.2	5 40.0	8 31.8
26	16 13 4.6	2 29.9	26 8.3	5♑29.0	6 11.7	5 51.8	24 7.8	20 41.0	5 4.2	20 14.7	5 38.6	8 30.4
27	16 17 1.1	3 30.6	26 5.3	22 9.3	8 30.5	7 11.0	24 18.8	20 48.6	4 59.5	20 12.2	5 37.1	8 29.0
28	16 20 57.7	4 31.4	26 2.3	7♒50.0	10 49.5	8 30.1	24 29.0	20 56.0	4 54.9	20 9.7	5 35.7	8 27.7
29	16 24 54.3	5 32.4	25 59.3	22 12.9	13 8.3	9 49.0	24 38.6	21 3.4	4 50.2	20 7.1	5 34.2	8 26.3
30	16 28 50.8	6 33.5	25 56.3	5♓20.4	15 26.5	11 7.9	24 47.5	21 10.6	4 45.6	20 4.6	5 32.7	8 25.0
31	16 32 47.4	7 34.7	25 53.2	17 26.4	17 43.9	12 26.6	24 55.6	21 17.7	4 40.9	20 2.0	5 31.2	8 23.7

DECLINATION

DAY	EPHEM. SID. TIME	☉	☊	☽	☿	♀	♂	♃	♄	♅	♆	♇
1	14 34 30.7	14N55.3	0N11.8	23S10.0	4N58.7	21N49.5	23S43.5	6S40.3	19S41.3	23S16.6	22S13.4	2N41.6
4	14 46 20.3	15 49.1	0 11.8	8 1.1	7 1.6	22 34.0	23 43.9	6 28.2	19 39.4	23 16.4	22 13.4	2 42.9
7	14 58 10.0	16 40.4	0 11.7	9N14.5	9 11.0	23 13.0	23 44.6	6 16.3	19 37.5	23 16.1	22 13.4	2 44.1
10	15 9 59.7	17 29.3	0 11.6	22 57.0	11 25.2	23 46.0	23 45.8	6 4.8	19 35.5	23 15.8	22 13.5	2 45.2
13	15 21 49.3	18 15.6	0 11.6	28 5.6	13 42.0	24 13.1	23 47.6	5 53.8	19 33.5	23 15.4	22 13.6	2 46.2
16	15 33 39.0	18 59.0	0 11.5	21 53.3	15 58.3	24 33.9	23 50.2	5 43.1	19 31.4	23 15.1	22 13.6	2 47.1
19	15 45 28.7	19 39.6	0 11.5	6 18.0	18 10.2	24 48.4	23 53.6	5 32.8	19 29.3	23 14.7	22 13.7	2 47.9
22	15 57 18.3	20 17.1	0 11.4	13S20.3	20 12.5	24 56.5	23 58.0	5 23.0	19 27.2	23 14.3	22 13.8	2 48.5
25	16 9 8.0	20 51.5	0 11.3	27 1.4	21 59.9	24 58.2	24 3.6	5 13.7	19 25.1	23 13.8	22 14.0	2 49.1
28	16 20 57.7	21 22.7	0 11.3	24 14.2	23 27.5	24 53.5	24 10.3	5 4.8	19 23.0	23 13.4	22 14.1	2 49.5
31	16 32 47.4	21 50.6	0 11.2	9 20.3	24 31.9	24 42.3	24 18.3	4 56.4	19 21.0	23 13.0	22 14.2	2 49.7

JUNE 1986

LONGITUDE

DAY	EPHEM. SID. TIME h m s	☉ ° ′	☊ ° ′	☽ ° ′	☿ ° ′	♀ ° ′	♂ ° ′	♃ ° ′	♄ ° ′	♅ ° ′	♆ ° ′	♇ ° ′
1	16 36 43.9	10♊13.5	27♈49.5	27♓32.1	20♊55.5	12♋29.2	22♑43.2	20♓10.9	6♐ 6.8	20♐48.4	5♑ 5.2	5♏ 2.7
2	16 40 40.5	11 11.0	27 46.3	9♈56.4	22 58.2	13 40.7	22 48.7	20 18.2	6R 2.3	20R46.0	5R 3.7	5R 1.4
3	16 44 37.0	12 8.5	27 43.1	22 6.3	24 58.9	14 52.2	22 53.4	20 25.3	5 57.9	20 43.6	5 2.3	5 .2
4	16 48 33.6	13 6.0	27 39.9	4♉ 5.9	26 57.4	16 3.5	22 57.5	20 32.3	5 53.5	20 41.2	5 .8	4 58.9
5	16 52 30.2	14 3.4	27 36.7	15 599	28 53.5	17 14.9	23 .8	20 39.1	5 49.1	20 38.7	4 59.3	4 57.7
6	16 56 26.7	15 .9	27 33.6	27 48.4	0♋47.3	18 26.2	23 3.4	20 45.7	5 44.7	20 36.3	4 57.8	4 56.5
7	17 0 23.3	15 58.3	27 30.4	9♊37.1	2 38.7	19 37.4	23 5.2	20 52.3	5 40.3	20 33.8	4 56.3	4 55.3
8	17 4 19.8	16 55.7	27 27.2	21 27.0	4 27.6	20 48.6	23 6.3	20 58.6	5 36.0	20 31.4	4 54.8	4 54.2
9	17 8 16.4	17 53.2	27 24.0	3♋20.0	6 13.9	21 59.7	23 6.7	21 4.8	5 31.7	20 28.9	4 53.3	4 53.1
10	17 12 13.0	18 50.5	27 20.9	15 17.7	7 57.7	23 10.7	23R 6.3	21 10.8	5 27.4	20 26.4	4 51.8	4 52.0
11	17 16 9.5	19 47.9	27 17.7	27 21.9	9 38.9	24 21.7	23 5.1	21 16.7	5 23.1	20 24.0	4 50.2	4 50.9
12	17 20 6.1	20 45.3	27 14.5	9♌34.7	11 17.4	25 32.6	23 3.2	21 22.4	5 18.9	20 21.5	4 48.6	4 49.8
13	17 24 2.6	21 42.6	27 11.3	21 58.4	12 53.4	26 43.4	23 .6	21 27.9	5 14.7	20 19.0	4 47.1	4 48.8
14	17 27 59.2	22 40.0	27 8.2	4♍36.0	14 26.6	27 54.2	22 57.2	21 33.3	5 10.5	20 16.6	4 45.5	4 47.8
15	17 31 55.7	23 37.3	27 5.0	17 30.6	15 57.2	29 4.9	22 53.0	21 38.5	5 6.4	20 14.1	4 43.9	4 46.9
16	17 35 52.3	24 34.6	27 1.8	0♎45.4	17 25.1	0♌15.5	22 48.1	21 43.5	5 2.3	20 11.7	4 42.3	4 45.9
17	17 39 48.9	25 31.9	26 58.6	14 23.4	18 50.3	1 26.1	22 42.5	21 48.4	4 58.3	20 9.2	4 40.8	4 45.0
18	17 43 45.4	26 29.1	26 55.5	28 26.4	20 12.7	2 36.5	22 36.1	21 53.1	4 54.3	20 6.8	4 39.2	4 44.1
19	17 47 42.0	27 26.4	26 52.3	12♏54.4	21 32.3	3 46.9	22 29.1	21 57.6	4 50.3	20 4.3	4 37.6	4 43.3
20	17 51 38.5	28 23.7	26 49.1	27 44.5	22 49.2	4 57.3	22 21.3	22 2.0	4 46.5	20 2.0	4 36.0	4 42.5
21	17 55 35.1	29 20.9	26 45.9	12♐51.1	24 3.1	6 7.5	22 12.8	22 6.2	4 42.6	19 59.5	4 34.4	4 41.7
22	17 59 31.7	0♋18.2	26 42.7	28 5.3	25 14.0	7 17.7	22 3.7	22 10.2	4 38.8	19 57.1	4 32.8	4 40.9
23	18 3 28.2	1 15.4	26 39.6	13♑16.7	26 22.0	8 27.8	21 53.8	22 14.0	4 35.0	19 54.7	4 31.2	4 40.2
24	18 7 24.8	2 12.6	26 36.4	28 14.8	27 26.8	9 37.7	21 43.3	22 17.7	4 31.3	19 52.3	4 29.5	4 39.5
25	18 11 21.3	3 9.8	26 33.2	12♒50.8	28 28.5	10 47.6	21 32.2	22 21.1	4 27.7	19 49.9	4 27.9	4 38.8
26	18 15 17.9	4 7.0	26 30.0	26 59.3	29 27.0	11 57.5	21 20.4	22 24.4	4 24.1	19 47.6	4 26.3	4 38.2
27	18 19 14.5	5 4.2	26 26.9	10♓38.0	0♌22.2	13 7.2	21 8.0	22 27.5	4 20.6	19 45.2	4 24.7	4 37.6
28	18 23 11.0	6 1.4	26 23.7	23 47.9	1 13.9	14 16.8	20 55.0	22 30.4	4 17.1	19 42.9	4 23.1	4 37.0
29	18 27 7.6	6 58.6	26 20.5	6♈32.2	2 2.1	15 26.4	20 41.4	22 33.2	4 13.7	19 40.6	4 21.4	4 36.4
30	18 31 4.1	7 55.8	26 17.3	18 55.4	2 46.7	16 35.9	20 27.3	22 35.7	4 10.4	19 38.3	4 19.8	4 35.9

LATITUDE

DAY	SID. TIME	☉	☊	☽	☿	♀	♂	♃	♄	♅	♆	♇
1	16 36 43.9	0 .0	0 .0	2S44.3	1N40.1	1N46.3	2S51.9	1S 5.7	2N 1.4	0S 5.3	1N 6.5	16N58.6
4	16 48 33.6	0 .0	0 .0	0N25.7	1 55.2	1 49.9	3 4.4	1 6.4	2 1.2	0 5.4	1 6.5	16 57.4
7	17 0 23.3	0 .0	0 .0	3 19.9	2 3.5	1 52.9	3 17.1	1 7.2	2 .9	0 5.4	1 6.5	16 56.2
10	17 12 13.0	0 .0	0 .0	4 57.9	2 5.0	1 55.1	3 30.2	1 8.1	2 .6	0 5.4	1 6.6	16 54.9
13	17 24 2.6	0 .0	0 .0	4 40.9	1 59.6	1 56.6	3 43.5	1 8.9	2 .3	0 5.5	1 6.6	16 53.6
16	17 35 52.3	0 .0	0 .0	2 22.0	1 47.7	1 57.4	3 56.8	1 9.7	1 59.9	0 5.5	1 6.6	16 52.2
19	17 47 42.0	0 .0	0 .0	1S17.3	1 29.6	1 57.3	4 10.2	1 10.6	1 59.5	0 5.5	1 6.5	16 50.8
22	17 59 31.7	0 .0	0 .0	4 23.5	1 5.7	1 56.5	4 23.4	1 11.5	1 59.0	0 5.6	1 6.5	16 49.3
25	18 11 21.3	0 .0	0 .0	4 52.9	0 36.3	1 54.8	4 36.3	1 12.4	1 58.5	0 5.6	1 6.5	16 47.7
28	18 23 11.0	0 .0	0 .0	2 48.5	0 2.0	1 52.2	4 48.6	1 13.3	1 58.0	0 5.6	1 6.5	16 46.2

RIGHT ASCENSION

DAY	SID. TIME	☉	☊	☽	☿	♀	♂	♃	♄	♅	♆	♇
1	16 36 43.9	8♊36.1	25♈50.2	28♓49.6	19♊60.0	13♋45.1	25♑ 3.1	21♓24.6	4♐36.2	19♐59.4	5♑29.7	8♏22.4
2	16 40 40.5	9 37.5	25 47.2	9♈48.8	22 14.5	15 3.5	25 9.7	21 31.4	4R31.6	19R56.7	5R28.1	8R21.1
3	16 44 37.0	10 39.0	25 44.2	20 41.1	24 27.3	16 21.6	25 15.7	21 38.1	4 26.9	19 54.1	5 26.6	8 19.8
4	16 48 33.6	11 40.6	25 41.2	1♉41.8	26 38.0	17 39.6	25 20.8	21 44.6	4 22.3	19 51.5	5 25.0	8 18.6
5	16 52 30.2	12 42.3	25 38.1	13 3.9	28 46.4	18 57.3	25 25.2	21 51.0	4 17.7	19 48.8	5 23.4	8 17.4
6	16 56 26.7	13 44.1	25 35.1	24 56.6	0♋52.4	20 14.8	25 28.8	21 57.2	4 13.1	19 46.2	5 21.8	8 16.1
7	17 0 23.3	14 46.0	25 32.1	7♊24.2	2 55.7	21 32.0	25 31.6	22 3.3	4 8.5	19 43.5	5 20.2	8 14.9
8	17 4 19.8	15 47.9	25 29.1	20 24.0	4 56.2	22 49.0	25 33.6	22 9.3	4 4.0	19 40.8	5 18.5	8 13.8
9	17 8 16.4	16 49.9	25 26.1	3♋45.8	6 53.8	24 5.7	25 34.8	22 15.1	3 59.5	19 38.2	5 16.9	8 12.6
10	17 12 13.0	17 52.0	25 23.1	17 14.0	8 48.3	25 22.1	25 35.2	22 20.8	3 55.0	19 35.5	5 15.2	8 11.5
11	17 16 9.5	18 54.2	25 20.1	0♌32.1	10 39.8	26 38.2	25R34.8	22 26.3	3 50.5	19 32.8	5 13.5	8 10.4
12	17 20 6.1	19 56.4	25 17.0	13 27.8	12 28.0	27 54.1	25 33.6	22 31.7	3 46.1	19 30.1	5 11.9	8 9.3
13	17 24 2.6	20 58.6	25 14.0	25 56.2	14 13.0	29 9.6	25 31.5	22 36.9	3 41.7	19 27.5	5 10.2	8 8.2
14	17 27 59.2	22 .9	25 11.0	8♍ .4	15 54.7	0♌24.8	25 28.7	22 41.9	3 37.3	19 24.8	5 8.5	8 7.2
15	17 31 55.7	23 3.2	25 8.0	19 49.6	17 33.0	1 39.6	25 25.0	22 46.8	3 33.0	19 22.1	5 6.8	8 6.1
16	17 35 52.3	24 5.5	25 5.0	1♎38.2	19 7.9	2 54.1	25 20.5	22 51.6	3 28.7	19 19.5	5 5.1	8 5.1
17	17 39 48.9	25 7.9	25 2.0	13 43.5	20 39.4	4 8.2	25 15.2	22 56.2	3 24.5	19 16.8	5 3.3	8 4.2
18	17 43 45.4	26 10.2	24 59.0	26 25.1	22 7.5	5 22.0	25 9.2	23 .6	3 20.3	19 14.2	5 1.6	8 3.2
19	17 47 42.0	27 12.6	24 55.9	10♏ 2.8	23 32.0	6 35.4	25 2.3	23 4.9	3 16.2	19 11.5	4 59.9	8 2.3
20	17 51 38.5	28 15.0	24 52.9	24 51.9	24 53.0	7 48.5	24 54.7	23 9.1	3 12.1	19 8.9	4 58.2	8 1.4
21	17 55 35.1	29 17.4	24 49.9	10♐54.4	26 10.4	9 1.2	24 46.2	23 13.0	3 8.1	19 6.3	4 56.5	8 .5
22	17 59 31.7	0♋19.8	24 46.9	27 50.7	27 24.2	10 13.5	24 37.0	23 16.8	3 4.1	19 3.7	4 54.7	7 59.7
23	18 3 28.2	1 22.2	24 43.9	14♑58.3	28 34.3	11 25.4	24 27.0	23 20.5	3 .2	19 1.1	4 53.0	7 58.8
24	18 7 24.8	2 24.5	24 40.9	1♒28.6	29 40.7	12 36.9	24 16.3	23 24.0	2 56.3	18 58.5	4 51.2	7 58.0
25	18 11 21.3	3 26.8	24 37.9	16 47.8	0♌43.4	13 48.0	24 4.8	23 27.3	2 52.5	18 55.9	4 49.5	7 57.2
26	18 15 17.9	4 29.1	24 34.9	0♓46.4	1 42.2	14 58.8	23 52.7	23 30.4	2 48.7	18 53.3	4 47.7	7 56.5
27	18 19 14.5	5 31.4	24 31.9	13 33.1	2 37.2	16 9.1	23 39.8	23 33.4	2 45.0	18 50.8	4 46.0	7 55.8
28	18 23 11.0	6 33.7	24 28.9	25 25.4	3 28.2	17 19.1	23 26.2	23 36.2	2 41.4	18 48.3	4 44.2	7 55.1
29	18 27 7.6	7 35.9	24 25.9	6♈43.0	4 15.2	18 28.7	23 12.0	23 38.8	2 37.8	18 45.7	4 42.5	7 54.4
30	18 31 4.1	8 38.0	24 22.8	17 44.7	4 58.1	19 37.9	22 57.2	23 41.3	2 34.3	18 43.2	4 40.7	7 53.7

DECLINATION

DAY	SID. TIME	☉	☊	☽	☿	♀	♂	♃	♄	♅	♆	♇
1	16 36 43.9	21N59.2	0N11.2	3S29.5	24N47.9	24N37.2	24S21.2	4S53.8	19S20.3	23S12.8	22S14.3	2N49.8
4	16 48 33.6	22 22.5	0 11.1	13N17.4	25 19.7	24 17.7	24 31.1	4 46.1	19 18.2	23 12.3	22 14.4	2 49.9
7	17 0 23.3	22 42.3	0 11.1	25 11.4	25 28.5	23 52.1	24 42.4	4 38.9	19 16.2	23 11.8	22 14.6	2 49.9
10	17 12 13.0	22 58.5	0 11.0	27 29.9	25 17.0	23 20.6	24 55.0	4 32.4	19 14.3	23 11.3	22 14.7	2 49.8
13	17 24 2.6	23 11.0	0 11.0	18 36.7	24 48.2	22 43.3	25 9.1	4 26.4	19 12.4	23 10.8	22 14.9	2 49.5
16	17 35 52.3	23 19.9	0 10.9	1 52.2	24 5.3	22 .6	25 24.4	4 21.0	19 10.6	23 10.3	22 15.1	2 49.1
19	17 47 42.0	23 25.1	0 10.8	16S56.6	23 11.7	21 12.6	25 40.8	4 16.2	19 8.8	23 9.8	22 15.2	2 48.5
22	17 59 31.7	23 26.6	0 10.8	27 49.2	22 10.2	20 19.7	25 58.0	4 12.1	19 7.2	23 9.3	22 15.4	2 47.9
25	18 11 21.3	23 24.3	0 10.7	21 38.1	21 3.8	19 22.1	26 15.9	4 8.6	19 5.7	23 8.8	22 15.6	2 47.1
28	18 23 11.0	23 18.4	0 10.7	5 2.5	19 55.2	18 20.2	26 34.1	4 5.7	19 4.2	23 8.3	22 15.8	2 46.1

JULY 1986

DAY	EPHEM. SID. TIME	☉	☊	☽	☿	♀	♂	♃	♄	♅	♆	♇
	h m s	° ′	° ′	° ′	° ′	° ′	° ′	° ′	° ′	° ′	° ′	° ′
		LONGITUDE										
1	18 35 .7	8♋53.1	26♈14.2	1♉ 2.5	3♌27.5	17♌45.3	20♑12.7	22♓38.1	4♐ 7.1	19♐36.0	4♑18.2	4♏35.4
2	18 38 57.2	9 50.3	26 11.0	12 58.7	4 4.4	18 54.5	19R57.6	22 40.2	4R 3.9	19R33.7	4R16.6	4R35.0
3	18 42 53.8	10 47.5	26 7.8	24 48.8	4 37.3	20 3.7	19 42.1	22 42.2	4 .8	19 31.5	4 15.0	4 34.6
4	18 46 50.4	11 44.7	26 4.6	6♊36.8	5 6.0	21 12.8	19 26.2	22 44.0	3 57.7	19 29.3	4 13.4	4 34.2
5	18 50 46.9	12 41.9	26 1.5	18 26.3	5 30.5	22 21.8	19 9.9	22 45.6	3 54.7	19 27.1	4 11.8	4 33.8
6	18 54 43.5	13 39.1	25 58.3	0♋19.7	5 50.6	23 30.8	18 53.3	22 47.0	3 51.8	19 24.9	4 10.2	4 33.5
7	18 58 40.0	14 36.4	25 55.1	12 19.2	6 6.2	24 39.6	18 36.5	22 48.2	3 49.0	19 22.7	4 8.6	4 33.2
8	19 2 36.6	15 33.6	25 51.9	24 25.9	6 17.3	25 48.3	18 19.4	22 49.2	3 46.2	19 20.6	4 7.0	4 32.9
9	19 6 33.2	16 30.8	25 48.8	6♌41.0	6 23.6	26 56.8	18 2.1	22 50.0	3 43.5	19 18.5	4 5.4	4 32.7
10	19 10 29.7	17 28.0	25 45.6	19 5.3	6 25.3	28 5.3	17 44.7	22 50.7	3 40.9	19 16.4	4 3.8	4 32.5
11	19 14 26.3	18 25.3	25 42.4	1♍39.9	6R22.2	29 13.8	17 27.3	22 51.1	3 38.4	19 14.4	4 2.3	4 32.4
12	19 18 22.8	19 22.5	25 39.2	14 26.2	6 14.4	0♍22.0	17 9.7	22 51.4	3 36.0	19 12.4	4 .8	4 32.3
13	19 22 19.4	20 19.8	25 36.0	27 26.1	6 1.9	1 30.1	16 52.2	22 51.4	3 33.6	19 10.4	3 59.2	4 32.2
14	19 26 15.9	21 17.0	25 32.9	10♎41.8	5 44.9	2 38.1	16 34.8	22R51.2	3 31.4	19 8.4	3 57.7	4 32.1
15	19 30 12.5	22 14.2	25 29.7	24 15.6	5 23.5	3 46.0	16 17.4	22 50.9	3 29.2	19 6.5	3 56.2	4 32.1
16	19 34 9.1	23 11.4	25 26.5	8♏ 9.4	4 57.9	4 53.8	16 .2	22 50.3	3 27.1	19 4.6	3 54.7	4 32.1
17	19 38 5.6	24 8.7	25 23.3	22 23.9	4 28.4	6 1.4	15 43.2	22 49.6	3 25.0	19 2.7	3 53.2	4D32.2
18	19 42 2.2	25 5.9	25 20.2	6♐57.7	3 55.6	7 8.9	15 26.5	22 48.6	3 23.1	19 .9	3 51.7	4 32.3
19	19 45 58.7	26 3.1	25 17.0	21 47.2	3 19.7	8 16.2	15 10.0	22 47.5	3 21.3	18 59.1	3 50.2	4 32.4
20	19 49 55.3	27 .4	25 13.8	6♑45.8	2 41.3	9 23.4	14 53.9	22 46.2	3 19.5	18 57.3	3 48.7	4 32.5
21	19 53 51.9	27 57.6	25 10.6	21 44.9	2 1.1	10 30.5	14 38.1	22 44.7	3 17.8	18 55.6	3 47.3	4 32.7
22	19 57 48.4	28 54.9	25 7.5	6♒34.8	1 19.7	11 37.4	14 22.7	22 43.0	3 16.3	18 53.9	3 45.9	4 32.9
23	20 1 45.0	29 52.1	25 4.3	21 7.1	0 37.8	12 44.1	14 7.8	22 41.1	3 14.8	18 52.2	3 44.4	4 33.2
24	20 5 41.5	0♌49.4	25 1.1	5♓15.2	29♋56.1	13 50.7	13 53.3	22 39.0	3 13.4	18 50.6	3 43.0	4 33.5
25	20 9 38.1	1 46.7	24 57.9	18 55.8	29 15.4	14 57.1	13 39.4	22 36.7	3 12.1	18 49.0	3 41.7	4 33.8
26	20 13 34.6	2 44.0	24 54.8	2♈ 8.5	28 36.4	16 3.4	13 25.9	22 34.2	3 10.9	18 47.5	3 40.3	4 34.1
27	20 17 31.2	3 41.3	24 51.6	14 55.6	27 59.9	17 9.5	13 13.1	22 31.5	3 9.7	18 46.0	3 38.9	4 34.5
28	20 21 27.8	4 38.6	24 48.4	27 20.9	27 26.5	18 15.5	13 .8	22 28.7	3 8.7	18 44.5	3 37.6	4 34.9
29	20 25 24.3	5 36.0	24 45.2	9♉29.4	26 56.9	19 21.3	12 49.2	22 25.6	3 7.8	18 43.1	3 36.3	4 35.4
30	20 29 20.9	6 33.3	24 42.0	21 26.3	26 31.6	20 26.9	12 38.2	22 22.4	3 6.9	18 41.7	3 35.0	4 35.9
31	20 33 17.4	7 30.7	24 38.9	3♊17.0	26 11.3	21 32.3	12 27.9	22 19.0	3 6.2	18 40.3	3 33.7	4 36.4
		LATITUDE										
1	18 35 .7	0 .0	0 .0	0N19.6	0S36.8	1N48.7	5S .4	1S14.2	1N57.5	0S 5.6	1N 6.4	16N44.5
4	18 46 50.4	0 .0	0 .0	3 12.2	1 19.1	1 44.4	5 11.3	1 15.1	1 57.0	0 5.7	1 6.4	16 42.9
7	18 58 40.0	0 .0	0 .0	4 51.0	2 3.8	1 39.1	5 21.2	1 16.0	1 56.4	0 5.7	1 6.4	16 41.2
10	19 10 29.7	0 .0	0 .0	4 36.6	2 49.0	1 33.0	5 29.9	1 16.9	1 55.8	0 5.7	1 6.3	16 39.5
13	19 22 19.4	0 .0	0 .0	2 23.3	3 32.2	1 25.9	5 37.4	1 17.8	1 55.2	0 5.7	1 6.3	16 37.8
16	19 34 9.1	0 .0	0 .0	1S 5.4	4 10.2	1 17.9	5 43.5	1 18.7	1 54.5	0 5.7	1 6.2	16 36.0
19	19 45 58.7	0 .0	0 .0	4 10.5	4 39.2	1 8.9	5 48.2	1 19.6	1 53.9	0 5.8	1 6.1	16 34.3
22	19 57 48.4	0 .0	0 .0	4 54.2	4 55.5	0 59.1	5 51.4	1 20.5	1 53.2	0 5.8	1 6.1	16 32.5
25	20 9 38.1	0 .0	0 .0	2 56.1	4 56.8	0 48.4	5 53.1	1 21.4	1 52.6	0 5.8	1 6.0	16 30.8
28	20 21 27.8	0 .0	0 .0	0N15.2	4 42.5	0 36.8	5 53.5	1 22.2	1 51.9	0 5.8	1 5.9	16 29.0
31	20 33 17.4	0 .0	0 .0	3 10.1	4 14.4	0 24.3	5 52.6	1 23.1	1 51.2	0 5.8	1 5.8	16 27.3
		RIGHT ASCENSION										
1	18 35 .7	9♋40.1	24♈19.8	28♈47.4	5♌36.8	20♌46.7	22♑41.7	23♓43.6	2♐30.9	18♐40.8	4♑39.0	7♏53.1
2	18 38 57.2	10 42.2	24 16.8	10♉ 5.7	6 11.3	21 55.1	22R25.7	23 45.7	2R27.5	18R38.3	4R37.2	7R52.5
3	18 42 53.8	11 44.2	24 13.8	21 51.0	6 41.4	23 3.1	22 9.2	23 47.6	2 24.2	18 35.9	4 35.5	7 52.0
4	18 46 50.4	12 46.1	24 10.8	4♊10.0	7 7.1	24 10.7	21 52.2	23 49.4	2 21.0	18 33.5	4 33.8	7 51.4
5	18 50 46.9	13 48.0	24 7.8	17 2.9	7 28.3	25 18.0	21 34.7	23 51.0	2 17.8	18 31.1	4 32.0	7 50.9
6	18 54 43.5	14 49.7	24 4.8	0♋22.3	7 45.0	26 24.9	21 16.9	23 52.4	2 14.8	18 28.7	4 30.3	7 50.4
7	18 58 40.0	15 51.4	24 1.8	13 53.6	7 56.9	27 31.4	20 58.7	23 53.6	2 11.8	18 26.4	4 28.6	7 50.0
8	19 2 36.6	16 53.0	23 58.8	27 19.5	8 4.2	28 37.5	20 40.2	23 54.7	2 8.9	18 24.1	4 26.9	7 49.6
9	19 6 33.2	17 54.5	23 55.8	10♌25.0	8 6.8	29 43.3	20 21.4	23 55.5	2 6.1	18 21.8	4 25.2	7 49.2
10	19 10 29.7	18 55.9	23 52.8	23 2.1	8R 4.6	0♍48.6	20 2.5	23 56.2	2 3.3	18 19.5	4 23.5	7 48.8
11	19 14 26.3	19 57.2	23 49.8	5♍10.7	7 57.8	1 53.7	19 43.5	23 56.8	2 .7	18 17.4	4 21.9	7 48.5
12	19 18 22.8	20 58.4	23 46.8	16 57.8	7 46.3	2 58.4	19 24.3	23 57.1	1 58.1	18 15.2	4 20.2	7 48.2
13	19 22 19.4	21 59.4	23 43.8	28 35.8	7 30.2	4 2.6	19 5.1	23 57.3	1 55.6	18 13.0	4 18.5	7 48.0
14	19 26 15.9	23 .3	23 40.8	10♎20.6	7 9.7	5 6.6	18 45.9	23R57.2	1 53.2	18 10.9	4 16.9	7 47.7
15	19 30 12.5	24 1.1	23 37.8	22 30.6	6 45.0	6 10.2	18 26.8	23 57.0	1 50.9	18 8.8	4 15.2	7 47.5
16	19 34 9.1	25 1.8	23 34.8	5♏25.2	6 16.5	7 13.4	18 7.8	23 56.7	1 48.7	18 6.7	4 13.6	7 47.3
17	19 38 5.6	26 2.4	23 31.8	19 22.1	5 44.3	8 16.3	17 49.0	23 56.1	1 46.5	18 4.7	4 12.0	7 47.2
18	19 42 2.2	27 2.8	23 28.8	4♐31.2	5 9.0	9 18.8	17 30.4	23 55.3	1 44.5	18 2.7	4 10.4	7 47.1
19	19 45 58.7	28 3.0	23 25.8	20 46.2	4 31.0	10 21.0	17 12.2	23 54.4	1 42.5	18 .8	4 8.8	7 47.0
20	19 49 55.3	29 3.2	23 22.8	7♑38.4	3 50.8	11 22.9	16 54.2	23 53.3	1 40.7	17 58.8	4 7.2	7 46.9
21	19 53 51.9	0♌ 3.2	23 19.8	24 23.1	3 9.1	12 24.4	16 36.6	23 52.0	1 38.9	17 57.0	4 5.6	7 46.9
22	19 57 48.4	1 3.0	23 16.8	10♒18.3	2 26.5	13 25.7	16 19.4	23 50.6	1 37.2	17 55.1	4 4.1	7 46.9
23	20 1 45.0	2 2.7	23 13.8	25 1.3	1 43.8	14 26.6	16 2.7	23 48.9	1 35.6	17 53.3	4 2.6	7 46.9
24	20 5 41.5	3 2.3	23 10.8	8♓30.7	1 1.6	15 27.2	15 46.5	23 47.1	1 34.1	17 51.6	4 1.0	7D47.0
25	20 9 38.1	4 1.7	23 7.8	20 58.9	0 20.7	16 27.5	15 30.8	23 45.1	1 32.7	17 49.9	3 59.5	7 47.1
26	20 13 34.6	5 1.0	23 4.8	2♈43.7	29♋41.8	17 27.5	15 15.7	23 43.0	1 31.4	17 48.2	3 58.1	7 47.2
27	20 17 31.2	6 .1	23 1.8	14 4.1	29 5.7	18 27.2	15 1.3	23 40.6	1 30.2	17 46.5	3 56.6	7 47.4
28	20 21 27.8	6 59.1	22 58.8	25 17.5	28 33.0	19 26.6	14 47.4	23 38.1	1 29.1	17 45.0	3 55.2	7 47.6
29	20 25 24.3	7 58.0	22 55.8	6♉39.4	28 4.4	20 25.8	14 34.3	23 35.4	1 28.1	17 43.4	3 53.7	7 47.8
30	20 29 20.9	8 56.6	22 52.8	18 22.4	27 40.5	21 24.7	14 21.9	23 32.6	1 27.2	17 41.9	3 52.3	7 48.0
31	20 33 17.4	9 55.2	22 49.8	0♊35.3	27 21.7	22 23.3	14 10.2	23 29.5	1 26.4	17 40.4	3 51.0	7 48.3
		DECLINATION										
1	18 35 .7	23N 8.7	0N10.6	12N 8.7	18N47.3	17N14.3	26S52.3	4S 3.5	19S 2.9	23S 7.8	22S16.0	2N45.1
4	18 46 50.4	22 55.4	0 10.5	24 34.3	17 42.9	16 4.7	27 10.0	4 2.0	19 1.7	23 7.3	22 16.2	2 43.9
7	18 58 40.0	22 38.6	0 10.5	27 42.1	16 45.0	14 51.7	27 27.1	4 1.2	19 .7	23 6.8	22 16.4	2 42.7
10	19 10 29.7	22 18.2	0 10.4	19 28.7	15 56.5	13 35.6	27 43.0	4 1.1	18 59.8	23 6.3	22 16.6	2 41.3
13	19 22 19.4	21 54.3	0 10.4	3 12.7	15 20.3	12 16.7	27 57.3	4 1.6	18 59.0	23 5.8	22 16.8	2 39.7
16	19 34 9.1	21 27.0	0 10.3	15S15.6	14 58.7	10 55.5	28 10.0	4 2.9	18 58.4	23 5.4	22 17.0	2 38.1
19	19 45 58.7	20 56.5	0 10.2	27 21.3	14 53.1	9 32.1	28 20.7	4 4.8	18 57.9	23 4.9	22 17.2	2 36.4
22	19 57 48.4	20 22.8	0 10.2	23 22.5	15 3.5	8 7.0	28 29.3	4 7.4	18 57.7	23 4.5	22 17.4	2 34.5
25	20 9 38.1	19 46.0	0 10.1	7 4.8	15 28.0	6 40.3	28 35.8	4 10.7	18 57.5	23 4.1	22 17.6	2 32.6
28	20 21 27.8	19 6.3	0 10.1	10N46.1	16 3.3	5 12.5	28 40.1	4 14.7	18 57.6	23 3.8	22 17.7	2 30.6
31	20 33 17.4	18 23.8	0 10.0	23 55.5	16 45.0	3 43.7	28 42.5	4 19.3	18 57.8	23 3.4	22 17.9	2 28.5

AUGUST 1986

LONGITUDE

DAY	EPHEM. SID. TIME (h m s)	☉ (° ′)	☊ (° ′)	☽ (° ′)	☿ (° ′)	♀ (° ′)	♂ (° ′)	♃ (° ′)	♄ (° ′)	♅ (° ′)	♆ (° ′)	♇ (° ′)
1	20 37 14.0	8♌28.2	24♈35.7	15♊ 6.5	25♋56.3	22♍37.6	12♑18.4	22♓15.4	3♐ 5.6	18♐39.1	3♑32.5	4♏37.0
2	20 41 10.5	9 25.6	24 32.5	26 58.7	25 R 47.0	23 42.6	12 R 9.5	22 R 11.7	3 R 5.1	18 R 37.8	3 R 31.2	4 37.6
3	20 45 7.1	10 23.0	24 29.3	8♋57.2	25 43.7	24 47.5	12 1.5	22 7.7	3 4.6	18 36.6	3 30.0	4 38.2
4	20 49 3.7	11 20.5	24 26.2	21 4.5	25 D 46.7	25 52.2	11 54.1	22 3.6	3 4.2	18 35.4	3 28.8	4 38.9
5	20 53 .2	12 17.9	24 23.0	3♌22.3	25 56.1	26 56.7	11 47.6	21 59.3	3 4.0	18 34.3	3 27.6	4 39.6
6	20 56 56.8	13 15.4	24 19.8	15 51.4	26 12.1	28 .9	11 41.9	21 54.8	3 3.8	18 33.2	3 26.5	4 40.3
7	21 0 53.3	14 12.9	24 16.6	28 31.9	26 34.7	29 5.0	11 37.0	21 50.1	3 3.8	18 32.2	3 25.4	4 41.1
8	21 4 49.9	15 10.4	24 13.5	11♍23.9	27 4.0	0♎ 8.8	11 32.9	21 45.3	3 3.8	18 31.2	3 24.2	4 41.9
9	21 8 46.4	16 8.0	24 10.3	24 27.2	27 40.0	1 12.4	11 29.7	21 40.3	3 D 3.9	18 30.2	3 23.2	4 42.7
10	21 12 43.0	17 5.5	24 7.1	7♎42.0	28 22.6	2 15.8	11 27.3	21 35.2	3 4.2	18 29.3	3 22.1	4 43.5
11	21 16 39.5	18 3.1	24 3.9	21 8.6	29 11.7	3 19.0	11 25.7	21 29.9	3 4.5	18 28.5	3 21.1	4 44.4
12	21 20 36.1	19 .6	24 .7	4♏47.9	0♌ 7.1	4 21.8	11 25.0	21 24.5	3 4.9	18 27.7	3 20.0	4 45.4
13	21 24 32.7	19 58.2	23 57.6	18 40.5	1 8.9	5 24.5	11 D 25.2	21 18.9	3 5.4	18 26.9	3 19.0	4 46.3
14	21 28 29.2	20 55.8	23 54.4	2♐46.8	2 16.7	6 26.8	11 26.2	21 13.1	3 6.1	18 26.2	3 18.1	4 47.3
15	21 32 25.8	21 53.5	23 51.2	17 5.7	3 30.4	7 28.9	11 28.0	21 7.2	3 6.8	18 25.5	3 17.1	4 48.3
16	21 36 22.3	22 51.1	23 48.0	1♑35.0	4 49.6	8 30.7	11 30.7	21 1.2	3 7.6	18 24.9	3 16.2	4 49.4
17	21 40 18.9	23 48.8	23 44.9	16 10.2	6 14.2	9 32.2	11 34.2	20 55.0	3 8.5	18 24.3	3 15.3	4 50.5
18	21 44 15.4	24 46.4	23 41.7	0♒45.5	7 43.8	10 33.4	11 38.5	20 48.7	3 9.5	18 23.8	3 14.5	4 51.6
19	21 48 12.0	25 44.1	23 38.5	15 13.9	9 18.0	11 34.3	11 43.7	20 42.3	3 10.6	18 23.3	3 13.6	4 52.7
20	21 52 8.5	26 41.8	23 35.3	29 28.9	10 56.4	12 34.9	11 49.6	20 35.8	3 11.8	18 22.9	3 12.8	4 53.9
21	21 56 5.1	27 39.6	23 32.1	13♓24.7	12 38.8	13 35.1	11 56.3	20 29.1	3 13.1	18 22.6	3 12.1	4 55.1
22	22 0 1.7	28 37.4	23 29.0	26 58.1	14 24.6	14 35.0	12 3.9	20 22.4	3 14.5	18 22.3	3 11.4	4 56.4
23	22 3 58.2	29 35.2	23 25.8	10♈ 7.6	16 13.3	15 34.6	12 12.2	20 15.5	3 16.0	18 22.0	3 10.6	4 57.7
24	22 7 54.8	0♍33.0	23 22.6	22 54.2	18 4.6	16 33.8	12 21.3	20 8.5	3 17.6	18 21.8	3 9.9	4 59.0
25	22 11 51.3	1 30.8	23 19.4	5♉20.6	19 58.1	17 32.6	12 31.1	20 1.4	3 19.3	18 21.6	3 9.3	5 .3
26	22 15 47.9	2 28.7	23 16.3	17 30.9	21 53.3	18 31.0	12 41.6	19 54.2	3 21.0	18 21.5	3 8.6	5 1.6
27	22 19 44.4	3 26.6	23 13.1	29 29.7	23 49.8	19 29.1	12 52.9	19 47.0	3 22.9	18 21.4	3 8.0	5 3.0
28	22 23 41.0	4 24.5	23 9.9	11♊22.2	25 47.2	20 26.7	13 5.0	19 39.6	3 24.9	18 21.4	3 7.5	5 4.4
29	22 27 37.5	5 22.5	23 6.7	23 13.4	27 45.3	21 23.9	13 17.7	19 32.1	3 26.9	18 D 21.5	3 6.9	5 5.9
30	22 31 34.1	6 20.5	23 3.6	5♋ 8.2	29 43.7	22 20.7	13 31.2	19 24.6	3 29.0	18 21.5	3 6.4	5 7.3
31	22 35 30.6	7 18.5	23 .4	17 10.7	1♍42.1	23 17.1	13 45.3	19 17.0	3 31.3	18 21.7	3 5.9	5 8.8

LATITUDE

DAY	EPHEM. SID. TIME	☉	☊	☽	☿	♀	♂	♃	♄	♅	♆	♇
1	20 37 14.0	0 .0	0 .0	3N54.3	4S 2.5	0N20.0	5S52.0	1S23.3	1N51.0	0S 5.8	1N 5.8	16N26.7
4	20 49 3.7	0 .0	0 .0	5 .8	3 21.0	0 6.4	5 49.4	1 24.2	1 50.3	0 5.9	1 5.7	16 24.9
7	21 0 53.3	0 .0	0 .0	4 6.8	2 33.9	0S 8.0	5 45.9	1 24.9	1 49.5	0 5.9	1 5.6	16 23.2
10	21 12 43.0	0 .0	0 .0	1 20.2	1 44.6	0 23.2	5 41.4	1 25.7	1 48.8	0 5.9	1 5.5	16 21.5
13	21 24 32.7	0 .0	0 .0	2S12.7	0 56.2	0 39.1	5 36.1	1 26.4	1 48.1	0 5.9	1 5.4	16 19.8
16	21 36 22.3	0 .0	0 .0	4 44.0	0 11.4	0 55.8	5 30.1	1 27.1	1 47.4	0 5.9	1 5.3	16 18.2
19	21 48 12.0	0 .0	0 .0	4 41.0	0N27.7	1 13.1	5 23.5	1 27.7	1 46.7	0 5.9	1 5.1	16 16.5
22	22 0 1.7	0 .0	0 .0	2 10.4	0 59.5	1 31.0	5 16.5	1 28.3	1 46.0	0 6.0	1 5.0	16 14.9
25	22 11 51.3	0 .0	0 .0	1N11.1	1 23.1	1 49.4	5 9.1	1 28.8	1 45.3	0 6.0	1 4.9	16 13.4
28	22 23 41.0	0 .0	0 .0	3 54.3	1 38.3	2 8.4	5 1.5	1 29.3	1 44.6	0 6.0	1 4.8	16 11.9
31	22 35 30.6	0 .0	0 .0	5 7.3	1 45.6	2 27.9	4 53.6	1 29.7	1 43.9	0 6.0	1 4.7	16 10.4

RIGHT ASCENSION

DAY	EPHEM. SID. TIME	☉	☊	☽	☿	♀	♂	♃	♄	♅	♆	♇
1	20 37 14.0	10♌53.6	22♈46.8	13♊21.1	27♋ 8.6	23♍21.7	13♑59.4	23♓26.4	1♐25.7	17♐39.1	3♑49.6	7♏48.7
2	20 41 10.5	11 51.9	22 43.8	26 35.5	27 R 1.5	24 19.7	13 R 49.3	23 R 23.0	1 R 25.1	17 R 37.7	3 R 48.3	7 49.0
3	20 45 7.1	12 50.0	22 40.8	10♋ 6.8	27 .8	25 17.6	13 40.1	23 19.5	1 24.6	17 36.4	3 47.0	7 49.4
4	20 49 3.7	13 48.0	22 37.8	23 38.9	27 D 6.6	26 15.1	13 31.7	23 15.8	1 24.1	17 35.1	3 45.7	7 49.8
5	20 53 .2	14 45.8	22 34.8	6♌56.0	27 19.3	27 12.4	13 24.3	23 11.9	1 23.8	17 33.9	3 44.4	7 50.2
6	20 56 56.8	15 43.4	22 31.8	19 47.4	27 38.8	28 9.5	13 17.7	23 7.9	1 23.6	17 32.7	3 43.2	7 50.7
7	21 0 53.3	16 40.9	22 28.8	2♍10.1	28 5.4	29 6.4	13 12.0	23 3.7	1 23.5	17 31.6	3 41.9	7 51.2
8	21 4 49.9	17 38.3	22 25.8	14 8.3	28 38.9	0♎ 2.9	13 7.2	22 59.4	1 23.5	17 30.5	3 40.7	7 51.8
9	21 8 46.4	18 35.5	22 22.8	25 52.3	29 19.5	0 59.3	13 3.4	22 54.9	1 D 23.6	17 29.5	3 39.6	7 52.3
10	21 12 43.0	19 32.6	22 19.8	7♎35.9	0♌ 7.0	1 55.4	13 .6	22 50.2	1 23.8	17 28.5	3 38.4	7 52.9
11	21 16 39.5	20 29.5	22 16.8	19 35.8	1 1.2	2 51.3	12 58.6	22 45.5	1 24.0	17 27.6	3 37.3	7 53.5
12	21 20 36.1	21 26.2	22 13.8	2♏ 9.6	2 2.2	3 46.9	12 57.7	22 40.5	1 24.4	17 26.7	3 36.2	7 54.2
13	21 24 32.7	22 22.8	22 10.8	15 34.3	3 9.5	4 42.3	12 57.6	22 35.5	1 24.9	17 25.9	3 35.1	7 54.9
14	21 28 29.2	23 19.3	22 7.8	0♐ 1.7	4 23.1	5 37.5	12 D 58.6	22 30.2	1 25.5	17 25.1	3 34.1	7 55.6
15	21 32 25.8	24 15.7	22 4.9	15 32.0	5 42.5	6 32.4	13 .4	22 24.9	1 26.2	17 24.4	3 33.1	7 56.3
16	21 36 22.3	25 11.8	22 1.9	1♑47.4	7 7.5	7 27.1	13 3.2	22 19.4	1 27.0	17 23.7	3 32.1	7 57.1
17	21 40 18.9	26 7.9	21 58.9	18 13.2	8 37.7	8 21.5	13 7.0	22 13.8	1 27.9	17 23.1	3 31.1	7 57.9
18	21 44 15.4	27 3.8	21 55.9	4♒10.1	10 12.7	9 15.7	13 11.6	22 8.1	1 28.9	17 22.5	3 30.2	7 58.7
19	21 48 12.0	27 59.6	21 52.9	19 10.1	11 51.9	10 9.6	13 17.2	22 2.3	1 30.0	17 22.0	3 29.3	7 59.6
20	21 52 8.5	28 55.3	21 49.9	3♓ 3.9	13 35.0	11 3.3	13 23.6	21 56.3	1 31.2	17 21.6	3 28.4	8 .5
21	21 56 5.1	29 50.9	21 46.9	15 57.4	15 21.4	11 56.8	13 31.0	21 50.3	1 32.5	17 21.2	3 27.6	8 1.4
22	22 0 1.7	0♍46.3	21 43.9	28 4.9	17 10.7	12 50.1	13 39.2	21 44.1	1 34.0	17 20.9	3 26.8	8 2.4
23	22 3 58.2	1 41.7	21 40.9	9♈43.3	19 2.2	13 43.0	13 48.3	21 37.8	1 35.5	17 20.6	3 26.1	8 3.4
24	22 7 54.8	2 36.9	21 37.9	21 9.4	20 55.4	14 35.7	13 58.2	21 31.5	1 37.0	17 20.4	3 25.3	8 4.4
25	22 11 51.3	3 32.0	21 34.9	2♉38.5	22 50.0	15 28.1	14 9.0	21 25.0	1 38.7	17 20.2	3 24.6	8 5.4
26	22 15 47.9	4 27.0	21 32.0	14 23.4	24 45.3	16 20.3	14 20.5	21 18.4	1 40.5	17 20.0	3 23.9	8 6.5
27	22 19 44.4	5 21.9	21 29.0	26 33.6	26 41.1	17 12.2	14 32.9	21 11.8	1 42.4	17 20.0	3 23.3	8 7.6
28	22 23 41.0	6 16.8	21 26.0	9♊13.7	28 36.9	18 3.8	14 46.1	21 5.0	1 44.4	17 19.9	3 22.6	8 8.7
29	22 27 37.5	7 11.5	21 23.0	22 21.6	0♍32.4	18 55.2	15 .1	20 58.2	1 46.5	17 D 20.0	3 22.0	8 9.9
30	22 31 34.1	8 6.1	21 20.0	5♋48.7	2 27.3	19 46.2	15 14.8	20 51.3	1 48.7	17 20.1	3 21.5	8 11.1
31	22 35 30.6	9 .7	21 17.0	19 21.2	4 21.3	20 37.0	15 30.3	20 44.3	1 50.9	17 20.2	3 21.0	8 12.3

DECLINATION

DAY	EPHEM. SID. TIME	☉	☊	☽	☿	♀	♂	♃	♄	♅	♆	♇
1	20 37 14.0	18N 8.9	0N10.0	26N29.5	16N59.4	3N14.0	28S42.8	4S20.9	18S57.9	23S 3.3	22S18.0	2N27.7
4	20 49 3.7	17 22.8	0 9.9	26 44.6	17 42.0	1 44.4	28 42.6	4 26.3	18 58.3	23 3.0	22 18.2	2 25.5
7	21 0 53.3	16 34.1	0 9.9	15 50.4	18 19.5	0 14.5	28 40.6	4 32.4	18 58.9	23 2.8	22 18.4	2 23.2
10	21 12 43.0	15 42.9	0 9.8	1S49.6	18 46.9	1S15.3	28 37.0	4 39.0	18 59.7	23 2.5	22 18.6	2 20.8
13	21 24 32.7	14 49.6	0 9.7	19 30.5	18 59.5	2 44.8	28 31.9	4 46.1	19 .6	23 2.4	22 18.8	2 18.3
16	21 36 22.3	13 54.1	0 9.7	28 10.0	18 52.6	4 13.8	28 25.5	4 53.6	19 1.7	23 2.2	22 18.9	2 15.8
19	21 48 12.0	12 56.6	0 9.6	20 44.5	18 22.6	5 41.9	28 17.8	5 1.7	19 3.0	23 2.1	22 19.1	2 13.2
22	22 0 1.7	11 57.3	0 9.6	3 12.0	17 27.6	7 8.8	28 8.9	5 10.0	19 4.4	23 2.0	22 19.3	2 10.5
25	22 11 51.3	10 56.3	0 9.5	14N25.3	16 8.5	8 34.3	27 59.0	5 18.8	19 6.0	23 2.0	22 19.5	2 7.8
28	22 23 41.0	9 53.7	0 9.4	26 .9	14 28.1	9 58.2	27 48.0	5 27.8	19 7.7	23 2.0	22 19.6	2 5.1
31	22 35 30.6	8 49.7	0 9.4	27 25.1	12 30.9	11 20.2	27 35.9	5 37.0	19 9.6	23 2.0	22 19.8	2 2.3

SEPTEMBER 1986

LONGITUDE

DAY	EPHEM. SID. TIME h m s	☉ ° ′	☊ ° ′	☽ ° ′	☿ ° ′	♀ ° ′	♂ ° ′	♃ ° ′	♄ ° ′	♅ ° ′	♆ ° ′	♇ ° ′
1	22 39 27.2	8♍16.5	22♈57.2	29♋24.4	3♍40.4	24♎13.0	14♑ .1	19♓ 9.4	3♐33.6	18♐21.9	3♑ 5.4	5♏10.4
2	22 43 23.8	9 14.6	22 54.0	11♌51.7	5 38.2	25 8.4	14 15.7	19R 1.7	3 36.0	18 22.1	3R 5.0	5 11.9
3	22 47 20.3	10 12.7	22 50.8	24 34.2	7 35.6	26 3.3	14 31.8	18 53.9	3 38.5	18 22.4	3 4.6	5 13.5
4	22 51 16.9	11 10.9	22 47.7	7♍32.1	9 32.2	26 57.8	14 48.7	18 46.1	3 41.1	18 22.7	3 4.3	5 15.1
5	22 55 13.4	12 9.0	22 44.5	20 44.7	11 28.0	27 51.6	15 6.2	18 38.2	3 43.8	18 23.1	3 3.9	5 16.8
6	22 59 10.0	13 7.2	22 41.3	4♎10.9	13 23.0	28 45.0	15 24.3	18 30.3	3 46.6	18 23.6	3 3.6	5 18.4
7	23 3 6.5	14 5.5	22 38.1	17 48.8	15 16.9	29 37.7	15 43.0	18 22.4	3 49.5	18 24.1	3 3.4	5 20.1
8	23 7 3.1	15 3.7	22 35.0	1♏36.7	17 9.9	0♏29.9	16 2.4	18 14.4	3 52.4	18 24.6	3 3.1	5 21.8
9	23 10 59.6	16 2.0	22 31.8	15 32.8	19 1.8	1 21.4	16 22.3	18 6.5	3 55.5	18 25.2	3 2.9	5 23.6
10	23 14 56.2	17 .3	22 28.6	29 35.8	20 52.6	2 12.3	16 42.9	17 58.5	3 58.6	18 25.9	3 2.8	5 25.3
11	23 18 52.7	17 58.6	22 25.4	13♐44.1	22 42.3	3 2.6	17 4.0	17 50.5	4 1.8	18 26.6	3 2.6	5 27.1
12	23 22 49.3	18 57.0	22 22.2	27 56.2	24 30.9	3 52.1	17 25.7	17 42.6	4 5.2	18 27.4	3 2.6	5 29.0
13	23 26 45.9	19 55.4	22 19.1	12♑10.0	26 18.4	4 40.9	17 47.9	17 34.7	4 8.6	18 28.2	3 2.5	5 30.8
14	23 30 42.4	20 53.8	22 15.9	26 22.7	28 4.7	5 29.0	18 10.6	17 26.7	4 12.0	18 29.1	3 2.4	5 32.6
15	23 34 39.0	21 52.2	22 12.7	10♒31.2	29 50.0	6 16.2	18 33.8	17 18.8	4 15.6	18 30.0	3 2.4	5 34.5
16	23 38 35.5	22 50.7	22 9.5	24 31.7	1♎34.1	7 2.7	18 57.6	17 10.9	4 19.2	18 30.9	3D 2.5	5 36.4
17	23 42 32.1	23 49.1	22 6.4	8♓20.5	3 17.2	7 48.2	19 21.8	17 3.0	4 22.9	18 31.9	3 2.5	5 38.3
18	23 46 28.6	24 47.7	22 3.2	21 54.2	4 59.2	8 32.9	19 46.5	16 55.2	4 26.7	18 33.0	3 2.6	5 40.3
19	23 50 25.2	25 46.2	21 60.0	5♈10.8	6 40.2	9 16.7	20 11.7	16 47.4	4 30.6	18 34.1	3 2.7	5 42.3
20	23 54 21.7	26 44.8	21 56.8	18 8.9	8 20.2	9 59.5	20 37.3	16 39.6	4 34.5	18 35.3	3 2.9	5 44.2
21	23 58 18.3	27 43.4	21 53.6	0♉48.9	9 59.1	10 41.4	21 3.4	16 32.0	4 38.6	18 36.5	3 3.1	5 46.2
22	0 2 14.8	28 42.1	21 50.5	13 12.4	11 37.0	11 22.2	21 29.9	16 24.3	4 42.7	18 37.7	3 3.3	5 48.3
23	0 6 11.4	29 40.7	21 47.3	25 22.0	13 14.0	12 1.9	21 56.8	16 16.8	4 46.9	18 39.0	3 3.6	5 50.3
24	0 10 7.9	0♎39.5	21 44.1	7♊21.4	14 50.0	12 40.5	22 24.2	16 9.3	4 51.1	18 40.4	3 3.8	5 52.4
25	0 14 4.5	1 38.2	21 40.9	19 14.7	16 25.1	13 18.0	22 51.9	16 1.9	4 55.5	18 41.8	3 4.2	5 54.5
26	0 18 1.0	2 37.0	21 37.8	1♋ 6.6	17 59.2	13 54.2	23 20.1	15 54.5	4 59.9	18 43.2	3 4.5	5 56.6
27	0 21 57.6	3 35.8	21 34.6	13 1.9	19 32.4	14 29.3	23 48.6	15 47.3	5 4.4	18 44.7	3 4.9	5 58.7
28	0 25 54.2	4 34.7	21 31.4	25 5.2	21 4.7	15 3.0	24 17.5	15 40.1	5 8.9	18 46.3	3 5.3	6 .8
29	0 29 50.7	5 33.6	21 28.2	7♌20.9	22 36.1	15 35.4	24 46.8	15 33.1	5 13.5	18 47.9	3 5.8	6 3.0
30	0 33 47.3	6 32.6	21 25.0	19 52.6	24 6.5	16 6.4	25 16.5	15 26.1	5 18.2	18 49.5	3 6.3	6 5.1

LATITUDE

DAY	SID. TIME	☉	☊	☽	☿	♀	♂	♃	♄	♅	♆	♇
1	22 39 27.2	0 .0	0 .0	5N 5.6	1N46.5	2S34.4	4S50.9	1S29.8	1N43.7	0S 6.0	1N 4.6	16N 9.9
4	22 51 16.9	0 .0	0 .0	3 34.7	1 44.9	2 54.4	4 42.8	1 30.2	1 43.0	0 6.0	1 4.5	16 8.5
7	23 3 6.5	0 .0	0 .0	0 18.7	1 37.9	3 14.6	4 34.6	1 30.4	1 42.4	0 6.0	1 4.4	16 7.1
10	23 14 56.2	0 .0	0 .0	3S13.8	1 26.7	3 35.0	4 26.3	1 30.6	1 41.7	0 6.0	1 4.2	16 5.8
13	23 26 45.9	0 .0	0 .0	5 8.4	1 12.0	3 55.6	4 18.1	1 30.8	1 41.1	0 6.1	1 4.1	16 4.6
16	23 38 35.5	0 .0	0 .0	4 21.1	0 54.8	4 16.1	4 9.8	1 30.9	1 40.4	0 6.1	1 4.0	16 3.4
19	23 50 25.2	0 .0	0 .0	1 25.5	0 35.7	4 36.4	4 1.6	1 30.9	1 39.8	0 6.1	1 3.8	16 2.2
22	0 2 14.8	0 .0	0 .0	1N59.6	0 15.1	4 56.5	3 53.4	1 30.9	1 39.2	0 6.1	1 3.7	16 1.2
25	0 14 4.5	0 .0	0 .0	4 28.4	0S 6.3	5 16.0	3 45.3	1 30.7	1 38.6	0 6.1	1 3.6	16 .2
28	0 25 54.2	0 .0	0 .0	5 14.8	0 28.2	5 34.8	3 37.3	1 30.6	1 38.1	0 6.1	1 3.4	15 59.2

RIGHT ASCENSION

DAY	SID. TIME	☉	☊	☽	☿	♀	♂	♃	♄	♅	♆	♇
1	22 39 27.2	9♍55.2	21♈14.0	2♌44.1	6♍14.4	21♎27.4	15♑46.6	20♓37.3	1♐53.3	17♐20.4	3♑20.5	8♏13.5
2	22 43 23.8	10 49.6	21 11.0	15 46.1	8 6.3	22 17.5	16 3.6	20R30.2	1 55.8	17 20.7	3R20.0	8 14.7
3	22 47 20.3	11 44.0	21 8.1	28 22.4	9 56.9	23 7.2	16 21.3	20 23.1	1 58.3	17 21.0	3 19.6	8 16.0
4	22 51 16.9	12 38.2	21 5.1	10♍35.1	11 46.1	23 56.6	16 39.7	20 15.9	2 1.0	17 21.4	3 19.2	8 17.3
5	22 55 13.4	13 32.5	21 2.1	22 32.4	13 33.9	24 45.6	16 58.8	20 8.7	2 3.8	17 21.8	3 18.8	8 18.7
6	22 59 10.0	14 26.6	20 59.1	4♎26.6	15 20.3	25 34.3	17 18.6	20 1.4	2 6.6	17 22.3	3 18.5	8 20.0
7	23 3 6.5	15 20.7	20 56.1	16 32.7	17 5.2	26 22.5	17 39.1	19 54.1	2 9.5	17 22.8	3 18.2	8 21.4
8	23 7 3.1	16 14.8	20 53.1	29 7.2	18 48.7	27 10.3	18 .2	19 46.8	2 12.6	17 23.4	3 18.0	8 22.8
9	23 10 59.6	17 8.8	20 50.1	12♏25.4	20 30.7	27 57.6	18 21.9	19 39.5	2 15.7	17 24.1	3 17.7	8 24.3
10	23 14 56.2	18 2.7	20 47.2	26 38.7	22 11.3	28 44.5	18 44.3	19 32.1	2 18.9	17 24.8	3 17.6	8 25.7
11	23 18 52.7	18 56.6	20 44.2	11♐48.2	23 50.6	29 30.9	19 7.3	19 24.8	2 22.2	17 25.5	3 17.4	8 27.2
12	23 22 49.3	19 50.5	20 41.2	27 40.0	25 28.6	0♏16.7	19 30.9	19 17.5	2 25.7	17 26.4	3 17.4	8 28.8
13	23 26 45.9	20 44.4	20 38.2	13♑45.2	27 5.3	1 2.0	19 55.0	19 10.1	2 29.2	17 27.3	3 17.3	8 30.3
14	23 30 42.4	21 38.2	20 35.2	29 29.0	28 40.7	1 46.7	20 19.6	19 2.8	2 32.7	17 28.2	3 17.2	8 31.9
15	23 34 39.0	22 32.0	20 32.2	14♒24.6	0♎15.0	2 30.7	20 44.8	18 55.4	2 36.4	17 29.2	3 17.2	8 33.4
16	23 38 35.5	23 25.8	20 29.3	28 20.6	1 48.2	3 14.1	21 10.5	18 48.1	2 40.1	17 30.2	3D17.3	8 35.0
17	23 42 32.1	24 19.6	20 26.3	11♓20.0	3 20.3	3 56.8	21 36.7	18 40.8	2 44.0	17 31.3	3 17.3	8 36.7
18	23 46 28.6	25 13.3	20 23.3	23 34.3	4 51.4	4 38.8	22 3.4	18 33.6	2 47.9	17 32.5	3 17.4	8 38.3
19	23 50 25.2	26 7.1	20 20.3	5♈19.1	6 21.6	5 20.0	22 30.6	18 26.4	2 51.9	17 33.7	3 17.6	8 40.0
20	23 54 21.7	27 .9	20 17.3	16 50.1	7 50.8	6 .5	22 58.2	18 19.2	2 55.9	17 34.9	3 17.7	8 41.7
21	23 58 18.3	27 54.7	20 14.3	28 22.0	9 19.2	6 40.0	23 26.2	18 12.1	3 .1	17 36.2	3 17.9	8 43.4
22	0 2 14.8	28 48.5	20 11.4	10♉ 7.4	10 46.8	7 18.7	23 54.7	18 5.0	3 4.4	17 37.6	3 18.2	8 45.1
23	0 6 11.4	29 42.3	20 8.4	22 15.6	12 13.6	7 56.5	24 23.6	17 58.0	3 8.7	17 39.0	3 18.4	8 46.9
24	0 10 7.9	0♎36.2	20 5.4	4♊51.4	13 39.8	8 33.3	24 52.8	17 51.0	3 13.1	17 40.5	3 18.8	8 48.6
25	0 14 4.5	1 30.1	20 2.4	17 53.8	15 5.2	9 9.1	25 22.5	17 44.1	3 17.6	17 42.0	3 19.1	8 50.4
26	0 18 1.0	2 24.1	19 59.4	1♋15.4	16 30.0	9 43.8	25 52.6	17 37.3	3 22.1	17 43.6	3 19.5	8 52.2
27	0 21 57.6	3 18.1	19 56.5	14 43.9	17 54.2	10 17.3	26 23.0	17 30.6	3 26.8	17 45.2	3 19.9	8 54.1
28	0 25 54.2	4 12.1	19 53.5	28 5.5	19 17.7	10 49.7	26 53.7	17 23.9	3 31.5	17 46.9	3 20.4	8 55.9
29	0 29 50.7	5 6.2	19 50.5	11♌ 9.0	20 40.8	11 20.8	27 24.9	17 17.3	3 36.3	17 48.6	3 20.9	8 57.8
30	0 33 47.3	6 .4	19 47.5	23 49.4	22 3.3	11 50.7	27 56.3	17 10.8	3 41.2	17 50.4	3 21.4	8 59.6

DECLINATION

DAY	SID. TIME	☉	☊	☽	☿	♀	♂	♃	♄	♅	♆	♇
1	22 39 27.2	8N28.1	0N 9.3	25N15.4	11N49.0	11S47.1	27S31.7	5S40.2	19S10.3	23S 2.0	22S19.8	2N 1.4
4	22 51 16.9	7 22.4	0 9.3	12 3.8	9 36.9	13 6.1	27 18.2	5 49.6	19 12.4	23 2.1	22 20.0	1 58.6
7	23 3 6.5	6 15.6	0 9.2	6S42.1	7 18.3	14 22.6	27 3.7	5 59.2	19 14.6	23 2.2	22 20.2	1 55.7
10	23 14 56.2	5 8.0	0 9.2	23 13.3	4 56.7	15 36.2	26 48.1	6 8.7	19 16.9	23 2.4	22 20.3	1 52.9
13	23 26 45.9	3 59.5	0 9.1	28 .2	2 34.2	16 46.7	26 31.3	6 18.2	19 19.4	23 2.6	22 20.4	1 50.0
16	23 38 35.5	2 50.4	0 9.0	17 26.8	0 12.8	17 53.8	26 13.4	6 27.5	19 21.9	23 2.9	22 20.6	1 47.1
19	23 50 25.2	1 40.9	0 9.0	0N45.0	2S 6.2	18 57.0	25 54.3	6 36.7	19 24.6	23 3.1	22 20.7	1 44.2
22	0 2 14.8	0 31.0	0 8.9	17 42.3	4 21.8	19 56.2	25 34.0	6 45.6	19 27.4	23 3.5	22 20.8	1 41.3
25	0 14 4.5	0S39.1	0 8.9	27 28.0	6 33.2	20 51.0	25 12.4	6 54.3	19 30.3	23 3.8	22 20.9	1 38.5
28	0 25 54.2	1 49.2	0 8.8	26 16.6	8 39.7	21 40.9	24 49.5	7 2.6	19 33.2	23 4.2	22 21.0	1 35.6

OCTOBER 1986

DAY	EPHEM. SID. TIME	☉	☊	☽	☿	♀	♂	♃	♄	♅	♆	♇
	LONGITUDE											
	h m s	° ′	° ′	° ′	° ′	° ′	° ′	° ′	° ′	° ′	° ′	° ′
1	0 37 43.8	7♎31.5	21♈21.9	2♍42.9	25♎36.1	16♏36.0	25♑46.5	15♓19.3	5♐23.0	18♐51.2	3♑ 6.8	6♏ 7.3
2	0 41 40.4	8 30.6	21 18.7	15 53.3	27 4.8	17 4.0	26 16.9	15 R 12.6	5 27.9	18 52.9	3 7.3	6 9.5
3	0 45 36.9	9 29.7	21 15.5	29 23.7	28 32.6	17 30.5	26 47.6	15 6.0	5 32.8	18 54.8	3 8.0	6 11.8
4	0 49 33.5	10 28.8	21 12.3	13♎12.5	29 59.4	17 55.4	27 18.7	14 59.5	5 37.8	18 56.6	3 8.6	6 14.0
5	0 53 30.0	11 27.9	21 9.2	27 16.7	1♏25.3	18 18.5	27 50.0	14 53.2	5 42.8	18 58.5	3 9.2	6 16.2
6	0 57 26.6	12 27.0	21 6.0	11♏32.3	2 50.3	18 40.0	28 21.7	14 47.0	5 47.9	19 .4	3 9.9	6 18.5
7	1 1 23.1	13 26.2	21 2.8	25 54.8	4 14.3	18 59.6	28 53.8	14 40.9	5 53.1	19 2.4	3 10.6	6 20.8
8	1 5 19.7	14 25.4	20 59.6	10♐19.3	5 37.2	19 17.3	29 26.1	14 35.0	5 58.3	19 4.4	3 11.4	6 23.1
9	1 9 16.2	15 24.7	20 56.4	24 41.9	6 59.2	19 33.0	29 58.7	14 29.2	6 3.6	19 6.4	3 12.2	6 25.3
10	1 13 12.8	16 24.0	20 53.3	8♑58.8	8 20.0	19 46.8	0♒31.6	14 23.5	6 9.0	19 8.5	3 13.0	6 27.7
11	1 17 9.4	17 23.3	20 50.1	23 7.6	9 39.7	19 58.5	1 4.8	14 18.0	6 14.4	19 10.7	3 13.8	6 30.0
12	1 21 5.9	18 22.6	20 46.9	7♒ 6.1	10 58.2	20 8.0	1 38.2	14 12.7	6 19.9	19 12.9	3 14.7	6 32.3
13	1 25 2.5	19 22.0	20 43.7	20 53.2	12 15.5	20 15.3	2 12.0	14 7.6	6 25.4	19 15.1	3 15.6	6 34.6
14	1 28 59.0	20 21.4	20 40.6	4♓27.8	13 31.4	20 20.4	2 45.9	14 2.6	6 31.0	19 17.3	3 16.5	6 37.0
15	1 32 55.6	21 20.8	20 37.4	17 49.4	14 45.9	20 23.2	3 20.2	13 57.7	6 36.7	19 19.6	3 17.5	6 39.3
16	1 36 52.1	22 20.2	20 34.2	0♈57.6	15 58.8	20 23.7	3 54.6	13 53.1	6 42.4	19 22.0	3 18.5	6 41.7
17	1 40 48.7	23 19.7	20 31.0	13 52.1	17 10.1	20 R 21.7	4 29.3	13 48.6	6 48.1	19 24.4	3 19.5	6 44.1
18	1 44 45.2	24 19.2	20 27.8	26 33.0	18 19.6	20 17.4	5 4.3	13 44.3	6 53.9	19 26.8	3 20.6	6 46.4
19	1 48 41.8	25 18.8	20 24.7	9♉ 1.0	19 27.1	20 10.6	5 39.4	13 40.1	6 59.8	19 29.3	3 21.7	6 48.8
20	1 52 38.3	26 18.4	20 21.5	21 16.9	20 32.5	20 1.5	6 14.8	13 36.2	7 5.7	19 31.8	3 22.8	6 51.2
21	1 56 34.9	27 18.0	20 18.3	3♊22.6	21 35.6	19 49.9	6 50.3	13 32.4	7 11.7	19 34.3	3 24.0	6 53.6
22	2 0 31.5	28 17.7	20 15.1	15 20.3	22 36.0	19 35.9	7 26.1	13 28.8	7 17.7	19 36.9	3 25.1	6 56.0
23	2 4 28.0	29 17.3	20 12.0	27 13.0	23 33.7	19 19.5	8 2.1	13 25.4	7 23.8	19 39.5	3 26.3	6 58.4
24	2 8 24.6	0♏17.1	20 8.8	9♋ 4.3	24 28.3	19 .8	8 38.3	13 22.3	7 29.9	19 42.2	3 27.6	7 .9
25	2 12 21.1	1 16.9	20 5.6	20 58.4	25 19.3	18 39.9	9 14.7	13 19.3	7 36.1	19 44.9	3 28.9	7 3.3
26	2 16 17.7	2 16.7	20 2.4	2♌59.7	26 6.6	18 16.8	9 51.2	13 16.4	7 42.3	19 47.6	3 30.2	7 5.7
27	2 20 14.2	3 16.5	19 59.3	15 12.7	26 49.6	17 51.6	10 27.9	13 13.8	7 48.5	19 50.4	3 31.5	7 8.2
28	2 24 10.8	4 16.4	19 56.1	27 42.2	27 27.8	17 24.5	11 4.9	13 11.4	7 54.8	19 53.2	3 32.9	7 10.6
29	2 28 7.3	5 16.3	19 52.9	10♍31.9	28 .9	16 55.6	11 42.0	13 9.2	8 1.1	19 56.0	3 34.2	7 13.0
30	2 32 3.9	6 16.3	19 49.7	23 45.1	28 28.2	16 25.0	12 19.2	13 7.1	8 7.5	19 58.9	3 35.6	7 15.4
31	2 36 .5	7 16.3	19 46.5	7♎23.2	28 49.1	15 53.0	12 56.6	13 5.3	8 13.9	20 1.8	3 37.1	7 17.9
	LATITUDE											
1	0 37 43.8	0 .0	0 .0	3N55.7	0S50.2	5S52.7	3S29.4	1S30.4	1N37.5	0S 6.1	1N 3.3	15N58.3
4	0 49 33.5	0 .0	0 .0	0 42.3	1 12.0	6 9.1	3 21.6	1 30.1	1 36.9	0 6.1	1 3.2	15 57.5
7	1 1 23.1	0 .0	0 .0	3S 2.2	1 33.2	6 23.9	3 13.9	1 29.8	1 36.4	0 6.2	1 3.0	15 56.8
10	1 13 12.8	0 .0	0 .0	5 10.2	1 53.4	6 36.4	3 6.3	1 29.4	1 35.9	0 6.2	1 2.9	15 56.2
13	1 25 2.5	0 .0	0 .0	4 34.7	2 12.2	6 46.1	2 58.8	1 29.0	1 35.4	0 6.2	1 2.8	15 55.6
16	1 36 52.1	0 .0	0 .0	1 48.3	2 29.0	6 52.3	2 51.5	1 28.5	1 34.9	0 6.2	1 2.6	15 55.1
19	1 48 41.8	0 .0	0 .0	1N38.8	2 43.3	6 54.1	2 44.2	1 28.0	1 34.5	0 6.2	1 2.5	15 54.6
22	2 0 31.5	0 .0	0 .0	4 17.9	2 54.2	6 50.8	2 37.2	1 27.4	1 34.0	0 6.2	1 2.4	15 54.3
25	2 12 21.1	0 .0	0 .0	5 16.4	3 .5	6 41.5	2 30.2	1 26.9	1 33.6	0 6.2	1 2.3	15 54.0
28	2 24 10.8	0 .0	0 .0	4 13.3	3 .7	6 25.6	2 23.4	1 26.3	1 33.2	0 6.3	1 2.2	15 53.8
31	2 36 .5	0 .0	0 .0	1 13.9	2 52.8	6 2.9	2 16.7	1 25.6	1 32.8	0 6.3	1 2.0	15 53.7
	RIGHT ASCENSION											
1	0 37 43.8	6♎54.7	19♈44.5	6♍ 7.9	23♎25.2	12♏19.2	28♑28.1	17♓ 4.5	3♐46.1	17♐52.2	3♑21.9	9♏ 1.5
2	0 41 40.4	7 49.0	19 41.6	18 11.9	24 46.7	12 46.2	29 .2	16 R 58.2	3 51.1	17 54.1	3 22.5	9 3.5
3	0 45 36.9	8 43.4	19 38.6	0♎12.9	26 7.7	13 11.8	29 32.7	16 52.0	3 56.3	17 56.1	3 23.2	9 5.4
4	0 49 33.5	9 37.9	19 35.6	12 25.6	27 28.1	13 35.8	0♒ 5.4	16 46.0	4 1.5	17 58.0	3 23.9	9 7.4
5	0 53 30.0	10 32.4	19 32.6	25 6.1	28 48.0	13 58.2	0 38.4	16 40.0	4 6.7	18 .1	3 24.6	9 9.3
6	0 57 26.6	11 27.1	19 29.7	8♏30.1	0♏ 7.5	14 18.9	1 11.7	16 34.2	4 12.0	18 2.1	3 25.3	9 11.3
7	1 1 23.1	12 21.8	19 26.7	22 48.7	1 26.3	14 37.8	1 45.2	16 28.5	4 17.4	18 4.3	3 26.1	9 13.3
8	1 5 19.7	13 16.6	19 23.7	8♐ 3.6	2 44.7	14 54.8	2 19.0	16 23.0	4 22.8	18 6.5	3 26.9	9 15.3
9	1 9 16.2	14 11.6	19 20.7	24 .5	4 2.4	15 9.9	2 53.1	16 17.5	4 28.3	18 8.7	3 27.8	9 17.3
10	1 13 12.8	15 6.6	19 17.8	10♑10.2	5 19.5	15 23.1	3 27.3	16 12.2	4 33.9	18 11.0	3 28.6	9 19.4
11	1 17 9.4	16 1.8	19 14.8	25 57.1	6 35.9	15 34.2	4 1.8	16 7.1	4 39.5	18 13.3	3 29.6	9 21.4
12	1 21 5.9	16 57.0	19 11.8	10♒54.0	7 51.6	15 43.1	4 36.6	16 2.1	4 45.3	18 15.6	3 30.5	9 23.5
13	1 25 2.5	17 52.4	19 8.8	24 49.2	9 6.5	15 49.9	5 11.5	15 57.2	4 51.0	18 18.0	3 31.5	9 25.5
14	1 28 59.0	18 47.9	19 5.9	7♓46.0	10 20.5	15 54.5	5 46.6	15 52.5	4 56.8	18 20.5	3 32.5	9 27.6
15	1 32 55.6	19 43.5	19 2.9	19 56.3	11 33.4	15 56.8	6 21.9	15 47.9	5 2.7	18 23.0	3 33.5	9 29.7
16	1 36 52.1	20 39.3	18 59.9	1♈35.9	12 45.3	15 56.8	6 57.4	15 43.5	5 8.7	18 25.5	3 34.6	9 31.8
17	1 40 48.7	21 35.2	18 56.9	13 .9	13 55.9	15 R 54.4	7 33.0	15 39.3	5 14.7	18 28.1	3 35.7	9 33.9
18	1 44 45.2	22 31.3	18 54.0	24 26.2	15 5.2	15 49.7	8 8.8	15 35.2	5 20.8	18 30.8	3 36.9	9 36.1
19	1 48 41.8	23 27.5	18 51.0	6♉ 4.7	16 12.8	15 42.6	8 44.7	15 31.3	5 26.9	18 33.4	3 38.1	9 38.2
20	1 52 38.3	24 23.8	18 48.0	18 6.3	17 18.7	15 33.1	9 20.8	15 27.6	5 33.1	18 36.1	3 39.3	9 40.3
21	1 56 34.9	25 20.3	18 45.1	0♊36.1	18 22.5	15 21.3	9 57.0	15 24.0	5 39.3	18 38.9	3 40.5	9 42.5
22	2 0 31.5	26 17.0	18 42.1	13 33.5	19 24.1	15 7.2	10 33.4	15 20.6	5 45.6	18 41.7	3 41.8	9 44.6
23	2 4 28.0	27 13.9	18 39.1	26 51.1	20 23.1	14 50.9	11 9.9	15 17.3	5 51.9	18 44.5	3 43.1	9 46.8
24	2 8 24.6	28 11.0	18 36.1	10♋16.4	21 19.3	14 32.4	11 46.5	15 14.3	5 58.3	18 47.5	3 44.5	9 49.0
25	2 12 21.1	29 8.2	18 33.2	23 35.0	22 12.2	14 11.8	12 23.2	15 11.4	6 4.8	18 50.4	3 45.9	9 51.2
26	2 16 17.7	0♏ 5.6	18 30.2	6♌35.2	23 1.3	13 49.3	13 .0	15 8.7	6 11.3	18 53.3	3 47.3	9 53.4
27	2 20 14.2	1 3.1	18 27.2	19 11.2	23 46.4	13 24.8	13 37.0	15 6.2	6 17.8	18 56.3	3 48.7	9 55.6
28	2 24 10.8	2 .9	18 24.3	1♍24.1	24 26.8	12 58.7	14 14.0	15 3.9	6 24.4	18 59.3	3 50.2	9 57.8
29	2 28 7.3	2 58.8	18 21.3	13 20.8	25 2.0	12 31.0	14 51.1	15 1.7	6 31.0	19 2.4	3 51.6	9 60.0
30	2 32 3.9	3 57.0	18 18.3	25 13.1	25 31.4	12 2.0	15 28.3	14 59.7	6 37.7	19 5.5	3 53.2	10 2.2
31	2 36 .5	4 55.3	18 15.4	7♎16.2	25 54.4	11 31.7	16 5.6	14 58.0	6 44.4	19 8.7	3 54.7	10 4.4
	DECLINATION											
1	0 37 43.8	2S59.2	0N 8.7	14N10.2	10S40.7	22S25.6	24S25.3	7S10.5	19S36.3	23S 4.6	22S21.1	1N32.8
4	0 49 33.5	4 9.0	0 8.7	4S34.0	12 35.6	23 4.5	23 59.7	7 17.9	19 39.4	23 5.1	22 21.2	1 29.9
7	1 1 23.1	5 18.3	0 8.6	22 11.2	14 23.8	23 36.9	23 32.7	7 24.8	19 42.6	23 5.6	22 21.3	1 27.2
10	1 13 12.8	6 27.0	0 8.5	28 17.8	16 4.4	24 2.2	23 4.3	7 31.1	19 45.8	23 6.1	22 21.4	1 24.4
13	1 25 2.5	7 34.9	0 8.5	18 52.2	17 36.9	24 19.5	22 34.5	7 36.9	19 49.1	23 6.7	22 21.5	1 21.7
16	1 36 52.1	8 41.8	0 8.4	1 16.5	19 .0	24 27.7	22 3.3	7 42.1	19 52.4	23 7.2	22 21.5	1 19.1
19	1 48 41.8	9 47.6	0 8.4	16N 3.8	20 12.9	24 25.9	21 30.8	7 46.6	19 55.8	23 7.8	22 21.5	1 16.5
22	2 0 31.5	10 52.2	0 8.3	26 54.5	21 13.8	24 12.9	20 56.8	7 50.4	19 59.1	23 8.4	22 21.6	1 13.9
25	2 12 21.1	11 55.3	0 8.3	27 .9	22 1.0	23 48.2	20 21.5	7 53.6	20 2.5	23 9.1	22 21.6	1 11.5
28	2 24 10.8	12 56.8	0 8.2	16 14.0	22 31.8	23 11.3	19 44.9	7 56.1	20 5.9	23 9.7	22 21.6	1 9.1
31	2 36 .5	13 56.5	0 8.1	1S48.0	22 42.5	22 22.6	19 6.9	7 57.8	20 9.3	23 10.4	22 21.6	1 6.7

NOVEMBER 1986

LONGITUDE

DAY	EPHEM. SID. TIME	☉	☊	☽	☿	♀	♂	♃	♄	♅	♆	♇
	h m s	° ′	° ′	° ′	° ′	° ′	° ′	° ′	° ′	° ′	° ′	° ′
1	2 39 57.0	8♏16.3	19♈43.4	21♎25.9	29♏ 3.0	15♏19.6	13♒34.2	13♓ 3.7	8♐20.4	20♐ 4.7	3♑38.5	7♏20.3
2	2 43 53.6	9 16.3	19 40.2	5♏50.3	29 9.4	14R45.2	14 12.0	13R 2.3	8 26.9	20 7.6	3 40.0	7 22.7
3	2 47 50.1	10 16.4	19 37.0	20 31.5	29R 7.5	14 10.0	14 49.9	13 1.0	8 33.4	20 10.6	3 41.5	7 25.2
4	2 51 46.7	11 16.5	19 33.8	5♐22.3	28 56.8	13 34.0	15 28.0	13 .0	8 40.0	20 13.6	3 43.1	7 27.6
5	2 55 43.2	12 16.7	19 30.7	20 14.6	28 36.7	12 57.7	16 6.2	12 59.2	8 46.6	20 16.7	3 44.6	7 30.0
6	2 59 39.8	13 16.9	19 27.5	5♑ .8	28 7.0	12 21.2	16 44.6	12 58.6	8 53.2	20 19.8	3 46.2	7 32.4
7	3 3 36.3	14 17.1	19 24.3	19 34.2	27 27.6	11 44.8	17 23.1	12 58.2	8 59.9	20 22.9	3 47.8	7 34.8
8	3 7 32.9	15 17.3	19 21.1	3♒50.3	26 38.5	11 8.8	18 1.8	12 58.1	9 6.6	20 26.0	3 49.5	7 37.3
9	3 11 29.5	16 17.5	19 17.9	17 47.0	25 40.3	10 33.3	18 40.5	12 58.1	9 13.3	20 29.2	3 51.1	7 39.7
10	3 15 26.0	17 17.8	19 14.8	1♓23.9	24 34.0	9 58.6	19 19.4	12D58.3	9 20.0	20 32.4	3 52.8	7 42.1
11	3 19 22.6	18 18.1	19 11.6	14 42.0	23 21.2	9 25.0	19 58.5	12 58.8	9 26.8	20 35.6	3 54.5	7 44.5
12	3 23 19.1	19 18.4	19 8.4	27 43.1	22 3.5	8 52.6	20 37.6	12 59.4	9 33.6	20 38.8	3 56.2	7 46.9
13	3 27 15.7	20 18.7	19 5.2	10♈29.5	20 43.5	8 21.7	21 16.8	13 .2	9 40.4	20 42.1	3 58.0	7 49.3
14	3 31 12.2	21 19.2	19 2.1	23 3.3	19 23.6	7 52.5	21 56.2	13 1.3	9 47.4	20 45.4	3 59.8	7 51.7
15	3 35 8.8	22 19.6	18 58.9	5♉26.3	18 6.4	7 25.1	22 35.7	13 2.6	9 54.2	20 48.7	4 1.6	7 54.1
16	3 39 5.4	23 20.0	18 55.7	17 40.2	16 54.4	6 59.7	23 15.3	13 4.1	10 1.1	20 52.0	4 3.4	7 56.4
17	3 43 1.9	24 20.4	18 52.5	29 46.3	15 49.9	6 36.4	23 54.9	13 5.7	10 8.1	20 55.4	4 5.3	7 58.8
18	3 46 58.5	25 20.9	18 49.4	11♊46.0	14 54.8	6 15.2	24 34.7	13 7.6	10 15.0	20 58.7	4 7.1	8 1.1
19	3 50 55.0	26 21.4	18 46.2	23 40.8	14 10.2	5 56.5	25 14.5	13 9.6	10 22.0	21 2.1	4 9.0	8 3.5
20	3 54 51.6	27 21.9	18 43.0	5♋32.6	13 37.1	5 40.1	25 54.5	13 11.9	10 28.9	21 5.5	4 10.9	8 5.8
21	3 58 48.1	28 22.5	18 39.8	17 23.8	13 15.7	5 26.1	26 34.5	13 14.4	10 35.9	21 8.9	4 12.8	8 8.1
22	4 2 44.7	29 23.0	18 36.7	29 17.2	13 5.8	5 14.6	27 14.6	13 17.0	10 42.9	21 12.4	4 14.7	8 10.4
23	4 6 41.3	0♐23.7	18 33.5	11♌16.6	13D 7.2	5 5.6	27 54.8	13 19.9	10 50.0	21 15.8	4 16.7	8 12.7
24	4 10 37.8	1 24.3	18 30.3	23 25.9	13 19.1	4 59.1	28 35.0	13 23.0	10 57.0	21 19.3	4 18.6	8 15.0
25	4 14 34.4	2 25.0	18 27.1	5♍49.9	13 40.7	4 55.1	29 15.4	13 26.2	11 4.1	21 22.8	4 20.6	8 17.3
26	4 18 30.9	3 25.7	18 23.9	18 33.0	14 11.3	4 53.6	29 55.8	13 29.7	11 11.1	21 26.3	4 22.6	8 19.5
27	4 22 27.5	4 26.4	18 20.8	1♎39.8	14 49.7	4D54.5	0♓36.3	13 33.3	11 18.2	21 29.8	4 24.7	8 21.8
28	4 26 24.0	5 27.1	18 17.6	15 13.5	15 35.3	4 57.9	1 16.9	13 37.1	11 25.3	21 33.4	4 26.7	8 24.0
29	4 30 20.6	6 27.9	18 14.4	29 15.8	16 27.2	5 3.6	1 57.5	13 41.2	11 32.4	21 36.9	4 28.7	8 26.2
30	4 34 17.2	7 28.7	18 11.2	13♏45.7	17 24.5	5 11.7	2 38.3	13 45.4	11 39.5	21 40.5	4 30.8	8 28.4

LATITUDE

DAY	EPHEM. SID. TIME	☉	☊	☽	☿	♀	♂	♃	♄	♅	♆	♇
1	2 39 57.0	0 .0	0 .0	0S 3.0	2S47.9	5S53.7	2S14.5	1S25.4	1N32.7	0S 6.3	1N 2.0	15N53.7
4	2 51 46.7	0 .0	0 .0	3 41.0	2 25.0	5 22.0	2 8.0	1 24.8	1 32.3	0 6.3	1 1.9	15 53.7
7	3 3 36.3	0 .0	0 .0	5 14.1	1 47.9	4 44.4	2 1.6	1 24.1	1 32.0	0 6.3	1 1.8	15 53.7
10	3 15 26.0	0 .0	0 .0	3 58.3	0 56.4	4 2.2	1 55.3	1 23.4	1 31.7	0 6.3	1 1.7	15 53.9
13	3 27 15.7	0 .0	0 .0	0 55.8	0N 4.3	3 17.1	1 49.2	1 22.7	1 31.4	0 6.3	1 1.6	15 54.1
16	3 39 5.4	0 .0	0 .0	2N21.7	1 3.4	2 30.9	1 43.2	1 22.1	1 31.1	0 6.4	1 1.5	15 54.4
19	3 50 55.0	0 .0	0 .0	4 37.1	1 49.7	1 45.0	1 37.4	1 21.4	1 30.8	0 6.4	1 1.4	15 54.8
22	4 2 44.7	0 .0	0 .0	5 5.7	2 18.2	1 .9	1 31.7	1 20.7	1 30.6	0 6.4	1 1.3	15 55.2
25	4 14 34.4	0 .0	0 .0	3 36.1	2 30.0	0 19.4	1 26.1	1 20.0	1 30.3	0 6.4	1 1.2	15 55.7
28	4 26 24.0	0 .0	0 .0	0 25.9	2 28.8	0N18.7	1 20.7	1 19.3	1 30.1	0 6.4	1 1.2	15 56.3

RIGHT ASCENSION

DAY	EPHEM. SID. TIME	☉	☊	☽	☿	♀	♂	♃	♄	♅	♆	♇
1	2 39 57.0	5♏53.9	18♈12.4	19♎47.2	26♏10.3	11♏ .6	16♒43.0	14♓56.4	6♐51.2	19♐11.8	3♑56.3	10♏ 6.6
2	2 43 53.6	6 52.6	18 9.4	3♏ 3.8	26 18.4	10R28.6	17 20.4	14R55.0	6 58.0	19 15.0	3 57.9	10 8.8
3	2 47 50.1	7 51.6	18 6.4	17 20.9	26R18.3	9 56.1	17 58.0	14 53.7	7 4.9	19 18.3	3 59.5	10 11.0
4	2 51 46.7	8 50.7	18 3.5	2♐43.7	26 9.1	9 23.4	18 35.6	14 52.7	7 11.7	19 21.5	4 1.2	10 13.2
5	2 55 43.2	9 50.1	18 .5	19 .7	25 50.6	8 50.5	19 13.2	14 51.9	7 18.7	19 24.9	4 2.9	10 15.4
6	2 59 39.8	10 49.6	17 57.5	5♑40.7	25 22.5	8 17.9	19 51.0	14 51.2	7 25.6	19 28.2	4 4.6	10 17.7
7	3 3 36.3	11 49.4	17 54.6	22 1.5	24 44.6	7 45.6	20 28.7	14 50.8	7 32.6	19 31.6	4 6.3	10 19.9
8	3 7 32.9	12 49.3	17 51.6	7♒28.1	23 57.4	7 14.0	21 6.6	14 50.5	7 39.7	19 35.0	4 8.1	10 22.1
9	3 11 29.5	13 49.5	17 48.6	21 44.6	23 1.3	6 43.2	21 44.5	14 50.5	7 46.7	19 38.4	4 9.9	10 24.3
10	3 15 26.0	14 49.9	17 45.7	4♓53.0	21 57.7	6 13.5	22 22.4	14D50.6	7 53.8	19 41.8	4 11.7	10 26.5
11	3 19 22.6	15 50.4	17 42.7	17 6.8	20 48.0	5 45.1	23 .3	14 50.9	8 1.0	19 45.3	4 13.6	10 28.7
12	3 23 19.1	16 51.2	17 39.8	28 43.3	19 34.1	5 18.1	23 38.3	14 51.4	8 8.1	19 48.8	4 15.4	10 30.9
13	3 27 15.7	17 52.2	17 36.8	10♈ .5	18 18.5	4 52.7	24 16.3	14 52.1	8 15.3	19 52.4	4 17.3	10 33.2
14	3 31 12.2	18 53.5	17 33.8	21 15.0	17 3.5	4 29.1	24 54.4	14 53.1	8 22.6	19 56.0	4 19.3	10 35.4
15	3 35 8.8	19 54.9	17 30.9	2♉41.1	15 51.6	4 7.4	25 32.4	14 54.1	8 29.8	19 59.6	4 21.2	10 37.6
16	3 39 5.4	20 56.5	17 27.9	14 30.2	14 45.1	3 47.8	26 10.5	14 55.4	8 37.1	20 3.2	4 23.2	10 39.8
17	3 43 1.9	21 58.3	17 24.9	26 49.1	13 46.1	3 30.2	26 48.6	14 56.9	8 44.4	20 6.8	4 25.2	10 42.0
18	3 46 58.5	23 .4	17 22.0	9♊38.6	12 56.1	3 14.8	27 26.7	14 58.5	8 51.7	20 10.5	4 27.2	10 44.2
19	3 50 55.0	24 2.6	17 19.0	22 52.1	12 16.2	3 1.7	28 4.8	15 .3	8 59.1	20 14.1	4 29.2	10 46.3
20	3 54 51.6	25 5.1	17 16.0	6♋16.6	11 47.1	2 50.9	28 42.9	15 2.4	9 6.4	20 17.8	4 31.3	10 48.5
21	3 58 48.1	26 7.8	17 13.1	19 36.1	11 28.9	2 42.4	29 21.1	15 4.6	9 13.8	20 21.6	4 33.3	10 50.7
22	4 2 44.7	27 10.6	17 10.1	2♌36.4	11 21.6	2 36.2	29 59.2	15 7.0	9 21.2	20 25.3	4 35.4	10 52.8
23	4 6 41.3	28 13.7	17 7.2	15 9.6	11D24.7	2 32.4	0♓37.3	15 9.5	9 28.6	20 29.0	4 37.5	10 55.0
24	4 10 37.8	29 17.0	17 4.2	27 15.0	11 37.5	2 30.8	1 15.5	15 12.3	9 36.1	20 32.8	4 39.7	10 57.1
25	4 14 34.4	0♐20.5	17 1.2	8♍58.8	11 59.4	2D31.6	1 53.6	15 15.2	9 43.5	20 36.6	4 41.8	10 59.2
26	4 18 30.9	1 24.2	16 58.3	20 32.2	12 29.7	2 34.7	2 31.8	15 18.4	9 51.0	20 40.4	4 44.0	11 1.4
27	4 22 27.5	2 28.0	16 55.3	2♎10.4	13 7.4	2 40.0	3 9.9	15 21.7	9 58.4	20 44.3	4 46.2	11 3.5
28	4 26 24.0	3 32.1	16 52.3	14 11.2	13 51.9	2 47.4	3 48.1	15 25.1	10 5.9	20 48.1	4 48.3	11 5.6
29	4 30 20.6	4 36.3	16 49.4	26 54.4	14 42.4	2 57.0	4 26.3	15 28.8	10 13.4	20 51.9	4 50.6	11 7.7
30	4 34 17.2	5 40.7	16 46.4	10♏39.2	15 38.2	3 8.8	5 4.4	15 32.6	10 20.9	20 55.8	4 52.8	11 9.7

DECLINATION

DAY	EPHEM. SID. TIME	☉	☊	☽	☿	♀	♂	♃	♄	♅	♆	♇
1	2 39 57.0	14S15.9	0N 8.1	8S24.3	22S40.8	22S 3.9	18S54.0	7S58.3	20S10.5	23S10.6	22S21.6	1N 6.0
4	2 51 46.7	15 12.9	0 8.0	24 49.5	22 17.1	21 1.6	18 14.3	7 59.1	20 13.9	23 11.3	22 21.6	1 3.7
7	3 3 36.3	16 7.7	0 8.0	27 11.7	21 20.8	19 51.9	17 33.4	7 59.1	20 17.3	23 12.0	22 21.6	1 1.6
10	3 15 26.0	16 60.0	0 7.9	14 41.3	19 49.6	18 38.2	16 51.2	7 58.5	20 20.6	23 12.7	22 21.5	0 59.5
13	3 27 15.7	17 49.7	0 7.8	3N17.9	17 52.1	17 24.2	16 8.0	7 57.1	20 24.0	23 13.4	22 21.5	0 57.6
16	3 39 5.4	18 36.6	0 7.8	19 22.2	15 52.6	16 13.5	15 23.6	7 55.0	20 27.3	23 14.1	22 21.4	0 55.7
19	3 50 55.0	19 20.5	0 7.7	27 54.3	14 20.8	15 9.3	14 38.3	7 52.2	20 30.5	23 14.8	22 21.3	0 53.9
22	4 2 44.7	20 1.3	0 7.6	25 17.0	13 34.5	14 13.7	13 52.0	7 48.7	20 33.7	23 15.5	22 21.2	0 52.3
25	4 14 34.4	20 38.8	0 7.6	12 43.3	13 33.7	13 28.1	13 4.7	7 44.6	20 36.9	23 16.2	22 21.1	0 50.7
28	4 26 24.0	21 12.9	0 7.5	5S35.9	14 8.1	12 53.1	12 16.6	7 39.7	20 40.0	23 16.9	22 21.0	0 49.3

DECEMBER 1986

DAY	EPHEM. SID. TIME	☉	☊	☾	☿	♀	♂	♃	♄	♅	♆	♇
	h m s	° ′	° ′	° ′	° ′	° ′	° ′	° ′	° ′	° ′	° ′	° ′
		LONGITUDE										
1	4 38 13.7	8♐29.5	18♈ 8.1	28♏39.1	18♏26.6	5♏22.0	3♓19.1	13♓49.8	11♐46.6	21♐44.1	4♑32.9	8♏30.6
2	4 42 10.3	9 30.4	18 4.9	13♐48.3	19 32.9	5 34.5	3 59.9	13 54.4	11 53.7	21 47.6	4 35.0	8 32.7
3	4 46 6.8	10 31.2	18 1.7	29 3.4	20 42.8	5 49.1	4 40.8	13 59.2	12 .8	21 51.2	4 37.1	8 34.9
4	4 50 3.4	11 32.1	17 58.5	14♑13.5	21 55.8	6 5.8	5 21.8	14 4.1	12 7.9	21 54.8	4 39.2	8 37.0
5	4 53 60.0	12 33.0	17 55.4	29 8.6	23 11.5	6 24.6	6 2.9	14 9.3	12 15.1	21 58.5	4 41.4	8 39.2
6	4 57 56.5	13 33.9	17 52.2	13♒41.3	24 29.5	6 45.3	6 44.0	14 14.7	12 22.2	22 2.1	4 43.5	8 41.3
7	5 1 53.1	14 34.9	17 49.0	27 47.7	25 49.5	7 7.8	7 25.2	14 20.2	12 29.3	22 5.7	4 45.7	8 43.3
8	5 5 49.6	15 35.8	17 45.8	11♓27.2	27 11.1	7 32.2	8 6.4	14 25.9	12 36.4	22 9.4	4 47.8	8 45.4
9	5 9 46.2	16 36.7	17 42.7	24 41.3	28 34.2	7 58.4	8 47.6	14 31.7	12 43.5	22 13.0	4 50.0	8 47.4
10	5 13 42.8	17 37.7	17 39.5	7♈33.4	29 58.5	8 26.2	9 28.9	14 37.8	12 50.6	22 16.6	4 52.2	8 49.4
11	5 17 39.3	18 38.6	17 36.3	20 7.5	1♐23.9	8 55.7	10 10.3	14 44.0	12 57.7	22 20.3	4 54.4	8 51.4
12	5 21 35.9	19 39.6	17 33.1	2♉27.4	2 50.3	9 26.8	10 51.7	14 50.3	13 4.8	22 23.9	4 56.6	8 53.4
13	5 25 32.4	20 40.6	17 29.9	14 37.0	4 17.4	9 59.5	11 33.1	14 56.9	13 11.9	22 27.6	4 58.8	8 55.4
14	5 29 29.0	21 41.6	17 26.8	26 39.2	5 45.2	10 33.6	12 14.5	15 3.6	13 19.0	22 31.2	5 1.0	8 57.3
15	5 33 25.5	22 42.6	17 23.6	8♊36.5	7 13.7	11 9.1	12 56.0	15 10.5	13 26.0	22 34.9	5 3.2	8 59.2
16	5 37 22.1	23 43.6	17 20.4	20 30.7	8 42.6	11 46.0	13 37.5	15 17.5	13 33.1	22 38.5	5 5.5	9 1.1
17	5 41 18.7	24 44.6	17 17.2	2♋23.4	10 12.1	12 24.2	14 19.1	15 24.7	13 40.1	22 42.2	5 7.7	9 2.9
18	5 45 15.2	25 45.7	17 14.1	14 15.7	11 41.9	13 3.7	15 .6	15 32.1	13 47.1	22 45.8	5 9.9	9 4.8
19	5 49 11.8	26 46.7	17 10.9	26 9.2	13 12.1	13 44.4	15 42.2	15 39.6	13 54.1	22 49.5	5 12.2	9 6.6
20	5 53 8.3	27 47.8	17 7.7	8♌ 5.5	14 42.7	14 26.3	16 23.9	15 47.3	14 1.1	22 53.1	5 14.5	9 8.3
21	5 57 4.9	28 48.9	17 4.5	20 7.1	16 13.6	15 9.3	17 5.5	15 55.1	14 8.1	22 56.7	5 16.7	9 10.1
22	6 1 1.5	29 50.0	17 1.4	2♍16.9	17 44.8	15 53.4	17 47.2	16 3.1	14 15.0	23 .4	5 19.0	9 11.8
23	6 4 58.0	0♑51.1	16 58.2	14 38.7	19 16.2	16 38.5	18 28.9	16 11.2	14 22.0	23 4.0	5 21.2	9 13.5
24	6 8 54.6	1 52.2	16 55.0	27 16.6	20 47.9	17 24.6	19 10.6	16 19.5	14 28.9	23 7.6	5 23.5	9 15.2
25	6 12 51.1	2 53.3	16 51.8	10♎15.1	22 19.9	18 11.7	19 52.4	16 27.9	14 35.8	23 11.2	5 25.8	9 16.9
26	6 16 47.7	3 54.5	16 48.7	23 38.5	23 52.2	18 59.8	20 34.2	16 36.5	14 42.7	23 14.9	5 28.1	9 18.5
27	6 20 44.3	4 55.6	16 45.5	7♏29.7	25 24.8	19 48.7	21 16.0	16 45.2	14 49.5	23 18.5	5 30.4	9 20.1
28	6 24 40.8	5 56.8	16 42.3	21 49.9	26 57.6	20 38.5	21 57.8	16 54.0	14 56.3	23 22.1	5 32.6	9 21.7
29	6 28 37.4	6 58.0	16 39.1	6♐37.0	28 30.6	21 29.0	22 39.6	17 3.0	15 3.1	23 25.6	5 34.9	9 23.3
30	6 32 33.9	7 59.1	16 36.0	21 45.5	0♑ 4.0	22 20.4	23 21.5	17 12.2	15 9.9	23 29.2	5 37.2	9 24.8
31	6 36 30.5	9 .3	16 32.8	7♑ 5.9	1 37.6	23 12.4	24 3.3	17 21.4	15 16.6	23 32.8	5 39.4	9 26.2
		LATITUDE										
1	4 38 13.7	0 .0	0 .0	3S12.6	2N18.8	0N53.3	1S15.4	1S18.6	1N29.9	0S 6.5	1N 1.1	15N57.0
4	4 50 3.4	0 .0	0 .0	5 4.7	2 3.0	1 24.2	1 10.2	1 17.9	1 29.8	0 6.5	1 1.0	15 57.8
7	5 1 53.1	0 .0	0 .0	3 59.9	1 43.7	1 51.4	1 5.2	1 17.3	1 29.6	0 6.5	1 1.0	15 58.6
10	5 13 42.8	0 .0	0 .0	1 2.1	1 22.4	2 15.1	1 .2	1 16.6	1 29.5	0 6.5	1 .9	15 59.5
13	5 25 32.4	0 .0	0 .0	2N11.0	1 .1	2 35.5	0 55.4	1 16.0	1 29.4	0 6.6	1 .9	16 .4
16	5 37 22.1	0 .0	0 .0	4 26.2	0 37.5	2 52.7	0 50.8	1 15.3	1 29.3	0 6.6	1 .8	16 1.4
19	5 49 11.8	0 .0	0 .0	4 58.3	0 15.2	3 7.1	0 46.2	1 14.7	1 29.2	0 6.6	1 .8	16 2.5
22	6 1 1.5	0 .0	0 .0	3 35.4	0S 6.4	3 18.7	0 41.8	1 14.1	1 29.1	0 6.7	1 .7	16 3.7
25	6 12 51.1	0 .0	0 .0	0 38.6	0 27.0	3 27.8	0 37.5	1 13.5	1 29.1	0 6.7	1 .7	16 4.8
28	6 24 40.8	0 .0	0 .0	2S50.4	0 46.4	3 34.6	0 33.4	1 13.0	1 29.1	0 6.7	1 .7	16 6.1
31	6 36 30.5	0 .0	0 .0	4 55.6	1 4.3	3 39.3	0 29.3	1 12.4	1 29.0	0 6.7	1 .6	16 7.4
		RIGHT ASCENSION										
1	4 38 13.7	6♐45.3	16♈43.5	25♏39.0	16♏38.8	3♏22.5	5♓42.6	15♓36.6	10♐28.5	20♐59.7	4♑55.0	11♏11.8
2	4 42 10.3	7 50.0	16 40.5	11♐52.8	17 43.6	3 38.2	6 20.7	15 40.8	10 36.0	21 3.6	4 57.3	11 13.9
3	4 46 6.8	8 55.0	16 37.5	28 56.0	18 52.0	3 55.8	6 58.9	15 45.2	10 43.5	21 7.5	4 59.6	11 15.9
4	4 50 3.4	10 .0	16 34.6	16♑ 3.2	20 3.8	4 15.3	7 37.1	15 49.7	10 51.1	21 11.4	5 1.9	11 17.9
5	4 53 60.0	11 5.3	16 31.6	2♒26.1	21 18.6	4 36.6	8 15.3	15 54.5	10 58.6	21 15.4	5 4.2	11 20.0
6	4 57 56.5	12 10.6	16 28.7	17 35.1	22 35.9	4 59.6	8 53.4	15 59.3	11 6.2	21 19.3	5 6.5	11 22.0
7	5 1 53.1	13 16.1	16 25.7	1♓24.6	23 55.5	5 24.3	9 31.6	16 4.4	11 13.7	21 23.3	5 8.9	11 24.0
8	5 5 49.6	14 21.7	16 22.8	14 6.1	25 17.2	5 50.7	10 9.7	16 9.6	11 21.3	21 27.2	5 11.2	11 25.9
9	5 9 46.2	15 27.4	16 19.8	25 58.2	26 40.7	6 18.6	10 47.8	16 15.0	11 28.8	21 31.1	5 13.6	11 27.9
10	5 13 42.8	16 33.2	16 16.8	7♈20.9	28 6.0	6 48.0	11 26.0	16 20.5	11 36.3	21 35.1	5 15.9	11 29.8
11	5 17 39.3	17 39.1	16 13.9	18 33.1	29 32.8	7 19.0	12 4.1	16 26.2	11 43.8	21 39.1	5 18.3	11 31.7
12	5 21 35.9	18 45.2	16 10.9	29 51.1	1♐ .9	7 51.3	12 42.2	16 32.0	11 51.4	21 43.0	5 20.7	11 33.6
13	5 25 32.4	19 51.3	16 8.0	11♉28.5	2 30.4	8 25.1	13 20.3	16 38.0	11 58.9	21 47.0	5 23.1	11 35.5
14	5 29 29.0	20 57.5	16 5.0	23 34.5	4 1.0	9 .2	13 58.3	16 44.2	12 6.4	21 51.0	5 25.4	11 37.4
15	5 33 25.5	22 3.7	16 2.1	6♊12.7	5 32.8	9 36.5	14 36.4	16 50.5	12 13.9	21 54.9	5 27.9	11 39.2
16	5 37 22.1	23 10.1	15 59.1	19 19.2	7 5.5	10 14.2	15 14.4	16 56.9	12 21.3	21 58.9	5 30.3	11 41.0
17	5 41 18.7	24 16.5	15 56.1	2♋42.2	8 39.2	10 53.0	15 52.5	17 3.5	12 28.8	22 2.9	5 32.7	11 42.9
18	5 45 15.2	25 22.9	15 53.2	16 5.1	10 13.8	11 33.1	16 30.5	17 10.3	12 36.3	22 6.8	5 35.1	11 44.6
19	5 49 11.8	26 29.4	15 50.2	29 11.5	11 49.3	12 14.3	17 8.5	17 17.2	12 43.7	22 10.8	5 37.5	11 46.4
20	5 53 8.3	27 35.9	15 47.3	11♌49.9	13 25.5	12 56.6	17 46.5	17 24.2	12 51.1	22 14.7	5 40.0	11 48.2
21	5 57 4.9	28 42.5	15 44.3	23 56.6	15 2.5	13 39.9	18 24.5	17 31.4	12 58.6	22 18.7	5 42.4	11 49.9
22	6 1 1.5	29 49.1	15 41.4	5♍35.4	16 40.2	14 24.3	19 2.5	17 38.7	13 5.9	22 22.6	5 44.8	11 51.6
23	6 4 58.0	0♑55.7	15 38.4	16 55.9	18 18.6	15 9.7	19 40.5	17 46.2	13 13.3	22 26.6	5 47.3	11 53.3
24	6 8 54.6	2 2.3	15 35.5	28 11.9	19 57.7	15 56.1	20 18.4	17 53.8	13 20.7	22 30.5	5 49.7	11 54.9
25	6 12 51.1	3 8.9	15 32.5	9♎40.5	21 37.4	16 43.5	20 56.4	18 1.5	13 28.0	22 34.5	5 52.2	11 56.5
26	6 16 47.7	4 15.5	15 29.6	21 40.8	23 17.7	17 31.8	21 34.4	18 9.4	13 35.4	22 38.4	5 54.7	11 58.2
27	6 20 44.3	5 22.1	15 26.6	4♏33.5	24 58.6	18 20.9	22 12.4	18 17.4	13 42.6	22 42.4	5 57.1	11 59.8
28	6 24 40.8	6 28.6	15 23.7	18 37.4	26 40.0	19 10.9	22 50.3	18 25.5	13 49.9	22 46.3	5 59.6	12 1.4
29	6 28 37.4	7 35.2	15 20.7	4♐ 3.2	28 21.9	20 1.8	23 28.3	18 33.8	13 57.1	22 50.2	6 2.1	12 2.9
30	6 32 33.9	8 41.6	15 17.7	20 42.7	0♑ 4.3	20 53.4	24 6.2	18 42.1	14 4.3	22 54.0	6 4.5	12 4.4
31	6 36 30.5	9 48.0	15 14.8	8♑ 1.7	1 47.2	21 45.9	24 44.2	18 50.6	14 11.5	22 57.9	6 7.0	12 5.9
		DECLINATION										
1	4 38 13.7	21S43.4	0N 7.4	22S59.5	15S 5.7	12S28.5	11S27.7	7S34.2	20S43.1	23S17.6	22S20.8	0N47.9
4	4 50 3.4	22 10.2	0 7.4	27 44.0	16 16.3	12 13.9	10 38.1	7 28.1	20 46.0	23 18.3	22 20.7	0 46.7
7	5 1 53.1	22 33.1	0 7.3	15 59.4	17 32.2	12 8.4	9 47.7	7 21.3	20 48.9	23 19.0	22 20.5	0 45.6
10	5 13 42.8	22 52.0	0 7.3	2N 2.8	18 48.4	12 11.1	8 56.7	7 13.9	20 51.8	23 19.6	22 20.4	0 44.6
13	5 25 32.4	23 6.9	0 7.2	18 18.7	20 1.3	12 21.2	8 5.2	7 5.9	20 54.5	23 20.3	22 20.2	0 43.8
16	5 37 22.1	23 17.7	0 7.1	27 31.7	21 8.4	12 37.6	7 13.3	6 57.3	20 57.2	23 20.9	22 20.0	0 43.0
19	5 49 11.8	23 24.2	0 7.1	25 48.2	22 8.1	12 59.3	6 20.9	6 48.2	20 59.8	23 21.5	22 19.7	0 42.4
22	6 1 1.5	23 26.6	0 7.0	14 .7	22 59.1	13 25.5	5 28.2	6 38.5	21 2.3	23 22.2	22 19.5	0 42.0
25	6 12 51.1	23 24.7	0 6.9	3S28.1	23 40.3	13 55.3	4 35.2	6 28.3	21 4.7	23 22.8	22 19.3	0 41.6
28	6 24 40.8	23 18.6	0 6.9	20 58.1	24 10.9	14 27.8	3 42.0	6 17.6	21 7.1	23 23.3	22 19.0	0 41.3
31	6 36 30.5	23 8.2	0 6.8	28 10.3	24 30.3	15 2.2	2 48.6	6 6.4	21 9.3	23 23.9	22 18.8	0 41.2

JANUARY 1987

LONGITUDE

DAY	EPHEM. SID. TIME	☉	☊	☽	☿	♀	♂	♃	♄	♅	♆	♇
	h m s	° ′	° ′	° ′	° ′	° ′	° ′	° ′	° ′	° ′	° ′	° ′
1	6 40 27.0	10♑ 1.5	16♈ 29.6	22♑ 26.8	3♑ 11.5	24♏ 5.3	24♓ 45.2	17♓ 30.8	15♐ 23.3	23♐ 36.3	5♑ 41.7	9♏ 27.7
2	6 44 23.6	11 2.7	16 26.4	7♒ 36.1	4 45.7	24 58.7	25 27.1	17 40.3	15 30.0	23 39.8	5 44.0	9 29.1
3	6 48 20.2	12 3.8	16 23.2	22 24.2	6 20.3	25 52.9	26 9.0	17 50.0	15 36.6	23 43.4	5 46.2	9 30.5
4	6 52 16.7	13 5.0	16 20.1	6♓ 44.5	7 55.2	26 47.7	26 50.9	17 59.8	15 43.2	23 46.9	5 48.5	9 31.9
5	6 56 13.3	14 6.2	16 16.9	20 34.6	9 30.4	27 43.1	27 32.9	18 9.7	15 49.8	23 50.3	5 50.7	9 33.2
6	7 0 9.8	15 7.4	16 13.7	3♈ 55.2	11 6.0	28 39.1	28 14.8	18 19.7	15 56.3	23 53.8	5 53.0	9 34.5
7	7 4 6.4	16 8.5	16 10.5	16 49.4	12 42.0	29 35.6	28 56.7	18 29.9	16 2.8	23 57.3	5 55.2	9 35.8
8	7 8 3.0	17 9.7	16 7.4	29 21.9	14 18.4	0♐ 32.7	29 38.7	18 40.2	16 9.3	24 .7	5 57.5	9 37.0
9	7 11 59.5	18 10.8	16 4.2	11♉ 37.5	15 55.1	1 30.3	0♈ 20.6	18 50.6	16 15.7	24 4.1	5 59.7	9 38.2
10	7 15 56.1	19 11.9	16 1.0	23 41.2	17 32.3	2 28.5	1 2.6	19 1.1	16 22.0	24 7.5	6 1.9	9 39.4
11	7 19 52.6	20 13.1	15 57.8	5♊ 37.3	19 9.9	3 27.1	1 44.5	19 11.7	16 28.4	24 10.9	6 4.2	9 40.5
12	7 23 49.2	21 14.2	15 54.7	17 29.5	20 48.0	4 26.2	2 26.5	19 22.4	16 34.7	24 14.3	6 6.4	9 41.6
13	7 27 45.7	22 15.3	15 51.5	29 20.8	22 26.6	5 25.8	3 8.4	19 33.3	16 40.9	24 17.6	6 8.6	9 42.7
14	7 31 42.3	23 16.4	15 48.3	11♋ 13.2	24 5.6	6 25.8	3 50.4	19 44.2	16 47.1	24 20.9	6 10.8	9 43.7
15	7 35 38.9	24 17.5	15 45.1	23 8.2	25 45.1	7 26.2	4 32.3	19 55.3	16 53.2	24 24.2	6 13.0	9 44.7
16	7 39 35.4	25 18.6	15 42.0	5♌ 7.3	27 25.1	8 27.1	5 14.3	20 6.5	16 59.4	24 27.5	6 15.2	9 45.7
17	7 43 32.0	26 19.7	15 38.8	17 11.2	29 5.5	9 28.4	5 56.2	20 17.7	17 5.5	24 30.8	6 17.3	9 46.6
18	7 47 28.5	27 20.8	15 35.6	29 21.4	0♒ 46.5	10 30.0	6 38.1	20 29.1	17 11.5	24 34.0	6 19.5	9 47.5
19	7 51 25.1	28 21.9	15 32.4	11♍ 39.4	2 27.9	11 32.0	7 20.0	20 40.5	17 17.4	24 37.2	6 21.6	9 48.4
20	7 55 21.7	29 22.9	15 29.2	24 7.6	4 9.8	12 34.4	8 1.9	20 52.1	17 23.3	24 40.3	6 23.8	9 49.2
21	7 59 18.2	0♒ 24.0	15 26.1	6♎ 48.8	5 52.2	13 37.1	8 43.8	21 3.8	17 29.2	24 43.5	6 25.9	9 50.0
22	8 3 14.8	1 25.1	15 22.9	19 46.5	7 34.9	14 40.1	9 25.7	21 15.5	17 35.0	24 46.6	6 28.0	9 50.8
23	8 7 11.3	2 26.1	15 19.7	3♏ 4.0	9 18.1	15 43.5	10 7.6	21 27.3	17 40.7	24 49.7	6 30.1	9 51.5
24	8 11 7.9	3 27.1	15 16.5	16 44.5	11 1.6	16 47.2	10 49.5	21 39.3	17 46.4	24 52.7	6 32.2	9 52.2
25	8 15 4.4	4 28.2	15 13.4	0♐ 49.8	12 45.3	17 51.2	11 31.3	21 51.3	17 52.0	24 55.8	6 34.2	9 52.8
26	8 19 1.0	5 29.2	15 10.2	15 19.6	14 29.3	18 55.5	12 13.2	22 3.4	17 57.6	24 58.8	6 36.3	9 53.5
27	8 22 57.6	6 30.2	15 7.0	0♑ 10.5	16 13.4	20 .0	12 55.0	22 15.6	18 3.1	25 1.7	6 38.3	9 54.0
28	8 26 54.1	7 31.2	15 3.8	15 16.0	17 57.5	21 4.8	13 36.9	22 27.9	18 8.5	25 4.7	6 40.3	9 54.6
29	8 30 50.7	8 32.2	15 .7	0♒ 26.6	19 41.5	22 9.9	14 18.7	22 40.2	18 13.9	25 7.6	6 42.3	9 55.1
30	8 34 47.2	9 33.2	14 57.5	15 31.8	21 25.1	23 15.2	15 .5	22 52.7	18 19.2	25 10.4	6 44.3	9 55.6
31	8 38 43.8	10 34.1	14 54.3	0♓ 21.3	23 8.2	24 20.8	15 42.4	23 5.2	18 24.5	25 13.3	6 46.3	9 56.0

LATITUDE

DAY	EPHEM. SID. TIME	☉	☊	☽	☿	♀	♂	♃	♄	♅	♆	♇
1	6 40 27.0	0 .0	0 .0	4S 58.6	1S 9.9	3N 40.5	0S 28.0	1S 12.3	1N 29.1	0S 6.8	1N .6	16N 7.8
4	6 52 16.7	0 .0	0 .0	3 12.5	1 25.4	3 42.6	0 24.1	1 11.7	1 29.1	0 6.8	1 .6	16 9.2
7	7 4 6.4	0 .0	0 .0	0N 2.7	1 38.8	3 43.1	0 20.3	1 11.2	1 29.1	0 6.8	1 .6	16 10.6
10	7 15 56.1	0 .0	0 .0	3 3.4	1 49.9	3 41.9	0 16.6	1 10.7	1 29.2	0 6.9	1 .6	16 12.0
13	7 27 45.7	0 .0	0 .0	4 47.3	1 58.4	3 39.2	0 13.0	1 10.3	1 29.2	0 6.9	1 .6	16 13.5
16	7 39 35.4	0 .0	0 .0	4 41.3	2 3.8	3 35.2	0 9.6	1 9.8	1 29.3	0 6.9	1 .6	16 15.0
19	7 51 25.1	0 .0	0 .0	2 43.8	2 5.8	3 29.9	0 6.2	1 9.4	1 29.4	0 7.0	1 .6	16 16.5
22	8 3 14.8	0 .0	0 .0	0S 28.5	2 3.9	3 23.5	0 3.0	1 9.0	1 29.5	0 7.0	1 .6	16 18.0
25	8 15 4.4	0 .0	0 .0	3 40.0	1 57.5	3 16.1	0N .2	1 8.6	1 29.7	0 7.0	1 .7	16 19.6
28	8 26 54.1	0 .0	0 .0	5 2.2	1 45.9	3 7.9	0 3.2	1 8.2	1 29.8	0 7.1	1 .7	16 21.2
31	8 38 43.8	0 .0	0 .0	3 27.7	1 28.6	2 58.8	0 6.2	1 7.9	1 30.0	0 7.1	1 .7	16 22.8

RIGHT ASCENSION

DAY	EPHEM. SID. TIME	☉	☊	☽	☿	♀	♂	♃	♄	♅	♆	♇
1	6 40 27.0	10♑ 54.4	15♈ 11.8	25♑ 8.9	3♑ 30.6	22♏ 39.1	25♓ 22.2	18♓ 59.3	14♐ 18.6	23♐ 1.8	6♑ 9.4	12♏ 7.4
2	6 44 23.6	12 .6	15 8.9	11♒ 18.5	5 14.3	23 33.1	26 .1	19 8.0	14 25.8	23 5.6	6 11.8	12 8.8
3	6 48 20.2	13 6.8	15 5.9	26 8.8	6 58.4	24 27.8	26 38.1	19 16.9	14 32.8	23 9.4	6 14.3	12 10.2
4	6 52 16.7	14 12.9	15 3.0	9♓ 41.6	8 42.9	25 23.2	27 16.1	19 25.9	14 39.9	23 13.2	6 16.7	12 11.6
5	6 56 13.3	15 18.9	15 .0	22 12.4	10 27.8	26 19.3	27 54.1	19 35.0	14 46.9	23 17.0	6 19.2	12 12.9
6	7 0 9.8	16 24.8	14 57.1	4♈ 1.6	12 12.9	27 16.1	28 32.1	19 44.2	14 53.8	23 20.8	6 21.6	12 14.3
7	7 4 6.4	17 30.5	14 54.1	15 29.2	13 58.3	28 13.5	29 10.0	19 53.5	15 .8	23 24.6	6 24.0	12 15.6
8	7 8 3.0	18 36.2	14 51.2	26 53.5	15 44.0	29 11.6	29 48.0	20 2.9	15 7.6	23 28.3	6 26.4	12 16.8
9	7 11 59.5	19 41.7	14 48.2	8♉ 29.6	17 29.9	0♐ 10.4	0♈ 26.0	20 12.5	15 14.5	23 32.0	6 28.8	12 18.1
10	7 15 56.1	20 47.0	14 45.3	20 29.1	19 16.1	1 9.7	1 4.0	20 22.1	15 21.3	23 35.7	6 31.2	12 19.3
11	7 19 52.6	21 52.3	14 42.3	2♊ 58.4	21 2.4	2 9.7	1 42.0	20 31.9	15 28.0	23 39.4	6 33.6	12 20.5
12	7 23 49.2	22 57.4	14 39.4	15 56.7	22 48.8	3 10.3	2 20.1	20 41.7	15 34.8	23 43.1	6 36.0	12 21.6
13	7 27 45.7	24 2.3	14 36.4	29 15.6	24 35.3	4 11.4	3 36.1	21 1.7	15 48.0	23 50.3	6 40.8	12 23.9
14	7 31 42.3	25 7.1	14 33.5	12♋ 40.3	26 22.0	5 13.1	4 14.2	21 11.9	15 54.6	23 53.9	6 43.1	12 24.9
15	7 35 38.9	26 11.7	14 30.5	25 53.9	28 8.6	6 15.4	4 52.3	21 22.1	16 1.2	23 57.5	6 45.5	12 26.0
16	7 39 35.4	27 16.2	14 27.6	8♌ 42.7	29 55.4	7 18.3	5 30.3	21 32.5	16 7.7	24 1.0	6 47.9	12 27.0
17	7 43 32.0	28 20.5	14 24.6	20 59.8	1♒ 42.0	8 21.7	6 8.4	21 42.9	16 14.1	24 4.5	6 50.2	12 28.0
18	7 47 28.5	29 24.6	14 21.7	2♍ 45.9	3 28.6	9 25.6	6 46.5	21 53.4	16 20.4	24 8.0	6 52.5	12 28.9
19	7 51 25.1	0♒ 28.6	14 18.7	14 8.1	5 15.1	10 30.1	7 24.6	22 4.0	16 26.7	24 11.5	6 54.8	12 29.9
20	7 55 21.7	1 32.3	14 15.8	25 18.2	7 1.4	11 35.0	8 2.8	22 14.7	16 33.0	24 14.9	6 57.1	12 30.7
21	7 59 18.2	2 35.9	14 12.9	6♎ 31.2	8 47.5	12 40.4	8 40.9	22 25.5	16 39.2	24 18.3	6 59.4	12 31.6
22	8 3 14.8	3 39.3	14 9.9	18 4.4	10 33.3	13 46.3	9 19.1	22 36.3	16 45.3	24 21.6	7 1.6	12 32.4
23	8 7 11.3	4 42.5	14 7.0	0♏ 16.8	12 18.7	14 52.7	9 57.3	22 47.3	16 51.4	24 25.0	7 3.9	12 33.2
24	8 11 7.9	5 45.5	14 4.0	13 27.4	14 3.8	15 59.5	10 35.6	22 58.3	16 57.4	24 28.2	7 6.1	12 34.0
25	8 15 4.4	6 48.4	14 1.1	27 51.3	15 48.3	17 6.7	11 13.8	23 9.4	17 3.4	24 31.5	7 8.3	12 34.7
26	8 19 1.0	7 51.0	13 58.1	13♐ 31.8	17 32.3	18 14.4	11 52.1	23 20.6	17 9.3	24 34.7	7 10.5	12 35.4
27	8 22 57.6	8 53.5	13 55.2	0♑ 11.9	19 15.5	19 22.5	12 30.4	23 31.8	17 15.1	24 37.9	7 12.7	12 36.0
28	8 26 54.1	9 55.7	13 52.2	17 12.7	20 58.0	20 31.0	13 8.8	23 43.2	17 20.9	24 41.1	7 14.9	12 36.7
29	8 30 50.7	10 57.8	13 49.3	3♒ 47.0	22 39.4	21 39.8	13 47.2	23 54.6	17 26.6	24 44.2	7 17.0	12 37.2
30	8 34 47.2	11 59.6	13 46.3	19 20.5	24 19.7	22 49.0	14 25.6	24 6.1	17 32.2	24 47.3	7 19.1	12 37.8
31	8 38 43.8	13 1.3	13 43.4	3♓ 41.4	25 58.6	23 58.6						

DECLINATION

DAY	EPHEM. SID. TIME	☉	☊	☽	☿	♀	♂	♃	♄	♅	♆	♇
1	6 40 27.0	23S 3.9	0N 6.8	26S 28.9	24S 34.1	15S 14.0	2S 30.8	6S 2.6	21S 10.0	23S 24.1	22S 18.7	0N 41.2
4	6 52 16.7	22 48.0	0 6.7	12 1.0	24 37.6	15 49.9	1 37.3	5 50.8	21 12.1	23 24.6	22 18.4	0 41.3
7	7 4 6.4	22 28.0	0 6.7	6N 39.2	24 28.6	16 26.0	0 43.8	5 38.5	21 14.1	23 25.1	22 18.1	0 41.5
10	7 15 56.1	22 4.1	0 6.6	21 39.4	24 6.6	17 1.9	0N 9.7	5 25.9	21 16.0	23 25.6	22 17.8	0 41.8
13	7 27 45.7	21 36.3	0 6.5	28 13.8	23 31.2	17 36.9	1 3.0	5 12.8	21 17.8	23 26.1	22 17.5	0 42.2
16	7 39 35.4	21 4.7	0 6.5	23 32.1	22 42.2	18 10.5	1 56.1	4 59.3	21 19.5	23 26.6	22 17.2	0 42.7
19	7 51 25.1	20 29.5	0 6.4	9 43.0	21 39.3	18 42.2	2 48.9	4 45.5	21 21.1	23 27.0	22 16.9	0 43.4
22	8 3 14.8	19 50.8	0 6.3	8S 10.5	20 22.4	19 11.5	3 41.5	4 31.4	21 22.7	23 27.4	22 16.6	0 44.2
25	8 15 4.4	19 8.8	0 6.3	23 54.7	18 51.7	19 37.9	4 33.6	4 16.9	21 24.1	23 27.8	22 16.2	0 45.0
28	8 26 54.1	18 23.6	0 6.2	27 34.3	17 7.9	20 1.2	5 25.4	4 2.1	21 25.4	23 28.2	22 15.9	0 46.0
31	8 38 43.8	17 35.4	0 6.2	14 35.1	15 12.2	20 20.8	6 16.6	3 47.0	21 26.6	23 28.5	22 15.6	0 47.1

FEBRUARY 1987

DAY	EPHEM. SID. TIME	☉	☊	☽	☿	♀	♂	♃	♄	♅	♆	♇
	h m s	° ′	° ′	° ′	° ′	° ′	° ′	° ′	° ′	° ′	° ′	° ′
		LONGITUDE										
1	8 42 40.3	11♒35.1	14♈51.1	14♓47.4	24♒50.6	25♐26.5	16♈24.2	23♓17.8	18♐29.7	25♐16.1	6♑48.3	9♏56.4
2	8 46 36.9	12 36.0	14 47.9	28 45.6	26 32.0	26 32.5	17 6.0	23 30.5	18 34.8	25 18.8	6 50.2	9 56.8
3	8 50 33.5	13 36.9	14 44.8	12♈14.7	28 12.0	27 38.7	17 47.7	23 43.2	18 39.9	25 21.6	6 52.1	9 57.1
4	8 54 30.0	14 37.8	14 41.6	25 16.4	29 50.3	28 45.1	18 29.5	23 56.0	18 44.9	25 24.2	6 54.0	9 57.4
5	8 58 26.6	15 38.6	14 38.4	7♉54.4	1♓26.5	29 51.7	19 11.2	24 8.9	18 49.8	25 26.9	6 55.9	9 57.6
6	9 2 23.1	16 39.5	14 35.2	20 13.2	3 .1	0♑58.6	19 53.0	24 21.9	18 54.7	25 29.6	6 57.8	9 57.9
7	9 6 19.7	17 40.3	14 32.1	2♊18.0	4 30.5	2 5.6	20 34.7	24 35.0	18 59.4	25 32.2	6 59.6	9 58.1
8	9 10 16.2	18 41.1	14 28.9	14 13.7	5 57.2	3 12.7	21 16.4	24 48.1	19 4.1	25 34.7	7 1.4	9 58.2
9	9 14 12.8	19 41.8	14 25.7	26 5.1	7 19.5	4 20.1	21 58.1	25 1.2	19 8.8	25 37.2	7 3.2	9 58.3
10	9 18 9.3	20 42.6	14 22.5	7♋56.1	8 36.7	5 27.6	22 39.7	25 14.4	19 13.3	25 39.7	7 5.0	9 58.4
11	9 22 5.9	21 43.3	14 19.4	19 50.0	9 48.2	6 35.2	23 21.3	25 27.7	19 17.8	25 42.1	7 6.8	9 58.4
12	9 26 2.5	22 44.0	14 16.2	1♌49.2	10 53.2	7 43.1	24 2.9	25 41.0	19 22.2	25 44.5	7 8.5	9 58.4
13	9 29 59.0	23 44.6	14 13.0	13 55.6	11 50.9	8 51.1	24 44.5	25 54.4	19 26.5	25 46.8	7 10.2	9 58.4
14	9 33 55.6	24 45.3	14 9.8	26 10.2	12 40.6	9 59.2	25 26.1	26 7.8	19 30.8	25 49.1	7 11.9	9R58.3
15	9 37 52.1	25 45.9	14 6.6	8♍34.0	13 21.7	11 7.5	26 7.6	26 21.3	19 35.0	25 51.4	7 13.5	9 58.2
16	9 41 48.7	26 46.4	14 3.5	21 7.6	13 53.6	12 16.0	26 49.1	26 34.9	19 39.1	25 53.6	7 15.2	9 58.1
17	9 45 45.2	27 47.0	14 .3	3♎51.9	14 15.7	13 24.5	27 30.6	26 48.5	19 43.1	25 55.8	7 16.8	9 57.9
18	9 49 41.8	28 47.6	13 57.1	16 47.9	14 27.8	14 33.3	28 12.1	27 2.1	19 47.0	25 57.9	7 18.4	9 57.7
19	9 53 38.3	29 48.1	13 53.9	29 57.1	14 29.5	15 42.1	28 53.5	27 15.8	19 50.9	26 .0	7 19.9	9 57.4
20	9 57 34.9	0♓48.6	13 50.8	13♏21.0	14R20.9	16 51.1	29 34.9	27 29.6	19 54.6	26 2.0	7 21.5	9 57.1
21	10 1 31.5	1 49.1	13 47.6	27 1.2	14 2.3	18 .2	0♉16.3	27 43.4	19 58.3	26 4.0	7 23.0	9 56.8
22	10 5 28.0	2 49.5	13 44.4	10♐58.6	13 34.1	19 9.4	0 57.7	27 57.2	20 1.9	26 6.0	7 24.5	9 56.4
23	10 9 24.6	3 49.9	13 41.2	25 12.9	12 57.0	20 18.8	1 39.1	28 11.1	20 5.4	26 7.9	7 25.9	9 56.1
24	10 13 21.1	4 50.4	13 38.1	9♑42.3	12 11.9	21 28.2	2 20.4	28 25.0	20 8.9	26 9.8	7 27.4	9 55.6
25	10 17 17.7	5 50.7	13 34.9	24 22.5	11 20.1	22 37.8	3 1.7	28 39.0	20 12.2	26 11.6	7 28.8	9 55.2
26	10 21 14.2	6 51.1	13 31.7	9♒ 7.6	10 22.9	23 47.5	3 43.0	28 53.0	20 15.5	26 13.4	7 30.1	9 54.7
27	10 25 10.8	7 51.5	13 28.5	23 50.2	9 21.9	24 57.3	4 24.3	29 7.1	20 18.7	26 15.1	7 31.5	9 54.2
28	10 29 7.3	8 51.8	13 25.3	8♓22.7	8 18.6	26 7.1	5 5.6	29 21.2	20 21.7	26 16.8	7 32.9	9 53.6
		LATITUDE										
1	8 42 40.3	0 .0	0 .0	2S25.9	1S21.4	2N55.6	0N 7.1	1S 7.8	1N30.0	0S 7.1	1N .7	16N23.3
4	8 54 30.0	0 .0	0 .0	1N 3.5	0 55.4	2 45.6	0 9.9	1 7.5	1 30.2	0 7.2	1 .7	16 24.9
7	9 6 19.7	0 .0	0 .0	3 51.2	0 22.5	2 35.0	0 12.7	1 7.2	1 30.4	0 7.2	1 .8	16 26.5
10	9 18 9.3	0 .0	0 .0	5 4.3	0N17.1	2 23.8	0 15.3	1 6.9	1 30.6	0 7.3	1 .8	16 28.1
13	9 29 59.0	0 .0	0 .0	4 21.5	1 2.2	2 12.3	0 17.9	1 6.6	1 30.8	0 7.3	1 .9	16 29.6
16	9 41 48.7	0 .0	0 .0	1 51.1	1 49.9	2 .5	0 20.3	1 6.4	1 31.0	0 7.3	1 .9	16 31.2
19	9 53 38.3	0 .0	0 .0	1S34.9	2 35.9	1 48.3	0 22.7	1 6.2	1 31.3	0 7.4	1 1.0	16 32.7
22	10 5 28.0	0 .0	0 .0	4 25.6	3 13.9	1 36.1	0 25.0	1 6.0	1 31.5	0 7.4	1 1.0	16 34.2
25	10 17 17.7	0 .0	0 .0	5 3.3	3 37.7	1 23.7	0 27.2	1 5.8	1 31.8	0 7.5	1 1.1	16 35.7
28	10 29 7.3	0 .0	0 .0	2 51.8	3 42.5	1 11.3	0 29.3	1 5.6	1 32.0	0 7.5	1 1.2	16 37.1
		RIGHT ASCENSION										
1	8 42 40.3	14♒ 2.7	13♈40.4	16♓56.5	27♒36.0	25♐ 8.5	15♈ 4.0	24♓17.6	17♐37.8	24♐50.4	7♑21.2	12♏38.3
2	8 46 36.9	15 3.9	13 37.5	29 22.3	29 11.6	26 18.7	15 42.5	24 29.2	17 43.3	24 53.4	7 23.3	12 38.8
3	8 50 33.5	16 4.9	13 34.6	11♈17.9	0♓45.0	27 29.2	16 21.1	24 40.9	17 48.7	24 56.4	7 25.4	12 39.3
4	8 54 30.0	17 5.7	13 31.6	23 1.6	2 16.1	28 40.1	16 59.6	24 52.7	17 54.0	24 59.3	7 27.4	12 39.7
5	8 58 26.6	18 6.3	13 28.7	4♉49.5	3 44.3	29 51.2	17 38.2	25 4.5	17 59.3	25 2.2	7 29.5	12 40.1
6	9 2 23.1	19 6.8	13 25.7	16 54.0	5 9.4	1♑ 2.6	18 16.9	25 16.4	18 4.6	25 5.1	7 31.5	12 40.5
7	9 6 19.7	20 7.0	13 22.8	29 23.0	6 30.8	2 14.2	18 55.6	25 28.3	18 9.7	25 7.9	7 33.5	12 40.8
8	9 10 16.2	21 7.0	13 19.8	12♊18.3	7 47.9	3 26.1	19 34.3	25 40.3	18 14.7	25 10.7	7 35.4	12 41.1
9	9 14 12.8	22 6.7	13 16.9	25 34.2	9 .4	4 38.2	20 13.0	25 52.4	18 19.7	25 13.4	7 37.4	12 41.4
10	9 18 9.3	23 6.3	13 13.9	8♋58.9	10 7.7	5 50.5	20 51.8	26 4.5	18 24.6	25 16.1	7 39.3	12 41.6
11	9 22 5.9	24 5.7	13 11.0	22 17.1	11 9.0	7 3.0	21 30.7	26 16.6	18 29.4	25 18.7	7 41.2	12 41.8
12	9 26 2.5	25 4.9	13 8.1	5♌15.0	12 3.9	8 15.7	22 9.5	26 28.8	18 34.1	25 21.3	7 43.0	12 42.0
13	9 29 59.0	26 3.9	13 5.1	17 44.1	12 51.7	9 28.6	22 48.5	26 41.1	18 38.7	25 23.9	7 44.9	12 42.1
14	9 33 55.6	27 2.7	13 2.2	29 43.1	13 31.9	10 41.6	23 27.4	26 53.4	18 43.3	25 26.4	7 46.7	12 42.2
15	9 37 52.1	28 1.3	12 59.2	11♍16.7	14 3.9	11 54.8	24 6.4	27 5.8	18 47.8	25 28.9	7 48.5	12 42.2
16	9 41 48.7	28 59.8	12 56.3	22 34.9	14 27.3	13 8.1	24 45.5	27 18.2	18 52.2	25 31.3	7 50.3	12 42.3
17	9 45 45.2	29 58.0	12 53.3	3♎50.6	14 41.7	14 21.5	25 24.6	27 30.6	18 56.5	25 33.6	7 52.0	12R42.2
18	9 49 41.8	0♓56.1	12 50.4	15 19.2	14 46.9	15 35.0	26 3.7	27 43.1	19 .7	25 36.0	7 53.7	12 42.2
19	9 53 38.3	1 54.0	12 47.5	27 17.5	14R42.8	16 48.7	26 42.9	27 55.7	19 4.8	25 38.2	7 55.4	12 42.1
20	9 57 34.9	2 51.8	12 44.5	10♏ 2.7	14 29.6	18 2.4	27 22.2	28 8.3	19 8.9	25 40.5	7 57.0	12 42.0
21	10 1 31.5	3 49.4	12 41.6	23 49.0	14 7.5	19 16.1	28 1.5	28 20.9	19 12.8	25 42.6	7 58.7	12 41.9
22	10 5 28.0	4 46.8	12 38.6	8♐42.7	13 37.0	20 29.9	28 40.9	28 33.6	19 16.7	25 44.8	8 .3	12 41.7
23	10 9 24.6	5 44.1	12 35.7	24 35.1	12 58.9	21 43.8	29 20.3	28 46.3	19 20.5	25 46.9	8 1.8	12 41.5
24	10 13 21.1	6 41.2	12 32.8	10♑59.1	12 14.2	22 57.6	29 59.8	28 59.0	19 24.2	25 48.9	8 3.4	12 41.3
25	10 17 17.7	7 38.2	12 29.8	27 16.4	11 24.0	24 11.5	0♉39.3	29 11.8	19 27.7	25 50.9	8 4.9	12 41.0
26	10 21 14.2	8 35.0	12 26.9	12♒52.5	10 29.6	25 25.3	1 18.9	29 24.7	19 31.2	25 52.8	8 6.4	12 40.7
27	10 25 10.8	9 31.7	12 23.9	27 29.3	9 32.3	26 39.2	1 58.6	29 37.6	19 34.7	25 54.7	8 7.9	12 40.4
28	10 29 7.3	10 28.3	12 21.0	11♓ 6.4	8 33.7	27 53.0	2 38.3	29 50.5	19 38.0	25 56.5	8 9.3	12 40.0
		DECLINATION										
1	8 42 40.3	17S18.7	0N 6.1	8S14.0	14S31.3	20S26.4	6N33.6	3S42.0	21S27.0	23S28.7	22S15.5	0N47.5
4	8 54 30.0	16 26.8	0 6.1	10N45.9	12 23.7	20 40.7	7 24.1	3 26.5	21 28.1	23 29.0	22 15.2	0 48.7
7	9 6 19.7	15 32.3	0 6.0	24 24.0	10 12.5	20 50.7	8 14.1	3 10.8	21 29.1	23 29.3	22 14.8	0 50.1
10	9 18 9.3	14 35.5	0 5.9	28 16.1	8 4.6	20 56.1	9 3.3	2 54.9	21 30.1	23 29.6	22 14.5	0 51.5
13	9 29 59.0	13 36.5	0 5.9	20 49.2	6 9.7	20 56.8	9 51.7	2 38.8	21 30.9	23 29.9	22 14.2	0 53.0
16	9 41 48.7	12 35.5	0 5.8	5 13.2	4 38.7	20 52.7	10 39.4	2 22.5	21 31.6	23 30.1	22 13.9	0 54.5
19	9 53 38.3	11 32.6	0 5.7	12S56.2	3 42.5	20 43.6	11 26.2	2 6.0	21 32.3	23 30.4	22 13.5	0 56.2
22	10 5 28.0	10 28.1	0 5.7	26 28.5	3 28.6	20 29.4	12 12.1	1 49.4	21 32.9	23 30.6	22 13.2	0 57.9
25	10 17 17.7	9 22.2	0 5.6	26 13.1	3 57.4	20 10.1	12 57.0	1 32.6	21 33.4	23 30.8	22 12.9	0 59.7
28	10 29 7.3	8 14.9	0 5.5	11 5.0	5 .8	19 45.7	13 41.0	1 15.6	21 33.8	23 31.0	22 12.7	1 1.5

MARCH 1987

LONGITUDE

DAY	EPHEM. SID. TIME	☉	☊	☽	☿	♀	♂	♃	♄	♅	♆	♇
	h m s	° ′	° ′	° ′	° ′	° ′	° ′	° ′	° ′	° ′	° ′	° ′
1	10 33 3.9	9♓52.1	13♈22.2	22♓38.3	7♓14.5	27♑17.1	5♉46.8	29♓35.3	20♐24.7	26♐18.4	7♑34.1	9♏53.0
2	10 37 .4	10 52.3	13 19.0	6♈32.3	6 R 11.3	28 27.1	6 28.0	29 49.4	20 27.6	26 20.0	7 35.4	9 R 52.4
3	10 40 57.0	11 52.6	13 15.8	20 2.0	5 10.2	29 37.2	7 9.2	0♈ 3.6	20 30.4	26 21.5	7 36.6	9 51.8
4	10 44 53.6	12 52.8	13 12.6	3♉ 7.5	4 12.6	0♒47.4	7 50.3	0 17.8	20 33.1	26 23.0	7 37.8	9 51.1
5	10 48 50.1	13 52.9	13 9.5	15 50.5	3 19.6	1 57.7	8 31.4	0 32.0	20 35.7	26 24.4	7 39.0	9 50.3
6	10 52 46.7	14 53.0	13 6.3	28 14.3	2 31.8	3 8.0	9 12.5	0 46.3	20 38.3	26 25.8	7 40.2	9 49.6
7	10 56 43.2	15 53.1	13 3.1	10♊23.0	1 50.0	4 18.4	9 53.6	1 .6	20 40.7	26 27.1	7 41.3	9 48.8
8	11 0 39.8	16 53.2	12 59.9	22 21.5	1 14.6	5 28.9	10 34.7	1 14.9	20 43.0	26 28.4	7 42.4	9 48.0
9	11 4 36.3	17 53.2	12 56.7	4♋14.6	0 45.7	6 39.5	11 15.7	1 29.2	20 45.2	26 29.6	7 43.4	9 47.1
10	11 8 32.9	18 53.1	12 53.6	16 6.8	0 23.6	7 50.1	11 56.7	1 43.6	20 47.4	26 30.8	7 44.4	9 46.3
11	11 12 29.4	19 53.1	12 50.4	28 2.5	0 8.2	9 .8	12 37.6	1 57.9	20 49.4	26 31.9	7 45.4	9 45.4
12	11 16 26.0	20 53.0	12 47.2	10♌ 5.2	29♒59.4	10 11.5	13 18.6	2 12.3	20 51.4	26 33.0	7 46.4	9 44.4
13	11 20 22.5	21 52.9	12 44.0	22 18.0	29 57.0	11 22.4	13 59.5	2 26.7	20 53.2	26 34.0	7 47.3	9 43.5
14	11 24 19.1	22 52.7	12 40.9	4♍42.9	0♓ .7	12 33.3	14 40.3	2 41.2	20 55.0	26 35.0	7 48.2	9 42.5
15	11 28 15.7	23 52.5	12 37.7	17 21.2	0 D 10.3	13 44.2	15 21.2	2 55.6	20 56.6	26 35.9	7 49.1	9 41.5
16	11 32 12.2	24 52.3	12 34.5	0♎13.5	0 25.5	14 55.2	16 2.0	3 10.0	20 58.2	26 36.8	7 49.9	9 40.4
17	11 36 8.8	25 52.0	12 31.3	13 19.8	0 46.0	16 6.3	16 42.8	3 24.5	20 59.7	26 37.6	7 50.7	9 39.3
18	11 40 5.3	26 51.7	12 28.1	26 39.3	1 11.5	17 17.4	17 23.5	3 39.0	21 1.0	26 38.4	7 51.5	9 38.2
19	11 44 1.9	27 51.4	12 25.0	10♏11.3	1 41.6	18 28.6	18 4.3	3 53.5	21 2.3	26 39.1	7 52.3	9 37.1
20	11 47 58.4	28 51.1	12 21.8	23 54.8	2 16.2	19 39.9	18 45.0	4 8.0	21 3.5	26 39.8	7 53.0	9 36.0
21	11 51 55.0	29 50.7	12 18.6	7♐48.5	2 54.9	20 51.2	19 25.7	4 22.5	21 4.6	26 40.4	7 53.7	9 34.8
22	11 55 51.5	0♈50.3	12 15.4	21 51.2	3 37.5	22 2.5	20 6.3	4 37.0	21 5.5	26 41.0	7 54.3	9 33.6
23	11 59 48.1	1 49.8	12 12.3	6♑ 1.3	4 23.8	23 13.9	20 46.9	4 51.6	21 6.4	26 41.5	7 54.9	9 32.4
24	12 3 44.6	2 49.4	12 9.1	20 16.7	5 13.5	24 25.4	21 27.5	5 6.1	21 7.2	26 41.9	7 55.5	9 31.1
25	12 7 41.2	3 48.9	12 5.9	4♒34.8	6 6.4	25 36.9	22 8.1	5 20.6	21 7.9	26 42.3	7 56.1	9 29.9
26	12 11 37.7	4 48.3	12 2.7	18 52.2	7 2.3	26 48.4	22 48.6	5 35.1	21 8.4	26 42.7	7 56.6	9 28.6
27	12 15 34.3	5 47.8	11 59.5	3♓ 5.1	8 1.2	28 .0	23 29.1	5 49.7	21 8.9	26 43.0	7 57.0	9 27.3
28	12 19 30.8	6 47.2	11 56.4	17 9.4	9 2.7	29 11.6	24 9.6	6 4.2	21 9.3	26 43.2	7 57.5	9 25.9
29	12 23 27.4	7 46.6	11 53.2	1♈ 1.3	10 6.8	0♓23.3	24 50.1	6 18.7	21 9.5	26 43.4	7 57.9	9 24.6
30	12 27 24.0	8 45.9	11 50.0	14 37.5	11 13.3	1 35.0	25 30.5	6 33.2	21 9.7	26 43.5	7 58.3	9 23.2
31	12 31 20.5	9 45.2	11 46.8	27 55.9	12 22.2	2 46.7	26 10.9	6 47.8	21 9.7	26 43.6	7 58.6	9 21.8

LATITUDE

DAY	EPHEM. SID. TIME	☉	☊	☽	☿	♀	♂	♃	♄	♅	♆	♇
1	10 33 3.9	0 .0	0 .0	1S42.3	3N39.7	1N 7.2	0N30.0	1S 5.6	1N32.1	0S 7.5	1N 1.2	16N37.6
4	10 44 53.6	0 .0	0 .0	1N54.5	3 19.5	0 54.9	0 32.1	1 5.4	1 32.4	0 7.6	1 1.2	16 39.0
7	10 56 43.2	0 .0	0 .0	4 28.1	2 45.9	0 42.7	0 34.0	1 5.3	1 32.7	0 7.6	1 1.3	16 40.3
10	11 8 32.9	0 .0	0 .0	5 13.0	2 5.0	0 30.7	0 35.9	1 5.2	1 32.9	0 7.7	1 1.4	16 41.6
13	11 20 22.5	0 .0	0 .0	3 58.6	1 21.9	0 19.0	0 37.8	1 5.1	1 33.2	0 7.7	1 1.4	16 42.9
16	11 32 12.2	0 .0	0 .0	1 1.8	0 39.8	0 7.6	0 39.5	1 5.1	1 33.5	0 7.8	1 1.5	16 44.0
19	11 44 1.9	0 .0	0 .0	2S32.0	0 .8	0S 3.4	0 41.2	1 5.0	1 33.8	0 7.8	1 1.6	16 45.1
22	11 55 51.5	0 .0	0 .0	4 57.9	0S34.2	0 14.1	0 42.8	1 5.0	1 34.1	0 7.9	1 1.7	16 46.2
25	12 7 41.2	0 .0	0 .0	4 51.3	1 4.8	0 24.2	0 44.4	1 5.0	1 34.4	0 7.9	1 1.8	16 47.2
28	12 19 30.8	0 .0	0 .0	2 10.8	1 30.8	0 33.9	0 45.9	1 5.0	1 34.6	0 8.0	1 1.8	16 48.1
31	12 31 20.5	0 .0	0 .0	1N29.8	1 52.3	0 43.0	0 47.3	1 5.0	1 34.9	0 8.0	1 1.9	16 48.9

RIGHT ASCENSION

DAY	EPHEM. SID. TIME	☉	☊	☽	☿	♀	♂	♃	♄	♅	♆	♇
1	10 33 3.9	11♓24.7	12♈18.0	23♓55.0	7♓35.1	29♑ 6.8	3♉18.1	0♈ 3.4	19♐41.2	25♐58.3	8♑10.7	12♏39.6
2	10 37 .4	12 21.0	12 15.1	6♈11.3	6 R 37.9	0♒20.5	3 57.9	0 16.3	19 44.3	26 .0	8 12.1	12 R 39.2
3	10 40 57.0	13 17.1	12 12.2	18 12.5	5 43.3	1 34.1	4 37.8	0 29.3	19 47.3	26 1.7	8 13.4	12 38.8
4	10 44 53.6	14 13.1	12 9.2	0♉14.1	4 52.5	2 47.6	5 17.8	0 42.3	19 50.2	26 3.3	8 14.7	12 38.3
5	10 48 50.1	15 9.1	12 6.3	12 28.5	4 6.3	4 1.1	5 57.8	0 55.4	19 53.0	26 4.9	8 16.0	12 37.7
6	10 52 46.7	16 4.9	12 3.4	25 4.0	3 25.4	5 14.4	6 37.9	1 8.5	19 55.7	26 6.4	8 17.2	12 37.2
7	10 56 43.2	17 .5	12 .4	8♊ 3.1	2 50.4	6 27.6	7 18.0	1 21.5	19 58.3	26 7.8	8 18.4	12 36.6
8	11 0 39.8	17 56.1	11 57.5	21 21.5	2 21.6	7 40.8	7 58.2	1 34.7	20 .8	26 9.2	8 19.6	12 36.0
9	11 4 36.3	18 51.6	11 54.5	4♋48.7	1 59.2	8 53.8	8 38.5	1 47.8	20 3.3	26 10.5	8 20.7	12 35.4
10	11 8 32.9	19 47.0	11 51.6	18 10.9	1 43.3	10 6.6	9 18.8	2 .9	20 5.6	26 11.8	8 21.8	12 34.7
11	11 12 29.4	20 42.3	11 48.7	1♌14.9	1 33.8	11 19.4	9 59.2	2 14.1	20 7.8	26 13.1	8 22.9	12 34.0
12	11 16 26.0	21 37.5	11 45.7	13 52.2	1 30.5	12 32.0	10 39.6	2 27.3	20 9.8	26 14.2	8 23.9	12 33.3
13	11 20 22.5	22 32.6	11 42.8	26 .9	1 D 33.3	13 44.4	11 20.1	2 40.5	20 11.8	26 15.3	8 24.9	12 32.5
14	11 24 19.1	23 27.6	11 39.8	7♍44.8	1 41.9	14 56.7	12 .7	2 53.7	20 13.7	26 16.4	8 25.9	12 31.7
15	11 28 15.7	24 22.6	11 36.9	19 12.8	1 56.1	16 8.8	12 41.3	3 7.0	20 15.5	26 17.4	8 26.8	12 30.9
16	11 32 12.2	25 17.5	11 34.0	0♎37.0	2 15.5	17 20.8	13 22.0	3 20.2	20 17.2	26 18.3	8 27.7	12 30.1
17	11 36 8.8	26 12.4	11 31.0	12 11.9	2 39.8	18 32.6	14 2.8	3 33.5	20 18.8	26 19.2	8 28.6	12 29.2
18	11 40 5.3	27 7.2	11 28.1	24 13.1	3 8.7	19 44.3	14 43.6	3 46.8	20 20.2	26 20.1	8 29.4	12 28.3
19	11 44 1.9	28 2.0	11 25.2	6♏56.5	3 42.0	20 55.8	15 24.5	4 .1	20 21.6	26 20.8	8 30.2	12 27.4
20	11 47 58.4	28 56.8	11 22.2	20 35.1	4 19.3	22 7.1	16 5.5	4 13.4	20 22.9	26 21.6	8 31.0	12 26.5
21	11 51 55.0	29 51.5	11 19.3	5♐14.5	5 .4	23 18.3	16 46.5	4 26.7	20 24.1	26 22.3	8 31.7	12 25.5
22	11 55 51.5	0♈46.1	11 16.3	20 47.2	5 44.9	24 29.2	17 27.5	4 40.0	20 25.1	26 22.9	8 32.4	12 24.6
23	11 59 48.1	1 40.8	11 13.4	6♑49.8	6 32.7	25 40.0	18 8.7	4 53.4	20 26.1	26 23.4	8 33.1	12 23.5
24	12 3 44.6	2 35.4	11 10.5	22 48.3	7 23.5	26 50.6	18 49.9	5 6.7	20 26.9	26 23.9	8 33.7	12 22.5
25	12 7 41.2	3 30.0	11 7.5	8♒11.2	8 17.2	28 1.1	19 31.1	5 20.0	20 27.6	26 24.4	8 34.3	12 21.4
26	12 11 37.7	4 24.6	11 4.6	22 40.6	9 13.4	29 11.3	20 12.4	5 33.4	20 28.2	26 24.7	8 34.8	12 20.3
27	12 15 34.3	5 19.2	11 1.7	6♓14.6	10 12.1	0♓21.4	20 53.8	5 46.7	20 28.7	26 25.1	8 35.3	12 19.2
28	12 19 30.8	6 13.8	10 58.7	19 2.5	11 13.0	1 31.3	21 35.3	6 .1	20 29.1	26 25.3	8 35.8	12 18.1
29	12 23 27.4	7 8.5	10 55.8	1♈19.2	12 16.1	2 41.0	22 16.8	6 13.4	20 29.4	26 25.5	8 36.3	12 17.0
30	12 27 24.0	8 3.1	10 52.9	13 21.1	13 21.2	3 50.6	22 58.4	6 26.8	20 29.6	26 25.7	8 36.7	12 15.8
31	12 31 20.5	8 57.7	10 49.9	25 23.4	14 28.1	4 59.9	23 40.0	6 40.1	20 29.7	26 25.8	8 37.0	12 14.6

DECLINATION

DAY	EPHEM. SID. TIME	☉	☊	☽	☿	♀	♂	♃	♄	♅	♆	♇
1	10 33 3.9	7S52.2	0N 5.5	4S29.3	5S27.1	19S36.5	13N55.4	1S10.0	21S33.9	23S31.1	22S12.6	1N 2.1
4	10 44 53.6	6 43.5	0 5.5	14N21.0	6 52.1	19 5.5	14 37.9	0 52.9	21 34.3	23 31.2	22 12.3	1 4.0
7	10 56 43.2	5 34.0	0 5.4	26 25.7	8 14.4	18 29.6	15 19.3	0 35.8	21 34.5	23 31.4	22 12.0	1 6.0
10	11 8 32.9	4 23.9	0 5.3	27 38.9	9 23.1	17 49.1	15 59.5	0 18.6	21 34.7	23 31.5	22 11.8	1 7.9
13	11 20 22.5	3 13.3	0 5.3	17 50.3	10 12.8	17 4.0	16 38.5	0 1.4	21 34.8	23 31.7	22 11.5	1 9.9
16	11 32 12.2	2 2.3	0 5.2	0 51.3	10 42.2	16 14.5	17 16.2	0N15.9	21 34.9	23 31.8	22 11.3	1 11.9
19	11 44 1.9	0 51.2	0 5.1	17S16.8	10 51.7	15 20.8	17 52.6	0 33.2	21 34.9	23 31.9	22 11.1	1 14.0
22	11 55 51.5	0N20.0	0 5.1	28 8.9	10 42.6	14 23.2	18 27.6	0 50.5	21 34.8	23 32.0	22 10.9	1 16.0
25	12 7 41.2	1 31.0	0 5.0	23 49.8	10 16.6	13 21.9	19 1.2	1 7.7	21 34.7	23 32.1	22 10.7	1 18.0
28	12 19 30.8	2 41.7	0 4.9	7 4.9	9 35.0	12 17.1	19 33.4	1 25.0	21 34.5	23 32.1	22 10.6	1 20.0
31	12 31 20.5	3 51.9	0 4.9	12N 8.3	8 39.0	11 9.3	20 4.0	1 42.2	21 34.2	23 32.2	22 10.4	1 22.0

APRIL 1987

LONGITUDE

DAY	EPHEM. SID. TIME h m s	☉ ° ′	☊ ° ′	☽ ° ′	☿ ° ′	♀ ° ′	♂ ° ′	♃ ° ′	♄ ° ′	♅ ° ′	♆ ° ′	♇ ° ′
1	12 35 17.1	10♈44.5	11♈43.7	10♉55.5	13♓33.3	3♓58.5	26♉51.3	7♈ 2.3	21♐ 9.7	26♐43.6	7♑58.9	9♏20.4
2	12 39 13.6	11 43.7	11 40.5	23 36.8	14 46.5	5 10.3	27 31.7	7 16.8	21R 9.6	26 43.6	7 59.2	9R18.9
3	12 43 10.2	12 42.9	11 37.3	6♊ 1.5	16 1.8	6 22.1	28 12.0	7 31.3	21 9.3	26R43.5	7 59.5	9 17.5
4	12 47 6.7	13 42.1	11 34.1	18 12.2	17 19.0	7 34.0	28 52.3	7 45.8	21 9.0	26 43.4	7 59.7	9 16.0
5	12 51 3.3	14 41.2	11 30.9	0♋12.7	18 38.2	8 45.9	29 32.5	8 .2	21 8.6	26 43.2	7 59.8	9 14.5
6	12 54 59.8	15 40.3	11 27.8	12 7.2	19 59.2	9 57.8	0♊12.8	8 14.7	21 8.0	26 43.0	7 60.0	9 13.0
7	12 58 56.4	16 39.3	11 24.6	24 .2	21 22.0	11 9.7	0 53.0	8 29.2	21 7.4	26 42.7	8 .1	9 11.5
8	13 2 52.9	17 38.3	11 21.4	5♌56.4	22 46.5	12 21.7	1 33.2	8 43.6	21 6.7	26 42.4	8 .2	9 9.9
9	13 6 49.5	18 37.3	11 18.2	18 .3	24 12.8	13 33.7	2 13.3	8 58.0	21 5.8	26 42.0	8 .2	9 8.4
10	13 10 46.0	19 36.3	11 15.1	0♍16.0	25 40.8	14 45.7	2 53.5	9 12.5	21 5.0	26 41.6	8 .3	9 6.9
11	13 14 42.6	20 35.2	11 11.9	12 47.1	27 10.5	15 57.8	3 33.6	9 26.8	21 3.9	26 41.1	8R .2	9 5.3
12	13 18 39.2	21 34.0	11 8.7	25 35.9	28 41.7	17 9.8	4 13.6	9 41.2	21 2.8	26 40.6	8 .2	9 3.7
13	13 22 35.7	22 32.9	11 5.5	8♎44.0	0♈14.6	18 21.9	4 53.7	9 55.5	21 1.6	26 40.0	8 .1	9 2.1
14	13 26 32.3	23 31.7	11 2.3	22 11.3	1 49.2	19 34.0	5 33.7	10 9.8	21 .3	26 39.4	7 60.0	9 .5
15	13 30 28.8	24 30.4	10 59.2	5♏56.4	3 25.3	20 46.2	6 13.6	10 24.1	20 58.9	26 38.7	7 59.8	8 58.9
16	13 34 25.4	25 29.1	10 56.0	19 56.5	5 3.1	21 58.4	6 53.6	10 38.4	20 57.4	26 37.9	7 59.6	8 57.2
17	13 38 21.9	26 27.8	10 52.8	4♐ 7.7	6 42.4	23 10.5	7 33.5	10 52.7	20 55.8	26 37.2	7 59.4	8 55.6
18	13 42 18.5	27 26.5	10 49.6	18 25.8	8 23.4	24 22.8	8 13.4	11 6.9	20 54.2	26 36.3	7 59.2	8 54.0
19	13 46 15.0	28 25.1	10 46.5	2♑46.3	10 6.0	25 35.0	8 53.2	11 21.1	20 52.4	26 35.5	7 58.9	8 52.3
20	13 50 11.6	29 23.7	10 43.3	17 5.2	11 50.2	26 47.3	9 33.1	11 35.2	20 50.5	26 34.5	7 58.6	8 50.6
21	13 54 8.1	0♉22.3	10 40.1	1♒19.2	13 36.1	27 59.6	10 12.9	11 49.4	20 48.6	26 33.6	7 58.2	8 49.0
22	13 58 4.7	1 20.9	10 36.9	15 25.9	15 23.6	29 11.9	10 52.6	12 3.5	20 46.5	26 32.5	7 57.8	8 47.3
23	14 2 1.3	2 19.4	10 33.8	29 23.7	17 12.7	0♈24.2	11 32.4	12 17.6	20 44.4	26 31.5	7 57.4	8 45.6
24	14 5 57.8	3 17.9	10 30.6	13♓11.4	19 3.5	1 36.6	12 12.1	12 31.6	20 42.2	26 30.4	7 57.0	8 43.9
25	14 9 54.4	4 16.4	10 27.4	26 48.0	20 56.0	2 48.9	12 51.8	12 45.6	20 39.9	26 29.2	7 56.5	8 42.2
26	14 13 50.9	5 14.8	10 24.2	10♈12.8	22 50.1	4 1.3	13 31.5	12 59.6	20 37.5	26 28.0	7 56.0	8 40.5
27	14 17 47.5	6 13.2	10 21.0	23 25.0	24 45.9	5 13.7	14 11.2	13 13.5	20 35.1	26 26.8	7 55.5	8 38.8
28	14 21 44.0	7 11.6	10 17.9	6♉24.1	26 43.3	6 26.2	14 50.8	13 27.4	20 32.5	26 25.5	7 54.9	8 37.1
29	14 25 40.6	8 10.0	10 14.7	19 9.6	28 42.3	7 38.6	15 30.4	13 41.3	20 29.9	26 24.2	7 54.3	8 35.5
30	14 29 37.1	9 8.3	10 11.5	1♊41.6	0♉42.9	8 51.0	16 10.0	13 55.1	20 27.2	26 22.8	7 53.7	8 33.8

LATITUDE

DAY	EPHEM. SID. TIME	☉	☊	☽	☿	♀	♂	♃	♄	♅	♆	♇
1	12 35 17.1	0 .0	0 .0	2N36.0	1S58.4	0S45.9	0N47.8	1S 5.0	1N35.0	0S 8.0	1N 1.9	16N49.1
4	12 47 6.7	0 .0	0 .0	4 51.1	2 13.8	0 54.3	0 49.1	1 5.1	1 35.3	0 8.1	1 2.0	16 49.9
7	12 58 56.4	0 .0	0 .0	5 9.3	2 24.6	1 2.0	0 50.4	1 5.2	1 35.5	0 8.1	1 2.1	16 50.5
10	13 10 46.0	0 .0	0 .0	3 29.1	2 30.8	1 9.1	0 51.7	1 5.3	1 35.8	0 8.2	1 2.2	16 51.0
13	13 22 35.7	0 .0	0 .0	0 15.6	2 32.5	1 15.6	0 52.9	1 5.4	1 36.0	0 8.2	1 2.2	16 51.5
16	13 34 25.4	0 .0	0 .0	3S16.4	2 29.5	1 21.3	0 54.0	1 5.5	1 36.3	0 8.3	1 2.3	16 51.9
19	13 46 15.0	0 .0	0 .0	5 11.6	2 22.0	1 26.4	0 55.1	1 5.6	1 36.5	0 8.3	1 2.4	16 52.1
22	13 58 4.7	0 .0	0 .0	4 21.4	2 9.8	1 30.7	0 56.1	1 5.8	1 36.7	0 8.4	1 2.5	16 52.3
25	14 9 54.4	0 .0	0 .0	1 19.9	1 53.1	1 34.4	0 57.1	1 6.0	1 36.9	0 8.4	1 2.5	16 52.4
28	14 21 44.0	0 .0	0 .0	2N12.5	1 32.1	1 37.3	0 58.1	1 6.2	1 37.0	0 8.5	1 2.6	16 52.4

RIGHT ASCENSION

DAY	EPHEM. SID. TIME	☉	☊	☽	☿	♀	♂	♃	♄	♅	♆	♇
1	12 35 17.1	9♈52.4	10♈47.0	7♉39.0	15♓36.8	6♓ 9.1	24♉21.7	6♈53.4	20♐29.6	26♐25.8	8♑37.4	12♏13.4
2	12 39 13.6	10 47.0	10 44.1	20 16.5	16 47.2	7 18.2	25 3.5	7 6.8	20R29.5	26 25.8	8 37.7	12R12.1
3	12 43 10.2	11 41.7	10 41.1	3♊18.7	17 59.1	8 27.0	25 45.3	7 20.1	20 29.3	26R25.7	8 37.9	12 10.9
4	12 47 6.7	12 36.5	10 38.2	16 41.6	19 12.6	9 35.7	26 27.2	7 33.4	20 28.9	26 25.5	8 38.2	12 9.6
5	12 51 3.3	13 31.2	10 35.3	0♋14.5	20 27.5	10 44.3	27 9.1	7 46.8	20 28.4	26 25.3	8 38.3	12 8.3
6	12 54 59.8	14 26.0	10 32.3	13 43.0	21 43.8	11 52.7	27 51.1	8 .1	20 27.9	26 25.1	8 38.5	12 7.0
7	12 58 56.4	15 20.9	10 29.4	26 53.3	23 1.4	13 1.0	28 33.1	8 13.4	20 27.2	26 24.8	8 38.6	12 5.7
8	13 2 52.9	16 15.8	10 26.5	9♌36.4	24 20.3	14 9.1	29 15.2	8 26.7	20 26.4	26 24.4	8 38.7	12 4.4
9	13 6 49.5	17 10.7	10 23.5	21 49.6	25 40.6	15 17.1	29 57.4	8 39.9	20 25.5	26 24.0	8 38.7	12 3.0
10	13 10 46.0	18 5.8	10 20.6	3♍36.9	27 2.1	16 25.0	0♊39.6	8 53.2	20 24.6	26 23.6	8 38.8	12 1.7
11	13 14 42.6	19 .8	10 17.7	15 7.0	28 24.9	17 32.7	1 21.8	9 6.5	20 23.5	26 23.0	8 38.8	12 .3
12	13 18 39.2	19 56.0	10 14.7	26 32.3	29 48.9	18 40.3	2 4.1	9 19.7	20 22.3	26 22.5	8R38.7	11 58.9
13	13 22 35.7	20 51.2	10 11.8	8♎ 7.5	1♈14.1	19 47.8	2 46.4	9 32.9	20 21.0	26 21.8	8 38.6	11 57.5
14	13 26 32.3	21 46.4	10 8.9	20 8.8	2 40.6	20 55.3	3 28.8	9 46.1	20 19.6	26 21.1	8 38.5	11 56.1
15	13 30 28.8	22 41.8	10 5.9	2♏52.7	4 8.4	22 2.6	4 11.2	9 59.3	20 18.1	26 20.4	8 38.3	11 54.6
16	13 34 25.4	23 37.2	10 3.0	16 33.2	5 37.4	23 9.8	4 53.7	10 12.5	20 16.5	26 19.6	8 38.1	11 53.2
17	13 38 21.9	24 32.8	10 .1	1♐16.9	7 7.8	24 17.0	5 36.2	10 25.6	20 14.9	26 18.7	8 37.9	11 51.7
18	13 42 18.5	25 28.4	9 57.1	16 56.9	8 39.6	25 24.1	6 18.7	10 38.8	20 13.1	26 17.8	8 37.6	11 50.2
19	13 46 15.0	26 24.1	9 54.2	3♑ 8.7	10 12.7	26 31.1	7 1.3	10 51.9	20 11.2	26 16.9	8 37.3	11 48.7
20	13 50 11.6	27 20.0	9 51.3	19 16.0	11 47.2	27 38.1	7 43.9	11 5.0	20 9.2	26 15.9	8 37.0	11 47.3
21	13 54 8.1	28 15.9	9 48.3	4♒44.9	13 23.2	28 45.1	8 26.6	11 18.0	20 7.1	26 14.8	8 36.6	11 45.8
22	13 58 4.7	29 12.0	9 45.4	19 16.0	15 .8	29 52.0	9 9.3	11 31.1	20 4.9	26 13.7	8 36.2	11 44.2
23	14 2 1.3	0♉ 8.1	9 42.5	2♓47.2	16 39.9	0♈58.8	9 52.0	11 44.1	20 2.7	26 12.5	8 35.7	11 42.7
24	14 5 57.8	1 4.4	9 39.5	15 28.4	18 20.6	2 5.7	10 34.8	11 57.1	20 .3	26 11.3	8 35.3	11 41.2
25	14 9 54.4	2 .8	9 36.6	27 35.6	20 3.0	3 12.5	11 17.6	12 10.0	19 57.8	26 10.1	8 34.7	11 39.7
26	14 13 50.9	2 57.4	9 33.7	9♈25.9	21 47.2	4 19.3	12 .4	12 22.9	19 55.3	26 8.8	8 34.2	11 38.1
27	14 17 47.5	3 54.0	9 30.8	21 15.8	23 33.2	5 26.2	12 43.3	12 35.8	19 52.6	26 7.4	8 33.6	11 36.6
28	14 21 44.0	4 50.8	9 27.8	3♉19.2	25 21.1	6 33.0	13 26.1	12 48.7	19 49.9	26 6.0	8 33.0	11 35.0
29	14 25 40.6	5 47.7	9 24.9	15 46.4	27 10.8	7 39.9	14 9.1	13 1.5	19 47.1	26 4.6	8 32.4	11 33.5
30	14 29 37.1	6 44.7	9 22.0	28 41.9	29 2.5	8 46.8	14 52.0	13 14.3	19 44.2	26 3.1	8 31.7	11 31.9

DECLINATION

DAY	EPHEM. SID. TIME	☉	☊	☽	☿	♀	♂	♃	♄	♅	♆	♇
1	12 35 17.1	4N15.1	0N 4.9	17N34.5	8S17.3	10S46.0	20N13.9	1N47.9	21S34.1	23S32.2	22S10.4	1N22.7
4	12 47 6.7	5 24.4	0 4.8	27 45.1	7 3.8	9 34.3	20 42.6	2 5.0	21 33.8	23 32.3	22 10.2	1 24.7
7	12 58 56.4	6 32.9	0 4.7	26 23.1	5 38.3	8 20.2	21 9.7	2 22.1	21 33.4	23 32.3	22 10.1	1 26.6
10	13 10 46.0	7 40.3	0 4.7	14 38.3	4 1.4	7 3.9	21 35.1	2 39.0	21 33.0	23 32.3	22 10.0	1 28.5
13	13 22 35.7	8 46.5	0 4.6	3S13.5	2 14.0	5 45.6	21 59.0	2 55.8	21 32.6	23 32.3	22 10.0	1 30.3
16	13 34 25.4	9 51.4	0 4.5	20 52.8	0 16.8	4 25.8	22 21.1	3 12.5	21 32.1	23 32.3	22 9.9	1 32.1
19	13 46 15.0	10 54.8	0 4.5	28 36.4	1N49.4	3 4.6	22 41.6	3 29.1	21 31.5	23 32.3	22 9.9	1 33.8
22	13 58 4.7	11 56.7	0 4.4	20 22.2	4 3.9	1 42.4	23 .4	3 45.5	21 30.9	23 32.3	22 9.9	1 35.5
25	14 9 54.4	12 56.8	0 4.3	2 29.6	6 25.4	0 19.4	23 17.4	4 1.7	21 30.2	23 32.2	22 9.9	1 37.1
28	14 21 44.0	13 55.0	0 4.3	15N44.4	8 52.4	1N 4.0	23 32.7	4 17.7	21 29.6	23 32.2	22 9.9	1 38.6

MAY 1987

LONGITUDE

DAY	EPHEM. SID. TIME h m s	☉ ° ′	☊ ° ′	☽ ° ′	☿ ° ′	♀ ° ′	♂ ° ′	♃ ° ′	♄ ° ′	♅ ° ′	♆ ° ′	♇ ° ′
1	14 33 33.7	10♉ 6.6	10♈ 8.3	14♊ 1.1	2♉45.1	10♈ 3.5	16♊49.6	14♈ 8.9	20♐24.4	26♐21.4	7♑53.1	8♏32.1
2	14 37 30.3	11 4.9	10 5.2	26 9.3	4 48.7	11 16.0	17 29.2	14 22.6	20 R 21.6	26 R 20.0	7 R 52.4	8 R 30.4
3	14 41 26.8	12 3.1	10 2.0	8♋ 8.9	6 53.7	12 28.5	18 8.7	14 36.3	20 18.6	26 18.5	7 51.7	8 28.7
4	14 45 23.4	13 1.3	9 58.8	20 2.9	9 .0	13 41.0	18 48.2	14 50.0	20 15.6	26 16.9	7 51.0	8 27.0
5	14 49 19.9	13 59.5	9 55.6	1♌55.1	11 7.5	14 53.5	19 27.6	15 3.5	20 12.5	26 15.4	7 50.2	8 25.3
6	14 53 16.5	14 57.6	9 52.4	13 50.1	13 15.9	16 6.0	20 7.1	15 17.1	20 9.4	26 13.8	7 49.4	8 23.6
7	14 57 13.0	15 55.7	9 49.3	25 52.6	15 25.2	17 18.5	20 46.5	15 30.6	20 6.2	26 12.1	7 48.6	8 22.0
8	15 1 9.6	16 53.8	9 46.1	8♍ 7.3	17 35.1	18 31.1	21 25.9	15 44.0	20 2.9	26 10.4	7 47.7	8 20.3
9	15 5 6.1	17 51.8	9 42.9	20 39.0	19 45.5	19 43.6	22 5.2	15 57.4	19 59.5	26 8.7	7 46.8	8 18.6
10	15 9 2.7	18 49.8	9 39.7	3♎31.6	21 55.9	20 56.2	22 44.5	16 10.7	19 56.1	26 6.9	7 45.9	8 17.0
11	15 12 59.3	19 47.8	9 36.6	16 47.8	24 6.3	22 8.7	23 23.8	16 24.0	19 52.6	26 5.2	7 45.0	8 15.3
12	15 16 55.8	20 45.7	9 33.4	0♏28.8	26 16.2	23 21.3	24 3.1	16 37.2	19 49.1	26 3.3	7 44.1	8 13.7
13	15 20 52.4	21 43.7	9 30.2	14 33.4	28 25.4	24 33.9	24 42.4	16 50.4	19 45.5	26 1.5	7 43.1	8 12.0
14	15 24 48.9	22 41.5	9 27.0	28 58.2	0♊33.7	25 46.5	25 21.6	17 3.5	19 41.8	25 59.6	7 42.1	8 10.4
15	15 28 45.5	23 39.4	9 23.9	13♐37.1	2 40.7	26 59.1	26 .8	17 16.5	19 38.1	25 57.7	7 41.0	8 8.8
16	15 32 42.0	24 37.2	9 20.7	28 23.0	4 46.2	28 11.8	26 40.0	17 29.5	19 34.3	25 55.7	7 40.0	8 7.2
17	15 36 38.6	25 35.1	9 17.5	13♑ 8.0	6 49.9	29 24.4	27 19.1	17 42.4	19 30.5	25 53.7	7 38.9	8 5.6
18	15 40 35.2	26 32.9	9 14.3	27 45.0	8 51.6	0♉37.1	27 58.3	17 55.3	19 26.6	25 51.7	7 37.8	8 4.0
19	15 44 31.7	27 30.6	9 11.1	12♒ 8.8	10 51.0	1 49.7	28 37.4	18 8.1	19 22.7	25 49.7	7 36.7	8 2.4
20	15 48 28.3	28 28.4	9 8.0	26 16.4	12 48.2	3 2.4	29 16.5	18 20.8	19 18.7	25 47.6	7 35.5	8 .8
21	15 52 24.8	29 26.2	9 4.8	10♓ 6.4	14 42.7	4 15.1	29 55.5	18 33.5	19 14.7	25 45.5	7 34.4	7 59.3
22	15 56 21.4	0♊23.9	9 1.6	23 39.5	16 34.7	5 27.9	0♋34.6	18 46.1	19 10.7	25 43.4	7 33.2	7 57.8
23	16 0 17.9	1 21.6	8 58.4	6♈56.7	18 23.9	6 40.6	1 13.7	18 58.6	19 6.6	25 41.3	7 32.0	7 56.3
24	16 4 14.5	2 19.3	8 55.3	19 59.8	20 10.2	7 53.4	1 52.7	19 11.1	19 2.5	25 39.1	7 30.8	7 54.7
25	16 8 11.1	3 17.0	8 52.1	2♉50.3	21 53.5	9 6.2	2 31.7	19 23.5	18 58.3	25 36.9	7 29.5	7 53.3
26	16 12 7.6	4 14.7	8 48.9	15 29.4	23 33.9	10 18.9	3 10.7	19 35.8	18 54.1	25 34.7	7 28.2	7 51.8
27	16 16 4.2	5 12.3	8 45.7	27 58.2	25 11.3	11 31.7	3 49.6	19 48.0	18 49.9	25 32.5	7 26.9	7 50.3
28	16 20 .7	6 9.9	8 42.6	10♊17.3	26 45.6	12 44.5	4 28.5	20 .1	18 45.6	25 30.2	7 25.6	7 48.9
29	16 23 57.3	7 7.5	8 39.4	22 27.6	28 16.8	13 57.3	5 7.5	20 12.2	18 41.3	25 27.9	7 24.3	7 47.5
30	16 27 53.9	8 5.1	8 36.2	4♋30.0	29 44.8	15 10.1	5 46.4	20 24.2	18 37.0	25 25.6	7 22.9	7 46.0
31	16 31 50.4	9 2.6	8 33.0	16 26.1	1♋ 9.6	16 22.9	6 25.2	20 36.1	18 32.6	25 23.3	7 21.6	7 44.7

LATITUDE

DAY	SID. TIME	☉	☊	☽	☿	♀	♂	♃	♄	♅	♆	♇
1	14 33 33.7	0 .0	0 .0	4N37.7	1S 7.0	1S39.5	0N59.0	1S 6.4	1N37.2	0S 8.5	1N 2.7	16N52.3
4	14 45 23.4	0 .0	0 .0	5 8.1	0 38.5	1 41.0	0 59.9	1 6.6	1 37.3	0 8.6	1 2.7	16 52.1
7	14 57 13.0	0 .0	0 .0	3 41.3	0 7.7	1 41.8	1 .7	1 6.9	1 37.4	0 8.6	1 2.8	16 51.9
10	15 9 2.7	0 .0	0 .0	0 40.8	0N23.9	1 41.9	1 1.4	1 7.2	1 37.5	0 8.7	1 2.9	16 51.5
13	15 20 52.4	0 .0	0 .0	2S51.5	0 54.6	1 41.4	1 2.2	1 7.5	1 37.6	0 8.7	1 2.9	16 51.0
16	15 32 42.0	0 .0	0 .0	5 1.2	1 22.2	1 40.2	1 2.9	1 7.8	1 37.6	0 8.7	1 3.0	16 50.5
19	15 44 31.7	0 .0	0 .0	4 22.5	1 45.1	1 38.3	1 3.5	1 8.1	1 37.6	0 8.8	1 3.0	16 49.8
22	15 56 21.4	0 .0	0 .0	1 29.2	2 1.9	1 35.8	1 4.1	1 8.5	1 37.6	0 8.8	1 3.0	16 49.1
25	16 8 11.1	0 .0	0 .0	1N57.1	2 11.8	1 32.8	1 4.7	1 8.8	1 37.5	0 8.9	1 3.1	16 48.3
28	16 20 .7	0 .0	0 .0	4 24.3	2 14.5	1 29.1	1 5.3	1 9.2	1 37.5	0 8.9	1 3.1	16 47.4
31	16 31 50.4	0 .0	0 .0	5 1.6	2 9.8	1 25.0	1 5.8	1 9.6	1 37.4	0 8.9	1 3.1	16 46.5

RIGHT ASCENSION

DAY	SID. TIME	☉	☊	☽	☿	♀	♂	♃	♄	♅	♆	♇
1	14 33 33.7	7♉41.9	9♈19.0	12♊ 2.8	0♉56.3	9♈53.7	15♊35.0	13♈27.2	19♐41.3	26♐ 1.6	8♑31.0	11♏30.4
2	14 37 30.3	8 39.2	9 16.1	25 38.7	2 51.9	11 .7	16 18.0	13 39.9	19 R 38.2	25 R 60.0	8 R 30.3	11 R 28.9
3	14 41 26.8	9 36.7	9 13.2	9♋13.9	4 49.6	12 7.7	17 1.0	13 52.6	19 35.1	25 58.4	8 29.5	11 27.3
4	14 45 23.4	10 34.2	9 10.2	22 32.2	6 49.3	13 14.8	17 44.0	14 5.2	19 31.8	25 56.7	8 28.7	11 25.7
5	14 49 19.9	11 31.9	9 7.3	5♌21.9	8 50.9	14 21.9	18 27.0	14 17.8	19 28.5	25 55.0	8 27.9	11 24.2
6	14 53 16.5	12 29.7	9 4.4	17 38.8	10 54.4	15 29.1	19 10.0	14 30.4	19 25.2	25 53.2	8 27.0	11 22.6
7	14 57 13.0	13 27.7	9 1.5	29 25.7	12 59.6	16 36.4	19 53.0	14 42.9	19 21.7	25 51.4	8 26.2	11 21.1
8	15 1 9.6	14 25.8	8 58.5	10♍51.1	15 6.4	17 43.9	20 36.1	14 55.4	19 18.2	25 49.6	8 25.2	11 19.5
9	15 5 6.1	15 24.0	8 55.6	22 7.5	17 14.7	18 51.4	21 19.1	15 7.9	19 14.6	25 47.7	8 24.3	11 17.9
10	15 9 2.7	16 22.4	8 52.7	3♎30.4	19 24.3	19 59.0	22 2.1	15 20.2	19 10.9	25 45.8	8 23.3	11 16.4
11	15 12 59.3	17 20.9	8 49.8	15 16.7	21 34.9	21 6.7	22 45.2	15 32.6	19 7.2	25 43.8	8 22.3	11 14.8
12	15 16 55.8	18 19.6	8 46.8	27 44.9	23 46.2	22 14.6	23 28.2	15 44.9	19 3.4	25 41.8	8 21.3	11 13.3
13	15 20 52.4	19 18.4	8 43.9	11♏12.2	25 57.9	23 22.6	24 11.2	15 57.1	18 59.5	25 39.8	8 20.2	11 11.8
14	15 24 48.9	20 17.3	8 41.0	25 50.0	28 9.8	24 30.8	24 54.3	16 9.3	18 55.6	25 37.7	8 19.1	11 10.2
15	15 28 45.5	21 16.4	8 38.0	11♐36.7	0♊21.5	25 39.1	25 37.3	16 21.5	18 51.6	25 35.6	8 18.0	11 8.7
16	15 32 42.0	22 15.6	8 35.1	28 10.1	2 32.7	26 47.6	26 20.3	16 33.6	18 47.6	25 33.5	8 16.9	11 7.2
17	15 36 38.6	23 15.0	8 32.2	14♑50.2	4 43.0	27 56.3	27 3.3	16 45.6	18 43.5	25 31.3	8 15.7	11 5.6
18	15 40 35.2	24 14.5	8 29.3	0♒54.4	6 52.2	29 5.2	27 46.2	16 57.6	18 39.4	25 29.2	8 14.5	11 4.1
19	15 44 31.7	25 14.1	8 26.3	15 55.3	8 60.0	0♉14.2	28 29.2	17 9.6	18 35.2	25 26.9	8 13.3	11 2.6
20	15 48 28.3	26 13.9	8 23.4	29 46.7	11 6.0	1 23.5	29 12.2	17 21.5	18 30.9	25 24.7	8 12.1	11 1.1
21	15 52 24.8	27 13.9	8 20.5	12♓37.9	13 10.0	2 32.9	29 55.1	17 33.3	18 26.6	25 22.4	8 10.8	10 59.6
22	15 56 21.4	28 14.0	8 17.6	24 46.1	15 11.8	3 42.7	0♋38.1	17 45.1	18 22.4	25 20.1	8 9.6	10 58.2
23	16 0 17.9	29 14.2	8 14.6	6♈30.1	17 11.1	4 52.5	1 21.0	17 56.8	18 18.0	25 17.8	8 8.3	10 56.7
24	16 4 14.5	0♊14.6	8 11.7	18 8.3	19 7.7	6 2.7	2 3.8	18 8.4	18 13.5	25 15.4	8 6.9	10 55.3
25	16 8 11.1	1 15.1	8 8.8	29 56.5	21 1.5	7 13.0	2 46.7	18 20.0	18 9.1	25 13.0	8 5.6	10 53.8
26	16 12 7.6	2 15.7	8 5.9	12♉ 7.2	22 52.4	8 23.6	3 29.5	18 31.5	18 4.6	25 10.6	8 4.2	10 52.4
27	16 16 4.2	3 16.4	8 2.9	24 47.5	24 40.0	9 34.4	4 12.3	18 43.0	18 .0	25 8.2	8 2.8	10 51.0
28	16 20 .7	4 17.3	8 .0	7♊57.5	26 24.5	10 45.5	4 55.0	18 54.4	17 55.5	25 5.7	8 1.4	10 49.6
29	16 23 57.3	5 18.2	7 57.1	21 28.8	28 5.5	11 56.8	5 37.7	19 5.7	17 50.9	25 3.2	7 60.0	10 48.2
30	16 27 53.9	6 19.3	7 54.2	5♋ 5.9	29 43.1	13 8.3	6 20.4	19 16.9	17 46.3	25 .7	7 58.5	10 46.8
31	16 31 50.4	7 20.5	7 51.2	18 30.8	1♋17.1	14 20.2	7 3.1	19 28.1	17 41.6	24 58.2	7 57.0	10 45.4

DECLINATION

DAY	SID. TIME	☉	☊	☽	☿	♀	♂	♃	♄	♅	♆	♇
1	14 33 33.7	14N51.1	0N 4.2	27N 4.9	11N22.8	2N27.6	23N46.2	4N33.6	21S28.8	23S32.1	22S10.0	1N40.0
4	14 45 23.4	15 45.0	0 4.1	27 1.4	13 53.5	3 50.9	23 57.9	4 49.3	21 28.1	23 32.0	22 10.0	1 41.4
7	14 57 13.0	16 36.5	0 4.1	16 21.8	16 20.3	5 13.8	24 7.9	5 4.7	21 27.3	23 31.9	22 10.1	1 42.6
10	15 9 2.7	17 25.6	0 4.0	0S46.7	18 38.3	6 35.9	24 16.0	5 19.8	21 26.5	23 31.8	22 10.2	1 43.8
13	15 20 52.4	18 12.0	0 3.9	18 56.2	20 42.0	7 56.9	24 22.4	5 34.8	21 25.6	23 31.7	22 10.3	1 44.8
16	15 32 42.0	18 55.7	0 3.9	28 27.2	22 26.4	9 16.5	24 26.9	5 49.4	21 24.7	23 31.6	22 10.4	1 45.7
19	15 44 31.7	19 36.4	0 3.8	21 21.1	23 48.6	10 34.4	24 29.7	6 3.8	21 23.8	23 31.4	22 10.6	1 46.6
22	15 56 21.4	20 14.3	0 3.7	3 53.0	24 47.3	11 50.4	24 30.7	6 17.9	21 22.9	23 31.3	22 10.7	1 47.3
25	16 8 11.1	20 49.0	0 3.7	14N17.5	25 23.3	13 4.0	24 29.8	6 31.7	21 21.9	23 31.1	22 10.9	1 47.9
28	16 20 .7	21 20.4	0 3.6	26 21.2	25 38.7	14 14.9	24 27.3	6 45.1	21 20.9	23 30.9	22 11.1	1 48.3
31	16 31 50.4	21 48.6	0 3.6	27 25.2	25 36.1	15 22.9	24 22.9	6 58.3	21 19.9	23 30.7	22 11.3	1 48.7

LONGITUDE

DAY	EPHEM. SID. TIME (h m s)	☉	☊	☽	☿	♀	♂	♃	♄	♅	♆	♇
1	16 35 47.0	10♊.2	8♈29.9	28♋18.2	2♋31.2	17♉35.8	7♋4.1	20♈47.9	18♐28.3	25♐21.0	7♑20.2	7♏43.3
2	16 39 43.5	10 57.7	8 26.7	10♌9.0	3 49.6	18 48.6	7 42.9	20 59.6	18R23.9	25R18.6	7R18.8	7R41.9
3	16 43 40.1	11 55.2	8 23.5	22 2.3	5 4.6	20 1.4	8 21.8	21 11.3	18 19.5	25 16.3	7 17.4	7 40.6
4	16 47 36.6	12 52.6	8 20.3	4♍2.6	6 16.3	21 14.3	9 .6	21 22.8	18 15.1	25 13.9	7 15.9	7 39.3
5	16 51 33.2	13 50.1	8 17.1	16 14.6	7 24.5	22 27.2	9 39.3	21 34.3	18 10.7	25 11.5	7 14.5	7 38.0
6	16 55 29.8	14 47.5	8 14.0	28 43.3	8 29.3	23 40.0	10 18.1	21 45.7	18 6.2	25 9.1	7 13.0	7 36.8
7	16 59 26.3	15 44.9	8 10.8	11♎33.8	9 30.5	24 52.9	10 56.8	21 57.0	18 1.8	25 6.7	7 11.6	7 35.5
8	17 3 22.9	16 42.3	8 7.6	24 50.0	10 28.1	26 5.8	11 35.6	22 8.2	17 57.4	25 4.3	7 10.1	7 34.3
9	17 7 19.4	17 39.7	8 4.4	8♏34.5	11 22.0	27 18.7	12 14.3	22 19.2	17 52.9	25 1.9	7 8.6	7 33.1
10	17 11 16.0	18 37.1	8 1.3	22 47.4	12 12.2	28 31.7	12 52.9	22 30.2	17 48.5	24 59.4	7 7.1	7 31.9
11	17 15 12.6	19 34.4	7 58.1	7♐25.7	12 58.4	29 44.6	13 31.6	22 41.1	17 44.0	24 57.0	7 5.6	7 30.8
12	17 19 9.1	20 31.8	7 54.9	22 23.3	13 40.7	0♊57.6	14 10.3	22 52.0	17 39.6	24 54.6	7 4.1	7 29.7
13	17 23 5.7	21 29.1	7 51.7	7♑31.0	14 18.9	2 10.6	14 48.9	23 2.7	17 35.2	24 52.2	7 2.5	7 28.6
14	17 27 2.2	22 26.4	7 48.6	22 38.5	14 53.0	3 23.5	15 27.5	23 13.3	17 30.8	24 49.7	7 1.0	7 27.6
15	17 30 58.8	23 23.7	7 45.4	7♒36.0	15 22.8	4 36.5	16 6.1	23 23.8	17 26.4	24 47.3	6 59.4	7 26.5
16	17 34 55.4	24 21.0	7 42.2	22 15.6	15 48.3	5 49.5	16 44.7	23 34.2	17 22.0	24 44.8	6 57.9	7 25.5
17	17 38 51.9	25 18.3	7 39.0	6♓32.8	16 9.4	7 2.6	17 23.3	23 44.5	17 17.6	24 42.3	6 56.3	7 24.5
18	17 42 48.5	26 15.5	7 35.9	20 25.8	16 26.0	8 15.6	18 1.8	23 54.7	17 13.2	24 39.9	6 54.7	7 23.6
19	17 46 45.0	27 12.8	7 32.7	3♈55.5	16 38.1	9 28.7	18 40.4	24 4.7	17 8.9	24 37.4	6 53.1	7 22.6
20	17 50 41.6	28 10.1	7 29.5	17 4.1	16 45.6	10 41.8	19 18.9	24 14.7	17 4.5	24 35.0	6 51.5	7 21.7
21	17 54 38.1	29 7.3	7 26.3	29 54.8	16 48.6	11 54.9	19 57.4	24 24.5	17 .2	24 32.5	6 49.9	7 20.8
22	17 58 34.7	0♋4.6	7 23.2	12♉30.9	16R47.0	13 8.0	20 35.9	24 34.2	16 56.0	24 30.1	6 48.3	7 20.0
23	18 2 31.3	1 1.9	7 20.0	24 55.1	16 41.0	14 21.1	21 14.4	24 43.8	16 51.7	24 27.6	6 46.7	7 19.2
24	18 6 27.8	1 59.1	7 16.8	7♊9.9	16 30.5	15 34.3	21 52.9	24 53.3	16 47.5	24 25.2	6 45.1	7 18.4
25	18 10 24.4	2 56.4	7 13.6	19 17.2	16 15.9	16 47.5	22 31.4	25 2.7	16 43.3	24 22.8	6 43.5	7 17.6
26	18 14 20.9	3 53.6	7 10.4	1♋18.3	15 57.3	18 .6	23 9.8	25 11.9	16 39.1	24 20.4	6 41.8	7 16.9
27	18 18 17.5	4 50.9	7 7.3	13 14.6	15 34.9	19 13.8	23 48.3	25 21.1	16 35.0	24 18.0	6 40.2	7 16.2
28	18 22 14.1	5 48.1	7 4.1	25 7.2	15 9.0	20 27.1	24 26.7	25 30.1	16 30.9	24 15.6	6 38.6	7 15.5
29	18 26 10.6	6 45.3	7 .9	6♌57.8	14 40.1	21 40.3	25 5.1	25 38.9	16 26.9	24 13.2	6 37.0	7 14.8
30	18 30 7.2	7 42.5	6 57.7	18 48.6	14 8.6	22 53.5	25 43.5	25 47.7	16 22.9	24 10.8	6 35.4	7 14.2

LATITUDE

DAY	SID. TIME	☉	☊	☽	☿	♀	♂	♃	♄	♅	♆	♇
1	16 35 47.0	0 .0	0 .0	4N47.6	2N 6.6	1 S23.5	1N 5.9	1 S 9.8	1N37.3	0 S 9.0	1N 3.1	16N46.1
4	16 47 36.6	0 .0	0 .0	2 55.7	1 52.2	1 18.7	1 6.4	1 10.2	1 37.2	0 9.0	1 3.2	16 45.0
7	16 59 26.3	0 .0	0 .0	0S12.7	1 30.6	1 13.5	1 6.8	1 10.7	1 37.0	0 9.1	1 3.2	16 43.9
10	17 11 16.0	0 .0	0 .0	3 29.5	1 2.1	1 7.8	1 7.2	1 11.2	1 36.8	0 9.1	1 3.2	16 42.7
13	17 23 5.7	0 .0	0 .0	5 1.3	0 27.1	1 1.8	1 7.5	1 11.6	1 36.6	0 9.1	1 3.2	16 41.4
16	17 34 55.4	0 .0	0 .0	3 37.3	0S13.7	0 55.4	1 7.9	1 12.2	1 36.3	0 9.1	1 3.2	16 40.1
19	17 46 45.0	0 .0	0 .0	0 22.2	0 59.3	0 48.8	1 8.2	1 12.7	1 36.0	0 9.2	1 3.2	16 38.7
22	17 58 34.7	0 .0	0 .0	2N50.9	1 47.8	0 41.9	1 8.4	1 13.2	1 35.7	0 9.2	1 3.2	16 37.3
25	18 10 24.4	0 .0	0 .0	4 44.6	2 36.9	0 34.8	1 8.7	1 13.8	1 35.4	0 9.2	1 3.2	16 35.8
28	18 22 14.1	0 .0	0 .0	4 44.6	3 23.2	0 27.6	1 8.9	1 14.4	1 35.0	0 9.2	1 3.1	16 34.2

RIGHT ASCENSION

DAY	SID. TIME	☉	☊	☽	☿	♀	♂	♃	♄	♅	♆	♇
1	16 35 47.0	8♊21.8	7♈48.3	1♌28.6	2♋47.5	15♉32.2	7♋45.7	19♈39.2	17♐36.9	24♐55.7	7♑55.5	10♏44.1
2	16 39 43.5	9 23.2	7 45.4	13 51.6	4 14.1	16 44.6	8 28.2	19 50.2	17R32.3	24R53.1	7R54.0	10R42.8
3	16 43 40.1	10 24.7	7 42.5	25 40.2	5 36.8	17 57.2	9 10.8	20 1.1	17 27.6	24 50.5	7 52.5	10 41.4
4	16 47 36.6	11 26.3	7 39.5	7♍1.4	6 55.7	19 10.1	9 53.2	20 12.0	17 22.8	24 47.9	7 51.0	10 40.1
5	16 51 33.2	12 28.0	7 36.6	18 7.0	8 10.5	20 23.2	10 35.6	20 22.7	17 18.1	24 45.3	7 49.4	10 38.8
6	16 55 29.8	13 29.7	7 33.7	29 11.7	9 21.3	21 36.7	11 18.0	20 33.4	17 13.4	24 42.7	7 47.8	10 37.6
7	16 59 26.3	14 31.6	7 30.8	10♎32.9	10 27.9	22 50.4	12 .3	20 44.1	17 8.6	24 40.1	7 46.2	10 36.3
8	17 3 22.9	15 33.4	7 27.8	22 29.6	11 30.3	24 4.3	12 42.6	20 54.6	17 3.9	24 37.5	7 44.6	10 35.1
9	17 7 19.4	16 35.4	7 24.9	5♏21.6	12 28.3	25 18.6	13 24.8	21 5.0	16 59.1	24 34.8	7 43.0	10 33.9
10	17 11 16.0	17 37.4	7 22.0	19 26.0	13 22.0	26 33.1	14 6.9	21 15.4	16 54.4	24 32.2	7 41.4	10 32.7
11	17 15 12.6	18 39.5	7 19.1	4♐50.6	14 11.2	27 47.9	14 49.0	21 25.7	16 49.6	24 29.5	7 39.8	10 31.5
12	17 19 9.1	19 41.7	7 16.1	21 24.0	14 55.8	29 3.2	15 31.1	21 35.9	16 44.9	24 26.9	7 38.2	10 30.4
13	17 23 5.7	20 43.9	7 13.2	8♑30.4	15 35.8	0♊18.4	16 13.1	21 46.0	16 40.2	24 24.2	7 36.5	10 29.3
14	17 27 2.2	21 46.1	7 10.3	25 20.6	16 11.0	1 34.0	16 55.0	21 56.0	16 35.4	24 21.6	7 34.8	10 28.2
15	17 30 58.8	22 48.4	7 7.4	11♒13.4	16 41.5	2 49.9	17 36.8	22 5.9	16 30.7	24 18.9	7 33.1	10 27.1
16	17 34 55.4	23 50.7	7 4.5	25 51.1	17 7.1	4 6.1	18 18.6	22 15.7	16 26.0	24 16.2	7 31.4	10 26.0
17	17 38 51.9	24 53.0	7 1.5	9♓17.6	17 27.8	5 22.5	19 .3	22 25.5	16 21.3	24 13.5	7 29.8	10 25.0
18	17 42 48.5	25 55.4	6 58.6	21 48.8	17 43.6	6 39.2	19 41.9	22 35.1	16 16.6	24 10.9	7 28.0	10 23.9
19	17 46 45.0	26 57.8	6 55.7	3♈44.9	17 54.4	7 56.1	20 23.5	22 44.6	16 12.0	24 8.2	7 26.3	10 22.9
20	17 50 41.6	28 .2	6 52.8	15 25.7	18 .3	9 13.3	21 5.0	22 54.0	16 7.4	24 5.5	7 24.6	10 22.0
21	17 54 38.1	29 2.6	6 49.8	27 9.0	18 1.4	10 30.8	21 46.5	23 3.3	16 2.7	24 2.9	7 22.9	10 21.0
22	17 58 34.7	0♋4.8	6 46.9	9♉9.3	17R57.5	11 48.4	22 27.8	23 12.6	15 58.2	24 .2	7 21.1	10 20.1
23	18 2 31.3	1 7.4	6 44.0	21 36.3	17 49.0	13 6.3	23 9.1	23 21.7	15 53.6	23 57.5	7 19.4	10 19.2
24	18 6 27.8	2 9.8	6 41.1	4♊33.3	17 35.9	14 24.4	23 50.4	23 30.7	15 49.1	23 54.9	7 17.7	10 18.3
25	18 10 24.4	3 12.2	6 38.2	17 55.1	17 18.4	15 42.7	24 31.5	23 39.6	15 44.6	23 52.2	7 15.9	10 17.5
26	18 14 20.9	4 14.6	6 35.2	1♋28.7	16 56.7	17 1.2	25 12.6	23 48.3	15 40.2	23 49.6	7 14.2	10 16.6
27	18 18 17.5	5 16.9	6 32.3	14 56.4	16 31.3	18 19.9	25 53.6	23 57.0	15 35.8	23 47.0	7 12.4	10 15.8
28	18 22 14.1	6 19.2	6 29.4	28 1.3	16 2.3	19 38.7	26 34.6	24 5.5	15 31.4	23 44.4	7 10.7	10 15.0
29	18 26 10.6	7 21.4	6 26.5	10♌32.5	15 30.0	20 57.8	27 15.4	24 14.0	15 27.1	23 41.8	7 8.9	10 14.3
30	18 30 7.2	8 23.6	6 23.6	22 27.2	14 55.8	22 16.9	27 56.2	24 22.3	15 22.8	23 39.2	7 7.2	10 13.6

DECLINATION

DAY	SID. TIME	☉	☊	☽	☿	♀	♂	♃	♄	♅	♆	♇
1	16 35 47.0	21N57.2	0N 3.5	25N11.8	25N31.7	15N44.9	24N21.1	7N 2.6	21S19.6	23S30.6	22S11.4	1N48.8
4	16 47 36.6	22 20.8	0 3.5	12 45.3	25 9.7	16 48.4	24 14.4	7 15.2	21 18.8	23 30.4	22 11.6	1 49.0
7	16 59 26.3	22 40.8	0 3.4	4S46.1	24 36.5	17 48.2	24 6.1	7 27.5	21 17.6	23 30.2	22 11.8	1 49.0
10	17 11 16.0	22 57.3	0 3.3	21 50.8	23 54.8	18 44.0	23 56.0	7 39.5	21 16.6	23 30.0	22 12.0	1 48.9
13	17 23 5.7	23 10.2	0 3.3	28 14.6	23 7.4	19 35.4	23 44.3	7 51.0	21 15.7	23 29.7	22 12.3	1 48.8
16	17 34 55.4	23 19.3	0 3.2	17 31.0	22 19.9	20 22.3	23 31.0	8 2.2	21 14.7	23 29.5	22 12.5	1 48.4
19	17 46 45.0	23 24.8	0 3.1	1N13.3	21 25.6	21 4.3	23 16.0	8 12.9	21 13.8	23 29.2	22 12.7	1 48.0
22	17 58 34.7	23 26.6	0 3.1	18 18.5	20 36.4	21 41.2	22 59.5	8 23.2	21 12.9	23 28.9	22 13.0	1 47.4
25	18 10 24.4	23 24.6	0 3.0	27 44.3	19 51.4	22 12.6	22 41.4	8 33.1	21 11.9	23 28.6	22 13.3	1 46.7
28	18 22 14.1	23 19.0	0 2.9	25 46.6	19 13.1	22 38.5	22 21.8	8 42.5	21 11.1	23 28.3	22 13.5	1 45.9

JULY 1987

DAY	EPHEM. SID. TIME	☉	☊	☾	☿	♀	♂	♃	♄	♅	♆	♇
		LONGITUDE										
	h m s	° ′	° ′	° ′	° ′	° ′	° ′	° ′	° ′	° ′	° ′	° ′
1	18 34 3.7	8♋39.8	6♈54.6	0♍42.3	13♋35.0	24♊ 6.8	26♋21.9	25♈56.3	16♐19.0	24♐ 8.5	6♑33.7	7♏13.7
2	18 38 .3	9 37.0	6 51.4	12 42.5	12 R 59.7	25 20.1	27 .3	26 4.7	16 R 15.1	24 R 6.1	6 R 32.1	7 R 13.1
3	18 41 56.9	10 34.2	6 48.2	24 53.5	12 23.5	26 33.4	27 38.7	26 13.1	16 11.2	24 3.8	6 30.5	7 12.6
4	18 45 53.4	11 31.4	6 45.0	7♎19.9	11 46.9	27 46.7	28 17.1	26 21.3	16 7.4	24 1.5	6 28.9	7 12.2
5	18 49 50.0	12 28.6	6 41.9	20 6.7	11 10.4	29 .1	28 55.4	26 29.4	16 3.7	23 59.2	6 27.3	7 11.7
6	18 53 46.5	13 25.8	6 38.7	3♏18.4	10 34.9	0♋13.4	29 33.7	26 37.3	15 60.0	23 57.0	6 25.7	7 11.3
7	18 57 43.1	14 23.0	6 35.5	16 58.4	10 .7	1 26.8	0♌12.1	26 45.1	15 56.4	23 54.7	6 24.1	7 10.9
8	19 1 39.6	15 20.2	6 32.3	1♐ 8.3	9 28.7	2 40.1	0 50.4	26 52.7	15 52.8	23 52.5	6 22.5	7 10.5
9	19 5 36.2	16 17.4	6 29.2	15 46.5	8 59.3	3 53.5	1 28.7	27 .2	15 49.3	23 50.3	6 20.9	7 10.2
10	19 9 32.8	17 14.5	6 26.0	0♑47.8	8 33.1	5 6.9	2 7.0	27 7.6	15 45.8	23 48.1	6 19.3	7 9.9
11	19 13 29.3	18 11.7	6 22.8	16 3.5	8 10.5	6 20.4	2 45.2	27 14.8	15 42.4	23 45.9	6 17.7	7 9.7
12	19 17 25.9	19 8.9	6 19.6	1♒22.8	7 52.0	7 33.8	3 23.5	27 21.8	15 39.1	23 43.8	6 16.2	7 9.5
13	19 21 22.4	20 6.1	6 16.4	16 34.1	7 38.0	8 47.3	4 1.8	27 28.7	15 35.8	23 41.7	6 14.6	7 9.3
14	19 25 19.0	21 3.3	6 13.3	1♓27.8	7 28.7	10 .8	4 40.0	27 35.5	15 32.6	23 39.6	6 13.0	7 9.1
15	19 29 15.6	22 .5	6 10.1	15 57.2	7 24.4	11 14.3	5 18.3	27 42.1	15 29.5	23 37.5	6 11.5	7 9.0
16	19 33 12.1	22 57.7	6 6.9	29 59.3	7 D 25.3	12 27.8	5 56.5	27 48.5	15 26.4	23 35.5	6 10.0	7 8.9
17	19 37 8.7	23 54.9	6 3.7	13♈33.9	7 31.7	13 41.4	6 34.7	27 54.8	15 23.4	23 33.4	6 8.4	7 8.8
18	19 41 5.2	24 52.2	6 .6	26 43.3	7 43.5	14 54.9	7 13.0	28 .9	15 20.5	23 31.5	6 6.9	7 8.8
19	19 45 1.8	25 49.4	5 57.4	9♉31.1	8 .8	16 8.6	7 51.2	28 6.9	15 17.6	23 29.5	6 5.4	7 8.8
20	19 48 58.3	26 46.7	5 54.2	22 1.2	8 23.8	17 22.2	8 29.4	28 12.7	15 14.9	23 27.6	6 3.9	7 D 8.9
21	19 52 54.9	27 43.9	5 51.0	4♊17.7	8 52.4	18 35.8	9 7.6	28 18.4	15 12.2	23 25.7	6 2.4	7 9.0
22	19 56 51.5	28 41.2	5 47.9	16 24.1	9 26.6	19 49.5	9 45.8	28 23.8	15 9.5	23 23.8	6 .9	7 9.1
23	20 0 48.0	29 38.5	5 44.7	28 23.5	10 6.5	21 3.2	10 24.0	28 29.1	15 7.0	23 22.0	5 59.5	7 9.2
24	20 4 44.6	0♌35.9	5 41.5	10♋18.3	10 51.9	22 17.0	11 2.3	28 34.3	15 4.6	23 20.3	5 58.1	7 9.5
25	20 8 41.1	1 33.2	5 38.3	22 10.5	11 42.8	23 30.7	11 40.5	28 39.3	15 2.2	23 18.5	5 56.7	7 9.7
26	20 12 37.7	2 30.5	5 35.2	4♌ 1.7	12 39.1	24 44.4	12 18.7	28 44.1	14 59.9	23 16.8	5 55.3	7 9.9
27	20 16 34.2	3 27.8	5 32.0	15 53.4	13 40.8	25 58.2	12 56.9	28 48.7	14 57.7	23 15.1	5 53.9	7 10.2
28	20 20 30.8	4 25.2	5 28.8	27 47.5	14 47.8	27 12.0	13 35.1	28 53.1	14 55.6	23 13.5	5 52.5	7 10.5
29	20 24 27.4	5 22.5	5 25.6	9♍45.8	15 59.9	28 25.8	14 13.2	28 57.4	14 53.6	23 11.8	5 51.1	7 10.9
30	20 28 23.9	6 19.9	5 22.4	21 51.0	17 17.0	29 39.7	14 51.4	29 1.5	14 51.6	23 10.3	5 49.8	7 11.3
31	20 32 20.5	7 17.3	5 19.3	4♎ 6.2	18 39.1	0♌53.5	15 29.6	29 5.4	14 49.8	23 8.7	5 48.4	7 11.7
		LATITUDE										
1	18 34 3.7	0 .0	0 .0	2N56.2	4S 2.7	0S20.2	1N 9.0	1S15.0	1N34.6	0S 9.3	1N 3.1	16N32.6
4	18 45 53.4	0 .0	0 .0	0S 5.2	4 31.9	0 12.8	1 9.2	1 15.6	1 34.2	0 9.3	1 3.1	16 31.0
7	18 57 43.1	0 .0	0 .0	3 17.1	4 47.8	0 5.4	1 9.3	1 16.2	1 33.7	0 9.3	1 3.0	16 29.4
10	19 9 32.8	0 .0	0 .0	4 59.6	4 49.4	0N 2.0	1 9.4	1 16.9	1 33.3	0 9.3	1 3.0	16 27.7
13	19 21 22.4	0 .0	0 .0	3 47.4	4 37.4	0 9.3	1 9.5	1 17.5	1 32.8	0 9.3	1 2.9	16 26.0
16	19 33 12.1	0 .0	0 .0	0 27.8	4 13.6	0 16.5	1 9.5	1 18.2	1 32.3	0 9.4	1 2.9	16 24.3
19	19 45 1.8	0 .0	0 .0	2N51.3	3 40.8	0 23.5	1 9.5	1 18.9	1 31.8	0 9.4	1 2.8	16 22.5
22	19 56 51.5	0 .0	0 .0	4 46.9	3 1.6	0 30.4	1 9.5	1 19.6	1 31.2	0 9.4	1 2.8	16 20.8
25	20 8 41.1	0 .0	0 .0	4 48.3	2 18.6	0 36.9	1 9.4	1 20.3	1 30.7	0 9.4	1 2.7	16 19.0
28	20 20 30.8	0 .0	0 .0	2 59.9	1 34.1	0 43.2	1 9.4	1 21.1	1 30.1	0 9.4	1 2.6	16 17.3
31	20 32 20.5	0 .0	0 .0	0S 1.7	0 50.3	0 49.2	1 9.3	1 21.8	1 29.5	0 9.4	1 2.5	16 15.5
		RIGHT ASCENSION										
1	18 34 3.7	9♋25.7	6♈20.6	3♍50.0	14♋19.3	23♊36.3	28♋36.9	24♈30.5	15♐18.6	23♐36.6	7♑ 5.4	10♏12.9
2	18 38 .3	10 27.8	6 17.7	14 50.6	13 R 41.2	24 55.7	29 17.5	24 38.5	15 R 14.4	23 R 34.1	7 R 3.7	10 R 12.2
3	18 41 56.9	11 29.8	6 14.8	25 42.6	13 2.4	26 15.3	29 58.1	24 46.5	15 10.3	23 31.6	7 2.0	10 11.6
4	18 45 53.4	12 31.7	6 11.9	6♎41.9	12 23.2	27 35.0	0♌38.5	24 54.3	15 6.3	23 29.1	7 .2	10 11.0
5	18 49 50.0	13 33.6	6 9.0	18 6.6	11 44.5	28 54.8	1 18.9	25 2.0	15 2.2	23 26.6	6 58.5	10 10.4
6	18 53 46.5	14 35.3	6 6.0	0♏16.5	11 6.8	0♋14.6	1 59.1	25 9.6	14 58.3	23 24.1	6 56.8	10 9.9
7	18 57 43.1	15 37.0	6 3.1	13 31.0	10 30.8	1 34.5	2 39.3	25 17.0	14 54.4	23 21.7	6 55.0	10 9.3
8	19 1 39.6	16 38.6	6 .2	28 4.8	9 57.1	2 54.4	3 19.4	25 24.3	14 50.6	23 19.2	6 53.3	10 8.8
9	19 5 36.2	17 40.0	5 57.3	13♐59.6	9 26.3	4 14.4	3 59.5	25 31.5	14 46.8	23 16.8	6 51.6	10 8.4
10	19 9 32.8	18 41.4	5 54.4	0♑54.1	8 58.9	5 34.5	4 39.4	25 38.5	14 43.1	23 14.4	6 49.9	10 7.9
11	19 13 29.3	19 42.7	5 51.4	18 4.8	8 35.4	6 54.5	5 19.2	25 45.4	14 39.4	23 12.1	6 48.2	10 7.5
12	19 17 25.9	20 43.8	5 48.5	4♒42.4	8 16.2	8 14.5	5 59.0	25 52.1	14 35.9	23 9.7	6 46.5	10 7.1
13	19 21 22.4	21 44.8	5 45.6	20 13.8	8 1.8	9 34.5	6 38.7	25 58.7	14 32.4	23 7.4	6 44.8	10 6.8
14	19 25 19.0	22 45.8	5 42.7	4♓30.9	7 52.5	10 54.5	7 18.3	26 5.2	14 28.9	23 5.2	6 43.1	10 6.5
15	19 29 15.6	23 46.6	5 39.8	17 43.6	7 48.4	12 14.5	7 57.8	26 11.6	14 25.6	23 2.9	6 41.4	10 6.2
16	19 33 12.1	24 47.3	5 36.8	0♈10.4	7 D 49.9	13 34.4	8 37.2	26 17.7	14 22.3	23 .7	6 39.8	10 5.9
17	19 37 8.7	25 47.8	5 33.9	12 11.7	7 57.2	14 54.2	9 16.6	26 23.8	14 19.1	22 58.5	6 38.1	10 5.7
18	19 41 5.2	26 48.3	5 31.0	24 6.3	8 10.3	16 14.0	9 55.8	26 29.7	14 15.9	22 56.3	6 36.5	10 5.5
19	19 45 1.8	27 48.6	5 28.1	6♉10.2	8 29.3	17 33.6	10 35.0	26 35.4	14 12.9	22 54.2	6 34.9	10 5.3
20	19 48 58.3	28 48.8	5 25.2	18 34.8	8 54.4	18 53.2	11 14.1	26 41.0	14 9.9	22 52.1	6 33.3	10 5.1
21	19 52 54.9	29 48.8	5 22.2	1♊25.7	9 25.6	20 12.6	11 53.1	26 46.4	14 7.0	22 50.1	6 31.7	10 5.0
22	19 56 51.5	0♌48.8	5 19.3	14 41.0	10 2.9	21 31.9	12 32.1	26 51.7	14 4.2	22 48.0	6 30.1	10 5.0
23	20 0 48.0	1 48.5	5 16.4	28 10.6	10 46.2	22 51.1	13 10.9	26 56.8	14 1.5	22 46.1	6 28.5	10 4.9
24	20 4 44.6	2 48.2	5 13.5	11♋38.9	11 35.7	24 10.2	13 49.7	27 1.8	13 58.9	22 44.2	6 27.0	10 4.9
25	20 8 41.1	3 47.7	5 10.6	24 49.1	12 31.1	25 29.0	14 28.4	27 6.6	13 56.4	22 42.2	6 25.5	10 4.9
26	20 12 37.7	4 47.1	5 7.6	7♌28.7	13 32.4	26 47.7	15 7.0	27 11.2	13 53.9	22 40.4	6 23.9	10 D 5.0
27	20 16 34.2	5 46.3	5 4.7	19 32.6	14 39.6	28 6.1	15 45.5	27 15.7	13 51.5	22 38.5	6 22.4	10 5.1
28	20 20 30.8	6 45.3	5 1.8	1♍ 2.6	15 52.6	29 24.4	16 24.0	27 20.0	13 49.2	22 36.7	6 20.9	10 5.2
29	20 24 27.4	7 44.2	4 58.9	12 6.5	17 11.2	0♌42.5	17 2.3	27 24.1	13 47.1	22 35.0	6 19.5	10 5.3
30	20 28 23.9	8 42.9	4 56.0	22 56.0	18 35.2	2 .4	17 40.6	27 28.1	13 45.0	22 33.3	6 18.0	10 5.5
31	20 32 20.5	9 41.5	4 53.0	3♎45.3	20 4.5	3 18.0	18 18.8	27 31.9	13 43.0	22 31.6	6 16.6	10 5.7
		DECLINATION										
1	18 34 3.7	23N 9.6	0N 2.9	13N58.2	18N43.5	22N58.5	22N .8	8N51.4	21S10.3	23S28.1	22S13.8	1N44.9
4	18 45 53.4	22 56.6	0 2.8	2S59.4	18 24.4	23 12.6	21 38.3	8 59.9	21 9.5	23 27.8	22 14.1	1 43.9
7	18 57 43.1	22 40.0	0 2.7	20 3.3	18 16.9	23 20.7	21 14.4	9 7.8	21 8.8	23 27.5	22 14.3	1 42.7
10	19 9 32.8	22 19.9	0 2.7	28 26.1	18 21.2	23 22.6	20 49.1	9 15.3	21 8.2	23 27.2	22 14.6	1 41.4
13	19 21 22.4	21 56.3	0 2.6	19 29.1	18 36.5	23 18.4	20 22.6	9 22.3	21 7.6	23 26.9	22 14.9	1 40.0
16	19 33 12.1	21 29.3	0 2.5	0 25.8	19 .9	23 8.0	19 54.7	9 28.7	21 7.1	23 26.6	22 15.2	1 38.4
19	19 45 1.8	20 59.1	0 2.5	17N22.2	19 31.7	22 51.4	19 25.7	9 34.6	21 6.7	23 26.4	22 15.4	1 36.8
22	19 56 51.5	20 25.6	0 2.4	27 30.3	20 5.3	22 28.8	18 55.4	9 40.0	21 6.4	23 26.1	22 15.7	1 35.1
25	20 8 41.1	19 49.0	0 2.3	26 21.4	20 37.5	22 .2	18 23.9	9 44.8	21 6.1	23 25.8	22 16.0	1 33.2
28	20 20 30.8	19 9.5	0 2.3	15 3.3	21 3.8	21 25.8	17 51.4	9 49.0	21 5.9	23 25.6	22 16.2	1 31.3
31	20 32 20.5	18 27.2	0 2.2	1S39.5	21 18.9	20 45.8	17 17.8	9 52.6	21 5.9	23 25.4	22 16.5	1 29.3

AUGUST 1987

DAY	EPHEM. SID. TIME	☉	☊	☽	☿	♀	♂	♃	♄	♅	♆	♇
	h m s	° ′	° ′	° ′	° ′	° ′	° ′	° ′	° ′	° ′	° ′	° ′
		LONGITUDE										
1	20 36 17.0	8♌14.7	5♈16.1	16♎35.3	20♋ 5.8	2♌ 7.4	16♌ 7.8	29♈ 9.1	14♐48.0	23♐ 7.2	5♑47.1	7♏12.2
2	20 40 13.6	9 12.1	5 12.9	29 22.1	21 37.1	3 21.3	16 45.9	29 12.6	14 R46.3	23 R 5.8	5 R45.8	7 12.7
3	20 44 10.1	10 9.5	5 9.7	12♏30.7	23 12.7	4 35.2	17 24.1	29 16.0	14 44.7	23 4.4	5 44.6	7 13.2
4	20 48 6.7	11 6.9	5 6.6	26 4.5	24 52.4	5 49.1	18 2.2	29 19.1	14 43.2	23 3.0	5 43.3	7 13.8
5	20 52 3.3	12 4.3	5 3.4	10♐ 5.4	26 35.9	7 3.0	18 40.4	29 22.1	14 41.8	23 1.7	5 42.1	7 14.4
6	20 55 59.8	13 1.8	5 .2	24 33.0	28 22.9	8 17.0	19 18.5	29 24.9	14 40.5	23 .4	5 40.9	7 15.0
7	20 59 56.4	13 59.2	4 57.0	9♑23.9	0♌13.0	9 31.0	19 56.7	29 27.5	14 39.3	22 59.1	5 39.7	7 15.6
8	21 3 52.9	14 56.7	4 53.9	24 31.4	2 6.0	10 45.0	20 34.8	29 29.9	14 38.1	22 57.9	5 38.5	7 16.3
9	21 7 49.5	15 54.2	4 50.7	9♒46.2	4 1.5	11 59.0	21 13.0	29 32.1	14 37.1	22 56.7	5 37.4	7 17.1
10	21 11 46.0	16 51.7	4 47.5	24 57.6	5 59.0	13 13.0	21 51.1	29 34.2	14 36.2	22 55.6	5 36.3	7 17.8
11	21 15 42.6	17 49.2	4 44.3	9♓55.4	7 58.2	14 27.1	22 29.2	29 36.0	14 35.3	22 54.6	5 35.2	7 18.6
12	21 19 39.2	18 46.7	4 41.1	24 31.9	9 58.8	15 41.1	23 7.4	29 37.7	14 34.6	22 53.5	5 34.1	7 19.4
13	21 23 35.7	19 44.3	4 38.0	8♈42.1	12 .4	16 55.2	23 45.5	29 39.1	14 33.9	22 52.5	5 33.0	7 20.3
14	21 27 32.3	20 41.9	4 34.8	22 24.5	14 2.7	18 9.4	24 23.7	29 40.4	14 33.4	22 51.7	5 32.0	7 21.2
15	21 31 28.8	21 39.5	4 31.6	5♉39.9	16 5.2	19 23.5	25 1.9	29 41.5	14 32.9	22 50.8	5 31.0	7 22.2
16	21 35 25.4	22 37.1	4 28.4	18 31.1	18 7.8	20 37.7	25 40.0	29 42.3	14 32.5	22 49.9	5 30.1	7 23.1
17	21 39 21.9	23 34.8	4 25.3	1♊ 2.2	20 10.2	21 51.8	26 18.1	29 43.0	14 32.3	22 49.1	5 29.1	7 24.1
18	21 43 18.5	24 32.5	4 22.1	13 17.3	22 12.2	23 6.0	26 56.3	29 43.5	14 32.1	22 48.4	5 28.2	7 25.1
19	21 47 15.0	25 30.2	4 18.9	25 20.9	24 13.6	24 20.3	27 34.5	29 43.7	14 32.0	22 47.7	5 27.3	7 26.2
20	21 51 11.6	26 27.9	4 15.7	7♋16.9	26 14.2	25 34.5	28 12.6	29 43.8	14 32.0	22 47.0	5 26.4	7 27.3
21	21 55 8.2	27 25.7	4 12.6	19 8.9	28 14.0	26 48.7	28 50.8	29 R43.7	14 D32.1	22 46.4	5 25.6	7 28.4
22	21 59 4.7	28 23.5	4 9.4	0♌59.9	0♍12.7	28 3.0	29 28.9	29 43.3	14 32.3	22 45.8	5 24.7	7 29.5
23	22 3 1.3	29 21.3	4 6.2	12 52.3	2 10.3	29 17.3	0♍ 7.1	29 42.8	14 32.6	22 45.3	5 23.9	7 30.7
24	22 6 57.8	0♍19.1	4 3.0	24 48.2	4 6.7	0♍31.6	0 45.3	29 42.1	14 33.0	22 44.9	5 23.2	7 31.9
25	22 10 54.4	1 17.0	3 59.8	6♍49.3	6 2.0	1 45.9	1 23.5	29 41.1	14 33.6	22 44.5	5 22.4	7 33.2
26	22 14 50.9	2 14.9	3 56.7	18 57.3	7 55.9	3 .3	2 1.6	29 40.0	14 34.2	22 44.1	5 21.7	7 34.4
27	22 18 47.5	3 12.8	3 53.5	1♎13.9	9 48.6	4 14.6	2 39.8	29 38.7	14 34.9	22 43.8	5 21.0	7 35.7
28	22 22 44.0	4 10.7	3 50.3	13 41.0	11 40.1	5 29.0	3 18.0	29 37.1	14 35.6	22 43.5	5 20.4	7 37.1
29	22 26 40.6	5 8.7	3 47.1	26 20.9	13 30.2	6 43.4	3 56.2	29 35.4	14 36.5	22 43.3	5 19.8	7 38.4
30	22 30 37.1	6 6.7	3 44.0	9♏15.9	15 19.0	7 57.7	4 34.4	29 33.5	14 37.5	22 43.2	5 19.2	7 39.8
31	22 34 33.7	7 4.7	3 40.8	22 28.5	17 6.5	9 12.2	5 12.6	29 31.3	14 38.6	22 43.1	5 18.6	7 41.2
		LATITUDE										
1	20 36 17.0	0 .0	0 .0	1S 8.2	0S36.1	0N51.1	1N 9.2	1S22.1	1N29.3	0S 9.4	1N 2.5	16N14.9
4	20 48 6.7	0 .0	0 .0	4 3.3	0N 3.8	0 56.6	1 9.1	1 22.8	1 28.7	0 9.4	1 2.4	16 13.2
7	20 59 56.4	0 .0	0 .0	5 5.4	0 38.5	1 1.7	1 9.0	1 23.6	1 28.1	0 9.4	1 2.3	16 11.4
10	21 11 46.0	0 .0	0 .0	3 11.1	1 6.5	1 6.3	1 8.8	1 24.3	1 27.5	0 9.5	1 2.2	16 9.7
13	21 23 35.7	0 .0	0 .0	0N30.2	1 27.1	1 10.5	1 8.6	1 25.1	1 26.9	0 9.5	1 2.1	16 8.0
16	21 35 25.4	0 .0	0 .0	3 41.1	1 39.9	1 14.2	1 8.4	1 25.8	1 26.3	0 9.5	1 2.0	16 6.3
19	21 47 15.0	0 .0	0 .0	5 7.5	1 45.4	1 17.4	1 8.1	1 26.6	1 25.7	0 9.5	1 1.9	16 4.7
22	21 59 4.7	0 .0	0 .0	4 34.0	1 44.5	1 20.0	1 7.9	1 27.3	1 25.1	0 9.5	1 1.8	16 3.0
25	22 10 54.4	0 .0	0 .0	2 15.8	1 38.2	1 22.1	1 7.6	1 28.0	1 24.4	0 9.5	1 1.7	16 1.5
28	22 22 44.0	0 .0	0 .0	1S 1.0	1 27.4	1 23.6	1 7.2	1 28.7	1 23.8	0 9.5	1 1.6	15 59.9
31	22 34 33.7	0 .0	0 .0	4 .8	1 12.9	1 24.5	1 6.9	1 29.4	1 23.2	0 9.5	1 1.4	15 58.4
		RIGHT ASCENSION										
1	20 36 17.0	10♌39.9	4♈50.1	14♎50.7	21♋38.8	4♌35.4	18♌56.9	27♈35.5	13♐41.0	22♐30.0	6♑15.2	10♏ 5.9
2	20 40 13.6	11 38.2	4 47.2	26 30.1	23 17.9	5 52.6	19 35.0	27 38.9	13 R39.2	22 R28.4	6 R13.8	10 6.2
3	20 44 10.1	12 36.3	4 44.3	9♏ 2.1	25 1.5	7 9.5	20 12.9	27 42.2	13 37.5	22 26.8	6 12.4	10 6.5
4	20 48 6.7	13 34.3	4 41.4	22 43.0	26 49.3	8 26.2	20 50.8	27 45.3	13 35.9	22 25.3	6 11.1	10 6.8
5	20 52 3.3	14 32.1	4 38.5	7♐41.5	28 40.7	9 42.6	21 28.6	27 48.2	13 34.4	22 23.9	6 9.7	10 7.2
6	20 55 59.8	15 29.8	4 35.5	23 49.6	0♌35.6	10 58.8	22 6.3	27 51.0	13 32.9	22 22.5	6 8.4	10 7.5
7	20 59 56.4	16 27.2	4 32.6	10♑38.0	2 33.3	12 14.7	22 43.9	27 53.5	13 31.6	22 21.1	6 7.2	10 8.0
8	21 3 52.9	17 24.6	4 29.7	27 22.8	4 33.4	13 30.4	23 21.5	27 55.9	13 30.4	22 19.8	6 5.9	10 8.4
9	21 7 49.5	18 21.8	4 26.8	13♒24.0	6 35.5	14 45.7	23 59.0	27 58.1	13 29.3	22 18.6	6 4.7	10 8.9
10	21 11 46.0	19 18.8	4 23.9	28 21.2	8 39.0	16 .9	24 36.4	28 .1	13 28.2	22 17.3	6 3.4	10 9.4
11	21 15 42.6	20 15.7	4 20.9	12♓14.5	10 43.5	17 15.7	25 13.7	28 2.0	13 27.3	22 16.2	6 2.3	10 10.0
12	21 19 39.2	21 12.5	4 18.0	25 17.2	12 48.6	18 30.3	25 51.0	28 3.6	13 26.5	22 15.0	6 1.1	10 10.5
13	21 23 35.7	22 9.1	4 15.1	7♈47.7	14 53.8	19 44.6	26 28.2	28 5.1	13 25.7	22 14.0	5 60.0	10 11.1
14	21 27 32.3	23 5.7	4 12.2	20 4.5	16 58.7	20 58.7	27 5.4	28 6.4	13 25.2	22 13.0	5 58.9	10 11.8
15	21 31 28.8	24 2.0	4 9.3	2♉23.9	19 2.9	22 12.5	27 42.4	28 7.5	13 24.6	22 12.0	5 57.8	10 12.5
16	21 35 25.4	24 58.3	4 6.4	14 58.3	21 6.2	23 26.0	28 19.4	28 8.4	13 24.2	22 11.1	5 56.8	10 13.2
17	21 39 21.9	25 54.4	4 3.4	27 54.4	23 8.4	24 39.3	28 56.4	28 9.2	13 23.9	22 10.3	5 55.7	10 13.9
18	21 43 18.5	26 50.3	4 .5	11♊12.2	25 9.1	25 52.3	29 33.2	28 9.7	13 23.7	22 9.4	5 54.7	10 14.7
19	21 47 15.0	27 46.2	3 57.6	24 43.6	27 8.3	27 5.0	0♍10.0	28 10.0	13 23.6	22 8.7	5 53.8	10 15.4
20	21 51 11.6	28 41.9	3 54.7	8♋15.0	29 5.8	28 17.5	0 46.8	28 10.2	13 23.6	22 8.0	5 52.8	10 16.3
21	21 55 8.2	29 37.5	3 51.8	21 30.8	1♍ 1.4	29 29.8	1 23.4	28 10.2	13 D23.7	22 7.3	5 51.9	10 17.1
22	21 59 4.7	0♍33.0	3 48.9	4♌18.7	2 55.3	0♍41.8	2 .1	28 R 9.9	13 23.9	22 6.7	5 51.0	10 18.0
23	22 3 1.3	1 28.4	3 45.9	16 32.2	4 47.3	1 53.5	2 36.6	28 9.5	13 24.2	22 6.1	5 50.2	10 18.9
24	22 6 57.8	2 23.7	3 43.0	28 12.1	6 37.3	3 5.1	3 13.1	28 8.9	13 24.6	22 5.6	5 49.3	10 19.8
25	22 10 54.4	3 18.9	3 40.1	9♍24.5	8 25.5	4 16.3	3 49.6	28 8.1	13 25.1	22 5.2	5 48.5	10 20.8
26	22 14 50.9	4 13.9	3 37.2	20 19.7	10 11.9	5 27.4	4 26.0	28 7.1	13 25.7	22 4.8	5 47.8	10 21.8
27	22 18 47.5	5 8.9	3 34.3	1♎10.6	11 56.4	6 38.2	5 2.3	28 5.9	13 26.4	22 4.5	5 47.0	10 22.8
28	22 22 44.0	6 3.7	3 31.3	12 11.7	13 39.1	7 48.9	5 38.6	28 4.5	13 27.2	22 4.2	5 46.3	10 23.9
29	22 26 40.6	6 58.5	3 28.4	23 39.1	15 20.1	8 59.3	6 14.8	28 3.0	13 28.2	22 4.0	5 45.7	10 24.9
30	22 30 37.1	7 53.2	3 25.5	5♏49.3	16 59.4	10 9.5	6 51.0	28 1.2	13 29.2	22 3.8	5 45.0	10 26.1
31	22 34 33.7	8 47.7	3 22.6	18 57.6	18 37.0	11 19.5	7 27.1	27 59.3	13 30.3	22 3.7	5 44.4	10 27.2
		DECLINATION										
1	20 36 17.0	18N12.4	0N 2.2	7S34.2	21N20.6	20N31.2	17N 6.4	9N53.7	21S 5.9	23S25.3	22S16.6	1N28.6
4	20 48 6.7	17 26.5	0 2.1	23 12.8	21 13.2	19 44.1	16 31.4	9 56.5	21 5.9	23 25.1	22 16.8	1 26.4
7	20 59 56.4	16 38.0	0 2.1	28 11.2	20 44.1	18 51.8	15 55.5	9 58.8	21 6.1	23 24.9	22 17.1	1 24.2
10	21 11 46.0	15 47.1	0 2.0	16 12.1	19 51.2	17 54.8	15 18.7	10 .4	21 6.3	23 24.7	22 17.3	1 21.9
13	21 23 35.7	14 53.9	0 1.9	3N54.8	18 35.3	16 53.2	14 40.9	10 1.5	21 6.7	23 24.6	22 17.6	1 19.6
16	21 35 25.4	13 58.6	0 1.9	20 52.8	16 58.9	15 47.4	14 2.4	10 1.9	21 7.1	23 24.4	22 17.8	1 17.1
19	21 47 15.0	13 1.3	0 1.8	28 29.0	15 6.3	14 37.6	13 23.0	10 1.7	21 7.7	23 24.3	22 18.0	1 14.6
22	21 59 4.7	12 2.1	0 1.7	24 23.5	13 1.7	13 24.3	12 42.9	10 .8	21 8.3	23 24.2	22 18.2	1 12.0
25	22 10 54.4	11 1.2	0 1.7	11 6.6	10 49.3	12 7.6	12 2.0	9 59.4	21 9.1	23 24.1	22 18.4	1 9.4
28	22 22 44.0	9 58.7	0 1.6	6S20.2	8 32.1	10 47.9	11 20.5	9 57.3	21 9.9	23 24.1	22 18.6	1 6.8
31	22 34 33.7	8 54.8	0 1.5	22 16.2	6 12.7	9 25.6	10 38.4	9 54.6	21 10.9	23 24.1	22 18.8	1 4.1

SEPTEMBER 1987

LONGITUDE

DAY	EPHEM. SID. TIME	☉	☊	☽	☿	♀	♂	♃	♄	♅	♆	♇
	h m s	° ′	° ′	° ′	° ′	° ′	° ′	° ′	° ′	° ′	° ′	° ′
1	22 38 30.3	8♍ 2.7	3♈37.6	6♐ .8	18♍52.8	10♍26.6	5♍50.8	29♈29.0	14♐39.8	22♐43.0	5♑18.1	7♏42.7
2	22 42 26.8	9 .8	3 34.4	19 54.1	20 37.7	11 41.0	6 29.0	29 R 26.5	14 41.1	22 43.0	5 R 17.6	7 44.2
3	22 46 23.4	9 58.8	3 31.2	4♑ 8.3	22 21.5	12 55.4	7 7.2	29 23.8	14 42.5	22 D 43.1	5 17.1	7 45.7
4	22 50 19.9	10 57.0	3 28.1	18 41.4	24 4.0	14 9.9	7 45.4	29 20.9	14 44.0	22 43.2	5 16.7	7 47.2
5	22 54 16.5	11 55.1	3 24.9	3♒29.0	25 45.2	15 24.4	8 23.6	29 17.8	14 45.6	22 43.4	5 16.3	7 48.8
6	22 58 13.0	12 53.2	3 21.7	18 24.6	27 25.3	16 38.8	9 1.9	29 14.5	14 47.2	22 43.6	5 15.9	7 50.4
7	23 2 9.6	13 51.4	3 18.5	3♓20.1	29 4.1	17 53.3	9 40.1	29 11.1	14 49.0	22 43.8	5 15.6	7 52.0
8	23 6 6.1	14 49.6	3 15.4	18 7.4	0♎41.8	19 7.8	10 18.3	29 7.4	14 50.8	22 44.1	5 15.3	7 53.6
9	23 10 2.7	15 47.8	3 12.2	2♈39.0	2 18.3	20 22.3	10 56.5	29 3.6	14 52.8	22 44.5	5 15.0	7 55.3
10	23 13 59.2	16 46.1	3 9.0	16 49.3	3 53.6	21 36.8	11 34.8	28 59.5	14 54.8	22 44.9	5 14.7	7 57.0
11	23 17 55.8	17 44.4	3 5.8	0♉35.0	5 27.8	22 51.3	12 13.0	28 55.3	14 56.9	22 45.3	5 14.5	7 58.7
12	23 21 52.4	18 42.7	3 2.6	13 55.5	7 .8	24 5.8	12 51.3	28 51.0	14 59.2	22 45.8	5 14.3	8 .4
13	23 25 48.9	19 41.1	2 59.5	26 51.8	8 32.8	25 20.4	13 29.5	28 46.4	15 1.5	22 46.4	5 14.2	8 2.2
14	23 29 45.5	20 39.4	2 56.3	9♊26.8	10 3.6	26 34.9	14 7.8	28 41.7	15 3.9	22 47.0	5 14.0	8 4.0
15	23 33 42.0	21 37.9	2 53.1	21 44.4	11 33.3	27 49.5	14 46.1	28 36.8	15 6.4	22 47.7	5 14.0	8 5.8
16	23 37 38.6	22 36.3	2 49.9	3♋48.8	13 1.8	29 4.1	15 24.4	28 31.7	15 9.0	22 48.4	5 13.9	8 7.6
17	23 41 35.1	23 34.8	2 46.8	15 44.6	14 29.2	0♎18.7	16 2.7	28 26.4	15 11.6	22 49.1	5 13.9	8 9.5
18	23 45 31.7	24 33.4	2 43.6	27 36.3	15 55.5	1 33.3	16 41.0	28 21.0	15 14.4	22 50.0	5 13.9	8 11.4
19	23 49 28.2	25 31.9	2 40.4	9♌27.8	17 20.6	2 47.9	17 19.3	28 15.5	15 17.3	22 50.8	5 13.9	8 13.3
20	23 53 24.8	26 30.6	2 37.2	21 22.7	18 44.5	4 2.5	17 57.7	28 9.8	15 20.2	22 51.7	5 D 14.0	8 15.2
21	23 57 21.3	27 29.2	2 34.0	3♍24.2	20 7.2	5 17.1	18 36.0	28 3.9	15 23.2	22 52.7	5 14.1	8 17.1
22	0 1 17.9	28 27.9	2 30.9	15 34.6	21 28.7	6 31.8	19 14.4	27 57.9	15 26.4	22 53.7	5 14.2	8 19.1
23	0 5 14.4	29 26.6	2 27.7	27 55.8	22 48.8	7 46.4	19 52.7	27 51.7	15 29.6	22 54.8	5 14.4	8 21.1
24	0 9 11.0	0♎25.3	2 24.5	10♎29.0	24 7.7	9 1.1	20 31.1	27 45.4	15 32.9	22 55.9	5 14.6	8 23.1
25	0 13 7.5	1 24.1	2 21.3	23 15.1	25 25.2	10 15.8	21 9.5	27 39.0	15 36.3	22 57.1	5 14.9	8 25.2
26	0 17 4.1	2 23.0	2 18.2	6♏14.7	26 41.3	11 30.4	21 47.9	27 32.5	15 39.7	22 58.3	5 15.2	8 27.2
27	0 21 .7	3 21.8	2 15.0	19 28.0	27 55.8	12 45.1	22 26.3	27 25.8	15 43.3	22 59.6	5 15.5	8 29.3
28	0 24 57.2	4 20.7	2 11.8	2♐55.0	29 8.7	13 59.7	23 4.7	27 18.9	15 46.9	23 .9	5 15.8	8 31.4
29	0 28 53.8	5 19.6	2 8.6	16 35.8	0♏20.0	15 14.4	23 43.1	27 12.0	15 50.6	23 2.3	5 16.2	8 33.5
30	0 32 50.3	6 18.5	2 5.4	0♑29.7	1 29.4	16 29.1	24 21.6	27 5.0	15 54.4	23 3.7	5 16.6	8 35.6

LATITUDE

DAY	EPHEM. SID. TIME	☉	☊	☽	☿	♀	♂	♃	♄	♅	♆	♇
1	22 38 30.3	0 .0	0 .0	4S41.5	1N 7.4	1N24.7	1N 6.8	1S29.7	1N23.0	0S 9.5	1N 1.4	15N57.9
4	22 50 19.9	0 .0	0 .0	5 2.2	0 49.3	1 24.9	1 6.4	1 30.3	1 22.4	0 9.5	1 1.3	15 56.4
7	23 2 9.6	0 .0	0 .0	2 33.4	0 29.2	1 24.5	1 6.0	1 31.0	1 21.8	0 9.5	1 1.1	15 55.0
10	23 13 59.2	0 .0	0 .0	1N19.0	0 7.5	1 23.5	1 5.6	1 31.6	1 21.2	0 9.5	1 1.0	15 53.7
13	23 25 48.9	0 .0	0 .0	4 17.7	0S15.2	1 21.9	1 5.1	1 32.1	1 20.6	0 9.5	1 .9	15 52.4
16	23 37 38.6	0 .0	0 .0	5 16.4	0 38.5	1 19.8	1 4.7	1 32.7	1 20.0	0 9.5	1 .8	15 51.1
19	23 49 28.2	0 .0	0 .0	4 12.9	1 2.1	1 17.1	1 4.2	1 33.2	1 19.4	0 9.5	1 .6	15 49.9
22	0 1 17.9	0 .0	0 .0	1 31.8	1 25.5	1 13.9	1 3.6	1 33.6	1 18.8	0 9.5	1 .5	15 48.8
25	0 13 7.5	0 .0	0 .0	1S53.3	1 48.4	1 10.1	1 3.1	1 34.0	1 18.3	0 9.5	1 .4	15 47.7
28	0 24 57.2	0 .0	0 .0	4 36.2	2 10.4	1 5.8	1 2.5	1 34.3	1 17.7	0 9.5	1 .3	15 46.7

RIGHT ASCENSION

DAY	EPHEM. SID. TIME	☉	☊	☽	☿	♀	♂	♃	♄	♅	♆	♇
1	22 38 30.3	9♍42.2	3♈19.7	3♐13.3	20♍13.2	12♍29.3	8♍ 3.2	27♈57.1	13♐31.6	22♐ 3.6	5♑43.9	10♏28.4
2	22 42 26.8	10 36.6	3 16.8	18 34.5	21 47.8	13 39.0	8 39.2	27 R 54.8	13 32.9	22 3.6	5 R 43.3	10 29.5
3	22 46 23.4	11 31.0	3 13.8	4♑41.8	23 20.9	14 48.5	9 15.1	27 52.3	13 34.3	22 D 3.7	5 42.8	10 30.8
4	22 50 19.9	12 25.3	3 10.9	21 1.1	24 52.7	15 57.8	9 51.1	27 49.7	13 35.9	22 3.8	5 42.4	10 32.1
5	22 54 16.5	13 19.5	3 8.0	6♒56.0	26 23.2	17 7.0	10 27.0	27 46.8	13 37.6	22 4.0	5 42.0	10 33.3
6	22 58 13.0	14 13.6	3 5.1	22 2.0	27 52.4	18 16.0	11 2.8	27 43.8	13 39.3	22 4.2	5 41.5	10 34.6
7	23 2 9.6	15 7.7	3 2.2	6♓12.6	29 20.3	19 24.9	11 38.6	27 40.6	13 41.2	22 4.5	5 41.2	10 35.9
8	23 6 6.1	16 1.7	2 59.3	19 35.4	0♎47.1	20 33.7	12 14.4	27 37.2	13 43.1	22 4.8	5 40.8	10 37.3
9	23 10 2.7	16 55.6	2 56.3	2♈25.3	2 12.8	21 42.3	12 50.1	27 33.6	13 45.2	22 5.2	5 40.5	10 38.7
10	23 13 59.2	17 49.6	2 53.4	14 59.6	3 37.3	22 50.8	13 25.7	27 29.8	13 47.3	22 5.6	5 40.3	10 40.1
11	23 17 55.8	18 43.5	2 50.5	27 34.1	5 .9	23 59.3	14 1.4	27 25.9	13 49.6	22 6.1	5 40.0	10 41.5
12	23 21 52.4	19 37.3	2 47.6	10♉21.6	6 23.4	25 7.7	14 37.0	27 21.8	13 51.9	22 6.7	5 39.8	10 43.0
13	23 25 48.9	20 31.2	2 44.7	23 29.2	7 45.0	26 15.9	15 12.6	27 17.6	13 54.4	22 7.3	5 39.7	10 44.4
14	23 29 45.5	21 25.0	2 41.8	6♊57.2	9 5.6	27 24.2	15 48.1	27 13.2	13 56.9	22 7.9	5 39.5	10 45.9
15	23 33 42.0	22 18.8	2 38.8	20 38.5	10 25.3	28 32.3	16 23.6	27 8.6	13 59.5	22 8.7	5 39.4	10 47.5
16	23 37 38.6	23 12.6	2 35.9	4♋19.7	11 44.2	29 40.5	16 59.1	27 3.8	14 2.3	22 9.4	5 39.4	10 49.0
17	23 41 35.1	24 6.4	2 33.0	17 45.4	13 2.1	0♎48.6	17 34.6	26 58.9	14 5.1	22 10.3	5 39.3	10 50.6
18	23 45 31.7	25 .2	2 30.1	0♌43.2	14 19.1	1 56.6	18 10.0	26 53.9	14 8.0	22 11.2	5 D 39.4	10 52.2
19	23 49 28.2	25 54.0	2 27.2	13 6.5	15 35.3	3 4.7	18 45.5	26 48.7	14 11.1	22 12.1	5 39.4	10 53.8
20	23 53 24.8	26 47.8	2 24.3	24 55.7	16 50.6	4 12.7	19 20.9	26 43.3	14 14.2	22 13.1	5 39.5	10 55.4
21	23 57 21.3	27 41.6	2 21.3	6♍16.6	18 5.0	5 20.8	19 56.2	26 37.8	14 17.4	22 14.1	5 39.6	10 57.1
22	0 1 17.9	28 35.5	2 18.4	17 19.2	19 18.5	6 28.9	20 31.6	26 32.1	14 20.7	22 15.3	5 39.7	10 58.8
23	0 5 14.4	29 29.3	2 15.5	28 15.8	20 31.0	7 37.0	21 7.0	26 26.4	14 24.1	22 16.4	5 39.9	11 .5
24	0 9 11.0	0♎23.2	2 12.6	9♎20.4	21 42.6	8 45.2	21 42.3	26 20.4	14 27.6	22 17.6	5 40.2	11 2.2
25	0 13 7.5	1 17.2	2 9.7	20 48.2	22 53.2	9 53.4	22 17.6	26 14.4	14 31.2	22 19.0	5 40.5	11 4.0
26	0 17 4.1	2 11.2	2 6.8	2♏54.5	24 2.7	11 1.7	22 52.9	26 8.3	14 34.9	22 20.3	5 40.8	11 5.7
27	0 21 .7	3 5.2	2 3.9	15 53.2	25 11.1	12 10.0	23 28.2	26 2.0	14 38.7	22 21.7	5 41.1	11 7.5
28	0 24 57.2	3 59.2	2 .9	29 52.9	26 18.2	13 18.4	24 3.5	25 55.6	14 42.5	22 23.1	5 41.5	11 9.3
29	0 28 53.8	4 53.3	1 58.0	14♐51.9	27 24.1	14 26.9	24 38.7	25 49.1	14 46.5	22 24.6	5 41.9	11 11.2
30	0 32 50.3	5 47.5	1 55.1	0♑33.7	28 28.5	15 35.5	25 14.0	25 42.4	14 50.5	22 26.1	5 42.3	11 13.0

DECLINATION

DAY	EPHEM. SID. TIME	☉	☊	☽	☿	♀	♂	♃	♄	♅	♆	♇
1	22 38 30.3	8N33.2	0N 1.5	25S55.9	5N26.1	8N57.6	10N24.2	9N53.6	21S11.2	23S24.1	22S18.9	1N 3.2
4	22 50 19.9	7 27.7	0 1.4	27 7.6	3 6.7	7 32.3	9 41.3	9 50.1	21 12.3	23 24.1	22 19.1	1 .4
7	23 2 9.6	6 21.0	0 1.4	12 40.0	0 49.0	6 5.1	8 57.9	9 46.1	21 13.5	23 24.1	22 19.2	0 57.6
10	23 13 59.2	5 13.5	0 1.3	7N49.7	1S26.0	4 36.3	8 13.9	9 41.4	21 14.7	23 24.2	22 19.4	0 54.8
13	23 25 48.9	4 5.1	0 1.2	23 38.1	3 37.3	3 6.4	7 29.6	9 36.3	21 16.1	23 24.3	22 19.5	0 52.0
16	23 37 38.6	2 56.1	0 1.2	28 39.6	5 44.3	1 35.5	6 44.8	9 30.6	21 17.5	23 24.4	22 19.7	0 49.2
19	23 49 28.2	1 46.6	0 1.1	21 56.8	7 46.0	0 4.0	5 59.6	9 24.4	21 19.0	23 24.5	22 19.8	0 46.4
22	0 1 17.9	0 36.6	0 1.0	7 5.8	9 41.9	1S27.7	5 14.1	9 17.7	21 20.5	23 24.7	22 19.9	0 43.5
25	0 13 7.5	0S33.5	0 1.0	10S47.4	11 30.9	2 59.4	4 28.3	9 10.6	21 22.1	23 24.9	22 20.0	0 40.7
28	0 24 57.2	1 43.6	0 .9	25 15.6	13 12.2	4 30.6	3 42.3	9 3.1	21 23.8	23 25.1	22 20.1	0 37.9

OCTOBER 1987

DAY	EPHEM. SID. TIME	☉	☊	☽	☿	♀	♂	♃	♄	♅	♆	♇
	h m s	° ′	° ′	° ′	° ′	° ′	° ′	° ′	° ′	° ′	° ′	° ′
		LONGITUDE										
1	0 36 46.9	7♎17.4	2♈ 2.3	14♑36.0	2♏36.9	17♎43.8	24♍60.0	26♈57.8	15♐58.3	23♐ 5.2	5♑17.0	8♏37.7
2	0 40 43.4	8 16.4	1 59.1	28 52.8	3 42.4	18 58.4	25 38.4	26R50.5	16 2.2	23 6.7	5 17.5	8 39.9
3	0 44 40.0	9 15.4	1 55.9	13♒17.7	4 45.6	20 13.1	26 16.9	26 43.2	16 6.3	23 8.2	5 18.0	8 42.1
4	0 48 36.5	10 14.5	1 52.7	27 47.0	5 46.5	21 27.8	26 55.3	26 35.8	16 10.4	23 9.8	5 18.6	8 44.3
5	0 52 33.1	11 13.5	1 49.6	12♓16.2	6 44.8	22 42.5	27 33.8	26 28.2	16 14.6	23 11.5	5 19.1	8 46.5
6	0 56 29.6	12 12.6	1 46.4	26 40.0	7 40.3	23 57.1	28 12.3	26 20.6	16 18.8	23 13.2	5 19.7	8 48.7
7	1 0 26.2	13 11.8	1 43.2	10♈53.3	8 32.7	25 11.8	28 50.8	26 12.9	16 23.2	23 14.9	5 20.4	8 50.9
8	1 4 22.7	14 10.9	1 40.0	24 51.4	9 21.8	26 26.5	29 29.3	26 5.2	16 27.6	23 16.7	5 21.0	8 53.2
9	1 8 19.3	15 10.1	1 36.9	8♉30.8	10 7.2	27 41.2	0♎ 7.8	25 57.4	16 32.1	23 18.6	5 21.7	8 55.4
10	1 12 15.9	16 9.4	1 33.7	21 49.3	10 48.7	28 55.9	0 46.3	25 49.5	16 36.6	23 20.4	5 22.5	8 57.7
11	1 16 12.4	17 8.7	1 30.5	4♊46.7	11 25.9	0♏10.5	1 24.9	25 41.6	16 41.2	23 22.4	5 23.2	8 60.0
12	1 20 9.0	18 8.0	1 27.3	17 24.0	11 58.2	1 25.2	2 3.4	25 33.6	16 45.9	23 24.3	5 24.0	9 2.3
13	1 24 5.5	19 7.3	1 24.1	29 43.9	12 25.4	2 39.9	2 42.0	25 25.6	16 50.7	23 26.4	5 24.9	9 4.6
14	1 28 2.1	20 6.7	1 21.0	11♋50.0	12 46.9	3 54.6	3 20.6	25 17.6	16 55.5	23 28.4	5 25.7	9 6.9
15	1 31 58.6	21 6.1	1 17.8	23 46.5	13 2.3	5 9.3	3 59.2	25 9.5	17 .4	23 30.5	5 26.6	9 9.2
16	1 35 55.2	22 5.7	1 14.6	5♌38.3	13 11.0	6 24.1	4 37.9	25 1.4	17 5.5	23 32.7	5 27.6	9 11.6
17	1 39 51.7	23 5.2	1 11.4	17 30.1	13 12.4	7 38.8	5 16.5	24 53.3	17 10.5	23 34.9	5 28.5	9 13.9
18	1 43 48.3	24 4.7	1 8.3	29 26.5	13R 6.1	8 53.5	5 55.2	24 45.2	17 15.6	23 37.1	5 29.5	9 16.3
19	1 47 44.8	25 4.3	1 5.1	11♍32.0	12 51.7	10 8.2	6 33.8	24 37.1	17 20.8	23 39.4	5 30.5	9 18.7
20	1 51 41.4	26 3.9	1 1.9	23 50.1	12 28.8	11 22.9	7 12.5	24 29.0	17 26.0	23 41.7	5 31.6	9 21.0
21	1 55 38.0	27 3.6	0 58.7	6♎23.6	11 57.1	12 37.6	7 51.2	24 20.8	17 31.3	23 44.1	5 32.7	9 23.4
22	1 59 34.5	28 3.3	0 55.5	19 14.2	11 16.7	13 52.4	8 29.9	24 12.7	17 36.7	23 46.5	5 33.8	9 25.8
23	2 3 31.1	29 3.0	0 52.4	2♏22.2	10 27.7	15 7.1	9 8.6	24 4.7	17 42.1	23 48.9	5 34.9	9 28.2
24	2 7 27.6	0♏ 2.7	0 49.2	15 47.1	9 30.7	16 21.8	9 47.3	23 56.6	17 47.5	23 51.4	5 36.1	9 30.6
25	2 11 24.2	1 2.5	0 46.0	29 26.8	8 26.6	17 36.5	10 26.1	23 48.6	17 53.1	23 53.9	5 37.3	9 33.0
26	2 15 20.7	2 2.3	0 42.8	13♐18.6	7 16.6	18 51.2	11 4.8	23 40.7	17 58.7	23 56.4	5 38.5	9 35.4
27	2 19 17.3	3 2.2	0 39.7	27 19.4	6 2.4	20 5.9	11 43.6	23 32.7	18 4.3	23 59.0	5 39.7	9 37.8
28	2 23 13.8	4 2.1	0 36.5	11♑26.0	4 46.1	21 20.6	12 22.4	23 24.9	18 10.0	24 1.6	5 41.0	9 40.3
29	2 27 10.4	5 2.0	0 33.3	25 35.6	3 29.8	22 35.4	13 1.1	23 17.1	18 15.8	24 4.3	5 42.3	9 42.7
30	2 31 7.0	6 1.9	0 30.1	9♒45.9	2 15.9	23 50.1	13 40.0	23 9.3	18 21.6	24 7.0	5 43.7	9 45.1
31	2 35 3.5	7 1.9	0 26.9	23 55.0	1 6.7	25 4.7	14 18.8	23 1.7	18 27.5	24 9.7	5 45.0	9 47.5
		LATITUDE										
1	0 36 46.9	0 .0	0 .0	5S 9.8	2S30.8	1N 1.0	1N 1.9	1S34.6	1N17.2	0S 9.5	1N .1	15N45.7
4	0 48 36.5	0 .0	0 .0	3 .3	2 49.1	0 55.8	1 1.3	1 34.8	1 16.6	0 9.5	0 60.0	15 44.9
7	1 0 26.2	0 .0	0 .0	0N46.9	3 4.4	0 50.2	1 .7	1 35.0	1 16.1	0 9.5	0 59.9	15 44.1
10	1 12 15.9	0 .0	0 .0	4 .4	3 15.4	0 44.2	0 60.0	1 35.1	1 15.6	0 9.5	0 59.7	15 43.3
13	1 24 5.5	0 .0	0 .0	5 15.3	3 20.6	0 37.8	0 59.3	1 35.1	1 15.1	0 9.5	0 59.6	15 42.7
16	1 35 55.2	0 .0	0 .0	4 23.6	3 17.7	0 31.1	0 58.6	1 35.1	1 14.6	0 9.5	0 59.5	15 42.1
19	1 47 44.8	0 .0	0 .0	1 52.0	3 3.8	0 24.1	0 57.8	1 35.0	1 14.2	0 9.5	0 59.4	15 41.6
22	1 59 34.5	0 .0	0 .0	1S31.5	2 35.8	0 16.9	0 57.0	1 34.8	1 13.7	0 9.6	0 59.3	15 41.1
25	2 11 24.2	0 .0	0 .0	4 23.1	1 52.0	0 9.5	0 56.2	1 34.5	1 13.3	0 9.6	0 59.1	15 40.8
28	2 23 13.8	0 .0	0 .0	5 7.8	0 55.0	0 1.9	0 55.4	1 34.2	1 12.8	0 9.6	0 59.0	15 40.5
31	2 35 3.5	0 .0	0 .0	3 12.4	0N 6.7	0S 5.7	0 54.5	1 33.8	1 12.4	0 9.6	0 58.9	15 40.3
		RIGHT ASCENSION										
1	0 36 46.9	6♎41.7	1♈52.2	16♑29.0	29♎31.5	16♎44.3	25♍49.2	25♈35.7	14♐54.6	22♐27.7	5♑42.8	11♏14.9
2	0 40 43.4	7 35.9	1 49.3	2♒ 5.0	0♏32.8	17 53.1	26 24.5	25R28.9	14 58.8	22 29.4	5 43.3	11 16.7
3	0 44 40.0	8 30.3	1 46.4	16 58.7	1 32.2	19 2.1	26 59.7	25 22.0	15 3.1	22 31.1	5 43.9	11 18.6
4	0 48 36.5	9 24.7	1 43.4	1♓ 2.3	2 29.7	20 11.2	27 34.9	25 15.0	15 7.5	22 32.8	5 44.4	11 20.5
5	0 52 33.1	10 19.2	1 40.5	14 21.3	3 24.9	21 20.4	28 10.2	25 7.9	15 11.9	22 34.6	5 45.1	11 22.5
6	0 56 29.6	11 13.8	1 37.6	27 9.1	4 17.8	22 29.8	28 45.4	25 .7	15 16.5	22 36.4	5 45.7	11 24.4
7	1 0 26.2	12 8.4	1 34.7	9♈42.1	5 7.9	23 39.4	29 20.6	24 53.5	15 21.1	22 38.3	5 46.4	11 26.4
8	1 4 22.7	13 3.2	1 31.8	22 16.3	5 55.1	24 49.2	29 55.9	24 46.2	15 25.8	22 40.3	5 47.1	11 28.4
9	1 8 19.3	13 58.1	1 28.9	5♉ 5.2	6 38.9	25 59.2	0♎31.1	24 38.9	15 30.5	22 42.3	5 47.9	11 30.3
10	1 12 15.9	14 53.1	1 25.9	18 17.0	7 19.2	27 9.3	1 6.4	24 31.5	15 35.4	22 44.3	5 48.7	11 32.4
11	1 16 12.4	15 48.2	1 23.0	1♊53.0	7 55.4	28 19.7	1 41.6	24 24.0	15 40.3	22 46.4	5 49.5	11 34.4
12	1 20 9.0	16 43.4	1 20.1	15 46.0	8 27.2	29 30.3	2 16.9	24 16.5	15 45.3	22 48.6	5 50.4	11 36.4
13	1 24 5.5	17 38.7	1 17.2	29 41.7	8 54.1	0♏41.1	2 52.2	24 9.0	15 50.4	22 50.8	5 51.3	11 38.5
14	1 28 2.1	18 34.2	1 14.3	13♋23.0	9 15.7	1 52.2	3 27.5	24 1.4	15 55.6	22 53.0	5 52.2	11 40.5
15	1 31 58.6	19 29.8	1 11.4	26 35.2	9 31.4	3 3.5	4 2.9	23 53.8	16 .8	22 55.3	5 53.1	11 42.6
16	1 35 55.2	20 25.6	1 8.5	9♌10.5	9 40.8	4 15.1	4 38.3	23 46.2	16 6.1	22 57.7	5 54.2	11 44.7
17	1 39 51.7	21 21.5	1 5.5	21 8.5	9 43.3	5 26.9	5 13.6	23 38.6	16 11.5	23 .1	5 55.2	11 46.8
18	1 43 48.3	22 17.6	1 2.6	2♍35.3	9R38.5	6 39.0	5 49.0	23 30.9	16 17.0	23 2.5	5 56.3	11 48.9
19	1 47 44.8	23 13.8	0 59.7	13 41.1	9 26.0	7 51.3	6 24.4	23 23.3	16 22.5	23 5.0	5 57.4	11 51.0
20	1 51 41.4	24 10.1	0 56.8	24 38.9	9 5.5	9 3.9	6 59.9	23 15.6	16 28.1	23 7.5	5 58.5	11 53.2
21	1 55 38.0	25 6.6	0 53.9	5♎43.3	8 36.9	10 16.8	7 35.3	23 8.0	16 33.7	23 10.1	5 59.7	11 55.3
22	1 59 34.5	26 3.3	0 51.0	17 10.0	8 .2	11 30.0	8 10.8	23 .3	16 39.5	23 12.7	6 .9	11 57.4
23	2 3 31.1	27 .2	0 48.0	29 14.9	7 15.8	12 43.5	8 46.3	22 52.7	16 45.2	23 15.3	6 2.1	11 59.6
24	2 7 27.6	27 57.2	0 45.1	12♏12.6	6 24.2	13 57.3	9 21.9	22 45.1	16 51.1	23 18.0	6 3.4	12 1.8
25	2 11 24.2	28 54.4	0 42.2	26 12.4	5 26.5	15 11.4	9 57.5	22 37.6	16 57.0	23 20.7	6 4.7	12 3.9
26	2 15 20.7	29 51.8	0 39.3	11♐13.1	4 23.8	16 25.8	10 33.1	22 30.1	17 3.0	23 23.5	6 6.0	12 6.1
27	2 19 17.3	0♏49.3	0 36.4	26 57.8	3 17.8	17 40.5	11 8.7	22 22.6	17 9.0	23 26.3	6 7.4	12 8.3
28	2 23 13.8	1 47.0	0 33.5	12♑55.7	2 10.5	18 55.5	11 44.4	22 15.2	17 15.1	23 29.2	6 8.7	12 10.5
29	2 27 10.4	2 44.9	0 30.6	28 32.5	1 3.8	20 10.8	12 20.1	22 7.8	17 21.3	23 32.1	6 10.2	12 12.7
30	2 31 7.0	3 43.0	0 27.6	13♒23.4	29♎59.9	21 26.4	12 55.9	22 .5	17 27.5	23 35.0	6 11.6	12 14.9
31	2 35 3.5	4 41.3	0 24.7	27 20.3	29 .8	22 42.3	13 31.6	21 53.3	17 33.8	23 38.0	6 13.1	12 17.1
		DECLINATION										
1	0 36 46.9	2S53.6	0N .8	27S46.5	14S44.5	6S 1.1	2N56.1	8N55.3	21S25.5	23S25.3	22S20.2	0N35.1
4	0 48 36.5	4 3.4	0 .8	15 3.8	16 6.4	7 30.4	2 9.7	8 47.1	21 27.3	23 25.5	22 20.3	0 32.3
7	1 0 26.2	5 12.7	0 .7	5N 1.7	17 15.7	8 58.3	1 23.2	8 38.8	21 29.1	23 25.8	22 20.3	0 29.5
10	1 12 15.9	6 21.3	0 .7	22 5.5	18 9.8	10 24.5	0 36.6	8 30.2	21 31.0	23 26.1	22 20.4	0 26.8
13	1 24 5.5	7 29.3	0 .6	28 41.9	18 45.0	11 48.5	0S10.0	8 21.5	21 32.8	23 26.4	22 20.4	0 24.1
16	1 35 55.2	8 36.4	0 .5	23 7.3	18 56.3	13 10.0	0 56.7	8 12.8	21 34.7	23 26.7	22 20.4	0 21.5
19	1 47 44.8	9 42.3	0 .5	8 57.9	18 37.1	14 28.7	1 43.3	8 4.0	21 36.6	23 27.0	22 20.4	0 18.9
22	1 59 34.5	10 47.0	0 .4	8S56.6	17 41.0	15 44.2	2 29.8	7 55.3	21 38.6	23 27.4	22 20.4	0 16.4
25	2 11 24.2	11 50.3	0 .3	24 18.9	16 5.3	16 56.1	3 16.2	7 46.7	21 40.5	23 27.7	22 20.4	0 13.9
28	2 23 13.8	12 52.0	0 .3	28 3.7	13 58.6	18 4.2	4 2.4	7 38.2	21 42.4	23 28.1	22 20.3	0 11.5
31	2 35 3.5	13 51.8	0 .2	16 34.5	11 45.5	19 7.9	4 48.4	7 30.0	21 44.4	23 28.4	22 20.3	0 9.1

NOVEMBER 1987

LONGITUDE

DAY	EPHEM. SID. TIME h m s	☉ ° ′	☊ ° ′	☽ ° ′	☿ ° ′	♀ ° ′	♂ ° ′	♃ ° ′	♄ ° ′	♅ ° ′	♆ ° ′	♇ ° ′
1	2 39 .1	8 ♏ 1.8	0 ♈ 23.8	8 ♓ 1.2	0 ♏ 4.4	26 ♏ 19.4	14 ♎ 57.6	22 ♈ 54.1	18 ♐ 33.4	24 ♐ 12.5	5 ♑ 46.4	9 ♏ 50.0
2	2 42 56.6	9 1.8	0 20.6	22 2.9	29 ♎ 10.8	27 34.1	15 36.4	22 R 46.6	18 39.4	24 15.3	5 47.9	9 52.4
3	2 46 53.2	10 1.9	0 17.4	5 ♈ 58.4	28 R 27.3	28 48.8	16 15.3	22 39.2	18 45.4	24 18.1	5 49.3	9 54.8
4	2 50 49.7	11 2.0	0 14.2	19 45.2	27 54.8	0 ♐ 3.5	16 54.2	22 31.9	18 51.5	24 21.0	5 50.8	9 57.2
5	2 54 46.3	12 2.0	0 11.1	3 ♉ 21.1	27 33.8	1 18.2	17 33.0	22 24.7	18 57.6	24 23.9	5 52.3	9 59.7
6	2 58 42.8	13 2.2	0 7.9	16 43.7	27 24.5	2 32.9	18 12.0	22 17.6	19 3.8	24 26.8	5 53.9	10 2.2
7	3 2 39.4	14 2.4	0 4.7	29 50.9	27 D 26.6	3 47.5	18 50.9	22 10.6	19 10.0	24 29.8	5 55.4	10 4.6
8	3 6 36.0	15 2.6	0 1.5	12 ♊ 41.5	27 39.5	5 2.2	19 29.8	22 3.8	19 16.2	24 32.8	5 57.0	10 7.0
9	3 10 32.5	16 2.8	29 ♓ 58.4	25 15.6	28 2.6	6 16.9	20 8.8	21 57.0	19 22.5	24 35.8	5 58.6	10 9.4
10	3 14 29.1	17 3.0	29 55.2	7 ♋ 34.3	28 35.1	7 31.5	20 47.8	21 50.4	19 28.8	24 38.8	6 .2	10 11.8
11	3 18 25.6	18 3.3	29 52.0	19 40.0	29 16.1	8 46.2	21 26.7	21 43.9	19 35.2	24 41.9	6 1.9	10 14.3
12	3 22 22.2	19 3.6	29 48.8	1 ♌ 36.1	0 ♏ 4.7	10 .8	22 5.7	21 37.5	19 41.6	24 45.0	6 3.5	10 16.7
13	3 26 18.7	20 4.0	29 45.6	13 27.0	0 59.7	11 15.5	22 44.8	21 31.3	19 48.1	24 48.1	6 5.2	10 19.1
14	3 30 15.3	21 4.4	29 42.5	25 17.5	2 1.1	12 30.1	23 23.8	21 25.2	19 54.6	24 51.3	6 6.9	10 21.5
15	3 34 11.9	22 4.8	29 39.3	7 ♍ 13.0	3 7.4	13 44.8	24 2.8	21 19.3	20 1.1	24 54.5	6 8.7	10 23.9
16	3 38 8.4	23 5.2	29 36.1	19 18.5	4 18.1	14 59.4	24 41.9	21 13.5	20 7.6	24 57.7	6 10.5	10 26.2
17	3 42 5.0	24 5.7	29 32.9	1 ♎ 39.1	5 32.6	16 14.0	25 21.0	21 7.8	20 14.2	25 .9	6 12.2	10 28.6
18	3 46 1.5	25 6.2	29 29.8	14 19.0	6 50.4	17 28.7	26 .1	21 2.4	20 20.9	25 4.2	6 14.0	10 31.0
19	3 49 58.1	26 6.7	29 26.6	27 21.0	8 10.9	18 43.3	26 39.2	20 57.1	20 27.5	25 7.5	6 15.9	10 33.4
20	3 53 54.6	27 7.3	29 23.4	10 ♏ 46.4	9 33.8	19 57.9	27 18.4	20 51.9	20 34.2	25 10.8	6 17.7	10 35.7
21	3 57 51.2	28 7.9	29 20.2	24 34.2	10 58.5	21 12.6	27 57.5	20 47.0	20 40.9	25 14.1	6 19.6	10 38.1
22	4 1 47.8	29 8.5	29 17.1	8 ♐ 41.3	12 25.0	22 27.2	28 36.7	20 42.2	20 47.7	25 17.4	6 21.5	10 40.4
23	4 5 44.3	0 ♐ 9.1	29 13.9	23 2.6	13 52.7	23 41.8	29 15.8	20 37.6	20 54.5	25 20.8	6 23.4	10 42.7
24	4 9 40.9	1 9.8	29 10.7	7 ♑ 31.6	15 21.6	24 56.4	29 55.0	20 33.2	21 1.3	25 24.2	6 25.3	10 45.1
25	4 13 37.4	2 10.5	29 7.5	22 2.0	16 51.5	26 11.0	0 ♏ 34.2	20 28.9	21 8.1	25 27.6	6 27.3	10 47.4
26	4 17 34.0	3 11.2	29 4.4	6 ♒ 27.0	18 22.0	27 25.5	1 13.5	20 24.9	21 15.0	25 31.0	6 29.2	10 49.6
27	4 21 30.5	4 11.9	29 1.2	20 45.3	19 53.3	28 40.3	1 52.7	20 21.1	21 21.9	25 34.5	6 31.2	10 52.0
28	4 25 27.1	5 12.7	28 58.0	4 ♓ 51.8	21 25.0	29 54.8	2 32.0	20 17.4	21 28.8	25 38.0	6 33.2	10 54.2
29	4 29 23.7	6 13.4	28 54.8	18 46.5	22 57.1	1 ♑ 9.4	3 11.3	20 13.9	21 35.7	25 41.4	6 35.3	10 56.5
30	4 33 20.2	7 14.2	28 51.6	2 ♈ 29.7	24 29.5	2 23.9	3 50.5	20 10.6	21 42.6	25 44.9	6 37.3	10 58.7

LATITUDE

DAY	EPHEM. SID. TIME h m s	☉	☊	☽	☿	♀	♂	♃	♄	♅	♆	♇
1	2 39 .1	0 .0	0 .0	2 S 6.7	0 N 26.3	0 S 8.3	0 N 54.2	1 S 33.7	1 N 12.3	0 S 9.6	0 N 58.9	15 N 40.2
4	2 50 49.7	0 .0	0 .0	1 N 35.1	1 17.5	0 16.0	0 53.3	1 33.2	1 11.9	0 9.6	0 58.8	15 40.1
7	3 2 39.4	0 .0	0 .0	4 22.3	1 53.0	0 23.8	0 52.4	1 32.7	1 11.5	0 9.6	0 58.7	15 40.1
10	3 14 29.1	0 .0	0 .0	5 6.2	2 12.5	0 31.4	0 51.4	1 32.1	1 11.1	0 9.6	0 58.6	15 40.1
13	3 26 18.7	0 .0	0 .0	3 48.2	2 18.7	0 39.0	0 50.4	1 31.5	1 10.8	0 9.6	0 58.5	15 40.3
16	3 38 8.4	0 .0	0 .0	1 3.2	2 14.9	0 46.4	0 49.4	1 30.8	1 10.5	0 9.6	0 58.4	15 40.5
19	3 49 58.1	0 .0	0 .0	2 S 15.7	2 4.2	0 53.6	0 48.3	1 30.1	1 10.1	0 9.7	0 58.3	15 40.7
22	4 1 47.8	0 .0	0 .0	4 42.0	1 48.9	1 .6	0 47.2	1 29.3	1 9.8	0 9.7	0 58.3	15 41.1
25	4 13 37.4	0 .0	0 .0	4 42.3	1 30.5	1 7.2	0 46.0	1 28.5	1 9.5	0 9.7	0 58.1	15 41.5
28	4 25 27.1	0 .0	0 .0	2 10.0	1 10.4	1 13.5	0 44.9	1 27.7	1 9.2	0 9.7	0 58.0	15 42.1

RIGHT ASCENSION

DAY	EPHEM. SID. TIME h m s	☉	☊	☽	☿	♀	♂	♃	♄	♅	♆	♇
1	2 39 .1	5 ♏ 39.8	0 ♈ 21.8	10 ♓ 28.9	28 ♎ 8.2	23 ♏ 58.6	14 ♎ 7.5	21 ♈ 46.2	17 ♐ 40.1	23 ♐ 41.0	6 ♑ 14.6	12 ♏ 19.3
2	2 42 56.6	6 38.4	0 18.9	23 3.1	27 R 23.8	25 15.1	14 43.3	21 R 39.1	17 43.4	23 44.0	6 16.1	12 21.5
3	2 46 53.2	7 37.3	0 16.0	5 ♈ 20.3	26 48.6	26 31.9	15 19.3	21 32.1	17 53.0	23 47.1	6 17.7	12 23.7
4	2 50 49.7	8 36.3	0 13.1	17 37.7	26 23.4	27 49.1	15 55.2	21 25.2	17 59.5	23 50.2	6 19.3	12 25.9
5	2 54 46.3	9 35.6	0 10.2	0 ♉ 10.4	26 8.5	29 6.5	16 31.2	21 18.4	18 6.0	23 53.4	6 20.9	12 28.2
6	2 58 42.8	10 35.1	0 7.2	13 9.3	26 4.0	0 ♐ 24.3	17 7.3	21 11.7	18 12.7	23 56.6	6 22.6	12 30.4
7	3 2 39.4	11 34.8	0 4.3	26 38.3	26 D 9.6	1 42.3	17 43.4	21 5.1	18 19.3	23 59.9	6 24.3	12 32.7
8	3 6 36.0	12 34.7	0 1.4	10 ♊ 32.5	26 24.7	3 .7	18 19.6	20 58.6	18 26.0	24 3.1	6 26.0	12 34.9
9	3 10 32.5	13 34.7	29 ♓ 58.5	24 37.7	26 48.9	4 19.3	18 55.8	20 52.2	18 32.7	24 6.4	6 27.7	12 37.1
10	3 14 29.1	14 35.1	29 55.6	8 ♋ 54.5	27 21.4	5 38.2	19 32.1	20 45.9	18 39.5	24 9.7	6 29.5	12 39.3
11	3 18 25.6	15 35.6	29 52.7	23 21.8	28 1.4	6 57.3	20 8.4	20 39.8	18 46.4	24 13.1	6 31.3	12 41.6
12	3 22 22.2	16 36.3	29 49.7	7 ♌ 55.3	28 48.1	8 16.7	20 44.8	20 33.7	18 53.2	24 16.4	6 33.1	12 43.8
13	3 26 18.7	17 37.3	29 46.8	17 4.6	29 40.9	9 36.4	21 21.2	20 27.8	19 .2	24 19.9	6 34.9	12 46.0
14	3 30 15.3	18 38.4	29 43.9	28 37.0	0 ♏ 39.0	10 56.3	21 57.7	20 22.1	19 7.1	24 23.3	6 36.8	12 48.2
15	3 34 11.9	19 39.8	29 41.0	9 ♍ 42.8	1 41.9	12 16.5	22 34.3	20 16.4	19 14.1	24 26.8	6 38.6	12 50.4
16	3 38 8.4	20 41.4	29 38.1	20 35.3	2 48.8	13 36.9	23 11.0	20 11.0	19 21.2	24 30.3	6 40.6	12 52.6
17	3 42 5.0	21 43.3	29 35.2	1 ♎ 29.9	3 59.4	14 57.5	23 47.7	20 5.6	19 28.2	24 33.9	6 42.5	12 54.9
18	3 46 1.5	22 45.3	29 32.3	12 43.3	5 13.6	16 18.3	24 24.4	20 .4	19 35.4	24 37.3	6 44.4	12 57.1
19	3 49 58.1	23 47.5	29 29.3	24 33.2	6 29.6	17 39.2	25 1.3	19 55.4	19 42.5	24 40.9	6 46.4	12 59.3
20	3 53 54.6	24 50.0	29 26.4	7 ♏ 16.8	7 48.5	19 .4	25 38.2	19 50.5	19 49.7	24 44.5	6 48.4	13 1.5
21	3 57 51.2	25 52.6	29 23.5	21 7.5	9 9.5	20 21.7	26 15.1	19 45.8	19 56.9	24 48.1	6 50.4	13 3.7
22	4 1 47.8	26 55.5	29 20.6	6 ♐ 8.9	10 32.4	21 43.2	26 52.2	19 41.2	20 4.2	24 51.8	6 52.5	13 5.8
23	4 5 44.3	27 58.6	29 17.7	22 7.5	11 56.9	23 4.8	27 29.3	19 36.8	20 11.5	24 55.4	6 54.5	13 8.0
24	4 9 40.9	29 1.8	29 14.8	8 ♑ 31.1	13 22.9	24 26.5	28 6.5	19 32.6	20 18.8	24 59.1	6 56.6	13 10.2
25	4 13 37.4	0 ♐ 5.3	29 11.9	24 38.6	14 50.4	25 48.4	28 43.7	19 28.5	20 26.1	25 2.8	6 58.7	13 12.5
26	4 17 34.0	1 8.9	29 8.9	9 ♒ 57.4	16 18.6	27 10.3	29 21.1	19 24.6	20 33.5	25 6.6	7 .8	13 14.5
27	4 21 30.5	2 12.8	29 6.0	24 49.1	17 48.1	28 32.3	29 58.5	19 21.0	20 40.9	25 10.4	7 3.0	13 16.7
28	4 25 27.1	3 16.8	29 3.1	7 ♓ 31.1	19 18.6	29 54.3	0 ♏ 36.0	19 17.5	20 48.3	25 14.1	7 5.2	13 18.8
29	4 29 23.7	4 21.0	29 .2	20 4.4	20 50.0	1 ♑ 16.4	1 13.5	19 14.1	20 55.8	25 17.9	7 7.3	13 20.9
30	4 33 20.2	5 25.3	28 57.3	2 ♈ 12.2	22 22.2	2 38.4	1 51.2	19 10.9	21 3.3	25 21.7	7 9.5	13 23.1

DECLINATION

DAY	EPHEM. SID. TIME h m s	☉	☊	☽	☿	♀	♂	♃	♄	♅	♆	♇
1	2 39 .1	14 S 11.3	0 N .2	10 S 31.3	11 S 5.3	19 S 28.1	5 S 3.7	7 N 27.4	21 S 45.0	23 S 28.6	22 S 20.2	0 N 8.4
4	2 50 49.7	15 8.4	0 .1	9 N 11.7	9 31.7	20 25.6	5 49.3	7 19.6	21 46.9	23 28.9	22 20.1	0 6.1
7	3 2 39.4	16 3.3	0 .0	24 48.4	8 54.5	21 18.1	6 34.6	7 12.2	21 48.8	23 29.3	22 20.0	0 4.0
10	3 14 29.1	16 55.8	0 .0	28 19.3	8 54.5	22 5.2	7 19.6	7 5.2	21 50.7	23 29.7	22 19.9	0 1.9
13	3 26 18.7	17 45.7	0 S .1	20 25.7	9 39.4	22 46.5	8 4.1	6 58.7	21 52.5	23 30.1	22 19.8	0 S .1
16	3 38 8.4	18 32.8	0 .2	5 12.1	10 50.3	23 22.0	8 48.2	6 52.6	21 54.3	23 30.5	22 19.7	0 2.0
19	3 49 58.1	19 17.1	0 .2	13 S 38.5	12 16.6	23 51.3	9 31.8	6 47.2	21 56.1	23 30.9	22 19.5	0 3.8
22	4 1 47.8	19 58.2	0 .3	26 23.7	13 50.2	24 14.2	10 14.9	6 42.3	21 57.8	23 31.2	22 19.3	0 5.5
25	4 13 37.4	20 36.0	0 .4	26 17.0	15 25.7	24 30.5	10 57.3	6 38.1	21 59.4	23 31.6	22 19.1	0 7.1
28	4 25 27.1	21 10.4	0 .4	11 44.7	16 59.2	24 40.1	11 39.1	6 34.5	22 1.1	23 32.0	22 18.9	0 8.6

DECEMBER 1987

LONGITUDE

DAY	EPHEM. SID. TIME	☉	☊	☽	☿	♀	♂	♃	♄	♅	♆	♇
	h m s	° ′	° ′	° ′	° ′	° ′	° ′	° ′	° ′	° ′	° ′	° ′
1	4 37 16.8	8♐15.0	28♓48.5	16♈ 1.7	26♏ 2.2	3♑38.5	4♏29.8	20♈ 7.6	21♐49.6	25♐48.4	6♑39.3	11♏ 1.0
2	4 41 13.3	9 15.8	28 45.3	29 23.3	27 35.1	4 53.0	5 9.1	20 R 4.7	21 56.6	25 51.9	6 41.4	11 3.2
3	4 45 9.9	10 16.6	28 42.1	12♉34.4	29 8.1	6 7.5	5 48.4	20 2.0	22 3.6	25 55.5	6 43.5	11 5.4
4	4 49 6.5	11 17.4	28 38.9	25 34.7	0♐41.2	7 22.0	6 27.8	19 59.5	22 10.6	25 59.0	6 45.5	11 7.5
5	4 53 3.0	12 18.2	28 35.8	8♊23.6	2 14.5	8 36.5	7 7.1	19 57.2	22 17.6	26 2.5	6 47.6	11 9.7
6	4 56 59.6	13 19.1	28 32.6	21 .5	3 47.8	9 50.9	7 46.5	19 55.2	22 24.6	26 6.1	6 49.8	11 11.8
7	5 0 56.1	14 20.0	28 29.4	3♋25.1	5 21.2	11 5.4	8 25.9	19 53.3	22 31.7	26 9.7	6 51.9	11 14.0
8	5 4 52.7	15 20.9	28 26.2	15 37.9	6 54.6	12 19.8	9 5.3	19 51.6	22 38.7	26 13.3	6 54.0	11 16.1
9	5 8 49.2	16 21.8	28 23.1	27 40.1	8 28.1	13 34.3	9 44.7	19 50.2	22 45.8	26 16.9	6 56.2	11 18.2
10	5 12 45.8	17 22.8	28 19.9	9♌34.0	10 1.6	14 48.7	10 24.2	19 48.9	22 52.9	26 20.5	6 58.3	11 20.2
11	5 16 42.4	18 23.7	28 16.7	21 23.1	11 35.2	16 3.1	11 3.6	19 47.9	22 59.9	26 24.1	7 .5	11 22.3
12	5 20 38.9	19 24.7	28 13.5	3♍11.6	13 8.9	17 17.5	11 43.1	19 47.1	23 7.0	26 27.7	7 2.7	11 24.3
13	5 24 35.5	20 25.7	28 10.4	15 4.4	14 42.6	18 31.8	12 22.6	19 46.4	23 14.1	26 31.3	7 4.9	11 26.3
14	5 28 32.0	21 26.7	28 7.2	27 6.9	16 16.4	19 46.2	13 2.1	19 46.0	23 21.2	26 34.9	7 7.1	11 28.3
15	5 32 28.6	22 27.7	28 4.0	9♎24.8	17 50.3	21 .5	13 41.6	19 45.8	23 28.3	26 38.5	7 9.3	11 30.3
16	5 36 25.2	23 28.8	28 .8	22 3.2	19 24.2	22 14.8	14 21.2	19 45.8	23 35.4	26 42.2	7 11.5	11 32.2
17	5 40 21.7	24 29.8	27 57.6	5♏ 6.7	20 58.3	23 29.2	15 .7	19 D 46.0	23 42.5	26 45.8	7 13.7	11 34.2
18	5 44 18.3	25 31.0	27 54.5	18 37.9	22 32.5	24 43.5	15 40.4	19 46.5	23 49.7	26 49.5	7 16.0	11 36.1
19	5 48 14.8	26 32.1	27 51.3	2♐37.2	24 6.9	25 57.8	16 20.0	19 47.1	23 56.7	26 53.1	7 18.2	11 38.0
20	5 52 11.4	27 33.2	27 48.1	17 1.9	25 41.3	27 12.0	16 59.6	19 48.0	24 3.8	26 56.8	7 20.5	11 39.8
21	5 56 8.0	28 34.3	27 44.9	1♑46.1	27 16.0	28 26.3	17 39.2	19 49.0	24 10.9	27 .4	7 22.7	11 41.7
22	6 0 4.5	29 35.4	27 41.8	16 41.7	28 50.8	29 40.5	18 18.8	19 50.3	24 18.0	27 4.0	7 25.0	11 43.5
23	6 4 1.1	0♑36.5	27 38.6	1♒39.1	0♑25.8	0♒54.7	18 58.5	19 51.7	24 25.1	27 7.7	7 27.2	11 45.3
24	6 7 57.6	1 37.7	27 35.4	16 29.4	2 1.0	2 8.8	19 38.1	19 53.4	24 32.2	27 11.3	7 29.5	11 47.0
25	6 11 54.2	2 38.8	27 32.2	1♓ 5.7	3 36.5	3 23.0	20 17.8	19 55.3	24 39.2	27 14.9	7 31.8	11 48.7
26	6 15 50.8	3 39.9	27 29.1	15 23.8	5 12.2	4 37.1	20 57.5	19 57.4	24 46.3	27 18.5	7 34.0	11 50.4
27	6 19 47.3	4 41.1	27 25.9	29 22.0	6 48.1	5 51.2	21 37.2	19 59.7	24 53.3	27 22.2	7 36.3	11 52.1
28	6 23 43.9	5 42.2	27 22.7	13♈ .7	8 24.2	7 5.2	22 16.9	20 2.1	25 .3	27 25.8	7 38.6	11 53.8
29	6 27 40.4	6 43.4	27 19.5	26 21.7	10 .7	8 19.2	22 56.7	20 4.8	25 7.3	27 29.4	7 40.8	11 55.4
30	6 31 37.0	7 44.5	27 16.4	9♉27.2	11 37.4	9 33.2	23 36.4	20 7.7	25 14.3	27 33.0	7 43.1	11 57.0
31	6 35 33.5	8 45.6	27 13.2	22 19.4	13 14.4	10 47.2	24 16.2	20 10.8	25 21.3	27 36.6	7 45.4	11 58.5

LATITUDE

DAY	EPHEM. SID. TIME	☉	☊	☽	☿	♀	♂	♃	♄	♅	♆	♇
1	4 37 16.8	0 .0	0 .0	1 N 23.6	0 N 49.4	1 S 19.5	0 N 43.7	1 S 26.8	1 N 9.0	0 S 9.7	0 N 58.0	15 N 42.6
4	4 49 6.5	0 .0	0 .0	4 9.5	0 28.0	1 24.9	0 42.4	1 26.0	1 8.7	0 9.7	0 57.9	15 43.3
7	5 0 56.1	0 .0	0 .0	4 59.6	0 6.8	1 30.0	0 41.1	1 25.1	1 8.5	0 9.8	0 57.8	15 44.0
10	5 12 45.8	0 .0	0 .0	3 47.9	0 S 13.8	1 34.5	0 39.8	1 24.1	1 8.3	0 9.8	0 57.8	15 44.8
13	5 24 35.5	0 .0	0 .0	1 10.0	0 33.6	1 38.4	0 38.4	1 23.2	1 8.1	0 9.8	0 57.7	15 45.7
16	5 36 25.2	0 .0	0 .0	2 S 1.5	0 52.3	1 41.8	0 37.0	1 22.3	1 7.9	0 9.8	0 57.6	15 46.6
19	5 48 14.8	0 .0	0 .0	4 31.4	1 9.6	1 44.6	0 35.6	1 21.4	1 7.7	0 9.9	0 57.6	15 47.6
22	6 0 4.5	0 .0	0 .0	4 43.4	1 25.3	1 46.7	0 34.1	1 20.4	1 7.5	0 9.9	0 57.6	15 48.6
25	6 11 54.2	0 .0	0 .0	2 12.5	1 39.0	1 48.1	0 32.5	1 19.5	1 7.4	0 9.9	0 57.5	15 49.7
28	6 23 43.9	0 .0	0 .0	1 N 23.3	1 50.5	1 48.8	0 30.9	1 18.5	1 7.3	0 9.9	0 57.5	15 50.9
31	6 35 33.5	0 .0	0 .0	4 8.3	1 59.5	1 48.8	0 29.3	1 17.6	1 7.1	0 10.0	0 57.5	15 52.1

RIGHT ASCENSION

DAY	EPHEM. SID. TIME	☉	☊	☽	☿	♀	♂	♃	♄	♅	♆	♇
1	4 37 16.8	6♐29.8	28♓54.4	14♈13.5	23♏55.1	4♑ .5	2♏28.9	19♈ 8.0	21♐10.7	25♐25.5	7♑11.7	13♏25.2
2	4 41 13.3	7 34.5	28 51.5	26 25.4	25 28.8	5 22.5	3 6.7	19 R 5.2	21 18.2	25 29.4	7 14.0	13 27.3
3	4 45 9.9	8 39.3	28 48.5	9♉ 1.7	27 3.2	6 44.5	3 44.5	19 2.6	21 25.8	25 33.2	7 16.2	13 29.3
4	4 49 6.5	9 44.3	28 45.6	22 10.0	28 38.2	8 6.4	4 22.5	19 .1	21 33.3	25 37.1	7 18.5	13 31.4
5	4 53 3.0	10 49.4	28 42.7	5♊49.7	0♐13.9	9 28.3	5 .5	18 57.9	21 40.9	25 40.9	7 20.7	13 33.5
6	4 56 59.6	11 54.7	28 39.8	19 50.1	1 50.2	10 50.1	5 38.7	18 55.8	21 48.4	25 44.8	7 23.0	13 35.5
7	5 0 56.1	13 .1	28 36.9	3♋52.3	3 27.1	12 11.8	6 16.9	18 54.0	21 56.0	25 48.7	7 25.3	13 37.5
8	5 4 52.7	14 5.7	28 34.0	17 35.2	5 4.6	13 33.4	6 55.2	18 52.3	22 3.6	25 52.6	7 27.6	13 39.5
9	5 8 49.2	15 11.3	28 31.1	0♌42.1	6 42.6	14 54.8	7 33.6	18 50.9	22 11.2	25 56.5	7 29.9	13 41.5
10	5 12 45.8	16 17.1	28 28.1	13 5.6	8 21.2	16 16.1	8 12.0	18 49.6	22 18.8	26 .5	7 32.3	13 43.5
11	5 16 42.4	17 23.0	28 25.2	24 47.3	10 .4	17 37.2	8 50.6	18 48.5	22 26.5	26 4.4	7 34.6	13 45.5
12	5 20 38.9	18 29.0	28 22.3	5♍55.5	11 40.1	18 58.1	9 29.3	18 47.6	22 34.1	26 8.3	7 37.0	13 47.4
13	5 24 35.5	19 35.1	28 19.4	16 42.6	13 20.3	20 18.9	10 8.0	18 46.9	22 41.7	26 12.3	7 39.3	13 49.4
14	5 28 32.0	20 41.3	28 16.5	27 23.9	15 1.0	21 39.4	10 46.9	18 46.4	22 49.4	26 16.2	7 41.7	13 51.3
15	5 32 28.6	21 47.6	28 13.6	8♎16.0	16 42.2	22 59.7	11 25.8	18 46.1	22 57.0	26 20.2	7 44.1	13 53.2
16	5 36 25.2	22 53.9	28 10.7	19 37.3	18 23.9	24 19.8	12 4.8	18 46.0	23 4.7	26 24.1	7 46.5	13 55.1
17	5 40 21.7	24 .3	28 7.7	1♏46.6	20 6.1	25 39.6	12 44.0	18 46.0	23 12.3	26 28.1	7 48.9	13 56.9
18	5 44 18.3	25 6.9	28 4.8	15 1.9	21 48.8	26 59.2	13 23.2	18 D 46.3	23 20.0	26 32.1	7 51.3	13 58.8
19	5 48 14.8	26 13.4	28 1.9	29 34.7	23 31.9	28 18.5	14 2.5	18 46.8	23 27.7	26 36.1	7 53.7	14 .6
20	5 52 11.4	27 20.0	27 59.0	15♐22.3	25 15.5	29 37.6	14 41.9	18 47.5	23 35.3	26 40.1	7 56.2	14 2.5
21	5 56 8.0	28 26.6	27 56.1	2♑ .2	26 59.4	0♒56.3	15 21.4	18 48.3	23 43.0	26 44.0	7 58.6	14 4.2
22	6 0 4.5	29 33.2	27 53.2	18 45.5	28 43.8	2 14.7	16 1.0	18 49.4	23 50.6	26 48.0	8 1.0	14 6.0
23	6 4 1.1	0♑39.8	27 50.3	4♒54.0	0♑28.5	3 32.9	16 40.7	18 50.6	23 58.3	26 52.0	8 3.5	14 7.7
24	6 7 57.6	1 46.5	27 47.3	19 59.1	2 13.5	4 50.7	17 20.5	18 52.1	24 5.9	26 55.9	8 5.9	14 9.5
25	6 11 54.2	2 53.1	27 44.4	3♓56.4	3 58.9	6 8.1	18 .4	18 53.7	24 13.5	26 59.9	8 8.3	14 11.2
26	6 15 50.8	3 59.7	27 41.5	16 57.2	5 44.5	7 25.3	18 40.3	18 55.5	24 21.1	27 3.8	8 10.8	14 12.8
27	6 19 47.3	5 6.2	27 38.6	29 20.2	7 30.4	8 42.1	19 20.4	18 57.6	24 28.7	27 7.8	8 13.2	14 14.5
28	6 23 43.9	6 12.8	27 35.7	11♈25.6	9 16.6	9 58.5	20 .5	18 59.8	24 36.3	27 11.7	8 15.7	14 16.1
29	6 27 40.4	7 19.3	27 32.8	23 32.0	11 2.9	11 14.6	20 40.8	19 2.2	24 43.8	27 15.6	8 18.1	14 17.7
30	6 31 37.0	8 25.7	27 29.8	5♉55.2	12 49.4	12 30.4	21 21.1	19 4.7	24 51.4	27 19.6	8 20.6	14 19.3
31	6 35 33.5	9 32.1	27 26.9	18 46.0	14 36.0	13 45.8	22 1.5	19 7.5	24 58.9	27 23.5	8 23.0	14 20.9

DECLINATION

DAY	EPHEM. SID. TIME	☉	☊	☽	☿	♀	♂	♃	♄	♅	♆	♇
1	4 37 16.8	21 S 41.1	0 S .5	7 N 35.6	18 S 28.0	24 S 43.0	12 S 20.2	6 N 31.6	22 S 2.6	23 S 32.3	22 S 18.7	0 S 10.0
4	4 49 6.5	22 8.2	0 .6	23 11.6	19 50.5	24 39.1	13 .5	6 29.4	22 4.1	23 32.7	22 18.4	0 11.3
7	5 0 56.1	22 31.4	0 .6	28 23.5	21 5.2	24 28.5	13 40.1	6 27.9	22 5.6	23 33.0	22 18.2	0 12.4
10	5 12 45.8	22 50.6	0 .7	21 31.1	22 11.1	24 11.1	14 18.8	6 27.1	22 6.9	23 33.3	22 17.9	0 13.5
13	5 24 35.5	23 5.8	0 .8	6 57.5	23 7.4	23 47.2	14 56.6	6 27.0	22 8.2	23 33.7	22 17.6	0 14.4
16	5 36 25.2	23 16.9	0 .8	10 S 28.2	23 53.4	23 16.8	15 33.5	6 27.7	22 9.5	23 34.0	22 17.3	0 15.2
19	5 48 14.8	23 23.9	0 .9	25 7.2	24 28.3	22 40.2	16 9.4	6 29.0	22 10.7	23 34.2	22 17.0	0 15.9
22	6 0 4.5	23 26.5	0 1.0	27 5.2	24 51.5	21 57.6	16 44.3	6 31.1	22 11.8	23 34.5	22 16.7	0 16.5
25	6 11 54.2	23 25.0	0 1.0	13 9.0	25 2.6	21 9.2	17 18.1	6 33.8	22 12.8	23 34.8	22 16.3	0 16.9
28	6 23 43.9	23 19.2	0 1.1	6 N 25.1	25 .9	20 15.4	17 50.7	6 37.3	22 13.7	23 35.0	22 16.0	0 17.3
31	6 35 33.5	23 9.2	0 1.2	22 21.0	24 46.0	19 16.5	18 22.1	6 41.4	22 14.6	23 35.3	22 15.6	0 17.5

JANUARY 1988

DAY	EPHEM. SID. TIME	☉	☊	☽	☿	♀	♂	♃	♄	♅	♆	♇
	h m s	° ′	° ′	° ′	° ′	° ′	° ′	° ′	° ′	° ′	° ′	° ′
		LONGITUDE										
1	6 39 30.1	9♑46.8	27♓10.0	4♊60.0	14♑51.7	12♒ 1.1	24♏55.9	20♈14.1	25♐28.3	27♐40.1	7♑47.6	12♏ .1
2	6 43 26.7	10 47.9	27 6.8	17 30.2	16 29.2	13 14.9	25 35.7	20 17.6	25 35.2	27 43.7	7 49.9	12 1.6
3	6 47 23.2	11 49.0	27 3.7	29 51.0	18 7.1	14 28.8	26 15.5	20 21.3	25 42.1	27 47.3	7 52.2	12 3.0
4	6 51 19.8	12 50.2	27 .5	12♋ 3.0	19 45.2	15 42.5	26 55.3	20 25.2	25 49.1	27 50.8	7 54.4	12 4.5
5	6 55 16.3	13 51.3	26 57.3	24 6.8	21 23.5	16 56.3	27 35.2	20 29.2	25 55.9	27 54.3	7 56.7	12 5.9
6	6 59 12.9	14 52.5	26 54.1	6♌ 3.4	23 2.1	18 10.0	28 15.0	20 33.5	26 2.8	27 57.9	7 59.0	12 7.3
7	7 3 9.5	15 53.6	26 50.9	17 54.4	24 40.9	19 23.7	28 54.9	20 37.9	26 9.6	28 1.4	8 1.2	12 8.6
8	7 7 6.0	16 54.8	26 47.8	29 42.3	26 19.9	20 37.3	29 34.8	20 42.6	26 16.5	28 4.9	8 3.5	12 10.0
9	7 11 2.6	17 55.9	26 44.6	11♍30.2	27 59.0	21 50.9	0♐14.7	20 47.4	26 23.3	28 8.4	8 5.8	12 11.3
10	7 14 59.1	18 57.0	26 41.4	23 22.0	29 38.1	23 4.4	0 54.6	20 52.4	26 30.0	28 11.9	8 8.0	12 12.6
11	7 18 55.7	19 58.2	26 38.2	5♎22.6	1♒17.2	24 17.9	1 34.6	20 57.6	26 36.7	28 15.3	8 10.2	12 13.8
12	7 22 52.3	20 59.3	26 35.1	17 37.0	2 56.2	25 31.4	2 14.5	21 2.9	26 43.4	28 18.7	8 12.5	12 15.0
13	7 26 48.8	22 .4	26 31.9	0♏10.6	4 34.9	26 44.8	2 54.5	21 8.5	26 50.1	28 22.2	8 14.7	12 16.1
14	7 30 45.4	23 1.6	26 28.7	13 8.4	6 13.3	27 58.1	3 34.5	21 14.2	26 56.7	28 25.5	8 16.9	12 17.3
15	7 34 41.9	24 2.7	26 25.5	26 34.3	7 51.1	29 11.4	4 14.5	21 20.1	27 3.3	28 28.9	8 19.1	12 18.4
16	7 38 38.5	25 3.8	26 22.4	10♐30.4	9 28.2	0♓24.7	4 54.5	21 26.1	27 9.9	28 32.3	8 21.3	12 19.4
17	7 42 35.0	26 5.0	26 19.2	24 55.7	11 4.3	1 37.9	5 34.5	21 32.3	27 16.4	28 35.6	8 23.5	12 20.5
18	7 46 31.6	27 6.1	26 16.0	9♑46.0	12 39.2	2 51.0	6 14.5	21 38.8	27 22.9	28 38.9	8 25.7	12 21.5
19	7 50 28.2	28 7.2	26 12.8	24 53.6	14 12.5	4 4.1	6 54.6	21 45.3	27 29.4	28 42.2	8 27.9	12 22.4
20	7 54 24.7	29 8.3	26 9.7	10♒ 8.3	15 43.8	5 17.1	7 34.7	21 52.1	27 35.8	28 45.5	8 30.0	12 23.3
21	7 58 21.3	0♒ 9.4	26 6.5	25 19.2	17 12.8	6 30.1	8 14.7	21 59.0	27 42.2	28 48.7	8 32.2	12 24.2
22	8 2 17.8	1 10.5	26 3.3	10♓16.8	18 39.0	7 43.0	8 54.8	22 6.0	27 48.5	28 52.0	8 34.3	12 25.1
23	8 6 14.4	2 11.6	26 .1	24 54.0	20 1.7	8 55.8	9 34.9	22 13.3	27 54.8	28 55.1	8 36.4	12 25.9
24	8 10 10.9	3 12.6	25 56.9	9♈ 6.9	21 20.4	10 8.6	10 15.0	22 20.7	28 1.1	28 58.3	8 38.5	12 26.7
25	8 14 7.5	4 13.6	25 53.8	22 54.5	22 34.4	11 21.3	10 55.1	22 28.2	28 7.3	29 1.5	8 40.6	12 27.5
26	8 18 4.1	5 14.6	25 50.6	6♉18.2	23 43.0	12 33.9	11 35.2	22 35.9	28 13.4	29 4.6	8 42.7	12 28.2
27	8 22 .6	6 15.6	25 47.4	19 20.4	24 45.4	13 46.5	12 15.4	22 43.7	28 19.5	29 7.7	8 44.8	12 28.8
28	8 25 57.2	7 16.6	25 44.2	2♊ 4.5	25 40.7	14 58.9	12 55.5	22 51.7	28 25.6	29 10.7	8 46.9	12 29.5
29	8 29 53.7	8 17.6	25 41.1	14 33.8	26 28.2	16 11.4	13 35.7	22 59.9	28 31.7	29 13.8	8 48.9	12 30.1
30	8 33 50.3	9 18.6	25 37.9	26 51.0	27 6.9	17 23.6	14 15.9	23 8.2	28 37.6	29 16.8	8 51.0	12 30.7
31	8 37 46.8	10 19.5	25 34.7	8♋59.0	27 36.1	18 35.9	14 56.1	23 16.7	28 43.5	29 19.8	8 53.0	12 31.3
		LATITUDE										
1	6 39 30.1	0 .0	0 .0	4N39.5	2S 1.8	1S48.6	0N28.7	1S17.3	1N 7.1	0S10.0	0N57.5	15N52.5
4	6 51 19.8	0 .0	0 .0	4 49.0	2 6.8	1 47.6	0 27.0	1 16.4	1 7.0	0 10.0	0 57.4	15 53.8
7	7 3 9.5	0 .0	0 .0	3 4.8	2 8.2	1 45.8	0 25.3	1 15.5	1 6.9	0 10.0	0 57.4	15 55.1
10	7 14 59.1	0 .0	0 .0	0 10.4	2 5.4	1 43.3	0 23.4	1 14.6	1 6.8	0 10.1	0 57.4	15 56.5
13	7 26 48.8	0 .0	0 .0	2S54.9	1 57.8	1 40.0	0 21.6	1 13.7	1 6.8	0 10.1	0 57.4	15 57.9
16	7 38 38.5	0 .0	0 .0	4 55.0	1 44.5	1 36.0	0 19.7	1 12.9	1 6.7	0 10.2	0 57.4	15 59.3
19	7 50 28.2	0 .0	0 .0	4 23.7	1 24.7	1 31.1	0 17.7	1 12.0	1 6.7	0 10.2	0 57.4	16 .8
22	8 2 17.8	0 .0	0 .0	1 14.9	0 57.6	1 25.5	0 15.6	1 11.2	1 6.6	0 10.2	0 57.4	16 2.3
25	8 14 7.5	0 .0	0 .0	2N27.5	0 22.5	1 19.1	0 13.5	1 10.4	1 6.6	0 10.3	0 57.4	16 3.8
28	8 25 57.2	0 .0	0 .0	4 45.3	0N20.4	1 12.0	0 11.4	1 9.6	1 6.6	0 10.3	0 57.4	16 5.3
31	8 37 46.8	0 .0	0 .0	4 57.7	1 9.7	1 4.2	0 9.2	1 8.9	1 6.6	0 10.4	0 57.5	16 6.8
		RIGHT ASCENSION										
1	6 39 30.1	10♑38.4	27♓24.0	2♊ 7.5	16♑22.7	15♒ .8	22♏42.1	19♈10.5	25♐ 6.4	27♐27.4	8♑25.5	14♏22.4
2	6 43 26.7	11 44.6	27 21.1	15 53.9	18 9.4	16 15.5	23 22.7	19 13.6	25 13.9	27 31.3	8 27.9	14 23.9
3	6 47 23.2	12 50.8	27 18.2	29 49.8	19 56.1	17 29.8	24 3.4	19 16.9	25 21.4	27 35.1	8 30.4	14 25.4
4	6 51 19.8	13 56.9	27 15.3	13♋35.3	21 42.7	18 43.7	24 44.2	19 20.4	25 28.9	27 39.0	8 32.8	14 26.8
5	6 55 16.3	15 2.8	27 12.4	26 51.6	23 29.1	19 57.3	25 25.1	19 24.1	25 36.3	27 42.9	8 35.3	14 28.3
6	6 59 12.9	16 8.7	27 9.4	9♌27.5	25 15.3	21 10.6	26 6.1	19 28.0	25 43.7	27 46.7	8 37.7	14 29.7
7	7 3 9.5	17 14.5	27 6.5	21 20.6	27 1.3	22 23.4	26 47.3	19 32.0	25 51.1	27 50.5	8 40.1	14 31.0
8	7 7 6.0	18 20.2	27 3.6	2♍36.1	28 46.9	23 36.0	27 28.5	19 36.2	25 58.5	27 54.4	8 42.6	14 32.4
9	7 11 2.6	19 25.7	27 .7	13 24.3	0♒32.0	24 48.1	28 9.8	19 40.6	26 5.8	27 58.2	8 45.0	14 33.8
10	7 14 59.1	20 31.1	26 57.8	23 58.7	2 16.5	25 60.0	28 51.2	19 45.2	26 13.1	28 2.0	8 47.5	14 35.0
11	7 18 55.7	21 36.4	26 54.9	4♎34.9	4 .3	27 11.4	29 32.7	19 49.9	26 20.4	28 5.7	8 49.9	14 36.3
12	7 22 52.3	22 41.5	26 51.9	15 29.6	5 43.4	28 22.5	0♐14.2	19 54.8	26 27.6	28 9.5	8 52.3	14 37.5
13	7 26 48.8	23 46.5	26 49.0	27 1.4	7 25.4	29 33.3	0 55.9	19 59.8	26 34.8	28 13.2	8 54.7	14 38.8
14	7 30 45.4	24 51.4	26 46.1	9♏28.8	9 6.4	0♓43.8	1 37.7	20 5.1	26 42.0	28 16.9	8 57.1	14 39.9
15	7 34 41.9	25 56.1	26 43.2	23 8.1	10 46.0	1 53.9	2 19.5	20 10.5	26 49.1	28 20.6	8 59.4	14 41.1
16	7 38 38.5	27 .6	26 40.3	8♐ 6.7	12 24.0	3 3.7	3 1.4	20 16.0	26 56.2	28 24.3	9 1.8	14 42.2
17	7 42 35.0	28 5.0	26 37.4	24 15.2	14 .3	4 13.2	3 43.5	20 21.8	27 3.2	28 27.9	9 4.2	14 43.3
18	7 46 31.6	29 9.2	26 34.5	11♑ 2.0	15 34.5	5 22.3	4 25.6	20 27.6	27 10.3	28 31.5	9 6.5	14 44.3
19	7 50 28.2	0♒13.2	26 31.5	27 42.2	17 6.3	6 31.2	5 7.7	20 33.7	27 17.2	28 35.1	9 8.9	14 45.4
20	7 54 24.7	1 17.0	26 28.6	13♒36.9	18 35.3	7 39.8	5 50.0	20 39.9	27 24.2	28 38.7	9 11.2	14 46.4
21	7 58 21.3	2 20.7	26 25.7	28 27.6	20 1.2	8 48.1	6 32.4	20 46.2	27 31.1	28 42.2	9 13.5	14 47.3
22	8 2 17.8	3 24.2	26 22.8	12♓16.4	21 23.4	9 56.1	7 14.8	20 52.8	27 37.9	28 45.7	9 15.8	14 48.3
23	8 6 14.4	4 27.5	26 19.9	25 18.0	22 41.6	11 3.8	7 57.3	20 59.4	27 44.7	28 49.2	9 18.1	14 49.2
24	8 10 10.9	5 30.5	26 17.0	7♈51.3	23 55.0	12 11.2	8 39.9	21 6.2	27 51.5	28 52.7	9 20.4	14 50.0
25	8 14 7.5	6 33.4	26 14.0	20 15.7	25 3.2	13 18.4	9 22.5	21 13.2	27 58.2	28 56.1	9 22.6	14 50.9
26	8 18 4.1	7 36.1	26 11.1	2♉47.7	26 5.4	14 25.3	10 5.3	21 20.3	28 4.8	28 59.5	9 24.9	14 51.7
27	8 22 .6	8 38.6	26 8.2	15 39.4	27 1.0	15 31.9	10 48.1	21 27.6	28 11.4	29 2.9	9 27.1	14 52.5
28	8 25 57.2	9 40.8	26 5.3	28 56.4	27 49.3	16 38.3	11 30.9	21 35.0	28 18.0	29 6.2	9 29.3	14 53.2
29	8 29 53.7	10 42.9	26 2.4	12♊35.7	28 29.5	17 44.6	12 13.9	21 42.6	28 24.5	29 9.6	9 31.6	14 54.0
30	8 33 50.3	11 44.8	25 59.4	26 25.8	29 1.0	18 50.5	12 56.9	21 50.2	28 31.0	29 12.8	9 33.8	14 54.6
31	8 37 46.8	12 46.4	25 56.5	10♋ 9.3	29 23.1	19 56.2	13 40.0	21 58.1	28 37.3	29 16.1	9 35.9	14 55.3
		DECLINATION										
1	6 39 30.1	23S 4.9	0S 1.2	25N42.9	24S38.0	18S55.8	18S32.3	6N42.9	22S14.9	23S35.3	22S15.5	0S17.5
4	6 51 19.8	22 49.4	0 1.2	27 41.6	24 4.8	17 50.5	19 2.1	6 47.9	22 15.7	23 35.6	22 15.1	0 17.6
7	7 3 9.5	22 29.8	0 1.3	18 23.8	23 17.6	16 40.9	19 30.6	6 53.5	22 16.4	23 35.8	22 14.7	0 17.5
10	7 14 59.1	22 6.2	0 1.4	2 47.6	22 16.4	15 27.3	19 57.7	6 59.8	22 17.0	23 35.9	22 14.3	0 17.3
13	7 26 48.8	21 38.7	0 1.4	14S15.8	21 1.5	14 10.0	20 23.5	7 6.6	22 17.6	23 36.1	22 13.9	0 17.0
16	7 38 38.5	21 7.4	0 1.5	26 53.4	19 33.9	12 49.5	20 47.8	7 14.0	22 18.1	23 36.3	22 13.5	0 16.5
19	7 50 28.2	20 32.5	0 1.6	25 28.6	17 55.3	11 26.0	21 10.6	7 21.9	22 18.5	23 36.4	22 13.1	0 16.0
22	8 2 17.8	19 54.0	0 1.6	8 52.2	16 9.1	9 59.9	21 31.9	7 30.4	22 18.9	23 36.5	22 12.7	0 15.3
25	8 14 7.5	19 12.2	0 1.7	11N11.5	14 20.8	8 31.6	21 51.7	7 39.4	22 19.2	23 36.7	22 12.2	0 14.5
28	8 25 57.2	18 27.3	0 1.8	25 14.2	12 38.5	7 1.4	22 9.9	7 48.8	22 19.4	23 36.8	22 11.8	0 13.6
31	8 37 46.8	17 39.4	0 1.8	28 5.3	11 13.0	5 29.7	22 26.4	7 58.7	22 19.6	23 36.9	22 11.4	0 12.7

FEBRUARY 1988

LONGITUDE

DAY	EPHEM. SID. TIME	☉	☊	☽	☿	♀	♂	♃	♄	♅	♆	♇
	h m s	° ′	° ′	° ′	° ′	° ′	° ′	° ′	° ′	° ′	° ′	° ′
1	8 41 43.4	11♒20.4	25♓31.5	20♋59.7	27♒55.2	19♓48.0	15♐36.3	23♈25.2	28♐49.4	29♐22.7	8♑55.0	12♏31.8
2	8 45 40.0	12 21.3	25 28.4	2♌54.9	28 3.6	21 .0	16 16.5	23 33.9	28 55.2	29 25.6	8 57.0	12 32.2
3	8 49 36.5	13 22.1	25 25.2	14 46.4	28R .9	22 12.0	16 56.7	23 42.8	29 .9	29 28.5	8 58.9	12 32.7
4	8 53 33.1	14 23.0	25 22.0	26 35.6	27 47.0	23 23.8	17 36.9	23 51.8	29 6.6	29 31.3	9 .9	12 33.0
5	8 57 29.6	15 23.8	25 18.8	8♍24.6	27 22.1	24 35.6	18 17.2	24 .9	29 12.3	29 34.1	9 2.8	12 33.4
6	9 1 26.2	16 24.6	25 15.6	20 15.5	26 46.6	25 47.2	18 57.4	24 10.2	29 17.8	29 36.9	9 4.7	12 33.7
7	9 5 22.7	17 25.4	25 12.5	2♎11.3	26 1.5	26 58.8	19 37.7	24 19.5	29 23.4	29 39.6	9 6.6	12 34.0
8	9 9 19.3	18 26.2	25 9.3	14 15.2	25 7.9	28 10.2	20 18.0	24 29.0	29 28.8	29 42.3	9 8.4	12 34.3
9	9 13 15.9	19 26.9	25 6.1	26 31.4	24 7.2	29 21.6	20 58.3	24 38.7	29 34.2	29 45.0	9 10.3	12 34.5
10	9 17 12.4	20 27.7	25 2.9	9♏ 4.0	23 1.2	0♈32.8	21 38.6	24 48.4	29 39.6	29 47.6	9 12.1	12 34.6
11	9 21 9.0	21 28.4	24 59.8	21 57.4	21 51.8	1 44.0	22 18.9	24 58.3	29 44.8	29 50.2	9 13.9	12 34.8
12	9 25 5.5	22 29.1	24 56.6	5♐15.3	20 41.0	2 55.0	22 59.2	25 8.3	29 50.1	29 52.8	9 15.7	12 34.9
13	9 29 2.1	23 29.8	24 53.4	19 .5	19 30.7	4 5.9	23 39.6	25 18.4	29 55.2	29 55.3	9 17.5	12 34.9
14	9 32 58.6	24 30.5	24 50.2	3♑13.6	18 22.6	5 16.7	24 19.9	25 28.7	0♑ .3	29 57.8	9 19.2	12 35.0
15	9 36 55.2	25 31.1	24 47.1	17 52.6	17 18.4	6 27.4	25 .3	25 39.0	0 5.3	0♑ .2	9 20.9	12 35.0
16	9 40 51.7	26 31.8	24 43.9	2♒52.4	16 19.3	7 38.0	25 40.7	25 49.5	0 10.2	0 2.6	9 22.6	12R34.9
17	9 44 48.3	27 32.4	24 40.7	18 4.8	15 26.3	8 48.5	26 21.1	26 .1	0 15.1	0 4.9	9 24.3	12 34.8
18	9 48 44.9	28 33.0	24 37.5	3♓20.0	14 40.3	9 58.8	27 1.5	26 10.8	0 19.9	0 7.3	9 25.9	12 34.7
19	9 52 41.4	29 33.6	24 34.3	18 27.7	14 1.6	11 9.1	27 41.9	26 21.6	0 24.7	0 9.6	9 27.6	12 34.6
20	9 56 38.0	0♓34.1	24 31.2	3♈18.8	13 30.6	12 19.1	28 22.3	26 32.5	0 29.4	0 11.8	9 29.2	12 34.4
21	10 0 34.5	1 34.6	24 28.0	17 47.0	13 7.1	13 29.1	29 2.7	26 43.5	0 34.0	0 14.0	9 30.8	12 34.2
22	10 4 31.1	2 35.1	24 24.8	1♉48.7	12 51.2	14 38.8	29 43.1	26 54.6	0 38.5	0 16.1	9 32.3	12 34.0
23	10 8 27.6	3 35.5	24 21.6	15 23.3	12 42.6	15 48.5	0♑23.5	27 5.9	0 42.9	0 18.2	9 33.8	12 33.7
24	10 12 24.2	4 35.9	24 18.5	28 32.2	12 41.1	16 58.0	1 3.9	27 17.2	0 47.3	0 20.3	9 35.3	12 33.3
25	10 16 20.7	5 36.3	24 15.3	11♊18.4	12D46.2	18 7.3	1 44.3	27 28.6	0 51.5	0 22.3	9 36.8	12 33.0
26	10 20 17.3	6 36.7	24 12.1	23 45.7	12 57.6	19 16.5	2 24.8	27 40.1	0 55.8	0 24.3	9 38.2	12 32.6
27	10 24 13.8	7 37.0	24 8.9	5♋58.1	13 15.0	20 25.5	3 5.2	27 51.6	0 59.9	0 26.2	9 39.6	12 32.2
28	10 28 10.4	8 37.3	24 5.7	17 59.5	13 37.8	21 34.4	3 45.6	28 3.3	1 3.9	0 28.1	9 41.0	12 31.7
29	10 32 7.0	9 37.5	24 2.6	29 53.5	14 5.9	22 43.0	4 26.1	28 15.1	1 7.9	0 29.9	9 42.4	12 31.2

LATITUDE

DAY	EPHEM. SID. TIME	☉	☊	☽	☿	♀	♂	♃	♄	♅	♆	♇
1	8 41 43.4	0 .0	0 .0	4N34.6	1N26.9	1S 1.4	0N 8.4	1S 8.6	1N 6.6	0S10.4	0N57.5	16N 7.3
4	8 53 33.1	0 .0	0 .0	2 20.7	2 18.3	0 52.6	0 6.1	1 7.9	1 6.7	0 10.4	0 57.5	16 8.9
7	9 5 22.7	0 .0	0 .0	0S47.7	3 3.1	0 43.2	0 3.7	1 7.2	1 6.7	0 10.5	0 57.5	16 10.4
10	9 17 12.4	0 .0	0 .0	3 44.0	3 33.0	0 33.2	0 1.3	1 6.5	1 6.7	0 10.5	0 57.6	16 12.0
13	9 29 2.1	0 .0	0 .0	5 12.4	3 42.3	0 22.5	0S 1.3	1 5.8	1 6.8	0 10.6	0 57.6	16 13.5
16	9 40 51.7	0 .0	0 .0	4 2.0	3 31.2	0 11.3	0 3.9	1 5.1	1 6.9	0 10.6	0 57.6	16 15.1
19	9 52 41.4	0 .0	0 .0	0 25.9	3 4.6	0N .4	0 6.5	1 4.5	1 6.9	0 10.7	0 57.7	16 16.6
22	10 4 31.1	0 .0	0 .0	3N17.4	2 29.2	0 12.6	0 9.3	1 3.9	1 7.0	0 10.7	0 57.7	16 18.1
25	10 16 20.7	0 .0	0 .0	5 9.2	1 50.2	0 25.3	0 12.1	1 3.3	1 7.1	0 10.8	0 57.8	16 19.5
28	10 28 10.4	0 .0	0 .0	4 47.0	1 11.1	0 38.2	0 15.0	1 2.7	1 7.2	0 10.8	0 57.8	16 21.0

RIGHT ASCENSION

DAY	EPHEM. SID. TIME	☉	☊	☽	☿	♀	♂	♃	♄	♅	♆	♇
1	8 41 43.4	13♒47.9	25♓53.6	23♋28.9	29♒35.4	21♓ 1.8	14♐23.2	22♈ 6.0	28♐43.7	29♐19.3	9♑38.1	14♏55.9
2	8 45 40.0	14 49.1	25 50.7	6♌12.2	29 37.3	22 7.1	15 6.4	22 14.1	28 49.9	29 22.4	9 40.2	14 56.5
3	8 49 36.5	15 50.1	25 47.8	18 14.5	29R28.7	23 12.2	15 49.7	22 22.3	28 56.2	29 25.6	9 42.3	14 57.0
4	8 53 33.1	16 51.0	25 44.9	29 38.9	29 9.6	24 17.1	15 33.0	22 30.7	29 2.3	29 28.7	9 44.4	14 57.5
5	8 57 29.6	17 51.6	25 41.9	10♍33.4	28 40.3	25 21.9	17 16.4	22 39.2	29 8.4	29 31.7	9 46.5	14 58.0
6	9 1 26.2	18 52.0	25 39.0	21 9.7	28 1.3	26 26.5	17 59.9	22 47.8	29 14.4	29 34.8	9 48.5	14 58.4
7	9 5 22.7	19 52.2	25 36.1	1♎41.5	27 13.5	27 30.9	18 43.4	22 56.5	29 20.4	29 37.8	9 50.5	14 58.9
8	9 9 19.3	20 52.3	25 33.2	12 23.7	26 18.2	28 35.2	19 27.0	23 5.3	29 26.3	29 40.7	9 52.6	14 59.2
9	9 13 15.9	21 52.1	25 30.3	23 32.7	25 16.7	29 39.3	20 10.6	23 14.3	29 32.1	29 43.6	9 54.5	14 59.6
10	9 17 12.4	22 51.7	25 27.4	5♏25.4	24 10.8	0♈43.3	20 54.3	23 23.4	29 37.9	29 46.5	9 56.5	14 59.9
11	9 21 9.0	23 51.2	25 24.4	18 17.7	23 2.3	1 47.2	21 38.0	23 32.6	29 43.6	29 49.3	9 58.5	15 .2
12	9 25 5.5	24 50.4	25 21.5	2♐20.5	21 53.0	2 51.0	22 21.8	23 42.0	29 49.3	29 52.1	10 .4	15 .4
13	9 29 2.1	25 49.5	25 18.6	17 33.6	20 44.8	3 54.6	23 5.6	23 51.4	29 54.8	29 54.8	10 2.3	15 .6
14	9 32 58.6	26 48.4	25 15.7	3♑39.5	19 39.3	4 58.2	23 49.5	24 1.0	0♑ .3	29 57.5	10 4.1	15 .8
15	9 36 55.2	27 47.1	25 12.8	20 4.4	18 38.0	6 1.7	24 33.4	24 10.7	0 5.7	0♑ .2	10 6.0	15 .9
16	9 40 51.7	28 45.6	25 9.8	6♒10.1	17 42.0	7 5.1	25 17.3	24 20.5	0 11.1	0 2.8	10 7.8	15 1.1
17	9 44 48.3	29 44.0	25 6.9	21 29.8	16 52.5	8 8.4	26 1.3	24 30.4	0 16.3	0 5.4	10 9.6	15 1.1
18	9 48 44.9	0♓42.1	25 4.0	5♓55.3	16 9.9	9 11.6	26 45.3	24 40.4	0 21.5	0 7.9	10 11.4	15 1.2
19	9 52 41.4	1 40.2	25 1.1	19 33.7	15 34.9	10 14.9	27 29.4	24 50.6	0 26.7	0 10.5	10 13.2	15 1.2
20	9 56 38.0	2 38.0	24 58.2	2♈40.3	15 7.5	11 18.0	28 13.4	25 .8	0 31.7	0 12.9	10 14.9	15 1.2
21	10 0 34.5	3 35.6	24 55.2	15 33.0	14 47.7	12 21.1	28 57.5	25 11.1	0 36.7	0 15.3	10 16.6	15R 1.1
22	10 4 31.1	4 33.1	24 52.3	28 28.0	14 35.6	13 24.1	29 41.6	25 21.5	0 41.6	0 17.6	10 18.3	15 1.0
23	10 8 27.6	5 30.4	24 49.4	11♉37.7	14 30.8	14 27.1	0♑25.7	25 32.1	0 46.4	0 19.9	10 19.9	15 .9
24	10 12 24.2	6 27.6	24 46.5	25 8.3	14D33.0	15 30.1	1 9.8	25 42.7	0 51.1	0 22.2	10 21.5	15 .8
25	10 16 20.7	7 24.5	24 43.6	8♊57.6	14 41.9	16 33.1	1 53.9	25 53.4	0 55.7	0 24.4	10 23.1	15 .6
26	10 20 17.3	8 21.4	24 40.6	22 55.4	14 57.1	17 36.0	2 38.0	26 4.2	1 .3	0 26.5	10 24.6	15 .4
27	10 24 13.8	9 18.1	24 37.7	6♋45.8	15 18.2	18 38.9	3 22.2	26 15.1	1 4.7	0 28.6	10 26.2	15 .1
28	10 28 10.4	10 14.6	24 34.8	20 12.2	15 44.7	19 41.8	4 6.3	26 26.1	1 9.1	0 30.7	10 27.6	14 59.8
29	10 32 7.0	11 11.0	24 31.9	3♌ 2.9	16 16.4	20 44.7	4 50.5	26 37.2	1 13.4	0 32.7	10 29.1	14 59.5

DECLINATION

DAY	EPHEM. SID. TIME	☉	☊	☽	☿	♀	♂	♃	♄	♅	♆	♇
1	8 41 43.4	17S22.8	0S 1.9	26N19.4	10S50.3	4S58.9	22S31.6	8N 2.1	22S19.6	23S36.9	22S11.3	0S12.3
4	8 53 33.1	16 31.1	0 1.9	14 51.4	10 4.8	3 25.7	22 45.9	8 12.6	22 19.8	23 37.0	22 10.8	0 11.2
7	9 5 22.7	15 36.9	0 2.0	1S36.0	9 58.3	1 51.7	22 58.6	8 23.5	22 19.8	23 37.0	22 10.4	0 10.0
10	9 17 12.4	14 40.2	0 2.1	18 3.4	10 29.3	0 17.4	23 9.5	8 34.7	22 19.8	23 37.1	22 10.0	0 8.7
13	9 29 2.1	13 41.4	0 2.1	28 10.6	11 26.9	1N17.1	23 18.8	8 46.2	22 19.8	23 37.2	22 9.6	0 7.3
16	9 40 51.7	12 40.5	0 2.2	23 26.6	12 35.2	2 51.4	23 26.2	8 58.1	22 19.7	23 37.2	22 9.2	0 5.8
19	9 52 41.4	11 37.7	0 2.3	4 57.7	13 40.4	4 25.2	23 31.9	9 10.3	22 19.6	23 37.3	22 8.8	0 4.3
22	10 4 31.1	10 33.3	0 2.3	15N11.4	14 34.3	5 58.1	23 35.8	9 22.8	22 19.5	23 37.3	22 8.4	0 2.7
25	10 16 20.7	9 27.4	0 2.4	27 14.5	15 13.1	7 29.9	23 38.0	9 35.5	22 19.3	23 37.3	22 8.1	0 1.0
28	10 28 10.4	8 20.3	0 2.5	26 58.4	15 36.1	9 .1	23 38.4	9 48.5	22 19.2	23 37.4	22 7.7	0N .7

MARCH 1988

LONGITUDE

DAY	EPHEM. SID. TIME h m s	☉ ° ′	☊ ° ′	☽ ° ′	☿ ° ′	♀ ° ′	♂ ° ′	♃ ° ′	♄ ° ′	♅ ° ′	♆ ° ′	♇ ° ′
1	10 36 3.5	10♓37.7	23♓59.4	11♌43.5	14♒38.7	23♈51.5	5♑ 6.5	28♈26.9	1♑11.8	0♑31.7	9♑43.7	12♏30.7
2	10 40 .1	11 37.9	23 56.2	23 32.2	15 15.9	24 59.8	5 47.0	28 38.9	1 15.6	0 33.4	9 45.0	12 R 30.1
3	10 43 56.6	12 38.1	23 53.0	5♍22.0	15 57.3	26 8.0	6 27.5	28 50.9	1 19.3	0 35.1	9 46.3	12 29.5
4	10 47 53.2	13 38.2	23 49.9	17 15.1	16 42.6	27 15.9	7 7.9	29 3.0	1 22.9	0 36.8	9 47.5	12 28.9
5	10 51 49.7	14 38.3	23 46.7	29 13.4	17 31.4	28 23.7	7 48.4	29 15.2	1 26.5	0 38.4	9 48.8	12 28.2
6	10 55 46.3	15 38.3	23 43.5	11♎19.0	18 23.6	29 31.2	8 28.9	29 27.4	1 30.0	0 39.9	9 50.0	12 27.5
7	10 59 42.8	16 38.4	23 40.3	23 33.8	19 18.8	0♉38.6	9 9.4	29 39.8	1 33.4	0 41.4	9 51.1	12 26.8
8	11 3 39.4	17 38.4	23 37.2	6♏ .3	20 16.9	1 45.7	9 49.9	29 52.2	1 36.7	0 42.9	9 52.2	12 26.0
9	11 7 35.9	18 38.4	23 34.0	18 41.0	21 17.8	2 52.6	10 30.4	0♉ 4.7	1 39.9	0 44.3	9 53.3	12 25.2
10	11 11 32.5	19 38.3	23 30.8	1♐38.3	22 21.2	3 59.3	11 10.9	0 17.2	1 43.0	0 45.6	9 54.4	12 24.4
11	11 15 29.1	20 38.3	23 27.6	14 54.9	23 27.0	5 5.9	11 51.5	0 29.9	1 46.1	0 47.0	9 55.5	12 23.6
12	11 19 25.6	21 38.2	23 24.4	28 32.4	24 35.1	6 12.1	12 32.0	0 42.6	1 49.0	0 48.2	9 56.5	12 22.7
13	11 23 22.2	22 38.1	23 21.3	12♑32.0	25 45.3	7 18.2	13 12.5	0 55.3	1 51.9	0 49.4	9 57.5	12 21.8
14	11 27 18.7	23 37.9	23 18.1	26 52.9	26 57.5	8 24.0	13 53.0	1 8.2	1 54.6	0 50.6	9 58.4	12 20.9
15	11 31 15.3	24 37.7	23 14.9	11♒32.5	28 11.7	9 29.6	14 33.6	1 21.1	1 57.3	0 51.7	9 59.3	12 19.9
16	11 35 11.8	25 37.5	23 11.7	26 25.9	29 27.7	10 34.9	15 14.1	1 34.0	1 59.9	0 52.7	10 .2	12 18.9
17	11 39 8.4	26 37.2	23 8.6	11♓26.2	0♓45.5	11 39.9	15 54.6	1 47.0	2 2.4	0 53.7	10 1.1	12 17.9
18	11 43 4.9	27 37.0	23 5.4	26 25.2	2 5.0	12 44.7	16 35.1	2 .1	2 4.8	0 54.7	10 1.9	12 16.9
19	11 47 1.5	28 36.7	23 2.2	11♈14.3	3 26.1	13 49.3	17 15.6	2 13.3	2 7.1	0 55.5	10 2.7	12 15.8
20	11 50 58.0	29 36.3	22 59.0	25 46.3	4 48.8	14 53.5	17 56.1	2 26.5	2 9.3	0 56.4	10 3.4	12 14.7
21	11 54 54.6	0♈35.9	22 55.8	9♉55.6	6 13.1	15 57.5	18 36.6	2 39.7	2 11.4	0 57.2	10 4.2	12 13.6
22	11 58 51.1	1 35.5	22 52.7	23 39.2	7 38.9	17 1.2	19 17.1	2 53.0	2 13.4	0 57.9	10 4.8	12 12.4
23	12 2 47.7	2 35.1	22 49.5	6♊56.6	9 6.1	18 4.5	19 57.6	3 6.4	2 15.3	0 58.6	10 5.5	12 11.2
24	12 6 44.3	3 34.6	22 46.3	19 49.2	10 34.8	19 7.6	20 38.1	3 19.8	2 17.1	0 59.2	10 6.1	12 10.0
25	12 10 40.8	4 34.0	22 43.1	2♋20.2	12 5.0	20 10.3	21 18.5	3 33.2	2 18.8	0 59.8	10 6.7	12 8.8
26	12 14 37.4	5 33.5	22 40.0	14 33.7	13 36.6	21 12.7	21 59.0	3 46.7	2 20.5	1 .3	10 7.3	12 7.5
27	12 18 33.9	6 32.8	22 36.8	26 34.2	15 9.5	22 14.7	22 39.4	4 .3	2 22.0	1 .8	10 7.8	12 6.3
28	12 22 30.5	7 32.2	22 33.6	8♌26.4	16 43.9	23 16.3	23 19.9	4 13.9	2 23.4	1 1.2	10 8.3	12 5.0
29	12 26 27.0	8 31.5	22 30.4	20 14.8	18 19.7	24 17.6	24 .3	4 27.5	2 24.8	1 1.6	10 8.8	12 3.6
30	12 30 23.6	9 30.8	22 27.2	2♍ 3.4	19 56.8	25 18.6	24 40.8	4 41.2	2 26.0	1 1.9	10 9.2	12 2.3
31	12 34 20.1	10 30.0	22 24.1	13 55.9	21 35.4	26 19.1	25 21.2	4 54.9	2 27.1	1 2.2	10 9.6	12 .9

LATITUDE

DAY	EPHEM. SID. TIME h m s	☉	☊	☽	☿	♀	♂	♃	♄	♅	♆	♇
1	10 36 3.5	0 .0	0 .0	3N29.4	0N45.9	0N47.1	0S16.9	1S 2.4	1N 7.3	0S10.9	0N57.9	16N21.9
4	10 47 53.2	0 .0	0 .0	0 32.1	0 10.5	1 .5	0 20.0	1 1.8	1 7.4	0 10.9	0 57.9	16 23.3
7	10 59 42.8	0 .0	0 .0	2S41.5	0S21.7	1 14.2	0 23.1	1 1.3	1 7.5	0 11.0	0 58.0	16 24.6
10	11 11 32.5	0 .0	0 .0	4 55.8	0 50.3	1 28.0	0 26.3	1 .8	1 7.6	0 11.0	0 58.1	16 25.9
13	11 23 22.2	0 .0	0 .0	4 59.7	1 15.1	1 41.8	0 29.6	1 .3	1 7.7	0 11.1	0 58.1	16 27.1
16	11 35 11.8	0 .0	0 .0	2 22.9	1 36.2	1 55.7	0 32.9	0 59.9	1 7.8	0 11.1	0 58.2	16 28.3
19	11 47 1.5	0 .0	0 .0	1N39.1	1 53.5	2 9.5	0 36.4	0 59.5	1 8.0	0 11.2	0 58.3	16 29.4
22	11 58 51.1	0 .0	0 .0	4 36.5	2 6.8	2 23.2	0 39.9	0 59.0	1 8.1	0 11.2	0 58.3	16 30.5
25	12 10 40.8	0 .0	0 .0	5 12.9	2 16.1	2 36.6	0 43.5	0 58.6	1 8.2	0 11.3	0 58.4	16 31.5
28	12 22 30.5	0 .0	0 .0	3 42.9	2 21.4	2 49.7	0 47.3	0 58.3	1 8.4	0 11.4	0 58.5	16 32.4
31	12 34 20.1	0 .0	0 .0	0 50.6	2 22.5	3 2.4	0 51.1	0 57.9	1 8.5	0 11.4	0 58.5	16 33.2

RIGHT ASCENSION

DAY	EPHEM. SID. TIME h m s	☉	☊	☽	☿	♀	♂	♃	♄	♅	♆	♇
1	10 36 3.5	12♓ 7.3	24♓29.0	15♌13.2	16♒52.7	21♈47.5	5♑34.7	26♈48.4	1♑17.6	0♑34.6	10♑30.5	14♏59.1
2	10 40 .1	13 3.5	24 26.0	26 45.4	17 33.4	22 50.4	6 18.8	26 59.7	1 21.7	0 36.5	10 31.9	14 R 58.8
3	10 43 56.6	13 59.5	24 23.1	7♍47.1	18 18.2	23 53.3	7 3.0	27 11.0	1 25.7	0 38.3	10 33.3	14 58.4
4	10 47 53.2	14 55.4	24 20.2	18 29.0	19 6.6	24 56.2	7 47.2	27 22.5	1 29.6	0 40.1	10 34.7	14 57.9
5	10 51 49.7	15 51.2	24 17.3	29 3.6	19 58.4	25 59.0	8 31.3	27 34.0	1 33.5	0 41.9	10 36.0	14 57.4
6	10 55 46.3	16 46.9	24 14.4	9♎45.0	20 53.3	27 1.9	9 15.5	27 45.6	1 37.2	0 43.6	10 37.2	14 56.9
7	10 59 42.8	17 42.5	24 11.4	20 47.6	21 51.1	28 4.9	9 59.6	27 57.2	1 40.9	0 45.2	10 38.5	14 56.4
8	11 3 39.4	18 37.9	24 8.5	2♏26.6	22 51.6	29 7.8	10 43.7	28 9.0	1 44.5	0 46.8	10 39.7	14 55.8
9	11 7 35.9	19 33.3	24 5.6	14 55.9	23 54.5	0♉10.7	11 27.9	28 20.8	1 47.9	0 48.3	10 40.9	14 55.2
10	11 11 32.5	20 28.7	24 2.7	28 25.7	24 59.6	1 13.7	12 12.0	28 32.7	1 51.3	0 49.8	10 42.0	14 54.6
11	11 15 29.1	21 23.9	23 59.8	12♐57.8	26 6.9	2 16.7	12 56.1	28 44.8	1 54.6	0 51.3	10 43.2	14 54.0
12	11 19 25.6	22 19.1	23 56.8	28 20.6	27 16.0	3 19.7	13 40.1	28 56.8	1 57.8	0 52.6	10 44.3	14 53.3
13	11 23 22.2	23 14.2	23 53.9	14♑ 8.9	28 26.9	4 22.7	14 24.2	29 8.9	2 .9	0 53.9	10 45.3	14 52.6
14	11 27 18.7	24 9.2	23 51.0	29 51.4	29 39.5	5 25.8	15 8.2	29 21.1	2 3.9	0 55.2	10 46.3	14 51.8
15	11 31 15.3	25 4.2	23 48.1	15♒ 2.4	0♓53.6	6 28.8	15 52.1	29 33.4	2 6.8	0 56.4	10 47.3	14 51.1
16	11 35 11.8	25 59.1	23 45.2	29 30.2	2 9.1	7 31.9	16 36.1	29 45.7	2 9.6	0 57.5	10 48.3	14 50.3
17	11 39 8.4	26 53.9	23 42.2	13♓17.3	3 26.0	8 34.9	17 19.9	29 58.1	2 12.2	0 58.6	10 49.2	14 49.5
18	11 43 4.9	27 48.8	23 39.3	26 35.5	4 44.1	9 38.0	18 3.8	0♉10.6	2 14.8	0 59.7	10 50.1	14 48.6
19	11 47 1.5	28 43.5	23 36.4	9♈40.9	6 3.4	10 41.1	18 47.6	0 23.1	2 17.3	1 .6	10 50.9	14 47.7
20	11 50 58.0	29 38.3	23 33.5	22 49.5	7 23.8	11 44.1	19 31.3	0 35.7	2 19.7	1 1.5	10 51.7	14 46.8
21	11 54 54.6	0♈33.0	23 30.5	6♉14.0	8 45.3	12 47.2	20 15.0	0 48.4	2 22.0	1 2.4	10 52.5	14 45.9
22	11 58 51.1	1 27.6	23 27.6	20 1.4	10 7.9	13 50.2	20 58.7	1 1.1	2 24.1	1 3.2	10 53.2	14 44.9
23	12 2 47.7	2 22.3	23 24.7	4♊ 9.7	11 31.4	14 53.2	21 42.3	1 13.9	2 26.2	1 4.0	10 53.9	14 43.9
24	12 6 44.3	3 16.9	23 21.8	18 28.1	12 55.9	15 56.1	22 25.8	1 26.7	2 28.2	1 4.7	10 54.6	14 42.9
25	12 10 40.8	4 11.5	23 18.9	2♋39.1	14 21.3	16 59.0	23 9.3	1 39.6	2 30.0	1 5.3	10 55.2	14 41.9
26	12 14 37.4	5 6.1	23 15.9	16 24.6	15 47.6	18 1.8	23 52.7	1 52.5	2 31.8	1 5.9	10 55.8	14 40.9
27	12 18 33.9	6 .7	23 13.0	29 31.3	17 14.8	19 4.5	24 36.1	2 5.5	2 33.4	1 6.4	10 56.4	14 39.8
28	12 22 30.5	6 55.2	23 10.1	11♌54.3	18 43.0	20 7.1	25 19.4	2 18.5	2 35.0	1 6.8	10 56.9	14 38.7
29	12 26 27.0	7 49.8	23 7.2	23 36.1	20 12.0	21 9.6	26 2.7	2 31.6	2 36.4	1 7.3	10 57.4	14 37.6
30	12 30 23.6	8 44.4	23 4.2	4♍44.7	21 42.0	22 11.9	26 45.8	2 44.7	2 37.7	1 7.6	10 57.9	14 36.4
31	12 34 20.1	9 39.0	23 1.3	15 31.5	23 12.9	23 14.2	27 29.0	2 57.9	2 39.0	1 7.9	10 58.3	14 35.2

DECLINATION

DAY	EPHEM. SID. TIME h m s	☉	☊	☽	☿	♀	♂	♃	♄	♅	♆	♇
1	10 36 3.5	7S35.0	0S 2.5	20N37.4	15S42.6	9N59.4	23S37.6	9N57.2	22S19.0	23S37.4	22S 7.5	0N 1.9
4	10 47 53.2	6 26.1	0 2.6	5 31.8	15 39.8	11 26.5	23 35.0	10 10.5	22 18.8	23 37.4	22 7.1	0 3.7
7	10 59 42.8	5 16.5	0 2.6	11S39.1	15 22.5	12 51.4	23 30.7	10 23.9	22 18.6	23 37.5	22 6.8	0 5.6
10	11 11 32.5	4 6.2	0 2.7	25 19.1	14 51.3	14 13.8	23 24.5	10 37.5	22 18.3	23 37.5	22 6.5	0 7.5
13	11 23 22.2	2 55.4	0 2.8	27 49.4	14 6.9	15 33.3	23 16.7	10 51.2	22 18.1	23 37.5	22 6.2	0 9.4
16	11 35 11.8	1 44.4	0 2.8	14 56.7	13 9.9	16 49.8	23 7.1	11 5.1	22 17.9	23 37.6	22 5.9	0 11.3
19	11 47 1.5	0 33.1	0 2.9	5N58.0	12 .7	18 3.0	22 55.8	11 19.0	22 17.6	23 37.6	22 5.7	0 13.3
22	11 58 51.1	0N38.0	0 3.0	23 8.9	10 39.8	19 12.5	22 42.9	11 33.0	22 17.4	23 37.6	22 5.5	0 15.3
25	12 10 40.8	1 48.9	0 3.0	28 38.3	9 7.6	20 18.2	22 28.3	11 47.0	22 17.2	23 37.7	22 5.2	0 17.2
28	12 22 30.5	2 59.5	0 3.1	21 44.5	7 24.6	21 19.9	22 12.2	12 1.1	22 17.0	23 37.7	22 5.1	0 19.2
31	12 34 20.1	4 9.5	0 3.2	7 6.1	5 31.1	22 17.3	21 54.5	12 15.2	22 16.8	23 37.8	22 4.9	0 21.1

APRIL 1988

DAY	EPHEM. SID. TIME	☉	☊	☽	☿	♀	♂	♃	♄	♅	♆	♇
	h m s	° ′	° ′	° ′	° ′	° ′	° ′	° ′	° ′	° ′	° ′	° ′
		LONGITUDE										
1	12 38 16.7	11♈29.3	22♓20.9	25♍55.3	23♓15.4	27♉19.2	26♑ 1.7	5♉ 8.7	2♑28.2	1♑ 2.5	10♑10.0	11♏59.6
2	12 42 13.2	12 28.4	22 17.7	8♎ 3.9	24 56.7	28 18.9	26 42.1	5 22.5	2 29.2	1 2.6	10 10.3	11R58.2
3	12 46 9.8	13 27.6	22 14.5	20 23.4	26 39.5	29 18.2	27 22.5	5 36.3	2 30.0	1 2.7	10 10.6	11 56.8
4	12 50 6.3	14 26.7	22 11.4	2♏55.2	28 23.7	0♊17.0	28 2.9	5 50.1	2 30.7	1 2.8	10 10.9	11 55.4
5	12 54 2.9	15 25.7	22 8.2	15 40.0	0♈ 9.3	1 15.3	28 43.3	6 4.0	2 31.4	1 2.8	10 11.1	11 53.9
6	12 57 59.4	16 24.8	22 5.0	28 38.3	1 56.3	2 13.2	29 23.7	6 18.0	2 31.9	1 2.8	10 11.3	11 52.4
7	13 1 56.0	17 23.8	22 1.8	11♐50.4	3 44.8	3 10.6	0♒ 4.1	6 31.9	2 32.4	1R 2.7	10 11.4	11 50.9
8	13 5 52.6	18 22.8	21 58.6	25 16.6	5 34.8	4 7.5	0 44.4	6 45.9	2 32.7	1 2.5	10 11.6	11 49.4
9	13 9 49.1	19 21.7	21 55.5	8♑56.9	7 26.3	5 3.9	1 24.8	6 59.9	2 33.0	1 2.3	10 11.6	11 47.9
10	13 13 45.7	20 20.6	21 52.3	22 51.1	9 19.2	5 59.7	2 5.1	7 14.0	2 33.1	1 2.1	10 11.7	11 46.4
11	13 17 42.2	21 19.5	21 49.1	6♒58.8	11 13.6	6 55.0	2 45.4	7 28.0	2 33.2	1 1.8	10 11.7	11 44.8
12	13 21 38.8	22 18.4	21 45.9	21 18.6	13 9.5	7 49.7	3 25.7	7 42.1	2R33.1	1 1.4	10 11.7	11 43.3
13	13 25 35.3	23 17.2	21 42.8	5♓48.0	15 6.8	8 43.9	4 6.0	7 56.3	2 33.0	1 1.0	10 11.7	11 41.7
14	13 29 31.9	24 16.0	21 39.6	20 23.2	17 5.6	9 37.4	4 46.3	8 10.4	2 32.7	1 .6	10R11.6	11 40.1
15	13 33 28.4	25 14.8	21 36.4	4♈59.3	19 5.8	10 30.3	5 26.5	8 24.6	2 32.4	1 .1	10 11.5	11 38.5
16	13 37 25.0	26 13.5	21 33.2	19 30.4	21 7.3	11 22.6	6 6.7	8 38.7	2 31.9	0 59.5	10 11.4	11 36.9
17	13 41 21.5	27 12.3	21 30.0	3♉50.2	23 10.2	12 14.2	6 46.9	8 52.9	2 31.4	0 58.9	10 11.2	11 35.3
18	13 45 18.1	28 10.9	21 26.9	17 53.2	25 14.2	13 5.0	7 27.0	9 7.2	2 30.8	0 58.3	10 11.0	11 33.6
19	13 49 14.7	29 9.6	21 23.7	1♊35.4	27 19.3	13 55.2	8 7.2	9 21.4	2 30.0	0 57.6	10 10.8	11 32.0
20	13 53 11.2	0♉ 8.2	21 20.5	14 54.4	29 25.5	14 44.6	8 47.2	9 35.7	2 29.2	0 56.8	10 10.5	11 30.3
21	13 57 7.8	1 6.8	21 17.3	27 50.0	1♉32.4	15 33.2	9 27.3	9 49.9	2 28.2	0 56.0	10 10.2	11 28.7
22	14 1 4.3	2 5.3	21 14.2	10♋24.2	3 40.1	16 21.0	10 7.4	10 4.2	2 27.3	0 55.2	10 9.9	11 27.1
23	14 5 .9	3 3.8	21 11.0	22 40.0	5 48.2	17 7.9	10 47.4	10 18.5	2 26.1	0 54.3	10 9.5	11 25.4
24	14 8 57.4	4 2.3	21 7.8	4♌41.8	7 56.5	17 54.0	11 27.4	10 32.8	2 24.9	0 53.4	10 9.1	11 23.7
25	14 12 54.0	5 .7	21 4.6	16 34.5	10 4.7	18 39.1	12 7.3	10 47.1	2 23.6	0 52.4	10 8.7	11 22.1
26	14 16 50.5	5 59.1	21 1.5	28 23.2	12 12.6	19 23.2	12 47.2	11 1.4	2 22.2	0 51.4	10 8.3	11 20.4
27	14 20 47.1	6 57.5	20 58.3	10♍13.0	14 19.9	20 6.4	13 27.0	11 15.7	2 20.7	0 50.3	10 7.8	11 18.7
28	14 24 43.7	7 55.8	20 55.1	22 8.6	16 26.3	20 48.6	14 6.9	11 30.1	2 19.1	0 49.2	10 7.3	11 17.0
29	14 28 40.2	8 54.1	20 51.9	4♎14.1	18 31.5	21 29.6	14 46.7	11 44.4	2 17.4	0 48.0	10 6.7	11 15.3
30	14 32 36.8	9 52.4	20 48.7	16 32.8	20 35.2	22 9.6	15 26.4	11 58.7	2 15.7	0 46.8	10 6.1	11 13.6
		LATITUDE										
1	12 38 16.7	0 .0	0 .0	0S15.5	2S21.9	3N 6.6	0S52.4	0S57.8	1N 8.5	0S11.4	0N58.6	16N33.5
4	12 50 6.3	0 .0	0 .0	3 22.1	2 17.2	3 18.6	0 56.3	0 57.4	1 8.7	0 11.5	0 58.6	16 34.2
7	13 1 56.0	0 .0	0 .0	5 8.3	2 8.0	3 30.0	1 .4	0 57.1	1 8.8	0 11.5	0 58.7	16 34.9
10	13 13 45.7	0 .0	0 .0	4 32.0	1 54.3	3 40.7	1 4.5	0 56.8	1 8.9	0 11.6	0 58.8	16 35.5
13	13 25 35.3	0 .0	0 .0	1 32.2	1 36.0	3 50.5	1 8.7	0 56.5	1 9.0	0 11.7	0 58.9	16 35.9
16	13 37 25.0	0 .0	0 .0	2N20.5	1 13.4	3 59.3	1 13.0	0 56.3	1 9.2	0 11.7	0 58.9	16 36.4
19	13 49 14.7	0 .0	0 .0	4 50.5	0 46.8	4 7.1	1 17.4	0 56.0	1 9.3	0 11.8	0 59.0	16 36.7
22	14 1 4.3	0 .0	0 .0	4 55.6	0 16.9	4 13.6	1 21.9	0 55.8	1 9.4	0 11.8	0 59.1	16 36.9
25	14 12 54.0	0 .0	0 .0	3 1.8	0N14.9	4 18.7	1 26.6	0 55.6	1 9.5	0 11.9	0 59.1	16 37.0
28	14 24 43.7	0 .0	0 .0	0 1.1	0 47.0	4 22.2	1 31.3	0 55.4	1 9.5	0 11.9	0 59.2	16 37.1
		RIGHT ASCENSION										
1	12 38 16.7	10♈33.7	22♓58.4	26♍ 9.3	24♓44.8	24♉16.3	28♑12.1	3♉11.2	2♑40.2	1♑ 8.2	10♑58.7	14♏34.1
2	12 42 13.2	11 28.4	22 55.5	6♎52.1	26 17.6	25 18.2	28 55.0	3 24.5	2 41.2	1 8.4	10 59.1	14R32.9
3	12 46 9.8	12 23.1	22 52.5	17 54.4	27 51.4	26 19.8	29 38.0	3 37.8	2 42.1	1 8.5	10 59.4	14 31.7
4	12 50 6.3	13 17.8	22 49.6	29 30.8	29 26.2	27 21.3	0♒20.8	3 51.1	2 42.9	1 8.5	10 59.7	14 30.4
5	12 54 2.9	14 12.6	22 46.7	11♏54.5	1♈ 2.1	28 22.5	1 3.6	4 4.5	2 43.6	1 8.6	10 59.9	14 29.2
6	12 57 59.4	15 7.4	22 43.8	25 14.9	2 39.1	29 23.5	1 46.3	4 18.0	2 44.2	1R 8.5	11 .1	14 27.9
7	13 1 56.0	16 2.2	22 40.8	9♐33.2	4 17.2	0♊24.2	2 28.9	4 31.4	2 44.6	1 8.4	11 .3	14 26.6
8	13 5 52.6	16 57.2	22 37.9	24 38.5	5 56.4	1 24.5	3 11.4	4 45.0	2 45.0	1 8.2	11 .4	14 25.3
9	13 9 49.1	17 52.2	22 35.0	10♑ 7.3	7 37.0	2 24.6	3 53.9	4 58.5	2 45.3	1 8.0	11 .5	14 23.9
10	13 13 45.7	18 47.2	22 32.1	25 30.5	9 18.7	3 24.3	4 36.3	5 12.1	2 45.4	1 7.8	11 .6	14 22.6
11	13 17 42.2	19 42.4	22 29.1	10♒24.1	11 1.9	4 23.6	5 18.6	5 25.7	2 45.5	1 7.4	11 .6	14 21.2
12	13 21 38.8	20 37.6	22 26.2	24 36.7	12 46.3	5 22.5	6 .8	5 39.4	2R45.4	1 7.0	11 .6	14 19.8
13	13 25 35.3	21 32.9	22 23.3	8♓10.0	14 32.2	6 20.9	6 42.9	5 53.1	2 45.3	1 6.6	11 .6	14 18.4
14	13 29 31.9	22 28.2	22 20.4	21 15.4	16 19.5	7 18.9	7 24.9	6 6.8	2 45.0	1 6.1	11R .5	14 17.0
15	13 33 28.4	23 23.7	22 17.4	4♈ 8.6	18 8.3	8 16.4	8 6.8	6 20.6	2 44.6	1 5.6	11 .4	14 15.6
16	13 37 25.0	24 19.2	22 14.5	17 6.3	19 58.7	9 13.3	8 48.7	6 34.4	2 44.2	1 5.0	11 .2	14 14.2
17	13 41 21.5	25 14.9	22 11.6	0♉23.3	21 50.5	10 9.7	9 30.4	6 48.2	2 43.6	1 4.3	11 .0	14 12.7
18	13 45 18.1	26 10.6	22 8.7	14 8.9	23 43.8	11 5.4	10 12.0	7 2.0	2 42.9	1 3.6	10 59.8	14 11.2
19	13 49 14.7	27 6.5	22 5.7	28 23.8	25 38.7	12 .5	10 53.5	7 15.9	2 42.1	1 2.8	10 59.5	14 9.8
20	13 53 11.2	28 2.4	22 2.8	12♊58.1	27 35.0	12 54.9	11 35.0	7 29.8	2 41.2	1 2.0	10 59.3	14 8.3
21	13 57 7.8	28 58.4	21 59.9	27 32.6	29 32.7	13 48.6	12 16.3	7 43.7	2 40.2	1 1.1	10 58.9	14 6.8
22	14 1 4.3	29 54.6	21 57.0	11♋45.1	1♉31.7	14 41.5	12 57.6	7 57.7	2 39.1	1 .3	10 58.6	14 5.3
23	14 5 .9	0♉50.9	21 54.0	25 17.7	3 31.9	15 33.5	13 38.7	8 11.6	2 37.9	0 59.3	10 58.2	14 3.8
24	14 8 57.4	1 47.3	21 51.1	8♌ 2.1	5 33.1	16 24.7	14 19.7	8 25.6	2 36.6	0 58.3	10 57.8	14 2.3
25	14 12 54.0	2 43.7	21 48.2	19 59.5	7 35.2	17 14.9	15 .6	8 39.6	2 35.2	0 57.2	10 57.3	14 .8
26	14 16 50.5	3 40.3	21 45.3	1♍17.8	9 37.9	18 4.2	15 41.4	8 53.6	2 33.6	0 56.1	10 56.8	13 59.2
27	14 20 47.1	4 37.1	21 42.3	12 9.1	11 41.0	18 52.4	16 22.1	9 7.6	2 32.0	0 54.9	10 56.3	13 57.7
28	14 24 43.7	5 33.9	21 39.4	22 47.5	13 44.2	19 39.5	17 2.6	9 21.7	2 30.3	0 53.7	10 55.8	13 56.2
29	14 28 40.2	6 30.9	21 36.5	3♎27.8	15 47.3	20 25.5	17 43.1	9 35.7	2 28.5	0 52.4	10 55.2	13 54.6
30	14 32 36.8	7 27.9	21 33.6	14 25.6	17 49.9	21 10.3	18 23.5	9 49.8	2 26.6	0 51.1	10 54.5	13 53.1
		DECLINATION										
1	12 38 16.7	4N32.7	0S 3.2	1N23.1	4S51.0	22N35.4	21S48.2	12N19.9	22S16.7	23S37.8	22S 4.8	0N21.7
4	12 50 6.3	5 41.7	0 3.2	15S39.0	2 44.2	23 26.9	21 28.5	12 34.0	22 16.5	23 37.9	22 4.7	0 23.7
7	13 1 56.0	6 49.9	0 3.3	27 18.1	0 28.1	24 13.7	21 7.3	12 48.0	22 16.4	23 37.9	22 4.6	0 25.5
10	13 13 45.7	7 57.0	0 3.4	25 58.6	1N56.6	24 55.9	20 44.8	13 2.0	22 16.2	23 38.0	22 4.5	0 27.4
13	13 25 35.3	9 2.9	0 3.4	10 48.8	4 28.7	25 33.3	20 20.8	13 16.0	22 16.1	23 38.0	22 4.4	0 29.2
16	13 37 25.0	10 7.5	0 3.5	9N48.1	7 6.5	26 5.9	19 55.6	13 29.9	22 16.0	23 38.1	22 4.4	0 30.9
19	13 49 14.7	11 10.6	0 3.6	25 13.2	9 47.7	26 33.8	19 29.2	13 43.7	22 15.9	23 38.2	22 4.3	0 32.6
22	14 1 4.3	12 12.1	0 3.6	27 56.8	12 28.6	26 56.8	19 1.6	13 57.4	22 15.9	23 38.2	22 4.3	0 34.3
25	14 12 54.0	13 11.7	0 3.7	18 45.6	15 4.6	27 15.2	18 32.9	14 11.0	22 15.9	23 38.3	22 4.4	0 35.8
28	14 24 43.7	14 9.3	0 3.8	3 8.0	17 30.4	27 29.0	18 3.1	14 24.5	22 15.9	23 38.4	22 4.4	0 37.3

MAY 1988

LONGITUDE

DAY	EPHEM. SID. TIME	☉	☊	☽	☿	♀	♂	♃	♄	♅	♆	♇
	h m s	° ′	° ′	° ′	° ′	° ′	° ′	° ′	° ′	° ′	° ′	° ′
1	14 36 33.3	10♉50.6	20♓45.6	29♎ 7.0	22♉37.0	22♊48.4	16♒ 6.1	12♉13.0	2♑13.8	0♑45.5	10♑ 5.5	11♏11.9
2	14 40 29.9	11 48.8	20 42.4	11♏57.6	24 36.7	23 26.0	16 45.8	12 27.3	2R11.9	0R44.2	10R 4.9	11R10.2
3	14 44 26.4	12 47.0	20 39.2	25 4.7	26 34.0	24 2.3	17 25.5	12 41.7	2 9.8	0 42.9	10 4.2	11 8.5
4	14 48 23.0	13 45.1	20 36.0	8♐26.9	28 28.7	24 37.3	18 5.0	12 56.0	2 7.7	0 41.5	10 3.5	11 6.8
5	14 52 19.5	14 43.2	20 32.9	22 2.2	0♊20.6	25 11.1	18 44.6	13 10.3	2 5.5	0 40.1	10 2.8	11 5.1
6	14 56 16.1	15 41.3	20 29.7	5♑48.4	2 9.5	25 43.4	19 24.1	13 24.6	2 3.2	0 38.6	10 2.0	11 3.5
7	15 0 12.7	16 39.4	20 26.5	19 42.9	3 55.2	26 14.3	20 3.6	13 38.9	2 .8	0 37.1	10 1.3	11 1.8
8	15 4 9.2	17 37.4	20 23.3	3♒43.7	5 37.6	26 43.7	20 43.0	13 53.2	1 58.4	0 35.6	10 .4	11 .1
9	15 8 5.8	18 35.5	20 20.1	17 49.3	7 16.6	27 11.5	21 22.3	14 7.5	1 55.8	0 34.0	9 59.6	10 58.4
10	15 12 2.3	19 33.5	20 17.0	1♓58.2	8 52.0	27 37.8	22 1.6	14 21.8	1 53.2	0 32.4	9 58.7	10 56.7
11	15 15 58.9	20 31.4	20 13.8	16 9.4	10 23.8	28 2.4	22 40.9	14 36.1	1 50.5	0 30.7	9 57.9	10 55.1
12	15 19 55.4	21 29.4	20 10.6	0♈21.1	11 52.0	28 25.3	23 20.1	14 50.3	1 47.7	0 29.1	9 56.9	10 53.4
13	15 23 52.0	22 27.4	20 7.4	14 31.2	13 16.4	28 46.4	23 59.2	15 4.7	1 44.9	0 27.4	9 56.0	10 51.8
14	15 27 48.6	23 25.3	20 4.3	28 36.6	14 37.0	29 5.7	24 38.3	15 18.9	1 42.0	0 25.6	9 55.1	10 50.1
15	15 31 45.1	24 23.2	20 1.1	12♉33.5	15 53.8	29 23.1	25 17.2	15 33.1	1 39.0	0 23.8	9 54.1	10 48.5
16	15 35 41.7	25 21.1	19 57.9	26 18.0	17 6.5	29 38.6	25 56.1	15 47.3	1 35.9	0 22.0	9 53.1	10 46.9
17	15 39 38.2	26 18.9	19 54.7	9♊46.6	18 15.4	29 52.0	26 35.0	16 1.5	1 32.8	0 20.1	9 52.0	10 45.3
18	15 43 34.8	27 16.7	19 51.6	22 56.8	19 20.1	0♋ 3.3	27 13.7	16 15.7	1 29.6	0 18.2	9 50.9	10 43.6
19	15 47 31.3	28 14.5	19 48.4	5♋47.5	20 20.8	0 12.6	27 52.4	16 29.9	1 26.3	0 16.3	9 49.8	10 42.1
20	15 51 27.9	29 12.3	19 45.2	18 19.2	21 17.3	0 19.6	28 30.9	16 44.0	1 22.9	0 14.3	9 48.7	10 40.5
21	15 55 24.5	0♊10.0	19 42.0	0♌34.2	22 9.5	0 24.3	29 9.4	16 58.1	1 19.5	0 12.3	9 47.6	10 38.9
22	15 59 21.0	1 7.7	19 38.9	12 35.7	22 57.4	0 26.8	29 47.9	17 12.2	1 16.1	0 10.3	9 46.4	10 37.3
23	16 3 17.6	2 5.4	19 35.7	24 28.4	23 41.0	0 27.0	0♓26.2	17 26.3	1 12.5	0 8.3	9 45.3	10 35.8
24	16 7 14.1	3 3.1	19 32.5	6♍17.2	24 20.1	0R24.7	1 4.4	17 40.3	1 8.9	0 6.2	9 44.0	10 34.2
25	16 11 10.7	4 .7	19 29.3	18 7.6	24 54.7	0 20.1	1 42.5	17 54.3	1 5.3	0 4.1	9 42.8	10 32.7
26	16 15 7.2	4 58.3	19 26.1	0♎ 4.9	25 24.8	0 13.0	2 20.6	18 8.3	1 1.6	0 2.0	9 41.6	10 31.2
27	16 19 3.8	5 55.9	19 23.0	12 14.2	25 50.2	0 3.5	2 58.5	18 22.3	0 57.8	29♐59.8	9 40.3	10 29.7
28	16 23 .4	6 53.5	19 19.8	24 39.9	26 10.9	29♊51.5	3 36.4	18 36.2	0 54.0	29 57.7	9 39.0	10 28.3
29	16 26 56.9	7 51.0	19 16.6	7♏25.0	26 26.9	29 37.1	4 14.1	18 50.1	0 50.1	29 55.5	9 37.7	10 26.8
30	16 30 53.5	8 48.5	19 13.4	20 31.3	26 38.3	29 20.3	4 51.8	19 3.9	0 46.2	29 53.3	9 36.4	10 25.4
31	16 34 50.0	9 46.0	19 10.3	3♐58.5	26 44.9	29 1.2	5 29.3	19 17.8	0 42.3	29 51.0	9 35.1	10 23.9

LATITUDE

DAY	EPHEM. SID. TIME	☉	☊	☽	☿	♀	♂	♃	♄	♅	♆	♇
1	14 36 33.3	0 .0	0 .0	3S 5.1	1N17.3	4N23.9	1S36.1	0S55.2	1N 9.6	0S12.0	0N59.3	16N37.0
4	14 48 23.0	0 .0	0 .0	4 57.9	1 43.8	4 23.5	1 41.0	0 55.0	1 9.7	0 12.1	0 59.3	16 36.9
7	15 0 12.7	0 .0	0 .0	4 30.0	2 4.8	4 20.9	1 46.0	0 54.8	1 9.7	0 12.1	0 59.4	16 36.6
10	15 12 2.3	0 .0	0 .0	1 42.2	2 19.2	4 15.8	1 51.0	0 54.7	1 9.7	0 12.2	0 59.4	16 36.3
13	15 23 52.0	0 .0	0 .0	2N .2	2 26.0	4 7.8	1 56.2	0 54.6	1 9.8	0 12.2	0 59.5	16 35.9
16	15 35 41.7	0 .0	0 .0	4 35.6	2 24.7	3 56.6	2 1.5	0 54.4	1 9.8	0 12.3	0 59.5	16 35.4
19	15 47 31.3	0 .0	0 .0	4 52.3	2 15.2	3 41.8	2 6.8	0 54.4	1 9.7	0 12.3	0 59.6	16 34.8
22	15 59 21.0	0 .0	0 .0	3 5.8	1 57.1	3 23.2	2 12.3	0 54.3	1 9.7	0 12.3	0 59.6	16 34.1
25	16 11 10.7	0 .0	0 .0	0 10.8	1 30.6	3 .4	2 17.8	0 54.2	1 9.7	0 12.4	0 59.6	16 33.4
28	16 23 .4	0 .0	0 .0	2S52.1	0 56.0	2 33.3	2 23.5	0 54.1	1 9.6	0 12.4	0 59.7	16 32.5
31	16 34 50.0	0 .0	0 .0	4 49.7	0 14.0	2 1.9	2 29.2	0 54.1	1 9.5	0 12.5	0 59.7	16 31.6

RIGHT ASCENSION

DAY	EPHEM. SID. TIME	☉	☊	☽	☿	♀	♂	♃	♄	♅	♆	♇
1	14 36 33.3	8♉25.2	21♓30.6	25♎56.5	19♉51.7	21♊53.9	19♒ 3.7	10♉ 3.9	2♑24.6	0♑49.7	10♑53.9	13♏51.5
2	14 40 29.9	9 22.5	21 27.7	8♏15.0	21 52.5	22 36.1	19 43.9	10 17.9	2R22.5	0R48.3	10R53.2	13R49.9
3	14 44 26.4	10 20.0	21 24.8	21 32.0	23 51.9	23 17.0	20 23.9	10 32.0	2 20.3	0 46.8	10 52.5	13 48.4
4	14 48 23.0	11 17.6	21 21.9	5♐50.1	25 49.6	23 56.4	21 3.8	10 46.1	2 18.0	0 45.3	10 51.7	13 46.8
5	14 52 19.5	12 15.4	21 18.9	20 59.0	27 45.3	24 34.4	21 43.7	11 .2	2 15.6	0 43.8	10 50.9	13 45.2
6	14 56 16.1	13 13.3	21 16.0	6♑34.2	29 38.8	25 10.8	22 23.4	11 14.4	2 13.1	0 42.2	10 50.1	13 43.7
7	15 0 12.7	14 11.4	21 13.1	22 3.7	1♊29.8	25 45.6	23 2.9	11 28.5	2 10.5	0 40.5	10 49.3	13 42.1
8	15 4 9.2	15 9.6	21 10.1	7♒ .3	3 18.1	26 18.8	23 42.4	11 42.6	2 7.9	0 38.9	10 48.4	13 40.5
9	15 8 5.8	16 7.9	21 7.2	21 10.5	5 3.5	26 50.2	24 21.8	11 56.7	2 5.2	0 37.1	10 47.5	13 39.0
10	15 12 2.3	17 6.4	21 4.3	4♓35.5	6 45.7	27 19.8	25 1.0	12 10.9	2 2.3	0 35.4	10 46.6	13 37.4
11	15 15 58.9	18 5.1	21 1.4	17 26.6	8 24.6	27 47.6	25 40.1	12 25.0	1 59.4	0 33.6	10 45.6	13 35.8
12	15 19 55.4	19 3.9	20 58.4	0♈ .4	10 .1	28 13.4	26 19.1	12 39.1	1 56.4	0 31.7	10 44.6	13 34.3
13	15 23 52.0	20 2.9	20 55.5	12 35.1	11 31.9	28 37.2	26 58.0	12 53.3	1 53.4	0 29.9	10 43.7	13 32.8
14	15 27 48.6	21 1.9	20 52.6	25 27.3	12 60.0	28 58.9	27 36.7	13 7.4	1 50.2	0 28.0	10 42.6	13 31.2
15	15 31 45.1	22 1.2	20 49.6	8♉50.1	14 24.1	29 18.5	28 15.3	13 21.6	1 47.0	0 26.0	10 41.6	13 29.7
16	15 35 41.7	23 .6	20 46.7	22 48.8	15 44.2	29 35.9	28 53.7	13 35.7	1 43.6	0 24.0	10 40.5	13 28.1
17	15 39 38.2	24 .1	20 43.8	7♊18.0	17 .1	29 51.0	29 32.0	13 49.8	1 40.3	0 22.0	10 39.3	13 26.6
18	15 43 34.8	24 59.7	20 40.9	22 .9	18 11.7	0♋ 3.7	0♓10.2	14 3.9	1 36.8	0 19.9	10 38.2	13 25.1
19	15 47 31.3	25 59.5	20 37.9	6♋33.0	19 18.9	0 14.1	0 48.3	14 18.0	1 33.2	0 17.8	10 37.0	13 23.5
20	15 51 27.9	26 59.4	20 35.0	20 31.1	20 21.6	0 21.9	1 26.2	14 32.1	1 29.6	0 15.6	10 35.8	13 22.0
21	15 55 24.5	27 59.5	20 32.1	3♌41.0	21 19.7	0 27.3	2 3.9	14 46.1	1 25.9	0 13.5	10 34.6	13 20.5
22	15 59 21.0	28 59.7	20 29.1	15 59.3	22 13.0	0 30.0	2 41.6	15 .2	1 22.2	0 11.3	10 33.3	13 19.0
23	16 3 17.6	0♊ .0	20 26.2	27 32.0	23 1.5	0 30.1	3 19.0	15 14.3	1 18.4	0 9.0	10 32.0	13 17.5
24	16 7 14.1	1 .4	20 23.3	8♍30.5	23 45.0	0R27.6	3 56.4	15 28.3	1 14.5	0 6.8	10 30.7	13 16.0
25	16 11 10.7	2 1.0	20 20.4	19 9.2	24 23.6	0 22.4	4 33.6	15 42.3	1 10.5	0 4.5	10 29.4	13 14.6
26	16 15 7.2	3 1.7	20 17.4	29 43.6	24 57.1	0 14.5	5 10.7	15 56.3	1 6.5	0 2.2	10 28.1	13 13.1
27	16 19 3.8	4 2.5	20 14.5	10♎30.3	25 25.4	0 3.9	5 47.6	16 10.3	1 2.5	29♐59.8	10 26.7	13 11.7
28	16 23 .4	5 3.4	20 11.6	21 46.2	25 48.6	29♊50.6	6 24.4	16 24.2	0 58.3	29 57.4	10 25.3	13 10.2
29	16 26 56.9	6 4.4	20 8.6	3♏47.8	26 6.5	29 34.6	7 1.0	16 38.1	0 54.2	29 55.1	10 23.9	13 8.8
30	16 30 53.5	7 5.5	20 5.7	16 49.5	26 19.4	29 16.0	7 37.5	16 52.1	0 50.0	29 52.6	10 22.5	13 7.4
31	16 34 50.0	8 6.8	20 2.8	0♐58.7	26 27.0	28 54.9	8 13.9	17 5.9	0 45.7	29 50.2	10 21.1	13 6.0

DECLINATION

DAY	EPHEM. SID. TIME	☉	☊	☽	☿	♀	♂	♃	♄	♅	♆	♇
1	14 36 33.3	15N 4.9	0S 3.8	14S 2.7	19N40.4	27N38.3	17S32.4	14N37.8	22S15.9	23S38.5	22S 4.5	0N38.7
4	14 48 23.0	15 58.1	0 3.9	26 37.1	21 30.7	27 43.3	17 .8	14 51.0	22 15.9	23 38.5	22 4.6	0 40.0
7	15 0 12.7	16 49.1	0 4.0	26 26.7	22 58.8	27 44.2	16 28.4	15 4.0	22 16.0	23 38.6	22 4.7	0 41.3
10	15 12 2.3	17 37.5	0 4.0	12 21.9	24 4.4	27 41.1	15 55.2	15 16.8	22 16.1	23 38.7	22 4.8	0 42.4
13	15 23 52.0	18 23.2	0 4.1	7N34.3	24 48.6	27 34.0	15 21.3	15 29.5	22 16.1	23 38.8	22 5.0	0 43.4
16	15 35 41.7	19 6.2	0 4.2	23 47.4	25 13.2	27 23.1	14 46.8	15 42.0	22 16.3	23 38.8	22 5.1	0 44.4
19	15 47 31.3	19 46.3	0 4.2	28 11.0	25 20.3	27 8.4	14 11.9	15 54.3	22 16.4	23 38.9	22 5.3	0 45.2
22	15 59 21.0	20 23.3	0 4.3	19 59.9	25 12.3	26 49.8	13 36.5	16 6.3	22 16.5	23 38.9	22 5.5	0 45.9
25	16 11 10.7	20 57.2	0 4.4	4 51.3	24 51.3	26 27.0	13 .8	16 18.2	22 16.7	23 39.0	22 5.8	0 46.5
28	16 23 .4	21 27.8	0 4.4	12S13.4	24 19.3	25 59.9	12 24.8	16 29.8	22 16.8	23 39.0	22 6.0	0 47.0
31	16 34 50.0	21 55.1	0 4.5	25 41.3	23 38.2	25 28.3	11 48.7	16 41.1	22 17.0	23 39.1	22 6.3	0 47.4

JUNE 1988

LONGITUDE

DAY	EPHEM. SID. TIME h m s	☉ ° ′	☊ ° ′	☽ ° ′	☿ ° ′	♀ ° ′	♂ ° ′	♃ ° ′	♄ ° ′	♅ ° ′	♆ ° ′	♇ ° ′
1	16 38 46.6	10♊43.5	19♓ 7.1	17♐44.7	26♊46.9	28♊39.8	6♓ 6.8	19♉31.5	0♑38.3	29♐48.8	9♑33.7	10♏22.5
2	16 42 43.1	11 41.0	19 3.9	1♑46.2	26 R 44.4	28 R 16.2	6 44.1	19 45.3	0 R 34.3	29 R 46.5	9 R 32.3	10 R 21.2
3	16 46 39.7	12 38.5	19 .7	15 58.0	26 37.5	27 50.5	7 21.3	19 59.1	0 30.2	29 44.2	9 31.0	10 19.8
4	16 50 36.3	13 35.9	18 57.6	0♒15.1	26 26.4	27 22.8	7 58.4	20 12.8	0 26.1	29 41.9	9 29.6	10 18.5
5	16 54 32.8	14 33.4	18 54.4	14 33.0	26 11.1	26 53.3	8 35.4	20 26.4	0 22.0	29 39.6	9 28.2	10 17.2
6	16 58 29.4	15 30.8	18 51.2	28 48.2	25 52.2	26 22.0	9 12.2	20 40.0	0 17.8	29 37.3	9 26.7	10 15.9
7	17 2 25.9	16 28.2	18 48.0	12♓58.3	25 29.7	25 49.2	9 48.9	20 53.6	0 13.5	29 34.9	9 25.3	10 14.6
8	17 6 22.5	17 25.6	18 44.9	27 2.3	25 4.2	25 15.1	10 25.5	21 7.1	0 9.3	29 32.5	9 23.8	10 13.3
9	17 10 19.1	18 23.0	18 41.7	10♈59.4	24 36.1	24 39.9	11 1.9	21 20.6	0 5.0	29 30.2	9 22.3	10 12.1
10	17 14 15.6	19 20.3	18 38.5	24 49.1	24 5.7	24 3.8	11 38.2	21 34.0	0 .7	29 27.8	9 20.8	10 10.9
11	17 18 12.2	20 17.7	18 35.3	8♉30.7	23 33.7	23 26.9	12 14.3	21 47.4	29♐56.4	29 25.4	9 19.3	10 9.7
12	17 22 8.7	21 15.1	18 32.1	22 2.8	23 .6	22 49.6	12 50.2	22 .8	29 52.0	29 23.0	9 17.8	10 8.5
13	17 26 5.3	22 12.4	18 29.0	5♊23.7	22 26.9	22 12.1	13 26.0	22 14.1	29 47.7	29 20.5	9 16.3	10 7.4
14	17 30 1.9	23 9.8	18 25.8	18 31.8	21 53.2	21 34.6	14 1.6	22 27.3	29 43.3	29 18.1	9 14.7	10 6.3
15	17 33 58.4	24 7.1	18 22.6	1♋25.3	21 20.1	20 57.3	14 37.0	22 40.5	29 38.9	29 15.7	9 13.2	10 5.2
16	17 37 55.0	25 4.4	18 19.4	14 3.6	20 48.1	20 20.5	15 12.3	22 53.6	29 34.5	29 13.2	9 11.6	10 4.1
17	17 41 51.5	26 1.7	18 16.3	26 26.8	20 17.9	19 44.4	15 47.4	23 6.7	29 30.1	29 10.8	9 10.1	10 3.1
18	17 45 48.1	26 59.0	18 13.1	8♌36.3	19 49.8	19 9.2	16 22.2	23 19.7	29 25.6	29 8.3	9 8.5	10 2.0
19	17 49 44.6	27 56.3	18 9.9	20 34.7	19 24.4	18 35.2	16 56.9	23 32.7	29 21.2	29 5.9	9 6.9	10 1.0
20	17 53 41.2	28 53.6	18 6.7	2♍25.5	19 2.2	18 2.5	17 31.4	23 45.6	29 16.8	29 3.4	9 5.3	10 .1
21	17 57 37.8	29 50.8	18 3.6	14 13.3	18 43.4	17 31.3	18 5.7	23 58.5	29 12.3	29 1.0	9 3.7	9 59.2
22	18 1 34.3	0♋48.1	18 .4	26 3.0	18 28.4	17 1.8	18 39.8	24 11.3	29 7.9	28 58.5	9 2.1	9 58.2
23	18 5 30.9	1 45.3	17 57.2	8♎ .1	18 17.6	16 34.1	19 13.6	24 24.0	29 3.4	28 56.1	9 .5	9 57.4
24	18 9 27.4	2 42.6	17 54.0	20 10.1	18 11.1	16 8.5	19 47.3	24 36.7	28 59.1	28 53.7	8 59.0	9 56.6
25	18 13 24.0	3 39.8	17 50.9	2♏37.9	18 9.1	15 44.8	20 20.7	24 49.3	28 54.7	28 51.2	8 57.4	9 55.8
26	18 17 20.6	4 37.0	17 47.7	15 27.6	18 D 11.7	15 23.4	20 53.9	25 1.9	28 50.3	28 48.8	8 55.8	9 55.0
27	18 21 17.1	5 34.2	17 44.5	28 42.1	18 19.0	15 4.1	21 26.9	25 14.3	28 45.9	28 46.4	8 54.1	9 54.2
28	18 25 13.7	6 31.4	17 41.3	12♐22.0	18 31.2	14 47.2	21 59.6	25 26.7	28 41.5	28 44.0	8 52.5	9 53.5
29	18 29 10.2	7 28.6	17 38.1	26 25.5	18 48.2	14 32.7	22 32.1	25 39.1	28 37.1	28 41.6	8 50.9	9 52.8
30	18 33 6.8	8♋25.8	17 35.0	10♑48.4	19♊10.0	14♊20.5	23 4.3	25 51.3	28♐32.8	28♐39.1	8♑49.3	9♏52.1

LATITUDE

DAY	EPHEM. SID. TIME	☉	☊	☽	☿	♀	♂	♃	♄	♅	♆	♇
1	16 38 46.6	0 .0	0 .0	5S .5	0S 1.4	1N50.5	2S31.1	0S54.1	1N 9.5	0S12.5	0N59.7	16N31.3
4	16 50 36.3	0 .0	0 .0	3 46.7	0 50.7	1 13.8	2 36.9	0 54.1	1 9.4	0 12.5	0 59.7	16 30.2
7	17 2 25.9	0 .0	0 .0	0 30.9	1 42.4	0 34.0	2 42.8	0 54.1	1 9.2	0 12.6	0 59.7	16 29.1
10	17 14 15.6	0 .0	0 .0	2N57.9	2 32.8	0S 7.8	2 48.7	0 54.1	1 9.1	0 12.6	0 59.7	16 28.0
13	17 26 5.3	0 .0	0 .0	4 52.8	3 18.0	0 50.3	2 54.8	0 54.1	1 8.9	0 12.6	0 59.7	16 26.7
16	17 37 55.0	0 .0	0 .0	4 29.7	3 54.1	1 31.9	3 .9	0 54.1	1 8.7	0 12.7	0 59.7	16 25.4
19	17 49 44.6	0 .0	0 .0	2 16.5	4 18.5	2 11.3	3 7.1	0 54.2	1 8.5	0 12.7	0 59.7	16 24.1
22	18 1 34.3	0 .0	0 .0	0S46.5	4 30.3	2 47.3	3 13.3	0 54.2	1 8.2	0 12.7	0 59.7	16 22.7
25	18 13 24.0	0 .0	0 .0	3 36.4	4 29.7	3 18.9	3 19.6	0 54.3	1 8.0	0 12.8	0 59.7	16 21.2
28	18 25 13.7	0 .0	0 .0	5 1.6	4 18.1	3 45.8	3 25.9	0 54.4	1 7.7	0 12.8	0 59.7	16 19.7

RIGHT ASCENSION

DAY	EPHEM. SID. TIME	☉	☊	☽	☿	♀	♂	♃	♄	♅	♆	♇
1	16 38 46.6	9♊ 8.1	19♓59.8	16♐ 9.7	26♊29.7	28♊31.4	8♓50.1	17♉19.8	0♑41.4	29♐47.7	10♑19.6	13♏ 4.6
2	16 42 43.1	10 9.6	19 56.9	2♑ .2	26 R 27.3	28 R 5.4	9 26.1	17 33.6	0 R 37.0	29 R 45.3	10 R 18.1	13 R 3.3
3	16 46 39.7	11 11.1	19 54.0	17 54.9	26 20.3	27 37.3	10 2.1	17 47.5	0 32.7	29 42.8	10 16.7	13 2.0
4	16 50 36.3	12 12.8	19 51.1	3♒19.5	26 8.7	27 7.1	10 37.8	18 1.3	0 28.2	29 40.3	10 15.2	13 .6
5	16 54 32.8	13 14.5	19 48.1	17 53.5	25 52.7	26 34.9	11 13.4	18 15.0	0 23.7	29 37.7	10 13.6	12 59.3
6	16 58 29.4	14 16.3	19 45.2	1♓33.8	25 32.8	26 1.0	11 48.8	18 28.7	0 19.2	29 35.2	10 12.1	12 58.0
7	17 2 25.9	15 18.2	19 42.3	14 30.2	25 9.3	25 25.6	12 24.1	18 42.4	0 14.6	29 32.6	10 10.5	12 56.7
8	17 6 22.5	16 20.1	19 39.3	26 59.7	24 42.5	24 48.9	12 59.2	18 56.1	0 10.0	29 30.0	10 9.0	12 55.5
9	17 10 19.1	17 22.2	19 36.4	9♈21.1	24 13.1	24 11.0	13 34.1	19 9.7	0 5.4	29 27.4	10 7.4	12 54.2
10	17 14 15.6	18 24.3	19 33.5	21 52.7	23 41.4	23 32.4	14 8.8	19 23.3	0 .8	29 24.8	10 5.8	12 53.0
11	17 18 12.2	19 26.5	19 30.5	4♉50.1	23 8.1	22 53.1	14 43.4	19 36.9	29♐56.1	29 22.2	10 4.1	12 51.8
12	17 22 8.7	20 28.7	19 27.6	18 22.7	22 33.6	22 13.5	15 17.8	19 50.4	29 51.4	29 19.6	10 2.5	12 50.6
13	17 26 5.3	21 30.9	19 24.7	2♊30.7	21 58.6	21 33.8	15 52.0	20 3.8	29 46.7	29 16.9	10 .9	12 49.4
14	17 30 1.9	22 33.3	19 21.7	17 2.5	21 23.8	20 54.2	16 26.0	20 17.3	29 41.9	29 14.3	9 59.2	12 48.3
15	17 33 58.4	23 35.6	19 18.8	1♋36.6	20 49.6	20 15.1	16 59.8	20 30.6	29 37.2	29 11.6	9 57.5	12 47.1
16	17 37 55.0	24 38.0	19 15.9	15 47.8	20 16.6	19 36.6	17 33.4	20 44.0	29 32.4	29 8.9	9 55.9	12 46.0
17	17 41 51.5	25 40.4	19 12.9	29 16.9	19 45.4	18 59.0	18 6.8	20 57.3	29 27.6	29 6.3	9 54.2	12 44.9
18	17 45 48.1	26 42.8	19 10.0	11♌55.0	19 16.5	18 22.6	18 40.1	21 10.5	29 22.8	29 3.6	9 52.5	12 43.9
19	17 49 44.6	27 45.2	19 7.1	23 43.9	18 50.4	17 47.4	19 13.1	21 23.7	29 18.1	29 .9	9 50.8	12 42.8
20	17 53 41.2	28 47.6	19 4.1	4♍52.6	18 27.5	17 13.8	19 45.9	21 36.9	29 13.3	28 58.2	9 49.1	12 41.8
21	17 57 37.8	29 50.0	19 1.2	15 34.3	18 8.1	16 41.8	20 18.5	21 50.0	29 8.5	28 55.6	9 47.3	12 40.8
22	18 1 34.3	0♋52.4	18 58.3	26 4.0	17 52.7	16 11.7	20 50.9	22 3.0	29 3.7	28 52.9	9 45.6	12 39.8
23	18 5 30.9	1 54.8	18 55.3	6♎38.3	17 41.4	15 43.6	21 23.0	22 16.0	28 58.9	28 50.2	9 43.9	12 38.9
24	18 9 27.4	2 57.2	18 52.4	17 34.0	17 34.6	15 17.6	21 55.0	22 29.0	28 54.2	28 47.6	9 42.2	12 38.0
25	18 13 24.0	3 59.5	18 49.5	29 8.8	17 32.3	14 53.8	22 26.7	22 41.8	28 49.4	28 44.9	9 40.5	12 37.1
26	18 17 20.6	5 1.8	18 46.5	11♏39.5	17 D 34.8	14 32.3	22 58.2	22 54.6	28 44.6	28 42.3	9 38.7	12 36.2
27	18 21 17.1	6 4.1	18 43.6	25 18.8	17 42.2	14 13.1	23 29.5	23 7.4	28 39.9	28 39.6	9 37.0	12 35.4
28	18 25 13.7	7 6.3	18 40.7	10♐ 9.3	17 54.5	13 56.4	24 .5	23 20.1	28 35.1	28 37.0	9 35.3	12 34.6
29	18 29 10.2	8 8.4	18 37.7	25 57.1	18 11.8	13 42.1	24 31.3	23 32.7	28 30.4	28 34.4	9 33.5	12 33.8
30	18 33 6.8	9♋10.5	18 34.8	12♑10.3	18♊34.2	13♊30.2	25 1.9	23 45.2	28♐25.7	28♐31.7	9♑31.8	12♏33.0

DECLINATION

DAY	EPHEM. SID. TIME	☉	☊	☽	☿	♀	♂	♃	♄	♅	♆	♇
1	16 38 46.6	22N 3.4	0S 4.5	27S51.9	23N22.8	25N16.7	11S36.6	16N44.9	22S17.0	23S39.1	22S 6.4	0N47.5
4	16 50 36.3	22 26.1	0 4.6	23 47.3	22 33.0	24 38.8	11 .3	16 55.9	22 17.2	23 39.1	22 6.6	0 47.7
7	17 2 25.9	22 45.3	0 4.6	7 9.9	21 39.6	23 56.6	10 24.1	17 6.7	22 17.4	23 39.1	22 6.9	0 47.8
10	17 14 15.6	23 .9	0 4.7	12N22.2	20 46.0	23 10.8	9 48.0	17 17.3	22 17.5	23 39.1	22 7.2	0 47.8
13	17 26 5.3	23 12.8	0 4.8	26 .3	19 56.0	22 22.6	9 12.1	17 27.6	22 17.7	23 39.1	22 7.5	0 47.6
16	17 37 55.0	23 21.1	0 4.8	27 10.2	19 13.9	21 33.8	8 36.6	17 37.6	22 17.9	23 39.1	22 7.9	0 47.3
19	17 49 44.6	23 25.6	0 4.9	16 47.4	18 43.5	20 46.3	8 1.5	17 47.3	22 18.0	23 39.1	22 8.2	0 46.9
22	18 1 34.3	23 26.4	0 5.0	0 51.6	18 27.3	20 2.1	7 26.9	17 56.7	22 18.2	23 39.1	22 8.5	0 46.4
25	18 13 24.0	23 23.5	0 5.0	15S46.3	18 26.2	19 23.0	6 53.0	18 5.9	22 18.3	23 39.0	22 8.9	0 45.7
28	18 25 13.7	23 16.9	0 5.1	27 15.8	18 39.6	18 50.1	6 19.7	18 14.8	22 18.5	23 39.0	22 9.2	0 45.0

JULY 1988

LONGITUDE

DAY	EPHEM. SID. TIME h m s	☉ ° ′	☊ ° ′	☽ ° ′	☿ ° ′	♀ ° ′	♂ ° ′	♃ ° ′	♄ ° ′	♅ ° ′	♆ ° ′	♇ ° ′
1	18 37 3.4	9♋23.0	17♓31.8	25♑24.4	19♊36.7	14♊10.8	23♓36.3	26♉ 3.5	28♐28.5	28♐36.8	8♑47.6	9♏51.5
2	18 40 59.9	10 20.1	17 28.6	10♒ 6.3	20 8.3	14R 3.4	24 8.0	26 15.6	28R24.2	28R34.4	8R46.0	9R50.9
3	18 44 56.5	11 17.3	17 25.4	24 47.0	20 44.6	13 58.5	24 39.5	26 27.7	28 19.9	28 32.0	8 44.4	9 50.3
4	18 48 53.0	12 14.5	17 22.3	9♓20.4	21 25.6	13 55.9	25 10.6	26 39.6	28 15.7	28 29.6	8 42.8	9 49.7
5	18 52 49.6	13 11.7	17 19.1	23 42.4	22 11.3	13 55.7	25 41.5	26 51.5	28 11.4	28 27.3	8 41.2	9 49.2
6	18 56 46.1	14 8.9	17 15.9	7♈50.8	23 1.7	13D57.8	26 12.1	27 3.3	28 7.3	28 25.0	8 39.5	9 48.7
7	19 0 42.7	15 6.1	17 12.7	21 44.5	23 56.7	14 2.2	26 42.3	27 15.1	28 3.1	28 22.6	8 37.9	9 48.3
8	19 4 39.3	16 3.3	17 9.6	5♉23.9	24 56.2	14 8.8	27 12.3	27 26.7	27 59.0	28 20.3	8 36.3	9 47.9
9	19 8 35.8	17 .5	17 6.4	18 49.5	26 .1	14 17.6	27 41.9	27 38.3	27 54.9	28 18.1	8 34.7	9 47.5
10	19 12 32.4	17 57.7	17 3.2	2♊ 1.8	27 8.4	14 28.5	28 11.2	27 49.7	27 50.9	28 15.8	8 33.1	9 47.1
11	19 16 28.9	18 55.0	17 .0	15 1.4	28 21.1	14 41.4	28 40.1	28 1.1	27 46.9	28 13.6	8 31.5	9 46.8
12	19 20 25.5	19 52.2	16 56.9	27 48.5	29 38.1	14 56.3	29 8.6	28 12.4	27 42.9	28 11.3	8 29.9	9 46.5
13	19 24 22.1	20 49.4	16 53.7	10♋23.2	0♋59.3	15 13.2	29 36.8	28 23.7	27 39.0	28 9.1	8 28.4	9 46.3
14	19 28 18.6	21 46.7	16 50.5	22 45.9	2 24.6	15 31.9	0♈ 4.6	28 34.8	27 35.2	28 6.9	8 26.8	9 46.0
15	19 32 15.2	22 44.0	16 47.3	4♌57.3	3 54.0	15 52.5	0 32.1	28 45.9	27 31.4	28 4.8	8 25.3	9 45.9
16	19 36 11.7	23 41.2	16 44.2	16 58.6	5 27.3	16 14.8	0 59.1	28 56.8	27 27.7	28 2.7	8 23.7	9 45.7
17	19 40 8.3	24 38.5	16 41.0	28 51.9	7 4.5	16 38.8	1 25.7	29 7.6	27 24.0	28 .6	8 22.2	9 45.6
18	19 44 4.8	25 35.7	16 37.8	10♍39.9	8 45.3	17 4.3	1 52.0	29 18.4	27 20.3	27 58.5	8 20.6	9 45.5
19	19 48 1.4	26 33.0	16 34.6	22 26.3	10 29.7	17 31.5	2 17.7	29 29.0	27 16.7	27 56.5	8 19.1	9 45.5
20	19 51 58.0	27 30.3	16 31.4	4♎15.3	12 17.4	18 .2	2 43.1	29 39.5	27 13.2	27 54.4	8 17.6	9 45.5
21	19 55 54.5	28 27.5	16 28.3	16 11.7	14 8.3	18 30.3	3 8.0	29 50.0	27 9.7	27 52.4	8 16.1	9 45.5
22	19 59 51.1	29 24.8	16 25.1	28 20.6	16 2.1	19 1.8	3 32.4	0♊ .3	27 6.3	27 50.5	8 14.6	9 45.5
23	20 3 47.6	0♌22.1	16 21.9	10♏47.0	17 58.5	19 34.7	3 56.4	0 10.5	27 3.0	27 48.5	8 13.1	9D45.6
24	20 7 44.2	1 19.4	16 18.7	23 35.6	19 57.2	20 8.9	4 19.9	0 20.6	26 59.7	27 46.6	8 11.7	9 45.7
25	20 11 40.8	2 16.7	16 15.6	6♐50.0	21 58.0	20 44.3	4 42.9	0 30.6	26 56.5	27 44.7	8 10.2	9 45.9
26	20 15 37.3	3 14.0	16 12.4	20 32.0	24 .5	21 21.0	5 5.5	0 40.5	26 53.4	27 42.9	8 8.8	9 46.1
27	20 19 33.9	4 11.3	16 9.2	4♑41.2	26 4.4	21 58.8	5 27.5	0 50.3	26 50.3	27 41.1	8 7.4	9 46.3
28	20 23 30.4	5 8.6	16 6.0	19 14.3	28 9.3	22 37.7	5 49.0	0 60.0	26 47.3	27 39.3	8 6.0	9 46.6
29	20 27 27.0	6 5.9	16 2.9	4♒ 5.3	0♌14.9	23 17.8	6 10.0	1 9.5	26 44.4	27 37.6	8 4.6	9 46.8
30	20 31 23.5	7 3.3	15 59.7	19 6.1	2 20.9	23 58.9	6 30.5	1 19.0	26 41.5	27 35.9	8 3.2	9 47.2
31	20 35 20.1	8 .6	15 56.5	4♓ 7.8	4 27.1	24 41.0	6 50.4	1 28.3	26 38.8	27 34.2	8 1.8	9 47.5

LATITUDE

DAY	EPHEM. SID. TIME	☉	☊	☽	☿	♀	♂	♃	♄	♅	♆	♇
1	18 37 3.4	0 .0	0 .0	3S55.7	3S57.4	4S 7.9	3S32.3	0S54.5	1N 7.4	0S12.8	0N59.7	16N18.2
4	18 48 53.0	0 .0	0 .0	0 36.1	3 29.3	4 25.3	3 38.6	0 54.6	1 7.1	0 12.8	0 59.6	16 16.6
7	19 0 42.7	0 .0	0 .0	2N58.3	2 55.7	4 38.3	3 45.0	0 54.7	1 6.8	0 12.8	0 59.6	16 15.0
10	19 12 32.4	0 .0	0 .0	4 56.2	2 18.3	4 47.5	3 51.5	0 54.8	1 6.4	0 12.9	0 59.6	16 13.3
13	19 24 22.1	0 .0	0 .0	4 37.1	1 38.7	4 53.2	3 57.9	0 55.0	1 6.0	0 12.9	0 59.5	16 11.6
16	19 36 11.7	0 .0	0 .0	2 25.1	0 58.5	4 55.8	4 4.4	0 55.2	1 5.6	0 12.9	0 59.5	16 9.9
19	19 48 1.4	0 .0	0 .0	0S40.1	0 19.5	4 55.7	4 10.8	0 55.3	1 5.2	0 12.9	0 59.4	16 8.2
22	19 59 51.1	0 .0	0 .0	3 33.0	0N16.6	4 53.4	4 17.1	0 55.5	1 4.8	0 12.9	0 59.3	16 6.5
25	20 11 40.8	0 .0	0 .0	5 6.9	0 47.9	4 48.9	4 23.4	0 55.7	1 4.4	0 12.9	0 59.3	16 4.7
28	20 23 30.4	0 .0	0 .0	4 15.8	1 13.1	4 42.7	4 29.6	0 55.9	1 3.9	0 12.9	0 59.2	16 3.0
31	20 35 20.1	0 .0	0 .0	0 56.2	1 31.2	4 35.0	4 35.6	0 56.1	1 3.5	0 12.9	0 59.1	16 1.2

RIGHT ASCENSION

DAY	EPHEM. SID. TIME	☉	☊	☽	☿	♀	♂	♃	♄	♅	♆	♇
1	18 37 3.4	10♋12.6	18♓31.8	28♑ 9.8	19♊ 1.6	13♊20.8	25♓32.1	23♉57.7	28♐21.1	28♐29.1	9♑30.0	12♏32.3
2	18 40 59.9	11 14.6	18 28.9	13♒24.7	19 34.1	13R13.9	26 2.2	24 10.1	28R16.4	28R26.5	9R28.3	12R31.5
3	18 44 56.5	12 16.5	18 26.0	27 42.8	20 11.7	13 9.5	26 32.0	24 22.5	28 11.8	28 23.9	9 26.5	12 30.9
4	18 48 53.0	13 18.3	18 23.0	11♓ 8.8	20 54.4	13 7.4	27 1.5	24 34.8	28 7.2	28 21.4	9 24.8	12 30.2
5	18 52 49.6	14 20.1	18 20.1	23 57.4	21 42.2	13D 7.8	27 30.7	24 47.0	28 2.7	28 18.8	9 23.0	12 29.6
6	18 56 46.1	15 21.8	18 17.2	6♈27.4	22 35.0	13 10.5	27 59.6	24 59.1	27 58.1	28 16.2	9 21.3	12 28.9
7	19 0 42.7	16 23.4	18 14.2	18 57.9	23 32.8	13 15.6	28 28.3	25 11.2	27 53.7	28 13.7	9 19.6	12 28.4
8	19 4 39.3	17 24.9	18 11.3	1♉45.5	24 35.7	13 22.9	28 56.6	25 23.2	27 49.2	28 11.2	9 17.8	12 27.8
9	19 8 35.8	18 26.4	18 8.4	15 1.8	25 43.5	13 32.4	29 24.7	25 35.1	27 44.8	28 8.7	9 16.1	12 27.3
10	19 12 32.4	19 27.7	18 5.4	28 51.0	26 56.2	13 44.0	29 52.4	25 46.9	27 40.4	28 6.2	9 14.4	12 26.8
11	19 16 28.9	20 28.9	18 2.5	13♊ 6.4	28 13.9	13 57.7	0♈19.8	25 58.7	27 36.1	28 3.8	9 12.7	12 26.3
12	19 20 25.5	21 30.0	17 59.5	27 31.1	29 36.5	14 13.5	0 46.8	26 10.3	27 31.8	28 1.4	9 11.0	12 25.9
13	19 24 22.1	22 31.0	17 56.6	11♋42.2	1♋ 3.8	14 31.2	1 13.5	26 21.9	27 27.6	27 59.0	9 9.3	12 25.5
14	19 28 18.6	23 31.9	17 53.7	25 19.3	2 35.9	14 50.8	1 39.9	26 33.4	27 23.5	27 56.6	9 7.6	12 25.1
15	19 32 15.2	24 32.7	17 50.7	8♌ 9.9	4 12.7	15 12.3	2 5.9	26 44.8	27 19.4	27 54.3	9 5.9	12 24.8
16	19 36 11.7	25 33.3	17 47.8	20 11.8	5 54.0	15 35.6	2 31.5	26 56.1	27 15.3	27 51.9	9 4.3	12 24.5
17	19 40 8.3	26 33.8	17 44.9	1♍31.0	7 39.6	16 .6	2 56.8	27 7.3	27 11.3	27 49.6	9 2.6	12 24.2
18	19 44 4.8	27 34.2	17 41.9	12 18.3	9 29.5	16 27.2	3 21.7	27 18.4	27 7.4	27 47.4	9 .9	12 24.0
19	19 48 1.4	28 34.4	17 39.0	22 47.5	11 23.3	16 55.5	3 46.1	27 29.4	27 3.5	27 45.1	8 59.3	12 23.7
20	19 51 58.0	29 34.5	17 36.0	3♎13.7	13 20.8	17 25.3	4 10.2	27 40.3	26 59.7	27 42.9	8 57.7	12 23.6
21	19 55 54.5	0♌34.5	17 33.1	13 52.7	15 21.7	17 56.7	4 33.8	27 51.1	26 56.0	27 40.7	8 56.0	12 23.4
22	19 59 51.1	1 34.3	17 30.2	25 1.6	17 25.7	18 29.6	4 57.1	28 1.8	26 52.3	27 38.6	8 54.4	12 23.3
23	20 3 47.6	2 33.9	17 27.2	6♏57.0	19 32.4	19 3.8	5 19.9	28 12.4	26 48.7	27 36.5	8 52.8	12 23.2
24	20 7 44.2	3 33.4	17 24.3	19 54.2	21 41.4	19 39.5	5 42.2	28 22.9	26 45.1	27 34.4	8 51.3	12 23.1
25	20 11 40.8	4 32.8	17 21.3	4♐ 2.1	23 52.2	20 16.5	6 4.2	28 33.3	26 41.7	27 32.3	8 49.7	12 23.1
26	20 15 37.3	5 32.0	17 18.4	19 17.1	26 4.4	20 54.7	6 25.6	28 43.6	26 38.3	27 30.3	8 48.2	12 23.0
27	20 19 33.9	6 31.0	17 15.5	5♑18.1	28 17.6	21 34.2	6 46.6	28 53.8	26 34.9	27 28.3	8 46.6	12D23.1
28	20 23 30.4	7 29.9	17 12.5	21 29.9	0♌31.1	22 15.0	7 7.1	29 3.8	26 31.7	27 26.4	8 45.1	12 23.1
29	20 27 27.0	8 28.6	17 9.6	7♒16.5	2 44.8	22 56.9	7 27.2	29 13.7	26 28.5	27 24.5	8 43.6	12 23.2
30	20 31 23.5	9 27.2	17 6.6	22 15.2	4 58.0	23 40.0	7 46.7	29 23.6	26 25.5	27 22.6	8 42.2	12 23.3
31	20 35 20.1	10 25.7	17 3.7	6♓21.7	7 10.5	24 24.1	8 5.7	29 33.3	26 22.5	27 20.8	8 40.7	12 23.5

DECLINATION

DAY	EPHEM. SID. TIME	☉	☊	☽	☿	♀	♂	♃	♄	♅	♆	♇
1	18 37 3.4	23N 6.6	0S 5.2	24S55.2	19N 5.5	18N24.1	5S47.2	18N23.4	22S18.7	23S39.0	22S 9.5	0N44.1
4	18 48 53.0	22 52.7	0 5.2	8 37.6	19 41.1	18 5.1	5 15.6	18 31.6	22 18.8	23 38.9	22 9.9	0 43.1
7	19 0 42.7	22 35.3	0 5.3	11N13.8	20 22.7	17 52.9	4 45.1	18 39.6	22 19.0	23 38.8	22 10.2	0 42.0
10	19 12 32.4	22 14.2	0 5.4	25 24.3	21 6.4	17 46.8	4 15.6	18 47.3	22 19.1	23 38.8	22 10.6	0 40.7
13	19 24 22.1	21 49.8	0 5.4	27 38.4	21 47.6	17 46.0	3 47.5	18 54.7	22 19.3	23 38.7	22 11.0	0 39.4
16	19 36 11.7	21 21.9	0 5.5	18 3.3	22 21.3	17 49.7	3 20.7	19 1.8	22 19.5	23 38.6	22 11.3	0 37.9
19	19 48 1.4	20 50.8	0 5.5	2 23.2	22 42.3	17 57.0	2 55.3	19 8.6	22 19.7	23 38.5	22 11.6	0 36.3
22	19 59 51.1	20 16.6	0 5.6	14S12.0	22 45.3	18 7.0	2 31.5	19 15.0	22 19.9	23 38.4	22 12.0	0 34.7
25	20 11 40.8	19 39.3	0 5.7	26 29.6	22 26.4	18 18.9	2 9.3	19 21.2	22 20.1	23 38.4	22 12.3	0 32.9
28	20 23 30.4	18 59.1	0 5.7	26 16.9	21 43.6	18 32.0	1 48.9	19 27.0	22 20.3	23 38.3	22 12.7	0 31.0
31	20 35 20.1	18 16.0	0 5.8	10 52.1	20 37.6	18 45.4	1 30.2	19 32.6	22 20.6	23 38.2	22 13.0	0 29.1

AUGUST 1988

DAY	EPHEM. SID. TIME	☉	☊	☽	☿	♀	♂	♃	♄	♅	♆	♇
	h m s	° ′	° ′	° ′	° ′	° ′	° ′	° ′	° ′	° ′	° ′	° ′
		LONGITUDE										
1	20 39 16.7	8♌58.0	15♓53.3	19♓ 2.0	6♌33.1	25♊24.1	7♈ 9.7	1♊37.5	26♐36.1	27♐32.5	8♑ .5	9♏47.9
2	20 43 13.2	9 55.4	15 50.1	3♈42.1	8 38.7	26 8.1	7 28.5	1 46.6	26 R 33.5	27 R 30.9	7 R 59.2	9 48.3
3	20 47 9.8	10 52.8	15 47.0	18 3.5	10 43.6	26 53.1	7 46.6	1 55.5	26 30.9	27 29.4	7 57.9	9 48.8
4	20 51 6.3	11 50.2	15 43.8	2♉ 4.2	12 47.8	27 38.9	8 4.1	2 4.4	26 28.4	27 27.9	7 56.6	9 49.3
5	20 55 2.9	12 47.7	15 40.6	15 43.8	14 51.1	28 25.6	8 21.1	2 13.1	26 26.1	27 26.4	7 55.4	9 49.9
6	20 58 59.4	13 45.2	15 37.4	29 3.2	16 53.2	29 13.1	8 37.3	2 21.7	26 23.8	27 25.0	7 54.1	9 50.4
7	21 2 56.0	14 42.7	15 34.3	12♊ 4.3	18 54.2	0♋ 1.3	8 52.9	2 30.2	26 21.6	27 23.6	7 52.9	9 51.0
8	21 6 52.5	15 40.2	15 31.1	24 49.2	20 53.8	0 50.3	9 7.9	2 38.5	26 19.5	27 22.2	7 51.7	9 51.7
9	21 10 49.1	16 37.7	15 27.9	7♋19.9	22 52.2	1 40.1	9 22.1	2 46.6	26 17.4	27 20.9	7 50.5	9 52.3
10	21 14 45.7	17 35.3	15 24.7	19 38.6	24 49.1	2 30.5	9 35.6	2 54.7	26 15.5	27 19.6	7 49.4	9 53.0
11	21 18 42.2	18 32.9	15 21.6	1♌47.0	26 44.6	3 21.6	9 48.4	3 2.6	26 13.6	27 18.4	7 48.2	9 53.8
12	21 22 38.8	19 30.5	15 18.4	13 47.0	28 38.6	4 13.3	10 .5	3 10.3	26 11.8	27 17.2	7 47.1	9 54.5
13	21 26 35.3	20 28.1	15 15.2	25 40.4	0♍31.2	5 5.7	10 11.8	3 18.0	26 10.1	27 16.0	7 46.0	9 55.3
14	21 30 31.9	21 25.7	15 12.0	7♍29.2	2 22.3	5 58.6	10 22.4	3 25.4	26 8.5	27 14.9	7 45.0	9 56.1
15	21 34 28.4	22 23.4	15 8.8	19 15.7	4 11.9	6 52.2	10 32.2	3 32.8	26 7.0	27 13.9	7 43.9	9 57.0
16	21 38 25.0	23 21.1	15 5.7	1♎ 2.6	6 .1	7 46.3	10 41.3	3 40.0	26 5.6	27 12.8	7 42.9	9 57.9
17	21 42 21.6	24 18.8	15 2.5	12 53.3	7 46.8	8 40.9	10 49.6	3 47.0	26 4.3	27 11.9	7 41.9	9 58.8
18	21 46 18.1	25 16.5	14 59.3	24 51.3	9 32.1	9 36.1	10 57.0	3 53.9	26 3.0	27 10.9	7 41.0	9 59.8
19	21 50 14.7	26 14.2	14 56.1	7♏ .8	11 15.9	10 31.8	11 3.7	4 .6	26 1.9	27 10.1	7 40.0	10 .8
20	21 54 11.2	27 11.9	14 53.0	19 26.1	12 58.3	11 27.9	11 9.6	4 7.2	26 .9	27 9.2	7 39.1	10 1.8
21	21 58 7.8	28 9.7	14 49.8	2♐11.5	14 39.3	12 24.6	11 14.7	4 13.6	25 59.9	27 8.5	7 38.2	10 2.9
22	22 2 4.3	29 7.5	14 46.6	15 20.8	16 18.8	13 21.7	11 18.9	4 19.8	25 59.1	27 7.7	7 37.3	10 4.0
23	22 6 .9	0♍ 5.3	14 43.4	28 56.6	17 57.0	14 19.3	11 22.3	4 25.9	25 58.3	27 7.0	7 36.5	10 5.1
24	22 9 57.4	1 3.1	14 40.3	12♑59.9	19 33.9	15 17.3	11 24.9	4 31.9	25 57.6	27 6.4	7 35.7	10 6.2
25	22 13 54.0	2 1.0	14 37.1	27 29.3	21 9.3	16 15.7	11 26.7	4 37.7	25 57.1	27 5.8	7 34.9	10 7.4
26	22 17 50.5	2 58.9	14 33.9	12♒20.6	22 43.4	17 14.6	11 27.7	4 43.3	25 56.6	27 5.3	7 34.2	10 8.7
27	22 21 47.1	3 56.8	14 30.7	27 26.9	24 16.2	18 13.8	11 27.7	4 48.8	25 56.3	27 4.8	7 33.5	10 9.9
28	22 25 43.7	4 54.7	14 27.5	12♓39.3	25 47.5	19 13.5	11 R 27.0	4 54.1	25 56.0	27 4.4	7 32.8	10 11.2
29	22 29 40.2	5 52.6	14 24.4	27 48.3	27 17.5	20 13.5	11 25.4	4 59.2	25 55.8	27 4.0	7 32.1	10 12.5
30	22 33 36.8	6 50.6	14 21.2	12♈44.9	28 46.2	21 13.9	11 22.9	5 4.1	25 55.7	27 3.6	7 31.5	10 13.8
31	22 37 33.3	7 48.6	14 18.0	27 22.2	0♎13.5	22 14.7	11 19.7	5 8.9	25 55.7	27 3.3	7 30.9	10 15.2
		LATITUDE										
1	20 39 16.7	0 .0	0 .0	0N24.9	1N35.6	4S32.1	4S37.6	0S56.2	1N 3.3	0S12.9	0N59.1	16N .6
4	20 51 6.3	0 .0	0 .0	3 51.3	1 44.1	4 22.6	4 43.4	0 56.4	1 2.9	0 12.9	0 59.0	15 58.9
7	21 2 56.0	0 .0	0 .0	5 12.8	1 46.0	4 12.1	4 49.0	0 56.7	1 2.4	0 12.9	0 58.9	15 57.1
10	21 14 45.7	0 .0	0 .0	4 15.8	1 42.0	4 .6	4 54.4	0 56.9	1 1.9	0 12.9	0 58.8	15 55.4
13	21 26 35.3	0 .0	0 .0	1 39.8	1 33.0	3 48.3	4 59.4	0 57.2	1 1.4	0 12.9	0 58.7	15 53.7
16	21 38 25.0	0 .0	0 .0	1S32.3	1 19.8	3 35.4	5 4.0	0 57.5	1 .9	0 12.9	0 58.6	15 52.0
19	21 50 14.7	0 .0	0 .0	4 12.6	1 3.2	3 21.9	5 8.2	0 57.7	1 .4	0 12.9	0 58.5	15 50.4
22	22 2 4.3	0 .0	0 .0	5 16.6	0 43.9	3 7.9	5 11.8	0 58.0	0 59.9	0 12.9	0 58.4	15 48.7
25	22 13 54.0	0 .0	0 .0	3 50.6	0 22.3	2 53.6	5 14.7	0 58.3	0 59.4	0 12.9	0 58.3	15 47.1
28	22 25 43.7	0 .0	0 .0	0 7.8	0S .9	2 39.0	5 16.9	0 58.6	0 58.9	0 12.9	0 58.2	15 45.5
31	22 37 33.3	0 .0	0 .0	3N38.1	0 25.5	2 24.2	5 18.2	0 58.9	0 58.4	0 12.9	0 58.1	15 44.0
		RIGHT ASCENSION										
1	20 39 16.7	11♌24.0	17♓ .7	19♓45.4	9♌21.9	25♊ 9.4	8♈24.2	29♉42.8	26♐19.5	27♐19.0	8♑39.3	12♏23.7
2	20 43 13.2	12 22.1	16 57.8	2♈42.8	11 31.9	25 55.6	8 42.2	29 52.3	26 R 16.7	27 R 17.3	8 R 37.8	12 23.9
3	20 47 9.8	13 20.1	16 54.9	15 32.2	13 40.3	26 42.9	8 59.5	0♊ 1.6	26 13.9	27 15.6	8 36.4	12 24.1
4	20 51 6.3	14 17.9	16 51.9	28 30.7	15 46.8	27 31.2	9 16.4	0 10.8	26 11.3	27 13.9	8 35.1	12 24.4
5	20 55 2.9	15 15.7	16 49.0	11♉50.7	17 51.5	28 20.4	9 32.6	0 20.0	26 8.8	27 12.3	8 33.7	12 24.7
6	20 58 59.4	16 13.2	16 46.0	25 37.7	19 53.9	29 10.5	9 48.3	0 28.9	26 6.3	27 10.8	8 32.4	12 25.1
7	21 2 56.0	17 10.7	16 43.1	9♊47.9	21 54.2	0♋ 1.4	10 3.3	0 37.7	26 3.9	27 9.2	8 31.1	12 25.4
8	21 6 52.5	18 7.9	16 40.1	24 7.7	23 52.3	0 53.2	10 17.7	0 46.4	26 1.6	27 7.7	8 29.8	12 25.8
9	21 10 49.1	19 5.0	16 37.2	8♋17.1	25 48.1	1 45.8	10 31.4	0 55.0	25 59.3	27 6.3	8 28.5	12 26.3
10	21 14 45.7	20 2.0	16 34.3	21 56.6	27 41.7	2 39.2	10 44.5	1 3.4	25 57.2	27 4.9	8 27.3	12 26.7
11	21 18 42.2	20 58.9	16 31.3	4♌53.4	29 32.9	3 33.3	10 56.9	1 11.6	25 55.2	27 3.6	8 26.1	12 27.2
12	21 22 38.8	21 55.6	16 28.4	17 3.5	1♍22.0	4 28.1	11 8.6	1 19.7	25 53.3	27 2.3	8 24.9	12 27.8
13	21 26 35.3	22 52.1	16 25.4	28 30.8	3 8.9	5 23.7	11 19.7	1 27.7	25 51.4	27 1.0	8 23.7	12 28.3
14	21 30 31.9	23 48.6	16 22.5	9♍24.5	4 53.6	6 19.9	11 30.0	1 35.5	25 49.7	26 59.8	8 22.5	12 28.9
15	21 34 28.4	24 44.8	16 19.5	19 56.6	6 36.2	7 16.8	11 39.6	1 43.2	25 48.1	26 58.6	8 21.4	12 29.5
16	21 38 25.0	25 41.0	16 16.6	0♎20.7	8 16.9	8 14.3	11 48.5	1 50.7	25 46.5	26 57.5	8 20.3	12 30.2
17	21 42 21.6	26 37.0	16 13.6	10 51.4	9 55.5	9 12.4	11 56.6	1 58.1	25 45.1	26 56.5	8 19.2	12 30.8
18	21 46 18.1	27 32.9	16 10.7	21 43.9	11 32.3	10 11.0	12 4.0	2 5.3	25 43.8	26 55.5	8 18.2	12 31.6
19	21 50 14.7	28 28.7	16 7.7	3♏13.5	13 7.2	11 10.2	12 10.7	2 12.4	25 42.5	26 54.5	8 17.2	12 32.3
20	21 54 11.2	29 24.3	16 4.8	15 34.7	14 40.3	12 10.0	12 16.6	2 19.2	25 41.4	26 53.6	8 16.2	12 33.1
21	21 58 7.8	0♍19.8	16 1.9	28 58.3	16 11.8	13 10.3	12 21.7	2 26.0	25 40.4	26 52.7	8 15.2	12 33.9
22	22 2 4.3	1 15.2	15 58.9	13♐26.5	17 41.5	14 11.0	12 26.0	2 32.5	25 39.4	26 51.9	8 14.3	12 34.7
23	22 6 .9	2 10.5	15 56.0	28 48.1	19 9.6	15 12.2	12 29.5	2 38.9	25 38.6	26 51.2	8 13.4	12 35.6
24	22 9 57.4	3 5.6	15 53.0	14♑37.7	20 36.2	16 13.9	12 32.3	2 45.2	25 37.9	26 50.5	8 12.6	12 36.5
25	22 13 54.0	4 .7	15 50.1	0♒23.2	22 1.3	17 16.0	12 34.3	2 51.2	25 37.3	26 49.8	8 11.7	12 37.4
26	22 17 50.5	4 55.7	15 47.1	15 38.3	23 25.0	18 18.6	12 35.5	2 57.2	25 36.8	26 49.3	8 11.0	12 38.4
27	22 21 47.1	5 50.5	15 44.2	0♓10.9	24 47.1	19 21.6	12 35.8	3 2.9	25 36.4	26 48.8	8 10.2	12 39.4
28	22 25 43.7	6 45.3	15 41.2	14 3.7	26 7.9	20 24.9	12 R 35.4	3 8.5	25 36.1	26 48.3	8 9.4	12 40.4
29	22 29 40.2	7 39.9	15 38.3	27 29.1	27 27.4	21 28.6	12 34.1	3 13.8	25 35.9	26 47.8	8 8.7	12 41.4
30	22 33 36.8	8 34.5	15 35.3	10♈43.6	28 45.4	22 32.6	12 32.1	3 19.0	25 35.8	26 47.5	8 8.0	12 42.5
31	22 37 33.3	9 29.0	15 32.4	24 3.6	0♎ 2.2	23 36.9	12 29.2	3 24.1	25 35.8	26 47.1	8 7.4	12 43.6
		DECLINATION										
1	20 39 16.7	18N 1.1	0S 5.8	3S57.5	20N10.8	18N49.9	1S24.4	19N34.3	22S20.6	23S38.2	22S13.1	0N28.4
4	20 51 6.3	17 14.5	0 5.9	15N48.5	18 38.2	19 2.8	1 8.4	19 39.5	22 20.9	23 38.1	22 13.4	0 26.4
7	21 2 56.0	16 25.4	0 6.0	27 24.5	16 50.3	19 14.5	0 54.4	19 44.3	22 21.2	23 38.0	22 13.7	0 24.2
10	21 14 45.7	15 33.9	0 6.0	26 13.4	14 51.2	19 24.6	0 42.6	19 48.8	22 21.5	23 37.9	22 14.0	0 22.0
13	21 26 35.3	14 40.1	0 6.1	14 31.7	12 44.4	19 32.5	0 33.1	19 53.0	22 21.9	23 37.8	22 14.3	0 19.7
16	21 38 25.0	13 44.2	0 6.2	1S49.6	10 32.9	19 37.9	0 25.9	19 56.9	22 22.2	23 37.8	22 14.6	0 17.3
19	21 50 14.7	12 46.4	0 6.2	17 49.9	8 19.0	19 40.2	0 21.0	20 .5	22 22.6	23 37.7	22 14.9	0 14.9
22	22 2 4.3	11 46.8	0 6.3	27 52.9	6 4.5	19 39.3	0 18.4	20 3.7	22 23.1	23 37.7	22 15.1	0 12.4
25	22 13 54.0	10 45.5	0 6.3	24 26.0	3 50.9	19 34.8	0 18.1	20 6.7	22 23.5	23 37.6	22 15.4	0 9.8
28	22 25 43.7	9 42.7	0 6.4	6 39.5	1 39.5	19 26.4	0 20.0	20 9.4	22 24.0	23 37.6	22 15.6	0 7.2
31	22 37 33.3	8 38.5	0 6.5	13N55.7	0S28.7	19 14.0	0 24.0	20 11.7	22 24.5	23 37.6	22 15.8	0 4.6

SEPTEMBER 1988

LONGITUDE

DAY	EPHEM. SID. TIME h m s	☉ ° ′	☊ ° ′	☽ ° ′	☿ ° ′	♀ ° ′	♂ ° ′	♃ ° ′	♄ ° ′	♅ ° ′	♆ ° ′	♇ ° ′
1	22 41 29.9	8♍46.6	14♓14.8	11♉35.5	1♎39.3	23♋15.8	11♈15.5	5♊13.5	25♐55.9	27♐ 3.1	7♑30.3	10♏16.6
2	22 45 26.4	9 44.7	14 11.7	25 23.1	3 3.8	24 17.3	11 R 10.5	5 17.9	25 D 56.1	27 R 2.9	7 R 29.8	10 18.0
3	22 49 23.0	10 42.8	14 8.5	8♊45.2	4 26.9	25 19.1	11 4.7	5 22.1	25 56.4	27 2.7	7 29.2	10 19.4
4	22 53 19.5	11 40.9	14 5.3	21 44.0	5 48.5	26 21.3	10 58.0	5 26.2	25 56.8	27 2.6	7 28.8	10 20.9
5	22 57 16.1	12 39.1	14 2.1	4♋22.4	7 8.6	27 23.7	10 50.6	5 30.1	25 57.3	27 2.6	7 28.3	10 22.4
6	23 1 12.6	13 37.3	13 58.9	16 43.9	8 27.1	28 26.5	10 42.3	5 33.8	25 57.9	27 2.6	7 27.9	10 23.9
7	23 5 9.2	14 35.5	13 55.8	28 52.2	9 44.1	29 29.6	10 33.2	5 37.3	25 58.6	27 D 2.7	7 27.5	10 25.5
8	23 9 5.8	15 33.8	13 52.6	10♌50.7	10 59.5	0♌32.9	10 23.4	5 40.6	25 59.4	27 2.8	7 27.1	10 27.1
9	23 13 2.3	16 32.1	13 49.4	22 42.7	12 13.1	1 36.6	10 12.8	5 43.8	26 .2	27 2.9	7 26.8	10 28.7
10	23 16 58.9	17 30.4	13 46.2	4♍30.8	13 25.0	2 40.5	10 1.5	5 46.7	26 1.2	27 3.1	7 26.5	10 30.3
11	23 20 55.4	18 28.7	13 43.1	16 17.7	14 35.0	3 44.7	9 49.5	5 49.5	26 2.3	27 3.4	7 26.2	10 32.0
12	23 24 52.0	19 27.1	13 39.9	28 5.7	15 43.0	4 49.1	9 36.8	5 52.1	26 3.5	27 3.7	7 26.0	10 33.7
13	23 28 48.5	20 25.6	13 36.7	9♎56.9	16 49.0	5 53.8	9 23.5	5 54.5	26 4.8	27 4.1	7 25.8	10 35.4
14	23 32 45.1	21 24.0	13 33.5	21 53.7	17 52.7	6 58.7	9 9.6	5 56.6	26 6.2	27 4.5	7 25.6	10 37.1
15	23 36 41.6	22 22.5	13 30.3	3♏58.5	18 54.2	8 3.9	8 55.1	5 58.6	26 7.6	27 5.0	7 25.5	10 38.9
16	23 40 38.2	23 21.0	13 27.2	16 14.1	19 53.1	9 9.4	8 40.2	6 .5	26 9.3	27 5.5	7 25.4	10 40.8
17	23 44 34.7	24 19.6	13 24.0	28 43.1	20 49.4	10 15.0	8 24.8	6 2.1	26 10.9	27 6.1	7 25.3	10 42.6
18	23 48 31.3	25 18.1	13 20.8	11♐28.8	21 42.8	11 20.9	8 8.9	6 3.5	26 12.7	27 6.7	7 25.3	10 44.4
19	23 52 27.8	26 16.7	13 17.6	24 34.2	22 33.1	12 27.0	7 52.6	6 4.7	26 14.5	27 7.4	7 25.3	10 46.3
20	23 56 24.4	27 15.3	13 14.5	8♑ 1.8	23 20.2	13 33.3	7 36.0	6 5.7	26 16.5	27 8.2	7 25.3	10 48.1
21	0 0 20.9	28 14.0	13 11.3	21 53.3	24 3.6	14 39.8	7 19.1	6 6.5	26 18.5	27 8.9	7 D 25.4	10 50.1
22	0 4 17.5	29 12.6	13 8.1	6♒ 9.0	24 43.2	15 46.5	7 1.9	6 7.1	26 20.7	27 9.8	7 25.5	10 52.0
23	0 8 14.1	0♎11.3	13 4.9	20 47.0	25 18.7	16 53.4	6 44.5	6 7.5	26 22.9	27 10.6	7 25.6	10 53.9
24	0 12 10.6	1 10.0	13 1.7	5♓42.9	25 49.6	18 .5	6 27.0	6 7.7	26 25.2	27 11.6	7 25.7	10 55.9
25	0 16 7.2	2 8.8	12 58.6	20 50.0	26 15.7	19 7.9	6 9.3	6 7.7	26 27.7	27 12.5	7 25.9	10 57.9
26	0 20 3.7	3 7.6	12 55.4	5♈59.5	26 36.5	20 15.4	5 51.6	6 R 7.6	26 30.2	27 13.6	7 26.2	10 59.9
27	0 24 .3	4 6.4	12 52.2	21 2.1	26 51.7	21 23.1	5 33.9	6 7.2	26 32.8	27 14.7	7 26.4	11 1.9
28	0 27 56.8	5 5.3	12 49.0	5♉48.9	27 .8	22 31.0	5 16.2	6 6.6	26 35.5	27 15.8	7 26.7	11 4.0
29	0 31 53.4	6 4.2	12 45.9	20 13.2	27 3.4	23 39.1	4 58.5	6 5.8	26 38.2	27 17.0	7 27.0	11 6.0
30	0 35 49.9	7 3.1	12 42.7	4♊10.8	26 R 59.2	24 47.4	4 41.0	6 4.8	26 41.1	27 18.2	7 27.4	11 8.1

LATITUDE

DAY	EPHEM. SID. TIME h m s	☉	☊	☽	☿	♀	♂	♃	♄	♅	♆	♇
1	22 41 29.9	0 .0	0 .0	4N28.2	0S33.8	2S19.3	5S18.4	0S59.0	0N58.2	0S12.9	0N58.0	15N43.5
4	22 53 19.5	0 .0	0 .0	5 14.9	0 59.4	2 4.4	5 18.5	0 59.3	0 57.7	0 12.9	0 57.9	15 42.0
7	23 5 9.2	0 .0	0 .0	3 45.9	1 25.2	1 49.5	5 17.4	0 59.6	0 57.2	0 12.9	0 57.8	15 40.6
10	23 16 58.9	0 .0	0 .0	0 53.1	1 50.8	1 34.7	5 15.2	0 59.9	0 56.7	0 12.9	0 57.7	15 39.2
13	23 28 48.5	0 .0	0 .0	2S18.7	2 15.8	1 20.0	5 11.7	1 .2	0 56.2	0 12.9	0 57.6	15 37.8
16	23 40 38.2	0 .0	0 .0	4 40.6	2 39.6	1 5.6	5 6.8	1 .5	0 55.7	0 12.9	0 57.4	15 36.6
19	23 52 27.8	0 .0	0 .0	5 11.6	3 1.4	0 51.3	5 .6	1 .8	0 55.2	0 12.9	0 57.3	15 35.3
22	0 4 17.5	0 .0	0 .0	3 14.9	3 20.2	0 37.5	4 53.0	1 1.1	0 54.7	0 12.9	0 57.2	15 34.2
25	0 16 7.2	0 .0	0 .0	0N37.3	3 34.4	0 24.0	4 44.1	1 1.4	0 54.2	0 12.9	0 57.1	15 33.0
28	0 27 56.8	0 .0	0 .0	4 8.1	3 42.2	0 10.9	4 34.1	1 1.7	0 53.7	0 12.9	0 56.9	15 32.0

RIGHT ASCENSION

DAY	EPHEM. SID. TIME h m s	☉	☊	☽	☿	♀	♂	♃	♄	♅	♆	♇
1	22 41 29.9	10♍23.4	15♓29.4	7♉41.7	1♎17.7	24♋41.6	12♈25.5	3♊28.9	25♐35.9	26♐46.9	8♑ 6.8	12♏44.7
2	22 45 26.4	11 17.8	15 26.5	21 43.9	2 31.9	25 46.6	12 R 21.0	3 33.6	25 D 36.1	26 R 46.7	8 R 6.2	12 45.8
3	22 49 23.0	12 12.1	15 23.5	6♊ 7.0	3 44.7	26 51.8	12 15.6	3 38.0	25 36.4	26 46.5	8 5.6	12 47.0
4	22 53 19.5	13 6.3	15 20.6	20 37.8	4 56.3	27 57.3	12 9.5	3 42.3	25 36.9	26 46.4	8 5.1	12 48.2
5	22 57 16.1	14 .4	15 17.6	4♋57.0	6 6.6	29 3.0	12 2.5	3 46.4	25 37.4	26 46.4	8 4.6	12 49.4
6	23 1 12.6	14 54.6	15 14.7	18 45.6	7 15.5	0♌ 9.0	11 54.8	3 50.3	25 38.1	26 46.4	8 4.1	12 50.7
7	23 5 9.2	15 48.6	15 11.7	1♌50.9	8 23.1	1 15.1	11 46.3	3 54.0	25 38.8	26 46.4	8 3.7	12 52.0
8	23 9 5.8	16 42.6	15 8.8	14 8.8	9 29.3	2 21.5	11 37.0	3 57.5	25 39.7	26 D 46.5	8 3.3	12 53.3
9	23 13 2.3	17 36.6	15 5.8	25 43.0	10 34.0	3 28.0	11 27.1	4 .9	25 40.6	26 46.7	8 3.0	12 54.6
10	23 16 58.9	18 30.6	15 2.9	6♍42.4	11 37.3	4 34.7	11 16.3	4 4.0	25 41.7	26 46.9	8 2.6	12 56.0
11	23 20 55.4	19 24.5	14 59.9	17 18.6	12 38.9	5 41.5	11 4.9	4 6.9	25 42.8	26 47.2	8 2.4	12 57.4
12	23 24 52.0	20 18.3	14 57.0	27 44.5	13 38.9	6 48.5	10 52.9	4 9.6	25 44.1	26 47.6	8 2.1	12 58.8
13	23 28 48.5	21 12.2	14 54.0	8♎13.8	14 37.2	7 55.5	10 40.2	4 12.1	25 45.5	26 48.0	8 1.9	13 .3
14	23 32 45.1	22 6.0	14 51.1	19 .3	15 33.6	9 2.7	10 26.9	4 14.5	25 47.0	26 48.4	8 1.7	13 1.7
15	23 36 41.6	22 59.8	14 48.1	0♏17.9	16 28.0	10 10.0	10 13.0	4 16.6	25 48.6	26 49.0	8 1.6	13 3.2
16	23 40 38.2	23 53.7	14 45.1	12 19.7	17 20.3	11 17.4	9 58.6	4 18.5	25 50.3	26 49.6	8 1.5	13 4.8
17	23 44 34.7	24 47.5	14 42.2	25 15.3	18 10.3	12 24.8	9 43.7	4 20.2	25 52.1	26 50.2	8 1.4	13 6.3
18	23 48 31.3	25 41.3	14 39.2	9♐ 7.9	18 57.8	13 32.3	9 28.3	4 21.7	25 54.0	26 50.9	8 1.4	13 7.9
19	23 52 27.8	26 35.1	14 36.3	23 50.6	19 42.6	14 39.8	9 12.6	4 23.0	25 56.0	26 51.6	8 1.4	13 9.5
20	23 56 24.4	27 28.9	14 33.3	9♑ 4.3	20 24.6	15 47.4	8 56.4	4 24.1	25 58.1	26 52.4	8 1.4	13 11.1
21	0 0 20.9	28 22.7	14 30.4	24 23.3	21 3.4	16 55.0	8 39.9	4 24.9	26 .3	26 53.3	8 D 1.5	13 12.7
22	0 4 17.5	29 16.5	14 27.4	9♒23.8	21 38.7	18 2.6	8 23.1	4 25.6	26 2.7	26 54.2	8 1.6	13 14.4
23	0 8 14.1	0♎10.4	14 24.5	23 52.3	22 10.4	19 10.3	8 6.1	4 26.0	26 5.1	26 55.1	8 1.7	13 16.0
24	0 12 10.6	1 4.3	14 21.5	7♓48.0	22 38.1	20 17.9	7 48.9	4 26.3	26 7.6	26 56.1	8 1.9	13 17.7
25	0 16 7.2	1 58.2	14 18.6	21 20.0	23 1.4	21 25.6	7 31.5	4 26.3	26 10.2	26 57.2	8 2.1	13 19.5
26	0 20 3.7	2 52.1	14 15.6	4♈43.1	23 20.0	22 33.3	7 14.0	4 R 26.1	26 12.9	26 58.3	8 2.3	13 21.2
27	0 24 .3	3 46.1	14 12.6	18 13.3	23 33.5	23 41.0	6 56.4	4 25.7	26 15.7	26 59.5	8 2.6	13 23.0
28	0 27 56.8	4 40.2	14 9.7	2♉ 4.3	23 41.6	24 48.6	6 38.8	4 25.1	26 18.6	27 .7	8 2.9	13 24.7
29	0 31 53.4	5 34.3	14 6.7	16 23.2	23 43.9	25 56.3	6 21.2	4 24.3	26 21.6	27 2.0	8 3.3	13 26.5
30	0 35 49.9	6 28.5	14 3.8	1♊ 7.5	23 R 40.0	27 3.9	6 3.7	4 23.3	26 24.7	27 3.4	8 3.7	13 28.4

DECLINATION

DAY	EPHEM. SID. TIME h m s	☉	☊	☽	☿	♀	♂	♃	♄	♅	♆	♇
1	22 41 29.9	8N16.8	0S 6.5	19N33.6	1S10.6	19N 9.0	0S25.8	20N12.5	22S24.7	23S37.6	22S15.9	0N 3.7
4	22 53 19.5	7 11.0	0 6.6	28 25.4	3 12.9	18 50.9	0 32.7	20 14.4	22 25.2	23 37.5	22 16.1	0 1.0
7	2 5 9.2	6 4.1	0 6.6	24 4.3	5 9.7	18 28.5	0 41.4	20 16.1	22 25.8	23 37.5	22 16.3	0S 1.7
10	23 16 58.9	4 56.2	0 6.7	10 40.8	6 59.9	18 1.7	0 51.7	20 17.4	22 26.3	23 37.5	22 16.5	0 4.4
13	23 28 48.5	3 47.6	0 6.7	6S 4.0	8 42.0	17 30.5	1 3.3	20 18.4	22 27.0	23 37.5	22 16.6	0 7.2
16	23 40 38.2	2 38.4	0 6.8	21 10.2	10 14.4	16 54.9	1 15.7	20 19.2	22 27.6	23 37.6	22 16.8	0 9.9
19	23 52 27.8	1 28.8	0 6.9	28 31.3	11 34.9	16 15.0	1 28.7	20 19.6	22 28.2	23 37.6	22 16.9	0 12.7
22	0 4 17.5	0 18.8	0 6.9	21 53.0	12 40.7	15 30.8	1 41.7	20 19.7	22 28.9	23 37.7	22 17.0	0 15.5
25	0 16 7.2	0S51.2	0 7.0	3 3.7	13 28.0	14 42.6	1 54.3	20 19.6	22 29.6	23 37.7	22 17.1	0 18.3
28	0 27 56.8	2 1.3	0 7.1	17N21.5	13 51.7	13 50.3	2 6.0	20 19.1	22 30.3	23 37.8	22 17.2	0 21.0

OCTOBER 1988

LONGITUDE

DAY	EPHEM. SID. TIME	☉	☊	☽	☿	♀	♂	♃	♄	♅	♆	♇
	h m s	° ′	° ′	° ′	° ′	° ′	° ′	° ′	° ′	° ′	° ′	° ′
1	0 39 46.5	8♎ 2.1	12♓39.5	17♊40.4	26♎47.8	25♌55.8	4♈23.6	6♊ 3.6	26♐44.1	27♐19.5	7♑27.8	11♏10.2
2	0 43 43.0	9 1.1	12 36.3	0♋43.1	26 R 28.9	27 4.4	4 R 6.4	6 R 2.2	26 47.1	27 20.8	7 28.2	11 12.3
3	0 47 39.6	10 .1	12 33.1	13 22.0	26 2.2	28 13.2	3 49.5	6 .6	26 50.2	27 22.2	7 28.7	11 14.5
4	0 51 36.1	10 59.2	12 30.0	25 41.2	25 27.8	29 22.2	3 32.9	5 58.8	26 53.4	27 23.6	7 29.1	11 16.6
5	0 55 32.7	11 58.3	12 26.8	7♌45.3	24 45.7	0♍31.3	3 16.6	5 56.8	26 56.7	27 25.1	7 29.7	11 18.8
6	0 59 29.3	12 57.5	12 23.6	19 39.2	23 56.2	1 40.6	3 .8	5 54.6	27 .1	27 26.6	7 30.2	11 21.0
7	1 3 25.8	13 56.7	12 20.4	1♍27.3	22 60.0	2 50.1	2 45.4	5 52.2	27 3.7	27 28.2	7 30.9	11 23.3
8	1 7 22.4	14 56.0	12 17.3	13 13.6	21 57.8	3 59.6	2 30.4	5 49.6	27 7.2	27 29.8	7 31.5	11 25.5
9	1 11 18.9	15 55.3	12 14.1	25 1.6	20 50.9	5 9.4	2 15.9	5 46.8	27 10.8	27 31.5	7 32.1	11 27.7
10	1 15 15.5	16 54.6	12 10.9	6♎54.3	19 40.8	6 19.3	2 2.0	5 43.9	27 14.6	27 33.2	7 32.8	11 30.0
11	1 19 12.0	17 53.9	12 7.7	18 53.7	18 29.2	7 29.3	1 48.7	5 40.7	27 18.4	27 34.9	7 33.5	11 32.2
12	1 23 8.6	18 53.3	12 4.5	1♏ 1.7	17 18.0	8 39.4	1 36.0	5 37.3	27 22.3	27 36.7	7 34.3	11 34.5
13	1 27 5.1	19 52.7	12 1.4	13 19.5	16 9.3	9 49.7	1 23.9	5 33.7	27 26.2	27 38.6	7 35.1	11 36.8
14	1 31 1.7	20 52.1	11 58.2	25 48.4	15 5.0	11 .1	1 12.5	5 30.0	27 30.3	27 40.5	7 35.9	11 39.1
15	1 34 58.2	21 51.6	11 55.0	8♐29.4	14 7.1	12 10.6	1 1.8	5 26.0	27 34.4	27 42.4	7 36.7	11 41.4
16	1 38 54.8	22 51.1	11 51.8	21 23.7	13 17.2	13 21.3	0 51.8	5 21.9	27 38.6	27 44.4	7 37.6	11 43.7
17	1 42 51.4	23 50.7	11 48.7	4♑32.7	12 36.6	14 32.1	0 42.6	5 17.6	27 42.9	27 46.4	7 38.5	11 46.0
18	1 46 47.9	24 50.2	11 45.5	17 57.9	12 6.4	15 43.0	0 34.1	5 13.1	27 47.2	27 48.5	7 39.5	11 48.4
19	1 50 44.5	25 49.8	11 42.3	1♒40.5	11 47.1	16 54.0	0 26.4	5 8.4	27 51.7	27 50.6	7 40.4	11 50.7
20	1 54 41.0	26 49.4	11 39.1	15 41.4	11 39.1	18 5.1	0 19.4	5 3.5	27 56.2	27 52.8	7 41.4	11 53.1
21	1 58 37.6	27 49.1	11 36.0	0♓ .3	11 D 42.2	19 16.4	0 13.3	4 58.5	28 .7	27 55.0	7 42.5	11 55.4
22	2 2 34.1	28 48.8	11 32.8	14 35.5	11 56.1	20 27.7	0 8.0	4 53.4	28 5.4	27 57.2	7 43.5	11 57.8
23	2 6 30.7	29 48.5	11 29.6	29 22.9	12 20.4	21 39.2	0 3.4	4 48.0	28 10.1	27 59.5	7 44.6	12 .2
24	2 10 27.2	0♏48.2	11 26.4	14♈16.6	12 54.3	22 50.8	29♓59.7	4 42.5	28 14.9	28 1.8	7 45.7	12 2.6
25	2 14 23.8	1 48.0	11 23.2	29 8.7	13 37.1	24 2.4	29 56.7	4 36.8	28 19.8	28 4.2	7 46.9	12 5.0
26	2 18 20.3	2 47.8	11 20.1	13♉51.0	14 27.9	25 14.2	29 54.6	4 31.0	28 24.7	28 6.6	7 48.1	12 7.4
27	2 22 16.9	3 47.6	11 16.9	28 15.6	15 25.8	26 26.1	29 53.2	4 25.0	28 29.7	28 9.0	7 49.3	12 9.8
28	2 26 13.5	4 47.5	11 13.7	12♊16.9	16 30.2	27 38.2	29 52.7	4 19.0	28 34.8	28 11.5	7 50.6	12 12.2
29	2 30 10.0	5 47.4	11 10.5	25 51.5	17 40.0	28 50.3	29 D 52.9	4 12.7	28 39.9	28 14.0	7 51.9	12 14.7
30	2 34 6.6	6 47.4	11 7.4	8♋59.1	18 54.7	0♎ 2.5	29 53.9	4 6.3	28 45.1	28 16.6	7 53.2	12 17.1
31	2 38 3.1	7 47.4	11 4.2	21 41.6	20 13.5	1 14.8	29 55.7	3 59.8	28 50.3	28 19.2	7 54.5	12 19.5

LATITUDE

DAY	EPHEM. SID. TIME	☉	☊	☽	☿	♀	♂	♃	♄	♅	♆	♇
1	0 39 46.5	0 .0	0 .0	5N14.3	3S40.6	0N 1.7	4S23.0	1S 1.9	0N53.3	0S12.9	0N56.8	15N31.0
4	0 51 36.1	0 .0	0 .0	3 54.9	3 26.4	0 13.7	4 11.0	1 2.2	0 52.8	0 12.9	0 56.7	15 30.1
7	1 3 25.8	0 .0	0 .0	1 7.9	2 56.6	0 25.2	3 58.2	1 2.4	0 52.3	0 12.8	0 56.6	15 29.2
10	1 15 15.5	0 .0	0 .0	2S 2.4	2 10.3	0 36.0	3 44.8	1 2.6	0 51.9	0 12.8	0 56.5	15 28.4
13	1 27 5.1	0 .0	0 .0	4 28.4	1 12.0	0 46.2	3 31.0	1 2.8	0 51.4	0 12.8	0 56.3	15 27.7
16	1 38 54.8	0 .0	0 .0	5 7.2	0 10.7	0 55.7	3 17.0	1 3.0	0 51.0	0 12.8	0 56.2	15 27.1
19	1 50 44.5	0 .0	0 .0	3 26.2	0N43.8	1 4.5	3 3.0	1 3.1	0 50.6	0 12.8	0 56.1	15 26.5
22	2 2 34.1	0 .0	0 .0	0N 7.2	1 25.4	1 12.5	2 49.0	1 3.2	0 50.1	0 12.8	0 56.0	15 26.0
25	2 14 23.8	0 .0	0 .0	3 41.7	1 52.3	1 19.8	2 35.2	1 3.2	0 49.7	0 12.8	0 55.9	15 25.6
28	2 26 13.5	0 .0	0 .0	5 6.7	2 5.8	1 26.3	2 21.8	1 3.3	0 49.3	0 12.8	0 55.8	15 25.2
31	2 38 3.1	0 .0	0 .0	3 58.1	2 8.6	1 32.0	2 8.8	1 3.3	0 48.9	0 12.8	0 55.6	15 25.0

RIGHT ASCENSION

DAY	EPHEM. SID. TIME	☉	☊	☽	☿	♀	♂	♃	♄	♅	♆	♇
1	0 39 46.5	7♎22.7	14♓ .8	16♊ 3.3	23♎29.8	28♌11.5	5♈46.3	4♊22.0	26♐27.9	27♐ 4.8	8♑ 4.1	13♏30.2
2	0 43 43.0	8 17.1	13 57.9	0♋48.8	23 R 12.9	29 19.1	5 R 29.0	4 R 20.6	26 31.2	27 6.2	8 4.5	13 32.0
3	0 47 39.6	9 11.5	13 54.9	15 2.0	22 49.2	0♍26.6	5 11.9	4 18.9	26 34.6	27 7.7	8 5.0	13 33.9
4	0 51 36.1	10 6.0	13 51.9	28 27.7	22 18.8	1 34.2	4 55.1	4 17.0	26 38.0	27 9.3	8 5.6	13 35.8
5	0 55 32.7	11 .6	13 49.0	11♌ 1.2	21 41.8	2 41.6	4 38.5	4 15.0	26 41.6	27 10.9	8 6.1	13 37.7
6	0 59 29.3	11 55.2	13 46.0	22 46.6	20 58.6	3 49.1	4 22.3	4 12.7	26 45.3	27 12.5	8 6.7	13 39.7
7	1 3 25.8	12 50.1	13 43.1	3♍53.4	20 9.8	4 56.5	4 6.4	4 10.2	26 49.1	27 14.3	8 7.4	13 41.6
8	1 7 22.4	13 45.0	13 40.1	14 34.0	19 16.3	6 3.9	3 51.0	4 7.5	26 52.9	27 16.1	8 8.1	13 43.6
9	1 11 18.9	14 39.9	13 37.2	25 2.2	18 19.3	7 11.2	3 35.9	4 4.6	26 56.9	27 17.9	8 8.8	13 45.6
10	1 15 15.5	15 35.1	13 34.2	5♎31.8	17 20.0	8 18.5	3 21.4	4 1.4	27 .9	27 19.7	8 9.5	13 47.6
11	1 19 12.0	16 30.3	13 31.2	16 16.8	16 20.1	9 25.7	3 7.3	3 58.1	27 5.0	27 21.7	8 10.3	13 49.6
12	1 23 8.6	17 25.6	13 28.3	27 30.9	15 21.2	10 32.9	2 53.9	3 54.6	27 9.2	27 23.6	8 11.1	13 51.6
13	1 27 5.1	18 21.1	13 25.3	9♏26.3	14 25.0	11 40.0	2 40.9	3 50.8	27 13.5	27 25.6	8 12.0	13 53.6
14	1 31 1.7	19 16.7	13 22.4	22 12.1	13 33.3	12 47.1	2 28.6	3 46.9	27 17.9	27 27.7	8 12.9	13 55.7
15	1 34 58.2	20 12.4	13 19.4	5♐50.9	12 47.6	13 54.2	2 17.0	3 42.8	27 22.3	27 29.8	8 13.8	13 57.7
16	1 38 54.8	21 8.3	13 16.4	20 15.5	12 9.3	15 1.2	2 6.0	3 38.5	27 26.9	27 32.0	8 14.7	13 59.8
17	1 42 51.4	22 4.3	13 13.5	5♑ 8.4	11 39.3	16 8.2	1 55.6	3 33.9	27 31.5	27 34.2	8 15.7	14 1.9
18	1 46 47.9	23 .5	13 10.5	20 5.6	11 18.5	17 15.2	1 46.0	3 29.2	27 36.2	27 36.5	8 16.7	14 4.0
19	1 50 44.5	23 56.8	13 7.6	4♒45.0	11 7.4	18 22.1	1 37.0	3 24.3	27 41.0	27 38.8	8 17.8	14 6.1
20	1 54 41.0	24 53.3	13 4.6	18 54.0	11 6.0	19 29.0	1 28.8	3 19.3	27 45.9	27 41.1	8 18.9	14 8.2
21	1 58 37.6	25 49.9	13 1.6	2♓31.4	11 D 14.3	20 35.9	1 21.3	3 14.0	27 50.8	27 43.5	8 20.0	14 10.4
22	2 2 34.1	26 46.6	12 58.7	15 45.8	11 31.9	21 42.8	1 14.6	3 8.6	27 55.9	27 45.9	8 21.1	14 12.5
23	2 6 30.7	27 43.6	12 55.7	28 51.8	11 58.4	22 49.7	1 8.6	3 3.0	28 1.0	27 48.4	8 22.3	14 14.6
24	2 10 27.2	28 40.7	12 52.7	12♈ 6.1	12 33.2	23 56.5	1 3.3	2 57.3	28 6.2	27 51.0	8 23.5	14 16.8
25	2 14 23.8	29 38.0	12 49.8	25 44.6	13 15.5	25 3.4	0 58.8	2 51.3	28 11.4	27 53.5	8 24.8	14 19.0
26	2 18 20.3	0♏35.4	12 46.8	9♉58.1	14 4.7	26 10.3	0 55.0	2 45.2	28 16.8	27 56.2	8 26.1	14 21.1
27	2 22 16.9	1 33.1	12 43.9	24 48.1	15 .0	27 17.2	0 52.0	2 39.0	28 22.2	27 58.8	8 27.4	14 23.3
28	2 26 13.5	2 31.0	12 40.9	10♊ 2.9	16 .8	28 24.2	0 49.7	2 32.6	28 27.7	28 1.6	8 28.8	14 25.6
29	2 30 10.0	3 29.0	12 37.9	25 18.7	17 6.3	29 31.1	0 48.2	2 26.1	28 33.2	28 4.3	8 30.1	14 27.7
30	2 34 6.6	4 27.2	12 35.0	10♋ 7.7	18 16.0	0♎38.1	0 47.4	2 19.4	28 38.9	28 7.1	8 31.5	14 29.9
31	2 38 3.1	5 25.6	12 32.0	24 8.3	19 29.2	1 45.2	0 47.3	2 12.6	28 44.5	28 9.9	8 33.0	14 32.2

DECLINATION

DAY	EPHEM. SID. TIME	☉	☊	☽	☿	♀	♂	♃	♄	♅	♆	♇
1	0 39 46.5	3S11.3	0S 7.1	28N 5.2	13S45.5	12N54.2	2S16.6	20N18.3	22S30.9	23S37.8	22S17.2	0S23.8
4	0 51 36.1	4 20.9	0 7.2	24 51.3	13 3.0	11 54.5	2 25.7	20 17.3	22 31.6	23 37.9	22 17.3	0 26.5
7	1 3 25.8	5 30.1	0 7.3	12 1.0	11 40.4	10 51.4	2 32.8	20 15.9	22 32.3	23 38.0	22 17.3	0 29.2
10	1 15 15.5	6 38.7	0 7.3	4S36.9	9 42.6	9 45.1	2 37.7	20 14.2	22 33.0	23 38.1	22 17.3	0 31.9
13	1 27 5.1	7 46.5	0 7.4	20 6.2	7 27.8	8 35.9	2 40.3	20 12.3	22 33.7	23 38.2	22 17.3	0 34.5
16	1 38 54.8	8 53.3	0 7.4	28 16.3	5 24.6	7 24.0	2 40.2	20 10.1	22 34.4	23 38.3	22 17.3	0 37.1
19	1 50 44.5	9 58.9	0 7.5	23 8.3	3 59.3	6 9.8	2 37.4	20 7.5	22 35.0	23 38.4	22 17.3	0 39.7
22	2 2 34.1	11 3.2	0 7.6	5 57.4	3 24.5	4 53.4	2 31.9	20 4.8	22 35.6	23 38.5	22 17.2	0 42.2
25	2 14 23.8	12 6.1	0 7.6	14N37.5	3 39.0	3 35.3	2 23.7	20 1.7	22 36.2	23 38.6	22 17.1	0 44.6
28	2 26 13.5	13 7.2	0 7.7	27 20.2	4 33.2	2 15.6	2 13.0	19 58.4	22 36.8	23 38.7	22 17.0	0 47.0
31	2 38 3.1	14 6.6	0 7.8	25 36.7	5 55.1	0 54.7	1 59.9	19 54.9	22 37.3	23 38.8	22 16.9	0 49.3

NOVEMBER 1988

DAY	EPHEM. SID. TIME	☉	☊	☾	☿	♀	♂	♃	♄	♅	♆	♇
		LONGITUDE										
	h m s	° ′	° ′	° ′	° ′	° ′	° ′	° ′	° ′	° ′	° ′	° ′
1	2 41 59.7	8♏47.4	11♓ 1.0	4♌ 2.7	21♎35.7	2♎27.1	29♓58.3	3♊53.1	28♐55.7	28♐21.8	7♑55.8	12♏21.9
2	2 45 56.2	9 47.4	10 57.8	16 7.3	23 .9	3 39.6	0♈ 1.6	3 R 46.3	29 1.0	28 24.5	7 57.2	12 24.3
3	2 49 52.8	10 47.5	10 54.6	28 .5	24 28.6	4 52.2	0 5.7	3 39.4	29 6.5	28 27.2	7 58.6	12 26.8
4	2 53 49.3	11 47.6	10 51.5	9♍48.0	25 58.3	6 4.8	0 10.6	3 32.3	29 12.0	28 29.9	8 .1	12 29.2
5	2 57 45.9	12 47.8	10 48.3	21 34.8	27 29.6	7 17.6	0 16.2	3 25.2	29 17.5	28 32.7	8 1.5	12 31.6
6	3 1 42.5	13 48.0	10 45.1	3♎25.6	29 2.3	8 30.4	0 22.5	3 17.9	29 23.1	28 35.5	8 3.0	12 34.1
7	3 5 39.0	14 48.2	10 41.9	15 24.0	0♏36.1	9 43.3	0 29.6	3 10.5	29 28.8	28 38.3	8 4.5	12 36.5
8	3 9 35.6	15 48.4	10 38.8	27 33.1	2 10.6	10 56.3	0 37.4	3 3.1	29 34.5	28 41.2	8 6.1	12 38.9
9	3 13 32.1	16 48.7	10 35.6	9♏54.8	3 45.9	12 9.3	0 46.0	2 55.5	29 40.3	28 44.1	8 7.6	12 41.3
10	3 17 28.7	17 49.0	10 32.4	22 29.8	5 21.6	13 22.5	0 55.2	2 47.9	29 46.1	28 47.0	8 9.2	12 43.8
11	3 21 25.2	18 49.4	10 29.2	5♐18.3	6 57.6	14 35.6	1 5.1	2 40.2	29 52.0	28 50.0	8 10.8	12 46.2
12	3 25 21.8	19 49.7	10 26.1	18 19.5	8 33.9	15 48.9	1 15.7	2 32.4	29 58.0	28 53.0	8 12.5	12 48.6
13	3 29 18.4	20 50.1	10 22.9	1♑32.4	10 10.3	17 2.2	1 27.0	2 24.5	0♑ 4.0	28 56.0	8 14.2	12 51.0
14	3 33 14.9	21 50.6	10 19.7	14 56.3	11 46.7	18 15.6	1 39.0	2 16.6	0 10.0	28 59.0	8 15.8	12 53.4
15	3 37 11.5	22 51.0	10 16.5	28 30.4	13 23.2	19 29.1	1 51.5	2 8.6	0 16.1	29 2.1	8 17.6	12 55.8
16	3 41 8.0	23 51.5	10 13.3	12♒14.8	14 59.5	20 42.6	2 4.8	2 .6	0 22.2	29 5.2	8 19.3	12 58.2
17	3 45 4.6	24 51.9	10 10.2	26 9.4	16 35.8	21 56.1	2 18.6	1 52.5	0 28.4	29 8.3	8 21.0	13 .6
18	3 49 1.1	25 52.5	10 7.0	10♓14.4	18 12.1	23 9.8	2 33.1	1 44.5	0 34.7	29 11.5	8 22.9	13 3.0
19	3 52 57.7	26 53.0	10 3.8	24 29.2	19 48.1	24 23.5	2 48.1	1 36.3	0 40.9	29 14.7	8 24.7	13 5.4
20	3 56 54.3	27 53.6	10 .6	8♈52.2	21 24.0	25 37.2	3 3.8	1 28.2	0 47.3	29 17.9	8 26.5	13 7.8
21	4 0 50.8	28 54.1	9 57.5	23 20.2	22 59.7	26 51.0	3 19.9	1 20.0	0 53.6	29 21.2	8 28.3	13 10.2
22	4 4 47.4	29 54.7	9 54.3	7♉48.2	24 35.2	28 4.8	3 36.7	1 11.8	0 60.0	29 24.4	8 30.2	13 12.5
23	4 8 43.9	0♐55.3	9 51.1	22 10.4	26 10.6	29 18.7	3 53.9	1 3.7	1 6.4	29 27.7	8 32.1	13 14.9
24	4 12 40.5	1 56.0	9 47.9	6♊20.3	27 45.8	0♏32.7	4 11.7	0 55.5	1 12.9	29 31.0	8 34.0	13 17.2
25	4 16 37.0	2 56.6	9 44.8	20 12.3	29 20.9	1 46.7	4 29.9	0 47.3	1 19.4	29 34.3	8 35.9	13 19.5
26	4 20 33.6	3 57.3	9 41.6	3♋42.5	0♐55.8	3 .7	4 48.7	0 39.1	1 25.9	29 37.7	8 37.8	13 21.8
27	4 24 30.2	4 58.0	9 38.4	16 49.0	2 30.5	4 14.8	5 8.0	0 31.0	1 32.5	29 41.0	8 39.8	13 24.1
28	4 28 26.7	5 58.8	9 35.2	29 32.5	4 5.2	5 28.9	5 27.7	0 22.9	1 39.1	29 44.4	8 41.7	13 26.4
29	4 32 23.3	6 59.5	9 32.1	11♌55.3	5 39.7	6 43.1	5 47.8	0 14.8	1 45.8	29 47.8	8 43.7	13 28.7
30	4 36 19.8	8 .3	9 28.9	24 1.4	7 14.1	7 57.4	6 8.5	0 6.7	1 52.4	29 51.2	8 45.7	13 30.9
		LATITUDE										
1	2 41 59.7	0 .0	0 .0	3N11.0	2N 7.6	1N33.7	2S 4.5	1S 3.3	0N48.8	0S12.8	0N55.6	15N24.9
4	2 53 49.3	0 .0	0 .0	0 14.1	2 .2	1 38.3	1 52.1	1 3.2	0 48.4	0 12.8	0 55.5	15 24.7
7	3 5 39.0	0 .0	0 .0	2S46.6	1 47.7	1 42.2	1 40.2	1 3.1	0 48.1	0 12.8	0 55.4	15 24.6
10	3 17 28.7	0 .0	0 .0	4 45.4	1 31.7	1 45.2	1 28.9	1 3.0	0 47.7	0 12.8	0 55.3	15 24.6
13	3 29 18.4	0 .0	0 .0	4 43.6	1 13.4	1 47.4	1 18.1	1 2.8	0 47.4	0 12.8	0 55.2	15 24.7
16	3 41 8.0	0 .0	0 .0	2 26.1	0 53.7	1 48.8	1 7.8	1 2.5	0 47.0	0 12.8	0 55.1	15 24.8
19	3 52 57.7	0 .0	0 .0	1N11.0	0 33.3	1 49.5	0 58.0	1 2.2	0 46.7	0 12.9	0 55.0	15 25.0
22	4 4 47.4	0 .0	0 .0	4 13.0	0 12.7	1 49.4	0 48.8	1 1.9	0 46.4	0 12.9	0 54.9	15 25.3
25	4 16 37.0	0 .0	0 .0	4 55.9	0S 7.7	1 48.5	0 40.1	1 1.6	0 46.1	0 12.9	0 54.9	15 25.7
28	4 28 26.7	0 .0	0 .0	3 14.7	0 27.6	1 46.9	0 32.0	1 1.1	0 45.8	0 12.9	0 54.8	15 26.1
		RIGHT ASCENSION										
1	2 41 59.7	6♏24.3	12♓29.0	7♌10.9	20♎45.6	2♎52.3	0♈48.0	2♊ 5.6	28♐50.3	28♐12.8	8♑34.4	14♏34.4
2	2 45 56.2	7 23.1	12 26.1	19 17.6	22 4.5	3 59.4	0 D 49.4	1 R 58.5	28 56.1	28 15.7	8 35.9	14 36.6
3	2 49 52.8	8 22.1	12 23.1	0♍38.2	23 25.8	5 6.6	0 51.5	1 51.2	29 2.0	28 18.7	8 37.5	14 38.8
4	2 53 49.3	9 21.4	12 20.1	11 26.2	24 48.9	6 13.9	0 54.3	1 43.9	29 8.0	28 21.6	8 39.0	14 41.0
5	2 57 45.9	10 20.8	12 17.2	21 56.7	26 13.7	7 21.2	0 57.9	1 36.4	29 14.0	28 24.7	8 40.6	14 43.3
6	3 1 42.5	11 20.5	12 14.2	2♎24.9	27 39.9	8 28.6	1 2.1	1 28.8	29 20.1	28 27.7	8 42.2	14 45.5
7	3 5 39.0	12 20.3	12 11.2	13 6.0	29 7.3	9 36.1	1 7.1	1 21.1	29 26.2	28 30.8	8 43.8	14 47.7
8	3 9 35.6	13 20.4	12 8.3	24 14.8	0♏35.7	10 43.8	1 12.7	1 13.4	29 32.4	28 33.9	8 45.5	14 50.0
9	3 13 32.1	14 20.7	12 5.3	6♏ 4.7	2 5.0	11 51.5	1 19.0	1 5.5	29 38.7	28 37.1	8 47.2	14 52.2
10	3 17 28.7	15 21.2	12 2.3	18 46.3	3 35.1	12 59.3	1 26.0	0 57.5	29 45.0	28 40.3	8 48.9	14 54.4
11	3 21 25.2	16 21.9	11 59.4	2♐23.2	5 5.9	14 7.2	1 33.6	0 49.4	29 51.4	28 43.5	8 50.6	14 56.7
12	3 25 21.8	17 22.9	11 56.4	16 48.8	6 37.3	15 15.3	1 41.9	0 41.3	29 57.8	28 46.8	8 52.4	14 58.9
13	3 29 18.4	18 24.0	11 53.4	1♑44.5	8 9.3	16 23.5	1 50.9	0 33.1	0♑ 4.3	28 50.1	8 54.2	15 1.1
14	3 33 14.9	19 25.4	11 50.5	16 44.1	9 41.7	17 31.8	2 .4	0 24.9	0 10.8	28 53.4	8 56.0	15 3.4
15	3 37 11.5	20 26.9	11 47.5	1♒22.9	11 14.6	18 40.3	2 10.6	0 16.6	0 17.4	28 56.8	8 57.9	15 5.6
16	3 41 8.0	21 28.7	11 44.5	15 26.0	12 48.0	19 48.9	2 21.4	0 8.2	0 24.1	29 .2	8 59.8	15 7.8
17	3 45 4.6	22 30.7	11 41.6	28 51.2	14 21.8	20 57.7	2 32.8	29♉59.8	0 30.8	29 3.6	9 1.7	15 10.0
18	3 49 1.1	23 32.9	11 38.6	11♓47.0	15 56.0	22 6.7	2 44.8	29 51.4	0 37.6	29 7.1	9 3.6	15 12.3
19	3 52 57.7	24 35.3	11 35.6	24 28.3	17 30.6	23 15.8	2 57.3	29 42.9	0 44.4	29 10.6	9 5.6	15 14.5
20	3 56 54.3	25 37.9	11 32.7	7♈12.7	19 5.6	24 25.2	3 10.4	29 34.4	0 51.2	29 14.1	9 7.5	15 16.7
21	4 0 50.8	26 40.6	11 29.7	20 18.4	20 41.0	25 34.7	3 24.1	29 25.9	0 58.1	29 17.6	9 9.5	15 18.9
22	4 4 47.4	27 43.6	11 26.7	4♉ .3	22 16.8	26 44.4	3 38.2	29 17.4	1 5.0	29 21.2	9 11.5	15 21.1
23	4 8 43.9	28 46.8	11 23.8	18 26.0	23 53.0	27 54.3	3 52.9	29 8.9	1 12.0	29 24.7	9 13.6	15 23.3
24	4 12 40.5	29 50.1	11 20.8	3♊31.0	25 29.6	29 4.5	4 8.0	29 .4	1 19.0	29 28.3	9 15.6	15 25.5
25	4 16 37.0	0♐53.7	11 17.8	18 56.0	27 6.6	0♏14.9	4 23.7	28 51.9	1 26.0	29 32.0	9 17.7	15 27.7
26	4 20 33.6	1 57.4	11 14.8	4♋11.2	28 44.0	1 25.5	4 39.8	28 43.4	1 33.1	29 35.6	9 19.8	15 29.9
27	4 24 30.2	3 1.4	11 11.9	18 47.4	0♐21.9	2 36.3	4 56.4	28 34.9	1 40.3	29 39.3	9 21.9	15 32.1
28	4 28 26.7	4 5.5	11 8.9	2♌26.6	2 .2	3 47.4	5 13.4	28 26.5	1 47.4	29 43.0	9 24.0	15 34.2
29	4 32 23.3	5 9.8	11 5.9	15 4.5	3 38.9	4 58.7	5 30.9	28 18.1	1 54.6	29 46.7	9 26.1	15 36.4
30	4 36 19.8	6 14.3	11 3.0	26 48.0	5 18.0	6 10.3	5 48.9	28 9.7	2 1.8	29 50.4	9 28.3	15 38.5
		DECLINATION										
1	2 41 59.7	14S25.9	0S 7.8	22N20.4	6S26.8	0N27.5	1S54.9	19N53.6	22S37.5	23S38.8	22S16.8	0S50.1
4	2 53 49.3	15 22.5	0 7.8	8 6.8	8 9.9	0S54.6	1 38.7	19 49.8	22 38.0	23 38.9	22 16.7	0 52.3
7	3 5 39.0	16 16.8	0 7.9	8S37.5	10 .1	2 17.2	1 20.2	19 45.8	22 38.5	23 39.0	22 16.5	0 54.5
10	3 17 28.7	17 8.7	0 8.0	22 59.6	11 52.2	3 39.9	0 59.6	19 41.6	22 38.9	23 39.1	22 16.3	0 56.5
13	3 29 18.4	17 58.0	0 8.0	28 9.7	13 42.5	5 2.4	0 37.0	19 37.2	22 39.2	23 39.2	22 16.1	0 58.5
16	3 41 8.0	18 44.4	0 8.1	19 27.9	15 28.8	6 24.4	0 12.6	19 32.7	22 39.5	23 39.2	22 15.9	1 .4
19	3 52 57.7	19 27.8	0 8.2	1 6.3	17 9.4	7 45.5	0N13.6	19 28.2	22 39.8	23 39.3	22 15.7	1 2.2
22	4 4 47.4	20 8.1	0 8.2	18N 5.9	18 42.9	9 5.4	0 41.3	19 23.5	22 40.0	23 39.4	22 15.4	1 3.9
25	4 16 37.0	20 45.0	0 8.3	27 59.9	20 8.4	10 23.8	1 10.5	19 18.9	22 40.1	23 39.4	22 15.1	1 5.5
28	4 28 26.7	21 18.5	0 8.4	23 25.3	21 25.2	11 40.2	1 40.9	19 14.2	22 40.2	23 39.5	22 14.8	1 7.0

DECEMBER 1988

DAY	EPHEM. SID. TIME	☉	☊	☽	☿	♀	♂	♃	♄	♅	♆	♇
		LONGITUDE										
	h m s	° ′	° ′	° ′	° ′	° ′	° ′	° ′	° ′	° ′	° ′	° ′
1	4 40 16.4	9♐ 1.1	9♓25.7	5♍55.9	8♐48.4	9♏11.6	6♈29.5	29♉58.7	1♑59.1	29♐54.6	8♑47.8	13♏33.2
2	4 44 13.0	10 1.9	9 22.5	17 44.2	10 22.7	10 26.0	6 51.0	29R50.8	2 5.9	29 58.1	8 49.8	13 35.4
3	4 48 9.5	11 2.8	9 19.3	29 32.0	11 56.9	11 40.3	7 12.9	29 42.9	2 12.6	0♑ 1.6	8 51.9	13 37.7
4	4 52 6.1	12 3.7	9 16.2	11♎24.7	13 31.1	12 54.7	7 35.3	29 35.1	2 19.4	0 5.0	8 53.9	13 39.9
5	4 56 2.6	13 4.6	9 13.0	23 27.1	15 5.3	14 9.1	7 58.0	29 27.3	2 26.2	0 8.5	8 56.0	13 42.1
6	4 59 59.2	14 5.5	9 9.8	5♏43.3	16 39.4	15 23.6	8 21.1	29 19.6	2 33.1	0 12.1	8 58.1	13 44.2
7	5 3 55.7	15 6.4	9 6.6	18 16.1	18 13.6	16 38.1	8 44.6	29 12.0	2 40.0	0 15.6	9 .2	13 46.4
8	5 7 52.3	16 7.4	9 3.5	1♐ 6.9	19 47.7	17 52.7	9 8.5	29 4.5	2 46.8	0 19.1	9 2.3	13 48.5
9	5 11 48.9	17 8.4	9 .3	14 15.4	21 22.0	19 7.3	9 32.8	28 57.1	2 53.8	0 22.7	9 4.5	13 50.7
10	5 15 45.4	18 9.4	8 57.1	27 40.1	22 56.2	20 21.9	9 57.4	28 49.8	3 .7	0 26.3	9 6.7	13 52.8
11	5 19 42.0	19 10.4	8 53.9	11♑18.4	24 30.5	21 36.5	10 22.4	28 42.6	3 7.7	0 29.8	9 8.8	13 54.9
12	5 23 38.5	20 11.4	8 50.8	25 6.9	26 4.9	22 51.1	10 47.7	28 35.4	3 14.7	0 33.4	9 11.0	13 57.0
13	5 27 35.1	21 12.4	8 47.6	9♒ 2.4	27 39.3	24 5.8	11 13.3	28 28.4	3 21.6	0 37.0	9 13.2	13 59.0
14	5 31 31.7	22 13.5	8 44.4	23 2.5	29 13.8	25 20.5	11 39.3	28 21.6	3 28.6	0 40.6	9 15.3	14 1.0
15	5 35 28.2	23 14.5	8 41.2	7♓ 5.2	0♑48.4	26 35.2	12 5.6	28 14.8	3 35.7	0 44.2	9 17.5	14 3.0
16	5 39 24.8	24 15.6	8 38.1	21 9.5	2 23.1	27 49.9	12 32.1	28 8.2	3 42.7	0 47.8	9 19.7	14 5.0
17	5 43 21.3	25 16.6	8 34.9	5♈14.6	3 57.8	29 4.7	12 59.0	28 1.7	3 49.7	0 51.4	9 22.0	14 7.0
18	5 47 17.9	26 17.7	8 31.7	19 19.9	5 32.6	0♐19.5	13 26.2	27 55.4	3 56.8	0 55.0	9 24.2	14 8.9
19	5 51 14.5	27 18.8	8 28.5	3♉23.9	7 7.4	1 34.3	13 53.6	27 49.2	4 3.8	0 58.6	9 26.4	14 10.8
20	5 55 11.0	28 19.8	8 25.3	17 24.5	8 42.3	2 49.1	14 21.3	27 43.2	4 10.9	1 2.2	9 28.6	14 12.7
21	5 59 7.6	29 20.9	8 22.2	1♊18.6	10 17.1	4 3.9	14 49.3	27 37.3	4 18.0	1 5.8	9 30.9	14 14.6
22	6 3 4.1	0♑22.0	8 19.0	15 2.8	11 51.9	5 18.8	15 17.5	27 31.5	4 25.1	1 9.5	9 33.1	14 16.4
23	6 7 .7	1 23.1	8 15.8	28 33.3	13 26.7	6 33.6	15 46.0	27 26.0	4 32.1	1 13.1	9 35.4	14 18.3
24	6 10 57.2	2 24.2	8 12.6	11♋47.4	15 1.3	7 48.5	16 14.7	27 20.5	4 39.2	1 16.7	9 37.6	14 20.1
25	6 14 53.8	3 25.3	8 9.5	24 43.1	16 35.7	9 3.4	16 43.6	27 15.3	4 46.3	1 20.3	9 39.9	14 21.8
26	6 18 50.4	4 26.4	8 6.3	7♌20.4	18 9.8	10 18.3	17 12.8	27 10.2	4 53.4	1 23.9	9 42.2	14 23.6
27	6 22 46.9	5 27.5	8 3.1	19 40.4	19 43.6	11 33.3	17 42.2	27 5.3	5 .5	1 27.6	9 44.4	14 25.3
28	6 26 43.5	6 28.6	7 59.9	1♍45.9	21 16.9	12 48.2	18 11.8	27 .6	5 7.6	1 31.2	9 46.7	14 27.0
29	6 30 40.0	7 29.8	7 56.8	13 40.7	22 49.5	14 3.2	18 41.6	26 56.0	5 14.7	1 34.8	9 49.0	14 28.7
30	6 34 36.6	8 31.0	7 53.6	25 29.6	24 21.3	15 18.2	19 11.7	26 51.7	5 21.9	1 38.4	9 51.3	14 30.4
31	6 38 33.2	9 32.1	7 50.4	7♎17.7	25 52.1	16 33.2	19 41.9	26 47.5	5 28.9	1 42.0	9 53.5	14 32.0
		LATITUDE										
1	4 40 16.4	0 .0	0 .0	0N19.1	0S46.6	1N44.6	0S24.3	1S .7	0N45.5	0S12.9	0N54.7	15N26.7
4	4 52 6.1	0 .0	0 .0	2S40.1	1 4.5	1 41.7	0 17.0	1 .2	0 45.2	0 12.9	0 54.6	15 27.2
7	5 3 55.7	0 .0	0 .0	4 41.0	1 21.0	1 38.1	0 10.2	0 59.7	0 44.9	0 12.9	0 54.6	15 27.9
10	5 15 45.4	0 .0	0 .0	4 43.7	1 35.8	1 33.9	0 3.8	0 59.1	0 44.7	0 13.0	0 54.5	15 28.6
13	5 27 35.1	0 .0	0 .0	2 26.5	1 48.7	1 29.2	0N 2.3	0 58.5	0 44.4	0 13.0	0 54.4	15 29.4
16	5 39 24.8	0 .0	0 .0	1N 9.7	1 59.1	1 24.0	0 7.9	0 57.8	0 44.2	0 13.0	0 54.4	15 30.3
19	5 51 14.5	0 .0	0 .0	4 10.0	2 6.9	1 18.3	0 13.2	0 57.2	0 44.0	0 13.0	0 54.3	15 31.2
22	6 3 4.1	0 .0	0 .0	4 59.5	2 11.4	1 12.1	0 18.2	0 56.5	0 43.7	0 13.0	0 54.3	15 32.2
25	6 14 53.8	0 .0	0 .0	3 23.8	2 12.2	1 5.6	0 22.9	0 55.8	0 43.5	0 13.1	0 54.3	15 33.2
28	6 26 43.5	0 .0	0 .0	0 25.8	2 8.4	0 58.8	0 27.3	0 55.0	0 43.3	0 13.1	0 54.2	15 34.3
31	6 38 33.2	0 .0	0 .0	2S37.1	1 59.2	0 51.6	0 31.4	0 54.3	0 43.1	0 13.1	0 54.2	15 35.4
		RIGHT ASCENSION										
1	4 40 16.4	7♐18.9	10♓60.0	7♍50.1	6♐57.6	7♏22.2	6♈ 7.2	28♉ 1.4	2♑ 9.1	29♐54.2	9♑30.5	15♏40.6
2	4 44 13.0	8 23.7	10 57.0	18 26.3	8 37.6	8 34.3	6 26.0	27R53.1	2 16.4	29 57.9	9 32.7	15 42.7
3	4 48 9.5	9 28.7	10 54.0	28 53.0	10 18.1	9 46.7	6 45.2	27 44.9	2 23.7	0♑ 1.7	9 34.9	15 44.8
4	4 52 6.1	10 33.8	10 51.1	9♎26.4	11 59.0	10 59.4	7 4.8	27 36.8	2 31.1	0 5.5	9 37.1	15 46.9
5	4 56 2.6	11 39.1	10 48.1	20 22.7	13 40.3	12 12.3	7 24.8	27 28.7	2 38.5	0 9.3	9 39.4	15 49.0
6	4 59 59.2	12 44.5	10 45.1	1♏57.7	15 22.0	13 25.6	7 45.2	27 20.7	2 45.9	0 13.2	9 41.6	15 51.1
7	5 3 55.7	13 50.1	10 42.1	14 24.6	17 4.2	14 39.1	8 5.9	27 12.8	2 53.3	0 17.0	9 43.9	15 53.2
8	5 7 52.3	14 55.7	10 39.2	27 51.4	18 46.7	15 52.9	8 27.1	27 5.0	3 .8	0 20.9	9 46.2	15 55.2
9	5 11 48.9	16 1.6	10 36.2	12♐15.9	20 29.7	17 7.1	8 48.6	26 57.4	3 8.4	0 24.8	9 48.6	15 57.3
10	5 15 45.4	17 7.5	10 33.2	27 21.9	22 12.9	18 21.5	9 10.5	26 49.8	3 15.9	0 28.7	9 50.9	15 59.3
11	5 19 42.0	18 13.5	10 30.2	12♑41.6	23 56.5	19 36.2	9 32.7	26 42.3	3 23.4	0 32.6	9 53.2	16 1.3
12	5 23 38.5	19 19.6	10 27.3	27 44.7	25 40.4	20 51.1	9 55.2	26 34.9	3 30.9	0 36.5	9 55.5	16 3.3
13	5 27 35.1	20 25.8	10 24.3	12♒ 9.6	27 24.6	22 6.4	10 18.1	26 27.6	3 38.5	0 40.4	9 57.9	16 5.2
14	5 31 31.7	21 32.1	10 21.3	25 49.4	29 9.0	23 22.0	10 41.3	26 20.5	3 46.1	0 44.3	10 .2	16 7.2
15	5 35 28.2	22 38.4	10 18.3	8♓49.9	0♑53.6	24 37.8	11 4.8	26 13.5	3 53.7	0 48.2	10 2.6	16 9.1
16	5 39 24.8	23 44.8	10 15.4	21 25.2	2 38.3	25 54.0	11 28.7	26 6.6	4 1.3	0 52.2	10 5.0	16 11.0
17	5 43 21.3	24 51.3	10 12.4	3♈53.3	4 23.2	27 10.4	11 52.8	25 59.9	4 8.9	0 56.1	10 7.4	16 12.9
18	5 47 17.9	25 57.7	10 9.4	16 33.1	6 8.1	28 27.2	12 17.3	25 53.3	4 16.6	1 .0	10 9.8	16 14.8
19	5 51 14.5	27 4.3	10 6.4	29 41.5	7 53.0	29 44.2	12 42.0	25 46.9	4 24.2	1 4.0	10 12.2	16 16.7
20	5 55 11.0	28 10.8	10 3.5	13♉30.7	9 37.8	1♐ 1.5	13 7.0	25 40.6	4 31.9	1 7.9	10 14.6	16 18.5
21	5 59 7.6	29 17.4	10 .5	28 3.4	11 22.4	2 19.1	13 32.3	25 34.5	4 39.5	1 11.9	10 17.0	16 20.3
22	6 3 4.1	0♑24.0	9 57.5	13♊ 8.6	13 6.8	3 36.9	13 57.8	25 28.6	4 47.2	1 15.8	10 19.4	16 22.1
23	6 7 .7	1 30.6	9 54.5	28 22.0	14 50.9	4 55.1	14 23.7	25 22.8	4 54.9	1 19.8	10 21.8	16 23.9
24	6 10 57.2	2 37.1	9 51.5	13♋13.6	16 34.5	6 13.5	14 49.7	25 17.1	5 2.6	1 23.7	10 24.3	16 25.7
25	6 14 53.8	3 43.7	9 48.6	27 18.7	18 17.6	7 32.1	15 16.1	25 11.7	5 10.3	1 27.7	10 26.7	16 27.4
26	6 18 50.4	4 50.2	9 45.6	10♌25.4	19 60.0	8 51.0	15 42.6	25 6.4	5 17.9	1 31.6	10 29.1	16 29.1
27	6 22 46.9	5 56.8	9 42.6	22 34.5	21 41.5	10 10.2	16 9.4	25 1.3	5 25.6	1 35.6	10 31.6	16 30.8
28	6 26 43.5	7 3.3	9 39.6	3♍55.7	23 22.0	11 29.6	16 36.5	24 56.4	5 33.3	1 39.5	10 34.0	16 32.5
29	6 30 40.0	8 9.7	9 36.6	14 43.0	25 1.3	12 49.2	17 3.7	24 51.7	5 41.0	1 43.5	10 36.5	16 34.1
30	6 34 36.6	9 16.2	9 33.7	25 12.3	26 39.3	14 9.2	17 31.3	24 47.2	5 48.7	1 47.5	10 39.0	16 35.8
31	6 38 33.2	10 22.5	9 30.7	5♎39.6	28 15.5	15 29.2	17 59.0	24 42.8	5 56.4	1 51.4	10 41.4	16 37.4
		DECLINATION										
1	4 40 16.4	21S48.3	0S 8.4	9N38.0	22S32.4	12S54.4	2N12.4	19N 9.6	22S40.2	23S39.5	22S14.5	1S 8.4
4	4 52 6.1	22 14.4	0 8.5	6S58.2	23 29.6	14 6.0	2 45.1	19 5.1	22 40.2	23 39.5	22 14.1	1 9.7
7	5 3 55.7	22 36.6	0 8.5	21 46.0	24 16.0	15 14.6	3 18.7	19 .7	22 40.0	23 39.5	22 13.8	1 10.9
10	5 15 45.4	22 54.9	0 8.6	28 9.0	24 51.0	16 19.9	3 53.2	18 56.4	22 39.9	23 39.5	22 13.4	1 12.0
13	5 27 35.1	23 9.1	0 8.7	20 21.2	25 14.0	17 21.4	4 28.5	18 52.3	22 39.6	23 39.5	22 13.0	1 12.9
16	5 39 24.8	23 19.1	0 8.7	2 26.3	25 24.4	18 18.9	5 4.5	18 48.5	22 39.3	23 39.4	22 12.6	1 13.8
19	5 51 14.5	23 24.9	0 8.8	16N33.8	25 21.8	19 12.0	5 41.1	18 44.9	22 38.9	23 39.4	22 12.2	1 14.5
22	6 3 4.1	23 26.5	0 8.9	27 33.9	25 5.7	20 .4	6 18.2	18 41.6	22 38.4	23 39.3	22 11.8	1 15.1
25	6 14 53.8	23 23.9	0 8.9	24 31.6	24 35.9	20 43.8	6 55.6	18 38.6	22 37.9	23 39.2	22 11.3	1 15.6
28	6 26 43.5	23 17.0	0 9.0	11 15.0	23 52.4	21 21.9	7 33.4	18 36.0	22 37.3	23 39.1	22 10.9	1 16.0
31	6 38 33.2	23 6.0	0 9.0	5S18.0	22 55.7	21 54.5	8 11.4	18 33.8	22 36.7	23 39.0	22 10.4	1 16.2

JANUARY 1989

DAY	EPHEM. SID. TIME	☉	☊	☽	☿	♀	♂	♃	♄	♅	♆	♇
		LONGITUDE										
	h m s	° ′	° ′	° ′	° ′	° ′	° ′	° ′	° ′	° ′	° ′	° ′
1	6 42 29.7	10♑33.3	7♓47.2	19♎10.6	27♑21.6	17♐48.3	20♈12.3	26♉43.5	5♑36.0	1♑45.6	9♑55.8	14♏33.6
2	6 46 26.3	11 34.4	7 44.1	1♏13.6	28 49.7	19 3.3	20 42.9	26 R 39.7	5 43.1	1 49.2	9 58.1	14 35.1
3	6 50 22.8	12 35.6	7 40.9	13 31.5	0♒15.8	20 18.3	21 13.7	26 36.1	5 50.2	1 52.8	10 .4	14 36.6
4	6 54 19.4	13 36.8	7 37.7	26 8.5	1 39.8	21 33.4	21 44.7	26 32.7	5 57.2	1 56.4	10 2.6	14 38.1
5	6 58 16.0	14 37.9	7 34.5	9♐ 7.1	3 1.1	22 48.4	22 15.9	26 29.4	6 4.3	1 59.9	10 4.9	14 39.6
6	7 2 12.5	15 39.1	7 31.4	22 28.3	4 19.3	24 3.5	22 47.2	26 26.4	6 11.3	2 3.5	10 7.2	14 41.1
7	7 6 9.1	16 40.3	7 28.2	6♑11.1	5 33.7	25 18.6	23 18.7	26 23.6	6 18.4	2 7.0	10 9.4	14 42.5
8	7 10 5.6	17 41.5	7 25.0	20 12.3	6 43.8	26 33.7	23 50.4	26 20.9	6 25.4	2 10.6	10 11.7	14 43.8
9	7 14 2.2	18 42.6	7 21.8	4♒27.5	7 48.9	27 48.8	24 22.3	26 18.5	6 32.4	2 14.1	10 13.9	14 45.2
10	7 17 58.7	19 43.8	7 18.6	18 51.0	8 48.2	29 3.9	24 54.3	26 16.3	6 39.4	2 17.6	10 16.2	14 46.5
11	7 21 55.3	20 44.9	7 15.5	3♓17.5	9 40.8	0♑19.0	25 26.4	26 14.3	6 46.3	2 21.1	10 18.4	14 47.8
12	7 25 51.9	21 46.1	7 12.3	17 42.0	10 25.9	1 34.1	25 58.8	26 12.4	6 53.3	2 24.5	10 20.7	14 49.0
13	7 29 48.4	22 47.2	7 9.1	2♈ .9	11 2.6	2 49.2	26 31.2	26 10.8	7 .2	2 28.0	10 22.9	14 50.3
14	7 33 45.0	23 48.4	7 5.9	16 11.9	11 30.0	4 4.3	27 3.8	26 9.4	7 7.1	2 31.4	10 25.1	14 51.5
15	7 37 41.5	24 49.5	7 2.8	0♉13.5	11 47.3	5 19.4	27 36.6	26 8.2	7 14.0	2 34.9	10 27.4	14 52.6
16	7 41 38.1	25 50.6	6 59.6	14 5.0	11 53.7	6 34.5	28 9.4	26 7.3	7 20.9	2 38.3	10 29.6	14 53.7
17	7 45 34.7	26 51.7	6 56.4	27 45.7	11 R 48.7	7 49.6	28 42.4	26 6.5	7 27.7	2 41.7	10 31.8	14 54.8
18	7 49 31.2	27 52.7	6 53.2	11♊15.1	11 32.0	9 4.7	29 15.5	26 5.9	7 34.5	2 45.0	10 34.0	14 55.9
19	7 53 27.8	28 53.8	6 50.1	24 32.6	11 3.7	10 19.8	29 48.8	26 5.6	7 41.3	2 48.4	10 36.1	14 56.9
20	7 57 24.3	29 54.9	6 46.9	7♋37.4	10 24.1	11 35.0	0♉22.2	26 5.4	7 48.1	2 51.8	10 38.4	14 57.9
21	8 1 20.9	0♒55.9	6 43.7	20 28.8	9 34.0	12 50.1	0 55.6	26 D 5.5	7 54.9	2 55.1	10 40.5	14 58.9
22	8 5 17.4	1 57.0	6 40.5	3♌ 6.4	8 34.8	14 5.2	1 29.2	26 5.8	8 1.6	2 58.3	10 42.7	14 59.8
23	8 9 14.0	2 58.0	6 37.4	15 30.6	7 28.1	15 20.3	2 2.9	26 6.2	8 8.3	3 1.6	10 44.8	15 .7
24	8 13 10.6	3 59.0	6 34.2	27 42.4	6 15.9	16 35.4	2 36.7	26 6.9	8 14.9	3 4.9	10 46.9	15 1.5
25	8 17 7.1	4 60.0	6 31.0	9♍43.5	5 .4	17 50.5	3 10.5	26 7.8	8 21.5	3 8.1	10 49.1	15 2.3
26	8 21 3.7	6 1.0	6 27.8	21 36.6	3 44.0	19 5.6	3 44.5	26 8.8	8 28.1	3 11.3	10 51.2	15 3.1
27	8 25 .2	7 1.9	6 24.6	3♎25.2	2 28.9	20 20.8	4 18.6	26 10.1	8 34.6	3 14.4	10 53.3	15 3.9
28	8 28 56.8	8 2.9	6 21.5	15 13.4	1 17.2	21 35.9	4 52.7	26 11.6	8 41.1	3 17.6	10 55.3	15 4.6
29	8 32 53.3	9 3.8	6 18.3	27 5.8	0 10.5	22 51.0	5 27.0	26 13.3	8 47.6	3 20.7	10 57.4	15 5.3
30	8 36 49.9	10 4.8	6 15.1	9♏ 7.4	29♑10.4	24 6.1	6 1.3	26 15.2	8 54.0	3 23.8	10 59.5	15 5.9
31	8 40 46.5	11 5.7	6 11.9	21 23.1	28 17.8	25 21.2	6 35.8	26 17.2	9 .4	3 26.8	11 1.5	15 6.5
		LATITUDE										
1	6 42 29.7	0 .0	0 .0	3 S 28.1	1 S 54.8	0 N 49.2	0 N 32.7	0 S 54.0	0 N 43.1	0 S 13.1	0 N 54.2	15 N 35.8
4	6 54 19.4	0 .0	0 .0	5 1.7	1 36.9	0 41.7	0 36.5	0 53.2	0 42.9	0 13.2	0 54.2	15 37.0
7	7 6 9.1	0 .0	0 .0	4 25.4	1 11.0	0 34.1	0 40.0	0 52.5	0 42.7	0 13.2	0 54.1	15 38.3
10	7 17 58.7	0 .0	0 .0	1 29.5	0 36.3	0 26.4	0 43.3	0 51.7	0 42.5	0 13.2	0 54.1	15 39.6
13	7 29 48.4	0 .0	0 .0	2 N 18.1	0 N 7.7	0 18.6	0 46.4	0 50.9	0 42.4	0 13.3	0 54.1	15 40.9
16	7 41 38.1	0 .0	0 .0	4 48.9	0 59.5	0 10.8	0 49.3	0 50.1	0 42.2	0 13.3	0 54.1	15 42.3
19	7 53 27.8	0 .0	0 .0	4 53.5	1 54.8	0 3.0	0 52.0	0 49.3	0 42.1	0 13.3	0 54.1	15 43.7
22	8 5 17.4	0 .0	0 .0	2 45.7	2 45.3	0 S 4.7	0 54.6	0 48.5	0 42.0	0 13.4	0 54.1	15 45.1
25	8 17 7.1	0 .0	0 .0	0 S 25.7	3 21.0	0 12.3	0 56.9	0 47.7	0 41.8	0 13.4	0 54.1	15 46.6
28	8 28 56.8	0 .0	0 .0	3 23.2	3 35.2	0 19.8	0 59.1	0 46.9	0 41.7	0 13.5	0 54.1	15 48.1
31	8 40 46.5	0 .0	0 .0	5 6.1	3 28.3	0 27.0	1 1.2	0 46.1	0 41.6	0 13.5	0 54.2	15 49.5
		RIGHT ASCENSION										
1	6 42 29.7	11♑28.8	9♓27.7	16♎21.5	29♑49.8	16♐49.5	18♈27.0	24♉38.6	6♑ 4.1	1♑55.3	10♑43.8	16♏39.0
2	6 46 26.3	12 35.0	9 24.7	27 34.5	1♒21.8	18 10.0	18 55.2	24 R 34.7	6 11.7	1 59.2	10 46.3	16 40.5
3	6 50 22.8	13 41.1	9 21.7	9♏33.8	2 51.2	19 30.6	19 23.6	24 30.9	6 19.4	2 3.1	10 48.7	16 42.1
4	6 54 19.4	14 47.2	9 18.8	22 31.8	4 17.7	20 51.4	19 52.2	24 27.3	6 27.0	2 7.0	10 51.2	16 43.6
5	6 58 16.0	15 53.1	9 15.8	6♐32.9	5 40.6	22 12.4	20 21.0	24 23.9	6 34.7	2 10.9	10 53.6	16 45.0
6	7 2 12.5	16 58.9	9 12.8	21 29.3	6 59.6	23 33.5	20 50.0	24 20.8	6 42.3	2 14.8	10 56.1	16 46.5
7	7 6 9.1	18 4.6	9 9.8	6♑58.2	8 14.1	24 54.7	21 19.3	24 17.8	6 49.9	2 18.7	10 58.5	16 47.9
8	7 10 5.6	19 10.2	9 6.8	22 27.6	9 23.5	26 16.1	21 48.7	24 15.0	6 57.5	2 22.5	11 .9	16 49.3
9	7 14 2.2	20 15.7	9 3.8	7♒28.8	10 27.0	27 37.5	22 18.4	24 12.5	7 5.1	2 26.4	11 3.4	16 50.7
10	7 17 58.7	21 21.0	9 .9	21 45.8	11 24.0	28 59.0	22 48.2	24 10.1	7 12.6	2 30.2	11 5.8	16 52.0
11	7 21 55.3	22 26.2	8 57.9	5♓17.9	12 13.7	0♑20.6	23 18.2	24 8.0	7 20.2	2 34.0	11 8.2	16 53.3
12	7 25 51.9	23 31.3	8 54.9	18 15.9	12 55.2	1 42.2	23 48.5	24 6.1	7 27.7	2 37.8	11 10.6	16 54.6
13	7 29 48.4	24 36.2	8 51.9	0♈56.0	13 27.7	3 3.9	24 18.9	24 4.4	7 35.2	2 41.6	11 13.0	16 55.9
14	7 33 45.0	25 40.9	8 48.9	13 36.7	13 50.6	4 25.6	24 49.5	24 2.9	7 42.7	2 45.3	11 15.4	16 57.1
15	7 37 41.5	26 45.4	8 45.9	26 35.4	14 2.9	5 47.3	25 20.3	24 1.6	7 50.1	2 49.1	11 17.8	16 58.3
16	7 41 38.1	27 49.8	8 42.9	10♉ 5.6	14 4.1	7 9.0	25 51.2	24 .5	7 57.5	2 52.8	11 20.2	16 59.5
17	7 45 34.7	28 54.0	8 40.0	24 13.5	13 R 53.9	8 30.7	26 22.4	23 59.6	8 4.9	2 56.5	11 22.5	17 .6
18	7 49 31.2	29 58.1	8 37.0	8♊54.0	13 31.9	9 52.4	26 53.7	23 59.0	8 12.3	3 .1	11 24.9	17 1.7
19	7 53 27.8	1♒ 1.9	8 34.0	23 49.6	12 58.4	11 13.9	27 25.1	23 58.5	8 19.6	3 3.8	11 27.3	17 2.8
20	7 57 24.3	2 5.6	8 31.0	8♋35.0	12 13.9	12 35.5	27 56.8	23 58.4	8 27.0	3 7.5	11 29.6	17 3.9
21	8 1 20.9	3 9.1	8 28.0	22 45.4	11 19.2	13 57.0	28 28.6	23 58.4	8 34.3	3 11.1	11 32.0	17 4.9
22	8 5 17.4	4 12.4	8 25.0	6♌ 5.4	10 15.7	15 18.3	29 .6	23 D 58.6	8 41.5	3 14.7	11 34.3	17 5.9
23	8 9 14.0	5 15.4	8 22.0	18 31.0	9 5.1	16 39.6	29 32.7	23 59.0	8 48.7	3 18.2	11 36.6	17 6.8
24	8 13 10.6	6 18.3	8 19.0	0♍ 7.7	7 49.5	18 .7	0♉ 4.9	23 59.6	8 55.9	3 21.8	11 38.9	17 7.7
25	8 17 7.1	7 21.0	8 16.1	11 6.9	6 31.1	19 21.7	0 37.4	24 .4	9 3.1	3 25.3	11 41.2	17 8.6
26	8 21 3.7	8 23.5	8 13.1	21 42.3	5 12.3	20 42.6	1 9.9	24 1.4	9 10.2	3 28.8	11 43.4	17 9.5
27	8 25 .2	9 25.8	8 10.1	2♎ 8.8	3 55.2	22 3.3	1 42.7	24 2.7	9 17.2	3 32.2	11 45.7	17 10.3
28	8 28 56.8	10 27.9	8 7.1	12 41.7	2 41.9	23 23.8	2 15.6	24 4.1	9 24.3	3 35.7	11 47.9	17 11.1
29	8 32 53.3	11 29.9	8 4.1	23 36.6	1 34.1	24 44.1	2 48.6	24 5.8	9 31.3	3 39.1	11 50.1	17 11.9
30	8 36 49.9	12 31.6	8 1.1	5♏ 8.4	0 33.3	26 4.3	3 21.8	24 7.7	9 38.2	3 42.4	11 52.3	17 12.6
31	8 40 46.5	13 33.1	7 58.1	17 30.6	29♑40.5	27 24.2	3 55.1	24 9.7	9 45.1	3 45.8	11 54.5	17 13.3
		DECLINATION										
1	6 42 29.7	23 S 1.4	0 S 9.1	10 S 43.0	22 S 34.0	22 S 4.0	8 N 24.1	18 N 33.1	22 S 36.4	23 S 39.0	22 S 10.2	1 S 16.3
4	6 54 19.4	22 44.8	0 9.1	24 10.5	21 22.0	22 28.8	9 2.4	18 31.3	22 35.7	23 38.9	22 9.7	1 16.4
7	7 6 9.1	22 24.1	0 9.2	27 43.0	20 1.8	22 47.5	9 40.7	18 30.0	22 34.9	23 38.8	22 9.3	1 16.3
10	7 17 58.7	21 59.5	0 9.2	16 35.6	18 38.7	22 60.0	10 19.0	18 29.1	22 34.0	23 38.6	22 8.8	1 16.2
13	7 29 48.4	21 31.0	0 9.3	2 N 54.8	17 20.2	23 6.2	10 57.2	18 28.6	22 33.1	23 38.5	22 8.2	1 15.9
16	7 41 38.1	20 58.8	0 9.4	20 39.5	16 16.4	23 6.0	11 35.3	18 28.5	22 32.2	23 38.3	22 7.7	1 15.6
19	7 53 27.8	20 23.0	0 9.4	28 13.1	15 36.9	22 59.5	12 13.2	18 28.9	22 31.2	23 38.1	22 7.2	1 15.1
22	8 5 17.4	19 43.7	0 9.5	22 9.1	15 27.5	22 46.6	12 50.7	18 29.7	22 30.1	23 38.0	22 6.7	1 14.5
25	8 17 7.1	19 1.1	0 9.6	7 31.6	15 45.9	22 27.4	13 27.9	18 31.0	22 29.0	23 37.8	22 6.2	1 13.8
28	8 28 56.8	18 15.5	0 9.6	9 S 7.2	16 22.5	22 2.1	14 4.7	18 32.6	22 27.9	23 37.6	22 5.7	1 13.0
31	8 40 46.5	17 26.8	0 9.7	23 1.8	17 6.2	21 30.7	14 41.0	18 34.7	22 26.7	23 37.4	22 5.1	1 12.1

FEBRUARY 1989

LONGITUDE

DAY	EPHEM. SID. TIME	☉	☊	☾	☿	♀	♂	♃	♄	♅	♆	♇
	h m s	° ′	° ′	° ′	° ′	° ′	° ′	° ′	° ′	° ′	° ′	° ′
1	8 44 43.0	12♒ 6.6	6♓ 8.8	3♐57.5	27♑33.5	26♑36.4	7♉10.3	26♉19.5	9♑ 6.8	3♑29.9	11♑ 3.5	15♏ 7.1
2	8 48 39.6	13 7.5	6 5.6	16 54.5	26 R 57.7	27 51.5	7 44.9	26 22.0	9 13.1	3 32.9	11 5.5	15 7.6
3	8 52 36.1	14 8.4	6 2.4	0♑16.6	26 30.5	29 6.6	8 19.5	26 24.7	9 19.4	3 35.8	11 7.5	15 8.1
4	8 56 32.7	15 9.2	5 59.2	14 4.6	26 11.9	0♒21.7	8 54.3	26 27.6	9 25.6	3 38.8	11 9.5	15 8.6
5	9 0 29.2	16 10.1	5 56.1	28 16.8	26 1.5	1 36.9	9 29.2	26 30.6	9 31.8	3 41.7	11 11.4	15 9.0
6	9 4 25.8	17 10.9	5 52.9	12♒49.3	25 58.9	2 52.0	10 4.1	26 33.9	9 37.9	3 44.6	11 13.3	15 9.4
7	9 8 22.3	18 11.8	5 49.7	27 35.7	26 D 3.8	4 7.1	10 39.1	26 37.4	9 44.0	3 47.4	11 15.2	15 9.7
8	9 12 18.9	19 12.5	5 46.5	12♓28.8	26 15.5	5 22.2	11 14.1	26 41.0	9 50.0	3 50.2	11 17.1	15 10.0
9	9 16 15.5	20 13.3	5 43.3	27 20.5	26 33.7	6 37.3	11 49.3	26 44.8	9 56.0	3 53.0	11 19.0	15 10.3
10	9 20 12.0	21 14.1	5 40.2	12♈ 4.0	26 57.9	7 52.4	12 24.5	26 48.9	10 2.0	3 55.8	11 20.9	15 10.6
11	9 24 8.6	22 14.8	5 37.0	26 33.7	27 27.4	9 7.5	12 59.8	26 53.1	10 7.9	3 58.5	11 22.8	15 10.8
12	9 28 5.1	23 15.5	5 33.8	10♉46.1	28 2.0	10 22.6	13 35.2	26 57.5	10 13.7	4 1.2	11 24.6	15 11.0
13	9 32 1.7	24 16.2	5 30.6	24 39.4	28 41.2	11 37.6	14 10.6	27 2.1	10 19.5	4 3.8	11 26.4	15 11.1
14	9 35 58.2	25 16.8	5 27.5	8♊13.5	29 24.7	12 52.7	14 46.0	27 6.9	10 25.2	4 6.4	11 28.1	15 11.2
15	9 39 54.8	26 17.4	5 24.3	21 29.2	0♒12.0	14 7.7	15 21.5	27 11.8	10 30.8	4 9.0	11 29.9	15 11.2
16	9 43 51.3	27 18.0	5 21.1	4♋28.1	1 2.9	15 22.8	15 57.1	27 16.9	10 36.4	4 11.5	11 31.6	15 11.3
17	9 47 47.9	28 18.5	5 17.9	17 12.0	1 57.1	16 37.8	16 32.7	27 22.2	10 42.0	4 14.0	11 33.3	15 11.3
18	9 51 44.5	29 19.1	5 14.8	29 42.6	2 54.3	17 52.8	17 8.4	27 27.7	10 47.5	4 16.4	11 35.0	15 R 11.2
19	9 55 41.0	0♓19.6	5 11.6	12♌ 1.7	3 54.3	19 7.8	17 44.1	27 33.3	10 52.9	4 18.8	11 36.6	15 11.1
20	9 59 37.6	1 20.0	5 8.4	24 10.9	4 56.9	20 22.8	18 19.9	27 39.1	10 58.3	4 21.2	11 38.3	15 11.0
21	10 3 34.1	2 20.5	5 5.2	6♍12.0	6 1.9	21 37.8	18 55.7	27 45.1	11 3.6	4 23.5	11 39.9	15 10.8
22	10 7 30.7	3 20.9	5 2.0	18 6.8	7 9.2	22 52.8	19 31.5	27 51.2	11 8.8	4 25.8	11 41.5	15 10.7
23	10 11 27.2	4 21.3	4 58.9	29 57.2	8 18.5	24 7.8	20 7.4	27 57.5	11 14.0	4 28.0	11 43.0	15 10.4
24	10 15 23.8	5 21.6	4 55.7	11♎45.7	9 29.9	25 22.7	20 43.3	28 4.0	11 19.1	4 30.2	11 44.5	15 10.2
25	10 19 20.3	6 22.0	4 52.5	23 35.2	10 43.0	26 37.7	21 19.3	28 10.6	11 24.2	4 32.4	11 46.1	15 9.9
26	10 23 16.9	7 22.3	4 49.3	5♏28.9	11 58.0	27 52.7	21 55.3	28 17.3	11 29.1	4 34.5	11 47.5	15 9.5
27	10 27 13.5	8 22.6	4 46.2	17 30.7	13 14.6	29 7.6	22 31.4	28 24.3	11 34.0	4 36.6	11 49.0	15 9.2
28	10 31 10.0	9 22.8	4 43.0	29 44.5	14 32.8	0♓22.5	23 7.4	28 31.4	11 38.9	4 38.6	11 50.4	15 8.8

LATITUDE

DAY	EPHEM. SID. TIME	☉	☊	☾	☿	♀	♂	♃	♄	♅	♆	♇
1	8 44 43.0	0 .0	0 .0	5S15.0	3N22.3	0S29.3	1N 1.9	0S45.8	0N41.6	0S13.5	0N54.2	15N50.0
4	8 56 32.7	0 .0	0 .0	4 5.0	2 56.5	0 36.2	1 3.8	0 45.1	0 41.5	0 13.6	0 54.2	15 51.5
7	9 8 22.3	0 .0	0 .0	0 40.2	2 23.8	0 42.7	1 5.5	0 44.3	0 41.4	0 13.6	0 54.2	15 53.1
10	9 20 12.0	0 .0	0 .0	3N11.8	1 48.5	0 48.9	1 7.2	0 43.6	0 41.3	0 13.7	0 54.2	15 54.6
13	9 32 1.7	0 .0	0 .0	5 12.0	1 13.3	0 54.8	1 8.7	0 42.8	0 41.2	0 13.7	0 54.3	15 56.1
16	9 43 51.3	0 .0	0 .0	4 36.1	0 39.6	1 .2	1 10.1	0 42.1	0 41.2	0 13.8	0 54.3	15 57.6
19	9 55 41.0	0 .0	0 .0	2 3.5	0 8.2	1 5.1	1 11.4	0 41.4	0 41.1	0 13.8	0 54.3	15 59.0
22	10 7 30.7	0 .0	0 .0	1S13.0	0S20.6	1 9.6	1 12.6	0 40.7	0 41.0	0 13.9	0 54.4	16 .5
25	10 19 20.3	0 .0	0 .0	3 59.0	0 46.5	1 13.6	1 13.7	0 40.0	0 41.0	0 14.0	0 54.4	16 1.9
28	10 31 10.0	0 .0	0 .0	5 16.3	1 9.3	1 17.1	1 14.7	0 39.3	0 40.9	0 14.0	0 54.5	16 3.4

RIGHT ASCENSION

DAY	EPHEM. SID. TIME	☉	☊	☾	☿	♀	♂	♃	♄	♅	♆	♇
1	8 44 43.0	14♒34.4	7♓55.1	0♐52.1	28♑56.2	28♑44.0	4♉28.6	24♉12.0	9♑52.0	3♑49.1	11♑56.7	17♏14.0
2	8 48 39.6	15 35.5	7 52.1	15 12.5	28 R 20.9	0♒ 3.5	5 2.2	24 14.5	9 58.8	3 52.4	11 58.8	17 14.6
3	8 52 36.1	16 36.4	7 49.1	0♑18.8	27 54.7	1 22.8	5 36.0	24 17.2	10 5.5	3 55.6	12 1.0	17 15.2
4	8 56 32.7	17 37.1	7 46.1	15 46.0	27 37.4	2 41.8	6 9.9	24 20.1	10 12.3	3 58.8	12 3.1	17 15.7
5	9 0 29.2	18 37.6	7 43.1	1♒ 4.7	27 28.6	4 .6	6 44.0	24 23.2	10 18.9	4 2.0	12 5.2	17 16.3
6	9 4 25.8	19 37.9	7 40.2	15 52.8	27 28.1	5 19.1	7 18.2	24 26.5	10 25.5	4 5.1	12 7.3	17 16.8
7	9 8 22.3	20 38.0	7 37.2	0♓ 1.4	27 D 35.3	6 37.4	7 52.5	24 30.0	10 32.1	4 8.2	12 9.3	17 17.2
8	9 12 18.9	21 37.9	7 34.2	13 34.7	27 49.8	7 55.4	8 27.0	24 33.6	10 38.6	4 11.3	12 11.3	17 17.7
9	9 16 15.5	22 37.6	7 31.2	26 45.5	28 11.0	9 13.1	9 1.6	24 37.5	10 45.1	4 14.3	12 13.4	17 18.1
10	9 20 12.0	23 37.2	7 28.2	9♈50.3	28 38.4	10 30.6	9 36.5	24 41.6	10 51.5	4 17.4	12 15.4	17 18.5
11	9 24 8.6	24 36.5	7 25.2	23 5.6	29 11.5	11 47.8	10 11.4	24 45.9	10 57.9	4 20.3	12 17.4	17 18.8
12	9 28 5.1	25 35.6	7 22.2	6♉44.9	29 49.8	13 4.6	10 46.4	24 50.4	11 4.2	4 23.2	12 19.3	17 19.1
13	9 32 1.7	26 34.5	7 19.2	20 54.8	0♒33.0	14 21.2	11 21.6	24 55.0	11 10.4	4 26.1	12 21.2	17 19.4
14	9 35 58.2	27 33.2	7 16.2	5♊31.9	1 20.5	15 37.5	11 56.9	24 59.9	11 16.6	4 28.9	12 23.1	17 19.6
15	9 39 54.8	28 31.8	7 13.2	20 22.0	2 12.0	16 53.5	12 32.3	25 4.9	11 22.7	4 31.7	12 25.0	17 19.8
16	9 43 51.3	29 30.1	7 10.2	5♋ 2.7	3 7.1	18 9.1	13 7.8	25 10.1	11 28.7	4 34.5	12 26.9	17 19.9
17	9 47 47.9	0♓28.3	7 7.2	19 11.9	4 5.6	19 24.5	13 43.5	25 15.5	11 34.7	4 37.2	12 28.7	17 20.1
18	9 51 44.5	1 26.3	7 4.2	2♌34.6	5 7.1	20 39.6	14 19.3	25 21.0	11 40.6	4 39.9	12 30.5	17 20.2
19	9 55 41.0	2 24.1	7 1.2	15 5.9	6 11.5	21 54.4	14 55.2	25 26.8	11 46.4	4 42.5	12 32.3	17 20.2
20	9 59 37.6	3 21.7	6 58.2	26 49.6	7 18.3	23 8.9	15 31.3	25 32.7	11 52.2	4 45.1	12 34.0	17 20.2
21	10 3 34.1	4 19.2	6 55.2	7♍55.4	8 27.5	24 23.1	16 7.4	25 38.8	11 57.9	4 47.6	12 35.8	17 20.2
22	10 7 30.7	5 16.5	6 52.2	18 35.6	9 38.7	25 37.0	16 43.7	25 45.1	12 3.6	4 50.1	12 37.5	17 20.2
23	10 11 27.2	6 13.7	6 49.2	29 3.7	10 52.0	26 50.7	17 20.1	25 51.5	12 9.2	4 52.5	12 39.1	17 R 20.1
24	10 15 23.8	7 10.7	6 46.2	9♎33.6	12 6.9	28 4.1	17 56.6	25 58.1	12 14.7	4 54.9	12 40.8	17 20.0
25	10 19 20.3	8 7.5	6 43.2	20 19.3	13 23.6	29 17.1	18 33.2	26 4.9	12 20.1	4 57.3	12 42.4	17 19.9
26	10 23 16.9	9 4.3	6 40.2	1♏34.3	14 41.7	0♓30.0	19 9.9	26 11.8	12 25.5	4 59.6	12 44.0	17 19.7
27	10 27 13.5	10 .8	6 37.2	13 31.0	16 1.2	1 42.5	19 46.8	26 18.9	12 30.7	5 1.9	12 45.5	17 19.5
28	10 31 10.0	10 57.3	6 34.2	26 18.4	17 22.0	2 54.8	20 23.7	26 26.2	12 36.0	5 4.1	12 47.1	17 19.3

DECLINATION

DAY	EPHEM. SID. TIME	☉	☊	☾	☿	♀	♂	♃	♄	♅	♆	♇
1	8 44 43.0	17S 9.9	0S 9.7	26S 5.8	17S20.7	21S19.0	14N53.0	18N35.5	22S26.3	23S37.3	22S 5.0	1S11.7
4	8 56 32.7	16 17.6	0 9.8	26 45.5	18 1.4	20 39.9	15 28.5	18 38.1	22 25.1	23 37.1	22 4.5	1 10.7
7	9 8 22.3	15 22.7	0 9.8	12 56.3	18 35.1	19 55.3	16 3.5	18 41.1	22 23.9	23 36.9	22 4.0	1 9.6
10	9 20 12.0	14 25.4	0 9.9	7N42.7	18 59.6	19 5.5	16 37.8	18 44.5	22 22.6	23 36.8	22 3.4	1 8.3
13	9 32 1.7	13 26.0	0 9.9	23 58.5	19 13.8	18 10.6	17 11.3	18 48.3	22 21.4	23 36.6	22 3.0	1 7.0
16	9 43 51.3	12 24.7	0 10.0	27 58.0	19 17.0	17 11.1	17 44.0	18 52.3	22 20.1	23 36.4	22 2.5	1 5.7
19	9 55 41.0	11 21.5	0 10.1	19 9.9	19 8.9	16 7.2	18 15.9	18 56.7	22 18.9	23 36.2	22 2.0	1 4.2
22	10 7 30.7	10 16.8	0 10.1	3 34.9	18 49.2	14 59.3	18 46.8	19 1.4	22 17.6	23 36.0	22 1.5	1 2.7
25	10 19 20.3	9 10.6	0 10.2	12S51.5	18 17.7	13 47.7	19 16.8	19 6.4	22 16.4	23 35.9	22 1.1	1 1.1
28	10 31 10.0	8 3.2	0 10.2	25 14.7	17 34.6	12 32.6	19 45.7	19 11.7	22 15.2	23 35.7	22 .7	0 59.4

MARCH 1989

LONGITUDE

DAY	EPHEM. SID. TIME (h m s)	☉ (° ′)	☊ (° ′)	☽ (° ′)	☿ (° ′)	♀ (° ′)	♂ (° ′)	♃ (° ′)	♄ (° ′)	♅ (° ′)	♆ (° ′)	♇ (° ′)
1	10 35 6.6	10♓23.0	4♓39.8	12♐14.8	15♒52.5	1♓37.5	23♉43.6	28♉38.6	11♑43.7	4♑40.6	11♑51.8	15♏ 8.3
2	10 39 3.1	11 23.3	4 36.6	25 5.6	17 13.7	2 52.4	24 19.7	28 46.0	11 48.4	4 42.5	11 53.2	15R 7.9
3	10 42 59.7	12 23.5	4 33.4	8♑20.5	18 36.3	4 7.4	24 56.0	28 53.6	11 53.0	4 44.5	11 54.6	15 7.4
4	10 46 56.2	13 23.7	4 30.3	22 1.8	20 .3	5 22.3	25 32.2	29 1.2	11 57.6	4 46.3	11 55.9	15 6.9
5	10 50 52.8	14 23.8	4 27.1	6♒10.1	21 25.5	6 37.2	26 8.5	29 9.1	12 2.1	4 48.1	11 57.2	15 6.3
6	10 54 49.3	15 23.9	4 23.9	20 43.5	22 52.1	7 52.1	26 44.8	29 17.0	12 6.5	4 49.9	11 58.4	15 5.7
7	10 58 45.9	16 24.0	4 20.7	5♓37.5	24 19.9	9 6.9	27 21.1	29 25.2	12 10.8	4 51.6	11 59.7	15 5.1
8	11 2 42.4	17 24.0	4 17.6	20 44.7	25 49.0	10 21.8	27 57.5	29 33.4	12 15.1	4 53.2	12 .9	15 4.4
9	11 6 39.0	18 24.0	4 14.4	5♈56.0	27 19.2	11 36.7	28 33.9	29 41.8	12 19.2	4 54.8	12 2.1	15 3.7
10	11 10 35.5	19 24.0	4 11.2	21 1.8	28 50.7	12 51.5	29 10.4	29 50.3	12 23.3	4 56.4	12 3.2	15 3.0
11	11 14 32.1	20 24.0	4 8.0	5♉53.2	0♓23.4	14 6.3	29 46.8	29 59.0	12 27.4	4 57.9	12 4.3	15 2.2
12	11 18 28.7	21 23.9	4 4.8	20 23.6	1 57.2	15 21.1	0♊23.3	0♊ 7.8	12 31.3	4 59.4	12 5.4	15 1.4
13	11 22 25.2	22 23.8	4 1.7	4♊29.0	3 32.3	16 35.9	0 59.8	0 16.7	12 35.1	5 .8	12 6.4	15 .6
14	11 26 21.8	23 23.6	3 58.5	18 8.3	5 8.5	17 50.7	1 36.4	0 25.7	12 38.9	5 2.2	12 7.5	14 59.8
15	11 30 18.3	24 23.4	3 55.3	1♋22.6	6 45.9	19 5.5	2 13.0	0 34.9	12 42.6	5 3.5	12 8.4	14 58.9
16	11 34 14.9	25 23.2	3 52.1	14 14.4	8 24.6	20 20.2	2 49.5	0 44.2	12 46.2	5 4.8	12 9.4	14 58.0
17	11 38 11.4	26 22.9	3 49.0	26 47.2	10 4.4	21 35.0	3 26.2	0 53.6	12 49.7	5 6.0	12 10.3	14 57.0
18	11 42 8.0	27 22.6	3 45.8	9♌ 4.8	11 45.4	22 49.7	4 2.8	1 3.1	12 53.2	5 7.2	12 11.2	14 56.1
19	11 46 4.5	28 22.2	3 42.6	21 10.8	13 27.7	24 4.4	4 39.4	1 12.8	12 56.5	5 8.3	12 12.1	14 55.1
20	11 50 1.1	29 21.8	3 39.4	3♍ 8.6	15 11.2	25 19.0	5 16.1	1 22.5	12 59.8	5 9.3	12 12.9	14 54.0
21	11 53 57.6	0♈21.4	3 36.2	15 1.0	16 56.0	26 33.7	5 52.8	1 32.4	13 3.0	5 10.4	12 13.7	14 53.0
22	11 57 54.2	1 21.0	3 33.1	26 50.6	18 42.0	27 48.4	6 29.5	1 42.4	13 6.1	5 11.3	12 14.5	14 51.9
23	12 1 50.7	2 20.5	3 29.9	8♎39.5	20 29.3	29 3.0	7 6.2	1 52.5	13 9.1	5 12.3	12 15.2	14 50.8
24	12 5 47.3	3 20.0	3 26.7	20 29.9	22 17.9	0♈17.7	7 43.0	2 2.7	13 12.0	5 13.2	12 16.0	14 49.7
25	12 9 43.9	4 19.4	3 23.5	2♏23.4	24 7.8	1 32.3	8 19.7	2 13.0	13 14.9	5 14.0	12 16.7	14 48.6
26	12 13 40.4	5 18.9	3 20.4	14 22.3	25 58.9	2 46.9	8 56.5	2 23.5	13 17.6	5 14.7	12 17.3	14 47.4
27	12 17 37.0	6 18.2	3 17.2	26 28.9	27 51.4	4 1.5	9 33.2	2 34.0	13 20.2	5 15.5	12 17.9	14 46.2
28	12 21 33.5	7 17.6	3 14.0	8♐45.9	29 45.2	5 16.0	10 10.0	2 44.6	13 22.8	5 16.1	12 18.5	14 45.0
29	12 25 30.1	8 16.9	3 10.8	21 16.4	1♈40.3	6 30.6	10 46.8	2 55.3	13 25.3	5 16.7	12 19.0	14 43.7
30	12 29 26.6	9 16.2	3 7.6	4♑ 3.7	3 36.7	7 45.1	11 23.7	3 6.1	13 27.6	5 17.3	12 19.5	14 42.4
31	12 33 23.2	10 15.5	3 4.5	17 11.4	5 34.3	8 59.6	12 .5	3 17.0	13 29.9	5 17.8	12 20.0	14 41.1

LATITUDE

DAY	EPHEM. SID. TIME (h m s)	☉	☊	☽	☿	♀	♂	♃	♄	♅	♆	♇
1	10 35 6.6	0 .0	0 .0	5S15.0	1S16.2	1S18.2	1N15.0	0S39.1	0N40.9	0S14.0	0N54.5	16N 3.8
4	10 46 56.2	0 .0	0 .0	3 36.2	1 34.8	1 20.9	1 16.0	0 38.5	0 40.8	0 14.1	0 54.5	16 5.2
7	10 58 45.9	0 .0	0 .0	0N 4.0	1 50.0	1 23.1	1 16.8	0 37.8	0 40.8	0 14.2	0 54.6	16 6.5
10	11 10 35.5	0 .0	0 .0	3 48.6	2 1.9	1 24.8	1 17.6	0 37.2	0 40.8	0 14.2	0 54.7	16 7.8
13	11 22 25.2	0 .0	0 .0	5 16.2	2 10.1	1 25.8	1 18.3	0 36.6	0 40.7	0 14.3	0 54.7	16 9.1
16	11 34 14.9	0 .0	0 .0	4 4.3	2 14.5	1 26.3	1 18.9	0 36.0	0 40.7	0 14.3	0 54.8	16 10.2
19	11 46 4.5	0 .0	0 .0	1 14.7	2 15.0	1 26.3	1 19.5	0 35.4	0 40.7	0 14.4	0 54.8	16 11.4
22	11 57 54.2	0 .0	0 .0	1S58.0	2 11.4	1 25.6	1 20.0	0 34.9	0 40.6	0 14.5	0 54.8	16 12.5
25	12 9 43.9	0 .0	0 .0	4 24.6	2 3.4	1 24.4	1 20.4	0 34.3	0 40.6	0 14.5	0 54.9	16 13.5
28	12 21 33.5	0 .0	0 .0	5 11.2	1 50.8	1 22.6	1 20.8	0 33.8	0 40.6	0 14.6	0 55.0	16 14.4
31	12 33 23.2	0 .0	0 .0	3 49.0	1 33.7	1 20.2	1 21.1	0 33.3	0 40.6	0 14.7	0 55.1	16 15.3

RIGHT ASCENSION

DAY	EPHEM. SID. TIME (h m s)	☉	☊	☽	☿	♀	♂	♃	♄	♅	♆	♇
1	10 35 6.6	11♓53.6	6♓31.2	9♐59.2	18♒43.9	4♓ 6.8	21♉ .8	26♉33.6	12♑41.1	5♑ 6.2	12♑48.6	17♏19.0
2	10 39 3.1	12 49.8	6 28.2	24 26.7	20 6.9	5 18.6	21 38.0	26 41.2	12 46.2	5 8.4	12 50.1	17R18.7
3	10 42 59.7	13 45.9	6 25.2	9♑23.5	21 31.0	6 30.2	22 15.3	26 49.0	12 51.2	5 10.5	12 51.5	17 18.4
4	10 46 56.2	14 41.9	6 22.2	24 26.3	22 56.0	7 41.5	22 52.7	26 56.9	12 56.1	5 12.5	12 53.0	17 18.0
5	10 50 52.8	15 37.7	6 19.2	9♒13.5	24 21.8	8 52.6	23 30.2	27 4.9	13 .9	5 14.5	12 54.3	17 17.6
6	10 54 49.3	16 33.5	6 16.2	23 33.0	25 48.5	10 3.4	24 7.8	27 13.1	13 5.7	5 16.4	12 55.7	17 17.2
7	10 58 45.9	17 29.1	6 13.2	7♓24.2	27 16.0	11 14.1	24 45.6	27 21.5	13 10.3	5 18.2	12 57.0	17 16.8
8	11 2 42.4	18 24.7	6 10.2	20 55.7	28 44.2	12 24.5	25 23.4	27 30.0	13 14.9	5 20.0	12 58.3	17 16.3
9	11 6 39.0	19 20.1	6 7.2	4♈21.8	0♓13.1	13 34.7	26 1.4	27 38.6	13 19.4	5 21.8	12 59.6	17 15.7
10	11 10 35.5	20 15.5	6 4.2	17 58.2	1 42.7	14 44.8	26 39.4	27 47.4	13 23.8	5 23.5	13 .8	17 15.2
11	11 14 32.1	21 10.7	6 1.2	1♉58.2	3 13.0	15 54.6	27 17.5	27 56.3	13 28.1	5 25.2	13 2.0	17 14.6
12	11 18 28.7	22 5.9	5 58.2	16 28.7	4 43.9	17 4.3	27 55.8	28 5.4	13 32.4	5 26.8	13 3.1	17 14.0
13	11 22 25.2	23 1.0	5 55.1	1♊26.1	6 15.5	18 13.8	28 34.1	28 14.6	13 36.5	5 28.3	13 4.3	17 13.3
14	11 26 21.8	23 56.0	5 52.1	16 35.4	7 47.6	19 23.1	29 12.6	28 24.0	13 40.6	5 29.8	13 5.4	17 12.7
15	11 30 18.3	24 51.0	5 49.1	1♋33.4	9 20.4	20 32.3	29 51.1	28 33.5	13 44.5	5 31.2	13 6.4	17 12.0
16	11 34 14.9	25 45.9	5 46.1	15 56.7	10 53.9	21 41.4	0♊29.7	28 43.1	13 48.4	5 32.6	13 7.4	17 11.2
17	11 38 11.4	26 40.8	5 43.1	29 30.3	12 27.9	22 50.3	1 8.4	28 52.8	13 52.2	5 34.0	13 8.4	17 10.5
18	11 42 8.0	27 35.5	5 40.1	12♌ 9.5	14 2.7	23 59.1	1 47.2	29 2.7	13 55.9	5 35.2	13 9.4	17 9.7
19	11 46 4.5	28 30.3	5 37.1	23 58.8	15 38.0	25 7.8	2 26.1	29 12.7	13 59.5	5 36.5	13 10.3	17 8.9
20	11 50 1.1	29 25.0	5 34.1	5♍ 8.3	17 14.1	26 16.4	3 5.0	29 22.8	14 3.0	5 37.6	13 11.2	17 8.0
21	11 53 57.6	0♈19.6	5 31.1	15 50.6	18 50.9	27 24.9	3 44.1	29 33.0	14 6.4	5 38.7	13 12.1	17 7.2
22	11 57 54.2	1 14.3	5 28.1	26 19.3	20 28.4	28 33.3	4 23.2	29 43.4	14 9.7	5 39.8	13 12.9	17 6.3
23	12 1 50.7	2 8.9	5 25.1	6♎47.9	22 6.7	29 41.6	5 2.4	29 53.9	14 13.0	5 40.8	13 13.7	17 5.4
24	12 5 47.3	3 3.5	5 22.0	17 29.7	23 45.8	0♈50.0	5 41.7	0♊ 4.5	14 16.1	5 41.8	13 14.5	17 4.5
25	12 9 43.9	3 58.1	5 19.0	28 37.3	25 25.6	1 58.2	6 21.1	0 15.2	14 19.2	5 42.7	13 15.2	17 3.5
26	12 13 40.4	4 52.7	5 16.0	10♏21.8	27 6.4	3 6.4	7 .5	0 26.1	14 22.1	5 43.5	13 15.9	17 2.5
27	12 17 37.0	5 47.2	5 13.0	22 51.4	28 48.0	4 14.6	7 40.0	0 37.0	14 25.0	5 44.3	13 16.5	17 1.5
28	12 21 33.5	6 41.8	5 10.0	6♐ 8.6	0♈30.6	5 22.8	8 19.5	0 48.1	14 27.7	5 45.0	13 17.2	17 .4
29	12 25 30.1	7 36.4	5 7.0	20 7.9	2 14.0	6 31.0	8 59.2	0 59.2	14 30.3	5 45.7	13 17.7	16 59.4
30	12 29 26.6	8 31.0	5 4.0	4♑35.0	3 58.5	7 39.2	9 38.9	1 10.5	14 32.9	5 46.3	13 18.3	16 58.3
31	12 33 23.2	9 25.6	5 1.0	19 10.4	5 44.0	8 47.4	10 18.7	1 21.9	14 35.3	5 46.8	13 18.8	16 57.2

DECLINATION

DAY	EPHEM. SID. TIME (h m s)	☉	☊	☽	☿	♀	♂	♃	♄	♅	♆	♇
1	10 35 6.6	7S40.5	0S10.3	27S28.0	17S17.6	12S 6.9	19N55.1	19N13.5	22S14.8	23S35.7	22S .5	0S58.9
4	10 46 56.2	6 31.7	0 10.3	25 11.8	16 18.8	10 47.9	20 22.7	19 19.1	22 13.6	23 35.5	22 .1	0 57.2
7	10 58 45.9	5 22.1	0 10.4	9 23.3	15 8.6	9 26.2	20 49.1	19 24.8	22 12.5	23 35.4	21 59.7	0 55.4
10	11 10 35.5	4 11.8	0 10.4	11N44.2	13 46.8	8 2.3	21 14.3	19 30.8	22 11.4	23 35.3	21 59.4	0 53.6
13	11 22 25.2	3 1.0	0 10.5	26 13.1	12 13.9	6 36.5	21 38.3	19 37.0	22 10.3	23 35.2	21 59.0	0 51.7
16	11 34 14.9	1 50.0	0 10.6	26 43.8	10 29.8	5 9.1	22 1.0	19 43.3	22 9.3	23 35.1	21 58.7	0 49.9
19	11 46 4.5	0 38.9	0 10.6	15 37.2	8 34.8	3 40.5	22 22.5	19 49.7	22 8.3	23 35.0	21 58.4	0 48.0
22	11 57 54.2	0N32.2	0 10.7	0S32.9	6 29.1	2 10.9	22 42.6	19 56.2	22 7.4	23 34.9	21 58.1	0 46.1
25	12 9 43.9	1 43.1	0 10.7	16 26.4	4 13.2	0 40.7	23 1.3	20 2.9	22 6.6	23 34.9	21 57.8	0 44.3
28	12 21 33.5	2 53.7	0 10.8	26 53.2	1 47.5	0N49.7	23 18.6	20 9.5	22 5.8	23 34.9	21 57.6	0 42.4
31	12 33 23.2	4 3.8	0 10.9	26 7.3	0N46.8	2 20.2	23 34.4	20 16.3	22 5.2	23 34.9	21 57.4	0 40.5

APRIL 1989

LONGITUDE

DAY	EPHEM. SID. TIME	☉	☊	☽	☿	♀	♂	♃	♄	♅	♆	♇
	h m s	° ′	° ′	° ′	° ′	° ′	° ′	° ′	° ′	° ′	° ′	° ′
1	12 37 19.7	11♈14.7	3♓ 1.3	0♒42.4	7♈33.2	10♈14.2	12♊37.3	3♊28.0	13♑32.1	5♑18.2	12♑20.4	14♏39.8
2	12 41 16.3	12 13.9	2 58.1	14 38.7	9 33.3	11 28.6	13 14.2	3 39.1	13 34.2	5 18.6	12 20.8	14 R 38.5
3	12 45 12.8	13 13.1	2 54.9	29 .6	11 34.4	12 43.1	13 51.1	3 50.3	13 36.2	5 19.0	12 21.2	14 37.1
4	12 49 9.4	14 12.2	2 51.8	13♓45.8	13 36.6	13 57.6	14 28.0	4 1.5	13 38.1	5 19.3	12 21.6	14 35.7
5	12 53 5.9	15 11.3	2 48.6	28 49.3	15 39.8	15 12.1	15 4.9	4 12.9	13 39.9	5 19.5	12 21.9	14 34.3
6	12 57 2.5	16 10.4	2 45.4	14♈ 3.1	17 43.7	16 26.5	15 41.8	4 24.3	13 41.6	5 19.7	12 22.1	14 32.9
7	13 0 59.1	17 9.5	2 42.2	29 16.9	19 48.2	17 40.9	16 18.7	4 35.9	13 43.2	5 19.9	12 22.4	14 31.5
8	13 4 55.6	18 8.5	2 39.0	14♉20.4	21 53.2	18 55.3	16 55.7	4 47.5	13 44.7	5 19.9	12 22.6	14 30.0
9	13 8 52.2	19 7.5	2 35.9	29 4.4	23 58.5	20 9.7	17 32.6	4 59.2	13 46.1	5 20.0	12 22.8	14 28.5
10	13 12 48.7	20 6.4	2 32.7	13♊22.5	26 3.8	21 24.1	18 9.6	5 11.0	13 47.4	5 20.0	12 22.9	14 27.1
11	13 16 45.3	21 5.3	2 29.5	27 11.6	28 8.8	22 38.4	18 46.6	5 22.8	13 48.6	5 R 19.9	12 23.0	14 25.5
12	13 20 41.8	22 4.2	2 26.3	10♋31.7	0♉13.2	23 52.8	19 23.6	5 34.7	13 49.7	5 19.8	12 23.1	14 24.0
13	13 24 38.4	23 3.0	2 23.2	23 25.3	2 16.8	25 7.1	20 .6	5 46.7	13 50.8	5 19.6	12 23.1	14 22.5
14	13 28 34.9	24 1.8	2 20.0	5♌56.3	4 19.2	26 21.4	20 37.6	5 58.8	13 51.7	5 19.4	12 23.2	14 21.0
15	13 32 31.5	25 .6	2 16.8	18 9.5	6 20.0	27 35.7	21 14.6	6 11.0	13 52.6	5 19.2	12 23.2	14 19.4
16	13 36 28.0	25 59.3	2 13.6	0♍ 9.9	8 18.9	28 49.9	21 51.6	6 23.2	13 53.3	5 18.8	12 R 23.1	14 17.9
17	13 40 24.6	26 58.0	2 10.4	12 2.1	10 15.6	0♉ 4.2	22 28.6	6 35.4	13 53.9	5 18.5	12 23.0	14 16.3
18	13 44 21.1	27 56.6	2 7.3	23 50.3	12 9.8	1 18.4	23 5.7	6 47.8	13 54.4	5 18.0	12 22.9	14 14.7
19	13 48 17.7	28 55.2	2 4.1	5♎38.1	14 1.1	2 32.6	23 42.7	7 .2	13 54.9	5 17.6	12 22.7	14 13.1
20	13 52 14.3	29 53.8	2 .9	17 28.3	15 49.2	3 46.7	24 19.7	7 12.6	13 55.2	5 17.0	12 22.5	14 11.4
21	13 56 10.8	0♉52.4	1 57.7	29 23.1	17 33.9	5 .9	24 56.8	7 25.1	13 55.4	5 16.5	12 22.3	14 9.8
22	14 0 7.4	1 50.9	1 54.6	11♏24.1	19 14.9	6 15.0	25 33.8	7 37.7	13 55.6	5 15.9	12 22.1	14 8.2
23	14 4 3.9	2 49.3	1 51.4	23 32.5	20 52.1	7 29.1	26 10.8	7 50.4	13 55.6	5 15.2	12 21.8	14 6.5
24	14 8 .5	3 47.8	1 48.2	5♐49.6	22 25.2	8 43.3	26 47.9	8 3.1	13 55.6	5 14.5	12 21.5	14 4.9
25	14 11 57.0	4 46.2	1 45.0	18 16.7	23 54.2	9 57.3	27 24.9	8 15.8	13 R 55.4	5 13.7	12 21.1	14 3.2
26	14 15 53.6	5 44.6	1 41.9	0♑55.2	25 18.7	11 11.4	28 2.0	8 28.6	13 55.2	5 12.9	12 20.7	14 1.6
27	14 19 50.1	6 43.0	1 38.7	13 47.1	26 38.8	12 25.5	28 39.1	8 41.5	13 54.8	5 12.0	12 20.3	13 59.9
28	14 23 46.7	7 41.3	1 35.5	26 54.8	27 54.3	13 39.5	29 16.1	8 54.4	13 54.4	5 11.1	12 19.9	13 58.2
29	14 27 43.3	8 39.6	1 32.3	10♒20.7	29 5.2	14 53.5	29 53.2	9 7.3	13 53.8	5 10.2	12 19.4	13 56.5
30	14 31 39.8	9 37.9	1 29.1	24 6.9	0♊11.2	16 7.6	0♋30.3	9 20.4	13 53.2	5 9.2	12 18.9	13 54.8

LATITUDE

DAY	EPHEM. SID. TIME	☉	☊	☽	☿	♀	♂	♃	♄	♅	♆	♇
1	12 37 19.7	0 .0	0 .0	2 S 53.0	1 S 26.9	1 S 19.3	1 N 21.2	0 S 33.1	0 N 40.6	0 S 14.7	0 N 55.1	16 N 15.6
4	12 49 9.4	0 .0	0 .0	0 N 51.0	1 3.6	1 16.3	1 21.5	0 32.6	0 40.5	0 14.8	0 55.2	16 16.4
7	13 0 59.1	0 .0	0 .0	4 13.9	0 36.1	1 12.7	1 21.7	0 32.1	0 40.5	0 14.8	0 55.2	16 17.1
10	13 12 48.7	0 .0	0 .0	5 4.5	0 5.2	1 8.7	1 21.9	0 31.6	0 40.5	0 14.9	0 55.3	16 17.7
13	13 24 38.4	0 .0	0 .0	3 20.1	0 N 27.7	1 4.2	1 22.1	0 31.2	0 40.4	0 15.0	0 55.4	16 18.2
16	13 36 28.0	0 .0	0 .0	0 19.3	1 1.0	0 59.2	1 22.2	0 30.7	0 40.4	0 15.0	0 55.4	16 18.7
19	13 48 17.7	0 .0	0 .0	2 S 42.5	1 32.3	0 53.9	1 22.2	0 30.3	0 40.4	0 15.1	0 55.5	16 19.1
22	14 0 7.4	0 .0	0 .0	4 42.4	1 59.6	0 48.2	1 22.2	0 29.9	0 40.3	0 15.1	0 55.6	16 19.3
25	14 11 57.0	0 .0	0 .0	4 52.6	2 21.1	0 42.1	1 22.2	0 29.4	0 40.3	0 15.2	0 55.6	16 19.5
28	14 23 46.7	0 .0	0 .0	2 57.2	2 35.2	0 35.7	1 22.1	0 29.0	0 40.3	0 15.3	0 55.7	16 19.7

RIGHT ASCENSION

DAY	EPHEM. SID. TIME	☉	☊	☽	☿	♀	♂	♃	♄	♅	♆	♇
1	12 37 19.7	10♈20.3	4♓58.0	3♒35.6	7♈30.5	9♈55.6	10♊58.5	1♊33.3	14♑37.7	5♑47.3	13♑19.3	16♏56.0
2	12 41 16.3	11 14.9	4 54.9	17 38.9	9 18.1	11 3.8	11 38.4	1 44.9	14 39.9	5 47.8	13 19.7	16 R 54.9
3	12 45 12.8	12 9.7	4 51.9	1♓18.9	11 6.6	12 12.2	12 18.4	1 56.6	14 42.1	5 48.1	13 20.1	16 53.7
4	12 49 9.4	13 4.4	4 48.9	14 42.8	12 56.2	13 20.5	12 58.4	2 8.4	14 44.1	5 48.5	13 20.5	16 52.5
5	12 53 5.9	13 59.2	4 45.9	28 3.8	14 46.8	14 29.0	13 38.5	2 20.2	14 46.0	5 48.7	13 20.8	16 51.3
6	12 57 2.5	14 54.0	4 42.9	11♈38.1	16 38.3	15 37.5	14 18.6	2 32.2	14 47.9	5 48.9	13 21.1	16 50.0
7	13 0 59.1	15 48.9	4 39.9	25 40.5	18 30.7	16 46.1	14 58.8	2 44.3	14 49.6	5 49.1	13 21.3	16 48.8
8	13 4 55.6	16 43.9	4 36.8	10♉20.6	20 23.8	17 54.8	15 39.1	2 56.5	14 51.2	5 49.2	13 21.6	16 47.5
9	13 8 52.2	17 38.9	4 33.8	25 37.6	22 17.6	19 3.6	16 19.4	3 8.7	14 52.7	5 49.2	13 21.7	16 46.2
10	13 12 48.7	18 33.9	4 30.8	11♊16.2	24 11.9	20 12.6	16 59.8	3 21.1	14 54.1	5 49.2	13 21.9	16 44.9
11	13 16 45.3	19 29.0	4 27.8	26 49.7	26 6.5	21 21.6	17 40.2	3 33.5	14 55.5	5 R 49.1	13 22.0	16 43.5
12	13 20 41.8	20 24.2	4 24.8	11♋49.1	28 1.2	22 30.8	18 20.6	3 46.0	14 56.7	5 49.0	13 22.1	16 42.2
13	13 24 38.4	21 19.5	4 21.8	25 53.9	29 55.8	23 40.1	19 1.1	3 58.6	14 57.7	5 48.8	13 22.1	16 40.8
14	13 28 34.9	22 14.9	4 18.7	8♌56.9	1♉50.1	24 49.7	19 41.7	4 11.3	14 58.8	5 48.6	13 22.2	16 39.5
15	13 32 31.5	23 10.3	4 15.7	21 2.5	3 43.6	25 59.3	20 22.2	4 24.1	14 59.7	5 48.3	13 R 22.1	16 38.1
16	13 36 28.0	24 5.8	4 12.7	2♍21.8	5 36.1	27 9.1	21 2.8	4 36.9	15 .5	5 48.0	13 22.1	16 36.7
17	13 40 24.6	25 1.4	4 9.7	13 8.9	7 27.3	28 19.1	21 43.4	4 49.8	15 1.1	5 47.6	13 22.0	16 35.3
18	13 44 21.1	25 57.0	4 6.7	23 38.7	9 16.9	29 29.3	22 24.1	5 2.8	15 1.7	5 47.1	13 21.9	16 33.8
19	13 48 17.7	26 52.8	4 3.6	4♎ 5.8	11 4.6	0♉39.7	23 4.8	5 15.9	15 2.2	5 46.6	13 21.7	16 32.4
20	13 52 14.3	27 48.7	4 .6	14 44.1	12 50.1	1 50.3	23 45.5	5 29.0	15 2.5	5 46.0	13 21.5	16 30.9
21	13 56 10.8	28 44.7	3 57.6	25 46.9	14 33.0	3 1.1	24 26.2	5 42.2	15 2.8	5 45.4	13 21.2	16 29.5
22	14 0 7.4	29 40.7	3 54.6	7♏25.4	16 13.2	4 12.1	25 6.9	5 55.5	15 2.9	5 44.8	13 21.0	16 28.0
23	14 4 3.9	0♉36.9	3 51.6	19 47.9	17 50.2	5 23.3	25 47.7	6 8.9	15 3.0	5 44.0	13 20.7	16 26.5
24	14 8 .5	1 33.3	3 48.5	2♐56.8	19 23.9	6 34.8	26 28.5	6 22.3	15 R 2.9	5 43.2	13 20.3	16 25.0
25	14 11 57.0	2 29.7	3 45.5	16 46.4	20 54.1	7 46.5	27 9.3	6 35.7	15 2.7	5 42.4	13 19.9	16 23.5
26	14 15 53.6	3 26.2	3 42.5	1♑ 2.3	22 20.4	8 58.5	27 50.1	6 49.3	15 2.5	5 41.5	13 19.5	16 22.0
27	14 19 50.1	4 22.9	3 39.5	15 24.6	23 42.8	10 10.7	28 30.9	7 2.9	15 2.1	5 40.6	13 19.1	16 20.4
28	14 23 46.7	5 19.7	3 36.5	29 34.6	25 1.0	11 23.2	29 11.7	7 16.6	15 1.6	5 39.6	13 18.6	16 18.9
29	14 27 43.3	6 16.7	3 33.4	13♒20.5	26 14.8	12 35.9	29 52.5	7 30.3	15 1.0	5 38.6	13 18.1	16 17.4
30	14 31 39.8	7 13.8	3 30.4	26 40.6	27 24.2	13 48.9	0♋33.4	7 44.1	15 .3	5 37.5	13 17.6	16 15.8

DECLINATION

DAY	EPHEM. SID. TIME	☉	☊	☽	☿	♀	♂	♃	♄	♅	♆	♇
1	12 37 19.7	4 N 27.0	0 S 10.9	22 S 49.0	1 N 40.0	2 N 50.2	23 N 39.4	20 N 18.6	22 S 4.9	23 S 34.9	21 S 57.3	0 S 39.9
4	12 49 9.4	5 36.1	0 10.9	5 36.1	4 23.7	4 20.1	23 53.3	20 25.3	22 4.4	23 34.9	21 57.2	0 38.0
7	13 0 59.1	6 44.4	0 11.0	15 N 10.5	7 11.3	5 49.2	24 5.7	20 32.1	22 3.9	23 34.9	21 57.0	0 36.2
10	13 12 48.7	7 51.6	0 11.1	27 26.6	9 59.1	7 17.1	24 16.5	20 38.9	22 3.5	23 35.0	21 56.9	0 34.4
13	13 24 38.4	8 57.7	0 11.1	24 41.8	12 42.1	8 43.6	24 25.8	20 45.7	22 3.1	23 35.1	21 56.8	0 32.6
16	13 36 28.0	10 2.4	0 11.2	11 43.0	15 14.5	10 8.3	24 33.6	20 52.4	22 2.9	23 35.2	21 56.8	0 30.9
19	13 48 17.7	11 5.5	0 11.2	4 S 43.5	17 31.0	11 30.8	24 39.7	20 59.1	22 2.8	23 35.3	21 56.7	0 29.2
22	14 0 7.4	12 7.1	0 11.3	19 43.5	19 27.5	12 50.9	24 44.3	21 5.7	22 2.7	23 35.4	21 56.7	0 27.6
25	14 11 57.0	13 6.8	0 11.4	27 47.0	21 1.7	14 8.2	24 47.2	21 12.2	22 2.8	23 35.6	21 56.8	0 26.1
28	14 23 46.7	14 4.6	0 11.4	23 40.4	22 13.0	15 22.4	24 48.6	21 18.6	22 3.0	23 35.7	21 56.8	0 24.6

MAY 1989

LONGITUDE

DAY	EPHEM. SID. TIME	☉	☊	☽	☿	♀	♂	♃	♄	♅	♆	♇
	h m s	° ′	° ′	° ′	° ′	° ′	° ′	° ′	° ′	° ′	° ′	° ′
1	14 35 36.4	10♉36.2	1♓26.0	8♓14.7	1♊12.4	17♉21.6	1♋ 7.4	9♊33.4	13♑52.4	5♑ 8.1	12♑18.4	13♏53.2
2	14 39 32.9	11 34.4	1 22.8	22 43.7	2 8.7	18 35.5	1 44.5	9 46.5	13R51.6	5R 7.0	12R17.8	13R51.5
3	14 43 29.5	12 32.6	1 19.6	7♈30.8	3 .1	19 49.5	2 21.6	9 59.7	13 50.6	5 5.9	12 17.2	13 49.8
4	14 47 26.0	13 30.8	1 16.4	22 30.5	3 46.3	21 3.5	2 58.7	10 12.9	13 49.6	5 4.7	12 16.6	13 48.1
5	14 51 22.6	14 29.0	1 13.3	7♉34.6	4 27.6	22 17.5	3 35.9	10 26.1	13 48.5	5 3.6	12 16.0	13 46.4
6	14 55 19.1	15 27.2	1 10.1	22 33.3	5 3.6	23 31.4	4 13.0	10 39.4	13 47.3	5 2.3	12 15.3	13 44.7
7	14 59 15.7	16 25.3	1 6.9	7♊17.1	5 34.4	24 45.3	4 50.1	10 52.7	13 46.0	5 1.0	12 14.6	13 43.0
8	15 3 12.3	17 23.4	1 3.7	21 38.3	6 .1	25 59.2	5 27.3	11 6.1	13 44.6	4 59.6	12 13.9	13 41.4
9	15 7 8.8	18 21.4	1 .6	5♋32.3	6 20.5	27 13.1	6 4.4	11 19.5	13 43.1	4 58.2	12 13.1	13 39.7
10	15 11 5.4	19 19.4	0 57.4	18 57.5	6 35.7	28 26.9	6 41.6	11 32.9	13 41.5	4 56.8	12 12.3	13 38.0
11	15 15 1.9	20 17.4	0 54.2	1♌55.2	6 45.7	29 40.7	7 18.7	11 46.4	13 39.8	4 55.3	12 11.5	13 36.3
12	15 18 58.5	21 15.4	0 51.0	14 28.9	6 50.7	0♊54.6	7 55.8	11 59.8	13 38.1	4 53.8	12 10.6	13 34.6
13	15 22 55.0	22 13.3	0 47.8	26 43.2	6 50.7	2 8.4	8 33.0	12 13.4	13 36.2	4 52.3	12 9.7	13 33.0
14	15 26 51.6	23 11.2	0 44.7	8♍43.6	6R45.8	3 22.1	9 10.2	12 26.9	13 34.3	4 50.7	12 8.8	13 31.3
15	15 30 48.2	24 9.1	0 41.5	20 35.3	6 36.3	4 35.9	9 47.3	12 40.5	13 32.2	4 49.0	12 7.9	13 29.6
16	15 34 44.7	25 6.9	0 38.3	2♎23.5	6 22.3	5 49.6	10 24.5	12 54.1	13 30.1	4 47.4	12 6.9	13 28.0
17	15 38 41.3	26 4.7	0 35.1	14 12.6	6 4.3	7 3.4	11 1.6	13 7.7	13 27.9	4 45.7	12 6.0	13 26.4
18	15 42 37.8	27 2.5	0 32.0	26 6.3	5 42.5	8 17.1	11 38.8	13 21.4	13 25.6	4 43.9	12 4.9	13 24.7
19	15 46 34.4	28 .3	0 28.8	8♏ 7.4	5 17.4	9 30.7	12 16.0	13 35.1	13 23.2	4 42.2	12 3.9	13 23.1
20	15 50 30.9	28 58.0	0 25.6	20 18.0	4 49.4	10 44.4	12 53.1	13 48.8	13 20.8	4 40.4	12 2.9	13 21.5
21	15 54 27.5	29 55.7	0 22.4	2♐39.1	4 19.0	11 58.1	13 30.3	14 2.5	13 18.2	4 38.5	12 1.8	13 19.9
22	15 58 24.1	0♊53.4	0 19.3	15 11.2	3 46.8	13 11.7	14 7.5	14 16.2	13 15.6	4 36.7	12 .7	13 18.3
23	16 2 20.6	1 51.1	0 16.1	27 54.4	3 13.3	14 25.3	14 44.6	14 30.0	13 12.9	4 34.8	11 59.6	13 16.7
24	16 6 17.2	2 48.7	0 12.9	10♑48.8	2 39.1	15 38.9	15 21.8	14 43.8	13 10.2	4 32.8	11 58.4	13 15.1
25	16 10 13.7	3 46.3	0 9.7	23 54.7	2 4.8	16 52.5	15 59.0	14 57.5	13 7.3	4 30.9	11 57.2	13 13.6
26	16 14 10.3	4 44.0	0 6.5	7♒12.6	1 31.1	18 6.1	16 36.2	15 11.4	13 4.5	4 28.9	11 56.1	13 12.1
27	16 18 6.8	5 41.6	0 3.4	20 43.6	0 58.5	19 19.7	17 13.4	15 25.2	13 1.5	4 26.9	11 54.9	13 10.5
28	16 22 3.4	6 39.2	0 .2	4♓28.6	0 27.5	20 33.2	17 50.6	15 39.1	12 58.4	4 24.9	11 53.6	13 9.0
29	16 25 60.0	7 36.8	29♒57.0	18 28.7	29♉58.6	21 46.8	18 27.8	15 52.9	12 55.3	4 22.8	11 52.4	13 7.5
30	16 29 56.5	8 34.3	29 53.8	2♈43.6	29 32.4	23 .3	19 5.0	16 6.8	12 52.1	4 20.7	11 51.1	13 6.0
31	16 33 53.1	9 31.8	29 50.7	17 11.9	29 9.2	24 13.8	19 42.2	16 20.7	12 48.8	4 18.6	11 49.8	13 4.6

LATITUDE

DAY	EPHEM. SID. TIME	☉	☊	☽	☿	♀	♂	♃	♄	♅	♆	♇
1	14 35 36.4	0 .0	0 .0	0N31.0	2N41.0	0S29.1	1N22.1	0S28.6	0N40.2	0S15.3	0N55.7	16N19.7
4	14 47 26.0	0 .0	0 .0	3 52.9	2 37.6	0 22.2	1 21.9	0 28.3	0 40.2	0 15.4	0 55.8	16 19.6
7	14 59 15.7	0 .0	0 .0	5 .2	2 24.3	0 15.2	1 21.8	0 27.9	0 40.1	0 15.5	0 55.8	16 19.4
10	15 11 5.4	0 .0	0 .0	3 24.2	2 .9	0 8.0	1 21.6	0 27.5	0 40.0	0 15.5	0 55.9	16 19.2
13	15 22 55.0	0 .0	0 .0	0 24.0	1 27.5	0 .7	1 21.4	0 27.2	0 40.0	0 15.6	0 55.9	16 18.8
16	15 34 44.7	0 .0	0 .0	2S36.8	0 45.3	0N 6.6	1 21.1	0 26.8	0 39.9	0 15.6	0 56.0	16 18.4
19	15 46 34.4	0 .0	0 .0	4 37.1	0S 3.6	0 13.9	1 20.8	0 26.5	0 39.8	0 15.7	0 56.0	16 17.9
22	15 58 24.1	0 .0	0 .0	4 49.6	0 56.0	0 21.2	1 20.5	0 26.2	0 39.7	0 15.7	0 56.1	16 17.3
25	16 10 13.7	0 .0	0 .0	2 56.3	1 47.7	0 28.5	1 20.2	0 25.8	0 39.6	0 15.8	0 56.1	16 16.6
28	16 22 3.4	0 .0	0 .0	0N25.9	2 34.5	0 35.6	1 19.9	0 25.5	0 39.5	0 15.8	0 56.1	16 15.8
31	16 33 53.1	0 .0	0 .0	3 43.5	3 13.0	0 42.5	1 19.5	0 25.2	0 39.3	0 15.9	0 56.2	16 15.0

RIGHT ASCENSION

DAY	EPHEM. SID. TIME	☉	☊	☽	☿	♀	♂	♃	♄	♅	♆	♇
1	14 35 36.4	8♉11.0	3♓27.4	9♓41.8	28♉28.9	15♉ 2.2	1♋14.2	7♊57.9	14♑59.6	5♑36.3	13♑17.0	16♏14.3
2	14 39 32.9	9 8.3	3 24.4	22 37.5	29 28.7	16 15.7	1 55.1	8 11.8	14R58.7	5R35.2	13R16.4	16R12.7
3	14 43 29.5	10 5.8	3 21.3	5♈44.6	0♊23.7	17 29.6	2 35.9	8 25.8	14 57.7	5 33.9	13 15.7	16 11.1
4	14 47 26.0	11 3.5	3 18.3	19 20.4	1 13.6	18 43.7	3 16.8	8 39.8	14 56.6	5 32.6	13 15.1	16 9.6
5	14 51 22.6	12 1.3	3 15.3	3♉39.1	1 58.4	19 58.1	3 57.7	8 53.9	14 55.4	5 31.3	13 14.4	16 8.0
6	14 55 19.1	12 59.2	3 12.3	18 46.4	2 37.9	21 12.8	4 38.5	9 8.0	14 54.1	5 30.0	13 13.7	16 6.5
7	14 59 15.7	13 57.3	3 9.2	4♊33.1	3 12.0	22 27.7	5 19.4	9 22.2	14 52.7	5 28.5	13 12.9	16 4.9
8	15 3 12.3	14 55.4	3 6.2	20 33.8	3 40.8	23 43.0	6 .2	9 36.4	14 51.2	5 27.1	13 12.1	16 3.3
9	15 7 8.8	15 53.8	3 3.2	6♋13.8	4 4.2	24 58.5	6 41.0	9 50.6	14 49.6	5 25.6	13 11.3	16 1.7
10	15 11 5.4	16 52.3	3 .1	21 3.1	4 22.2	26 14.3	7 21.8	10 4.9	14 47.9	5 24.0	13 10.4	16 .2
11	15 15 1.9	17 50.9	2 57.1	4♌46.4	4 34.9	27 30.3	8 2.6	10 19.3	14 46.1	5 22.4	13 9.5	15 58.6
12	15 18 58.5	18 49.6	2 54.1	17 23.6	4 42.2	28 46.6	8 43.4	10 33.6	14 44.2	5 20.7	13 8.6	15 57.0
13	15 22 55.0	19 48.5	2 51.1	29 5.0	4 44.4	0♊ 3.2	9 24.1	10 48.0	14 42.2	5 19.0	13 7.7	15 55.5
14	15 26 51.6	20 47.6	2 48.0	10♍ 5.6	4R41.6	1 20.1	10 4.9	11 2.5	14 40.1	5 17.3	13 6.7	15 53.9
15	15 30 48.2	21 46.7	2 45.0	20 41.6	4 34.1	2 37.2	10 45.5	11 17.0	14 37.9	5 15.5	13 5.7	15 52.3
16	15 34 44.7	22 46.0	2 42.0	1♎ 9.2	4 22.0	3 54.6	11 26.2	11 31.5	14 35.6	5 13.7	13 4.7	15 50.8
17	15 38 41.3	23 45.5	2 38.9	11 43.9	4 5.8	5 12.2	12 6.9	11 46.1	14 33.3	5 11.9	13 3.6	15 49.2
18	15 42 37.8	24 45.1	2 35.9	22 40.1	3 45.9	6 30.1	12 47.5	12 .7	14 30.8	5 10.0	13 2.5	15 47.7
19	15 46 34.4	25 44.8	2 32.9	4♏10.9	3 22.5	7 48.2	13 28.0	12 15.3	14 28.3	5 8.0	13 1.4	15 46.1
20	15 50 30.9	26 44.6	2 29.9	16 26.3	2 56.3	9 6.6	14 8.6	12 30.0	14 25.6	5 6.1	13 .3	15 44.6
21	15 54 27.5	27 44.6	2 26.8	29 30.5	2 27.8	10 25.1	14 49.1	12 44.6	14 22.9	5 4.1	12 59.1	15 43.0
22	15 58 24.1	28 44.7	2 23.8	13♐19.3	1 57.6	11 43.9	15 29.5	12 59.3	14 20.1	5 2.0	12 58.0	15 41.5
23	16 2 20.6	29 45.0	2 20.8	27 38.4	1 26.1	13 2.9	16 10.0	13 14.1	14 17.2	4 60.0	12 56.7	15 40.0
24	16 6 17.2	0♊45.4	2 17.7	12♑ 6.3	0 54.1	14 22.0	16 50.3	13 28.8	14 14.2	4 57.9	12 55.5	15 38.5
25	16 10 13.7	1 45.9	2 14.7	26 21.1	0 22.0	15 41.4	17 30.7	13 43.6	14 11.2	4 55.7	12 54.2	15 37.0
26	16 14 10.3	2 46.6	2 11.7	10♒ 7.9	29♉50.6	17 1.0	18 11.0	13 58.5	14 8.1	4 53.6	12 53.0	15 35.5
27	16 18 6.8	3 47.4	2 8.6	23 22.7	29 20.3	18 20.7	18 51.3	14 13.3	14 4.9	4 51.4	12 51.7	15 34.1
28	16 22 3.4	4 48.3	2 5.6	6♓11.0	28 51.6	19 40.5	19 31.5	14 28.2	14 1.6	4 49.2	12 50.4	15 32.6
29	16 25 60.0	5 49.3	2 2.6	18 45.9	28 25.0	21 .5	20 11.7	14 43.1	13 58.2	4 46.9	12 49.0	15 31.1
30	16 29 56.5	6 50.4	1 59.5	1♈24.2	28 1.0	22 20.6	20 51.8	14 58.0	13 54.8	4 44.6	12 47.7	15 29.7
31	16 33 53.1	7 51.7	1 56.5	14 24.3	27 40.0	23 40.9	21 31.9	15 12.9	13 51.3	4 42.3	12 46.3	15 28.2

DECLINATION

DAY	EPHEM. SID. TIME	☉	☊	☽	☿	♀	♂	♃	♄	♅	♆	♇
1	14 35 36.4	15N .3	0S11.5	7S60.0	23N 1.8	16N33.1	24N48.3	21N24.9	22S 3.2	23S35.9	21S56.9	0S23.2
4	14 47 26.0	15 53.9	0 11.5	12N21.6	23 29.2	17 40.0	24 46.5	21 31.1	22 3.5	23 36.1	21 57.0	0 21.8
7	14 59 15.7	16 45.0	0 11.6	26 27.7	23 36.2	18 42.9	24 43.0	21 37.1	22 4.0	23 36.3	21 57.1	0 20.6
10	15 11 5.4	17 33.6	0 11.7	25 28.2	23 23.9	19 41.2	24 37.9	21 43.0	22 4.5	23 36.5	21 57.3	0 19.4
13	15 22 55.0	18 19.6	0 11.7	12 59.1	22 53.6	20 34.8	24 31.2	21 48.8	22 5.1	23 36.8	21 57.5	0 18.4
16	15 34 44.7	19 2.8	0 11.8	3S20.9	22 7.2	21 23.4	24 22.9	21 54.3	22 5.8	23 37.0	21 57.7	0 17.4
19	15 46 34.4	19 43.1	0 11.8	18 35.0	21 7.6	22 6.6	24 13.1	21 59.7	22 6.6	23 37.2	21 57.9	0 16.6
22	15 58 24.1	20 20.3	0 11.9	27 24.9	19 59.6	22 44.2	24 1.7	22 5.0	22 7.4	23 37.5	21 58.2	0 15.8
25	16 10 13.7	20 54.5	0 12.0	24 13.2	18 49.3	23 16.0	23 48.8	22 10.0	22 8.3	23 37.7	21 58.4	0 15.1
28	16 22 3.4	21 25.4	0 12.0	9 28.1	17 43.9	23 41.8	23 34.3	22 14.8	22 9.3	23 38.0	21 58.7	0 14.6
31	16 33 53.1	21 53.0	0 12.1	10N11.7	16 49.8	24 1.5	23 18.4	22 19.4	22 10.4	23 38.2	21 59.0	0 14.2

JUNE 1989

LONGITUDE

DAY	EPHEM. SID. TIME	☉	☊	☽	☿	♀	♂	♃	♄	♅	♆	♇
	h m s	° ′	° ′	° ′	° ′	° ′	° ′	° ′	° ′	° ′	° ′	° ′
1	16 37 49.6	10♊29.4	29♒47.5	1♉50.0	28♉49.4	25♊27.3	20♋19.4	16♊34.6	12♑45.4	4♑16.4	11♑48.5	13♏ 3.1
2	16 41 46.2	11 26.9	29 44.3	16 32.1	28 R 33.3	26 40.8	20 56.7	16 48.5	12 R 42.0	4 R 14.3	11 R 47.2	13 R 1.7
3	16 45 42.7	12 24.4	29 41.1	1♊11.0	28 21.2	27 54.2	21 33.9	17 2.4	12 38.6	4 12.1	11 45.8	13 .3
4	16 49 39.3	13 21.9	29 38.0	15 39.1	28 13.2	29 7.7	22 11.1	17 16.3	12 35.0	4 9.8	11 44.5	12 58.9
5	16 53 35.9	14 19.3	29 34.8	29 49.6	28 9.6	0♋21.1	22 48.4	17 30.2	12 31.5	4 7.6	11 43.1	12 57.5
6	16 57 32.4	15 16.8	29 31.6	13♋37.4	28 D 10.3	1 34.6	23 25.6	17 44.1	12 27.8	4 5.3	11 41.7	12 56.1
7	17 1 29.0	16 14.2	29 28.4	27 .1	28 15.5	2 48.0	24 2.9	17 58.0	12 24.1	4 3.1	11 40.3	12 54.8
8	17 5 25.5	17 11.7	29 25.3	9♌57.9	28 25.2	4 1.4	24 40.2	18 11.9	12 20.4	4 .8	11 38.8	12 53.4
9	17 9 22.1	18 9.1	29 22.1	22 33.0	28 39.4	5 14.7	25 17.4	18 25.8	12 16.5	3 58.5	11 37.4	12 52.1
10	17 13 18.7	19 6.4	29 18.9	4♍49.3	28 58.1	6 28.1	25 54.7	18 39.7	12 12.7	3 56.1	11 35.9	12 50.9
11	17 17 15.2	20 3.8	29 15.7	16 51.5	29 21.2	7 41.4	26 32.0	18 53.6	12 8.8	3 53.8	11 34.4	12 49.6
12	17 21 11.8	21 1.1	29 12.5	28 45.0	29 48.7	8 54.7	27 9.3	19 7.5	12 4.8	3 51.4	11 33.0	12 48.4
13	17 25 8.3	21 58.5	29 9.4	10♎34.9	0♊20.5	10 8.0	27 46.5	19 21.4	12 .8	3 49.1	11 31.5	12 47.2
14	17 29 4.9	22 55.8	29 6.2	22 26.5	0 56.6	11 21.3	28 23.8	19 35.3	11 56.8	3 46.7	11 30.0	12 46.0
15	17 33 1.5	23 53.1	29 3.0	4♏24.0	1 36.9	12 34.5	29 1.1	19 49.2	11 52.7	3 44.3	11 28.4	12 44.8
16	17 36 58.0	24 50.4	28 59.8	16 31.3	2 21.3	13 47.8	29 38.5	20 3.1	11 48.7	3 42.0	11 26.9	12 43.7
17	17 40 54.6	25 47.7	28 56.7	28 50.9	3 9.7	15 1.0	0♌15.8	20 17.0	11 44.5	3 39.6	11 25.4	12 42.6
18	17 44 51.1	26 45.0	28 53.5	11♐24.5	4 2.0	16 14.2	0 53.1	20 30.9	11 40.3	3 37.1	11 23.9	12 41.5
19	17 48 47.7	27 42.2	28 50.3	24 12.7	4 58.2	17 27.4	1 30.4	20 44.7	11 36.1	3 34.7	11 22.3	12 40.5
20	17 52 44.2	28 39.5	28 47.1	7♑15.1	5 58.3	18 40.6	2 7.7	20 58.5	11 31.9	3 32.3	11 20.7	12 39.4
21	17 56 40.8	29 36.7	28 44.0	20 30.6	7 2.1	19 53.7	2 45.0	21 12.3	11 27.6	3 29.9	11 19.1	12 38.4
22	18 0 37.4	0♋33.9	28 40.8	3♒57.9	8 9.6	21 6.8	3 22.3	21 26.1	11 23.3	3 27.4	11 17.6	12 37.4
23	18 4 33.9	1 31.2	28 37.6	17 35.6	9 20.7	22 19.9	3 59.7	21 39.9	11 19.0	3 25.0	11 16.0	12 36.5
24	18 8 30.5	2 28.4	28 34.4	1♓22.5	10 35.4	23 33.0	4 37.0	21 53.7	11 14.7	3 22.5	11 14.4	12 35.5
25	18 12 27.0	3 25.6	28 31.3	15 17.7	11 53.7	24 46.1	5 14.3	22 7.4	11 10.3	3 20.1	11 12.8	12 34.6
26	18 16 23.6	4 22.8	28 28.1	29 20.7	13 15.5	25 59.1	5 51.7	22 21.2	11 5.9	3 17.7	11 11.2	12 33.8
27	18 20 20.2	5 20.0	28 24.9	13♈30.4	14 40.8	27 12.2	6 29.1	22 34.9	11 1.5	3 15.2	11 9.6	12 32.9
28	18 24 16.7	6 17.3	28 21.7	27 45.5	16 9.6	28 25.2	7 6.4	22 48.6	10 57.1	3 12.8	11 7.9	12 32.1
29	18 28 13.3	7 14.5	28 18.5	12♉ 3.5	17 41.7	29 38.2	7 43.8	23 2.2	10 52.7	3 10.3	11 6.3	12 31.3
30	18 32 9.8	8 11.7	28 15.4	26 20.9	19 17.1	0♌51.2	8 21.2	23 15.9	10 48.3	3 7.9	11 4.7	12 30.6

LATITUDE

DAY	EPHEM. SID. TIME	☉	☊	☽	☿	♀	♂	♃	♄	♅	♆	♇
1	16 37 49.6	0 .0	0 .0	4N27.4	3S23.6	0N44.7	1N19.4	0S25.1	0N39.3	0S15.9	0N56.2	16N14.7
4	16 49 39.3	0 .0	0 .0	4 48.4	3 48.3	0 51.3	1 18.9	0 24.8	0 39.2	0 15.9	0 56.2	16 13.7
7	17 1 29.0	0 .0	0 .0	2 38.3	4 2.0	0 57.7	1 18.5	0 24.5	0 39.0	0 16.0	0 56.2	16 12.7
10	17 13 18.7	0 .0	0 .0	0S34.3	4 5.4	1 3.7	1 18.0	0 24.3	0 38.8	0 16.0	0 56.2	16 11.6
13	17 25 8.3	0 .0	0 .0	3 24.9	3 59.5	1 9.3	1 17.6	0 24.0	0 38.7	0 16.1	0 56.2	16 10.4
16	17 36 58.0	0 .0	0 .0	4 57.4	3 45.7	1 14.6	1 17.1	0 23.7	0 38.5	0 16.1	0 56.2	16 9.2
19	17 48 47.7	0 .0	0 .0	4 31.6	3 25.1	1 19.4	1 16.5	0 23.5	0 38.3	0 16.1	0 56.2	16 7.9
22	18 0 37.4	0 .0	0 .0	2 .7	2 58.9	1 23.7	1 16.0	0 23.2	0 38.1	0 16.2	0 56.2	16 6.6
25	18 12 27.0	0 .0	0 .0	1N36.0	2 28.2	1 27.6	1 15.4	0 23.0	0 37.9	0 16.2	0 56.2	16 5.2
28	18 24 16.7	0 .0	0 .0	4 28.0	1 54.2	1 30.8	1 14.8	0 22.7	0 37.6	0 16.2	0 56.2	16 3.7

RIGHT ASCENSION

DAY	EPHEM. SID. TIME	☉	☊	☽	☿	♀	♂	♃	♄	♅	♆	♇
1	16 37 49.6	8♊53.0	1♓53.4	28♈ 3.7	27♉22.2	25♊ 1.2	22♋11.9	15♊27.8	13♑47.7	4♑40.0	12♑44.9	15♏26.8
2	16 41 46.2	9 54.5	1 50.4	12♉33.9	27 R 8.0	26 21.6	22 51.9	15 42.7	13 R 44.1	4 R 37.6	12 R 43.4	15 R 25.4
3	16 45 42.7	10 56.0	1 47.4	27 55.1	26 57.6	27 42.1	23 31.9	15 57.7	13 40.3	4 35.2	12 42.0	15 24.0
4	16 49 39.3	11 57.7	1 44.3	13♊50.6	26 51.1	29 2.6	24 11.7	16 12.6	13 36.5	4 32.8	12 40.5	15 22.6
5	16 53 35.9	12 59.4	1 41.3	29 48.2	26 48.7	0♋23.2	24 51.6	16 27.6	13 32.7	4 30.3	12 39.0	15 21.3
6	16 57 32.4	14 1.2	1 38.3	15♋12.0	26 D 50.4	1 43.8	25 31.3	16 42.6	13 28.8	4 27.9	12 37.5	15 19.9
7	17 1 29.0	15 3.1	1 35.2	29 36.2	26 56.5	3 4.4	26 11.1	16 57.6	13 24.8	4 25.4	12 36.0	15 18.6
8	17 5 25.5	16 5.1	1 32.2	12♌52.0	27 6.8	4 25.0	26 50.7	17 12.6	13 20.8	4 22.9	12 34.5	15 17.3
9	17 9 22.1	17 7.1	1 29.1	25 4.6	27 21.4	5 45.5	27 30.3	17 27.6	13 16.7	4 20.4	12 32.9	15 16.0
10	17 13 18.7	18 9.2	1 26.1	6♍27.5	27 40.3	7 6.1	28 9.9	17 42.6	13 12.5	4 17.8	12 31.3	15 14.7
11	17 17 15.2	19 11.4	1 23.1	17 16.9	28 3.6	8 26.5	28 49.3	17 57.6	13 8.3	4 15.3	12 29.8	15 13.4
12	17 21 11.8	20 13.6	1 20.0	27 49.8	28 31.1	9 46.9	29 28.8	18 12.6	13 4.1	4 12.7	12 28.2	15 12.2
13	17 25 8.3	21 15.8	1 17.0	8♎22.6	29 2.8	11 7.2	0♌ 8.1	18 27.6	12 59.8	4 10.1	12 26.6	15 10.9
14	17 29 4.9	22 18.1	1 13.9	19 11.2	29 38.7	12 27.4	0 47.4	18 42.6	12 55.5	4 7.5	12 24.9	15 9.7
15	17 33 1.5	23 20.4	1 10.9	0♏30.2	0♊18.8	13 47.5	1 26.6	18 57.5	12 51.1	4 4.9	12 23.3	15 8.5
16	17 36 58.0	24 22.7	1 7.9	12 31.9	1 3.1	15 7.5	2 5.8	19 12.6	12 46.7	4 2.4	12 21.7	15 7.4
17	17 40 54.6	25 25.1	1 4.8	25 24.2	1 51.5	16 27.3	2 44.9	19 27.6	12 42.3	3 59.7	12 20.0	15 6.3
18	17 44 51.1	26 27.5	1 1.8	9♐ 6.6	2 43.9	17 46.9	3 24.0	19 42.5	12 37.8	3 57.1	12 18.4	15 5.2
19	17 48 47.7	27 29.8	0 58.7	23 28.3	3 40.4	19 6.4	4 2.9	19 57.5	12 33.2	3 54.5	12 16.7	15 4.0
20	17 52 44.2	28 32.2	0 55.7	8♑ 8.1	4 41.0	20 25.6	4 41.8	20 12.4	12 28.7	3 51.8	12 15.0	15 3.0
21	17 56 40.8	29 34.6	0 52.7	22 41.2	5 45.6	21 44.7	5 20.6	20 27.4	12 24.1	3 49.1	12 13.3	15 1.9
22	18 0 37.4	0♋37.0	0 49.6	6♒47.7	6 54.2	23 3.6	5 59.4	20 42.3	12 19.5	3 46.5	12 11.6	15 .9
23	18 4 33.9	1 39.4	0 46.6	20 18.5	8 6.8	24 22.2	6 38.1	20 57.2	12 14.8	3 43.8	12 9.9	14 59.8
24	18 8 30.5	2 41.7	0 43.5	3♓15.8	9 23.5	25 40.6	7 16.7	21 12.1	12 10.1	3 41.2	12 8.2	14 58.9
25	18 12 27.0	3 44.1	0 40.5	15 50.5	10 44.2	26 58.8	7 55.3	21 27.0	12 5.5	3 38.5	12 6.5	14 57.9
26	18 16 23.6	4 46.4	0 37.4	28 18.6	12 9.0	28 16.7	8 33.8	21 41.9	12 .7	3 35.8	12 4.7	14 56.9
27	18 20 20.2	5 48.7	0 34.4	10♈58.2	13 37.8	29 34.4	9 12.2	21 56.7	11 56.0	3 33.2	12 3.0	14 56.0
28	18 24 16.7	6 50.9	0 31.3	24 7.2	15 10.7	0♌51.8	9 50.6	22 11.6	11 51.3	3 30.5	12 1.3	14 55.1
29	18 28 13.3	7 53.1	0 28.3	8♉ .2	16 47.6	2 8.9	10 28.9	22 26.4	11 46.5	3 27.8	11 59.5	14 54.3
30	18 32 9.8	8 55.3	0 25.2	22 43.5	18 28.6	3 25.8	11 7.1	22 41.2	11 41.8	3 25.2	11 57.8	14 53.4

DECLINATION

DAY	EPHEM. SID. TIME	☉	☊	☽	☿	♀	♂	♃	♄	♅	♆	♇
1	16 37 49.6	22N 1.4	0S12.1	16N17.3	16N35.2	24N 6.6	23N12.7	22N20.9	22S10.7	23S38.3	21S59.1	0S14.1
4	16 49 39.3	22 24.4	0 12.2	27 26.9	16 3.3	24 17.7	22 54.8	22 25.3	22 11.8	23 38.6	21 59.5	0 13.8
7	17 1 29.0	22 43.9	0 12.2	23 20.9	15 50.5	24 22.5	22 35.5	22 29.4	22 13.0	23 38.8	21 59.8	0 13.6
10	17 13 18.7	22 59.7	0 12.3	9 12.7	15 56.3	24 20.7	22 14.7	22 33.3	22 14.2	23 39.1	22 .2	0 13.6
13	17 25 8.3	23 11.9	0 12.3	7S19.8	16 19.2	24 12.5	21 52.6	22 37.0	22 15.5	23 39.3	22 .6	0 13.7
16	17 36 58.0	23 20.5	0 12.4	21 31.4	16 56.8	23 57.9	21 29.1	22 40.5	22 16.7	23 39.5	22 .9	0 13.9
19	17 48 47.7	23 25.3	0 12.4	27 50.3	17 46.0	23 36.9	21 4.3	22 43.8	22 18.0	23 39.8	22 1.3	0 14.2
22	18 0 37.4	23 26.5	0 12.5	21 13.2	18 43.6	23 9.8	20 38.2	22 46.8	22 19.3	23 40.0	22 1.8	0 14.6
25	18 12 27.0	23 23.9	0 12.6	4 19.2	19 46.2	22 36.7	20 10.8	22 49.6	22 20.6	23 40.2	22 2.2	0 15.2
28	18 24 16.7	23 17.6	0 12.6	14N50.6	20 49.8	21 57.8	19 42.3	22 52.2	22 22.0	23 40.4	22 2.6	0 15.9

JULY 1989

LONGITUDE

DAY	EPHEM. SID. TIME h m s	☉ ° ′	☊ ° ′	☽ ° ′	☿ ° ′	♀ ° ′	♂ ° ′	♃ ° ′	♄ ° ′	♅ ° ′	♆ ° ′	♇ ° ′
1	18 36 6.4	9♋ 9.0	28♒12.2	10♊33.3	20♊55.9	2♌ 4.2	8♌58.6	23♊29.5	10♑43.8	3♑ 5.5	11♑ 3.1	12♏29.8
2	18 40 3.0	10 6.2	28 9.0	24 36.1	22 37.9	3 17.1	9 36.1	23 43.1	10R39.4	3R 3.0	11R 1.5	12R29.1
3	18 43 59.5	11 3.4	28 5.8	8♋24.6	24 23.0	4 30.0	10 13.5	23 56.7	10 35.0	3 .6	10 59.8	12 28.5
4	18 47 56.1	12 .6	28 2.7	21 55.3	26 11.2	5 43.0	10 50.9	24 10.2	10 30.5	2 58.2	10 58.2	12 27.8
5	18 51 52.6	12 57.9	27 59.5	5♌ 6.1	28 2.3	6 55.8	11 28.4	24 23.7	10 26.1	2 55.8	10 56.6	12 27.2
6	18 55 49.2	13 55.1	27 56.3	17 56.7	29 56.3	8 8.7	12 5.8	24 37.2	10 21.7	2 53.4	10 55.0	12 26.6
7	18 59 45.7	14 52.4	27 53.1	0♍28.3	1♋52.9	9 21.6	12 43.3	24 50.7	10 17.3	2 51.1	10 53.4	12 26.1
8	19 3 42.3	15 49.6	27 50.0	12 43.5	3 51.8	10 34.4	13 20.8	25 4.1	10 12.9	2 48.7	10 51.8	12 25.6
9	19 7 38.9	16 46.8	27 46.8	24 46.1	5 53.0	11 47.2	13 58.3	25 17.5	10 8.5	2 46.4	10 50.2	12 25.2
10	19 11 35.4	17 44.0	27 43.6	6♎40.6	7 56.2	13 .0	14 35.8	25 30.8	10 4.1	2 44.1	10 48.5	12 24.7
11	19 15 32.0	18 41.2	27 40.4	18 31.9	10 1.0	14 12.8	15 13.3	25 44.1	9 59.7	2 41.7	10 46.9	12 24.3
12	19 19 28.5	19 38.4	27 37.3	0♏24.9	12 7.3	15 25.5	15 50.8	25 57.4	9 55.4	2 39.4	10 45.3	12 23.9
13	19 23 25.1	20 35.6	27 34.1	12 24.4	14 14.7	16 38.2	16 28.3	26 10.6	9 51.1	2 37.1	10 43.7	12 23.6
14	19 27 21.7	21 32.9	27 30.9	24 35.0	16 22.9	17 50.8	17 5.9	26 23.8	9 46.8	2 34.9	10 42.1	12 23.2
15	19 31 18.2	22 30.1	27 27.7	7♐ .0	18 31.6	19 3.5	17 43.4	26 36.9	9 42.5	2 32.6	10 40.6	12 23.0
16	19 35 14.8	23 27.3	27 24.6	19 42.3	20 40.5	20 16.1	18 21.0	26 50.0	9 38.2	2 30.4	10 39.0	12 22.7
17	19 39 11.3	24 24.5	27 21.4	2♑43.1	22 49.4	21 28.7	18 58.5	27 3.0	9 34.0	2 28.2	10 37.4	12 22.5
18	19 43 7.9	25 21.7	27 18.2	16 2.6	24 57.9	22 41.2	19 36.1	27 16.0	9 29.8	2 26.0	10 35.9	12 22.3
19	19 47 4.4	26 19.0	27 15.0	29 39.3	27 5.8	23 53.7	20 13.7	27 29.0	9 25.7	2 23.8	10 34.3	12 22.1
20	19 51 1.0	27 16.2	27 11.8	13♒30.9	29 13.0	25 6.2	20 51.3	27 41.9	9 21.6	2 21.7	10 32.8	12 22.0
21	19 54 57.6	28 13.5	27 8.7	27 34.1	1♌19.2	26 18.7	21 28.9	27 54.8	9 17.5	2 19.6	10 31.2	12 21.9
22	19 58 54.1	29 10.7	27 5.5	11♓45.3	3 24.3	27 31.1	22 6.5	28 7.6	9 13.4	2 17.5	10 29.7	12 21.9
23	20 2 50.7	0♌ 8.0	27 2.3	26 1.0	5 28.1	28 43.5	22 44.1	28 20.3	9 9.5	2 15.4	10 28.2	12 21.9
24	20 6 47.2	1 5.3	26 59.1	10♈18.1	7 30.6	29 55.9	23 21.7	28 33.0	9 5.5	2 13.4	10 26.7	12 21.9
25	20 10 43.8	2 2.6	26 56.0	24 33.6	9 31.6	1♍ 8.2	23 59.4	28 45.7	9 1.6	2 11.3	10 25.2	12 21.9
26	20 14 40.3	2 59.9	26 52.8	8♉45.3	11 31.1	2 20.6	24 37.1	28 58.3	8 57.7	2 9.4	10 23.8	12D22.0
27	20 18 36.9	3 57.2	26 49.6	22 50.9	13 29.0	3 32.9	25 14.8	29 10.8	8 53.9	2 7.4	10 22.3	12 22.2
28	20 22 33.5	4 54.6	26 46.4	6♊48.6	15 25.3	4 45.2	25 52.5	29 23.4	8 50.2	2 5.5	10 20.9	12 22.4
29	20 26 30.0	5 52.0	26 43.3	20 36.3	17 20.0	5 57.4	26 30.2	29 35.8	8 46.5	2 3.6	10 19.5	12 22.5
30	20 30 26.6	6 49.4	26 40.1	4♋12.2	19 13.1	7 9.6	27 8.0	29 48.2	8 42.8	2 1.8	10 18.1	12 22.8
31	20 34 23.1	7 46.8	26 36.9	17 34.6	21 4.5	8 21.8	27 45.7	0♋ .5	8 39.2	1 59.9	10 16.7	12 23.0

LATITUDE

DAY	SID. TIME	☉	☊	☽	☿	♀	♂	♃	♄	♅	♆	♇
1	18 36 6.4	0 .0	0 .0	4N58.5	1S18.1	1N33.5	1N14.2	0S22.5	0N37.4	0S16.2	0N56.1	16N 2.2
4	18 47 56.1	0 .0	0 .0	2 55.3	0 41.2	1 35.6	1 13.6	0 22.3	0 37.1	0 16.3	0 56.1	16 .7
7	18 59 45.7	0 .0	0 .0	0S22.2	0 5.3	1 37.1	1 13.0	0 22.0	0 36.9	0 16.3	0 56.1	15 59.1
10	19 11 35.4	0 .0	0 .0	3 21.4	0N27.9	1 37.9	1 12.3	0 21.8	0 36.6	0 16.3	0 56.0	15 57.5
13	19 23 25.1	0 .0	0 .0	5 2.2	0 56.7	1 38.1	1 11.6	0 21.6	0 36.3	0 16.3	0 56.0	15 55.8
16	19 35 14.8	0 .0	0 .0	4 45.8	1 19.6	1 37.6	1 10.9	0 21.4	0 36.0	0 16.3	0 56.0	15 54.2
19	19 47 4.4	0 .0	0 .0	2 18.9	1 35.8	1 36.4	1 10.2	0 21.2	0 35.7	0 16.3	0 55.9	15 52.5
22	19 58 54.1	0 .0	0 .0	1N25.8	1 45.0	1 34.5	1 9.4	0 21.0	0 35.4	0 16.3	0 55.8	15 50.8
25	20 10 43.8	0 .0	0 .0	4 28.5	1 47.6	1 31.9	1 8.7	0 20.8	0 35.0	0 16.4	0 55.8	15 49.0
28	20 22 33.5	0 .0	0 .0	5 8.9	1 44.3	1 28.6	1 7.9	0 20.6	0 34.7	0 16.4	0 55.7	15 47.3
31	20 34 23.1	0 .0	0 .0	3 15.3	1 35.7	1 24.7	1 7.1	0 20.4	0 34.4	0 16.4	0 55.6	15 45.6

RIGHT ASCENSION

DAY	SID. TIME	☉	☊	☽	☿	♀	♂	♃	♄	♅	♆	♇
1	18 36 6.4	9♋57.4	0♓22.2	8♊ 9.5	20♊13.6	4♌42.3	11♌45.3	22♊55.9	11♑37.0	3♑22.5	11♑56.1	14♏52.6
2	18 40 3.0	10 59.4	0 19.1	23 54.6	22 2.6	5 58.6	12 23.4	23 10.7	11R32.2	3R19.9	11R54.3	14R51.8
3	18 43 59.5	12 1.4	0 16.1	9♋25.5	23 55.4	7 14.5	13 1.4	23 25.4	11 27.4	3 17.3	11 52.6	14 51.0
4	18 47 56.1	13 3.3	0 13.0	24 11.8	25 52.0	8 30.1	13 39.4	23 40.1	11 22.6	3 14.6	11 50.8	14 50.3
5	18 51 52.6	14 5.2	0 10.0	7♌56.5	27 52.2	9 45.5	14 17.3	23 54.7	11 17.9	3 12.0	11 49.1	14 49.6
6	18 55 49.2	15 6.9	0 6.9	20 37.7	29 55.9	11 .5	14 55.1	24 9.3	11 13.1	3 9.4	11 47.3	14 48.9
7	18 59 45.7	16 8.6	0 3.9	2♍24.4	2♋ 2.9	12 15.2	15 32.9	24 24.0	11 8.4	3 6.9	11 45.6	14 48.3
8	19 3 42.3	17 10.2	0 .8	13 30.9	4 12.8	13 29.5	16 10.7	24 38.5	11 3.6	3 4.3	11 43.9	14 47.7
9	19 7 38.9	18 11.6	29♒57.8	24 13.2	6 25.4	14 43.6	16 48.3	24 53.0	10 58.9	3 1.7	11 42.2	14 47.1
10	19 11 35.4	19 13.0	29 54.7	4♎47.8	8 40.2	15 57.3	17 25.9	25 7.5	10 54.2	2 59.2	11 40.4	14 46.5
11	19 15 32.0	20 14.2	29 51.7	15 30.4	10 57.0	17 10.6	18 3.4	25 21.9	10 49.5	2 56.6	11 38.7	14 46.0
12	19 19 28.5	21 15.3	29 48.6	26 36.5	13 15.3	18 23.7	18 40.8	25 36.3	10 44.8	2 54.1	11 37.0	14 45.4
13	19 23 25.1	22 16.3	29 45.6	8♏19.6	15 34.6	19 36.4	19 18.2	25 50.7	10 40.1	2 51.6	11 35.3	14 45.0
14	19 27 21.7	23 17.2	29 42.5	20 50.4	17 54.6	20 48.7	19 55.5	26 5.0	10 35.5	2 49.1	11 33.6	14 44.5
15	19 31 18.2	24 18.0	29 39.5	4♐13.3	20 14.7	22 .8	20 32.7	26 19.3	10 30.9	2 46.7	11 31.9	14 44.1
16	19 35 14.8	25 18.6	29 36.4	18 23.1	22 34.6	23 12.5	21 9.9	26 33.5	10 26.3	2 44.2	11 30.2	14 43.7
17	19 39 11.3	26 19.1	29 33.4	3♑ 3.6	24 53.9	24 23.9	21 47.0	26 47.7	10 21.8	2 41.8	11 28.5	14 43.3
18	19 43 7.9	27 19.5	29 30.3	17 50.7	27 12.1	25 35.0	22 24.1	27 1.8	10 17.3	2 39.4	11 26.8	14 43.0
19	19 47 4.4	28 19.7	29 27.3	2♒20.9	29 29.0	26 45.7	23 1.0	27 15.9	10 12.8	2 37.1	11 25.1	14 42.7
20	19 51 1.0	29 19.8	29 24.2	16 19.2	1♌44.2	27 56.2	23 38.0	27 29.9	10 8.4	2 34.7	11 23.5	14 42.4
21	19 54 57.6	0♌19.7	29 21.1	29 42.4	3 57.5	29 6.3	24 14.8	27 43.9	10 4.0	2 32.4	11 21.8	14 42.2
22	19 58 54.1	1 19.5	29 18.1	12♓37.5	6 8.7	0♍16.2	24 51.6	27 57.8	9 59.6	2 30.1	11 20.2	14 41.9
23	20 2 50.7	2 19.2	29 15.0	25 18.1	8 17.7	1 25.7	25 28.4	28 11.7	9 55.3	2 27.9	11 18.6	14 41.8
24	20 6 47.2	3 18.8	29 12.0	8♈ 1.0	10 24.3	2 35.0	26 5.1	28 25.5	9 51.0	2 25.6	11 17.0	14 41.6
25	20 10 43.8	4 18.2	29 8.9	21 3.5	12 28.4	3 43.9	26 41.7	28 39.2	9 46.8	2 23.4	11 15.4	14 41.5
26	20 14 40.3	5 17.4	29 5.9	4♉40.4	14 29.9	4 52.6	27 18.3	28 52.9	9 42.7	2 21.3	11 13.8	14 41.4
27	20 18 36.9	6 16.5	29 2.8	19 .2	16 29.0	6 1.1	27 54.9	29 6.6	9 38.6	2 19.1	11 12.2	14 41.3
28	20 22 33.5	7 15.5	28 59.7	4♊ .2	18 25.5	7 9.3	28 31.4	29 20.2	9 34.5	2 17.1	11 10.7	14D41.4
29	20 26 30.0	8 14.4	28 56.7	19 23.8	20 19.4	8 17.2	29 7.8	29 33.7	9 30.5	2 15.0	11 9.2	14 41.4
30	20 30 26.6	9 13.0	28 53.6	4♋43.6	22 10.7	9 24.8	29 44.2	29 47.1	9 26.6	2 13.0	11 7.7	14 41.4
31	20 34 23.1	10 11.5	28 50.6	19 31.0	23 59.6	10 32.2	0♍20.5	0♋ .5	9 22.7	2 11.0	11 6.2	14 41.5

DECLINATION

DAY	SID. TIME	☉	☊	☽	☿	♀	♂	♃	♄	♅	♆	♇
1	18 36 6.4	23N 7.6	0S12.7	26N57.3	21N50.1	21N13.2	19N12.5	22N54.5	22S23.3	23S40.6	22S 3.0	0S16.7
4	18 47 56.1	22 54.0	0 12.7	24 32.5	22 42.1	20 23.4	18 41.6	22 56.6	22 24.6	23 40.8	22 3.4	0 17.6
7	18 59 45.7	22 36.7	0 12.8	10 57.7	22 20.5	19 28.5	18 9.6	22 58.5	22 25.9	23 41.0	22 3.9	0 18.6
10	19 11 35.4	22 16.0	0 12.8	5S44.0	23 40.2	18 28.8	17 36.5	23 .2	22 27.2	23 41.2	22 4.3	0 19.7
13	19 23 25.1	21 51.8	0 12.9	20 21.2	23 37.3	17 24.7	17 2.4	23 1.7	22 28.4	23 41.3	22 4.7	0 21.0
16	19 35 14.8	21 24.3	0 13.0	27 47.5	23 9.8	16 16.5	16 27.3	23 2.9	22 29.7	23 41.5	22 5.2	0 22.3
19	19 47 4.4	20 53.5	0 13.0	22 29.3	22 18.5	15 4.4	15 51.2	23 4.0	22 30.9	23 41.6	22 5.6	0 23.8
22	19 58 54.1	20 19.5	0 13.1	5 50.0	21 5.9	13 48.9	15 14.3	23 4.8	22 32.0	23 41.7	22 6.0	0 25.4
25	20 10 43.8	19 42.4	0 13.1	13N40.6	19 35.9	12 30.2	14 36.4	23 5.5	22 33.2	23 41.8	22 6.4	0 27.0
28	20 22 33.5	19 2.4	0 13.2	26 31.3	17 52.5	11 8.7	13 57.7	23 5.9	22 34.3	23 41.9	22 6.8	0 28.8
31	20 34 23.1	18 19.6	0 13.2	25 30.9	15 59.2	9 44.6	13 18.1	23 6.2	22 35.3	23 42.0	22 7.2	0 30.7

AUGUST 1989

LONGITUDE

DAY	EPHEM. SID. TIME h m s	☉ ° ′	☊ ° ′	☽ ° ′	☿ ° ′	♀ ° ′	♂ ° ′	♃ ° ′	♄ ° ′	♅ ° ′	♆ ° ′	♇ ° ′
1	20 38 19.7	8♌44.2	26♒33.7	0♌42.3	22♌54.2	9♍34.0	28♌23.5	0♋12.7	8♑35.7	1♑58.1	10♑15.3	12♏23.3
2	20 42 16.2	9 41.6	26 30.5	13 34.7	24 42.3	10 46.1	29 1.3	0 24.9	8 R 32.2	1 R 56.3	10 R 13.9	12 23.6
3	20 46 12.8	10 39.1	26 27.4	26 11.7	26 28.8	11 58.1	29 39.1	0 37.0	8 28.8	1 54.6	10 12.6	12 24.0
4	20 50 9.4	11 36.5	26 24.2	8♍34.4	28 13.6	13 10.2	0♍16.9	0 49.0	8 25.5	1 52.9	10 11.2	12 24.4
5	20 54 5.9	12 34.0	26 21.0	20 44.6	29 56.8	14 22.2	0 54.8	1 1.0	8 22.2	1 51.3	10 9.9	12 24.8
6	20 58 2.5	13 31.5	26 17.8	2♎44.9	1♍38.3	15 34.2	1 32.6	1 12.9	8 19.0	1 49.6	10 8.6	12 25.3
7	21 1 59.0	14 29.0	26 14.7	14 38.6	3 18.3	16 46.1	2 10.5	1 24.7	8 15.8	1 48.1	10 7.3	12 25.8
8	21 5 55.6	15 26.5	26 11.5	26 29.6	4 56.7	17 58.0	2 48.3	1 36.4	8 12.7	1 46.5	10 6.1	12 26.3
9	21 9 52.1	16 24.0	26 8.3	8♏22.4	6 33.4	19 9.9	3 26.2	1 48.1	8 9.7	1 45.0	10 4.9	12 26.9
10	21 13 48.7	17 21.5	26 5.1	20 21.5	8 8.6	20 21.7	4 4.1	1 59.7	8 6.8	1 43.5	10 3.7	12 27.5
11	21 17 45.2	18 19.1	26 2.0	2♐31.6	9 42.2	21 33.4	4 42.1	2 11.2	8 3.9	1 42.1	10 2.5	12 28.1
12	21 21 41.8	19 16.6	25 58.8	14 56.9	11 14.2	22 45.2	5 20.0	2 22.7	8 1.2	1 40.7	10 1.3	12 28.8
13	21 25 38.4	20 14.2	25 55.6	27 41.2	12 44.6	23 56.9	5 58.0	2 34.0	7 58.5	1 39.4	10 .1	12 29.5
14	21 29 34.9	21 11.8	25 52.4	10♑47.2	14 13.4	25 8.5	6 35.9	2 45.3	7 55.8	1 38.1	9 59.0	12 30.2
15	21 33 31.5	22 9.4	25 49.2	24 16.3	15 40.5	26 20.1	7 13.9	2 56.5	7 53.3	1 36.8	9 57.9	12 31.0
16	21 37 28.0	23 7.1	25 46.1	8♒ 7.9	17 6.1	27 31.6	7 51.9	3 7.6	7 50.8	1 35.6	9 56.8	12 31.8
17	21 41 24.6	24 4.7	25 42.9	22 19.7	18 29.9	28 43.1	8 30.0	3 18.6	7 48.4	1 34.4	9 55.8	12 32.6
18	21 45 21.1	25 2.4	25 39.7	6♓47.6	19 52.1	29 54.6	9 8.0	3 29.6	7 46.2	1 33.3	9 54.8	12 33.5
19	21 49 17.7	26 .1	25 36.5	21 25.7	21 12.6	1♎ 6.0	9 46.1	3 40.4	7 44.0	1 32.2	9 53.8	12 34.4
20	21 53 14.2	26 57.9	25 33.4	6♈ 7.8	22 31.3	2 17.4	10 24.2	3 51.1	7 41.8	1 31.2	9 52.8	12 35.3
21	21 57 10.8	27 55.6	25 30.2	20 47.3	23 48.2	3 28.7	11 2.3	4 1.8	7 39.8	1 30.2	9 51.9	12 36.3
22	22 1 7.4	28 53.4	25 27.0	5♉18.7	25 3.2	4 39.9	11 40.4	4 12.3	7 37.8	1 29.2	9 50.9	12 37.3
23	22 5 3.9	29 51.2	25 23.8	19 37.6	26 16.3	5 51.2	12 18.5	4 22.8	7 36.0	1 28.3	9 50.0	12 38.3
24	22 9 .5	0♍49.0	25 20.6	3♊41.4	27 27.4	7 2.3	12 56.7	4 33.2	7 34.2	1 27.4	9 49.1	12 39.4
25	22 12 57.0	1 46.9	25 17.5	17 28.6	28 36.4	8 13.4	13 34.9	4 43.4	7 32.5	1 26.6	9 48.3	12 40.5
26	22 16 53.6	2 44.8	25 14.3	0♋59.1	29 43.3	9 24.5	14 13.1	4 53.6	7 30.9	1 25.9	9 47.5	12 41.6
27	22 20 50.1	3 42.7	25 11.1	14 13.5	0♎47.9	10 35.5	14 51.3	5 3.7	7 29.4	1 25.1	9 46.7	12 42.7
28	22 24 46.7	4 40.7	25 7.9	27 12.8	1 50.1	11 46.5	15 29.6	5 13.6	7 27.9	1 24.5	9 45.9	12 43.9
29	22 28 43.2	5 38.6	25 4.8	9♌58.1	2 49.8	12 57.4	16 7.9	5 23.5	7 26.6	1 23.8	9 45.2	12 45.1
30	22 32 39.8	6 36.6	25 1.6	22 30.8	3 46.9	14 8.3	16 46.2	5 33.2	7 25.4	1 23.2	9 44.5	12 46.4
31	22 36 36.3	7 34.7	24 58.4	4♍52.0	4 41.2	15 19.1	17 24.5	5 42.8	7 24.2	1 22.7	9 43.8	12 47.6

LATITUDE

DAY	SID. TIME	☉	☊	☽	☿	♀	♂	♃	♄	♅	♆	♇
1	20 38 19.7	0 .0	0 .0	2N14.0	1N31.8	1N23.2	1N 6.8	0S20.3	0N34.3	0S16.4	0N55.6	15N45.0
4	20 50 9.4	0 .0	0 .0	1S10.2	1 17.3	1 18.3	1 6.0	0 20.1	0 33.9	0 16.4	0 55.5	15 43.2
7	21 1 59.0	0 .0	0 .0	3 58.6	0 59.3	1 12.7	1 5.2	0 19.9	0 33.6	0 16.4	0 55.5	15 41.5
10	21 13 48.7	0 .0	0 .0	5 15.3	0 38.2	1 6.4	1 4.3	0 19.7	0 33.2	0 16.4	0 55.4	15 39.8
13	21 25 38.4	0 .0	0 .0	4 29.3	0 14.7	0 59.6	1 3.4	0 19.6	0 32.8	0 16.4	0 55.3	15 38.1
16	21 37 28.0	0 .0	0 .0	1 36.5	0S10.8	0 52.1	1 2.5	0 19.4	0 32.5	0 16.3	0 55.2	15 36.4
19	21 49 17.7	0 .0	0 .0	2N17.4	0 37.8	0 44.0	1 1.6	0 19.2	0 32.1	0 16.3	0 55.1	15 34.7
22	22 1 7.4	0 .0	0 .0	4 57.1	1 5.9	0 35.3	1 .7	0 19.0	0 31.7	0 16.3	0 55.0	15 33.0
25	22 12 57.0	0 .0	0 .0	4 54.7	1 34.6	0 26.2	0 59.7	0 18.8	0 31.3	0 16.3	0 54.9	15 31.4
28	22 24 46.7	0 .0	0 .0	2 32.1	2 3.5	0 16.5	0 58.8	0 18.6	0 30.9	0 16.3	0 54.8	15 29.8
31	22 36 36.3	0 .0	0 .0	0S49.7	2 31.9	0 6.4	0 57.8	0 18.5	0 30.6	0 16.3	0 54.7	15 28.3

RIGHT ASCENSION

DAY	SID. TIME	☉	☊	☽	☿	♀	♂	♃	♄	♅	♆	♇
1	20 38 19.7	11♌ 9.9	28♒47.5	3♌26.2	25♌46.0	11♍39.4	0♍56.8	0♋13.8	9♑18.9	2♑ 9.0	11♑ 4.7	14♏41.6
2	20 42 16.2	12 8.1	28 44.4	16 22.8	27 30.0	12 46.4	1 33.0	0 27.0	9 R 15.2	2 R 7.1	11 R 3.2	14 41.7
3	20 46 12.8	13 6.2	28 41.4	28 25.5	29 11.6	13 53.1	2 9.2	0 40.2	9 11.5	2 5.2	11 1.8	14 41.8
4	20 50 9.4	14 4.1	28 38.3	9♍45.5	0♍51.0	14 59.6	2 45.4	0 53.3	9 7.9	2 3.3	11 .3	14 42.0
5	20 54 5.9	15 1.9	28 35.2	20 37.1	2 28.1	16 6.0	3 21.5	1 6.3	9 4.3	2 1.5	10 58.9	14 42.3
6	20 58 2.5	15 59.5	28 32.2	1♎15.4	4 3.1	17 12.1	3 57.5	1 19.2	9 .9	1 59.7	10 57.5	14 42.5
7	21 1 59.0	16 56.9	28 29.1	11 55.3	5 35.9	18 18.0	4 33.5	1 32.1	8 57.5	1 58.0	10 56.2	14 42.8
8	21 5 55.6	17 54.2	28 26.0	22 51.3	7 6.7	19 23.8	5 9.5	1 44.9	8 54.1	1 56.3	10 54.8	14 43.1
9	21 9 52.1	18 51.4	28 23.0	4♏17.0	8 35.4	20 29.4	5 45.4	1 57.5	8 50.9	1 54.7	10 53.5	14 43.5
10	21 13 48.7	19 48.4	28 19.9	16 23.9	10 2.2	21 34.8	6 21.3	2 10.1	8 47.7	1 53.1	10 52.2	14 43.9
11	21 17 45.2	20 45.3	28 16.9	29 19.0	11 27.1	22 40.1	6 57.1	2 22.7	8 44.7	1 51.5	10 50.9	14 44.3
12	21 21 41.8	21 42.0	28 13.8	13♐ 2.1	12 50.1	23 45.2	7 32.9	2 35.1	8 41.7	1 50.0	10 49.6	14 44.7
13	21 25 38.4	22 38.5	28 10.7	27 23.4	14 11.2	24 50.3	8 8.7	2 47.4	8 38.7	1 48.5	10 48.4	14 45.2
14	21 29 34.9	23 34.9	28 7.6	12♑ 4.2	15 30.5	25 55.1	8 44.4	2 59.7	8 35.9	1 47.1	10 47.2	14 45.7
15	21 33 31.5	24 31.2	28 4.6	26 42.3	16 48.1	26 59.9	9 20.1	3 11.8	8 33.2	1 45.7	10 46.0	14 46.2
16	21 37 28.0	25 27.4	28 1.5	10♒59.5	18 3.8	28 4.6	9 55.8	3 23.9	8 30.5	1 44.4	10 44.9	14 46.8
17	21 41 24.6	26 23.4	27 58.4	24 47.7	19 17.8	29 9.1	10 31.4	3 35.9	8 27.9	1 43.1	10 43.7	14 47.4
18	21 45 21.1	27 19.3	27 55.4	8♓ 9.0	20 30.1	0♎13.7	11 7.0	3 47.8	8 25.5	1 41.9	10 42.7	14 48.1
19	21 49 17.7	28 15.1	27 52.3	21 13.5	21 40.6	1 18.1	11 42.6	3 59.6	8 23.1	1 40.7	10 41.6	14 48.7
20	21 53 14.2	29 10.7	27 49.2	4♈15.9	22 49.3	2 22.4	12 18.1	4 11.3	8 20.8	1 39.6	10 40.5	14 49.4
21	21 57 10.8	0♍ 6.3	27 46.2	17 32.4	23 56.3	3 26.7	12 53.6	4 22.8	8 18.6	1 38.5	10 39.5	14 50.2
22	22 1 7.4	1 1.7	27 43.1	1♉17.1	25 1.4	4 30.9	13 29.1	4 34.3	8 16.5	1 37.4	10 38.5	14 50.9
23	22 5 3.9	1 57.0	27 40.0	15 38.4	26 4.7	5 35.2	14 4.6	4 45.7	8 14.5	1 36.4	10 37.6	14 51.7
24	22 9 .5	2 52.2	27 36.9	0♊34.8	27 6.2	6 39.4	14 40.0	4 56.9	8 12.5	1 35.5	10 36.6	14 52.5
25	22 12 57.0	3 47.3	27 33.9	15 52.3	28 5.7	7 43.5	15 15.5	5 8.1	8 10.7	1 34.6	10 35.7	14 53.4
26	22 16 53.6	4 42.3	27 30.8	1♋ 6.6	29 3.2	8 47.7	15 50.9	5 19.1	8 9.0	1 33.8	10 34.8	14 54.2
27	22 20 50.1	5 37.2	27 27.7	15 51.6	29 58.6	9 51.9	16 26.3	5 30.0	8 7.4	1 33.0	10 34.0	14 55.1
28	22 24 46.7	6 32.0	27 24.7	29 48.3	0♎51.9	10 56.1	17 1.7	5 40.9	8 5.8	1 32.2	10 33.1	14 56.1
29	22 28 43.2	7 26.7	27 21.6	12♌49.5	1 42.9	12 .3	17 37.0	5 51.5	8 4.4	1 31.6	10 32.3	14 57.0
30	22 32 39.8	8 21.4	27 18.5	24 58.2	2 31.5	13 4.6	18 12.4	6 2.1	8 3.1	1 30.9	10 31.6	14 58.0
31	22 36 36.3	9 15.9	27 15.4	6♍24.3	3 17.7	14 8.9	18 47.7	6 12.6	8 1.8	1 30.3	10 30.8	14 59.1

DECLINATION

DAY	SID. TIME	☉	☊	☽	☿	♀	♂	♃	♄	♅	♆	♇
1	20 38 19.7	18N 4.7	0S13.3	22N10.9	15N19.8	9N16.1	13N 4.8	23N 6.3	22S35.7	23S42.0	22S 7.3	0S31.3
4	20 50 9.4	17 18.3	0 13.3	7 16.2	13 18.1	7 49.1	12 24.2	23 6.3	22 36.7	23 42.1	22 7.7	0 33.3
7	21 1 59.0	16 29.3	0 13.4	9S26.2	11 13.0	6 20.4	11 42.9	23 6.2	22 37.6	23 42.2	22 8.1	0 35.3
10	21 13 48.7	15 38.0	0 13.4	22 53.9	9 6.5	4 50.2	11 1.0	23 5.9	22 38.5	23 42.2	22 8.5	0 37.4
13	21 25 38.4	14 44.5	0 13.5	27 54.6	7 .3	3 18.9	10 18.4	23 5.5	22 39.4	23 42.3	22 8.8	0 39.6
16	21 37 28.0	13 48.8	0 13.5	19 47.4	4 55.8	1 46.8	9 35.3	23 5.0	22 40.2	23 42.3	22 9.2	0 41.9
19	21 49 17.7	12 51.2	0 13.6	1 17.6	2 54.4	0 14.1	8 51.5	23 4.3	22 41.0	23 42.4	22 9.5	0 44.3
22	22 1 7.4	11 51.7	0 13.7	17N57.3	0 57.5	1S18.8	8 7.3	23 3.6	22 41.7	23 42.4	22 9.8	0 46.7
25	22 12 57.0	10 50.5	0 13.7	27 44.5	0S53.6	2 51.7	7 22.5	23 2.7	22 42.4	23 42.4	22 10.1	0 49.1
28	22 24 46.7	9 47.8	0 13.8	23 12.3	2 37.1	4 24.2	6 37.3	23 1.7	22 43.1	23 42.4	22 10.4	0 51.6
31	22 36 36.3	8 43.7	0 13.8	8 57.4	4 11.2	5 56.1	5 51.7	23 .7	22 43.6	23 42.4	22 10.6	0 54.2

SEPTEMBER 1989

LONGITUDE

DAY	EPHEM. SID. TIME h m s	☉ ° ′	☊ ° ′	☽ ° ′	☿ ° ′	♀ ° ′	♂ ° ′	♃ ° ′	♄ ° ′	♅ ° ′	♆ ° ′	♇ ° ′
1	22 40 32.9	8♍32.7	24♒55.2	17♍ 3.2	5♎32.5	16♎29.9	18♍ 2.8	5♋52.3	7♑23.2	1♑22.2	9♑43.1	12♏48.9
2	22 44 29.5	9 30.8	24 52.1	29 5.9	6 20.6	17 40.6	18 41.2	6 1.7	7R22.2	1R21.8	9R42.5	12 50.3
3	22 48 26.0	10 28.9	24 48.9	11♎ 2.0	7 5.4	18 51.3	19 19.6	6 11.0	7 21.4	1 21.4	9 41.9	12 51.6
4	22 52 22.6	11 27.1	24 45.7	22 53.8	7 46.5	20 1.8	19 58.0	6 20.2	7 20.6	1 21.1	9 41.3	12 53.0
5	22 56 19.1	12 25.3	24 42.5	4♏44.1	8 23.8	21 12.4	20 36.4	6 29.2	7 19.9	1 20.8	9 40.8	12 54.5
6	23 0 15.7	13 23.4	24 39.3	16 36.2	8 57.1	22 22.8	21 14.9	6 38.2	7 19.4	1 20.6	9 40.3	12 55.9
7	23 4 12.2	14 21.7	24 36.2	28 33.9	9 25.9	23 33.2	21 53.4	6 47.0	7 18.9	1 20.4	9 39.8	12 57.4
8	23 8 8.8	15 20.0	24 33.0	10♐41.5	9 50.1	24 43.6	22 31.9	6 55.7	7 18.6	1 20.3	9 39.4	12 58.9
9	23 12 5.3	16 18.2	24 29.8	23 3.3	10 9.2	25 53.9	23 10.4	7 4.3	7 18.3	1 20.3	9 39.0	13 .5
10	23 16 1.9	17 16.5	24 26.6	5♑43.7	10 23.1	27 4.1	23 49.0	7 12.7	7 18.1	1 20.2	9 38.7	13 2.0
11	23 19 58.4	18 14.8	24 23.5	18 46.7	10 31.3	28 14.2	24 27.5	7 21.0	7 18.1	1D20.3	9 38.3	13 3.6
12	23 23 55.0	19 13.2	24 20.3	2♒15.1	10 33.6	29 24.3	25 6.1	7 29.1	7 18.1	1 20.3	9 38.0	13 5.2
13	23 27 51.5	20 11.5	24 17.1	16 10.3	10R29.6	0♏34.3	25 44.7	7 37.2	7D18.2	1 20.5	9 37.7	13 6.9
14	23 31 48.1	21 9.9	24 13.9	0♓31.2	10 19.1	1 44.2	26 23.4	7 45.1	7 18.4	1 20.6	9 37.5	13 8.5
15	23 35 44.7	22 8.4	24 10.7	15 14.3	10 1.9	2 54.0	27 2.0	7 52.8	7 18.7	1 20.9	9 37.2	13 10.2
16	23 39 41.2	23 6.8	24 7.6	0♈13.1	9 37.8	4 3.7	27 40.7	8 .4	7 19.1	1 21.1	9 37.1	13 11.9
17	23 43 37.8	24 5.3	24 4.4	15 19.2	9 6.9	5 13.4	28 19.4	8 7.9	7 19.7	1 21.5	9 36.9	13 13.7
18	23 47 34.3	25 3.8	24 1.2	0♉23.0	8 29.2	6 23.0	28 58.1	8 15.3	7 20.3	1 21.8	9 36.8	13 15.5
19	23 51 30.9	26 2.4	23 58.0	15 15.6	7 45.0	7 32.5	29 36.9	8 22.5	7 21.0	1 22.3	9 36.7	13 17.2
20	23 55 27.4	27 1.0	23 54.9	29 50.0	6 54.8	8 41.9	0♎15.7	8 29.5	7 21.8	1 22.8	9 36.6	13 19.1
21	23 59 24.0	27 59.6	23 51.7	14♊ 1.8	5 59.2	9 51.2	0 54.5	8 36.4	7 22.7	1 23.3	9 36.6	13 20.9
22	0 3 20.5	28 58.3	23 48.5	27 49.4	4 59.1	11 .5	1 33.3	8 43.2	7 23.7	1 23.9	9 36.6	13 22.8
23	0 7 17.1	29 57.0	23 45.3	11♋13.3	3 55.8	12 9.6	2 12.2	8 49.8	7 24.8	1 24.5	9D36.7	13 24.6
24	0 11 13.6	0♎55.7	23 42.1	24 15.7	2 50.4	13 18.7	2 51.1	8 56.2	7 26.0	1 25.2	9 36.7	13 26.5
25	0 15 10.2	1 54.5	23 39.0	6♌59.6	1 44.6	14 27.7	3 30.0	9 2.5	7 27.3	1 26.0	9 36.8	13 28.5
26	0 19 6.7	2 53.3	23 35.8	19 28.4	0 40.0	15 36.6	4 9.0	9 8.7	7 28.7	1 26.7	9 37.0	13 30.4
27	0 23 3.3	3 52.2	23 32.6	1♍45.1	29♍38.2	16 45.4	4 48.0	9 14.7	7 30.2	1 27.6	9 37.2	13 32.4
28	0 26 59.8	4 51.1	23 29.4	13 52.6	28 40.9	17 54.1	5 27.0	9 20.5	7 31.7	1 28.5	9 37.4	13 34.4
29	0 30 56.4	5 50.1	23 26.3	25 53.2	27 49.8	19 2.8	6 6.1	9 26.2	7 33.5	1 29.5	9 37.6	13 36.4
30	0 34 53.0	6 49.0	23 23.1	7♎48.8	27 6.0	20 11.3	6 45.2	9 31.7	7 35.2	1 30.5	9 37.9	13 38.5

LATITUDE

DAY	SID. TIME	☉	☊	☽	☿	♀	♂	♃	♄	♅	♆	♇
1	22 40 32.9	0 .0	0 .0	1S54.6	2S41.1	0N 3.0	0N57.4	0S18.4	0N30.4	0S16.3	0N54.6	15N27.7
4	22 52 22.6	0 .0	0 .0	4 25.1	3 7.7	0S 7.7	0 56.4	0 18.2	0 30.0	0 16.3	0 54.5	15 26.2
7	23 4 12.2	0 .0	0 .0	5 14.7	3 31.4	0 18.6	0 55.4	0 18.1	0 29.7	0 16.3	0 54.4	15 24.8
10	23 16 1.9	0 .0	0 .0	4 1.3	3 50.7	0 29.9	0 54.3	0 17.9	0 29.3	0 16.2	0 54.3	15 23.3
13	23 27 51.5	0 .0	0 .0	0 52.2	4 3.2	0 41.4	0 53.3	0 17.7	0 28.9	0 16.2	0 54.2	15 21.9
16	23 39 41.2	0 .0	0 .0	2N58.0	4 5.8	0 53.0	0 52.2	0 17.5	0 28.5	0 16.2	0 54.1	15 20.6
19	23 51 30.9	0 .0	0 .0	5 7.5	3 54.9	1 4.8	0 51.1	0 17.3	0 28.1	0 16.2	0 54.0	15 19.3
22	0 3 20.5	0 .0	0 .0	4 23.8	3 27.5	1 16.6	0 49.9	0 17.1	0 27.8	0 16.2	0 53.8	15 18.1
25	0 15 10.2	0 .0	0 .0	1 38.8	2 43.4	1 28.4	0 48.8	0 17.0	0 27.4	0 16.2	0 53.7	15 16.9
28	0 26 59.8	0 .0	0 .0	1S38.6	1 47.0	1 40.1	0 47.6	0 16.8	0 27.0	0 16.1	0 53.6	15 15.8

RIGHT ASCENSION

DAY	SID. TIME	☉	☊	☽	☿	♀	♂	♃	♄	♅	♆	♇
1	22 40 32.9	10♍10.4	27♒12.4	17♍20.7	4♎ 1.1	15♎13.3	19♍23.1	6♋22.9	8♑ .7	1♑29.8	10♑30.1	15♏ .1
2	22 44 29.5	11 4.8	27 9.3	28 1.3	4 41.8	16 17.7	19 58.4	6 33.1	7R59.7	1R29.4	10R29.5	15 1.2
3	22 48 26.0	11 59.1	27 6.2	8♎39.9	5 19.5	17 22.2	20 33.7	6 43.2	7 58.8	1 28.9	10 28.8	15 2.3
4	22 52 22.6	12 53.4	27 3.1	19 30.0	5 54.0	18 26.7	21 9.0	6 53.1	7 57.9	1 28.6	10 28.2	15 3.4
5	22 56 19.1	13 47.5	27 .0	0♏44.0	6 25.1	19 31.4	21 44.3	7 3.0	7 57.2	1 28.3	10 27.7	15 4.6
6	23 0 15.7	14 41.7	26 57.0	12 32.6	6 52.6	20 36.1	22 19.7	7 12.6	7 56.6	1 28.0	10 27.1	15 5.8
7	23 4 12.2	15 35.8	26 53.9	25 3.2	7 16.2	21 41.0	22 55.0	7 22.2	7 56.1	1 27.8	10 26.6	15 7.0
8	23 8 8.8	16 29.8	26 50.8	8♐17.5	7 35.8	22 46.0	23 30.3	7 31.7	7 55.8	1 27.7	10 26.2	15 8.3
9	23 12 5.3	17 23.8	26 47.7	22 9.6	7 50.9	23 51.0	24 5.6	7 40.9	7 55.5	1 27.7	10 25.8	15 9.6
10	23 16 1.9	18 17.7	26 44.7	6♑26.1	8 1.4	24 56.2	24 40.9	7 50.1	7 55.3	1 27.6	10 25.4	15 10.9
11	23 19 58.4	19 11.6	26 41.6	20 49.0	8 6.9	26 1.5	25 16.2	7 59.1	7 55.3	1 27.6	10 25.0	15 12.2
12	23 23 55.0	20 5.5	26 38.5	5♒ 1.6	8 7.4	27 7.0	25 51.6	8 7.9	7 55.3	1D27.7	10 24.7	15 13.6
13	23 27 51.5	20 59.3	26 35.4	18 54.1	8R 2.4	28 12.5	26 26.9	8 16.6	7D55.4	1 27.9	10 24.4	15 15.0
14	23 31 48.1	21 53.1	26 32.3	2♓25.7	7 51.8	29 18.3	27 2.2	8 25.2	7 55.7	1 28.1	10 24.1	15 16.4
15	23 35 44.7	22 46.9	26 29.2	15 43.8	7 35.5	0♏24.1	27 37.6	8 33.6	7 56.0	1 28.3	10 23.8	15 17.8
16	23 39 41.2	23 40.6	26 26.2	29 1.2	7 13.5	1 30.2	28 12.9	8 41.9	7 56.5	1 28.6	10 23.7	15 19.3
17	23 43 37.8	24 34.4	26 23.1	12♈33.0	6 45.7	2 36.4	28 48.3	8 50.0	7 57.0	1 29.0	10 23.5	15 20.7
18	23 47 34.3	25 28.2	26 20.0	26 33.5	6 12.3	3 42.8	29 23.7	8 58.0	7 57.7	1 29.4	10 23.4	15 22.2
19	23 51 30.9	26 22.0	26 16.9	11♉11.4	5 33.7	4 49.3	29 59.1	9 5.8	7 58.5	1 29.9	10 23.3	15 23.8
20	23 55 27.4	27 15.7	26 13.8	26 25.5	4 50.3	5 56.0	0♎34.6	9 13.4	7 59.3	1 30.4	10 23.2	15 25.3
21	23 59 24.0	28 9.6	26 10.7	12♊ 1.1	4 2.8	7 2.9	1 10.0	9 20.9	8 .3	1 31.0	10 23.2	15 26.9
22	0 3 20.5	29 3.4	26 7.7	27 32.7	3 12.0	8 10.0	1 45.5	9 28.2	8 1.4	1 31.6	10 23.2	15 28.5
23	0 7 17.1	29 57.3	26 4.6	12♋32.6	2 18.9	9 17.3	2 21.0	9 35.4	8 2.6	1 32.3	10 23.2	15 30.1
24	0 11 13.6	0♎51.0	26 1.5	26 40.8	1 24.8	10 24.8	2 56.5	9 42.4	8 3.9	1 33.1	10D23.3	15 31.8
25	0 15 10.2	1 45.1	25 58.4	9♌50.1	0 30.9	11 32.5	3 32.1	9 49.2	8 5.3	1 33.9	10 23.4	15 33.4
26	0 19 6.7	2 39.1	25 55.3	22 4.1	29♍38.7	12 40.4	4 7.7	9 55.8	8 6.8	1 34.7	10 23.6	15 35.1
27	0 23 3.3	3 33.1	25 52.2	3♍33.2	28 49.6	13 48.5	4 43.4	10 2.3	8 8.5	1 35.7	10 23.8	15 36.9
28	0 26 59.8	4 27.2	25 49.1	14 30.8	28 4.9	14 56.8	5 19.0	10 8.6	8 10.2	1 36.6	10 24.0	15 38.6
29	0 30 56.4	5 21.3	25 46.0	25 11.0	27 26.0	16 5.4	5 54.8	10 14.8	8 12.1	1 37.7	10 24.3	15 40.4
30	0 34 53.0	6 15.5	25 43.0	5♎47.5	26 54.0	17 14.1	6 30.5	10 20.7	8 14.0	1 38.8	10 24.6	15 42.2

DECLINATION

DAY	SID. TIME	☉	☊	☽	☿	♀	♂	♃	♄	♅	♆	♇
1	22 40 32.9	8N22.0	0S13.8	3N21.2	4S40.0	6S26.5	5N36.4	23N .4	22S43.8	23S42.4	22S10.7	0S55.0
4	22 52 22.6	7 16.2	0 13.9	13S .2	5 57.5	7 57.0	4 50.3	22 59.3	22 44.4	23 42.4	22 11.0	0 57.6
7	23 4 12.2	6 9.4	0 14.0	24 57.3	6 58.6	9 26.2	4 3.9	22 58.1	22 44.8	23 42.4	22 11.2	1 .2
10	23 16 1.9	5 1.6	0 14.0	27 20.2	7 38.9	10 53.7	3 17.3	22 56.9	22 45.3	23 42.4	22 11.4	1 2.9
13	23 27 51.5	3 53.1	0 14.1	16 49.3	7 52.9	12 19.2	2 30.4	22 55.8	22 45.6	23 42.4	22 11.6	1 5.6
16	23 39 41.2	2 44.0	0 14.1	2N48.5	7 34.9	13 42.4	1 43.3	22 54.6	22 46.0	23 42.4	22 11.7	1 8.3
19	23 51 30.9	1 34.5	0 14.2	21 18.6	6 40.3	15 2.9	0 56.0	22 53.4	22 46.2	23 42.3	22 11.9	1 11.0
22	0 3 20.5	0 24.5	0 14.2	27 49.3	5 9.3	16 20.7	0 8.7	22 52.2	22 46.5	23 42.3	22 12.0	1 13.7
25	0 15 10.2	0S45.6	0 14.3	20 7.1	3 11.6	17 35.2	0S38.7	22 51.1	22 46.6	23 42.3	22 12.1	1 16.4
28	0 26 59.8	1 55.7	0 14.3	4 49.6	1 6.7	18 46.2	1 26.2	22 50.1	22 46.8	23 42.2	22 12.2	1 19.1

OCTOBER 1989

LONGITUDE

DAY	EPHEM. SID. TIME	☉	☊	☾	☿	♀	♂	♃	♄	♅	♆	♇
	h m s	° ′	° ′	° ′	° ′	° ′	° ′	° ′	° ′	° ′	° ′	° ′
1	0 38 49.5	7♎48.0	23♒19.9	19♎41.2	26♍30.9	21♏19.7	7♎24.3	9♋37.0	7♑37.1	1♑31.5	9♑38.2	13♏40.5
2	0 42 46.1	8 47.1	23 16.7	1♏31.9	26R 5.2	22 28.0	8 3.4	9 42.1	7 39.1	1 32.6	9 38.6	13 42.6
3	0 46 42.6	9 46.1	23 13.5	13 22.9	25 49.6	23 36.2	8 42.5	9 47.1	7 41.2	1 33.7	9 38.9	13 44.7
4	0 50 39.2	10 45.2	23 10.4	25 16.3	25 44.4	24 44.2	9 21.7	9 51.9	7 43.3	1 34.9	9 39.4	13 46.8
5	0 54 35.7	11 44.3	23 7.2	7♐14.8	25D49.8	25 52.2	10 .9	9 56.6	7 45.6	1 36.2	9 39.8	13 48.9
6	0 58 32.3	12 43.5	23 4.0	19 21.5	26 5.6	27 .0	10 40.2	10 1.1	7 47.9	1 37.5	9 40.3	13 51.0
7	1 2 28.8	13 42.7	23 .8	1♑40.4	26 31.4	28 7.7	11 19.4	10 5.3	7 50.4	1 38.8	9 40.8	13 53.2
8	1 6 25.4	14 41.9	22 57.7	14 15.5	27 6.8	29 15.3	11 58.7	10 9.5	7 52.9	1 40.2	9 41.3	13 55.4
9	1 10 21.9	15 41.1	22 54.5	27 11.3	27 51.1	0♐22.8	12 38.0	10 13.4	7 55.5	1 41.6	9 41.9	13 57.6
10	1 14 18.5	16 40.4	22 51.3	10♒31.6	28 43.7	1 30.0	13 17.4	10 17.1	7 58.2	1 43.1	9 42.5	13 59.8
11	1 18 15.0	17 39.7	22 48.1	24 19.4	29 43.7	2 37.2	13 56.8	10 20.7	8 1.0	1 44.7	9 43.1	14 2.0
12	1 22 11.6	18 39.0	22 44.9	8♓35.7	0♎50.5	3 44.2	14 36.2	10 24.1	8 3.9	1 46.2	9 43.8	14 4.2
13	1 26 8.2	19 38.4	22 41.8	23 18.7	2 3.2	4 51.0	15 15.6	10 27.3	8 6.9	1 47.9	9 44.5	14 6.5
14	1 30 4.7	20 37.8	22 38.6	8♈23.2	3 21.1	5 57.7	15 55.1	10 30.3	8 10.0	1 49.6	9 45.2	14 8.7
15	1 34 1.3	21 37.2	22 35.4	23 40.7	4 43.5	7 4.2	16 34.6	10 33.2	8 13.2	1 51.3	9 46.0	14 11.0
16	1 37 57.8	22 36.6	22 32.2	9♉ .4	6 9.8	8 10.6	17 14.1	10 35.8	8 16.4	1 53.0	9 46.8	14 13.3
17	1 41 54.4	23 36.1	22 29.1	24 10.7	7 39.3	9 16.8	17 53.6	10 38.3	8 19.7	1 54.9	9 47.6	14 15.6
18	1 45 50.9	24 35.7	22 25.9	9♊ 1.9	9 11.5	10 22.8	18 33.2	10 40.5	8 23.2	1 56.7	9 48.5	14 17.9
19	1 49 47.5	25 35.2	22 22.7	23 27.1	10 46.0	11 28.6	19 12.9	10 42.6	8 26.7	1 58.6	9 49.4	14 20.2
20	1 53 44.0	26 34.9	22 19.5	7♋23.4	12 22.2	12 34.3	19 52.6	10 44.5	8 30.3	2 .6	9 50.4	14 22.6
21	1 57 40.6	27 34.5	22 16.3	20 50.6	13 59.9	13 39.7	20 32.2	10 46.2	8 34.0	2 2.6	9 51.3	14 24.9
22	2 1 37.1	28 34.2	22 13.2	3♌51.5	15 38.6	14 45.0	21 12.0	10 47.7	8 37.7	2 4.6	9 52.3	14 27.3
23	2 5 33.7	29 33.9	22 10.0	16 30.1	17 18.2	15 50.0	21 51.7	10 49.0	8 41.5	2 6.7	9 53.3	14 29.6
24	2 9 30.3	0♏33.7	22 6.8	28 50.9	18 58.4	16 54.9	22 31.5	10 50.1	8 45.5	2 8.8	9 54.4	14 32.0
25	2 13 26.8	1 33.5	22 3.6	10♍58.6	20 38.9	17 59.5	23 11.3	10 51.0	8 49.5	2 11.0	9 55.5	14 34.4
26	2 17 23.4	2 33.3	22 .5	22 57.4	22 19.7	19 3.9	23 51.2	10 51.7	8 53.5	2 13.2	9 56.6	14 36.7
27	2 21 19.9	3 33.2	21 57.3	4♎50.9	24 .5	20 8.1	24 31.1	10 52.2	8 57.7	2 15.4	9 57.7	14 39.1
28	2 25 16.5	4 33.1	21 54.1	16 41.9	25 41.4	21 12.0	25 11.0	10 52.5	9 1.9	2 17.7	9 58.9	14 41.5
29	2 29 13.0	5 33.0	21 50.9	28 32.7	27 22.1	22 15.7	25 50.9	10 52.6	9 6.2	2 20.1	10 .1	14 43.9
30	2 33 9.6	6 33.0	21 47.8	10♏24.8	29 2.6	23 19.2	26 30.9	10R52.5	9 10.6	2 22.4	10 1.3	14 46.3
31	2 37 6.1	7 33.0	21 44.6	22 19.5	0♏42.9	24 22.4	27 10.9	10 52.2	9 15.1	2 24.8	10 2.6	14 48.7

LATITUDE

DAY	EPHEM. SID. TIME	☉	☊	☾	☿	♀	♂	♃	♄	♅	♆	♇
1	0 38 49.5	0 .0	0 .0	4S11.3	0S46.3	1S51.6	0N46.4	0S16.6	0N26.6	0S16.1	0N53.5	15N14.8
4	0 50 39.2	0 .0	0 .0	5 7.4	0N10.1	2 3.0	0 45.2	0 16.4	0 26.3	0 16.1	0 53.4	15 13.8
7	1 2 28.8	0 .0	0 .0	4 5.3	0 56.2	2 14.0	0 44.0	0 16.2	0 25.9	0 16.1	0 53.2	15 12.9
10	1 14 18.5	0 .0	0 .0	1 14.3	1 29.5	2 24.6	0 42.7	0 16.0	0 25.6	0 16.1	0 53.1	15 12.0
13	1 26 8.2	0 .0	0 .0	2N28.1	1 50.1	2 34.8	0 41.4	0 15.8	0 25.2	0 16.1	0 53.0	15 11.2
16	1 37 57.8	0 .0	0 .0	4 53.9	1 59.6	2 44.5	0 40.1	0 15.6	0 24.9	0 16.1	0 52.9	15 10.5
19	1 49 47.5	0 .0	0 .0	4 24.4	2 .2	2 53.5	0 38.8	0 15.3	0 24.5	0 16.0	0 52.8	15 9.9
22	2 1 37.1	0 .0	0 .0	1 43.1	1 53.9	3 1.8	0 37.5	0 15.1	0 24.2	0 16.0	0 52.7	15 9.3
25	2 13 26.8	0 .0	0 .0	1S31.1	1 42.7	3 9.4	0 36.1	0 14.9	0 23.8	0 16.0	0 52.5	15 8.8
28	2 25 16.5	0 .0	0 .0	4 2.3	1 27.8	3 16.0	0 34.7	0 14.6	0 23.5	0 16.0	0 52.4	15 8.4
31	2 37 6.1	0 .0	0 .0	5 .1	1 10.6	3 21.7	0 33.3	0 14.4	0 23.2	0 16.0	0 52.3	15 8.0

RIGHT ASCENSION

DAY	EPHEM. SID. TIME	☉	☊	☾	☿	♀	♂	♃	♄	♅	♆	♇
1	0 38 49.5	7♎ 9.8	25♒39.9	16♎33.5	26♍29.7	18♏23.0	7♎ 6.3	10♋26.5	8♑16.0	1♑39.9	10♑25.0	15♏44.0
2	0 42 46.1	8 4.1	25 36.8	27 40.6	26R13.9	19 32.1	7 42.1	10 32.1	8 18.2	1 41.1	10 25.3	15 45.8
3	0 46 42.6	8 58.5	25 33.7	9♏18.9	26 7.1	20 41.3	8 18.0	10 37.5	8 20.4	1 42.4	10 25.7	15 47.6
4	0 50 39.2	9 53.0	25 30.6	21 35.1	26D 9.5	21 50.8	8 53.9	10 42.7	8 22.8	1 43.7	10 26.2	15 49.5
5	0 54 35.7	10 47.6	25 27.5	4♐30.6	26 21.1	23 .5	9 29.8	10 47.7	8 25.2	1 45.0	10 26.7	15 51.3
6	0 58 32.3	11 42.3	25 24.4	18 .4	26 41.7	24 10.3	10 5.8	10 52.6	8 27.8	1 46.5	10 27.2	15 53.2
7	1 2 28.8	12 37.0	25 21.3	1♑52.9	27 11.0	25 20.3	10 41.9	10 57.2	8 30.4	1 47.9	10 27.7	15 55.1
8	1 6 25.4	13 31.9	25 18.2	15 52.4	27 48.4	26 30.5	11 18.0	11 1.7	8 33.2	1 49.4	10 28.3	15 57.1
9	1 10 21.9	14 26.8	25 15.1	29 44.4	28 33.5	27 40.8	11 54.1	11 5.9	8 36.0	1 5..0	.0 28.9	15 59.0
10	1 14 18.5	15 21.9	25 12.0	13♒20.0	29 25.6	28 51.2	12 30.3	11 10.0	8 39.0	1 52.6	10 29.6	16 1.0
11	1 18 15.0	16 17.0	25 8.9	26 37.9	0♎24.0	0♐ 1.8	13 6.6	11 13.9	8 42.0	1 54.3	10 30.3	16 2.9
12	1 22 11.6	17 12.3	25 5.8	9♓44.9	1 27.9	1 12.5	13 42.9	11 17.5	8 45.2	1 56.0	10 31.0	16 4.9
13	1 26 8.2	18 7.7	25 2.8	22 53.0	2 36.8	2 23.4	14 19.2	11 21.0	8 48.4	1 57.8	10 31.8	16 6.9
14	1 30 4.7	19 3.3	24 59.7	6♈17.9	3 50.0	3 34.3	14 55.6	11 24.3	8 51.7	1 59.6	10 32.6	16 9.0
15	1 34 1.3	19 58.9	24 56.6	20 15.5	5 6.9	4 45.4	15 32.1	11 27.3	8 55.2	2 1.5	10 33.4	16 11.0
16	1 37 57.8	20 54.7	24 53.5	4♉57.7	6 26.8	5 56.5	16 8.7	11 30.2	8 58.7	2 3.4	10 34.3	16 13.0
17	1 41 54.4	21 50.7	24 50.4	20 26.7	7 49.5	7 7.6	16 45.3	11 32.9	9 2.3	2 5.4	10 35.2	16 15.1
18	1 45 50.9	22 46.8	24 47.3	6♊29.4	9 14.3	8 18.9	17 22.0	11 35.3	9 6.0	2 7.5	10 36.1	16 17.2
19	1 49 47.5	23 43.0	24 44.2	22 37.4	10 40.9	9 30.2	17 58.7	11 37.6	9 9.8	2 9.5	10 37.1	16 19.3
20	1 53 44.0	24 39.5	24 41.1	8♋16.5	12 9.0	10 41.5	18 35.6	11 39.7	9 13.7	2 11.7	10 38.1	16 21.4
21	1 57 40.6	25 36.0	24 38.0	22 60.0	13 38.3	11 52.8	19 12.5	11 41.5	9 17.7	2 13.9	10 39.1	16 23.5
22	2 1 37.1	26 32.8	24 34.9	6♌36.6	15 8.5	13 4.1	19 49.5	11 43.1	9 21.8	2 16.1	10 40.2	16 25.6
23	2 5 33.7	27 29.7	24 31.8	19 9.2	16 39.5	14 15.4	20 26.5	11 44.5	9 25.9	2 18.4	10 41.3	16 27.8
24	2 9 30.3	28 26.8	24 28.7	0♍49.3	18 11.1	15 26.7	21 3.6	11 45.7	9 30.2	2 20.7	10 42.4	16 29.9
25	2 13 26.8	29 24.1	24 25.6	11 52.0	19 43.2	16 37.9	21 40.8	11 46.7	9 34.5	2 23.1	10 43.6	16 32.1
26	2 17 23.4	0♏21.5	24 22.5	22 33.0	21 15.6	17 49.0	22 18.1	11 47.4	9 38.9	2 25.5	10 44.8	16 34.2
27	2 21 19.9	1 19.2	24 19.4	3♎ 7.3	22 48.3	19 .0	22 55.5	11 48.0	9 43.4	2 27.9	10 46.0	16 36.4
28	2 25 16.5	2 17.0	24 16.3	13 48.9	24 21.1	20 10.9	23 33.0	11 48.3	9 48.0	2 30.4	10 47.3	16 38.6
29	2 29 13.0	3 15.0	24 13.2	24 50.4	25 54.2	21 21.7	24 10.5	11 48.4	9 52.7	2 33.0	10 48.6	16 40.8
30	2 33 9.6	4 13.2	24 10.1	6♏22.3	27 27.4	22 32.2	24 48.1	11R48.3	9 57.5	2 35.5	10 49.9	16 42.9
31	2 37 6.1	5 11.6	24 7.0	18 31.3	29 .7	23 42.6	25 25.8	11 48.0	10 2.3	2 38.2	10 51.3	16 45.2

DECLINATION

DAY	EPHEM. SID. TIME	☉	☊	☾	☿	♀	♂	♃	♄	♅	♆	♇
1	0 38 49.5	3S 5.7	0S14.4	11S34.6	0N40.7	19S53.4	2S13.7	22N49.1	22S46.8	23S42.2	22S12.2	1S21.8
4	0 50 39.2	4 15.4	0 14.4	24 3.2	1 50.9	20 56.6	3 1.1	22 48.2	22 46.8	23 42.1	22 12.3	1 24.5
7	1 2 28.8	5 24.7	0 14.5	27 31.2	2 14.6	21 55.3	3 48.4	22 47.4	22 46.8	23 42.0	22 12.3	1 27.2
10	1 14 18.5	6 33.3	0 14.6	18 47.5	1 52.5	22 49.4	4 35.5	22 46.7	22 46.7	23 42.0	22 12.3	1 29.8
13	1 26 8.2	7 41.0	0 14.6	0 23.3	0 52.1	23 38.7	5 22.4	22 46.1	22 46.5	23 41.9	22 12.2	1 32.4
16	1 37 57.8	8 47.9	0 14.7	19N 8.2	0S37.0	24 22.8	6 9.1	22 45.7	22 46.2	23 41.8	22 12.2	1 35.0
19	1 49 47.5	9 53.6	0 14.7	27 41.0	2 25.1	25 1.6	6 55.5	22 45.4	22 45.9	23 41.7	22 12.1	1 37.5
22	2 1 37.1	10 58.1	0 14.8	20 57.6	4 24.3	25 34.9	7 41.5	22 45.2	22 45.6	23 41.6	22 12.0	1 40.0
25	2 13 26.8	12 1.0	0 14.8	6 2.7	6 28.7	26 2.6	8 27.2	22 45.1	22 45.1	23 41.5	22 11.9	1 42.4
28	2 25 16.5	13 2.4	0 14.9	10S17.5	8 34.0	26 24.6	9 12.4	22 45.2	22 44.6	23 41.4	22 11.7	1 44.8
31	2 37 6.1	14 1.9	0 14.9	23 11.0	10 37.3	26 40.9	9 57.2	22 45.5	22 44.1	23 41.2	22 11.6	1 47.1

NOVEMBER 1989

LONGITUDE

DAY	EPHEM. SID. TIME	☉	☊	☽	☿	♀	♂	♃	♄	♅	♆	♇
	h m s	° ′	° ′	° ′	° ′	° ′	° ′	° ′	° ′	° ′	° ′	° ′
1	2 41 2.7	8♏33.0	21♒41.4	4♐18.3	2♏22.9	25♐25.3	27♎51.0	10♋51.7	9♑19.6	2♑27.3	10♑ 3.9	14♏51.1
2	2 44 59.3	9 33.1	21 38.2	16 22.6	4 2.6	26 27.9	28 31.1	10 R 51.0	9 24.2	2 29.8	10 5.2	14 53.6
3	2 48 55.8	10 33.1	21 35.0	28 34.3	5 41.9	27 30.3	29 11.2	10 50.0	9 28.9	2 32.3	10 6.5	14 56.0
4	2 52 52.4	11 33.3	21 31.9	10♑56.1	7 20.8	28 32.3	29 51.3	10 48.9	9 33.7	2 34.9	10 7.9	14 58.4
5	2 56 48.9	12 33.4	21 28.7	23 31.0	8 59.4	29 34.0	0♏31.5	10 47.6	9 38.5	2 37.5	10 9.3	15 .8
6	3 0 45.5	13 33.6	21 25.5	6♒22.8	10 37.6	0♑35.4	1 11.7	10 46.1	9 43.4	2 40.1	10 10.7	15 3.3
7	3 4 42.0	14 33.8	21 22.3	19 35.3	12 15.4	1 36.4	1 52.0	10 44.4	9 48.4	2 42.8	10 12.2	15 5.7
8	3 8 38.6	15 34.0	21 19.2	3♓11.9	13 52.8	2 37.0	2 32.2	10 42.5	9 53.4	2 45.5	10 13.7	15 8.1
9	3 12 35.1	16 34.2	21 16.0	17 15.0	15 29.8	3 37.3	3 12.5	10 40.3	9 58.5	2 48.2	10 15.2	15 10.5
10	3 16 31.7	17 34.5	21 12.8	1♈44.7	17 6.5	4 37.3	3 52.9	10 38.1	10 3.7	2 51.0	10 16.8	15 13.0
11	3 20 28.3	18 34.8	21 9.6	16 37.8	18 42.8	5 36.8	4 33.3	10 35.6	10 8.9	2 53.8	10 18.3	15 15.4
12	3 24 24.8	19 35.1	21 6.5	1♉48.0	20 18.8	6 35.8	5 13.7	10 32.9	10 14.2	2 56.7	10 19.9	15 17.9
13	3 28 21.4	20 35.5	21 3.3	17 5.6	21 54.4	7 34.5	5 54.1	10 30.0	10 19.6	2 59.6	10 21.5	15 20.3
14	3 32 17.9	21 35.8	21 .1	2♊19.2	23 29.8	8 32.6	6 34.6	10 26.9	10 25.0	3 2.5	10 23.1	15 22.7
15	3 36 14.5	22 36.2	20 56.9	17 17.8	25 4.8	9 30.4	7 15.1	10 23.6	10 30.5	3 5.4	10 24.8	15 25.1
16	3 40 11.0	23 36.7	20 53.7	1♋52.7	26 39.5	10 27.6	7 55.7	10 20.2	10 36.0	3 8.4	10 26.5	15 27.5
17	3 44 7.6	24 37.1	20 50.6	15 58.6	28 14.0	11 24.3	8 36.2	10 16.5	10 41.6	3 11.3	10 28.2	15 29.9
18	3 48 4.2	25 37.6	20 47.4	29 34.2	29 48.3	12 20.5	9 16.9	10 12.7	10 47.2	3 14.4	10 29.9	15 32.3
19	3 52 .7	26 38.1	20 44.2	12♌40.9	1♐22.3	13 16.1	9 57.5	10 8.6	10 52.9	3 17.4	10 31.6	15 34.7
20	3 55 57.3	27 38.7	20 41.0	25 22.4	2 56.1	14 11.2	10 38.2	10 4.4	10 58.7	3 20.5	10 33.4	15 37.1
21	3 59 53.8	28 39.3	20 37.9	7♍43.6	4 29.7	15 5.8	11 18.9	10 .0	11 4.5	3 23.6	10 35.2	15 39.5
22	4 3 50.4	29 39.9	20 34.7	19 49.7	6 3.1	15 59.7	11 59.7	9 55.5	11 10.4	3 26.7	10 37.0	15 41.9
23	4 7 46.9	0♐40.5	20 31.5	1♎46.0	7 36.3	16 53.0	12 40.5	9 50.7	11 16.3	3 29.9	10 38.8	15 44.2
24	4 11 43.5	1 41.2	20 28.3	13 36.9	9 9.4	17 45.6	13 21.3	9 45.8	11 22.3	3 33.1	10 40.7	15 46.6
25	4 15 40.1	2 41.8	20 25.2	25 26.6	10 42.3	18 37.6	14 2.2	9 40.7	11 28.3	3 36.3	10 42.6	15 48.9
26	4 19 36.6	3 42.6	20 22.0	7♏18.1	12 15.1	19 28.8	14 43.1	9 35.5	11 34.4	3 39.5	10 44.4	15 51.3
27	4 23 33.2	4 43.3	20 18.8	19 13.7	13 47.8	20 19.3	15 24.0	9 30.0	11 40.5	3 42.8	10 46.4	15 53.6
28	4 27 29.7	5 44.1	20 15.6	1♐15.0	15 20.3	21 9.1	16 5.0	9 24.5	11 46.7	3 46.1	10 48.3	15 55.9
29	4 31 26.3	6 44.8	20 12.4	13 23.2	16 52.7	21 58.0	16 46.0	9 18.7	11 52.9	3 49.4	10 50.2	15 58.2
30	4 35 22.9	7 45.6	20 9.3	25 38.9	18 24.9	22 46.1	17 27.1	9 12.8	11 59.1	3 52.7	10 52.2	16 .5

LATITUDE

DAY	EPHEM. SID. TIME	☉	☊	☽	☿	♀	♂	♃	♄	♅	♆	♇
1	2 41 2.7	0 .0	0 .0	4 S 53.7	1 N 4.4	3 S 23.4	0 N 32.8	0 S 14.3	0 N 23.1	0 S 16.0	0 N 52.3	15 N 7.9
4	2 52 52.4	0 .0	0 .0	3 17.9	0 45.2	3 27.6	0 31.4	0 14.0	0 22.8	0 16.0	0 52.2	15 7.7
7	3 4 42.0	0 .0	0 .0	0 11.7	0 25.2	3 30.6	0 29.9	0 13.8	0 22.5	0 16.0	0 52.1	15 7.5
10	3 16 31.7	0 .0	0 .0	3 N 14.0	0 4.9	3 32.3	0 28.4	0 13.5	0 22.2	0 16.0	0 52.0	15 7.4
13	3 28 21.4	0 .0	0 .0	4 59.1	0 S 15.2	3 32.5	0 26.9	0 13.2	0 21.9	0 16.0	0 51.9	15 7.3
16	3 40 11.0	0 .0	0 .0	3 46.7	0 34.9	3 31.3	0 25.4	0 12.9	0 21.6	0 16.0	0 51.8	15 7.4
19	3 52 .7	0 .0	0 .0	0 41.4	0 53.8	3 28.3	0 23.8	0 12.6	0 21.3	0 16.0	0 51.7	15 7.5
22	4 3 50.4	0 .0	0 .0	2 S 28.2	1 11.6	3 23.6	0 22.2	0 12.3	0 21.0	0 16.0	0 51.6	15 7.7
25	4 15 40.1	0 .0	0 .0	4 33.1	1 28.1	3 17.0	0 20.6	0 11.9	0 20.7	0 16.0	0 51.5	15 8.0
28	4 27 29.7	0 .0	0 .0	4 54.0	1 42.9	3 8.2	0 18.9	0 11.6	0 20.4	0 16.0	0 51.5	15 8.3

RIGHT ASCENSION

DAY	EPHEM. SID. TIME	☉	☊	☽	☿	♀	♂	♃	♄	♅	♆	♇
1	2 41 2.7	6♏10.2	24♒ 3.9	1♐19.3	0♏34.1	24♐52.8	26♎ 3.6	11♋47.5	10♑ 7.2	2♑40.8	10♑52.7	16♏47.4
2	2 44 59.3	7 9.0	24 .8	14 40.8	2 7.6	26 2.8	26 41.5	11 R 46.7	10 12.2	2 43.6	10 54.1	16 49.6
3	2 48 55.8	8 8.0	23 57.7	28 23.7	3 41.2	27 12.4	27 19.5	11 45.7	10 17.3	2 46.3	10 55.5	16 51.8
4	2 52 52.4	9 7.2	23 54.6	12♑11.5	5 14.9	28 21.8	27 57.6	11 44.5	10 22.4	2 49.1	10 57.0	16 54.0
5	2 56 48.9	10 6.6	23 51.4	25 49.2	6 48.7	29 30.9	28 35.7	11 43.1	10 27.7	2 52.0	10 58.5	16 56.2
6	3 0 45.5	11 6.2	23 48.3	9♒ 7.2	8 22.7	0♑39.6	29 14.0	11 41.5	10 33.0	2 54.8	11 .1	16 58.5
7	3 4 42.0	12 6.0	23 45.2	22 4.1	9 56.7	1 47.9	29 52.4	11 39.6	10 38.3	2 57.7	11 1.6	17 .7
8	3 8 38.6	13 6.0	23 42.1	4♓46.1	11 31.0	2 55.8	0♏30.8	11 37.6	10 43.8	3 .7	11 3.2	17 2.9
9	3 12 35.1	14 6.2	23 39.0	17 25.6	13 5.4	4 3.3	1 9.4	11 35.3	10 49.3	3 3.7	11 4.9	17 5.2
10	3 16 31.7	15 6.7	23 35.9	0♈18.8	14 40.0	5 10.4	1 48.1	11 32.8	10 54.9	3 6.8	11 6.6	17 7.5
11	3 20 28.3	16 7.3	23 32.8	13 43.4	16 14.8	6 16.9	2 26.8	11 30.1	11 .6	3 9.8	11 8.2	17 9.7
12	3 24 24.8	17 8.1	23 29.7	27 56.1	17 49.9	7 22.9	3 5.7	11 27.2	11 6.3	3 12.9	11 9.9	17 12.0
13	3 28 21.4	18 9.2	23 26.6	13♉ 6.6	19 25.2	8 28.4	3 44.7	11 24.1	11 12.1	3 16.1	11 11.7	17 14.2
14	3 32 17.9	19 10.4	23 23.5	29 10.2	21 .8	9 33.3	4 23.7	11 20.8	11 18.0	3 19.2	11 13.4	17 16.4
15	3 36 14.5	20 11.9	23 20.4	15♊43.0	22 36.6	10 37.5	5 2.9	11 17.2	11 23.9	3 22.4	11 15.2	17 18.7
16	3 40 11.0	21 13.6	23 17.3	2♋ 6.4	24 12.8	11 41.1	5 42.2	11 13.5	11 29.9	3 25.7	11 17.0	17 20.9
17	3 44 7.6	22 15.5	23 14.1	17 42.4	25 49.2	12 44.1	6 21.6	11 9.6	11 35.9	3 28.9	11 18.9	17 23.2
18	3 48 4.2	23 17.6	23 11.0	2♌ 8.5	27 26.0	13 46.4	7 1.1	11 5.4	11 42.0	3 32.2	11 20.7	17 25.4
19	3 52 .7	24 19.9	23 7.9	15 21.1	29 3.2	14 47.9	7 40.7	11 1.1	11 48.2	3 35.6	11 22.6	17 27.6
20	3 55 57.3	25 22.4	23 4.8	27 29.8	0♐40.6	15 48.7	8 20.5	10 56.5	11 54.4	3 38.9	11 24.5	17 29.9
21	3 59 53.8	26 25.2	23 1.7	8♍50.7	2 18.5	16 48.7	9 .3	10 51.8	12 .7	3 42.3	11 26.4	17 32.1
22	4 3 50.4	27 28.1	22 58.6	19 41.0	3 56.6	17 47.9	9 40.3	10 46.8	12 7.1	3 45.7	11 28.4	17 34.3
23	4 7 46.9	28 31.3	22 55.5	0♎17.8	5 35.2	18 46.2	10 20.4	10 41.7	12 13.5	3 49.2	11 30.4	17 36.5
24	4 11 43.5	29 34.6	22 52.4	10 56.8	7 14.0	19 43.7	11 .6	10 36.4	12 19.9	3 52.7	11 32.4	17 38.8
25	4 15 40.1	0♐38.2	22 49.2	21 52.3	8 53.2	20 40.2	11 41.0	10 30.9	12 26.4	3 56.2	11 34.4	17 41.0
26	4 19 36.6	1 41.9	22 46.1	3♏16.4	10 32.7	21 35.8	12 21.4	10 25.2	12 33.0	3 59.7	11 36.4	17 43.2
27	4 23 33.2	2 45.9	22 43.0	15 18.2	12 12.6	22 30.4	13 2.0	10 19.3	12 39.6	4 3.2	11 38.5	17 45.4
28	4 27 29.7	3 50.0	22 39.9	28 1.1	13 52.7	23 24.0	13 42.7	10 13.3	12 46.3	4 6.8	11 40.6	17 47.6
29	4 31 26.3	4 54.3	22 36.8	11♐21.3	15 33.0	24 16.5	14 23.5	10 7.1	12 53.0	4 10.4	11 42.7	17 49.7
30	4 35 22.9	5 58.7	22 33.7	25 6.6	17 13.6	25 7.9	15 4.4	10 .7	12 59.8	4 14.0	11 44.8	17 51.9

DECLINATION

DAY	EPHEM. SID. TIME	☉	☊	☽	☿	♀	♂	♃	♄	♅	♆	♇
1	2 41 2.7	14 S 21.3	0 S 15.0	25 S 48.9	11 S 17.6	26 S 45.0	10 S 12.0	22 N 45.6	22 S 43.8	23 S 41.2	22 S 11.5	1 S 47.8
4	2 52 52.4	15 18.1	0 15.0	26 16.7	13 15.2	26 53.6	10 56.0	22 46.1	22 43.2	23 41.0	22 11.3	1 50.1
7	3 4 42.0	16 12.6	0 15.1	15 7.8	15 7.0	26 56.5	11 39.4	22 46.8	22 42.4	23 40.9	22 11.1	1 52.2
10	3 16 31.7	17 4.6	0 15.1	3 N 39.6	16 52.0	26 53.8	12 22.1	22 47.5	22 41.6	23 40.7	22 10.8	1 54.3
13	3 28 21.4	17 54.1	0 15.2	21 43.0	18 29.4	26 45.7	13 4.0	22 48.5	22 40.7	23 40.5	22 10.6	1 56.3
16	3 40 11.0	18 40.7	0 15.2	27 12.4	19 58.6	26 32.4	13 45.2	22 49.5	22 39.7	23 40.3	22 10.3	1 58.2
19	3 52 .7	19 24.4	0 15.3	17 40.0	21 18.9	26 14.1	14 25.6	22 50.7	22 38.6	23 40.1	22 9.9	1 60.0
22	4 3 50.4	20 4.9	0 15.3	1 45.4	22 29.7	25 51.2	15 5.1	22 52.0	22 37.4	23 39.8	22 9.6	2 1.7
25	4 15 40.1	20 42.1	0 15.4	14 S 4.5	23 30.5	25 23.9	15 43.6	22 53.4	22 36.2	23 39.6	22 9.2	2 3.4
28	4 27 29.7	21 15.9	0 15.4	25 12.4	24 20.5	24 52.7	16 21.0	22 54.9	22 34.9	23 39.3	22 8.9	2 4.9

DECEMBER 1989

LONGITUDE

DAY	EPHEM. SID. TIME h m s	☉ ° ′	☊ ° ′	☾ ° ′	☿ ° ′	♀ ° ′	♂ ° ′	♃ ° ′	♄ ° ′	♅ ° ′	♆ ° ′	♇ ° ′
1	4 39 19.4	8♐46.5	20♒ 6.1	8♑ 3.1	19♐57.1	23♑33.4	18♏ 8.2	9♋ 6.8	12♑ 5.5	3♑56.1	10♑54.2	16♏ 2.9
2	4 43 16.0	9 47.4	20 2.9	20 36.8	21 29.0	24 19.8	18 49.3	9R .6	12 11.8	3 59.4	10 56.2	16 5.1
3	4 47 12.5	10 48.2	19 59.7	3♒21.5	23 .8	25 5.2	19 30.5	8 54.3	12 18.2	4 2.8	10 58.3	16 7.4
4	4 51 9.1	11 49.1	19 56.6	16 19.4	24 32.4	25 49.6	20 11.7	8 47.9	12 24.7	4 6.2	11 .3	16 9.6
5	4 55 5.6	12 50.0	19 53.4	29 32.9	26 3.8	26 32.9	20 52.9	8 41.3	12 31.1	4 9.6	11 2.3	16 11.9
6	4 59 2.2	13 50.9	19 50.2	13♓ 4.7	27 35.0	27 15.2	21 34.1	8 34.5	12 37.6	4 13.0	11 4.4	16 14.1
7	5 2 58.8	14 51.8	19 47.0	26 56.8	29 5.9	27 56.4	22 15.4	8 27.7	12 44.2	4 16.5	11 6.5	16 16.3
8	5 6 55.3	15 52.7	19 43.9	11♈ 9.8	0♑36.4	28 36.3	22 56.7	8 20.7	12 50.7	4 20.0	11 8.6	16 18.5
9	5 10 51.9	16 53.6	19 40.7	25 42.4	2 6.6	29 15.1	23 38.1	8 13.7	12 57.4	4 23.4	11 10.7	16 20.6
10	5 14 48.4	17 54.6	19 37.5	10♉30.8	3 36.2	29 52.6	24 19.5	8 6.5	13 4.0	4 26.9	11 12.8	16 22.8
11	5 18 45.0	18 55.5	19 34.3	25 28.0	5 5.4	0♒28.7	25 .9	7 59.2	13 10.7	4 30.4	11 14.9	16 24.9
12	5 22 41.6	19 56.5	19 31.2	10♊25.5	6 33.8	1 3.4	25 42.4	7 51.8	13 17.4	4 33.9	11 17.1	16 27.0
13	5 26 38.1	20 57.5	19 28.0	25 13.7	8 1.5	1 36.8	26 23.9	7 44.4	13 24.1	4 37.5	11 19.2	16 29.1
14	5 30 34.7	21 58.5	19 24.8	9♋44.2	9 28.2	2 8.6	27 5.4	7 36.8	13 30.9	4 41.0	11 21.4	16 31.2
15	5 34 31.2	22 59.5	19 21.6	23 50.9	10 53.8	2 38.8	27 47.0	7 29.2	13 37.7	4 44.5	11 23.5	16 33.3
16	5 38 27.8	24 .5	19 18.4	7♌30.7	12 18.0	3 7.5	28 28.6	7 21.5	13 44.5	4 48.1	11 25.7	16 35.3
17	5 42 24.3	25 1.5	19 15.3	20 43.3	13 40.7	3 34.5	29 10.2	7 13.7	13 51.3	4 51.7	11 27.9	16 37.3
18	5 46 20.9	26 2.6	19 12.1	3♍30.7	15 1.6	3 59.7	29 51.9	7 5.9	13 58.2	4 55.2	11 30.1	16 39.3
19	5 50 17.5	27 3.7	19 8.9	15 56.9	16 20.3	4 23.2	0♐33.6	6 58.0	14 5.1	4 58.8	11 32.3	16 41.3
20	5 54 14.0	28 4.7	19 5.7	28 6.5	17 36.4	4 44.8	1 15.4	6 50.0	14 12.0	5 2.4	11 34.5	16 43.3
21	5 58 10.6	29 5.8	19 2.6	10♎ 4.8	18 49.5	5 4.4	1 57.2	6 42.0	14 18.9	5 6.0	11 36.8	16 45.2
22	6 2 7.1	0♑ 7.0	18 59.4	21 56.9	19 59.2	5 22.2	2 39.1	6 34.0	14 25.9	5 9.6	11 39.1	16 47.2
23	6 6 3.7	1 8.1	18 56.2	3♏47.5	21 4.8	5 37.8	3 20.9	6 25.9	14 32.9	5 13.2	11 41.3	16 49.1
24	6 10 .3	2 9.3	18 53.0	15 40.8	22 5.7	5 51.4	4 2.8	6 17.8	14 39.9	5 16.8	11 43.5	16 50.9
25	6 13 56.8	3 10.4	18 49.9	27 40.2	23 1.2	6 2.7	4 44.8	6 9.7	14 46.9	5 20.4	11 45.8	16 52.8
26	6 17 53.4	4 11.5	18 46.7	9♐48.3	23 50.5	6 11.9	5 26.8	6 1.6	14 53.9	5 24.1	11 48.0	16 54.6
27	6 21 49.9	5 12.7	18 43.5	22 6.8	24 32.8	6 18.7	6 8.8	5 53.4	15 1.0	5 27.7	11 50.3	16 56.4
28	6 25 46.5	6 13.9	18 40.3	4♑36.7	25 7.1	6 23.2	6 50.8	5 45.2	15 8.0	5 31.3	11 52.6	16 58.1
29	6 29 43.1	7 15.0	18 37.2	17 18.3	25 32.6	6 25.3	7 32.9	5 37.1	15 15.1	5 34.9	11 54.8	16 59.9
30	6 33 39.6	8 16.2	18 34.0	0♒11.6	25 48.4	6R25.0	8 15.0	5 29.0	15 22.1	5 38.5	11 57.1	17 1.6
31	6 37 36.2	9 17.4	18 30.8	13 16.5	25 53.7	6 22.2	8 57.2	5 20.8	15 29.2	5 42.1	11 59.4	17 3.3

LATITUDE

DAY	EPHEM. SID. TIME	☉	☊	☾	☿	♀	♂	♃	♄	♅	♆	♇
1	4 39 19.4	0 .0	0 .0	3S17.9	1S55.8	2S57.2	0N17.3	0S11.3	0N20.2	0S16.0	0N51.4	15N 8.7
4	4 51 9.1	0 .0	0 .0	0 12.9	2 6.2	2 43.9	0 15.6	0 10.9	0 19.9	0 16.0	0 51.3	15 9.2
7	5 2 58.8	0 .0	0 .0	3N 8.6	2 13.8	2 27.9	0 13.8	0 10.5	0 19.6	0 16.0	0 51.3	15 9.8
10	5 14 48.4	0 .0	0 .0	5 .9	2 17.9	2 9.1	0 12.1	0 10.1	0 19.4	0 16.0	0 51.2	15 10.4
13	5 26 38.1	0 .0	0 .0	4 2.8	2 17.9	1 47.4	0 10.3	0 9.8	0 19.1	0 16.0	0 51.1	15 11.1
16	5 38 27.8	0 .0	0 .0	0 54.8	2 12.9	1 22.6	0 8.5	0 9.4	0 18.9	0 16.1	0 51.1	15 11.9
19	5 50 17.5	0 .0	0 .0	2S25.6	2 1.7	0 54.5	0 6.7	0 9.0	0 18.6	0 16.1	0 51.0	15 12.7
22	6 2 7.1	0 .0	0 .0	4 37.3	1 43.0	0 22.9	0 4.8	0 8.5	0 18.4	0 16.1	0 51.0	15 13.6
25	6 13 56.8	0 .0	0 .0	5 2.8	1 15.4	0N12.2	0 2.9	0 8.1	0 18.2	0 16.1	0 50.9	15 14.5
28	6 25 46.5	0 .0	0 .0	3 28.6	0 37.7	0 50.7	0 1.0	0 7.7	0 18.0	0 16.1	0 50.9	15 15.5
31	6 37 36.2	0 .0	0 .0	0 19.5	0N10.5	1 32.3	0S 1.0	0 7.3	0 17.7	0 16.2	0 50.9	15 16.6

RIGHT ASCENSION

DAY	EPHEM. SID. TIME	☉	☊	☾	☿	♀	♂	♃	♄	♅	♆	♇
1	4 39 19.4	7♐ 3.4	22♒30.5	8♑59.3	18♐54.4	25♑58.3	15♏45.5	9♋54.2	13♑ 6.6	4♑17.7	11♑47.0	17♏54.1
2	4 43 16.0	8 8.2	22 27.4	22 41.2	20 35.4	26 47.4	16 26.7	9R47.6	13 13.5	4 21.4	11 49.1	17 56.3
3	4 47 12.5	9 13.1	22 24.3	5♒59.7	22 16.4	27 35.3	17 8.0	9 40.7	13 20.4	4 25.1	11 51.3	17 58.4
4	4 51 9.1	10 18.2	22 21.2	18 50.8	23 57.4	28 21.9	17 49.4	9 33.7	13 27.3	4 28.8	11 53.5	18 .5
5	4 55 5.6	11 23.5	22 18.1	1♓19.1	25 38.4	29 7.3	18 31.0	9 26.6	13 34.3	4 32.5	11 55.7	18 2.7
6	4 59 2.2	12 28.8	22 15.0	13 35.9	27 19.3	29 51.2	19 12.6	9 19.3	13 41.3	4 36.3	11 57.9	18 4.8
7	5 2 58.8	13 34.3	22 11.8	25 56.9	28 60.0	0♒33.8	19 54.4	9 11.9	13 48.4	4 40.0	12 .1	18 6.9
8	5 6 55.3	14 39.9	22 8.7	8♈40.3	0♑40.4	1 14.9	20 36.3	9 4.4	13 55.4	4 43.8	12 2.4	18 8.9
9	5 10 51.9	15 45.7	22 5.6	22 4.7	2 20.4	1 54.5	21 18.4	8 56.7	14 2.6	4 47.6	12 4.7	18 11.0
10	5 14 48.4	16 51.5	22 2.5	6♉25.7	3 59.8	2 32.6	22 .5	8 48.9	14 9.7	4 51.4	12 6.9	18 13.1
11	5 18 45.0	17 57.4	21 59.4	21 49.0	5 38.6	3 9.1	22 42.8	8 41.0	14 16.9	4 55.2	12 9.2	18 15.1
12	5 22 41.6	19 3.5	21 56.2	8♊ 3.6	7 16.5	3 43.9	23 25.2	8 33.1	14 24.2	4 59.1	12 11.5	18 17.1
13	5 26 38.1	20 9.6	21 53.1	24 38.2	8 53.4	4 17.0	24 7.7	8 25.0	14 31.4	5 2.9	12 13.8	18 19.2
14	5 30 34.7	21 15.8	21 50.0	10♋51.0	10 29.0	4 48.4	24 50.4	8 16.8	14 38.7	5 6.8	12 16.2	18 21.2
15	5 34 31.2	22 22.1	21 46.9	26 7.0	12 3.2	5 17.9	25 33.2	8 8.5	14 46.0	5 10.6	12 18.5	18 23.1
16	5 38 27.8	23 28.4	21 43.7	10♌10.0	13 35.6	5 45.6	26 16.1	8 .1	14 53.4	5 14.5	12 20.9	18 25.1
17	5 42 24.3	24 34.8	21 40.6	23 1.8	15 6.0	6 11.4	26 59.1	7 51.7	15 .7	5 18.4	12 23.2	18 27.1
18	5 46 20.9	25 41.3	21 37.5	4♍55.2	16 34.1	6 35.2	27 42.3	7 43.2	15 8.1	5 22.3	12 25.6	18 29.0
19	5 50 17.5	26 47.8	21 34.4	16 7.5	17 59.3	6 57.0	28 25.6	7 34.6	15 15.6	5 26.2	12 28.0	18 30.9
20	5 54 14.0	27 54.4	21 31.2	26 56.5	19 21.4	7 16.7	29 9.0	7 26.0	15 23.0	5 30.1	12 30.3	18 32.8
21	5 58 10.6	29 1.0	21 28.1	7♎39.2	20 39.8	7 34.3	29 52.5	7 17.3	15 30.5	5 34.0	12 32.7	18 34.7
22	6 2 7.1	0♑ 7.6	21 25.0	18 31.4	21 54.0	7 49.7	0♐36.3	7 8.6	15 38.0	5 38.0	12 35.2	18 36.6
23	6 6 3.7	1 14.2	21 21.9	29 46.9	23 3.3	8 2.9	1 20.0	6 59.9	15 45.5	5 41.9	12 37.6	18 38.4
24	6 10 .3	2 20.9	21 18.7	11♏37.1	24 7.1	8 13.7	2 4.0	6 51.1	15 53.0	5 45.9	12 40.0	18 40.2
25	6 13 56.8	3 27.5	21 15.6	24 8.9	25 4.6	8 22.2	2 48.0	6 42.3	16 .6	5 49.8	12 42.4	18 42.0
26	6 17 53.4	4 34.1	21 12.5	7♐22.1	25 55.1	8 28.2	3 32.1	6 33.4	16 8.1	5 53.7	12 44.9	18 43.8
27	6 21 49.9	5 40.7	21 9.3	21 7.9	26 37.6	8 31.9	4 16.4	6 24.6	16 15.7	5 57.7	12 47.3	18 45.6
28	6 25 46.5	6 47.2	21 6.2	5♑ 9.6	27 11.4	8 33.0	5 .8	6 15.7	16 23.3	6 1.6	12 49.7	18 47.3
29	6 29 43.1	7 53.7	21 3.1	19 7.0	27 35.4	8R31.6	5 45.3	6 6.9	16 30.9	6 5.5	12 52.2	18 49.0
30	6 33 39.6	9 .1	20 59.9	2♒43.4	27 48.9	8 27.7	6 29.9	5 58.0	16 38.5	6 9.5	12 54.6	18 50.7
31	6 37 36.2	10 6.5	20 56.8	15 50.3	27 51.0	8 21.2	7 14.6	5 49.2	16 46.1	6 13.4	12 57.0	18 52.4

DECLINATION

DAY	EPHEM. SID. TIME	☉	☊	☾	☿	♀	♂	♃	♄	♅	♆	♇
1	4 39 19.4	21S46.0	0S15.5	26S29.4	24S59.2	24S17.8	16S57.5	22N56.5	22S33.5	23S39.0	22S 8.5	2S 6.3
4	4 51 9.1	22 12.4	0 15.5	16 9.1	25 25.9	23 39.9	17 32.7	22 58.2	22 32.0	23 38.7	22 8.0	2 7.7
7	5 2 58.8	22 35.0	0 15.6	1N40.2	25 40.2	22 59.5	18 6.8	22 59.8	22 30.4	23 38.4	22 7.6	2 8.9
10	5 14 48.4	22 53.5	0 15.6	19 44.0	25 41.5	22 16.9	18 39.6	23 1.5	22 28.7	23 38.1	22 7.1	2 10.0
13	5 26 38.1	23 8.0	0 15.7	27 24.0	25 29.6	21 32.9	19 11.0	23 3.2	22 27.0	23 37.7	22 6.6	2 11.0
16	5 38 27.8	23 18.4	0 15.7	19 16.7	25 4.7	20 48.0	19 41.1	23 4.9	22 25.2	23 37.4	22 6.1	2 11.9
19	5 50 17.5	23 24.6	0 15.8	3 18.4	24 27.4	20 2.8	20 9.7	23 6.6	22 23.3	23 37.0	22 5.6	2 12.7
22	6 2 7.1	23 26.5	0 15.8	12S50.1	23 39.2	19 17.9	20 36.9	23 8.2	22 21.3	23 36.6	22 5.1	2 13.4
25	6 13 56.8	23 24.2	0 15.9	24 33.3	22 43.1	18 34.0	21 2.4	23 9.8	22 19.3	23 36.2	22 4.6	2 14.0
28	6 25 46.5	23 17.7	0 15.9	26 50.2	21 43.8	17 51.7	21 26.4	23 11.4	22 17.2	23 35.8	22 4.0	2 14.4
31	6 37 36.2	23 7.0	0 16.0	17 8.9	20 47.9	17 11.6	21 48.7	23 12.8	22 15.0	23 35.3	22 3.4	2 14.8

JANUARY 1990

LONGITUDE

DAY	EPHEM. SID. TIME	☉	☊	☽	☿	♀	♂	♃	♄	♅	♆	♇
	h m s	° ′	° ′	° ′	° ′	° ′	° ′	° ′	° ′	° ′	° ′	° ′
1	6 41 32.7	10♑18.5	18♒27.6	26♒32.9	25♑47.6	6♒16.9	9♐39.4	5♋12.7	15♑36.3	5♑45.7	12♑ 1.6	17♏ 4.9
2	6 45 29.3	11 19.7	18 24.5	10♓ 1.1	25 R 29.9	6 R 9.0	10 21.6	5 R 4.7	15 43.4	5 49.3	12 3.9	17 6.6
3	6 49 25.8	12 20.9	18 21.3	23 41.5	25 .3	5 58.7	11 3.9	4 56.6	15 50.5	5 52.9	12 6.2	17 8.2
4	6 53 22.4	13 22.0	18 18.1	7♈34.2	24 19.0	5 45.8	11 46.2	4 48.6	15 57.6	5 56.5	12 8.5	17 9.8
5	6 57 19.0	14 23.2	18 14.9	21 39.0	23 26.8	5 30.5	12 28.5	4 40.7	16 4.7	6 .1	12 10.8	17 11.3
6	7 1 15.5	15 24.4	18 11.7	5♉54.9	22 24.8	5 12.7	13 10.9	4 32.8	16 11.8	6 3.7	12 13.0	17 12.9
7	7 5 12.1	16 25.5	18 8.6	20 19.3	21 14.8	4 52.5	13 53.3	4 25.0	16 19.0	6 7.2	12 15.3	17 14.3
8	7 9 8.6	17 26.6	18 5.4	4♊48.4	19 58.8	4 30.0	14 35.7	4 17.3	16 26.1	6 10.8	12 17.6	17 15.8
9	7 13 5.2	18 27.8	18 2.2	19 16.9	18 39.3	4 5.3	15 18.1	4 9.6	16 33.2	6 14.3	12 19.8	17 17.2
10	7 17 1.8	19 28.9	17 59.0	3♋38.9	17 19.0	3 38.5	16 .6	4 2.0	16 40.3	6 17.9	12 22.1	17 18.6
11	7 20 58.3	20 30.0	17 55.9	17 48.6	16 .3	3 9.7	16 43.2	3 54.4	16 47.4	6 21.4	12 24.3	17 20.0
12	7 24 54.9	21 31.1	17 52.7	1♌41.2	14 45.6	2 39.1	17 25.7	3 47.0	16 54.5	6 24.9	12 26.6	17 21.3
13	7 28 51.4	22 32.2	17 49.5	15 13.3	13 36.9	2 7.0	18 8.3	3 39.7	17 1.6	6 28.4	12 28.8	17 22.7
14	7 32 48.0	23 33.3	17 46.3	28 23.6	12 35.7	1 33.5	18 51.0	3 32.4	17 8.7	6 31.9	12 31.1	17 23.9
15	7 36 44.5	24 34.4	17 43.2	11♍12.5	11 43.2	0 58.8	19 33.7	3 25.3	17 15.7	6 35.4	12 33.3	17 25.2
16	7 40 41.1	25 35.5	17 40.0	23 42.1	11 .1	0 23.1	20 16.4	3 18.2	17 22.8	6 38.9	12 35.5	17 26.4
17	7 44 37.7	26 36.6	17 36.8	5♎55.6	10 26.5	29♑46.8	20 59.1	3 11.3	17 29.9	6 42.3	12 37.8	17 27.6
18	7 48 34.2	27 37.7	17 33.6	17 57.2	10 2.4	29 10.0	21 41.9	3 4.5	17 36.9	6 45.8	12 40.0	17 28.7
19	7 52 30.8	28 38.8	17 30.5	29 51.6	9 47.7	28 33.1	22 24.7	2 57.8	17 43.9	6 49.2	12 42.2	17 29.8
20	7 56 27.3	29 39.8	17 27.3	11♏43.7	9 41.9	27 56.2	23 7.6	2 51.3	17 51.0	6 52.6	12 44.4	17 30.9
21	8 0 23.9	0♒40.9	17 24.1	23 38.1	9 D 44.5	27 19.6	23 50.5	2 44.9	17 58.0	6 56.0	12 46.6	17 32.0
22	8 4 20.4	1 42.0	17 20.9	5♐39.3	9 54.8	26 43.7	24 33.5	2 38.6	18 5.0	6 59.4	12 48.8	17 33.0
23	8 8 17.0	2 43.1	17 17.7	17 51.1	10 12.3	26 8.6	25 16.5	2 32.5	18 12.0	7 2.7	12 51.0	17 34.0
24	8 12 13.6	3 44.1	17 14.6	0♑16.6	10 36.4	25 34.5	25 59.5	2 26.5	18 18.9	7 6.1	12 53.1	17 35.0
25	8 16 10.1	4 45.1	17 11.4	12 57.8	11 6.5	25 1.7	26 42.5	2 20.7	18 25.9	7 9.4	12 55.3	17 35.9
26	8 20 6.7	5 46.2	17 8.2	25 55.7	11 42.0	24 30.4	27 25.6	2 15.0	18 32.8	7 12.7	12 57.4	17 36.7
27	8 24 3.2	6 47.2	17 5.0	9♒10.2	12 22.5	24 .7	28 8.7	2 9.4	18 39.7	7 15.9	12 59.5	17 37.6
28	8 27 59.8	7 48.2	17 1.9	22 40.3	13 7.4	23 32.9	28 51.8	2 4.1	18 46.5	7 19.2	13 1.6	17 38.4
29	8 31 56.3	8 49.1	16 58.7	6♓23.8	13 56.4	23 7.0	29 35.0	1 58.8	18 53.4	7 22.4	13 3.7	17 39.2
30	8 35 52.9	9 50.1	16 55.5	20 18.4	14 49.1	22 43.3	0♑18.2	1 53.8	19 .2	7 25.6	13 5.8	17 39.9
31	8 39 49.5	10 51.1	16 52.3	4♈21.2	15 45.2	22 21.7	1 1.4	1 48.9	19 7.0	7 28.7	13 7.9	17 40.6

LATITUDE

DAY	EPHEM. SID. TIME	☉	☊	☽	☿	♀	♂	♃	♄	♅	♆	♇
1	6 41 32.7	0 .0	0 .0	0N52.6	0N28.6	1N46.8	0S 1.6	0S 7.1	0N17.7	0S16.2	0N50.9	15N17.0
4	6 53 22.4	0 .0	0 .0	4 1.8	1 26.1	2 31.7	0 3.6	0 6.7	0 17.4	0 16.2	0 50.8	15 18.1
7	7 5 12.1	0 .0	0 .0	5 11.7	2 21.0	3 18.0	0 5.7	0 6.2	0 17.2	0 16.3	0 50.8	15 19.2
10	7 17 1.8	0 .0	0 .0	3 33.7	3 2.2	4 4.5	0 7.7	0 5.7	0 17.0	0 16.3	0 50.7	15 20.4
13	7 28 51.4	0 .0	0 .0	0 7.2	3 22.0	4 49.4	0 9.8	0 5.3	0 16.8	0 16.3	0 50.7	15 21.7
16	7 40 41.1	0 .0	0 .0	3S10.6	3 20.6	5 31.0	0 11.9	0 4.9	0 16.6	0 16.4	0 50.7	15 23.0
19	7 52 30.8	0 .0	0 .0	5 2.2	3 3.7	6 7.5	0 14.0	0 4.4	0 16.4	0 16.4	0 50.7	15 24.3
22	8 4 20.4	0 .0	0 .0	4 58.3	2 37.9	6 37.7	0 16.2	0 4.0	0 16.2	0 16.5	0 50.7	15 25.7
25	8 16 10.1	0 .0	0 .0	2 54.9	2 7.6	7 .5	0 18.4	0 3.5	0 16.0	0 16.5	0 50.7	15 27.1
28	8 27 59.8	0 .0	0 .0	0N34.4	1 36.0	7 15.7	0 20.6	0 3.1	0 15.8	0 16.6	0 50.7	15 28.5
31	8 39 49.5	0 .0	0 .0	3 55.4	1 4.7	7 23.6	0 22.8	0 2.7	0 15.6	0 16.6	0 50.7	15 29.9

RIGHT ASCENSION

DAY	EPHEM. SID. TIME	☉	☊	☽	☿	♀	♂	♃	♄	♅	♆	♇
1	6 41 32.7	11♑12.8	20♒53.7	28♒28.4	27♑41.1	8♒12.1	7♐59.4	5♋40.4	16♑53.7	6♑17.3	12♑59.5	18♏54.0
2	6 45 29.3	12 19.1	20 50.6	10♓46.5	27 R 18.8	8 R .4	8 44.4	5 R 31.6	17 1.3	6 21.3	13 1.9	18 55.6
3	6 49 25.8	13 25.2	20 47.4	22 58.4	26 44.1	7 46.1	9 29.4	5 22.9	17 8.9	6 25.2	13 4.4	18 57.2
4	6 53 22.4	14 31.2	20 44.3	5♈21.0	25 57.2	7 29.2	10 14.6	5 14.2	17 16.6	6 29.1	13 6.8	18 58.8
5	6 57 19.0	15 37.2	20 41.2	18 12.4	24 59.1	7 9.9	10 59.8	5 5.6	17 24.2	6 33.0	13 9.3	19 .4
6	7 1 15.5	16 43.0	20 38.0	1♉49.4	23 51.0	6 48.1	11 45.2	4 57.0	17 31.9	6 36.9	13 11.7	19 1.9
7	7 5 12.1	17 48.8	20 34.9	16 22.7	22 34.8	6 23.8	12 30.6	4 48.5	17 39.5	6 40.8	13 14.2	19 3.4
8	7 9 8.6	18 54.3	20 31.7	1♊51.3	21 12.7	5 57.4	13 16.2	4 40.1	17 47.1	6 44.7	13 16.6	19 4.8
9	7 13 5.2	19 59.8	20 28.6	17 56.7	19 47.3	5 28.7	14 1.9	4 31.7	17 54.8	6 48.6	13 19.0	19 6.3
10	7 17 1.8	21 5.1	20 25.5	4♋ 5.1	18 21.4	4 58.0	14 47.6	4 23.5	18 2.4	6 52.4	13 21.5	19 7.7
11	7 20 58.3	22 10.3	20 22.3	19 39.8	16 57.6	4 25.5	15 33.5	4 15.3	18 10.0	6 56.3	13 23.9	19 9.1
12	7 24 54.9	23 15.3	20 19.2	4♌15.2	15 38.3	3 51.2	16 19.4	4 7.2	18 17.6	7 .1	13 26.3	19 10.4
13	7 28 51.4	24 20.2	20 16.1	17 43.4	14 25.6	3 15.5	17 5.4	3 59.2	18 25.2	7 3.9	13 28.7	19 11.8
14	7 32 48.0	25 25.0	20 12.9	0♍10.3	13 21.0	2 38.6	17 51.6	3 51.3	18 32.8	7 7.7	13 31.1	19 13.1
15	7 36 44.5	26 29.5	20 9.8	11 49.6	12 25.6	2 .6	18 37.8	3 43.6	18 40.4	7 11.5	13 33.5	19 14.3
16	7 40 41.1	27 34.0	20 6.6	22 57.7	11 40.2	1 21.8	19 24.1	3 35.9	18 47.9	7 15.3	13 35.9	19 15.6
17	7 44 37.7	28 38.2	20 3.5	3♎51.1	11 5.1	0 42.5	20 10.4	3 28.4	18 55.5	7 19.0	13 38.3	19 16.8
18	7 48 34.2	29 42.3	20 .4	14 45.7	10 40.1	0 2.9	20 56.9	3 21.0	19 3.0	7 22.8	13 40.7	19 18.0
19	7 52 30.8	0♒46.2	19 57.2	25 56.0	10 25.1	29♑23.4	21 43.5	3 13.7	19 10.6	7 26.5	13 43.0	19 19.1
20	7 56 27.3	1 49.9	19 54.1	7♏34.3	10 19.5	28 44.1	22 30.1	3 6.6	19 18.1	7 30.2	13 45.4	19 20.3
21	8 0 23.9	2 53.5	19 50.9	19 49.9	10 D 22.9	28 5.3	23 16.8	2 59.6	19 25.6	7 33.9	13 47.7	19 21.4
22	8 4 20.4	3 56.9	19 47.8	2♐46.5	10 34.6	27 27.3	24 3.6	2 52.8	19 33.1	7 37.6	13 50.1	19 22.5
23	8 8 17.0	5 .0	19 44.7	16 20.2	10 54.0	26 50.3	24 50.4	2 46.1	19 40.6	7 41.3	13 52.5	19 23.5
24	8 12 13.6	6 3.0	19 41.5	0♑18.6	11 20.5	26 14.6	25 37.3	2 39.6	19 48.0	7 44.9	13 54.8	19 24.5
25	8 16 10.1	7 5.8	19 38.4	14 23.9	11 53.4	25 40.3	26 24.3	2 33.2	19 55.4	7 48.5	13 57.1	19 25.5
26	8 20 6.7	8 8.4	19 35.2	28 17.7	12 32.2	25 7.6	27 11.3	2 27.0	20 2.8	7 52.1	13 59.4	19 26.4
27	8 24 3.2	9 10.8	19 32.1	11♒47.6	13 16.4	24 36.8	27 58.3	2 21.0	20 10.2	7 55.6	14 1.7	19 27.3
28	8 27 59.8	10 13.0	19 28.9	24 49.8	14 5.4	24 8.0	28 45.5	2 15.2	20 17.5	7 59.2	14 3.9	19 28.2
29	8 31 56.3	11 15.0	19 25.8	7♓28.9	14 58.8	23 41.3	29 32.6	2 9.5	20 24.8	8 2.7	14 6.2	19 29.1
30	8 35 52.9	12 16.7	19 22.6	19 56.1	15 56.3	23 16.9	0♑19.8	2 4.0	20 32.1	8 6.1	14 8.4	19 29.9
31	8 39 49.5	13 18.3	19 19.5	2♈26.0	16 57.3	22 54.8	1 7.1	1 58.7	20 39.4	8 9.6	14 10.6	19 30.6

DECLINATION

DAY	EPHEM. SID. TIME	☉	☊	☽	☿	♀	♂	♃	♄	♅	♆	♇
1	6 41 32.7	23S 2.5	0S16.0	11S50.6	20S31.2	16S58.9	21S55.7	23N13.3	22S14.2	23S35.2	22S 3.2	2S14.8
4	6 53 22.4	22 46.2	0 16.1	6N42.3	19 50.6	16 22.9	22 15.6	23 14.6	22 12.0	23 34.7	22 2.6	2 15.0
7	7 5 12.1	22 25.9	0 16.1	22 49.8	19 26.5	15 50.6	22 33.8	23 15.9	22 9.7	23 34.3	22 2.1	2 15.1
10	7 17 1.8	22 1.7	0 16.2	26 57.1	19 18.5	15 22.6	22 50.1	23 17.1	22 7.3	23 33.8	22 1.5	2 15.1
13	7 28 51.4	21 33.5	0 16.2	16 23.3	19 23.8	14 59.3	23 4.5	23 18.2	22 4.8	23 33.4	22 .9	2 14.9
16	7 40 41.1	21 1.6	0 16.3	0S24.9	19 39.3	14 40.7	23 17.0	23 19.2	22 2.4	23 32.9	22 .3	2 14.6
19	7 52 30.8	20 26.1	0 16.3	16 7.9	20 1.6	14 27.0	23 27.5	23 20.1	21 59.8	23 32.4	21 59.7	2 14.2
22	8 4 20.4	19 47.1	0 16.4	26 8.6	20 26.9	14 18.2	23 36.0	23 21.0	21 57.2	23 31.9	21 59.0	2 13.7
25	8 16 10.1	19 4.7	0 16.4	25 42.7	20 51.5	14 13.9	23 42.4	23 21.8	21 54.6	23 31.4	21 58.4	2 13.1
28	8 27 59.8	18 19.2	0 16.5	13 25.1	21 12.2	14 13.8	23 46.8	23 22.5	21 52.0	23 30.9	21 57.8	2 12.4
31	8 39 49.5	17 30.8	0 16.5	5N19.8	21 26.5	14 17.3	23 49.1	23 23.1	21 49.3	23 30.4	21 57.2	2 11.6

FEBRUARY 1990

LONGITUDE

DAY	EPHEM. SID. TIME	☉	☊	☽	☿	♀	♂	♃	♄	♅	♆	♇
	h m s	° ′	° ′	° ′	° ′	° ′	° ′	° ′	° ′	° ′	° ′	° ′
1	8 43 46.0	11 ♒ 52.0	16 ♒ 49.2	18 ♈ 29.6	16 ♑ 44.3	22 ♑ 2.4	1 ♑ 44.6	1 ♋ 44.2	19 ♑ 13.7	7 ♑ 31.9	13 ♑ 9.9	17 ♏ 41.3
2	8 47 42.6	12 52.9	16 46.0	2 ♉ 40.9	17 46.1	21 R 45.5	2 27.9	1 R 39.7	19 20.5	7 35.0	13 12.0	17 41.9
3	8 51 39.1	13 53.7	16 42.8	16 52.8	18 50.5	21 31.0	3 11.3	1 35.4	19 27.2	7 38.1	13 14.0	17 42.5
4	8 55 35.7	14 54.6	16 39.6	1 ♊ 2.9	19 57.2	21 18.9	3 54.6	1 31.2	19 33.8	7 41.1	13 16.0	17 43.1
5	8 59 32.2	15 55.4	16 36.4	15 9.1	21 6.1	21 9.3	4 38.0	1 27.3	19 40.5	7 44.2	13 18.0	17 43.6
6	9 3 28.8	16 56.2	16 33.3	29 9.1	22 16.9	21 2.2	5 21.4	1 23.5	19 47.1	7 47.2	13 20.0	17 44.1
7	9 7 25.4	17 57.0	16 30.1	13 ♋ .5	23 29.6	20 57.5	6 4.8	1 19.9	19 53.6	7 50.1	13 21.9	17 44.5
8	9 11 21.9	18 57.8	16 26.9	26 41.1	24 44.0	20 55.4	6 48.3	1 16.5	20 .2	7 53.1	13 23.9	17 44.9
9	9 15 18.5	19 58.5	16 23.7	10 ♌ 8.7	25 59.9	20 D 55.7	7 31.8	1 13.3	20 6.7	7 56.0	13 25.8	17 45.3
10	9 19 15.0	20 59.2	16 20.6	23 21.8	27 17.4	20 58.3	8 15.4	1 10.2	20 13.1	7 58.9	13 27.7	17 45.6
11	9 23 11.6	21 59.9	16 17.4	6 ♍ 19.1	28 36.2	21 3.4	8 58.9	1 7.4	20 19.6	8 1.7	13 29.6	17 46.0
12	9 27 8.1	23 .6	16 14.2	19 .8	29 56.5	21 10.8	9 42.6	1 4.8	20 26.0	8 4.6	13 31.5	17 46.3
13	9 31 4.7	24 1.3	16 11.0	1 ♎ 27.3	1 ♒ 17.9	21 20.5	10 26.2	1 2.3	20 32.3	8 7.3	13 33.3	17 46.5
14	9 35 1.2	25 1.9	16 7.9	13 40.6	2 40.6	21 32.3	11 9.9	1 .1	20 38.6	8 10.1	13 35.1	17 46.7
15	9 38 57.8	26 2.5	16 4.7	25 43.3	4 4.5	21 46.3	11 53.6	0 58.0	20 44.9	8 12.8	13 36.9	17 46.9
16	9 42 54.4	27 3.1	16 1.5	7 ♏ 38.9	5 29.5	22 2.4	12 37.3	0 56.2	20 51.1	8 15.5	13 38.7	17 47.0
17	9 46 50.9	28 3.7	15 58.3	19 31.5	6 55.6	22 20.5	13 21.1	0 54.5	20 57.3	8 18.1	13 40.5	17 47.1
18	9 50 47.5	29 4.2	15 55.1	1 ♐ 25.6	8 22.8	22 40.6	14 4.9	0 53.1	21 3.4	8 20.7	13 42.2	17 47.1
19	9 54 44.0	0 ♓ 4.7	15 52.0	13 25.9	9 51.0	23 2.5	14 48.7	0 51.8	21 9.4	8 23.3	13 43.9	17 47.2
20	9 58 40.6	1 5.2	15 48.8	25 37.0	11 20.2	23 26.3	15 32.6	0 50.7	21 15.5	8 25.8	13 45.6	17 R 47.1
21	10 2 37.1	2 5.7	15 45.6	8 ♑ 3.5	12 50.5	23 51.9	16 16.5	0 49.9	21 21.4	8 28.3	13 47.3	17 47.1
22	10 6 33.7	3 6.2	15 42.4	20 48.8	14 21.7	24 19.1	17 .4	0 49.2	21 27.4	8 30.8	13 48.9	17 47.0
23	10 10 30.2	4 6.6	15 39.3	3 ♒ 55.5	15 54.0	24 47.9	17 44.4	0 48.8	21 33.2	8 33.2	13 50.6	17 46.9
24	10 14 26.8	5 7.0	15 36.1	17 24.7	17 27.2	25 18.3	18 28.4	0 48.5	21 39.0	8 35.6	13 52.1	17 46.7
25	10 18 23.3	6 7.4	15 32.9	1 ♓ 15.6	19 1.5	25 50.2	19 12.4	0 48.4	21 44.8	8 37.9	13 53.7	17 46.5
26	10 22 19.9	7 7.8	15 29.7	15 25.4	20 36.7	26 23.5	19 56.4	0 D 48.6	21 50.5	8 40.2	13 55.3	17 46.3
27	10 26 16.5	8 8.1	15 26.5	29 49.6	22 12.9	26 58.2	20 40.4	0 48.9	21 56.2	8 42.4	13 56.8	17 46.0
28	10 30 13.0	9 8.4	15 23.4	14 ♈ 22.3	23 50.2	27 34.3	21 24.5	0 49.5	22 1.8	8 44.7	13 58.3	17 45.7

LATITUDE

DAY	EPHEM. SID. TIME	☉	☊	☽	☿	♀	♂	♃	♄	♅	♆	♇
1	8 43 46.0	0 .0	0 .0	4 N 40.1	0 N 54.5	7 N 24.7	0 S 23.5	0 S 2.5	0 N 15.5	0 S 16.6	0 N 50.7	15 N 30.4
4	8 55 35.7	0 .0	0 .0	5 6.9	0 24.9	7 23.8	0 25.8	0 2.1	0 15.3	0 16.7	0 50.7	15 31.8
7	9 7 25.4	0 .0	0 .0	2 55.2	0 S 2.7	7 17.5	0 28.1	0 1.7	0 15.1	0 16.7	0 50.8	15 33.3
10	9 19 15.0	0 .0	0 .0	0 S 38.0	0 28.1	7 6.7	0 30.4	0 1.3	0 15.0	0 16.8	0 50.8	15 34.8
13	9 31 4.7	0 .0	0 .0	3 44.1	0 51.1	6 52.3	0 32.8	0 .9	0 14.8	0 16.8	0 50.8	15 36.2
16	9 42 54.4	0 .0	0 .0	5 12.7	1 11.5	6 35.2	0 35.1	0 .5	0 14.6	0 16.9	0 50.8	15 37.7
19	9 54 44.0	0 .0	0 .0	4 41.9	1 29.1	6 16.0	0 37.5	0 .1	0 14.4	0 16.9	0 50.9	15 39.1
22	10 6 33.7	0 .0	0 .0	2 17.1	1 43.9	5 55.4	0 39.9	0 N .3	0 14.3	0 17.0	0 50.9	15 40.6
25	10 18 23.3	0 .0	0 .0	1 N 20.6	1 55.5	5 33.7	0 42.3	0 .7	0 14.1	0 17.1	0 50.9	15 42.0
28	10 30 13.0	0 .0	0 .0	4 26.5	2 3.9	5 11.3	0 44.7	0 1.0	0 13.9	0 17.1	0 51.0	15 43.4

RIGHT ASCENSION

DAY	EPHEM. SID. TIME	☉	☊	☽	☿	♀	♂	♃	♄	♅	♆	♇
1	8 43 46.0	14 ♒ 19.7	19 ♒ 16.3	15 ♈ 14.9	18 ♑ 1.7	22 ♑ 35.1	1 ♑ 54.4	1 ♋ 53.6	20 ♑ 46.6	8 ♑ 13.0	14 ♑ 12.8	19 ♏ 31.4
2	8 47 42.6	15 20.8	19 13.2	28 38.5	19 9.0	22 R 17.9	2 41.7	1 R 48.7	20 53.8	8 16.4	14 15.0	19 32.1
3	8 51 39.1	16 21.8	19 10.0	12 ♉ 47.8	20 19.0	22 3.3	3 29.1	1 43.9	21 .9	8 19.8	14 17.2	19 32.8
4	8 55 35.7	17 22.5	19 6.9	27 45.0	21 31.5	21 51.2	4 16.5	1 39.4	21 8.1	8 23.1	14 19.3	19 33.4
5	8 59 32.2	18 23.0	19 3.7	13 ♊ 18.4	22 46.2	21 41.7	5 3.9	1 35.1	21 15.1	8 26.4	14 21.5	19 34.1
6	9 3 28.8	19 23.4	19 .6	29 2.8	24 2.9	21 34.8	5 51.3	1 31.0	21 22.2	8 29.7	14 23.6	19 34.6
7	9 7 25.4	20 23.5	18 57.4	14 ♋ 26.9	25 21.5	21 30.5	6 38.8	1 27.0	21 29.2	8 32.9	14 25.7	19 35.2
8	9 11 21.9	21 23.4	18 54.3	29 5.2	26 41.8	21 28.8	7 26.3	1 23.3	21 36.2	8 36.1	14 27.8	19 35.7
9	9 15 18.5	22 23.1	18 51.1	12 ♌ 45.5	28 3.6	21 D 29.6	8 13.8	1 19.8	21 43.1	8 39.3	14 29.8	19 36.2
10	9 19 15.0	23 22.6	18 48.0	25 28.9	29 26.9	21 33.0	9 1.3	1 16.5	21 50.0	8 42.4	14 31.9	19 36.6
11	9 23 11.6	24 21.9	18 44.8	7 ♍ 24.8	0 ♒ 51.4	21 38.8	9 48.8	1 13.4	21 56.8	8 45.5	14 33.9	19 37.0
12	9 27 8.1	25 21.1	18 41.7	18 47.2	2 17.1	21 47.1	10 36.4	1 10.6	22 3.6	8 48.6	14 35.9	19 37.5
13	9 31 4.7	26 20.1	18 38.5	29 50.8	3 43.9	21 57.7	11 24.0	1 7.9	22 10.4	8 51.6	14 37.9	19 37.8
14	9 35 1.2	27 18.8	18 35.4	10 ♎ 50.4	5 11.7	22 10.6	12 11.5	1 5.5	22 17.1	8 54.6	14 39.9	19 38.1
15	9 38 57.8	28 17.4	18 32.2	21 59.5	6 40.4	22 25.7	12 59.1	1 3.3	22 23.8	8 57.6	14 41.8	19 38.4
16	9 42 54.4	29 15.8	18 29.1	3 ♏ 30.2	8 9.9	22 43.0	13 46.6	1 1.2	22 30.4	9 .5	14 43.7	19 38.7
17	9 46 50.9	0 ♓ 14.0	18 25.9	15 31.8	9 40.2	23 2.4	14 34.2	0 59.4	22 36.9	9 3.4	14 45.6	19 38.9
18	9 50 47.5	1 12.0	18 22.8	28 9.7	11 11.2	23 23.9	15 21.7	0 57.8	22 43.5	9 6.2	14 47.4	19 39.1
19	9 54 44.0	2 9.9	18 19.6	11 ♐ 23.1	12 42.9	23 47.3	16 9.2	0 56.5	22 49.9	9 9.0	14 49.3	19 39.2
20	9 58 40.6	3 7.6	18 16.4	25 4.3	14 15.2	24 12.6	16 56.7	0 55.3	22 56.3	9 11.8	14 51.1	19 39.3
21	10 2 37.1	4 5.2	18 13.3	8 ♑ 59.6	15 48.0	24 39.7	17 44.2	0 54.4	23 2.7	9 14.5	14 52.9	19 39.4
22	10 6 33.7	5 2.6	18 10.1	22 53.2	17 21.4	25 8.6	18 31.7	0 53.6	23 9.0	9 17.1	14 54.6	19 39.4
23	10 10 30.2	5 59.8	18 7.0	6 ♒ 32.0	18 55.3	25 39.2	19 19.1	0 53.1	23 15.2	9 19.8	14 56.4	19 39.4
24	10 14 26.8	6 56.9	18 3.8	19 49.9	20 29.7	26 11.4	20 6.6	0 52.9	23 21.4	9 22.4	14 58.1	19 39.4
25	10 18 23.3	7 53.8	18 .6	2 ♓ 48.4	22 4.6	26 45.2	20 54.0	0 52.8	23 27.5	9 24.9	14 59.7	19 39.4
26	10 22 19.9	8 50.6	17 57.5	15 35.7	23 39.9	27 20.5	21 41.3	0 D 53.0	23 33.6	9 27.4	15 1.4	19 R 39.3
27	10 26 16.5	9 47.3	17 54.3	28 24.3	25 15.6	27 57.1	22 28.6	0 53.3	23 39.6	9 29.9	15 3.0	19 39.1
28	10 30 13.0	10 43.8	17 51.2	11 ♈ 29.1	26 51.8	28 35.2	23 15.9	0 53.9	23 45.5	9 32.3	15 4.6	19 39.0

DECLINATION

DAY	EPHEM. SID. TIME	☉	☊	☽	☿	♀	♂	♃	♄	♅	♆	♇
1	8 43 46.0	17 S 14.0	0 S 16.5	11 N 33.7	21 S 29.6	14 S 19.2	23 S 49.4	23 N 23.3	21 S 48.4	23 S 30.3	21 S 57.0	2 S 11.3
4	8 55 35.7	16 21.9	0 16.6	25 22.4	21 32.9	14 26.5	23 48.9	23 23.9	21 45.8	23 29.8	21 56.4	2 10.4
7	9 7 25.4	15 27.2	0 16.6	25 42.8	21 26.6	14 35.9	23 46.2	23 24.4	21 43.1	23 29.3	21 55.8	2 9.4
10	9 19 15.0	14 30.2	0 16.7	13 8.1	21 9.8	14 46.5	23 41.5	23 25.0	21 40.4	23 28.9	21 55.2	2 8.3
13	9 31 4.7	13 31.0	0 16.7	4 S .3	20 42.2	14 57.5	23 34.6	23 25.4	21 37.7	23 28.4	21 54.6	2 7.1
16	9 42 54.4	12 29.8	0 16.8	18 59.1	20 3.3	15 8.1	23 25.5	23 25.9	21 35.1	23 28.0	21 54.0	2 5.8
19	9 54 44.0	11 26.8	0 16.8	27 4.6	19 12.9	15 17.5	23 14.4	23 26.3	21 32.4	23 27.5	21 53.4	2 4.5
22	10 6 33.7	10 22.1	0 16.9	24 5.3	18 10.8	15 25.3	23 1.2	23 26.7	21 29.8	23 27.1	21 52.9	2 3.0
25	10 18 23.3	9 16.0	0 16.9	9 46.4	16 57.0	15 30.8	22 45.8	23 27.1	21 27.2	23 26.7	21 52.4	2 1.5
28	10 30 13.0	8 8.6	0 17.0	9 N 45.5	15 31.6	15 33.6	22 28.5	23 27.4	21 24.7	23 26.3	21 51.9	1 60.0

MARCH 1990

LONGITUDE

DAY	EPHEM. SID. TIME h m s	☉ ° ′	☊ ° ′	☾ ° ′	☿ ° ′	♀ ° ′	♂ ° ′	♃ ° ′	♄ ° ′	♅ ° ′	♆ ° ′	♇ ° ′
1	10 34 9.6	10♓ 8.6	15♒ 20.2	28♈ 57.1	25♒ 28.4	28♑ 11.6	22♑ 8.6	0♋ 50.2	22♑ 7.3	8♑ 46.8	13♑ 59.7	17♏ 45.4
2	10 38 6.1	11 8.9	15 17.0	13♉ 28.0	27 7.7	28 50.1	22 52.8	0 51.2	22 12.8	8 49.0	14 1.2	17R 45.0
3	10 42 2.7	12 9.1	15 13.8	27 50.2	28 48.0	29 29.8	23 36.9	0 52.3	22 18.2	8 51.0	14 2.6	17 44.6
4	10 45 59.2	13 9.2	15 10.7	12♊ .4	0♓ 29.3	0♒ 10.6	24 21.1	0 53.6	22 23.5	8 53.1	14 4.0	17 44.2
5	10 49 55.8	14 9.4	15 7.5	25 56.9	2 11.8	0 52.5	25 5.3	0 55.2	22 28.9	8 55.1	14 5.4	17 43.7
6	10 53 52.3	15 9.5	15 4.3	9♋ 39.0	3 55.2	1 35.4	25 49.6	0 57.0	22 34.1	8 57.1	14 6.7	17 43.2
7	10 57 48.9	16 9.5	15 1.1	23 7.0	5 39.8	2 19.4	26 33.8	0 58.9	22 39.2	8 59.0	14 8.0	17 42.7
8	11 1 45.4	17 9.6	14 57.9	6♌ 21.7	7 25.5	3 4.3	27 18.1	1 1.0	22 44.3	9 .8	14 9.3	17 42.1
9	11 5 42.0	18 9.5	14 54.8	19 23.8	9 12.2	3 50.1	28 2.4	1 3.3	22 49.4	9 2.6	14 10.5	17 41.5
10	11 9 38.5	19 9.5	14 51.6	2♍ 14.0	11 .1	4 36.8	28 46.7	1 5.8	22 54.3	9 4.4	14 11.7	17 40.9
11	11 13 35.1	20 9.4	14 48.4	14 52.7	12 49.2	5 24.4	29 31.0	1 8.5	22 59.2	9 6.1	14 12.9	17 40.2
12	11 17 31.7	21 9.3	14 45.2	27 20.5	14 39.3	6 12.8	0♒ 15.4	1 11.3	23 4.0	9 7.8	14 14.1	17 39.5
13	11 21 28.2	22 9.2	14 42.1	9♎ 38.0	16 30.6	7 2.0	0 59.8	1 14.4	23 8.8	9 9.4	14 15.2	17 38.8
14	11 25 24.8	23 9.0	14 38.9	21 46.1	18 23.1	7 52.0	1 44.2	1 17.6	23 13.5	9 11.0	14 16.3	17 38.0
15	11 29 21.3	24 8.8	14 35.7	3♏ 46.4	20 16.6	8 42.7	2 28.7	1 21.0	23 18.1	9 12.6	14 17.4	17 37.2
16	11 33 17.9	25 8.5	14 32.5	15 41.1	22 11.3	9 34.1	3 13.1	1 24.6	23 22.6	9 14.0	14 18.4	17 36.4
17	11 37 14.4	26 8.3	14 29.3	27 33.1	24 7.1	10 26.2	3 57.6	1 28.4	23 27.1	9 15.5	14 19.4	17 35.5
18	11 41 11.0	27 8.0	14 26.2	9♐ 26.1	26 3.9	11 19.0	4 42.1	1 32.4	23 31.5	9 16.9	14 20.4	17 34.7
19	11 45 7.5	28 7.6	14 23.0	21 24.3	28 1.7	12 12.3	5 26.7	1 36.5	23 35.8	9 18.2	14 21.3	17 33.7
20	11 49 4.1	29 7.3	14 19.8	3♑ 32.4	0♈ .4	13 6.3	6 11.2	1 40.8	23 40.0	9 19.5	14 22.2	17 32.8
21	11 53 .6	0♈ 6.9	14 16.6	15 55.5	1 60.0	14 .9	6 55.8	1 45.3	23 44.2	9 20.7	14 23.1	17 31.8
22	11 56 57.2	1 6.5	14 13.5	28 38.1	4 .2	14 56.0	7 40.4	1 50.0	23 48.3	9 21.9	14 23.9	17 30.8
23	12 0 53.7	2 6.0	14 10.3	11♒ 44.5	6 1.1	15 51.6	8 25.0	1 54.8	23 52.3	9 23.1	14 24.8	17 29.8
24	12 4 50.3	3 5.6	14 7.1	25 17.4	8 2.3	16 47.8	9 9.6	1 59.8	23 56.2	9 24.2	14 25.5	17 28.8
25	12 8 46.8	4 5.1	14 3.9	9♓ 17.5	10 3.8	17 44.4	9 54.3	2 4.9	24 .1	9 25.2	14 26.3	17 27.7
26	12 12 43.4	5 4.6	14 .7	23 43.0	12 5.4	18 41.6	10 39.0	2 10.3	24 3.9	9 26.2	14 27.1	17 26.6
27	12 16 40.0	6 4.0	13 57.6	8♈ 28.7	14 6.6	19 39.2	11 23.7	2 15.8	24 7.6	9 27.2	14 27.8	17 25.5
28	12 20 36.5	7 3.4	13 54.4	23 27.1	16 7.3	20 37.2	12 8.4	2 21.5	24 11.2	9 28.1	14 28.4	17 24.3
29	12 24 33.1	8 2.8	13 51.2	8♉ 28.8	18 7.1	21 35.7	12 53.1	2 27.3	24 14.7	9 28.9	14 29.0	17 23.1
30	12 28 29.6	9 2.1	13 48.0	23 24.4	20 5.8	22 34.5	13 37.8	2 33.3	24 18.1	9 29.7	14 29.6	17 21.9
31	12 32 26.2	10 1.4	13 44.9	8♊ 5.8	22 2.8	23 33.7	14 22.5	2 39.4	24 21.4	9 30.4	14 30.2	17 20.7

LATITUDE

DAY	EPHEM. SID. TIME h m s	☉ ° ′	☊ ° ′	☾ ° ′	☿ ° ′	♀ ° ′	♂ ° ′	♃ ° ′	♄ ° ′	♅ ° ′	♆ ° ′	♇ ° ′
1	10 34 9.6	0 .0	0 .0	4N 59.6	2S 6.0	5N 3.7	0S 45.5	0N 1.2	0N 13.8	0S 17.1	0N 51.0	15N 43.8
4	10 45 59.2	0 .0	0 .0	4 42.7	2 9.7	4 40.8	0 47.9	0 1.5	0 13.7	0 17.2	0 51.0	15 45.2
7	10 57 48.9	0 .0	0 .0	2 3.5	2 9.6	4 17.7	0 50.4	0 1.9	0 13.5	0 17.3	0 51.1	15 46.5
10	11 9 38.5	0 .0	0 .0	1S 26.0	2 5.4	3 54.7	0 52.8	0 2.2	0 13.3	0 17.3	0 51.1	15 47.8
13	11 21 28.2	0 .0	0 .0	4 9.8	1 56.9	3 31.9	0 55.3	0 2.6	0 13.2	0 17.4	0 51.2	15 49.0
16	11 33 17.9	0 .0	0 .0	5 9.5	1 43.8	3 9.4	0 57.8	0 2.9	0 13.0	0 17.5	0 51.2	15 50.2
19	11 45 7.5	0 .0	0 .0	4 11.2	1 25.8	2 47.3	1 .2	0 3.2	0 12.8	0 17.5	0 51.3	15 51.4
22	11 56 57.2	0 .0	0 .0	1 30.3	1 3.0	2 25.7	1 2.7	0 3.6	0 12.6	0 17.6	0 51.3	15 52.5
25	12 8 46.8	0 .0	0 .0	2N 4.2	0 35.5	2 4.6	1 5.1	0 3.9	0 12.5	0 17.7	0 51.4	15 53.5
28	12 20 36.5	0 .0	0 .0	4 44.3	0 4.0	1 44.2	1 7.6	0 4.2	0 12.3	0 17.8	0 51.5	15 54.5
31	12 32 26.2	0 .0	0 .0	4 41.2	0N 30.2	1 24.5	1 10.0	0 4.5	0 12.1	0 17.8	0 51.5	15 55.4

RIGHT ASCENSION

DAY	EPHEM. SID. TIME h m s	☉ ° ′	☊ ° ′	☾ ° ′	☿ ° ′	♀ ° ′	♂ ° ′	♃ ° ′	♄ ° ′	♅ ° ′	♆ ° ′	♇ ° ′
1	10 34 9.6	11♓ 40.1	17♒ 48.0	25♈ 4.2	28♒ 28.3	29♑ 14.5	24♑ 3.1	0♋ 54.7	23♑ 51.4	9♑ 34.6	15♑ 6.2	19♏ 38.8
2	10 38 6.1	12 36.4	17 44.8	9♉ 20.1	0♓ 5.3	29 55.2	24 50.3	0 55.8	23 57.2	9 36.9	15 7.7	19R 38.6
3	10 42 2.7	13 32.5	17 41.7	24 18.4	1 42.6	0♒ 37.0	25 37.5	0 57.0	24 3.0	9 39.2	15 9.2	19 38.3
4	10 45 59.2	14 28.5	17 38.5	9♊ 48.3	3 20.4	1 19.9	26 24.6	0 58.5	24 8.6	9 41.4	15 10.7	19 38.0
5	10 49 55.8	15 24.4	17 35.3	25 26.8	4 58.7	2 4.0	27 11.7	1 .2	24 14.3	9 43.6	15 12.2	19 37.8
6	10 53 52.3	16 20.1	17 32.2	10♋ 45.1	6 37.3	2 49.1	27 58.7	1 2.1	24 19.8	9 45.8	15 13.6	19 37.4
7	10 57 48.9	17 15.8	17 29.0	25 19.7	8 16.4	3 35.2	28 45.6	1 4.2	24 25.3	9 47.8	15 15.0	19 37.0
8	11 1 45.4	18 11.3	17 25.8	8♌ 59.1	9 55.9	4 22.3	29 32.5	1 6.5	24 30.7	9 49.9	15 16.4	19 36.6
9	11 5 42.0	19 6.7	17 22.7	21 43.5	11 35.9	5 10.3	0♒ 19.3	1 9.0	24 36.0	9 51.8	15 17.7	19 36.2
10	11 9 38.5	20 2.1	17 19.5	3♍ 41.8	13 16.4	5 59.1	1 6.1	1 11.7	24 41.3	9 53.8	15 19.0	19 35.7
11	11 13 35.1	20 57.3	17 16.3	15 6.7	14 57.4	6 48.8	1 52.8	1 14.7	24 46.5	9 55.6	15 20.3	19 35.2
12	11 17 31.7	21 52.5	17 13.2	26 12.2	16 39.0	7 39.3	2 39.4	1 17.8	24 51.6	9 57.4	15 21.5	19 34.6
13	11 21 28.2	22 47.6	17 10.0	7♎ 12.1	18 21.0	8 30.5	3 26.0	1 21.1	24 56.6	9 59.2	15 22.7	19 34.1
14	11 25 24.8	23 42.6	17 6.8	18 19.1	20 3.7	9 22.5	4 12.5	1 24.6	25 1.6	10 .9	15 23.9	19 33.5
15	11 29 21.3	24 37.6	17 3.7	29 44.4	21 46.9	10 15.1	4 58.9	1 28.4	25 6.5	10 2.6	15 25.0	19 32.8
16	11 33 17.9	25 32.5	17 .5	11♏ 36.8	23 30.7	11 8.4	5 45.3	1 32.3	25 11.3	10 4.2	15 26.1	19 32.2
17	11 37 14.4	26 27.3	16 57.3	24 1.4	25 15.1	12 2.3	6 31.6	1 36.4	25 16.0	10 5.8	15 27.2	19 31.5
18	11 41 11.0	27 22.1	16 54.2	6♐ 57.9	27 .1	12 56.8	7 17.9	1 40.7	25 20.7	10 7.3	15 28.3	19 30.8
19	11 45 7.5	28 16.9	16 51.0	20 20.4	28 45.6	13 51.8	8 4.0	1 45.2	25 25.3	10 8.8	15 29.3	19 30.0
20	11 49 4.1	29 11.6	16 47.8	3♑ 57.7	0♈ 31.7	14 47.4	8 50.1	1 49.9	25 29.7	10 10.2	15 30.2	19 29.3
21	11 53 .6	0♈ 6.3	16 44.6	17 36.5	2 18.4	15 43.4	9 36.1	1 54.8	25 34.2	10 11.5	15 31.2	19 28.5
22	11 56 57.2	1 1.0	16 41.5	1♒ 5.3	4 5.5	16 39.9	10 22.1	1 59.9	25 38.5	10 12.8	15 32.1	19 27.6
23	12 0 53.7	1 55.7	16 38.3	14 18.2	5 53.0	17 36.9	11 7.9	2 5.2	25 42.7	10 14.1	15 33.0	19 26.8
24	12 4 50.3	2 50.3	16 35.1	27 15.9	7 40.8	18 34.2	11 53.7	2 10.6	25 46.9	10 15.2	15 33.8	19 25.9
25	12 8 46.8	3 44.9	16 31.9	10♓ 5.4	9 28.9	19 31.9	12 39.4	2 16.2	25 50.9	10 16.4	15 34.6	19 25.0
26	12 12 43.4	4 39.6	16 28.8	22 58.6	11 17.0	20 30.0	13 25.1	2 22.1	25 55.0	10 17.5	15 35.4	19 24.1
27	12 16 40.0	5 34.2	16 25.6	6♈ 9.9	13 5.0	21 28.4	14 10.6	2 28.1	25 58.9	10 18.5	15 36.2	19 23.1
28	12 20 36.5	6 28.8	16 22.4	19 54.2	14 52.7	22 27.1	14 56.0	2 34.3	26 2.7	10 19.5	15 36.8	19 22.1
29	12 24 33.1	7 23.4	16 19.2	4♉ 22.9	16 39.9	23 26.1	15 41.4	2 40.6	26 6.4	10 20.4	15 37.5	19 21.1
30	12 28 29.6	8 18.0	16 16.1	19 38.6	18 26.2	24 25.3	16 26.6	2 47.1	26 10.0	10 21.3	15 38.1	19 20.1
31	12 32 26.2	9 12.6	16 12.9	5♊ 30.1	20 11.5	25 24.8	17 11.8	2 53.8	26 13.6	10 22.1	15 38.7	19 19.0

DECLINATION

DAY	EPHEM. SID. TIME h m s	☉ ° ′	☊ ° ′	☾ ° ′	☿ ° ′	♀ ° ′	♂ ° ′	♃ ° ′	♄ ° ′	♅ ° ′	♆ ° ′	♇ ° ′
1	10 34 9.6	7S 45.9	0S 17.0	15N 46.0	15S .5	15S 33.8	22S 22.2	23N 27.6	21S 23.9	23S 26.2	21S 51.7	1S 59.5
4	10 45 59.2	6 37.2	0 17.1	26 54.1	13 19.4	15 32.4	22 2.2	23 27.9	21 21.4	23 25.9	21 51.2	1 57.8
7	10 57 48.9	5 27.7	0 17.1	23 29.5	11 26.6	15 27.4	21 40.1	23 28.2	21 19.0	23 25.5	21 50.8	1 56.2
10	11 9 38.5	4 17.5	0 17.2	9 20.6	9 22.5	15 18.7	21 16.1	23 28.5	21 16.7	23 25.2	21 50.3	1 54.5
13	11 21 28.2	3 6.8	0 17.2	7S 38.6	7 7.2	15 5.9	20 50.3	23 28.8	21 14.5	23 24.9	21 49.9	1 52.7
16	11 33 17.9	1 55.8	0 17.2	21 28.1	4 41.3	14 48.9	20 22.6	23 29.0	21 12.3	23 24.7	21 49.5	1 51.0
19	11 45 7.5	0 44.7	0 17.3	27 20.5	2 5.8	14 27.6	19 53.1	23 29.2	21 10.2	23 24.5	21 49.1	1 49.2
22	11 56 57.2	0N 26.5	0 17.3	21 54.6	0N 37.7	14 2.1	19 21.8	23 29.3	21 8.2	23 24.3	21 48.8	1 47.4
25	12 8 46.8	1 37.4	0 17.4	6 10.1	3 26.5	13 32.3	18 48.9	23 29.4	21 6.4	23 24.1	21 48.5	1 45.6
28	12 20 36.5	2 48.1	0 17.4	13N 30.4	6 16.8	12 58.3	18 14.3	23 29.5	21 4.6	23 24.0	21 48.2	1 43.8
31	12 32 26.2	3 58.2	0 17.5	26 17.1	9 3.4	12 20.2	17 38.2	23 29.4	21 3.0	23 23.9	21 48.0	1 41.9

APRIL 1990

DAY	EPHEM. SID. TIME	☉	☊	☽	☿	♀	♂	♃	♄	♅	♆	♇
LONGITUDE												
	h m s	° ′	° ′	° ′	° ′	° ′	° ′	° ′	° ′	° ′	° ′	° ′
1	12 36 22.7	11♈ .7	13♒41.7	22♊27.8	23♈57.9	24♒33.3	15♒ 7.2	2♋45.7	24♑24.7	9♑31.1	14♑30.7	17♏19.5
2	12 40 19.3	11 59.9	13 38.5	6♋27.7	25 50.7	25 33.3	15 52.0	2 52.1	24 27.9	9 31.7	14 31.2	17R18.2
3	12 44 15.8	12 59.0	13 35.3	20 5.4	27 40.6	26 33.6	16 36.7	2 58.7	24 30.9	9 32.3	14 31.6	17 16.9
4	12 48 12.4	13 58.2	13 32.1	3♌22.6	29 27.5	27 34.2	17 21.5	3 5.4	24 33.9	9 32.8	14 32.1	17 15.6
5	12 52 8.9	14 57.3	13 29.0	16 21.9	1♉10.8	28 35.2	18 6.3	3 12.3	24 36.8	9 33.3	14 32.4	17 14.2
6	12 56 5.5	15 56.3	13 25.8	29 6.1	2 50.3	29 36.5	18 51.1	3 19.4	24 39.6	9 33.7	14 32.8	17 12.9
7	13 0 2.0	16 55.3	13 22.6	11♍37.9	4 25.6	0♓38.1	19 35.8	3 26.5	24 42.4	9 34.1	14 33.1	17 11.5
8	13 3 58.6	17 54.3	13 19.4	23 59.8	5 56.3	1 40.1	20 20.6	3 33.8	24 45.0	9 34.4	14 33.4	17 10.1
9	13 7 55.1	18 53.3	13 16.3	6♎13.3	7 22.3	2 42.3	21 5.5	3 41.3	24 47.5	9 34.7	14 33.7	17 8.7
10	13 11 51.7	19 52.2	13 13.1	18 19.9	8 43.2	3 44.8	21 50.3	3 48.9	24 50.0	9 34.9	14 33.9	17 7.2
11	13 15 48.3	20 51.1	13 9.9	0♏20.7	9 58.9	4 47.5	22 35.1	3 56.6	24 52.3	9 35.1	14 34.1	17 5.8
12	13 19 44.8	21 49.9	13 6.7	12 16.8	11 9.1	5 50.6	23 20.0	4 4.5	24 54.6	9 35.2	14 34.2	17 4.3
13	13 23 41.4	22 48.7	13 3.5	24 9.8	12 13.7	6 53.8	24 4.8	4 12.5	24 56.8	9 35.3	14 34.4	17 2.8
14	13 27 37.9	23 47.5	13 .4	6♐ 1.4	13 12.6	7 57.4	24 49.7	4 20.6	24 58.9	9 35.3	14 34.5	17 1.3
15	13 31 34.5	24 46.3	12 57.2	17 54.4	14 5.6	9 1.2	25 34.5	4 28.8	25 .8	9R35.2	14 34.5	16 59.8
16	13 35 31.0	25 45.0	12 54.0	29 52.2	14 52.6	10 5.2	26 19.4	4 37.2	25 2.8	9 35.2	14 34.6	16 58.3
17	13 39 27.6	26 43.7	12 50.8	11♑58.7	15 33.6	11 9.5	27 4.3	4 45.7	25 4.6	9 35.1	14 34.6	16 56.8
18	13 43 24.1	27 42.4	12 47.7	24 18.5	16 8.5	12 13.9	27 49.2	4 54.3	25 6.3	9 34.9	14R34.5	16 55.2
19	13 47 20.7	28 41.0	12 44.5	6♒56.6	16 37.2	13 18.6	28 34.1	5 3.1	25 7.9	9 34.6	14 34.5	16 53.6
20	13 51 17.2	29 39.7	12 41.3	19 57.8	16 59.8	14 23.4	29 18.9	5 11.9	25 9.4	9 34.3	14 34.4	16 52.1
21	13 55 13.8	0♉38.2	12 38.1	3♓26.1	17 16.3	15 28.5	0♓ 3.8	5 20.9	25 10.8	9 34.0	14 34.2	16 50.5
22	13 59 10.4	1 36.8	12 34.9	17 23.7	17 26.8	16 33.8	0 48.7	5 30.0	25 12.1	9 33.6	14 34.0	16 48.8
23	14 3 6.9	2 35.3	12 31.8	1♈50.3	17 31.3	17 39.2	1 33.6	5 39.2	25 13.3	9 33.2	14 33.8	16 47.2
24	14 7 3.5	3 33.8	12 28.6	16 42.2	17R30.1	18 44.8	2 18.5	5 48.6	25 14.5	9 32.7	14 33.6	16 45.6
25	14 11 .0	4 32.3	12 25.4	1♉52.1	17 23.3	19 50.6	3 3.3	5 58.0	25 15.5	9 32.1	14 33.3	16 44.0
26	14 14 56.6	5 30.8	12 22.2	17 9.7	17 11.3	20 56.6	3 48.2	6 7.5	25 16.4	9 31.5	14 33.0	16 42.3
27	14 18 53.1	6 29.2	12 19.1	2♊23.5	16 54.2	22 2.7	4 33.0	6 17.2	25 17.2	9 30.9	14 32.7	16 40.7
28	14 22 49.7	7 27.5	12 15.9	17 23.0	16 32.6	23 8.9	5 17.9	6 26.9	25 18.0	9 30.2	14 32.3	16 39.0
29	14 26 46.2	8 25.9	12 12.7	2♋ .3	16 6.9	24 15.4	6 2.7	6 36.8	25 18.6	9 29.5	14 31.9	16 37.3
30	14 30 42.8	9 24.2	12 9.5	16 11.2	15 37.5	25 21.9	6 47.5	6 46.8	25 19.1	9 28.7	14 31.5	16 35.7
LATITUDE												
1	12 36 22.7	0 .0	0 .0	4N 2.6	0N42.0	1N18.1	1S10.9	0N 4.6	0N12.1	0S17.9	0N51.5	15N55.7
4	12 48 12.4	0 .0	0 .0	1 .7	1 17.1	0 59.4	1 13.3	0 4.9	0 11.9	0 17.9	0 51.6	15 56.5
7	13 0 2.0	0 .0	0 .0	2S18.0	1 50.0	0 41.4	1 15.7	0 5.2	0 11.7	0 18.0	0 51.7	15 57.2
10	13 11 51.7	0 .0	0 .0	4 31.7	2 18.6	0 24.3	1 18.1	0 5.4	0 11.5	0 18.1	0 51.7	15 57.9
13	13 23 41.4	0 .0	0 .0	4 56.6	2 40.6	0 8.0	1 20.5	0 5.7	0 11.4	0 18.2	0 51.8	15 58.5
16	13 35 31.0	0 .0	0 .0	3 28.3	2 54.3	0S 7.3	1 22.8	0 6.0	0 11.2	0 18.2	0 51.8	15 59.0
19	13 47 20.7	0 .0	0 .0	0 33.2	2 57.9	0 21.8	1 25.1	0 6.3	0 11.0	0 18.3	0 51.9	15 59.4
22	13 59 10.4	0 .0	0 .0	2N50.2	2 50.3	0 35.3	1 27.4	0 6.6	0 10.8	0 18.4	0 51.9	15 59.8
25	14 11 .0	0 .0	0 .0	4 55.0	2 30.7	0 47.9	1 29.7	0 6.8	0 10.6	0 18.4	0 52.0	16 .0
28	14 22 49.7	0 .0	0 .0	4 6.2	1 59.4	0 59.5	1 31.9	0 7.1	0 10.4	0 18.5	0 52.1	16 .2
RIGHT ASCENSION												
1	12 36 22.7	10♈ 7.3	16♒ 9.7	21♊32.2	21♈55.5	26♒24.5	17♒56.9	3♋ .7	26♑17.0	10♑22.8	15♑39.3	19♏18.0
2	12 40 19.3	11 2.0	16 6.5	7♋12.6	23 37.7	27 24.5	18 41.9	3 7.7	26 20.3	10 23.5	15 39.8	19R16.9
3	12 44 15.8	11 56.7	16 3.3	22 4.8	25 17.9	28 24.6	19 26.8	3 14.9	26 23.6	10 24.1	15 40.3	19 15.7
4	12 48 12.4	12 51.4	16 .2	5♌55.9	26 55.7	29 24.9	20 11.6	3 22.2	26 26.8	10 24.7	15 40.7	19 14.6
5	12 52 8.9	13 46.1	15 57.0	18 46.7	28 30.8	0♓25.4	20 56.4	3 29.7	26 29.8	10 25.2	15 41.2	19 13.4
6	12 56 5.5	14 40.9	15 53.8	0♍47.0	0♉ 2.8	1 26.1	21 41.0	3 37.4	26 32.8	10 25.7	15 41.5	19 12.2
7	13 0 2.0	15 35.8	15 50.6	12 10.8	1 31.4	2 26.9	22 25.6	3 45.2	26 35.7	10 26.1	15 41.9	19 11.0
8	13 3 58.6	16 30.7	15 47.4	23 13.0	2 56.3	3 27.9	23 10.0	3 53.2	26 38.5	10 26.4	15 42.2	19 9.8
9	13 7 55.1	17 25.6	15 44.3	4♎ 8.0	4 17.2	4 29.0	23 54.4	4 1.3	26 41.2	10 26.7	15 42.5	19 8.5
10	13 11 51.7	18 20.6	15 41.1	15 9.1	5 33.9	5 30.2	24 38.7	4 9.6	26 43.8	10 27.0	15 42.7	19 7.2
11	13 15 48.3	19 15.7	15 37.9	26 27.5	6 45.9	6 31.5	25 22.9	4 18.0	26 46.3	10 27.2	15 42.9	19 5.9
12	13 19 44.8	20 10.9	15 34.7	8♏12.1	7 53.2	7 33.0	26 7.0	4 26.6	26 48.7	10 27.3	15 43.1	19 4.6
13	13 23 41.4	21 6.1	15 31.5	20 27.9	8 55.5	8 34.5	26 51.0	4 35.3	26 51.0	10 27.4	15 43.2	19 3.3
14	13 27 37.9	22 1.4	15 28.3	3♐14.6	9 52.6	9 36.2	27 35.0	4 44.1	26 53.2	10 27.4	15 43.3	19 2.0
15	13 31 34.5	22 56.8	15 25.2	16 26.1	10 44.4	10 37.9	28 18.9	4 53.1	26 55.3	10R27.3	15 43.3	19 .6
16	13 35 31.0	23 52.3	15 22.0	29 51.3	11 30.6	11 39.7	29 2.7	5 2.3	26 57.3	10 27.3	15 43.4	18 59.3
17	13 39 27.6	24 47.9	15 18.8	13♑16.8	12 11.3	12 41.6	29 46.4	5 11.5	26 59.2	10 27.1	15 43.4	18 57.9
18	13 43 24.1	25 43.5	15 15.6	26 31.5	12 46.2	13 43.6	0♓30.0	5 20.9	27 1.0	10 26.9	15 43.4	18 56.5
19	13 47 20.7	26 39.3	15 12.4	9♒29.3	13 15.3	14 45.6	1 13.5	5 30.5	27 2.7	10 26.7	15R43.3	18 55.1
20	13 51 17.2	27 35.2	15 9.2	22 10.8	13 38.6	15 47.7	1 57.0	5 40.1	27 4.3	10 26.4	15 43.2	18 53.6
21	13 55 13.8	28 31.2	15 6.0	4♓43.1	13 56.2	16 49.8	2 40.3	5 49.9	27 5.8	10 26.0	15 43.0	18 52.2
22	13 59 10.4	29 27.3	15 2.9	17 18.0	14 8.0	17 52.0	3 23.6	5 59.8	27 7.2	10 25.6	15 42.8	18 50.7
23	14 3 6.9	0♉23.5	14 59.7	0♈10.8	14 14.2	18 54.2	4 6.8	6 9.8	27 8.5	10 25.1	15 42.6	18 49.3
24	14 7 3.5	1 19.8	14 56.5	13 38.3	14 14.9	19 56.5	4 49.9	6 20.0	27 9.7	10 24.6	15 42.4	18 47.8
25	14 11 .0	2 16.2	14 53.3	27 55.6	14R10.4	20 58.9	5 32.9	6 30.3	27 10.8	10 24.0	15 42.1	18 46.3
26	14 14 56.6	3 12.8	14 50.1	13♉10.7	14 1.0	22 1.2	6 15.8	6 40.7	27 11.8	10 23.3	15 41.7	18 44.8
27	14 18 53.1	4 9.5	14 46.9	29 17.5	13 46.9	23 3.7	6 58.7	6 51.2	27 12.7	10 22.6	15 41.4	18 43.3
28	14 22 49.7	5 6.3	14 43.7	15♊51.3	13 28.6	24 6.2	7 41.4	7 1.8	27 13.4	10 21.9	15 41.0	18 41.8
29	14 26 46.2	6 3.2	14 40.5	2♋14.4	13 6.5	25 8.7	8 24.1	7 12.5	27 14.1	10 21.1	15 40.6	18 40.2
30	14 30 42.8	7 .3	14 37.3	17 50.9	12 41.3	26 11.3	9 6.7	7 23.4	27 14.7	10 20.2	15 40.1	18 38.7
DECLINATION												
1	12 36 22.7	4N21.5	0S17.5	27N15.8	9N57.0	12S 6.6	17S25.9	23N29.4	21S 2.5	23S23.9	21S47.9	1S41.3
4	12 48 12.4	5 30.7	0 17.6	20 23.2	12 29.0	11 23.3	16 47.8	23 29.3	21 1.0	23 23.8	21 47.7	1 39.5
7	13 0 2.0	6 39.0	0 17.6	5 4.5	14 43.4	10 36.2	16 8.4	23 29.0	20 59.7	23 23.8	21 47.5	1 37.8
10	13 11 51.7	7 46.3	0 17.6	11S22.3	16 35.8	9 45.5	15 27.7	23 28.7	20 58.5	23 23.8	21 47.4	1 36.0
13	13 23 41.4	8 52.4	0 17.7	23 36.1	18 3.3	8 51.4	14 45.7	23 28.3	20 57.5	23 23.9	21 47.3	1 34.3
16	13 35 31.0	9 57.2	0 17.7	26 54.8	19 4.6	7 54.0	14 2.5	23 27.7	20 56.5	23 23.9	21 47.2	1 32.6
19	13 47 20.7	11 .5	0 17.8	19 4.5	19 38.8	6 54.0	13 18.2	23 27.0	20 55.8	23 24.0	21 47.1	1 31.0
22	13 59 10.4	12 2.2	0 17.8	2 22.1	19 45.8	5 50.8	12 32.9	23 26.2	20 55.2	23 24.2	21 47.1	1 29.4
25	14 11 .0	13 2.1	0 17.9	16N44.0	19 26.0	4 45.4	11 46.7	23 25.3	20 54.8	23 24.4	21 47.1	1 27.9
28	14 22 49.7	14 .1	0 17.9	26 55.7	18 41.4	3 37.8	10 59.7	23 24.2	20 54.5	23 24.6	21 47.2	1 26.4

MAY 1990

LONGITUDE

DAY	EPHEM. SID. TIME	☉	☊	☽	☿	♀	♂	♃	♄	♅	♆	♇
	h m s	° ′	° ′	° ′	° ′	° ′	° ′	° ′	° ′	° ′	° ′	° ′
1	14 34 39.3	10♉22.5	12♒ 6.4	29♋54.7	15♉ 5.1	26♓28.6	7♓32.3	6♋56.8	25♑19.5	9♑27.9	14♑31.0	16♏34.0
2	14 38 35.9	11 20.7	12 3.2	13♌12.4	14 R 30.3	27 35.4	8 17.1	7 7.0	25 19.9	9 R 27.0	14 R 30.6	16 R 32.3
3	14 42 32.5	12 18.9	11 60.0	26 7.6	13 53.7	28 42.4	9 1.9	7 17.2	25 20.1	9 26.1	14 30.0	16 30.6
4	14 46 29.0	13 17.1	11 56.8	8♍44.2	13 16.0	29 49.4	9 46.6	7 27.6	25 20.2	9 25.1	14 29.5	16 29.0
5	14 50 25.6	14 15.2	11 53.6	21 6.3	12 37.8	0♈56.7	10 31.4	7 38.0	25 20.3	9 24.1	14 28.9	16 27.3
6	14 54 22.1	15 13.3	11 50.5	3♎17.5	11 60.0	2 4.0	11 16.1	7 48.5	25 R 20.2	9 23.0	14 28.3	16 25.6
7	14 58 18.7	16 11.5	11 47.3	15 21.1	11 23.1	3 11.5	12 .9	7 59.2	25 20.1	9 21.9	14 27.7	16 24.0
8	15 2 15.2	17 9.5	11 44.1	27 19.3	10 47.7	4 19.1	12 45.6	8 9.9	25 19.9	9 20.8	14 27.0	16 22.3
9	15 6 11.8	18 7.5	11 40.9	9♏14.2	10 14.5	5 26.8	13 30.3	8 20.7	25 19.5	9 19.6	14 26.3	16 20.6
10	15 10 8.4	19 5.5	11 37.8	21 7.2	9 43.9	6 34.6	14 15.0	8 31.6	25 19.1	9 18.4	14 25.6	16 18.9
11	15 14 4.9	20 3.5	11 34.6	2♐59.6	9 16.5	7 42.5	14 59.6	8 42.5	25 18.5	9 17.1	14 24.9	16 17.2
12	15 18 1.5	21 1.4	11 31.4	14 53.1	8 52.6	8 50.5	15 44.3	8 53.6	25 17.9	9 15.8	14 24.1	16 15.5
13	15 21 58.0	21 59.3	11 28.2	26 49.3	8 32.5	9 58.6	16 28.9	9 4.7	25 17.1	9 14.4	14 23.3	16 13.8
14	15 25 54.6	22 57.2	11 25.1	8♑50.7	8 16.5	11 6.9	17 13.5	9 15.9	25 16.3	9 13.0	14 22.4	16 12.2
15	15 29 51.1	23 55.1	11 21.9	21 .2	8 4.9	12 15.2	17 58.1	9 27.2	25 15.4	9 11.6	14 21.6	16 10.5
16	15 33 47.7	24 52.9	11 18.7	3♒21.7	7 57.7	13 23.7	18 42.6	9 38.5	25 14.3	9 10.1	14 20.7	16 8.8
17	15 37 44.2	25 50.8	11 15.5	15 59.1	7 55.0	14 32.2	19 27.1	9 50.0	25 13.2	9 8.6	14 19.8	16 7.2
18	15 41 40.8	26 48.6	11 12.3	28 57.0	7 D 56.9	15 40.8	20 11.7	10 1.5	25 12.0	9 7.0	14 18.8	16 5.5
19	15 45 37.4	27 46.4	11 9.2	12♓19.3	8 3.4	16 49.5	20 56.1	10 13.0	25 10.7	9 5.4	14 17.8	16 3.9
20	15 49 33.9	28 44.2	11 6.0	26 9.0	8 14.5	17 58.4	21 40.6	10 24.7	25 9.3	9 3.8	14 16.9	16 2.2
21	15 53 30.5	29 41.9	11 2.8	10♈26.9	8 30.0	19 7.2	22 25.0	10 36.4	25 7.8	9 2.1	14 15.8	16 .6
22	15 57 27.0	0♊39.6	10 59.6	25 10.9	8 50.0	20 16.2	23 9.4	10 48.2	25 6.2	9 .4	14 14.8	15 59.0
23	16 1 23.6	1 37.4	10 56.5	10♉15.5	9 14.4	21 25.3	23 53.8	10 60.0	25 4.6	8 58.6	14 13.7	15 57.4
24	16 5 20.1	2 35.1	10 53.3	25 31.7	9 42.9	22 34.4	24 38.1	11 11.9	25 2.8	8 56.9	14 12.6	15 55.8
25	16 9 16.7	3 32.7	10 50.1	10♊48.5	10 15.6	23 43.6	25 22.3	11 23.9	25 1.0	8 55.1	14 11.5	15 54.2
26	16 13 13.3	4 30.4	10 46.9	25 54.8	10 52.3	24 52.9	26 6.6	11 35.9	24 59.0	8 53.2	14 10.4	15 52.6
27	16 17 9.8	5 28.0	10 43.8	10♋41.3	11 32.9	26 2.3	26 50.8	11 48.0	24 57.0	8 51.3	14 9.2	15 51.0
28	16 21 6.4	6 25.7	10 40.6	25 2.0	12 17.3	27 11.7	27 35.0	12 .2	24 54.9	8 49.5	14 8.1	15 49.5
29	16 25 2.9	7 23.3	10 37.4	8♌54.2	13 5.4	28 21.2	28 19.1	12 12.4	24 52.7	8 47.5	14 6.9	15 48.0
30	16 28 59.5	8 20.9	10 34.2	22 18.3	13 57.0	29 30.7	29 3.1	12 24.7	24 50.4	8 45.6	14 5.6	15 46.5
31	16 32 56.1	9 18.4	10 31.0	5♍17.0	14 52.1	0♉40.4	29 47.1	12 37.0	24 48.1	8 43.6	14 4.4	15 44.9

LATITUDE

DAY	EPHEM. SID. TIME	☉	☊	☽	☿	♀	♂	♃	♄	♅	♆	♇
1	14 34 39.3	0 .0	0 .0	1N 3.6	1N17.7	1S10.1	1S34.1	0N 7.3	0N10.3	0S18.6	0N52.1	16N .3
4	14 46 29.0	0 .0	0 .0	2S16.0	0 28.8	1 19.8	1 36.2	0 7.6	0 10.1	0 18.6	0 52.2	16 .3
7	14 58 18.7	0 .0	0 .0	4 29.1	0S23.2	1 28.5	1 38.3	0 7.9	0 9.9	0 18.7	0 52.2	16 .2
10	15 10 8.4	0 .0	0 .0	4 54.9	1 13.8	1 36.2	1 40.3	0 8.1	0 9.7	0 18.8	0 52.2	16 .0
13	15 21 58.0	0 .0	0 .0	3 28.0	1 59.2	1 43.0	1 42.2	0 8.4	0 9.5	0 18.8	0 52.3	15 59.8
16	15 33 47.7	0 .0	0 .0	0 36.4	2 36.9	1 48.7	1 44.1	0 8.6	0 9.3	0 18.9	0 52.3	15 59.4
19	15 45 37.4	0 .0	0 .0	2N41.4	3 5.5	1 53.5	1 45.9	0 8.9	0 9.0	0 19.0	0 52.4	15 59.0
22	15 57 27.0	0 .0	0 .0	4 52.4	3 25.0	1 57.4	1 47.7	0 9.1	0 8.8	0 19.0	0 52.4	15 58.4
25	16 9 16.7	0 .0	0 .0	4 18.9	3 35.7	2 .4	1 49.4	0 9.4	0 8.6	0 19.1	0 52.4	15 57.8
28	16 21 6.4	0 .0	0 .0	1 15.0	3 38.2	2 2.4	1 51.0	0 9.6	0 8.4	0 19.1	0 52.5	15 57.1
31	16 32 56.1	0 .0	0 .0	2S14.4	3 33.4	2 3.6	1 52.6	0 9.9	0 8.2	0 19.2	0 52.5	15 56.3

RIGHT ASCENSION

DAY	EPHEM. SID. TIME	☉	☊	☽	☿	♀	♂	♃	♄	♅	♆	♇
1	14 34 39.3	7♉57.5	14♒34.1	2♌19.8	12♉13.3	27♓13.9	9♓49.2	7♋34.3	27♑15.1	10♑19.3	15♑39.6	18♏37.1
2	14 38 35.9	8 54.8	14 30.9	15 38.6	11 R 43.4	28 16.6	10 31.7	7 45.4	27 15.5	10 R 18.4	15 R 39.1	18 R 35.6
3	14 42 32.5	9 52.3	14 27.7	27 56.8	11 11.9	29 19.3	11 14.0	7 56.5	27 15.8	10 17.4	15 38.5	18 34.0
4	14 46 29.0	10 49.8	14 24.5	9♍29.9	10 39.7	0♈22.1	11 56.3	8 7.8	27 15.9	10 16.3	15 37.9	18 32.5
5	14 50 25.6	11 47.5	14 21.4	20 34.7	10 7.3	1 24.9	12 38.5	8 19.1	27 16.0	10 15.2	15 37.3	18 30.9
6	14 54 22.1	12 45.4	14 18.2	1♎27.5	9 35.4	2 27.8	13 20.6	8 30.6	27 R 15.9	10 14.1	15 36.6	18 29.3
7	14 58 18.7	13 43.4	14 15.0	12 22.8	9 4.6	3 30.9	14 2.7	8 42.2	27 15.8	10 12.9	15 36.0	18 27.8
8	15 2 15.2	14 41.6	14 11.8	23 33.5	8 35.4	4 33.9	14 44.7	8 53.8	27 15.6	10 11.7	15 35.3	18 26.2
9	15 6 11.8	15 39.8	14 8.6	5♏ 9.6	8 8.3	5 37.1	15 26.6	9 5.6	27 15.2	10 10.4	15 34.5	18 24.7
10	15 10 8.4	16 38.2	14 5.4	17 17.4	7 43.7	6 40.3	16 8.5	9 17.4	27 14.7	10 9.0	15 33.8	18 23.1
11	15 14 4.9	17 36.8	14 2.2	29 57.6	7 22.1	7 43.6	16 50.3	9 29.3	27 14.2	10 7.6	15 33.0	18 21.5
12	15 18 1.5	18 35.5	13 59.0	13♐ 4.5	7 3.7	8 47.1	17 32.0	9 41.3	27 13.5	10 6.2	15 32.1	18 19.9
13	15 21 58.0	19 34.3	13 55.8	26 26.6	6 48.9	9 50.6	18 13.6	9 53.4	27 12.8	10 4.7	15 31.3	18 18.4
14	15 25 54.6	20 33.3	13 52.6	9♑49.2	6 37.8	10 54.2	18 55.2	10 5.6	27 11.9	10 3.2	15 30.4	18 16.8
15	15 29 51.1	21 32.4	13 49.4	22 59.3	6 30.7	11 57.9	19 36.8	10 17.8	27 10.9	10 1.6	15 29.4	18 15.2
16	15 33 47.7	22 31.7	13 46.2	5♒48.9	6 27.5	13 1.8	20 18.2	10 30.1	27 9.9	10 .0	15 28.5	18 13.6
17	15 37 44.2	23 31.1	13 43.0	18 17.3	6 D 28.4	14 5.7	20 59.6	10 42.6	27 8.7	9 58.4	15 27.5	18 12.1
18	15 41 40.8	24 30.7	13 39.8	0♓30.6	6 33.3	15 9.8	21 41.0	10 55.0	27 7.4	9 56.7	15 26.5	18 10.5
19	15 45 37.4	25 30.4	13 36.6	12 40.2	6 42.4	16 14.1	22 22.2	11 7.6	27 6.1	9 55.0	15 25.4	18 8.9
20	15 49 33.9	26 30.3	13 33.4	25 1.4	6 55.5	17 18.4	23 3.5	11 20.2	27 4.6	9 53.2	15 24.4	18 7.4
21	15 53 30.5	27 30.3	13 30.2	7♈52.0	7 12.6	18 22.9	23 44.6	11 32.9	27 3.1	9 51.4	15 23.3	18 5.8
22	15 57 27.0	28 30.4	13 27.0	21 29.9	7 33.7	19 27.6	24 25.7	11 45.7	27 1.4	9 49.5	15 22.2	18 4.3
23	16 1 23.6	29 30.7	13 23.8	6♉ 9.9	7 58.7	20 32.4	25 6.8	11 58.6	26 59.7	9 47.6	15 21.0	18 2.7
24	16 5 20.1	0♊31.1	13 20.6	21 55.7	8 27.4	21 37.4	25 47.7	12 11.5	26 57.8	9 45.7	15 19.8	18 1.2
25	16 9 16.7	1 31.6	13 17.4	8♊32.7	8 59.9	22 42.5	26 28.7	12 24.4	26 55.9	9 43.7	15 18.6	17 59.6
26	16 13 13.3	2 32.3	13 14.1	25 25.6	9 36.0	23 47.8	27 9.5	12 37.5	26 53.9	9 41.7	15 17.4	17 58.1
27	16 17 9.8	3 33.0	13 10.9	11♋50.4	10 15.6	24 53.2	27 50.3	12 50.6	26 51.7	9 39.7	15 16.2	17 56.6
28	16 21 6.4	4 34.0	13 7.7	27 13.3	10 58.8	25 58.9	28 31.1	13 3.8	26 49.6	9 37.6	15 15.0	17 55.2
29	16 25 2.9	5 35.0	13 4.5	11♌20.5	11 45.4	27 4.8	29 11.8	13 17.0	26 47.3	9 35.5	15 13.7	17 53.7
30	16 28 59.5	6 36.1	13 1.3	24 16.8	12 35.3	28 10.8	29 52.4	13 30.3	26 44.9	9 33.4	15 12.4	17 52.2
31	16 32 56.1	7 37.3	12 58.1	6♍16.6	13 28.5	29 17.0	0♈33.0	13 43.6	26 42.4	9 31.2	15 11.0	17 50.7

DECLINATION

DAY	EPHEM. SID. TIME	☉	☊	☽	☿	♀	♂	♃	♄	♅	♆	♇
1	14 34 39.3	14N56.0	0S18.0	21N12.5	17N36.1	2S28.4	10S11.8	23N22.9	20S54.4	23S24.8	21S47.3	1S25.0
4	14 46 29.0	15 49.7	0 18.0	6 11.6	16 16.8	1 17.4	9 23.3	23 21.5	20 54.5	23 25.1	21 47.4	1 23.7
7	14 58 18.7	16 41.0	0 18.1	10S10.8	14 52.8	0 5.1	8 34.2	23 19.9	20 54.7	23 25.4	21 47.5	1 22.5
10	15 10 8.4	17 29.8	0 18.1	22 46.7	13 33.8	1N 8.3	7 44.5	23 18.2	20 55.1	23 25.7	21 47.7	1 21.3
13	15 21 58.0	18 16.0	0 18.2	26 52.2	12 28.2	2 22.4	6 54.3	23 16.2	20 55.6	23 26.0	21 47.9	1 20.2
16	15 33 47.7	18 59.4	0 18.2	19 59.9	11 41.4	3 37.1	6 3.8	23 14.1	20 56.3	23 26.4	21 48.2	1 19.2
19	15 45 37.4	19 40.0	0 18.3	4 27.1	11 16.0	4 51.9	5 13.0	23 11.8	20 57.2	23 26.8	21 48.4	1 18.3
22	15 57 27.0	20 17.5	0 18.3	14N16.6	11 12.4	6 6.5	4 21.9	23 9.2	20 58.2	23 27.2	21 48.7	1 17.6
25	16 9 16.7	20 51.9	0 18.3	26 20.4	11 28.9	7 20.8	3 30.8	23 6.5	20 59.4	23 27.6	21 49.0	1 16.9
28	16 21 6.4	21 23.1	0 18.4	22 21.5	12 3.6	8 34.3	2 39.6	23 3.6	21 .7	23 28.0	21 49.3	1 16.3
31	16 32 56.1	21 50.9	0 18.4	7 29.4	12 53.8	9 46.7	1 48.4	23 .4	21 2.1	23 28.4	21 49.7	1 15.8

JUNE 1990

LONGITUDE

DAY	EPHEM. SID. TIME h m s	☉ ° ′	☊ ° ′	☽ ° ′	☿ ° ′	♀ ° ′	♂ ° ′	♃ ° ′	♄ ° ′	♅ ° ′	♆ ° ′	♇ ° ′
1	16 36 52.6	10♊15.9	10♒27.9	17♍54.2	15♉50.5	1♉50.0	0♈31.1	12♋49.4	24♑45.6	8♑41.5	14♑ 3.1	15♏43.4
2	16 40 49.2	11 13.4	10 24.7	0♎14.4	16 52.3	2 59.8	1 15.0	13 1.8	24 R 43.1	8 R 39.5	14 R 1.8	15 R 42.0
3	16 44 45.7	12 10.9	10 21.5	12 22.0	17 57.3	4 9.6	1 58.9	13 14.3	24 40.5	8 37.4	14 .5	15 40.5
4	16 48 42.3	13 8.3	10 18.3	24 21.1	19 5.5	5 19.4	2 42.7	13 26.8	24 37.8	8 35.3	13 59.2	15 39.1
5	16 52 38.8	14 5.8	10 15.2	6♏15.3	20 16.7	6 29.3	3 26.5	13 39.3	24 35.0	8 33.2	13 57.9	15 37.6
6	16 56 35.4	15 3.2	10 12.0	18 7.4	21 31.0	7 39.3	4 10.2	13 51.9	24 32.2	8 31.0	13 56.5	15 36.2
7	17 0 32.0	16 .6	10 8.8	29 59.8	22 48.3	8 49.4	4 53.8	14 4.6	24 29.3	8 28.9	13 55.2	15 34.8
8	17 4 28.5	16 58.0	10 5.6	11♐54.4	24 8.6	9 59.5	5 37.5	14 17.3	24 26.3	8 26.7	13 53.8	15 33.4
9	17 8 25.1	17 55.4	10 2.5	23 52.6	25 31.8	11 9.6	6 21.0	14 30.0	24 23.2	8 24.5	13 52.4	15 32.1
10	17 12 21.6	18 52.7	9 59.3	5♑56.2	26 57.8	12 19.8	7 4.5	14 42.8	24 20.1	8 22.2	13 50.9	15 30.7
11	17 16 18.2	19 50.1	9 56.1	18 6.6	28 26.8	13 30.1	7 48.0	14 55.6	24 16.9	8 20.0	13 49.5	15 29.4
12	17 20 14.8	20 47.4	9 52.9	0♒25.8	29 58.6	14 40.4	8 31.3	15 8.5	24 13.6	8 17.7	13 48.0	15 28.1
13	17 24 11.3	21 44.7	9 49.8	12 56.4	1♊33.2	15 50.8	9 14.7	15 21.4	24 10.3	8 15.4	13 46.6	15 26.9
14	17 28 7.9	22 42.0	9 46.6	25 41.0	3 10.6	17 1.3	9 57.9	15 34.3	24 6.9	8 13.1	13 45.1	15 25.6
15	17 32 4.4	23 39.4	9 43.4	8♓42.7	4 50.8	18 11.8	10 41.1	15 47.3	24 3.4	8 10.8	13 43.6	15 24.4
16	17 36 1.0	24 36.7	9 40.2	22 4.5	6 33.8	19 22.3	11 24.3	16 .3	23 59.9	8 8.4	13 42.1	15 23.2
17	17 39 57.5	25 34.0	9 37.0	5♈48.6	8 19.5	20 33.0	12 7.3	16 13.3	23 56.3	8 6.1	13 40.6	15 22.0
18	17 43 54.1	26 31.3	9 33.9	19 56.1	10 8.0	21 43.7	12 50.4	16 26.4	23 52.7	8 3.8	13 39.1	15 20.9
19	17 47 50.7	27 28.6	9 30.7	4♉25.7	11 59.0	22 54.4	13 33.3	16 39.5	23 49.0	8 1.4	13 37.6	15 19.7
20	17 51 47.2	28 25.9	9 27.5	19 13.7	13 52.6	24 5.2	14 16.1	16 52.6	23 45.3	7 59.0	13 36.0	15 18.6
21	17 55 43.8	29 23.2	9 24.3	4♊13.6	15 48.7	25 16.0	14 58.9	17 5.8	23 41.5	7 56.6	13 34.5	15 17.5
22	17 59 40.3	0♋20.5	9 21.2	19 16.8	17 47.2	26 26.9	15 41.6	17 19.0	23 37.6	7 54.2	13 32.9	15 16.5
23	18 3 36.9	1 17.7	9 18.0	4♋14.0	19 47.9	27 37.8	16 24.2	17 32.2	23 33.7	7 51.8	13 31.3	15 15.4
24	18 7 33.5	2 15.0	9 14.8	18 56.6	21 50.6	28 48.8	17 6.7	17 45.4	23 29.8	7 49.4	13 29.7	15 14.4
25	18 11 30.0	3 12.2	9 11.6	3♌17.7	23 55.3	29 59.8	17 49.1	17 58.7	23 25.8	7 46.9	13 28.2	15 13.5
26	18 15 26.6	4 9.5	9 8.5	17 13.5	26 1.6	1♊10.8	18 31.4	18 11.9	23 21.7	7 44.5	13 26.6	15 12.5
27	18 19 23.1	5 6.7	9 5.3	0♍42.7	28 9.4	2 21.9	19 13.7	18 25.2	23 17.7	7 42.1	13 25.0	15 11.6
28	18 23 19.7	6 4.0	9 2.1	13 46.6	0♋18.3	3 33.0	19 55.8	18 38.5	23 13.5	7 39.6	13 23.4	15 10.7
29	18 27 16.2	7 1.2	8 58.9	26 27.9	2 28.2	4 44.2	20 37.9	18 51.9	23 9.4	7 37.2	13 21.7	15 9.8
30	18 31 12.8	7 58.4	8 55.8	8♎50.6	4 38.6	5 55.5	21 19.8	19 5.2	23 5.2	7 34.8	13 20.1	15 9.0

LATITUDE

DAY	EPHEM. SID. TIME	☉	☊	☽	☿	♀	♂	♃	♄	♅	♆	♇
1	16 36 52.6	0 .0	0 .0	3S11.2	3S30.3	2S 3.8	1S53.1	0N 9.9	0N 8.1	0S19.2	0N52.5	15N56.1
4	16 48 42.3	0 .0	0 .0	4 55.1	3 16.8	2 3.9	1 54.5	0 10.2	0 7.9	0 19.3	0 52.5	15 55.2
7	17 0 32.0	0 .0	0 .0	4 44.3	2 57.7	2 3.1	1 55.8	0 10.4	0 7.6	0 19.3	0 52.5	15 54.2
10	17 12 21.6	0 .0	0 .0	2 44.1	2 33.7	2 1.5	1 57.1	0 10.7	0 7.4	0 19.4	0 52.5	15 53.2
13	17 24 11.3	0 .0	0 .0	0N26.3	2 5.6	1 59.2	1 58.2	0 10.9	0 7.2	0 19.4	0 52.6	15 52.1
16	17 36 1.0	0 .0	0 .0	3 35.4	1 34.3	1 56.2	1 59.3	0 11.2	0 6.9	0 19.4	0 52.6	15 51.0
19	17 47 50.7	0 .0	0 .0	5 9.1	1 .8	1 52.5	2 .2	0 11.4	0 6.7	0 19.5	0 52.6	15 49.7
22	17 59 40.3	0 .0	0 .0	3 52.6	0 26.3	1 48.2	2 1.1	0 11.7	0 6.5	0 19.5	0 52.5	15 48.4
25	18 11 30.0	0 .0	0 .0	0 23.6	0N 7.4	1 43.3	2 1.9	0 12.0	0 6.2	0 19.6	0 52.5	15 47.1
28	18 23 19.7	0 .0	0 .0	3S 4.7	0 38.5	1 37.8	2 2.5	0 12.2	0 5.9	0 19.6	0 52.5	15 45.7

RIGHT ASCENSION

DAY	EPHEM. SID. TIME	☉	☊	☽	☿	♀	♂	♃	♄	♅	♆	♇
1	16 36 52.6	8♊38.6	12♒54.9	17♍37.9	14♉25.0	0♉23.4	1♈13.5	13♋57.0	26♑39.8	9♑29.0	15♑ 9.7	17♏49.2
2	16 40 49.2	9 40.1	12 51.7	28 38.5	15 24.7	1 30.1	1 54.0	14 10.5	26 R 37.2	9 R 26.8	15 R 8.3	17 R 47.8
3	16 44 45.7	10 41.6	12 48.5	9♎34.8	16 27.6	2 36.9	2 34.4	14 23.9	26 34.4	9 24.5	15 6.9	17 46.4
4	16 48 42.3	11 43.2	12 45.3	20 41.4	17 33.7	3 44.0	3 14.8	14 37.5	26 31.6	9 22.2	15 5.5	17 44.9
5	16 52 38.8	12 44.8	12 42.1	2♏10.2	18 42.9	4 51.3	3 55.1	14 51.1	26 28.7	9 19.9	15 4.0	17 43.5
6	16 56 35.4	13 46.6	12 38.9	14 9.5	19 55.4	5 58.8	4 35.4	15 4.7	26 25.7	9 17.6	15 2.6	17 42.1
7	17 0 32.0	14 48.4	12 35.6	26 42.6	21 11.0	7 6.5	5 15.6	15 18.3	26 22.7	9 15.2	15 1.1	17 40.8
8	17 4 28.5	15 50.4	12 32.4	9♐45.9	22 29.8	8 14.6	5 55.8	15 32.1	26 19.5	9 12.8	14 59.6	17 39.4
9	17 8 25.1	16 52.3	12 29.2	23 8.8	23 51.9	9 22.8	6 36.0	15 45.8	26 16.3	9 10.4	14 58.1	17 38.0
10	17 12 21.6	17 54.4	12 26.0	6♑36.1	25 17.2	10 31.3	7 16.1	15 59.6	26 13.0	9 8.0	14 56.6	17 36.7
11	17 16 18.2	18 56.5	12 22.8	19 52.5	26 45.8	11 40.1	7 56.1	16 13.4	26 9.7	9 5.5	14 55.0	17 35.4
12	17 20 14.8	19 58.7	12 19.6	2♒47.2	28 17.8	12 49.1	8 36.1	16 27.3	26 6.2	9 3.1	14 53.5	17 34.1
13	17 24 11.3	21 .9	12 16.4	15 16.6	29 53.1	13 58.4	9 16.1	16 41.2	26 2.7	9 .6	14 51.9	17 32.8
14	17 28 7.9	22 3.1	12 13.2	27 24.3	1♊31.8	15 8.0	9 56.1	16 55.1	25 59.1	8 58.1	14 50.3	17 31.6
15	17 32 4.4	23 5.4	12 9.9	9♓20.2	3 14.0	16 17.9	10 36.0	17 9.1	25 55.5	8 55.5	14 48.7	17 30.3
16	17 36 1.0	24 7.8	12 6.7	21 18.4	4 59.6	17 28.0	11 15.8	17 23.1	25 51.8	8 53.0	14 47.1	17 29.1
17	17 39 57.5	25 10.1	12 3.5	3♈35.7	6 48.7	18 38.4	11 55.6	17 37.1	25 48.0	8 50.4	14 45.5	17 27.9
18	17 43 54.1	26 12.6	12 .3	16 30.7	8 41.4	19 49.2	12 35.4	17 51.2	25 44.3	8 47.9	14 43.9	17 26.7
19	17 47 50.7	27 15.0	11 57.1	0♉20.6	10 37.5	21 .1	13 15.1	18 5.3	25 40.4	8 45.3	14 42.3	17 25.6
20	17 51 47.2	28 17.4	11 53.9	15 17.0	12 37.0	22 11.4	13 54.8	18 19.4	25 36.4	8 42.7	14 40.6	17 24.4
21	17 55 43.8	29 19.9	11 50.6	1♊17.5	14 39.9	23 22.9	14 34.5	18 33.6	25 32.4	8 40.1	14 38.9	17 23.3
22	17 59 40.3	0♋22.3	11 47.4	17 59.5	16 46.1	24 34.8	15 14.0	18 47.8	25 28.3	8 37.5	14 37.3	17 22.2
23	18 3 36.9	1 24.7	11 44.2	4♋42.9	18 55.3	25 46.9	15 53.6	19 1.9	25 24.2	8 34.9	14 35.6	17 21.1
24	18 7 33.5	2 27.1	11 41.0	20 45.8	21 7.5	26 59.2	16 33.1	19 16.1	25 20.1	8 32.3	14 33.9	17 20.1
25	18 11 30.0	3 29.5	11 37.8	5♌41.6	23 22.4	28 11.9	17 12.5	19 30.4	25 15.9	8 29.6	14 32.2	17 19.0
26	18 15 26.6	4 31.9	11 34.5	19 24.0	25 39.6	29 24.9	17 51.9	19 44.6	25 11.6	8 27.0	14 30.5	17 18.0
27	18 19 23.1	5 34.2	11 31.3	2♍ 2.2	27 59.0	0♊38.1	18 31.2	19 58.9	25 7.3	8 24.3	14 28.7	17 17.0
28	18 23 19.7	6 36.4	11 28.1	13 52.1	0♋20.0	1 51.6	19 10.5	20 13.1	25 3.0	8 21.7	14 27.0	17 16.1
29	18 27 16.2	7 38.7	11 24.9	25 11.7	2 42.4	3 5.3	19 49.8	20 27.4	24 58.6	8 19.0	14 25.3	17 15.1
30	18 31 12.8	8 40.8	11 21.7	6♎18.5	5 5.8	4 19.4	20 29.0	20 41.7	24 54.2	8 16.4	14 23.6	17 14.2

DECLINATION

DAY	EPHEM. SID. TIME	☉	☊	☽	☿	♀	♂	♃	♄	♅	♆	♇
1	16 36 52.6	21N59.4	0S18.4	1N50.9	13N13.6	10N10.5	1S31.4	22N59.3	21S 2.6	23S28.6	21S49.8	1S15.7
4	16 48 42.3	22 22.7	0 18.5	14S .6	14 20.4	11 21.1	0 40.4	22 55.9	21 4.3	23 29.1	21 50.2	1 15.3
7	17 0 32.0	22 42.4	0 18.5	24 46.7	15 36.5	12 29.9	0N10.4	22 52.3	21 6.0	23 29.5	21 50.6	1 15.1
10	17 12 21.6	22 58.6	0 18.6	26 2.5	16 59.2	13 36.6	1 1.0	22 48.4	21 7.8	23 30.0	21 51.0	1 15.0
13	17 24 11.3	23 11.1	0 18.6	16 30.7	18 25.4	14 40.9	1 51.1	22 44.3	21 9.8	23 30.5	21 51.5	1 15.0
16	17 36 1.0	23 20.0	0 18.7	0N 9.3	19 51.5	15 42.5	2 40.9	22 40.1	21 11.8	23 30.9	21 51.9	1 15.2
19	17 47 50.7	23 25.1	0 18.7	17 50.5	21 13.5	16 41.2	3 30.2	22 35.6	21 14.0	23 31.4	21 52.4	1 15.4
22	17 59 40.3	23 26.5	0 18.8	26 52.3	22 26.6	17 36.5	4 18.9	22 30.8	21 16.2	23 31.9	21 52.9	1 15.8
25	18 11 30.0	23 24.2	0 18.8	19 48.2	23 25.5	18 28.2	5 6.9	22 25.9	21 18.4	23 32.3	21 53.4	1 16.2
28	18 23 19.7	23 18.2	0 18.8	3 32.3	24 5.0	19 15.9	5 54.1	22 20.8	21 20.7	23 32.8	21 53.8	1 16.8

JULY 1990

LONGITUDE

DAY	EPHEM. SID. TIME h m s	☉ ° ′	☊ ° ′	☽ ° ′	☿ ° ′	♀ ° ′	♂ ° ′	♃ ° ′	♄ ° ′	♅ ° ′	♆ ° ′	♇ ° ′
1	18 35 9.4	8♋55.6	8♒52.6	20♎59.2	6♋49.4	7♊ 6.7	22♈ 1.7	19♋18.6	23♑ 1.0	7♑32.3	13♑18.5	15♏ 8.1
2	18 39 5.9	9 52.8	8 49.4	2♏58.2	9 .3	8 18.0	22 43.4	19 32.0	22 R56.7	7 R29.9	13 R16.9	15 R 7.4
3	18 43 2.5	10 50.0	8 46.2	14 51.7	11 10.9	9 29.4	23 25.1	19 45.3	22 52.5	7 27.5	13 15.3	15 6.6
4	18 46 59.0	11 47.2	8 43.1	26 43.8	13 21.1	10 40.8	24 6.7	19 58.7	22 48.2	7 25.0	13 13.6	15 5.9
5	18 50 55.6	12 44.4	8 39.9	8♐37.7	15 30.5	11 52.2	24 48.1	20 12.2	22 43.8	7 22.6	13 12.0	15 5.2
6	18 54 52.2	13 41.6	8 36.7	20 36.2	17 39.0	13 3.7	25 29.5	20 25.6	22 39.5	7 20.2	13 10.4	15 4.5
7	18 58 48.7	14 38.8	8 33.5	2♑41.6	19 46.4	14 15.2	26 10.7	20 39.0	22 35.1	7 17.8	13 8.8	15 3.9
8	19 2 45.3	15 36.0	8 30.3	14 55.7	21 52.5	15 26.8	26 51.8	20 52.4	22 30.7	7 15.4	13 7.2	15 3.3
9	19 6 41.8	16 33.2	8 27.2	27 19.7	23 57.3	16 38.5	27 32.9	21 5.9	22 26.4	7 13.0	13 5.6	15 2.8
10	19 10 38.4	17 30.4	8 24.0	9♒54.9	26 .4	17 50.2	28 13.8	21 19.4	22 22.0	7 10.6	13 4.0	15 2.2
11	19 14 34.9	18 27.6	8 20.8	22 42.4	28 1.9	19 1.9	28 54.6	21 32.8	22 17.5	7 8.3	13 2.3	15 1.7
12	19 18 31.5	19 24.8	8 17.6	5♓43.3	0♌ 1.7	20 13.7	29 35.3	21 46.3	22 13.1	7 5.9	13 .7	15 1.2
13	19 22 28.1	20 22.0	8 14.5	18 58.5	1 59.8	21 25.5	0♉15.9	21 59.8	22 8.7	7 3.5	12 59.1	15 .8
14	19 26 24.6	21 19.2	8 11.3	2♈29.1	3 56.1	22 37.3	0 56.3	22 13.2	22 4.2	7 1.2	12 57.5	15 .4
15	19 30 21.2	22 16.4	8 8.1	16 15.6	5 50.6	23 49.2	1 36.6	22 26.7	21 59.8	6 58.9	12 55.9	15 .0
16	19 34 17.7	23 13.7	8 4.9	0♉18.0	7 43.2	25 1.2	2 16.8	22 40.1	21 55.3	6 56.6	12 54.3	14 59.7
17	19 38 14.3	24 10.9	8 1.8	14 34.9	9 34.0	26 13.2	2 56.9	22 53.6	21 50.9	6 54.3	12 52.7	14 59.3
18	19 42 10.9	25 8.2	7 58.6	29 3.8	11 22.9	27 25.2	3 36.8	23 7.1	21 46.5	6 52.0	12 51.2	14 59.1
19	19 46 7.4	26 5.4	7 55.4	13♊40.6	13 10.0	28 37.3	4 16.5	23 20.5	21 42.0	6 49.7	12 49.6	14 58.8
20	19 50 4.0	27 2.7	7 52.2	28 19.6	14 55.3	29 49.5	4 56.2	23 34.0	21 37.6	6 47.5	12 48.0	14 58.6
21	19 54 .5	28 .0	7 49.1	12♋54.8	16 38.7	1♋ 1.6	5 35.7	23 47.4	21 33.2	6 45.3	12 46.5	14 58.4
22	19 57 57.1	28 57.3	7 45.9	27 19.7	18 20.2	2 13.9	6 15.0	24 .9	21 28.8	6 43.1	12 44.9	14 58.3
23	20 1 53.6	29 54.6	7 42.7	11♌28.8	19 60.0	3 26.1	6 54.2	24 14.3	21 24.4	6 40.9	12 43.4	14 58.1
24	20 5 50.2	0♌51.9	7 39.5	25 18.1	21 37.9	4 38.4	7 33.2	24 27.7	21 20.1	6 38.7	12 41.8	14 58.1
25	20 9 46.8	1 49.3	7 36.3	8♍45.3	23 13.9	5 50.8	8 12.0	24 41.1	21 15.7	6 36.6	12 40.3	14 58.0
26	20 13 43.3	2 46.6	7 33.2	21 50.1	24 48.2	7 3.2	8 50.7	24 54.5	21 11.4	6 34.5	12 38.8	14 58.0
27	20 17 39.9	3 43.9	7 30.0	4♎33.7	26 20.6	8 15.6	9 29.2	25 7.9	21 7.1	6 32.4	12 37.3	14 58.0
28	20 21 36.4	4 41.3	7 26.8	16 59.1	27 51.1	9 28.0	10 7.6	25 21.2	21 2.8	6 30.4	12 35.9	14 D58.1
29	20 25 33.0	5 38.6	7 23.6	29 9.7	29 19.8	10 40.6	10 45.8	25 34.6	20 58.6	6 28.3	12 34.4	14 58.2
30	20 29 29.5	6 36.0	7 20.5	11♏ 9.8	0♍46.7	11 53.2	11 23.8	25 48.0	20 54.4	6 26.4	12 33.0	14 58.3
31	20 33 26.1	7 33.4	7 17.3	23 4.0	2 11.6	13 5.7	12 1.7	26 1.3	20 50.3	6 24.4	12 31.5	14 58.5

LATITUDE

DAY	EPHEM. SID. TIME	☉	☊	☽	☿	♀	♂	♃	♄	♅	♆	♇
1	18 35 9.4	0 .0	0 .0	4S59.9	1N 5.4	1S31.9	2S 3.0	0N12.5	0N 5.7	0S19.6	0N52.5	15N44.3
4	18 46 59.0	0 .0	0 .0	4 55.7	1 26.5	1 25.5	2 3.5	0 12.7	0 5.4	0 19.6	0 52.5	15 42.8
7	18 58 48.7	0 .0	0 .0	2 58.8	1 41.1	1 18.6	2 3.7	0 13.0	0 5.2	0 19.7	0 52.4	15 41.2
10	19 10 38.4	0 .0	0 .0	0N14.5	1 49.0	1 11.5	2 3.9	0 13.3	0 4.9	0 19.7	0 52.4	15 39.7
13	19 22 28.1	0 .0	0 .0	3 30.2	1 50.3	1 4.0	2 4.0	0 13.6	0 4.7	0 19.7	0 52.4	15 38.1
16	19 34 17.7	0 .0	0 .0	5 13.6	1 45.7	0 56.2	2 3.9	0 13.8	0 4.4	0 19.7	0 52.3	15 36.4
19	19 46 7.4	0 .0	0 .0	4 14.8	1 35.8	0 48.3	2 3.7	0 14.1	0 4.1	0 19.7	0 52.3	15 34.8
22	19 57 57.1	0 .0	0 .0	0 54.8	1 21.1	0 40.2	2 3.4	0 14.4	0 3.9	0 19.7	0 52.2	15 33.1
25	20 9 46.8	0 .0	0 .0	2S45.8	1 2.4	0 32.0	2 2.9	0 14.7	0 3.6	0 19.7	0 52.2	15 31.4
28	20 21 36.4	0 .0	0 .0	4 57.3	0 40.1	0 23.8	2 2.3	0 15.0	0 3.3	0 19.7	0 52.1	15 29.7
31	20 33 26.1	0 .0	0 .0	5 5.1	0 14.9	0 15.5	2 1.6	0 15.3	0 3.1	0 19.7	0 52.0	15 28.0

RIGHT ASCENSION

DAY	EPHEM. SID. TIME	☉	☊	☽	☿	♀	♂	♃	♄	♅	♆	♇
1	18 35 9.4	9♋42.9	11♒18.4	17♎28.1	7♋29.6	5♊33.7	21♈ 8.1	20♋56.0	24♑49.7	8♑13.7	14♑21.8	17♏13.3
2	18 39 5.9	10 45.0	11 15.2	28 53.8	9 53.4	6 48.3	21 47.2	21 10.4	24 R45.2	8 R11.1	14 R20.1	17 R12.5
3	18 43 2.5	11 46.9	11 12.0	10♏46.1	12 16.9	8 3.1	22 26.2	21 24.7	24 40.7	8 8.4	14 18.4	17 11.6
4	18 46 59.0	12 48.8	11 8.8	23 10.8	14 39.7	9 18.2	23 5.2	21 39.0	24 36.2	8 5.8	14 16.6	17 10.8
5	18 50 55.6	13 50.6	11 5.5	6♐ 7.4	17 1.3	10 33.5	23 44.2	21 53.3	24 31.6	8 3.1	14 14.9	17 10.0
6	18 54 52.2	14 52.4	11 2.3	19 28.4	19 21.5	11 49.1	24 23.1	22 7.7	24 27.0	8 .5	14 13.1	17 9.3
7	18 58 48.7	15 54.0	10 59.1	3♑ .2	21 39.9	13 4.9	25 1.9	22 22.0	24 22.4	7 57.9	14 11.4	17 8.5
8	19 2 45.3	16 55.5	10 55.9	16 26.8	23 56.3	14 20.9	25 40.7	22 36.4	24 17.8	7 55.2	14 9.7	17 7.8
9	19 6 41.8	17 57.0	10 52.6	29 34.9	26 10.5	15 37.2	26 19.5	22 50.8	24 13.2	7 52.7	14 8.0	17 7.2
10	19 10 38.4	18 58.4	10 49.4	12♒17.5	28 22.2	16 53.7	26 58.2	23 5.1	24 8.5	7 50.1	14 6.2	17 6.6
11	19 14 34.9	19 59.6	10 46.2	24 35.3	0♌31.4	18 10.4	27 36.8	23 19.4	24 3.8	7 47.5	14 4.5	17 5.9
12	19 18 31.5	21 .7	10 42.9	6♓35.3	2 38.0	19 27.3	28 15.4	23 33.8	23 59.1	7 44.9	14 2.8	17 5.4
13	19 22 28.1	22 1.8	10 39.7	18 29.6	4 41.8	20 44.4	28 53.9	23 48.1	23 54.4	7 42.4	14 1.0	17 4.8
14	19 26 24.6	23 2.7	10 36.5	0♈33.4	6 42.9	22 1.7	29 32.3	24 2.5	23 49.7	7 39.8	13 59.3	17 4.3
15	19 30 21.2	24 3.5	10 33.3	13 3.6	8 41.2	23 19.1	0♉10.7	24 16.8	23 45.0	7 37.3	13 57.6	17 3.8
16	19 34 17.7	25 4.2	10 30.0	26 17.3	10 36.8	24 36.7	0 49.0	24 31.1	23 40.3	7 34.8	13 55.9	17 3.3
17	19 38 14.3	26 4.7	10 26.8	10♉28.0	12 29.5	25 54.5	1 27.3	24 45.4	23 35.6	7 32.3	13 54.2	17 2.8
18	19 42 10.9	27 5.2	10 23.6	25 40.4	14 19.5	27 12.4	2 5.4	24 59.7	23 30.9	7 29.8	13 52.5	17 2.4
19	19 46 7.4	28 5.5	10 20.3	11♊43.3	16 6.7	28 30.4	2 43.5	25 14.0	23 26.2	7 27.3	13 50.8	17 2.0
20	19 50 4.0	29 5.6	10 17.1	28 7.8	17 51.3	29 48.6	3 21.5	25 28.3	23 21.6	7 24.9	13 49.1	17 1.7
21	19 54 .5	0♌ 5.7	10 13.9	14♋15.8	19 33.2	1♋ 6.8	3 59.5	25 42.5	23 16.9	7 22.4	13 47.5	17 1.3
22	19 57 57.1	1 5.5	10 10.6	29 34.9	21 12.5	2 25.1	4 37.3	25 56.8	23 12.2	7 20.0	13 45.8	17 1.0
23	20 1 53.6	2 5.3	10 7.4	13♌49.6	22 49.2	3 43.6	5 15.1	26 11.0	23 7.6	7 17.7	13 44.2	17 .8
24	20 5 50.2	3 4.9	10 4.2	27 .8	24 23.5	5 2.0	5 52.7	26 25.2	23 3.0	7 15.3	13 42.5	17 .5
25	20 9 46.8	4 4.4	10 .9	9♍19.7	25 55.2	6 20.5	6 30.3	26 39.4	22 58.4	7 13.0	13 40.9	17 .3
26	20 13 43.3	5 3.7	9 57.7	21 2.3	27 24.6	7 39.1	7 7.8	26 53.6	22 53.8	7 10.7	13 39.3	17 .2
27	20 17 39.9	6 2.8	9 54.5	2♎24.9	28 51.5	8 57.7	7 45.1	27 7.7	22 49.2	7 8.4	13 37.7	17 .0
28	20 21 36.4	7 1.8	9 51.2	13 43.2	0♍16.1	10 16.3	8 22.4	27 21.9	22 44.7	7 6.2	13 36.1	16 59.9
29	20 25 33.0	8 .7	9 48.0	25 11.1	1 38.4	11 34.9	8 59.5	27 36.0	22 40.2	7 4.0	13 34.5	16 59.8
30	20 29 29.5	8 59.4	9 44.7	6♏59.7	2 58.4	12 53.5	9 36.6	27 50.1	22 35.8	7 1.9	13 33.0	16 59.8
31	20 33 26.1	9 57.9	9 41.5	19 16.5	4 16.1	14 12.0	10 13.6	28 4.1	22 31.4	6 59.7	13 31.5	16 59.8

DECLINATION

DAY	EPHEM. SID. TIME	☉	☊	☽	☿	♀	♂	♃	♄	♅	♆	♇
1	18 35 9.4	23N 8.5	0S18.9	12S49.1	24N21.2	19N59.4	6N40.7	22N15.4	21S23.1	23S33.2	21S54.3	1S17.5
4	18 46 59.0	22 55.2	0 18.9	24 13.1	24 12.4	20 38.4	7 26.3	22 9.9	21 25.5	23 33.7	21 54.9	1 18.4
7	18 58 48.7	22 38.2	0 19.0	26 23.6	23 39.1	21 12.7	8 11.1	22 4.2	21 27.9	23 34.1	21 55.4	1 19.3
10	19 10 38.4	22 17.8	0 19.0	17 31.9	22 44.0	21 41.9	8 55.0	21 58.2	21 30.3	23 34.5	21 55.9	1 20.3
13	19 22 28.1	21 53.9	0 19.1	1 8.3	21 30.5	22 6.0	9 37.8	21 52.1	21 32.7	23 34.9	21 56.4	1 21.5
16	19 34 17.7	21 26.6	0 19.1	16N28.0	20 2.6	22 24.7	10 19.6	21 45.8	21 35.1	23 35.3	21 56.9	1 22.7
19	19 46 7.4	20 56.0	0 19.2	26 39.5	18 23.8	22 37.8	11 .3	21 39.3	21 37.5	23 35.6	21 57.4	1 24.1
22	19 57 57.1	20 22.3	0 19.2	21 35.5	16 37.2	22 45.2	11 39.8	21 32.7	21 39.8	23 36.0	21 57.9	1 25.6
25	20 9 46.8	19 45.4	0 19.2	5 43.5	14 45.5	22 46.8	12 18.1	21 25.9	21 42.1	23 36.3	21 58.4	1 27.1
28	20 21 36.4	19 5.6	0 19.3	11S14.8	12 50.9	22 42.5	12 55.2	21 18.9	21 44.4	23 36.6	21 58.8	1 28.8
31	20 33 26.1	18 23.0	0 19.3	23 27.4	10 55.6	22 32.4	13 31.0	21 11.8	21 46.6	23 36.9	21 59.3	1 30.6

AUGUST 1990

LONGITUDE

DAY	EPHEM. SID. TIME h m s	☉ ° ′	☊ ° ′	☾ ° ′	☿ ° ′	♀ ° ′	♂ ° ′	♃ ° ′	♄ ° ′	♅ ° ′	♆ ° ′	♇ ° ′
1	20 37 22.7	8♌30.8	7♒14.1	4♐56.7	3♍34.5	14♋18.4	12♉39.3	26♋14.6	20♑46.1	6♑22.5	12♑30.1	14♏58.7
2	20 41 19.2	9 28.2	7 10.9	16 52.3	4 55.5	15 31.0	13 16.8	26 27.8	20 R 42.1	6 R 20.6	12 R 28.7	14 58.9
3	20 45 15.8	10 25.6	7 7.8	28 54.6	6 14.5	16 43.7	13 54.1	26 41.1	20 38.0	6 18.7	12 27.3	14 59.2
4	20 49 12.3	11 23.0	7 4.6	11♑ 6.9	7 31.4	17 56.5	14 31.2	26 54.3	20 34.0	6 16.8	12 26.0	14 59.5
5	20 53 8.9	12 20.4	7 1.4	23 31.8	8 46.3	19 9.3	15 8.1	27 7.5	20 30.0	6 15.0	12 24.6	14 59.8
6	20 57 5.4	13 17.9	6 58.2	6♒11.0	9 58.9	20 22.1	15 44.8	27 20.7	20 26.1	6 13.2	12 23.3	15 .1
7	21 1 2.0	14 15.3	6 55.0	19 5.5	11 9.4	21 35.0	16 21.3	27 33.8	20 22.2	6 11.5	12 21.9	15 .5
8	21 4 58.5	15 12.8	6 51.9	2♓15.4	12 17.5	22 47.9	16 57.7	27 46.9	20 18.4	6 9.8	12 20.6	15 1.0
9	21 8 55.1	16 10.3	6 48.7	15 39.9	13 23.2	24 .9	17 33.8	28 .0	20 14.6	6 8.1	12 19.3	15 1.4
10	21 12 51.7	17 7.8	6 45.5	29 17.8	14 26.4	25 13.9	18 9.7	28 13.1	20 10.9	6 6.4	12 18.1	15 1.9
11	21 16 48.2	18 5.4	6 42.3	13♈ 7.5	15 27.0	26 27.0	18 45.4	28 26.1	20 7.2	6 4.8	12 16.8	15 2.5
12	21 20 44.8	19 2.9	6 39.2	27 6.7	16 24.9	27 40.1	19 20.9	28 39.1	20 3.6	6 3.3	12 15.6	15 3.0
13	21 24 41.3	20 .5	6 36.0	11♉13.5	17 20.0	28 53.2	19 56.1	28 52.1	20 .1	6 1.7	12 14.4	15 3.6
14	21 28 37.9	20 58.1	6 32.8	25 25.7	18 12.0	0♌ 6.4	20 31.1	29 5.0	19 56.6	6 .2	12 13.2	15 4.3
15	21 32 34.4	21 55.7	6 29.6	9♊40.7	19 .9	1 19.7	21 5.9	29 17.9	19 53.2	5 58.8	12 12.1	15 4.9
16	21 36 31.0	22 53.4	6 26.4	23 56.2	19 46.5	2 32.9	21 40.5	29 30.8	19 49.8	5 57.4	12 10.9	15 5.6
17	21 40 27.5	23 51.1	6 23.3	8♋ 9.4	20 28.6	3 46.3	22 14.8	29 43.6	19 46.5	5 56.0	12 9.8	15 6.4
18	21 44 24.1	24 48.8	6 20.1	22 17.2	21 7.0	4 59.6	22 48.8	29 56.4	19 43.3	5 54.7	12 8.7	15 7.1
19	21 48 20.7	25 46.5	6 16.9	6♌16.3	21 41.4	6 13.0	23 22.6	0♌ 9.1	19 40.1	5 53.4	12 7.7	15 7.9
20	21 52 17.2	26 44.3	6 13.7	20 3.6	22 11.8	7 26.5	23 56.1	0 21.9	19 37.1	5 52.2	12 6.7	15 8.8
21	21 56 13.8	27 42.1	6 10.6	3♍36.3	22 37.8	8 40.0	24 29.4	0 34.5	19 34.0	5 51.0	12 5.6	15 9.7
22	22 0 10.3	28 39.9	6 7.4	16 52.4	22 59.1	9 53.5	25 2.3	0 47.2	19 31.1	5 49.8	12 4.6	15 10.6
23	22 4 6.9	29 37.8	6 4.2	29 50.6	23 15.6	11 7.1	25 35.0	0 59.7	19 28.2	5 48.7	12 3.7	15 11.5
24	22 8 3.4	0♍35.6	6 1.0	12♎31.3	23 27.0	12 20.7	26 7.4	1 12.2	19 25.4	5 47.6	12 2.7	15 12.5
25	22 11 60.0	1 33.5	5 57.9	24 55.6	23 33.1	13 34.3	26 39.5	1 24.7	19 22.7	5 46.6	12 1.8	15 13.5
26	22 15 56.5	2 31.4	5 54.7	7♏ 6.2	23 33.6	14 48.0	27 11.2	1 37.1	19 20.1	5 45.6	12 .9	15 14.5
27	22 19 53.1	3 29.3	5 51.5	19 6.3	23 R 28.3	16 1.7	27 42.7	1 49.5	19 17.5	5 44.6	12 .1	15 15.5
28	22 23 49.6	4 27.2	5 48.3	1♐ .2	23 17.0	17 15.5	28 13.9	2 1.8	19 15.0	5 43.8	11 59.2	15 16.6
29	22 27 46.2	5 25.2	5 45.1	12 52.4	22 59.8	18 29.2	28 44.8	2 14.0	19 12.6	5 42.9	11 58.4	15 17.8
30	22 31 42.8	6 23.1	5 42.0	24 47.8	22 36.4	19 43.1	29 15.3	2 26.2	19 10.3	5 42.1	11 57.6	15 18.9
31	22 35 39.3	7 21.1	5 38.8	6♑51.3	22 7.0	20 56.9	29 45.5	2 38.4	19 8.1	5 41.4	11 56.9	15 20.1

LATITUDE

DAY	SID. TIME	☉	☊	☾	☿	♀	♂	♃	♄	♅	♆	♇
1	20 37 22.7	0 .0	0 .0	4S40.9	0N 5.9	0S12.8	2S 1.3	0N15.4	0N 3.0	0S19.7	0N52.0	15N27.4
4	20 49 12.3	0 .0	0 .0	2 20.2	0S22.7	0 4.6	2 .4	0 15.7	0 2.7	0 19.7	0 51.9	15 25.7
7	21 1 2.0	0 .0	0 .0	1N 4.8	0 53.1	0N 3.5	1 59.3	0 16.0	0 2.4	0 19.7	0 51.9	15 24.0
10	21 12 51.7	0 .0	0 .0	4 9.5	1 25.0	0 11.5	1 58.0	0 16.3	0 2.2	0 19.7	0 51.8	15 22.2
13	21 24 41.3	0 .0	0 .0	5 15.3	1 57.7	0 19.2	1 56.6	0 16.6	0 1.9	0 19.7	0 51.7	15 20.5
16	21 36 31.0	0 .0	0 .0	3 37.0	2 30.5	0 26.7	1 55.1	0 16.9	0 1.6	0 19.7	0 51.6	15 18.8
19	21 48 20.7	0 .0	0 .0	0 5.6	3 2.6	0 33.9	1 53.4	0 17.3	0 1.4	0 19.7	0 51.5	15 17.1
22	22 0 10.3	0 .0	0 .0	3S20.8	3 32.6	0 40.7	1 51.5	0 17.6	0 1.1	0 19.7	0 51.4	15 15.5
25	22 11 60.0	0 .0	0 .0	5 6.7	3 58.7	0 47.2	1 49.4	0 18.0	0 .9	0 19.6	0 51.3	15 13.8
28	22 23 49.6	0 .0	0 .0	4 46.5	4 18.3	0 53.3	1 47.2	0 18.3	0 .6	0 19.6	0 51.2	15 12.2
31	22 35 39.3	0 .0	0 .0	2 37.7	4 28.2	0 59.0	1 44.7	0 18.7	0 .3	0 19.6	0 51.1	15 10.7

RIGHT ASCENSION

DAY	SID. TIME	☉	☊	☾	☿	♀	♂	♃	♄	♅	♆	♇
1	20 37 22.7	10♌56.3	9♒38.3	2♐ 3.8	5♍31.6	15♋30.5	10♉50.4	28♋18.2	22♑27.0	6♑57.6	13♑30.0	16♏59.8
2	20 41 19.2	11 54.5	9 35.0	15 17.4	6 44.8	16 49.0	11 27.1	28 32.1	22 R 22.7	6 R 55.5	13 R 28.5	16 D 59.9
3	20 45 15.8	12 52.6	9 31.8	28 46.9	7 55.7	18 7.4	12 3.7	28 46.1	22 18.4	6 53.5	13 27.0	16 60.0
4	20 49 12.3	13 50.5	9 28.5	12♑18.1	9 4.3	19 25.7	12 40.1	29 .0	22 14.1	6 51.4	13 25.5	17 .1
5	20 53 8.9	14 48.3	9 25.3	25 37.3	10 10.7	20 43.9	13 16.4	29 13.9	22 9.9	6 49.5	13 24.0	17 .2
6	20 57 5.4	15 45.9	9 22.1	8♒35.5	11 14.8	22 2.1	13 52.6	29 27.8	22 5.8	6 47.5	13 22.6	17 .4
7	21 1 2.0	16 43.3	9 18.8	21 10.2	12 16.5	23 20.1	14 28.7	29 41.6	22 1.6	6 45.6	13 21.2	17 .6
8	21 4 58.5	17 40.7	9 15.6	3♓25.9	13 15.9	24 38.0	15 4.6	29 55.4	21 57.6	6 43.7	13 19.8	17 .8
9	21 8 55.1	18 37.8	9 12.3	15 32.1	14 12.8	25 55.8	15 40.4	0♌ 9.1	21 53.6	6 41.9	13 18.4	17 1.1
10	21 12 51.7	19 34.8	9 9.1	27 42.0	15 7.3	27 13.5	16 16.0	0 22.8	21 49.6	6 40.1	13 17.1	17 1.4
11	21 16 48.2	20 31.7	9 5.8	10♈10.7	15 59.2	28 31.0	16 51.5	0 36.5	21 45.7	6 38.4	13 15.7	17 1.7
12	21 20 44.8	21 28.5	9 2.6	23 13.7	16 48.5	29 48.3	17 26.8	0 50.2	21 41.9	6 36.6	13 14.4	17 2.1
13	21 24 41.3	22 25.1	8 59.3	7♉ 3.7	17 35.0	1♌ 5.5	18 1.9	1 3.7	21 38.1	6 35.0	13 13.1	17 2.5
14	21 28 37.9	23 21.5	8 56.1	21 46.9	18 18.7	2 22.5	18 36.9	1 17.3	21 34.4	6 33.3	13 11.9	17 2.9
15	21 32 34.4	24 17.9	8 52.9	7♊16.8	18 59.5	3 39.4	19 11.7	1 30.8	21 30.8	6 31.8	13 10.6	17 3.4
16	21 36 31.0	25 14.1	8 49.6	23 12.7	19 37.1	4 56.0	19 46.3	1 44.3	21 27.2	6 30.2	13 9.4	17 3.9
17	21 40 27.5	26 10.2	8 46.4	9♋ 3.3	20 11.6	6 12.5	20 20.7	1 57.7	21 23.7	6 28.7	13 8.2	17 4.4
18	21 44 24.1	27 6.1	8 43.1	24 18.7	20 42.6	7 28.7	20 54.8	2 11.0	21 20.3	6 27.3	13 7.0	17 4.9
19	21 48 20.7	28 2.0	8 39.9	8♌40.7	21 10.1	8 44.8	21 28.8	2 24.3	21 16.9	6 25.9	13 5.9	17 5.5
20	21 52 17.2	28 57.7	8 36.6	22 5.5	21 33.9	10 .7	22 2.6	2 37.7	21 13.7	6 24.5	13 4.8	17 6.2
21	21 56 13.8	29 53.3	8 33.4	4♍40.0	21 53.8	11 16.3	22 36.2	2 50.9	21 10.4	6 23.2	13 3.7	17 6.8
22	22 0 10.3	0♍48.8	8 30.1	16 37.3	22 9.6	12 31.7	23 9.5	3 4.0	21 7.3	6 22.0	13 2.7	17 7.5
23	22 4 6.9	1 44.1	8 26.9	28 11.9	22 21.1	13 46.9	23 42.5	3 17.1	21 4.3	6 20.7	13 1.6	17 8.2
24	22 8 3.4	2 39.4	8 23.6	9♎38.4	22 28.1	15 1.8	24 15.3	3 30.2	21 1.3	6 19.6	13 .6	17 8.9
25	22 11 60.0	3 34.5	8 20.4	21 9.9	22 30.4	16 16.5	24 47.9	3 43.1	20 58.4	6 18.4	12 59.6	17 9.7
26	22 15 56.5	4 29.5	8 17.1	2♏57.3	22 R 27.9	17 31.0	25 20.2	3 56.1	20 55.6	6 17.4	12 58.7	17 10.5
27	22 19 53.1	5 24.5	8 13.8	15 8.5	22 20.4	18 45.3	25 52.2	4 8.9	20 52.9	6 16.3	12 57.7	17 11.3
28	22 23 49.6	6 19.3	8 10.6	27 46.8	22 7.9	19 59.3	26 24.0	4 21.7	20 50.2	6 15.4	12 56.8	17 12.2
29	22 27 46.2	7 14.0	8 7.3	10♐50.1	21 50.3	21 13.0	26 55.5	4 34.4	20 47.7	6 14.5	12 56.0	17 13.1
30	22 31 42.8	8 8.6	8 4.1	24 10.7	21 27.6	22 26.6	27 26.7	4 47.1	20 45.3	6 13.6	12 55.1	17 14.0
31	22 35 39.3	9 3.2	8 .8	7♑36.9	20 59.9	23 39.9	27 57.6	4 59.7	20 42.9	6 12.8	12 54.3	17 15.0

DECLINATION

DAY	SID. TIME	☉	☊	☾	☿	♀	♂	♃	♄	♅	♆	♇
1	20 37 22.7	18N 8.2	0S19.3	25S43.6	10N17.3	22N27.8	13N42.7	21N 9.4	21S47.3	23S37.0	21S59.5	1S31.2
4	20 49 12.3	17 22.0	0 19.4	25 18.3	8 23.8	22 9.8	14 16.8	21 2.1	21 49.4	23 37.3	21 59.9	1 33.0
7	21 1 2.0	16 33.3	0 19.4	14 4.5	6 33.8	21 46.2	14 49.6	20 54.7	21 51.4	23 37.5	22 .4	1 35.0
10	21 12 51.7	15 42.2	0 19.5	3N32.1	4 49.1	21 16.8	15 21.0	20 47.2	21 53.4	23 37.8	22 .8	1 37.0
13	21 24 41.3	14 48.8	0 19.5	20 11.3	3 11.9	20 41.9	15 51.2	20 39.6	21 55.2	23 38.0	22 1.2	1 39.1
16	21 36 31.0	13 53.3	0 19.5	26 55.0	1 44.5	20 1.5	16 19.9	20 31.9	21 57.0	23 38.1	22 1.6	1 41.3
19	21 48 20.7	12 55.8	0 19.6	18 47.9	0 29.9	19 16.0	16 47.4	20 24.1	21 58.7	23 38.3	22 2.0	1 43.5
22	22 0 10.3	11 56.4	0 19.6	2 6.0	0S28.2	18 25.5	17 13.4	20 16.3	22 .2	23 38.5	22 2.4	1 45.8
25	22 11 60.0	10 55.3	0 19.7	14S24.2	1 5.6	17 30.3	17 38.2	20 8.4	22 1.7	23 38.6	22 2.7	1 48.2
28	22 23 49.6	9 52.7	0 19.7	25 1.9	1 17.3	16 30.6	18 1.6	20 .5	22 3.0	23 38.7	22 3.1	1 50.6
31	22 35 39.3	8 48.7	0 19.8	25 53.3	0 58.8	15 26.8	18 23.7	19 52.5	22 4.2	23 38.8	22 3.4	1 53.0

SEPTEMBER 1990

LONGITUDE

DAY	EPHEM. SID. TIME h m s	☉ ° ′	☊ ° ′	☽ ° ′	☿ ° ′	♀ ° ′	♂ ° ′	♃ ° ′	♄ ° ′	♅ ° ′	♆ ° ′	♇ ° ′
1	22 39 35.9	8♍19.1	5♒35.6	19♑ 7.2	21♍31.8	22♌10.8	0♊15.4	2♌50.5	19♑ 6.0	5♑40.7	11♑56.2	15♏21.3
2	22 43 32.4	9 17.2	5 32.4	1♒39.3	20 R 51.0	23 24.7	0 45.0	3 2.5	19 R 3.9	5 R 40.0	11 R 55.5	15 22.6
3	22 47 29.0	10 15.3	5 29.3	14 30.5	20 5.0	24 38.7	1 14.1	3 14.4	19 1.9	5 39.4	11 54.8	15 23.8
4	22 51 25.5	11 13.4	5 26.1	27 42.3	19 14.5	25 52.7	1 43.0	3 26.3	19 .1	5 38.8	11 54.2	15 25.1
5	22 55 22.1	12 11.5	5 22.9	11♓14.6	18 20.3	27 6.7	2 11.5	3 38.2	18 58.3	5 38.3	11 53.6	15 26.5
6	22 59 18.6	13 9.6	5 19.7	25 5.4	17 23.2	28 20.7	2 39.6	3 49.9	18 56.6	5 37.9	11 53.0	15 27.8
7	23 3 15.2	14 7.8	5 16.5	9♈11.3	16 24.4	29 34.8	3 7.3	4 1.6	18 55.0	5 37.5	11 52.4	15 29.2
8	23 7 11.7	15 6.0	5 13.4	23 27.7	15 25.1	0♍49.0	3 34.7	4 13.3	18 53.5	5 37.1	11 51.9	15 30.6
9	23 11 8.3	16 4.3	5 10.2	7♉49.3	14 26.5	2 3.1	4 1.7	4 24.8	18 52.0	5 36.8	11 51.4	15 32.1
10	23 15 4.8	17 2.6	5 7.0	22 11.3	13 30.2	3 17.4	4 28.3	4 36.4	18 50.8	5 36.6	11 51.0	15 33.6
11	23 19 1.4	18 .9	5 3.8	6♊29.4	12 37.3	4 31.6	4 54.4	4 47.8	18 49.5	5 36.3	11 50.6	15 35.1
12	23 22 58.0	18 59.2	5 .7	20 40.8	11 49.1	5 45.9	5 20.2	4 59.1	18 48.4	5 36.2	11 50.2	15 36.7
13	23 26 54.5	19 57.6	4 57.5	4♋43.7	11 7.0	7 .2	5 45.4	5 10.4	18 47.3	5 36.1	11 49.8	15 38.2
14	23 30 51.1	20 56.0	4 54.3	18 37.1	10 31.8	8 14.5	6 10.3	5 21.6	18 46.4	5 36.0	11 49.5	15 39.8
15	23 34 47.6	21 54.5	4 51.1	2♌20.6	10 4.6	9 28.9	6 34.7	5 32.7	18 45.5	5 36.0	11 49.2	15 41.4
16	23 38 44.2	22 53.0	4 47.9	15 53.8	9 46.0	10 43.3	6 58.6	5 43.8	18 44.8	5 36.0	11 48.9	15 43.1
17	23 42 40.7	23 51.5	4 44.8	29 16.0	9 36.6	11 57.8	7 22.0	5 54.7	18 44.1	5 D 36.1	11 48.7	15 44.7
18	23 46 37.3	24 50.1	4 41.6	12♍26.7	9 36.6	13 12.2	7 45.0	6 5.6	18 43.5	5 36.3	11 48.5	15 46.4
19	23 50 33.8	25 48.6	4 38.4	25 24.9	9 D 46.2	14 26.7	8 7.4	6 16.4	18 43.1	5 36.5	11 48.3	15 48.1
20	23 54 30.4	26 47.3	4 35.2	8♎ 9.9	10 5.3	15 41.2	8 29.4	6 27.1	18 42.7	5 36.7	11 48.2	15 49.9
21	23 58 26.9	27 45.9	4 32.1	20 41.5	10 33.8	16 55.8	8 50.8	6 37.7	18 42.4	5 37.0	11 48.1	15 51.6
22	0 2 23.5	28 44.6	4 28.9	3♏ .2	11 11.4	18 10.4	9 11.6	6 48.2	18 42.3	5 37.4	11 48.0	15 53.4
23	0 6 20.0	29 43.3	4 25.7	15 7.2	11 57.6	19 25.0	9 32.0	6 58.6	18 42.2	5 37.8	11 48.0	15 55.3
24	0 10 16.6	0♎42.1	4 22.5	27 5.1	12 51.9	20 39.6	9 51.8	7 8.9	18 42.2	5 38.2	11 48.0	15 57.1
25	0 14 13.1	1 40.8	4 19.3	8♐57.0	13 53.7	21 54.2	10 11.0	7 19.2	18 D 42.4	5 38.7	11 48.0	15 59.0
26	0 18 9.7	2 39.6	4 16.2	20 47.2	15 2.4	23 8.9	10 29.6	7 29.3	18 42.6	5 39.3	11 48.0	16 .8
27	0 22 6.2	3 38.5	4 13.0	2♑40.3	16 17.3	24 23.6	10 47.7	7 39.3	18 42.9	5 39.9	11 D 48.1	16 2.7
28	0 26 2.8	4 37.3	4 9.8	14 41.6	17 37.8	25 38.3	11 5.2	7 49.3	18 43.4	5 40.5	11 48.3	16 4.7
29	0 29 59.4	5 36.2	4 6.6	26 56.3	19 3.1	26 53.0	11 22.0	7 59.1	18 43.9	5 41.2	11 48.4	16 6.6
30	0 33 55.9	6 35.1	4 3.5	9♒29.5	20 32.7	28 7.8	11 38.3	8 8.8	18 44.5	5 42.0	11 48.6	16 8.6

LATITUDE

DAY	EPHEM. SID. TIME	☉	☊	☽	☿	♀	♂	♃	♄	♅	♆	♇
1	22 39 35.9	0 .0	0 .0	1 S 36.5	4 S 28.7	1 N .8	1 S 43.9	0 N 18.8	0 N .3	0 S 19.6	0 N 51.1	15 N 10.1
4	22 51 25.5	0 .0	0 .0	1 N 50.3	4 19.9	1 5.8	1 41.2	0 19.2	0 .0	0 19.6	0 51.0	15 8.6
7	23 3 15.2	0 .0	0 .0	4 34.9	3 54.0	1 10.3	1 38.2	0 19.6	0 S .2	0 19.6	0 50.9	15 7.1
10	23 15 4.8	0 .0	0 .0	4 58.4	3 11.9	1 14.3	1 35.1	0 19.9	0 .5	0 19.5	0 50.8	15 5.6
13	23 26 54.5	0 .0	0 .0	2 43.5	2 17.8	1 17.8	1 31.7	0 20.3	0 .7	0 19.5	0 50.7	15 4.2
16	23 38 44.2	0 .0	0 .0	0 S 50.3	1 19.0	1 20.7	1 28.2	0 20.7	0 1.0	0 19.5	0 50.6	15 2.9
19	23 50 33.8	0 .0	0 .0	3 52.0	0 22.4	1 23.0	1 24.3	0 21.2	0 1.2	0 19.5	0 50.4	15 1.5
22	0 2 23.5	0 .0	0 .0	5 5.1	0 N 26.5	1 24.7	1 20.2	0 21.6	0 1.5	0 19.4	0 50.3	15 .3
25	0 14 13.1	0 .0	0 .0	4 15.5	1 4.9	1 25.9	1 15.8	0 22.0	0 1.7	0 19.4	0 50.2	14 59.0
28	0 26 2.8	0 .0	0 .0	1 48.7	1 31.9	1 26.4	1 11.1	0 22.5	0 2.0	0 19.4	0 50.1	14 57.9

RIGHT ASCENSION

DAY	EPHEM. SID. TIME	☉	☊	☽	☿	♀	♂	♃	♄	♅	♆	♇
1	22 39 35.9	9♍57.6	7♒57.6	20♑56.7	20♍27.4	24♌52.9	28♉28.2	5♌12.2	20♑40.6	6♑12.0	12♑53.6	17♏15.9
2	22 43 32.4	10 52.0	7 54.3	4♒ 1.0	19 R 50.4	26 5.8	28 58.5	5 24.7	20 R 38.4	6 R 11.3	12 R 52.8	17 17.0
3	22 47 29.0	11 46.3	7 51.1	16 46.2	19 9.4	27 18.4	29 28.4	5 37.1	20 36.3	6 10.6	12 52.1	17 18.0
4	22 51 25.5	12 40.6	7 47.8	29 14.9	18 24.9	28 30.8	29 58.1	5 49.4	20 34.4	6 10.0	12 51.4	17 19.1
5	22 55 22.1	13 34.7	7 44.5	11♓34.9	17 37.7	29 42.9	0♊27.4	6 1.7	20 32.5	6 9.5	12 50.8	17 20.2
6	22 59 18.6	14 28.8	7 41.3	23 57.8	16 48.6	0♍54.9	0 56.3	6 13.9	20 30.7	6 8.9	12 50.2	17 21.3
7	23 3 15.2	15 22.9	7 38.0	6♈37.4	15 58.6	2 6.6	1 24.9	6 26.0	20 29.0	6 8.5	12 49.6	17 22.4
8	23 7 11.7	16 16.9	7 34.8	19 48.0	15 8.8	3 18.1	1 53.2	6 38.0	20 27.3	6 8.1	12 49.0	17 23.6
9	23 11 8.3	17 10.9	7 31.5	3♉41.5	14 20.2	4 29.4	2 21.0	6 49.9	20 25.8	6 7.8	12 48.5	17 24.8
10	23 15 4.8	18 4.8	7 28.2	18 23.2	13 34.2	5 40.6	2 48.6	7 1.8	20 24.5	6 7.5	12 48.1	17 26.1
11	23 19 1.4	18 58.7	7 25.0	3♊47.1	12 51.7	6 51.5	3 15.6	7 13.6	20 23.2	6 7.3	12 47.6	17 27.4
12	23 22 58.0	19 52.6	7 21.7	19 34.1	12 14.0	8 2.2	3 42.3	7 25.3	20 22.0	6 7.1	12 47.2	17 28.7
13	23 26 54.5	20 46.4	7 18.5	5♋15.6	11 42.1	9 12.8	4 8.5	7 37.0	20 20.9	6 7.0	12 46.8	17 30.0
14	23 30 51.1	21 40.3	7 15.2	20 24.1	11 16.8	10 23.2	4 34.3	7 48.5	20 19.9	6 6.9	12 46.4	17 31.3
15	23 34 47.6	22 34.1	7 11.9	4♌42.3	10 58.9	11 33.4	4 59.6	7 60.0	20 18.9	6 6.9	12 46.1	17 32.7
16	23 38 44.2	23 27.9	7 8.7	18 5.9	10 49.0	12 43.4	5 24.5	8 11.3	20 18.1	6 D 7.0	12 45.8	17 34.1
17	23 42 40.7	24 21.7	7 5.4	0♍41.0	10 47.6	13 53.3	5 48.9	8 22.6	20 17.5	6 7.0	12 45.6	17 35.5
18	23 46 37.3	25 15.5	7 2.1	12 39.6	10 D 54.7	15 3.1	6 12.8	8 33.8	20 16.9	6 7.2	12 45.4	17 37.0
19	23 50 33.8	26 9.3	6 58.9	24 15.5	11 10.6	16 12.7	6 36.2	8 44.9	20 16.4	6 7.4	12 45.2	17 38.4
20	23 54 30.4	27 3.1	6 55.6	5♎42.6	11 35.1	17 22.2	6 59.0	8 55.9	20 16.0	6 7.7	12 45.1	17 39.9
21	23 58 26.9	27 57.0	6 52.3	17 13.3	12 8.0	18 31.5	7 21.4	9 6.8	20 15.7	6 8.0	12 44.9	17 41.5
22	0 2 23.5	28 50.8	6 49.1	28 58.3	12 48.9	19 40.7	7 43.2	9 17.5	20 15.6	6 8.4	12 44.9	17 43.0
23	0 6 20.0	29 44.7	6 45.8	11♏ 4.8	13 37.4	20 49.9	8 4.4	9 28.2	20 15.5	6 8.8	12 44.8	17 44.6
24	0 10 16.6	0♎38.6	6 42.5	23 36.3	14 33.0	21 58.9	8 25.1	9 38.8	20 15.5	6 9.3	12 44.8	17 46.2
25	0 14 13.1	1 32.5	6 39.3	6♐30.8	15 35.0	23 7.8	8 45.2	9 49.3	20 D 15.7	6 9.9	12 D 44.9	17 47.8
26	0 18 9.7	2 26.5	6 36.0	19 41.7	16 42.8	24 16.7	9 4.7	9 59.7	20 16.0	6 10.5	12 44.9	17 49.4
27	0 22 6.2	3 20.5	6 32.7	2♑58.4	17 55.8	25 25.5	9 23.6	10 10.0	20 16.3	6 11.1	12 45.0	17 51.1
28	0 26 2.8	4 14.5	6 29.5	16 10.1	19 13.4	26 34.2	9 41.8	10 20.2	20 16.8	6 11.8	12 45.2	17 52.8
29	0 29 59.4	5 8.6	6 26.2	29 8.3	20 34.9	27 42.8	9 59.5	10 30.2	20 17.4	6 12.6	12 45.3	17 54.5
30	0 33 55.9	6 2.8	6 22.9	11♒49.8	21 59.7	28 51.4	10 16.5	10 40.2	20 18.1	6 13.4	12 45.6	17 56.2

DECLINATION

DAY	EPHEM. SID. TIME	☉	☊	☽	☿	♀	♂	♃	♄	♅	♆	♇
1	22 39 35.9	8 N 27.1	0 S 19.8	23 S 40.2	0 S 45.4	15 N 4.6	18 N 30.8	19 N 49.9	22 S 4.6	23 S 38.8	22 S 3.5	1 S 53.8
4	22 51 25.5	7 21.4	0 19.8	10 32.7	0 N 16.4	13 55.6	18 51.3	19 42.0	22 5.7	23 38.9	22 3.7	1 56.4
7	23 3 15.2	6 14.7	0 19.8	7 N 51.1	1 46.2	12 43.1	19 10.6	19 34.0	22 6.7	23 38.9	22 4.0	1 58.9
10	23 15 4.8	5 7.1	0 19.9	23 7.1	3 32.0	11 27.3	19 28.8	19 26.2	22 7.5	23 38.9	22 4.2	2 1.5
13	23 26 54.5	3 58.6	0 19.9	26 4.8	5 16.3	10 8.7	19 45.8	19 18.3	22 8.2	23 38.9	22 4.5	2 4.1
16	23 38 44.2	2 49.5	0 20.0	15 16.4	6 41.3	8 47.5	20 1.7	19 10.6	22 8.8	23 38.9	22 4.6	2 6.7
19	23 50 33.8	1 39.9	0 20.0	1 S 43.6	7 33.7	7 24.0	20 16.7	19 2.9	22 9.3	23 38.8	22 4.8	2 9.3
22	0 2 23.5	0 30.0	0 20.0	17 17.2	7 46.7	5 58.6	20 30.6	18 55.3	22 9.6	23 38.8	22 4.9	2 12.0
25	0 14 13.1	0 S 40.1	0 20.1	25 60.0	7 20.1	4 31.6	20 43.8	18 47.9	22 9.9	23 38.7	22 5.1	2 14.6
28	0 26 2.8	1 50.2	0 20.1	24 26.0	6 17.9	3 3.3	20 56.1	18 40.6	22 10.0	23 38.6	22 5.1	2 17.3

OCTOBER 1990

LONGITUDE

DAY	EPHEM. SID. TIME (h m s)	☉ (° ′)	☊ (° ′)	☽ (° ′)	☿ (° ′)	♀ (° ′)	♂ (° ′)	♃ (° ′)	♄ (° ′)	♅ (° ′)	♆ (° ′)	♇ (° ′)
1	0 37 52.5	7♎34.1	4♒ .3	22♒25.2	22♍ 6.0	29♍22.6	11♊53.9	8♌18.5	18♑45.3	5♑42.9	11♑48.9	16♏10.6
2	0 41 49.0	8 33.1	3 57.1	5♓46.4	23 42.2	0♎37.4	12 8.9	8 28.0	18 46.1	5 43.7	11 49.1	16 12.6
3	0 45 45.6	9 32.1	3 53.9	19 33.6	25 21.0	1 52.2	12 23.2	8 37.4	18 47.1	5 44.6	11 49.4	16 14.7
4	0 49 42.1	10 31.1	3 50.7	3♈45.2	27 1.8	3 7.1	12 36.9	8 46.7	18 48.1	5 45.6	11 49.8	16 16.7
5	0 53 38.7	11 30.2	3 47.6	18 16.5	28 44.2	4 21.9	12 49.9	8 55.9	18 49.2	5 46.6	11 50.1	16 18.8
6	0 57 35.2	12 29.3	3 44.4	3♉ .6	0♎27.8	5 36.8	13 2.1	9 5.0	18 50.4	5 47.7	11 50.5	16 20.9
7	1 1 31.8	13 28.5	3 41.2	17 49.3	2 12.4	6 51.7	13 13.7	9 13.9	18 51.7	5 48.8	11 50.9	16 23.0
8	1 5 28.3	14 27.6	3 38.0	2♊34.3	3 57.6	8 6.6	13 24.6	9 22.8	18 53.2	5 49.9	11 51.4	16 25.1
9	1 9 24.9	15 26.9	3 34.9	17 9.0	5 43.2	9 21.5	13 34.7	9 31.5	18 54.7	5 51.1	11 51.9	16 27.2
10	1 13 21.4	16 26.1	3 31.7	1♋28.6	7 28.9	10 36.5	13 44.1	9 40.1	18 56.3	5 52.4	11 52.4	16 29.4
11	1 17 18.0	17 25.4	3 28.5	15 31.1	9 14.7	11 51.5	13 52.7	9 48.6	18 58.0	5 53.7	11 53.0	16 31.6
12	1 21 14.6	18 24.7	3 25.3	29 16.2	11 .4	13 6.5	14 .5	9 56.9	18 59.8	5 55.0	11 53.6	16 33.7
13	1 25 11.1	19 24.1	3 22.1	12♌45.0	12 45.8	14 21.5	14 7.5	10 5.1	19 1.7	5 56.4	11 54.2	16 35.9
14	1 29 7.7	20 23.5	3 19.0	25 59.2	14 30.9	15 36.5	14 13.7	10 13.2	19 3.7	5 57.9	11 54.8	16 38.2
15	1 33 4.2	21 23.0	3 15.8	9♍ .4	16 15.5	16 51.6	14 19.1	10 21.2	19 5.8	5 59.4	11 55.5	16 40.4
16	1 37 .8	22 22.5	3 12.6	21 50.0	17 59.7	18 6.7	14 23.7	10 29.0	19 8.0	6 .9	11 56.3	16 42.6
17	1 40 57.3	23 22.0	3 9.4	4♎29.0	19 43.4	19 21.7	14 27.4	10 36.7	19 10.3	6 2.5	11 57.0	16 44.9
18	1 44 53.9	24 21.5	3 6.3	16 57.8	21 26.5	20 36.8	14 30.3	10 44.3	19 12.6	6 4.2	11 57.8	16 47.2
19	1 48 50.4	25 21.1	3 3.1	29 16.7	23 9.1	21 52.0	14 32.3	10 51.7	19 15.1	6 5.9	11 58.6	16 49.5
20	1 52 47.0	26 20.8	2 59.9	11♏26.3	24 51.0	23 7.1	14 33.4	10 59.0	19 17.7	6 7.6	11 59.5	16 51.7
21	1 56 43.5	27 20.4	2 56.7	23 27.4	26 32.4	24 22.2	14 33.7	11 6.1	19 20.3	6 9.4	12 .3	16 54.1
22	2 0 40.1	28 20.2	2 53.5	5♐21.5	28 13.2	25 37.4	14R33.1	11 13.1	19 23.1	6 11.3	12 1.3	16 56.4
23	2 4 36.6	29 19.9	2 50.4	17 11.0	29 53.4	26 52.6	14 31.7	11 20.0	19 26.0	6 13.1	12 2.3	16 58.8
24	2 8 33.2	0♏19.6	2 47.2	28 59.1	1♏33.0	28 7.7	14 29.3	11 26.7	19 28.9	6 15.1	12 3.2	17 1.1
25	2 12 29.8	1 19.4	2 44.0	10♑49.8	3 12.0	29 22.9	14 26.0	11 33.2	19 31.9	6 17.0	12 4.2	17 3.4
26	2 16 26.3	2 19.2	2 40.8	22 47.9	4 50.4	0♏38.1	14 21.8	11 39.6	19 35.0	6 19.0	12 5.3	17 5.8
27	2 20 22.9	3 19.1	2 37.7	4♒58.8	6 28.3	1 53.3	14 16.8	11 45.9	19 38.3	6 21.1	12 6.3	17 8.2
28	2 24 19.4	4 18.9	2 34.5	17 27.9	8 5.6	3 8.5	14 10.9	11 52.0	19 41.5	6 23.2	12 7.4	17 10.5
29	2 28 16.0	5 18.8	2 31.3	0♓20.3	9 42.4	4 23.7	14 4.0	11 57.9	19 44.9	6 25.3	12 8.6	17 12.9
30	2 32 12.5	6 18.7	2 28.1	13 40.2	11 18.7	5 38.9	13 56.3	12 3.7	19 48.4	6 27.5	12 9.7	17 15.3
31	2 36 9.1	7 18.7	2 25.0	27 29.8	12 54.5	6 54.1	13 47.8	12 9.3	19 51.9	6 29.7	12 10.9	17 17.7

LATITUDE

DAY	EPHEM. SID. TIME	☉	☊	☽	☿	♀	♂	♃	♄	♅	♆	♇
1	0 37 52.5	0 .0	0 .0	1N29.2	1N47.9	1N26.4	1S 6.0	0N22.9	0S 2.2	0S19.4	0N50.0	14N56.8
4	0 49 42.1	0 .0	0 .0	4 18.7	1 54.5	1 25.7	1 .7	0 23.4	0 2.4	0 19.3	0 49.9	14 55.7
7	1 1 31.8	0 .0	0 .0	4 54.4	1 53.4	1 24.5	0 55.0	0 23.8	0 2.6	0 19.3	0 49.8	14 54.8
10	1 13 21.4	0 .0	0 .0	2 44.9	1 46.4	1 22.7	0 49.0	0 24.3	0 2.9	0 19.3	0 49.7	14 53.8
13	1 25 11.1	0 .0	0 .0	0S44.3	1 34.8	1 20.3	0 42.6	0 24.8	0 3.1	0 19.3	0 49.5	14 53.0
16	1 37 .8	0 .0	0 .0	3 42.8	1 19.9	1 17.4	0 35.9	0 25.3	0 3.3	0 19.2	0 49.4	14 52.2
19	1 48 50.4	0 .0	0 .0	4 58.8	1 2.7	1 13.9	0 28.7	0 25.8	0 3.5	0 19.2	0 49.3	14 51.5
22	2 0 40.1	0 .0	0 .0	4 13.7	0 44.0	1 10.0	0 21.2	0 26.4	0 3.8	0 19.2	0 49.2	14 50.8
25	2 12 29.8	0 .0	0 .0	1 52.3	0 24.3	1 5.6	0 13.3	0 26.9	0 4.0	0 19.2	0 49.1	14 50.3
28	2 24 19.4	0 .0	0 .0	1N17.9	0 4.1	1 .8	0 5.0	0 27.5	0 4.2	0 19.1	0 49.0	14 49.8
31	2 36 9.1	0 .0	0 .0	4 7.2	0S16.2	0 55.5	0N 3.5	0 28.0	0 4.4	0 19.1	0 48.9	14 49.3

RIGHT ASCENSION

DAY	EPHEM. SID. TIME	☉	☊	☽	☿	♀	♂	♃	♄	♅	♆	♇
1	0 37 52.5	6♎57.0	6♒19.7	24♒16.9	23♍27.4	0♎ .1	10♊32.9	10♌50.1	20♑18.9	6♑14.4	12♑45.9	17♏58.0
2	0 41 49.0	7 51.3	6 16.4	6♓36.9	24 57.2	1 8.6	10 48.5	10 59.8	20 19.8	6 15.3	12 46.1	17 59.8
3	0 45 45.6	8 45.6	6 13.1	19 1.2	26 28.9	2 17.2	11 3.5	11 9.4	20 20.8	6 16.3	12 46.5	18 1.6
4	0 49 42.1	9 40.1	6 9.8	1♈43.6	28 2.0	3 25.7	11 17.8	11 18.9	20 21.9	6 17.3	12 46.8	18 3.4
5	0 53 38.7	10 34.6	6 6.6	14 58.9	29 36.2	4 34.2	11 31.3	11 28.3	20 23.1	6 18.5	12 47.2	18 5.2
6	0 57 35.2	11 29.2	6 3.3	28 59.9	1♎11.1	5 42.8	11 44.2	11 37.6	20 24.4	6 19.6	12 47.6	18 7.1
7	1 1 31.8	12 23.9	6 .0	13♉53.0	2 46.6	6 51.4	11 56.3	11 46.7	20 25.8	6 20.8	12 48.1	18 8.9
8	1 5 28.3	13 18.7	5 56.7	29 32.6	4 22.4	8 .0	12 7.6	11 55.7	20 27.4	6 22.1	12 48.6	18 10.8
9	1 9 24.9	14 13.6	5 53.5	15♊38.3	5 58.3	9 8.7	12 18.1	12 4.6	20 29.0	6 23.4	12 49.1	18 12.7
10	1 13 21.4	15 8.6	5 50.2	1♋38.6	7 34.3	10 17.5	12 27.9	12 13.4	20 30.7	6 24.8	12 49.7	18 14.6
11	1 17 18.0	16 3.8	5 46.9	17 2.7	9 10.1	11 26.3	12 36.8	12 22.1	20 32.6	6 26.2	12 50.3	18 16.6
12	1 21 14.6	16 59.0	5 43.6	1♌31.2	10 45.9	12 35.2	12 44.9	12 30.6	20 34.5	6 27.7	12 50.9	18 18.5
13	1 25 11.1	17 54.4	5 40.4	14 59.9	12 21.4	13 44.2	12 52.1	12 38.9	20 36.6	6 29.2	12 51.6	18 20.5
14	1 29 7.7	18 49.9	5 37.1	27 35.6	13 56.6	14 53.3	12 58.5	12 47.2	20 38.7	6 30.8	12 52.3	18 22.5
15	1 33 4.2	19 45.6	5 33.8	9♍31.4	15 31.6	16 2.5	13 4.0	12 55.3	20 41.0	6 32.4	12 53.0	18 24.5
16	1 37 .8	20 41.4	5 30.5	21 2.1	17 6.3	17 11.8	13 8.6	13 3.3	20 43.3	6 34.1	12 53.8	18 26.5
17	1 40 57.3	21 37.3	5 27.3	2♎22.6	18 40.7	18 21.3	13 12.3	13 11.1	20 45.8	6 35.8	12 54.6	18 28.6
18	1 44 53.9	22 33.4	5 24.0	13 46.0	20 14.8	19 30.9	13 15.1	13 18.8	20 48.3	6 37.6	12 55.5	18 30.6
19	1 48 50.4	23 29.7	5 20.7	25 23.5	21 48.7	20 40.6	13 16.9	13 26.4	20 51.0	6 39.5	12 56.4	18 32.7
20	1 52 47.0	24 26.1	5 17.4	7♏22.9	23 22.2	21 50.5	13 17.8	13 33.8	20 53.7	6 41.4	12 57.3	18 34.8
21	1 56 43.5	25 22.7	5 14.1	19 47.7	24 55.6	23 .6	13 17.8	13 41.0	20 56.6	6 43.3	12 58.2	18 36.8
22	2 0 40.1	26 19.4	5 10.9	2♐36.3	26 28.8	24 10.9	13R16.9	13 48.2	20 59.6	6 45.4	12 59.3	18 39.0
23	2 4 36.6	27 16.3	5 7.6	15 41.4	28 1.7	25 21.3	13 15.0	13 55.2	21 2.6	6 47.4	13 .3	18 41.1
24	2 8 33.2	28 13.4	5 4.3	28 52.1	29 34.5	26 31.9	13 12.1	14 2.0	21 5.8	6 49.5	13 1.4	18 43.2
25	2 12 29.8	29 10.6	5 1.0	11♑56.7	1♏ 7.2	27 42.8	13 8.2	14 8.6	21 9.0	6 51.6	13 2.4	18 45.4
26	2 16 26.3	0♏ 8.0	4 57.7	24 46.1	2 39.8	28 53.8	13 3.4	14 15.1	21 12.3	6 53.8	13 3.6	18 47.5
27	2 20 22.9	1 5.6	4 54.4	7♒16.6	4 12.3	0♏ 5.1	12 57.7	14 21.5	21 15.8	6 56.0	13 4.7	18 49.7
28	2 24 19.4	2 3.3	4 51.2	19 30.2	5 44.8	1 16.6	12 50.9	14 27.7	21 19.3	6 58.3	13 5.9	18 51.8
29	2 28 16.0	3 1.2	4 47.9	1♓34.4	7 17.3	2 28.3	12 43.2	14 33.7	21 22.9	7 .7	13 7.1	18 54.0
30	2 32 12.5	3 59.4	4 44.6	13 40.7	8 49.8	3 40.2	12 34.6	14 39.6	21 26.6	7 3.0	13 8.4	18 56.2
31	2 36 9.1	4 57.7	4 41.3	26 3.9	10 22.4	4 52.4	12 25.0	14 45.3	21 30.4	7 5.4	13 9.6	18 58.4

DECLINATION

DAY	EPHEM. SID. TIME	☉	☊	☽	☿	♀	♂	♃	♄	♅	♆	♇
1	0 37 52.5	3S .2	0S20.2	12S38.0	4N47.2	1N34.1	21N 7.6	18N33.5	22S 9.9	23S38.5	22S 5.2	2S19.9
4	0 49 42.1	4 9.9	0 20.2	5N26.8	2 56.0	0 4.3	21 18.5	18 26.6	22 9.8	23 38.3	22 5.2	2 22.5
7	1 1 31.8	5 19.1	0 20.2	21 51.1	0 51.4	1S25.8	21 28.8	18 19.9	22 9.5	23 38.1	22 5.2	2 25.1
10	1 13 21.4	6 27.8	0 20.3	26 11.0	1S20.4	2 55.9	21 38.4	18 13.4	22 9.1	23 38.0	22 5.2	2 27.7
13	1 25 11.1	7 35.6	0 20.3	16 16.6	3 35.2	4 25.7	21 47.6	18 7.1	22 8.5	23 37.8	22 5.2	2 30.3
16	1 37 .8	8 42.6	0 20.4	0S10.4	5 49.7	5 54.7	21 56.1	18 1.1	22 7.9	23 37.5	22 5.1	2 32.8
19	1 48 50.4	9 48.5	0 20.4	15 52.3	8 1.6	7 22.6	22 4.2	17 55.4	22 7.1	23 37.3	22 5.0	2 35.3
22	2 0 40.1	10 53.1	0 20.4	25 21.4	10 9.5	8 49.2	22 11.8	17 50.1	22 6.2	23 37.0	22 4.9	2 37.7
25	2 12 29.8	11 56.2	0 20.5	24 51.9	12 12.1	10 13.9	22 18.8	17 45.0	22 5.1	23 36.7	22 4.7	2 40.1
28	2 24 19.4	12 57.6	0 20.5	14 21.8	14 8.6	11 36.6	22 25.3	17 40.4	22 3.9	23 36.4	22 4.5	2 42.5
31	2 36 9.1	13 57.2	0 20.5	2N47.1	15 58.3	12 56.8	22 31.0	17 36.1	22 2.6	23 36.1	22 4.3	2 44.8

NOVEMBER 1990

LONGITUDE

DAY	EPHEM. SID. TIME (h m s)	☉ (° ′)	☊ (° ′)	☽ (° ′)	☿ (° ′)	♀ (° ′)	♂ (° ′)	♃ (° ′)	♄ (° ′)	♅ (° ′)	♆ (° ′)	♇ (° ′)
1	2 40 5.6	8♏18.6	2♒21.8	11♈48.7	14♏29.8	8♏ 9.4	13♊38.3	12♌14.7	19♑55.6	6♑32.0	12♑12.1	17♏20.1
2	2 44 2.2	9 18.7	2 18.6	26 33.0	16 4.7	9 24.6	13R28.0	12 20.0	19 59.3	6 34.3	12 13.4	17 22.5
3	2 47 58.8	10 18.7	2 15.4	11♉35.4	17 39.1	10 39.8	13 16.9	12 25.2	20 3.1	6 36.6	12 14.7	17 24.9
4	2 51 55.3	11 18.7	2 12.2	26 46.1	19 13.1	11 55.1	13 4.9	12 30.1	20 7.0	6 39.0	12 16.0	17 27.3
5	2 55 51.9	12 18.8	2 9.1	11♊54.3	20 46.7	13 10.3	12 52.1	12 34.9	20 10.9	6 41.4	12 17.3	17 29.7
6	2 59 48.4	13 19.0	2 5.9	26 50.4	22 19.8	14 25.6	12 38.5	12 39.5	20 15.0	6 43.8	12 18.7	17 32.1
7	3 3 45.0	14 19.1	2 2.7	11♋27.3	23 52.6	15 40.9	12 24.1	12 44.0	20 19.1	6 46.3	12 20.0	17 34.5
8	3 7 41.5	15 19.3	1 59.5	25 41.1	25 25.1	16 56.1	12 8.9	12 48.3	20 23.3	6 48.9	12 21.5	17 37.0
9	3 11 38.1	16 19.6	1 56.4	9♌30.7	26 57.1	18 11.4	11 53.0	12 52.4	20 27.6	6 51.4	12 22.9	17 39.4
10	3 15 34.6	17 19.8	1 53.2	22 57.6	28 28.8	19 26.7	11 36.3	12 56.3	20 31.9	6 54.1	12 24.4	17 41.8
11	3 19 31.2	18 20.1	1 50.0	6♍ 4.2	0♐ .2	20 42.0	11 19.0	13 .1	20 36.3	6 56.7	12 25.9	17 44.2
12	3 23 27.8	19 20.5	1 46.8	18 53.6	1 31.3	21 57.4	11 1.0	13 3.7	20 40.9	6 59.4	12 27.4	17 46.7
13	3 27 24.3	20 20.9	1 43.6	1♎28.9	3 2.0	23 12.7	10 42.4	13 7.1	20 45.5	7 2.1	12 29.0	17 49.1
14	3 31 20.9	21 21.3	1 40.5	13 52.6	4 32.3	24 28.0	10 23.2	13 10.3	20 50.1	7 4.9	12 30.5	17 51.5
15	3 35 17.4	22 21.7	1 37.3	26 7.1	6 2.3	25 43.4	10 3.4	13 13.3	20 54.9	7 7.7	12 32.1	17 54.0
16	3 39 14.0	23 22.2	1 34.1	8♏13.7	7 31.9	26 58.7	9 43.1	13 16.1	20 59.7	7 10.5	12 33.8	17 56.4
17	3 43 10.5	24 22.7	1 30.9	20 13.9	9 1.2	28 14.0	9 22.3	13 18.8	21 4.6	7 13.3	12 35.4	17 58.8
18	3 47 7.1	25 23.2	1 27.8	2♐ 8.7	10 30.0	29 29.4	9 1.1	13 21.2	21 9.5	7 16.2	12 37.1	18 1.2
19	3 51 3.7	26 23.7	1 24.6	13 59.5	11 58.4	0♐44.7	8 39.5	13 23.5	21 14.5	7 19.1	12 38.8	18 3.6
20	3 55 .2	27 24.3	1 21.4	25 48.0	13 26.4	2 .1	8 17.7	13 25.6	21 19.6	7 22.0	12 40.5	18 6.0
21	3 58 56.8	28 24.8	1 18.2	7♑36.5	14 53.9	3 15.4	7 55.5	13 27.5	21 24.7	7 25.0	12 42.2	18 8.4
22	4 2 53.3	29 25.5	1 15.1	19 28.0	16 20.8	4 30.8	7 33.1	13 29.2	21 30.0	7 28.0	12 44.0	18 10.8
23	4 6 49.9	0♐26.1	1 11.9	1♒26.3	17 47.1	5 46.1	7 10.6	13 30.7	21 35.2	7 31.0	12 45.8	18 13.2
24	4 10 46.4	1 26.7	1 8.7	13 35.8	19 12.8	7 1.5	6 47.9	13 32.0	21 40.6	7 34.1	12 47.6	18 15.6
25	4 14 43.0	2 27.4	1 5.5	26 1.5	20 37.7	8 16.8	6 25.2	13 33.1	21 46.0	7 37.2	12 49.4	18 17.9
26	4 18 39.6	3 28.1	1 2.4	8♓48.1	22 1.7	9 32.2	6 2.5	13 34.0	21 51.4	7 40.3	12 51.2	18 20.3
27	4 22 36.1	4 28.8	0 59.2	22 .5	23 24.8	10 47.5	5 39.8	13 34.7	21 57.0	7 43.4	12 53.1	18 22.6
28	4 26 32.7	5 29.5	0 56.0	5♈41.7	24 46.7	12 2.9	5 17.2	13 35.3	22 2.6	7 46.6	12 55.0	18 25.0
29	4 30 29.2	6 30.2	0 52.8	19 53.0	26 7.4	13 18.2	4 54.7	13 35.6	22 8.2	7 49.8	12 56.9	18 27.3
30	4 34 25.8	7 31.0	0 49.6	4♉32.6	27 26.6	14 33.5	4 32.5	13 35.7	22 13.9	7 53.0	12 58.8	18 29.6

LATITUDE

DAY	EPHEM. SID. TIME	☉	☊	☽	☿	♀	♂	♃	♄	♅	♆	♇
1	2 40 5.6	0 .0	0 .0	4N41.9	0S22.9	0N53.7	0N 6.5	0N28.2	0S 4.5	0S19.1	0N48.9	14N49.2
4	2 51 55.3	0 .0	0 .0	4 32.5	0 42.7	0 47.9	0 15.4	0 28.8	0 4.7	0 19.1	0 48.8	14 48.9
7	3 3 45.0	0 .0	0 .0	1 43.1	1 1.8	0 41.8	0 24.6	0 29.4	0 4.9	0 19.1	0 48.7	14 48.6
10	3 15 34.6	0 .0	0 .0	1S52.1	1 19.9	0 35.4	0 33.9	0 30.0	0 5.1	0 19.1	0 48.6	14 48.4
13	3 27 24.3	0 .0	0 .0	4 22.8	1 36.7	0 28.8	0 43.3	0 30.6	0 5.3	0 19.1	0 48.5	14 48.3
16	3 39 14.0	0 .0	0 .0	4 59.1	1 51.8	0 21.9	0 52.7	0 31.2	0 5.5	0 19.1	0 48.4	14 48.2
19	3 51 3.7	0 .0	0 .0	3 38.3	2 4.9	0 14.9	1 1.9	0 31.8	0 5.7	0 19.0	0 48.3	14 48.3
22	4 2 53.3	0 .0	0 .0	0 54.5	2 15.4	0 7.8	1 11.0	0 32.4	0 5.9	0 19.0	0 48.2	14 48.4
25	4 14 43.0	0 .0	0 .0	2N16.4	2 22.9	0 .6	1 19.7	0 33.1	0 6.1	0 19.0	0 48.1	14 48.6
28	4 26 32.7	0 .0	0 .0	4 40.5	2 26.7	0S 6.6	1 28.0	0 33.7	0 6.3	0 19.0	0 48.0	14 48.8

RIGHT ASCENSION

DAY	EPHEM. SID. TIME	☉	☊	☽	☿	♀	♂	♃	♄	♅	♆	♇
1	2 40 5.6	5♏56.2	4♒38.0	9♈ .2	11♏55.0	6♏ 4.9	12♊14.5	14♌50.8	21♑34.3	7♑ 7.9	13♑11.0	19♏ .6
2	2 44 2.2	6 54.9	4 34.7	22 45.9	13 27.8	7 17.6	12R 3.0	14 56.2	21 38.3	7 10.4	13 12.3	19 2.8
3	2 47 58.8	7 53.8	4 31.4	7♉32.2	15 .6	8 30.6	11 50.7	15 1.4	21 42.3	7 13.0	13 13.7	19 5.0
4	2 51 55.3	8 52.9	4 28.2	23 19.3	16 33.6	9 43.9	11 37.4	15 6.5	21 46.5	7 15.5	13 15.1	19 7.2
5	2 55 51.9	9 52.2	4 24.9	9♊49.7	18 6.8	10 57.5	11 23.2	15 11.4	21 50.7	7 18.2	13 16.5	19 9.4
6	2 59 48.4	10 51.7	4 21.6	26 28.8	19 40.1	12 11.3	11 8.2	15 16.1	21 55.0	7 20.9	13 18.0	19 11.7
7	3 3 45.0	11 51.4	4 18.3	12♋37.0	21 13.7	13 25.5	10 52.3	15 20.6	21 59.5	7 23.6	13 19.5	19 13.9
8	3 7 41.5	12 51.4	4 15.0	27 45.7	22 47.4	14 39.9	10 35.5	15 25.0	22 3.9	7 26.3	13 21.0	19 16.1
9	3 11 38.1	13 51.5	4 11.7	11♌45.1	24 21.3	15 54.6	10 17.9	15 29.2	22 8.5	7 29.1	13 22.5	19 18.4
10	3 15 34.6	14 51.9	4 8.4	24 40.7	25 55.5	17 9.7	9 59.6	15 33.2	22 13.2	7 32.0	13 24.1	19 20.6
11	3 19 31.2	15 52.5	4 5.1	6♍46.6	27 29.8	18 25.0	9 40.5	15 37.0	22 17.9	7 34.9	13 25.7	19 22.9
12	3 23 27.8	16 53.4	4 1.8	18 19.8	29 4.4	19 40.7	9 20.8	15 40.7	22 22.8	7 37.8	13 27.4	19 25.2
13	3 27 24.3	17 54.4	3 58.6	29 36.8	0♐39.1	20 56.7	9 .3	15 44.2	22 27.7	7 40.8	13 29.1	19 27.4
14	3 31 20.9	18 55.6	3 55.3	10♎52.7	2 14.0	22 13.0	8 39.1	15 47.4	22 32.6	7 43.8	13 30.8	19 29.7
15	3 35 17.4	19 57.1	3 52.0	22 20.4	3 49.1	23 29.6	8 17.4	15 50.5	22 37.7	7 46.8	13 32.5	19 31.9
16	3 39 14.0	20 58.8	3 48.7	4♏ 9.5	5 24.2	24 46.5	7 55.1	15 53.4	22 42.8	7 49.9	13 34.2	19 34.2
17	3 43 10.5	22 .6	3 45.4	16 25.3	6 59.5	26 3.7	7 32.4	15 56.2	22 48.0	7 53.0	13 36.0	19 36.4
18	3 47 7.1	23 2.7	3 42.1	29 7.4	8 34.7	27 21.2	7 9.1	15 58.7	22 53.3	7 56.1	13 37.8	19 38.7
19	3 51 3.7	24 5.0	3 38.8	12♐ 9.3	10 10.0	28 39.0	6 45.5	16 1.0	22 58.6	7 59.3	13 39.6	19 40.9
20	3 55 .2	25 7.5	3 35.5	25 19.4	11 45.2	29 57.1	6 21.6	16 3.2	23 4.1	8 2.5	13 41.5	19 43.2
21	3 58 56.8	26 10.3	3 32.2	8♑24.3	13 20.2	1♐15.5	5 57.3	16 5.1	23 9.6	8 5.7	13 43.3	19 45.4
22	4 2 53.3	27 13.2	3 28.9	21 12.7	14 55.0	2 34.2	5 32.9	16 6.9	23 15.1	8 9.0	13 45.2	19 47.7
23	4 6 49.9	28 16.3	3 25.6	3♒38.4	16 29.5	3 53.2	5 8.2	16 8.5	23 20.7	8 12.3	13 47.1	19 49.9
24	4 10 46.4	29 19.6	3 22.3	15 41.9	18 3.5	5 12.4	4 43.5	16 9.8	23 26.4	8 15.6	13 49.1	19 52.1
25	4 14 43.0	0♐23.0	3 19.0	27 29.4	19 37.0	6 31.9	4 18.7	16 11.0	23 32.2	8 19.0	13 51.0	19 54.4
26	4 18 39.6	1 26.7	3 15.7	9♓11.8	21 9.7	7 51.7	3 53.9	16 12.0	23 38.0	8 22.3	13 53.0	19 56.6
27	4 22 36.1	2 30.6	3 12.4	21 3.7	22 41.5	9 11.7	3 29.2	16 12.8	23 43.9	8 25.8	13 55.0	19 58.8
28	4 26 32.7	3 34.6	3 9.1	3♈21.9	24 12.3	10 32.0	3 4.6	16 13.4	23 49.9	8 29.2	13 57.1	20 1.0
29	4 30 29.2	4 38.8	3 5.8	16 24.7	25 41.7	11 52.5	2 40.2	16 13.8	23 55.9	8 32.7	13 59.1	20 3.2
30	4 34 25.8	5 43.2	3 2.5	0♉28.8	27 9.7	13 13.3	2 16.0	16 14.0	24 1.9	8 36.2	14 1.2	20 5.4

DECLINATION

DAY	EPHEM. SID. TIME	☉	☊	☽	☿	♀	♂	♃	♄	♅	♆	♇
1	2 40 5.6	14S16.7	0S20.6	8N59.5	16S33.2	13S22.9	22N32.8	17N34.7	22S 2.2	23S35.9	22S 4.2	2S45.5
4	2 51 55.3	15 13.6	0 20.6	23 51.0	18 12.9	14 39.2	22 37.6	17 30.9	22 .7	23 35.6	22 4.0	2 47.7
7	3 3 45.0	16 8.2	0 20.6	24 39.6	19 44.5	15 52.2	22 41.4	17 27.6	21 59.1	23 35.2	22 3.7	2 49.8
10	3 15 34.6	17 .5	0 20.7	12 6.0	21 7.3	17 1.5	22 44.3	17 24.7	21 57.4	23 34.8	22 3.4	2 51.9
13	3 27 24.3	17 50.2	0 20.7	4S36.4	22 20.8	18 6.8	22 46.1	17 22.2	21 55.5	23 34.3	22 3.1	2 53.9
16	3 39 14.0	18 37.1	0 20.7	18 57.7	23 24.4	19 7.7	22 46.7	17 20.2	21 53.6	23 33.9	22 2.7	2 55.8
19	3 51 3.7	19 21.0	0 20.8	26 5.7	24 17.4	20 3.9	22 46.1	17 18.7	21 51.5	23 33.4	22 2.3	2 57.7
22	4 2 53.3	20 1.8	0 20.8	22 55.6	24 59.2	20 55.0	22 44.4	17 17.6	21 49.3	23 32.9	22 1.9	2 59.4
25	4 14 43.0	20 39.3	0 20.9	10 42.3	25 29.2	21 40.8	22 41.5	17 17.1	21 46.9	23 32.4	22 1.5	3 1.1
28	4 26 32.7	21 13.3	0 20.9	6N33.2	25 46.9	22 20.8	22 37.7	17 17.1	21 44.5	23 31.8	22 1.0	3 2.6

DECEMBER 1990

DAY	EPHEM. SID. TIME	☉	☊	☽	☿	♀	♂	♃	♄	♅	♆	♇
	h m s	° ′	° ′	° ′	° ′	° ′	° ′	° ′	° ′	° ′	° ′	° ′
		LONGITUDE										
1	4 38 22.3	8♐31.8	0♒46.5	19♉35.0	28♐44.1	15♐48.9	4♊10.5	13♌35.6	22♑19.7	7♑56.2	13♑ .8	18♏32.0
2	4 42 18.9	9 32.5	0 43.3	4♊51.4	29 59.7	17 4.2	3R48.8	13R35.4	22 25.5	7 59.5	13 2.7	18 34.3
3	4 46 15.5	10 33.4	0 40.1	20 10.9	1♑13.1	18 19.6	3 27.4	13 35.0	22 31.4	8 2.8	13 4.7	18 36.6
4	4 50 12.0	11 34.2	0 36.9	5♋22.4	2 24.0	19 35.0	3 6.4	13 34.3	22 37.3	8 6.1	13 6.7	18 38.9
5	4 54 8.6	12 35.1	0 33.8	20 16.5	3 31.9	20 50.3	2 45.8	13 33.5	22 43.3	8 9.4	13 8.7	18 41.1
6	4 58 5.1	13 35.9	0 30.6	4♌46.6	4 36.4	22 5.6	2 25.6	13 32.4	22 49.3	8 12.8	13 10.8	18 43.4
7	5 2 1.7	14 36.8	0 27.4	18 49.7	5 37.0	23 21.0	2 5.9	13 31.2	22 55.4	8 16.1	13 12.8	18 45.6
8	5 5 58.3	15 37.8	0 24.2	2♍25.6	6 33.1	24 36.3	1 46.8	13 29.7	23 1.5	8 19.5	13 14.9	18 47.9
9	5 9 54.8	16 38.7	0 21.1	15 36.2	7 24.2	25 51.7	1 28.2	13 28.1	23 7.7	8 22.9	13 16.9	18 50.1
10	5 13 51.4	17 39.6	0 17.9	28 24.8	8 9.5	27 7.0	1 10.2	13 26.2	23 13.9	8 26.3	13 19.0	18 52.3
11	5 17 47.9	18 40.6	0 14.7	10♎55.3	8 48.2	28 22.4	0 52.8	13 24.2	23 20.1	8 29.7	13 21.1	18 54.4
12	5 21 44.5	19 41.6	0 11.5	23 11.5	9 19.5	29 37.7	0 36.1	13 22.0	23 26.4	8 33.2	13 23.2	18 56.6
13	5 25 41.0	20 42.6	0 8.4	5♏17.1	9 42.6	0♑53.1	0 20.1	13 19.5	23 32.8	8 36.6	13 25.4	18 58.7
14	5 29 37.6	21 43.6	0 5.2	17 15.1	9 56.5	2 8.4	0 4.7	13 16.9	23 39.2	8 40.1	13 27.5	19 .9
15	5 33 34.2	22 44.7	0 2.0	29 8.2	10 .4	3 23.8	29♉50.1	13 14.1	23 45.6	8 43.6	13 29.7	19 3.0
16	5 37 30.7	23 45.7	29♑58.8	10♐58.6	9R53.6	4 39.1	29 36.3	13 11.1	23 52.1	8 47.1	13 31.8	19 5.1
17	5 41 27.3	24 46.8	29 55.6	22 48.2	9 35.5	5 54.4	29 23.2	13 7.9	23 58.6	8 50.6	13 34.0	19 7.1
18	5 45 23.8	25 47.9	29 52.5	4♑38.6	9 5.8	7 9.8	29 10.9	13 4.5	24 5.1	8 54.1	13 36.2	19 9.2
19	5 49 20.4	26 49.0	29 49.3	16 31.8	8 24.5	8 25.1	28 59.4	13 .9	24 11.7	8 57.6	13 38.4	19 11.2
20	5 53 17.0	27 50.1	29 46.1	28 29.8	7 32.1	9 40.5	28 48.8	12 57.2	24 18.4	9 1.2	13 40.6	19 13.2
21	5 57 13.5	28 51.2	29 42.9	10♒35.1	6 29.6	10 55.8	28 38.9	12 53.3	24 25.0	9 4.7	13 42.8	19 15.2
22	6 1 10.1	29 52.3	29 39.8	22 50.7	5 18.6	12 11.1	28 29.9	12 49.1	24 31.7	9 8.3	13 45.0	19 17.2
23	6 5 6.6	0♑53.4	29 36.6	5♓20.0	4 1.2	13 26.4	28 21.7	12 44.8	24 38.4	9 11.8	13 47.2	19 19.2
24	6 9 3.2	1 54.6	29 33.4	18 6.7	2 39.9	14 41.8	28 14.4	12 40.4	24 45.2	9 15.5	13 49.5	19 21.1
25	6 12 59.7	2 55.7	29 30.2	1♈14.3	1 17.3	15 57.1	28 7.9	12 35.8	24 52.0	9 19.0	13 51.7	19 23.0
26	6 16 56.3	3 56.8	29 27.1	14 45.9	29♐56.3	17 12.4	28 2.2	12 31.0	24 58.8	9 22.6	13 54.0	19 24.9
27	6 20 52.9	4 58.0	29 23.9	28 43.2	28 39.4	18 27.7	27 57.3	12 26.0	25 5.6	9 26.2	13 56.2	19 26.8
28	6 24 49.4	5 59.1	29 20.7	13♉ 6.0	27 28.9	19 42.9	27 53.3	12 20.9	25 12.5	9 29.8	13 58.5	19 28.6
29	6 28 46.0	7 .2	29 17.5	27 51.4	26 26.6	20 58.2	27 50.1	12 15.6	25 19.4	9 33.4	14 .7	19 30.4
30	6 32 42.5	8 1.3	29 14.4	12♊53.5	25 33.6	22 13.4	27 47.7	12 10.1	25 26.3	9 37.0	14 3.0	19 32.2
31	6 36 39.1	9 2.5	29 11.2	28 4.1	24 50.9	23 28.7	27 46.1	12 4.5	25 33.2	9 40.6	14 5.2	19 33.9
		LATITUDE										
1	4 38 22.3	0 .0	0 .0	4N47.8	2S25.7	0S13.9	1N35.8	0N34.4	0S 6.5	0S19.0	0N48.0	14N49.2
4	4 50 12.0	0 .0	0 .0	2 3.6	2 19.0	0 21.0	1 43.0	0 35.0	0 6.7	0 19.0	0 47.9	14 49.5
7	5 2 1.7	0 .0	0 .0	1S45.7	2 5.0	0 28.1	1 49.5	0 35.7	0 6.9	0 19.0	0 47.8	14 50.0
10	5 13 51.4	0 .0	0 .0	4 27.4	1 42.0	0 35.0	1 55.5	0 36.3	0 7.1	0 19.0	0 47.8	14 50.5
13	5 25 41.0	0 .0	0 .0	5 8.1	1 8.2	0 41.7	2 .7	0 37.0	0 7.3	0 19.1	0 47.7	14 51.1
16	5 37 30.7	0 .0	0 .0	3 49.3	0 22.7	0 48.2	2 5.4	0 37.6	0 7.5	0 19.1	0 47.6	14 51.8
19	5 49 20.4	0 .0	0 .0	1 3.4	0N33.1	0 54.4	2 9.4	0 38.2	0 7.7	0 19.1	0 47.6	14 52.6
22	6 1 10.1	0 .0	0 .0	2N11.4	1 32.6	1 .3	2 12.8	0 38.9	0 7.9	0 19.1	0 47.5	14 53.3
25	6 12 59.7	0 .0	0 .0	4 40.8	2 24.3	1 5.8	2 15.6	0 39.5	0 8.1	0 19.1	0 47.5	14 54.2
28	6 24 49.4	0 .0	0 .0	5 4.5	2 57.5	1 10.9	2 18.0	0 40.1	0 8.3	0 19.1	0 47.5	14 55.1
31	6 36 39.1	0 .0	0 .0	2 38.1	3 9.1	1 15.6	2 19.8	0 40.7	0 8.5	0 19.1	0 47.4	14 56.1
		RIGHT ASCENSION										
1	4 38 22.3	6♐47.7	2♒59.2	15♉43.9	28♐35.7	14♐34.2	1♊52.1	16♌14.0	24♑ 8.1	8♑39.7	14♑ 3.3	20♏ 7.6
2	4 42 18.9	7 52.4	2 55.9	2♊ 4.4	29 59.7	15 55.4	1R28.5	16R13.8	24 14.2	8 43.2	14 5.4	20 9.8
3	4 46 15.5	8 57.3	2 52.6	19 3.2	1♑21.2	17 16.8	1 5.3	16 13.4	24 20.5	8 46.8	14 7.5	20 12.0
4	4 50 12.0	10 2.3	2 49.3	5♋56.8	2 39.7	18 38.3	0 42.5	16 12.8	24 26.8	8 50.4	14 9.7	20 14.2
5	4 54 8.6	11 7.5	2 46.0	22 3.4	3 54.9	20 .0	0 20.1	16 12.0	24 33.2	8 54.0	14 11.8	20 16.4
6	4 58 5.1	12 12.8	2 42.7	6♌59.3	5 6.1	21 21.9	29♉58.3	16 11.1	24 39.6	8 57.7	14 14.0	20 18.5
7	5 2 1.7	13 18.2	2 39.4	20 41.7	6 12.9	22 43.9	29 37.0	16 9.9	24 46.0	9 1.3	14 16.2	20 20.6
8	5 5 58.3	14 23.8	2 36.1	3 21.9	7 14.6	24 6.0	29 16.3	16 8.5	24 52.5	9 5.0	14 18.4	20 22.7
9	5 9 54.8	15 29.5	2 32.8	15 17.4	8 10.5	25 28.3	28 56.2	16 6.9	24 59.1	9 8.7	14 20.6	20 24.9
10	5 13 51.4	16 35.3	2 29.5	26 46.2	8 59.8	26 50.6	28 36.7	16 5.1	25 5.7	9 12.4	14 22.9	20 27.0
11	5 17 47.9	17 41.3	2 26.2	8♎ 5.5	9 41.6	28 13.1	28 18.0	16 3.1	25 12.3	9 16.1	14 25.1	20 29.0
12	5 21 44.5	18 47.3	2 22.9	19 30.0	10 15.1	29 35.6	27 59.9	16 1.0	25 19.0	9 19.9	14 27.4	20 31.1
13	5 25 41.0	19 53.5	2 19.6	1♏11.5	10 39.3	0♑58.1	27 42.6	15 58.6	25 25.7	9 23.6	14 29.7	20 33.2
14	5 29 37.6	20 59.7	2 16.3	13 17.9	10 53.4	2 20.7	27 26.1	15 56.0	25 32.5	9 27.4	14 32.0	20 35.2
15	5 33 34.2	22 6.0	2 13.0	25 51.6	10 56.4	3 43.3	27 10.4	15 53.3	25 39.3	9 31.2	14 34.3	20 37.2
16	5 37 30.7	23 12.4	2 9.7	8♐48.6	10R47.7	5 5.9	26 55.4	15 50.3	25 46.2	9 35.0	14 36.6	20 39.3
17	5 41 27.3	24 18.8	2 6.4	21 58.8	10 26.6	6 28.5	26 41.3	15 47.1	25 53.1	9 38.8	14 38.9	20 41.3
18	5 45 23.8	25 25.3	2 3.1	5♑ 8.4	9 52.9	7 51.1	26 28.1	15 43.8	26 .1	9 42.7	14 41.3	20 43.2
19	5 49 20.4	26 31.8	1 59.8	18 4.0	9 6.8	9 13.6	26 15.7	15 40.3	26 7.0	9 46.5	14 43.6	20 45.2
20	5 53 17.0	27 38.4	1 56.4	0♒36.4	8 8.9	10 36.0	26 4.2	15 36.6	26 14.0	9 50.4	14 46.0	20 47.2
21	5 57 13.5	28 45.0	1 53.1	12 43.0	7 .4	11 58.4	25 53.6	15 32.7	26 21.1	9 54.2	14 48.4	20 49.1
22	6 1 10.1	29 51.6	1 49.8	24 27.6	5 43.1	13 20.7	25 43.9	15 28.6	26 28.2	9 58.1	14 50.8	20 51.0
23	6 5 6.6	0♑58.2	1 46.5	5♓59.0	4 19.1	14 42.8	25 35.0	15 24.3	26 35.3	10 2.0	14 53.1	20 52.9
24	6 9 3.2	2 4.9	1 43.2	17 30.0	2 51.4	16 4.9	25 27.1	15 20.0	26 42.5	10 5.9	14 55.6	20 54.8
25	6 12 59.7	3 11.5	1 39.9	29 16.2	1 22.7	17 26.7	25 20.0	15 15.4	26 49.7	10 9.8	14 58.0	20 56.7
26	6 16 56.3	4 18.1	1 36.6	11♈35.3	29♐56.0	18 48.4	25 13.9	15 10.6	26 56.9	10 13.7	15 .4	20 58.5
27	6 20 52.9	5 24.6	1 33.3	24 45.1	28 34.0	20 10.0	25 8.6	15 5.6	27 4.1	10 17.6	15 2.8	21 .3
28	6 24 49.4	6 31.1	1 30.0	9♉ .8	27 18.9	21 31.3	25 4.2	15 .5	27 11.3	10 21.5	15 5.2	21 2.1
29	6 28 46.0	7 37.6	1 26.6	24 28.2	26 12.7	22 52.4	25 .6	14 55.2	27 18.6	10 25.4	15 7.6	21 3.9
30	6 32 42.5	8 44.0	1 23.3	10♊55.7	25 16.5	24 13.3	24 58.0	14 49.8	27 25.9	10 29.3	15 10.1	21 5.6
31	6 36 39.1	9 50.3	1 20.0	27 51.1	24 31.1	25 34.0	24 56.2	14 44.2	27 33.2	10 33.2	15 12.5	21 7.4
		DECLINATION										
1	4 38 22.3	21S43.7	0S20.9	22N14.6	25S51.9	22S55.0	22N33.0	17N17.6	21S41.9	23S31.2	22S .6	3S 4.1
4	4 50 12.0	22 10.4	0 21.0	25 23.5	25 44.2	23 22.9	22 27.8	17 18.6	21 39.2	23 30.6	22 .1	3 5.5
7	5 2 1.7	22 33.3	0 21.0	13 30.4	25 24.2	23 44.5	22 22.3	17 20.1	21 36.4	23 30.0	21 59.5	3 6.7
10	5 13 51.4	22 52.2	0 21.0	3S27.5	24 53.2	23 59.6	22 16.7	17 22.2	21 33.5	23 29.4	21 59.0	3 7.9
13	5 25 41.0	23 7.0	0 21.1	18 7.1	24 13.2	24 8.0	22 11.4	17 24.7	21 30.5	23 28.7	21 58.4	3 8.9
16	5 37 30.7	23 17.7	0 21.1	25 52.5	23 26.9	24 9.8	22 6.5	17 27.8	21 27.4	23 28.1	21 57.8	3 9.9
19	5 49 20.4	23 24.2	0 21.1	23 28.0	22 37.4	24 4.7	22 2.4	17 31.3	21 24.2	23 27.4	21 57.2	3 10.7
22	6 1 10.1	23 26.5	0 21.2	11 49.9	21 47.5	23 53.0	21 59.1	17 35.2	21 20.9	23 26.6	21 56.6	3 11.5
25	6 12 59.7	23 24.5	0 21.2	4N47.1	21 1.8	23 34.6	21 56.9	17 39.6	21 17.4	23 25.9	21 55.9	3 12.1
28	6 24 49.4	23 18.4	0 21.2	20 36.2	20 27.6	23 9.7	21 55.9	17 44.4	21 13.9	23 25.2	21 55.3	3 12.6
31	6 36 39.1	23 8.0	0 21.3	26 3.8	20 11.5	22 38.5	21 56.0	17 49.6	21 10.3	23 24.4	21 54.6	3 13.0

JANUARY 1991

LONGITUDE

DAY	EPHEM. SID. TIME	☉	☊	☽	☿	♀	♂	♃	♄	♅	♆	♇
	h m s	° ′	° ′	° ′	° ′	° ′	° ′	° ′	° ′	° ′	° ′	° ′
1	6 40 35.7	10♑ 3.6	29♑ 8.0	13♋13.4	24♐18.6	24♑43.9	27♉45.3	11♌58.8	25♑40.2	9♑44.2	14♑ 7.5	19♏35.7
2	6 44 32.2	11 4.7	29 4.8	28 11.9	23R56.7	25 59.2	27R45.2	11R52.9	25 47.1	9 47.8	14 9.8	19 37.4
3	6 48 28.8	12 5.8	29 1.6	12♌51.5	23 44.9	27 14.4	27D46.0	11 46.8	25 54.1	9 51.4	14 12.1	19 39.1
4	6 52 25.3	13 7.0	28 58.5	27 6.6	23 42.7	28 29.6	27 47.5	11 40.6	26 1.1	9 54.9	14 14.3	19 40.7
5	6 56 21.9	14 8.1	28 55.3	10♍54.6	23D49.4	29 44.8	27 49.7	11 34.3	26 8.2	9 58.5	14 16.6	19 42.3
6	7 0 18.4	15 9.3	28 52.1	24 15.5	24 4.3	0♒60.0	27 52.7	11 27.9	26 15.2	10 2.1	14 18.9	19 43.9
7	7 4 15.0	16 10.4	28 48.9	7♎11.2	24 26.7	2 15.2	27 56.5	11 21.3	26 22.3	10 5.7	14 21.1	19 45.5
8	7 8 11.6	17 11.5	28 45.8	19 45.2	24 55.9	3 30.3	28 .9	11 14.6	26 29.3	10 9.3	14 23.4	19 47.1
9	7 12 8.1	18 12.7	28 42.6	2♏ 1.7	25 31.3	4 45.5	28 6.1	11 7.8	26 36.4	10 12.8	14 25.7	19 48.6
10	7 16 4.7	19 13.8	28 39.4	14 5.0	26 12.2	6 .7	28 11.9	11 .9	26 43.5	10 16.4	14 28.0	19 50.0
11	7 20 1.2	20 15.0	28 36.2	25 59.5	26 58.0	7 15.8	28 18.5	10 53.8	26 50.6	10 20.0	14 30.2	19 51.5
12	7 23 57.8	21 16.1	28 33.1	7♐49.3	27 48.2	8 30.9	28 25.7	10 46.7	26 57.7	10 23.5	14 32.5	19 52.9
13	7 27 54.4	22 17.3	28 29.9	19 37.9	28 42.4	9 46.1	28 33.6	10 39.5	27 4.8	10 27.1	14 34.7	19 54.3
14	7 31 50.9	23 18.5	28 26.7	1♑28.4	29 40.3	11 1.2	28 42.2	10 32.2	27 12.0	10 30.6	14 37.0	19 55.7
15	7 35 47.5	24 19.6	28 23.5	13 23.3	0♑41.2	12 16.3	28 51.4	10 24.8	27 19.1	10 34.2	14 39.3	19 57.1
16	7 39 44.0	25 20.8	28 20.4	25 24.8	1 45.0	13 31.4	29 1.2	10 17.3	27 26.3	10 37.7	14 41.5	19 58.4
17	7 43 40.6	26 21.9	28 17.2	7♒34.5	2 51.3	14 46.5	29 11.6	10 9.7	27 33.4	10 41.2	14 43.8	19 59.6
18	7 47 37.1	27 23.0	28 14.0	19 54.0	3 60.0	16 1.5	29 22.7	10 2.1	27 40.6	10 44.7	14 46.0	20 .9
19	7 51 33.7	28 24.1	28 10.8	2♓24.8	5 10.7	17 16.6	29 34.3	9 54.3	27 47.7	10 48.1	14 48.2	20 2.1
20	7 55 30.3	29 25.2	28 7.6	15 8.3	6 23.4	18 31.6	29 46.6	9 46.6	27 54.8	10 51.6	14 50.5	20 3.2
21	7 59 26.8	0♒26.3	28 4.5	28 6.1	7 37.8	19 46.6	29 59.3	9 38.8	28 2.0	10 55.0	14 52.7	20 4.4
22	8 3 23.4	1 27.3	28 1.3	11♈19.7	8 53.8	21 1.6	0♊12.7	9 30.9	28 9.1	10 58.5	14 54.9	20 5.5
23	8 7 19.9	2 28.4	27 58.1	24 50.4	10 11.2	22 16.5	0 26.6	9 23.0	28 16.2	11 1.9	14 57.1	20 6.6
24	8 11 16.5	3 29.4	27 54.9	8♉39.2	11 29.9	23 31.5	0 41.0	9 15.0	28 23.4	11 5.3	14 59.2	20 7.6
25	8 15 13.0	4 30.4	27 51.8	22 45.8	12 49.9	24 46.4	0 55.9	9 7.1	28 30.5	11 8.7	15 1.4	20 8.6
26	8 19 9.6	5 31.4	27 48.6	7♊ 9.2	14 11.1	26 1.3	1 11.3	8 59.1	28 37.6	11 12.0	15 3.6	20 9.6
27	8 23 6.2	6 32.4	27 45.4	21 46.1	15 33.4	27 16.1	1 27.2	8 51.1	28 44.7	11 15.4	15 5.7	20 10.5
28	8 27 2.7	7 33.4	27 42.2	6♋32.0	16 56.7	28 31.0	1 43.6	8 43.1	28 51.8	11 18.7	15 7.9	20 11.4
29	8 30 59.3	8 34.3	27 39.1	21 20.6	18 21.0	29 45.8	2 .5	8 35.0	28 58.8	11 22.0	15 10.0	20 12.3
30	8 34 55.8	9 35.2	27 35.9	6♌ 4.6	19 46.2	1♓ .6	2 17.8	8 27.0	29 5.9	11 25.3	15 12.1	20 13.1
31	8 38 52.4	10 36.1	27 32.7	20 37.0	21 12.4	2 15.3	2 35.5	8 19.0	29 13.0	11 28.5	15 14.2	20 13.9

LATITUDE

DAY	EPHEM. SID. TIME	☉	☊	☽	☿	♀	♂	♃	♄	♅	♆	♇
1	6 40 35.7	0 .0	0 .0	1N21.0	3N 8.8	1S17.1	2N20.3	0N40.9	0S 8.6	0S19.2	0N47.4	14N56.4
4	6 52 25.3	0 .0	0 .0	2S34.2	2 58.2	1 21.1	2 21.6	0 41.5	0 8.8	0 19.2	0 47.4	14 57.4
7	7 4 15.0	0 .0	0 .0	4 56.3	2 38.0	1 24.7	2 22.5	0 42.1	0 9.0	0 19.2	0 47.4	14 58.5
10	7 16 4.7	0 .0	0 .0	5 4.9	2 12.5	1 27.7	2 23.2	0 42.6	0 9.2	0 19.2	0 47.3	14 59.7
13	7 27 54.4	0 .0	0 .0	3 17.5	1 44.8	1 30.2	2 23.5	0 43.1	0 9.4	0 19.3	0 47.3	15 .8
16	7 39 44.0	0 .0	0 .0	0 14.5	1 16.5	1 32.0	2 23.6	0 43.6	0 9.6	0 19.3	0 47.3	15 2.1
19	7 51 33.7	0 .0	0 .0	2N59.7	0 48.6	1 33.3	2 23.4	0 44.1	0 9.9	0 19.3	0 47.3	15 3.3
22	8 3 23.4	0 .0	0 .0	5 4.3	0 21.8	1 34.0	2 23.1	0 44.5	0 10.1	0 19.4	0 47.3	15 4.6
25	8 15 13.0	0 .0	0 .0	4 48.6	0S 3.5	1 34.0	2 22.6	0 44.9	0 10.3	0 19.4	0 47.3	15 5.9
28	8 27 2.7	0 .0	0 .0	1 56.7	0 27.0	1 33.4	2 22.0	0 45.3	0 10.5	0 19.5	0 47.3	15 7.3
31	8 38 52.4	0 .0	0 .0	2S 1.9	0 48.6	1 32.2	2 21.2	0 45.7	0 10.7	0 19.5	0 47.3	15 8.6

RIGHT ASCENSION

DAY	EPHEM. SID. TIME	☉	☊	☽	☿	♀	♂	♃	♄	♅	♆	♇
1	6 40 35.7	10♑56.6	1♒16.7	14♋30.7	23♐56.7	26♑54.5	24♉55.2	14♌38.5	27♑40.6	10♑37.1	15♑14.9	21♏ 9.1
2	6 44 32.2	12 2.8	1 13.4	0♌17.9	23R33.4	28 14.7	24R55.0	14R32.6	27 47.9	10 41.0	15 17.4	21 10.7
3	6 48 28.8	13 9.0	1 10.1	14 55.6	23 20.7	29 34.6	24D55.7	14 26.5	27 55.3	10 44.9	15 19.8	21 12.4
4	6 52 25.3	14 15.0	1 6.8	28 25.6	23 18.1	0♒54.3	24 57.2	14 20.3	28 2.7	10 48.8	15 22.2	21 14.0
5	6 56 21.9	15 21.0	1 3.4	11♍ 1.1	23D24.9	2 13.7	24 59.5	14 14.0	28 10.1	10 52.7	15 24.7	21 15.7
6	7 0 18.4	16 26.8	1 .1	22 59.4	23 40.4	3 32.8	25 2.5	14 7.6	28 17.5	10 56.6	15 27.1	21 17.2
7	7 4 15.0	17 32.5	0 56.8	4♎38.0	24 4.0	4 51.6	25 6.4	14 1.0	28 25.0	11 .5	15 29.5	21 18.8
8	7 8 11.6	18 38.2	0 53.5	16 12.8	24 34.9	6 10.2	25 11.0	13 54.3	28 32.4	11 4.4	15 32.0	21 20.3
9	7 12 8.1	19 43.7	0 50.2	27 57.1	25 12.4	7 28.4	25 16.4	13 47.4	28 39.9	11 8.3	15 34.4	21 21.9
10	7 16 4.7	20 49.1	0 46.9	10♏ .4	25 55.8	8 46.3	25 22.5	13 40.5	28 47.3	11 12.1	15 36.8	21 23.3
11	7 20 1.2	21 54.3	0 43.5	22 28.0	26 44.7	10 3.9	25 29.3	13 33.4	28 54.8	11 16.0	15 39.3	21 24.8
12	7 23 57.8	22 59.4	0 40.2	5♐18.9	27 38.4	11 21.2	25 36.9	13 26.2	29 2.3	11 19.9	15 41.7	21 26.2
13	7 27 54.4	24 4.4	0 36.9	18. 26.2	28 36.6	12 38.2	25 45.2	13 19.0	29 9.8	11 23.7	15 44.1	21 27.6
14	7 31 50.9	25 9.3	0 33.6	1♑38.1	29 38.7	13 54.8	25 54.2	13 11.6	29 17.3	11 27.6	15 46.6	21 29.1
15	7 35 47.5	26 13.9	0 30.3	14 41.5	0♑44.4	15 11.2	26 3.9	13 4.2	29 24.8	11 31.4	15 49.0	21 30.4
16	7 39 44.0	27 18.4	0 26.9	27 25.5	1 53.3	16 27.2	26 14.2	12 56.6	29 32.3	11 35.2	15 51.4	21 31.7
17	7 43 40.6	28 22.7	0 23.6	9♒44.8	3 5.1	17 42.8	26 25.2	12 49.0	29 39.8	11 39.0	15 53.8	21 33.0
18	7 47 37.1	29 26.9	0 20.3	21 40.3	4 19.6	18 58.1	26 36.8	12 41.2	29 47.3	11 42.8	15 56.2	21 34.3
19	7 51 33.7	0♒30.9	0 17.0	3♓18.2	5 36.5	20 13.1	26 49.1	12 33.5	29 54.8	11 46.6	15 58.6	21 35.5
20	7 55 30.3	1 34.6	0 13.6	14 48.9	6 55.5	21 27.8	27 2.0	12 25.6	0♒ 2.3	11 50.4	16 .9	21 36.7
21	7 59 26.8	2 38.2	0 10.3	26 25.9	8 16.5	22 42.1	27 15.6	12 17.7	0 9.8	11 54.1	16 3.3	21 37.9
22	8 3 23.4	3 41.6	0 7.0	8♈24.4	9 39.3	23 56.1	27 29.7	12 9.8	0 17.3	11 57.8	16 5.7	21 39.0
23	8 7 19.9	4 44.8	0 3.7	21 .9	11 3.8	25 9.8	27 44.4	12 1.8	0 24.8	12 1.5	16 8.0	21 40.1
24	8 11 16.5	5 47.9	0 .3	4♉30.3	12 29.7	26 23.2	27 59.7	11 53.7	0 32.3	12 5.2	16 10.3	21 41.2
25	8 15 13.0	6 50.7	29♑57.0	19 2.2	13 57.0	27 36.2	28 15.5	11 45.7	0 39.7	12 8.9	16 12.7	21 42.3
26	8 19 9.6	7 53.3	29 53.7	4♊34.7	15 25.5	28 49.0	28 31.9	11 37.6	0 47.2	12 12.5	16 15.0	21 43.3
27	8 23 6.2	8 55.7	29 50.4	20 49.4	16 55.2	0♓ 1.4	28 48.8	11 29.4	0 54.6	12 16.1	16 17.3	21 44.3
28	8 27 2.7	9 57.9	29 47.0	7♋13.3	18 25.9	1 13.5	29 6.2	11 21.3	1 2.1	12 19.8	16 19.6	21 45.3
29	8 30 59.3	10 59.9	29 43.7	23 10.4	19 57.6	2 25.3	29 24.2	11 13.2	1 9.5	12 23.3	16 21.9	21 46.2
30	8 34 55.8	12 1.7	29 40.4	8♌15.8	21 30.2	3 36.9	29 42.6	11 5.0	1 16.9	12 26.9	16 24.1	21 47.1
31	8 38 52.4	13 3.2	29 37.1	22 21.1	23 3.6	4 48.1	0♊ 1.5	10 56.9	1 24.2	12 30.4	16 26.4	21 47.9

DECLINATION

DAY	EPHEM. SID. TIME	☉	☊	☽	☿	♀	♂	♃	♄	♅	♆	♇
1	6 40 35.7	23S 3.6	0S21.3	24N 7.7	20S10.6	22S26.7	21N56.3	17N51.4	21S 9.1	23S24.2	21S54.4	3S13.1
4	6 52 25.3	22 47.7	0 21.3	10 3.6	20 19.5	21 47.3	21 58.1	17 57.0	21 5.4	23 23.4	21 53.7	3 13.4
7	7 4 15.0	22 27.7	0 21.4	7S23.2	20 41.7	21 2.1	22 1.0	18 2.9	21 1.7	23 22.6	21 53.0	3 13.5
10	7 16 4.7	22 3.8	0 21.4	20 54.7	21 10.7	20 11.2	22 5.2	18 9.0	20 57.8	23 21.8	21 52.3	3 13.6
13	7 27 54.4	21 35.9	0 21.4	26 19.0	21 41.3	19 15.1	22 10.3	18 15.4	20 53.9	23 21.0	21 51.6	3 13.5
16	7 39 44.0	21 4.3	0 21.5	21 17.8	22 9.3	18 14.1	22 16.6	18 21.9	20 49.9	23 20.2	21 50.9	3 13.3
19	7 51 33.7	20 29.0	0 21.5	7 49.1	22 31.8	17 8.4	22 23.7	18 28.6	20 45.9	23 19.4	21 50.2	3 13.0
22	8 3 23.4	19 50.2	0 21.5	9N 8.7	22 46.8	15 58.4	22 31.7	18 35.3	20 41.9	23 18.6	21 49.5	3 12.6
25	8 15 13.0	19 8.2	0 21.6	23 6.7	22 52.8	14 44.5	22 40.3	18 42.0	20 37.8	23 17.8	21 48.7	3 12.1
28	8 27 2.7	18 23.0	0 21.6	25 13.4	22 48.9	13 27.1	22 49.6	18 48.7	20 33.7	23 17.0	21 48.0	3 11.5
31	8 38 52.4	17 34.8	0 21.6	12 41.6	22 34.2	12 6.4	22 59.3	18 55.3	20 29.5	23 16.2	21 47.3	3 10.8

FEBRUARY 1991

LONGITUDE

DAY	EPHEM. SID. TIME (h m s)	☉ (° ′)	☊ (° ′)	☾ (° ′)	☿ (° ′)	♀ (° ′)	♂ (° ′)	♃ (° ′)	♄ (° ′)	♅ (° ′)	♆ (° ′)	♇ (° ′)
1	8 42 48.9	11 ♒ 37.0	27 ♑ 29.5	4 ♍ 51.4	22 ♑ 39.4	3 ♓ 30.1	2 ♊ 53.7	8 ♌ 11.0	29 ♑ 20.0	11 ♑ 31.8	15 ♑ 16.3	20 ♏ 14.7
2	8 46 45.5	12 37.9	27 26.3	18 43.6	24 7.2	4 44.8	3 12.2	8 R 3.0	29 27.0	11 35.0	15 18.4	20 15.4
3	8 50 42.0	13 38.8	27 23.2	2 ♎ 11.1	25 35.9	5 59.5	3 31.2	7 55.1	29 34.0	11 38.2	15 20.4	20 16.1
4	8 54 38.6	14 39.7	27 20.0	15 14.1	27 5.5	7 14.2	3 50.7	7 47.2	29 41.1	11 41.4	15 22.5	20 16.8
5	8 58 35.2	15 40.5	27 16.8	27 54.2	28 35.8	8 28.8	4 10.4	7 39.3	29 48.0	11 44.5	15 24.6	20 17.4
6	9 2 31.7	16 41.3	27 13.6	10 ♏ 14.9	0 ♒ 7.0	9 43.4	4 30.6	7 31.4	29 55.0	11 47.6	15 26.6	20 18.0
7	9 6 28.3	17 42.1	27 10.5	22 20.3	1 38.9	10 58.0	4 51.1	7 23.6	0 ♒ 1.9	11 50.7	15 28.6	20 18.6
8	9 10 24.8	18 42.9	27 7.3	4 ♐ 15.3	3 11.6	12 12.5	5 12.0	7 15.9	0 8.8	11 53.8	15 30.6	20 19.1
9	9 14 21.4	19 43.7	27 4.1	16 4.7	4 45.1	13 27.0	5 33.3	7 8.2	0 15.7	11 56.8	15 32.5	20 19.6
10	9 18 17.9	20 44.4	27 .9	27 53.4	6 19.4	14 41.5	5 54.9	7 .6	0 22.5	11 59.8	15 34.5	20 20.0
11	9 22 14.5	21 45.2	26 57.8	9 ♑ 45.8	7 54.5	15 56.0	6 16.8	6 53.0	0 29.4	12 2.8	15 36.4	20 20.4
12	9 26 11.0	22 45.9	26 54.6	21 45.6	9 30.4	17 10.4	6 39.1	6 45.5	0 36.2	12 5.7	15 38.3	20 20.8
13	9 30 7.6	23 46.6	26 51.4	3 ♒ 55.9	11 7.2	18 24.8	7 1.7	6 38.1	0 43.0	12 8.6	15 40.2	20 21.1
14	9 34 4.2	24 47.2	26 48.2	16 19.1	12 44.8	19 39.1	7 24.6	6 30.8	0 49.7	12 11.5	15 42.1	20 21.4
15	9 38 .7	25 47.9	26 45.0	28 56.4	14 23.2	20 53.5	7 47.8	6 23.6	0 56.4	12 14.4	15 43.9	20 21.7
16	9 41 57.3	26 48.5	26 41.9	11 ♓ 48.4	16 2.5	22 7.8	8 11.3	6 16.5	1 3.1	12 17.2	15 45.8	20 21.9
17	9 45 53.8	27 49.1	26 38.7	24 54.7	17 42.6	23 22.0	8 35.1	6 9.4	1 9.8	12 20.0	15 47.6	20 22.1
18	9 49 50.4	28 49.7	26 35.5	8 ♈ 14.5	19 23.7	24 36.2	8 59.2	6 2.5	1 16.4	12 22.7	15 49.4	20 22.3
19	9 53 46.9	29 50.2	26 32.3	21 46.7	21 5.6	25 50.4	9 23.6	5 55.7	1 23.0	12 25.4	15 51.1	20 22.4
20	9 57 43.5	0 ♓ 50.8	26 29.2	5 ♉ 29.9	22 48.4	27 4.5	9 48.3	5 49.0	1 29.5	12 28.1	15 52.9	20 22.5
21	10 1 40.0	1 51.2	26 26.0	19 22.9	24 32.2	28 18.6	10 13.2	5 42.5	1 36.0	12 30.8	15 54.6	20 22.5
22	10 5 36.6	2 51.7	26 22.8	3 ♊ 24.5	26 16.9	29 32.7	10 38.4	5 36.0	1 42.5	12 33.4	15 56.3	20 22.5
23	10 9 33.2	3 52.1	26 19.6	17 33.6	28 2.6	0 ♈ 46.7	11 3.9	5 29.7	1 48.9	12 35.9	15 58.0	20 22.5
24	10 13 29.7	4 52.5	26 16.4	1 ♋ 48.7	29 49.2	2 .6	11 29.5	5 23.6	1 55.3	12 38.5	15 59.6	20 R 22.4
25	10 17 26.3	5 52.9	26 13.3	16 7.8	1 ♓ 36.8	3 14.6	11 55.5	5 17.6	2 1.7	12 41.0	16 1.3	20 22.4
26	10 21 22.8	6 53.2	26 10.1	0 ♌ 27.8	3 25.3	4 28.4	12 21.7	5 11.7	2 8.0	12 43.5	16 2.9	20 22.2
27	10 25 19.4	7 53.5	26 6.9	14 45.0	5 14.8	5 42.2	12 48.0	5 5.9	2 14.2	12 45.9	16 4.5	20 22.1
28	10 29 15.9	8 53.8	26 3.7	28 55.0	7 5.3	6 56.0	13 14.6	5 .3	2 20.5	12 48.3	16 6.0	20 21.9

LATITUDE

DAY	EPHEM. SID. TIME	☉	☊	☾	☿	♀	♂	♃	♄	♅	♆	♇
1	8 42 48.9	0 .0	0 .0	3 S 10.1	0 S 55.3	1 S 31.7	2 N 20.9	0 N 45.8	0 S 10.8	0 S 19.5	0 N 47.3	15 N 9.1
4	8 54 38.6	0 .0	0 .0	5 8.5	1 13.9	1 29.6	2 20.1	0 46.1	0 11.0	0 19.6	0 47.3	15 10.5
7	9 6 28.3	0 .0	0 .0	4 47.9	1 30.0	1 26.9	2 19.1	0 46.4	0 11.3	0 19.6	0 47.3	15 11.9
10	9 18 17.9	0 .0	0 .0	2 38.4	1 43.5	1 23.5	2 18.0	0 46.6	0 11.5	0 19.7	0 47.3	15 13.3
13	9 30 7.6	0 .0	0 .0	0 N 32.7	1 54.2	1 19.5	2 16.9	0 46.8	0 11.7	0 19.7	0 47.3	15 14.7
16	9 41 57.3	0 .0	0 .0	3 37.4	2 1.8	1 14.9	2 15.8	0 47.0	0 12.0	0 19.8	0 47.3	15 16.1
19	9 53 46.9	0 .0	0 .0	5 10.5	2 6.0	1 9.8	2 14.6	0 47.2	0 12.2	0 19.9	0 47.4	15 17.5
22	10 5 36.6	0 .0	0 .0	4 13.1	2 6.6	1 4.0	2 13.3	0 47.3	0 12.5	0 19.9	0 47.4	15 18.9
25	10 17 26.3	0 .0	0 .0	1 1.9	2 3.2	0 57.7	2 12.0	0 47.4	0 12.7	0 20.0	0 47.4	15 20.3
28	10 29 15.9	0 .0	0 .0	2 S 41.9	1 55.5	0 50.9	2 10.7	0 47.5	0 13.0	0 20.1	0 47.5	15 21.6

RIGHT ASCENSION

DAY	EPHEM. SID. TIME	☉	☊	☾	☿	♀	♂	♃	♄	♅	♆	♇
1	8 42 48.9	14 ♒ 4.6	29 ♑ 33.7	5 ♍ 32.3	24 ♑ 37.7	5 ♓ 59.1	0 ♊ 20.9	10 ♌ 48.7	1 ♒ 31.6	12 ♑ 33.9	16 ♑ 28.6	21 ♏ 48.8
2	8 46 45.5	15 5.8	29 30.4	18 2.2	26 12.5	7 9.8	0 40.8	10 R 40.6	1 39.0	12 37.4	16 30.8	21 49.6
3	8 50 42.0	16 6.8	29 27.1	0 ♎ 6.7	27 47.9	8 20.2	1 1.1	10 32.5	1 46.3	12 40.9	16 33.0	21 50.3
4	8 54 38.6	17 7.6	29 23.7	12 .7	29 24.0	9 30.4	1 21.9	10 24.5	1 53.6	12 44.4	16 35.3	21 51.1
5	8 58 35.2	18 8.2	29 20.4	23 57.5	1 ♒ .5	10 40.4	1 43.0	10 16.4	2 .9	12 47.8	16 37.4	21 51.8
6	9 2 31.7	19 8.6	29 17.1	6 ♏ 7.1	2 37.5	11 50.1	2 4.6	10 8.4	2 8.2	12 51.1	16 39.6	21 52.5
7	9 6 28.3	20 8.7	29 13.7	18 35.7	4 15.0	12 59.5	2 26.7	10 .5	2 15.4	12 54.5	16 41.7	21 53.1
8	9 10 24.8	21 8.7	29 10.4	1 ♐ 24.3	5 52.9	14 8.8	2 49.1	9 52.6	2 22.6	12 57.8	16 43.9	21 53.7
9	9 14 21.4	22 8.5	29 7.1	14 28.5	7 31.2	15 17.8	3 11.9	9 44.7	2 29.8	13 1.1	16 46.0	21 54.3
10	9 18 17.9	23 8.1	29 3.7	27 39.2	9 9.9	16 26.6	3 35.1	9 36.9	2 37.0	13 4.4	16 48.0	21 54.8
11	9 22 14.5	24 7.5	29 .4	10 ♑ 45.3	10 48.8	17 35.3	3 58.8	9 29.2	2 44.1	13 7.6	16 50.1	21 55.3
12	9 26 11.0	25 6.7	28 57.1	23 36.6	12 28.1	18 43.8	4 22.8	9 21.5	2 51.2	13 10.8	16 52.1	21 55.8
13	9 30 7.6	26 5.8	28 53.7	6 ♒ 7.1	14 7.7	19 52.0	4 47.1	9 14.0	2 58.3	13 13.9	16 54.2	21 56.2
14	9 34 4.2	27 4.6	28 50.4	18 15.9	15 47.6	21 .2	5 11.8	9 6.5	3 5.3	13 17.1	16 56.2	21 56.6
15	9 38 .7	28 3.3	28 47.1	0 ♓ 7.5	17 27.8	22 8.1	5 36.9	8 59.1	3 12.3	13 20.1	16 58.1	21 57.0
16	9 41 57.3	29 1.7	28 43.7	11 50.2	19 8.2	23 16.0	6 2.4	8 51.8	3 19.3	13 23.2	17 .1	21 57.3
17	9 45 53.8	0 ♓ .0	28 40.4	23 35.6	20 48.8	24 23.6	6 28.1	8 44.6	3 26.2	13 26.2	17 2.0	21 57.6
18	9 49 50.4	0 58.1	28 37.1	5 ♈ 37.1	22 29.7	25 31.2	6 54.2	8 37.5	3 33.1	13 29.2	17 3.9	21 57.9
19	9 53 46.9	1 56.1	28 33.7	18 8.8	24 10.8	26 38.7	7 20.7	8 30.5	3 40.0	13 32.1	17 5.8	21 58.1
20	9 57 43.5	2 53.8	28 30.4	1 ♉ 23.8	25 52.2	27 46.0	7 47.4	8 23.6	3 46.8	13 35.0	17 7.7	21 58.3
21	10 1 40.0	3 51.4	28 27.0	15 30.8	27 33.8	28 53.2	8 14.5	8 16.9	3 53.5	13 37.9	17 9.5	21 58.5
22	10 5 36.6	4 48.8	28 23.7	0 ♊ 29.8	29 15.7	0 ♈ .4	8 41.9	8 10.3	4 .3	13 40.7	17 11.3	21 58.6
23	10 9 33.2	5 46.1	28 20.4	16 8.1	0 ♓ 57.8	1 7.5	9 9.5	8 3.8	4 7.0	13 43.5	17 13.1	21 58.7
24	10 13 29.7	6 43.2	28 17.0	2 ♋ .6	2 40.1	2 14.5	9 37.5	7 57.5	4 13.6	13 46.3	17 14.9	21 58.7
25	10 17 26.3	7 40.2	28 13.7	17 37.8	4 22.7	3 21.5	10 5.8	7 51.3	4 20.3	13 49.0	17 16.7	21 58.8
26	10 21 22.8	8 37.0	28 10.3	2 ♌ 36.2	6 5.5	4 28.4	10 34.3	7 45.2	4 26.8	13 51.7	17 18.4	21 58.8
27	10 25 19.4	9 33.6	28 7.0	16 45.1	7 48.6	5 35.2	11 3.0	7 39.3	4 33.3	13 54.3	17 20.1	21 58.8
28	10 29 15.9	10 30.1	28 3.7	0 ♍ 6.1	9 31.9	6 42.1	11 32.1	7 33.6	4 39.8	13 56.9	17 21.7	21 R 58.7

DECLINATION

DAY	EPHEM. SID. TIME	☉	☊	☾	☿	♀	♂	♃	♄	♅	♆	♇
1	8 42 48.9	17 S 18.1	0 S 21.6	6 N 46.8	22 S 26.8	11 S 38.9	23 N 2.6	18 N 57.5	20 S 28.1	23 S 15.9	21 S 47.1	3 S 10.6
4	8 54 38.6	16 26.2	0 21.7	10 S 44.3	21 57.0	10 14.4	23 12.8	19 4.0	20 23.9	23 15.1	21 46.4	3 9.7
7	9 6 28.3	15 31.7	0 21.7	22 59.4	21 15.5	8 47.6	23 23.1	19 10.3	20 19.8	23 14.4	21 45.7	3 8.8
10	9 18 17.9	14 34.9	0 21.7	26 3.9	20 21.9	7 18.7	23 33.6	19 16.4	20 15.6	23 13.6	21 45.0	3 7.8
13	9 30 7.6	13 35.8	0 21.8	18 44.6	19 16.1	5 48.2	23 44.1	19 22.3	20 11.4	23 12.9	21 44.3	3 6.7
16	9 41 57.3	12 34.7	0 21.8	3 47.0	17 58.0	4 16.2	23 54.5	19 27.9	20 7.3	23 12.1	21 43.6	3 5.6
19	9 53 46.9	11 31.8	0 21.8	13 N 17.0	16 27.5	2 43.2	24 4.7	19 33.2	20 3.1	23 11.4	21 43.0	3 4.3
22	10 5 36.6	10 27.3	0 21.9	24 58.6	14 44.5	1 9.6	24 14.6	19 38.2	19 59.1	23 10.8	21 42.3	3 3.0
25	10 17 26.3	9 21.3	0 21.9	23 29.4	12 49.2	0 N 24.4	24 24.1	19 42.8	19 55.0	23 10.1	21 41.7	3 1.6
28	10 29 15.9	8 14.1	0 21.9	9 19.3	10 41.8	1 58.4	24 33.2	19 47.1	19 51.0	23 9.5	21 41.1	3 .2

MARCH 1991

LONGITUDE

DAY	EPHEM. SID. TIME h m s	☉ ° ′	☊ ° ′	☽ ° ′	☿ ° ′	♀ ° ′	♂ ° ′	♃ ° ′	♄ ° ′	♅ ° ′	♆ ° ′	♇ ° ′
1	10 33 12.5	9♓54.0	26♑ .6	12♍53.1	8♓56.7	8♈ 9.7	13♊41.4	4♌54.9	2♒26.6	12♑50.6	16♑ 7.6	20♏21.6
2	10 37 9.0	10 54.2	25 57.4	26 35.1	10 49.0	9 23.3	14 8.4	4R49.6	2 32.8	12 52.9	16 9.1	20R21.4
3	10 41 5.6	11 54.4	25 54.2	9♎58.0	12 42.3	10 36.9	14 35.6	4 44.4	2 38.8	12 55.2	16 10.5	20 21.1
4	10 45 2.1	12 54.5	25 51.0	23 .1	14 36.3	11 50.5	15 3.0	4 39.5	2 44.9	12 57.4	16 12.0	20 20.7
5	10 48 58.7	13 54.7	25 47.8	5♏41.7	16 31.1	13 4.0	15 30.6	4 34.6	2 50.8	12 59.6	16 13.4	20 20.3
6	10 52 55.2	14 54.8	25 44.7	18 4.7	18 26.7	14 17.4	15 58.4	4 30.0	2 56.8	13 1.7	16 14.8	20 19.9
7	10 56 51.8	15 54.8	25 41.5	0♐12.1	20 22.8	15 30.8	16 26.4	4 25.5	3 2.6	13 3.8	16 16.2	20 19.5
8	11 0 48.4	16 54.9	25 38.3	12 8.4	22 19.4	16 44.2	16 54.6	4 21.2	3 8.5	13 5.9	16 17.5	20 19.0
9	11 4 44.9	17 54.9	25 35.1	23 58.4	24 16.4	17 57.5	17 22.9	4 17.1	3 14.2	13 7.9	16 18.8	20 18.5
10	11 8 41.5	18 54.9	25 32.0	5♑47.6	26 13.4	19 10.7	17 51.4	4 13.1	3 19.9	13 9.8	16 20.1	20 18.0
11	11 12 38.0	19 54.8	25 28.8	17 41.0	28 10.5	20 23.9	18 20.1	4 9.3	3 25.6	13 11.8	16 21.4	20 17.4
12	11 16 34.6	20 54.7	25 25.6	29 43.9	0♈ 7.2	21 37.0	18 48.9	4 5.7	3 31.2	13 13.6	16 22.6	20 16.8
13	11 20 31.1	21 54.6	25 22.4	12♒ .4	2 3.4	22 50.1	19 18.0	4 2.3	3 36.7	13 15.5	16 23.8	20 16.1
14	11 24 27.7	22 54.5	25 19.2	24 34.1	3 58.6	24 3.1	19 47.1	3 59.0	3 42.2	13 17.3	16 25.0	20 15.5
15	11 28 24.2	23 54.4	25 16.1	7♓26.9	5 52.6	25 16.1	20 16.5	3 56.0	3 47.6	13 19.0	16 26.1	20 14.8
16	11 32 20.8	24 54.2	25 12.9	20 39.4	7 45.0	26 29.0	20 46.0	3 53.1	3 53.0	13 20.7	16 27.2	20 14.0
17	11 36 17.3	25 53.9	25 9.7	4♈10.5	9 35.4	27 41.8	21 15.6	3 50.4	3 58.3	13 22.3	16 28.3	20 13.3
18	11 40 13.9	26 53.7	25 6.5	17 57.4	11 23.2	28 54.6	21 45.4	3 47.9	4 3.6	13 24.0	16 29.4	20 12.5
19	11 44 10.4	27 53.4	25 3.4	1♉56.3	13 8.1	0♉ 7.3	22 15.4	3 45.6	4 8.7	13 25.5	16 30.4	20 11.7
20	11 48 7.0	28 53.1	25 .2	16 3.0	14 49.6	1 20.0	22 45.4	3 43.5	4 13.8	13 27.0	16 31.4	20 10.8
21	11 52 3.5	29 52.8	24 57.0	0♊13.3	16 27.2	2 32.5	23 15.6	3 41.6	4 18.9	13 28.5	16 32.3	20 9.9
22	11 56 .1	0♈52.3	24 53.8	14 24.0	18 .5	3 45.0	23 46.0	3 39.9	4 23.8	13 29.9	16 33.3	20 9.0
23	11 59 56.6	1 51.9	24 50.6	28 32.7	19 28.9	4 57.5	24 16.4	3 38.3	4 28.7	13 31.2	16 34.2	20 8.1
24	12 3 53.2	2 51.4	24 47.5	12♋38.2	20 52.2	6 9.8	24 47.0	3 37.0	4 33.6	13 32.5	16 35.0	20 7.1
25	12 7 49.8	3 50.9	24 44.3	26 39.5	22 9.8	7 22.1	25 17.7	3 35.8	4 38.3	13 33.8	16 35.9	20 6.1
26	12 11 46.3	4 50.3	24 41.1	10♌36.0	23 21.5	8 34.3	25 48.6	3 34.9	4 43.0	13 35.0	16 36.7	20 5.1
27	12 15 42.9	5 49.8	24 37.9	24 26.5	24 26.8	9 46.4	26 19.5	3 34.1	4 47.6	13 36.2	16 37.4	20 4.0
28	12 19 39.4	6 49.1	24 34.8	8♍ 9.5	25 25.7	10 58.5	26 50.6	3 33.5	4 52.2	13 37.3	16 38.1	20 2.9
29	12 23 36.0	7 48.4	24 31.6	21 42.9	26 17.7	12 10.4	27 21.8	3 33.1	4 56.6	13 38.3	16 38.8	20 1.8
30	12 27 32.5	8 47.7	24 28.4	5♎ 4.3	27 2.7	13 22.3	27 53.0	3 32.9	5 1.0	13 39.3	16 39.5	20 .7
31	12 31 29.1	9 47.0	24 25.2	18 11.3	27 40.5	14 34.1	28 24.4	3 32.9	5 5.4	13 40.3	16 40.2	19 59.5

LATITUDE

DAY	EPHEM. SID. TIME h m s	☉	☊	☽	☿	♀	♂	♃	♄	♅	♆	♇
1	10 33 12.5	0 .0	0 .0	3S40.8	1S51.9	0S48.6	2N10.3	0N47.5	0S13.1	0S20.1	0N47.5	15N22.1
4	10 45 2.1	0 .0	0 .0	5 7.6	1 37.8	0 41.1	2 9.0	0 47.5	0 13.3	0 20.1	0 47.5	15 23.4
7	10 56 51.8	0 .0	0 .0	4 17.7	1 18.7	0 33.2	2 7.6	0 47.5	0 13.6	0 20.2	0 47.5	15 24.7
10	11 8 41.5	0 .0	0 .0	1 50.5	0 54.3	0 24.9	2 6.3	0 47.5	0 13.9	0 20.3	0 47.6	15 26.0
13	11 20 31.1	0 .0	0 .0	1N21.0	0 24.9	0 16.3	2 4.9	0 47.5	0 14.1	0 20.4	0 47.6	15 27.2
16	11 32 20.8	0 .0	0 .0	4 7.3	0N 8.9	0 7.3	2 3.5	0 47.4	0 14.4	0 20.4	0 47.7	15 28.4
19	11 44 10.4	0 .0	0 .0	5 2.2	0 45.8	0N 1.9	2 2.1	0 47.4	0 14.7	0 20.5	0 47.7	15 29.6
22	11 56 .1	0 .0	0 .0	3 21.1	1 23.6	0 11.4	2 .7	0 47.3	0 15.0	0 20.6	0 47.8	15 30.7
25	12 7 49.8	0 .0	0 .0	0S 5.5	1 60.0	0 21.0	1 59.3	0 47.2	0 15.2	0 20.7	0 47.8	15 31.7
28	12 19 39.4	0 .0	0 .0	3 25.4	2 32.0	0 30.7	1 57.9	0 47.1	0 15.5	0 20.7	0 47.9	15 32.7
31	12 31 29.1	0 .0	0 .0	4 59.0	2 56.9	0 40.5	1 56.5	0 47.0	0 15.8	0 20.8	0 47.9	15 33.7

RIGHT ASCENSION

DAY	EPHEM. SID. TIME h m s	☉	☊	☽	☿	♀	♂	♃	♄	♅	♆	♇
1	10 33 12.5	11♓26.5	28♑ .3	12♍48.8	11♓15.5	7♈48.9	12♊ 1.4	7♌27.9	4♒46.2	13♑59.4	17♑23.4	21♏58.6
2	10 37 9.0	12 22.7	27 57.0	25 6.4	12 59.2	8 55.7	12 30.9	7R22.5	4 52.5	14 1.9	17 25.0	21R58.5
3	10 41 5.6	13 18.8	27 53.6	7♎12.6	14 43.2	10 2.6	13 .7	7 17.2	4 58.9	14 4.4	17 26.6	21 58.3
4	10 45 2.1	14 14.8	27 50.3	19 19.6	16 27.4	11 9.4	13 30.7	7 12.1	5 5.1	14 6.8	17 28.1	21 58.1
5	10 48 58.7	15 10.7	27 46.9	1♏37.1	18 11.8	12 16.3	14 .9	7 7.1	5 11.3	14 9.2	17 29.6	21 57.8
6	10 52 55.2	16 6.5	27 43.6	14 10.9	19 56.2	13 23.2	14 31.4	7 2.3	5 17.5	14 11.5	17 31.1	21 57.6
7	10 56 51.8	17 2.1	27 40.3	27 2.2	21 40.7	14 30.2	15 2.1	6 57.7	5 23.6	14 13.7	17 32.6	21 57.3
8	11 0 48.4	17 57.7	27 36.9	10♐ 7.1	23 25.2	15 37.2	15 33.0	6 53.2	5 29.6	14 16.0	17 34.0	21 56.9
9	11 4 44.9	18 53.2	27 33.6	23 17.7	25 9.5	16 44.3	16 4.1	6 48.9	5 35.6	14 18.1	17 35.4	21 56.6
10	11 8 41.5	19 48.6	27 30.2	6♑23.9	26 53.7	17 51.4	16 35.4	6 44.8	5 41.5	14 20.3	17 36.8	21 56.2
11	11 12 38.0	20 43.9	27 26.9	19 16.7	28 37.4	18 58.7	17 7.0	6 40.9	5 47.4	14 22.3	17 38.1	21 55.7
12	11 16 34.6	21 39.1	27 23.5	1♒50.5	0♈20.6	20 6.0	17 38.7	6 37.2	5 53.2	14 24.4	17 39.4	21 55.3
13	11 20 31.1	22 34.2	27 20.2	14 4.7	2 3.1	21 13.5	18 10.7	6 33.6	5 58.9	14 26.4	17 40.7	21 54.8
14	11 24 27.7	23 29.3	27 16.8	26 3.2	3 44.6	22 21.0	18 42.8	6 30.3	6 4.6	14 28.3	17 42.0	21 54.3
15	11 28 24.2	24 24.3	27 13.5	7♓53.9	5 24.8	23 28.7	19 15.1	6 27.1	6 10.2	14 30.2	17 43.2	21 53.7
16	11 32 20.8	25 19.3	27 10.1	19 47.8	7 3.5	24 36.5	19 47.6	6 24.1	6 15.7	14 32.0	17 44.3	21 53.1
17	11 36 17.3	26 14.2	27 6.8	1♈57.5	8 40.4	25 44.5	20 20.3	6 21.3	6 21.2	14 33.8	17 45.5	21 52.5
18	11 40 13.9	27 9.1	27 3.4	14 36.6	10 15.1	26 52.7	20 53.2	6 18.8	6 26.7	14 35.6	17 46.7	21 51.9
19	11 44 10.4	28 3.9	27 .1	27 57.1	11 47.2	28 .9	21 26.3	6 16.4	6 32.0	14 37.2	17 47.8	21 51.2
20	11 48 7.0	28 58.6	26 56.7	12♉ 6.9	13 16.3	29 9.3	21 59.5	6 14.2	6 37.3	14 38.9	17 48.8	21 50.5
21	11 52 3.5	29 53.3	26 53.4	27 5.0	14 42.1	0♉17.9	22 32.8	6 12.2	6 42.5	14 40.4	17 49.8	21 49.8
22	11 56 .1	0♈48.0	26 50.0	12♊38.5	16 4.2	1 26.6	23 6.3	6 10.4	6 47.7	14 42.0	17 50.8	21 49.0
23	11 59 56.6	1 42.7	26 46.7	28 23.2	17 22.1	2 35.6	23 40.0	6 8.8	6 52.7	14 43.4	17 51.8	21 48.2
24	12 3 53.2	2 37.3	26 43.3	13♋51.0	18 35.5	3 44.7	24 13.8	6 7.4	6 57.7	14 44.9	17 52.7	21 47.4
25	12 7 49.8	3 31.9	26 40.0	28 40.2	19 44.1	4 54.0	24 47.8	6 6.2	7 2.7	14 46.2	17 53.6	21 46.6
26	12 11 46.3	4 26.5	26 36.6	12♌40.8	20 47.4	6 3.4	25 21.9	6 5.2	7 7.5	14 47.5	17 54.4	21 45.7
27	12 15 42.9	5 21.1	26 33.3	25 54.8	21 45.2	7 13.1	25 56.1	6 4.4	7 12.3	14 48.8	17 55.2	21 44.8
28	12 19 39.4	6 15.6	26 29.9	8♍31.7	22 37.3	8 23.0	26 30.5	6 3.8	7 17.0	14 50.0	17 56.0	21 43.9
29	12 23 36.0	7 10.2	26 26.5	20 44.3	23 23.3	9 33.1	27 4.9	6 3.4	7 21.6	14 51.1	17 56.7	21 42.9
30	12 27 32.5	8 4.8	26 23.2	2♎46.4	24 3.1	10 43.4	27 39.5	6 3.1	7 26.1	14 52.2	17 57.5	21 41.9
31	12 31 29.1	8 59.4	26 19.8	14 50.3	24 36.6	11 53.9	28 14.3	6 3.1	7 30.6	14 53.3	17 58.1	21 40.9

DECLINATION

DAY	EPHEM. SID. TIME h m s	☉	☊	☽	☿	♀	♂	♃	♄	♅	♆	♇
1	10 33 12.5	7S51.5	0S21.9	3N19.3	9S56.7	2N29.6	24N36.1	19N48.4	19S49.7	23S 9.3	21S40.9	2S59.7
4	10 45 2.1	6 42.9	0 22.0	13S41.9	7 34.0	4 3.1	24 44.4	19 52.2	19 45.8	23 8.7	21 40.4	2 58.2
7	10 56 51.8	5 33.4	0 22.0	24 23.4	5 1.0	5 35.8	24 52.0	19 55.5	19 42.0	23 8.1	21 39.8	2 56.6
10	11 8 41.5	4 23.2	0 22.0	25 9.3	2 19.9	7 7.5	24 58.9	19 58.5	19 38.2	23 7.6	21 39.3	2 55.0
13	11 20 31.1	3 12.5	0 22.1	15 53.8	0N26.2	8 37.7	25 5.1	20 1.0	19 34.6	23 7.1	21 38.8	2 53.4
16	11 32 20.8	2 1.5	0 22.1	0N 5.3	3 12.7	10 6.3	25 10.4	20 3.2	19 31.1	23 6.7	21 38.4	2 51.7
19	11 44 10.4	0 50.3	0 22.1	16 52.1	5 53.4	11 32.8	25 14.8	20 4.8	19 27.6	23 6.3	21 37.9	2 50.0
22	11 56 .1	0N20.8	0 22.2	25 51.5	8 21.1	12 56.8	25 18.3	20 6.1	19 24.3	23 5.9	21 37.5	2 48.3
25	12 7 49.8	1 31.8	0 22.2	20 44.2	10 29.1	14 18.2	25 20.7	20 7.0	19 21.1	23 5.6	21 37.2	2 46.5
28	12 19 39.4	2 42.4	0 22.2	5 20.0	12 11.5	15 36.5	25 22.1	20 7.4	19 18.1	23 5.3	21 36.8	2 44.8
31	12 31 29.1	3 52.6	0 22.2	11S44.2	13 23.9	16 51.4	25 22.4	20 7.4	19 15.2	23 5.1	21 36.5	2 43.1

APRIL 1991

LONGITUDE

DAY	EPHEM. SID. TIME (h m s)	☉ ° ′	☊ ° ′	☽ ° ′	☿ ° ′	♀ ° ′	♂ ° ′	♃ ° ′	♄ ° ′	♅ ° ′	♆ ° ′	♇ ° ′
1	12 35 25.6	10♈46.2	24♑22.0	1♏ 2.6	28♈11.1	15♉45.9	28♊55.9	3♌33.1	5♒ 9.6	13♑41.2	16♑40.8	19♏58.4
2	12 39 22.2	11 45.4	24 18.9	13 37.5	28 34.5	16 57.5	29 27.5	3D33.5	5 13.8	13 42.1	16 41.3	19R57.2
3	12 43 18.7	12 44.6	24 15.7	25 56.8	28 50.5	18 9.1	29 59.1	3 34.0	5 17.9	13 42.9	16 41.9	19 55.9
4	12 47 15.3	13 43.7	24 12.5	8♐ 2.6	28 59.3	19 20.5	0♋30.9	3 34.8	5 21.9	13 43.6	16 42.4	19 54.7
5	12 51 11.8	14 42.8	24 9.3	19 58.3	29 1.1	20 31.9	1 2.8	3 35.7	5 25.8	13 44.3	16 42.8	19 53.4
6	12 55 8.4	15 41.9	24 6.2	1♑48.0	28R56.0	21 43.2	1 34.7	3 36.9	5 29.7	13 45.0	16 43.3	19 52.1
7	12 59 4.9	16 40.9	24 3.0	13 36.7	28 44.4	22 54.4	2 6.8	3 38.2	5 33.4	13 45.6	16 43.7	19 50.8
8	13 3 1.5	17 40.0	23 59.8	25 30.0	28 26.6	24 5.6	2 39.0	3 39.7	5 37.2	13 46.2	16 44.1	19 49.5
9	13 6 58.1	18 39.0	23 56.6	7♒33.2	28 3.0	25 16.6	3 11.2	3 41.4	5 40.8	13 46.7	16 44.4	19 48.1
10	13 10 54.6	19 37.9	23 53.4	19 51.7	27 34.3	26 27.6	3 43.6	3 43.3	5 44.3	13 47.2	16 44.8	19 46.8
11	13 14 51.2	20 36.9	23 50.3	2♓30.0	27 1.1	27 38.5	4 16.0	3 45.4	5 47.7	13 47.6	16 45.0	19 45.4
12	13 18 47.7	21 35.7	23 47.1	15 31.3	26 24.0	28 49.2	4 48.5	3 47.6	5 51.1	13 47.9	16 45.3	19 44.0
13	13 22 44.3	22 34.6	23 43.9	28 57.2	25 43.9	29 59.9	5 21.1	3 50.0	5 54.4	13 48.2	16 45.5	19 42.5
14	13 26 40.8	23 33.4	23 40.7	12♈46.8	25 1.5	1♊10.5	5 53.7	3 52.6	5 57.5	13 48.4	16 45.6	19 41.1
15	13 30 37.4	24 32.2	23 37.6	26 56.9	24 17.7	2 20.9	6 26.5	3 55.4	6 .6	13 48.6	16 45.8	19 39.6
16	13 34 33.9	25 31.0	23 34.4	11♉22.1	23 33.3	3 31.3	6 59.3	3 58.4	6 3.6	13 48.8	16 45.9	19 38.1
17	13 38 30.5	26 29.7	23 31.2	25 55.6	22 49.2	4 41.6	7 32.2	4 1.5	6 6.5	13 48.9	16 46.0	19 36.6
18	13 42 27.0	27 28.4	23 28.0	10♊30.5	22 6.2	5 51.8	8 5.2	4 4.8	6 9.4	13 48.9	16 46.0	19 35.1
19	13 46 23.6	28 27.1	23 24.8	25 .8	21 25.0	7 1.8	8 38.3	4 8.3	6 12.1	13 48.9	16 46.0	19 33.6
20	13 50 20.1	29 25.7	23 21.7	9♋22.0	20 46.2	8 11.8	9 11.4	4 12.0	6 14.7	13R48.8	16 46.0	19 32.0
21	13 54 16.7	0♉24.3	23 18.5	23 31.7	20 10.5	9 21.6	9 44.6	4 15.8	6 17.3	13 48.7	16R45.9	19 30.5
22	13 58 13.3	1 22.9	23 15.3	7♌28.9	19 38.5	10 31.3	10 17.9	4 19.8	6 19.8	13 48.5	16 45.8	19 28.9
23	14 2 9.8	2 21.4	23 12.1	21 13.6	19 10.4	11 40.9	10 51.2	4 24.0	6 22.1	13 48.3	16 45.7	19 27.3
24	14 6 6.4	3 19.9	23 9.0	4♍46.4	18 46.7	12 50.4	11 24.6	4 28.3	6 24.4	13 48.1	16 45.6	19 25.7
25	14 10 2.9	4 18.3	23 5.8	18 7.8	18 27.6	13 59.7	11 58.1	4 32.9	6 26.6	13 47.7	16 45.4	19 24.1
26	14 13 59.5	5 16.7	23 2.6	1♎17.9	18 13.3	15 9.0	12 31.6	4 37.5	6 28.7	13 47.4	16 45.1	19 22.5
27	14 17 56.0	6 15.1	22 59.4	14 16.6	18 3.9	16 18.0	13 5.2	4 42.3	6 30.7	13 47.0	16 44.9	19 20.9
28	14 21 52.6	7 13.4	22 56.2	27 3.5	17 59.4	17 27.0	13 38.8	4 47.3	6 32.6	13 46.5	16 44.6	19 19.2
29	14 25 49.1	8 11.8	22 53.1	9♏38.1	17D59.9	18 35.9	14 12.6	4 52.5	6 34.4	13 46.0	16 44.3	19 17.7
30	14 29 45.7	9 10.1	22 49.9	22 .3	18 5.2	19 44.6	14 46.3	4 57.8	6 36.2	13 45.5	16 44.0	19 16.0

LATITUDE

DAY	SID. TIME	☉	☊	☽	☿	♀	♂	♃	♄	♅	♆	♇
1	12 35 25.6	0 .0	0 .0	4S59.3	3N 3.1	0N43.8	1N56.0	0N46.9	0S15.9	0S20.8	0N47.9	15N34.0
4	12 47 15.3	0 .0	0 .0	3 38.4	3 14.4	0 53.6	1 54.6	0 46.8	0 16.2	0 20.9	0 48.0	15 34.8
7	12 59 4.9	0 .0	0 .0	0 55.4	3 13.0	1 3.4	1 53.2	0 46.7	0 16.5	0 21.0	0 48.0	15 35.6
10	13 10 54.6	0 .0	0 .0	2N11.8	2 57.5	1 13.0	1 51.8	0 46.6	0 16.8	0 21.1	0 48.1	15 36.3
13	13 22 44.3	0 .0	0 .0	4 33.2	2 28.2	1 22.4	1 50.4	0 46.4	0 17.1	0 21.2	0 48.1	15 36.9
16	13 34 33.9	0 .0	0 .0	4 45.5	1 47.5	1 31.5	1 49.0	0 46.3	0 17.5	0 21.2	0 48.2	15 37.5
19	13 46 23.6	0 .0	0 .0	2 21.0	0 59.5	1 40.4	1 47.5	0 46.1	0 17.8	0 21.3	0 48.2	15 37.9
22	13 58 13.3	0 .0	0 .0	1S17.2	0 9.0	1 48.9	1 46.1	0 46.0	0 18.1	0 21.4	0 48.3	15 38.3
25	14 10 2.9	0 .0	0 .0	4 9.0	0S39.6	1 56.9	1 44.7	0 45.8	0 18.4	0 21.5	0 48.3	15 38.7
28	14 21 52.6	0 .0	0 .0	4 59.9	1 23.3	2 4.4	1 43.3	0 45.7	0 18.8	0 21.6	0 48.4	15 38.9

RIGHT ASCENSION

DAY	SID. TIME	☉	☊	☽	☿	♀	♂	♃	♄	♅	♆	♇
1	12 35 25.6	9♈54.0	26♑16.5	27♎ 5.9	25♈ 3.6	13♉ 4.6	28♊49.1	6♌ 3.3	7♒35.0	14♑54.3	17♑58.8	21♏39.9
2	12 39 22.2	10 48.6	26 13.1	9♏39.1	25 24.1	14 15.5	29 24.0	6D 3.7	7 39.3	14 55.2	17 59.4	21R38.9
3	12 43 18.7	11 43.3	26 9.8	22 31.3	25 38.1	15 26.6	29 59.0	6 4.3	7 43.5	14 56.1	17 60.0	21 37.8
4	12 47 15.3	12 38.0	26 6.4	5♐38.1	25 45.7	16 38.0	0♋34.2	6 5.0	7 47.7	14 56.9	18 .5	21 36.7
5	12 51 11.8	13 32.8	26 3.0	18 51.1	25 47.0	17 49.6	1 9.4	6 6.0	7 51.7	14 57.7	18 1.0	21 35.6
6	12 55 8.4	14 27.5	25 59.7	1♑59.4	25R42.3	19 1.4	1 44.8	6 7.2	7 55.7	14 58.4	18 1.5	21 34.4
7	12 59 4.9	15 22.4	25 56.3	14 53.2	25 31.8	20 13.4	2 20.2	6 8.5	7 59.6	14 59.0	18 1.9	21 33.3
8	13 3 1.5	16 17.3	25 53.0	27 26.7	25 16.1	21 25.7	2 55.8	6 10.1	8 3.5	14 59.7	18 2.3	21 32.1
9	13 6 58.1	17 12.3	25 49.6	9♒38.8	24 55.4	22 38.2	3 31.4	6 11.8	8 7.2	15 .2	18 2.7	21 30.9
10	13 10 54.6	18 7.3	25 46.3	21 33.9	24 30.4	23 50.9	4 7.1	6 13.8	8 10.8	15 .7	18 3.0	21 29.7
11	13 14 51.2	19 2.4	25 42.9	3♓20.1	24 1.8	25 3.8	4 42.9	6 15.9	8 14.4	15 1.1	18 3.3	21 28.5
12	13 18 47.7	19 57.6	25 39.5	15 8.8	23 30.0	26 16.9	5 18.7	6 18.2	8 17.9	15 1.5	18 3.6	21 27.2
13	13 22 44.3	20 52.8	25 36.2	27 13.6	22 56.0	27 30.2	5 54.7	6 20.7	8 21.2	15 1.8	18 3.8	21 25.9
14	13 26 40.8	21 48.1	25 32.8	9♈48.9	22 20.4	28 43.7	6 30.7	6 23.4	8 24.5	15 2.1	18 4.0	21 24.6
15	13 30 37.4	22 43.5	25 29.4	23 8.6	21 44.0	29 57.4	7 6.8	6 26.2	8 27.7	15 2.3	18 4.1	21 23.3
16	13 34 33.9	23 39.0	25 26.1	7♉22.4	21 7.6	1♊11.3	7 42.9	6 29.3	8 30.8	15 2.5	18 4.2	21 21.9
17	13 38 30.5	24 34.6	25 22.7	22 31.2	20 31.8	2 25.4	8 19.2	6 32.5	8 33.8	15 2.6	18 4.3	21 20.6
18	13 42 27.0	25 30.3	25 19.4	8♊22.0	19 57.4	3 39.6	8 55.5	6 35.9	8 36.8	15 2.6	18 4.3	21 19.2
19	13 46 23.6	26 26.0	25 16.0	24 28.1	19 24.9	4 54.0	9 31.8	6 39.5	8 39.6	15 2.6	18 4.3	21 17.8
20	13 50 20.1	27 21.9	25 12.6	10♋17.0	18 54.9	6 8.6	10 8.2	6 43.3	8 42.3	15R 2.5	18 4.3	21 16.4
21	13 54 16.7	28 17.8	25 9.3	25 22.5	18 27.9	7 23.3	10 44.6	6 47.3	8 45.0	15 2.4	18R 4.2	21 15.0
22	13 58 13.3	29 13.9	25 5.9	9♌32.7	18 4.4	8 38.1	11 21.1	6 51.4	8 47.5	15 2.2	18 4.1	21 13.6
23	14 2 9.8	0♉10.1	25 2.5	22 49.3	17 44.5	9 53.0	11 57.7	6 55.7	8 50.0	15 2.0	18 4.0	21 12.1
24	14 6 6.4	1 6.3	24 59.2	5♍22.9	17 28.6	11 8.0	12 34.2	7 .2	8 52.3	15 1.7	18 3.8	21 10.7
25	14 10 2.9	2 2.7	24 55.8	17 27.9	17 16.9	12 23.1	13 10.9	7 4.8	8 54.6	15 1.4	18 3.6	21 9.2
26	14 13 59.5	2 59.2	24 52.4	29 19.4	17 9.3	13 38.3	13 47.5	7 9.6	8 56.8	15 1.0	18 3.4	21 7.7
27	14 17 56.0	3 55.8	24 49.1	11♎11.3	17 6.2	14 53.5	14 24.2	7 14.6	8 58.8	15 .6	18 3.1	21 6.2
28	14 21 52.6	4 52.6	24 45.7	23 14.8	17D 7.3	16 8.8	15 .9	7 19.7	9 .8	15 .1	18 2.8	21 4.7
29	14 25 49.1	5 49.5	24 42.3	5♏37.8	17 12.8	17 24.2	15 37.7	7 25.0	9 2.8	14 59.6	18 2.5	21 3.3
30	14 29 45.7	6 46.5	24 39.0	18 22.7	17 22.4	18 39.5	16 14.4	7 30.5	9 4.5	14 59.0	18 2.2	21 1.8

DECLINATION

DAY	SID. TIME	☉	☊	☽	☿	♀	♂	♃	♄	♅	♆	♇
1	12 35 25.6	4N15.8	0S22.2	16S30.4	13N40.7	17N15.6	25N22.2	20N 7.4	19S14.2	23S 5.0	21S36.5	2S42.5
4	12 47 15.3	5 25.0	0 22.3	25 14.6	14 8.6	18 25.5	25 21.0	20 6.8	19 11.5	23 4.8	21 36.2	2 40.8
7	12 59 4.9	6 33.4	0 22.3	23 39.9	14 1.9	19 31.3	25 18.7	20 5.9	19 9.0	23 4.7	21 36.0	2 39.1
10	13 10 54.6	7 40.9	0 22.3	12 46.4	13 22.2	20 32.8	25 15.1	20 4.6	19 6.6	23 4.6	21 35.8	2 37.4
13	13 22 44.3	8 47.1	0 22.4	3N45.6	12 14.7	21 29.6	25 10.3	20 2.9	19 4.5	23 4.6	21 35.7	2 35.7
16	13 34 33.9	9 52.1	0 22.4	19 45.8	10 48.8	22 21.5	25 4.2	20 .8	19 2.5	23 4.6	21 35.6	2 34.1
19	13 46 23.6	10 55.5	0 22.4	25 41.8	9 16.3	23 8.1	24 56.9	19 58.3	19 .7	23 4.7	21 35.5	2 32.5
22	13 58 13.3	11 57.3	0 22.4	17 9.5	7 49.4	23 49.4	24 48.3	19 55.4	18 59.1	23 4.8	21 35.5	2 30.9
25	14 10 2.9	12 57.4	0 22.5	0 52.3	6 37.5	24 25.0	24 38.5	19 52.1	18 57.7	23 5.0	21 35.5	2 29.4
28	14 21 52.6	13 55.5	0 22.5	15S 4.9	5 46.4	24 54.8	24 27.3	19 48.5	18 56.5	23 5.2	21 35.5	2 28.0

MAY 1991

LONGITUDE

DAY	EPHEM. SID. TIME h m s	☉ ° ′	☊ ° ′	☽ ° ′	☿ ° ′	♀ ° ′	♂ ° ′	♃ ° ′	♄ ° ′	♅ ° ′	♆ ° ′	♇ ° ′
1	14 33 42.2	10♉ 8.3	22♑46.7	4♐10.9	18♈15.4	20♊53.1	15♋20.1	5♌ 3.3	6♒37.8	13♑44.9	16♑43.6	19♏14.4
2	14 37 38.8	11 6.5	22 43.5	16 11.3	18 30.3	22 1.5	15 54.0	5 8.9	6 39.3	13 R 44.2	16 R 43.2	19 R 12.7
3	14 41 35.4	12 4.7	22 40.4	28 4.0	18 49.7	23 9.8	16 27.9	5 14.6	6 40.7	13 43.5	16 42.8	19 11.0
4	14 45 31.9	13 2.9	22 37.2	9♑52.2	19 13.7	24 17.9	17 1.9	5 20.6	6 42.1	13 42.8	16 42.3	19 9.4
5	14 49 28.5	14 1.1	22 34.0	21 40.1	19 41.9	25 25.8	17 35.9	5 26.6	6 43.3	13 42.0	16 41.8	19 7.7
6	14 53 25.0	14 59.2	22 30.8	3♒32.7	20 14.2	26 33.7	18 10.0	5 32.8	6 44.4	13 41.1	16 41.2	19 6.0
7	14 57 21.6	15 57.3	22 27.7	15 35.0	20 50.6	27 41.3	18 44.2	5 39.2	6 45.5	13 40.2	16 40.7	19 4.3
8	15 1 18.1	16		22 24.5	27 52.5	21 30.8	19 18.3	5 45.7	6 46.4	13 39.3	16 40.1	19 2.7
9	15 5 14.7	17 53.4	22 21.3	10♓30.3	22 14.7	29 56.2	19 52.6	5 52.3	6 47.3	13 38.3	16 39.5	19 1.0
10	15 9 11.2	18 51.4	22 18.1	23 32.5	23 2.2	1♋ 3.4	20 26.9	5 59.1	6 48.0	13 37.3	16 38.8	18 59.3
11	15 13 7.8	19 49.4	22 14.9	7♈ 1.9	23 53.1	2 10.4	21 1.3	6 6.0	6 48.7	13 36.2	16 38.1	18 57.6
12	15 17 4.4	20 47.4	22 11.8	20 58.9	24 47.3	3 17.2	21 35.7	6 13.0	6 49.2	13 35.1	16 37.4	18 55.9
13	15 21 .9	21 45.4	22 8.6	5♉21.0	25 44.7	4 23.9	22 10.1	6 20.2	6 49.7	13 33.9	16 36.7	18 54.2
14	15 24 57.5	22 43.3	22 5.4	20 3.0	26 45.1	5 30.4	22 44.6	6 27.5	6 50.0	13 32.7	16 35.9	18 52.5
15	15 28 54.0	23 41.2	22 2.2	4♊57.2	27 48.5	6 36.7	23 19.2	6 35.0	6 50.3	13 31.4	16 35.1	18 50.9
16	15 32 50.6	24 39.1	21 59.1	19 54.8	28 54.8	7 42.9	23 53.8	6 42.5	6 50.4	13 30.1	16 34.3	18 49.2
17	15 36 47.1	25 37.0	21 55.9	4♋47.4	0♉ 3.9	8 48.8	24 28.5	6 50.3	6 50.5	13 28.8	16 33.4	18 47.5
18	15 40 43.7	26 34.8	21 52.7	19 27.8	1 15.7	9 54.5	25 3.2	6 58.1	6 R 50.4	13 27.4	16 32.5	18 45.9
19	15 44 40.3	27 32.6	21 49.5	3♌51.5	2 30.1	11 .1	25 37.9	7 6.1	6 50.3	13 26.0	16 31.6	18 44.2
20	15 48 36.8	28 30.4	21 46.4	17 56.3	3 47.2	12 5.4	26 12.7	7 14.2	6 50.1	13 24.6	16 30.8	18 42.6
21	15 52 33.4	29 28.2	21 43.2	1♍41.5	5 6.8	13 10.5	26 47.6	7 22.4	6 49.8	13 23.1	16 29.8	18 40.9
22	15 56 29.9	0♊25.9	21 40.0	15 8.1	6 28.9	14 15.4	27 22.4	7 30.7	6 49.3	13 21.6	16 28.8	18 39.3
23	16 0 26.5	1 23.6	21 36.8	28 17.8	7 53.4	15 20.1	27 57.4	7 39.1	6 48.8	13 20.0	16 27.8	18 37.7
24	16 4 23.0	2 21.3	21 33.6	11♎12.3	9 20.4	16 24.5	28 32.3	7 47.7	6 48.2	13 18.4	16 26.8	18 36.0
25	16 8 19.6	3 18.9	21 30.5	23 53.3	10 49.8	17 28.6	29 7.3	7 56.4	6 47.4	13 16.7	16 25.7	18 34.4
26	16 12 16.2	4 16.5	21 27.3	6♏22.3	12 21.6	18 32.5	29 42.4	8 5.1	6 46.6	13 15.1	16 24.6	18 32.8
27	16 16 12.7	5 14.1	21 24.1	18 40.6	13 55.7	19 36.2	0♌17.4	8 14.0	6 45.7	13 13.3	16 23.5	18 31.2
28	16 20 9.3	6 11.7	21 20.9	0♐49.3	15 32.3	20 39.6	0 52.5	8 23.0	6 44.7	13 11.6	16 22.4	18 29.6
29	16 24 5.8	7 9.3	21 17.8	12 49.8	17 11.2	21 42.7	1 27.7	8 32.1	6 43.6	13 9.8	16 21.3	18 28.1
30	16 28 2.4	8 6.8	21 14.6	24 43.7	18 52.5	22 45.5	2 2.9	8 41.3	6 42.4	13 8.0	16 20.1	18 26.5
31	16 31 58.9	9 4.3	21 11.4	6♑32.9	20 36.1	23 48.1	2 38.1	8 50.6	6 41.1	13 6.1	16 18.9	18 25.0

LATITUDE

DAY	EPHEM. SID. TIME	☉	☊	☽	☿	♀	♂	♃	♄	♅	♆	♇
1	14 33 42.2	0 .0	0 .0	3S42.4	2S .1	2N11.4	1N41.9	0N45.6	0S19.1	0S21.6	0N48.4	15N39.0
4	14 45 31.9	0 .0	0 .0	1 .1	2 29.5	2 17.7	1 40.5	0 45.4	0 19.4	0 21.7	0 48.5	15 39.1
7	14 57 21.6	0 .0	0 .0	2N 6.4	2 51.2	2 23.4	1 39.1	0 45.3	0 19.8	0 21.8	0 48.5	15 39.1
10	15 9 11.2	0 .0	0 .0	4 30.6	3 5.6	2 28.3	1 37.7	0 45.2	0 20.1	0 21.9	0 48.6	15 39.0
13	15 21 .9	0 .0	0 .0	4 54.9	3 13.0	2 32.4	1 36.3	0 45.0	0 20.5	0 21.9	0 48.6	15 38.8
16	15 32 50.6	0 .0	0 .0	2 35.3	3 13.9	2 35.6	1 34.9	0 44.9	0 20.8	0 22.0	0 48.7	15 38.5
19	15 44 40.3	0 .0	0 .0	1S12.6	3 8.8	2 37.8	1 33.5	0 44.8	0 21.2	0 22.1	0 48.7	15 38.1
22	15 56 29.9	0 .0	0 .0	4 12.2	2 58.0	2 39.1	1 32.1	0 44.7	0 21.5	0 22.1	0 48.7	15 37.7
25	16 8 19.6	0 .0	0 .0	5 7.1	2 42.1	2 39.3	1 30.7	0 44.6	0 21.9	0 22.2	0 48.7	15 37.1
28	16 20 9.3	0 .0	0 .0	3 52.5	2 21.3	2 38.4	1 29.3	0 44.5	0 22.2	0 22.3	0 48.8	15 36.5
31	16 31 58.9	0 .0	0 .0	1 9.2	1 56.4	2 36.3	1 27.9	0 44.5	0 22.6	0 22.3	0 48.8	15 35.8

RIGHT ASCENSION

DAY	EPHEM. SID. TIME	☉	☊	☽	☿	♀	♂	♃	♄	♅	♆	♇
1	14 33 42.2	7♉43.6	24♑35.6	1♐26.4	17♈36.3	19♊54.9	16♋51.2	7♌36.1	9♒ 6.2	14♑58.3	18♑ 1.7	21♏ .2
2	14 37 38.8	8 40.9	24 32.2	14 40.1	17 54.1	21 10.2	17 28.0	7 41.9	9 7.8	14 R 57.6	18 R 1.3	20 R 58.7
3	14 41 35.4	9 38.3	24 28.9	27 51.6	18 15.9	22 25.5	18 4.8	7 47.8	9 9.3	14 56.8	18 .8	20 57.2
4	14 45 31.9	10 35.8	24 25.5	10♑49.2	18 41.5	23 40.8	18 41.7	7 53.9	9 10.7	14 56.0	18 .3	20 55.6
5	14 49 28.5	11 33.5	24 22.1	23 24.5	19 10.8	24 55.9	19 18.5	8 .1	9 12.0	14 55.2	17 59.8	20 54.0
6	14 53 25.0	12 31.3	24 18.8	5♒35.1	19 43.6	26 11.1	19 55.4	8 6.5	9 13.2	14 54.2	17 59.2	20 52.5
7	14 57 21.6	13 29.3	24 15.4	17 24.2	20 19.9	27 26.1	20 32.3	8 13.0	9 14.3	14 53.3	17 58.6	20 50.9
8	15 1 18.1	14 27.4	24 12.0	28 59.4	20 59.4	28 41.0	21 9.2	8 19.6	9 15.3	14 52.3	17 58.0	20 49.3
9	15 5 14.7	15 25.6	24 8.6	10♓32.5	21 42.1	29 55.7	21 46.1	8 26.5	9 16.2	14 51.2	17 57.3	20 47.8
10	15 9 11.2	16 24.0	24 5.3	22 17.3	22 27.9	1♋10.4	22 23.0	8 33.4	9 17.0	14 50.1	17 56.6	20 46.2
11	15 13 7.8	17 22.6	24 1.9	4♈29.6	23 16.6	2 24.8	22 59.9	8 40.5	9 17.7	14 48.9	17 55.9	20 44.6
12	15 17 4.4	18 21.3	23 58.5	17 25.8	24 8.2	3 39.1	23 36.8	8 47.7	9 18.2	14 47.7	17 55.1	20 43.0
13	15 21 .9	19 20.1	23 55.2	1♉20.1	25 2.7	4 53.2	24 13.7	8 55.1	9 18.7	14 46.5	17 54.3	20 41.4
14	15 24 57.5	20 19.1	23 51.8	16 19.5	25 59.8	6 7.0	24 50.6	9 2.6	9 19.1	14 45.2	17 53.5	20 39.9
15	15 28 54.0	21 18.3	23 48.4	2♊17.2	26 59.5	7 20.6	25 27.5	9 10.2	9 19.4	14 43.8	17 52.6	20 38.3
16	15 32 50.6	22 17.5	23 45.0	18 48.6	28 1.9	8 34.0	26 4.4	9 18.0	9 19.6	14 42.4	17 51.8	20 36.7
17	15 36 47.1	23 17.0	23 41.7	5♋16.3	29 6.8	9 47.0	26 41.3	9 25.9	9 19.7	14 41.0	17 50.9	20 35.1
18	15 40 43.7	24 16.5	23 38.3	21 4.6	0♉14.2	10 59.8	27 18.2	9 33.9	9 19.7	14 39.5	17 49.9	20 33.5
19	15 44 40.3	25 16.2	23 34.9	5♌52.7	1 24.2	12 12.2	27 55.1	9 42.0	9 R 19.6	14 37.9	17 48.9	20 31.9
20	15 48 36.8	26 16.1	23 31.5	19 37.6	2 36.6	13 24.4	28 32.0	9 50.4	9 19.4	14 36.4	17 48.0	20 30.4
21	15 52 33.4	27 16.0	23 28.2	2♍28.7	3 51.5	14 36.1	29 8.9	9 58.7	9 19.1	14 34.8	17 47.0	20 28.8
22	15 56 29.9	28 16.1	23 24.8	14 41.3	5 8.9	15 47.5	29 45.7	10 7.2	9 18.7	14 33.2	17 45.9	20 27.3
23	16 0 26.5	29 16.3	23 21.4	26 32.4	6 28.8	16 58.5	0♌22.6	10 15.9	9 18.2	14 31.5	17 44.8	20 25.7
24	16 4 23.0	0♊16.6	23 18.0	8♎17.6	7 51.2	18 9.0	0 59.4	10 24.6	9 17.6	14 29.7	17 43.7	20 24.1
25	16 8 19.6	1 17.1	23 14.7	20 10.3	9 16.1	19 19.2	1 36.2	10 33.4	9 16.9	14 27.9	17 42.6	20 22.6
26	16 12 16.2	2 17.7	23 11.3	2♏20.4	10 43.6	20 28.8	2 12.9	10 42.4	9 16.1	14 26.1	17 41.5	20 21.0
27	16 16 12.7	3 18.4	23 7.9	14 53.2	12 13.8	21 38.1	2 49.6	10 51.5	9 15.1	14 24.3	17 40.3	20 19.5
28	16 20 9.3	4 19.2	23 4.5	27 47.9	13 46.7	22 46.8	3 26.4	11 .6	9 14.1	14 22.4	17 39.1	20 18.0
29	16 24 5.8	5 20.1	23 1.1	10♐57.3	15 22.3	23 55.1	4 3.0	11 9.9	9 13.1	14 20.4	17 37.9	20 16.5
30	16 28 2.4	6 21.2	22 57.8	24 9.7	17 .7	25 2.8	4 39.7	11 19.3	9 11.9	14 18.5	17 36.6	20 14.9
31	16 31 58.9	7 22.3	22 54.4	7♑11.6	18 41.9	26 10.0	5 16.3	11 28.8	9 10.6	14 16.5	17 35.3	20 13.4

DECLINATION

DAY	EPHEM. SID. TIME	☉	☊	☽	☿	♀	♂	♃	♄	♅	♆	♇
1	14 33 42.2	14N51.6	0S22.5	24S37.5	5N18.4	25N18.8	24N14.8	19N44.5	18S55.5	23S 5.4	21S35.6	2S26.6
4	14 45 31.9	15 45.4	0 22.6	24 4.4	5 13.3	25 36.7	24 1.1	19 40.2	18 54.8	23 5.7	21 35.7	2 25.3
7	14 57 21.6	16 36.9	0 22.6	14 9.2	5 29.5	25 48.6	23 46.0	19 35.5	18 54.3	23 6.0	21 35.9	2 24.1
10	15 9 11.2	17 26.0	0 22.6	1N34.7	6 4.9	25 54.5	23 29.7	19 30.4	18 53.9	23 6.4	21 36.0	2 22.9
13	15 21 .9	18 12.4	0 22.6	17 56.1	6 57.1	25 54.4	23 12.0	19 25.1	18 53.9	23 6.8	21 36.3	2 21.8
16	15 32 50.6	18 56.0	0 22.7	25 38.3	8 3.9	25 48.3	22 53.1	19 19.3	18 54.0	23 7.3	21 36.5	2 20.8
19	15 44 40.3	19 36.8	0 22.7	18 6.8	9 23.1	25 36.4	22 32.9	19 13.3	18 54.4	23 7.8	21 36.8	2 19.9
22	15 56 29.9	20 14.6	0 22.7	1 58.7	10 52.7	25 18.9	22 11.5	19 6.9	18 55.0	23 8.3	21 37.1	2 19.1
25	16 8 19.6	20 49.2	0 22.7	14S 1.4	12 30.5	24 55.9	21 48.8	19 .2	18 55.8	23 8.8	21 37.5	2 18.4
28	16 20 9.3	21 20.6	0 22.8	24 6.8	14 14.4	24 27.7	21 25.0	18 53.2	18 56.8	23 9.4	21 37.8	2 17.8
31	16 31 58.9	21 48.7	0 22.8	24 25.9	16 1.9	23 54.6	20 59.9	18 45.9	18 58.0	23 10.0	21 38.2	2 17.3

JUNE 1991

LONGITUDE

DAY	EPHEM. SID. TIME	☉	☊	☽	☿	♀	♂	♃	♄	♅	♆	♇
	h m s	° ′	° ′	° ′	° ′	° ′	° ′	° ′	° ′	° ′	° ′	° ′
1	16 35 55.5	10♊ 1.8	21♑ 8.2	18♑20.1	22♉22.1	24♋50.3	3♌13.4	9♌ .0	6♒39.8	13♑ 4.3	16♑17.7	18♏23.4
2	16 39 52.1	10 59.3	21 5.1	0♒ 8.6	24 10.4	25 52.3	3 48.7	9 9.6	6R38.3	13R 2.4	16R16.5	18R21.9
3	16 43 48.6	11 56.8	21 1.9	12 2.2	26 1.0	26 53.9	4 24.0	9 19.2	6 36.7	13 .4	16 15.2	18 20.4
4	16 47 45.2	12 54.3	20 58.7	24 5.1	27 53.9	27 55.3	4 59.4	9 28.9	6 35.1	12 58.4	16 13.9	18 18.9
5	16 51 41.7	13 51.7	20 55.5	6♓22.2	29 49.1	28 56.3	5 34.8	9 38.7	6 33.3	12 56.4	16 12.6	18 17.4
6	16 55 38.3	14 49.1	20 52.3	18 58.2	1♊46.4	29 57.0	6 10.3	9 48.6	6 31.5	12 54.4	16 11.3	18 16.0
7	16 59 34.8	15 46.6	20 49.2	1♈57.3	3 45.9	0♌57.3	6 45.8	9 58.6	6 29.6	12 52.4	16 10.0	18 14.5
8	17 3 31.4	16 44.0	20 46.0	15 22.9	5 47.5	1 57.3	7 21.3	10 8.7	6 27.6	12 50.3	16 8.6	18 13.1
9	17 7 28.0	17 41.4	20 42.8	29 16.6	7 50.9	2 56.9	7 56.9	10 18.8	6 25.5	12 48.2	16 7.3	18 11.7
10	17 11 24.5	18 38.8	20 39.6	13♉37.7	9 56.3	3 56.2	8 32.6	10 29.1	6 23.3	12 46.1	16 5.9	18 10.3
11	17 15 21.1	19 36.2	20 36.5	28 22.1	12 3.1	4 55.1	9 8.2	10 39.5	6 21.0	12 43.9	16 4.5	18 9.0
12	17 19 17.6	20 33.6	20 33.3	13♊23.6	14 11.5	5 53.6	9 43.9	10 49.9	6 18.7	12 41.8	16 3.1	18 7.6
13	17 23 14.2	21 31.0	20 30.1	28 33.1	16 21.0	6 51.6	10 19.6	11 .5	6 16.3	12 39.6	16 1.7	18 6.3
14	17 27 10.8	22 28.3	20 26.9	13♋41.2	18 31.6	7 49.3	10 55.4	11 11.1	6 13.7	12 37.3	16 .3	18 5.0
15	17 31 7.3	23 25.7	20 23.8	28 38.9	20 42.9	8 46.4	11 31.2	11 21.8	6 11.1	12 35.1	15 58.8	18 3.7
16	17 35 3.9	24 23.0	20 20.6	13♌19.0	22 54.6	9 43.2	12 7.0	11 32.5	6 8.5	12 32.8	15 57.3	18 2.4
17	17 39 .4	25 20.3	20 17.4	27 37.1	25 6.5	10 39.5	12 42.9	11 43.4	6 5.7	12 30.6	15 55.8	18 1.2
18	17 42 57.0	26 17.6	20 14.2	11♍31.0	27 18.4	11 35.2	13 18.8	11 54.3	6 2.9	12 28.3	15 54.3	17 59.9
19	17 46 53.5	27 14.9	20 11.1	25 1.0	29 29.9	12 30.5	13 54.8	12 5.3	5 60.0	12 26.0	15 52.8	17 58.7
20	17 50 50.1	28 12.2	20 7.9	8♎ 8.6	1♋40.8	13 25.2	14 30.8	12 16.3	5 57.0	12 23.6	15 51.3	17 57.6
21	17 54 46.7	29 9.4	20 4.7	20 56.4	3 50.8	14 19.4	15 6.8	12 27.5	5 53.9	12 21.3	15 49.8	17 56.4
22	17 58 43.2	0♋ 6.7	20 1.5	3♏27.4	5 59.7	15 13.0	15 42.8	12 38.7	5 50.8	12 19.0	15 48.2	17 55.3
23	18 2 39.8	1 3.9	19 58.4	15 44.8	8 7.3	16 6.0	16 18.9	12 50.0	5 47.6	12 16.6	15 46.7	17 54.2
24	18 6 36.3	2 1.1	19 55.2	27 51.3	10 13.5	16 58.5	16 55.0	13 1.3	5 44.3	12 14.2	15 45.1	17 53.1
25	18 10 32.9	2 58.3	19 52.0	9♐49.6	12 18.1	17 50.3	17 31.1	13 12.7	5 41.0	12 11.8	15 43.5	17 52.0
26	18 14 29.5	3 55.5	19 48.8	21 42.2	14 21.0	18 41.4	18 7.3	13 24.2	5 37.6	12 9.5	15 42.0	17 51.0
27	18 18 26.0	4 52.8	19 45.6	3♑31.4	16 22.0	19 31.8	18 43.5	13 35.7	5 34.2	12 7.1	15 40.4	17 50.0
28	18 22 22.6	5 50.0	19 42.5	15 19.2	18 21.2	20 21.6	19 19.7	13 47.3	5 30.6	12 4.7	15 38.8	17 49.0
29	18 26 19.1	6 47.1	19 39.3	27 8.1	20 18.4	21 10.6	19 56.0	13 59.0	5 27.1	12 2.2	15 37.2	17 48.1
30	18 30 15.7	7 44.3	19 36.1	9♒ .4	22 13.6	21 58.9	20 32.3	14 10.7	5 23.4	11 59.8	15 35.6	17 47.1

LATITUDE

DAY	EPHEM. SID. TIME	☉	☊	☽	☿	♀	♂	♃	♄	♅	♆	♇
1	16 35 55.5	0 .0	0 .0	0S 5.6	1S47.2	2N35.3	1N27.4	0N44.4	0S22.7	0S22.4	0N48.8	15N35.5
4	16 47 45.2	0 .0	0 .0	2N58.2	1 17.7	2 31.5	1 26.0	0 44.4	0 23.0	0 22.4	0 48.8	15 34.7
7	16 59 34.8	0 .0	0 .0	4 58.5	0 45.9	2 26.4	1 24.6	0 44.3	0 23.4	0 22.5	0 48.8	15 33.9
10	17 11 24.5	0 .0	0 .0	4 45.2	0 13.1	2 19.9	1 23.2	0 44.3	0 23.7	0 22.5	0 48.8	15 32.9
13	17 23 14.2	0 .0	0 .0	1 50.4	0N19.1	2 11.9	1 21.8	0 44.2	0 24.1	0 22.6	0 48.9	15 31.9
16	17 35 3.9	0 .0	0 .0	2S 9.6	0 48.8	2 2.4	1 20.3	0 44.2	0 24.4	0 22.6	0 48.9	15 30.8
19	17 46 53.5	0 .0	0 .0	4 48.0	1 14.2	1 51.3	1 18.9	0 44.1	0 24.8	0 22.7	0 48.9	15 29.6
22	17 58 43.2	0 .0	0 .0	5 5.6	1 34.0	1 38.6	1 17.5	0 44.1	0 25.1	0 22.7	0 48.9	15 28.4
25	18 10 32.9	0 .0	0 .0	3 19.7	1 47.4	1 24.1	1 16.1	0 44.1	0 25.4	0 22.7	0 48.8	15 27.1
28	18 22 22.6	0 .0	0 .0	0 19.8	1 54.0	1 7.9	1 14.7	0 44.1	0 25.8	0 22.8	0 48.8	15 25.8

RIGHT ASCENSION

DAY	EPHEM. SID. TIME	☉	☊	☽	☿	♀	♂	♃	♄	♅	♆	♇
1	16 35 55.5	8♊23.6	22♑51.0	19♑52.5	20♉26.1	27♋16.7	5♌52.9	11♌38.3	9♒ 9.2	14♑14.4	17♑34.0	20♏11.9
2	16 39 52.1	9 25.0	22 47.6	2♒ 6.7	22 13.2	28 22.9	6 29.5	11 48.0	9R 7.7	14R12.4	17R32.7	20R10.5
3	16 43 48.6	10 26.5	22 44.3	13 55.1	24 3.4	29 28.4	7 6.0	11 57.8	9 6.2	14 10.3	17 31.4	20 9.0
4	16 47 45.2	11 28.0	22 40.9	25 23.7	25 56.6	0♌33.5	7 42.6	12 7.7	9 4.5	14 8.1	17 30.0	20 7.5
5	16 51 41.7	12 29.7	22 37.5	6♓43.0	27 52.9	1 37.9	8 19.1	12 17.6	9 2.7	14 6.0	17 28.6	20 6.1
6	16 55 38.3	13 31.5	22 34.1	18 6.1	29 52.3	2 41.7	8 55.5	12 27.7	9 .9	14 3.8	17 27.2	20 4.6
7	16 59 34.8	14 33.3	22 30.7	29 48.6	1♊54.7	3 44.9	9 31.9	12 37.8	8 59.0	14 1.6	17 25.8	20 3.2
8	17 3 31.4	15 35.2	22 27.3	12♈ 7.6	4 .1	4 47.5	10 8.3	12 48.0	8 56.9	13 59.3	17 24.4	20 1.8
9	17 7 28.0	16 37.3	22 24.0	25 20.0	6 8.5	5 49.5	10 44.7	12 58.4	8 54.8	13 57.0	17 22.9	20 .4
10	17 11 24.5	17 39.4	22 20.6	9♉39.2	8 19.8	6 50.8	11 21.1	13 8.8	8 52.6	13 54.8	17 21.5	19 59.1
11	17 15 21.1	18 41.5	22 17.2	25 8.6	10 33.6	7 51.5	11 57.4	13 19.3	8 50.4	13 52.5	17 20.0	19 57.7
12	17 19 17.6	19 43.7	22 13.8	11♊34.5	12 49.9	8 51.5	12 33.7	13 29.9	8 48.0	13 50.1	17 18.5	19 56.4
13	17 23 14.2	20 45.9	22 10.4	28 24.0	15 8.4	9 50.8	13 9.9	13 40.5	8 45.5	13 47.7	17 16.9	19 55.0
14	17 27 10.8	21 48.2	22 7.0	14♋55.2	17 28.8	10 49.4	13 46.1	13 51.2	8 42.9	13 45.3	17 15.4	19 53.7
15	17 31 7.3	22 50.6	22 3.7	0♌35.0	19 50.7	11 47.3	14 22.3	14 2.0	8 40.3	13 42.9	17 13.8	19 52.4
16	17 35 3.9	23 52.9	22 .3	15 8.8	22 13.9	12 44.4	14 58.5	14 12.9	8 37.6	13 40.4	17 12.3	19 51.1
17	17 39 .4	24 55.3	21 56.9	28 40.0	24 38.0	13 40.9	15 34.6	14 23.9	8 34.8	13 38.0	17 10.7	19 49.9
18	17 42 57.0	25 57.7	21 53.5	11♍21.8	27 2.4	14 36.5	16 10.6	14 34.9	8 31.9	13 35.5	17 9.1	19 48.6
19	17 46 53.5	27 .1	21 50.1	23 31.3	29 26.9	15 31.4	16 46.7	14 46.0	8 29.0	13 33.0	17 7.5	19 47.4
20	17 50 50.1	28 2.5	21 46.7	5♎25.5	1♋51.0	16 25.5	17 22.7	14 57.1	8 25.9	13 30.5	17 5.8	19 46.2
21	17 54 46.7	29 4.9	21 43.3	17 19.4	4 14.3	17 18.8	17 58.6	15 8.4	8 22.8	13 28.0	17 4.2	19 45.0
22	17 58 43.2	0♋ 7.3	21 40.0	29 24.8	6 36.5	18 11.3	18 34.5	15 19.6	8 19.7	13 25.4	17 2.5	19 43.9
23	18 2 39.8	1 9.6	21 36.6	11♏49.4	8 57.2	19 2.9	19 10.4	15 31.0	8 16.4	13 22.9	17 .9	19 42.7
24	18 6 36.3	2 12.0	21 33.2	24 35.1	11 16.1	19 53.7	19 46.3	15 42.4	8 13.1	13 20.3	16 59.2	19 41.6
25	18 10 32.9	3 14.4	21 29.8	7♐38.0	13 33.1	20 43.7	20 22.1	15 53.9	8 9.7	13 17.7	16 57.5	19 40.5
26	18 14 29.5	4 16.7	21 26.4	20 48.1	15 47.8	21 32.7	20 57.9	16 5.4	8 6.2	13 15.1	16 55.9	19 39.4
27	18 18 26.0	5 18.9	21 23.0	3♑52.8	18 .0	22 20.9	21 33.6	16 17.0	8 2.7	13 12.5	16 54.2	19 38.4
28	18 22 22.6	6 21.2	21 19.6	16 39.9	20 9.7	23 8.1	22 9.3	16 28.6	7 59.1	13 9.9	16 52.5	19 37.4
29	18 26 19.1	7 23.4	21 16.2	29 1.8	22 16.6	23 54.4	22 44.9	16 40.3	7 55.5	13 7.3	16 50.8	19 36.4
30	18 30 15.7	8 25.5	21 12.8	10♒56.4	24 20.7	24 39.7	23 20.6	16 52.1	7 51.8	13 4.7	16 49.0	19 35.4

DECLINATION

DAY	EPHEM. SID. TIME	☉	☊	☽	☿	♀	♂	♃	♄	♅	♆	♇
1	16 35 55.5	21N57.4	0S22.8	22S16.7	16N38.1	23N42.5	20N51.3	18N43.3	18S58.5	23S10.2	21S38.4	2S17.1
4	16 47 45.2	22 20.9	0 22.8	10 41.4	18 25.8	23 3.2	20 24.7	18 35.6	19 .0	23 10.8	21 38.8	2 16.8
7	16 59 34.8	22 40.9	0 22.9	5N20.5	20 9.2	22 19.6	19 56.9	18 27.6	19 1.7	23 11.5	21 39.3	2 16.5
10	17 11 24.5	22 57.4	0 22.9	20 27.6	21 43.5	21 32.2	19 28.0	18 19.3	19 3.6	23 12.1	21 39.7	2 16.3
13	17 23 14.2	23 10.2	0 22.9	25 16.4	23 3.4	20 41.2	18 58.0	18 10.7	19 5.7	23 12.8	21 40.2	2 16.3
16	17 35 3.9	23 19.3	0 22.9	14 45.1	24 3.8	19 47.0	18 26.9	18 1.8	19 8.0	23 13.5	21 40.7	2 16.3
19	17 46 53.5	23 24.8	0 23.0	2S25.6	24 40.6	18 50.0	17 54.7	17 52.6	19 10.4	23 14.1	21 41.3	2 16.5
22	17 58 43.2	23 26.5	0 23.0	17 27.1	24 52.2	17 50.6	17 21.6	17 43.2	19 13.0	23 14.8	21 41.8	2 16.8
25	18 10 32.9	23 24.5	0 23.0	25 13.0	24 39.2	16 49.3	16 47.5	17 33.5	19 15.8	23 15.5	21 42.4	2 17.2
28	18 22 22.6	23 18.8	0 23.0	22 53.3	24 4.0	15 46.5	16 12.5	17 23.6	19 18.6	23 16.2	21 42.9	2 17.7

JULY 1991

LONGITUDE

DAY	EPHEM. SID. TIME (h m s)	☉	☊	☽	☿	♀	♂	♃	♄	♅	♆	♇
1	18 34 12.2	8♋41.6	19♑32.9	20♒59.2	24♋ 6.8	22♌46.5	21♌ 8.7	14♌22.5	5♒19.8	11♑57.4	15♑34.0	17♏46.3
2	18 38 8.8	9 38.8	19 29.8	3♓ 7.3	25 57.9	23 33.2	21 45.1	14 34.4	5R16.0	11R55.0	15R32.4	17R45.4
3	18 42 5.4	10 36.0	19 26.6	15 28.2	27 46.9	24 19.0	22 21.5	14 46.2	5 12.2	11 52.6	15 30.8	17 44.6
4	18 46 1.9	11 33.2	19 23.4	28 5.6	29 33.8	25 4.1	22 57.9	14 58.2	5 8.4	11 50.2	15 29.2	17 43.8
5	18 49 58.5	12 30.4	19 20.2	11♈ 3.0	1♌18.7	25 48.2	23 34.4	15 10.2	5 4.5	11 47.7	15 27.6	17 43.0
6	18 53 55.0	13 27.6	19 17.1	24 23.3	3 1.5	26 31.3	24 10.9	15 22.2	5 .5	11 45.3	15 25.9	17 42.2
7	18 57 51.6	14 24.8	19 13.9	8♉ 8.7	4 42.1	27 13.6	24 47.4	15 34.3	4 56.5	11 42.9	15 24.3	17 41.5
8	19 1 48.2	15 22.0	19 10.7	22 19.6	6 20.7	27 54.8	25 24.0	15 46.5	4 52.5	11 40.5	15 22.7	17 40.8
9	19 5 44.7	16 19.2	19 7.5	6♊54.1	7 57.2	28 35.0	26 .6	15 58.7	4 48.4	11 38.0	15 21.1	17 40.2
10	19 9 41.3	17 16.5	19 4.4	21 47.8	9 31.6	29 14.1	26 37.3	16 10.9	4 44.3	11 35.6	15 19.4	17 39.5
11	19 13 37.8	18 13.7	19 1.2	6♋54.0	11 3.8	29 52.1	27 14.0	16 23.2	4 40.1	11 33.2	15 17.8	17 38.9
12	19 17 34.4	19 10.9	18 58.0	22 3.9	12 33.9	0♍28.9	27 50.7	16 35.6	4 35.9	11 30.8	15 16.2	17 38.4
13	19 21 30.9	20 8.2	18 54.8	7♌ 8.4	14 1.9	1 4.6	28 27.4	16 47.9	4 31.7	11 28.4	15 14.6	17 37.8
14	19 25 27.5	21 5.4	18 51.6	21 58.6	15 27.7	1 39.0	29 4.2	17 .4	4 27.4	11 26.0	15 13.0	17 37.3
15	19 29 24.1	22 2.7	18 48.5	6♍28.0	16 51.4	2 12.0	29 41.1	17 12.8	4 23.1	11 23.6	15 11.4	17 36.9
16	19 33 20.6	22 59.9	18 45.3	20 32.2	18 12.7	2 43.7	0♍17.9	17 25.3	4 18.8	11 21.3	15 9.7	17 36.4
17	19 37 17.2	23 57.2	18 42.1	4♎ 9.9	19 31.9	3 14.0	0 54.8	17 37.9	4 14.5	11 18.9	15 8.1	17 36.0
18	19 41 13.7	24 54.4	18 38.9	17 21.5	20 48.7	3 42.8	1 31.8	17 50.4	4 10.1	11 16.6	15 6.5	17 35.6
19	19 45 10.3	25 51.7	18 35.8	0♏ 9.6	22 3.1	4 10.1	2 8.7	18 3.1	4 5.7	11 14.2	15 5.0	17 35.3
20	19 49 6.8	26 48.9	18 32.6	12 37.7	23 15.1	4 35.8	2 45.7	18 15.7	4 1.3	11 11.9	15 3.4	17 35.0
21	19 53 3.4	27 46.2	18 29.4	24 49.9	24 24.5	4 59.9	3 22.7	18 28.4	3 56.9	11 9.6	15 1.8	17 34.7
22	19 56 60.0	28 43.5	18 26.2	6♐50.3	25 31.5	5 22.3	3 59.8	18 41.1	3 52.5	11 7.4	15 .3	17 34.5
23	20 0 56.5	29 40.7	18 23.1	18 42.9	26 35.7	5 42.9	4 36.9	18 53.9	3 48.1	11 5.1	14 58.7	17 34.3
24	20 4 53.1	0♌38.0	18 19.9	0♑31.4	27 37.2	6 1.6	5 14.0	19 6.6	3 43.7	11 2.9	14 57.2	17 34.1
25	20 8 49.6	1 35.3	18 16.7	12 19.0	28 35.8	6 18.5	5 51.2	19 19.4	3 39.2	11 .6	14 55.6	17 34.0
26	20 12 46.2	2 32.6	18 13.5	24 8.7	29 31.4	6 33.4	6 28.4	19 32.2	3 34.7	10 58.4	14 54.1	17 33.8
27	20 16 42.7	3 29.9	18 10.3	6♒ 2.7	0♍23.9	6 46.4	7 5.6	19 45.1	3 30.3	10 56.3	14 52.6	17 33.8
28	20 20 39.3	4 27.2	18 7.2	18 3.3	1 13.1	6 57.3	7 42.9	19 58.0	3 25.8	10 54.1	14 51.1	17 33.7
29	20 24 35.9	5 24.5	18 4.0	0♓12.4	1 59.0	7 6.0	8 20.1	20 10.9	3 21.4	10 52.0	14 49.6	17 33.7
30	20 28 32.4	6 21.9	18 .8	12 31.8	2 41.4	7 12.6	8 57.5	20 23.8	3 16.9	10 49.8	14 48.1	17 33.7
31	20 32 29.0	7 19.2	17 57.6	25 3.4	3 20.0	7 17.0	9 34.8	20 36.7	3 12.5	10 47.7	14 46.6	17D33.8

LATITUDE

DAY	SID. TIME	☉	☊	☽	☿	♀	♂	♃	♄	♅	♆	♇
1	18 34 12.2	0 .0	0 .0	2N48.9	1N54.2	0N49.7	1N13.2	0N44.2	0S26.1	0S22.8	0N48.8	15N24.4
4	18 46 1.9	0 .0	0 .0	4 56.9	1 48.2	0 29.6	1 11.8	0 44.2	0 26.4	0 22.8	0 48.8	15 23.0
7	18 57 51.6	0 .0	0 .0	5 .1	1 36.7	0 7.4	1 10.4	0 44.2	0 26.7	0 22.9	0 48.8	15 21.5
10	19 9 41.3	0 .0	0 .0	2 25.3	1 20.1	0S16.8	1 8.9	0 44.3	0 27.0	0 22.9	0 48.7	15 20.0
13	19 21 30.9	0 .0	0 .0	1S39.5	0 59.0	0 43.2	1 7.5	0 44.3	0 27.3	0 22.9	0 48.7	15 18.4
16	19 33 20.6	0 .0	0 .0	4 39.6	0 33.9	1 11.9	1 6.0	0 44.4	0 27.6	0 22.9	0 48.7	15 16.9
19	19 45 10.3	0 .0	0 .0	5 11.6	0 5.2	1 42.7	1 4.6	0 44.5	0 27.9	0 22.9	0 48.6	15 15.2
22	19 56 60.0	0 .0	0 .0	3 33.2	0S26.6	2 15.7	1 3.1	0 44.5	0 28.2	0 22.9	0 48.6	15 13.6
25	20 8 49.6	0 .0	0 .0	0 36.9	1 .9	2 50.8	1 1.7	0 44.6	0 28.5	0 22.9	0 48.5	15 11.9
28	20 20 39.3	0 .0	0 .0	2N34.1	1 37.1	3 27.8	1 .2	0 44.8	0 28.7	0 22.9	0 48.4	15 10.3
31	20 32 29.0	0 .0	0 .0	4 48.8	2 14.5	4 6.2	0 58.7	0 44.9	0 29.0	0 22.9	0 48.4	15 8.6

RIGHT ASCENSION

DAY	SID. TIME	☉	☊	☽	☿	♀	♂	♃	♄	♅	♆	♇
1	18 34 12.2	9♋27.7	21♑ 9.5	22♒27.5	26♋22.0	25♌24.1	23♌56.2	17♌ 3.9	7♒48.1	13♑ 2.1	16♑47.4	19♏34.5
2	18 38 8.8	10 29.7	21 6.1	3♓43.1	28 20.3	26 7.5	24 31.8	17 15.8	7R44.2	12R59.5	16R45.7	19R33.5
3	18 42 5.4	11 31.7	21 2.7	14 54.9	0♌15.7	26 49.8	25 7.3	17 27.7	7 40.4	12 56.8	16 43.9	19 32.6
4	18 46 1.9	12 33.6	20 59.3	26 16.8	2 8.1	27 31.1	25 42.8	17 39.6	7 36.4	12 54.2	16 42.2	19 31.7
5	18 49 58.5	13 35.5	20 55.9	8♈ 4.8	3 57.5	28 11.3	26 18.2	17 51.6	7 32.4	12 51.6	16 40.5	19 30.9
6	18 53 55.0	14 37.2	20 52.5	20 35.4	5 43.9	28 50.4	26 53.6	18 3.6	7 28.4	12 48.9	16 38.7	19 30.1
7	18 57 51.6	15 38.9	20 49.1	4♉ 4.2	7 27.5	29 28.5	27 29.0	18 15.7	7 24.3	12 46.3	16 37.0	19 29.3
8	19 1 48.2	16 40.5	20 45.7	18 41.3	9 8.0	0♍ 5.3	28 4.4	18 27.8	7 20.2	12 43.7	16 35.3	19 28.5
9	19 5 44.7	17 42.0	20 42.3	4♊24.6	10 45.7	0 41.0	28 39.7	18 40.0	7 16.0	12 41.0	16 33.5	19 27.7
10	19 9 41.3	18 43.4	20 38.9	20 54.3	12 20.5	1 15.5	29 15.1	18 52.2	7 11.8	12 38.4	16 31.8	19 27.0
11	19 13 37.8	19 44.7	20 35.5	7♋34.6	13 52.4	1 48.8	29 50.3	19 4.5	7 7.5	12 35.8	16 30.1	19 26.3
12	19 17 34.4	20 46.0	20 32.1	23 47.2	15 21.5	2 20.7	0♍25.6	19 16.7	7 3.2	12 33.2	16 28.3	19 25.6
13	19 21 30.9	21 47.0	20 28.7	9♌ 6.0	16 47.8	2 51.4	1 .8	19 29.1	6 58.9	12 30.6	16 26.6	19 25.0
14	19 25 27.5	22 48.0	20 25.3	23 23.4	18 11.3	3 20.7	1 36.0	19 41.4	6 54.5	12 28.0	16 24.9	19 24.4
15	19 29 24.1	23 48.9	20 21.9	6♍46.2	19 31.9	3 48.6	2 11.2	19 53.8	6 50.1	12 25.4	16 23.1	19 23.8
16	19 33 20.6	24 49.6	20 18.5	19 28.5	20 49.8	4 15.1	2 46.3	20 6.2	6 45.7	12 22.9	16 21.4	19 23.2
17	19 37 17.2	25 50.2	20 15.2	1♎46.7	22 4.9	4 40.1	3 21.5	20 18.6	6 41.3	12 20.3	16 19.7	19 22.7
18	19 41 13.7	26 50.6	20 11.8	13 56.3	23 17.2	5 3.5	3 56.6	20 31.1	6 36.8	12 17.8	16 18.0	19 22.2
19	19 45 10.3	27 50.9	20 8.4	26 9.9	24 26.7	5 25.4	4 31.6	20 43.6	6 32.3	12 15.2	16 16.3	19 21.8
20	19 49 6.8	28 51.1	20 5.0	8♏36.7	25 33.4	5 45.6	5 6.7	20 56.1	6 27.8	12 12.7	16 14.6	19 21.3
21	19 53 3.4	29 51.2	20 1.6	21 20.8	26 37.2	6 4.2	5 41.7	21 8.7	6 23.2	12 10.2	16 12.9	19 20.9
22	19 56 60.0	0♌51.1	19 58.2	4♐20.5	27 38.2	6 21.1	6 16.7	21 21.3	6 18.7	12 7.8	16 11.3	19 20.6
23	20 0 56.5	1 50.8	19 54.8	17 28.7	28 36.2	6 36.2	6 51.7	21 33.9	6 14.2	12 5.3	16 9.6	19 20.2
24	20 4 53.1	2 50.4	19 51.4	0♑34.6	29 31.3	6 49.5	7 26.7	21 46.5	6 9.6	12 2.9	16 8.0	19 19.9
25	20 8 49.6	3 49.9	19 48.0	13 26.9	0♍23.2	7 .9	8 1.6	21 59.2	6 5.0	12 .5	16 6.3	19 19.6
26	20 12 46.2	4 49.2	19 44.6	25 57.0	1 12.1	7 10.3	8 36.5	22 11.8	6 .4	11 58.1	16 4.7	19 19.4
27	20 16 42.7	5 48.4	19 41.2	8♒ 1.2	1 57.8	7 17.9	9 11.4	22 24.5	5 55.8	11 55.7	16 3.1	19 19.2
28	20 20 39.3	6 47.4	19 37.8	19 41.2	2 40.2	7 23.4	9 46.3	22 37.2	5 51.2	11 53.4	16 1.4	19 19.0
29	20 24 35.9	7 46.2	19 34.4	1♓ 3.0	3 19.2	7 26.9	10 21.2	22 49.9	5 46.7	11 51.1	15 59.8	19 18.8
30	20 28 32.4	8 44.9	19 31.0	12 16.4	3 54.7	7 28.3	10 56.0	23 2.6	5 42.1	11 48.8	15 58.2	19 18.7
31	20 32 29.0	9 43.5	19 27.6	23 33.3	4 26.6	7R27.6	11 30.9	23 15.4	5 37.5	11 46.5	15 56.7	19 18.6

DECLINATION

DAY	SID. TIME	☉	☊	☽	☿	♀	♂	♃	♄	♅	♆	♇
1	18 34 12.2	23N 9.4	0S23.1	11S50.0	23N 9.8	14N42.5	15N36.5	17N13.4	19S21.6	23S16.9	21S43.5	2S18.3
4	18 46 1.9	22 56.3	0 23.1	3N46.9	22 .4	13 37.9	14 59.6	17 3.0	19 24.7	23 17.6	21 44.1	2 19.1
7	18 57 51.6	22 39.7	0 23.1	18 57.1	20 39.2	12 33.1	14 21.9	16 52.4	19 27.8	23 18.2	21 44.6	2 19.9
10	19 9 41.3	22 19.5	0 23.1	25 36.2	19 9.4	11 28.7	13 43.3	16 41.5	19 31.1	23 18.9	21 45.2	2 20.9
13	19 21 30.9	21 55.9	0 23.1	16 53.0	17 33.6	10 25.1	13 4.0	16 30.4	19 34.4	23 19.5	21 45.8	2 21.9
16	19 33 20.6	21 28.8	0 23.2	0S32.2	15 54.6	9 23.1	12 23.8	16 19.1	19 37.8	23 20.2	21 46.4	2 23.1
19	19 45 10.3	20 58.5	0 23.2	16 23.1	14 14.5	8 23.2	11 43.0	16 7.6	19 41.2	23 20.8	21 47.0	2 24.3
22	19 56 60.0	20 25.0	0 23.2	24 57.3	12 35.8	7 26.2	11 1.4	15 55.9	19 44.5	23 21.4	21 47.5	2 25.7
25	20 8 49.6	19 48.5	0 23.2	23 29.0	11 .7	6 33.0	10 19.3	15 44.1	19 47.9	23 21.9	21 48.1	2 27.2
28	20 20 39.3	19 9.0	0 23.3	12 58.5	9 31.7	5 44.5	9 36.5	15 32.0	19 51.3	23 22.5	21 48.7	2 28.7
31	20 32 29.0	18 26.6	0 23.3	2N27.3	8 11.6	5 1.4	8 53.1	15 19.8	19 54.7	23 23.0	21 49.2	2 30.4

AUGUST 1991

LONGITUDE

DAY	EPHEM. SID. TIME h m s	☉ ° ′	☊ ° ′	☽ ° ′	☿ ° ′	♀ ° ′	♂ ° ′	♃ ° ′	♄ ° ′	♅ ° ′	♆ ° ′	♇ ° ′
1	20 36 25.5	8♌16.6	17♑54.5	7♈49.1	3♍54.8	7♍19.2	10♍12.2	20♌49.7	3♒ 8.0	10♑45.7	14♑45.1	17♏33.9
2	20 40 22.1	9 14.0	17 51.3	20 50.9	4 25.5	7R19.0	10 49.6	21 2.7	3R 3.6	10R43.6	14R43.7	17 34.0
3	20 44 18.6	10 11.4	17 48.1	4♉10.5	4 52.0	7 16.6	11 27.1	21 15.7	2 59.2	10 41.6	14 42.3	17 34.2
4	20 48 15.2	11 8.8	17 44.9	17 49.6	5 14.1	7 11.8	12 4.6	21 28.7	2 54.8	10 39.6	14 40.8	17 34.3
5	20 52 11.7	12 6.3	17 41.8	1♊48.8	5 31.5	7 4.6	12 42.2	21 41.7	2 50.4	10 37.7	14 39.4	17 34.6
6	20 56 8.3	13 3.8	17 38.6	16 7.8	5 44.2	6 55.1	13 19.7	21 54.8	2 46.0	10 35.7	14 38.1	17 34.8
7	21 0 4.9	14 1.2	17 35.4	0♋44.2	5 51.9	6 43.2	13 57.4	22 7.8	2 41.7	10 33.8	14 36.7	17 35.1
8	21 4 1.4	14 58.8	17 32.2	15 34.0	5 54.5	6 28.9	14 35.0	22 20.9	2 37.3	10 32.0	14 35.3	17 35.5
9	21 7 58.0	15 56.3	17 29.0	0♌31.0	5R51.8	6 12.4	15 12.7	22 34.0	2 33.1	10 30.1	14 34.0	17 35.8
10	21 11 54.5	16 53.8	17 25.9	15 27.3	5 43.8	5 53.5	15 50.4	22 47.1	2 28.8	10 28.3	14 32.7	17 36.2
11	21 15 51.1	17 51.4	17 22.7	0♍14.8	5 30.3	5 32.4	16 28.2	23 .2	2 24.6	10 26.6	14 31.4	17 36.6
12	21 19 47.6	18 49.0	17 19.5	14 45.9	5 11.5	5 9.2	17 6.1	23 13.3	2 20.4	10 24.9	14 30.2	17 37.2
13	21 23 44.2	19 46.6	17 16.3	28 54.6	4 47.3	4 43.9	17 43.9	23 26.5	2 16.3	10 23.2	14 28.9	17 37.7
14	21 27 40.7	20 44.3	17 13.2	12♎37.6	4 17.9	4 16.6	18 21.8	23 39.6	2 12.1	10 21.5	14 27.7	17 38.2
15	21 31 37.3	21 41.9	17 10.0	25 54.0	3 43.6	3 47.5	18 59.7	23 52.7	2 8.0	10 19.9	14 26.5	17 38.8
16	21 35 33.9	22 39.6	17 6.8	8♏45.2	3 4.7	3 16.7	19 37.6	24 5.9	2 4.0	10 18.3	14 25.3	17 39.4
17	21 39 30.4	23 37.2	17 3.6	21 14.4	2 21.8	2 44.3	20 15.6	24 19.0	2 .0	10 16.7	14 24.1	17 40.0
18	21 43 27.0	24 34.9	17 .4	3♐25.9	1 35.3	2 10.5	20 53.7	24 32.1	1 56.1	10 15.2	14 23.0	17 40.7
19	21 47 23.5	25 32.6	16 57.3	15 24.5	0 46.0	1 35.6	21 31.7	24 45.2	1 52.2	10 13.8	14 21.8	17 41.4
20	21 51 20.1	26 30.3	16 54.1	27 15.2	29♌54.8	0 59.8	22 9.8	24 58.4	1 48.3	10 12.3	14 20.7	17 42.1
21	21 55 16.6	27 28.1	16 50.9	9♑ 2.7	29 2.5	0 23.2	22 47.9	25 11.5	1 44.5	10 10.9	14 19.6	17 42.9
22	21 59 13.2	28 25.8	16 47.7	20 51.5	28 10.3	29♌46.1	23 26.1	25 24.6	1 40.8	10 9.6	14 18.6	17 43.7
23	22 3 9.7	29 23.6	16 44.6	2♒45.3	27 19.0	29 8.8	24 4.3	25 37.7	1 37.1	10 8.3	14 17.6	17 44.5
24	22 7 6.3	0♍21.4	16 41.4	14 47.1	26 29.8	28 31.5	24 42.5	25 50.8	1 33.4	10 7.0	14 16.6	17 45.4
25	22 11 2.8	1 19.2	16 38.2	26 59.2	25 43.8	27 54.4	25 20.8	26 3.9	1 29.9	10 5.8	14 15.6	17 46.3
26	22 14 59.4	2 17.1	16 35.0	9♓23.1	25 2.0	27 17.7	25 59.1	26 17.0	1 26.4	10 4.6	14 14.6	17 47.2
27	22 18 56.0	3 15.0	16 31.9	21 59.6	24 25.2	26 41.8	26 37.5	26 30.1	1 22.9	10 3.4	14 13.7	17 48.2
28	22 22 52.5	4 12.9	16 28.7	4♈49.0	23 54.4	26 6.9	27 15.9	26 43.2	1 19.5	10 2.3	14 12.8	17 49.2
29	22 26 49.1	5 10.8	16 25.5	17 51.3	23 30.3	25 33.1	27 54.3	26 56.2	1 16.2	10 1.3	14 11.9	17 50.2
30	22 30 45.6	6 8.8	16 22.3	1♉ 6.4	23 13.6	25 .6	28 32.8	27 9.3	1 12.9	10 .3	14 11.1	17 51.2
31	22 34 42.2	7 6.7	16 19.1	14 34.2	23 4.6	24 29.7	29 11.3	27 22.3	1 9.8	9 59.3	14 10.2	17 52.3

LATITUDE

DAY	EPHEM. SID. TIME h m s	☉ ° ′	☊ ° ′	☽ ° ′	☿ ° ′	♀ ° ′	♂ ° ′	♃ ° ′	♄ ° ′	♅ ° ′	♆ ° ′	♇ ° ′
1	20 36 25.5	0 .0	0 .0	5N 9.7	2S27.0	4S19.3	0N58.2	0N44.9	0S29.1	0S22.9	0N48.4	15N 8.0
4	20 48 15.2	0 .0	0 .0	4 35.8	3 4.2	4 58.9	0 56.8	0 45.1	0 29.3	0 22.9	0 48.3	15 6.3
7	21 0 4.9	0 .0	0 .0	1 37.9	3 39.4	5 38.4	0 55.3	0 45.2	0 29.5	0 22.9	0 48.2	15 4.6
10	21 11 54.5	0 .0	0 .0	2S21.1	4 10.3	6 16.7	0 53.8	0 45.4	0 29.8	0 22.9	0 48.2	15 2.9
13	21 23 44.2	0 .0	0 .0	4 54.6	4 33.6	6 52.5	0 52.3	0 45.5	0 30.0	0 22.9	0 48.1	15 1.2
16	21 35 33.9	0 .0	0 .0	4 53.4	4 45.9	7 24.2	0 50.7	0 45.7	0 30.2	0 22.9	0 48.0	14 59.5
19	21 47 23.5	0 .0	0 .0	2 50.7	4 43.4	7 50.4	0 49.2	0 45.9	0 30.4	0 22.9	0 47.9	14 57.8
22	21 59 13.2	0 .0	0 .0	0N12.9	4 24.2	8 9.7	0 47.7	0 46.1	0 30.6	0 22.8	0 47.8	14 56.2
25	22 11 2.8	0 .0	0 .0	3 13.4	3 48.9	8 21.1	0 46.2	0 46.4	0 30.7	0 22.8	0 47.7	14 54.5
28	22 22 52.5	0 .0	0 .0	4 59.9	3 1.0	8 24.5	0 44.6	0 46.6	0 30.9	0 22.8	0 47.6	14 52.9
31	22 34 42.2	0 .0	0 .0	4 34.8	2 6.3	8 20.0	0 43.1	0 46.8	0 31.1	0 22.8	0 47.6	14 51.3

RIGHT ASCENSION

DAY	EPHEM. SID. TIME h m s	☉ ° ′	☊ ° ′	☽ ° ′	☿ ° ′	♀ ° ′	♂ ° ′	♃ ° ′	♄ ° ′	♅ ° ′	♆ ° ′	♇ ° ′
1	20 36 25.5	10♌41.9	19♑24.2	5♈ 7.6	4♍54.8	7♍24.8	12♍ 5.7	23♌28.1	5♒32.9	11♑44.2	15♑55.1	19♏18.5
2	20 40 22.1	11 40.1	19 20.8	17 14.2	5 19.1	7R19.8	12 40.5	23 40.9	5R28.3	11R42.0	15R53.6	19 18.5
3	20 44 18.6	12 38.3	19 17.4	0♉ 7.5	5 39.4	7 12.6	13 15.4	23 53.6	5 23.8	11 39.8	15 52.0	19 18.5
4	20 48 15.2	13 36.2	19 14.0	13 59.0	5 55.6	7 3.3	13 50.2	24 6.4	5 19.3	11 37.7	15 50.5	19 18.5
5	20 52 11.7	14 34.0	19 10.5	28 51.9	6 7.5	6 51.7	14 25.0	24 19.2	5 14.7	11 35.5	15 49.0	19 18.5
6	20 56 8.3	15 31.7	19 7.1	14♊36.6	6 15.1	6 38.0	14 59.8	24 32.0	5 10.2	11 33.4	15 47.5	19D18.6
7	21 0 4.9	16 29.2	19 3.7	0♋48.8	6 18.1	6 22.2	15 34.6	24 44.8	5 5.7	11 31.4	15 46.1	19 18.8
8	21 4 1.4	17 26.6	19 .3	16 55.7	6R16.5	6 4.2	16 9.4	24 57.6	5 1.3	11 29.4	15 44.6	19 18.9
9	21 7 58.0	18 23.9	18 56.9	2♌28.6	6 10.2	5 44.2	16 44.2	25 10.4	4 56.9	11 27.4	15 43.2	19 19.1
10	21 11 54.5	19 21.0	18 53.5	17 12.1	5 59.2	5 22.1	17 19.0	25 23.2	4 52.5	11 25.4	15 41.8	19 19.3
11	21 15 51.1	20 17.9	18 50.1	1♍ 5.5	5 43.4	4 58.1	17 53.8	25 36.0	4 48.1	11 23.5	15 40.4	19 19.6
12	21 19 47.6	21 14.8	18 46.7	14 17.9	5 23.0	4 32.2	18 28.7	25 48.9	4 43.8	11 21.6	15 39.1	19 19.9
13	21 23 44.2	22 11.4	18 43.3	27 2.7	4 58.0	4 4.5	19 3.5	26 1.7	4 39.5	11 19.8	15 37.8	19 20.2
14	21 27 40.7	23 8.0	18 39.9	9♎34.0	4 28.5	3 35.2	19 38.3	26 14.5	4 35.2	11 18.0	15 36.5	19 20.5
15	21 31 37.3	24 4.3	18 36.5	22 4.4	3 55.0	3 4.4	20 13.2	26 27.3	4 31.0	11 16.2	15 35.2	19 20.9
16	21 35 33.9	25 .6	18 33.1	4♏42.9	3 17.7	2 32.2	20 48.0	26 40.1	4 26.8	11 14.5	15 33.9	19 21.3
17	21 39 30.4	25 56.7	18 29.7	17 34.3	2 37.1	1 58.8	21 22.9	26 52.9	4 22.7	11 12.8	15 32.6	19 21.8
18	21 43 27.0	26 52.7	18 26.3	0♐38.1	1 53.8	1 24.3	21 57.7	27 5.7	4 18.6	11 11.2	15 31.4	19 22.3
19	21 47 23.5	27 48.5	18 22.9	13 49.0	1 8.4	0 49.1	22 32.6	27 18.5	4 14.6	11 9.6	15 30.2	19 22.8
20	21 51 20.1	28 44.2	18 19.5	26 57.8	0 21.8	0 13.2	23 7.5	27 31.2	4 10.6	11 8.0	15 29.0	19 23.3
21	21 55 16.6	29 39.8	18 16.0	9♑54.5	29♌34.7	29♌36.9	23 42.3	27 44.0	4 6.7	11 6.5	15 27.9	19 23.9
22	21 59 13.2	0♍35.3	18 12.6	22 31.1	28 48.2	29 .5	24 17.3	27 56.7	4 2.8	11 5.0	15 26.7	19 24.5
23	22 3 9.7	1 30.6	18 9.2	4♒43.9	28 3.1	28 24.1	24 52.2	28 9.5	3 59.0	11 3.6	15 25.6	19 25.1
24	22 7 6.3	2 25.8	18 5.8	16 33.5	27 20.4	27 47.9	25 27.1	28 22.2	3 55.2	11 2.2	15 24.6	19 25.7
25	22 11 2.8	3 21.0	18 2.4	28 5.1	26 41.1	27 12.3	26 2.1	28 34.9	3 51.5	11 .9	15 23.5	19 26.4
26	22 14 59.4	4 16.0	17 59.0	9♓26.9	26 6.2	26 37.4	26 37.1	28 47.6	3 47.9	10 59.6	15 22.5	19 27.2
27	22 18 56.0	5 10.9	17 55.6	20 49.7	25 36.4	26 3.4	27 12.1	29 .2	3 44.3	10 58.3	15 21.5	19 27.9
28	22 22 52.5	6 5.7	17 52.2	2♈25.7	25 12.5	25 30.6	27 47.1	29 12.9	3 40.8	10 57.1	15 20.5	19 28.7
29	22 26 49.1	7 .5	17 48.8	14 28.1	24 55.2	24 59.2	28 22.2	29 25.5	3 37.3	10 56.0	15 19.6	19 29.5
30	22 30 45.6	7 55.1	17 45.3	27 9.5	24 45.2	24 29.2	28 57.3	29 38.2	3 34.0	10 54.9	15 18.7	19 30.4
31	22 34 42.2	8 49.7	17 41.9	10♉39.9	24 42.7	24 1.0	29 32.4	29 50.8	3 30.7	10 53.8	15 17.8	19 31.2

DECLINATION

DAY	EPHEM. SID. TIME h m s	☉ ° ′	☊ ° ′	☽ ° ′	☿ ° ′	♀ ° ′	♂ ° ′	♃ ° ′	♄ ° ′	♅ ° ′	♆ ° ′	♇ ° ′
1	20 36 25.5	18N11.9	0S23.3	7N50.5	7N47.4	4N48.5	8N38.5	15N15.7	19S55.8	23S23.2	21S49.4	2S30.9
4	20 48 15.2	17 25.9	0 23.3	21 33.3	6 44.1	4 14.4	7 54.4	15 3.4	19 59.1	23 23.6	21 49.9	2 32.7
7	21 0 4.9	16 37.3	0 23.3	25 4.3	5 57.5	3 48.1	7 9.7	14 50.8	20 2.3	23 24.1	21 50.5	2 34.5
10	21 11 54.5	15 46.4	0 23.4	13 57.3	5 31.8	3 30.4	6 24.6	14 38.2	20 5.5	23 24.5	21 51.0	2 36.5
13	21 23 44.2	14 53.1	0 23.4	4S 4.3	5 30.4	3 22.1	5 39.0	14 25.4	20 8.5	23 24.9	21 51.4	2 38.5
16	21 35 33.9	13 57.8	0 23.4	19 2.7	5 55.7	3 23.5	4 53.1	14 12.5	20 11.5	23 25.3	21 51.9	2 40.5
19	21 47 23.5	13 .4	0 23.4	25 28.2	6 46.8	3 34.4	4 6.8	13 59.6	20 14.3	23 25.6	21 52.4	2 42.7
22	21 59 13.2	12 1.2	0 23.4	21 36.6	7 58.5	3 54.0	3 20.2	13 46.5	20 17.1	23 25.9	21 52.8	2 44.9
25	22 11 2.8	11 .4	0 23.5	9 29.1	9 21.0	4 21.0	2 33.3	13 33.5	20 19.7	23 26.2	21 53.2	2 47.1
28	22 22 52.5	9 57.9	0 23.5	6N30.0	10 42.2	4 53.4	1 46.2	13 20.3	20 22.1	23 26.4	21 53.6	2 49.4
31	22 34 42.2	8 54.0	0 23.5	20 34.9	11 50.2	5 29.3	0 58.9	13 7.1	20 24.4	23 26.6	21 54.0	2 51.8

SEPTEMBER 1991

DAY	EPHEM. SID. TIME	☉	☊	☽	☿	♀	♂	♃	♄	♅	♆	♇
		LONGITUDE										
	h m s	° ′	° ′	° ′	° ′	° ′	° ′	° ′	° ′	° ′	° ′	° ′
1	22 38 38.7	8 ♍ 4.8	16 ♑ 16.0	28 ♉ 14.7	23 ♌ 3.7	24 ♌ .6	29 ♍ 49.8	27 ♌ 35.3	1 ♒ 6.6	9 ♑ 58.4	14 ♑ 9.4	17 ♏ 53.5
2	22 42 35.3	9 2.9	16 12.8	12 ♊ 8.2	23 D 11.3	23 R 33.3	0 ♎ 28.5	27 48.4	1 R 3.6	9 R 57.5	14 R 8.7	17 54.7
3	22 46 31.8	10 1.0	16 9.6	26 14.4	23 27.3	23 8.0	1 7.1	28 1.4	1 .7	9 56.7	14 8.0	17 55.8
4	22 50 28.4	10 59.1	16 6.4	10 ♋ 32.5	23 51.8	22 44.8	1 45.8	28 14.3	0 57.8	9 55.9	14 7.3	17 57.1
5	22 54 24.9	11 57.2	16 3.3	25 .5	24 24.7	22 23.8	2 24.5	28 27.3	0 55.0	9 55.2	14 6.6	17 58.3
6	22 58 21.5	12 55.4	16 .1	9 ♌ 34.9	25 5.8	22 5.1	3 3.2	28 40.2	0 52.2	9 54.5	14 5.9	17 59.6
7	23 2 18.0	13 53.6	15 56.9	24 10.7	25 54.8	21 48.7	3 42.0	28 53.1	0 49.6	9 53.9	14 5.3	18 .9
8	23 6 14.6	14 51.9	15 53.7	8 ♍ 41.6	26 51.5	21 34.7	4 20.9	29 6.0	0 47.0	9 53.3	14 4.7	18 2.2
9	23 10 11.2	15 50.2	15 50.5	23 1.0	27 55.3	21 23.1	4 59.8	29 18.8	0 44.5	9 52.7	14 4.1	18 3.6
10	23 14 7.7	16 48.5	15 47.4	7 ♎ 2.9	29 5.9	21 13.8	5 38.7	29 31.7	0 42.1	9 52.3	14 3.6	18 5.0
11	23 18 4.3	17 46.8	15 44.2	20 43.0	0 ♍ 22.6	21 7.0	6 17.7	29 44.5	0 39.7	9 51.8	14 3.1	18 6.4
12	23 22 .8	18 45.2	15 41.0	3 ♏ 59.0	1 45.0	21 2.6	6 56.7	29 57.2	0 37.5	9 51.4	14 2.6	18 7.8
13	23 25 57.4	19 43.5	15 37.8	16 51.1	3 12.6	21 .5	7 35.7	0 ♍ 10.0	0 35.3	9 51.1	14 2.2	18 9.3
14	23 29 53.9	20 42.0	15 34.7	29 21.3	4 44.7	21 D .8	8 14.8	0 22.7	0 33.3	9 50.8	14 1.8	18 10.8
15	23 33 50.5	21 40.4	15 31.5	11 ♐ 33.4	6 20.8	21 3.5	8 53.9	0 35.3	0 31.3	9 50.5	14 1.4	18 12.4
16	23 37 47.0	22 38.9	15 28.3	23 32.1	8 .3	21 8.4	9 33.1	0 48.0	0 29.4	9 50.3	14 1.1	18 13.9
17	23 41 43.6	23 37.4	15 25.1	5 ♑ 22.7	9 42.6	21 15.5	10 12.3	1 .6	0 27.6	9 50.2	14 .7	18 15.5
18	23 45 40.1	24 35.9	15 21.9	17 10.7	11 27.4	21 24.8	10 51.6	1 13.1	0 25.9	9 50.1	14 .5	18 17.1
19	23 49 36.7	25 34.4	15 18.8	29 1.2	13 14.1	21 36.3	11 30.9	1 25.6	0 24.3	9 50.1	14 .2	18 18.8
20	23 53 33.2	26 33.0	15 15.6	10 ♒ 59.0	15 2.3	21 49.8	12 10.2	1 38.1	0 22.8	9 50.1	13 60.0	18 20.4
21	23 57 29.8	27 31.6	15 12.4	23 8.2	16 51.6	22 5.4	12 49.6	1 50.6	0 21.3	9 50.1	13 59.8	18 22.1
22	0 1 26.3	28 30.3	15 9.2	5 ♓ 31.6	18 41.7	22 22.9	13 29.0	2 3.0	0 20.0	9 D 50.3	13 59.7	18 23.8
23	0 5 22.9	29 29.0	15 6.1	18 11.2	20 32.4	22 42.5	14 8.5	2 15.4	0 18.8	9 50.5	13 59.6	18 25.6
24	0 9 19.4	0 ♎ 27.7	15 2.9	1 ♈ 7.2	22 23.2	23 3.8	14 48.0	2 27.7	0 17.7	9 50.7	13 59.5	18 27.4
25	0 13 16.0	1 26.4	14 59.7	14 18.9	24 14.0	23 26.9	15 27.5	2 39.9	0 16.6	9 50.9	13 59.4	18 29.2
26	0 17 12.6	2 25.2	14 56.5	27 44.4	26 4.7	23 51.8	16 7.1	2 52.1	0 15.7	9 51.3	13 59.4	18 31.0
27	0 21 9.1	3 24.0	14 53.3	11 ♉ 21.6	27 55.1	24 18.4	16 46.7	3 4.3	0 14.8	9 51.6	13 59.4	18 32.8
28	0 25 5.7	4 22.8	14 50.2	25 7.7	29 45.1	24 46.6	17 26.4	3 16.4	0 14.1	9 52.0	13 D 59.5	18 34.7
29	0 29 2.2	5 21.7	14 47.0	9 ♊ .9	1 ♎ 34.5	25 16.3	18 6.1	3 28.5	0 13.4	9 52.5	13 59.5	18 36.6
30	0 32 58.8	6 20.6	14 43.8	22 59.5	3 23.3	25 47.6	18 45.9	3 40.5	0 12.9	9 53.0	13 59.7	18 38.5
		LATITUDE										
1	22 38 38.7	0 .0	0 .0	3 N 54.2	1 S 47.6	8 S 16.8	0 N 42.6	0 N 46.9	0 S 31.1	0 S 22.8	0 N 47.5	14 N 50.8
4	22 50 28.4	0 .0	0 .0	0 38.2	0 52.6	8 3.1	0 41.0	0 47.2	0 31.3	0 22.7	0 47.4	14 49.3
7	23 2 18.0	0 .0	0 .0	3 S 2.9	0 2.7	7 43.7	0 39.4	0 47.5	0 31.4	0 22.7	0 47.3	14 47.7
10	23 14 7.7	0 .0	0 .0	4 59.9	0 N 39.1	7 20.0	0 37.9	0 47.8	0 31.6	0 22.7	0 47.2	14 46.3
13	23 25 57.4	0 .0	0 .0	4 23.9	1 11.3	6 53.1	0 36.3	0 48.1	0 31.7	0 22.6	0 47.1	14 44.8
16	23 37 47.0	0 .0	0 .0	1 59.9	1 33.5	6 24.0	0 34.7	0 48.4	0 31.8	0 22.6	0 47.0	14 43.4
19	23 49 36.7	0 .0	0 .0	1 N 5.7	1 46.2	5 53.6	0 33.1	0 48.7	0 31.9	0 22.6	0 46.9	14 42.1
22	0 1 26.3	0 .0	0 .0	3 49.1	1 50.6	5 22.6	0 31.5	0 49.1	0 32.0	0 22.5	0 46.8	14 40.8
25	0 13 16.0	0 .0	0 .0	5 1.0	1 48.1	4 51.5	0 29.9	0 49.5	0 32.1	0 22.5	0 46.7	14 39.5
28	0 25 5.7	0 .0	0 .0	3 52.0	1 40.3	4 20.8	0 28.2	0 49.8	0 32.2	0 22.5	0 46.6	14 38.3
		RIGHT ASCENSION										
1	22 38 38.7	9 ♍ 44.2	17 ♑ 38.5	25 ♉ 3.0	24 ♌ 48.1	23 ♌ 34.6	0 ♎ 7.6	0 ♍ 3.3	3 ♒ 27.4	10 ♑ 52.8	15 ♑ 17.0	19 ♏ 32.1
2	22 42 35.3	10 38.6	17 35.1	10 ♊ 12.6	25 D 1.6	23 R 10.2	0 42.8	0 15.9	3 R 24.3	10 R 51.9	15 R 16.2	19 33.1
3	22 46 31.8	11 33.0	17 31.7	25 50.7	25 23.2	22 47.8	1 18.1	0 28.5	3 21.2	10 51.0	15 15.4	19 34.1
4	22 50 28.4	12 27.2	17 28.3	11 ♋ 31.3	25 53.0	22 27.6	1 53.3	0 41.0	3 18.2	10 50.2	15 14.6	19 35.1
5	22 54 24.9	13 21.4	17 24.9	26 49.5	26 30.7	22 9.7	2 28.7	0 53.4	3 15.3	10 49.4	15 13.9	19 36.1
6	22 58 21.5	14 15.6	17 21.4	11 ♌ 29.5	27 16.2	21 54.0	3 4.0	1 5.9	3 12.5	10 48.6	15 13.2	19 37.2
7	23 2 18.0	15 9.7	17 18.0	25 27.5	28 9.0	21 40.7	3 39.4	1 18.3	3 9.7	10 47.9	15 12.6	19 38.2
8	23 6 14.6	16 3.8	17 14.6	8 ♍ 49.1	29 8.9	21 29.8	4 14.9	1 30.7	3 7.0	10 47.3	15 11.9	19 39.4
9	23 10 11.2	16 57.8	17 11.2	21 45.4	0 ♍ 15.2	21 21.3	4 50.4	1 43.1	3 4.4	10 46.7	15 11.3	19 40.5
10	23 14 7.7	17 51.8	17 7.8	4 ♎ 28.9	1 27.6	21 15.1	5 25.9	1 55.4	3 1.9	10 46.2	15 10.8	19 41.7
11	23 18 4.3	18 45.7	17 4.4	17 11.1	2 45.4	21 11.4	6 1.5	2 7.7	2 59.5	10 45.7	15 10.2	19 42.9
12	23 22 .8	19 39.6	17 1.0	0 ♏ .9	4 8.0	21 10.0	6 37.1	2 20.0	2 57.2	10 45.3	15 9.7	19 44.1
13	23 25 57.4	20 33.5	16 57.5	13 2.8	5 34.9	21 D 11.0	7 12.8	2 32.2	2 55.0	10 44.9	15 9.3	19 45.3
14	23 29 53.9	21 27.3	16 54.1	26 16.0	7 5.5	21 14.3	7 48.6	2 44.4	2 52.8	10 44.6	15 8.8	19 46.6
15	23 33 50.5	22 21.1	16 50.7	9 ♐ 35.1	8 39.1	21 19.8	8 24.4	2 56.6	2 50.8	10 44.3	15 8.4	19 47.9
16	23 37 47.0	23 14.9	16 47.3	22 51.1	10 15.3	21 27.6	9 .2	3 8.7	2 48.8	10 44.1	15 8.0	19 49.3
17	23 41 43.6	24 8.7	16 43.9	5 ♑ 54.2	11 53.5	21 37.6	9 36.1	3 20.7	2 46.9	10 43.9	15 7.7	19 50.6
18	23 45 40.1	25 2.5	16 40.4	18 36.8	13 33.3	21 49.7	10 12.1	3 32.8	2 45.2	10 43.8	15 7.4	19 52.0
19	23 49 36.7	25 56.3	16 37.0	0 ♒ 55.3	15 14.1	22 3.9	10 48.2	3 44.8	2 43.5	10 43.8	15 7.2	19 53.4
20	23 53 33.2	26 50.1	16 33.6	12 50.6	16 55.7	22 20.1	11 24.2	3 56.7	2 41.9	10 43.8	15 6.9	19 54.9
21	23 57 29.8	27 43.9	16 30.2	24 28.0	18 37.8	22 38.3	12 .4	4 8.6	2 40.4	10 D 43.9	15 6.7	19 56.3
22	0 1 26.3	28 37.7	16 26.8	5 ♓ 55.6	20 19.9	22 58.4	12 36.6	4 20.5	2 39.0	10 44.0	15 6.6	19 57.8
23	0 5 22.9	29 31.5	16 23.3	17 24.2	22 2.1	23 20.4	13 13.0	4 32.3	2 37.8	10 44.2	15 6.5	19 59.4
24	0 9 19.4	0 ♎ 25.4	16 19.9	29 5.5	23 43.9	23 44.2	13 49.3	4 44.1	2 36.6	10 44.4	15 6.4	20 .9
25	0 13 16.0	1 19.3	16 16.5	11 ♈ 12.2	25 25.3	24 9.7	14 25.8	4 55.8	2 35.5	10 44.7	15 6.3	20 2.5
26	0 17 12.6	2 13.2	16 13.1	23 56.2	27 6.3	24 36.8	15 2.3	5 7.4	2 34.6	10 45.1	15 6.3	20 4.1
27	0 21 9.1	3 7.2	16 9.7	7 ♉ 26.7	28 46.6	25 5.5	15 38.9	5 19.1	2 33.7	10 45.5	15 6.3	20 5.7
28	0 25 5.7	4 1.2	16 6.2	21 46.4	0 ♎ 26.2	25 35.8	16 15.5	5 30.6	2 32.9	10 45.9	15 D 6.4	20 7.3
29	0 29 2.2	4 55.3	16 2.8	6 ♊ 48.5	2 5.1	26 7.6	16 52.3	5 42.1	2 32.2	10 46.4	15 6.5	20 9.0
30	0 32 58.8	5 49.4	15 59.4	22 15.4	3 43.3	26 40.8	17 29.1	5 53.6	2 31.6	10 47.0	15 6.6	20 10.7
		DECLINATION										
1	22 38 38.7	8 N 32.4	0 S 23.5	23 N 34.4	12 N 8.2	5 N 41.6	0 N 43.1	13 N 2.7	20 S 25.1	23 S 26.7	21 S 54.1	2 S 52.6
4	22 50 28.4	7 26.8	0 23.5	23 39.4	12 44.4	6 18.7	0 S 4.4	12 49.5	20 27.2	23 26.8	21 54.4	2 55.0
7	23 2 18.0	6 20.2	0 23.5	10 35.2	12 50.4	6 54.7	0 52.1	12 36.3	20 29.2	23 27.0	21 54.7	2 57.5
10	23 14 7.7	5 12.5	0 23.6	7 S 23.2	12 24.0	7 28.0	1 39.8	12 23.0	20 30.9	23 27.0	21 55.0	2 59.9
13	23 25 57.4	4 4.1	0 23.6	21 5.0	11 26.3	7 57.7	2 27.5	12 9.9	20 32.5	23 27.1	21 55.2	3 2.4
16	23 37 47.0	2 55.1	0 23.6	25 16.7	10 .8	8 22.9	3 15.2	11 56.7	20 33.9	23 27.1	21 55.5	3 5.0
19	23 49 36.7	1 45.6	0 23.6	19 17.1	8 13.4	8 43.0	4 2.8	11 43.6	20 35.1	23 27.1	21 55.6	3 7.5
22	0 1 26.3	0 35.7	0 23.6	5 55.9	6 10.1	8 57.7	4 50.3	11 30.6	20 36.1	23 27.1	21 55.8	3 10.1
25	0 13 16.0	0 S 34.4	0 23.7	10 N 15.9	3 56.7	9 6.7	5 37.6	11 17.7	20 36.9	23 27.0	21 55.9	3 12.7
28	0 25 5.7	1 44.5	0 23.7	22 48.0	1 37.9	9 9.8	6 24.8	11 4.8	20 37.6	23 26.9	21 56.0	3 15.2

OCTOBER 1991

LONGITUDE

DAY	EPHEM. SID. TIME h m s	☉ ° ′	☊ ° ′	☽ ° ′	☿ ° ′	♀ ° ′	♂ ° ′	♃ ° ′	♄ ° ′	♅ ° ′	♆ ° ′	♇ ° ′
1	0 36 55.3	7♎19.6	14♑40.6	7♋ 2.6	5♎11.4	26♌20.4	19♎25.7	3♍52.4	0♒12.4	9♑53.6	13♑59.8	18♏40.4
2	0 40 51.9	8 18.6	14 37.5	21 9.5	6 58.8	26 54.6	20 5.5	4 4.4	0 R 12.0	9 54.2	13 60.0	18 42.4
3	0 44 48.4	9 17.6	14 34.3	5♌19.3	8 45.5	27 30.1	20 45.4	4 16.2	0 11.8	9 54.9	14 .2	18 44.3
4	0 48 45.0	10 16.7	14 31.1	19 30.6	10 31.4	28 6.9	21 25.4	4 28.0	0 11.6	9 55.6	14 .4	18 46.3
5	0 52 41.5	11 15.8	14 27.9	3♍40.8	12 16.4	28 45.0	22 5.4	4 39.7	0 11.5	9 56.4	14 .7	18 48.3
6	0 56 38.1	12 14.9	14 24.7	17 46.4	14 .7	29 24.3	22 45.4	4 51.4	0 D 11.6	9 57.2	14 1.0	18 50.4
7	1 0 34.6	13 14.1	14 21.6	1♎43.2	15 44.2	0♍ 4.7	23 25.5	5 3.0	0 11.7	9 58.1	14 1.4	18 52.4
8	1 4 31.2	14 13.3	14 18.4	15 26.7	17 26.9	0 46.3	24 5.6	5 14.5	0 12.0	9 59.0	14 1.7	18 54.5
9	1 8 27.7	15 12.6	14 15.2	28 53.2	19 8.8	1 28.9	24 45.8	5 26.0	0 12.3	10 .0	14 2.1	18 56.6
10	1 12 24.3	16 11.8	14 12.0	12♏ .2	20 49.9	2 12.6	25 26.0	5 37.4	0 12.7	10 1.0	14 2.6	18 58.7
11	1 16 20.9	17 11.2	14 8.9	24 47.0	22 30.2	2 57.3	26 6.3	5 48.7	0 13.3	10 2.1	14 3.1	19 .8
12	1 20 17.4	18 10.5	14 5.7	7♐14.5	24 9.8	3 42.9	26 46.6	5 59.9	0 13.9	10 3.2	14 3.6	19 2.9
13	1 24 14.0	19 9.9	14 2.5	19 25.4	25 48.6	4 29.4	27 27.0	6 11.1	0 14.7	10 4.4	14 4.1	19 5.1
14	1 28 10.5	20 9.3	13 59.3	1♑23.7	27 26.7	5 16.9	28 7.4	6 22.3	0 15.6	10 5.7	14 4.8	19 7.3
15	1 32 7.1	21 8.8	13 56.1	13 14.0	29 4.1	6 5.2	28 47.8	6 33.3	0 16.5	10 7.0	14 5.4	19 9.5
16	1 36 3.6	22 8.2	13 53.0	25 1.8	0♏40.8	6 54.3	29 28.3	6 44.2	0 17.6	10 8.3	14 6.0	19 11.7
17	1 40 .2	23 7.7	13 49.8	6♒52.7	2 16.9	7 44.2	0♏ 8.9	6 55.1	0 18.7	10 9.7	14 6.7	19 13.9
18	1 43 56.7	24 7.2	13 46.6	18 52.1	3 52.3	8 34.9	0 49.4	7 5.9	0 20.0	10 11.1	14 7.4	19 16.1
19	1 47 53.3	25 6.8	13 43.4	1♓ 4.9	5 27.0	9 26.4	1 30.1	7 16.6	0 21.3	10 12.6	14 8.1	19 18.4
20	1 51 49.8	26 6.4	13 40.3	13 35.1	7 1.1	10 18.6	2 10.7	7 27.2	0 22.8	10 14.1	14 8.9	19 20.6
21	1 55 46.4	27 6.0	13 37.1	26 25.5	8 34.6	11 11.4	2 51.4	7 37.8	0 24.3	10 15.7	14 9.7	19 22.9
22	1 59 42.9	28 5.6	13 33.9	9♈37.1	10 7.5	12 5.0	3 32.2	7 48.2	0 26.0	10 17.3	14 10.5	19 25.2
23	2 3 39.5	29 5.3	13 30.7	23 9.2	11 39.8	12 59.2	4 13.0	7 58.6	0 27.7	10 18.9	14 11.4	19 27.5
24	2 7 36.1	0♏ 5.0	13 27.5	6♉58.9	13 11.5	13 54.0	4 53.9	8 8.8	0 29.5	10 20.6	14 12.3	19 29.8
25	2 11 32.6	1 4.8	13 24.4	21 2.4	14 42.7	14 49.5	5 34.7	8 19.0	0 31.5	10 22.4	14 13.2	19 32.1
26	2 15 29.2	2 4.6	13 21.2	5♊14.6	16 13.3	15 45.6	6 15.7	8 29.1	0 33.5	10 24.2	14 14.2	19 34.4
27	2 19 25.7	3 4.4	13 18.0	19 30.8	17 43.4	16 42.2	6 56.7	8 39.1	0 35.6	10 26.0	14 15.2	19 36.7
28	2 23 22.3	4 4.2	13 14.8	3♋47.0	19 12.8	17 39.4	7 37.7	8 49.0	0 37.9	10 27.9	14 16.2	19 39.1
29	2 27 18.8	5 4.1	13 11.7	18 .2	20 41.8	18 37.1	8 18.8	8 58.8	0 40.2	10 29.8	14 17.3	19 41.4
30	2 31 15.4	6 4.0	13 8.5	2♌ 8.6	22 10.1	19 35.4	8 59.9	9 8.4	0 42.6	10 31.8	14 18.4	19 43.8
31	2 35 11.9	7 4.0	13 5.3	16 11.1	23 37.9	20 34.1	9 41.1	9 18.0	0 45.1	10 33.8	14 19.5	19 46.2

LATITUDE

DAY	EPHEM. SID. TIME	☉	☊	☽	☿	♀	♂	♃	♄	♅	♆	♇
1	0 36 55.3	0 .0	0 .0	0N42.8	1N28.3	3S50.6	0N26.6	0N50.2	0S32.3	0S22.4	0N46.5	14N37.1
4	0 48 45.0	0 .0	0 .0	2S50.9	1 13.1	3 21.3	0 24.9	0 50.7	0 32.4	0 22.4	0 46.4	14 36.0
7	1 0 34.6	0 .0	0 .0	4 52.8	0 55.8	2 52.9	0 23.3	0 51.1	0 32.5	0 22.4	0 46.3	14 35.0
10	1 12 24.3	0 .0	0 .0	4 25.8	0 36.8	2 25.6	0 21.6	0 51.5	0 32.5	0 22.3	0 46.1	14 34.0
13	1 24 14.0	0 .0	0 .0	2 4.6	0 16.9	1 59.4	0 19.9	0 52.0	0 32.6	0 22.3	0 46.0	14 33.1
16	1 36 3.6	0 .0	0 .0	1N .1	0S 3.6	1 34.4	0 18.2	0 52.5	0 32.7	0 22.3	0 45.9	14 32.3
19	1 47 53.3	0 .0	0 .0	3 43.5	0 24.2	1 10.6	0 16.5	0 53.0	0 32.8	0 22.2	0 45.8	14 31.5
22	1 59 42.9	0 .0	0 .0	5 1.0	0 44.6	0 48.1	0 14.8	0 53.5	0 32.8	0 22.2	0 45.7	14 30.8
25	2 11 32.6	0 .0	0 .0	3 56.7	1 4.5	0 26.8	0 13.1	0 54.0	0 32.9	0 22.2	0 45.6	14 30.1
28	2 23 22.3	0 .0	0 .0	0 44.9	1 23.6	0 6.9	0 11.4	0 54.6	0 33.0	0 22.1	0 45.5	14 29.6
31	2 35 11.9	0 .0	0 .0	2S50.5	1 41.4	0N11.8	0 9.7	0 55.1	0 33.0	0 22.1	0 45.4	14 29.1

RIGHT ASCENSION

DAY	EPHEM. SID. TIME	☉	☊	☽	☿	♀	♂	♃	♄	♅	♆	♇
1	0 36 55.3	6♎43.6	15♑56.0	7♋42.7	5♎20.8	27♌15.4	18♎ 6.0	6♍ 5.0	2♒31.2	10♑47.6	15♑ 6.8	20♏12.4
2	0 40 51.9	7 37.9	15 52.6	22 47.1	6 57.6	27 51.3	18 43.0	6 16.3	2 R 30.8	10 48.3	15 7.0	20 14.1
3	0 44 48.4	8 32.3	15 49.1	7♌14.2	8 33.6	28 28.4	19 20.1	6 27.6	2 30.5	10 49.0	15 7.2	20 15.8
4	0 48 45.0	9 26.7	15 45.7	21 .9	10 9.0	29 6.7	19 57.3	6 38.8	2 30.4	10 49.8	15 7.4	20 17.6
5	0 52 41.5	10 21.2	15 42.3	4♍12.8	11 43.7	29 46.2	20 34.5	6 49.9	2 30.3	10 50.7	15 7.7	20 19.4
6	0 56 38.1	11 15.9	15 38.9	17 .9	13 17.8	0♍26.8	21 11.9	7 1.0	2 30.3	10 51.6	15 8.1	20 21.2
7	1 0 34.6	12 10.6	15 35.4	29 37.9	14 51.3	1 8.4	21 49.4	7 12.1	2 D 30.5	10 52.5	15 8.5	20 23.0
8	1 4 31.2	13 5.4	15 32.0	12♎15.8	16 24.2	1 51.0	22 26.9	7 23.0	2 30.7	10 53.5	15 8.9	20 24.9
9	1 8 27.7	14 .3	15 28.6	25 3.9	17 56.6	2 34.6	23 4.6	7 33.9	2 31.1	10 54.6	15 9.3	20 26.7
10	1 12 24.3	14 55.4	15 25.2	8♏ 7.3	19 28.5	3 19.0	23 42.3	7 44.7	2 31.6	10 55.7	15 9.8	20 28.6
11	1 16 20.9	15 50.5	15 21.7	21 25.7	21 .0	4 4.3	24 20.2	7 55.5	2 32.2	10 56.9	15 10.3	20 30.5
12	1 20 17.4	16 45.7	15 18.3	4♐53.0	22 31.2	4 50.5	24 58.1	8 6.2	2 32.8	10 58.1	15 10.9	20 32.4
13	1 24 14.0	17 41.1	15 14.9	18 18.9	24 1.9	5 37.4	25 36.1	8 16.8	2 33.6	10 59.4	15 11.4	20 34.4
14	1 28 10.5	18 36.7	15 11.5	1♑32.0	25 32.4	6 25.2	26 14.3	8 27.4	2 34.6	11 .8	15 12.1	20 36.4
15	1 32 7.1	19 32.3	15 8.0	14 22.8	27 2.5	7 13.6	26 52.6	8 37.8	2 35.6	11 2.1	15 12.8	20 38.3
16	1 36 3.6	20 28.1	15 4.6	26 46.9	28 32.4	8 2.7	27 30.9	8 48.2	2 36.7	11 3.6	15 13.5	20 40.3
17	1 40 .2	21 23.9	15 1.2	8♒44.9	0♏ 2.1	8 52.5	28 9.4	8 58.5	2 37.9	11 5.1	15 14.2	20 42.3
18	1 43 56.7	22 20.0	14 57.8	20 22.1	1 31.6	9 42.9	28 48.0	9 8.7	2 39.2	11 6.6	15 15.0	20 44.4
19	1 47 53.3	23 16.2	14 54.3	1♓47.3	3 .9	10 33.9	29 26.7	9 18.9	2 40.6	11 8.2	15 15.8	20 46.4
20	1 51 49.8	24 12.5	14 50.9	13 11.8	4 30.1	11 25.4	0♏ 5.5	9 28.9	2 42.1	11 9.9	15 16.6	20 48.4
21	1 55 46.4	25 9.0	14 47.5	24 48.4	5 59.2	12 17.6	0 44.4	9 38.9	2 43.7	11 11.6	15 17.5	20 50.5
22	1 59 42.9	26 5.6	14 44.0	6♈50.8	7 28.2	13 10.2	1 23.4	9 48.8	2 45.4	11 13.3	15 18.4	20 52.6
23	2 3 39.5	27 2.4	14 40.6	19 32.4	8 57.2	14 3.4	2 2.5	9 58.6	2 47.2	11 15.1	15 19.3	20 54.7
24	2 7 36.1	27 59.4	14 37.2	3♉ 3.8	10 26.1	14 57.0	2 41.8	10 8.3	2 49.2	11 17.0	15 20.3	20 56.8
25	2 11 32.6	28 56.6	14 33.8	17 29.4	11 55.0	15 51.2	3 21.2	10 18.0	2 51.2	11 18.9	15 21.3	20 58.9
26	2 15 29.2	29 53.9	14 30.3	2♊43.0	13 23.9	16 45.7	4 .7	10 27.5	2 53.3	11 20.8	15 22.3	21 1.0
27	2 19 25.7	0♏51.4	14 26.9	18 25.4	14 52.7	17 40.7	4 40.3	10 36.9	2 55.5	11 22.8	15 23.4	21 3.2
28	2 23 22.3	1 49.1	14 23.5	4♋ 8.8	16 21.6	18 36.2	5 20.1	10 46.3	2 57.9	11 24.9	15 24.5	21 5.3
29	2 27 18.8	2 47.0	14 20.0	19 25.9	17 50.4	19 32.0	5 59.9	10 55.6	3 .3	11 27.0	15 25.6	21 7.5
30	2 31 15.4	3 45.1	14 16.6	3♌59.8	19 19.2	20 28.2	6 40.0	11 4.7	3 2.8	11 29.1	15 26.8	21 9.6
31	2 35 11.9	4 43.4	14 13.2	17 46.3	20 47.9	21 24.7	7 20.1	11 13.8	3 5.4	11 31.3	15 28.0	21 11.8

DECLINATION

DAY	EPHEM. SID. TIME	☉	☊	☽	☿	♀	♂	♃	♄	♅	♆	♇
1	0 36 55.3	2S54.5	0S23.7	23N58.0	0S42.7	9N 7.2	7S11.6	10N52.1	20S38.0	23S26.7	21S56.1	3S17.8
4	0 48 45.0	4 4.2	0 23.7	12 15.7	3 2.7	8 58.8	7 58.2	10 39.6	20 38.3	23 26.5	21 56.2	3 20.4
7	1 0 34.6	5 13.5	0 23.7	5S 9.6	5 20.1	8 44.8	8 44.3	10 27.2	20 38.3	23 26.3	21 56.2	3 22.9
10	1 12 24.3	6 22.3	0 23.8	19 39.0	7 33.8	8 25.3	9 30.1	10 14.9	20 38.2	23 26.0	21 56.1	3 25.4
13	1 24 14.0	7 30.2	0 23.8	25 5.4	9 42.7	8 .7	10 15.4	10 2.9	20 37.9	23 25.8	21 56.1	3 27.9
16	1 36 3.6	8 37.3	0 23.8	20 8.6	11 46.0	7 30.9	11 .1	9 51.1	20 37.3	23 25.4	21 56.0	3 30.4
19	1 47 53.3	9 43.2	0 23.8	7 36.3	13 43.2	6 56.4	11 44.3	9 39.5	20 36.6	23 25.1	21 55.9	3 32.8
22	1 59 42.9	10 47.8	0 23.8	8N25.2	15 33.6	6 17.3	12 27.8	9 28.2	20 35.6	23 24.7	21 55.7	3 35.2
25	2 11 32.6	11 51.0	0 23.8	21 49.3	17 16.8	5 33.9	13 10.6	9 17.2	20 34.5	23 24.2	21 55.6	3 37.6
28	2 23 22.3	12 52.6	0 23.9	24 8.1	18 52.2	4 46.3	13 52.6	9 6.5	20 33.2	23 23.8	21 55.3	3 39.9
31	2 35 11.9	13 52.4	0 23.9	13 16.3	20 19.1	3 55.1	14 33.8	8 56.1	20 31.7	23 23.3	21 55.1	3 42.2

NOVEMBER 1991

LONGITUDE

DAY	EPHEM. SID. TIME h m s	☉ ° ′	☊ ° ′	☽ ° ′	☿ ° ′	♀ ° ′	♂ ° ′	♃ ° ′	♄ ° ′	♅ ° ′	♆ ° ′	♇ ° ′
1	2 39 8.5	8♏ 4.0	13♑ 2.1	0♍ 7.2	25♏ 5.1	21♍33.4	10♏22.4	9♍27.5	0♒47.7	10♑35.9	14♑20.6	19♏48.5
2	2 43 5.0	9 4.0	12 58.9	13 56.0	26 31.6	22 33.1	11 3.7	9 36.9	0 50.4	10 38.0	14 21.8	19 50.9
3	2 47 1.6	10 4.1	12 55.8	27 36.5	27 57.5	23 33.2	11 45.0	9 46.2	0 53.2	10 40.1	14 23.0	19 53.3
4	2 50 58.2	11 4.2	12 52.6	11♎ 7.1	29 22.8	24 33.9	12 26.4	9 55.4	0 56.1	10 42.4	14 24.3	19 55.7
5	2 54 54.7	12 4.4	12 49.4	24 25.9	0♐47.4	25 34.9	13 7.9	10 4.4	0 59.1	10 44.6	14 25.5	19 58.1
6	2 58 51.3	13 4.5	12 46.2	7♏31.0	2 11.1	26 36.3	13 49.3	10 13.4	1 2.2	10 46.9	14 26.8	20 .5
7	3 2 47.8	14 4.7	12 43.1	20 21.1	3 34.1	27 38.1	14 30.9	10 22.2	1 5.3	10 49.2	14 28.2	20 2.9
8	3 6 44.4	15 5.0	12 39.9	2♐55.7	4 56.1	28 40.3	15 12.5	10 30.9	1 8.6	10 51.6	14 29.5	20 5.4
9	3 10 40.9	16 5.2	12 36.7	15 15.3	6 17.2	29 42.9	15 54.1	10 39.4	1 11.9	10 53.9	14 30.9	20 7.8
10	3 14 37.5	17 5.5	12 33.5	27 21.6	7 37.2	0♎45.8	16 35.7	10 47.9	1 15.3	10 56.4	14 32.3	20 10.2
11	3 18 34.0	18 5.8	12 30.4	9♑17.3	8 56.0	1 49.1	17 17.5	10 56.2	1 18.8	10 58.8	14 33.7	20 12.6
12	3 22 30.6	19 6.2	12 27.2	21 6.4	10 13.5	2 52.7	17 59.2	11 4.4	1 22.4	11 1.4	14 35.2	20 15.0
13	3 26 27.2	20 6.5	12 24.0	2♒53.3	11 29.6	3 56.6	18 41.0	11 12.5	1 26.1	11 3.9	14 36.7	20 17.4
14	3 30 23.7	21 6.9	12 20.8	14 43.1	12 44.0	5 .9	19 22.9	11 20.5	1 29.9	11 6.5	14 38.2	20 19.9
15	3 34 20.3	22 7.3	12 17.6	26 41.2	13 56.6	6 5.4	20 4.8	11 28.3	1 33.7	11 9.1	14 39.7	20 22.3
16	3 38 16.8	23 7.7	12 14.5	8♓52.9	15 7.1	7 10.3	20 46.8	11 36.0	1 37.7	11 11.8	14 41.3	20 24.7
17	3 42 13.4	24 8.2	12 11.3	21 23.1	16 15.3	8 15.4	21 28.7	11 43.5	1 41.7	11 14.4	14 42.9	20 27.1
18	3 46 9.9	25 8.7	12 8.1	4♈15.5	17 20.9	9 20.8	22 10.8	11 50.9	1 45.8	11 17.2	14 44.5	20 29.5
19	3 50 6.5	26 9.2	12 4.9	17 32.8	18 23.5	10 26.5	22 52.9	11 58.2	1 50.0	11 19.9	14 46.1	20 31.9
20	3 54 3.1	27 9.7	12 1.8	1♉15.3	19 22.7	11 32.5	23 35.0	12 5.4	1 54.2	11 22.7	14 47.8	20 34.3
21	3 57 59.6	28 10.2	11 58.6	15 21.0	20 18.1	12 38.7	24 17.2	12 12.4	1 58.5	11 25.5	14 49.5	20 36.7
22	4 1 56.2	29 10.8	11 55.4	29 45.8	21 9.1	13 45.2	24 59.4	12 19.2	2 3.0	11 28.4	14 51.2	20 39.1
23	4 5 52.7	0♐11.4	11 52.2	14♊23.5	21 55.3	14 51.9	25 41.7	12 25.9	2 7.4	11 31.3	14 52.9	20 41.5
24	4 9 49.3	1 12.0	11 49.1	29 7.0	22 36.0	15 58.9	26 24.0	12 32.5	2 12.0	11 34.2	14 54.6	20 43.9
25	4 13 45.8	2 12.7	11 45.9	13♋49.3	23 10.5	17 6.1	27 6.5	12 39.0	2 16.7	11 37.2	14 56.5	20 46.4
26	4 17 42.4	3 13.3	11 42.7	28 24.4	23 38.0	18 13.6	27 48.9	12 45.3	2 21.4	11 40.1	14 58.3	20 48.7
27	4 21 39.0	4 14.0	11 39.5	12♌48.0	23 57.8	19 21.2	28 31.4	12 51.4	2 26.2	11 43.1	15 .1	20 51.1
28	4 25 35.5	5 14.8	11 36.3	26 57.5	24 9.1	20 29.1	29 13.9	12 57.3	2 31.1	11 46.2	15 1.9	20 53.5
29	4 29 32.1	6 15.5	11 33.2	10♍51.6	24 11.1	21 37.2	29 56.5	13 3.2	2 36.0	11 49.2	15 3.8	20 55.8
30	4 33 28.6	7 16.3	11 30.0	24 30.2	24 R 3.0	22 45.5	0♐39.1	13 8.8	2 41.0	11 52.3	15 5.6	20 58.2

LATITUDE

DAY	SID. TIME	☉	☊	☽	☿	♀	♂	♃	♄	♅	♆	♇
1	2 39 8.5	0 .0	0 .0	3S46.4	1S47.1	0N17.7	0N 9.1	0N55.3	0S33.1	0S22.1	0N45.4	14N28.9
4	2 50 58.2	0 .0	0 .0	5 4.0	2 2.7	0 34.6	0 7.3	0 55.9	0 33.1	0 22.1	0 45.3	14 28.5
7	3 2 47.8	0 .0	0 .0	3 57.3	2 16.3	0 50.3	0 5.6	0 56.5	0 33.2	0 22.1	0 45.2	14 28.1
10	3 14 37.5	0 .0	0 .0	1 12.9	2 27.1	1 4.6	0 3.8	0 57.2	0 33.3	0 22.0	0 45.1	14 27.9
13	3 26 27.2	0 .0	0 .0	1N55.3	2 34.6	1 17.7	0 2.0	0 57.8	0 33.3	0 22.0	0 45.0	14 27.7
16	3 38 16.8	0 .0	0 .0	4 22.0	2 37.9	1 29.5	0 .3	0 58.5	0 33.4	0 22.0	0 44.9	14 27.6
19	3 50 6.5	0 .0	0 .0	5 6.9	2 35.6	1 40.0	0S 1.5	0 59.1	0 33.5	0 22.0	0 44.8	14 27.5
22	4 1 56.2	0 .0	0 .0	3 22.4	2 26.4	1 49.3	0 3.3	0 59.8	0 33.6	0 22.0	0 44.7	14 27.5
25	4 13 45.8	0 .0	0 .0	0S19.1	2 8.3	1 57.4	0 5.1	1 .6	0 33.6	0 21.9	0 44.7	14 27.6
28	4 25 35.5	0 .0	0 .0	3 47.4	1 39.1	2 4.2	0 7.0	1 1.3	0 33.7	0 21.9	0 44.6	14 27.8

RIGHT ASCENSION

DAY	SID. TIME	☉	☊	☽	☿	♀	♂	♃	♄	♅	♆	♇
1	2 39 8.5	5♏41.9	14♑ 9.8	0♍51.9	22♏16.6	22♍21.6	8♏ .4	11♍22.7	3♒ 8.1	11♑33.5	15♑29.2	21♏14.0
2	2 43 5.0	6 40.6	14 6.3	13 28.7	23 45.2	23 18.9	8 40.8	11 31.6	3 11.0	11 35.8	15 30.5	21 16.2
3	2 47 1.6	7 39.5	14 2.9	25 51.1	25 13.6	24 16.5	9 21.3	11 40.4	3 13.9	11 38.2	15 31.8	21 18.4
4	2 50 58.2	8 38.6	13 59.5	8♎12.9	26 41.9	25 14.4	10 2.0	11 49.1	3 16.9	11 40.6	15 33.1	21 20.6
5	2 54 54.7	9 37.9	13 56.0	20 45.4	28 9.9	26 12.6	10 42.8	11 57.6	3 20.0	11 43.0	15 34.5	21 22.9
6	2 58 51.3	10 37.4	13 52.6	3♏36.0	29 37.6	27 11.1	11 23.8	12 6.0	3 23.2	11 45.5	15 35.9	21 25.1
7	3 2 47.8	11 37.2	13 49.2	16 46.7	1♐ 4.9	28 9.8	12 4.8	12 14.4	3 26.5	11 48.0	15 37.3	21 27.3
8	3 6 44.4	12 37.1	13 45.7	0♐12.6	2 31.8	29 8.9	12 46.1	12 22.6	3 29.9	11 50.5	15 38.8	21 29.6
9	3 10 40.9	13 37.2	13 42.3	13 43.5	3 58.0	0♎ 8.2	13 27.4	12 30.7	3 33.4	11 53.1	15 40.2	21 31.8
10	3 14 37.5	14 37.6	13 38.9	27 5.7	5 23.5	1 7.8	14 8.9	12 38.7	3 37.0	11 55.8	15 41.7	21 34.0
11	3 18 34.0	15 38.1	13 35.4	10♑ 7.2	6 48.2	2 7.6	14 50.5	12 46.6	3 40.6	11 58.5	15 43.3	21 36.3
12	3 22 30.6	16 38.9	13 32.0	22 40.1	8 11.8	3 7.7	15 32.3	12 54.3	3 44.4	12 1.2	15 44.8	21 38.5
13	3 26 27.2	17 39.9	13 28.6	4♒42.9	9 34.2	4 8.0	16 14.2	13 1.9	3 48.2	12 3.9	15 46.4	21 40.8
14	3 30 23.7	18 41.1	13 25.1	16 19.5	10 55.1	5 8.6	16 56.2	13 9.5	3 52.1	12 6.7	15 48.1	21 43.1
15	3 34 20.3	19 42.4	13 21.7	27 38.4	12 14.3	6 9.4	17 38.4	13 16.8	3 56.1	12 9.6	15 49.7	21 45.3
16	3 38 16.8	20 44.0	13 18.3	8♓50.9	13 31.5	7 10.5	18 20.7	13 24.1	4 .2	12 12.5	15 51.4	21 47.6
17	3 42 13.4	21 45.9	13 14.8	20 10.5	14 46.4	8 11.8	19 3.1	13 31.2	4 4.4	12 15.4	15 53.1	21 49.8
18	3 46 9.9	22 47.9	13 11.4	1♈52.1	15 58.6	9 13.3	19 45.7	13 38.3	4 8.7	12 18.3	15 54.8	21 52.1
19	3 50 6.5	23 50.1	13 8.0	14 11.1	17 7.7	10 15.1	20 28.5	13 45.1	4 13.0	12 21.3	15 56.6	21 54.4
20	3 54 3.1	24 52.5	13 4.5	27 21.8	18 13.3	11 17.1	21 11.3	13 51.9	4 17.5	12 24.3	15 58.4	21 56.6
21	3 57 59.6	25 55.1	13 1.1	11♉34.0	19 14.7	12 19.4	21 54.4	13 58.5	4 22.0	12 27.4	16 .2	21 58.9
22	4 1 56.2	26 57.9	12 57.7	26 47.3	20 11.4	13 21.9	22 37.5	14 5.0	4 26.6	12 30.5	16 2.0	22 1.1
23	4 5 52.7	28 .9	12 54.2	12♊46.5	21 2.8	14 24.6	23 20.8	14 11.3	4 31.2	12 33.6	16 3.8	22 3.4
24	4 9 49.3	29 4.2	12 50.8	29 1.8	21 48.2	15 27.6	24 4.3	14 17.6	4 36.0	12 36.8	16 5.7	22 5.6
25	4 13 45.8	0♐ 7.6	12 47.4	14♋58.5	22 26.7	16 30.9	24 47.9	14 23.7	4 40.8	12 40.0	16 7.7	22 7.9
26	4 17 42.4	1 11.2	12 43.9	0♌10.4	22 57.6	17 34.4	25 31.6	14 29.6	4 45.7	12 43.3	16 9.6	22 10.2
27	4 21 39.0	2 15.0	12 40.5	14 27.0	23 20.0	18 38.2	26 15.5	14 35.4	4 50.7	12 46.5	16 11.6	22 12.4
28	4 25 35.5	3 19.0	12 37.1	27 51.7	23 33.0	19 42.2	26 59.5	14 41.1	4 55.8	12 49.8	16 13.5	22 14.7
29	4 29 32.1	4 23.2	12 33.6	10♍36.9	23 35.7	20 46.4	27 43.7	14 46.6	5 .9	12 53.1	16 15.5	22 16.9
30	4 33 28.6	5 27.6	12 30.2	22 58.1	23 R 27.6	21 50.9	28 28.0	14 52.0	5 6.1	12 56.5	16 17.5	22 19.1

DECLINATION

DAY	SID. TIME	☉	☊	☽	☿	♀	♂	♃	♄	♅	♆	♇
1	2 39 8.5	14S11.9	0S23.9	7N53.8	20S46.2	3N37.2	14S47.3	8N52.7	20S31.2	23S23.1	21S55.0	3S42.9
4	2 50 58.2	15 9.0	0 23.9	9S 3.5	22 1.0	2 41.3	15 27.3	8 42.7	20 29.4	23 22.6	21 54.7	3 45.1
7	3 2 47.8	16 3.9	0 23.9	21 38.6	23 5.9	1 42.5	16 6.3	8 33.1	20 27.4	23 22.0	21 54.4	3 47.2
10	3 14 37.5	16 56.4	0 23.9	24 37.8	24 .1	0 41.1	16 44.3	8 24.0	20 25.3	23 21.4	21 54.0	3 49.3
13	3 26 27.2	17 46.3	0 23.9	17 38.6	24 42.9	0S22.7	17 21.1	8 15.2	20 23.0	23 20.7	21 53.7	3 51.2
16	3 38 16.8	18 33.4	0 24.0	4 11.4	25 13.5	1 28.6	17 56.7	8 6.9	20 20.5	23 20.0	21 53.2	3 53.2
19	3 50 6.5	19 17.5	0 24.0	11N36.6	25 31.0	2 36.0	18 31.1	7 59.0	20 17.8	23 19.3	21 52.8	3 55.0
22	4 1 56.2	19 58.5	0 24.0	23 23.7	25 34.8	3 44.8	19 4.2	7 51.6	20 15.0	23 18.6	21 52.3	3 56.7
25	4 13 45.8	20 36.3	0 24.0	22 24.4	25 24.0	4 54.6	19 35.8	7 44.7	20 12.0	23 17.8	21 51.8	3 58.4
28	4 25 35.5	21 10.6	0 24.0	8 57.7	24 57.7	6 5.0	20 6.0	7 38.4	20 8.8	23 17.0	21 51.3	3 60.0

DECEMBER 1991

LONGITUDE

DAY	EPHEM. SID. TIME h m s	☉ ° ′	☊ ° ′	☽ ° ′	☿ ° ′	♀ ° ′	♂ ° ′	♃ ° ′	♄ ° ′	♅ ° ′	♆ ° ′	♇ ° ′
1	4 37 25.2	8♐17.1	11♑26.8	7♎53.8	23♐44.3	23♎53.9	1♐21.8	13♍14.3	2♒46.1	11♑55.4	15♑ 7.5	21♏ .5
2	4 41 21.7	9 17.9	11 23.6	21 3.2	23R14.6	25 2.6	2 4.5	13 19.6	2 51.2	11 58.6	15 9.5	21 2.8
3	4 45 18.3	10 18.7	11 20.5	3♏58.8	22 33.8	26 11.4	2 47.3	13 24.8	2 56.4	12 1.7	15 11.4	21 5.2
4	4 49 14.9	11 19.6	11 17.3	16 41.5	21 42.3	27 20.5	3 30.1	13 29.8	3 1.7	12 4.9	15 13.4	21 7.5
5	4 53 11.4	12 20.5	11 14.1	29 11.8	20 40.7	28 29.7	4 13.0	13 34.7	3 7.0	12 8.1	15 15.3	21 9.8
6	4 57 8.0	13 21.4	11 10.9	11♐30.5	19 30.6	29 39.0	4 55.9	13 39.3	3 12.4	12 11.4	15 17.3	21 12.0
7	5 1 4.5	14 22.3	11 7.8	23 38.6	18 13.7	0♏48.5	5 38.8	13 43.8	3 17.9	12 14.6	15 19.3	21 14.3
8	5 5 1.1	15 23.3	11 4.6	5♑37.5	16 52.4	1 58.2	6 21.9	13 48.2	3 23.4	12 17.9	15 21.3	21 16.6
9	5 8 57.6	16 24.2	11 1.4	17 29.5	15 29.4	3 8.0	7 4.9	13 52.3	3 29.0	12 21.2	15 23.4	21 18.8
10	5 12 54.2	17 25.2	10 58.2	29 17.0	14 7.6	4 18.0	7 48.0	13 56.3	3 34.6	12 24.5	15 25.4	21 21.0
11	5 16 50.8	18 26.2	10 55.0	11♒ 3.6	12 49.5	5 28.1	8 31.2	14 .1	3 40.3	12 27.9	15 27.5	21 23.3
12	5 20 47.3	19 27.2	10 51.9	22 53.0	11 37.8	6 38.3	9 14.4	14 3.8	3 46.1	12 31.2	15 29.6	21 25.5
13	5 24 43.9	20 28.2	10 48.7	4♓49.8	10 34.4	7 48.7	9 57.6	14 7.2	3 51.9	12 34.6	15 31.7	21 27.7
14	5 28 40.4	21 29.2	10 45.5	16 58.7	9 40.8	8 59.2	10 40.9	14 10.5	3 57.8	12 38.0	15 33.8	21 29.8
15	5 32 37.0	22 30.2	10 42.3	29 24.5	8 57.9	10 9.8	11 24.2	14 13.6	4 3.7	12 41.4	15 35.9	21 32.0
16	5 36 33.6	23 31.3	10 39.2	12♈11.8	8 26.2	11 20.5	12 7.7	14 16.5	4 9.7	12 44.9	15 38.1	21 34.2
17	5 40 30.1	24 32.3	10 36.0	25 23.9	8 5.5	12 31.4	12 51.1	14 19.2	4 15.8	12 48.3	15 40.2	21 36.3
18	5 44 26.7	25 33.4	10 32.8	9♉ 3.3	7 55.6	13 42.4	13 34.5	14 21.8	4 21.9	12 51.8	15 42.4	21 38.4
19	5 48 23.2	26 34.4	10 29.6	23 9.9	7D55.9	14 53.4	14 18.1	14 24.1	4 28.0	12 55.2	15 44.5	21 40.5
20	5 52 19.8	27 35.5	10 26.5	7♊41.3	8 5.8	16 4.6	15 1.6	14 26.3	4 34.2	12 58.7	15 46.7	21 42.5
21	5 56 16.3	28 36.6	10 23.3	22 32.3	8 24.4	17 15.9	15 45.2	14 28.3	4 40.4	13 2.2	15 48.9	21 44.6
22	6 0 12.9	29 37.6	10 20.1	7♋35.3	8 50.9	18 27.3	16 28.9	14 30.1	4 46.7	13 5.7	15 51.1	21 46.6
23	6 4 9.5	0♑38.7	10 16.9	22 41.5	9 24.6	19 38.8	17 12.6	14 31.7	4 53.0	13 9.2	15 53.3	21 48.6
24	6 8 6.0	1 39.8	10 13.8	7♌41.9	10 4.7	20 50.4	17 56.3	14 33.1	4 59.3	13 12.7	15 55.5	21 50.6
25	6 12 2.6	2 40.9	10 10.6	22 28.8	10 50.4	22 2.1	18 40.1	14 34.4	5 5.7	13 16.3	15 57.7	21 52.5
26	6 15 59.1	3 42.0	10 7.4	6♍56.5	11 41.2	23 13.9	19 23.9	14 35.4	5 12.2	13 19.8	15 60.0	21 54.5
27	6 19 55.7	4 43.1	10 4.2	21 1.8	12 36.4	24 25.8	20 7.8	14 36.3	5 18.7	13 23.4	16 2.2	21 56.4
28	6 23 52.2	5 44.3	10 1.0	4♎43.7	13 35.6	25 37.8	20 51.7	14 36.9	5 25.2	13 26.9	16 4.4	21 58.3
29	6 27 48.8	6 45.4	9 57.9	18 3.1	14 38.3	26 49.9	21 35.7	14 37.4	5 31.8	13 30.5	16 6.7	22 .2
30	6 31 45.4	7 46.6	9 54.7	1♏ 1.9	15 44.0	28 2.0	22 19.7	14 37.6	5 38.4	13 34.0	16 8.9	22 2.0
31	6 35 41.9	8 47.7	9 51.5	13 43.0	16 52.4	29 14.2	23 3.8	14 37.7	5 45.0	13 37.6	16 11.2	22 3.8

LATITUDE

DAY	EPHEM. SID. TIME	☉	☊	☽	☿	♀	♂	♃	♄	♅	♆	♇
1	4 37 25.2	0 .0	0 .0	5S12.3	0S57.1	2N 9.9	0S 8.8	1N 2.0	0S33.8	0S21.9	0N44.5	14N28.0
4	4 49 14.9	0 .0	0 .0	4 11.5	0 2.9	2 14.4	0 10.6	1 2.8	0 33.9	0 21.9	0 44.4	14 28.3
7	5 1 4.5	0 .0	0 .0	1 28.2	0N57.7	2 17.8	0 12.4	1 3.6	0 34.0	0 21.9	0 44.4	14 28.7
10	5 12 54.2	0 .0	0 .0	1N45.2	1 53.2	2 20.1	0 14.2	1 4.3	0 34.1	0 21.9	0 44.3	14 29.1
13	5 24 43.9	0 .0	0 .0	4 19.2	2 32.5	2 21.4	0 16.1	1 5.1	0 34.2	0 21.9	0 44.2	14 29.6
16	5 36 33.6	0 .0	0 .0	5 16.5	2 51.2	2 21.6	0 17.9	1 5.9	0 34.3	0 21.9	0 44.2	14 30.2
19	5 48 23.2	0 .0	0 .0	3 51.0	2 52.4	2 20.8	0 19.8	1 6.8	0 34.4	0 21.9	0 44.1	14 30.9
22	6 0 12.9	0 .0	0 .0	0 12.4	2 41.2	2 19.1	0 21.6	1 7.6	0 34.5	0 21.9	0 44.1	14 31.6
25	6 12 2.6	0 .0	0 .0	3S35.7	2 22.6	2 16.6	0 23.5	1 8.4	0 34.7	0 21.9	0 44.0	14 32.3
28	6 23 52.2	0 .0	0 .0	5 16.7	1 59.8	2 13.2	0 25.3	1 9.2	0 34.8	0 22.0	0 44.0	14 33.1
31	6 35 41.9	0 .0	0 .0	4 24.3	1 34.9	2 9.0	0 27.1	1 10.1	0 34.9	0 22.0	0 43.9	14 34.0

RIGHT ASCENSION

DAY	EPHEM. SID. TIME	☉	☊	☽	☿	♀	♂	♃	♄	♅	♆	♇
1	4 37 25.2	6♐32.1	12♑26.7	5♎10.9	23♐ 7.9	22♎55.7	29♏12.5	14♍57.2	5♒11.3	12♑59.8	16♑19.6	22♏21.3
2	4 41 21.7	7 36.8	12 23.3	17 29.0	22R36.3	24 .7	29 57.1	15 2.2	5 16.7	13 3.2	16 21.6	22 23.5
3	4 45 18.3	8 41.7	12 19.9	0♏ 2.6	21 52.9	25 6.0	0♐41.8	15 7.1	5 22.1	13 6.7	16 23.7	22 25.7
4	4 49 14.9	9 46.7	12 16.4	12 56.9	20 58.0	26 11.5	1 26.7	15 11.9	5 27.5	13 10.1	16 25.8	22 27.9
5	4 53 11.4	10 51.9	12 13.0	26 10.6	19 52.7	27 17.4	2 11.7	15 16.5	5 33.1	13 13.6	16 27.9	22 30.1
6	4 57 8.0	11 57.2	12 9.6	9♐35.9	18 38.6	28 23.4	2 56.8	15 21.0	5 38.7	13 17.1	16 30.0	22 32.3
7	5 1 4.5	13 2.7	12 6.1	22 59.9	17 17.6	29 29.8	3 42.1	15 25.2	5 44.3	13 20.6	16 32.2	22 34.5
8	5 5 1.1	14 8.2	12 2.7	6♑ 8.8	15 52.5	0♏36.4	4 27.5	15 29.4	5 50.0	13 24.2	16 34.3	22 36.6
9	5 8 57.6	15 13.9	11 59.2	18 51.5	14 26.0	1 43.3	5 13.1	15 33.3	5 55.8	13 27.8	16 36.5	22 38.8
10	5 12 54.2	16 19.8	11 55.8	1♒ 3.1	13 1.0	2 50.5	5 58.8	15 37.2	6 1.7	13 31.4	16 38.7	22 40.9
11	5 16 50.8	17 25.7	11 52.4	12 44.5	11 40.4	3 58.0	6 44.6	15 40.8	6 7.6	13 35.0	16 40.9	22 43.0
12	5 20 47.3	18 31.7	11 48.9	24 2.0	10 26.6	5 5.7	7 30.5	15 44.3	6 13.5	13 38.6	16 43.2	22 45.2
13	5 24 43.9	19 37.8	11 45.5	5♓ 5.6	9 21.5	6 13.7	8 16.6	15 47.6	6 19.6	13 42.3	16 45.4	22 47.2
14	5 28 40.4	20 44.0	11 42.0	16 7.9	8 26.6	7 22.1	9 2.8	15 50.7	6 25.6	13 46.0	16 47.7	22 49.3
15	5 32 37.0	21 50.3	11 38.6	27 23.4	7 42.7	8 30.7	9 49.1	15 53.7	6 31.8	13 49.6	16 49.9	22 51.4
16	5 36 33.6	22 56.7	11 35.2	9♈ 7.9	7 10.2	9 39.6	10 35.6	15 56.6	6 38.0	13 53.4	16 52.3	22 53.5
17	5 40 30.1	24 3.1	11 31.7	21 37.4	6 49.0	10 48.9	11 22.1	15 59.2	6 44.2	13 57.1	16 54.6	22 55.6
18	5 44 26.7	25 9.5	11 28.3	5♉ 6.6	6 38.8	11 58.4	12 8.8	16 1.7	6 50.5	14 .9	16 56.9	22 57.6
19	5 48 23.2	26 16.0	11 24.8	19 43.5	6D38.9	13 8.2	12 55.5	16 4.0	6 56.9	14 4.6	16 59.2	22 59.6
20	5 52 19.8	27 22.5	11 21.4	5♊24.0	6 48.7	14 18.4	13 42.4	16 6.1	7 3.2	14 8.4	17 1.5	23 1.6
21	5 56 16.3	28 29.1	11 18.0	21 46.7	7 7.5	15 28.8	14 29.4	16 8.1	7 9.7	14 12.2	17 3.9	23 3.6
22	6 0 12.9	29 35.6	11 14.5	8♋16.5	7 34.5	16 39.6	15 16.6	16 9.8	7 16.1	14 16.0	17 6.2	23 5.5
23	6 4 9.5	0♑42.2	11 11.1	24 17.6	8 8.8	17 50.7	16 3.8	16 11.4	7 22.7	14 19.8	17 8.6	23 7.5
24	6 8 6.0	1 48.8	11 7.6	9♌26.9	8 49.8	19 2.1	16 51.1	16 12.9	7 29.2	14 23.6	17 11.0	23 9.4
25	6 12 2.6	2 55.4	11 4.2	23 38.7	9 36.8	20 13.8	17 38.5	16 14.1	7 35.8	14 27.4	17 13.3	23 11.3
26	6 15 59.1	4 1.9	11 .8	7♍ .7	10 29.2	21 25.8	18 26.1	16 15.2	7 42.5	14 31.2	17 15.7	23 13.2
27	6 19 55.7	5 8.5	10 57.3	19 47.1	11 26.4	22 38.2	19 13.7	16 16.1	7 49.2	14 35.1	17 18.1	23 15.1
28	6 23 52.2	6 15.0	10 53.9	2♎14.0	12 28.0	23 50.9	20 1.5	16 16.8	7 55.9	14 38.9	17 20.5	23 16.9
29	6 27 48.8	7 21.5	10 50.4	14 36.4	13 33.4	25 3.9	20 49.3	16 17.3	8 2.6	14 42.8	17 22.9	23 18.8
30	6 31 45.4	8 28.0	10 47.0	27 6.3	14 42.3	26 17.2	21 37.2	16 17.7	8 9.5	14 46.6	17 25.3	23 20.6
31	6 35 41.9	9 34.4	10 43.5	9♏51.4	15 54.4	27 30.8	22 25.2	16 17.9	8 16.3	14 50.5	17 27.7	23 22.4

DECLINATION

DAY	EPHEM. SID. TIME	☉	☊	☽	☿	♀	♂	♃	♄	♅	♆	♇
1	4 37 25.2	21S41.4	0S24.0	7S54.8	24S14.6	7S15.6	20S34.7	7N32.5	20S 5.4	23S16.2	21S50.7	4S 1.5
4	4 49 14.9	22 8.4	0 24.0	20 50.4	23 13.8	8 26.2	21 1.7	7 27.3	20 1.9	23 15.3	21 50.2	4 2.9
7	5 1 4.5	22 31.5	0 24.1	24 45.4	21 57.7	9 36.1	21 27.1	7 22.6	19 58.3	23 14.4	21 49.6	4 4.1
10	5 12 54.2	22 50.7	0 24.1	18 35.2	20 37.3	10 45.3	21 50.8	7 18.5	19 54.5	23 13.5	21 48.9	4 5.3
13	5 24 43.9	23 5.9	0 24.1	5 42.9	19 31.1	11 53.1	22 12.6	7 15.0	19 50.5	23 12.6	21 48.3	4 6.4
16	5 36 33.6	23 16.9	0 24.1	9N40.4	18 53.6	12 59.4	22 32.6	7 12.2	19 46.4	23 11.6	21 47.6	4 7.4
19	5 48 23.2	23 23.8	0 24.1	22 17.3	18 47.8	14 3.6	22 50.7	7 10.0	19 42.2	23 10.6	21 46.9	4 8.3
22	6 0 12.9	23 26.4	0 24.1	23 25.8	19 7.3	15 5.5	23 6.7	7 8.4	19 37.8	23 9.6	21 46.2	4 9.1
25	6 12 2.6	23 24.8	0 24.1	10 37.2	19 43.1	16 4.6	23 20.8	7 7.6	19 33.3	23 8.6	21 45.4	4 9.8
28	6 23 52.2	23 19.0	0 24.2	6S43.3	20 27.1	17 .7	23 32.8	7 7.3	19 28.7	23 7.5	21 44.7	4 10.4
31	6 35 41.9	23 8.9	0 24.2	20 9.4	21 13.1	17 53.3	23 42.6	7 7.8	19 24.0	23 6.5	21 43.9	4 10.9

JANUARY 1992

LONGITUDE

DAY	EPHEM. SID. TIME (h m s)	☉	☊	☾	☿	♀	♂	♃	♄	♅	♆	♇
		° ′	° ′	° ′	° ′	° ′	° ′	° ′	° ′	° ′	° ′	° ′
1	6 39 38.5	9♑48.9	9♑48.3	26♏ 9.0	18♐ 3.3	0♐26.5	23♐47.9	14♍37.6	5♒51.7	13♑41.2	16♑13.5	22♏ 5.6
2	6 43 35.0	10 50.1	9 45.2	8♐22.8	19 16.3	1 38.9	24 32.1	14 R37.3	5 58.4	13 44.8	16 15.7	22 7.4
3	6 47 31.6	11 51.2	9 42.0	20 27.0	20 31.2	2 51.3	25 16.3	14 36.7	6 5.1	13 48.4	16 18.0	22 9.2
4	6 51 28.2	12 52.4	9 38.8	2♑23.8	21 47.7	4 3.8	26 .5	14 36.0	6 11.9	13 51.9	16 20.3	22 10.9
5	6 55 24.7	13 53.6	9 35.6	14 15.5	23 5.8	5 16.4	26 44.8	14 35.1	6 18.7	13 55.5	16 22.5	22 12.6
6	6 59 21.3	14 54.8	9 32.5	26 4.1	24 25.3	6 29.1	27 29.2	14 34.1	6 25.6	13 59.1	16 24.9	22 14.3
7	7 3 17.8	15 56.0	9 29.3	7♒51.6	25 46.0	7 41.8	28 13.6	14 32.8	6 32.5	14 2.7	16 27.1	22 15.9
8	7 7 14.4	16 57.2	9 26.1	19 40.3	27 7.8	8 54.5	28 58.0	14 31.3	6 39.4	14 6.3	16 29.4	22 17.6
9	7 11 10.9	17 58.3	9 22.9	1♓32.9	28 30.6	10 7.3	29 42.4	14 29.6	6 46.3	14 9.9	16 31.7	22 19.1
10	7 15 7.5	18 59.5	9 19.8	13 32.2	29 54.3	11 20.2	0♑26.9	14 27.7	6 53.2	14 13.5	16 34.0	22 20.7
11	7 19 4.1	20 .6	9 16.6	25 41.8	1♑18.9	12 33.1	1 11.5	14 25.6	7 .2	14 17.0	16 36.2	22 22.2
12	7 23 .6	21 1.8	9 13.4	8♈ 5.4	2 44.3	13 46.0	1 56.0	14 23.4	7 7.1	14 20.6	16 38.5	22 23.7
13	7 26 57.2	22 2.9	9 10.2	20 47.0	4 10.5	14 59.0	2 40.7	14 20.9	7 14.1	14 24.2	16 40.8	22 25.2
14	7 30 53.7	23 4.0	9 7.0	3♉50.3	5 37.4	16 12.1	3 25.3	14 18.3	7 21.2	14 27.7	16 43.0	22 26.6
15	7 34 50.3	24 5.2	9 3.9	17 18.4	7 5.0	17 25.1	4 10.0	14 15.5	7 28.2	14 31.3	16 45.3	22 28.1
16	7 38 46.8	25 6.3	9 .7	1♊13.2	8 33.2	18 38.3	4 54.7	14 12.5	7 35.3	14 34.8	16 47.5	22 29.4
17	7 42 43.4	26 7.3	8 57.5	15 34.8	10 2.0	19 51.4	5 39.5	14 9.3	7 42.3	14 38.3	16 49.8	22 30.8
18	7 46 40.0	27 8.4	8 54.3	0♋20.6	11 31.5	21 4.7	6 24.3	14 5.9	7 49.4	14 41.9	16 52.0	22 32.1
19	7 50 36.5	28 9.5	8 51.2	15 24.9	13 1.5	22 17.9	7 9.2	14 2.4	7 56.5	14 45.4	16 54.3	22 33.4
20	7 54 33.1	29 10.5	8 48.0	0♌39.7	14 32.2	23 31.2	7 54.1	13 58.6	8 3.6	14 48.9	16 56.5	22 34.7
21	7 58 29.6	0♒11.6	8 44.8	15 55.0	16 3.4	24 44.5	8 39.0	13 54.7	8 10.8	14 52.4	16 58.7	22 35.9
22	8 2 26.2	1 12.6	8 41.6	1♍ .6	17 35.3	25 57.9	9 24.0	13 50.7	8 17.9	14 55.8	17 1.0	22 37.1
23	8 6 22.7	2 13.6	8 38.5	15 47.6	19 7.7	27 11.3	10 9.0	13 46.4	8 25.0	14 59.3	17 3.2	22 38.2
24	8 10 19.3	3 14.7	8 35.3	0♎ 9.9	20 40.7	28 24.8	10 54.0	13 42.0	8 32.2	15 2.7	17 5.4	22 39.4
25	8 14 15.9	4 15.7	8 32.1	14 4.2	22 14.3	29 38.3	11 39.1	13 37.4	8 39.4	15 6.2	17 7.6	22 40.5
26	8 18 12.4	5 16.7	8 28.9	27 30.2	23 48.6	0♑51.8	12 24.2	13 32.7	8 46.5	15 9.6	17 9.8	22 41.5
27	8 22 9.0	6 17.7	8 25.7	10♏30.1	25 23.5	2 5.4	13 9.4	13 27.8	8 53.7	15 13.1	17 12.0	22 42.6
28	8 26 5.5	7 18.7	8 22.6	23 7.3	26 58.9	3 19.0	13 54.6	13 22.7	9 .9	15 16.5	17 14.2	22 43.6
29	8 30 2.1	8 19.7	8 19.4	5♐26.1	28 35.1	4 32.6	14 39.9	13 17.5	9 8.1	15 19.8	17 16.3	22 44.6
30	8 33 58.6	9 20.6	8 16.2	17 31.0	0♒11.8	5 46.2	15 25.2	13 12.1	9 15.3	15 23.2	17 18.5	22 45.5
31	8 37 55.2	10 21.6	8 13.0	29 26.2	1 49.3	6 59.9	16 10.5	13 6.6	9 22.5	15 26.5	17 20.6	22 46.4

LATITUDE

DAY	SID. TIME	☉	☊	☾	☿	♀	♂	♃	♄	♅	♆	♇
1	6 39 38.5	0 .0	0 .0	3 S 40.1	1 N 26.5	2 N 7.4	0 S 27.7	1 N 10.3	0 S 35.0	0 S 22.0	0 N 43.9	14 N 34.3
4	6 51 28.2	0 .0	0 .0	0 41.4	1 .9	2 2.3	0 29.6	1 11.2	0 35.1	0 22.0	0 43.9	14 35.3
7	7 3 17.8	0 .0	0 .0	2 N 29.5	0 35.7	1 56.5	0 31.4	1 12.0	0 35.3	0 22.0	0 43.9	14 36.3
10	7 15 7.5	0 .0	0 .0	4 44.7	0 11.3	1 50.1	0 33.2	1 12.8	0 35.4	0 22.1	0 43.8	14 37.3
13	7 26 57.2	0 .0	0 .0	5 11.4	0 S 11.8	1 43.1	0 35.1	1 13.6	0 35.6	0 22.1	0 43.8	14 38.4
16	7 38 46.8	0 .0	0 .0	3 18.1	0 33.4	1 35.7	0 36.9	1 14.4	0 35.8	0 22.1	0 43.8	14 39.5
19	7 50 36.5	0 .0	0 .0	0 S 30.9	0 53.3	1 27.8	0 38.7	1 15.2	0 35.9	0 22.1	0 43.8	14 40.7
22	8 2 26.2	0 .0	0 .0	4 6.3	1 11.2	1 19.6	0 40.5	1 15.9	0 36.1	0 22.2	0 43.8	14 41.9
25	8 14 15.9	0 .0	0 .0	5 14.2	1 27.0	1 11.1	0 42.2	1 16.7	0 36.3	0 22.2	0 43.8	14 43.1
28	8 26 5.5	0 .0	0 .0	3 48.7	1 40.4	1 2.3	0 44.0	1 17.4	0 36.5	0 22.3	0 43.7	14 44.4
31	8 37 55.2	0 .0	0 .0	0 56.0	1 51.3	0 53.3	0 45.7	1 18.1	0 36.7	0 22.3	0 43.7	14 45.7

RIGHT ASCENSION

DAY	SID. TIME	☉	☊	☾	☿	♀	♂	♃	♄	♅	♆	♇
1	6 39 38.5	10♑40.7	10♑40.1	22♏53.8	17♐ 9.2	28♏44.8	23♐13.3	16♍17.9	8♒23.2	14♑54.4	17♑30.1	23♏24.1
2	6 43 35.0	11 47.0	10 36.7	6♐ 9.3	18 26.7	29 59.0	24 1.5	16 R17.7	8 30.1	14 58.2	17 32.6	23 25.9
3	6 47 31.6	12 53.2	10 33.2	19 28.1	19 46.4	1♐13.6	24 49.7	16 17.3	8 37.0	15 2.1	17 35.0	23 27.6
4	6 51 28.2	13 59.3	10 29.8	2♑37.6	21 8.2	2 28.4	25 38.1	16 16.7	8 44.0	15 6.0	17 37.4	23 29.3
5	6 55 24.7	15 5.3	10 26.3	15 26.2	22 31.9	3 43.5	26 26.5	16 16.0	8 50.9	15 9.8	17 39.8	23 31.0
6	6 59 21.3	16 11.3	10 22.9	27 46.4	23 57.4	4 59.0	27 15.0	16 15.1	8 58.0	15 13.8	17 42.3	23 32.7
7	7 3 17.8	17 17.1	10 19.4	9♒36.5	25 24.5	6 14.7	28 3.5	16 14.0	9 5.1	15 17.6	17 44.8	23 34.3
8	7 7 14.4	18 22.7	10 16.0	20 60.0	26 53.0	7 30.7	28 52.1	16 12.7	9 12.1	15 21.5	17 47.2	23 35.9
9	7 11 10.9	19 28.3	10 12.5	2♓ 4.5	28 22.8	8 46.9	29 40.8	16 11.3	9 19.2	15 25.4	17 49.6	23 37.5
10	7 15 7.5	20 33.7	10 9.1	13 .6	29 53.8	10 3.4	0♑29.5	16 9.6	9 26.4	15 29.2	17 52.0	23 39.0
11	7 19 4.1	21 39.0	10 5.7	24 .9	1♑26.0	11 20.2	1 18.2	16 7.8	9 33.5	15 33.1	17 54.5	23 40.6
12	7 23 .6	22 44.1	10 2.2	5♈19.7	2 59.2	12 37.2	2 7.0	16 5.8	9 40.7	15 37.0	17 56.9	23 42.1
13	7 26 57.2	23 49.1	9 58.8	17 12.0	4 33.4	13 54.4	2 55.9	16 3.7	9 47.8	15 40.8	17 59.3	23 43.5
14	7 30 53.7	24 54.0	9 55.3	29 52.9	6 8.4	15 11.9	3 44.7	16 1.3	9 55.0	15 44.6	18 1.7	23 45.0
15	7 34 50.3	25 58.6	9 51.9	13♉34.4	7 44.3	16 29.6	4 33.7	15 58.8	10 2.2	15 48.5	18 4.2	23 46.4
16	7 38 46.8	27 3.1	9 48.4	28 21.3	9 20.9	17 47.5	5 22.6	15 56.1	10 9.5	15 52.3	18 6.6	23 47.8
17	7 42 43.4	28 7.4	9 45.0	14♊ 5.3	10 58.2	19 5.6	6 11.6	15 53.2	10 16.7	15 56.1	18 9.0	23 49.2
18	7 46 40.0	29 11.6	9 41.5	0♋22.5	12 36.2	20 23.9	7 .6	15 50.2	10 24.0	15 59.9	18 11.4	23 50.5
19	7 50 36.5	0♒15.6	9 38.1	16 39.8	14 14.8	21 42.4	7 49.6	15 47.0	10 31.2	16 3.7	18 13.8	23 51.8
20	7 54 33.1	1 19.3	9 34.6	2♌26.6	15 53.9	23 1.0	8 38.6	15 43.6	10 38.5	16 7.5	18 16.1	23 53.1
21	7 58 29.6	2 23.0	9 31.2	17 25.7	17 33.5	24 19.9	9 27.7	15 40.1	10 45.8	16 11.3	18 18.5	23 54.3
22	8 2 26.2	3 26.4	9 27.7	1♍35.2	19 13.7	25 38.8	10 16.8	15 36.4	10 53.1	16 15.0	18 20.9	23 55.6
23	8 6 22.7	4 29.6	9 24.3	15 3.8	20 54.2	26 57.9	11 5.9	15 32.5	11 .4	16 18.8	18 23.3	23 56.8
24	8 10 19.3	5 32.6	9 20.8	28 5.1	22 35.2	28 17.2	11 55.0	15 28.5	11 7.7	16 22.5	18 25.6	23 57.9
25	8 14 15.9	6 35.5	9 17.4	10♎53.3	24 16.6	29 36.5	12 44.1	15 24.4	11 15.0	16 26.2	18 28.0	23 59.1
26	8 18 12.4	7 38.2	9 13.9	23 40.5	25 58.3	0♑56.0	13 33.2	15 20.0	11 22.3	16 29.9	18 30.3	24 .2
27	8 22 9.0	8 40.7	9 10.5	6♏35.4	27 40.3	2 15.5	14 22.3	15 15.6	11 29.7	16 33.6	18 32.7	24 1.3
28	8 26 5.5	9 42.9	9 7.0	19 41.4	29 22.6	3 35.1	15 11.4	15 11.0	11 37.0	16 37.3	18 35.0	24 2.3
29	8 30 2.1	10 45.0	9 3.6	2♐56.6	1♒ 5.2	4 54.8	16 .5	15 6.2	11 44.4	16 40.9	18 37.3	24 3.3
30	8 33 58.6	11 46.9	9 .2	16 13.8	2 48.0	6 14.5	16 49.5	15 1.2	11 51.7	16 44.5	18 39.6	24 4.3
31	8 37 55.2	12 48.5	8 56.7	29 22.9	4 31.0	7 34.2	17 38.6	14 56.2	11 59.0	16 48.1	18 41.8	24 5.2

DECLINATION

DAY	SID. TIME	☉	☊	☾	☿	♀	♂	♃	♄	♅	♆	♇
1	6 39 38.5	23 S 4.7	0 S 24.2	22 S 51.3	21 S 28.1	18 S 10.0	23 S 45.4	7 N 8.1	19 S 22.4	23 S 6.1	21 S 43.7	4 S 11.0
4	6 51 28.2	22 49.1	0 24.2	24 6.6	22 10.4	18 57.5	23 52.4	7 9.5	19 17.5	23 5.0	21 42.9	4 11.3
7	7 3 17.8	22 29.4	0 24.2	15 53.8	22 46.7	19 40.7	23 57.1	7 11.5	19 12.5	23 3.9	21 42.1	4 11.5
10	7 15 7.5	22 5.7	0 24.2	2 5.3	23 15.1	20 19.4	23 59.6	7 14.2	19 7.4	23 2.8	21 41.3	4 11.6
13	7 26 57.2	21 38.1	0 24.2	12 N 55.1	23 34.3	20 53.2	23 59.9	7 17.6	19 2.3	23 1.7	21 40.5	4 11.6
16	7 38 46.8	21 6.8	0 24.2	23 38.1	23 43.2	21 21.9	23 57.8	7 21.6	18 57.0	23 .6	21 39.7	4 11.5
19	7 50 36.5	20 31.9	0 24.2	22 2.3	23 41.2	21 45.3	23 53.5	7 26.2	18 51.7	22 59.4	21 38.9	4 11.3
22	8 2 26.2	19 53.4	0 24.2	7 16.5	23 27.7	22 3.2	23 46.8	7 31.4	18 46.4	22 58.3	21 38.0	4 11.0
25	8 14 15.9	19 11.7	0 24.3	10 S 22.3	23 2.2	22 15.4	23 37.9	7 37.2	18 40.9	22 57.2	21 37.2	4 10.6
28	8 26 5.5	18 26.7	0 24.3	22 14.5	22 24.3	22 21.7	23 26.6	7 43.5	18 35.5	22 56.1	21 36.4	4 10.1
31	8 37 55.2	17 38.7	0 24.3	24 22.3	21 33.8	22 22.1	23 13.1	7 50.3	18 30.0	22 55.0	21 35.6	4 9.5

FEBRUARY 1992

LONGITUDE

DAY	EPHEM. SID. TIME h m s	☉ ° ′	☊ ° ′	☾ ° ′	☿ ° ′	♀ ° ′	♂ ° ′	♃ ° ′	♄ ° ′	♅ ° ′	♆ ° ′	♇ ° ′
1	8 41 51.8	11♒22.5	8♑ 9.9	11♑15.7	3♒27.4	8♑13.6	16♑55.8	13♍ .9	9♒29.6	15♑29.8	17♑22.7	22♏47.2
2	8 45 48.3	12 23.5	8 6.7	23 2.8	5 6.2	9 27.3	17 41.2	12R55.1	9 36.8	15 33.1	17 24.8	22 48.1
3	8 49 44.9	13 24.4	8 3.5	4♒50.2	6 45.7	10 41.1	18 26.7	12 49.1	9 44.0	15 36.4	17 26.9	22 48.9
4	8 53 41.4	14 25.2	8 .3	16 40.2	8 25.9	11 54.8	19 12.1	12 43.0	9 51.2	15 39.7	17 29.0	22 49.6
5	8 57 38.0	15 26.1	7 57.2	28 34.5	10 6.9	13 8.6	19 57.6	12 36.8	9 58.3	15 42.9	17 31.1	22 50.3
6	9 1 34.5	16 27.0	7 54.0	10♓34.9	11 48.6	14 22.4	20 43.1	12 30.4	10 5.5	15 46.1	17 33.1	22 51.0
7	9 5 31.1	17 27.8	7 50.8	22 42.9	13 31.1	15 36.2	21 28.7	12 24.0	10 12.6	15 49.3	17 35.2	22 51.7
8	9 9 27.6	18 28.6	7 47.6	5♈ .4	15 14.4	16 50.1	22 14.2	12 17.4	10 19.8	15 52.5	17 37.2	22 52.3
9	9 13 24.2	19 29.4	7 44.4	17 29.4	16 58.4	18 3.9	22 59.9	12 10.7	10 26.9	15 55.6	17 39.2	22 52.9
10	9 17 20.8	20 30.1	7 41.3	0♉12.5	18 43.2	19 17.8	23 45.5	12 3.8	10 34.0	15 58.7	17 41.2	22 53.4
11	9 21 17.3	21 30.9	7 38.1	13 12.3	20 28.9	20 31.7	24 31.2	11 56.9	10 41.1	16 1.8	17 43.2	22 53.9
12	9 25 13.9	22 31.6	7 34.9	26 31.7	22 15.2	21 45.5	25 16.9	11 49.9	10 48.2	16 4.8	17 45.1	22 54.4
13	9 29 10.4	23 32.2	7 31.7	10♊13.2	24 2.4	22 59.4	26 2.6	11 42.8	10 55.3	16 7.9	17 47.0	22 54.8
14	9 33 7.0	24 32.9	7 28.6	24 18.0	25 50.3	24 13.3	26 48.3	11 35.6	11 2.3	16 10.9	17 49.0	22 55.2
15	9 37 3.5	25 33.5	7 25.4	8♋46.1	27 39.0	25 27.3	27 34.1	11 28.3	11 9.4	16 13.8	17 50.9	22 55.6
16	9 41 .1	26 34.1	7 22.2	23 34.7	29 28.4	26 41.2	28 19.9	11 21.0	11 16.4	16 16.8	17 52.7	22 55.9
17	9 44 56.6	27 34.7	7 19.0	8♌38.4	1♓18.5	27 55.2	29 5.8	11 13.6	11 23.4	16 19.7	17 54.6	22 56.2
18	9 48 53.2	28 35.3	7 15.8	23 48.8	3 9.1	29 9.1	29 51.7	11 6.1	11 30.4	16 22.6	17 56.5	22 56.5
19	9 52 49.7	29 35.8	7 12.7	8♍56.1	5 .3	0♒23.1	0♒37.6	10 58.6	11 37.4	16 25.5	17 58.3	22 56.7
20	9 56 46.3	0♓36.3	7 9.5	23 50.2	6 51.9	1 37.1	1 23.5	10 51.0	11 44.3	16 28.3	18 .1	22 56.9
21	10 0 42.9	1 36.7	7 6.3	8♎22.6	8 43.9	2 51.1	2 9.4	10 43.3	11 51.2	16 31.1	18 1.9	22 57.0
22	10 4 39.4	2 37.2	7 3.1	22 27.7	10 36.1	4 5.1	2 55.4	10 35.6	11 58.1	16 33.8	18 3.6	22 57.2
23	10 8 36.0	3 37.6	6 60.0	6♏ 3.3	12 28.2	5 19.1	3 41.4	10 27.9	12 5.0	16 36.6	18 5.4	22 57.2
24	10 12 32.5	4 38.0	6 56.8	19 10.1	14 20.3	6 33.1	4 27.5	10 20.1	12 11.8	16 39.2	18 7.1	22 57.3
25	10 16 29.1	5 38.3	6 53.6	1♐51.0	16 11.9	7 47.2	5 13.5	10 12.3	12 18.6	16 41.9	18 8.8	22 57.3
26	10 20 25.6	6 38.7	6 50.4	14 10.7	18 2.8	9 1.2	5 59.6	10 4.4	12 25.4	16 44.5	18 10.4	22R57.2
27	10 24 22.2	7 39.0	6 47.3	26 14.3	19 52.8	10 15.3	6 45.7	9 56.6	12 32.1	16 47.1	18 12.1	22 57.2
28	10 28 18.7	8 39.3	6 44.1	8♑ 7.1	21 41.4	11 29.4	7 31.8	9 48.7	12 38.8	16 49.6	18 13.7	22 57.1
29	10 32 15.3	9 39.6	6 40.9	19 54.4	23 28.3	12 43.4	8 18.0	9 40.8	12 45.5	16 52.1	18 15.3	22 56.9

LATITUDE

DAY	EPHEM. SID. TIME	☉	☊	☾	☿	♀	♂	♃	♄	♅	♆	♇
1	8 41 51.8	0 .0	0 .0	0N 8.7	1S54.2	0N50.3	0S46.3	1N18.3	0S36.8	0S22.3	0N43.7	14N46.1
4	8 53 41.4	0 .0	0 .0	3 8.3	2 1.1	0 41.2	0 48.0	1 18.9	0 37.0	0 22.4	0 43.7	14 47.5
7	9 5 31.1	0 .0	0 .0	4 57.5	2 4.7	0 32.1	0 49.7	1 19.5	0 37.2	0 22.4	0 43.8	14 48.8
10	9 17 20.8	0 .0	0 .0	4 49.1	2 4.7	0 22.9	0 51.4	1 20.0	0 37.5	0 22.5	0 43.8	14 50.1
13	9 29 10.4	0 .0	0 .0	2 29.2	2 .6	0 13.8	0 53.1	1 20.6	0 37.7	0 22.5	0 43.8	14 51.5
16	9 41 .1	0 .0	0 .0	1S18.4	1 52.0	0 4.8	0 54.7	1 21.0	0 38.0	0 22.6	0 43.8	14 52.9
19	9 52 49.7	0 .0	0 .0	4 26.8	1 38.4	0S 4.0	0 56.3	1 21.4	0 38.2	0 22.7	0 43.8	14 54.2
22	10 4 39.4	0 .0	0 .0	4 57.4	1 19.5	0 12.6	0 57.8	1 21.8	0 38.5	0 22.7	0 43.8	14 55.6
25	10 16 29.1	0 .0	0 .0	3 1.9	0 54.9	0 20.9	0 59.4	1 22.1	0 38.8	0 22.8	0 43.8	14 56.9
28	10 28 18.7	0 .0	0 .0	0N .1	0 24.6	0 28.9	1 .9	1 22.3	0 39.1	0 22.8	0 43.9	14 58.2

RIGHT ASCENSION

DAY	EPHEM. SID. TIME	☉	☊	☾	☿	♀	♂	♃	♄	♅	♆	♇
1	8 41 51.8	13♒50.0	8♑53.3	12♑14.0	6♒14.2	8♑54.0	18♑27.6	14♍51.0	12♒ 6.3	16♑51.7	18♑44.1	24♏ 6.2
2	8 45 48.3	14 51.3	8 49.8	24 39.7	7 57.6	10 13.7	19 16.6	14R45.6	12 13.6	16 55.3	18 46.4	24 7.0
3	8 49 44.9	15 52.4	8 46.4	6♒37.5	9 41.2	11 33.4	20 5.6	14 40.1	12 20.9	16 58.8	18 48.6	24 7.9
4	8 53 41.4	16 53.2	8 42.9	18 9.3	11 24.9	12 53.1	20 54.6	14 34.5	12 28.2	17 2.3	18 50.8	24 8.7
5	8 57 38.0	17 53.9	8 39.5	29 21.1	13 8.8	14 12.7	21 43.5	14 28.8	12 35.5	17 5.8	18 53.0	24 9.5
6	9 1 34.5	18 54.3	8 36.0	10♓21.4	14 52.7	15 32.3	22 32.3	14 23.0	12 42.8	17 9.3	18 55.2	24 10.2
7	9 5 31.1	19 54.6	8 32.5	21 21.2	16 36.8	16 51.8	23 21.2	14 17.0	12 50.1	17 12.7	18 57.4	24 11.0
8	9 9 27.6	20 54.6	8 29.1	2♈32.4	18 21.0	18 11.2	24 10.0	14 10.9	12 57.3	17 16.1	18 59.5	24 11.7
9	9 13 24.2	21 54.5	8 25.6	14 8.0	20 5.2	19 30.6	24 58.7	14 4.7	13 4.6	17 19.5	19 1.7	24 12.3
10	9 17 20.8	22 54.1	8 22.2	26 21.1	21 49.5	20 49.8	25 47.4	13 58.5	13 11.8	17 22.9	19 3.8	24 12.9
11	9 21 17.3	23 53.6	8 18.7	9♉23.0	23 33.8	22 8.9	26 36.0	13 52.1	13 19.0	17 26.2	19 5.9	24 13.5
12	9 25 13.9	24 52.8	8 15.3	23 20.6	25 18.2	23 27.8	27 24.6	13 45.6	13 26.2	17 29.5	19 8.0	24 14.1
13	9 29 10.4	25 51.8	8 11.8	8♊11.9	27 2.6	24 46.6	28 13.1	13 39.0	13 33.4	17 32.7	19 10.0	24 14.6
14	9 33 7.0	26 50.7	8 8.4	23 43.8	28 46.9	26 5.3	29 1.6	13 32.4	13 40.6	17 36.0	19 12.1	24 15.1
15	9 37 3.5	27 49.4	8 4.9	9♋32.7	0♓31.2	27 23.7	29 50.0	13 25.6	13 47.7	17 39.2	19 14.1	24 15.5
16	9 41 .1	28 47.8	8 1.5	25 12.2	2 15.4	28 42.0	0♒38.3	13 18.8	13 54.8	17 42.4	19 16.1	24 15.9
17	9 44 56.6	29 46.2	7 58.0	10♌22.4	3 59.6	0♒ .2	1 26.6	13 12.0	14 2.0	17 45.5	19 18.1	24 16.4
18	9 48 53.2	0♓44.3	7 54.6	24 54.9	5 43.5	1 18.1	2 14.8	13 5.0	14 9.0	17 48.7	19 20.1	24 16.7
19	9 52 49.7	1 42.2	7 51.1	8♍52.0	7 27.2	2 35.9	3 3.0	12 58.0	14 16.1	17 51.7	19 22.0	24 17.0
20	9 56 46.3	2 40.0	7 47.7	22 23.1	9 10.7	3 53.4	3 51.0	12 50.9	14 23.1	17 54.8	19 23.9	24 17.3
21	10 0 42.9	3 37.6	7 44.2	5♎39.7	10 53.7	5 10.7	4 39.0	12 43.8	14 30.1	17 57.8	19 25.8	24 17.5
22	10 4 39.4	4 35.0	7 40.8	18 52.8	12 36.2	6 27.8	5 26.9	12 36.6	14 37.1	18 .7	19 27.7	24 17.8
23	10 8 36.0	5 32.3	7 37.3	2♏10.2	14 18.1	7 44.6	6 14.8	12 29.4	14 44.0	18 3.7	19 29.5	24 17.9
24	10 12 32.5	6 29.4	7 33.9	15 35.1	15 59.2	9 1.2	7 2.5	12 22.2	14 50.9	18 6.6	19 31.4	24 18.1
25	10 16 29.1	7 26.4	7 30.4	29 5.2	17 39.3	10 17.6	7 50.2	12 14.9	14 57.8	18 9.4	19 33.2	24 18.2
26	10 20 25.6	8 23.3	7 26.9	12♐34.0	19 18.3	11 33.7	8 37.8	12 7.6	15 4.7	18 12.2	19 34.9	24 18.3
27	10 24 22.2	9 20.0	7 23.5	25 52.1	20 55.9	12 49.6	9 25.3	12 .3	15 11.5	18 15.0	19 36.7	24 18.3
28	10 28 18.7	10 16.5	7 20.0	8♑50.3	22 31.8	14 5.3	10 12.8	11 52.9	15 18.3	18 17.7	19 38.4	24 18.3
29	10 32 15.3	11 13.0	7 16.6	21 22.5	24 5.6	15 20.7	11 .1	11 45.6	15 25.0	18 20.4	19 40.1	24 18.3

DECLINATION

DAY	EPHEM. SID. TIME	☉	☊	☾	☿	♀	♂	♃	♄	♅	♆	♇
1	8 41 51.8	17S22.1	0S24.3	22S49.1	21S14.1	22S20.9	23S 8.0	7N52.7	18S28.1	22S54.6	21S35.3	4S 9.3
4	8 53 41.4	16 30.4	0 24.3	12 50.7	20 6.3	22 13.3	22 51.5	8 .1	18 22.6	22 53.5	21 34.5	4 8.6
7	9 5 31.1	15 36.1	0 24.3	1N39.9	18 45.4	21 59.8	22 32.7	8 8.0	18 17.0	22 52.4	21 33.7	4 7.8
10	9 17 20.8	14 39.4	0 24.3	16 3.1	17 11.4	21 40.5	22 11.7	8 16.2	18 11.4	22 51.4	21 32.9	4 6.9
13	9 29 10.4	13 40.5	0 24.3	24 26.5	15 24.3	21 15.3	21 48.6	8 24.7	18 5.8	22 50.3	21 32.1	4 5.9
16	9 41 .1	12 39.6	0 24.3	20 5.7	13 24.3	20 44.4	21 23.3	8 33.4	18 .3	22 49.3	21 31.4	4 4.8
19	9 52 49.7	11 36.9	0 24.3	4 5.7	11 12.2	20 8.0	20 56.0	8 42.3	17 54.7	22 48.3	21 30.6	4 3.7
22	10 4 39.4	10 32.5	0 24.4	13S20.2	8 49.1	19 26.4	20 26.7	8 51.4	17 49.2	22 47.4	21 29.9	4 2.5
25	10 16 29.1	9 26.7	0 24.4	23 30.1	6 17.3	18 39.6	19 55.4	9 .5	17 43.7	22 46.4	21 29.2	4 1.2
28	10 28 18.7	8 19.5	0 24.4	23 11.4	3 40.3	17 47.9	19 22.2	9 9.7	17 38.3	22 45.5	21 28.5	3 59.8

MARCH 1992

LONGITUDE

DAY	EPHEM. SID. TIME h m s	☉ ° ′	☊ ° ′	☽ ° ′	☿ ° ′	♀ ° ′	♂ ° ′	♃ ° ′	♄ ° ′	♅ ° ′	♆ ° ′	♇ ° ′
1	10 36 11.8	10♓39.8	6♑37.7	1♒40.6	25♓13.0	13♒57.5	9♒ 4.2	9♍32.9	12♒52.2	16♑54.6	18♑16.8	22♏56.8
2	10 40 8.4	11 40.0	6 34.5	13 29.5	26 55.1	15 11.6	9 50.4	9R25.1	12 58.8	16 57.0	18 18.4	22R56.6
3	10 44 4.9	12 40.2	6 31.4	25 24.1	28 34.0	16 25.7	10 36.6	9 17.2	13 5.4	16 59.4	18 19.9	22 56.3
4	10 48 1.5	13 40.4	6 28.2	7♓26.7	0♈ 9.2	17 39.8	11 22.8	9 9.3	13 11.9	17 1.8	18 21.4	22 56.0
5	10 51 58.1	14 40.5	6 25.0	19 38.5	1 40.2	18 53.9	12 9.1	9 1.5	13 18.4	17 4.1	18 22.8	22 55.7
6	10 55 54.6	15 40.6	6 21.8	2♈ .4	3 6.3	20 8.0	12 55.3	8 53.7	13 24.9	17 6.4	18 24.3	22 55.4
7	10 59 51.2	16 40.7	6 18.7	14 32.9	4 27.1	21 22.1	13 41.6	8 46.0	13 31.3	17 8.6	18 25.7	22 55.0
8	11 3 47.7	17 40.7	6 15.5	27 16.3	5 41.9	22 36.2	14 27.9	8 38.2	13 37.6	17 10.8	18 27.1	22 54.6
9	11 7 44.3	18 40.8	6 12.3	10♉11.3	6 50.3	23 50.3	15 14.3	8 30.6	13 44.0	17 13.0	18 28.5	22 54.2
10	11 11 40.8	19 40.8	6 9.1	23 18.8	7 51.7	25 4.4	16 .6	8 23.0	13 50.3	17 15.1	18 29.8	22 53.7
11	11 15 37.4	20 40.7	6 5.9	6♊40.1	8 45.8	26 18.5	16 47.0	8 15.4	13 56.6	17 17.1	18 31.1	22 53.2
12	11 19 33.9	21 40.6	6 2.8	20 16.8	9 32.0	27 32.6	17 33.3	8 7.9	14 2.8	17 19.1	18 32.4	22 52.6
13	11 23 30.5	22 40.4	5 59.6	4♋10.4	10 10.2	28 46.7	18 19.7	8 .5	14 8.9	17 21.1	18 33.6	22 52.1
14	11 27 27.0	23 40.3	5 56.4	18 21.5	10 40.1	0♓ .7	19 6.1	7 53.1	14 15.0	17 23.0	18 34.8	22 51.4
15	11 31 23.6	24 40.0	5 53.2	2♌49.1	11 1.5	1 14.8	19 52.4	7 45.8	14 21.1	17 24.9	18 36.0	22 50.8
16	11 35 20.1	25 39.8	5 50.1	17 30.3	11 14.3	2 28.9	20 38.8	7 38.6	14 27.1	17 26.8	18 37.1	22 50.1
17	11 39 16.7	26 39.5	5 46.9	2♍19.7	11 18.7	3 43.0	21 25.3	7 31.5	14 33.0	17 28.6	18 38.3	22 49.4
18	11 43 13.2	27 39.2	5 43.7	17 9.9	11R14.7	4 57.0	22 11.7	7 24.5	14 38.9	17 30.3	18 39.4	22 48.7
19	11 47 9.8	28 38.8	5 40.5	1♎52.3	11 2.7	6 11.1	22 58.1	7 17.6	14 44.8	17 32.0	18 40.4	22 47.9
20	11 51 6.3	29 38.4	5 37.3	16 18.7	10 43.0	7 25.2	23 44.6	7 10.7	14 50.6	17 33.7	18 41.5	22 47.1
21	11 55 2.9	0♈38.0	5 34.2	0♏22.7	10 16.3	8 39.3	24 31.0	7 4.0	14 56.3	17 35.3	18 42.5	22 46.3
22	11 58 59.5	1 37.5	5 31.0	14 .4	9 43.1	9 53.3	25 17.5	6 57.4	15 2.0	17 36.9	18 43.4	22 45.4
23	12 2 56.0	2 37.0	5 27.8	27 11.1	9 4.4	11 7.4	26 3.9	6 50.9	15 7.6	17 38.4	18 44.4	22 44.5
24	12 6 52.6	3 36.5	5 24.6	9♐56.3	8 20.9	12 21.5	26 50.4	6 44.5	15 13.2	17 39.8	18 45.3	22 43.6
25	12 10 49.1	4 36.0	5 21.4	22 19.6	7 33.7	13 35.5	27 36.9	6 38.3	15 18.7	17 41.3	18 46.1	22 42.7
26	12 14 45.7	5 35.4	5 18.3	4♑25.9	6 43.8	14 49.6	28 23.4	6 32.1	15 24.1	17 42.6	18 47.0	22 41.7
27	12 18 42.2	6 34.8	5 15.1	16 20.6	5 52.3	16 3.7	29 9.9	6 26.1	15 29.5	17 44.0	18 47.8	22 40.7
28	12 22 38.8	7 34.1	5 11.9	28 9.3	5 .3	17 17.7	29 56.4	6 20.2	15 34.9	17 45.2	18 48.6	22 39.7
29	12 26 35.3	8 33.5	5 8.7	9♒57.1	4 8.8	18 31.8	0♓43.0	6 14.5	15 40.1	17 46.5	18 49.3	22 38.6
30	12 30 31.9	9 32.8	5 5.6	21 49.1	3 19.0	19 45.9	1 29.5	6 9.0	15 45.4	17 47.7	18 50.1	22 37.6
31	12 34 28.4	10 32.1	5 2.4	3♓49.0	2 31.5	20 60.0	2 16.0	6 3.5	15 50.5	17 48.8	18 50.8	22 36.5

LATITUDE

DAY	EPHEM. SID. TIME h m s	☉	☊	☽	☿	♀	♂	♃	♄	♅	♆	♇
1	10 36 11.8	0 .0	0 .0	2N 2.5	0S 1.4	0S34.0	1S 1.8	1N22.5	0S39.3	0S22.9	0N43.9	14N59.1
4	10 48 1.5	0 .0	0 .0	4 21.8	0N36.9	0 41.4	1 3.3	1 22.6	0 39.6	0 23.0	0 43.9	15 .4
7	10 59 51.2	0 .0	0 .0	4 59.3	1 17.9	0 48.4	1 4.7	1 22.8	0 39.9	0 23.0	0 44.0	15 1.7
10	11 11 40.8	0 .0	0 .0	3 28.0	1 58.8	0 55.0	1 6.0	1 22.8	0 40.2	0 23.1	0 44.0	15 2.9
13	11 23 30.5	0 .0	0 .0	0 12.6	2 36.2	1 1.0	1 7.3	1 22.8	0 40.5	0 23.2	0 44.0	15 4.1
16	11 35 20.1	0 .0	0 .0	3S18.6	3 6.5	1 6.6	1 8.6	1 22.8	0 40.9	0 23.3	0 44.1	15 5.3
19	11 47 9.8	0 .0	0 .0	4 59.8	3 25.6	1 11.6	1 9.8	1 22.7	0 41.2	0 23.3	0 44.1	15 6.4
22	11 58 59.5	0 .0	0 .0	3 55.8	3 30.2	1 16.1	1 10.9	1 22.5	0 41.5	0 23.4	0 44.1	15 7.5
25	12 10 49.1	0 .0	0 .0	1 7.8	3 18.5	1 20.0	1 12.0	1 22.3	0 41.9	0 23.5	0 44.2	15 8.6
28	12 22 38.8	0 .0	0 .0	1N58.2	2 51.2	1 23.3	1 13.0	1 22.1	0 42.3	0 23.6	0 44.2	15 9.5
31	12 34 28.4	0 .0	0 .0	4 17.9	2 11.9	1 26.0	1 14.0	1 21.8	0 42.7	0 23.7	0 44.3	15 10.5

RIGHT ASCENSION

DAY	EPHEM. SID. TIME h m s	☉	☊	☽	☿	♀	♂	♃	♄	♅	♆	♇
1	10 36 11.8	12♓ 9.3	7♑13.1	3♒26.8	25♓37.2	16♒35.8	11♒47.4	11♍38.2	15♒31.7	18♑23.1	19♑41.8	24♏18.3
2	10 40 8.4	13 5.4	7 9.7	15 5.3	27 6.0	17 50.7	12 34.6	11R30.8	15 38.4	18 25.7	19 43.4	24R18.2
3	10 44 4.9	14 1.5	7 6.2	26 23.9	28 31.7	19 5.3	13 21.7	11 23.5	15 45.1	18 28.3	19 45.0	24 18.0
4	10 48 1.5	14 57.4	7 2.8	7♓30.8	29 53.8	20 19.6	14 8.7	11 16.1	15 51.7	18 30.8	19 46.6	24 17.9
5	10 51 58.1	15 53.3	6 59.3	18 36.0	1♈11.9	21 33.7	14 55.6	11 8.8	15 58.2	18 33.3	19 48.1	24 17.7
6	10 55 54.6	16 49.0	6 55.9	29 50.5	2 25.5	22 47.5	15 42.4	11 1.5	16 4.8	18 35.8	19 49.7	24 17.5
7	10 59 51.2	17 44.6	6 52.4	11♈25.9	3 34.2	24 1.0	16 29.1	10 54.2	16 11.2	18 38.2	19 51.2	24 17.2
8	11 3 47.7	18 40.1	6 48.9	23 33.5	4 37.5	25 14.3	17 15.7	10 47.0	16 17.7	18 40.5	19 52.6	24 16.9
9	11 7 44.3	19 35.6	6 45.5	6♉22.7	5 35.0	26 27.4	18 2.3	10 39.8	16 24.1	18 42.9	19 54.1	24 16.6
10	11 11 40.8	20 30.9	6 42.0	19 59.1	6 26.2	27 40.2	18 48.7	10 32.6	16 30.4	18 45.1	19 55.5	24 16.3
11	11 15 37.4	21 26.1	6 38.6	4♊21.2	7 10.8	28 52.7	19 35.1	10 25.5	16 36.7	18 47.4	19 56.9	24 15.9
12	11 19 33.9	22 21.3	6 35.1	19 18.7	7 48.5	0♓ 5.0	20 21.3	10 18.5	16 43.0	18 49.5	19 58.3	24 15.5
13	11 23 30.5	23 16.4	6 31.7	4♋33.3	8 19.1	1 17.0	21 7.4	10 11.5	16 49.2	18 51.7	19 59.6	24 15.0
14	11 27 27.0	24 11.4	6 28.2	19 44.0	8 42.3	2 28.7	21 53.5	10 4.5	16 55.3	18 53.7	20 .9	24 14.6
15	11 31 23.6	25 6.3	6 24.7	4♌34.0	8 58.0	3 40.3	22 39.4	9 57.7	17 1.4	18 55.8	20 2.1	24 14.0
16	11 35 20.1	26 1.2	6 21.3	18 55.1	9 6.4	4 51.6	23 25.3	9 50.9	17 7.5	18 57.7	20 3.3	24 13.5
17	11 39 16.7	26 56.0	6 17.8	2♍48.3	9 7.3	6 2.7	24 11.0	9 44.2	17 13.5	18 59.7	20 4.5	24 12.9
18	11 43 13.2	27 50.8	6 14.4	16 20.9	9R 1.1	7 13.5	24 56.7	9 37.6	17 19.4	19 1.6	20 5.7	24 12.3
19	11 47 9.8	28 45.5	6 10.9	29 43.4	8 48.0	8 24.2	25 42.3	9 31.0	17 25.3	19 3.4	20 6.8	24 11.7
20	11 51 6.3	29 40.2	6 7.5	13♎ 6.2	8 28.5	9 34.6	26 27.7	9 24.6	17 31.1	19 5.2	20 7.9	24 11.0
21	11 55 2.9	0♈34.9	6 4.0	26 36.9	8 3.2	10 44.8	27 13.1	9 18.2	17 36.9	19 6.9	20 9.0	24 10.3
22	11 58 59.5	1 29.5	6 .5	10♏18.3	7 32.6	11 54.9	27 58.4	9 12.0	17 42.6	19 8.6	20 10.0	24 9.6
23	12 2 56.0	2 24.1	5 57.1	24 7.7	6 57.6	13 4.7	28 43.6	9 5.8	17 48.2	19 10.2	20 11.0	24 8.9
24	12 6 52.6	3 18.7	5 53.6	7♐56.8	6 19.1	14 14.4	29 28.7	8 59.8	17 53.8	19 11.8	20 12.0	24 8.1
25	12 10 49.1	4 13.3	5 50.2	21 34.5	5 37.8	15 23.9	0♓13.7	8 53.8	17 59.4	19 13.3	20 12.9	24 7.3
26	12 14 45.7	5 7.9	5 46.7	4♑49.9	4 54.8	16 33.2	0 58.7	8 48.0	18 4.9	19 14.8	20 13.8	24 6.5
27	12 18 42.2	6 2.5	5 43.3	17 35.9	4 11.1	17 42.4	1 43.5	8 42.3	18 10.3	19 16.3	20 14.7	24 5.6
28	12 22 38.8	6 57.0	5 39.8	29 50.3	3 27.5	18 51.5	2 28.3	8 36.7	18 15.6	19 17.6	20 15.5	24 4.7
29	12 26 35.3	7 51.7	5 36.3	11♒35.9	2 45.0	20 .4	3 12.9	8 31.3	18 20.9	19 19.0	20 16.3	24 3.8
30	12 30 31.9	8 46.3	5 32.9	22 59.2	2 4.5	21 9.2	3 57.6	8 26.0	18 26.2	19 20.3	20 17.1	24 2.9
31	12 34 28.4	9 41.0	5 29.4	4♓ 9.1	1 26.5	22 17.9	4 42.1	8 20.8	18 31.3	19 21.5	20 17.8	24 1.9

DECLINATION

DAY	EPHEM. SID. TIME h m s	☉	☊	☽	☿	♀	♂	♃	♄	♅	♆	♇
1	10 36 11.8	7S34.1	0S24.4	17S47.7	1S55.3	17S11.0	18S59.0	9N15.8	17S34.7	22S45.0	21S28.1	3S58.9
4	10 48 1.5	6 25.2	0 24.4	4 43.4	0N37.5	16 11.9	18 22.8	9 24.8	17 29.4	22 44.1	21 27.4	3 57.5
7	10 59 51.2	5 15.5	0 24.4	10N19.8	2 57.6	15 8.7	17 44.9	9 33.7	17 24.1	22 43.3	21 26.8	3 56.0
10	11 11 40.8	4 5.2	0 24.4	21 57.3	4 56.3	14 1.7	17 5.3	9 42.4	17 18.9	22 42.6	21 26.2	3 54.5
13	11 23 30.5	2 54.5	0 24.4	23 35.1	6 25.3	12 51.2	16 24.2	9 50.8	17 13.9	22 41.9	21 25.7	3 53.0
16	11 35 20.1	1 43.4	0 24.4	12 26.0	7 18.3	11 37.6	15 41.6	9 59.0	17 8.9	22 41.2	21 25.2	3 51.4
19	11 47 9.8	0 32.3	0 24.4	5S19.7	7 31.3	10 21.1	14 57.6	10 6.7	17 4.1	22 40.6	21 24.7	3 49.8
22	11 58 59.5	0N38.8	0 24.4	19 47.5	7 4.3	9 2.1	14 12.3	10 14.1	16 59.4	22 40.1	21 24.2	3 48.1
25	12 10 49.1	1 49.7	0 24.4	24 20.8	6 2.3	7 40.9	13 25.7	10 21.0	16 54.8	22 39.6	21 23.8	3 46.5
28	12 22 38.8	3 .2	0 24.4	18 36.0	4 36.5	6 17.8	12 38.0	10 27.5	16 50.3	22 39.2	21 23.4	3 44.8
31	12 34 28.4	4 10.3	0 24.4	6 6.1	3 1.3	4 53.1	11 49.1	10 33.4	16 46.0	22 38.8	21 23.1	3 43.2

APRIL 1992

DAY	EPHEM. SID. TIME	☉	☊	☽	☿	♀	♂	♃	♄	♅	♆	♇
	h m s	° ′	° ′	° ′	° ′	° ′	° ′	° ′	° ′	° ′	° ′	° ′
		LONGITUDE										
1	12 38 25.0	11♈31.3	4♑59.2	15♓59.8	1♈47.2	22♓14.0	3♓ 2.6	5♍58.2	15♒55.6	17♑49.9	18♑51.4	22♏35.4
2	12 42 21.5	12 30.5	4 56.0	28 23.6	1R 6.8	23 28.1	3 49.1	5R53.0	16 .6	17 50.9	18 52.1	22R34.2
3	12 46 18.1	13 29.7	4 52.8	11♈ 1.0	0 30.8	24 42.1	4 35.6	5 48.0	16 5.5	17 51.9	18 52.6	22 33.0
4	12 50 14.6	14 28.9	4 49.7	23 52.0	29♓59.7	25 56.1	5 22.1	5 43.2	16 10.4	17 52.8	18 53.2	22 31.8
5	12 54 11.2	15 28.0	4 46.5	6♉55.8	29 33.8	27 10.2	6 8.6	5 38.5	16 15.2	17 53.7	18 53.7	22 30.6
6	12 58 7.7	16 27.0	4 43.3	20 11.2	29 13.2	28 24.2	6 55.1	5 34.0	16 19.9	17 54.6	18 54.2	22 29.3
7	13 2 4.3	17 26.1	4 40.1	3♊37.2	28 58.1	29 38.2	7 41.6	5 29.6	16 24.5	17 55.3	18 54.7	22 28.0
8	13 6 .9	18 25.1	4 37.0	17 12.9	28 48.5	0♈52.2	8 28.1	5 25.4	16 29.1	17 56.1	18 55.1	22 26.8
9	13 9 57.4	19 24.0	4 33.8	0♋58.1	28 44.3	2 6.2	9 14.6	5 21.4	16 33.6	17 56.7	18 55.5	22 25.4
10	13 13 54.0	20 23.0	4 30.6	14 52.8	28D45.6	3 20.2	10 1.1	5 17.5	16 38.0	17 57.4	18 55.8	22 24.1
11	13 17 50.5	21 21.8	4 27.4	28 57.0	28 52.1	4 34.2	10 47.6	5 13.8	16 42.4	17 57.9	18 56.1	22 22.7
12	13 21 47.1	22 20.7	4 24.2	13♌10.0	29 3.7	5 48.1	11 34.0	5 10.3	16 46.7	17 58.5	18 56.4	22 21.4
13	13 25 43.6	23 19.5	4 21.1	27 30.2	29 20.2	7 2.1	12 20.5	5 7.0	16 50.9	17 58.9	18 56.7	22 20.0
14	13 29 40.2	24 18.2	4 17.9	11♍54.4	29 41.5	8 16.0	13 6.9	5 3.8	16 55.0	17 59.3	18 56.9	22 18.5
15	13 33 36.7	25 17.0	4 14.7	26 18.1	0♈ 7.4	9 30.0	13 53.3	5 .8	16 59.0	17 59.7	18 57.1	22 17.1
16	13 37 33.3	26 15.7	4 11.5	10♎35.6	0 37.6	10 43.9	14 39.8	4 58.0	17 3.0	18 .0	18 57.2	22 15.7
17	13 41 29.8	27 14.3	4 8.4	24 41.0	1 11.9	11 57.8	15 26.2	4 55.4	17 6.9	18 .3	18 57.4	22 14.2
18	13 45 26.4	28 13.0	4 5.2	8♏29.3	1 50.3	13 11.8	16 12.6	4 53.0	17 10.7	18 .5	18 57.5	22 12.7
19	13 49 22.9	29 11.6	4 2.0	21 56.9	2 32.4	14 25.7	16 59.0	4 50.7	17 14.4	18 .7	18 57.5	22 11.2
20	13 53 19.5	0♉10.2	3 58.8	5♐ 2.1	3 18.2	15 39.6	17 45.4	4 48.7	17 18.1	18 .9	18 57.6	22 9.8
21	13 57 16.0	1 8.7	3 55.6	17 45.6	4 7.3	16 53.5	18 31.7	4 46.8	17 21.6	18 .9	18 57.6	22 8.2
22	14 1 12.6	2 7.2	3 52.5	0♑ 9.5	4 59.8	18 7.5	19 18.1	4 45.0	17 25.1	18 .9	18R57.5	22 6.7
23	14 5 9.2	3 5.7	3 49.3	12 17.5	5 55.4	19 21.3	20 4.4	4 43.5	17 28.5	18 .9	18 57.5	22 5.1
24	14 9 5.7	4 4.1	3 46.1	24 14.4	6 53.9	20 35.2	20 50.7	4 42.1	17 31.8	18R .8	18 57.4	22 3.6
25	14 13 2.3	5 2.6	3 42.9	6♒ 5.2	7 55.4	21 49.1	21 37.1	4 41.0	17 35.0	18 .7	18 57.2	22 2.0
26	14 16 58.8	6 1.0	3 39.8	17 55.2	8 59.6	23 3.0	22 23.3	4 40.0	17 38.1	18 .5	18 57.0	22 .4
27	14 20 55.4	6 59.3	3 36.6	29 49.7	10 6.5	24 16.9	23 9.6	4 39.2	17 41.2	18 .2	18 56.8	21 58.8
28	14 24 51.9	7 57.7	3 33.4	11♓53.2	11 16.0	25 30.8	23 55.9	4 38.6	17 44.1	17 60.0	18 56.6	21 57.2
29	14 28 48.5	8 56.0	3 30.2	24 9.7	12 27.9	26 44.6	24 42.1	4 38.2	17 47.0	17 59.6	18 56.3	21 55.6
30	14 32 45.0	9 54.3	3 27.1	6♈42.2	13 42.2	27 58.5	25 28.3	4 37.9	17 49.8	17 59.2	18 56.0	21 53.9
		LATITUDE										
1	12 38 25.0	0 .0	0 .0	4N44.6	1N57.0	1S26.7	1S14.3	1N21.7	0S42.8	0S23.7	0N44.3	15N10.8
4	12 50 14.6	0 .0	0 .0	4 42.8	1 9.6	1 28.6	1 15.2	1 21.4	0 43.2	0 23.8	0 44.3	15 11.6
7	13 2 4.3	0 .0	0 .0	2 31.5	0 21.7	1 29.9	1 16.0	1 21.0	0 43.6	0 23.9	0 44.4	15 12.4
10	13 13 54.0	0 .0	0 .0	0S59.7	0S23.1	1 30.6	1 16.8	1 20.6	0 44.0	0 24.0	0 44.4	15 13.1
13	13 25 43.6	0 .0	0 .0	4 5.5	1 3.0	1 30.6	1 17.5	1 20.2	0 44.4	0 24.0	0 44.5	15 13.7
16	13 37 33.3	0 .0	0 .0	4 59.9	1 37.0	1 30.1	1 18.1	1 19.8	0 44.8	0 24.1	0 44.5	15 14.3
19	13 49 22.9	0 .0	0 .0	3 18.2	2 4.6	1 28.9	1 18.7	1 19.3	0 45.2	0 24.2	0 44.6	15 14.8
22	14 1 12.6	0 .0	0 .0	0 12.1	2 26.0	1 27.2	1 19.2	1 18.8	0 45.7	0 24.3	0 44.6	15 15.2
25	14 13 2.3	0 .0	0 .0	2N50.3	2 41.4	1 24.9	1 19.6	1 18.3	0 46.1	0 24.4	0 44.6	15 15.6
28	14 24 51.9	0 .0	0 .0	4 47.2	2 50.8	1 22.1	1 19.9	1 17.8	0 46.6	0 24.5	0 44.7	15 15.8
		RIGHT ASCENSION										
1	12 38 25.0	10♈35.6	5♑26.0	15♓16.5	0♈51.8	23♓26.4	5♓26.5	8♍15.7	18♒36.4	19♑22.7	20♑18.5	24♏ 1.0
2	12 42 21.5	11 30.3	5 22.5	26 32.6	0R20.9	24 34.8	6 10.8	8R10.8	18 41.5	19 23.8	20 19.2	23R59.9
3	12 46 18.1	12 25.1	5 19.0	8♈ 9.6	29♓54.2	25 43.2	6 55.0	8 6.0	18 46.4	19 24.8	20 19.8	23 58.9
4	12 50 14.6	13 19.8	5 15.6	20 18.5	29 32.1	26 51.4	7 39.2	8 1.4	18 51.3	19 25.8	20 20.4	23 57.8
5	12 54 11.2	14 14.6	5 12.1	3♉ 8.7	29 14.7	27 59.6	8 23.3	7 56.9	18 56.1	19 26.8	20 20.9	23 56.7
6	12 58 7.7	15 9.5	5 8.7	16 45.0	29 2.1	29 7.7	9 7.3	7 52.6	19 .9	19 27.7	20 21.4	23 55.6
7	13 2 4.3	16 4.4	5 5.2	1♊ 5.1	28 54.5	0♈15.8	9 51.2	7 48.4	19 5.5	19 28.5	20 21.9	23 54.5
8	13 6 .9	16 59.3	5 1.7	15 57.5	28 51.9	1 23.8	10 35.0	7 44.4	19 10.1	19 29.3	20 22.4	23 53.3
9	13 9 57.4	17 54.3	4 58.3	1♋ 3.4	28D54.0	2 31.7	11 18.7	7 40.6	19 14.6	19 30.0	20 22.8	23 52.2
10	13 13 54.0	18 49.4	4 54.8	16 2.0	29 .9	3 39.7	12 2.4	7 36.9	19 19.1	19 30.7	20 23.2	23 51.0
11	13 17 50.5	19 44.5	4 51.4	0♌37.0	29 12.4	4 47.6	12 46.0	7 33.3	19 23.5	19 31.3	20 23.5	23 49.7
12	13 21 47.1	20 39.7	4 47.9	14 41.3	29 28.4	5 55.5	13 29.5	7 29.9	19 27.8	19 31.9	20 23.8	23 48.5
13	13 25 43.6	21 35.0	4 44.4	28 16.6	29 48.6	7 3.4	14 13.0	7 26.7	19 32.0	19 32.4	20 24.1	23 47.2
14	13 29 40.2	22 30.4	4 41.0	11♍31.4	0♈12.9	8 11.3	14 56.4	7 23.7	19 36.1	19 32.8	20 24.3	23 46.0
15	13 33 36.7	23 25.8	4 37.5	24 37.1	0 41.1	9 19.3	15 39.7	7 20.8	19 40.2	19 33.2	20 24.5	23 44.7
16	13 37 33.3	24 21.3	4 34.1	7♎45.3	1 13.1	10 27.2	16 22.9	7 18.1	19 44.1	19 33.6	20 24.7	23 43.4
17	13 41 29.8	25 16.9	4 30.6	21 5.7	1 48.5	11 35.2	17 6.1	7 15.6	19 48.0	19 33.9	20 24.8	23 42.0
18	13 45 26.4	26 12.6	4 27.1	4♏43.4	2 27.3	12 43.3	17 49.2	7 13.2	19 51.9	19 34.1	20 24.9	23 40.7
19	13 49 22.9	27 8.4	4 23.7	18 36.9	3 9.3	13 51.4	18 32.3	7 11.0	19 55.6	19 34.3	20 24.9	23 39.3
20	13 53 19.5	28 4.3	4 20.2	2♐38.1	3 54.4	14 59.7	19 15.3	7 9.0	19 59.3	19 34.5	20 25.0	23 38.0
21	13 57 16.0	29 .3	4 16.8	16 34.0	4 42.4	16 7.9	19 58.3	7 7.1	20 2.9	19 34.6	20 25.0	23 36.6
22	14 1 12.6	29 56.5	4 13.3	0♑10.3	5 33.0	17 16.3	20 41.2	7 5.4	20 6.4	19 34.6	20 25.0	23 35.2
23	14 5 9.2	0♉52.7	4 9.8	13 16.4	6 26.3	18 24.8	21 24.0	7 3.9	20 9.8	19R34.5	20R24.9	23 33.7
24	14 9 5.7	1 49.1	4 6.4	25 47.1	7 22.1	19 33.4	22 6.8	7 2.6	20 13.1	19 34.5	20 24.8	23 32.3
25	14 13 2.3	2 45.5	4 2.9	7♒44.0	8 20.3	20 42.1	22 49.5	7 1.4	20 16.4	19 34.3	20 24.6	23 30.8
26	14 16 58.8	3 42.2	3 59.5	19 13.1	9 20.8	21 50.9	23 32.2	7 .4	20 19.5	19 34.1	20 24.4	23 29.4
27	14 20 55.4	4 38.9	3 56.0	0♓24.0	10 23.5	22 59.9	24 14.8	6 59.6	20 22.6	19 33.9	20 24.2	23 27.9
28	14 24 51.9	5 35.7	3 52.5	11 28.2	11 28.3	24 9.1	24 57.4	6 59.0	20 25.6	19 33.6	20 23.9	23 26.4
29	14 28 48.5	6 32.7	3 49.1	22 38.4	12 35.2	25 18.4	25 40.0	6 58.5	20 28.4	19 33.2	20 23.7	23 24.9
30	14 32 45.0	7 29.9	3 45.6	4♈ 7.7	13 44.2	26 27.8	26 22.4	6 58.2	20 31.2	19 32.8	20 23.3	23 23.4
		DECLINATION										
1	12 38 25.0	4N33.5	0S24.4	1S 8.9	2N30.0	4S24.6	11S32.7	10N35.3	16S44.7	22S38.6	21S23.0	3S42.6
4	12 50 14.6	5 42.5	0 24.5	13N38.4	1 3.7	2 58.3	10 42.6	10 40.5	16 40.6	22 38.3	21 22.7	3 41.0
7	13 2 4.3	6 50.7	0 24.5	23 21.4	0S 4.7	1 31.2	9 51.6	10 45.2	16 36.7	22 38.1	21 22.4	3 39.3
10	13 13 54.0	7 57.8	0 24.5	21 37.3	0 50.8	0 3.5	8 59.9	10 49.3	16 33.0	22 37.9	21 22.2	3 37.7
13	13 25 43.6	9 3.7	0 24.5	8 29.7	1 13.6	1N24.3	8 7.5	10 52.8	16 29.6	22 37.8	21 22.1	3 36.1
16	13 37 33.3	10 8.2	0 24.5	8S47.3	1 14.0	2 52.0	7 14.5	10 55.7	16 26.3	22 37.7	21 21.9	3 34.6
19	13 49 22.9	11 11.3	0 24.5	21 26.6	0 53.8	4 19.3	6 20.9	10 57.9	16 23.2	22 37.7	21 21.9	3 33.0
22	14 1 12.6	12 12.6	0 24.5	23 38.5	0 15.0	5 45.8	5 26.9	10 59.5	16 20.4	22 37.8	21 21.8	3 31.6
25	14 13 2.3	13 12.2	0 24.5	15 60.0	0N40.3	7 11.3	4 32.6	11 .6	16 17.8	22 37.9	21 21.8	3 30.1
28	14 24 51.9	14 9.8	0 24.5	2 40.5	1 50.2	8 35.4	3 38.0	11 1.0	16 15.4	22 38.1	21 21.8	3 28.7

MAY 1992

DAY	EPHEM. SID. TIME	LONGITUDE ☉	☊	☾	☿	♀	♂	♃	♄	♅	♆	♇
	h m s	° ′	° ′	° ′	° ′	° ′	° ′	° ′	° ′	° ′	° ′	° ′
1	14 36 41.6	10 ♉ 52.6	3 ♑ 23.9	19 ♈ 32.1	14 ♈ 58.8	29 ♈ 12.3	26 ♓ 14.5	4 ♍ 37.9	17 ♒ 52.5	17 ♑ 58.8	18 ♑ 55.7	21 ♏ 52.3
2	14 40 38.1	11 50.8	3 20.7	2 ♉ 39.9	16 17.7	0 ♉ 26.2	27 .6	4 D 38.0	17 55.1	17 R 58.3	18 R 55.3	21 R 50.7
3	14 44 34.7	12 49.0	3 17.5	16 4.3	17 38.9	1 40.0	27 46.8	4 38.3	17 57.6	17 57.8	18 54.9	21 49.0
4	14 48 31.3	13 47.2	3 14.3	29 43.3	19 2.1	2 53.9	28 32.9	4 38.8	17 60.0	17 57.2	18 54.5	21 47.4
5	14 52 27.8	14 45.4	3 11.2	13 ♊ 34.0	20 27.6	4 7.7	29 19.0	4 39.5	18 2.3	17 56.6	18 54.1	21 45.7
6	14 56 24.4	15 43.5	3 8.0	27 33.3	21 55.1	5 21.5	0 ♈ 5.0	4 40.4	18 4.5	17 55.9	18 53.6	21 44.0
7	15 0 20.9	16 41.6	3 4.8	11 ♋ 38.6	23 24.6	6 35.3	0 51.0	4 41.4	18 6.6	17 55.2	18 53.0	21 42.4
8	15 4 17.5	17 39.6	3 1.6	25 47.3	24 56.3	7 49.2	1 37.0	4 42.7	18 8.7	17 54.4	18 52.5	21 40.7
9	15 8 14.0	18 37.7	2 58.5	9 ♌ 57.6	26 29.9	9 3.0	2 23.0	4 44.1	18 10.6	17 53.6	18 51.9	21 39.0
10	15 12 10.6	19 35.7	2 55.3	24 7.9	28 5.6	10 16.7	3 8.9	4 45.7	18 12.5	17 52.7	18 51.3	21 37.3
11	15 16 7.1	20 33.7	2 52.1	8 ♍ 16.5	29 43.4	11 30.6	3 54.8	4 47.5	18 14.3	17 51.8	18 50.7	21 35.7
12	15 20 3.7	21 31.6	2 48.9	22 21.3	1 ♉ 23.1	12 44.3	4 40.7	4 49.4	18 15.9	17 50.9	18 50.0	21 34.0
13	15 24 .3	22 29.5	2 45.7	6 ♎ 20.1	3 4.8	13 58.1	5 26.5	4 51.6	18 17.5	17 49.9	18 49.3	21 32.3
14	15 27 56.8	23 27.4	2 42.6	20 10.0	4 48.6	15 11.9	6 12.3	4 53.9	18 19.0	17 48.8	18 48.6	21 30.7
15	15 31 53.4	24 25.2	2 39.4	3 ♏ 48.3	6 34.3	16 25.6	6 58.1	4 56.4	18 20.3	17 47.7	18 47.9	21 29.0
16	15 35 49.9	25 23.0	2 36.2	17 12.3	8 22.1	17 39.4	7 43.8	4 59.0	18 21.6	17 46.6	18 47.1	21 27.3
17	15 39 46.5	26 20.8	2 33.0	0 ♐ 20.2	10 11.9	18 53.1	8 29.5	5 1.8	18 22.8	17 45.4	18 46.3	21 25.7
18	15 43 43.0	27 18.6	2 29.9	13 11.1	12 3.8	20 6.8	9 15.1	5 4.8	18 23.8	17 44.2	18 45.4	21 24.0
19	15 47 39.6	28 16.4	2 26.7	25 45.2	13 57.6	21 20.6	10 .7	5 8.0	18 24.8	17 42.9	18 44.6	21 22.3
20	15 51 36.2	29 14.1	2 23.5	8 ♑ 3.9	15 53.4	22 34.3	10 46.3	5 11.3	18 25.7	17 41.6	18 43.7	21 20.7
21	15 55 32.7	0 ♊ 11.8	2 20.3	20 10.0	17 51.2	23 48.0	11 31.9	5 14.8	18 26.5	17 40.3	18 42.8	21 19.0
22	15 59 29.3	1 9.5	2 17.2	2 ♒ 6.7	19 50.9	25 1.7	12 17.4	5 18.5	18 27.2	17 38.9	18 41.8	21 17.4
23	16 3 25.8	2 7.1	2 14.0	13 58.2	21 52.5	26 15.5	13 2.8	5 22.3	18 27.8	17 37.4	18 40.9	21 15.7
24	16 7 22.4	3 4.8	2 10.8	25 49.3	23 55.8	27 29.2	13 48.3	5 26.3	18 28.3	17 36.0	18 39.9	21 14.1
25	16 11 18.9	4 2.4	2 7.6	7 ♓ 44.7	26 .8	28 42.9	14 33.7	5 30.4	18 28.7	17 34.5	18 38.8	21 12.4
26	16 15 15.5	5 .1	2 4.4	19 49.3	28 7.4	29 56.6	15 19.0	5 34.8	18 29.0	17 32.9	18 37.8	21 10.8
27	16 19 12.0	5 57.7	2 1.3	2 ♈ 7.5	0 ♊ 15.4	1 ♊ 10.4	16 4.3	5 39.2	18 29.2	17 31.4	18 36.7	21 9.2
28	16 23 8.6	6 55.3	1 58.1	14 43.2	2 24.7	2 24.1	16 49.6	5 43.9	18 29.3	17 29.7	18 35.6	21 7.6
29	16 27 5.2	7 52.8	1 54.9	27 39.2	4 35.0	3 37.8	17 34.8	5 48.6	18 29.3	17 28.1	18 34.5	21 6.0
30	16 31 1.7	8 50.4	1 51.7	10 ♉ 56.9	6 46.1	4 51.5	18 19.9	5 53.6	18 R 29.2	17 26.4	18 33.4	21 4.4
31	16 34 58.3	9 47.9	1 48.6	24 36.0	8 57.8	6 5.3	19 5.0	5 58.7	18 29.0	17 24.7	18 32.2	21 2.9

DAY	SID. TIME	LATITUDE ☉	☊	☾	☿	♀	♂	♃	♄	♅	♆	♇
1	14 36 41.6	0 .0	0 .0	4 N 52.0	2 S 54.7	1 S 18.8	1 S 20.1	1 N 17.3	0 S 47.0	0 S 24.6	0 N 44.7	15 N 16.0
4	14 48 31.3	0 .0	0 .0	2 42.5	2 53.1	1 14.9	1 20.3	1 16.8	0 47.5	0 24.6	0 44.8	15 16.1
7	15 0 20.9	0 .0	0 .0	0 S 55.0	2 46.3	1 10.6	1 20.4	1 16.3	0 47.9	0 24.7	0 44.8	15 16.1
10	15 12 10.6	0 .0	0 .0	4 6.9	2 34.5	1 5.8	1 20.4	1 15.7	0 48.4	0 24.8	0 44.8	15 16.0
13	15 24 .3	0 .0	0 .0	5 8.9	2 18.0	1 .7	1 20.4	1 15.2	0 48.9	0 24.9	0 44.9	15 15.9
16	15 35 49.9	0 .0	0 .0	3 35.6	1 57.0	0 55.1	1 20.2	1 14.7	0 49.4	0 25.0	0 44.9	15 15.6
19	15 47 39.6	0 .0	0 .0	0 28.1	1 32.0	0 49.2	1 20.0	1 14.1	0 49.9	0 25.0	0 44.9	15 15.3
22	15 59 29.3	0 .0	0 .0	2 N 42.8	1 3.6	0 43.0	1 19.6	1 13.6	0 50.3	0 25.1	0 45.0	15 14.9
25	16 11 18.9	0 .0	0 .0	4 48.8	0 32.8	0 36.6	1 19.2	1 13.1	0 50.8	0 25.2	0 45.0	15 14.4
28	16 23 8.6	0 .0	0 .0	5 5.1	0 .9	0 29.9	1 18.7	1 12.6	0 51.3	0 25.3	0 45.0	15 13.8
31	16 34 58.3	0 .0	0 .0	3 6.0	0 N 30.4	0 23.1	1 18.1	1 12.1	0 51.8	0 25.3	0 45.0	15 13.2

DAY	SID. TIME	RIGHT ASCENSION ☉	☊	☾	☿	♀	♂	♃	♄	♅	♆	♇
1	14 36 41.6	8 ♉ 27.1	3 ♑ 42.2	16 ♈ 9.1	14 ♈ 55.2	27 ♈ 37.4	27 ♓ 4.9	6 ♍ 58.1	20 ♒ 34.0	19 ♑ 32.3	20 ♑ 23.0	23 ♏ 21.9
2	14 40 38.1	9 24.5	3 38.7	28 53.8	16 8.1	28 47.3	27 47.3	6 58.1	20 36.6	19 R 31.8	20 R 22.6	23 R 20.3
3	14 44 34.7	10 22.1	3 35.2	12 ♉ 29.0	17 23.0	29 57.3	28 29.7	6 D 58.4	20 39.1	19 31.2	20 22.2	23 18.8
4	14 48 31.3	11 19.7	3 31.8	26 54.1	18 39.8	1 ♉ 7.5	29 12.0	6 58.8	20 41.5	19 30.6	20 21.7	23 17.3
5	14 52 27.8	12 17.6	3 28.3	11 ♊ 58.0	19 58.5	2 17.9	29 54.3	6 59.4	20 43.9	19 29.9	20 21.2	23 15.7
6	14 56 24.4	13 15.5	3 24.9	27 19.7	21 19.1	3 28.5	0 ♈ 36.6	7 .1	20 46.1	19 29.2	20 20.7	23 14.2
7	15 0 20.9	14 13.6	3 21.4	12 ♋ 34.3	22 41.7	4 39.3	1 18.8	7 1.1	20 48.3	19 28.4	20 20.1	23 12.6
8	15 4 17.5	15 11.8	3 17.9	27 21.3	24 6.3	5 50.4	2 1.0	7 2.2	20 50.4	19 27.6	20 19.6	23 11.0
9	15 8 14.0	16 10.2	3 14.5	11 ♌ 30.7	25 32.8	7 1.7	2 43.2	7 3.4	20 52.3	19 26.7	20 18.9	23 9.4
10	15 12 10.6	17 8.7	3 11.0	25 3.5	27 1.4	8 13.2	3 25.3	7 4.9	20 54.2	19 25.8	20 18.3	23 7.9
11	15 16 7.1	18 7.4	3 7.6	8 ♍ 8.4	28 32.1	9 25.0	4 7.4	7 6.5	20 56.0	19 24.9	20 17.7	23 6.3
12	15 20 3.7	19 6.1	3 4.1	20 57.9	0 ♉ 4.8	10 37.0	4 49.5	7 8.3	20 57.7	19 23.8	20 16.9	23 4.7
13	15 24 .3	20 5.1	3 .6	3 ♎ 45.8	1 39.7	11 49.3	5 31.6	7 10.3	20 59.3	19 22.8	20 16.2	23 3.2
14	15 27 56.8	21 4.1	2 57.2	16 44.2	3 16.9	13 1.8	6 13.6	7 12.4	21 .8	19 21.6	20 15.4	23 1.6
15	15 31 53.4	22 3.3	2 53.7	0 ♏ 1.2	4 56.3	14 14.6	6 55.6	7 14.7	21 2.2	19 20.5	20 14.6	22 60.0
16	15 35 49.9	23 2.6	2 50.2	13 39.5	6 38.1	15 27.6	7 37.6	7 17.1	21 3.5	19 19.3	20 13.8	22 58.4
17	15 39 46.5	24 2.1	2 46.8	27 34.0	8 22.4	16 40.9	8 19.6	7 19.7	21 4.8	19 18.0	20 12.9	22 56.8
18	15 43 43.0	25 1.7	2 43.3	11 ♐ 33.1	10 9.1	17 54.5	9 1.5	7 22.5	21 5.9	19 16.7	20 12.0	22 55.2
19	15 47 39.6	26 1.5	2 39.9	25 21.4	11 58.4	19 8.4	9 43.5	7 25.4	21 6.9	19 15.3	20 11.1	22 53.6
20	15 51 36.2	27 1.4	2 36.4	8 ♑ 44.2	13 50.2	20 22.6	10 25.4	7 28.5	21 7.8	19 13.9	20 10.2	22 52.0
21	15 55 32.7	28 1.4	2 32.9	21 32.6	15 44.8	21 37.0	11 7.4	7 31.7	21 8.7	19 12.5	20 9.2	22 50.5
22	15 59 29.3	29 1.6	2 29.5	3 ♒ 44.2	17 42.0	22 51.7	11 49.3	7 35.1	21 9.4	19 11.0	20 8.2	22 48.9
23	16 3 25.8	0 ♊ 1.9	2 26.0	15 22.8	19 41.9	24 6.7	12 31.2	7 38.7	21 10.0	19 9.5	20 7.2	22 47.3
24	16 7 22.4	1 2.3	2 22.6	26 36.8	21 44.4	25 22.0	13 13.1	7 42.4	21 10.6	19 7.9	20 6.1	22 45.7
25	16 11 18.9	2 2.9	2 19.1	7 ♓ 37.6	23 49.7	26 37.5	13 55.0	7 46.3	21 11.0	19 6.3	20 5.0	22 44.2
26	16 15 15.5	3 3.5	2 15.6	18 37.9	25 57.5	27 53.4	14 36.9	7 50.3	21 11.4	19 4.6	20 3.9	22 42.6
27	16 19 12.0	4 4.4	2 12.2	29 51.7	28 7.8	29 9.5	15 18.8	7 54.5	21 11.6	19 2.9	20 2.8	22 41.0
28	16 23 8.6	5 5.3	2 8.7	11 ♈ 33.2	0 ♊ 20.4	0 ♊ 25.9	16 .7	7 58.8	21 11.8	19 1.2	20 1.6	22 39.5
29	16 27 5.2	6 6.4	2 5.2	23 56.4	2 35.2	1 42.5	16 42.6	8 3.2	21 11.8	18 59.4	20 .4	22 37.9
30	16 31 1.7	7 7.5	2 1.8	7 ♉ 12.3	4 52.0	2 59.5	17 24.5	8 7.8	21 11.8	18 57.6	19 59.2	22 36.4
31	16 34 58.3	8 8.8	1 58.3	21 25.6	7 10.4	4 16.7	18 6.4	8 12.6	21 R 11.6	18 55.8	19 58.0	22 34.9

DAY	SID. TIME	DECLINATION ☉	☊	☾	☿	♀	♂	♃	♄	♅	♆	♇
1	14 36 41.6	15 N 5.4	0 S 24.5	12 N 8.7	3 N 12.9	9 N 57.9	2 S 43.2	11 N .7	16 S 13.3	22 S 38.3	21 S 21.9	3 S 27.4
4	14 48 31.3	15 58.7	0 24.5	22 44.2	4 47.0	11 18.3	1 48.3	10 59.9	16 11.4	22 38.6	21 22.1	3 26.1
7	15 0 20.9	16 49.6	0 24.5	22 1.0	6 31.0	12 36.3	0 53.5	10 58.5	16 9.8	22 39.0	21 22.2	3 24.9
10	15 12 10.6	17 37.9	0 24.5	9 35.6	8 23.4	13 51.6	0 N 1.3	10 56.4	16 8.4	22 39.4	21 22.4	3 23.8
13	15 24 .3	18 23.7	0 24.5	7 S 14.4	10 22.6	15 4.0	0 55.9	10 53.7	16 7.3	22 39.8	21 22.7	3 22.8
16	15 35 49.9	19 6.6	0 24.5	20 24.9	12 26.9	16 13.0	1 50.3	10 50.5	16 6.5	22 40.3	21 22.9	3 21.8
19	15 47 39.6	19 46.6	0 24.5	23 50.4	14 34.0	17 18.3	2 44.4	10 46.7	16 6.0	22 40.9	21 23.2	3 20.9
22	15 59 29.3	20 23.5	0 24.5	17 2.8	16 40.8	18 19.7	3 38.1	10 42.4	16 5.7	22 41.5	21 23.6	3 20.1
25	16 11 18.9	20 57.4	0 24.5	4 11.7	18 43.7	19 16.7	4 31.3	10 37.5	16 5.7	22 42.1	21 24.0	3 19.4
28	16 23 8.6	21 28.0	0 24.5	10 N 29.2	20 37.8	20 9.2	5 24.0	10 32.1	16 6.0	22 42.8	21 24.4	3 18.8
31	16 34 58.3	21 55.2	0 24.5	21 55.5	22 17.7	20 56.7	6 16.1	10 26.2	16 6.6	22 43.5	21 24.8	3 18.3

JUNE 1992

LONGITUDE

DAY	EPHEM. SID. TIME	☉	☊	☽	☿	♀	♂	♃	♄	♅	♆	♇
	h m s	° ′	° ′	° ′	° ′	° ′	° ′	° ′	° ′	° ′	° ′	° ′
1	16 38 54.8	10♊45.5	1♑45.4	8♊34.7	11♊ 9.9	7♊19.0	19♈50.2	6♍ 4.0	18♒28.7	17♑22.9	18♑31.1	21♏ 1.4
2	16 42 51.4	11 43.0	1 42.2	22 49.2	13 22.0	8 32.8	20 35.2	6 9.4	18 R 28.3	17 R 21.2	18 R 29.9	20 R 59.8
3	16 46 47.9	12 40.5	1 39.0	7♋14.7	15 33.8	9 46.5	21 20.1	6 14.9	18 27.8	17 19.3	18 28.7	20 58.3
4	16 50 44.5	13 38.0	1 35.9	21 46.0	17 45.2	11 .2	22 5.0	6 20.6	18 27.2	17 17.5	18 27.4	20 56.8
5	16 54 41.1	14 35.4	1 32.7	6♌17.6	19 55.8	12 13.9	22 49.9	6 26.5	18 26.6	17 15.6	18 26.2	20 55.3
6	16 58 37.6	15 32.9	1 29.5	20 44.8	22 5.4	13 27.6	23 34.7	6 32.5	18 25.8	17 13.7	18 24.9	20 53.8
7	17 2 34.2	16 30.3	1 26.3	5♍ 4.0	24 13.7	14 41.3	24 19.4	6 38.6	18 24.9	17 11.7	18 23.6	20 52.3
8	17 6 30.7	17 27.7	1 23.2	19 12.3	26 20.5	15 55.0	25 4.1	6 44.9	18 23.9	17 9.7	18 22.3	20 50.9
9	17 10 27.3	18 25.1	1 20.0	3♎ 8.0	28 25.8	17 8.7	25 48.7	6 51.3	18 22.9	17 7.7	18 20.9	20 49.4
10	17 14 23.9	19 22.4	1 16.8	16 50.1	0♋29.2	18 22.4	26 33.3	6 57.8	18 21.7	17 5.7	18 19.6	20 48.0
11	17 18 20.4	20 19.8	1 13.6	0♏18.0	2 30.6	19 36.1	27 17.8	7 4.5	18 20.4	17 3.6	18 18.2	20 46.6
12	17 22 17.0	21 17.1	1 10.4	13 31.8	4 30.0	20 49.8	28 2.2	7 11.3	18 19.1	17 1.5	18 16.8	20 45.2
13	17 26 13.5	22 14.4	1 7.3	26 31.4	6 27.3	22 3.5	28 46.6	7 18.3	18 17.6	16 59.4	18 15.4	20 43.8
14	17 30 10.1	23 11.7	1 4.1	9♐17.2	8 22.4	23 17.2	29 31.0	7 25.4	18 16.1	16 57.3	18 14.0	20 42.5
15	17 34 6.6	24 9.0	1 .9	21 49.8	10 15.2	24 30.9	0♉15.2	7 32.6	18 14.5	16 55.1	18 12.5	20 41.2
16	17 38 3.2	25 6.3	0 57.7	4♑10.2	12 5.6	25 44.6	0 59.5	7 39.9	18 12.8	16 53.0	18 11.1	20 39.9
17	17 41 59.8	26 3.5	0 54.6	16 19.8	13 53.8	26 58.3	1 43.6	7 47.4	18 11.0	16 50.8	18 9.6	20 38.6
18	17 45 56.3	27 .8	0 51.4	28 20.6	15 39.5	28 12.0	2 27.7	7 54.9	18 9.1	16 48.6	18 8.1	20 37.3
19	17 49 52.9	27 58.0	0 48.2	10♒14.9	17 22.9	29 25.7	3 11.7	8 2.6	18 7.1	16 46.3	18 6.6	20 36.1
20	17 53 49.4	28 55.3	0 45.0	22 5.8	19 3.9	0♋39.4	3 55.7	8 10.5	18 5.0	16 44.1	18 5.1	20 34.9
21	17 57 46.0	29 52.5	0 41.9	3♓56.9	20 42.5	1 53.1	4 39.6	8 18.4	18 2.9	16 41.8	18 3.6	20 33.7
22	18 1 42.5	0♋49.8	0 38.7	15 52.3	22 18.7	3 6.9	5 23.5	8 26.5	18 .7	16 39.5	18 2.1	20 32.5
23	18 5 39.1	1 47.0	0 35.5	27 56.2	23 52.4	4 20.6	6 7.3	8 34.7	17 58.3	16 37.2	18 .6	20 31.4
24	18 9 35.7	2 44.3	0 32.3	10♈13.0	25 23.7	5 34.3	6 51.0	8 43.0	17 55.9	16 34.9	17 59.1	20 30.3
25	18 13 32.2	3 41.5	0 29.1	22 47.1	26 52.5	6 48.1	7 34.6	8 51.4	17 53.4	16 32.6	17 57.5	20 29.2
26	18 17 28.8	4 38.7	0 26.0	5♉42.2	28 18.8	8 1.8	8 18.2	8 59.9	17 50.9	16 30.2	17 55.9	20 28.1
27	18 21 25.3	5 36.0	0 22.8	19 1.1	29 42.6	9 15.5	9 1.7	9 8.6	17 48.2	16 27.9	17 54.4	20 27.0
28	18 25 21.9	6 33.2	0 19.6	2♊45.2	1♌ 3.9	10 29.3	9 45.2	9 17.3	17 45.5	16 25.5	17 52.8	20 26.0
29	18 29 18.5	7 30.4	0 16.4	16 53.7	2 22.6	11 43.0	10 28.5	9 26.2	17 42.7	16 23.1	17 51.2	20 25.0
30	18 33 15.0	8 27.7	0 13.3	1♋23.6	3 38.6	12 56.8	11 11.8	9 35.1	17 39.8	16 20.7	17 49.6	20 24.0

LATITUDE

DAY	EPHEM. SID. TIME	☉	☊	☽	☿	♀	♂	♃	♄	♅	♆	♇
1	16 38 54.8	0 .0	0 .0	1N59.0	0N40.4	0S20.8	1S17.9	1N11.9	0S52.0	0S25.4	0N45.0	15N12.9
4	16 50 44.5	0 .0	0 .0	1S53.9	1 7.9	0 13.7	1 17.2	1 11.4	0 52.5	0 25.4	0 45.1	15 12.2
7	17 2 34.2	0 .0	0 .0	4 45.3	1 30.7	0 6.6	1 16.5	1 10.9	0 53.0	0 25.5	0 45.1	15 11.4
10	17 14 23.9	0 .0	0 .0	5 4.1	1 47.4	0N .5	1 15.6	1 10.5	0 53.4	0 25.5	0 45.1	15 10.4
13	17 26 13.5	0 .0	0 .0	2 58.1	1 57.5	0 7.6	1 14.6	1 10.0	0 53.9	0 25.6	0 45.1	15 9.5
16	17 38 3.2	0 .0	0 .0	0N19.5	2 .9	0 14.7	1 13.6	1 9.6	0 54.4	0 25.6	0 45.1	15 8.4
19	17 49 52.9	0 .0	0 .0	3 22.5	1 57.7	0 21.7	1 12.5	1 9.1	0 54.9	0 25.7	0 45.1	15 7.3
22	18 1 42.5	0 .0	0 .0	5 6.8	1 48.1	0 28.6	1 11.2	1 8.7	0 55.3	0 25.7	0 45.1	15 6.2
25	18 13 32.2	0 .0	0 .0	4 54.1	1 32.7	0 35.2	1 9.9	1 8.3	0 55.8	0 25.8	0 45.1	15 4.9
28	18 25 21.9	0 .0	0 .0	2 29.0	1 11.9	0 41.6	1 8.6	1 7.9	0 56.2	0 25.8	0 45.1	15 3.6

RIGHT ASCENSION

DAY	EPHEM. SID. TIME	☉	☊	☽	☿	♀	♂	♃	♄	♅	♆	♇
1	16 38 54.8	9♊10.3	1♑54.9	6♊30.5	9♊30.2	5♊34.2	18♈48.4	8♍17.5	21♒11.4	18♑53.9	19♑56.8	22♏33.4
2	16 42 51.4	10 11.7	1 51.4	22 8.3	11 51.1	6 51.9	19 30.3	8 22.6	21 R 11.1	18 R 52.0	19 R 55.5	22 R 31.9
3	16 46 47.9	11 13.3	1 47.9	7♋51.2	14 12.7	8 9.8	20 12.2	8 27.7	21 10.7	18 50.0	19 54.2	22 30.4
4	16 50 44.5	12 15.0	1 44.5	23 11.9	16 34.5	9 28.0	20 54.1	8 33.1	21 10.1	18 48.0	19 52.9	22 28.9
5	16 54 41.1	13 16.7	1 41.0	7♌52.9	18 56.4	10 46.4	21 36.0	8 38.5	21 9.5	18 46.0	19 51.5	22 27.5
6	16 58 37.6	14 18.6	1 37.5	21 49.9	21 17.8	12 5.0	22 17.9	8 44.1	21 8.8	18 43.9	19 50.1	22 26.0
7	17 2 34.2	15 20.5	1 34.1	5♍ 9.3	23 38.4	13 23.9	22 59.9	8 49.8	21 8.0	18 41.8	19 48.8	22 24.6
8	17 6 30.7	16 22.4	1 30.6	18 3.3	25 57.9	14 42.9	23 41.8	8 55.7	21 7.1	18 39.7	19 47.3	22 23.1
9	17 10 27.3	17 24.5	1 27.2	0♎46.3	28 15.9	16 2.2	24 23.7	9 1.7	21 6.0	18 37.6	19 45.9	22 21.7
10	17 14 23.9	18 26.6	1 23.7	13 32.2	0♋32.2	17 21.6	25 5.7	9 7.8	21 5.0	18 35.4	19 44.5	22 20.3
11	17 18 20.4	19 28.7	1 20.2	26 31.6	2 46.5	18 41.2	25 47.6	9 14.0	21 3.8	18 33.2	19 43.0	22 18.9
12	17 22 17.0	20 30.9	1 16.8	9♏50.5	4 58.5	20 .9	26 29.6	9 20.4	21 2.5	18 30.9	19 41.5	22 17.5
13	17 26 13.5	21 33.1	1 13.3	23 28.2	7 8.1	21 20.8	27 11.6	9 26.9	21 1.1	18 28.7	19 40.0	22 16.2
14	17 30 10.1	22 35.4	1 9.9	7♐16.9	9 15.1	22 40.8	27 53.6	9 33.5	20 59.6	18 26.4	19 38.5	22 14.8
15	17 34 6.6	23 37.7	1 6.4	21 3.1	11 19.4	24 .9	28 35.6	9 40.2	20 58.1	18 24.0	19 37.0	22 13.5
16	17 38 3.2	24 40.0	1 2.9	4♑32.0	13 20.8	25 21.2	29 17.6	9 47.1	20 56.4	18 21.7	19 35.4	22 12.2
17	17 41 59.8	25 42.3	0 59.5	17 31.5	15 19.2	26 41.6	29 59.6	9 54.0	20 54.7	18 19.3	19 33.9	22 10.9
18	17 45 56.3	26 44.7	0 56.0	29 55.8	17 14.6	28 2.0	0♉41.7	10 1.1	20 52.9	18 17.0	19 32.3	22 9.6
19	17 49 52.9	27 47.1	0 52.5	11♒45.4	19 6.9	29 22.5	1 23.7	10 8.3	20 50.9	18 14.6	19 30.7	22 8.3
20	17 53 49.4	28 49.5	0 49.1	23 6.0	20 56.1	0♋43.1	2 5.8	10 15.6	20 48.9	18 12.1	19 29.1	22 7.1
21	17 57 46.0	29 51.8	0 45.6	4♓ 7.3	22 42.1	2 3.7	2 47.9	10 23.0	20 46.9	18 9.7	19 27.5	22 5.9
22	18 1 42.5	0♋54.3	0 42.2	15 1.0	24 25.0	3 24.4	3 30.1	10 30.6	20 44.7	18 7.3	19 25.9	22 4.7
23	18 5 39.1	1 56.7	0 38.7	26 .2	26 4.6	4 45.0	4 12.3	10 38.2	20 42.5	18 4.8	19 24.3	22 3.6
24	18 9 35.7	2 59.0	0 35.2	7♈19.2	27 41.0	6 5.7	4 54.4	10 46.0	20 40.1	18 2.3	19 22.7	22 2.4
25	18 13 32.2	4 1.4	0 31.8	19 12.5	29 14.1	7 26.3	5 36.6	10 53.8	20 37.7	17 59.8	19 21.0	22 1.3
26	18 17 28.8	5 3.7	0 28.3	1♉53.5	0♌44.1	8 47.0	6 18.8	11 1.8	20 35.2	17 57.3	19 19.3	22 .1
27	18 21 25.3	6 6.0	0 24.8	15 32.1	2 10.7	10 7.5	7 1.0	11 9.8	20 32.6	17 54.7	19 17.7	21 59.1
28	18 25 21.9	7 8.2	0 21.4	0♊10.2	3 34.1	11 28.0	7 43.2	11 18.0	20 30.0	17 52.2	19 16.0	21 58.0
29	18 29 18.5	8 10.4	0 17.9	15 37.6	4 54.2	12 48.5	8 25.4	11 26.2	20 27.2	17 49.6	19 14.3	21 56.9
30	18 33 15.0	9 12.6	0 14.5	1♋31.1	6 11.1	14 8.8	9 7.7	11 34.6	20 24.4	17 47.0	19 12.6	21 55.9

DECLINATION

DAY	EPHEM. SID. TIME	☉	☊	☽	☿	♀	♂	♃	♄	♅	♆	♇
1	16 38 54.8	22N 3.6	0S24.5	23N41.6	22N47.0	21N11.5	6N33.3	10N24.0	16S 6.8	22S43.8	21S25.0	3S18.2
4	16 50 44.5	22 26.2	0 24.5	19 48.4	24 .2	21 52.0	7 24.4	10 17.4	16 7.7	22 44.5	21 25.5	3 17.8
7	17 2 34.2	22 45.4	0 24.5	5 13.5	24 49.4	22 27.1	8 14.7	10 10.3	16 8.9	22 45.3	21 26.0	3 17.5
10	17 14 23.9	23 .9	0 24.5	11S17.5	25 13.8	22 56.4	9 4.1	10 2.7	16 10.4	22 46.2	21 26.5	3 17.3
13	17 26 13.5	23 12.8	0 24.5	22 15.8	25 14.4	23 19.8	9 52.6	9 54.7	16 12.1	22 47.0	21 27.1	3 17.3
16	17 38 3.2	23 21.0	0 24.5	23 3.0	24 53.8	23 37.0	10 40.2	9 46.2	16 14.0	22 47.9	21 27.6	3 17.3
19	17 49 52.9	23 25.5	0 24.5	14 25.4	24 15.3	23 48.0	11 26.6	9 37.3	16 16.2	22 48.7	21 28.2	3 17.4
22	18 1 42.5	23 26.3	0 24.5	0 51.3	23 22.3	23 52.8	12 12.0	9 28.0	16 18.7	22 49.6	21 28.8	3 17.7
25	18 13 32.2	23 23.3	0 24.5	13N24.5	22 18.0	23 51.1	12 56.2	9 18.3	16 21.3	22 50.5	21 29.4	3 18.1
28	18 25 21.9	23 16.7	0 24.5	23 8.7	21 5.5	23 43.1	13 39.1	9 8.2	16 24.2	22 51.4	21 30.1	3 18.5

JULY 1992

DAY	EPHEM. SID. TIME	☉	☊	☽	☿	♀	♂	♃	♄	♅	♆	♇
	h m s	° ′	° ′	° ′	° ′	° ′	° ′	° ′	° ′	° ′	° ′	° ′
		LONGITUDE										
1	18 37 11.6	9♋24.9	0♑10.1	16♋ 9.7	4♌52.0	14♋10.5	11♉55.0	9♍44.2	17♒36.8	16♑18.3	17♑48.0	20♏23.1
2	18 41 8.1	10 22.1	0 6.9	1♌ 4.8	6 2.6	15 24.3	12 38.1	9 53.4	17 R33.8	16 R15.9	17 R46.4	20 R22.2
3	18 45 4.7	11 19.3	0 3.7	16 .9	7 10.4	16 38.1	13 21.2	10 2.6	17 30.6	16 13.5	17 44.8	20 21.3
4	18 49 1.2	12 16.6	0 .6	0♍50.2	8 15.3	17 51.8	14 4.1	10 12.0	17 27.5	16 11.1	17 43.2	20 20.4
5	18 52 57.8	13 13.8	29♐57.4	15 25.9	9 17.2	19 5.6	14 47.0	10 21.5	17 24.2	16 8.7	17 41.6	20 19.6
6	18 56 54.4	14 11.0	29 54.2	29 43.4	10 16.0	20 19.3	15 29.8	10 31.0	17 20.9	16 6.3	17 39.9	20 18.8
7	19 0 50.9	15 8.2	29 51.0	13♎40.2	11 11.7	21 33.1	16 12.5	10 40.7	17 17.5	16 3.8	17 38.3	20 18.0
8	19 4 47.5	16 5.4	29 47.9	27 15.8	12 4.1	22 46.9	16 55.2	10 50.4	17 14.0	16 1.4	17 36.7	20 17.2
9	19 8 44.0	17 2.6	29 44.7	10♏31.1	12 53.1	24 .6	17 37.7	11 .3	17 10.5	15 59.0	17 35.1	20 16.5
10	19 12 40.6	17 59.8	29 41.5	23 28.1	13 38.5	25 14.4	18 20.2	11 10.2	17 6.9	15 56.6	17 33.4	20 15.8
11	19 16 37.1	18 57.0	29 38.3	6♐ 9.0	14 20.3	26 28.2	19 2.6	11 20.2	17 3.3	15 54.2	17 31.8	20 15.2
12	19 20 33.7	19 54.2	29 35.1	18 36.4	14 58.3	27 41.9	19 44.9	11 30.3	16 59.6	15 51.7	17 30.2	20 14.6
13	19 24 30.3	20 51.4	29 32.0	0♑52.6	15 32.4	28 55.8	20 27.2	11 40.6	16 55.9	15 49.4	17 28.6	20 14.0
14	19 28 26.8	21 48.6	29 28.8	12 59.7	16 2.3	0♌ 9.5	21 9.3	11 50.8	16 52.1	15 47.0	17 27.0	20 13.4
15	19 32 23.4	22 45.8	29 25.6	24 59.8	16 28.0	1 23.3	21 51.3	12 1.2	16 48.3	15 44.6	17 25.4	20 12.9
16	19 36 19.9	23 43.0	29 22.4	6♒54.7	16 49.4	2 37.1	22 33.3	12 11.6	16 44.4	15 42.2	17 23.8	20 12.4
17	19 40 16.5	24 40.3	29 19.3	18 46.3	17 6.2	3 50.9	23 15.2	12 22.1	16 40.4	15 39.8	17 22.2	20 11.9
18	19 44 13.0	25 37.5	29 16.1	0♓36.9	17 18.4	5 4.6	23 56.9	12 32.7	16 36.4	15 37.4	17 20.6	20 11.5
19	19 48 9.6	26 34.7	29 12.9	12 28.9	17 25.9	6 18.4	24 38.6	12 43.4	16 32.4	15 35.0	17 19.0	20 11.1
20	19 52 6.2	27 32.0	29 9.7	24 25.2	17 28.5	7 32.2	25 20.2	12 54.2	16 28.3	15 32.7	17 17.4	20 10.7
21	19 56 2.7	28 29.2	29 6.6	6♈29.2	17 R26.2	8 46.0	26 1.8	13 5.0	16 24.2	15 30.3	17 15.8	20 10.4
22	19 59 59.3	29 26.5	29 3.4	18 44.6	17 19.0	9 59.8	26 43.2	13 15.9	16 20.0	15 28.0	17 14.2	20 10.1
23	20 3 55.8	0♌23.8	29 .2	1♉15.5	17 6.8	11 13.6	27 24.5	13 26.8	16 15.8	15 25.7	17 12.6	20 9.8
24	20 7 52.4	1 21.1	28 57.0	14 6.0	16 49.9	12 27.4	28 5.7	13 37.9	16 11.5	15 23.4	17 11.0	20 9.5
25	20 11 48.9	2 18.4	28 53.8	27 19.7	16 28.1	13 41.2	28 46.9	13 49.0	16 7.3	15 21.1	17 9.5	20 9.3
26	20 15 45.5	3 15.7	28 50.7	10♊59.5	16 1.9	14 55.0	29 27.9	14 .2	16 3.0	15 18.8	17 7.9	20 9.2
27	20 19 42.1	4 13.1	28 47.5	25 6.3	15 31.5	16 8.8	0♊ 8.8	14 11.4	15 58.6	15 16.6	17 6.4	20 9.0
28	20 23 38.6	5 10.4	28 44.3	9♋38.9	14 57.1	17 22.6	0 49.7	14 22.7	15 54.3	15 14.3	17 4.9	20 8.9
29	20 27 35.2	6 7.8	28 41.1	24 33.0	14 19.4	18 36.5	1 30.4	14 34.1	15 49.9	15 12.1	17 3.4	20 8.8
30	20 31 31.7	7 5.2	28 38.0	9♌41.5	13 38.7	19 50.3	2 11.0	14 45.6	15 45.5	15 9.9	17 1.8	20 8.8
31	20 35 28.3	8 2.6	28 34.8	24 54.9	12 55.8	21 4.1	2 51.5	14 57.1	15 41.1	15 7.7	17 .4	20 8.8
		LATITUDE										
1	18 37 11.6	0 .0	0 .0	1S24.7	0N46.0	0N47.8	1S 7.1	1N 7.6	0S56.7	0S25.9	0N45.0	15N 2.3
4	18 49 1.2	0 .0	0 .0	4 34.8	0 15.5	0 53.7	1 5.5	1 7.2	0 57.1	0 25.9	0 45.0	15 .9
7	19 0 50.9	0 .0	0 .0	5 8.3	0S19.1	0 59.2	1 3.9	1 6.9	0 57.5	0 25.9	0 45.0	14 59.5
10	19 12 40.6	0 .0	0 .0	3 11.5	0 57.2	1 4.3	1 2.2	1 6.6	0 57.9	0 25.9	0 45.0	14 58.0
13	19 24 30.3	0 .0	0 .0	0N 1.0	1 37.9	1 9.0	1 .4	1 6.3	0 58.3	0 26.0	0 44.9	14 56.5
16	19 36 19.9	0 .0	0 .0	3 6.2	2 20.3	1 13.3	0 58.5	1 6.0	0 58.7	0 26.0	0 44.9	14 55.0
19	19 48 9.6	0 .0	0 .0	4 58.1	3 2.6	1 17.1	0 56.5	1 5.7	0 59.1	0 26.0	0 44.8	14 53.4
22	19 59 59.3	0 .0	0 .0	4 57.2	3 42.6	1 20.4	0 54.4	1 5.4	0 59.4	0 26.0	0 44.8	14 51.8
25	20 11 48.9	0 .0	0 .0	2 50.7	4 17.3	1 23.2	0 52.3	1 5.2	0 59.8	0 26.0	0 44.7	14 50.2
28	20 23 38.6	0 .0	0 .0	0S50.6	4 43.0	1 25.4	0 50.1	1 5.0	1 .1	0 26.0	0 44.7	14 48.5
31	20 35 28.3	0 .0	0 .0	4 13.8	4 56.1	1 27.0	0 47.8	1 4.8	1 .4	0 26.0	0 44.6	14 46.9
		RIGHT ASCENSION										
1	18 37 11.6	10♋14.7	0♑11.0	17♋20.9	7♌24.5	15♋29.0	9♉49.9	11♍43.0	20♒21.5	17♑44.4	19♑10.9	21♏54.9
2	18 41 8.1	11 16.7	0 7.5	2♌41.5	8 34.7	16 49.2	10 32.2	11 51.6	20 R18.5	17 R41.9	19 R 9.2	21 R53.9
3	18 45 4.7	12 18.6	0 4.1	17 19.8	9 41.4	18 9.2	11 14.5	12 .2	20 15.5	17 39.3	19 7.4	21 53.0
4	18 49 1.2	13 20.5	0 .6	1♍15.3	10 44.8	19 29.0	11 56.7	12 8.9	20 12.4	17 36.7	19 5.7	21 52.1
5	18 52 57.8	14 22.3	29♐57.1	14 37.2	11 44.6	20 48.7	12 39.0	12 17.8	20 9.2	17 34.1	19 4.0	21 51.2
6	18 56 54.4	15 24.0	29 53.7	27 38.6	12 40.9	22 8.2	13 21.3	12 26.7	20 5.9	17 31.4	19 2.3	21 50.3
7	19 0 50.9	16 25.6	29 50.2	10♎33.3	13 33.6	23 27.5	14 3.6	12 35.7	20 2.6	17 28.8	19 .5	21 49.4
8	19 4 47.5	17 27.1	29 46.8	23 33.1	14 22.7	24 46.7	14 45.9	12 44.7	19 59.2	17 26.2	18 58.8	21 48.6
9	19 8 44.0	18 28.5	29 43.3	6♏45.7	15 8.0	26 5.6	15 28.2	12 53.9	19 55.8	17 23.6	18 57.1	21 47.8
10	19 12 40.6	19 29.8	29 39.8	20 13.3	15 49.5	27 24.3	16 10.5	13 3.1	19 52.2	17 21.0	18 55.4	21 47.0
11	19 16 37.1	20 31.0	29 36.4	3♐51.6	16 27.0	28 42.8	16 52.9	13 12.5	19 48.7	17 18.4	18 53.6	21 46.3
12	19 20 33.7	21 32.1	29 32.9	17 30.5	17 .6	0♌ 1.1	17 35.2	13 21.9	19 45.0	17 15.8	18 51.9	21 45.6
13	19 24 30.3	22 33.1	29 29.4	0♑57.3	17 30.2	1 19.1	18 17.6	13 31.4	19 41.4	17 13.2	18 50.2	21 44.9
14	19 28 26.8	23 33.9	29 26.0	14 .1	17 55.4	2 36.9	18 59.9	13 40.9	19 37.7	17 10.6	18 48.5	21 44.3
15	19 32 23.4	24 34.6	29 22.5	26 31.5	18 16.4	3 54.4	19 42.2	13 50.6	19 33.9	17 8.1	18 46.8	21 43.7
16	19 36 19.9	25 35.2	29 19.1	8♒29.7	18 33.1	5 11.7	20 24.5	14 .3	19 30.0	17 5.5	18 45.1	21 43.1
17	19 40 16.5	26 35.7	29 15.6	19 58.0	18 45.2	6 28.6	21 6.9	14 10.0	19 26.1	17 2.9	18 43.3	21 42.5
18	19 44 13.0	27 36.0	29 12.1	1♓ 3.9	18 52.8	7 45.3	21 49.2	14 19.9	19 22.2	17 .3	18 41.6	21 41.9
19	19 48 9.6	28 36.2	29 8.7	11 57.1	18 55.8	9 1.8	22 31.5	14 29.8	19 18.2	16 57.8	18 39.9	21 41.4
20	19 52 6.2	29 36.3	29 5.2	22 49.3	18 R54.1	10 17.9	23 13.8	14 39.8	19 14.2	16 55.2	18 38.2	21 40.9
21	19 56 2.7	0♌36.2	29 1.8	3♈53.2	18 47.8	11 33.8	23 56.1	14 49.8	19 10.1	16 52.7	18 36.5	21 40.5
22	19 59 59.3	1 36.0	28 58.3	15 22.3	18 36.8	12 49.3	24 38.4	14 59.9	19 6.0	16 50.2	18 34.9	21 40.0
23	20 3 55.8	2 35.6	28 54.8	27 29.7	18 21.2	14 4.6	25 20.7	15 10.1	19 1.8	16 47.7	18 33.2	21 39.7
24	20 7 52.4	3 35.1	28 51.4	10♉27.0	18 1.1	15 19.6	26 3.0	15 20.4	18 57.6	16 45.2	18 31.5	21 39.3
25	20 11 48.9	4 34.5	28 47.9	24 20.8	17 36.7	16 34.3	26 45.2	15 30.7	18 53.4	16 42.7	18 29.8	21 38.9
26	20 15 45.5	5 33.7	28 44.4	9♊ 9.3	17 8.3	17 48.7	27 27.5	15 41.1	18 49.1	16 40.3	18 28.2	21 38.6
27	20 19 42.1	6 32.8	28 41.0	24 38.9	16 36.0	19 2.8	28 9.7	15 51.5	18 44.9	16 37.9	18 26.6	21 38.4
28	20 23 38.6	7 31.7	28 37.5	10♋25.9	16 .4	20 16.6	28 51.9	16 2.0	18 40.5	16 35.4	18 24.9	21 38.1
29	20 27 35.2	8 30.5	28 34.1	26 4.0	15 21.8	21 30.1	29 34.0	16 12.5	18 36.2	16 33.1	18 23.3	21 37.9
30	20 31 31.7	9 29.2	28 30.6	11♌13.5	14 40.8	22 43.3	0♊16.1	16 23.1	18 31.8	16 30.7	18 21.7	21 37.7
31	20 35 28.3	10 27.6	28 27.1	25 46.1	13 58.0	23 56.3	0 58.2	16 33.8	18 27.4	16 28.3	18 20.1	21 37.6
		DECLINATION										
1	18 37 11.6	23N 6.4	0S24.5	21N 3.7	19N47.6	23N28.7	14N20.8	8N57.7	16S27.3	22S52.3	21S30.7	3S19.1
4	18 49 1.2	22 52.4	0 24.5	6 53.4	18 27.1	23 8.1	15 1.1	8 46.9	16 30.5	22 53.2	21 31.4	3 19.8
7	19 0 50.9	22 34.9	0 24.5	10S 7.5	17 6.7	22 41.3	15 40.0	8 35.7	16 34.0	22 54.1	21 32.0	3 20.6
10	19 12 40.6	22 13.8	0 24.5	21 43.7	15 49.1	22 8.6	16 17.5	8 24.2	16 37.6	22 55.0	21 32.7	3 21.5
13	19 24 30.3	21 49.3	0 24.5	23 25.2	14 37.1	21 30.0	16 53.5	8 12.3	16 41.3	22 55.9	21 33.3	3 22.5
16	19 36 19.9	21 21.5	0 24.5	15 32.4	13 33.9	20 45.9	17 28.1	8 .2	16 45.2	22 56.8	21 34.0	3 23.6
19	19 48 9.6	20 50.4	0 24.5	2 16.9	12 42.6	19 56.5	18 1.0	7 47.8	16 49.1	22 57.6	21 34.7	3 24.8
22	19 59 59.3	20 16.1	0 24.5	11N55.3	12 6.5	19 2.0	18 32.5	7 35.1	16 53.2	22 58.4	21 35.3	3 26.1
25	20 11 48.9	19 38.8	0 24.5	22 20.0	11 48.4	18 2.7	19 2.3	7 22.1	16 57.4	22 59.2	21 36.0	3 27.5
28	20 23 38.6	18 58.5	0 24.5	22 14.9	11 50.2	16 58.9	19 30.5	7 8.9	17 1.5	23 .0	21 36.6	3 28.9
31	20 35 28.3	18 15.4	0 24.5	9 13.7	12 11.8	15 50.9	19 57.0	6 55.4	17 5.8	23 .7	21 37.2	3 30.5

AUGUST 1992

LONGITUDE

DAY	EPHEM. SID. TIME (h m s)	☉ (° ′)	☊ (° ′)	☾ (° ′)	☿ (° ′)	♀ (° ′)	♂ (° ′)	♃ (° ′)	♄ (° ′)	♅ (° ′)	♆ (° ′)	♇ (° ′)
1	20 39 24.8	9♌ .0	28♐31.6	10♍ 2.9	12♌11.2	22♌17.9	3♊31.9	15♍ 8.6	15♒36.6	15♑ 5.6	16♑58.9	20♏ 8.8
2	20 43 21.4	9 57.5	28 28.4	24 56.1	11 R 25.8	23 31.8	4 12.2	15 20.3	15 R 32.2	15 R 3.5	16 R 57.4	20 D 8.9
3	20 47 18.0	10 54.9	28 25.3	9♎27.2	10 40.5	24 45.6	4 52.4	15 32.0	15 27.7	15 1.4	16 56.0	20 9.0
4	20 51 14.5	11 52.4	28 22.1	23 32.2	9 55.9	25 59.4	5 32.5	15 43.7	15 23.3	14 59.3	16 54.6	20 9.1
5	20 55 11.1	12 49.8	28 18.9	7♏10.0	9 12.9	27 13.3	6 12.4	15 55.5	15 18.8	14 57.3	16 53.1	20 9.3
6	20 59 7.6	13 47.3	28 15.7	20 22.1	8 32.4	28 27.1	6 52.2	16 7.3	15 14.3	14 55.2	16 51.7	20 9.5
7	21 3 4.2	14 44.8	28 12.5	3♐11.5	7 55.2	29 40.9	7 31.9	16 19.2	15 9.8	14 53.2	16 50.3	20 9.7
8	21 7 .7	15 42.3	28 9.4	15 42.1	7 22.1	0♍54.7	8 11.5	16 31.2	15 5.3	14 51.3	16 49.0	20 10.0
9	21 10 57.3	16 39.8	28 6.2	27 57.9	6 53.6	2 8.5	8 51.0	16 43.2	15 .8	14 49.3	16 47.6	20 10.3
10	21 14 53.8	17 37.3	28 3.0	10♑ 2.9	6 30.5	3 22.3	9 30.4	16 55.2	14 56.3	14 47.4	16 46.3	20 10.6
11	21 18 50.4	18 34.9	27 59.8	22 .5	6 13.3	4 36.0	10 9.6	17 7.3	14 51.8	14 45.5	16 44.9	20 11.0
12	21 22 46.9	19 32.4	27 56.7	3♒53.7	6 2.3	5 49.8	10 48.7	17 19.4	14 47.4	14 43.7	16 43.6	20 11.4
13	21 26 43.5	20 30.0	27 53.5	15 44.8	5 58.1	7 3.6	11 27.7	17 31.6	14 42.9	14 41.9	16 42.3	20 11.8
14	21 30 40.1	21 27.6	27 50.3	27 35.7	6 D .8	8 17.4	12 6.6	17 43.8	14 38.5	14 40.1	16 41.1	20 12.3
15	21 34 36.6	22 25.2	27 47.1	9♓28.2	6 10.6	9 31.1	12 45.4	17 56.1	14 34.0	14 38.3	16 39.8	20 12.8
16	21 38 33.2	23 22.9	27 44.0	21 23.9	6 27.7	10 44.9	13 24.0	18 8.4	14 29.6	14 36.6	16 38.6	20 13.3
17	21 42 29.7	24 20.5	27 40.8	3♈24.7	6 52.2	11 58.7	14 2.5	18 20.7	14 25.2	14 34.9	16 37.4	20 13.9
18	21 46 26.3	25 18.2	27 37.6	15 32.6	7 24.0	13 12.4	14 40.9	18 33.1	14 20.8	14 33.3	16 36.2	20 14.5
19	21 50 22.8	26 15.9	27 34.4	27 50.3	8 3.1	14 26.2	15 19.1	18 45.5	14 16.5	14 31.7	16 35.1	20 15.1
20	21 54 19.4	27 13.7	27 31.2	10♉21.1	8 49.3	15 39.9	15 57.2	18 58.0	14 12.2	14 30.1	16 33.9	20 15.8
21	21 58 15.9	28 11.4	27 28.1	23 8.6	9 42.5	16 53.7	16 35.2	19 10.5	14 7.9	14 28.6	16 32.8	20 16.5
22	22 2 12.5	29 9.2	27 24.9	6♊16.3	10 42.5	18 7.4	17 13.0	19 23.0	14 3.6	14 27.1	16 31.7	20 17.2
23	22 6 9.0	0♍ 7.1	27 21.7	19 47.7	11 49.1	19 21.2	17 50.7	19 35.6	13 59.4	14 25.6	16 30.6	20 18.0
24	22 10 5.6	1 5.0	27 18.5	3♋45.1	13 1.9	20 35.0	18 28.3	19 48.2	13 55.2	14 24.2	16 29.7	20 18.8
25	22 14 2.2	2 2.8	27 15.4	18 8.9	14 20.5	21 48.7	19 5.7	20 .8	13 51.0	14 22.9	16 28.6	20 19.7
26	22 17 58.7	3 .8	27 12.2	2♌56.8	15 44.7	23 2.4	19 43.0	20 13.5	13 46.9	14 21.5	16 27.6	20 20.5
27	22 21 55.3	3 58.7	27 9.0	18 3.1	17 14.0	24 16.2	20 20.1	20 26.1	13 42.8	14 20.2	16 26.7	20 21.4
28	22 25 51.8	4 56.7	27 5.8	3♍19.2	18 47.9	25 29.9	20 57.1	20 38.9	13 38.8	14 19.0	16 25.7	20 22.4
29	22 29 48.4	5 54.7	27 2.6	18 34.1	20 26.0	26 43.6	21 33.9	20 51.6	13 34.8	14 17.8	16 24.8	20 23.3
30	22 33 44.9	6 52.7	26 59.5	3♎36.9	22 7.8	27 57.3	22 10.5	21 4.3	13 30.9	14 16.6	16 23.9	20 24.3
31	22 37 41.5	7 50.7	26 56.3	18 18.3	23 52.9	29 11.0	22 47.0	21 17.1	13 27.0	14 15.5	16 23.0	20 25.3

LATITUDE

DAY	EPHEM. SID. TIME	☉	☊	☾	☿	♀	♂	♃	♄	♅	♆	♇
1	20 39 24.8	0 .0	0 .0	4S51.5	4S57.1	1N27.4	0S47.0	1N 4.7	1S .5	0S26.0	0N44.6	14N46.3
4	20 51 14.5	0 .0	0 .0	4 44.2	4 49.4	1 28.3	0 44.5	1 4.5	1 .8	0 26.0	0 44.6	14 44.6
7	21 3 4.2	0 .0	0 .0	2 19.5	4 25.8	1 28.5	0 42.0	1 4.3	1 1.0	0 26.0	0 44.5	14 43.0
10	21 14 53.8	0 .0	0 .0	0N54.6	3 48.8	1 28.2	0 39.4	1 4.2	1 1.3	0 26.0	0 44.4	14 41.3
13	21 26 43.5	0 .0	0 .0	3 41.0	3 2.5	1 27.2	0 36.7	1 4.0	1 1.5	0 26.0	0 44.3	14 39.6
16	21 38 33.2	0 .0	0 .0	5 2.3	2 11.4	1 25.7	0 33.9	1 3.9	1 1.7	0 25.9	0 44.3	14 37.9
19	21 50 22.8	0 .0	0 .0	4 27.1	1 19.6	1 23.5	0 31.1	1 3.8	1 1.9	0 25.9	0 44.2	14 36.3
22	22 2 12.5	0 .0	0 .0	1 56.9	0 30.5	1 20.7	0 28.1	1 3.7	1 2.1	0 25.9	0 44.1	14 34.6
25	22 14 2.2	0 .0	0 .0	1S41.7	0N13.0	1 17.3	0 25.1	1 3.7	1 2.2	0 25.9	0 44.0	14 33.0
28	22 25 51.8	0 .0	0 .0	4 34.5	0 49.1	1 13.3	0 21.9	1 3.6	1 2.3	0 25.8	0 43.9	14 31.4
31	22 37 41.5	0 .0	0 .0	4 43.8	1 16.5	1 8.7	0 18.7	1 3.6	1 2.4	0 25.8	0 43.9	14 29.8

RIGHT ASCENSION

DAY	EPHEM. SID. TIME	☉	☊	☾	☿	♀	♂	♃	♄	♅	♆	♇
1	20 39 24.8	11♌26.0	28♐23.7	9♍44.7	13♌14.1	25♌ 8.9	1♊40.2	16♍44.5	18♒23.0	16♑26.0	18♑18.5	21♏37.5
2	20 43 21.4	12 24.1	28 20.2	23 18.6	12 R 29.7	26 21.3	2 22.2	16 55.3	18 R 18.6	16 R 23.7	18 R 17.0	21 R 37.4
3	20 47 18.0	13 22.2	28 16.7	6♎39.7	11 45.8	27 33.4	3 4.2	17 6.1	18 14.2	16 21.5	18 15.5	21 37.4
4	20 51 14.5	14 20.1	28 13.3	19 59.1	11 3.0	28 45.2	3 46.1	17 17.0	18 9.8	16 19.3	18 13.9	21 37.3
5	20 55 11.1	15 17.8	28 9.8	3♏24.7	10 22.1	29 56.7	4 28.0	17 27.9	18 5.3	16 17.0	18 12.4	21 37.3
6	20 59 7.6	16 15.3	28 6.4	16 59.3	9 44.1	1♍ 8.0	5 9.8	17 38.8	18 .9	16 14.8	18 10.9	21 D 37.4
7	21 3 4.2	17 12.7	28 2.9	0♐40.2	9 9.7	2 18.9	5 51.5	17 49.9	17 56.4	16 12.7	18 9.4	21 37.5
8	21 7 .7	18 10.0	27 59.4	14 19.6	8 39.5	3 29.7	6 33.2	18 .9	17 51.9	16 10.6	18 8.0	21 37.6
9	21 10 57.3	19 7.1	27 56.0	27 46.7	8 14.3	4 40.1	7 14.9	18 12.0	17 47.5	16 8.5	18 6.5	21 37.7
10	21 14 53.8	20 4.0	27 52.5	10♑51.4	7 54.6	5 50.3	7 56.4	18 23.1	17 43.0	16 6.4	18 5.1	21 37.9
11	21 18 50.4	21 .8	27 49.0	23 26.7	7 41.0	7 .3	8 38.0	18 34.3	17 38.5	16 4.4	18 3.7	21 38.1
12	21 22 46.9	21 57.5	27 45.6	5♒30.6	7 34.0	8 10.0	9 19.4	18 45.5	17 34.1	16 2.4	18 2.3	21 38.3
13	21 26 43.5	22 54.0	27 42.1	17 5.3	7 33.8	9 19.6	10 .8	18 56.8	17 29.6	16 .4	18 .9	21 38.6
14	21 30 40.1	23 50.4	27 38.7	28 17.0	7 D 40.7	10 28.9	10 42.1	19 8.0	17 25.2	15 58.5	17 59.6	21 38.8
15	21 34 36.6	24 46.6	27 35.2	9♓14.2	7 55.0	11 37.9	11 23.3	19 19.4	17 20.8	15 56.6	17 58.3	21 39.2
16	21 38 33.2	25 42.7	27 31.7	20 6.9	8 16.7	12 46.8	12 4.5	19 30.7	17 16.4	15 54.7	17 57.0	21 39.5
17	21 42 29.7	26 38.7	27 28.3	1♈ 6.4	8 45.9	13 55.5	12 45.5	19 42.1	17 12.0	15 52.9	17 55.7	21 39.9
18	21 46 26.3	27 34.6	27 24.8	12 24.3	9 22.6	15 4.0	13 26.5	19 53.6	17 7.6	15 51.1	17 54.4	21 40.3
19	21 50 22.8	28 30.3	27 21.3	24 12.2	10 6.6	16 12.4	14 7.4	20 5.0	17 3.3	15 49.4	17 53.2	21 40.8
20	21 54 19.4	29 25.9	27 17.9	6♉40.6	10 57.9	17 20.5	14 48.2	20 16.5	16 58.9	15 47.7	17 52.0	21 41.3
21	21 58 15.9	0♍21.4	27 14.4	19 56.8	11 56.1	18 28.6	15 28.9	20 28.0	16 54.6	15 46.0	17 50.8	21 41.8
22	22 2 12.5	1 16.8	27 11.0	4♊ 2.2	13 1.0	19 36.4	16 9.5	20 39.6	16 50.4	15 44.4	17 49.6	21 42.4
23	22 6 9.0	2 12.1	27 7.5	18 49.9	14 12.3	20 44.2	16 50.0	20 51.2	16 46.1	15 42.8	17 48.5	21 42.9
24	22 10 5.6	3 7.3	27 4.0	4♋ 4.4	15 29.6	21 51.8	17 30.4	21 2.8	16 42.0	15 41.3	17 47.4	21 43.6
25	22 14 2.2	4 2.4	27 .6	19 25.1	16 52.4	22 59.3	18 10.7	21 14.5	16 37.8	15 39.9	17 46.3	21 44.2
26	22 17 58.7	4 57.4	26 57.1	4♌33.1	18 20.4	24 6.7	18 50.9	21 26.1	16 33.7	15 38.4	17 45.3	21 44.9
27	22 21 55.3	5 52.3	26 53.6	19 17.1	19 52.9	25 14.0	19 30.9	21 37.8	16 29.6	15 37.0	17 44.2	21 45.6
28	22 25 51.8	6 47.1	26 50.2	3♍35.3	21 29.4	26 21.2	20 10.8	21 49.5	16 25.5	15 35.6	17 43.2	21 46.4
29	22 29 48.4	7 41.8	26 46.7	17 32.8	23 9.5	27 28.3	20 50.5	22 1.3	16 21.5	15 34.3	17 42.3	21 47.1
30	22 33 44.9	8 36.4	26 43.3	1♎18.9	24 52.6	28 35.4	21 30.1	22 13.0	16 17.6	15 33.1	17 41.3	21 47.9
31	22 37 41.5	9 30.9	26 39.8	15 2.9	26 38.0	29 42.4	22 9.6	22 24.8	16 13.7	15 31.9	17 40.4	21 488

DECLINATION

DAY	EPHEM. SID. TIME	☉	☊	☾	☿	♀	♂	♃	♄	♅	♆	♇
1	20 39 24.8	18N .4	0S24.5	3N17.9	12N23.0	15N27.4	20N 5.5	6N50.9	17S 7.2	23S 1.0	21S37.4	3S31.1
4	20 51 14.5	17 13.8	0 24.5	13S32.2	13 6.6	14 14.4	20 29.9	6 37.1	17 11.4	23 1.7	21 38.0	3 32.8
7	21 3 4.2	16 24.6	0 24.5	23 4.6	14 .3	12 58.0	20 52.6	6 23.2	17 15.7	23 2.4	21 38.6	3 34.5
10	21 14 53.8	15 33.1	0 24.5	22 9.1	14 57.1	11 38.4	21 13.7	6 9.0	17 19.9	23 3.0	21 39.2	3 36.4
13	21 26 43.5	14 39.4	0 24.5	12 35.7	15 49.9	10 16.2	21 33.1	5 54.7	17 24.0	23 3.6	21 39.7	3 38.3
16	21 38 33.2	13 43.6	0 24.5	1N13.3	16 32.2	8 51.4	21 50.8	5 40.2	17 28.1	23 4.1	21 40.3	3 40.3
19	21 50 22.8	12 45.8	0 24.5	14 51.5	16 58.4	7 24.6	22 7.0	5 25.6	17 32.1	23 4.7	21 40.8	3 42.3
22	22 2 12.5	11 46.1	0 24.5	23 16.5	17 3.6	5 56.0	22 21.6	5 10.8	17 36.0	23 5.1	21 41.3	3 44.4
25	22 14 2.2	10 44.8	0 24.5	20 31.8	16 44.2	4 25.9	22 34.6	4 55.9	17 39.8	23 5.6	21 41.7	3 46.6
28	22 25 51.8	9 41.9	0 24.5	6 1.2	15 58.1	2 54.6	22 46.0	4 40.9	17 43.5	23 5.9	21 42.2	3 48.8
31	22 37 41.5	8 37.6	0 24.5	11S32.8	14 45.8	1 22.5	22 55.9	4 25.8	17 47.0	23 6.3	21 42.6	3 51.1

SEPTEMBER 1992

LONGITUDE

DAY	EPHEM. SID. TIME (h m s)	☉ (° ′)	☊ (° ′)	☽ (° ′)	☿ (° ′)	♀ (° ′)	♂ (° ′)	♃ (° ′)	♄ (° ′)	♅ (° ′)	♆ (° ′)	♇ (° ′)
1	22 41 38.0	8♍48.8	26♐53.1	2♏32.5	25♌40.7	0♎24.7	23♊23.3	21♍29.9	13♒23.1	14♑14.4	16♑22.2	20♏26.4
2	22 45 34.6	9 46.9	26 49.9	16 16.9	27 30.8	1 38.4	23 59.4	21 42.7	13R19.3	14R13.4	16R21.4	20 27.5
3	22 49 31.1	10 45.0	26 46.8	29 32.3	29 22.8	2 52.0	24 35.4	21 55.6	13 15.6	14 12.4	16 20.6	20 28.6
4	22 53 27.7	11 43.1	26 43.6	12♐21.9	1♍16.2	4 5.7	25 11.2	22 8.4	13 11.9	14 11.4	16 19.9	20 29.8
5	22 57 24.2	12 41.3	26 40.4	24 49.9	3 10.7	5 19.3	25 46.9	22 21.3	13 8.3	14 10.5	16 19.1	20 31.0
6	23 1 20.8	13 39.5	26 37.2	7♑1.5	5 6.0	6 33.0	26 22.4	22 34.2	13 4.8	14 9.7	16 18.4	20 32.2
7	23 5 17.3	14 37.7	26 34.0	19 1.5	7 1.6	7 46.6	26 57.7	22 47.1	13 1.3	14 8.9	16 17.8	20 33.4
8	23 9 13.9	15 35.9	26 30.9	0♒54.7	8 57.4	9 .2	27 32.8	23 .0	12 57.8	14 8.1	16 17.1	20 34.7
9	23 13 10.5	16 34.2	26 27.7	12 44.8	10 53.1	10 13.8	28 7.7	23 12.9	12 54.5	14 7.4	16 16.5	20 36.0
10	23 17 7.0	17 32.5	26 24.5	24 35.1	12 48.5	11 27.4	28 42.5	23 25.9	12 51.2	14 6.7	16 16.0	20 37.3
11	23 21 3.6	18 30.8	26 21.3	6♓28.1	14 43.4	12 41.0	29 17.1	23 38.8	12 48.0	14 6.1	16 15.4	20 38.7
12	23 25 .1	19 29.1	26 18.2	18 25.5	16 37.8	13 54.5	29 51.5	23 51.8	12 44.8	14 5.5	16 14.9	20 40.1
13	23 28 56.7	20 27.5	26 15.0	0♈28.6	18 31.5	15 8.1	0♋25.7	24 4.7	12 41.8	14 5.0	16 14.4	20 41.5
14	23 32 53.2	21 25.9	26 11.8	12 38.6	20 24.5	16 21.6	0 59.7	24 17.8	12 38.8	14 4.6	16 14.0	20 43.0
15	23 36 49.8	22 24.4	26 8.6	24 56.3	22 16.5	17 35.2	1 33.6	24 30.7	12 35.9	14 4.2	16 13.6	20 44.5
16	23 40 46.3	23 22.9	26 5.4	7♉23.2	24 7.6	18 48.7	2 7.2	24 43.7	12 33.0	14 3.8	16 13.2	20 46.0
17	23 44 42.9	24 21.4	26 2.3	20 1.1	25 57.8	20 2.2	2 40.6	24 56.7	12 30.3	14 3.5	16 12.8	20 47.5
18	23 48 39.4	25 19.9	25 59.1	2♊52.3	27 47.1	21 15.6	3 13.8	25 9.7	12 27.6	14 3.2	16 12.5	20 49.1
19	23 52 36.0	26 18.5	25 55.9	15 59.7	29 35.3	22 29.1	3 46.9	25 22.7	12 25.0	14 3.0	16 12.2	20 50.7
20	23 56 32.5	27 17.1	25 52.7	29 26.0	1♎22.5	23 42.6	4 19.6	25 35.6	12 22.4	14 2.8	16 11.9	20 52.3
21	0 0 29.1	28 15.8	25 49.5	13♋13.8	3 8.8	24 56.0	4 52.2	25 48.6	12 20.0	14 2.7	16 11.7	20 53.9
22	0 4 25.6	29 14.5	25 46.4	27 24.2	4 54.0	26 9.5	5 24.6	26 1.6	12 17.6	14 2.6	16 11.5	20 55.6
23	0 8 22.2	0♎13.2	25 43.2	11♌56.5	6 38.2	27 22.9	5 56.7	26 14.6	12 15.4	14 2.6	16 11.3	20 57.3
24	0 12 18.7	1 12.0	25 40.0	26 47.1	8 21.5	28 36.3	6 28.6	26 27.6	12 13.2	14 2.6	16 11.2	20 59.0
25	0 16 15.3	2 10.8	25 36.8	11♍49.4	10 3.8	29 49.7	7 .3	26 40.5	12 11.1	14D 2.7	16 11.1	21 .7
26	0 20 11.8	3 9.6	25 33.7	26 54.4	11 45.1	1♏3.1	7 31.7	26 53.5	12 9.1	14 2.8	16 11.0	21 2.5
27	0 24 8.4	4 8.5	25 30.5	11♎51.9	13 25.6	2 16.5	8 2.8	27 6.4	12 7.2	14 3.0	16 11.0	21 4.3
28	0 28 5.0	5 7.4	25 27.3	26 32.5	15 5.0	3 29.9	8 33.7	27 19.4	12 5.4	14 3.3	16 11.0	21 6.1
29	0 32 1.5	6 6.3	25 24.1	10♏49.0	16 43.6	4 43.3	9 4.4	27 32.3	12 3.6	14 3.5	16 11.0	21 7.9
30	0 35 58.1	7 5.3	25 20.9	24 37.5	18 21.3	5 56.6	9 34.8	27 45.2	12 2.0	14 3.9	16 11.0	21 9.8

LATITUDE

DAY	EPHEM. SID. TIME	☉	☊	☽	☿	♀	♂	♃	♄	♅	♆	♇
1	22 41 38.0	0 .0	0 .0	4S 9.2	1N23.7	1N 7.1	0S17.6	1N 3.6	1S 2.5	0S25.8	0N43.8	14N29.3
4	22 53 27.7	0 .0	0 .0	1 20.4	1 39.3	1 1.8	0 14.2	1 3.6	1 2.6	0 25.8	0 43.7	14 27.7
7	23 5 17.3	0 .0	0 .0	1N50.6	1 46.7	0 56.0	0 10.7	1 3.6	1 2.6	0 25.7	0 43.6	14 26.2
10	23 17 7.0	0 .0	0 .0	4 13.1	1 47.1	0 49.8	0 7.1	1 3.6	1 2.7	0 25.7	0 43.5	14 24.7
13	23 28 56.7	0 .0	0 .0	4 59.0	1 41.7	0 43.1	0 3.4	1 3.6	1 2.7	0 25.6	0 43.4	14 23.3
16	23 40 46.3	0 .0	0 .0	3 46.2	1 31.6	0 35.9	0N .4	1 3.7	1 2.7	0 25.6	0 43.3	14 21.9
19	23 52 36.0	0 .0	0 .0	0 52.2	1 17.9	0 28.4	0 4.3	1 3.8	1 2.8	0 25.6	0 43.2	14 20.5
22	0 4 25.6	0 .0	0 .0	2S38.1	1 1.5	0 20.5	0 8.3	1 3.9	1 2.8	0 25.5	0 43.1	14 19.2
25	0 16 15.3	0 .0	0 .0	4 52.0	0 43.1	0 12.3	0 12.5	1 4.0	1 2.7	0 25.5	0 43.0	14 17.9
28	0 28 5.0	0 .0	0 .0	4 16.7	0 23.3	0 3.8	0 16.8	1 4.1	1 2.7	0 25.4	0 42.9	14 16.7

RIGHT ASCENSION

DAY	EPHEM. SID. TIME	☉	☊	☽	☿	♀	♂	♃	♄	♅	♆	♇
1	22 41 38.0	10♍25.4	26♐36.3	28♎51.7	28♌25.4	0♎49.3	22♊48.9	22♍36.6	16♒ 9.8	15♑30.7	17♑39.5	21♏49.6
2	22 45 34.6	11 19.8	26 32.9	12♏47.5	0♍14.2	1 56.3	23 28.1	22 48.4	16R 6.0	15R29.6	17R38.6	21 50.5
3	22 49 31.1	12 14.1	26 29.4	26 47.0	2 3.9	3 3.2	24 7.1	23 .2	16 2.3	15 28.5	17 37.8	21 51.4
4	22 53 27.7	13 8.3	26 26.0	10♐41.9	3 54.2	4 10.0	24 46.0	23 12.1	15 58.6	15 27.5	17 37.0	21 52.4
5	22 57 24.2	14 2.5	26 22.5	24 21.6	5 44.7	5 16.9	25 24.7	23 23.9	15 55.0	15 26.5	17 36.2	21 53.4
6	23 1 20.8	14 56.6	26 19.0	7♑36.1	7 35.1	6 23.8	26 3.2	23 35.8	15 51.4	15 25.6	17 35.5	21 54.4
7	23 5 17.3	15 50.6	26 15.6	20 19.4	9 25.0	7 30.7	26 41.6	23 47.7	15 47.9	15 24.7	17 34.8	21 55.4
8	23 9 13.9	16 44.6	26 12.1	2♒29.9	11 14.4	8 37.6	27 19.8	23 59.6	15 44.4	15 23.9	17 34.1	21 56.5
9	23 13 10.5	17 38.5	26 8.6	14 10.5	13 3.0	9 44.5	27 57.8	24 11.5	15 41.1	15 23.1	17 33.5	21 57.6
10	23 17 7.0	18 32.4	26 5.2	25 27.5	14 50.6	10 51.5	28 35.6	24 23.4	15 37.8	15 22.4	17 32.8	21 58.7
11	23 21 3.6	19 26.3	26 1.7	6♓29.3	16 37.2	11 58.5	29 13.3	24 35.3	15 34.5	15 21.7	17 32.3	21 59.9
12	23 25 .1	20 20.2	25 58.3	17 25.7	18 22.7	13 5.7	29 50.7	24 47.2	15 31.4	15 21.1	17 31.7	22 1.1
13	23 28 56.7	21 14.0	25 54.8	28 27.0	20 7.0	14 12.9	0♋28.0	24 59.1	15 28.3	15 20.5	17 31.2	22 2.3
14	23 32 53.2	22 7.8	25 51.3	9♈44.1	21 50.2	15 20.2	1 5.1	25 11.1	15 25.3	15 20.1	17 30.8	22 3.6
15	23 36 49.8	23 1.6	25 47.9	21 27.1	23 32.1	16 27.6	1 42.0	25 23.0	15 22.3	15 19.6	17 30.3	22 4.8
16	23 40 46.3	23 55.4	25 44.4	3♉44.9	25 12.9	17 35.1	2 18.6	25 35.0	15 19.5	15 19.2	17 29.9	22 6.1
17	23 44 42.9	24 49.2	25 41.0	16 43.6	26 52.5	18 42.7	2 55.1	25 46.9	15 16.7	15 18.9	17 29.5	22 7.5
18	23 48 39.4	25 42.9	25 37.5	0♊24.3	28 31.0	19 50.4	3 31.3	25 58.9	15 14.0	15 18.6	17 29.2	22 8.8
19	23 52 36.0	26 36.7	25 34.0	14 41.5	0♎ 8.3	20 58.3	4 7.3	26 10.8	15 11.3	15 18.3	17 28.9	22 10.2
20	23 56 32.5	27 30.5	25 30.6	29 23.1	1 44.6	22 6.4	4 43.1	26 22.7	15 8.8	15 18.1	17 28.6	22 11.6
21	0 0 29.1	28 24.4	25 27.1	14♋12.8	3 19.9	23 14.6	5 18.6	26 34.7	15 6.3	15 18.0	17 28.3	22 13.0
22	0 4 25.6	29 18.2	25 23.7	28 55.6	4 54.2	24 23.0	5 54.0	26 46.6	15 3.9	15 17.9	17 28.1	22 14.5
23	0 8 22.2	0♎12.1	25 20.2	13♌21.9	6 27.6	25 31.5	6 29.0	26 58.5	15 1.6	15 17.9	17 27.9	22 16.0
24	0 12 18.7	1 6.0	25 16.7	27 29.5	8 .1	26 40.3	7 3.8	27 10.5	14 59.4	15 17.9	17 27.8	22 17.5
25	0 16 15.3	1 60.0	25 13.3	11♍22.9	9 31.8	27 49.2	7 38.4	27 22.4	14 57.3	15D18.0	17 27.7	22 19.0
26	0 20 11.8	2 54.0	25 9.8	25 10.3	11 2.7	28 58.4	8 12.6	27 34.3	14 55.3	15 18.2	17 27.6	22 20.5
27	0 24 8.4	3 48.0	25 6.4	9♎ .8	12 32.9	0♏ 7.8	8 46.6	27 46.2	14 53.4	15 18.4	17 27.6	22 22.1
28	0 28 5.0	4 42.1	25 2.9	23 1.5	14 2.4	1 17.4	9 20.4	27 58.1	14 51.5	15 18.6	17 27.6	22 23.7
29	0 32 1.5	5 36.3	24 59.4	7♏14.7	15 31.3	2 27.2	9 53.8	28 10.0	14 49.8	15 18.9	17 27.6	22 25.4
30	0 35 58.1	6 30.5	24 56.0	21 36.2	16 59.5	3 37.3	10 26.9	28 21.9	14 48.1	15 19.3	17D27.7	22 27.0

DECLINATION

DAY	EPHEM. SID. TIME	☉	☊	☽	☿	♀	♂	♃	♄	♅	♆	♇
1	22 41 38.0	8N15.9	0S24.5	16S15.1	14N16.4	0N51.7	22N58.9	4N20.7	17S48.1	23S 6.4	21S42.7	3S51.9
4	22 53 27.7	7 10.1	0 24.5	23 36.4	12 34.1	0S40.9	23 7.0	4 5.5	17 51.4	23 6.7	21 43.1	3 54.2
7	23 5 17.3	6 3.2	0 24.5	20 15.9	10 35.0	2 13.6	23 13.6	3 50.2	17 54.5	23 6.9	21 43.4	3 56.6
10	23 17 7.0	4 55.4	0 24.5	9 20.8	8 24.1	3 46.1	23 18.9	3 34.9	17 57.4	23 7.1	21 43.7	3 59.0
13	23 28 56.7	3 46.9	0 24.5	4N45.7	6 5.9	5 18.0	23 22.9	3 19.5	18 .1	23 7.2	21 44.0	4 1.4
16	23 40 46.3	2 37.7	0 24.5	17 32.3	3 44.1	6 49.0	23 25.8	3 4.1	18 2.6	23 7.3	21 44.3	4 3.8
19	23 52 36.0	1 28.1	0 24.5	23 34.1	1 21.3	8 18.7	23 27.5	2 48.8	18 4.9	23 7.4	21 44.5	4 6.3
22	0 4 25.6	0 18.1	0 24.5	18 5.7	1S .3	9 46.9	23 28.1	2 33.4	18 7.0	23 7.4	21 44.7	4 8.8
25	0 16 15.3	0S52.0	0 24.5	2 37.5	3 19.5	11 13.2	23 27.8	2 18.0	18 8.8	23 7.3	21 44.8	4 11.3
28	0 28 5.0	2 2.1	0 24.5	14S13.3	5 35.1	12 37.3	23 26.6	2 2.7	18 10.4	23 7.2	21 44.9	4 13.8

OCTOBER 1992

DAY	EPHEM. SID. TIME	☉	☊	☽	☿	♀	♂	♃	♄	♅	♆	♇
	h m s	° ′	° ′	° ′	° ′	° ′	° ′	° ′	° ′	° ′	° ′	° ′
		LONGITUDE										
1	0 39 54.6	8♎ 4.3	25♐17.8	7♐57.5	19♎58.2	7♏ 9.9	10♋ 4.9	27♍58.1	12♒ .5	14♑ 4.3	16♑11.1	21♏11.7
2	0 43 51.2	9 3.3	25 14.6	20 50.8	21 34.1	8 23.2	10 34.8	28 11.0	11 R 59.0	14 4.7	16 D 11.3	21 13.6
3	0 47 47.7	10 2.4	25 11.4	3♑21.3	23 9.3	9 36.5	11 4.3	28 23.8	11 57.7	14 5.2	16 11.4	21 15.5
4	0 51 44.3	11 1.5	25 8.2	15 34.0	24 43.6	10 49.8	11 33.7	28 36.7	11 56.4	14 5.7	16 11.6	21 17.4
5	0 55 40.8	12 .6	25 5.1	27 34.1	26 17.1	12 3.1	12 2.7	28 49.6	11 55.3	14 6.4	16 11.9	21 19.5
6	0 59 37.4	12 59.8	25 1.9	9♒26.9	27 49.8	13 16.3	12 31.5	29 2.4	11 54.3	14 7.0	16 12.2	21 21.4
7	1 3 33.9	13 59.0	24 58.7	21 17.1	29 21.7	14 29.5	12 59.9	29 15.1	11 53.3	14 7.7	16 12.5	21 23.5
8	1 7 30.5	14 58.2	24 55.5	3♓ 8.9	0♏52.9	15 42.7	13 28.0	29 27.9	11 52.4	14 8.5	16 12.8	21 25.5
9	1 11 27.0	15 57.4	24 52.3	15 5.5	2 23.2	16 55.9	13 55.9	29 40.6	11 51.7	14 9.3	16 13.2	21 27.5
10	1 15 23.6	16 56.7	24 49.2	27 9.4	3 52.7	18 9.0	14 23.4	29 53.3	11 51.0	14 10.1	16 13.5	21 29.6
11	1 19 20.1	17 56.0	24 46.0	9♈22.2	5 21.5	19 22.2	14 50.6	0♎ 6.0	11 50.5	14 11.0	16 14.0	21 31.7
12	1 23 16.7	18 55.3	24 42.8	21 44.9	6 49.5	20 35.3	15 17.5	0 18.6	11 50.0	14 12.0	16 14.4	21 33.8
13	1 27 13.2	19 54.7	24 39.6	4♉17.7	8 16.7	21 48.3	15 44.1	0 31.3	11 49.6	14 13.0	16 14.9	21 35.9
14	1 31 9.8	20 54.1	24 36.5	17 1.0	9 43.1	23 1.4	16 10.4	0 43.9	11 49.4	14 14.0	16 15.5	21 38.0
15	1 35 6.4	21 53.5	24 33.3	29 55.0	11 8.6	24 14.5	16 36.3	0 56.4	11 49.2	14 15.1	16 16.0	21 40.2
16	1 39 2.9	22 53.0	24 30.1	13♊ .4	12 33.3	25 27.5	17 1.8	1 8.9	11 49.2	14 16.3	16 16.6	21 42.3
17	1 42 59.5	23 52.5	24 26.9	26 18.0	13 57.2	26 40.5	17 27.0	1 21.4	11 49.2	14 17.5	16 17.2	21 44.5
18	1 46 56.0	24 52.1	24 23.7	9♋49.1	15 20.1	27 53.5	17 51.8	1 33.9	11 D 49.3	14 18.7	16 17.9	21 46.7
19	1 50 52.6	25 51.7	24 20.6	23 35.1	16 42.1	29 6.4	18 16.3	1 46.3	11 49.6	14 20.0	16 18.6	21 48.9
20	1 54 49.1	26 51.3	24 17.4	7♌36.6	18 3.1	0♐19.4	18 40.4	1 58.6	11 49.9	14 21.3	16 19.3	21 51.2
21	1 58 45.7	27 50.9	24 14.2	21 53.2	19 23.0	1 32.3	19 4.1	2 11.0	11 50.4	14 22.7	16 20.1	21 53.4
22	2 2 42.2	28 50.7	24 11.0	6♍22.8	20 41.8	2 45.2	19 27.4	2 23.3	11 50.9	14 24.2	16 20.9	21 55.6
23	2 6 38.8	29 50.4	24 7.9	21 1.2	21 59.4	3 58.1	19 50.2	2 35.5	11 51.6	14 25.7	16 21.7	21 57.9
24	2 10 35.3	0♏50.2	24 4.7	5♎42.3	23 15.7	5 10.9	20 12.7	2 47.7	11 52.4	14 27.2	16 22.5	22 .2
25	2 14 31.9	1 50.0	24 1.5	20 18.8	24 30.7	6 23.8	20 34.7	2 59.9	11 53.2	14 28.8	16 23.4	22 2.5
26	2 18 28.4	2 49.9	23 58.3	4♏43.3	25 44.1	7 36.6	20 56.3	3 12.0	11 54.2	14 30.5	16 24.4	22 4.8
27	2 22 25.0	3 49.8	23 55.1	18 49.3	26 55.8	8 49.4	21 17.5	3 24.1	11 55.3	14 32.1	16 25.3	22 7.1
28	2 26 21.6	4 49.7	23 52.0	2♐32.7	28 5.7	10 2.2	21 38.2	3 36.1	11 56.5	14 33.9	16 26.3	22 9.5
29	2 30 18.1	5 49.6	23 48.8	15 51.6	29 13.5	11 15.0	21 58.4	3 48.1	11 57.7	14 35.6	16 27.3	22 11.8
30	2 34 14.7	6 49.6	23 45.6	28 46.5	0♐19.1	12 27.7	22 18.1	3 60.0	11 59.1	14 37.4	16 28.4	22 14.1
31	2 38 11.2	7 49.6	23 42.4	11♑19.8	1 22.2	13 40.3	22 37.4	4 11.8	12 .6	14 39.3	16 29.5	22 16.5
		LATITUDE										
1	0 39 54.6	0 .0	0 .0	1S27.4	0N 2.5	0S 4.8	0N21.3	1N 4.3	1S 2.7	0S25.4	0N42.8	14N15.5
4	0 51 44.3	0 .0	0 .0	1N48.5	0S18.8	0 13.6	0 25.9	1 4.4	1 2.6	0 25.3	0 42.7	14 14.4
7	1 3 33.9	0 .0	0 .0	4 13.3	0 40.1	0 22.6	0 30.6	1 4.6	1 2.6	0 25.3	0 42.6	14 13.3
10	1 15 23.6	0 .0	0 .0	5 1.5	1 1.3	0 31.5	0 35.6	1 4.8	1 2.5	0 25.3	0 42.5	14 12.3
13	1 27 13.2	0 .0	0 .0	3 49.5	1 21.9	0 40.6	0 40.6	1 5.0	1 2.4	0 25.2	0 42.4	14 11.4
16	1 39 2.9	0 .0	0 .0	0 54.0	1 41.5	0 49.5	0 45.9	1 5.3	1 2.3	0 25.2	0 42.3	14 10.5
19	1 50 52.6	0 .0	0 .0	2S35.4	1 59.9	0 58.4	0 51.3	1 5.5	1 2.3	0 25.1	0 42.2	14 9.7
22	2 2 42.2	0 .0	0 .0	4 53.2	2 16.5	1 7.1	0 56.9	1 5.8	1 2.2	0 25.1	0 42.1	14 8.9
25	2 14 31.9	0 .0	0 .0	4 31.5	2 30.8	1 15.5	1 2.8	1 6.1	1 2.1	0 25.1	0 42.0	14 8.2
28	2 26 21.6	0 .0	0 .0	1 44.7	2 42.1	1 23.7	1 8.8	1 6.4	1 2.0	0 25.0	0 41.9	14 7.6
31	2 38 11.2	0 .0	0 .0	1N41.0	2 49.5	1 31.6	1 15.1	1 6.8	1 1.9	0 25.0	0 41.8	14 7.1
		RIGHT ASCENSION										
1	0 39 54.6	7♎24.8	24♐52.5	5♐56.0	18♎27.2	4♏47.6	10♋59.8	28♍33.7	14♒46.6	15♑19.7	17♑27.8	22♏28.7
2	0 43 51.2	8 19.1	24 49.1	20 .8	19 54.4	5 58.1	11 32.4	28 45.6	14 R 45.1	15 20.2	17 27.9	22 30.4
3	0 47 47.7	9 13.6	24 45.6	3♑38.1	21 21.1	7 8.9	12 4.6	28 57.4	14 43.7	15 20.7	17 28.1	22 32.1
4	0 51 44.3	10 8.1	24 42.1	16 40.0	22 47.3	8 20.0	12 36.6	29 9.2	14 42.5	15 21.3	17 28.3	22 33.8
5	0 55 40.8	11 2.7	24 38.7	29 4.4	24 13.1	9 31.4	13 8.3	29 21.0	14 41.3	15 22.0	17 28.6	22 35.6
6	0 59 37.4	11 57.4	24 35.2	10♒54.6	25 38.6	10 43.0	13 39.6	29 32.8	14 40.3	15 22.7	17 28.9	22 37.4
7	1 3 33.9	12 52.1	24 31.8	22 17.6	27 3.6	11 54.9	14 10.6	29 44.5	14 39.3	15 23.4	17 29.2	22 39.2
8	1 7 30.5	13 47.0	24 28.3	3♓23.0	28 28.3	13 7.0	14 41.3	29 56.3	14 38.4	15 24.2	17 29.6	22 41.1
9	1 11 27.0	14 42.0	24 24.8	14 21.2	29 52.7	14 19.4	15 11.6	0♎ 8.0	14 37.6	15 25.1	17 30.0	22 42.9
10	1 15 23.6	15 37.0	24 21.4	25 23.5	1♏16.7	15 32.2	15 41.6	0 19.7	14 37.0	15 26.0	17 30.4	22 44.8
11	1 19 20.1	16 32.2	24 17.9	6♈41.0	2 40.4	16 45.2	16 11.2	0 31.3	14 36.4	15 27.0	17 30.9	22 46.6
12	1 23 16.7	17 27.5	24 14.5	18 24.0	4 3.8	17 58.5	16 40.5	0 43.0	14 35.9	15 28.0	17 31.4	22 48.5
13	1 27 13.2	18 23.0	24 11.0	0♉41.5	5 26.9	19 12.1	17 9.4	0 54.6	14 35.5	15 29.1	17 31.9	22 50.5
14	1 31 9.8	19 18.5	24 7.6	13 38.8	6 49.7	20 26.0	17 38.0	1 6.1	14 35.3	15 30.2	17 32.5	22 52.4
15	1 35 6.4	20 14.3	24 4.1	27 16.3	8 12.1	21 40.1	18 6.2	1 17.7	14 35.1	15 31.4	17 33.1	22 54.3
16	1 39 2.9	21 10.1	24 .6	11♊27.2	9 34.2	22 54.6	18 34.0	1 29.2	14 35.0	15 32.6	17 33.7	22 56.3
17	1 42 59.5	22 6.1	23 57.2	25 58.6	10 55.9	24 9.4	19 1.4	1 40.7	14 D 35.1	15 33.9	17 34.4	22 58.3
18	1 46 56.0	23 2.3	23 53.7	10♋34.0	12 17.2	25 24.5	19 28.4	1 52.1	14 35.2	15 35.3	17 35.1	23 .3
19	1 50 52.6	23 58.6	23 50.3	24 58.8	13 38.0	26 39.8	19 55.0	2 3.6	14 35.5	15 36.7	17 35.8	23 2.3
20	1 54 49.1	24 55.0	23 46.8	9♌ 4.3	14 58.4	27 55.5	20 21.2	2 15.0	14 35.8	15 38.1	17 36.6	23 4.4
21	1 58 45.7	25 51.7	23 43.4	22 49.5	16 18.1	29 11.4	20 47.0	2 26.3	14 36.2	15 39.6	17 37.4	23 6.4
22	2 2 42.2	26 48.5	23 39.9	6♍19.8	17 37.2	0♐27.7	21 12.3	2 37.6	14 36.8	15 41.2	17 38.3	23 8.5
23	2 6 38.8	27 45.5	23 36.4	19 44.7	18 55.5	1 44.2	21 37.2	2 48.9	14 37.4	15 42.8	17 39.2	23 10.5
24	2 10 35.3	28 42.6	23 33.0	3♎15.3	20 12.9	3 .9	22 1.6	3 .1	14 38.2	15 44.4	17 40.1	23 12.6
25	2 14 31.9	29 39.9	23 29.5	17 1.0	21 29.4	4 18.0	22 25.6	3 11.3	14 39.1	15 46.1	17 41.0	23 14.7
26	2 18 28.4	0♏37.5	23 26.1	1♏ 7.2	22 44.7	5 35.3	22 49.1	3 22.5	14 40.1	15 48.0	17 42.1	23 16.9
27	2 22 25.0	1 35.2	23 22.6	15 32.1	23 58.8	6 52.9	23 12.1	3 33.6	14 41.1	15 49.8	17 43.1	23 19.0
28	2 26 21.6	2 33.1	23 19.2	0♐ 6.5	25 11.3	8 10.7	23 34.6	3 44.7	14 42.3	15 51.6	17 44.1	23 21.2
29	2 30 18.1	3 31.2	23 15.7	14 34.8	26 22.0	9 28.7	23 56.6	3 55.7	14 43.6	15 53.5	17 45.2	23 23.3
30	2 34 14.7	4 29.4	23 12.2	28 40.2	27 30.8	10 47.0	24 18.1	4 6.7	14 45.0	15 55.5	17 46.3	23 25.5
31	2 38 11.2	5 27.9	23 8.8	12♑ 9.9	28 37.4	12 5.4	24 39.1	4 17.6	14 46.4	15 57.5	17 47.5	23 27.7
		DECLINATION										
1	0 39 54.6	3S12.1	0S24.5	23S 4.5	7S46.2	13S58.8	23N24.6	1N47.4	18S11.7	23S 7.1	21S45.0	4S16.2
4	0 51 44.3	4 21.8	0 24.5	20 44.2	9 52.1	15 17.4	23 22.0	1 32.2	18 12.8	23 6.9	21 45.1	4 18.7
7	1 3 33.9	5 30.9	0 24.4	10 24.2	11 52.4	16 32.8	23 18.8	1 17.1	18 13.6	23 6.6	21 45.1	4 21.2
10	1 15 23.6	6 39.4	0 24.4	3N28.8	13 46.4	17 44.5	23 15.1	1 2.1	18 14.2	23 6.3	21 45.0	4 23.7
13	1 27 13.2	7 47.1	0 24.4	16 33.0	15 33.4	18 52.2	23 11.1	0 47.2	18 14.5	23 6.0	21 45.0	4 26.1
16	1 39 2.9	8 53.9	0 24.4	23 15.2	17 13.1	19 55.7	23 6.8	0 32.5	18 14.6	23 5.6	21 44.9	4 28.5
19	1 50 52.6	9 59.5	0 24.4	18 49.7	18 44.6	20 54.5	23 2.4	0 17.9	18 14.4	23 5.1	21 44.7	4 30.9
22	2 2 42.2	11 3.8	0 24.4	4 37.5	20 7.2	21 48.4	22 58.1	0 3.4	18 13.9	23 4.6	21 44.6	4 33.2
25	2 14 31.9	12 6.7	0 24.4	12S 7.5	21 20.0	22 37.1	22 53.9	0S10.8	18 13.2	23 4.1	21 44.3	4 35.5
28	2 26 21.6	13 7.9	0 24.4	22 22.9	22 22.1	23 20.1	22 50.0	0 24.9	18 12.2	23 3.5	21 44.1	4 37.7
31	2 38 11.2	14 7.2	0 24.4	21 16.8	23 12.0	23 57.4	22 46.6	0 38.8	18 10.9	23 2.9	21 43.8	4 39.9

NOVEMBER 1992

DAY	EPHEM. SID. TIME	☉	☊	☽	☿	♀	♂	♃	♄	♅	♆	♇
	h m s	° ′	° ′	° ′	° ′	° ′	° ′	° ′	° ′	° ′	° ′	° ′
LONGITUDE												
1	2 42 7.8	8♏49.6	23♐39.3	23♑35.3	2♐22.6	14♐53.0	22♋56.2	4♎23.6	12♒ 2.1	14♑41.2	16♑30.6	22♏18.8
2	2 46 4.3	9 49.7	23 36.1	5♒37.8	3 19.8	16 5.6	23 14.4	4 35.3	12 3.8	14 43.2	16 31.7	22 21.2
3	2 50 .9	10 49.8	23 32.9	17 32.2	4 13.7	17 18.2	23 32.2	4 47.0	12 5.6	14 45.2	16 32.9	22 23.6
4	2 53 57.4	11 49.9	23 29.7	29 23.6	5 3.7	18 30.8	23 49.4	4 58.6	12 7.4	14 47.2	16 34.1	22 25.9
5	2 57 54.0	12 50.0	23 26.6	11♓16.9	5 49.4	19 43.3	24 6.1	5 10.1	12 9.4	14 49.3	16 35.3	22 28.3
6	3 1 50.5	13 50.2	23 23.4	23 16.3	6 30.3	20 55.7	24 22.3	5 21.6	12 11.5	14 51.4	16 36.5	22 30.7
7	3 5 47.1	14 50.4	23 20.2	5♈25.2	7 5.9	22 8.2	24 37.9	5 33.0	12 13.6	14 53.6	16 37.8	22 33.1
8	3 9 43.7	15 50.6	23 17.0	17 46.3	7 35.5	23 20.6	24 53.0	5 44.3	12 15.9	14 55.8	16 39.1	22 35.5
9	3 13 40.2	16 50.8	23 13.8	0♉21.2	7 58.5	24 32.9	25 7.4	5 55.6	12 18.3	14 58.0	16 40.5	22 37.9
10	3 17 36.8	17 51.1	23 10.7	13 10.6	8 14.3	25 45.2	25 21.3	6 6.8	12 20.7	15 .3	16 41.8	22 40.3
11	3 21 33.3	18 51.4	23 7.5	26 14.1	8 22.0	26 57.5	25 34.6	6 17.9	12 23.3	15 2.6	16 43.2	22 42.7
12	3 25 29.9	19 51.7	23 4.3	9♊31.0	8 R 21.2	28 9.7	25 47.3	6 29.0	12 25.9	15 5.0	16 44.6	22 45.1
13	3 29 26.4	20 52.0	23 1.1	23 .0	8 11.0	29 21.9	25 59.4	6 39.9	12 28.6	15 7.4	16 46.1	22 47.5
14	3 33 23.0	21 52.4	22 58.0	6♋39.7	7 51.0	0♑34.0	26 10.8	6 50.8	12 31.5	15 9.8	16 47.6	22 49.9
15	3 37 19.6	22 52.8	22 54.8	20 28.7	7 20.8	1 46.1	26 21.6	7 1.7	12 34.4	15 12.3	16 49.1	22 52.4
16	3 41 16.1	23 53.3	22 51.6	4♌26.0	6 40.3	2 58.2	26 31.8	7 12.5	12 37.5	15 14.9	16 50.6	22 54.8
17	3 45 12.7	24 53.8	22 48.4	18 30.3	5 49.7	4 10.2	26 41.2	7 23.1	12 40.6	15 17.4	16 52.2	22 57.2
18	3 49 9.2	25 54.3	22 45.2	2♍40.3	4 49.7	5 22.2	26 50.0	7 33.7	12 43.8	15 20.0	16 53.8	22 59.6
19	3 53 5.8	26 54.9	22 42.1	16 54.1	3 41.3	6 34.1	26 58.1	7 44.2	12 47.1	15 22.6	16 55.4	23 2.0
20	3 57 2.3	27 55.4	22 38.9	1♎ 9.1	2 26.3	7 45.9	27 5.4	7 54.6	12 50.4	15 25.3	16 57.0	23 4.5
21	4 0 58.9	28 56.0	22 35.7	15 22.1	1 6.8	8 57.7	27 12.0	8 4.9	12 53.9	15 28.0	16 58.6	23 6.9
22	4 4 55.4	29 56.7	22 32.5	29 29.2	29♏45.1	10 9.5	27 17.9	8 15.1	12 57.5	15 30.7	17 .3	23 9.3
23	4 8 52.0	0♐57.3	22 29.4	13♏26.2	28 24.1	11 21.2	27 23.0	8 25.3	13 1.1	15 33.5	17 2.0	23 11.7
24	4 12 48.6	1 58.0	22 26.2	27 9.5	27 6.5	12 32.8	27 27.4	8 35.3	13 4.8	15 36.3	17 3.7	23 14.1
25	4 16 45.1	2 58.7	22 23.0	10♐36.1	25 54.7	13 44.4	27 30.9	8 45.2	13 8.7	15 39.1	17 5.5	23 16.4
26	4 20 41.7	3 59.4	22 19.8	23 44.2	24 50.9	14 55.9	27 33.7	8 55.1	13 12.6	15 42.0	17 7.2	23 18.8
27	4 24 38.2	5 .2	22 16.7	6♑33.5	23 56.8	16 7.3	27 35.7	9 4.8	13 16.5	15 44.9	17 9.0	23 21.2
28	4 28 34.8	6 .9	22 13.5	19 5.1	23 13.6	17 18.7	27 36.9	9 14.5	13 20.6	15 47.8	17 10.8	23 23.6
29	4 32 31.3	7 1.7	22 10.3	1♒21.1	22 41.8	18 30.0	27 37.3	9 24.0	13 24.8	15 50.8	17 12.7	23 25.9
30	4 36 27.9	8 2.5	22 7.1	13 25.0	22 21.6	19 41.2	27 R 36.9	9 33.4	13 29.0	15 53.8	17 14.5	23 28.3
LATITUDE												
1	2 42 7.8	0 .0	0 .0	2N41.1	2S51.0	1S34.1	1N17.2	1N 6.9	1S 1.9	0S25.0	0N41.8	14N 6.9
4	2 53 57.4	0 .0	0 .0	4 45.8	2 51.3	1 41.5	1 23.8	1 7.3	1 1.8	0 24.9	0 41.7	14 6.4
7	3 5 47.1	0 .0	0 .0	5 1.9	2 44.4	1 48.3	1 30.6	1 7.6	1 1.7	0 24.9	0 41.6	14 6.0
10	3 17 36.8	0 .0	0 .0	3 14.6	2 27.8	1 54.7	1 37.6	1 8.1	1 1.6	0 24.9	0 41.5	14 5.7
13	3 29 26.4	0 .0	0 .0	0S 7.2	1 59.1	2 .5	1 44.9	1 8.5	1 1.5	0 24.8	0 41.4	14 5.5
16	3 41 16.1	0 .0	0 .0	3 33.2	1 16.3	2 5.6	1 52.4	1 8.9	1 1.4	0 24.8	0 41.3	14 5.3
19	3 53 5.8	0 .0	0 .0	5 12.9	0 20.8	2 10.1	2 .1	1 9.4	1 1.3	0 24.8	0 41.3	14 5.2
22	4 4 55.4	0 .0	0 .0	4 8.3	0N40.5	2 13.8	2 8.1	1 9.9	1 1.2	0 24.8	0 41.2	14 5.1
25	4 16 45.1	0 .0	0 .0	0 59.7	1 35.6	2 16.7	2 16.2	1 10.4	1 1.2	0 24.7	0 41.1	14 5.2
28	4 28 34.8	0 .0	0 .0	2N26.7	2 14.5	2 18.8	2 24.6	1 10.9	1 1.1	0 24.7	0 41.0	14 5.3
RIGHT ASCENSION												
1	2 42 7.8	6♏26.5	23♐ 5.3	24♑58.0	29♏41.3	13♐24.1	24♋59.6	4♎28.4	14♒48.0	15♑59.6	17♑48.7	23♏29.8
2	2 46 4.3	7 25.3	23 1.9	7♒ 5.7	0♐42.3	14 42.9	25 19.5	4 39.3	14 49.7	16 1.7	17 49.9	23 32.0
3	2 50 .9	8 24.4	22 58.4	18 39.7	1 39.9	16 1.9	25 38.8	4 50.0	14 51.5	16 3.8	17 51.1	23 34.2
4	2 53 57.4	9 23.6	22 55.0	29 50.0	2 33.7	17 21.0	25 57.7	5 .7	14 53.3	16 6.0	17 52.4	23 36.4
5	2 57 54.0	10 23.1	22 51.5	10♓48.2	3 23.1	18 40.3	26 15.9	5 11.4	14 55.3	16 8.3	17 53.7	23 38.7
6	3 1 50.5	11 22.7	22 48.1	21 46.8	4 7.6	19 59.7	26 33.6	5 21.9	14 57.4	16 10.5	17 55.1	23 40.9
7	3 5 47.1	12 22.5	22 44.6	2♈58.2	4 46.6	21 19.3	26 50.7	5 32.5	14 59.6	16 12.9	17 56.5	23 43.1
8	3 9 43.7	13 22.6	22 41.2	14 34.5	5 19.3	22 38.9	27 7.2	5 42.9	15 1.9	16 15.3	17 57.9	23 45.3
9	3 13 40.2	14 22.8	22 37.7	26 46.4	5 45.2	23 58.6	27 23.1	5 53.3	15 4.2	16 17.7	17 59.3	23 47.6
10	3 17 36.8	15 23.3	22 34.2	9♉41.4	6 3.4	25 18.3	27 38.3	6 3.7	15 6.7	16 20.2	18 .7	23 49.8
11	3 21 33.3	16 24.0	22 30.8	23 21.4	6 13.3	26 38.1	27 53.0	6 13.9	15 9.3	16 22.7	18 2.2	23 52.1
12	3 25 29.9	17 24.9	22 27.3	7♊40.1	6 14.0	27 58.0	28 7.0	6 24.1	15 11.9	16 25.2	18 3.8	23 54.3
13	3 29 26.4	18 26.0	22 23.9	22 23.1	6 R 5.0	29 17.8	28 20.3	6 34.3	15 14.7	16 27.8	18 5.3	23 56.6
14	3 33 23.0	19 27.3	22 20.4	7♋10.9	5 45.7	0♑37.7	28 33.0	6 44.4	15 17.5	16 30.4	18 6.9	23 58.8
15	3 37 19.6	20 28.9	22 17.0	21 44.9	5 15.8	1 57.5	28 44.9	6 54.4	15 20.4	16 33.1	18 8.5	24 1.1
16	3 41 16.1	21 30.7	22 13.5	5♌53.4	4 35.5	3 17.3	28 56.3	7 4.3	15 23.5	16 35.9	18 10.2	24 3.4
17	3 45 12.7	22 32.6	22 10.1	19 33.7	3 44.8	4 37.1	29 6.9	7 14.2	15 26.7	16 38.6	18 11.8	24 5.7
18	3 49 9.2	23 34.8	22 6.6	2♍50.9	2 44.7	5 56.7	29 16.7	7 24.0	15 29.9	16 41.4	18 13.5	24 8.0
19	3 53 5.8	24 37.2	22 3.2	15 55.4	1 36.5	7 16.3	29 25.8	7 33.7	15 33.2	16 44.3	18 15.2	24 10.2
20	3 57 2.3	25 39.8	21 59.7	28 59.8	0 21.9	8 35.7	29 34.2	7 43.3	15 36.6	16 47.1	18 17.0	24 12.5
21	4 0 58.9	26 42.6	21 56.3	12♎16.5	29♏ 3.1	9 55.1	29 41.8	7 52.9	15 40.1	16 50.0	18 18.7	24 14.8
22	4 4 55.4	27 45.6	21 52.8	25 54.4	27 42.8	11 14.3	29 48.6	8 2.3	15 43.6	16 53.0	18 20.5	24 17.0
23	4 8 52.0	28 48.9	21 49.4	9♏57.2	26 23.6	12 33.3	29 54.6	8 11.7	15 47.3	16 56.0	18 22.3	24 19.3
24	4 12 48.6	29 52.3	21 45.9	24 20.3	25 8.2	13 52.1	29 59.8	8 21.0	15 51.0	16 59.0	18 24.2	24 21.6
25	4 16 45.1	0♐55.9	21 42.5	8♐50.9	23 58.9	15 10.8	0♌ 4.2	8 30.2	15 54.9	17 2.0	18 26.1	24 23.8
26	4 20 41.7	1 59.7	21 39.0	23 11.4	22 57.7	16 29.2	0 7.8	8 39.4	15 58.8	17 5.1	18 27.9	24 26.1
27	4 24 38.2	3 3.7	21 35.6	7♑ 4.2	22 6.2	17 47.4	0 10.5	8 48.4	16 2.8	17 8.3	18 29.9	24 28.3
28	4 28 34.8	4 7.8	21 32.1	20 17.8	21 25.3	19 5.4	0 12.4	8 57.3	16 6.9	17 11.4	18 31.8	24 30.6
29	4 32 31.3	5 12.2	21 28.7	2♒48.6	20 55.5	20 23.1	0 13.4	9 6.2	16 11.1	17 14.6	18 33.7	24 32.8
30	4 36 27.9	6 16.6	21 25.2	14 40.0	20 36.9	21 40.5	0 13.6	9 14.9	16 15.3	17 17.8	18 35.7	24 35.1
DECLINATION												
1	2 42 7.8	14S26.5	0S24.4	18S44.1	23S25.7	24S 8.5	22N45.6	0S43.4	18S10.5	23S 2.7	21S43.7	4S40.7
4	2 53 57.4	15 23.1	0 24.4	7 13.1	23 57.0	24 37.7	22 42.9	0 56.9	18 8.9	23 2.0	21 43.4	4 42.8
7	3 5 47.1	16 17.3	0 24.4	6N46.2	24 11.7	25 .5	22 41.0	1 10.2	18 7.0	23 1.2	21 43.0	4 44.9
10	3 17 36.8	17 9.2	0 24.4	18 53.1	24 6.7	25 16.9	22 40.0	1 23.2	18 5.0	23 .4	21 42.6	4 46.9
13	3 29 26.4	17 58.3	0 24.4	23 8.1	23 37.9	25 26.8	22 40.0	1 35.9	18 2.6	22 59.6	21 42.2	4 48.8
16	3 41 16.1	18 44.7	0 24.3	15 42.0	22 40.7	25 30.0	22 41.2	1 48.3	18 .1	22 58.7	21 41.7	4 50.7
19	3 53 5.8	19 28.1	0 24.3	0 21.9	21 13.8	25 26.5	22 43.7	2 .4	17 57.3	22 57.8	21 41.2	4 52.5
22	4 4 55.4	20 8.3	0 24.3	15S 9.6	19 26.3	25 16.5	22 47.6	2 12.2	17 54.2	22 56.9	21 40.6	4 54.2
25	4 16 45.1	20 45.3	0 24.3	23 1.3	17 41.2	24 59.9	22 53.0	2 23.6	17 51.0	22 55.9	21 40.1	4 55.8
28	4 28 34.8	21 18.7	0 24.3	19 39.6	16 24.5	24 36.8	22 60.0	2 34.6	17 47.5	22 54.8	21 39.5	4 57.4

DECEMBER 1992

DAY	EPHEM. SID. TIME	☉	☊	☽	☿	♀	♂	♃	♄	♅	♆	♇
	h m s	° ′	° ′	° ′	° ′	° ′	° ′	° ′	° ′	° ′	° ′	° ′
		LONGITUDE										
1	4 40 24.5	9♐ 3.3	22♐ 4.0	25♒20.7	22♏12.8	20♑52.4	27♋35.6	9♎42.8	13♒33.3	15♑56.8	17♑16.4	23♏30.6
2	4 44 21.0	10 4.2	22 .8	7♓12.9	22 D 14.7	22 3.5	27 R 33.5	9 52.0	13 37.7	15 59.8	17 18.3	23 33.0
3	4 48 17.6	11 5.0	21 57.6	19 6.2	22 26.9	23 14.5	27 30.6	10 1.1	13 42.2	16 2.9	17 20.2	23 35.3
4	4 52 14.1	12 5.9	21 54.4	1♈ 5.5	22 48.3	24 25.4	27 26.9	10 10.1	13 46.7	16 6.0	17 22.1	23 37.6
5	4 56 10.7	13 6.7	21 51.2	13 15.2	23 18.2	25 36.2	27 22.3	10 18.9	13 51.4	16 9.1	17 24.1	23 39.9
6	5 0 7.2	14 7.6	21 48.1	25 39.1	23 55.6	26 46.9	27 16.8	10 27.7	13 56.1	16 12.2	17 26.0	23 42.2
7	5 4 3.8	15 8.6	21 44.9	8♉20.5	24 39.9	27 57.5	27 10.6	10 36.4	14 .9	16 15.4	17 28.1	23 44.6
8	5 8 .4	16 9.5	21 41.7	21 21.1	25 30.0	29 8.1	27 3.5	10 44.9	14 5.7	16 18.6	17 30.1	23 46.8
9	5 11 56.9	17 10.4	21 38.5	4♊41.5	26 25.4	0♒18.5	26 55.5	10 53.3	14 10.6	16 21.8	17 32.1	23 49.1
10	5 15 53.5	18 11.4	21 35.4	18 20.8	27 25.4	1 28.8	26 46.7	11 1.6	14 15.6	16 25.1	17 34.1	23 51.3
11	5 19 50.0	19 12.3	21 32.2	2♋16.7	28 29.4	2 38.9	26 37.0	11 9.8	14 20.7	16 28.3	17 36.1	23 53.6
12	5 23 46.6	20 13.3	21 29.0	16 25.5	29 36.9	3 49.0	26 26.5	11 17.8	14 25.8	16 31.6	17 38.2	23 55.8
13	5 27 43.1	21 14.3	21 25.8	0♌43.0	0♐47.4	4 59.0	26 15.2	11 25.7	14 31.0	16 34.9	17 40.3	23 58.0
14	5 31 39.7	22 15.3	21 22.7	15 4.6	2 .6	6 8.8	26 3.0	11 33.5	14 36.3	16 38.2	17 42.4	24 .2
15	5 35 36.3	23 16.3	21 19.5	29 26.1	3 16.1	7 18.5	25 50.1	11 41.1	14 41.6	16 41.6	17 44.5	24 2.4
16	5 39 32.8	24 17.3	21 16.3	13♍43.6	4 33.5	8 28.1	25 36.3	11 48.6	14 47.0	16 44.9	17 46.6	24 4.5
17	5 43 29.4	25 18.4	21 13.1	27 54.3	5 52.8	9 37.6	25 21.7	11 56.0	14 52.5	16 48.3	17 48.7	24 6.7
18	5 47 25.9	26 19.5	21 9.9	11♎56.2	7 13.5	10 46.9	25 6.4	12 3.3	14 58.0	16 51.7	17 50.9	24 8.8
19	5 51 22.5	27 20.6	21 6.8	25 47.8	8 35.5	11 56.1	24 50.3	12 10.4	15 3.6	16 55.1	17 53.0	24 10.9
20	5 55 19.1	28 21.7	21 3.6	9♏28.1	9 58.8	13 5.2	24 33.5	12 17.3	15 9.2	16 58.5	17 55.2	24 13.0
21	5 59 15.6	29 22.8	21 .4	22 56.5	11 23.0	14 14.1	24 15.9	12 24.1	15 14.9	17 2.0	17 57.4	24 15.1
22	6 3 12.2	0♑23.9	20 57.2	6♐12.3	12 48.1	15 22.9	23 57.7	12 30.8	15 20.7	17 5.4	17 59.5	24 17.1
23	6 7 8.7	1 25.0	20 54.1	19 15.0	14 14.1	16 31.5	23 38.8	12 37.3	15 26.5	17 8.9	18 1.7	24 19.2
24	6 11 5.3	2 26.2	20 50.9	2♑ 4.5	15 40.7	17 40.0	23 19.2	12 43.7	15 32.4	17 12.3	18 3.9	24 21.2
25	6 15 1.8	3 27.3	20 47.7	14 40.7	17 8.0	18 48.2	22 59.1	12 49.9	15 38.3	17 15.8	18 6.1	24 23.2
26	6 18 58.4	4 28.5	20 44.5	27 4.1	18 35.9	19 56.4	22 38.4	12 56.0	15 44.3	17 19.3	18 8.4	24 25.2
27	6 22 55.0	5 29.6	20 41.4	9♒16.1	20 4.4	21 4.3	22 17.3	13 1.9	15 50.4	17 22.8	18 10.6	24 27.1
28	6 26 51.5	6 30.8	20 38.2	21 18.4	21 33.3	22 12.1	21 55.6	13 7.7	15 56.5	17 26.4	18 12.9	24 29.1
29	6 30 48.1	7 32.0	20 35.0	3♓13.8	23 2.7	23 19.7	21 33.5	13 13.4	16 2.7	17 29.9	18 15.1	24 31.0
30	6 34 44.6	8 33.1	20 31.8	15 5.5	24 32.5	24 27.0	21 11.0	13 18.8	16 8.9	17 33.5	18 17.4	24 32.9
31	6 38 41.2	9 34.3	20 28.7	26 57.6	26 2.7	25 34.2	20 48.2	13 24.1	16 15.1	17 37.0	18 19.6	24 34.7
		LATITUDE										
1	4 40 24.5	0 .0	0 .0	4N44.2	2N34.5	2S20.1	2N33.0	1N11.5	1S 1.0	0S24.7	0N41.0	14N 5.4
4	4 52 14.1	0 .0	0 .0	5 12.4	2 38.5	2 20.4	2 41.6	1 12.0	1 1.0	0 24.7	0 40.9	14 5.7
7	5 4 3.8	0 .0	0 .0	3 37.1	2 31.0	2 19.8	2 50.2	1 12.6	1 .9	0 24.7	0 40.8	14 6.0
10	5 15 53.5	0 .0	0 .0	0 17.5	2 16.1	2 18.1	2 58.8	1 13.2	1 .9	0 24.7	0 40.7	14 6.3
13	5 27 43.1	0 .0	0 .0	3S20.9	1 56.7	2 15.5	3 7.3	1 13.8	1 .9	0 24.7	0 40.7	14 6.8
16	5 39 32.8	0 .0	0 .0	5 14.3	1 34.8	2 11.8	3 15.7	1 14.5	1 .8	0 24.7	0 40.6	14 7.3
19	5 51 22.5	0 .0	0 .0	4 22.3	1 11.7	2 6.9	3 23.7	1 15.2	1 .8	0 24.7	0 40.6	14 7.8
22	6 3 12.2	0 .0	0 .0	1 24.0	0 48.2	2 1.0	3 31.3	1 15.8	1 .8	0 24.7	0 40.5	14 8.5
25	6 15 1.8	0 .0	0 .0	2N 4.6	0 24.9	1 53.9	3 38.5	1 16.5	1 .8	0 24.7	0 40.5	14 9.2
28	6 26 51.5	0 .0	0 .0	4 33.2	0 2.4	1 45.7	3 45.0	1 17.2	1 .8	0 24.7	0 40.4	14 9.9
31	6 38 41.2	0 .0	0 .0	5 13.9	0S19.1	1 36.2	3 50.8	1 18.0	1 .8	0 24.7	0 40.4	14 10.7
		RIGHT ASCENSION										
1	4 40 24.5	7♐21.3	21♐21.8	26♒ .5	20♏29.2	22♑57.6	0♌12.8	9♎23.6	16♒19.7	17♑21.0	18♑37.7	24♏37.3
2	4 44 21.0	8 26.1	21 18.3	7♓ 1.3	20 D 32.0	24 14.4	0 R 11.2	9 32.1	16 24.1	17 24.3	18 39.7	24 39.5
3	4 48 17.6	9 31.1	21 14.9	17 55.2	20 44.5	25 30.8	0 8.8	9 40.6	16 28.5	17 27.6	18 41.8	24 41.8
4	4 52 14.1	10 36.2	21 11.4	28 55.5	21 6.0	26 47.0	0 5.4	9 49.0	16 33.1	17 31.0	18 43.8	24 44.0
5	4 56 10.7	11 41.5	21 8.0	10♈15.6	21 35.7	28 2.7	0 1.1	9 57.2	16 37.8	17 34.3	18 45.9	24 46.2
6	5 0 7.2	12 46.8	21 4.5	22 8.3	22 12.8	29 18.2	29♋55.9	10 5.4	16 42.5	17 37.7	18 48.0	24 48.4
7	5 4 3.8	13 52.4	21 1.1	4♉44.7	22 56.6	0♒33.2	29 49.9	10 13.4	16 47.3	17 41.2	18 50.2	24 50.6
8	5 8 .4	14 58.0	20 57.6	18 10.9	23 46.4	1 47.9	29 42.9	10 21.4	16 52.2	17 44.6	18 52.3	24 52.8
9	5 11 56.9	16 3.8	20 54.2	2♊25.9	24 41.4	3 2.2	29 35.0	10 29.2	16 57.1	17 48.1	18 54.5	24 55.0
10	5 15 53.5	17 9.7	20 50.7	17 18.2	25 41.2	4 16.0	29 26.2	10 36.9	17 2.1	17 51.6	18 56.7	24 57.1
11	5 19 50.0	18 15.6	20 47.3	2♋27.8	26 45.2	5 29.4	29 16.5	10 44.5	17 7.2	17 55.1	18 58.8	24 59.3
12	5 23 46.6	19 21.7	20 43.8	17 31.4	27 52.9	6 42.4	29 5.8	10 52.0	17 12.3	17 58.6	19 1.0	25 1.4
13	5 27 43.1	20 27.8	20 40.4	2♌10.3	29 4.0	7 55.0	28 54.3	10 59.4	17 17.5	18 2.1	19 3.3	25 3.5
14	5 31 39.7	21 34.1	20 36.9	16 15.8	0♐18.1	9 7.2	28 41.8	11 6.6	17 22.8	18 5.7	19 5.5	25 5.7
15	5 35 36.3	22 40.4	20 33.5	29 49.4	1 34.9	10 18.9	28 28.5	11 13.8	17 28.1	18 9.3	19 7.7	25 7.8
16	5 39 32.8	23 46.8	20 30.0	12♍59.7	2 54.0	11 30.1	28 14.3	11 20.8	17 33.5	18 12.9	19 10.0	25 9.8
17	5 43 29.4	24 53.2	20 26.6	25 59.2	4 15.3	12 41.0	27 59.2	11 27.7	17 39.0	18 16.5	19 12.3	25 11.9
18	5 47 25.9	25 59.7	20 23.1	9♎ 1.0	5 38.6	13 51.3	27 43.2	11 34.4	17 44.5	18 20.2	19 14.5	25 14.0
19	5 51 22.5	27 6.2	20 19.7	22 16.7	7 3.7	15 1.2	27 26.4	11 41.1	17 50.1	18 23.9	19 16.8	25 16.0
20	5 55 19.1	28 12.8	20 16.2	5♏53.2	8 30.4	16 10.7	27 8.7	11 47.6	17 55.8	18 27.5	19 19.1	25 18.0
21	5 59 15.6	29 19.4	20 12.8	19 51.4	9 58.6	17 19.7	26 50.3	11 54.0	18 1.5	18 31.2	19 21.5	25 20.1
22	6 3 12.2	0♑26.0	20 9.3	4♐ 4.1	11 28.1	18 28.2	26 31.0	12 .2	18 7.2	18 34.9	19 23.8	25 22.0
23	6 7 8.7	1 32.7	20 5.9	18 17.5	12 58.9	19 36.2	26 11.1	12 6.3	18 13.1	18 38.7	19 26.1	25 24.0
24	6 11 5.3	2 39.3	20 2.5	2♑14.7	14 30.8	20 43.8	25 50.4	12 12.3	18 18.9	18 42.4	19 28.5	25 26.0
25	6 15 1.8	3 45.9	19 59.0	15 41.5	16 3.8	21 50.9	25 29.0	12 18.1	18 24.9	18 46.2	19 30.8	25 27.9
26	6 18 58.4	4 52.5	19 55.6	28 29.7	17 37.8	22 57.5	25 6.9	12 23.8	18 30.8	18 49.9	19 33.2	25 29.9
27	6 22 55.0	5 59.1	19 52.1	10♒38.3	19 12.8	24 3.7	24 44.3	12 29.4	18 36.9	18 53.7	19 35.6	25 31.8
28	6 26 51.5	7 5.6	19 48.7	22 12.5	20 48.7	25 9.4	24 21.1	12 34.9	18 43.0	18 57.5	19 38.0	25 33.7
29	6 30 48.1	8 12.1	19 45.2	3♓21.1	22 25.3	26 14.5	23 57.4	12 40.1	18 49.2	19 1.3	19 40.4	25 35.6
30	6 34 44.6	9 18.5	19 41.8	14 15.4	24 2.7	27 19.2	23 33.2	12 45.2	18 55.3	19 5.1	19 42.8	25 37.4
31	6 38 41.2	10 24.9	19 38.3	25 7.8	25 40.8	28 23.4	23 8.6	12 50.2	19 1.6	19 8.9	19 45.2	25 39.2
		DECLINATION										
1	4 40 24.5	21S48.5	0S24.3	8S36.4	15S49.9	24S 7.6	23N 8.6	2S45.2	17S43.8	22S53.8	21S38.8	4S58.8
4	4 52 14.1	22 14.5	0 24.3	5N12.6	15 55.0	23 32.2	23 18.7	2 55.3	17 39.8	22 52.7	21 38.2	5 .2
7	5 4 3.8	22 36.7	0 24.3	17 42.5	16 29.6	22 51.1	23 30.4	3 5.1	17 35.7	22 51.5	21 37.5	5 1.5
10	5 15 53.5	22 54.9	0 24.3	23 13.1	17 22.5	22 4.5	23 43.5	3 14.4	17 31.4	22 50.3	21 36.8	5 2.7
13	5 27 43.1	23 9.0	0 24.3	16 43.6	18 24.8	21 12.7	23 58.0	3 23.3	17 26.9	22 49.1	21 36.0	5 3.8
16	5 39 32.8	23 19.0	0 24.2	1 33.6	19 29.9	20 15.9	24 13.5	3 31.6	17 22.1	22 47.9	21 35.2	5 4.8
19	5 51 22.5	23 24.8	0 24.2	14S 2.2	20 33.4	19 14.6	24 30.0	3 39.5	17 17.3	22 46.6	21 34.5	5 5.7
22	6 3 12.2	23 26.3	0 24.2	22 43.4	21 32.2	18 9.0	24 47.0	3 46.8	17 12.2	22 45.3	21 33.7	5 6.5
25	6 15 1.8	23 23.7	0 24.2	20 34.0	22 24.2	16 59.5	25 4.2	3 53.6	17 7.0	22 44.0	21 32.8	5 7.2
28	6 26 51.5	23 16.7	0 24.2	10 4.9	23 7.8	15 46.5	25 21.3	3 59.9	17 1.5	22 42.6	21 32.0	5 7.8
31	6 38 41.2	23 5.6	0 24.2	3N35.5	23 42.0	14 30.4	25 37.8	4 5.5	16 56.0	22 41.3	21 31.1	5 8.3

JANUARY 1993

DAY	EPHEM. SID. TIME h m s	☉ ° ′	☊ ° ′	☽ ° ′	☿ ° ′	♀ ° ′	♂ ° ′	♃ ° ′	♄ ° ′	♅ ° ′	♆ ° ′	♇ ° ′
		LONGITUDE										
1	6 42 37.7	10♑35.5	20♐25.5	8♈54.5	27♐33.4	26♒41.1	20♋25.0	13♎29.2	16♒21.4	17♑40.5	18♑21.9	24♏36.6
2	6 46 34.3	11 36.6	20 22.3	21 1.0	29 4.4	27 47.8	20 R 1.6	13 34.2	16 27.7	17 44.1	18 24.1	24 38.4
3	6 50 30.9	12 37.8	20 19.1	3♉21.8	0♑35.7	28 54.3	19 38.0	13 39.0	16 34.1	17 47.7	18 26.4	24 40.2
4	6 54 27.4	13 38.9	20 15.9	16 1.3	2 7.5	0♓ .5	19 14.2	13 43.6	16 40.6	17 51.2	18 28.7	24 41.9
5	6 58 24.0	14 40.0	20 12.8	29 3.2	3 39.7	1 6.5	18 50.3	13 48.1	16 47.0	17 54.8	18 30.9	24 43.7
6	7 2 20.5	15 41.2	20 9.6	12♊29.8	5 12.2	2 12.2	18 26.4	13 52.4	16 53.5	17 58.3	18 33.2	24 45.4
7	7 6 17.1	16 42.3	20 6.4	26 21.6	6 45.1	3 17.7	18 2.4	13 56.5	17 .1	18 1.9	18 35.5	24 47.1
8	7 10 13.7	17 43.4	20 3.2	10♋36.9	8 18.4	4 22.9	17 38.5	14 .4	17 6.7	18 5.5	18 37.7	24 48.7
9	7 14 10.2	18 44.5	20 .1	25 11.3	9 52.1	5 27.8	17 14.6	14 4.2	17 13.3	18 9.0	18 40.0	24 50.4
10	7 18 6.8	19 45.7	19 56.9	9♌58.3	11 26.3	6 32.4	16 50.9	14 7.8	17 20.0	18 12.6	18 42.3	24 52.0
11	7 22 3.3	20 46.8	19 53.7	24 50.0	13 .8	7 36.7	16 27.3	14 11.3	17 26.7	18 16.2	18 44.6	24 53.5
12	7 25 59.9	21 47.9	19 50.5	9♍38.3	14 35.8	8 40.7	16 3.9	14 14.5	17 33.4	18 19.7	18 46.8	24 55.1
13	7 29 56.4	22 49.0	19 47.4	24 16.0	16 11.3	9 44.4	15 40.8	14 17.6	17 40.2	18 23.3	18 49.1	24 56.6
14	7 33 53.0	23 50.1	19 44.2	8♎38.0	17 47.2	10 47.8	15 18.0	14 20.5	17 47.0	18 26.9	18 51.4	24 58.1
15	7 37 49.6	24 51.2	19 41.0	22 41.2	19 23.6	11 50.8	14 55.5	14 23.2	17 53.8	18 30.4	18 53.6	24 59.6
16	7 41 46.1	25 52.3	19 37.8	6♏25.1	21 .5	12 53.4	14 33.5	14 25.8	18 .7	18 34.0	18 55.9	25 1.0
17	7 45 42.7	26 53.4	19 34.6	19 50.2	22 38.0	13 55.8	14 11.8	14 28.1	18 7.5	18 37.5	18 58.2	25 2.4
18	7 49 39.2	27 54.6	19 31.5	2♐58.5	24 16.0	14 57.7	13 50.7	14 30.3	18 14.5	18 41.1	19 .5	25 3.8
19	7 53 35.8	28 55.7	19 28.3	15 51.8	25 54.5	15 59.3	13 30.0	14 32.3	18 21.5	18 44.6	19 2.7	25 5.2
20	7 57 32.3	29 56.8	19 25.1	28 32.4	27 33.5	17 .5	13 9.8	14 34.1	18 28.4	18 48.1	19 5.0	25 6.5
21	8 1 28.9	0♒57.8	19 21.9	11♑ 2.0	29 13.1	18 1.2	12 50.2	14 35.7	18 35.4	18 51.7	19 7.2	25 7.7
22	8 5 25.4	1 58.9	19 18.8	23 22.0	0♒53.3	19 1.5	12 31.3	14 37.1	18 42.5	18 55.2	19 9.4	25 9.0
23	8 9 22.0	2 60.0	19 15.6	5♒33.6	2 34.1	20 1.4	12 12.9	14 38.3	18 49.5	18 58.7	19 11.7	25 10.2
24	8 13 18.6	4 1.0	19 12.4	17 37.9	4 15.5	21 .8	11 55.3	14 39.4	18 56.6	19 2.1	19 13.9	25 11.4
25	8 17 15.1	5 2.0	19 9.2	29 36.1	5 57.5	21 59.8	11 38.3	14 40.2	19 3.6	19 5.6	19 16.1	25 12.5
26	8 21 11.7	6 3.1	19 6.1	11♓29.7	7 40.1	22 58.2	11 22.0	14 40.9	19 10.7	19 9.1	19 18.3	25 13.7
27	8 25 8.2	7 4.1	19 2.9	23 20.8	9 23.2	23 56.1	11 6.5	14 41.3	19 17.9	19 12.5	19 20.5	25 14.7
28	8 29 4.8	8 5.0	18 59.7	5♈12.2	11 7.0	24 53.5	10 51.7	14 41.6	19 25.0	19 15.9	19 22.7	25 15.8
29	8 33 1.3	9 6.0	18 56.5	17 7.4	12 51.3	25 50.4	10 37.6	14 41.7	19 32.1	19 19.4	19 24.8	25 16.8
30	8 36 57.9	10 7.0	18 53.3	29 10.5	14 36.2	26 46.7	10 24.4	14 R 41.6	19 39.3	19 22.8	19 27.0	25 17.8
31	8 40 54.5	11 7.9	18 50.2	11♉26.1	16 21.6	27 42.3	10 11.9	14 41.3	19 46.5	19 26.1	19 29.1	25 18.7
		LATITUDE										
1	6 42 37.7	0 .0	0 .0	5N .8	0S26.0	1S32.8	3N52.5	1N18.2	1S .9	0S24.7	0N40.4	14N11.0
4	6 54 27.4	0 .0	0 .0	3 2.7	0 45.8	1 21.9	3 57.2	1 19.0	1 .9	0 24.7	0 40.3	14 11.9
7	7 6 17.1	0 .0	0 .0	0S27.1	1 3.9	1 9.7	4 .9	1 19.7	1 .9	0 24.7	0 40.3	14 12.8
10	7 18 6.8	0 .0	0 .0	3 55.2	1 20.2	0 56.3	4 3.7	1 20.5	1 1.0	0 24.7	0 40.3	14 13.8
13	7 29 56.4	0 .0	0 .0	5 11.9	1 34.4	0 41.7	4 5.6	1 21.3	1 1.1	0 24.8	0 40.2	14 14.8
16	7 41 46.1	0 .0	0 .0	3 39.7	1 46.3	0 25.9	4 6.6	1 22.1	1 1.2	0 24.8	0 40.2	14 15.8
19	7 53 35.8	0 .0	0 .0	0 28.5	1 55.6	0 8.8	4 6.6	1 22.9	1 1.3	0 24.8	0 40.2	14 16.9
22	8 5 25.4	0 .0	0 .0	2N45.9	2 1.9	0N 9.4	4 5.8	1 23.7	1 1.4	0 24.9	0 40.2	14 18.1
25	8 17 15.1	0 .0	0 .0	4 47.2	2 4.9	0 28.8	4 4.2	1 24.5	1 1.5	0 24.9	0 40.2	14 19.3
28	8 29 4.8	0 .0	0 .0	4 57.0	2 4.2	0 49.3	4 2.0	1 25.3	1 1.6	0 24.9	0 40.2	14 20.5
31	8 40 54.5	0 .0	0 .0	3 12.5	1 59.3	1 11.0	3 59.1	1 26.1	1 1.8	0 25.0	0 40.2	14 21.7
		RIGHT ASCENSION										
1	6 42 37.7	11♑31.1	19♐34.9	6♈11.5	27♐19.7	29♒27.2	22♋43.6	12♎55.1	19♒ 7.8	19♑12.7	19♑47.6	25♏41.0
2	6 46 34.3	12 37.3	19 31.4	17 39.8	28 59.1	0♓30.4	22 R 18.2	12 59.7	19 14.2	19 16.6	19 50.0	25 42.8
3	6 50 30.9	13 43.4	19 28.0	29 45.1	0♑39.2	1 33.1	21 52.6	13 4.3	19 20.5	19 20.4	19 52.4	25 44.6
4	6 54 27.4	14 49.4	19 24.6	12♉37.5	2 19.8	2 35.4	21 26.7	13 8.6	19 26.9	19 24.2	19 54.8	25 46.3
5	6 58 24.0	15 55.3	19 21.1	26 21.9	4 .9	3 37.1	21 .7	13 12.9	19 33.4	19 28.0	19 57.3	25 48.0
6	7 2 20.5	17 1.1	19 17.7	10♊55.0	5 42.6	4 38.4	20 34.6	13 16.9	19 39.9	19 31.9	19 59.7	25 49.7
7	7 6 17.1	18 6.8	19 14.2	26 2.9	7 24.7	5 39.1	20 8.4	13 20.9	19 46.4	19 35.7	20 2.1	25 51.4
8	7 10 13.7	19 12.3	19 10.8	11♋23.9	9 7.3	6 39.4	19 42.1	13 24.6	19 52.9	19 39.5	20 4.5	25 53.0
9	7 14 10.2	20 17.7	19 7.3	26 35.1	10 50.3	7 39.2	19 16.0	13 28.2	19 59.5	19 43.3	20 6.9	25 54.7
10	7 18 6.8	21 23.0	19 3.9	11♌20.0	12 33.7	8 38.5	18 49.9	13 31.6	20 6.2	19 47.2	20 9.4	25 56.2
11	7 22 3.3	22 28.2	19 .5	25 32.7	14 17.4	9 37.3	18 23.9	13 34.9	20 12.8	19 51.0	20 11.8	25 57.8
12	7 25 59.9	23 33.2	18 57.0	9♍16.4	16 1.5	10 35.5	17 58.2	13 38.0	20 19.5	19 54.8	20 14.2	25 59.4
13	7 29 56.4	24 38.0	18 53.6	22 40.7	17 45.9	11 33.3	17 32.7	13 41.0	20 26.2	19 58.7	20 16.6	26 .9
14	7 33 53.0	25 42.7	18 50.1	5♎57.4	19 30.6	12 30.6	17 7.5	13 43.8	20 33.0	20 2.5	20 19.0	26 2.4
15	7 37 49.6	26 47.3	18 46.7	19 17.7	21 15.5	13 27.4	16 42.6	13 46.4	20 39.8	20 6.3	20 21.5	26 3.8
16	7 41 46.1	27 51.6	18 43.2	2♏49.9	23 .6	14 23.7	16 18.1	13 48.8	20 46.6	20 10.1	20 23.9	26 5.3
17	7 45 42.7	28 55.9	18 39.8	16 36.9	24 46.0	15 19.6	15 54.1	13 51.1	20 53.4	20 13.9	20 26.3	26 6.7
18	7 49 39.2	29 60.0	18 36.4	0♐35.3	26 31.6	16 14.9	15 30.6	13 53.2	21 .3	20 17.7	20 28.7	26 8.1
19	7 53 35.8	1♒ 3.8	18 32.9	14 35.7	28 17.2	17 9.7	15 7.6	13 55.2	21 7.2	20 21.5	20 31.1	26 9.5
20	7 57 32.3	2 7.5	18 29.5	28 25.0	0♒ 3.0	18 4.0	14 45.2	13 56.9	21 14.2	20 25.3	20 33.5	26 10.8
21	8 1 28.9	3 11.0	18 26.0	11♑50.5	1 48.9	18 57.8	14 23.4	13 58.5	21 21.1	20 29.1	20 35.9	26 12.1
22	8 5 25.4	4 14.3	18 22.6	24 43.3	3 34.9	19 51.0	14 2.2	13 59.9	21 28.1	20 32.8	20 38.3	26 13.4
23	8 9 22.0	5 17.5	18 19.2	7♒ .5	5 20.9	20 43.7	13 41.7	14 1.2	21 35.0	20 36.6	20 40.6	26 14.6
24	8 13 18.6	6 20.4	18 15.7	18 44.3	7 6.9	21 35.9	13 22.0	14 2.2	21 42.0	20 40.3	20 43.0	26 15.8
25	8 17 15.1	7 23.1	18 12.3	0♓ 1.2	8 52.9	22 27.6	13 3.0	14 3.1	21 49.0	20 44.0	20 45.3	26 17.0
26	8 21 11.7	8 25.7	18 8.8	11 .3	10 38.8	23 18.7	12 44.8	14 3.8	21 56.1	20 47.7	20 47.7	26 18.2
27	8 25 8.2	9 28.0	18 5.4	21 52.1	12 24.7	24 9.2	12 27.4	14 4.4	22 3.1	20 51.4	20 50.0	26 19.3
28	8 29 4.8	10 30.1	18 2.0	2♈48.1	14 10.4	24 59.2	12 10.8	14 4.7	22 10.2	20 55.1	20 52.3	26 20.4
29	8 33 1.3	11 32.0	17 58.5	14 .2	15 56.0	25 48.5	11 55.0	14 4.9	22 17.2	20 58.8	20 54.6	26 21.4
30	8 36 57.9	12 33.7	17 55.1	25 39.8	17 41.4	26 37.3	11 40.2	14 4.9	22 24.3	21 2.4	20 56.9	26 22.4
31	8 40 54.5	13 35.2	17 51.6	7♉57.5	19 26.4	27 25.4	11 26.1	14 R 4.7	22 31.4	21 6.0	20 59.2	26 23.4
		DECLINATION										
1	6 42 37.7	23S 1.0	0S24.2	8N 8.2	23S51.1	14S 4.4	25N43.1	4S 7.3	16S54.1	22S40.8	21S30.8	5S 8.4
4	6 54 27.4	22 44.4	0 24.2	19 32.8	24 11.1	12 44.7	25 58.3	4 12.2	16 48.4	22 39.4	21 29.9	5 8.8
7	7 6 17.1	22 23.7	0 24.2	22 56.2	24 19.9	11 22.8	26 12.2	4 16.5	16 42.5	22 38.0	21 29.0	5 9.0
10	7 18 6.8	21 59.1	0 24.1	13 58.2	24 16.8	9 59.0	26 24.4	4 20.1	16 36.5	22 36.6	21 28.1	5 9.2
13	7 29 56.4	21 30.6	0 24.1	2S29.8	24 1.3	8 33.6	26 35.0	4 23.2	16 30.4	22 35.2	21 27.2	5 9.2
16	7 41 46.1	20 58.3	0 24.1	17 6.8	23 32.9	7 7.1	26 43.7	4 25.6	16 24.2	22 33.7	21 26.3	5 9.1
19	7 53 35.8	20 22.5	0 24.1	23 9.7	22 51.5	5 39.8	26 50.6	4 27.4	16 17.8	22 32.3	21 25.4	5 9.0
22	8 5 25.4	19 43.1	0 24.1	18 41.5	21 56.6	4 12.0	26 55.7	4 28.5	16 11.4	22 30.9	21 24.5	5 8.7
25	8 17 15.1	19 .5	0 24.1	7 7.4	20 48.0	2 44.1	26 59.1	4 29.0	16 4.9	22 29.4	21 23.5	5 8.4
28	8 29 4.8	18 14.7	0 24.1	6N36.6	19 25.7	1 16.5	27 .9	4 28.8	15 58.4	22 28.0	21 22.6	5 7.9
31	8 40 54.5	17 26.1	0 24.1	18 18.7	17 49.8	0N10.4	27 1.3	4 28.0	15 51.8	22 26.6	21 21.7	5 7.4

FEBRUARY 1993

LONGITUDE

DAY	EPHEM. SID. TIME	☉	☊	☽	☿	♀	♂	♃	♄	♅	♆	♇
	h m s	° ′	° ′	° ′	° ′	° ′	° ′	° ′	° ′	° ′	° ′	° ′
1	8 44 51.0	12♒ 8.8	18♐47.0	23♉59.3	18♒ 7.4	28♓37.4	10♋ .2	14♎40.8	19♒53.6	19♑29.5	19♑31.3	25♏19.7
2	8 48 47.6	13 9.7	18 43.8	6♊54.7	19 53.7	29 31.8	9R49.3	14R40.1	20 .8	19 32.9	19 33.4	25 20.5
3	8 52 44.1	14 10.5	18 40.6	20 16.3	21 40.3	0♈25.5	9 39.3	14 39.3	20 8.0	19 36.2	19 35.5	25 21.4
4	8 56 40.7	15 11.3	18 37.5	4♋ 6.7	23 27.2	1 18.5	9 30.0	14 38.2	20 15.3	19 39.5	19 37.6	25 22.2
5	9 0 37.2	16 12.2	18 34.3	18 26.0	25 14.2	2 10.8	9 21.5	14 36.9	20 22.5	19 42.8	19 39.7	25 23.0
6	9 4 33.8	17 12.9	18 31.1	3♌11.1	27 1.2	3 2.3	9 13.9	14 35.5	20 29.7	19 46.1	19 41.8	25 23.7
7	9 8 30.3	18 13.7	18 27.9	18 15.5	28 48.1	3 53.1	9 7.0	14 33.9	20 36.9	19 49.3	19 43.8	25 24.4
8	9 12 26.9	19 14.5	18 24.8	3♍29.8	0♓34.7	4 43.1	9 1.0	14 32.1	20 44.2	19 52.6	19 45.9	25 25.2
9	9 16 23.4	20 15.2	18 21.6	18 42.9	2 20.7	5 32.2	8 55.7	14 30.1	20 51.4	19 55.8	19 48.0	25 25.8
10	9 20 20.0	21 15.9	18 18.4	3♎44.3	4 5.9	6 20.4	8 51.3	14 27.9	20 58.6	19 59.0	19 50.0	25 26.4
11	9 24 16.6	22 16.6	18 15.2	18 25.6	5 50.0	7 7.7	8 47.6	14 25.6	21 5.9	20 2.1	19 52.0	25 27.0
12	9 28 13.1	23 17.3	18 12.0	2♏41.8	7 32.5	7 54.1	8 44.7	14 23.0	21 13.1	20 5.3	19 54.0	25 27.5
13	9 32 9.7	24 18.0	18 8.9	16 31.4	9 13.2	8 39.6	8 42.5	14 20.3	21 20.3	20 8.4	19 55.9	25 28.0
14	9 36 6.2	25 18.6	18 5.7	29 55.3	10 51.6	9 24.0	8 41.1	14 17.3	21 27.6	20 11.5	19 57.9	25 28.5
15	9 40 2.8	26 19.2	18 2.5	12♐56.4	12 27.1	10 7.3	8 40.5	14 14.2	21 34.8	20 14.5	19 59.8	25 28.9
16	9 43 59.3	27 19.8	17 59.3	25 38.5	13 59.2	10 49.6	8D40.7	14 11.0	21 42.0	20 17.5	20 1.7	25 29.3
17	9 47 55.9	28 20.4	17 56.2	8♑ 5.4	15 27.4	11 30.8	8 41.5	14 7.5	21 49.2	20 20.5	20 3.6	25 29.6
18	9 51 52.4	29 20.9	17 53.0	20 20.8	16 50.9	12 10.8	8 43.1	14 3.9	21 56.4	20 23.5	20 5.5	25 30.0
19	9 55 49.0	0♓21.5	17 49.8	2♒27.8	18 9.1	12 49.5	8 45.5	14 .1	22 3.6	20 26.5	20 7.3	25 30.2
20	9 59 45.5	1 22.0	17 46.6	14 28.6	19 21.4	13 27.0	8 48.5	13 56.1	22 10.8	20 29.4	20 9.1	25 30.5
21	10 3 42.1	2 22.5	17 43.4	26 25.2	20 27.0	14 3.2	8 52.3	13 51.9	22 17.9	20 32.3	20 10.9	25 30.7
22	10 7 38.7	3 22.9	17 40.3	8♓19.0	21 25.3	14 38.0	8 56.7	13 47.6	22 25.1	20 35.1	20 12.7	25 30.9
23	10 11 35.2	4 23.3	17 37.1	20 11.1	22 15.8	15 11.4	9 1.8	13 43.1	22 32.2	20 37.9	20 14.5	25 31.0
24	10 15 31.8	5 23.7	17 33.9	2♈ 3.0	22 57.8	15 43.3	9 7.6	13 38.5	22 39.3	20 40.7	20 16.2	25 31.1
25	10 19 28.3	6 24.1	17 30.7	13 56.3	23 30.8	16 13.6	9 14.1	13 33.7	22 46.5	20 43.5	20 18.0	25 31.2
26	10 23 24.9	7 24.5	17 27.6	25 53.4	23 54.4	16 42.4	9 21.2	13 28.7	22 53.5	20 46.2	20 19.6	25 31.2
27	10 27 21.4	8 24.8	17 24.4	7♉57.3	24 8.5	17 9.4	9 29.0	13 23.6	23 .6	20 48.9	20 21.3	25 31.2
28	10 31 18.0	9 25.0	17 21.2	20 11.8	24 12.9	17 34.8	9 37.3	13 18.3	23 7.7	20 51.5	20 23.0	25 31.2

LATITUDE

DAY	EPHEM. SID. TIME	☉	☊	☽	☿	♀	♂	♃	♄	♅	♆	♇
1	8 44 51.0	0 .0	0 .0	2N15.6	1S56.6	1N18.5	3N58.0	1N26.3	1S 1.8	0S25.0	0N40.2	14N22.1
4	8 56 40.7	0 .0	0 .0	1S14.4	1 45.2	1 41.7	3 54.5	1 27.1	1 2.0	0 25.0	0 40.2	14 23.3
7	9 8 30.3	0 .0	0 .0	4 19.6	1 28.2	2 5.9	3 50.7	1 27.9	1 2.2	0 25.1	0 40.2	14 24.6
10	9 20 20.0	0 .0	0 .0	4 54.5	1 5.1	2 31.2	3 46.5	1 28.6	1 2.3	0 25.2	0 40.2	14 25.9
13	9 32 9.7	0 .0	0 .0	2 44.6	0 35.7	2 57.5	3 42.1	1 29.4	1 2.5	0 25.2	0 40.2	14 27.2
16	9 43 59.3	0 .0	0 .0	0N34.4	0N .1	3 24.6	3 37.5	1 30.1	1 2.8	0 25.3	0 40.2	14 28.5
19	9 55 49.0	0 .0	0 .0	3 28.1	0 41.3	3 52.6	3 32.8	1 30.8	1 3.0	0 25.3	0 40.2	14 29.8
22	10 7 38.7	0 .0	0 .0	4 55.6	1 26.1	4 21.2	3 28.0	1 31.4	1 3.2	0 25.4	0 40.2	14 31.1
25	10 19 28.3	0 .0	0 .0	4 29.6	2 11.0	4 50.3	3 23.3	1 32.1	1 3.5	0 25.5	0 40.2	14 32.4
28	10 31 18.0	0 .0	0 .0	2 18.1	2 51.8	5 19.5	3 18.5	1 32.6	1 3.8	0 25.5	0 40.2	14 33.7

RIGHT ASCENSION

DAY	EPHEM. SID. TIME	☉	☊	☽	☿	♀	♂	♃	♄	♅	♆	♇
1	8 44 51.0	14♒36.5	17♐48.2	21♉ .9	21♒11.2	28♓13.0	11♋13.0	14♎ 4.4	22♒38.5	21♑ 9.7	21♑ 1.5	26♏24.4
2	8 48 47.6	15 37.6	17 44.8	4♊51.9	22 55.6	28 59.8	11R .8	14R 3.9	22 45.6	21 13.2	21 3.8	26 25.3
3	8 52 44.1	16 38.5	17 41.3	19 25.0	24 39.4	29 46.1	10 49.4	14 3.1	22 52.7	21 16.8	21 6.0	26 26.2
4	8 56 40.7	17 39.2	17 37.9	4♋26.3	26 22.8	0♈31.6	10 39.0	14 2.3	22 59.9	21 20.4	21 8.2	26 27.1
5	9 0 37.2	18 39.6	17 34.5	19 36.9	28 5.4	1 16.4	10 29.4	14 1.2	23 7.0	21 23.9	21 10.4	26 27.9
6	9 4 33.8	19 39.9	17 31.0	4♌38.7	29 47.2	2 .5	10 20.8	13 60.0	23 14.1	21 27.4	21 12.7	26 28.7
7	9 8 30.3	20 39.9	17 27.6	19 20.3	1♓28.1	2 43.8	10 13.0	13 58.6	23 21.2	21 30.9	21 14.8	26 29.5
8	9 12 26.9	21 39.8	17 24.1	3♍38.9	3 7.9	3 26.5	10 6.2	13 57.0	23 28.4	21 34.4	21 17.1	26 30.3
9	9 16 23.4	22 39.5	17 20.7	17 38.8	4 46.3	4 8.2	10 .2	13 55.3	23 35.5	21 37.8	21 19.2	26 31.0
10	9 20 20.0	23 38.9	17 17.3	1♎28.3	6 23.2	4 49.2	9 55.1	13 53.4	23 42.7	21 41.2	21 21.3	26 31.7
11	9 24 16.6	24 38.2	17 13.8	15 16.8	7 58.3	5 29.3	9 50.9	13 51.3	23 49.8	21 44.6	21 23.5	26 32.3
12	9 28 13.1	25 37.3	17 10.4	29 11.0	9 31.3	6 8.6	9 47.5	13 49.0	23 56.9	21 47.9	21 25.6	26 32.9
13	9 32 9.7	26 36.2	17 7.0	13♏13.5	11 1.8	6 47.0	9 45.0	13 46.6	24 4.0	21 51.3	21 27.7	26 33.5
14	9 36 6.2	27 34.9	17 3.5	27 21.2	12 29.6	7 24.4	9 43.3	13 44.0	24 11.2	21 54.6	21 29.7	26 34.0
15	9 40 2.8	28 33.5	17 .1	11♐25.9	13 54.1	8 .8	9 42.5	13 41.2	24 18.3	21 57.8	21 31.8	26 34.5
16	9 43 59.3	29 31.8	16 56.6	25 16.3	15 14.9	8 36.3	9D42.6	13 38.2	24 25.4	22 1.1	21 33.8	26 35.0
17	9 47 55.9	0♓30.0	16 53.2	8♑42.0	16 31.5	9 10.7	9 43.4	13 35.1	24 32.5	22 4.3	21 35.8	26 35.4
18	9 51 52.4	1 28.0	16 49.8	21 35.7	17 43.4	9 44.1	9 45.1	13 31.9	24 39.5	22 7.5	21 37.8	26 35.8
19	9 55 49.0	2 25.9	16 46.3	3♒55.1	18 50.1	10 16.3	9 47.6	13 28.4	24 46.6	22 10.6	21 39.7	26 36.2
20	9 59 45.5	3 23.5	16 42.9	15 42.5	19 51.0	10 47.4	9 50.9	13 24.8	24 53.7	22 13.7	21 41.7	26 36.5
21	10 3 42.1	4 21.1	16 39.5	27 3.8	20 45.6	11 17.2	9 54.9	13 21.1	25 .7	22 16.8	21 43.6	26 36.8
22	10 7 38.7	5 18.4	16 36.0	8♓ 6.9	21 33.3	11 45.8	9 59.7	13 17.2	25 7.7	22 19.9	21 45.5	26 37.1
23	10 11 35.2	6 15.6	16 32.6	19 1.2	22 13.7	12 13.1	10 5.3	13 13.1	25 14.7	22 22.9	21 47.4	26 37.3
24	10 15 31.8	7 12.7	16 29.2	29 56.8	22 46.3	12 39.0	10 11.7	13 8.9	25 21.7	22 25.9	21 49.2	26 37.5
25	10 19 28.3	8 9.5	16 25.7	11♈ 3.7	23 10.8	13 3.5	10 18.7	13 4.6	25 28.7	22 28.8	21 51.0	26 37.7
26	10 23 24.9	9 6.3	16 22.3	22 32.0	23 26.9	13 26.6	10 26.5	13 .1	25 35.7	22 31.7	21 52.8	26 37.8
27	10 27 21.4	10 2.9	16 18.9	4♉30.4	23 34.4	13 48.1	10 35.0	12 55.4	25 42.6	22 34.6	21 54.6	26 37.9
28	10 31 18.0	10 59.3	16 15.4	17 5.9	23R33.3	14 8.0	10 44.1	12 50.6	25 49.5	22 37.4	21 56.4	26 37.9

DECLINATION

DAY	EPHEM. SID. TIME	☉	☊	☽	☿	♀	♂	♃	♄	♅	♆	♇
1	8 44 51.0	17S 9.2	0S24.0	20N57.5	17S14.8	0N39.1	27N 1.1	4S27.5	15S49.5	22S26.1	21S21.4	5S 7.2
4	8 56 40.7	16 16.9	0 24.0	22 8.2	15 21.4	2 4.5	26 59.9	4 25.8	15 42.8	22 24.8	21 20.5	5 6.5
7	9 8 30.3	15 22.0	0 24.0	11 14.2	13 16.1	3 28.2	26 57.7	4 23.4	15 36.1	22 23.4	21 19.6	5 5.8
10	9 20 20.0	14 24.7	0 24.0	5S59.3	11 1.1	4 49.9	26 54.6	4 20.4	15 29.3	22 22.0	21 18.7	5 5.0
13	9 32 9.7	13 25.3	0 24.0	19 24.2	8 39.8	6 9.1	26 50.8	4 16.8	15 22.6	22 20.7	21 17.9	5 4.0
16	9 43 59.3	12 24.0	0 24.0	22 47.6	6 17.9	7 25.3	26 46.4	4 12.5	15 15.8	22 19.4	21 17.0	5 3.1
19	9 55 49.0	11 20.8	0 24.0	16 13.8	4 3.0	8 38.1	26 41.4	4 7.7	15 9.0	22 18.1	21 16.2	5 2.0
22	10 7 38.7	10 16.0	0 23.9	3 52.7	2 5.0	9 46.7	26 35.8	4 2.3	15 2.2	22 16.9	21 15.4	5 .9
25	10 19 28.3	9 9.8	0 23.9	9N38.2	0 34.2	10 50.6	26 29.8	3 56.3	14 55.5	22 15.7	21 14.6	4 59.7
28	10 31 18.0	8 2.3	0 23.9	20 .6	0N19.9	11 49.0	26 23.4	3 49.8	14 48.8	22 14.5	21 13.8	4 58.4

MARCH 1993

LONGITUDE

DAY	EPHEM. SID. TIME h m s	☉ ° ′	☊ ° ′	☽ ° ′	☿ ° ′	♀ ° ′	♂ ° ′	♃ ° ′	♄ ° ′	♅ ° ′	♆ ° ′	♇ ° ′
1	10 35 14.5	10♓25.3	17♐18.0	2♊41.2	24♓ 7.6	17♈58.4	9♋46.3	13♎13.0	23♒14.8	20♑54.2	20♑24.6	25♏31.2
2	10 39 11.1	11 25.5	17 14.8	15 30.1	23 R 52.9	18 20.1	9 55.9	13 R 7.4	23 21.8	20 56.8	20 26.2	25 R 31.0
3	10 43 7.6	12 25.7	17 11.7	28 43.1	23 29.2	18 39.9	10 6.1	13 1.8	23 28.7	20 59.3	20 27.8	25 30.9
4	10 47 4.2	13 25.8	17 8.5	12♋23.8	22 57.1	18 57.6	10 16.8	12 55.9	23 35.7	21 1.8	20 29.4	25 30.7
5	10 51 .7	14 26.0	17 5.3	26 34.2	22 17.4	19 13.4	10 28.1	12 50.0	23 42.6	21 4.3	20 30.9	25 30.5
6	10 54 57.3	15 26.0	17 2.1	11♌13.0	21 31.2	19 27.0	10 39.9	12 43.9	23 49.5	21 6.7	20 32.4	25 30.3
7	10 58 53.8	16 26.1	16 59.0	26 15.8	20 39.6	19 38.4	10 52.2	12 37.7	23 56.4	21 9.1	20 33.9	25 30.0
8	11 2 50.4	17 26.1	16 55.8	11♍34.0	19 43.9	19 47.6	11 5.1	12 31.4	24 3.3	21 11.5	20 35.3	25 29.7
9	11 6 47.0	18 26.0	16 52.6	26 56.6	18 45.5	19 54.5	11 18.5	12 25.0	24 10.1	21 13.8	20 36.7	25 29.3
10	11 10 43.5	19 26.0	16 49.4	12♎11.5	17 45.8	19 59.0	11 32.3	12 18.4	24 16.9	21 16.1	20 38.1	25 28.9
11	11 14 40.1	20 25.9	16 46.2	27 8.1	16 46.2	20 1.2	11 46.7	12 11.8	24 23.7	21 18.3	20 39.5	25 28.5
12	11 18 36.6	21 25.7	16 43.1	11♏39.1	15 47.8	20 R .9	12 1.5	12 5.0	24 30.4	21 20.5	20 40.8	25 28.0
13	11 22 33.2	22 25.6	16 39.9	25 40.6	14 52.1	19 58.2	12 16.8	11 58.2	24 37.1	21 22.7	20 42.1	25 27.6
14	11 26 29.7	23 25.4	16 36.7	9♐12.7	13 59.8	19 53.0	12 32.5	11 51.2	24 43.7	21 24.8	20 43.4	25 27.0
15	11 30 26.3	24 25.2	16 33.5	22 17.8	13 12.0	19 45.3	12 48.7	11 44.2	24 50.4	21 26.9	20 44.7	25 26.5
16	11 34 22.8	25 25.0	16 30.4	4♑59.7	12 29.3	19 35.2	13 5.3	11 37.1	24 57.0	21 28.9	20 45.9	25 25.9
17	11 38 19.4	26 24.7	16 27.2	17 23.3	11 52.2	19 22.5	13 22.3	11 29.9	25 3.5	21 30.9	20 47.1	25 25.3
18	11 42 15.9	27 24.4	16 24.0	29 33.2	11 21.0	19 7.4	13 39.8	11 22.6	25 10.0	21 32.8	20 48.3	25 24.6
19	11 46 12.5	28 24.1	16 20.8	11♒33.7	10 56.0	18 49.9	13 57.7	11 15.3	25 16.5	21 34.7	20 49.4	25 24.0
20	11 50 9.0	29 23.8	16 17.6	23 28.4	10 37.3	18 30.0	14 15.9	11 7.9	25 22.9	21 36.6	20 50.5	25 23.3
21	11 54 5.6	0♈23.4	16 14.5	5♓20.4	10 24.8	18 7.8	14 34.6	11 .4	25 29.3	21 38.4	20 51.6	25 22.5
22	11 58 2.1	1 23.0	16 11.3	17 11.8	10 18.4	17 43.5	14 53.7	10 52.9	25 35.7	21 40.2	20 52.7	25 21.8
23	12 1 58.7	2 22.6	16 8.1	29 4.4	10 18.0	17 16.9	15 13.1	10 45.4	25 42.0	21 41.9	20 53.7	25 21.0
24	12 5 55.2	3 22.1	16 4.9	10♈59.4	10 D 23.4	16 48.5	15 32.9	10 37.8	25 48.2	21 43.6	20 54.7	25 20.2
25	12 9 51.8	4 21.6	16 1.8	22 58.3	10 34.3	16 18.1	15 53.0	10 30.1	25 54.4	21 45.2	20 55.6	25 19.3
26	12 13 48.3	5 21.0	15 58.6	5♉ 2.4	10 50.5	15 46.1	16 13.5	10 22.4	26 .6	21 46.8	20 56.6	25 18.4
27	12 17 44.9	6 20.5	15 55.4	17 13.7	11 11.7	15 12.6	16 34.3	10 14.7	26 6.7	21 48.3	20 57.4	25 17.5
28	12 21 41.4	7 19.8	15 52.2	29 34.7	11 37.7	14 37.8	16 55.5	10 7.0	26 12.8	21 49.8	20 58.3	25 16.5
29	12 25 38.0	8 19.2	15 49.0	12♊ 8.3	12 8.3	14 1.9	17 16.9	9 59.3	26 18.8	21 51.2	20 59.1	25 15.6
30	12 29 34.6	9 18.5	15 45.9	24 58.1	12 43.1	13 25.1	17 38.8	9 51.5	26 24.7	21 52.6	20 59.9	25 14.6
31	12 33 31.1	10 17.7	15 42.7	8♋ 8.0	13 21.9	12 47.7	18 .9	9 43.8	26 30.6	21 54.0	21 .7	25 13.5

LATITUDE

DAY	SID. TIME	☉	☊	☽	☿	♀	♂	♃	♄	♅	♆	♇
1	10 35 14.5	0 .0	0 .0	1N16.6	3N 3.5	5N29.3	3N16.9	1N32.8	1S 3.9	0S25.5	0N40.2	14N34.1
4	10 47 4.2	0 .0	0 .0	2S 8.3	3 30.1	5 58.3	3 12.1	1 33.4	1 4.1	0 25.6	0 40.3	14 35.4
7	10 58 53.8	0 .0	0 .0	4 40.9	3 40.4	6 26.6	3 7.4	1 33.9	1 4.4	0 25.7	0 40.3	14 36.6
10	11 10 43.5	0 .0	0 .0	4 30.6	3 32.1	6 53.6	3 2.8	1 34.3	1 4.8	0 25.8	0 40.3	14 37.8
13	11 22 33.2	0 .0	0 .0	1 45.7	3 6.9	7 18.3	2 58.3	1 34.7	1 5.1	0 25.8	0 40.3	14 39.0
16	11 34 22.8	0 .0	0 .0	1N38.2	2 29.6	7 39.9	2 53.8	1 35.0	1 5.4	0 25.9	0 40.4	14 40.2
19	11 46 12.5	0 .0	0 .0	4 8.9	1 45.9	7 57.2	2 49.5	1 35.3	1 5.8	0 26.0	0 40.4	14 41.3
22	11 58 2.1	0 .0	0 .0	5 .2	1 .8	8 8.9	2 45.2	1 35.5	1 6.2	0 26.1	0 40.4	14 42.4
25	12 9 51.8	0 .0	0 .0	3 56.9	0 17.6	8 14.0	2 41.0	1 35.7	1 6.5	0 26.2	0 40.5	14 43.4
28	12 21 41.4	0 .0	0 .0	1 17.7	0S21.9	8 11.4	2 36.9	1 35.8	1 6.9	0 26.3	0 40.5	14 44.4
31	12 33 31.1	0 .0	0 .0	2S 3.3	0 56.7	8 .7	2 33.0	1 35.8	1 7.3	0 26.4	0 40.5	14 45.3

RIGHT ASCENSION

DAY	SID. TIME	☉	☊	☽	☿	♀	♂	♃	♄	♅	♆	♇
1	10 35 14.5	11♓55.7	16♐12.0	0♊21.4	23♓23.9	14♈26.2	10♋54.0	12♎45.8	25♒56.5	22♑40.3	21♑58.1	26♏38.0
2	10 39 11.1	12 51.9	16 8.6	14 14.4	23 R 6.3	14 42.8	11 4.5	12 R 40.7	26 3.4	22 43.0	21 59.8	26 38.0
3	10 43 7.6	13 48.0	16 5.1	28 36.8	22 41.0	14 57.5	11 15.7	12 35.5	26 10.2	22 45.8	22 1.5	26 38.0
4	10 47 4.2	14 43.9	16 1.7	13♋15.7	22 8.7	15 10.4	11 27.4	12 30.2	26 17.0	22 48.5	22 3.1	26 R 37.9
5	10 51 .7	15 39.7	15 58.3	27 57.4	21 30.1	15 21.5	11 39.8	12 24.8	26 23.8	22 51.1	22 4.8	26 37.8
6	10 54 57.3	16 35.4	15 54.8	12♌31.6	20 46.4	15 30.5	11 52.8	12 19.3	26 30.6	22 53.7	22 6.3	26 37.6
7	10 58 53.8	17 31.0	15 51.4	26 53.9	19 58.5	15 37.6	12 6.3	12 13.6	26 37.3	22 56.3	22 7.9	26 37.5
8	11 2 50.4	18 26.5	15 48.0	11♍ 6.2	19 7.6	15 42.6	12 20.4	12 7.8	26 44.0	22 58.8	22 9.4	26 37.2
9	11 6 47.0	19 21.9	15 44.6	25 14.4	18 15.1	15 45.6	12 35.1	12 2.0	26 50.7	23 1.2	22 10.9	26 37.0
10	11 10 43.5	20 17.2	15 41.1	9♎26.0	17 22.0	15 46.4	12 50.3	11 56.0	26 57.4	23 3.7	22 12.4	26 36.7
11	11 14 40.1	21 12.5	15 37.7	23 46.6	16 29.7	15 R 45.0	13 6.0	11 49.9	27 4.0	23 6.1	22 13.9	26 36.4
12	11 18 36.6	22 7.6	15 34.3	8♏17.5	15 39.3	15 41.5	13 22.2	11 43.7	27 10.6	23 8.4	22 15.3	26 36.1
13	11 22 33.2	23 2.7	15 30.8	22 53.9	14 51.7	15 35.7	13 39.0	11 37.5	27 17.1	23 10.7	22 16.7	26 35.7
14	11 26 29.7	23 57.7	15 27.4	7♐25.3	14 7.8	15 27.8	13 56.2	11 31.1	27 23.6	23 13.0	22 18.0	26 35.3
15	11 30 26.3	24 52.7	15 24.0	21 38.8	13 28.4	15 17.7	14 13.9	11 24.7	27 30.1	23 15.2	22 19.4	26 34.9
16	11 34 22.8	25 47.6	15 20.5	5♑22.5	12 54.0	15 5.4	14 32.0	11 18.1	27 36.6	23 17.4	22 20.7	26 34.4
17	11 38 19.4	26 42.4	15 17.1	18 29.3	12 25.0	14 50.9	14 50.6	11 11.5	27 43.0	23 19.5	22 21.9	26 33.9
18	11 42 15.9	27 37.3	15 13.7	0♒57.5	12 1.6	14 34.3	15 9.7	11 4.9	27 49.3	23 21.6	22 23.2	26 33.4
19	11 46 12.5	28 32.0	15 10.3	12 50.5	11 44.0	14 15.7	15 29.2	10 58.1	27 55.7	23 23.6	22 24.4	26 32.8
20	11 50 9.0	29 26.8	15 6.8	24 15.4	11 32.3	13 55.1	15 49.1	10 51.4	28 1.9	23 25.6	22 25.5	26 32.3
21	11 54 5.6	0♈21.5	15 3.4	5♓20.8	11 26.4	13 32.6	16 9.4	10 44.5	28 8.2	23 27.5	22 26.7	26 31.6
22	11 58 2.1	1 16.2	14 60.0	16 16.6	11 26.1	13 8.4	16 30.2	10 37.7	28 14.4	23 29.4	22 27.8	26 31.0
23	12 1 58.7	2 10.8	14 56.6	27 12.8	11 D 31.3	12 42.5	16 51.4	10 30.7	28 20.6	23 31.3	22 28.9	26 30.4
24	12 5 55.2	3 5.5	14 53.1	8♈19.3	11 41.8	12 15.0	17 12.9	10 23.7	28 26.7	23 33.1	22 29.9	26 29.6
25	12 9 51.8	4 .1	14 49.7	19 45.2	11 57.4	11 46.2	17 34.8	10 16.7	28 32.7	23 34.8	22 31.0	26 28.9
26	12 13 48.3	4 54.7	14 46.3	1♉38.4	12 17.7	11 16.2	17 57.0	10 9.7	28 38.7	23 36.5	22 31.9	26 28.1
27	12 17 44.9	5 49.3	14 42.8	14 4.4	12 42.6	10 45.2	18 19.6	10 2.6	28 44.7	23 38.1	22 32.9	26 27.3
28	12 21 41.4	6 43.9	14 39.4	27 4.9	13 11.7	10 13.3	18 42.6	9 55.5	28 50.6	23 39.7	22 33.8	26 26.5
29	12 25 38.0	7 38.5	14 36.0	10♊37.1	13 44.8	9 40.9	19 5.9	9 48.4	28 56.5	23 41.2	22 34.7	26 25.7
30	12 29 34.6	8 33.1	14 32.6	24 33.5	14 21.7	9 8.1	19 29.5	9 41.3	29 2.3	23 42.7	22 35.5	26 24.8
31	12 33 31.1	9 27.7	14 29.1	8♋43.1	15 2.2	8 35.1	19 53.4	9 34.1	29 8.0	23 44.2	22 36.3	26 23.9

DECLINATION

DAY	SID. TIME	☉	☊	☽	☿	♀	♂	♃	♄	♅	♆	♇
1	10 35 14.5	7S39.6	0S23.9	21N56.9	0N28.6	12N 7.1	26N21.1	3S47.5	14S46.5	22S14.1	21S13.5	4S58.0
4	10 47 4.2	6 30.8	0 23.9	20 43.9	0 25.2	12 56.7	26 14.0	3 40.4	14 39.9	22 13.0	21 12.8	4 56.7
7	10 58 53.8	5 21.2	0 23.9	8 21.3	0S19.4	13 38.4	26 6.5	3 32.9	14 33.3	22 12.0	21 12.1	4 55.3
10	11 10 43.5	4 11.0	0 23.9	8S58.1	1 34.8	14 11.2	25 58.4	3 25.0	14 26.8	22 11.0	21 11.5	4 53.9
13	11 22 33.2	3 .3	0 23.8	20 53.3	3 5.1	14 33.7	25 49.8	3 16.7	14 20.3	22 10.0	21 10.8	4 52.4
16	11 34 22.8	1 49.3	0 23.8	21 42.6	4 34.2	14 44.7	25 40.7	3 8.2	14 14.0	22 9.1	21 10.2	4 50.9
19	11 46 12.5	0 38.1	0 23.8	13 19.5	5 49.9	14 43.2	25 31.0	2 59.4	14 7.7	22 8.3	21 9.7	4 49.4
22	11 58 2.1	0N33.0	0 23.8	0 26.8	6 45.9	14 28.4	25 20.6	2 50.5	14 1.6	22 7.5	21 9.1	4 47.9
25	12 9 51.8	1 44.0	0 23.8	12N35.6	7 19.9	13 59.9	25 9.6	2 41.4	13 55.6	22 6.8	21 8.6	4 46.3
28	12 21 41.4	2 54.6	0 23.8	21 19.5	7 32.4	13 18.3	24 57.8	2 32.3	13 49.8	22 6.1	21 8.2	4 44.8
31	12 33 31.1	4 4.6	0 23.7	21 8.3	7 24.7	12 25.3	24 45.2	2 23.1	13 44.1	22 5.5	21 7.8	4 43.2

APRIL 1993

LONGITUDE

DAY	EPHEM. SID. TIME h m s	☉ ° ′	☊ ° ′	☽ ° ′	☿ ° ′	♀ ° ′	♂ ° ′	♃ ° ′	♄ ° ′	♅ ° ′	♆ ° ′	♇ ° ′
1	12 37 27.7	11♈17.0	15♐39.5	21♋41.0	14♓ 4.5	12♈10.0	18♋23.3	9♎36.1	26♒36.5	21♑55.3	21♑ 1.4	25♏12.5
2	12 41 24.2	12 16.2	15 36.3	5♌39.6	14 50.8	11 R 32.1	18 46.0	9 R 28.3	26 42.3	21 56.5	21 2.1	25 R 11.4
3	12 45 20.8	13 15.3	15 33.2	20 3.8	15 40.5	10 54.4	19 9.0	9 20.6	26 48.0	21 57.7	21 2.8	25 10.3
4	12 49 17.3	14 14.4	15 30.0	4♍50.9	16 33.3	10 17.0	19 32.3	9 12.9	26 53.7	21 58.8	21 3.4	25 9.1
5	12 53 13.9	15 13.5	15 26.8	19 55.0	17 29.3	9 40.3	19 55.8	9 5.2	26 59.3	21 59.9	21 4.0	25 8.0
6	12 57 10.4	16 12.5	15 23.6	5♎ 7.3	18 28.1	9 4.4	20 19.6	8 57.6	27 4.9	22 1.0	21 4.6	25 6.8
7	13 1 7.0	17 11.5	15 20.4	20 17.0	19 29.7	8 29.7	20 43.7	8 50.0	27 10.4	22 2.0	21 5.1	25 5.6
8	13 5 3.5	18 10.5	15 17.3	5♏13.9	20 33.9	7 56.3	21 8.0	8 42.4	27 15.8	22 2.9	21 5.6	25 4.4
9	13 9 .1	19 9.4	15 14.1	19 49.5	21 40.6	7 24.4	21 32.6	8 34.9	27 21.2	22 3.8	21 6.1	25 3.1
10	13 12 56.6	20 8.3	15 10.9	3♐58.5	22 49.7	6 54.3	21 57.4	8 27.4	27 26.5	22 4.7	21 6.5	25 1.9
11	13 16 53.2	21 7.2	15 7.7	17 38.8	24 1.2	6 26.0	22 22.4	8 20.0	27 31.8	22 5.5	21 6.9	25 .6
12	13 20 49.7	22 6.1	15 4.5	0♑51.5	25 14.9	5 59.8	22 47.7	8 12.7	27 37.0	22 6.3	21 7.4	24 59.3
13	13 24 46.3	23 4.9	15 1.4	13 39.3	26 30.7	5 35.6	23 13.2	8 5.4	27 42.1	22 7.0	21 7.7	24 58.0
14	13 28 42.8	24 3.7	14 58.2	26 6.5	27 48.6	5 13.7	23 39.0	7 58.2	27 47.2	22 7.6	21 8.0	24 56.6
15	13 32 39.4	25 2.5	14 55.0	8♒17.9	29 8.4	4 54.2	24 4.9	7 51.0	27 52.2	22 8.2	21 8.3	24 55.2
16	13 36 36.0	26 1.2	14 51.8	20 18.1	0♈30.3	4 37.0	24 31.1	7 43.9	27 57.1	22 8.8	21 8.5	24 53.8
17	13 40 32.5	26 59.9	14 48.7	2♓11.8	1 54.0	4 22.2	24 57.5	7 36.9	28 1.9	22 9.3	21 8.7	24 52.4
18	13 44 29.1	27 58.6	14 45.5	14 2.8	3 19.7	4 9.8	25 24.1	7 30.0	28 6.7	22 9.7	21 8.9	24 51.0
19	13 48 25.6	28 57.2	14 42.3	25 54.5	4 47.1	3 59.9	25 50.8	7 23.2	28 11.4	22 10.1	21 9.0	24 49.5
20	13 52 22.2	29 55.8	14 39.1	7♈49.6	6 16.4	3 52.4	26 17.8	7 16.5	28 16.1	22 10.4	21 9.1	24 48.1
21	13 56 18.7	0♉54.4	14 35.9	19 50.0	7 47.5	3 47.4	26 45.0	7 9.9	28 20.6	22 10.7	21 9.2	24 46.6
22	14 0 15.3	1 53.0	14 32.8	1♉57.3	9 20.3	3 44.8	27 12.4	7 3.4	28 25.1	22 11.0	21 9.3	24 45.1
23	14 4 11.8	2 51.5	14 29.6	14 12.9	10 54.9	3 44.6	27 40.0	6 57.0	28 29.5	22 11.2	21 9.3	24 43.6
24	14 8 8.4	3 50.0	14 26.4	26 37.7	12 31.2	3 D 46.7	28 7.7	6 50.8	28 33.9	22 11.3	21 R 9.2	24 42.1
25	14 12 4.9	4 48.4	14 23.2	9♊13.2	14 9.3	3 51.2	28 35.7	6 44.6	28 38.1	22 11.4	21 9.2	24 40.5
26	14 16 1.5	5 46.9	14 20.1	22 .7	15 49.1	3 57.8	29 3.8	6 38.6	28 42.3	22 11.4	21 9.1	24 39.0
27	14 19 58.0	6 45.2	14 16.9	5♋ 2.2	17 30.7	4 6.7	29 32.1	6 32.7	28 46.4	22 11.4	21 9.0	24 37.4
28	14 23 54.6	7 43.6	14 13.7	18 19.4	19 14.0	4 17.7	0♌ .6	6 26.9	28 50.5	22 11.4	21 8.8	24 35.8
29	14 27 51.2	8 41.9	14 10.5	1♌54.1	20 59.0	4 30.7	0 29.2	6 21.3	28 54.4	22 R 11.2	21 8.6	24 34.2
30	14 31 47.7	9 40.2	14 7.4	15 47.5	22 45.8	4 45.8	0 58.0	6 15.8	28 58.3	22 11.1	21 8.4	24 32.6

LATITUDE

DAY	EPHEM. SID. TIME	☉	☊	☽	☿	♀	♂	♃	♄	♅	♆	♇
1	12 37 27.7	0 .0	0 .0	3S 5.3	1S 7.2	7N55.3	2N31.7	1N35.8	1S 7.5	0S26.4	0N40.6	14N45.6
4	12 49 17.3	0 .0	0 .0	5 .4	1 35.3	7 33.9	2 27.8	1 35.8	1 7.9	0 26.5	0 40.6	14 46.5
7	13 1 7.0	0 .0	0 .0	4 5.0	1 58.2	7 5.5	2 24.1	1 35.7	1 8.4	0 26.6	0 40.6	14 47.3
10	13 12 56.6	0 .0	0 .0	0 50.7	2 16.0	6 31.3	2 20.4	1 35.5	1 8.8	0 26.7	0 40.7	14 48.0
13	13 24 46.3	0 .0	0 .0	2N35.1	2 28.8	5 53.0	2 16.8	1 35.3	1 9.3	0 26.7	0 40.7	14 48.7
16	13 36 36.0	0 .0	0 .0	4 43.2	2 36.6	5 12.2	2 13.3	1 35.1	1 9.8	0 26.8	0 40.8	14 49.3
19	13 48 25.6	0 .0	0 .0	5 .1	2 39.6	4 30.4	2 9.9	1 34.7	1 10.2	0 26.9	0 40.8	14 49.8
22	14 0 15.3	0 .0	0 .0	3 22.0	2 37.7	3 48.8	2 6.6	1 34.3	1 10.7	0 27.0	0 40.8	14 50.3
25	14 12 4.9	0 .0	0 .0	0 18.1	2 31.0	3 8.4	2 3.3	1 33.9	1 11.3	0 27.1	0 40.9	14 50.7
28	14 23 54.6	0 .0	0 .0	3S 2.6	2 19.7	2 29.7	2 .1	1 33.4	1 11.8	0 27.2	0 40.9	14 51.0

RIGHT ASCENSION

DAY	EPHEM. SID. TIME	☉	☊	☽	☿	♀	♂	♃	♄	♅	♆	♇
1	12 37 27.7	10♈22.4	14♐25.7	22♋55.0	15♓45.9	8♈ 2.2	20♋17.6	9♎27.0	29♒13.8	23♑45.5	22♑37.1	26♏23.0
2	12 41 24.2	11 17.0	14 22.3	7♌ 1.2	16 32.8	7 R 29.5	20 42.1	9 R 19.9	29 19.4	23 46.9	22 37.8	26 R 22.0
3	12 45 20.8	12 11.7	14 18.9	20 59.2	17 22.5	6 57.4	21 6.9	9 12.8	29 25.0	23 48.1	22 38.5	26 21.0
4	12 49 17.3	13 6.5	14 15.5	4♍51.6	18 15.0	6 26.0	21 32.0	9 5.7	29 30.5	23 49.4	22 39.2	26 20.0
5	12 53 13.9	14 1.2	14 12.0	18 45.4	19 10.1	5 55.6	21 57.3	8 58.6	29 36.0	23 50.5	22 39.8	26 19.0
6	12 57 10.4	14 56.0	14 8.6	2♎48.9	20 7.5	5 26.3	22 23.0	8 51.6	29 41.4	23 51.7	22 40.4	26 17.9
7	13 1 7.0	15 50.9	14 5.2	17 9.7	21 7.2	4 58.4	22 48.8	8 44.6	29 46.8	23 52.7	22 41.0	26 16.9
8	13 5 3.5	16 45.8	14 1.8	1♏50.5	22 9.1	4 31.9	23 14.9	8 37.6	29 52.1	23 53.7	22 41.5	26 15.8
9	13 9 .1	17 40.7	13 58.3	16 47.4	23 13.0	4 7.1	23 41.2	8 30.6	29 57.4	23 54.7	22 42.0	26 14.6
10	13 12 56.6	18 35.7	13 54.9	1♐48.5	24 18.8	3 44.2	24 7.8	8 23.8	0♓ 2.5	23 55.6	22 42.5	26 13.5
11	13 16 53.2	19 30.8	13 51.5	16 36.8	25 26.5	3 23.1	24 34.6	8 16.9	0 7.7	23 56.5	22 42.9	26 12.3
12	13 20 49.7	20 26.1	13 48.1	0♑55.5	26 36.0	3 4.1	25 1.6	8 10.2	0 12.8	23 57.3	22 43.3	26 11.2
13	13 24 46.3	21 21.3	13 44.7	14 33.1	27 47.1	2 47.2	25 28.9	8 3.4	0 17.8	23 58.1	22 43.7	26 10.0
14	13 28 42.8	22 16.7	13 41.2	27 25.6	28 59.9	2 32.5	25 56.3	7 56.7	0 22.7	23 58.8	22 44.0	26 8.7
15	13 32 39.4	23 12.1	13 37.8	9♒35.8	0♈14.2	2 20.0	26 23.9	7 50.1	0 27.6	23 59.4	22 44.3	26 7.5
16	13 36 36.0	24 7.6	13 34.4	21 11.3	1 30.1	2 9.7	26 51.7	7 43.6	0 32.4	24 .0	22 44.6	26 6.2
17	13 40 32.5	25 3.2	13 31.0	2♓22.3	2 47.5	2 1.6	27 19.7	7 37.1	0 37.1	24 .5	22 44.8	26 4.9
18	13 44 29.1	25 58.9	13 27.6	13 19.9	4 6.4	1 55.9	27 47.9	7 30.7	0 41.8	24 1.0	22 45.0	26 3.6
19	13 48 25.6	26 54.7	13 24.1	24 15.5	5 26.8	1 52.4	28 16.3	7 24.4	0 46.4	24 1.4	22 45.1	26 2.3
20	13 52 22.2	27 50.6	13 20.7	5♈20.1	6 48.7	1 51.1	28 44.9	7 18.2	0 50.9	24 1.8	22 45.2	26 .9
21	13 56 18.7	28 46.7	13 17.3	16 43.6	8 12.0	1 D 52.1	29 13.6	7 12.1	0 55.3	24 2.1	22 45.3	25 59.6
22	14 0 15.3	29 42.8	13 13.9	28 34.7	9 36.8	1 55.2	29 42.5	7 6.1	0 59.7	24 2.4	22 45.3	25 58.2
23	14 4 11.8	0♉39.0	13 10.5	10♉59.1	11 3.1	2 .4	0♌11.5	7 .2	1 4.0	24 2.6	22 45.3	25 56.8
24	14 8 8.4	1 35.4	13 7.0	23 58.3	12 30.9	2 7.8	0 40.7	6 54.3	1 8.3	24 2.7	22 45.3	25 55.4
25	14 12 4.9	2 31.9	13 3.6	7♊28.8	14 .3	2 17.2	1 10.0	6 48.6	1 12.4	24 2.8	22 R 45.2	25 54.0
26	14 16 1.5	3 28.5	13 .2	21 21.6	15 31.3	2 28.5	1 39.5	6 43.0	1 16.5	24 2.9	22 45.1	25 52.5
27	14 19 58.0	4 25.2	12 56.8	5♋24.3	17 3.8	2 41.8	2 9.2	6 37.5	1 20.5	24 2.9	22 45.0	25 51.1
28	14 23 54.6	5 22.0	12 53.4	19 24.7	18 38.1	2 57.0	2 38.9	6 32.2	1 24.5	24 R 2.8	22 44.8	25 49.6
29	14 27 51.2	6 19.0	12 50.0	3♌14.3	20 14.1	3 13.9	3 8.8	6 26.9	1 28.3	24 2.7	22 44.6	25 48.1
30	14 31 47.7	7 16.0	12 46.5	16 50.7	21 51.8	3 32.6	3 38.8	6 21.8	1 32.1	24 2.5	22 44.4	25 46.6

DECLINATION

DAY	EPHEM. SID. TIME	☉	☊	☽	☿	♀	♂	♃	♄	♅	♆	♇
1	12 37 27.7	4N27.8	0S23.7	18N38.6	7S18.0	12N 5.5	24N40.9	2S20.1	13S42.2	22S 5.4	21S 7.7	4S42.7
4	12 49 17.3	5 36.9	0 23.7	5 4.1	6 46.2	11 1.3	24 27.3	2 11.1	13 36.7	22 4.9	21 7.3	4 41.1
7	13 1 7.0	6 45.1	0 23.7	11S42.3	5 58.2	9 52.8	24 12.8	2 2.1	13 31.4	22 4.5	21 7.0	4 39.6
10	13 12 56.6	7 52.3	0 23.7	21 46.4	4 55.7	8 43.6	23 57.5	1 53.4	13 26.3	22 4.1	21 6.8	4 38.0
13	13 24 46.3	8 58.3	0 23.7	20 10.0	3 39.7	7 37.2	23 41.4	1 44.9	13 21.3	22 3.8	21 6.6	4 36.5
16	13 36 36.0	10 3.0	0 23.6	10 14.2	2 11.6	6 36.5	23 24.3	1 36.7	13 16.6	22 3.6	21 6.4	4 35.0
19	13 48 25.6	11 6.2	0 23.6	2N57.9	0 32.4	5 43.5	23 6.2	1 28.9	13 12.1	22 3.5	21 6.3	4 33.5
22	14 0 15.0	12 7.7	0 23.6	15 18.6	1N17.0	4 59.3	22 47.2	1 21.4	13 7.8	22 3.5	21 6.2	4 32.1
25	14 12 4.9	13 7.4	0 23.6	22 7.9	3 15.6	4 24.7	22 27.3	1 14.4	13 3.7	22 3.5	21 6.2	4 30.7
28	14 23 54.6	14 5.2	0 23.6	19 10.2	5 22.4	3 59.8	22 6.3	1 7.8	12 59.9	22 3.6	21 6.2	4 29.4

MAY 1993

LONGITUDE

DAY	EPHEM. SID. TIME	☉	☊	☽	☿	♀	♂	♃	♄	♅	♆	♇
	h m s	° ′	° ′	° ′	° ′	° ′	° ′	° ′	° ′	° ′	° ′	° ′
1	14 35 44.3	10♉38.4	14♐ 4.2	29♌59.5	24♈34.4	5♈ 2.9	1♌26.9	6♎10.4	29♒ 2.1	22♑10.9	21♑ 8.1	24♏31.0
2	14 39 40.8	11 36.7	14 1.0	14♍28.3	26 24.7	5 21.8	1 56.0	6R 5.2	29 5.8	22R10.6	21R 7.9	24R29.4
3	14 43 37.4	12 34.9	13 57.8	29 10.2	28 16.9	5 42.6	2 25.3	6 .2	29 9.4	22 10.3	21 7.6	24 27.9
4	14 47 33.9	13 33.0	13 54.6	13♎59.0	0♉10.8	6 5.2	2 54.7	5 55.3	29 13.0	22 10.0	21 7.2	24 26.2
5	14 51 30.5	14 31.2	13 51.5	28 47.4	2 6.5	6 29.4	3 24.2	5 50.5	29 16.4	22 9.6	21 6.9	24 24.6
6	14 55 27.0	15 29.2	13 48.3	13♏27.5	4 3.9	6 55.4	3 53.9	5 45.9	29 19.8	22 9.1	21 6.4	24 22.9
7	14 59 23.6	16 27.3	13 45.1	27 52.3	6 3.0	7 22.9	4 23.7	5 41.4	29 23.1	22 8.6	21 6.0	24 21.3
8	15 3 20.1	17 25.3	13 41.9	11♐56.4	8 3.8	7 52.0	4 53.7	5 37.1	29 26.3	22 8.0	21 5.5	24 19.6
9	15 7 16.7	18 23.3	13 38.8	25 36.6	10 6.3	8 22.6	5 23.7	5 33.0	29 29.4	22 7.4	21 5.0	24 18.0
10	15 11 13.3	19 21.3	13 35.6	8♑52.3	12 10.3	8 54.6	5 53.9	5 29.0	29 32.4	22 6.8	21 4.5	24 16.3
11	15 15 9.8	20 19.3	13 32.4	21 44.6	14 15.8	9 27.9	6 24.3	5 25.2	29 35.3	22 6.1	21 3.9	24 14.6
12	15 19 6.4	21 17.2	13 29.2	4♒16.4	16 22.7	10 2.6	6 54.8	5 21.5	29 38.2	22 5.3	21 3.3	24 13.0
13	15 23 2.9	22 15.2	13 26.0	16 31.5	18 30.8	10 38.6	7 25.4	5 18.1	29 40.9	22 4.5	21 2.7	24 11.3
14	15 26 59.5	23 13.1	13 22.9	28 34.5	20 40.0	11 15.8	7 56.1	5 14.7	29 43.6	22 3.7	21 2.1	24 9.6
15	15 30 56.0	24 10.9	13 19.7	10♓29.8	22 50.0	11 54.2	8 26.9	5 11.6	29 46.2	22 2.8	21 1.4	24 8.0
16	15 34 52.6	25 8.8	13 16.5	22 22.0	25 .7	12 33.6	8 57.9	5 8.6	29 48.6	22 1.9	21 .7	24 6.3
17	15 38 49.1	26 6.6	13 13.3	4♈15.4	27 11.9	13 14.2	9 29.0	5 5.8	29 51.0	22 .9	20 59.9	24 4.6
18	15 42 45.7	27 4.4	13 10.2	16 13.6	29 23.2	13 55.8	10 .2	5 3.2	29 53.3	21 59.9	20 59.2	24 2.9
19	15 46 42.3	28 2.2	13 7.0	28 19.7	1♊34.4	14 38.4	10 31.5	5 .8	29 55.5	21 58.8	20 58.4	24 1.3
20	15 50 38.8	29 .0	13 3.8	10♉36.2	3 45.3	15 21.9	11 3.0	4 58.5	29 57.6	21 57.7	20 57.5	23 59.6
21	15 54 35.4	29 57.8	13 .6	23 4.8	5 55.5	16 6.4	11 34.5	4 56.4	29 59.6	21 56.6	20 56.7	23 57.9
22	15 58 31.9	0♊55.5	12 57.5	5♊46.5	8 4.7	16 51.7	12 6.2	4 54.5	0♓ 1.6	21 55.4	20 55.8	23 56.3
23	16 2 28.5	1 53.2	12 54.3	18 41.9	10 12.8	17 37.9	12 38.0	4 52.8	0 3.4	21 54.1	20 54.9	23 54.6
24	16 6 25.0	2 50.9	12 51.1	1♋51.0	12 19.4	18 24.9	13 9.9	4 51.3	0 5.2	21 52.9	20 54.0	23 53.0
25	16 10 21.6	3 48.6	12 47.9	15 13.6	14 24.4	19 12.7	13 41.9	4 49.9	0 6.8	21 51.6	20 53.1	23 51.4
26	16 14 18.2	4 46.2	12 44.7	28 49.2	16 27.4	20 1.2	14 14.0	4 48.7	0 8.3	21 50.2	20 52.1	23 49.7
27	16 18 14.7	5 43.9	12 41.6	12♌37.0	18 28.4	20 50.4	14 46.2	4 47.7	0 9.8	21 48.8	20 51.1	23 48.1
28	16 22 11.3	6 41.4	12 38.4	26 36.1	20 27.1	21 40.3	15 18.5	4 46.9	0 11.1	21 47.4	20 50.1	23 46.5
29	16 26 7.8	7 39.0	12 35.2	10♍45.0	22 23.5	22 30.9	15 50.9	4 46.2	0 12.3	21 45.9	20 49.0	23 44.9
30	16 30 4.4	8 36.6	12 32.0	25 1.8	24 17.4	23 22.1	16 23.4	4 45.8	0 13.5	21 44.4	20 47.9	23 43.3
31	16 34 .9	9 34.1	12 28.9	9♎23.5	26 8.8	24 13.9	16 56.0	4 45.5	0 14.5	21 42.8	20 46.8	23 41.7

LATITUDE

DAY	EPHEM. SID. TIME	☉	☊	☽	☿	♀	♂	♃	♄	♅	♆	♇
1	14 35 44.3	0 .0	0 .0	5S 4.8	2S 3.7	1N53.1	1N57.0	1N32.9	1S12.3	0S27.3	0N40.9	14N51.2
4	14 47 33.9	0 .0	0 .0	4 26.5	1 43.4	1 19.0	1 54.0	1 32.4	1 12.9	0 27.4	0 41.0	14 51.3
7	14 59 23.6	0 .0	0 .0	1 18.2	1 18.9	0 47.4	1 51.0	1 31.8	1 13.4	0 27.5	0 41.0	14 51.4
10	15 11 13.3	0 .0	0 .0	2N21.2	0 51.0	0 18.3	1 48.1	1 31.1	1 14.0	0 27.6	0 41.0	14 51.4
13	15 23 2.9	0 .0	0 .0	4 43.8	0 20.6	0S 8.3	1 45.2	1 30.5	1 14.6	0 27.7	0 41.1	14 51.3
16	15 34 52.6	0 .0	0 .0	5 10.4	0N10.9	0 32.4	1 42.4	1 29.8	1 15.1	0 27.7	0 41.1	14 51.1
19	15 46 42.3	0 .0	0 .0	3 39.0	0 41.9	0 54.3	1 39.6	1 29.1	1 15.7	0 27.8	0 41.1	14 50.9
22	15 58 31.9	0 .0	0 .0	0 35.2	1 10.3	1 13.9	1 36.9	1 28.4	1 16.3	0 27.9	0 41.1	14 50.5
25	16 10 21.6	0 .0	0 .0	2S53.1	1 34.3	1 31.4	1 34.2	1 27.6	1 16.9	0 28.0	0 41.2	14 50.1
28	16 22 11.3	0 .0	0 .0	5 5.3	1 52.5	1 46.8	1 31.5	1 26.9	1 17.5	0 28.1	0 41.2	14 49.6
31	16 34 .9	0 .0	0 .0	4 42.0	2 4.2	2 .3	1 28.9	1 26.1	1 18.2	0 28.1	0 41.2	14 49.0

RIGHT ASCENSION

DAY	EPHEM. SID. TIME	☉	☊	☽	☿	♀	♂	♃	♄	♅	♆	♇
1	14 35 44.3	8♉13.3	12♐43.1	0♍17.1	23♈31.4	3♈53.0	4♌ 9.0	6♎16.8	1♓35.8	24♑ 2.3	22♑44.1	25♏45.1
2	14 39 40.8	9 10.6	12 39.7	13 41.7	25 12.8	4 15.1	4 39.2	6R12.0	1 39.4	24R 2.0	22R43.8	25R43.6
3	14 43 37.4	10 8.1	12 36.3	27 15.0	26 56.3	4 38.8	5 9.6	6 7.3	1 43.0	24 1.8	22 43.5	25 42.2
4	14 47 33.9	11 5.7	12 32.9	11♎ 7.4	28 41.8	5 3.9	5 40.1	6 2.7	1 46.5	24 1.4	22 43.2	25 40.6
5	14 51 30.5	12 3.4	12 29.5	25 26.2	0♉29.3	5 30.5	6 10.6	5 58.3	1 49.9	24 .9	22 42.8	25 39.1
6	14 55 27.0	13 1.3	12 26.1	10♏12.3	2 19.0	5 58.6	6 41.3	5 53.9	1 53.2	24 .5	22 42.3	25 37.5
7	14 59 23.6	13 59.3	12 22.6	25 17.8	4 10.8	6 28.0	7 12.0	5 49.8	1 56.4	23 59.9	22 41.8	25 36.0
8	15 3 20.1	14 57.5	12 19.2	10♐25.8	6 4.9	6 58.7	7 42.8	5 45.7	1 59.5	23 59.3	22 41.3	25 34.4
9	15 7 16.7	15 55.8	12 15.8	25 15.6	8 1.3	7 30.6	8 13.7	5 41.9	2 2.6	23 58.7	22 40.8	25 32.9
10	15 11 13.3	16 54.2	12 12.4	9♑29.2	9 59.9	8 3.8	8 44.7	5 38.1	2 5.5	23 58.0	22 40.2	25 31.3
11	15 15 9.8	17 52.8	12 9.0	22 56.2	12 .8	8 38.2	9 15.8	5 34.5	2 8.4	23 57.3	22 39.6	25 29.7
12	15 19 6.4	18 51.6	12 5.6	5♒35.2	14 3.9	9 13.7	9 47.0	5 31.1	2 11.2	23 56.5	22 39.0	25 28.1
13	15 23 2.9	19 50.5	12 2.2	17 32.0	16 9.2	9 50.2	10 18.2	5 27.8	2 13.9	23 55.6	22 38.4	25 26.6
14	15 26 59.5	20 49.5	11 58.8	28 56.6	18 16.6	10 27.8	10 49.5	5 24.7	2 16.6	23 54.8	22 37.7	25 25.0
15	15 30 56.0	21 48.7	11 55.4	10♓ .7	20 25.9	11 6.4	11 20.9	5 21.7	2 19.1	23 53.8	22 36.9	25 23.4
16	15 34 52.6	22 48.0	11 51.9	20 57.0	22 36.9	11 45.9	11 52.4	5 18.9	2 21.5	23 52.8	22 36.2	25 21.8
17	15 38 49.1	23 47.5	11 48.5	1♈57.8	24 49.6	12 26.3	12 23.9	5 16.2	2 23.9	23 51.8	22 35.4	25 20.2
18	15 42 45.7	24 47.1	11 45.1	13 14.8	27 3.5	13 7.6	12 55.5	5 13.7	2 26.2	23 50.7	22 34.6	25 18.6
19	15 46 42.3	25 46.9	11 41.7	24 58.5	29 18.5	13 49.7	13 27.2	5 11.4	2 28.4	23 49.6	22 33.7	25 17.0
20	15 50 38.8	26 46.8	11 38.3	7♉16.7	1♊34.3	14 32.7	13 58.9	5 9.2	2 30.4	23 48.4	22 32.9	25 15.4
21	15 54 35.4	27 46.8	11 34.9	20 13.2	3 50.5	15 16.4	14 30.7	5 7.2	2 32.5	23 47.2	22 32.0	25 13.8
22	15 58 31.9	28 47.0	11 31.5	3♊45.9	6 6.8	16 .9	15 2.5	5 5.3	2 34.4	23 45.9	22 31.0	25 12.2
23	16 2 28.5	29 47.3	11 28.1	17 46.0	8 22.9	16 46.1	15 34.4	5 3.7	2 36.2	23 44.6	22 30.1	25 10.6
24	16 6 25.0	0♊47.8	11 24.7	1♋59.4	10 38.4	17 32.0	16 6.4	5 2.2	2 38.0	23 43.3	22 29.1	25 9.1
25	16 10 21.6	1 48.3	11 21.3	16 10.7	12 52.9	18 18.6	16 38.3	5 .8	2 39.6	23 41.9	22 28.1	25 7.5
26	16 14 18.2	2 49.0	11 17.9	0♌ 7.8	15 6.2	19 5.8	17 10.4	4 59.6	2 41.1	23 40.4	22 27.1	25 5.9
27	16 18 14.7	3 49.8	11 14.5	13 45.4	17 17.9	19 53.6	17 42.5	4 58.6	2 42.6	23 38.9	22 26.0	25 4.3
28	16 22 11.3	4 50.7	11 11.1	27 5.0	19 27.8	20 42.1	18 14.6	4 57.8	2 43.9	23 37.4	22 24.9	25 2.8
29	16 26 7.8	5 51.7	11 7.7	10♍14.1	21 35.6	21 31.1	18 46.8	4 57.1	2 45.2	23 35.8	22 23.8	25 1.2
30	16 30 4.4	6 52.8	11 4.2	23 23.8	23 41.1	22 20.7	19 19.0	4 56.6	2 46.4	23 34.2	22 22.7	24 59.6
31	16 34 .9	7 54.1	11 .8	6♎45.9	25 44.1	23 10.9	19 51.2	4 56.2	2 47.4	23 32.6	22 21.5	24 58.1

DECLINATION

DAY	EPHEM. SID. TIME	☉	☊	☽	☿	♀	♂	♃	♄	♅	♆	♇
1	14 35 44.3	15N .9	0S23.6	6N42.8	7N36.1	3N44.2	21N44.3	1S 1.8	12S56.4	22S 3.7	21S 6.3	4S28.1
4	14 47 33.9	15 54.4	0 23.5	9S36.4	9 55.3	3 37.6	21 21.4	0 56.3	12 53.1	22 4.0	21 6.4	4 26.8
7	14 59 23.6	16 45.4	0 23.5	20 57.4	12 17.8	3 39.3	20 57.4	0 51.4	12 50.0	22 4.3	21 6.5	4 25.7
10	15 11 13.3	17 34.0	0 23.5	20 47.7	14 40.7	3 48.8	20 32.5	0 47.0	12 47.3	22 4.7	21 6.7	4 24.6
13	15 23 2.9	18 19.9	0 23.5	11 22.0	17 .4	4 5.2	20 6.6	0 43.3	12 44.8	22 5.1	21 7.0	4 23.5
16	15 34 52.6	19 3.5	0 23.4	1N43.5	19 11.8	4 27.9	19 39.7	0 40.2	12 42.7	22 5.6	21 7.3	4 22.5
19	15 46 42.3	19 43.4	0 23.4	14 17.2	21 9.6	4 56.2	19 11.8	0 37.7	12 40.8	22 6.2	21 7.6	4 21.7
22	15 58 31.9	20 20.6	0 23.4	21 50.8	22 48.7	5 29.3	18 42.9	0 35.9	12 39.2	22 6.8	21 7.9	4 20.9
25	16 10 21.6	20 54.7	0 23.4	19 42.1	24 5.3	6 6.7	18 13.0	0 34.7	12 37.9	22 7.5	21 8.3	4 20.2
28	16 22 11.3	21 25.6	0 23.4	7 51.5	24 58.0	6 47.7	17 42.2	0 34.2	12 37.0	22 8.3	21 8.8	4 19.5
31	16 34 .9	21 53.1	0 23.3	8S 2.4	25 27.1	7 31.8	17 10.4	0 34.4	12 36.3	22 9.1	21 9.2	4 19.0

JUNE 1993

LONGITUDE

DAY	EPHEM. SID. TIME h m s	☉ ° ′	☊ ° ′	☾ ° ′	☿ ° ′	♀ ° ′	♂ ° ′	♃ ° ′	♄ ° ′	♅ ° ′	♆ ° ′	♇ ° ′
1	16 37 57.5	10♊31.6	12♐25.7	23♎46.8	27♊57.5	25♈ 6.4	17♌28.7	4♎45.4	0♓15.5	21♑41.2	20♑45.7	23♏40.1
2	16 41 54.1	11 29.0	12 22.5	8♏ 7.5	29 43.6	25 59.4	18 1.5	4D45.5	0 16.3	21R39.6	20R44.5	23R38.5
3	16 45 50.6	12 26.5	12 19.3	22 21.0	1♋26.9	26 53.0	18 34.3	4 45.8	0 17.1	21 37.9	20 43.4	23 37.0
4	16 49 47.2	13 23.9	12 16.2	6♐23.1	3 7.5	27 47.1	19 7.3	4 46.2	0 17.7	21 36.2	20 42.2	23 35.4
5	16 53 43.7	14 21.4	12 13.0	20 9.9	4 45.3	28 41.7	19 40.3	4 46.8	0 18.3	21 34.5	20 41.0	23 33.9
6	16 57 40.3	15 18.8	12 9.8	3♑38.8	6 20.3	29 36.9	20 13.4	4 47.6	0 18.7	21 32.7	20 39.7	23 32.3
7	17 1 36.8	16 16.2	12 6.6	16 48.4	7 52.4	0♉32.5	20 46.6	4 48.6	0 19.1	21 30.9	20 38.5	23 30.8
8	17 5 33.4	17 13.5	12 3.4	29 38.7	9 21.7	1 28.6	21 19.9	4 49.8	0 19.4	21 29.1	20 37.2	23 29.3
9	17 9 30.0	18 10.9	12 .3	12♒10.9	10 48.1	2 25.2	21 53.3	4 51.1	0 19.5	21 27.2	20 35.9	23 27.9
10	17 13 26.5	19 8.3	11 57.1	24 27.7	12 11.5	3 22.2	22 26.8	4 52.6	0 19.6	21 25.3	20 34.6	23 26.4
11	17 17 23.1	20 5.6	11 53.9	6♓32.4	13 32.0	4 19.7	23 .3	4 54.3	0 19.6	21 23.4	20 33.3	23 24.9
12	17 21 19.6	21 3.0	11 50.7	18 29.1	14 49.5	5 17.5	23 33.9	4 56.1	0R19.4	21 21.4	20 31.9	23 23.5
13	17 25 16.2	22 .3	11 47.6	0♈22.4	16 4.0	6 15.7	24 7.6	4 58.2	0 19.2	21 19.4	20 30.6	23 22.1
14	17 29 12.7	22 57.7	11 44.4	12 16.7	17 15.4	7 14.4	24 41.5	5 .4	0 18.9	21 17.5	20 29.2	23 20.7
15	17 33 9.3	23 55.0	11 41.2	24 16.7	18 23.6	8 13.4	25 15.4	5 2.8	0 18.5	21 15.4	20 27.8	23 19.4
16	17 37 5.9	24 52.3	11 38.0	6♉26.5	19 28.6	9 12.8	25 49.3	5 5.4	0 18.0	21 13.4	20 26.4	23 18.0
17	17 41 2.4	25 49.6	11 34.9	18 49.7	20 30.3	10 12.5	26 23.3	5 8.1	0 17.3	21 11.3	20 25.0	23 16.7
18	17 44 59.0	26 46.9	11 31.7	1♊29.1	21 28.7	11 12.5	26 57.5	5 11.0	0 16.6	21 9.2	20 23.6	23 15.3
19	17 48 55.5	27 44.2	11 28.5	14 26.4	22 23.5	12 12.8	27 31.7	5 14.0	0 15.8	21 7.0	20 22.1	23 14.0
20	17 52 52.1	28 41.5	11 25.3	27 42.2	23 14.9	13 13.5	28 5.9	5 17.3	0 14.9	21 4.9	20 20.6	23 12.8
21	17 56 48.6	29 38.8	11 22.2	11♋15.7	24 2.5	14 14.4	28 40.3	5 20.7	0 13.9	21 2.7	20 19.1	23 11.5
22	18 0 45.2	0♋36.1	11 19.0	25 4.8	24 46.4	15 15.7	29 14.7	5 24.2	0 12.8	21 .5	20 17.6	23 10.3
23	18 4 41.8	1 33.3	11 15.8	9♌ 6.5	25 26.5	16 17.2	29 49.2	5 28.0	0 11.6	20 58.3	20 16.1	23 9.0
24	18 8 38.3	2 30.6	11 12.6	23 16.9	26 2.5	17 19.0	0♍23.8	5 31.8	0 10.3	20 56.0	20 14.6	23 7.9
25	18 12 34.9	3 27.8	11 9.4	7♍32.3	26 34.5	18 21.1	0 58.5	5 35.9	0 8.9	20 53.8	20 13.1	23 6.7
26	18 16 31.4	4 25.1	11 6.3	21 49.0	27 2.2	19 23.4	1 33.2	5 40.1	0 7.4	20 51.5	20 11.5	23 5.5
27	18 20 28.0	5 22.3	11 3.1	6♎ 3.8	27 25.7	20 25.9	2 8.0	5 44.5	0 5.8	20 49.2	20 10.0	23 4.4
28	18 24 24.5	6 19.5	10 59.9	20 14.1	27 44.7	21 28.7	2 42.8	5 49.0	0 4.1	20 46.9	20 8.4	23 3.3
29	18 28 21.1	7 16.7	10 56.7	4♏18.1	27 59.2	22 31.8	3 17.8	5 53.7	0 2.4	20 44.6	20 6.8	23 2.3
30	18 32 17.7	8 13.9	10 53.6	18 14.0	28 9.1	23 35.0	3 52.8	5 58.5	0 .5	20 42.2	20 5.3	23 1.2

LATITUDE

DAY	SID. TIME	☉	☊	☾	☿	♀	♂	♃	♄	♅	♆	♇
1	16 37 57.5	0 .0	0 .0	3S57.3	2N 6.5	2S 4.4	1N28.1	1N25.9	1S18.4	0S28.2	0N41.2	14N48.8
4	16 49 47.2	0 .0	0 .0	0 32.1	2 8.8	2 15.5	1 25.6	1 25.1	1 19.0	0 28.2	0 41.2	14 48.1
7	17 1 36.8	0 .0	0 .0	3N .4	2 4.1	2 24.9	1 23.1	1 24.4	1 19.6	0 28.3	0 41.2	14 47.4
10	17 13 26.5	0 .0	0 .0	5 1.8	1 52.5	2 32.7	1 20.6	1 23.6	1 20.2	0 28.4	0 41.2	14 46.6
13	17 25 16.2	0 .0	0 .0	5 .8	1 34.3	2 38.9	1 18.2	1 22.8	1 20.8	0 28.4	0 41.2	14 45.7
16	17 37 5.9	0 .0	0 .0	3 5.1	1 9.8	2 43.7	1 15.7	1 22.1	1 21.4	0 28.5	0 41.2	14 44.7
19	17 48 55.5	0 .0	0 .0	0S12.3	0 39.3	2 47.1	1 13.4	1 21.3	1 22.0	0 28.5	0 41.2	14 43.7
22	18 0 45.2	0 .0	0 .0	3 34.8	0 3.4	2 49.2	1 11.0	1 20.6	1 22.6	0 28.6	0 41.2	14 42.6
25	18 12 34.9	0 .0	0 .0	5 13.5	0S37.4	2 50.0	1 8.7	1 19.8	1 23.2	0 28.6	0 41.2	14 41.4
28	18 24 24.5	0 .0	0 .0	4 7.3	1 22.0	2 49.7	1 6.4	1 19.1	1 23.8	0 28.7	0 41.2	14 40.2

RIGHT ASCENSION

DAY	SID. TIME	☉	☊	☾	☿	♀	♂	♃	♄	♅	♆	♇
1	16 37 57.5	8♊55.4	10♐57.4	20♎31.1	27♊44.4	24♈ 1.7	20♌23.5	4♎56.0	2♓48.4	23♑30.9	22♑20.3	24♏56.6
2	16 41 54.1	9 56.8	10 54.0	4♏45.3	29 41.8	24 52.9	20 55.8	4 56.0	2 49.3	23R29.1	22R19.1	24R55.0
3	16 45 50.6	10 58.3	10 50.6	19 27.0	1♋36.3	25 44.8	21 28.1	4D56.1	2 50.1	23 27.4	22 17.8	24 53.5
4	16 49 47.2	11 59.9	10 47.2	4♐25.3	3 27.7	26 37.1	22 .5	4 56.4	2 50.8	23 25.5	22 16.6	24 52.0
5	16 53 43.7	13 1.6	10 43.8	19 21.5	5 15.9	27 29.9	22 32.9	4 56.9	2 51.4	23 23.7	22 15.3	24 50.5
6	16 57 40.3	14 3.4	10 40.4	3♑55.0	7 .9	28 23.3	23 5.3	4 57.5	2 51.9	23 21.8	22 14.0	24 49.0
7	17 1 36.8	15 5.2	10 37.0	17 49.6	8 42.4	29 17.1	23 37.7	4 58.3	2 52.4	23 19.9	22 12.7	24 47.5
8	17 5 33.4	16 7.2	10 33.6	0♒57.6	10 20.6	0♉11.4	24 10.2	4 59.3	2 52.7	23 18.0	22 11.3	24 46.0
9	17 9 30.0	17 9.2	10 30.2	13 20.1	11 55.3	1 6.2	24 42.7	5 .4	2 52.9	23 16.0	22 9.9	24 44.6
10	17 13 26.5	18 11.2	10 26.8	25 4.2	13 26.4	2 1.4	25 15.2	5 1.7	2 53.0	23 13.9	22 8.5	24 43.1
11	17 17 23.1	19 13.4	10 23.4	6♓20.7	14 53.9	2 57.2	25 47.8	5 3.2	2 53.1	23 11.9	22 7.1	24 41.7
12	17 21 19.6	20 15.6	10 20.0	17 21.9	16 17.8	3 53.3	26 20.4	5 4.8	2R53.0	23 9.8	22 5.7	24 40.3
13	17 25 16.2	21 17.8	10 16.6	28 20.6	17 37.9	4 49.9	26 53.0	5 6.5	2 52.9	23 7.7	22 4.3	24 38.9
14	17 29 12.7	22 20.1	10 13.2	9♈29.5	18 54.4	5 47.0	27 25.6	5 8.5	2 52.7	23 5.6	22 2.8	24 37.5
15	17 33 9.3	23 22.5	10 9.8	21 .3	20 7.0	6 44.5	27 58.3	5 10.6	2 52.4	23 3.4	22 1.4	24 36.1
16	17 37 5.9	24 24.8	10 6.4	3♉ 3.4	21 15.7	7 42.4	28 31.0	5 12.8	2 51.9	23 1.2	21 59.9	24 34.8
17	17 41 2.4	25 27.2	10 3.0	15 45.7	22 20.5	8 40.7	29 3.7	5 15.2	2 51.4	22 59.0	21 58.3	24 33.4
18	17 44 59.0	26 29.6	9 59.6	29 9.2	23 21.2	9 39.5	29 36.4	5 17.8	2 50.8	22 56.8	21 56.8	24 32.1
19	17 48 55.5	27 32.0	9 56.2	13♊ 8.6	24 17.9	10 38.7	0♍ 9.1	5 20.5	2 50.1	22 54.5	21 55.3	24 30.8
20	17 52 52.1	28 34.5	9 52.8	27 31.5	25 10.5	11 38.2	0 41.9	5 23.3	2 49.3	22 52.2	21 53.7	24 29.5
21	17 56 48.6	29 36.9	9 49.4	12♋ .9	25 58.8	12 38.2	1 14.7	5 26.4	2 48.4	22 49.8	21 52.1	24 28.2
22	18 0 45.2	0♋39.3	9 46.0	26 20.9	26 42.8	13 38.6	1 47.5	5 29.5	2 47.4	22 47.5	21 50.5	24 27.0
23	18 4 41.8	1 41.7	9 42.6	10♌20.8	27 22.5	14 39.4	2 20.3	5 32.9	2 46.3	22 45.1	21 48.9	24 25.7
24	18 8 38.3	2 44.1	9 39.2	23 58.0	27 57.7	15 40.5	2 53.2	5 36.3	2 45.1	22 42.7	21 47.3	24 24.5
25	18 12 34.9	3 46.5	9 35.8	7♍17.0	28 28.4	16 42.1	3 26.0	5 40.0	2 43.9	22 40.3	21 45.7	24 23.3
26	18 16 31.4	4 48.8	9 32.4	20 26.9	28 54.4	17 44.0	3 58.9	5 43.7	2 42.5	22 37.9	21 44.1	24 22.1
27	18 20 28.0	5 51.1	9 29.1	3♎39.5	29 15.8	18 46.4	4 31.8	5 47.6	2 41.1	22 35.5	21 42.4	24 21.0
28	18 24 24.5	6 53.3	9 25.7	17 6.1	29 32.4	19 49.1	5 4.8	5 51.7	2 39.5	22 33.0	21 40.8	24 19.9
29	18 28 21.1	7 55.5	9 22.3	0♏55.0	29 44.2	20 52.2	5 37.7	5 55.9	2 37.9	22 30.5	21 39.1	24 18.8
30	18 32 17.7	8 57.6	9 18.9	15 9.0	29 51.3	21 55.7	6 10.7	6 .3	2 36.2	22 28.0	21 37.4	24 17.7

DECLINATION

DAY	SID. TIME	☉	☊	☾	☿	♀	♂	♃	♄	♅	♆	♇
1	16 37 57.5	22N 1.5	0S23.3	12S54.1	25N31.9	7N47.1	16N59.6	0S34.6	12S36.2	22S 9.3	21S 9.4	4S18.8
4	16 49 47.2	22 24.4	0 23.3	21 54.1	25 32.9	8 34.6	16 26.6	0 35.6	12 36.0	22 10.2	21 9.9	4 18.4
7	17 1 36.8	22 43.9	0 23.3	19 23.9	25 16.2	9 23.9	15 52.8	0 37.2	12 36.0	22 11.1	21 10.5	4 18.1
10	17 13 26.5	22 59.7	0 23.3	8 37.2	24 44.8	10 14.7	15 18.1	0 39.5	12 36.4	22 12.1	21 11.0	4 17.9
13	17 25 16.2	23 11.9	0 23.2	4N44.8	24 2.0	11 6.4	14 42.5	0 42.4	12 37.2	22 13.0	21 11.6	4 17.8
16	17 37 5.9	23 20.4	0 23.2	16 34.7	23 10.6	11 58.6	14 6.0	0 46.0	12 38.2	22 14.0	21 12.3	4 17.8
19	17 48 55.5	23 25.2	0 23.2	22 19.7	22 13.5	12 50.9	13 28.7	0 50.1	12 39.5	22 15.1	21 12.9	4 17.9
22	18 0 45.2	23 26.2	0 23.2	17 35.7	21 13.6	13 42.8	12 50.7	0 54.8	12 41.1	22 16.1	21 13.6	4 18.1
25	18 12 34.9	23 23.6	0 23.2	3 53.2	20 13.6	14 34.0	12 11.9	1 .1	12 43.1	22 17.2	21 14.3	4 18.3
28	18 24 24.5	23 17.3	0 23.1	11S43.3	19 16.4	15 24.0	11 32.3	1 6.0	12 45.3	22 18.3	21 15.0	4 18.7

JULY 1993

DAY	EPHEM. SID. TIME	☉	☊	☽	☿	♀	♂	♃	♄	♅	♆	♇
		LONGITUDE										
	h m s	° ′	° ′	° ′	° ′	° ′	° ′	° ′	° ′	° ′	° ′	° ′
1	18 36 14.2	9♋11.1	10♐50.4	2♐ .5	28♋14.4	24♉38.5	4♍27.8	6♎ 3.5	29♒58.6	20♑39.9	20♑ 3.7	23♏ .2
2	18 40 10.8	10 8.3	10 47.2	15 36.1	28 15.1	25 42.2	5 3.0	6 8.6	29 R 56.5	20 R 37.5	20 R 2.1	22 R 59.2
3	18 44 7.3	11 5.5	10 44.0	28 59.4	28 R 11.1	26 46.2	5 38.2	6 13.9	29 54.4	20 35.2	20 .5	22 58.2
4	18 48 3.9	12 2.6	10 40.9	12♑ 9.3	28 2.5	27 50.3	6 13.4	6 19.4	29 52.2	20 32.8	19 58.9	22 57.3
5	18 52 .5	12 59.9	10 37.7	25 5.0	27 49.5	28 54.7	6 48.8	6 25.0	29 50.0	20 30.5	19 57.3	22 56.4
6	18 55 57.0	13 57.0	10 34.5	7♒45.9	27 32.1	29 59.3	7 24.2	6 30.7	29 47.6	20 28.1	19 55.7	22 55.5
7	18 59 53.6	14 54.2	10 31.3	20 12.7	27 10.6	1♊ 4.1	7 59.7	6 36.6	29 45.2	20 25.7	19 54.1	22 54.7
8	19 3 50.1	15 51.4	10 28.1	2♓26.6	26 45.3	2 9.0	8 35.2	6 42.6	29 42.6	20 23.3	19 52.5	22 53.8
9	19 7 46.7	16 48.6	10 25.0	14 30.0	26 16.4	3 14.2	9 10.8	6 48.7	29 40.0	20 20.8	19 50.9	22 53.0
10	19 11 43.2	17 45.8	10 21.8	26 26.1	25 44.4	4 19.5	9 46.4	6 55.0	29 37.3	20 18.4	19 49.3	22 52.3
11	19 15 39.8	18 43.0	10 18.6	8♈18.6	25 9.7	5 25.0	10 22.2	7 1.5	29 34.5	20 16.0	19 47.6	22 51.5
12	19 19 36.4	19 40.2	10 15.4	20 12.1	24 33.0	6 30.7	10 57.9	7 8.0	29 31.7	20 13.6	19 46.0	22 50.8
13	19 23 32.9	20 37.4	10 12.3	2♉11.4	23 54.7	7 36.6	11 33.8	7 14.7	29 28.7	20 11.2	19 44.4	22 50.1
14	19 27 29.5	21 34.7	10 9.1	14 21.4	23 15.5	8 42.6	12 9.7	7 21.6	29 25.7	20 8.8	19 42.8	22 49.5
15	19 31 26.0	22 31.9	10 5.9	26 46.8	22 36.1	9 48.8	12 45.7	7 28.5	29 22.6	20 6.3	19 41.1	22 48.9
16	19 35 22.6	23 29.2	10 2.7	9♊31.6	21 57.1	10 55.1	13 21.8	7 35.6	29 19.4	20 3.9	19 39.5	22 48.3
17	19 39 19.1	24 26.4	9 59.6	22 38.8	21 19.3	12 1.6	13 57.9	7 42.8	29 16.2	20 1.5	19 37.9	22 47.7
18	19 43 15.7	25 23.7	9 56.4	6♋ 9.8	20 43.3	13 8.3	14 34.1	7 50.2	29 12.9	19 59.1	19 36.3	22 47.2
19	19 47 12.2	26 21.0	9 53.2	20 3.8	20 9.7	14 15.1	15 10.3	7 57.7	29 9.5	19 56.7	19 34.7	22 46.7
20	19 51 8.8	27 18.3	9 50.0	4♌18.0	19 39.2	15 22.1	15 46.6	8 5.3	29 6.1	19 54.3	19 33.0	22 46.2
21	19 55 5.4	28 15.5	9 46.9	18 47.1	19 12.4	16 29.1	16 23.0	8 13.0	29 2.6	19 51.9	19 31.4	22 45.8
22	19 59 1.9	29 12.8	9 43.7	3♍24.6	18 49.7	17 36.4	16 59.5	8 20.9	28 59.0	19 49.6	19 29.8	22 45.4
23	20 2 58.5	0♌10.2	9 40.5	18 3.3	18 31.7	18 43.7	17 36.0	8 28.8	28 55.4	19 47.2	19 28.3	22 45.0
24	20 6 55.0	1 7.5	9 37.3	2♎36.8	18 18.7	19 51.2	18 12.5	8 36.9	28 51.7	19 44.8	19 26.7	22 44.7
25	20 10 51.6	2 4.8	9 34.1	16 59.9	18 11.0	20 58.8	18 49.2	8 45.1	28 48.0	19 42.5	19 25.1	22 44.4
26	20 14 48.1	3 2.1	9 31.0	1♏ 9.7	18 8.9	22 6.6	19 25.9	8 53.5	28 44.2	19 40.2	19 23.6	22 44.1
27	20 18 44.7	3 59.5	9 27.8	15 4.6	18 D 12.6	23 14.5	20 2.6	9 1.9	28 40.4	19 37.9	19 22.0	22 43.9
28	20 22 41.3	4 56.8	9 24.6	28 44.6	18 22.3	24 22.5	20 39.4	9 10.5	28 36.4	19 35.6	19 20.4	22 43.7
29	20 26 37.8	5 54.2	9 21.4	12♐10.5	18 38.1	25 30.6	21 16.3	9 19.1	28 32.5	19 33.3	19 18.9	22 43.5
30	20 30 34.4	6 51.5	9 18.3	25 23.5	19 .1	26 38.8	21 53.2	9 27.9	28 28.5	19 31.0	19 17.4	22 43.4
31	20 34 30.9	7 48.9	9 15.1	8♑24.3	19 28.3	27 47.2	22 30.2	9 36.8	28 24.4	19 28.7	19 15.9	22 43.3
		LATITUDE										
1	18 36 14.2	0 .0	0 .0	0S54.9	2S 8.7	2S48.3	1N 4.1	1N18.4	1S24.4	0S28.7	0N41.2	14N38.9
4	18 48 3.9	0 .0	0 .0	2N37.2	2 55.5	2 45.8	1 1.9	1 17.7	1 25.0	0 28.8	0 41.2	14 37.6
7	18 59 53.6	0 .0	0 .0	4 49.6	3 39.2	2 42.4	0 59.6	1 17.0	1 25.5	0 28.8	0 41.2	14 36.2
10	19 11 43.2	0 .0	0 .0	5 .7	4 16.2	2 38.1	0 57.4	1 16.3	1 26.1	0 28.8	0 41.1	14 34.8
13	19 23 32.9	0 .0	0 .0	3 17.5	4 42.7	2 33.0	0 55.2	1 15.7	1 26.6	0 28.9	0 41.1	14 33.4
16	19 35 22.6	0 .0	0 .0	0 11.1	4 55.5	2 27.1	0 53.1	1 15.0	1 27.1	0 28.9	0 41.1	14 31.9
19	19 47 12.2	0 .0	0 .0	3S12.7	4 53.3	2 20.5	0 50.9	1 14.4	1 27.6	0 28.9	0 41.0	14 30.4
22	19 59 1.9	0 .0	0 .0	5 4.5	4 36.6	2 13.3	0 48.8	1 13.8	1 28.1	0 28.9	0 41.0	14 28.8
25	20 10 51.6	0 .0	0 .0	4 8.6	4 7.5	2 5.5	0 46.6	1 13.2	1 28.6	0 28.9	0 40.9	14 27.2
28	20 22 41.3	0 .0	0 .0	1 4.7	3 29.3	1 57.2	0 44.5	1 12.6	1 29.0	0 28.9	0 40.9	14 25.6
31	20 34 30.9	0 .0	0 .0	2N21.8	2 45.2	1 48.4	0 42.4	1 12.0	1 29.4	0 28.9	0 40.8	14 24.0
		RIGHT ASCENSION										
1	18 36 14.2	9♋59.7	9♐15.5	29♏43.1	29♋53.4	22♉59.6	6♍43.6	6♎ 4.7	2♓34.4	22♑25.5	21♑35.7	24♏16.6
2	18 40 10.8	11 1.7	9 12.1	14♐24.2	29 R 50.8	24 3.8	7 16.6	6 9.4	2 R 32.5	22 R 23.0	21 R 34.1	24 R 15.6
3	18 44 7.3	12 3.6	9 8.7	28 54.7	29 43.5	25 8.5	7 49.6	6 14.1	2 30.6	22 20.5	21 32.4	24 14.5
4	18 48 3.9	13 5.5	9 5.3	12♑57.5	29 31.5	26 13.5	8 22.7	6 19.0	2 28.5	22 17.9	21 30.7	24 13.6
5	18 52 .5	14 7.3	9 1.9	26 21.3	29 15.0	27 19.0	8 55.7	6 24.1	2 26.5	22 15.4	21 29.0	24 12.6
6	18 55 57.0	15 9.0	8 58.5	9♒ 2.3	28 54.2	28 24.8	9 28.8	6 29.3	2 24.2	22 12.9	21 27.3	24 11.7
7	18 59 53.6	16 10.6	8 55.1	21 4.1	28 29.4	29 30.9	10 1.9	6 34.6	2 22.0	22 10.3	21 25.6	24 10.8
8	19 3 50.1	17 12.1	8 51.7	2♓34.4	28 .7	0♊37.4	10 35.0	6 40.0	2 19.6	22 7.8	21 23.9	24 9.9
9	19 7 46.7	18 13.5	8 48.3	13 43.8	27 28.7	1 44.3	11 8.1	6 45.6	2 17.1	22 5.2	21 22.1	24 9.0
10	19 11 43.2	19 14.9	8 44.9	24 44.2	26 53.8	2 51.6	11 41.3	6 51.3	2 14.6	22 2.6	21 20.4	24 8.2
11	19 15 39.8	20 16.1	8 41.6	5♈47.5	26 16.4	3 59.2	12 14.4	6 57.1	2 12.0	22 .0	21 18.7	24 7.3
12	19 19 36.4	21 17.2	8 38.2	17 5.8	25 37.1	5 7.2	12 47.6	7 3.0	2 9.3	21 57.4	21 17.0	24 6.6
13	19 23 32.9	22 18.2	8 34.8	28 50.0	24 56.5	6 15.5	13 20.8	7 9.1	2 6.6	21 54.9	21 15.3	24 5.8
14	19 27 29.5	23 19.1	8 31.4	11♉ 9.3	24 15.3	7 24.1	13 54.1	7 15.3	2 3.7	21 52.3	21 13.5	24 5.1
15	19 31 26.0	24 19.9	8 28.0	24 9.2	23 34.1	8 33.1	14 27.3	7 21.6	2 .8	21 49.7	21 11.8	24 4.4
16	19 35 22.6	25 20.5	8 24.6	7♊49.6	22 53.6	9 42.5	15 .6	7 28.0	1 57.8	21 47.1	21 10.1	24 3.7
17	19 39 19.1	26 21.1	8 21.2	22 3.2	22 14.6	10 52.1	15 33.9	7 34.6	1 54.8	21 44.5	21 8.4	24 3.0
18	19 43 15.7	27 21.5	8 17.8	6♋36.3	21 37.6	12 2.1	16 7.3	7 41.3	1 51.7	21 41.9	21 6.7	24 2.4
19	19 47 12.2	28 21.7	8 14.4	21 12.4	21 3.4	13 12.4	16 40.7	7 48.1	1 48.5	21 39.4	21 4.9	24 1.8
20	19 51 8.8	29 21.9	8 11.1	5♌37.4	20 32.5	14 23.0	17 14.1	7 55.0	1 45.2	21 36.8	21 3.2	24 1.2
21	19 55 5.4	0♌21.9	8 7.7	19 43.3	20 5.6	15 33.9	17 47.5	8 2.0	1 41.9	21 34.3	21 1.5	24 .7
22	19 59 1.9	1 21.7	8 4.3	3♍29.6	19 43.1	16 45.0	18 21.0	8 9.1	1 38.6	21 31.7	20 59.8	24 .2
23	20 2 58.5	2 21.4	8 .9	17 2.0	19 25.6	17 56.5	18 54.5	8 16.4	1 35.1	21 29.2	20 58.1	23 59.7
24	20 6 55.0	3 21.0	7 57.5	0♎29.9	19 13.4	19 8.2	19 28.0	8 23.8	1 31.6	21 26.7	20 56.5	23 59.3
25	20 10 51.6	4 20.4	7 54.1	14 3.3	19 6.9	20 20.2	20 1.6	8 31.2	1 28.1	21 24.1	20 54.8	23 58.9
26	20 14 48.1	5 19.7	7 50.7	27 50.5	19 6.4	21 32.5	20 35.2	8 38.9	1 24.5	21 21.7	20 53.2	23 58.5
27	20 18 44.7	6 18.8	7 47.4	11♏55.3	19 D 12.1	22 45.0	21 8.9	8 46.5	1 20.9	21 19.2	20 51.5	23 58.2
28	20 22 41.3	7 17.7	7 44.0	26 15.5	19 24.1	23 57.7	21 42.5	8 54.3	1 17.2	21 16.7	20 49.9	23 57.8
29	20 26 37.8	8 16.5	7 40.6	10♐42.2	19 42.6	25 10.6	22 16.2	9 2.2	1 13.4	21 14.3	20 48.2	23 57.5
30	20 30 34.4	9 15.2	7 37.2	25 1.6	20 7.7	26 23.8	22 50.0	9 10.2	1 9.6	21 11.9	20 46.6	23 57.3
31	20 34 30.9	10 13.6	7 33.8	8♑59.3	20 39.5	27 37.2	23 23.7	9 18.3	1 5.7	21 9.4	20 45.0	23 57.1
		DECLINATION										
1	18 36 14.2	23N 7.2	0S23.1	21S27.6	18N24.7	16N12.5	10N52.1	1S12.4	12S47.8	22S19.4	21S15.7	4S19.3
4	18 48 3.9	22 53.6	0 23.1	20 16.4	17 41.2	16 59.0	10 11.2	1 19.3	12 50.6	22 20.5	21 16.4	4 19.9
7	18 59 53.6	22 36.4	0 23.1	10 9.8	17 8.3	17 43.4	9 29.6	1 26.7	12 53.6	22 21.6	21 17.1	4 20.6
10	19 11 43.2	22 15.6	0 23.0	3N10.9	16 47.9	18 25.0	8 47.5	1 34.6	12 56.9	22 22.7	21 17.8	4 21.4
13	19 23 32.9	21 51.4	0 23.0	15 19.3	16 40.9	19 3.8	8 4.7	1 43.0	13 .4	22 23.8	21 18.6	4 22.3
16	19 35 22.6	21 23.8	0 23.0	22 3.7	16 47.2	19 39.2	7 21.4	1 51.9	13 4.1	22 24.9	21 19.3	4 23.3
19	19 47 12.2	20 52.9	0 23.0	18 45.7	17 5.4	20 11.0	6 37.5	2 1.1	13 8.1	22 26.0	21 20.0	4 24.4
22	19 59 1.9	20 18.9	0 22.9	5 31.2	17 33.0	20 39.0	5 53.1	2 10.8	13 12.2	22 27.1	21 20.8	4 25.6
25	20 10 51.6	19 41.8	0 22.9	10S30.1	18 6.9	21 2.7	5 8.3	2 20.9	13 16.5	22 28.1	21 21.5	4 26.9
28	20 22 41.3	19 1.7	0 22.9	20 55.9	18 43.3	21 22.1	4 23.1	2 31.4	13 20.9	22 29.1	21 22.2	4 28.3
31	20 34 30.9	18 18.9	0 22.9	20 48.9	19 18.0	21 36.8	3 37.5	2 42.3	13 25.5	22 30.1	21 22.9	4 29.8

AUGUST 1993

LONGITUDE

DAY	EPHEM. SID. TIME h m s	☉ ° ′	☊ ° ′	☽ ° ′	☿ ° ′	♀ ° ′	♂ ° ′	♃ ° ′	♄ ° ′	♅ ° ′	♆ ° ′	♇ ° ′
1	20 38 27.5	8♌46.2	9♐11.9	21♑13.6	20♋ 2.7	28♊55.7	23♍ 7.2	9♎45.7	28♒20.3	19♑26.5	19♑14.3	22♏43.2
2	20 42 24.0	9 43.6	9 8.7	3♒51.9	20 43.2	0♋ 4.2	23 44.3	9 54.8	28 R 16.2	19 R 24.3	19 R 12.8	22 R 43.1
3	20 46 20.6	10 41.0	9 5.5	16 19.3	21 29.9	1 13.0	24 21.5	10 4.0	28 12.0	19 22.1	19 11.4	22 43.1
4	20 50 17.1	11 38.4	9 2.4	28 36.4	22 22.7	2 21.8	24 58.7	10 13.3	28 7.8	19 19.9	19 9.9	22 D 43.2
5	20 54 13.7	12 35.9	8 59.2	10♓43.9	23 21.4	3 30.7	25 36.0	10 22.7	28 3.6	19 17.7	19 8.4	22 43.2
6	20 58 10.3	13 33.3	8 56.0	22 43.3	24 25.9	4 39.8	26 13.3	10 32.1	27 59.3	19 15.6	19 7.0	22 43.3
7	21 2 6.8	14 30.8	8 52.8	4♈36.8	25 36.0	5 49.0	26 50.7	10 41.7	27 54.9	19 13.5	19 5.5	22 43.4
8	21 6 3.4	15 28.3	8 49.7	16 27.5	26 51.7	6 58.2	27 28.1	10 51.4	27 50.6	19 11.4	19 4.1	22 43.6
9	21 9 59.9	16 25.8	8 46.5	28 19.1	28 12.7	8 7.6	28 5.7	11 1.1	27 46.2	19 9.3	19 2.7	22 43.8
10	21 13 56.5	17 23.3	8 43.3	10♉16.2	29 38.7	9 17.1	28 43.2	11 11.0	27 41.8	19 7.3	19 1.3	22 44.0
11	21 17 53.0	18 20.9	8 40.1	22 23.9	1♌ 9.6	10 26.7	29 20.9	11 20.9	27 37.4	19 5.3	18 60.0	22 44.3
12	21 21 49.6	19 18.5	8 37.0	4♊47.3	2 44.9	11 36.5	29 58.6	11 31.0	27 32.9	19 3.3	18 58.6	22 44.6
13	21 25 46.1	20 16.1	8 33.8	17 31.4	4 24.4	12 46.3	0♎36.3	11 41.1	27 28.5	19 1.3	18 57.3	22 44.9
14	21 29 42.7	21 13.7	8 30.6	0♋40.5	6 7.8	13 56.2	1 14.1	11 51.3	27 24.0	18 59.4	18 56.0	22 45.3
15	21 33 39.2	22 11.3	8 27.4	14 17.1	7 54.5	15 6.2	1 52.0	12 1.6	27 19.5	18 57.5	18 54.7	22 45.7
16	21 37 35.8	23 9.1	8 24.2	28 21.9	9 44.4	16 16.4	2 30.0	12 12.1	27 15.0	18 55.7	18 53.4	22 46.2
17	21 41 32.4	24 6.8	8 21.1	12♌52.0	11 36.9	17 26.6	3 8.0	12 22.5	27 10.5	18 53.9	18 52.2	22 46.6
18	21 45 28.9	25 4.5	8 17.9	27 41.8	13 31.6	18 36.9	3 46.1	12 33.1	27 6.0	18 52.1	18 50.9	22 47.1
19	21 49 25.5	26 2.2	8 14.7	12♍42.7	15 28.1	19 47.3	4 24.2	12 43.7	27 1.4	18 50.3	18 49.7	22 47.7
20	21 53 22.0	27 .0	8 11.5	27 45.1	17 26.1	20 57.8	5 2.4	12 54.4	26 56.9	18 48.6	18 48.5	22 48.3
21	21 57 18.6	27 57.8	8 8.4	12♎39.5	19 25.2	22 8.3	5 40.6	13 5.2	26 52.4	18 46.9	18 47.4	22 48.9
22	22 1 15.1	28 55.6	8 5.2	27 18.3	21 25.0	23 19.0	6 18.9	13 16.1	26 47.8	18 45.2	18 46.2	22 49.5
23	22 5 11.7	29 53.4	8 2.0	11♏37.0	23 25.1	24 29.7	6 57.3	13 27.0	26 43.3	18 43.6	18 45.1	22 50.2
24	22 9 8.2	0♍51.3	7 58.8	25 33.7	25 25.4	25 40.6	7 35.7	13 38.0	26 38.8	18 42.0	18 44.0	22 50.9
25	22 13 4.8	1 49.1	7 55.6	9♐ 8.9	27 25.6	26 51.5	8 14.2	13 49.1	26 34.3	18 40.4	18 42.9	22 51.6
26	22 17 1.3	2 47.0	7 52.5	22 24.6	29 25.4	28 2.5	8 52.7	14 .3	26 29.8	18 38.9	18 41.8	22 52.4
27	22 20 57.9	3 44.9	7 49.3	5♑23.2	1♍24.7	29 13.6	9 31.3	14 11.5	26 25.3	18 37.4	18 40.8	22 53.2
28	22 24 54.4	4 42.8	7 46.1	18 7.6	3 23.3	0♌24.7	10 9.9	14 22.8	26 20.9	18 36.0	18 39.8	22 54.0
29	22 28 51.0	5 40.8	7 42.9	0♒40.2	5 21.1	1 36.0	10 48.6	14 34.1	26 16.4	18 34.6	18 38.8	22 54.9
30	22 32 47.6	6 38.8	7 39.8	13 2.8	7 18.0	2 47.3	11 27.4	14 45.6	26 12.0	18 33.2	18 37.9	22 55.8
31	22 36 44.1	7 36.8	7 36.6	25 16.8	9 13.8	3 58.8	12 6.2	14 57.0	26 7.6	18 31.9	18 36.9	22 56.7

LATITUDE

DAY	SID. TIME	☉	☊	☽	☿	♀	♂	♃	♄	♅	♆	♇
1	20 38 27.5	0 .0	0 .0	3N18.2	2S29.7	1S45.4	0N41.7	1N11.9	1S29.5	0S28.9	0N40.8	14N23.5
4	20 50 17.1	0 .0	0 .0	4 57.0	1 42.5	1 36.2	0 39.7	1 11.3	1 29.9	0 28.9	0 40.8	14 21.8
7	21 2 6.8	0 .0	0 .0	4 35.5	0 56.0	1 26.7	0 37.6	1 10.8	1 30.3	0 28.9	0 40.7	14 20.2
10	21 13 56.5	0 .0	0 .0	2 29.1	0 12.5	1 16.9	0 35.5	1 10.3	1 30.6	0 28.9	0 40.6	14 18.6
13	21 25 46.1	0 .0	0 .0	0S42.3	0N25.8	1 7.0	0 33.5	1 9.8	1 30.9	0 28.9	0 40.6	14 16.9
16	21 37 35.8	0 .0	0 .0	3 48.2	0 57.3	0 56.9	0 31.5	1 9.4	1 31.2	0 28.9	0 40.5	14 15.3
19	21 49 25.5	0 .0	0 .0	5 .4	1 21.1	0 46.8	0 29.4	1 8.9	1 31.4	0 28.8	0 40.4	14 13.6
22	22 1 15.1	0 .0	0 .0	3 19.0	1 36.7	0 36.7	0 27.4	1 8.5	1 31.6	0 28.8	0 40.3	14 12.0
25	22 13 4.8	0 .0	0 .0	0N 4.0	1 44.7	0 26.6	0 25.4	1 8.1	1 31.8	0 28.8	0 40.3	14 10.4
28	22 24 54.4	0 .0	0 .0	3 13.3	1 45.8	0 16.7	0 23.5	1 7.7	1 32.0	0 28.7	0 40.2	14 8.8
31	22 36 44.1	0 .0	0 .0	4 52.6	1 41.1	0 7.0	0 21.5	1 7.4	1 32.1	0 28.7	0 40.1	14 7.2

RIGHT ASCENSION

DAY	SID. TIME	☉	☊	☽	☿	♀	♂	♃	♄	♅	♆	♇
1	20 38 27.5	11♌12.0	7♐30.4	22♑24.3	21♋17.8	28♊50.8	23♍57.5	9♎26.5	1♓ 1.8	21♑ 7.0	20♑43.4	23♏56.9
2	20 42 24.0	12 10.1	7 27.1	5♒11.6	22 2.8	0♋ 4.6	24 31.4	9 34.8	0 R 57.9	21 R 4.7	20 R 41.8	23 R 56.7
3	20 46 20.6	13 8.1	7 23.7	17 22.2	22 54.3	1 18.5	25 5.3	9 43.2	0 53.9	21 2.3	20 40.2	23 56.5
4	20 50 17.1	14 6.0	7 20.3	29 1.5	23 52.3	2 32.7	25 39.2	9 51.6	0 49.9	20 60.0	20 38.6	23 56.4
5	20 54 13.7	15 3.7	7 16.9	10♓18.2	24 56.6	3 47.0	26 13.2	10 .2	0 45.8	20 57.6	20 37.1	23 56.4
6	20 58 10.3	16 1.3	7 13.5	21 22.3	26 7.1	5 1.4	26 47.2	10 8.9	0 41.7	20 55.4	20 35.6	23 56.3
7	21 2 6.8	16 58.7	7 10.1	2♈24.3	27 23.5	6 16.0	27 21.2	10 17.6	0 37.6	20 53.1	20 34.0	23 56.3
8	21 6 3.4	17 56.0	7 6.8	13 35.0	28 45.7	7 30.7	27 55.3	10 26.5	0 33.5	20 50.9	20 32.5	23 56.3
9	21 9 59.9	18 53.1	7 3.4	25 4.7	0♌13.2	8 45.5	28 29.5	10 35.4	0 29.3	20 48.6	20 31.0	23 D 56.4
10	21 13 56.5	19 50.1	7 .0	7♉ 2.4	1 45.9	10 .5	29 3.7	10 44.4	0 25.1	20 46.5	20 29.6	23 56.5
11	21 17 53.0	20 47.0	6 56.6	19 34.9	3 23.4	11 15.5	29 38.0	10 53.5	0 20.8	20 44.3	20 28.1	23 56.6
12	21 21 49.6	21 43.7	6 53.2	2♊45.2	5 5.2	12 30.6	0♎12.3	11 2.7	0 16.6	20 42.2	20 26.7	23 56.7
13	21 25 46.1	22 40.3	6 49.9	16 30.7	6 51.0	13 45.8	0 46.6	11 12.0	0 12.3	20 40.1	20 25.3	23 56.9
14	21 29 42.7	23 36.7	6 46.5	0♋43.5	8 40.2	15 1.0	1 21.1	11 21.4	0 8.0	20 38.0	20 23.9	23 57.1
15	21 33 39.2	24 33.1	6 43.1	15 11.1	10 32.4	16 16.2	1 55.6	11 30.8	0 3.7	20 36.0	20 22.5	23 57.4
16	21 37 35.8	25 29.3	6 39.7	29 40.4	12 27.1	17 31.6	2 30.1	11 40.4	29♒59.4	20 34.0	20 21.2	23 57.7
17	21 41 32.4	26 25.3	6 36.4	14♌ 1.6	14 23.7	18 46.9	3 4.7	11 50.0	29 55.0	20 32.0	20 19.9	23 58.0
18	21 45 28.9	27 21.3	6 33.0	28 10.5	16 21.9	20 2.2	3 39.4	11 59.7	29 50.7	20 30.1	20 18.6	23 58.3
19	21 49 25.5	28 17.1	6 29.6	12♍ 8.9	18 21.0	21 17.5	4 14.1	12 9.4	29 46.3	20 28.2	20 17.3	23 58.7
20	21 53 22.0	29 12.8	6 26.2	26 2.9	20 20.6	22 32.7	4 48.9	12 19.3	29 42.0	20 26.4	20 16.0	23 59.1
21	21 57 18.6	0♍ 8.3	6 22.9	10♎ .1	22 20.5	23 48.0	5 23.8	12 29.2	29 37.6	20 24.5	20 14.8	23 59.6
22	22 1 15.1	1 3.8	6 19.5	24 7.1	24 20.0	25 3.1	5 58.7	12 39.2	29 33.3	20 22.7	20 13.5	24 .0
23	22 5 11.7	1 59.1	6 16.1	8♏26.8	26 19.1	26 18.3	6 33.7	12 49.2	29 28.9	20 21.0	20 12.3	24 .5
24	22 9 8.2	2 54.3	6 12.7	22 56.6	28 17.3	27 33.4	7 8.8	12 59.3	29 24.6	20 19.3	20 11.2	24 1.1
25	22 13 4.8	3 49.4	6 9.4	7♐27.9	0♍14.4	28 48.3	7 43.9	13 9.5	29 20.2	20 17.6	20 10.0	24 1.6
26	22 17 1.3	4 44.4	6 6.0	21 48.7	2 10.3	0♌ 3.3	8 19.1	13 19.8	29 15.9	20 16.0	20 8.9	24 2.2
27	22 20 57.9	5 39.3	6 2.6	5♑46.1	4 4.9	1 18.1	8 54.4	13 30.1	29 11.6	20 14.4	20 7.8	24 2.8
28	22 24 54.4	6 34.0	5 59.2	19 10.9	5 57.9	2 32.8	9 29.7	13 40.5	29 7.2	20 12.9	20 6.7	24 3.5
29	22 28 51.0	7 28.7	5 55.9	1♒59.1	7 49.3	3 47.4	10 5.1	13 51.0	29 3.0	20 11.4	20 5.7	24 4.2
30	22 32 47.6	8 23.3	5 52.5	14 11.7	9 39.2	5 1.9	10 40.6	14 1.5	28 58.7	20 9.9	20 4.7	24 4.9
31	22 36 44.1	9 17.8	5 49.1	25 54.0	11 27.4	6 16.3	11 16.2	14 12.1	28 54.4	20 8.5	20 3.7	24 5.7

DECLINATION

DAY	SID. TIME	☉	☊	☽	☿	♀	♂	♃	♄	♅	♆	♇
1	20 38 27.5	18N 4.0	0S22.9	18S30.0	19N28.5	21N40.7	3N22.2	2S46.0	13S27.1	22S30.4	21S23.1	4S30.3
4	20 50 17.1	17 17.6	0 22.8	7 18.7	19 53.8	21 48.9	2 36.1	2 57.2	13 31.8	22 31.4	21 23.8	4 31.9
7	21 2 6.8	16 28.7	0 22.8	6N 2.8	20 6.3	21 52.1	1 49.8	3 8.8	13 36.6	22 32.3	21 24.5	4 33.5
10	21 13 56.5	15 37.4	0 22.8	17 15.4	20 1.3	21 50.1	1 3.2	3 20.8	13 41.4	22 33.1	21 25.1	4 35.3
13	21 25 46.1	14 43.8	0 22.8	22 9.1	19 34.6	21 42.9	0 16.3	3 33.0	13 46.3	22 34.0	21 25.8	4 37.1
16	21 37 35.8	13 48.0	0 22.7	16 45.7	18 43.9	21 30.4	0S30.8	3 45.5	13 51.2	22 34.7	21 26.4	4 39.0
19	21 49 25.5	12 50.3	0 22.7	2 9.6	17 29.3	21 12.5	1 18.0	3 58.2	13 56.1	22 35.5	21 26.9	4 40.9
22	22 1 15.1	11 50.8	0 22.7	13S36.4	15 53.4	20 49.4	2 5.3	4 11.1	14 1.0	22 36.1	21 27.5	4 42.9
25	22 13 4.8	10 49.6	0 22.7	21 45.4	14 .2	20 21.0	2 52.6	4 24.3	14 5.8	22 36.8	21 28.0	4 45.0
28	22 24 54.4	9 46.9	0 22.6	19 1.1	11 54.4	19 47.4	3 40.0	4 37.7	14 10.6	22 37.3	21 28.5	4 47.1
31	22 36 44.1	8 42.8	0 22.6	8 29.7	9 40.2	19 8.8	4 27.3	4 51.3	14 15.2	22 37.9	21 29.0	4 49.3

SEPTEMBER 1993

LONGITUDE

DAY	EPHEM. SID. TIME h m s	☉ ° ′	☊ ° ′	☽ ° ′	☿ ° ′	♀ ° ′	♂ ° ′	♃ ° ′	♄ ° ′	♅ ° ′	♆ ° ′	♇ ° ′
1	22 40 40.7	8♍34.8	7♐33.4	7♓23.4	11♍ 8.6	5♌10.3	12♎45.0	15♎ 8.6	26♒ 3.2	18♑30.7	18♑36.0	22♏57.7
2	22 44 37.2	9 32.8	7 30.2	19 23.5	13 2.3	6 21.9	13 24.0	15 20.2	25R58.9	18R29.4	18R35.2	22 58.7
3	22 48 33.8	10 30.9	7 27.0	1♈18.3	14 54.8	7 33.5	14 3.0	15 31.8	25 54.6	18 28.2	18 34.3	22 59.7
4	22 52 30.3	11 29.0	7 23.9	13 9.4	16 46.1	8 45.3	14 42.0	15 43.6	25 50.3	18 27.1	18 33.5	23 .8
5	22 56 26.9	12 27.2	7 20.7	24 59.0	18 36.3	9 57.1	15 21.1	15 55.3	25 46.0	18 26.0	18 32.7	23 1.9
6	23 0 23.4	13 25.4	7 17.5	6♉50.1	20 25.3	11 9.1	16 .3	16 7.2	25 41.9	18 25.0	18 32.0	23 3.0
7	23 4 20.0	14 23.6	7 14.3	18 46.4	22 13.1	12 21.1	16 39.5	16 19.1	25 37.7	18 23.9	18 31.2	23 4.2
8	23 8 16.5	15 21.8	7 11.2	0♊52.4	23 59.7	13 33.2	17 18.8	16 31.1	25 33.5	18 23.0	18 30.5	23 5.4
9	23 12 13.1	16 20.1	7 8.0	13 13.0	25 45.1	14 45.3	17 58.2	16 43.0	25 29.5	18 22.1	18 29.8	23 6.6
10	23 16 9.6	17 18.4	7 4.8	25 53.4	27 29.4	15 57.5	18 37.6	16 55.1	25 25.4	18 21.2	18 29.2	23 7.8
11	23 20 6.2	18 16.7	7 1.6	8♋58.3	29 12.5	17 9.8	19 17.0	17 7.2	25 21.4	18 20.3	18 28.6	23 9.1
12	23 24 2.7	19 15.1	6 58.4	22 31.4	0♎54.5	18 22.2	19 56.6	17 19.3	25 17.5	18 19.6	18 28.0	23 10.4
13	23 27 59.3	20 13.5	6 55.3	6♌34.6	2 35.4	19 34.7	20 36.2	17 31.5	25 13.6	18 18.8	18 27.4	23 11.7
14	23 31 55.8	21 11.9	6 52.1	21 6.6	4 15.2	20 47.2	21 15.8	17 43.8	25 9.7	18 18.1	18 26.9	23 13.1
15	23 35 52.4	22 10.4	6 48.9	6♍ 2.7	5 53.9	21 59.8	21 55.5	17 56.0	25 5.9	18 17.5	18 26.4	23 14.5
16	23 39 48.9	23 8.9	6 45.7	21 14.6	7 31.5	23 12.5	22 35.3	18 8.4	25 2.2	18 16.9	18 25.9	23 15.9
17	23 43 45.5	24 7.5	6 42.6	6♎31.8	9 8.1	24 25.2	23 15.1	18 20.7	24 58.5	18 16.3	18 25.4	23 17.3
18	23 47 42.1	25 6.0	6 39.4	21 42.9	10 43.6	25 38.0	23 55.0	18 33.1	24 54.9	18 15.8	18 25.0	23 18.8
19	23 51 38.6	26 4.6	6 36.2	6♏38.3	12 18.2	26 50.9	24 35.0	18 45.6	24 51.4	18 15.4	18 24.7	23 20.3
20	23 55 35.2	27 3.3	6 33.0	21 11.0	13 51.7	28 3.8	25 15.0	18 58.1	24 47.9	18 15.0	18 24.3	23 21.9
21	23 59 31.7	28 1.9	6 29.8	5♐17.8	15 24.2	29 16.8	25 55.0	19 10.6	24 44.5	18 14.6	18 24.0	23 23.4
22	0 3 28.3	29 .6	6 26.7	18 58.1	16 55.6	0♍29.8	26 35.2	19 23.2	24 41.2	18 14.3	18 23.7	23 25.0
23	0 7 24.8	29 59.3	6 23.5	2♑13.9	18 26.1	1 42.9	27 15.4	19 35.8	24 37.9	18 14.1	18 23.5	23 26.6
24	0 11 21.4	0♎58.1	6 20.3	15 8.3	19 55.6	2 56.1	27 55.6	19 48.4	24 34.7	18 13.9	18 23.3	23 28.3
25	0 15 17.9	1 56.8	6 17.1	27 45.1	21 24.1	4 9.3	28 35.9	20 1.0	24 31.6	18 13.8	18 23.1	23 29.9
26	0 19 14.5	2 55.6	6 13.9	10♒ 7.8	22 51.5	5 22.6	29 16.3	20 13.7	24 28.5	18 13.7	18 22.9	23 31.6
27	0 23 11.0	3 54.5	6 10.8	22 19.8	24 18.0	6 36.0	29 56.7	20 26.5	24 25.6	18 13.7	18 22.8	23 33.4
28	0 27 7.6	4 53.4	6 7.6	4♓23.8	25 43.4	7 49.4	0♏37.2	20 39.2	24 22.7	18 13.7	18 22.8	23 35.1
29	0 31 4.1	5 52.3	6 4.4	16 22.0	27 7.7	9 2.8	1 17.7	20 52.0	24 19.9	18 13.7	18 22.7	23 36.9
30	0 35 .7	6 51.2	6 1.2	28 16.3	28 31.0	10 16.3	1 58.3	21 4.8	24 17.2	18D13.8	18 22.7	23 38.7

LATITUDE

DAY	EPHEM. SID. TIME	☉	☊	☽	☿	♀	♂	♃	♄	♅	♆	♇
1	22 40 40.7	0 .0	0 .0	4N59.6	1N38.4	0S 3.8	0N20.8	1N 7.3	1S32.2	0S28.7	0N40.1	14N 6.7
4	22 52 30.3	0 .0	0 .0	4 2.7	1 27.5	0N 5.7	0 18.8	1 6.9	1 32.3	0 28.7	0 40.0	14 5.1
7	23 4 20.0	0 .0	0 .0	1 33.0	1 13.1	0 14.9	0 16.9	1 6.6	1 32.3	0 28.6	0 39.9	14 3.6
10	23 16 9.6	0 .0	0 .0	1S40.3	0 56.0	0 23.7	0 14.9	1 6.3	1 32.4	0 28.6	0 39.8	14 2.1
13	23 27 59.3	0 .0	0 .0	4 22.1	0 36.8	0 32.1	0 13.0	1 6.0	1 32.4	0 28.5	0 39.7	14 .6
16	23 39 48.9	0 .0	0 .0	4 51.1	0 16.1	0 40.2	0 11.0	1 5.7	1 32.4	0 28.5	0 39.6	13 59.2
19	23 51 38.6	0 .0	0 .0	2 27.0	0S 5.6	0 47.7	0 9.1	1 5.5	1 32.3	0 28.4	0 39.5	13 57.8
22	0 3 28.3	0 .0	0 .0	1N11.1	0 28.0	0 54.8	0 7.2	1 5.3	1 32.3	0 28.4	0 39.4	13 56.5
25	0 15 17.9	0 .0	0 .0	4 1.1	0 50.6	1 1.4	0 5.3	1 5.1	1 32.2	0 28.3	0 39.3	13 55.2
28	0 27 7.6	0 .0	0 .0	5 3.7	1 13.1	1 7.4	0 3.4	1 4.9	1 32.1	0 28.3	0 39.3	13 53.9

RIGHT ASCENSION

DAY	EPHEM. SID. TIME	☉	☊	☽	☿	♀	♂	♃	♄	♅	♆	♇
1	22 40 40.7	10♍12.3	5♐45.7	7♓13.8	13♍13.9	7♌30.6	11♎51.9	14♎22.7	28♒50.2	20♑ 7.1	20♑ 2.7	24♏ 6.5
2	22 44 37.2	11 6.6	5 42.4	18 20.2	14 58.8	8 44.7	12 27.6	14 33.4	28R46.0	20R 5.8	20R 1.8	24 7.3
3	22 48 33.8	12 .9	5 39.0	29 22.7	16 42.1	9 58.7	13 3.4	14 44.2	28 41.8	20 4.5	20 .9	24 8.1
4	22 52 30.3	12 55.1	5 35.6	10♈30.8	18 23.9	11 12.6	13 39.3	14 55.0	28 37.7	20 3.3	20 .0	24 9.0
5	22 56 26.9	13 49.3	5 32.3	21 53.4	20 4.1	12 26.3	14 15.3	15 5.9	28 33.6	20 2.1	19 59.2	24 9.9
6	23 0 23.4	14 43.5	5 28.9	3♉38.5	21 42.8	13 39.9	14 51.5	15 16.8	28 29.5	20 1.0	19 58.4	24 10.9
7	23 4 20.0	15 37.5	5 25.5	15 52.0	23 20.2	14 53.2	15 27.6	15 27.8	28 25.5	19 59.9	19 57.6	24 11.9
8	23 8 16.5	16 31.5	5 22.2	28 37.0	24 56.1	16 6.5	16 3.9	15 38.9	28 21.5	19 58.9	19 56.9	24 12.9
9	23 12 13.1	17 25.5	5 18.8	11♊52.9	26 30.7	17 19.5	16 40.3	15 49.9	28 17.5	19 57.9	19 56.2	24 13.9
10	23 16 9.6	18 19.4	5 15.4	25 34.7	28 4.1	18 32.4	17 16.7	16 1.1	28 13.6	19 56.9	19 55.5	24 14.9
11	23 20 6.2	19 13.3	5 12.1	9♋34.1	29 36.3	19 45.2	17 53.3	16 12.3	28 9.7	19 56.0	19 54.8	24 16.0
12	23 24 2.7	20 7.2	5 8.7	23 41.9	1♎ 7.3	20 57.7	18 29.9	16 23.5	28 5.9	19 55.2	19 54.2	24 17.1
13	23 27 59.3	21 1.1	5 5.3	7♌50.3	2 37.2	22 10.1	19 6.7	16 34.8	28 2.1	19 54.4	19 53.6	24 18.3
14	23 31 55.8	21 54.9	5 2.0	21 55.4	4 6.1	23 22.3	19 43.6	16 46.2	27 58.3	19 53.6	19 53.0	24 19.5
15	23 35 52.4	22 48.7	4 58.6	5♍58.0	5 34.0	24 34.3	20 20.5	16 57.5	27 54.7	19 52.9	19 52.5	24 20.7
16	23 39 48.9	23 42.6	4 55.2	20 2.8	7 1.0	25 46.2	20 57.6	17 9.0	27 51.0	19 52.3	19 52.0	24 21.9
17	23 43 45.5	24 36.4	4 51.9	4♎16.3	8 27.1	26 57.9	21 34.8	17 20.4	27 47.5	19 51.7	19 51.5	24 23.2
18	23 47 42.1	25 30.2	4 48.5	18 44.1	9 52.3	28 9.4	22 12.1	17 32.0	27 43.9	19 51.2	19 51.1	24 24.4
19	23 51 38.6	26 24.0	4 45.1	3♏28.2	11 16.7	29 20.7	22 49.5	17 43.5	27 40.5	19 50.7	19 50.7	24 25.8
20	23 55 35.2	27 17.8	4 41.8	18 24.3	12 40.3	0♍31.8	23 27.0	17 55.1	27 37.1	19 50.3	19 50.3	24 27.1
21	23 59 31.7	28 11.7	4 38.4	3♐22.0	14 3.1	1 42.8	24 4.7	18 6.7	27 33.8	19 49.9	19 50.0	24 28.5
22	0 3 28.3	29 5.5	4 35.0	18 6.6	15 25.3	2 53.6	24 42.4	18 18.4	27 30.5	19 49.6	19 49.7	24 29.9
23	0 7 24.8	29 59.4	4 31.7	2♑23.5	16 46.7	4 4.3	25 20.3	18 30.1	27 27.3	19 49.3	19 49.5	24 31.3
24	0 11 21.4	0♎53.3	4 28.3	16 2.6	18 7.4	5 14.7	25 58.3	18 41.9	27 24.2	19 49.1	19 49.2	24 32.7
25	0 15 17.9	1 47.2	4 24.9	29 .2	19 27.5	6 25.1	26 36.3	18 53.6	27 21.1	19 48.9	19 49.0	24 34.2
26	0 19 14.5	2 41.2	4 21.6	11♒18.5	20 46.8	7 35.2	27 14.6	19 5.5	27 18.2	19 48.8	19 48.9	24 35.7
27	0 23 11.0	3 35.2	4 18.2	23 4.0	22 5.6	8 45.3	27 52.9	19 17.3	27 15.3	19 48.8	19 48.8	24 37.3
28	0 27 7.6	4 29.3	4 14.9	4♓25.1	23 23.7	9 55.2	28 31.4	19 29.2	27 12.5	19 48.8	19 48.7	24 38.8
29	0 31 4.1	5 23.4	4 11.5	15 31.8	24 41.1	11 4.9	29 10.0	19 41.1	27 9.7	19D48.9	19 48.7	24 40.4
30	0 35 .7	6 17.5	4 8.1	26 33.8	25 57.8	12 14.5	29 48.7	19 53.0	27 7.0	19 49.0	19 48.7	24 42.0

DECLINATION

DAY	EPHEM. SID. TIME	☉	☊	☽	☿	♀	♂	♃	♄	♅	♆	♇
1	22 40 40.7	8N21.2	0S22.6	4S 9.5	8N54.2	18N54.9	4S43.0	4S55.8	14S16.7	22S38.0	21S29.2	4S50.0
4	22 52 30.3	7 15.4	0 22.6	8N55.1	6 34.0	18 9.8	5 30.2	5 9.6	14 21.2	22 38.5	21 29.6	4 52.2
7	23 4 20.0	6 8.6	0 22.5	18 53.9	4 12.4	17 20.0	6 17.3	5 23.5	14 25.6	22 38.9	21 30.0	4 54.5
10	23 16 9.6	5 .9	0 22.5	21 42.3	1 51.3	16 25.8	7 4.1	5 37.6	14 29.7	22 39.2	21 30.4	4 56.8
13	23 27 59.3	3 52.3	0 22.5	14 23.7	0S28.0	15 27.3	7 50.7	5 51.8	14 33.8	22 39.5	21 30.7	4 59.1
16	23 39 48.9	2 43.2	0 22.5	0S59.4	2 44.4	14 24.9	8 37.1	6 6.0	14 37.6	22 39.7	21 31.0	5 1.5
19	23 51 38.6	1 33.6	0 22.4	16 2.6	4 56.9	13 18.7	9 23.0	6 20.4	14 41.2	22 39.9	21 31.3	5 3.8
22	0 3 28.3	0 23.6	0 22.4	21 48.0	7 4.9	12 9.1	10 8.6	6 34.8	14 44.6	22 39.9	21 31.5	5 6.2
25	0 15 17.9	0S46.5	0 22.4	16 40.2	9 7.7	10 56.3	10 53.6	6 49.3	14 47.7	22 40.0	21 31.7	5 8.6
28	0 27 7.6	1 56.6	0 22.3	5 10.8	11 4.6	9 40.7	11 38.2	7 3.8	14 50.6	22 39.9	21 31.8	5 11.0

OCTOBER 1993

DAY	EPHEM. SID. TIME	☉	☊	☽	☿	♀	♂	♃	♄	♅	♆	♇
		LONGITUDE										
	h m s	° ′	° ′	° ′	° ′	° ′	° ′	° ′	° ′	° ′	° ′	° ′
1	0 38 57.2	7♎50.1	5♐58.1	10♈ 8.0	29♎53.2	11♍29.9	2♏38.9	21♎17.6	24♒14.5	18♑14.0	18♑22.7	23♏40.5
2	0 42 53.8	8 49.1	5 54.9	21 58.8	1♏14.2	12 43.5	3 19.7	21 30.4	24R11.9	18 14.2	18D22.8	23 42.3
3	0 46 50.3	9 48.1	5 51.7	3♉50.4	2 34.0	13 57.2	4 .4	21 43.3	24 9.5	18 14.4	18 22.8	23 44.2
4	0 50 46.9	10 47.2	5 48.5	15 45.0	3 52.5	15 11.0	4 41.2	21 56.2	24 7.1	18 14.7	18 22.9	23 46.0
5	0 54 43.4	11 46.3	5 45.3	27 45.2	5 9.8	16 24.8	5 22.1	22 9.1	24 4.8	18 15.1	18 23.1	23 47.9
6	0 58 40.0	12 45.4	5 42.2	9♊54.4	6 25.7	17 38.6	6 3.1	22 22.0	24 2.5	18 15.5	18 23.3	23 49.9
7	1 2 36.5	13 44.6	5 39.0	22 16.5	7 40.1	18 52.5	6 44.1	22 34.9	24 .4	18 16.0	18 23.5	23 51.8
8	1 6 33.1	14 43.8	5 35.8	4♋55.8	8 53.0	20 6.5	7 25.1	22 47.9	23 58.4	18 16.5	18 23.7	23 53.8
9	1 10 29.7	15 43.0	5 32.6	17 56.6	10 4.2	21 20.5	8 6.3	23 .9	23 56.4	18 17.1	18 24.0	23 55.8
10	1 14 26.2	16 42.3	5 29.5	1♌22.6	11 13.7	22 34.5	8 47.4	23 13.8	23 54.6	18 17.7	18 24.3	23 57.8
11	1 18 22.8	17 41.7	5 26.3	15 16.2	12 21.3	23 48.6	9 28.7	23 26.8	23 52.8	18 18.3	18 24.7	23 59.8
12	1 22 19.3	18 41.0	5 23.1	29 37.6	13 26.7	25 2.8	10 10.0	23 39.8	23 51.1	18 19.0	18 25.0	24 1.8
13	1 26 15.9	19 40.4	5 19.9	14♍24.0	14 30.0	26 17.0	10 51.4	23 52.9	23 49.5	18 19.8	18 25.5	24 3.9
14	1 30 12.4	20 39.9	5 16.7	29 29.4	15 30.7	27 31.3	11 32.8	24 5.9	23 48.1	18 20.6	18 25.9	24 6.0
15	1 34 9.0	21 39.3	5 13.6	14♎44.5	16 28.8	28 45.5	12 14.3	24 18.9	23 46.7	18 21.5	18 26.4	24 8.1
16	1 38 5.5	22 38.8	5 10.4	29 58.9	17 24.0	29 59.9	12 55.9	24 32.0	23 45.4	18 22.4	18 26.9	24 10.2
17	1 42 2.1	23 38.4	5 7.2	15♏ 2.0	18 15.9	1♎14.3	13 37.5	24 45.0	23 44.2	18 23.4	18 27.4	24 12.3
18	1 45 58.6	24 38.0	5 4.0	29 45.4	19 4.3	2 28.7	14 19.2	24 58.1	23 43.2	18 24.5	18 28.1	24 14.5
19	1 49 55.2	25 37.6	5 .9	14♐ 3.4	19 48.7	3 43.2	15 .9	25 11.1	23 42.2	18 25.5	18 28.7	24 16.7
20	1 53 51.7	26 37.2	4 57.7	27 53.9	20 28.7	4 57.6	15 42.7	25 24.2	23 41.3	18 26.7	18 29.3	24 18.8
21	1 57 48.3	27 36.9	4 54.5	11♑17.2	21 4.0	6 12.2	16 24.6	25 37.2	23 40.6	18 27.8	18 30.0	24 21.0
22	2 1 44.8	28 36.6	4 51.3	24 15.8	21 34.1	7 26.7	17 6.5	25 50.3	23 39.9	18 29.0	18 30.7	24 23.2
23	2 5 41.4	29 36.3	4 48.1	6♒53.2	21 58.3	8 41.3	17 48.4	26 3.3	23 39.3	18 30.3	18 31.5	24 25.5
24	2 9 38.0	0♏36.1	4 45.0	19 13.6	22 16.2	9 55.9	18 30.5	26 16.4	23 38.8	18 31.6	18 32.2	24 27.7
25	2 13 34.5	1 35.8	4 41.8	1♓21.2	22 27.2	11 10.6	19 12.5	26 29.4	23 38.5	18 33.0	18 33.1	24 30.0
26	2 17 31.1	2 35.7	4 38.6	13 20.0	22 30.6	12 25.3	19 54.7	26 42.4	23 38.2	18 34.4	18 33.9	24 32.2
27	2 21 27.6	3 35.5	4 35.4	25 13.4	22R26.0	13 40.0	20 36.9	26 55.4	23 38.0	18 35.9	18 34.8	24 34.5
28	2 25 24.2	4 35.4	4 32.3	7♈ 4.5	22 12.8	14 54.7	21 19.1	27 8.4	23 38.0	18 37.4	18 35.7	24 36.8
29	2 29 20.7	5 35.2	4 29.1	18 55.7	21 50.6	16 9.5	22 1.4	27 21.4	23 38.0	18 38.9	18 36.6	24 39.1
30	2 33 17.3	6 35.2	4 25.9	0♉49.1	21 19.1	17 24.3	22 43.8	27 34.4	23D38.2	18 40.5	18 37.6	24 41.4
31	2 37 13.8	7 35.1	4 22.7	12 46.5	20 38.2	18 39.1	23 26.2	27 47.4	23 38.4	18 42.2	18 38.6	24 43.7
		LATITUDE										
1	0 38 57.2	0 .0	0 .0	4N 7.8	1S35.1	1N12.8	0N 1.5	1N 4.7	1S32.0	0S28.2	0N39.2	13N52.7
4	0 50 46.9	0 .0	0 .0	1 37.2	1 56.2	1 17.7	0S .4	1 4.5	1 31.8	0 28.2	0 39.1	13 51.6
7	1 2 36.5	0 .0	0 .0	1S36.3	2 15.9	1 21.9	0 2.3	1 4.4	1 31.7	0 28.1	0 39.0	13 50.5
10	1 14 26.2	0 .0	0 .0	4 20.0	2 33.8	1 25.4	0 4.1	1 4.3	1 31.5	0 28.1	0 38.9	13 49.4
13	1 26 15.9	0 .0	0 .0	5 3.7	2 49.1	1 28.4	0 6.0	1 4.2	1 31.3	0 28.0	0 38.8	13 48.4
16	1 38 5.5	0 .0	0 .0	2 52.0	3 .9	1 30.6	0 7.8	1 4.1	1 31.1	0 28.0	0 38.7	13 47.5
19	1 49 55.2	0 .0	0 .0	0N57.0	3 8.0	1 32.3	0 9.7	1 4.0	1 30.9	0 27.9	0 38.6	13 46.6
22	2 1 44.8	0 .0	0 .0	4 1.8	3 8.7	1 33.2	0 11.5	1 4.0	1 30.6	0 27.9	0 38.5	13 45.8
25	2 13 34.5	0 .0	0 .0	5 12.0	3 .6	1 33.5	0 13.3	1 4.0	1 30.4	0 27.8	0 38.4	13 45.1
28	2 25 24.2	0 .0	0 .0	4 20.1	2 41.1	1 33.2	0 15.1	1 4.0	1 30.1	0 27.8	0 38.3	13 44.4
31	2 37 13.8	0 .0	0 .0	1 49.2	2 7.2	1 32.2	0 16.9	1 4.0	1 29.9	0 27.7	0 38.2	13 43.8
		RIGHT ASCENSION										
1	0 38 57.2	7♎11.8	4♐ 4.8	7♈40.6	27♎13.8	13♍24.0	0♏27.5	20♎ 5.0	27♒ 4.4	19♑49.1	19♑48.7	24♏43.6
2	0 42 53.8	8 6.1	4 1.4	19 .8	28 29.0	14 33.3	1 6.5	20 17.0	27R 1.9	19 49.4	19 48.7	24 45.3
3	0 46 50.3	9 .4	3 58.1	0♉41.4	29 43.5	15 42.6	1 45.6	20 29.0	26 59.5	19 49.6	19D48.8	24 46.9
4	0 50 46.9	9 54.9	3 54.7	12 47.4	0♏57.2	16 51.7	2 24.8	20 41.0	26 57.1	19 50.0	19 48.9	24 48.6
5	0 54 43.4	10 49.4	3 51.4	25 21.0	2 10.0	18 .8	3 4.1	20 53.1	26 54.8	19 50.3	19 49.1	24 50.3
6	0 58 40.0	11 44.1	3 48.0	8♊20.7	3 21.8	19 9.7	3 43.6	21 5.2	26 52.7	19 50.8	19 49.3	24 52.1
7	1 2 36.5	12 38.8	3 44.6	21 41.4	4 32.7	20 18.6	4 23.3	21 17.3	26 50.6	19 51.3	19 49.5	24 53.8
8	1 6 33.1	13 33.7	3 41.3	5♋16.0	5 42.4	21 27.4	5 3.0	21 29.4	26 48.6	19 51.8	19 49.8	24 55.6
9	1 10 29.7	14 28.6	3 37.9	18 56.5	6 50.8	22 36.1	5 42.9	21 41.6	26 46.6	19 52.4	19 50.1	24 57.4
10	1 14 26.2	15 23.7	3 34.6	2♌37.3	7 57.9	23 44.8	6 23.0	21 53.7	26 44.8	19 53.1	19 50.4	24 59.2
11	1 18 22.8	16 18.9	3 31.2	16 16.2	9 3.5	24 53.4	7 3.2	22 5.9	26 43.1	19 53.8	19 50.8	25 1.0
12	1 22 19.3	17 14.2	3 27.9	29 55.5	10 7.4	26 2.0	7 43.5	22 18.1	26 41.4	19 54.6	19 51.2	25 2.9
13	1 26 15.9	18 9.7	3 24.5	13♍41.0	11 9.5	27 10.5	8 24.0	22 30.3	26 39.8	19 55.4	19 51.7	25 4.8
14	1 30 12.4	19 5.2	3 21.2	27 40.9	12 9.4	28 19.0	9 4.7	22 42.6	26 38.4	19 56.3	19 52.1	25 6.7
15	1 34 9.0	20 1.0	3 17.8	12♎ 2.8	13 7.0	29 27.5	9 45.5	22 54.8	26 37.0	19 57.2	19 52.7	25 8.6
16	1 38 5.5	20 56.8	3 14.5	26 51.2	14 2.0	0♎35.9	10 26.4	23 7.1	26 35.7	19 58.2	19 53.2	25 10.5
17	1 42 2.1	21 52.8	3 11.1	12♏ 3.6	14 54.0	1 44.4	11 7.5	23 19.3	26 34.6	19 59.2	19 53.8	25 12.5
18	1 45 58.6	22 49.0	3 7.7	27 29.2	15 42.7	2 52.9	11 48.7	23 31.7	26 33.5	20 .4	19 54.5	25 14.5
19	1 49 55.2	23 45.3	3 4.4	12♐49.6	16 27.7	4 1.4	12 30.1	23 43.9	26 32.5	20 1.5	19 55.1	25 16.5
20	1 53 51.7	24 41.7	3 1.0	27 44.8	17 8.6	5 9.9	13 11.7	23 56.2	26 31.7	20 2.7	19 55.8	25 18.5
21	1 57 48.3	25 38.4	2 57.7	11♑59.2	17 44.9	6 18.5	13 53.3	24 8.5	26 30.9	20 4.0	19 56.6	25 20.5
22	2 1 44.8	26 35.1	2 54.3	25 25.4	18 16.0	7 27.0	14 35.2	24 20.8	26 30.2	20 5.3	19 57.3	25 22.5
23	2 5 41.4	27 32.0	2 51.0	8♒ 4.5	18 41.5	8 35.7	15 17.1	24 33.1	26 29.6	20 6.6	19 58.1	25 24.6
24	2 9 38.0	23 29.1	2 47.6	20 3.1	19 .8	9 44.4	15 59.3	24 45.4	26 29.1	20 8.0	19 58.9	25 26.6
25	2 13 34.5	29 26.4	2 44.3	1♓31.3	19 13.2	10 53.1	16 41.6	24 57.7	26 28.7	20 9.5	19 59.8	25 28.7
26	2 17 31.1	0♏23.8	2 40.9	12 40.5	19 18.2	12 2.0	17 24.0	25 10.0	26 28.4	20 11.0	20 .7	25 30.8
27	2 21 27.6	1 21.4	2 37.6	23 41.9	19R15.2	13 10.9	18 6.6	25 22.3	26 28.2	20 12.6	20 1.6	25 32.9
28	2 25 24.2	2 19.2	2 34.3	4♈46.4	19 3.8	14 19.9	18 49.3	25 34.6	26 28.1	20 14.2	20 2.6	25 35.0
29	2 29 20.7	3 17.2	2 30.9	16 3.4	18 43.6	15 29.1	19 32.2	25 46.9	26D28.2	20 15.9	20 3.6	25 37.2
30	2 33 17.3	4 15.4	2 27.6	27 41.1	18 14.3	16 38.3	20 15.3	25 59.2	26 28.3	20 17.6	20 4.7	25 39.3
31	2 37 13.8	5 13.8	2 24.2	9♉44.9	17 36.1	17 47.7	20 58.5	26 11.5	26 28.5	20 19.4	20 5.7	25 41.5
		DECLINATION										
1	0 38 57.2	3S 6.5	0S22.3	7N48.6	12S54.9	8N22.4	12S22.1	7S18.3	14S53.2	22S39.8	21S31.9	5S13.4
4	0 50 46.9	4 16.1	0 22.3	18 6.3	14 37.9	7 1.9	13 5.4	7 32.9	14 55.5	22 39.7	21 32.0	5 15.8
7	1 2 36.5	5 25.3	0 22.2	21 36.7	16 12.6	5 39.4	13 47.9	7 47.4	14 57.6	22 39.5	21 32.0	5 18.2
10	1 14 26.2	6 33.9	0 22.2	15 37.4	17 38.0	4 15.2	14 29.7	8 1.9	14 59.4	22 39.2	21 32.0	5 20.6
13	1 26 15.9	7 41.8	0 22.2	1 28.0	18 52.8	2 49.7	15 10.6	8 16.3	15 .9	22 38.8	21 31.9	5 23.0
16	1 38 5.5	8 48.6	0 22.2	14S 8.8	19 55.0	1 23.2	15 50.7	8 30.7	15 2.0	22 38.4	21 31.8	5 25.3
19	1 49 55.2	9 54.4	0 22.1	21 32.6	20 42.3	0S 4.0	16 29.7	8 45.1	15 2.9	22 38.0	21 31.7	5 27.6
22	2 1 44.8	10 58.8	0 22.1	17 17.6	21 11.4	1 31.6	17 7.6	8 59.4	15 3.4	22 37.4	21 31.5	5 29.9
25	2 13 34.5	12 1.7	0 22.1	6 7.7	21 17.5	2 59.2	17 44.4	9 13.5	15 3.7	22 36.8	21 31.2	5 32.1
28	2 25 24.2	13 3.0	0 22.0	6N47.3	20 54.9	4 26.5	18 20.0	9 27.6	15 3.6	22 36.2	21 31.0	5 34.3
31	2 37 13.8	14 2.5	0 22.0	17 24.4	19 57.2	5 53.2	18 54.3	9 41.5	15 3.2	22 35.5	21 30.7	5 36.5

NOVEMBER 1993

LONGITUDE

DAY	EPHEM. SID. TIME	☉	☊	☽	☿	♀	♂	♃	♄	♅	♆	♇
	h m s	° ′	° ′	° ′	° ′	° ′	° ′	° ′	° ′	° ′	° ′	° ′
1	2 41 10.4	8♏35.1	4♐19.5	24♉49.7	19♏48.1	19♎54.0	24♏ 8.7	28♎ .3	23♒38.7	18♑43.9	18♑39.6	24♏46.0
2	2 45 6.9	9 35.1	4 16.4	7♊ .4	18 R 49.5	21 8.9	24 51.2	28 13.2	23 39.2	18 45.6	18 40.7	24 48.3
3	2 49 3.5	10 35.2	4 13.2	19 20.7	17 43.3	22 23.8	25 33.8	28 26.2	23 39.8	18 47.4	18 41.8	24 50.7
4	2 53 .0	11 35.3	4 10.0	1♋52.9	16 31.0	23 38.8	26 16.5	28 39.1	23 40.4	18 49.3	18 42.9	24 53.0
5	2 56 56.6	12 35.4	4 6.8	14 39.5	15 14.3	24 53.8	26 59.2	28 51.9	23 41.2	18 51.1	18 44.0	24 55.4
6	3 0 53.2	13 35.6	4 3.7	27 43.4	13 55.6	26 8.8	27 42.0	29 4.8	23 42.0	18 53.1	18 45.2	24 57.7
7	3 4 49.7	14 35.7	4 .5	11♌ 6.9	12 37.2	27 23.8	28 24.8	29 17.6	23 43.0	18 55.0	18 46.4	25 .1
8	3 8 46.3	15 36.0	3 57.3	24 51.9	11 21.7	28 38.9	29 7.8	29 30.5	23 44.1	18 57.1	18 47.7	25 2.5
9	3 12 42.8	16 36.3	3 54.1	8♍58.9	10 11.4	29 54.0	29 50.7	29 43.3	23 45.3	18 59.1	18 49.0	25 4.9
10	3 16 39.4	17 36.6	3 51.0	23 26.5	9 8.6	1♏ 9.1	0♐33.7	29 56.1	23 46.6	19 1.2	18 50.3	25 7.3
11	3 20 35.9	18 36.9	3 47.8	8♎11.3	8 15.1	2 24.3	1 16.8	0♏ 8.8	23 48.0	19 3.4	18 51.6	25 9.7
12	3 24 32.5	19 37.3	3 44.6	23 7.3	7 32.1	3 39.4	1 60.0	0 21.5	23 49.4	19 5.5	18 53.0	25 12.1
13	3 28 29.0	20 37.7	3 41.4	8♏ 6.8	7 .4	4 54.6	2 43.2	0 34.2	23 51.0	19 7.8	18 54.3	25 14.5
14	3 32 25.6	21 38.1	3 38.2	23 1.1	6 40.5	6 9.8	3 26.4	0 46.8	23 52.7	19 10.0	18 55.7	25 16.9
15	3 36 22.2	22 38.5	3 35.1	7♐42.0	6 32.2	7 25.0	4 9.7	0 59.4	23 54.5	19 12.3	18 57.2	25 19.3
16	3 40 18.7	23 39.0	3 31.9	22 3.1	6 D 35.1	8 40.2	4 53.1	1 12.0	23 56.4	19 14.7	18 58.6	25 21.7
17	3 44 15.3	24 39.5	3 28.7	6♑ .1	6 48.7	9 55.5	5 36.5	1 24.5	23 58.4	19 17.0	19 .1	25 24.1
18	3 48 11.8	25 40.0	3 25.5	19 31.2	7 12.1	11 10.7	6 20.0	1 37.0	24 .5	19 19.5	19 1.7	25 26.5
19	3 52 8.4	26 40.5	3 22.4	2♒37.0	7 44.5	12 26.0	7 3.5	1 49.5	24 2.7	19 21.9	19 3.2	25 28.9
20	3 56 4.9	27 41.1	3 19.2	15 19.8	8 25.0	13 41.3	7 47.1	2 1.9	24 5.0	19 24.4	19 4.8	25 31.3
21	4 0 1.5	28 41.7	3 16.0	27 43.2	9 12.7	14 56.6	8 30.7	2 14.3	24 7.3	19 27.0	19 6.4	25 33.7
22	4 3 58.0	29 42.3	3 12.8	9♓51.6	10 6.7	16 11.9	9 14.4	2 26.6	24 9.8	19 29.5	19 8.0	25 36.1
23	4 7 54.6	0♐42.9	3 9.6	21 49.4	11 6.3	17 27.2	9 58.2	2 38.9	24 12.4	19 32.1	19 9.6	25 38.5
24	4 11 51.2	1 43.5	3 6.5	3♈41.3	12 10.7	18 42.5	10 42.0	2 51.1	24 15.1	19 34.8	19 11.3	25 40.9
25	4 15 47.7	2 44.2	3 3.3	15 31.4	13 19.4	19 57.9	11 25.8	3 3.3	24 17.9	19 37.4	19 13.0	25 43.3
26	4 19 44.3	3 44.9	3 .1	27 23.6	14 31.6	21 13.2	12 9.7	3 15.4	24 20.7	19 40.2	19 14.7	25 45.7
27	4 23 40.8	4 45.6	2 56.9	9♉21.0	15 46.9	22 28.6	12 53.7	3 27.5	24 23.7	19 42.9	19 16.4	25 48.1
28	4 27 37.4	5 46.3	2 53.8	21 26.2	17 4.9	23 43.9	13 37.7	3 39.5	24 26.8	19 45.7	19 18.2	25 50.5
29	4 31 33.9	6 47.1	2 50.6	3♊41.4	18 25.2	24 59.4	14 21.8	3 51.5	24 29.9	19 48.5	19 20.0	25 52.9
30	4 35 30.5	7 47.8	2 47.4	16 7.8	19 47.3	26 14.8	15 5.9	4 3.4	24 33.2	19 51.4	19 21.8	25 55.3

LATITUDE

DAY	EPHEM. SID. TIME	☉	☊	☽	☿	♀	♂	♃	♄	♅	♆	♇
1	2 41 10.4	0 .0	0 .0	0N45.1	1S52.5	1N31.8	0S17.5	1N 4.0	1S29.8	0S27.7	0N38.2	13N43.6
4	2 53 .0	0 .0	0 .0	2S32.5	0 59.2	1 30.0	0 19.3	1 4.0	1 29.6	0 27.7	0 38.1	13 43.0
7	3 4 49.7	0 .0	0 .0	4 53.2	0N 2.1	1 27.6	0 21.0	1 4.1	1 29.3	0 27.6	0 38.0	13 42.6
10	3 16 39.4	0 .0	0 .0	4 56.6	1 .2	1 24.6	0 22.8	1 4.1	1 29.0	0 27.6	0 37.9	13 42.2
13	3 28 29.0	0 .0	0 .0	2 13.7	1 45.1	1 21.1	0 24.5	1 4.2	1 28.8	0 27.6	0 37.8	13 41.8
16	3 40 18.7	0 .0	0 .0	1N43.8	2 12.7	1 17.1	0 26.2	1 4.3	1 28.5	0 27.5	0 37.7	13 41.6
19	3 52 8.4	0 .0	0 .0	4 34.0	2 24.4	1 12.6	0 27.9	1 4.4	1 28.3	0 27.5	0 37.7	13 41.4
22	4 3 58.0	0 .0	0 .0	5 15.3	2 23.9	1 7.6	0 29.5	1 4.6	1 28.0	0 27.4	0 37.6	13 41.3
25	4 15 47.7	0 .0	0 .0	3 54.5	2 14.8	1 2.2	0 31.2	1 4.8	1 27.8	0 27.4	0 37.5	13 41.2
28	4 27 37.4	0 .0	0 .0	1 4.1	2 .0	0 56.5	0 32.8	1 4.9	1 27.5	0 27.4	0 37.4	13 41.2

RIGHT ASCENSION

DAY	EPHEM. SID. TIME	☉	☊	☽	☿	♀	♂	♃	♄	♅	♆	♇
1	2 41 10.4	6♏12.3	2♐20.9	22♉16.8	16♏49.1	18♎57.2	21♏41.8	26♎23.8	26♒28.8	20♑21.2	20♑ 6.8	25♏43.6
2	2 45 6.9	7 11.1	2 17.5	5♊14.6	15 R 54.2	20 6.9	22 25.4	26 36.1	26 29.2	20 23.0	20 8.0	25 45.8
3	2 49 3.5	8 10.1	2 14.2	18 32.3	14 52.5	21 16.7	23 9.0	26 48.3	26 29.7	20 25.0	20 9.1	25 48.0
4	2 53 .0	9 9.2	2 10.8	2♋ .7	13 45.2	22 26.7	23 52.9	27 .6	26 30.3	20 26.9	20 10.3	25 50.2
5	2 56 56.6	10 8.6	2 7.5	15 30.6	12 34.5	23 36.9	24 36.9	27 12.8	26 31.1	20 28.9	20 11.5	25 52.4
6	3 0 53.2	11 8.2	2 4.1	28 55.1	11 22.3	24 47.2	25 21.0	27 25.0	26 31.9	20 31.0	20 12.8	25 54.6
7	3 4 49.7	12 8.0	2 .8	12♌11.9	10 11.0	25 57.8	26 5.3	27 37.2	26 32.8	20 33.1	20 14.1	25 56.8
8	3 8 46.3	13 8.1	1 57.5	25 23.5	9 3.0	27 8.6	26 49.8	27 49.5	26 33.8	20 35.3	20 15.5	25 59.1
9	3 12 42.8	14 8.3	1 54.1	8♍36.8	8 .3	28 19.5	27 34.4	28 1.6	26 35.0	20 37.5	20 16.8	26 1.3
10	3 16 39.4	15 8.8	1 50.8	22 1.5	7 4.8	29 30.7	28 19.2	28 13.8	26 36.2	20 39.7	20 18.2	26 3.5
11	3 20 35.9	16 9.4	1 47.4	5♎48.4	6 18.2	0♏42.1	29 4.2	28 25.9	26 37.5	20 42.0	20 19.6	26 5.8
12	3 24 32.5	17 10.3	1 44.1	20 6.6	5 41.4	1 53.7	29 49.2	28 38.1	26 38.9	20 44.4	20 21.1	26 8.0
13	3 28 29.0	18 11.4	1 40.8	4♏59.7	5 15.1	3 5.6	0♐34.5	28 50.2	26 40.4	20 46.7	20 22.5	26 10.3
14	3 32 25.6	19 12.7	1 37.4	20 22.5	4 59.5	4 17.7	1 19.9	29 2.2	26 42.0	20 49.2	20 24.1	26 12.6
15	3 36 22.2	20 14.3	1 34.1	5♐59.4	4 54.6	5 30.1	2 5.4	29 14.3	26 43.8	20 51.6	20 25.6	26 14.8
16	3 40 18.7	21 16.0	1 30.7	21 27.5	4 D 59.8	6 42.7	2 51.1	29 26.3	26 45.6	20 54.1	20 27.1	26 17.1
17	3 44 15.3	22 17.9	1 27.4	6♑23.9	5 14.8	7 55.6	3 36.9	29 38.3	26 47.5	20 56.7	20 28.7	26 19.4
18	3 48 11.8	23 20.1	1 24.1	20 32.8	5 38.6	9 8.7	4 22.9	29 50.2	26 49.5	20 59.3	20 30.4	26 21.6
19	3 52 8.4	24 22.4	1 20.7	3♒49.2	6 10.7	10 22.2	5 9.1	0♏ 2.2	26 51.6	21 1.9	20 32.0	26 23.9
20	3 56 4.9	25 25.0	1 17.4	16 16.7	6 50.2	11 35.9	5 55.3	0 14.0	26 53.8	21 4.6	20 33.7	26 26.2
21	4 0 1.5	26 27.8	1 14.1	28 4.7	7 36.4	12 49.8	6 41.7	0 25.9	26 56.1	21 7.3	20 35.4	26 28.5
22	4 3 58.0	27 30.7	1 10.7	9♓25.3	8 28.4	14 4.1	7 28.3	0 37.7	26 58.5	21 10.0	20 37.1	26 30.7
23	4 7 54.6	28 33.8	1 7.4	20 30.9	9 25.8	15 18.6	8 15.0	0 49.5	27 1.0	21 12.8	20 38.8	26 33.0
24	4 11 51.2	29 37.2	1 4.1	1♈34.1	10 27.8	16 33.5	9 1.8	1 1.3	27 3.6	21 15.7	20 40.6	26 35.3
25	4 15 47.7	0♐40.7	1 .7	12 46.2	11 33.9	17 48.6	9 48.7	1 13.0	27 6.2	21 18.5	20 42.4	26 37.6
26	4 19 44.3	1 44.4	0 57.4	24 17.2	12 43.6	19 4.0	10 35.8	1 24.6	27 9.0	21 21.4	20 44.2	26 39.8
27	4 23 40.8	2 48.3	0 54.1	6♉14.8	13 56.5	20 19.8	11 23.0	1 36.2	27 11.9	21 24.4	20 46.1	26 42.1
28	4 27 37.4	3 52.4	0 50.7	18 43.0	15 12.2	21 35.8	12 10.4	1 47.8	27 14.8	21 27.3	20 48.0	26 44.4
29	4 31 33.9	4 56.7	0 47.4	1♊41.4	16 30.4	22 52.2	12 57.9	1 59.4	27 17.9	21 30.4	20 49.9	26 46.7
30	4 35 30.5	6 1.1	0 44.1	15 4.3	17 50.8	24 8.8	13 45.5	2 10.9	27 21.0	21 33.4	20 51.8	26 48.9

DECLINATION

DAY	EPHEM. SID. TIME	☉	☊	☽	☿	♀	♂	♃	♄	♅	♆	♇
1	2 41 10.4	14S21.8	0S22.0	19N42.3	19S29.6	6S21.9	19S 5.4	9S46.1	15S 3.1	22S35.2	21S30.6	5S37.2
4	2 53 .0	15 18.5	0 22.0	20 53.1	17 43.2	7 47.2	19 37.9	9 59.9	15 2.3	22 34.4	21 30.2	5 39.3
7	3 4 49.7	16 13.0	0 21.9	12 44.0	15 35.5	9 11.0	20 8.9	10 13.4	15 1.1	22 33.6	21 29.8	5 41.3
10	3 16 39.4	17 5.1	0 21.9	1S56.2	13 35.5	10 33.1	20 38.4	10 26.9	14 59.7	22 32.7	21 29.4	5 43.3
13	3 28 29.0	17 54.5	0 21.9	16 19.1	12 11.8	11 53.0	21 6.2	10 40.1	14 58.0	22 31.7	21 28.9	5 45.2
16	3 40 18.7	18 41.1	0 21.8	21 28.4	11 37.5	13 10.4	21 32.4	10 53.2	14 56.0	22 30.7	21 28.4	5 47.0
19	3 52 8.4	19 24.7	0 21.8	15 7.5	11 48.9	14 25.0	21 56.8	11 6.0	14 53.6	22 29.6	21 27.8	5 48.8
22	4 3 58.0	20 5.2	0 21.8	3 .0	12 34.3	15 36.2	22 19.3	11 18.6	14 51.0	22 28.5	21 27.2	5 50.5
25	4 15 47.7	20 42.4	0 21.7	9N42.9	13 41.7	16 43.9	22 40.0	11 31.0	14 48.1	22 27.3	21 26.6	5 52.1
28	4 27 37.4	21 16.1	0 21.7	19 9.1	15 1.0	17 47.6	22 58.7	11 43.1	14 44.9	22 26.1	21 25.9	5 53.7

DECEMBER 1993

LONGITUDE

DAY	EPHEM. SID. TIME h m s	☉ ° ′	☊ ° ′	☽ ° ′	☿ ° ′	♀ ° ′	♂ ° ′	♃ ° ′	♄ ° ′	♅ ° ′	♆ ° ′	♇ ° ′
1	4 39 27.1	8♐48.6	2♐44.2	28♊46.6	21♏11.1	27♏30.2	15♐50.1	4♏15.3	24♒36.5	19♑54.2	19♑23.6	25♏57.6
2	4 43 23.6	9 49.4	2 41.1	11♋38.3	22 36.3	28 45.6	16 34.3	4 27.1	24 39.9	19 57.1	19 25.5	25 60.0
3	4 47 20.2	10 50.2	2 37.9	24 43.4	24 2.7	0♐ 1.0	17 18.6	4 38.9	24 43.4	20 .1	19 27.3	26 2.3
4	4 51 16.7	11 51.1	2 34.7	8♌ 2.1	25 30.0	1 16.4	18 3.0	4 50.5	24 47.0	20 3.0	19 29.2	26 4.6
5	4 55 13.3	12 52.0	2 31.5	21 34.5	26 58.2	2 31.8	18 47.4	5 2.2	24 50.7	20 6.0	19 31.1	26 7.0
6	4 59 9.8	13 52.8	2 28.3	5♍20.5	28 27.1	3 47.3	19 31.8	5 13.7	24 54.5	20 9.0	19 33.0	26 9.3
7	5 3 6.4	14 53.8	2 25.2	19 19.8	29 56.6	5 2.8	20 16.3	5 25.2	24 58.4	20 12.1	19 35.0	26 11.6
8	5 7 3.0	15 54.7	2 22.0	3♎31.3	1♐26.6	6 18.2	21 .9	5 36.6	25 2.3	20 15.2	19 36.9	26 13.9
9	5 10 59.5	16 55.6	2 18.8	17 53.0	2 57.0	7 33.7	21 45.5	5 48.0	25 6.4	20 18.3	19 38.9	26 16.2
10	5 14 56.1	17 56.6	2 15.6	2♏22.0	4 27.8	8 49.2	22 30.1	5 59.2	25 10.5	20 21.4	19 40.9	26 18.5
11	5 18 52.6	18 57.6	2 12.5	16 54.1	5 59.0	10 4.7	23 14.8	6 10.4	25 14.7	20 24.5	19 42.9	26 20.7
12	5 22 49.2	19 58.6	2 9.3	1♐24.2	7 30.4	11 20.2	23 59.6	6 21.6	25 18.9	20 27.7	19 44.9	26 23.0
13	5 26 45.7	20 59.7	2 6.1	15 46.6	9 2.0	12 35.7	24 44.4	6 32.6	25 23.3	20 30.9	19 47.0	26 25.2
14	5 30 42.3	22 .7	2 2.9	29 55.9	10 33.9	13 51.2	25 29.3	6 43.6	25 27.8	20 34.1	19 49.0	26 27.5
15	5 34 38.9	23 1.7	1 59.8	13♑47.4	12 6.0	15 6.7	26 14.2	6 54.5	25 32.3	20 37.4	19 51.1	26 29.7
16	5 38 35.4	24 2.8	1 56.6	27 18.1	13 38.2	16 22.2	26 59.2	7 5.3	25 36.9	20 40.6	19 53.2	26 31.9
17	5 42 32.0	25 3.9	1 53.4	10♒26.5	15 10.6	17 37.7	27 44.2	7 16.0	25 41.6	20 43.9	19 55.3	26 34.0
18	5 46 28.5	26 5.0	1 50.2	23 13.2	16 43.2	18 53.2	28 29.2	7 26.7	25 46.3	20 47.2	19 57.4	26 36.2
19	5 50 25.1	27 6.0	1 47.1	5♓40.3	18 16.0	20 8.7	29 14.3	7 37.2	25 51.2	20 50.5	19 59.5	26 38.4
20	5 54 21.6	28 7.2	1 43.9	17 51.2	19 49.0	21 24.2	29 59.5	7 47.7	25 56.1	20 53.9	20 1.7	26 40.5
21	5 58 18.2	29 8.3	1 40.7	29 50.2	21 22.1	22 39.8	0♑44.7	7 58.1	26 1.1	20 57.3	20 3.9	26 42.7
22	6 2 14.8	0♑ 9.4	1 37.5	11♈42.0	22 55.4	23 55.3	1 30.0	8 8.4	26 6.1	21 .6	20 6.0	26 44.8
23	6 6 11.3	1 10.5	1 34.3	23 31.9	24 28.8	25 10.8	2 15.2	8 18.6	26 11.3	21 4.0	20 8.2	26 46.8
24	6 10 7.9	2 11.6	1 31.2	5♉24.5	26 2.5	26 26.3	3 .6	8 28.7	26 16.4	21 7.4	20 10.4	26 48.9
25	6 14 4.4	3 12.7	1 28.0	17 24.6	27 36.4	27 41.8	3 45.9	8 38.7	26 21.7	21 10.8	20 12.6	26 50.9
26	6 18 1.0	4 13.8	1 24.8	29 36.1	29 10.5	28 57.3	4 31.4	8 48.6	26 27.0	21 14.3	20 14.8	26 53.0
27	6 21 57.6	5 14.9	1 21.6	12♊ 1.9	0♑44.8	0♑12.8	5 16.8	8 58.4	26 32.4	21 17.7	20 17.0	26 55.0
28	6 25 54.1	6 16.0	1 18.5	24 44.3	2 19.4	1 28.3	6 2.3	9 8.1	26 37.9	21 21.2	20 19.2	26 56.9
29	6 29 50.7	7 17.1	1 15.3	7♋43.9	3 54.3	2 43.8	6 47.9	9 17.6	26 43.4	21 24.6	20 21.4	26 58.9
30	6 33 47.2	8 18.3	1 12.1	21 .3	5 29.4	3 59.2	7 33.5	9 27.1	26 49.0	21 28.1	20 23.6	27 .8
31	6 37 43.8	9 19.4	1 8.9	4♌31.9	7 4.8	5 14.7	8 19.1	9 36.5	26 54.6	21 31.6	20 25.9	27 2.8

LATITUDE

DAY	EPHEM. SID. TIME	☉	☊	☽	☿	♀	♂	♃	♄	♅	♆	♇
1	4 39 27.1	0 .0	0 .0	2S18.1	1N41.6	0N50.4	0S34.4	1N 5.1	1S27.3	0S27.4	0N37.4	13N41.3
4	4 51 16.7	0 .0	0 .0	4 47.5	1 21.1	0 44.0	0 36.0	1 5.3	1 27.0	0 27.3	0 37.3	13 41.5
7	5 3 6.4	0 .0	0 .0	5 4.2	0 59.5	0 37.3	0 37.6	1 5.6	1 26.8	0 27.3	0 37.2	13 41.7
10	5 14 56.1	0 .0	0 .0	2 41.8	0 37.6	0 30.5	0 39.1	1 5.8	1 26.6	0 27.3	0 37.2	13 42.0
13	5 26 45.7	0 .0	0 .0	1N 9.9	0 15.7	0 23.4	0 40.6	1 6.1	1 26.4	0 27.3	0 37.1	13 42.3
16	5 38 35.4	0 .0	0 .0	4 16.3	0S 5.6	0 16.3	0 42.1	1 6.4	1 26.2	0 27.3	0 37.0	13 42.7
19	5 50 25.1	0 .0	0 .0	5 14.2	0 26.0	0 9.1	0 43.6	1 6.7	1 26.0	0 27.3	0 37.0	13 43.2
22	6 2 14.8	0 .0	0 .0	4 4.9	0 45.3	0 1.8	0 45.0	1 7.0	1 25.9	0 27.3	0 36.9	13 43.8
25	6 14 4.4	0 .0	0 .0	1 23.6	1 3.2	0S 5.4	0 46.4	1 7.4	1 25.7	0 27.3	0 36.9	13 44.4
28	6 25 54.1	0 .0	0 .0	1S56.9	1 19.4	0 12.6	0 47.8	1 7.7	1 25.6	0 27.3	0 36.8	13 45.0
31	6 37 43.8	0 .0	0 .0	4 34.3	1 33.8	0 19.7	0 49.1	1 8.1	1 25.4	0 27.3	0 36.8	13 45.7

RIGHT ASCENSION

DAY	EPHEM. SID. TIME	☉	☊	☽	☿	♀	♂	♃	♄	♅	♆	♇
1	4 39 27.1	7♐ 5.7	0♐40.7	28♊41.4	19♏13.2	25♏25.7	14♐33.2	2♏22.3	27♒24.2	21♑36.5	20♑53.8	26♏51.2
2	4 43 23.6	8 10.4	0 37.4	12♋20.9	20 37.3	26 43.0	15 21.0	2 33.7	27 27.6	21 39.6	20 55.7	26 53.5
3	4 47 20.2	9 15.3	0 34.1	25 52.6	22 3.0	28 .5	16 9.0	2 45.0	27 30.9	21 42.7	20 57.7	26 55.7
4	4 51 16.7	10 20.4	0 30.7	9♌10.8	23 30.1	29 18.3	16 57.1	2 56.3	27 34.4	21 45.9	20 59.7	26 57.9
5	4 55 13.3	11 25.6	0 27.4	22 15.9	24 58.6	0♐36.5	17 45.3	3 7.5	27 38.0	21 49.1	21 1.7	27 .2
6	4 59 9.8	12 31.0	0 24.1	5♍13.3	26 28.2	1 54.9	18 33.5	3 18.7	27 41.6	21 52.3	21 3.8	27 2.4
7	5 3 6.4	13 36.5	0 20.7	18 12.5	27 58.9	3 13.6	19 21.9	3 29.8	27 45.4	21 55.6	21 5.9	27 4.6
8	5 7 3.0	14 42.1	0 17.4	1♎25.0	29 30.7	4 32.5	20 10.5	3 40.9	27 49.2	21 58.8	21 7.9	27 6.8
9	5 10 59.5	15 47.9	0 14.1	15 2.4	1♐ 3.4	5 51.8	20 59.1	3 51.9	27 53.1	22 2.2	21 10.0	27 9.0
10	5 14 56.1	16 53.7	0 10.8	29 13.2	2 37.0	7 11.3	21 47.8	4 2.8	27 57.0	22 5.5	21 12.2	27 11.2
11	5 18 52.6	17 59.7	0 7.4	13♏59.8	4 11.4	8 31.1	22 36.6	4 13.7	28 1.1	22 8.9	21 14.3	27 13.4
12	5 22 49.2	19 5.8	0 4.1	29 15.0	5 46.6	9 51.1	23 25.5	4 24.5	28 5.2	22 12.2	21 16.5	27 15.6
13	5 26 45.7	20 12.0	0 .8	14♐41.4	7 22.5	11 11.4	24 14.4	4 35.2	28 9.5	22 15.7	21 18.6	27 17.7
14	5 30 42.3	21 18.2	29♏57.5	29 55.6	8 59.2	12 31.9	25 3.5	4 45.9	28 13.7	22 19.1	21 20.8	27 19.9
15	5 34 38.9	22 24.6	29 54.1	14♑36.2	10 36.5	13 52.6	25 52.6	4 56.4	28 18.1	22 22.6	21 23.0	27 22.0
16	5 38 35.4	23 30.9	29 50.8	28 29.6	12 14.5	15 13.5	26 41.9	5 7.0	28 22.6	22 26.0	21 25.2	27 24.1
17	5 42 32.0	24 37.4	29 47.5	11♒32.7	13 53.1	16 34.6	27 31.2	5 17.4	28 27.1	22 29.6	21 27.5	27 26.3
18	5 46 28.5	25 43.9	29 44.2	23 50.4	15 32.4	17 55.9	28 20.5	5 27.8	28 31.7	22 33.1	21 29.7	27 28.4
19	5 50 25.1	26 50.4	29 40.8	5♓32.6	17 12.2	19 17.4	29 9.9	5 38.0	28 36.4	22 36.6	21 32.0	27 30.4
20	5 54 21.6	27 57.0	29 37.5	16 51.3	18 52.6	20 39.1	29 59.5	5 48.3	28 41.1	22 40.2	21 34.3	27 32.6
21	5 58 18.2	29 3.6	29 34.2	27 59.3	20 33.5	22 .9	0♑49.0	5 58.4	28 45.9	22 43.8	21 36.6	27 34.6
22	6 2 14.8	0♑10.2	29 30.9	9♈ 8.9	22 15.0	23 22.8	1 38.6	6 8.4	28 50.8	22 47.4	21 38.9	27 36.7
23	6 6 11.3	1 16.8	29 27.6	20 31.4	23 56.9	24 44.9	2 28.2	6 18.4	28 55.8	22 51.0	21 41.2	27 38.7
24	6 10 7.9	2 23.4	29 24.2	2♉16.8	25 39.3	26 7.0	3 17.9	6 28.2	29 .8	22 54.7	21 43.5	27 40.7
25	6 14 4.4	3 30.0	29 20.9	14 32.0	27 22.2	27 29.2	4 7.6	6 38.0	29 5.9	22 58.3	21 45.8	27 42.7
26	6 18 1.0	4 36.5	29 17.6	27 20.2	29 5.5	28 51.6	4 57.4	6 47.7	29 11.0	23 2.0	21 48.2	27 44.6
27	6 21 57.6	5 43.0	29 14.3	10♊39.1	0♑49.3	0♑13.9	5 47.2	6 57.3	29 16.2	23 5.7	21 50.5	27 46.6
28	6 25 54.1	6 49.5	29 11.0	24 21.0	2 33.5	1 36.3	6 37.0	7 6.8	29 21.5	23 9.4	21 52.9	27 48.5
29	6 29 50.7	7 56.0	29 7.6	8♋13.9	4 18.0	2 58.8	7 26.9	7 16.1	29 26.8	23 13.1	21 55.2	27 50.5
30	6 33 47.2	9 2.4	29 4.3	22 5.0	6 2.9	4 21.3	8 16.7	7 25.4	29 32.2	23 16.8	21 57.6	27 52.4
31	6 37 43.8	10 8.7	29 1.0	5♌44.6	7 48.1	5 43.7	9 6.6	7 34.6	29 37.6	23 20.5	21 60.0	27 54.2

DECLINATION

DAY	EPHEM. SID. TIME	☉	☊	☽	☿	♀	♂	♃	♄	♅	♆	♇
1	4 39 27.1	21S46.2	0S21.7	21N 7.9	16S25.2	18S47.1	23S15.4	11S55.0	14S41.4	22S24.8	21S25.2	5S55.2
4	4 51 16.7	22 12.5	0 21.7	13 37.5	17 49.3	19 41.8	23 30.0	12 6.5	14 37.6	22 23.5	21 24.5	5 56.5
7	5 3 6.4	22 35.0	0 21.6	0S26.5	19 10.1	20 31.6	23 42.4	12 17.9	14 33.6	22 22.2	21 23.7	5 57.8
10	5 14 56.1	22 53.5	0 21.6	14 49.5	20 25.1	21 16.2	23 52.7	12 28.9	14 29.4	22 20.8	21 23.0	5 59.0
13	5 26 45.7	23 7.9	0 21.6	21 31.3	21 32.7	21 55.1	24 .7	12 39.6	14 24.8	22 19.3	21 22.1	6 .1
16	5 38 35.4	23 18.3	0 21.5	16 30.5	22 31.7	22 28.3	24 6.4	12 50.0	14 20.1	22 17.8	21 21.3	6 1.2
19	5 50 25.1	23 24.4	0 21.5	4 33.4	23 21.1	22 55.3	24 9.8	13 .0	14 15.0	22 16.3	21 20.4	6 2.1
22	6 2 14.8	23 26.3	0 21.5	8N22.9	24 .2	23 16.1	24 10.8	13 9.8	14 9.8	22 14.8	21 19.5	6 2.9
25	6 14 4.4	23 24.0	0 21.4	18 21.9	24 28.2	23 30.6	24 9.5	13 19.1	14 4.3	22 13.2	21 18.6	6 3.7
28	6 25 54.1	23 17.4	0 21.4	21 23.2	24 44.5	23 38.5	24 5.8	13 28.2	13 58.7	22 11.6	21 17.7	6 4.3
31	6 37 43.8	23 6.6	0 21.4	14 41.1	24 48.6	23 39.8	23 59.7	13 36.8	13 52.8	22 9.9	21 16.7	6 4.8

JANUARY 1994

DAY	EPHEM. SID. TIME	☉	☊	☽	☿	♀	♂	♃	♄	♅	♆	♇
	h m s	° ′	° ′	° ′	° ′	° ′	° ′	° ′	° ′	° ′	° ′	° ′
		LONGITUDE										
1	6 41 40.3	10 ♑ 20.5	1 ♐ 5.8	18 ♌ 16.3	8 ♑ 40.6	6 ♑ 30.2	9 ♑ 4.8	9 ♏ 45.8	27 ♒ .3	21 ♑ 35.1	20 ♑ 28.1	27 ♏ 4.7
2	6 45 36.9	11 21.6	1 2.6	2 ♍ 10.4	10 16.6	7 45.7	9 50.5	9 55.0	27 6.1	21 38.6	20 30.4	27 6.5
3	6 49 33.5	12 22.8	0 59.4	16 11.4	11 53.1	9 1.2	10 36.3	10 4.0	27 11.9	21 42.1	20 32.6	27 8.4
4	6 53 30.0	13 23.9	0 56.2	0 ♎ 16.6	13 29.8	10 16.7	11 22.1	10 12.9	27 17.8	21 45.7	20 34.9	27 10.2
5	6 57 26.6	14 25.1	0 53.0	14 23.9	15 7.0	11 32.2	12 7.9	10 21.8	27 23.8	21 49.2	20 37.1	27 12.0
6	7 1 23.1	15 26.2	0 49.9	28 31.8	16 44.5	12 47.7	12 53.8	10 30.5	27 29.7	21 52.7	20 39.4	27 13.8
7	7 5 19.7	16 27.4	0 46.7	12 ♏ 39.0	18 22.4	14 3.2	13 39.7	10 39.1	27 35.8	21 56.3	20 41.7	27 15.5
8	7 9 16.2	17 28.5	0 43.5	26 44.0	20 .7	15 18.7	14 25.7	10 47.5	27 41.9	21 59.8	20 44.0	27 17.3
9	7 13 12.8	18 29.7	0 40.3	10 ♐ 44.9	21 39.4	16 34.2	15 11.7	10 55.9	27 48.1	22 3.4	20 46.2	27 19.0
10	7 17 9.4	19 30.9	0 37.2	24 39.6	23 18.6	17 49.7	15 57.8	11 4.1	27 54.3	22 7.0	20 48.5	27 20.7
11	7 21 5.9	20 32.1	0 34.0	8 ♑ 25.0	24 58.1	19 5.2	16 43.9	11 12.2	28 .6	22 10.5	20 50.8	27 22.3
12	7 25 2.5	21 33.2	0 30.8	21 58.1	26 38.0	20 20.7	17 30.1	11 20.2	28 6.9	22 14.1	20 53.1	27 23.9
13	7 28 59.0	22 34.4	0 27.6	5 ♒ 16.1	28 18.3	21 36.2	18 16.2	11 28.0	28 13.2	22 17.7	20 55.4	27 25.5
14	7 32 55.6	23 35.5	0 24.5	18 17.2	29 59.0	22 51.7	19 2.4	11 35.7	28 19.7	22 21.2	20 57.7	27 27.1
15	7 36 52.1	24 36.6	0 21.3	1 ♓ .5	1 ♒ 40.0	24 7.1	19 48.7	11 43.3	28 26.1	22 24.8	20 59.9	27 28.6
16	7 40 48.7	25 37.8	0 18.1	13 26.7	3 21.3	25 22.6	20 34.9	11 50.7	28 32.6	22 28.3	21 2.2	27 30.1
17	7 44 45.3	26 38.9	0 14.9	25 37.7	5 2.8	26 38.0	21 21.2	11 58.0	28 39.1	22 31.9	21 4.5	27 31.6
18	7 48 41.8	27 40.0	0 11.8	7 ♈ 36.9	6 44.6	27 53.5	22 7.6	12 5.1	28 45.7	22 35.4	21 6.7	27 33.1
19	7 52 38.4	28 41.1	0 8.6	19 28.5	8 26.5	29 8.9	22 54.0	12 12.1	28 52.3	22 39.0	21 9.0	27 34.5
20	7 56 34.9	29 42.1	0 5.4	1 ♉ 17.4	10 8.4	0 ♒ 24.3	23 40.4	12 19.0	28 59.0	22 42.5	21 11.2	27 35.9
21	8 0 31.5	0 ♒ 43.2	0 2.2	13 9.1	11 50.3	1 39.8	24 26.8	12 25.7	29 5.7	22 46.0	21 13.5	27 37.2
22	8 4 28.0	1 44.2	29 ♏ 59.0	25 8.8	13 31.9	2 55.2	25 13.2	12 32.3	29 12.4	22 49.6	21 15.7	27 38.6
23	8 8 24.6	2 45.3	29 55.9	7 ♊ 21.9	15 13.3	4 10.6	25 59.7	12 38.7	29 19.2	22 53.1	21 18.0	27 39.9
24	8 12 21.1	3 46.3	29 52.7	19 52.8	16 54.0	5 26.0	26 46.2	12 45.0	29 26.0	22 56.6	21 20.2	27 41.1
25	8 16 17.7	4 47.3	29 49.5	2 ♋ 44.9	18 34.0	6 41.3	27 32.8	12 51.1	29 32.8	23 .1	21 22.4	27 42.4
26	8 20 14.3	5 48.2	29 46.3	15 59.9	20 13.0	7 56.7	28 19.4	12 57.0	29 39.7	23 3.6	21 24.7	27 43.6
27	8 24 10.8	6 49.2	29 43.2	29 37.5	21 50.7	9 12.1	29 6.0	13 2.9	29 46.6	23 7.1	21 26.9	27 44.7
28	8 28 7.4	7 50.1	29 40.0	13 ♌ 35.2	23 26.7	10 27.4	29 52.6	13 8.5	29 53.5	23 10.5	21 29.1	27 45.9
29	8 32 3.9	8 51.1	29 36.8	27 48.7	25 .6	11 42.7	0 ♒ 39.2	13 14.0	0 ♓ .4	23 14.0	21 31.3	27 47.0
30	8 36 .5	9 52.0	29 33.6	12 ♍ 11.9	26 31.9	12 58.1	1 25.9	13 19.4	0 7.4	23 17.4	21 33.5	27 48.0
31	8 39 57.0	10 52.9	29 30.4	26 38.7	28 .2	14 13.4	2 12.7	13 24.6	0 14.5	23 20.9	21 35.7	27 49.1
		LATITUDE										
1	6 41 40.3	0 .0	0 .0	5 S .9	1 S 38.1	0 S 22.0	0 S 49.5	1 N 8.2	1 S 25.4	0 S 27.3	0 N 36.8	13 N 46.0
4	6 53 30.0	0 .0	0 .0	4 34.0	1 49.5	0 28.9	0 50.8	1 8.6	1 25.3	0 27.3	0 36.7	13 46.7
7	7 5 19.7	0 .0	0 .0	1 44.2	1 58.3	0 35.5	0 52.1	1 9.1	1 25.2	0 27.3	0 36.7	13 47.6
10	7 17 9.4	0 .0	0 .0	1 N 58.0	2 4.1	0 41.9	0 53.3	1 9.5	1 25.1	0 27.3	0 36.7	13 48.5
13	7 28 59.0	0 .0	0 .0	4 34.1	2 6.6	0 48.0	0 54.4	1 9.9	1 25.0	0 27.3	0 36.6	13 49.4
16	7 40 48.7	0 .0	0 .0	4 59.4	2 5.1	0 53.8	0 55.5	1 10.4	1 25.0	0 27.3	0 36.6	13 50.4
19	7 52 38.4	0 .0	0 .0	3 24.3	1 59.2	0 59.3	0 56.6	1 10.9	1 25.0	0 27.4	0 36.6	13 51.4
22	8 4 28.0	0 .0	0 .0	0 32.3	1 48.1	1 4.3	0 57.6	1 11.4	1 24.9	0 27.4	0 36.6	13 52.4
25	8 16 17.7	0 .0	0 .0	2 S 40.0	1 31.0	1 8.9	0 58.6	1 11.9	1 24.9	0 27.4	0 36.5	13 53.5
28	8 28 7.4	0 .0	0 .0	4 49.2	1 7.4	1 13.0	0 59.6	1 12.4	1 24.9	0 27.5	0 36.5	13 54.6
31	8 39 57.0	0 .0	0 .0	4 30.9	0 36.4	1 16.7	1 .4	1 12.9	1 25.0	0 27.5	0 36.5	13 55.8
		RIGHT ASCENSION										
1	6 41 40.3	11 ♑ 15.0	28 ♏ 57.7	19 ♌ 8.3	9 ♑ 33.6	7 ♑ 6.2	9 ♑ 56.5	7 ♏ 43.7	29 ♒ 43.1	23 ♑ 24.2	22 ♑ 2.4	27 ♏ 56.1
2	6 45 36.9	12 21.1	28 54.4	2 ♍ 18.1	11 19.4	8 28.6	10 46.5	7 52.7	29 48.7	23 28.0	22 4.8	27 57.9
3	6 49 33.5	13 27.3	28 51.1	15 20.7	13 5.5	9 51.0	11 36.4	8 1.6	29 54.3	23 31.7	22 7.2	27 59.8
4	6 53 30.0	14 33.3	28 47.7	28 26.0	14 51.8	11 13.3	12 26.3	8 10.4	29 60.0	23 35.5	22 9.5	28 1.6
5	6 57 26.6	15 39.2	28 44.4	11 ♎ 45.0	16 38.2	12 35.5	13 16.3	8 19.1	0 ♓ 5.7	23 39.2	22 11.9	28 3.3
6	7 1 23.1	16 45.0	28 41.1	25 27.4	18 24.8	13 57.7	14 6.2	8 27.6	0 11.5	23 43.0	22 14.4	28 5.1
7	7 5 19.7	17 50.8	28 37.8	9 ♏ 39.0	20 11.6	15 19.7	14 56.1	8 36.1	0 17.3	23 46.8	22 16.8	28 6.8
8	7 9 16.2	18 56.4	28 34.5	24 18.6	21 58.4	16 41.6	15 46.0	8 44.4	0 23.2	23 50.6	22 19.2	28 8.5
9	7 13 12.8	20 1.9	28 31.2	9 ♐ 16.6	23 45.3	18 3.4	16 35.9	8 52.6	0 29.1	23 54.3	22 21.6	28 10.2
10	7 17 9.4	21 7.3	28 27.9	24 16.1	25 32.2	19 25.1	17 25.9	9 .8	0 35.2	23 58.2	22 24.1	28 11.9
11	7 21 5.9	22 12.5	28 24.5	8 ♑ 57.4	27 19.0	20 46.5	18 15.8	9 8.8	0 41.2	24 2.0	22 26.5	28 13.6
12	7 25 2.5	23 17.6	28 21.2	23 4.5	29 5.8	22 7.8	19 5.6	9 16.6	0 47.3	24 5.7	22 28.9	28 15.2
13	7 28 59.0	24 22.5	28 17.9	6 ♒ 28.9	0 ♒ 52.4	23 28.9	19 55.4	9 24.3	0 53.4	24 9.5	22 31.3	28 16.8
14	7 32 55.6	25 27.3	28 14.6	19 10.2	2 38.7	24 49.8	20 45.2	9 31.9	0 59.5	24 13.3	22 33.7	28 18.3
15	7 36 52.1	26 31.9	28 11.3	1 ♓ 14.1	4 24.8	26 10.5	21 34.9	9 39.4	1 5.8	24 17.1	22 36.1	28 19.9
16	7 40 48.7	27 36.3	28 8.0	12 49.8	6 10.6	27 30.9	22 24.6	9 46.7	1 12.0	24 20.9	22 38.5	28 21.4
17	7 44 45.3	28 40.6	28 4.7	24 8.5	7 55.9	28 51.1	23 14.3	9 54.0	1 18.3	24 24.7	22 40.9	28 22.8
18	7 48 41.8	29 44.6	28 1.4	5 ♈ 21.5	9 40.7	0 ♒ 11.1	24 3.9	10 1.0	1 24.6	24 28.4	22 43.3	28 24.3
19	7 52 38.4	0 ♒ 48.5	27 58.1	16 39.8	11 24.9	1 30.8	24 53.4	10 8.0	1 31.0	24 32.2	22 45.7	28 25.7
20	7 56 34.9	1 52.3	27 54.8	28 13.8	13 8.3	2 50.2	25 42.9	10 14.8	1 37.4	24 36.0	22 48.1	28 27.1
21	8 0 31.5	2 55.8	27 51.4	10 ♉ 11.9	14 50.9	4 9.4	26 32.4	10 21.4	1 43.8	24 39.7	22 50.5	28 28.5
22	8 4 28.0	3 59.1	27 48.1	22 39.8	16 32.5	5 28.2	27 21.8	10 27.9	1 50.3	24 43.5	22 52.9	28 29.8
23	8 8 24.6	5 2.3	27 44.8	5 ♊ 39.4	18 12.9	6 46.8	28 11.1	10 34.3	1 56.8	24 47.2	22 55.3	28 31.1
24	8 12 21.1	6 5.2	27 41.5	19 7.5	19 51.9	8 5.1	29 .3	10 40.5	2 3.3	24 51.0	22 57.6	28 32.4
25	8 16 17.7	7 7.9	27 38.2	2 ♋ 56.2	21 29.3	9 23.1	29 49.5	10 46.6	2 9.9	24 54.7	22 60.0	28 33.7
26	8 20 14.3	8 10.5	27 34.9	16 54.3	23 4.9	10 40.8	0 ♒ 38.6	10 52.6	2 16.5	24 58.4	23 2.3	28 34.9
27	8 24 10.8	9 12.8	27 31.6	0 ♌ 50.9	24 38.3	11 58.2	1 27.7	10 58.3	2 23.1	25 2.1	23 4.7	28 36.1
28	8 28 7.4	10 14.9	27 28.3	14 38.6	26 9.3	13 15.3	2 16.6	11 4.0	2 29.7	25 5.8	23 7.0	28 37.3
29	8 32 3.9	11 16.9	27 25.0	28 14.8	27 37.4	14 32.1	3 5.5	11 9.5	2 36.4	25 9.5	23 9.3	28 38.4
30	8 36 .5	12 18.6	27 21.7	11 ♍ 42.2	29 2.3	15 48.5	3 54.3	11 14.8	2 43.1	25 13.1	23 11.7	28 39.5
31	8 39 57.0	13 20.2	27 18.4	25 7.6	0 ♓ 23.5	17 4.7	4 43.1	11 20.0	2 49.9	25 16.8	23 14.0	28 40.6
		DECLINATION										
1	6 41 40.3	23 S 2.1	0 S 21.3	10 N 34.5	24 S 47.2	23 S 38.7	23 S 57.1	13 S 39.6	13 S 50.8	22 S 9.4	21 S 16.4	6 S 5.0
4	6 53 30.0	22 45.8	0 21.3	4 S 18.0	24 34.2	23 31.2	23 47.8	13 47.7	13 44.7	22 7.7	21 15.4	6 5.4
7	7 5 19.7	22 25.5	0 21.3	17 17.3	24 7.9	23 17.2	23 36.0	13 55.5	13 38.4	22 6.0	21 14.4	6 5.7
10	7 17 9.4	22 1.1	0 21.2	21 22.0	23 27.9	22 56.6	23 21.9	14 2.8	13 31.9	22 4.3	21 13.4	6 5.9
13	7 28 59.0	21 32.9	0 21.2	14 30.9	22 33.9	22 29.7	23 5.4	14 9.8	13 25.3	22 2.6	21 12.4	6 6.0
16	7 40 48.7	21 .9	0 21.2	1 53.8	21 26.0	21 56.7	22 46.6	14 16.3	13 18.5	22 .9	21 11.4	6 6.0
19	7 52 38.4	20 25.4	0 21.1	10 N 46.2	20 4.2	21 17.7	22 25.5	14 22.3	13 11.6	21 59.2	21 10.4	6 6.0
22	8 4 28.0	19 46.3	0 21.1	19 34.4	18 29.1	20 32.9	22 2.1	14 28.0	13 4.5	21 57.4	21 9.4	6 5.8
25	8 16 17.7	19 4.0	0 21.1	20 44.6	16 42.2	19 42.7	21 36.5	14 33.2	12 57.4	21 55.7	21 8.4	6 5.5
28	8 28 7.4	18 18.6	0 21.0	12 7.4	14 45.8	18 47.3	21 8.8	14 37.9	12 50.1	21 54.0	21 7.3	6 5.1
31	8 39 57.0	17 30.1	0 21.0	2 S 48.5	12 44.2	17 47.1	20 38.9	14 42.3	12 42.7	21 52.3	21 6.3	6 4.7

FEBRUARY 1994

LONGITUDE

DAY	EPHEM. SID. TIME (h m s)	☉ (° ′)	☊ (° ′)	☽ (° ′)	☿ (° ′)	♀ (° ′)	♂ (° ′)	♃ (° ′)	♄ (° ′)	♅ (° ′)	♆ (° ′)	♇ (° ′)
1	8 43 53.6	11♒53.8	29♏27.3	11♎ 3.3	29♒24.8	15♒28.7	2♒59.4	13♏29.6	0♓21.5	23♑24.3	21♑37.9	27♏50.1
2	8 47 50.1	12 54.7	29 24.1	25 21.6	0♓45.1	16 44.1	3 46.2	13 34.5	0 28.6	23 27.8	21 40.0	27 51.1
3	8 51 46.7	13 55.6	29 20.9	9♏30.8	2 .5	17 59.3	4 33.0	13 39.2	0 35.6	23 31.1	21 42.2	27 52.1
4	8 55 43.3	14 56.4	29 17.7	23 30.0	3 10.1	19 14.6	5 19.8	13 43.7	0 42.7	23 34.5	21 44.3	27 53.0
5	8 59 39.8	15 57.3	29 14.6	7♐18.9	4 13.2	20 29.9	6 6.6	13 48.1	0 49.9	23 37.9	21 46.4	27 53.8
6	9 3 36.4	16 58.1	29 11.4	20 57.9	5 9.0	21 45.2	6 53.5	13 52.3	0 57.0	23 41.2	21 48.5	27 54.7
7	9 7 32.9	17 58.9	29 8.2	4♑27.2	5 56.8	23 .4	7 40.4	13 56.3	1 4.2	23 44.6	21 50.6	27 55.5
8	9 11 29.5	18 59.7	29 5.0	17 46.8	6 35.8	24 15.7	8 27.3	14 .2	1 11.4	23 47.9	21 52.7	27 56.2
9	9 15 26.0	20 .5	29 1.9	0♒55.8	7 5.4	25 30.9	9 14.2	14 3.9	1 18.6	23 51.1	21 54.8	27 57.0
10	9 19 22.6	21 1.2	28 58.7	13 53.4	7 24.9	26 46.1	10 1.2	14 7.4	1 25.8	23 54.4	21 56.8	27 57.7
11	9 23 19.1	22 2.0	28 55.5	26 38.4	7 33.9	28 1.4	10 48.2	14 10.7	1 33.0	23 57.7	21 58.8	27 58.3
12	9 27 15.7	23 2.7	28 52.3	9♓10.3	7R32.3	29 16.5	11 35.1	14 13.8	1 40.2	24 .9	22 .9	27 59.0
13	9 31 12.2	24 3.3	28 49.1	21 29.0	7 20.0	0♓31.7	12 22.1	14 16.8	1 47.5	24 4.1	22 2.9	27 59.6
14	9 35 8.8	25 4.0	28 46.0	3♈35.7	6 57.3	1 46.9	13 9.2	14 19.6	1 54.7	24 7.3	22 4.9	28 .1
15	9 39 5.4	26 4.6	28 42.8	15 32.4	6 24.6	3 2.0	13 56.2	14 22.2	2 2.0	24 10.4	22 6.8	28 .6
16	9 43 1.9	27 5.2	28 39.6	27 22.4	5 42.7	4 17.2	14 43.2	14 24.6	2 9.3	24 13.6	22 8.8	28 1.1
17	9 46 58.5	28 5.8	28 36.4	9♉ 9.9	4 52.8	5 32.3	15 30.3	14 26.8	2 16.6	24 16.7	22 10.7	28 1.6
18	9 50 55.0	29 6.4	28 33.3	20 59.7	3 56.3	6 47.4	16 17.4	14 28.9	2 23.8	24 19.7	22 12.6	28 2.0
19	9 54 51.6	0♓ 6.9	28 30.1	2♊57.2	2 54.5	8 2.4	17 4.4	14 30.8	2 31.1	24 22.8	22 14.5	28 2.4
20	9 58 48.1	1 7.4	28 26.9	15 8.2	1 49.3	9 17.5	17 51.5	14 32.5	2 38.4	24 25.8	22 16.4	28 2.7
21	10 2 44.7	2 7.9	28 23.7	27 37.9	0 42.4	10 32.6	18 38.7	14 34.0	2 45.8	24 28.9	22 18.3	28 3.1
22	10 6 41.2	3 8.3	28 20.5	10♋31.0	29♒35.5	11 47.6	19 25.8	14 35.3	2 53.1	24 31.8	22 20.1	28 3.3
23	10 10 37.8	4 8.7	28 17.4	23 50.7	28 30.2	13 2.6	20 12.9	14 36.4	3 .4	24 34.8	22 22.0	28 3.6
24	10 14 34.3	5 9.1	28 14.2	7♌38.1	27 28.0	14 17.5	21 .0	14 37.4	3 7.7	24 37.7	22 23.8	28 3.8
25	10 18 30.9	6 9.4	28 11.0	21 51.4	26 30.1	15 32.5	21 47.2	14 38.2	3 14.9	24 40.6	22 25.5	28 4.0
26	10 22 27.4	7 9.7	28 7.8	6♍25.9	25 37.5	16 47.4	22 34.3	14 38.7	3 22.2	24 43.4	22 27.3	28 4.1
27	10 26 24.0	8 10.0	28 4.7	21 14.4	24 51.1	18 2.3	23 21.4	14 39.1	3 29.5	24 46.2	22 29.0	28 4.2
28	10 30 20.5	9 10.2	28 1.5	6♎ 8.2	24 11.3	19 17.2	24 8.6	14 39.3	3 36.8	24 49.0	22 30.7	28 4.2

LATITUDE

DAY	EPHEM. SID. TIME	☉	☊	☽	☿	♀	♂	♃	♄	♅	♆	♇
1	8 43 53.6	0 .0	0 .0	3S48.7	0S24.5	1S17.8	1S .7	1N13.1	1S25.0	0S27.5	0N36.5	13N56.2
4	8 55 43.3	0 .0	0 .0	0 34.1	0N16.1	1 20.8	1 1.5	1 13.6	1 25.0	0 27.6	0 36.5	13 57.4
7	9 7 32.9	0 .0	0 .0	2N51.8	1 2.6	1 23.2	1 2.3	1 14.2	1 25.1	0 27.6	0 36.5	13 58.6
10	9 19 22.6	0 .0	0 .0	4 49.4	1 52.1	1 25.1	1 3.0	1 14.8	1 25.2	0 27.7	0 36.5	13 59.8
13	9 31 12.2	0 .0	0 .0	4 37.0	2 39.5	1 26.5	1 3.7	1 15.3	1 25.3	0 27.7	0 36.5	14 1.0
16	9 43 1.9	0 .0	0 .0	2 35.4	3 17.8	1 27.2	1 4.3	1 15.9	1 25.4	0 27.8	0 36.5	14 2.2
19	9 54 51.6	0 .0	0 .0	0S25.2	3 40.0	1 27.4	1 4.8	1 16.4	1 25.6	0 27.8	0 36.5	14 3.5
22	10 6 41.2	0 .0	0 .0	3 24.0	3 41.9	1 27.0	1 5.3	1 17.0	1 25.8	0 27.9	0 36.5	14 4.7
25	10 18 30.9	0 .0	0 .0	4 59.3	3 24.7	1 26.0	1 5.7	1 17.6	1 25.9	0 28.0	0 36.5	14 6.0
28	10 30 20.5	0 .0	0 .0	3 54.4	2 53.5	1 24.4	1 6.1	1 18.1	1 26.1	0 28.0	0 36.5	14 7.2

RIGHT ASCENSION

DAY	EPHEM. SID. TIME	☉	☊	☽	☿	♀	♂	♃	♄	♅	♆	♇
1	8 43 53.6	14♒21.5	27♏15.1	8♎39.4	1♓40.5	18♒20.5	5♒31.8	11♏25.0	2♓56.6	25♑20.5	23♑16.3	28♏41.7
2	8 47 50.1	15 22.6	27 11.8	22 25.7	2 52.7	19 36.1	6 20.4	11 29.9	3 3.4	25 24.1	23 18.6	28 42.7
3	8 51 46.7	16 23.6	27 8.5	6♏31.8	3 59.5	20 51.3	7 8.8	11 34.6	3 10.2	25 27.7	23 20.9	28 43.7
4	8 55 43.3	17 24.3	27 5.2	20 57.7	5 .3	22 6.2	7 57.2	11 39.1	3 17.0	25 31.3	23 23.1	28 44.6
5	8 59 39.8	18 24.8	27 1.9	5♐37.2	5 54.5	23 20.8	8 45.6	11 43.5	3 23.8	25 34.9	23 25.4	28 45.5
6	9 3 36.4	19 25.1	26 58.6	20 18.0	6 41.5	24 35.1	9 33.8	11 47.7	3 30.6	25 38.4	23 27.6	28 46.4
7	9 7 32.9	20 25.3	26 55.3	4♑45.0	7 20.5	25 49.1	10 21.9	11 51.7	3 37.5	25 41.9	23 29.8	28 47.3
8	9 11 29.5	21 25.2	26 52.0	18 44.9	7 51.1	27 2.8	11 10.0	11 55.6	3 44.4	25 45.4	23 32.0	28 48.1
9	9 15 26.0	22 25.0	26 48.7	2♒ 9.3	8 12.6	28 16.2	11 57.9	11 59.2	3 51.3	25 48.9	23 34.2	28 48.9
10	9 19 22.6	23 24.5	26 45.4	14 56.3	8 24.7	29 29.3	12 45.8	12 2.8	3 58.2	25 52.4	23 36.4	28 49.6
11	9 23 19.1	24 23.9	26 42.1	27 9.1	8 27.1	0♓42.1	13 33.5	12 6.1	4 5.1	25 55.9	23 38.5	28 50.4
12	9 27 15.7	25 23.0	26 38.8	8♓54.5	8R19.7	1 54.7	14 21.2	12 9.3	4 12.0	25 59.3	23 40.7	28 51.0
13	9 31 12.2	26 22.0	26 35.5	20 21.6	8 2.5	3 6.9	15 8.7	12 12.3	4 19.0	26 2.7	23 42.8	28 51.7
14	9 35 8.8	27 20.8	26 32.2	1♈39.8	7 36.0	4 18.9	15 56.2	12 15.1	4 25.9	26 6.0	23 44.9	28 52.3
15	9 39 5.4	28 19.4	26 28.9	12 58.7	7 .7	5 30.7	16 43.5	12 17.7	4 32.8	26 9.4	23 47.0	28 52.9
16	9 43 1.9	29 17.8	26 25.6	24 27.3	6 17.4	6 42.1	17 30.8	12 20.1	4 39.8	26 12.7	23 49.0	28 53.5
17	9 46 58.5	0♓16.0	26 22.3	6♉13.5	5 27.3	7 53.3	18 17.9	12 22.4	4 46.8	26 16.0	23 51.1	28 54.0
18	9 50 55.0	1 14.1	26 19.0	18 23.1	4 31.6	9 4.3	19 5.0	12 24.5	4 53.7	26 19.3	23 53.1	28 54.5
19	9 54 51.6	2 11.9	26 15.7	0♊59.5	3 31.7	10 15.0	19 51.9	12 26.4	5 .7	26 22.5	23 55.1	28 54.9
20	9 58 48.1	3 9.6	26 12.4	14 2.4	2 29.4	11 25.5	20 38.7	12 28.1	5 7.7	26 25.7	23 57.1	28 55.3
21	10 2 44.7	4 7.2	26 9.1	27 28.0	1 26.1	12 35.9	21 25.5	12 29.7	5 14.7	26 29.0	23 59.1	28 55.8
22	10 6 41.2	5 4.6	26 5.8	11♋ 9.3	0 23.5	13 45.9	22 12.1	12 31.1	5 21.6	26 32.1	24 1.0	28 56.1
23	10 10 37.8	6 1.8	26 2.5	24 58.3	29♒23.0	14 55.8	22 58.7	12 32.3	5 28.6	26 35.2	24 3.0	28 56.4
24	10 14 34.3	6 58.8	25 59.2	8♌48.3	28 25.9	16 5.5	23 45.1	12 33.3	5 35.6	26 38.3	24 4.9	28 56.7
25	10 18 30.9	7 55.7	25 56.0	22 35.8	27 33.4	17 15.0	24 31.4	12 34.1	5 42.5	26 41.4	24 6.7	28 56.9
26	10 22 27.4	8 52.4	25 52.7	6♍21.3	26 46.4	18 24.3	25 17.6	12 34.7	5 49.5	26 44.4	24 8.6	28 57.2
27	10 26 24.0	9 49.0	25 49.4	20 8.9	26 5.5	19 33.4	26 3.7	12 35.1	5 56.4	26 47.4	24 10.4	28 57.3
28	10 30 20.5	10 45.5	25 46.1	4♎ 4.7	25 31.2	20 42.4	26 49.7	12 35.4	6 3.4	26 50.3	24 12.2	28 57.5

DECLINATION

DAY	EPHEM. SID. TIME	☉	☊	☽	☿	♀	♂	♃	♄	♅	♆	♇
1	8 43 53.6	17S13.3	0S21.0	7S52.8	12S 3.6	17S26.0	20S28.5	14S43.6	12S40.2	21S51.7	21S 6.0	6S 4.5
4	8 55 43.3	16 21.2	0 20.9	19 11.9	10 5.6	16 19.8	19 55.8	14 47.3	12 32.8	21 50.0	21 5.0	6 4.0
7	9 7 32.9	15 26.5	0 20.9	20 30.2	8 21.6	15 9.5	19 21.3	14 50.5	12 25.2	21 48.3	21 4.0	6 3.3
10	9 19 22.6	14 29.4	0 20.9	12 2.1	7 3.1	13 55.4	18 44.8	14 53.2	12 17.6	21 46.7	21 3.0	6 2.6
13	9 31 12.2	13 30.1	0 20.8	0N52.0	6 20.9	12 38.0	18 6.5	14 55.5	12 9.9	21 45.0	21 2.0	6 1.8
16	9 43 1.9	12 28.9	0 20.8	12 57.2	6 20.9	11 17.5	17 26.5	14 57.2	12 2.2	21 43.4	21 1.1	6 .9
19	9 54 51.6	11 25.9	0 20.8	20 20.2	7 .8	9 54.3	16 44.8	14 58.5	11 54.5	21 41.9	21 .1	5 59.9
22	10 6 41.2	10 21.2	0 20.7	19 38.0	8 8.9	8 28.8	16 1.6	14 59.3	11 46.7	21 40.3	20 59.2	5 58.9
25	10 18 30.9	9 15.2	0 20.7	9 29.8	9 28.3	7 1.2	15 16.8	14 59.6	11 38.9	21 38.8	20 58.3	5 57.8
28	10 30 20.5	8 7.9	0 20.7	6S 1.4	10 43.8	5 32.1	14 30.7	14 59.4	11 31.2	21 37.4	20 57.5	5 56.7

MARCH 1994

LONGITUDE

DAY	EPHEM. SID. TIME h m s	☉ ° ′	☊ ° ′	☽ ° ′	☿ ° ′	♀ ° ′	♂ ° ′	♃ ° ′	♄ ° ′	♅ ° ′	♆ ° ′	♇ ° ′
1	10 34 17.1	10♓10.5	27♏58.3	20♎58.4	23♒38.5	20♓32.1	24♒55.8	14♏39.3	3♓44.1	24♑51.8	22♑32.4	28♏ 4.3
2	10 38 13.7	11 10.7	27 55.1	5♏38.0	23R12.8	21 46.9	25 42.9	14R39.1	3 51.3	24 54.5	22 34.1	28 4.3
3	10 42 10.2	12 10.8	27 51.9	20 2.0	22 54.2	23 1.8	26 30.1	14 38.8	3 58.6	24 57.2	22 35.7	28R 4.2
4	10 46 6.8	13 11.0	27 48.8	4♐ 8.1	22 42.5	24 16.6	27 17.3	14 38.2	4 5.8	24 59.9	22 37.3	28 4.1
5	10 50 3.3	14 11.1	27 45.6	17 55.9	22 37.7	25 31.3	28 4.5	14 37.5	4 13.0	25 2.5	22 38.9	28 4.0
6	10 53 59.9	15 11.2	27 42.4	1♑26.4	22D39.3	26 46.1	28 51.7	14 36.5	4 20.3	25 5.1	22 40.5	28 3.9
7	10 57 56.4	16 11.3	27 39.2	14 41.4	22 47.2	28 .9	29 38.9	14 35.4	4 27.5	25 7.6	22 42.0	28 3.7
8	11 1 53.0	17 11.3	27 36.1	27 42.5	23 .9	29 15.6	0♓26.1	14 34.1	4 34.6	25 10.1	22 43.5	28 3.5
9	11 5 49.5	18 11.3	27 32.9	10♒31.3	23 20.2	0♈30.3	1 13.2	14 32.6	4 41.8	25 12.6	22 45.0	28 3.2
10	11 9 46.1	19 11.3	27 29.7	23 8.8	23 44.6	1 45.0	2 .4	14 30.9	4 49.0	25 15.1	22 46.5	28 2.9
11	11 13 42.6	20 11.3	27 26.5	5♓35.7	24 13.9	2 59.6	2 47.6	14 29.0	4 56.1	25 17.5	22 47.9	28 2.6
12	11 17 39.2	21 11.2	27 23.3	17 52.6	24 47.8	4 14.3	3 34.8	14 27.0	5 3.2	25 19.8	22 49.3	28 2.2
13	11 21 35.7	22 11.1	27 20.2	0D .1	25 25.9	5 28.9	4 22.0	14 24.7	5 10.3	25 22.2	22 50.7	28 1.8
14	11 25 32.3	23 11.0	27 17.0	11♈59.3	26 8.0	6 43.5	5 9.2	14 22.3	5 17.5	25 24.5	22 52.1	28 1.5
15	11 29 28.8	24 10.8	27 13.8	23 51.7	26 53.8	7 58.1	5 56.4	14 19.7	5 24.5	25 26.7	22 53.4	28 1.0
16	11 33 25.4	25 10.6	27 10.6	5♉39.7	27 43.1	9 12.6	6 43.6	14 17.0	5 31.5	25 28.9	22 54.7	28 .5
17	11 37 21.9	26 10.4	27 7.5	17 26.3	28 35.6	10 27.1	7 30.7	14 14.0	5 38.6	25 31.1	22 56.0	27 60.0
18	11 41 18.5	27 10.1	27 4.3	29 15.6	29 31.2	11 41.6	8 17.9	14 10.8	5 45.5	25 33.2	22 57.2	27 59.4
19	11 45 15.0	28 9.8	27 1.1	11♊12.1	0♓29.7	12 56.0	9 5.0	14 7.5	5 52.5	25 35.3	22 58.4	27 58.8
20	11 49 11.6	29 9.4	26 57.9	23 20.9	1 30.8	14 10.4	9 52.2	14 4.0	5 59.4	25 37.3	22 59.6	27 58.2
21	11 53 8.1	0♈ 9.0	26 54.7	5♋47.4	2 34.5	15 24.8	10 39.3	14 .4	6 6.3	25 39.3	23 .7	27 57.6
22	11 57 4.7	1 8.6	26 51.6	18 36.4	3 40.6	16 39.2	11 26.4	13 56.5	6 13.2	25 41.3	23 1.9	27 56.9
23	12 1 1.3	2 8.1	26 48.4	1♌52.2	4 49.0	17 53.5	12 13.5	13 52.5	6 20.0	25 43.2	23 2.9	27 56.2
24	12 4 57.8	3 7.6	26 45.2	15 37.1	5 59.6	19 7.8	13 .6	13 48.4	6 26.8	25 45.0	23 4.0	27 55.4
25	12 8 54.4	4 7.1	26 42.0	29 51.1	7 12.3	20 22.0	13 47.6	13 44.1	6 33.5	25 46.9	23 5.0	27 54.6
26	12 12 50.9	5 6.5	26 38.8	14♍31.0	8 27.0	21 36.3	14 34.7	13 39.6	6 40.3	25 48.6	23 6.0	27 53.8
27	12 16 47.5	6 5.9	26 35.7	29 30.3	9 43.6	22 50.5	15 21.7	13 35.0	6 47.0	25 50.4	23 7.0	27 53.0
28	12 20 44.0	7 5.2	26 32.5	14♎40.0	11 2.0	24 4.6	16 8.7	13 30.2	6 53.6	25 52.1	23 7.9	27 52.1
29	12 24 40.6	8 4.6	26 29.3	29 50.0	12 22.3	25 18.7	16 55.8	13 25.2	7 .2	25 53.7	23 8.8	27 51.2
30	12 28 37.1	9 3.8	26 26.1	14♏50.7	13 44.3	26 32.8	17 42.7	13 20.1	7 6.8	25 55.3	23 9.7	27 50.3
31	12 32 33.7	10 3.1	26 23.0	29 34.5	15 8.0	27 46.9	18 29.7	13 14.9	7 13.4	25 56.8	23 10.6	27 49.4

LATITUDE

DAY	EPHEM. SID. TIME	☉	☊	☽	☿	♀	♂	♃	♄	♅	♆	♇
1	10 34 17.1	0 .0	0 .0	2S57.9	2N41.1	1S23.7	1S 6.2	1N18.3	1S26.2	0S28.0	0N36.5	14N 7.6
4	10 46 6.8	0 .0	0 .0	0N38.4	2 .8	1 21.4	1 6.4	1 18.9	1 26.4	0 28.1	0 36.6	14 8.8
7	10 57 56.4	0 .0	0 .0	3 45.1	1 19.2	1 18.5	1 6.6	1 19.4	1 26.7	0 28.2	0 36.6	14 10.0
10	11 9 46.1	0 .0	0 .0	5 1.8	0 39.1	1 15.0	1 6.8	1 19.9	1 26.9	0 28.3	0 36.6	14 11.2
13	11 21 35.7	0 .0	0 .0	4 10.9	0 2.0	1 11.0	1 6.9	1 20.4	1 27.2	0 28.3	0 36.6	14 12.4
16	11 33 25.4	0 .0	0 .0	1 43.5	0S31.4	1 6.5	1 6.9	1 20.9	1 27.5	0 28.4	0 36.6	14 13.5
19	11 45 15.0	0 .0	0 .0	1S24.0	1 .7	1 1.5	1 6.8	1 21.4	1 27.8	0 28.5	0 36.7	14 14.6
22	11 57 4.7	0 .0	0 .0	4 6.6	1 25.9	0 56.1	1 6.7	1 21.8	1 28.1	0 28.6	0 36.7	14 15.7
25	12 8 54.4	0 .0	0 .0	5 6.1	1 46.8	0 50.2	1 6.5	1 22.2	1 28.5	0 28.7	0 36.7	14 16.7
28	12 20 44.0	0 .0	0 .0	3 18.7	2 3.5	0 43.9	1 6.3	1 22.6	1 28.9	0 28.8	0 36.7	14 17.7
31	12 32 33.7	0 .0	0 .0	0N26.9	2 15.9	0 37.2	1 5.9	1 22.9	1 29.3	0 28.9	0 36.8	14 18.6

RIGHT ASCENSION

DAY	EPHEM. SID. TIME	☉	☊	☽	☿	♀	♂	♃	♄	♅	♆	♇
1	10 34 17.1	11♓41.8	25♏42.8	18♎14.6	25♒ 3.8	21♓51.2	27♒35.7	12♏35.4	6♓10.3	26♑53.3	24♑14.0	28♏57.6
2	10 38 13.7	12 38.0	25 39.5	2♏42.0	24R43.4	22 60.0	28 21.5	12R35.3	6 17.2	26 56.1	24 15.7	28 57.7
3	10 42 10.2	13 34.1	25 36.2	17 25.1	24 29.9	24 8.6	29 7.2	12 35.0	6 24.1	26 59.0	24 17.5	28 57.7
4	10 46 6.8	14 30.1	25 32.9	2♐16.4	24 23.2	25 17.0	29 52.8	12 34.5	6 31.0	27 1.8	24 19.2	28 57.7
5	10 50 3.3	15 25.9	25 29.6	17 3.5	24 23.1	26 25.4	0♓38.3	12 33.8	6 37.9	27 4.6	24 20.8	28 57.7
6	10 53 59.9	16 21.7	25 26.3	1♑32.2	24D29.3	27 33.7	1 23.8	12 33.0	6 44.8	27 7.3	24 22.5	28R57.6
7	10 57 56.4	17 17.3	25 23.1	15 30.8	24 41.5	28 41.9	2 9.1	12 31.9	6 51.7	27 10.0	24 24.1	28 57.5
8	11 1 53.0	18 12.9	25 19.8	28 52.8	24 59.3	29 50.0	2 54.3	12 30.7	6 58.5	27 12.7	24 25.7	28 57.4
9	11 5 49.5	19 8.3	25 16.5	11♒37.5	25 22.5	0♈58.1	3 39.5	12 29.2	7 5.4	27 15.3	24 27.3	28 57.3
10	11 9 46.1	20 3.7	25 13.2	23 48.9	25 50.6	2 6.1	4 24.5	12 27.6	7 12.2	27 17.9	24 28.8	28 57.1
11	11 13 42.6	20 59.0	25 9.9	5♓34.1	26 23.3	3 14.1	5 9.5	12 25.8	7 19.0	27 20.5	24 30.3	28 56.8
12	11 17 39.2	21 54.2	25 6.6	17 1.5	27 .3	4 22.1	5 54.4	12 23.8	7 25.8	27 23.0	24 31.8	28 56.6
13	11 21 35.7	22 49.4	25 3.3	28 20.2	27 41.3	5 30.0	6 39.1	12 21.7	7 32.5	27 25.4	24 33.3	28 56.3
14	11 25 32.3	23 44.5	25 .1	9♈38.8	28 26.0	6 38.0	7 23.9	12 19.4	7 39.3	27 27.9	24 34.7	28 56.0
15	11 29 28.8	24 39.5	24 56.8	21 5.1	29 14.1	7 45.9	8 8.5	12 16.8	7 46.0	27 30.3	24 36.1	28 55.7
16	11 33 25.4	25 34.4	24 53.5	2♉45.9	0♓ 5.3	8 53.9	8 53.0	12 14.1	7 52.7	27 32.6	24 37.5	28 55.3
17	11 37 21.9	26 29.3	24 50.2	14 45.9	0 59.4	10 1.9	9 37.4	12 11.2	7 59.4	27 34.9	24 38.8	28 54.8
18	11 41 18.5	27 24.1	24 46.9	27 7.7	1 56.3	11 9.9	10 21.8	12 8.2	8 6.0	27 37.1	24 40.1	28 54.4
19	11 45 15.0	28 18.9	24 43.7	9♊51.1	2 55.6	12 17.9	11 6.0	12 4.9	8 12.6	27 39.3	24 41.4	28 53.9
20	11 49 11.6	29 13.6	24 40.4	22 53.1	3 57.3	13 26.0	11 50.2	12 1.5	8 19.2	27 41.5	24 42.7	28 53.4
21	11 53 8.1	0♈ 8.3	24 37.1	6♋ 9.1	5 1.1	14 34.2	12 34.3	11 58.0	8 25.8	27 43.6	24 43.9	28 52.8
22	11 57 4.7	1 2.9	24 33.8	19 33.5	6 6.9	15 42.4	13 18.3	11 54.2	8 32.3	27 45.7	24 45.1	28 52.3
23	12 1 1.3	1 57.6	24 30.5	3♌ 2.2	7 14.6	16 50.7	14 2.3	11 50.3	8 38.8	27 47.7	24 46.2	28 51.7
24	12 4 57.8	2 52.2	24 27.3	16 33.4	8 24.1	17 59.1	14 46.1	11 46.3	8 45.2	27 49.7	24 47.3	28 51.0
25	12 8 54.4	3 46.8	24 24.0	0♍ 8.8	9 35.2	19 7.6	15 29.9	11 42.0	8 51.7	27 51.6	24 48.4	28 50.4
26	12 12 50.9	4 41.3	24 20.7	13 52.8	10 47.8	20 16.2	16 13.6	11 37.7	8 58.1	27 53.5	24 49.5	28 49.7
27	12 16 47.5	5 35.9	24 17.4	27 51.9	12 2.0	21 25.0	16 57.3	11 33.1	9 4.4	27 55.3	24 50.5	28 48.9
28	12 20 44.0	6 30.5	24 14.1	12♎12.5	13 17.5	22 33.8	17 40.9	11 28.4	9 10.8	27 57.1	24 51.5	28 48.2
29	12 24 40.6	7 25.0	24 10.9	26 58.1	14 34.3	23 42.9	18 24.4	11 23.6	9 17.0	27 58.8	24 52.4	28 47.4
30	12 28 37.1	8 19.6	24 7.6	12♏ 6.7	15 52.4	24 52.0	19 7.8	11 18.6	9 23.3	28 .5	24 53.3	28 46.6
31	12 32 33.7	9 14.2	24 4.3	27 28.7	17 11.7	26 1.4	19 51.2	11 13.5	9 29.5	28 2.1	24 54.2	28 45.8

DECLINATION

DAY	EPHEM. SID. TIME	☉	☊	☽	☿	♀	♂	♃	♄	♅	♆	♇
1	10 34 17.1	7S45.2	0S20.6	10S55.9	11S 6.2	5S 2.0	14S15.0	14S59.2	11S28.6	21S36.9	20S57.2	5S56.3
4	10 46 6.8	6 36.5	0 20.6	20 20.6	12 2.5	3 31.1	13 27.2	14 58.4	11 20.9	21 35.5	20 56.4	5 55.0
7	10 57 56.4	5 26.9	0 20.6	18 53.9	12 40.3	1 59.4	12 38.1	14 57.0	11 13.2	21 34.2	20 55.6	5 53.8
10	11 9 46.1	4 16.7	0 20.5	9 2.7	12 59.4	0 27.1	11 47.9	14 55.2	11 5.6	21 32.9	20 54.9	5 52.5
13	11 21 35.7	3 6.0	0 20.5	3N50.2	13 .7	1N 5.4	10 56.8	14 52.9	10 58.0	21 31.7	20 54.1	5 51.1
16	11 33 25.4	1 55.0	0 20.4	15 2.1	12 45.4	2 37.9	10 4.7	14 50.2	10 50.5	21 30.5	20 53.5	5 49.7
19	11 45 15.0	0 43.8	0 20.4	20 44.0	12 14.7	4 9.8	9 11.7	14 46.9	10 43.0	21 29.5	20 52.8	5 48.3
22	11 57 4.7	0N27.3	0 20.4	18 4.4	11 29.6	5 40.9	8 18.1	14 43.3	10 35.7	21 28.4	20 52.2	5 46.9
25	12 8 54.4	1 38.2	0 20.3	6 44.5	10 31.1	7 11.0	7 23.8	14 39.2	10 28.5	21 27.5	20 51.7	5 45.4
28	12 20 44.0	2 48.8	0 20.3	8S49.9	9 19.9	8 39.5	6 29.0	14 34.7	10 21.4	21 26.6	20 51.1	5 43.9
31	12 32 33.7	3 58.9	0 20.3	19 37.3	7 56.7	10 6.3	5 33.7	14 29.8	10 14.4	21 25.8	20 50.7	5 42.4

APRIL 1994

LONGITUDE

DAY	EPHEM. SID. TIME h m s	☉ ° ′	☊ ° ′	☽ ° ′	☿ ° ′	♀ ° ′	♂ ° ′	♃ ° ′	♄ ° ′	♅ ° ′	♆ ° ′	♇ ° ′
1	12 36 30.2	11♈ 2.3	26♏19.8	13♐56.5	16♓33.3	29♈ .9	19♓16.7	13♏ 9.5	7♓19.9	25♑58.3	23♑11.4	27♏48.4
2	12 40 26.8	12 1.5	26 16.6	27 54.9	18 .2	0♉14.9	20 3.6	13R 4.0	7 26.3	25 59.8	23 12.2	27R47.4
3	12 44 23.3	13 .7	26 13.4	11♑29.6	19 28.8	1 28.9	20 50.6	12 58.4	7 32.7	26 1.2	23 12.9	27 46.4
4	12 48 19.9	13 59.9	26 10.2	24 42.7	20 58.9	2 42.9	21 37.5	12 52.6	7 39.2	26 2.6	23 13.7	27 45.4
5	12 52 16.4	14 59.0	26 7.1	7♒36.6	22 30.6	3 56.8	22 24.4	12 46.7	7 45.5	26 3.9	23 14.3	27 44.3
6	12 56 13.0	15 58.0	26 3.9	20 14.1	24 3.8	5 10.7	23 11.3	12 40.7	7 51.8	26 5.2	23 15.0	27 43.2
7	13 0 9.5	16 57.1	26 .7	2♓38.2	25 38.5	6 24.6	23 58.2	12 34.5	7 58.0	26 6.4	23 15.6	27 42.0
8	13 4 6.1	17 56.1	25 57.5	14 51.2	27 14.8	7 38.4	24 45.0	12 28.2	8 4.2	26 7.5	23 16.2	27 40.9
9	13 8 2.6	18 55.1	25 54.4	26 55.3	28 52.5	8 52.2	25 31.8	12 21.8	8 10.3	26 8.7	23 16.8	27 39.7
10	13 11 59.2	19 54.0	25 51.2	8♈52.5	0♈31.8	10 5.9	26 18.6	12 15.3	8 16.4	26 9.7	23 17.3	27 38.5
11	13 15 55.7	20 53.0	25 48.0	20 44.5	2 12.6	11 19.7	27 5.4	12 8.7	8 22.4	26 10.7	23 17.8	27 37.3
12	13 19 52.3	21 51.9	25 44.8	2♉33.1	3 54.9	12 33.4	27 52.1	12 2.0	8 28.4	26 11.7	23 18.2	27 36.0
13	13 23 48.9	22 50.7	25 41.6	14 20.4	5 38.7	13 47.0	28 38.8	11 55.2	8 34.4	26 12.6	23 18.6	27 34.7
14	13 27 45.4	23 49.5	25 38.5	26 8.7	7 24.1	15 .6	29 25.5	11 48.3	8 40.2	26 13.5	23 19.0	27 33.4
15	13 31 42.0	24 48.3	25 35.3	8♊ 1.1	9 11.0	16 14.2	0♈12.1	11 41.3	8 46.1	26 14.3	23 19.4	27 32.1
16	13 35 38.5	25 47.1	25 32.1	20 .9	10 59.5	17 27.8	0 58.8	11 34.3	8 51.8	26 15.1	23 19.7	27 30.8
17	13 39 35.1	26 45.8	25 28.9	2♋12.0	12 49.5	18 41.3	1 45.3	11 27.1	8 57.5	26 15.8	23 20.0	27 29.4
18	13 43 31.6	27 44.4	25 25.8	14 38.6	14 41.1	19 54.7	2 31.9	11 19.9	9 3.2	26 16.5	23 20.2	27 28.1
19	13 47 28.2	28 43.1	25 22.6	27 25.1	16 34.3	21 8.2	3 18.4	11 12.6	9 8.7	26 17.1	23 20.5	27 26.7
20	13 51 24.7	29 41.7	25 19.4	10♌35.3	18 29.0	22 21.6	4 4.9	11 5.3	9 14.3	26 17.6	23 20.6	27 25.3
21	13 55 21.3	0♉40.3	25 16.2	24 12.1	20 25.3	23 34.9	4 51.4	10 57.9	9 19.7	26 18.2	23 20.8	27 23.8
22	13 59 17.8	1 38.8	25 13.0	8♍16.6	22 23.2	24 48.2	5 37.8	10 50.5	9 25.1	26 18.6	23 20.9	27 22.4
23	14 3 14.4	2 37.3	25 9.9	22 47.5	24 22.6	26 1.5	6 24.2	10 43.0	9 30.5	26 19.0	23 21.0	27 20.9
24	14 7 10.9	3 35.7	25 6.7	7♎40.6	26 23.5	27 14.7	7 10.5	10 35.5	9 35.7	26 19.4	23 21.1	27 19.4
25	14 11 7.5	4 34.2	25 3.5	22 49.0	28 25.9	28 27.9	7 56.9	10 28.0	9 41.0	26 19.8	23 21.1	27 18.0
26	14 15 4.0	5 32.6	25 .3	8♏ 3.3	0♉29.6	29 41.1	8 43.2	10 20.4	9 46.1	26 20.0	23 21.1	27 16.5
27	14 19 .6	6 30.9	24 57.2	23 13.5	2 34.6	0♊54.2	9 29.5	10 12.8	9 51.2	26 20.2	23 21.1	27 15.0
28	14 22 57.2	7 29.3	24 54.0	8♐10.6	4 40.7	2 7.2	10 15.7	10 5.1	9 56.2	26 20.4	23R21.0	27 13.4
29	14 26 53.7	8 27.6	24 50.8	22 47.4	6 48.0	3 20.3	11 1.9	9 57.5	10 1.2	26 20.5	23 20.9	27 11.9
30	14 30 50.3	9 25.9	24 47.6	6♑59.3	8 56.1	4 33.2	11 48.0	9 49.8	10 6.0	26 20.6	23 20.8	27 10.3

LATITUDE

DAY	SID. TIME	☉	☊	☽	☿	♀	♂	♃	♄	♅	♆	♇
1	12 36 30.2	0 .0	0 .0	1N42.9	2S19.1	0S34.9	1S 5.8	1N23.0	1S29.4	0S28.9	0N36.8	14N18.9
4	12 48 19.9	0 .0	0 .0	4 29.4	2 25.7	0 27.8	1 5.4	1 23.3	1 29.8	0 29.0	0 36.8	14 19.8
7	13 0 9.5	0 .0	0 .0	5 7.4	2 27.9	0 20.4	1 4.9	1 23.5	1 30.2	0 29.1	0 36.8	14 20.6
10	13 11 59.2	0 .0	0 .0	3 41.5	2 25.8	0 12.8	1 4.4	1 23.7	1 30.7	0 29.2	0 36.9	14 21.3
13	13 23 48.9	0 .0	0 .0	0 52.4	2 19.1	0 5.0	1 3.7	1 23.9	1 31.1	0 29.3	0 36.9	14 22.0
16	13 35 38.5	0 .0	0 .0	2S18.5	2 7.8	0N 3.0	1 3.1	1 24.0	1 31.6	0 29.4	0 36.9	14 22.7
19	13 47 28.2	0 .0	0 .0	4 42.0	1 52.0	0 11.0	1 2.3	1 24.1	1 32.1	0 29.5	0 37.0	14 23.2
22	13 59 17.8	0 .0	0 .0	5 5.5	1 31.8	0 19.1	1 1.5	1 24.1	1 32.6	0 29.6	0 37.0	14 23.7
25	14 11 7.5	0 .0	0 .0	2 43.1	1 7.4	0 27.3	1 .6	1 24.0	1 33.2	0 29.7	0 37.0	14 24.1
28	14 22 57.2	0 .0	0 .0	1N18.8	0 39.5	0 35.3	0 59.7	1 23.9	1 33.7	0 29.8	0 37.1	14 24.5

RIGHT ASCENSION

DAY	SID. TIME	☉	☊	☽	☿	♀	♂	♃	♄	♅	♆	♇
1	12 36 30.2	10♈ 8.8	24♏ 1.0	12♐48.0	18♓32.2	27♈10.9	20♓34.6	11♏ 8.2	9♓35.7	28♑ 3.7	24♑55.1	28♏44.9
2	12 40 26.8	11 3.5	23 57.8	27 46.5	19 53.8	28 20.6	21 17.9	11R 2.8	9 41.8	28 5.3	24 55.9	28R44.0
3	12 44 23.3	11 58.2	23 54.5	12♑ 9.1	21 16.6	29 30.4	22 1.1	10 57.3	9 47.9	28 6.8	24 56.7	28 43.1
4	12 48 19.9	12 53.0	23 51.2	25 48.1	22 40.6	0♉40.5	22 44.3	10 51.7	9 54.0	28 8.2	24 57.5	28 42.2
5	12 52 16.4	13 47.7	23 47.9	8♒43.0	24 5.6	1 50.8	23 27.5	10 45.9	10 .0	28 9.6	24 58.2	28 41.2
6	12 56 13.0	14 42.6	23 44.7	20 59.1	25 31.7	3 1.3	24 10.5	10 40.0	10 6.0	28 11.0	24 58.9	28 40.2
7	13 0 9.5	15 37.4	23 41.4	2♓45.1	26 58.9	4 12.0	24 53.6	10 33.9	10 11.9	28 12.3	24 59.5	28 39.2
8	13 4 6.1	16 32.4	23 38.1	14 10.8	28 27.2	5 22.9	25 36.6	10 27.8	10 17.8	28 13.5	25 .2	28 38.2
9	13 8 2.6	17 27.4	23 34.9	25 26.4	29 56.6	6 34.1	26 19.5	10 21.5	10 23.6	28 14.7	25 .7	28 37.1
10	13 11 59.2	18 22.4	23 31.6	6♈41.4	1♈27.2	7 45.5	27 2.4	10 15.1	10 29.4	28 15.8	25 1.3	28 36.0
11	13 15 55.7	19 17.5	23 28.3	18 3.9	2 58.9	8 57.1	27 45.3	10 8.7	10 35.2	28 16.9	25 1.8	28 34.9
12	13 19 52.3	20 12.7	23 25.0	29 40.8	4 31.8	10 9.0	28 28.1	10 2.1	10 40.8	28 17.9	25 2.3	28 33.7
13	13 23 48.9	21 8.0	23 21.8	11♉36.5	6 6.0	11 21.1	29 10.9	9 55.4	10 46.5	28 18.9	25 2.7	28 32.6
14	13 27 45.4	22 3.3	23 18.5	23 52.7	7 41.4	12 33.5	29 53.6	9 48.7	10 52.1	28 19.8	25 3.1	28 31.4
15	13 31 42.0	22 58.7	23 15.2	6♊28.3	9 18.2	13 46.1	0♈36.3	9 41.8	10 57.6	28 20.7	25 3.5	28 30.2
16	13 35 38.5	23 54.2	23 12.0	19 19.3	10 56.3	14 59.0	1 19.0	9 34.9	11 3.1	28 21.5	25 3.8	28 29.0
17	13 39 35.1	24 49.8	23 8.7	2♋20.4	12 35.8	16 12.2	2 1.6	9 27.9	11 8.5	28 22.3	25 4.1	28 27.7
18	13 43 31.6	25 45.5	23 5.4	15 25.8	14 16.8	17 25.6	2 44.2	9 20.9	11 13.8	28 23.0	25 4.4	28 26.4
19	13 47 28.2	26 41.3	23 2.2	28 31.7	15 59.4	18 39.3	3 26.8	9 13.8	11 19.2	28 23.6	25 4.6	28 25.2
20	13 51 24.7	27 37.2	22 58.9	11♌37.2	17 43.4	19 53.3	4 9.4	9 6.6	11 24.4	28 24.2	25 4.8	28 23.8
21	13 55 21.3	28 33.1	22 55.6	24 44.9	19 29.2	21 7.5	4 51.9	8 59.3	11 29.6	28 24.8	25 5.0	28 22.5
22	13 59 17.8	29 29.2	22 52.4	8♍ .9	21 16.6	22 22.0	5 34.5	8 52.1	11 34.7	28 25.3	25 5.1	28 21.2
23	14 3 14.4	0♉25.4	22 49.1	21 33.7	23 5.7	23 36.7	6 16.9	8 44.7	11 39.8	28 25.7	25 5.2	28 19.8
24	14 7 10.9	1 21.7	22 45.9	5♎32.5	24 56.6	24 51.7	6 59.4	8 37.4	11 44.8	28 26.1	25 5.3	28 18.5
25	14 11 7.5	2 18.1	22 42.6	20 4.6	26 49.3	26 7.1	7 41.9	8 30.0	11 49.8	28 26.5	25 5.3	28 17.1
26	14 15 4.0	3 14.6	22 39.3	5♏12.3	28 43.7	27 22.6	8 24.4	8 22.6	11 54.7	28 26.8	25 5.3	28 15.7
27	14 19 .6	4 11.3	22 36.1	20 49.1	0♉40.0	28 38.4	9 6.8	8 15.2	11 59.5	28 27.0	25 5.3	28 14.3
28	14 22 57.2	5 8.1	22 32.8	6♐38.6	2 38.0	29 54.4	9 49.3	8 7.7	12 4.3	28 27.2	25R 5.2	28 12.9
29	14 26 53.7	6 5.0	22 29.5	22 17.9	4 37.8	1♊10.7	10 31.7	8 .2	12 9.0	28 27.3	25 5.1	28 11.4
30	14 30 50.3	7 2.0	22 26.3	7♑24.5	6 39.2	2 27.3	11 14.1	7 52.7	12 13.7	28 27.4	25 4.9	28 10.0

DECLINATION

DAY	SID. TIME	☉	☊	☽	☿	♀	♂	♃	♄	♅	♆	♇
1	12 36 30.2	4N22.1	0S20.2	20S46.2	7S26.5	10N34.8	5S15.2	14S28.1	10S12.1	21S25.5	20S50.5	5S42.0
4	12 48 19.9	5 31.3	0 20.2	16 45.7	5 48.4	11 58.7	4 19.3	14 22.8	10 5.2	21 24.8	20 50.1	5 40.5
7	13 0 9.5	6 39.6	0 20.2	5 44.9	3 59.7	13 20.1	3 23.3	14 17.1	9 58.6	21 24.2	20 49.8	5 39.0
10	13 11 59.2	7 46.9	0 20.1	6N54.6	2 1.1	14 38.6	2 27.1	14 11.1	9 52.1	21 23.7	20 49.4	5 37.5
13	13 23 48.9	8 53.0	0 20.1	16 58.5	0N 6.8	15 53.8	1 30.8	14 4.8	9 45.8	21 23.2	20 49.2	5 36.1
16	13 35 38.5	9 57.8	0 20.0	20 45.7	2 23.3	17 5.4	0 34.5	13 58.3	9 39.7	21 22.9	20 49.0	5 34.6
19	13 47 28.2	11 1.1	0 20.0	16 3.9	4 47.3	18 13.2	0N21.7	13 51.6	9 33.8	21 22.6	20 48.8	5 33.2
22	13 59 17.8	12 2.7	0 20.0	3 44.3	7 17.5	19 16.7	1 17.7	13 44.8	9 28.1	21 22.4	20 48.7	5 31.9
25	14 11 7.5	13 2.6	0 19.9	11S23.8	9 52.0	20 15.6	2 13.5	13 37.8	9 22.6	21 22.3	20 48.6	5 30.5
28	14 22 57.2	14 .5	0 19.9	20 22.4	12 27.7	21 9.7	3 8.9	13 30.8	9 17.3	21 22.2	20 48.6	5 29.2

MAY 1994

DAY	EPHEM. SID. TIME	☉	☊	☽	☿	♀	♂	♃	♄	♅	♆	♇
	h m s	° ′	° ′	° ′	° ′	° ′	° ′	° ′	° ′	° ′	° ′	° ′
		LONGITUDE										
1	14 34 46.8	10♉24.1	24♏44.4	20♑44.7	11♉ 5.0	5♊46.2	12♈34.1	9♏42.2	10♓10.8	26♑20.6	23♑20.6	27♏ 8.8
2	14 38 43.4	11 22.3	24 41.3	4♒ 4.2	13 14.3	6 59.1	13 20.2	9R34.5	10 15.6	26R20.5	23R20.4	27R 7.2
3	14 42 39.9	12 20.5	24 38.1	16 59.9	15 23.9	8 11.9	14 6.2	9 26.9	10 20.2	26 20.5	23 20.2	27 5.6
4	14 46 36.5	13 18.7	24 34.9	29 35.2	17 33.5	9 24.8	14 52.3	9 19.2	10 24.8	26 20.3	23 19.9	27 4.0
5	14 50 33.0	14 16.9	24 31.7	11♓53.9	19 42.9	10 37.5	15 38.2	9 11.6	10 29.3	26 20.1	23 19.6	27 2.4
6	14 54 29.6	15 15.0	24 28.6	23 59.7	21 51.7	11 50.3	16 24.1	9 4.0	10 33.7	26 19.9	23 19.3	27 .8
7	14 58 26.1	16 13.1	24 25.4	5♈56.3	23 59.6	13 3.0	17 10.0	8 56.4	10 38.1	26 19.6	23 18.9	26 59.1
8	15 2 22.7	17 11.2	24 22.2	17 47.0	26 6.4	14 15.7	17 55.9	8 48.9	10 42.4	26 19.3	23 18.5	26 57.5
9	15 6 19.3	18 9.3	24 19.0	29 34.8	28 11.7	15 28.3	18 41.7	8 41.4	10 46.6	26 18.9	23 18.1	26 55.9
10	15 10 15.8	19 7.3	24 15.8	11♉22.4	0♊15.4	16 40.9	19 27.4	8 33.9	10 50.7	26 18.5	23 17.6	26 54.2
11	15 14 12.4	20 5.3	24 12.7	23 11.9	2 17.0	17 53.4	20 13.1	8 26.5	10 54.8	26 18.0	23 17.1	26 52.6
12	15 18 8.9	21 3.3	24 9.5	5♊ 5.8	4 16.5	19 5.9	20 58.8	8 19.2	10 58.7	26 17.4	23 16.6	26 50.9
13	15 22 5.5	22 1.2	24 6.3	17 6.1	6 13.5	20 18.3	21 44.4	8 11.9	11 2.6	26 16.9	23 16.1	26 49.2
14	15 26 2.0	22 59.2	24 3.1	29 15.1	8 8.0	21 30.7	22 30.0	8 4.7	11 6.4	26 16.2	23 15.5	26 47.6
15	15 29 58.6	23 57.1	23 60.0	11♋35.3	9 59.7	22 43.1	23 15.5	7 57.5	11 10.1	26 15.6	23 14.9	26 45.9
16	15 33 55.1	24 55.0	23 56.8	24 9.4	11 48.5	23 55.4	24 1.1	7 50.5	11 13.8	26 14.9	23 14.3	26 44.3
17	15 37 51.7	25 52.8	23 53.6	7♌ .0	13 34.3	25 7.7	24 46.5	7 43.5	11 17.3	26 14.1	23 13.6	26 42.6
18	15 41 48.3	26 50.6	23 50.4	20 9.8	15 17.0	26 19.9	25 31.9	7 36.5	11 20.8	26 13.3	23 12.9	26 41.0
19	15 45 44.8	27 48.4	23 47.3	3♍40.9	16 56.4	27 32.0	26 17.2	7 29.7	11 24.2	26 12.4	23 12.2	26 39.3
20	15 49 41.4	28 46.2	23 44.1	17 34.7	18 32.7	28 44.1	27 2.5	7 23.0	11 27.5	26 11.5	23 11.4	26 37.6
21	15 53 37.9	29 43.9	23 40.9	1♎50.9	20 5.6	29 56.2	27 47.7	7 16.3	11 30.7	26 10.6	23 10.7	26 36.0
22	15 57 34.5	0♊41.6	23 37.7	16 27.5	21 35.2	1♋ 8.2	28 32.9	7 9.8	11 33.8	26 9.6	23 9.8	26 34.3
23	16 1 31.0	1 39.3	23 34.5	1♏20.0	23 1.4	2 20.1	29 18.0	7 3.4	11 36.8	26 8.5	23 9.0	26 32.6
24	16 5 27.6	2 36.9	23 31.4	16 22.0	24 24.1	3 32.0	0♉ 3.1	6 57.1	11 39.8	26 7.5	23 8.2	26 31.0
25	16 9 24.1	3 34.5	23 28.2	1♐25.3	25 43.3	4 43.8	0 48.1	6 50.8	11 42.6	26 6.3	23 7.3	26 29.3
26	16 13 20.7	4 32.2	23 25.0	16 21.2	26 59.0	5 55.6	1 33.1	6 44.8	11 45.4	26 5.2	23 6.3	26 27.7
27	16 17 17.3	5 29.7	23 21.8	1♑ 1.9	28 11.2	7 7.3	2 18.0	6 38.8	11 48.1	26 3.9	23 5.4	26 26.0
28	16 21 13.8	6 27.3	23 18.7	15 20.9	29 19.6	8 18.9	3 2.9	6 32.9	11 50.6	26 2.7	23 4.4	26 24.4
29	16 25 10.4	7 24.9	23 15.5	29 14.5	0♋24.4	9 30.5	3 47.7	6 27.2	11 53.1	26 1.4	23 3.4	26 22.8
30	16 29 6.9	8 22.4	23 12.3	12♒41.4	1 25.4	10 42.1	4 32.5	6 21.6	11 55.5	26 .1	23 2.4	26 21.2
31	16 33 3.5	9 19.9	23 9.1	25 42.6	2 22.6	11 53.6	5 17.2	6 16.1	11 57.8	25 58.7	23 1.4	26 19.5
		LATITUDE										
1	14 34 46.8	0 .0	0 .0	4N25.8	0S 8.8	0N43.3	0S58.7	1N23.7	1S34.3	0S29.9	0N37.1	14N24.8
4	14 46 36.5	0 .0	0 .0	5 15.6	0N22.9	0 51.2	0 57.6	1 23.5	1 34.9	0 30.0	0 37.1	14 25.0
7	14 58 26.1	0 .0	0 .0	3 55.6	0 54.1	0 58.8	0 56.5	1 23.3	1 35.5	0 30.1	0 37.1	14 25.1
10	15 10 15.8	0 .0	0 .0	1 8.4	1 22.5	1 6.2	0 55.3	1 23.0	1 36.1	0 30.1	0 37.2	14 25.1
13	15 22 5.5	0 .0	0 .0	2S 6.1	1 46.5	1 13.3	0 54.0	1 22.6	1 36.7	0 30.2	0 37.2	14 25.1
16	15 33 55.1	0 .0	0 .0	4 36.5	2 4.5	1 20.0	0 52.7	1 22.2	1 37.3	0 30.3	0 37.2	14 25.0
19	15 45 44.8	0 .0	0 .0	5 13.1	2 15.6	1 26.4	0 51.3	1 21.7	1 38.0	0 30.4	0 37.2	14 24.8
22	15 57 34.5	0 .0	0 .0	3 13.1	2 19.3	1 32.3	0 49.9	1 21.2	1 38.6	0 30.5	0 37.3	14 24.5
25	16 9 24.1	0 .0	0 .0	0N42.1	2 15.3	1 37.7	0 48.4	1 20.7	1 39.3	0 30.6	0 37.3	14 24.2
28	16 21 13.8	0 .0	0 .0	4 8.6	2 3.6	1 42.6	0 46.9	1 20.1	1 40.0	0 30.7	0 37.3	14 23.7
31	16 33 3.5	0 .0	0 .0	5 16.6	1 44.1	1 46.9	0 45.3	1 19.5	1 40.7	0 30.8	0 37.3	14 23.2
		RIGHT ASCENSION										
1	14 34 46.8	7♉59.2	22♏23.0	21♑43.7	8♉42.2	3♊44.1	11♈56.6	7♏45.2	12♓18.2	28♑27.4	25♑ 4.7	28♏ 8.5
2	14 38 43.4	8 56.5	22 19.8	5♒11.0	10 46.6	5 1.1	12 39.0	7R37.8	12 22.7	28 27.4	25R 4.5	28R 7.0
3	14 42 39.9	9 53.9	22 16.5	17 50.2	12 52.3	6 18.3	13 21.4	7 30.3	12 27.2	28R27.3	25 4.3	28 5.5
4	14 46 36.5	10 51.5	22 13.3	29 50.6	14 59.0	7 35.8	14 3.9	7 22.8	12 31.5	28 27.1	25 4.0	28 4.0
5	14 50 33.0	11 49.3	22 10.0	11♓23.4	17 6.5	8 53.5	14 46.3	7 15.3	12 35.8	28 26.9	25 3.7	28 2.5
6	14 54 29.6	12 47.1	22 6.7	22 40.6	19 14.6	10 11.3	15 28.7	7 7.9	12 40.1	28 26.7	25 3.3	28 .9
7	14 58 26.1	13 45.1	22 3.5	3♈53.3	21 22.9	11 29.4	16 11.2	7 .5	12 44.2	28 26.4	25 2.9	27 59.4
8	15 2 22.7	14 43.3	22 .2	15 11.5	23 31.2	12 47.7	16 53.6	6 53.1	12 48.3	28 26.1	25 2.5	27 57.9
9	15 6 19.3	15 41.6	21 57.0	26 43.3	25 39.2	14 6.1	17 36.1	6 45.8	12 52.3	28 25.7	25 2.1	27 56.3
10	15 10 15.8	16 40.1	21 53.7	8♉34.4	27 46.5	15 24.7	18 18.6	6 38.5	12 56.3	28 25.2	25 1.6	27 54.7
11	15 14 12.4	17 38.7	21 50.5	20 47.5	29 52.8	16 43.4	19 1.1	6 31.3	13 .1	28 24.7	25 1.1	27 53.2
12	15 18 8.9	18 37.4	21 47.2	3♊21.6	1♊57.8	18 2.3	19 43.6	6 24.1	13 3.9	28 24.1	25 .5	27 51.6
13	15 22 5.5	19 36.3	21 44.0	16 12.1	4 1.2	19 21.3	20 26.1	6 17.0	13 7.6	28 23.5	24 59.9	27 50.0
14	15 26 2.0	20 35.3	21 40.7	29 12.2	6 2.8	20 40.4	21 8.6	6 9.9	13 11.3	28 22.9	24 59.3	27 48.4
15	15 29 58.6	21 34.5	21 37.5	12♋14.3	8 2.2	21 59.6	21 51.2	6 2.9	13 14.8	28 22.2	24 58.7	27 46.8
16	15 33 55.1	22 33.8	21 34.2	25 12.7	9 59.3	23 18.9	22 33.8	5 56.0	13 18.3	28 21.5	24 58.1	27 45.3
17	15 37 51.7	23 33.3	21 31.0	8♌ 4.9	11 53.8	24 38.2	23 16.4	5 49.2	13 21.7	28 20.7	24 57.4	27 43.7
18	15 41 48.3	24 32.9	21 27.7	20 52.6	13 45.4	25 57.6	23 59.0	5 42.4	13 25.1	28 19.8	24 56.6	27 42.1
19	15 45 44.8	25 32.6	21 24.5	3♍41.7	15 34.1	27 17.0	24 41.6	5 35.7	13 28.3	28 18.9	24 55.9	27 40.5
20	15 49 41.4	26 32.4	21 21.2	16 41.2	17 19.7	28 36.4	25 24.3	5 29.2	13 31.5	28 18.0	24 55.1	27 38.9
21	15 53 37.9	27 32.4	21 18.0	0♎ 1.9	19 1.9	29 55.8	26 6.9	5 22.7	13 34.6	28 17.0	24 54.2	27 37.3
22	15 57 34.5	28 32.5	21 14.7	13 54.8	20 40.8	1♋15.2	26 49.6	5 16.3	13 37.6	28 15.9	24 53.4	27 35.7
23	16 1 31.0	29 32.7	21 11.5	28 27.7	22 16.1	2 34.5	27 32.3	5 10.0	13 40.5	28 14.8	24 52.5	27 34.1
24	16 5 27.6	0♊33.1	21 8.2	13♏41.6	23 47.7	3 53.8	28 15.1	5 3.8	13 43.3	28 13.7	24 51.6	27 32.5
25	16 9 24.1	1 33.5	21 5.0	29 27.2	25 15.5	5 13.0	28 57.9	4 57.7	13 46.1	28 12.5	24 50.7	27 30.9
26	16 13 20.7	2 34.2	21 1.7	15♐24.0	26 39.5	6 32.2	29 40.7	4 51.8	13 48.7	28 11.3	24 49.7	27 29.3
27	16 17 17.3	3 34.9	20 58.5	1♑ 5.8	27 59.4	7 51.2	0♉23.5	4 45.9	13 51.3	28 10.0	24 48.7	27 27.7
28	16 21 13.8	4 35.7	20 55.2	16 9.5	29 15.3	9 10.2	1 6.4	4 40.2	13 53.8	28 8.7	24 47.7	27 26.1
29	16 25 10.4	5 36.7	20 52.0	0♒21.5	0♋27.0	10 29.0	1 49.3	4 34.6	13 56.2	28 7.3	24 46.6	27 24.6
30	16 29 6.9	6 37.8	20 48.7	13 39.8	1 34.5	11 47.6	2 32.3	4 29.1	13 58.5	28 5.9	24 45.5	27 23.0
31	16 33 3.5	7 39.0	20 45.5	26 10.5	2 37.5	13 6.1	3 15.2	4 23.8	14 .8	28 4.5	24 44.5	27 21.4
		DECLINATION										
1	14 34 46.8	14N56.4	0S19.8	17S27.4	15N .7	21N58.7	4N 3.9	13S23.7	9S12.3	21S22.3	20S48.7	5S28.0
4	14 46 36.5	15 50.1	0 19.8	6 41.1	17 26.2	22 42.3	4 58.4	13 16.7	9 7.6	21 22.4	20 48.8	5 26.8
7	14 58 26.1	16 41.3	0 19.8	5N57.8	19 38.6	23 20.1	5 52.4	13 9.7	9 3.1	21 22.7	20 48.9	5 25.6
10	15 10 15.8	17 30.1	0 19.7	16 19.6	21 32.9	23 52.2	6 45.7	13 2.9	8 58.8	21 23.0	20 49.1	5 24.6
13	15 22 5.5	18 16.3	0 19.7	20 43.3	23 5.7	24 18.1	7 38.2	12 56.1	8 54.9	21 23.4	20 49.3	5 23.6
16	15 33 55.1	18 59.7	0 19.6	16 44.5	24 15.5	24 37.9	8 30.0	12 49.6	8 51.2	21 23.8	20 49.6	5 22.6
19	15 45 44.8	19 40.2	0 19.6	5 17.3	25 2.8	24 51.3	9 20.9	12 43.4	8 47.9	21 24.4	20 49.9	5 21.7
22	15 57 34.5	20 17.7	0 19.6	9S26.4	25 29.3	24 58.3	10 10.8	12 37.4	8 44.8	21 25.0	20 50.3	5 20.9
25	16 9 24.1	20 52.0	0 19.5	19 45.4	25 37.4	24 58.8	10 59.8	12 31.7	8 42.0	21 25.7	20 50.7	5 20.2
28	16 21 13.8	21 23.1	0 19.5	18 26.3	25 29.8	24 53.0	11 47.6	12 26.4	8 39.6	21 26.5	20 51.2	5 19.6
31	16 33 3.5	21 50.9	0 19.4	7 58.6	25 9.1	24 40.8	12 34.4	12 21.5	8 37.5	21 27.3	20 51.6	5 19.0

JUNE 1994

LONGITUDE

DAY	EPHEM. SID. TIME	☉	☊	☽	☿	♀	♂	♃	♄	♅	♆	♇
	h m s	° ′	° ′	° ′	° ′	° ′	° ′	° ′	° ′	° ′	° ′	° ′
1	16 37 .0	10♊17.4	23♏ 6.0	8♓20.7	3♋16.0	13♋ 5.0	6♉ 1.9	6♏10.8	12♓ .0	25♑57.3	23♑ .3	26♏17.9
2	16 40 56.6	11 14.9	23 2.8	20 39.6	4 5.3	14 16.4	6 46.5	6R 5.6	12 2.2	25R55.8	22R59.2	26R16.3
3	16 44 53.2	12 12.4	22 59.6	2♈43.8	4 50.6	15 27.7	7 31.1	6 .6	12 4.2	25 54.3	22 58.1	26 14.7
4	16 48 49.7	13 9.9	22 56.4	14 37.9	5 31.7	16 38.9	8 15.6	5 55.7	12 6.1	25 52.8	22 57.0	26 13.2
5	16 52 46.3	14 7.4	22 53.2	26 26.4	6 8.7	17 50.1	9 .1	5 51.0	12 7.9	25 51.2	22 55.8	26 11.6
6	16 56 42.8	15 4.9	22 50.1	8♉13.5	6 41.4	19 1.3	9 44.5	5 46.4	12 9.7	25 49.7	22 54.7	26 10.1
7	17 0 39.4	16 2.3	22 46.9	20 2.9	7 9.6	20 12.4	10 28.9	5 42.0	12 11.3	25 48.0	22 53.5	26 8.5
8	17 4 35.9	16 59.7	22 43.7	1♊57.6	7 33.5	21 23.4	11 13.2	5 37.7	12 12.9	25 46.3	22 52.3	26 7.0
9	17 8 32.5	17 57.1	22 40.5	14 .1	7 52.8	22 34.4	11 57.4	5 33.5	12 14.3	25 44.6	22 51.0	26 5.5
10	17 12 29.1	18 54.5	22 37.4	26 12.6	8 7.6	23 45.3	12 41.6	5 29.6	12 15.7	25 42.9	22 49.8	26 4.0
11	17 16 25.6	19 51.9	22 34.2	8♋36.4	8 17.8	24 56.1	13 25.7	5 25.8	12 16.9	25 41.1	22 48.5	26 2.5
12	17 20 22.2	20 49.3	22 31.0	21 12.6	8 23.4	26 6.9	14 9.7	5 22.1	12 18.1	25 39.3	22 47.2	26 1.0
13	17 24 18.7	21 46.6	22 27.8	4♌ 2.1	8 24.5	27 17.6	14 53.7	5 18.7	12 19.1	25 37.4	22 45.9	25 59.6
14	17 28 15.3	22 44.0	22 24.7	17 5.7	8R21.1	28 28.2	15 37.6	5 15.4	12 20.1	25 35.6	22 44.5	25 58.1
15	17 32 11.8	23 41.3	22 21.5	0♍24.0	8 13.3	29 38.7	16 21.5	5 12.2	12 20.9	25 33.6	22 43.2	25 56.7
16	17 36 8.4	24 38.6	22 18.3	13 57.5	8 1.2	0♌49.2	17 5.3	5 9.3	12 21.7	25 31.7	22 41.8	25 55.3
17	17 40 5.0	25 35.9	22 15.1	27 46.7	7 45.1	1 59.6	17 49.0	5 6.5	12 22.3	25 29.7	22 40.4	25 53.9
18	17 44 1.5	26 33.2	22 11.9	11♎51.4	7 25.2	3 9.9	18 32.7	5 3.9	12 22.9	25 27.8	22 39.0	25 52.5
19	17 47 58.1	27 30.5	22 8.8	26 10.6	7 1.8	4 20.1	19 16.3	5 1.5	12 23.3	25 25.7	22 37.6	25 51.2
20	17 51 54.6	28 27.7	22 5.6	10♏42.1	6 35.3	5 30.2	19 59.9	4 59.2	12 23.7	25 23.7	22 36.1	25 49.8
21	17 55 51.2	29 25.0	22 2.4	25 22.1	6 6.0	6 40.3	20 43.4	4 57.1	12 23.9	25 21.6	22 34.7	25 48.5
22	17 59 47.7	0♋22.2	21 59.2	10♐ 5.5	5 34.5	7 50.3	21 26.8	4 55.2	12 24.1	25 19.5	22 33.2	25 47.2
23	18 3 44.3	1 19.4	21 56.1	24 45.6	5 1.3	9 .1	22 10.2	4 53.5	12 24.1	25 17.4	22 31.7	25 45.9
24	18 7 40.9	2 16.6	21 52.9	9♑15.7	4 26.8	10 9.9	22 53.5	4 51.9	12 24.1	25 15.3	22 30.3	25 44.7
25	18 11 37.4	3 13.8	21 49.7	23 29.5	3 51.8	11 19.6	23 36.7	4 50.6	12R23.9	25 13.1	22 28.8	25 43.5
26	18 15 34.0	4 11.0	21 46.5	7♒21.9	3 16.7	12 29.2	24 19.9	4 49.4	12 23.7	25 10.9	22 27.2	25 42.3
27	18 19 30.5	5 8.3	21 43.4	20 50.3	2 42.3	13 38.8	25 3.1	4 48.4	12 23.4	25 8.8	22 25.8	25 41.1
28	18 23 27.1	6 5.5	21 40.2	3♓54.0	2 9.0	14 48.2	25 46.1	4 47.6	12 23.0	25 6.5	22 24.2	25 40.0
29	18 27 23.6	7 2.7	21 37.0	16 34.6	1 37.5	15 57.6	26 29.1	4 46.9	12 22.4	25 4.3	22 22.7	25 38.8
30	18 31 20.2	7 59.9	21 33.8	28 55.2	1 8.3	17 6.8	27 12.0	4 46.5	12 21.8	25 2.0	22 21.1	25 37.7

LATITUDE

DAY	EPHEM. SID. TIME	☉	☊	☽	☿	♀	♂	♃	♄	♅	♆	♇
1	16 37 .0	0 .0	0 .0	5N 6.5	1N35.9	1N48.2	0S44.7	1N19.3	1S40.9	0S30.8	0N37.3	14N23.0
4	16 48 49.7	0 .0	0 .0	3 20.0	1 6.4	1 51.6	0 43.1	1 18.6	1 41.6	0 30.9	0 37.3	14 22.4
7	17 0 39.4	0 .0	0 .0	0 20.7	0 29.9	1 54.4	0 41.4	1 17.9	1 42.3	0 31.0	0 37.3	14 21.7
10	17 12 29.1	0 .0	0 .0	2S49.1	0S12.9	1 56.5	0 39.6	1 17.2	1 43.0	0 31.0	0 37.3	14 21.0
13	17 24 18.7	0 .0	0 .0	4 55.4	1 .5	1 57.8	0 37.8	1 16.5	1 43.7	0 31.1	0 37.3	14 20.2
16	17 36 8.4	0 .0	0 .0	4 53.3	1 50.8	1 58.3	0 35.9	1 15.7	1 44.5	0 31.2	0 37.3	14 19.3
19	17 47 58.1	0 .0	0 .0	2 23.5	2 40.6	1 58.1	0 34.0	1 14.9	1 45.2	0 31.2	0 37.3	14 18.3
22	17 59 47.7	0 .0	0 .0	1N29.7	3 26.3	1 57.0	0 32.1	1 14.2	1 45.9	0 31.3	0 37.3	14 17.3
25	18 11 37.4	0 .0	0 .0	4 29.7	4 3.8	1 55.0	0 30.1	1 13.4	1 46.6	0 31.3	0 37.3	14 16.2
28	18 23 27.1	0 .0	0 .0	5 4.3	4 29.8	1 52.2	0 28.0	1 12.6	1 47.3	0 31.4	0 37.3	14 15.1

RIGHT ASCENSION

DAY	EPHEM. SID. TIME	☉	☊	☽	☿	♀	♂	♃	♄	♅	♆	♇
1	16 37 .0	8♊40.3	20♏42.3	8♓ 4.4	3♋36.1	14♋24.5	3♉58.3	4♏18.5	14♓ 2.9	28♑ 3.0	24♑43.3	27♏19.8
2	16 40 56.6	9 41.7	20 39.0	19 34.2	4 30.2	15 42.6	4 41.3	4R13.5	14 5.0	28R 1.5	24R42.2	27R18.3
3	16 44 53.2	10 43.3	20 35.8	0♈52.2	5 19.7	17 .5	5 24.4	4 8.5	14 7.0	27 59.9	24 41.0	27 16.7
4	16 48 49.7	11 44.9	20 32.5	12 10.0	6 4.4	18 18.3	6 7.5	4 3.7	14 8.9	27 58.3	24 39.8	27 15.2
5	16 52 46.3	12 46.6	20 29.3	23 37.6	6 44.3	19 35.8	6 50.7	3 59.0	14 10.7	27 56.6	24 38.6	27 13.6
6	16 56 42.8	13 48.4	20 26.0	5♉22.8	7 19.4	20 53.1	7 34.0	3 54.6	14 12.4	27 55.0	24 37.4	27 12.2
7	17 0 39.4	14 50.3	20 22.8	17 30.4	7 49.6	22 10.1	8 17.2	3 50.2	14 14.0	27 53.2	24 36.1	27 10.6
8	17 4 35.9	15 52.3	20 19.6	0♊ 1.4	8 14.7	23 26.8	9 .5	3 46.0	14 15.6	27 51.5	24 34.8	27 9.1
9	17 8 32.5	16 54.3	20 16.3	12 52.6	8 34.8	24 43.2	9 43.8	3 41.9	14 17.0	27 49.7	24 33.5	27 7.6
10	17 12 29.1	17 56.4	20 13.1	25 57.4	8 49.9	25 59.4	10 27.2	3 38.0	14 18.4	27 47.8	24 32.2	27 6.2
11	17 16 25.6	18 58.5	20 9.9	9♋ 6.8	8 59.9	27 15.3	11 10.5	3 34.3	14 19.6	27 46.0	24 30.8	27 4.7
12	17 20 22.2	20 .7	20 6.6	22 12.7	9 4.9	28 30.8	11 54.0	3 30.7	14 20.8	27 44.0	24 29.4	27 3.2
13	17 24 18.7	21 3.0	20 3.4	5♌ 9.7	9 5.0	29 46.0	12 37.4	3 27.2	14 21.8	27 42.1	24 28.1	27 1.8
14	17 28 15.3	22 5.3	20 .1	17 56.9	9R .2	1♌ .9	13 20.9	3 24.0	14 22.8	27 40.1	24 26.6	27 .3
15	17 32 11.8	23 7.6	19 56.9	0♍38.0	8 50.7	2 15.4	14 4.4	3 20.9	14 23.7	27 38.1	24 25.2	26 58.9
16	17 36 8.4	24 9.9	19 53.7	13 20.6	8 36.7	3 29.6	14 48.0	3 17.9	14 24.5	27 36.1	24 23.8	26 57.5
17	17 40 5.0	25 12.3	19 50.4	26 14.8	8 18.4	4 43.5	15 31.6	3 15.2	14 25.2	27 34.0	24 22.3	26 56.1
18	17 44 1.5	26 14.7	19 47.2	9♎32.2	7 56.1	5 57.0	16 15.2	3 12.6	14 25.8	27 31.9	24 20.8	26 54.8
19	17 47 58.1	27 17.0	19 44.0	23 23.2	7 30.3	7 10.1	16 58.9	3 10.1	14 26.3	27 29.8	24 19.3	26 53.4
20	17 51 54.6	28 19.4	19 40.7	7♏54.4	7 1.1	8 22.8	17 42.6	3 7.9	14 26.7	27 27.6	24 17.8	26 52.1
21	17 55 51.2	29 21.8	19 37.5	23 4.4	6 29.3	9 35.1	18 26.3	3 5.8	14 27.1	27 25.4	24 16.3	26 50.7
22	17 59 47.7	0♋24.2	19 34.3	8♐41.5	5 55.2	10 47.1	19 10.1	3 3.8	14 27.3	27 23.2	24 14.7	26 49.4
23	18 3 44.3	1 26.6	19 31.0	24 24.4	5 19.3	11 58.6	19 53.9	3 2.1	14 27.5	27 21.0	24 13.1	26 48.1
24	18 7 40.9	2 28.9	19 27.8	9♑48.2	4 42.4	13 9.8	20 37.7	3 .5	14 27.5	27 18.7	24 11.6	26 46.9
25	18 11 37.4	3 31.2	19 24.6	24 32.9	4 5.0	14 20.6	21 21.6	2 59.1	14 27.5	27 16.4	24 10.0	26 45.6
26	18 15 34.0	4 33.5	19 21.3	8♒28.1	3 27.7	15 31.0	22 5.5	2 57.9	14R27.3	27 14.1	24 8.4	26 44.4
27	18 19 30.5	5 35.9	19 18.1	21 33.9	2 51.2	16 41.0	22 49.4	2 56.8	14 27.2	27 11.9	24 6.8	26 43.2
28	18 23 27.1	6 38.1	19 14.9	3♓57.1	2 15.9	17 50.6	23 33.4	2 55.9	14 26.8	27 9.5	24 5.2	26 42.0
29	18 27 23.6	7 40.3	19 11.7	15 48.7	1 42.7	18 59.8	24 17.4	2 55.2	14 26.4	27 7.1	24 3.6	26 40.9
30	18 31 20.2	8 42.4	19 8.4	27 20.7	1 11.9	20 8.6	25 1.4	2 54.7	14 25.9	27 4.8	24 1.9	26 39.7

DECLINATION

DAY	EPHEM. SID. TIME	☉	☊	☽	☿	♀	♂	♃	♄	♅	♆	♇
1	16 37 .0	21N59.4	0S19.4	3S41.9	24N59.8	24N35.3	12N49.7	12S20.0	8S36.9	21S27.6	20S51.8	5S18.9
4	16 48 49.7	22 22.7	0 19.4	8N50.3	24 25.8	24 14.8	13 34.8	12 15.6	8 35.2	21 28.5	20 52.4	5 18.4
7	17 0 39.4	22 42.4	0 19.3	18 5.1	23 44.5	23 48.2	14 18.6	12 11.7	8 33.8	21 29.5	20 52.9	5 18.1
10	17 12 29.1	22 58.5	0 19.3	20 34.0	22 58.5	23 15.7	15 1.1	12 8.3	8 32.8	21 30.5	20 53.5	5 17.9
13	17 24 18.7	23 11.0	0 19.3	14 27.4	22 9.9	22 37.5	15 42.2	12 5.4	8 32.2	21 31.6	20 54.2	5 17.7
16	17 36 8.4	23 19.8	0 19.2	1 47.7	21 21.1	21 53.9	16 21.8	12 3.0	8 31.9	21 32.7	20 54.9	5 17.6
19	17 47 58.1	23 24.9	0 19.2	12S20.0	20 34.7	21 5.1	16 59.9	12 1.1	8 31.9	21 33.9	20 55.5	5 17.7
22	17 59 47.7	23 26.2	0 19.1	20 29.0	19 53.1	20 11.5	17 36.4	11 59.8	8 32.3	21 35.1	20 56.3	5 17.8
25	18 11 37.4	23 23.9	0 19.1	16 57.8	19 19.3	19 13.3	18 11.4	11 59.0	8 33.0	21 36.3	20 57.0	5 18.1
28	18 23 27.1	23 17.9	0 19.0	5 20.8	18 55.5	18 10.8	18 44.7	11 58.7	8 34.0	21 37.5	20 57.8	5 18.4

JULY 1994

DAY	EPHEM. SID. TIME h m s	☉ ° ′	☊ ° ′	☽ ° ′	☿ ° ′	♀ ° ′	♂ ° ′	♃ ° ′	♄ ° ′	♅ ° ′	♆ ° ′	♇ ° ′
		LONGITUDE										
1	18 35 16.8	8♋57.1	21♏30.7	11♈ .2	0♋41.9	18♌16.0	27♉54.9	4♏46.2	12♓21.1	24♑59.8	22♑19.6	25♏36.6
2	18 39 13.3	9 54.3	21 27.5	22 54.4	0 R 18.8	19 25.0	28 37.7	4 R 46.0	12 R 20.2	24 R 57.5	22 R 18.0	25 R 35.5
3	18 43 9.9	10 51.5	21 24.3	4♉43.1	29♊59.4	20 34.0	29 20.4	4 D 46.1	12 19.3	24 55.2	22 16.4	25 34.5
4	18 47 6.4	11 48.7	21 21.1	16 31.3	29 44.1	21 42.8	0♊ 3.1	4 46.4	12 18.3	24 52.8	22 14.8	25 33.5
5	18 51 3.0	12 46.0	21 17.9	28 23.8	29 33.1	22 51.6	0 45.7	4 46.8	12 17.2	24 50.5	22 13.2	25 32.5
6	18 54 59.5	13 43.2	21 14.8	10♊24.5	29 26.7	24 .2	1 28.2	4 47.4	12 15.9	24 48.2	22 11.6	25 31.5
7	18 58 56.1	14 40.4	21 11.6	22 36.9	29 25.1	25 8.7	2 10.7	4 48.2	12 14.6	24 45.8	22 10.0	25 30.6
8	19 2 52.7	15 37.6	21 8.4	5♋ 3.1	29 D 28.5	26 17.2	2 53.1	4 49.2	12 13.2	24 43.4	22 8.4	25 29.7
9	19 6 49.2	16 34.9	21 5.2	17 44.5	29 37.0	27 25.5	3 35.4	4 50.3	12 11.7	24 41.1	22 6.8	25 28.8
10	19 10 45.8	17 32.1	21 2.1	0♌41.2	29 50.7	28 33.7	4 17.7	4 51.6	12 10.1	24 38.7	22 5.2	25 28.0
11	19 14 42.3	18 29.3	20 58.9	13 52.5	0♋ 9.6	29 41.7	4 59.9	4 53.1	12 8.4	24 36.3	22 3.6	25 27.1
12	19 18 38.9	19 26.6	20 55.7	27 17.0	0 33.7	0♍49.7	5 42.0	4 54.8	12 6.6	24 33.9	22 1.9	25 26.3
13	19 22 35.4	20 23.8	20 52.5	10♍53.0	1 3.0	1 57.5	6 24.0	4 56.7	12 4.7	24 31.5	22 .3	25 25.6
14	19 26 32.0	21 21.0	20 49.4	24 39.0	1 37.6	3 5.2	7 6.0	4 58.7	12 2.8	24 29.1	21 58.7	25 24.8
15	19 30 28.6	22 18.3	20 46.2	8♎33.4	2 17.4	4 12.8	7 47.9	5 .9	12 .7	24 26.7	21 57.1	25 24.1
16	19 34 25.1	23 15.5	20 43.0	22 35.4	3 2.3	5 20.2	8 29.7	5 3.3	11 58.6	24 24.3	21 55.4	25 23.4
17	19 38 21.7	24 12.7	20 39.8	6♏44.0	3 52.4	6 27.5	9 11.4	5 5.9	11 56.3	24 21.8	21 53.8	25 22.8
18	19 42 18.2	25 10.0	20 36.6	20 58.1	4 47.5	7 34.7	9 53.2	5 8.7	11 54.1	24 19.5	21 52.2	25 22.2
19	19 46 14.8	26 7.2	20 33.5	5♐15.8	5 47.6	8 41.7	10 34.8	5 11.6	11 51.7	24 17.1	21 50.6	25 21.6
20	19 50 11.3	27 4.5	20 30.3	19 34.6	6 52.6	9 48.6	11 16.3	5 14.6	11 49.2	24 14.7	21 49.0	25 21.1
21	19 54 7.9	28 1.7	20 27.1	3♑50.6	8 2.5	10 55.2	11 57.7	5 17.9	11 46.6	24 12.3	21 47.4	25 20.6
22	19 58 4.5	28 59.0	20 23.9	17 59.2	9 17.2	12 1.8	12 39.1	5 21.3	11 43.9	24 9.9	21 45.8	25 20.1
23	20 2 1.0	29 56.2	20 20.8	1♒55.7	10 36.5	13 8.1	13 20.4	5 24.8	11 41.2	24 7.5	21 44.2	25 19.6
24	20 5 57.6	0♌53.5	20 17.6	15 35.6	12 .4	14 14.3	14 1.7	5 28.6	11 38.4	24 5.1	21 42.6	25 19.2
25	20 9 54.1	1 50.8	20 14.4	28 55.9	13 28.7	15 20.4	14 42.8	5 32.5	11 35.5	24 2.7	21 41.0	25 18.8
26	20 13 50.7	2 48.1	20 11.2	11♓55.0	15 1.3	16 26.2	15 23.9	5 36.5	11 32.5	24 .3	21 39.4	25 18.4
27	20 17 47.2	3 45.4	20 8.1	24 33.4	16 38.0	17 31.9	16 4.9	5 40.7	11 29.5	23 57.9	21 37.8	25 18.1
28	20 21 43.8	4 42.7	20 4.9	6♈53.3	18 18.6	18 37.4	16 45.9	5 45.1	11 26.3	23 55.6	21 36.2	25 17.8
29	20 25 40.3	5 40.1	20 1.7	18 58.1	20 2.9	19 42.7	17 26.7	5 49.6	11 23.1	23 53.2	21 34.7	25 17.5
30	20 29 36.9	6 37.4	19 58.5	0♉52.4	21 50.6	20 47.9	18 7.5	5 54.3	11 19.9	23 50.9	21 33.1	25 17.3
31	20 33 33.5	7 34.8	19 55.3	12 41.4	23 41.5	21 52.8	18 48.3	5 59.2	11 16.5	23 48.6	21 31.5	25 17.0
		LATITUDE										
1	18 35 16.8	0 .0	0 .0	3N27.1	4S42.4	1N48.5	0S26.0	1N11.8	1S48.0	0S31.4	0N37.3	14N13.9
4	18 47 6.4	0 .0	0 .0	0 34.2	4 41.5	1 43.8	0 23.9	1 10.9	1 48.7	0 31.5	0 37.3	14 12.6
7	18 58 56.1	0 .0	0 .0	2S33.3	4 28.2	1 38.2	0 21.7	1 10.1	1 49.4	0 31.5	0 37.3	14 11.3
10	19 10 45.8	0 .0	0 .0	4 44.0	3 4.7	1 31.8	0 19.5	1 9.3	1 50.1	0 31.6	0 37.2	14 10.0
13	19 22 35.4	0 .0	0 .0	4 49.0	3 33.1	1 24.3	0 17.3	1 8.5	1 50.8	0 31.6	0 37.2	14 8.6
16	19 34 25.1	0 .0	0 .0	2 29.6	2 55.8	1 16.0	0 15.0	1 7.7	1 51.4	0 31.6	0 37.2	14 7.1
19	19 46 14.8	0 .0	0 .0	1N11.2	2 15.0	1 6.7	0 12.7	1 6.9	1 52.1	0 31.6	0 37.1	14 5.7
22	19 58 4.5	0 .0	0 .0	4 12.9	1 32.5	0 56.6	0 10.3	1 6.1	1 52.7	0 31.7	0 37.1	14 4.2
25	20 9 54.1	0 .0	0 .0	4 59.7	0 50.2	0 45.5	0 8.0	1 5.4	1 53.3	0 31.7	0 37.1	14 2.7
28	20 21 43.8	0 .0	0 .0	3 30.2	0 10.2	0 33.5	0 5.6	1 4.6	1 53.9	0 31.7	0 37.0	14 1.1
31	20 33 33.5	0 .0	0 .0	0 41.7	0N25.8	0 20.6	0 3.1	1 3.9	1 54.4	0 31.7	0 37.0	13 59.6
		RIGHT ASCENSION										
1	18 35 16.8	9♋44.5	19♏ 5.2	8♈45.1	0♋44.1	21♌17.0	25♉45.4	2♏54.3	14♓25.3	27♑ 2.3	24♑ .3	26♏38.6
2	18 39 13.3	10 46.6	19 2.0	20 12.9	0 R 19.8	22 25.1	26 29.5	2 R 54.1	14 R 24.7	26 R 59.9	23 R 58.6	26 R 37.5
3	18 43 9.9	11 48.5	18 58.7	1♉53.2	29♊59.4	23 32.7	27 13.6	2 54.1	14 23.9	26 57.5	23 56.9	26 36.4
4	18 47 6.4	12 50.5	18 55.5	13 53.1	29 43.2	24 40.0	27 57.7	2 D 54.2	14 23.0	26 55.0	23 55.3	26 35.3
5	18 51 3.0	13 52.3	18 52.3	26 16.2	29 31.6	25 46.8	28 41.9	2 54.5	14 22.1	26 52.6	23 53.6	26 34.3
6	18 54 59.5	14 54.0	18 49.1	9♊ 2.2	29 24.9	26 53.3	29 26.0	2 55.0	14 21.0	26 50.1	23 51.9	26 33.3
7	18 58 56.1	15 55.7	18 45.8	22 6.7	29 23.2	27 59.4	0♊10.2	2 55.7	14 19.9	26 47.6	23 50.2	26 32.3
8	19 2 52.7	16 57.3	18 42.6	5♋21.8	29 D 26.8	29 5.1	0 54.4	2 56.5	14 18.6	26 45.1	23 48.5	26 31.3
9	19 6 49.2	17 58.8	18 39.4	18 38.9	29 35.7	0♍10.5	1 38.6	2 57.6	14 17.3	26 42.6	23 46.8	26 30.4
10	19 10 45.8	19 .2	18 36.2	1♌50.2	29 50.2	1 15.5	2 22.8	2 58.7	14 15.9	26 40.0	23 45.1	26 29.5
11	19 14 42.3	20 1.4	18 33.0	14 51.7	0♋10.1	2 20.1	3 7.0	3 .1	14 14.4	26 37.5	23 43.4	26 28.6
12	19 18 38.9	21 2.6	18 29.7	27 44.1	0 35.7	3 24.3	3 51.2	3 1.6	14 12.8	26 35.0	23 41.7	26 27.7
13	19 22 35.4	22 3.7	18 26.5	10♍32.0	1 6.9	4 28.2	4 35.4	3 3.3	14 11.2	26 32.4	23 39.9	26 26.9
14	19 26 32.0	23 4.6	18 23.3	23 23.4	1 43.7	5 31.7	5 19.6	3 5.2	14 9.4	26 29.9	23 38.2	26 26.1
15	19 30 28.6	24 5.4	18 20.1	6♎28.4	2 26.2	6 34.9	6 3.8	3 7.2	14 7.6	26 27.3	23 36.5	26 25.3
16	19 34 25.1	25 6.0	18 16.8	19 57.0	3 14.4	7 37.7	6 48.1	3 9.5	14 5.6	26 24.8	23 34.8	26 24.6
17	19 38 21.7	26 6.6	18 13.6	3♏56.9	4 8.1	8 40.2	7 32.3	3 11.8	14 3.6	26 22.2	23 33.1	26 23.8
18	19 42 18.2	27 7.0	18 10.4	18 30.9	5 7.5	9 42.3	8 16.5	3 14.4	14 1.6	26 19.7	23 31.4	26 23.2
19	19 46 14.8	28 7.3	18 7.2	3♐33.7	6 12.3	10 44.1	9 .7	3 17.1	13 59.4	26 17.2	23 29.7	26 22.5
20	19 50 11.3	29 7.4	18 4.0	18 51.6	7 22.6	11 45.5	9 44.9	3 20.0	13 57.2	26 14.6	23 28.0	26 21.9
21	19 54 7.9	0♌ 7.4	18 .8	4♑ 4.9	8 38.3	12 46.6	10 29.1	3 23.0	13 54.9	26 12.1	23 26.3	26 21.3
22	19 58 4.5	1 7.3	17 57.5	18 54.0	9 59.3	13 47.4	11 13.3	3 26.2	13 52.5	26 9.5	23 24.6	26 20.7
23	20 2 1.0	2 6.9	17 54.3	3♒ 4.9	11 25.5	14 47.9	11 57.4	3 29.6	13 50.0	26 7.0	23 22.9	26 20.1
24	20 5 57.6	3 6.5	17 51.1	16 32.5	12 56.8	15 48.0	12 41.6	3 33.1	13 47.4	26 4.4	23 21.2	26 19.6
25	20 9 54.1	4 5.9	17 47.9	29 19.0	14 32.9	16 47.9	13 25.7	3 36.8	13 44.8	26 1.9	23 19.5	26 19.1
26	20 13 50.7	5 5.2	17 44.7	11♓31.6	16 13.8	17 47.4	14 9.8	3 40.6	13 42.1	25 59.4	23 17.8	26 18.7
27	20 17 47.2	6 4.3	17 41.5	23 20.4	17 59.0	18 46.6	14 53.8	3 44.6	13 39.3	25 56.9	23 16.2	26 18.2
28	20 21 43.8	7 3.3	17 38.2	4♈56.0	19 48.5	19 45.6	15 37.9	3 48.7	13 36.5	25 54.4	23 14.5	26 17.8
29	20 25 40.3	8 2.1	17 35.0	16 28.7	21 41.8	20 44.2	16 21.9	3 53.0	13 33.5	25 51.9	23 12.8	26 17.4
30	20 29 36.9	9 .8	17 31.8	28 7.9	23 38.5	21 42.6	17 5.9	3 57.5	13 30.6	25 49.4	23 11.2	26 17.1
31	20 33 33.5	9 59.3	17 28.6	10♉ 1.4	25 38.4	22 40.7	17 49.9	4 2.1	13 27.5	25 46.9	23 9.6	26 16.8
		DECLINATION										
1	18 35 16.8	23N 8.1	0S19.0	7N31.7	18N43.8	17N 4.4	19N16.4	11S59.0	8S35.4	21S38.8	20S58.5	5S18.8
4	18 47 6.4	22 54.8	0 19.0	17 19.3	18 44.8	15 54.3	19 46.3	11 59.9	8 37.1	21 40.1	20 59.3	5 19.4
7	18 58 56.1	22 37.8	0 18.9	20 40.9	18 58.0	14 40.9	20 14.5	12 1.2	8 39.2	21 41.4	21 .1	5 20.0
10	19 10 45.8	22 17.3	0 18.9	15 22.7	19 21.6	13 24.5	20 40.9	12 3.1	8 41.5	21 42.7	21 .9	5 20.7
13	19 22 35.4	21 53.4	0 18.8	3 1.5	19 52.9	12 5.4	21 5.6	12 5.6	8 44.2	21 44.0	21 1.7	5 21.6
16	19 34 25.1	21 26.0	0 18.8	11S 6.2	20 28.4	10 43.9	21 28.4	12 8.5	8 47.2	21 45.3	21 2.5	5 22.5
19	19 46 14.8	20 55.4	0 18.7	20 .6	21 3.8	9 20.4	21 49.4	12 12.0	8 50.4	21 46.6	21 3.3	5 23.5
22	19 58 4.5	20 21.7	0 18.7	18 3.1	21 34.5	7 55.2	22 8.5	12 16.0	8 53.9	21 47.9	21 4.1	5 24.6
25	20 9 54.1	19 44.9	0 18.6	7 9.5	21 55.4	6 28.6	22 25.8	12 20.4	8 57.7	21 49.2	21 4.9	5 25.8
28	20 21 43.8	19 5.1	0 18.6	5N57.0	22 1.1	5 .8	22 41.3	12 25.3	9 1.7	21 50.4	21 5.7	5 27.1
31	20 33 33.5	18 22.5	0 18.6	16 18.5	21 47.1	3 32.2	22 54.9	12 30.7	9 6.0	21 51.6	21 6.5	5 28.5

AUGUST 1994

DAY	EPHEM. SID. TIME	☉	☊	☽	☿	♀	♂	♃	♄	♅	♆	♇
	h m s	° ′	° ′	° ′	° ′	° ′	° ′	° ′	° ′	° ′	° ′	° ′
		LONGITUDE										
1	20 37 30.0	8♌32.2	19♏52.2	24♉30.6	25♋35.3	22♍57.6	19♊28.9	6♏ 4.2	11♓13.1	23♑46.3	21♑30.0	25♏16.9
2	20 41 26.6	9 29.6	19 49.0	6♊25.2	27 31.6	24 2.1	20 9.5	6 9.4	11R 9.6	23R44.0	21R28.5	25R16.7
3	20 45 23.1	10 27.0	19 45.8	18 30.4	29 30.0	25 6.4	20 49.9	6 14.7	11 6.1	23 41.7	21 27.0	25 16.6
4	20 49 19.7	11 24.5	19 42.6	0♋50.2	1♌30.3	26 10.6	21 30.4	6 20.1	11 2.5	23 39.4	21 25.4	25 16.6
5	20 53 16.2	12 21.9	19 39.5	13 27.9	3 32.0	27 14.5	22 10.7	6 25.7	10 58.8	23 37.2	21 24.0	25 16.5
6	20 57 12.8	13 19.4	19 36.3	26 25.1	5 34.9	28 18.2	22 50.9	6 31.5	10 55.1	23 34.9	21 22.5	25 16.5
7	21 1 9.3	14 16.9	19 33.1	9♌41.9	7 38.5	29 21.7	23 31.1	6 37.4	10 51.3	23 32.7	21 21.0	25 16.5
8	21 5 5.9	15 14.5	19 29.9	23 16.6	9 42.7	0♎25.0	24 11.2	6 43.5	10 47.5	23 30.6	21 19.6	25D16.7
9	21 9 2.4	16 12.0	19 26.7	7♍ 6.2	11 46.9	1 28.0	24 51.2	6 49.7	10 43.6	23 28.4	21 18.2	25 16.8
10	21 12 59.0	17 9.6	19 23.6	21 6.6	13 51.0	2 30.7	25 31.1	6 56.1	10 39.6	23 26.3	21 16.7	25 16.9
11	21 16 55.6	18 7.1	19 20.4	5♎13.8	15 54.8	3 33.2	26 11.0	7 2.5	10 35.6	23 24.1	21 15.3	25 17.1
12	21 20 52.1	19 4.7	19 17.2	19 24.0	17 58.0	4 35.4	26 50.7	7 9.2	10 31.6	23 22.0	21 13.9	25 17.3
13	21 24 48.7	20 2.3	19 14.0	3♏34.4	20 .5	5 37.3	27 30.4	7 15.9	10 27.5	23 20.0	21 12.5	25 17.5
14	21 28 45.2	20 59.9	19 10.9	17 43.2	22 2.0	6 39.0	28 9.9	7 22.8	10 23.3	23 17.9	21 11.2	25 17.8
15	21 32 41.8	21 57.6	19 7.7	1♐49.1	24 2.6	7 40.4	28 49.4	7 29.9	10 19.1	23 15.9	21 9.8	25 18.1
16	21 36 38.3	22 55.2	19 4.5	15 51.4	26 2.0	8 41.4	29 28.8	7 37.0	10 14.9	23 13.9	21 8.5	25 18.4
17	21 40 34.9	23 52.9	19 1.3	29 49.1	28 .3	9 42.1	0♋ 8.1	7 44.3	10 10.6	23 11.9	21 7.2	25 18.8
18	21 44 31.4	24 50.5	18 58.1	13♑40.7	29 57.2	10 42.6	0 47.3	7 51.8	10 6.3	23 10.0	21 5.9	25 19.2
19	21 48 28.0	25 48.2	18 55.0	27 24.1	1♍52.9	11 42.6	1 26.5	7 59.3	10 2.0	23 8.1	21 4.7	25 19.6
20	21 52 24.5	26 45.9	18 51.8	10♒56.7	3 47.2	12 42.3	2 5.5	8 7.0	9 57.6	23 6.2	21 3.4	25 20.1
21	21 56 21.1	27 43.7	18 48.6	24 16.1	5 40.2	13 41.7	2 44.5	8 14.8	9 53.2	23 4.4	21 2.2	25 20.6
22	22 0 17.6	28 41.4	18 45.4	7♓19.9	7 31.8	14 40.7	3 23.4	8 22.7	9 48.8	23 2.6	21 1.0	25 21.1
23	22 4 14.2	29 39.2	18 42.3	20 6.9	9 22.0	15 39.3	4 2.1	8 30.8	9 44.3	23 .8	20 59.8	25 21.7
24	22 8 10.8	0♍37.0	18 39.1	2♈37.2	11 10.9	16 37.5	4 40.8	8 38.9	9 39.9	22 59.0	20 58.6	25 22.3
25	22 12 7.3	1 34.9	18 35.9	14 52.0	12 58.4	17 35.4	5 19.4	8 47.2	9 35.4	22 57.3	20 57.5	25 22.9
26	22 16 3.9	2 32.7	18 32.7	26 54.0	14 44.5	18 32.8	5 58.0	8 55.6	9 30.9	22 55.6	20 56.4	25 23.6
27	22 20 .4	3 30.6	18 29.5	8♉46.8	16 29.3	19 29.7	6 36.4	9 4.2	9 26.3	22 54.0	20 55.3	25 24.3
28	22 23 57.0	4 28.5	18 26.4	20 35.0	18 12.8	20 26.3	7 14.7	9 12.8	9 21.8	22 52.4	20 54.2	25 25.0
29	22 27 53.5	5 26.5	18 23.2	2♊23.8	19 55.0	21 22.4	7 53.0	9 21.6	9 17.3	22 50.8	20 53.2	25 25.8
30	22 31 50.1	6 24.5	18 20.0	14 18.6	21 35.9	22 18.0	8 31.2	9 30.5	9 12.7	22 49.3	20 52.2	25 26.6
31	22 35 46.6	7 22.5	18 16.8	26 24.8	23 15.5	23 13.1	9 9.2	9 39.4	9 8.1	22 47.8	20 51.2	25 27.5
		LATITUDE										
1	20 37 30.0	0 .0	0 .0	0S21.0	0N36.6	0N16.1	0S 2.3	1N 3.6	1S54.6	0S31.7	0N36.9	13N59.0
4	20 49 19.7	0 .0	0 .0	3 16.3	1 4.7	0 2.1	0N .2	1 2.9	1 55.1	0 31.7	0 36.9	13 57.4
7	21 1 9.3	0 .0	0 .0	4 56.0	1 25.6	0S12.7	0 2.7	1 2.1	1 55.6	0 31.7	0 36.8	13 55.8
10	21 12 59.0	0 .0	0 .0.	4 16.3	1 38.9	0 28.4	0 5.3	1 1.4	1 56.1	0 31.7	0 36.8	13 54.2
13	21 24 48.7	0 .0	0 .0	1 21.4	1 45.1	0 44.7	0 7.9	1 .7	1 56.5	0 31.6	0 36.7	13 52.6
16	21 36 38.3	0 .0	0 .0	2N16.4	1 44.9	1 1.8	0 10.6	1 .1	1 57.0	0 31.6	0 36.7	13 51.0
19	21 48 28.0	0 .0	0 .0	4 40.4	1 39.0	1 19.6	0 13.2	0 59.4	1 57.3	0 31.6	0 36.6	13 49.4
22	22 0 17.6	0 .0	0 .0	4 44.6	1 28.6	1 38.0	0 15.9	0 58.8	1 57.7	0 31.6	0 36.5	13 47.8
25	22 12 7.3	0 .0	0 .0	2 44.8	1 14.4	1 57.1	0 18.7	0 58.1	1 58.0	0 31.5	0 36.4	13 46.2
28	22 23 57.0	0 .0	0 .0	0S15.6	0 57.1	2 16.6	0 21.5	0 57.5	1 58.2	0 31.5	0 36.4	13 44.6
31	22 35 46.6	0 .0	0 .0	3 11.0	0 37.4	2 36.6	0 24.3	0 56.9	1 58.5	0 31.5	0 36.3	13 43.0
		RIGHT ASCENSION										
1	20 37 30.0	10♌57.7	17♏25.4	22♉14.2	27♋40.9	23♍38.5	18♊33.8	4♏ 6.9	13♓24.4	25♑44.5	23♑ 7.9	26♏16.5
2	20 41 26.6	11 55.9	17 22.2	4♊48.6	29 45.7	24 36.0	19 17.6	4 11.8	13R21.2	25R42.1	23R 6.3	26R16.2
3	20 45 23.1	12 54.0	17 19.0	17 43.3	1♌52.2	25 33.3	20 1.5	4 16.8	13 17.9	25 39.6	23 4.7	26 16.0
4	20 49 19.7	13 51.9	17 15.8	0♋53.4	3 60.0	26 30.3	20 45.3	4 22.0	13 14.6	25 37.2	23 3.1	26 15.8
5	20 53 16.2	14 49.7	17 12.5	14 11.9	6 8.6	27 27.0	21 29.0	4 27.4	13 11.3	25 34.8	23 1.5	26 15.7
6	20 57 12.8	15 47.4	17 9.3	27 31.7	8 17.5	28 23.5	22 12.7	4 32.9	13 7.8	25 32.5	22 60.0	26 15.5
7	21 1 9.3	16 44.9	17 6.1	10♌47.4	10 26.4	29 19.8	22 56.3	4 38.5	13 4.3	25 30.1	22 58.4	26 15.4
8	21 5 5.9	17 42.3	17 2.9	23 57.0	12 34.8	0♎15.8	23 39.9	4 44.3	13 .8	25 27.9	22 56.9	26 15.4
9	21 9 2.4	18 39.5	16 59.7	7♍ 2.5	14 42.4	1 11.5	24 23.4	4 50.3	12 57.2	25 25.6	22 55.4	26 15.4
10	21 12 59.0	19 36.5	16 56.5	20 9.2	16 49.0	2 7.0	25 6.9	4 56.3	12 53.6	25 23.3	22 53.9	26 15.4
11	21 16 55.6	20 33.4	16 53.3	3♎24.5	18 54.1	3 2.2	25 50.2	5 2.6	12 49.9	25 21.0	22 52.4	26 15.4
12	21 20 52.1	21 30.2	16 50.1	16 56.6	20 57.7	3 57.2	26 33.5	5 8.9	12 46.2	25 18.8	22 50.9	26D15.5
13	21 24 48.7	22 26.8	16 46.9	0♏51.9	22 59.5	4 51.9	27 16.8	5 15.4	12 42.4	25 16.6	22 49.5	26 15.6
14	21 28 45.2	23 23.3	16 43.7	15 13.2	24 59.5	5 46.4	27 59.9	5 22.0	12 38.5	25 14.4	22 48.0	26 15.7
15	21 32 41.8	24 19.6	16 40.5	29 57.1	26 57.5	6 40.6	28 43.0	5 28.8	12 34.7	25 12.3	22 46.6	26 15.9
16	21 36 38.3	25 15.8	16 37.3	14♐53.9	28 53.5	7 34.5	29 26.0	5 35.6	12 30.7	25 10.1	22 45.2	26 16.1
17	21 40 34.9	26 11.8	16 34.1	29 48.4	0♍47.5	8 28.2	0♋ 8.9	5 42.7	12 26.8	25 8.0	22 43.8	26 16.3
18	21 44 31.4	27 7.7	16 30.9	14♑24.8	2 39.3	9 21.6	0 51.7	5 49.8	12 22.8	25 6.0	22 42.5	26 16.6
19	21 48 28.0	28 3.5	16 27.6	28 30.9	4 29.2	10 14.8	1 34.4	5 57.1	12 18.8	25 3.9	22 41.1	26 16.9
20	21 52 24.5	28 59.2	16 24.4	12♒ .5	6 17.0	11 7.7	2 17.0	6 4.5	12 14.7	25 2.0	22 39.8	26 17.2
21	21 56 21.1	29 54.8	16 21.2	24 53.9	8 2.8	12 .3	2 59.6	6 12.0	12 10.6	24 60.0	22 38.5	26 17.5
22	22 0 17.6	0♍50.2	16 18.0	7♓16.1	9 46.6	12 52.6	3 42.0	6 19.6	12 6.5	24 58.1	22 37.3	26 17.9
23	22 4 14.2	1 45.5	16 14.8	19 14.7	11 28.6	13 44.6	4 24.4	6 27.4	12 2.4	24 56.2	22 36.0	26 18.4
24	22 8 10.8	2 40.7	16 11.6	0♈58.7	13 8.7	14 36.4	5 6.7	6 35.3	11 58.2	24 54.3	22 34.8	26 18.8
25	22 12 7.3	3 35.8	16 8.4	12 37.0	14 47.1	15 27.8	5 48.8	6 43.3	11 54.1	24 52.5	22 33.6	26 19.3
26	22 16 3.9	4 30.8	16 5.2	24 17.8	16 23.7	16 19.0	6 30.9	6 51.4	11 49.9	24 50.7	22 32.4	26 19.8
27	22 20 .4	5 25.7	16 2.0	6♉ 8.1	17 58.7	17 9.8	7 12.8	6 59.7	11 45.6	24 48.9	22 31.2	26 20.4
28	22 23 57.0	6 20.5	15 58.8	18 13.1	19 32.1	18 .3	7 54.6	7 8.0	11 41.4	24 47.2	22 30.1	26 20.9
29	22 27 53.5	7 15.3	15 55.6	0♊35.6	21 4.0	18 50.6	8 36.4	7 16.6	11 37.2	24 45.6	22 29.1	26 21.6
30	22 31 50.1	8 9.9	15 52.4	13 15.7	22 34.4	19 40.4	9 18.0	7 25.2	11 32.9	24 44.0	22 28.0	26 22.2
31	22 35 46.6	9 4.5	15 49.2	26 11.0	24 3.4	20 29.9	9 59.5	7 33.9	11 28.7	24 42.4	22 26.9	26 22.9
		DECLINATION										
1	20 37 30.0	18N 7.6	0S18.5	18N33.4	21N37.4	3N 2.5	22N59.0	12S32.6	9S 7.5	21S52.0	21S 6.8	5S29.0
4	20 49 19.7	17 21.4	0 18.5	20 9.9	20 52.5	1 33.1	23 10.2	12 38.5	9 12.0	21 53.2	21 7.5	5 30.4
7	21 1 9.3	16 32.7	0 18.5	13 3.8	19 44.2	0 3.6	23 19.5	12 44.9	9 16.7	21 54.3	21 8.3	5 32.0
10	21 12 59.0	15 41.5	0 18.4	0S24.2	18 14.9	1S26.0	23 27.1	12 51.6	9 21.6	21 55.4	21 9.0	5 33.6
13	21 24 48.7	14 48.1	0 18.4	13 58.9	16 28.4	2 55.1	23 32.8	12 58.8	9 26.6	21 56.5	21 9.7	5 35.3
16	21 36 38.3	13 52.6	0 18.3	20 25.6	14 29.0	4 23.6	23 36.8	13 6.2	9 31.8	21 57.5	21 10.4	5 37.1
19	21 48 28.0	12 55.1	0 18.3	16 5.6	12 20.8	5 51.1	23 39.1	13 14.1	9 37.0	21 58.5	21 11.0	5 39.0
22	22 0 17.6	11 55.7	0 18.2	4 24.7	10 6.9	7 17.5	23 39.6	13 22.2	9 42.3	21 59.4	21 11.7	5 40.9
25	22 12 7.3	10 54.7	0 18.2	8N23.4	7 50.0	8 42.4	23 38.5	13 30.6	9 47.7	22 .2	21 12.3	5 42.8
28	22 23 57.0	9 52.1	0 18.1	17 38.8	5 32.2	10 5.5	23 35.8	13 39.3	9 53.0	22 1.0	21 12.9	5 44.8
31	22 35 46.6	8 48.1	0 18.1	20 12.4	3 15.0	11 26.7	23 31.6	13 48.3	9 58.4	22 1.7	21 13.4	5 46.9

SEPTEMBER 1994

LONGITUDE

DAY	EPHEM. SID. TIME h m s	☉ ° ′	☊ ° ′	☽ ° ′	☿ ° ′	♀ ° ′	♂ ° ′	♃ ° ′	♄ ° ′	♅ ° ′	♆ ° ′	♇ ° ′
1	22 39 43.2	8♍20.6	18♏13.7	8♋47.4	24♍53.8	24♎ 7.7	9♋47.2	9♏48.5	9♓ 3.6	22♑46.4	20♑50.2	25♏28.3
2	22 43 39.7	9 18.6	18 10.5	21 30.5	26 30.9	25 1.8	10 25.0	9 57.7	8R59.0	22R44.9	20R49.3	25 29.2
3	22 47 36.3	10 16.8	18 7.3	4♌36.8	28 6.7	25 55.4	11 2.8	10 7.0	8 54.4	22 43.6	20 48.4	25 30.2
4	22 51 32.8	11 14.9	18 4.1	18 7.2	29 41.3	26 48.4	11 40.5	10 16.4	8 49.8	22 42.2	20 47.5	25 31.1
5	22 55 29.4	12 13.1	18 .9	2♍ .2	1♎14.7	27 40.8	12 18.0	10 25.9	8 45.3	22 40.9	20 46.6	25 32.1
6	22 59 25.9	13 11.3	17 57.8	16 12.2	2 46.8	28 32.6	12 55.5	10 35.5	8 40.7	22 39.7	20 45.8	25 33.2
7	23 3 22.5	14 9.5	17 54.6	0♎37.7	4 17.8	29 23.8	13 32.8	10 45.3	8 36.1	22 38.5	20 45.0	25 34.2
8	23 7 19.0	15 7.7	17 51.4	15 10.4	5 47.5	0♏14.3	14 10.1	10 55.1	8 31.6	22 37.3	20 44.2	25 35.3
9	23 11 15.6	16 6.0	17 48.2	29 43.9	7 15.9	1 4.2	14 47.2	11 5.0	8 27.1	22 36.2	20 43.4	25 36.4
10	23 15 12.1	17 4.3	17 45.1	14♏12.8	8 43.2	1 53.4	15 24.2	11 15.0	8 22.6	22 35.1	20 42.7	25 37.6
11	23 19 8.7	18 2.7	17 41.9	28 33.3	10 9.1	2 41.8	16 1.1	11 25.1	8 18.1	22 34.0	20 42.0	25 38.8
12	23 23 5.3	19 1.0	17 38.7	12♐43.0	11 33.8	3 29.4	16 37.9	11 35.3	8 13.6	22 33.0	20 41.3	25 40.0
13	23 27 1.8	19 59.4	17 35.5	26 40.9	12 57.2	4 16.3	17 14.6	11 45.6	8 9.2	22 32.1	20 40.7	25 41.2
14	23 30 58.4	20 57.8	17 32.3	10♑26.7	14 19.3	5 2.3	17 51.2	11 55.9	8 4.8	22 31.2	20 40.1	25 42.5
15	23 34 54.9	21 56.2	17 29.2	24 .4	15 40.0	5 47.4	18 27.7	12 6.4	8 .4	22 30.3	20 39.5	25 43.8
16	23 38 51.5	22 54.7	17 26.0	7♒22.0	16 59.3	6 31.7	19 4.0	12 16.9	7 56.0	22 29.5	20 39.0	25 45.2
17	23 42 48.0	23 53.2	17 22.8	20 31.3	18 17.2	7 15.0	19 40.3	12 27.6	7 51.7	22 28.8	20 38.5	25 46.5
18	23 46 44.6	24 51.7	17 19.6	3♓27.9	19 33.6	7 57.3	20 16.4	12 38.3	7 47.5	22 28.1	20 38.0	25 47.9
19	23 50 41.1	25 50.3	17 16.5	16 11.7	20 48.4	8 38.7	20 52.5	12 49.1	7 43.3	22 27.4	20 37.6	25 49.4
20	23 54 37.7	26 48.9	17 13.3	28 42.3	22 1.6	9 19.0	21 28.4	12 60.0	7 39.1	22 26.8	20 37.1	25 50.8
21	23 58 34.2	27 47.5	17 10.1	11♈ .2	23 13.1	9 58.1	22 4.1	13 10.9	7 34.9	22 26.3	20 36.7	25 52.3
22	0 2 30.8	28 46.1	17 6.9	23 6.6	24 22.7	10 36.2	22 39.8	13 22.0	7 30.8	22 25.7	20 36.4	25 53.8
23	0 6 27.3	29 44.8	17 3.7	5♉ 3.5	25 30.4	11 13.0	23 15.3	13 33.1	7 26.7	22 25.3	20 36.1	25 55.3
24	0 10 23.9	0♎43.5	17 .6	16 53.5	26 36.1	11 48.6	23 50.8	13 44.3	7 22.7	22 24.8	20 35.8	25 56.9
25	0 14 20.4	1 42.3	16 57.4	28 40.4	27 39.6	12 23.0	24 26.1	13 55.5	7 18.8	22 24.5	20 35.5	25 58.5
26	0 18 17.0	2 41.1	16 54.2	10♊28.3	28 40.7	12 56.0	25 1.2	14 6.9	7 14.9	22 24.1	20 35.3	26 .1
27	0 22 13.5	3 39.9	16 51.0	22 22.2	29 39.3	13 27.7	25 36.3	14 18.3	7 11.0	22 23.9	20 35.1	26 1.7
28	0 26 10.1	4 38.8	16 47.9	4♋27.0	0♏35.2	13 57.9	26 11.2	14 29.7	7 7.2	22 23.6	20 34.9	26 3.4
29	0 30 6.6	5 37.7	16 44.7	16 48.0	1 28.2	14 26.7	26 46.0	14 41.3	7 3.5	22 23.5	20 34.7	26 5.1
30	0 34 3.2	6 36.6	16 41.5	29 29.8	2 18.0	14 53.9	27 20.6	14 52.9	6 59.8	22 23.3	20 34.6	26 6.8

LATITUDE

DAY	EPHEM. SID. TIME	☉	☊	☽	☿	♀	♂	♃	♄	♅	♆	♇
1	22 39 43.2	0 .0	0 .0	3S57.4	0N30.5	2S43.4	0N25.2	0N56.7	1S58.5	0S31.5	0N36.3	13N42.5
4	22 51 32.8	0 .0	0 .0	5 3.4	0 8.5	3 3.9	0 28.1	0 56.1	1 58.7	0 31.4	0 36.2	13 40.9
7	23 3 22.5	0 .0	0 .0	3 39.5	0S14.8	3 24.7	0 31.0	0 55.6	1 58.8	0 31.4	0 36.1	13 39.4
10	23 15 12.1	0 .0	0 .0	0 12.3	0 38.8	3 45.7	0 34.0	0 55.0	1 58.9	0 31.3	0 36.0	13 37.9
13	23 27 1.8	0 .0	0 .0	3N18.3	1 3.1	4 6.7	0 37.0	0 54.5	1 59.0	0 31.3	0 35.9	13 36.5
16	23 38 51.5	0 .0	0 .0	5 2.8	1 27.5	4 27.8	0 40.1	0 54.0	1 59.0	0 31.2	0 35.8	13 35.0
19	23 50 41.1	0 .0	0 .0	4 25.2	1 51.5	4 48.7	0 43.2	0 53.5	1 59.0	0 31.2	0 35.8	13 33.6
22	0 2 30.8	0 .0	0 .0	1 58.3	2 14.6	5 9.3	0 46.3	0 53.0	1 59.0	0 31.1	0 35.7	13 32.3
25	0 14 20.4	0 .0	0 .0	1S11.0	2 36.2	5 29.2	0 49.5	0 52.6	1 58.9	0 31.1	0 35.6	13 31.0
28	0 26 10.1	0 .0	0 .0	3 55.1	2 55.7	5 48.4	0 52.8	0 52.1	1 58.8	0 31.0	0 35.5	13 29.7

RIGHT ASCENSION

DAY	EPHEM. SID. TIME	☉	☊	☽	☿	♀	♂	♃	♄	♅	♆	♇
1	22 39 43.2	9♍58.9	15♏46.0	9♋17.4	25♍31.1	21♎19.1	10♋40.8	7♏42.7	11♓24.4	24♑40.8	22♑25.9	26♏23.6
2	22 43 39.7	10 53.3	15 42.8	22 29.8	26 57.4	22 7.8	11 22.1	7 51.6	11R20.1	24R39.3	22R24.9	26 24.4
3	22 47 36.3	11 47.7	15 39.6	5♌44.2	28 22.4	22 56.2	12 3.2	8 .6	11 15.8	24 37.8	22 23.9	26 25.1
4	22 51 32.8	12 42.0	15 36.5	18 58.7	29 46.2	23 44.2	12 44.2	8 9.8	11 11.5	24 36.4	22 23.0	26 25.9
5	22 55 29.4	13 36.2	15 33.3	2♍14.5	1♎ 8.9	24 31.7	13 25.0	8 19.0	11 7.3	24 35.0	22 22.1	26 26.8
6	22 59 25.9	14 30.3	15 30.1	15 35.4	2 30.3	25 18.8	14 5.7	8 28.4	11 3.0	24 33.7	22 21.2	26 27.6
7	23 3 22.5	15 24.4	15 26.9	29 7.2	3 50.7	26 5.4	14 46.3	8 37.8	10 58.7	24 32.4	22 20.3	26 28.5
8	23 7 19.0	16 18.5	15 23.7	12♎56.2	5 10.0	26 51.6	15 26.7	8 47.4	10 54.5	24 31.1	22 19.5	26 29.4
9	23 11 15.6	17 12.5	15 20.5	27 7.3	6 28.2	27 37.2	16 7.0	8 57.1	10 50.2	24 29.9	22 18.7	26 30.4
10	23 15 12.1	18 6.4	15 17.3	11♏41.4	7 45.3	28 22.3	16 47.1	9 6.8	10 46.0	24 28.8	22 17.9	26 31.4
11	23 19 8.7	19 .3	15 14.1	26 34.0	9 1.3	29 6.8	17 27.1	9 16.7	10 41.8	24 27.7	22 17.2	26 32.4
12	23 23 5.3	19 54.2	15 10.9	11♐34.5	10 16.3	29 50.7	18 6.9	9 26.6	10 37.6	24 26.6	22 16.5	26 33.4
13	23 27 1.8	20 48.1	15 7.7	26 28.3	11 30.3	0♏33.9	18 46.6	9 36.7	10 33.4	24 25.6	22 15.8	26 34.5
14	23 30 58.4	21 41.9	15 4.5	11♑ 1.1	12 43.2	1 16.5	19 26.1	9 46.8	10 29.3	24 24.6	22 15.2	26 35.6
15	23 34 54.9	22 35.7	15 1.3	25 2.2	13 55.0	1 58.4	20 5.4	9 57.1	10 25.2	24 23.7	22 14.6	26 36.8
16	23 38 51.5	23 29.5	14 58.1	8♒27.1	15 5.7	2 39.5	20 44.6	10 7.4	10 21.1	24 22.9	22 14.0	26 37.9
17	23 42 48.0	24 23.3	14 55.0	21 16.9	16 15.2	3 19.8	21 23.7	10 17.8	10 17.0	24 22.1	22 13.5	26 39.1
18	23 46 44.6	25 17.0	14 51.8	3♓36.9	17 23.6	3 59.3	22 2.6	10 28.3	10 13.0	24 21.3	22 13.0	26 40.3
19	23 50 41.1	26 10.8	14 48.6	15 34.8	18 30.8	4 38.0	22 41.3	10 39.0	10 9.0	24 20.6	22 12.5	26 41.6
20	23 54 37.7	27 4.6	14 45.4	27 19.0	19 36.6	5 15.8	23 19.9	10 49.6	10 5.1	24 20.0	22 12.1	26 42.9
21	23 58 34.2	27 58.4	14 42.2	8♈57.7	20 41.1	5 52.5	23 58.3	11 .4	10 1.1	24 19.4	22 11.7	26 44.2
22	0 2 30.8	28 52.2	14 39.0	20 38.4	21 44.1	6 28.3	24 36.5	11 11.3	9 57.2	24 18.8	22 11.3	26 45.5
23	0 6 27.3	29 46.1	14 35.8	2♉27.0	22 45.6	7 3.0	25 14.5	11 22.2	9 53.4	24 18.3	22 11.0	26 46.9
24	0 10 23.9	0♎39.9	14 32.6	14 27.8	23 45.4	7 36.6	25 52.4	11 33.2	9 49.6	24 17.8	22 10.6	26 48.3
25	0 14 20.4	1 33.8	14 29.5	26 42.9	24 43.4	8 9.1	26 30.1	11 44.3	9 45.9	24 17.4	22 10.4	26 49.7
26	0 18 17.0	2 27.8	14 26.3	9♊12.0	25 39.4	8 40.4	27 7.6	11 55.4	9 42.2	24 17.1	22 10.1	26 51.1
27	0 22 13.5	3 21.8	14 23.1	21 53.0	26 33.3	9 10.3	27 45.0	12 6.7	9 38.5	24 16.8	22 9.9	26 52.6
28	0 26 10.1	4 15.8	14 19.9	4♋42.6	27 24.9	9 39.0	28 22.1	12 18.0	9 34.9	24 16.5	22 9.7	26 54.1
29	0 30 6.6	5 9.9	14 16.7	17 37.2	28 13.9	10 6.3	28 59.1	12 29.4	9 31.4	24 16.4	22 9.6	26 55.6
30	0 34 3.2	6 4.1	14 13.5	0♌34.6	29 .2	10 32.1	29 35.9	12 40.9	9 27.9	24 16.2	22 9.5	26 57.1

DECLINATION

DAY	EPHEM. SID. TIME	☉	☊	☽	☿	♀	♂	♃	♄	♅	♆	♇
1	22 39 43.2	8N26.5	0S18.1	19N12.0	2N29.6	11S53.3	23N29.8	13S51.4	10S .2	22S 2.0	21S13.6	5S47.6
4	22 51 32.8	7 20.8	0 18.0	10 34.9	0 15.2	13 11.4	23 23.5	14 .7	10 5.5	22 2.6	21 14.1	5 49.7
7	23 3 22.5	6 14.0	0 18.0	3S36.4	1S56.0	14 26.8	23 15.8	14 10.2	10 10.8	22 3.2	21 14.5	5 51.9
10	23 15 12.1	5 6.3	0 17.9	16 17.9	4 3.0	15 39.3	23 6.7	14 19.9	10 16.0	22 3.7	21 14.9	5 54.1
13	23 27 1.8	3 57.9	0 17.9	20 5.6	6 5.1	16 48.6	22 56.3	14 29.8	10 21.1	22 4.1	21 15.3	5 56.3
16	23 38 51.5	2 48.8	0 17.8	13 32.7	8 1.3	17 54.3	22 44.6	14 39.9	10 26.0	22 4.5	21 15.7	5 58.5
19	23 50 41.1	1 39.3	0 17.8	1 22.2	9 50.7	18 56.1	22 31.7	14 50.1	10 30.8	22 4.8	21 16.0	6 .8
22	0 2 30.8	0 29.4	0 17.7	10N48.7	11 32.1	19 53.5	22 17.7	15 .4	10 35.4	22 5.0	21 16.2	6 3.1
25	0 14 20.4	0S40.7	0 17.7	18 42.5	13 4.2	20 46.3	22 2.6	15 10.9	10 39.9	22 5.2	21 16.5	6 5.4
28	0 26 10.1	1 50.8	0 17.7	19 26.8	14 25.1	21 33.8	21 46.5	15 21.4	10 44.1	22 5.3	21 16.6	6 7.7

OCTOBER 1994

LONGITUDE

DAY	EPHEM. SID. TIME	☉	☊	☽	☿	♀	♂	♃	♄	♅	♆	♇
	h m s	° ′	° ′	° ′	° ′	° ′	° ′	° ′	° ′	° ′	° ′	° ′
1	0 37 59.7	7♎35.6	16♏38.3	12♌36.1	3♏ 4.3	15♏19.5	27♋55.2	15♏ 4.6	6♓56.2	22♑23.3	20♑34.6	26♏ 8.5
2	0 41 56.3	8 34.6	16 35.1	26 9.1	3 46.9	15 43.5	28 29.5	15 16.3	6R52.6	22R23.2	20R34.5	26 10.3
3	0 45 52.8	9 33.6	16 32.0	10♍ 8.9	4 25.5	16 5.8	29 3.8	15 28.1	6 49.1	22D23.3	20 34.5	26 12.0
4	0 49 49.4	10 32.7	16 28.8	24 32.6	4 59.5	16 26.2	29 37.9	15 40.0	6 45.7	22 23.3	20D34.6	26 13.9
5	0 53 46.0	11 31.8	16 25.6	9♎15.2	5 28.8	16 44.9	0♌11.8	15 51.9	6 42.4	22 23.5	20 34.6	26 15.7
6	0 57 42.5	12 31.0	16 22.4	24 9.3	5 52.8	17 1.7	0 45.6	16 3.9	6 39.1	22 23.6	20 34.7	26 17.5
7	1 1 39.1	13 30.2	16 19.2	9♏ 6.5	6 11.0	17 16.5	1 19.2	16 16.0	6 35.9	22 23.9	20 34.9	26 19.4
8	1 5 35.6	14 29.4	16 16.1	23 58.8	6 23.2	17 29.2	1 52.7	16 28.1	6 32.8	22 24.2	20 35.0	26 21.3
9	1 9 32.2	15 28.7	16 12.9	8♐39.4	6 28.6	17 39.9	2 26.1	16 40.3	6 29.8	22 24.5	20 35.2	26 23.2
10	1 13 28.7	16 28.0	16 9.7	23 3.8	6R27.0	17 48.5	2 59.3	16 52.5	6 26.9	22 24.9	20 35.5	26 25.2
11	1 17 25.3	17 27.3	16 6.5	7♑ 9.1	6 17.8	17 54.8	3 32.3	17 4.8	6 24.0	22 25.4	20 35.8	26 27.2
12	1 21 21.8	18 26.7	16 3.4	20 54.7	6 .7	17 58.8	4 5.2	17 17.1	6 21.2	22 25.8	20 36.1	26 29.2
13	1 25 18.4	19 26.0	16 .2	4♒21.0	5 35.3	18 .5	4 37.9	67 29.5	6 18.5	22 26.4	20 36.4	26 31.2
14	1 29 14.9	20 25.4	15 57.0	17 29.4	5 1.6	17R59.9	5 10.4	17 41.9	6 15.8	22 27.0	20 36.8	26 33.2
15	1 33 11.5	21 24.9	15 53.8	0♓21.7	4 19.6	17 56.9	5 42.7	17 54.4	6 13.3	22 27.6	20 37.2	26 35.2
16	1 37 8.0	22 24.3	15 50.6	12 59.6	3 29.5	17 51.5	6 14.9	18 6.9	6 10.8	22 28.30	20 37.6	26 37.3
17	1 41 4.6	23 23.8	15 47.5	25 24.9	2 32.0	17 43.6	6 47.0	18 19.4	6 8.5	22 29.0	20 38.1	26 39.4
18	1 45 1.1	24 23.3	15 44.3	7♈39.3	1 28.0	17 33.3	7 18.8	18 32.0	6 6.2	22 29.8	20 38.6	26 41.4
19	1 48 57.7	25 22.9	15 41.1	19 44.3	0 18.7	17 20.6	7 50.5	18 44.6	6 4.0	22 30.7	20 39.1	26 43.6
20	1 52 54.2	26 22.5	15 37.9	1♉41.6	29♎ 5.8	17 5.4	8 22.0	18 57.3	6 1.9	22 31.6	20 39.7	26 45.7
21	1 56 50.8	27 22.1	15 34.8	13 33.1	27 51.1	16 48.0	8 53.3	19 10.0	5 59.9	22 32.5	20 40.3	26 47.8
22	2 0 47.3	28 21.7	15 31.6	25 20.9	26 36.9	16 28.2	9 24.4	19 22.8	5 58.0	22 33.5	20 40.9	26 50.0
23	2 4 43.9	29 21.4	15 28.4	7♊ 7.8	25 25.4	16 6.2	9 55.3	19 35.6	5 56.2	22 34.6	20 41.6	26 52.2
24	2 8 40.5	0♏21.2	15 25.2	18 56.9	24 18.7	15 42.0	10 26.1	19 48.4	5 54.5	22 35.7	20 42.2	26 54.3
25	2 12 37.0	1 20.9	15 22.0	0♋51.7	23 18.8	15 15.9	10 56.6	20 1.3	5 52.9	22 36.8	20 43.0	26 56.5
26	2 16 33.6	2 20.7	15 18.9	12 56.5	22 27.5	14 47.8	11 27.0	20 14.2	5 51.4	22 38.0	20 43.7	26 58.8
27	2 20 30.1	3 20.6	15 15.7	25 15.4	21 46.2	14 18.0	11 57.1	20 27.1	5 49.9	22 39.2	20 44.5	27 1.0
28	2 24 26.7	4 20.4	15 12.5	7♌52.9	21 15.7	13 46.7	12 27.1	20 40.0	5 48.6	22 40.5	20 45.4	27 3.2
29	2 28 23.2	5 20.3	15 9.3	20 53.1	20 56.6	13 13.9	12 56.8	20 53.0	5 47.4	22 41.9	20 46.2	27 5.5
30	2 32 19.8	6 20.3	15 6.2	4♍19.1	20 49.0	12 40.0	13 26.3	21 6.0	5 46.3	22 43.2	20 47.1	27 7.8
31	2 36 16.3	7 20.3	15 3.0	18 12.6	20D52.8	12 5.1	13 55.6	21 19.1	5 45.3	22 44.7	20 48.1	27 10.1

LATITUDE

DAY	EPHEM. SID. TIME	☉	☊	☽	☿	♀	♂	♃	♄	♅	♆	♇
1	0 37 59.7	0 .0	0 .0	5S11.2	3S12.1	6S 6.4	0N56.1	0N51.7	1S58.7	0S30.9	0N35.4	13N28.5
4	0 49 49.4	0 .0	0 .0	4 1.6	3 24.0	6 22.8	0 59.5	0 51.3	1 58.5	0 30.9	0 35.3	13 27.3
7	1 1 39.1	0 .0	0 .0	0 32.5	3 29.7	6 37.2	1 2.9	0 50.9	1 58.3	0 30.8	0 35.2	13 26.1
10	1 13 28.7	0 .0	0 .0	3N13.9	3 26.6	6 49.1	1 6.4	0 50.5	1 58.0	0 30.8	0 35.1	13 25.1
13	1 25 18.4	0 .0	0 .0	5 9.2	3 11.5	6 57.6	1 10.0	0 50.2	1 57.8	0 30.7	0 35.0	13 24.0
16	1 37 8.0	0 .0	0 .0	4 38.1	2 41.5	7 2.2	1 13.7	0 49.8	1 57.5	0 30.6	0 34.9	13 23.1
19	1 48 57.7	0 .0	0 .0	2 14.1	1 55.4	7 1.8	1 17.4	0 49.5	1 57.2	0 30.6	0 34.9	13 22.1
22	2 0 47.3	0 .0	0 .0	0S58.4	0 57.0	6 55.6	1 21.2	0 49.2	1 56.9	0 30.5	0 34.8	13 21.3
25	2 12 37.0	0 .0	0 .0	3 48.9	0N 4.4	6 42.9	1 25.1	0 48.9	1 56.5	0 30.5	0 34.7	13 20.5
28	2 24 26.7	0 .0	0 .0	5 15.4	0 58.4	6 23.2	1 29.1	0 48.6	1 56.2	0 30.4	0 34.6	13 19.7
31	2 36 16.3	0 .0	0 .0	4 25.6	1 38.3	5 56.5	1 33.2	0 48.3	1 55.8	0 30.4	0 34.5	13 19.1

RIGHT ASCENSION

DAY	EPHEM. SID. TIME	☉	☊	☽	☿	♀	♂	♃	♄	♅	♆	♇
1	0 37 59.7	6♎58.4	14♏10.4	13♌34.5	29♎43.4	10♏56.4	0♌12.5	12♏52.4	9♓24.4	24♑16.1	22♑ 9.4	26♏58.7
2	0 41 56.3	7 52.7	14 7.2	26 39.1	0♏23.2	11 19.1	0 48.9	13 4.1	9R21.1	24 16.1	22 9.4	27 .3
3	0 45 52.8	8 47.1	14 4.0	9♍53.4	0 59.4	11 40.2	1 25.2	13 15.8	9 17.8	24 16.1	22 9.4	27 1.9
4	0 49 49.4	9 41.5	14 .8	23 23.8	1 31.5	11 59.6	2 1.2	13 27.5	9 14.5	24D16.2	22 9.4	27 3.5
5	0 53 46.0	10 36.1	13 57.6	7♎17.5	1 59.2	12 17.2	2 37.0	13 39.3	9 11.3	24 16.3	22D 9.5	27 5.2
6	0 57 42.5	11 30.8	13 54.5	21 39.9	2 22.0	12 32.9	3 12.6	13 51.2	9 8.2	24 16.5	22 9.6	27 6.9
7	1 1 39.1	12 25.5	13 51.3	6♏32.3	2 39.6	12 46.8	3 48.0	14 3.2	9 5.2	24 16.8	22 9.8	27 8.6
8	1 5 35.6	13 20.4	13 48.1	21 48.9	2 51.5	12 58.6	4 23.2	14 15.2	9 2.2	24 17.1	22 9.9	27 10.3
9	1 9 32.2	14 15.3	13 44.9	7♐16.8	2 57.2	13 8.4	58.2	14 27.3	8 59.3	24 17.4	22 10.2	27 12.1
10	1 13 28.7	15 10.4	13 41.7	22 37.6	2R56.4	13 16.1	5 33.0	14 39.5	8 56.5	24 17.9	22 10.5	27 13.9
11	1 17 25.3	16 5.6	13 38.6	7♑33.1	2 48.6	13 21.6	6 7.6	14 51.7	8 53.8	24 18.3	22 10.7	27 15.7
12	1 21 21.8	17 .8	13 35.4	21 50.7	2 33.5	13 24.9	6 42.0	15 4.0	8 51.1	2 18.9	22 11.1	27 17.5
13	1 25 18.4	17 56.2	13 32.2	5♒25.2	2 10.9	13 25.9	7 16.1	15 16.3	8 48.5	24 19.4	22 11.4	27 19.3
14	1 29 14.9	18 51.8	13 29.0	18 18.9	1 40.9	13R24.6	7 50.0	15 28.7	8 46.00	24 20.0	22 11.8	27 21.2
15	1 33 11.5	19 47.4	13 25.9	0♓38.4	1 3.3	13 21.0	8 23.7	15 41.2	8 43.5	24 20.7	22 12.2	27 23.0
16	1 37 8.0	20 43.2	13 22.7	12 33.0	0 18.8	13 15.0	8 57.2	15 53.7	8 41.2	24 21.5	22 12.7	27 24.9
17	1 41 4.6	21 39.1	13 19.5	24 12.4	29♎27.9	13 6.7	5 30.5	16 6.2	8 38.9	24 22.2	22 13.2	27 26.9
18	1 45 1.1	22 35.2	13 16.3	5♈46.0	28 31.5	12 56.1	10 3.6	16 18.8	8 36.7	24 23.1	22 13.7	27 28.8
19	1 48 57.7	23 31.4	13 13.2	17 21.9	27 30.9	12 43.1	10 36.4	16 31.4	8 34.6	24 24.0	22 14.3	27 30.7
20	1 52 54.2	24 27.8	13 10.0	29 6.4	26 27.7	12 27.9	11 9.0	16 44.1	8 32.6	24 24.9	22 14.9	27 32.7
21	1 56 50.8	25 24.3	13 6.8	11♉ 3.6	25 23.6	12 10.5	11 41.3	16 56.9	8 30.6	24 25.9	22 15.6	27 34.7
22	2 0 47.3	26 21.0	13 3.6	23 15.2	24 20.4	11 50.9	12 13.5	17 9.7	8 28.8	24 27.0	22 16.2	27 36.7
23	2 4 43.9	27 17.8	13 .5	5♊40.0	23 20.3	11 29.4	12 45.4	17 22.5	8 27.0	24 28.1	22 16.9	27 38.7
24	2 8 40.5	28 14.9	12 57.3	18 14.7	22 24.9	11 5.9	13 17.0	17 35.4	8 25.4	24 29.2	22 17.7	27 40.7
25	2 12 37.0	29 12.1	12 54.1	0♋54.8	21 36.1	10 40.7	13 48.5	17 48.3	8 23.8	24 30.5	22 18.5	27 42.8
26	2 16 33.6	0♏ 9.5	12 51.0	13 36.2	20 55.1	10 13.8	14 19.6	18 1.3	8 22.3	24 31.7	22 19.3	27 44.8
27	2 20 30.1	1 7.1	12 47.8	26 16.1	20 23.2	9 45.5	14 50.6	18 14.3	8 20.9	24 33.0	22 20.1	27 46.9
28	2 24 26.7	2 4.8	12 44.6	8♌54.5	20 .9	9 15.9	15 21.3	18 27.3	8 19.6	24 34.4	22 21.0	27 49.0
29	2 28 23.2	3 2.8	12 41.5	21 34.6	19 48.7	8 45.3	15 51.7	18 40.4	8 18.4	24 35.8	22 21.9	27 51.1
30	2 32 19.8	4 .9	12 38.3	4♍22.2	19 46.6	8 13.9	16 21.9	18 53.5	8 17.3	24 37.3	22 22.9	27 53.2
31	2 36 16.3	4 59.3	12 35.1	17 25.9	19D54.5	7 41.9	16 51.9	19 6.7	8 16.3	24 38.9	22 23.9	27 55.4

DECLINATION

DAY	EPHEM. SID. TIME	☉	☊	☽	☿	♀	♂	♃	♄	♅	♆	♇
1	0 37 59.7	3S .8	0S17.6	12N 2.6	15S32.6	22S15.7	21N29.6	15S32.0	10S48.0	22S 5.3	21S16.8	6S10.0
4	0 49 49.4	4 10.5	0 17.6	1S31.8	16 23.2	22 51.3	21 11.8	15 42.7	10 51.8	22 5.2	21 16.9	6 12.4
7	1 1 39.1	5 19.7	0 17.5	15 2.6	16 52.7	23 19.8	20 53.2	15 53.4	10 55.2	22 5.0	21 16.9	6 14.7
10	1 13 28.7	6 28.4	0 17.5	20 1.7	16 55.1	23 40.4	20 34.0	16 4.1	10 58.4	22 4.8	21 16.9	6 17.0
13	1 25 18.4	7 36.3	0 17.4	14 9.7	16 23.5	23 52.1	20 14.2	16 14.9	11 1.2	22 4.5	21 16.9	6 19.3
16	1 37 8.0	8 43.2	0 17.4	2 23.8	15 12.5	23 53.8	19 53.9	16 25.6	11 3.8	22 4.1	21 16.8	6 21.5
19	1 48 57.7	9 49.0	0 17.3	9N47.3	13 22.8	23 44.5	19 33.2	16 36.4	11 6.1	22 3.7	21 16.6	6 23.7
22	2 0 47.3	10 53.5	0 17.3	18 9.3	11 9.0	23 23.2	19 12.2	16 47.0	11 8.0	22 3.2	21 16.4	6 26.0
25	2 12 37.0	11 56.6	0 17.2	19 37.2	8 59.3	22 49.5	18 50.9	16 57.7	11 9.6	22 2.6	21 16.2	6 28.1
28	2 24 26.7	12 58.0	0 17.2	13 12.7	7 23.4	22 3.5	18 29.5	17 8.3	11 10.8	22 1.9	21 15.9	6 30.3
31	2 36 16.3	13 57.6	0 17.1	0 35.1	6 37.9	21 6.5	18 8.1	17 18.8	11 11.7	22 1.1	21 15.6	6 32.4

NOVEMBER 1994

LONGITUDE

DAY	EPHEM. SID. TIME	☉	☊	☽	☿	♀	♂	♃	♄	♅	♆	♇
	h m s	° ′	° ′	° ′	° ′	° ′	° ′	° ′	° ′	° ′	° ′	° ′
1	2 40 12.9	8 ♏ 20.3	14 ♏ 59.8	2 ♎ 32.9	21 ♎ 7.3	11 ♏ 29.5	14 ♌ 24.7	21 ♏ 32.2	5 ♓ 44.4	22 ♑ 46.2	20 ♑ 49.0	27 ♏ 12.4
2	2 44 9.4	9 20.4	14 56.6	17 16.8	21 32.1	10 R 53.3	14 53.5	21 45.3	5 R 43.5	22 47.7	20 50.0	27 14.7
3	2 48 6.0	10 20.5	14 53.4	2 ♏ 18.4	22 6.3	10 16.9	15 22.1	21 58.4	5 42.8	22 49.3	20 51.0	27 17.0
4	2 52 2.6	11 20.6	14 50.3	17 29.2	22 49.1	9 40.5	15 50.5	22 11.5	5 42.2	22 50.9	20 52.1	27 19.3
5	2 55 59.1	12 20.7	14 47.1	2 ♐ 39.7	23 39.5	9 4.2	16 18.6	22 24.7	5 41.7	22 52.6	20 53.2	27 21.6
6	2 59 55.7	13 20.9	14 43.9	17 40.6	24 36.8	8 28.4	16 46.4	22 37.9	5 41.3	22 54.3	20 54.3	27 24.0
7	3 3 52.2	14 21.1	14 40.7	2 ♑ 24.2	25 40.0	7 53.3	17 14.0	22 51.1	5 41.0	22 56.1	20 55.4	27 26.3
8	3 7 48.8	15 21.4	14 37.6	16 45.1	26 48.5	7 19.2	17 41.4	23 4.3	5 40.8	22 57.9	20 56.6	27 28.7
9	3 11 45.3	16 21.6	14 34.4	0 ♒ 40.6	28 1.4	6 46.1	18 8.4	23 17.5	5 40.7	22 59.8	20 57.8	27 31.0
10	3 15 41.9	17 21.9	14 31.2	14 10.5	29 18.2	6 14.5	18 35.2	23 30.7	5 40.7	23 1.7	20 59.0	27 33.4
11	3 19 38.4	18 22.2	14 28.0	27 16.4	0 ♏ 38.2	5 44.3	19 1.8	23 44.0	5 D 40.9	23 3.6	21 .3	27 35.7
12	3 23 35.0	19 22.5	14 24.9	10 ♓ 1.1	2 1.0	5 15.9	19 28.0	23 57.2	5 41.1	23 5.6	21 1.6	27 38.1
13	3 27 31.5	20 22.9	14 21.7	22 28.2	3 26.1	4 49.4	19 54.0	24 10.5	5 41.4	23 7.6	21 2.9	27 40.5
14	3 31 28.1	21 23.3	14 18.5	4 ♈ 41.2	4 53.2	4 24.8	20 19.7	24 23.8	5 41.9	23 9.7	21 4.2	27 42.9
15	3 35 24.7	22 23.7	14 15.3	16 43.6	6 21.8	4 2.5	20 45.1	24 37.1	5 42.4	23 11.8	21 5.6	27 45.3
16	3 39 21.2	23 24.1	14 12.1	28 38.5	7 51.8	3 42.3	21 10.1	24 50.3	5 43.1	23 14.0	21 7.0	27 47.7
17	3 43 17.8	24 24.5	14 9.0	10 ♉ 28.7	9 22.8	3 24.5	21 34.9	25 3.6	5 43.8	23 16.2	21 8.4	27 50.0
18	3 47 14.3	25 25.0	14 5.8	22 16.8	10 54.6	3 9.2	21 59.4	25 16.9	5 44.7	23 18.4	21 9.9	27 52.4
19	3 51 10.9	26 25.5	14 2.6	4 ♊ 4.8	12 27.2	2 56.2	22 23.6	25 30.2	5 45.6	23 20.7	21 11.3	27 54.8
20	3 55 7.4	27 26.0	13 59.4	15 55.0	14 .3	2 45.7	22 47.4	25 43.5	5 46.7	23 23.0	21 12.8	27 57.2
21	3 59 4.0	28 26.6	13 56.3	27 49.4	15 33.9	2 37.8	23 11.0	25 56.8	5 47.9	23 25.4	21 14.4	27 59.7
22	4 3 .5	29 27.2	13 53.1	9 ♋ 50.4	17 7.7	2 32.3	23 34.1	26 10.1	5 49.2	23 27.8	21 16.0	28 2.1
23	4 6 57.1	0 ♐ 27.8	13 49.9	22 .3	18 41.8	2 29.4	23 57.0	26 23.4	5 50.6	23 30.2	21 17.6	28 4.5
24	4 10 53.7	1 28.4	13 46.7	4 ♌ 22.3	20 16.0	2 28.9	24 19.4	26 36.7	5 52.1	23 32.7	21 19.2	28 6.9
25	4 14 50.2	2 29.1	13 43.5	16 59.3	21 50.3	2 D 30.8	24 41.5	26 50.0	5 53.6	23 35.2	21 20.8	28 9.2
26	4 18 46.8	3 29.8	13 40.4	29 54.8	23 24.7	2 35.1	25 3.3	27 3.3	5 55.3	23 37.7	21 22.5	28 11.6
27	4 22 43.3	4 30.5	13 37.2	13 ♍ 11.6	24 59.2	2 41.8	25 24.6	27 16.5	5 57.1	23 40.3	21 24.1	28 14.0
28	4 26 39.9	5 31.3	13 34.0	26 52.4	26 33.6	2 50.8	25 45.6	27 29.8	5 59.0	23 42.9	21 25.8	28 16.4
29	4 30 36.4	6 32.0	13 30.8	10 ♎ 58.1	28 8.0	3 2.1	26 6.2	27 43.0	6 1.0	23 45.6	21 27.6	28 18.8
30	4 34 33.0	7 32.8	13 27.7	25 28.2	29 42.4	3 15.5	26 26.3	27 56.2	6 3.1	23 48.3	21 29.3	28 21.2

LATITUDE

DAY	EPHEM. SID. TIME	☉	☊	☽	☿	♀	♂	♃	♄	♅	♆	♇
1	2 40 12.9	0 .0	0 .0	3 S 34.1	1 N 48.0	5 S 46.0	1 N 34.6	0 N 48.2	1 S 55.7	0 S 30.3	0 N 34.5	13 N 18.9
4	2 52 2.6	0 .0	0 .0	0 N 15.0	2 7.4	5 10.7	1 38.9	0 47.9	1 55.3	0 30.3	0 34.4	13 18.3
7	3 3 52.2	0 .0	0 .0	3 55.3	2 14.1	4 30.2	1 43.2	0 47.7	1 54.9	0 30.2	0 34.3	13 17.7
10	3 15 41.9	0 .0	0 .0	5 18.2	2 11.2	3 46.2	1 47.7	0 47.5	1 54.5	0 30.2	0 34.2	13 17.3
13	3 27 31.5	0 .0	0 .0	4 12.2	2 1.4	3 .3	1 52.3	0 47.3	1 54.1	0 30.1	0 34.1	13 16.9
16	3 39 21.2	0 .0	0 .0	1 28.9	1 46.9	2 14.3	1 57.0	0 47.1	1 53.6	0 30.1	0 34.1	13 16.5
19	3 51 10.9	0 .0	0 .0	1 S 44.8	1 29.3	1 29.4	2 1.9	0 46.9	1 53.2	0 30.0	0 34.0	13 16.3
22	4 3 .5	0 .0	0 .0	4 19.8	1 9.9	0 46.9	2 6.9	0 46.7	1 52.8	0 30.0	0 33.9	13 16.1
25	4 14 50.2	0 .0	0 .0	5 16.0	0 49.3	0 7.3	2 12.0	0 46.5	1 52.4	0 30.0	0 33.8	13 16.0
28	4 26 39.9	0 .0	0 .0	3 54.5	0 28.4	0 N 28.9	2 17.3	0 46.4	1 51.9	0 29.9	0 33.8	13 15.9

RIGHT ASCENSION

DAY	EPHEM. SID. TIME	☉	☊	☽	☿	♀	♂	♃	♄	♅	♆	♇
1	2 40 12.9	5 ♏ 57.9	12 ♏ 32.0	0 ♎ 55.0	20 ♎ 11.8	7 ♏ 9.4	17 ♌ 21.5	19 ♏ 19.9	8 ♓ 15.4	24 ♑ 40.4	22 ♑ 24.9	27 ♏ 57.5
2	2 44 9.4	6 56.6	12 28.8	14 58.8	20 37.9	6 R 36.8	17 50.9	19 33.2	8 R 14.6	24 42.1	22 26.0	27 59.7
3	2 48 6.0	7 55.6	12 25.6	29 42.8	21 12.3	6 4.3	18 20.0	19 46.4	8 13.9	24 43.7	22 27.0	28 1.9
4	2 52 2.6	8 54.8	12 22.5	15 ♏ 5.7	21 54.1	5 32.0	18 48.9	19 59.7	8 13.2	24 45.5	22 28.2	28 4.0
5	2 55 59.1	9 54.1	12 19.3	0 ♐ 56.2	22 42.6	5 .4	19 17.4	20 13.0	8 12.7	24 47.2	22 29.3	28 6.2
6	2 59 55.7	10 53.7	12 16.1	16 53.4	23 37.1	4 29.4	19 45.7	20 26.4	8 12.3	24 49.1	22 30.5	28 8.4
7	3 3 52.2	11 53.5	12 13.0	2 ♑ 32.6	24 36.9	3 59.4	20 13.7	20 39.8	8 11.9	24 50.9	22 31.7	28 10.6
8	3 7 48.8	12 53.5	12 9.8	17 33.2	25 41.3	3 30.6	20 41.4	20 53.2	8 11.7	24 52.9	22 32.9	28 12.8
9	3 11 45.3	13 53.7	12 6.7	1 ♒ 44.1	26 49.7	3 3.1	21 8.8	21 6.6	8 11.6	24 54.8	22 34.2	28 15.1
10	3 15 41.9	14 54.0	12 3.5	15 4.6	28 1.7	2 37.2	21 35.9	21 20.0	8 11.5	24 56.8	22 35.5	28 17.3
11	3 19 38.4	15 54.6	12 .3	27 41.2	29 16.8	2 12.9	22 2.8	21 33.5	8 D 11.6	24 58.9	22 36.9	28 19.5
12	3 23 35.0	16 55.5	11 57.2	9 ♓ 44.3	0 ♏ 34.5	1 50.4	22 29.3	21 47.0	8 11.8	25 1.0	22 38.2	28 21.8
13	3 27 31.5	17 56.5	11 54.0	21 25.6	1 54.5	1 29.9	22 55.5	22 .5	8 12.0	25 3.2	22 39.6	28 24.0
14	3 31 28.1	18 57.7	11 50.9	2 ♈ 56.3	3 16.5	1 11.4	23 21.4	22 14.0	8 12.4	25 5.4	22 41.1	28 26.3
15	3 35 24.7	19 59.1	11 47.7	14 26.6	4 40.2	0 55.1	23 47.0	22 27.5	8 12.8	25 7.6	22 42.5	28 28.5
16	3 39 21.2	21 .8	11 44.5	26 4.5	6 5.4	0 40.9	24 12.3	22 41.1	8 13.4	25 9.9	22 44.0	28 30.8
17	3 43 17.8	22 2.6	11 41.4	7 ♉ 55.8	7 32.0	0 29.0	24 37.2	22 54.7	8 14.1	25 12.2	22 45.5	28 33.1
18	3 47 14.3	23 4.7	11 38.2	20 3.2	8 59.8	0 19.4	25 1.8	23 8.2	8 14.8	25 14.6	22 47.1	28 35.4
19	3 51 10.9	24 6.9	11 35.1	2 ♊ 26.1	10 28.6	0 12.1	25 26.1	23 21.8	8 15.7	25 17.0	22 48.6	28 37.6
20	3 55 7.4	25 9.4	11 31.9	15 .7	11 58.3	0 7.1	25 50.1	23 35.4	8 16.6	25 19.5	22 50.2	28 39.9
21	3 59 4.0	26 12.1	11 28.8	27 41.5	13 29.0	0 4.5	26 13.8	23 49.1	8 17.7	25 22.0	22 51.9	28 42.2
22	4 3 .5	27 15.0	11 25.6	10 ♋ 22.0	15 .3	0 4.1	26 37.0	24 2.7	8 18.9	25 24.6	22 53.6	28 44.5
23	4 6 57.1	28 18.1	11 22.4	22 57.5	16 32.4	0 D 6.1	26 59.9	24 16.3	8 20.2	25 27.2	22 55.2	28 46.8
24	4 10 53.7	29 21.4	11 19.3	5 ♌ 26.1	18 5.2	0 10.2	27 22.5	24 29.9	8 21.5	25 29.8	22 57.0	28 49.1
25	4 14 50.2	0 ♐ 24.9	11 16.1	17 49.3	19 38.6	0 16.6	27 44.7	24 43.5	8 23.0	25 32.4	22 58.7	28 51.4
26	4 18 46.8	1 28.6	11 13.0	0 ♍ 12.5	21 12.6	0 25.2	28 6.5	24 57.2	8 24.5	25 35.1	23 .4	28 53.6
27	4 22 43.3	2 32.4	11 9.8	12 44.1	22 47.1	0 35.8	28 27.9	25 10.8	8 26.1	25 37.9	23 2.2	28 55.9
28	4 26 39.9	3 36.5	11 6.7	25 34.6	24 22.3	0 48.6	28 49.0	25 24.4	8 27.9	25 40.7	23 4.0	28 58.2
29	4 30 36.4	4 40.7	11 3.5	8 ♎ 55.7	25 57.9	1 3.3	29 9.6	25 38.0	8 29.7	25 43.5	23 5.9	29 .5
30	4 34 33.0	5 45.1	11 .4	22 57.6	27 34.1	1 20.0	29 29.8	25 51.6	8 31.6	25 46.3	23 7.7	29 2.8

DECLINATION

DAY	EPHEM. SID. TIME	☉	☊	☽	☿	♀	♂	♃	♄	♅	♆	♇
1	2 40 12.9	14 S 17.1	0 S 17.1	4 S 17.3	6 S 34.3	20 S 45.3	18 N .9	17 S 22.2	11 S 11.9	22 S .9	21 S 15.5	6 S 33.1
4	2 52 2.6	15 14.0	0 17.1	16 48.6	6 54.0	19 36.9	17 39.6	17 32.6	11 12.3	22 .0	21 15.1	6 35.1
7	3 3 52.2	16 8.6	0 17.0	19 29.7	7 50.3	18 23.7	17 18.5	17 42.9	11 12.4	21 59.1	21 14.7	6 37.1
10	3 15 41.9	17 .9	0 17.0	11 29.6	9 10.8	17 9.3	16 57.7	17 53.0	11 12.1	21 58.1	21 14.2	6 39.0
13	3 27 31.5	17 50.5	0 16.9	0 N 52.4	10 45.4	15 57.5	16 37.2	18 3.0	11 11.5	21 57.1	21 13.7	6 40.9
16	3 39 21.2	18 37.3	0 16.9	12 22.6	12 26.6	14 51.3	16 17.3	18 12.9	11 10.5	21 56.0	21 13.2	6 42.7
19	3 51 10.9	19 21.2	0 16.8	19 14.7	14 9.3	13 53.4	15 58.1	18 22.6	11 9.1	21 54.8	21 12.6	6 44.4
22	4 3 .5	20 1.9	0 16.8	18 45.3	15 49.9	13 5.2	15 39.5	18 32.2	11 7.4	21 53.5	21 11.9	6 46.1
25	4 14 50.2	20 39.4	0 16.7	10 43.0	17 25.8	12 27.5	15 21.8	18 41.6	11 5.4	21 52.2	21 11.3	6 47.7
28	4 26 39.9	21 13.4	0 16.7	2 S 20.6	18 55.5	12 .4	15 5.1	18 50.8	11 3.0	21 50.8	21 10.5	6 49.3

DECEMBER 1994

DAY	EPHEM. SID. TIME	☉	☊	☽	☿	♀	♂	♃	♄	♅	♆	♇
		LONGITUDE										
	h m s	° ′	° ′	° ′	° ′	° ′	° ′	° ′	° ′	° ′	° ′	° ′
1	4 38 29.6	8♐33.6	13♏24.5	10♏19.3	1♐16.8	3♏31.1	26♌46.1	28♏ 9.5	6♓ 5.3	23♑51.0	21♑31.1	28♏23.5
2	4 42 26.1	9 34.5	13 21.3	25 25.4	2 51.1	3 48.7	27 5.4	28 22.7	6 7.6	23 53.8	21 32.9	28 25.9
3	4 46 22.7	10 35.3	13 18.1	10♐37.9	4 25.4	4 8.3	27 24.3	28 35.8	6 10.0	23 56.6	21 34.7	28 28.3
4	4 50 19.2	11 36.2	13 15.0	25 47.2	5 59.6	4 29.9	27 42.7	28 49.0	6 12.5	23 59.4	21 36.5	28 30.6
5	4 54 15.8	12 37.1	13 11.8	10♑43.4	7 33.8	4 53.3	28 .7	29 2.1	6 15.1	24 2.2	21 38.4	28 32.9
6	4 58 12.3	13 38.0	13 8.6	25 18.5	9 8.0	5 18.5	28 18.3	29 15.3	6 17.8	24 5.1	21 40.3	28 35.3
7	5 2 8.9	14 39.0	13 5.4	9♒27.0	10 42.1	5 45.4	28 35.3	29 28.4	6 20.6	24 8.0	21 42.2	28 37.6
8	5 6 5.5	15 39.9	13 2.2	23 6.9	12 16.3	6 14.0	28 51.9	29 41.4	6 23.5	24 11.0	21 44.1	28 39.9
9	5 10 2.0	16 40.9	12 59.1	6♓18.6	13 50.4	6 44.2	29 8.0	29 54.5	6 26.5	24 13.9	21 46.0	28 42.2
10	5 13 58.6	17 41.8	12 55.9	19 4.9	15 24.6	7 16.0	29 23.6	0♐ 7.5	6 29.5	24 16.9	21 48.0	28 44.5
11	5 17 55.1	18 42.8	12 52.7	1♈29.8	16 58.7	7 49.3	29 38.6	0 20.5	6 32.7	24 20.0	21 49.9	28 46.8
12	5 21 51.7	19 43.8	12 49.5	13 38.2	18 33.0	8 24.0	29 53.2	0 33.5	6 36.0	24 23.1	21 52.0	28 49.1
13	5 25 48.2	20 44.8	12 46.4	25 34.9	20 7.3	9 .2	0♍ 7.3	0 46.4	6 39.4	24 26.1	21 54.0	28 51.4
14	5 29 44.8	21 45.8	12 43.2	7♉24.5	21 41.7	9 37.6	0 20.8	0 59.3	6 42.9	24 29.2	21 56.0	28 53.7
15	5 33 41.4	22 46.8	12 40.0	19 11.2	23 16.2	10 16.3	0 33.7	1 12.2	6 46.4	24 32.4	21 58.0	28 55.9
16	5 37 37.9	23 47.9	12 36.8	0♊58.7	24 50.7	10 56.3	0 46.1	1 25.0	6 50.0	24 35.5	22 .1	28 58.1
17	5 41 34.5	24 48.9	12 33.7	12 49.6	26 25.4	11 37.5	0 57.9	1 37.8	6 53.8	24 38.7	22 2.1	29 .3
18	5 45 31.0	25 49.9	12 30.5	24 46.4	28 .2	12 19.8	1 9.2	1 50.5	6 57.6	24 41.9	22 4.2	29 2.5
19	5 49 27.6	26 51.0	12 27.3	6♋50.6	29 35.2	13 3.3	1 19.8	2 3.3	7 1.5	24 45.1	22 6.3	29 4.7
20	5 53 24.1	27 52.0	12 24.1	19 3.5	1♑10.4	13 47.8	1 29.9	2 15.9	7 5.4	24 48.4	22 8.4	29 6.9
21	5 57 20.7	28 53.1	12 21.0	1♌26.2	2 45.7	14 33.3	1 39.3	2 28.6	7 9.5	24 51.6	22 10.5	29 9.0
22	6 1 17.3	29 54.2	12 17.8	13 59.8	4 21.2	15 19.9	1 48.1	2 41.1	7 13.7	24 54.9	22 12.7	29 11.2
23	6 5 13.8	0♑55.3	12 14.6	26 45.6	5 56.9	16 7.3	1 56.2	2 53.7	7 17.9	24 58.2	22 14.8	29 13.3
24	6 9 10.4	1 56.4	12 11.4	9♍45.0	7 32.8	16 55.7	2 3.7	3 6.2	7 22.2	25 1.5	22 17.0	29 15.4
25	6 13 6.9	2 57.5	12 8.2	23 .0	9 8.9	17 45.0	2 10.6	3 18.6	7 26.6	25 4.9	22 19.1	29 17.5
26	6 17 3.5	3 58.7	12 5.1	6♎32.5	10 45.1	18 35.1	2 16.7	3 31.0	7 31.1	25 8.2	22 21.3	29 19.6
27	6 21 .0	4 59.8	12 1.9	20 24.0	12 21.6	19 26.0	2 22.2	3 43.4	7 35.7	25 11.6	22 23.5	29 21.6
28	6 24 56.6	6 .9	11 58.7	4♏35.2	13 58.3	20 17.7	2 27.0	3 55.6	7 40.3	25 15.0	22 25.7	29 23.6
29	6 28 53.2	7 2.1	11 55.5	19 5.2	15 35.1	21 10.1	2 31.0	4 7.9	7 45.0	25 18.4	22 27.9	29 25.7
30	6 32 49.7	8 3.3	11 52.4	3♐50.9	17 12.1	22 3.2	2 34.3	4 20.1	7 49.8	25 21.8	22 30.1	29 27.6
31	6 36 46.3	9 4.4	11 49.2	18 46.9	18 49.2	22 57.0	2 36.9	4 32.2	7 54.7	25 25.2	22 32.3	29 29.6
		LATITUDE										
1	4 38 29.6	0 .0	0 .0	0S24.2	0N 7.4	1N 1.5	2N22.7	0N46.3	1S51.5	0S29.9	0N33.7	13N15.9
4	4 50 19.2	0 .0	0 .0	3N27.1	0S13.0	1 30.6	2 28.3	0 46.2	1 51.1	0 29.9	0 33.6	13 16.0
7	5 2 8.9	0 .0	0 .0	5 12.4	0 32.8	1 56.1	2 34.1	0 46.0	1 50.7	0 29.8	0 33.6	13 16.1
10	5 13 58.6	0 .0	0 .0	4 18.0	0 51.5	2 18.2	2 40.0	0 45.9	1 50.3	0 29.8	0 33.5	13 16.3
13	5 25 48.2	0 .0	0 .0	1 41.2	1 8.9	2 37.2	2 46.1	0 45.9	1 49.9	0 29.8	0 33.4	13 16.6
16	5 37 37.9	0 .0	0 .0	1S29.0	1 24.7	2 53.2	2 52.3	0 45.8	1 49.5	0 29.8	0 33.4	13 16.9
19	5 49 27.6	0 .0	0 .0	4 6.1	1 38.7	3 6.5	2 58.7	0 45.7	1 49.2	0 29.7	0 33.3	13 17.3
22	6 1 17.3	0 .0	0 .0	5 8.2	1 50.6	3 17.2	3 5.2	0 45.7	1 48.8	0 29.7	0 33.3	13 17.7
25	6 13 6.9	0 .0	0 .0	3 58.2	1 60.0	3 25.6	3 11.9	0 45.7	1 48.5	0 29.7	0 33.2	13 18.2
28	6 24 56.6	0 .0	0 .0	0 47.8	2 6.5	3 31.8	3 18.7	0 45.6	1 48.2	0 29.7	0 33.2	13 18.8
31	6 36 46.3	0 .0	0 .0	2N57.6	2 9.6	3 36.0	3 25.5	0 45.6	1 47.8	0 29.7	0 33.1	13 19.4
		RIGHT ASCENSION										
1	4 38 29.6	6♐49.7	10♏57.2	7♏46.5	29♏10.8	1♏38.6	29♌49.7	26♏ 5.3	8♓33.7	25♑49.2	23♑ 9.6	29♏ 5.0
2	4 42 26.1	7 54.5	10 54.1	23 19.8	0♐48.1	1 59.0	0♍ 9.1	26 18.9	8 35.8	25 52.1	23 11.5	29 7.3
3	4 46 22.7	8 59.4	10 50.9	9♐23.1	2 25.8	2 21.2	0 28.1	26 32.5	8 38.0	25 55.1	23 13.4	29 9.6
4	4 50 19.2	10 4.5	10 47.8	25 31.6	4 4.0	2 45.0	0 46.6	26 46.0	8 40.3	25 58.1	23 15.4	29 11.8
5	4 54 15.8	11 9.7	10 44.6	11♑17.6	5 42.7	3 10.6	1 4.7	26 59.6	8 42.7	26 1.1	23 17.4	29 14.1
6	4 58 12.3	12 15.1	10 41.5	26 19.8	7 21.9	3 37.7	1 22.3	27 13.2	8 45.2	26 4.1	23 19.3	29 16.3
7	5 2 8.9	13 20.6	10 38.3	10♒28.3	9 1.6	4 6.4	1 39.5	27 26.7	8 47.8	26 7.2	23 21.4	29 18.6
8	5 6 5.5	14 26.2	10 35.2	23 44.5	10 41.8	4 36.6	1 56.2	27 40.2	8 50.5	26 10.3	23 23.4	29 20.8
9	5 10 2.0	15 31.9	10 32.0	6♓16.7	12 22.4	5 8.2	2 12.4	27 53.7	8 53.3	26 13.5	23 25.4	29 23.0
10	5 13 58.6	16 37.7	10 28.9	18 16.8	14 3.5	5 41.2	2 28.2	28 7.2	8 56.1	26 16.7	23 27.5	29 25.3
11	5 17 55.1	17 43.7	10 25.8	29 57.3	15 45.1	6 15.5	2 43.5	28 20.7	8 59.1	26 19.9	23 29.6	29 27.5
12	5 21 51.7	18 49.7	10 22.6	11♈30.1	17 27.2	6 51.2	2 58.3	28 34.2	9 2.2	26 23.2	23 31.7	29 29.7
13	5 25 48.2	19 55.9	10 19.5	23 5.1	19 9.6	7 28.1	3 12.5	28 47.6	9 5.3	26 26.4	23 33.9	29 31.9
14	5 29 44.8	21 2.1	10 16.3	4♉50.5	20 52.5	8 6.2	3 26.3	29 1.0	9 8.5	26 29.7	23 36.0	29 34.1
15	5 33 41.4	22 8.3	10 13.2	16 51.5	22 35.8	8 45.6	3 39.5	29 14.3	9 11.8	26 33.0	23 38.2	29 36.3
16	5 37 37.9	23 14.7	10 10.0	29 9.6	24 19.5	9 26.0	3 52.2	29 27.7	9 15.2	26 36.4	23 40.3	29 38.4
17	5 41 34.5	24 21.1	10 6.9	11♊43.1	26 3.5	10 7.6	4 4.3	29 41.0	9 18.7	26 39.7	23 42.5	29 40.6
18	5 45 31.0	25 27.5	10 3.8	24 26.8	27 47.9	10 50.2	4 15.9	29 54.2	9 22.2	26 43.1	23 44.7	29 42.7
19	5 49 27.6	26 34.0	10 .6	7♋13.7	29 32.7	11 33.9	4 26.9	0♐ 7.5	9 25.8	26 46.5	23 46.9	29 44.8
20	5 53 24.1	27 40.5	9 57.5	19 56.9	1♑17.7	12 18.7	4 37.3	0 20.7	9 29.5	26 49.9	23 49.2	29 46.9
21	5 57 20.7	28 47.1	9 54.3	2♌31.8	3 3.0	13 4.3	4 47.2	0 33.8	9 33.3	26 53.4	23 51.4	29 49.0
22	6 1 17.3	29 53.7	9 51.2	14 57.1	4 48.6	13 51.0	4 56.4	0 47.0	9 37.2	26 56.9	23 53.7	29 51.1
23	6 5 13.8	1♑ .3	9 48.1	27 15.7	6 34.4	14 38.6	5 5.0	1 .1	9 41.2	27 .4	23 56.0	29 53.2
24	6 9 10.4	2 6.9	9 44.9	9♍33.6	8 20.3	15 27.1	5 13.1	1 13.1	9 45.2	27 3.9	23 58.2	29 55.2
25	6 13 6.9	3 13.5	9 41.8	22 .3	10 6.4	16 16.4	5 20.4	1 26.1	9 49.3	27 7.4	24 .5	29 57.3
26	6 17 3.5	4 20.0	9 38.6	4♎46.6	11 52.5	17 6.6	5 27.2	1 39.1	9 53.5	27 11.0	24 2.8	29 59.3
27	6 21 .0	5 26.6	9 35.5	18 4.1	13 38.7	17 57.7	5 33.2	1 52.0	9 57.7	27 14.5	24 5.1	0♐ 1.3
28	6 24 56.6	6 33.1	9 32.4	2♏ 2.5	15 24.8	18 49.5	5 38.6	2 4.8	10 2.1	27 18.1	24 7.5	0 3.3
29	6 28 53.2	7 39.6	9 29.2	16 46.5	17 10.9	19 42.1	5 43.4	2 17.6	10 6.5	27 21.7	24 9.8	0 5.3
30	6 32 49.7	8 46.1	9 26.1	2♐12.1	18 56.8	20 35.5	5 47.4	2 30.4	10 11.0	27 25.3	24 12.2	0 7.2
31	6 36 46.3	9 52.5	9 23.0	18 4.0	20 42.4	21 29.6	5 50.7	2 43.1	10 15.5	27 28.9	24 14.5	0 9.2
		DECLINATION										
1	4 38 29.6	21S43.8	0S16.6	15S17.9	20S17.6	11S43.4	14N49.5	18S59.8	11S .3	21S49.4	21S 9.8	6S50.7
4	4 50 19.2	22 10.4	0 16.6	19 55.3	21 31.2	11 35.9	14 35.2	19 8.6	10 57.3	21 47.9	21 9.0	6 52.1
7	5 2 8.9	22 33.2	0 16.5	12 51.7	22 35.4	11 36.9	14 22.3	19 17.2	10 53.9	21 46.4	21 8.2	6 53.4
10	5 13 58.6	22 52.1	0 16.5	0 21.8	23 29.5	11 45.5	14 10.9	19 25.6	10 50.2	21 44.8	21 7.3	6 54.6
13	5 25 48.2	23 6.9	0 16.4	11N27.6	24 12.9	12 .8	14 1.1	19 33.8	10 46.2	21 43.2	21 6.4	6 55.7
16	5 37 37.9	23 17.5	0 16.4	18 54.1	24 44.9	12 21.8	13 53.1	19 41.7	10 41.9	21 41.5	21 5.5	6 56.8
19	5 49 27.6	23 24.0	0 16.3	19 9.9	25 5.0	12 47.5	13 47.0	19 49.5	10 37.3	21 39.7	21 4.6	6 57.7
22	6 1 17.3	23 26.3	0 16.3	11 42.2	25 12.5	13 17.2	13 42.9	19 56.9	10 32.4	21 38.0	21 3.6	6 58.6
25	6 13 6.9	23 24.3	0 16.2	0S52.2	25 7.0	13 49.9	13 41.0	20 4.2	10 27.2	21 36.2	21 2.6	6 59.3
28	6 24 56.6	23 18.0	0 16.2	13 48.0	24 48.1	14 24.9	13 41.4	20 11.2	10 21.8	21 34.3	21 1.6	7 .0
31	6 36 46.3	23 7.6	0 16.1	20 .8	24 15.3	15 1.5	13 44.1	20 17.9	10 16.2	21 32.4	21 .5	7 .6

JANUARY 1995

DAY	EPHEM. SID. TIME	☉	☊	☾	☿	♀	♂	♃	♄	♅	♆	♇
	h m s	° ′	° ′	° ′	° ′	° ′	° ′	° ′	° ′	° ′	° ′	° ′
		LONGITUDE										
1	6 40 42.8	10♑ 5.6	11♏46.0	3♑45.2	20♑26.4	23♏51.5	2♍38.7	4♐44.3	7♓59.7	25♑28.7	22♑34.6	29♏31.6
2	6 44 39.4	11 6.9	11 42.8	18 36.9	22 3.6	24 46.7	2 39.8	4 56.3	8 4.7	25 32.2	22 36.9	29 34.5
3	6 48 35.9	12 8.0	11 39.7	3♒13.1	23 40.8	25 42.4	2 40.1	5 8.3	8 9.8	25 35.6	22 39.1	29 36.4
4	6 52 32.5	13 9.2	11 36.5	17 26.8	25 17.9	26 38.6	2R39.6	5 20.1	8 15.0	25 39.1	22 41.4	29 38.3
5	6 56 29.1	14 10.4	11 33.3	1♓13.5	26 54.8	27 35.5	2 38.4	5 31.9	8 20.2	25 42.6	22 43.6	29 40.2
6	7 0 25.6	15 11.6	11 30.1	14 32.0	28 31.3	28 32.8	2 36.3	5 43.7	8 25.5	25 46.1	22 45.9	29 42.0
7	7 4 22.2	16 12.7	11 26.9	27 23.7	0♒ 7.5	29 30.7	2 33.5	5 55.4	8 30.9	25 49.6	22 48.2	29 43.8
8	7 8 18.7	17 13.9	11 23.8	9♈51.9	1 43.0	0♐29.1	2 29.9	6 7.0	8 36.4	25 53.1	22 50.4	29 45.6
9	7 12 15.3	18 15.0	11 20.6	22 1.6	3 17.7	1 28.0	2 25.5	6 18.5	8 41.9	25 56.6	22 52.7	29 47.4
10	7 16 11.8	19 16.2	11 17.4	3♉58.1	4 51.5	2 27.3	2 20.2	6 29.9	8 47.5	26 .1	22 55.0	29 49.1
11	7 20 8.4	20 17.3	11 14.2	15 47.0	6 23.9	3 27.1	2 14.2	6 41.3	8 53.1	26 3.7	22 57.2	29 50.8
12	7 24 5.0	21 18.4	11 11.1	27 33.4	7 54.8	4 27.3	2 7.4	6 52.6	8 58.8	26 7.2	22 59.5	29 52.5
13	7 28 1.5	22 19.6	11 7.9	9♊22.2	9 23.7	5 28.0	1 59.7	7 3.9	9 4.6	26 10.7	23 1.8	29 54.1
14	7 31 58.1	23 20.7	11 4.7	21 17.3	10 50.3	6 29.0	1 51.3	7 15.0	9 10.4	26 14.3	23 4.1	29 55.8
15	7 35 54.6	24 21.8	11 1.5	3♋21.8	12 14.1	7 30.4	1 42.0	7 26.1	9 16.3	26 17.8	23 6.3	29 57.4
16	7 39 51.2	25 22.9	10 58.4	15 37.6	13 34.5	8 32.2	1 32.0	7 37.0	9 22.2	26 21.4	23 8.6	29 59.0
17	7 43 47.7	26 24.0	10 55.2	28 5.9	14 51.0	9 34.4	1 21.1	7 47.9	9 28.2	26 24.9	23 10.9	0♐ .5
18	7 47 44.3	27 25.0	10 52.0	10♌46.8	16 2.8	10 36.9	1 9.5	7 58.7	9 34.3	26 28.4	23 13.2	0 2.0
19	7 51 40.8	28 26.1	10 48.8	23 39.8	17 9.3	11 39.8	0 57.1	8 9.5	9 40.4	26 32.0	23 15.4	0 3.5
20	7 55 37.4	29 27.2	10 45.6	6♍44.3	18 9.6	12 43.0	0 43.9	8 20.1	9 46.5	26 35.5	23 17.7	0 5.0
21	7 59 34.0	0♒28.2	10 42.5	19 59.6	19 3.0	13 46.6	0 29.9	8 30.6	9 52.8	26 39.1	23 20.0	0 6.4
22	8 3 30.5	1 29.3	10 39.3	3♎25.6	19 48.6	14 50.4	0 15.3	8 41.1	9 59.1	26 42.6	23 22.3	0 7.9
23	8 7 27.1	2 30.3	10 36.1	17 2.3	20 25.4	15 54.6	29♌59.8	8 51.5	10 5.4	26 46.2	23 24.5	0 9.3
24	8 11 23.6	3 31.4	10 32.9	0♏50.3	20 52.7	16 59.0	29 43.6	9 1.8	10 11.7	26 49.7	23 26.8	0 10.6
25	8 15 20.2	4 32.4	10 29.8	14 50.2	21 9.7	18 3.7	29 26.7	9 11.9	10 18.2	26 53.2	23 29.0	0 11.9
26	8 19 16.7	5 33.4	10 26.6	29 1.9	21 15.9	19 8.7	29 9.2	9 22.0	10 24.6	26 56.7	23 31.3	0 13.2
27	8 23 13.3	6 34.4	10 23.4	13♐24.3	21R10.7	20 13.9	28 50.9	9 32.0	10 31.1	27 .3	23 33.5	0 14.5
28	8 27 9.8	7 35.4	10 20.2	27 54.4	20 54.1	21 19.4	28 32.1	9 41.8	10 37.7	27 3.8	23 35.7	0 15.7
29	8 31 6.4	8 36.4	10 17.1	12♑27.6	20 26.2	22 25.1	28 12.6	9 51.6	10 44.3	27 7.3	23 37.9	0 16.9
30	8 35 3.0	9 37.4	10 13.9	26 57.5	19 47.6	23 31.0	27 52.5	10 1.2	10 50.9	27 10.7	23 40.1	0 18.0
31	8 38 59.5	10 38.3	10 10.7	11♒17.2	18 59.0	24 37.1	27 31.9	10 10.8	10 57.6	27 14.2	23 42.3	0 19.2
		LATITUDE										
1	6 40 42.8	0 .0	0 .0	3N56.0	2S 9.8	3N36.9	3N27.8	0N45.6	1S47.7	0S29.7	0N33.1	13N19.6
4	6 52 32.5	0 .0	0 .0	5 3.8	2 7.5	3 38.6	3 34.7	0 45.6	1 47.5	0 29.7	0 33.0	13 20.1
7	7 4 22.2	0 .0	0 .0	3 36.6	2 .3	3 38.7	3 41.5	0 45.6	1 47.2	0 29.7	0 33.0	13 20.8
10	7 16 11.8	0 .0	0 .0	0 45.2	1 47.4	3 37.2	3 48.2	0 45.6	1 46.9	0 29.7	0 33.0	13 21.6
13	7 28 1.5	0 .0	0 .0	2S18.1	1 27.8	3 34.3	3 54.8	0 45.7	1 46.7	0 29.8	0 32.9	13 22.5
16	7 39 51.2	0 .0	0 .0	4 30.3	1 .4	3 30.1	4 1.2	0 45.7	1 46.5	0 29.8	0 32.9	13 23.3
19	7 51 40.8	0 .0	0 .0	4 54.0	0 24.7	3 24.7	4 7.2	0 45.8	1 46.3	0 29.8	0 32.9	13 24.3
22	8 3 30.5	0 .0	0 .0	3 4.0	0N19.4	3 18.2	4 12.9	0 45.9	1 46.1	0 29.8	0 32.8	13 25.2
25	8 15 20.2	0 .0	0 .0	0N21.3	1 10.2	3 10.8	4 18.0	0 45.9	1 45.9	0 29.8	0 32.8	13 26.2
28	8 27 9.8	0 .0	0 .0	3 41.5	2 3.6	3 2.4	4 22.6	0 46.0	1 45.8	0 29.9	0 32.8	13 27.3
31	8 38 59.5	0 .0	0 .0	5 .2	2 52.0	2 53.3	4 26.4	0 46.1	1 45.7	0 29.9	0 32.8	13 28.3
		RIGHT ASCENSION										
1	6 40 42.8	10♑58.8	9♏19.8	3♑58.3	22♑27.7	22♏24.5	5♍53.3	2♐55.8	10♓20.2	27♑32.6	24♑16.9	0♐11.1
2	6 44 39.4	12 5.1	9 16.7	19 29.7	24 12.6	23 20.0	5 55.2	3 8.4	10 24.9	27 36.2	24 19.3	0 13.9
3	6 48 35.9	13 11.3	9 13.6	4♒19.4	25 57.0	24 16.3	5 56.4	3 20.9	10 29.7	27 39.9	24 21.7	0 15.8
4	6 52 32.5	14 17.4	9 10.4	18 19.6	27 40.6	25 13.2	5 56.8	3 33.4	10 34.5	27 43.6	24 24.1	0 17.6
5	6 56 29.1	15 23.4	9 7.3	1♓32.2	29 23.5	26 10.7	5R56.4	3 45.8	10 39.4	27 47.3	24 26.5	0 19.5
6	7 0 25.6	16 29.3	9 4.2	14 5.4	1♒ 5.4	27 8.9	5 55.3	3 58.2	10 44.3	27 51.0	24 28.9	0 21.3
7	7 4 22.2	17 35.0	9 1.0	26 10.4	2 46.2	28 7.7	5 53.5	4 10.4	10 49.4	27 54.7	24 31.3	0 23.1
8	7 8 18.7	18 40.7	8 57.9	7♈58.8	4 25.7	29 7.1	5 50.8	4 22.6	10 54.5	27 58.4	24 33.7	0 24.8
9	7 12 15.3	19 46.2	8 54.8	19 41.4	6 3.7	0♐ 7.1	5 47.4	4 34.8	10 59.6	28 2.1	24 36.1	0 26.6
10	7 16 11.8	20 51.5	8 51.6	1♉27.5	7 39.8	1 7.6	5 43.3	4 46.8	11 4.8	28 5.8	24 38.5	0 28.3
11	7 20 8.4	21 56.8	8 48.5	13 24.3	9 13.9	2 8.8	5 38.3	4 58.8	11 10.1	28 9.5	24 40.9	0 30.0
12	7 24 5.0	23 1.9	8 45.4	25 36.0	10 45.6	3 10.5	5 32.6	5 10.7	11 15.4	28 13.3	24 43.3	0 31.7
13	7 28 1.5	24 6.8	8 42.2	8♊ 3.6	12 14.6	4 12.8	5 26.1	5 22.6	11 20.8	28 17.0	24 45.7	0 33.3
14	7 31 58.1	25 11.6	8 39.1	20 44.5	13 40.4	5 15.6	5 18.8	5 34.3	11 26.2	28 20.7	24 48.1	0 35.0
15	7 35 54.6	26 16.2	8 36.0	3♋33.5	15 2.6	6 19.0	5 10.7	5 46.0	11 31.7	28 24.5	24 50.5	0 36.6
16	7 39 51.2	27 20.6	8 32.9	16 24.4	16 20.6	7 22.9	5 1.8	5 57.6	11 37.3	28 28.2	24 52.9	0 38.1
17	7 43 47.7	28 24.9	8 29.7	29 11.0	17 34.0	8 27.3	4 52.1	6 9.1	11 42.9	28 31.9	24 55.3	0 39.7
18	7 47 44.3	29 29.0	8 26.6	11♌50.0	18 42.0	9 32.2	4 41.7	6 20.5	11 48.6	28 35.7	24 57.7	0 41.2
19	7 51 40.8	0♒32.9	8 23.5	24 21.1	19 44.0	10 37.5	4 30.5	6 31.9	11 54.3	28 39.4	25 .1	0 42.7
20	7 55 37.4	1 36.6	8 20.3	6♍47.7	20 39.4	11 43.4	4 18.5	6 43.1	12 .0	28 43.1	25 2.5	0 44.2
21	7 59 34.0	2 40.2	8 17.2	19 16.2	21 27.3	12 49.7	4 5.7	6 54.3	12 5.8	28 46.9	25 4.8	0 45.6
22	8 3 30.5	3 43.6	8 14.1	1♎55.4	22 7.0	13 56.5	3 52.2	7 5.4	12 11.7	28 50.6	25 7.3	0 47.1
23	8 7 27.1	4 46.8	8 11.0	14 54.9	22 37.8	15 3.8	3 38.0	7 16.3	12 17.6	28 54.4	25 9.7	0 48.5
24	8 11 23.6	5 49.8	8 7.8	28 23.9	22 58.9	16 11.4	3 22.9	7 27.2	12 23.6	28 58.1	25 12.0	0 49.8
25	8 15 20.2	6 52.6	8 4.7	12♏28.9	23 9.7	17 19.5	3 7.2	7 38.0	12 29.6	29 1.8	25 14.4	0 51.2
26	8 19 16.7	7 55.3	8 1.6	27 10.5	23 9.9	18 27.9	2 50.8	7 48.6	12 35.6	29 5.5	25 16.8	0 52.5
27	8 23 13.3	8 57.7	7 58.5	12♐21.6	22R59.1	19 36.8	2 33.7	7 59.2	12 41.7	29 9.2	25 19.1	0 53.7
28	8 27 9.8	9 59.9	7 55.4	27 46.9	22 37.2	20 46.0	2 15.9	8 9.7	12 47.8	29 12.9	25 21.5	0 55.0
29	8 31 6.4	11 1.9	7 52.2	13♑ 6.4	22 4.6	21 55.6	1 57.5	8 20.0	12 54.0	29 16.6	25 23.8	0 56.2
30	8 35 3.0	12 3.8	7 49.1	28 1.5	21 21.8	23 5.5	1 38.4	8 30.3	13 .2	29 20.2	25 26.1	0 57.4
31	8 38 59.5	13 5.4	7 46.0	12♒20.1	20 29.8	24 15.8	1 18.8	8 40.4	13 6.4	29 23.9	25 28.5	0 58.5
		DECLINATION										
1	6 40 42.8	23S 3.2	0S16.1	19S27.2	24S 1.3	15S13.9	13N45.6	20S20.1	10S14.2	21S31.8	21S .2	7S .7
4	6 52 32.5	22 47.3	0 16.0	10 46.6	23 9.9	15 51.5	13 51.7	20 26.5	10 8.2	21 29.9	20 59.2	7 1.6
7	7 4 22.2	22 27.2	0 16.0	2N16.6	22 4.9	16 29.0	14 .3	20 32.7	10 2.0	21 28.0	20 58.1	7 2.0
10	7 16 11.8	22 3.2	0 15.9	13 33.0	20 47.2	17 6.0	14 11.4	20 38.6	9 55.5	21 26.0	20 57.0	7 2.2
13	7 28 1.5	21 35.3	0 15.9	19 34.8	19 18.7	17 41.8	14 24.9	20 44.2	9 48.9	21 24.0	20 55.9	7 2.4
16	7 39 51.2	21 3.7	0 15.8	18 2.8	17 42.8	18 16.0	14 40.9	20 49.6	9 42.0	21 22.0	20 54.8	7 2.5
19	7 51 40.8	20 28.4	0 15.8	9 .1	16 5.1	18 48.1	14 59.1	20 54.8	9 34.9	21 20.0	20 53.7	7 2.5
22	8 3 30.5	19 49.6	0 15.7	4S10.6	14 34.0	19 17.6	15 19.3	20 59.7	9 27.7	21 18.0	20 52.5	7 2.4
25	8 15 20.2	19 7.6	0 15.7	15 56.9	13 20.1	19 44.1	15 41.4	21 4.3	9 20.3	21 16.0	20 51.4	7 2.2
28	8 27 9.8	18 22.3	0 15.6	19 43.8	12 34.4	20 7.2	16 5.0	21 8.7	9 12.8	21 14.0	20 50.3	7 1.9
31	8 38 59.5	17 34.1	0 15.6	12 34.5	12 24.3	20 26.5	16 29.6	21 12.8	9 5.1	21 12.0	20 49.2	7 1.5

FEBRUARY 1995

LONGITUDE

DAY	EPHEM. SID. TIME h m s	☉ ° ′	☊ ° ′	☽ ° ′	☿ ° ′	♀ ° ′	♂ ° ′	♃ ° ′	♄ ° ′	♅ ° ′	♆ ° ′	♇ ° ′
1	8 42 56.1	11♒39.3	10♏ 7.5	25♒20.2	18♒ 1.8	25♐43.5	27♌10.8	10♐20.2	11♓ 4.3	27♑17.7	23♑44.5	0♐20.3
2	8 46 52.6	12 40.2	10 4.3	9♓ 1.7	16 R 57.6	26 50.1	26 R 49.2	10 29.5	11 11.1	27 21.1	23 46.7	0 21.3
3	8 50 49.2	13 41.1	10 1.2	22 19.0	15 48.3	27 56.8	26 27.2	10 38.7	11 17.9	27 24.6	23 48.9	0 22.4
4	8 54 45.7	14 42.0	9 58.0	5♈12.1	14 35.9	29 3.8	26 4.8	10 47.8	11 24.7	27 28.0	23 51.1	0 23.3
5	8 58 42.3	15 42.8	9 54.8	17 42.9	13 22.5	0♑10.9	25 42.0	10 56.8	11 31.6	27 31.4	23 53.2	0 24.3
6	9 2 38.8	16 43.7	9 51.6	29 55.2	12 10.2	1 18.2	25 19.0	11 5.6	11 38.5	27 34.8	23 55.3	0 25.2
7	9 6 35.4	17 44.5	9 48.5	11♉53.8	11 .9	2 25.7	24 55.6	11 14.3	11 45.4	27 38.2	23 57.5	0 26.1
8	9 10 32.0	18 45.2	9 45.3	23 44.2	9 56.1	3 33.3	24 32.1	11 23.0	11 52.4	27 41.6	23 59.6	0 27.0
9	9 14 28.5	19 46.0	9 42.1	5♊32.0	8 57.2	4 41.1	24 8.4	11 31.4	11 59.3	27 44.9	24 1.7	0 27.8
10	9 18 25.1	20 46.7	9 38.9	17 22.5	8 5.2	5 49.1	23 44.5	11 39.8	12 6.4	27 48.3	24 3.8	0 28.6
11	9 22 21.6	21 47.5	9 35.7	29 20.8	7 20.7	6 57.2	23 20.6	11 48.0	12 13.4	27 51.6	24 5.8	0 29.4
12	9 26 18.2	22 48.2	9 32.6	11♋31.0	6 44.2	8 5.5	22 56.7	11 56.2	12 20.5	27 54.9	24 7.9	0 30.1
13	9 30 14.7	23 48.8	9 29.4	23 56.0	6 15.7	9 13.9	22 32.8	12 4.1	12 27.6	27 58.2	24 10.0	0 30.8
14	9 34 11.3	24 49.5	9 26.2	6♌37.7	5 55.2	10 22.4	22 8.9	12 12.0	12 34.8	28 1.5	24 12.0	0 31.5
15	9 38 7.8	25 50.1	9 23.0	19 36.3	5 42.5	11 31.1	21 45.0	12 19.7	12 41.9	28 4.7	24 14.0	0 32.1
16	9 42 4.4	26 50.7	9 19.9	2♍50.9	5 37.4	12 39.9	21 21.4	12 27.2	12 49.1	28 7.9	24 16.0	0 32.7
17	9 46 .9	27 51.2	9 16.7	16 19.4	5 D 39.4	13 48.8	20 57.9	12 34.7	12 56.3	28 11.1	24 18.0	0 33.2
18	9 49 57.5	28 51.7	9 13.5	29 59.3	5 48.2	14 57.9	20 34.7	12 42.0	13 3.5	28 14.3	24 20.0	0 33.7
19	9 53 54.0	29 52.3	9 10.3	13♎47.8	6 3.3	16 7.1	20 11.7	12 49.1	13 10.7	28 17.5	24 21.9	0 34.2
20	9 57 50.6	0♓52.8	9 7.1	27 42.7	6 24.2	17 16.4	19 49.0	12 56.1	13 17.9	28 20.6	24 23.8	0 34.6
21	10 1 47.2	1 53.2	9 4.0	11♏42.3	6 50.7	18 25.8	19 26.7	13 3.0	13 25.2	28 23.7	24 25.7	0 35.1
22	10 5 43.7	2 53.7	9 .8	25 45.5	7 22.2	19 35.4	19 4.7	13 9.7	13 32.5	28 26.8	24 27.6	0 35.4
23	10 9 40.3	3 54.1	8 57.6	9♐51.5	7 58.3	20 45.0	18 43.2	13 16.3	13 39.8	28 29.8	24 29.5	0 35.8
24	10 13 36.8	4 54.5	8 54.4	23 59.6	8 38.8	21 54.8	18 22.2	13 22.7	13 47.1	28 32.8	24 31.3	0 36.1
25	10 17 33.4	5 54.9	8 51.3	8♑ 8.0	9 23.3	23 4.7	18 1.6	13 29.0	13 54.4	28 35.8	24 33.1	0 36.3
26	10 21 29.9	6 55.2	8 48.1	22 14.6	10 11.5	24 14.6	17 41.6	13 35.1	14 1.7	28 38.8	24 35.0	0 36.6
27	10 25 26.5	7 55.6	8 44.9	6♒16.1	11 3.1	25 24.6	17 22.1	13 41.1	14 9.1	28 41.8	24 36.7	0 36.7
28	10 29 23.0	8 55.9	8 41.7	20 8.5	11 57.8	26 34.8	17 3.3	13 46.9	14 16.4	28 44.7	24 38.5	0 36.9

LATITUDE

DAY	EPHEM. SID. TIME	☉	☊	☽	☿	♀	♂	♃	♄	♅	♆	♇
1	8 42 56.1	0 .0	0 .0	4 N 49.6	3 N 5.4	2 N 50.2	4 N 27.4	0 N 46.2	1 S 45.6	0 S 29.9	0 N 32.8	13 N 28.7
4	8 54 45.7	0 .0	0 .0	2 50.3	3 33.3	2 40.2	4 30.1	0 46.3	1 45.5	0 30.0	0 32.8	13 29.8
7	9 6 35.4	0 .0	0 .0	0 S 13.5	3 39.6	2 29.6	4 31.9	0 46.4	1 45.5	0 30.0	0 32.8	13 30.9
10	9 18 25.1	0 .0	0 .0	3 7.1	3 26.0	2 18.5	4 32.7	0 46.5	1 45.4	0 30.0	0 32.8	13 32.1
13	9 30 14.7	0 .0	0 .0	4 51.3	2 58.6	2 7.1	4 32.5	0 46.7	1 45.4	0 30.1	0 32.7	13 33.2
16	9 42 4.4	0 .0	0 .0	4 34.5	2 23.7	1 55.4	4 31.4	0 46.8	1 45.4	0 30.1	0 32.7	13 34.4
19	9 53 54.0	0 .0	0 .0	2 4.2	1 46.1	1 43.4	4 29.3	0 47.0	1 45.4	0 30.2	0 32.7	13 35.6
22	10 5 43.7	0 .0	0 .0	1 N 34.1	1 8.8	1 31.3	4 26.3	0 47.1	1 45.4	0 30.3	0 32.7	13 36.8
25	10 17 33.4	0 .0	0 .0	4 25.1	0 33.3	1 19.1	4 22.5	0 47.3	1 45.5	0 30.3	0 32.7	13 38.0
28	10 29 23.0	0 .0	0 .0	4 56.9	0 .5	1 6.8	4 17.9	0 47.4	1 45.6	0 30.4	0 32.8	13 39.1

RIGHT ASCENSION

DAY	EPHEM. SID. TIME	☉	☊	☽	☿	♀	♂	♃	♄	♅	♆	♇
1	8 42 56.1	14♒ 6.8	7♏42.9	25♒58.2	19♒29.9	25♐26.4	0♍58.6	8♐50.4	13♓12.7	29♑27.5	25♑30.8	0♐59.7
2	8 46 52.6	15 8.0	7 39.8	8♓58.8	18 R 23.7	26 37.3	0 R 37.9	9 .3	13 19.0	29 31.2	25 33.1	1 .8
3	8 50 49.2	16 9.0	7 36.6	21 29.2	17 13.1	27 48.5	0 16.7	9 10.1	13 25.3	29 34.8	25 35.4	1 1.8
4	8 54 45.7	17 9.9	7 33.5	3♈38.7	16 .0	28 59.9	29♌55.1	9 19.7	13 31.7	29 38.4	25 37.6	1 2.8
5	8 58 42.3	18 10.4	7 30.4	15 36.8	14 46.6	0♑11.6	29 33.1	9 29.3	13 38.1	29 42.0	25 39.9	1 3.8
6	9 2 38.8	19 10.8	7 27.3	27 32.1	13 34.8	1 23.6	29 10.7	9 38.7	13 44.5	29 45.6	25 42.2	1 4.8
7	9 6 35.4	20 11.0	7 24.2	9♉31.8	12 26.3	2 35.8	28 47.9	9 48.0	13 51.0	29 49.1	25 44.4	1 5.7
8	9 10 32.0	21 11.0	7 21.0	21 41.0	11 22.8	3 48.2	28 24.9	9 57.1	13 57.5	29 52.7	25 46.6	1 6.6
9	9 14 28.5	22 10.8	7 17.9	4♊ 2.3	10 25.4	5 .9	28 1.7	10 6.2	14 4.0	29 56.2	25 48.8	1 7.5
10	9 18 25.1	23 10.3	7 14.8	16 35.6	9 35.2	6 13.7	27 38.2	10 15.1	14 10.6	29 59.7	25 51.0	1 8.3
11	9 22 21.6	24 9.7	7 11.7	29 18.5	8 52.8	7 26.7	27 14.6	10 23.8	14 17.2	0♒ 3.2	25 53.2	1 9.1
12	9 26 18.2	25 8.9	7 8.6	12♋ 7.0	8 18.5	8 39.9	26 51.0	10 32.5	14 23.8	0 6.7	25 55.4	1 10.0
13	9 30 14.7	26 7.9	7 5.5	24 56.4	7 52.5	9 53.3	26 27.2	10 41.0	14 30.4	0 10.2	25 57.6	1 10.7
14	9 34 11.3	27 6.7	7 2.3	7♌43.5	7 34.6	11 6.7	26 3.5	10 49.4	14 37.1	0 13.6	25 59.7	1 11.4
15	9 38 7.8	28 5.3	6 59.2	20 27.1	7 24.8	12 20.3	25 39.7	10 57.6	14 43.7	0 17.0	26 1.8	1 12.1
16	9 42 4.4	29 3.8	6 56.1	3♍ 8.7	7 22.7	13 34.1	25 16.0	11 5.6	14 50.4	0 20.4	26 3.9	1 12.7
17	9 46 .9	0♓ 2.0	6 53.0	15 52.6	7 D 27.8	14 47.9	24 52.5	11 13.6	14 57.1	0 23.7	26 6.0	1 13.3
18	9 49 57.5	1 .1	6 49.9	28 45.0	7 39.9	16 1.8	24 29.1	11 21.4	15 3.9	0 27.1	26 8.1	1 13.9
19	9 53 54.0	1 58.0	6 46.8	11♎53.2	7 58.4	17 15.8	24 5.9	11 29.0	15 10.6	0 30.4	26 10.1	1 14.4
20	9 57 50.6	2 55.7	6 43.7	25 24.2	8 22.9	18 29.8	23 43.0	11 36.5	15 17.4	0 33.7	26 12.1	1 14.9
21	10 1 47.2	3 53.3	6 40.6	9♏22.7	8 52.9	19 43.9	23 20.3	11 43.8	15 24.1	0 36.9	26 14.1	1 15.4
22	10 5 43.7	4 50.7	6 37.4	23 49.1	9 28.1	20 58.0	22 58.0	11 51.0	15 30.9	0 40.1	26 16.1	1 15.8
23	10 9 40.3	5 47.9	6 34.3	8♐38.0	10 7.9	22 12.2	22 36.0	11 58.0	15 37.7	0 43.4	26 18.1	1 16.2
24	10 13 36.8	6 45.0	6 31.2	23 38.0	10 52.1	23 26.3	22 14.5	12 4.9	15 44.5	0 46.5	26 20.0	1 16.6
25	10 17 33.4	7 42.0	6 28.1	8♑34.1	11 40.3	24 40.5	21 53.4	12 11.6	15 51.3	0 49.7	26 22.0	1 16.9
26	10 21 29.9	8 38.8	6 25.0	23 11.9	12 32.1	25 54.6	21 32.8	12 18.2	15 58.2	0 52.8	26 23.9	1 17.2
27	10 25 26.5	9 35.5	6 21.9	7♒21.2	13 27.2	27 8.7	21 12.7	12 24.5	16 5.0	0 55.9	26 25.7	1 17.5
28	10 29 23.0	10 32.0	6 18.8	20 57.8	14 25.4	28 22.7	20 53.1	12 30.8	16 11.9	0 58.9	26 27.6	1 17.7

DECLINATION

DAY	EPHEM. SID. TIME	☉	☊	☽	☿	♀	♂	♃	♄	♅	♆	♇
1	8 42 56.1	17 S 17.3	0 S 15.6	8 S 31.4	12 S 29.0	20 S 32.1	16 N 38.0	21 S 14.1	9 S 2.5	21 S 11.3	20 S 48.8	7 S 1.4
4	8 54 45.7	16 25.4	0 15.5	4 N 40.3	13 3.0	20 45.9	17 3.3	21 18.0	8 54.6	21 9.3	20 47.7	7 .9
7	9 6 35.4	15 30.9	0 15.4	15 11.4	13 56.6	20 55.4	17 28.7	21 21.5	8 46.7	21 7.4	20 46.6	7 .3
10	9 18 25.1	14 34.0	0 15.4	19 44.1	14 55.5	21 .2	17 53.5	21 24.9	8 38.6	21 5.4	20 45.5	6 59.7
13	9 30 14.7	13 34.9	0 15.3	16 32.1	15 49.3	21 .2	18 17.3	21 28.0	8 30.4	21 3.5	20 44.4	6 59.0
16	9 42 4.4	12 33.9	0 15.3	6 11.2	16 32.5	20 55.2	18 39.7	21 30.8	8 22.2	21 1.6	20 43.4	6 58.2
19	9 53 54.0	11 31.0	0 15.2	7 S 21.0	17 2.6	20 45.2	19 .3	21 33.5	8 13.9	20 59.7	20 42.4	6 57.3
22	10 5 43.7	10 26.5	0 15.2	17 40.3	17 19.1	20 30.1	19 18.9	21 35.9	8 5.5	20 57.9	20 41.4	6 56.4
25	10 17 33.4	9 20.5	0 15.1	18 46.7	17 22.1	20 9.9	19 35.2	21 38.1	7 57.2	20 56.1	20 40.4	6 55.4
28	10 29 23.0	8 13.2	0 15.1	10 4.1	17 11.7	19 44.6	19 49.0	21 40.1	7 48.7	20 54.4	20 39.4	6 54.3

MARCH 1995

LONGITUDE

DAY	EPHEM. SID. TIME	☉	☊	☽	☿	♀	♂	♃	♄	♅	♆	♇
	h m s	° ′	° ′	° ′	° ′	° ′	° ′	° ′	° ′	° ′	° ′	° ′
1	10 33 19.6	9♓56.1	8♏38.5	3♓47.9	12♒55.5	27♑45.0	16♌45.0	13♐52.6	14♓23.7	28♑47.6	24♑40.2	0♐37.0
2	10 37 16.1	10 56.4	8 35.4	17 11.1	13 56.0	28 55.3	16 R 27.4	13 58.1	14 31.1	28 50.4	24 42.0	0 37.1
3	10 41 12.7	11 56.6	8 32.2	0♈15.7	14 59.0	0♒ 5.7	16 10.5	14 3.4	14 38.5	28 53.2	24 43.7	0 37.2
4	10 45 9.2	12 56.8	8 29.0	13 1.2	16 4.4	1 16.1	15 54.3	14 8.6	14 45.8	28 56.0	24 45.3	0 37.2
5	10 49 5.8	13 57.0	8 25.8	25 28.5	17 12.0	2 26.7	15 38.8	14 13.7	14 53.3	28 58.8	24 47.0	0 37.2
6	10 53 2.3	14 57.1	8 22.7	7♉39.9	18 21.8	3 37.3	15 24.0	14 18.5	15 .6	29 1.6	24 48.6	0 R 37.1
7	10 56 58.9	15 57.2	8 19.5	19 39.2	19 33.5	4 47.9	15 10.0	14 23.2	15 8.0	29 4.2	24 50.2	0 37.1
8	11 0 55.4	16 57.3	8 16.3	1♊30.7	20 47.1	5 58.6	14 56.7	14 27.7	15 15.4	29 6.9	24 51.8	0 36.9
9	11 4 52.0	17 57.3	8 13.1	13 19.5	22 2.6	7 9.4	14 44.2	14 32.0	15 22.7	29 9.5	24 53.4	0 36.8
10	11 8 48.5	18 57.2	8 9.9	25 10.9	23 19.7	8 20.3	14 32.4	14 36.2	15 30.1	29 12.1	24 54.9	0 36.6
11	11 12 45.1	19 57.2	8 6.8	7♋10.2	24 38.5	9 31.2	14 21.5	14 40.2	15 37.4	29 14.7	24 56.4	0 36.3
12	11 16 41.7	20 57.1	8 3.6	19 22.1	25 58.9	10 42.2	14 11.3	14 44.0	15 44.8	29 17.2	24 57.9	0 36.1
13	11 20 38.2	21 57.0	8 .4	1♌50.8	27 20.8	11 53.2	14 1.9	14 47.7	15 52.1	29 19.7	24 59.3	0 35.8
14	11 24 34.8	22 56.8	7 57.2	14 39.2	28 44.2	13 4.3	13 53.3	14 51.2	15 59.5	29 22.1	25 .7	0 35.5
15	11 28 31.3	23 56.6	7 54.1	27 48.9	0♓ 9.1	14 15.4	13 45.5	14 54.5	16 6.8	29 24.5	25 2.1	0 35.1
16	11 32 27.9	24 56.4	7 50.9	11♍19.4	1 35.3	15 26.6	13 38.5	14 57.6	16 14.1	29 26.9	25 3.5	0 34.7
17	11 36 24.4	25 56.1	7 47.7	25 8.9	3 3.0	16 37.9	13 32.2	15 .6	16 21.4	29 29.2	25 4.8	0 34.3
18	11 40 21.0	26 55.8	7 44.5	9♎13.8	4 32.0	17 49.2	13 26.7	15 3.3	16 28.7	29 31.5	25 6.1	0 33.8
19	11 44 17.5	27 55.5	7 41.3	23 29.6	6 2.4	19 .5	13 22.1	15 5.9	16 36.0	29 33.8	25 7.4	0 33.3
20	11 48 14.1	28 55.1	7 38.2	7♏51.3	7 34.0	20 11.9	13 18.1	15 8.3	16 43.3	29 36.0	25 8.6	0 32.8
21	11 52 10.6	29 54.7	7 35.0	22 14.3	9 7.1	21 23.4	13 15.0	15 10.6	16 50.5	29 38.1	25 9.9	0 32.2
22	11 56 7.2	0♈54.3	7 31.8	6♐34.9	10 41.4	22 34.9	13 12.6	15 12.6	16 57.7	29 40.3	25 11.1	0 31.6
23	12 0 3.7	1 53.8	7 28.6	20 50.1	12 17.0	23 46.5	13 10.9	15 14.5	17 5.0	29 42.4	25 12.2	0 31.0
24	12 4 .3	2 53.3	7 25.4	4♑57.9	13 54.0	24 58.1	13 10.0	15 16.2	17 12.2	29 44.4	25 13.4	0 30.3
25	12 7 56.8	3 52.8	7 22.3	18 56.8	15 32.2	26 9.7	13 9.9	15 17.7	17 19.3	29 46.4	25 14.5	0 29.7
26	12 11 53.4	4 52.3	7 19.1	2♒45.7	17 11.9	27 21.5	13 D 10.5	15 19.0	17 26.5	29 48.4	25 15.6	0 29.0
27	12 15 49.9	5 51.8	7 15.9	16 23.6	18 52.8	28 33.2	13 11.8	15 20.2	17 33.7	29 50.3	25 16.6	0 28.2
28	12 19 46.5	6 51.2	7 12.7	29 49.5	20 35.0	29 45.0	13 13.8	15 21.1	17 40.8	29 52.2	25 17.7	0 27.5
29	12 23 43.0	7 50.5	7 9.6	13♓ 2.3	22 18.5	0♓56.8	13 16.5	15 21.8	17 47.9	29 54.0	25 18.6	0 26.7
30	12 27 39.6	8 49.9	7 6.4	26 1.3	24 3.5	2 8.6	13 19.9	15 22.4	17 55.0	29 55.8	25 19.6	0 25.8
31	12 31 36.1	9 49.2	7 3.2	8♈46.0	25 49.7	3 20.5	13 24.0	15 22.8	18 2.0	29 57.6	25 20.5	0 24.9

LATITUDE

DAY	EPHEM. SID. TIME	☉	☊	☽	☿	♀	♂	♃	♄	♅	♆	♇
1	10 33 19.6	0 .0	0 .0	4N32.5	0S 9.8	1N 2.8	4N16.2	0N47.5	1S45.6	0S30.4	0N32.8	13N39.5
4	10 45 9.2	0 .0	0 .0	2 3.9	0 38.4	0 50.6	4 10.8	0 47.7	1 45.7	0 30.5	0 32.8	13 40.7
7	10 56 58.9	0 .0	0 .0	1S 9.2	1 3.7	0 38.6	4 4.9	0 47.8	1 45.8	0 30.6	0 32.8	13 41.9
10	11 8 48.5	0 .0	0 .0	3 51.6	1 25.5	0 26.9	3 58.5	0 48.0	1 46.0	0 30.6	0 32.8	13 43.0
13	11 20 38.2	0 .0	0 .0	5 7.9	1 43.7	0 15.3	3 51.9	0 48.2	1 46.2	0 30.7	0 32.8	13 44.1
16	11 32 27.9	0 .0	0 .0	4 13.5	1 58.3	0 4.1	3 45.1	0 48.4	1 46.4	0 30.8	0 32.8	13 45.2
19	11 44 17.5	0 .0	0 .0	1 7.6	2 9.2	0S 6.7	3 38.1	0 48.5	1 46.6	0 30.9	0 32.8	13 46.3
22	11 56 7.2	0 .0	0 .0	2N39.2	2 16.1	0 17.1	3 31.0	0 48.7	1 46.8	0 31.0	0 32.9	13 47.3
25	12 7 56.8	0 .0	0 .0	4 59.0	2 19.1	0 27.0	3 24.0	0 48.9	1 47.1	0 31.1	0 32.9	13 48.4
28	12 19 46.5	0 .0	0 .0	4 46.0	2 18.0	0 36.5	3 16.9	0 49.1	1 47.4	0 31.1	0 32.9	13 49.3
31	12 31 36.1	0 .0	0 .0	2 22.3	2 12.5	0 45.3	3 10.0	0 49.2	1 47.7	0 31.2	0 32.9	13 50.2

RIGHT ASCENSION

DAY	EPHEM. SID. TIME	☉	☊	☽	☿	♀	♂	♃	♄	♅	♆	♇
1	10 33 19.6	11♓28.4	6♏15.7	4♓ 2.9	15♒26.3	29♑36.7	20♌34.2	12♐36.8	16♓18.7	1♒ 2.0	26♑29.4	1♐17.9
2	10 37 16.1	12 24.7	6 12.6	16 41.8	16 29.9	0♒50.6	20 R 15.8	12 42.7	16 25.6	1 5.0	26 31.2	1 18.1
3	10 41 12.7	13 20.8	6 9.5	29 1.6	17 35.8	2 4.5	19 58.2	12 48.4	16 32.4	1 7.9	26 33.0	1 18.2
4	10 45 9.2	14 16.9	6 6.4	11♈10.1	18 43.8	3 18.2	19 41.1	12 53.9	16 39.3	1 10.9	26 34.8	1 18.3
5	10 49 5.8	15 12.8	6 3.3	23 14.4	19 53.9	4 31.9	19 24.9	12 59.3	16 46.2	1 13.8	26 36.5	1 18.4
6	10 53 2.3	16 8.6	6 .2	5♉20.2	21 5.7	5 45.4	19 9.3	13 4.5	16 53.1	1 16.7	26 38.3	1 18.4
7	10 56 58.9	17 4.3	5 57.0	17 31.8	22 19.2	6 58.8	18 54.4	13 9.5	16 59.9	1 19.5	26 39.9	1 18.4
8	11 0 55.4	17 59.9	5 53.9	29 51.4	23 34.3	8 12.1	18 40.2	13 14.4	17 6.8	1 22.3	26 41.6	1 18.4
9	11 4 52.0	18 55.4	5 50.8	12♊19.3	24 50.8	9 25.3	18 26.9	13 19.0	17 13.7	1 25.0	26 43.2	1 R 18.3
10	11 8 48.5	19 50.7	5 47.7	24 54.0	26 8.7	10 38.3	18 14.3	13 23.5	17 20.5	1 27.7	26 44.8	1 18.2
11	11 12 45.1	20 46.0	5 44.6	7♋33.1	27 27.8	11 51.1	18 2.4	13 27.8	17 27.4	1 30.4	26 46.4	1 18.0
12	11 16 41.7	21 41.2	5 41.5	20 14.0	28 48.1	13 3.8	17 51.4	13 31.9	17 34.2	1 33.1	26 47.9	1 17.8
13	11 20 38.2	22 36.4	5 38.4	2♌55.0	0♓ 9.4	14 16.4	17 41.1	13 35.8	17 41.1	1 35.7	26 49.4	1 17.6
14	11 24 34.8	23 31.4	5 35.3	15 36.3	1 31.8	15 28.8	17 31.7	13 39.5	17 47.9	1 38.2	26 50.9	1 17.4
15	11 28 31.3	24 26.4	5 32.2	28 19.8	2 55.2	16 41.0	17 23.0	13 43.1	17 54.7	1 40.7	26 52.4	1 17.1
16	11 32 27.9	25 21.3	5 29.1	11♍ 9.8	4 19.5	17 53.1	17 15.2	13 46.4	18 1.5	1 43.2	26 53.8	1 16.8
17	11 36 24.4	26 16.2	5 26.0	24 12.1	5 44.6	19 4.9	17 8.1	13 49.6	18 8.4	1 45.7	26 55.2	1 16.5
18	11 40 21.0	27 11.0	5 22.9	7♎33.3	7 10.7	20 16.7	17 1.8	13 52.6	18 15.1	1 48.1	26 56.6	1 16.1
19	11 44 17.5	28 5.7	5 19.8	21 19.1	8 37.5	21 28.2	16 56.3	13 55.4	18 21.9	1 50.4	26 57.9	1 15.7
20	11 48 14.1	29 .4	5 16.7	5♏32.9	10 5.2	22 39.6	16 51.6	13 58.0	18 28.7	1 52.7	26 59.3	1 15.2
21	11 52 10.6	29 55.1	5 13.6	20 13.1	11 33.7	23 50.7	16 47.7	14 .4	18 35.4	1 55.0	27 .5	1 14.8
22	11 56 7.2	0♈49.8	5 10.5	5♐12.3	13 3.0	25 1.8	16 44.5	14 2.6	18 42.2	1 57.3	27 1.8	1 14.3
23	12 0 3.7	1 44.4	5 7.4	20 17.7	14 33.0	26 12.6	16 42.1	14 4.6	18 48.9	1 59.4	27 3.0	1 13.7
24	12 4 .3	2 39.0	5 4.3	5♑13.9	16 3.9	27 23.2	16 40.4	14 6.4	18 55.6	2 1.6	27 4.2	1 13.2
25	12 7 56.8	3 33.7	5 1.2	19 47.2	17 35.5	28 33.7	16 39.6	14 8.0	19 2.3	2 3.7	27 5.4	1 12.6
26	12 11 53.4	4 28.3	4 58.1	3♒49.2	19 8.0	29 44.0	16 39.5	14 9.4	19 9.0	2 5.8	27 6.5	1 12.0
27	12 15 49.9	5 22.9	4 55.0	17 17.2	20 41.3	0♓54.1	16 D 40.0	14 10.7	19 15.7	2 7.8	27 7.6	1 11.4
28	12 19 46.5	6 17.5	4 52.0	0♓14.2	22 15.4	2 4.1	16 41.4	14 11.7	19 22.3	2 9.8	27 8.7	1 10.7
29	12 23 43.0	7 12.1	4 48.9	12 46.4	23 50.4	3 13.8	16 43.4	14 12.5	19 28.9	2 11.7	27 9.7	1 10.0
30	12 27 39.6	8 6.7	4 45.8	25 1.3	25 26.2	4 23.4	16 46.2	14 13.1	19 35.5	2 13.6	27 10.7	1 9.2
31	12 31 36.1	9 1.4	4 42.7	7♈ 6.9	27 3.0	5 32.8	16 49.6	14 13.5	19 42.0	2 15.4	27 11.7	1 8.5

DECLINATION

DAY	EPHEM. SID. TIME	☉	☊	☽	☿	♀	♂	♃	♄	♅	♆	♇
1	10 33 19.6	7S50.6	0S15.1	5S52.7	17S 5.3	19S35.1	19N53.0	21S40.7	7S45.9	20S53.8	20S39.1	6S54.0
4	10 45 9.2	6 41.9	0 15.0	7N 2.6	16 37.7	19 3.1	20 3.3	21 42.4	7 37.5	20 52.1	20 38.2	6 52.9
7	10 56 58.9	5 32.4	0 15.0	16 32.1	15 57.6	18 26.3	20 11.0	21 43.9	7 29.0	20 50.5	20 37.3	6 51.7
10	11 8 48.5	4 22.2	0 14.9	19 29.5	15 5.2	17 44.8	20 16.2	21 45.3	7 20.6	20 49.0	20 36.5	6 50.5
13	11 20 38.2	3 11.6	0 14.8	14 44.5	14 1.0	16 58.7	20 18.8	21 46.4	7 12.2	20 47.5	20 35.7	6 49.2
16	11 32 27.9	2 .6	0 14.8	3 24.4	12 45.0	16 8.3	20 19.2	21 47.3	7 3.8	20 46.0	20 34.9	6 47.9
19	11 44 17.5	0 49.5	0 14.7	10S10.2	11 17.8	15 13.8	20 17.3	21 48.1	6 55.5	20 44.7	20 34.2	6 46.6
22	11 56 7.2	0N21.6	0 14.7	18 47.5	9 39.4	14 15.3	20 13.3	21 48.6	6 47.3	20 43.4	20 33.5	6 45.3
25	12 7 56.8	1 32.6	0 14.6	17 9.8	7 50.3	13 13.2	20 7.3	21 49.0	6 39.1	20 42.2	20 32.9	6 43.9
28	12 19 46.5	2 43.2	0 14.6	7 3.9	5 50.7	12 7.7	19 59.4	21 49.2	6 31.0	20 41.0	20 32.3	6 42.5
31	12 31 36.1	3 53.4	0 14.5	5N39.3	3 41.1	10 59.1	19 49.8	21 49.2	6 23.0	20 40.0	20 31.7	6 41.2

APRIL 1995

LONGITUDE

DAY	EPHEM. SID. TIME h m s	☉ ° ′	☊ ° ′	☽ ° ′	☿ ° ′	♀ ° ′	♂ ° ′	♃ ° ′	♄ ° ′	♅ ° ′	♆ ° ′	♇ ° ′
1	12 35 32.7	10♈48.4	7♏ .0	21♈16.6	27♓37.4	4♓32.4	13♌28.8	15♐23.0	18♓ 9.0	29♑59.3	25♑21.4	0♐24.1
2	12 39 29.2	11 47.7	6 56.8	3♉34.0	29 26.4	5 44.3	13 34.2	15 23.0	18 16.0	0♒ .9	25 22.3	0 R 23.1
3	12 43 25.8	12 46.9	6 53.7	15 39.8	1♈16.8	6 56.3	13 40.3	15 R 22.8	18 22.9	0 2.5	25 23.1	0 22.2
4	12 47 22.3	13 46.0	6 50.5	27 36.5	3 8.7	8 8.3	13 47.1	15 22.4	18 29.9	0 4.1	25 23.9	0 21.2
5	12 51 18.9	14 45.2	6 47.3	9♊27.4	5 1.9	9 20.3	13 54.4	15 21.8	18 36.7	0 5.6	25 24.6	0 20.2
6	12 55 15.5	15 44.2	6 44.1	21 16.3	6 56.5	10 32.3	14 2.4	15 21.0	18 43.6	0 7.1	25 25.4	0 19.2
7	12 59 12.0	16 43.3	6 41.0	3♋ 7.8	8 52.5	11 44.4	14 11.0	15 20.1	18 50.4	0 8.5	25 26.1	0 18.1
8	13 3 8.6	17 42.3	6 37.8	15 6.5	10 49.9	12 56.5	14 20.3	15 19.0	18 57.2	0 9.8	25 26.7	0 17.0
9	13 7 5.1	18 41.3	6 34.6	27 17.3	12 48.6	14 8.6	14 30.0	15 17.7	19 4.0	0 11.2	25 27.4	0 15.9
10	13 11 1.7	19 40.2	6 31.4	9♌44.6	14 48.6	15 20.7	14 40.4	15 16.1	19 10.7	0 12.4	25 28.0	0 14.8
11	13 14 58.2	20 39.1	6 28.2	22 32.4	16 49.9	16 32.9	14 51.3	15 14.5	19 17.3	0 13.7	25 28.5	0 13.6
12	13 18 54.8	21 38.0	6 25.1	5♍43.7	18 52.4	17 45.0	15 2.8	15 12.6	19 24.0	0 14.8	25 29.1	0 12.4
13	13 22 51.3	22 36.8	6 21.9	19 19.7	20 56.0	18 57.2	15 14.8	15 10.5	19 30.6	0 16.0	25 29.6	0 11.2
14	13 26 47.9	23 35.6	6 18.7	3♎19.7	23 .6	20 9.4	15 27.3	15 8.3	19 37.1	0 17.1	25 30.0	0 10.0
15	13 30 44.4	24 34.3	6 15.5	17 41.0	25 6.1	21 21.7	15 40.3	15 5.9	19 43.6	0 18.1	25 30.5	0 8.7
16	13 34 41.0	25 33.1	6 12.4	2♏18.6	27 12.4	22 34.0	15 53.9	15 3.3	19 50.1	0 19.1	25 30.9	0 7.5
17	13 38 37.5	26 31.8	6 9.2	17 5.9	29 19.1	23 46.3	16 8.0	15 .6	19 56.6	0 20.1	25 31.3	0 6.2
18	13 42 34.1	27 30.5	6 6.0	1♐55.8	1♉26.1	24 58.6	16 22.5	14 57.6	20 2.9	0 20.9	25 31.6	0 4.9
19	13 46 30.6	28 29.1	6 2.8	16 41.0	3 33.2	26 10.9	16 37.4	14 54.5	20 9.3	0 21.8	25 31.9	0 3.6
20	13 50 27.2	29 27.7	5 59.6	1♑15.7	5 40.1	27 23.3	16 52.9	14 51.2	20 15.6	0 22.6	25 32.2	0 2.2
21	13 54 23.7	0♉26.2	5 56.5	15 35.4	7 46.5	28 35.7	17 8.7	14 47.7	20 21.8	0 23.3	25 32.5	0 .9
22	13 58 20.3	1 24.8	5 53.3	29 37.5	9 52.1	29 48.1	17 25.1	14 44.1	20 28.0	0 24.0	25 32.7	29♏59.5
23	14 2 16.8	2 23.3	5 50.1	13♒21.0	11 56.6	1♈ .5	17 41.8	14 40.3	20 34.1	0 24.6	25 32.8	29 58.1
24	14 6 13.4	3 21.8	5 46.9	26 46.1	13 59.7	2 12.9	17 59.0	14 36.3	20 40.2	0 25.2	25 33.0	29 56.6
25	14 10 10.0	4 20.3	5 43.8	9♓53.9	16 1.0	3 25.4	18 16.6	14 32.2	20 46.2	0 25.8	25 33.1	29 55.2
26	14 14 6.5	5 18.7	5 40.6	22 45.8	18 .3	4 37.8	18 34.6	14 27.9	20 52.2	0 26.2	25 33.2	29 53.7
27	14 18 3.1	6 17.1	5 37.4	5♈23.5	19 57.2	5 50.3	18 53.1	14 23.4	20 58.2	0 26.7	25 33.2	29 52.3
28	14 21 59.6	7 15.5	5 34.2	17 48.7	21 51.5	7 2.8	19 11.9	14 18.8	21 4.0	0 27.1	25 33.2	29 50.8
29	14 25 56.2	8 13.8	5 31.0	0♉ 3.1	23 42.9	8 15.4	19 31.1	14 14.0	21 9.8	0 27.4	25 33.2	29 49.3
30	14 29 52.7	9 12.2	5 27.9	12 8.3	25 31.2	9 27.9	19 50.7	14 9.1	21 15.6	0 27.7	25 R 33.1	29 47.7

LATITUDE

DAY	EPHEM. SID. TIME	☉	☊	☽	☿	♀	♂	♃	♄	♅	♆	♇
1	12 35 32.7	0 .0	0 .0	1N18.2	2S 9.7	0S48.2	3N 7.7	0N49.3	1S47.8	0S31.3	0N32.9	13N50.5
4	12 47 22.3	0 .0	0 .0	1S58.4	1 58.3	0 56.3	3 .9	0 49.4	1 48.1	0 31.4	0 32.9	13 51.4
7	12 59 12.0	0 .0	0 .0	4 26.8	1 42.3	1 3.8	2 54.2	0 49.5	1 48.5	0 31.5	0 33.0	13 52.2
10	13 11 1.7	0 .0	0 .0	5 15.6	1 21.8	1 10.7	2 47.7	0 49.7	1 48.9	0 31.6	0 33.0	13 53.0
13	13 22 51.3	0 .0	0 .0	3 49.2	0 56.9	1 16.9	2 41.3	0 49.8	1 49.3	0 31.7	0 33.0	13 53.7
16	13 34 41.0	0 .0	0 .0	0 18.1	0 28.3	1 22.4	2 35.2	0 49.9	1 49.7	0 31.8	0 33.0	13 54.3
19	13 46 30.6	0 .0	0 .0	3N29.0	0N 3.1	1 27.2	2 29.1	0 49.9	1 50.2	0 31.9	0 33.1	13 54.9
22	13 58 20.3	0 .0	0 .0	5 15.9	0 35.7	1 31.3	2 23.3	0 50.0	1 50.6	0 32.0	0 33.1	13 55.4
25	14 10 10.0	0 .0	0 .0	4 22.6	1 7.6	1 34.8	2 17.6	0 50.0	1 51.1	0 32.1	0 33.1	13 55.9
28	14 21 59.6	0 .0	0 .0	1 37.3	1 36.6	1 37.5	2 12.1	0 50.0	1 51.6	0 32.2	0 33.1	13 56.3

RIGHT ASCENSION

DAY	EPHEM. SID. TIME	☉	☊	☽	☿	♀	♂	♃	♄	♅	♆	♇
1	12 35 32.7	9♈56.0	4♏39.6	19♈10.0	28♓40.8	6♓42.0	16♌53.7	14♐13.7	19♓48.6	2♒17.2	27♑12.6	1♐ 7.7
2	12 39 29.2	10 50.7	4 36.5	1♉16.1	0♈19.5	7 51.1	16 58.6	14 13.7	19 55.1	2 18.9	27 13.5	1 R 6.8
3	12 43 25.8	11 45.4	4 33.4	13 28.4	1 59.3	8 60.0	17 4.0	14 R 13.5	20 1.5	2 20.6	27 14.4	1 6.0
4	12 47 22.3	12 40.2	4 30.3	25 48.3	3 40.1	10 8.7	17 10.2	14 13.1	20 8.0	2 22.2	27 15.2	1 5.1
5	12 51 18.9	13 34.9	4 27.2	8♊14.9	5 22.1	11 17.3	17 17.0	14 12.5	20 14.4	2 23.8	27 16.0	1 4.2
6	12 55 15.5	14 29.8	4 24.1	20 45.8	7 5.2	12 25.7	17 24.4	14 11.7	20 20.8	2 25.3	27 16.8	1 3.2
7	12 59 12.0	15 24.6	4 21.0	3♋18.0	8 49.5	13 34.0	17 32.4	14 10.7	20 27.1	2 26.8	27 17.5	1 2.3
8	13 3 8.6	16 19.5	4 17.9	15 49.0	10 35.0	14 42.1	17 41.0	14 9.4	20 33.5	2 28.3	27 18.2	1 1.3
9	13 7 5.1	17 14.5	4 14.8	28 17.6	12 21.8	15 50.1	17 50.2	14 8.0	20 39.8	2 29.7	27 18.9	1 .3
10	13 11 1.7	18 9.5	4 11.8	10♌44.8	14 9.9	16 58.0	18 .0	14 6.4	20 46.0	2 31.0	27 19.5	0 59.2
11	13 14 58.2	19 4.6	4 8.7	23 13.9	15 59.3	18 5.8	18 10.4	14 4.6	20 52.2	2 32.3	27 20.1	0 58.2
12	13 18 54.8	19 59.7	4 5.6	5♍50.4	17 49.9	19 13.4	18 21.3	14 2.6	20 58.4	2 33.5	27 20.7	0 57.1
13	13 22 51.3	20 54.9	4 2.5	18 41.7	19 41.9	20 21.0	18 32.7	14 .4	21 4.6	2 34.7	27 21.2	0 56.0
14	13 26 47.9	21 50.2	3 59.4	1♎55.8	21 35.2	21 28.4	18 44.6	13 58.1	21 10.7	2 35.8	27 21.7	0 54.9
15	13 30 44.4	22 45.6	3 56.3	15 40.6	23 29.7	22 35.8	18 57.1	13 55.5	21 16.7	2 36.9	27 22.1	0 53.7
16	13 34 41.0	23 41.0	3 53.2	0♏ 1.1	25 25.4	23 43.1	19 10.1	13 52.8	21 22.8	2 38.0	27 22.6	0 52.6
17	13 38 37.5	24 36.6	3 50.1	14 56.8	27 22.1	24 50.3	19 23.6	13 49.8	21 28.8	2 39.0	27 23.0	0 51.4
18	13 42 34.1	25 32.2	3 47.1	0♐19.7	29 19.7	25 57.4	19 37.5	13 46.6	21 34.7	2 39.9	27 23.4	0 50.2
19	13 46 30.6	26 27.9	3 44.0	15 54.0	1♉18.1	27 4.5	19 51.8	13 43.3	21 40.6	2 40.8	27 23.7	0 48.9
20	13 50 27.2	27 23.8	3 40.9	1♑19.8	3 17.2	28 11.5	20 6.7	13 39.8	21 46.5	2 41.6	27 24.0	0 47.7
21	13 54 23.7	28 19.7	3 37.8	16 18.7	5 16.5	29 18.4	20 21.9	13 36.1	21 52.3	2 42.4	27 24.2	0 46.4
22	13 58 20.3	29 15.8	3 34.7	0♒39.0	7 16.0	0♈25.4	20 37.6	13 32.2	21 58.1	2 43.1	27 24.4	0 45.1
23	14 2 16.8	0♉12.0	3 31.6	14 17.4	9 15.4	1 32.3	20 53.8	13 28.1	22 3.8	2 43.8	27 24.6	0 43.8
24	14 6 13.4	1 8.2	3 28.6	27 17.5	11 14.4	2 39.2	21 10.3	13 23.9	22 9.5	2 44.4	27 24.7	0 42.4
25	14 10 10.0	2 4.7	3 25.5	9♓47.2	13 12.6	3 46.1	21 27.2	13 19.4	22 15.1	2 45.0	27 24.9	0 41.1
26	14 14 6.5	3 1.2	3 22.4	21 55.9	15 9.8	4 53.0	21 44.5	13 14.8	22 20.7	2 45.5	27 24.9	0 39.7
27	14 18 3.1	3 57.8	3 19.3	3♈53.3	17 5.6	5 59.9	22 2.2	13 10.1	22 26.3	2 46.0	27 25.0	0 38.3
28	14 21 59.6	4 54.6	3 16.2	15 47.9	18 59.8	7 6.8	22 20.3	13 5.1	22 31.7	2 46.4	27 25.0	0 36.9
29	14 25 56.2	5 51.5	3 13.2	27 46.5	20 52.1	8 13.7	22 38.8	13 .0	22 37.2	2 46.7	27 R 24.9	0 35.5
30	14 29 52.7	6 48.6	3 10.1	9♉53.3	22 42.1	9 20.7	22 57.6	12 54.7	22 42.6	2 47.0	27 24.9	0 34.1

DECLINATION

DAY	EPHEM. SID. TIME	☉	☊	☽	☿	♀	♂	♃	♄	♅	♆	♇
1	12 35 32.7	4N16.6	0S14.5	9N30.4	2S55.7	10S35.6	19N46.2	21S49.2	6S20.3	20S39.7	20S31.6	6S40.7
4	12 47 22.3	5 25.9	0 14.4	17 42.2	0 33.5	9 23.3	19 34.4	21 49.0	6 12.5	20 38.7	20 31.1	6 39.3
7	12 59 12.0	6 34.3	0 14.4	18 57.4	1N57.0	8 8.6	19 21.0	21 48.6	6 4.7	20 37.9	20 30.7	6 37.9
10	13 11 1.7	7 41.7	0 14.3	12 44.1	4 34.7	6 51.7	19 6.1	21 48.1	5 57.1	20 37.1	20 30.3	6 36.5
13	13 22 51.3	8 47.8	0 14.3	0 42.6	7 17.4	5 33.0	18 49.9	21 47.4	5 49.7	20 36.5	20 30.0	6 35.1
16	13 34 41.0	9 52.7	0 14.2	12S33.5	10 2.2	4 12.7	18 32.2	21 46.5	5 42.4	20 35.9	20 29.7	6 33.8
19	13 46 30.6	10 56.1	0 14.2	19 18.3	12 44.9	2 51.1	18 13.4	21 45.4	5 35.3	20 35.4	20 29.5	6 32.5
22	13 58 20.3	11 57.9	0 14.1	15 4.6	15 20.1	1 28.6	17 53.2	21 44.2	5 28.3	20 35.1	20 29.3	6 31.1
25	14 10 10.0	12 57.9	0 14.1	3 48.0	17 42.5	0 5.3	17 31.9	21 42.8	5 21.6	20 34.8	20 29.2	6 29.9
28	14 21 59.6	13 56.1	0 14.0	8N29.2	19 47.1	1N18.3	17 9.4	21 41.2	5 15.1	20 34.6	20 29.2	6 28.6

MAY 1995

LONGITUDE

DAY	EPHEM. SID. TIME h m s	☉ ° ′	☊ ° ′	☽ ° ′	☿ ° ′	♀ ° ′	♂ ° ′	♃ ° ′	♄ ° ′	♅ ° ′	♆ ° ′	♇ ° ′
1	14 33 49.3	10♉10.5	5♏24.7	24♉ 6.1	27♉16.2	10♈40.4	20♌10.6	14♐ 4.0	21♓21.3	0♒27.9	25♑33.0	29♏46.2
2	14 37 45.8	11 8.7	5 21.5	5♊58.6	28 57.7	11 53.0	20 30.9	13 R 58.8	21 26.9	0 28.1	25 R 32.9	29 R 44.7
3	14 41 42.4	12 6.9	5 18.3	17 48.1	0♊35.5	13 5.5	20 51.6	13 53.4	21 32.5	0 28.2	25 32.7	29 43.1
4	14 45 38.9	13 5.1	5 15.2	29 37.4	2 9.6	14 18.1	21 12.6	13 47.9	21 38.0	0 28.3	25 32.6	29 41.5
5	14 49 35.5	14 3.3	5 12.0	11♋29.6	3 39.9	15 30.7	21 34.0	13 42.3	21 43.5	0 28.3	25 32.3	29 40.0
6	14 53 32.0	15 1.5	5 8.8	23 28.5	5 6.1	16 43.3	21 55.7	13 36.5	21 48.9	0 28.3	25 32.1	29 38.4
7	14 57 28.6	15 59.6	5 5.6	5♌38.1	6 28.3	17 55.9	22 17.7	13 30.6	21 54.2	0 28.3	25 31.8	29 36.8
8	15 1 25.2	16 57.7	5 2.4	18 2.5	7 46.4	19 8.5	22 40.1	13 24.6	21 59.5	0 R 28.2	25 31.5	29 35.2
9	15 5 21.7	17 55.7	4 59.3	0♍46.0	9 .2	20 21.2	23 2.7	13 18.5	22 4.7	0 28.0	25 31.2	29 33.6
10	15 9 18.3	18 53.7	4 56.1	13 52.3	10 9.8	21 33.8	23 25.6	13 12.2	22 9.8	0 27.8	25 30.8	29 32.0
11	15 13 14.8	19 51.7	4 52.9	27 24.2	11 15.0	22 46.4	23 48.9	13 5.9	22 14.9	0 27.5	25 30.4	29 30.3
12	15 17 11.4	20 49.6	4 49.7	11♎22.8	12 15.8	23 59.1	24 12.4	12 59.4	22 19.9	0 27.2	25 29.9	29 28.7
13	15 21 7.9	21 47.6	4 46.6	25 47.1	13 12.1	25 11.7	24 36.2	12 52.8	22 24.8	0 26.9	25 29.5	29 27.1
14	15 25 4.5	22 45.4	4 43.4	10♏33.4	14 3.9	26 24.4	25 .3	12 46.1	22 29.6	0 26.5	25 29.0	29 25.4
15	15 29 1.0	23 43.3	4 40.2	25 35.5	14 51.1	27 37.1	25 24.7	12 39.4	22 34.4	0 26.0	25 28.4	29 23.8
16	15 32 57.6	24 41.1	4 37.0	10♐44.8	15 33.6	28 49.8	25 49.3	12 32.5	22 39.1	0 25.5	25 27.9	29 22.1
17	15 36 54.2	25 39.0	4 33.8	25 51.8	16 11.4	0♉ 2.5	26 14.1	12 25.6	22 43.7	0 24.9	25 27.3	29 20.5
18	15 40 50.7	26 36.8	4 30.7	10♑47.5	16 44.5	1 15.2	26 39.3	12 18.5	22 48.3	0 24.3	25 26.7	29 18.8
19	15 44 47.3	27 34.5	4 27.5	25 24.4	17 12.7	2 27.9	27 4.7	12 11.4	22 52.8	0 23.7	25 26.0	29 17.2
20	15 48 43.8	28 32.3	4 24.3	9♒38.0	17 36.1	3 40.7	27 30.3	12 4.3	22 57.2	0 23.0	25 25.3	29 15.5
21	15 52 40.4	29 30.0	4 21.1	23 26.1	17 54.7	4 53.4	27 56.2	11 57.0	23 1.5	0 22.3	25 24.6	29 13.8
22	15 56 36.9	0♊27.7	4 18.0	6♓49.1	18 8.4	6 6.2	28 22.3	11 49.7	23 5.8	0 21.5	25 23.9	29 12.2
23	16 0 33.5	1 25.4	4 14.8	19 49.3	18 17.2	7 19.0	28 48.6	11 42.3	23 9.9	0 20.6	25 23.1	29 10.5
24	16 4 30.0	2 23.1	4 11.6	2♈29.6	18 21.3	8 31.8	29 15.2	11 34.9	23 14.0	0 19.7	25 22.3	29 8.8
25	16 8 26.6	3 20.8	4 8.4	14 53.6	18 R 20.8	9 44.6	29 42.0	11 27.5	23 18.0	0 18.8	25 21.5	29 7.2
26	16 12 23.2	4 18.4	4 5.3	27 5.0	18 15.6	10 57.4	0♍ 9.0	11 19.9	23 22.0	0 17.9	25 20.7	29 5.5
27	16 16 19.7	5 16.1	4 2.1	9♉ 6.9	18 6.1	12 10.2	0 36.2	11 12.4	23 25.8	0 16.8	25 19.8	29 3.9
28	16 20 16.3	6 13.7	3 58.9	21 2.4	17 52.4	13 23.1	1 3.8	11 4.9	23 29.6	0 15.8	25 18.9	29 2.3
29	16 24 12.8	7 11.3	3 55.7	2♊53.7	17 34.8	14 36.0	1 31.4	10 57.3	23 33.3	0 14.7	25 18.0	29 .6
30	16 28 9.4	8 8.9	3 52.5	14 43.1	17 13.6	15 48.9	1 59.3	10 49.6	23 36.9	0 13.6	25 17.0	28 59.0
31	16 32 5.9	9 6.5	3 49.4	26 32.6	16 49.2	17 1.7	2 27.4	10 42.0	23 40.4	0 12.4	25 16.1	28 57.4

LATITUDE

DAY	EPHEM. SID. TIME h m s	☉ ° ′	☊ ° ′	☽ ° ′	☿ ° ′	♀ ° ′	♂ ° ′	♃ ° ′	♄ ° ′	♅ ° ′	♆ ° ′	♇ ° ′
1	14 33 49.3	0 .0	0 .0	1S41.0	2N 1.0	1S39.5	2N 6.8	0N50.0	1S52.2	0S32.3	0N33.2	13N56.6
4	14 45 38.9	0 .0	0 .0	4 17.0	2 19.0	1 40.8	2 1.6	0 50.0	1 52.7	0 32.4	0 33.2	13 56.8
7	14 57 28.6	0 .0	0 .0	5 17.0	2 29.7	1 41.4	1 56.6	0 49.9	1 53.3	0 32.5	0 33.2	13 57.0
10	15 9 18.3	0 .0	0 .0	4 8.9	2 32.1	1 41.3	1 51.7	0 49.8	1 53.9	0 32.6	0 33.2	13 57.1
13	15 21 7.9	0 .0	0 .0	0 54.0	2 26.0	1 40.6	1 47.0	0 49.7	1 54.5	0 32.7	0 33.2	13 57.1
16	15 32 57.6	0 .0	0 .0	3N 2.2	2 10.8	1 39.2	1 42.5	0 49.6	1 55.1	0 32.8	0 33.3	13 57.0
19	15 44 47.3	0 .0	0 .0	5 10.4	1 46.4	1 37.2	1 38.0	0 49.4	1 55.8	0 32.9	0 33.3	13 56.9
22	15 56 36.9	0 .0	0 .0	4 29.1	1 13.1	1 34.5	1 33.7	0 49.2	1 56.4	0 33.0	0 33.3	13 56.7
25	16 8 26.6	0 .0	0 .0	1 50.7	0 31.7	1 31.3	1 29.5	0 48.9	1 57.1	0 33.1	0 33.3	13 56.4
28	16 20 16.3	0 .0	0 .0	1S24.4	0S16.3	1 27.6	1 25.4	0 48.7	1 57.8	0 33.2	0 33.3	13 56.1
31	16 32 5.9	0 .0	0 .0	4 3.3	1 8.0	1 23.3	1 21.4	0 48.4	1 58.5	0 33.2	0 33.3	13 55.6

RIGHT ASCENSION

DAY	EPHEM. SID. TIME h m s	☉ ° ′	☊ ° ′	☽ ° ′	☿ ° ′	♀ ° ′	♂ ° ′	♃ ° ′	♄ ° ′	♅ ° ′	♆ ° ′	♇ ° ′
1	14 33 49.3	7♉45.8	3♏ 7.0	22♉ 9.8	24♉29.6	10♈27.7	23♌16.7	12♐49.3	22♓47.9	2♒47.3	27♑24.8	0♐32.6
2	14 37 45.8	8 43.1	3 3.9	4♊34.9	26 14.3	11 34.7	23 36.2	12 R 43.7	22 53.2	2 47.5	27 R 24.7	0 R 31.2
3	14 41 42.4	9 40.5	3 .8	17 5.2	27 56.0	12 41.8	23 56.1	12 38.0	22 58.4	2 47.6	27 24.5	0 29.7
4	14 45 38.9	10 38.1	2 57.8	29 36.1	29 34.6	13 49.0	24 16.2	12 32.1	23 3.5	2 47.7	27 24.3	0 28.2
5	14 49 35.5	11 35.8	2 54.7	12♋ 3.6	1♊ 9.7	14 56.3	24 36.7	12 26.1	23 8.6	2 47.8	27 24.1	0 26.7
6	14 53 32.0	12 33.6	2 51.6	24 24.9	2 41.2	16 3.6	24 57.5	12 19.9	23 13.7	2 47.8	27 23.8	0 25.2
7	14 57 28.6	13 31.6	2 48.5	6♌40.2	4 8.9	17 11.0	25 18.6	12 13.7	23 18.7	2 47.8	27 23.5	0 23.7
8	15 1 25.2	14 29.8	2 45.5	18 52.4	5 32.7	18 18.6	25 39.9	12 7.3	23 23.6	2 R 47.6	27 23.2	0 22.2
9	15 5 21.7	15 28.0	2 42.4	1♍ 7.2	6 52.4	19 26.2	26 1.6	12 .7	23 28.5	2 47.5	27 22.8	0 20.7
10	15 9 18.3	16 26.4	2 39.3	13 32.8	8 7.8	20 33.9	26 23.5	11 54.0	23 33.3	2 47.3	27 22.4	0 19.1
11	15 13 14.8	17 24.9	2 36.2	26 19.1	9 18.8	21 41.8	26 45.7	11 47.2	23 38.0	2 47.0	27 22.0	0 17.6
12	15 17 11.4	18 23.6	2 33.2	9♎36.5	10 25.3	22 49.8	27 8.1	11 40.3	23 42.7	2 46.7	27 21.5	0 16.0
13	15 21 7.9	19 22.4	2 30.1	23 34.3	11 27.2	23 57.9	27 30.8	11 33.3	23 47.3	2 46.3	27 21.0	0 14.4
14	15 25 4.5	20 21.3	2 27.0	8♏17.2	12 24.3	25 6.2	27 53.7	11 26.2	23 51.8	2 45.9	27 20.5	0 12.9
15	15 29 1.0	21 20.4	2 23.9	23 42.5	13 16.6	26 14.7	28 16.9	11 19.0	23 56.3	2 45.4	27 20.0	0 11.3
16	15 32 57.6	22 19.7	2 20.9	9♐36.8	14 3.9	27 23.3	28 40.3	11 11.6	24 .7	2 44.9	27 19.4	0 9.7
17	15 36 54.2	23 19.0	2 17.8	25 37.6	14 46.1	28 32.2	29 3.9	11 4.2	24 5.1	2 44.3	27 18.7	0 8.1
18	15 40 50.7	24 18.5	2 14.7	11♑19.8	15 23.2	29 41.2	29 27.7	10 56.7	24 9.4	2 43.7	27 18.1	0 6.5
19	15 44 47.3	25 18.2	2 11.6	26 23.3	15 55.1	0♉50.4	29 51.8	10 49.2	24 13.6	2 43.0	27 17.4	0 4.9
20	15 48 43.8	26 18.0	2 8.6	10♒38.6	16 21.8	1 59.8	0♍16.0	10 41.5	24 17.7	2 42.3	27 16.7	0 3.3
21	15 52 40.4	27 17.9	2 5.5	24 6.1	16 43.2	3 9.4	0 40.5	10 33.8	24 21.8	2 41.5	27 15.9	0 1.7
22	15 56 36.9	28 18.0	2 2.4	6♓53.2	16 59.3	4 19.2	1 5.1	10 26.0	24 25.8	2 40.7	27 15.2	0 .1
23	16 0 33.5	29 18.3	1 59.4	19 10.3	17 10.3	5 29.3	1 30.0	10 18.1	24 29.7	2 39.9	27 14.4	29♏58.5
24	16 4 30.0	0♊18.6	1 56.3	1♈ 9.0	17 16.1	6 39.5	1 55.1	10 10.2	24 33.6	2 39.0	27 13.5	29 56.9
25	16 8 26.6	1 19.1	1 53.2	12 59.7	17 16.8	7 50.0	2 20.3	10 2.3	24 37.4	2 38.0	27 12.7	29 55.3
26	16 12 23.2	2 19.7	1 50.2	24 51.2	17 R 12.7	9 .8	2 45.7	9 54.3	24 41.1	2 37.0	27 11.8	29 53.7
27	16 16 19.7	3 20.5	1 47.1	6♉50.1	17 3.9	10 11.8	3 11.3	9 46.2	24 44.7	2 35.9	27 10.9	29 52.1
28	16 20 16.3	4 21.4	1 44.0	18 59.7	16 50.8	11 23.1	3 37.2	9 38.2	24 48.3	2 34.9	27 10.0	29 50.5
29	16 24 12.8	5 22.4	1 41.0	1♊20.2	16 33.5	12 34.6	4 3.1	9 30.1	24 51.8	2 33.7	27 9.0	29 48.9
30	16 28 9.4	6 23.5	1 37.9	13 48.9	16 12.5	13 46.3	4 29.3	9 22.0	24 55.2	2 32.5	27 8.0	29 47.3
31	16 32 5.9	7 24.7	1 34.8	26 20.8	15 48.1	14 58.3	4 55.6	9 13.9	24 58.5	2 31.3	27 7.0	29 45.7

DECLINATION

DAY	EPHEM. SID. TIME h m s	☉ ° ′	☊ ° ′	☽ ° ′	☿ ° ′	♀ ° ′	♂ ° ′	♃ ° ′	♄ ° ′	♅ ° ′	♆ ° ′	♇ ° ′
1	14 33 49.3	14N52.1	0S14.0	17N 9.9	21N30.6	2N41.9	16N45.7	21S39.5	5S 8.7	20S34.5	20S29.2	6S27.4
4	14 45 38.9	15 45.9	0 13.9	19 9.3	22 51.7	4 5.4	16 20.9	21 37.7	5 2.6	20 34.5	20 29.3	6 26.3
7	14 57 28.6	16 37.4	0 13.8	13 44.0	23 50.7	5 28.3	15 55.0	21 35.6	4 56.8	20 34.6	20 29.4	6 25.2
10	15 9 18.3	17 26.4	0 13.8	2 30.7	24 28.8	6 50.3	15 28.0	21 33.5	4 51.2	20 34.8	20 29.5	6 24.1
13	15 21 7.9	18 12.8	0 13.7	10S48.1	24 47.7	8 11.2	15 .1	21 31.2	4 45.8	20 35.1	20 29.8	6 23.2
16	15 32 57.6	18 56.4	0 13.7	19 2.9	24 49.3	9 30.7	14 31.1	21 28.7	4 40.7	20 35.5	20 30.0	6 22.2
19	15 44 47.3	19 37.1	0 13.6	15 58.1	24 35.3	10 48.4	14 1.1	21 26.2	4 35.9	20 36.0	20 30.4	6 21.4
22	15 56 36.9	20 14.8	0 13.6	4 50.3	24 7.3	12 4.0	13 30.2	21 23.5	4 31.4	20 36.6	20 30.7	6 20.6
25	16 8 26.6	20 49.4	0 13.5	7N34.1	23 27.1	13 17.2	12 58.4	21 20.8	4 27.1	20 37.2	20 31.1	6 19.9
28	16 20 16.3	21 20.8	0 13.5	16 39.6	22 36.9	14 27.8	12 25.6	21 18.0	4 23.2	20 38.0	20 31.6	6 19.3
31	16 32 5.9	21 48.9	0 13.4	19 20.4	21 39.4	15 35.3	11 51.9	21 15.1	4 19.6	20 38.8	20 32.1	6 18.7

JUNE 1995

LONGITUDE

DAY	EPHEM. SID. TIME	☉	☊	☾	☿	♀	♂	♃	♄	♅	♆	♇
	h m s	° ′	° ′	° ′	° ′	° ′	° ′	° ′	° ′	° ′	° ′	° ′
1	16 36 2.5	10♊ 4.0	3♏46.2	8♋24.2	16♊22.0	18♉14.6	2♍55.7	10♐34.4	23♓43.9	0♒11.2	25♑15.1	28♏55.7
2	16 39 59.0	11 1.5	3 43.0	20 19.8	15 R 52.4	19 27.5	3 24.2	10 R 26.7	23 47.2	0 R 9.9	25 R 14.0	28 R 54.1
3	16 43 55.6	11 59.0	3 39.8	2♌22.1	15 21.0	20 40.4	3 52.8	10 19.1	23 50.4	0 8.6	25 13.0	28 52.5
4	16 47 52.2	12 56.5	3 36.7	14 33.8	14 48.4	21 53.3	4 21.7	10 11.4	23 53.6	0 7.2	25 11.9	28 50.9
5	16 51 48.7	13 54.0	3 33.5	26 58.3	14 15.0	23 6.2	4 50.8	10 3.8	23 56.7	0 5.8	25 10.8	28 49.3
6	16 55 45.3	14 51.4	3 30.3	9♍39.0	13 41.4	24 19.2	5 20.0	9 56.2	23 59.7	0 4.4	25 9.7	28 47.7
7	16 59 41.8	15 48.8	3 27.1	22 39.7	13 8.3	25 32.1	5 49.4	9 48.6	24 2.6	0 2.9	25 8.5	28 46.2
8	17 3 38.4	16 46.2	3 24.0	6♎ 3.7	12 36.2	26 45.1	6 19.0	9 41.0	24 5.4	0 1.4	25 7.4	28 44.6
9	17 7 34.9	17 43.6	3 20.8	19 53.5	12 5.6	27 58.0	6 48.8	9 33.5	24 8.1	29♑59.8	25 6.2	28 43.1
10	17 11 31.5	18 41.0	3 17.6	4♏ 9.8	11 37.1	29 11.0	7 18.7	9 26.0	24 10.7	29 58.3	25 5.0	28 41.5
11	17 15 28.1	19 38.3	3 14.4	18 51.1	11 11.1	0♊24.0	7 48.8	9 18.6	24 13.2	29 56.6	25 3.7	28 40.0
12	17 19 24.6	20 35.6	3 11.2	3♐52.6	10 48.0	1 37.0	8 19.1	9 11.2	24 15.7	29 55.0	25 2.5	28 38.5
13	17 23 21.2	21 32.9	3 8.1	19 6.6	10 28.4	2 50.0	8 49.5	9 3.9	24 18.0	29 53.3	25 1.2	28 37.0
14	17 27 17.7	22 30.2	3 4.9	4♑23.1	10 12.4	4 3.0	9 20.1	8 56.6	24 20.2	29 51.6	24 59.9	28 35.5
15	17 31 14.3	23 27.5	3 1.7	19 31.4	10 .3	5 16.0	9 50.8	8 49.4	24 22.4	29 49.8	24 58.6	28 34.0
16	17 35 10.8	24 24.8	2 58.5	4♒21.7	9 52.4	6 29.1	10 21.7	8 42.2	24 24.5	29 48.0	24 57.3	28 32.6
17	17 39 7.4	25 22.1	2 55.4	18 47.1	9 48.9	7 42.1	10 52.7	8 35.2	24 26.4	29 46.2	24 55.9	28 31.1
18	17 43 4.0	26 19.4	2 52.2	2♓43.8	9 D 49.9	8 55.3	11 23.9	8 28.2	24 28.3	29 44.4	24 54.6	28 29.8
19	17 47 .5	27 16.7	2 49.0	16 11.5	9 55.5	10 8.4	11 55.2	8 21.3	24 30.1	29 42.5	24 53.2	28 28.4
20	17 50 57.1	28 13.9	2 45.8	29 12.1	10 5.6	11 21.5	12 26.7	8 14.5	24 31.8	29 40.6	24 51.8	28 27.0
21	17 54 53.6	29 11.2	2 42.7	11♈49.4	10 20.4	12 34.6	12 58.3	8 7.7	24 33.4	29 38.7	24 50.4	28 25.6
22	17 58 50.2	0♋ 8.5	2 39.5	24 8.0	10 39.9	13 47.8	13 30.1	8 1.1	24 34.8	29 36.7	24 49.0	28 24.3
23	18 2 46.7	1 5.7	2 36.3	6♉12.8	11 4.0	15 1.0	14 2.0	7 54.6	24 36.2	29 34.7	24 47.6	28 22.9
24	18 6 43.3	2 3.0	2 33.1	18 8.3	11 32.7	16 14.1	14 34.1	7 48.1	24 37.5	29 32.7	24 46.1	28 21.6
25	18 10 39.9	3 .2	2 30.0	29 58.5	12 6.0	17 27.4	15 6.3	7 41.8	24 38.7	29 30.6	24 44.6	28 20.3
26	18 14 36.4	3 57.4	2 26.8	11♊46.8	12 43.7	18 40.6	15 38.6	7 35.6	24 39.8	29 28.5	24 43.1	28 19.1
27	18 18 33.0	4 54.7	2 23.6	23 36.1	13 25.9	19 53.8	16 11.0	7 29.5	24 40.7	29 26.4	24 41.6	28 17.8
28	18 22 29.5	5 51.9	2 20.4	5♋28.3	14 12.5	21 7.1	16 43.6	7 23.5	24 41.6	29 24.3	24 40.1	28 16.6
29	18 26 26.1	6 49.2	2 17.2	17 25.3	15 3.4	22 20.3	17 16.4	7 17.6	24 42.4	29 22.1	24 38.6	28 15.4
30	18 30 22.6	7 46.4	2 14.1	29 28.4	15 58.5	23 33.6	17 49.2	7 11.9	24 43.1	29 20.0	24 37.1	28 14.2

LATITUDE

DAY	EPHEM. SID. TIME	☉	☊	☾	☿	♀	♂	♃	♄	♅	♆	♇
1	16 36 2.5	0 .0	0 .0	4S37.9	1S25.5	1S21.8	1N20.1	0N48.2	1S58.8	0S33.3	0N33.3	13N55.5
4	16 47 52.2	0 .0	0 .0	5 6.3	2 16.6	1 16.9	1 16.2	0 47.9	1 59.5	0 33.4	0 33.3	13 54.9
7	16 59 41.8	0 .0	0 .0	3 28.8	3 2.3	1 11.5	1 12.5	0 47.5	2 .2	0 33.4	0 33.4	13 54.3
10	17 11 31.5	0 .0	0 .0	0 3.6	3 39.1	1 5.8	1 8.8	0 47.1	2 1.0	0 33.5	0 33.4	13 53.6
13	17 23 21.2	0 .0	0 .0	3N36.0	4 4.7	0 59.7	1 5.3	0 46.7	2 1.8	0 33.6	0 33.4	13 52.9
16	17 35 10.8	0 .0	0 .0	5 7.5	4 18.3	0 53.2	1 1.8	0 46.2	2 2.5	0 33.7	0 33.4	13 52.1
19	17 47 .5	0 .0	0 .0	3 48.9	4 20.4	0 46.6	0 58.4	0 45.7	2 3.3	0 33.8	0 33.4	13 51.2
22	17 58 50.2	0 .0	0 .0	0 53.7	4 12.2	0 39.6	0 55.1	0 45.2	2 4.1	0 33.8	0 33.3	13 50.2
25	18 10 39.9	0 .0	0 .0	2S13.7	3 55.1	0 32.5	0 51.8	0 44.7	2 4.9	0 33.9	0 33.3	13 49.2
28	18 22 29.5	0 .0	0 .0	4 27.5	3 30.9	0 25.3	0 48.6	0 44.1	2 5.7	0 33.9	0 33.3	13 48.1

RIGHT ASCENSION

DAY	EPHEM. SID. TIME	☉	☊	☾	☿	♀	♂	♃	♄	♅	♆	♇
1	16 36 2.5	8♊26.0	1♏31.8	8♋50.2	15♊20.9	16♉10.6	5♍22.0	9♐ 5.8	25♓ 1.8	2♒30.0	27♑ 5.9	29♏44.2
2	16 39 59.0	9 27.4	1 28.7	21 12.7	14 R 51.3	17 23.1	5 48.6	8 R 57.6	25 5.0	2 R 28.7	27 R 4.8	29 R 42.6
3	16 43 55.6	10 28.9	1 25.6	3♌25.9	14 19.8	18 36.0	6 15.4	8 49.5	25 8.1	2 27.3	27 3.7	29 41.0
4	16 47 52.2	11 30.5	1 22.6	15 30.8	13 47.1	19 49.0	6 42.3	8 41.4	25 11.1	2 25.9	27 2.6	29 39.4
5	16 51 48.7	12 32.2	1 19.5	27 31.8	13 13.7	21 2.4	7 9.4	8 33.2	25 14.0	2 24.5	27 1.4	29 37.9
6	16 55 45.3	13 33.9	1 16.5	9♍36.1	12 40.2	22 16.0	7 36.6	8 25.1	25 16.8	2 23.0	27 .2	29 36.3
7	16 59 41.8	14 35.8	1 13.4	21 53.2	12 7.2	23 29.9	8 4.0	8 17.1	25 19.6	2 21.5	26 59.0	29 34.8
8	17 3 38.4	15 37.7	1 10.3	4♎34.4	11 35.3	24 44.1	8 31.5	8 9.1	25 22.3	2 19.9	26 57.8	29 33.2
9	17 7 34.9	16 39.6	1 7.3	17 51.2	11 4.9	25 58.5	8 59.1	8 1.1	25 24.9	2 18.3	26 56.6	29 31.7
10	17 11 31.5	17 41.7	1 4.2	1♏53.3	10 36.7	27 13.3	9 26.8	7 53.1	25 27.4	2 16.6	26 55.3	29 30.2
11	17 15 28.1	18 43.8	1 1.1	16 45.2	10 11.0	28 28.2	9 54.7	7 45.2	25 29.8	2 14.9	26 54.0	29 28.7
12	17 19 24.6	19 45.9	0 58.1	2♐22.3	9 48.2	29 43.5	10 22.7	7 37.4	25 32.1	2 13.2	26 52.7	29 27.2
13	17 23 21.2	20 48.1	0 55.0	18 28.1	9 28.8	0♊59.1	10 50.8	7 29.6	25 34.4	2 11.5	26 51.3	29 25.7
14	17 27 17.7	21 50.3	0 52.0	4♑37.4	9 13.1	2 14.9	11 19.1	7 21.8	25 36.6	2 9.7	26 50.0	29 24.2
15	17 31 14.3	22 52.6	0 48.9	20 23.2	9 1.3	3 30.9	11 47.4	7 14.2	25 38.6	2 7.8	26 48.6	29 22.8
16	17 35 10.8	23 54.9	0 45.9	5♒26.3	8 53.6	4 47.3	12 15.9	7 6.6	25 40.6	2 6.0	26 47.2	29 21.3
17	17 39 7.4	24 57.2	0 42.8	19 39.0	8 50.2	6 3.9	12 44.5	6 59.1	25 42.5	2 4.1	26 45.8	29 19.9
18	17 43 4.0	25 59.6	0 39.7	3♓ 3.6	8 D 51.4	7 20.8	13 13.2	6 51.7	25 44.4	2 2.2	26 44.4	29 18.5
19	17 47 .5	27 2.0	0 36.7	15 48.7	8 57.0	8 37.9	13 42.0	6 44.4	25 46.1	2 .2	26 43.0	29 17.1
20	17 50 57.1	28 4.4	0 33.6	28 5.7	9 7.3	9 55.3	14 11.0	6 37.1	25 47.8	1 58.2	26 41.5	29 15.7
21	17 54 53.6	29 6.8	0 30.6	10♈ 6.2	9 22.3	11 12.8	14 40.0	6 30.0	25 49.3	1 56.2	26 40.0	29 14.4
22	17 58 50.2	0♋ 9.2	0 27.5	22 .7	9 41.9	12 30.7	15 9.1	6 22.9	25 50.8	1 54.1	26 38.5	29 13.0
23	18 2 46.7	1 11.6	0 24.5	3♉57.4	10 6.3	13 48.7	15 38.4	6 16.0	25 52.2	1 52.1	26 37.0	29 11.7
24	18 6 43.3	2 14.0	0 21.4	16 2.1	10 35.3	15 6.9	16 7.8	6 9.1	25 53.5	1 49.9	26 35.5	29 10.3
25	18 10 39.9	3 16.4	0 18.4	28 17.3	11 9.0	16 25.4	16 37.2	6 2.4	25 54.7	1 47.8	26 33.9	29 9.0
26	18 14 36.4	4 18.7	0 15.3	10♊42.4	11 47.4	17 44.0	17 6.8	5 55.8	25 55.8	1 45.6	26 32.4	29 7.7
27	18 18 33.0	5 21.0	0 12.2	23 13.7	12 30.5	19 2.9	17 36.5	5 49.4	25 56.8	1 43.4	26 30.8	29 6.5
28	18 22 29.5	6 23.3	0 9.2	5♋46.0	13 18.2	20 21.8	18 6.3	5 43.0	25 57.7	1 41.2	26 29.2	29 5.2
29	18 26 26.1	7 25.6	0 6.1	18 13.6	14 10.5	21 41.0	18 36.2	5 36.8	25 58.5	1 39.0	26 27.6	29 4.0
30	18 30 22.6	8 27.7	0 3.1	0♌32.6	15 7.4	23 .3	19 6.2	5 30.7	25 59.2	1 36.7	26 26.0	29 2.8

DECLINATION

DAY	EPHEM. SID. TIME	☉	☊	☾	☿	♀	♂	♃	♄	♅	♆	♇
1	16 36 2.5	21N57.5	0S13.4	18N32.9	21N19.3	15N57.0	11N40.4	21S14.1	4S18.4	20S39.1	20S32.3	6S18.5
4	16 47 52.2	22 21.0	0 13.3	11 34.4	20 18.6	16 60.0	11 5.6	21 11.2	4 15.2	20 40.0	20 32.8	6 18.1
7	16 59 41.8	22 40.9	0 13.3	0S17.2	19 21.6	17 59.1	10 29.9	21 8.2	4 12.4	20 41.0	20 33.5	6 17.7
10	17 11 31.5	22 57.3	0 13.2	12 57.8	18 33.5	18 54.2	9 53.4	21 5.3	4 9.8	20 42.1	20 34.1	6 17.5
13	17 23 21.2	23 10.1	0 13.1	19 24.1	17 58.8	19 44.9	9 16.1	21 2.3	4 7.6	20 43.2	20 34.8	6 17.3
16	17 35 10.8	23 19.2	0 13.1	14 11.1	17 40.2	20 30.9	8 38.1	20 59.5	4 5.8	20 44.4	20 35.5	6 17.2
19	17 47 .5	23 24.6	0 13.0	1 55.8	17 38.6	21 12.0	7 59.4	20 56.7	4 4.2	20 45.6	20 36.2	6 17.2
22	17 58 50.2	23 26.3	0 13.0	10N11.5	17 53.0	21 47.9	7 20.0	20 54.0	4 3.1	20 46.9	20 37.0	6 17.3
25	18 10 39.9	23 24.2	0 12.9	17 58.0	18 21.3	22 18.4	6 39.9	20 51.4	4 2.3	20 48.2	20 37.8	6 17.5
28	18 22 29.5	23 18.5	0 12.9	18 52.2	19 .7	22 43.2	5 59.1	20 49.0	4 1.8	20 49.6	20 38.6	6 17.8

JULY 1995

DAY	EPHEM. SID. TIME	LONGITUDE										
		☉	☊	☽	☿	♀	♂	♃	♄	♅	♆	♇
	h m s	° ′	° ′	° ′	° ′	° ′	° ′	° ′	° ′	° ′	° ′	° ′
1	18 34 19.2	8♋43.6	2♏10.9	11♌38.9	16♊57.8	24♊46.9	18♍22.2	7♐ 6.3	24♓43.7	29♑17.8	24♑35.5	28♏13.1
2	18 38 15.8	9 40.8	2 7.7	23 58.6	18 1.3	26 .2	18 55.3	7R .9	24 44.1	29R15.6	24R34.0	28R11.9
3	18 42 12.3	10 38.0	2 4.5	6♍29.2	19 8.8	27 13.6	19 28.6	6 55.5	24 44.5	29 13.3	24 32.4	28 10.8
4	18 46 8.9	11 35.3	2 1.4	19 13.2	20 20.4	28 26.9	20 2.0	6 50.4	24 44.8	29 11.1	24 30.9	28 9.7
5	18 50 5.4	12 32.5	1 58.2	2♎13.4	21 36.0	29 40.3	20 35.4	6 45.3	24 45.0	29 8.8	24 29.3	28 8.7
6	18 54 2.0	13 29.7	1 55.0	15 32.7	22 55.4	0♋53.7	21 9.1	6 40.5	24 45.1	29 6.6	24 27.7	28 7.6
7	18 57 58.5	14 26.8	1 51.8	29 13.8	24 18.8	2 7.1	21 42.8	6 35.7	24R45.0	29 4.3	24 26.1	28 6.6
8	19 1 55.1	15 24.0	1 48.7	13♏18.4	25 46.0	3 20.5	22 16.6	6 31.2	24 44.9	29 2.0	24 24.5	28 5.6
9	19 5 51.7	16 21.3	1 45.5	27 46.4	27 16.9	4 33.9	22 50.6	6 26.8	24 44.7	28 59.7	24 23.0	28 4.7
10	19 9 48.2	17 18.5	1 42.3	12♐34.9	28 51.5	5 47.4	23 24.7	6 22.5	24 44.4	28 57.3	24 21.3	28 3.8
11	19 13 44.8	18 15.6	1 39.1	27 38.4	0♋29.7	7 .8	23 58.9	6 18.4	24 44.0	28 55.0	24 19.7	28 2.9
12	19 17 41.3	19 12.8	1 35.9	12♑48.1	2 11.4	8 14.3	24 33.1	6 14.5	24 43.5	28 52.6	24 18.1	28 2.0
13	19 21 37.9	20 10.0	1 32.8	27 54.0	3 56.4	9 27.8	25 7.5	6 10.7	24 42.8	28 50.3	24 16.5	28 1.2
14	19 25 34.4	21 7.2	1 29.6	12♒45.8	5 44.7	10 41.3	25 42.0	6 7.1	24 42.1	28 47.9	24 14.9	28 .4
15	19 29 31.0	22 4.4	1 26.4	27 15.3	7 36.0	11 54.9	26 16.7	6 3.6	24 41.3	28 45.5	24 13.3	27 59.6
16	19 33 27.6	23 1.6	1 23.2	11♓17.2	9 30.2	13 8.4	26 51.4	6 .4	24 40.4	28 43.1	24 11.6	27 58.8
17	19 37 24.1	23 58.8	1 20.1	24 49.7	11 27.1	14 22.0	27 26.2	5 57.3	24 39.4	28 40.7	24 10.0	27 58.1
18	19 41 20.7	24 56.1	1 16.9	7♈53.9	13 26.3	15 35.6	28 1.1	5 54.3	24 38.3	28 38.4	24 8.4	27 57.4
19	19 45 17.2	25 53.3	1 13.7	20 33.2	15 27.6	16 49.2	28 36.2	5 51.6	24 37.0	28 35.9	24 6.8	27 56.7
20	19 49 13.8	26 50.5	1 10.5	2♉52.3	17 30.7	18 2.9	29 11.3	5 49.0	24 35.7	28 33.5	24 5.1	27 56.0
21	19 53 10.3	27 47.8	1 7.4	14 56.2	19 35.3	19 16.5	29 46.5	5 46.6	24 34.3	28 31.1	24 3.5	27 55.4
22	19 57 6.9	28 45.1	1 4.2	26 50.4	21 41.1	20 30.2	0♎21.9	5 44.3	24 32.8	28 28.7	24 1.9	27 54.8
23	20 1 3.4	29 42.4	1 1.0	8♊39.8	23 47.7	21 44.0	0 57.4	5 42.3	24 31.2	28 26.3	24 .3	27 54.3
24	20 5 .0	0♌39.7	0 57.8	20 28.5	25 54.9	22 57.7	1 32.9	5 40.4	24 29.5	28 23.9	23 58.7	27 53.8
25	20 8 56.6	1 37.0	0 54.6	2♋20.3	28 2.4	24 11.4	2 8.6	5 38.7	24 27.8	28 21.5	23 57.1	27 53.3
26	20 12 53.1	2 34.3	0 51.5	14 17.8	0♌ 9.8	25 25.2	2 44.3	5 37.2	24 25.9	28 19.1	23 55.4	27 52.8
27	20 16 49.7	3 31.6	0 48.3	26 22.9	2 16.9	26 39.0	3 20.2	5 35.9	24 23.9	28 16.7	23 53.8	27 52.4
28	20 20 46.2	4 29.0	0 45.1	8♌36.9	4 23.4	27 52.8	3 56.2	5 34.7	24 21.8	28 14.3	23 52.3	27 52.0
29	20 24 42.8	5 26.3	0 41.9	21 .5	6 29.3	29 6.7	4 32.3	5 33.8	24 19.7	28 11.9	23 50.7	27 51.6
30	20 28 39.3	6 23.8	0 38.8	3♍34.1	8 34.2	0♌20.6	5 8.5	5 33.1	24 17.5	28 9.6	23 49.1	27 51.3
31	20 32 35.9	7 21.2	0 35.6	16 18.4	10 38.0	1 34.4	5 44.7	5 32.5	24 15.2	28 7.2	23 47.6	27 51.0
		LATITUDE										
1	18 34 19.2	0 .0	0 .0	4S59.6	3S 1.0	0S17.9	0N45.5	0N43.5	2S 6.5	0S34.0	0N33.3	13N47.0
4	18 46 8.9	0 .0	0 .0	3 29.6	2 26.8	0 10.5	0 42.4	0 42.9	2 7.3	0 34.0	0 33.3	13 45.8
7	18 57 58.5	0 .0	0 .0	0 18.7	1 49.7	0 3.1	0 39.4	0 42.3	2 8.1	0 34.1	0 33.3	13 44.6
10	19 9 48.2	0 .0	0 .0	3N14.5	1 11.2	0N 4.2	0 36.5	0 41.7	2 8.8	0 34.1	0 33.2	13 43.3
13	19 21 37.9	0 .0	0 .0	5 .4	0 32.8	0 11.5	0 33.6	0 41.1	2 9.6	0 34.2	0 33.2	13 42.0
16	19 33 27.6	0 .0	0 .0	3 53.1	0N 3.7	0 18.7	0 30.8	0 40.5	2 10.4	0 34.2	0 33.2	13 40.6
19	19 45 17.2	0 .0	0 .0	0 58.2	0 36.5	0 25.6	0 28.0	0 39.8	2 11.2	0 34.2	0 33.2	13 39.2
22	19 57 6.9	0 .0	0 .0	2S 9.3	1 4.0	0 32.4	0 25.2	0 39.2	2 11.9	0 34.2	0 33.1	13 37.8
25	20 8 56.6	0 .0	0 .0	4 23.3	1 24.9	0 38.9	0 22.5	0 38.5	2 12.7	0 34.3	0 33.1	13 36.3
28	20 20 46.2	0 .0	0 .0	4 57.0	1 38.7	0 45.1	0 19.9	0 37.9	2 13.4	0 34.3	0 33.0	13 34.9
31	20 32 35.9	0 .0	0 .0	3 28.6	1 45.6	0 50.9	0 17.3	0 37.2	2 14.1	0 34.3	0 33.0	13 33.3
		RIGHT ASCENSION										
1	18 34 19.2	9♋29.9	0♏ .0	12♌41.7	16♊ 8.9	24♊19.7	19♍36.3	5♐24.8	25♓59.9	1♒34.4	26♑24.4	29♏ 1.6
2	18 38 15.8	10 31.9	29♎57.0	24 42.6	17 15.0	25 39.3	20 6.5	5R19.0	26 .4	1R32.1	26R22.7	29R .4
3	18 42 12.3	11 33.9	29 53.9	6♍40.6	18 25.6	26 58.9	20 36.7	5 13.4	26 .9	1 29.8	26 21.1	28 59.3
4	18 46 8.9	12 35.9	29 50.9	18 43.3	19 40.8	28 18.7	21 7.1	5 7.9	26 1.2	1 27.4	26 19.4	28 58.2
5	18 50 5.4	13 37.7	29 47.8	1♎ .8	21 .5	29 38.5	21 37.6	5 2.5	26 1.5	1 25.1	26 17.8	28 57.1
6	18 54 2.0	14 39.4	29 44.8	13 44.0	22 24.7	0♋58.4	22 8.2	4 57.4	26 1.7	1 22.7	26 16.1	28 56.0
7	18 57 58.5	15 41.1	29 41.7	27 3.8	23 53.4	2 18.4	22 38.9	4 52.3	26 1.8	1 20.3	26 14.4	28 54.9
8	19 1 55.1	16 42.7	29 38.7	11♏ 8.6	25 26.5	3 38.4	23 9.6	4 47.5	26R 1.7	1 17.9	26 12.8	28 53.9
9	19 5 51.7	17 44.2	29 35.6	26 .9	27 4.1	4 58.5	23 40.5	4 42.8	26 1.7	1 15.5	26 11.1	28 53.0
10	19 9 48.2	18 45.6	29 32.6	11♐33.8	28 46.0	6 18.6	24 11.5	4 38.3	26 1.5	1 13.0	26 9.4	28 52.0
11	19 13 44.8	19 46.8	29 29.5	27 30.3	0♋32.1	7 38.6	24 42.5	4 33.9	26 1.2	1 10.6	26 7.8	28 51.0
12	19 17 41.3	20 47.9	29 26.5	13♑26.1	2 22.4	8 58.7	25 13.7	4 29.8	26 .8	1 8.1	26 6.1	28 50.1
13	19 21 37.9	21 49.0	29 23.4	28 57.3	4 16.6	10 18.7	25 44.9	4 25.7	26 .4	1 5.7	26 4.4	28 49.2
14	19 25 34.4	22 49.9	29 20.4	13♒48.2	6 14.5	11 38.7	26 16.2	4 21.9	25 59.8	1 3.2	26 2.6	28 48.3
15	19 29 31.0	23 50.7	29 17.4	27 53.2	8 16.0	12 58.6	26 47.6	4 18.2	25 59.2	1 .7	26 .9	28 47.5
16	19 33 27.6	24 51.4	29 14.3	11♓15.4	10 20.7	14 18.5	27 19.1	4 14.7	25 58.4	0 58.2	25 59.2	28 46.6
17	19 37 24.1	25 51.9	29 11.3	24 3.2	12 28.4	15 38.3	27 50.7	4 11.4	25 57.6	0 55.7	25 57.5	28 45.8
18	19 41 20.7	26 52.3	29 8.2	6♈26.9	14 38.6	16 58.0	28 22.4	4 8.3	25 56.7	0 53.2	25 55.8	28 45.1
19	19 45 17.2	27 52.6	29 5.2	18 36.9	16 51.0	18 17.7	28 54.2	4 5.4	25 55.7	0 50.6	25 54.1	28 44.3
20	19 49 13.8	28 52.8	29 2.1	0♉42.2	19 5.2	19 37.2	29 26.1	4 2.6	25 54.6	0 48.1	25 52.4	28 43.6
21	19 53 10.3	29 52.8	28 59.1	12 49.7	21 20.6	20 56.5	29 58.1	4 .0	25 53.4	0 45.6	25 50.7	28 42.9
22	19 57 6.9	0♌52.7	28 56.0	25 3.9	23 36.9	22 15.8	0♎30.1	3 57.6	25 52.1	0 43.1	25 49.0	28 42.2
23	20 1 3.4	1 52.5	28 53.0	7♊26.3	25 53.6	23 34.9	1 2.3	3 55.4	25 50.7	0 40.6	25 47.3	28 41.6
24	20 5 .0	2 52.1	28 50.0	19 55.5	28 10.2	24 53.8	1 34.6	3 53.4	25 49.3	0 38.0	25 45.6	28 41.0
25	20 8 56.6	3 51.6	28 46.9	2♋28.0	0♌26.4	26 12.6	2 6.9	3 51.6	25 47.7	0 35.5	25 43.9	28 40.4
26	20 12 53.1	4 50.9	28 43.9	14 59.3	2 41.7	27 31.1	2 39.4	3 50.0	25 46.1	0 33.0	25 42.2	28 39.9
27	20 16 49.7	5 50.1	28 40.8	27 25.1	4 55.8	28 49.5	3 12.0	3 48.5	25 44.4	0 30.5	25 40.5	28 39.4
28	20 20 46.2	6 49.1	28 37.8	9♌42.9	7 8.5	0♌ 7.7	3 44.7	3 47.3	25 42.6	0 28.0	25 38.8	28 38.9
29	20 24 42.8	7 48.0	28 34.7	21 52.7	9 19.5	1 25.7	4 17.4	3 46.3	25 40.7	0 25.5	25 37.2	28 38.4
30	20 28 39.3	8 46.8	28 31.7	3♍57.6	11 28.6	2 43.5	4 50.3	3 45.5	25 38.7	0 23.0	25 35.6	28 38.1
31	20 32 35.9	9 45.4	28 28.7	16 2.9	13 35.5	4 1.0	5 23.3	3 44.8	25 36.7	0 20.5	25 33.9	28 37.7
		DECLINATION										
1	18 34 19.2	23N 9.0	0S12.8	12N29.3	19N47.8	23N 2.2	5N17.8	20S46.8	4S 1.8	20S51.0	20S39.4	6S18.1
4	18 46 8.9	22 55.9	0 12.8	1 3.1	20 38.7	23 15.2	4 35.9	20 44.7	4 2.0	20 52.5	20 40.2	6 18.6
7	18 57 58.5	22 39.3	0 12.7	11S29.5	21 29.3	23 22.1	3 53.4	20 42.8	4 2.7	20 53.9	20 41.1	6 19.2
10	19 9 48.2	22 19.1	0 12.6	19 5.3	22 14.8	23 22.9	3 10.4	20 41.2	4 3.7	20 55.4	20 42.0	6 19.8
13	19 21 37.9	21 55.4	0 12.6	15 40.2	22 40.9	23 17.5	2 27.0	20 39.8	4 5.0	20 56.9	20 42.8	6 20.6
16	19 33 27.6	21 28.4	0 12.5	3 44.1	23 9.5	23 5.9	1 43.2	20 38.6	4 6.7	20 58.4	20 43.7	6 21.4
19	19 45 17.2	20 58.0	0 12.5	8N55.6	23 8.8	22 48.2	0 59.0	20 37.7	4 8.7	20 59.9	20 44.6	6 22.4
22	19 57 6.9	20 24.5	0 12.4	17 21.1	22 44.6	22 24.4	0 14.4	20 37.1	4 11.1	21 1.4	20 45.5	6 23.4
25	20 8 56.6	19 47.9	0 12.3	19 1.8	21 56.3	21 54.7	0S30.5	20 36.8	4 13.8	21 2.9	20 46.3	6 24.5
28	20 20 46.2	19 8.3	0 12.3	13 19.4	20 45.5	21 19.2	1 15.6	20 36.7	4 16.8	21 4.3	20 47.2	6 25.7
31	20 32 35.9	18 25.9	0 12.2	2 11.9	19 15.7	20 38.1	2 1.0	20 37.0	4 20.1	21 5.8	20 48.1	6 27.0

AUGUST 1995

DAY	EPHEM. SID. TIME	☉	☊	☽	☿	♀	♂	♃	♄	♅	♆	♇
	h m s	° ′	° ′	° ′	° ′	° ′	° ′	° ′	° ′	° ′	° ′	° ′
		LONGITUDE										
1	20 36 32.4	8♌18.5	0♏32.4	29♍14.1	12♌40.7	2♌48.3	6♎21.1	5♐32.1	24♓12.7	28♑ 4.9	23♑46.0	27♏50.8
2	20 40 29.0	9 16.0	0 29.2	12♎22.7	14 42.0	4 2.2	6 57.6	5 R 31.8	24 R 10.2	28 R 2.5	23 R 44.4	27 R 50.5
3	20 44 25.6	10 13.4	0 26.0	25 45.7	16 42.0	5 16.2	7 34.1	5 31.8	24 7.6	28 .2	23 42.9	27 50.3
4	20 48 22.1	11 10.8	0 22.9	9♏24.9	18 40.5	6 30.1	8 10.7	5 D 32.0	24 5.0	27 57.9	23 41.4	27 50.2
5	20 52 18.7	12 8.2	0 19.7	23 21.6	20 37.5	7 44.1	8 47.5	5 32.3	24 2.2	27 55.5	23 39.8	27 50.0
6	20 56 15.2	13 5.7	0 16.5	7♐36.2	22 33.1	8 58.1	9 24.3	5 32.8	23 59.4	27 53.2	23 38.3	27 49.9
7	21 0 11.8	14 3.1	0 13.3	22 7.1	24 27.1	10 12.0	10 1.2	5 33.5	23 56.5	27 51.0	23 36.8	27 49.9
8	21 4 8.3	15 .6	0 10.2	6♑50.5	26 19.5	11 26.0	10 38.2	5 34.4	23 53.5	27 48.7	23 35.3	27 49.8
9	21 8 4.9	15 58.1	0 7.0	21 40.4	28 10.4	12 40.1	11 15.3	5 35.5	23 50.4	27 46.4	23 33.9	27 49.8
10	21 12 1.4	16 55.6	0 3.8	6♒28.8	29 59.7	13 54.1	11 52.5	5 36.7	23 47.2	27 44.2	23 32.4	27 D 49.9
11	21 15 58.0	17 53.1	0 .6	21 7.2	1♍47.5	15 8.2	12 29.8	5 38.2	23 44.0	27 42.0	23 31.0	27 49.9
12	21 19 54.5	18 50.6	29♎57.5	5♓28.0	3 33.8	16 22.3	13 7.1	5 39.8	23 40.7	27 39.8	23 29.5	27 50.0
13	21 23 51.1	19 48.2	29 54.3	19 25.6	5 18.5	17 36.4	13 44.6	5 41.6	23 37.3	27 37.6	23 28.1	27 50.2
14	21 27 47.7	20 45.8	29 51.1	2♈57.1	7 1.7	18 50.5	14 22.1	5 43.5	23 33.9	27 35.5	23 26.7	27 50.3
15	21 31 44.2	21 43.4	29 47.9	16 2.5	8 43.5	20 4.6	14 59.7	5 45.7	23 30.4	27 33.3	23 25.3	27 50.5
16	21 35 40.8	22 41.0	29 44.7	28 43.9	10 23.7	21 18.8	15 37.4	5 48.0	23 26.8	27 31.2	23 23.9	27 50.8
17	21 39 37.3	23 38.6	29 41.6	11♉ 5.2	12 2.5	22 32.9	16 15.2	5 50.5	23 23.2	27 29.2	23 22.6	27 51.0
18	21 43 33.9	24 36.3	29 38.4	23 11.0	13 39.8	23 47.1	16 53.1	5 53.2	23 19.5	27 27.1	23 21.3	27 51.3
19	21 47 30.4	25 34.0	29 35.2	5♊ 6.8	15 15.6	25 1.4	17 31.1	5 56.1	23 15.7	27 25.1	23 19.9	27 51.7
20	21 51 27.0	26 31.8	29 32.0	16 57.6	16 50.0	26 15.6	18 9.2	5 59.1	23 11.9	27 23.1	23 18.7	27 52.1
21	21 55 23.5	27 29.5	29 28.9	28 48.4	18 23.0	27 29.9	18 47.3	6 2.3	23 8.1	27 21.1	23 17.4	27 52.5
22	21 59 20.1	28 27.3	29 25.7	10♋43.6	19 54.5	28 44.2	19 25.6	6 5.7	23 4.1	27 19.2	23 16.2	27 52.9
23	22 3 16.6	29 25.1	29 22.5	22 46.6	21 24.5	29 58.4	20 3.9	6 9.3	23 .1	27 17.2	23 14.9	27 53.4
24	22 7 13.2	0♍23.0	29 19.3	5♌ .1	22 53.1	1♍12.8	20 42.3	6 13.0	22 56.1	27 15.4	23 13.7	27 53.9
25	22 11 9.7	1 20.8	29 16.1	17 25.9	24 20.2	2 27.1	21 20.8	6 16.9	22 52.0	27 13.5	23 12.5	27 54.4
26	22 15 6.3	2 18.7	29 13.0	0♍ 4.6	25 45.8	3 41.4	21 59.4	6 20.9	22 47.8	27 11.7	23 11.3	27 55.0
27	22 19 2.8	3 16.6	29 9.8	12 56.2	27 9.9	4 55.8	22 38.0	6 25.2	22 43.6	27 9.9	23 10.2	27 55.6
28	22 22 59.4	4 14.6	29 6.6	26 .3	28 32.4	6 10.1	23 16.8	6 29.6	22 39.4	27 8.1	23 9.0	27 56.3
29	22 26 56.0	5 12.5	29 3.4	9♎16.1	29 53.4	7 24.5	23 55.6	6 34.1	22 35.1	27 6.4	23 7.9	27 56.9
30	22 30 52.5	6 10.5	29 .3	22 42.9	1♎12.8	8 38.9	24 34.6	6 38.8	22 30.8	27 4.7	23 6.9	27 57.6
31	22 34 49.1	7 8.5	28 57.1	6♏20.4	2 30.5	9 53.3	25 13.6	6 43.7	22 26.5	27 3.0	23 5.8	27 58.4
		LATITUDE										
1	20 36 32.4	0 .0	0 .0	2 S 34.6	1 N 46.4	0 N 52.8	0 N 16.4	0 N 37.0	2 S 14.3	0 S 34.3	0 N 33.0	13 N 32.8
4	20 48 22.1	0 .0	0 .0	0 N 50.2	1 44.9	0 58.2	0 13.9	0 36.4	2 15.0	0 34.3	0 32.9	13 31.3
7	21 0 11.8	0 .0	0 .0	3 59.5	1 38.0	1 3.1	0 11.4	0 35.7	2 15.6	0 34.3	0 32.9	13 29.7
10	21 12 1.4	0 .0	0 .0	4 59.4	1 26.4	1 7.6	0 8.9	0 35.1	2 16.2	0 34.3	0 32.8	13 28.2
13	21 23 51.1	0 .0	0 .0	3 13.0	1 11.0	1 11.7	0 6.5	0 34.4	2 16.8	0 34.3	0 32.8	13 26.6
16	21 35 40.8	0 .0	0 .0	0 .2	0 52.4	1 15.2	0 4.1	0 33.8	2 17.4	0 34.2	0 32.7	13 25.0
19	21 47 30.4	0 .0	0 .0	3 S 1.2	0 31.2	1 18.2	0 1.8	0 33.2	2 17.9	0 34.2	0 32.6	13 23.4
22	21 59 20.1	0 .0	0 .0	4 50.0	0 8.0	1 20.7	0 S .5	0 32.6	2 18.4	0 34.2	0 32.6	13 21.8
25	22 11 9.7	0 .0	0 .0	4 47.5	0 S 16.8	1 22.6	0 2.8	0 32.0	2 18.9	0 34.2	0 32.5	13 20.3
28	22 22 59.4	0 .0	0 .0	2 41.1	0 42.8	1 24.0	0 5.1	0 31.4	2 19.3	0 34.1	0 32.4	13 18.7
31	22 34 49.1	0 .0	0 .0	0 N 47.2	1 9.5	1 24.8	0 7.3	0 30.8	2 19.7	0 34.1	0 32.4	13 17.2
		RIGHT ASCENSION										
1	20 36 32.4	10♌43.8	28♎25.6	28♍16.4	15♌40.2	5♌18.3	5♎56.4	3♐44.3	25♓34.6	0♒18.0	25♑32.3	28♏37.3
2	20 40 29.0	11 42.1	28 22.6	10♎47.3	17 42.6	6 35.4	6 29.6	3 R 44.1	25 R 32.3	0 R 15.6	25 R 30.6	28 R 37.0
3	20 44 25.6	12 40.2	28 19.5	23 44.9	19 42.6	7 52.2	7 2.8	3 44.0	25 30.0	0 13.1	25 29.0	28 36.7
4	20 48 22.1	13 38.2	28 16.5	7♏17.5	21 40.3	9 8.7	7 36.2	3 D 44.1	25 27.7	0 10.7	25 27.4	28 36.4
5	20 52 18.7	14 36.0	28 13.5	21 29.9	23 35.5	10 25.0	8 9.7	3 44.4	25 25.2	0 8.2	25 25.8	28 36.2
6	20 56 15.2	15 33.6	28 10.4	6♐20.6	25 28.3	11 41.0	8 43.3	3 44.9	25 22.7	0 5.8	25 24.2	28 35.9
7	21 0 11.8	16 31.1	28 7.4	21 40.2	27 18.7	12 56.8	9 17.0	3 45.6	25 20.1	0 3.4	25 22.6	28 35.8
8	21 4 8.3	17 28.4	28 4.4	7♑11.9	29 6.8	14 12.3	9 50.8	3 46.5	25 17.4	0 1.1	25 21.0	28 35.6
9	21 8 4.9	18 25.6	28 1.3	22 35.9	0♍52.6	15 27.6	10 24.7	3 47.6	25 14.7	29♑58.7	25 19.5	28 35.5
10	21 12 1.4	19 22.6	27 58.3	7♒35.1	2 36.2	16 42.5	10 58.7	3 48.9	25 11.9	29 56.3	25 18.0	28 35.4
11	21 15 58.0	20 19.5	27 55.3	21 59.5	4 17.6	17 57.2	11 32.8	3 50.3	25 9.0	29 54.0	25 16.4	28 35.4
12	21 19 54.5	21 16.3	27 52.2	5♓46.9	5 56.9	19 11.6	12 7.0	3 52.0	25 6.0	29 51.7	25 14.9	28 35.4
13	21 23 51.1	22 12.9	27 49.2	19 1.2	7 34.2	20 25.8	12 41.4	3 53.8	25 3.0	29 49.4	25 13.4	28 35.4
14	21 27 47.7	23 9.4	27 46.1	1♈49.7	9 9.4	21 39.7	13 15.8	3 55.9	24 59.9	29 47.2	25 12.0	28 35.4
15	21 31 44.2	24 5.7	27 43.1	14 20.6	10 42.7	22 53.3	13 50.4	3 58.1	24 56.8	29 44.9	25 10.5	28 D 35.5
16	21 35 40.8	25 1.9	27 40.1	26 42.0	12 14.2	24 6.7	14 25.0	4 .5	24 53.5	29 42.7	25 9.1	28 35.6
17	21 39 37.3	25 58.0	27 37.0	9♉ .5	13 43.8	25 19.8	14 59.8	4 3.1	24 50.3	29 40.5	25 7.6	28 35.8
18	21 43 33.9	26 54.0	27 34.0	21 20.6	15 11.7	26 32.7	15 34.7	4 5.9	24 46.9	29 38.3	25 6.2	28 35.9
19	21 47 30.4	27 49.8	27 31.0	3♊44.9	16 37.9	27 45.2	16 9.7	4 8.9	24 43.5	29 36.2	25 4.9	28 36.1
20	21 51 27.0	28 45.6	27 27.9	16 13.4	18 2.5	28 57.6	16 44.9	4 12.1	24 40.1	29 34.1	25 3.5	28 36.4
21	21 55 23.5	29 41.2	27 24.9	28 44.5	19 25.4	0♍ 9.7	17 20.2	4 15.4	24 36.6	29 32.0	25 2.2	28 36.7
22	21 59 20.1	0♍36.7	27 21.9	11♋15.4	20 46.7	1 21.6	17 55.6	4 18.9	24 33.0	29 30.0	25 .9	28 37.0
23	22 3 16.6	1 32.0	27 18.9	23 43.2	22 6.4	2 33.2	18 31.1	4 22.6	24 29.4	29 28.0	24 59.6	28 37.3
24	22 7 13.2	2 27.3	27 15.8	6♌ 6.0	23 24.6	3 44.6	19 6.8	4 26.5	24 25.8	29 26.0	24 58.3	28 37.7
25	22 11 9.7	3 22.4	27 12.8	18 23.6	24 41.4	4 55.7	19 42.5	4 30.6	24 22.0	29 24.0	24 57.0	28 38.1
26	22 15 6.3	4 17.5	27 9.8	0♍38.1	25 56.6	6 6.6	20 18.4	4 34.8	24 18.3	29 22.1	24 55.8	28 38.5
27	22 19 2.8	5 12.4	27 6.7	12 53.6	27 10.3	7 17.3	20 54.5	4 39.2	24 14.5	29 20.2	24 54.6	28 39.0
28	22 22 59.4	6 7.3	27 3.7	25 16.1	28 22.6	8 27.8	21 30.6	4 43.8	24 10.6	29 18.3	24 53.4	28 39.5
29	22 26 56.0	7 2.1	27 .7	7♎52.7	29 33.4	9 38.1	22 6.9	4 48.6	24 6.7	29 16.5	24 52.2	28 40.0
30	22 30 52.5	7 56.7	26 57.6	20 50.9	0♎42.7	10 48.2	22 43.3	4 53.6	24 2.8	29 14.7	24 51.1	28 40.6
31	22 34 49.1	8 51.3	26 54.6	4♏17.0	1 50.4	11 58.1	23 19.9	4 58.7	23 58.8	29 13.0	24 50.0	28 41.2
		DECLINATION										
1	20 36 32.4	18 N 11.2	0 S 12.2	2 S 3.6	18 N 42.2	20 N 23.2	2 S 16.2	20 S 37.1	4 S 21.2	21 S 6.2	20 S 48.4	6 S 27.4
4	20 48 22.1	17 25.2	0 12.2	13 50.1	16 53.3	19 35.1	3 1.9	20 37.7	4 24.9	21 7.6	20 49.2	6 28.8
7	21 0 11.8	16 36.7	0 12.1	19 13.1	14 54.6	18 41.9	3 47.6	20 38.6	4 28.9	21 9.0	20 50.0	6 30.3
10	21 12 1.4	15 45.7	0 12.0	13 48.9	12 49.2	17 44.0	4 33.5	20 39.8	4 33.1	21 10.3	20 50.8	6 31.8
13	21 23 51.1	14 52.5	0 12.0	1 13.5	10 39.9	16 41.6	5 19.3	20 41.3	4 37.6	21 11.6	20 51.6	6 33.4
16	21 35 40.8	13 57.2	0 11.9	11 N 1.6	8 28.7	15 35.0	6 5.2	20 43.0	4 42.3	21 12.9	20 52.4	6 35.1
19	21 47 30.4	12 59.8	0 11.9	18 10.7	6 17.3	14 24.5	6 50.9	20 45.1	4 47.2	21 14.1	20 53.1	6 36.8
22	21 59 20.1	12 .6	0 11.8	18 11.1	4 7.1	13 10.4	7 36.6	20 47.3	4 52.2	21 15.2	20 53.8	6 38.6
25	22 11 9.7	10 59.7	0 11.7	11 2.4	1 59.5	11 53.1	8 22.1	20 49.8	4 57.4	21 16.3	20 54.5	6 40.4
28	22 22 59.4	9 57.2	0 11.7	0 S 52.6	0 S 4.4	10 32.9	9 7.4	20 52.6	5 2.8	21 17.3	20 55.1	6 42.4
31	22 34 49.1	8 53.3	0 11.6	12 53.4	2 3.6	9 10.1	9 52.3	20 55.6	5 8.2	21 18.3	20 55.8	6 44.3

SEPTEMBER 1995

LONGITUDE

DAY	EPHEM. SID. TIME	☉	☊	☾	☿	♀	♂	♃	♄	♅	♆	♇
	h m s	° ′	° ′	° ′	° ′	° ′	° ′	° ′	° ′	° ′	° ′	° ′
1	22 38 45.6	8♍ 6.6	28♎53.9	20♏ 8.5	3♎46.5	11♍ 7.7	25♎52.6	6♐48.8	22♓22.1	27♑ 1.4	23♑ 4.8	27♏59.1
2	22 42 42.2	9 4.6	28 50.7	4♐ 6.8	5 .7	12 22.1	26 31.8	6 54.0	22R17.6	26R59.8	23R 3.8	27 60.0
3	22 46 38.7	10 2.7	28 47.5	18 15.0	6 13.1	13 36.6	27 11.1	6 59.4	22 13.2	26 58.2	23 2.8	28 .8
4	22 50 35.3	11 .8	28 44.4	2♑31.7	7 23.5	14 51.0	27 50.4	7 4.9	22 8.7	26 56.7	23 1.8	28 1.7
5	22 54 31.8	11 58.9	28 41.2	16 54.4	8 32.0	16 5.5	28 29.8	7 10.6	22 4.2	26 55.2	23 .9	28 2.6
6	22 58 28.4	12 57.1	28 38.0	1♒19.2	9 38.4	17 19.9	29 9.3	7 16.4	21 59.7	26 53.8	22 60.0	28 3.5
7	23 2 24.9	13 55.2	28 34.8	15 41.2	10 42.5	18 34.4	29 48.8	7 22.4	21 55.1	26 52.4	22 59.1	28 4.5
8	23 6 21.5	14 53.4	28 31.6	29 54.8	11 44.3	19 48.9	0♏28.5	7 28.5	21 50.6	26 51.1	22 58.2	28 5.5
9	23 10 18.0	15 51.6	28 28.5	13♓54.7	12 43.6	21 3.3	1 8.2	7 34.8	21 46.0	26 49.7	22 57.4	28 6.5
10	23 14 14.6	16 49.9	28 25.3	27 36.6	13 40.3	22 17.9	1 48.0	7 41.3	21 41.5	26 48.5	22 56.7	28 7.6
11	23 18 11.1	17 48.2	28 22.1	10♈57.9	14 34.1	23 32.4	2 27.9	7 47.8	21 36.8	26 47.3	22 55.9	28 8.7
12	23 22 7.7	18 46.6	28 18.9	23 57.7	15 24.9	24 46.9	3 7.9	7 54.6	21 32.2	26 46.1	22 55.2	28 9.8
13	23 26 4.2	19 44.9	28 15.8	6♉37.1	16 12.5	26 1.4	3 47.9	8 1.4	21 27.6	26 45.0	22 54.5	28 11.0
14	23 30 .8	20 43.3	28 12.6	18 58.5	16 56.7	27 16.0	4 28.0	8 8.4	21 23.0	26 43.9	22 53.8	28 12.1
15	23 33 57.3	21 41.7	28 9.4	1♊ 5.7	17 37.1	28 30.5	5 8.2	8 15.6	21 18.4	26 42.8	22 53.1	28 13.3
16	23 37 53.9	22 40.2	28 6.2	13 3.0	18 13.6	29 45.1	5 48.4	8 22.8	21 13.7	26 41.8	22 52.5	28 14.6
17	23 41 50.4	23 38.7	28 3.0	24 55.2	18 45.8	0♎59.7	6 28.8	8 30.2	21 9.1	26 40.8	22 51.9	28 15.9
18	23 45 47.0	24 37.2	27 59.9	6♋47.5	19 13.4	2 14.2	7 9.2	8 37.8	21 4.5	26 39.9	22 51.3	28 17.2
19	23 49 43.5	25 35.7	27 56.7	18 44.5	19 36.0	3 28.8	7 49.7	8 45.5	20 59.9	26 39.0	22 50.8	28 18.5
20	23 53 40.1	26 34.3	27 53.5	0♌50.5	19 53.3	4 43.4	8 30.3	8 53.3	20 55.3	26 38.2	22 50.3	28 19.9
21	23 57 36.7	27 33.0	27 50.3	13 9.3	20 5.0	5 58.0	9 11.0	9 1.3	20 50.7	26 37.4	22 49.8	28 21.2
22	0 1 33.2	28 31.7	27 47.2	25 43.6	20 10.6	7 12.6	9 51.7	9 9.3	20 46.1	26 36.6	22 49.4	28 22.7
23	0 5 29.8	29 30.4	27 44.0	8♍34.9	20R 9.8	8 27.3	10 32.6	9 17.6	20 41.6	26 36.0	22 49.0	28 24.1
24	0 9 26.3	0♎29.1	27 40.8	21 43.7	20 2.3	9 41.9	11 13.5	9 25.9	20 37.0	26 35.3	22 48.6	28 25.6
25	0 13 22.9	1 27.9	27 37.6	5♎ 9.2	19 47.7	10 56.5	11 54.4	9 34.4	20 32.5	26 34.7	22 48.3	28 27.1
26	0 17 19.4	2 26.7	27 34.4	18 49.5	19 25.9	12 11.2	12 35.5	9 43.0	20 28.0	26 34.2	22 47.9	28 28.6
27	0 21 16.0	3 25.5	27 31.3	2♏42.0	18 56.7	13 25.8	13 16.6	9 51.7	20 23.6	26 33.7	22 47.7	28 30.2
28	0 25 12.5	4 24.4	27 28.1	16 44.0	18 20.1	14 40.5	13 57.8	10 .5	20 19.1	26 33.2	22 47.4	28 31.7
29	0 29 9.1	5 23.3	27 24.9	0♐52.4	17 36.4	15 55.1	14 39.1	10 9.5	20 14.7	26 32.8	22 47.2	28 33.4
30	0 33 5.6	6 22.2	27 21.7	15 4.5	16 45.8	17 9.8	15 20.5	10 18.5	20 10.4	26 32.5	22 47.0	28 35.0

LATITUDE

DAY	SID. TIME	☉	☊	☾	☿	♀	♂	♃	♄	♅	♆	♇
1	22 38 45.6	0 .0	0 .0	1N58.7	1S18.5	1N24.9	0S 8.0	0N30.6	2S19.8	0S34.1	0N32.3	13N16.6
4	22 50 35.3	0 .0	0 .0	4 39.8	1 45.5	1 24.9	0 10.1	0 30.0	2 20.1	0 34.0	0 32.3	13 15.1
7	23 2 24.9	0 .0	0 .0	4 52.9	2 12.1	1 24.3	0 12.3	0 29.4	2 20.4	0 34.0	0 32.2	13 13.6
10	23 14 14.6	0 .0	0 .0	2 32.4	2 37.9	1 23.2	0 14.4	0 28.9	2 20.6	0 33.9	0 32.1	13 12.1
13	23 26 4.2	0 .0	0 .0	0S52.6	3 1.8	1 21.4	0 16.4	0 28.3	2 20.8	0 33.9	0 32.0	13 10.7
16	23 37 53.9	0 .0	0 .0	3 45.4	3 23.1	1 19.1	0 18.5	0 27.8	2 20.9	0 33.8	0 32.0	13 9.2
19	23 49 43.5	0 .0	0 .0	5 9.4	3 40.0	1 16.2	0 20.4	0 27.3	2 21.0	0 33.8	0 31.9	13 7.8
22	0 1 33.2	0 .0	0 .0	4 33.9	3 50.6	1 12.8	0 22.4	0 26.8	2 21.1	0 33.7	0 31.8	13 6.5
25	0 13 22.9	0 .0	0 .0	1 55.0	3 52.0	1 8.9	0 24.3	0 26.3	2 21.1	0 33.7	0 31.7	13 5.1
28	0 25 12.5	0 .0	0 .0	1N48.9	3 40.9	1 4.5	0 26.2	0 25.8	2 21.1	0 33.6	0 31.6	13 3.8

RIGHT ASCENSION

DAY	SID. TIME	☉	☊	☾	☿	♀	♂	♃	♄	♅	♆	♇
1	22 38 45.6	9♍45.8	26♎51.6	18♏14.9	2♎56.6	13♍ 7.9	23♎56.6	5♐ 4.0	23♓54.9	29♑11.2	24♑48.9	28♏41.8
2	22 42 42.2	10 40.2	26 48.6	2♐43.4	4 1.2	14 17.4	24 33.4	5 9.4	23R50.8	29R 9.6	24R47.8	28 42.5
3	22 46 38.7	11 34.5	26 45.5	17 35.8	5 4.2	15 26.8	25 10.4	5 15.1	23 46.8	29 7.9	24 46.8	28 43.2
4	22 50 35.3	12 28.8	26 42.5	2♑39.7	6 5.5	16 36.0	25 47.5	5 20.9	23 42.7	29 6.3	24 45.8	28 43.9
5	22 54 31.8	13 23.0	26 39.5	17 40.0	7 5.0	17 45.1	26 24.7	5 26.8	23 38.6	29 4.8	24 44.8	28 44.7
6	22 58 28.4	14 17.1	26 36.5	2♒23.2	8 2.7	18 54.0	27 2.1	5 33.0	23 34.4	29 3.3	24 43.9	28 45.5
7	23 2 24.9	15 11.2	26 33.4	16 40.4	8 58.5	20 2.8	27 39.6	5 39.3	23 30.3	29 1.8	24 42.9	28 46.3
8	23 6 21.5	16 5.2	26 30.4	0♓28.3	9 52.2	21 11.5	28 17.2	5 45.7	23 26.1	29 .4	24 42.0	28 47.1
9	23 10 18.0	16 59.2	26 27.4	13 49.1	10 43.7	22 20.0	28 55.0	5 52.3	23 21.9	28 59.0	24 41.2	28 48.0
10	23 14 14.6	17 53.1	26 24.4	26 47.9	11 33.0	23 28.5	29 33.0	5 59.1	23 17.8	28 57.7	24 40.4	28 49.0
11	23 18 11.1	18 47.0	26 21.3	9♈31.0	12 19.8	24 36.9	0♏11.1	6 6.1	23 13.5	28 56.4	24 39.6	28 49.9
12	23 22 7.7	19 40.9	26 18.3	22 5.0	13 3.9	25 45.2	0 49.3	6 13.1	23 9.3	28 55.1	24 38.8	28 50.9
13	23 26 4.2	20 34.7	26 15.3	4♉35.0	13 45.3	26 53.4	1 27.7	6 20.4	23 5.1	28 53.9	24 38.1	28 51.9
14	23 30 .8	21 28.5	26 12.3	17 4.6	14 23.6	28 1.6	2 6.2	6 27.7	23 .8	28 52.7	24 37.3	28 52.9
15	23 33 57.3	22 22.3	26 9.2	29 35.3	14 58.6	29 9.7	2 44.9	6 35.3	22 56.6	28 51.6	24 36.7	28 54.0
16	23 37 53.9	23 16.1	26 6.2	12♊ 7.2	15 30.1	0♎17.8	3 23.7	6 43.0	22 52.3	28 50.5	24 36.0	28 55.1
17	23 41 50.4	24 9.9	26 3.2	24 38.7	15 57.9	1 25.8	4 2.7	6 50.8	22 48.1	28 49.5	24 35.4	28 56.2
18	23 45 47.0	25 3.7	26 .2	7♋ 7.9	16 21.5	2 33.9	4 41.9	6 58.8	22 43.8	28 48.5	24 34.8	28 57.3
19	23 49 43.5	25 57.5	25 57.1	19 33.1	16 40.8	3 41.9	5 21.2	7 6.9	22 39.6	28 47.6	24 34.2	28 58.5
20	23 53 40.1	26 51.3	25 54.1	1♌53.5	16 55.4	4 49.9	6 .6	7 15.2	22 35.3	28 46.7	24 33.7	28 59.7
21	23 57 36.7	27 45.1	25 51.1	14 10.1	17 5.0	5 58.0	6 40.3	7 23.6	22 31.1	28 45.9	24 33.2	29 .9
22	0 1 33.2	28 38.9	25 48.1	26 25.7	17 9.3	7 6.1	7 20.0	7 32.1	22 26.9	28 45.1	24 32.8	29 2.2
23	0 5 29.8	29 32.8	25 45.1	8♍44.8	17R 7.9	8 14.2	7 60.0	7 40.8	22 22.7	28 44.4	24 32.3	29 3.5
24	0 9 26.3	0♎26.7	25 42.0	21 13.4	17 .6	9 22.3	8 40.1	7 49.6	22 18.5	28 43.7	24 31.9	29 4.8
25	0 13 22.9	1 20.6	25 39.0	3♎58.1	16 47.2	10 30.5	9 20.4	7 58.6	22 14.3	28 43.1	24 31.6	29 6.2
26	0 17 19.4	2 14.6	25 36.0	17 5.8	16 27.5	11 38.8	10 .8	8 7.7	22 10.2	28 42.5	24 31.2	29 7.5
27	0 21 16.0	3 8.6	25 33.0	0♏41.8	16 1.5	12 47.2	10 41.4	8 16.9	22 6.1	28 42.0	24 31.0	29 8.9
28	0 25 12.5	4 2.6	25 30.0	14 48.2	15 29.3	13 55.6	11 22.2	8 26.3	22 2.0	28 41.5	24 30.7	29 10.4
29	0 29 9.1	4 56.8	25 27.0	29 22.3	14 51.1	15 4.2	12 3.1	8 35.8	21 57.9	28 41.1	24 30.5	29 11.8
30	0 33 5.6	5 50.9	25 23.9	14♐15.7	14 7.4	16 12.8	12 44.2	8 45.4	21 53.9	28 40.7	24 30.3	29 13.3

DECLINATION

DAY	SID. TIME	☉	☊	☾	☿	♀	♂	♃	♄	♅	♆	♇
1	22 38 45.6	8N31.7	0S11.6	15S52.3	2S42.1	8N42.0	10S 7.3	20S56.6	5S10.1	21S18.6	20S56.0	6S45.0
4	22 50 35.3	7 26.1	0 11.5	18 45.1	4 32.9	7 16.3	10 51.8	20 59.9	5 15.7	21 19.4	20 56.5	6 47.0
7	23 2 24.9	6 19.5	0 11.5	11 27.9	6 15.8	5 48.8	11 35.8	21 3.3	5 21.3	21 20.2	20 57.0	6 49.0
10	23 14 14.6	5 11.9	0 11.4	1N22.9	7 49.1	4 19.7	12 19.4	21 6.9	5 26.9	21 20.9	20 57.5	6 51.1
13	23 26 4.2	4 3.6	0 11.4	12 53.8	9 10.3	2 49.6	13 2.4	21 10.7	5 32.5	21 21.6	20 58.0	6 53.3
16	23 37 53.9	2 54.5	0 11.3	18 38.2	10 16.4	1 18.5	13 44.8	21 14.6	5 38.2	21 22.1	20 58.4	6 55.4
19	23 49 43.5	1 45.0	0 11.2	17 1.1	11 3.6	0S13.0	14 26.5	21 18.7	5 43.7	21 22.6	20 58.7	6 57.6
22	0 1 33.2	0 35.1	0 11.2	8 38.5	11 26.5	1 44.8	15 7.4	21 22.8	5 49.2	21 23.0	20 59.0	6 59.8
25	0 13 22.9	0S35.0	0 11.1	3S48.4	11 19.2	3 16.4	15 47.5	21 27.1	5 54.6	21 23.3	20 59.3	7 2.0
28	0 25 12.5	1 45.1	0 11.1	15 5.7	10 35.4	4 47.5	16 26.7	21 31.4	5 59.8	21 23.5	20 59.5	7 4.2

OCTOBER 1995

LONGITUDE

DAY	EPHEM. SID. TIME	☉	☊	☽	☿	♀	♂	♃	♄	♅	♆	♇
	h m s	° ′	° ′	° ′	° ′	° ′	° ′	° ′	° ′	° ′	° ′	° ′
1	0 37 2.2	7♎21.2	27♎18.6	29♐17.8	15♎49.2	18♎24.5	16♏ 2.0	10♐27.8	20♓ 6.1	26♑32.2	22♑46.9	28♏36.7
2	0 40 58.7	8 20.2	27 15.4	13♑29.9	14 R 47.4	19 39.1	16 43.5	10 37.1	20 R 1.8	26 R 32.0	22 R 46.8	28 38.4
3	0 44 55.3	9 19.2	27 12.2	27 38.8	13 41.5	20 53.8	17 25.1	10 46.5	19 57.6	26 31.8	22 46.7	28 40.1
4	0 48 51.8	10 18.3	27 9.0	11♒42.0	12 33.0	22 8.4	18 6.7	10 56.0	19 53.4	26 31.6	22 46.7	28 41.8
5	0 52 48.4	11 17.3	27 5.8	25 37.5	11 23.7	23 23.1	18 48.4	11 5.6	19 49.3	26 31.5	22 46.6	28 43.6
6	0 56 44.9	12 16.4	27 2.7	9♓22.6	10 15.2	24 37.7	19 30.2	11 15.3	19 45.2	26 31.5	22 D 46.7	28 45.4
7	1 0 41.5	13 15.6	26 59.5	22 55.4	9 9.6	25 52.4	20 12.1	11 25.2	19 41.1	26 31.5	22 46.7	28 47.2
8	1 4 38.0	14 14.8	26 56.3	6♈13.8	8 8.6	27 7.0	20 54.0	11 35.1	19 37.1	26 31.5	22 46.8	28 49.0
9	1 8 34.6	15 14.0	26 53.1	19 16.7	7 14.0	28 21.7	21 36.0	11 45.2	19 33.2	26 D 31.6	22 46.9	28 50.8
10	1 12 31.1	16 13.2	26 49.9	2♉ 3.5	6 27.3	29 36.4	22 18.1	11 55.3	19 29.3	26 31.8	22 47.1	28 52.7
11	1 16 27.7	17 12.5	26 46.8	14 34.9	5 49.8	0♏51.0	23 .3	12 5.6	19 25.5	26 32.0	22 47.2	28 54.6
12	1 20 24.2	18 11.8	26 43.6	26 52.3	5 22.3	2 5.7	23 42.5	12 15.9	19 21.7	26 32.3	22 47.5	28 56.5
13	1 24 20.8	19 11.1	26 40.4	8♊57.9	5 5.5	3 20.3	24 24.8	12 26.4	19 18.0	26 32.6	22 47.7	28 58.5
14	1 28 17.3	20 10.5	26 37.2	20 55.1	4 59.7	4 35.0	25 7.1	12 36.9	19 14.4	26 32.9	22 48.0	29 .4
15	1 32 13.9	21 9.9	26 34.1	2♋47.5	5 D 4.9	5 49.7	25 49.6	12 47.5	19 10.8	26 33.3	22 48.3	29 2.4
16	1 36 10.5	22 9.4	26 30.9	14 39.6	5 20.7	7 4.3	26 32.1	12 58.3	19 7.3	26 33.8	22 48.6	29 4.4
17	1 40 7.0	23 8.9	26 27.7	26 36.0	5 46.7	8 19.0	27 14.7	13 9.1	19 3.9	26 34.3	22 49.0	29 6.4
18	1 44 3.6	24 8.4	26 24.5	8♌41.2	6 22.2	9 33.7	27 57.3	13 20.0	19 .5	26 34.9	22 49.4	29 8.4
19	1 48 .1	25 8.0	26 21.3	20 59.9	7 6.7	10 48.4	28 40.1	13 31.0	18 57.3	26 35.5	22 49.9	29 10.5
20	1 51 56.7	26 7.6	26 18.2	3♍35.9	7 59.2	12 3.0	29 22.9	13 42.1	18 54.1	26 36.2	22 50.4	29 12.6
21	1 55 53.2	27 7.2	26 15.0	16 32.3	8 58.9	13 17.7	0♐ 5.8	13 53.2	18 50.9	26 36.9	22 50.9	29 14.6
22	1 59 49.8	28 7.0	26 11.8	29 51.0	10 5.2	14 32.4	0 48.7	14 4.5	18 47.9	26 37.7	22 51.5	29 16.8
23	2 3 46.3	29 6.7	26 8.6	13♎31.9	11 17.0	15 47.1	1 31.8	14 15.9	18 45.0	26 38.5	22 52.1	29 18.9
24	2 7 42.9	0♏ 6.4	26 5.5	27 33.5	12 33.7	17 1.8	2 14.9	14 27.3	18 42.1	26 39.4	22 52.7	29 21.1
25	2 11 39.4	1 6.2	26 2.3	11♏52.2	13 54.5	18 16.5	2 58.0	14 38.8	18 39.3	26 40.3	22 53.3	29 23.2
26	2 15 36.0	2 6.1	25 59.1	26 22.9	15 19.0	19 31.2	3 41.2	14 50.4	18 36.6	26 41.3	22 54.0	29 25.4
27	2 19 32.5	3 5.9	25 55.9	10♐59.5	16 46.4	20 45.9	4 24.5	15 2.0	18 33.9	26 42.3	22 54.7	29 27.6
28	2 23 29.1	4 5.8	25 52.7	25 35.9	18 16.3	22 .5	5 7.9	15 13.7	18 31.4	26 43.3	22 55.5	29 29.8
29	2 27 25.6	5 5.7	25 49.6	10♑ 6.3	19 48.3	23 15.2	5 51.3	15 25.5	18 28.9	26 44.5	22 56.3	29 32.0
30	2 31 22.2	6 5.6	25 46.4	24 26.4	21 21.9	24 29.9	6 34.8	15 37.4	18 26.6	26 45.6	22 57.1	29 34.2
31	2 35 18.8	7 5.6	25 43.2	8♒33.3	22 56.8	25 44.6	7 18.4	15 49.3	18 24.3	26 46.9	22 57.9	29 36.4

LATITUDE

DAY	EPHEM. SID. TIME	☉	☊	☽	☿	♀	♂	♃	♄	♅	♆	♇
1	0 37 2.2	0 .0	0 .0	4N40.6	3S13.9	0N59.6	0S28.1	0N25.3	2S21.0	0S33.5	0N31.6	13N 2.6
4	0 48 51.8	0 .0	0 .0	5 4.8	2 30.2	0 54.3	0 29.9	0 24.8	2 20.9	0 33.5	0 31.5	13 1.4
7	1 0 41.5	0 .0	0 .0	2 55.1	1 33.6	0 48.5	0 31.7	0 24.4	2 20.7	0 33.4	0 31.4	13 .2
10	1 12 31.1	0 .0	0 .0	0S31.0	0 32.3	0 42.3	0 33.4	0 23.9	2 20.5	0 33.3	0 31.3	12 59.1
13	1 24 20.8	0 .0	0 .0	3 34.5	0N24.2	0 35.8	0 35.1	0 23.5	2 20.3	0 33.3	0 31.2	12 58.1
16	1 36 10.5	0 .0	0 .0	5 10.6	1 9.3	0 29.0	0 36.8	0 23.1	2 20.0	0 33.2	0 31.1	12 57.0
19	1 48 .1	0 .0	0 .0	4 48.9	1 40.4	0 22.0	0 38.4	0 22.7	2 19.7	0 33.1	0 31.0	12 56.1
22	1 59 49.8	0 .0	0 .0	2 22.7	1 58.3	0 14.7	0 40.0	0 22.2	2 19.3	0 33.1	0 31.0	12 55.2
25	2 11 39.4	0 .0	0 .0	1N24.2	2 5.0	0 7.2	0 41.6	0 21.8	2 18.9	0 33.0	0 30.9	12 54.3
28	2 23 29.1	0 .0	0 .0	4 32.1	2 2.9	0S .4	0 43.1	0 21.5	2 18.5	0 32.9	0 30.8	12 53.6
31	2 35 18.8	0 .0	0 .0	5 9.9	1 54.4	0 8.1	0 44.5	0 21.1	2 18.1	0 32.9	0 30.7	12 52.8

RIGHT ASCENSION

DAY	EPHEM. SID. TIME	☉	☊	☽	☿	♀	♂	♃	♄	♅	♆	♇
1	0 37 2.2	6♎45.2	25♎20.9	29♐15.6	13♎18.8	17♎21.6	13♏25.5	8♐55.2	21♓49.9	28♑40.4	24♑30.2	29♏14.9
2	0 40 58.7	7 39.5	25 17.9	14♑ 7.3	12 R 26.2	18 30.5	14 7.0	9 5.1	21 R 46.0	28 R 40.1	24 R 30.1	29 16.4
3	0 44 55.3	8 33.8	25 14.9	28 38.9	11 30.7	19 39.5	14 48.6	9 15.1	21 42.0	28 39.9	24 30.0	29 17.9
4	0 48 51.8	9 28.2	25 11.9	12♒43.3	10 33.7	20 48.7	15 30.3	9 25.2	21 38.1	28 39.8	24 29.9	29 19.5
5	0 52 48.4	10 22.7	25 8.9	26 19.1	9 36.4	21 58.0	16 12.3	9 35.5	21 34.3	28 39.7	24 29.9	29 21.1
6	0 56 44.9	11 17.3	25 5.8	9♓29.7	8 40.7	23 7.5	16 54.4	9 45.8	21 30.5	28 39.6	24 29.9	29 22.8
7	1 0 41.5	12 12.0	25 2.8	22 20.9	7 48.0	24 17.1	17 36.6	9 56.3	21 26.7	28 39.6	24 D 30.0	29 24.4
8	1 4 38.0	13 6.8	24 59.8	4♈59.6	6 59.8	25 27.0	18 19.1	10 6.9	21 23.0	28 D 39.7	24 30.1	29 26.1
9	1 8 34.6	14 1.6	24 56.8	17 32.3	6 17.7	26 37.0	19 1.7	10 17.6	21 19.3	28 39.8	24 30.2	29 27.8
10	1 12 31.1	14 56.6	24 53.8	0♉ 3.9	5 42.8	27 47.3	19 44.4	10 28.4	21 15.7	28 39.9	24 30.4	29 29.5
11	1 16 27.7	15 51.7	24 50.8	12 37.3	5 16.1	28 57.7	20 27.4	10 39.3	21 12.2	28 40.1	24 30.6	29 31.3
12	1 20 24.2	16 47.0	24 47.8	25 13.3	4 58.4	0♏ 8.4	21 10.5	10 50.3	21 8.7	28 40.4	24 30.8	29 33.0
13	1 24 20.8	17 42.3	24 44.8	7♊50.3	4 50.1	1 19.3	21 53.8	11 1.5	21 5.2	28 40.7	24 31.1	29 34.8
14	1 28 17.3	18 37.8	24 41.7	20 25.6	4 D 51.3	2 30.5	22 37.2	11 12.7	21 1.8	28 41.1	24 31.4	29 36.6
15	1 32 13.9	19 33.4	24 38.7	2♋56.1	5 1.9	3 41.9	23 20.9	11 24.1	20 58.5	28 41.5	24 31.7	29 38.5
16	1 36 10.5	20 29.1	24 35.7	15 19.4	5 21.8	4 53.5	24 4.7	11 35.5	20 55.2	28 42.0	24 32.1	29 40.3
17	1 40 7.0	21 25.0	24 32.7	27 34.8	5 50.4	6 5.4	24 48.6	11 47.1	20 52.0	28 42.5	24 32.5	29 42.2
18	1 44 3.6	22 21.1	24 29.7	9♌43.7	6 27.2	7 17.6	25 32.8	11 58.7	20 48.8	28 43.1	24 32.9	29 44.1
19	1 48 .1	23 17.3	24 26.7	21 49.7	7 11.5	8 30.1	26 17.1	12 10.5	20 45.8	28 43.8	24 33.4	29 46.0
20	1 51 56.7	24 13.7	24 23.7	3♍58.5	8 2.6	9 42.8	27 1.6	12 22.3	20 42.8	28 44.5	24 33.9	29 47.9
21	1 55 53.2	25 10.2	24 20.7	16 17.5	8 59.9	10 55.9	27 46.2	12 34.3	20 39.8	28 45.2	24 34.5	29 49.8
22	1 59 49.8	26 6.9	24 17.7	28 54.9	10 2.6	12 9.2	28 31.1	12 46.4	20 37.0	28 46.1	24 35.1	29 51.9
23	2 3 46.3	27 3.8	24 14.7	11♎59.2	11 10.0	13 22.9	29 16.1	12 58.5	20 34.2	28 46.9	24 35.7	29 53.8
24	2 7 42.9	28 .8	24 11.7	25 37.2	12 21.5	14 36.8	0♐ 1.2	13 10.7	20 31.5	28 47.8	24 36.4	29 55.8
25	2 11 39.4	28 58.0	24 8.6	9♏52.6	13 36.6	15 51.0	0 46.6	13 23.0	20 28.8	28 48.8	24 37.1	29 57.9
26	2 15 36.0	29 55.4	24 5.6	24 42.8	14 54.7	17 5.5	1 32.0	13 35.5	20 26.3	28 49.8	24 37.8	29 59.9
27	2 19 32.5	0♏52.9	24 2.6	9♐58.0	16 15.4	18 20.4	2 17.7	13 47.9	20 23.8	28 50.9	24 38.6	0♐ 1.9
28	2 23 29.1	1 50.7	23 59.6	25 21.8	17 38.2	19 35.5	3 3.5	14 .5	20 21.4	28 52.0	24 39.4	0 4.0
29	2 27 25.6	2 48.6	23 56.6	10♑35.3	19 2.8	20 50.9	3 49.5	14 13.2	20 19.1	28 53.2	24 40.2	0 6.1
30	2 31 22.2	3 46.7	23 53.6	25 23.0	20 29.0	22 6.7	4 35.6	14 25.9	20 16.8	28 54.4	24 41.1	0 8.2
31	2 35 18.8	4 45.0	23 50.6	9♒35.9	21 56.5	23 22.8	5 21.9	14 38.7	20 14.7	28 55.7	24 42.0	0 10.3

DECLINATION

DAY	EPHEM. SID. TIME	☉	☊	☽	☿	♀	♂	♃	♄	♅	♆	♇
1	0 37 2.2	2S55.1	0S11.0	18S45.6	9S12.4	6S17.8	17S 5.0	21S35.9	6S 4.9	21S23.6	20S59.7	7S 6.4
4	0 48 51.8	4 4.8	0 11.0	12 23.4	7 15.8	7 46.9	17 42.1	21 40.3	6 9.7	21 23.7	20 59.8	7 8.6
7	1 0 41.5	5 14.1	0 10.9	0 7.7	5 3.8	9 14.5	18 18.1	21 44.8	6 14.4	21 23.7	20 59.9	7 10.8
10	1 12 31.1	6 22.7	0 10.8	11N42.2	3 3.4	10 40.3	18 52.9	21 49.3	6 18.9	21 23.5	20 59.9	7 13.1
13	1 24 20.8	7 30.7	0 10.8	18 15.5	1 39.2	12 3.9	19 26.4	21 53.8	6 23.1	21 23.3	20 59.9	7 15.2
16	1 36 10.5	8 37.7	0 10.7	17 29.1	1 3.8	13 24.9	19 58.5	21 58.3	6 27.0	21 23.0	20 59.8	7 17.4
19	1 48 .1	9 43.6	0 10.7	9 55.7	1 17.1	14 43.1	20 29.2	22 2.8	6 30.7	21 22.6	20 59.7	7 19.6
22	1 59 49.8	10 48.2	0 10.6	2S 7.4	2 10.8	15 58.0	20 58.3	22 7.2	6 34.0	21 22.1	20 59.5	7 21.7
25	2 11 39.4	11 51.4	0 10.5	14 3.6	3 34.0	17 9.2	21 25.8	22 11.5	6 37.1	21 21.6	20 59.3	7 23.8
28	2 23 29.1	12 53.0	0 10.5	18 49.9	5 16.1	18 16.5	21 51.6	22 15.8	6 39.8	21 20.9	20 59.0	7 25.9
31	2 35 18.8	13 52.8	0 10.4	13 7.9	7 9.0	19 19.5	22 15.6	22 20.0	6 42.2	21 20.2	20 58.7	7 27.9

NOVEMBER 1995

LONGITUDE

DAY	EPHEM. SID. TIME	☉	☊	☾	☿	♀	♂	♃	♄	♅	♆	♇
	h m s	° ′	° ′	° ′	° ′	° ′	° ′	° ′	° ′	° ′	° ′	° ′
1	2 39 15.3	8♏ 5.6	25♎40.0	22♒25.3	24♎32.7	26♏59.2	8♐ 2.0	16♐ 1.4	18♓22.2	26♑48.1	22♑58.8	29♏38.7
2	2 43 11.9	9 5.6	25 36.9	6♓ 2.0	26 9.5	28 13.9	8 45.7	16 13.4	18 R 20.1	26 49.4	22 59.7	29 40.9
3	2 47 8.4	10 5.6	25 33.7	19 23.7	27 46.8	29 28.5	9 29.4	16 25.6	18 18.1	26 50.8	23 .7	29 43.2
4	2 51 5.0	11 5.7	25 30.5	2♈31.2	29 24.6	0♐43.2	10 13.3	16 37.8	18 16.2	26 52.2	23 1.6	29 45.5
5	2 55 1.5	12 5.8	25 27.3	15 25.2	1♏ 2.6	1 57.8	10 57.1	16 50.0	18 14.4	26 53.7	23 2.6	29 47.8
6	2 58 58.1	13 5.9	25 24.1	28 6.7	2 40.7	3 12.5	11 41.1	17 2.4	18 12.7	26 55.2	23 3.7	29 50.1
7	3 2 54.6	14 6.1	25 21.0	10♉36.5	4 18.9	4 27.1	12 25.1	17 14.8	18 11.2	26 56.7	23 4.7	29 52.4
8	3 6 51.2	15 6.3	25 17.8	22 55.6	5 57.1	5 41.7	13 9.1	17 27.2	18 9.7	26 58.3	23 5.8	29 54.7
9	3 10 47.7	16 6.5	25 14.6	5♊ 5.1	7 35.2	6 56.3	13 53.3	17 39.7	18 8.3	26 60.0	23 7.0	29 57.1
10	3 14 44.3	17 6.7	25 11.4	17 6.5	9 13.1	8 10.9	14 37.5	17 52.3	18 7.0	27 1.7	23 8.1	29 59.4
11	3 18 40.9	18 7.0	25 8.3	29 1.8	10 50.9	9 25.6	15 21.7	18 4.9	18 5.8	27 3.4	23 9.3	0♐ 1.7
12	3 22 37.4	19 7.4	25 5.1	10♋53.5	12 28.5	10 40.2	16 6.1	18 17.6	18 4.8	27 5.2	23 10.6	0 4.1
13	3 26 34.0	20 7.7	25 1.9	22 44.9	14 5.8	11 54.8	16 50.4	18 30.3	18 3.8	27 7.1	23 11.8	0 6.5
14	3 30 30.5	21 8.1	24 58.7	4♌39.6	15 42.9	13 9.4	17 34.9	18 43.1	18 2.9	27 8.9	23 13.1	0 8.8
15	3 34 27.1	22 8.5	24 55.6	16 41.9	17 19.7	14 24.0	18 19.4	18 55.9	18 2.1	27 10.9	23 14.4	0 11.2
16	3 38 23.6	23 8.9	24 52.4	28 56.5	18 56.3	15 38.6	19 4.0	19 8.8	18 1.5	27 12.8	23 15.7	0 13.6
17	3 42 20.2	24 9.4	24 49.2	11♍27.9	20 32.6	16 53.2	19 48.6	19 21.7	18 .9	27 14.8	23 17.1	0 16.0
18	3 46 16.7	25 9.9	24 46.0	24 20.6	22 8.7	18 7.8	20 33.3	19 34.7	18 .4	27 16.9	23 18.5	0 18.3
19	3 50 13.3	26 10.4	24 42.8	7♎38.0	23 44.5	19 22.4	21 18.0	19 47.7	18 .1	27 19.0	23 19.9	0 20.7
20	3 54 9.8	27 11.0	24 39.7	21 22.2	25 20.1	20 37.0	22 2.8	20 .7	17 59.8	27 21.1	23 21.3	0 23.1
21	3 58 6.4	28 11.6	24 36.5	5♏33.1	26 55.5	21 51.6	22 47.7	20 13.8	17 59.7	27 23.3	23 22.8	0 25.5
22	4 2 3.0	29 12.2	24 33.3	20 7.9	28 30.6	23 6.2	23 32.6	20 26.9	17 59.7	27 25.5	23 24.3	0 27.9
23	4 5 59.5	0♐12.8	24 30.1	5♐ .9	0♐ 5.5	24 20.7	24 17.6	20 40.1	17 59.7	27 27.7	23 25.8	0 30.3
24	4 9 56.1	1 13.5	24 27.0	20 3.9	1 40.3	25 35.3	25 2.7	20 53.3	17 D 59.9	27 30.0	23 27.3	0 32.6
25	4 13 52.6	2 14.2	24 23.8	5♑ 7.5	3 14.9	26 49.9	25 47.8	21 6.6	18 .2	27 32.4	23 28.9	0 35.0
26	4 17 49.2	3 14.9	24 20.6	20 2.3	4 49.3	28 4.4	26 32.9	21 19.8	18 .6	27 34.8	23 30.5	0 37.4
27	4 21 45.7	4 15.6	24 17.4	4♒40.8	6 23.5	29 19.0	27 18.1	21 33.2	18 1.1	27 37.2	23 32.1	0 39.8
28	4 25 42.3	5 16.4	24 14.2	18 58.0	7 57.7	0♑33.5	28 3.4	21 46.5	18 1.7	27 39.6	23 33.8	0 42.2
29	4 29 38.9	6 17.1	24 11.1	2♓51.8	9 31.7	1 48.0	28 48.7	21 59.9	18 2.5	27 42.1	23 35.5	0 44.6
30	4 33 35.4	7 17.9	24 7.9	16 22.5	11 5.6	3 2.5	29 34.1	22 13.3	18 3.3	27 44.6	23 37.2	0 46.9

LATITUDE

DAY	EPHEM. SID. TIME	☉	☊	☾	☿	♀	♂	♃	♄	♅	♆	♇
1	2 39 15.3	0 .0	0 .0	4N45.0	1N50.5	0S10.7	0S45.0	0N20.9	2S17.9	0S32.8	0N30.7	12N52.6
4	2 51 5.0	0 .0	0 .0	2 9.0	1 36.2	0 18.5	0 46.4	0 20.6	2 17.5	0 32.8	0 30.6	12 52.0
7	3 2 54.6	0 .0	0 .0	1S17.0	1 19.1	0 26.2	0 47.8	0 20.2	2 17.0	0 32.7	0 30.5	12 51.4
10	3 14 44.3	0 .0	0 .0	4 3.6	1 .3	0 33.9	0 49.2	0 19.9	2 16.5	0 32.7	0 30.4	12 50.8
13	3 26 34.0	0 .0	0 .0	5 13.5	0 40.4	0 41.4	0 50.4	0 19.5	2 15.9	0 32.6	0 30.4	12 50.4
16	3 38 23.6	0 .0	0 .0	4 24.3	0 20.1	0 48.8	0 51.7	0 19.2	2 15.4	0 32.5	0 30.3	12 50.0
19	3 50 13.3	0 .0	0 .0	1 40.3	0S .3	0 56.0	0 52.9	0 18.8	2 14.8	0 32.5	0 30.2	12 49.7
22	4 2 3.0	0 .0	0 .0	2N 6.7	0 20.4	1 2.9	0 54.0	0 18.5	2 14.3	0 32.4	0 30.1	12 49.4
25	4 13 52.6	0 .0	0 .0	4 50.5	0 39.8	1 9.5	0 55.1	0 18.2	2 13.7	0 32.4	0 30.1	12 49.2
28	4 25 42.3	0 .0	0 .0	4 45.8	0 58.2	1 15.7	0 56.2	0 17.9	2 13.1	0 32.3	0 30.0	12 49.0

RIGHT ASCENSION

DAY	EPHEM. SID. TIME	☉	☊	☾	☿	♀	♂	♃	♄	♅	♆	♇
1	2 39 15.3	5♏43.5	23♎47.6	23♒12.8	23♎25.0	24♏39.1	6♐ 8.3	14♐51.6	20♓12.6	28♑57.0	24♑42.9	0♐12.4
2	2 43 11.9	6 42.2	23 44.6	6♓18.3	24 54.4	25 55.8	6 54.9	15 4.6	20 R 10.6	28 58.4	24 43.9	0 14.5
3	2 47 8.4	7 41.0	23 41.6	19 .1	26 24.5	27 12.8	7 41.6	15 17.7	20 8.7	28 59.8	24 44.9	0 16.7
4	2 51 5.0	8 40.1	23 38.6	1♈27.4	27 55.3	28 30.0	8 28.5	15 30.8	20 6.9	29 1.3	24 45.9	0 18.8
5	2 55 1.5	9 39.4	23 35.6	13 48.3	29 26.6	29 47.6	9 15.6	15 44.0	20 5.2	29 2.9	24 47.0	0 21.0
6	2 58 58.1	10 38.9	23 32.6	26 9.8	0♏58.4	1♐ 5.5	10 2.7	15 57.2	20 3.6	29 4.4	24 48.1	0 23.2
7	3 2 54.6	11 38.5	23 29.6	8♉36.2	2 30.6	2 23.6	10 50.0	16 10.6	20 2.1	29 6.1	24 49.2	0 25.4
8	3 6 51.2	12 38.4	23 26.6	21 8.7	4 3.2	3 42.1	11 37.5	16 24.0	20 .6	29 7.7	24 50.3	0 27.6
9	3 10 47.7	13 38.5	23 23.6	3♊46.0	5 36.1	5 .8	12 25.1	16 37.4	19 59.3	29 9.5	24 51.5	0 29.8
10	3 14 44.3	14 38.8	23 20.6	16 24.3	7 9.3	6 19.8	13 12.8	16 51.0	19 58.0	29 11.3	24 52.8	0 32.0
11	3 18 40.9	15 39.4	23 17.6	28 58.7	8 42.8	7 39.1	14 .7	17 4.6	19 56.8	29 13.1	24 54.0	0 34.2
12	3 22 37.4	16 40.2	23 14.6	11♋24.8	10 16.7	8 58.6	14 48.7	17 18.3	19 55.8	29 15.0	24 55.4	0 36.5
13	3 26 34.0	17 41.1	23 11.6	23 39.7	11 50.7	10 18.4	15 36.8	17 32.0	19 54.8	29 16.9	24 56.7	0 38.7
14	3 30 30.5	18 42.3	23 8.6	5♌43.5	13 25.1	11 38.4	16 25.1	17 45.8	19 53.9	29 18.9	24 58.0	0 41.0
15	3 34 27.1	19 43.7	23 5.6	17 39.0	14 59.8	12 58.6	17 13.5	17 59.6	19 53.1	29 20.9	24 59.4	0 43.2
16	3 38 23.6	20 45.3	23 2.6	29 31.8	16 34.8	14 19.1	18 1.9	18 13.5	19 52.5	29 23.0	25 .8	0 45.5
17	3 42 20.2	21 47.1	22 59.6	11♍29.8	18 10.1	15 39.8	18 50.6	18 27.4	19 51.9	29 25.1	25 2.2	0 47.7
18	3 46 16.7	22 49.2	22 56.6	23 42.7	19 45.7	17 .6	19 39.3	18 41.4	19 51.4	29 27.2	25 3.7	0 50.0
19	3 50 13.3	23 51.4	22 53.6	6♎20.9	21 21.6	18 21.7	20 28.1	18 55.5	19 51.0	29 29.4	25 5.2	0 52.3
20	3 54 9.8	24 53.9	22 50.6	19 34.8	22 57.9	19 42.9	21 17.1	19 9.6	19 50.7	29 31.7	25 6.7	0 54.6
21	3 58 6.4	25 56.6	22 47.6	3♏32.4	24 34.5	21 4.3	22 6.1	19 23.7	19 50.5	29 33.9	25 8.3	0 56.9
22	4 2 3.0	26 59.4	22 44.6	18 16.6	26 11.5	22 25.8	22 55.3	19 37.9	19 50.4	29 36.3	25 9.9	0 59.1
23	4 5 59.5	28 2.5	22 41.6	3♐41.5	27 48.8	23 47.4	23 44.5	19 52.2	19 50.4	29 38.6	25 11.5	1 1.4
24	4 9 56.1	29 5.8	22 38.6	19 31.4	29 26.6	25 9.1	24 33.8	20 6.5	19 50.4	29 41.1	25 13.1	1 3.7
25	4 13 52.6	0♐ 9.3	22 35.6	5♑23.1	1♐ 4.7	26 31.0	25 23.3	20 20.8	19 D 50.6	29 43.5	25 14.8	1 6.0
26	4 17 49.2	1 12.9	22 32.6	20 53.3	2 43.2	27 52.9	26 12.8	20 35.2	19 50.9	29 46.0	25 16.5	1 8.3
27	4 21 45.7	2 16.8	22 29.6	5♒45.5	4 22.1	29 14.9	27 2.4	20 49.6	19 51.3	29 48.5	25 18.2	1 10.6
28	4 25 42.3	3 20.8	22 26.6	19 53.3	6 1.4	0♑36.9	27 52.0	21 4.0	19 51.8	29 51.1	25 19.9	1 12.9
29	4 29 38.9	4 25.0	22 23.6	3♓19.1	7 41.1	1 58.9	28 41.8	21 18.5	19 52.4	29 53.7	25 21.7	1 15.2
30	4 33 35.4	5 29.3	22 20.6	16 11.0	9 21.2	3 20.9	29 31.6	21 33.0	19 53.1	29 56.4	25 23.5	1 17.5

DECLINATION

DAY	EPHEM. SID. TIME	☉	☊	☾	☿	♀	♂	♃	♄	♅	♆	♇
1	2 39 15.3	14S12.3	0S10.4	9S32.5	7S47.8	19S39.4	22S23.2	22S21.4	6S42.9	21S19.9	20S58.6	7S28.6
4	2 51 5.0	15 9.4	0 10.3	2N58.5	9 45.7	20 36.1	22 44.8	22 25.5	6 44.8	21 19.1	20 58.2	7 30.6
7	3 2 54.6	16 4.2	0 10.3	13 47.1	11 42.9	21 27.6	23 4.3	22 29.4	6 46.3	21 18.1	20 57.7	7 32.5
10	3 14 44.3	16 56.6	0 10.2	18 46.2	13 36.8	22 13.7	23 21.9	22 33.3	6 47.5	21 17.1	20 57.3	7 34.4
13	3 26 34.0	17 46.5	0 10.1	16 21.8	15 25.5	22 54.0	23 37.4	22 37.0	6 48.2	21 16.0	20 56.7	7 36.2
16	3 38 23.6	18 33.5	0 10.1	7 42.5	17 7.8	23 28.4	23 50.7	22 40.5	6 48.6	21 14.8	20 56.1	7 38.0
19	3 50 13.3	19 17.7	0 10.0	4S33.9	18 42.7	23 56.6	24 1.9	22 43.9	6 48.7	21 13.6	20 55.5	7 39.7
22	4 2 3.0	19 58.7	0 10.0	15 44.3	20 9.4	24 18.3	24 10.8	22 47.1	6 48.3	21 12.2	20 54.8	7 41.4
25	4 13 52.6	20 36.4	0 9.9	18 30.0	21 27.3	24 33.4	24 17.3	22 50.2	6 47.6	21 10.8	20 54.1	7 42.9
28	4 25 42.3	21 10.7	0 9.8	10 36.3	22 35.5	24 41.9	24 21.5	22 53.1	6 46.5	21 9.3	20 53.4	7 44.4

DECEMBER 1995

LONGITUDE

DAY	EPHEM. SID. TIME	☉	☊	☽	☿	♀	♂	♃	♄	♅	♆	♇
	h m s	° ′	° ′	° ′	° ′	° ′	° ′	° ′	° ′	° ′	° ′	° ′
1	4 37 32.0	8♐18.7	24♎ 4.7	29♓31.9	12♐39.4	4♑17.0	0♑19.5	22♐26.7	18♓ 4.2	27♑47.2	23♑38.9	0♐49.3
2	4 41 28.5	9 19.5	24 1.5	12♈22.9	14 13.2	5 31.5	1 5.0	22 40.1	18 5.3	27 49.8	23 40.6	0 51.7
3	4 45 25.1	10 20.4	23 58.4	24 58.7	15 47.0	6 46.0	1 50.6	22 53.7	18 6.5	27 52.5	23 42.4	0 54.1
4	4 49 21.6	11 21.2	23 55.2	7♉22.3	17 20.6	8 .5	2 36.1	23 7.2	18 7.7	27 55.2	23 44.2	0 56.5
5	4 53 18.2	12 22.1	23 52.0	19 36.3	18 54.2	9 14.9	3 21.8	23 20.7	18 9.1	27 57.9	23 46.0	0 58.8
6	4 57 14.8	13 22.9	23 48.8	1♊42.7	20 27.9	10 29.3	4 7.4	23 34.2	18 10.5	28 .6	23 47.8	1 1.2
7	5 1 11.3	14 23.8	23 45.7	13 43.4	22 1.4	11 43.7	4 53.2	23 47.8	18 12.1	28 3.4	23 49.7	1 3.5
8	5 5 7.9	15 24.7	23 42.5	25 39.6	23 35.0	12 58.1	5 38.9	24 1.3	18 13.8	28 6.2	23 51.6	1 5.8
9	5 9 4.4	16 25.6	23 39.3	7♋32.8	25 8.6	14 12.5	6 24.7	24 14.9	18 15.6	28 9.0	23 53.4	1 8.2
10	5 13 1.0	17 26.6	23 36.1	19 24.4	26 42.1	15 26.8	7 10.6	24 28.5	18 17.4	28 11.8	23 55.3	1 10.5
11	5 16 57.5	18 27.5	23 32.9	1♌16.6	28 15.6	16 41.2	7 56.5	24 42.2	18 19.4	28 14.7	23 57.3	1 12.8
12	5 20 54.1	19 28.5	23 29.8	13 11.8	29 49.1	17 55.5	8 42.5	24 55.8	18 21.5	28 17.7	23 59.2	1 15.1
13	5 24 50.6	20 29.5	23 26.6	25 13.2	1♑22.6	19 9.8	9 28.5	25 9.4	18 23.7	28 20.6	24 1.2	1 17.4
14	5 28 47.2	21 30.5	23 23.4	7♍24.7	2 56.0	20 24.1	10 14.5	25 23.1	18 26.0	28 23.6	24 3.2	1 19.6
15	5 32 43.8	22 31.5	23 20.2	19 50.7	4 29.3	21 38.4	11 .6	25 36.8	18 28.4	28 26.6	24 5.2	1 21.9
16	5 36 40.3	23 32.6	23 17.1	2♎35.8	6 2.5	22 52.7	11 46.8	25 50.4	18 30.9	28 29.6	24 7.2	1 24.2
17	5 40 36.9	24 33.6	23 13.9	15 44.6	7 35.6	24 6.9	12 33.0	26 4.1	18 33.4	28 32.7	24 9.2	1 26.4
18	5 44 33.4	25 34.7	23 10.7	29 20.7	9 8.4	25 21.1	13 19.2	26 17.8	18 36.1	28 35.8	24 11.2	1 28.6
19	5 48 30.0	26 35.8	23 7.5	13♏26.1	10 40.9	26 35.3	14 5.5	26 31.5	18 38.9	28 38.9	24 13.3	1 30.8
20	5 52 26.5	27 36.9	23 4.4	28 .1	12 13.1	27 49.5	14 51.8	26 45.2	18 41.8	28 42.0	24 15.4	1 33.0
21	5 56 23.1	28 38.0	23 1.2	12♐58.4	13 44.8	29 3.7	15 38.2	26 58.9	18 44.8	28 45.2	24 17.5	1 35.2
22	6 0 19.7	29 39.1	22 58.0	28 13.3	15 15.9	0♒17.8	16 24.6	27 12.6	18 47.9	28 48.4	24 19.6	1 37.4
23	6 4 16.2	0♑40.3	22 54.8	13♑34.0	16 46.3	1 32.0	17 11.0	27 26.2	18 51.1	28 51.6	24 21.7	1 39.6
24	6 8 12.8	1 41.5	22 51.7	28 48.9	18 15.9	2 46.1	17 57.6	27 40.0	18 54.4	28 54.8	24 23.9	1 41.7
25	6 12 9.3	2 42.6	22 48.5	13♒47.2	19 44.4	4 .2	18 44.1	27 53.7	18 57.8	28 58.1	24 26.0	1 43.9
26	6 16 5.9	3 43.8	22 45.3	28 21.2	21 11.5	5 14.2	19 30.7	28 7.3	19 1.2	29 1.4	24 28.2	1 46.0
27	6 20 2.4	4 44.9	22 42.1	12♓26.7	22 37.1	6 28.2	20 17.3	28 21.0	19 4.8	29 4.6	24 30.3	1 48.1
28	6 23 59.0	5 46.1	22 38.9	26 3.2	24 .8	7 42.2	21 3.9	28 34.6	19 8.4	29 7.9	24 32.5	1 50.1
29	6 27 55.6	6 47.2	22 35.8	9♈12.9	25 22.3	8 56.1	21 50.6	28 48.3	19 12.2	29 11.3	24 34.7	1 52.2
30	6 31 52.1	7 48.4	22 32.6	21 59.4	26 41.1	10 10.0	22 37.3	29 1.9	19 16.0	29 14.6	24 36.9	1 54.2
31	6 35 48.7	8 49.5	22 29.4	4♉27.2	27 56.8	11 23.9	23 24.0	29 15.5	19 19.9	29 18.0	24 39.1	1 56.2

LATITUDE

DAY	EPHEM. SID. TIME	☉	☊	☽	☿	♀	♂	♃	♄	♅	♆	♇
1	4 37 32.0	0 .0	0 .0	2N17.7	1S15.4	1S21.6	0S57.2	0N17.6	2S12.6	0S32.3	0N29.9	12N49.0
4	4 49 21.6	0 .0	0 .0	1S 2.1	1 31.1	1 27.0	0 58.1	0 17.3	2 12.0	0 32.3	0 29.9	12 49.0
7	5 1 11.3	0 .0	0 .0	3 48.8	1 45.0	1 31.9	0 59.0	0 17.0	2 11.4	0 32.2	0 29.8	12 49.0
10	5 13 1.0	0 .0	0 .0	5 4.0	1 56.8	1 36.3	0 59.8	0 16.7	2 10.8	0 32.2	0 29.7	12 49.1
13	5 24 50.6	0 .0	0 .0	4 23.5	2 6.0	1 40.1	1 .6	0 16.4	2 10.3	0 32.1	0 29.7	12 49.3
16	5 36 40.3	0 .0	0 .0	1 54.8	2 12.2	1 43.3	1 1.4	0 16.1	2 9.7	0 32.1	0 29.6	12 49.5
19	5 48 30.0	0 .0	0 .0	1N38.8	2 14.7	1 45.9	1 2.0	0 15.9	2 9.2	0 32.1	0 29.6	12 49.8
22	6 0 19.7	0 .0	0 .0	4 32.3	2 13.1	1 47.8	1 2.6	0 15.6	2 8.6	0 32.1	0 29.5	12 50.2
25	6 12 9.3	0 .0	0 .0	4 44.4	2 6.2	1 49.0	1 3.2	0 15.3	2 8.1	0 32.0	0 29.5	12 50.6
28	6 23 59.0	0 .0	0 .0	2 20.3	1 53.2	1 49.6	1 3.7	0 15.1	2 7.6	0 32.0	0 29.4	12 51.1
31	6 35 48.7	0 .0	0 .0	0S57.7	1 32.8	1 49.4	1 4.1	0 14.8	2 7.1	0 32.0	0 29.4	12 51.6

RIGHT ASCENSION

DAY	EPHEM. SID. TIME	☉	☊	☽	☿	♀	♂	♃	♄	♅	♆	♇
1	4 37 32.0	6♐33.8	22♎17.6	28♓39.4	11♐ 1.7	4♑42.9	0♑21.4	21♐47.5	19♓53.9	29♑59.1	25♑25.3	1♐19.7
2	4 41 28.5	7 38.5	22 14.6	10♈54.9	12 42.5	6 4.9	1 11.4	22 2.1	19 54.8	0♒ 1.8	25 27.1	1 22.0
3	4 45 25.1	8 43.4	22 11.6	23 6.9	14 23.8	7 26.9	2 1.4	22 16.8	19 55.8	0 4.6	25 29.1	1 24.4
4	4 49 21.6	9 48.4	22 8.7	5♉22.1	16 5.4	8 48.8	2 51.4	22 31.4	19 56.9	0 7.4	25 30.9	1 26.6
5	4 53 18.2	10 53.6	22 5.7	17 44.4	17 47.3	10 10.6	3 41.5	22 46.1	19 58.1	0 10.2	25 32.9	1 28.9
6	4 57 14.8	11 58.8	22 2.7	0♊14.6	19 29.5	11 32.3	4 31.6	23 .7	19 59.4	0 13.1	25 34.8	1 31.2
7	5 1 11.3	13 4.3	21 59.7	12 49.9	21 12.1	12 53.9	5 21.8	23 15.5	20 .7	0 16.0	25 36.7	1 33.4
8	5 5 7.9	14 9.8	21 56.7	25 25.5	22 54.9	14 15.3	6 11.9	23 30.2	20 2.2	0 18.9	25 38.7	1 35.7
9	5 9 4.4	15 15.5	21 53.7	7♋55.5	24 37.9	15 36.6	7 2.2	23 44.9	20 3.8	0 21.9	25 40.7	1 37.9
10	5 13 1.0	16 21.3	21 50.7	20 15.1	26 21.1	16 57.8	7 52.4	23 59.7	20 5.4	0 24.9	25 42.7	1 40.2
11	5 16 57.5	17 27.1	21 47.7	2♌21.6	28 4.5	18 18.8	8 42.7	24 14.5	20 7.2	0 27.9	25 44.7	1 42.4
12	5 20 54.1	18 33.2	21 44.7	14 15.4	29 48.0	19 39.5	9 33.0	24 29.3	20 9.1	0 31.0	25 46.8	1 44.7
13	5 24 50.6	19 39.3	21 41.7	26 .3	1♑31.5	21 .1	10 23.3	24 44.1	20 11.0	0 34.1	25 48.9	1 46.9
14	5 28 47.2	20 45.4	21 38.7	7♍42.7	3 15.0	22 20.5	11 13.6	24 58.9	20 13.1	0 37.2	25 51.0	1 49.1
15	5 32 43.8	21 51.7	21 35.8	19 31.5	4 58.3	23 40.6	12 3.9	25 13.8	20 15.2	0 40.4	25 53.1	1 51.3
16	5 36 40.3	22 58.1	21 32.8	1♎37.3	6 41.5	25 .5	12 54.2	25 28.6	20 17.4	0 43.5	25 55.2	1 53.5
17	5 40 36.9	24 4.5	21 29.8	14 11.8	8 24.4	26 20.2	13 44.6	25 43.5	20 19.7	0 46.8	25 57.3	1 55.7
18	5 44 33.4	25 11.0	21 26.8	27 26.3	10 6.9	27 39.6	14 34.9	25 58.4	20 22.0	0 50.0	25 59.5	1 57.8
19	5 48 30.0	26 17.5	21 23.8	11♏29.5	11 49.0	28 58.7	15 25.2	26 13.2	20 24.7	0 53.2	26 1.7	2 .0
20	5 52 26.5	27 24.1	21 20.8	26 24.0	13 30.3	0♒17.5	16 15.5	26 28.1	20 27.3	0 56.5	26 3.8	2 2.2
21	5 56 23.1	28 30.7	21 17.8	12♐ 2.8	15 10.9	1 36.0	17 5.8	26 43.0	20 30.0	0 59.8	26 6.1	2 4.3
22	6 0 19.7	29 37.3	21 14.8	28 7.6	16 50.5	2 54.2	17 56.1	26 57.9	20 32.7	1 3.2	26 8.3	2 6.4
23	6 4 16.2	0♑43.9	21 11.9	14♑12.6	18 29.0	4 12.1	18 46.3	27 12.8	20 35.6	1 6.5	26 10.5	2 8.5
24	6 8 12.8	1 50.6	21 8.9	29 52.9	20 6.2	5 29.8	19 36.6	27 27.7	20 38.6	1 10.0	26 12.8	2 10.7
25	6 12 9.3	2 57.2	21 5.9	14♒51.7	21 41.6	6 47.0	20 26.7	27 42.6	20 41.7	1 13.4	26 15.1	2 12.8
26	6 16 5.9	4 3.8	21 2.9	29 3.7	23 15.2	8 3.9	21 16.9	27 57.4	20 44.8	1 16.8	26 17.3	2 14.8
27	6 20 2.4	5 10.4	20 59.9	12♓32.5	24 46.6	9 20.5	22 7.0	28 12.3	20 48.0	1 20.2	26 19.6	2 16.9
28	6 23 59.0	6 17.0	20 56.9	25 27.0	26 15.4	10 36.7	22 57.0	28 27.1	20 51.3	1 23.7	26 21.9	2 18.9
29	6 27 55.6	7 23.5	20 53.9	7♈58.3	27 41.2	11 52.6	23 47.0	28 42.0	20 54.7	1 27.2	26 24.2	2 20.9
30	6 31 52.1	8 29.9	20 51.0	20 16.7	29 3.7	13 8.1	24 37.0	28 56.8	20 58.2	1 30.7	26 26.5	2 22.9
31	6 35 48.7	9 36.3	20 48.0	2♉31.3	0♒22.2	14 23.3	25 26.9	29 11.6	21 1.7	1 34.2	26 28.8	2 24.9

DECLINATION

DAY	EPHEM. SID. TIME	☉	☊	☽	☿	♀	♂	♃	♄	♅	♆	♇
1	4 37 32.0	21S41.4	0S 9.8	1N55.1	23S33.6	24S43.6	24S23.4	22S55.8	6S45.0	21S 7.8	20S52.6	7S45.9
4	4 49 21.6	22 8.4	0 9.7	12 59.5	24 20.8	24 38.6	24 22.8	22 58.3	6 43.1	21 6.2	20 51.7	7 47.2
7	5 1 11.3	22 31.5	0 9.7	18 39.6	24 56.7	24 26.7	24 19.8	23 .5	6 40.8	21 4.5	20 50.8	7 48.5
10	5 13 1.0	22 50.7	0 9.6	17 1.0	25 20.5	24 8.2	24 14.3	23 2.6	6 38.2	21 2.8	20 49.9	7 49.7
13	5 24 50.6	23 5.8	0 9.5	8 58.4	25 31.8	23 43.2	24 6.4	23 4.5	6 35.2	21 1.0	20 49.0	7 50.9
16	5 36 40.3	23 16.8	0 9.5	2S47.3	25 30.0	23 11.7	23 56.0	23 6.2	6 31.9	20 59.1	20 48.0	7 51.9
19	5 48 30.0	23 23.6	0 9.4	14 18.0	25 14.8	22 34.0	23 43.2	23 7.6	6 28.2	20 57.2	20 47.0	7 52.9
22	6 0 19.7	23 26.2	0 9.3	18 53.3	24 46.0	21 50.4	23 27.9	23 8.9	6 24.2	20 55.2	20 45.9	7 53.7
25	6 12 9.3	23 24.6	0 9.3	12 8.5	24 4.0	21 1.1	23 10.2	23 9.9	6 19.9	20 53.2	20 44.8	7 54.5
28	6 23 59.0	23 18.7	0 9.2	0N34.7	23 9.7	20 6.4	22 50.2	23 10.7	6 15.2	20 51.1	20 43.7	7 55.2
31	6 35 48.7	23 8.6	0 9.2	12 5.9	22 5.2	19 6.6	22 27.8	23 11.3	6 10.2	20 49.1	20 42.6	7 55.8

JANUARY 1996

LONGITUDE

DAY	EPHEM. SID. TIME	☉	☊	☽	☿	♀	♂	♃	♄	♅	♆	♇
	h m s	° ′	° ′	° ′	° ′	° ′	° ′	° ′	° ′	° ′	° ′	° ′
1	6 39 45.2	9 ♑ 50.7	22 ♎ 26.2	16 ♉ 41.0	29 ♑ 8.8	12 ♒ 37.7	24 ♑ 10.8	29 ♐ 29.1	19 ♓ 23.9	29 ♑ 21.3	24 ♑ 41.3	1 ♐ 58.2
2	6 43 41.8	10 51.8	22 23.1	28 44.9	0 ♒ 16.5	13 51.5	24 57.6	29 42.7	19 28.0	29 24.7	24 43.5	2 .2
3	6 47 38.3	11 53.0	22 19.9	10 ♊ 42.4	1 19.3	15 5.3	25 44.4	29 56.3	19 32.2	29 28.1	24 45.7	2 2.2
4	6 51 34.9	12 54.1	22 16.7	22 36.3	2 16.3	16 19.0	26 31.3	0 ♑ 9.8	19 36.4	29 31.5	24 48.0	2 4.1
5	6 55 31.5	13 55.2	22 13.5	4 ♋ 28.7	3 6.8	17 32.6	27 18.1	0 23.4	19 40.8	29 35.0	24 50.2	2 6.0
6	6 59 28.0	14 56.4	22 10.4	16 21.2	3 49.8	18 46.3	28 5.1	0 36.9	19 45.2	29 38.4	24 52.5	2 7.9
7	7 3 24.6	15 57.5	22 7.2	28 15.0	4 24.6	19 59.8	28 52.0	0 50.3	19 49.7	29 41.9	24 54.7	2 9.8
8	7 7 21.1	16 58.6	22 4.0	10 ♌ 11.3	4 50.1	21 13.4	29 39.0	1 3.8	19 54.3	29 45.3	24 57.0	2 11.6
9	7 11 17.7	17 59.8	22 .8	22 11.6	5 5.5	22 26.8	0 ♒ 26.0	1 17.2	19 59.0	29 48.8	24 59.2	2 13.4
10	7 15 14.2	19 .9	21 57.6	4 ♍ 17.9	5 10.1	23 40.3	1 13.0	1 30.6	20 3.7	29 52.3	25 1.5	2 15.2
11	7 19 10.8	20 2.0	21 54.5	16 32.6	5 R 3.2	24 53.6	2 .0	1 44.0	20 8.5	29 55.8	25 3.8	2 17.0
12	7 23 7.4	21 3.2	21 51.3	28 59.2	4 44.5	26 7.0	2 47.1	1 57.4	20 13.4	29 59.3	25 6.0	2 18.8
13	7 27 3.9	22 4.3	21 48.1	11 ♎ 41.4	4 14.1	27 20.3	3 34.2	2 10.7	20 18.4	0 ♒ 2.8	25 8.3	2 20.5
14	7 31 .5	23 5.5	21 44.9	24 43.5	3 32.3	28 33.5	4 21.4	2 24.0	20 23.5	0 6.3	25 10.6	2 22.2
15	7 34 57.0	24 6.6	21 41.8	8 ♏ 9.4	2 39.9	29 46.7	5 8.5	2 37.3	20 28.6	0 9.8	25 12.9	2 23.9
16	7 38 53.6	25 7.7	21 38.6	22 1.9	1 38.2	0 ♓ 59.8	5 55.7	2 50.5	20 33.8	0 13.4	25 15.2	2 25.5
17	7 42 50.1	26 8.9	21 35.4	6 ♐ 22.1	0 29.1	2 12.9	6 42.9	3 3.7	20 39.1	0 16.9	25 17.4	2 27.2
18	7 46 46.7	27 10.0	21 32.2	21 8.2	29 ♑ 14.5	3 25.9	7 30.2	3 16.8	20 44.5	0 20.4	25 19.7	2 28.8
19	7 50 43.3	28 11.1	21 29.1	6 ♑ 14.6	27 57.0	4 38.9	8 17.4	3 29.9	20 49.9	0 23.9	25 22.0	2 30.3
20	7 54 39.8	29 12.2	21 25.9	21 32.2	26 38.8	5 51.8	9 4.7	3 43.0	20 55.4	0 27.5	25 24.3	2 31.9
21	7 58 36.4	0 ♒ 13.3	21 22.7	6 ♒ 49.9	25 22.4	7 4.6	9 51.9	3 56.0	21 .9	0 31.0	25 26.5	2 33.4
22	8 2 32.9	1 14.4	21 19.5	21 56.0	24 10.0	8 17.4	10 39.2	4 9.0	21 6.5	0 34.5	25 28.8	2 34.8
23	8 6 29.5	2 15.5	21 16.3	6 ♓ 14.6	23 3.2	9 30.1	11 26.6	4 21.9	21 12.2	0 38.1	25 31.1	2 36.3
24	8 10 26.0	3 16.5	21 13.2	20 58.0	22 3.6	10 42.7	12 13.9	4 34.8	21 18.0	0 41.6	25 33.3	2 37.7
25	8 14 22.6	4 17.6	21 10.0	4 ♈ 45.1	21 12.1	11 55.3	13 1.2	4 47.7	21 23.8	0 45.1	25 35.6	2 39.1
26	8 18 19.1	5 18.6	21 6.8	18 2.8	20 29.3	13 7.7	13 48.6	5 .4	21 29.6	0 48.7	25 37.9	2 40.5
27	8 22 15.7	6 19.6	21 3.6	0 ♉ 54.2	19 55.5	14 20.1	14 36.0	5 13.2	21 35.6	0 52.2	25 40.1	2 41.8
28	8 26 12.3	7 20.6	21 .5	13 23.8	19 30.8	15 32.4	15 23.3	5 25.8	21 41.5	0 55.7	25 42.3	2 43.1
29	8 30 8.8	8 21.6	20 57.3	25 36.7	19 14.9	16 44.7	16 10.7	5 38.5	21 47.6	0 59.2	25 44.6	2 44.4
30	8 34 5.4	9 22.5	20 54.1	7 ♊ 37.9	19 7.5	17 56.8	16 58.1	5 51.0	21 53.7	1 2.7	25 46.8	2 45.6
31	8 38 1.9	10 23.4	20 50.9	19 32.0	19 D 8.0	19 8.9	17 45.5	6 3.5	21 59.8	1 6.2	25 49.0	2 46.8

LATITUDE

DAY	EPHEM. SID. TIME	☉	☊	☽	☿	♀	♂	♃	♄	♅	♆	♇
1	6 39 45.2	0 .0	0 .0	1 S 59.4	1 S 24.1	1 S 49.1	1 S 4.3	0 N 14.7	2 S 6.9	0 S 32.0	0 N 29.4	12 N 51.8
4	6 51 34.9	0 .0	0 .0	4 18.9	0 51.9	1 47.9	1 4.6	0 14.5	2 6.4	0 32.0	0 29.3	12 52.4
7	7 3 24.6	0 .0	0 .0	4 57.8	0 10.0	1 45.9	1 4.9	0 14.2	2 6.0	0 32.0	0 29.3	12 53.1
10	7 15 14.2	0 .0	0 .0	3 41.8	0 N 41.1	1 43.2	1 5.2	0 14.0	2 5.5	0 32.0	0 29.2	12 53.8
13	7 27 3.9	0 .0	0 .0	0 52.0	1 37.3	1 39.6	1 5.4	0 13.7	2 5.1	0 32.0	0 29.2	12 54.5
16	7 38 53.6	0 .0	0 .0	2 N 33.4	2 30.8	1 35.3	1 5.5	0 13.5	2 4.7	0 32.0	0 29.2	12 55.3
19	7 50 43.3	0 .0	0 .0	4 50.3	3 10.8	1 30.2	1 5.5	0 13.3	2 4.3	0 32.0	0 29.1	12 56.1
22	8 2 32.9	0 .0	0 .0	4 17.2	3 29.6	1 24.3	1 5.5	0 13.0	2 3.9	0 32.0	0 29.1	12 57.0
25	8 14 22.6	0 .0	0 .0	1 21.6	3 26.9	1 17.7	1 5.4	0 12.8	2 3.6	0 32.1	0 29.1	12 57.9
28	8 26 12.3	0 .0	0 .0	1 S 59.1	3 8.1	1 10.3	1 5.3	0 12.6	2 3.2	0 32.1	0 29.1	12 58.9
31	8 38 1.9	0 .0	0 .0	4 20.4	2 39.9	1 2.2	1 5.1	0 12.3	2 2.9	0 32.1	0 29.0	12 59.9

RIGHT ASCENSION

DAY	EPHEM. SID. TIME	☉	☊	☽	☿	♀	♂	♃	♄	♅	♆	♇
1	6 39 45.2	10 ♑ 42.6	20 ♎ 45.0	14 ♉ 48.3	1 ♒ 36.2	15 ♒ 38.0	26 ♑ 16.7	29 ♐ 26.4	21 ♓ 5.4	1 ♒ 37.7	26 ♑ 31.2	2 ♐ 26.9
2	6 43 41.8	11 48.8	20 42.0	27 11.2	2 45.1	16 52.5	27 6.4	29 41.2	21 9.1	1 41.2	26 33.5	2 28.8
3	6 47 38.3	12 55.0	20 39.0	9 ♊ 40.1	3 48.2	18 6.5	27 56.1	29 56.0	21 12.9	1 44.8	26 35.8	2 30.7
4	6 51 34.9	14 1.1	20 36.0	22 12.1	4 44.8	19 20.2	28 45.8	0 ♑ 10.7	21 16.7	1 48.4	26 38.2	2 32.7
5	6 55 31.5	15 7.0	20 33.1	4 ♋ 42.6	5 34.0	20 33.6	29 35.3	0 25.4	21 20.7	1 51.9	26 40.6	2 34.5
6	6 59 28.0	16 12.9	20 30.1	17 6.3	6 15.1	21 46.5	0 ♒ 24.8	0 40.1	21 24.7	1 55.5	26 42.9	2 36.4
7	7 3 24.6	17 18.7	20 27.1	29 19.2	6 47.1	22 59.1	1 14.2	0 54.8	21 28.8	1 59.1	26 45.3	2 38.3
8	7 7 21.1	18 24.3	20 24.1	11 ♌ 19.4	7 9.2	24 11.4	2 3.6	1 9.4	21 33.0	2 2.8	26 47.7	2 40.1
9	7 11 17.7	19 29.8	20 21.1	23 8.0	7 20.7	25 23.3	2 52.8	1 24.0	21 37.3	2 6.4	26 50.0	2 41.9
10	7 15 14.2	20 35.2	20 18.2	4 ♍ 49.2	7 20.8	26 34.8	3 42.0	1 38.6	21 41.6	2 10.0	26 52.4	2 43.7
11	7 19 10.8	21 40.5	20 15.2	16 29.6	7 R 9.1	27 46.0	4 31.1	1 53.2	21 46.0	2 13.7	26 54.8	2 45.4
12	7 23 7.4	22 45.6	20 12.2	28 18.0	6 45.4	28 56.9	5 20.1	2 7.7	21 50.5	2 17.3	26 57.2	2 47.2
13	7 27 3.9	23 50.6	20 9.2	10 ♎ 24.6	6 9.6	0 ♓ 7.4	6 9.0	2 22.2	21 55.0	2 21.0	26 59.6	2 48.9
14	7 31 .5	24 55.5	20 6.2	23 .4	5 22.5	1 17.7	6 57.9	2 36.7	21 59.6	2 24.7	27 2.0	2 50.6
15	7 34 57.0	26 .1	20 3.3	6 ♏ 15.8	4 24.7	2 27.5	7 46.6	2 51.1	22 4.3	2 28.4	27 4.4	2 52.3
16	7 38 53.6	27 4.7	20 .3	20 18.0	3 17.9	3 37.1	8 35.3	3 5.5	22 9.1	2 32.0	27 6.8	2 53.9
17	7 42 50.1	28 9.0	19 57.3	5 ♐ 8.5	2 3.7	4 46.3	9 23.8	3 19.8	22 13.9	2 35.7	27 9.2	2 55.5
18	7 46 46.7	29 13.2	19 54.3	20 39.5	0 44.5	5 55.2	10 12.3	3 34.1	22 18.8	2 39.4	27 11.6	2 57.1
19	7 50 43.3	0 ♒ 17.2	19 51.3	6 ♑ 33.6	29 ♑ 22.6	7 3.8	11 .6	3 48.4	22 23.7	2 43.1	27 14.0	2 58.7
20	7 54 39.8	1 21.1	19 48.4	22 27.3	28 .5	8 12.1	11 48.9	4 2.6	22 28.7	2 46.8	27 16.4	3 .2
21	7 58 36.4	2 24.7	19 45.4	7 ♒ 58.7	26 40.7	9 20.2	12 37.1	4 16.7	22 33.8	2 50.5	27 18.8	3 1.8
22	8 2 32.9	3 28.2	19 42.4	22 53.7	25 25.2	10 27.9	13 25.1	4 30.9	22 38.9	2 54.1	27 21.2	3 3.2
23	8 6 29.5	4 31.4	19 39.4	7 ♓ 7.6	24 15.9	11 35.4	14 13.1	4 44.9	22 44.1	2 57.8	27 23.5	3 4.7
24	8 10 26.0	5 34.5	19 36.5	20 43.6	23 14.3	12 42.6	15 .9	4 58.9	22 49.4	3 1.5	27 25.9	3 6.1
25	8 14 22.6	6 37.4	19 33.5	3 ♈ 49.3	22 21.3	13 49.5	15 48.7	5 12.9	22 54.7	3 5.2	27 28.3	3 7.5
26	8 18 19.1	7 40.1	19 30.5	16 34.0	21 37.6	14 56.2	16 36.3	5 26.8	23 .0	3 8.9	27 30.7	3 8.9
27	8 22 15.7	8 42.5	19 27.5	29 6.3	21 3.3	16 2.6	17 23.8	5 40.6	23 5.5	3 12.5	27 33.0	3 10.3
28	8 26 12.3	9 44.8	19 24.5	11 ♉ 33.5	20 38.7	17 8.8	18 11.2	5 54.4	23 10.9	3 16.2	27 35.4	3 11.6
29	8 30 8.8	10 46.9	19 21.6	24 .2	20 23.3	18 14.7	18 58.5	6 8.1	23 16.5	3 19.9	27 37.7	3 12.9
30	8 34 5.4	11 48.7	19 18.6	6 ♊ 28.7	20 16.9	19 20.4	19 45.7	6 21.8	23 22.0	3 23.5	27 40.1	3 14.1
31	8 38 1.9	12 50.4	19 15.6	18 58.5	20 D 19.0	20 25.9	20 32.8	6 35.3	23 27.7	3 27.2	27 42.4	3 15.3

DECLINATION

DAY	EPHEM. SID. TIME	☉	☊	☽	☿	♀	♂	♃	♄	♅	♆	♇
1	6 39 45.2	23 S 4.3	0 S 9.1	14 N 54.8	21 S 41.9	18 S 45.6	22 S 19.8	23 S 11.4	6 S 8.5	20 S 48.3	20 S 42.2	7 S 56.0
4	6 51 34.9	22 48.7	0 9.1	18 55.4	20 29.7	17 39.6	21 54.3	23 11.7	6 3.1	20 46.2	20 41.1	7 56.5
7	7 3 24.6	22 29.0	0 9.0	15 38.7	19 19.0	16 29.3	21 26.7	23 11.8	5 57.5	20 44.0	20 39.9	7 56.9
10	7 15 14.2	22 5.3	0 9.0	6 29.2	18 18.6	15 15.1	20 56.8	23 11.7	5 51.6	20 41.8	20 38.7	7 57.2
13	7 27 3.9	21 37.8	0 8.9	5 S 25.3	17 37.3	13 57.3	20 24.8	23 11.4	5 45.4	20 39.6	20 37.6	7 57.4
16	7 38 53.6	21 6.4	0 8.8	15 48.2	17 20.5	12 36.2	19 50.7	23 10.9	5 38.9	20 37.4	20 36.3	7 57.5
19	7 50 43.3	20 31.4	0 8.8	18 27.4	17 27.2	11 12.3	19 14.7	23 10.2	5 32.2	20 35.1	20 35.1	7 57.6
22	8 2 32.9	19 52.9	0 8.7	10 8.1	17 50.2	9 45.8	18 36.8	23 9.3	5 25.3	20 32.8	20 33.9	7 57.5
25	8 14 22.6	19 11.1	0 8.6	3 N 8.2	18 21.5	8 17.2	17 57.1	23 8.2	5 18.2	20 30.6	20 32.7	7 57.4
28	8 26 12.3	18 26.1	0 8.6	13 57.9	18 54.9	6 46.8	17 15.6	23 7.0	5 10.9	20 28.3	20 31.5	7 57.2
31	8 38 1.9	17 38.1	0 8.5	18 41.8	19 26.0	5 14.9	16 32.5	23 5.6	5 3.4	20 26.0	20 30.3	7 56.9

FEBRUARY 1996

LONGITUDE

DAY	EPHEM. SID. TIME	☉	☊	☽	☿	♀	♂	♃	♄	♅	♆	♇
	h m s	° ′	° ′	° ′	° ′	° ′	° ′	° ′	° ′	° ′	° ′	° ′
1	8 41 58.5	11♒24.3	20♎47.7	1♋23.1	19♑16.1	20♓20.8	18♒32.9	6♑16.0	22♓ 6.1	1♒ 9.7	25♑51.2	2♐48.0
2	8 45 55.0	12 25.2	20 44.6	13 14.3	19 31.1	21 32.7	19 20.3	6 28.4	22 12.3	1 13.2	25 53.4	2 49.1
3	8 49 51.6	13 26.1	20 41.4	25 8.0	19 52.5	22 44.4	20 7.8	6 40.7	22 18.6	1 16.7	25 55.6	2 50.2
4	8 53 48.1	14 27.0	20 38.2	7♌ 6.1	20 19.9	23 56.2	20 55.2	6 53.0	22 25.0	1 20.2	25 57.9	2 51.4
5	8 57 44.7	15 27.8	20 35.0	19 9.7	20 52.7	25 7.7	21 42.7	7 5.2	22 31.5	1 23.6	26 .0	2 52.4
6	9 1 41.2	16 28.6	20 31.9	1♍19.9	21 30.3	26 19.2	22 30.1	7 17.4	22 37.9	1 27.1	26 2.2	2 53.4
7	9 5 37.8	17 29.4	20 28.7	13 37.6	22 12.5	27 30.5	23 17.6	7 29.4	22 44.4	1 30.5	26 4.4	2 54.4
8	9 9 34.4	18 30.2	20 25.5	26 4.2	22 58.8	28 41.8	24 5.0	7 41.4	22 51.0	1 33.9	26 6.5	2 55.4
9	9 13 30.9	19 31.0	20 22.3	8♎41.4	23 48.9	29 52.9	24 52.4	7 53.3	22 57.6	1 37.3	26 8.6	2 56.3
10	9 17 27.5	20 31.7	20 19.2	21 31.4	24 42.4	1♈ 4.0	25 39.9	8 5.2	23 4.2	1 40.7	26 10.8	2 57.2
11	9 21 24.0	21 32.4	20 16.0	4♏36.8	25 39.1	2 14.9	26 27.4	8 17.0	23 10.9	1 44.1	26 12.9	2 58.0
12	9 25 20.6	22 33.1	20 12.8	18 .5	26 38.6	3 25.7	27 14.8	8 28.7	23 17.6	1 47.5	26 15.0	2 58.8
13	9 29 17.1	23 33.8	20 9.6	1♐44.8	27 40.9	4 36.4	28 2.3	8 40.3	23 24.4	1 50.8	26 17.0	2 59.6
14	9 33 13.7	24 34.5	20 6.4	15 50.8	28 45.6	5 46.9	28 49.7	8 51.9	23 31.2	1 54.1	26 19.1	3 .3
15	9 37 10.2	25 35.1	20 3.3	0♑17.9	29 52.5	6 57.4	29 37.2	9 3.4	23 38.1	1 57.5	26 21.2	3 1.0
16	9 41 6.8	26 35.8	20 .1	15 2.9	1♒ 1.6	8 7.7	0♓24.6	9 14.7	23 45.0	2 .8	26 23.2	3 1.7
17	9 45 3.3	27 36.4	19 56.9	29 59.6	2 12.6	9 17.9	1 12.1	9 26.1	23 51.9	2 4.0	26 25.2	3 2.4
18	9 48 59.9	28 37.0	19 53.7	14♒59.7	3 25.5	10 27.9	1 59.5	9 37.3	23 58.8	2 7.3	26 27.2	3 3.0
19	9 52 56.4	29 37.5	19 50.6	29 53.8	4 40.1	11 37.9	2 47.0	9 48.4	24 5.8	2 10.5	26 29.2	3 3.5
20	9 56 53.0	0♓38.1	19 47.4	14♓32.9	5 56.4	12 47.7	3 34.4	9 59.5	24 12.8	2 13.7	26 31.2	3 4.1
21	10 0 49.6	1 38.6	19 44.2	28 50.1	7 14.1	13 57.3	4 21.9	10 10.4	24 19.9	2 16.9	26 33.1	3 4.6
22	10 4 46.1	2 39.0	19 41.0	12♈41.3	8 33.4	15 6.8	5 9.3	10 21.3	24 27.0	2 20.1	26 35.0	3 5.0
23	10 8 42.7	3 39.5	19 37.8	26 5.4	9 54.0	16 16.1	5 56.7	10 32.1	24 34.1	2 23.3	26 37.0	3 5.5
24	10 12 39.2	4 39.9	19 34.7	9♉ 3.6	11 16.0	17 25.3	6 44.1	10 42.7	24 41.2	2 26.4	26 38.9	3 5.9
25	10 16 35.8	5 40.3	19 31.5	21 39.2	12 39.3	18 34.4	7 31.5	10 53.4	24 48.4	2 29.5	26 40.8	3 6.3
26	10 20 32.3	6 40.7	19 28.3	3♊56.5	14 3.8	19 43.3	8 18.9	11 3.8	24 55.6	2 32.6	26 42.6	3 6.6
27	10 24 28.9	7 41.0	19 25.1	16 .3	15 29.6	20 51.9	9 6.3	11 14.2	25 2.8	2 35.7	26 44.5	3 6.9
28	10 28 25.4	8 41.3	19 22.0	27 55.7	16 56.5	22 .5	9 53.6	11 24.5	25 10.1	2 38.7	26 46.3	3 7.1
29	10 32 22.0	9 41.6	19 18.8	9♋47.3	18 24.6	23 8.8	10 40.9	11 34.7	25 17.3	2 41.7	26 48.1	3 7.3

LATITUDE

DAY	EPHEM. SID. TIME	☉	☊	☽	☿	♀	♂	♃	♄	♅	♆	♇
1	8 41 58.5	0 .0	0 .0	4S46.3	2N29.3	0S59.3	1S 5.0	0N12.3	2S 2.8	0S32.1	0N29.0	13N .2
4	8 53 48.1	0 .0	0 .0	4 47.7	1 56.0	0 50.3	1 4.8	0 12.0	2 2.6	0 32.2	0 29.0	13 1.2
7	9 5 37.8	0 .0	0 .0	2 55.6	1 22.2	0 40.6	1 4.4	0 11.8	2 2.3	0 32.2	0 29.0	13 2.3
10	9 17 27.5	0 .0	0 .0	0N15.1	0 49.5	0 30.3	1 4.0	0 11.6	2 2.1	0 32.2	0 29.0	13 3.3
13	9 29 17.1	0 .0	0 .0	3 29.6	0 18.6	0 19.3	1 3.5	0 11.3	2 1.9	0 32.3	0 29.0	13 4.4
16	9 41 6.8	0 .0	0 .0	5 5.8	0S10.0	0 7.8	1 3.0	0 11.1	2 1.7	0 32.3	0 29.0	13 5.5
19	9 52 56.4	0 .0	0 .0	3 49.3	0 35.9	0N 4.2	1 2.4	0 10.9	2 1.5	0 32.4	0 29.0	13 6.6
22	10 4 46.1	0 .0	0 .0	0 28.3	0 59.2	0 16.6	1 1.8	0 10.7	2 1.4	0 32.4	0 29.0	13 7.8
25	10 16 35.8	0 .0	0 .0	2S52.4	1 19.5	0 29.5	1 1.1	0 10.4	2 1.3	0 32.5	0 29.0	13 8.9
28	10 28 25.4	0 .0	0 .0	4 51.7	1 36.8	0 42.7	1 .3	0 10.2	2 1.2	0 32.6	0 29.0	13 10.0

RIGHT ASCENSION

DAY	EPHEM. SID. TIME	☉	☊	☽	☿	♀	♂	♃	♄	♅	♆	♇
1	8 41 58.5	13♒51.8	19♎12.6	1♋27.4	20♑29.0	21♓31.2	21♒19.8	6♑48.9	23♓33.4	3♒30.8	27♑44.7	3♐16.5
2	8 45 55.0	14 53.0	19 9.7	13 51.8	20 46.4	22 36.3	22 6.7	7 2.3	23 39.1	3 34.4	27 47.0	3 17.7
3	8 49 51.6	15 54.1	19 6.7	26 8.4	21 10.6	23 41.2	22 53.4	7 15.7	23 44.9	3 38.0	27 49.3	3 18.9
4	8 53 48.1	16 54.9	19 3.7	8♌15.2	21 41.1	24 45.9	23 40.1	7 29.1	23 50.7	3 41.7	27 51.7	3 20.0
5	8 57 44.7	17 55.5	19 .7	20 12.0	22 17.4	25 50.5	24 26.6	7 42.3	23 56.6	3 45.3	27 53.9	3 21.1
6	9 1 41.2	18 55.9	18 57.8	2♍ 1.2	22 58.9	26 54.8	25 13.1	7 55.5	24 2.5	3 48.9	27 56.2	3 22.1
7	9 5 37.8	19 56.2	18 54.8	13 47.3	23 45.1	27 59.0	25 59.4	8 8.6	24 8.5	3 52.5	27 58.5	3 23.1
8	9 9 34.4	20 56.2	18 51.8	25 36.9	24 35.7	29 3.1	26 45.6	8 21.6	24 14.5	3 56.0	28 .7	3 24.1
9	9 13 30.9	21 56.0	18 48.9	7♎37.9	25 30.3	0♈ 7.0	27 31.7	8 34.5	24 20.6	3 59.6	28 3.0	3 25.1
10	9 17 27.5	22 55.6	18 45.9	19 59.2	26 28.5	1 10.7	28 17.7	8 47.4	24 26.6	4 3.1	28 5.2	3 26.0
11	9 21 24.0	23 55.0	18 42.9	2♏49.6	27 30.0	2 14.4	29 3.6	9 .2	24 32.8	4 6.6	28 7.4	3 26.9
12	9 25 20.6	24 54.3	18 39.9	16 16.1	28 34.5	3 17.9	29 49.4	9 12.9	24 38.9	4 10.1	28 9.6	3 27.7
13	9 29 17.1	25 53.3	18 37.0	0♐22.5	29 41.7	4 21.3	0♓35.1	9 25.5	24 45.1	4 13.6	28 11.8	3 28.5
14	9 33 13.7	26 52.2	18 34.0	15 6.5	0♒51.3	5 24.6	1 20.7	9 38.0	24 51.4	4 17.1	28 13.9	3 29.3
15	9 37 10.2	27 50.9	18 31.0	0♑18.9	2 3.2	6 27.9	2 6.2	9 50.5	24 57.7	4 20.5	28 16.1	3 30.1
16	9 41 6.8	28 49.4	18 28.1	15 44.1	3 17.2	7 31.0	2 51.6	10 2.8	25 4.0	4 23.9	28 18.2	3 30.8
17	9 45 3.3	29 47.7	18 25.1	1♒ 4.6	4 33.1	8 34.1	3 36.9	10 15.1	25 10.3	4 27.3	28 20.3	3 31.5
18	9 48 59.9	0♓45.9	18 22.1	16 5.5	5 50.6	9 37.1	4 22.1	10 27.2	25 16.7	4 30.7	28 22.4	3 32.1
19	9 52 56.4	1 43.9	18 19.1	0♓38.1	7 9.7	10 40.1	5 7.2	10 39.3	25 23.1	4 34.1	28 24.5	3 32.8
20	9 56 53.0	2 41.7	18 16.2	14 40.5	8 30.3	11 42.9	5 52.2	10 51.3	25 29.5	4 37.4	28 26.6	3 33.3
21	10 0 49.6	3 39.3	18 13.2	28 15.6	9 52.1	12 45.8	6 37.2	11 3.1	25 36.0	4 40.8	28 28.6	3 33.9
22	10 4 46.1	4 36.8	18 10.2	11♈29.2	11 15.2	13 48.6	7 22.0	11 14.9	25 42.5	4 44.0	28 30.6	3 34.4
23	10 8 42.7	5 34.1	18 7.3	24 27.8	12 39.4	14 51.3	8 6.7	11 26.5	25 49.0	4 47.3	28 32.6	3 34.9
24	10 12 39.2	6 31.2	18 4.3	7♉16.8	14 4.6	15 54.0	8 51.3	11 38.1	25 55.6	4 50.6	28 34.6	3 35.3
25	10 16 35.8	7 28.3	18 1.3	20 .3	15 30.8	16 56.8	9 35.9	11 49.6	26 2.2	4 53.8	28 36.6	3 35.8
26	10 20 32.3	8 25.1	17 58.4	2♊40.3	16 57.8	17 59.4	10 20.4	12 .9	26 8.8	4 57.0	28 38.6	3 36.2
27	10 24 28.9	9 21.8	17 55.4	15 17.1	18 25.6	19 2.0	11 4.8	12 12.2	26 15.4	5 .2	28 40.5	3 36.5
28	10 28 25.4	10 18.4	17 52.4	27 49.3	19 54.2	20 4.6	11 49.0	12 23.3	26 22.1	5 3.3	28 42.4	3 36.8
29	10 32 22.0	11 14.8	17 49.5	10♋15.2	21 23.5	21 7.2	12 33.2	12 34.3	26 28.7	5 6.4	28 44.3	3 37.1

DECLINATION

DAY	EPHEM. SID. TIME	☉	☊	☽	☿	♀	♂	♃	♄	♅	♆	♇
1	8 41 58.5	17S21.4	0S 8.5	18N39.5	19S35.4	4S44.0	16S17.8	23S 5.1	5S .8	20S25.3	20S29.9	7S56.8
4	8 53 48.1	16 29.7	0 8.4	13 51.1	19 59.2	3 10.7	15 32.6	23 3.5	4 53.1	20 23.0	20 28.7	7 56.4
7	9 5 37.8	15 35.4	0 8.4	3 44.0	20 15.3	1 36.7	14 46.0	23 1.8	4 45.2	20 20.7	20 27.5	7 55.9
10	9 17 27.5	14 38.8	0 8.3	8S 9.5	20 22.3	0 2.3	13 58.1	22 59.9	4 37.1	20 18.5	20 26.3	7 55.3
13	9 29 17.1	13 39.9	0 8.3	17 5.2	20 19.2	1N32.1	13 8.9	22 57.9	4 29.0	20 16.3	20 25.1	7 54.7
16	9 41 6.8	12 38.9	0 8.2	17 31.4	20 5.4	3 6.2	12 18.5	22 55.8	4 20.7	20 14.1	20 24.0	7 54.0
19	9 52 56.4	11 36.2	0 8.1	7 55.6	19 40.6	4 39.8	11 27.1	22 53.6	4 12.2	20 12.0	20 22.8	7 53.2
22	10 4 46.1	10 31.7	0 8.1	5N26.8	19 4.4	6 12.5	10 34.7	22 51.4	4 3.7	20 9.9	20 21.7	7 52.4
25	10 16 35.8	9 25.8	0 8.0	15 24.0	18 16.8	7 44.0	9 41.4	22 49.1	3 55.1	20 7.8	20 20.6	7 51.5
28	10 28 25.4	8 18.7	0 7.9	18 33.7	17 17.6	9 13.9	8 47.4	22 46.7	3 46.5	20 5.8	20 19.6	7 50.6

MARCH 1996

DAY	EPHEM. SID. TIME	☉	☊	☽	☿	♀	♂	♃	♄	♅	♆	♇
	h m s	° ′	° ′	° ′	° ′	° ′	° ′	° ′	° ′	° ′	° ′	° ′
		LONGITUDE										
1	10 36 18.5	10♓41.8	19♎15.6	21♋39.3	19♒53.8	24♈16.9	11♓28.2	11♑44.7	25♓24.6	2♒44.6	26♑49.8	3♐ 7.5
2	10 40 15.1	11 42.0	19 12.4	3♌35.3	21 24.2	25 24.9	12 15.5	11 54.7	25 31.9	2 47.6	26 51.6	3 7.7
3	10 44 11.6	12 42.1	19 9.2	15 38.2	22 55.7	26 32.6	13 2.8	12 4.6	25 39.2	2 50.5	26 53.3	3 7.8
4	10 48 8.2	13 42.3	19 6.1	27 50.0	24 28.3	27 40.2	13 50.1	12 14.3	25 46.5	2 53.4	26 55.0	3 7.9
5	10 52 4.7	14 42.3	19 2.9	10♍12.0	26 2.0	28 47.5	14 37.3	12 23.9	25 53.9	2 56.2	26 56.7	3 7.9
6	10 56 1.3	15 42.4	18 59.7	22 45.2	27 36.8	29 54.6	15 24.5	12 33.5	26 1.2	2 59.1	26 58.4	3 7.9
7	10 59 57.8	16 42.4	18 56.5	5♎30.0	29 12.7	1♉ 1.6	16 11.8	12 42.9	26 8.6	3 1.8	27 .0	3 7.9
8	11 3 54.4	17 42.4	18 53.3	18 26.8	0♓49.7	2 8.3	16 58.9	12 52.2	26 16.0	3 4.6	27 1.6	3R 7.8
9	11 7 50.9	18 42.4	18 50.2	1♏35.8	2 27.9	3 14.7	17 46.1	13 1.4	26 23.4	3 7.3	27 3.2	3 7.7
10	11 11 47.5	19 42.3	18 47.0	14 57.5	4 7.2	4 21.0	18 33.3	13 10.4	26 30.8	3 10.0	27 4.8	3 7.6
11	11 15 44.0	20 42.3	18 43.8	28 32.3	5 47.6	5 27.0	19 20.4	13 19.4	26 38.2	3 12.7	27 6.3	3 7.4
12	11 19 40.6	21 42.2	18 40.6	12♐20.7	7 29.1	6 32.7	20 7.5	13 28.2	26 45.6	3 15.3	27 7.8	3 7.2
13	11 23 37.2	22 42.0	18 37.5	26 22.4	9 11.9	7 38.3	20 54.6	13 36.9	26 53.1	3 17.9	27 9.3	3 7.0
14	11 27 33.7	23 41.8	18 34.3	10♑36.4	10 55.8	8 43.5	21 41.7	13 45.5	27 .5	3 20.5	27 10.7	3 6.7
15	11 31 30.3	24 41.6	18 31.1	25 .5	12 40.9	9 48.6	22 28.7	13 53.9	27 7.9	3 23.0	27 12.2	3 6.4
16	11 35 26.8	25 41.4	18 27.9	9♒31.0	14 27.2	10 53.3	23 15.7	14 2.2	27 15.4	3 25.5	27 13.6	3 6.1
17	11 39 23.4	26 41.2	18 24.7	24 3.0	16 14.7	11 57.8	24 2.8	14 10.4	27 22.9	3 28.0	27 15.0	3 5.7
18	11 43 19.9	27 40.9	18 21.6	8♓30.4	18 3.4	13 2.0	24 49.7	14 18.5	27 30.3	3 30.4	27 16.4	3 5.3
19	11 47 16.5	28 40.6	18 18.4	22 47.5	19 53.4	14 5.9	25 36.7	14 26.4	27 37.8	3 32.8	27 17.7	3 4.9
20	11 51 13.0	29 40.3	18 15.2	6♈49.0	21 44.6	15 9.6	26 23.6	14 34.2	27 45.2	3 35.1	27 19.0	3 4.4
21	11 55 9.6	0♈39.9	18 12.0	20 31.0	23 37.0	16 12.9	27 10.5	14 41.8	27 52.7	3 37.4	27 20.2	3 3.9
22	11 59 6.1	1 39.5	18 8.9	3♉51.4	25 30.6	17 15.9	27 57.3	14 49.3	28 .1	3 39.7	27 21.5	3 3.4
23	12 3 2.7	2 39.0	18 5.7	16 50.1	27 25.5	18 18.5	28 44.2	14 56.7	28 7.5	3 41.9	27 22.7	3 2.8
24	12 6 59.2	3 38.5	18 2.5	29 28.6	29 21.6	19 20.9	29 31.0	15 3.9	28 15.0	3 44.0	27 23.9	3 2.2
25	12 10 55.8	4 38.0	17 59.3	11♊49.5	1♈18.8	20 22.8	0♈17.7	15 11.0	28 22.4	3 46.2	27 25.0	3 1.6
26	12 14 52.3	5 37.4	17 56.1	23 56.8	3 17.2	21 24.5	1 4.4	15 17.9	28 29.8	3 48.3	27 26.1	3 .9
27	12 18 48.9	6 36.8	17 53.0	5♋54.7	5 16.7	22 25.7	1 51.1	15 24.7	28 37.2	3 50.3	27 27.2	3 .2
28	12 22 45.4	7 36.2	17 49.8	17 47.9	7 17.1	23 26.6	2 37.8	15 31.3	28 44.6	3 52.3	27 28.3	2 59.5
29	12 26 42.0	8 35.5	17 46.6	29 41.1	9 18.5	24 27.0	3 24.4	15 37.8	28 52.0	3 54.3	27 29.3	2 58.8
30	12 30 38.5	9 34.8	17 43.4	11♌38.8	11 20.7	25 27.1	4 11.0	15 44.1	28 59.3	3 56.2	27 30.3	2 58.0
31	12 34 35.1	10 34.0	17 40.3	23 44.8	13 23.6	26 26.7	4 57.6	15 50.3	29 6.7	3 58.1	27 31.3	2 57.2
		LATITUDE										
1	10 36 18.5	0 .0	0 .0	5S 9.5	1S46.5	0N51.7	0S59.7	0N10.0	2S 1.2	0S32.6	0N29.0	13N10.7
4	10 48 8.2	0 .0	0 .0	3 57.2	1 58.4	1 5.4	0 58.9	0 9.8	2 1.1	0 32.7	0 29.0	13 11.9
7	10 59 57.8	0 .0	0 .0	1 4.0	2 6.9	1 19.4	0 57.9	0 9.6	2 1.1	0 32.8	0 29.0	13 13.0
10	11 11 47.5	0 .0	0 .0	2N26.0	2 11.8	1 33.4	0 57.0	0 9.3	2 1.1	0 32.8	0 29.0	13 14.1
13	11 23 37.2	0 .0	0 .0	4 53.6	2 12.8	1 47.5	0 55.9	0 9.1	2 1.2	0 32.9	0 29.0	13 15.1
16	11 35 26.8	0 .0	0 .0	4 51.1	2 9.7	2 1.6	0 54.8	0 8.8	2 1.2	0 33.0	0 29.0	13 16.2
19	11 47 16.5	0 .0	0 .0	2 10.2	2 2.4	2 15.6	0 53.7	0 8.6	2 1.3	0 33.1	0 29.0	13 17.2
22	11 59 6.1	0 .0	0 .0	1S31.2	1 50.5	2 29.5	0 52.5	0 8.3	2 1.4	0 33.2	0 29.0	13 18.2
25	12 10 55.8	0 .0	0 .0	4 18.4	1 34.0	2 43.1	0 51.3	0 8.1	2 1.6	0 33.2	0 29.0	13 19.2
28	12 22 45.4	0 .0	0 .0	5 16.6	1 12.7	2 56.4	0 50.0	0 7.8	2 1.8	0 33.3	0 29.0	13 20.1
31	12 34 35.1	0 .0	0 .0	4 14.6	0 46.9	3 9.2	0 48.6	0 7.6	2 2.0	0 33.4	0 29.1	13 21.0
		RIGHT ASCENSION										
1	10 36 18.5	12♓11.1	17♎46.5	22♋33.1	22♒53.4	22♈ 9.8	13♓17.3	12♑45.2	26♓35.4	5♒ 9.5	28♑46.1	3♐37.4
2	10 40 15.1	13 7.2	17 43.5	4♌42.1	24 24.0	23 12.4	14 1.4	12 55.9	26 42.1	5 12.6	28 48.0	3 37.6
3	10 44 11.6	14 3.2	17 40.6	16 43.0	25 55.2	24 14.9	14 45.3	13 6.6	26 48.8	5 15.6	28 49.8	3 37.8
4	10 48 8.2	14 59.1	17 37.6	28 38.2	27 27.0	25 17.5	15 29.2	13 17.1	26 55.5	5 18.6	28 51.6	3 37.9
5	10 52 4.7	15 54.9	17 34.6	10♍31.8	28 59.4	26 20.1	16 13.0	13 27.5	27 2.3	5 21.6	28 53.3	3 38.0
6	10 56 1.3	16 50.6	17 31.7	22 29.4	0♓32.3	27 22.6	16 56.7	13 37.8	27 9.0	5 24.5	28 55.0	3 38.1
7	10 59 57.8	17 46.2	17 28.7	4♎37.5	2 5.7	28 25.2	17 40.4	13 48.0	27 15.8	5 27.4	28 56.8	3 38.1
8	11 3 54.4	18 41.7	17 25.7	17 3.4	3 39.7	29 27.7	18 24.0	13 58.0	27 22.6	5 30.2	28 58.4	3 38.1
9	11 7 50.9	19 37.0	17 22.8	29 53.8	5 14.2	0♉30.3	19 7.5	14 7.9	27 29.4	5 33.1	29 .1	3 38.1
10	11 11 47.5	20 32.3	17 19.8	13♏13.8	6 49.2	1 32.9	19 51.0	14 17.7	27 36.2	5 35.9	29 1.7	3R38.0
11	11 15 44.0	21 27.6	17 16.8	27 5.8	8 24.8	2 35.4	20 34.4	14 27.4	27 43.0	5 38.6	29 3.3	3 37.9
12	11 19 40.6	22 22.7	17 13.9	11♐27.4	10 .9	3 38.0	21 17.7	14 36.9	27 49.8	5 41.4	29 4.9	3 37.8
13	11 23 37.2	23 17.8	17 10.9	26 11.4	11 37.7	4 40.6	22 1.0	14 46.3	27 56.7	5 44.0	29 6.5	3 37.6
14	11 27 33.7	24 12.8	17 7.9	11♑ 6.1	13 14.9	5 43.1	22 44.2	14 55.5	28 3.5	5 46.7	29 8.0	3 37.4
15	11 31 30.3	25 7.8	17 5.0	25 58.7	14 52.8	6 45.7	23 27.4	15 4.6	28 10.3	5 49.3	29 9.5	3 37.2
16	11 35 26.8	26 2.7	17 2.0	10♒37.9	16 31.3	7 48.3	24 10.5	15 13.6	28 17.2	5 51.9	29 11.0	3 37.0
17	11 39 23.4	26 57.6	16 59.1	24 57.1	18 10.5	8 50.9	24 53.6	15 22.4	28 24.1	5 54.5	29 12.4	3 36.7
18	11 43 19.9	27 52.4	16 56.1	8♓54.2	19 50.3	9 53.4	25 36.7	15 31.1	28 30.9	5 57.0	29 13.9	3 36.4
19	11 47 16.5	28 47.2	16 53.1	22 31.4	21 30.8	10 56.0	26 19.7	15 39.6	28 37.8	5 59.5	29 15.2	3 36.0
20	11 51 13.0	29 41.9	16 50.2	5♈53.1	23 12.0	11 58.4	27 2.6	15 48.0	28 44.6	6 1.9	29 16.6	3 35.6
21	11 55 9.6	0♈36.6	16 47.2	19 4.0	24 54.0	13 .9	27 45.5	15 56.2	28 51.5	6 4.3	29 17.9	3 35.2
22	11 59 6.1	1 31.3	16 44.2	2♉ 8.3	26 36.7	14 3.3	28 28.3	16 4.3	28 58.3	6 6.6	29 19.2	3 34.7
23	12 3 2.7	2 25.9	16 41.3	15 8.2	28 20.2	15 5.6	29 11.1	16 12.2	29 5.2	6 8.9	29 20.5	3 34.3
24	12 6 59.2	3 20.5	16 38.3	28 4.3	0♈ 4.5	16 7.9	29 53.9	16 20.0	29 12.0	6 11.2	29 21.7	3 33.7
25	12 10 55.8	4 15.2	16 35.4	10♊55.1	1 49.7	17 10.1	0♈36.6	16 27.6	29 18.8	6 13.4	29 22.9	3 33.2
26	12 14 52.3	5 9.8	16 32.4	23 38.4	3 35.7	18 12.2	1 19.4	16 35.1	29 25.6	6 15.5	29 24.1	3 32.6
27	12 18 48.9	6 4.4	16 29.4	6♋11.8	5 22.5	19 14.1	2 2.0	16 42.4	29 32.5	6 17.7	29 25.2	3 32.0
28	12 22 45.4	6 58.9	16 26.5	18 33.7	7 10.1	20 16.0	2 44.7	16 49.5	29 39.3	6 19.8	29 26.3	3 31.4
29	12 26 42.0	7 53.5	16 23.5	0♌44.1	8 58.6	21 17.7	3 27.3	16 56.5	29 46.1	6 21.8	29 27.4	3 30.7
30	12 30 38.5	8 48.1	16 20.6	12 44.6	10 47.8	22 19.2	4 9.9	17 3.3	29 52.9	6 23.8	29 28.4	3 30.0
31	12 34 35.1	9 42.8	16 17.6	24 38.9	12 37.7	23 20.5	4 52.4	17 9.9	29 59.6	6 25.8	29 29.4	3 29.2
		DECLINATION										
1	10 36 18.5	7S33.3	0S 7.9	16N36.0	16S31.8	10N12.9	8S10.9	22S45.1	3S40.7	20S 4.4	20S18.9	7S49.9
4	10 48 8.2	6 24.5	0 7.8	8 30.6	15 13.5	11 39.7	7 15.8	22 42.7	3 31.9	20 2.5	20 17.9	7 48.9
7	10 59 57.8	5 14.8	0 7.8	3S 9.9	13 43.7	13 4.2	6 20.1	22 40.3	3 23.1	20 .6	20 17.0	7 47.8
10	11 11 47.5	4 4.5	0 7.7	13 59.7	12 2.6	14 26.1	5 24.0	22 37.8	3 14.3	19 58.8	20 16.0	7 46.6
13	11 23 37.2	2 53.8	0 7.6	18 29.8	10 10.2	15 45.1	4 27.6	22 35.4	3 5.5	19 57.0	20 15.1	7 45.5
16	11 35 26.8	1 42.8	0 7.6	13 11.2	8 6.8	17 1.0	3 30.9	22 33.1	2 56.7	19 55.4	20 14.3	7 44.3
19	11 47 16.5	0 31.6	0 7.5	0 52.0	5 52.7	18 13.6	2 33.9	22 30.8	2 47.9	19 53.7	20 13.5	7 43.1
22	11 59 6.1	0N39.6	0 7.5	11N22.3	3 28.5	19 22.5	1 37.0	22 28.5	2 39.1	19 52.2	20 12.8	7 41.8
25	12 10 55.8	1 50.5	0 7.4	17 56.1	0 54.9	20 27.6	0 40.0	22 26.4	2 30.4	19 50.8	20 12.0	7 40.5
28	12 22 45.4	3 1.0	0 7.3	17 1.3	1N46.7	21 28.6	0N16.9	22 24.3	2 21.7	19 49.4	20 11.4	7 39.2
31	12 34 35.1	4 11.0	0 7.3	9 35.7	4 33.9	22 25.4	1 13.6	22 22.4	2 13.1	19 48.1	20 10.8	7 37.9

APRIL 1996

LONGITUDE

DAY	EPHEM. SID. TIME h m s	☉ ° ′	☊ ° ′	☽ ° ′	☿ ° ′	♀ ° ′	♂ ° ′	♃ ° ′	♄ ° ′	♅ ° ′	♆ ° ′	♇ ° ′
1	12 38 31.6	11♈33.2	17♎37.1	6♍ 2.5	15♈26.9	27♉25.9	5♈44.1	15♑56.3	29♓14.0	3♒60.0	27♑32.2	2♐56.3
2	12 42 28.2	12 32.4	17 33.9	18 34.4	17 30.6	28 24.7	6 30.6	16 2.1	29 21.4	4 1.8	27 33.1	2R55.4
3	12 46 24.7	13 31.5	17 30.7	1♎22.1	19 34.3	29 22.9	7 17.0	16 7.8	29 28.7	4 3.5	27 34.0	2 54.5
4	12 50 21.3	14 30.6	17 27.5	14 26.2	21 37.9	0♊20.7	8 3.4	16 13.4	29 36.0	4 5.2	27 34.8	2 53.6
5	12 54 17.8	15 29.7	17 24.4	27 46.3	23 41.0	1 18.0	8 49.8	16 18.8	29 43.2	4 6.9	27 35.6	2 52.7
6	12 58 14.4	16 28.7	17 21.2	11♏21.1	25 43.4	2 14.8	9 36.1	16 24.0	29 50.5	4 8.5	27 36.4	2 51.7
7	13 2 10.9	17 27.8	17 18.0	25 8.7	27 44.7	3 11.1	10 22.4	16 29.1	29 57.8	4 10.1	27 37.2	2 50.7
8	13 6 7.5	18 26.7	17 14.8	9♐ 6.6	29 44.5	4 6.8	11 8.7	16 34.0	0♈ 5.0	4 11.6	27 37.9	2 49.7
9	13 10 4.1	19 25.7	17 11.6	23 12.2	1♉42.5	5 2.0	11 54.9	16 38.7	0 12.2	4 13.1	27 38.6	2 48.6
10	13 14 .6	20 24.6	17 8.5	7♑22.8	3 38.4	5 56.5	12 41.1	16 43.3	0 19.3	4 14.6	27 39.2	2 47.5
11	13 17 57.2	21 23.5	17 5.3	21 36.0	5 31.8	6 50.5	13 27.2	16 47.7	0 26.4	4 15.9	27 39.9	2 46.4
12	13 21 53.7	22 22.3	17 2.1	5♒49.1	7 22.3	7 43.9	14 13.3	16 51.9	0 33.6	4 17.3	27 40.4	2 45.3
13	13 25 50.3	23 21.1	16 58.9	19 59.8	9 9.5	8 36.6	14 59.4	16 55.9	0 40.6	4 18.6	27 41.0	2 44.1
14	13 29 46.8	24 19.9	16 55.8	4♓ 5.6	10 53.3	9 28.6	15 45.4	16 59.8	0 47.7	4 19.8	27 41.5	2 43.0
15	13 33 43.4	25 18.7	16 52.6	18 3.9	12 33.3	10 20.0	16 31.4	17 3.5	0 54.7	4 21.0	27 42.0	2 41.8
16	13 37 39.9	26 17.4	16 49.4	1♈52.4	14 9.2	11 10.7	17 17.4	17 7.0	1 1.7	4 22.2	27 42.5	2 40.5
17	13 41 36.5	27 16.1	16 46.2	15 28.5	15 40.9	12 .6	18 3.3	17 10.4	1 8.7	4 23.3	27 42.9	2 39.3
18	13 45 33.0	28 14.8	16 43.0	28 50.4	17 8.1	12 49.8	18 49.1	17 13.5	1 15.6	4 24.3	27 43.3	2 38.0
19	13 49 29.6	29 13.5	16 39.9	11♉56.6	18 30.6	13 38.2	19 34.9	17 16.5	1 22.5	4 25.3	27 43.6	2 36.7
20	13 53 26.1	0♉12.1	16 36.7	24 46.5	19 48.3	14 25.7	20 20.7	17 19.3	1 29.4	4 26.3	27 43.9	2 35.4
21	13 57 22.7	1 10.6	16 33.5	7♊20.5	21 1.0	15 12.4	21 6.4	17 22.0	1 36.2	4 27.2	27 44.2	2 34.1
22	14 1 19.2	2 9.2	16 30.3	19 40.1	22 8.6	15 58.2	21 52.1	17 24.4	1 43.0	4 28.0	27 44.5	2 32.7
23	14 5 15.8	3 7.7	16 27.2	1♋47.6	23 11.1	16 43.1	22 37.7	17 26.6	1 49.7	4 28.8	27 44.7	2 31.3
24	14 9 12.3	4 6.2	16 24.0	13 46.2	24 8.3	17 27.0	23 23.3	17 28.7	1 56.5	4 29.6	27 44.9	2 30.0
25	14 13 8.9	5 4.6	16 20.8	25 39.9	25 .1	18 9.9	24 8.8	17 30.6	2 3.1	4 30.3	27 45.1	2 28.5
26	14 17 5.5	6 3.0	16 17.6	7♌33.1	25 46.5	18 51.8	24 54.3	17 32.3	2 9.8	4 30.9	27 45.2	2 27.1
27	14 21 2.0	7 1.4	16 14.4	19 30.5	26 27.4	19 32.6	25 39.7	17 33.8	2 16.3	4 31.5	27 45.3	2 25.7
28	14 24 58.6	7 59.7	16 11.3	1♍36.7	27 2.8	20 12.3	26 25.2	17 35.2	2 22.9	4 32.1	27 45.4	2 24.3
29	14 28 55.1	8 58.0	16 8.1	13 56.1	27 32.6	20 50.8	27 10.5	17 36.3	2 29.4	4 32.6	27 45.4	2 22.8
30	14 32 51.7	9 56.3	16 4.9	26 32.7	27 56.8	21 28.1	27 55.8	17 37.3	2 35.9	4 33.1	27 45.4	2 21.3

LATITUDE

DAY	EPHEM. SID. TIME	☉	☊	☽	☿	♀	♂	♃	♄	♅	♆	♇
1	12 38 31.6	0 .0	0 .0	3S28.6	0S37.4	3N13.4	0S48.2	0N 7.5	2S 2.0	0S33.5	0N29.1	13N21.3
4	12 50 21.3	0 .0	0 .0	0 14.9	0 6.4	3 25.6	0 46.8	0 7.2	2 2.3	0 33.6	0 29.1	13 22.2
7	13 2 10.9	0 .0	0 .0	3N15.6	0N26.9	3 37.1	0 45.3	0 6.9	2 2.5	0 33.7	0 29.1	13 23.0
10	13 14 .6	0 .0	0 .0	5 12.5	1 1.0	3 47.8	0 43.9	0 6.7	2 2.8	0 33.8	0 29.1	13 23.7
13	13 25 50.3	0 .0	0 .0	4 26.5	1 33.5	3 57.7	0 42.3	0 6.4	2 3.1	0 33.9	0 29.1	13 24.4
16	13 37 39.9	0 .0	0 .0	1 23.8	2 2.3	4 6.5	0 40.8	0 6.1	2 3.4	0 34.0	0 29.2	13 25.0
19	13 49 29.6	0 .0	0 .0	2S12.8	2 25.3	4 14.1	0 39.2	0 5.8	2 3.8	0 34.1	0 29.2	13 25.6
22	14 1 19.2	0 .0	0 .0	4 40.4	2 40.9	4 20.5	0 37.6	0 5.5	2 4.1	0 34.2	0 29.2	13 26.1
25	14 13 8.9	0 .0	0 .0	5 11.9	2 47.8	4 25.4	0 35.9	0 5.2	2 4.6	0 34.3	0 29.2	13 26.6
28	14 24 58.6	0 .0	0 .0	3 44.8	2 44.9	4 28.6	0 34.2	0 4.8	2 5.0	0 34.4	0 29.2	13 27.0

RIGHT ASCENSION

DAY	EPHEM. SID. TIME	☉	☊	☽	☿	♀	♂	♃	♄	♅	♆	♇
1	12 38 31.6	10♈37.4	16♎14.6	6♍31.9	14♈28.1	24♉21.7	5♈35.0	17♑16.4	0♈ 6.4	6♒27.7	29♑30.4	3♐28.5
2	12 42 28.2	11 32.1	16 11.7	18 30.3	16 19.1	25 22.6	6 17.5	17 22.7	0 13.1	6 29.5	29 31.3	3R27.7
3	12 46 24.7	12 26.8	16 8.7	0♎41.0	18 10.5	26 23.3	6 60.0	17 28.8	0 19.9	6 31.3	29 32.3	3 26.9
4	12 50 21.3	13 21.5	16 5.8	13 11.6	20 2.0	27 23.7	7 42.5	17 34.8	0 26.6	6 33.1	29 33.1	3 26.0
5	12 54 17.8	14 16.3	16 2.8	26 8.6	21 53.6	28 23.9	8 24.9	17 40.6	0 33.3	6 34.8	29 34.0	3 25.2
6	12 58 14.4	15 11.1	15 59.9	9♏36.7	23 45.0	29 23.7	9 7.4	17 46.2	0 40.0	6 36.5	29 34.8	3 24.3
7	13 2 10.9	16 6.0	15 56.9	23 36.8	25 35.9	0♊23.2	9 49.9	17 51.7	0 46.7	6 38.2	29 35.6	3 23.4
8	13 6 7.5	17 .9	15 53.9	8♐ 4.9	27 26.1	1 22.4	10 32.3	17 56.9	0 53.3	6 39.8	29 36.4	3 22.4
9	13 10 4.1	17 55.9	15 51.0	22 51.6	29 15.2	2 21.1	11 14.8	18 2.0	0 60.0	6 41.3	29 37.1	3 21.5
10	13 14 .6	18 51.0	15 48.0	7♑43.9	1♉ 3.0	3 19.5	11 57.2	18 6.9	1 6.6	6 42.8	29 37.7	3 20.5
11	13 17 57.2	19 46.1	15 45.1	22 28.6	2 49.1	4 17.4	12 39.7	18 11.7	1 13.2	6 44.2	29 38.4	3 19.4
12	13 21 53.7	20 41.3	15 42.1	6♒55.3	4 33.2	5 14.8	13 22.1	18 16.2	1 19.7	6 45.6	29 39.0	3 18.4
13	13 25 50.3	21 36.6	15 39.2	20 58.9	6 15.0	6 11.7	14 4.6	18 20.5	1 26.3	6 47.0	29 39.6	3 17.3
14	13 29 46.8	22 32.0	15 36.2	4♓39.5	7 54.2	7 8.1	14 47.0	18 24.7	1 32.8	6 48.3	29 40.1	3 16.2
15	13 33 43.4	23 27.4	15 33.2	18 1.2	9 30.5	8 4.0	15 29.5	18 28.7	1 39.3	6 49.5	29 40.6	3 15.1
16	13 37 39.9	24 23.0	15 30.3	1♈ 9.8	11 3.5	8 59.2	16 12.0	18 32.5	1 45.7	6 50.7	29 41.1	3 13.9
17	13 41 36.5	25 18.6	15 27.3	14 11.5	12 33.0	9 53.7	16 54.5	18 36.1	1 52.2	6 51.8	29 41.5	3 12.8
18	13 45 33.0	26 14.4	15 24.4	27 11.4	13 58.7	10 47.6	17 37.0	18 39.5	1 58.6	6 52.9	29 41.9	3 11.6
19	13 49 29.6	27 10.2	15 21.4	10♉12.1	15 20.5	11 40.8	18 19.5	18 42.7	2 4.9	6 54.0	29 42.3	3 10.4
20	13 53 26.1	28 6.2	15 18.5	23 13.8	16 38.0	12 33.2	19 2.0	18 45.7	2 11.3	6 55.0	29 42.6	3 9.1
21	13 57 22.7	29 2.2	15 15.5	6♊14.0	17 51.1	13 24.7	19 44.5	18 48.5	2 17.6	6 55.9	29 42.9	3 7.9
22	14 1 19.2	29 58.4	15 12.6	19 8.6	18 59.6	14 15.4	20 27.1	18 51.2	2 23.9	6 56.8	29 43.2	3 6.6
23	14 5 15.8	0♉54.7	15 9.6	1♋52.9	20 3.2	15 5.2	21 9.7	18 53.6	2 30.1	6 57.6	29 43.4	3 5.3
24	14 9 12.3	1 51.0	15 6.7	14 23.5	21 2.0	15 53.9	21 52.3	18 55.8	2 36.3	6 58.4	29 43.6	3 4.0
25	14 13 8.9	2 47.5	15 3.7	26 38.8	21 55.6	16 41.7	22 34.9	18 57.9	2 42.5	6 59.1	29 43.8	3 2.7
26	14 17 5.5	3 44.1	15 .8	8♌40.0	22 43.9	17 28.4	23 17.5	18 59.7	2 48.6	6 59.8	29 43.9	3 1.3
27	14 21 2.0	4 40.9	14 57.8	20 30.7	23 26.9	18 14.0	24 .2	19 1.3	2 54.7	7 .5	29 44.0	2 60.0
28	14 24 58.6	5 37.8	14 54.9	2♍16.8	24 4.6	18 58.4	24 42.9	19 2.8	3 .8	7 1.1	29 44.1	2 58.6
29	14 28 55.1	6 34.7	14 51.9	14 5.6	24 36.7	19 41.5	25 25.6	19 4.1	3 6.8	7 1.6	29 44.1	2 57.2
30	14 32 51.7	7 31.9	14 48.9	26 5.9	25 3.2	20 23.3	26 8.3	19 5.1	3 12.8	7 2.1	29 44.1	2 55.8

DECLINATION

DAY	EPHEM. SID. TIME	☉	☊	☽	☿	♀	♂	♃	♄	♅	♆	♇
1	12 38 31.6	4N34.2	0S 7.2	6N 3.6	5N30.4	22N43.3	1N32.4	22S21.7	2S10.2	19S47.7	20S10.6	7S37.5
4	12 50 21.3	5 43.2	0 7.2	5S55.3	8 19.9	23 34.2	2 28.7	22 20.0	2 1.7	19 46.6	20 10.1	7 36.2
7	13 2 10.9	6 51.3	0 7.1	15 53.1	11 5.4	24 20.5	3 24.7	22 18.3	1 53.3	19 45.5	20 9.6	7 34.9
10	13 14 .6	7 58.4	0 7.0	18 1.9	13 41.1	25 2.0	4 20.2	22 16.9	1 45.0	19 44.6	20 9.2	7 33.6
13	13 25 50.3	9 4.3	0 7.0	10 35.7	16 1.4	25 38.9	5 15.2	22 15.6	1 36.8	19 43.7	20 8.8	7 32.3
16	13 37 39.9	10 8.8	0 6.9	2N 1.5	18 1.8	26 11.0	6 9.6	22 14.5	1 28.7	19 42.9	20 8.5	7 31.0
19	13 49 29.6	11 11.9	0 6.9	13 18.5	19 39.6	26 38.3	7 3.4	22 13.6	1 20.7	19 42.3	20 8.3	7 29.8
22	14 1 19.2	12 13.2	0 6.8	18 22.6	20 53.6	27 .9	7 56.3	22 12.9	1 13.0	19 41.8	20 8.1	7 28.6
25	14 13 8.9	13 12.8	0 6.7	15 53.8	21 43.7	27 18.9	8 48.5	22 12.4	1 5.3	19 41.3	20 7.9	7 27.4
28	14 24 58.6	14 10.4	0 6.7	7 23.8	22 10.3	27 32.3	9 39.7	22 12.1	0 57.9	19 41.0	20 7.9	7 26.2

MAY 1996

DAY	EPHEM. SID. TIME	☉	☊	☾	☿	♀	♂	♃	♄	♅	♆	♇
	h m s	° ′	° ′	° ′	° ′	° ′	° ′	° ′	° ′	° ′	° ′	° ′
		LONGITUDE										
1	14 36 48.2	10♉54.5	16♎ 1.7	9♎29.4	28♉15.5	22♊ 4.1	28♈41.0	17♑38.1	2♈42.3	4♒33.5	27♑45.3	2♐19.8
2	14 40 44.8	11 52.7	15 58.6	22 47.8	28 28.6	22 38.8	29 26.2	17 38.7	2 48.6	4 33.9	27 45.3	2R18.3
3	14 44 41.3	12 50.9	15 55.4	6♏27.9	28 36.3	23 12.1	0♉11.4	17 39.0	2 55.0	4 34.2	27R45.2	2 16.8
4	14 48 37.9	13 49.0	15 52.2	20 27.6	28 38.6	23 44.1	0 56.4	17 39.3	3 1.2	4 34.4	27 45.0	2 15.2
5	14 52 34.4	14 47.1	15 49.0	4♐43.3	28R35.7	24 14.5	1 41.5	17 39.3	3 7.4	4 34.6	27 44.8	2 13.7
6	14 56 31.0	15 45.2	15 45.8	19 9.8	28 27.8	24 43.4	2 26.5	17R39.1	3 13.6	4 34.8	27 44.6	2 12.1
7	15 0 27.5	16 43.3	15 42.7	3♑41.1	28 15.2	25 10.8	3 11.4	17 38.8	3 19.7	4 34.9	27 44.4	2 10.5
8	15 4 24.1	17 41.3	15 39.5	18 11.3	27 58.2	25 36.5	3 56.3	17 38.2	3 25.8	4 34.9	27 44.1	2 9.0
9	15 8 20.7	18 39.3	15 36.3	2♒35.5	27 37.0	26 .6	4 41.1	17 37.5	3 31.8	4 34.9	27 43.8	2 7.4
10	15 12 17.2	19 37.3	15 33.1	16 49.9	27 12.2	26 22.9	5 25.9	17 36.6	3 37.7	4 34.9	27 43.5	2 5.8
11	15 16 13.8	20 35.3	15 30.0	0♓52.4	26 44.2	26 43.5	6 10.7	17 35.4	3 43.6	4R34.8	27 43.2	2 4.2
12	15 20 10.3	21 33.2	15 26.8	14 41.8	26 13.5	27 2.1	6 55.4	17 34.1	3 49.4	4 34.7	27 42.8	2 2.5
13	15 24 6.9	22 31.1	15 23.6	28 18.1	25 40.8	27 18.9	7 40.0	17 32.7	3 55.2	4 34.5	27 42.3	2 .9
14	15 28 3.4	23 29.0	15 20.4	11♈41.6	25 6.5	27 33.7	8 24.6	17 31.0	4 .9	4 34.2	27 41.9	1 59.3
15	15 31 60.0	24 26.9	15 17.2	24 52.6	24 31.3	27 46.4	9 9.2	17 29.1	4 6.6	4 33.9	27 41.4	1 57.6
16	15 35 56.5	25 24.8	15 14.1	7♉51.5	23 55.8	27 57.1	9 53.7	17 27.1	4 12.2	4 33.6	27 40.9	1 56.0
17	15 39 53.1	26 22.6	15 10.9	20 38.4	23 20.6	28 5.6	10 38.1	17 24.8	4 17.7	4 33.2	27 40.3	1 54.4
18	15 43 49.6	27 20.4	15 7.7	3♊13.5	22 46.4	28 11.9	11 22.5	17 22.4	4 23.2	4 32.8	27 39.8	1 52.7
19	15 47 46.2	28 18.3	15 4.5	15 37.2	22 13.8	28 16.1	12 6.9	17 19.9	4 28.6	4 32.3	27 39.2	1 51.1
20	15 51 42.8	29 16.0	15 1.4	27 50.2	21 43.2	28 17.8	12 51.1	17 17.1	4 34.0	4 31.8	27 38.6	1 49.5
21	15 55 39.3	0♊13.8	14 58.2	9♋54.0	21 15.1	28R17.2	13 35.4	17 14.1	4 39.2	4 31.2	27 37.9	1 47.8
22	15 59 35.9	1 11.5	14 55.0	21 50.6	20 50.0	28 14.3	14 19.5	17 11.0	4 44.5	4 30.6	27 37.2	1 46.1
23	16 3 32.4	2 9.2	14 51.8	3♌43.0	20 28.2	28 8.9	15 3.6	17 7.7	4 49.6	4 29.9	27 36.5	1 44.5
24	16 7 29.0	3 6.9	14 48.7	15 34.8	20 10.1	28 1.1	15 47.7	17 4.2	4 54.7	4 29.2	27 35.7	1 42.8
25	16 11 25.5	4 4.5	14 45.5	27 30.3	19 56.0	27 50.9	16 31.7	17 .6	4 59.7	4 28.4	27 34.9	1 41.2
26	16 15 22.1	5 2.1	14 42.3	9♍34.3	19 46.0	27 38.2	17 15.6	16 56.7	5 4.6	4 27.6	27 34.1	1 39.5
27	16 19 18.6	5 59.7	14 39.1	21 51.9	19 40.3	27 23.1	17 59.5	16 52.8	5 9.4	4 26.8	27 33.3	1 37.9
28	16 23 15.2	6 57.3	14 35.9	4♎27.7	19 39.0	27 5.6	18 43.3	16 48.6	5 14.2	4 25.9	27 32.4	1 36.2
29	16 27 11.8	7 54.8	14 32.8	17 26.1	19D42.2	26 45.8	19 27.1	16 44.3	5 18.9	4 24.9	27 31.5	1 34.6
30	16 31 8.3	8 52.4	14 29.6	0♏50.2	19 49.9	26 23.7	20 10.8	16 39.8	5 23.6	4 23.9	27 30.6	1 32.9
31	16 35 4.9	9 49.9	14 26.4	14 41.1	20 2.0	25 59.4	20 54.5	16 35.2	5 28.1	4 22.9	27 29.7	1 31.3
		LATITUDE										
1	14 36 48.2	0 .0	0 .0	0S41.6	2N31.5	4N29.9	0S32.5	0N 4.5	2S 5.4	0S34.5	0N29.2	13N27.3
4	14 48 37.9	0 .0	0 .0	2N53.0	2 7.1	4 29.0	0 30.7	0 4.2	2 5.9	0 34.6	0 29.3	13 27.5
7	15 0 27.5	0 .0	0 .0	5 4.3	1 32.3	4 25.7	0 28.9	0 3.8	2 6.4	0 34.7	0 29.3	13 27.7
10	15 12 17.2	0 .0	0 .0	4 30.5	0 48.3	4 19.6	0 27.1	0 3.5	2 6.9	0 34.8	0 29.3	13 27.8
13	15 24 6.9	0 .0	0 .0	1 39.0	0S 1.8	4 10.5	0 25.3	0 3.1	2 7.5	0 34.9	0 29.3	13 27.9
16	15 35 56.5	0 .0	0 .0	1S52.1	0 54.4	3 57.9	0 23.4	0 2.8	2 8.0	0 35.0	0 29.3	13 27.9
19	15 47 46.2	0 .0	0 .0	4 25.2	1 44.9	3 41.5	0 21.5	0 2.4	2 8.6	0 35.1	0 29.3	13 27.8
22	15 59 35.9	0 .0	0 .0	5 6.7	2 29.5	3 21.0	0 19.6	0 2.0	2 9.2	0 35.2	0 29.3	13 27.6
25	16 11 25.5	0 .0	0 .0	3 51.0	3 5.5	2 56.1	0 17.7	0 1.6	2 9.9	0 35.3	0 29.3	13 27.3
28	16 23 15.2	0 .0	0 .0	1 1.5	3 31.5	2 26.9	0 15.8	0 1.3	2 10.5	0 35.4	0 29.3	13 27.0
31	16 35 4.9	0 .0	0 .0	2N27.9	3 47.4	1 53.3	0 13.8	0 .9	2 11.2	0 35.5	0 29.4	13 26.6
		RIGHT ASCENSION										
1	14 36 48.2	8♉29.1	14♎46.0	8♎26.8	25♉24.2	21♊ 3.7	26♈51.1	19♑ 5.9	3♈18.8	7♒ 2.5	29♑44.1	2♐54.4
2	14 40 44.8	9 26.4	14 43.0	21 17.1	25 39.7	21 42.7	27 33.9	19 6.6	3 24.6	7 2.9	29R44.0	2R53.0
3	14 44 41.3	10 23.9	14 40.1	4♏43.5	25 49.7	22 20.3	28 16.7	19 7.0	3 30.5	7 3.2	29 43.9	2 51.5
4	14 48 37.9	11 21.6	14 37.1	18 48.9	25 54.4	22 56.2	28 59.5	19 7.3	3 36.3	7 3.5	29 43.7	2 50.0
5	14 52 34.4	12 19.3	14 34.2	3♐30.1	25R53.9	23 30.5	29 42.4	19 7.3	3 42.1	7 3.7	29 43.6	2 48.5
6	14 56 31.0	13 17.3	14 31.2	18 36.6	25 48.5	24 3.1	0♉25.4	19R 7.1	3 47.8	7 3.9	29 43.4	2 47.1
7	15 0 27.5	14 15.3	14 28.3	3♑52.0	25 38.3	24 34.0	1 8.3	19 6.8	3 53.5	7 4.0	29 43.1	2 45.5
8	15 4 24.1	15 13.5	14 25.3	18 58.4	25 23.8	25 3.1	1 51.3	19 6.2	3 59.1	7 4.1	29 42.8	2 44.0
9	15 8 20.7	16 11.9	14 22.4	3♒41.6	25 5.4	25 30.2	2 34.4	19 5.4	4 4.7	7 4.1	29 42.5	2 42.5
10	15 12 17.2	17 10.4	14 19.4	17 53.9	24 43.4	25 55.5	3 17.5	19 4.5	4 10.2	7R 4.0	29 42.2	2 41.0
11	15 16 13.8	18 9.0	14 16.5	1♓35.1	24 18.3	26 18.6	4 .6	19 3.3	4 15.7	7 4.0	29 41.8	2 39.4
12	15 20 10.3	19 7.8	14 13.6	14 50.3	23 50.8	26 39.7	4 43.8	19 1.9	4 21.1	7 3.8	29 41.4	2 37.9
13	15 24 6.9	20 6.8	14 10.6	27 47.2	23 21.4	26 58.7	5 27.0	19 .3	4 26.4	7 3.6	29 40.9	2 36.3
14	15 28 3.4	21 5.9	14 7.7	10♈34.3	22 50.6	27 15.4	6 10.2	18 58.6	4 31.8	7 3.4	29 40.5	2 34.7
15	15 31 60.0	22 5.1	14 4.7	23 19.1	22 19.0	27 29.8	6 53.5	18 56.6	4 37.0	7 3.1	29 39.9	2 33.2
16	15 35 56.5	23 4.5	14 1.8	6♉ 6.9	21 47.3	27 41.9	7 36.9	18 54.4	4 42.2	7 2.8	29 39.4	2 31.6
17	15 39 53.1	24 4.0	13 58.8	18 59.8	21 16.1	27 51.6	8 20.3	18 52.0	4 47.4	7 2.4	29 38.8	2 30.0
18	15 43 49.6	25 3.7	13 55.9	1♊56.6	20 45.8	27 58.8	9 3.7	18 49.5	4 52.5	7 1.9	29 38.2	2 28.4
19	15 47 46.2	26 3.5	13 52.9	14 53.1	20 17.2	28 3.5	9 47.2	18 46.7	4 57.6	7 1.5	29 37.6	2 26.8
20	15 51 42.8	27 3.4	13 50.0	27 43.6	19 50.5	28 5.5	10 30.8	18 43.8	5 2.6	7 1.0	29 37.0	2 25.2
21	15 55 39.3	28 3.5	13 47.0	10♋22.3	19 26.3	28R 5.0	11 14.3	18 40.6	5 7.5	7 .4	29 36.3	2 23.6
22	15 59 35.9	29 3.7	13 44.1	22 45.1	19 4.9	28 1.8	11 57.9	18 37.3	5 12.3	6 59.7	29 35.6	2 22.0
23	16 3 32.4	0♊ 4.0	13 41.1	4♌50.8	18 46.7	27 55.9	12 41.6	18 33.8	5 17.1	6 59.0	29 34.8	2 20.4
24	16 7 29.0	1 4.5	13 38.2	16 41.4	18 31.9	27 47.3	13 25.3	18 30.0	5 21.9	6 58.3	29 34.0	2 18.8
25	16 11 25.5	2 5.1	13 35.2	28 21.7	18 20.8	27 36.1	14 9.0	18 26.1	5 26.5	6 57.5	29 33.2	2 17.2
26	16 15 22.1	3 5.8	13 32.3	9♍58.8	18 13.6	27 22.1	14 52.8	18 22.1	5 31.1	6 56.7	29 32.4	2 15.6
27	16 19 18.6	4 6.6	13 29.4	21 42.0	18 10.3	27 5.6	15 36.6	18 17.8	5 35.7	6 55.8	29 31.5	2 14.0
28	16 23 15.2	5 7.5	13 26.4	3♎41.3	18D11.1	26 46.4	16 20.5	18 13.4	5 40.2	6 54.9	29 30.6	2 12.4
29	16 27 11.8	6 8.5	13 23.5	16 7.6	18 16.0	26 24.7	17 4.4	18 8.7	5 44.6	6 53.9	29 29.7	2 10.8
30	16 31 8.3	7 9.6	13 20.5	29 10.8	18 25.0	26 .6	17 48.3	18 4.0	5 48.9	6 52.9	29 28.7	2 9.2
31	16 35 4.9	8 10.9	13 17.6	12♏58.2	18 38.2	25 34.1	18 32.3	17 59.0	5 53.2	6 51.8	29 27.7	2 7.6
		DECLINATION										
1	14 36 48.2	15N 5.9	0S 6.6	4S23.9	22N13.9	27N41.3	10N30.0	22S12.0	0S50.6	19S40.7	20S 7.9	7S25.1
4	14 48 37.9	15 59.1	0 6.5	15 4.9	21 55.3	27 46.0	11 19.2	22 12.2	0 43.5	19 40.6	20 7.9	7 24.0
7	15 0 27.5	16 49.9	0 6.5	18 18.9	21 16.1	27 46.5	12 7.4	22 12.6	0 36.6	19 40.6	20 8.0	7 23.0
10	15 12 17.2	17 38.3	0 6.4	11 29.3	20 19.0	27 42.8	12 54.3	22 13.2	0 30.0	19 40.7	20 8.2	7 22.0
13	15 24 6.9	18 24.0	0 6.3	0N50.4	19 8.9	27 35.0	13 40.1	22 14.1	0 23.5	19 40.9	20 8.4	7 21.1
16	15 35 56.5	19 6.9	0 6.3	12 21.6	17 52.5	27 23.1	14 24.6	22 15.2	0 17.3	19 41.2	20 8.7	7 20.2
19	15 47 46.2	19 46.8	0 6.2	18 16.0	16 38.1	27 7.0	15 7.7	22 16.5	0 11.3	19 41.6	20 9.0	7 19.4
22	15 59 35.9	20 23.8	0 6.2	16 37.1	15 33.4	26 46.5	15 49.4	22 18.0	0 5.6	19 42.1	20 9.4	7 18.6
25	16 11 25.5	20 57.6	0 6.1	8 43.1	14 44.5	26 21.3	16 29.6	22 19.7	0 .2	19 42.8	20 9.8	7 18.0
28	16 23 15.2	21 28.2	0 6.0	2S42.8	14 14.9	25 51.1	17 8.4	22 21.6	0N 5.0	19 43.5	20 10.3	7 17.4
31	16 35 4.9	21 55.4	0 6.0	13 53.1	14 5.7	25 15.8	17 45.5	22 23.6	0 9.9	19 44.3	20 10.8	7 16.8

JUNE 1996

LONGITUDE

DAY	EPHEM. SID. TIME	☉	☊	☽	☿	♀	♂	♃	♄	♅	♆	♇
	h m s	° ′	° ′	° ′	° ′	° ′	° ′	° ′	° ′	° ′	° ′	° ′
1	16 39 1.4	10♊47.3	14♎23.2	28♏57.4	20♉18.7	25♊33.1	21♉38.1	16♑30.4	5♈32.6	4♒21.8	27♑28.7	1♐29.7
2	16 42 58.0	11 44.8	14 20.1	13♐34.8	20 39.7	25 R 4.8	22 21.6	16 R 25.4	5 37.0	4 R 20.7	27 R 27.7	1 R 28.0
3	16 46 54.5	12 42.2	14 16.9	28 26.6	21 5.1	24 34.6	23 5.1	16 20.4	5 41.3	4 19.5	27 26.7	1 26.4
4	16 50 51.1	13 39.7	14 13.7	13♑24.0	21 34.7	24 2.8	23 48.6	16 15.1	5 45.6	4 18.3	27 25.7	1 24.8
5	16 54 47.7	14 37.1	14 10.5	28 17.8	22 8.5	23 29.5	24 32.0	16 9.7	5 49.8	4 17.1	27 24.6	1 23.2
6	16 58 44.2	15 34.5	14 7.4	13♒ .3	22 46.5	22 55.0	25 15.3	16 4.2	5 53.9	4 15.8	27 23.5	1 21.6
7	17 2 40.8	16 31.9	14 4.2	27 25.8	23 28.4	22 19.3	25 58.6	15 58.6	5 57.9	4 14.4	27 22.4	1 20.0
8	17 6 37.3	17 29.3	14 1.0	11♓31.2	24 14.2	21 42.9	26 41.8	15 52.8	6 1.8	4 13.1	27 21.3	1 18.5
9	17 10 33.9	18 26.7	13 57.8	25 16.1	25 4.0	21 5.8	27 25.0	15 46.9	6 5.7	4 11.7	27 20.2	1 16.9
10	17 14 30.4	19 24.1	13 54.6	8♈41.3	25 57.4	20 28.3	28 8.1	15 40.9	6 9.5	4 10.3	27 19.0	1 15.4
11	17 18 27.0	20 21.4	13 51.5	21 49.1	26 54.4	19 50.7	28 51.2	15 34.7	6 13.2	4 8.8	27 17.8	1 13.9
12	17 22 23.6	21 18.8	13 48.3	4♉42.0	27 55.0	19 13.2	29 34.2	15 28.4	6 16.7	4 7.3	27 16.6	1 12.3
13	17 26 20.1	22 16.1	13 45.1	17 22.0	28 59.2	18 36.0	0♊17.2	15 22.0	6 20.3	4 5.7	27 15.3	1 10.8
14	17 30 16.7	23 13.5	13 41.9	29 51.3	0♊ 6.8	17 59.4	1 .1	15 15.5	6 23.7	4 4.1	27 14.1	1 9.3
15	17 34 13.2	24 10.8	13 38.8	12♊11.1	1 17.7	17 23.6	1 42.9	15 8.8	6 27.0	4 2.5	27 12.8	1 7.8
16	17 38 9.8	25 8.1	13 35.6	24 22.7	2 32.1	16 48.8	2 25.7	15 2.1	6 30.3	4 .8	27 11.5	1 6.3
17	17 42 6.3	26 5.4	13 32.4	6♋27.0	3 49.7	16 15.2	3 8.4	14 55.3	6 33.4	3 59.1	27 10.2	1 4.9
18	17 46 2.9	27 2.7	13 29.2	18 25.1	5 10.5	15 43.0	3 51.1	14 48.4	6 36.5	3 57.3	27 8.8	1 3.4
19	17 49 59.5	28 .0	13 26.1	0♌18.4	6 34.6	15 12.4	4 33.7	14 41.4	6 39.4	3 55.6	27 7.5	1 2.0
20	17 53 56.0	28 57.3	13 22.9	12 9.0	8 1.9	14 43.5	5 16.2	14 34.3	6 42.3	3 53.8	27 6.1	1 .6
21	17 57 52.6	29 54.5	13 19.7	23 59.8	9 32.3	14 16.5	5 58.7	14 27.1	6 45.1	3 51.9	27 4.7	0 59.2
22	18 1 49.1	0♋51.8	13 16.5	5♍54.1	11 5.9	13 51.5	6 41.2	14 19.9	6 47.8	3 50.1	27 3.3	0 57.8
23	18 5 45.7	1 49.0	13 13.3	17 56.3	12 42.6	13 28.7	7 23.5	14 12.6	6 50.4	3 48.2	27 1.9	0 56.4
24	18 9 42.2	2 46.3	13 10.2	0♎11.1	14 22.3	13 8.0	8 5.8	14 5.2	6 52.9	3 46.2	27 .5	0 55.1
25	18 13 38.8	3 43.5	13 7.0	12 43.6	16 5.0	12 49.5	8 48.1	13 57.8	6 55.3	3 44.3	26 59.0	0 53.8
26	18 17 35.4	4 40.7	13 3.8	25 38.8	17 50.7	12 33.4	9 30.3	13 50.3	6 57.7	3 42.3	26 57.5	0 52.5
27	18 21 31.9	5 37.9	13 .6	9♏ .8	19 39.3	12 19.6	10 12.4	13 42.8	6 59.9	3 40.3	26 56.1	0 51.2
28	18 25 28.5	6 35.1	12 57.5	22 52.0	21 30.7	12 8.2	10 54.5	13 35.2	7 2.0	3 38.3	26 54.6	0 49.9
29	18 29 25.0	7 32.3	12 54.3	7♐12.5	23 24.8	11 59.3	11 36.5	13 27.6	7 4.1	3 36.2	26 53.1	0 48.7
30	18 33 21.6	8♋29.5	12 51.1	21♐58.9	25♊21.5	11♊52.7	12♊18.5	13♑20.1	7 6.0	3♒34.2	26♑51.6	0♐47.5

LATITUDE

DAY	EPHEM. SID. TIME	☉	☊	☽	☿	♀	♂	♃	♄	♅	♆	♇
1	16 39 1.4	0 .0	0 .0	3N29.4	3S50.5	1N41.2	0S13.2	0N .7	2S11.4	0S35.6	0N29.4	13N26.5
4	16 50 51.1	0 .0	0 .0	5 4.5	3 53.7	1 2.8	0 11.2	0 .3	2 12.1	0 35.6	0 29.4	13 26.0
7	17 2 40.8	0 .0	0 .0	3 45.9	3 48.5	0 21.7	0 9.2	0S .1	2 12.8	0 35.7	0 29.4	13 25.4
10	17 14 30.4	0 .0	0 .0	0 34.1	3 36.0	0S20.8	0 7.2	0 .5	2 13.6	0 35.8	0 29.4	13 24.8
13	17 26 20.1	0 .0	0 .0	2S42.7	3 17.1	1 3.0	0 5.2	0 .9	2 14.3	0 35.9	0 29.4	13 24.1
16	17 38 9.8	0 .0	0 .0	4 43.0	2 52.8	1 43.6	0 3.2	0 1.3	2 15.1	0 36.0	0 29.4	13 23.3
19	17 49 59.5	0 .0	0 .0	4 49.1	2 24.1	2 21.2	0 1.1	0 1.8	2 15.9	0 36.1	0 29.3	13 22.5
22	18 1 49.1	0 .0	0 .0	3 5.0	1 51.8	2 54.9	0N .9	0 2.2	2 16.7	0 36.1	0 29.3	13 21.6
25	18 13 38.8	0 .0	0 .0	0 4.0	1 17.2	3 24.1	0 3.0	0 2.6	2 17.5	0 36.2	0 29.3	13 20.6
28	18 25 28.5	0 .0	0 .0	3N12.1	0 41.6	3 48.6	0 5.0	0 3.0	2 18.3	0 36.3	0 29.3	13 19.6

RIGHT ASCENSION

DAY	EPHEM. SID. TIME	☉	☊	☽	☿	♀	♂	♃	♄	♅	♆	♇
1	16 39 1.4	9♊12.2	13♎14.6	27♏31.7	18♉55.6	25♊ 5.4	19♉16.4	17♑53.9	5♈57.4	6♒50.7	29♑26.7	2♐ 6.0
2	16 42 58.0	10 13.7	13 11.7	12♐44.7	19 17.0	24 R 34.7	20 .5	17 R 48.6	6 1.5	6 R 49.6	29 R 25.7	2 R 4.4
3	16 46 54.5	11 15.2	13 8.7	28 21.8	19 42.5	24 2.1	20 44.6	17 43.1	6 5.6	6 48.4	29 24.6	2 2.8
4	16 50 51.1	12 16.8	13 5.8	14♑ 1.4	20 12.1	23 27.9	21 28.8	17 37.5	6 9.6	6 47.2	29 23.5	2 1.2
5	16 54 47.7	13 18.5	13 2.9	29 22.2	20 45.6	22 52.1	22 13.0	17 31.8	6 13.5	6 45.9	29 22.4	1 59.6
6	16 58 44.2	14 20.3	12 59.9	14♒ 9.9	21 23.0	22 15.1	22 57.2	17 25.9	6 17.4	6 44.5	29 21.3	1 58.0
7	17 2 40.8	15 22.2	12 57.0	28 19.2	22 4.2	21 37.1	23 41.5	17 19.8	6 21.1	6 43.2	29 20.1	1 56.5
8	17 6 37.3	16 24.2	12 54.0	11♓52.7	22 49.3	20 58.3	24 25.9	17 13.6	6 24.8	6 41.8	29 18.9	1 54.9
9	17 10 33.9	17 26.3	12 51.1	24 58.3	23 38.3	20 19.1	25 10.3	17 7.3	6 28.5	6 40.4	29 17.8	1 53.4
10	17 14 30.4	18 28.4	12 48.2	7♈45.4	24 30.9	19 39.6	25 54.7	17 .8	6 32.1	6 38.9	29 16.5	1 51.9
11	17 18 27.0	19 30.5	12 45.2	20 23.7	25 27.2	19 .1	26 39.2	16 54.2	6 35.5	6 37.4	29 15.3	1 50.4
12	17 22 23.6	20 32.7	12 42.3	3♉ .7	26 27.1	18 20.8	27 23.7	16 47.4	6 38.9	6 35.8	29 14.0	1 48.8
13	17 26 20.1	21 35.0	12 39.3	15 41.5	27 30.8	17 42.1	28 8.2	16 40.6	6 42.3	6 34.2	29 12.7	1 47.3
14	17 30 16.7	22 37.3	12 36.4	28 27.6	28 38.0	17 4.1	28 52.8	16 33.6	6 45.5	6 32.5	29 11.4	1 45.8
15	17 34 13.2	23 39.6	12 33.4	11♊17.1	29 49.0	16 27.1	29 37.3	16 26.5	6 48.7	6 30.9	29 10.1	1 44.4
16	17 38 9.8	24 42.0	12 30.5	24 5.3	1♊ 3.6	15 51.4	0♊22.0	16 19.2	6 51.7	6 29.1	29 8.7	1 42.9
17	17 42 6.3	25 44.4	12 27.6	6♋46.2	2 21.8	15 17.0	1 6.6	16 11.9	6 54.7	6 27.4	29 7.3	1 41.4
18	17 46 2.9	26 46.8	12 24.6	19 14.3	3 43.7	14 44.1	1 51.3	16 4.5	6 57.6	6 25.6	29 5.9	1 40.0
19	17 49 59.5	27 49.2	12 21.7	1♌26.0	5 9.4	14 13.1	2 36.0	15 56.9	7 .5	6 23.8	29 4.5	1 38.5
20	17 53 56.0	28 51.6	12 18.7	13 20.8	6 38.7	13 43.9	3 20.7	15 49.3	7 3.2	6 21.9	29 3.1	1 37.1
21	17 57 52.6	29 54.1	12 15.8	25 1.2	8 11.8	13 16.8	4 5.5	15 41.6	7 5.9	6 20.0	29 1.6	1 35.7
22	18 1 49.1	0♋56.5	12 12.9	6♍32.7	9 48.6	12 51.8	4 50.2	15 33.8	7 8.5	6 18.1	29 .1	1 34.3
23	18 5 45.7	1 58.8	12 9.9	18 3.3	11 29.3	12 29.0	5 35.0	15 26.0	7 11.0	6 16.1	28 58.7	1 33.0
24	18 9 42.2	3 1.2	12 7.0	29 42.4	13 13.7	12 8.5	6 19.8	15 18.1	7 13.4	6 14.2	28 57.2	1 31.6
25	18 13 38.8	4 3.5	12 4.1	11♎40.9	15 1.9	11 50.4	7 4.6	15 10.1	7 15.7	6 12.1	28 55.6	1 30.3
26	18 17 35.4	5 5.8	12 1.1	24 10.0	16 53.8	11 34.7	7 49.5	15 2.0	7 17.9	6 10.1	28 54.1	1 29.0
27	18 21 31.9	6 8.1	11 58.2	7♏20.2	18 49.4	11 21.4	8 34.3	14 53.9	7 20.1	6 8.0	28 52.6	1 27.7
28	18 25 28.5	7 10.3	11 55.2	21 18.5	20 48.6	11 10.5	9 19.1	14 45.8	7 22.1	6 5.9	28 51.0	1 26.4
29	18 29 25.0	8 12.4	11 52.3	6♐ 5.9	22 51.2	11 2.1	10 4.0	14 37.6	7 24.1	6 3.8	28 49.4	1 25.1
30	18 33 21.6	9♋14.6	11♎49.4	21♐34.2	24♊57.3	10♊56.2	10♊48.9	14♑29.5	7♈26.1	6♒ 1.7	28♑47.9	1♐23.9

DECLINATION

DAY	EPHEM. SID. TIME	☉	☊	☽	☿	♀	♂	♃	♄	♅	♆	♇
1	16 39 1.4	22N 3.7	0S 5.9	16S31.0	14N 7.1	25N 2.9	17N57.6	22S24.3	0N11.4	19S44.6	20S11.0	7S16.7
4	16 50 51.1	22 26.3	0 5.9	17 42.7	14 23.6	24 20.9	18 32.6	22 26.6	0 15.9	19 45.5	20 11.6	7 16.3
7	17 2 40.8	22 45.4	0 5.8	8 49.5	14 57.0	23 34.5	19 5.9	22 29.0	0 20.1	19 46.5	20 12.2	7 15.9
10	17 14 30.4	23 .9	0 5.7	3N58.0	15 44.6	22 45.0	19 37.6	22 31.4	0 24.0	19 47.6	20 12.9	7 15.7
13	17 26 20.1	23 12.7	0 5.7	14 24.7	16 43.4	21 54.1	20 7.5	22 34.0	0 27.6	19 48.7	20 13.6	7 15.5
16	17 38 9.8	23 20.9	0 5.6	18 36.3	17 50.4	21 3.9	20 35.6	22 36.7	0 30.9	19 50.0	20 14.3	7 15.4
19	17 49 59.5	23 25.3	0 5.6	15 22.4	19 2.3	20 16.6	21 1.9	22 39.4	0 33.8	19 51.3	20 15.1	7 15.4
22	18 1 49.1	23 26.1	0 5.5	6 28.6	20 15.5	19 34.0	21 26.3	22 42.2	0 36.3	19 52.7	20 15.9	7 15.5
25	18 13 38.8	23 23.1	0 5.4	5S 5.4	21 25.8	18 57.6	21 48.9	22 44.9	0 38.6	19 54.1	20 16.8	7 15.7
28	18 25 28.5	23 16.4	0 5.4	15 23.3	22 28.4	18 28.1	22 9.6	22 47.6	0 40.5	19 55.6	20 17.6	7 15.9

JULY 1996

LONGITUDE

DAY	EPHEM. SID. TIME	☉	☊	☽	☿	♀	♂	♃	♄	♅	♆	♇
	h m s	° ′	° ′	° ′	° ′	° ′	° ′	° ′	° ′	° ′	° ′	° ′
1	18 37 18.1	9♋26.7	12♎47.9	7♑ 4.3	27♊20.6	11♊48.5	13♊ .5	13♑12.4	7♈ 7.9	3♒32.1	26♑50.1	0♐46.3
2	18 41 14.7	10 23.9	12 44.8	22 18.9	29 21.9	11 R 46.6	13 42.3	13 R 4.8	7 9.6	3 R 29.9	26 R 48.5	0 R 45.2
3	18 45 11.3	11 21.1	12 41.6	7♒31.7	1♋25.2	11 D 47.1	14 24.1	12 57.1	7 11.3	3 27.8	26 47.0	0 44.0
4	18 49 7.8	12 18.2	12 38.4	22 32.3	3 30.2	11 49.9	15 5.8	12 49.4	7 12.8	3 25.6	26 45.4	0 42.9
5	18 53 4.4	13 15.4	12 35.2	7♓12.7	5 36.8	11 55.0	15 47.5	12 41.7	7 14.3	3 23.4	26 43.9	0 41.8
6	18 57 .9	14 12.6	12 32.1	21 28.4	7 44.6	12 2.3	16 29.1	12 34.0	7 15.6	3 21.2	26 42.3	0 40.7
7	19 0 57.5	15 9.8	12 28.9	5♈18.0	9 53.4	12 11.7	17 10.7	12 26.3	7 16.9	3 19.0	26 40.7	0 39.6
8	19 4 54.0	16 7.0	12 25.7	18 42.6	12 2.8	12 23.3	17 52.2	12 18.6	7 18.0	3 16.7	26 39.1	0 38.6
9	19 8 50.6	17 4.2	12 22.5	1♉45.2	14 12.6	12 36.8	18 33.7	12 10.9	7 19.1	3 14.4	26 37.5	0 37.6
10	19 12 47.2	18 1.4	12 19.3	14 29.1	16 22.5	12 52.4	19 15.1	12 3.3	7 20.0	3 12.2	26 35.9	0 36.6
11	19 16 43.7	18 58.6	12 16.2	26 58.1	18 32.2	13 9.9	19 56.4	11 55.7	7 20.9	3 9.9	26 34.3	0 35.7
12	19 20 40.3	19 55.9	12 13.0	9♊15.4	20 41.4	13 29.2	20 37.7	11 48.1	7 21.6	3 7.6	26 32.7	0 34.8
13	19 24 36.8	20 53.1	12 9.8	21 23.8	22 49.9	13 50.4	21 19.0	11 40.5	7 22.2	3 5.2	26 31.1	0 33.9
14	19 28 33.4	21 50.3	12 6.6	3♋25.5	24 57.5	14 13.2	22 .2	11 33.0	7 22.8	3 2.9	26 29.5	0 33.0
15	19 32 29.9	22 47.6	12 3.5	15 22.4	27 4.0	14 37.8	22 41.3	11 25.6	7 23.2	3 .5	26 27.9	0 32.1
16	19 36 26.5	23 44.8	12 .3	27 15.7	29 9.3	15 3.9	23 22.3	11 18.2	7 23.6	2 58.2	26 26.3	0 31.3
17	19 40 23.0	24 42.1	11 57.1	9♌ 6.8	1♌13.3	15 31.6	24 3.3	11 10.9	7 23.8	2 55.8	26 24.6	0 30.5
18	19 44 19.6	25 39.4	11 53.9	20 57.5	3 15.8	16 .8	24 44.3	11 3.6	7 23.9	2 53.4	26 23.0	0 29.8
19	19 48 16.2	26 36.6	11 50.8	2♍49.7	5 16.7	16 31.4	25 25.2	10 56.4	7 24.0	2 51.1	26 21.4	0 29.1
20	19 52 12.7	27 33.9	11 47.6	14 46.1	7 16.0	17 3.4	26 6.0	10 49.3	7 R 23.9	2 48.7	26 19.7	0 28.4
21	19 56 9.3	28 31.2	11 44.4	26 50.0	9 13.8	17 36.8	26 46.8	10 42.3	7 23.8	2 46.3	26 18.2	0 27.7
22	20 0 5.8	29 28.5	11 41.2	9♎ 5.3	11 9.7	18 11.4	27 27.5	10 35.3	7 23.5	2 43.9	26 16.5	0 27.1
23	20 4 2.4	0♌25.8	11 38.0	21 36.7	13 4.0	18 47.2	28 8.1	10 28.5	7 23.1	2 41.5	26 14.9	0 26.5
24	20 7 58.9	1 23.1	11 34.9	4♏28.6	14 56.5	19 24.3	28 48.7	10 21.7	7 22.6	2 39.1	26 13.3	0 25.9
25	20 11 55.5	2 20.4	11 31.7	17 45.5	16 47.3	20 2.5	29 29.2	10 15.1	7 22.0	2 36.7	26 11.7	0 25.4
26	20 15 52.0	3 17.7	11 28.5	1♐30.4	18 36.4	20 41.8	0♋ 9.7	10 8.5	7 21.4	2 34.3	26 10.1	0 24.9
27	20 19 48.6	4 15.0	11 25.3	15 44.5	20 23.7	21 22.2	0 50.1	10 2.1	7 20.6	2 31.9	26 8.5	0 24.4
28	20 23 45.2	5 12.3	11 22.2	0♑25.9	22 9.3	22 3.6	1 30.4	9 55.7	7 19.7	2 29.5	26 6.9	0 23.9
29	20 27 41.7	6 9.7	11 19.0	15 29.2	23 53.2	22 46.0	2 10.7	9 49.5	7 18.7	2 27.1	26 5.3	0 23.5
30	20 31 38.3	7 7.0	11 15.8	0♒45.7	25 35.3	23 29.3	2 51.0	9 43.4	7 17.6	2 24.7	26 3.7	0 23.1
31	20 35 34.8	8 4.4	11 12.6	16 4.5	27 15.8	24 13.6	3 31.1	9 37.4	7 16.5	2 22.3	26 2.1	0 22.7

LATITUDE

DAY	EPHEM. SID. TIME	☉	☊	☽	☿	♀	♂	♃	♄	♅	♆	♇
1	18 37 18.1	0 .0	0 .0	4N58.9	0S 6.4	4S 8.4	0N 7.1	0S 3.5	2S19.1	0S36.3	0N29.3	13N18.5
4	18 49 7.8	0 .0	0 .0	3 50.8	0N26.5	4 23.9	0 9.1	0 3.9	2 19.9	0 36.4	0 29.3	13 17.4
7	19 0 57.5	0 .0	0 .0	0 37.1	0 55.4	4 35.3	0 11.2	0 4.3	2 20.7	0 36.4	0 29.3	13 16.2
10	19 12 47.2	0 .0	0 .0	2S41.1	1 18.7	4 43.1	0 13.3	0 4.7	2 21.6	0 36.5	0 29.2	13 15.0
13	19 24 36.8	0 .0	0 .0	4 41.5	1 35.5	4 47.7	0 15.4	0 5.1	2 22.4	0 36.5	0 29.2	13 13.7
16	19 36 26.5	0 .0	0 .0	4 48.9	1 45.4	4 49.5	0 17.5	0 5.6	2 23.3	0 36.6	0 29.2	13 12.4
19	19 48 16.2	0 .0	0 .0	3 6.1	1 48.7	4 48.8	0 19.6	0 6.0	2 24.1	0 36.6	0 29.1	13 11.1
22	20 0 5.8	0 .0	0 .0	0 8.1	1 45.9	4 45.9	0 21.6	0 6.4	2 24.9	0 36.6	0 29.1	13 9.7
25	20 11 55.5	0 .0	0 .0	3N 4.1	1 37.8	4 41.2	0 23.7	0 6.7	2 25.7	0 36.6	0 29.1	13 8.3
28	20 23 45.2	0 .0	0 .0	4 59.0	1 24.9	4 34.7	0 25.8	0 7.1	2 26.5	0 36.7	0 29.0	13 6.8
31	20 35 34.8	0 .0	0 .0	4 5.7	1 8.0	4 26.9	0 27.9	0 7.5	2 27.3	0 36.7	0 29.0	13 5.4

RIGHT ASCENSION

DAY	EPHEM. SID. TIME	☉	☊	☽	☿	♀	♂	♃	♄	♅	♆	♇
1	18 37 18.1	10♋16.6	11♎46.4	7♑25.3	27♊ 6.4	10♊52.6	11♊33.8	14♑21.2	7♈27.9	5♒59.5	28♑46.3	1♐22.7
2	18 41 14.7	11 18.6	11 43.5	23 15.9	29 18.4	10 R 51.5	12 18.6	14 R 13.0	7 29.6	5 R 57.3	28 R 44.7	1 R 21.5
3	18 45 11.3	12 20.5	11 40.5	8♒44.4	1♋33.0	10 D 52.7	13 3.5	14 4.7	7 31.2	5 55.1	28 43.1	1 20.3
4	18 49 7.8	13 22.3	11 37.6	23 37.1	3 49.8	10 56.3	13 48.4	13 56.4	7 32.7	5 52.9	28 41.5	1 19.2
5	18 53 4.4	14 24.1	11 34.7	7♓50.2	6 8.6	11 2.1	14 33.2	13 48.1	7 34.2	5 50.6	28 39.8	1 18.0
6	18 57 .9	15 25.8	11 31.7	21 27.5	8 28.8	11 10.2	15 18.1	13 39.8	7 35.5	5 48.3	28 38.2	1 16.9
7	19 0 57.5	16 27.4	11 28.8	4♈37.1	10 50.1	11 20.4	16 3.0	13 31.5	7 36.8	5 46.0	28 36.5	1 15.8
8	19 4 54.0	17 28.9	11 25.9	17 28.6	13 12.0	11 32.8	16 47.8	13 23.2	7 37.9	5 43.7	28 34.9	1 14.8
9	19 8 50.6	18 30.3	11 22.9	0♉10.8	15 34.1	11 47.2	17 32.7	13 14.9	7 39.0	5 41.3	28 33.2	1 13.7
10	19 12 47.2	19 31.6	11 20.0	12 50.4	17 55.9	12 3.7	18 17.5	13 6.6	7 40.0	5 39.0	28 31.5	1 12.7
11	19 16 43.7	20 32.8	11 17.1	25 31.3	20 17.1	12 22.1	19 2.3	12 58.4	7 40.9	5 36.6	28 29.8	1 11.7
12	19 20 40.3	21 33.9	11 14.1	8♊14.4	22 37.3	12 42.4	19 47.1	12 50.2	7 41.7	5 34.2	28 28.2	1 10.7
13	19 24 36.8	22 34.9	11 11.2	20 57.3	24 56.1	13 4.4	20 31.8	12 42.1	7 42.4	5 31.8	28 26.5	1 9.8
14	19 28 33.4	23 35.7	11 8.2	3♋35.9	27 13.3	13 28.3	21 16.6	12 34.0	7 43.0	5 29.4	28 24.8	1 8.8
15	19 32 29.9	24 36.5	11 5.3	16 5.0	29 28.5	13 53.9	22 1.3	12 25.9	7 43.5	5 27.0	28 23.1	1 7.9
16	19 36 26.5	25 37.1	11 2.4	28 20.7	1♌41.5	14 21.1	22 46.0	12 17.9	7 43.9	5 24.5	28 21.4	1 7.1
17	19 40 23.0	26 37.6	10 59.4	10♌20.8	3 52.3	14 49.9	23 30.6	12 10.0	7 44.2	5 22.1	28 19.7	1 6.2
18	19 44 19.6	27 38.0	10 56.5	22 5.9	6 .6	15 20.3	24 15.2	12 2.1	7 44.5	5 19.6	28 18.0	1 5.4
19	19 48 16.2	28 38.2	10 53.6	3♍39.4	8 6.4	15 52.1	24 59.8	11 54.3	7 44.6	5 17.1	28 16.3	1 4.6
20	19 52 12.7	29 38.3	10 50.6	15 7.1	10 9.5	16 25.5	25 44.4	11 46.6	7 44.6	5 14.7	28 14.6	1 3.8
21	19 56 9.3	0♌38.3	10 47.7	26 36.8	12 10.0	17 .2	26 28.9	11 39.1	7 44.6	5 12.2	28 12.9	1 3.2
22	20 0 5.8	1 38.0	10 44.8	8♎17.8	14 7.8	17 36.3	27 13.3	11 31.6	7 R 44.5	5 9.8	28 11.2	1 2.5
23	20 4 2.4	2 37.7	10 41.8	20 20.4	16 3.0	18 13.6	27 57.7	11 24.1	7 44.2	5 7.3	28 9.5	1 1.8
24	20 7 58.9	3 37.2	10 38.9	2♏55.1	17 55.5	18 52.3	28 42.1	11 16.8	7 43.9	5 4.8	28 7.8	1 1.1
25	20 11 55.5	4 36.5	10 36.0	16 10.8	19 45.3	19 32.1	29 26.4	11 9.6	7 43.5	5 2.3	28 6.1	1 .5
26	20 15 52.0	5 35.7	10 33.0	0♐13.3	21 32.6	20 13.2	0♋10.6	11 2.5	7 43.0	4 59.8	28 4.5	0 59.9
27	20 19 48.6	6 34.8	10 30.1	15 1.9	23 17.3	20 55.4	0 54.8	10 55.5	7 42.4	4 57.3	28 2.8	0 59.3
28	20 23 45.2	7 33.7	10 27.2	0♑27.2	24 59.6	21 38.7	1 38.9	10 48.7	7 41.7	4 54.8	28 1.1	0 58.8
29	20 27 41.7	8 32.4	10 24.2	16 11.8	26 39.4	22 23.1	2 23.0	10 41.9	7 40.9	4 52.3	27 59.4	0 58.3
30	20 31 38.3	9 31.0	10 21.3	1♒54.7	28 16.8	23 8.5	3 6.9	10 35.3	7 40.0	4 49.9	27 57.8	0 57.8
31	20 35 34.8	10 29.4	10 18.4	17 17.1	29 51.9	23 55.0	3 50.9	10 28.9	7 39.0	4 47.4	27 56.1	0 57.4

DECLINATION

DAY	EPHEM. SID. TIME	☉	☊	☽	☿	♀	♂	♃	♄	♅	♆	♇
1	18 37 18.1	23N 6.1	0S 5.3	18S16.4	23N18.2	18N 5.8	22N28.5	22S50.3	0N42.0	19S57.1	20S18.5	7S16.3
4	18 49 7.8	22 52.1	0 5.2	10 21.6	23 50.0	17 50.7	22 45.3	22 53.0	0 43.2	19 58.6	20 19.4	7 16.8
7	19 0 57.5	22 34.5	0 5.2	2N40.4	23 59.3	17 42.2	23 .3	22 55.6	0 44.0	20 .2	20 20.4	7 17.3
10	19 12 47.2	22 13.4	0 5.1	13 36.9	23 44.1	17 39.5	23 13.4	22 58.1	0 44.5	20 1.9	20 21.3	7 17.9
13	19 24 36.8	21 48.9	0 5.0	18 28.6	23 4.4	17 41.8	23 24.5	23 .6	0 44.6	20 3.5	20 22.2	7 18.6
16	19 36 26.5	21 21.0	0 5.0	15 58.9	22 2.6	17 48.3	23 33.7	23 2.9	0 44.4	20 5.2	20 23.2	7 19.4
19	19 48 16.2	20 49.9	0 4.9	7 34.2	20 42.3	17 57.9	23 41.0	23 5.1	0 43.8	20 6.8	20 24.1	7 20.3
22	20 0 5.8	20 15.5	0 4.8	3S43.6	19 7.3	18 9.9	23 46.4	23 7.2	0 42.8	20 8.5	20 25.1	7 21.3
25	20 11 55.5	19 38.2	0 4.8	14 10.7	17 21.4	18 23.4	23 49.9	23 9.2	0 41.5	20 10.2	20 26.0	7 22.3
28	20 23 45.2	18 57.9	0 4.7	18 27.2	15 27.8	18 37.7	23 51.6	23 11.1	0 39.8	20 11.8	20 27.0	7 23.5
31	20 35 34.8	18 14.8	0 4.6	12 6.3	13 29.1	18 52.0	23 51.4	23 12.8	0 37.8	20 13.5	20 27.9	7 24.7

AUGUST 1996

LONGITUDE

DAY	EPHEM. SID. TIME h m s	☉ ° ′	☊ ° ′	☽ ° ′	☿ ° ′	♀ ° ′	♂ ° ′	♃ ° ′	♄ ° ′	♅ ° ′	♆ ° ′	♇ ° ′
1	20 39 31.4	9♌ 1.7	11♎ 9.4	1♓14.3	28♌54.5	24♊58.8	4♋11.2	9♑31.6	7♈15.2	2♒20.0	26♑ .5	0♐22.4
2	20 43 27.9	9 59.1	11 6.3	16 5.6	0♍31.6	25 44.9	4 51.3	9R25.9	7R13.8	2R17.6	25R59.0	0R22.1
3	20 47 24.5	10 56.5	11 3.1	0♈32.1	2 6.9	26 31.7	5 31.3	9 20.3	7 12.4	2 15.2	25 57.4	0 21.9
4	20 51 21.0	11 53.9	10 59.9	14 30.8	3 40.6	27 19.4	6 11.2	9 14.9	7 10.8	2 12.9	25 55.8	0 21.6
5	20 55 17.6	12 51.4	10 56.7	28 1.7	5 12.6	28 7.9	6 51.1	9 9.6	7 9.1	2 10.5	25 54.3	0 21.4
6	20 59 14.2	13 48.8	10 53.6	11♉ 7.0	6 42.9	28 57.1	7 31.0	9 4.4	7 7.4	2 8.2	25 52.8	0 21.3
7	21 3 10.7	14 46.3	10 50.4	23 50.5	8 11.5	29 47.0	8 10.7	8 59.4	7 5.5	2 5.8	25 51.3	0 21.1
8	21 7 7.3	15 43.8	10 47.2	6♊16.2	9 38.3	0♋37.6	8 50.4	8 54.6	7 3.6	2 3.5	25 49.7	0 21.0
9	21 11 3.8	16 41.4	10 44.0	18 28.3	11 3.4	1 28.9	9 30.1	8 49.9	7 1.5	2 1.2	25 48.2	0 21.0
10	21 15 .4	17 38.9	10 40.8	0♋30.7	12 26.8	2 20.8	10 9.7	8 45.3	6 59.4	1 58.9	25 46.8	0 20.9
11	21 18 56.9	18 36.5	10 37.7	12 26.8	13 48.4	3 13.4	10 49.3	8 41.0	6 57.2	1 56.7	25 45.3	0D21.0
12	21 22 53.5	19 34.1	10 34.5	24 19.3	15 8.1	4 6.5	11 28.8	8 36.8	6 54.9	1 54.4	25 43.9	0 21.0
13	21 26 50.0	20 31.7	10 31.3	6♌10.4	16 25.9	5 .3	12 8.2	8 32.7	6 52.5	1 52.2	25 42.4	0 21.1
14	21 30 46.6	21 29.4	10 28.1	18 2.1	17 41.8	5 54.5	12 47.5	8 28.8	6 50.0	1 50.0	25 41.0	0 21.2
15	21 34 43.1	22 27.0	10 25.0	29 56.0	18 55.7	6 49.3	13 26.8	8 25.1	6 47.4	1 47.8	25 39.6	0 21.3
16	21 38 39.7	23 24.7	10 21.8	11♍53.7	20 7.5	7 44.7	14 6.1	8 21.6	6 44.7	1 45.6	25 38.2	0 21.5
17	21 42 36.2	24 22.4	10 18.6	23 57.3	21 17.2	8 40.5	14 45.2	8 18.2	6 42.0	1 43.4	25 36.8	0 21.7
18	21 46 32.8	25 20.1	10 15.4	6♎ 9.1	22 24.7	9 36.8	15 24.3	8 15.0	6 39.1	1 41.3	25 35.5	0 21.9
19	21 50 29.4	26 17.9	10 12.3	18 31.7	23 29.9	10 33.6	16 3.4	8 12.0	6 36.2	1 39.2	25 34.1	0 22.2
20	21 54 25.9	27 15.6	10 9.1	1♏ 8.3	24 32.6	11 30.8	16 42.4	8 9.2	6 33.2	1 37.1	25 32.8	0 22.5
21	21 58 22.5	28 13.4	10 5.9	14 2.5	25 32.8	12 28.5	17 21.3	8 6.6	6 30.1	1 35.0	25 31.5	0 22.9
22	22 2 19.0	29 11.2	10 2.7	27 17.5	26 30.3	13 26.6	18 .2	8 4.1	6 27.0	1 33.0	25 30.2	0 23.2
23	22 6 15.6	0♍ 9.0	9 59.5	10♐56.1	27 25.1	14 25.1	18 39.0	8 1.8	6 23.7	1 30.9	25 28.9	0 23.6
24	22 10 12.1	1 6.8	9 56.4	24 59.6	28 16.8	15 24.1	19 17.7	7 59.8	6 20.4	1 28.9	25 27.7	0 24.1
25	22 14 8.7	2 4.7	9 53.2	9♑27.3	29 5.4	16 23.4	19 56.3	7 57.8	6 17.0	1 27.0	25 26.4	0 24.5
26	22 18 5.2	3 2.5	9 50.0	24 15.6	29 50.6	17 23.1	20 35.0	7 56.1	6 13.6	1 25.0	25 25.2	0 25.1
27	22 22 1.8	4 .4	9 46.8	9♒18.2	0♎32.4	18 23.2	21 13.5	7 54.6	6 10.1	1 23.1	25 24.1	0 25.6
28	22 25 58.3	4 58.3	9 43.6	24 26.5	1 10.3	19 23.7	21 52.0	7 53.3	6 6.5	1 21.3	25 22.9	0 26.2
29	22 29 54.9	5 56.3	9 40.5	9♓30.6	1 44.3	20 24.5	22 30.4	7 52.1	6 2.8	1 19.4	25 21.8	0 26.8
30	22 33 51.4	6 54.2	9 37.3	24 21.3	2 14.0	21 25.6	23 8.8	7 51.1	5 59.1	1 17.6	25 20.6	0 27.4
31	22 37 48.0	7 52.2	9 34.1	8♈51.3	2 39.1	22 27.1	23 47.0	7 50.4	5 55.3	1 15.8	25 19.5	0 28.1

LATITUDE

DAY	SID. TIME	☉	☊	☽	☿	♀	♂	♃	♄	♅	♆	♇
1	20 39 31.4	0 .0	0 .0	3N10.2	1N 1.5	4S24.0	0N28.6	0S 7.6	2S27.6	0S36.7	0N29.0	13N 4.9
4	20 51 21.0	0 .0	0 .0	0S25.9	0 40.2	4 14.6	0 30.7	0 8.0	2 28.4	0 36.7	0 28.9	13 3.4
7	21 3 10.7	0 .0	0 .0	3 34.0	0 16.1	4 4.1	0 32.9	0 8.4	2 29.2	0 36.7	0 28.9	13 1.9
10	21 15 .4	0 .0	0 .0	5 2.6	0S10.2	3 52.7	0 35.0	0 8.7	2 29.9	0 36.7	0 28.8	13 .4
13	21 26 50.0	0 .0	0 .0	4 33.1	0 38.3	3 40.5	0 37.1	0 9.1	2 30.6	0 36.7	0 28.8	12 58.8
16	21 38 39.7	0 .0	0 .0	2 19.4	1 7.7	3 27.8	0 39.2	0 9.4	2 31.3	0 36.6	0 28.7	12 57.3
19	21 50 29.4	0 .0	0 .0	0N53.6	1 37.9	3 14.4	0 41.3	0 9.7	2 32.0	0 36.6	0 28.7	12 55.7
22	22 2 19.0	0 .0	0 .0	3 53.9	2 8.3	3 .7	0 43.4	0 10.0	2 32.6	0 36.6	0 28.6	12 54.2
25	22 14 8.7	0 .0	0 .0	5 11.2	2 38.4	2 46.6	0 45.6	0 10.3	2 33.2	0 36.6	0 28.5	12 52.7
28	22 25 58.3	0 .0	0 .0	3 36.5	3 7.2	2 32.2	0 47.7	0 10.6	2 33.8	0 36.5	0 28.5	12 51.1
31	22 37 48.0	0 .0	0 .0	0S 3.4	3 33.5	2 17.7	0 49.8	0 10.9	2 34.3	0 36.5	0 28.4	12 49.6

RIGHT ASCENSION

DAY	SID. TIME	☉	☊	☽	☿	♀	♂	♃	♄	♅	♆	♇
1	20 39 31.4	11♌27.7	10♎15.4	2♓ 8.0	1♍24.7	24♊42.4	4♋34.7	10♑22.5	7♈37.9	4♒44.9	27♑54.5	0♐57.0
2	20 43 27.9	12 25.8	10 12.5	16 24.5	2 55.3	25 30.9	5 18.5	10R16.3	7R36.8	4R42.4	27R52.8	0R56.6
3	20 47 24.5	13 23.8	10 9.6	0♈10.1	4 23.7	26 20.2	6 2.2	10 10.3	7 35.5	4 40.0	27 51.2	0 56.2
4	20 51 21.0	14 21.6	10 6.6	13 31.7	5 50.0	27 10.4	6 45.9	10 4.4	7 34.2	4 37.5	27 49.6	0 55.9
5	20 55 17.6	15 19.3	10 3.7	26 36.9	7 14.2	28 1.6	7 29.5	9 58.6	7 32.8	4 35.1	27 47.9	0 55.6
6	20 59 14.2	16 16.8	10 .8	9♉32.4	8 36.3	28 53.5	8 13.0	9 53.1	7 31.3	4 32.7	27 46.3	0 55.4
7	21 3 10.7	17 14.2	9 57.8	22 22.7	9 56.5	29 46.3	8 56.4	9 47.6	7 29.7	4 30.2	27 44.7	0 55.1
8	21 7 7.3	18 11.4	9 54.9	5♊10.0	11 14.6	0♋39.8	9 39.7	9 42.4	7 28.0	4 27.8	27 43.2	0 54.9
9	21 11 3.8	19 8.5	9 52.0	17 53.9	12 30.8	1 34.1	10 23.0	9 37.3	7 26.2	4 25.4	27 41.6	0 54.8
10	21 15 .4	20 5.5	9 49.1	0♋32.3	13 45.0	2 29.1	11 6.1	9 32.4	7 24.3	4 23.1	27 40.0	0 54.7
11	21 18 56.9	21 2.4	9 46.1	13 1.8	14 57.3	3 24.8	11 49.3	9 27.7	7 22.4	4 20.7	27 38.6	0 54.6
12	21 22 53.5	21 59.1	9 43.2	25 19.4	16 7.6	4 21.2	12 32.2	9 23.1	7 20.4	4 18.4	27 37.0	0 54.5
13	21 26 50.0	22 55.6	9 40.3	7♌23.3	17 15.9	5 18.3	13 15.1	9 18.7	7 18.3	4 16.1	27 35.5	0 54.5
14	21 30 46.6	23 52.0	9 37.3	19 13.7	18 22.3	6 15.9	13 57.9	9 14.5	7 16.1	4 13.8	27 34.0	0 54.5
15	21 34 43.1	24 48.3	9 34.4	0♍52.8	19 26.6	7 14.2	14 40.6	9 10.5	7 13.8	4 11.5	27 32.5	0 54.5
16	21 38 39.7	25 44.5	9 31.5	12 24.9	20 28.9	8 13.0	15 23.2	9 6.6	7 11.4	4 9.2	27 31.1	0D54.6
17	21 42 36.2	26 40.5	9 28.5	23 56.0	21 29.1	9 12.4	16 5.7	9 3.0	7 9.0	4 6.9	27 29.6	0 54.7
18	21 46 32.8	27 36.4	9 25.6	5♎33.5	22 27.2	10 12.3	16 48.1	8 59.5	7 6.5	4 4.7	27 28.2	0 54.8
19	21 50 29.4	28 32.1	9 22.7	17 26.0	23 23.1	11 12.7	17 30.3	8 56.3	7 3.9	4 2.5	27 26.8	0 55.0
20	21 54 25.9	29 27.8	9 19.7	29 42.1	24 16.7	12 13.7	18 12.5	8 53.2	7 1.2	4 .3	27 25.4	0 55.1
21	21 58 22.5	0♍23.3	9 16.8	12♏30.1	25 7.9	13 15.1	18 54.6	8 50.3	6 58.5	3 58.2	27 24.0	0 55.4
22	22 2 19.0	1 18.7	9 13.9	25 56.0	25 56.6	14 16.9	19 36.5	8 47.7	6 55.6	3 56.0	27 22.7	0 55.6
23	22 6 15.6	2 13.9	9 11.0	10♐ 2.1	26 42.8	15 19.2	20 18.3	8 45.2	6 52.8	3 53.9	27 21.4	0 55.9
24	22 10 12.1	3 9.1	9 8.0	24 44.8	27 26.3	16 21.9	21 .0	8 42.9	6 49.8	3 51.9	27 20.1	0 56.2
25	22 14 8.7	4 4.1	9 5.1	9♑54.1	28 6.9	17 25.0	21 41.6	8 40.9	6 46.8	3 49.8	27 18.8	0 56.6
26	22 18 5.2	4 59.1	9 2.2	25 15.0	28 44.5	18 28.5	22 23.1	8 39.0	6 43.7	3 47.8	27 17.5	0 57.0
27	22 22 1.8	5 53.9	8 59.2	10♒31.6	29 18.9	19 32.3	23 4.5	8 37.3	6 40.5	3 45.8	27 16.3	0 57.4
28	22 25 58.3	6 48.7	8 56.3	25 31.4	29 50.0	20 36.5	23 45.7	8 35.9	6 37.3	3 43.9	27 15.1	0 57.8
29	22 29 54.9	7 43.3	8 53.4	10♓ 7.6	0♎17.5	21 41.0	24 26.8	8 34.6	6 34.0	3 42.0	27 13.9	0 58.3
30	22 33 51.4	8 37.9	8 50.4	24 19.3	0 41.2	22 45.9	25 7.8	8 33.6	6 30.7	3 40.1	27 12.7	0 58.8
31	22 37 48.0	9 32.4	8 47.5	8♈ 9.4	1 1.0	23 51.0	25 48.7	8 32.8	6 27.2	3 38.2	27 11.6	0 59.4

DECLINATION

DAY	SID. TIME	☉	☊	☽	☿	♀	♂	♃	♄	♅	♆	♇
1	20 39 31.4	17N59.9	0S 4.6	8S 4.1	12N48.9	18N56.7	23N50.9	23S13.3	0N37.1	20S14.0	20S28.2	7S25.1
4	20 51 21.0	17 13.2	0 4.6	5N19.4	10 46.9	19 10.1	23 48.3	23 14.9	0 34.6	20 15.6	20 29.1	7 26.4
7	21 3 10.7	16 24.1	0 4.5	15 16.5	8 44.8	19 22.2	23 43.9	23 16.3	0 31.8	20 17.2	20 30.0	7 27.8
10	21 15 .4	15 32.5	0 4.4	18 23.6	6 43.9	19 32.3	23 37.8	23 17.6	0 28.7	20 18.8	20 30.9	7 29.2
13	21 26 50.0	14 38.7	0 4.4	14 18.9	4 46.0	19 40.2	23 29.9	23 18.7	0 25.4	20 20.2	20 31.8	7 30.8
16	21 38 39.7	13 42.9	0 4.3	4 57.1	2 52.4	19 45.2	23 20.4	23 19.8	0 21.7	20 21.7	20 32.6	7 32.4
19	21 50 29.4	12 45.0	0 4.2	6S26.1	1 5.0	19 47.2	23 9.3	23 20.7	0 17.7	20 23.1	20 33.4	7 34.0
22	22 2 19.0	11 45.4	0 4.2	15 45.3	0S34.4	19 45.7	22 56.7	23 21.5	0 13.5	20 24.5	20 34.2	7 35.7
25	22 14 8.7	10 44.1	0 4.1	17 55.6	2 3.6	19 40.5	22 42.5	23 22.2	0 9.0	20 25.8	20 34.9	7 37.5
28	22 25 58.3	9 41.2	0 4.0	9 58.1	3 19.7	19 31.4	22 26.8	23 22.8	0 4.3	20 27.0	20 35.6	7 39.3
31	22 37 48.0	8 37.0	0 4.0	3N27.5	4 19.2	19 18.2	22 9.7	23 23.2	0S .6	20 28.2	20 36.3	7 41.2

SEPTEMBER 1996

DAY	EPHEM. SID. TIME	☉	☊	☽	☿	♀	♂	♃	♄	♅	♆	♇
	h m s	° ′	° ′	° ′	° ′	° ′	° ′	° ′	° ′	° ′	° ′	° ′
		LONGITUDE										
1	22 41 44.5	8♍50.3	9♎30.9	22♈56.1	2♎59.6	23♋29.0	24♋25.3	7♑49.8	5♈51.5	1♒14.1	25♑18.5	0♐28.8
2	22 45 41.1	9 48.4	9 27.8	6♉33.9	3 14.9	24 31.2	25 3.5	7 R 49.4	5 R 47.6	1 R 12.4	25 R 17.5	0 29.6
3	22 49 37.6	10 46.5	9 24.6	19 45.5	3 24.9	25 33.7	25 41.6	7 49.2	5 43.6	1 10.8	25 16.4	0 30.3
4	22 53 34.2	11 44.6	9 21.4	2♊33.4	3 29.2	26 36.5	26 19.7	7 49.2	5 39.6	1 9.1	25 15.4	0 31.2
5	22 57 30.7	12 42.7	9 18.2	15 1.4	3 R 27.6	27 39.6	26 57.7	7 D 49.4	5 35.5	1 7.5	25 14.5	0 32.0
6	23 1 27.3	13 40.9	9 15.0	27 13.7	3 19.9	28 43.0	27 35.6	7 49.7	5 31.4	1 5.9	25 13.5	0 32.9
7	23 5 23.8	14 39.1	9 11.9	9♋14.9	3 5.8	29 46.6	28 13.4	7 50.3	5 27.2	1 4.4	25 12.6	0 33.8
8	23 9 20.4	15 37.4	9 8.7	21 9.1	2 45.3	0♌50.6	28 51.2	7 51.0	5 23.0	1 2.9	25 11.7	0 34.7
9	23 13 17.0	16 35.7	9 5.5	3♌ .2	2 18.3	1 54.8	29 29.0	7 52.0	5 18.7	1 1.5	25 10.8	0 35.7
10	23 17 13.5	17 34.0	9 2.3	14 51.6	1 44.8	2 59.2	0♌ 6.6	7 53.1	5 14.4	1 .0	25 10.0	0 36.6
11	23 21 10.1	18 32.4	8 59.2	26 46.0	1 5.1	4 4.0	0 44.2	7 54.4	5 10.0	0 58.7	25 9.2	0 37.7
12	23 25 6.6	19 30.7	8 56.0	8♍45.8	0 19.5	5 8.9	1 21.7	7 55.9	5 5.6	0 57.3	25 8.4	0 38.7
13	23 29 3.2	20 29.1	8 52.8	20 53.0	29♍28.5	6 14.1	1 59.2	7 57.6	5 1.2	0 56.0	25 7.7	0 39.8
14	23 32 59.7	21 27.6	8 49.6	3♎ 9.0	28 33.0	7 19.6	2 36.6	7 59.5	4 56.7	0 54.8	25 6.9	0 40.9
15	23 36 56.3	22 26.1	8 46.4	15 35.3	27 33.7	8 25.2	3 13.9	8 1.6	4 52.2	0 53.6	25 6.2	0 42.1
16	23 40 52.8	23 24.6	8 43.3	28 13.3	26 32.0	9 31.1	3 51.1	8 3.8	4 47.7	0 52.4	25 5.6	0 43.3
17	23 44 49.4	24 23.1	8 40.1	11♏ 4.5	25 28.9	10 37.2	4 28.3	8 6.3	4 43.2	0 51.3	25 4.9	0 44.5
18	23 48 45.9	25 21.7	8 36.9	24 10.3	24 26.1	11 43.5	5 5.4	8 8.9	4 38.6	0 50.2	25 4.3	0 45.7
19	23 52 42.5	26 20.3	8 33.7	7♐32.2	23 25.1	12 50.1	5 42.4	8 11.7	4 34.0	0 49.2	25 3.7	0 47.0
20	23 56 39.0	27 18.9	8 30.6	21 11.3	22 27.2	13 56.8	6 19.4	8 14.7	4 29.4	0 48.2	25 3.2	0 48.3
21	0 0 35.6	28 17.5	8 27.4	5♑ 8.0	21 34.2	15 3.7	6 56.2	8 17.9	4 24.7	0 47.2	25 2.7	0 49.6
22	0 4 32.1	29 16.3	8 24.2	19 21.8	20 47.3	16 10.9	7 33.1	8 21.3	4 20.1	0 46.4	25 2.2	0 51.1
23	0 8 28.7	0♎15.0	8 21.0	3♒50.2	20 7.8	17 18.2	8 9.8	8 24.8	4 15.5	0 45.5	25 1.8	0 52.4
24	0 12 25.2	1 13.7	8 17.8	18 29.6	19 36.6	18 25.7	8 46.5	8 28.6	4 10.8	0 44.7	25 1.4	0 53.9
25	0 16 21.8	2 12.4	8 14.7	3♓14.3	19 14.7	19 33.4	9 23.0	8 32.5	4 6.1	0 44.0	25 1.0	0 55.3
26	0 20 18.3	3 11.2	8 11.5	17 57.9	19 2.4	20 41.3	9 59.5	8 36.5	4 1.4	0 43.3	25 .6	0 56.8
27	0 24 14.9	4 10.1	8 8.3	2♈33.2	19 .3	21 49.3	10 36.0	8 40.8	3 56.8	0 42.6	25 .3	0 58.3
28	0 28 11.4	5 8.9	8 5.1	16 53.9	19 D 8.3	22 57.6	11 12.3	8 45.2	3 52.1	0 42.0	24 60.0	0 59.8
29	0 32 8.0	6 7.8	8 1.9	0♉55.1	19 26.4	24 6.0	11 48.6	8 49.8	3 47.4	0 41.4	24 59.7	1 1.3
30	0 36 4.5	7 6.7	7 58.8	14 33.6	19 54.3	25 14.6	12 24.8	8 54.6	3 42.7	0 40.9	24 59.5	1 2.9
		LATITUDE										
1	22 41 44.5	0 .0	0 .0	1 S 19.8	3 S 41.4	2 S 12.8	0 N 50.6	0 S 11.0	2 S 34.5	0 S 36.5	0 N 28.4	12 N 49.1
4	22 53 34.2	0 .0	0 .0	4 15.3	4 1.5	1 58.2	0 52.7	0 11.3	2 34.9	0 36.4	0 28.3	12 47.6
7	23 5 23.8	0 .0	0 .0	5 14.2	4 13.9	1 43.6	0 54.9	0 11.6	2 35.4	0 36.4	0 28.2	12 46.1
10	23 17 13.5	0 .0	0 .0	4 12.3	4 15.0	1 29.0	0 57.0	0 11.8	2 35.8	0 36.3	0 28.2	12 44.7
13	23 29 3.2	0 .0	0 .0	1 33.0	4 1.5	1 14.6	0 59.2	0 12.1	2 36.1	0 36.3	0 28.1	12 43.2
16	23 40 52.8	0 .0	0 .0	1 N 49.8	3 30.9	1 .4	1 1.4	0 12.3	2 36.4	0 36.2	0 28.0	12 41.8
19	23 52 42.5	0 .0	0 .0	4 33.3	2 44.2	0 46.5	1 3.6	0 12.6	2 36.6	0 36.2	0 28.0	12 40.4
22	0 4 32.1	0 .0	0 .0	5 10.9	1 46.9	0 32.9	1 5.8	0 12.8	2 36.8	0 36.1	0 27.9	12 39.1
25	0 16 21.8	0 .0	0 .0	3 1.2	0 47.0	0 19.7	1 8.0	0 13.1	2 37.0	0 36.0	0 27.8	12 37.7
28	0 28 11.4	0 .0	0 .0	0 S 49.3	0 N 8.0	0 6.9	1 10.2	0 13.3	2 37.1	0 36.0	0 27.7	12 36.5
		RIGHT ASCENSION										
1	22 41 44.5	10♍26.8	8♎44.6	21♈42.9	1♎16.6	24♋56.5	26♋29.5	8♑32.2	6♈23.8	3♒36.4	27♑10.5	1♐ .0
2	22 45 41.1	11 21.1	8 41.7	5♉ 4.2	1 27.7	26 2.1	27 10.2	8 R 31.8	6 R 20.3	3 R 34.7	27 R 9.4	1 .6
3	22 49 37.6	12 15.4	8 38.7	18 16.6	1 34.2	27 8.1	27 50.7	8 31.5	6 16.7	3 32.9	27 8.3	1 1.3
4	22 53 34.2	13 9.6	8 35.8	1♊21.5	1 35.7	28 14.2	28 31.1	8 31.5	6 13.1	3 31.2	27 7.3	1 1.9
5	22 57 30.7	14 3.8	8 32.9	14 18.4	1 R 32.2	29 20.6	29 11.3	8 D 31.7	6 9.4	3 29.5	27 6.3	1 2.7
6	23 1 27.3	14 57.9	8 30.0	27 5.6	1 23.5	0♌27.2	29 51.5	8 32.1	6 5.7	3 27.9	27 5.3	1 3.4
7	23 5 23.8	15 51.9	8 27.0	9♋40.9	1 9.3	1 33.9	0♌31.5	8 32.7	6 1.9	3 26.3	27 4.3	1 4.2
8	23 9 20.4	16 45.9	8 24.1	22 2.5	0 49.8	2 40.9	1 11.4	8 33.5	5 58.1	3 24.7	27 3.4	1 5.0
9	23 13 17.0	17 39.9	8 21.2	4♌ 9.8	0 24.8	3 47.9	1 51.1	8 34.6	5 54.2	3 23.2	27 2.5	1 5.8
10	23 17 13.5	18 33.9	8 18.2	16 3.9	29♍54.5	4 55.2	2 30.7	8 35.8	5 50.3	3 21.7	27 1.6	1 6.7
11	23 21 10.1	19 27.8	8 15.3	27 47.4	29 19.2	6 2.5	3 10.2	8 37.2	5 46.4	3 20.3	27 .7	1 7.6
12	23 25 6.6	20 21.6	8 12.4	9♍24.5	28 39.1	7 10.0	3 49.5	8 38.9	5 42.4	3 18.9	26 59.9	1 8.5
13	23 29 3.2	21 15.5	8 9.5	21 .8	27 55.0	8 17.5	4 28.7	8 40.7	5 38.3	3 17.5	26 59.1	1 9.4
14	23 32 59.7	22 9.3	8 6.5	2♎42.8	27 7.3	9 25.2	5 7.8	8 42.8	5 34.3	3 16.2	26 58.4	1 10.4
15	23 36 56.3	23 3.1	8 3.6	14 37.7	26 17.1	10 32.9	5 46.7	8 45.0	5 30.2	3 15.0	26 57.6	1 11.5
16	23 40 52.8	23 56.9	8 .7	26 52.6	25 25.3	11 40.7	6 25.5	8 47.5	5 26.1	3 13.7	26 56.9	1 12.5
17	23 44 49.4	24 50.8	7 57.8	9♏34.0	24 33.1	12 48.5	7 4.2	8 50.1	5 21.9	3 12.6	26 56.3	1 13.6
18	23 48 45.9	25 44.6	7 54.8	22 46.3	23 41.7	13 56.4	7 42.7	8 53.0	5 17.8	3 11.4	26 55.6	1 14.7
19	23 52 42.5	26 38.4	7 51.9	6♐31.2	22 52.5	15 4.3	8 21.1	8 56.1	5 13.6	3 10.4	26 55.0	1 15.8
20	23 56 39.0	27 32.2	7 49.0	20 45.7	22 6.6	16 12.2	8 59.3	8 59.4	5 9.4	3 9.3	26 54.5	1 17.0
21	0 0 35.6	28 26.0	7 46.0	5♑22.7	21 25.4	17 20.1	9 37.4	9 2.8	5 5.1	3 8.3	26 53.9	1 18.2
22	0 4 32.1	29 19.9	7 43.1	20 11.3	20 50.1	18 28.1	10 15.3	9 6.5	5 .9	3 7.4	26 53.5	1 19.5
23	0 8 28.7	0♎13.7	7 40.2	5♒ .1	20 21.6	19 36.1	10 53.1	9 10.4	4 56.7	3 6.5	26 53.0	1 20.7
24	0 12 25.2	1 7.6	7 37.3	19 39.5	20 .8	20 44.1	11 30.8	9 14.4	4 52.4	3 5.7	26 52.6	1 22.0
25	0 16 21.8	2 1.5	7 34.3	4♓ 4.3	19 48.4	21 52.0	12 8.3	9 18.7	4 48.2	3 4.9	26 52.2	1 23.3
26	0 20 18.3	2 55.5	7 31.4	18 13.3	19 44.6	22 59.9	12 45.7	9 23.1	4 43.9	3 4.2	26 51.8	1 24.6
27	0 24 14.9	3 49.5	7 28.5	2♈ 8.6	19 D 49.9	24 7.9	13 22.9	9 27.7	4 39.6	3 3.5	26 51.4	1 26.0
28	0 28 11.4	4 43.5	7 25.6	15 53.5	20 4.1	25 15.8	14 .0	9 32.6	4 35.3	3 2.8	26 51.1	1 27.4
29	0 32 8.0	5 37.6	7 22.6	29 31.2	20 27.2	26 23.6	14 37.0	9 37.5	4 31.0	3 2.2	26 50.9	1 28.8
30	0 36 4.5	6 31.8	7 19.7	13♉ 3.3	20 58.8	27 31.5	15 13.8	9 42.7	4 26.8	3 1.7	26 50.6	1 30.3
		DECLINATION										
1	22 41 44.5	8 N 15.3	0 S 3.9	7 N 40.9	4 S 34.5	19 N 12.8	22 N 3.7	23 S 23.4	0 S 2.3	20 S 28.5	20 S 36.5	7 S 41.8
4	22 53 34.2	7 9.5	0 3.9	16 29.7	5 4.7	18 53.8	21 44.8	23 23.7	0 7.4	20 29.6	20 37.1	7 43.7
7	23 5 23.8	6 2.6	0 3.8	17 53.4	5 6.8	18 30.5	21 24.6	23 23.9	0 12.7	20 30.6	20 37.7	7 45.7
10	23 17 13.5	4 54.7	0 3.8	12 21.0	4 35.6	18 2.7	21 3.2	23 24.0	0 18.1	20 31.5	20 38.3	7 47.7
13	23 29 3.2	3 46.2	0 3.7	2 11.3	3 29.0	17 30.5	20 40.6	23 24.0	0 23.6	20 32.3	20 38.8	7 49.7
16	23 40 52.8	2 37.0	0 3.6	9 S 7.9	1 50.8	16 53.8	20 16.9	23 23.8	0 29.3	20 33.0	20 39.2	7 51.7
19	23 52 42.5	1 27.4	0 3.6	17 4.2	0 N 5.9	16 12.9	19 52.2	23 23.6	0 34.9	20 33.7	20 39.6	7 53.8
22	0 4 32.1	0 17.4	0 3.5	16 54.6	2 .7	15 27.7	19 26.4	23 23.2	0 40.6	20 34.2	20 40.0	7 55.9
25	0 16 21.8	0 S 52.7	0 3.4	7 30.0	3 32.2	14 38.4	18 59.8	23 22.8	0 46.3	20 34.7	20 40.3	7 58.0
28	0 28 11.4	2 2.7	0 3.4	5 N 52.8	4 25.3	13 45.2	18 32.2	23 22.2	0 51.9	20 35.1	20 40.5	8 .1

OCTOBER 1996

DAY	EPHEM. SID. TIME	LONGITUDE ☉	☊	☽	☿	♀	♂	♃	♄	♅	♆	♇
	h m s	° ′	° ′	° ′	° ′	° ′	° ′	° ′	° ′	° ′	° ′	° ′
1	0 40 1.1	8♎ 5.7	7♎55.6	27♉48.5	20♍31.5	26♌23.4	13♌ .9	8♑59.5	3♈38.1	0♒40.4	24♑59.3	1♐ 4.5
2	0 43 57.6	9 4.7	7 52.4	10♊40.5	21 17.5	27 32.3	13 37.0	9 4.6	3R33.4	0R40.0	24R59.1	1 6.2
3	0 47 54.2	10 3.7	7 49.2	23 12.2	22 11.7	28 41.4	14 13.0	9 9.9	3 28.8	0 39.6	24 59.0	1 7.8
4	0 51 50.7	11 2.8	7 46.1	5♋27.2	23 13.3	29 50.6	14 48.9	9 15.3	3 24.1	0 39.3	24 58.9	1 9.5
5	0 55 47.3	12 1.9	7 42.9	17 29.6	24 21.7	1♍ .0	15 24.7	9 20.9	3 19.5	0 39.0	24 58.8	1 11.2
6	0 59 43.9	13 1.1	7 39.7	29 24.0	25 36.1	2 9.6	16 .4	9 26.6	3 14.9	0 38.8	24 58.8	1 12.9
7	1 3 40.4	14 .2	7 36.5	11♌15.2	26 55.8	3 19.3	16 36.1	9 32.6	3 10.4	0 38.6	24 58.8	1 14.7
8	1 7 37.0	14 59.5	7 33.3	23 7.5	28 20.1	4 29.1	17 11.6	9 38.6	3 5.8	0 38.5	24 58.8	1 16.5
9	1 11 33.5	15 58.7	7 30.2	5♍ 5.0	29 48.3	5 39.1	17 47.1	9 44.9	3 1.3	0 38.4	24D58.9	1 18.3
10	1 15 30.1	16 58.0	7 27.0	17 11.0	1♎19.9	6 49.2	18 22.5	9 51.3	2 56.8	0 38.4	24 59.0	1 20.1
11	1 19 26.6	17 57.4	7 23.8	29 28.3	2 54.3	7 59.5	18 57.8	9 57.8	2 52.4	0 38.4	24 59.1	1 21.9
12	1 23 23.2	18 56.8	7 20.6	11♎59.0	4 30.9	9 9.9	19 33.0	10 4.6	2 48.0	0D38.5	24 59.3	1 23.8
13	1 27 19.7	19 56.2	7 17.5	24 44.1	6 9.4	10 20.5	20 8.2	10 11.5	2 43.6	0 38.7	24 59.5	1 25.7
14	1 31 16.3	20 55.7	7 14.3	7♏44.0	7 49.3	11 31.1	20 43.2	10 18.5	2 39.3	0 38.9	24 59.8	1 27.7
15	1 35 12.8	21 55.1	7 11.1	20 58.3	9 30.2	12 41.9	21 18.2	10 25.6	2 35.0	0 39.1	25 .0	1 29.6
16	1 39 9.4	22 54.6	7 7.9	4♐26.1	11 12.0	13 52.8	21 53.0	10 33.0	2 30.8	0 39.4	25 .3	1 31.5
17	1 43 5.9	23 54.2	7 4.7	18 6.2	12 54.4	15 3.8	22 27.7	10 40.4	2 26.6	0 39.7	25 .7	1 33.5
18	1 47 2.5	24 53.8	7 1.6	1♑57.0	14 37.1	16 14.9	23 2.4	10 48.0	2 22.4	0 40.1	25 1.0	1 35.5
19	1 50 59.0	25 53.3	6 58.4	15 57.1	16 20.0	17 26.1	23 36.9	10 55.8	2 18.3	0 40.6	25 1.4	1 37.5
20	1 54 55.6	26 53.0	6 55.2	0♒ 4.7	18 2.9	18 37.5	24 11.4	11 3.7	2 14.3	0 41.0	25 1.9	1 39.5
21	1 58 52.1	27 52.6	6 52.0	14 18.0	19 45.7	19 48.9	24 45.7	11 11.7	2 10.3	0 41.6	25 2.3	1 41.6
22	2 2 48.7	28 52.3	6 48.9	28 34.8	21 28.4	21 .4	25 20.0	11 19.9	2 6.4	0 42.2	25 2.8	1 43.7
23	2 6 45.2	29 52.0	6 45.7	12♓52.5	23 10.7	22 12.1	25 54.1	11 28.2	2 2.5	0 42.8	25 3.4	1 45.7
24	2 10 41.8	0♏51.8	6 42.5	27 7.7	24 52.8	23 23.9	26 28.2	11 36.6	1 58.7	0 43.5	25 3.9	1 47.8
25	2 14 38.4	1 51.5	6 39.3	11♈16.9	26 34.4	24 35.7	27 2.1	11 45.2	1 55.0	0 44.3	25 4.5	1 50.0
26	2 18 34.9	2 51.3	6 36.1	25 16.0	28 15.6	25 47.7	27 36.0	11 53.9	1 51.3	0 45.1	25 5.2	1 52.1
27	2 22 31.5	3 51.2	6 33.0	9♉ 1.5	29 56.4	26 59.7	28 9.7	12 2.7	1 47.7	0 45.9	25 5.8	1 54.2
28	2 26 28.0	4 51.0	6 29.8	22 30.2	1♏36.8	28 11.9	28 43.3	12 11.6	1 44.2	0 46.8	25 6.5	1 56.4
29	2 30 24.6	5 50.9	6 26.6	5♊40.2	3 16.7	29 24.1	29 16.8	12 20.7	1 40.7	0 47.7	25 7.3	1 58.6
30	2 34 21.1	6 50.9	6 23.4	18 31.0	4 56.1	0♎36.5	29 50.2	12 29.9	1 37.3	0 48.7	25 8.0	2 .8
31	2 38 17.7	7 50.8	6 20.3	1♋ 3.3	6 35.0	1 48.9	0♍23.5	12 39.2	1 34.0	0 49.8	25 8.8	2 3.0
		LATITUDE										
1	0 40 1.1	0 .0	0 .0	4S 2.8	0N53.0	0N 5.3	1N12.5	0S13.5	2S37.1	0S35.9	0N27.7	12N35.2
4	0 51 50.7	0 .0	0 .0	5 17.1	1 25.7	0 17.1	1 14.7	0 13.7	2 37.1	0 35.8	0 27.6	12 34.0
7	1 3 40.4	0 .0	0 .0	4 25.6	1 46.4	0 28.2	1 17.0	0 13.9	2 37.0	0 35.8	0 27.5	12 32.8
10	1 15 30.1	0 .0	0 .0	1 53.2	1 56.5	0 38.8	1 19.3	0 14.2	2 36.9	0 35.7	0 27.4	12 31.7
13	1 27 19.7	0 .0	0 .0	1N37.1	1 57.7	0 48.7	1 21.6	0 14.4	2 36.7	0 35.6	0 27.3	12 30.7
16	1 39 9.4	0 .0	0 .0	4 23.5	1 52.2	0 57.9	1 24.0	0 14.6	2 36.5	0 35.5	0 27.3	12 29.6
19	1 50 59.0	0 .0	0 .0	5 12.6	1 41.6	1 6.4	1 26.3	0 14.8	2 36.3	0 35.5	0 27.2	12 28.7
22	2 2 48.7	0 .0	0 .0	3 20.3	1 27.4	1 14.2	1 28.7	0 15.0	2 36.0	0 35.4	0 27.1	12 27.8
25	2 14 38.4	0 .0	0 .0	0S18.3	1 10.6	1 21.2	1 31.1	0 15.2	2 35.6	0 35.3	0 27.0	12 26.9
28	2 26 28.0	0 .0	0 .0	3 40.5	0 52.0	1 27.4	1 33.6	0 15.4	2 35.2	0 35.2	0 26.9	12 26.1
31	2 38 17.7	0 .0	0 .0	5 10.7	0 32.4	1 32.8	1 36.1	0 15.6	2 34.8	0 35.2	0 26.9	12 25.3
		RIGHT ASCENSION										
1	0 40 1.1	7♎26.1	7♎16.8	26♉29.3	21♍38.5	28♌39.3	15♌50.5	9♑48.1	4♈22.5	3♒ 1.2	26♑50.4	1♐31.7
2	0 43 57.6	8 20.4	7 13.9	9♊46.9	22 25.8	29 47.1	16 27.0	9 53.6	4R18.2	3R .7	26R50.2	1 33.2
3	0 47 54.2	9 14.8	7 10.9	22 52.5	23 20.0	0♍54.8	17 3.4	9 59.4	4 13.9	3 .3	26 50.1	1 34.8
4	0 51 50.7	10 9.3	7 8.0	5♋42.7	24 20.6	2 2.5	17 39.6	10 5.3	4 9.7	2 60.0	26 50.0	1 36.3
5	0 55 47.3	11 3.9	7 5.1	18 15.2	25 26.7	3 10.2	18 15.7	10 11.4	4 5.5	2 59.7	26 49.9	1 37.9
6	0 59 43.9	11 58.6	7 2.2	0♌29.6	26 37.9	4 17.8	18 51.7	10 17.6	4 1.3	2 59.5	26 49.9	1 39.5
7	1 3 40.4	12 53.3	6 59.2	12 27.7	27 53.3	5 25.3	19 27.5	10 24.1	3 57.1	2 59.3	26 49.9	1 41.1
8	1 7 37.0	13 48.2	6 56.3	24 13.1	29 12.5	6 32.8	20 3.2	10 30.7	3 52.9	2 59.1	26 49.9	1 42.7
9	1 11 33.5	14 43.2	6 53.4	5♍51.2	0♎34.7	7 40.3	20 38.7	10 37.5	3 48.7	2 59.1	26D50.0	1 44.4
10	1 15 30.1	15 38.3	6 50.5	17 28.5	1 59.6	8 47.7	21 14.1	10 44.4	3 44.6	2 59.0	26 50.1	1 46.1
11	1 19 26.6	16 33.6	6 47.6	29 12.1	3 26.7	9 55.1	21 49.3	10 51.5	3 40.5	2 59.0	26 50.3	1 47.8
12	1 23 23.2	17 28.9	6 44.6	11♎ 9.7	4 55.5	11 2.4	22 24.4	10 58.8	3 36.4	2D59.1	26 50.4	1 49.6
13	1 27 19.7	18 24.4	6 41.7	23 28.5	6 25.7	12 9.8	22 59.4	11 6.3	3 32.4	2 59.3	26 50.7	1 51.4
14	1 31 16.3	19 20.1	6 38.8	6♏14.4	7 57.0	13 17.0	23 34.1	11 14.0	3 28.4	2 59.5	26 51.0	1 53.1
15	1 35 12.8	20 15.8	6 35.9	19 31.0	9 29.1	14 24.2	24 8.8	11 21.7	3 24.5	2 59.7	26 51.3	1 55.0
16	1 39 9.4	21 11.7	6 32.9	3♐18.3	11 1.8	15 31.3	24 43.3	11 29.7	3 20.5	3 .0	26 51.6	1 56.8
17	1 43 5.9	22 7.7	6 30.0	17 31.8	12 35.0	16 38.5	25 17.6	11 37.8	3 16.7	3 .4	26 51.9	1 58.6
18	1 47 2.5	23 3.9	6 27.1	2♑ 2.7	14 8.5	17 45.5	25 51.8	11 46.0	3 12.8	3 .8	26 52.3	2 .5
19	1 50 59.0	24 .2	6 24.2	16 39.5	15 42.1	18 52.6	26 25.8	11 54.5	3 9.0	3 1.2	26 52.8	2 2.4
20	1 54 55.6	24 56.7	6 21.2	1♒11.5	17 15.9	19 59.6	26 59.7	12 3.0	3 5.3	3 1.7	26 53.2	2 4.3
21	1 58 52.1	25 53.3	6 18.3	15 30.6	18 49.8	21 6.6	27 33.4	12 11.7	3 1.6	3 2.3	26 53.7	2 6.2
22	2 2 48.7	26 50.1	6 15.4	29 33.5	20 23.6	22 13.6	28 7.0	12 20.6	2 57.9	3 2.9	26 54.2	2 8.1
23	2 6 45.2	27 47.0	6 12.5	13♓21.4	21 57.4	23 20.6	28 40.4	12 29.6	2 54.4	3 3.6	26 54.8	2 10.1
24	2 10 41.8	28 44.2	6 9.6	26 58.3	23 31.2	24 27.6	29 13.7	12 38.7	2 50.8	3 4.3	26 55.4	2 12.1
25	2 14 38.4	29 41.4	6 6.6	10♈29.5	25 4.9	25 34.5	29 46.9	12 48.0	2 47.4	3 5.0	26 56.1	2 14.1
26	2 18 34.9	0♏38.9	6 3.7	23 59.5	26 38.5	26 41.5	0♍19.9	12 57.4	2 43.9	3 5.9	26 56.7	2 16.1
27	2 22 31.5	1 36.6	6 .8	7♉31.1	28 12.1	27 48.5	0 52.7	13 7.0	2 40.6	3 6.7	26 57.4	2 18.1
28	2 26 28.0	2 34.4	5 57.9	21 4.0	29 45.7	28 55.6	1 25.4	13 16.7	2 37.3	3 7.7	26 58.2	2 20.2
29	2 30 24.6	3 32.4	5 54.9	4♊34.7	1♏19.2	0♎ 2.6	1 57.9	13 26.5	2 34.1	3 8.6	26 59.0	2 22.2
30	2 34 21.1	4 30.7	5 52.0	17 57.6	2 52.7	1 9.7	2 30.3	13 36.5	2 30.9	3 9.7	26 59.8	2 24.3
31	2 38 17.7	5 29.1	5 49.1	1♋ 6.4	4 26.2	2 16.8	3 2.6	13 46.6	2 27.8	3 10.8	27 .6	2 26.4
		DECLINATION										
1	0 40 1.1	3S12.6	0S 3.3	15N43.5	4N33.9	12N48.2	18N 3.9	23S21.4	0S57.5	20S35.3	20S40.7	8S 2.3
4	0 51 50.7	4 22.3	0 3.2	18 2.7	4 .2	11 47.5	17 34.8	23 20.6	1 3.0	20 35.5	20 40.9	8 4.4
7	1 3 40.4	5 31.4	0 3.2	13 8.3	2 50.9	10 43.6	17 5.0	23 19.6	1 8.4	20 35.6	20 41.0	8 6.5
10	1 15 30.1	6 39.9	0 3.1	3 19.5	1 15.1	9 36.4	16 34.6	23 18.4	1 13.7	20 35.6	20 41.0	8 8.6
13	1 27 19.7	7 47.7	0 3.0	8S10.0	0S38.6	8 26.5	16 3.6	23 17.1	1 18.8	20 35.4	20 41.0	8 10.7
16	1 39 9.4	8 54.5	0 3.0	16 42.5	2 42.6	7 13.9	15 32.2	23 15.6	1 23.7	20 35.2	20 40.9	8 12.8
19	1 50 59.0	10 .1	0 2.9	17 18.6	4 51.5	5 59.0	15 .3	23 14.0	1 28.4	20 34.9	20 40.8	8 14.9
22	2 2 48.7	11 4.4	0 2.8	8 50.0	7 1.3	4 42.0	14 28.1	23 12.2	1 32.9	20 34.4	20 40.6	8 16.9
25	2 14 38.4	12 7.1	0 2.8	4N10.9	9 9.1	3 23.3	13 55.5	23 10.2	1 37.1	20 33.9	20 40.4	8 18.9
28	2 26 28.0	13 8.3	0 2.7	14 50.3	11 13.2	2 3.2	13 22.8	23 8.0	1 41.0	20 33.3	20 40.1	8 20.9
31	2 38 17.7	14 7.5	0 2.6	18 15.3	13 12.1	0 41.8	12 49.8	23 5.6	1 44.6	20 32.6	20 39.7	8 22.9

NOVEMBER 1996

LONGITUDE

DAY	EPHEM. SID. TIME (h m s)	☉ (° ′)	☊ (° ′)	☽ (° ′)	☿ (° ′)	♀ (° ′)	♂ (° ′)	♃ (° ′)	♄ (° ′)	♅ (° ′)	♆ (° ′)	♇ (° ′)
1	2 42 14.2	8♏50.8	6♎17.1	13♋19.5	8♏13.4	3♎ 1.5	0♍56.7	12♑48.7	1♈30.8	0♒50.9	25♑ 9.7	2♐ 5.2
2	2 46 10.8	9 50.9	6 13.9	25 22.8	9 51.4	4 14.1	1 29.8	12 58.2	1R27.6	0 52.0	25 10.5	2 7.4
3	2 50 7.3	10 51.0	6 10.7	7♌17.6	11 29.0	5 26.8	2 2.8	13 8.0	1 24.6	0 53.3	25 11.5	2 9.7
4	2 54 3.9	11 51.1	6 7.5	19 8.4	13 6.1	6 39.6	2 35.6	13 17.8	1 21.6	0 54.5	25 12.4	2 11.9
5	2 58 .4	12 51.2	6 4.4	1♍ .4	14 42.8	7 52.5	3 8.3	13 27.7	1 18.7	0 55.8	25 13.4	2 14.2
6	3 1 57.0	13 51.4	6 1.2	12 58.6	16 19.1	9 5.5	3 40.9	13 37.7	1 15.9	0 57.1	25 14.3	2 16.5
7	3 5 53.6	14 51.6	5 58.0	25 7.7	17 54.9	10 18.5	4 13.4	13 47.8	1 13.1	0 58.5	25 15.4	2 18.8
8	3 9 50.1	15 51.9	5 54.8	7♎31.7	19 30.4	11 31.6	4 45.7	13 58.1	1 10.5	0 60.0	25 16.4	2 21.1
9	3 13 46.7	16 52.2	5 51.7	20 13.9	21 5.5	12 44.8	5 17.9	14 8.4	1 7.9	1 1.4	25 17.5	2 23.4
10	3 17 43.2	17 52.5	5 48.5	3♏15.9	22 40.3	13 58.0	5 50.0	14 18.9	1 5.5	1 3.0	25 18.6	2 25.7
11	3 21 39.8	18 52.8	5 45.3	16 38.0	24 14.7	15 11.3	6 21.9	14 29.5	1 3.1	1 4.5	25 19.8	2 28.0
12	3 25 36.3	19 53.2	5 42.1	0♐18.7	25 48.8	16 24.7	6 53.7	14 40.2	1 .8	1 6.2	25 20.9	2 30.3
13	3 29 32.9	20 53.6	5 38.9	14 15.0	27 22.6	17 38.1	7 25.3	14 50.9	0 58.7	1 7.8	25 22.1	2 32.7
14	3 33 29.4	21 54.0	5 35.8	28 22.5	28 56.1	18 51.6	7 56.8	15 1.8	0 56.6	1 9.6	25 23.4	2 35.0
15	3 37 26.0	22 54.4	5 32.6	12♑36.7	0♐29.4	20 5.2	8 28.2	15 12.8	0 54.6	1 11.3	25 24.6	2 37.4
16	3 41 22.5	23 54.9	5 29.4	26 52.8	2 2.4	21 18.8	8 59.3	15 23.9	0 52.7	1 13.1	25 25.9	2 39.7
17	3 45 19.1	24 55.4	5 26.2	11♒ 7.3	3 35.1	22 32.5	9 30.4	15 35.0	0 50.9	1 15.0	25 27.2	2 42.1
18	3 49 15.7	25 55.9	5 23.1	25 17.4	5 7.5	23 46.2	10 1.3	15 46.3	0 49.2	1 16.9	25 28.6	2 44.4
19	3 53 12.2	26 56.4	5 19.9	9♓21.5	6 39.8	24 60.0	10 32.0	15 57.6	0 47.6	1 18.8	25 30.0	2 46.8
20	3 57 8.8	27 57.0	5 16.7	23 18.7	8 11.8	26 13.8	11 2.6	16 9.1	0 46.2	1 20.8	25 31.4	2 49.2
21	4 1 5.3	28 57.6	5 13.5	7♈ 8.4	9 43.6	27 27.7	11 33.0	16 20.6	0 44.8	1 22.8	25 32.8	2 51.5
22	4 5 1.9	29 58.2	5 10.4	20 50.0	11 15.1	28 41.6	12 3.2	16 32.2	0 43.5	1 24.9	25 34.3	2 53.9
23	4 8 58.4	0♐58.8	5 7.2	4♉22.4	12 46.5	29 55.6	12 33.3	16 43.9	0 42.3	1 27.0	25 35.7	2 56.3
24	4 12 55.0	1 59.5	5 4.0	17 44.4	14 17.6	1♏ 9.7	13 3.3	16 55.7	0 41.3	1 29.2	25 37.3	2 58.7
25	4 16 51.6	3 .1	5 .8	0♊54.1	15 48.4	2 23.8	13 33.0	17 7.6	0 40.4	1 31.4	25 38.8	3 1.1
26	4 20 48.1	4 .8	4 57.6	13 50.3	17 19.0	3 37.9	14 2.6	17 19.6	0 39.5	1 33.7	25 40.4	3 3.5
27	4 24 44.7	5 1.5	4 54.5	26 31.9	18 49.4	4 52.1	14 32.0	17 31.6	0 38.8	1 35.9	25 42.0	3 5.8
28	4 28 41.2	6 2.2	4 51.3	8♋58.9	20 19.4	6 6.3	15 1.2	17 43.7	0 38.1	1 38.2	25 43.6	3 8.2
29	4 32 37.8	7 3.0	4 48.1	21 12.3	21 49.1	7 20.5	15 30.3	17 55.8	0 37.6	1 40.6	25 45.2	3 10.6
30	4 36 34.3	8 3.8	4 44.9	3♌14.1	23 18.4	8 34.8	15 59.1	18 8.1	0 37.1	1 43.0	25 46.9	3 12.9

LATITUDE

DAY	EPHEM. SID. TIME	☉	☊	☽	☿	♀	♂	♃	♄	♅	♆	♇
1	2 42 14.2	0 .0	0 .0	5S11.1	0N25.8	1N34.4	1N36.9	0S15.6	2S34.6	0S35.1	0N26.8	12N25.1
4	2 54 3.9	0 .0	0 .0	3 54.0	0 5.6	1 38.8	1 39.4	0 15.8	2 34.2	0 35.1	0 26.8	12 24.4
7	3 5 53.6	0 .0	0 .0	1 7.4	0S14.6	1 42.4	1 42.0	0 16.0	2 33.7	0 35.0	0 26.7	12 23.8
10	3 17 43.2	0 .0	0 .0	2N15.0	0 34.4	1 45.2	1 44.6	0 16.2	2 33.1	0 34.9	0 26.6	12 23.2
13	3 29 32.9	0 .0	0 .0	4 44.1	0 53.5	1 47.2	1 47.2	0 16.4	2 32.5	0 34.9	0 26.5	12 22.7
16	3 41 22.5	0 .0	0 .0	4 49.8	1 11.6	1 48.4	1 49.9	0 16.6	2 31.9	0 34.8	0 26.5	12 22.3
19	3 53 12.2	0 .0	0 .0	2 22.6	1 28.5	1 48.8	1 52.7	0 16.8	2 31.3	0 34.7	0 26.4	12 21.9
22	4 5 1.9	0 .0	0 .0	1S14.4	1 43.7	1 48.5	1 55.4	0 17.0	2 30.7	0 34.7	0 26.3	12 21.6
25	4 16 51.6	0 .0	0 .0	4 7.9	1 57.1	1 47.4	1 58.3	0 17.2	2 30.0	0 34.6	0 26.3	12 21.4
28	4 28 41.2	0 .0	0 .0	5 3.6	2 8.1	1 45.6	2 1.2	0 17.4	2 29.3	0 34.6	0 26.2	12 21.2

RIGHT ASCENSION

DAY	EPHEM. SID. TIME	☉	☊	☽	☿	♀	♂	♃	♄	♅	♆	♇
1	2 42 14.2	6♏27.7	5♎46.2	13♋56.1	5♏59.7	3♎24.0	3♍34.7	13♑56.8	2♈24.8	3♒11.9	27♑ 1.5	2♐28.5
2	2 46 10.8	7 26.5	5 43.3	26 24.0	7 33.3	4 31.3	4 6.6	14 7.2	2R21.8	3 13.1	27 2.4	2 30.6
3	2 50 7.3	8 25.6	5 40.3	8♌30.7	9 7.0	5 38.6	4 38.4	14 17.7	2 19.0	3 14.4	27 3.4	2 32.8
4	2 54 3.9	9 24.9	5 37.4	20 19.5	10 40.8	6 46.0	5 10.1	14 28.3	2 16.2	3 15.7	27 4.4	2 34.9
5	2 58 .4	10 24.3	5 34.5	1♍56.3	12 14.7	7 53.5	5 41.5	14 39.0	2 13.5	3 17.0	27 5.4	2 37.1
6	3 1 57.0	11 24.0	5 31.6	13 28.5	13 48.7	9 1.0	6 12.9	14 49.9	2 10.8	3 18.4	27 6.4	2 39.3
7	3 5 53.6	12 23.8	5 28.7	25 5.0	15 23.0	10 8.6	6 44.0	15 .9	2 8.2	3 19.8	27 7.5	2 41.4
8	3 9 50.1	13 23.9	5 25.7	6♎54.7	16 57.4	11 16.4	7 15.0	15 11.9	2 5.7	3 21.3	27 8.6	2 43.6
9	3 13 46.7	14 24.2	5 22.8	19 6.9	18 32.0	12 24.2	7 45.9	15 23.1	2 3.3	3 22.9	27 9.8	2 45.8
10	3 17 43.2	15 24.8	5 19.9	1♏49.3	20 6.8	13 32.1	8 16.5	15 34.4	2 1.0	3 24.4	27 10.9	2 48.0
11	3 21 39.8	16 25.5	5 17.0	15 7.5	21 41.9	14 40.2	8 47.1	15 45.9	1 58.7	3 26.1	27 12.1	2 50.3
12	3 25 36.3	17 26.4	5 14.1	29 2.5	23 17.3	15 48.4	9 17.4	15 57.4	1 56.6	3 27.8	27 13.4	2 52.5
13	3 29 32.9	18 27.6	5 11.1	13♐29.6	24 52.9	16 56.7	9 47.6	16 9.0	1 54.5	3 29.5	27 14.6	2 54.7
14	3 33 29.4	19 29.0	5 8.2	28 17.7	26 28.8	18 5.2	10 17.6	16 20.8	1 52.5	3 31.3	27 15.9	2 57.0
15	3 37 26.0	20 30.5	5 5.3	13♑11.9	28 5.0	19 13.8	10 47.5	16 32.6	1 50.6	3 33.1	27 17.3	2 59.2
16	3 41 22.5	21 32.3	5 2.4	27 57.3	29 41.5	20 22.6	11 17.1	16 44.5	1 48.8	3 35.0	27 18.6	3 1.5
17	3 45 19.1	22 34.3	4 59.5	12♒22.8	1♐18.3	21 31.5	11 46.6	16 56.6	1 47.1	3 36.9	27 20.0	3 3.7
18	3 49 15.7	23 36.5	4 56.5	26 24.0	2 55.4	22 40.7	12 16.0	17 8.7	1 45.5	3 38.9	27 21.4	3 6.0
19	3 53 12.2	24 38.9	4 53.6	10♓ 2.2	4 32.7	23 49.9	12 45.1	17 21.0	1 43.9	3 40.9	27 22.9	3 8.3
20	3 57 8.8	25 41.5	4 50.7	23 22.9	6 10.3	24 59.4	13 14.1	17 33.3	1 42.5	3 43.0	27 24.4	3 10.6
21	4 1 5.3	26 44.3	4 47.8	6♈34.0	7 48.2	26 9.1	13 42.9	17 45.7	1 41.1	3 45.1	27 25.9	3 12.8
22	4 5 1.9	27 47.2	4 44.9	19 42.9	9 26.3	27 19.0	14 11.6	17 58.2	1 39.9	3 47.2	27 27.4	3 15.1
23	4 8 58.4	28 50.4	4 42.0	2♉55.5	11 4.6	28 29.1	14 40.0	18 10.8	1 38.7	3 49.4	27 29.0	3 17.4
24	4 12 55.0	29 53.8	4 39.0	16 14.5	12 43.1	29 39.4	15 8.3	18 23.5	1 37.7	3 51.7	27 30.6	3 19.8
25	4 16 51.6	0♐57.4	4 36.1	29 38.8	14 21.8	0♏50.0	15 36.5	18 36.3	1 36.7	3 54.0	27 32.2	3 22.0
26	4 20 48.1	2 1.2	4 33.2	13♊ 3.6	16 .5	2 .7	16 4.4	18 49.1	1 35.8	3 56.3	27 33.9	3 24.3
27	4 24 44.7	3 5.1	4 30.3	26 21.5	17 39.3	3 11.8	16 32.1	19 2.0	1 35.1	3 58.7	27 35.5	3 26.6
28	4 28 41.2	4 9.2	4 27.4	9♋24.9	19 18.0	4 23.0	16 59.7	19 15.0	1 34.4	4 1.1	27 37.2	3 28.9
29	4 32 37.8	5 13.5	4 24.4	22 7.8	20 56.7	5 34.5	17 27.0	19 28.1	1 33.8	4 3.5	27 39.0	3 31.2
30	4 36 34.3	6 18.0	4 21.5	4♌27.4	22 35.2	6 46.3	17 54.2	19 41.3	1 33.3	4 6.0	27 40.7	3 33.5

DECLINATION

DAY	EPHEM. SID. TIME	☉	☊	☽	☿	♀	♂	♃	♄	♅	♆	♇
1	2 42 14.2	14S26.8	0S 2.6	17N36.6	13S50.4	0N14.5	12N38.8	23S 4.8	1S45.8	20S32.3	20S39.6	8S23.5
4	2 54 3.9	15 23.4	0 2.5	11 22.4	15 40.9	1S 7.9	12 5.7	23 2.1	1 49.0	20 31.4	20 39.2	8 25.4
7	3 5 53.6	16 17.6	0 2.5	0 54.3	17 24.1	2 30.7	11 32.6	22 59.3	1 51.9	20 30.5	20 38.7	8 27.3
10	3 17 43.2	17 9.4	0 2.4	10S29.1	18 59.5	3 53.6	10 59.5	22 56.2	1 54.4	20 29.5	20 38.2	8 29.1
13	3 29 32.9	17 58.6	0 2.3	17 48.3	20 26.4	5 16.2	10 26.6	22 52.9	1 56.6	20 28.3	20 37.6	8 30.8
16	3 41 22.5	18 45.0	0 2.3	16 2.2	21 44.2	6 38.2	9 53.8	22 49.4	1 58.4	20 27.1	20 37.0	8 32.5
19	3 53 12.2	19 28.3	0 2.2	5 51.4	22 52.4	7 59.3	9 21.3	22 45.7	1 59.9	20 25.8	20 36.4	8 34.2
22	4 5 1.9	20 8.5	0 2.2	6N59.0	23 50.3	9 19.1	8 49.0	22 41.7	2 .9	20 24.4	20 35.6	8 35.8
25	4 16 51.6	20 45.4	0 2.1	16 17.5	24 37.3	10 37.3	8 17.2	22 37.5	2 1.6	20 22.9	20 34.9	8 37.3
28	4 28 41.2	21 18.8	0 2.0	18 5.0	25 12.8	11 53.5	7 45.8	22 33.0	2 1.9	20 21.3	20 34.1	8 38.7

DECEMBER 1996

LONGITUDE

DAY	EPHEM. SID. TIME (h m s)	☉ (° ′)	☊ (° ′)	☾ (° ′)	☿ (° ′)	♀ (° ′)	♂ (° ′)	♃ (° ′)	♄ (° ′)	♅ (° ′)	♆ (° ′)	♇ (° ′)
1	4 40 30.9	9♐ 4.6	4♎41.8	15♌ 7.6	24♐47.3	9♏49.2	16♍27.8	18♑20.4	0♈36.8	1♒45.4	25♑48.6	3♐15.3
2	4 44 27.4	10 5.4	4 38.6	26 57.0	26 15.7	11 3.6	16 56.2	18 32.8	0R36.6	1 47.9	25 50.3	3 17.7
3	4 48 24.0	11 6.2	4 35.4	8♍47.1	27 43.5	12 18.0	17 24.5	18 45.3	0 36.5	1 50.4	25 52.0	3 20.0
4	4 52 20.6	12 7.1	4 32.2	20 43.2	29 10.7	13 32.4	17 52.5	18 57.8	0 36.5	1 52.9	25 53.8	3 22.4
5	4 56 17.1	13 8.0	4 29.1	2♎50.9	0♑37.1	14 46.9	18 20.4	19 10.4	0D36.6	1 55.5	25 55.5	3 24.7
6	5 0 13.7	14 8.9	4 25.9	15 15.3	2 2.7	16 1.5	18 48.0	19 23.1	0 36.8	1 58.1	25 57.3	3 27.1
7	5 4 10.2	15 9.8	4 22.7	28 1.1	3 27.2	17 16.0	19 15.4	19 35.8	0 37.2	2 .8	25 59.2	3 29.4
8	5 8 6.8	16 10.8	4 19.5	11♏11.5	4 50.6	18 30.6	19 42.6	19 48.6	0 37.6	2 3.5	26 1.0	3 31.8
9	5 12 3.3	17 11.8	4 16.3	24 47.7	6 12.5	19 45.3	20 9.6	20 1.5	0 38.1	2 6.2	26 2.9	3 34.1
10	5 15 59.9	18 12.7	4 13.2	8♐48.6	7 32.9	20 59.9	20 36.3	20 14.4	0 38.8	2 8.9	26 4.7	3 36.4
11	5 19 56.5	19 13.8	4 10.0	23 10.3	8 51.3	22 14.6	21 2.8	20 27.4	0 39.6	2 11.7	26 6.6	3 38.7
12	5 23 53.0	20 14.8	4 6.8	7♑46.5	10 7.5	23 29.3	21 29.0	20 40.4	0 40.4	2 14.5	26 8.6	3 41.0
13	5 27 49.6	21 15.8	4 3.6	22 29.4	11 21.1	24 44.0	21 55.0	20 53.5	0 41.4	2 17.4	26 10.5	3 43.3
14	5 31 46.1	22 16.8	4 .5	7♒11.2	12 31.7	25 58.8	22 20.7	21 6.6	0 42.5	2 20.2	26 12.5	3 45.6
15	5 35 42.7	23 17.9	3 57.3	21 45.0	13 38.8	27 13.6	22 46.2	21 19.9	0 43.8	2 23.2	26 14.5	3 47.9
16	5 39 39.2	24 19.0	3 54.1	6♓ 6.2	14 41.9	28 28.4	23 11.4	21 33.1	0 45.1	2 26.1	26 16.5	3 50.2
17	5 43 35.8	25 20.1	3 50.9	20 12.3	15 40.3	29 43.2	23 36.4	21 46.4	0 46.5	2 29.1	26 18.5	3 52.4
18	5 47 32.4	26 21.1	3 47.8	4♈ 2.8	16 33.3	0♐58.0	24 1.0	21 59.7	0 48.0	2 32.1	26 20.5	3 54.7
19	5 51 28.9	27 22.2	3 44.6	17 38.4	17 20.3	2 12.9	24 25.4	22 13.1	0 49.6	2 35.1	26 22.5	3 56.9
20	5 55 25.5	28 23.3	3 41.4	1♉ .5	18 .3	3 27.8	24 49.5	22 26.5	0 51.4	2 38.1	26 24.6	3 59.1
21	5 59 22.0	29 24.4	3 38.2	14 10.5	18 32.5	4 42.6	25 13.3	22 40.0	0 53.2	2 41.2	26 26.7	4 1.3
22	6 3 18.6	0♑25.5	3 35.0	27 9.3	18 56.0	5 57.5	25 36.8	22 53.5	0 55.2	2 44.3	26 28.8	4 3.5
23	6 7 15.1	1 26.6	3 31.9	9♊57.5	19 9.9	7 12.4	26 .0	23 7.1	0 57.2	2 47.4	26 30.8	4 5.7
24	6 11 11.7	2 27.7	3 28.7	22 35.1	19 13.3	8 27.4	26 22.9	23 20.7	0 59.4	2 50.6	26 33.0	4 7.8
25	6 15 8.3	3 28.8	3 25.5	5♋ 2.1	19R 5.7	9 42.3	26 45.5	23 34.3	1 1.6	2 53.7	26 35.1	4 10.0
26	6 19 4.8	4 29.9	3 22.3	17 18.6	18 46.3	10 57.3	27 7.8	23 47.9	1 4.0	2 56.9	26 37.2	4 12.1
27	6 23 1.4	5 31.0	3 19.2	29 25.0	18 15.2	12 12.2	27 29.8	24 1.6	1 6.4	3 .1	26 39.4	4 14.2
28	6 26 57.9	6 32.1	3 16.0	11♌22.8	17 32.4	13 27.2	27 51.4	24 15.4	1 9.0	3 3.3	26 41.5	4 16.3
29	6 30 54.5	7 33.3	3 12.8	23 14.0	16 38.7	14 42.2	28 12.6	24 29.1	1 11.7	3 6.6	26 43.7	4 18.4
30	6 34 51.0	8 34.4	3 9.6	5♍ 1.7	15 35.1	15 57.3	28 33.5	24 42.9	1 14.4	3 9.9	26 45.9	4 20.4
31	6 38 47.6	9 35.6	3 6.5	16 50.0	14 23.6	17 12.3	28 54.1	24 56.7	1 17.3	3 13.2	26 48.1	4 22.5

LATITUDE

DAY	EPHEM. SID. TIME	☉	☊	☾	☿	♀	♂	♃	♄	♅	♆	♇
1	4 40 30.9	0 .0	0 .0	3S55.4	2S16.2	1N43.2	2N 4.1	0S17.6	2S28.7	0S34.5	0N26.1	12N21.1
4	4 52 20.6	0 .0	0 .0	1 18.4	2 20.9	1 40.1	2 7.1	0 17.8	2 28.0	0 34.5	0 26.1	12 21.0
7	5 4 10.2	0 .0	0 .0	1N56.4	2 21.5	1 36.4	2 10.2	0 18.0	2 27.3	0 34.4	0 26.0	12 21.0
10	5 15 59.9	0 .0	0 .0	4 30.4	2 16.9	1 32.1	2 13.4	0 18.2	2 26.6	0 34.4	0 26.0	12 21.0
13	5 27 49.6	0 .0	0 .0	4 46.8	2 6.0	1 27.2	2 16.6	0 18.4	2 25.9	0 34.3	0 25.9	12 21.2
16	5 39 39.2	0 .0	0 .0	2 23.2	1 47.4	1 21.9	2 19.8	0 18.7	2 25.1	0 34.3	0 25.8	12 21.3
19	5 51 28.9	0 .0	0 .0	1S10.1	1 19.4	1 16.1	2 23.2	0 18.9	2 24.4	0 34.2	0 25.8	12 21.6
22	6 3 18.6	0 .0	0 .0	4 .7	0 40.7	1 9.8	2 26.6	0 19.1	2 23.7	0 34.2	0 25.7	12 21.9
25	6 15 8.3	0 .0	0 .0	4 59.4	0N 8.9	1 3.3	2 30.1	0 19.3	2 23.0	0 34.2	0 25.7	12 22.2
28	6 26 57.9	0 .0	0 .0	3 55.1	1 6.4	0 56.3	2 33.7	0 19.6	2 22.4	0 34.2	0 25.6	12 22.6
31	6 38 47.6	0 .0	0 .0	1 21.7	2 3.6	0 49.2	2 37.3	0 19.8	2 21.7	0 34.1	0 25.6	12 23.1

RIGHT ASCENSION

DAY	EPHEM. SID. TIME	☉	☊	☾	☿	♀	♂	♃	♄	♅	♆	♇
1	4 40 30.9	7♐22.6	4♎18.6	16♌24.6	24♐13.4	7♏58.3	18♍21.2	19♑54.5	1♈32.9	4♒ 8.5	27♑42.5	3♐35.8
2	4 44 27.4	8 27.4	4 15.7	28 3.8	25 51.2	9 10.7	18 48.0	20 7.8	1R32.6	4 11.1	27 44.3	3 38.1
3	4 48 24.0	9 32.4	4 12.8	9♍31.9	27 28.6	10 23.2	19 14.6	20 21.1	1 32.5	4 13.7	27 46.1	3 40.4
4	4 52 20.6	10 37.5	4 9.9	20 57.6	29 5.3	11 36.1	19 40.9	20 34.6	1 32.4	4 16.3	27 47.9	3 42.7
5	4 56 17.1	11 42.8	4 6.9	2♎31.0	0♑41.2	12 49.2	20 7.1	20 48.1	1 32.4	4 19.0	27 49.8	3 45.0
6	5 0 13.7	12 48.2	4 4.0	14 22.8	2 16.2	14 2.7	20 33.1	21 1.6	1D32.5	4 21.7	27 51.7	3 47.3
7	5 4 10.2	13 53.8	4 1.1	26 43.5	3 49.9	15 16.4	20 58.8	21 15.3	1 32.7	4 24.4	27 53.6	3 49.5
8	5 8 6.8	14 59.5	3 58.2	9♏42.0	5 22.3	16 30.4	21 24.4	21 29.0	1 33.0	4 27.2	27 55.5	3 51.8
9	5 12 3.3	16 5.3	3 55.3	23 24.1	6 53.0	17 44.7	21 49.7	21 42.7	1 33.4	4 30.0	27 57.5	3 54.1
10	5 15 59.9	17 11.2	3 52.3	7♐49.4	8 21.7	18 59.3	22 14.8	21 56.5	1 33.9	4 32.9	27 59.5	3 56.3
11	5 19 56.5	18 17.2	3 49.4	22 49.8	9 48.1	20 14.2	22 39.6	22 10.4	1 34.5	4 35.8	28 1.5	3 58.6
12	5 23 53.0	19 23.3	3 46.5	8♑ 9.3	11 11.8	21 29.4	23 4.2	22 24.3	1 35.2	4 38.7	28 3.5	4 .8
13	5 27 49.6	20 29.5	3 43.6	23 28.3	12 32.3	22 44.9	23 28.6	22 38.3	1 36.0	4 41.6	28 5.5	4 3.1
14	5 31 46.1	21 35.8	3 40.7	8♒28.8	13 49.3	24 .6	23 52.8	22 52.3	1 36.9	4 44.6	28 7.6	4 5.3
15	5 35 42.7	22 42.2	3 37.8	23 .2	15 2.1	25 16.7	24 16.7	23 6.5	1 38.0	4 47.7	28 9.7	4 7.6
16	5 39 39.2	23 48.6	3 34.8	6♓59.5	16 10.2	26 33.1	24 40.3	23 20.6	1 39.1	4 50.7	28 11.8	4 9.8
17	5 43 35.8	24 55.0	3 31.9	20 31.0	17 12.8	27 49.7	25 3.7	23 34.7	1 40.3	4 53.8	28 13.9	4 12.0
18	5 47 32.4	26 1.5	3 29.0	3♈42.3	18 9.2	29 6.7	25 26.9	23 49.0	1 41.6	4 56.9	28 16.0	4 14.2
19	5 51 28.9	27 8.1	3 26.1	16 42.8	18 58.6	0♐23.9	25 49.7	24 3.2	1 43.0	5 .0	28 18.2	4 16.4
20	5 55 25.5	28 14.6	3 23.2	29 40.7	19 40.1	1 41.4	26 12.3	24 17.5	1 44.5	5 3.2	28 20.3	4 18.5
21	5 59 22.0	29 21.2	3 20.3	12♉42.0	20 13.0	2 59.1	26 34.7	24 31.8	1 46.1	5 6.4	28 22.5	4 20.7
22	6 3 18.6	0♑27.8	3 17.3	25 49.3	20 36.1	4 17.2	26 56.8	24 46.2	1 47.8	5 9.6	28 24.7	4 22.8
23	6 7 15.1	1 34.4	3 14.4	9♊ 1.3	20 48.6	5 35.5	27 18.5	25 .6	1 49.6	5 12.8	28 26.9	4 25.0
24	6 11 11.7	2 40.9	3 11.5	22 12.9	20 49.8	6 54.1	27 40.1	25 15.0	1 51.5	5 16.0	28 29.1	4 27.1
25	6 15 8.3	3 47.5	3 8.6	5♋17.2	20R38.9	8 12.9	28 1.3	25 29.5	1 53.4	5 19.3	28 31.3	4 29.2
26	6 19 4.8	4 54.1	3 5.7	18 6.7	20 15.5	9 32.0	28 22.2	25 44.0	1 55.5	5 22.6	28 33.6	4 31.3
27	6 23 1.4	6 .6	3 2.8	0♌36.3	19 39.6	10 51.3	28 42.8	25 58.5	1 57.7	5 25.9	28 35.8	4 33.4
28	6 26 57.9	7 7.1	2 59.8	12 43.6	18 51.3	12 10.9	29 3.1	26 13.1	1 59.9	5 29.3	28 38.1	4 35.4
29	6 30 54.5	8 13.5	2 56.9	24 30.1	17 51.5	13 30.7	29 23.1	26 27.6	2 2.3	5 32.6	28 40.4	4 37.5
30	6 34 51.0	9 19.9	2 54.0	6♍ .3	16 41.6	14 50.7	29 42.8	26 42.3	2 4.7	5 36.0	28 42.7	4 39.5
31	6 38 47.6	10 26.2	2 51.1	17 21.4	15 23.4	16 10.9	0♎ 2.2	26 56.9	2 7.3	5 39.4	28 45.0	4 41.5

DECLINATION

DAY	EPHEM. SID. TIME	☉	☊	☾	☿	♀	♂	♃	♄	♅	♆	♇
1	4 40 30.9	21S48.5	0S 2.0	12N32.6	25S36.2	13S 7.4	7N14.9	22S28.3	2S 1.7	20S19.6	20S33.2	8S40.1
4	4 52 20.6	22 14.6	0 1.9	2 28.6	25 47.0	14 18.6	6 44.5	22 23.4	2 1.2	20 17.9	20 32.3	8 41.4
7	5 4 10.2	22 36.7	0 1.8	8S57.4	25 44.9	15 26.7	6 14.9	22 18.2	2 .3	20 16.1	20 31.3	8 42.7
10	5 15 59.9	22 54.9	0 1.8	17 18.9	25 30.0	16 31.4	5 45.9	22 12.7	1 59.0	20 14.2	20 30.4	8 43.8
13	5 27 49.6	23 8.9	0 1.7	16 50.6	25 2.7	17 32.4	5 17.8	22 7.1	1 57.3	20 12.3	20 29.3	8 44.9
16	5 39 39.2	23 18.9	0 1.6	7 3.2	24 24.3	18 29.2	4 50.6	22 1.1	1 55.2	20 10.3	20 28.3	8 45.9
19	5 51 28.9	23 24.7	0 1.6	5N50.6	23 37.5	19 21.6	4 24.4	21 54.9	1 52.8	20 8.2	20 27.2	8 46.9
22	6 3 18.6	23 26.2	0 1.5	15 36.8	22 46.3	20 9.2	3 59.1	21 48.5	1 49.9	20 6.1	20 26.1	8 47.7
25	6 15 8.3	23 23.5	0 1.4	18 21.2	21 55.8	20 51.7	3 35.1	21 41.9	1 46.7	20 3.9	20 24.9	8 48.5
28	6 26 57.9	23 16.6	0 1.4	13 35.6	21 11.4	21 28.8	3 12.2	21 35.0	1 43.2	20 1.6	20 23.7	8 49.2
31	6 38 47.6	23 5.4	0 1.3	3 56.6	20 36.7	22 .3	2 50.6	21 27.8	1 39.3	19 59.3	20 22.5	8 49.8

JANUARY 1997

LONGITUDE

DAY	EPHEM. SID. TIME h m s	☉ ° ′	☊ ° ′	☽ ° ′	☿ ° ′	♀ ° ′	♂ ° ′	♃ ° ′	♄ ° ′	♅ ° ′	♆ ° ′	♇ ° ′
1	6 42 44.2	10♑36.7	3♎ 3.3	28♍43.7	13♑ 6.2	18♐27.3	29♍14.3	25♑10.6	1♈20.2	3♒16.5	26♑50.3	4♐24.5
2	6 46 40.7	11 37.9	3 .1	10♎48.1	11 R 45.4	19 42.4	29 34.1	25 24.5	1 23.3	3 19.8	26 52.5	4 26.5
3	6 50 37.3	12 39.0	2 56.9	23 8.7	10 24.0	20 57.5	29 53.5	25 38.4	1 26.4	3 23.1	26 54.7	4 28.5
4	6 54 33.8	13 40.2	2 53.7	5♏50.9	9 4.5	22 12.6	0♎12.6	25 52.3	1 29.7	3 26.5	26 56.9	4 30.4
5	6 58 30.4	14 41.4	2 50.6	18 59.2	7 49.5	23 27.7	0 31.2	26 6.3	1 33.1	3 29.9	26 59.2	4 32.4
6	7 2 26.9	15 42.6	2 47.4	2♐36.4	6 40.9	24 42.8	0 49.5	26 20.3	1 36.5	3 33.3	27 1.4	4 34.3
7	7 6 23.5	16 43.8	2 44.2	16 43.1	5 40.3	25 57.9	1 7.3	26 34.3	1 40.1	3 36.7	27 3.7	4 36.2
8	7 10 20.0	17 44.9	2 41.0	1♑16.3	4 48.8	27 13.0	1 24.6	26 48.3	1 43.7	3 40.1	27 5.9	4 38.1
9	7 14 16.6	18 46.1	2 37.9	16 10.0	4 7.1	28 28.2	1 41.5	27 2.3	1 47.4	3 43.5	27 8.2	4 40.0
10	7 18 13.2	19 47.3	2 34.7	1♒15.2	3 35.4	29 43.3	1 58.0	27 16.4	1 51.2	3 47.0	27 10.4	4 41.8
11	7 22 9.7	20 48.4	2 31.5	16 21.6	3 13.5	0♑58.4	2 14.0	27 30.4	1 55.1	3 50.4	27 12.7	4 43.6
12	7 26 6.3	21 49.6	2 28.3	1♓19.4	3 1.3	2 13.6	2 29.5	27 44.5	1 59.1	3 53.9	27 15.0	4 45.4
13	7 30 2.8	22 50.8	2 25.2	16 1.2	2 58.2	3 28.7	2 44.6	27 58.6	2 3.2	3 57.3	27 17.2	4 47.1
14	7 33 59.4	23 51.9	2 22.0	0♈22.1	3 D 3.5	4 43.8	2 59.1	28 12.7	2 7.4	4 .8	27 19.5	4 48.9
15	7 37 55.9	24 53.0	2 18.8	14 20.4	3 16.7	5 59.0	3 13.2	28 26.8	2 11.7	4 4.3	27 21.8	4 50.6
16	7 41 52.5	25 54.1	2 15.6	27 56.6	3 37.2	7 14.1	3 26.7	28 40.9	2 16.0	4 7.8	27 24.1	4 52.3
17	7 45 49.1	26 55.2	2 12.4	11♉12.7	4 4.2	8 29.2	3 39.8	28 55.0	2 20.4	4 11.3	27 26.3	4 53.9
18	7 49 45.6	27 56.3	2 9.3	24 11.3	4 37.2	9 44.4	3 52.3	29 9.1	2 24.9	4 14.8	27 28.6	4 55.5
19	7 53 42.2	28 57.4	2 6.1	6♊55.1	5 15.7	10 59.5	4 4.2	29 23.2	2 29.5	4 18.3	27 30.9	4 57.1
20	7 57 38.7	29 58.4	2 2.9	19 26.6	5 58.9	12 14.7	4 15.7	29 37.4	2 34.2	4 21.8	27 33.2	4 58.7
21	8 1 35.3	0♒59.5	1 59.7	1♋47.7	6 46.6	13 29.8	4 26.5	29 51.5	2 39.0	4 25.3	27 35.4	5 .3
22	8 5 31.8	2 .5	1 56.6	13 59.9	7 38.3	14 44.9	4 36.8	0♒ 5.6	2 43.8	4 28.8	27 37.7	5 1.8
23	8 9 28.4	3 1.5	1 53.4	26 4.5	8 33.5	16 .1	4 46.5	0 19.7	2 48.7	4 32.4	27 40.0	5 3.3
24	8 13 24.9	4 2.6	1 50.2	8♌ 2.6	9 32.0	17 15.2	4 55.7	0 33.8	2 53.7	4 35.9	27 42.3	5 4.7
25	8 17 21.5	5 3.5	1 47.0	19 55.4	10 33.4	18 30.3	5 4.2	0 48.0	2 58.8	4 39.4	27 44.5	5 6.2
26	8 21 18.1	6 4.6	1 43.9	1♍44.6	11 37.5	19 45.5	5 12.2	1 2.1	3 3.9	4 43.0	27 46.8	5 7.6
27	8 25 14.6	7 5.5	1 40.7	13 32.4	12 43.9	21 .7	5 19.5	1 16.2	3 9.2	4 46.5	27 49.1	5 9.0
28	8 29 11.2	8 6.5	1 37.5	25 21.8	13 52.6	22 15.8	5 26.1	1 30.3	3 14.4	4 50.0	27 51.3	5 10.3
29	8 33 7.7	9 7.5	1 34.3	7♎16.4	15 3.3	23 31.0	5 32.1	1 44.4	3 19.8	4 53.5	27 53.6	5 11.7
30	8 37 4.3	10 8.4	1 31.1	19 20.6	16 15.8	24 46.1	5 37.5	1 58.4	3 25.2	4 57.0	27 55.8	5 12.9
31	8 41 .8	11 9.3	1 28.0	1♏39.0	17 30.1	26 1.2	5 42.1	2 12.5	3 30.7	5 .5	27 58.0	5 14.2

LATITUDE

DAY	SID. TIME	☉	☊	☽	☿	♀	♂	♃	♄	♅	♆	♇
1	6 42 44.2	0 .0	0 .0	0 S 19.7	2 N 20.6	0 N 46.7	2 N 38.6	0 S 19.9	2 S 21.5	0 S 34.1	0 N 25.6	12 N 23.2
4	6 54 33.8	0 .0	0 .0	2 N 47.3	2 59.6	0 39.3	2 42.3	0 20.1	2 20.8	0 34.1	0 25.5	12 23.8
7	7 6 23.5	0 .0	0 .0	4 51.0	3 16.8	0 31.6	2 46.2	0 20.4	2 20.2	0 34.1	0 25.5	12 24.4
10	7 18 13.2	0 .0	0 .0	4 22.5	3 13.9	0 23.9	2 50.1	0 20.6	2 19.5	0 34.1	0 25.5	12 25.0
13	7 30 2.8	0 .0	0 .0	1 19.8	2 57.0	0 16.1	2 54.1	0 20.9	2 18.9	0 34.1	0 25.4	12 25.7
16	7 41 52.5	0 .0	0 .0	2 S 17.5	2 32.0	0 8.3	2 58.1	0 21.2	2 18.3	0 34.1	0 25.4	12 26.4
19	7 53 42.2	0 .0	0 .0	4 37.8	2 3.2	0 .6	3 2.1	0 21.4	2 17.7	0 34.1	0 25.4	12 27.2
22	8 5 31.8	0 .0	0 .0	4 55.7	1 33.0	0 S 7.1	3 6.2	0 21.7	2 17.2	0 34.1	0 25.3	12 28.0
25	8 17 21.5	0 .0	0 .0	3 17.2	1 3.1	0 14.6	3 10.4	0 22.0	2 16.7	0 34.1	0 25.3	12 28.8
28	8 29 11.2	0 .0	0 .0	0 23.9	0 34.2	0 21.9	3 14.5	0 22.3	2 16.1	0 34.2	0 25.3	12 29.7
31	8 41 .8	0 .0	0 .0	2 N 43.5	0 6.9	0 29.1	3 18.6	0 22.6	2 15.6	0 34.2	0 25.3	12 30.6

RIGHT ASCENSION

DAY	SID. TIME	☉	☊	☽	☿	♀	♂	♃	♄	♅	♆	♇
1	6 42 44.2	11♑32.5	2♎48.2	28♍42.2	13♑59.4	17♐31.3	0♎21.2	27♑11.5	2♈ 9.9	5♒42.8	28♑47.3	4♐43.5
2	6 46 40.7	12 38.7	2 45.3	10♎13.1	12 R 32.2	18 51.9	0 39.9	27 26.2	2 12.6	5 46.3	28 49.6	4 45.5
3	6 50 37.3	13 44.8	2 42.4	22 5.0	11 4.6	20 12.7	0 58.2	27 40.9	2 15.4	5 49.7	28 51.9	4 47.4
4	6 54 33.8	14 50.8	2 39.4	4♏28.8	9 39.5	21 33.6	1 16.1	27 55.6	2 18.3	5 53.2	28 54.2	4 49.4
5	6 58 30.4	15 56.8	2 36.5	17 34.0	8 19.4	22 54.7	1 33.8	28 10.4	2 21.3	5 56.7	28 56.6	4 51.3
6	7 2 26.9	17 2.6	2 33.6	1♐26.1	7 6.2	24 15.9	1 51.0	28 25.1	2 24.4	6 .3	28 59.0	4 53.2
7	7 6 23.5	18 8.3	2 30.7	16 4.6	6 1.7	25 37.3	2 7.8	28 39.9	2 27.6	6 3.8	29 1.3	4 55.1
8	7 10 20.0	19 13.9	2 27.8	1♑20.1	5 7.0	26 58.7	2 24.2	28 54.6	2 30.8	6 7.3	29 3.7	4 57.0
9	7 14 16.6	20 19.4	2 24.9	16 55.4	4 22.7	28 20.2	2 40.3	29 9.4	2 34.1	6 10.8	29 6.0	4 58.8
10	7 18 13.2	21 24.7	2 21.9	2♒29.2	3 49.1	29 41.8	2 55.9	29 24.2	2 37.5	6 14.4	29 8.4	5 .6
11	7 22 9.7	22 29.9	2 19.0	17 43.2	3 26.0	1♑ 3.5	3 11.1	29 39.0	2 41.0	6 18.0	29 10.8	5 2.4
12	7 26 6.3	23 35.0	2 16.1	2♓26.6	3 13.1	2 25.2	3 25.8	29 53.8	2 44.6	6 21.5	29 13.1	5 4.2
13	7 30 2.8	24 39.8	2 13.2	16 36.9	3 9.9	3 46.9	3 40.2	0♒ 8.6	2 48.3	6 25.1	29 15.5	5 6.0
14	7 33 59.4	25 44.6	2 10.3	0♈18.5	3 D 15.8	5 8.7	3 54.0	0 23.4	2 52.0	6 28.7	29 17.9	5 7.7
15	7 37 55.9	26 49.1	2 7.4	13 39.0	3 30.1	6 30.4	4 7.5	0 38.2	2 55.9	6 32.3	29 20.3	5 9.4
16	7 41 52.5	27 53.5	2 4.4	26 46.8	3 52.2	7 52.2	4 20.4	0 53.0	2 59.8	6 35.9	29 22.7	5 11.1
17	7 45 49.1	28 57.7	2 1.5	9♉49.2	4 21.4	9 13.9	4 32.9	1 7.8	3 3.8	6 39.5	29 25.0	5 12.7
18	7 49 45.6	0♒ 1.7	1 58.6	22 51.0	4 57.1	10 35.5	4 44.9	1 22.5	3 7.8	6 43.1	29 27.4	5 14.4
19	7 53 42.2	1 5.6	1 55.7	5♊53.8	5 38.6	11 57.1	4 56.4	1 37.3	3 12.0	6 46.7	29 29.8	5 16.0
20	7 57 38.7	2 9.2	1 52.8	18 55.9	6 25.5	13 18.7	5 7.4	1 52.1	3 16.2	6 50.4	29 32.2	5 17.5
21	8 1 35.3	3 12.7	1 49.9	1♋53.0	7 17.1	14 40.1	5 17.9	2 6.9	3 20.5	6 54.0	29 34.6	5 19.1
22	8 5 31.8	4 16.0	1 47.0	14 39.7	8 13.2	16 1.4	5 27.9	2 21.6	3 24.8	6 57.6	29 36.9	5 20.6
23	8 9 28.4	5 19.1	1 44.0	27 11.0	9 13.1	17 22.6	5 37.4	2 36.3	3 29.2	7 1.3	29 39.3	5 22.1
24	8 13 24.9	6 21.9	1 41.1	9♌23.4	10 16.7	18 43.7	5 46.3	2 51.1	3 33.7	7 4.9	29 41.7	5 23.6
25	8 17 21.5	7 24.6	1 38.2	21 16.6	11 23.5	20 4.7	5 54.7	3 5.8	3 38.3	7 8.5	29 44.1	5 25.0
26	8 21 18.1	8 27.2	1 35.3	2♍52.8	12 33.2	21 25.5	6 2.5	3 20.5	3 43.0	7 12.2	29 46.5	5 26.5
27	8 25 14.6	9 29.5	1 32.4	14 16.7	13 45.6	22 46.2	6 9.7	3 35.2	3 47.7	7 15.8	29 48.8	5 27.9
28	8 29 11.2	10 31.6	1 29.5	25 35.2	15 .4	24 6.6	6 16.4	3 49.9	3 52.5	7 19.4	29 51.2	5 29.2
29	8 33 7.7	11 33.5	1 26.5	6♎56.7	16 17.3	25 26.9	6 22.4	4 4.5	3 57.3	7 23.1	29 53.5	5 30.6
30	8 37 4.3	12 35.2	1 23.6	18 30.6	17 36.3	26 47.0	6 27.9	4 19.2	4 2.2	7 26.7	29 55.9	5 31.9
31	8 41 .8	13 36.6	1 20.7	0♏26.8	18 57.1	28 6.8	6 32.7	4 33.8	4 7.2	7 30.3	29 58.2	5 33.2

DECLINATION

DAY	SID. TIME	☉	☊	☽	☿	♀	♂	♃	♄	♅	♆	♇
1	6 42 44.2	23 S .8	0 S 1.3	0 N 12.3	20 S 27.6	22 S 9.6	2 N 43.7	21 S 25.4	1 S 37.9	19 S 58.6	20 S 22.1	8 S 49.9
4	6 54 33.8	22 44.1	0 1.2	10 S 50.3	20 8.4	22 33.3	2 23.9	21 18.0	1 33.5	19 56.2	20 20.9	8 50.4
7	7 6 23.5	22 23.4	0 1.1	17 56.8	20 2.3	22 50.9	2 5.7	21 10.3	1 28.8	19 53.8	20 19.6	8 50.8
10	7 18 13.2	21 58.7	0 1.1	15 36.5	20 9.5	23 2.3	1 49.2	21 2.4	1 23.8	19 51.4	20 18.4	8 51.2
13	7 30 2.8	21 30.1	0 1.0	4 17.2	20 27.3	23 7.3	1 34.3	20 54.3	1 18.5	19 49.0	20 17.1	8 51.4
16	7 41 52.5	20 57.9	0 .9	8 N 36.1	20 51.3	23 6.0	1 21.3	20 46.1	1 12.8	19 46.5	20 15.8	8 51.5
19	7 53 42.2	20 22.0	0 .9	16 53.8	21 16.9	22 58.3	1 10.1	20 37.6	1 6.9	19 44.0	20 14.5	8 51.6
22	8 5 31.8	19 42.7	0 .8	17 47.9	21 40.2	22 44.3	1 1.0	20 28.9	1 .8	19 41.5	20 13.2	8 51.6
25	8 17 21.5	19 .0	0 .7	11 43.0	21 58.2	22 24.0	0 53.9	20 20.1	0 54.3	19 39.0	20 11.8	8 51.5
28	8 29 11.2	18 14.3	0 .7	1 28.6	22 8.8	21 57.5	0 49.1	20 11.1	0 47.6	19 36.4	20 10.5	8 51.3
31	8 41 .8	17 25.6	0 .6	9 S 29.3	22 10.6	21 25.1	0 46.5	20 2.0	0 40.7	19 33.9	20 9.2	8 51.0

FEBRUARY 1997

LONGITUDE

DAY	EPHEM. SID. TIME	☉	☊	☽	☿	♀	♂	♃	♄	♅	♆	♇
	h m s	° ′	° ′	° ′	° ′	° ′	° ′	° ′	° ′	° ′	° ′	° ′
1	8 44 57.4	12 ♒ 10.2	1 ♎ 24.8	14 ♏ 16.7	18 ♑ 46.0	27 ♑ 16.4	5 ♎ 46.1	2 ♒ 26.5	3 ♈ 36.3	5 ♒ 4.0	28 ♑ .3	5 ♐ 15.4
2	8 48 53.9	13 11.1	1 21.6	27 18.4	20 3.3	28 31.5	5 49.4	2 40.6	3 41.9	5 7.5	28 2.5	5 16.6
3	8 52 50.5	14 12.0	1 18.4	10 ♐ 47.7	21 22.0	29 46.7	5 52.0	2 54.6	3 47.6	5 11.0	28 4.7	5 17.8
4	8 56 47.1	15 12.9	1 15.3	24 46.6	22 42.0	1 ♒ 1.8	5 53.8	3 8.6	3 53.4	5 14.5	28 6.9	5 18.9
5	9 0 43.6	16 13.7	1 12.1	9 ♑ 14.2	24 3.2	2 16.9	5 54.9	3 22.5	3 59.2	5 18.0	28 9.1	5 20.0
6	9 4 40.2	17 14.6	1 8.9	24 6.4	25 25.6	3 32.1	5 55.3	3 36.5	4 5.1	5 21.5	28 11.3	5 21.1
7	9 8 36.7	18 15.4	1 5.7	9 ♒ 15.9	26 49.2	4 47.2	5 R 55.0	3 50.4	4 11.0	5 24.9	28 13.4	5 22.1
8	9 12 33.3	19 16.2	1 2.5	24 32.7	28 13.7	6 2.3	5 53.8	4 4.3	4 17.0	5 28.4	28 15.6	5 23.1
9	9 16 29.8	20 17.0	0 59.4	9 ♓ 45.9	29 39.3	7 17.4	5 52.0	4 18.2	4 23.1	5 31.8	28 17.8	5 24.0
10	9 20 26.4	21 17.7	0 56.2	24 45.8	1 ♒ 5.9	8 32.6	5 49.3	4 32.1	4 29.2	5 35.2	28 19.9	5 25.0
11	9 24 22.9	22 18.4	0 53.0	9 ♈ 24.9	2 33.5	9 47.7	5 45.9	4 45.9	4 35.4	5 38.6	28 22.0	5 25.9
12	9 28 19.5	23 19.1	0 49.8	23 39.0	4 2.0	11 2.8	5 41.7	4 59.7	4 41.7	5 42.0	28 24.1	5 26.7
13	9 32 16.0	24 19.8	0 46.7	7 ♉ 26.7	5 31.4	12 17.8	5 36.7	5 13.5	4 48.0	5 45.4	28 26.2	5 27.6
14	9 36 12.6	25 20.5	0 43.5	20 48.9	7 1.8	13 32.9	5 31.0	5 27.2	4 54.3	5 48.8	28 28.3	5 28.4
15	9 40 9.1	26 21.1	0 40.3	3 ♊ 48.1	8 33.1	14 48.0	5 24.5	5 40.9	5 .7	5 52.2	28 30.4	5 29.1
16	9 44 5.7	27 21.7	0 37.1	16 27.9	10 5.3	16 3.1	5 17.2	5 54.6	5 7.2	5 55.5	28 32.5	5 29.9
17	9 48 2.3	28 22.3	0 33.9	28 51.7	11 38.4	17 18.1	5 9.1	6 8.3	5 13.7	5 58.9	28 34.5	5 30.6
18	9 51 58.8	29 22.8	0 30.8	11 ♋ 3.1	13 12.4	18 33.2	5 .2	6 21.9	5 20.2	6 2.2	28 36.6	5 31.3
19	9 55 55.4	0 ♓ 23.3	0 27.6	23 5.2	14 47.2	19 48.2	4 50.6	6 35.4	5 26.8	6 5.5	28 38.6	5 31.9
20	9 59 51.9	1 23.8	0 24.4	5 ♌ .8	16 23.1	21 3.2	4 40.2	6 48.9	5 33.5	6 8.7	28 40.6	5 32.5
21	10 3 48.5	2 24.2	0 21.2	16 52.2	17 59.8	22 18.2	4 29.0	7 2.4	5 40.2	6 12.0	28 42.5	5 33.0
22	10 7 45.0	3 24.7	0 18.1	28 41.6	19 37.5	23 33.2	4 17.1	7 15.8	5 46.9	6 15.2	28 44.5	5 33.6
23	10 11 41.6	4 25.0	0 14.9	10 ♍ 30.8	21 16.1	24 48.2	4 4.4	7 29.2	5 53.7	6 18.4	28 46.4	5 34.0
24	10 15 38.1	5 25.4	0 11.7	22 21.8	22 55.6	26 3.2	3 51.0	7 42.6	6 .5	6 21.6	28 48.3	5 34.5
25	10 19 34.7	6 25.7	0 8.5	4 ♎ 16.8	24 36.2	27 18.2	3 36.8	7 55.9	6 7.3	6 24.8	28 50.2	5 34.9
26	10 23 31.2	7 26.1	0 5.3	16 18.2	26 17.7	28 33.1	3 21.9	8 9.1	6 14.2	6 27.9	28 52.1	5 35.3
27	10 27 27.8	8 26.3	0 2.2	28 29.0	28 .2	29 48.1	3 6.3	8 22.3	6 21.1	6 31.0	28 54.0	5 35.6
28	10 31 24.3	9 26.6	29 ♍ 59.0	10 ♏ 52.4	29 43.8	1 ♓ 3.1	2 50.0	8 35.5	6 28.1	6 34.1	28 55.8	5 35.9

LATITUDE

DAY	EPHEM. SID. TIME	☉	☊	☽	☿	♀	♂	♃	♄	♅	♆	♇
1	8 44 57.4	0 .0	0 .0	3 N 37.1	0 S 1.7	0 S 31.4	3 N 20.0	0 S 22.7	2 S 15.5	0 S 34.2	0 N 25.3	12 N 30.9
4	8 56 47.1	0 .0	0 .0	5 8.2	0 26.4	0 38.1	3 24.0	0 23.0	2 15.0	0 34.2	0 25.2	12 31.8
7	9 8 36.7	0 .0	0 .0	3 58.1	0 48.8	0 44.6	3 27.9	0 23.3	2 14.6	0 34.2	0 25.2	12 32.8
10	9 20 26.4	0 .0	0 .0	0 24.2	1 8.9	0 50.7	3 31.6	0 23.6	2 14.2	0 34.3	0 25.2	12 33.8
13	9 32 16.0	0 .0	0 .0	3 S 13.7	1 26.3	0 56.4	3 35.1	0 24.0	2 13.8	0 34.3	0 25.2	12 34.8
16	9 44 5.7	0 .0	0 .0	5 5.1	1 41.1	1 1.7	3 38.4	0 24.3	2 13.4	0 34.4	0 25.2	12 35.8
19	9 55 55.4	0 .0	0 .0	4 45.9	1 52.9	1 6.5	3 41.3	0 24.6	2 13.1	0 34.4	0 25.2	12 36.9
22	10 7 45.0	0 .0	0 .0	2 37.9	2 1.6	1 10.8	3 43.8	0 25.0	2 12.8	0 34.5	0 25.2	12 37.9
25	10 19 34.7	0 .0	0 .0	0 N 30.6	2 6.9	1 14.7	3 45.8	0 25.4	2 12.5	0 34.5	0 25.2	12 39.0
28	10 31 24.3	0 .0	0 .0	3 32.5	2 8.5	1 18.0	3 47.3	0 25.7	2 12.3	0 34.6	0 25.1	12 40.1

RIGHT ASCENSION

DAY	EPHEM. SID. TIME	☉	☊	☽	☿	♀	♂	♃	♄	♅	♆	♇
1	8 44 57.4	14 ♒ 37.9	1 ♎ 17.8	12 ♏ 55.0	20 ♑ 19.5	29 ♑ 26.5	6 ♎ 36.9	4 ♒ 48.3	4 ♈ 12.3	7 ♒ 33.9	0 ♒ .5	5 ♐ 34.4
2	8 48 53.9	15 39.0	1 14.9	26 3.2	21 43.4	0 ♒ 45.9	6 40.4	5 2.9	4 17.4	7 37.5	0 2.8	5 35.6
3	8 52 50.5	16 39.9	1 12.0	9 ♐ 55.8	23 8.7	2 5.0	6 43.3	5 17.4	4 22.5	7 41.1	0 5.1	5 36.8
4	8 56 47.1	17 40.6	1 9.0	24 31.3	24 35.3	3 24.0	6 45.5	5 31.9	4 27.8	7 44.7	0 7.4	5 38.0
5	9 0 43.6	18 41.1	1 6.1	9 ♑ 40.8	26 3.0	4 42.7	6 47.1	5 46.4	4 33.0	7 48.3	0 9.7	5 39.1
6	9 4 40.2	19 41.4	1 3.2	25 8.8	27 31.7	6 1.1	6 48.0	6 .9	4 38.4	7 51.8	0 12.0	5 40.2
7	9 8 36.7	20 41.5	1 .3	10 ♒ 37.1	29 1.4	7 19.2	6 48.1	6 15.3	4 43.8	7 55.4	0 14.3	5 41.2
8	9 12 33.3	21 41.4	0 57.4	25 50.4	0 ♒ 32.0	8 37.1	6 R 47.6	6 29.7	4 49.2	7 58.9	0 16.5	5 42.3
9	9 16 29.8	22 41.1	0 54.5	10 ♓ 39.5	2 3.4	9 54.7	6 46.4	6 44.0	4 54.8	8 2.5	0 18.8	5 43.3
10	9 20 26.4	23 40.6	0 51.6	25 2.0	3 35.5	11 12.0	6 44.4	6 58.3	5 .3	8 6.0	0 21.0	5 44.2
11	9 24 22.9	24 40.0	0 48.6	9 ♈ .9	5 8.3	12 29.0	6 41.8	7 12.6	5 5.9	8 9.5	0 23.2	5 45.1
12	9 28 19.5	25 39.1	0 45.7	22 41.6	6 41.7	13 45.8	6 38.4	7 26.8	5 11.6	8 13.0	0 25.4	5 46.0
13	9 32 16.0	26 38.0	0 42.8	6 ♉ 9.7	8 15.7	15 2.2	6 34.3	7 41.0	5 17.3	8 16.5	0 27.6	5 46.9
14	9 36 12.6	27 36.7	0 39.9	19 29.5	9 50.2	16 18.3	6 29.5	7 55.1	5 23.1	8 20.0	0 29.8	5 47.7
15	9 40 9.1	28 35.3	0 37.0	2 ♊ 43.1	11 25.3	17 34.2	6 23.9	8 9.2	5 28.9	8 23.4	0 31.9	5 48.5
16	9 44 5.7	29 33.6	0 34.1	15 50.2	13 .8	18 49.8	6 17.7	8 23.3	5 34.9	8 26.9	0 34.1	5 49.4
17	9 48 2.3	0 ♓ 31.8	0 31.1	28 48.4	14 36.7	20 5.0	6 10.7	8 37.4	5 40.8	8 30.3	0 36.3	5 50.1
18	9 51 58.8	1 29.8	0 28.2	11 ♋ 34.4	16 13.1	21 20.0	6 2.9	8 51.3	5 46.7	8 33.7	0 38.4	5 50.8
19	9 55 55.4	2 27.6	0 25.3	24 5.1	17 49.8	22 34.6	5 54.5	9 5.2	5 52.7	8 37.1	0 40.5	5 51.5
20	9 59 51.9	3 25.3	0 22.4	6 ♌ 18.5	19 26.9	23 49.0	5 45.3	9 19.1	5 58.8	8 40.5	0 42.5	5 52.1
21	10 3 48.5	4 22.7	0 19.5	18 14.5	21 4.4	25 3.1	5 35.4	9 32.9	6 4.9	8 43.8	0 44.6	5 52.7
22	10 7 45.0	5 20.0	0 16.6	29 54.8	22 42.2	26 16.9	5 24.7	9 46.7	6 11.0	8 47.1	0 46.6	5 53.3
23	10 11 41.6	6 17.2	0 13.7	11 ♍ 23.3	24 20.3	27 30.4	5 13.4	10 .4	6 17.2	8 50.4	0 48.7	5 53.8
24	10 15 38.1	7 14.2	0 10.7	22 45.4	25 58.8	28 43.6	5 1.3	10 14.0	6 23.4	8 53.7	0 50.7	5 54.3
25	10 19 34.7	8 11.1	0 7.8	4 ♎ 7.8	27 37.7	29 56.6	4 48.6	10 27.6	6 29.7	8 56.9	0 52.6	5 54.8
26	10 23 31.2	9 7.8	0 4.9	15 38.2	29 16.8	1 ♓ 9.2	4 35.2	10 41.2	6 35.9	9 .2	0 54.6	5 55.2
27	10 27 27.8	10 4.3	0 2.0	27 24.5	0 ♓ 56.3	2 21.7	4 21.1	10 54.7	6 42.3	9 3.4	0 56.6	5 55.6
28	10 31 24.3	11 .8	29 ♍ 59.1	9 ♏ 34.6	2 36.2	3 33.8	4 6.3	11 8.1	6 48.6	9 6.6	0 58.5	5 55.9

DECLINATION

DAY	EPHEM. SID. TIME	☉	☊	☽	☿	♀	♂	♃	♄	♅	♆	♇
1	8 44 57.4	17 S 8.7	0 S .6	12 S 39.8	22 S 9.1	21 S 13.0	0 N 46.2	19 S 58.9	0 S 38.4	19 S 33.1	20 S 8.8	8 S 50.9
4	8 56 47.1	16 16.3	0 .5	18 12.0	21 57.6	20 32.8	0 46.8	19 49.5	0 31.2	19 30.6	20 7.5	8 50.6
7	9 8 36.7	15 21.4	0 .5	14 6.4	21 35.4	19 47.2	0 49.9	19 40.1	0 23.8	19 28.1	20 6.2	8 50.1
10	9 20 26.4	14 24.1	0 .4	1 42.6	21 1.9	18 56.4	0 55.6	19 30.5	0 16.2	19 25.6	20 4.9	8 49.6
13	9 32 16.0	13 24.6	0 .3	10 N 56.4	20 16.9	18 .7	1 3.8	19 20.9	0 8.4	19 23.1	20 3.7	8 49.1
16	9 44 5.7	12 23.2	0 .3	17 41.3	19 20.3	17 .3	1 14.5	19 11.1	0 .5	19 20.6	20 2.4	8 48.4
19	9 55 55.4	11 20.1	0 .2	16 45.7	18 11.7	15 55.6	1 27.7	19 1.3	0 N 7.6	19 18.2	20 1.2	8 47.7
22	10 7 45.0	10 15.3	0 .1	9 27.5	16 51.2	14 46.9	1 43.3	18 51.4	0 15.8	19 15.9	19 60.0	8 47.0
25	10 19 34.7	9 9.1	0 .1	1 S 14.0	15 18.7	13 34.6	2 1.1	18 41.5	0 24.2	19 13.5	19 58.8	8 46.1
28	10 31 24.3	8 1.7	0 .0	11 43.1	13 34.3	12 18.9	2 21.0	18 31.6	0 32.6	19 11.2	19 57.7	8 45.3

MARCH 1997

DAY	EPHEM. SID. TIME	☉	☊	☽	☿	♀	♂	♃	♄	♅	♆	♇
	h m s	° ′	° ′	° ′	° ′	° ′	° ′	° ′	° ′	° ′	° ′	° ′
		LONGITUDE										
1	10 35 20.9	10♓26.8	29♍55.8	23♏32.1	1♓28.3	2♓18.0	2♎33.1	8♒48.6	6♈35.1	6♒37.2	28♑57.7	5♐36.2
2	10 39 17.4	11 27.0	29 52.6	6♐31.4	3 13.9	3 32.9	2 R 15.5	9 1.6	6 42.1	6 40.3	28 59.5	5 36.5
3	10 43 14.0	12 27.2	29 49.5	19 53.7	5 .6	4 47.9	1 57.2	9 14.6	6 49.2	6 43.3	29 1.3	5 36.7
4	10 47 10.5	13 27.4	29 46.3	3♑41.0	6 48.3	6 2.8	1 38.4	9 27.6	6 56.3	6 46.3	29 3.0	5 36.8
5	10 51 7.1	14 27.5	29 43.1	17 53.9	8 37.1	7 17.7	1 19.0	9 40.4	7 3.4	6 49.2	29 4.8	5 37.0
6	10 55 3.6	15 27.6	29 39.9	2♒30.3	10 26.9	8 32.6	0 59.0	9 53.3	7 10.6	6 52.2	29 6.5	5 37.1
7	10 59 .2	16 27.7	29 36.7	17 25.7	12 17.9	9 47.5	0 38.5	10 6.0	7 17.8	6 55.1	29 8.2	5 37.1
8	11 2 56.8	17 27.8	29 33.6	2♓32.9	14 9.8	11 2.3	0 17.5	10 18.7	7 25.0	6 58.0	29 9.8	5 37.2
9	11 6 53.3	18 27.8	29 30.4	17 43.0	16 2.9	12 17.3	29♍56.2	10 31.4	7 32.3	7 .9	29 11.5	5 37.2
10	11 10 49.9	19 27.8	29 27.2	2♈46.2	17 57.0	13 32.1	29 34.3	10 44.0	7 39.5	7 3.7	29 13.1	5 37.2
11	11 14 46.4	20 27.8	29 24.0	17 34.0	19 52.0	14 46.9	29 12.2	10 56.5	7 46.8	7 6.5	29 14.7	5 R 37.1
12	11 18 43.0	21 27.7	29 20.9	1♉59.8	21 48.0	16 1.8	28 49.7	11 8.9	7 54.1	7 9.3	29 16.3	5 37.0
13	11 22 39.5	22 27.6	29 17.7	15 59.7	23 44.9	17 16.6	28 26.9	11 21.3	8 1.5	7 12.0	29 17.9	5 36.8
14	11 26 36.1	23 27.4	29 14.5	29 32.6	25 42.5	18 31.4	28 3.8	11 33.5	8 8.8	7 14.7	29 19.4	5 36.7
15	11 30 32.6	24 27.2	29 11.3	12♊39.5	27 40.9	19 46.1	27 40.6	11 45.8	8 16.2	7 17.4	29 20.9	5 36.5
16	11 34 29.2	25 27.0	29 8.1	25 23.2	29 39.8	21 .9	27 17.3	11 57.9	8 23.6	7 20.0	29 22.3	5 36.2
17	11 38 25.7	26 26.7	29 5.0	7♋47.4	1♈39.2	22 15.6	26 53.8	12 10.0	8 31.0	7 22.6	29 23.8	5 35.9
18	11 42 22.3	27 26.4	29 1.8	19 56.4	3 38.9	23 30.4	26 30.3	12 22.0	8 38.4	7 25.1	29 25.2	5 35.6
19	11 46 18.8	28 26.1	28 58.6	1♌54.5	5 38.5	24 45.1	26 6.7	12 33.9	8 45.9	7 27.7	29 26.6	5 35.3
20	11 50 15.4	29 25.7	28 55.4	13 45.9	7 38.0	25 59.8	25 43.2	12 45.7	8 53.3	7 30.2	29 28.0	5 34.9
21	11 54 11.9	0♈25.3	28 52.2	25 34.2	9 37.1	27 14.4	25 19.8	12 57.5	9 .8	7 32.6	29 29.3	5 34.5
22	11 58 8.5	1 24.9	28 49.1	7♍22.9	11 35.3	28 29.1	24 56.5	13 9.1	9 8.3	7 35.0	29 30.6	5 34.0
23	12 2 5.0	2 24.4	28 45.9	19 14.6	13 32.5	29 43.7	24 33.3	13 20.7	9 15.7	7 37.4	29 31.9	5 33.5
24	12 6 1.6	3 23.9	28 42.7	1♎11.9	15 28.2	0♈58.4	24 10.4	13 32.2	9 23.2	7 39.7	29 33.1	5 33.0
25	12 9 58.1	4 23.3	28 39.5	13 16.7	17 22.0	2 13.0	23 47.6	13 43.6	9 30.7	7 42.0	29 34.3	5 32.5
26	12 13 54.7	5 22.7	28 36.4	25 30.8	19 13.5	3 27.6	23 25.2	13 54.9	9 38.2	7 44.3	29 35.5	5 31.9
27	12 17 51.2	6 22.1	28 33.2	7♏55.7	21 2.3	4 42.2	23 3.1	14 6.2	9 45.7	7 46.5	29 36.7	5 31.3
28	12 21 47.8	7 21.4	28 30.0	20 33.1	22 48.0	5 56.7	22 41.4	14 17.3	9 53.3	7 48.7	29 37.8	5 30.7
29	12 25 44.3	8 20.8	28 26.8	3♐24.5	24 30.2	7 11.3	22 20.0	14 28.4	10 .8	7 50.9	29 38.9	5 30.0
30	12 29 40.9	9 20.1	28 23.6	16 31.6	26 8.5	8 25.9	21 59.2	14 39.4	10 8.4	7 53.0	29 40.1	5 29.4
31	12 33 37.4	10 19.4	28 20.5	29 55.6	27 42.4	9 40.4	21 38.7	14 50.2	10 15.9	7 55.1	29 41.1	5 28.6
		LATITUDE										
1	10 35 20.9	0 .0	0 .0	4 N 18.8	2 S 8.2	1 S 19.0	3 N 47.6	0 S 25.9	2 S 12.2	0 S 34.6	0 N 25.1	12 N 40.4
4	10 47 10.5	0 .0	0 .0	5 15.6	2 4.6	1 21.6	3 48.2	0 26.3	2 12.0	0 34.7	0 25.1	12 41.5
7	10 59 .2	0 .0	0 .0	3 29.6	1 56.7	1 23.6	3 48.1	0 26.7	2 11.8	0 34.7	0 25.1	12 42.5
10	11 10 49.9	0 .0	0 .0	0 S 22.6	1 44.1	1 25.1	3 47.2	0 27.1	2 11.6	0 34.8	0 25.1	12 43.6
13	11 22 39.5	0 .0	0 .0	3 53.8	1 26.7	1 26.0	3 45.5	0 27.5	2 11.5	0 34.9	0 25.1	12 44.6
16	11 34 29.2	0 .0	0 .0	5 17.4	1 4.2	1 26.3	3 42.9	0 27.9	2 11.4	0 35.0	0 25.1	12 45.6
19	11 46 18.8	0 .0	0 .0	4 26.4	0 36.9	1 26.1	3 39.5	0 28.4	2 11.3	0 35.0	0 25.1	12 46.6
22	11 58 8.5	0 .0	0 .0	1 56.1	0 5.3	1 25.3	3 35.3	0 28.8	2 11.2	0 35.1	0 25.2	12 47.6
25	12 9 58.1	0 .0	0 .0	1 N 19.9	0 N 29.5	1 23.9	3 30.4	0 29.3	2 11.2	0 35.2	0 25.2	12 48.5
28	12 21 47.8	0 .0	0 .0	4 9.7	1 5.8	1 21.9	3 24.8	0 29.8	2 11.2	0 35.3	0 25.2	12 49.4
31	12 33 37.4	0 .0	0 .0	5 17.0	1 41.1	1 19.4	3 18.6	0 30.3	2 11.2	0 35.4	0 25.2	12 50.3
		RIGHT ASCENSION										
1	10 35 20.9	11♓57.1	29♍56.2	22♏15.6	4♓16.4	4♓45.7	3♎50.9	11♒21.5	6♈55.0	9♒9.7	1♒.4	5♐56.3
2	10 39 17.4	12 53.3	29 53.2	5♐32.1	5 57.0	5 57.4	3 R 34.9	11 34.8	7 1.4	9 12.8	1 2.3	5 56.6
3	10 43 14.0	13 49.3	29 50.3	19 25.4	7 37.9	7 8.8	3 18.3	11 48.0	7 7.9	9 15.9	1 4.1	5 56.8
4	10 47 10.5	14 45.3	29 47.4	3♑51.6	9 19.3	8 20.0	3 1.1	12 1.2	7 14.4	9 19.0	1 5.9	5 57.1
5	10 51 7.1	15 41.1	29 44.5	18 42.1	11 1.0	9 30.9	2 43.3	12 14.3	7 20.9	9 22.1	1 7.8	5 57.2
6	10 55 3.6	16 36.9	29 41.6	3♒44.8	12 43.1	10 41.7	2 25.0	12 27.3	7 27.5	9 25.1	1 9.5	5 57.4
7	10 59 .2	17 32.5	29 38.7	18 47.3	14 25.7	11 52.2	2 6.1	12 40.3	7 34.0	9 28.1	1 11.3	5 57.5
8	11 2 56.8	18 28.1	29 35.7	3♓40.1	16 8.7	13 2.6	1 46.8	12 53.2	7 40.6	9 31.0	1 13.0	5 57.6
9	11 6 53.3	19 23.6	29 32.8	18 18.4	17 52.1	14 12.7	1 27.1	13 6.1	7 47.3	9 34.0	1 14.8	5 57.7
10	11 10 49.9	20 18.9	29 29.9	2♈41.4	19 36.0	15 22.7	1 7.0	13 18.8	7 54.0	9 36.9	1 16.5	5 57.7
11	11 14 46.4	21 14.2	29 27.0	16 51.2	21 20.2	16 32.4	0 46.4	13 31.5	8 .7	9 39.8	1 18.2	5 57.7
12	11 18 43.0	22 9.4	29 24.1	0♉50.4	23 4.9	17 42.0	0 25.5	13 44.1	8 7.4	9 42.6	1 19.8	5 57.7
13	11 22 39.5	23 4.5	29 21.2	14 40.8	24 50.0	18 51.5	0 4.4	13 56.6	8 14.1	9 45.4	1 21.4	5 R 57.6
14	11 26 36.1	23 59.6	29 18.3	28 22.4	26 35.4	20 .7	29♍42.9	14 9.1	8 20.8	9 48.2	1 23.0	5 57.5
15	11 30 32.6	24 54.5	29 15.3	11♊53.2	28 21.1	21 9.9	29 21.3	14 21.5	8 27.6	9 50.9	1 24.5	5 57.3
16	11 34 29.2	25 49.4	29 12.4	25 10.0	0♈7.1	22 18.9	28 59.5	14 33.7	8 34.4	9 53.6	1 26.1	5 57.1
17	11 38 25.7	26 44.3	29 9.5	8♋9.5	1 53.2	23 27.7	28 37.5	14 45.9	8 41.1	9 56.3	1 27.6	5 56.9
18	11 42 22.3	27 39.1	29 6.6	20 49.1	3 39.3	24 36.5	28 15.4	14 58.0	8 48.0	9 58.9	1 29.0	5 56.7
19	11 46 18.8	28 33.8	29 3.7	3♌8.1	5 25.4	25 45.1	27 53.3	15 10.1	8 54.8	10 1.5	1 30.5	5 56.4
20	11 50 15.4	29 28.5	29 .8	15 7.5	7 11.2	26 53.7	27 31.2	15 22.0	9 1.6	10 4.0	1 31.9	5 56.1
21	11 54 11.9	0♈23.2	28 57.8	26 50.4	8 56.6	28 2.1	27 9.1	15 33.9	9 8.5	10 6.5	1 33.3	5 55.7
22	11 58 8.5	1 17.9	28 54.9	8♍21.3	10 41.4	29 10.5	26 47.1	15 45.6	9 15.3	10 9.0	1 34.6	5 55.3
23	12 2 5.0	2 12.5	28 52.0	19 46.1	12 25.3	0♈18.9	26 25.2	15 57.3	9 22.2	10 11.4	1 36.0	5 54.9
24	12 6 1.6	3 7.1	28 49.1	1♎11.4	14 8.0	1 27.1	26 3.4	16 8.9	9 29.1	10 13.8	1 37.3	5 54.5
25	12 9 58.1	4 1.6	28 46.2	12 44.2	15 49.2	2 35.4	25 41.8	16 20.4	9 36.0	10 16.2	1 38.5	5 54.0
26	12 13 54.7	4 56.2	28 43.3	24 31.5	17 28.6	3 43.6	25 20.4	16 31.8	9 42.9	10 18.5	1 39.8	5 53.5
27	12 17 51.2	5 50.8	28 40.3	6♏40.0	19 5.9	4 51.7	24 59.3	16 43.1	9 49.8	10 20.8	1 41.0	5 53.0
28	12 21 47.8	6 45.4	28 37.4	19 15.1	20 40.7	5 59.9	24 38.5	16 54.3	9 56.7	10 23.0	1 42.2	5 52.4
29	12 25 44.3	7 40.0	28 34.5	2♐19.9	22 12.6	7 8.1	24 18.0	17 5.4	10 3.6	10 25.2	1 43.3	5 51.8
30	12 29 40.9	8 34.6	28 31.6	15 54.5	23 41.4	8 16.3	23 58.0	17 16.4	10 10.6	10 27.4	1 44.5	5 51.2
31	12 33 37.4	9 29.2	28 28.7	29 55.4	25 6.5	9 24.5	23 38.3	17 27.3	10 17.5	10 29.6	1 45.6	5 50.6
		DECLINATION										
1	10 35 20.9	7 S 39.0	0 .0	14 S 28.5	12 S 56.8	11 S 53.0	2 N 28.0	18 S 28.3	0 N 35.4	19 S 10.5	19 S 57.3	8 S 45.0
4	10 47 10.5	6 30.2	0 N .1	18 7.7	10 56.5	10 33.4	2 50.3	18 18.4	0 44.0	19 8.3	19 56.2	8 44.0
7	10 59 .2	5 20.5	0 .2	12 16.8	8 44.6	9 11.3	3 14.0	18 8.4	0 52.7	19 6.1	19 55.2	8 43.0
10	11 10 49.9	4 10.3	0 .2	0 N 45.4	6 21.6	7 46.9	3 38.6	17 58.5	1 1.4	19 4.0	19 54.1	8 42.0
13	11 22 39.5	2 59.5	0 .3	12 53.4	3 48.6	6 20.8	4 3.9	17 48.7	1 10.2	19 2.0	19 53.2	8 40.9
16	11 34 29.2	1 48.5	0 .4	18 4.2	1 7.0	4 53.0	4 29.2	17 39.0	1 19.0	19 .0	19 52.2	8 39.8
19	11 46 18.8	0 37.3	0 .4	15 24.2	1 N 40.6	3 24.1	4 54.1	17 29.3	1 27.8	18 58.1	19 51.3	8 38.7
22	11 58 8.5	0 N 33.7	0 .5	7 .1	4 30.1	1 54.4	5 18.2	17 19.7	1 36.6	18 56.3	19 50.5	8 37.5
25	12 9 58.1	1 44.6	0 .6	4 S .9	7 16.4	0 24.1	5 41.0	17 10.3	1 45.5	18 54.6	19 49.7	8 36.4
28	12 21 47.8	2 55.2	0 .6	13 52.3	9 53.1	1 N 6.4	6 2.1	17 1.0	1 54.3	18 53.0	19 49.0	8 35.2
31	12 33 37.4	4 5.2	0 .7	18 9.2	12 13.8	2 36.9	6 21.2	16 51.9	2 3.1	18 51.4	19 48.3	8 34.0

APRIL 1997

LONGITUDE

DAY	EPHEM. SID. TIME	☉	☊	☾	☿	♀	♂	♃	♄	♅	♆	♇
	h m s	° ′	° ′	° ′	° ′	° ′	° ′	° ′	° ′	° ′	° ′	° ′
1	12 37 34.0	11♈18.6	28♍17.3	13♑37.7	29♈11.6	10♈54.9	21♍18.8	15♒ 1.0	10♈23.4	7♒57.1	29♑42.1	5♐27.9
2	12 41 30.5	12 17.8	28 14.1	27 38.3	0♉35.7	12 9.4	20R59.4	15 11.7	10 30.9	7 59.1	29 43.1	5R27.1
3	12 45 27.1	13 17.0	28 10.9	11♒56.5	1 54.6	13 23.9	20 40.5	15 22.2	10 38.4	8 1.0	29 44.0	5 26.3
4	12 49 23.6	14 16.1	28 7.8	26 30.0	3 7.9	14 38.3	20 22.3	15 32.7	10 46.0	8 2.9	29 45.0	5 25.4
5	12 53 20.2	15 15.2	28 4.6	11♓14.8	4 15.3	15 52.8	20 4.6	15 43.0	10 53.5	8 4.8	29 45.9	5 24.6
6	12 57 16.8	16 14.3	28 1.4	26 5.0	5 16.7	17 7.2	19 47.6	15 53.3	11 1.0	8 6.6	29 46.7	5 23.7
7	13 1 13.3	17 13.3	27 58.2	10♈53.7	6 11.9	18 21.6	19 31.3	16 3.4	11 8.5	8 8.3	29 47.5	5 22.7
8	13 5 9.9	18 12.3	27 55.0	25 33.3	7 .7	19 36.0	19 15.7	16 13.5	11 16.0	8 10.0	29 48.3	5 21.8
9	13 9 6.4	19 11.3	27 51.9	9♉57.0	7 43.1	20 50.4	19 .8	16 23.4	11 23.5	8 11.7	29 49.1	5 20.8
10	13 13 3.0	20 10.3	27 48.7	23 59.6	8 18.9	22 4.8	18 46.6	16 33.2	11 30.9	8 13.3	29 49.8	5 19.8
11	13 16 59.5	21 9.2	27 45.5	7♊37.8	8 48.1	23 19.1	18 33.2	16 42.9	11 38.4	8 14.9	29 50.5	5 18.7
12	13 20 56.1	22 8.1	27 42.3	20 50.7	9 10.7	24 33.5	18 20.5	16 52.4	11 45.9	8 16.5	29 51.2	5 17.7
13	13 24 52.6	23 6.9	27 39.2	3♋39.7	9 26.7	25 47.8	18 8.6	17 1.9	11 53.3	8 18.0	29 51.8	5 16.6
14	13 28 49.2	24 5.7	27 36.0	16 7.5	9 36.2	27 2.1	17 57.5	17 11.2	12 .7	8 19.4	29 52.4	5 15.5
15	13 32 45.7	25 4.4	27 32.8	28 18.2	9 39.3	28 16.3	17 47.2	17 20.4	12 8.1	8 20.8	29 53.0	5 14.3
16	13 36 42.3	26 3.2	27 29.6	10♌16.5	9R36.2	29 30.6	17 37.6	17 29.5	12 15.5	8 22.2	29 53.5	5 13.2
17	13 40 38.8	27 1.9	27 26.4	22 7.3	9 27.2	0♉44.8	17 28.9	17 38.5	12 22.9	8 23.5	29 54.0	5 12.0
18	13 44 35.4	28 .5	27 23.3	3♍55.4	9 12.5	1 59.0	17 20.9	17 47.4	12 30.3	8 24.7	29 54.5	5 10.8
19	13 48 31.9	28 59.1	27 20.1	15 45.3	8 52.6	3 13.2	17 13.7	17 56.1	12 37.6	8 25.9	29 54.9	5 9.6
20	13 52 28.5	29 57.7	27 16.9	27 41.2	8 28.0	4 27.4	17 7.4	18 4.7	12 44.9	8 27.1	29 55.4	5 8.4
21	13 56 25.0	0♉56.3	27 13.7	9♎46.1	7 59.0	5 41.6	17 1.8	18 13.2	12 52.2	8 28.2	29 55.8	5 7.1
22	14 0 21.6	1 54.8	27 10.5	22 2.6	7 26.3	6 55.7	16 57.0	18 21.5	12 59.5	8 29.3	29 56.1	5 5.8
23	14 4 18.1	2 53.3	27 7.4	4♏32.5	6 50.7	8 9.8	16 53.0	18 29.7	13 6.8	8 30.3	29 56.4	5 4.5
24	14 8 14.7	3 51.7	27 4.2	17 16.5	6 12.7	9 23.9	16 49.7	18 37.8	13 14.0	8 31.3	29 56.7	5 3.1
25	14 12 11.3	4 50.1	27 1.0	0♐14.8	5 33.1	10 38.0	16 47.2	18 45.7	13 21.2	8 32.2	29 56.9	5 1.8
26	14 16 7.8	5 48.5	26 57.8	13 26.8	4 52.6	11 52.1	16 45.5	18 53.5	13 28.3	8 33.1	29 57.1	5 .4
27	14 20 4.4	6 46.9	26 54.7	26 51.9	4 12.1	13 6.1	16 44.5	19 1.1	13 35.5	8 33.9	29 57.3	4 59.0
28	14 24 .9	7 45.2	26 51.5	10♑28.9	3 32.2	14 20.1	16 44.3	19 8.6	13 42.6	8 34.7	29 57.4	4 57.6
29	14 27 57.5	8 43.5	26 48.3	24 17.0	2 53.5	15 34.1	16D44.8	19 16.0	13 49.7	8 35.4	29 57.5	4 56.2
30	14 31 54.0	9 41.8	26 45.1	8♒15.2	2 16.9	16 48.1	16 46.1	19 23.2	13 56.7	8 36.1	29 57.6	4 54.8

LATITUDE

DAY	EPHEM. SID. TIME	☉	☊	☾	☿	♀	♂	♃	♄	♅	♆	♇
1	12 37 34.0	0 .0	0 .0	5N 6.4	1N52.3	1S18.5	3N16.4	0S30.4	2S11.2	0S35.4	0N25.2	12N50.6
4	12 49 23.6	0 .0	0 .0	2 49.2	2 22.6	1 15.3	3 9.5	0 30.9	2 11.3	0 35.5	0 25.2	12 51.4
7	13 1 13.3	0 .0	0 .0	1S 6.8	2 46.2	1 11.6	3 2.2	0 31.5	2 11.4	0 35.6	0 25.2	12 52.2
10	13 13 3.0	0 .0	0 .0	4 19.7	3 1.1	1 7.4	2 54.6	0 32.0	2 11.5	0 35.7	0 25.2	12 52.9
13	13 24 52.6	0 .0	0 .0	5 13.7	3 5.4	1 2.7	2 46.8	0 32.6	2 11.7	0 35.8	0 25.2	12 53.6
16	13 36 42.3	0 .0	0 .0	3 55.0	2 57.4	0 57.7	2 38.9	0 33.1	2 11.9	0 35.9	0 25.2	12 54.3
19	13 48 31.9	0 .0	0 .0	1 9.7	2 36.6	0 52.2	2 31.0	0 33.7	2 12.1	0 36.0	0 25.2	12 54.8
22	14 0 21.6	0 .0	0 .0	2N 5.0	2 3.5	0 46.4	2 23.0	0 34.3	2 12.3	0 36.2	0 25.2	12 55.4
25	14 12 11.3	0 .0	0 .0	4 34.6	1 20.2	0 40.2	2 15.2	0 34.9	2 12.6	0 36.3	0 25.3	12 55.8
28	14 24 .9	0 .0	0 .0	5 3.3	0 30.4	0 33.7	2 7.5	0 35.5	2 12.8	0 36.4	0 25.3	12 56.3

RIGHT ASCENSION

DAY	EPHEM. SID. TIME	☉	☊	☾	☿	♀	♂	♃	♄	♅	♆	♇
1	12 37 34.0	10♈23.9	28♍25.8	14♑15.5	26♈27.7	10♈32.8	23♍19.0	17♒38.1	10♈24.5	10♒31.6	1♒46.6	5♐49.9
2	12 41 30.5	11 18.5	28 22.8	28 46.0	27 44.6	11 41.1	23R .2	17 48.8	10 31.4	10 33.7	1 47.6	5R49.2
3	12 45 27.1	12 13.3	28 19.9	13♒18.0	28 57.0	12 49.4	22 41.9	17 59.4	10 38.3	10 35.7	1 48.6	5 48.4
4	12 49 23.6	13 8.0	28 17.0	27 45.5	0♉ 4.5	13 57.8	22 24.1	18 9.9	10 45.2	10 37.6	1 49.6	5 47.6
5	12 53 20.2	14 2.8	28 14.1	12♓ 5.5	1 7.0	15 6.3	22 6.8	18 20.3	10 52.2	10 39.5	1 50.5	5 46.8
6	12 57 16.8	14 57.7	28 11.2	26 18.6	2 4.1	16 14.9	21 50.2	18 30.5	10 59.1	10 41.3	1 51.4	5 46.0
7	13 1 13.3	15 52.6	28 8.3	10♈27.1	2 55.6	17 23.6	21 34.1	18 40.7	11 6.0	10 43.2	1 52.2	5 45.1
8	13 5 9.9	16 47.5	28 5.3	24 33.8	3 41.5	18 32.3	21 18.7	18 50.7	11 12.9	10 44.9	1 53.1	5 44.2
9	13 9 6.4	17 42.5	28 2.4	8♉39.6	4 21.5	19 41.2	21 3.9	19 .6	11 19.8	10 46.6	1 53.9	5 43.3
10	13 13 3.0	18 37.6	27 59.5	22 43.3	4 55.5	20 50.2	20 49.8	19 10.5	11 26.8	10 48.3	1 54.6	5 42.4
11	13 16 59.5	19 32.7	27 56.6	6♊40.4	5 23.4	21 59.3	20 36.3	19 20.1	11 33.6	10 49.9	1 55.3	5 41.4
12	13 20 56.1	20 27.9	27 53.7	20 24.8	5 45.3	23 8.6	20 23.6	19 29.7	11 40.5	10 51.5	1 56.0	5 40.4
13	13 24 52.6	21 23.2	27 50.8	3♋50.2	6 1.1	24 18.0	20 11.5	19 39.2	11 47.4	10 53.0	1 56.7	5 39.4
14	13 28 49.2	22 18.5	27 47.8	16 51.8	6 11.0	25 27.6	20 .2	19 48.5	11 54.3	10 54.5	1 57.3	5 38.4
15	13 32 45.7	23 14.0	27 44.9	29 27.4	6 14.9	26 37.4	19 49.6	19 57.7	12 1.1	10 55.9	1 57.9	5 37.3
16	13 36 42.3	24 9.5	27 42.0	11♌38.0	6R13.3	27 47.3	19 39.7	20 6.7	12 7.9	10 57.3	1 58.4	5 36.2
17	13 40 38.8	25 5.1	27 39.1	23 27.4	6 6.2	28 57.4	19 30.5	20 15.7	12 14.8	10 58.7	1 59.0	5 35.1
18	13 44 35.4	26 .8	27 36.2	5♍ 1.1	5 54.0	0♉ 7.7	19 22.1	20 24.5	12 21.6	10 60.0	1 59.5	5 34.0
19	13 48 31.9	26 56.6	27 33.3	16 26.2	5 37.1	1 18.2	19 14.4	20 33.2	12 28.4	11 1.2	1 59.9	5 32.8
20	13 52 28.5	27 52.5	27 30.3	27 50.7	5 16.1	2 28.9	19 7.5	20 41.8	12 35.2	11 2.4	2 .4	5 31.7
21	13 56 25.0	28 48.5	27 27.4	9♎22.6	4 51.3	3 39.8	19 1.2	20 50.3	12 41.9	11 3.6	2 .8	5 30.5
22	14 0 21.6	29 44.6	27 24.5	21 9.7	4 23.4	4 51.0	18 55.7	20 58.5	12 48.7	11 4.7	2 1.1	5 29.2
23	14 4 18.1	0♉40.8	27 21.6	3♏19.3	3 53.1	6 2.3	18 51.0	21 6.7	12 55.4	11 5.7	2 1.4	5 28.0
24	14 8 14.7	1 37.1	27 18.7	15 56.7	3 20.9	7 14.0	18 46.9	21 14.7	13 2.1	11 6.7	2 1.7	5 26.7
25	14 12 11.3	2 33.5	27 15.8	29 4.5	2 47.6	8 25.8	18 43.6	21 22.6	13 8.7	11 7.7	2 2.0	5 25.4
26	14 16 7.8	3 30.1	27 12.8	12♐41.6	2 13.8	9 37.9	18 40.9	21 30.4	13 15.4	11 8.6	2 2.2	5 24.1
27	14 20 4.4	4 26.8	27 9.9	26 42.7	1 40.3	10 50.3	18 39.0	21 38.0	13 22.0	11 9.4	2 2.3	5 22.8
28	14 24 .9	5 23.6	27 7.0	10♑59.0	1 7.6	12 2.9	18 37.8	21 45.5	13 28.6	11 10.2	2 2.5	5 21.5
29	14 27 57.5	6 20.5	27 4.1	25 20.1	0 36.4	13 15.7	18 37.3	21 52.8	13 35.2	11 11.0	2 2.6	5 20.1
30	14 31 54.0	7 17.6	27 1.2	9♒37.0	0 7.2	14 28.9	18D37.5	21 60.0	13 41.8	11 11.7	2 2.7	5 18.7

DECLINATION

DAY	EPHEM. SID. TIME	☉	☊	☾	☿	♀	♂	♃	♄	♅	♆	♇
1	12 37 34.0	4N28.4	0N .7	17S39.5	12N56.1	3N 6.9	6N27.1	16S48.9	2N 6.1	18S50.9	19S48.1	8S33.6
4	12 49 23.6	5 37.6	0 .8	10 1.6	14 47.3	4 36.7	6 43.0	16 40.0	2 14.8	18 49.5	19 47.5	8 32.4
7	13 1 13.3	6 45.8	0 .8	3N17.2	16 11.9	6 5.6	6 56.4	16 31.4	2 23.5	18 48.2	19 46.9	8 31.1
10	13 13 3.0	7 53.0	0 .9	14 34.3	17 7.9	7 33.4	7 7.0	16 23.0	2 32.2	18 47.0	19 46.4	8 29.9
13	13 24 52.6	8 59.0	0 1.0	18 9.6	17 33.9	8 59.6	7 14.7	16 14.8	2 40.7	18 45.9	19 46.0	8 28.7
16	13 36 42.3	10 3.6	0 1.0	13 53.5	17 29.4	10 23.9	7 19.6	16 6.9	2 49.2	18 44.9	19 45.6	8 27.5
19	13 48 31.9	11 6.8	0 1.1	4 32.7	16 55.7	11 46.1	7 21.6	15 59.4	2 57.6	18 44.0	19 45.3	8 26.4
22	14 0 21.6	12 8.3	0 1.2	6S39.0	15 56.2	13 5.7	7 20.9	15 52.1	3 5.9	18 43.3	19 45.1	8 25.2
25	14 12 11.3	13 7.9	0 1.2	15 43.4	14 37.8	14 22.5	7 17.5	15 45.2	3 14.1	18 42.6	19 44.9	8 24.1
28	14 24 .9	14 5.7	0 1.3	17 59.0	13 10.2	15 36.1	7 11.5	15 38.6	3 22.1	18 42.1	19 44.8	8 23.0

MAY 1997

LONGITUDE

DAY	EPHEM. SID. TIME h m s	☉ ° ′	☊ ° ′	☽ ° ′	☿ ° ′	♀ ° ′	♂ ° ′	♃ ° ′	♄ ° ′	♅ ° ′	♆ ° ′	♇ ° ′
1	14 35 50.6	10♉40.0	26♍41.9	22♒22.8	1♉42.8	18♉ 2.1	16♍48.0	19♒30.3	14♈ 3.7	8♒36.7	29♑57.6	4♐53.3
2	14 39 47.1	11 38.3	26 38.8	6♓38.2	1 R 11.8	19 16.1	16 50.7	19 37.2	14 10.7	8 37.3	29 57.7	4 R 51.9
3	14 43 43.7	12 36.5	26 35.6	20 59.7	0 44.3	20 30.0	16 54.1	19 44.0	14 17.7	8 37.8	29 R 57.6	4 50.4
4	14 47 40.2	13 34.7	26 32.4	5♈24.3	0 20.7	21 44.0	16 58.2	19 50.6	14 24.6	8 38.3	29 57.6	4 48.9
5	14 51 36.8	14 32.8	26 29.2	19 48.1	0 1.2	22 57.9	17 3.1	19 57.1	14 31.5	8 38.7	29 57.5	4 47.4
6	14 55 33.3	15 31.0	26 26.1	4♉ 6.1	29♈46.2	24 11.8	17 8.5	20 3.4	14 38.3	8 39.1	29 57.4	4 45.8
7	14 59 29.9	16 29.1	26 22.9	18 13.4	29 35.6	25 25.7	17 14.7	20 9.6	14 45.1	8 39.4	29 57.2	4 44.3
8	15 3 26.5	17 27.1	26 19.7	2♊ 4.9	29 29.8	26 39.6	17 21.5	20 15.6	14 51.9	8 39.7	29 57.0	4 42.7
9	15 7 23.0	18 25.2	26 16.5	15 37.1	29 28.6	27 53.4	17 29.0	20 21.4	14 58.6	8 39.9	29 56.8	4 41.2
10	15 11 19.6	19 23.2	26 13.4	28 47.7	29 D 32.1	29 7.3	17 37.2	20 27.1	15 5.3	8 40.1	29 56.5	4 39.6
11	15 15 16.1	20 21.2	26 10.2	11♋36.7	29 40.3	0♊21.1	17 46.0	20 32.6	15 12.0	8 40.2	29 56.3	4 38.1
12	15 19 12.7	21 19.2	26 7.0	24 5.5	29 53.1	1 34.9	17 55.4	20 38.0	15 18.6	8 40.3	29 56.0	4 36.5
13	15 23 9.2	22 17.1	26 3.8	6♌17.3	0♉10.4	2 48.7	18 5.4	20 43.2	15 25.1	8 40.3	29 55.6	4 34.9
14	15 27 5.8	23 15.0	26 .6	18 16.4	0 32.1	4 2.5	18 16.0	20 48.2	15 31.6	8 40.3	29 55.3	4 33.3
15	15 31 2.3	24 12.9	25 57.5	0♍ 7.6	0 58.1	5 16.2	18 27.2	20 53.0	15 38.1	8 R 40.2	29 54.9	4 31.7
16	15 34 58.9	25 10.8	25 54.3	11 56.3	1 28.3	6 29.9	18 38.9	20 57.7	15 44.5	8 40.1	29 54.4	4 30.1
17	15 38 55.4	26 8.6	25 51.1	23 47.8	2 2.6	7 43.7	18 51.3	21 2.2	15 50.9	8 39.9	29 53.9	4 28.4
18	15 42 52.0	27 6.4	25 47.9	5♎46.9	2 40.7	8 57.3	19 4.1	21 6.6	15 57.2	8 39.7	29 53.4	4 26.8
19	15 46 48.6	28 4.1	25 44.8	17 58.1	3 22.7	10 11.0	19 17.5	21 10.7	16 3.4	8 39.5	29 52.9	4 25.2
20	15 50 45.1	29 1.8	25 41.6	0♏24.9	4 8.4	11 24.7	19 31.5	21 14.7	16 9.6	8 39.1	29 52.4	4 23.5
21	15 54 41.7	29 59.6	25 38.4	13 9.5	4 57.6	12 38.3	19 45.9	21 18.5	16 15.8	8 38.8	29 51.8	4 21.9
22	15 58 38.2	0♊57.2	25 35.2	26 12.7	5 50.3	13 51.9	20 .9	21 22.2	16 21.9	8 38.4	29 51.1	4 20.2
23	16 2 34.8	1 54.9	25 32.0	9♐33.9	6 46.3	15 5.5	20 16.4	21 25.6	16 27.9	8 37.9	29 50.5	4 18.6
24	16 6 31.3	2 52.5	25 28.9	23 11.0	7 45.6	16 19.1	20 32.3	21 28.9	16 33.9	8 37.4	29 49.8	4 17.0
25	16 10 27.9	3 50.2	25 25.7	7♑ .9	8 48.0	17 32.6	20 48.7	21 32.0	16 39.9	8 36.8	29 49.1	4 15.3
26	16 14 24.4	4 47.8	25 22.5	20 60.0	9 53.4	18 46.2	21 5.6	21 35.0	16 45.7	8 36.2	29 48.4	4 13.7
27	16 18 21.0	5 45.4	25 19.3	5♒ 4.8	11 1.9	19 59.7	21 23.0	21 37.7	16 51.5	8 35.6	29 47.6	4 12.0
28	16 22 17.6	6 42.9	25 16.2	19 12.5	12 13.3	21 13.2	21 40.7	21 40.3	16 57.3	8 34.9	29 46.8	4 10.4
29	16 26 14.1	7 40.5	25 13.0	3♓20.9	13 27.6	22 26.7	21 59.0	21 42.6	17 3.0	8 34.1	29 46.0	4 8.7
30	16 30 10.7	8 38.0	25 9.8	17 28.6	14 44.7	23 40.2	22 17.6	21 44.8	17 8.6	8 33.4	29 45.2	4 7.1
31	16 34 7.2	9 35.6	25 6.6	1♈34.6	16 4.5	24 53.7	22 36.7	21 46.8	17 14.2	8 32.5	29 44.3	4 5.4

LATITUDE

DAY	EPHEM. SID. TIME	☉	☊	☽	☿	♀	♂	♃	♄	♅	♆	♇
1	14 35 50.6	0 .0	0 .0	3N 1.0	0S21.0	0S27.0	1N59.9	0S36.1	2S13.2	0S36.5	0N25.3	12N56.6
4	14 47 40.2	0 .0	0 .0	0S40.2	1 10.0	0 20.1	1 52.5	0 36.7	2 13.5	0 36.6	0 25.3	12 56.9
7	14 59 29.9	0 .0	0 .0	3 57.6	1 53.1	0 13.0	1 45.3	0 37.4	2 13.9	0 36.7	0 25.3	12 57.1
10	15 11 19.6	0 .0	0 .0	5 6.9	2 28.5	0 5.8	1 38.3	0 38.1	2 14.3	0 36.8	0 25.3	12 57.3
13	15 23 9.2	0 .0	0 .0	3 58.5	2 55.5	0N 1.5	1 31.5	0 38.7	2 14.7	0 36.9	0 25.3	12 57.4
16	15 34 58.9	0 .0	0 .0	1 20.4	3 14.1	0 8.9	1 24.9	0 39.4	2 15.1	0 37.0	0 25.3	12 57.4
19	15 46 48.6	0 .0	0 .0	1N49.4	3 24.6	0 16.2	1 18.6	0 40.1	2 15.6	0 37.1	0 25.3	12 57.2
22	15 58 38.2	0 .0	0 .0	4 21.8	3 27.6	0 23.5	1 12.5	0 40.8	2 16.1	0 37.3	0 25.3	12 57.0
25	16 10 27.9	0 .0	0 .0	4 57.7	3 23.8	0 30.7	1 6.6	0 41.6	2 16.6	0 37.4	0 25.3	12 56.7
28	16 22 17.6	0 .0	0 .0	3 1.9	3 13.8	0 37.8	1 .9	0 42.3	2 17.2	0 37.5	0 25.3	12 56.4
31	16 34 7.2	0 .0	0 .0	0S30.2	2 58.1	0 44.7	0 55.4	0 43.0	2 17.7	0 37.6	0 25.3	12 56.4

RIGHT ASCENSION

DAY	EPHEM. SID. TIME	☉	☊	☽	☿	♀	♂	♃	♄	♅	♆	♇
1	14 35 50.6	8♉14.8	26♍58.3	23♒44.3	29♈40.5	15♉42.3	18♍38.3	22♒ 7.0	13♈48.3	11♒12.3	2♒ 2.7	5♐17.3
2	14 39 47.1	9 12.2	26 55.3	7♓40.6	29 R 16.8	16 56.0	18 39.8	22 13.9	13 54.8	11 12.9	2 2.7	5 R 15.9
3	14 43 43.7	10 9.7	26 52.4	21 28.7	28 56.3	18 10.0	18 42.0	22 20.7	14 1.2	11 13.4	2 2.7	5 14.5
4	14 47 40.2	11 7.3	26 49.5	5♈13.6	28 39.4	19 24.2	18 44.9	22 27.3	14 7.7	11 13.9	2 R 2.6	5 13.1
5	14 51 36.8	12 5.1	26 46.6	19 .6	28 26.2	20 38.8	18 48.4	22 33.7	14 14.1	11 14.4	2 2.5	5 11.6
6	14 55 33.3	13 3.0	26 43.7	2♉53.6	28 17.0	21 53.6	18 52.5	22 40.0	14 20.4	11 14.8	2 2.4	5 10.1
7	14 59 29.9	14 1.1	26 40.8	16 53.5	28 11.8	23 8.7	18 57.3	22 46.1	14 26.8	11 15.1	2 2.3	5 8.7
8	15 3 26.5	14 59.3	26 37.8	0♊56.9	28 10.8	24 24.1	19 2.7	22 52.1	14 33.1	11 15.4	2 2.1	5 7.2
9	15 7 23.0	15 57.7	26 34.9	14 56.8	28 D 13.9	25 39.7	19 8.7	22 57.9	14 39.3	11 15.6	2 1.8	5 5.7
10	15 11 19.6	16 56.2	26 32.0	28 44.1	28 21.1	26 55.7	19 15.3	23 3.6	14 45.6	11 15.8	2 1.6	5 4.1
11	15 15 16.1	17 54.8	26 29.1	12♋10.2	28 32.4	28 11.9	19 22.6	23 9.1	14 51.8	11 16.0	2 1.3	5 2.7
12	15 19 12.7	18 53.6	26 26.2	25 9.1	28 47.7	29 28.4	19 30.4	23 14.4	14 58.0	11 16.1	2 1.0	5 1.1
13	15 23 9.2	19 52.5	26 23.3	7♌38.9	29 6.9	0♊45.1	19 38.8	23 19.6	15 4.1	11 16.1	2 .6	4 59.6
14	15 27 5.8	20 51.5	26 20.3	19 41.8	29 30.0	2 2.1	19 47.7	23 24.6	15 10.1	11 16.1	2 .2	4 58.0
15	15 31 2.3	21 50.7	26 17.4	1♍22.9	29 56.8	3 19.4	19 57.2	23 29.4	15 16.2	11 16.1	1 59.8	4 56.5
16	15 34 58.9	22 50.1	26 14.5	12 49.8	0♉27.3	4 36.9	20 7.2	23 34.1	15 22.1	11 R 15.9	1 59.4	4 54.9
17	15 38 55.4	23 49.5	26 11.6	24 11.3	1 1.3	5 54.7	20 17.8	23 38.6	15 28.1	11 15.8	1 58.9	4 53.3
18	15 42 52.0	24 49.1	26 8.7	5♎36.9	1 38.8	7 12.7	20 28.8	23 42.9	15 34.0	11 15.6	1 58.3	4 51.7
19	15 46 48.6	25 48.8	26 5.7	17 16.1	2 19.7	8 30.9	20 40.4	23 47.1	15 39.8	11 15.3	1 57.8	4 50.1
20	15 50 45.1	26 48.7	26 2.8	29 18.1	3 3.9	9 49.4	20 52.5	23 51.1	15 45.6	11 15.0	1 57.2	4 48.5
21	15 54 41.7	27 48.7	25 59.9	11♏50.3	3 51.2	11 8.0	21 5.0	23 54.9	15 51.4	11 14.6	1 56.6	4 46.9
22	15 58 38.2	28 48.8	25 57.0	24 57.2	4 41.7	12 26.9	21 18.0	23 58.6	15 57.1	11 14.2	1 56.0	4 45.3
23	16 2 34.8	29 49.1	25 54.1	8♐39.2	5 35.3	13 46.0	21 31.5	24 2.0	16 2.8	11 13.8	1 55.3	4 43.7
24	16 6 31.3	0♊49.5	25 51.2	22 50.9	6 31.8	15 5.2	21 45.4	24 5.3	16 8.4	11 13.2	1 54.6	4 42.1
25	16 10 27.9	1 50.0	25 48.2	7♑21.7	7 31.4	16 24.7	21 59.8	24 8.5	16 14.0	11 12.7	1 53.8	4 40.5
26	16 14 24.4	2 50.6	25 45.3	21 58.0	8 33.8	17 44.3	22 14.6	24 11.4	16 19.5	11 12.1	1 53.1	4 38.9
27	16 18 21.0	3 51.4	25 42.4	6♒26.9	9 39.2	19 4.0	22 29.8	24 14.2	16 24.9	11 11.4	1 52.3	4 37.3
28	16 22 17.6	4 52.3	25 39.5	20 39.8	10 47.4	20 24.0	22 45.5	24 16.8	16 30.3	11 10.7	1 51.5	4 35.7
29	16 26 14.1	5 53.3	25 36.6	4♓33.8	11 58.5	21 44.0	23 1.6	24 19.2	16 35.7	11 10.0	1 50.6	4 34.1
30	16 30 10.7	6 54.4	25 33.6	18 11.5	13 12.5	23 4.1	23 18.0	24 21.4	16 41.0	11 9.2	1 49.7	4 32.4
31	16 34 7.2	7 55.7	25 30.7	1♈38.8	14 29.3	24 24.4	23 34.9	24 23.4	16 46.2	11 8.3	1 48.8	4 30.8

DECLINATION

DAY	EPHEM. SID. TIME	☉	☊	☽	☿	♀	♂	♃	♄	♅	♆	♇
1	14 35 50.6	15N 1.4	0N 1.4	11S11.8	11N44.4	16N46.2	7N 3.1	15S32.4	3N30.0	18S41.6	19S44.7	8S21.9
4	14 47 40.2	15 54.8	0 1.4	1N31.9	10 30.0	17 52.4	6 52.3	15 26.6	3 37.7	18 41.3	19 44.7	8 20.9
7	14 59 29.9	16 45.9	0 1.5	13 26.8	9 33.8	18 54.4	6 39.2	15 21.2	3 45.3	18 41.1	19 44.8	8 19.9
10	15 11 19.6	17 34.4	0 1.6	18 19.0	8 59.4	19 51.9	6 24.0	15 16.3	3 52.7	18 41.1	19 44.9	8 19.0
13	15 23 9.2	18 20.4	0 1.6	14 50.8	8 47.4	20 44.7	6 6.7	15 11.8	3 59.9	18 41.1	19 45.1	8 18.1
16	15 34 58.9	19 3.5	0 1.7	5 50.6	8 56.9	21 32.3	5 47.5	15 7.8	4 6.9	18 41.3	19 45.3	8 17.3
19	15 46 48.6	19 43.7	0 1.8	5S21.7	9 25.9	22 14.5	5 26.6	15 4.3	4 13.8	18 41.5	19 45.7	8 16.5
22	15 58 38.2	20 20.9	0 1.8	15 3.5	10 12.0	22 51.1	5 3.9	15 1.3	4 20.4	18 41.9	19 46.0	8 15.8
25	16 10 27.9	20 54.9	0 1.9	18 17.8	11 12.7	23 21.8	4 39.7	14 58.8	4 26.8	18 42.4	19 46.4	8 15.2
28	16 22 17.6	21 25.7	0 2.0	12 10.7	12 25.6	23 46.5	4 13.9	14 56.9	4 32.9	18 43.0	19 46.9	8 14.6
31	16 34 7.2	21 53.2	0 2.0	0N 9.9	13 48.2	24 5.0	3 46.8	14 55.4	4 38.8	18 43.8	19 47.5	8 14.1

JUNE 1997

LONGITUDE

DAY	EPHEM. SID. TIME h m s	☉ ° ′	☊ ° ′	☽ ° ′	☿ ° ′	♀ ° ′	♂ ° ′	♃ ° ′	♄ ° ′	♅ ° ′	♆ ° ′	♇ ° ′
1	16 38 3.8	10♊33.1	25♍ 3.5	15♈37.9	17♉27.1	26♊ 7.2	22♍56.3	21♒48.7	17♈19.8	8♒31.7	29♑43.4	4♐ 3.8
2	16 42 .3	11 30.6	25 .3	29 36.9	18 52.4	27 20.6	23 16.2	21 50.3	17 25.2	8 R 30.8	29 R 42.5	4 R 2.2
3	16 45 56.9	12 28.1	24 57.1	13♉29.3	20 20.4	28 34.1	23 36.5	21 51.7	17 30.6	8 29.8	29 41.5	4 .6
4	16 49 53.5	13 25.6	24 53.9	27 12.5	21 51.0	29 47.5	23 57.3	21 53.0	17 35.9	8 28.8	29 40.6	3 58.9
5	16 53 50.0	14 23.1	24 50.7	10♊43.4	23 24.2	1♋ .9	24 18.4	21 54.0	17 41.2	8 27.7	29 39.6	3 57.3
6	16 57 46.6	15 20.5	24 47.6	23 59.2	25 .0	2 14.3	24 39.9	21 54.9	17 46.4	8 26.6	29 38.5	3 55.7
7	17 1 43.1	16 18.0	24 44.4	6♋58.1	26 38.5	3 27.6	25 1.8	21 55.6	17 51.5	8 25.5	29 37.5	3 54.1
8	17 5 39.7	17 15.4	24 41.2	19 39.3	28 19.5	4 41.0	25 24.0	21 56.0	17 56.5	8 24.3	29 36.4	3 52.5
9	17 9 36.2	18 12.8	24 38.0	2♌ 3.5	0♊ 3.1	5 54.3	25 46.6	21 56.3	18 1.5	8 23.1	29 35.3	3 50.9
10	17 13 32.8	19 10.2	24 34.9	14 12.7	1 49.3	7 7.6	26 9.6	21 56.4	18 6.4	8 21.8	29 34.2	3 49.4
11	17 17 29.4	20 7.5	24 31.7	26 10.5	3 38.0	8 20.9	26 32.9	21 R 56.3	18 11.2	8 20.5	29 33.0	3 47.8
12	17 21 25.9	21 4.9	24 28.5	8♍ 1.0	5 29.1	9 34.2	26 56.5	21 56.0	18 15.9	8 19.1	29 31.9	3 46.2
13	17 25 22.5	22 2.2	24 25.3	19 49.4	7 22.7	10 47.5	27 20.5	21 55.5	18 20.6	8 17.7	29 30.7	3 44.7
14	17 29 19.0	22 59.5	24 22.2	1♎41.0	9 18.7	12 .7	27 44.8	21 54.9	18 25.2	8 16.3	29 29.5	3 43.1
15	17 33 15.6	23 56.8	24 19.0	13 41.4	11 17.0	13 13.9	28 9.4	21 54.0	18 29.7	8 14.8	29 28.2	3 41.6
16	17 37 12.1	24 54.1	24 15.8	25 55.6	13 17.5	14 27.1	28 34.3	21 52.9	18 34.1	8 13.3	29 27.0	3 40.1
17	17 41 8.7	25 51.4	24 12.6	8♏28.1	15 20.0	15 40.3	28 59.6	21 51.7	18 38.5	8 11.8	29 25.7	3 38.6
18	17 45 5.3	26 48.7	24 9.4	21 22.2	17 24.4	16 53.5	29 25.1	21 50.3	18 42.8	8 10.2	29 24.4	3 37.1
19	17 49 1.8	27 45.9	24 6.3	4♐39.4	19 30.5	18 6.6	29 50.9	21 48.6	18 47.0	8 8.6	29 23.1	3 35.7
20	17 52 58.4	28 43.1	24 3.1	18 19.3	21 38.2	19 19.7	0♎17.0	21 46.8	18 51.1	8 6.9	29 21.8	3 34.2
21	17 56 54.9	29 40.4	23 59.9	2♑19.2	23 47.1	20 32.8	0 43.4	21 44.8	18 55.2	8 5.3	29 20.4	3 32.8
22	18 0 51.5	0♋37.6	23 56.7	16 34.5	25 57.1	21 45.9	1 10.1	21 42.7	18 59.2	8 3.6	29 19.1	3 31.4
23	18 4 48.0	1 34.9	23 53.6	0♒59.4	28 7.9	22 59.0	1 37.0	21 40.3	19 3.0	8 1.8	29 17.8	3 30.0
24	18 8 44.6	2 32.1	23 50.4	15 27.7	0♋19.1	24 12.0	2 4.2	21 37.8	19 6.8	8 .1	29 16.4	3 28.6
25	18 12 41.2	3 29.3	23 47.2	29 54.1	2 30.5	25 25.0	2 31.7	21 35.0	19 10.5	7 58.2	29 14.9	3 27.2
26	18 16 37.7	4 26.5	23 44.0	14♓14.5	4 41.8	26 38.0	2 59.4	21 32.1	19 14.1	7 56.4	29 13.5	3 25.9
27	18 20 34.3	5 23.7	23 40.9	28 26.2	6 52.8	27 51.0	3 27.3	21 29.0	19 17.7	7 54.5	29 12.1	3 24.6
28	18 24 30.8	6 20.9	23 37.7	12♈28.2	9 3.2	29 3.9	3 55.5	21 25.7	19 21.1	7 52.6	29 10.6	3 23.2
29	18 28 27.4	7 18.1	23 34.5	26 19.8	11 12.8	0♌16.9	4 24.0	21 22.3	19 24.5	7 50.7	29 9.1	3 21.9
30	18 32 23.9	8 15.4	23 31.3	10♉ 1.1	13 21.3	1 29.8	4 52.7	21 18.6	19 27.8	7 48.7	29 7.7	3 20.7

LATITUDE

DAY	EPHEM. SID. TIME	☉	☊	☽	☿	♀	♂	♃	♄	♅	♆	♇
1	16 38 3.8	0 .0	0 .0	1 S 42.8	2 S 51.7	0 N 46.9	0 N 53.6	0 S 43.3	2 S 17.9	0 S 37.6	0 N 25.3	12 N 56.3
4	16 49 53.5	0 .0	0 .0	4 25.5	2 29.4	0 53.5	0 48.4	0 44.0	2 18.5	0 37.7	0 25.3	12 55.8
7	17 1 43.1	0 .0	0 .0	4 54.5	2 3.0	0 59.7	0 43.3	0 44.8	2 19.1	0 37.8	0 25.3	12 55.3
10	17 13 32.8	0 .0	0 .0	3 15.9	1 33.1	1 5.7	0 38.4	0 45.5	2 19.8	0 37.9	0 25.3	12 54.8
13	17 25 22.5	0 .0	0 .0	0 24.4	1 .7	1 11.2	0 33.8	0 46.3	2 20.4	0 38.0	0 25.3	12 54.1
16	17 37 12.1	0 .0	0 .0	2 N 38.7	0 27.1	1 16.4	0 29.2	0 47.0	2 21.1	0 38.1	0 25.3	12 53.4
19	17 49 1.8	0 .0	0 .0	4 44.2	0 N 6.1	1 21.1	0 24.9	0 47.8	2 21.8	0 38.2	0 25.3	12 52.7
22	18 0 51.5	0 .0	0 .0	4 37.1	0 37.2	1 25.3	0 20.6	0 48.5	2 22.5	0 38.2	0 25.3	12 51.9
25	18 12 41.2	0 .0	0 .0	1 59.6	1 4.4	1 29.0	0 16.5	0 49.3	2 23.3	0 38.3	0 25.3	12 51.0
28	18 24 30.8	0 .0	0 .0	1 S 41.0	1 26.1	1 32.1	0 12.6	0 50.0	2 24.0	0 38.4	0 25.3	12 50.0

RIGHT ASCENSION

DAY	EPHEM. SID. TIME	☉	☊	☽	☿	♀	♂	♃	♄	♅	♆	♇
1	16 38 3.8	8♊57.1	25♍27.8	15♈ 3.6	15♉49.1	25♊44.8	23♍52.2	24♒25.3	16♈51.5	11♒ 7.5	1♒47.9	4♐29.3
2	16 42 .3	9 58.5	25 24.9	28 32.7	17 11.8	27 5.2	24 9.8	24 27.0	16 56.6	11 R 6.6	1 R 47.0	4 R 27.7
3	16 45 56.9	11 .1	25 22.0	12♉10.8	18 37.4	28 25.7	24 27.8	24 28.5	17 1.6	11 5.6	1 46.0	4 26.1
4	16 49 53.5	12 1.7	25 19.1	25 58.3	20 6.0	29 46.3	24 46.2	24 29.8	17 6.7	11 4.6	1 45.0	4 24.5
5	16 53 50.0	13 3.5	25 16.1	9♊51.2	21 37.7	1♋ 6.8	25 4.9	24 30.9	17 11.6	11 3.5	1 43.9	4 22.9
6	16 57 46.6	14 5.3	25 13.2	23 41.4	23 12.4	2 27.4	25 24.0	24 31.8	17 16.5	11 2.4	1 42.9	4 21.3
7	17 1 43.1	15 7.2	25 10.3	7♋19.0	24 50.2	3 48.0	25 43.5	24 32.6	17 21.3	11 1.2	1 41.8	4 19.7
8	17 5 39.7	16 9.2	25 7.4	20 34.9	26 31.2	5 8.5	26 3.2	24 33.1	17 26.1	11 .0	1 40.6	4 18.1
9	17 9 36.2	17 11.2	25 4.5	3♌23.1	28 15.4	6 29.0	26 23.4	24 33.5	17 30.7	10 58.8	1 39.5	4 16.5
10	17 13 32.8	18 13.3	25 1.5	15 42.4	0♊ 2.9	7 49.5	26 43.8	24 33.7	17 35.4	10 57.5	1 38.3	4 15.0
11	17 17 29.4	19 15.4	24 58.6	27 35.5	1 53.7	9 9.9	27 4.6	24 33.7	17 39.9	10 56.2	1 37.1	4 13.4
12	17 21 25.9	20 17.6	24 55.7	9♍ 8.3	3 47.8	10 30.2	27 25.7	24 R 33.5	17 44.4	10 54.8	1 35.9	4 11.9
13	17 25 22.5	21 19.9	24 52.8	20 29.3	5 45.1	11 50.5	27 47.1	24 33.1	17 48.8	10 53.4	1 34.7	4 10.3
14	17 29 19.0	22 22.1	24 49.9	1♎48.0	7 45.8	13 10.6	28 8.7	24 32.5	17 53.2	10 51.9	1 33.4	4 8.8
15	17 33 15.6	23 24.4	24 47.0	13 14.9	9 49.6	14 30.5	28 30.7	24 31.7	17 57.5	10 50.4	1 32.1	4 7.3
16	17 37 12.1	24 26.8	24 44.0	25 .4	11 56.6	15 50.4	28 53.0	24 30.8	18 1.7	10 48.9	1 30.8	4 5.8
17	17 41 8.7	25 29.1	24 41.1	7♏14.5	14 6.6	17 10.1	29 15.6	24 29.6	18 5.8	10 47.4	1 29.5	4 4.3
18	17 45 5.3	26 31.5	24 38.2	20 4.9	16 19.4	18 29.6	29 38.4	24 28.3	18 9.9	10 45.8	1 28.2	4 2.8
19	17 49 1.8	27 33.9	24 35.3	3♐35.8	18 34.8	19 48.9	0♎ 1.5	24 26.8	18 13.9	10 44.1	1 26.8	4 1.3
20	17 52 58.4	28 36.2	24 32.4	17 45.7	20 52.6	21 8.1	0 24.9	24 25.1	18 17.8	10 42.4	1 25.4	3 59.9
21	17 56 54.9	29 38.6	24 29.4	2♑26.2	23 12.5	22 27.0	0 48.6	24 23.3	18 21.6	10 40.7	1 24.0	3 58.4
22	18 0 51.5	0♋41.0	24 26.5	17 22.7	25 34.1	23 45.7	1 12.5	24 21.2	18 25.4	10 39.0	1 22.7	3 57.0
23	18 4 48.0	1 43.4	24 23.6	2♒18.5	27 57.1	25 4.2	1 36.7	24 19.0	18 29.1	10 37.2	1 21.2	3 55.6
24	18 8 44.6	2 45.7	24 20.7	16 59.3	0♋20.9	26 22.5	2 1.1	24 16.6	18 32.7	10 35.4	1 19.8	3 54.2
25	18 12 41.2	3 48.1	24 17.8	1♓17.1	2 45.3	27 40.5	2 25.7	24 14.0	18 36.3	10 33.6	1 18.3	3 52.9
26	18 16 37.7	4 50.4	24 14.8	15 11.0	5 9.9	28 58.2	2 50.6	24 11.2	18 39.7	10 31.7	1 16.8	3 51.5
27	18 20 34.3	5 52.6	24 11.9	28 45.3	7 34.1	0♌15.7	3 15.8	24 8.2	18 43.1	10 29.8	1 15.3	3 50.1
28	18 24 30.8	6 54.9	24 9.0	12♈ 7.6	9 57.6	1 32.9	3 41.2	24 5.1	18 46.4	10 27.9	1 13.8	3 48.8
29	18 28 27.4	7 57.1	24 6.1	25 26.1	12 20.0	2 49.8	4 6.8	24 1.8	18 49.6	10 25.9	1 12.3	3 47.5
30	18 32 23.9	8 59.2	24 3.2	8♉47.8	14 41.0	4 6.4	4 32.6	23 58.3	18 52.8	10 23.9	1 10.8	3 46.2

DECLINATION

DAY	EPHEM. SID. TIME	☉	☊	☽	☿	♀	♂	♃	♄	♅	♆	♇
1	16 38 3.8	22 N 1.6	0 N 2.1	4 N 34.3	14 N 17.5	24 N 9.7	3 N 37.4	14 S 55.1	4 N 40.8	18 S 44.0	19 S 47.6	8 S 13.9
4	16 49 53.5	22 24.5	0 2.1	15 13.4	15 49.2	24 19.7	3 8.5	14 54.4	4 46.4	18 44.9	19 48.2	8 13.5
7	17 1 43.1	22 43.9	0 2.2	18 21.1	17 24.5	24 23.2	2 38.3	14 54.2	4 51.7	18 45.8	19 48.9	8 13.2
10	17 13 32.8	22 59.7	0 2.3	13 26.2	19 .2	24 20.3	2 6.9	14 54.7	4 56.7	18 46.9	19 49.6	8 12.9
13	17 25 22.5	23 11.9	0 2.3	3 39.4	20 32.5	24 10.9	1 34.4	14 55.7	5 1.5	18 48.0	19 50.3	8 12.7
16	17 37 12.1	23 20.3	0 2.4	7 S 32.9	21 56.6	23 55.1	1 .9	14 57.2	5 6.0	18 49.3	19 51.1	8 12.6
19	17 49 1.8	23 25.1	0 2.5	16 24.5	23 7.4	23 33.1	0 26.4	14 59.3	5 10.2	18 50.6	19 51.9	8 12.6
22	18 0 51.5	23 26.1	0 2.5	17 49.5	23 59.7	23 4.9	0 S 9.0	15 2.0	5 14.2	18 51.9	19 52.7	8 12.6
25	18 12 41.2	23 23.5	0 2.6	9 38.3	24 29.2	22 30.7	0 45.1	15 5.2	5 17.8	18 53.4	19 53.6	8 12.8
28	18 24 30.8	23 17.1	0 2.6	3 N 22.6	24 33.5	21 50.7	1 22.1	15 8.9	5 21.1	18 54.9	19 54.5	8 13.0

JULY 1997

DAY	EPHEM. SID. TIME	☉	☊	☽	☿	♀	♂	♃	♄	♅	♆	♇
	h m s	° ′	° ′	° ′	° ′	° ′	° ′	° ′	° ′	° ′	° ′	° ′
		LONGITUDE										
1	18 36 20.5	9♋12.6	23♍28.2	23♉31.9	15♋28.6	2♌42.7	5♎21.7	21♒14.8	19♈30.9	7♒46.7	29♑ 6.2	3♐19.4
2	18 40 17.1	10 9.8	23 25.0	6♊51.6	17 34.5	3 55.6	5 50.9	21 R 10.8	19 34.0	7 R 44.7	29 R 4.7	3 R 18.2
3	18 44 13.6	11 7.0	23 21.8	19 59.4	19 38.9	5 8.5	6 20.3	21 6.6	19 37.0	7 42.7	29 3.1	3 17.0
4	18 48 10.2	12 4.2	23 18.6	2♋54.5	21 41.6	6 21.3	6 49.9	21 2.3	19 39.9	7 40.6	29 1.6	3 15.8
5	18 52 6.7	13 1.5	23 15.4	15 36.1	23 42.6	7 34.1	7 19.8	20 57.8	19 42.7	7 38.5	29 .1	3 14.6
6	18 56 3.3	13 58.7	23 12.3	28 3.9	25 41.8	8 47.0	7 49.9	20 53.1	19 45.4	7 36.4	28 58.5	3 13.5
7	18 59 59.8	14 55.9	23 9.1	10♌18.6	27 39.2	9 59.7	8 20.3	20 48.3	19 48.1	7 34.2	28 56.9	3 12.4
8	19 3 56.4	15 53.1	23 5.9	22 21.7	29 34.7	11 12.5	8 50.8	20 43.3	19 50.6	7 32.1	28 55.4	3 11.3
9	19 7 52.9	16 50.3	23 2.7	4♍15.7	1♌28.3	12 25.2	9 21.6	20 38.2	19 53.0	7 29.9	28 53.8	3 10.2
10	19 11 49.5	17 47.6	22 59.6	16 4.1	3 19.9	13 37.9	9 52.5	20 32.9	19 55.3	7 27.7	28 52.2	3 9.1
11	19 15 46.1	18 44.8	22 56.4	27 51.3	5 9.6	14 50.6	10 23.7	20 27.5	19 57.6	7 25.5	28 50.6	3 8.1
12	19 19 42.6	19 42.0	22 53.2	9♎42.0	6 57.3	16 3.3	10 55.1	20 21.9	19 59.7	7 23.2	28 49.0	3 7.1
13	19 23 39.2	20 39.3	22 50.0	21 41.7	8 43.2	17 15.9	11 26.7	20 16.2	20 1.8	7 21.0	28 47.5	3 6.2
14	19 27 35.7	21 36.5	22 46.9	3♏55.6	10 27.0	18 28.5	11 58.4	20 10.4	20 3.8	7 18.7	28 45.9	3 5.3
15	19 31 32.3	22 33.7	22 43.7	16 28.7	12 8.9	19 41.1	12 30.4	20 4.4	20 5.6	7 16.4	28 44.2	3 4.3
16	19 35 28.8	23 30.9	22 40.5	29 25.2	13 48.9	20 53.6	13 2.5	19 58.3	20 7.3	7 14.1	28 42.6	3 3.4
17	19 39 25.4	24 28.1	22 37.3	12♐47.7	15 26.9	22 6.1	13 34.9	19 52.0	20 9.0	7 11.8	28 41.0	3 2.6
18	19 43 22.0	25 25.4	22 34.1	26 36.8	17 3.0	23 18.6	14 7.4	19 45.7	20 10.5	7 9.5	28 39.4	3 1.8
19	19 47 18.5	26 22.6	22 31.0	10♑50.5	18 37.1	24 31.1	14 40.1	19 39.2	20 12.0	7 7.2	28 37.8	3 .9
20	19 51 15.1	27 19.8	22 27.8	25 24.1	20 9.3	25 43.5	15 12.9	19 32.6	20 13.3	7 4.8	28 36.1	3 .2
21	19 55 11.6	28 17.1	22 24.6	10♒10.9	21 39.4	26 55.8	15 46.0	19 25.9	20 14.6	7 2.5	28 34.5	2 59.4
22	19 59 8.2	29 14.3	22 21.4	25 2.7	23 7.7	28 8.2	16 19.2	19 19.1	20 15.7	7 .1	28 32.9	2 58.7
23	20 3 4.7	0♌11.6	22 18.3	9♓51.7	24 33.9	29 20.5	16 52.5	19 12.2	20 16.8	6 57.7	28 31.3	2 58.0
24	20 7 1.3	1 8.9	22 15.1	24 31.3	25 58.0	0♍32.8	17 26.1	19 5.2	20 17.7	6 55.3	28 29.6	2 57.3
25	20 10 57.8	2 6.1	22 11.9	8♈56.8	27 20.2	1 45.1	17 59.8	18 58.1	20 18.6	6 53.0	28 28.0	2 56.7
26	20 14 54.4	3 3.5	22 8.7	23 5.5	28 40.2	2 57.3	18 33.7	18 50.9	20 19.3	6 50.6	28 26.4	2 56.1
27	20 18 51.0	4 .8	22 5.5	6♉56.7	29 58.1	4 9.5	19 7.7	18 43.6	20 19.9	6 48.2	28 24.8	2 55.5
28	20 22 47.5	4 58.1	22 2.4	20 30.6	1♍13.8	5 21.6	19 41.9	18 36.3	20 20.5	6 45.8	28 23.2	2 55.0
29	20 26 44.1	5 55.5	21 59.2	3♊48.1	2 27.3	6 33.8	20 16.3	18 28.9	20 20.9	6 43.4	28 21.5	2 54.5
30	20 30 40.6	6 52.9	21 56.0	16 50.6	3 38.5	7 45.9	20 50.8	18 21.4	20 21.2	6 41.0	28 19.9	2 54.0
31	20 34 37.2	7 50.2	21 52.8	29 39.2	4 47.3	8 57.9	21 25.5	18 13.9	20 21.4	6 38.6	28 18.3	2 53.5
		LATITUDE										
1	18 36 20.5	0 .0	0 .0	4 S 23.8	1 N 41.4	1 N 34.6	0 N 8.7	0 S 50.8	2 S 24.8	0 S 38.4	0 N 25.2	12 N 49.0
4	18 48 10.2	0 .0	0 .0	4 57.1	1 50.0	1 36.6	0 5.1	0 51.5	2 25.6	0 38.5	0 25.2	12 48.0
7	18 59 59.8	0 .0	0 .0	3 21.8	1 52.1	1 37.9	0 1.5	0 52.2	2 26.4	0 38.6	0 25.2	12 46.9
10	19 11 49.5	0 .0	0 .0	0 30.0	1 48.1	1 38.5	0 S 2.0	0 52.9	2 27.2	0 38.6	0 25.2	12 45.7
13	19 23 39.2	0 .0	0 .0	2 N 33.7	1 38.5	1 38.5	0 5.3	0 53.5	2 28.0	0 38.7	0 25.2	12 44.5
16	19 35 28.8	0 .0	0 .0	4 43.7	1 24.0	1 37.8	0 8.6	0 54.2	2 28.8	0 38.7	0 25.1	12 43.3
19	19 47 18.5	0 .0	0 .0	4 48.4	1 5.1	1 36.4	0 11.7	0 54.8	2 29.7	0 38.8	0 25.1	12 42.0
22	19 59 8.2	0 .0	0 .0	2 14.2	0 42.4	1 34.3	0 14.8	0 55.4	2 30.5	0 38.8	0 25.1	12 40.7
25	20 10 57.8	0 .0	0 .0	1 S 36.5	0 16.4	1 31.5	0 17.8	0 55.9	2 31.3	0 38.8	0 25.0	12 39.4
28	20 22 47.5	0 .0	0 .0	4 27.3	0 S 12.5	1 28.0	0 20.6	0 56.5	2 32.2	0 38.8	0 25.0	12 38.0
31	20 34 37.2	0 .0	0 .0	5 5.4	0 43.7	1 23.8	0 23.4	0 57.0	2 33.0	0 38.9	0 25.0	12 36.6
		RIGHT ASCENSION										
1	18 36 20.5	10♋ 1.3	24♍ .2	22♉16.6	17♋ .3	5♌22.7	4♎58.7	23♒54.6	18♈55.8	10♒21.9	1♒ 9.2	3♐44.9
2	18 40 17.1	11 3.3	23 57.3	5♊52.3	19 17.6	6 38.8	5 25.1	23 R 50.8	18 58.8	10 R 19.8	1 R 7.6	3 R 43.7
3	18 44 13.6	12 5.3	23 54.4	19 30.5	21 32.7	7 54.5	5 51.6	23 46.8	19 1.7	10 17.7	1 6.0	3 42.4
4	18 48 10.2	13 7.2	23 51.5	3♋ 3.3	23 45.4	9 9.9	6 18.4	23 42.6	19 4.5	10 15.6	1 4.5	3 41.2
5	18 52 6.7	14 9.0	23 48.5	16 21.9	25 55.6	10 25.0	6 45.4	23 38.3	19 7.2	10 13.5	1 2.8	3 40.0
6	18 56 3.3	15 10.8	23 45.6	29 18.6	28 3.0	11 39.8	7 12.6	23 33.8	19 9.8	10 11.3	1 1.2	3 38.8
7	18 59 59.8	16 12.4	23 42.7	11♌49.2	0♌ 7.7	12 54.2	7 40.1	23 29.1	19 12.3	10 9.1	0 59.6	3 37.7
8	19 3 56.4	17 13.9	23 39.8	23 53.4	2 9.6	14 8.4	8 7.7	23 24.3	19 14.8	10 6.9	0 58.0	3 36.5
9	19 7 52.9	18 15.4	23 36.9	5♍34.6	4 8.7	15 22.2	8 35.6	23 19.3	19 17.2	10 4.7	0 56.3	3 35.4
10	19 11 49.5	19 16.7	23 33.9	16 59.0	6 4.8	16 35.6	9 3.7	23 14.2	19 19.4	10 2.4	0 54.7	3 34.4
11	19 15 46.1	20 18.0	23 31.0	28 15.0	7 58.1	17 48.8	9 32.0	23 8.9	19 21.6	10 .2	0 53.0	3 33.3
12	19 19 42.6	21 19.1	23 28.1	9♎32.2	9 48.6	19 1.6	10 .5	23 3.5	19 23.7	9 57.9	0 51.4	3 32.2
13	19 23 39.2	22 20.1	23 25.2	21 .9	11 36.2	20 14.1	10 29.3	22 58.0	19 25.8	9 55.6	0 49.8	3 31.3
14	19 27 35.7	23 21.0	23 22.3	2♏51.7	13 21.0	21 26.2	10 58.2	22 52.3	19 27.7	9 53.3	0 48.1	3 30.3
15	19 31 32.3	24 21.8	23 19.3	15 14.3	15 3.0	22 38.1	11 27.3	22 46.5	19 29.5	9 51.0	0 46.4	3 29.3
16	19 35 28.8	25 22.4	23 16.4	28 16.3	16 42.2	23 49.5	11 56.6	22 40.5	19 31.2	9 48.6	0 44.7	3 28.4
17	19 39 25.4	26 22.9	23 13.5	12♐ 1.3	18 18.8	25 .7	12 26.1	22 34.5	19 32.8	9 46.3	0 43.0	3 27.5
18	19 43 22.0	27 23.2	23 10.6	26 26.8	19 52.7	26 11.5	12 55.8	22 28.2	19 34.4	9 43.9	0 41.3	3 26.6
19	19 47 18.5	28 23.4	23 7.6	11♑22.8	21 23.9	27 22.1	13 25.7	22 21.9	19 35.8	9 41.5	0 39.7	3 25.7
20	19 51 15.1	29 23.5	23 4.7	26 33.6	22 52.6	28 32.3	13 55.7	22 15.5	19 37.2	9 39.1	0 38.0	3 24.9
21	19 55 11.6	0♌23.4	23 1.8	11♒41.8	24 18.7	29 42.2	14 26.0	22 8.9	19 38.5	9 36.7	0 36.3	3 24.1
22	19 59 8.2	1 23.2	22 58.9	26 33.7	25 42.2	0♍51.8	14 56.5	22 2.3	19 39.6	9 34.3	0 34.6	3 23.3
23	20 3 4.7	2 22.9	22 55.9	11♓ 1.9	27 3.3	2 1.1	15 27.1	21 55.5	19 40.7	9 31.8	0 32.9	3 22.5
24	20 7 1.3	3 22.4	22 53.0	25 6.2	28 21.8	3 10.1	15 58.0	21 48.7	19 41.7	9 29.4	0 31.2	3 21.8
25	20 10 57.8	4 21.8	22 50.1	8♈51.1	29 37.9	4 18.9	16 29.0	21 41.7	19 42.6	9 27.0	0 29.5	3 21.1
26	20 14 54.4	5 21.0	22 47.2	22 23.6	0♍51.5	5 27.4	17 .2	21 34.7	19 43.4	9 24.5	0 27.8	3 20.5
27	20 18 51.0	6 20.1	22 44.3	5♉50.6	2 2.6	6 35.6	17 31.6	21 27.6	19 44.1	9 22.1	0 26.1	3 19.8
28	20 22 47.5	7 19.1	22 41.3	19 17.3	3 11.3	7 43.5	18 3.2	21 20.4	19 44.7	9 19.6	0 24.4	3 19.2
29	20 26 44.1	8 17.9	22 38.4	2♊45.6	4 17.4	8 51.2	18 35.0	21 13.1	19 45.2	9 17.2	0 22.8	3 18.6
30	20 30 40.6	9 16.5	22 35.5	16 14.2	5 21.0	9 58.6	19 7.0	21 5.7	19 45.6	9 14.7	0 21.1	3 18.1
31	20 34 37.2	10 15.0	22 32.6	29 38.2	6 22.1	11 5.8	19 39.1	20 58.3	19 45.9	9 12.2	0 19.4	3 17.5
		DECLINATION										
1	18 36 20.5	23 N 7.0	0 N 2.7	14 N 23.6	24 N 13.1	21 N 5.2	1 S 59.8	15 S 13.1	5 N 24.0	18 S 56.5	19 S 55.4	8 S 13.3
4	18 48 10.2	22 53.3	0 2.8	18 27.3	23 30.0	20 14.4	2 38.1	15 17.8	5 26.7	18 58.2	19 56.4	8 13.7
7	18 59 59.8	22 36.0	0 2.8	14 24.9	22 27.6	19 18.7	3 17.0	15 22.9	5 29.0	18 59.8	19 57.4	8 14.2
10	19 11 49.5	22 15.2	0 2.9	5 2.1	21 9.6	18 18.2	3 56.5	15 28.5	5 31.0	19 1.6	19 58.4	8 14.8
13	19 23 39.2	21 51.0	0 3.0	6 S 4.7	19 39.8	17 13.4	4 36.5	15 34.4	5 32.7	19 3.3	19 59.4	8 15.4
16	19 35 28.8	21 23.4	0 3.0	15 24.2	18 1.1	16 4.4	5 16.9	15 40.7	5 34.0	19 5.1	20 .4	8 16.1
19	19 47 18.5	20 52.5	0 3.1	18 12.2	16 16.6	14 51.8	5 57.6	15 47.3	5 35.0	19 6.9	20 1.4	8 17.0
22	19 59 8.2	20 18.5	0 3.2	11 3.8	14 28.5	13 35.7	6 38.7	15 54.2	5 35.6	19 8.8	20 2.4	8 17.8
25	20 10 57.8	19 41.4	0 3.2	2 N 4.1	12 39.1	12 16.5	7 20.0	16 1.3	5 35.9	19 10.6	20 3.4	8 18.8
28	20 22 47.5	19 1.3	0 3.3	13 34.6	10 50.5	10 54.5	8 1.4	16 8.6	5 35.8	19 12.4	20 4.5	8 19.9
31	20 34 37.2	18 18.4	0 3.4	18 20.8	9 4.6	9 30.1	8 43.0	16 16.0	5 35.4	19 14.3	20 5.5	8 21.0

AUGUST 1997

LONGITUDE

DAY	EPHEM. SID. TIME h m s	☉ ° ′	☊ ° ′	☽ ° ′	☿ ° ′	♀ ° ′	♂ ° ′	♃ ° ′	♄ ° ′	♅ ° ′	♆ ° ′	♇ ° ′
1	20 38 33.7	8♌47.6	21♍49.7	12♋15.0	5♍53.6	10♍10.0	22♎ .4	18♒ 6.3	20♈21.6	6♒36.2	28♑16.7	2♐53.1
2	20 42 30.3	9 45.1	21 46.5	24 39.0	6 57.4	11 22.0	22 35.4	17 R 58.6	20 21.6	6 R 33.8	28 R 15.2	2 R 52.7
3	20 46 26.8	10 42.6	21 43.3	6♌52.3	7 58.6	12 34.0	23 10.6	17 51.0	20 R 21.5	6 31.4	28 13.6	2 52.4
4	20 50 23.4	11 40.0	21 40.1	18 55.9	8 57.0	13 45.9	23 45.9	17 43.3	20 21.3	6 29.0	28 12.0	2 52.1
5	20 54 20.0	12 37.5	21 37.0	0♍51.4	9 52.4	14 57.8	24 21.3	17 35.5	20 21.0	6 26.7	28 10.5	2 51.8
6	20 58 16.5	13 35.0	21 33.8	12 41.1	10 44.9	16 9.7	24 56.9	17 27.7	20 20.6	6 24.3	28 8.9	2 51.6
7	21 2 13.1	14 32.5	21 30.6	24 27.6	11 34.2	17 21.5	25 32.7	17 19.9	20 20.1	6 21.9	28 7.4	2 51.3
8	21 6 9.6	15 30.0	21 27.4	6♎14.3	12 20.1	18 33.3	26 8.6	17 12.1	20 19.5	6 19.5	28 5.8	2 51.1
9	21 10 6.2	16 27.5	21 24.2	18 5.1	13 2.5	19 45.0	26 44.6	17 4.2	20 18.8	6 17.2	28 4.3	2 51.0
10	21 14 2.7	17 25.1	21 21.1	0♏ 4.5	13 41.3	20 56.7	27 20.8	16 56.4	20 18.0	6 14.8	28 2.8	2 50.9
11	21 17 59.3	18 22.6	21 17.9	12 17.2	14 16.1	22 8.4	27 57.1	16 48.6	20 17.1	6 12.5	28 1.3	2 50.8
12	21 21 55.8	19 20.2	21 14.7	24 48.2	14 46.9	23 20.0	28 33.6	16 40.8	20 16.1	6 10.2	27 59.8	2 50.7
13	21 25 52.4	20 17.8	21 11.5	7♐41.7	15 13.4	24 31.5	29 10.2	16 33.0	20 14.9	6 7.9	27 58.3	2 50.7
14	21 29 48.9	21 15.4	21 8.4	21 1.2	15 35.4	25 43.1	29 46.9	16 25.2	20 13.7	6 5.6	27 56.9	2 50.7
15	21 33 45.5	22 13.0	21 5.2	4♑48.6	15 52.6	26 54.5	0♏23.8	16 17.4	20 12.4	6 3.3	27 55.4	2 50.7
16	21 37 42.0	23 10.6	21 2.0	19 3.4	16 4.9	28 5.9	1 .8	16 9.7	20 11.0	6 1.1	27 54.0	2 D 50.8
17	21 41 38.6	24 8.3	20 58.8	3♒42.2	16 12.0	29 17.3	1 37.9	16 2.0	20 9.5	5 58.8	27 52.5	2 50.9
18	21 45 35.2	25 5.9	20 55.6	18 39.2	16 13.8	0♎28.6	2 15.1	15 54.3	20 7.9	5 56.6	27 51.1	2 51.0
19	21 49 31.7	26 3.6	20 52.5	3♓46.0	16 R 10.0	1 39.9	2 52.5	15 46.7	20 6.2	5 54.4	27 49.8	2 51.2
20	21 53 28.3	27 1.4	20 49.3	18 53.4	16 .6	2 51.1	3 30.0	15 39.2	20 4.4	5 52.2	27 48.4	2 51.4
21	21 57 24.8	27 59.1	20 46.1	3♈52.5	15 45.4	4 2.2	4 7.6	15 31.7	20 2.5	5 50.0	27 47.0	2 51.7
22	22 1 21.4	28 56.9	20 42.9	18 36.0	15 24.4	5 13.3	4 45.3	15 24.3	20 .5	5 47.9	27 45.7	2 51.9
23	22 5 17.9	29 54.7	20 39.8	2♉58.9	14 57.7	6 24.4	5 23.2	15 16.9	19 58.4	5 45.7	27 44.4	2 52.2
24	22 9 14.5	0♍52.5	20 36.6	16 58.8	14 25.5	7 35.4	6 1.2	15 9.7	19 56.2	5 43.7	27 43.1	2 52.6
25	22 13 11.0	1 50.4	20 33.4	0♊35.2	13 48.0	8 46.4	6 39.3	15 2.5	19 54.0	5 41.6	27 41.8	2 53.0
26	22 17 7.6	2 48.3	20 30.2	13 49.3	13 5.5	9 57.3	7 17.5	14 55.3	19 51.6	5 39.5	27 40.6	2 53.4
27	22 21 4.1	3 46.2	20 27.0	26 43.2	12 18.7	11 8.1	7 55.9	14 48.3	19 49.1	5 37.5	27 39.3	2 53.9
28	22 25 .7	4 44.1	20 23.9	9♋19.9	11 28.1	12 18.9	8 34.4	14 41.4	19 46.6	5 35.5	27 38.1	2 54.3
29	22 28 57.2	5 42.1	20 20.7	21 42.0	10 34.7	13 29.7	9 12.9	14 34.5	19 43.9	5 33.5	27 36.9	2 54.8
30	22 32 53.8	6 40.1	20 17.5	3♌52.3	9 39.2	14 40.4	9 51.7	14 27.8	19 41.2	5 31.6	27 35.7	2 55.4
31	22 36 50.3	7 38.1	20 14.3	15 53.5	8 43.0	15 51.0	10 30.5	14 21.1	19 38.4	5 29.7	27 34.6	2 55.9

LATITUDE

DAY	SID. TIME	☉	☊	☽	☿	♀	♂	♃	♄	♅	♆	♇
1	20 38 33.7	0 .0	0 .0	4 S 47.4	0 S 54.5	1 N 22.2	0 S 24.3	0 S 57.1	2 S 33.3	0 S [illegible]	0 N 24.9	12 N 36.1
4	20 50 23.4	0 .0	0 .0	2 41.4	1 28.0	1 17.1	0 27.0	0 57.6	2 34.1	0 38.9	0 24.9	12 34.7
7	21 2 13.1	0 .0	0 .0	0 N 24.2	2 2.6	1 11.3	0 29.6	0 58.0	2 34.9	0 38.9	0 24.9	12 33.2
10	21 14 2.7	0 .0	0 .0	3 22.0	2 37.4	1 4.8	0 32.1	0 58.3	2 35.7	0 38.9	0 24.8	12 31.7
13	21 25 52.4	0 .0	0 .0	5 6.8	3 11.3	0 57.7	0 34.5	0 58.7	2 36.5	0 38.9	0 24.8	12 30.3
16	21 37 42.0	0 .0	0 .0	4 34.8	3 42.8	0 50.0	0 36.9	0 59.0	2 37.3	0 38.9	0 24.7	12 28.8
19	21 49 31.7	0 .0	0 .0	1 27.4	4 9.6	0 41.7	0 39.2	0 59.2	2 38.1	0 38.8	0 24.7	12 27.3
22	22 1 21.4	0 .0	0 .0	2 S 32.5	4 29.0	0 32.8	0 41.4	0 59.4	2 38.8	0 38.8	0 24.6	12 25.8
25	22 13 11.0	0 .0	0 .0	4 58.8	4 37.1	0 23.4	0 43.5	0 59.6	2 39.5	0 38.8	0 24.5	12 24.3
28	22 25 .7	0 .0	0 .0	4 58.4	4 30.5	0 13.6	0 45.6	0 59.7	2 40.2	0 38.8	0 24.5	12 22.8
31	22 36 50.3	0 .0	0 .0	2 56.8	4 6.9	0 3.3	0 47.6	0 59.8	2 40.9	0 38.7	0 24.4	12 21.3

RIGHT ASCENSION

DAY	SID. TIME	☉	☊	☽	☿	♀	♂	♃	♄	♅	♆	♇
1	20 38 33.7	11♌13.4	22♍29.6	12♋51.2	7♍20.5	12♍12.8	20♎11.5	20♒50.8	19♈46.1	9♒ 9.8	0♒17.8	3♐17.0
2	20 42 30.3	12 11.6	22 26.7	25 46.8	8 16.3	13 19.5	20 44.1	20 R 43.3	19 46.2	9 R 7.3	0 R 16.1	3 R 16.6
3	20 46 26.8	13 9.7	22 23.8	8♌20.3	9 9.5	14 26.1	21 16.8	20 35.8	19 46.3	9 4.9	0 14.5	3 16.2
4	20 50 23.4	14 7.6	22 20.9	20 30.1	9 59.8	15 32.4	21 49.8	20 28.1	19 R 46.2	9 2.5	0 12.9	3 15.8
5	20 54 20.0	15 5.3	22 17.9	2♍17.5	10 47.2	16 38.6	22 22.9	20 20.5	19 46.0	9 .0	0 11.2	3 15.4
6	20 58 16.5	16 2.9	22 15.0	13 46.8	11 31.7	17 44.5	22 56.2	20 12.8	19 45.8	8 57.6	0 9.6	3 15.1
7	21 2 13.1	17 .4	22 12.1	25 4.4	12 13.1	18 50.2	23 29.7	20 5.1	19 45.4	8 55.2	0 8.0	3 14.8
8	21 6 9.6	17 57.7	22 9.2	6♎18.2	12 51.3	19 55.8	24 3.4	19 57.4	19 44.9	8 52.7	0 6.4	3 14.5
9	21 10 6.2	18 54.8	22 6.2	17 37.1	13 26.2	21 1.2	24 37.3	19 49.6	19 44.4	8 50.3	0 4.8	3 14.3
10	21 14 2.7	19 51.8	22 3.3	29 10.6	13 57.6	22 6.5	25 11.3	19 41.9	19 43.7	8 47.9	0 3.2	3 14.0
11	21 17 59.3	20 48.7	22 .4	11♏ 8.0	14 25.5	23 11.6	25 45.6	19 34.1	19 43.0	8 45.5	0 1.7	3 13.9
12	21 21 55.8	21 45.4	21 57.5	23 37.9	14 49.6	24 16.6	26 20.0	19 26.4	19 42.1	8 43.1	0 .1	3 13.7
13	21 25 52.4	22 41.9	21 54.5	6♐46.5	15 9.7	25 21.4	26 54.6	19 18.6	19 41.2	8 40.8	29♑58.6	3 13.6
14	21 29 48.9	23 38.4	21 51.6	20 35.9	15 25.8	26 26.1	27 29.4	19 10.9	19 40.1	8 38.4	29 57.1	3 13.5
15	21 33 45.5	24 34.6	21 48.7	5♑ 2.8	15 37.6	27 30.7	28 4.4	19 3.2	19 39.0	8 36.1	29 55.5	3 13.5
16	21 37 42.0	25 30.8	21 45.7	19 57.5	15 45.0	28 35.2	28 39.6	18 55.5	19 37.8	8 33.7	29 54.0	3 13.4
17	21 41 38.6	26 26.8	21 42.8	5♒ 5.9	15 47.9	29 39.6	29 15.0	18 47.9	19 36.5	8 31.4	29 52.6	3 13.4
18	21 45 35.2	27 22.7	21 39.9	20 13.2	15 R 46.0	0♎44.0	29 50.5	18 40.3	19 35.1	8 29.1	29 51.1	3 D 13.5
19	21 49 31.7	28 18.4	21 37.0	5♓ 8.2	15 39.3	1 48.2	0♏26.3	18 32.7	19 33.6	8 26.9	29 49.7	3 13.6
20	21 53 28.3	29 14.0	21 34.0	19 45.2	15 27.8	2 52.4	1 2.2	18 25.2	19 32.0	8 24.6	29 48.2	3 13.7
21	21 57 24.8	0♍ 9.5	21 31.1	4♈ 3.9	15 11.3	3 56.5	1 38.3	18 17.7	19 30.3	8 22.4	29 46.8	3 13.8
22	22 1 21.4	1 4.9	21 28.2	18 7.7	14 49.9	5 .6	2 14.6	18 10.3	19 28.6	8 20.2	29 45.4	3 14.0
23	22 5 17.9	2 .2	21 25.3	2♉ 1.2	14 23.8	6 4.7	2 51.1	18 3.0	19 26.7	8 18.0	29 44.1	3 14.2
24	22 9 14.5	2 55.5	21 22.3	15 48.1	13 53.0	7 8.8	3 27.8	17 55.8	19 24.8	8 15.9	29 42.8	3 14.5
25	22 13 11.0	3 50.5	21 19.4	29 30.3	13 18.0	8 12.8	4 4.7	17 48.6	19 22.8	8 13.7	29 41.4	3 14.7
26	22 17 7.6	4 45.5	21 16.5	13♊ 6.6	12 39.0	9 16.8	4 41.7	17 41.5	19 20.7	8 11.6	29 40.1	3 15.0
27	22 21 4.1	5 40.4	21 13.5	26 33.8	11 56.6	10 20.9	5 19.0	17 34.4	19 18.5	8 9.5	29 38.8	3 15.4
28	22 25 .7	6 35.2	21 10.6	9♋47.2	11 11.4	11 24.9	5 56.4	17 27.5	19 16.2	8 7.5	29 37.5	3 15.7
29	22 28 57.2	7 29.9	21 7.7	22 42.3	10 24.2	12 29.0	6 34.1	17 20.6	19 13.8	8 5.4	29 36.3	3 16.2
30	22 32 53.8	8 24.6	21 4.8	5♌16.0	9 35.8	13 33.1	7 11.9	17 13.9	19 11.4	8 3.4	29 35.1	3 16.6
31	22 36 50.3	9 19.1	21 1.8	17 27.1	8 47.2	14 37.3	7 50.0	17 7.3	19 8.8	8 1.5	29 33.9	3 17.1

DECLINATION

DAY	SID. TIME	☉	☊	☽	☿	♀	♂	♃	♄	♅	♆	♇
1	20 38 33.7	18 N 3.5	0 N 3.4	18 N 6.1	8 N 30.3	9 N 1.5	8 S 56.8	16 S 18.5	5 N 35.2	19 S 14.9	20 S 5.8	8 S 21.4
4	20 50 23.4	17 17.1	0 3.5	12 35.3	6 51.2	7 34.2	9 38.5	16 26.0	5 34.3	19 16.7	20 6.8	8 22.6
7	21 2 13.1	16 28.1	0 3.5	2 34.2	5 20.0	6 5.3	10 20.1	16 33.6	5 33.1	19 18.5	20 7.8	8 23.9
10	21 14 2.7	15 36.8	0 3.6	8 S 20.6	3 59.5	4 34.9	11 1.6	16 41.0	5 31.6	19 20.2	20 8.7	8 25.3
13	21 25 52.4	14 43.2	0 3.7	16 32.6	2 52.9	3 3.5	11 43.0	16 48.5	5 29.7	19 21.9	20 9.7	8 26.7
16	21 37 42.0	13 47.5	0 3.7	17 32.8	2 4.0	1 31.3	12 24.1	16 55.7	5 27.5	19 23.6	20 10.6	8 28.2
19	21 49 31.7	12 49.8	0 3.8	8 46.1	1 37.2	0 S 1.4	13 4.9	17 2.8	5 25.0	19 25.3	20 11.5	8 29.7
22	22 1 21.4	11 50.3	0 3.9	4 N 56.2	1 36.9	1 34.3	13 45.3	17 9.7	5 22.1	19 26.8	20 12.3	8 31.3
25	22 13 11.0	10 49.1	0 3.9	15 23.9	2 6.3	3 7.1	14 25.3	17 16.3	5 19.0	19 28.4	20 13.1	8 33.0
28	22 25 .7	9 46.4	0 4.0	18 8.8	3 5.4	4 39.5	15 4.7	17 22.7	5 15.6	19 29.8	20 13.9	8 34.7
31	22 36 50.3	8 42.3	0 4.0	13 15.4	4 29.0	6 11.2	15 43.5	17 28.6	5 11.9	19 31.2	20 14.7	8 36.5

SEPTEMBER 1997

LONGITUDE

DAY	EPHEM. SID. TIME h m s	☉ ° ′	☊ ° ′	☽ ° ′	☿ ° ′	♀ ° ′	♂ ° ′	♃ ° ′	♄ ° ′	♅ ° ′	♆ ° ′	♇ ° ′
1	22 40 46.9	8♍36.2	20♍11.2	27♌47.7	7♍47.0	17♎ 1.6	11♏ 9.4	14♒14.6	19♈35.5	5♒27.8	27♑33.5	2♐56.6
2	22 44 43.4	9 34.3	20 8.0	9♍37.3	6R52.4	18 12.1	11 48.5	14R 8.2	19R32.5	5R25.9	27R32.3	2 57.2
3	22 48 40.0	10 32.4	20 4.8	21 24.4	6 .6	19 22.6	12 27.7	14 2.0	19 29.4	5 24.1	27 31.3	2 57.9
4	22 52 36.5	11 30.5	20 1.6	3♎11.3	5 12.7	20 33.0	13 7.0	13 55.8	19 26.3	5 22.3	27 30.2	2 58.6
5	22 56 33.1	12 28.7	19 58.4	15 .5	4 29.8	21 43.3	13 46.4	13 49.8	19 23.1	5 20.5	27 29.2	2 59.3
6	23 0 29.7	13 26.9	19 55.3	26 54.9	3 53.0	22 53.6	14 25.9	13 43.9	19 19.8	5 18.8	27 28.2	3 .1
7	23 4 26.2	14 25.1	19 52.1	8♏57.8	3 23.1	24 3.8	15 5.5	13 38.2	19 16.4	5 17.1	27 27.2	3 .9
8	23 8 22.8	15 23.4	19 48.9	21 12.6	3 1.0	25 13.9	15 45.3	13 32.6	19 12.9	5 15.5	27 26.2	3 1.7
9	23 12 19.3	16 21.6	19 45.7	3♐43.2	2 47.1	26 24.0	16 25.1	13 27.2	19 9.4	5 13.8	27 25.3	3 2.6
10	23 16 15.9	17 19.9	19 42.5	16 33.3	2 42.0	27 34.0	17 5.1	13 21.9	19 5.8	5 12.3	27 24.4	3 3.5
11	23 20 12.4	18 18.3	19 39.4	29 46.4	2D46.0	28 43.9	17 45.1	13 16.8	19 2.1	5 10.7	27 23.5	3 4.4
12	23 24 9.0	19 16.6	19 36.2	13♑25.0	2 59.0	29 53.7	18 25.3	13 11.8	18 58.4	5 9.2	27 22.6	3 5.4
13	23 28 5.5	20 15.0	19 33.0	27 30.0	3 21.2	1♏ 3.5	19 5.5	13 7.0	18 54.6	5 7.7	27 21.8	3 6.4
14	23 32 2.1	21 13.4	19 29.8	12♒ .3	3 52.3	2 13.2	19 45.9	13 2.4	18 50.8	5 6.4	27 21.1	3 7.5
15	23 35 58.6	22 11.9	19 26.7	26 52.0	4 32.2	3 22.8	20 26.4	12 57.9	18 46.9	5 5.0	27 20.3	3 8.5
16	23 39 55.2	23 10.3	19 23.5	11♓58.6	5 20.3	4 32.3	21 7.0	12 53.6	18 42.9	5 3.6	27 19.6	3 9.6
17	23 43 51.7	24 8.8	19 20.3	27 11.6	6 16.3	5 41.7	21 47.6	12 49.5	18 38.8	5 2.3	27 18.8	3 10.8
18	23 47 48.3	25 7.3	19 17.1	12♈21.3	7 19.7	6 51.0	22 28.4	12 45.5	18 34.7	5 1.0	27 18.2	3 11.9
19	23 51 44.8	26 5.9	19 13.9	27 18.6	8 29.9	8 .2	23 9.2	12 41.7	18 30.6	4 59.8	27 17.5	3 13.1
20	23 55 41.4	27 4.5	19 10.8	11♉55.9	9 46.3	9 9.4	23 50.2	12 38.1	18 26.4	4 58.6	27 16.9	3 14.3
21	23 59 37.9	28 3.1	19 7.6	26 8.3	11 8.3	10 18.4	24 31.3	12 34.7	18 22.1	4 57.5	27 16.3	3 15.5
22	0 3 34.5	29 1.7	19 4.4	9♊53.6	12 35.2	11 27.4	25 12.4	12 31.4	18 17.8	4 56.4	27 15.7	3 16.8
23	0 7 31.0	0♎ .4	19 1.2	23 12.0	14 6.4	12 36.3	25 53.7	12 28.3	18 13.5	4 55.3	27 15.2	3 18.1
24	0 11 27.6	0 59.2	18 58.1	6♋ 5.8	15 41.4	13 45.1	26 35.0	12 25.5	18 9.1	4 54.3	27 14.7	3 19.4
25	0 15 24.1	1 57.9	18 54.9	18 38.4	17 19.5	14 53.7	27 16.5	12 22.8	18 4.7	4 53.3	27 14.2	3 20.8
26	0 19 20.7	2 56.8	18 51.7	0♌53.9	19 .2	16 2.3	27 58.0	12 20.3	18 .2	4 52.4	27 13.8	3 22.2
27	0 23 17.2	3 55.6	18 48.5	12 56.6	20 43.0	17 10.8	28 39.6	12 18.0	17 55.7	4 51.6	27 13.4	3 23.6
28	0 27 13.8	4 54.5	18 45.3	24 50.3	22 27.5	18 19.2	29 21.4	12 15.8	17 51.2	4 50.7	27 13.0	3 25.0
29	0 31 10.3	5 53.4	18 42.2	6♍38.9	24 13.4	19 27.5	0♐ 3.2	12 13.9	17 46.6	4 49.9	27 12.6	3 26.5
30	0 35 6.9	6 52.4	18 39.0	18 25.6	26 .1	20 35.7	0 45.1	12 12.2	17 42.0	4 49.2	27 12.3	3 28.0

LATITUDE

DAY	SID. TIME	☉	☊	☽	☿	♀	♂	♃	♄	♅	♆	♇
1	22 40 46.9	0 .0	0 .0	1S58.6	3S55.3	0S .3	0S48.2	0S59.8	2S41.1	0S38.7	0N24.4	12N20.8
4	22 52 36.5	0 .0	0 .0	1N14.3	3 10.8	0 11.1	0 50.1	0 59.9	2 41.7	0 38.7	0 24.3	12 19.3
7	23 4 26.2	0 .0	0 .0	4 1.2	2 16.3	0 22.2	0 52.0	0 59.9	2 42.3	0 38.6	0 24.3	12 17.9
10	23 16 15.9	0 .0	0 .0	5 17.6	1 18.4	0 33.7	0 53.7	0 59.9	2 42.9	0 38.6	0 24.2	12 16.4
13	23 28 5.5	0 .0	0 .0	4 11.8	0 23.5	0 45.3	0 55.4	0 59.8	2 43.4	0 38.5	0 24.1	12 15.0
16	23 39 55.2	0 .0	0 .0	0 43.1	0N24.1	0 57.1	0 57.0	0 59.7	2 43.8	0 38.5	0 24.1	12 13.6
19	23 51 44.8	0 .0	0 .0	3S14.1	1 1.8	1 9.1	0 58.6	0 59.6	2 44.2	0 38.4	0 24.0	12 12.2
22	0 3 34.5	0 .0	0 .0	5 13.1	1 28.6	1 21.0	1 .1	0 59.5	2 44.6	0 38.3	0 23.9	12 10.9
25	0 15 24.1	0 .0	0 .0	4 38.2	1 45.0	1 33.0	1 1.5	0 59.3	2 44.9	0 38.3	0 23.9	12 9.5
28	0 27 13.8	0 .0	0 .0	2 14.0	1 52.2	1 44.8	1 2.9	0 59.1	2 45.2	0 38.2	0 23.8	12 8.3

RIGHT ASCENSION

DAY	SID. TIME	☉	☊	☽	☿	♀	♂	♃	♄	♅	♆	♇
1	22 40 46.9	10♍13.6	20♍58.9	29♌17.1	7♍59.5	15♎41.5	8♏28.2	17♒ .7	19♈ 6.2	7♒59.5	29♑32.7	3♐17.5
2	22 44 43.4	11 8.0	20 56.0	10♍49.7	7R13.6	16 45.8	9 6.6	16R54.3	19R 3.5	7R57.6	29R31.5	3 18.1
3	22 48 40.0	12 2.3	20 53.0	22 10.1	6 30.7	17 50.2	9 45.3	16 48.0	19 .8	7 55.7	29 30.4	3 18.6
4	22 52 36.5	12 56.5	20 50.1	3♎25.0	5 51.9	18 54.6	10 24.1	16 41.9	18 57.9	7 53.9	29 29.3	3 19.2
5	22 56 33.1	13 50.7	20 47.2	14 41.9	5 18.0	19 59.1	11 3.1	16 35.8	18 55.0	7 52.0	29 28.2	3 19.9
6	23 0 29.7	14 44.9	20 44.3	26 8.5	4 50.1	21 3.7	11 42.3	16 30.0	18 52.0	7 50.3	29 27.2	3 20.5
7	23 4 26.2	15 38.9	20 41.3	7♏52.8	4 28.8	22 8.5	12 21.8	16 24.2	18 48.9	7 48.5	29 26.1	3 21.2
8	23 8 22.8	16 33.0	20 38.4	20 2.2	4 14.9	23 13.3	13 1.4	16 18.6	18 45.8	7 46.8	29 25.1	3 22.0
9	23 12 19.3	17 26.9	20 35.5	2♐42.5	4 8.9	24 18.2	13 41.2	16 13.1	18 42.6	7 45.1	29 24.2	3 22.7
10	23 16 15.9	18 20.9	20 32.5	15 57.1	4D11.1	25 23.3	14 21.2	16 7.8	18 39.3	7 43.5	29 23.2	3 23.5
11	23 20 12.4	19 14.7	20 29.6	29 45.8	4 21.6	26 28.4	15 1.4	16 2.6	18 36.0	7 41.9	29 22.3	3 24.3
12	23 24 9.0	20 8.6	20 26.7	14♑ 3.8	4 40.7	27 33.7	15 41.8	15 57.6	18 32.6	7 40.3	29 21.4	3 25.2
13	23 28 5.5	21 2.4	20 23.7	28 42.7	5 8.1	28 39.2	16 22.4	15 52.8	18 29.1	7 38.8	29 20.6	3 26.1
14	23 32 2.1	21 56.3	20 20.8	13♒32.0	5 43.8	29 44.8	17 3.2	15 48.1	18 25.6	7 37.4	29 19.8	3 27.0
15	23 35 58.6	22 50.1	20 17.9	28 22.0	6 27.4	0♏50.6	17 44.2	15 43.6	18 22.0	7 36.0	29 19.0	3 28.0
16	23 39 55.2	23 43.8	20 14.9	13♓ 6.1	7 18.4	1 56.5	18 25.3	15 39.3	18 18.4	7 34.6	29 18.2	3 28.9
17	23 43 51.7	24 37.6	20 12.0	27 41.9	8 16.4	3 2.5	19 6.7	15 35.1	18 14.7	7 33.2	29 17.5	3 29.9
18	23 47 48.3	25 31.4	20 9.1	12♈ 9.7	9 20.8	4 8.7	19 48.2	15 31.1	18 10.9	7 31.9	29 16.8	3 31.0
19	23 51 44.8	26 25.1	20 6.1	26 31.4	10 31.1	5 15.1	20 30.0	15 27.2	18 7.1	7 30.6	29 16.1	3 32.0
20	23 55 41.4	27 18.9	20 3.2	10♉48.3	11 46.7	6 21.7	21 11.9	15 23.6	18 3.3	7 29.4	29 15.4	3 33.1
21	23 59 37.9	28 12.7	20 .3	24 59.8	13 6.8	7 28.4	21 54.1	15 20.1	17 59.4	7 28.2	29 14.8	3 34.3
22	0 3 34.5	29 6.5	19 57.4	9♊ 3.0	14 31.0	8 35.4	22 36.4	15 16.8	17 55.5	7 27.1	29 14.2	3 35.4
23	0 7 31.0	0♎ .4	19 54.4	22 52.7	15 58.5	9 42.5	23 18.9	15 13.7	17 51.5	7 26.0	29 13.7	3 36.6
24	0 11 27.6	0 54.3	19 51.5	6♋23.7	17 28.9	10 49.8	24 1.6	15 10.8	17 47.4	7 24.9	29 13.2	3 37.8
25	0 15 24.1	1 48.2	19 48.6	19 31.2	19 1.6	11 57.3	24 44.5	15 8.1	17 43.4	7 23.9	29 12.7	3 39.0
26	0 19 20.7	2 42.2	19 45.6	2♌12.9	20 36.1	13 5.0	25 27.6	15 5.5	17 39.3	7 23.0	29 12.2	3 40.3
27	0 23 17.2	3 36.2	19 42.7	14 28.9	22 12.0	14 12.9	26 10.9	15 3.2	17 35.1	7 22.1	29 11.8	3 41.6
28	0 27 13.8	4 30.3	19 39.8	26 21.9	23 49.0	15 21.0	26 54.4	15 1.0	17 31.0	7 21.2	29 11.4	3 42.9
29	0 31 10.3	5 24.4	19 36.8	7♍56.5	25 26.6	16 29.2	27 38.1	14 59.0	17 26.8	7 20.4	29 11.0	3 44.3
30	0 35 6.9	6 18.6	19 33.9	19 18.6	27 4.7	17 37.7	28 22.0	14 57.3	17 22.5	7 19.6	29 10.7	3 45.7

DECLINATION

DAY	SID. TIME	☉	☊	☽	☿	♀	♂	♃	♄	♅	♆	♇
1	22 40 46.9	8N20.6	0N 4.1	10N22.9	5N .5	6S41.5	15S56.3	17S30.6	5N10.6	19S31.7	20S14.9	8S37.0
4	22 52 36.5	7 14.8	0 4.1	0S 7.8	6 38.3	8 11.8	16 34.2	17 36.1	5 6.6	19 33.0	20 15.6	8 38.9
7	23 4 26.2	6 8.0	0 4.2	10 40.3	8 8.7	9 40.7	17 11.4	17 41.2	5 2.3	19 34.2	20 16.3	8 40.7
10	23 16 15.9	5 .2	0 4.3	17 29.4	9 17.5	11 7.8	17 47.6	17 45.8	4 57.8	19 35.3	20 16.9	8 42.6
13	23 28 5.5	3 51.7	0 4.3	16 32.5	9 54.7	12 32.9	18 22.9	17 50.0	4 53.2	19 36.4	20 17.5	8 44.5
16	23 39 55.2	2 42.6	0 4.4	6 24.3	9 55.6	13 55.7	18 57.2	17 53.8	4 48.3	19 37.3	20 18.0	8 46.5
19	23 51 44.8	1 33.1	0 4.5	7N29.6	9 20.2	15 15.9	19 30.3	17 57.0	4 43.3	19 38.2	20 18.4	8 48.4
22	0 3 34.5	0 23.2	0 4.5	16 46.2	8 12.0	16 33.1	20 2.2	17 59.8	4 38.1	19 39.0	20 18.8	8 50.4
25	0 15 24.1	0S46.9	0 4.6	17 32.8	6 37.1	17 47.1	20 32.8	18 2.1	4 32.8	19 39.6	20 19.2	8 52.4
28	0 27 13.8	1 57.0	0 4.7	11 8.1	4 42.6	18 57.5	21 2.0	18 3.9	4 27.5	19 40.2	20 19.5	8 54.4

OCTOBER 1997

DAY	EPHEM. SID. TIME	☉	☊	☽	☿	♀	♂	♃	♄	♅	♆	♇
	h m s	° ′	° ′	° ′	° ′	° ′	° ′	° ′	° ′	° ′	° ′	° ′
		LONGITUDE										
1	0 39 3.4	7♎51.4	18♍35.8	0♎13.2	27♍47.6	21♏43.7	1♐27.2	12♒10.6	17♈37.4	4♒48.5	27♑12.0	3♐29.5
2	0 43 .0	8 50.4	18 32.6	12 4.0	29 35.4	22 51.7	2 9.3	12R 9.3	17R32.7	4R47.9	27R11.8	3 31.1
3	0 46 56.6	9 49.4	18 29.5	24 .2	1♎23.3	23 59.5	2 51.5	12 8.2	17 28.1	4 47.3	27 11.6	3 32.7
4	0 50 53.1	10 48.5	18 26.3	6♏ 3.5	3 11.3	25 7.2	3 33.8	12 7.2	17 23.4	4 46.7	27 11.4	3 34.3
5	0 54 49.7	11 47.7	18 23.1	18 16.1	4 59.1	26 14.8	4 16.2	12 6.5	17 18.7	4 46.3	27 11.3	3 35.9
6	0 58 46.2	12 46.9	18 19.9	0♐39.7	6 46.6	27 22.3	4 58.7	12 6.0	17 14.0	4 45.9	27 11.2	3 37.6
7	1 2 42.8	13 46.0	18 16.7	13 16.5	8 33.6	28 29.6	5 41.2	12 5.7	17 9.3	4 45.5	27 11.1	3 39.3
8	1 6 39.3	14 45.3	18 13.6	26 8.9	10 20.2	29 36.7	6 23.9	12 5.5	17 4.5	4 45.1	27 11.0	3 41.0
9	1 10 35.9	15 44.5	18 10.4	9♑19.2	12 6.3	0♐43.8	7 6.6	12D 5.6	16 59.8	4 44.8	27 11.0	3 42.7
10	1 14 32.4	16 43.8	18 7.2	22 49.6	13 51.7	1 50.6	7 49.4	12 5.9	16 55.1	4 44.6	27 11.0	3 44.4
11	1 18 29.0	17 43.1	18 4.0	6♒41.6	15 36.5	2 57.4	8 32.3	12 6.3	16 50.3	4 44.4	27D11.1	3 46.2
12	1 22 25.5	18 42.4	18 .8	20 55.5	17 20.7	4 3.9	9 15.3	12 7.0	16 45.6	4 44.2	27 11.2	3 48.0
13	1 26 22.1	19 41.8	17 57.7	5♓29.8	19 4.2	5 10.3	9 58.4	12 7.8	16 40.8	4 44.2	27 11.3	3 49.8
14	1 30 18.6	20 41.2	17 54.5	20 20.9	20 46.9	6 16.5	10 41.5	12 8.9	16 36.1	4 44.1	27 11.4	3 51.7
15	1 34 15.2	21 40.6	17 51.3	5♈22.7	22 29.0	7 22.6	11 24.8	12 10.2	16 31.4	4 44.1	27 11.6	3 53.5
16	1 38 11.7	22 40.0	17 48.1	20 27.1	24 10.5	8 28.4	12 8.1	12 11.6	16 26.7	4D44.2	27 11.8	3 55.4
17	1 42 8.3	23 39.5	17 45.0	5♉24.9	25 51.2	9 34.1	12 51.4	12 13.3	16 22.0	4 44.3	27 12.1	3 57.3
18	1 46 4.8	24 39.1	17 41.8	20 7.4	27 31.3	10 39.5	13 34.9	12 15.1	16 17.3	4 44.4	27 12.4	3 59.3
19	1 50 1.4	25 38.6	17 38.6	4♊27.7	29 10.7	11 44.8	14 18.4	12 17.2	16 12.7	4 44.7	27 12.7	4 1.2
20	1 53 57.9	26 38.2	17 35.4	18 21.3	0♏49.4	12 49.9	15 2.0	12 19.4	16 8.1	4 44.9	27 13.1	4 3.2
21	1 57 54.5	27 37.8	17 32.2	1♋46.8	2 27.6	13 54.8	15 45.7	12 21.8	16 3.5	4 45.2	27 13.4	4 5.2
22	2 1 51.0	28 37.5	17 29.1	14 45.3	4 5.1	14 59.4	16 29.5	12 24.4	15 58.9	4 45.6	27 13.9	4 7.2
23	2 5 47.6	29 37.2	17 25.9	27 19.8	5 42.0	16 3.8	17 13.3	12 27.3	15 54.3	4 46.0	27 14.3	4 9.2
24	2 9 44.2	0♏37.0	17 22.7	9♌34.9	7 18.4	17 8.1	17 57.3	12 30.3	15 49.8	4 46.5	27 14.8	4 11.2
25	2 13 40.7	1 36.8	17 19.5	21 35.4	8 54.2	18 12.0	18 41.3	12 33.5	15 45.4	4 47.0	27 15.3	4 13.3
26	2 17 37.3	2 36.6	17 16.4	3♍26.6	10 29.4	19 15.8	19 25.4	12 36.9	15 41.0	4 47.6	27 15.9	4 15.4
27	2 21 33.8	3 36.5	17 13.2	15 13.3	12 4.2	20 19.3	20 9.5	12 40.5	15 36.6	4 48.2	27 16.5	4 17.5
28	2 25 30.4	4 36.4	17 10.0	26 60.0	13 38.4	21 22.5	20 53.8	12 44.2	15 32.2	4 48.9	27 17.1	4 19.6
29	2 29 26.9	5 36.3	17 6.8	8♎50.5	15 12.1	22 25.5	21 38.1	12 48.2	15 27.9	4 49.6	27 17.8	4 21.7
30	2 33 23.5	6 36.3	17 3.6	20 47.8	16 45.3	23 28.2	22 22.5	12 52.3	15 23.6	4 50.4	27 18.5	4 23.9
31	2 37 20.0	7 36.3	17 .5	2♏54.2	18 18.1	24 30.6	23 6.9	12 56.6	15 19.4	4 51.2	27 19.2	4 26.0
		LATITUDE										
1	0 39 3.4	0 .0	0 .0	0N57.5	1N51.8	1S56.4	1S 4.2	0S58.9	2S45.4	0S38.1	0N23.7	12N 7.0
4	0 50 53.1	0 .0	0 .0	3 48.5	1 45.4	2 7.9	1 5.4	0 58.7	2 45.6	0 38.0	0 23.7	12 5.8
7	1 2 42.8	0 .0	0 .0	5 12.8	1 34.4	2 19.0	1 6.5	0 58.5	2 45.7	0 38.0	0 23.6	12 4.6
10	1 14 32.4	0 .0	0 .0	4 22.9	1 20.0	2 29.7	1 7.6	0 58.2	2 45.7	0 37.9	0 23.5	12 3.5
13	1 26 22.1	0 .0	0 .0	1 16.1	1 3.2	2 39.9	1 8.6	0 58.0	2 45.7	0 37.8	0 23.4	12 2.4
16	1 38 11.7	0 .0	0 .0	2S41.4	0 44.6	2 49.6	1 9.6	0 57.7	2 45.7	0 37.7	0 23.4	12 1.4
19	1 50 1.4	0 .0	0 .0	5 1.4	0 25.0	2 58.6	1 10.5	0 57.4	2 45.5	0 37.6	0 23.3	12 .4
22	2 1 51.0	0 .0	0 .0	4 40.8	0 4.8	3 6.9	1 11.3	0 57.2	2 45.4	0 37.6	0 23.2	11 59.4
25	2 13 40.7	0 .0	0 .0	2 23.7	0S15.6	3 14.4	1 12.0	0 56.9	2 45.2	0 37.5	0 23.2	11 58.5
28	2 25 30.4	0 .0	0 .0	0N43.0	0 35.8	3 21.0	1 12.7	0 56.6	2 44.9	0 37.4	0 23.1	11 57.7
31	2 37 20.0	0 .0	0 .0	3 34.2	0 55.5	3 26.5	1 13.3	0 56.3	2 44.6	0 37.3	0 23.0	11 56.9
		RIGHT ASCENSION										
1	0 39 3.4	7♎12.9	19♍30.9	0♎35.0	28♍43.0	18♏46.3	29♏ 6.1	14♒55.7	17♈18.3	7♒18.9	29♑10.4	3♐47.1
2	0 43 .0	8 7.2	19 28.0	11 52.8	0♎21.3	19 55.2	29 50.3	14R54.3	17R14.0	7R18.3	29R10.2	3 48.5
3	0 46 56.6	9 1.6	19 25.1	23 19.3	1 59.4	21 4.2	0♐34.8	14 53.2	17 9.7	7 17.6	29 10.0	3 50.0
4	0 50 53.1	9 56.1	19 22.1	5♏ 1.3	3 37.4	22 13.4	1 19.4	14 52.2	17 5.3	7 17.1	29 9.8	3 51.5
5	0 54 49.7	10 50.8	19 19.2	17 5.0	5 15.0	23 22.8	2 4.2	14 51.5	17 1.1	7 16.6	29 9.7	3 53.0
6	0 58 46.2	11 45.4	19 16.3	29 34.6	6 52.3	24 32.4	2 49.2	14 50.9	16 56.7	7 16.2	29 9.6	3 54.6
7	1 2 42.8	12 40.2	19 13.3	12♐32.4	8 29.0	25 42.1	3 34.4	14 50.5	16 52.3	7 15.7	29 9.5	3 56.1
8	1 6 39.3	13 35.0	19 10.4	25 57.7	10 5.4	26 51.9	4 19.7	14 50.4	16 48.0	7 15.4	29 9.4	3 57.7
9	1 10 35.9	14 30.0	19 7.5	9♑46.7	11 41.2	28 1.9	5 5.3	14 50.4	16 43.6	7 15.1	29 9.4	3 59.3
10	1 14 32.4	15 25.1	19 4.5	23 53.0	13 16.6	29 12.0	5 51.0	14D50.7	16 39.2	7 14.8	29 9.4	4 1.0
11	1 18 29.0	16 20.2	19 1.6	8♒ 9.5	14 51.5	0♐22.3	6 36.8	14 51.1	16 34.8	7 14.6	29D 9.5	4 2.6
12	1 22 25.5	17 15.5	18 58.7	22 29.8	16 25.9	1 32.6	7 22.8	14 51.7	16 30.4	7 14.4	29 9.6	4 4.3
13	1 26 22.1	18 10.9	18 55.7	6♓50.1	17 59.9	2 43.1	8 9.0	14 52.6	16 26.0	7 14.3	29 9.7	4 6.0
14	1 30 18.6	19 6.5	18 52.8	21 9.8	19 33.5	3 53.6	8 55.4	14 53.6	16 21.7	7 14.3	29 9.9	4 7.8
15	1 34 15.2	20 2.2	18 49.9	5♈30.3	21 6.8	5 4.2	9 41.9	14 54.9	16 17.3	7 14.3	29 10.1	4 9.5
16	1 38 11.7	20 58.0	18 46.9	19 54.3	22 39.6	6 14.9	10 28.6	14 56.3	16 12.9	7 14.3	29 10.3	4 11.3
17	1 42 8.3	21 53.9	18 44.0	4♉23.2	24 12.2	7 25.6	11 15.4	14 58.0	16 8.6	7D14.5	29 10.6	4 13.1
18	1 46 4.8	22 50.0	18 41.0	18 55.8	25 44.5	8 36.4	12 2.4	14 59.8	16 4.2	7 14.6	29 10.9	4 14.9
19	1 50 1.4	23 46.3	18 38.1	3♊27.0	27 16.6	9 47.2	12 49.5	15 1.8	15 59.9	7 14.8	29 11.2	4 16.8
20	1 53 57.9	24 42.7	18 35.2	17 48.9	28 48.4	10 57.9	13 36.8	15 4.1	15 55.6	7 15.1	29 11.6	4 18.6
21	1 57 54.5	25 39.2	18 32.2	1♋52.1	0♏20.1	12 8.7	14 24.2	15 6.5	15 51.3	7 15.4	29 12.0	4 20.5
22	2 1 51.0	26 36.0	18 29.3	15 28.6	1 51.7	13 19.4	15 11.8	15 9.1	15 47.1	7 15.8	29 12.4	4 22.4
23	2 5 47.6	27 32.9	18 26.4	28 33.7	3 23.1	14 30.1	15 59.5	15 11.9	15 42.9	7 16.2	29 12.9	4 24.3
24	2 9 44.2	28 30.0	18 23.4	11♌ 6.7	4 54.5	15 40.7	16 47.3	15 14.9	15 38.7	7 16.7	29 13.4	4 26.3
25	2 13 40.7	29 27.3	18 20.5	23 10.7	6 25.8	16 51.3	17 35.3	15 18.1	15 34.5	7 17.2	29 14.0	4 28.2
26	2 17 37.3	0♏24.8	18 17.5	4♍51.2	7 57.2	18 1.8	18 23.5	15 21.5	15 30.4	7 17.8	29 14.6	4 30.2
27	2 21 33.8	1 22.4	18 14.6	16 15.5	9 28.5	19 12.1	19 11.8	15 25.1	15 26.3	7 18.4	29 15.2	4 32.2
28	2 25 30.4	2 20.2	18 11.7	27 31.9	10 59.8	20 22.2	20 .1	15 28.9	15 22.2	7 19.1	29 15.9	4 34.2
29	2 29 26.9	3 18.3	18 8.7	8♎48.7	12 31.3	21 32.2	20 48.6	15 32.8	15 18.2	7 19.9	29 16.6	4 36.3
30	2 33 23.5	4 16.5	18 5.8	20 14.2	14 2.7	22 42.0	21 37.2	15 37.0	15 14.2	7 20.6	29 17.3	4 38.3
31	2 37 20.0	5 14.9	18 2.9	1♏55.9	15 34.3	23 51.6	22 26.0	15 41.3	15 10.3	7 21.5	29 18.0	4 40.4
		DECLINATION										
1	0 39 3.4	3S 7.0	0N 4.7	0N47.5	2N35.3	20S 4.2	21S29.8	18S 5.1	4N22.0	19S40.6	20S19.8	8S56.4
4	0 50 53.1	4 16.7	0 4.8	9S56.6	0 20.7	21 6.7	21 56.0	18 5.9	4 16.6	19 41.0	20 20.0	8 58.5
7	1 2 42.8	5 25.9	0 4.9	17 13.0	1S56.9	22 4.8	22 20.6	18 6.1	4 11.1	19 41.2	20 20.1	9 .5
10	1 14 32.4	6 34.5	0 4.9	17 11.0	4 14.3	22 58.3	22 43.4	18 5.8	4 5.6	19 41.4	20 20.2	9 2.5
13	1 26 22.1	7 42.2	0 5.0	8 18.8	6 29.5	23 46.9	23 4.5	18 5.0	4 .2	19 41.4	20 20.2	9 4.5
16	1 38 11.7	8 49.0	0 5.0	5N29.8	8 41.0	24 30.4	23 23.7	18 3.7	3 54.9	19 41.3	20 20.2	9 6.5
19	1 50 1.4	9 54.7	0 5.1	16 5.5	10 47.5	25 8.6	23 40.8	18 1.9	3 49.6	19 41.1	20 20.1	9 8.5
22	2 1 51.0	10 59.1	0 5.2	17 58.1	12 48.3	25 41.3	23 56.0	17 59.6	3 44.5	19 40.8	20 19.9	9 10.4
25	2 13 40.7	12 2.0	0 5.2	12 2.3	14 42.6	26 8.4	24 9.1	17 56.8	3 39.5	19 40.4	20 19.7	9 12.4
28	2 25 30.4	13 3.3	0 5.3	1 51.1	16 30.0	26 29.9	24 20.0	17 53.4	3 34.8	19 39.9	20 19.4	9 14.3
31	2 37 20.0	14 2.8	0 5.4	9S 7.2	18 9.8	26 45.7	24 28.7	17 49.6	3 30.1	19 39.2	20 19.1	9 16.2

NOVEMBER 1997

LONGITUDE

DAY	EPHEM. SID. TIME h m s	☉ ° ′	☊ ° ′	☽ ° ′	☿ ° ′	♀ ° ′	♂ ° ′	♃ ° ′	♄ ° ′	♅ ° ′	♆ ° ′	♇ ° ′
1	2 41 16.6	8♏36.3	16♍57.3	15♏11.2	19♏50.3	25♐32.7	23♐51.4	13♒ 1.1	15♈15.3	4♒52.1	27♑19.9	4♐28.2
2	2 45 13.1	9 36.4	16 54.1	27 39.6	21 22.2	26 34.5	24 36.0	13 5.8	15R11.2	4 53.0	27 20.7	4 30.4
3	2 49 9.7	10 36.4	16 50.9	10♐19.8	22 53.6	27 35.9	25 20.7	13 10.7	15 7.1	4 54.0	27 21.5	4 32.6
4	2 53 6.2	11 36.6	16 47.8	23 12.0	24 24.5	28 37.1	26 5.4	13 15.7	15 3.1	4 55.0	27 22.4	4 34.8
5	2 57 2.8	12 36.7	16 44.6	6♑16.5	25 55.0	29 37.9	26 50.2	13 20.9	14 59.2	4 56.1	27 23.3	4 37.0
6	3 0 59.4	13 36.9	16 41.4	19 33.8	27 25.1	0♑38.3	27 35.1	13 26.3	14 55.3	4 57.2	27 24.2	4 39.3
7	3 4 55.9	14 37.1	16 38.2	3♒ 4.5	28 54.8	1 38.4	28 20.0	13 31.9	14 51.5	4 58.4	27 25.1	4 41.5
8	3 8 52.5	15 37.3	16 35.0	16 49.6	0♐23.9	2 38.0	29 5.0	13 37.7	14 47.8	4 59.6	27 26.1	4 43.8
9	3 12 49.0	16 37.5	16 31.9	0♓49.7	1 52.7	3 37.3	29 50.0	13 43.6	14 44.2	5 .9	27 27.1	4 46.0
10	3 16 45.6	17 37.8	16 28.7	15 4.6	3 20.9	4 36.1	0♑35.1	13 49.7	14 40.6	5 2.2	27 28.1	4 48.3
11	3 20 42.1	18 38.1	16 25.5	29 32.9	4 48.6	5 34.5	1 20.3	13 55.9	14 37.1	5 3.6	27 29.2	4 50.6
12	3 24 38.7	19 38.4	16 22.3	14♈11.5	6 15.9	6 32.4	2 5.5	14 2.3	14 33.6	5 5.0	27 30.3	4 52.9
13	3 28 35.2	20 38.7	16 19.2	28 55.0	7 42.5	7 29.8	2 50.8	14 8.9	14 30.3	5 6.4	27 31.4	4 55.2
14	3 32 31.8	21 39.1	16 16.0	13♉36.6	9 8.6	8 26.8	3 36.1	14 15.6	14 27.0	5 7.9	27 32.6	4 57.5
15	3 36 28.3	22 39.5	16 12.8	28 8.6	10 34.0	9 23.2	4 21.5	14 22.5	14 23.8	5 9.5	27 33.8	4 59.8
16	3 40 24.9	23 40.0	16 9.6	12♊23.9	11 58.8	10 19.1	5 7.0	14 29.6	14 20.7	5 11.1	27 35.1	5 2.2
17	3 44 21.5	24 40.4	16 6.5	26 17.0	13 22.7	11 14.4	5 52.6	14 36.8	14 17.7	5 12.8	27 36.3	5 4.5
18	3 48 18.0	25 40.9	16 3.3	9♋44.6	14 45.8	12 9.2	6 38.1	14 44.2	14 14.7	5 14.5	27 37.6	5 6.8
19	3 52 14.6	26 41.4	16 .1	22 46.4	16 7.9	13 3.4	7 23.7	14 51.7	14 11.9	5 16.2	27 38.9	5 9.2
20	3 56 11.1	27 42.0	15 56.9	5♌24.1	17 29.0	13 56.9	8 9.4	14 59.4	14 9.1	5 18.0	27 40.2	5 11.5
21	4 0 7.7	28 42.5	15 53.7	17 41.5	18 48.9	14 49.8	8 55.2	15 7.2	14 6.4	5 19.9	27 41.6	5 13.9
22	4 4 4.2	29 43.1	15 50.6	29 43.2	20 7.3	15 42.0	9 40.9	15 15.2	14 3.8	5 21.7	27 43.0	5 16.2
23	4 8 .8	0♐43.7	15 47.4	11♍34.9	21 24.3	16 33.6	10 26.8	15 23.3	14 1.3	5 23.6	27 44.4	5 18.6
24	4 11 57.3	1 44.4	15 44.2	23 22.0	22 39.5	17 24.4	11 12.7	15 31.5	13 58.9	5 25.6	27 45.8	5 20.9
25	4 15 53.9	2 45.1	15 41.0	5♎10.0	23 52.7	18 14.5	11 58.6	15 40.0	13 56.6	5 27.6	27 47.3	5 23.3
26	4 19 50.5	3 45.8	15 37.9	17 3.7	25 3.6	19 3.8	12 44.6	15 48.5	13 54.4	5 29.7	27 48.8	5 25.7
27	4 23 47.0	4 46.5	15 34.7	29 7.2	26 11.8	19 52.2	13 30.7	15 57.2	13 52.3	5 31.8	27 50.3	5 28.0
28	4 27 43.6	5 47.3	15 31.5	11♏23.7	27 17.1	20 39.9	14 16.8	16 6.0	13 50.3	5 33.9	27 51.9	5 30.4
29	4 31 40.1	6 48.0	15 28.3	23 54.9	28 19.0	21 26.6	15 2.9	16 15.0	13 48.4	5 36.1	27 53.5	5 32.8
30	4 35 36.7	7 48.9	15 25.2	6♐41.6	29 17.0	22 12.5	15 49.1	16 24.1	13 46.6	5 38.3	27 55.1	5 35.1

LATITUDE

DAY	SID. TIME	☉	☊	☽	☿	♀	♂	♃	♄	♅	♆	♇
1	2 41 16.6	0 .0	0 .0	4N16.1	1S 1.9	3S28.1	1S13.5	0S56.2	2S44.4	0S37.3	0N23.0	11N56.6
4	2 53 6.2	0 .0	0 .0	5 5.0	1 20.4	3 32.2	1 14.0	0 56.0	2 44.0	0 37.2	0 22.9	11 55.9
7	3 4 55.9	0 .0	0 .0	3 36.7	1 37.6	3 35.0	1 14.4	0 55.7	2 43.6	0 37.1	0 22.8	11 55.3
10	3 16 45.6	0 .0	0 .0	0 15.5	1 53.3	3 36.4	1 14.8	0 55.4	2 43.1	0 37.1	0 22.8	11 54.7
13	3 28 35.2	0 .0	0 .0	3S20.4	2 7.0	3 36.4	1 15.1	0 55.2	2 42.6	0 37.0	0 22.7	11 54.1
16	3 40 24.9	0 .0	0 .0	5 2.0	2 18.2	3 34.7	1 15.3	0 54.9	2 42.0	0 36.9	0 22.6	11 53.6
19	3 52 14.6	0 .0	0 .0	4 6.3	2 26.4	3 31.3	1 15.4	0 54.7	2 41.4	0 36.8	0 22.6	11 53.2
22	4 4 4.2	0 .0	0 .0	1 29.5	2 30.8	3 26.1	1 15.5	0 54.4	2 40.8	0 36.8	0 22.5	11 52.8
25	4 15 53.9	0 .0	0 .0	1N36.2	2 30.4	3 18.8	1 15.5	0 54.2	2 40.1	0 36.7	0 22.5	11 52.5
28	4 27 43.6	0 .0	0 .0	4 6.9	2 24.0	3 9.3	1 15.5	0 54.0	2 39.4	0 36.6	0 22.4	11 52.2

RIGHT ASCENSION

DAY	SID. TIME	☉	☊	☽	☿	♀	♂	♃	♄	♅	♆	♇
1	2 41 16.6	6♏13.5	17♍59.9	13♏59.9	17♏ 6.0	25♐ .9	23♐14.8	15♒45.8	15♈ 6.4	7♒22.4	29♑18.8	4♐42.4
2	2 45 13.1	7 12.3	17 57.0	26 30.4	18 37.8	26 10.0	24 3.8	15 50.5	15R 2.6	7 23.3	29 19.7	4 44.5
3	2 49 9.7	8 11.3	17 54.0	9♐28.6	20 9.7	27 18.7	24 52.8	15 55.3	14 58.8	7 24.3	29 20.5	4 46.6
4	2 53 6.2	9 10.5	17 51.1	22 52.2	21 41.7	28 27.1	25 42.0	16 .4	14 55.0	7 25.4	29 21.4	4 48.7
5	2 57 2.8	10 9.9	17 48.2	6♑35.6	23 13.8	29 35.2	26 31.2	16 5.6	14 51.4	7 26.5	29 22.3	4 50.9
6	3 0 59.4	11 9.5	17 45.2	20 30.9	24 46.1	0♑42.9	27 20.5	16 11.0	14 47.7	7 27.6	29 23.3	4 53.0
7	3 4 55.9	12 9.3	17 42.3	4♒30.3	26 18.4	1 50.2	28 10.0	16 16.6	14 44.2	7 28.8	29 24.3	4 55.2
8	3 8 52.5	13 9.4	17 39.3	18 27.6	27 50.8	2 57.0	28 59.4	16 22.3	14 40.7	7 30.1	29 25.3	4 57.3
9	3 12 49.0	14 9.6	17 36.4	2♓20.2	29 23.3	4 3.4	29 49.0	16 28.2	14 37.2	7 31.4	29 26.4	4 59.5
10	3 16 45.6	15 10.0	17 33.5	16 9.5	0♐55.8	5 9.2	0♑38.6	16 34.3	14 33.9	7 32.7	29 27.5	5 1.7
11	3 20 42.1	16 10.7	17 30.5	29 59.7	2 28.3	6 14.5	1 28.3	16 40.6	14 30.6	7 34.1	29 28.6	5 3.9
12	3 24 38.7	17 11.5	17 27.6	13♈56.3	4 .7	7 19.3	2 18.1	16 47.0	14 27.3	7 35.6	29 29.7	5 6.1
13	3 28 35.2	18 12.6	17 24.6	28 4.4	5 33.0	8 23.4	3 7.9	16 53.6	14 24.2	7 37.1	29 30.9	5 8.3
14	3 32 31.8	19 13.8	17 21.7	12♉26.2	7 5.1	9 26.9	3 57.8	17 .3	14 21.1	7 38.6	29 32.1	5 10.6
15	3 36 28.3	20 15.3	17 18.7	26 59.5	8 36.9	10 29.8	4 47.7	17 7.2	14 18.0	7 40.2	29 33.4	5 12.8
16	3 40 24.9	21 17.0	17 15.8	11♊36.6	10 8.5	11 32.0	5 37.7	17 14.3	14 15.1	7 41.9	29 34.7	5 15.1
17	3 44 21.5	22 18.9	17 12.9	26 5.8	11 39.5	12 33.4	6 27.7	17 21.5	14 12.3	7 43.6	29 36.0	5 17.3
18	3 48 18.0	23 21.0	17 9.9	10♋14.5	13 9.9	13 34.1	7 17.7	17 28.8	14 9.5	7 45.4	29 37.4	5 19.6
19	3 52 14.6	24 23.4	17 7.0	23 52.5	14 39.7	14 34.0	8 7.8	17 36.3	14 6.7	7 47.1	29 38.7	5 21.9
20	3 56 11.1	25 25.9	17 4.0	6♌54.8	16 8.5	15 33.1	8 57.9	17 44.0	14 4.1	7 49.0	29 40.1	5 24.1
21	4 0 7.7	26 28.6	17 1.1	19 21.6	17 36.3	16 31.4	9 48.0	17 51.7	14 1.5	7 50.8	29 41.6	5 26.4
22	4 4 4.2	27 31.6	16 58.2	1♍17.5	19 2.8	17 28.7	10 38.1	17 59.7	13 59.1	7 52.8	29 43.0	5 28.7
23	4 8 .8	28 34.7	16 55.2	12 50.0	20 27.9	18 25.2	11 28.2	18 7.8	13 56.7	7 54.7	29 44.5	5 31.0
24	4 11 57.3	29 38.1	16 52.3	24 8.5	21 51.1	19 20.6	12 18.4	18 16.0	13 54.4	7 56.8	29 46.0	5 33.3
25	4 15 53.9	0♐41.6	16 49.3	5♎22.6	23 12.2	20 15.1	13 8.6	18 24.4	13 52.2	7 58.8	29 47.6	5 35.6
26	4 19 50.5	1 45.4	16 46.4	16 42.5	24 30.9	21 8.6	13 58.7	18 32.9	13 50.0	8 .9	29 49.1	5 37.9
27	4 23 47.0	2 49.3	16 43.4	28 17.4	25 46.7	22 1.0	14 48.9	18 41.5	13 48.0	8 3.1	29 50.7	5 40.2
28	4 27 43.6	3 53.4	16 40.5	10♏15.6	26 59.2	22 52.3	15 39.1	18 50.3	13 46.0	8 5.2	29 52.4	5 42.5
29	4 31 40.1	4 57.7	16 37.5	22 43.3	28 8.0	23 42.5	16 29.2	18 59.2	13 44.2	8 7.5	29 54.0	5 44.8
30	4 35 36.7	6 2.2	16 34.6	5♐43.0	29 12.3	24 31.5	17 19.3	19 8.2	13 42.4	8 9.7	29 55.7	5 47.1

DECLINATION

DAY	SID. TIME	☉	☊	☽	☿	♀	♂	♃	♄	♅	♆	♇
1	2 41 16.6	14S22.2	0N 5.4	12S18.2	18S41.3	26S49.7	24S31.0	17S48.3	3N28.7	19S39.0	20S19.0	9S16.8
4	2 53 6.2	15 18.9	0 5.5	18 11.1	20 10.2	26 57.9	24 36.7	17 43.8	3 24.4	19 38.2	20 18.5	9 18.6
7	3 4 55.9	16 13.3	0 5.5	15 57.1	21 30.1	27 .5	24 40.0	17 38.9	3 20.3	19 37.3	20 18.1	9 20.4
10	3 16 45.6	17 5.3	0 5.6	5 38.5	22 40.6	26 57.7	24 40.9	17 33.6	3 16.5	19 36.3	20 17.5	9 22.1
13	3 28 35.2	17 54.7	0 5.7	7N57.8	23 40.9	26 49.5	24 39.4	17 27.7	3 13.0	19 35.2	20 17.0	9 23.8
16	3 40 24.9	18 41.3	0 5.7	17 17.2	24 30.4	26 36.2	24 35.5	17 21.5	3 9.9	19 34.0	20 16.3	9 25.5
19	3 52 14.6	19 24.9	0 5.8	17 27.8	25 8.5	26 18.1	24 29.2	17 14.8	3 7.0	19 32.7	20 15.6	9 27.1
22	4 4 4.2	20 5.3	0 5.8	10 10.3	25 34.5	25 55.4	24 20.3	17 7.6	3 4.5	19 31.3	20 14.9	9 28.6
25	4 15 53.9	20 42.5	0 5.9	0S34.9	25 47.9	25 28.6	24 9.1	17 .0	3 2.3	19 29.8	20 14.1	9 30.1
28	4 27 43.6	21 16.2	0 6.0	11 19.9	25 48.6	24 58.0	23 55.4	16 52.1	3 .5	19 28.2	20 13.3	9 31.5

DECEMBER 1997

LONGITUDE

DAY	EPHEM. SID. TIME	☉	☊	☾	☿	♀	♂	♃	♄	♅	♆	♇
	h m s	° ′	° ′	° ′	° ′	° ′	° ′	° ′	° ′	° ′	° ′	° ′
1	4 39 33.2	8♐49.7	15♍22.0	19♐43.1	0♑10.6	22♑57.3	16♑35.4	16♒33.3	13♈44.9	5♒40.5	27♑56.7	5♐37.5
2	4 43 29.8	9 50.5	15 18.8	2♑58.1	0 59.0	23 41.2	17 21.7	16 42.6	13 R 43.2	5 42.8	27 58.4	5 39.9
3	4 47 26.4	10 51.4	15 15.6	16 24.6	1 41.8	24 24.0	18 8.0	16 52.1	13 41.7	5 45.2	28 .0	5 42.2
4	4 51 22.9	11 52.2	15 12.4	0♒ .7	2 18.0	25 5.8	18 54.4	17 1.8	13 40.3	5 47.5	28 1.7	5 44.6
5	4 55 19.5	12 53.1	15 9.3	13 44.8	2 47.0	25 46.3	19 40.8	17 11.5	13 39.1	5 50.0	28 3.5	5 46.9
6	4 59 16.0	13 54.0	15 6.1	27 36.0	3 7.8	26 25.7	20 27.3	17 21.4	13 37.9	5 52.4	28 5.2	5 49.3
7	5 3 12.6	14 55.0	15 2.9	11♓33.8	3 19.7	27 4.0	21 13.8	17 31.4	13 36.8	5 54.9	28 7.0	5 51.7
8	5 7 9.1	15 55.9	14 59.7	25 38.0	3 21.7	27 40.8	22 .4	17 41.5	13 35.9	5 57.5	28 8.8	5 54.0
9	5 11 5.7	16 56.9	14 56.6	9♈48.0	3 R 13.2	28 16.3	22 46.9	17 51.7	13 35.0	6 .0	28 10.6	5 56.3
10	5 15 2.3	17 57.8	14 53.4	24 2.6	2 53.6	28 50.4	23 33.6	18 2.1	13 34.3	6 2.6	28 12.4	5 58.7
11	5 18 58.8	18 58.8	14 50.2	8♉19.1	2 22.6	29 23.1	24 20.2	18 12.5	13 33.6	6 5.3	28 14.3	6 1.0
12	5 22 55.4	19 59.7	14 47.0	22 33.8	1 40.1	29 54.2	25 6.9	18 23.1	13 33.1	6 7.9	28 16.2	6 3.3
13	5 26 51.9	21 .7	14 43.9	6♊41.5	0 46.7	0♒23.7	25 53.6	18 33.7	13 32.6	6 10.6	28 18.1	6 5.6
14	5 30 48.5	22 1.7	14 40.7	20 37.3	29♐43.4	0 51.6	26 40.3	18 44.5	13 32.3	6 13.4	28 20.0	6 7.9
15	5 34 45.0	23 2.7	14 37.5	4♋16.3	28 31.6	1 17.8	27 27.1	18 55.4	13 32.1	6 16.1	28 21.9	6 10.2
16	5 38 41.6	24 3.7	14 34.3	17 35.2	27 13.5	1 42.2	28 13.9	19 6.4	13 32.0	6 18.9	28 23.8	6 12.5
17	5 42 38.2	25 4.8	14 31.1	0♌32.7	25 51.6	2 4.8	29 .7	19 17.5	13 32.0	6 21.7	28 25.8	6 14.7
18	5 46 34.7	26 5.8	14 28.0	13 9.2	24 28.6	2 25.4	29 47.6	19 28.7	13 D 32.1	6 24.6	28 27.8	6 17.0
19	5 50 31.3	27 6.9	14 24.8	25 27.1	23 7.3	2 44.2	0♒34.5	19 40.0	13 32.4	6 27.5	28 29.8	6 19.2
20	5 54 27.8	28 8.0	14 21.6	7♍30.0	21 50.4	3 .9	1 21.4	19 51.4	13 32.7	6 30.4	28 31.8	6 21.5
21	5 58 24.4	29 9.0	14 18.4	19 22.8	20 40.2	3 15.5	2 8.3	20 2.9	13 33.2	6 33.3	28 33.8	6 23.7
22	6 2 20.9	0♑10.1	14 15.3	1♎10.8	19 38.4	3 28.0	2 55.3	20 14.5	13 33.7	6 36.3	28 35.9	6 25.9
23	6 6 17.5	1 11.3	14 12.1	12 59.6	18 46.4	3 38.2	3 42.3	20 26.1	13 34.4	6 39.3	28 38.0	6 28.1
24	6 10 14.1	2 12.4	14 8.9	24 54.8	18 4.9	3 46.3	4 29.4	20 37.9	13 35.2	6 42.3	28 40.0	6 30.3
25	6 14 10.6	3 13.5	14 5.7	7♏ 1.2	17 34.2	3 52.0	5 16.4	20 49.8	13 36.1	6 45.4	28 42.1	6 32.5
26	6 18 7.2	4 14.7	14 2.6	19 23.2	17 14.3	3 55.3	6 3.5	21 1.7	13 37.1	6 48.5	28 44.2	6 34.6
27	6 22 3.7	5 15.8	13 59.4	2♐ 3.7	17 4.6	3 56.2	6 50.6	21 13.8	13 38.2	6 51.6	28 46.4	6 36.7
28	6 26 .3	6 17.0	13 56.2	15 4.3	17 D 4.8	3 R 54.8	7 37.8	21 25.9	13 39.4	6 54.7	28 48.5	6 38.9
29	6 29 56.8	7 18.2	13 53.0	28 24.6	17 14.0	3 50.8	8 24.9	21 38.2	13 40.8	6 57.9	28 50.7	6 41.0
30	6 33 53.4	8 19.4	13 49.8	12♑ 2.8	17 31.6	3 44.4	9 12.1	21 50.4	13 42.2	7 1.1	28 52.8	6 43.1
31	6 37 50.0	9 20.5	13 46.7	25 55.4	17 56.7	3 35.4	9 59.3	22 2.8	13 43.7	7 4.3	28 55.0	6 45.2

LATITUDE

DAY	EPHEM. SID. TIME	☉	☊	☾	☿	♀	♂	♃	♄	♅	♆	♇
1	4 39 33.2	0 .0	0 .0	4N59.6	2S10.2	2S57.5	1S15.4	0S53.7	2S38.7	0S36.6	0N22.3	11N52.1
4	4 51 22.9	0 .0	0 .0	3 34.2	1 46.9	2 43.1	1 15.2	0 53.5	2 38.0	0 36.5	0 22.3	11 51.9
7	5 3 12.6	0 .0	0 .0	0 18.7	1 12.2	2 26.0	1 14.9	0 53.4	2 37.2	0 36.4	0 22.2	11 51.8
10	5 15 2.3	0 .0	0 .0	3S10.2	0 25.3	2 6.0	1 14.6	0 53.2	2 36.5	0 36.4	0 22.2	11 51.8
13	5 26 51.9	0 .0	0 .0	4 57.7	0N31.9	1 42.9	1 14.2	0 53.0	2 35.7	0 36.3	0 22.1	11 51.9
16	5 38 41.6	0 .0	0 .0	4 11.0	1 31.5	1 16.4	1 13.7	0 52.8	2 34.9	0 36.3	0 22.0	11 52.0
19	5 50 31.3	0 .0	0 .0	1 34.9	2 21.7	0 46.4	1 13.2	0 52.7	2 34.1	0 36.2	0 22.0	11 52.1
22	6 2 20.9	0 .0	0 .0	1N32.1	2 52.6	0 12.9	1 12.6	0 52.6	2 33.3	0 36.2	0 21.9	11 52.3
25	6 14 10.6	0 .0	0 .0	4 4.3	3 2.6	0N24.2	1 11.9	0 52.4	2 32.4	0 36.2	0 21.9	11 52.6
28	6 26 .3	0 .0	0 .0	5 2.6	2 56.3	1 4.6	1 11.2	0 52.3	2 31.6	0 36.1	0 21.9	11 52.9
31	6 37 50.0	0 .0	0 .0	3 40.9	2 39.4	1 47.9	1 10.4	0 52.2	2 30.8	0 36.1	0 21.8	11 53.3

RIGHT ASCENSION

DAY	EPHEM. SID. TIME	☉	☊	☾	☿	♀	♂	♃	♄	♅	♆	♇
1	4 39 33.2	7♐ 6.8	16♍31.7	19♐13.2	0♑11.7	25♑19.3	18♑ 9.5	19♒17.4	13♈40.7	8♒12.1	29♑57.4	5♐49.4
2	4 43 29.8	8 11.6	16 28.7	3♑ 7.3	1 5.4	26 5.8	18 59.5	19 26.7	13 R 39.2	8 14.4	29 59.1	5 51.7
3	4 47 26.4	9 16.5	16 25.8	17 14.8	1 52.5	26 51.0	19 49.6	19 36.1	13 37.7	8 16.8	0♒ .9	5 54.0
4	4 51 22.9	10 21.6	16 22.8	1♒24.2	2 32.5	27 34.8	20 39.6	19 45.6	13 36.3	8 19.2	0 2.7	5 56.3
5	4 55 19.5	11 26.9	16 19.9	15 26.1	3 4.2	28 17.2	21 29.6	19 55.3	13 35.0	8 21.7	0 4.5	5 58.6
6	4 59 16.0	12 32.3	16 16.9	29 15.5	3 26.8	28 58.1	22 19.6	20 5.1	13 33.8	8 24.2	0 6.3	6 .9
7	5 3 12.6	13 37.8	16 14.0	12♓52.4	3 39.6	29 37.6	23 9.5	20 15.0	13 32.8	8 26.8	0 8.2	6 3.2
8	5 7 9.1	14 43.4	16 11.0	26 21.6	3 41.4	0♒15.4	23 59.4	20 25.0	13 31.8	8 29.4	0 10.1	6 5.5
9	5 11 5.7	15 49.2	16 8.1	9♈50.1	3 R 31.7	0 51.7	24 49.2	20 35.2	13 30.9	8 32.0	0 12.0	6 7.8
10	5 15 2.3	16 55.0	16 5.2	23 26.1	3 9.8	1 26.2	25 39.0	20 45.4	13 30.1	8 34.7	0 13.9	6 10.0
11	5 18 58.8	18 1.0	16 2.2	7♉15.9	2 35.5	1 59.1	26 28.6	20 55.7	13 29.4	8 37.4	0 15.8	6 12.3
12	5 22 55.4	19 7.0	15 59.3	21 22.5	1 48.9	2 30.1	27 18.3	21 6.2	13 28.8	8 40.1	0 17.8	6 14.6
13	5 26 51.9	20 13.1	15 56.3	5♊43.2	0 50.7	2 59.3	28 7.8	21 16.7	13 28.3	8 42.9	0 19.7	6 16.8
14	5 30 48.5	21 19.3	15 53.4	20 9.8	29♐42.0	3 26.5	28 57.3	21 27.3	13 27.9	8 45.7	0 21.7	6 19.1
15	5 34 45.0	22 25.6	15 50.4	4♋29.6	28 24.5	3 51.9	29 46.7	21 38.1	13 27.6	8 48.5	0 23.8	6 21.3
16	5 38 41.6	23 32.0	15 47.5	18 29.3	27 .6	4 15.2	0♒36.1	21 48.9	13 27.4	8 51.4	0 25.8	6 23.6
17	5 42 38.2	24 38.4	15 44.5	1♌58.4	25 33.0	4 36.4	1 25.3	21 59.9	13 27.3	8 54.3	0 27.9	6 25.8
18	5 46 34.7	25 44.8	15 41.6	14 51.9	24 4.7	4 55.5	2 14.5	22 10.9	13 27.3	8 57.2	0 29.9	6 28.0
19	5 50 31.3	26 51.3	15 38.6	27 10.5	22 38.5	5 12.4	3 3.6	22 22.0	13 D 27.4	9 .2	0 32.0	6 30.2
20	5 54 27.8	27 57.9	15 35.7	8♍59.3	21 17.2	5 27.1	3 52.6	22 33.2	13 27.6	9 3.1	0 34.1	6 32.4
21	5 58 24.4	29 4.5	15 32.7	20 26.4	20 3.2	5 39.5	4 41.6	22 44.5	13 27.9	9 6.2	0 36.2	6 34.6
22	6 2 20.9	0♑11.1	15 29.8	1♎41.6	18 58.2	5 49.5	5 30.4	22 55.9	13 28.4	9 9.2	0 38.4	6 36.8
23	6 6 17.5	1 17.7	15 26.8	12 55.5	18 3.5	5 57.1	6 19.2	23 7.4	13 28.9	9 12.3	0 40.5	6 39.0
24	6 10 14.1	2 24.3	15 23.9	24 18.8	17 19.9	6 2.3	7 7.8	23 19.0	13 29.5	9 15.4	0 42.7	6 41.1
25	6 14 10.6	3 30.9	15 20.9	6♏ 1.8	16 47.6	6 5.0	7 56.4	23 30.6	13 30.2	9 18.5	0 44.9	6 43.3
26	6 18 7.2	4 37.5	15 18.0	18 13.3	16 26.4	6 5.2	8 44.9	23 42.4	13 31.0	9 21.6	0 47.1	6 45.4
27	6 22 3.7	5 44.0	15 15.0	0♐59.7	16 16.0	6 R 2.9	9 33.3	23 54.2	13 31.9	9 24.8	0 49.3	6 47.5
28	6 26 .3	6 50.6	15 12.1	14 23.0	16 15.8	5 58.0	10 21.6	24 6.1	13 33.0	9 28.1	0 51.6	6 49.7
29	6 29 56.8	7 57.1	15 9.1	28 19.7	16 D 25.1	5 50.4	11 9.8	24 18.1	13 34.1	9 31.3	0 53.8	6 51.8
30	6 33 53.4	9 3.5	15 6.2	12♑40.5	16 43.1	5 40.3	11 57.9	24 30.1	13 35.3	9 34.5	0 56.1	6 53.8
31	6 37 50.0	10 9.9	15 3.2	27 11.7	17 9.1	5 27.6	12 45.9	24 42.2	13 36.7	9 37.8	0 58.3	6 55.9

DECLINATION

DAY	EPHEM. SID. TIME	☉	☊	☾	☿	♀	♂	♃	♄	♅	♆	♇
1	4 39 33.2	21S46.2	0N 6.0	18S 3.6	25S36.4	24S24.0	23S39.2	16S43.6	2N59.1	19S26.5	20S12.4	9S32.8
4	4 51 22.9	22 12.6	0 6.1	16 39.3	25 11.9	23 47.1	23 20.6	16 34.8	2 58.0	19 24.7	20 11.4	9 34.1
7	5 3 12.6	22 35.0	0 6.2	6 56.2	24 35.9	23 7.8	22 59.7	16 25.6	2 57.4	19 22.8	20 10.4	9 35.3
10	5 15 2.3	22 53.5	0 6.2	6N22.6	23 49.6	22 26.7	22 36.4	16 16.0	2 57.1	19 20.8	20 9.4	9 36.5
13	5 26 51.9	23 8.0	0 6.3	16 32.0	22 54.2	21 44.3	22 10.8	16 6.1	2 57.2	19 18.8	20 8.3	9 37.5
16	5 38 41.6	23 18.2	0 6.4	18 7.9	21 52.9	21 1.2	21 43.0	15 55.8	2 57.7	19 16.7	20 7.2	9 38.5
19	5 50 31.3	23 24.3	0 6.4	11 32.7	20 54.0	20 18.0	21 13.0	15 45.1	2 58.6	19 14.5	20 6.1	9 39.5
22	6 2 20.9	23 26.2	0 6.5	0 56.3	20 9.9	19 35.2	20 40.8	15 34.1	2 59.8	19 12.3	20 4.9	9 40.3
25	6 14 10.6	23 23.9	0 6.6	10S .2	19 49.5	18 53.6	20 6.6	15 22.7	3 1.5	19 9.9	20 3.6	9 41.1
28	6 26 .3	23 17.3	0 6.6	17 35.3	19 53.1	18 13.6	19 30.4	15 11.0	3 3.5	19 7.5	20 2.4	9 41.8
31	6 37 50.0	23 6.5	0 6.7	17 20.5	20 14.7	17 36.0	18 52.3	14 59.0	3 5.9	19 5.1	20 1.1	9 42.4

JANUARY 1998

LONGITUDE

DAY	EPHEM. SID. TIME (h m s)	☉ (° ′)	☊ (° ′)	☾ (° ′)	☿ (° ′)	♀ (° ′)	♂ (° ′)	♃ (° ′)	♄ (° ′)	♅ (° ′)	♆ (° ′)	♇ (° ′)
1	6 41 46.5	10♑21.7	13♍43.5	9♒58.3	18♐28.7	3♒23.9	10♒46.5	22♒15.3	13♈45.4	7♒ 7.5	28♑57.2	6♐47.3
2	6 45 43.1	11 22.9	13 40.3	24 7.3	19 6.8	3R10.0	11 33.7	22 27.8	13 47.2	7 10.7	28 59.4	6 49.3
3	6 49 39.6	12 24.0	13 37.1	8♓18.6	19 50.4	2 53.5	12 21.0	22 40.4	13 49.0	7 14.0	29 1.6	6 51.3
4	6 53 36.2	13 25.2	13 34.0	22 29.4	20 38.9	2 34.7	13 8.2	22 53.1	13 51.0	7 17.2	29 3.8	6 53.3
5	6 57 32.7	14 26.4	13 30.8	6♈37.9	21 31.8	2 13.5	13 55.5	23 5.8	13 53.1	7 20.5	29 6.0	6 55.3
6	7 1 29.3	15 27.5	13 27.6	20 42.9	22 28.5	1 50.1	14 42.8	23 18.6	13 55.3	7 23.8	29 8.2	6 57.3
7	7 5 25.8	16 28.7	13 24.4	4♉43.6	23 28.7	1 24.5	15 30.0	23 31.5	13 57.6	7 27.2	29 10.4	6 59.2
8	7 9 22.4	17 29.8	13 21.3	18 38.8	24 32.0	0 56.8	16 17.3	23 44.5	13 60.0	7 30.5	29 12.7	7 1.1
9	7 13 19.0	18 30.9	13 18.1	2♊27.3	25 38.0	0 27.3	17 4.6	23 57.5	14 2.5	7 33.9	29 14.9	7 3.0
10	7 17 15.5	19 32.1	13 14.9	16 6.9	26 46.5	29♑56.1	17 51.9	24 10.6	14 5.1	7 37.2	29 17.2	7 4.9
11	7 21 12.1	20 33.2	13 11.7	29 35.5	27 57.2	29 23.3	18 39.2	24 23.7	14 7.8	7 40.6	29 19.4	7 6.8
12	7 25 8.6	21 34.3	13 8.5	12♋50.8	29 9.9	28 49.2	19 26.6	24 36.9	14 10.6	7 44.0	29 21.7	7 8.6
13	7 29 5.2	22 35.4	13 5.4	25 50.9	0♑24.3	28 14.1	20 13.9	24 50.2	14 13.5	7 47.4	29 23.9	7 10.4
14	7 33 1.7	23 36.5	13 2.2	8♌34.9	1 40.4	27 38.1	21 1.2	25 3.5	14 16.5	7 50.8	29 26.2	7 12.2
15	7 36 58.3	24 37.6	12 59.0	21 2.9	2 58.0	27 1.5	21 48.5	25 16.9	14 19.6	7 54.3	29 28.5	7 14.0
16	7 40 54.9	25 38.7	12 55.8	3♍16.2	4 16.9	26 24.6	22 35.9	25 30.3	14 22.8	7 57.7	29 30.7	7 15.7
17	7 44 51.4	26 39.8	12 52.7	15 17.4	5 37.0	25 47.6	23 23.2	25 43.8	14 26.1	8 1.2	29 33.0	7 17.4
18	7 48 48.0	27 40.9	12 49.5	27 10.1	6 58.4	25 10.9	24 10.6	25 57.4	14 29.5	8 4.7	29 35.3	7 19.1
19	7 52 44.5	28 42.0	12 46.3	8♎58.4	8 20.7	24 34.5	24 57.9	26 10.9	14 33.0	8 8.2	29 37.6	7 20.8
20	7 56 41.1	29 43.1	12 43.1	20 47.2	9 44.1	23 58.9	25 45.2	26 24.6	14 36.6	8 11.6	29 39.9	7 22.4
21	8 0 37.6	0♒44.1	12 40.0	2♏41.9	11 8.4	23 24.2	26 32.6	26 38.3	14 40.3	8 15.1	29 42.2	7 24.1
22	8 4 34.2	1 45.2	12 36.8	14 47.7	12 33.5	22 50.7	27 19.9	26 52.0	14 44.0	8 18.6	29 44.4	7 25.6
23	8 8 30.7	2 46.2	12 33.6	27 9.4	13 59.6	22 18.6	28 7.3	27 5.8	14 47.9	8 22.1	29 46.7	7 27.2
24	8 12 27.3	3 47.3	12 30.4	9♐51.1	15 26.4	21 48.0	28 54.6	27 19.6	14 51.8	8 25.6	29 49.0	7 28.7
25	8 16 23.9	4 48.3	12 27.2	22 55.9	16 54.0	21 19.2	29 41.9	27 33.4	14 55.9	8 29.1	29 51.3	7 30.2
26	8 20 20.4	5 49.3	12 24.1	6♑24.8	18 22.3	20 52.3	0♓29.3	27 47.3	15 .0	8 32.6	29 53.5	7 31.7
27	8 24 17.0	6 50.4	12 20.9	20 17.0	19 51.4	20 27.5	1 16.6	28 1.3	15 4.2	8 36.1	29 55.8	7 33.2
28	8 28 13.5	7 51.4	12 17.7	4♒29.5	21 21.3	20 4.8	2 3.9	28 15.2	15 8.5	8 39.6	29 58.1	7 34.6
29	8 32 10.1	8 52.3	12 14.5	18 57.2	22 51.8	19 44.4	2 51.2	28 29.3	15 12.9	8 43.1	0♒ .3	7 36.0
30	8 36 6.6	9 53.3	12 11.4	3♓33.9	24 23.0	19 26.3	3 38.5	28 43.3	15 17.4	8 46.7	0 2.6	7 37.3
31	8 40 3.2	10 54.3	12 8.2	18 13.0	25 55.0	19 10.6	4 25.8	28 57.4	15 22.0	8 50.2	0 4.8	7 38.6

LATITUDE

DAY	SID. TIME	☉	☊	☾	☿	♀	♂	♃	♄	♅	♆	♇
1	6 41 46.5	0 .0	0 .0	2N43.4	2N32.3	2N 2.9	1S10.1	0S52.2	2S30.6	0S36.1	0N21.8	11N53.4
4	6 53 36.2	0 .0	0 .0	0S54.6	2 8.1	2 48.9	1 9.2	0 52.1	2 29.8	0 36.1	0 21.8	11 53.9
7	7 5 25.8	0 .0	0 .0	4 3.5	1 41.7	3 35.6	1 8.3	0 52.1	2 29.0	0 36.1	0 21.7	11 54.4
10	7 17 15.5	0 .0	0 .0	5 5.4	1 14.7	4 21.5	1 7.3	0 52.0	2 28.2	0 36.0	0 21.7	11 54.9
13	7 29 5.2	0 .0	0 .0	3 40.0	0 47.9	5 4.7	1 6.3	0 52.0	2 27.4	0 36.0	0 21.6	11 55.5
16	7 40 54.9	0 .0	0 .0	0 43.2	0 22.0	5 43.6	1 5.1	0 52.0	2 26.7	0 36.0	0 21.6	11 56.1
19	7 52 44.5	0 .0	0 .0	2N24.9	0S 2.6	6 16.5	1 4.0	0 52.0	2 25.9	0 36.0	0 21.6	11 56.8
22	8 4 34.2	0 .0	0 .0	4 38.9	0 25.6	6 42.4	1 2.8	0 52.0	2 25.2	0 36.0	0 21.5	11 57.5
25	8 16 23.9	0 .0	0 .0	5 4.8	0 46.7	7 .9	1 1.5	0 52.0	2 24.5	0 36.0	0 21.5	11 58.3
28	8 28 13.5	0 .0	0 .0	3 5.4	1 5.8	7 12.0	1 .2	0 52.0	2 23.8	0 36.0	0 21.5	11 59.1
31	8 40 3.2	0 .0	0 .0	0S41.0	1 22.7	7 16.3	0 58.8	0 52.1	2 23.1	0 36.1	0 21.5	11 59.9

RIGHT ASCENSION

DAY	SID. TIME	☉	☊	☾	☿	♀	♂	♃	♄	♅	♆	♇
1	6 41 46.5	11♑16.2	15♍ .3	11♒39.5	17♐42.4	5♒12.3	13♒33.8	24♒54.4	13♈38.1	9♒41.1	1♒ .6	6♐57.9
2	6 45 43.1	12 22.5	14 57.3	25 53.5	18 22.2	4R54.4	14 21.6	25 6.6	13 39.6	9 44.4	1 2.9	6 59.9
3	6 49 39.6	13 28.6	14 54.4	9♓49.1	19 8.0	4 34.0	15 9.3	25 18.9	13 41.2	9 47.7	1 5.2	7 2.0
4	6 53 36.2	14 34.7	14 51.4	23 27.8	19 59.1	4 11.2	15 56.8	25 31.3	13 43.0	9 51.1	1 7.5	7 3.9
5	6 57 32.7	15 40.6	14 48.5	6♈55.5	20 55.0	3 46.1	16 44.3	25 43.7	13 44.8	9 54.4	1 9.8	7 5.9
6	7 1 29.3	16 46.4	14 45.5	20 20.2	21 55.2	3 18.7	17 31.6	25 56.2	13 46.7	9 57.8	1 12.1	7 7.9
7	7 5 25.8	17 52.1	14 42.6	3♉49.9	22 59.2	2 49.1	18 18.9	26 8.8	13 48.7	10 1.2	1 14.4	7 9.8
8	7 9 22.4	18 57.7	14 39.6	17 30.7	24 6.8	2 17.6	19 6.0	26 21.4	13 50.8	10 4.6	1 16.8	7 11.7
9	7 13 19.0	20 3.2	14 36.7	1♊24.5	25 17.5	1 44.3	19 53.0	26 34.1	13 53.0	10 8.1	1 19.1	7 13.6
10	7 17 15.5	21 8.5	14 33.7	15 28.4	26 31.1	1 9.3	20 39.9	26 46.8	13 55.3	10 11.5	1 21.4	7 15.5
11	7 21 12.1	22 13.7	14 30.8	29 34.2	27 47.3	0 32.9	21 26.7	26 59.6	13 57.7	10 15.0	1 23.8	7 17.3
12	7 25 8.6	23 18.7	14 27.8	13♋30.9	29 5.7	29♑55.4	22 13.3	27 12.4	14 .2	10 18.4	1 26.1	7 19.1
13	7 29 5.2	24 23.6	14 24.8	27 7.3	0♑26.4	29 16.9	22 59.9	27 25.3	14 2.8	10 21.9	1 28.5	7 20.9
14	7 33 1.7	25 28.3	14 21.9	10♌15.1	1 48.9	28 37.7	23 46.3	27 38.2	14 5.5	10 25.4	1 30.8	7 22.7
15	7 36 58.3	26 32.9	14 18.9	22 51.0	3 13.2	27 58.0	24 32.7	27 51.2	14 8.2	10 28.9	1 33.2	7 24.5
16	7 40 54.9	27 37.3	14 16.0	4♍56.2	4 39.1	27 18.2	25 18.9	28 4.2	14 11.1	10 32.4	1 35.6	7 26.2
17	7 44 51.4	28 41.5	14 13.0	16 36.0	6 6.5	26 38.5	26 5.0	28 17.3	14 14.0	10 36.0	1 37.9	7 27.9
18	7 48 48.0	29 45.6	14 10.1	27 58.0	7 35.3	25 59.3	26 51.1	28 30.4	14 17.1	10 39.5	1 40.4	7 29.7
19	7 52 44.5	0♒49.5	14 7.1	9♎11.6	9 5.2	25 20.6	27 37.0	28 43.6	14 20.2	10 43.1	1 42.7	7 31.4
20	7 56 41.1	1 53.2	14 4.2	20 26.9	10 36.3	24 42.8	28 22.8	28 56.8	14 23.4	10 46.6	1 45.1	7 33.0
21	8 0 37.6	2 56.7	14 1.2	1♏54.3	12 8.4	24 6.1	29 8.4	29 10.0	14 26.7	10 50.2	1 47.5	7 34.6
22	8 4 34.2	4 .1	13 58.2	13 43.6	13 41.5	23 30.8	29 54.0	29 23.2	14 30.1	10 53.7	1 49.8	7 36.2
23	8 8 30.7	5 3.2	13 55.3	26 3.6	15 15.4	22 57.1	0♓39.5	29 36.5	14 33.6	10 57.3	1 52.2	7 37.8
24	8 12 27.3	6 6.2	13 52.3	9♐ .2	16 50.2	22 25.1	1 24.9	29 49.9	14 37.2	11 .9	1 54.6	7 39.3
25	8 16 23.9	7 9.0	13 49.4	22 35.2	18 25.6	21 55.0	2 10.2	0♓ 3.2	14 40.8	11 4.4	1 56.9	7 40.8
26	8 20 20.4	8 11.6	13 46.4	6♑44.7	20 1.8	21 27.1	2 55.3	0 16.6	14 44.5	11 8.0	1 59.3	7 42.3
27	8 24 17.0	9 14.0	13 43.5	21 18.8	21 38.6	21 1.3	3 40.4	0 30.1	14 48.3	11 11.6	2 1.6	7 43.8
28	8 28 13.5	10 16.1	13 40.5	6♒ 3.7	23 16.0	20 37.8	4 25.4	0 43.5	14 52.2	11 15.2	2 4.0	7 45.2
29	8 32 10.1	11 18.1	13 37.5	20 45.6	24 53.8	20 16.8	5 10.3	0 57.0	14 56.2	11 18.8	2 6.4	7 46.6
30	8 36 6.6	12 19.9	13 34.6	5♓14.4	26 32.2	19 58.2	5 55.0	1 10.5	15 .3	11 22.3	2 8.7	7 48.0
31	8 40 3.2	13 21.5	13 31.6	19 26.0	28 11.0	19 42.1	6 39.7	1 24.0	15 4.4	11 25.9	2 11.0	7 49.3

DECLINATION

DAY	SID. TIME	☉	☊	☾	☿	♀	♂	♃	♄	♅	♆	♇
1	6 41 46.5	23S 1.9	0N 6.7	15S 7.3	20S24.5	17S24.1	18S39.2	14S54.9	3N 6.8	19S 4.3	20S .7	9S42.6
4	6 53 36.2	22 45.6	0 6.8	3 49.0	20 58.6	16 50.4	17 58.7	14 42.5	3 9.7	19 1.8	19 59.4	9 43.1
7	7 5 25.8	22 25.3	0 6.8	9N16.2	21 35.0	16 20.2	17 16.5	14 29.8	3 13.0	18 59.2	19 58.0	9 43.5
10	7 17 15.5	22 .9	0 6.9	17 38.9	22 9.2	15 54.0	16 32.6	14 16.8	3 16.6	18 56.6	19 56.7	9 43.8
13	7 29 5.2	21 32.7	0 7.0	17 22.2	22 38.3	15 32.1	15 47.2	14 3.5	3 20.6	18 54.0	19 55.3	9 44.1
16	7 40 54.9	21 .7	0 7.0	9 38.1	23 .1	15 14.5	15 .4	13 50.0	3 24.9	18 51.3	19 53.9	9 44.3
19	7 52 44.5	20 25.1	0 7.1	1S20.2	23 13.0	15 1.6	14 12.2	13 36.2	3 29.5	18 48.6	19 52.5	9 44.4
22	8 4 34.2	19 46.1	0 7.1	11 49.6	23 16.1	14 53.1	13 22.8	13 22.2	3 34.4	18 45.9	19 51.1	9 44.4
25	8 16 23.9	19 3.7	0 7.2	18 10.5	23 8.5	14 48.9	12 32.2	13 8.0	3 39.6	18 43.2	19 49.7	9 44.4
28	8 28 13.5	18 18.2	0 7.3	16 8.1	22 49.6	14 48.6	11 40.5	12 53.6	3 45.1	18 40.4	19 48.3	9 44.3
31	8 40 3.2	17 29.7	0 7.3	5 17.2	22 19.0	14 51.8	10 47.9	12 39.0	3 50.9	18 37.7	19 46.9	9 44.1

FEBRUARY 1998

LONGITUDE

DAY	EPHEM. SID. TIME h m s	☉ ° ′	☊ ° ′	☾ ° ′	☿ ° ′	♀ ° ′	♂ ° ′	♃ ° ′	♄ ° ′	♅ ° ′	♆ ° ′	♇ ° ′
1	8 43 59.7	11♒55.2	12♍ 5.0	2♈48.6	27♑27.6	18♑57.4	5♓13.1	29♒11.5	15♈26.6	8♒53.7	0♒ 7.1	7♐39.9
2	8 47 56.3	12 56.1	12 1.8	17 15.7	29 1.0	18R 46.6	6 .4	29 25.6	15 31.4	8 57.2	0 9.3	7 41.2
3	8 51 52.9	13 57.0	11 58.6	1♉31.1	0♒35.0	18 38.3	6 47.6	29 39.8	15 36.2	9 .7	0 11.5	7 42.4
4	8 55 49.4	14 57.9	11 55.5	15 32.7	2 9.8	18 32.4	7 34.8	29 54.0	15 41.1	9 4.2	0 13.7	7 43.6
5	8 59 46.0	15 58.7	11 52.3	29 19.9	3 45.3	18 29.0	8 22.1	0♓ 8.2	15 46.0	9 7.7	0 16.0	7 44.8
6	9 3 42.5	16 59.5	11 49.1	12♊52.4	5 21.5	18 28.0	9 9.3	0 22.5	15 51.1	9 11.2	0 18.2	7 46.0
7	9 7 39.1	18 .3	11 45.9	26 10.6	6 58.5	18D 29.5	9 56.5	0 36.7	15 56.2	9 14.6	0 20.4	7 47.1
8	9 11 35.6	19 1.1	11 42.8	9♋15.0	8 36.3	18 33.4	10 43.7	0 51.1	16 1.4	9 18.2	0 22.6	7 48.2
9	9 15 32.2	20 1.9	11 39.6	22 5.9	10 14.8	18 39.6	11 30.8	1 5.4	16 6.7	9 21.6	0 24.8	7 49.2
10	9 19 28.7	21 2.6	11 36.4	4♌43.9	11 54.2	18 48.0	12 18.0	1 19.7	16 12.0	9 25.1	0 26.9	7 50.3
11	9 23 25.3	22 3.3	11 33.2	17 9.8	13 34.3	18 58.7	13 5.1	1 34.0	16 17.5	9 28.5	0 29.1	7 51.2
12	9 27 21.8	23 3.9	11 30.1	29 24.3	15 15.2	19 11.6	13 52.2	1 48.4	16 22.9	9 32.0	0 31.2	7 52.2
13	9 31 18.4	24 4.6	11 26.9	11♍28.9	16 57.0	19 26.6	14 39.2	2 2.8	16 28.5	9 35.4	0 33.4	7 53.1
14	9 35 14.9	25 5.2	11 23.7	23 25.4	18 39.6	19 43.6	15 26.3	2 17.2	16 34.1	9 38.8	0 35.5	7 54.0
15	9 39 11.5	26 5.8	11 20.5	5♎16.3	20 23.1	20 2.7	16 13.3	2 31.6	16 39.8	9 42.2	0 37.6	7 54.8
16	9 43 8.1	27 6.4	11 17.3	17 4.6	22 7.5	20 23.6	17 .3	2 46.0	16 45.6	9 45.6	0 39.7	7 55.6
17	9 47 4.6	28 7.0	11 14.2	28 53.9	23 52.7	20 46.5	17 47.3	3 .4	16 51.4	9 49.0	0 41.7	7 56.4
18	9 51 1.2	29 7.5	11 11.0	10♏48.4	25 38.9	21 11.1	18 34.2	3 14.8	16 57.3	9 52.3	0 43.8	7 57.2
19	9 54 57.7	0♓ 8.0	11 7.8	22 52.7	27 25.9	21 37.5	19 21.2	3 29.3	17 3.2	9 55.7	0 45.9	7 57.9
20	9 58 54.3	1 8.5	11 4.6	5♐11.3	29 13.8	22 5.5	20 8.1	3 43.7	17 9.2	9 59.0	0 47.9	7 58.6
21	10 2 50.8	2 9.0	11 1.5	17 48.9	1♓ 2.7	22 35.1	20 55.0	3 58.1	17 15.3	10 2.4	0 49.9	7 59.2
22	10 6 47.4	3 9.5	10 58.3	0♑49.2	2 52.4	23 6.3	21 41.8	4 12.6	17 21.4	10 5.7	0 51.9	7 59.8
23	10 10 43.9	4 9.9	10 55.1	14 15.0	4 42.9	23 38.9	22 28.7	4 27.1	17 27.6	10 8.9	0 53.9	8 .4
24	10 14 40.5	5 10.3	10 51.9	28 7.5	6 34.3	24 13.0	23 15.5	4 41.5	17 33.8	10 12.2	0 55.9	8 .9
25	10 18 37.0	6 10.7	10 48.7	12♒25.4	8 26.5	24 48.4	24 2.3	4 56.0	17 40.1	10 15.5	0 57.8	8 1.5
26	10 22 33.6	7 11.1	10 45.6	27 5.0	10 19.4	25 25.1	24 49.0	5 10.4	17 46.5	10 18.7	0 59.7	8 1.9
27	10 26 30.1	8 11.4	10 42.4	12♓ .0	12 12.9	26 3.1	25 35.8	5 24.9	17 52.9	10 21.9	1 1.7	8 2.4
28	10 30 26.7	9 11.7	10 39.2	27 2.5	14 7.1	26 42.3	26 22.5	5 39.3	17 59.4	10 25.1	1 3.5	8 2.8

LATITUDE

DAY	SID. TIME	☉	☊	☾	☿	♀	♂	♃	♄	♅	♆	♇
1	8 43 59.7	0 .0	0 .0	1S58.3	1S27.8	7N16.4	0S58.4	0S52.1	2S22.9	0S36.1	0N21.4	12N .2
4	8 55 49.4	0 .0	0 .0	4 44.8	1 41.4	7 12.9	0 56.9	0 52.1	2 22.2	0 36.1	0 21.4	12 1.0
7	9 7 39.1	0 .0	0 .0	5 3.5	1 52.3	7 4.7	0 55.5	0 52.2	2 21.6	0 36.1	0 21.4	12 1.9
10	9 19 28.7	0 .0	0 .0	3 5.0	2 .2	6 52.6	0 54.0	0 52.3	2 21.0	0 36.1	0 21.4	12 2.8
13	9 31 18.4	0 .0	0 .0	0N 5.5	2 4.8	6 37.6	0 52.4	0 52.4	2 20.5	0 36.2	0 21.4	12 3.8
16	9 43 8.1	0 .0	0 .0	3 9.3	2 5.9	6 20.2	0 50.8	0 52.6	2 19.9	0 36.2	0 21.3	12 4.7
19	9 54 57.7	0 .0	0 .0	5 2.7	2 3.0	6 1.1	0 49.2	0 52.7	2 19.4	0 36.2	0 21.3	12 5.7
22	10 6 47.4	0 .0	0 .0	4 58.1	1 55.8	5 40.6	0 47.5	0 52.9	2 18.9	0 36.3	0 21.3	12 6.7
25	10 18 37.0	0 .0	0 .0	2 30.1	1 43.9	5 19.3	0 45.8	0 53.0	2 18.4	0 36.3	0 21.3	12 7.7
28	10 30 26.7	0 .0	0 .0	1S30.6	1 26.9	4 57.4	0 44.1	0 53.2	2 18.0	0 36.4	0 21.3	12 8.7

RIGHT ASCENSION

DAY	SID. TIME	☉	☊	☾	☿	♀	♂	♃	♄	♅	♆	♇
1	8 43 59.7	14♒22.8	13♍28.7	3♈21.7	29♑50.2	19♑28.6	7♓24.3	1♓37.6	15♈ 8.6	11♒29.5	2♒13.4	7♐50.6
2	8 47 56.3	15 24.0	13 25.7	17 6.6	1♒29.8	19R 17.7	8 8.8	1 51.2	15 12.9	11 33.0	2 15.7	7 51.9
3	8 51 52.9	16 24.9	13 22.7	0♉47.2	3 9.8	19 9.4	8 53.2	2 4.7	15 17.3	11 36.6	2 18.0	7 53.2
4	8 55 49.4	17 25.7	13 19.8	14 29.3	4 50.0	19 3.7	9 37.5	2 18.4	15 21.7	11 40.2	2 20.3	7 54.4
5	8 59 46.0	18 26.2	13 16.8	28 16.3	6 30.6	19 .5	10 21.7	2 32.0	15 26.2	11 43.7	2 22.6	7 55.6
6	9 3 42.5	19 26.5	13 13.9	12♊ 7.7	8 11.4	18 59.9	11 5.8	2 45.6	15 30.8	11 47.3	2 24.9	7 56.8
7	9 7 39.1	20 26.6	13 10.9	25 59.3	9 52.5	19D 1.8	11 49.9	2 59.3	15 35.5	11 50.8	2 27.2	7 57.9
8	9 11 35.6	21 26.6	13 7.9	9♋43.7	11 33.9	19 6.3	12 33.9	3 13.0	15 40.2	11 54.4	2 29.5	7 59.1
9	9 15 32.2	22 26.3	13 5.0	23 12.4	13 15.4	19 13.1	13 17.7	3 26.7	15 45.0	11 57.9	2 31.7	8 .1
10	9 19 28.7	23 25.8	13 2.0	6♌18.4	14 57.2	19 22.4	14 1.5	3 40.4	15 49.9	12 1.4	2 34.0	8 1.2
11	9 23 25.3	24 25.2	12 59.1	18 57.6	16 39.1	19 33.9	14 45.2	3 54.1	15 54.8	12 4.9	2 36.2	8 2.2
12	9 27 21.8	25 24.3	12 56.1	1♍ 9.5	18 21.3	19 47.8	15 28.8	4 7.8	15 59.8	12 8.4	2 38.5	8 3.2
13	9 31 18.4	26 23.2	12 53.1	12 57.1	20 3.6	20 3.8	16 12.4	4 21.5	16 4.9	12 11.9	2 40.7	8 4.1
14	9 35 14.9	27 22.0	12 50.2	24 25.9	21 46.1	20 22.0	16 55.9	4 35.2	16 10.0	12 15.4	2 42.9	8 5.0
15	9 39 11.5	28 20.5	12 47.2	5♎43.1	23 28.8	20 42.3	17 39.2	4 48.9	16 15.2	12 18.9	2 45.0	8 5.9
16	9 43 8.1	29 18.9	12 44.2	16 57.0	25 11.7	21 4.6	18 22.6	5 2.6	16 20.5	12 22.3	2 47.2	8 6.7
17	9 47 4.6	0♓17.1	12 41.3	28 16.5	26 54.7	21 28.9	19 5.8	5 16.4	16 25.8	12 25.7	2 49.4	8 7.6
18	9 51 1.2	1 15.2	12 38.3	9♏50.5	28 37.9	21 55.0	19 49.0	5 30.1	16 31.2	12 29.2	2 51.5	8 8.3
19	9 54 57.7	2 13.0	12 35.3	21 47.5	0♓21.2	22 23.0	20 32.2	5 43.8	16 36.6	12 32.6	2 53.6	8 9.1
20	9 58 54.3	3 10.7	12 32.4	4♐14.3	2 4.7	22 52.7	21 15.2	5 57.5	16 42.2	12 35.9	2 55.7	8 9.8
21	10 2 50.8	4 8.3	12 29.4	17 15.4	3 48.3	23 24.0	21 58.3	6 11.3	16 47.7	12 39.3	2 57.8	8 10.5
22	10 6 47.4	5 5.7	12 26.4	0♑51.6	5 32.1	23 57.0	22 41.2	6 25.0	16 53.3	12 42.7	2 59.9	8 11.1
23	10 10 43.9	6 2.9	12 23.5	14 58.8	7 15.9	24 31.5	23 24.1	6 38.7	16 59.0	12 46.0	3 2.0	8 11.8
24	10 14 40.5	6 60.0	12 20.5	29 28.5	8 59.9	25 7.5	24 7.0	6 52.4	17 4.7	12 49.3	3 4.0	8 12.3
25	10 18 37.0	7 56.9	12 17.6	14♒ 9.7	10 43.9	25 44.9	24 49.8	7 6.1	17 10.5	12 52.6	3 6.0	8 12.9
26	10 22 33.6	8 53.7	12 14.6	28 51.7	12 28.0	26 23.7	25 32.5	7 19.8	17 16.3	12 55.9	3 8.0	8 13.4
27	10 26 30.1	9 50.4	12 11.6	13♓27.1	14 12.0	27 3.8	26 15.2	7 33.5	17 22.2	12 59.2	3 10.0	8 13.9
28	10 30 26.7	10 46.9	12 8.7	27 53.1	15 55.9	27 45.1	26 57.9	7 47.2	17 28.2	13 2.4	3 12.0	8 14.3

DECLINATION

DAY	SID. TIME	☉	☊	☾	☿	♀	♂	♃	♄	♅	♆	♇
1	8 43 59.7	17S12.9	0N 7.4	0S41.5	22S 6.1	14S53.5	10S30.1	12S34.0	3N52.9	18S36.8	19S46.5	9S44.0
4	8 55 49.4	16 20.7	0 7.4	11N56.9	21 19.4	15 .2	9 36.3	12 19.2	3 59.0	18 34.0	19 45.1	9 43.7
7	9 7 39.1	15 26.0	0 7.5	18 19.6	20 20.3	15 8.7	8 41.8	12 4.2	4 5.4	18 31.3	19 43.7	9 43.3
10	9 19 28.7	14 28.9	0 7.6	16 5.1	19 8.6	15 18.3	7 46.6	11 49.0	4 12.0	18 28.5	19 42.3	9 42.9
13	9 31 18.4	13 29.7	0 7.6	7 20.5	17 44.2	15 28.0	6 50.9	11 33.7	4 18.9	18 25.8	19 40.9	9 42.4
16	9 43 8.1	12 28.5	0 7.7	3S47.5	16 7.1	15 37.3	5 54.7	11 18.3	4 25.9	18 23.1	19 39.6	9 41.8
19	9 54 57.7	11 25.4	0 7.7	13 36.3	14 17.2	15 45.3	4 58.1	11 2.8	4 33.1	18 20.4	19 38.3	9 41.2
22	10 6 47.4	10 20.8	0 7.8	18 28.0	12 14.9	15 51.6	4 1.2	10 47.1	4 40.5	18 17.8	19 37.0	9 40.5
25	10 18 37.0	9 14.7	0 7.9	14 40.3	10 .6	15 55.5	3 4.2	10 31.5	4 48.1	18 15.2	19 35.7	9 39.8
28	10 30 26.7	8 7.3	0 7.9	2 33.7	7 35.1	15 56.7	2 7.0	10 15.7	4 55.8	18 12.6	19 34.5	9 39.0

MARCH 1998

LONGITUDE

DAY	EPHEM. SID. TIME (h m s)	☉ ° ′	☊ ° ′	☽ ° ′	☿ ° ′	♀ ° ′	♂ ° ′	♃ ° ′	♄ ° ′	♅ ° ′	♆ ° ′	♇ ° ′
1	10 34 23.2	10 ♓ 12.0	10 ♍ 36.0	12 ♈ 3.7	16 ♓ 1.7	27 ♑ 22.7	27 ♓ 9.2	5 ♓ 53.8	18 ♈ 5.9	10 ♒ 28.3	1 ♒ 5.5	8 ♐ 3.2
2	10 38 19.8	11 12.3	10 32.9	26 55.3	17 56.6	28 4.1	27 55.8	6 8.3	18 12.5	10 31.4	1 7.3	8 3.5
3	10 42 16.4	12 12.5	10 29.7	11 ♉ 30.8	19 51.7	28 46.6	28 42.4	6 22.7	18 19.1	10 34.6	1 9.2	8 3.8
4	10 46 12.9	13 12.7	10 26.5	25 45.8	21 46.7	29 30.1	29 29.0	6 37.1	18 25.7	10 37.6	1 11.0	8 4.1
5	10 50 9.5	14 12.8	10 23.3	9 ♊ 38.2	23 41.5	0 ♒ 14.6	0 ♈ 15.5	6 51.5	18 32.4	10 40.7	1 12.8	8 4.3
6	10 54 6.0	15 12.9	10 20.1	23 8.0	25 35.7	0 60.0	1 2.0	7 5.9	18 39.2	10 43.8	1 14.5	8 4.5
7	10 58 2.6	16 13.0	10 17.0	6 ♋ 16.7	27 29.1	1 46.3	1 48.5	7 20.3	18 46.0	10 46.8	1 16.3	8 4.6
8	11 1 59.1	17 13.0	10 13.8	19 6.6	29 21.4	2 33.5	2 34.9	7 34.6	18 52.8	10 49.8	1 18.0	8 4.8
9	11 5 55.7	18 13.0	10 10.6	1 ♌ 40.4	1 ♈ 12.1	3 21.5	3 21.3	7 49.0	18 59.7	10 52.7	1 19.7	8 4.8
10	11 9 52.2	19 13.0	10 7.4	14 .9	3 .8	4 10.4	4 7.6	8 3.3	19 6.6	10 55.7	1 21.4	8 4.9
11	11 13 48.8	20 12.9	10 4.2	26 10.7	4 47.1	4 60.0	4 53.9	8 17.6	19 13.6	10 58.6	1 23.0	8 4.9
12	11 17 45.3	21 12.8	10 1.1	8 ♍ 12.2	6 30.5	5 50.4	5 40.2	8 31.9	19 20.5	11 1.5	1 24.7	8 4.9
13	11 21 41.9	22 12.7	9 57.9	20 7.6	8 10.6	6 41.4	6 26.4	8 46.1	19 27.6	11 4.3	1 26.3	8 R 4.8
14	11 25 38.4	23 12.5	9 54.7	1 ♎ 58.9	9 46.7	7 33.2	7 12.6	9 .4	19 34.6	11 7.1	1 27.9	8 4.8
15	11 29 35.0	24 12.3	9 51.5	13 48.2	11 18.5	8 25.6	7 58.7	9 14.6	19 41.7	11 9.9	1 29.4	8 4.6
16	11 33 31.5	25 12.0	9 48.4	25 37.6	12 45.4	9 18.7	8 44.8	9 28.8	19 48.9	11 12.7	1 31.0	8 4.5
17	11 37 28.1	26 11.8	9 45.2	7 ♏ 29.5	14 6.8	10 12.4	9 30.9	9 43.0	19 56.0	11 15.4	1 32.5	8 4.3
18	11 41 24.6	27 11.5	9 42.0	19 26.8	15 22.5	11 6.7	10 16.9	9 57.1	20 3.2	11 18.1	1 33.9	8 4.1
19	11 45 21.2	28 11.1	9 38.8	1 ♐ 32.7	16 31.9	12 1.6	11 2.9	10 11.2	20 10.4	11 20.8	1 35.4	8 3.8
20	11 49 17.7	29 10.8	9 35.6	13 50.7	17 34.7	12 57.0	11 48.9	10 25.3	20 17.7	11 23.4	1 36.8	8 3.5
21	11 53 14.3	0 ♈ 10.4	9 32.5	26 24.7	18 30.5	13 53.0	12 34.8	10 39.3	20 25.0	11 26.0	1 38.2	8 3.2
22	11 57 10.8	1 10.0	9 29.3	9 ♑ 18.7	19 19.1	14 49.5	13 20.7	10 53.4	20 32.3	11 28.6	1 39.7	8 2.9
23	12 1 7.4	2 9.6	9 26.1	22 36.0	20 .2	15 46.4	14 6.5	11 7.4	20 39.7	11 31.2	1 41.0	8 2.5
24	12 5 3.9	3 9.1	9 22.9	6 ♒ 19.1	20 33.6	16 43.8	14 52.3	11 21.4	20 47.0	11 33.7	1 42.3	8 2.1
25	12 9 .5	4 8.6	9 19.8	20 29.0	20 59.2	17 41.7	15 38.1	11 35.3	20 54.4	11 36.1	1 43.6	8 1.6
26	12 12 57.0	5 8.1	9 16.6	5 ♓ 4.3	21 17.1	18 40.0	16 23.8	11 49.2	21 1.8	11 38.5	1 44.9	8 1.2
27	12 16 53.6	6 7.5	9 13.4	20 .7	21 27.1	19 38.7	17 9.4	12 3.0	21 9.2	11 40.9	1 46.1	8 .6
28	12 20 50.1	7 6.9	9 10.2	5 ♈ 11.0	21 29.5	20 37.8	17 55.1	12 16.8	21 16.7	11 43.3	1 47.3	8 .1
29	12 24 46.7	8 6.3	9 7.0	20 25.9	21 R 24.5	21 37.3	18 40.6	12 30.6	21 24.1	11 45.6	1 48.5	7 59.5
30	12 28 43.3	9 5.7	9 3.9	5 ♉ 35.1	21 12.3	22 37.2	19 26.2	12 44.3	21 31.6	11 47.9	1 49.6	7 58.9
31	12 32 39.8	10 5.0	9 .7	20 29.2	20 53.3	23 37.4	20 11.7	12 57.9	21 39.1	11 50.1	1 50.8	7 58.3

LATITUDE

DAY	EPHEM. SID. TIME (h m s)	☉ ° ′	☊ ° ′	☽ ° ′	☿ ° ′	♀ ° ′	♂ ° ′	♃ ° ′	♄ ° ′	♅ ° ′	♆ ° ′	♇ ° ′
1	10 34 23.2	0 .0	0 .0	2 S 46.6	1 S 20.1	4 N 50.1	0 S 43.5	0 S 53.3	2 S 17.8	0 S 36.4	0 N 21.3	12 N 9.0
4	10 46 12.9	0 .0	0 .0	5 7.5	0 55.9	4 27.8	0 41.8	0 53.5	2 17.4	0 36.5	0 21.3	12 10.0
7	10 58 2.6	0 .0	0 .0	4 46.6	0 26.4	4 5.4	0 40.0	0 54.0	2 17.0	0 36.5	0 21.3	12 11.0
10	11 9 52.2	0 .0	0 .0	2 22.4	0 N 7.8	3 43.1	0 38.2	0 54.2	2 16.7	0 36.6	0 21.3	12 12.0
13	11 21 41.9	0 .0	0 .0	0 N 52.7	0 45.6	3 20.9	0 36.4	0 54.5	2 16.4	0 36.7	0 21.3	12 12.9
16	11 33 31.5	0 .0	0 .0	3 44.4	1 24.8	2 59.1	0 34.5	0 54.5	2 16.1	0 36.8	0 21.3	12 13.9
19	11 45 21.2	0 .0	0 .0	5 12.2	2 2.8	2 37.7	0 32.7	0 54.8	2 15.8	0 36.8	0 21.3	12 14.9
22	11 57 10.8	0 .0	0 .0	4 36.6	2 36.7	2 16.7	0 30.8	0 55.1	2 15.6	0 36.9	0 21.3	12 15.8
25	12 9 .5	0 .0	0 .0	1 47.8	3 3.1	1 56.3	0 28.9	0 55.4	2 15.3	0 37.0	0 21.3	12 16.7
28	12 20 50.1	0 .0	0 .0	2 S 12.0	3 19.0	1 36.5	0 27.0	0 55.8	2 15.2	0 37.1	0 21.3	12 17.6
31	12 32 39.8	0 .0	0 .0	4 55.0	3 21.6	1 17.4	0 25.0	0 56.1	2 15.0	0 37.2	0 21.3	12 18.4

RIGHT ASCENSION

DAY	EPHEM. SID. TIME (h m s)	☉ ° ′	☊ ° ′	☽ ° ′	☿ ° ′	♀ ° ′	♂ ° ′	♃ ° ′	♄ ° ′	♅ ° ′	♆ ° ′	♇ ° ′
1	10 34 23.2	11 ♓ 43.4	12 ♍ 5.7	12 ♈ 10.6	17 ♓ 39.7	28 ♑ 27.6	27 ♓ 40.6	8 ♓ .9	17 ♈ 34.2	13 ♒ 5.7	3 ♒ 14.0	8 ♐ 14.8
2	10 38 19.8	12 39.5	12 2.7	26 22.5	19 23.2	29 11.2	28 23.1	8 14.6	17 40.2	13 8.8	3 15.9	8 15.2
3	10 42 16.4	13 35.6	11 59.7	10 ♉ 32.2	21 6.4	29 55.9	29 5.7	8 28.2	17 46.3	13 12.0	3 17.8	8 15.5
4	10 46 12.9	14 31.6	11 56.8	24 41.1	22 49.0	0 ♒ 41.6	29 48.2	8 41.8	17 52.5	13 15.1	3 19.7	8 15.8
5	10 50 9.5	15 27.5	11 53.8	8 ♊ 47.9	24 31.0	1 28.4	0 ♈ 30.6	8 55.4	17 58.6	13 18.3	3 21.5	8 16.1
6	10 54 6.0	16 23.3	11 50.8	22 48.3	26 12.1	2 16.0	1 13.0	9 9.0	18 4.8	13 21.3	3 23.4	8 16.3
7	10 58 2.6	17 18.9	11 47.9	6 ♋ 36.0	27 52.1	3 4.6	1 55.4	9 22.6	18 11.1	13 24.4	3 25.2	8 16.5
8	11 1 59.1	18 14.5	11 44.9	20 4.6	29 30.7	3 54.0	2 37.8	9 36.1	18 17.4	13 27.4	3 26.9	8 16.7
9	11 5 55.7	19 9.9	11 41.9	3 ♌ 8.9	1 ♈ 7.7	4 44.2	3 20.1	9 49.6	18 23.8	13 30.5	3 28.7	8 16.8
10	11 9 52.2	20 5.3	11 39.0	15 46.4	2 42.8	5 35.2	4 2.4	10 3.1	18 30.1	13 33.4	3 30.4	8 16.9
11	11 13 48.8	21 .5	11 36.0	27 57.8	4 15.5	6 27.0	4 44.7	10 16.6	18 36.6	13 36.4	3 32.2	8 17.0
12	11 17 45.3	21 55.7	11 33.0	9 ♍ 46.1	5 45.6	7 19.5	5 26.9	10 30.0	18 43.0	13 39.3	3 33.9	8 17.0
13	11 21 41.9	22 50.8	11 30.1	21 16.4	7 12.6	8 12.6	6 9.1	10 43.5	18 49.5	13 42.2	3 35.5	8 17.0
14	11 25 38.4	23 45.8	11 27.1	2 ♎ 35.2	8 36.0	9 6.4	6 51.4	10 56.9	18 56.0	13 45.1	3 37.2	8 17.0
15	11 29 35.0	24 40.8	11 24.1	13 49.7	9 55.6	10 .8	7 33.6	11 10.2	19 2.6	13 47.9	3 38.8	8 R 16.9
16	11 33 31.5	25 35.7	11 21.1	25 7.4	11 10.8	10 55.8	8 15.7	11 23.6	19 9.2	13 50.7	3 40.4	8 16.8
17	11 37 28.1	26 30.6	11 18.2	6 ♏ 35.8	12 21.3	11 51.3	8 57.9	11 36.9	19 15.8	13 53.5	3 41.9	8 16.7
18	11 41 24.6	27 25.4	11 15.2	18 21.8	13 26.6	12 47.3	9 40.1	11 50.2	19 22.5	13 56.2	3 43.4	8 16.5
19	11 45 21.2	28 20.1	11 12.2	0 ♐ 31.2	14 26.4	13 43.9	10 22.2	12 3.4	19 29.2	13 58.9	3 44.9	8 16.3
20	11 49 17.7	29 14.9	11 9.2	13 8.2	15 20.4	14 40.8	11 4.4	12 16.6	19 35.9	14 1.6	3 46.4	8 16.1
21	11 53 14.3	0 ♈ 9.5	11 6.3	26 14.1	16 8.2	15 38.3	11 46.5	12 29.8	19 42.6	14 4.2	3 47.9	8 15.8
22	11 57 10.8	1 4.3	11 3.3	9 ♑ 47.6	16 49.6	16 36.1	12 28.7	12 43.0	19 49.5	14 6.8	3 49.4	8 15.6
23	12 1 7.4	1 58.9	11 .3	23 43.8	17 24.3	17 34.3	13 10.9	12 56.1	19 56.3	14 9.4	3 50.7	8 15.2
24	12 5 3.9	2 53.6	10 57.4	7 ♒ 56.3	17 52.3	18 32.9	13 53.1	13 9.2	20 3.1	14 11.9	3 52.1	8 14.9
25	12 9 .5	3 48.2	10 54.4	22 17.9	18 13.4	19 31.7	14 35.2	13 22.3	20 9.9	14 14.4	3 53.5	8 14.5
26	12 12 57.0	4 42.8	10 51.4	6 ♓ 43.4	18 27.7	20 30.9	15 17.4	13 35.3	20 16.8	14 16.9	3 54.8	8 14.0
27	12 16 53.6	5 37.4	10 48.4	21 9.9	18 35.1	21 30.4	15 59.6	13 48.2	20 23.7	14 19.3	3 56.0	8 13.6
28	12 20 50.1	6 32.0	10 45.5	5 ♈ 30.9	18 35.9	22 30.1	16 41.8	14 1.1	20 30.6	14 21.7	3 57.3	8 13.1
29	12 24 46.7	7 26.7	10 42.5	20 8.6	18 R 30.2	23 30.1	17 24.0	14 14.0	20 37.6	14 24.0	3 58.5	8 12.5
30	12 28 43.3	8 21.3	10 39.5	4 ♉ 44.0	18 18.3	24 30.3	18 6.2	14 26.8	20 44.5	14 26.3	3 59.7	8 12.0
31	12 32 39.8	9 15.9	10 36.5	19 23.3	18 .7	25 30.7	18 48.4	14 39.6	20 51.5	14 28.6	4 .8	8 11.4

DECLINATION

DAY	EPHEM. SID. TIME (h m s)	☉ ° ′	☊ ° ′	☽ ° ′	☿ ° ′	♀ ° ′	♂ ° ′	♃ ° ′	♄ ° ′	♅ ° ′	♆ ° ′	♇ ° ′
1	10 34 23.2	7 S 44.6	0 N 7.9	2 N 12.6	6 S 44.4	15 S 56.4	1 S 47.9	10 S 10.4	4 N 58.4	18 S 11.8	19 S 34.1	9 S 38.7
4	10 46 12.9	6 35.8	0 8.0	14 12.8	4 7.0	15 53.2	0 50.7	9 54.6	5 6.3	18 9.3	19 32.9	9 37.9
7	10 58 2.6	5 26.3	0 8.1	18 31.1	1 24.2	15 46.5	0 N 6.4	9 38.8	5 14.3	18 6.9	19 31.7	9 37.0
10	11 9 52.2	4 16.1	0 8.1	14 20.9	1 N 19.1	15 35.9	1 3.3	9 23.0	5 22.4	18 4.5	19 30.6	9 36.0
13	11 21 41.9	3 5.4	0 8.2	4 43.1	3 56.4	15 21.3	2 .0	9 7.2	5 30.6	18 2.2	19 29.5	9 35.1
16	11 33 31.5	1 54.4	0 8.3	6 S 25.1	6 20.4	15 2.6	2 56.3	8 51.4	5 38.9	17 60.0	19 28.5	9 34.1
19	11 45 21.2	0 43.3	0 8.3	15 22.2	8 23.3	14 39.6	3 52.3	8 35.6	5 47.2	17 57.8	19 27.5	9 33.0
22	11 57 10.8	0 N 27.9	0 8.4	18 30.7	9 58.6	14 12.3	4 47.7	8 19.9	5 55.6	17 55.7	19 26.6	9 32.0
25	12 9 .5	1 38.8	0 8.5	12 57.3	11 1.0	13 40.9	5 42.6	8 4.3	6 4.1	17 53.7	19 25.7	9 30.9
28	12 20 50.1	2 49.4	0 8.5	0 N 2.3	11 27.1	13 5.3	6 36.8	7 48.7	6 12.6	17 51.8	19 24.9	9 29.8
31	12 32 39.8	3 59.6	0 8.6	13 7.5	11 15.9	12 25.6	7 30.3	7 33.3	6 21.0	17 50.0	19 24.1	9 28.7

APRIL 1998

LONGITUDE

DAY	EPHEM. SID. TIME h m s	☉ ° ′	☊ ° ′	☽ ° ′	☿ ° ′	♀ ° ′	♂ ° ′	♃ ° ′	♄ ° ′	♅ ° ′	♆ ° ′	♇ ° ′
1	12 36 36.4	11♈ 4.2	8♍57.5	5♊ .7	20♈28.1	24♒38.0	20♈57.1	13♓11.6	21♈46.6	11♒52.3	1♒51.8	7♐57.6
2	12 40 32.9	12 3.4	8 54.3	19 5.3	19R57.3	25 38.9	21 42.5	13 25.1	21 54.1	11 54.4	1 52.9	7R56.9
3	12 44 29.5	13 2.6	8 51.1	2♋41.9	19 21.5	26 40.1	22 27.8	13 38.7	22 1.7	11 56.5	1 53.9	7 56.1
4	12 48 26.0	14 1.8	8 48.0	15 51.7	18 41.6	27 41.6	23 13.1	13 52.1	22 9.2	11 58.6	1 54.9	7 55.4
5	12 52 22.6	15 .9	8 44.8	28 37.9	17 58.3	28 43.4	23 58.4	14 5.6	22 16.8	12 .6	1 55.9	7 54.6
6	12 56 19.1	15 59.9	8 41.6	11♌ 4.4	17 12.7	29 45.6	24 43.6	14 18.9	22 24.3	12 2.6	1 56.8	7 53.8
7	13 0 15.7	16 59.0	8 38.4	23 15.6	16 25.7	0♓48.0	25 28.7	14 32.3	22 31.9	12 4.6	1 57.7	7 52.9
8	13 4 12.2	17 58.0	8 35.3	5♍15.8	15 38.1	1 50.6	26 13.8	14 45.5	22 39.5	12 6.5	1 58.6	7 52.0
9	13 8 8.8	18 56.9	8 32.1	17 8.9	14 50.9	2 53.6	26 58.8	14 58.7	22 47.1	12 8.3	1 59.4	7 51.1
10	13 12 5.3	19 55.8	8 28.9	28 58.2	14 5.0	3 56.8	27 43.8	15 11.9	22 54.7	12 10.1	2 .2	7 50.2
11	13 16 1.9	20 54.7	8 25.7	10♎46.7	13 21.2	5 .2	28 28.8	15 25.0	23 2.2	12 11.9	2 1.0	7 49.2
12	13 19 58.4	21 53.6	8 22.5	22 36.6	12 40.2	6 4.0	29 13.7	15 38.1	23 9.9	12 13.7	2 1.8	7 48.3
13	13 23 55.0	22 52.4	8 19.4	4♏29.6	12 2.7	7 7.9	29 58.6	15 51.0	23 17.5	12 15.4	2 2.5	7 47.3
14	13 27 51.5	23 51.2	8 16.2	16 27.6	11 29.1	8 12.0	0♉43.4	16 3.9	23 25.1	12 17.0	2 3.2	7 46.2
15	13 31 48.1	24 50.0	8 13.0	28 32.2	10 59.8	9 16.4	1 28.1	16 16.8	23 32.7	12 18.6	2 3.9	7 45.2
16	13 35 44.6	25 48.7	8 9.8	10♐45.2	10 35.3	10 21.0	2 12.8	16 29.6	23 40.3	12 20.2	2 4.5	7 44.1
17	13 39 41.2	26 47.4	8 6.7	23 8.8	10 15.7	11 25.8	2 57.5	16 42.3	23 47.9	12 21.7	2 5.1	7 43.0
18	13 43 37.7	27 46.1	8 3.5	5♑45.5	10 1.2	12 30.8	3 42.1	16 54.9	23 55.5	12 23.1	2 5.6	7 41.8
19	13 47 34.3	28 44.7	8 .3	18 38.2	9 51.9	13 36.1	4 26.6	17 7.5	24 3.1	12 24.5	2 6.1	7 40.7
20	13 51 30.9	29 43.3	7 57.1	1♒49.8	9 47.7	14 41.5	5 11.2	17 20.0	24 10.6	12 25.9	2 6.6	7 39.5
21	13 55 27.4	0♉41.9	7 53.9	15 23.3	9D48.7	15 47.0	5 55.6	17 32.4	24 18.2	12 27.2	2 7.1	7 38.3
22	13 59 24.0	1 40.5	7 50.8	29 20.6	9 54.7	16 52.8	6 40.0	17 44.8	24 25.8	12 28.5	2 7.5	7 37.0
23	14 3 20.5	2 39.0	7 47.6	13♓42.1	10 5.6	17 58.7	7 24.4	17 57.1	24 33.3	12 29.7	2 7.9	7 35.8
24	14 7 17.1	3 37.5	7 44.4	28 25.9	10 21.4	19 4.8	8 8.7	18 9.3	24 40.9	12 30.9	2 8.2	7 34.5
25	14 11 13.6	4 36.0	7 41.2	13♈27.0	10 41.8	20 11.1	8 53.0	18 21.4	24 48.4	12 32.0	2 8.6	7 33.2
26	14 15 10.2	5 34.4	7 38.1	28 37.8	11 6.6	21 17.5	9 37.2	18 33.5	24 55.9	12 33.1	2 8.8	7 31.9
27	14 19 6.7	6 32.8	7 34.9	13♉48.2	11 35.8	22 24.0	10 21.3	18 45.5	25 3.5	12 34.1	2 9.1	7 30.6
28	14 23 3.3	7 31.2	7 31.7	28 48.0	12 9.2	23 30.7	11 5.5	18 57.3	25 10.9	12 35.1	2 9.3	7 29.2
29	14 26 59.8	8 29.5	7 28.5	13♊28.0	12 46.4	24 37.5	11 49.5	19 9.2	25 18.4	12 36.0	2 9.5	7 27.9
30	14 30 56.4	9 27.9	7 25.3	27 41.8	13 27.5	25 44.5	12 33.5	19 20.9	25 25.9	12 36.9	2 9.7	7 26.5

LATITUDE

DAY	EPHEM. SID. TIME	☉	☊	☽	☿	♀	♂	♃	♄	♅	♆	♇
1	12 36 36.4	0 .0	0 .0	5S12.0	3N19.2	1N11.1	0S24.4	0S56.2	2S15.0	0S37.2	0N21.3	12N18.7
4	12 48 26.0	0 .0	0 .0	4 14.4	3 1.8	0 53.0	0 22.5	0 56.6	2 14.8	0 37.3	0 21.3	12 19.5
7	13 0 15.7	0 .0	0 .0	1 31.0	2 30.4	0 35.6	0 20.5	0 57.0	2 14.8	0 37.4	0 21.3	12 20.3
10	13 12 5.3	0 .0	0 .0	1N40.7	1 48.2	0 19.0	0 18.6	0 57.4	2 14.7	0 37.5	0 21.3	12 21.0
13	13 23 55.0	0 .0	0 .0	4 12.1	0 59.8	0 3.2	0 16.6	0 57.9	2 14.7	0 37.6	0 21.3	12 21.7
16	13 35 44.6	0 .0	0 .0	5 8.0	0 10.4	0S11.7	0 14.7	0 58.3	2 14.7	0 37.7	0 21.3	12 22.3
19	13 47 34.3	0 .0	0 .0	3 58.5	0S36.4	0 25.7	0 12.7	0 58.8	2 14.7	0 37.8	0 21.3	12 22.9
22	13 59 24.0	0 .0	0 .0	0 53.0	1 17.8	0 38.8	0 10.8	0 59.3	2 14.8	0 37.9	0 21.3	12 23.4
25	14 11 13.6	0 .0	0 .0	2S53.0	1 52.8	0 50.9	0 8.8	0 59.8	2 14.8	0 38.0	0 21.3	12 23.9
28	14 23 3.3	0 .0	0 .0	5 .5	2 20.7	1 2.1	0 6.9	1 .3	2 14.9	0 38.2	0 21.3	12 24.3

RIGHT ASCENSION

DAY	EPHEM. SID. TIME	☉	☊	☽	☿	♀	♂	♃	♄	♅	♆	♇
1	12 36 36.4	10♈10.6	10♍33.5	4♊ 2.6	17♈38.0	26♒31.3	19♈30.6	14♓52.4	20♈58.5	14♒30.8	4♒ 2.0	8♐10.8
2	12 40 32.9	11 5.3	10 30.6	18 34.6	17R10.5	27 32.1	20 12.9	15 5.0	21 5.5	14 33.0	4 3.1	8R10.1
3	12 44 29.5	12 .0	10 27.6	2♋50.2	16 39.2	28 33.1	20 55.2	15 17.7	21 12.5	14 35.1	4 4.1	8 9.5
4	12 48 26.0	12 54.8	10 24.6	16 41.0	16 4.6	29 34.2	21 37.5	15 30.3	21 19.6	14 37.2	4 5.1	8 8.7
5	12 52 22.6	13 49.5	10 21.6	0♌ 1.1	15 27.6	0♓35.4	22 19.8	15 42.8	21 26.6	14 39.2	4 6.1	8 8.0
6	12 56 19.1	14 44.3	10 18.7	12 48.5	14 49.1	1 36.8	23 2.1	15 55.3	21 33.7	14 41.3	4 7.1	8 7.2
7	13 0 15.7	15 39.2	10 15.7	25 5.0	14 9.8	2 38.3	23 44.5	16 7.7	21 40.7	14 43.2	4 8.0	8 6.4
8	13 4 12.2	16 34.1	10 12.7	6♍55.2	13 30.6	3 39.9	24 26.9	16 20.1	21 47.8	14 45.2	4 8.9	8 5.6
9	13 8 8.8	17 29.1	10 9.7	18 25.5	12 52.2	4 41.6	25 9.3	16 32.4	21 54.9	14 47.0	4 9.8	8 4.8
10	13 12 5.3	18 24.1	10 6.7	29 43.4	12 15.5	5 43.5	25 51.7	16 44.7	22 2.0	14 48.9	4 10.6	8 3.9
11	13 16 1.9	19 19.2	10 3.8	10♎56.7	11 41.0	6 45.4	26 34.2	16 56.9	22 9.1	14 50.7	4 11.4	8 3.0
12	13 19 58.4	20 14.4	10 .8	22 13.0	11 9.4	7 47.4	27 16.7	17 9.1	22 16.2	14 52.5	4 12.3	8 2.1
13	13 23 55.0	21 9.6	9 57.8	3♏39.6	10 41.1	8 49.5	27 59.3	17 21.1	22 23.3	14 54.2	4 13.0	8 1.2
14	13 27 51.5	22 4.9	9 54.8	15 22.6	10 16.6	9 51.6	28 41.8	17 33.2	22 30.5	14 55.8	4 13.7	8 .2
15	13 31 48.1	23 .3	9 51.8	27 27.0	9 56.1	10 53.8	29 24.4	17 45.1	22 37.6	14 57.5	4 14.4	7 59.2
16	13 35 44.6	23 55.8	9 48.9	9♐55.5	9 39.9	11 56.1	0♉ 7.1	17 57.0	22 44.7	14 59.0	4 15.0	7 58.1
17	13 39 41.2	24 51.4	9 45.9	22 48.5	9 28.1	12 58.5	0 49.7	18 8.9	22 51.8	15 .5	4 15.6	7 57.1
18	13 43 37.7	25 47.1	9 42.9	6♑ 3.7	9 20.9	14 .9	1 32.5	18 20.7	22 58.9	15 2.0	4 16.2	7 56.0
19	13 47 34.3	26 42.8	9 39.9	19 36.5	9 18.2	15 3.3	2 15.2	18 32.4	23 6.0	15 3.5	4 16.7	7 54.9
20	13 51 30.9	27 38.7	9 36.9	3♒21.3	9D20.0	16 5.8	2 58.0	18 44.0	23 13.1	15 4.8	4 17.2	7 53.8
21	13 55 27.4	28 34.7	9 34.0	17 13.1	9 26.4	17 8.3	3 40.9	18 55.6	23 20.3	15 6.2	4 17.7	7 52.6
22	13 59 24.0	29 30.8	9 31.0	1♓ 8.9	9 37.1	18 10.9	4 23.8	19 7.1	23 27.4	15 7.5	4 18.1	7 51.4
23	14 3 20.5	0♉27.0	9 28.0	15 8.3	9 52.0	19 13.5	5 6.7	19 18.5	23 34.5	15 8.7	4 18.5	7 50.2
24	14 7 17.1	1 23.4	9 25.0	29 14.0	10 11.1	20 16.2	5 49.7	19 29.9	23 41.5	15 9.9	4 18.9	7 49.0
25	14 11 13.6	2 19.8	9 22.0	13♈29.8	10 34.1	21 18.9	6 32.7	19 41.2	23 48.6	15 11.1	4 19.2	7 47.8
26	14 15 10.2	3 16.4	9 19.0	27 59.7	11 1.0	22 21.6	7 15.8	19 52.4	23 55.7	15 12.2	4 19.5	7 46.5
27	14 19 6.7	4 13.1	9 16.1	12♉45.0	11 31.5	23 24.4	7 58.9	20 3.5	24 2.8	15 13.2	4 19.8	7 45.2
28	14 23 3.3	5 9.9	9 13.1	27 42.4	12 5.5	24 27.2	8 42.1	20 14.5	24 9.8	15 14.2	4 20.0	7 43.9
29	14 26 59.8	6 6.9	9 10.1	12♊43.3	12 42.9	25 30.1	9 25.3	20 25.5	24 16.9	15 15.2	4 20.2	7 42.6
30	14 30 56.4	7 4.0	9 7.1	27 34.7	13 23.5	26 32.9	10 8.5	20 36.4	24 23.9	15 16.1	4 20.4	7 41.3

DECLINATION

DAY	EPHEM. SID. TIME	☉	☊	☽	☿	♀	♂	♃	♄	♅	♆	♇
1	12 36 36.4	4N22.8	0N 8.6	16N .8	11N 4.1	12S11.5	7N48.0	7S28.2	6N23.9	17S49.4	19S23.9	9S28.3
4	12 48 26.0	5 32.0	0 8.7	18 17.0	10 7.5	11 26.6	8 40.4	7 12.9	6 32.4	17 47.8	19 23.2	9 27.2
7	13 0 15.7	6 40.3	0 8.7	12 19.9	8 46.3	10 38.1	9 32.0	6 57.8	6 40.9	17 46.2	19 22.6	9 26.1
10	13 12 5.3	7 47.5	0 8.8	1 57.0	7 12.9	9 46.0	10 22.6	6 42.9	6 49.3	17 44.7	19 22.0	9 24.9
13	13 23 55.0	8 53.6	0 8.8	9S 3.4	5 40.7	8 50.5	11 12.2	6 28.1	6 57.7	17 43.4	19 21.5	9 23.8
16	13 35 44.6	9 58.4	0 8.9	16 58.4	4 21.0	7 52.0	12 .7	6 13.6	7 6.1	17 42.1	19 21.0	9 22.7
19	13 47 34.3	11 1.7	0 9.0	18 12.2	3 21.0	6 50.5	12 48.1	5 59.2	7 14.4	17 41.0	19 20.7	9 21.6
22	13 59 24.0	12 3.3	0 9.0	10 52.4	2 43.9	5 46.5	13 34.2	5 45.1	7 22.7	17 40.0	19 20.4	9 20.6
25	14 11 13.6	13 3.2	0 9.1	2N39.0	2 30.2	4 40.1	14 19.1	5 31.3	7 30.9	17 39.1	19 20.1	9 19.5
28	14 23 3.3	14 1.1	0 9.2	15 .0	2 38.6	3 31.6	15 2.7	5 17.7	7 38.9	17 38.3	19 19.9	9 18.5

MAY 1998

LONGITUDE

DAY	EPHEM. SID. TIME	☉	☊	☽	☿	♀	♂	♃	♄	♅	♆	♇
	h m s	° ′	° ′	° ′	° ′	° ′	° ′	° ′	° ′	° ′	° ′	° ′
1	14 34 52.9	10♉26.1	7♍22.2	11♋26.4	14♈12.3	26♓51.6	13♉17.5	19♓32.5	25♈33.3	12♒37.8	2♒ 9.8	7♐25.1
2	14 38 49.5	11 24.4	7 19.0	24 41.8	15 .5	27 58.8	14 1.4	19 44.0	25 40.8	12 38.5	2 9.9	7R23.7
3	14 42 46.0	12 22.7	7 15.8	7♌30.8	15 52.1	29 6.2	14 45.3	19 55.5	25 48.2	12 39.3	2 10.0	7 22.3
4	14 46 42.6	13 20.8	7 12.6	19 57.4	16 46.9	0♈13.6	15 29.1	20 6.9	25 55.6	12 40.0	2 10.0	7 20.8
5	14 50 39.2	14 19.0	7 9.5	2♍ 6.8	17 44.8	1 21.2	16 12.8	20 18.2	26 3.0	12 40.7	2 10.0	7 19.3
6	14 54 35.7	15 17.1	7 6.3	14 4.1	18 45.7	2 28.9	16 56.5	20 29.3	26 10.3	12 41.3	2 10.0	7 17.9
7	14 58 32.3	16 15.2	7 3.1	25 54.3	19 49.4	3 36.7	17 40.1	20 40.4	26 17.6	12 41.8	2R 9.9	7 16.4
8	15 2 28.8	17 13.2	6 59.9	7♎42.0	20 55.9	4 44.6	18 23.7	20 51.4	26 24.9	12 42.3	2 9.8	7 14.9
9	15 6 25.4	18 11.3	6 56.7	19 30.9	22 5.1	5 52.6	19 7.2	21 2.2	26 32.2	12 42.7	2 9.6	7 13.3
10	15 10 21.9	19 9.3	6 53.6	1♏23.9	23 16.9	7 .7	19 50.7	21 13.0	26 39.4	12 43.1	2 9.5	7 11.8
11	15 14 18.5	20 7.2	6 50.4	13 23.3	24 31.2	8 8.9	20 34.1	21 23.7	26 46.6	12 43.5	2 9.3	7 10.3
12	15 18 15.0	21 5.2	6 47.2	25 30.6	25 48.0	9 17.2	21 17.5	21 34.3	26 53.8	12 43.8	2 9.0	7 8.7
13	15 22 11.6	22 3.1	6 44.0	7♐46.9	27 7.2	10 25.6	22 .8	21 44.7	27 .9	12 44.0	2 8.8	7 7.1
14	15 26 8.1	23 1.0	6 40.9	20 12.8	28 28.8	11 34.1	22 44.1	21 55.1	27 8.0	12 44.2	2 8.5	7 5.6
15	15 30 4.7	23 58.8	6 37.7	2♑49.1	29 52.7	12 42.8	23 27.3	22 5.4	27 15.1	12 44.3	2 8.1	7 4.0
16	15 34 1.3	24 56.7	6 34.5	15 36.8	1♉18.9	13 51.5	24 10.4	22 15.5	27 22.2	12 44.4	2 7.8	7 2.4
17	15 37 57.8	25 54.5	6 31.3	28 37.1	2 47.4	15 .3	24 53.5	22 25.5	27 29.2	12 44.5	2 7.4	7 .8
18	15 41 54.4	26 52.3	6 28.2	11♒52.0	4 18.2	16 9.1	25 36.6	22 35.5	27 36.2	12 44.5	2 7.0	6 59.2
19	15 45 50.9	27 50.1	6 25.0	25 23.1	5 51.1	17 18.1	26 19.6	22 45.3	27 43.1	12R44.4	2 6.5	6 57.6
20	15 49 47.5	28 47.8	6 21.8	9♓12.4	7 26.3	18 27.1	27 2.6	22 55.0	27 50.0	12 44.3	2 6.0	6 56.0
21	15 53 44.0	29 45.6	6 18.6	23 20.8	9 3.8	19 36.3	27 45.5	23 4.5	27 56.9	12 44.2	2 5.5	6 54.3
22	15 57 40.6	0♊43.3	6 15.4	7♈47.6	10 43.4	20 45.5	28 28.4	23 14.0	28 3.7	12 44.0	2 5.0	6 52.7
23	16 1 37.1	1 41.0	6 12.3	22 30.1	12 25.2	21 54.8	29 11.2	23 23.3	28 10.5	12 43.7	2 4.4	6 51.1
24	16 5 33.7	2 38.8	6 9.1	7♉22.8	14 9.3	23 4.2	29 54.0	23 32.6	28 17.3	12 43.5	2 3.8	6 49.5
25	16 9 30.3	3 36.5	6 5.9	22 18.0	15 55.5	24 13.6	0♊36.7	23 41.7	28 24.0	12 43.1	2 3.2	6 47.8
26	16 13 26.8	4 34.1	6 2.7	7♊ 6.8	17 44.0	25 23.1	1 19.4	23 50.6	28 30.7	12 42.7	2 2.5	6 46.2
27	16 17 23.4	5 31.8	5 59.6	21 40.6	19 34.6	26 32.7	2 2.0	23 59.5	28 37.3	12 42.3	2 1.8	6 44.5
28	16 21 19.9	6 29.4	5 56.4	5♋52.3	21 27.4	27 42.3	2 44.5	24 8.2	28 43.9	12 41.8	2 1.1	6 42.9
29	16 25 16.5	7 27.0	5 53.2	19 37.7	23 22.3	28 52.0	3 27.0	24 16.8	28 50.4	12 41.3	2 .4	6 41.3
30	16 29 13.0	8 24.5	5 50.0	2♌55.6	25 19.3	0♉ 1.7	4 9.5	24 25.2	28 56.9	12 40.7	1 59.6	6 39.6
31	16 33 9.6	9 22.1	5 46.8	15 47.4	27 18.3	1 11.5	4 51.9	24 33.5	29 3.3	12 40.1	1 58.8	6 38.0

LATITUDE

DAY	EPHEM. SID. TIME	☉	☊	☽	☿	♀	♂	♃	♄	♅	♆	♇
1	14 34 52.9	0 .0	0 .0	4S16.2	2S41.7	1S12.4	0S 4.9	1S .9	2S15.1	0S38.3	0N21.3	12N24.7
4	14 46 42.6	0 .0	0 .0	1 36.5	2 55.9	1 21.7	0 3.0	1 1.4	2 15.3	0 38.4	0 21.3	12 25.0
7	14 58 32.3	0 .0	0 .0	1N32.3	3 3.7	1 30.0	0 1.0	1 2.0	2 15.5	0 38.5	0 21.3	12 25.3
10	15 10 21.9	0 .0	0 .0	4 2.9	3 5.4	1 37.4	0N .9	1 2.6	2 15.7	0 38.6	0 21.3	12 25.5
13	15 22 11.6	0 .0	0 .0	5 1.1	3 1.3	1 43.8	0 2.8	1 3.2	2 15.9	0 38.7	0 21.3	12 25.6
16	15 34 1.3	0 .0	0 .0	3 55.7	2 51.8	1 49.2	0 4.7	1 3.9	2 16.2	0 38.8	0 21.3	12 25.6
19	15 45 50.9	0 .0	0 .0	0 59.7	2 37.3	1 53.8	0 6.6	1 4.5	2 16.5	0 39.0	0 21.3	12 25.6
22	15 57 40.6	0 .0	0 .0	2S36.4	2 18.0	1 57.4	0 8.5	1 5.2	2 16.8	0 39.1	0 21.3	12 25.5
25	16 9 30.3	0 .0	0 .0	4 51.8	1 54.4	2 .1	0 10.4	1 5.9	2 17.2	0 39.2	0 21.3	12 25.4
28	16 21 19.9	0 .0	0 .0	4 20.6	1 27.1	2 1.9	0 12.3	1 6.6	2 17.6	0 39.3	0 21.3	12 25.2
31	16 33 9.6	0 .0	0 .0	1 42.2	0 56.9	2 2.8	0 14.1	1 7.3	2 18.0	0 39.4	0 21.3	12 24.9

RIGHT ASCENSION

DAY	EPHEM. SID. TIME	☉	☊	☽	☿	♀	♂	♃	♄	♅	♆	♇
1	14 34 52.9	8♉ 1.2	9♍ 4.1	12♋ 3.1	14♈ 7.2	27♓35.9	10♉51.8	20♓47.2	24♈30.9	15♒16.9	4♒20.5	7♐39.9
2	14 38 49.5	8 58.5	9 1.1	25 57.8	14 53.8	28 38.8	11 35.2	20 57.9	24 37.9	15 17.7	4 20.6	7R38.5
3	14 42 46.0	9 56.0	8 58.1	9♌13.6	15 43.3	29 41.9	12 18.6	21 8.6	24 45.0	15 18.5	4 20.7	7 37.2
4	14 46 42.6	10 53.6	8 55.2	21 50.7	16 35.5	0♈45.0	13 2.1	21 19.2	24 51.9	15 19.2	4 20.7	7 35.8
5	14 50 39.2	11 51.4	8 52.2	3♍54.1	17 30.4	1 48.1	13 45.5	21 29.6	24 58.9	15 19.9	4 20.7	7 34.4
6	14 54 35.7	12 49.2	8 49.2	15 31.3	18 27.8	2 51.3	14 29.1	21 40.0	25 5.8	15 20.5	4 20.7	7 32.9
7	14 58 32.3	13 47.2	8 46.2	26 51.2	19 27.6	3 54.6	15 12.6	21 50.3	25 12.7	15 21.0	4R20.6	7 31.5
8	15 2 28.8	14 45.4	8 43.2	8♎ 3.4	20 29.9	4 57.9	15 56.3	22 .5	25 19.6	15 21.5	4 20.5	7 30.0
9	15 6 25.4	15 43.6	8 40.2	19 16.8	21 34.6	6 1.3	16 39.9	22 10.6	25 26.5	15 22.0	4 20.3	7 28.5
10	15 10 21.9	16 42.1	8 37.2	0♏40.0	22 41.5	7 4.8	17 23.7	22 20.6	25 33.3	15 22.4	4 20.2	7 27.1
11	15 14 18.5	17 40.6	8 34.2	12 20.3	23 50.8	8 8.3	18 7.4	22 30.5	25 40.1	15 22.8	4 19.9	7 25.6
12	15 18 15.0	18 39.3	8 31.3	24 22.9	25 2.2	9 12.0	18 51.2	22 40.4	25 46.9	15 23.1	4 19.7	7 24.0
13	15 22 11.6	19 38.2	8 28.3	6♐50.9	26 16.0	10 15.8	19 35.1	22 50.1	25 53.7	15 23.3	4 19.4	7 22.5
14	15 26 8.1	20 37.2	8 25.3	19 43.8	27 31.9	11 19.6	20 19.0	22 59.7	26 .4	15 23.5	4 19.1	7 21.0
15	15 30 4.7	21 36.3	8 22.3	2♑58.2	28 50.2	12 23.6	21 3.0	23 9.3	26 7.1	15 23.7	4 18.8	7 19.4
16	15 34 1.3	22 35.6	8 19.3	16 27.6	0♉10.6	13 27.7	21 47.0	23 18.7	26 13.8	15 23.8	4 18.4	7 17.9
17	15 37 57.8	23 35.0	8 16.3	0♒ 4.6	1 33.4	14 31.9	22 31.0	23 28.0	26 20.5	15 23.9	4 18.0	7 16.3
18	15 41 54.4	24 34.6	8 13.3	13 42.9	2 58.4	15 36.2	23 15.1	23 37.2	26 27.1	15 23.9	4 17.6	7 14.8
19	15 45 50.9	25 34.3	8 10.3	27 18.8	4 25.8	16 40.7	23 59.3	23 46.4	26 33.7	15R23.8	4 17.1	7 13.2
20	15 49 47.5	26 34.2	8 7.3	10♓52.5	5 55.5	17 45.3	24 43.4	23 55.4	26 40.3	15 23.7	4 16.6	7 11.6
21	15 53 44.0	27 34.2	8 4.3	24 27.9	7 27.7	18 50.0	25 27.7	24 4.3	26 46.8	15 23.6	4 16.1	7 10.0
22	15 57 40.6	28 34.3	8 1.4	8♈11.2	9 2.3	19 54.9	26 12.0	24 13.1	26 53.3	15 23.4	4 15.5	7 8.4
23	16 1 37.1	29 34.6	7 58.4	22 9.5	10 39.5	20 59.9	26 56.3	24 21.7	26 59.8	15 23.2	4 14.9	7 6.8
24	16 5 33.7	0♊35.0	7 55.4	6♉28.7	12 19.3	22 5.2	27 40.7	24 30.4	27 6.2	15 22.9	4 14.3	7 5.2
25	16 9 30.3	1 35.6	7 52.4	21 10.3	14 1.8	23 10.5	28 25.1	24 38.8	27 12.6	15 22.6	4 13.7	7 3.6
26	16 13 26.8	2 36.2	7 49.4	6♊ 9.7	15 46.9	24 16.1	29 9.5	24 47.1	27 19.0	15 22.2	4 13.0	7 2.0
27	16 17 23.4	3 37.0	7 46.4	21 15.5	17 34.8	25 21.8	29 54.0	24 55.4	27 25.3	15 21.8	4 12.3	7 .4
28	16 21 19.9	4 37.9	7 43.4	6♋11.5	19 25.6	26 27.7	0♊38.5	25 3.5	27 31.5	15 21.3	4 11.5	6 58.8
29	16 25 16.5	5 38.9	7 40.4	20 41.5	21 19.2	27 33.7	1 23.1	25 11.4	27 37.8	15 20.8	4 10.7	6 57.2
30	16 29 13.0	6 40.1	7 37.4	4♌33.9	23 15.7	28 40.0	2 7.6	25 19.3	27 43.9	15 20.2	4 9.9	6 55.5
31	16 33 9.6	7 41.3	7 34.4	17 43.7	25 15.2	29 46.4	2 52.2	25 27.0	27 50.1	15 19.6	4 9.1	6 53.9

DECLINATION

DAY	EPHEM. SID. TIME	☉	☊	☽	☿	♀	♂	♃	♄	♅	♆	♇
1	14 34 52.9	14N57.0	0N 9.2	18N41.4	3N 6.9	2S21.3	15N44.9	5S 4.4	7N46.9	17S37.7	19S19.8	9S17.5
4	14 46 42.6	15 50.6	0 9.3	13 18.0	3 53.1	1 9.5	16 25.7	4 51.4	7 54.8	17 37.1	19 19.8	9 16.5
7	14 58 32.3	16 41.9	0 9.3	3 2.4	4 54.9	0N 3.5	17 5.0	4 38.8	8 2.6	17 36.8	19 19.8	9 15.6
10	15 10 21.9	17 30.6	0 9.4	8S 9.6	6 10.4	1 17.5	17 42.7	4 26.4	8 10.2	17 36.5	19 19.9	9 14.7
13	15 22 11.6	18 16.7	0 9.5	16 39.1	7 37.5	2 32.2	18 18.9	4 14.5	8 17.7	17 36.3	19 20.0	9 13.9
16	15 34 1.3	19 .1	0 9.5	18 37.3	9 14.6	3 47.3	18 53.4	4 2.9	8 25.0	17 36.3	19 20.3	9 13.1
19	15 45 50.9	19 40.5	0 9.6	12 7.2	10 59.8	5 2.5	19 26.2	3 51.8	8 32.2	17 36.4	19 20.6	9 12.4
22	15 57 40.6	20 18.0	0 9.7	0N41.8	12 51.2	6 17.4	19 57.4	3 41.0	8 39.2	17 36.7	19 20.9	9 11.7
25	16 9 30.3	20 52.3	0 9.7	13 38.3	14 46.6	7 31.9	20 26.8	3 30.7	8 46.0	17 37.0	19 21.3	9 11.1
28	16 21 19.9	21 23.4	0 9.8	18 58.1	16 43.3	8 45.6	20 54.4	3 20.9	8 52.7	17 37.5	19 21.8	9 10.6
31	16 33 9.6	21 51.2	0 9.8	14 28.4	18 37.9	9 58.1	21 20.2	3 11.5	8 59.2	17 38.1	19 22.3	9 10.1

JUNE 1998

LONGITUDE

DAY	EPHEM. SID. TIME h m s	☉ ° ′	☊ ° ′	☽ ° ′	☿ ° ′	♀ ° ′	♂ ° ′	♃ ° ′	♄ ° ′	♅ ° ′	♆ ° ′	♇ ° ′
1	16 37 6.2	10♊19.6	5♍43.7	28♌16.6	29♉19.4	2♉21.4	5♊34.2	24♓41.7	29♈ 9.7	12♒39.4	1♒57.9	6♐36.3
2	16 41 2.7	11 17.1	5 40.5	10♍27.7	1♊22.3	3 31.3	6 16.5	24 49.7	29 16.0	12R38.7	1R57.1	6R34.7
3	16 44 59.3	12 14.6	5 37.3	22 26.2	3 27.0	4 41.3	6 58.8	24 57.6	29 22.3	12 37.9	1 56.2	6 33.1
4	16 48 55.8	13 12.0	5 34.1	4♎17.3	5 33.4	5 51.4	7 41.0	25 5.3	29 28.5	12 37.1	1 55.3	6 31.4
5	16 52 52.4	14 9.5	5 31.0	16 6.3	7 41.2	7 1.5	8 23.1	25 12.9	29 34.7	12 36.2	1 54.3	6 29.8
6	16 56 48.9	15 6.9	5 27.8	27 57.6	9 50.4	8 11.6	9 5.2	25 20.4	29 40.8	12 35.3	1 53.4	6 28.2
7	17 0 45.5	16 4.3	5 24.6	9♏55.2	12 .6	9 21.8	9 47.2	25 27.7	29 46.8	12 34.4	1 52.4	6 26.6
8	17 4 42.0	17 1.7	5 21.4	22 2.0	14 11.7	10 32.1	10 29.2	25 34.9	29 52.8	12 33.4	1 51.4	6 25.0
9	17 8 38.6	17 59.1	5 18.3	4♐19.9	16 23.4	11 42.4	11 11.2	25 41.9	29 58.8	12 32.3	1 50.3	6 23.4
10	17 12 35.2	18 56.4	5 15.1	16 50.0	18 35.4	12 52.8	11 53.0	25 48.8	0♉ 4.7	12 31.2	1 49.3	6 21.8
11	17 16 31.7	19 53.8	5 11.9	29 32.5	20 47.5	14 3.2	12 34.9	25 55.5	0 10.5	12 30.1	1 48.2	6 20.2
12	17 20 28.3	20 51.1	5 8.7	12♑27.1	22 59.3	15 13.7	13 16.7	26 2.0	0 16.2	12 29.0	1 47.1	6 18.6
13	17 24 24.8	21 48.4	5 5.6	25 33.2	25 10.7	16 24.2	13 58.4	26 8.4	0 21.9	12 27.7	1 45.9	6 17.0
14	17 28 21.4	22 45.8	5 2.4	8♒50.6	27 21.4	17 34.8	14 40.1	26 14.8	0 27.6	12 26.5	1 44.8	6 15.5
15	17 32 17.9	23 43.1	4 59.2	22 19.0	29 31.1	18 45.5	15 21.8	26 20.8	0 33.2	12 25.3	1 43.6	6 14.0
16	17 36 14.5	24 40.4	4 56.0	5♓58.7	1♋39.5	19 56.2	16 3.4	26 26.8	0 38.7	12 23.9	1 42.5	6 12.4
17	17 40 11.1	25 37.6	4 52.8	19 50.0	3 46.6	21 6.9	16 44.9	26 32.6	0 44.1	12 22.6	1 41.2	6 10.9
18	17 44 7.6	26 34.9	4 49.7	3♈53.1	5 52.1	22 17.7	17 26.4	26 38.2	0 49.5	12 21.2	1 40.0	6 9.4
19	17 48 4.2	27 32.2	4 46.5	18 7.6	7 55.8	23 28.6	18 7.9	26 43.6	0 54.8	12 19.7	1 38.7	6 7.9
20	17 52 .7	28 29.5	4 43.3	2♉31.5	9 57.8	24 39.5	18 49.3	26 48.9	1 .1	12 18.2	1 37.4	6 6.4
21	17 55 57.3	29 26.8	4 40.1	17 1.4	11 57.8	25 50.4	19 30.6	26 54.0	1 5.2	12 16.7	1 36.1	6 4.9
22	17 59 53.8	0♋24.0	4 37.0	1♊32.2	13 55.8	27 1.4	20 11.9	26 59.0	1 10.3	12 15.1	1 34.8	6 3.5
23	18 3 50.4	1 21.3	4 33.8	15 57.8	15 51.7	28 12.5	20 53.2	27 3.7	1 15.4	12 13.5	1 33.5	6 2.0
24	18 7 47.0	2 18.6	4 30.6	0♋11.7	17 45.5	29 23.5	21 34.4	27 8.3	1 20.3	12 11.9	1 32.1	6 .6
25	18 11 43.5	3 15.8	4 27.4	14 8.3	19 37.2	0♊34.7	22 15.6	27 12.7	1 25.2	12 10.2	1 30.8	5 59.2
26	18 15 40.1	4 13.1	4 24.3	27 43.7	21 26.7	1 45.8	22 56.7	27 17.0	1 30.0	12 8.5	1 29.4	5 57.8
27	18 19 36.6	5 10.3	4 21.1	10♌56.0	23 14.0	2 57.1	23 37.8	27 21.0	1 34.8	12 6.8	1 28.0	5 56.4
28	18 23 33.2	6 7.5	4 17.9	23 45.5	24 59.1	4 8.3	24 18.8	27 24.9	1 39.4	12 5.0	1 26.5	5 55.0
29	18 27 29.7	7 4.8	4 14.7	6♍14.6	26 42.0	5 19.6	24 59.8	27 28.6	1 44.0	12 3.2	1 25.1	5 53.7
30	18 31 26.3	8 2.0	4 11.5	18 26.9	28 22.6	6 30.9	25 40.7	27 32.1	1 48.5	12 1.4	1 23.7	5 52.4

LATITUDE

DAY	EPHEM. SID. TIME	☉	☊	☽	☿	♀	♂	♃	♄	♅	♆	♇
1	16 37 6.2	0 .0	0 .0	0S38.0	0S46.4	2S 2.9	0N14.7	1S 7.6	2S18.1	0S39.4	0N21.3	12N24.8
4	16 48 55.8	0 .0	0 .0	2N26.4	0 14.2	2 2.7	0 16.6	1 8.3	2 18.6	0 39.5	0 21.3	12 24.4
7	17 0 45.5	0 .0	0 .0	4 32.8	0N17.8	2 1.7	0 18.4	1 9.1	2 19.0	0 39.6	0 21.3	12 24.0
10	17 12 35.2	0 .0	0 .0	4 54.1	0 47.7	2 .0	0 20.2	1 9.9	2 19.5	0 39.7	0 21.3	12 23.5
13	17 24 24.8	0 .0	0 .0	3 8.6	1 13.7	1 57.5	0 22.0	1 10.7	2 20.1	0 39.8	0 21.3	12 22.9
16	17 36 14.5	0 .0	0 .0	0S11.0	1 34.2	1 54.4	0 23.8	1 11.6	2 20.6	0 39.9	0 21.2	12 22.3
19	17 48 4.2	0 .0	0 .0	3 32.5	1 48.4	1 50.5	0 25.5	1 12.4	2 21.2	0 40.0	0 21.2	12 21.6
22	17 59 53.8	0 .0	0 .0	5 3.4	1 55.9	1 46.1	0 27.3	1 13.3	2 21.7	0 40.1	0 21.2	12 20.9
25	18 11 43.5	0 .0	0 .0	3 50.1	1 56.8	1 41.0	0 29.0	1 14.1	2 22.3	0 40.2	0 21.2	12 20.0
28	18 23 33.2	0 .0	0 .0	0 48.9	1 51.4	1 35.5	0 30.7	1 15.0	2 23.0	0 40.3	0 21.2	12 19.2

RIGHT ASCENSION

DAY	EPHEM. SID. TIME	☉	☊	☽	☿	♀	♂	♃	♄	♅	♆	♇
1	16 37 6.2	8♊42.6	7♍31.4	0♍12.9	27♉17.5	0♉53.1	3♊36.9	25♓34.6	27♈56.2	15♒18.9	4♒ 8.2	6♐52.3
2	16 41 2.7	9 44.0	7 28.4	12 8.0	29 22.7	1 60.0	4 21.5	25 42.1	28 2.2	15R18.2	4R 7.4	6R50.7
3	16 44 59.3	10 45.6	7 25.4	23 38.3	1♊30.7	3 7.1	5 6.2	25 49.4	28 8.2	15 17.4	4 6.4	6 49.1
4	16 48 55.8	11 47.2	7 22.4	4♎54.2	3 41.4	4 14.4	5 50.9	25 56.7	28 14.1	15 16.6	4 5.5	6 47.5
5	16 52 52.4	12 48.9	7 19.4	16 6.2	5 54.7	5 21.9	6 35.6	26 3.8	28 20.0	15 15.7	4 4.5	6 45.8
6	16 56 48.9	13 50.6	7 16.4	27 24.5	8 10.3	6 29.7	7 20.4	26 10.7	28 25.9	15 14.8	4 3.5	6 44.2
7	17 0 45.5	14 52.5	7 13.4	8♏58.3	10 28.0	7 37.7	8 5.2	26 17.5	28 31.7	15 13.9	4 2.5	6 42.6
8	17 4 42.0	15 54.4	7 10.5	20 54.8	12 47.6	8 45.9	8 49.9	26 24.2	28 37.4	15 12.9	4 1.5	6 41.0
9	17 8 38.6	16 56.4	7 7.5	3♐19.0	15 8.8	9 54.5	9 34.8	26 30.8	28 43.1	15 11.9	4 .4	6 39.5
10	17 12 35.2	17 58.4	7 4.5	16 12.1	17 31.2	11 3.2	10 19.6	26 37.2	28 48.8	15 10.8	3 59.3	6 37.9
11	17 16 31.7	19 .5	7 1.5	29 31.0	19 54.4	12 12.2	11 4.4	26 43.5	28 54.3	15 9.7	3 58.2	6 36.3
12	17 20 28.3	20 2.7	6 58.5	13♑ 8.6	22 18.1	13 21.5	11 49.2	26 49.6	28 59.9	15 8.5	3 57.0	6 34.7
13	17 24 24.8	21 4.9	6 55.5	26 55.1	24 41.9	14 31.1	12 34.1	26 55.6	29 5.3	15 7.3	3 55.8	6 33.2
14	17 28 21.4	22 7.2	6 52.5	10♒41.2	27 5.4	15 40.9	13 19.0	27 1.5	29 10.8	15 6.1	3 54.7	6 31.6
15	17 32 17.9	23 9.5	6 49.5	24 20.1	29 28.1	16 51.0	14 3.9	27 7.2	29 16.2	15 4.8	3 53.5	6 30.1
16	17 36 14.5	24 11.8	6 46.5	7♓49.6	1♋49.8	18 1.4	14 48.8	27 12.8	29 21.5	15 3.5	3 52.2	6 28.6
17	17 40 11.1	25 14.2	6 43.5	21 12.3	4 10.0	19 12.1	15 33.7	27 18.2	29 26.7	15 2.1	3 51.0	6 27.0
18	17 44 7.6	26 16.5	6 40.5	4♈34.4	6 28.6	20 23.0	16 18.5	27 23.5	29 31.9	15 .7	3 49.7	6 25.5
19	17 48 4.2	27 18.9	6 37.5	18 4.1	8 45.1	21 34.2	17 3.4	27 28.6	29 37.0	14 59.2	3 48.4	6 24.0
20	17 52 .7	28 21.4	6 34.5	1♉49.9	10 59.5	22 45.7	17 48.3	27 33.5	29 42.0	14 57.8	3 47.1	6 22.5
21	17 55 57.3	29 23.8	6 31.5	15 57.8	13 11.5	23 57.5	18 33.2	27 38.3	29 47.0	14 56.2	3 45.7	6 21.0
22	17 59 53.8	0♋26.2	6 28.5	0♊29.0	15 20.9	25 9.6	19 18.0	27 43.0	29 51.9	14 54.7	3 44.4	6 19.6
23	18 3 50.4	1 28.6	6 25.5	15 18.0	17 27.6	26 21.9	20 2.9	27 47.5	29 56.8	14 53.1	3 43.0	6 18.1
24	18 7 47.0	2 31.0	6 22.5	0♋12.4	19 31.4	27 34.6	20 47.7	27 51.8	0♉ 1.6	14 51.4	3 41.6	6 16.7
25	18 11 43.5	3 33.4	6 19.4	14 55.6	21 32.4	28 47.5	21 32.6	27 56.0	0 6.3	14 49.8	3 40.2	6 15.2
26	18 15 40.1	4 35.7	6 16.4	29 11.9	23 30.4	0♊ .7	22 17.4	27 60.0	0 11.0	14 48.0	3 38.7	6 13.8
27	18 19 36.6	5 38.0	6 13.4	12♌50.6	25 25.4	1 14.1	23 2.2	28 3.8	0 15.5	14 46.3	3 37.3	6 12.4
28	18 23 33.2	6 40.3	6 10.4	25 48.2	27 17.3	2 27.9	23 46.9	28 7.5	0 20.0	14 44.5	3 35.8	6 11.1
29	18 27 29.7	7 42.5	6 7.4	8♍ 7.3	29 6.2	3 41.9	24 31.7	28 11.0	0 24.5	14 42.7	3 34.3	6 9.7
30	18 31 26.3	8 44.7	6 4.4	19 55.2	0♌52.1	4 56.2	25 16.4	28 14.4	0 28.8	14 40.9	3 32.8	6 8.3

DECLINATION

DAY	EPHEM. SID. TIME	☉	☊	☽	☿	♀	♂	♃	♄	♅	♆	♇
1	16 37 6.2	21N59.7	0N 9.9	11N28.6	19N14.9	10N22.0	21N28.4	3S 8.5	9N 1.3	17S38.3	19S22.5	9S 9.9
4	16 48 55.8	22 22.9	0 9.9	0 32.1	20 59.8	11 32.5	21 51.7	2 59.8	9 7.4	17 39.1	19 23.1	9 9.5
7	17 0 45.5	22 42.5	0 10.0	10S28.2	22 31.4	12 41.2	22 13.2	2 51.7	9 13.4	17 39.9	19 23.7	9 9.2
10	17 12 35.2	22 58.6	0 10.0	17 54.4	23 44.4	13 47.7	22 32.7	2 44.0	9 19.2	17 40.9	19 24.4	9 8.9
13	17 24 24.8	23 11.0	0 10.1	17 56.3	24 34.6	14 51.8	22 50.4	2 36.9	9 24.7	17 42.0	19 25.2	9 8.7
16	17 36 14.5	23 19.8	0 10.2	9 29.3	24 59.8	15 53.1	23 6.1	2 30.4	9 30.0	17 43.2	19 26.0	9 8.6
19	17 48 4.2	23 24.8	0 10.2	3N49.9	25 .2	16 51.4	23 19.9	2 24.5	9 35.1	17 44.4	19 26.8	9 8.6
22	17 59 53.8	23 26.2	0 10.3	15 30.7	24 37.8	17 46.2	23 31.7	2 19.2	9 39.9	17 45.8	19 27.7	9 8.6
25	18 11 43.5	23 23.8	0 10.3	18 52.4	23 55.7	18 37.3	23 41.6	2 14.5	9 44.4	17 47.3	19 28.6	9 8.7
28	18 23 33.2	23 17.7	0 10.4	12 49.9	22 57.5	19 24.5	23 49.6	2 10.5	9 48.7	17 48.8	19 29.5	9 8.9

JULY 1998

LONGITUDE

DAY	EPHEM. SID. TIME	☉	☊	☽	☿	♀	♂	♃	♄	♅	♆	♇
	h m s	° ′	° ′	° ′	° ′	° ′	° ′	° ′	° ′	° ′	° ′	° ′
1	18 35 22.9	8♋59.2	4♍ 8.4	0♎26.9	0♌ 1.1	7♊42.3	26♊21.6	27♓35.5	1♉52.9	11♒59.5	1♒22.2	5♐51.1
2	18 39 19.4	9 56.4	4 5.2	12 19.7	1 37.3	8 53.7	27 2.4	27 38.6	1 57.2	11 R57.6	1 R20.7	5 R49.8
3	18 43 16.0	10 53.6	4 2.0	24 10.5	3 11.2	10 5.2	27 43.2	27 41.6	2 1.5	11 55.7	1 19.2	5 48.5
4	18 47 12.5	11 50.8	3 58.8	6♏ 4.3	4 42.9	11 16.7	28 24.0	27 44.4	2 5.7	11 53.8	1 17.7	5 47.3
5	18 51 9.1	12 48.0	3 55.7	18 5.6	6 12.4	12 28.3	29 4.7	27 47.1	2 9.8	11 51.8	1 16.3	5 46.1
6	18 55 5.6	13 45.2	3 52.5	0♐18.1	7 39.5	13 39.9	29 45.3	27 49.5	2 13.8	11 49.8	1 14.7	5 44.9
7	18 59 2.2	14 42.4	3 49.3	12 44.6	9 4.4	14 51.5	0♋25.9	27 51.7	2 17.8	11 47.8	1 13.2	5 43.7
8	19 2 58.8	15 39.6	3 46.1	25 27.0	10 26.8	16 3.2	1 6.5	27 53.7	2 21.6	11 45.7	1 11.6	5 42.5
9	19 6 55.3	16 36.8	3 43.0	8♑25.7	11 46.9	17 14.9	1 47.0	27 55.6	2 25.3	11 43.7	1 10.1	5 41.4
10	19 10 51.9	17 33.9	3 39.8	21 40.0	13 4.6	18 26.7	2 27.4	27 57.2	2 29.0	11 41.6	1 8.5	5 40.3
11	19 14 48.4	18 31.1	3 36.6	5♒ 8.7	14 19.8	19 38.5	3 7.8	27 58.7	2 32.6	11 39.4	1 7.0	5 39.2
12	19 18 45.0	19 28.3	3 33.4	18 49.5	15 32.4	20 50.3	3 48.2	27 60.0	2 36.1	11 37.3	1 5.4	5 38.2
13	19 22 41.5	20 25.5	3 30.2	2♓40.3	16 42.5	22 2.2	4 28.5	28 1.1	2 39.5	11 35.1	1 3.8	5 37.1
14	19 26 38.1	21 22.7	3 27.1	16 39.0	17 49.9	23 14.1	5 8.8	28 2.0	2 42.8	11 32.9	1 2.2	5 36.1
15	19 30 34.7	22 19.9	3 23.9	0♈43.6	18 54.5	24 26.1	5 49.0	28 2.7	2 46.0	11 30.7	1 .6	5 35.1
16	19 34 31.2	23 17.2	3 20.7	14 52.6	19 56.3	25 38.2	6 29.2	28 3.1	2 49.2	11 28.5	0 59.0	5 34.1
17	19 38 27.8	24 14.4	3 17.5	29 4.2	20 55.2	26 50.2	7 9.4	28 3.5	2 52.2	11 26.3	0 57.4	5 33.2
18	19 42 24.3	25 11.6	3 14.4	13♉16.5	21 51.0	28 2.4	7 49.5	28 3.6	2 55.2	11 24.0	0 55.8	5 32.3
19	19 46 20.9	26 8.9	3 11.2	27 27.3	22 43.7	29 14.5	8 29.6	28 R 3.5	2 58.0	11 21.7	0 54.1	5 31.4
20	19 50 17.4	27 6.2	3 8.0	11♊33.6	23 33.0	0♋26.7	9 9.6	28 3.2	3 .8	11 19.4	0 52.5	5 30.6
21	19 54 14.0	28 3.4	3 4.8	25 32.2	24 19.0	1 39.0	9 49.6	28 2.7	3 3.5	11 17.1	0 50.9	5 29.7
22	19 58 10.5	29 .7	3 1.7	9♋19.4	25 1.4	2 51.3	10 29.5	28 2.0	3 6.0	11 14.8	0 49.3	5 28.9
23	20 2 7.1	29 58.0	2 58.5	22 52.3	25 40.1	4 3.6	11 9.4	28 1.1	3 8.5	11 12.5	0 47.6	5 28.2
24	20 6 3.7	0♌55.4	2 55.3	6♌ 8.6	26 14.9	5 16.0	11 49.3	28 .1	3 10.9	11 10.1	0 46.0	5 27.4
25	20 10 .2	1 52.7	2 52.1	19 6.9	26 45.7	6 28.4	12 29.1	27 58.8	3 13.1	11 7.8	0 44.4	5 26.7
26	20 13 56.8	2 50.1	2 48.9	1♍47.5	27 12.3	7 41.0	13 8.9	27 57.4	3 15.4	11 5.5	0 42.8	5 26.1
27	20 17 53.3	3 47.4	2 45.8	14 11.5	27 34.4	8 53.5	13 48.6	27 55.7	3 17.5	11 3.1	0 41.2	5 25.4
28	20 21 49.9	4 44.7	2 42.6	26 21.6	27 52.0	10 6.0	14 28.3	27 53.8	3 19.4	11 .7	0 39.5	5 24.8
29	20 25 46.4	5 42.1	2 39.4	8♎21.2	28 4.9	11 18.6	15 8.0	27 51.8	3 21.3	10 58.3	0 37.9	5 24.2
30	20 29 43.0	6 39.5	2 36.2	20 14.4	28 13.0	12 31.2	15 47.5	27 49.5	3 23.1	10 55.9	0 36.3	5 23.6
31	20 33 39.5	7 36.8	2 33.1	2♏ 5.8	28 16.0	13 43.9	16 27.1	27 47.1	3 24.8	10 53.5	0 34.7	5 23.1

LATITUDE

DAY	EPHEM. SID. TIME	☉	☊	☽	☿	♀	♂	♃	♄	♅	♆	♇
1	18 35 22.9	0 .0	0 .0	2N22.5	1N40.2	1S29.4	0N32.4	1S15.9	2S23.6	0S40.3	0N21.2	12N18.2
4	18 47 12.5	0 .0	0 .0	4 34.7	1 23.6	1 23.0	0 34.1	1 16.8	2 24.3	0 40.4	0 21.2	12 17.3
7	18 59 2.2	0 .0	0 .0	5 2.6	1 2.1	1 16.1	0 35.8	1 17.7	2 25.0	0 40.5	0 21.1	12 16.2
10	19 10 51.9	0 .0	0 .0	3 20.7	0 36.3	1 8.9	0 37.5	1 18.6	2 25.7	0 40.5	0 21.1	12 15.2
13	19 22 41.5	0 .0	0 .0	0S 3.5	0 6.5	1 1.4	0 39.1	1 19.5	2 26.4	0 40.6	0 21.1	12 14.0
16	19 34 31.2	0 .0	0 .0	3 31.8	0S26.7	0 53.6	0 40.7	1 20.4	2 27.1	0 40.7	0 21.0	12 12.9
19	19 46 20.9	0 .0	0 .0	5 10.2	1 2.8	0 45.7	0 42.3	1 21.3	2 27.9	0 40.7	0 21.0	12 11.7
22	19 58 10.5	0 .0	0 .0	4 7.3	1 41.0	0 37.6	0 43.9	1 22.2	2 28.6	0 40.7	0 21.0	12 10.4
25	20 10 .2	0 .0	0 .0	1 7.9	2 20.6	0 29.4	0 45.5	1 23.1	2 29.4	0 40.8	0 21.0	12 9.1
28	20 21 49.9	0 .0	0 .0	2N11.8	3 .1	0 21.2	0 47.0	1 24.0	2 30.2	0 40.8	0 20.9	12 7.8
31	20 33 39.5	0 .0	0 .0	4 34.0	3 37.7	0 12.9	0 48.6	1 24.9	2 30.9	0 40.8	0 20.9	12 6.5

RIGHT ASCENSION

DAY	EPHEM. SID. TIME	☉	☊	☽	☿	♀	♂	♃	♄	♅	♆	♇
1	18 35 22.9	9♋46.8	6♍ 1.4	1♎21.4	2♌34.8	6♊10.7	26♊ 1.1	28♓17.6	0♉33.1	14♒39.0	3♒31.3	6♐ 7.0
2	18 39 19.4	10 48.8	5 58.4	12 36.7	4 14.5	7 25.5	26 45.7	28 20.6	0 37.3	14 R37.1	3 R29.8	6 R 5.7
3	18 43 16.0	11 50.8	5 55.4	23 51.9	5 51.2	8 40.5	27 30.3	28 23.4	0 41.5	14 35.2	3 28.2	6 4.4
4	18 47 12.5	12 52.7	5 52.4	5♏17.4	7 24.8	9 55.8	28 14.9	28 26.1	0 45.5	14 33.2	3 26.7	6 3.2
5	18 51 9.1	13 54.5	5 49.4	17 2.6	8 55.5	11 11.4	28 59.5	28 28.7	0 49.5	14 31.3	3 25.2	6 1.9
6	18 55 5.6	14 56.2	5 46.4	29 14.7	10 23.1	12 27.2	29 43.9	28 31.0	0 53.4	14 29.3	3 23.6	6 .7
7	18 59 2.2	15 57.9	5 43.4	11♐58.2	11 47.6	13 43.3	0♋28.4	28 33.2	0 57.3	14 27.2	3 22.0	5 59.5
8	19 2 58.8	16 59.4	5 40.4	25 12.8	13 9.2	14 59.5	1 12.8	28 35.2	1 1.0	14 25.1	3 20.4	5 58.3
9	19 6 55.3	18 .8	5 37.4	8♑53.7	14 27.8	16 16.0	1 57.1	28 37.0	1 4.7	14 23.1	3 18.8	5 57.2
10	19 10 51.9	19 2.2	5 34.4	22 51.4	15 43.3	17 32.6	2 41.4	28 38.6	1 8.3	14 20.9	3 17.2	5 56.0
11	19 14 48.4	20 3.4	5 31.4	6♒54.4	16 55.8	18 49.5	3 25.7	28 40.1	1 11.8	14 18.8	3 15.5	5 54.9
12	19 18 45.0	21 4.5	5 28.3	20 52.5	18 5.3	20 6.6	4 9.9	28 41.4	1 15.2	14 16.6	3 13.9	5 53.8
13	19 22 41.5	22 5.5	5 25.3	4♓39.3	19 11.7	21 23.8	4 54.0	28 42.5	1 18.5	14 14.4	3 12.3	5 52.7
14	19 26 38.1	23 6.4	5 22.3	18 13.7	20 15.0	22 41.3	5 38.1	28 43.4	1 21.8	14 12.2	3 10.6	5 51.6
15	19 30 34.7	24 7.2	5 19.3	1♈39.5	21 15.2	23 58.9	6 22.1	28 44.2	1 24.9	14 10.0	3 9.0	5 50.6
16	19 34 31.2	25 7.8	5 16.3	15 3.7	22 12.2	25 16.6	7 6.1	28 44.8	1 28.0	14 7.8	3 7.3	5 49.6
17	19 38 27.8	26 8.3	5 13.3	28 34.6	23 6.0	26 34.5	7 50.0	28 45.2	1 31.0	14 5.5	3 5.6	5 48.6
18	19 42 24.3	27 8.8	5 10.3	12♉19.7	23 56.4	27 52.6	8 33.8	28 45.4	1 33.9	14 3.2	3 4.0	5 47.7
19	19 46 20.9	28 9.0	5 7.3	26 23.5	24 43.5	29 10.7	9 17.6	28 45.4	1 36.7	14 .9	3 2.3	5 46.7
20	19 50 17.4	29 9.2	5 4.3	10♊45.3	25 27.2	0♋29.0	10 1.3	28 R45.3	1 39.4	13 58.6	3 .6	5 45.8
21	19 54 14.0	0♌ 9.2	5 1.2	25 18.3	26 7.3	1 47.4	10 44.9	28 45.0	1 42.1	13 56.3	2 58.9	5 45.0
22	19 58 10.5	1 9.1	4 58.2	9♋50.4	26 43.7	3 5.8	11 28.5	28 44.4	1 44.6	13 54.0	2 57.2	5 44.1
23	20 2 7.1	2 8.8	4 55.2	24 7.2	27 16.5	4 24.3	12 12.0	28 43.8	1 47.0	13 51.6	2 55.6	5 43.3
24	20 6 3.7	3 8.4	4 52.2	7♌56.4	27 45.3	5 42.9	12 55.4	28 42.9	1 49.4	13 49.2	2 53.9	5 42.5
25	20 10 .2	4 7.8	4 49.2	21 10.5	28 10.2	7 1.5	13 38.7	28 41.8	1 51.7	13 46.9	2 52.2	5 41.7
26	20 13 56.8	5 7.2	4 46.2	3♍48.1	28 31.1	8 20.2	14 22.0	28 40.6	1 53.9	13 44.5	2 50.5	5 41.0
27	20 17 53.3	6 6.3	4 43.2	15 52.9	28 47.7	9 38.8	15 5.1	28 39.2	1 56.0	13 42.1	2 48.9	5 40.3
28	20 21 49.9	7 5.3	4 40.2	27 32.0	28 59.9	10 57.5	15 48.2	28 37.6	1 57.9	13 39.7	2 47.2	5 39.6
29	20 25 46.4	8 4.2	4 37.1	8♎54.6	29 7.7	12 16.1	16 31.2	28 35.9	1 59.8	13 37.3	2 45.5	5 38.9
30	20 29 43.0	9 2.8	4 34.1	20 10.7	29 11.0	13 34.7	17 14.1	28 33.9	2 1.6	13 34.9	2 43.8	5 38.3
31	20 33 39.5	10 1.4	4 31.1	1♏30.5	29 R 9.7	14 53.3	17 56.9	28 31.8	2 3.3	13 32.5	2 42.2	5 37.7

DECLINATION

DAY	EPHEM. SID. TIME	☉	☊	☽	☿	♀	♂	♃	♄	♅	♆	♇
1	18 35 22.9	23N 8.0	0N10.5	2N .1	21N46.5	20N 7.3	23N55.7	2S 7.1	9N52.8	17S50.4	19S30.5	9S 9.2
4	18 47 12.5	22 54.5	0 10.5	9S13.1	20 26.1	20 45.6	23 59.8	2 4.4	9 56.5	17 52.1	19 31.5	9 9.6
7	18 59 2.2	22 37.6	0 10.6	17 19.2	18 59.1	21 19.1	24 2.0	2 2.3	9 60.0	17 53.8	19 32.5	9 10.0
10	19 10 51.9	22 17.0	0 10.6	18 23.4	17 28.2	21 47.5	24 2.3	2 .9	10 3.2	17 55.6	19 33.6	9 10.5
13	19 22 41.5	21 53.1	0 10.7	10 34.5	15 55.9	22 10.6	24 .7	2 .2	10 6.0	17 57.5	19 34.6	9 11.1
16	19 34 31.2	21 25.7	0 10.8	2N36.2	14 24.6	22 28.3	23 57.3	2 .3	10 8.6	17 59.3	19 35.7	9 11.8
19	19 46 20.9	20 55.1	0 10.8	14 33.0	12 56.9	22 40.4	23 52.1	2 1.0	10 10.9	18 1.3	19 36.8	9 12.5
22	19 58 10.5	20 21.3	0 10.9	18 59.8	11 35.5	22 46.8	23 45.1	2 2.4	10 12.9	18 3.2	19 37.9	9 13.3
25	20 10 .2	19 44.4	0 10.9	14 .8	10 23.3	22 47.4	23 36.3	2 4.5	10 14.6	18 5.2	19 39.0	9 14.2
28	20 21 49.9	19 4.6	0 11.0	3 27.8	9 23.7	22 42.1	23 25.8	2 7.3	10 16.0	18 7.2	19 40.0	9 15.2
31	20 33 39.5	18 21.9	0 11.1	7S54.6	8 40.1	22 30.9	23 13.6	2 10.7	10 17.1	18 9.1	19 41.1	9 16.3

AUGUST 1998

DAY	EPHEM. SID. TIME	☉	☊	☽	☿	♀	♂	♃	♄	♅	♆	♇
	h m s	° ′	° ′	° ′	° ′	° ′	° ′	° ′	° ′	° ′	° ′	° ′
		LONGITUDE										
1	20 37 36.1	8♌34.2	2♍29.9	14♏ .3	28♌14.0	14♋56.6	17♋ 6.6	27♓44.5	3♉26.3	10♒51.1	0♒33.1	5♐22.6
2	20 41 32.7	9 31.6	2 26.7	26 2.5	28R 6.7	16 9.3	17 46.1	27R41.6	3 27.8	10R48.8	0R31.5	5R22.1
3	20 45 29.2	10 29.0	2 23.5	8♐16.8	27 54.3	17 22.1	18 25.5	27 38.6	3 29.2	10 46.4	0 29.9	5 21.7
4	20 49 25.8	11 26.4	2 20.3	20 47.1	27 36.7	18 34.9	19 4.9	27 35.5	3 30.5	10 44.0	0 28.3	5 21.3
5	20 53 22.3	12 23.9	2 17.2	3♑36.3	27 14.0	19 47.7	19 44.2	27 32.1	3 31.6	10 41.6	0 26.7	5 20.9
6	20 57 18.9	13 21.3	2 14.0	16 45.8	26 46.4	21 .6	20 23.5	27 28.5	3 32.7	10 39.2	0 25.1	5 20.5
7	21 1 15.4	14 18.8	2 10.8	0♒15.9	26 14.1	22 13.6	21 2.7	27 24.8	3 33.7	10 36.8	0 23.5	5 20.2
8	21 5 12.0	15 16.2	2 7.6	14 5.0	25 37.5	23 26.6	21 41.9	27 20.9	3 34.5	10 34.4	0 22.0	5 19.9
9	21 9 8.5	16 13.7	2 4.5	28 10.3	24 57.1	24 39.6	22 21.1	27 16.8	3 35.3	10 32.0	0 20.4	5 19.7
10	21 13 5.1	17 11.2	2 1.3	12♓27.7	24 13.3	25 52.6	23 .2	27 12.5	3 35.9	10 29.6	0 18.9	5 19.5
11	21 17 1.6	18 8.7	1 58.1	26 52.5	23 27.0	27 5.8	23 39.3	27 8.1	3 36.5	10 27.3	0 17.3	5 19.3
12	21 20 58.2	19 6.3	1 54.9	11♈19.8	22 38.8	28 18.9	24 18.4	27 3.5	3 36.9	10 24.9	0 15.8	5 19.1
13	21 24 54.8	20 3.9	1 51.8	25 45.2	21 49.5	29 32.1	24 57.4	26 58.7	3 37.2	10 22.5	0 14.3	5 19.0
14	21 28 51.3	21 1.5	1 48.6	10♉ 4.9	21 .1	0♌45.3	25 36.4	26 53.8	3 37.5	10 20.2	0 12.8	5 18.9
15	21 32 47.9	21 59.1	1 45.4	24 16.1	20 11.6	1 58.6	26 15.3	26 48.7	3 37.6	10 17.9	0 11.3	5 18.8
16	21 36 44.4	22 56.8	1 42.2	8♊16.6	19 24.9	3 12.0	26 54.2	26 43.5	3 37.7	10 15.6	0 9.9	5D18.9
17	21 40 41.0	23 54.5	1 39.0	22 4.9	18 40.9	4 25.4	27 33.1	26 38.1	3R37.6	10 13.3	0 8.4	5 18.9
18	21 44 37.5	24 52.2	1 35.9	5♋40.2	18 .6	5 38.8	28 11.9	26 32.5	3 37.4	10 11.0	0 7.0	5 18.9
19	21 48 34.1	25 49.9	1 32.7	19 1.8	17 24.7	6 52.2	28 50.7	26 26.8	3 37.1	10 8.7	0 5.6	5 19.0
20	21 52 30.6	26 47.6	1 29.5	2♌ 9.5	16 54.2	8 5.7	29 29.4	26 20.9	3 36.7	10 6.4	0 4.1	5 19.1
21	21 56 27.2	27 45.4	1 26.3	15 3.1	16 29.8	9 19.3	0♌ 8.1	26 14.9	3 36.2	10 4.2	0 2.8	5 19.2
22	22 0 23.7	28 43.2	1 23.2	27 43.0	16 11.9	10 32.8	0 46.8	26 8.7	3 35.6	10 1.9	0 1.4	5 19.4
23	22 4 20.3	29 41.0	1 20.0	10♍ 9.8	16 1.1	11 46.5	1 25.4	26 2.4	3 34.9	9 59.7	0 .0	5 19.6
24	22 8 16.8	0♍38.9	1 16.8	22 24.6	15 57.7	13 .1	2 4.0	25 56.0	3 34.1	9 57.5	29♑58.7	5 19.9
25	22 12 13.4	1 36.7	1 13.6	4♎29.3	16D 2.1	14 13.8	2 42.5	25 49.5	3 33.1	9 55.3	29 57.3	5 20.2
26	22 16 10.0	2 34.6	1 10.4	16 26.1	16 14.4	15 27.5	3 21.0	25 42.8	3 32.1	9 53.2	29 56.0	5 20.5
27	22 20 6.5	3 32.6	1 7.3	28 18.2	16 34.7	16 41.3	3 59.5	25 36.0	3 31.0	9 51.0	29 54.7	5 20.8
28	22 24 3.1	4 30.5	1 4.1	10♏ 8.9	17 2.9	17 55.0	4 37.9	25 29.2	3 29.8	9 48.9	29 53.4	5 21.2
29	22 27 59.6	5 28.4	1 .9	22 2.5	17 39.1	19 8.9	5 16.3	25 22.2	3 28.4	9 46.8	29 52.2	5 21.6
30	22 31 56.2	6 26.4	0 57.7	4♐ 3.2	18 23.0	20 22.7	5 54.6	25 15.1	3 27.0	9 44.8	29 51.0	5 22.1
31	22 35 52.7	7 24.4	0 54.6	16 15.6	19 14.5	21 36.6	6 32.9	25 7.9	3 25.5	9 42.7	29 49.8	5 22.5
		LATITUDE										
1	20 37 36.1	0 .0	0 .0	5N .1	3S49.4	0S10.2	0N49.1	1S25.2	2S31.2	0S40.8	0N20.9	12N 6.0
4	20 49 25.8	0 .0	0 .0	4 57.6	4 20.5	0 2.1	0 50.6	1 26.0	2 32.0	0 40.9	0 20.8	12 4.7
7	21 1 15.4	0 .0	0 .0	2 43.9	4 42.7	0N 5.9	0 52.1	1 26.8	2 32.8	0 40.9	0 20.8	12 3.3
10	21 13 5.1	0 .0	0 .0	1S .6	4 52.3	0 13.8	0 53.6	1 27.6	2 33.6	0 40.9	0 20.7	12 1.8
13	21 24 54.8	0 .0	0 .0	4 17.4	4 46.2	0 21.4	0 55.0	1 28.4	2 34.4	0 40.9	0 20.7	12 .4
16	21 36 44.4	0 .0	0 .0	5 14.6	4 23.4	0 28.8	0 56.5	1 29.1	2 35.2	0 40.9	0 20.7	11 59.0
19	21 48 34.1	0 .0	0 .0	3 34.2	3 45.9	0 35.8	0 57.9	1 29.8	2 35.9	0 40.8	0 20.6	11 57.5
22	22 0 23.7	0 .0	0 .0	0 20.7	2 57.6	0 42.6	0 59.4	1 30.4	2 36.7	0 40.8	0 20.6	11 56.1
25	22 12 13.4	0 .0	0 .0	2N53.3	2 4.0	0 49.0	1 .8	1 31.0	2 37.5	0 40.8	0 20.5	11 54.6
28	22 24 3.1	0 .0	0 .0	4 55.6	1 9.9	0 54.9	1 2.2	1 31.6	2 38.2	0 40.8	0 20.4	11 53.2
31	22 35 52.7	0 .0	0 .0	5 6.7	0 19.6	1 .4	1 3.6	1 32.1	2 38.9	0 40.7	0 20.4	11 51.7
		RIGHT ASCENSION										
1	20 37 36.1	10♌59.7	4♍28.1	13♏ 3.7	29♌ 3.7	16♋11.9	18♋39.6	28♓29.5	2♉ 4.9	13♒30.1	2♒40.5	5♐37.2
2	20 41 32.7	11 58.0	4 25.1	24 59.2	28R53.0	17 30.3	19 22.2	28R27.0	2 6.4	13R27.6	2R38.8	5R36.6
3	20 45 29.2	12 56.0	4 22.1	7♐23.5	28 37.6	18 48.8	20 4.7	28 24.4	2 7.8	13 25.2	2 37.2	5 36.1
4	20 49 25.8	13 53.9	4 19.0	20 20.1	28 17.6	20 7.1	20 47.1	28 21.6	2 9.1	13 22.8	2 35.5	5 35.6
5	20 53 22.3	14 51.7	4 16.0	3♑48.0	27 53.2	21 25.3	21 29.4	28 18.6	2 10.3	13 20.4	2 33.9	5 35.2
6	20 57 18.9	15 49.3	4 13.0	17 41.4	27 24.4	22 43.4	22 11.7	28 15.4	2 11.4	13 17.9	2 32.2	5 34.8
7	21 1 15.4	16 46.7	4 10.0	1♒50.7	26 51.7	24 1.4	22 53.8	28 12.1	2 12.4	13 15.5	2 30.6	5 34.4
8	21 5 12.0	17 44.0	4 7.0	16 4.7	26 15.4	25 19.3	23 35.8	28 8.6	2 13.3	13 13.1	2 29.0	5 34.0
9	21 9 8.5	18 41.1	4 3.9	0♓13.9	25 35.8	26 37.1	24 17.7	28 5.0	2 14.1	13 10.7	2 27.4	5 33.7
10	21 13 5.1	19 38.1	4 .9	14 13.2	24 53.7	27 54.7	24 59.6	28 1.2	2 14.9	13 8.3	2 25.8	5 33.4
11	21 17 1.6	20 35.0	3 57.9	28 2.1	24 9.5	29 12.1	25 41.3	27 57.2	2 15.5	13 5.9	2 24.2	5 33.1
12	21 20 58.2	21 31.7	3 54.9	11♈44.5	23 24.1	0♌29.4	26 22.9	27 53.1	2 16.0	13 3.5	2 22.6	5 32.9
13	21 24 54.8	22 28.3	3 51.9	25 26.6	22 38.2	1 46.6	27 4.4	27 48.8	2 16.4	13 1.1	2 21.1	5 32.7
14	21 28 51.3	23 24.8	3 48.8	9♉14.6	21 52.6	3 3.5	27 45.8	27 44.4	2 16.7	12 58.7	2 19.5	5 32.5
15	21 32 47.9	24 21.1	3 45.8	23 13.3	21 8.3	4 20.3	28 27.1	27 39.8	2 16.9	12 56.3	2 18.0	5 32.4
16	21 36 44.4	25 17.3	3 42.8	7♊23.5	20 26.2	5 36.9	29 8.4	27 35.1	2 17.1	12 54.0	2 16.5	5 32.3
17	21 40 41.0	26 13.4	3 39.8	21 41.4	19 47.1	6 53.3	29 49.5	27 30.2	2 17.1	12 51.7	2 15.0	5 32.3
18	21 44 37.5	27 9.3	3 36.7	5♋58.7	19 11.9	8 9.5	0♌30.4	27 25.2	2R17.0	12 49.4	2 13.5	5 32.2
19	21 48 34.1	28 5.1	3 33.7	20 4.6	18 41.3	9 25.4	1 11.3	27 20.0	2 16.8	12 47.0	2 12.0	5 32.2
20	21 52 30.6	29 .8	3 30.7	3♌48.7	18 16.2	10 41.2	1 52.1	27 14.7	2 16.5	12 44.7	2 10.5	5 32.2
21	21 56 27.2	29 56.4	3 27.7	17 3.7	17 57.2	11 56.7	2 32.7	27 9.3	2 16.1	12 42.4	2 9.1	5D32.3
22	22 0 23.7	0♍51.9	3 24.6	29 46.8	17 44.8	13 12.0	3 13.3	27 3.7	2 15.6	12 40.2	2 7.6	5 32.4
23	22 4 20.3	1 47.2	3 21.6	11♍59.5	17 39.6	14 27.1	3 53.7	26 58.0	2 15.0	12 37.9	2 6.2	5 32.5
24	22 8 16.8	2 42.5	3 18.6	23 46.8	17D41.7	15 42.0	4 34.0	26 52.2	2 14.3	12 35.7	2 4.8	5 32.7
25	22 12 13.4	3 37.6	3 15.6	5♎15.9	17 51.5	16 56.6	5 14.2	26 46.3	2 13.5	12 33.5	2 3.5	5 32.8
26	22 16 10.0	4 32.6	3 12.5	16 34.9	18 9.2	18 10.9	5 54.3	26 40.2	2 12.6	12 31.3	2 2.1	5 33.1
27	22 20 6.5	5 27.5	3 9.5	27 52.9	18 34.7	19 25.1	6 34.3	26 34.1	2 11.6	12 29.1	2 .8	5 33.3
28	22 24 3.1	6 22.3	3 6.5	9♏18.6	19 8.1	20 39.0	7 14.1	26 27.8	2 10.6	12 27.0	1 59.4	5 33.6
29	22 27 59.6	7 17.1	3 3.5	21 .3	19 49.1	21 52.7	7 53.9	26 21.4	2 9.4	12 24.8	1 58.1	5 33.9
30	22 31 56.2	8 11.7	3 .4	3♐ 5.0	20 37.7	23 6.1	8 33.5	26 15.0	2 8.1	12 22.7	1 56.9	5 34.3
31	22 35 52.7	9 6.2	2 57.4	15 37.6	21 33.5	24 19.3	9 13.0	26 8.4	2 6.7	12 20.7	1 55.6	5 34.7
		DECLINATION										
1	20 37 36.1	18N 7.1	0N11.1	11S15.6	8N29.8	22N25.9	23N 9.2	2S12.0	10N17.4	18S 9.8	19S41.5	9S16.6
4	20 49 25.8	17 20.9	0 11.1	18 10.1	8 13.2	22 6.9	22 54.8	2 16.4	10 18.0	18 11.8	19 42.5	9 17.8
7	21 1 15.4	16 32.1	0 11.2	17 25.3	8 20.1	21 42.1	22 38.9	2 21.4	10 18.3	18 13.8	19 43.6	9 19.0
10	21 13 5.1	15 41.0	0 11.3	7 49.0	8 50.8	21 11.7	22 21.4	2 27.0	10 18.4	18 15.7	19 44.6	9 20.2
13	21 24 54.8	14 47.6	0 11.3	5N57.2	9 42.7	20 35.7	22 2.4	2 33.2	10 18.1	18 17.6	19 45.7	9 21.6
16	21 36 44.4	13 52.0	0 11.4	16 30.3	10 49.4	19 54.4	21 41.9	2 39.9	10 17.5	18 19.5	19 46.6	9 23.0
19	21 48 34.1	12 54.5	0 11.4	18 33.0	12 1.5	19 7.9	21 20.0	2 47.2	10 16.6	18 21.4	19 47.6	9 24.4
22	22 0 23.7	11 55.1	0 11.5	11 56.4	13 9.2	18 16.5	20 56.8	2 54.9	10 15.3	18 23.2	19 48.5	9 25.9
25	22 12 13.4	10 54.0	0 11.6	0 52.0	14 3.3	17 20.4	20 32.3	3 3.1	10 13.8	18 24.9	19 49.4	9 27.5
28	22 24 3.1	9 51.4	0 11.6	10S10.7	14 36.8	16 19.9	20 6.6	3 11.7	10 11.9	18 26.6	19 50.3	9 29.1
31	22 35 52.7	8 47.4	0 11.7	17 38.6	14 44.4	15 15.2	19 39.6	3 20.6	10 9.8	18 28.3	19 51.2	9 30.7

SEPTEMBER 1998

LONGITUDE

DAY	EPHEM. SID. TIME	☉	☊	☽	☿	♀	♂	♃	♄	♅	♆	♇
	h m s	° ′	° ′	° ′	° ′	° ′	° ′	° ′	° ′	° ′	° ′	° ′
1	22 39 49.3	8♍22.4	0♍51.4	28♐44.1	20♌13.2	22♌50.5	7♌11.1	25♓ .6	3♉23.8	9♒40.7	29♑48.6	5♐23.0
2	22 43 45.8	9 20.5	0 48.2	11♑32.7	21 18.8	24 4.5	7 49.3	24R53.2	3R22.1	9R38.7	29R47.4	5 23.6
3	22 47 42.4	10 18.6	0 45.0	24 44.4	22 30.8	25 18.5	8 27.5	24 45.8	3 20.3	9 36.8	29 46.3	5 24.2
4	22 51 38.9	11 16.7	0 41.8	8♒20.8	23 49.0	26 32.5	9 5.6	24 38.2	3 18.3	9 34.8	29 45.1	5 24.8
5	22 55 35.5	12 14.8	0 38.7	22 21.8	25 12.7	27 46.6	9 43.7	24 30.7	3 16.3	9 32.9	29 44.0	5 25.4
6	22 59 32.0	13 13.0	0 35.5	6♓44.8	26 41.6	29 .7	10 21.8	24 23.0	3 14.2	9 31.1	29 43.0	5 26.1
7	23 3 28.6	14 11.1	0 32.3	21 25.1	28 15.0	0♍14.8	10 59.8	24 15.3	3 12.0	9 29.3	29 42.0	5 26.9
8	23 7 25.1	15 9.3	0 29.1	6♈16.1	29 52.4	1 29.0	11 37.8	24 7.6	3 9.7	9 27.5	29 40.9	5 27.6
9	23 11 21.7	16 7.6	0 25.9	21 9.8	1♍33.4	2 43.2	12 15.7	23 59.7	3 7.3	9 25.7	29 39.9	5 28.4
10	23 15 18.2	17 5.8	0 22.8	5♉58.6	3 17.3	3 57.4	12 53.6	23 51.9	3 4.8	9 24.0	29 39.0	5 29.2
11	23 19 14.8	18 4.1	0 19.6	20 35.6	5 3.8	5 11.7	13 31.4	23 44.0	3 2.2	9 22.3	29 38.0	5 30.0
12	23 23 11.3	19 2.5	0 16.4	4♊55.9	6 52.2	6 26.0	14 9.3	23 36.0	2 59.5	9 20.6	29 37.1	5 30.9
13	23 27 7.9	20 .9	0 13.2	18 56.8	8 42.3	7 40.3	14 47.0	23 28.1	2 56.8	9 18.9	29 36.2	5 31.8
14	23 31 4.4	20 59.3	0 10.1	2♋37.4	10 33.6	8 54.6	15 24.8	23 20.1	2 53.9	9 17.3	29 35.3	5 32.7
15	23 35 1.0	21 57.7	0 6.9	15 58.4	12 25.8	10 9.0	16 2.5	23 12.1	2 51.0	9 15.8	29 34.5	5 33.7
16	23 38 57.5	22 56.2	0 3.7	29 1.4	14 18.5	11 23.5	16 40.2	23 4.1	2 48.0	9 14.3	29 33.7	5 34.7
17	23 42 54.1	23 54.7	0 .5	11♌48.7	16 11.4	12 37.9	17 17.8	22 56.1	2 44.8	9 12.8	29 32.9	5 35.7
18	23 46 50.7	24 53.3	29♌57.3	24 22.3	18 4.4	13 52.4	17 55.4	22 48.1	2 41.7	9 11.3	29 32.1	5 36.8
19	23 50 47.2	25 51.8	29 54.2	6♍44.3	19 57.3	15 6.9	18 32.9	22 40.1	2 38.4	9 9.9	29 31.4	5 37.9
20	23 54 43.8	26 50.5	29 51.0	18 56.7	21 49.8	16 21.5	19 10.4	22 32.2	2 35.0	9 8.5	29 30.7	5 39.0
21	23 58 40.3	27 49.1	29 47.8	1♎ 1.1	23 41.8	17 36.0	19 47.9	22 24.2	2 31.6	9 7.2	29 30.0	5 40.1
22	0 2 36.9	28 47.8	29 44.6	12 59.1	25 33.3	18 50.6	20 25.3	22 16.3	2 28.1	9 5.9	29 29.4	5 41.3
23	0 6 33.4	29 46.5	29 41.5	24 52.4	27 24.1	20 5.3	21 2.7	22 8.4	2 24.5	9 4.7	29 28.8	5 42.5
24	0 10 30.0	0♎45.2	29 38.3	6♏43.2	29 14.2	21 19.9	21 40.0	22 .6	2 20.8	9 3.5	29 28.2	5 43.8
25	0 14 26.5	1 44.0	29 35.1	18 33.7	1♎ 3.4	22 34.6	22 17.3	21 52.8	2 17.1	9 2.3	29 27.7	5 45.0
26	0 18 23.1	2 42.8	29 31.9	0♐27.0	2 51.9	23 49.3	22 54.5	21 45.1	2 13.3	9 1.2	29 27.1	5 46.3
27	0 22 19.6	3 41.7	29 28.7	12 26.4	4 39.5	25 4.0	23 31.8	21 37.5	2 9.5	9 .2	29 26.7	5 47.7
28	0 26 16.2	4 40.6	29 25.6	24 36.0	6 26.2	26 18.8	24 8.9	21 29.9	2 5.6	8 59.1	29 26.3	5 49.1
29	0 30 12.7	5 39.5	29 22.4	7♑ .0	8 12.0	27 33.5	24 46.0	21 22.4	2 1.6	8 58.2	29 25.8	5 50.5
30	0 34 9.3	6 38.4	29 19.2	19 42.9	9 56.9	28 48.3	25 23.1	21 14.9	1 57.6	8 57.2	29 25.4	5 51.9

LATITUDE

DAY	EPHEM. SID. TIME	☉	☊	☽	☿	♀	♂	♃	♄	♅	♆	♇
1	22 39 49.3	0 .0	0 .0	4N42.1	0S 4.2	1N 2.2	1N 4.0	1S32.2	2S39.2	0S40.7	0N20.4	11N51.2
4	22 51 38.9	0 .0	0 .0	2 4.8	0N36.7	1 7.0	1 5.4	1 32.6	2 39.9	0 40.7	0 20.3	11 49.8
7	23 3 28.6	0 .0	0 .0	1S48.1	1 8.5	1 11.4	1 6.7	1 33.0	2 40.5	0 40.6	0 20.3	11 48.4
10	23 15 18.2	0 .0	0 .0	4 45.4	1 30.9	1 15.2	1 8.1	1 33.3	2 41.2	0 40.6	0 20.2	11 47.0
13	23 27 7.9	0 .0	0 .0	5 1.1	1 44.0	1 18.5	1 9.4	1 33.5	2 41.8	0 40.5	0 20.1	11 45.6
16	23 38 57.5	0 .0	0 .0	2 49.3	1 49.1	1 21.3	1 10.7	1 33.7	2 42.4	0 40.5	0 20.1	11 44.2
19	23 50 47.2	0 .0	0 .0	0N29.1	1 47.3	1 23.4	1 12.1	1 33.7	2 42.9	0 40.4	0 20.0	11 42.8
22	0 2 36.9	0 .0	0 .0	3 28.3	1 40.0	1 25.0	1 13.4	1 33.8	2 43.4	0 40.4	0 20.0	11 41.5
25	0 14 26.5	0 .0	0 .0	5 4.7	1 28.5	1 26.0	1 14.7	1 33.7	2 43.9	0 40.3	0 19.9	11 40.2
28	0 26 16.2	0 .0	0 .0	4 45.9	1 13.7	1 26.3	1 15.9	1 33.6	2 44.3	0 40.2	0 19.8	11 38.9

RIGHT ASCENSION

DAY	EPHEM. SID. TIME	☉	☊	☽	☿	♀	♂	♃	♄	♅	♆	♇
1	22 39 49.3	10♍ .7	2♍54.4	28♐40.2	22♌36.1	25♌32.2	9♌52.4	26♓ 1.8	2♉ 5.2	12♒18.6	1♒54.4	5♐35.1
2	22 43 45.8	10 55.1	2 51.3	12♑10.9	23 45.1	26 45.0	10 31.6	25R55.1	2R 3.6	12R16.6	1R53.2	5 35.5
3	22 47 42.4	11 49.4	2 48.3	26 4.4	25 .1	27 57.5	11 10.8	25 48.3	2 2.0	12 14.6	1 52.0	5 36.0
4	22 51 38.9	12 43.6	2 45.3	10♒12.4	26 20.6	29 9.7	11 49.8	25 41.4	2 .2	12 12.6	1 50.8	5 36.5
5	22 55 35.5	13 37.8	2 42.2	24 26.4	27 45.9	0♍21.8	12 28.8	25 34.5	1 58.3	12 10.7	1 49.7	5 37.1
6	22 59 32.0	14 31.9	2 39.2	8♓39.9	29 15.7	1 33.6	13 7.6	25 27.5	1 56.4	12 8.9	1 48.6	5 37.7
7	23 3 28.6	15 26.0	2 36.2	22 49.8	0♍49.2	2 45.3	13 46.3	25 20.5	1 54.4	12 7.0	1 47.6	5 38.3
8	23 7 25.1	16 20.0	2 33.2	6♈56.8	2 25.8	3 56.7	14 24.9	25 13.4	1 52.3	12 5.1	1 46.5	5 39.0
9	23 11 21.7	17 13.9	2 30.1	21 4.0	4 5.2	5 7.9	15 3.4	25 6.2	1 50.1	12 3.3	1 45.5	5 39.7
10	23 15 18.2	18 7.8	2 27.1	5♉15.4	5 46.6	6 18.9	15 41.7	24 59.0	1 47.7	12 1.6	1 44.4	5 40.4
11	23 19 14.8	19 1.7	2 24.1	19 33.7	7 29.7	7 29.7	16 20.0	24 51.8	1 45.4	11 59.8	1 43.5	5 41.1
12	23 23 11.3	19 55.6	2 21.0	3♊58.3	9 13.9	8 40.3	16 58.1	24 44.5	1 42.9	11 58.1	1 42.5	5 41.9
13	23 27 7.9	20 49.4	2 18.0	18 25.0	10 58.9	9 50.8	17 36.2	24 37.2	1 40.3	11 56.4	1 41.6	5 42.7
14	23 31 4.4	21 43.2	2 15.0	2♋45.9	12 44.3	11 1.1	18 14.1	24 29.9	1 37.6	11 54.8	1 40.7	5 43.5
15	23 35 1.0	22 37.0	2 11.9	16 51.5	14 29.8	12 11.2	18 51.9	24 22.6	1 34.9	11 53.2	1 39.8	5 44.4
16	23 38 57.5	23 30.8	2 8.9	0♌33.3	16 15.2	13 21.2	19 29.6	24 15.3	1 32.1	11 51.7	1 39.0	5 45.3
17	23 42 54.1	24 24.6	2 5.8	13 45.7	18 .2	14 31.0	20 7.2	24 7.9	1 29.2	11 50.1	1 38.2	5 46.2
18	23 46 50.7	25 18.4	2 2.8	26 27.1	19 44.6	15 40.7	20 44.7	24 .6	1 26.2	11 48.7	1 37.4	5 47.2
19	23 50 47.2	26 12.2	1 59.8	8♍39.4	21 28.4	16 50.2	21 22.0	23 53.2	1 23.1	11 47.2	1 36.6	5 48.2
20	23 54 43.8	27 6.1	1 56.7	20 27.5	23 11.5	17 59.6	21 59.3	23 45.9	1 20.0	11 45.8	1 35.9	5 49.2
21	23 58 40.3	27 59.9	1 53.7	1♎57.8	24 53.7	19 8.9	22 36.4	23 38.6	1 16.8	11 44.5	1 35.2	5 50.2
22	0 2 36.9	28 53.7	1 50.7	13 17.8	26 35.0	20 18.1	23 13.5	23 31.3	1 13.5	11 43.1	1 34.5	5 51.3
23	0 6 33.4	29 47.6	1 47.6	24 35.2	28 15.4	21 27.1	23 50.4	23 24.0	1 10.2	11 41.9	1 33.9	5 52.4
24	0 10 30.0	0♎41.5	1 44.6	5♏57.7	29 54.8	22 36.1	24 27.2	23 16.8	1 6.7	11 40.6	1 33.3	5 53.6
25	0 14 26.5	1 35.4	1 41.5	17 32.2	1♎33.4	23 45.0	25 3.9	23 9.6	1 3.2	11 39.4	1 32.8	5 54.8
26	0 18 23.1	2 29.4	1 38.5	29 24.7	3 11.0	24 53.8	25 40.5	23 2.5	0 59.7	11 38.3	1 32.2	5 56.0
27	0 22 19.6	3 23.5	1 35.5	11♐39.7	4 47.8	26 2.6	26 17.0	22 55.5	0 56.1	11 37.2	1 31.8	5 57.2
28	0 26 16.2	4 17.5	1 32.4	24 19.3	6 23.7	27 11.3	26 53.4	22 48.4	0 52.4	11 36.2	1 31.3	5 58.5
29	0 30 12.7	5 11.6	1 29.4	7♑23.3	7 58.8	28 19.9	27 29.7	22 41.5	0 48.6	11 35.2	1 30.9	5 59.8
30	0 34 9.3	6 5.8	1 26.3	20 48.7	9 33.1	29 28.5	28 5.9	22 34.6	0 44.8	11 34.2	1 30.5	6 1.1

DECLINATION

DAY	EPHEM. SID. TIME	☉	☊	☽	☿	♀	♂	♃	♄	♅	♆	♇
1	22 39 49.3	8N25.8	0N11.7	18S43.8	14N40.6	14N52.8	19N30.4	3S23.6	10N 9.0	18S28.8	19S51.4	9S31.3
4	22 51 38.9	7 20.1	0 11.8	16 10.0	14 9.5	13 43.1	19 1.9	3 32.9	10 6.5	18 30.3	19 52.2	9 33.0
7	23 3 28.6	6 13.4	0 11.8	5 3.5	13 9.2	12 29.9	18 32.3	3 42.3	10 3.8	18 31.8	19 52.9	9 34.7
10	23 15 18.2	5 5.7	0 11.9	9N 1.2	11 42.6	11 13.5	18 1.8	3 51.8	10 .7	18 33.1	19 53.6	9 36.5
13	23 27 7.9	3 57.3	0 11.9	17 58.5	9 54.7	9 54.4	17 30.2	4 1.5	9 57.4	18 34.4	19 54.2	9 38.3
16	23 38 57.5	2 48.2	0 12.0	17 35.4	7 51.2	8 32.7	16 57.8	4 11.1	9 53.9	18 35.6	19 54.8	9 40.2
19	23 50 47.2	1 38.6	0 12.0	9 29.3	5 37.3	7 8.8	16 24.5	4 20.7	9 50.1	18 36.7	19 55.4	9 42.0
22	0 2 36.9	0 28.7	0 12.1	1S55.6	3 17.8	5 43.0	15 50.4	4 30.1	9 46.1	18 37.7	19 55.8	9 43.9
25	0 14 26.5	0S41.4	0 12.2	12 27.7	0 55.9	4 15.7	15 15.5	4 39.3	9 42.0	18 38.6	19 56.3	9 45.8
28	0 26 16.2	1 51.5	0 12.2	18 34.0	1S25.6	2 47.2	14 39.9	4 48.3	9 37.6	18 39.3	19 56.6	9 47.7

OCTOBER 1998

DAY	EPHEM. SID. TIME	☉	☊	☽	☿	♀	♂	♃	♄	♅	♆	♇
	h m s	° ′	° ′	° ′	° ′	° ′	° ′	° ′	° ′	° ′	° ′	° ′
		LONGITUDE										
1	0 38 5.8	7♎37.3	29♌16.0	2♒48.9	11♎40.9	0♎ 3.1	26♌ .1	21♓ 7.5	1♉53.5	8♒56.3	29♑25.1	5♐53.3
2	0 42 2.4	8 36.3	29 12.9	16 21.1	13 24.0	1 17.9	26 37.1	21R .3	1R49.3	8R55.5	29R24.7	5 54.8
3	0 45 58.9	9 35.3	29 9.7	0♓21.2	15 6.3	2 32.7	27 14.0	20 53.1	1 45.1	8 54.7	29 24.4	5 56.3
4	0 49 55.5	10 34.4	29 6.5	14 48.6	16 47.7	3 47.6	27 50.9	20 46.0	1 40.8	8 53.9	29 24.2	5 57.8
5	0 53 52.0	11 33.4	29 3.3	29 39.3	18 28.2	5 2.4	28 27.8	20 39.0	1 36.5	8 53.2	29 24.0	5 59.3
6	0 57 48.6	12 32.5	29 .1	14♈46.7	20 7.9	6 17.3	29 4.6	20 32.2	1 32.2	8 52.6	29 23.8	6 .9
7	1 1 45.1	13 31.7	28 57.0	0♉ 1.1	21 46.9	7 32.2	29 41.3	20 25.4	1 27.7	8 52.0	29 23.6	6 2.5
8	1 5 41.7	14 30.8	28 53.8	15 12.1	23 25.0	8 47.1	0♍18.0	20 18.8	1 23.3	8 51.4	29 23.5	6 4.1
9	1 9 38.2	15 30.0	28 50.6	0♊ 9.5	25 2.3	10 2.1	0 54.7	20 12.3	1 18.8	8 50.9	29 23.4	6 5.8
10	1 13 34.8	16 29.3	28 47.4	14 45.8	26 38.9	11 17.0	1 31.4	20 5.9	1 14.3	8 50.4	29 23.3	6 7.5
11	1 17 31.3	17 28.6	28 44.2	28 56.5	28 14.7	12 32.0	2 7.9	19 59.6	1 9.7	8 50.0	29 23.3	6 9.2
12	1 21 27.9	18 27.9	28 41.1	12♋40.0	29 49.8	13 47.0	2 44.5	19 53.5	1 5.1	8 49.6	29 23.3	6 10.9
13	1 25 24.5	19 27.3	28 37.9	25 57.7	1♏24.2	15 2.0	3 21.0	19 47.5	1 .5	8 49.3	29 23.3	6 12.6
14	1 29 21.0	20 26.7	28 34.7	8♌52.4	2 57.9	16 17.1	3 57.4	19 41.7	0 55.8	8 49.1	29 23.3	6 14.4
15	1 33 17.6	21 26.1	28 31.5	21 28.0	4 31.0	17 32.1	4 33.9	19 36.0	0 51.1	8 48.8	29D23.4	6 16.2
16	1 37 14.1	22 25.6	28 28.4	3♍48.5	6 3.3	18 47.2	5 10.2	19 30.5	0 46.4	8 48.7	29 23.6	6 18.0
17	1 41 10.7	23 25.1	28 25.2	15 57.6	7 35.0	20 2.3	5 46.5	19 25.1	0 41.7	8 48.5	29 23.7	6 19.9
18	1 45 7.2	24 24.7	28 22.0	27 58.8	9 6.1	21 17.4	6 22.8	19 19.9	0 37.0	8 48.5	29 24.0	6 21.8
19	1 49 3.8	25 24.3	28 18.8	9♎54.6	10 36.5	22 32.6	6 59.1	19 14.9	0 32.2	8 48.5	29 24.2	6 23.6
20	1 53 .3	26 23.9	28 15.6	21 47.3	12 6.2	23 47.7	7 35.2	19 10.0	0 27.5	8D48.6	29 24.5	6 25.5
21	1 56 56.9	27 23.6	28 12.5	3♏38.5	13 35.3	25 2.8	8 11.3	19 5.3	0 22.7	8 48.6	29 24.8	6 27.5
22	2 0 53.4	28 23.3	28 9.3	15 29.8	15 3.7	26 18.0	8 47.4	19 .8	0 17.9	8 48.8	29 25.1	6 29.4
23	2 4 50.0	29 23.0	28 6.1	27 22.7	16 31.4	27 33.1	9 23.4	18 56.4	0 13.1	8 49.0	29 25.5	6 31.4
24	2 8 46.5	0♏22.7	28 2.9	9♐18.9	17 58.5	28 48.3	9 59.3	18 52.3	0 8.3	8 49.2	29 25.9	6 33.4
25	2 12 43.1	1 22.5	27 59.8	21 20.8	19 24.9	0♏ 3.5	10 35.2	18 48.3	0 3.5	8 49.5	29 26.4	6 35.4
26	2 16 39.6	2 22.3	27 56.6	3♑31.1	20 50.5	1 18.7	11 11.1	18 44.5	29♈58.7	8 49.8	29 26.8	6 37.4
27	2 20 36.2	3 22.2	27 53.4	15 53.4	22 15.4	2 33.9	11 46.9	18 40.8	29 53.9	8 50.2	29 27.3	6 39.4
28	2 24 32.8	4 22.1	27 50.2	28 31.7	23 39.5	3 49.1	12 22.6	18 37.4	29 49.1	8 50.7	29 27.9	6 41.5
29	2 28 29.3	5 22.0	27 47.0	11♒30.0	25 2.8	5 4.3	12 58.3	18 34.2	29 44.3	8 51.2	29 28.4	6 43.5
30	2 32 25.9	6 21.9	27 43.9	24 52.5	26 25.3	6 19.5	13 33.9	18 31.2	29 39.6	8 51.7	29 29.0	6 45.6
31	2 36 22.4	7 21.8	27 40.7	8♓42.2	27 46.8	7 34.7	14 9.5	18 28.3	29 34.8	8 52.3	29 29.7	6 47.7
		LATITUDE										
1	0 38 5.8	0 .0	0 .0	2N27.2	0N56.6	1N26.1	1N17.2	1S33.5	2S44.7	0S40.1	0N19.8	11N37.7
4	0 49 55.5	0 .0	0 .0	1S14.6	0 37.7	1 25.3	1 18.5	1 33.2	2 45.1	0 40.1	0 19.7	11 36.4
7	1 1 45.1	0 .0	0 .0	4 25.8	0 17.7	1 23.9	1 19.7	1 32.9	2 45.3	0 40.0	0 19.6	11 35.3
10	1 13 34.8	0 .0	0 .0	4 59.1	0S 2.9	1 21.9	1 21.0	1 32.6	2 45.6	0 39.9	0 19.6	11 34.1
13	1 25 24.5	0 .0	0 .0	2 54.7	0 23.8	1 19.4	1 22.2	1 32.2	2 45.7	0 39.8	0 19.5	11 33.0
16	1 37 14.1	0 .0	0 .0	0N18.5	0 44.6	1 16.3	1 23.5	1 31.7	2 45.9	0 39.7	0 19.4	11 32.0
19	1 49 3.8	0 .0	0 .0	3 15.4	1 4.9	1 12.8	1 24.7	1 31.2	2 45.9	0 39.6	0 19.4	11 31.0
22	2 0 53.4	0 .0	0 .0	4 54.4	1 24.5	1 8.7	1 25.9	1 30.7	2 45.9	0 39.6	0 19.3	11 30.0
25	2 12 43.1	0 .0	0 .0	4 41.3	1 43.0	1 4.2	1 27.1	1 30.1	2 45.9	0 39.5	0 19.2	11 29.1
28	2 24 32.8	0 .0	0 .0	2 34.5	1 60.0	0 59.2	1 28.3	1 29.5	2 45.8	0 39.4	0 19.2	11 28.2
31	2 36 22.4	0 .0	0 .0	0S51.6	2 15.0	0 53.8	1 29.5	1 28.9	2 45.6	0 39.3	0 19.1	11 27.4
		RIGHT ASCENSION										
1	0 38 5.8	6♎60.0	1♍23.3	4♒30.8	11♎ 6.6	0♎37.1	28♌41.9	22♓27.8	0♉41.0	11♒33.3	1♒30.1	6♐ 2.4
2	0 42 2.4	7 54.3	1 20.3	18 24.1	12 39.5	1 45.6	29 17.9	22R21.1	0R37.1	11R32.4	1R29.8	6 3.8
3	0 45 58.9	8 48.6	1 17.2	2♓24.4	14 11.7	2 54.2	29 53.7	22 14.4	0 33.1	11 31.6	1 29.4	6 5.2
4	0 49 55.5	9 43.1	1 14.2	16 29.7	15 43.2	4 2.7	0♍29.5	22 7.8	0 29.1	11 30.9	1 29.2	6 6.6
5	0 53 52.0	10 37.6	1 11.1	0♈40.5	17 14.2	5 11.2	1 5.1	22 1.4	0 25.0	11 30.1	1 28.9	6 8.1
6	0 57 48.6	11 32.2	1 8.1	14 59.5	18 44.7	6 19.8	1 40.7	21 55.0	0 20.9	11 29.4	1 28.7	6 9.6
7	1 1 45.1	12 26.9	1 5.0	29 29.8	20 14.7	7 28.4	2 16.2	21 48.7	0 16.7	11 28.8	1 28.6	6 11.1
8	1 5 41.7	13 21.7	1 2.0	14♉12.9	21 44.3	8 37.1	2 51.5	21 42.6	0 12.5	11 28.2	1 28.4	6 12.6
9	1 9 38.2	14 16.6	0 59.0	29 6.4	23 13.4	9 45.8	3 26.8	21 36.5	0 8.3	11 27.7	1 28.3	6 14.2
10	1 13 34.8	15 11.6	0 55.9	14♊ 3.4	24 42.2	10 54.6	4 1.9	21 30.6	0 4.0	11 27.2	1 28.3	6 15.7
11	1 17 31.3	16 6.7	0 52.9	28 53.0	26 10.7	12 3.4	4 37.0	21 24.7	29♈59.7	11 26.8	1 28.2	6 17.3
12	1 21 27.9	17 2.0	0 49.8	13♋23.0	27 38.9	13 12.3	5 12.0	21 19.0	29 55.3	11 26.4	1 28.2	6 19.0
13	1 25 24.5	17 57.4	0 46.8	27 23.0	29 6.8	14 21.4	5 46.9	21 13.5	29 51.0	11 26.1	1D28.3	6 20.6
14	1 29 21.0	18 52.9	0 43.7	10♌47.2	0♏34.5	15 30.5	6 21.7	21 8.0	29 46.6	11 25.8	1 28.4	6 22.3
15	1 33 17.6	19 48.6	0 40.7	23 34.9	2 2.0	16 39.8	6 56.4	21 2.7	29 42.1	11 25.6	1 28.5	6 24.0
16	1 37 14.1	20 44.4	0 37.6	5♍49.4	3 29.2	17 49.2	7 31.0	20 57.5	29 37.7	11 25.4	1 28.6	6 25.7
17	1 41 10.7	21 40.3	0 34.6	17 37.0	4 56.4	18 58.7	8 5.5	20 52.5	29 33.2	11 25.3	1 28.8	6 27.5
18	1 45 7.2	22 36.5	0 31.5	29 5.5	6 23.4	20 8.4	8 40.0	20 47.7	29 28.7	11 25.2	1 29.0	6 29.3
19	1 49 3.8	23 32.7	0 28.5	10♎23.2	7 50.2	21 18.2	9 14.3	20 43.0	29 24.2	11 25.2	1 29.3	6 31.1
20	1 53 .3	24 29.1	0 25.4	21 38.1	9 16.9	22 28.2	9 48.5	20 38.4	29 19.7	11D25.3	1 29.6	6 32.9
21	1 56 56.9	25 25.7	0 22.4	2♏57.9	10 43.4	23 38.4	10 22.7	20 34.0	29 15.2	11 25.3	1 29.9	6 34.7
22	2 0 53.4	26 22.4	0 19.3	14 29.2	12 9.9	24 48.7	10 56.7	20 29.7	29 10.6	11 25.5	1 30.3	6 36.6
23	2 4 50.0	27 19.3	0 16.3	26 17.2	13 36.1	25 59.2	11 30.7	20 25.6	29 6.1	11 25.6	1 30.6	6 38.5
24	2 8 46.5	28 16.4	0 13.2	8♐25.2	15 2.3	27 10.0	12 4.6	20 21.7	29 1.5	11 25.9	1 31.1	6 40.4
25	2 12 43.1	29 13.6	0 10.2	20 54.2	16 28.2	28 20.9	12 38.3	20 17.9	28 56.9	11 26.2	1 31.5	6 42.3
26	2 16 39.6	0♏11.0	0 7.1	3♑43.0	17 54.0	29 32.1	13 12.0	20 14.3	28 52.4	11 26.5	1 32.0	6 44.2
27	2 20 36.2	1 8.6	0 4.1	16 48.3	19 19.5	0♏43.4	13 45.6	20 10.9	28 47.8	11 26.9	1 32.6	6 46.2
28	2 24 32.8	2 6.4	0 1.0	0♒ 5.8	20 44.7	1 55.0	14 19.1	20 7.6	28 43.3	11 27.4	1 33.1	6 48.1
29	2 28 29.3	3 4.4	29♌58.0	13 31.3	22 9.6	3 6.9	14 52.6	20 4.6	28 38.8	11 27.9	1 33.7	6 50.1
30	2 32 25.9	4 2.5	29 54.9	27 2.2	23 34.1	4 19.0	15 25.9	20 1.7	28 34.2	11 28.4	1 34.4	6 52.1
31	2 36 22.4	5 .8	29 51.9	10♓38.8	24 58.1	5 31.3	15 59.2	19 59.0	28 29.7	11 29.0	1 35.0	6 54.2
		DECLINATION										
1	0 38 5.8	3S 1.4	0N12.3	17S 8.3	3S45.1	1N17.8	14N 3.7	4S57.0	9N33.1	18S40.0	19S56.9	9S49.6
4	0 49 55.5	4 11.1	0 12.3	7 7.7	6 1.1	0S12.2	13 26.8	5 5.2	9 28.5	18 40.6	19 57.2	9 51.5
7	1 1 45.1	5 20.3	0 12.4	7N19.6	8 12.8	1 42.4	12 49.5	5 13.1	9 23.7	18 41.0	19 57.4	9 53.5
10	1 13 34.8	6 28.9	0 12.5	17 36.8	10 19.3	3 12.4	12 11.6	5 20.5	9 18.9	18 41.3	19 57.5	9 55.4
13	1 25 24.5	7 36.8	0 12.5	18 5.5	12 20.0	4 42.1	11 33.3	5 27.3	9 14.0	18 41.5	19 57.6	9 57.3
16	1 37 14.1	8 43.7	0 12.6	10 23.9	14 14.4	6 10.9	10 54.5	5 33.6	9 9.0	18 41.6	19 57.6	9 59.2
19	1 49 3.8	9 49.5	0 12.6	0S55.8	16 1.9	7 38.7	10 15.4	5 39.3	9 4.0	18 41.6	19 57.5	10 1.1
22	2 0 53.4	10 54.0	0 12.7	11 46.8	17 41.9	9 5.0	9 36.0	5 44.3	8 59.0	18 41.4	19 57.4	10 2.9
25	2 12 43.1	11 57.1	0 12.7	18 28.5	19 14.0	10 29.4	8 56.4	5 48.7	8 54.1	18 41.2	19 57.2	10 4.8
28	2 24 32.8	12 58.5	0 12.8	17 55.9	20 37.3	11 51.7	8 16.6	5 52.4	8 49.2	18 40.8	19 56.9	10 6.6
31	2 36 22.4	13 58.1	0 12.9	9 6.2	21 51.3	13 11.4	7 36.6	5 55.4	8 44.3	18 40.2	19 56.6	10 8.4

NOVEMBER 1998

LONGITUDE

DAY	EPHEM. SID. TIME h m s	☉ ° ′	☊ ° ′	☽ ° ′	☿ ° ′	♀ ° ′	♂ ° ′	♃ ° ′	♄ ° ′	♅ ° ′	♆ ° ′	♇ ° ′
1	2 40 19.0	8♏21.8	27♌37.5	23♓ .3	29♏ 7.2	8♏49.9	14♍45.0	18♓25.7	29♈30.1	8♒53.0	29♑30.4	6♐49.8
2	2 44 15.5	9 21.8	27 34.3	7♈45.0	0♐26.6	10 5.1	15 20.4	18 R 23.2	29 R 25.4	8 53.7	29 31.1	6 52.0
3	2 48 12.1	10 21.8	27 31.2	22 51.3	1 44.9	11 20.4	15 55.8	18 21.0	29 20.8	8 54.4	29 31.8	6 54.1
4	2 52 8.6	11 21.9	27 28.0	8♉10.5	3 1.8	12 35.6	16 31.1	18 18.9	29 16.1	8 55.2	29 32.6	6 56.3
5	2 56 5.2	12 22.0	27 24.8	23 31.3	4 17.3	13 50.9	17 6.4	18 17.1	29 11.5	8 56.1	29 33.4	6 58.5
6	3 0 1.7	13 22.1	27 21.6	8♊42.0	5 31.2	15 6.1	17 41.6	18 15.4	29 6.9	8 57.0	29 34.2	7 .6
7	3 3 58.3	14 22.3	27 18.4	23 32.5	6 43.4	16 21.4	18 16.8	18 14.0	29 2.4	8 57.9	29 35.1	7 2.8
8	3 7 54.8	15 22.5	27 15.3	7♋55.9	7 53.8	17 36.7	18 52.0	18 12.8	28 57.9	8 59.0	29 36.0	7 5.1
9	3 11 51.4	16 22.7	27 12.1	21 49.1	9 1.9	18 52.0	19 27.0	18 11.8	28 53.5	9 .0	29 36.9	7 7.3
10	3 15 48.0	17 23.0	27 8.9	5♌12.4	10 7.6	20 7.2	20 2.0	18 10.9	28 49.0	9 1.1	29 37.9	7 9.6
11	3 19 44.5	18 23.3	27 5.7	18 8.8	11 10.6	21 22.5	20 36.9	18 10.3	28 44.6	9 2.3	29 38.9	7 11.8
12	3 23 41.1	19 23.6	27 2.6	0♍42.5	12 10.5	22 37.8	21 11.8	18 9.9	28 40.3	9 3.5	29 39.9	7 14.1
13	3 27 37.6	20 24.0	26 59.4	12 58.5	13 7.0	23 53.1	21 46.6	18 9.7	28 36.0	9 4.7	29 41.0	7 16.3
14	3 31 34.2	21 24.4	26 56.2	25 1.9	13 59.7	25 8.4	22 21.3	18 9.7	28 31.8	9 6.0	29 42.1	7 18.6
15	3 35 30.7	22 24.8	26 53.0	6♎57.3	14 48.0	26 23.8	22 55.9	18 D 9.9	28 27.6	9 7.4	29 43.2	7 20.9
16	3 39 27.3	23 25.2	26 49.9	18 48.4	15 31.4	27 39.1	23 30.5	18 10.3	28 23.5	9 8.8	29 44.3	7 23.2
17	3 43 23.8	24 25.7	26 46.7	0♏38.5	16 9.3	28 54.4	24 5.0	18 10.9	28 19.4	9 10.2	29 45.5	7 25.5
18	3 47 20.4	25 26.2	26 43.5	12 30.0	16 41.1	0♐ 9.7	24 39.5	18 11.7	28 15.4	9 11.7	29 46.7	7 27.8
19	3 51 17.0	26 26.7	26 40.3	24 24.4	17 6.0	1 25.1	25 13.9	18 12.8	28 11.5	9 13.3	29 48.0	7 30.1
20	3 55 13.5	27 27.3	26 37.1	6♐23.1	17 23.3	2 40.4	25 48.1	18 14.0	28 7.6	9 14.8	29 49.2	7 32.4
21	3 59 10.1	28 27.9	26 34.0	18 27.1	17 32.2	3 55.7	26 22.4	18 15.4	28 3.8	9 16.5	29 50.5	7 34.8
22	4 3 6.6	29 28.5	26 30.8	0♑37.5	17 R 32.1	5 11.1	26 56.5	18 17.1	28 .1	9 18.1	29 51.8	7 37.1
23	4 7 3.2	0♐29.1	26 27.6	12 55.9	17 22.1	6 26.4	27 30.6	18 19.0	27 56.4	9 19.9	29 53.2	7 39.4
24	4 10 59.7	1 29.8	26 24.4	25 24.4	17 1.8	7 41.8	28 4.6	18 21.0	27 52.9	9 21.6	29 54.6	7 41.8
25	4 14 56.3	2 30.5	26 21.3	8♒ 5.6	16 30.8	8 57.1	28 38.5	18 23.3	27 49.3	9 23.5	29 56.0	7 44.1
26	4 18 52.8	3 31.1	26 18.1	21 2.8	15 49.0	10 12.5	29 12.3	18 25.7	27 45.9	9 25.3	29 57.4	7 46.5
27	4 22 49.4	4 31.8	26 14.9	4♓19.3	14 56.7	11 27.8	29 46.0	18 28.4	27 42.6	9 27.2	29 58.9	7 48.8
28	4 26 46.0	5 32.6	26 11.7	17 58.2	13 54.7	12 43.1	0♎19.7	18 31.3	27 39.3	9 29.2	0♒ .4	7 51.1
29	4 30 42.5	6 33.4	26 8.6	2♈ 1.7	12 44.4	13 58.5	0 53.3	18 34.4	27 36.2	9 31.2	0 1.9	7 53.5
30	4 34 39.1	7 34.1	26 5.4	16 29.5	11 27.5	15 13.8	1 26.8	18 37.6	27 33.1	9 33.2	0 3.5	7 55.9

LATITUDE

DAY	EPHEM. SID. TIME	☉	☊	☽	☿	♀	♂	♃	♄	♅	♆	♇
1	2 40 19.0	0 .0	0 .0	2S 4.0	2S19.5	0N51.9	1N29.9	1S28.7	2S45.6	0S39.3	0N19.1	11N27.1
4	2 52 8.6	0 .0	0 .0	4 42.8	2 31.2	0 46.1	1 31.1	1 28.0	2 45.3	0 39.2	0 19.0	11 26.4
7	3 3 58.3	0 .0	0 .0	4 32.4	2 39.4	0 39.9	1 32.3	1 27.3	2 45.1	0 39.1	0 19.0	11 25.7
10	3 15 48.0	0 .0	0 .0	1 56.7	2 43.3	0 33.4	1 33.5	1 26.6	2 44.7	0 39.0	0 18.9	11 25.0
13	3 27 37.6	0 .0	0 .0	1N19.4	2 41.6	0 26.7	1 34.7	1 25.9	2 44.3	0 38.9	0 18.8	11 24.4
16	3 39 27.3	0 .0	0 .0	3 54.6	2 32.6	0 19.8	1 35.9	1 25.1	2 43.9	0 38.8	0 18.8	11 23.9
19	3 51 17.0	0 .0	0 .0	4 58.9	2 14.3	0 12.8	1 37.1	1 24.4	2 43.4	0 38.8	0 18.7	11 23.4
22	4 3 6.6	0 .0	0 .0	4 7.7	1 44.2	0 5.6	1 38.3	1 23.6	2 42.9	0 38.7	0 18.7	11 23.0
25	4 14 56.3	0 .0	0 .0	1 32.5	1 .7	0S 1.6	1 39.5	1 22.9	2 42.3	0 38.6	0 18.6	11 22.6
28	4 26 46.0	0 .0	0 .0	1S54.0	0 5.1	0 8.9	1 40.7	1 22.1	2 41.7	0 38.5	0 18.5	11 22.3

RIGHT ASCENSION

DAY	EPHEM. SID. TIME	☉	☊	☽	☿	♀	♂	♃	♄	♅	♆	♇
1	2 40 19.0	5♏59.3	29♌48.8	24♓23.8	26♏21.6	6♏43.9	16♍32.3	19♓56.4	28♈25.2	11♒29.7	1♒35.7	6♐56.2
2	2 44 15.5	6 58.0	29 45.8	8♈22.2	27 44.4	7 56.8	17 5.4	19 R 54.1	28 R 20.8	11 30.4	1 36.5	6 58.3
3	2 48 12.1	7 56.9	29 42.7	22 39.7	29 6.4	9 9.9	17 38.4	19 51.9	28 16.3	11 31.1	1 37.2	7 .3
4	2 52 8.6	8 56.1	29 39.7	7♉20.7	0♐27.4	10 23.3	18 11.4	19 49.9	28 11.9	11 31.9	1 38.0	7 2.4
5	2 56 5.2	9 55.4	29 36.6	22 25.2	1 47.4	11 37.0	18 44.2	19 48.1	28 7.5	11 32.8	1 38.9	7 4.5
6	3 0 1.7	10 54.9	29 33.5	7♊46.8	3 6.1	12 51.0	19 17.0	19 46.5	28 3.2	11 33.7	1 39.8	7 6.6
7	3 3 58.3	11 54.6	29 30.5	23 12.0	4 23.3	14 5.3	19 49.7	19 45.1	27 58.8	11 34.7	1 40.7	7 8.8
8	3 7 54.8	12 54.6	29 27.4	8♋23.4	5 38.9	15 20.0	20 22.3	19 43.9	27 54.6	11 35.7	1 41.7	7 10.9
9	3 11 51.4	13 54.8	29 24.4	23 4.5	6 52.4	16 34.8	20 54.9	19 42.9	27 50.3	11 36.8	1 42.6	7 13.1
10	3 15 48.0	14 55.2	29 21.3	7♌ 4.2	8 3.6	17 50.0	21 27.3	19 42.0	27 46.1	11 37.9	1 43.6	7 15.3
11	3 19 44.5	15 55.7	29 18.3	20 18.8	9 12.1	19 5.5	21 59.7	19 41.3	27 41.9	11 39.1	1 44.7	7 17.4
12	3 23 41.1	16 56.6	29 15.2	2♍51.4	10 17.6	20 21.3	22 32.0	19 40.8	27 37.7	11 40.3	1 45.7	7 19.6
13	3 27 37.6	17 57.6	29 12.1	14 49.1	11 19.5	21 37.5	23 4.2	19 40.6	27 33.6	11 41.5	1 46.8	7 21.8
14	3 31 34.2	18 58.8	29 9.1	26 21.5	12 17.4	22 53.9	23 36.4	19 40.5	27 29.6	11 42.9	1 48.0	7 24.0
15	3 35 30.7	20 .3	29 6.0	7♎38.6	13 10.7	24 10.6	24 8.5	19 40.5	27 25.6	11 44.2	1 49.1	7 26.3
16	3 39 27.3	21 2.0	29 3.0	18 50.3	13 58.8	25 27.7	24 40.5	19 D 40.8	27 21.7	11 45.6	1 50.3	7 28.5
17	3 43 23.8	22 3.8	28 59.9	0♏ 5.9	14 41.0	26 45.0	25 12.4	19 41.3	27 17.8	11 47.1	1 51.6	7 30.7
18	3 47 20.4	23 5.9	28 56.8	11 33.0	15 16.6	28 2.7	25 44.2	19 42.0	27 13.9	11 48.6	1 52.8	7 33.0
19	3 51 17.0	24 8.2	28 53.8	23 17.8	15 44.7	29 20.6	26 15.9	19 42.8	27 10.2	11 50.2	1 54.1	7 35.2
20	3 55 13.5	25 10.8	28 50.7	5♐23.8	16 4.7	0♐38.9	26 47.6	19 43.9	27 6.4	11 51.8	1 55.4	7 37.5
21	3 59 10.1	26 13.5	28 47.7	17 51.9	16 15.5	1 57.5	27 19.2	19 45.1	27 2.8	11 53.4	1 56.8	7 39.8
22	4 3 6.6	27 16.4	28 44.6	0♑39.7	16 16.5	3 16.3	27 50.7	19 46.5	26 59.2	11 55.1	1 58.2	7 42.0
23	4 7 3.2	28 19.5	28 41.5	13 42.0	16 R 7.0	4 35.4	28 22.1	19 48.1	26 55.7	11 56.8	1 59.6	7 44.3
24	4 10 59.7	29 22.8	28 38.5	26 52.6	15 46.4	5 54.8	28 53.5	19 49.9	26 52.2	11 58.6	2 1.0	7 46.6
25	4 14 56.3	0♐26.3	28 35.4	10♒ 5.7	15 14.4	7 14.4	29 24.8	19 51.9	26 48.9	12 .5	2 2.5	7 48.9
26	4 18 52.8	1 30.0	28 32.3	23 17.6	14 31.0	8 34.4	29 56.0	19 54.1	26 45.5	12 2.4	2 4.0	7 51.2
27	4 22 49.4	2 33.8	28 29.3	6♓28.2	13 36.6	9 54.5	0♎27.1	19 56.5	26 42.3	12 4.3	2 5.5	7 53.5
28	4 26 46.0	3 37.9	28 26.2	19 41.0	12 32.3	11 14.9	0 58.1	19 59.0	26 39.2	12 6.3	2 7.1	7 55.8
29	4 30 42.5	4 42.1	28 23.2	3♈ 2.7	11 19.6	12 35.6	1 29.1	20 1.8	26 36.1	12 8.3	2 8.7	7 58.1
30	4 34 39.1	5 46.5	28 20.1	16 41.6	10 .4	13 56.5	1 59.9	20 4.7	26 33.1	12 10.4	2 10.3	8 .4

DECLINATION

DAY	EPHEM. SID. TIME	☉	☊	☽	☿	♀	♂	♃	♄	♅	♆	♇
1	2 40 19.0	14S17.5	0N12.9	4S40.5	22S13.8	13S37.3	7N23.3	5S56.2	8N42.7	18S40.0	19S56.5	10S 9.0
4	2 52 8.6	15 14.4	0 12.9	9N46.0	23 14.0	14 53.1	6 43.2	5 58.2	8 38.0	18 39.4	19 56.1	10 10.7
7	3 3 58.3	16 9.0	0 13.0	18 44.7	24 2.9	16 5.4	6 3.0	5 59.5	8 33.5	18 38.6	19 55.6	10 12.4
10	3 15 48.0	17 1.2	0 13.0	17 4.7	24 39.5	17 14.1	5 22.9	6 .0	8 29.1	18 37.6	19 55.1	10 14.1
13	3 27 37.6	17 50.8	0 13.1	7 54.5	25 2.6	18 18.6	4 42.8	5 59.9	8 24.9	18 36.6	19 54.5	10 15.7
16	3 39 27.3	18 37.6	0 13.2	3S44.8	25 10.8	19 18.7	4 2.7	5 58.9	8 20.9	18 35.5	19 53.9	10 17.3
19	3 51 17.0	19 21.4	0 13.2	14 2.2	25 2.3	20 14.0	3 22.9	5 57.3	8 17.1	18 34.2	19 53.2	10 18.8
22	4 3 6.6	20 2.2	0 13.3	19 18.4	24 34.9	21 4.2	2 43.2	5 54.9	8 13.6	18 32.8	19 52.4	10 20.3
25	4 14 56.3	20 39.6	0 13.3	16 45.1	23 45.7	21 49.0	2 3.7	5 51.8	8 10.3	18 31.3	19 51.6	10 21.7
28	4 26 46.0	21 13.6	0 13.4	6 30.3	22 33.1	22 28.0	1 24.5	5 48.0	8 7.3	18 29.7	19 50.7	10 23.1

DECEMBER 1998

DAY	EPHEM. SID. TIME	☉	☊	☽	☿	♀	♂	♃	♄	♅	♆	♇
	h m s	° ′	° ′	° ′	° ′	° ′	° ′	° ′	° ′	° ′	° ′	° ′
		LONGITUDE										
1	4 38 35.6	8♐34.9	26♌ 2.2	1♉18.8	10♐ 6.3	16♐29.2	2♎ .1	18♓41.1	27♈30.1	9♒35.3	0♒ 5.0	7♐58.2
2	4 42 32.2	9 35.7	25 59.0	16 23.6	8 R 43.6	17 44.5	2 33.5	18 44.7	27 R 27.2	9 37.4	0 6.6	8 .6
3	4 46 28.7	10 36.5	25 55.8	1♊34.5	7 22.1	18 59.8	3 6.7	18 48.6	27 24.3	9 39.6	0 8.2	8 2.9
4	4 50 25.3	11 37.3	25 52.7	16 41.1	6 4.5	20 15.1	3 39.8	18 52.6	27 21.6	9 41.8	0 9.9	8 5.3
5	4 54 21.9	12 38.2	25 49.5	1♋32.8	4 53.4	21 30.5	4 12.9	18 56.8	27 18.9	9 44.0	0 11.5	8 7.6
6	4 58 18.4	13 39.0	25 46.3	16 1.4	3 50.7	22 45.8	4 45.8	19 1.2	27 16.4	9 46.3	0 13.2	8 10.0
7	5 2 15.0	14 39.9	25 43.1	0♌ 2.1	2 58.0	24 1.1	5 18.7	19 5.8	27 13.9	9 48.6	0 14.9	8 12.3
8	5 6 11.5	15 40.8	25 40.0	13 33.2	2 16.2	25 16.4	5 51.4	19 10.6	27 11.6	9 51.0	0 16.7	8 14.7
9	5 10 8.1	16 41.7	25 36.8	26 36.3	1 45.7	26 31.8	6 24.1	19 15.5	27 9.3	9 53.4	0 18.4	8 17.0
10	5 14 4.6	17 42.7	25 33.6	9♍14.9	1 26.6	27 47.1	6 56.7	19 20.7	27 7.1	9 55.8	0 20.2	8 19.3
11	5 18 1.2	18 43.6	25 30.4	21 33.7	1 18.5	29 2.4	7 29.1	19 26.0	27 5.1	9 58.3	0 22.0	8 21.6
12	5 21 57.8	19 44.6	25 27.3	3♎38.0	1 D 20.9	0♑17.7	8 1.5	19 31.5	27 3.4	10 .8	0 23.8	8 24.0
13	5 25 54.3	20 45.6	25 24.1	15 33.0	1 32.9	1 33.1	8 33.7	19 37.2	27 1.2	10 3.3	0 25.7	8 26.3
14	5 29 50.9	21 46.6	25 20.9	27 23.5	1 53.9	2 48.4	9 5.9	19 43.0	26 59.5	10 5.9	0 27.6	8 28.6
15	5 33 47.4	22 47.7	25 17.7	9♏13.8	2 22.8	4 3.7	9 37.9	19 49.1	26 57.8	10 8.5	0 29.4	8 30.9
16	5 37 44.0	23 48.7	25 14.5	21 7.1	2 59.0	5 19.0	10 9.8	19 55.3	26 56.3	10 11.1	0 31.3	8 33.2
17	5 41 40.5	24 49.8	25 11.4	3♐ 6.2	3 41.7	6 34.4	10 41.6	20 1.7	26 54.8	10 13.8	0 33.3	8 35.5
18	5 45 37.1	25 50.9	25 8.2	15 12.7	4 30.0	7 49.7	11 13.3	20 8.2	26 53.5	10 16.5	0 35.2	8 37.7
19	5 49 33.7	26 52.0	25 5.0	27 27.7	5 23.4	9 5.0	11 44.9	20 14.9	26 52.3	10 19.3	0 37.2	8 40.0
20	5 53 30.2	27 53.1	25 1.8	9♑52.1	6 21.2	10 20.4	12 16.4	20 21.8	26 51.2	10 22.1	0 39.2	8 42.3
21	5 57 26.8	28 54.2	24 58.7	22 26.1	7 22.9	11 35.7	12 47.7	20 28.9	26 50.2	10 24.9	0 41.2	8 44.5
22	6 1 23.3	29 55.3	24 55.5	5♒10.4	8 28.0	12 51.0	13 18.9	20 36.1	26 49.3	10 27.8	0 43.2	8 46.8
23	6 5 19.9	0♑56.5	24 52.3	18 5.9	9 36.1	14 6.3	13 49.9	20 43.5	26 48.5	10 30.6	0 45.2	8 49.0
24	6 9 16.4	1 57.6	24 49.1	1♓13.9	10 46.8	15 21.6	14 20.8	20 51.0	26 47.8	10 33.5	0 47.3	8 51.2
25	6 13 13.0	2 58.7	24 46.0	14 36.0	11 59.9	16 36.9	14 51.6	20 58.7	26 47.2	10 36.5	0 49.3	8 53.4
26	6 17 9.6	3 59.8	24 42.8	28 14.0	13 14.9	17 52.1	15 22.3	21 6.5	26 46.8	10 39.4	0 51.4	8 55.6
27	6 21 6.1	5 1.0	24 39.6	12♈ 8.9	14 31.8	19 7.4	15 52.8	21 14.5	26 46.4	10 42.4	0 53.5	8 57.7
28	6 25 2.7	6 2.1	24 36.4	26 20.9	15 50.2	20 22.7	16 23.1	21 22.6	26 46.2	10 45.4	0 55.6	8 59.9
29	6 28 59.2	7 3.2	24 33.2	10♉48.6	17 10.1	21 37.9	16 53.4	21 30.9	26 46.0	10 48.5	0 57.7	9 2.0
30	6 32 55.8	8 4.4	24 30.1	25 28.0	18 31.2	22 53.1	17 23.4	21 39.4	26 46.0	10 51.5	0 59.8	9 4.1
31	6 36 52.3	9 5.5	24 26.9	10♊13.5	19 53.4	24 8.4	17 53.4	21 47.9	26 D 46.1	10 54.6	1 2.0	9 6.3
		LATITUDE										
1	4 38 35.6	0 .0	0 .0	4 S 34.7	0 N 55.9	0 S 16.1	1 N 41.9	1 S 21.4	2 S 41.0	0 S 38.4	0 N 18.5	11 N 22.0
4	4 50 25.3	0 .0	0 .0	4 40.3	1 50.2	0 23.2	1 43.0	1 20.7	2 40.3	0 38.4	0 18.4	11 21.8
7	5 2 15.0	0 .0	0 .0	2 6.9	2 27.4	0 30.3	1 44.2	1 19.9	2 39.6	0 38.3	0 18.4	11 21.7
10	5 14 4.6	0 .0	0 .0	1 N 16.8	2 44.9	0 37.1	1 45.4	1 19.2	2 38.8	0 38.2	0 18.3	11 21.6
13	5 25 54.3	0 .0	0 .0	3 56.4	2 45.9	0 43.8	1 46.6	1 18.5	2 38.1	0 38.2	0 18.3	11 21.6
16	5 37 44.0	0 .0	0 .0	5 3.0	2 35.5	0 50.2	1 47.7	1 17.8	2 37.3	0 38.1	0 18.2	11 21.6
19	5 49 33.7	0 .0	0 .0	4 13.0	2 18.0	0 56.3	1 48.9	1 17.1	2 36.4	0 38.1	0 18.2	11 21.7
22	6 1 23.3	0 .0	0 .0	1 35.5	1 56.4	1 2.1	1 50.1	1 16.4	2 35.6	0 38.0	0 18.1	11 21.8
25	6 13 13.0	0 .0	0 .0	1 S 52.4	1 32.7	1 7.5	1 51.2	1 15.8	2 34.8	0 38.0	0 18.1	11 22.0
28	6 25 2.7	0 .0	0 .0	4 35.1	1 8.1	1 12.6	1 52.4	1 15.1	2 33.9	0 37.9	0 18.0	11 22.3
31	6 36 52.3	0 .0	0 .0	4 54.5	0 43.6	1 17.1	1 53.6	1 14.5	2 33.0	0 37.9	0 18.0	11 22.6
		RIGHT ASCENSION										
1	4 38 35.6	6♐51.1	28♌17.0	0♉46.3	8♐37.2	15♐17.5	2♎30.7	20♓ 7.8	26♈30.2	12♒12.5	2♒11.9	8♐ 2.7
2	4 42 32.2	7 55.8	28 14.0	15 22.6	7 R 12.8	16 38.8	3 1.4	20 11.1	26 R 27.4	12 14.6	2 13.6	8 5.0
3	4 46 28.7	9 .6	28 10.9	0♊30.5	5 50.1	18 .2	3 32.1	20 14.5	26 24.6	12 16.8	2 15.3	8 7.3
4	4 50 25.3	10 5.7	28 7.8	16 1.4	4 31.9	19 21.8	4 2.6	20 18.2	26 22.0	12 19.0	2 17.0	8 9.6
5	4 54 21.9	11 10.8	28 4.8	1♋38.1	3 20.4	20 43.6	4 33.1	20 22.0	26 19.4	12 21.3	2 18.7	8 11.9
6	4 58 18.4	12 16.1	28 1.7	16 59.0	2 17.7	22 5.6	5 3.5	20 25.9	26 16.9	12 23.6	2 20.5	8 14.2
7	5 2 15.0	13 21.6	27 58.6	1♌44.7	1 25.2	23 27.6	5 33.8	20 30.1	26 14.5	12 25.9	2 22.2	8 16.5
8	5 6 11.5	14 27.1	27 55.5	15 43.7	0 43.7	24 49.8	6 4.0	20 34.4	26 12.2	12 28.3	2 24.0	8 18.8
9	5 10 8.1	15 32.8	27 52.5	28 53.5	0 13.5	26 12.1	6 34.2	20 38.9	26 9.9	12 30.8	2 25.9	8 21.1
10	5 14 4.6	16 38.7	27 49.4	11♍19.1	29♏54.6	27 34.5	7 4.2	20 43.5	26 7.8	12 33.2	2 27.7	8 23.4
11	5 18 1.2	17 44.6	27 46.3	23 9.6	29 46.7	28 56.9	7 34.2	20 48.4	26 5.8	12 35.7	2 29.6	8 25.7
12	5 21 57.8	18 50.6	27 43.3	4♎36.2	29 D 49.2	0♑19.4	8 4.1	20 53.3	26 3.8	12 38.2	2 31.5	8 28.0
13	5 25 54.3	19 56.8	27 40.2	15 50.5	0♐ 1.3	1 42.0	8 33.9	20 58.5	26 2.0	12 40.8	2 33.4	8 30.3
14	5 29 50.9	21 3.0	27 37.1	27 3.4	0 22.3	3 4.6	9 3.6	21 3.8	26 .2	12 43.4	2 35.4	8 32.6
15	5 33 47.4	22 9.3	27 34.1	8♏24.8	0 51.4	4 27.2	9 33.2	21 9.3	25 58.6	12 46.1	2 37.3	8 34.8
16	5 37 44.0	23 15.6	27 31.0	20 2.9	1 27.9	5 49.8	10 2.8	21 14.9	25 57.0	12 48.8	2 39.3	8 37.1
17	5 41 40.5	24 22.1	27 27.9	2♐ 3.6	2 10.9	7 12.3	10 32.2	21 20.7	25 55.6	12 51.5	2 41.3	8 39.3
18	5 45 37.1	25 28.6	27 24.8	14 29.5	2 59.9	8 34.8	11 1.5	21 26.7	25 54.2	12 54.2	2 43.3	8 41.6
19	5 49 33.7	26 35.1	27 21.8	27 19.2	3 54.1	9 57.3	11 30.8	21 32.8	25 52.9	12 57.0	2 45.3	8 43.8
20	5 53 30.2	27 41.7	27 18.7	10♑27.6	4 53.1	11 19.7	11 59.9	21 39.1	25 51.8	12 59.9	2 47.4	8 46.1
21	5 57 26.8	28 48.3	27 15.6	23 46.5	5 56.3	12 42.0	12 29.0	21 45.5	25 50.8	13 2.7	2 49.5	8 48.3
22	6 1 23.3	29 54.9	27 12.5	7♒ 7.4	7 3.2	14 4.2	12 57.9	21 52.1	25 49.8	13 5.6	2 51.6	8 50.5
23	6 5 19.9	1♑ 1.5	27 9.5	20 23.4	8 13.5	15 26.3	13 26.7	21 58.8	25 49.0	13 8.5	2 53.7	8 52.7
24	6 9 16.4	2 8.1	27 6.4	3♓31.4	9 26.9	16 48.2	13 55.4	22 5.6	25 48.2	13 11.4	2 55.8	8 54.9
25	6 13 13.0	3 14.7	27 3.3	16 32.8	10 43.0	18 10.0	14 24.0	22 12.6	25 47.6	13 14.4	2 58.0	8 57.1
26	6 17 9.6	4 21.3	27 .2	29 33.2	12 1.5	19 31.6	14 52.5	22 19.8	25 47.0	13 17.4	3 .1	8 59.2
27	6 21 6.1	5 27.9	26 57.2	12♈41.0	13 22.3	20 53.0	15 20.9	22 27.0	25 46.6	13 20.4	3 2.3	9 1.4
28	6 25 2.7	6 34.4	26 54.1	26 6.4	14 45.0	22 14.2	15 49.2	22 34.5	25 46.3	13 23.4	3 4.5	9 3.5
29	6 28 59.2	7 40.8	26 51.0	9♉58.5	16 9.7	23 35.2	16 17.3	22 42.0	25 46.1	13 26.5	3 6.7	9 5.7
30	6 32 55.8	8 47.3	26 47.9	24 23.5	17 35.9	24 56.0	16 45.4	22 49.7	25 45.9	13 29.6	3 8.9	9 7.8
31	6 36 52.3	9 53.6	26 44.8	9♊20.7	19 3.8	26 16.6	17 13.3	22 57.5	25 45.9	13 32.7	3 11.1	9 9.9
		DECLINATION										
1	4 38 35.6	21 S 44.0	0 N 13.4	7 N 38.0	21 S 2.5	23 S 1.1	0 N 45.7	5 S 43.5	8 N 4.6	18 S 28.0	19 S 49.8	10 S 24.4
4	4 50 25.3	22 10.6	0 13.5	18 7.3	19 30.7	23 27.9	0 7.2	5 38.3	8 2.3	18 26.2	19 48.8	10 25.6
7	5 2 15.0	22 33.3	0 13.6	18 4.4	18 20.3	23 48.3	0 S 30.9	5 32.4	8 .2	18 24.3	19 47.8	10 26.8
10	5 14 4.6	22 52.1	0 13.6	9 17.2	17 45.3	24 2.2	1 8.6	5 25.9	7 58.5	18 22.3	19 46.7	10 27.9
13	5 25 54.3	23 6.9	0 13.7	2 S 29.0	17 45.6	24 9.5	1 45.7	5 18.8	7 57.1	18 20.3	19 45.6	10 29.0
16	5 37 44.0	23 17.5	0 13.7	13 9.5	18 12.6	24 10.0	2 22.4	5 11.0	7 56.1	18 18.1	19 44.4	10 30.0
19	5 49 33.7	23 24.0	0 13.8	19 11.8	18 56.1	24 3.8	2 58.4	5 2.7	7 55.4	18 15.8	19 43.2	10 30.9
22	6 1 23.3	23 26.2	0 13.8	17 25.7	19 47.9	23 50.8	3 33.9	4 53.7	7 55.1	18 13.5	19 42.0	10 31.7
25	6 13 13.0	23 24.2	0 13.9	7 47.4	20 41.7	23 31.3	4 8.7	4 44.2	7 55.2	18 11.1	19 40.7	10 32.5
28	6 25 2.7	23 18.0	0 13.9	5 N 53.4	21 33.3	23 5.2	4 42.7	4 34.2	7 55.6	18 8.6	19 39.4	10 33.1
31	6 36 52.3	23 7.5	0 14.0	17 7.3	22 19.6	22 32.9	5 16.1	4 23.6	7 56.4	18 6.0	19 38.0	10 33.8

JANUARY 1999

DAY	EPHEM. SID. TIME	☉	☊	☽	☿	♀	♂	♃	♄	♅	♆	♇
	LONGITUDE											
	h m s	° ′	° ′	° ′	° ′	° ′	° ′	° ′	° ′	° ′	° ′	° ′
1	6 40 48.9	10♑ 6.6	24♌23.7	24♊57.4	21♐16.7	25♑23.6	18♎23.1	21♓56.7	26♈46.3	10♒57.7	1♒ 4.1	9♐ 8.3
2	6 44 45.5	11 7.7	24 20.5	9♋32.0	22 40.9	26 38.8	18 52.8	22 5.5	26 46.7	11 .8	1 6.3	9 10.4
3	6 48 42.0	12 8.9	24 17.4	23 50.1	24 5.9	27 54.0	19 22.2	22 14.5	26 47.1	11 4.0	1 8.4	9 12.5
4	6 52 38.6	13 10.0	24 14.2	7♌46.4	25 31.6	29 9.2	19 51.5	22 23.6	26 47.6	11 7.2	1 10.6	9 14.5
5	6 56 35.1	14 11.1	24 11.0	21 18.2	26 58.1	0♒24.3	20 20.7	22 32.9	26 48.3	11 10.4	1 12.8	9 16.5
6	7 0 31.7	15 12.3	24 7.8	4♍25.0	28 25.2	1 39.5	20 49.7	22 42.3	26 49.0	11 13.6	1 15.0	9 18.5
7	7 4 28.2	16 13.4	24 4.7	17 8.7	29 53.0	2 54.7	21 18.5	22 51.8	26 49.9	11 16.8	1 17.2	9 20.5
8	7 8 24.8	17 14.5	24 1.5	29 32.5	1♑21.3	4 9.8	21 47.1	23 1.5	26 50.9	11 20.1	1 19.5	9 22.5
9	7 12 21.4	18 15.7	23 58.3	11♎41.0	2 50.2	5 24.9	22 15.6	23 11.3	26 52.0	11 23.4	1 21.7	9 24.4
10	7 16 17.9	19 16.9	23 55.1	23 38.9	4 19.7	6 40.1	22 43.9	23 21.2	26 53.3	11 26.7	1 24.0	9 26.4
11	7 20 14.5	20 18.0	23 51.9	5♏31.2	5 49.7	7 55.2	23 12.0	23 31.3	26 54.6	11 30.0	1 26.2	9 28.3
12	7 24 11.0	21 19.1	23 48.8	17 22.8	7 20.2	9 10.3	23 39.9	23 41.4	26 56.0	11 33.3	1 28.4	9 30.2
13	7 28 7.6	22 20.3	23 45.6	29 18.1	8 51.2	10 25.4	24 7.6	23 51.7	26 57.5	11 36.7	1 30.7	9 32.0
14	7 32 4.1	23 21.4	23 42.4	11♐20.7	10 22.7	11 40.5	24 35.2	24 2.1	26 59.2	11 40.1	1 33.0	9 33.9
15	7 36 .7	24 22.6	23 39.2	23 33.7	11 54.7	12 55.6	25 2.5	24 12.6	27 .9	11 43.4	1 35.2	9 35.7
16	7 39 57.2	25 23.7	23 36.1	5♑59.0	13 27.2	14 10.6	25 29.5	24 23.2	27 2.8	11 46.8	1 37.5	9 37.5
17	7 43 53.8	26 24.8	23 32.9	18 37.9	15 .2	15 25.7	25 56.4	24 34.0	27 4.8	11 50.2	1 39.8	9 39.3
18	7 47 50.4	27 25.9	23 29.7	1♒30.8	16 33.7	16 40.7	26 23.1	24 44.8	27 6.8	11 53.6	1 42.0	9 41.0
19	7 51 46.9	28 27.0	23 26.5	14 37.1	18 7.8	17 55.7	26 49.5	24 55.8	27 9.0	11 57.0	1 44.3	9 42.7
20	7 55 43.5	29 28.1	23 23.4	27 56.3	19 42.3	19 10.7	27 15.7	25 6.8	27 11.3	12 .5	1 46.6	9 44.4
21	7 59 40.0	0♒29.2	23 20.2	11♓27.3	21 17.5	20 25.7	27 41.7	25 18.0	27 13.7	12 3.9	1 48.9	9 46.1
22	8 3 36.6	1 30.3	23 17.0	25 9.0	22 53.1	21 40.6	28 7.4	25 29.3	27 16.2	12 7.4	1 51.1	9 47.7
23	8 7 33.1	2 31.3	23 13.8	9♈ .6	24 29.4	22 55.5	28 32.9	25 40.6	27 18.8	12 10.8	1 53.4	9 49.4
24	8 11 29.7	3 32.4	23 10.6	23 .9	26 6.2	24 10.5	28 58.1	25 52.1	27 21.5	12 14.3	1 55.7	9 50.9
25	8 15 26.3	4 33.4	23 7.5	7♉ 8.7	27 43.6	25 25.3	29 23.1	26 3.7	27 24.3	12 17.8	1 58.0	9 52.5
26	8 19 22.8	5 34.4	23 4.3	21 22.2	29 21.6	26 40.2	29 47.9	26 15.4	27 27.2	12 21.2	2 .2	9 54.0
27	8 23 19.4	6 35.4	23 1.1	5♊39.1	1♒ .2	27 55.0	0♏12.3	26 27.1	27 30.2	12 24.7	2 2.5	9 55.6
28	8 27 15.9	7 36.4	22 57.9	19 56.2	2 39.5	29 9.8	0 36.5	26 39.0	27 33.4	12 28.2	2 4.8	9 57.0
29	8 31 12.5	8 37.3	22 54.8	4♋ 9.6	4 19.4	0♓24.6	1 .5	26 50.9	27 36.6	12 31.7	2 7.0	9 58.5
30	8 35 9.0	9 38.2	22 51.6	18 15.0	6 .0	1 39.4	1 24.1	27 2.9	27 39.9	12 35.2	2 9.3	9 59.9
31	8 39 5.6	10 39.2	22 48.4	2♌ 8.4	7 41.3	2 54.1	1 47.5	27 15.1	27 43.3	12 38.7	2 11.6	10 1.4
	LATITUDE											
1	6 40 48.9	0 .0	0 .0	4S21.6	0N35.5	1S18.6	1N53.9	1S14.3	2S32.7	0S37.9	0N18.0	11N22.7
4	6 52 38.6	0 .0	0 .0	1 19.7	0 11.9	1 22.5	1 55.1	1 13.7	2 31.9	0 37.8	0 17.9	11 23.0
7	7 4 28.2	0 .0	0 .0	2N 9.7	0S10.8	1 25.9	1 56.2	1 13.2	2 31.0	0 37.8	0 17.9	11 23.4
10	7 16 17.9	0 .0	0 .0	4 33.3	0 32.0	1 28.8	1 57.4	1 12.6	2 30.1	0 37.8	0 17.8	11 23.9
13	7 28 7.6	0 .0	0 .0	5 10.1	0 51.7	1 31.1	1 58.5	1 12.1	2 29.2	0 37.8	0 17.8	11 24.4
16	7 39 57.2	0 .0	0 .0	3 46.6	1 9.5	1 32.8	1 59.6	1 11.5	2 28.4	0 37.8	0 17.8	11 24.9
19	7 51 46.9	0 .0	0 .0	0 41.4	1 25.3	1 33.9	2 .7	1 11.0	2 27.5	0 37.7	0 17.7	11 25.5
22	8 3 36.6	0 .0	0 .0	2S51.9	1 38.9	1 34.4	2 1.8	1 10.6	2 26.7	0 37.7	0 17.7	11 26.2
25	8 15 26.3	0 .0	0 .0	5 4.9	1 49.9	1 34.3	2 2.8	1 10.1	2 25.8	0 37.7	0 17.7	11 26.8
28	8 27 15.9	0 .0	0 .0	4 39.7	1 58.2	1 33.5	2 3.8	1 9.7	2 25.0	0 37.7	0 17.6	11 27.5
31	8 39 5.6	0 .0	0 .0	1 48.3	2 3.3	1 32.1	2 4.8	1 9.3	2 24.2	0 37.7	0 17.6	11 28.3
	RIGHT ASCENSION											
1	6 40 48.9	10♑59.9	26♌41.8	24♊40.9	20♐33.0	27♑36.9	17♎41.1	23♓ 5.5	25♈46.0	13♒35.8	3♒13.3	9♐11.9
2	6 44 45.5	12 6.1	26 38.7	10♋ 6.3	22 3.5	28 56.9	18 8.8	23 13.5	25D46.2	13 39.0	3 15.6	9 14.0
3	6 48 42.0	13 12.2	26 35.6	25 15.4	23 35.2	0♒16.7	18 36.3	23 21.8	25 46.5	13 42.2	3 17.8	9 16.0
4	6 52 38.6	14 18.2	26 32.5	9♌49.7	25 8.0	1 36.2	19 3.8	23 30.1	25 46.9	13 45.4	3 20.1	9 18.1
5	6 56 35.1	15 24.2	26 29.4	23 38.7	26 41.9	2 55.4	19 31.1	23 38.5	25 47.4	13 48.6	3 22.4	9 20.1
6	7 0 31.7	16 30.0	26 26.4	6♍40.8	28 16.7	4 14.4	19 58.2	23 47.1	25 48.0	13 51.9	3 24.7	9 22.1
7	7 4 28.2	17 35.7	26 23.3	19 1.3	29 52.3	5 33.0	20 25.3	23 55.8	25 48.8	13 55.2	3 26.9	9 24.1
8	7 8 24.8	18 41.3	26 20.2	0♎49.5	1♑28.8	6 51.4	20 52.1	24 4.6	25 49.6	13 58.5	3 29.2	9 26.0
9	7 12 21.4	19 46.8	26 17.1	12 16.7	3 6.1	8 9.4	21 18.9	24 13.5	25 50.5	14 1.8	3 31.6	9 28.0
10	7 16 17.9	20 52.2	26 14.0	23 34.5	4 44.1	9 27.2	21 45.5	24 22.6	25 51.6	14 5.1	3 33.9	9 29.9
11	7 20 14.5	21 57.5	26 10.9	4♏53.7	6 22.8	10 44.6	22 12.0	24 31.8	25 52.7	14 8.5	3 36.2	9 31.8
12	7 24 11.0	23 2.6	26 7.9	16 24.4	8 2.0	12 1.7	22 38.2	24 41.1	25 54.0	14 11.8	3 38.6	9 33.7
13	7 28 7.6	24 7.5	26 4.8	28 14.8	9 41.9	13 18.4	23 4.4	24 50.4	25 55.3	14 15.2	3 40.9	9 35.6
14	7 32 4.1	25 12.3	26 1.7	10♐30.4	11 22.2	14 34.9	23 30.3	24 59.9	25 56.7	14 18.6	3 43.2	9 37.4
15	7 36 .7	26 17.0	25 58.6	23 13.0	13 3.1	15 51.0	23 56.1	25 9.5	25 58.3	14 22.0	3 45.6	9 39.2
16	7 39 57.2	27 21.5	25 55.5	6♑20.2	14 44.4	17 6.8	24 21.7	25 19.2	25 59.9	14 25.4	3 47.9	9 41.0
17	7 43 53.8	28 25.8	25 52.4	19 45.4	16 26.2	18 22.3	24 47.1	25 29.0	26 1.7	14 28.9	3 50.3	9 42.8
18	7 47 50.4	29 29.9	25 49.3	3♒19.3	18 8.3	19 37.4	25 12.4	25 38.9	26 3.5	14 32.3	3 52.6	9 44.6
19	7 51 46.9	0♒33.9	25 46.2	16 52.5	19 50.8	20 52.2	25 37.4	25 49.0	26 5.5	14 35.7	3 55.0	9 46.3
20	7 55 43.5	1 37.7	25 43.2	0♓18.1	21 33.7	22 6.7	26 2.3	25 59.1	26 7.6	14 39.2	3 57.3	9 48.0
21	7 59 40.0	2 41.2	25 40.1	13 33.6	23 16.8	23 20.8	26 26.9	26 9.3	26 9.7	14 42.7	3 59.7	9 49.7
22	8 3 36.6	3 44.7	25 37.0	26 41.3	25 .2	24 34.6	26 51.4	26 19.6	26 12.0	14 46.2	4 2.1	9 51.3
23	8 7 33.1	4 47.9	25 33.9	9♈47.2	26 43.9	25 48.1	27 15.6	26 29.9	26 14.3	14 49.6	4 4.4	9 53.0
24	8 11 29.7	5 50.9	25 30.8	22 59.9	28 27.8	27 1.3	27 39.6	26 40.4	26 16.8	14 53.1	4 6.8	9 54.6
25	8 15 26.3	6 53.7	25 27.7	6♉28.7	0♒11.9	28 14.2	28 3.4	26 51.0	26 19.3	14 56.6	4 9.1	9 56.1
26	8 19 22.8	7 56.3	25 24.6	20 21.2	1 56.2	29 26.7	28 27.0	27 1.6	26 22.0	15 .1	4 11.5	9 57.7
27	8 23 19.4	8 58.7	25 21.5	4♊41.0	3 40.6	0♓38.9	28 50.4	27 12.4	26 24.7	15 3.6	4 13.8	9 59.2
28	8 27 15.9	10 .9	25 18.4	19 25.4	5 25.2	1 50.9	29 13.5	27 23.2	26 27.5	15 7.2	4 16.2	10 .7
29	8 31 12.5	11 2.9	25 15.3	4♋24.1	7 9.9	3 2.5	29 36.4	27 34.1	26 30.5	15 10.7	4 18.5	10 2.2
30	8 35 9.0	12 4.6	25 12.3	19 20.9	8 54.7	4 13.9	29 59.0	27 45.1	26 33.5	15 14.2	4 20.9	10 3.6
31	8 39 5.6	13 6.3	25 9.2	3♌58.5	10 39.6	5 25.0	0♏21.5	27 56.2	26 36.7	15 17.8	4 23.2	10 5.1
	DECLINATION											
1	6 40 48.9	23S 3.1	0N14.0	18N59.0	22S33.6	22S20.7	5S27.0	4S20.0	7N56.7	18S 5.2	19S37.6	10S33.9
4	6 52 38.6	22 47.1	0 14.1	17 2.4	23 9.8	21 40.2	5 59.3	4 8.8	7 58.0	18 2.5	19 36.2	10 34.5
7	7 4 28.2	22 27.1	0 14.1	7 4.0	23 37.0	20 54.0	6 30.8	3 57.1	7 59.7	17 59.9	19 34.8	10 34.9
10	7 16 17.9	22 3.1	0 14.2	4S56.6	23 54.0	20 2.2	7 1.5	3 45.0	8 1.7	17 57.1	19 33.4	10 35.3
13	7 28 7.6	21 35.1	0 14.2	14 56.9	24 .1	19 5.2	7 31.2	3 32.4	8 4.0	17 54.3	19 31.9	10 35.6
16	7 39 57.2	21 3.5	0 14.3	19 31.7	23 54.6	18 3.2	7 60.0	3 19.5	8 6.7	17 51.5	19 30.5	10 35.8
19	7 51 46.9	20 28.2	0 14.4	15 47.1	23 37.2	16 56.8	8 27.8	3 6.1	8 9.7	17 48.6	19 29.0	10 35.9
22	8 3 36.6	19 49.4	0 14.4	4 33.4	23 7.3	15 46.1	8 54.6	2 52.4	8 13.1	17 45.7	19 27.5	10 36.0
25	8 15 26.3	19 7.3	0 14.5	9N 5.3	22 24.6	14 31.5	9 20.3	2 38.3	8 16.8	17 42.8	19 26.0	10 36.0
28	8 27 15.9	18 22.0	0 14.5	18 24.5	21 28.9	13 13.4	9 45.0	2 23.9	8 20.8	17 39.9	19 24.5	10 35.9
31	8 39 5.6	17 33.8	0 14.6	17 55.3	20 19.9	11 52.2	10 8.6	2 9.1	8 25.1	17 36.9	19 23.0	10 35.7

FEBRUARY 1999

LONGITUDE

DAY	EPHEM. SID. TIME	☉	☊	☽	☿	♀	♂	♃	♄	♅	♆	♇
	h m s	° ′	° ′	° ′	° ′	° ′	° ′	° ′	° ′	° ′	° ′	° ′
1	8 43 2.1	11♒40.1	22♌45.2	15♌46.2	9♒23.3	4♓ 8.8	2♏10.6	27♓27.3	27♈46.8	12♒42.2	2♒13.9	10♐ 2.7
2	8 46 58.7	12 41.0	22 42.1	29 6.1	11 6.0	5 23.5	2 33.4	27 39.6	27 50.4	12 45.7	2 16.1	10 4.1
3	8 50 55.2	13 41.8	22 38.9	12♍ 7.1	12 49.3	6 38.1	2 55.9	27 51.9	27 54.1	12 49.2	2 18.4	10 5.4
4	8 54 51.8	14 42.7	22 35.7	24 49.3	14 33.4	7 52.7	3 18.1	28 4.4	27 57.9	12 52.7	2 20.6	10 6.7
5	8 58 48.4	15 43.5	22 32.5	7♎14.6	16 18.2	9 7.3	3 40.0	28 16.9	28 1.8	12 56.2	2 22.8	10 7.9
6	9 2 44.9	16 44.3	22 29.3	19 25.6	18 3.7	10 21.9	4 1.5	28 29.5	28 5.7	12 59.7	2 25.1	10 9.1
7	9 6 41.5	17 45.1	22 26.2	1♏26.1	19 49.9	11 36.4	4 22.7	28 42.1	28 9.8	13 3.2	2 27.3	10 10.3
8	9 10 38.0	18 45.9	22 23.0	13 20.3	21 36.8	12 50.9	4 43.6	28 54.9	28 13.9	13 6.7	2 29.5	10 11.5
9	9 14 34.6	19 46.6	22 19.8	25 12.8	23 24.3	14 5.4	5 4.1	29 7.7	28 18.2	13 10.2	2 31.7	10 12.6
10	9 18 31.1	20 47.4	22 16.6	7♐ 8.5	25 12.4	15 19.8	5 24.2	29 20.6	28 22.5	13 13.7	2 33.9	10 13.7
11	9 22 27.7	21 48.1	22 13.5	19 11.8	27 1.0	16 34.2	5 44.0	29 33.5	28 26.9	13 17.1	2 36.0	10 14.7
12	9 26 24.2	22 48.8	22 10.3	1♑27.0	28 50.2	17 48.6	6 3.4	29 46.5	28 31.4	13 20.6	2 38.2	10 15.8
13	9 30 20.8	23 49.5	22 7.1	13 57.6	0♓39.7	19 2.9	6 22.5	29 59.6	28 36.0	13 24.1	2 40.4	10 16.8
14	9 34 17.3	24 50.2	22 3.9	26 46.1	2 29.6	20 17.2	6 41.1	0♈12.8	28 40.6	13 27.5	2 42.5	10 17.7
15	9 38 13.9	25 50.9	22 .7	9♒53.8	4 19.6	21 31.5	6 59.3	0 26.0	28 45.4	13 31.0	2 44.7	10 18.7
16	9 42 10.5	26 51.5	21 57.6	23 20.7	6 9.6	22 45.7	7 17.1	0 39.3	28 50.2	13 34.4	2 46.8	10 19.6
17	9 46 7.0	27 52.1	21 54.4	7♓ 5.4	7 59.5	23 59.9	7 34.5	0 52.6	28 55.1	13 37.8	2 48.9	10 20.4
18	9 50 3.6	28 52.7	21 51.2	21 5.0	9 49.0	25 14.1	7 51.5	1 6.0	29 .1	13 41.2	2 51.0	10 21.3
19	9 54 .1	29 53.2	21 48.0	5♈15.7	11 37.8	26 28.2	8 8.0	1 19.5	29 5.2	13 44.6	2 53.1	10 22.1
20	9 57 56.7	0♓53.8	21 44.9	19 33.1	13 25.8	27 42.3	8 24.1	1 33.0	29 10.3	13 48.0	2 55.1	10 22.8
21	10 1 53.2	1 54.3	21 41.7	3♉53.0	15 12.4	28 56.4	8 39.8	1 46.6	29 15.6	13 51.4	2 57.2	10 23.6
22	10 5 49.8	2 54.8	21 38.5	18 11.4	16 57.4	0♈10.3	8 54.9	2 .2	29 20.9	13 54.8	2 59.3	10 24.3
23	10 9 46.3	3 55.2	21 35.3	2♊25.0	18 40.2	1 24.3	9 9.6	2 13.8	29 26.2	13 58.1	3 1.3	10 25.0
24	10 13 42.9	4 55.6	21 32.1	16 31.5	20 20.5	2 38.2	9 23.8	2 27.5	29 31.7	14 1.5	3 3.3	10 25.6
25	10 17 39.4	5 56.0	21 29.0	0♋29.1	21 57.7	3 52.0	9 37.5	2 41.3	29 37.2	14 4.8	3 5.3	10 26.2
26	10 21 36.0	6 56.3	21 25.8	14 16.7	23 31.2	5 5.8	9 50.7	2 55.1	29 42.8	14 8.1	3 7.3	10 26.7
27	10 25 32.5	7 56.6	21 22.6	27 53.4	25 .5	6 19.5	10 3.4	3 8.9	29 48.4	14 11.3	3 9.2	10 27.3
28	10 29 29.1	8 56.9	21 19.4	11♌18.3	26 25.0	7 33.2	10 15.5	3 22.8	29 54.1	14 14.6	3 11.2	10 27.7

LATITUDE

DAY	EPHEM. SID. TIME	☉	☊	☽	☿	♀	♂	♃	♄	♅	♆	♇
1	8 43 2.1	0 .0	0 .0	0S35.0	2S 4.3	1S31.5	2N 5.2	1S 9.1	2S23.9	0S37.8	0N17.6	11N28.5
4	8 54 51.8	0 .0	0 .0	2N51.6	2 4.7	1 29.2	2 6.1	1 8.7	2 23.1	0 37.8	0 17.6	11 29.3
7	9 6 41.5	0 .0	0 .0	4 56.8	2 1.1	1 26.3	2 7.0	1 8.4	2 22.4	0 37.8	0 17.6	11 30.1
10	9 18 31.1	0 .0	0 .0	5 6.5	1 53.0	1 22.7	2 7.9	1 8.0	2 21.6	0 37.8	0 17.5	11 30.9
13	9 30 20.8	0 .0	0 .0	3 16.5	1 39.9	1 18.6	2 8.6	1 7.7	2 20.9	0 37.8	0 17.5	11 31.8
16	9 42 10.5	0 .0	0 .0	0S 6.6	1 21.2	1 13.8	2 9.3	1 7.4	2 20.2	0 37.9	0 17.5	11 32.7
19	9 54 .1	0 .0	0 .0	3 36.8	0 56.8	1 8.4	2 10.0	1 7.1	2 19.5	0 37.9	0 17.5	11 33.6
22	10 5 49.8	0 .0	0 .0	5 15.8	0 26.3	1 2.5	2 10.5	1 6.8	2 18.8	0 37.9	0 17.5	11 34.5
25	10 17 39.4	0 .0	0 .0	4 8.4	0N 9.8	0 56.0	2 10.9	1 6.6	2 18.2	0 38.0	0 17.4	11 35.4
28	10 29 29.1	0 .0	0 .0	0 59.6	0 50.4	0 49.0	2 11.2	1 6.4	2 17.6	0 38.0	0 17.4	11 36.3

RIGHT ASCENSION

DAY	EPHEM. SID. TIME	☉	☊	☽	☿	♀	♂	♃	♄	♅	♆	♇
1	8 43 2.1	14♒ 7.6	25♌ 6.1	18♌ 3.0	12♒24.6	6♓35.8	0♏43.6	28♓ 7.4	26♈39.9	15♒21.3	4♒25.6	10♐ 6.5
2	8 46 58.7	15 8.8	25 3.0	1♍27.7	14 9.5	7 46.3	1 5.5	28 18.6	26 43.2	15 24.8	4 27.9	10 7.8
3	8 50 55.2	16 9.8	24 59.9	14 12.5	15 54.6	8 56.6	1 27.1	28 29.9	26 46.6	15 28.3	4 30.2	10 9.2
4	8 54 51.8	17 10.5	24 56.8	26 23.1	17 39.6	10 6.6	1 48.4	28 41.2	26 50.0	15 31.8	4 32.5	10 10.5
5	8 58 48.4	18 11.1	24 53.7	8♎ 7.9	19 24.5	11 16.3	2 9.4	28 52.7	26 53.6	15 35.4	4 34.8	10 11.7
6	9 2 44.9	19 11.5	24 50.6	19 37.0	21 9.5	12 25.9	2 30.2	29 4.2	26 57.2	15 38.9	4 37.1	10 13.0
7	9 6 41.5	20 11.6	24 47.5	1♏ .7	22 54.3	13 35.2	2 50.6	29 15.8	27 1.0	15 42.4	4 39.4	10 14.2
8	9 10 38.0	21 11.6	24 44.4	12 28.9	24 39.1	14 44.3	3 10.7	29 27.4	27 4.8	15 45.9	4 41.7	10 15.4
9	9 14 34.6	22 11.4	24 41.3	24 10.5	26 23.7	15 53.2	3 30.5	29 39.1	27 8.7	15 49.4	4 44.0	10 16.5
10	9 18 31.1	23 11.0	24 38.2	6♐12.4	28 8.1	17 1.9	3 50.0	29 50.9	27 12.7	15 52.9	4 46.2	10 17.6
11	9 22 27.7	24 10.4	24 35.1	18 39.2	29 52.2	18 10.4	4 9.1	0♈ 2.7	27 16.8	15 56.4	4 48.5	10 18.7
12	9 26 24.2	25 9.6	24 32.0	1♑32.0	1♓36.0	19 18.7	4 27.9	0 14.6	27 21.0	15 59.9	4 50.7	10 19.8
13	9 30 20.8	26 8.6	24 28.9	14 47.9	3 19.5	20 26.9	4 46.3	0 26.6	27 25.2	16 3.3	4 53.0	10 20.8
14	9 34 17.3	27 7.4	24 25.8	28 20.6	5 2.4	21 34.9	5 4.4	0 38.6	27 29.5	16 6.8	4 55.2	10 21.8
15	9 38 13.9	28 6.1	24 22.7	12♒ 1.5	6 44.7	22 42.7	5 22.1	0 50.7	27 33.9	16 10.3	4 57.4	10 22.7
16	9 42 10.5	29 4.5	24 19.6	25 42.8	8 26.4	23 50.4	5 39.3	1 2.8	27 38.4	16 13.7	4 59.6	10 23.7
17	9 46 7.0	0♓ 2.8	24 16.5	9♓19.2	10 7.1	24 58.0	5 56.2	1 15.0	27 43.0	16 17.1	5 1.8	10 24.6
18	9 50 3.6	1 .9	24 13.4	22 49.3	11 46.8	26 5.5	6 12.7	1 27.3	27 47.6	16 20.6	5 3.9	10 25.4
19	9 54 .1	1 58.9	24 10.3	6♈15.6	13 25.2	27 12.8	6 28.8	1 39.6	27 52.4	16 24.0	5 6.1	10 26.2
20	9 57 56.7	2 56.6	24 7.2	19 43.9	15 2.1	28 20.1	6 44.4	1 51.9	27 57.1	16 27.4	5 8.2	10 27.0
21	10 1 53.2	3 54.3	24 4.1	3♉21.1	16 37.2	29 27.3	6 59.6	2 4.4	28 2.1	16 30.8	5 10.4	10 27.9
22	10 5 49.8	4 51.7	24 1.0	17 13.4	18 10.3	0♈34.3	7 14.4	2 16.8	28 7.0	16 34.2	5 12.5	10 28.6
23	10 9 46.3	5 49.0	23 57.9	1♊24.1	19 40.9	1 41.3	7 28.7	2 29.3	28 12.0	16 37.5	5 14.6	10 29.3
24	10 13 42.9	6 46.1	23 54.8	15 52.2	21 8.6	2 48.3	7 42.5	2 41.9	28 17.1	16 40.9	5 16.6	10 29.9
25	10 17 39.4	7 43.0	23 51.7	0♋30.8	22 33.1	3 55.2	7 55.9	2 54.5	28 22.2	16 44.2	5 18.7	10 30.6
26	10 21 36.0	8 39.8	23 48.5	15 8.3	23 54.0	5 2.0	8 8.8	3 7.1	28 27.5	16 47.5	5 20.7	10 31.2
27	10 25 32.5	9 36.4	23 45.4	29 31.4	25 10.7	6 8.8	8 21.1	3 19.7	28 32.7	16 50.8	5 22.7	10 31.7
28	10 29 29.1	10 33.0	23 42.3	13♌28.6	26 22.7	7 15.6	8 33.0	3 32.5	28 38.1	16 54.1	5 24.7	10 32.2

DECLINATION

DAY	EPHEM. SID. TIME	☉	☊	☽	☿	♀	♂	♃	♄	♅	♆	♇
1	8 43 2.1	17S17.1	0N14.6	15N33.0	19S53.9	11S24.5	10S16.2	2S 4.2	8N26.6	17S35.9	19S22.5	10S35.7
4	8 54 51.8	16 25.1	0 14.6	4 41.0	18 27.1	9 59.6	10 38.2	1 49.1	8 31.2	17 33.0	19 21.0	10 35.4
7	9 6 41.5	15 30.6	0 14.7	7S19.7	16 46.8	8 32.4	10 59.1	1 33.7	8 36.2	17 30.0	19 19.5	10 35.1
10	9 18 31.1	14 33.8	0 14.7	16 27.7	14 53.5	7 3.1	11 18.7	1 18.1	8 41.4	17 27.0	19 18.1	10 34.8
13	9 30 20.8	13 34.7	0 14.8	19 26.9	12 47.6	5 32.3	11 37.1	1 2.3	8 46.8	17 24.1	19 16.6	10 34.3
16	9 42 10.5	12 33.6	0 14.9	13 50.4	10 30.6	4 .1	11 54.2	0 46.2	8 52.5	17 21.2	19 15.2	10 33.8
19	9 54 .1	11 30.6	0 14.9	1 13.7	8 4.5	2 27.0	12 10.0	0 30.0	8 58.4	17 18.3	19 13.8	10 33.3
22	10 5 49.8	10 26.1	0 15.0	12N11.0	5 33.2	0 53.2	12 24.4	0 13.5	9 4.5	17 15.4	19 12.3	10 32.7
25	10 17 39.4	9 20.1	0 15.0	19 17.8	3 2.3	0N40.8	12 37.4	0N 3.0	9 10.9	17 12.5	19 11.0	10 32.0
28	10 29 29.1	8 12.9	0 15.1	16 25.8	0 39.2	2 14.8	12 49.0	0 19.7	9 17.4	17 9.7	19 9.6	10 31.3

MARCH 1999

DAY	EPHEM. SID. TIME	☉	☊	☾	☿	♀	♂	♃	♄	♅	♆	♇
	h m s	° ′	° ′	° ′	° ′	° ′	° ′	° ′	° ′	° ′	° ′	° ′
		LONGITUDE										
1	10 33 25.6	9♓57.1	21♌16.3	24♌30.7	27♓44.0	8♈46.9	10♏27.2	3♈36.7	29♈59.9	14♒17.8	3♒13.1	10♐28.2
2	10 37 22.2	10 57.3	21 13.1	7♍30.0	28 57.0	10 .5	10 38.2	3 50.7	0♉ 5.8	14 21.1	3 15.0	10 28.6
3	10 41 18.7	11 57.5	21 9.9	20 15.9	0♈ 3.3	11 14.0	10 48.8	4 4.7	0 11.7	14 24.3	3 16.9	10 29.0
4	10 45 15.3	12 57.6	21 6.7	2♎48.6	1 2.4	12 27.5	10 58.7	4 18.7	0 17.7	14 27.4	3 18.7	10 29.4
5	10 49 11.9	13 57.8	21 3.5	15 8.7	1 53.8	13 40.9	11 8.1	4 32.8	0 23.7	14 30.6	3 20.6	10 29.7
6	10 53 8.4	14 57.9	21 .4	27 17.7	2 37.1	14 54.2	11 16.9	4 46.9	0 29.8	14 33.7	3 22.4	10 30.0
7	10 57 5.0	15 57.9	20 57.2	9♏17.9	3 11.8	16 7.6	11 25.1	5 1.0	0 36.0	14 36.9	3 24.2	10 30.2
8	11 1 1.5	16 58.0	20 54.0	21 12.3	3 37.7	17 20.8	11 32.7	5 15.2	0 42.2	14 40.0	3 26.0	10 30.4
9	11 4 58.1	17 58.0	20 50.8	3♐ 4.6	3 54.7	18 34.0	11 39.6	5 29.4	0 48.4	14 43.0	3 27.7	10 30.6
10	11 8 54.6	18 58.0	20 47.7	14 59.2	4 2.6	19 47.2	11 46.0	5 43.6	0 54.8	14 46.1	3 29.5	10 30.7
11	11 12 51.2	19 57.9	20 44.5	27 .7	4R 1.5	21 .3	11 51.6	5 57.8	1 1.2	14 49.1	3 31.2	10 30.9
12	11 16 47.7	20 57.8	20 41.3	9♑13.9	3 51.7	22 13.3	11 56.6	6 12.1	1 7.6	14 52.1	3 32.9	10 30.9
13	11 20 44.3	21 57.7	20 38.1	21 43.6	3 33.5	23 26.3	12 .9	6 26.4	1 14.1	14 55.0	3 34.5	10 31.0
14	11 24 40.8	22 57.7	20 34.9	4♒33.7	3 7.4	24 39.2	12 4.6	6 40.8	1 20.7	14 58.0	3 36.2	10 31.0
15	11 28 37.4	23 57.5	20 31.8	17 47.3	2 34.1	25 52.1	12 7.5	6 55.1	1 27.3	15 .9	3 37.9	10 31.0
16	11 32 33.9	24 57.3	20 28.6	1♓25.7	1 54.5	27 4.9	12 9.8	7 9.5	1 33.9	15 3.8	3 39.5	10R30.9
17	11 36 30.5	25 57.1	20 25.4	15 28.2	1 9.5	28 17.6	12 11.3	7 23.9	1 40.6	15 6.7	3 41.0	10 30.8
18	11 40 27.0	26 56.9	20 22.2	29 51.6	0 20.1	29 30.3	12 12.1	7 38.3	1 47.4	15 9.5	3 42.6	10 30.7
19	11 44 23.6	27 56.6	20 19.1	14♈30.3	29♓27.5	0♉42.9	12 12.1	7 52.8	1 54.1	15 12.3	3 44.1	10 30.5
20	11 48 20.1	28 56.3	20 15.9	29 17.1	28 33.0	1 55.4	12R11.4	8 7.2	2 1.0	15 15.1	3 45.6	10 30.3
21	11 52 16.7	29 55.9	20 12.7	14♉ 3.9	27 37.7	3 7.9	12 10.0	8 21.7	2 7.8	15 17.8	3 47.1	10 30.1
22	11 56 13.2	0♈55.5	20 9.5	28 43.5	26 42.8	4 20.3	12 7.8	8 36.1	2 14.8	15 20.5	3 48.5	10 29.8
23	12 0 9.8	1 55.1	20 6.3	13♊10.1	25 49.4	5 32.6	12 4.8	8 50.6	2 21.7	15 23.2	3 49.9	10 29.5
24	12 4 6.3	2 54.6	20 3.2	27 20.1	24 58.5	6 44.8	12 1.1	9 5.1	2 28.7	15 25.8	3 51.3	10 29.2
25	12 8 2.9	3 54.1	19 60.0	11♋12.0	24 11.0	7 57.0	11 56.7	9 19.6	2 35.7	15 28.4	3 52.7	10 28.8
26	12 11 59.4	4 53.6	19 56.8	24 46.1	23 27.6	9 9.1	11 51.5	9 34.1	2 42.8	15 31.0	3 54.0	10 28.4
27	12 15 56.0	5 53.0	19 53.6	8♌ 3.7	22 48.9	10 21.1	11 45.5	9 48.6	2 49.9	15 33.5	3 55.3	10 28.0
28	12 19 52.6	6 52.4	19 50.4	21 6.5	22 15.4	11 33.0	11 38.7	10 3.1	2 57.1	15 36.0	3 56.6	10 27.5
29	12 23 49.1	7 51.7	19 47.3	3♍56.4	21 47.3	12 44.8	11 31.2	10 17.6	3 4.2	15 38.4	3 57.8	10 27.0
30	12 27 45.7	8 51.0	19 44.1	16 34.8	21 25.0	13 56.6	11 22.9	10 32.1	3 11.4	15 40.9	3 59.0	10 26.5
31	12 31 42.2	9 50.3	19 40.9	29 3.0	21 8.4	15 8.3	11 13.9	10 46.7	3 18.7	15 43.3	4 .2	10 26.0
		LATITUDE										
1	10 33 25.6	0 .0	0 .0	0N13.0	1N 4.6	0S46.6	2N11.3	1S 6.3	2S17.4	0S38.1	0N17.4	11N36.6
4	10 45 15.3	0 .0	0 .0	3 25.5	1 47.5	0 39.0	2 11.4	1 6.1	2 16.8	0 38.1	0 17.4	11 37.5
7	10 57 5.0	0 .0	0 .0	5 6.3	2 28.4	0 30.9	2 11.3	1 5.9	2 16.2	0 38.2	0 17.4	11 38.5
10	11 8 54.6	0 .0	0 .0	4 48.6	3 3.0	0 22.5	2 11.0	1 5.7	2 15.7	0 38.2	0 17.4	11 39.4
13	11 20 44.3	0 .0	0 .0	2 37.6	3 26.8	0 13.7	2 10.5	1 5.6	2 15.2	0 38.3	0 17.4	11 40.3
16	11 32 33.9	0 .0	0 .0	0S52.0	3 35.5	0 4.6	2 9.8	1 5.5	2 14.7	0 38.4	0 17.4	11 41.2
19	11 44 23.6	0 .0	0 .0	4 7.7	3 27.1	0N 4.8	2 8.7	1 5.4	2 14.3	0 38.4	0 17.3	11 42.1
22	11 56 13.2	0 .0	0 .0	5 7.7	3 2.1	0 14.4	2 7.3	1 5.3	2 13.9	0 38.5	0 17.3	11 43.0
25	12 8 2.9	0 .0	0 .0	3 20.4	2 24.5	0 24.1	2 5.6	1 5.2	2 13.5	0 38.6	0 17.3	11 43.9
28	12 19 52.6	0 .0	0 .0	0 1.6	1 39.7	0 34.0	2 3.5	1 5.2	2 13.1	0 38.7	0 17.3	11 44.7
31	12 31 42.2	0 .0	0 .0	3N 8.5	0 52.8	0 43.9	2 .9	1 5.1	2 12.8	0 38.8	0 17.3	11 45.5
		RIGHT ASCENSION										
1	10 33 25.6	11♓29.3	23♌39.2	26♌52.9	27♓29.6	8♈22.4	8♏44.4	3♈45.2	28♈43.5	16♒57.3	5♒26.7	10♐32.7
2	10 37 22.2	12 25.6	23 36.1	9♍43.1	28 30.8	9 29.1	8 55.2	3 58.0	28 49.0	17 .6	5 28.7	10 33.2
3	10 41 18.7	13 21.7	23 33.0	22 2.1	29 25.9	10 35.9	9 5.5	4 10.8	28 54.5	17 3.8	5 30.6	10 33.6
4	10 45 15.3	14 17.7	23 29.9	3♎56.4	0♈14.5	11 42.7	9 15.2	4 23.6	29 .1	17 6.9	5 32.5	10 34.0
5	10 49 11.9	15 13.5	23 26.8	15 33.9	0 56.1	12 49.6	9 24.3	4 36.5	29 5.8	17 10.1	5 34.4	10 34.4
6	10 53 8.4	16 9.3	23 23.7	27 3.2	1 30.3	13 56.4	9 32.9	4 49.5	29 11.5	17 13.3	5 36.3	10 34.7
7	10 57 5.0	17 5.0	23 20.6	8♏33.0	1 57.0	15 3.4	9 40.9	5 2.4	29 17.3	17 16.4	5 38.2	10 35.0
8	11 1 1.5	18 .5	23 17.5	20 10.9	2 15.8	16 10.3	9 48.3	5 15.4	29 23.2	17 19.5	5 40.0	10 35.2
9	11 4 58.1	18 56.0	23 14.3	2♐ 3.6	2 26.7	17 17.4	9 55.1	5 28.4	29 29.1	17 22.6	5 41.8	10 35.4
10	11 8 54.6	19 51.4	23 11.2	14 16.1	2 29.8	18 24.5	10 1.2	5 41.4	29 35.0	17 25.6	5 43.6	10 35.6
11	11 12 51.2	20 46.7	23 8.1	26 50.7	2R25.1	19 31.8	10 6.7	5 54.5	29 41.0	17 28.6	5 45.4	10 35.8
12	11 16 47.7	21 41.9	23 5.0	9♑47.1	2 12.9	20 39.1	10 11.5	6 7.6	29 47.1	17 31.6	5 47.1	10 35.9
13	11 20 44.3	22 37.1	23 1.9	23 2.1	1 53.6	21 46.5	10 15.7	6 20.7	29 53.2	17 34.6	5 48.8	10 36.0
14	11 24 40.8	23 32.2	22 58.8	6♒30.6	1 27.8	22 54.1	10 19.2	6 33.9	29 59.4	17 37.6	5 50.6	10 36.1
15	11 28 37.4	24 27.2	22 55.7	20 6.7	0 56.0	24 1.8	10 22.0	6 47.1	0♉ 5.7	17 40.5	5 52.2	10 36.1
16	11 32 33.9	25 22.2	22 52.5	3♓46.0	0 19.2	25 9.6	10 24.1	7 .3	0 11.9	17 43.4	5 53.9	10 36.1
17	11 36 30.5	26 17.1	22 49.4	17 26.3	29♓38.2	26 17.6	10 25.5	7 13.5	0 18.2	17 46.3	5 55.5	10R36.0
18	11 40 27.0	27 11.9	22 46.3	1♈ 8.8	28 54.1	27 25.7	10 26.1	7 26.7	0 24.6	17 49.1	5 57.1	10 35.9
19	11 44 23.6	28 6.7	22 43.2	14 57.1	28 7.8	28 33.9	10 26.1	7 40.0	0 31.0	17 51.9	5 58.6	10 35.8
20	11 48 20.1	29 1.5	22 40.1	28 55.9	27 20.4	29 42.3	10R25.2	7 53.3	0 37.5	17 54.7	6 .2	10 35.6
21	11 52 16.7	29 56.2	22 37.0	13♉ 9.5	26 33.1	0♉50.9	10 23.7	8 6.5	0 44.0	17 57.4	6 1.7	10 35.4
22	11 56 13.2	0♈50.9	22 33.8	27 39.5	25 46.7	1 59.7	10 21.4	8 19.8	0 50.6	18 .1	6 3.2	10 35.2
23	12 0 9.8	1 45.6	22 30.7	12♊22.7	25 2.3	3 8.6	10 18.3	8 33.2	0 57.1	18 2.8	6 4.6	10 35.0
24	12 4 6.3	2 40.2	22 27.6	27 11.1	24 20.6	4 17.7	10 14.5	8 46.5	1 3.8	18 5.4	6 6.1	10 34.7
25	12 8 2.9	3 34.8	22 24.5	11♋52.9	23 42.4	5 27.0	10 10.0	8 59.8	1 10.4	18 8.0	6 7.5	10 34.4
26	12 11 59.4	4 29.4	22 21.4	26 15.6	23 8.3	6 36.5	10 4.7	9 13.2	1 17.2	18 10.6	6 8.8	10 34.0
27	12 15 56.0	5 24.0	22 18.2	10♌ 9.4	22 38.7	7 46.2	9 58.6	9 26.5	1 23.9	18 13.1	6 10.2	10 33.6
28	12 19 52.6	6 18.6	22 15.1	23 29.2	22 13.9	8 56.1	9 51.8	9 39.9	1 30.7	18 15.6	6 11.5	10 33.2
29	12 23 49.1	7 13.2	22 12.0	6♍14.9	21 54.3	10 6.2	9 44.2	9 53.2	1 37.5	18 18.1	6 12.8	10 32.7
30	12 27 45.7	8 7.8	22 8.9	18 30.6	21 39.9	11 16.5	9 35.8	10 6.6	1 44.4	18 20.5	6 14.0	10 32.3
31	12 31 42.2	9 2.4	22 5.8	0♎22.8	21 30.9	12 27.0	9 26.7	10 20.0	1 51.2	18 22.9	6 15.2	10 31.7
		DECLINATION										
1	10 33 25.6	7S50.2	0N15.1	13N33.3	0N 5.2	2N46.0	12S52.6	0N25.3	9N19.6	17S 8.8	19S 9.2	10S31.1
4	10 45 15.3	6 41.6	0 15.1	2 1.6	2 3.5	4 19.4	13 2.2	0 42.1	9 26.3	17 6.0	19 7.9	10 30.3
7	10 57 5.0	5 32.1	0 15.2	9S44.7	3 32.5	5 52.0	13 10.4	0 59.1	9 33.2	17 3.4	19 6.7	10 29.5
10	11 8 54.6	4 22.0	0 15.2	17 48.7	4 24.4	7 23.5	13 17.0	1 16.1	9 40.2	17 .7	19 5.5	10 28.7
13	11 20 44.3	3 11.3	0 15.3	19 5.4	4 34.6	8 53.5	13 22.1	1 33.2	9 47.3	16 58.2	19 4.3	10 27.8
16	11 32 33.9	2 .3	0 15.4	11 46.5	4 3.3	10 21.7	13 25.5	1 50.3	9 54.6	16 55.6	19 3.2	10 26.9
19	11 44 23.6	0 49.1	0 15.4	1N54.6	2 57.0	11 47.8	13 27.2	2 7.5	10 2.0	16 53.2	19 2.1	10 25.9
22	11 56 13.2	0N22.1	0 15.5	14 52.0	1 28.8	13 11.4	13 27.2	2 24.6	10 9.4	16 50.9	19 1.1	10 25.0
25	12 8 2.9	1 33.0	0 15.5	19 38.2	0S 5.9	14 32.3	13 25.5	2 41.8	10 16.9	16 48.6	19 .1	10 24.0
28	12 19 52.6	2 43.7	0 15.6	14 26.2	1 32.7	15 50.1	13 22.0	2 58.9	10 24.5	16 46.4	18 59.2	10 23.0
31	12 31 42.2	3 53.8	0 15.6	3 15.6	2 42.2	17 4.4	13 16.9	3 16.0	10 32.2	16 44.4	18 58.3	10 22.0

APRIL 1999

LONGITUDE

DAY	EPHEM. SID. TIME h m s	☉ ° ′	☊ ° ′	☽ ° ′	☿ ° ′	♀ ° ′	♂ ° ′	♃ ° ′	♄ ° ′	♅ ° ′	♆ ° ′	♇ ° ′
1	12 35 38.8	10♈49.5	19♌37.7	11♎22.0	20♓57.7	16♉19.8	11♏ 4.1	11♈ 1.2	3♉25.9	15♒45.6	4♒ 1.4	10♐25.4
2	12 39 35.3	11 48.7	19 34.6	23 32.6	20R52.7	17 31.3	10R53.6	11 15.7	3 33.2	15 47.9	4 2.5	10R24.8
3	12 43 31.9	12 47.9	19 31.4	5♏35.8	20D53.3	18 42.7	10 42.3	11 30.2	3 40.6	15 50.2	4 3.6	10 24.1
4	12 47 28.4	13 47.1	19 28.2	17 33.1	20 59.5	19 54.1	10 30.3	11 44.8	3 48.0	15 52.5	4 4.7	10 23.5
5	12 51 25.0	14 46.2	19 25.0	29 26.2	21 10.9	21 5.3	10 17.5	11 59.3	3 55.3	15 54.7	4 5.8	10 22.8
6	12 55 21.5	15 45.2	19 21.8	11♐17.8	21 27.3	22 16.5	10 4.0	12 13.8	4 2.7	15 56.8	4 6.8	10 22.0
7	12 59 18.1	16 44.3	19 18.7	23 11.3	21 48.7	23 27.5	9 49.8	12 28.3	4 10.2	15 59.0	4 7.8	10 21.2
8	13 3 14.6	17 43.3	19 15.5	5♑10.9	22 14.7	24 38.5	9 34.9	12 42.8	4 17.6	16 1.0	4 8.7	10 20.5
9	13 7 11.2	18 42.3	19 12.3	17 21.0	22 45.1	25 49.3	9 19.3	12 57.3	4 25.1	16 3.1	4 9.6	10 19.6
10	13 11 7.7	19 41.2	19 9.1	29 46.7	23 19.8	27 .1	9 3.0	13 11.7	4 32.6	16 5.1	4 10.5	10 18.8
11	13 15 4.3	20 40.1	19 6.0	12♒32.9	23 58.4	28 10.8	8 46.2	13 26.2	4 40.1	16 7.0	4 11.4	10 17.9
12	13 19 .8	21 39.0	19 2.8	25 43.9	24 40.8	29 21.4	8 28.7	13 40.7	4 47.6	16 8.9	4 12.2	10 17.0
13	13 22 57.4	22 37.9	18 59.6	9♓22.8	25 26.9	0♊31.8	8 10.6	13 55.1	4 55.2	16 10.8	4 13.0	10 16.0
14	13 26 53.9	23 36.7	18 56.4	23 30.3	26 16.3	1 42.2	7 51.9	14 9.5	5 2.7	16 12.6	4 13.8	10 15.1
15	13 30 50.5	24 35.5	18 53.2	8♈ 4.4	27 9.0	2 52.5	7 32.7	14 23.9	5 10.3	16 14.4	4 14.5	10 14.1
16	13 34 47.0	25 34.3	18 50.1	22 59.6	28 4.8	4 2.7	7 13.0	14 38.3	5 17.9	16 16.1	4 15.2	10 13.1
17	13 38 43.6	26 33.1	18 46.9	8♉ 7.5	29 3.5	5 12.7	6 52.9	14 52.7	5 25.5	16 17.8	4 15.9	10 12.0
18	13 42 40.2	27 31.8	18 43.7	23 17.6	0♈ 5.1	6 22.7	6 32.3	15 7.0	5 33.1	16 19.5	4 16.5	10 10.9
19	13 46 36.7	28 30.4	18 40.5	8♊19.6	1 9.3	7 32.5	6 11.3	15 21.3	5 40.8	16 21.1	4 17.1	10 9.9
20	13 50 33.3	29 29.1	18 37.4	23 4.7	2 16.1	8 42.3	5 50.0	15 35.6	5 48.4	16 22.7	4 17.7	10 8.7
21	13 54 29.8	0♉27.7	18 34.2	7♋27.4	3 25.4	9 51.9	5 28.4	15 49.9	5 56.1	16 24.2	4 18.2	10 7.6
22	13 58 26.4	1 26.2	18 31.0	21 25.2	4 37.1	11 1.4	5 6.6	16 4.2	6 3.7	16 25.6	4 18.7	10 6.4
23	14 2 22.9	2 24.8	18 27.8	4♌58.4	5 51.1	12 10.7	4 44.5	16 18.4	6 11.4	16 27.1	4 19.2	10 5.2
24	14 6 19.5	3 23.3	18 24.6	18 9.2	7 7.4	13 20.0	4 22.3	16 32.6	6 19.0	16 28.4	4 19.6	10 4.0
25	14 10 16.0	4 21.8	18 21.5	1♍ 1.0	8 25.8	14 29.1	3 59.9	16 46.8	6 26.7	16 29.8	4 20.0	10 2.9
26	14 14 12.6	5 20.2	18 18.3	13 37.1	9 46.4	15 38.1	3 37.5	17 1.0	6 34.4	16 31.1	4 20.4	10 1.6
27	14 18 9.1	6 18.6	18 15.1	26 .8	11 8.9	16 46.9	3 15.0	17 15.1	6 42.1	16 32.3	4 20.8	10 .3
28	14 22 5.7	7 16.9	18 11.9	8♎15.0	12 33.6	17 55.6	2 52.5	17 29.1	6 49.7	16 33.5	4 21.1	9 59.0
29	14 26 2.2	8 15.2	18 8.8	20 21.9	14 .2	19 4.2	2 30.0	17 43.2	6 57.4	16 34.7	4 21.3	9 57.7
30	14 29 58.8	9 13.5	18 5.6	2♏23.1	15 28.8	20 12.6	2 7.7	17 57.2	7 5.1	16 35.7	4 21.6	9 56.4

LATITUDE

DAY	EPHEM. SID. TIME h m s	☉	☊	☽	☿	♀	♂	♃	♄	♅	♆	♇
1	12 35 38.8	0 .0	0 .0	3N55.8	0N37.3	0N47.2	1N60.0	1S 5.1	2S12.7	0S38.8	0N17.3	11N45.8
4	12 47 28.4	0 .0	0 .0	5 5.0	0S 6.8	0 57.0	1 56.8	1 5.1	2 12.4	0 38.9	0 17.3	11 46.6
7	12 59 18.1	0 .0	0 .0	4 17.0	0 46.4	1 6.8	1 53.1	1 5.1	2 12.1	0 39.0	0 17.3	11 47.3
10	13 11 7.7	0 .0	0 .0	1 47.2	1 20.6	1 16.5	1 48.9	1 5.2	2 11.8	0 39.1	0 17.3	11 48.0
13	13 22 57.4	0 .0	0 .0	1S40.3	1 49.1	1 25.9	1 44.1	1 5.2	2 11.6	0 39.2	0 17.3	11 48.7
16	13 34 47.0	0 .0	0 .0	4 30.2	2 11.8	1 35.1	1 38.8	1 5.3	2 11.4	0 39.3	0 17.3	11 49.3
19	13 46 36.7	0 .0	0 .0	4 46.4	2 28.9	1 43.9	1 33.0	1 5.4	2 11.3	0 39.4	0 17.3	11 49.9
22	13 58 26.4	0 .0	0 .0	2 21.8	2 40.5	1 52.4	1 26.7	1 5.5	2 11.1	0 39.5	0 17.3	11 50.4
25	14 10 16.0	0 .0	0 .0	1N 2.2	2 46.7	2 .4	1 20.0	1 5.6	2 11.0	0 39.6	0 17.3	11 50.9
28	14 22 5.7	0 .0	0 .0	3 48.4	2 47.6	2 7.9	1 12.8	1 5.8	2 11.0	0 39.7	0 17.3	11 51.3

RIGHT ASCENSION

DAY	EPHEM. SID. TIME h m s	☉	☊	☽	☿	♀	♂	♃	♄	♅	♆	♇
1	12 35 38.8	9♈57.0	22♌ 2.6	11♎59.3	21♓27.0	13♉37.7	9♏16.8	10♈33.4	1♉58.2	18♒25.2	6♒16.4	10♐31.2
2	12 39 35.3	10 51.7	21 59.5	23 28.0	21D28.4	14 48.6	9R 6.2	10 46.7	2 5.1	18 27.5	6 17.6	10R30.6
3	12 43 31.9	11 46.4	21 56.4	4♏56.9	21 34.8	15 59.8	8 54.8	11 .1	2 12.1	18 29.8	6 18.7	10 30.0
4	12 47 28.4	12 41.1	21 53.3	16 32.8	21 46.1	17 11.2	8 42.8	11 13.6	2 19.1	18 32.1	6 19.9	10 29.4
5	12 51 25.0	13 35.9	21 50.1	28 21.2	22 2.0	18 22.8	8 29.9	11 26.9	2 26.2	18 34.3	6 20.9	10 28.8
6	12 55 21.5	14 30.7	21 47.0	10♐25.9	22 22.4	19 34.5	8 16.4	11 40.3	2 33.2	18 36.5	6 22.0	10 28.1
7	12 59 18.1	15 25.5	21 43.9	22 48.9	22 47.1	20 46.6	8 2.1	11 53.7	2 40.3	18 38.6	6 23.0	10 27.4
8	13 3 14.6	16 20.4	21 40.8	5♑29.6	23 15.8	21 58.8	7 47.2	12 7.1	2 47.4	18 40.7	6 24.0	10 26.6
9	13 7 11.2	17 15.4	21 37.6	18 25.6	23 48.3	23 11.2	7 31.5	12 20.5	2 54.6	18 42.7	6 24.9	10 25.8
10	13 11 7.7	18 10.4	21 34.5	1♒33.2	24 24.5	24 23.9	7 15.3	12 33.9	3 1.7	18 44.7	6 25.8	10 25.0
11	13 15 4.3	19 5.5	21 31.4	14 48.7	25 4.1	25 36.7	6 58.4	12 47.2	3 8.9	18 46.7	6 26.7	10 24.2
12	13 19 .8	20 .7	21 28.3	28 9.5	25 46.9	26 49.8	6 40.8	13 .6	3 16.1	18 48.6	6 27.6	10 23.3
13	13 22 57.4	20 55.9	21 25.1	11♓35.4	26 32.7	28 3.0	6 22.7	13 13.9	3 23.3	18 50.4	6 28.4	10 22.4
14	13 26 53.9	21 51.3	21 22.0	25 8.7	27 21.4	29 16.5	6 4.1	13 27.3	3 30.6	18 52.3	6 29.2	10 21.5
15	13 30 50.5	22 46.7	21 18.9	8♈53.9	28 12.8	0♊30.1	5 44.9	13 40.6	3 37.8	18 54.1	6 29.9	10 20.5
16	13 34 47.0	23 42.2	21 15.7	22 56.8	29 6.8	1 44.0	5 25.2	13 53.9	3 45.1	18 55.8	6 30.6	10 19.6
17	13 38 43.6	24 37.8	21 12.6	7♉22.3	0♈ 3.2	2 57.9	5 5.1	14 7.2	3 52.4	18 57.5	6 31.3	10 18.6
18	13 42 40.2	25 33.5	21 9.5	22 12.0	1 1.9	4 12.1	4 44.6	14 20.5	3 59.7	18 59.2	6 32.0	10 17.5
19	13 46 36.7	26 29.3	21 6.3	7♊22.1	2 2.8	5 26.4	4 23.7	14 33.8	4 7.1	19 .8	6 32.6	10 16.5
20	13 50 33.3	27 25.1	21 3.2	22 41.7	3 5.9	6 40.8	4 2.4	14 47.1	4 14.4	19 2.3	6 33.1	10 15.4
21	13 54 29.8	28 21.1	21 .1	7♋55.0	4 11.0	7 55.4	3 40.9	15 .3	4 21.7	19 3.8	6 33.7	10 14.3
22	13 58 26.4	29 17.2	20 56.9	22 45.5	5 18.0	9 10.1	3 19.1	15 13.6	4 29.1	19 5.3	6 34.2	10 13.2
23	14 2 22.9	0♉13.4	20 53.8	7♌ .4	6 26.9	10 24.9	2 57.1	15 26.8	4 36.5	19 6.7	6 34.7	10 12.0
24	14 6 19.5	1 9.7	20 50.7	20 33.7	7 37.7	11 39.7	2 34.9	15 40.0	4 43.8	19 8.1	6 35.1	10 10.9
25	14 10 16.0	2 6.1	20 47.5	3♍26.1	8 50.3	12 54.7	2 12.6	15 53.2	4 51.2	19 9.5	6 35.6	10 9.7
26	14 14 12.6	3 2.6	20 44.4	15 43.0	10 4.6	14 9.7	1 50.3	16 6.3	4 58.6	19 10.8	6 36.0	10 8.5
27	14 18 9.1	3 59.3	20 41.3	27 32.8	11 20.7	15 24.8	1 27.8	16 19.4	5 6.0	19 12.0	6 36.3	10 7.3
28	14 22 5.7	4 56.0	20 38.1	9♎ 4.7	12 38.5	16 39.9	1 5.4	16 32.5	5 13.4	19 13.2	6 36.6	10 6.0
29	14 26 2.2	5 52.9	20 35.0	20 28.1	13 58.0	17 55.0	0 43.1	16 45.6	5 20.8	19 14.4	6 36.9	10 4.8
30	14 29 58.8	6 49.9	20 31.9	1♏51.6	15 19.3	19 10.1	0 20.8	16 58.6	5 28.2	19 15.5	6 37.2	10 3.5

DECLINATION

DAY	EPHEM. SID. TIME h m s	☉	☊	☽	☿	♀	♂	♃	♄	♅	♆	♇
1	12 35 38.8	4N17.0	0N15.6	0S52.7	3S .6	17N28.4	13S14.8	3N21.7	10N34.7	16S43.7	18S58.1	10S21.6
4	12 47 28.4	5 26.3	0 15.7	12 11.0	3 40.5	18 37.7	13 7.3	3 38.7	10 42.4	16 41.7	18 57.3	10 20.6
7	12 59 18.1	6 34.7	0 15.7	18 59.1	3 57.5	19 42.9	12 58.2	3 55.7	10 50.1	16 39.9	18 56.6	10 19.6
10	13 11 7.7	7 42.0	0 15.8	18 26.9	3 52.9	20 43.6	12 47.5	4 12.5	10 57.8	16 38.2	18 55.9	10 18.5
13	13 22 57.4	8 48.2	0 15.8	9 36.1	3 28.7	21 39.6	12 35.3	4 29.3	11 5.6	16 36.6	18 55.3	10 17.5
16	13 34 47.0	9 53.1	0 15.9	4N45.1	2 46.8	22 30.7	12 21.8	4 45.9	11 13.3	16 35.1	18 54.8	10 16.5
19	13 46 36.7	10 56.6	0 15.9	16 58.7	1 49.1	23 16.5	12 7.2	5 2.4	11 21.0	16 33.7	18 54.4	10 15.5
22	13 58 26.4	11 58.4	0 16.0	19 23.9	0 37.2	23 56.9	11 51.7	5 18.8	11 28.6	16 32.4	18 54.0	10 14.5
25	14 10 16.0	12 58.4	0 16.0	12 4.9	0N47.4	24 31.7	11 35.8	5 35.0	1' 36.3	16 31.3	18 53.7	10 13.5
28	14 22 5.7	13 56.5	0 16.1	0 13.7	2 23.3	25 .7	11 19.6	5 51.1	11 43.8	16 30.2	18 53.4	10 12.6

MAY 1999

DAY	EPHEM. SID. TIME	☉	☊	☽	☿	♀	♂	♃	♄	♅	♆	♇
	h m s	° ′	° ′	° ′	° ′	° ′	° ′	° ′	° ′	° ′	° ′	° ′
		LONGITUDE										
1	14 33 55.3	10♉11.8	18♌ 2.4	14♏20.0	16♈59.3	21♊20.8	1♏45.4	18♈11.1	7♉12.7	16♒36.8	4♒21.8	9♐55.0
2	14 37 51.9	11 10.0	17 59.2	26 13.8	18 31.8	22 28.9	1R23.4	18 25.1	7 20.4	16 37.8	4 21.9	9R53.7
3	14 41 48.5	12 8.2	17 56.0	8♐ 6.0	20 6.1	23 36.9	1 1.5	18 39.0	7 28.0	16 38.7	4 22.1	9 52.3
4	14 45 45.0	13 6.4	17 52.9	19 58.2	21 42.4	24 44.7	0 40.0	18 52.8	7 35.7	16 39.6	4 22.2	9 50.9
5	14 49 41.6	14 4.5	17 49.7	1♑53.0	23 20.6	25 52.3	0 18.7	19 6.6	7 43.3	16 40.5	4 22.3	9 49.5
6	14 53 38.1	15 2.6	17 46.5	13 53.5	25 .7	26 59.8	29♎57.8	19 20.4	7 51.0	16 41.3	4 22.3	9 48.0
7	14 57 34.7	16 .7	17 43.3	26 3.4	26 42.6	28 7.1	29 37.2	19 34.2	7 58.6	16 42.1	4 22.3	9 46.6
8	15 1 31.2	16 58.8	17 40.2	8♒27.2	28 26.5	29 14.3	29 17.1	19 47.8	8 6.2	16 42.8	4 22.3	9 45.1
9	15 5 27.8	17 56.9	17 37.0	21 9.6	0♉12.3	0♋21.3	28 57.4	20 1.5	8 13.8	16 43.4	4R22.2	9 43.7
10	15 9 24.3	18 54.9	17 33.8	4♓15.4	1 60.0	1 28.1	28 38.2	20 15.1	8 21.4	16 44.0	4 22.1	9 42.2
11	15 13 20.9	19 52.9	17 30.6	17 48.2	3 49.6	2 34.7	28 19.6	20 28.6	8 29.0	16 44.6	4 22.0	9 40.7
12	15 17 17.4	20 50.9	17 27.4	1♈50.4	5 41.1	3 41.2	28 1.5	20 42.1	8 36.5	16 45.1	4 21.9	9 39.1
13	15 21 14.0	21 48.8	17 24.3	16 21.3	7 34.5	4 47.4	27 44.0	20 55.6	8 44.1	16 45.6	4 21.7	9 37.6
14	15 25 10.6	22 46.8	17 21.1	1♉17.1	9 29.8	5 53.5	27 27.1	21 9.0	8 51.6	16 46.0	4 21.5	9 36.1
15	15 29 7.1	23 44.7	17 17.9	16 30.0	11 27.0	6 59.4	27 10.9	21 22.3	8 59.1	16 46.3	4 21.2	9 34.5
16	15 33 3.7	24 42.6	17 14.7	1♊49.6	13 26.0	8 5.2	26 55.3	21 35.7	9 6.7	16 46.7	4 21.0	9 33.0
17	15 37 .2	25 40.5	17 11.6	17 4.3	15 26.8	9 10.7	26 40.5	21 48.9	9 14.2	16 46.9	4 20.7	9 31.4
18	15 40 56.8	26 38.4	17 8.4	2♋ 3.4	17 29.4	10 15.9	26 26.4	22 2.1	9 21.6	16 47.2	4 20.3	9 29.8
19	15 44 53.3	27 36.2	17 5.2	16 39.2	19 33.6	11 21.0	26 13.0	22 15.2	9 29.1	16 47.3	4 19.9	9 28.3
20	15 48 49.9	28 34.0	17 2.0	0♌47.6	21 39.4	12 25.8	26 .3	22 28.3	9 36.5	16 47.4	4 19.5	9 26.7
21	15 52 46.4	29 31.7	16 58.9	14 27.7	23 46.6	13 30.4	25 48.5	22 41.3	9 43.9	16 47.5	4 19.1	9 25.1
22	15 56 43.0	0♊29.4	16 55.7	27 41.3	25 55.1	14 34.8	25 37.4	22 54.2	9 51.2	16 47.5	4 18.6	9 23.4
23	16 0 39.6	1 27.1	16 52.5	10♍32.0	28 4.7	15 38.9	25 27.1	23 7.1	9 58.6	16 47.5	4 18.1	9 21.8
24	16 4 36.1	2 24.8	16 49.3	23 3.7	0♊15.2	16 42.8	25 17.6	23 19.9	10 5.9	16R47.4	4 17.6	9 20.2
25	16 8 32.7	3 22.5	16 46.1	5♎21.0	2 26.4	17 46.4	25 9.0	23 32.6	10 13.1	16 47.3	4 17.0	9 18.6
26	16 12 29.2	4 20.1	16 43.0	17 27.7	4 38.1	18 49.8	25 1.1	23 45.3	10 20.4	16 47.1	4 16.4	9 17.0
27	16 16 25.8	5 17.7	16 39.8	29 27.2	6 50.0	19 52.8	24 54.1	23 57.9	10 27.6	16 46.8	4 15.8	9 15.3
28	16 20 22.3	6 15.3	16 36.6	11♏22.3	9 1.7	20 55.6	24 47.8	24 10.4	10 34.8	16 46.6	4 15.2	9 13.7
29	16 24 18.9	7 12.8	16 33.4	23 15.2	11 13.2	21 58.1	24 42.4	24 22.9	10 42.0	16 46.2	4 14.5	9 12.1
30	16 28 15.5	8 10.4	16 30.3	5♐ 7.6	13 23.9	23 .3	24 37.8	24 35.3	10 49.1	16 45.9	4 13.8	9 10.4
31	16 32 12.0	9 7.9	16 27.1	17 1.0	15 33.8	24 2.2	24 34.0	24 47.6	10 56.2	16 45.4	4 13.0	9 8.8
		LATITUDE										
1	14 33 55.3	0 .0	0 .0	4N59.0	2S43.6	2N14.7	1N 5.4	1S 5.9	2S10.9	0S39.8	0N17.3	11N51.7
4	14 45 45.0	0 .0	0 .0	4 14.3	2 34.5	2 21.0	0 57.7	1 6.1	2 10.9	0 40.0	0 17.3	11 52.0
7	14 57 34.7	0 .0	0 .0	1 50.4	2 20.7	2 26.5	0 49.8	1 6.3	2 10.9	0 40.1	0 17.3	11 52.3
10	15 9 24.3	0 .0	0 .0	1S27.8	2 2.3	2 31.3	0 41.8	1 6.5	2 10.9	0 40.2	0 17.3	11 52.5
13	15 21 14.0	0 .0	0 .0	4 18.6	1 39.7	2 35.2	0 33.7	1 6.7	2 11.0	0 40.3	0 17.3	11 52.7
16	15 33 3.7	0 .0	0 .0	4 50.2	1 13.3	2 38.2	0 25.8	1 7.0	2 11.1	0 40.4	0 17.3	11 52.8
19	15 44 53.3	0 .0	0 .0	2 29.8	0 43.9	2 40.2	0 18.0	1 7.3	2 11.2	0 40.5	0 17.2	11 52.8
22	15 56 43.0	0 .0	0 .0	1N .2	0 12.6	2 41.3	0 10.3	1 7.5	2 11.3	0 40.7	0 17.2	11 52.8
25	16 8 32.7	0 .0	0 .0	3 49.2	0N19.0	2 41.2	0 2.9	1 7.9	2 11.5	0 40.8	0 17.2	11 52.7
28	16 20 22.3	0 .0	0 .0	5 .7	0 49.1	2 40.0	0S 4.2	1 8.2	2 11.7	0 40.9	0 17.2	11 52.5
31	16 32 12.0	0 .0	0 .0	4 16.9	1 15.9	2 37.5	0 11.1	1 8.5	2 11.9	0 41.0	0 17.2	11 52.3
		RIGHT ASCENSION										
1	14 33 55.3	7♉47.1	20♌28.7	13♏22.6	16♈42.3	20♊25.2	29♎58.6	17♈11.6	5♉35.6	19♒16.5	6♒37.4	10♐ 2.2
2	14 37 51.9	8 44.3	20 25.6	25 6.6	18 7.0	21 40.3	29R36.6	17 24.6	5 43.0	19 17.5	6 37.6	10R .8
3	14 41 48.5	9 41.7	20 22.5	7♐ 7.3	19 33.6	22 55.3	29 14.9	17 37.6	5 50.4	19 18.5	6 37.7	9 59.5
4	14 45 45.0	10 39.3	20 19.3	19 25.6	21 1.9	24 10.3	28 53.4	17 50.5	5 57.8	19 19.4	6 37.8	9 58.1
5	14 49 41.6	11 37.0	20 16.2	1♑59.9	22 32.1	25 25.2	28 32.2	18 3.4	6 5.2	19 20.2	6 37.9	9 56.7
6	14 53 38.1	12 34.8	20 13.0	14 46.7	24 4.2	26 40.0	28 11.3	18 16.2	6 12.6	19 21.1	6 37.9	9 55.3
7	14 57 34.7	13 32.8	20 9.9	27 41.4	25 38.2	27 54.7	27 50.8	18 29.1	6 19.9	19 21.8	6 37.9	9 53.9
8	15 1 31.2	14 30.9	20 6.8	10♒39.7	27 14.2	29 9.2	27 30.6	18 41.8	6 27.3	19 22.5	6 37.9	9 52.5
9	15 5 27.8	15 29.2	20 3.6	23 39.3	28 52.2	0♋23.6	27 11.0	18 54.6	6 34.7	19 23.2	6 37.9	9 51.0
10	15 9 24.3	16 27.6	20 .5	6♓40.6	0♉32.4	1 37.9	26 51.8	19 7.3	6 42.0	19 23.8	6R37.8	9 49.6
11	15 13 20.9	17 26.2	19 57.3	19 47.2	2 14.8	2 51.9	26 33.1	19 20.0	6 49.4	19 24.4	6 37.6	9 48.1
12	15 17 17.4	18 24.9	19 54.2	3♈ 5.5	3 59.4	4 5.8	26 14.9	19 32.6	6 56.7	19 24.9	6 37.5	9 46.6
13	15 21 14.0	19 23.7	19 51.0	16 43.5	5 46.3	5 19.4	25 57.4	19 45.2	7 4.1	19 25.4	6 37.3	9 45.1
14	15 25 10.6	20 22.7	19 47.9	0♉49.7	7 35.6	6 32.8	25 40.4	19 57.8	7 11.4	19 25.8	6 37.1	9 43.6
15	15 29 7.1	21 21.9	19 44.8	15 29.8	9 27.3	7 45.9	25 24.0	20 10.3	7 18.7	19 26.2	6 36.8	9 42.1
16	15 33 3.7	22 21.2	19 41.6	0♊44.0	11 21.5	8 58.8	25 8.4	20 22.8	7 26.0	19 26.5	6 36.6	9 40.6
17	15 37 .2	23 20.6	19 38.5	16 23.6	13 18.2	10 11.4	24 53.3	20 35.2	7 33.3	19 26.8	6 36.2	9 39.0
18	15 40 56.8	24 20.2	19 35.3	2♋11.0	15 17.4	11 23.6	24 39.0	20 47.6	7 40.5	19 27.0	6 35.9	9 37.5
19	15 44 53.3	25 19.9	19 32.2	17 43.8	17 19.1	12 35.5	24 25.4	20 59.9	7 47.8	19 27.2	6 35.5	9 35.9
20	15 48 49.9	26 19.7	19 29.0	2♌41.8	19 23.2	13 47.1	24 12.5	21 12.2	7 55.0	19 27.3	6 35.1	9 34.4
21	15 52 46.4	27 19.7	19 25.9	16 52.7	21 29.8	14 58.3	24 .3	21 24.4	8 2.2	19 27.4	6 34.6	9 32.8
22	15 56 43.0	28 19.8	19 22.7	0♍13.8	23 38.8	16 9.0	23 48.9	21 36.6	8 9.4	19 27.4	6 34.1	9 31.2
23	16 0 39.6	29 20.0	19 19.6	12 49.8	25 49.9	17 19.4	23 38.3	21 48.7	8 16.5	19 27.4	6 33.6	9 29.6
24	16 4 36.1	0♊20.4	19 16.4	24 50.0	28 3.1	18 29.3	23 28.4	22 .7	8 23.7	19R27.3	6 33.1	9 28.0
25	16 8 32.7	1 20.9	19 13.3	6♎25.4	0♊18.1	19 38.8	23 19.3	22 12.7	8 30.8	19 27.2	6 32.5	9 26.4
26	16 12 29.2	2 21.5	19 10.1	17 47.4	2 34.7	20 47.8	23 11.0	22 24.6	8 37.8	19 27.0	6 31.9	9 24.8
27	16 16 25.8	3 22.2	19 7.0	29 6.2	4 52.6	21 56.4	23 3.5	22 36.5	8 44.9	19 26.8	6 31.3	9 23.2
28	16 20 22.3	4 23.0	19 3.8	10♏30.9	7 11.5	23 4.4	22 56.7	22 48.3	8 51.9	19 26.6	6 30.6	9 21.6
29	16 24 18.9	5 24.0	19 .7	22 8.9	9 31.0	24 11.9	22 50.7	23 .1	8 58.9	19 26.2	6 29.9	9 20.0
30	16 28 15.5	6 25.0	18 57.5	4♐ 4.6	11 50.9	25 18.9	22 45.5	23 11.8	9 5.9	19 25.9	6 29.2	9 18.3
31	16 32 12.0	7 26.2	18 54.4	16 19.9	14 10.7	26 25.4	22 41.1	23 23.4	9 12.8	19 25.5	6 28.4	9 16.7
		DECLINATION										
1	14 33 55.3	14N52.5	0N16.2	11S22.4	4N 9.3	25N23.8	11S 3.7	6N 6.9	11N51.3	16S29.4	18S53.3	10S11.7
4	14 45 45.0	15 46.3	0 16.2	18 49.9	6 4.2	25 40.9	10 48.2	6 22.5	11 58.7	16 28.6	18 53.2	10 10.8
7	14 57 34.7	16 37.7	0 16.3	19 7.7	8 6.6	25 51.9	10 33.7	6 38.0	12 6.1	16 28.0	18 53.2	10 9.9
10	15 9 24.3	17 26.7	0 16.3	11 18.7	10 15.2	25 57.0	10 20.3	6 53.2	12 13.4	16 27.5	18 53.2	10 9.1
13	15 21 14.0	18 13.1	0 16.4	2N27.0	12 27.9	25 56.1	10 8.5	7 8.2	12 20.5	16 27.2	18 53.3	10 8.3
16	15 33 3.7	18 56.7	0 16.4	15 47.0	14 42.3	25 49.3	9 58.4	7 22.9	12 27.6	16 26.9	18 53.5	10 7.6
19	15 44 53.3	19 37.4	0 16.5	19 55.3	16 55.0	25 36.8	9 50.4	7 37.4	12 34.5	16 26.8	18 53.7	10 6.9
22	15 56 43.0	20 15.1	0 16.5	13 13.0	19 1.8	25 18.7	9 44.6	7 51.6	12 41.3	16 26.9	18 54.1	10 6.3
25	16 8 32.7	20 49.7	0 16.6	1 22.9	20 57.5	24 55.2	9 41.2	8 5.4	12 48.0	16 27.1	18 54.4	10 5.7
28	16 20 22.3	21 21.0	0 16.6	10S28.2	22 36.7	24 26.6	9 40.1	8 19.0	12 54.6	16 27.4	18 54.9	10 5.2
31	16 32 12.0	21 49.1	0 16.7	18 32.6	23 54.7	23 53.1	9 41.5	8 32.3	13 1.0	16 27.8	18 55.4	10 4.7

JUNE 1999

DAY	EPHEM. SID. TIME	☉	☊	☾	☿	♀	♂	♃	♄	♅	♆	♇
	h m s	° ′	° ′	° ′	° ′	° ′	° ′	° ′	° ′	° ′	° ′	° ′
		LONGITUDE										
1	16 36 8.6	10♊ 5.4	16♌23.9	28♐56.9	17♊42.5	25♋ 3.8	24♎31.0	24♈59.8	11♉ 3.2	16♒45.0	4♒12.3	9♐ 7.2
2	16 40 5.1	11 2.9	16 20.7	10♑57.0	19 49.9	26 5.0	24R28.8	25 12.0	11 10.2	16R44.5	4R11.5	9R 5.5
3	16 44 1.7	12 .4	16 17.6	23 3.5	21 55.6	27 5.9	24 27.4	25 24.1	11 17.2	16 43.9	4 10.7	9 3.9
4	16 47 58.2	12 57.8	16 14.4	5♒19.1	23 59.5	28 6.5	24 26.8	25 36.1	11 24.2	16 43.3	4 9.8	9 2.3
5	16 51 54.8	13 55.3	16 11.2	17 47.2	26 1.5	29 6.7	24D27.0	25 48.0	11 31.1	16 42.6	4 9.0	9 .6
6	16 55 51.3	14 52.7	16 8.0	0♓31.4	28 1.5	0♌ 6.6	24 28.1	25 59.9	11 38.0	16 42.0	4 8.1	8 59.1
7	16 59 47.9	15 50.2	16 4.8	13 35.7	29 59.2	1 6.1	24 29.8	26 11.7	11 44.8	16 41.2	4 7.2	8 57.4
8	17 3 44.5	16 47.6	16 1.7	27 3.5	1♋54.7	2 5.2	24 32.3	26 23.3	11 51.6	16 40.4	4 6.2	8 55.8
9	17 7 41.0	17 45.0	15 58.5	10♈57.2	3 47.8	3 4.0	24 35.6	26 34.9	11 58.3	16 39.6	4 5.2	8 54.2
10	17 11 37.6	18 42.4	15 55.3	25 17.2	5 38.4	4 2.3	24 39.6	26 46.4	12 5.0	16 38.7	4 4.2	8 52.6
11	17 15 34.1	19 39.8	15 52.1	10♉ 1.2	7 26.6	5 .2	24 44.4	26 57.8	12 11.7	16 37.8	4 3.2	8 51.0
12	17 19 30.7	20 37.1	15 49.0	25 3.4	9 12.4	5 57.7	24 49.9	27 9.1	12 18.3	16 36.8	4 2.2	8 49.4
13	17 23 27.2	21 34.5	15 45.8	10♊15.3	10 55.5	6 54.7	24 56.2	27 20.4	12 24.8	16 35.8	4 1.1	8 47.8
14	17 27 23.8	22 31.9	15 42.6	25 26.5	12 36.2	7 51.3	25 3.1	27 31.5	12 31.3	16 34.7	3 60.0	8 46.2
15	17 31 20.4	23 29.2	15 39.4	10♋26.7	14 14.3	8 47.4	25 10.8	27 42.5	12 37.8	16 33.6	3 58.9	8 44.7
16	17 35 16.9	24 26.5	15 36.3	25 7.1	15 49.8	9 43.0	25 19.2	27 53.5	12 44.2	16 32.5	3 57.7	8 43.1
17	17 39 13.5	25 23.8	15 33.1	9♌22.2	17 22.7	10 38.1	25 28.3	28 4.3	12 50.5	16 31.3	3 56.6	8 41.5
18	17 43 10.0	26 21.1	15 29.9	23 9.5	18 53.0	11 32.7	25 38.1	28 15.0	12 56.8	16 30.1	3 55.4	8 40.0
19	17 47 6.6	27 18.4	15 26.7	6♍29.5	20 20.7	12 26.7	25 48.5	28 25.7	13 3.1	16 28.8	3 54.2	8 38.5
20	17 51 3.2	28 15.7	15 23.5	19 24.5	21 45.7	13 20.1	25 59.6	28 36.2	13 9.3	16 27.5	3 52.9	8 37.0
21	17 54 59.7	29 13.0	15 20.4	1♎58.4	23 8.0	14 13.0	26 11.3	28 46.6	13 15.4	16 26.1	3 51.7	8 35.5
22	17 58 56.3	0♋10.2	15 17.2	14 15.6	24 27.5	15 5.2	26 23.7	28 56.9	13 21.5	16 24.7	3 50.4	8 34.0
23	18 2 52.8	1 7.5	15 14.0	26 20.7	25 44.3	15 56.8	26 36.7	29 7.1	13 27.5	16 23.3	3 49.1	8 32.5
24	18 6 49.4	2 4.7	15 10.8	8♏17.8	26 58.3	16 47.8	26 50.3	29 17.2	13 33.5	16 21.8	3 47.8	8 31.0
25	18 10 45.9	3 1.9	15 7.7	20 10.7	28 9.3	17 38.0	27 4.5	29 27.2	13 39.4	16 20.3	3 46.5	8 29.6
26	18 14 42.5	3 59.1	15 4.5	2♐ 2.6	29 17.4	18 27.6	27 19.3	29 37.1	13 45.2	16 18.8	3 45.1	8 28.1
27	18 18 39.1	4 56.4	15 1.3	13 56.1	0♌22.6	19 16.4	27 34.7	29 46.9	13 51.0	16 17.2	3 43.8	8 26.8
28	18 22 35.6	5 53.6	14 58.1	25 53.4	1 24.6	20 4.5	27 50.6	29 56.5	13 56.7	16 15.6	3 42.4	8 25.4
29	18 26 32.2	6 50.8	14 55.0	7♑56.1	2 23.4	20 51.7	28 7.0	0♉ 6.0	14 2.4	16 14.0	3 41.0	8 24.0
30	18 30 28.7	7 48.0	14 51.8	20 5.9	3 18.9	21 38.1	28 24.0	0 15.4	14 8.0	16 12.3	3 39.6	8 22.6
		LATITUDE										
1	16 36 8.6	0 .0	0 .0	3N38.2	1N23.7	2N36.4	0S13.4	1S 8.6	2S12.0	0S41.0	0N17.2	11N52.2
4	16 47 58.2	0 .0	0 .0	0 49.9	1 43.5	2 32.3	0 19.9	1 9.0	2 12.2	0 41.1	0 17.2	11 51.9
7	16 59 47.9	0 .0	0 .0	2S28.2	1 56.8	2 26.7	0 26.1	1 9.4	2 12.5	0 41.3	0 17.2	11 51.5
10	17 11 37.6	0 .0	0 .0	4 48.8	2 3.3	2 19.7	0 32.0	1 9.8	2 12.8	0 41.4	0 17.2	11 51.0
13	17 23 27.2	0 .0	0 .0	4 35.2	2 3.0	2 11.2	0 37.6	1 10.2	2 13.2	0 41.5	0 17.2	11 50.5
16	17 35 16.9	0 .0	0 .0	1 39.6	1 56.1	2 1.2	0 42.8	1 10.7	2 13.5	0 41.6	0 17.2	11 50.0
19	17 47 6.6	0 .0	0 .0	1N58.7	1 42.8	1 49.5	0 47.8	1 11.1	2 13.9	0 41.7	0 17.1	11 49.3
22	17 58 56.3	0 .0	0 .0	4 28.8	1 23.5	1 36.1	0 52.5	1 11.6	2 14.3	0 41.8	0 17.1	11 48.7
25	18 10 45.9	0 .0	0 .0	5 7.2	0 58.6	1 20.8	0 57.0	1 12.1	2 14.7	0 41.8	0 17.1	11 47.9
28	18 22 35.6	0 .0	0 .0	3 48.9	0 28.6	1 3.7	1 1.2	1 12.6	2 15.2	0 41.9	0 17.1	11 47.1
		RIGHT ASCENSION										
1	16 36 8.6	8♊27.5	18♌51.2	28♐53.1	16♊30.1	27♋31.3	22♎37.5	23♈35.0	9♉19.7	19♒25.0	6♒27.6	9♐15.1
2	16 40 5.1	9 28.9	18 48.1	11♑39.6	18 48.7	28 36.6	22R34.6	23 46.5	9 26.6	19R24.5	6R26.8	9R13.5
3	16 44 1.7	10 30.3	18 44.9	24 33.3	21 6.1	29 41.4	22 32.4	23 57.9	9 33.5	19 24.0	6 26.0	9 11.9
4	16 47 58.2	11 31.9	18 41.8	7♒27.8	23 22.2	0♌45.5	22 31.1	24 9.3	9 40.3	19 23.4	6 25.1	9 10.2
5	16 51 54.8	12 33.6	18 38.6	20 18.9	25 36.6	1 49.0	22 30.5	24 20.6	9 47.0	19 22.7	6 24.2	9 8.6
6	16 55 51.3	13 35.4	18 35.5	3♓ 5.6	27 49.0	2 52.0	22D30.7	24 31.8	9 53.8	19 22.1	6 23.4	9 7.0
7	16 59 47.9	14 37.2	18 32.3	15 50.6	29 59.1	3 54.2	22 31.6	24 43.0	10 .5	19 21.4	6 22.4	9 5.4
8	17 3 44.5	15 39.2	18 29.2	28 40.3	2♋ 6.9	4 55.9	22 33.2	24 54.1	10 7.2	19 20.6	6 21.4	9 3.8
9	17 7 41.0	16 41.2	18 26.0	11♈43.8	4 12.0	5 56.8	22 35.5	25 5.1	10 13.8	19 19.8	6 20.4	9 2.2
10	17 11 37.6	17 43.2	18 22.9	25 11.8	6 14.4	6 57.1	22 38.6	25 16.0	10 20.4	19 18.9	6 19.4	9 .6
11	17 15 34.1	18 45.4	18 19.7	9♉14.1	8 14.0	7 56.7	22 42.4	25 26.8	10 26.9	19 18.0	6 18.3	8 59.0
12	17 19 30.7	19 47.5	18 16.5	23 57.1	10 10.5	8 55.6	22 47.0	25 37.6	10 33.4	19 17.0	6 17.3	8 57.4
13	17 23 27.2	20 49.8	18 13.4	9♊19.8	12 4.0	9 53.8	22 52.2	25 48.2	10 39.9	19 16.0	6 16.2	8 55.8
14	17 27 23.8	21 52.1	18 10.2	25 10.5	13 54.3	10 51.2	22 58.1	25 58.8	10 46.3	19 15.0	6 15.0	8 54.2
15	17 31 20.4	22 54.4	18 7.1	11♋ 7.4	15 41.5	11 47.9	23 4.7	26 9.3	10 52.7	19 13.9	6 13.9	8 52.7
16	17 35 16.9	23 56.8	18 3.9	26 44.9	17 25.4	12 43.9	23 12.0	26 19.7	10 59.0	19 12.8	6 12.7	8 51.1
17	17 39 13.5	24 59.1	18 .8	11♌41.6	19 5.9	13 39.0	23 20.0	26 30.1	11 5.2	19 11.6	6 11.5	8 49.5
18	17 43 10.0	26 1.5	17 57.6	25 46.5	20 43.2	14 33.4	23 28.6	26 40.3	11 11.5	19 10.4	6 10.3	8 48.0
19	17 47 6.6	27 3.9	17 54.4	8♍59.2	22 17.1	15 27.0	23 37.9	26 50.4	11 17.6	19 9.1	6 9.0	8 46.5
20	17 51 3.2	28 6.3	17 51.3	21 26.8	23 47.6	16 19.7	23 47.8	27 .5	11 23.7	19 7.8	6 7.8	8 44.9
21	17 54 59.7	29 8.8	17 48.1	3♎20.2	25 14.6	17 11.6	23 58.4	27 10.4	11 29.8	19 6.5	6 6.5	8 43.4
22	17 58 56.3	0♋11.1	17 44.9	14 51.7	26 38.2	18 2.7	24 9.6	27 20.3	11 35.8	19 5.1	6 5.2	8 41.9
23	18 2 52.8	1 13.5	17 41.8	26 13.2	27 58.3	18 52.8	24 21.3	27 30.0	11 41.8	19 3.7	6 3.9	8 40.4
24	18 6 49.4	2 15.9	17 38.6	7♏35.7	29 14.9	19 42.1	24 33.7	27 39.7	11 47.7	19 2.2	6 2.5	8 39.0
25	18 10 45.9	3 18.2	17 35.5	19 8.3	0♌28.0	20 30.4	24 46.7	27 49.2	11 53.5	19 .8	6 1.1	8 37.5
26	18 14 42.5	4 20.6	17 32.3	0♐57.8	1 37.4	21 17.8	25 .2	27 58.7	11 59.3	18 59.2	5 59.8	8 36.0
27	18 18 39.1	5 22.9	17 29.1	13 7.9	2 43.3	22 4.3	25 14.3	28 8.0	12 5.0	18 57.7	5 58.4	8 34.6
28	18 22 35.6	6 25.1	17 26.0	25 38.8	3 45.4	22 49.8	25 29.0	28 17.3	12 10.7	18 56.1	5 57.0	8 33.2
29	18 26 32.2	7 27.3	17 22.8	8♑26.9	4 43.8	23 34.2	25 44.2	28 26.4	12 16.3	18 54.5	5 55.6	8 31.8
30	18 30 28.7	8 29.4	17 19.6	21 25.3	5 38.4	24 17.7	25 59.9	28 35.4	12 21.9	18 52.8	5 54.1	8 30.4
		DECLINATION										
1	16 36 8.6	21N57.6	0N16.7	19S47.8	24N15.5	23N40.9	9S42.4	8N36.7	13N 3.0	16S28.0	18S55.6	10S 4.6
4	16 47 58.2	22 21.1	0 16.7	18 7.8	25 1.4	23 1.4	9 47.0	8 49.5	13 9.2	16 28.6	18 56.2	10 4.2
7	16 59 47.9	22 41.0	0 16.8	8 43.8	25 23.0	22 17.8	9 53.8	9 2.0	13 15.3	16 29.4	18 56.8	10 3.9
10	17 11 37.6	22 57.4	0 16.8	5N17.8	25 22.2	21 30.4	10 2.9	9 14.2	13 21.1	16 30.2	18 57.5	10 3.7
13	17 23 27.2	23 10.2	0 16.9	17 26.7	25 1.9	20 39.5	10 14.2	9 26.0	13 26.8	16 31.2	18 58.3	10 3.5
16	17 35 16.9	23 19.2	0 16.9	19 28.5	24 25.2	19 45.6	10 27.5	9 37.4	13 32.3	16 32.3	18 59.1	10 3.4
19	17 47 6.6	23 24.6	0 17.0	10 58.0	23 35.4	18 49.1	10 42.8	9 48.4	13 37.6	16 33.5	18 59.9	10 3.3
22	17 58 56.3	23 26.2	0 17.0	1S29.4	22 35.8	17 50.3	11 .0	9 59.0	13 42.7	16 34.8	19 .8	10 3.3
25	18 10 45.9	23 24.2	0 17.1	12 51.0	21 29.2	16 49.8	11 18.9	10 9.2	13 47.6	16 36.2	19 1.8	10 3.4
28	18 22 35.6	23 18.4	0 17.1	19 33.7	20 18.5	15 47.8	11 39.5	10 19.0	13 52.3	16 37.7	19 2.7	10 3.6

JULY 1999

DAY	EPHEM. SID. TIME	☉	☊	☽	☿	♀	♂	♃	♄	♅	♆	♇
	h m s	° ′	° ′	° ′	° ′	° ′	° ′	° ′	° ′	° ′	° ′	° ′
		LONGITUDE										
1	18 34 25.3	8♋45.1	14♌48.6	2♒24.1	4♌11.0	22♌23.7	28♎41.6	0♉24.7	14♉13.5	16♒10.6	3♒38.2	8♐21.2
2	18 38 21.8	9 42.3	14 45.4	14 52.5	4 59.6	23 8.4	28 59.6	0 33.9	14 18.9	16R 8.8	3R36.7	8R19.9
3	18 42 18.4	10 39.5	14 42.2	27 33.0	5 44.7	23 52.2	29 18.2	0 42.9	14 24.3	16 7.0	3 35.3	8 18.6
4	18 46 15.0	11 36.7	14 39.1	10♓27.6	6 26.0	24 35.0	29 37.2	0 51.8	14 29.6	16 5.2	3 33.8	8 17.3
5	18 50 11.5	12 33.9	14 35.9	23 38.7	7 3.4	25 16.9	29 56.8	1 .6	14 34.9	16 3.4	3 32.3	8 16.0
6	18 54 8.1	13 31.1	14 32.7	7♈ 8.3	7 36.9	25 57.7	0♏16.8	1 9.2	14 40.1	16 1.5	3 30.8	8 14.8
7	18 58 4.6	14 28.3	14 29.5	20 57.8	8 6.3	26 37.5	0 37.3	1 17.8	14 45.2	15 59.6	3 29.3	8 13.5
8	19 2 1.2	15 25.5	14 26.4	5♉ 7.4	8 31.4	27 16.2	0 58.2	1 26.1	14 50.2	15 57.7	3 27.8	8 12.3
9	19 5 57.7	16 22.7	14 23.2	19 35.4	8 52.1	27 53.7	1 19.7	1 34.4	14 55.2	15 55.7	3 26.3	8 11.1
10	19 9 54.3	17 19.9	14 20.0	4♊18.1	9 8.4	28 30.1	1 41.5	1 42.5	15 .1	15 53.7	3 24.7	8 9.9
11	19 13 50.9	18 17.2	14 16.8	19 9.7	9 20.1	29 5.2	2 3.9	1 50.5	15 4.9	15 51.7	3 23.2	8 8.8
12	19 17 47.4	19 14.4	14 13.7	4♋ 2.5	9 27.1	29 39.1	2 26.6	1 58.3	15 9.6	15 49.6	3 21.6	8 7.7
13	19 21 44.0	20 11.6	14 10.5	18 48.5	9 29.4	0♍11.7	2 49.8	2 6.0	15 14.3	15 47.6	3 20.0	8 6.6
14	19 25 40.5	21 8.9	14 7.3	3♌20.2	9R26.9	0 42.9	3 13.4	2 13.5	15 18.9	15 45.5	3 18.5	8 5.5
15	19 29 37.1	22 6.1	14 4.1	17 31.7	9 19.6	1 12.6	3 37.4	2 20.9	15 23.4	15 43.4	3 16.9	8 4.4
16	19 33 33.6	23 3.4	14 .9	1♍19.5	9 7.6	1 40.9	4 1.9	2 28.2	15 27.8	15 41.2	3 15.3	8 3.4
17	19 37 30.2	24 .6	13 57.8	14 42.5	8 51.0	2 7.7	4 26.7	2 35.3	15 32.1	15 39.1	3 13.7	8 2.4
18	19 41 26.7	24 57.9	13 54.6	27 41.6	8 29.9	2 32.8	4 52.0	2 42.3	15 36.4	15 36.9	3 12.1	8 1.5
19	19 45 23.3	25 55.2	13 51.4	10♎19.3	8 4.5	2 56.3	5 17.6	2 49.1	15 40.6	15 34.7	3 10.5	8 .5
20	19 49 19.9	26 52.4	13 48.2	22 39.2	7 35.1	3 18.1	5 43.5	2 55.7	15 44.7	15 32.5	3 8.9	7 59.6
21	19 53 16.4	27 49.7	13 45.1	4♏45.7	7 2.1	3 38.1	6 9.9	3 2.2	15 48.7	15 30.3	3 7.3	7 58.7
22	19 57 13.0	28 46.9	13 41.9	16 43.3	6 26.0	3 56.2	6 36.6	3 8.5	15 52.6	15 28.0	3 5.7	7 57.8
23	20 1 9.5	29 44.2	13 38.7	28 36.3	5 47.2	4 12.4	7 3.6	3 14.7	15 56.4	15 25.8	3 4.0	7 57.0
24	20 5 6.1	0♌41.5	13 35.5	10♐29.0	5 6.5	4 26.7	7 31.0	3 20.7	16 .1	15 23.5	3 2.4	7 56.1
25	20 9 2.6	1 38.8	13 32.4	22 24.8	4 24.3	4 38.9	7 58.7	3 26.6	16 3.8	15 21.2	3 .8	7 55.3
26	20 12 59.2	2 36.1	13 29.2	4♑27.1	3 41.6	4 49.0	8 26.7	3 32.2	16 7.4	15 18.9	2 59.1	7 54.6
27	20 16 55.8	3 33.3	13 26.0	16 38.2	2 58.9	4 57.1	8 55.1	3 37.8	16 10.8	15 16.5	2 57.5	7 53.8
28	20 20 52.3	4 30.7	13 22.8	29 .1	2 17.0	5 2.9	9 23.8	3 43.1	16 14.2	15 14.2	2 55.9	7 53.1
29	20 24 48.9	5 28.0	13 19.6	11♒34.1	1 36.8	5 6.5	9 52.8	3 48.3	16 17.5	15 11.9	2 54.3	7 52.5
30	20 28 45.4	6 25.3	13 16.5	24 21.2	0 59.0	5 7.8	10 22.1	3 53.3	16 20.7	15 9.5	2 52.6	7 51.8
31	20 32 42.0	7 22.6	13 13.3	7♓21.7	0 24.4	5R 6.8	10 51.7	3 58.1	16 23.8	15 7.1	2 51.0	7 51.2
		LATITUDE										
1	18 34 25.3	0 .0	0 .0	0N58.6	0S 6.2	0N44.6	1S 5.1	1S13.1	2S15.6	0S42.0	0N17.1	11N46.3
4	18 46 15.0	0 .0	0 .0	2S23.6	0 45.1	0 23.5	1 8.8	1 13.7	2 16.1	0 42.1	0 17.0	11 45.3
7	18 58 4.6	0 .0	0 .0	4 50.1	1 27.3	0 .2	1 12.3	1 14.3	2 16.6	0 42.2	0 17.0	11 44.4
10	19 9 54.3	0 .0	0 .0	4 52.5	2 11.5	0S25.2	1 15.6	1 14.8	2 17.2	0 42.2	0 17.0	11 43.4
13	19 21 44.0	0 .0	0 .0	2 9.2	2 55.9	0 52.9	1 18.7	1 15.4	2 17.7	0 42.3	0 17.0	11 42.3
16	19 33 33.6	0 .0	0 .0	1N39.4	3 38.1	1 22.8	1 21.6	1 16.1	2 18.3	0 42.4	0 16.9	11 41.2
19	19 45 23.3	0 .0	0 .0	4 25.9	4 14.7	1 55.1	1 24.3	1 16.7	2 18.9	0 42.4	0 16.9	11 40.1
22	19 57 13.0	0 .0	0 .0	5 15.3	4 42.1	2 29.5	1 26.8	1 17.3	2 19.5	0 42.5	0 16.9	11 38.9
25	20 9 2.6	0 .0	0 .0	4 4.4	4 56.7	3 6.0	1 29.2	1 18.0	2 20.1	0 42.5	0 16.8	11 37.7
28	20 20 52.3	0 .0	0 .0	1 16.4	4 56.0	3 44.2	1 31.4	1 18.6	2 20.7	0 42.5	0 16.8	11 36.5
31	20 32 42.0	0 .0	0 .0	2S11.4	4 39.6	4 23.7	1 33.5	1 19.3	2 21.4	0 42.6	0 16.8	11 35.2
		RIGHT ASCENSION										
1	18 34 25.3	9♋31.5	17♌16.5	4♒26.4	6♌29.1	25♌ .1	26♎16.2	28♈44.3	12♉27.3	18♒51.1	5♒52.6	8♐29.1
2	18 38 21.8	10 33.6	17 13.3	17 23.2	7 15.8	25 41.4	26 33.0	28 53.1	12 32.8	18R49.4	5R51.2	8R27.7
3	18 42 18.4	11 35.5	17 10.1	0♓11.9	7 58.6	26 21.6	26 50.3	29 1.8	12 38.1	18 47.6	5 49.7	8 26.4
4	18 46 15.0	12 37.4	17 7.0	12 53.0	8 37.2	27 .8	27 8.0	29 10.3	12 43.4	18 45.8	5 48.1	8 25.0
5	18 50 11.5	13 39.2	17 3.8	25 30.8	9 11.7	27 38.7	27 26.3	29 18.8	12 48.6	18 44.0	5 46.6	8 23.7
6	18 54 8.1	14 41.0	17 .6	8♈13.4	9 41.9	28 15.5	27 45.1	29 27.1	12 53.8	18 42.1	5 45.1	8 22.4
7	18 58 4.6	15 42.7	16 57.5	21 11.0	10 7.7	28 51.1	28 4.4	29 35.3	12 58.9	18 40.2	5 43.5	8 21.2
8	19 2 1.2	16 44.2	16 54.3	4♉34.9	10 29.2	29 25.5	28 24.1	29 43.4	13 3.9	18 38.3	5 42.0	8 19.9
9	19 5 57.7	17 45.7	16 51.1	18 34.7	10 46.1	29 58.6	28 44.3	29 51.3	13 8.8	18 36.4	5 40.4	8 18.7
10	19 9 54.3	18 47.1	16 47.9	3♊15.6	10 58.4	0♍30.4	29 5.0	29 59.2	13 13.7	18 34.4	5 38.8	8 17.5
11	19 13 50.9	19 48.4	16 44.8	18 34.6	11 6.0	1 .8	29 26.1	0♉ 6.8	13 18.5	18 32.4	5 37.2	8 16.3
12	19 17 47.4	20 49.6	16 41.6	4♋17.8	11 9.0	1 29.9	29 47.7	0 14.4	13 23.2	18 30.3	5 35.6	8 15.2
13	19 21 44.0	21 50.7	16 38.4	20 2.9	11R 7.3	1 57.6	0♏ 9.7	0 21.8	13 27.9	18 28.3	5 34.0	8 14.0
14	19 25 40.5	22 51.6	16 35.3	5♌25.4	11 .9	2 23.8	0 32.2	0 29.1	13 32.4	18 26.2	5 32.4	8 12.9
15	19 29 37.1	23 52.5	16 32.1	20 6.3	10 49.9	2 48.5	0 55.1	0 36.3	13 36.9	18 24.1	5 30.7	8 11.8
16	19 33 33.6	24 53.2	16 28.9	3♍57.4	10 34.2	3 11.6	1 18.5	0 43.3	13 41.4	18 22.0	5 29.1	8 10.7
17	19 37 30.2	25 53.8	16 25.7	16 59.9	10 14.2	3 33.1	1 42.2	0 50.2	13 45.7	18 19.8	5 27.4	8 9.7
18	19 41 26.7	26 54.3	16 22.6	29 21.5	9 50.0	3 53.1	2 6.4	0 56.9	13 50.0	18 17.7	5 25.8	8 8.7
19	19 45 23.3	27 54.6	16 19.4	11♎13.3	9 21.7	4 11.3	2 31.0	1 3.5	13 54.2	18 15.5	5 24.2	8 7.7
20	19 49 19.9	28 54.8	16 16.2	22 47.4	8 49.8	4 27.7	2 56.0	1 10.0	13 58.3	18 13.3	5 22.5	8 6.8
21	19 53 16.4	29 54.8	16 13.0	4♏15.1	8 14.6	4 42.4	3 21.4	1 16.2	14 2.3	18 11.1	5 20.9	8 5.8
22	19 57 13.0	0♌54.7	16 9.9	15 47.0	7 36.6	4 55.2	3 47.2	1 22.4	14 6.2	18 8.8	5 19.2	8 4.9
23	20 1 9.5	1 54.4	16 6.7	27 31.5	6 56.4	5 6.1	4 13.4	1 28.4	14 10.1	18 6.6	5 17.5	8 4.0
24	20 5 6.1	2 54.0	16 3.5	9♐34.7	6 14.5	5 15.0	4 39.9	1 34.2	14 13.8	18 4.3	5 15.8	8 3.1
25	20 9 2.6	3 53.4	16 .3	21 59.2	5 31.6	5 22.0	5 6.8	1 39.9	14 17.5	18 2.0	5 14.2	8 2.3
26	20 12 59.2	4 52.7	15 57.1	4♑43.9	4 48.4	5 26.9	5 34.1	1 45.4	14 21.1	17 59.7	5 12.5	8 1.5
27	20 16 55.8	5 51.9	15 54.0	17 43.9	4 5.6	5 29.8	6 1.8	1 50.8	14 24.6	17 57.4	5 10.8	8 .7
28	20 20 52.3	6 50.9	15 50.8	0♒51.8	3 24.1	5 30.5	6 29.8	1 56.0	14 28.0	17 55.1	5 9.1	7 59.9
29	20 24 48.9	7 49.7	15 47.6	13 59.5	2 44.5	5R29.1	6 58.1	2 1.1	14 31.3	17 52.7	5 7.5	7 59.2
30	20 28 45.4	8 48.4	15 44.4	27 .9	2 7.6	5 25.5	7 26.8	2 6.0	14 34.5	17 50.4	5 5.8	7 58.5
31	20 32 42.0	9 46.9	15 41.2	9♓53.3	1 34.1	5 19.7	7 55.9	2 10.7	14 37.7	17 48.0	5 4.1	7 57.8
		DECLINATION										
1	18 34 25.3	23N 8.9	0N17.2	18S40.3	19N 6.5	14N45.0	12S 1.4	10N28.4	13N56.8	16S39.3	19S 3.7	10S 3.9
4	18 46 15.0	22 55.8	0 17.2	9 51.6	17 56.1	13 41.7	12 24.7	10 37.3	14 1.0	16 41.0	19 4.8	10 4.2
7	18 58 4.6	22 39.1	0 17.3	3N41.7	16 50.0	12 38.6	12 49.1	10 45.8	14 5.1	16 42.7	19 5.8	10 4.6
10	19 9 54.3	22 18.8	0 17.3	16 12.5	15 51.2	11 36.0	13 14.6	10 53.8	14 8.9	16 44.6	19 6.9	10 5.1
13	19 21 44.0	21 55.1	0 17.4	19 59.1	15 2.9	10 34.6	13 41.1	11 1.3	14 12.5	16 46.5	19 8.0	10 5.6
16	19 33 33.6	21 28.1	0 17.4	12 33.0	14 27.9	9 35.1	14 8.5	11 8.3	14 15.8	16 48.4	19 9.2	10 6.2
19	19 45 23.3	20 57.7	0 17.5	0S .5	14 8.5	8 38.1	14 36.6	11 14.9	14 18.9	16 50.4	19 10.3	10 6.9
22	19 57 13.0	20 24.1	0 17.5	11 47.4	14 6.4	7 44.5	15 5.3	11 20.9	14 21.8	16 52.4	19 11.4	10 7.7
25	20 9 2.6	19 47.5	0 17.5	19 9.2	14 21.1	6 55.1	15 34.4	11 26.4	14 24.4	16 54.5	19 12.6	10 8.5
28	20 20 52.3	19 7.9	0 17.6	19 6.6	14 50.4	6 10.8	16 4.0	11 31.3	14 26.8	16 56.6	19 13.8	10 9.4
31	20 32 42.0	18 25.5	0 17.6	10 50.3	15 30.5	5 32.5	16 33.8	11 35.8	14 28.9	16 58.7	19 14.9	10 10.4

AUGUST 1999

DAY	EPHEM. SID. TIME	☉	☊	☽	☿	♀	♂	♃	♄	♅	♆	♇
	LONGITUDE											
	h m s	° ′	° ′	° ′	° ′	° ′	° ′	° ′	° ′	° ′	° ′	° ′
1	20 36 38.5	8♌20.0	13♌10.1	20♓35.9	29♋53.5	5♍ 3.4	11♏21.6	4♉ 2.8	16♉26.8	15♒ 4.8	2♒49.4	7♐50.6
2	20 40 35.1	9 17.4	13 6.9	4♈ 3.8	29R27.0	4R57.7	11 51.8	4 7.3	16 29.8	15R 2.4	2R47.8	7R50.0
3	20 44 31.6	10 14.8	13 3.8	17 45.2	29 5.5	4 49.6	12 22.2	4 11.6	16 32.6	15 .0	2 46.2	7 49.5
4	20 48 28.2	11 12.2	13 .6	1♉39.3	28 49.4	4 39.2	12 53.0	4 15.8	16 35.3	14 57.6	2 44.6	7 49.0
5	20 52 24.7	12 9.6	12 57.4	15 45.2	28 39.2	4 26.4	13 24.0	4 19.7	16 38.0	14 55.2	2 42.9	7 48.6
6	20 56 21.3	13 7.1	12 54.2	0♊ 1.1	28 35.1	4 11.2	13 55.3	4 23.5	16 40.5	14 52.8	2 41.3	7 48.1
7	21 0 17.9	14 4.6	12 51.1	14 24.4	28D37.4	3 53.7	14 26.9	4 27.1	16 42.9	14 50.4	2 39.8	7 47.7
8	21 4 14.4	15 2.1	12 47.9	28 51.6	28 46.4	3 34.1	14 58.7	4 30.6	16 45.3	14 48.1	2 38.2	7 47.4
9	21 8 11.0	15 59.6	12 44.7	13♋18.2	29 2.1	3 12.1	15 30.8	4 33.8	16 47.6	14 45.7	2 36.6	7 47.0
10	21 12 7.5	16 57.2	12 41.5	27 39.4	29 24.6	2 48.1	16 3.2	4 36.8	16 49.7	14 43.3	2 35.1	7 46.7
11	21 16 4.1	17 54.7	12 38.3	11♌50.3	29 54.0	2 22.0	16 35.8	4 39.7	16 51.8	14 40.9	2 33.5	7 46.5
12	21 20 .6	18 52.3	12 35.2	25 46.5	0♌30.2	1 54.0	17 8.7	4 42.3	16 53.7	14 38.5	2 32.0	7 46.2
13	21 23 57.2	19 49.9	12 32.0	9♍24.7	1 13.1	1 24.3	17 41.8	4 44.8	16 55.5	14 36.1	2 30.4	7 46.0
14	21 27 53.7	20 47.5	12 28.8	22 42.8	2 2.7	0 52.9	18 15.2	4 47.1	16 57.3	14 33.8	2 28.9	7 45.8
15	21 31 50.3	21 45.2	12 25.6	5♎40.6	2 58.9	0 20.0	18 48.8	4 49.1	16 58.9	14 31.4	2 27.4	7 45.7
16	21 35 46.8	22 42.8	12 22.5	18 18.9	4 1.3	29♌45.9	19 22.6	4 51.0	17 .4	14 29.0	2 25.9	7 45.6
17	21 39 43.4	23 40.5	12 19.3	0♏40.3	5 10.0	29 10.7	19 56.7	4 52.7	17 1.8	14 26.6	2 24.4	7 45.5
18	21 43 40.0	24 38.2	12 16.1	12 48.1	6 24.5	28 34.6	20 30.9	4 54.2	17 3.2	14 24.3	2 22.9	7 45.4
19	21 47 36.5	25 35.9	12 12.9	24 46.3	7 44.7	27 57.9	21 5.5	4 55.5	17 4.4	14 22.0	2 21.4	7 45.4
20	21 51 33.1	26 33.6	12 9.7	6♐39.6	9 10.1	27 20.7	21 40.2	4 56.6	17 5.5	14 19.6	2 20.0	7 45.4
21	21 55 29.6	27 31.4	12 6.6	18 32.6	10 40.6	26 43.4	22 15.1	4 57.5	17 6.5	14 17.3	2 18.5	7D45.5
22	21 59 26.2	28 29.1	12 3.4	0♑29.8	12 15.6	26 6.1	22 50.3	4 58.2	17 7.4	14 15.0	2 17.1	7 45.6
23	22 3 22.7	29 26.9	12 .2	12 35.5	13 54.7	25 29.2	23 25.6	4 58.7	17 8.2	14 12.7	2 15.7	7 45.7
24	22 7 19.3	0♍24.7	11 57.0	24 53.4	15 37.6	24 52.8	24 1.2	4 59.1	17 8.9	14 10.4	2 14.3	7 45.8
25	22 11 15.8	1 22.5	11 53.9	7♒26.3	17 23.8	24 17.1	24 37.0	4 59.2	17 9.5	14 8.2	2 12.9	7 46.0
26	22 15 12.4	2 20.4	11 50.7	20 16.1	19 12.9	23 42.5	25 12.9	4R59.1	17 9.9	14 5.9	2 11.6	7 46.2
27	22 19 8.9	3 18.2	11 47.5	3♓23.6	21 4.4	23 9.1	25 49.1	4 58.8	17 10.3	14 3.7	2 10.2	7 46.5
28	22 23 5.5	4 16.1	11 44.3	16 48.3	22 57.8	22 37.1	26 25.4	4 58.3	17 10.6	14 1.5	2 8.9	7 46.7
29	22 27 2.0	5 14.1	11 41.1	0♈28.6	24 52.9	22 6.8	27 2.0	4 57.7	17 10.8	13 59.4	2 7.6	7 47.1
30	22 30 58.6	6 12.0	11 38.0	14 21.9	26 49.1	21 38.2	27 38.7	4 56.8	17 10.8	13 57.2	2 6.4	7 47.5
31	22 34 55.1	7 10.0	11 34.8	28 24.9	28 46.1	21 11.5	28 15.5	4 55.7	17 10.8	13 55.1	2 5.1	7 47.8
	LATITUDE											
1	20 36 38.5	0 .0	0 .0	3S14.0	4S30.9	4S37.0	1S34.2	1S19.5	2S21.6	0S42.6	0N16.8	11N34.8
4	20 48 28.2	0 .0	0 .0	5 11.0	3 56.8	5 17.1	1 36.0	1 20.2	2 22.3	0 42.6	0 16.7	11 33.5
7	21 0 17.9	0 .0	0 .0	4 30.7	3 13.5	5 56.3	1 37.8	1 20.9	2 22.9	0 42.6	0 16.7	11 32.1
10	21 12 7.5	0 .0	0 .0	1 23.9	2 25.0	6 33.6	1 39.4	1 21.6	2 23.6	0 42.6	0 16.6	11 30.8
13	21 23 57.2	0 .0	0 .0	2N21.4	1 34.9	7 7.3	1 40.8	1 22.3	2 24.3	0 42.6	0 16.6	11 29.4
16	21 35 46.8	0 .0	0 .0	4 47.9	0 46.5	7 36.0	1 42.2	1 23.0	2 25.0	0 42.6	0 16.6	11 28.0
19	21 47 36.5	0 .0	0 .0	5 9.6	0 2.2	7 58.2	1 43.4	1 23.7	2 25.7	0 42.6	0 16.5	11 26.6
22	21 59 26.2	0 .0	0 .0	3 33.6	0N35.8	8 13.0	1 44.5	1 24.4	2 26.4	0 42.6	0 16.5	11 25.2
25	22 11 15.8	0 .0	0 .0	0 30.5	1 6.0	8 19.8	1 45.5	1 25.1	2 27.1	0 42.6	0 16.4	11 23.8
28	22 23 5.5	0 .0	0 .0	2S55.6	1 27.7	8 18.7	1 46.4	1 25.8	2 27.8	0 42.6	0 16.4	11 22.4
31	22 34 55.1	0 .0	0 .0	5 4.0	1 41.0	8 10.2	1 47.2	1 26.5	2 28.5	0 42.5	0 16.3	11 21.0
	RIGHT ASCENSION											
1	20 36 38.5	10♌45.3	15♌38.0	22♓38.5	1♌ 4.7	5♍11.8	8♏25.3	2♉15.3	14♉40.7	17♒45.7	5♒ 2.4	7♐57.2
2	20 40 35.1	11 43.5	15 34.9	5♈21.8	0R40.0	5R 1.6	8 55.1	2 19.7	14 43.7	17R43.3	5R .8	7R56.6
3	20 44 31.6	12 41.6	15 31.7	18 11.7	0 20.5	4 49.2	9 25.1	2 23.9	14 46.6	17 40.9	4 59.1	7 56.0
4	20 48 28.2	13 39.6	15 28.5	1♉18.1	0 6.7	4 34.6	9 55.6	2 28.0	14 49.3	17 38.5	4 57.5	7 55.4
5	20 52 24.7	14 37.4	15 25.3	14 50.7	29♋59.1	4 17.9	10 26.3	2 31.8	14 52.0	17 36.1	4 55.8	7 54.9
6	20 56 21.3	15 35.0	15 22.1	28 56.8	29 58.0	3 59.0	10 57.4	2 35.6	14 54.6	17 33.7	4 54.2	7 54.4
7	21 0 17.9	16 32.5	15 18.9	13♊37.8	0♌ 3.5	3 38.1	11 28.8	2 39.1	14 57.1	17 31.3	4 52.5	7 53.9
8	21 4 14.4	17 29.9	15 15.8	28 47.5	0D16.1	3 15.2	12 .6	2 42.5	14 59.5	17 29.0	4 50.9	7 53.5
9	21 8 11.0	18 27.2	15 12.6	14♋10.5	0 35.6	2 50.3	12 32.7	2 45.7	15 1.8	17 26.6	4 49.3	7 53.1
10	21 12 7.5	19 24.2	15 9.4	29 26.5	1 2.3	2 23.6	13 5.1	2 48.7	15 4.0	17 24.2	4 47.7	7 52.7
11	21 16 4.1	20 21.2	15 6.2	14♌16.1	1 36.1	1 55.2	13 37.8	2 51.5	15 6.1	17 21.8	4 46.1	7 52.4
12	21 20 .6	21 18.0	15 3.0	28 26.4	2 17.0	1 25.1	14 10.9	2 54.1	15 8.0	17 19.4	4 44.5	7 52.1
13	21 23 57.2	22 14.6	14 59.8	11♍53.0	3 4.9	0 53.6	14 44.2	2 56.6	15 9.9	17 17.0	4 42.9	7 51.8
14	21 27 53.7	23 11.1	14 56.6	24 39.1	3 59.7	0 20.8	15 17.9	2 58.9	15 11.7	17 14.6	4 41.3	7 51.6
15	21 31 50.3	24 7.5	14 53.4	6♎52.5	5 1.2	29♌46.8	15 51.8	3 .9	15 13.4	17 12.3	4 39.8	7 51.3
16	21 35 46.8	25 3.7	14 50.2	18 43.2	6 9.1	29 11.9	16 26.1	3 2.8	15 15.0	17 9.9	4 38.2	7 51.1
17	21 39 43.4	25 59.8	14 47.1	0♏21.9	7 23.3	28 36.2	17 .7	3 4.6	15 16.5	17 7.5	4 36.7	7 51.0
18	21 43 40.0	26 55.8	14 43.9	11 58.6	8 43.3	27 59.9	17 35.6	3 6.1	15 17.8	17 5.2	4 35.1	7 50.9
19	21 47 36.5	27 51.6	14 40.7	23 42.3	10 8.7	27 23.3	18 10.8	3 7.4	15 19.1	17 2.8	4 33.6	7 50.8
20	21 51 33.1	28 47.3	14 37.5	5♐39.9	11 39.3	26 46.6	18 46.3	3 8.5	15 20.3	17 .5	4 32.1	7 50.7
21	21 55 29.6	29 42.9	14 34.3	17 55.9	13 14.5	26 10.0	19 22.0	3 9.5	15 21.3	16 58.2	4 30.7	7 50.7
22	21 59 26.2	0♍38.4	14 31.1	0♑31.7	14 53.8	25 33.7	19 58.1	3 10.3	15 22.3	16 55.9	4 29.2	7 50.7
23	22 3 22.7	1 33.7	14 27.9	13 25.0	16 36.8	24 58.0	20 34.4	3 10.8	15 23.1	16 53.6	4 27.7	7D50.8
24	22 7 19.3	2 28.9	14 24.7	26 30.8	18 22.9	24 23.1	21 11.0	3 11.2	15 23.9	16 51.3	4 26.3	7 50.8
25	22 11 15.8	3 24.0	14 21.5	9♒42.5	20 11.5	23 49.2	21 47.9	3 11.4	15 24.5	16 49.0	4 24.9	7 50.9
26	22 15 12.4	4 19.0	14 18.3	22 53.5	22 2.3	23 16.4	22 25.1	3 11.4	15 25.1	16 46.8	4 23.5	7 51.1
27	22 19 8.9	5 14.0	14 15.1	5♓59.8	23 54.6	22 45.1	23 2.5	3R11.2	15 25.5	16 44.6	4 22.1	7 51.3
28	22 23 5.5	6 8.8	14 11.9	19 .5	25 48.0	22 15.3	23 40.3	3 10.8	15 25.8	16 42.3	4 20.7	7 51.5
29	22 27 2.0	7 3.5	14 8.7	1♈58.7	27 42.2	21 47.4	24 18.3	3 10.3	15 26.1	16 40.2	4 19.5	7 51.7
30	22 30 58.6	7 58.2	14 5.5	15 .2	29 36.5	21 21.2	24 56.5	3 9.5	15 26.2	16 38.0	4 18.1	7 52.0
31	22 34 55.1	8 52.7	14 2.3	28 12.8	1♍30.7	20 57.1	25 35.1	3 8.5	15 26.2	16 35.9	4 16.8	7 52.3
	DECLINATION											
1	20 36 38.5	18N10.8	0N17.7	6S41.8	15N45.3	5N21.3	16S43.8	11N37.1	14N29.5	16S59.4	19S15.3	10S10.7
4	20 48 28.2	17 24.8	0 17.7	7N10.9	16 31.7	4 52.7	17 13.7	11 40.8	14 31.3	17 1.5	19 16.4	10 11.8
7	21 0 17.9	16 36.2	0 17.8	18 2.6	17 16.5	4 32.3	17 43.7	11 44.0	14 32.8	17 3.6	19 17.6	10 12.9
10	21 12 7.5	15 45.2	0 17.8	19 15.4	17 54.5	4 20.9	18 13.6	11 46.6	14 34.0	17 5.8	19 18.7	10 14.1
13	21 23 57.2	14 52.0	0 17.8	10 13.4	18 20.5	4 18.6	18 43.2	11 48.6	14 35.0	17 7.9	19 19.8	10 15.3
16	21 35 46.8	13 56.6	0 17.9	2S44.4	18 29.7	4 25.6	19 12.6	11 50.0	14 35.7	17 9.9	19 20.8	10 16.6
19	21 47 36.5	12 59.2	0 17.9	13 57.0	18 17.8	4 41.3	19 41.5	11 50.8	14 36.1	17 12.0	19 21.9	10 18.0
22	21 59 26.2	12 .0	0 18.0	19 52.6	17 41.5	5 4.4	20 9.9	11 51.1	14 36.3	17 14.0	19 22.9	10 19.4
25	22 11 15.8	10 59.1	0 18.0	17 55.1	16 40.0	5 33.3	20 37.6	11 50.7	14 36.2	17 16.0	19 23.9	10 20.8
28	22 23 5.5	9 56.6	0 18.1	7 54.3	15 14.5	6 6.2	21 4.6	11 49.8	14 35.8	17 17.9	19 24.8	10 22.3
31	22 34 55.1	8 52.7	0 18.1	6N10.3	13 28.7	6 41.0	21 30.7	11 48.3	14 35.2	17 19.7	19 25.7	10 23.9

SEPTEMBER 1999

LONGITUDE

DAY	EPHEM. SID. TIME	☉	☊	☽	☿	♀	♂	♃	♄	♅	♆	♇
	h m s	° ′	° ′	° ′	° ′	° ′	° ′	° ′	° ′	° ′	° ′	° ′
1	22 38 51.7	8♍ 8.0	11♌31.6	12♉34.3	0♍43.6	20♌46.8	28♏52.6	4♉54.4	17♉10.6	13♒53.0	2♒ 3.9	7♐48.3
2	22 42 48.3	9 6.1	11 28.4	26 46.9	2 41.4	20 R 24.3	29 29.8	4 R 53.0	17 R 10.3	13 R 50.9	2 R 2.6	7 48.7
3	22 46 44.8	10 4.1	11 25.3	10♊59.9	4 39.1	20 4.1	0♐ 7.3	4 51.3	17 10.0	13 48.8	2 1.4	7 49.2
4	22 50 41.4	11 2.2	11 22.1	25 10.9	6 36.6	19 46.1	0 44.9	4 49.4	17 9.5	13 46.7	2 .3	7 49.7
5	22 54 37.9	12 .4	11 18.9	9♋18.0	8 33.6	19 30.5	1 22.6	4 47.3	17 8.9	13 44.7	1 59.1	7 50.2
6	22 58 34.5	12 58.6	11 15.7	23 19.4	10 30.0	19 17.2	2 .6	4 45.0	17 8.2	13 42.7	1 58.0	7 50.8
7	23 2 31.0	13 56.8	11 12.5	7♌13.3	12 25.8	19 6.4	2 38.7	4 42.6	17 7.4	13 40.7	1 56.9	7 51.4
8	23 6 27.6	14 55.0	11 9.4	20 57.9	14 20.7	18 58.0	3 17.0	4 39.9	17 6.5	13 38.8	1 55.8	7 52.1
9	23 10 24.1	15 53.3	11 6.2	4♍31.0	16 14.7	18 52.1	3 55.4	4 37.0	17 5.5	13 36.9	1 54.7	7 52.8
10	23 14 20.7	16 51.6	11 3.0	17 50.8	18 7.7	18 48.5	4 34.0	4 34.0	17 4.4	13 35.0	1 53.7	7 53.5
11	23 18 17.2	17 49.9	10 59.8	0♎55.7	19 59.7	18 47.3	5 12.8	4 30.7	17 3.2	13 33.1	1 52.6	7 54.2
12	23 22 13.8	18 48.3	10 56.7	13 44.8	21 50.7	18 D 48.4	5 51.7	4 27.3	17 1.8	13 31.3	1 51.7	7 55.0
13	23 26 10.3	19 46.6	10 53.5	26 18.3	23 40.6	18 51.8	6 30.8	4 23.6	17 .4	13 29.5	1 50.7	7 55.8
14	23 30 6.9	20 45.1	10 50.3	8♏37.1	25 29.5	18 57.5	7 10.1	4 19.8	16 58.9	13 27.8	1 49.8	7 56.7
15	23 34 3.4	21 43.5	10 47.1	20 43.6	27 17.2	19 5.4	7 49.5	4 15.8	16 57.2	13 26.1	1 48.8	7 57.5
16	23 37 60.0	22 42.0	10 43.9	2♐40.8	29 3.9	19 15.5	8 29.0	4 11.6	16 55.5	13 24.4	1 48.0	7 58.4
17	23 41 56.5	23 40.5	10 40.8	14 33.0	0♎49.5	19 27.7	9 8.7	4 7.3	16 53.7	13 22.7	1 47.1	7 59.4
18	23 45 53.1	24 39.0	10 37.6	26 24.6	2 34.0	19 41.9	9 48.5	4 2.7	16 51.7	13 21.1	1 46.3	8 .3
19	23 49 49.6	25 37.6	10 34.4	8♑20.7	4 17.5	19 58.2	10 28.5	3 58.1	16 49.7	13 19.6	1 45.5	8 1.4
20	23 53 46.2	26 36.2	10 31.2	20 26.4	5 59.9	20 16.4	11 8.6	3 53.2	16 47.6	13 18.0	1 44.8	8 2.4
21	23 57 42.7	27 34.8	10 28.0	2♒46.3	7 41.3	20 36.4	11 48.9	3 48.1	16 45.4	13 16.5	1 44.0	8 3.5
22	0 1 39.3	28 33.4	10 24.9	15 24.9	9 21.7	20 58.3	12 29.3	3 42.9	16 43.1	13 15.1	1 43.3	8 4.6
23	0 5 35.8	29 32.1	10 21.7	28 25.1	11 1.0	21 22.0	13 9.8	3 37.5	16 40.6	13 13.6	1 42.6	8 5.7
24	0 9 32.4	0♎30.8	10 18.5	11♓48.6	12 39.4	21 47.4	13 50.4	3 32.0	16 38.1	13 12.3	1 42.0	8 6.8
25	0 13 29.0	1 29.5	10 15.3	25 34.8	14 16.9	22 14.4	14 31.2	3 26.3	16 35.5	13 10.9	1 41.3	8 8.0
26	0 17 25.5	2 28.3	10 12.2	9♈41.1	15 53.4	22 43.0	15 12.0	3 20.5	16 32.8	13 9.6	1 40.7	8 9.2
27	0 21 22.1	3 27.1	10 9.0	24 2.9	17 28.9	23 13.2	15 53.1	3 14.5	16 30.0	13 8.4	1 40.2	8 10.5
28	0 25 18.6	4 25.9	10 5.8	8♉33.8	19 3.6	23 44.9	16 34.2	3 8.3	16 27.2	13 7.1	1 39.6	8 11.7
29	0 29 15.2	5 24.8	10 2.6	23 7.3	20 37.4	24 18.1	17 15.4	3 2.1	16 24.2	13 6.0	1 39.1	8 13.0
30	0 33 11.7	6 23.7	9 59.4	7♊37.2	22 10.2	24 52.6	17 56.8	2 55.7	16 21.2	13 4.8	1 38.7	8 14.4

LATITUDE

DAY	EPHEM. SID. TIME	☉	☊	☽	☿	♀	♂	♃	♄	♅	♆	♇
1	22 38 51.7	0 .0	0 .0	5S13.7	1N43.6	8S 5.9	1S47.4	1S26.7	2S28.7	0S42.5	0N16.3	11N20.5
4	22 50 41.4	0 .0	0 .0	3 51.6	1 46.9	7 49.1	1 48.0	1 27.4	2 29.4	0 42.5	0 16.3	11 19.1
7	23 2 31.0	0 .0	0 .0	0 30.2	1 43.8	7 27.6	1 48.5	1 28.0	2 30.1	0 42.5	0 16.2	11 17.8
10	23 14 20.7	0 .0	0 .0	2N59.7	1 35.7	7 2.6	1 48.9	1 28.6	2 30.7	0 42.4	0 16.2	11 16.4
13	23 26 10.3	0 .0	0 .0	4 58.1	1 23.6	6 35.1	1 49.2	1 29.2	2 31.4	0 42.4	0 16.1	11 15.0
16	23 37 60.0	0 .0	0 .0	4 50.5	1 8.2	6 6.0	1 49.4	1 29.7	2 32.0	0 42.3	0 16.0	11 13.7
19	23 49 49.6	0 .0	0 .0	2 52.6	0 50.5	5 36.0	1 49.5	1 30.2	2 32.6	0 42.2	0 16.0	11 12.3
22	0 1 39.3	0 .0	0 .0	0S17.7	0 31.0	5 5.7	1 49.6	1 30.7	2 33.1	0 42.2	0 15.9	11 11.0
25	0 13 29.0	0 .0	0 .0	3 32.0	0 10.4	4 35.5	1 49.5	1 31.1	2 33.7	0 42.1	0 15.9	11 9.7
28	0 25 18.6	0 .0	0 .0	5 5.5	0S11.1	4 5.7	1 49.3	1 31.5	2 34.2	0 42.0	0 15.8	11 8.5

RIGHT ASCENSION

DAY	EPHEM. SID. TIME	☉	☊	☽	☿	♀	♂	♃	♄	♅	♆	♇
1	22 38 51.7	9♍47.2	13♌59.1	11♉44.5	3♍24.6	20♌35.1	26♏13.8	3♉ 7.4	15♉26.1	16♒33.7	4♒15.6	7♐52.6
2	22 42 48.3	10 41.6	13 55.9	25 41.6	5 17.8	20 R 15.3	26 52.9	3 R 6.0	15 R 26.0	16 R 31.6	4 R 14.3	7 53.0
3	22 46 44.8	11 35.9	13 52.7	10♊ 6.1	7 10.1	19 57.8	27 32.2	3 4.5	15 25.6	16 29.6	4 13.1	7 53.4
4	22 50 41.4	12 30.2	13 49.5	24 54.0	9 1.5	19 42.6	28 11.7	3 2.7	15 25.2	16 27.5	4 11.8	7 53.9
5	22 54 37.9	13 24.4	13 46.3	9♋54.3	10 51.6	19 29.8	28 51.6	3 .8	15 24.7	16 25.5	4 10.6	7 54.3
6	22 58 34.5	14 18.5	13 43.1	24 51.4	12 40.5	19 19.4	29 31.6	2 58.7	15 24.1	16 23.4	4 9.5	7 54.8
7	23 2 31.0	15 12.6	13 39.9	9♌29.3	14 28.1	19 11.5	0♐12.0	2 56.4	15 23.4	16 21.5	4 8.3	7 55.4
8	23 6 27.6	16 6.7	13 36.7	23 36.0	16 14.3	19 5.9	0 52.6	2 53.9	15 22.5	16 19.5	4 7.2	7 55.9
9	23 10 24.1	17 .7	13 33.5	7♍ 6.0	17 59.1	19 2.7	1 33.4	2 51.2	15 21.6	16 17.6	4 6.1	7 56.5
10	23 14 20.7	17 54.6	13 30.3	20 .1	19 42.6	19 2.0	2 14.5	2 48.3	15 20.6	16 15.7	4 5.0	7 57.1
11	23 18 17.2	18 48.6	13 27.1	2♎23.6	21 24.7	19 D 3.5	2 55.8	2 45.2	15 19.4	16 13.8	4 4.0	7 57.8
12	23 22 13.8	19 42.5	13 23.9	14 24.7	23 5.4	19 7.4	3 37.4	2 42.0	15 18.2	16 12.0	4 3.0	7 58.5
13	23 26 10.3	20 36.3	13 20.7	26 12.1	24 44.8	19 13.6	4 19.2	2 38.6	15 16.8	16 10.2	4 2.0	7 59.2
14	23 30 6.9	21 30.2	13 17.5	7♏54.8	26 23.0	19 22.0	5 1.3	2 35.0	15 15.3	16 8.4	4 1.0	7 60.0
15	23 34 3.4	22 24.0	13 14.3	19 40.6	27 59.9	19 32.6	5 43.6	2 31.2	15 13.8	16 6.7	4 .1	8 .8
16	23 37 60.0	23 17.8	13 11.1	1♐36.1	29 35.7	19 45.3	6 26.1	2 27.2	15 12.1	16 5.0	3 59.2	8 1.6
17	23 41 56.5	24 11.6	13 7.9	13 45.7	1♎10.3	20 .0	7 8.8	2 23.1	15 10.4	16 3.3	3 58.3	8 2.5
18	23 45 53.1	25 5.4	13 4.7	26 11.7	2 43.8	20 16.8	7 51.8	2 18.8	15 8.5	16 1.7	3 57.5	8 3.3
19	23 49 49.6	25 59.2	13 1.4	8♑53.5	4 16.4	20 35.6	8 35.0	2 14.4	15 6.6	16 .2	3 56.7	8 4.3
20	23 53 46.2	26 53.0	12 58.2	21 48.1	5 47.9	20 56.2	9 18.4	2 9.7	15 4.5	15 58.6	3 55.9	8 5.3
21	23 57 42.7	27 46.8	12 55.0	4♒51.2	7 18.5	21 18.6	10 2.0	2 4.9	15 2.4	15 57.1	3 55.1	8 6.2
22	0 1 39.3	28 40.6	12 51.8	17 58.1	8 48.3	21 42.8	10 45.8	1 60.0	15 .1	15 55.6	3 54.4	8 7.3
23	0 5 35.8	29 34.4	12 48.6	1♓ 5.4	10 17.2	22 8.7	11 29.8	1 54.9	14 57.8	15 54.2	3 53.7	8 8.3
24	0 9 32.4	0♎28.2	12 45.4	14 12.4	11 45.3	22 36.3	12 14.0	1 49.6	14 55.4	15 52.8	3 53.0	8 9.4
25	0 13 29.0	1 22.1	12 42.2	27 21.0	13 12.8	23 5.5	12 58.4	1 44.2	14 52.8	15 51.4	3 52.4	8 10.5
26	0 17 25.5	2 16.1	12 39.0	10♈35.9	14 39.5	23 36.2	13 42.9	1 38.6	14 50.2	15 50.1	3 51.8	8 11.6
27	0 21 22.1	3 10.0	12 35.8	24 3.5	16 5.6	24 8.4	14 27.7	1 32.9	14 47.5	15 48.8	3 51.2	8 12.8
28	0 25 18.6	4 4.0	12 32.5	7♉50.4	17 31.1	24 41.9	15 12.7	1 27.1	14 44.7	15 47.6	3 50.6	8 13.9
29	0 29 15.2	4 58.1	12 29.3	22 1.2	18 55.9	25 16.9	15 57.8	1 21.1	14 41.8	15 46.4	3 50.1	8 15.2
30	0 33 11.7	5 52.2	12 26.1	6♊36.6	20 20.3	25 53.1	16 43.1	1 15.0	14 38.9	15 45.2	3 49.6	8 16.4

DECLINATION

DAY	EPHEM. SID. TIME	☉	☊	☽	☿	♀	♂	♃	♄	♅	♆	♇
1	22 38 51.7	8N31.1	0N18.1	10N37.4	12N49.8	6N52.7	21S39.2	11N47.7	14N35.0	17S20.3	19S26.0	10S24.4
4	22 50 41.4	7 25.6	0 18.2	19 29.5	10 44.4	7 27.1	22 4.0	11 45.4	14 34.0	17 22.1	19 26.9	10 26.0
7	23 2 31.0	6 18.9	0 18.2	17 58.7	8 29.7	7 59.6	22 27.7	11 42.5	14 32.8	17 23.8	19 27.7	10 27.7
10	23 14 20.7	5 11.3	0 18.3	7 33.6	6 9.7	8 28.8	22 50.1	11 39.1	14 31.3	17 25.4	19 28.5	10 29.3
13	23 26 10.3	4 2.9	0 18.3	5S31.0	3 47.4	8 54.1	23 11.3	11 35.1	14 29.6	17 26.9	19 29.2	10 31.0
16	23 37 60.0	2 53.8	0 18.4	15 56.6	1 24.9	9 14.6	23 31.1	11 30.5	14 27.6	17 28.3	19 29.8	10 32.8
19	23 49 49.6	1 44.3	0 18.4	20 18.2	0S56.0	9 30.1	23 49.4	11 25.5	14 25.4	17 29.6	19 30.4	10 34.5
22	0 1 39.3	0 34.4	0 18.5	16 29.7	3 14.0	9 40.3	24 6.1	11 19.9	14 23.0	17 30.8	19 31.0	10 36.3
25	0 13 29.0	0S35.6	0 18.5	4 59.9	5 28.3	9 45.0	24 21.1	11 13.9	14 20.4	17 32.0	19 31.5	10 38.1
28	0 25 18.6	1 45.7	0 18.6	9N31.8	7 38.1	9 44.1	24 34.4	11 7.5	14 17.5	17 33.0	19 31.9	10 39.9

OCTOBER 1999

LONGITUDE

DAY	EPHEM. SID. TIME	☉	☊	☽	☿	♀	♂	♃	♄	♅	♆	♇
	h m s	° ′	° ′	° ′	° ′	° ′	° ′	° ′	° ′	° ′	° ′	° ′
1	0 37 8.3	7♎22.6	9♌56.3	21♊58.8	23♎42.2	25♌28.5	18♐38.3	2♉49.1	16♉18.0	13♒ 3.7	1♒38.2	8♐15.7
2	0 41 4.8	8 21.6	9 53.1	6♋ 9.0	25 13.3	26 5.7	19 19.9	2 R 42.4	16 R 14.8	13 R 2.7	1 R 37.8	8 17.1
3	0 45 1.4	9 20.6	9 49.9	20 6.4	26 43.6	26 44.1	20 1.6	2 35.6	16 11.5	13 1.7	1 37.4	8 18.5
4	0 48 57.9	10 19.7	9 46.7	3♌51.0	28 12.9	27 23.7	20 43.5	2 28.7	16 8.1	13 .7	1 37.1	8 20.0
5	0 52 54.5	11 18.8	9 43.6	17 23.2	29 41.5	28 4.5	21 25.4	2 21.7	16 4.6	12 59.8	1 36.8	8 21.4
6	0 56 51.0	12 17.9	9 40.4	0♍43.7	1♏ 9.1	28 46.4	22 7.5	2 14.5	16 1.1	12 58.9	1 36.5	8 22.9
7	1 0 47.6	13 17.1	9 37.2	13 52.9	2 35.8	29 29.3	22 49.7	2 7.3	15 57.5	12 58.1	1 36.3	8 24.4
8	1 4 44.1	14 16.3	9 34.0	26 51.0	4 1.7	0♍13.3	23 32.0	1 59.9	15 53.8	12 57.3	1 36.0	8 26.0
9	1 8 40.7	15 15.5	9 30.8	9♎37.7	5 26.6	0 58.2	24 14.4	1 52.5	15 50.0	12 56.6	1 35.9	8 27.6
10	1 12 37.2	16 14.9	9 27.7	22 12.8	6 50.6	1 44.2	24 57.0	1 45.0	15 46.2	12 56.0	1 35.7	8 29.2
11	1 16 33.8	17 14.2	9 24.5	4♏36.2	8 13.6	2 31.0	25 39.6	1 37.4	15 42.3	12 55.4	1 35.6	8 30.8
12	1 20 30.3	18 13.5	9 21.3	16 48.3	9 35.6	3 18.7	26 22.3	1 29.7	15 38.4	12 54.8	1 35.5	8 32.5
13	1 24 26.9	19 12.9	9 18.1	28 50.5	10 56.5	4 7.2	27 5.1	1 21.9	15 34.3	12 54.2	1 35.5	8 34.1
14	1 28 23.4	20 12.3	9 15.0	10♐45.0	12 16.3	4 56.6	27 48.1	1 14.1	15 30.3	12 53.8	1 35.5	8 35.8
15	1 32 20.0	21 11.8	9 11.8	22 34.7	13 35.0	5 46.7	28 31.1	1 6.2	15 26.1	12 53.3	1 35.5	8 37.6
16	1 36 16.6	22 11.2	9 8.6	4♑23.9	14 52.4	6 37.6	29 14.2	0 58.3	15 21.9	12 52.9	1 D 35.6	8 39.3
17	1 40 13.1	23 10.7	9 5.4	16 17.1	16 8.5	7 29.2	29 57.4	0 50.3	15 17.6	12 52.6	1 35.6	8 41.1
18	1 44 9.7	24 10.3	9 2.2	28 19.6	17 23.1	8 21.6	0♑40.8	0 42.3	15 13.3	12 52.3	1 35.8	8 42.9
19	1 48 6.2	25 9.8	8 59.1	10♒36.9	18 36.3	9 14.6	1 24.2	0 34.2	15 8.9	12 52.1	1 35.9	8 44.7
20	1 52 2.8	26 9.4	8 55.9	23 14.1	19 47.7	10 8.3	2 7.6	0 26.1	15 4.5	12 51.9	1 36.1	8 46.5
21	1 55 59.3	27 9.0	8 52.7	6♓15.7	20 57.4	11 2.7	2 51.2	0 18.0	15 .1	12 51.8	1 36.3	8 48.4
22	1 59 55.9	28 8.7	8 49.5	19 44.8	22 5.2	11 57.6	3 34.9	0 9.9	14 55.6	12 51.7	1 36.6	8 50.2
23	2 3 52.4	29 8.3	8 46.4	3♈42.1	23 10.7	12 53.2	4 18.6	0 1.8	14 51.0	12 51.7	1 36.9	8 52.1
24	2 7 49.0	0♏ 8.0	8 43.2	18 5.4	24 14.0	13 49.3	5 2.4	29♈53.6	14 46.4	12 51.7	1 37.2	8 54.1
25	2 11 45.5	1 7.8	8 40.0	2♉49.4	25 14.6	14 46.1	5 46.3	29 45.5	14 41.8	12 51.7	1 37.5	8 56.0
26	2 15 42.1	2 7.6	8 36.8	17 46.0	26 12.3	15 43.3	6 30.3	29 37.4	14 37.2	12 D 51.9	1 37.9	8 57.9
27	2 19 38.6	3 7.4	8 33.6	2♊45.8	27 6.9	16 41.1	7 14.4	29 29.3	14 32.5	12 52.0	1 38.3	8 59.9
28	2 23 35.2	4 7.2	8 30.5	17 39.4	27 58.0	17 39.5	7 58.5	29 21.2	14 27.8	12 52.2	1 38.8	9 1.9
29	2 27 31.7	5 7.1	8 27.3	2♋19.3	28 45.1	18 38.3	8 42.7	29 13.1	14 23.0	12 52.5	1 39.3	9 3.9
30	2 31 28.3	6 7.0	8 24.1	16 40.7	29 27.9	19 37.6	9 27.0	29 5.1	14 18.3	12 52.8	1 39.8	9 6.0
31	2 35 24.9	7 7.0	8 20.9	0♌41.5	0♐ 5.9	20 37.4	10 11.4	28 57.2	14 13.5	12 53.3	1 40.4	9 8.0

LATITUDE

DAY	EPHEM. SID. TIME	☉	☊	☽	☿	♀	♂	♃	♄	♅	♆	♇
1	0 37 8.3	0 .0	0 .0	3S52.6	0S32.9	3S36.5	1S49.0	1S31.8	2S34.7	0S42.0	0N15.8	11N 7.2
4	0 48 57.9	0 .0	0 .0	0 39.9	0 54.7	3 8.2	1 48.7	1 32.1	2 35.1	0 41.9	0 15.7	11 6.0
7	1 0 47.6	0 .0	0 .0	2N44.5	1 16.1	2 40.8	1 48.2	1 32.3	2 35.5	0 41.8	0 15.6	11 4.8
10	1 12 37.2	0 .0	0 .0	4 46.7	1 36.9	2 14.5	1 47.6	1 32.5	2 35.9	0 41.7	0 15.6	11 3.7
13	1 24 26.9	0 .0	0 .0	4 46.4	1 56.5	1 49.3	1 47.0	1 32.6	2 36.2	0 41.6	0 15.5	11 2.6
16	1 36 16.6	0 .0	0 .0	2 56.2	2 14.6	1 25.2	1 46.3	1 32.6	2 36.5	0 41.5	0 15.5	11 1.5
19	1 48 6.2	0 .0	0 .0	0S 4.2	2 30.6	1 2.4	1 45.5	1 32.6	2 36.7	0 41.4	0 15.4	11 .5
22	1 59 55.9	0 .0	0 .0	3 14.5	2 43.9	0 40.7	1 44.6	1 32.5	2 36.9	0 41.3	0 15.3	10 59.5
25	2 11 45.5	0 .0	0 .0	4 58.6	2 53.6	0 20.3	1 43.6	1 32.3	2 37.0	0 41.3	0 15.3	10 58.6
28	2 23 35.2	0 .0	0 .0	3 54.4	2 58.6	0 1.1	1 42.6	1 32.0	2 37.1	0 41.2	0 15.2	10 57.7
31	2 35 24.9	0 .0	0 .0	0 41.4	2 57.2	0N16.9	1 41.5	1 31.7	2 37.1	0 41.1	0 15.2	10 56.9

RIGHT ASCENSION

DAY	EPHEM. SID. TIME	☉	☊	☽	☿	♀	♂	♃	♄	♅	♆	♇
1	0 37 8.3	6♎46.4	12♌22.9	21♊31.0	21♎44.1	26♌30.7	17♐28.6	1♉ 8.8	14♉35.8	15♒44.1	3♒49.2	8♐17.7
2	0 41 4.8	7 40.7	12 19.7	6♋33.1	23 7.4	27 9.4	18 14.2	1 R 2.4	14 R 32.7	15 R 43.1	3 R 48.8	8 19.0
3	0 45 1.4	8 35.1	12 16.5	21 27.7	24 30.3	27 49.2	19 .1	0 56.0	14 29.5	15 42.1	3 48.4	8 20.3
4	0 48 57.9	9 29.5	12 13.3	6♌ .2	25 52.7	28 30.1	19 46.1	0 49.4	14 26.2	15 41.1	3 48.0	8 21.7
5	0 52 54.5	10 24.0	12 10.0	20 .3	27 14.6	29 12.1	20 32.2	0 42.7	14 22.8	15 40.2	3 47.7	8 23.1
6	0 56 51.0	11 18.7	12 6.8	3♍24.0	28 36.1	29 55.1	21 18.5	0 35.9	14 19.3	15 39.3	3 47.4	8 24.5
7	1 0 47.6	12 13.4	12 3.6	16 13.0	29 57.1	0♍39.0	22 5.0	0 28.9	14 15.8	15 38.5	3 47.2	8 25.9
8	1 4 44.1	13 8.2	12 .4	28 33.3	1♏17.7	1 23.9	22 51.6	0 21.9	14 12.2	15 37.7	3 46.9	8 27.4
9	1 8 40.7	14 3.1	11 57.2	10♎32.5	2 37.8	2 9.5	23 38.4	0 14.8	14 8.5	15 36.9	3 46.8	8 28.9
10	1 12 37.2	14 58.2	11 54.0	22 19.3	3 57.5	2 56.1	24 25.3	0 7.7	14 4.8	15 36.3	3 46.7	8 30.5
11	1 16 33.8	15 53.3	11 50.7	4♏ 2.0	5 16.6	3 43.4	25 12.4	0 .5	14 1.0	15 35.6	3 46.5	8 32.0
12	1 20 30.3	16 48.6	11 47.5	15 47.6	6 35.2	4 31.4	25 59.6	29♈53.1	13 57.1	15 35.0	3 46.5	8 33.6
13	1 24 26.9	17 44.0	11 44.3	27 41.8	7 53.1	5 20.2	26 46.8	29 45.7	13 53.2	15 34.5	3 46.4	8 35.2
14	1 28 23.4	18 39.5	11 41.1	9♐48.3	9 10.5	6 9.6	27 34.3	29 38.3	13 49.1	15 34.0	3 46.4	8 36.8
15	1 32 20.0	19 35.1	11 37.8	22 8.4	10 27.1	6 59.7	28 21.8	29 30.7	13 45.1	15 33.6	3 46.4	8 38.5
16	1 36 16.6	20 30.9	11 34.6	4♑41.3	11 42.9	7 50.4	29 9.4	29 23.2	13 41.0	15 33.2	3 D 46.5	8 40.1
17	1 40 13.1	21 26.8	11 31.4	17 24.1	12 57.9	8 41.7	29 57.2	29 15.6	13 36.8	15 32.8	3 46.6	8 41.8
18	1 44 9.7	22 22.8	11 28.2	0♒13.2	14 11.8	9 33.6	0♑45.0	29 7.9	13 32.5	15 32.5	3 46.7	8 43.5
19	1 48 6.2	23 19.0	11 25.0	13 5.1	15 24.7	10 26.0	1 33.0	29 .2	13 28.3	15 32.3	3 46.9	8 45.3
20	1 52 2.8	24 15.4	11 21.7	25 58.1	16 36.3	11 18.9	2 21.0	28 52.5	13 23.9	15 32.1	3 47.1	8 47.0
21	1 55 59.3	25 11.9	11 18.5	8♓52.5	17 46.5	12 12.3	3 9.1	28 44.8	13 19.6	15 31.9	3 47.3	8 48.8
22	1 59 55.9	26 8.5	11 15.3	21 51.5	18 55.1	13 6.2	3 57.3	28 37.1	13 15.1	15 31.9	3 47.6	8 50.6
23	2 3 52.4	27 5.4	11 12.1	5♈ .8	20 1.9	14 .5	4 45.5	28 29.3	13 10.7	15 31.8	3 47.9	8 52.5
24	2 7 49.0	28 2.3	11 8.8	18 27.8	21 6.7	14 55.3	5 33.9	28 21.5	13 6.2	15 31.8	3 48.2	8 54.3
25	2 11 45.5	28 59.5	11 5.6	2♉20.1	22 9.1	15 50.5	6 22.2	28 13.8	13 1.7	15 D 31.9	3 48.6	8 56.2
26	2 15 42.1	29 56.8	11 2.4	16 43.2	23 8.9	16 46.1	7 10.7	28 6.1	12 57.1	15 32.0	3 49.0	8 58.1
27	2 19 38.6	0♏54.4	10 59.2	1♊38.0	24 5.7	17 42.1	7 59.2	27 58.3	12 52.5	15 32.1	3 49.4	8 60.0
28	2 23 35.2	1 52.1	10 55.9	16 57.9	24 59.1	18 38.5	8 47.7	27 50.6	12 47.9	15 32.4	3 49.9	9 1.9
29	2 27 31.7	2 49.9	10 52.7	2♋28.4	25 48.7	19 35.2	9 36.3	27 42.9	12 43.2	15 32.6	3 50.4	9 3.9
30	2 31 28.3	3 48.0	10 49.5	17 50.2	26 34.1	20 32.3	10 24.9	27 35.3	12 38.5	15 32.9	3 50.9	9 5.8
31	2 35 24.9	4 46.4	10 46.2	2♌44.6	27 14.6	21 29.8	11 13.6	27 27.7	12 33.9	15 33.4	3 51.6	9 7.9

DECLINATION

DAY	EPHEM. SID. TIME	☉	☊	☽	☿	♀	♂	♃	♄	♅	♆	♇
1	0 37 8.3	2S55.6	0N18.6	19N19.5	9S42.6	9N37.6	24S45.7	11N .6	14N14.5	17S33.9	19S32.3	10S41.7
4	0 48 57.9	4 5.3	0 18.6	18 38.6	11 41.4	9 25.7	24 55.2	10 53.4	14 11.2	17 34.7	19 32.6	10 43.5
7	1 0 47.6	5 14.6	0 18.7	8 52.1	13 33.9	9 8.3	25 2.6	10 45.9	14 7.8	17 35.3	19 32.8	10 45.3
10	1 12 37.2	6 23.4	0 18.7	4S12.7	15 19.4	8 45.7	25 8.0	10 38.1	14 4.3	17 35.8	19 33.0	10 47.1
13	1 24 26.9	7 31.3	0 18.8	15 14.3	16 57.1	8 18.0	25 11.3	10 30.1	14 .5	17 36.2	19 33.1	10 48.9
16	1 36 16.6	8 38.3	0 18.8	20 25.7	18 26.4	7 45.5	25 12.4	10 21.9	13 56.7	17 36.5	19 33.2	10 50.7
19	1 48 6.2	9 44.2	0 18.9	17 38.5	19 46.3	7 8.4	25 11.3	10 13.5	13 52.8	17 36.7	19 33.1	10 52.5
22	1 59 55.9	10 48.8	0 18.9	7 2.5	20 55.6	6 26.9	25 7.9	10 5.2	13 48.7	17 36.7	19 33.0	10 54.3
25	2 11 45.5	11 52.0	0 18.9	7N46.2	21 52.9	5 41.2	25 2.3	9 56.8	13 44.6	17 36.6	19 32.9	10 56.0
28	2 23 35.2	12 53.5	0 19.0	18 58.5	22 36.3	4 51.6	24 54.3	9 48.5	13 40.4	17 36.4	19 32.7	10 57.8
31	2 35 24.9	13 53.2	0 19.0	19 19.6	23 3.3	3 58.5	24 44.0	9 40.3	13 36.2	17 36.0	19 32.4	10 59.5

NOVEMBER 1999

LONGITUDE

DAY	EPHEM. SID. TIME	☉	☊	☽	☿	♀	♂	♃	♄	♅	♆	♇
	h m s	° ′	° ′	° ′	° ′	° ′	° ′	° ′	° ′	° ′	° ′	° ′
1	2 39 21.4	8♏ 7.0	8♌17.8	14♌21.9	0♐38.5	21♍37.7	10♑55.9	28♈49.2	14♉ 8.7	12♒53.7	1♒41.0	9♐10.1
2	2 43 18.0	9 7.0	8 14.6	27 43.6	1 5.2	22 38.3	11 40.4	28R41.3	14R 3.9	12 54.2	1 41.6	9 12.2
3	2 47 14.5	10 7.1	8 11.4	10♍48.9	1 25.4	23 39.4	12 25.0	28 33.5	13 59.1	12 54.7	1 42.3	9 14.3
4	2 51 11.1	11 7.2	8 8.2	23 40.1	1 38.3	24 40.9	13 9.6	28 25.7	13 54.2	12 55.3	1 43.0	9 16.4
5	2 55 7.6	12 7.3	8 5.0	6♎19.5	1 43.5	25 42.8	13 54.3	28 18.1	13 49.4	12 55.9	1 43.7	9 18.5
6	2 59 4.2	13 7.5	8 1.9	18 48.5	1R40.2	26 45.1	14 39.1	28 10.4	13 44.5	12 56.6	1 44.4	9 20.7
7	3 3 .7	14 7.7	7 58.7	1♏ 8.1	1 27.8	27 47.7	15 24.0	28 2.9	13 39.7	12 57.3	1 45.2	9 22.8
8	3 6 57.3	15 7.9	7 55.5	13 19.3	1 6.0	28 50.7	16 8.9	27 55.5	13 34.8	12 58.1	1 46.0	9 25.0
9	3 10 53.8	16 8.1	7 52.3	25 22.6	0 34.2	29 54.1	16 53.9	27 48.1	13 30.0	12 58.9	1 46.9	9 27.2
10	3 14 50.4	17 8.4	7 49.2	7♐19.1	29♏52.6	0♎57.7	17 39.0	27 40.9	13 25.1	12 59.8	1 47.8	9 29.4
11	3 18 47.0	18 8.7	7 46.0	19 10.3	29 1.3	2 1.7	18 24.1	27 33.7	13 20.3	13 .7	1 48.7	9 31.6
12	3 22 43.5	19 9.1	7 42.8	0♑58.4	28 1.0	3 6.0	19 9.3	27 26.7	13 15.5	13 1.7	1 49.6	9 33.8
13	3 26 40.1	20 9.5	7 39.6	12 46.3	26 52.8	4 10.7	19 54.5	27 19.8	13 10.7	13 2.8	1 50.6	9 36.0
14	3 30 36.6	21 9.8	7 36.4	24 38.0	25 38.3	5 15.6	20 39.8	27 13.0	13 5.9	13 3.8	1 51.6	9 38.2
15	3 34 33.2	22 10.3	7 33.3	6♒38.0	24 19.5	6 20.8	21 25.2	27 6.3	13 1.1	13 5.0	1 52.7	9 40.5
16	3 38 29.7	23 10.7	7 30.1	18 51.5	22 58.8	7 26.2	22 10.6	26 59.8	12 56.4	13 6.2	1 53.8	9 42.8
17	3 42 26.3	24 11.1	7 26.9	1♓23.7	21 38.9	8 32.0	22 56.0	26 53.4	12 51.7	13 7.4	1 54.9	9 45.0
18	3 46 22.8	25 11.6	7 23.7	14 19.8	20 22.4	9 38.0	23 41.5	26 47.1	12 47.0	13 8.7	1 56.0	9 47.3
19	3 50 19.4	26 12.1	7 20.6	27 44.0	19 11.7	10 44.2	24 27.0	26 41.0	12 42.3	13 10.0	1 57.2	9 49.6
20	3 54 16.0	27 12.6	7 17.4	11♈38.5	18 9.1	11 50.7	25 12.6	26 35.0	12 37.7	13 11.4	1 58.4	9 51.9
21	3 58 12.5	28 13.2	7 14.2	26 2.9	17 16.2	12 57.5	25 58.3	26 29.3	12 33.2	13 12.9	1 59.6	9 54.2
22	4 2 9.1	29 13.8	7 11.0	10♉53.2	16 34.2	14 4.5	26 44.0	26 23.6	12 28.6	13 14.3	2 .9	9 56.5
23	4 6 5.6	0♐14.4	7 7.9	26 1.9	16 3.6	15 11.7	27 29.7	26 18.1	12 24.1	13 15.8	2 2.2	9 58.8
24	4 10 2.2	1 15.0	7 4.7	11♊18.6	15 44.8	16 19.2	28 15.5	26 12.8	12 19.7	13 17.4	2 3.5	10 1.1
25	4 13 58.7	2 15.6	7 1.5	26 32.3	15 37.4	17 26.8	29 1.3	26 7.7	12 15.3	13 19.0	2 4.8	10 3.5
26	4 17 55.3	3 16.3	6 58.3	11♋32.6	15D41.1	18 34.7	29 47.1	26 2.7	12 10.9	13 20.7	2 6.2	10 5.8
27	4 21 51.9	4 17.0	6 55.1	26 12.2	15 55.0	19 42.8	0♒33.0	25 57.8	12 6.6	13 22.4	2 7.6	10 8.1
28	4 25 48.4	5 17.7	6 52.0	10♌26.8	16 18.4	20 51.1	1 18.9	25 53.2	12 2.3	13 24.1	2 9.0	10 10.4
29	4 29 45.0	6 18.4	6 48.8	24 15.5	16 50.4	21 59.6	2 4.9	25 48.8	11 58.1	13 25.9	2 10.4	10 12.8
30	4 33 41.5	7 19.2	6 45.6	7♍39.4	17 30.1	23 8.3	2 50.9	25 44.5	11 54.0	13 27.8	2 11.9	10 15.1

LATITUDE

DAY	EPHEM. SID. TIME	☉	☊	☽	☿	♀	♂	♃	♄	♅	♆	♇
1	2 39 21.4	0 .0	0 .0	0N30.7	2S54.9	0N22.6	1S41.1	1S31.6	2S37.1	0S41.0	0N15.2	10N56.6
4	2 51 11.1	0 .0	0 .0	3 34.1	2 41.6	0 38.9	1 39.8	1 31.2	2 37.1	0 40.9	0 15.1	10 55.8
7	3 3 .7	0 .0	0 .0	4 57.7	2 16.3	0 53.9	1 38.5	1 30.8	2 37.0	0 40.9	0 15.0	10 55.1
10	3 14 50.4	0 .0	0 .0	4 20.0	1 36.6	1 7.7	1 37.2	1 30.3	2 36.8	0 40.8	0 15.0	10 54.4
13	3 26 40.1	0 .0	0 .0	2 3.3	0 43.2	1 20.2	1 35.7	1 29.7	2 36.6	0 40.7	0 14.9	10 53.8
16	3 38 29.7	0 .0	0 .0	1S 4.1	0N17.9	1 31.5	1 34.2	1 29.1	2 36.4	0 40.6	0 14.9	10 53.2
19	3 50 19.4	0 .0	0 .0	3 56.5	1 15.5	1 41.6	1 32.6	1 28.4	2 36.0	0 40.5	0 14.8	10 52.7
22	4 2 9.1	0 .0	0 .0	5 1.8	1 58.9	1 50.4	1 31.0	1 27.7	2 35.7	0 40.4	0 14.8	10 52.2
25	4 13 58.7	0 .0	0 .0	3 12.5	2 24.0	1 58.0	1 29.3	1 27.0	2 35.3	0 40.3	0 14.7	10 51.8
28	4 25 48.4	0 .0	0 .0	0N25.8	2 32.7	2 4.5	1 27.6	1 26.2	2 34.8	0 40.2	0 14.6	10 51.4

RIGHT ASCENSION

DAY	EPHEM. SID. TIME	☉	☊	☽	☿	♀	♂	♃	♄	♅	♆	♇
1	2 39 21.4	5♏44.9	10♌43.0	16♌59.2	27♏49.8	22♍27.5	12♑ 2.3	27♈20.1	12♉29.2	15♒33.8	3♒52.2	9♐ 9.9
2	2 43 18.0	6 43.6	10 39.8	0♍30.0	28 18.8	23 25.6	12 51.1	27R12.6	12R24.4	15 34.2	3 52.8	9 11.9
3	2 47 14.5	7 42.4	10 36.5	13 19.8	28 41.3	24 23.9	13 39.8	27 5.1	12 19.7	15 34.8	3 53.5	9 13.9
4	2 51 11.1	8 41.5	10 33.3	25 36.4	28 56.3	25 22.6	14 28.6	26 57.7	12 14.9	15 35.3	3 54.2	9 16.0
5	2 55 7.6	9 40.9	10 30.1	7♎29.3	29 3.4	26 21.5	15 17.4	26 50.4	12 10.1	15 36.0	3 55.0	9 18.0
6	2 59 4.2	10 40.4	10 26.9	19 8.7	29R 1.7	27 20.6	16 6.2	26 43.1	12 5.4	15 36.6	3 55.8	9 20.1
7	3 3 .7	11 40.1	10 23.6	0♏44.1	28 50.8	28 20.1	16 55.0	26 35.9	12 .6	15 37.4	3 56.6	9 22.2
8	3 6 57.3	12 40.0	10 20.4	12 23.4	28 30.3	29 19.8	17 43.8	26 28.8	11 55.8	15 38.1	3 57.4	9 24.3
9	3 10 53.8	13 40.2	10 17.2	24 12.6	27 59.7	0♎19.7	18 32.6	26 21.8	11 51.0	15 39.0	3 58.3	9 26.5
10	3 14 50.4	14 40.5	10 13.9	6♐15.5	27 19.3	1 19.9	19 21.4	26 14.9	11 46.3	15 39.8	3 59.2	9 28.6
11	3 18 47.0	15 41.1	10 10.7	18 32.7	26 29.4	2 20.3	20 10.2	26 8.1	11 41.5	15 40.8	4 .2	9 30.8
12	3 22 43.5	16 41.9	10 7.4	1♑ 2.3	25 30.7	3 21.0	20 58.9	26 1.3	11 36.8	15 41.7	4 1.2	9 32.9
13	3 26 40.1	17 42.9	10 4.2	13 40.1	24 24.5	4 21.9	21 47.7	25 54.7	11 32.0	15 42.8	4 2.2	9 35.1
14	3 30 36.6	18 44.1	10 1.0	26 21.3	23 12.5	5 23.0	22 36.4	25 48.2	11 27.3	15 43.9	4 3.3	9 37.3
15	3 34 33.2	19 45.5	9 57.7	9♒ 1.3	21 56.8	6 24.3	23 25.1	25 41.9	11 22.6	15 45.0	4 4.3	9 39.5
16	3 38 29.7	20 47.1	9 54.5	21 37.8	20 39.7	7 25.9	24 13.8	25 35.6	11 18.0	15 46.2	4 5.4	9 41.7
17	3 42 26.3	21 48.9	9 51.3	4♓11.6	19 24.0	8 27.7	25 2.4	25 29.5	11 13.3	15 47.4	4 6.6	9 43.9
18	3 46 22.8	22 50.9	9 48.0	16 46.5	18 12.0	9 29.7	25 50.9	25 23.5	11 8.7	15 48.7	4 7.8	9 46.1
19	3 50 19.4	23 53.2	9 44.8	29 29.4	17 6.0	10 32.0	26 39.5	25 17.6	11 4.1	15 50.0	4 9.0	9 48.4
20	3 54 16.0	24 55.6	9 41.5	12♈29.7	16 8.0	11 34.5	27 27.9	25 11.9	10 59.6	15 51.4	4 10.2	9 50.6
21	3 58 12.5	25 58.3	9 38.3	25 57.8	15 19.5	12 37.2	28 16.4	25 6.4	10 55.1	15 52.9	4 11.5	9 52.9
22	4 2 9.1	27 1.1	9 35.1	10♉ 3.3	14 41.3	13 40.2	29 4.8	25 1.0	10 50.6	15 54.3	4 12.8	9 55.2
23	4 6 5.6	28 4.1	9 31.8	24 51.9	14 14.1	14 43.3	29 53.1	24 55.7	10 46.1	15 55.8	4 14.2	9 57.5
24	4 10 2.2	29 7.4	9 28.6	10♊21.5	13 58.0	15 46.8	0♒41.3	24 50.6	10 41.7	15 57.4	4 15.5	9 59.7
25	4 13 58.7	0♐10.8	9 25.3	26 19.0	13 52.6	16 50.4	1 29.4	24 45.6	10 37.4	15 59.0	4 16.9	10 2.0
26	4 17 55.3	1 14.4	9 22.1	12♋21.4	13D57.5	17 54.3	2 17.5	24 40.8	10 33.1	16 .7	4 18.3	10 4.3
27	4 21 51.9	2 18.2	9 18.9	28 2.5	14 12.1	18 58.4	3 5.6	24 36.2	10 28.8	16 2.4	4 19.8	10 6.6
28	4 25 48.4	3 22.2	9 15.6	13♌ 1.1	14 35.6	20 2.8	3 53.5	24 31.7	10 24.6	16 4.1	4 21.3	10 8.9
29	4 29 45.0	4 26.4	9 12.4	27 7.4	15 7.3	21 7.5	4 41.4	24 27.4	10 20.5	16 5.9	4 22.8	10 11.2
30	4 33 41.5	5 30.7	9 9.1	10♍22.0	15 46.3	22 12.3	5 29.2	24 23.3	10 16.4	16 7.8	4 24.3	10 13.5

DECLINATION

DAY	EPHEM. SID. TIME	☉	☊	☽	☿	♀	♂	♃	♄	♅	♆	♇
1	2 39 21.4	14S12.7	0N19.0	17N .6	23S 8.0	3N40.0	24S40.0	9N37.6	13N34.8	17S35.8	19S32.3	11S .0
4	2 51 11.1	15 9.8	0 19.1	5 47.4	23 7.5	2 42.5	24 26.6	9 29.6	13 30.6	17 35.3	19 31.9	11 1.7
7	3 3 .7	16 4.6	0 19.1	7S12.7	22 40.5	1 42.1	24 10.8	9 21.9	13 26.4	17 34.6	19 31.4	11 3.3
10	3 14 50.4	16 57.1	0 19.2	17 15.3	21 41.8	0 39.2	23 52.7	9 14.6	13 22.3	17 33.8	19 30.9	11 4.9
13	3 26 40.1	17 46.9	0 19.2	20 46.7	20 9.6	0S26.0	23 32.4	9 7.6	13 18.2	17 32.9	19 30.3	11 6.4
16	3 38 29.7	18 34.0	0 19.3	16 11.2	18 13.6	1 33.0	23 9.7	9 1.0	13 14.2	17 31.9	19 29.7	11 8.0
19	3 50 19.4	19 18.1	0 19.3	4 31.0	16 18.7	2 41.5	22 44.9	8 54.9	13 10.3	17 30.7	19 29.0	11 9.4
22	4 2 9.1	19 59.0	0 19.3	10N18.4	14 53.4	3 51.3	22 17.8	8 49.3	13 6.5	17 29.4	19 28.2	11 10.8
25	4 13 58.7	20 36.7	0 19.4	20 11.1	14 13.1	5 1.8	21 48.6	8 44.2	13 2.9	17 27.9	19 27.4	11 12.2
28	4 25 48.4	21 10.9	0 19.4	18 2.0	14 16.5	6 12.9	21 17.3	8 39.7	12 59.4	17 26.4	19 26.5	11 13.5

DECEMBER 1999

LONGITUDE

DAY	EPHEM. SID. TIME	☉	☊	☽	☿	♀	♂	♃	♄	♅	♆	♇
	h m s	° ′	° ′	° ′	° ′	° ′	° ′	° ′	° ′	° ′	° ′	° ′
1	4 37 38.1	8♐20.0	6♌42.4	20♍41.4	18♏16.6	24♎17.2	3♒36.9	25♈40.4	11♉49.9	13♒29.6	2♒13.4	10♐17.4
2	4 41 34.6	9 20.8	6 39.3	3♎25.0	19 9.2	25 26.2	4 23.0	25R36.5	11R45.9	13 31.6	2 15.0	10 19.8
3	4 45 31.2	10 21.7	6 36.1	15 53.5	20 7.1	26 35.5	5 9.0	25 32.8	11 41.9	13 33.5	2 16.5	10 22.1
4	4 49 27.8	11 22.5	6 32.9	28 10.2	21 9.5	27 44.8	5 55.2	25 29.2	11 38.0	13 35.6	2 18.1	10 24.4
5	4 53 24.3	12 23.4	6 29.7	10♏17.7	22 16.0	28 54.4	6 41.3	25 25.9	11 34.2	13 37.6	2 19.7	10 26.8
6	4 57 20.9	13 24.3	6 26.6	22 18.3	23 25.9	0♏ 4.1	7 27.5	25 22.8	11 30.5	13 39.7	2 21.3	10 29.1
7	5 1 17.4	14 25.2	6 23.4	4♐13.6	24 38.8	1 14.0	8 13.8	25 19.9	11 26.8	13 41.8	2 23.0	10 31.5
8	5 5 14.0	15 26.2	6 20.2	16 5.2	25 54.3	2 24.0	9 .0	25 17.1	11 23.2	13 44.0	2 24.7	10 33.8
9	5 9 10.5	16 27.1	6 17.0	27 54.7	27 12.1	3 34.1	9 46.3	25 14.6	11 19.7	13 46.3	2 26.4	10 36.1
10	5 13 7.1	17 28.1	6 13.8	9♑43.6	28 31.8	4 44.4	10 32.6	25 12.3	11 16.3	13 48.5	2 28.1	10 38.4
11	5 17 3.7	18 29.1	6 10.7	21 34.2	29 53.1	5 54.8	11 18.9	25 10.2	11 12.9	13 50.8	2 29.8	10 40.8
12	5 21 .2	19 30.1	6 7.5	3♒29.3	1♐15.9	7 5.4	12 5.3	25 8.3	11 9.7	13 53.2	2 31.7	10 43.1
13	5 24 56.8	20 31.2	6 4.3	15 32.0	2 39.8	8 16.0	12 51.7	25 6.6	11 6.5	13 55.6	2 33.5	10 45.5
14	5 28 53.3	21 32.2	6 1.1	27 46.5	4 4.9	9 26.8	13 38.1	25 5.1	11 3.4	13 58.0	2 35.3	10 47.8
15	5 32 49.9	22 33.2	5 58.0	10♓17.0	5 30.8	10 37.7	14 24.5	25 3.9	11 .4	14 .5	2 37.1	10 50.1
16	5 36 46.4	23 34.2	5 54.8	23 8.2	6 57.6	11 48.7	15 10.9	25 2.8	10 57.5	14 2.9	2 39.0	10 52.4
17	5 40 43.0	24 35.3	5 51.6	6♈24.0	8 25.0	12 59.8	15 57.4	25 1.9	10 54.7	14 5.5	2 40.8	10 54.6
18	5 44 39.6	25 36.3	5 48.4	20 7.5	9 53.1	14 11.0	16 43.8	25 1.3	10 51.9	14 8.0	2 42.7	10 56.9
19	5 48 36.1	26 37.4	5 45.3	4♉19.6	11 21.7	15 22.3	17 30.3	25 .8	10 49.3	14 10.6	2 44.7	10 59.2
20	5 52 32.7	27 38.5	5 42.1	18 58.7	12 50.8	16 33.8	18 16.8	25 .6	10 46.8	14 13.3	2 46.6	11 1.5
21	5 56 29.2	28 39.5	5 38.9	3♊59.5	14 20.3	17 45.3	19 3.2	25 .6	10 44.3	14 15.9	2 48.5	11 3.7
22	6 0 25.8	29 40.6	5 35.7	19 14.0	15 50.3	18 56.9	19 49.7	25D .8	10 42.0	14 18.6	2 50.5	11 6.0
23	6 4 22.3	0♑41.7	5 32.6	4♋31.6	17 20.6	20 8.6	20 36.2	25 1.2	10 39.8	14 21.4	2 52.5	11 8.2
24	6 8 18.9	1 42.8	5 29.4	19 41.8	18 51.2	21 20.4	21 22.7	25 1.8	10 37.6	14 24.1	2 54.5	11 10.4
25	6 12 15.5	2 43.9	5 26.2	4♌35.2	20 22.2	22 32.3	22 9.2	25 2.6	10 35.6	14 26.9	2 56.5	11 12.6
26	6 16 12.0	3 45.0	5 23.0	19 5.0	21 53.4	23 44.3	22 55.8	25 3.6	10 33.6	14 29.7	2 58.6	11 14.8
27	6 20 8.6	4 46.1	5 19.8	3♍ 7.7	23 25.0	24 56.4	23 42.3	25 4.8	10 31.8	14 32.6	3 .6	11 17.0
28	6 24 5.1	5 47.2	5 16.7	16 42.7	24 56.9	26 8.6	24 28.8	25 6.2	10 30.1	14 35.5	3 2.7	11 19.2
29	6 28 1.7	6 48.3	5 13.5	29 51.6	26 29.0	27 20.8	25 15.3	25 7.9	10 28.4	14 38.4	3 4.8	11 21.4
30	6 31 58.2	7 49.5	5 10.3	12♎37.7	28 1.5	28 33.2	26 1.9	25 9.7	10 26.9	14 41.3	3 6.8	11 23.5
31	6 35 54.8	8 50.6	5 7.1	25 4.8	29 34.3	29 45.6	26 48.4	25 11.8	10 25.5	14 44.3	3 9.0	11 25.6

LATITUDE

DAY	EPHEM. SID. TIME	☉	☊	☽	☿	♀	♂	♃	♄	♅	♆	♇
1	4 37 38.1	0 .0	0 .0	3N37.1	2N29.2	2N 9.8	1S25.7	1S25.4	2S34.3	0S40.1	0N14.6	10N51.1
4	4 49 27.8	0 .0	0 .0	5 3.2	2 17.4	2 14.0	1 23.9	1 24.5	2 33.7	0 40.1	0 14.5	10 50.8
7	5 1 17.4	0 .0	0 .0	4 27.0	2 .3	2 17.0	1 22.0	1 23.6	2 33.1	0 40.0	0 14.5	10 50.6
10	5 13 7.1	0 .0	0 .0	2 9.3	1 40.1	2 19.0	1 20.0	1 22.7	2 32.5	0 39.9	0 14.4	10 50.5
13	5 24 56.8	0 .0	0 .0	1S .1	1 18.2	2 20.0	1 18.0	1 21.8	2 31.8	0 39.8	0 14.4	10 50.4
16	5 36 46.4	0 .0	0 .0	3 54.1	0 55.5	2 20.0	1 16.0	1 20.9	2 31.1	0 39.8	0 14.3	10 50.4
19	5 48 36.1	0 .0	0 .0	5 11.2	0 32.7	2 19.0	1 13.9	1 20.0	2 30.3	0 39.7	0 14.3	10 50.4
22	6 0 25.8	0 .0	0 .0	3 40.2	0 10.4	2 17.1	1 11.7	1 19.0	2 29.6	0 39.7	0 14.3	10 50.4
25	6 12 15.5	0 .0	0 .0	0N 3.5	0S11.2	2 14.3	1 9.6	1 18.1	2 28.8	0 39.6	0 14.2	10 50.5
28	6 24 5.1	0 .0	0 .0	3 33.5	0 31.6	2 10.8	1 7.4	1 17.1	2 28.0	0 39.5	0 14.2	10 50.7
31	6 35 54.8	0 .0	0 .0	5 10.6	0 50.7	2 6.4	1 5.2	1 16.2	2 27.1	0 39.5	0 14.1	10 50.9

RIGHT ASCENSION

DAY	EPHEM. SID. TIME	☉	☊	☽	☿	♀	♂	♃	♄	♅	♆	♇
1	4 37 38.1	6♐35.2	9♌ 5.9	22♍52.8	16♏31.8	23♎17.5	6♒16.9	24♈19.3	10♉12.3	16♒ 9.6	4♒25.8	10♐15.8
2	4 41 34.6	7 39.9	9 2.6	4♎51.1	17 23.3	24 22.9	7 4.5	24R15.6	10R 8.3	16 11.6	4 27.4	10 18.1
3	4 45 31.2	8 44.8	8 59.4	16 29.2	18 19.9	25 28.5	7 52.1	24 12.0	10 4.4	16 13.5	4 29.0	10 20.4
4	4 49 27.8	9 49.8	8 56.1	27 58.7	19 21.2	26 34.4	8 39.6	24 8.5	10 .6	16 15.5	4 30.7	10 22.7
5	4 53 24.3	10 55.0	8 52.9	9♏29.8	20 26.6	27 40.6	9 27.0	24 5.3	9 56.8	16 17.6	4 32.3	10 25.0
6	4 57 20.9	12 .3	8 49.7	21 10.6	21 35.6	28 47.0	10 14.3	24 2.2	9 53.1	16 19.7	4 34.0	10 27.3
7	5 1 17.4	13 5.8	8 46.4	3♐ 6.2	22 47.9	29 53.7	11 1.5	23 59.4	9 49.4	16 21.8	4 35.7	10 29.6
8	5 5 14.0	14 11.4	8 43.2	15 18.7	24 3.0	1♏ .7	11 48.6	23 56.7	9 45.8	16 24.0	4 37.5	10 31.9
9	5 9 10.5	15 17.1	8 39.9	27 46.5	25 20.7	2 8.0	12 35.6	23 54.2	9 42.3	16 26.2	4 39.2	10 34.2
10	5 13 7.1	16 22.9	8 36.7	10♑24.8	26 40.7	3 15.5	13 22.6	23 51.9	9 38.9	16 28.5	4 41.0	10 36.5
11	5 17 3.7	17 28.9	8 33.4	23 7.0	28 2.8	4 23.3	14 9.4	23 49.8	9 35.6	16 30.8	4 42.8	10 38.8
12	5 21 .2	18 34.9	8 30.2	5♒46.4	29 26.7	5 31.4	14 56.2	23 48.0	9 32.4	16 33.2	4 44.7	10 41.2
13	5 24 56.8	19 41.1	8 26.9	18 18.3	0♐52.3	6 39.8	15 42.8	23 46.3	9 29.2	16 35.6	4 46.6	10 43.5
14	5 28 53.3	20 47.3	8 23.7	0♓41.3	2 19.4	7 48.4	16 29.4	23 44.7	9 26.1	16 38.0	4 48.5	10 45.8
15	5 32 49.9	21 53.5	8 20.4	12 58.1	3 47.9	8 57.4	17 15.8	23 43.4	9 23.1	16 40.4	4 50.4	10 48.1
16	5 36 46.4	22 59.9	8 17.2	25 14.9	5 17.7	10 6.7	18 2.1	23 42.3	9 20.2	16 42.9	4 52.3	10 50.3
17	5 40 43.0	24 6.3	8 13.9	7♈41.3	6 48.7	11 16.2	18 48.4	23 41.4	9 17.4	16 45.5	4 54.2	10 52.6
18	5 44 39.6	25 12.7	8 10.7	20 28.7	8 20.7	12 26.0	19 34.5	23 40.6	9 14.6	16 48.0	4 56.2	10 54.9
19	5 48 36.1	26 19.2	8 7.4	3♉49.8	9 53.8	13 36.2	20 20.5	23 40.1	9 12.0	16 50.6	4 58.2	10 57.1
20	5 52 32.7	27 25.7	8 4.1	17 55.7	11 27.8	14 46.7	21 6.4	23 39.8	9 9.4	16 53.2	5 .2	10 59.4
21	5 56 29.2	28 32.3	8 .9	2♊52.4	13 2.7	15 57.4	21 52.2	23 39.6	9 7.0	16 55.9	5 2.2	11 1.6
22	6 0 25.8	29 38.8	7 57.6	18 36.2	14 38.5	17 8.5	22 37.9	23D39.7	9 4.6	16 58.6	5 4.2	11 3.8
23	6 4 22.3	0♑45.4	7 54.4	4♋50.3	16 15.1	18 19.9	23 23.5	23 40.0	9 2.3	17 1.3	5 6.3	11 6.1
24	6 8 18.9	1 52.0	7 51.1	21 7.0	17 52.4	19 31.6	24 9.0	23 40.4	9 .2	17 4.1	5 8.3	11 8.3
25	6 12 15.5	2 58.6	7 47.9	6♌56.4	19 30.4	20 43.7	24 54.3	23 41.1	8 58.1	17 6.9	5 10.4	11 10.5
26	6 16 12.0	4 5.1	7 44.6	21 57.0	21 9.1	21 56.0	25 39.6	23 41.9	8 56.1	17 9.7	5 12.5	11 12.7
27	6 20 8.6	5 11.7	7 41.4	6♍ .6	22 48.5	23 8.7	26 24.8	23 42.9	8 54.3	17 12.5	5 14.6	11 14.9
28	6 24 5.1	6 18.2	7 38.1	19 10.3	24 28.5	24 21.7	27 9.8	23 44.2	8 52.5	17 15.4	5 16.8	11 17.0
29	6 28 1.7	7 24.7	7 34.8	1♎36.1	26 9.0	25 35.0	27 54.8	23 45.6	8 50.8	17 18.3	5 18.9	11 19.2
30	6 31 58.2	8 31.1	7 31.6	13 31.0	27 50.1	26 48.6	28 39.7	23 47.2	8 49.3	17 21.3	5 21.1	11 21.3
31	6 35 54.8	9 37.5	7 28.3	25 8.1	29 31.8	28 2.5	29 24.4	23 49.0	8 47.8	17 24.2	5 23.3	11 23.5

DECLINATION

DAY	EPHEM. SID. TIME	☉	☊	☽	☿	♀	♂	♃	♄	♅	♆	♇
1	4 37 38.1	21S41.6	0N19.5	7N .8	14S52.8	7S24.2	20S44.0	8N35.8	12N56.1	17S24.7	19S25.6	11S14.7
4	4 49 27.8	22 8.6	0 19.5	6S 5.8	15 50.2	8 35.2	20 8.7	8 32.6	12 53.0	17 22.9	19 24.6	11 15.9
7	5 1 17.4	22 31.7	0 19.6	16 36.8	16 59.1	9 45.6	19 31.6	8 30.0	12 50.2	17 21.1	19 23.5	11 17.1
10	5 13 7.1	22 50.8	0 19.6	20 55.9	18 12.2	10 55.0	18 52.6	8 28.1	12 47.6	17 19.1	19 22.4	11 18.2
13	5 24 56.8	23 5.9	0 19.6	17 8.1	19 24.8	12 3.0	18 11.8	8 26.9	12 45.2	17 17.0	19 21.2	11 19.2
16	5 36 46.4	23 16.9	0 19.7	6 18.4	20 33.5	13 9.4	17 29.5	8 26.3	12 43.1	17 14.8	19 20.0	11 20.1
19	5 48 36.1	23 23.7	0 19.7	8N 4.4	21 36.1	14 13.6	16 45.5	8 26.5	12 41.3	17 12.5	19 18.8	11 21.0
22	6 0 25.8	23 26.2	0 19.8	19 20.6	22 30.8	15 15.4	16 .1	8 27.3	12 39.8	17 10.1	19 17.5	11 21.8
25	6 12 15.5	23 24.5	0 19.8	19 10.2	23 16.4	16 14.3	15 13.3	8 28.9	12 38.6	17 7.6	19 16.1	11 22.6
28	6 24 5.1	23 18.6	0 19.8	8 31.3	23 52.1	17 10.1	14 25.2	8 31.1	12 37.6	17 5.1	19 14.8	11 23.2
31	6 35 54.8	23 8.5	0 19.9	4S53.0	24 16.9	18 2.3	13 35.9	8 34.0	12 37.0	17 2.5	19 13.4	11 23.8